SCOTT

1997 Standard Postage Stamp Catalogue

ONE HUNDRED AND FIFTY-THIRD EDITION IN SIX VOLUMES

VOLUME 2

EUROPEAN COUNTRIES and COLONIES,
INDEPENDENT NATIONS of
AFRICA, ASIA, LATIN AMERICA

A-C

Released June 1996

Scott Publishing Co.

911 Vandemark Road, Sidney, OH 45365-0828

A division of AMOS PRESS, INC., publishers of *Linn's Stamp News, Coin World, Cars & Parts* magazine, *Moneycard Collector* and *The Sidney Daily News.*

Table of Contents

See Volume 1A for United States and affiliated territories, United Nations, Canada and British America.
See Volume 1B for the British Commonwealth of Nations other than British America.
See Volumes 3, 4 and 5 for nations of Africa, Asia, Europe, Latin America and their affiliated territories.

Scott Publishing Mission Statement

The Scott Publishing Team exists to serve the recreational, educational and commercial hobby needs of stamp collectors and dealers.

We strive to set the industry standard for philatelic information and products by developing and providing goods that help collectors identify, value, organize and present their collections.

Quality customer service is, and will continue to be, our highest priority. We aspire toward achieving total customer satisfaction.

Copyright Notice

Trademark Notice

ISBN 0-89487-220-6

Library of Congress Card No. 2-3301

Scott Publishing Co.

SCOTT

911 VANDEMARK ROAD, P. O. Box 828, SIDNEY, OHIO 45365-0828 513-498-0802

Dear Catalogue User:

The big news is that this is the first edition of the Scott standard catalogue to contain values for stamps in the grade of very fine. In the past we have listed values for stamps of a grade of fine to very fine. You will find that the change in grade has significantly affected values throughout the volume, particularly for 19th-century material.

With the 1997 edition of the *Scott Standard Postage Stamp Catalogue,* Scott values also reflect the world market. We have factored the prices stamps sell for in their respective home markets into our values. For example, the editors now take into consideration the price paid in Vienna for a WIPA sheet, Austria Scott B111.

And now, with your permission, I'll ask myself a few key questions.

Why the move to World Market values?

It is time that Scott abandons its isolationist policy of valuing for the U.S. market only. Scott must use values that reflect the world market because overseas buyers have changed the nature of the stamp business. The prices that collectors in the United States pay for stamps is strongly influenced by the home market for the same stamps.

But how does this affect me?

When values of foreign stamps are well below prices paid abroad, many nice stamps are dispatched across the ocean to buyers who are quite willing to pay the higher price. When the next U.S. collector goes to buy the same foreign item, he has to compete not only with the overseas demand but an even thinner supply here in this country. It is a vicious circle.

Will the change to market values mean that Scott values will be the equivalent in dollars to Stanley Gibbons, Michel, Yvert or other foreign catalogue values?

Good question! Each of these catalogues has its own unique method of valuing stamps. Michel uses reference values that are highly discounted by dealers when selling. So do most of the other overseas catalogues. Scott uses a retail value that represents what a collector might actually expect to pay for a specific stamp in the specified condition.

Have these changes made an impact on China values? Is China still hot?

Yes. Molten.

More than 10,000 of the 23,000 value changes in Volume 2 are found in China. In stamps from the Imperial era, Scott 3, the 1878 5¢ Large Dragon, climbs to $450 unused and $67.50 used for very fine from $300 unused, $50 used for fine to very fine examples in the 1996 catalogue. Scott 24, the 1894 24¢ Empress Dowager, jumps to $190 unused and $40 used from $140 unused and $30 used. The 1912 Foochow overprints, Scott 134-137, leap to $6,450 unused and $4,320 used from $5,395 unused and $3,205 used. In the early Republic era, Scott 178-189, the 1912 Sun Yat-Sen issue, charges to $610.25 unused and $424.50 used from $403 unused and $336.15 used. The 1932-34 Martyrs issue zooms to $8.25 unused from $5.15 last year.

The stamps of the People's Republic of China, which showed numerous decreases last year, make up for that this year with some rather significant increases. Scott 12-20, the first Gate of Heavenly Peace issue, leaps to $75.55 unused from $49.60 last year, and the 1950 Sino-Soviet Treaty issue, Scott 74-76, doubles to $28.50 unused from $14.25. The 1963 Yellow Mountains landscapes, Scott 716-731, shoot to $256 unused, $60 used from $176 unused, $30.26 used. Many of the sets of the Cultural Revolution period again push much higher. The 1967 Thoughts of Mao set, Scott 938-948, charges to $385 unused, $154 used, from $264 unused and $77 used, and the Poems of Mao set, Scott 967-980, zips to $567.50 unused from $391 used.

What are the other Volume 2 countries doing?

Plenty. In Austria, nearly 2,500 values change. Scott 11, the type II 15kr Emperor Franz Josef of 1858, charges to $550 unused and $2 used from $250 unused and $1 used. The 15kr of the 1863 Arms, Scott 21, also leaps considerably, to $950 unused and $10 used from $550 unused and $5.50 used. The 1910 Birthday Jubilee issue, Scott 128-144, jumps to $425 unused and $580 used from $365.50 unused and $514.90 used and the 1936 Dollfuss 10s, Scott 380, zips to $650 hinged, $900 never hinged, $800 used from $575 hinged, $775 never hinged and $675 used.

In Belgium, Scott 3, the 10¢ Leopold I of 1850 with framed watermark, marches to $1,500 unused and $67.50 used from $1,000 unused and $55 used. The 1919 King Albert in Trench Helmet set, Scott 124-137, leaps to $630 unused and $642.40 used from $357.63 unused and $342.60 used. The 1910 St. Martin semi-postals, Scott B1-B8, shoot to $42.15 unused from $20.85 last year, and the 1933 Orval Abbey set, Scott B132-B143, charges to $607.50 unused and $635 used from $450 unused and $437.50 used.

Brazil's Bullseyes are higher. Scott 1, the 30r, leaps to $2,250 unused and $550 used from $1,650 unused and $400 used. The 1878-79 Dom Pedro set, Scott 68-77, zooms to $756 unused and $186.75 used from $411 unused and $155.10 used. The 1920-22 definitives, Scott 218-230, charge to $80.90 unused and $8.50 used from $44.20 unused and $4.45 used.

Large increases can be found in Cambodia. The 1951-52 set, Scott 1-17, leaps to $73.80 never hinged from $41.89 last year, and the 1954-55 set, Scott 18-37, soars to $38.20 never hinged from $17.36 never hinged.

Any Editorial changes?

Many minor varieties have been added throughout Volume 2. Nine on-cover bisects have been added in Austria and seven in Brazil.

A subset of China's 1897 small numeral surcharges has been added as Scott 25a-37b. These nine stamps have the numerals 4mm below the Chinese characters, as opposed to 2 1/2 mm below on the majors.

Most other added items are shades or perforation-omitted varieties.

Renumberings affect Argentina's 1992-94 Mushrooms set, the 1992-94 Arms set of Belarus and the 1994 Image of the Republic non-denominated issue of Brazil.

Two more important things.

Set totals for three and four stamps sets have been added throughout Volume 2. This change will certainly make your life with the catalogue much easier.

Pronunciations for each country return to the standard catalogues this year. Now you'll know how to pronounce Cilicia.

Happy Collecting,

Stuart Morrissey

Stuart Morrissey, Publisher

Acknowledgments

Our appreciation and gratitude go to the following individuals and organizations who have assisted us in preparing information included in the 1997 Scott Catalogues. Some helpers prefer anonymity. These individuals have generously shared their stamp knowledge with others through the medium of the Scott Catalogue.

Those who follow provided information that is in addition to the hundreds of dealer price lists and advertisements and scores of auction catalogues and realizations which were used in producing the catalogue values. It is from those noted here that we have been able to obtain information on items not normally seen in published lists and advertisements. Support from these people of course goes beyond data leading to catalogue values, for they also are key to editorial changes.

George F. Ackermann
Michael E. Aldrich
A. R. Allison
B. J. Ammel
David J. Armacost
Mike Armus
Robert Ausubel
Don Bakos
Alfredo V. Basurto
Jules K. Beck
Vladimir Berrio-Lemm
Kenneth R. Berry
John Birkinbine II
Rex Dean Bishop
Torbjorn Bjork
John R. Boker, Jr.
George W. Brett
Roger Brody
Randall Brooksbank
Lawrence A. Bustillo
Peter Bylen
A. Bryan Camarda
Nathan Carlin
Dr. Herman J. Cestero, Jr.
E. J. Chamberlin
Richard A. Champagne
Albert F. Chang
Henry Chlanda
Andrew Cronin
James A. Cross
William T. Crowe
Dan Demetriade
Bob Dumaine
William S. Dunn
Victor E. Engstrom
J. A. Farrington
Leon Finik
Henry Fisher
Joseph E. Foley
Marvin Frey
Richard Friedberg
Eugene A. Garrett
Peter Georgiadis
Richard B. Graham
Brian M. Green
Fred F. Gregory
Gary Griffith
Harry Hagendorf
Calvet M. Hahn
Rudolf Hamar
Erich E. Hamm
John B. Head
Dale Hendricks
Clifford O. Herrick
Lee H. Hill, Jr.
W. Wilson Hulme II
Eric Jackson
Michael Jaffe
John I. Jamieson
Peter C. Jeannopoulos
Clyde Jennings
Donald B. Johnstone
Henry Karen
Stanford M. Katz
Lewis Kaufman
Dr. James Kerr
Charles F. Kezbers
Robert Kitson
William Langs
Lester Lanphear III
Richard F. Larkin
Ken Lawrence
Ronald E. Lesher, Sr.
Pedro Llach
William Thomas Lockard
David Mac Donnell
Walter J. Mader
Robert L. Markovits
F. Brian Marshall
Timothy M. Mc Ree
Dr. Hector Mena
Giorgio Migliavacca
Jack Molesworth
Chuck O. Moo
William E. Mooz
Gary M. Morris
Peter Mosiondz, Jr.
Bruce M. Moyer
Gregg Nelson
Robert Odenweller
John C. Olson
Victor Ostolaza
Souren Panirian
Sheldon Paris
John E. Pearson
Otto Peetoom
Donald J. Peterson
Vernon Pickering
Stanley M. Piller
S. Pinchot
Peter A. Robertson
Jon Rose
Frans H. A. Rummens
Richard H. Salz
Byron Sandfield
Jacques C. Schiff, Jr.
F. Burton Sellers
Jeff Siddiqui
Dr. Hubert Skinner
Roger D. Skinner
Merle Spencer
Sherwood Springer
Richard Stambaugh
Mark Stucker
R. J. Thoden
David Torre
Scott Trepel
Ming W. Tsang
James O. Vadeboncoeur
Xavier Verbeck
Jerome S. Wagshal
Richard A. Washburn
Giana Wayman
Raymond H. Weill
Irwin Weinberg
Larry S. Weiss
William R. Weiss, Jr.
Hans A. Westphal
Greg Winston
Robert F. Yacano
Clarke Yarbrough
Val Zabijaka
Nathan Zankel

A special acknowledgment to Liane and Sergio Sismondo of The Classic Collector for their extraordinary assistance and knowledge sharing that has aided in the preparation of this year's Standard Catalogues.

American Air Mail Society
Stephen Reinhard, PO Box 110,
Mineola, NY 11501

American Philatelic Society
PO Box 8000, State College, PA 16803

American Revenue Association
Bruce Miller, Suite 332, 701 South
First Ave., Arcadia, CA 91006

American Stamp Dealers' Association
3 School St., Glen Cove, NY 11542

American Topical Association
PO Box 630, Johnstown, PA 15907

Booklet Collectors Club
James Natale, PO Box 2461,
Cinnaminson, NJ 08077-5461

Bureau Issues Association
George V.H. Godin, PO Box 23707,
Belleville, IL 62223

Confederate Stamp Alliance Authentication Service
Richard L. Calhoun, 1749 W. Golf Rd.,
Suite 366, Mt. Prospect, IL 60056

Errors, Freaks, and Oddities Collectors Club
Jim McDevitt, 138 Lakemont Dr. East,
Kingsland, GA 31548-8921

International Society of Worldwide Stamp Collectors
2505 Second St.,
Caddo Mills, TX 75135

Junior Philatelists of America
Ellie Chapman, PO Box 850,
Boalsburg, PA 16827-0850

National Duck Stamp Collectors Society
PO Box 43, Harleysville, PA 19438

No-Value-Identified Collectors Club
Albert Sauvanet, Le Clos Royal B,
Boulevard des Pas Enchantes, 44230
St. Sebastien-sur-Loire, France

Plate Number Coil Collectors Club
Joann Lenz, 37211 Alper Drive,
Sterling Heights, MI 48312-2203

Precancel Stamp Society
1750 Skippack Pk. #1603,
Center Square, PA 19422

Royal Philatelic Society
41 Devonshire Place,
London, U.K. W1N 1PE

Royal Philatelic Society of Canada
PO Box 929, Station Q,
Toronto ON, CANADA M4T 2P1

United Postal Stationery Society
Joann Thomas, PO Box 48,
Redlands, CA 92373

US Philatelic Classics Society
W. Wilson Hulme II, PO Box 5368,
Naperville, IL 60567-5368

US Possessions Philatelic Society
Charles A. Richmond, PO Box 26724,
Columbus, OH 43226

Society for the New Republics of the Former USSR (Armenia, etc.)
Michael Padwee, 163 Joralemon St.,
PO Box 1520, Brooklyn, NY 11201-1520

American Belgian Philatelic Society
Kenneth L. Costilow,
621 Virginius Dr.,
Virginia Beach, VA 23452-4417

Belize Philatelic Study Circle
Charles R. Gambill, 730 Collingswood,
Corpus Christi, TX 78412

Bermuda Collectors Society
Thomas J. McMahon, 86 Nash Road,
Purdys, NY 10578

Brazil Philatelic Association
Kurt Ottenheimer,
462 West Walnut St.,
Long Beach, NY 11561

British Caribbean Philatelic Study Group
Gale J. Raymond, PO Box 35695,
Houston, TX 77235

British North America Philatelic Society
Jerome C. Jarnick, 108 Duncan Drive,
Troy, MI 48098

Burma Philatelic Study Circle
A. Meech, 7208 91st Ave.,
Edmonton, AB, CANADA T6B 0R8

Canal Zone Study Group
Richard H. Salz, 60 27th Ave.,
San Francisco, CA 94121

China Stamp Society
Paul H. Gault, 140 West 18th Ave.,
Columbus, OH 43210

COPAPHIL (Colombia & Panama)
PO Box 2245, El Cajon, CA 92021

Society of Costa Rica Collectors
Dr. Hector Mena, PO Box 14831,
Baton Rouge, LA 70808

Croatian Philatelic Society (Croatia and other Balkan areas)
Eck Spahich, 1512 Lancelot Rd., Borger, TX 79007

Cuban Philatelic Society of America
PO Box 450207, Miami, FL 33245-0207

Society for Czechoslovak Philately
Robert T. Cossaboom, PO Box 332, Scott AFB, IL 62225

Estonian Philatleic Soc.
Rudolf Hamar, 1912 Nugget Dr. Felton, CA 95018

Ethiopian Philatelic Society
Huguette Gagnon, PO Box 8110-45, Blaine, WA 98230

Falkland Islands Philatelic Study Group
James Driscoll, PO Box 172, South Dennis, NJ 08245

France & Colonies Philatelic Society
Walter Parshall, 103 Spruce St., Bloomfield, NJ 07003

Germany Philatelic Society
PO Box 779, Arnold, MD 21012-4779

GDR Study Group of German Philatelic Society
Ken Lawrence, PO Box 8040, State College, PA 16803-8040

Great Britain Collectors Club
Frank J. Koch, PO Box 309, Batavia, OH 45103-0309

Hawaiian Philatelic Society
Karen E. Awong, PO Box 10115, Honolulu, HI 96816-0115

Hellenic Philatelic Society of America (Greece and related areas)
Dr. Nicholas Asimakopulos, 541 Cedar Hill Ave., Wyckoff, NJ 07481

International Society of Guatemala Collectors
Mrs. Mae Vignola, 105 22nd Ave., San Francisco, CA 94121

Haiti Philatelic Society
Dwight Bishop, 2385 Cartegena Way, Oceanside, CA 92056

Hong Kong Stamp Society
Dr. An-Min Chung, 120 Deerfield Rd., Broomall, PA 19008

Hungary Philatelic Society
Thomas Phillips, PO Box 1162, Samp Mortar Sta., Fairfield, CT 06432

India Study Circle
John Warren, PO Box 70775, Washington, DC 20024

Society of Indochina Philatelists
Paul Blake, 1466 Hamilton Way, San Jose, CA 95125

Iran Philatelic Study Circle
David J. Armacost, PO Box 33381, Phoenix, AZ 85067

Eire Philatelic Association (Ireland)
Michael J. Conway, 74 Woodside Circle, Fairfield, CT 06430

Society of Israel Philatelists
Howard D. Chapman, 28650 Settlers Lane, Pepper Pike, OH 44124

Italy and Colonies Study Circle
David F. Emery, PO Box 86, Philipsburg, NJ 08865

International Society for Japanese Philately
Kenneth Kamholz, PO Box 1283, Haddonfield, NJ 08033

Korea Stamp Society
William A. Matthews, PO Box 15306, Columbus, OH 43215

Latin American Philatelic Society
Piet Steen, 197 Pembina Ave., Hinton, AB, CANADA T7V 2B2

Cuyahoga Latvian Philatelist Club
Arturs Rubenis, 1460 West Clifton Blvd., Lakewood, OH 44107-3309

Liberian Philatelic Society
William Thomas Lockard, PO Box 267, Wellston, OH 45692

Liechtenstudy USA (Liechtenstein)
Max Rheinberger, 100 Elizabeth St. #112, Duluth, MN 55803

Lithuanian Philatelic Society of New York
Vincent M. Alones, 217 McKee St., Floral Park, NY 11001-1314

Plebiscite-Memel-Saar Study Group
Clay Wallace, 158 Arapaho Circle, San Ramon, CA 94583

Mexico-Elmhurst Philatelic Society International
Juan Jose Vidrio, PO Box 435360, San Ysidro, CA 92143-5360

Nepal & Tibet Philatelic Study Group
Roger D. Skinner, 1020 Covington Rd., Los Altos, CA 94022

American Society of Netherlands Philately
Jan Enthoven, W6428 Riverview Drive, Onalaska, WI 54650

Nicaragua Study Group
Clyde R. Maxwell, Airport Plaza, 2041 Business Center Drive, Suite 101, Irvine, CA 92715

Society of Australasian Specialists / Oceania
Henry Bateman, PO Box 4862, Monroe, LA 71211

Orange Free State Study Circle
J. R. Stroud, 28 Oxford St., Burnham-on-sea, Somerset, U.K. TA8 1LQ

Pakistan Study Circle
Jeff Siddiqui, PO Box 7002, Lynnwood, WA 98046

International Philippine Philatelic Society
Eugene A. Garrett, 446 Stratford Ave., Elmhurst, IL 60126-4123

American Society of Polar Philatelists (Antarctic areas)
Richard Julian, 1153 Fairview Dr., York, PA 17403

Pitcairn Islands Study Group
Nelson A.L. Weller, 2940 Wesleyan Lane, Winston-Salem, NC 27106

Polonus Philatelic Society (Poland)
PO Box 458, Berwyn, IL 60402

International Society for Portuguese Philately
Michael Bryne, Adirondack Stamps, PO Box 13100, Mexico Beach, FL 32410

Rhodesian Study Circle
William R. Wallace, PO Box 16381, San Francisco, CA 94116

Romanian Chapter of Croatian Philatelic Society
Dan Demetriade, PO Box 10182, Detroit, MI 48210

Rossica Society of Russian Philately
Gary Combs, 8241 Chalet Ct., Millersville, MD 21108

Canadian Society of Russian Philately
Andrew Cronin, PO Box 5722, Station A, Toronto, ON, CANADA M5W 1P2

Ryukyu Philatelic Specialist Society
Carmine J. DiVincenzo, PO Box 381, Clayton, CA 94517-0381

St. Helena, Ascension & Tristan Society
Dr. Russell V. Skavaril, 222 East Torrance Road, Columbus, OH 43214-3834

St. Pierre & Miquelon Study Group
David Salovey, Box 464, New York NY 10014-0464

Associated Collectors of El Salvador

Honduras Collectors Club
Jeff Brasor, Box 173, Coconut Creek, FL 33097

Sarawak Specialists' Society
Art Bunce, PO Box 2516, Escondido, CA 92033

Arabian Philatelic Association
ARAMCO Box 1929, Dhahran 31311, SAUDI ARABIA

Scandinavian Collectors Club
Robert W. Lang, PO Box 125, Newark, DE 19715-0125

Philatelic Society for Greater Southern Africa
William C. Brooks VI, PO Box 2698, San Bernardino, CA 92406-2698

Slovakia Stamp Society
Jack Benchik, PO Box 555, Notre Dame, IN 46556

Spanish Philatelic Society
Robert H. Penn, RD #3, Box 3349-1, Bangor, PA 18013

American Helvetia Philatelic Society (Switzerland, Liechtenstein)
Richard T. Hall, PO Box 666, Manhattan Beach, CA 90267-0666

Tannu Tuva Collectors Society
Kenneth R. Simon, 513 Sixth Ave. So., Lake Worth, FL 33460-4507

Society for Thai Philately
H.R. Blakeney, PO Box 25644, Oklahoma City, OK 73125

Tonga/Tin Can Mail Study Circle
Tom Jackson, 121 Mullingar Ct. #1A, Schaumburg, IL 60193

Turkey and Ottoman Philatelic Society
Gary F. Paiste, 4249 Berritt St., Fairfax, VA 22030

Tuvalu & Kiribati Philatelic Society
Frank Caprio, PO Box 218071, Nashville, TN 37221

Ukrainian Philatelic & Numismatic Society
Bohdan O. Pauk, PO Box 11184, Chicago, IL 60611-0184

United Nations Philatelists
Alex Bereson, 18 Portola Drive, San Francisco CA 94131-1518

Vatican Philatelic Society
Louis Padavan, PO Box 127, Remsenburg, NY 11960

Yugoslavia Study Group
Michael Lenard, 1514 North 3rd Ave., Wausau, WI 54401

Expertizing Services

American Philatelic Expertizing Service
PO Box 8000, State College, PA 16803

Confederate Stamp Alliance Authorization Service
10833 Greencrest Dr., Baton Rouge, LA 70811

Philatelic Foundation
501 Fifth Ave., Rm. 1901, New York, NY 10017

Professional Stamp Experts
1 Datran Center, Suite 1149, 9100 South Dadeland Blvd., Miami, FL 33156

Information on Catalogue Values, Grade and Condition

Catalogue Value

The Scott Catalogue value is a retail value; that is, an amount you could expect to pay for a stamp in a grade of Very Fine with no faults. Any exceptions to the grade valued will be noted in the text. The general introduction on the following pages and the individual section introductions further explain the type of material that is valued. The value listed for any given stamp is a reference that reflects recent actual dealer selling prices for that item.

Dealer retail price lists, public auction results, published prices in advertising and individual solicitation of retail prices from dealers, collectors and specialty organizations have been used in establishing the values found in this catalogue. Scott Publishing Co. values stamps, but Scott is not a company engaged in the business of buying and selling stamps as a dealer.

Use this catalogue as a guide for buying and selling. The actual price you pay for a stamp may be higher or lower than the catalogue value because of many different factors, including the amount of personal service a dealer offers, or increased or decreased interest in the country or topic represented by a stamp or set. An item may occasionally be offered at a lower price as a "loss leader," or as part of a special sale. You also may obtain an item inexpensively at public auction because of little interest at that time or as part of a large lot.

Copies of stamps that are of a lesser grade than Very Fine, or those with condition problems, trade at lower prices than those given in this catalogue. Stamps of exceptional quality in both grade and condition often command higher prices than those listed.

Values for pre-1900 unused issues are for stamps with at least most of their original gum. On rarer stamps, it may be expected that the original gum will be somewhat more disturbed than it will be on more common issues. Post-1900 unused issues are assumed to have full original gum. From breakpoints in most countries' listings, stamps are valued as never hinged, due to the wide availability of stamps in that condition. These notations are prominently placed in the listings and in the country information preceding the listings. Some countries also feature listings with dual values for hinged and never-hinged stamps.

Grade

A stamp's grade and condition are crucial to its value. The accompanying illustrations show examples of Very Fine stamps from different time periods, along with examples of stamps in Fine to Very Fine and Extremely Fine grades as points of reference.

FINE stamps (illustrations not shown) have designs that are noticeably off center on two sides. Imperforate stamps may have small margins, and earlier issues may show the design touching one edge of the stamp design. For perforated stamps, perfs may barely clear the design on one side, and very early issues normally will have the perforations slightly cutting into the design. Used stamps may have heavier than usual cancellations.

FINE-VERY FINE stamps may be somewhat off center on one side, or slightly off center on two sides. Imperforate stamps will have two margins of at least normal size, and the design will not touch any edge. For perforated stamps, the perfs are well clear of the design, but are still noticeably off center. *However, early issues of a country may be printed in such a way that the design naturally is very close to the edges. In these cases, the perforations may cut into the design very slightly.* Used stamps will not have a cancellation that detracts from the design.

VERY FINE stamps may be slightly off center on one side, but the design will be well clear of the edge. The stamp will present a nice, balanced appearance. Imperforate stamps will have three normal-sized margins. *However, early issues of many countries may be printed in such a way that the perforations may touch the design on one or more sides. Where this is the case, a boxed note will be found defining the centering and margins of the stamps being valued.* Used stamps will have light or otherwise neat cancellations. This is the grade used to establish Scott Catalogue values.

EXTREMELY FINE stamps are close to being perfectly centered. Imperforate stamps will have even margins that are larger than normal. Even the earliest perforated issues will have perforations clear of the design on all sides.

Condition

Grade addresses only centering and (for used stamps) cancellation. *Condition* refers to factors other than grade that affect a stamp's desirability.

Factors that can increase the value of a stamp include exceptionally wide margins, particularly fresh color, the presence of selvage, and plate or die varieties. Unusual cancels on used stamps (particularly those of the 19th century) can greatly enhance their value as well.

Factors other than faults that decrease the value of a stamp include loss of original gum, regumming, a hinge remnant or foreign object adhering to the gum, natural inclusions, straight edges, and markings or notations applied by collectors or dealers.

Faults include missing pieces, tears, pin or other holes, surface scuffs, thin spots, creases, toning, short or pulled perforations, clipped perforations, oxidation or other forms of color changelings, soiling, stains, and such man-made changes as reperforations or the chemical removal or lightening of a cancellation.

Scott Publishing Co. recognizes that there is no formally enforced grading scheme for postage stamps, and that the final price you pay or obtain for a stamp will be determined by individual agreement at the time of transaction.

On the following two pages are illustrations of various stamps from countries appearing in Volume 2. These stamps are arranged by country, and they represent early or important issues that are often found in widely different grades in the marketplace. The editors believe the illustrations will prove useful in showing the margin size and centering that will be seen on the various issues.

In addition to the matters of margin size and centering, collectors are reminded that the very fine stamps valued in the Scott catalogues also will possess fresh color and intact perforations, and they will be free from defects.

The three grades shown for each stamp except Brazil No. 1 are computer manipulated using a single digitized master illustration.

Fine-Very Fine
SCOTT CATALOGUES VALUE STAMPS IN THIS GRADE
Very Fine
Extremely Fine
Fine-Very Fine
SCOTT CATALOGUES VALUE STAMPS IN THIS GRADE
Very Fine
Extremely Fine

Fine-Very Fine
SCOTT CATALOGUES VALUE STAMPS IN THIS GRADE
Very Fine
Extremely Fine
Fine-Very Fine
SCOTT CATALOGUES VALUE STAMPS IN THIS GRADE
Very Fine
Extremely Fine

Catalogue Listing Policy

It is the intent of Scott Publishing Co. to list all postage stamps of the world in the *Scott Standard Postage Stamp Catalogue.* The only strict criteria for listing is that stamps be decreed legal for postage by the issuing country. Whether the primary intent of issuing a given stamp or set was for sale to postal patrons or to stamp collectors is not part of our listing criteria. Scott's role is to provide basic comprehensive postage stamp information. It is up to each stamp collector to choose which items to include in a collection.

It is Scott's objective to seek reasons why a stamp should be listed, rather than why it should not. Nevertheless, there are certain types of items that will not be listed. These include the following:

1. Unissued items that are not officially distributed or released by the issuing postal authority. Even if such a stamp is "accidentally" distributed to the philatelic or even postal market, it remains unissued. If such items are officially issued at a later date by the country, they will be listed. Unissued items consist of those that have been printed and then held from sale for reasons such as change in government, errors found on stamps or something deemed objectionable about a stamp subject or design.

2. Stamps "issued" by non-existent postal entities or fantasy countries, such as Nagaland, Occusi-Ambeno, Staffa, Sedang, Torres Straits and others.

3. Semi-official or unofficial items not required for postage. Examples include items issued by private agencies for their own express services. When such items are required for delivery, or are valid as prepayment of postage, they are listed.

4. Local stamps issued for local use only. Postage stamps issued by governments specifically for "domestic" use, such as Haiti Scott 219-228, or the United States non-denominated stamps, are not considered to be locals, since they are valid for postage throughout the country of origin.

5. Items not valid for postal use. For example, a few countries have issued souvenir sheets that are not valid for postage. This area also includes a number of worldwide charity labels (some denominated) that do not pay postage.

6. Intentional varieties, such as imperforate stamps that look like their perforated counterparts and are issued in very small quantities. These are often controlled issues intended for speculation.

7. Items distributed by the issuing government only to a limited group, such as a stamp club, philatelic exhibition or a single stamp dealer, and later brought to market at inflated prices. These items normally will be included in a footnote.

The fact that a stamp has been used successfully as postage, even on international mail, is not in itself sufficient proof that it was legitimately issued. Numerous examples of so-called stamps from non-existent countries are known to have been used to post letters that have successfully passed through the international mail system.

There are certain items that are subject to interpretation. When a stamp falls outside our specifications, it may be listed along with a cautionary footnote.

A number of factors are considered in our approach to analyzing how a stamp is listed. The following list of factors is presented to share with you, the catalogue user, the complexity of the listing process.

Additional printings — "Additional printings" of a previously issued stamp may range from an item that is totally different to cases where it is impossible to differentiate from the original. At least a minor number (a small-letter suffix) is assigned if there is a distinct change in stamp shade, noticeably redrawn design, or a significantly different perforation measurement. A major number (numeral or numeral and capital-letter combination) is assigned if the editors feel the "additional printing" is sufficiently different from the original that it constitutes a different issue.

Commemoratives — Where practical, commemoratives with the same theme are placed in a set. For example, the U.S. Civil War Centenniel set of 1961-65 and the Constitution Bicentennial series of 1989-90 appear as sets. Countries such as Japan and Korea issue such material on a regular basis, with an announced, or at least predictable, number of stamps known in advance. Occasionally, however, stamp sets that were released over a period of years have been separated. Appropriately placed footnotes will guide you to each set's continuation.

Definitive sets — Blocks of numbers generally have been reserved for definitive sets, based on previous experience with any given country. If a few more stamps were issued in a set than originally expected, they often have been inserted into the original set with a capital-letter suffix, such as U.S. Scott 1059A. If it appears that many more stamps than the originally allotted block will be released before the set is completed, a new block of numbers will be reserved, with the original one being closed off. In some cases, such as the British Machin Head series or the U.S. Transportation and Great Americans series, several blocks of numbers exist. Appropriately placed footnotes will guide you to each set's continuation.

New country — Membership in the Universal Postal Union is not a consideration for listing status or order of placement within the catalogue. The index will tell you in what volume or page number the listings begin.

"No release date" items — The amount of information available for any given stamp issue varies greatly from country to country and even from time to time. Extremely comprehensive information about new stamps is available from some countries well before the stamps are released. By contrast some countries do not provide information about stamps or release dates. Most countries, however, fall between these extremes. A country may provide denominations or subjects of stamps from upcoming issues that are not issued as planned. Sometimes, philatelic agencies, those private firms hired to represent countries, add these later-issued items to sets well after the formal release date. This time period can range from weeks to years. If these items were officially released by the country, they will be added to the appropriate spot in the set. In many cases, the specific release date of a stamp or set of stamps may never be known.

Overprints — The color of an overprint is always noted if it is other than black. Where more than one color of ink has been used on overprints of a single set, the color used is noted. Early overprint and surcharge illustrations were altered to prevent their use by forgers.

Se-tenants — Connected stamps of differing features (se-tenants) will be listed in the format most commonly collected. This includes pairs, blocks or larger multiples. Se-tenant units are not always symmetrical. An example is Australia Scott 508, which is a block of seven stamps. If the stamps are primarily collected as a unit, the major number may be assigned to the multiple, with minors going to each component stamp. In cases where continuous-design or other unit se-tenants will receive significant postal use, each stamp is given a major Scott number listing. This includes issues from the United States, Canada, Germany and Great Britain, for example.

Understanding the Listings

On the opposite page is an enlarged "typical" listing from this catalogue. Below are detailed explanations of each of the highlighted parts of the listing.

1 Scott number — Scott catalogue numbers are used to identify specific items when buying, selling or trading stamps. Each listed postage stamp from every country has a unique Scott catalogue number. Therefore, Germany Scott 99, for example, can only refer to a single stamp. Although the Scott catalogue usually lists stamps in chronological order by date of issue, there are exceptions. When a country has issued a set of stamps over a period of time, those stamps within the set are kept together without regard to date of issue. This follows the normal collecting approach of keeping stamps in their natural sets.

When a country issues a set of stamps over a period of time, a group of consecutive catalogue numbers is reserved for the stamps in that set, as issued. If that group of numbers proves to be too few, capital-letter suffixes, such as "A" or "B," may be added to existing numbers to create enough catalogue numbers to cover all items in the set. A capital-letter suffix indicates a major Scott catalogue number listing. Scott uses a suffix letter only once. Therefore, a catalogue number listing with a capital-letter prefix will not also be found with the same letter (lower case) used as a minor-letter listing. If there is a Scott 16A in a set, for example, there will not also be a Scott 16a.

Suffix letters are not cumulative. A minor variety of Scott 16A would be Scott 16b, not Scott 16Ab. Any exceptions, such as Great Britain Scott 358cp, are clearly indicated.

There are times when a reserved block of Scott catalogue numbers is too large for a set, leaving some numbers unused. Such gaps in the numbering sequence also occur when the catalogue editors move an item's listing elsewhere or have removed it entirely from the catalogue. Scott does not attempt to account for every possible number, but rather attempts to assure that each stamp is assigned its own number.

Scott numbers designating regular postage normally are only numerals. Scott numbers for other types of stamps, such as air post, semi-postal, postal tax, postage due, occupation and others have a prefix consisting of one or more capital letters or a combination of numerals and capital letters.

2 Illustration number — Illustration or design-type numbers are used to identify each catalogue illustration. For most sets, the lowest face-value stamp is shown. It then serves as an example of the basic design approach for other stamps not illustrated. Where more than one stamp use the same illustration number, but have differences in design, the design paragraph or the description line clearly indicates the design on each stamp not illustrated. Where there are both vertical and horizontal designs in a set, a single illustration may be used, with the exceptions noted in the design paragraph or description line.

When an illustration is followed by a lower-case letter in parentheses, such as "A2(b)," the trailing letter indicates which overprint or surcharge illustration applies.

Illustrations normally are 75 percent of the original size of the stamp. An effort has been made to note all illustrations not illustrated at that percentage. Virtually all souvenir sheet illustrations are reduced even more. Overprints and surcharges are shown at 100 percent of their original size, unless otherwise noted. In some cases, the illustration will be placed above the set, between listings or omitted completely. Overprint and surcharge illustrations are not placed in this catalogue for purposes of expertizing stamps.

3 Paper color — The color of a stamp's paper is noted in italic type when the paper used is not white.

4 Listing styles — There are two principal types of catalogue listings: major and minor.

Major listings are in a larger type style than minor listings. The catalogue number is a numeral that can be found with or without a capital-letter suffix, and with or without a prefix.

Minor listings are in a smaller type style and have a small-letter suffix or (if the listing immediately follows that of the major number) may show only the letter. These listings identify a variety of the major item. Examples include perforation, color, watermark or printing method differences, multiples (some souvenir sheets, booklet panes and se-tenant combinations), and singles of multiples.

Examples of major number listings include 16, 28A, B97, C13A, 10N5, and 10N6A. Examples of minor numbers are 16a and C13b.

5 Basic information about a stamp or set — Introducing each stamp issue is a small section (usually a line listing) of basic information about a stamp or set. This section normally includes the date of issue, method of printing, perforation, watermark and, sometimes, some additional information of note. *Printing method, perforation and watermark apply to the following sets until a change is noted.* Stamps created by overprinting or surcharging previous issues are assumed to have the same perforation, watermark and printing method as the original. Dates of issue are as precise as Scott is able to confirm and often reflect the dates on first-day covers, rather than the actual date of release.

6 Denomination — This normally refers to the face value of the stamp; that is, the cost of the unused stamp at the post office at the time of issue. When a denomination is shown in parentheses, it does not appear on the stamp. This includes the non-denominated stamps of the United States, Brazil and Great Britain, for example.

7 Color or other description — This area provides information to solidify identification of a stamp. In many recent cases, a description of the stamp design appears in this space, rather than a listing of colors.

8 Year of issue — In stamp sets that have been released in a period that spans more than a year, the number shown in parentheses is the year that stamp first appeared. Stamps without a date appeared during the first year of the issue. Dates are not always given for minor varieties.

9 Value unused and Value used — The Scott catalogue values are based on stamps that are in a grade of Very Fine unless stated otherwise. Unused values refer to items that have not seen postal, revenue or any other duty for which they were intended. Pre-1900 unused stamps that were issued with gum must have at least most of their original gum. Later issues are assumed to have full original gum. From breakpoints specified in most countries' listings, stamps are valued as never hinged. Stamps issued without gum are noted. Modern issues with PVA or other synthetic adhesives may appear ungummed. Self-adhesive stamps are valued as appearing undisturbed on their original backing paper. For a more detailed explanation of these values, please see the "Catalogue Value," "Condition" and "Understanding Valuing Notations" elsewhere in this introduction.

In some cases, where used stamps are more valuable than unused stamps, the value is for an example with a contemporaneous cancel, rather than a modern cancel or a smudge or other unclear marking. For those stamps that were released for postal and fiscal purposes, the used value represents a postally used stamp. Stamps with revenue cancels generally sell for less.

10 Changes in basic set information — Bold type is used to show any changes in the basic data given for a set of stamps. This includes perforation differences from one stamp to the next or a different paper, printing method or watermark.

11 Total value of a set — The total value of sets of three or more stamps issued after 1900 are shown. The set line also notes the range of Scott numbers and total number of stamps included in the grouping. *Set value* is the term used to indicate the value of a stamp set when its combined total is less than the sum of the individual stamps. This happens when some of the stamps in a set have the minimum catalogue value.

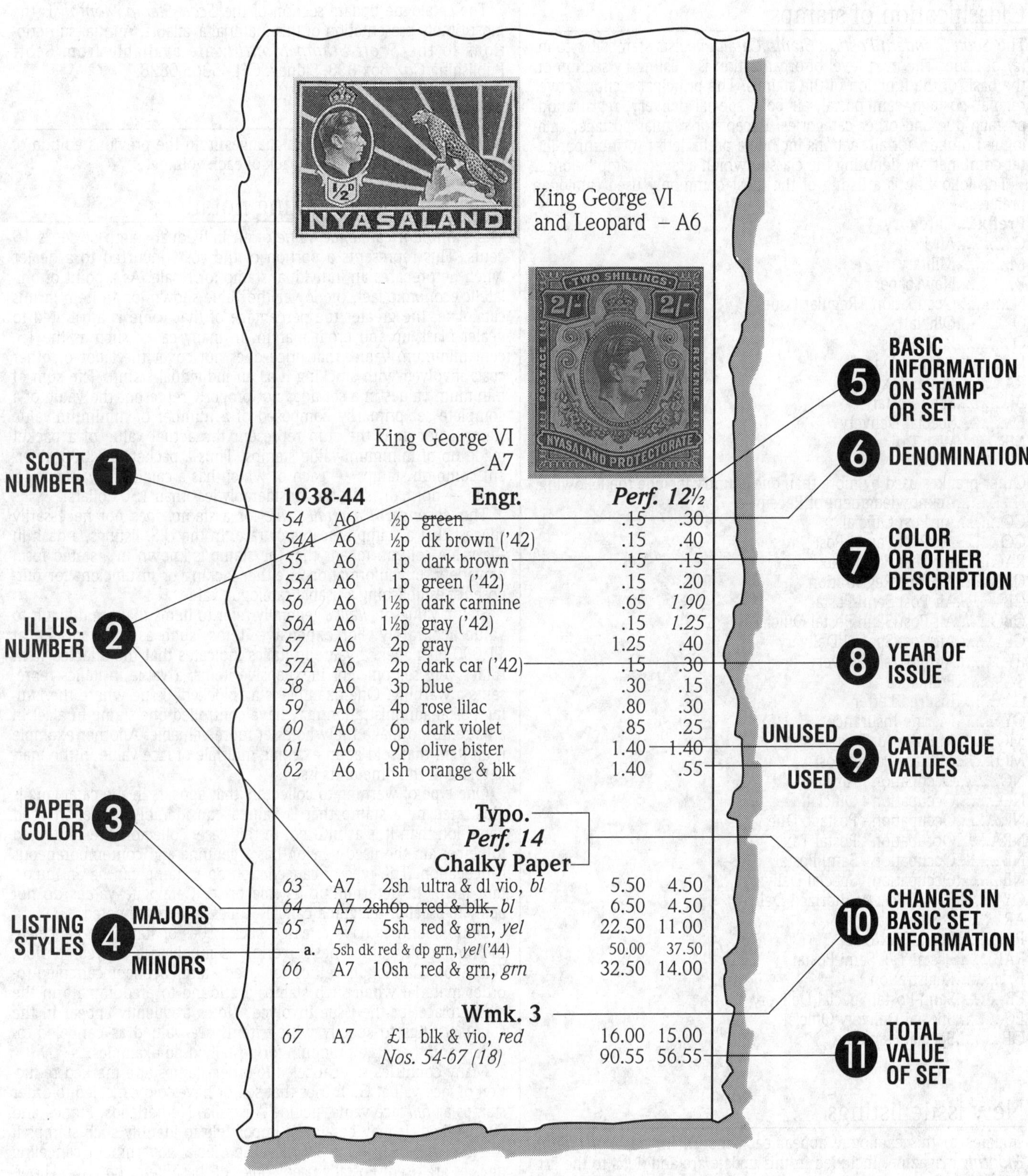
NYASALAND
1/2D
King George VI
and Leopard – A6
TWO SHILLINGS
2/-
2/-
POSTAGE
REVENUE
NYASALAND PROTECTORATE
King George VI
A7
1938-44 Engr. Perf. 12½
54 A6 ½p green .15 .30
54A A6 ½p dk brown ('42) .15 .40
55 A6 1p dark brown .15 .15
55A A6 1p green ('42) .15 .20
56 A6 1½p dark carmine .65 1.90
56A A6 1½p gray ('42) .15 1.25
57 A6 2p gray 1.25 .40
57A A6 2p dark car ('42) .15 .30
58 A6 3p blue .30 .15
59 A6 4p rose lilac .80 .30
60 A6 6p dark violet .85 .25
61 A6 9p olive bister 1.40 1.40
62 A6 1sh orange & blk 1.40 .55
Typo.
Perf. 14
Chalky Paper
63 A7 2sh ultra & dl vio, bl 5.50 4.50
64 A7 2sh6p red & blk, bl 6.50 4.50
65 A7 5sh red & grn, yel 22.50 11.00
a. 5sh dk red & dp grn, yel ('44) 50.00 37.50
66 A7 10sh red & grn, grn 32.50 14.00
Wmk. 3
67 A7 £1 blk & vio, red 16.00 15.00
Nos. 54-67 (18) 90.55 56.55
1 SCOTT NUMBER
2 ILLUS. NUMBER
3 PAPER COLOR
4 LISTING STYLES
MAJORS
MINORS
5 BASIC INFORMATION ON STAMP OR SET
6 DENOMINATION
7 COLOR OR OTHER DESCRIPTION
8 YEAR OF ISSUE
9 CATALOGUE VALUES
UNUSED
USED
10 CHANGES IN BASIC SET INFORMATION
11 TOTAL VALUE OF SET

Special Notices

Classification of stamps

The *Scott Standard Postage Stamp Catalogue* lists stamps by country of issue. The next level of organization is a listing by section on the basis of the function of the stamps. The principal sections cover regular postage, semi-postal, air post, special delivery, registration, postage due and other categories. Except for regular postage, catalogue numbers for all sections include a prefix letter (or number-letter combination) denoting the class to which a given stamp belongs.

The following is a listing of the most commonly used catalogue prefixes.

Prefix....Category
C ....Air Post
M...........Military
P............Newspaper
N ....Occupation - Regular Issues
O ....Official
Q ....Parcel Post
J.............Postage Due
RA ....Postal Tax
B............Semi-Postal
E............Special Delivery
MR ....War Tax

Other prefixes used by more than one country include the following:
H ....Acknowledgment of Receipt
CO.........Air Post Official
CQ.........Air Post Parcel Post
RAC ....Air Post Postal Tax
CF..........Air Post Registration
CB ....Air Post Semi-Postal
CBO.......Air Post Semi-Postal Official
CE ....Air Post Special Delivery
EY..........Authorized Delivery
S ....Franchise
G ....Insured Letter
GY ....Marine Insurance
MC ....Military Air Post
MQ........Military Parcel Post
NC.........Occupation - Air Post
NO.........Occupation - Official
NJ ....Occupation - Postage Due
NRA.......Occupation - Postal Tax
NB ....Occupation - Semi-Postal
NE ....Occupation - Special Delivery
QY ....Parcel Post Authorized Delivery
AR ....Postal-fiscal
RAJ ....Postal Tax Due
RAB ....Postal Tax Semi-Postal
F ....Registration
EB..........Semi-Postal Special Delivery
EO ....Special Delivery Official
QE ....Special Handling

New issue listings

Updates to this catalogue appear each month in the *Scott Stamp Monthly* magazine. Included in this update are additions to the listings of countries found in the *Scott Standard Postage Stamp Catalogue* and the *Specialized Catalogue of United States Stamps*, as well as corrections and updates to current editions of this catalogue.

From time to time there will be changes in the final listings of stamps from the *Scott Stamp Monthly* to the next edition of the catalogue. This occurs as more information about certain stamps or sets becomes available.

The catalogue update section of the *Scott Stamp Monthly* is the most timely presentation of this material available. Annual subscriptions to the *Scott Stamp Monthly* are available from Scott Publishing Co., Box 828, Sidney, OH 45365-0828.

Number changes

A listing of catalogue number changes from the previous edition of the catalogue appears at the back of each volume.

Understanding valuing notations

The *minimum catalogue value* of an individual stamp or set is 15 cents. This represents a portion of the costs incurred to a dealer when he prepares an individual stamp for resale. As a point of philatelic-economic fact, the lower the value shown for an item in this catalogue, the greater the percentage of that value is attributed to dealer mark up and profit margin. In many cases, such as the 15-cent minimum value, that price does not cover the labor or other costs involved with stocking it as an individual stamp. The sum of minimum values in a set does not properly represent the value of a complete set primarily composed of a number of minimum-value stamps, nor does the sum represent the actual value of a packet made up of minimum-value stamps. Thus a packet of 1,000 different common stamps — each of which has a catalogue value of 15 cents — normally sells for considerably less than 150 dollars!

The *absence of a retail value* for a stamp does not necessarily suggest that a stamp is scarce or rare. In the U.S. listings, a dash in the value column means that the stamp is known in a stated form or variety, but information is either lacking or insufficient for purposes of establishing a usable catalogue value.

Stamp values in *italics* generally refer to items that are difficult to value accurately. For expensive items, such as those priced at $1,000 or higher, a value in italics indicates that the affected item trades very seldom. For inexpensive items, a value in italics represents a warning. One example is a "blocked" issue where the issuing postal administration may have controlled one stamp in a set in an attempt to make the whole set more valuable. Another example is an item that sold at an extreme multiple of face value in the marketplace at the time of its issue.

One type of warning to collectors that appears in the catalogue is illustrated by a stamp that is valued considerably higher in used condition than it is as unused. In this case, collectors are cautioned to be certain the used version has a genuine and contemporaneous cancellation. The type of cancellation on a stamp can be an important factor in determining its sale price. Catalogue values do not apply to fiscal or telegraph cancels, unless otherwise noted.

Some countries have released back issues of stamps in canceled-to-order form, sometimes covering as much as a 10-year period. The Scott Catalogue values for used stamps reflect canceled-to-order material when such stamps are found to predominate in the marketplace for the issue involved. Notes frequently appear in the stamp listings to specify which items are valued as canceled-to-order, or if there is a premium for postally used examples.

Many countries sell canceled-to-order stamps at a marked reduction of face value. Countries that sell or have sold canceled-to-order stamps at *full* face value include Australia, Netherlands, France and Switzerland. It may be almost impossible to identify such stamps if the gum has been removed, because official government canceling devices are used. Postally used copies of these items on cover, however, are usually worth more than the canceled-to-order stamps with original gum.

Abbreviations

Scott Publishing Co. uses a consistent set of abbreviations throughout this catalogue to conserve space, while still providing necessary information.

COLOR ABBREVIATIONS

amb	amber	crim	crimson	ol	olive
anil	aniline	cr	cream	olvn	olivine
ap	apple	dk	dark	org	orange
aqua	aquamarine	dl	dull	pck	peacock
az	azure	dp	deep	pnksh	pinkish
bis	bister	db	drab	Prus	Prussian
bl	blue	emer	emerald	pur	purple
bld	blood	gldn	golden	redsh	reddish
blk	black	grysh	grayish	res	reseda
bril	brilliant	grn	green	ros	rosine
brn	brown	grnsh	greenish	ryl	royal
brnsh	brownish	hel	heliotrope	sal	salmon
brnz	bronze	hn	henna	saph	sapphire
brt	bright	ind	indigo	scar	scarlet
brnt	burnt	int	intense	sep	sepia
car	carmine	lav	lavender	sien	sienna
cer	cerise	lem	lemon	sil	silver
chlky	chalky	lil	lilac	sl	slate
cham	chamois	lt	light	stl	steel
chnt	chestnut	mag	magenta	turq	turquoise
choc	chocolate	man	manila	ultra	ultramarine
chr	chrome	mar	maroon	Ven	Venetian
cit	citron	mv	mauve	ver	vermilion
cl	claret	multi	multicolored	vio	violet
cob	cobalt	mlky	milky	yel	yellow
cop	copper	myr	myrtle	yelsh	yellowish

When no color is given for an overprint or surcharge, black is the color used. Abbreviations for colors used for overprints and surcharges include: "(B)" or "(Blk)," black; "(Bl)," blue; "(R)," red; and "(G)," green.

Additional abbreviations in this catalogue are shown below:

Adm. ....Administration
AFL ....American Federation of Labor
Anniv. ....Anniversary
APS ....American Philatelic Society
Assoc. ....Association
ASSR. ....Autonomous Soviet Socialist Republic
b. ....Born
BEP ....Bureau of Engraving and Printing
Bicent. ....Bicentennial
Bklt. ....Booklet
Brit. ....British
btwn. ....Between
Bur. ....Bureau
c. or ca. ....Circa
Cat. ....Catalogue
Cent. ....Centennial, century, centenary
CIO ....Congress of Industrial Organizations
Conf. ....Conference
Cong. ....Congress
Cpl. ....Corporal
CTO ....Canceled to order
d. ....Died
Dbl. ....Double
EKU ....Earliest known use
Engr. ....Engraved
Exhib. ....Exhibition
Expo. ....Exposition
Fed. ....Federation
GB ....Great Britain
Gen. ....General
GPO ....General post office
Horiz. ....Horizontal
Imperf. ....Imperforate
Impt. ....Imprint
Intl. ....International
Invtd. ....Inverted
L. ....Left
Lieut., lt. ....Lieutenant
Litho. ....Lithographed
LL ....Lower left
LR ....Lower right
mm ....Millimeter
Ms. ....Manuscript
Natl. ....National
No. ....Number
NY ....New York
NYC ....New York City
Ovpt. ....Overprint
Ovptd. ....Overprinted
P ....Plate number
Perf. ....Perforated, perforation
Phil. ....Philatelic
Photo. ....Photogravure
PO ....Post office
Pr. ....Pair
P.R. ....Puerto Rico
Prec. ....Precancel, precanceled
Pres. ....President
PTT ....Post, Telephone and Telegraph
Rio ....Rio de Janeiro
Sgt. ....Sergeant
Soc. ....Society
Souv. ....Souvenir
SSR ....Soviet Socialist Republic, see ASSR
St. ....Saint, street
Surch. ....Surcharge
Typo. ....Typographed
UL ....Upper left
Unwmkd. ....Unwatermarked
UPU ....Universal Postal Union
UR ....Upper Right
US ....United States
USPOD ....United States Post Office Department
USSR ....Union of Soviet Socialist Republics
Vert. ....Vertical
VP ....Vice president
Wmk. ....Watermark
Wmkd. ....Watermarked
WWI ....World War I
WWII ....World War II

Examination

Scott Publishing Co. will not comment upon the genuineness, grade or condition of stamps, because of the time and responsibility involved. Rather, there are several expertizing groups that undertake this work for both collectors and dealers. Neither will Scott Publishing Co. appraise or identify philatelic material. The company cannot take responsibility for unsolicited stamps or covers sent by individuals.

How to order from your dealer

When ordering stamps from a dealer, it is not necessary to write the full description of a stamp as listed in this catalogue. All you need is the name of the country, the Scott catalogue number and whether the desired item is unused or used. For example, "Japan Scott 422 unused" is sufficient to identify the unused stamp of Japan listed as "422 A206 5y brown."

Basic Stamp Information

A stamp collector's knowledge of the combined elements that make a given stamp issue unique determines his or her ability to identify stamps. These elements include paper, watermark, method of separation, printing, design and gum. On the following pages each of these important areas is briefly described.

Paper

Paper is an organic material composed of a compacted weave of cellulose fibers and generally formed into sheets. Paper used to print stamps may be manufactured in sheets, or it may have been part of a large roll (called a web) before being cut to size. The fibers most often used to create paper on which stamps are printed include bark, wood, straw and certain grasses. In many cases, linen or cotton rags have been added for greater strength and durability. Grinding, bleaching, cooking and rinsing these raw fibers reduces them to a slushy pulp, referred to by paper makers as "stuff." Sizing and, sometimes, coloring matter is added to the pulp to make different types of finished paper.

After the stuff is prepared, it is poured onto sieve-like frames that allow the water to run off, while retaining the matted pulp. As fibers fall onto the screen and are held by gravity, they form a natural weave that will later hold the paper together. If the screen has metal bits that are formed into letters or images attached, it leaves slightly thinned areas on the paper. These are called watermarks.

When the stuff is almost dry, it is passed under pressure through smooth or engraved rollers - dandy rolls - or placed between cloth in a press to be flattened and dried.

Stamp paper falls broadly into two types: wove and laid. The nature of the surface of the frame onto which the pulp is first deposited causes the differences in appearance between the two. If the surface is smooth and even, the paper will be of fairly uniform texture throughout. This is known as *wove paper.* Early papermaking machines poured the pulp onto a continuously circulating web of felt, but modern machines feed the pulp onto a cloth-like screen made of closely interwoven fine wires. This paper, when held to a light, will show little dots or points very close together. The proper name for this is "wire wove," but the type is still considered wove. Any U.S. or British stamp printed after 1880 will serve as an example of wire wove paper.

Closely spaced parallel wires, with cross wires at wider intervals, make up the frames used for what is known as *laid paper.* A greater thickness of the pulp will settle between the wires. The paper, when held to a light, will show alternate light and dark lines. The spacing and the thickness of the lines may vary, but on any one sheet of paper they are all alike. See Russia Scott 31-38 for examples of laid paper.

Batonne, from the French word meaning "a staff," is a term used if the lines in the paper are spaced quite far apart, like the printed ruling on a writing tablet. Batonne paper may be either wove or laid. If laid, fine laid lines can be seen between the batons. The laid lines, which are a form of watermark, may be geometrical figures such as squares, diamonds, rectangles or wavy lines.

Quadrille is the term used when the lines in the paper form little squares. *Oblong quadrille* is the term used when rectangles, rather than squares, are formed. See Mexico-Guadalajara Scott 35-37 for examples of oblong quadrille paper.

Paper also is classified as thick or thin, hard or soft, and by color if dye is added during manufacture. Such colors may include yellowish, greenish, bluish and reddish.

Brief explanations of other types of paper used for printing stamps, as well as examples, follow.

Pelure — Pelure paper is a very thin, hard and often brittle paper that is sometimes bluish or grayish in appearance. See Serbia Scott 169-170.

Native — This is a term applied to handmade papers used to produce some of the early stamps of the Indian states. Stamps printed on native paper may be expected to display various natural inclusions that are normal and do not negatively affect value. Japanese paper, originally made of mulberry fibers and rice flour, is part of this group. See Japan Scott 1-18.

Manila — This type of paper is often used to make stamped envelopes and wrappers. It is a coarse-textured stock, usually smooth on one side and rough on the other. A variety of colors of manila paper exist, but the most common range is yellowish-brown.

Silk — Introduced by the British in 1847 as a safeguard against counterfeiting, silk paper contains bits of colored silk thread scattered throughout. The density of these fibers varies greatly and can include as few as one fiber per stamp or hundreds. U.S. revenue Scott R152 is a good example of an easy-to-identify silk paper stamp.

Silk-thread paper has uninterrupted threads of colored silk arranged so that one or more threads run through the stamp or postal stationery. See Great Britain Scott 5-6 and Switzerland Scott 14-19.

Granite — Filled with minute cloth or colored paper fibers of various colors and lengths, granite paper should not be confused with either type of silk paper. Austria Scott 172-175 and a number of Swiss stamps are examples of granite paper.

Chalky — A chalk-like substance coats the surface of chalky paper to discourage the cleaning and reuse of canceled stamps, as well as to provide a smoother, more acceptable printing surface. Because the designs of stamps printed on chalky paper are imprinted on what is often a water-soluble coating, any attempt to remove a cancellation will destroy the stamp. *Do not soak these stamps in any fluid.* To remove a stamp printed on chalky paper from an envelope, wet the paper from underneath the stamp until the gum dissolves enough to release the stamp from the paper. See St. Kitts-Nevis Scott 89-90 for examples of stamps printed on this type of chalky paper.

India — Another name for this paper, originally introduced from China about 1750, is "China Paper." It is a thin, opaque paper often used for plate and die proofs by many countries.

Double — In philately, the term double paper has two distinct meanings. The first is a two-ply paper, usually a combination of a thick and a thin sheet, joined during manufacture. This type was used experimentally as a means to discourage the reuse of stamps.

The design is printed on the thin paper. Any attempt to remove a cancellation would destroy the design. U.S. Scott 158 and other Banknote-era stamps exist on this form of double paper.

The second type of double paper occurs on a rotary press, when the end of one paper roll, or web, is affixed to the next roll to save time feeding the paper through the press. Stamp designs are printed over the joined paper and, if overlooked by inspectors, may get into post office stocks.

Goldbeater's Skin — This type of paper was used for the 1866 issue of Prussia, and was a tough, translucent paper. The design was printed in reverse on the back of the stamp, and the gum applied over the printing. It is impossible to remove stamps printed on this type of paper from the paper to which they are affixed without destroying the design.

Ribbed — Ribbed paper has an uneven, corrugated surface made by passing the paper through ridged rollers. This type exists on some copies of U.S. Scott 156-165.

Various other substances, or substrates, have been used for stamp manufacture, including wood, aluminum, copper, silver and gold foil, plastic, and silk and cotton fabrics.

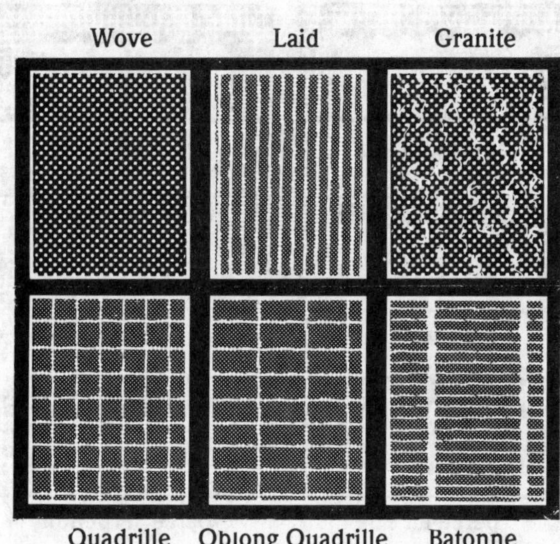

Watermarks

Watermarks are an integral part of some papers. They are formed in the process of paper manufacture. Watermarks consist of small designs, formed of wire or cut from metal and soldered to the surface of the mold or, sometimes, on the dandy roll. The designs may be in the form of crowns, stars, anchors, letters or other characters or symbols. These pieces of metal - known in the paper-making industry as "bits" - impress a design into the paper. The design sometimes may be seen by holding the stamp to the light. Some are more easily seen with a watermark detector. This important tool is a small black tray into which a stamp is placed face down and dampened with a fast-evaporating watermark detection fluid that brings up the watermark image in the form of dark lines against a lighter background. These dark lines are the thinner areas of the paper known as the watermark. Some watermarks are extremely difficult to locate, due to either a faint impression, watermark location or the color of the stamp. There also are electric watermark detectors that come with plastic filter disks of various colors. The disks neutralize the color of the stamp, permitting the watermark to be seen more easily.

Multiple watermarks of Crown Agents and Burma

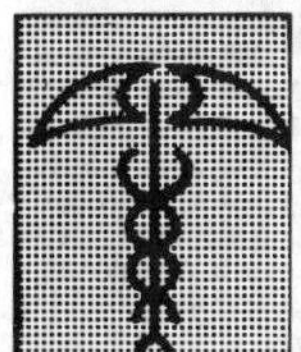

Watermarks of Uruguay, Vatican City and Jamaica

WARNING: Some inks used in the photogravure process dissolve in watermark fluids (Please see the section on Soluble Printing Inks). Also, see "chalky paper."

Watermarks may be found normal, reversed, inverted, reversed and inverted, sideways or diagonal, as seen from the back of the stamp. The relationship of watermark to stamp design depends on the position of the printing plates or how paper is fed through the press. On machine-made paper, watermarks normally are read from right to left. The design is repeated closely throughout the sheet in a "multiple-watermark design." In a "sheet watermark," the design appears only once on the sheet, but extends over many stamps. Individual stamps may carry only a small fraction or none of the watermark.

"Marginal watermarks" occur in the margins of sheets or panes of stamps. They occur on the outside border of paper (ostensibly outside the area where stamps are to be printed). A large row of letters may spell the name of the country or the manufacturer of the paper, or a border of lines may appear. Careless press feeding may cause parts of these letters and/or lines to show on stamps of the outer row of a pane.

Soluble Printing Inks

WARNING: Most stamp colors are permanent; that is, they are not seriously affected by short-term exposure to light or water. Many colors, especially of modern inks, fade from excessive exposure to light. There are stamps printed with inks that dissolve easily in water or in fluids used to detect watermarks. Use of these inks was intentional to prevent the removal of cancellations. Water affects all aniline inks, those on so-called safety paper and some photogravure printings - all such inks are known as *fugitive colors. Removal from paper of such stamps requires care and alternatives to traditional soaking.*

Separation

"Separation" is the general term used to describe methods used to separate stamps. The three standard forms currently in use are perforating, rouletting and die-cutting. These methods are done during the stamp production process, after printing. Sometimes these methods are done on-press or sometimes as a separate step. The earliest issues, such as the 1840 Penny Black of Great Britain (Scott 1), did not have any means provided for separation. It was expected the stamps would be cut apart with scissors or folded and torn. These are examples of imperforate stamps. Many stamps were first issued in imperforate formats and were later issued with perforations. Therefore, care must be observed in buying single imperforate stamps to be certain they were issued imperforate and are not perforated copies that have been altered by having the perforations trimmed away. Stamps issued imperforate usually are valued as singles. However, imperforate varieties of normally perforated stamps should be collected in pairs or larger pieces as indisputable evidence of their imperforate character.

PERFORATION

The chief style of separation of stamps, and the one that is in almost universal use today, is perforating. By this process, paper between the stamps is cut away in a line of holes, usually round, leaving little bridges of paper between the stamps to hold them together. Some types of perforation, such as hyphen-hole perfs, can be confused with roulettes, but a close visual inspection reveals that paper has been removed. The little perforation bridges, which project from the stamp when it is torn from the pane, are called the teeth of the perforation.

As the size of the perforation is sometimes the only way to differentiate between two otherwise identical stamps, it is necessary to be able to accurately measure and describe them. This is done with a perforation gauge, usually a ruler-like device that has dots or graduated lines to show how many perforations may be counted in the space of two centimeters. Two centimeters is the space universally adopted in which to measure perforations.

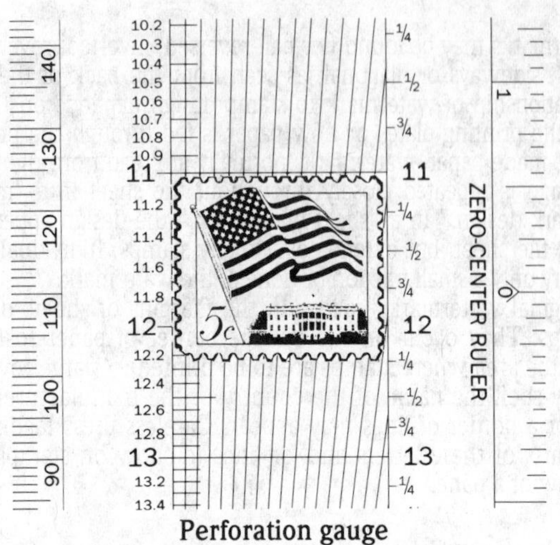

Perforation gauge

To measure a stamp, run it along the gauge until the dots on it fit exactly into the perforations of the stamp. If you are using a graduated-line perforation gauge, simply slide the stamp along the surface until the lines on the gauge perfectly project from the center of the bridges or holes. The number to the side of the line of dots or lines that fit the stamp's perforation is the measurement. For example, an "11" means that 11 perforations fit between two centimeters. The description of the stamp therefore is "perf. 11." If the gauge of the perforations on the top and bottom of a stamp differs from that on the sides, the result is what is known as *compound perforations.* In measuring compound perforations, the gauge at top and bottom is always given first, then the sides. Thus, a stamp that measures 11 at top and bottom and 10 1/2 at the sides is "perf. 11 x 10 1/2." See U.S. Scott 632-642 for examples of compound perforations.

Stamps also are known with perforations different on three or all four sides. Descriptions of such items are clockwise, beginning with the top of the stamp.

A perforation with small holes and teeth close together is a "fine perforation." One with large holes and teeth far apart is a "coarse perforation." Holes that are jagged, rather than clean-cut, are "rough perforations." *Blind perforations* are the slight impressions left by the perforating pins if they fail to puncture the paper. Multiples of stamps showing blind perforations may command a slight premium over normally perforated stamps.

The term *syncopated perfs* describes intentional irregularities in the perforations. The earliest form was used by the Netherlands from 1925-33, where holes were omitted to create distinctive patterns. Beginning in 1992, Great Britain has used an oval perforation to help prevent counterfeiting. Several other countries have started using the oval perfs.

A new type of perforation, still primarily used for postal stationery, is known as microperfs. Microperfs are tiny perforations (in some cases hundreds of holes per two centimeters) that allows items to be intentionally separated very easily, while not accidentally breaking apart as easily as standard perforations. These are not currently measured or differentiated by size, as are standard perforations.

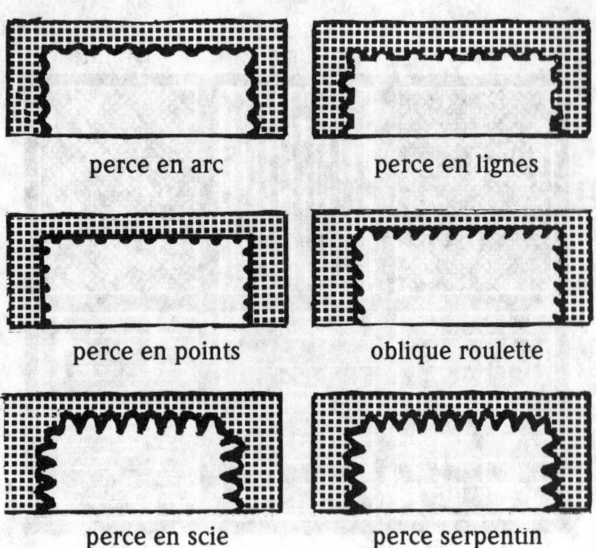

ROULETTING

In rouletting, the stamp paper is cut partly or wholly through, with no paper removed. In perforating, some paper is removed. Rouletting derives its name from the French roulette, a spur-like wheel. As the wheel is rolled over the paper, each point makes a small cut. The number of cuts made in a two-centimeter space determines the gauge of the roulette, just as the number of perforations in two centimeters determines the gauge of the perforation.

The shape and arrangement of the teeth on the wheels varies. Various roulette types generally carry French names:

Perce en lignes - rouletted in lines. The paper receives short, straight cuts in lines. This is the most common type of rouletting. See Mexico Scott 500.

Perce en points - pin-rouletted. This differs from a small perforation because no paper is removed, although round, equidistant holes are pricked through the paper. See Mexico Scott 242-256.

Perce en arc and *perce en scie* - pierced in an arc or saw-toothed designs, forming half circles or small triangles. See Hanover (German States) Scott 25-29.

Perce en serpentin - serpentine roulettes. The cuts form a serpentine or wavy line. See Brunswick (German States) Scott 13-18.

Once again, no paper is removed by these processes, leaving the stamps easily separated, but closely attached.

DIE-CUTTING

The third major form of stamp separation is die-cutting. This is a method where a die in the pattern of separation is created that later cuts the stamp paper in a stroke motion. Although some standard stamps bear die-cut perforations, this process is primarily used for self-adhesive postage stamps. Die-cutting can appear in straight lines, such as U.S. Scott 2522, shapes, such as U.S. Scott 1551, or imitating the appearance of perforations, such as New Zealand Scott 935A and 935B.

Printing Processes

ENGRAVING (Intaglio, Line-engraving, Etching)

Master die - The initial operation in the process of line engraving is making the master die. The die is a small, flat block of softened steel upon which the stamp design is recess engraved in reverse.

Master die

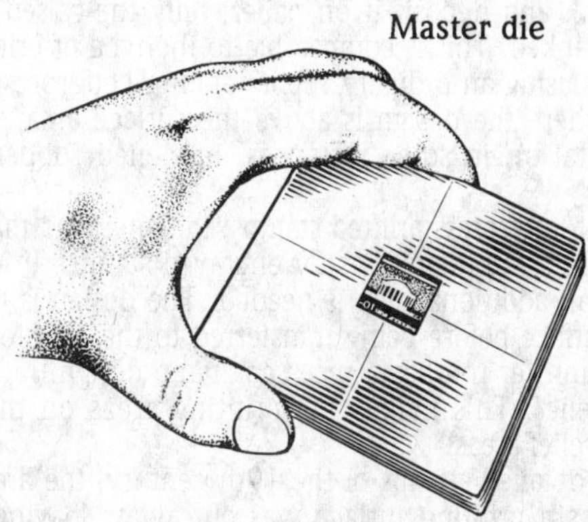

Photographic reduction of the original art is made to the appropriate size. It then serves as a tracing guide for the initial outline of the design. The engraver lightly traces the design on the steel with his graver, then slowly works the design until it is completed. At various points during the engraving process, the engraver hand-inks the die and makes an impression to check his progress. These are known as progressive die proofs. After completion of the engraving, the die is hardened to withstand the stress and pressures of later transfer operations.

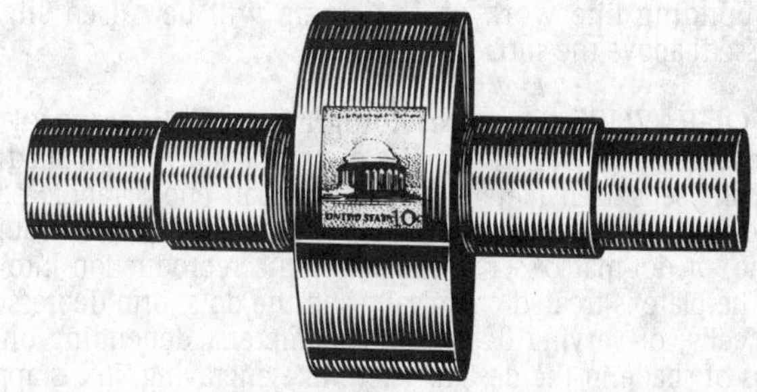

Transfer roll

Transfer roll — Next is production of the transfer roll that, as the name implies, is the medium used to transfer the subject from the master die to the printing plate. A blank roll of soft steel, mounted on a mandrel, is placed under the bearers of the transfer press to allow it to roll freely on its axis. The hardened die is placed on the bed of the press and the face of the transfer roll is applied to the die, under pressure. The bed or the roll is then rocked back and forth under increasing pressure, until the soft steel of the roll is forced into every engraved line of the die. The resulting impression on the roll is known as a "relief" or a "relief transfer." The engraved image is now positive in appearance and stands out from the steel. After the required number of reliefs are "rocked in," the soft steel transfer roll is hardened.

Different flaws may occur during the relief process. A defective relief may occur during the rocking in process because of a minute piece of foreign material lodging on the die, or some other cause. Imperfections in the steel of the transfer roll may result in a breaking away of parts of the design. This is known as a relief break, which will show up on finished stamps as small, unprinted areas. If a damaged relief remains in use, it will transfer a repeating defect to the plate. Deliberate alterations of reliefs sometimes occur. "Altered reliefs" designate these changed conditions.

Plate — The final step in pre-printing production is the making of the printing plate. A flat piece of soft steel replaces the die on the bed of the transfer press. One of the reliefs on the transfer roll is positioned over this soft steel. Position, or layout, dots determine the correct position on the plate. The dots have been lightly marked on the plate in advance. After the correct position of the relief is determined, the design is rocked in by following the same method used in making the transfer roll. The difference is that this time the image is being transferred from the transfer roll, rather than to it. Once the design is entered on the plate, it appears in reverse and is recessed. There are as many transfers entered on the plate as there are subjects printed on the sheet of stamps. It is during this process that double and shifted transfers occur, as well as re-entries. These are the result of improperly entered images that have not been properly burnished out prior to rocking in a new image.

Modern siderography processes, such as those used by the U.S. Bureau of Engraving and Printing, involve an automated form of rocking designs in on preformed cylindrical printing sleeves. The same process also allows for easier removal and re-entry of worn images right on the sleeve.

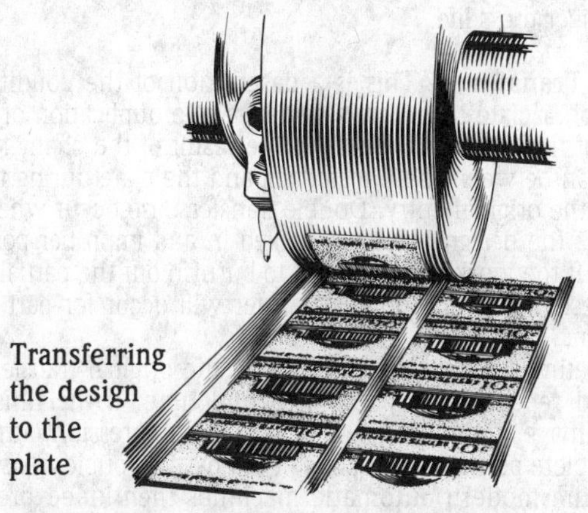

Transferring the design to the plate

Following the entering of the required transfers on the plate, the position dots, layout dots and lines, scratches and other markings generally are burnished out. Added at this time by the siderographer are any required *guide lines, plate numbers* or other *marginal markings.* The plate is then hand-inked and a proof impression is taken. This is known as a plate proof. If the impression is approved, the plate is machined for fitting onto the press, is hardened and sent to the plate vault ready for use.

On press, the plate is inked and the surface is automatically wiped clean, leaving ink only in the recessed lines. Paper is then forced under pressure into the engraved recessed lines, thereby receiving the ink. Thus, the ink lines on engraved stamps are slightly raised, and slight depressions (debossing) occur on the back of the stamp. Prior to the advent of modern high-speed presses and more advanced ink formulations, paper had to be dampened before receiving the ink. This sometimes led to uneven shrinkage by the time the stamps were perforated, resulting in improperly perforated stamps, or misperfs. Newer presses use drier paper, thus both *wet* and *dry printings* exist on some stamps.

Rotary Press — Until 1914, only flat plates were used to print engraved stamps. Rotary press printing was introduced in 1914, and slowly spread. Some countries still use flat-plate printing.

After approval of the plate proof, older *rotary press plates* require additional machining. They are curved to fit the press cylinder. "Gripper slots" are cut into the back of each plate to receive the "grippers," which hold the plate securely on the press. The plate is then hardened. Stamps printed from these bent rotary press plates are longer or wider than the same stamps printed from flat-plate presses. The stretching of the plate during the curving process is what causes this distortion.

Re-entry — To execute a re-entry on a flat plate, the transfer roll is re-applied to the plate, often at some time after its first use on the press. Worn-out designs can be resharpened by carefully burnishing out the original image and re-entering it from the transfer roll. If the original impression has not been sufficiently removed and the transfer roll is not precisely in line with the remaining impression, the resulting double transfer will make the re-entry obvious. If the registration is true, a re-entry may be difficult or impossible to distinguish. Sometimes a stamp printed from a successful re-entry is identified by having a much sharper and clearer impression than its neighbors. With the advent of rotary presses, post-press re-entries were not possible. After a plate was curved for the rotary press, it was impossible to make a re-entry. This is because the plate had already been bent once (with the design distorted).

However, with the introduction of the previously mentioned modern-style siderography machines, entries are made to the preformed cylindrical printing sleeve. Such sleeves are dechromed and softened. This allows individual images to be burnished out and re-entered on the curved sleeve. The sleeve is then rechromed, resulting in longer press life.

Double Transfer — This is a description of the condition of a transfer on a plate that shows evidence of a duplication of all, or a portion of the design. It usually is the result of the changing of the registration between the transfer roll and the plate during the rocking in of the original entry. Double transfers also occur when only a portion of the design has been rocked in and improper positioning is noted. If the worker elected not to burnish out the partial or completed design, a strong double transfer will occur for part or all of the design.

It sometimes is necessary to remove the original transfer from a plate and repeat the process a second time. If the finished reworked image shows traces of the original impression, attributable to incomplete burnishing, the result is a partial double transfer.

With the modern automatic machines mentioned previously, double transfers are all but impossible to create. Those partially doubled images on stamps printed from such sleeves are more than likely re-entries, rather than true double transfers.

Re-engraved — Alterations to a stamp design are sometimes necessary after some stamps have been printed. In some cases, either the original die or the actual printing plate may have its "temper" drawn (softened), and the design will be re-cut. The resulting impressions from such a re-engraved die or plate may differ slightly from the original issue, and are known as "re-engraved." If the alteration was made to the master die, all future printings will be consistently different from the original. If alterations were made to the printing plate, each altered stamp on the plate will be slightly different from each other, allowing specialists to reconstruct a complete printing plate.

Dropped Transfers — If an impression from the transfer roll has not been properly placed, a dropped transfer may occur. The final stamp image will appear obviously out of line with its neighbors.

Short Transfer — Sometimes a transfer roll is not rocked its entire length when entering a transfer onto a plate. As a result, the finished transfer on the plate fails to show the complete design, and the finished stamp will have an incomplete design printed. This is known as a "short transfer." U.S. Scott No. 8 is a good example of a short transfer.

TYPOGRAPHY (Letterpress, Surface Printing, Flexography, Dry Offset, High Etch)

Although the word "Typography" is obsolete as a term describing a printing method, it was the accepted term throughout the first century of postage stamps. Therefore, appropriate Scott listings in this catalogue refer to typographed stamps. The current term for this form of printing, however, is "letterpress."

As it relates to the production of postage stamps, letterpress printing is the reverse of engraving. Rather than having recessed areas trap the ink and deposit it on paper, only the raised areas of the design are inked. This is comparable to the type of printing seen by inking and using an ordinary rubber stamp. Letterpress includes all printing where the design is above the surface area, whether it is wood, metal or, in some instances, hardened rubber or polymer plastic.

For most letterpress-printed stamps, the engraved master is made in much the same manner as for engraved stamps. In this instance, however, an additional step is needed. The design is transferred to another surface before being transferred to the transfer roll. In this way, the transfer roll has a recessed stamp design, rather than one done in relief. This makes the printing areas on the final plate raised, or relief areas.

For less-detailed stamps of the 19th century, the area on the die not used as a printing surface was cut away, leaving the surface area raised. The original die was then reproduced by stereotyping or electrotyping. The resulting electrotypes were assembled in the required number and format of the desired sheet of stamps. The plate used in printing the stamps was an electroplate of these assembled electrotypes.

Once the final letterpress plates are created, ink is applied to the raised surface and the pressure of the press transfers the ink impression to the paper. In contrast to engraving, the fine lines of letterpress are impressed on the surface of the stamp, leaving a debossed surface. When viewed from the back (as on a typewritten page), the corresponding line work on the stamp will be raised slightly (embossed) above the surface.

PHOTOGRAVURE (Gravure, Rotogravure, Heliogravure)

In this process, the basic principles of photography are applied to a chemically sensitized metal plate, rather than photographic paper. The design is transferred photographically to the plate through a halftone, or dot-matrix screen, breaking the reproduction into tiny dots. The plate is treated chemically and the dots form depressions, called cells, of varying depths and diameters, depending on the degrees of shade in the design. Then, like engraving, ink is applied to the plate and the surface is wiped clean. This leaves ink in the tiny cells that is lifted out and deposited on the paper when it is pressed against the plate.

Gravure is most often used for multicolored stamps, generally using the three primary colors (red, yellow and blue) and black. By varying the dot matrix pattern and density of these colors, virtually any color can be reproduced. A typical full-color gravure stamp will be created from four printing cylinders (one for each color). The original multicolored image will have been photographically separated into its component colors.

For examples of the first photogravure stamps printed (1914), see Bavaria Scott 94-114.

LITHOGRAPHY (Offset Lithography, Stone Lithography, Dilitho, Planography, Collotype)

The principle that oil and water do not mix is the basis for lithography. The stamp design is drawn by hand or transferred from engraving to the surface of a lithographic stone or metal plate in a greasy (oily) substance. This oily substance holds the ink, which will later be transferred to the paper. The stone (or plate) is wet with an acid fluid, causing it to repel the printing ink in all areas not covered by the greasy substance.

Transfer paper is used to transfer the design from the original stone or plate. A series of duplicate transfers are grouped and, in turn, transferred to the final printing plate.

Photolithography — The application of photographic processes to lithography. This process allows greater flexibility of design, related to use of halftone screens combined with line work. Unlike photogravure or engraving, this process can allow large, solid areas to be printed.

Offset — A refinement of the lithographic process. A rubber-covered blanket cylinder takes the impression from the inked lithographic plate. From the "blanket" the impression is *offset* or transferred to the paper. Greater flexibility and speed are the principal reasons offset printing has largely displaced lithography. The term "lithography" covers both processes, and results are almost identical.

EMBOSSED (Relief) Printing

Embossing, not considered one of the four main printing types, is a method in which the design first is sunk into the metal of the die. Printing is done against a yielding platen, such as leather or linoleum. The platen is forced into the depression of the die, thus forming the design on the paper in relief. This process is often used for metallic inks.

Embossing may be done without color (see Sardinia Scott 4-6); with color printed around the embossed area (see Great Britain Scott 5 and most U.S. envelopes); and with color in exact registration with the embossed subject (see Canada Scott 656-657).

COMBINATION PRINTINGS

Sometimes two or even three printing methods are combined in producing stamps. In these cases, such as Austria Scott 933, the stamp's dual printing technique can be determined by studying the individual characteristics of each printing type (intaglio and offset). A few stamps, such as Singapore Scott 684-684A, combine as many as three of the four major printing types (offset, intaglio and letterpress). When this is done it often indicates the incorporation of security devices against counterfeiting.

INK COLORS

Inks or colored papers used in stamp printing often are of mineral origin, although there are numerous examples of organic-based pigments. As a general rule, organic-based pigments are far more subject to varieties and change than those of mineral-based origin.

The appearance of any given color on a stamp may be affected by many aspects, including printing variations, light, color of paper, aging and chemical alterations.

Numerous printing variations may be observed. Heavier pressure or inking will cause a more intense color, while slight interruptions in the ink feed or lighter impressions will cause a lighter appearance. Stamps printed in the same color by water-based and solvent-based inks can differ significantly in appearance. This affects several stamps in the U.S. Prominent Americans series. Hand-mixed ink formulas (primarily from the 19th century) produced under different conditions (humidity and temperature) account for notable color variations in early printings of the same stamp (see U.S. Scott 248-250, 279B, for example). Different sources of pigment can also result in significant differences in color.

Light exposure and aging are closely related in the way they affect stamp color. Both eventually break down the ink and fade colors, so that a carefully kept stamp may differ significantly in color from an identical copy that has been exposed to light. If stamps are exposed to light either intentionally or accidentally, their colors can be faded or completely changed in some cases.

Papers of different quality and consistency used for the same stamp printing may affect color appearance. Most pelure papers, for example, show a richer color when compared with wove or laid papers. See Russia Scott 181a, for an example of this effect.

The very nature of the printing processes can cause a variety of differences in shades or hues of the same stamp. Some of these shades are scarcer than others, and are of particular interest to the advanced collector.

Luminescence

All forms of tagged stamps fall under the general category of luminescence. Within this broad category is fluorescence, dealing with forms of tagging visible under longwave ultraviolet light, and phosphorescence, which deals with tagging visible only under shortwave light. Phosphorescence leaves an afterglow and fluorescence does not. These treated stamps show up in a range of different colors when exposed to UV light. The differing wavelengths of the light activates the tagging material, making it glow in various colors that usually serve different mail processing purposes.

Intentional tagging is a post-World War II phenomenon, brought about by the increased literacy rate and rapidly growing mail volume. It was one of several answers to the problem of the need for more automated mail processes. Early tagged stamps served the purpose of triggering machines to separate different types of mail. A natural outgrowth was to also use the signal to trigger machines that faced all envelopes the same way and canceled them.

Tagged stamps come many different ways and in different forms. Some tagged stamps have luminescent shapes or images imprinted on them as a form of security device. Others have blocks (United States), stripes, frames (South Africa and Canada), overall coatings (United States), bars (Great Britain and Canada) and many other types. Some types of tagging are even mixed in with the pigmented printing ink (Australia Scott 366, Netherlands Scott 478 and U.S. Scott 1359 and 2443). Each form of tagging has a different purpose, some to give different machines different types of signals, and others as adaptive forms of technological growth.

The means of applying taggant to stamps differs as much as the intended purposes for the stamps. The most common form of tagging is a coating applied to the surface of the printed stamp. Since the taggant ink is frequently invisible except under UV light, it does not interfere with the appearance of the stamp. Another common application is the use of phosphored papers. In this case the paper itself either has a coating of taggant applied before the stamp is printed or has taggant applied during the papermaking process, incorporating it into the fibers. This is currently in use in the United States. A similar form is the application of a fluorescent coating either to the finished paper or during the papermaking process. This type of tagging has been extensively used by Australia and Germany.

Many countries now use tagging in various forms to either expedite mail handling or to serve as a printing security device against counterfeiting. Following the introduction of tagged stamps for public use in 1959 by Great Britain, other countries have steadily joined the parade. Among those are Germany (1961); Canada and Denmark (1962); United States, Australia, France and Switzerland (1963); Belgium and Japan (1966); Sweden and Norway (1967); Italy (1968); and Russia (1969). Since then, many other countries have begun using forms of tagging, including Brazil, China, Czechoslovakia, Hong Kong, Guatemala, Indonesia, Israel, Lithuania, Luxembourg, Netherlands, Penrhyn Islands, Portugal, St. Vincent, Singapore, South Africa, Spain and Sweden to name a few.

In some cases, including United States, Canada, Great Britain and Switzerland, stamps were released both with and without tagging. Many of these were released during each country's experimental period. Tagged and untagged versions are listed for the aforementioned countries and are noted in some other countries' listings. For at least a few stamps, the experimentally tagged version is worth far more than its untagged counterpart, such as the 1963 experimental tagged version of France Scott 1024.

In some cases luminescent varieties of stamps were inadvertently created. Several Russian stamps, for example, sport highly fluorescent ink that was not intended as a form of tagging. Older stamps, such as early U.S. postage dues, can be positively identified by the use of UV light, since the organic ink used has become slightly fluorescent over time. Other stamps, such as Austria Scott 70a-82a (varnish bars) and Obock Scott 46-64 (printed quadrille lines), have become fluorescent over time.

Various fluorescent substances have been added to paper to make it appear brighter. These optical brightners, as they are known, greatly affect the appearance of the stamp under UV light. The brightest of these is known as Hi-Brite paper. These paper varieties are beyond the scope of the Scott Catalogue.

Shortwave UV light also is used extensively in expertizing, since each form of paper has its own fluorescent characteristics that are impossible to perfectly match. It is therefore a simple matter to detect filled thins, added perforation teeth and other alterations that involve the addition of paper. UV light also is used to examine stamps that have had cancels chemically removed and for other purposes as well.

Gum

The gum on the back of a stamp may be shiny, dull, smooth, rough, dark, white, colored or tinted. Most stamp gumming adhesives use gum arabic or dextrine as a base. Certain polymers such as polyvinyl alcohol (PVA) have been used extensively since World War II.

The *Scott Standard Postage Stamp Catalogue* does not list items by types of gum. The *Scott Specialized Catalogue of United States Stamps* does differentiate among some types of gum for certain issues.

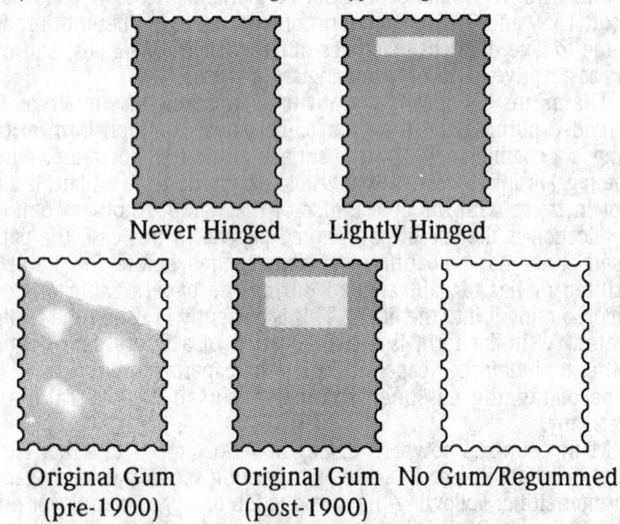

For purposes of determining the condition of an unused stamp, Scott Publishing Co. presents the following definitions (with accompanying illustrations): **Never Hinged (NH)** - Full original gum with no hinge mark or disturbance. The presence of an expertizer's mark does not disqualify a stamp from this designation; **Lightly Hinged (LH)** - Full original gum with a light disturbance of the gum from the removal of a peelable hinge; **Original Gum (OG)** - Pre-1900 stamps should have at least most of their original gum. On rarer stamps, it may be expected that the original gum will be somewhat more disturbed than it will be on more common issues. Post-1900 stamps should have full original gum. Original gum will show some disturbance caused by previous hinge, which may be present or entirely removed. **No Gum (NG) or Regummed (RE)** - A stamp with no gum. A regummed stamp is considered the same as a stamp with none of its original gum for purposes of grading.

Reprints of stamps may have gum differing from the original issues. In addition, some countries have used different gum formulas for different seasons. These adhesives have different properties that may become more apparent over time.

Many stamps have been issued without gum, and the catalogue will note this fact. See United States Scott PR33-PR56. Sometimes, gum may have been removed to preserve the stamp. Germany Scott B68, for example, has a highly acidic gum that eventually destroys the stamps. This item is valued in the catalogue with gum removed.

Reprints and Reissues

These are impressions of stamps (usually obsolete) made from the original plates or stones. If they are valid for postage and reproduce obsolete issues (such as U.S. Scott 102-111), the stamps are *reissues.* If they are from current issues, they are designated as *second, third,* etc., *printing.* If designated for a particular purpose, they are called *special printings.*

When special printings are not valid for postage, but are made from original dies and plates by authorized persons, they are *official reprints. Private reprints* are made from the original plates and dies by private hands. An example of a private reprint is that of the 1871-1932 reprints made from the original die of the 1845 New Haven, Conn., postmaster's provisional. *Official reproductions* or imitations are made from new dies and plates by government authorization. Scott will list those reissues that are valid for postage if they differ significantly from the original printing.

The U.S. government made special printings of its first postage stamps in 1875. Produced were official imitations of the first two stamps (listed as Scott 3-4), reprints of the demonetized pre-1861 issues (Scott 40-47) and reissues of the 1861 stamps, the 1869 stamps and the then-current 1875 denominations. Even though the official imitations and the reprints were not valid for postage, Scott lists all of these U.S. special printings.

Most reprints or reissues differ slightly from the original stamp in some characteristic, such as gum, paper, perforation, color or watermark. Sometimes the details are followed so meticulously that only a student of that specific stamp is able to distinguish the reprint or reissue from the original.

Remainders and Canceled to Order

Some countries sell their stock of old stamps when a new issue replaces them. To avoid postal use, the *remainders* usually are canceled with a punch hole, a heavy line or bar, or a more-or-less regular-looking cancellation. The most famous merchant of remainders was Nicholas F. Seebeck. In the 1880s and 1890s, he arranged printing contracts between the Hamilton Bank Note Co., of which he was a director, and several Central and South American countries. The contracts provided that the plates and all remainders of the yearly issues became the property of Hamilton. Seebeck saw to it that ample stock remained. The "Seebecks," both remainders and reprints, were standard packet fillers for decades.

Some countries also issue stamps *canceled-to-order (CTO),* either in sheets with original gum or stuck onto pieces of paper or envelopes and canceled. Such CTO items generally are worth less than postally used stamps. In cases where the CTO material is far more prevalent in the marketplace than postally used examples, the catalogue value relates to the CTO examples, with postally used examples noted as premium items. Most CTOs can be detected by the presence of gum. However, as the CTO practice goes back at least to 1885, the gum inevitably has been soaked off some stamps so they could pass as postally used. The normally applied postmarks usually differ slightly from standard postmarks, and specialists are able to tell the difference. When applied individually to envelopes by philatelically minded persons, CTO material is known as *favor canceled* and generally sells at large discounts.

Cinderellas and Facsimiles

Cinderella is a catch-all term used by stamp collectors to describe phantoms, fantasies, bogus items, municipal issues, exhibition seals, local revenues, transportation stamps, labels, poster stamps and many other types of items. Some cinderella collectors include in their collections local postage issues, telegraph stamps, essays and proofs, forgeries and counterfeits.

A *fantasy* is an adhesive created for a nonexistent stamp-issuing authority. Fantasy items range from imaginary countries (Occusi-Ambeno, Kingdom of Sedang, Principality of Trinidad or Torres Straits), to non-existent locals (Winans City Post), or nonexistent transportation lines (McRobish & Co.'s Acapulco-San Francisco Line).

On the other hand, if the entity exists and could have issued stamps (but did not) or was known to have issued other stamps, the items are considered *bogus* stamps. These would include the Mormon postage stamps of Utah, S. Allan Taylor's Guatemala and Paraguay inventions, the propaganda issues for the South Moluccas and the adhesives of the Page & Keyes local post of Boston.

Phantoms is another term for both fantasy and bogus issues.

Facsimiles are copies or imitations made to represent original stamps, but which do not pretend to be originals. A catalogue illustration is such a facsimile. Illustrations from the Moens catalogue of the last century were occasionally colored and passed off as stamps. Since the beginning of stamp collecting, facsimiles have been made for collectors as space fillers or for reference. They often carry the word "facsimile," "falsch" (German), "sanko" or "mozo" (Japanese), or "faux" (French) overprinted on the face or stamped on the back. Unfortunately, over the years a number of these items have had fake cancels applied over the facsimile notation and have been passed off as genuine.

Forgeries and Counterfeits

Forgeries and counterfeits have been with philately virtually from the beginning of stamp production. Over time, the terminology for the two has been used interchangeably. Although both forgeries and counterfeits are reproductions of stamps, the purposes behind their creation differ considerably.

Among specialists there is an increasing movement to more specifically define such items. Although there is no universally accepted terminology, we feel the following definitions most closely mirror the items and their purposes as they are currently defined.

Forgeries (also often referred to as *Counterfeits*) are reproductions of genuine stamps that have been created to defraud collectors. Such spurious items first appeared on the market around 1860, and most old-time collections contain one or more. Many are crude and easily spotted, but some can deceive experts.

An important supplier of these early philatelic forgeries was the Hamburg printer Gebruder Spiro. Many others with reputations in this craft included S. Allan Taylor, George Hussey, James Chute, George Forune, Benjamin & Sarpy, Julius Goldner, E. Oneglia and L.H. Mercier. Among the noted 20th-century forgers were Francois Fournier, Jean Sperati and the prolific Raoul DeThuin.

Forgeries may be complete replications, or they may be genuine stamps altered to resemble a scarcer (and more valuable) type. Most forgeries, particularly those of rare stamps, are worth only a small fraction of the value of a genuine example, but a few types, created by some of the most notable forgers, such as Sperati, can be worth as much or more than the genuine. Fraudulently produced copies are known of most classic rarities and many medium-priced stamps.

In addition to rare stamps, large numbers of common 19th- and early 20th-century stamps were forged to supply stamps to the early packet trade. Many can still be easily found. Few new philatelic forgeries have appeared in recent decades. Successful imitation of well-engraved work is virtually impossible. It has proven far easier to produce a fake by altering a genuine stamp than to duplicate a stamp completely.

Counterfeit (also often referred to as *Postal Counterfeit* or *Postal Forgery*) is the term generally applied to reproductions of stamps that have been created to defraud the government of revenue. Such items usually are created at the time a stamp is current and, in some cases, are hard to detect. Because most counterfeits are seized when the perpetrator is captured, postal counterfeits, particularly used on cover, are usually worth much more than a genuine example to specialists. The first postal counterfeit was of Spain's 4-cuarto carmine of 1854 (the real one is Scott 25). Apparently, the counterfeiters were not satisfied with their first version, which is now very scarce, and they soon created an engraved counterfeit, which is common. Postal counterfeits quickly followed in Austria, Naples, Sardinia and the Roman States. They have since been created in many other countries as well, including the United States.

An infamous counterfeit to defraud the government is the 1-shilling Great Britain "Stock Exchange" forgery of 1872, used on telegraph forms at the exchange that year. The stamp escaped detection until a stamp dealer noticed it in 1898.

Fakes

Fakes are genuine stamps altered in some way to make them more desirable. One student of this part of stamp collecting has estimated that by the 1950s more than 30,000 varieties of fakes were known. That number has grown greatly since then. The widespread existence of fakes makes it important for stamp collectors to study their philatelic holdings and use relevant literature. Likewise, collectors should buy from reputable dealers who guarantee their stamps and make full and prompt refunds should a purchased item be declared faked or altered by some mutually agreed-upon authority. Because fakes always have some genuine characteristics, it is not always possible to obtain unanimous agreement among experts regarding specific items. These students may change their opinions as philatelic knowledge increases. More than 80 percent of all fakes on the philatelic market today are regummed, reperforated (or perforated for the first time), or bear forged overprints, surcharges or cancellations.

Stamps can be chemically treated to alter or eliminate colors. For example, a pale rose stamp can be re-colored to resemble a blue shade of high market value. In other cases, treated stamps can be made to resemble missing color varieties. Designs may be changed by painting, or a stroke or a dot added or bleached out to turn an ordinary variety into a seemingly scarcer stamp. Part of a stamp can be bleached and reprinted in a different version, achieving an inverted center or frame. Margins can be added or repairs done so deceptively that the stamps move from the "repaired" into the "fake" category.

Fakers have not left the backs of the stamps untouched either. They may create false watermarks, add fake grills or press out genuine grills. A thin India paper proof may be glued onto a thicker backing to create the appearance an issued stamp, or a proof printed on cardboard may be shaved down and perforated to resemble a stamp. Silk threads are impressed into paper and stamps have been split so that a rare paper variety is added to an otherwise inexpensive stamp. The most common treatment to the back of a stamp, however, is regumming.

Some in the business of faking stamps have openly advertised fool-proof application of "original gum" to stamps that lack it, although most publications now ban such ads from their pages. It is believed that very few early stamps have survived without being hinged. The large number of never-hinged examples of such earlier material offered for sale thus suggests the widespread extent of regumming activity. Regumming also may be used to hide repairs or thin spots. Dipping the stamp into watermark fluid, or examining it under longwave ultraviolet light often will reveal these flaws.

Fakers also tamper with separations. Ingenious ways to add margins are known. Perforated wide-margin stamps may be falsely represented as imperforate when trimmed. Reperforating is commonly done to create scarce coil or perforation varieties, and to eliminate the naturally occurring straight-edge stamps found in sheet margin positions of many earlier issues. Custom has made straight-edged stamps less desirable. Fakers have obliged by perforating straight-edged stamps so that many are now uncommon, if not rare.

Another fertile field for the faker is that of overprints, surcharges and cancellations. The forging of rare surcharges or overprints began in the 1880s or 1890s. These forgeries are sometimes difficult to detect, but experts have identified almost all. Occasionally, overprints or cancellations are removed to create non-overprinted stamps or seemingly unused items. This is most commonly done by removing a manuscript cancel to make a stamp resemble an unused example. "SPECIMEN" overprints may be removed by scraping and repainting to create non-overprinted varieties. Fakers use inexpensive revenues or pen-canceled stamps to generate unused stamps for further faking by adding other markings. The quartz lamp or UV lamp and a high-powered magnifying glass help to easily detect removed cancellations.

The bigger problem, however, is the addition of overprints, surcharges or cancellations - many with such precision that they are very difficult to ascertain. Plating of the stamps or the overprint can be an important method of detection.

Fake postmarks may range from many spurious fancy cancellations to a host of markings applied to transatlantic covers, to adding normally appearing postmarks to definitives of some countries with stamps that are valued far higher used than unused. With the increased popularity of cover collecting, and the widespread interest in postal history, a fertile new field for fakers has come about. Some have tried to create entire covers. Others specialize in adding stamps, tied by fake cancellations, to genuine stampless covers, or replacing less expensive or damaged stamps with more valuable ones. Detailed study of postal rates in effect at the time a cover in question was mailed, including the analysis of each handstamp used during the period, ink analysis and similar techniques, usually will unmask the fraud.

Restoration and Repairs

Scott Publishing Co. bases its catalogue values on stamps that are free of defects and otherwise meet the standards set forth earlier in this introduction. Most stamp collectors desire to have the finest copy of an item possible. Even within given grading categories there are variances. This leads to a controversial practice that is not defined in any universal manner: stamp *restoration.*

There are broad differences of opinion about what is permissible when it comes to restoration. Carefully applying a soft eraser to a stamp or cover to remove light soiling is one form of restoration, as is washing a stamp in mild soap and water to clean it. These are fairly accepted forms of restoration. More severe forms of restoration include pressing out creases or removing stains caused by tape. To what degree each of these is acceptable is dependent upon the individual situation. Further along the spectrum is the freshening of a stamp's color by removing oxide build-up or the effects of wax paper left next to stamps shipped to the tropics.

At some point in this spectrum the concept of *repair* replaces that of restoration. Repairs include filling thin spots, mending tears by reweaving or adding a missing perforation tooth. Regumming stamps may have been acceptable as a restoration or repair technique many decades ago, but today it is considered a form of fakery.

Restored stamps may or may not sell at a discount, and it is possible that the value of individual restored items may be enhanced over that of their pre-restoration state. Specific situations dictate the resultant value of such an item. Repaired stamps sell at substantial discounts from the value of sound stamps.

Terminology

Booklets — Many countries have issued stamps in small booklets for the convenience of users. This idea continues to become increasingly popular in many countries. Booklets have been issued in many sizes and forms, often with advertising on the covers, the panes of stamps or on the interleaving.

The panes used in booklets may be printed from special plates or made from regular sheets. All panes from booklets issued by the United States and many from those of other countries contain stamps that are straight edged on the sides, but perforated between. Others are distinguished by orientation of watermark or other identifying features. Any stamp-like unit in the pane, either printed or blank, that is not a postage stamp is considered to be a *label* in the catalogue listings.

Scott lists and values booklet panes only. Complete booklets are listed and valued in only a few cases, such as Grenada Scott 1055 and some forms of British prestige booklets. Individual booklet panes are listed only when they are not fashioned from existing sheet stamps and, therefore, are identifiable from their sheet stamp counterparts.

Panes usually do not have a used value assigned to them because there is little market activity for used booklet panes, even though many exist used and there is some demand for them.

Cancellations — The marks or obliterations put on stamps by postal authorities to show that they have performed service and to prevent their reuse are known as cancellations. If the marking is made with a pen, it is considered a "pen cancel." When the location of the post office appears in the marking, it is a "town cancellation." A "postmark" is technically any postal marking, but in practice the term generally is applied to a town cancellation with a date. When calling attention to a cause or celebration, the marking is known as a "slogan cancellation." Many other types and styles of cancellations exist, such as duplex, numerals, targets, fancy and others. See also "precancels," below.

Coil Stamps — These are stamps that are issued in rolls for use in dispensers, affixing and vending machines. Those coils of the United States, Canada, Sweden and some other countries are perforated horizontally or vertically only, with the outer edges imperforate. Coil stamps of some countries, such as Great Britain and Germany, are perforated on all four sides and may in some cases be distinguished from their sheet stamp counterparts by watermarks, counting numbers on the reverse or other means.

Covers — Entire envelopes, with or without adhesive postage stamps, that have passed through the mail and bear postal or other markings of philatelic interest are known as covers. Before the introduction of envelopes in about 1840, people folded letters and wrote the address on the outside. Some people covered their letters with an extra sheet of paper on the outside for the address, producing the term "cover." Used airletter sheets, stamped envelopes and other items of postal stationery also are considered covers.

Errors — Stamps that have some major, consistent, unintentional deviation from the normal are considered errors. Errors include, but are not limited to, missing or wrong colors, wrong paper, wrong watermarks, inverted centers or frames on multicolor printing, inverted or missing surcharges or overprints, double impressions, missing perforations and others. Factually wrong or misspelled information, if it appears on all examples of a stamp, are not considered errors in the true sense of the word. They are errors of design. Inconsistent or randomly appearing items, such as misperfs or color shifts, are classified as freaks.

Overprints and Surcharges — Overprinting involves applying wording or design elements over an already existing stamp. Overprints can be used to alter the place of use (such as "Canal Zone" on U.S. stamps), to adapt them for a special purpose ("Porto" on Denmark's 1913-20 regular issues for use as postage due stamps, Scott J1-J7) or to commemorate a special occasion (United States Scott 647-648).

A *surcharge* is a form of overprint that changes or restates the face value of a stamp or piece of postal stationery.

Surcharges and overprints may be handstamped, typeset or, occasionally, lithographed or engraved. A few hand-written overprints and surcharges are known.

Precancels — Stamps that are canceled before they are placed in the mail are known as precancels. Precanceling usually is done to expedite the handling of large mailings and generally allow the affected mail pieces to skip certain phases of mail handling.

In the United States, precancellations generally identified the point of origin; that is, the city and state. This information appeared across the face of the stamp, usually centered between parallel lines. More recently, bureau precancels retained the parallel lines, but the city and state designations were dropped. Recent coils have a service inscription that is present on the original printing plate. These show the mail service paid for by the stamp. Since these stamps are not intended to receive further cancellations when used as intended, they are considered precancels. Such items often do not have parallel lines as part of the precancellation.

In France, the abbreviation *Affranchts* in a semicircle together with the word *Postes* is the general form of precancel in use. Belgian precancellations usually appear in a box in which the name of the city appears. Netherlands precancels have the name of the city enclosed between concentric circles, sometimes called a "lifesaver." Precancellations of other countries usually follow these patterns, but may be any arrangement of bars, boxes and city names.

Precancels are listed in the Scott catalogues only if the precancel changes the denomination (Belgium Scott 477-478); if the precanceled stamp is different from the non-precanceled version (such as untagged U.S. precancels); or if the stamp exists only precanceled (France Scott 1096-1099, U.S. Scott 2265).

Proofs and Essays — Proofs are impressions taken from an approved die, plate or stone in which the design and color are the same as the stamp issued to the public. Trial color proofs are impressions taken from approved dies, plates or stones in colors that vary from the final version. An essay is the impression of a design that differs in some way from the issued stamp. "Progressive die proofs" generally are considered to be essays.

Provisionals — These are stamps that are issued on short notice and intended for temporary use pending the arrival of regular issues. They usually are issued to meet such contingencies as changes in government or currency, shortage of necessary postage values or military occupation.

During the 1840s, postmasters in certain American cities issued stamps that were valid only at specific post offices. In 1861, postmasters of the Confederate States also issued stamps with limited validity. Both of these examples are known as "postmaster's provisionals."

Se-tenant — This term refers to an unsevered pair, strip or block of stamps that differ in design, denomination or overprint.

Unless the se-tenant item has a continuous design (see U.S. Scott 1451a, 1694a) the stamps do not have to be in the same order as shown in the catalogue (see U.S. Scott 2158a).

Specimens — The Universal Postal Union required member nations to send samples of all stamps they released into service to the International Bureau in Switzerland. Member nations of the UPU received these specimens as samples of what stamps were valid for postage. Many are overprinted, handstamped or initial-perforated "Specimen," "Canceled" or "Muestra." Some are marked with bars across the denominations (China-Taiwan), punched holes (Czechoslovakia) or back inscriptions (Mongolia).

Stamps distributed to government officials or for publicity purposes, and stamps submitted by private security printers for official approval, also may receive such defacements.

The previously described defacement markings prevent postal use, and all such items generally are known as "specimens."

Tete Beche — This term describes a pair of stamps in which one is upside down in relation to the other. Some of these are the result of intentional sheet arrangements, such as Morocco Scott B10-B11. Others occurred when one or more electrotypes accidentally were placed upside down on the plate, such as Colombia Scott 57a. Separation of the tete-beche stamps, of course, destroys the tete beche variety.

Currency Conversion

Country	Dollar	Pound	S Franc	Guilder	Yen	Lira	HK Dollar	D-Mark	Fr Franc	Cdn Dollar	Aust Dollar
Australia	1.3251	2.0321	1.0972	0.8016	0.0124	0.0008	0.1714	0.8976	0.2611	0.9656	....
Canada	1.3723	2.1044	1.1363	0.8302	0.0129	0.0009	0.1775	0.9296	0.2704	....	1.0356
France	5.0758	7.7838	4.2029	3.0707	0.0475	0.0032	0.6565	3.4382	....	3.6988	3.8305
Germany	1.4763	2.2639	1.2224	0.8931	0.0138	0.0009	0.1910	....	0.2909	1.0758	1.1141
Hong Kong	7.7313	11.8560	6.4017	4.6771	0.0724	0.0049	....	5.2369	1.5232	5.6338	5.8345
Italy	1569.25	2406.46	1229.37	949.33	14.6975	....	202.97	1062.96	309.16	1143.52	1184.25
Japan	106.77	163.73	88.4077	64.5917	....	0.0680	13.8101	72.3227	21.0351	77.8037	80.5751
Netherlands	1.6531	2.5349	1.3687	....	0.0155	0.0011	0.2138	1.1197	0.3257	1.2045	1.2475
Switzerland	1.2077	1.8520	....	0.7306	0.0113	0.0008	0.1562	0.8181	0.2379	0.8801	0.9114
U.K.	0.6521	....	0.5400	0.3945	0.0061	0.0004	0.0843	0.4417	0.1285	0.4752	0.4921
U.S.	....	1.5335	0.8280	0.6050	0.0094	0.0006	0.1293	0.6774	0.1970	0.7287	0.7547

Country	Currency	U.S. $ Equiv.
Afghanistan	afghani	.00021
Albania	lek	.01
Algeria	dinar	.0191
Andorra (French)	franc	.1970
Andorra (Spanish)	peseta	.008
Angola	kwanza	.000176
Argentina	peso	1.00
Aruba	guilder	.5586
Austria	schilling	.0963
Belgium	franc	.0329
Benin	Community of French Africa (CFA) franc	.0019
Bhutan	ngultrum	.027
Bolivia	boliviano	.20
Brazil	real	1.02
Bulgaria	lev	.014
Burkina Faso	CFA franc	.0019
Burundi	franc	.0039
Cameroun	CFA franc	.0019
Cape Verde	escudo	.012
Central African Republic	CFA franc	.0019
Chad	CFA franc	.0019
Chile	peso	.0024
China (Taiwan)	dollar	.036
China (People's Republic)	yuan	.1203
Colombia	peso	.001
Comoro Islands	CFA franc	.0019
Congo	CFA franc	.0019
Costa Rica	colon	.005
Czech Republic	koruna	.036

Source: ***Wall Street Journal*** *Feb. 12, 1996. Figures reflect values as of Feb. 9, 1996.*

Colonies, Former Colonies, Offices, Territories Controlled by Parent States

Belgium
Belgian Congo
Ruanda-Urundi

Denmark
Danish West Indies
Faroe Islands
Greenland
Iceland

Finland
Aland Islands

France
COLONIES PAST AND PRESENT, CONTROLLED TERRITORIES
Afars & Issas, Territory of
Alaouites
Alexandretta
Algeria
Alsace & Lorraine
Ajouan
Annam & Tonkin
Benin
Cambodia (Khmer)
Cameroun
Castellorizo
Chad
Cilicia
Cochin China
Comoro Islands
Dahomey
Diego Suarez
Djibouti (Somali Coast)
Fezzan
French Congo
French Equatorial Africa
French Guiana
French Guinea
French India
French Morocco
French Polynesia (Oceania)
French Southern & Antarctic Territories
French Sudan
French West Africa
Gabon
Germany
Ghadames
Grand Comoro
Guadeloupe
Indo-China
Inini
Ivory Coast
Laos
Latakia
Lebanon
Madagascar
Martinique
Mauritania
Mayotte
Memel
Middle Congo
Moheli
New Caledonia
New Hebrides
Niger Territory
Nossi-Be
Obock
Reunion
Rouad, Ile
Ste.-Marie de Madagascar
St. Pierre & Miquelon
Senegal
Senegambia & Niger
Somali Coast
Syria
Tahiti
Togo
Tunisia
Ubangi-Shari
Upper Senegal & Niger
Upper Volta
Viet Nam
Wallis & Futuna Islands

POST OFFICES IN FOREIGN COUNTRIES
China
Crete
Egypt
Turkish Empire
Zanzibar

Germany
EARLY STATES
Baden
Bavaria
Bergedorf
Bremen
Brunswick
Hamburg
Hanover
Lubeck
Mecklenburg-Schwerin
Mecklenburg-Strelitz
Oldenburg
Prussia
Saxony
Schleswig-Holstein
Wurttemberg

FORMER COLONIES
Cameroun (Kamerun)
Caroline Islands
German East Africa
German New Guinea
German South-West Africa
Kiauchau
Mariana Islands
Marshall Islands
Samoa
Togo

Italy
EARLY STATES
Modena
Parma
Romagna
Roman States
Sardinia
Tuscany
Two Sicilies
  Naples
  Neapolitan Provinces
  Sicily

FORMER COLONIES, CONTROLLED TERRITORIES, OCCUPATION AREAS
Aegean Islands
  Calimno (Calino)
  Caso
  Cos (Coo)
  Karki (Carchi)
  Leros (Lero)
  Lipso
  Nisiros (Nisiro)
  Patmos (Patmo)
  Piscopi
  Rodi (Rhodes)
  Scarpanto
  Simi
  Stampalia
Castellorizo
Corfu
Cyrenaica
Eritrea
Ethiopia (Abyssinia)
Fiume
Ionian Islands
  Cephalonia
  Ithaca
  Paxos
Italian East Africa
Libya
Oltre Giuba
Saseno
Somalia (Italian Somaliland)
Tripolitania

POST OFFICES IN FOREIGN COUNTRIES
"ESTERO"*
Austria
China
  Peking
  Tientsin
Crete
Tripoli
Turkish Empire
  Constantinople
  Durazzo
  Janina
Jerusalem
Salonika
Scutari
Smyrna
Valona

*Stamps overprinted "ESTERO" were used in various parts of the world.

Netherlands
Aruba
Netherlands Antilles (Curacao)
Netherlands Indies
Netherlands New Guinea
Surinam (Dutch Guiana)

Portugal
COLONIES PAST AND PRESENT, CONTROLLED TERRITORIES
Angola
Angra
Azores
Cape Verde
Funchal
Horta
Inhambane
Kionga
Lourenco Marques
Macao
Madeira
Mozambique
Mozambique Co.
Nyassa
Ponta Delgada
Portuguese Africa
Portuguese Congo
Portuguese Guinea
Portuguese India
Quelimane
St. Thomas & Prince Islands
Tete
Timor
Zambezia

Russia
ALLIED TERRITORIES AND REPUBLICS, OCCUPATION AREAS
Armenia
Aunus (Olonets)
Azerbaijan
Batum
Estonia
Far Eastern Republic
Georgia
Karelia
Latvia
Lithuania
North Ingermanland
Ostland
Russian Turkestan
Siberia
South Russia
Tannu Tuva
Transcaucasian Fed. Republics
Ukraine
Wenden (Livonia)
Western Ukraine

Spain
COLONIES PAST AND PRESENT, CONTROLLED TERRITORIES
Aguera, La
Cape Juby
Cuba
Elobey, Annobon & Corisco
Fernando Po
Ifni
Mariana Islands
Philippines
Puerto Rico
Rio de Oro
Rio Muni
Spanish Guinea
Spanish Morocco
Spanish Sahara
Spanish West Africa

POST OFFICES IN FOREIGN COUNTRIES
Morocco
Tangier
Tetuan

Common Design Types

Pictured in this section are issues where one illustration has been used for a number of countries in the Catalogue. Not included in this section are overprinted stamps or those issues which are illustrated in each country.

EUROPA

Europa Issue, 1956

The design symbolizing the cooperation among the six countries comprising the Coal and Steel Community is illustrated in each country.

Belgium....496-497
France....805-806
Germany....748-749
Italy....715-716
Luxembourg....318-320
Netherlands....368-369

Europa Issue, 1958

"E" and Dove – CD1

European Postal Union at the service of European integration.

1958, Sept. 13

Belgium....527-528
France....889-890
Germany....790-791
Italy....750-751
Luxembourg....341-343
Netherlands....375-376
Saar....317-318

Europa Issue, 1959

6-Link Endless Chain – CD2

1959, Sept. 19

Belgium....536-537
France....929-930
Germany....805-806
Italy....791-792
Luxembourg....354-355
Netherlands....379-380

Europa Issue, 1960

19-Spoke Wheel – CD3

First anniversary of the establishment of C.E.P.T. (Conference Europeenne des Administrations des Postes et des Telecommunications.)

The spokes symbolize the 19 founding members of the Conference.

1960, Sept.

Belgium....553-554
Denmark....379
Finland....376-377
France....970-971
Germany....818-820
Great Britain....377-378
Greece....688
Iceland....327-328
Ireland....175-176
Italy....809-810
Luxembourg....374-375
Netherlands....385-386
Norway....387
Portugal....866-867
Spain....941-942
Sweden....562-563
Switzerland....400-401
Turkey....1493-1494

Europa Issue, 1961

19 Doves Flying as One – CD4

The 19 doves represent the 19 members of the Conference of European Postal and Telecommunications Administrations C.E.P.T.

1961-62

Belgium....572-573
Cyprus....201-203
France....1005-1006
Germany....844-845
Great Britain....383-384
Greece....718-719
Iceland....340-341
Italy....845-846
Luxembourg....382-383
Netherlands....387-388
Spain....1010-1011
Switzerland....410-411
Turkey....1518-1520

Europa Issue, 1962

Young Tree with 19 Leaves – CD5

The 19 leaves represent the 19 original members of C.E.P.T.

1962-63

Belgium....582-583
Cyprus....219-221
France....1045-1046
Germany....852-853
Greece....739-740
Iceland....348-349
Ireland....184-185
Italy....860-861
Luxembourg....386-387
Netherlands....394-395
Norway....414-415
Switzerland....416-417
Turkey....1553-1555

Europa Issue, 1963

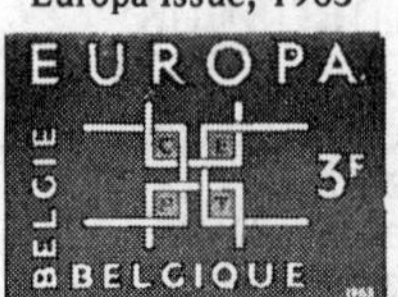

Stylized Links, Symbolizing Unity – CD6

1963, Sept.

Belgium....598-599
Cyprus....229-231
Finland....419
France....1074-1075
Germany....867-868
Greece....768-769
Iceland....357-358
Ireland....188-189
Italy....880-881
Luxembourg....403-404
Netherlands....416-417
Norway....441-442
Switzerland....429
Turkey....1602-1603

Europa Issue, 1964

Symbolic Daisy – CD7

5th anniversary of the establishment of C.E.P.T. The 22 petals of the flower symbolize the 22 members of the Conference.

1964, Sept.

Austria....738
Belgium....614-615
Cyprus....244-246
France....1109-1110
Germany....897-898
Greece....801-802
Iceland....367-368
Ireland....196-197
Italy....894-895
Luxembourg....411-412
Monaco....590-591
Netherlands....428-429
Norway....458
Portugal....931-933
Spain....1262-1263
Switzerland....438-439
Turkey....1628-1629

Europa Issue, 1965

Leaves and "Fruit" – CD8

1965

Belgium....636-637
Cyprus....262-264
Finland....437
France....1131-1132
Germany....934-935
Greece....833-834
Iceland....375-376
Ireland....204-205
Italy....915-916
Luxembourg....432-433
Monaco....616-617
Netherlands....438-439
Norway....475-476
Portugal....958-960
Switzerland....469
Turkey....1665-1666

Europa Issue, 1966

Symbolic Sailboat – CD9

1966, Sept.

Andorra, French....172
Belgium....675-676
Cyprus....275-277
France....1163-1164
Germany....963-964
Greece....862-863
Iceland....384-385
Ireland....216-217
Italy....942-943
Liechtenstein....415
Luxembourg....440-441
Monaco....639-640
Netherlands....441-442
Norway....496-497
Portugal....980-982
Switzerland....477-478
Turkey....1718-1719

Europa Issue, 1967

Cogwheels – CD10

1967

Andorra, French....174-175
Belgium....688-689
Cyprus....297-299
France....1178-1179
Greece....891-892
Germany....969-970
Iceland....389-390
Ireland....232-233
Italy....951-952
Liechtenstein....420
Luxembourg....449-450
Monaco....669-670
Netherlands....444-447
Norway....504-505
Portugal....994-996
Spain....1465-1466
Switzerland....482
Turkey....B120-B121

Europa Issue, 1968

Golden Key with C.E.P.T. Emblem CD11

1968

Andorra, French....182-183
Belgium....705-706
Cyprus....314-316
France....1209-1210
Germany....983-984
Greece....916-917
Iceland....395-396
Ireland....242-243
Italy....979-980
Liechtenstein....442
Luxembourg....466-467
Monaco....689-691
Netherlands....452-453
Portugal....1019-1021
San Marino....687
Spain....1526
Turkey....1775-1776

Europa Issue, 1969

"EUROPA" and "CEPT" – CD12

Tenth anniversary of C.E.P.T.

1969

Andorra, French....188-189
Austria....837
Belgium....718-719
Cyprus....326-328
Denmark....458
Finland....483
France....1245-1246
Germany....996-997
Great Britain....585
Greece....947-948
Iceland....406-407
Ireland....270-271

Italy....1000-1001
Liechtenstein....453
Luxembourg....474-475
Monaco....722-724
Netherlands....475-476
Norway....533-534
Portugal....1038-1040
San Marino....701-702
Spain....1567
Sweden....814-816
Switzerland....500-501
Turkey....1799-1800
Vatican....470-472
Yugoslavia....1003-1004

Europa Issue, 1970

Interwoven Threads CD13

1970

Andorra, French....196-197
Belgium....741-742
Cyprus....340-342
France....1271-1272
Germany....1018-1019
Greece....985, 987
Iceland....420-421
Ireland....279-281
Italy....1013-1014
Liechtenstein....470
Luxembourg....489-490
Monaco....768-770
Netherlands....483-484
Portugal....1060-1062
San Marino....729-730
Spain....1607
Switzerland....515-516
Turkey....1848-1849
Yugoslavia....1024-1025

Europa Issue, 1971

"Fraternity, Cooperation, Common Effort" – CD14

1971

Andorra, French....205-206
Belgium....803-804
Cyprus....365-367
Finland....504
France....1304
Germany....1064-1065
Greece....1029-1030
Iceland....429-430
Ireland....305-306
Italy....1038-1039
Liechtenstein....485
Luxembourg....500-501
Malta....425-427
Monaco....797-799
Netherlands....488-489
Portugal....1094-1096
San Marino....749-750
Spain....1675-1676
Switzerland....531-532
Turkey....1876-1877
Yugoslavia....1052-1053

Europa Issue, 1972

Sparkles, Symbolic of Communications CD15

1972

Andorra, French....210-211
Andorra, Spanish....62
Belgium....825-826
Cyprus....380-382
Finland....512-513
France....1341
Germany....1089-1090
Greece....1049-1050
Iceland....439-440
Ireland....316-317
Italy....1065-1066
Liechtenstein....504
Luxembourg....512-513
Malta....450-453
Monaco....831-832
Netherlands....494-495
Portugal....1141-1143
San Marino....771-772
Spain....1718
Switzerland....544-545
Turkey....1907-1908
Yugoslavia....1100-1101

Europa Issue, 1973

Post Horn and Arrows CD16

1973

Andorra, French....319-320
Andorra, Spanish....76
Belgium....839-840
Cyprus....396-398
Finland....526
France....1367
Germany....1114-1115
Greece....1090-1092
Iceland....447-448
Ireland....329-330
Italy....1108-1109
Liechtenstein....528-529
Luxembourg....523-524
Malta....469-471
Monaco....866-867
Netherlands....504-505
Norway....604-605
Portugal....1170-1172
San Marino....802-803
Spain....1753
Switzerland....580-581
Turkey....1935-1936
Yugoslavia....1138-1139

PORTUGAL & COLONIES

Vasco da Gama Issue

Fleet Departing – CD20

Fleet Arriving at Calicut – CD21

Embarking at Rastello – CD22

Muse of History – CD23

San Gabriel, da Gama and Camoens – CD24

Archangel Gabriel, the Patron Saint CD25

Flagshig San Gabriel CD26

Vasco da Gama CD27

Fourth centenary of Vasco da Gama's discovery of the route to India.

1898

Azores....93-100
Macao....67-74
Madeira....37-44
Portugal....147-154
Port. Africa....1-8
Port. India....189-196
Timor....45-52

Pombal Issue

POSTAL TAX

Marquis de Pombal CD28

Planning Reconstruction of Lisbon, 1755 CD29

Pombal Monument, Lisbon – CD30

Sebastiao Jose de Carvalho e Mello, Marquis de Pombal (1699-1782), statesman, rebuilt Lisbon after earthquake of 1755. Tax was for the erection of Pombal monument. Obligatory on all mail on certain days throughout the year.

1925

Angola....RA1-RA3
Azores....RA9-RA11
Cape Verde....RA1-RA3
Macao....RA1-RA3
Madeira....RA1-RA3
Mozambique....RA1-RA3
Portugal....RA11-RA13
Port. Guinea....RA1-RA3
Port. India....RA1-RA3
St. Thomas & Prince Islands....RA1-RA3
Timor....RA1-RA3

Pombal Issue

POSTAL TAX DUES

CD31 CD32

CD33

1925

Angola....RAJ1-RAJ3
Azores....RAJ2-RAJ4
Cape Verde....RAJ1-RAJ3
Macao....RAJ1-RAJ3
Madeira....RAJ1-RAJ3
Mozambique....RAJ1-RAJ3
Portugal....RAJ2-RAJ4
Port. Guinea....RAJ1-RAJ3
Port. India....RAJ1-RAJ3
St. Thomas & Prince Islands....RAJ1-RAJ3
Timor....RAJ1-RAJ3

Vasco da Gama CD34

Mousinho de Albuquerque CD35

Dam CD36

Prince Henry the Navigator – CD37

Affonso de Albuquerque CD38

Plane over Globe CD39

1938-39

Angola....274-291
Cape Verde....234-251
Macao....289-305
Mozambique....270-287
Port. Guinea....233-250
Port. India....439-453
St. Thomas & Prince Islands....302-319, 323-340
Timor....223-239

1938-39

Angola....C1-C9
Cape Verde....C1-C9

Macao	C7-C15
Mozambique	C1-C9
Port. Guinea	C1-C9
Port. India	C1-C8
St. Thomas & Prince Islands	C1-C18
Timor	C1-C9

Lady of Fatima Issue

Our Lady of the Rosary, Fatima, Portugal CD40

1948-49

Angola	315-318
Cape Verde	266
Macao	336
Mozambique	325-328
Port. Guinea	271
Port. India	480
St. Thomas & Prince Islands	351
Timor	254

A souvenir sheet of 9 stamps was issued in 1951 to mark the extension of the 1950 Holy Year. The sheet contains: Angola No. 316, Cape Verde No. 266, Macao No. 336, Mozambique No. 325, Portuguese Guinea No. 271, Portugese India Nos. 480, 485, St. Thomas & Prince Islands No. 351, Timor No. 254.

The sheet also contains a portrait of Pope Pius XII and is inscribed "Encerramento do Ano Santo, Fatima 1951." It was sold for 11 escudos.

Holy Year Issue

Church Bells and Dove CD41

Angel Holding Candelabra CD42

Holy Year, 1950.

1950-51

Angola	331-332
Cape Verde	268-269
Macao	339-340
Mozambique	330-331
Port. Guinea	273-274
Port. India	490-491, 496-503
St. Thomas & Prince Islands	353-354
Timor	258-259

A souvenir sheet of 8 stamps was issued in 1951 to mark the extension of the Holy Year. The sheet contains: Angola No. 331, Cape Verde No. 269, Macao No. 340, Mozambique No. 331, Portuguese Guinea No. 275, Portuguese India No. 490, St. Thomas & Prince Islands No. 354, Timor No. 258, some with colors changed. The sheet contains doves and is inscribed "Encerramento do Ano Santo, Fatima 1951." It was sold for 17 escudos.

Holy Year Conclusion Issue

Our Lady of Fatima CD43

Conclusion of Holy Year. Sheets contain alternate vertical rows of stamps and labels bearing quotation from Pope Pius XII, different for each colony.

1951

Angola	357
Cape Verde	270
Macao	352
Mozambique	356
Port. Guinea	275
Port. India	506
St. Thomas & Prince Islands	355
Timor	270

Medical Congress Issue

Medical Examination CD44

First National Congress of Tropical Medicine, Lisbon, 1952.

Each stamp has a different design.

1952

Angola	358
Cape Verde	287
Macao	364
Mozambique	359
Port. Guinea	276
Port. India	516
St. Thomas & Prince Islands	356
Timor	271

POSTAGE DUE STAMPS

CD45

1952

Angola	J37-J42
Cape Verde	J31-J36
Macao	J53-J58
Mozambique	J51-J56
Port. Guinea	J40-J45
Port. India	J47-J52
St. Thomas & Prince Islands	J52-J57
Timor	J31-J36

Sao Paulo Issue

Father Manuel de Nobrega and View of Sao Paulo – CD46

400th anniversary of the founding of Sao Paulo, Brazil.

1954

Angola	385
Cape Verde	297
Macao	382
Mozambique	395
Port. Guinea	291
Port. India	530
St. Thomas & Prince Islands	369
Timor	279

Tropical Medicine Congress Issue

Securidaca Longipedunculata – CD47

Sixth International Congress for Tropical Medicine and Malaria, Lisbon, Sept. 1958.

Each stamp shows a different plant.

1958

Angola	409
Cape Verde	303
Macao	392
Mozambique	404
Port. Guinea	295
Port. India	569
St. Thomas & Prince Islands	371
Timor	289

Sports Issue

Flying – CD48

Each stamp shows a different sport.

1962

Angola	433-438
Cape Verde	320-325
Macao	394-399
Mozambique	424-429
Port. Guinea	299-304
St. Thomas & Prince Islands	374-379
Timor	313-318

Anti-Malaria Issue

Anopheles Funestus and Malaria Eradication Symbol – CD49

World Health Organization drive to eradicate malaria.

1962

Angola	439
Cape Verde	326
Macao	400
Mozambique	430
Port. Guinea	305
St. Thomas & Prince Islands	380
Timor	319

Airline Anniversary Issue

Map of Africa, Super Constellation and Jet Liner – CD50

Tenth anniversary of Transportes Aereos Portugueses (TAP).

1963

Angola	490
Cape Verde	327
Mozambique	434
Port. Guinea	318
St. Thomas & Prince Islands	381

National Overseas Bank Issue

Antonio Teixeira de Sousa – CD51

Centenary of the National Overseas Bank of Portugal.

1964, May 16

Angola	509
Cape Verde	328
Port. Guinea	319
St. Thomas & Prince Islands	382
Timor	320

ITU Issue

ITU Emblem and St. Gabriel CD52

Centenary of the International Communications Union.

1965, May 17

Angola	511
Cape Verde	329
Macao	402
Mozambique	464
Port. Guinea	320
St. Thomas & Prince Islands	383
Timor	321

National Revolution Issue

St. Paul's Hospital, and Commercial and Industrial School – CD53

40th anniversary of the National Revolution.

Different buildings on each stamp.

1966, May 28

Angola	525
Cape Verde	338
Macao	403
Mozambique	465
Port. Guinea	329
St. Thomas & Prince Islands	392
Timor	322

Navy Club Issue

Mendes Barata and Cruiser Dom Carlos I – CD54

Centenary of Portugal's Navy Club.

Each stamp has a different design.

1967, Jan. 31

Angola	527-528
Cape Verde	339-340
Macao	412-413
Mozambique	478-479
Port. Guinea	330-331
St. Thomas & Prince Islands	393-394
Timor	323-324

Admiral Coutinho Issue

Admiral Gago Coutinho and his First Ship – CD55

Centenary of the birth of Admiral Carlos Viegas Gago Coutinho (1869-1959), explorer and aviation pioneer.

Each stamp has a different design.

1969, Feb. 17

Angola	547
Cape Verde	355
Macao	417
Mozambique	484
Port. Guinea	335
St. Thomas & Prince Islands	397
Timor	335

Administration Reform Issue

Luiz Augusto Rebello da Silva – CD56

Centenary of the administration reforms of the overseas territories.

1969, Sept. 25

Angola	549
Cape Verde	357
Macao	419
Mozambique	491
Port. Guinea	337
St. Thomas & Prince Islands	399
Timor	338

Marshal Carmona Issue

Marshal A.O. Carmona CD57

Birth centenary of Marshal Antonio Oscar Carmona de Fragoso (1869-1951), President of Portugal.

Each stamp has a different design.

1970, Nov. 15

Angola	563
Cape Verde	359
Macao	422
Mozambique	493
Port. Guinea	340
St. Thomas & Prince Islands	403
Timor	341

Olympic Games Issue

Racing Yachts and Olympic Emblem CD59

20th Olympic Games, Munich, Aug. 26-Sept. 11.

Each stamp shows a different sport.

1972, June 20

Angola	569
Cape Verde	361
Macao	426
Mozambique	504
Port. Guinea	342
St. Thomas & Prince Islands	408
Timor	343

Lisbon-Rio de Janeiro Flight Issue

"Santa Cruz" over Fernando de Noronha – CD60

50th anniversary of the Lisbon to Rio de Janeiro flight by Arturo de Sacadura and Coutinho, March 30-June 5, 1922.

Each stamp shows a different stage of the flight.

1972, Sept. 20

Angola	570
Cape Verde	362
Macao	427
Mozambique	505
Port. Guinea	343
St. Thomas & Prince Islands	409
Timor	344

WMO Centenary Issue

WMO Emblem – CD61

Centenary of international meterological cooperation.

1973, Dec. 15

Angola	571
Cape Verde	363
Macao	429
Mozambique	509
Port. Guinea	344
St. Thomas & Prince Islands	410
Timor	345

FRENCH COMMUNITY

Upper Volta can be found under Burkina Faso in Vol. 2

Colonial Exposition Issue

People of French Empire – CD70

Women's Heads – CD71

France Showing Way to Civilization CD72

"Colonial Commerce" – CD73

International Colonial Exposition, Paris 1931.

1931

Cameroun	213-216
Chad	60-63
Dahomey	97-100
Fr. Guiana	152-155
Fr. Guinea	116-119
Fr. India	100-103
Fr. Polynesia	76-79
Fr. Sudan	102-105
Gabon	120-123
Guadeloupe	138-141
Indo-China	140-142
Ivory Coast	92-95
Madagascar	169-172
Martinique	129-132
Mauritania	65-68
Middle Congo	61-64
New Caledonia	176-179
Niger	73-76
Reunion	122-125
St. Pierre & Miquelon	132-135
Senegal	138-141
Somali Coast	135-138
Togo	254-257
Ubangi-Shari	82-85
Upper Volta	66-69
Wallis & Futuna Isls.	85-88

Paris International Exposition Issue
Colonial Arts Exposition Issue

"Colonial Resources" CD74 CD77

Overseas Commerce – CD75

Exposition Building and Women – CD76

"France and the Empire" – CD78

Cultural Treasures of the Colonies CD79

Souvenir sheets contain one imperf. stamp.

1937

Cameroun	217-222A
Dahomey	101-107
Fr. Equatorial Africa	27-32, 73
Fr. Guiana	162-168
Fr. Guinea	120-126
Fr. India	104-110
Fr. Polynesia	117-123
Fr. Sudan	106-112
Guadeloupe	148-154
Indo-China	193-199
Inini	41
Ivory Coast	152-158
Kwangchowan	132
Madagascar	191-197
Martinique	179-185
Mauritania	69-75
New Caledonia	208-214
Niger	72-83
Reunion	167-173
St. Pierre & Miquelon	165-171
Senegal	172-178
Somali Coast	139-145
Togo	258-264
Wallis & Futuna Isls.	89

Curie Issue

Pierre and Marie Curie – CD80

40th anniversary of the discovery of radium. The surtax was for the benefit of the International Union for the Control of Cancer.

1938

Cameroun	B1
Cuba	B1-B2
Dahomey	B2
France	B76
Fr. Equatorial Africa	B1
Fr. Guiana	B3
Fr. Guinea	B2
Fr. India	B6
Fr. Polynesia	B5
Fr. Sudan	B1
Guadeloupe	B3
Indo-China	B14
Ivory Coast	B2
Madagascar	B2
Martinique	B2
Mauritania	B3
New Caledonia	B4
Niger	B1
Reunion	B4
St. Pierre & Miquelon	B3
Senegal	B3
Somali Coast	B2
Togo	B1

Caillie Issue

Rene Caille and Map of Northwestern Africa – CD81

Death centenary of Rene Caillie (1799-1838), French explorer.

All three denominations exist with colony name omitted.

1939

Dahomey	108-110
Fr. Guinea	161-163
Fr. Sudan	113-115
Ivory Coast	160-162
Mauritania	109-111
Niger	84-86
Senegal	188-190
Togo	265-267

New York World's Fair Issue

Natives and New York Skyline – CD82

1939

Cameroun	223-224
Dahomey	111-112
Fr. Equatorial Africa	78-79
Fr. Guiana	169-170
Fr. Guinea	164-165
Fr. India	111-112
Fr. Polynesia	124-125
Fr. Sudan	116-117
Guadeloupe	155-156
Indo-China	203-204
Inini	42-43
Ivory Coast	163-164
Kwangchowan	121-122
Madagascar	209-210
Martinique	186-187
Mauritania	112-113
New Caledonia	215-216
Niger	87-88
Reunion	174-175
St. Pierre & Miquelon	205-206
Senegal	191-192
Somali Coast	179-180
Togo	268-269
Wallis & Futuna Isls.	90-91

French Revolution Issue

Storming of the Bastille – CD83

150th anniversary of the French Revolution. The surtax was for the defense of the colonies.

1939

Cameroun	B2-B6
Dahomey	B3-B7
Fr. Equatorial Africa	B4-B8, CB1
Fr. Guiana	B4-B8, CB1
Fr. Guinea	B3-B7
Fr. India	B7-B11
Fr. Polynesia	B6-B10, CB1
Fr. Sudan	B2-B6
Guadeloupe	B4-B8
Indo-China	B15-B19, CB1
Inini	B1-B5
Ivory Coast	B3-B7
Kwangchowan	B1-B5
Madagascar	B3-B7, CB1
Martinique	B3-B7
Mauritania	B4-B8
New Caledonia	B5-B9, CB1
Niger	B2-B6
Reunion	B5-B9, CB1
St. Pierre & Miquelon	B4-B8
Senegal	B4-B8, CB1
Somali Coast	B3-B7
Togo	B2-B6
Wallis & Futuna Isls.	B1-B5

Plane over Coastal Area – CD85

All five denominations exist with colony name omitted.

1940

Dahomey	C1-C5
Fr. Guinea	C1-C5
Fr. Sudan	C1-C5
Ivory Coast	C1-C5
Mauritania	C1-C5
Niger	C1-C5
Senegal	C12-C16
Togo	C1-C5

Colonial Infantryman CD86

1941

Cameroun	B13B
Dahomey	B13
Fr. Equatorial Africa	B8B
Fr. Guiana	B10
Fr. Guinea	B13
Fr. India	B13
Fr. Polynesia	B12
Fr. Sudan	B12
Guadeloupe	B10
Indo-China	B19B
Inini	B7
Ivory Coast	B13
Kwangchowan	B7
Madagascar	B9
Martinique	B9
Mauritania	B14
New Caledonia	B11
Niger	B12
Reunion	B11
St. Pierre & Miquelon	B8B
Senegal	B14
Somali Coast	B9
Togo	B10B
Wallis & Futuna Isls.	B7

Cross of Lorraine and Four-motor Plane – CD87

1941-5

Cameroun	C1-C7
Fr. Equatorial Africa	C17-C23
Fr. Guiana	C9-C10
Fr. India	C1-C6
Fr. Polynesia	C3-C9
Fr. West Africa	C1-C3
Guadeloupe	C1-C2
Madagascar	C37-C43
Martinique	C1-C2
New Caledonia	C7-C13
Reunion	C18-C24
St. Pierre & Miquelon	C1-C7
Somali Coast	C1-C7

Transport Plane CD88

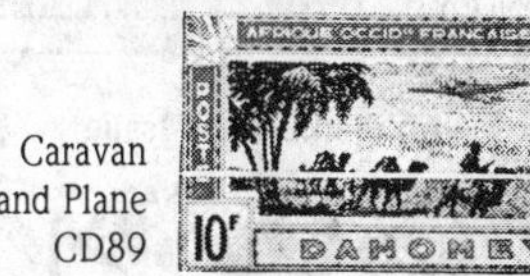

Caravan and Plane CD89

1942

Dahomey	C6-C13
Fr. Guinea	C6-C13
Fr. Sudan	C6-C13
Ivory Coast	C6-C13
Mauritania	C6-C13
Niger	C6-C13
Senegal	C17-C25
Togo	C6-C13

Red Cross Issue

Marianne CD90

The surtax was for the French Red Cross and national relief.

1944

Cameroun	B28
Fr. Equatorial Africa	B38
Fr. Guiana	B12
Fr. India	B14
Fr. Polynesia	B13
Fr. West Africa	B1
Guadeloupe	B12
Madagascar	B15
Martinique	B11
New Caledonia	B13
Reunion	B15
St. Pierre & Miquelon	B13
Somali Coast	B13
Wallis & Futuna Isls.	B9

Eboue Issue

Felix Eboue – CD91

Felix Eboue, first French colonial administrator to proclaim resistance to Germany after French surrender in World War II.

1945

Cameroun	296-297
Fr. Equatorial Africa	156-157
Fr. Guiana	171-172
Fr. India	210-211
Fr. Polynesia	150-151
Fr. West Africa	15-16
Guadeloupe	187-188
Madagascar	259-260
Martinique	196-197
New Caledonia	274-275
Reunion	238-239
St. Pierre & Miquelon	322-323
Somali Coast	238-239

Victory Issue

Victory – CD92

European victory of the Allied Nations in World War II.

1946, May 8

Cameroun	C8
Fr. Equatorial Africa	C24
Fr. Guiana	C11
Fr. India	C7
Fr. Polynesia	C10
Fr. West Africa	C4
Guadeloupe	C3
Indo-China	C19
Madagascar	C44
Martinique	C3
New Caledonia	C14
Reunion	C25
St. Pierre & Miquelon	C8
Somali Coast	C8
Wallis & Futuna Isls.	C1

Chad to Rhine Issue

Leclerc's Departure from Chad – CD93

Battle at Cufra Oasis – CD94

Tanks in Action, Mareth – CD95

Normandy Invasion – CD96

Entering Paris – CD97

Liberation of Strasbourg – CD98

"Chad to the Rhine" march, 1942-44, by Gen. Jacques Leclerc's column, later French 2nd Armored Division.

1946, June 6

Cameroun	C9-C14
Fr. Equatorial Africa	C25-C30
Fr. Guiana	C12-C17
Fr. India	C8-C13
Fr. Polynesia	C11-C16
Fr. West Africa	C5-C10
Guadeloupe	C4-C9
Indo-China	C20-C25
Madagascar	C45-C50
Martinique	C4-C9
New Caledonia	C15-C20
Reunion	C26-C31
St. Pierre & Miquelon	C9-C14
Somali Coast	C9-C14
Wallis & Futuna Isls.	C2-C7

UPU Issue

French Colonials, Globe and Plane CD99

75th anniversary of the Universal Postal Union.

1949, July 4

Cameroun	C29
Fr. Equatorial Africa	C34
Fr. India	C17
Fr. Polynesia	C20
Fr. West Africa	C15
Indo-China	C26

Madagascar.......................................C55
New Caledonia.......................................C24
St. Pierre & Miquelon.......................................C18
Somali Coast.......................................C18
Togo.......................................C18
Wallis & Futuna Isls.......................................C10

Tropical Medicine Issue

Doctor Treating Infant – CD100

The surtax was for charitable work.

1950

Cameroun.......................................B29
Fr. Equatorial Africa.......................................B39
Fr. India.......................................B15
Fr. Polynesia.......................................B14
Fr. West Africa.......................................B3
Madagascar.......................................B17
New Caledonia.......................................B14
St. Pierre & Miquelon.......................................B14
Somali Coast.......................................B14
Togo.......................................B11

Military Medal Issue

Medal, Early Marine and Colonial Soldier – CD101

Centenary of the creation of the French Military Medal.

1952

Cameroun.......................................332
Comoro Isls.......................................39
Fr. Equatorial Africa.......................................186
Fr. India.......................................233
Fr. Polynesia.......................................179
Fr. West Africa.......................................57
Madagascar.......................................286
New Caledonia.......................................295
St. Pierre & Miquelon.......................................345
Somali Coast.......................................267
Togo.......................................327
Wallis & Futuna Isls.......................................149

Liberation Issue

Allied Landing, Victory Sign and Cross of Lorraine – CD102

10th anniversary of the liberation of France.

1954, June 6

Cameroun.......................................C32
Comoro Isls.......................................C4
Fr. Equatorial Africa.......................................C38
Fr. India.......................................C18
Fr. Polynesia.......................................C23
Fr. West Africa.......................................C17
Madagascar.......................................C57
New Caledonia.......................................C25
St. Pierre & Miquelon.......................................C19
Somali Coast.......................................C19
Togo.......................................C19
Wallis & Futuna Isls.......................................C11

FIDES Issue

Plowmen CD103

Efforts of FIDES, the Economic and Social Development Fund for Overseas Possessions (Fonds d' Investissement pour le Developpement Economique et Social).

Each stamp has a different design.

1956

Cameroun.......................................326-329
Comoro Isls.......................................43
Fr. Polynesia.......................................181
Madagascar.......................................292-295
New Caledonia.......................................303
Somali Coast.......................................268
Togo.......................................331

Flower Issue

Euadania CD104

Each stamp shows a different flower.

1958-9

Cameroun.......................................333
Comoro Isls.......................................45
Fr. Equatorial Africa.......................................200-201
Fr. Polynesia.......................................192
Fr. So. & Antarctic Terr.......................................11
Fr. West Africa.......................................79-83
Madagascar.......................................301-302
New Caledonia.......................................304-305
St. Pierre & Miquelon.......................................357
Somali Coast.......................................270
Togo.......................................348-349
Wallis & Futuna Isls.......................................152

Human Rights Issue

Sun, Dove and U.N. Emblem – CD105

10th anniversary of the signing of the Universal Declaration of Human Rights.

1958

Comoro Isls.......................................44
Fr. Equatorial Africa.......................................202
Fr. Polynesia.......................................191
Fr. West Africa.......................................85
Madagascar.......................................300
New Caledonia.......................................306
St. Pierre & Miquelon.......................................356
Somali Coast.......................................274
Wallis & Futuna Isls.......................................153

C.C.T.A. Issue

Map of Africa & Cogwheels – CD106

10th anniversary of the Commission for Technical Cooperation in Africa south of the Sahara.

1960

Cameroun.......................................335
Cent. African Rep.......................................3
Chad.......................................66
Congo, P.R.......................................90
Dahomey.......................................138
Gabon.......................................150
Ivory Coast.......................................180
Madagascar.......................................317
Mali.......................................9
Mauritania.......................................117
Niger.......................................104
Upper Volta.......................................89

Air Afrique Issue, 1961

Modern and Ancient Africa, Map and Planes – CD107

Founding of Air Afrique (African Airlines).

1961-62

Cameroun.......................................C37
Cent. African Rep.......................................C5
Chad.......................................C7
Congo, P.R.......................................C5
Dahomey.......................................C17
Gabon.......................................C5
Ivory Coast.......................................C18
Mauritania.......................................C17
Niger.......................................C22
Senegal.......................................C31
Upper Volta.......................................C4

Anti-Malaria Issue

Malaria Eradication Emblem – CD108

World Health Organization drive to eradicate malaria.

1962, Apr. 7

Cameroun.......................................B36
Cent. African Rep.......................................B1
Chad.......................................B1
Comoro Isls.......................................B1
Congo, P.R.......................................B3
Dahomey.......................................B15
Gabon.......................................B4
Ivory Coast.......................................B15
Madagascar.......................................B19
Mali.......................................B1
Mauritania.......................................B16
Niger.......................................B14
Senegal.......................................B16
Somali Coast.......................................B15
Upper Volta.......................................B1

Abidjan Games Issue

Relay Race – CD109

Abidjan Games, Ivory Coast, Dec. 24-31, 1961.

Each stamp shows a different sport.

1962

Chad.......................................83-84
Cent. African Rep.......................................19-20
Congo, P.R.......................................103-104
Gabon.......................................163-164
Niger.......................................109-111
Upper Volta.......................................103-105

African and Malagasy Union Issue

Flag of Union – CD110

First anniversary of the Union.

1962, Sept. 8

Cameroun.......................................373
Cent. African Rep.......................................21
Chad.......................................85
Congo, P.R.......................................105
Dahomey.......................................155
Gabon.......................................165
Ivory Coast.......................................198
Madagascar.......................................332
Mauritania.......................................170
Niger.......................................112
Senegal.......................................211
Upper Volta.......................................106

Telstar Issue

Telstar and Globe Showing Andover and Pleumeur-Bodou – CD111

First television connection of the United States and Europe through the Telstar satellite, July 11-12, 1962.

1962-63

Andorra, French.......................................154
Comoro Isls.......................................C7
Fr. Polynesia.......................................C29
Fr. So. & Antarctic Terr.......................................C5
New Caledonia.......................................C33
Somali Coast.......................................C31
St. Pierre & Miquelon.......................................C26
Wallis & Futuna Isls.......................................C17

Freedom From Hunger Issue

World Map and Wheat Emblem – CD112

United Nations Food and Agriculture Organization's "Freedom from Hunger" campaign.

1963, Mar. 21

Cameroun.......................................B37-B38
Cent. African Rep.......................................B2
Chad.......................................B2
Congo, P.R.......................................B4
Dahomey.......................................B16
Gabon.......................................B5
Ivory Coast.......................................B16
Madagascar.......................................B21
Mauritania.......................................B17
Niger.......................................B15
Senegal.......................................B17
Upper Volta.......................................B2

Red Cross Centenary Issue

Centenary Emblem – CD113

Centenary of the International Red Cross.

1963, Sept. 2

Comoro Isls. 55
Fr. Polynesia 205
New Caledonia 328
St. Pierre & Miquelon 367
Somali Coast 297
Wallis & Futuna Isls. 165

African Postal Union Issue

UAMPT Emblem, Radio Masts, Plane and Mail – CD114

Establishment of the African and Malagasy Posts and Telecommunications Union, UAMPT.

1963, Sept. 8

Cameroun C47
Cent. African Rep. C10
Chad C9
Congo, P.R. C13
Dahomey C19
Gabon C13
Ivory Coast C25
Madagascar C75
Mauritania C22
Niger C27
Rwanda 36
Senegal C32
Upper Volta C9

Air Afrique Issue, 1963

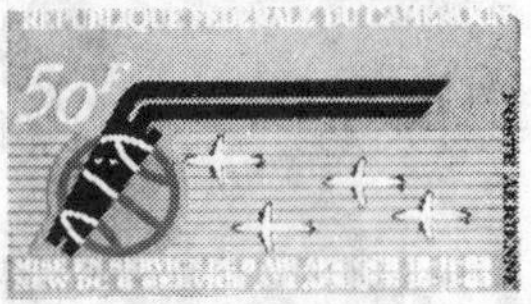

Symbols of Flight – CD115

First anniversary of Air Afrique and inauguration of DC-8 service.

1963, Nov. 19

Cameroun C48
Chad C10
Congo, P.R. C14
Gabon C18
Ivory Coast C26
Mauritania C26
Niger C35
Senegal C33

Europafrica Issue

Europe and Africa Linked – CD116

Signing of an economic agreement between the European Economic Community and the African and Malagasy Union, Yaounde, Cameroun, July 20, 1963.

1963-64

Cameroun 402
Chad C11
Cent. African Rep. C12
Congo, P.R. C16
Gabon C19
Ivory Coast 217
Niger C43
Upper Volta C11

Human Rights Issue

Scales of Justice and Globe – CD117

15th anniversary of the Universal Declaration of Human Rights.

1963, Dec. 10

Comoro Isls. 58
Fr. Polynesia 206
New Caledonia 329
St. Pierre & Miquelon 368
Somali Coast 300
Wallis & Futuna Isls. 166

PHILATEC Issue

Stamp Album, Champs Elysees Palace and Horses of Marly – CD118

"PHILATEC," International Philatelic and Postal Techniques Exhibition, Paris, June 5-21, 1964.

1963-64

Comoro Isls. 60
France 1078
Fr. Polynesia 207
New Caledonia 341
St. Pierre & Miquelon 369
Somali Coast 301
Wallis & Futuna Isls. 167

Cooperation Issue

Maps of France and Africa and Clasped Hands – CD119

Cooperation between France and the French-speaking countries of Africa and Madagascar.

1964

Cameroun 409-410
Cent. African Rep. 39
Chad 103
Congo, P.R. 121
Dahomey 193
France 1111
Gabon 175
Ivory Coast 221
Madagascar 360
Mauritania 181
Niger 143
Senegal 236
Togo 495

ITU Issue

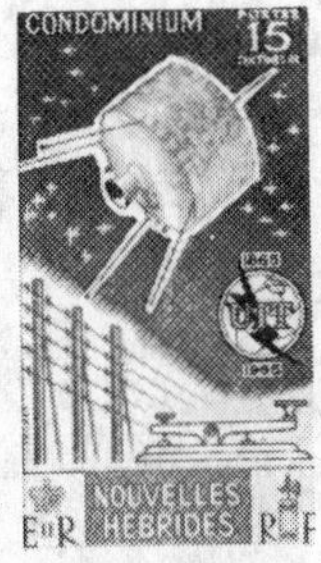

Telegraph, Syncom Satellite and ITU Emblem – CD120

Centenary of the International Telecommunication Union.

1965, May 17

Comoro Isls. C14
Fr. Polynesia C33
Fr. So. & Antarctic Terr. C8
New Caledonia C40
New Hebrides 124-125
St. Pierre & Miquelon C29
Somali Coast C36
Wallis & Futuna Isls. C20

French Satellite A-1 Issue

Diamant Rocket and Launching Installation – CD121

Launching of France's first satellite, Nov. 26, 1965.

1965-66

Comoro Isls. C15-C16
France 1137-1138
Fr. Polynesia C40-C41
Fr. So. & Antarctic Terr. C9-C10
New Caledonia C44-C45
St. Pierre & Miquelon C30-C31
Somali Coast C39-C40
Wallis & Futuna Isls. C22-C23

French Satellite D-1 Issue

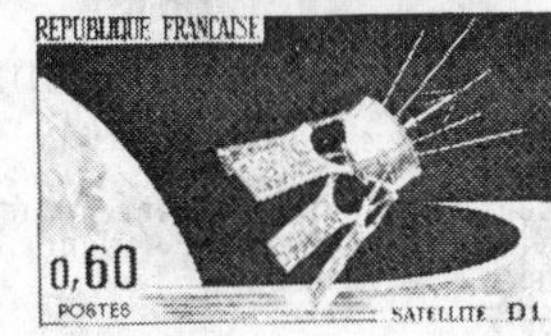

D-1 Satellite in Orbit – CD122

Launching of the D-1 satellite at Hammaguir, Algeria, Feb. 17, 1966.

1966

Comoro Isls. C17
France 1148
Fr. Polynesia C42
Fr. So. & Antarctic Terr. C11
New Caledonia C46
St. Pierre & Miquelon C32
Somali Coast C49
Wallis & Futuna Isls. C24

Air Afrique Issue, 1966

Planes and Air Afrique Emblem – CD123

Introduction of DC-8F planes by Air Afrique.

1966

Cameroun C79
Cent. African Rep. C35
Chad C26
Congo, P.R. C42
Dahomey C42
Gabon C47
Ivory Coast C32
Mauritania C57
Niger C63
Senegal C47
Togo C54
Upper Volta C31

African Postal Union, 1967

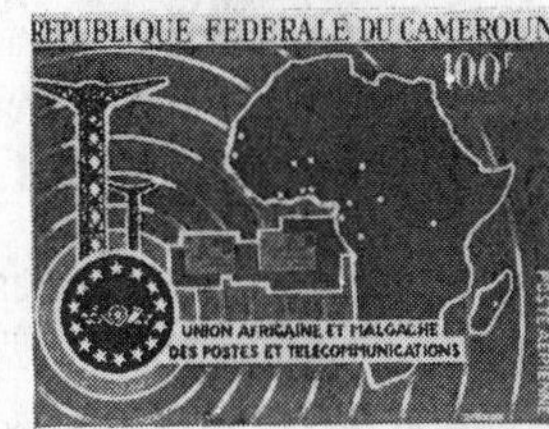

Telecommunications Symbols and Map of Africa – CD124

Fifth anniversary of the establishment of the African and Malagasy Union of Posts and Telecommunications, UAMPT.

1967

Cameroun C90
Cent. African Rep. C46
Chad C37
Congo, P.R. C57
Dahomey C61
Gabon C58
Ivory Coast C34
Madagascar C85
Mauritania C65
Niger C75
Rwanda C1-C3
Senegal C60
Togo C81
Upper Volta C50

Monetary Union Issue

Gold Token of the Ashantis, 17-18th Centuries – CD125

Fifth anniversary of the West African Monetary Union.

1967, Nov. 4

Dahomey 244
Ivory Coast 259
Mauritania 238
Niger 204
Senegal 294
Togo 623
Upper Volta 181

WHO Anniversary Issue

Sun, Flowers and WHO Emblem CD126

20th anniversary of the World Health Organization.

1968, May 4

Afars & Issas 317
Comoro Isls. 73
Fr. Polynesia 241-242

Fr. So. & Antarctic Terr. 31
New Caledonia 367
St. Pierre & Miquelon 377
Wallis & Futuna Isls. 169

Human Rights Year Issue

Human Rights Flame – CD127

International Human Rights Year.

1968, Aug. 10
Afars & Issas 322-323
Comoro Isls. 76
Fr. Polynesia 243-244
Fr. So. & Antarctic Terr. 32
New Caledonia 369
St. Pierre & Miquelon 382
Wallis & Futuna Isls. 170

2nd PHILEXAFRIQUE Issue

Gabon No. 131 and Industrial Plant CD128

Opening of PHILEXAFRIQUE, Abidjan, Feb. 14. Each stamp shows a local scene and stamp.

1969, Feb. 14
Cameroun C118
Cent. African Rep. C65
Chad C48
Congo, P.R. C77
Dahomey C94
Gabon C82
Ivory Coast C38-C40
Madagascar C92
Mali C65
Mauritania C80
Niger C104
Senegal C68
Togo C104
Upper Volta C62

Concorde Issue

Concorde in Flight – CD129

First flight of the prototpye Concorde super-sonic plane at Toulouse, Mar. 1, 1969.

1969
Afars & Issas C56
Comoro Isls. C29
France C42
Fr. Polynesia C50
Fr. So. & Antarctic Terr. C18
New Caledonia C63
St. Pierre & Miquelon C40
Wallis & Futuna Isls. C30

Development Bank Issue

Bank Emblem CD130

Fifth anniversary of the African Development Bank.

1969
Cameroun 499
Chad 217
Congo, P.R. 181-182
Ivory Coast 281
Mali 127-128
Mauritania 267
Niger 220
Senegal 317-318
Upper Volta 201

ILO Issue

ILO Headquarters, Geneva, and Emblem – CD131

50th anniversary of the International Labor Organization.

1969-70
Afars & Issas 337
Comoro Isls. 83
Fr. Polynesia 251-252
Fr. So. & Antarctic Terr. 35
New Caledonia 379
St. Pierre & Miquelon 396
Wallis & Futuna Isls. 172

ASECNA Issue

Map of Africa, Plane and Airport – CD132

10th anniversary of the Agency for the Security of Aerial Navigation in Africa and Madagascar (ASECNA, Agence pour la Securite de la Navigation Aerienne en Afrique et a Madagascar).

1969-70
Cameroun 500
Cent. African Rep. 119
Chad 222
Congo, P.R. 197
Dahomey 269
Gabon 260
Ivory Coast 287
Mali 130
Niger 221
Senegal 321
Upper Volta 204

U.P.U. Headquarters Issue

U.P.U. Headquarters and Emblem CD133

New Universal Postal Union headquarters, Bern, Switzerland.

1970
Afars & Issas 342
Algeria 443
Cameroun 503-504
Cent. African Rep. 125
Chad 225
Comoro Isls. 84
Congo, P.R. 216
Fr. Polynesia 261-262
Fr. So. & Antarctic Terr. 36
Gabon 258
Ivory Coast 295
Madagascar 444
Mali 134-135
Mauritania 283
New Caledonia 382
Niger 231-232
St. Pierre & Miquelon 397-398
Senegal 328-329
Tunisia 535
Wallis & Futuna Isls. 173

De Gaulle Issue

General de Gaulle 1940 – CD134

First anniversay of the death of Charles de Gaulle, (1890-1970), President of France.

1971-72
Afars & Issas 356-357
Comoro Isls. 104-105
France 1322-1325
Fr. Polynesia 270-271
Fr. So. & Antarctic Terr. 52-53
New Caledonia 393-394
Reunion 377, 380
St. Pierre & Miquelon 417-418
Wallis & Futuna Isls. 177-178

African Postal Union Issue, 1971

Carved Stool, UAMPT Building, Brazzaville, Congo – CD135

10th anniversary of the establishment of the African and Malagasy Posts and Telecommunications Union, UAMPT.

Each stamp has a different native design.

1971, Nov. 13
Cameroun C177
Cent. African Rep. C89
Chad C94
Congo, P.R. C136
Dahomey C146
Gabon C120
Ivory Coast C47
Mauritania C113
Niger C164
Rwanda C8
Senegal C105
Togo C166
Upper Volta C97

West African Monetary Union Issue

African Couple, City, Village and Commemorative Coin – CD136

10th anniversary of the West African Monetary Union.

1972, Nov. 2
Dahomey 300
Ivory Coast 331
Mauritania 299
Niger 258
Senegal 374
Togo 825
Upper Volta 280

African Postal Union Issue, 1973

Telecommunications Symbols and Map of Africa – CD137

11th anniversary of the African and Malagasy Posts and Telecommunications Union (UAMPT).

1973, Sept. 12
Cameroun 574
Cent. African Rep. 194
Chad 272
Congo, P.R. 289
Dahomey 311
Gabon 320
Ivory Coast 361
Madagascar 500
Mauritania 304
Niger 287
Rwanda 540
Senegal 393
Togo 849
Upper Volta 285

Philexafrique II — Essen Issue

Buffalo and Dahomey No. C33 – CD138

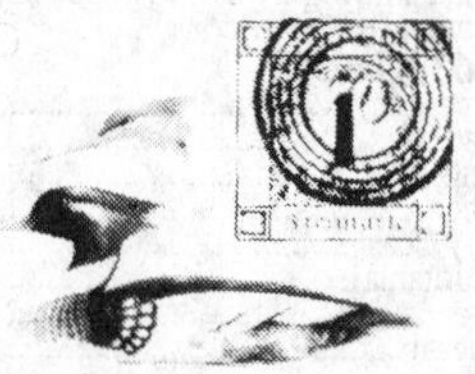

Wild Ducks and Baden No. 1 – CD139

Designs: Indigenous fauna, local and German stamps.

Types CD138-CD139 printed horizontally and vertically se-tenant in sheets of 10 (2x5). Label between horizontal pairs alternately commemoratives Philexafrique II, Libreville, Gabon, June 1978, and 2nd International Stamp Fair, Essen, Germany, Nov. 1-5.

1978-1979
Benin C285-C286
Central Africa C200-C201
Chad C238-C239
Congo Republic C245-C246
Djibouti C121-C122
Gabon C215-C216
Ivory Coast C64-C65
Mali C356-C357
Mauritania C185-C186
Niger C291-C292
Rwanda C12-C13
Senegal C146-C147
Togo C363-C364
Upper Volta C253-C254

ABU DHABI

ˌä-bü-ˈthä-bē

LOCATION — Arabia, on Persian Gulf
GOVT. — Sheikdom under British protection
POP. — 25,000 (estimated)
CAPITAL — Abu Dhabi

Abu Dhabi is one of six Persian Gulf sheikdoms to join the United Arab Emirates, which proclaimed its independence Dec. 2, 1971. See United Arab Emirates.

100 Naye Paise = 1 Rupee
1000 Fils = 1 Dinar (1966)

Catalogue values for all unused stamps in this country are for Never Hinged items.

Sheik Shakbut bin Sultan — A1

Palace — A2

Designs: 40np, 50np, 75np, Gazelle. 5r, 10r, Oil rig and camels.

Perf. 14½

1964, Mar. 30 Photo. Unwmk.

1	A1	5np brt yel green	.15	.15
2	A1	15np brown	.30	.15
3	A1	20np brt ultra	.40	.20
4	A1	30np red orange	.50	.25
5	A1	40np brt violet	.65	.35
6	A1	50np brown olive	.75	.35
7	A1	75np gray	1.25	.55

Engr. *Perf. 13x13½*

8	A2	1r light green	1.75	.75
9	A2	2r black	4.00	1.75
10	A2	5r carmine rose	10.00	4.75
11	A2	10r dark blue	22.50	12.00
		Nos. 1-11 (11)	42.25	21.25

For surcharges see Nos. 15-25.

Falcon Perched on Wrist — A3

Designs: 40np, Falcon facing left. 2r, Falcon facing right.

1965, Mar. 30 Photo. *Perf. 14½*

12	A3	20np chlky blue & brn	1.50	.50
13	A3	40np ultra & brown	3.50	2.00
14	A3	2r brt blue grn & gray brn	15.00	15.00
		Nos. 12-14 (3)	20.00	17.50

Nos. 1-11 Surcharged

5Fils ٥ فلس
a

Fils فلس
b

100 Fils ١٠٠ فلس
c

1966, Oct. 1 Photo. *Perf. 14½*

15	A1 (a)	5f on 5np	.20	.20
16	A1 (a)	15f on 15np	.65	.45
17	A1 (a)	20f on 20np	.90	.60
18	A1 (a)	30f on 30np	1.00	.75
19	A1 (b)	40f on 40np	1.75	1.00
20	A1 (b)	50f on 50np	7.50	9.00
21	A1 (b)	75f on 75np	9.00	9.00

Engr.

Perf. 13x13½

22	A2 (c)	100f on 1r	9.00	6.00
23	A2 (c)	200f on 2r	20.00	12.50
24	A2 (c)	500f on 5r	45.00	42.50
25	A2 (c)	1d on 10r	87.50	95.00
		Nos. 15-25 (11)	182.50	177.00

Overprint on #25 has "1 Dinar" on 1 line and 3 bars through old denomination.

Sheik Zaid bin Sultan al Nahayan
A4 A6

Dorcas Gazelle — A5

Designs: 5f, 15f, 20f, 35f, Crossed flags of Abu Dhabi. 200f, Falcon. 500f, 1d, Palace.

Engr.; Flags Litho.

1967, Apr. 1 *Perf. 13x13½*

26	A4	5f dull grn & red	.15	.15
27	A4	15f dk brown & red	.30	.20
28	A4	20f dk blue & red	.35	.25
29	A4	35f purple & red	.65	.45

Engr.

30	A4	40f green	.75	.55
31	A4	50f brown	1.00	.70
32	A4	60f blue	1.30	.80
33	A4	100f car rose	2.25	1.50

Litho.

34	A5	125f green & brn ol	2.75	1.90
35	A5	200f sky blue & brn	4.50	3.00
36	A5	500f org & brt pur	11.00	7.50
37	A5	1d green & vio bl	25.00	15.00
		Nos. 26-37 (12)	50.00	32.00

In 1969, the 15f was surcharged "25" in Arabic in black with a numbering machine.

1967, Aug. 6 Photo. *Perf. 14½x14*

38	A6	40f Prussian green	1.40	1.10
39	A6	50f brown	1.40	.75
40	A6	60f blue	2.25	1.00
41	A6	100f carmine rose	4.00	1.90
		Nos. 38-41 (4)	9.05	4.75

Human Rights Flame and Sheik Zaid A6a

Perf. 14½x14

1968, Apr. 1 Photo. Unwmk.

Emblem in Red and Green

42	A6a	35f peacock bl & gold	1.25	.60
43	A6a	60f dk blue & gold	2.00	.75
44	A6a	150f dk brown & gold	4.75	1.75
		Nos. 42-44 (3)	8.00	3.10

International Human Rights Year.

Sheik Zaid and Coat of Arms A7

Perf. 14x14½

1968, Aug. 6 Photo. Unwmk.

45	A7	5f green, sil, red & blk	.40	.15
46	A7	10f brn org, sil, red & blk	.60	.20
47	A7	100f lilac, gold, red & blk	3.75	1.50
48	A7	125f lt blue, gold, red & blk	5.50	2.25
		Nos. 45-48 (4)	10.25	4.10

Accession of Sheik Zaid, 2nd anniversary.

Abu Dhabi Airport A8

Designs: 5f, Buildings under construction and earth-moving equipment. 35f, New bridge and falcon. Each stamp shows different portrait of Sheik Zaid.

Perf. 12, 12½x13 (10f)

1969, Mar. 28 Litho.

Size: 5f, 35f, 59x34mm

49	A8	5f multicolored	1.00	.25
50	A8	10f multicolored	1.50	.60
51	A8	35f multicolored	6.00	2.50
		Nos. 49-51 (3)	8.50	3.35

Issued to publicize progress made in Abu Dhabi during preceding 2 years.

Sheik Zaid and Abu Dhabi Petroleum Co. — A9

Designs: 60f, Abu Dhabi Marine Areas drilling platform and helicopter. 125f, Zakum Field separator at night. 200f, Tank farm.

1969, Aug. 6 Litho. *Perf. 14x13½*

52	A9	35f olive grn & multi	.65	.25
53	A9	60f yel brown & multi	1.25	.55
54	A9	125f multicolored	2.75	1.10
55	A9	200f red brown & multi	5.00	2.00
		Nos. 52-55 (4)	9.65	3.90

Accession of Sheik Zaid, 3rd anniversary.

Sheik Zaid — A10

Sheik Zaid and Stallion A11

Designs: 5f, 25f, 60f, 90f, Oval frame around portrait. 150f, Gazelle and Sheik. 500f, Fort Jahili and Sheik. 1d, Grand Mosque and Sheik.

1970-71 Litho. *Perf. 14*

56	A10	5f lt green & multi	.15	.15
57	A10	10f bister & multi	.30	.15
58	A10	25f lilac & multi	.65	.20
59	A10	35f violet & multi	.90	.30
60	A10	50f sepia & multi	1.50	.40
61	A10	60f violet & multi	1.75	.45
62	A10	70f rose red & multi	2.25	.60
63	A10	90f car rose & multi	2.50	.70
64	A11	125f multi ('71)	3.00	.85
65	A11	150f multi ('71)	3.50	1.00
66	A11	500f multi ('71)	11.00	3.50
67	A11	1d multi ('71)	22.50	6.50
		Nos. 56-67 (12)	50.00	14.80

For surcharge see No. 80.

Sheik Zaid and Mt. Fuji — A12

1970, Aug. Litho. *Perf. 13½x13*

68	A12	25f multicolored	1.75	1.00
69	A12	35f multicolored	2.00	1.25
70	A12	60f multicolored	3.75	1.75
		Nos. 68-70 (3)	7.50	4.00

Issued to publicize EXPO '70 International Exhibition, Osaka, Japan, Mar. 15-Sept. 13.

Abu Dhabi Airport A13

Designs: 60f, Airport entrance. 150f, Aerial view of Abu Dhabi Town, vert.

Perf. 14x13½, 13½x14

1970, Sept. 22 Litho.

71	A13	25f multicolored	1.25	.50
72	A13	60f multicolored	4.00	1.25
73	A13	150f multicolored	7.25	3.00
		Nos. 71-73 (3)	12.50	4.75

Accession of Sheik Zaid, 4th anniversary.

Gamal Abdel Nasser — A14

1971, May 3 Litho. *Perf. 14*

74	A14	25f deep rose & blk	2.75	2.00
75	A14	35f rose violet & blk	4.00	3.00

In memory of Gamal Abdel Nasser (1918-1970), President of UAR.

Scout Cars — A15

Designs: 60f, Patrol boat. 125f, Armored car in desert. 150f, Meteor jet fighters.

1971, Aug. 6 Litho. *Perf. 13*

76	A15	35f multicolored	2.25	1.00
77	A15	60f multicolored	3.25	1.50
78	A15	125f multicolored	4.50	2.25
79	A15	150f multicolored	5.00	3.00
		Nos. 76-79 (4)	15.00	7.75

Accession of Sheik Zaid, 5th anniversary.

٥ فلوس

No. 60 Surcharged in Green

5 Fils

1971, Dec. 8 *Perf. 14*

80	A10	5f on 50f multi	*65.00*	*30.00*

Dome of the Rock, Jerusalem — A16

Designs: Different views of Dome of the Rock.

1972, June 3 *Perf. 13*

81	A16	35f lt violet & multi	8.50	2.00
82	A16	60f lt violet & multi	12.50	2.50
83	A16	125f lilac & multi	24.00	5.50
		Nos. 81-83 (3)	45.00	10.00

Nos. 80-83 were issued after Abu Dhabi joined the United Arab Emirates Dec. 2, 1971. Stamps of UAE replaced those of Abu Dhabi. UAE Nos. 1-12 were used only in Abu Dhabi except the 10f and 25f which were issued later in Dubai and Sharjah.

AFARS AND ISSAS

French Territory of the

'ä–,fär(z) and ē–'sä(z)

LOCATION — East Africa
GOVT. — French Overseas Territory
AREA — 8,880 sq. mi.
POP. — 150,000 (est. 1974)
CAPITAL — Djibouti (Jibuti)

The French overseas territory of Somali Coast was renamed the French Territory of the Afars and Issas in 1967. It became the Djibouti Republic (which see) on June 27, 1977.

100 Centimes = 1 Franc

Catalogue values for all unused stamps in this country are for Never Hinged items.

Imperforates
Most stamps of Afars and Issas exist imperforate in issued and trial colors, and also in small presentation sheets in issued colors.

Grayheaded Kingfisher A48

Designs: 15fr, Oystercatcher. 50fr, Greenshanks. 55fr, Abyssinian roller. 60fr, Ground squirrel, vert.

1967 **Engr.** **Unwmk.** *Perf. 13*

310	A48	10fr brt bl, gray grn & blk	1.25	1.10
311	A48	15fr dk brn, bl, ol & ocher	2.00	1.75
312	A48	50fr blk, sl grn & brn	7.75	4.00
313	A48	55fr vio, brt bl & gray grn	9.50	5.00
314	A48	60fr ocher, brt grn & sl grn	13.00	8.00
		Nos. 310-314 (5)	33.50	19.85

Dates of Issue: 10fr, 55fr, Aug. 21; 15fr, 50fr, 60fr, Sept. 25. See No. C50.

Soccer — A49

1967, Dec. 18 **Engr.** *Perf. 13*

315	A49	25fr shown	1.50	1.00
316	A49	30fr Basketball	2.00	1.75

WHO Anniversary Issue
Common Design Type

1968, May 4 **Engr.** *Perf. 13*

317	CD126	15fr multi	1.10	.75

20th anniv. of WHO.

Damerdjog Fortress — A50

Administration Buildings: 25fr, Ali Adde. 30fr, Dorra. 40fr, Assamo.

1968, May 17 **Engr.** *Perf. 13*

318	A50	20fr sl, brn & emer	.90	.50
319	A50	25fr brt grn, bl & brn	.95	.50
320	A50	30fr brn ol, brn org & sl	1.10	.75
321	A50	40fr brn ol, sl & brt grn	2.00	1.50
		Nos. 318-321 (4)	4.95	3.25

Common Design Types
Pictured in section at front of book.

Human Rights Year Issue
Common Design Type

1968, Aug. 10 **Engr.** *Perf. 13*

322	CD127	10fr pur, ver & org	.75	.60
323	CD127	70fr grn, pur & org	1.50	1.10

International Human Rights Year.

Radio-television Station, Djibouti — A52

High Commission Palace, Djibouti — A53

Designs: 2fr, Justice Building. 5fr, Chamber of Deputies. 8fr, Great Mosque. 15fr, Monument of Free French Forces (vert.). 40fr, Djibouti Post Office. 70fr, Residence of Gov. Léonce Lagarde at Obock. No. 332, Djibouti Harbormaster's Building. No. 333, Control tower, Djibouti Airport.

1968-70 **Engr.** *Perf. 13*

324	A52	1fr dk red, sky bl & ind ('69)	.20	.15
325	A52	2fr grn, bl & ind ('69)	.20	.15
326	A52	5fr brn, sky bl & grn ('69)	.28	.20
327	A52	8fr choc, emer & gray ('69)	.32	.20
328	A52	15fr grn, sky bl & yel brn ('69)	2.25	1.75
329	A52	40fr grn, brn & sl ('70)	1.50	.85
330	A53	60fr multi	1.75	1.40
331	A53	70fr dl grn, gray & ol bis ('69)	2.25	1.75
332	A53	85fr multi ('69)	3.00	2.00
333	A52	85fr dk grn, bl & gray ('70)	3.50	2.25
		Nos. 324-333 (10)	15.25	10.70

Locust — A54

Designs: 50fr, Pest control by helicopter. 55fr, Pest control by plane.

1969, Oct. 6 **Engr.** *Perf. 13*

334	A54	15fr brn, grn & slate	1.10	.65
335	A54	50fr dk grn, bl & ol brn	1.75	1.00
336	A54	55fr red brn, bl & brn	2.25	1.75
		Nos. 334-336 (3)	5.10	3.40

Campaign against locusts.

ILO Issue
Common Design Type

1969, Nov. 24 **Engr.** *Perf. 13*

337	CD131	30fr org, gray & lil	1.25	.80

Afar Dagger in Ornamental Scabbard A56

1970, Apr. 3 **Engr.** *Perf. 13*

338	A56	10fr yel grn, dk grn & org brn	.50	.25
339	A56	15fr yel grn, bl & org brn	.60	.25
340	A56	20fr yel grn, red & org brn	.65	.40
341	A56	25fr yel grn, plum & org brn	1.10	.40
		Nos. 338-341 (4)	2.85	1.30

See No. 364.

UPU Headquarters Issue
Common Design Type

1970, May 20 **Engr.** *Perf. 13*

342	CD133	25fr brn, brt grn & choc	1.00	.60

Trapshooting A57

Motorboats A58

Designs: 50fr, Steeplechase. 55fr, Sailboat, vert. 60fr, Equestrians.

1970 **Engr.** *Perf. 13*

343	A57	30fr dp brn, yel grn & brt bl	1.40	1.00
344	A58	48fr bl & multi	1.50	.80
345	A58	50fr cop red, bl & pur	1.75	1.10
346	A58	55fr red brn, bl & ol	1.50	1.00
347	A58	60fr ol, blk & red brn	2.25	1.75
		Nos. 343-347 (5)	8.40	5.65

Issue dates: 30fr, June 5; 48fr, Oct. 9; 50fr, 60fr, Nov. 6.

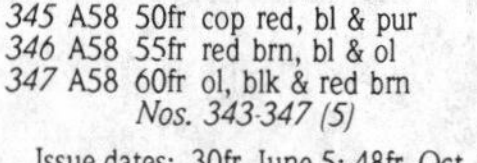

Automatic Ferry, Tadjourah A59

1970, Nov. 25

348	A59	48fr blue, brn & grn	1.40	.75

Volcanic Geode — A60

Diabase and Chrysolite A61

Designs: 10fr, Doleritic basalt. 15fr, Olivine basalt.

1971 **Photo.** *Perf. 13*

349	A61	10fr blk & multi	.40	.35
350	A61	15fr blk & multi	.50	.35
351	A60	25fr blk, crim & brn	1.10	.80
352	A61	40fr blk & multi	2.00	1.40
		Nos. 349-352 (4)	4.00	2.90

Issue dates: 10fr, Nov. 22; 15fr, Oct. 8; 25fr, Apr. 26; 40fr, Jan. 25.

Manta Ray — A62

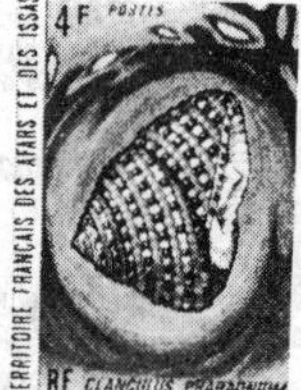

Strawberry Top — A63

Fishes: 5fr, Dolphinfish. 9fr, Smalltooth sawfish.

1971, July 1 **Photo.** *Perf. 12x12½*

353	A62	4fr green & multi	.45	.25
354	A62	5fr blue & multi	.45	.25
355	A62	9fr red & multi	.75	.55
		Nos. 353-355 (3)	1.65	1.05

See No. C60.

De Gaulle Issue
Common Design Type

Designs: 60fr, Gen. Charles de Gaulle, 1940. 85fr, Pres. de Gaulle, 1970.

1971, Nov. 9 **Engr.** *Perf. 13*

356	CD134	60fr dk vio bl & blk	1.50	1.25
357	CD134	85fr dk vio bl & blk	2.00	1.25

1972, Mar. 8 **Photo.** *Perf. 12½x13*

Shells: 9fr, Cypraea pantherina. 20fr, Bullmouth helmet. 50fr, Ethiopian volute.

358	A63	4fr olive & multi	.32	.22
359	A63	9fr dk blue & multi	.42	.40
360	A63	20fr dp green & multi	1.00	.55
361	A63	50fr dp claret & multi	2.00	1.00
		Nos. 358-361 (4)	3.74	2.17

Shepherd — A64

Design: 10fr, Dromedary breeding.

1973, Apr. 11 Photo. *Perf. 13*

362 A64 9fr blue & multi .50 .30
363 A64 10fr blue & multi .50 .30

Afar Dagger — A65

1974, Jan. 29 Engr. *Perf. 13*

364 A65 30fr sl grn & dk brn 1.10 .65

For surcharge see No. 379.

Flamingos, Lake Abbe — A66

Designs: Flamingos and different views of Lake Abbe.

1974, Feb. 22 Photo. *Perf. 13*

370 A66 5fr multicolored .28 .20
371 A66 15fr multicolored .50 .22
372 A66 50fr multicolored 1.50 .75
Nos. 370-372 (3) 2.28 1.17

Soccer Ball — A67

1974, May 24 Engr. *Perf. 13*

373 A67 25fr black & emer 1.25 .80

World Cup Soccer Championship, Munich, June 13-July 7.

Letters Around UPU Emblem A68 — Oleo Chrysophylla A69

1974, Oct. 9 Engr. *Perf. 13*

374 A68 20fr multicolored 1.10 .60
375 A68 100fr multicolored 2.75 2.25

Centenary of Universal Postal Union.

1974, Nov. 22 Photo.

376 A69 10fr *shown* .35 .28
377 A69 15fr *Ficus species* .50 .40
378 A69 20fr *Solanum adoense* 1.10 .80
Nos. 376-378 (3) 1.95 1.48

Day Primary Forest.

No. 364 Surcharged with New Value and Two Bars in Red

1975, Jan. 1 Engr. *Perf. 13*

379 A65 40fr on 30fr multi 1.50 .90

Treasury — A70

Design: 25fr, Government buildings.

1975, Jan. 7 Engr. *Perf. 13*

380 A70 8fr bl, gray & red .40 .28
381 A70 25fr red, bl & ind .75 .60

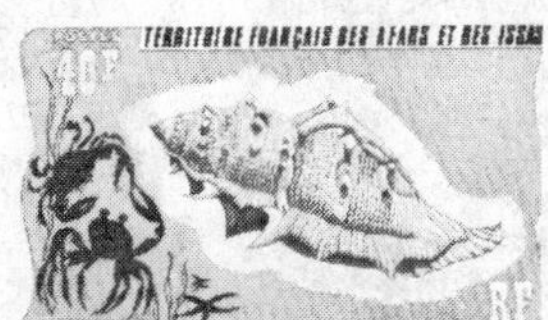

Ranella Spinosa — A71

Sea Shells: No. 382, Darioconus textile. No. 383, Murex palmarosa. 10fr, Conus sumatrensis. 15fr, Cypraea pulchra. No. 386, 45fr, Murex scolopax. No. 387, Cypraea exhusta. 55fr, Cypraea erythraensis. 60fr, Conus taeniatus.

1975-76 Engr. *Perf. 13*

382 A71 5fr bl grn & brn .38 .20
383 A71 5fr bl & multi ('76) .28 .15
384 A71 10fr lil, blk & brn .40 .28
385 A71 15fr bl, indigo & brn .75 .38
386 A71 20fr pur & lt brn 1.10 .75
387 A71 20fr brt grn & multi ('76) .38 .22
388 A71 40fr grn & brn 2.00 1.00
389 A71 45fr grn, bl & bis 1.75 1.00
390 A71 55fr turq & multi ('76) 1.10 .75
391 A71 60fr buff & sepia ('76) 2.00 1.10
Nos. 382-391 (10) 10.14 5.83

Hypolimnas Misippus A72

Butterflies: 40fr, Papilio nireus. 50fr, Acraea anemosa. 65fr, Holocerina smilax menieri. 70fr, Papilio demodocus. No. 397, Papilio dardanus. No. 398, Balachowsky gonimbrasca. 150fr, Vanessa cardui.

1975-76 Photo. *Perf. 13*

392 A72 25fr emer & multi 1.00 .75
393 A72 40fr yel & multi 1.10 .75
394 A72 50fr ultra & multi ('76) 1.40 1.00
395 A72 65fr ol & multi ('76) 1.75 1.00
396 A72 70fr vio & multi 2.25 2.00
397 A72 100fr bl & multi 3.00 2.00
398 A72 100fr Prus bl & multi ('76) 2.25 1.75
399 A72 150fr grn & multi ('76) 3.00 2.00
Nos. 392-399 (8) 15.75 11.25

Mongoose — A73

Animals: 10fr, Hyena. No. 401, Catarrhine monkeys, vert. No. 402, Wild ass, vert. 30fr, Antelope. 60fr, Porcupines, vert. 70fr, Skunks. 200fr, Aardvarks.

Perf. 13x12½, 12½x13

1975-76 Photo.

400 A73 10fr lt vio & multi ('76) .28 .20
401 A73 15fr yel grn & multi .60 .38
402 A73 15fr grn & multi ('76) .40 .28
403 A73 30fr bl & multi ('76) .65 .50
404 A73 50fr dp org & multi 1.75 1.00
405 A73 60fr yel brn & multi 2.00 1.25
406 A73 70fr blk & brn 3.00 1.75
407 A73 200fr bl gray & multi 4.00 3.00
Nos. 400-407 (8) 12.68 8.36

Pin-tailed Whydah — A74 — Palms — A75

Birds: 25fr, Rose-ringed parakeet. 50fr, Variable sunbird. 60fr, Purple heron. No. 417, Hammerhead. No. 418, Turtle dove. 300fr, African spoonbill.

1975-76 Photo. *Perf. 12½x13*

413 A74 20fr lil, blk & org .65 .50
414 A74 25fr car rose & multi ('76) .65 .28
415 A74 50fr bl & multi 1.40 .85
416 A74 60fr multi 2.00 1.10
417 A74 100fr lt grn & multi 2.50 1.75
418 A74 100fr lt yel & multi ('76) 2.00 1.40
419 A74 300fr multi ('76) 5.50 3.75
Nos. 413-419 (7) 14.70 9.63

1975, Dec. 19 Engr. *Perf. 13*

421 A75 20fr brt bl & multi .50 .28

Satellite and Alexander Graham Bell — A76

1976, Mar. 10 Engr. *Perf. 13*

422 A76 200fr dp bl, org & sl grn 3.00 2.00

Centenary of the first telephone call by Alexander Graham Bell, Mar. 10, 1876.

Basketball A77

1976, July 7 Litho. *Perf. 12½*

423 A77 10fr shown .26 .15
424 A77 15fr Bicycling .55 .30
425 A77 40fr Soccer 1.00 .70
426 A77 60fr Running 1.65 1.10
Nos. 423-426 (4) 3.46 2.25

21st Olympic Games, Montreal, Canada, July 17-Aug. 1.

Turkeyfish — A78

1976, Aug. 10 Photo. *Perf. 13x13½*

428 A78 45fr bl & multi 1.40 1.00

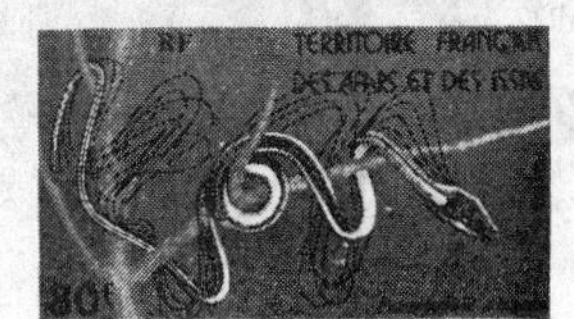

Psammophis Elegans — A79

Design: 70fr, Naja nigricollis, vert.

Perf. 13x13½, 13½x13

1976, Sept. 27 Photo.

430 A79 70fr ocher & multi 1.75 1.50
431 A79 80fr emer & multi 2.00 1.75

Motorcyclist — A80

1977, Jan. 27 Litho. *Perf. 12x12½*

432 A80 200fr multi 3.75 2.75

Moto-Cross motorcycle race.

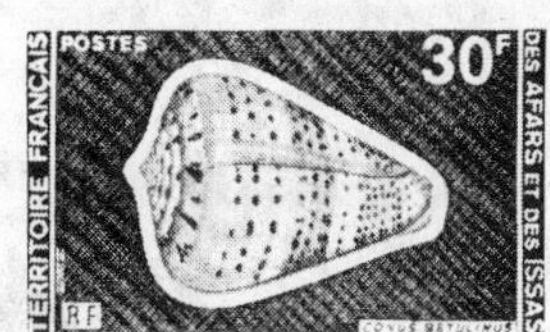

Conus Betulinus — A81

Sea Shells: 5fr, Cyprea tigris. 70fr, Conus striatus. 85fr, Cyprea mauritiana.

1977 Engr. *Perf. 13*

433 A81 5fr multi .45 .28
434 A81 30fr multi .60 .38
435 A81 70fr multi 2.25 1.10
436 A81 85fr multi 3.25 2.00
Nos. 433-436 (4) 6.55 3.76

Gaterin Gaterinus A82

1977, Apr. 15 Photo. *Perf. 13x12½*

437 A82 15fr shown .55 .28
438 A82 65fr Barracudas 1.50 .80

Stamps of the French Territory of the Afars and Issas were replaced in 1977 by those of the Republic of Djibouti.

AIR POST STAMPS

Tawny Eagles AP16 — Parachutists AP17

Unwmk.

1967, Aug. 21 Engr. *Perf. 13*

C50 AP16 200fr multi 12.00 7.50

1968 Engr. *Perf. 13*

Design: 85fr, Water skier and skin diver.

C51 AP17 48fr brn ol, Prus bl & brn 2.75 1.50
C52 AP17 85fr dk brn, ol & Prus bl 3.50 2.25

Issue dates: 48fr, Jan. 5; 85fr, Mar. 15.

Aerial Map of the Territory — AP18

1968, Nov. 15 Engr. *Perf. 13*

C53 AP18 500fr bl, dk brn & ocher 26.00 8.00

Buildings Type of Regular Issue

Designs: 100fr, Cathedral, vert. 200fr, Sayed Hassan Mosque, vert.

1969 Engr. *Perf. 13*

C54 A53 100fr multi 2.50 1.25
C55 A53 200fr multi 5.00 2.75

Issue dates: 100fr, Apr. 4; 200fr, May 8.

Concorde Issue

Common Design Type

1969, Apr. 17

C56 CD129 100fr org red & olive 17.50 10.00

Arta Ionospheric Station — AP19

Japanese Sword Guard, Fish Design — AP20

1970, May 8 Engr. *Perf. 13*

C57 AP19 70fr multi 2.50 2.00

Gold embossed

1970, Sept. 29 *Perf. 12½*

Design: 200fr, Japanese sword guard, horse design.

C58 AP20 100fr multi 7.50 5.00
C59 AP20 200fr multi 9.50 5.50

EXPO '70 International Exposition, Osaka, Japan, Mar. 15-Sept. 13.

Parrotfish AP21

1971, July 1 Photo. *Perf. 12½*

C60 AP21 30fr blk & multi 2.00 1.75

Djibouti Harbor AP22

1971, Nov. 26

C61 AP22 100fr bl & multi 3.25 2.00

New Djibouti harbor.

Lichtenstein's Sandgrouse AP23

Running, Olympic Rings AP24

Birds: 49fr, Hoopoe. 66fr, Great snipe. 500fr, Tawny-breasted francolin.

1972 Photo. *Perf. 12½x13*

C62 AP23 30fr multi 1.90 1.40
C63 AP23 49fr multi 2.75 2.50
C64 AP23 66fr bl & multi 3.75 2.50
C65 AP23 500fr multi 17.50 8.00
Nos. C62-C65 (4) 25.90 14.40

Issue dates: #C65, Nov. 3, others Apr. 21.

1972, June 8 Engr. *Perf. 13*

Designs (Olympic Rings and): 10fr, Basketball. 55fr, Swimming, horiz. 60fr, Olympic torch and Greek frieze, horiz.

C66 AP24 5fr multi .30 .20
C67 AP24 10fr multi .38 .20
C68 AP24 55fr multi 1.40 .75
C69 AP24 60fr multi 1.90 .90
Nos. C66-C69 (4) 3.98 2.05

20th Olympic Games, Munich, Aug. 26-Sept. 11.

Louis Pasteur — AP25

Design: 100fr, Albert Calmette and C. Guérin.

1972, Oct. 5 Engr. *Perf. 13*

C70 AP25 20fr multi .80 .50
C71 AP25 100fr multi 3.00 2.25

Pasteur, Calmette, Guerin, chemists and bacteriologists, benefactors of mankind.

Map and Views of Territory — AP26

Design: 200fr, Woman and Mosque of Djibouti, vert.

1973, Jan. 15 Photo. *Perf. 13*

C72 AP26 30fr brn & multi 3.25 2.75
C73 AP26 200fr multi 7.25 5.75

Visit of Pres. Georges Pompidou of France, Jan. 15-17.

Oryx AP27

1973, Feb. 26 Photo. *Perf. 13x12½*

C74 AP27 30fr shown 1.00 .75
C75 AP27 50fr Dik-dik 1.75 1.00
C76 AP27 66fr Caracal 2.50 2.00
Nos. C74-C76 (3) 5.25 3.75

See Nos. C94-C96.

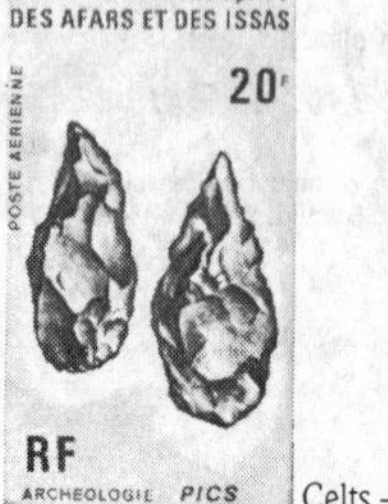

Celts — AP28

Designs: Various pre-historic flint tools. 40fr, 60fr, horiz.

1973 *Perf. 13*

C77 AP28 20fr yel grn, blk & brn 1.50 1.10
C78 AP28 40fr yel & multi 1.50 1.10
C79 AP28 49fr lil & multi 2.50 1.75
C80 AP28 60fr bl & multi 2.50 1.75
Nos. C77-C80 (4) 8.00 5.70

Issued: 20fr, 49fr, Mar. 16; 40fr, 60fr, Sept. 7.

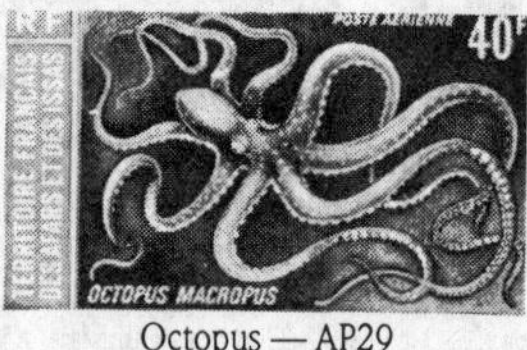

Octopus — AP29

1973, Mar. 16

C81 AP29 40fr shown 1.50 .80
C82 AP29 60fr Dugong 2.75 1.75

Copernicus — AP30

Baboons — AP31

Designs: 8fr, Nicolaus Copernicus, Polish astronomer. 9fr, William C. Roentgen, physicist, X-ray discoverer. No. C85, Edward Jenner, physician, discoverer of vaccination. No. C86, Marie Curie, discoverer of radium and polonium. 49fr, Robert Koch, physician and bacteriologist. 50fr, Clement Ader (1841-1925), French aviation pioneer. 55fr, Guglielmo Marconi, Italian electrical engineer, inventor. 85fr, Moliere, French playwright. 100fr, Henri Farman (1874-1937), French aviation pioneer. 150fr, Andre-Marie Ampere (1775-1836), French physicist. 250fr, Michelangelo Buonarroti (1475-1564), Italian sculptor, painter and architect.

1973-75 Engr. *Perf. 13*

C83 AP30 8fr multi .50 .28
C84 AP30 9fr multi .40 .28
C85 AP30 10fr multi .40 .28
C86 AP30 10fr multi .50 .28
C87 AP30 49fr multi 2.50 1.75
C88 AP30 50fr multi 2.00 1.40
C89 AP30 55fr multi 1.75 1.40
C90 AP30 85fr multi 3.50 2.25
C91 AP30 100fr multi 3.25 2.75
C92 AP30 150fr multi 3.25 2.75
C93 AP30 250fr multi 5.50 4.00
Nos. C83-C93 (11) 23.55 17.42

Issue dates: 8fr, 85fr, May 9, 1973. 9fr, No. C85, 49fr, Oct. 12, 1973. 100fr, Jan. 29, 1974. 55fr, Mar. 22, 1974. No. C86, Aug. 23, 1974. 150fr, July 24, 1975. 250fr, June 26, 1975. 50fr, Sept. 25, 1975.

Perf. 12½x13, 13x12½

1973, Dec. 12 Photo.

C94 AP31 20fr shown .80 .60
C95 AP31 50fr Genets, horiz. 1.75 .80
C96 AP31 66fr Hares 2.75 1.75
Nos. C94-C96 (3) 5.30 3.15

Spearfishing — AP32

1974, Apr. 14 Engr. *Perf. 13*

C97 AP32 200fr multi 5.00 4.25

No. C97 was prepared for release in Nov. 1972, for the 3rd Underwater Spearfishing Contest in the Red Sea. Dates were obliterated with a rectangle and the stamp was not issued without this obliteration.

Rock Carvings, Balho — AP33

1974, Apr. 26

C98 AP33 200fr car & slate 6.25 4.25

Lake Assal AP34

Designs (Lake Assal): 50fr, Rock formations on shore. 85fr, Crystallized wood.

1974, Oct. 25 Photo. *Perf. 13*

C99 AP34 49fr multi 1.00 .80
C100 AP34 50fr multi 1.25 1.00
C101 AP34 85fr multi 2.25 2.00
Nos. C99-C101 (3) 4.50 3.80

Guinea Dove — AP35

1975, May 23 Photo. *Perf. 13*

C102 AP35 500fr multi 11.00 6.00

Djibouti Airport — AP36

1977, Mar. 1 Litho. *Perf. 12*

C103 AP36 500fr multi 9.00 7.50

Opening of new Djibouti Airport.

Thomas A. Edison and Phonograph — AP37

Design: 75fr, Alexander Volta, electric train, lines and light bulb.

1977, May 5 Engr. *Perf. 13*

C104 AP37 55fr multi 2.00 1.40
C105 AP37 75fr multi 3.25 2.25

Famous inventors: Thomas Alva Edison and Alexander Volta (1745-1827).

POSTAGE DUE STAMPS

Nomad's Milk Jug — D3

Perf. 14x13

1969, Dec. 15 Engr. Unwmk.

J49	D3	1fr red brn, red lil & slate	.15	.15
J50	D3	2fr red brn, emer & slate	.15	.15
J51	D3	5fr red brn, bl & slate	.28	.28
J52	D3	10fr red brn, brn & slate	.60	.60
		Nos. J49-J52 (4)	1.18	1.18

AFGHANISTAN

af-'ga-nə-,stan

LOCATION — Central Asia, bounded by Iran, Russian Turkestan, Pakistan, Baluchistan and China
GOVT. — Republic
AREA — 251,773 sq. mi.
POP. — 17,150,000 (1984 est.)
CAPITAL — Kabul

Afghanistan changed from a constitutional monarchy to a republic in July 1973.

12 Shahi = 6 Sanar = 3 Abasi =
2 Krans = 1 Rupee Kabuli
60 Paisas = 1 Rupee (1921)
100 Pouls = 1 Rupee Afghani (1927)

Catalogue values for unused stamps in this country are for Never Hinged items, beginning with Scott 364 in the regular postage section, Scott B1 in the semi-postal section, Scott C7 in the airpost section, Scott O8 in officials section, and Scott RA6 in the postal tax section.

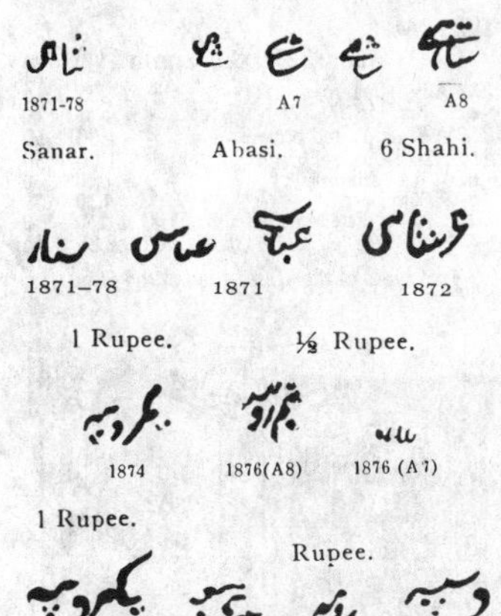

From 1871 to 1892 and 1898 the Moslem year date appears on the stamp. Numerals as follows:

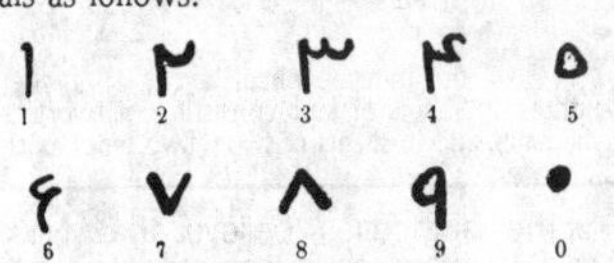

Until 1891 cancellation consisted of cutting or tearing a piece from the stamps. Such copies should not be considered as damaged.

Values are for cut square examples of good color. Cut to shape or faded copies sell for much less, particularly Nos. 2-10.

Nos. 2-108 are on laid paper of varying thickness except where wove is noted.

Until 1907 all stamps were issued ungummed.

The tiger's head on types A2 to A11 symbolizes the name of the contemporary amir, Sher (Tiger) Ali.

Kingdom of Kabul

Tiger's Head
A2

(Both circles dotted)

1871 Unwmk. Litho. *Imperf.*

Dated "1288"

2	A2	1sh black	110.00	22.50
3	A2	1sa black	75.00	20.00
4	A2	1ab black	37.50	20.00

Thirty varieties of the shahi, 10 of the sanar and 5 of the abasi.

Similar designs without the tiger's head in the center are revenues.

A3

(Outer circle dotted)

Dated "1288"

5	A3	1sh black	175.00	35.00
6	A3	1sa black	75.00	22.50
7	A3	1ab black	37.50	22.50

Five varieties of each.

A4

1872

Toned Wove Paper

Dated "1289"

8	A4	6sh violet	*850.*	*550.*
9	A4	1rup violet	*1,200.*	*650.*

Two varieties of each. Date varies in location. Printed in sheets of 4 (2x2) containing two of each denomination.

Most used copies are smeared with a greasy ink cancel.

A4a

1873

White Laid Paper

Dated "1290"

10	A4a	1sh black	10.00	4.50
a.		Corner ornament missing	*450.00*	*375.00*
b.		Corner ornament retouched	*60.00*	*25.00*

15 varieties. Nos. 10a, 10b are the sixth stamp on the sheet.

A5

1873

11	A5	1sh black	2.25	2.00
11A	A5	1sh violet	*500.00*	

Sixty varieties of each.

1874

Dated "1291"

12	A5	1ab black	40.00	25.00
13	A5	½rup black	20.00	17.50
14	A5	1rup black	22.50	20.00
		Nos. 12-14 (3)	82.50	62.50

Five varieties of each.

Nos. 12-14 were printed on the same sheet. Se-tenant varieties exist.

A6

A7

1875

Dated "1292"

15	A6	1sa black	*160.00*	*125.00*
a.		Wide outer circle	*600.00*	
16	A6	1ab black	225.00	175.00
17	A6	1sa brown violet	22.50	22.50
a.		Wide outer circle	110.00	
18	A6	1ab brown violet	40.00	25.00

Ten varieties of the sanar, five of the abasi.

Nos. 15-16 and 17-18 were printed in the same sheets. Se-tenant pairs exist.

1876

Dated "1293"

19	A7	1sh black	300.00	150.00
20	A7	1sa black	375.00	200.00
21	A7	1ab black	600.00	325.00
22	A7	½rup black	375.00	200.00
23	A7	1rup black	550.00	200.00
24	A7	1sh violet	375.00	200.00
25	A7	1sa violet	350.00	200.00
26	A7	1ab violet	425.00	200.00
27	A7	½rup violet	90.00	55.00
28	A7	1rup violet	90.00	75.00

12 varieties of the shahi and 3 each of the other values.

A8

1876

Dated "1293"

29	A8	1sh gray	5.00	4.00
30	A8	1sa gray	7.50	4.00
31	A8	1ab gray	15.00	7.50
32	A8	½rup gray	17.50	10.00
33	A8	1rup gray	22.50	10.00
34	A8	1sh olive blk	125.00	
35	A8	1sa olive blk	175.00	
36	A8	1ab olive blk	350.00	
37	A8	½rup olive blk	250.00	
38	A8	1rup olive blk	275.00	
39	A8	1sh green	22.50	3.75
40	A8	1sa green	35.00	15.00
41	A8	1ab green	50.00	37.50
42	A8	½rup green	100.00	40.00
43	A8	1rup green	100.00	80.00
44	A8	1sh ocher	22.50	7.50
45	A8	1sa ocher	35.00	15.00
46	A8	1ab ocher	60.00	27.50
47	A8	½rup ocher	75.00	60.00
48	A8	1rup ocher	125.00	110.00
49	A8	1sh violet	22.50	5.50
50	A8	1sa violet	22.50	7.50
51	A8	1ab violet	35.00	10.00
52	A8	½rup violet	60.00	22.50
53	A8	1rup violet	75.00	35.00

12 varieties of the sanar, 6 of the abasi and 3 each of the ½ rupee and rupee.

24 varieties of the shahi, 4 of which show denomination written:

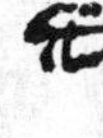

A9

1877

Dated "1294"

54	A9	1sh gray	3.50	2.25
55	A9	1sa gray	6.00	3.00
56	A9	1ab gray	9.00	6.00
57	A9	½rup gray	12.00	12.00
58	A9	1rup gray	12.00	12.00
59	A9	1sh black	10.00	
60	A9	1sa black	17.50	
61	A9	1ab black	42.50	
62	A9	½rup black	45.00	
63	A9	1rup black	45.00	
64	A9	1sh green	4.50	3.50
a.		Wove paper	12.00	
65	A9	1sa green	7.50	3.50
a.		Wove paper	16.00	12.00
66	A9	1ab green	10.00	10.00
a.		Wove paper	27.50	
67	A9	½rup green	14.00	14.00
a.		Wove paper	30.00	30.00
68	A9	1rup green	14.00	14.00
a.		Wove paper	30.00	30.00
69	A9	1sh ocher	3.50	2.00
70	A9	1sa ocher	10.00	3.50
71	A9	1ab ocher	17.50	16.00
72	A9	½rup ocher	30.00	30.00
73	A9	1rup ocher	30.00	30.00
74	A9	1sh violet	3.75	2.00
75	A9	1sa violet	7.50	2.75
76	A9	1ab violet	11.00	7.50
77	A9	½rup violet	17.50	14.00
78	A9	1rup violet	17.50	14.00

25 varieties of the shahi, 8 of the sanar, 3 of the abasi and 2 each of the ½rupee and rupee.

A10

A11

1878

Dated "1295"

79	A10	1sh gray	1.50	1.50
80	A10	1sa gray	1.75	1.75
81	A10	1ab gray	3.75	3.75
82	A10	½rup gray	10.00	7.50
83	A10	1rup gray	10.00	7.50
84	A10	1sh black	3.00	
85	A10	1sa black	3.00	
86	A10	1ab black	10.00	
87	A10	½rup black	20.00	
88	A10	1rup black	20.00	
89	A10	1sh green	21.00	20.00
90	A10	1sa green	3.00	3.00
91	A10	1ab green	11.00	10.00
92	A10	½rup green	21.00	17.50
93	A10	1rup green	21.00	17.50
94	A10	1sh ocher	10.00	3.00
95	A10	1sa ocher	3.00	2.25
96	A10	1ab ocher	11.00	10.00
97	A10	½rup ocher	21.00	21.00
98	A10	1rup ocher	16.00	16.00
99	A10	1sh violet	1.75	1.75
100	A10	1sa violet	1.75	1.75
101	A10	1ab violet	5.50	5.50
102	A10	½rup violet	21.00	17.50
103	A10	1rup violet	21.00	17.50
104	A11	1sh gray	2.00	1.75
105	A11	1sh black	*90.00*	
106	A11	1sh green	1.75	1.75
107	A11	1sh ocher	1.40	1.40
108	A11	1sh violet	2.00	1.75

40 varieties of the shahi, 30 of the sanar, 6 of the abasi and 2 each of the ½ rupee and 1 rupee.

The 1876, 1877 and 1878 issues were printed in separate colors for each main post office on the Peshawar-Kabul-Khulm (Tashkurghan) postal route. Some specialists consider the black printings to be proofs or trial colors.

There are many shades of these colors.

1ab, Type I
(26mm) — A12

1ab, Type II
(28mm) — A13

A14

A15

Dated "1298", numerals scattered through design

Handstamped, in watercolor

1881-90

Thin White Laid Batonne Paper

109 A12 1ab violet 1.75 1.10
109A A13 1ab violet 3.50 2.50
110 A12 1ab black brn 3.50 1.75
111 A12 1ab rose 2.00 2.00
b. Se-tenant with No. 111A 16.00
111A A13 1ab rose 2.50 2.00
112 A14 2ab violet 1.75 1.50
113 A14 2ab black brn 5.00 4.00
114 A14 2ab rose 3.00 3.00
115 A15 1rup violet 2.50 1.50
116 A15 1rup black brn 6.50 6.50
117 A15 1rup rose 3.00 3.00

Thin White Wove Batonne Paper

118 A12 1ab violet 6.50 4.00
119 A12 1ab vermilion 4.25
120 A12 1ab rose
121 A14 2ab violet
122 A14 2ab vermilion 5.00
122A A14 2ab black brn
123 A15 1rup violet 8.25
124 A15 1rup vermilion 6.50
125 A15 1rup black brn 8.25

Thin White Laid Batonne Paper

126 A12 1ab brown org 2.50 2.50
126A A13 1ab brn org (II) 3.50 3.50
127 A12 1ab carmine lake 2.50 2.50
a. Laid paper
128 A14 2ab brown org 2.50 2.50
129 A14 2ab carmine lake 3.00 3.00
130 A15 1rup brown org 10.00 10.00
131 A15 1rup car lake 4.25 4.25

Yellowish Laid Batonne Paper

132 A12 1ab purple 3.50
133 A12 1ab red 6.50 3.50

1884

Colored Wove Paper

133A A13 1ab purple, *yel* (II) 17.50 17.50
134 A12 1ab purple, *grn* 20.00
135 A12 1ab purple, *blue* 32.50 21.00
136 A12 1ab red, *grn* 37.50
137 A12 1ab red, *yel* 1.75
139 A12 1ab red, *rose* 6.00
140 A14 2ab red, *yel* 6.00
142 A14 2ab red, *rose* 5.50
143 A15 1rup red, *yel* 6.50 6.50
145 A15 1rup red, *rose* 7.00 7.00

Thin Colored Ribbed Paper

146 A14 2ab red, *yellow* 3.00
147 A15 1rup red, *yellow* 8.25
148 A12 1ab lake, *lilac* 4.00
149 A14 2ab lake, *lilac* 5.00
150 A15 1rup lake, *lilac* 4.00
151 A12 1ab lake, *green* 2.00
152 A14 2ab lake, *green* 4.00
153 A15 1rup lake, *green* 4.00

1886-88

Colored Wove Paper

155 A12 1ab black, *magenta* 27.50
156 A12 1ab claret brn, *org* 20.00
156A A12 1ab red, *org* 2.00
156B A14 2ab red, *org* 4.75
156C A15 1rup red, *org* 3.50

Laid Batonné Paper

157 A12 1ab black, *lavender* 2.75
158 A12 1ab cl brn, *grn* 6.50
159 A12 1ab black, *pink* 17.50
160 A14 2ab black, *pink* 35.00
161 A15 1rup black, *pink* 20.00

Laid Paper

162 A12 1ab black, *pink* 6.50
163 A14 2ab black, *pink* 6.50
164 A15 1rup black, *pink* 6.50
165 A12 1ab brown, *yel* 6.50
166 A14 2ab brown, *yel* 6.50
167 A15 1rup brown, *yel* 6.50
168 A12 1ab blue, *grn* 6.50
169 A14 2ab blue, *grn* 6.50
170 A15 1rup blue, *grn* 6.50

1891

Colored Wove Paper

175 A12 1ab green, *rose* 22.50
176 A15 1rup pur, *grn batonne* 22.50

Nos. 109-176 fall into three categories:

1. Those regularly issued and in normal postal use from 1881 on, handstamped on thin white laid or wove paper in strip sheets containing 12 or more impressions of the same denomination arranged in two irregular rows, with the impressions often touching or overlappng.

2. The 1884 postal issues provisionally printed on smooth or ribbed colored wove paper as needed to supplement low stocks of the normal white paper stamps.

3. The "special" printings made in a range of colors on several types of laid or wove colored papers, most of which were never used for normal printings. These were produced periodically from 1886 to 1891 to meet philatelic demands. Although nominally valid for postage, most of the special printings were exported directly to fill dealers' orders, and few were ever postally used. Many of the sheets contained all three denominations with impressions separated by ruled lines. Sometimes different colors were used, so se-tenant multiples of denomination or color exist. Many combinations of stamp and paper colors exist besides those listed.

Various shades of each color exist.

Type A12 is known dated "1297."

Counterfeits, lithographed or typographed, are plentiful.

Kingdom of Afghanistan

A16

A17

A18

Dated "1309"

1891 Pelure Paper Litho.

177 A16 1ab slate blue .85 .85
a. Tete beche pair 14.00
178 A17 2ab slate blue 6.00 5.00
179 A18 1rup slate blue 12.25 10.00
Nos. 177-179 (3) 19.10 15.85

Revenue stamps of similar design exist in various colors.

Nos. 177-179 were printed in panes on the same sheet, so se-tenant gutter pairs exist. Examples in black or red are proofs.

A Mosque Gate and Crossed Cannons (National Seal) — A19

Dated "1310" in Upper Right Corner

1892

Flimsy Wove Paper

180 A19 1ab black, *green* 2.00 1.60
181 A19 1ab black, *orange* 2.50 2.50
182 A19 1ab black, *yellow* 2.00 1.60
183 A19 1ab black, *pink* 2.50 1.60
184 A19 1ab black, *lil rose* 2.50 2.50
185 A19 1ab black, *blue* 4.25 3.50
186 A19 1ab black, *salmon* 2.50 2.00
187 A19 1ab black, *magenta* 2.50 2.50
188 A19 1ab black, *violet* 2.50 2.50
188A A19 1ab black, *scarlet* 2.50 1.75

Many shades exist.

A20

A21

Undated

1894

Flimsy Wove Paper

189 A20 2ab black, *green* 6.50 6.50
190 A21 1rup black, *green* 10.00 10.00

24 varieties of the 2 abasi and 12 varieties of the rupee.

Nos. 189-190 and F3 were printed se-tenant in the same sheet. Pairs exist.

A21a

Dated "1316"

1898

Flimsy Wove Paper

191 A21a 2ab black, *pink* 2.50
192 A21a 2ab black, *magenta* 2.50
193 A21a 2ab black, *yellow* 1.10
193A A21a 2ab black, *salmon* 3.00
194 A21a 2ab black, *green* 1.40
195 A21a 2ab black, *purple* 1.75
195A A21a 2ab black, *blue* 17.50
Nos. 191-195A (7) 29.75

Nos. 191-195A were not regularly issued. Genuinely used copies are scarce. No. 195A was found in remainder stocks and probably was never released.

A22

A23

A24

1907 Engr. *Imperf.*

Medium Wove Paper

196 A22 1ab blue green 3.75 2.50
a. 1ab emerald 8.50 5.00
197 A22 1ab brt blue 10.00 10.00
198 A23 2ab deep blue 1.85 1.25
199 A24 1rup green 3.00 2.50
a. 1rup blue green 6.00 6.00

Zigzag Roulette 10

200 A22 1ab green 60.00
201 A23 2ab blue 80.00
201A A24 1rup blue green *110.00*

1908 *Perf. 12*

202 A22 1ab green 10.00 6.25
203 A23 2ab deep blue 1.25 1.25
204 A24 1rup blue green 3.00 3.00
Nos. 202-204 (3) 14.25 10.50

Twelve varieties of the 1 abasi, 6 of the 2 abasi, 4 of the 1 rupee.

Nos. 196-204 were issued in small sheets containing 3 or 4 panes. Gutter pairs, normal and tête bêche, exist.

A25

A26

A27

1909-19 Typo. *Perf. 12*

205 A25 1ab ultra .35 .22
a. Imperf., pair 5.00
206 A25 1ab red ('16) .22 .15
a. Imperf.
207 A25 1ab rose ('18) .22 .15
208 A26 2ab green .50 .25
a. Imperf., pair 3.00
b. Horiz. pair, imperf. btwn.
208C A26 2ab yellow ('16) 1.25 1.25
209 A26 2ab bis ('18-'19) .90 .90
210 A27 1rup lilac brn 1.50 1.50
a. 1rup red brown 2.50 2.00
211 A27 1rup ol bis ('16) 1.50 1.50
Nos. 205-211 (8) 6.44 5.92

A28

1913

212 A28 2pa drab brown 1.25 1.25
a. 2pa red brown 1.25 1.25

No. 212 is inscribed "Tiket waraq dak" (Postal card stamps). It was usable only on postcards and not accepted for postage on letters.

Nos. 196-212 sometimes show letters of a papermaker's watermark, "Howard & Jones, London."

Royal Star — A29

1920, Aug. 24 *Perf. 12*

Size: 39x47mm

214 A29 10pa rose 20.00 12.00
215 A29 20pa red brown 45.00 18.00
216 A29 30pa green 90.00 60.00
Nos. 214-216 (3) 155.00 90.00

Issued in sheets of two.

1921, Mar.

Size: 22 1/2x28 1/4mm

217 A29 10pa rose .35 .16
a. Perf. 11 ('27) .65 1.00
218 A29 20pa red brown 1.00 .50
219 A29 30pa yel green 1.00 .50
a. Tete beche pair 6.00 5.50
b. 30pa green 1.50 .75
c. As "b," Tete beche pair 6.50 6.50
Nos. 217-219 (3) 2.35 1.16

Two types of the 10pa, three of the 20pa.

Crest of King Amanullah — A32
A30 A32

1924, Feb. 26 *Perf. 12*

220 A30 10pa chocolate 10.00 6.00
a. Tete beche pair 20.00 16.00

6th Independence Day.

Printed in sheets of four consisting of two tete beche pairs, and in sheets of two. Two types exist.

Some authorities believe that Nos. Q15-Q16 were issued as regular postage stamps.

1925, Feb. 26 *Perf. 12*

Size: 29x37mm

222 A32 10pa light brown 10.00 6.00

7th Independence Day.

Printed in sheets of 8 (two panes of 4).

1926, Feb. 28

Wove Paper

Size: 26x33mm

224 A32 10pa dark blue 1.40 1.40
a. Imperf., pair 6.00
b. Horiz. pair, imperf. btwn. 8.00
c. Vert. pair, imperf. btwn. 8.00
d. Laid paper 6.50 5.00

7th anniv. of Independence. Printed in sheets of 4, and in sheets of 8 (two panes of 4). Tete beche gutter pairs exist.

Tughra and Crest of Amanullah — A33

1927, Feb.

225 A33 10pa magenta	10.00	4.25
a. Vertical pair, imperf. between	20.00	

Dotted Background

226 A33 10pa magenta	5.50	4.25
a. Horiz. pair, imperf. between	15.00	

The surface of No. 226 is covered by a net of fine dots.

8th anniv. of Independence. Printed in sheets of 8 (two panes of 4). Tete beche gutter pairs exist.

National Seal — A34

A35

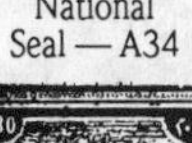

A35a

A36

1927, Oct. ***Imperf.***

227 A34 15p pink	.35	.35
228 A35 30p Prus green	.80	.40
229 A36 60p light blue	1.50	1.50
a. Tete beche pair	4.50	
Nos. 227-229 (3)	2.65	2.25

1927-30 ***Perf. 11, 12***

230 A34 15p pink	.22	.16
231 A34 15p ultra ('29)	.50	.30
232 A35 30p Prus green	.35	.35
233 A35a 30p dp green ('30)	.75	.70
234 A36 60p bright blue	1.50	1.00
a. Tete beche pair	5.00	
235 A36 60p black ('29)	1.40	.65
Nos. 230-235 (6)	4.72	3.16

Nos. 230, 232 and 234 are usually imperforate on one or two sides.

No. 233 has been redrawn. A narrow border of pearls has been added and "30," in European and Arabic numerals, inserted in the upper spandrels.

Tughra and Crest of Amanullah A37

1928, Feb. 27

236 A37 15p pink	2.00	2.00
a. Tete beche pair	7.50	
b. Horiz. pair, imperf. vert.	6.00	
c. As "a," imperf. vert., block of 4	10.00	

9th anniv. of Independence. This stamp is always imperforate on one or two sides.

A 15p blue of somewhat similar design was prepared for the 10th anniv., but was not issued due to Amanullah's dethronement. Value, $15.

A38

A39

A40

A41

A42

1928-30 ***Perf. 11, 12***

237 A38 2p dull blue	2.50	1.60
a. Vertical pair, imperf. between		
238 A38 2p lt rose ('30)	.25	.25
239 A39 10p gray green	.25	.15
a. Tete beche pair	5.00	5.00
b. Vert. pair, imperf. horiz.	.65	
c. Vertical pair, imperf. between	1.00	
240 10p choc ('30)	.50	.50
a. 10p brown purple ('29)	10.00	2.50
241 A40 25p car rose	.35	.25
242 A40 25p Prus green ('29)	.75	.60
243 A41 40p ultra	.40	.35
a. Tete beche pair	5.00	
244 A41 40p rose ('29)	1.00	1.00
a. Tete beche pair	7.00	
b. Vert. pair, imperf. horiz.	3.50	
245 A42 50p red	.30	.30
246 A42 50p dk blue ('29)	1.50	1.00
Nos. 237-246 (10)	7.80	6.00

The sheets of these stamps are often imperforate at the outer margins.

Nos. 237-238 are newspaper stamps.

This handstamp was used for ten months by the Revolutionary Gov't in Kabul as a control mark on outgoing mail. It occasionally fell on the stamps but there is no evidence that it was officially used as an overprint. Unused copies were privately made.

Independence Monument — A46

Wmk. Large Seal in the Sheet

1931, Aug. Litho. ***Perf. 12***

Laid Paper

Without Gum

262 A46 20p red	1.00	.60

13th Independence Day.

National Assembly Chamber — A47

A48

A50

National Assembly Building A49

National Assembly Chamber A51

National Assembly Building — A52

1932 Unwmk. Typo. ***Perf. 12***

Wove Paper

263 A47 40p olive	1.00	.40
264 A48 60p violet	.65	.50
265 A49 80p dark red	1.00	.80
266 A50 1af black	10.00	4.25
267 A51 2af ultra	3.50	2.75
268 A52 3af gray green	4.25	3.50
Nos. 263-268 (6)	20.40	12.20

Formation of the Natl. Council. Imperforate or perforated examples on ungummed chalky paper are proofs.

See Nos. 304-305.

Mosque at Balkh — A53

Kabul Fortress — A54

Parliament House, Darul Funun — A55

Parliament House, Darul Funun — A56

Arch of Qalai Bist — A57

Memorial Pillar of Knowledge and Ignorance — A58

Independence Monument — A59

Minaret at Herat — A60

Arch of Paghman — A61

Ruins at Balkh — A62

Minarets of Herat — A63

Great Buddha at Bamian — A64

1932 Typo. ***Perf. 12***

269 A53 10p brown	.50	.15
270 A54 15p dk brown	.60	.15
271 A55 20p red	.28	.16
272 A56 25p dk green	.75	.15
273 A57 30p red	.40	.28
274 A58 40p orange	.65	.35
275 A59 50p blue	.80	.35
a. Tete beche pair	5.50	
276 A60 60p blue	1.50	.50
277 A61 80p violet	1.75	1.00
278 A62 1af dark blue	2.75	.60
279 A63 2af dk red violet	3.75	2.00
280 A64 3af claret	4.25	2.50
Nos. 269-280 (12)	17.98	8.19

Counterfeits of types A53-A65 exist.

See Nos. 290-295, 298-299, 302-303.

Entwined 2's — A65

Two types:

Type I - Numerals shaded. Size about 21x29mm.

Type II - Numerals unshaded. Size about 21¾x30mm.

1931-38 ***Perf. 12, 11x12***

281 A65 2p red brn (I)	.25	.15
282 A65 2p olive blk (I) ('34)	.25	.15
283 A65 2p grnsh gray (I) ('34)	.35	.15
283A A65 2p black (II) ('36)	.35	.15
284 A65 2p salmon (II) ('38)	.25	.15
284A A65 2p rose (I) ('38)	.25	.15
b. Imperf., pair	3.00	

Imperf

285 A65 2p black (II) ('37)	.75	.15
286 A65 2p salmon (II) ('38)	.25	.15
Nos. 281-286 (8)	2.70	
Set value		.70

The newspaper rate was 2 pouls.

Independence Monument — A66

1932, Aug. ***Perf. 12***

287 A66 1af deep rose	2.75	1.50

14th Independence Day.

1929 Liberation Monument, Kabul — A67

1932, Oct. **Typo.**

288 A67 80p red brown	.85	.50

Arch of Paghman A68

1933, Aug.

289 A68 50p light ultra	1.25	1.25

15th Independence Day.

Types of 1932 and

Royal Palace, Kabul — A69

Darrah- Shikari Pass, Hindu Kush — A70

1934-38 Typo. *Perf. 12*

290 A53 10p deep violet .16 .15
291 A54 15p turq green .20 .15
292 A55 20p magenta .22 .15
293 A56 25p deep rose .28 .16
294 A57 30p orange .40 .20
295 A58 40p blue black .75 .28
296 A69 45p dark blue 1.50 1.00
297 A69 45p red ('38) .50 .16
298 A59 50p orange .28 .16
299 A60 60p purple .85 .16
300 A70 75p red 1.00 .35
301 A70 75p dk blue ('38) .60 .40
302 A61 80p brown vio 1.00 .50
303 A62 1af red violet 1.65 1.00
304 A51 2af gray black 3.00 2.00
305 A52 3af ultra 5.00 3.00
Nos. 290-305 (16) 17.39 9.82

Nos. 290, 292, 300, 304, 305 exist imperf.

Independence Monument — A71

1934, Aug. Litho.

Without Gum

306 A71 50p pale green 2.50 1.25
a. Tete beche pair 10.00 3.50

16th year of Independence. Each sheet of 40 (4x10) included 4 tete beche pairs as lower half of sheet was inverted.

Independence Monument A74

Fireworks Display A75

1935, Aug. 15

Laid Paper

309 A74 50p dark blue 1.25 1.25

17th year of Independence.

1936, Aug. 15 *Perf. 12*

Wove Paper

310 A75 50p red violet 1.25 1.00

18th year of Independence.

Independence Monument and Nadir Shah — A76

1937

311 A76 50p vio & bis brn 1.00 .60
a. Imperf., pair 2.25

19th year of Independence.

Mohammed Nadir Shah
A77 A78

1938 *Perf. 11x12*

Without Gum

315 A77 50p brt blue & sepia 5.00 2.50
a. Imperf. pair 20.00

20th year of Independence.

1939 *Perf. 11, 12x11*

317 A78 50p deep salmon 1.75 1.00

21st year of Independence.

National Arms A79

Parliament House, Darul Funun A80

Royal Palace, Kabul A81

Independence Monument A82

Independence Monument and Nadir Shah — A83

Mohammed Zahir Shah — A84

Mohammed Zahir Shah — A85

Perf. 11, 11x12, 12x11, 12

1939-61 Typo.

318 A79 2p intense blk .15 .15
318A A79 2p brt pink ('61) 1.50 .50
319 A80 10p brt purple .15 .15
320 A80 15p brt green .15 .15
321 A80 20p red lilac .15 .15
322 A81 25p rose red 1.00 .25
322A A81 25p green ('41) .50 .15
323 A81 30p orange .20 .15
324 A81 40p dk gray .20 .15
325 A82 45p brt carmine .20 .15
326 A82 50p dp orange .30 .20
327 A82 60p violet .60 .20
328 A83 75p ultra 3.00 .75
328A A83 75p red vio ('41) .75 .30
328C A83 75p brt red ('44) 3.00 3.00
328D A83 75p chnt brn ('49) 4.00 3.00
329 A83 80p chocolate .50 .50
a. 80p dull red violet (error)
330 A84 1af brt red violet 1.50 .75
330A A85 1af brt red vio ('44) 3.00 1.50
331 A85 2af copper red 1.75 .50
a. 2af dp rose red 2.50 1.35
332 A84 3af deep blue 3.75 1.60
Nos. 318-332 (21) 26.35 14.25

Many shades exist in this issue.
On No. 332 the King faces slightly left.
No. 318A issued with and without gum.
See #795A-795B. For similar design see #907A.

Mohammed Nadir Shah — A86

1940, Aug. 23 *Perf. 11*

333 A86 50p gray green .75 .60

22nd year of Independence.

Independence Monument A87

Arch of Paghman A88

1941, Aug. 23 *Perf. 12*

334 A87 15p gray green 8.00 2.75
335 A88 50p red brown 1.25 .85

23rd year of Independence.

Sugar Factory, Baghlan — A89

1942, Apr. *Perf. 12*

336 A89 1.25af blue (shades) 2.00 1.00
a. 1.25af ultra .75 .50

In 1949, a 1.50af brown, type A89, was sold for 3af by the Philatelic Office, Kabul. It was not valid for postage. Value $3.50.

Independence Monument A90

Mohammed Nadir Shah and Arch of Paghman A91

1942, Aug. 23 *Perf. 12*

337 A90 35p bright green 2.75 2.00
338 A91 125p chalky blue 1.40 1.10

24th year of Independence.

Independence Monument and Nadir Shah — A92

Mohammed Nadir Shah — A93

Perf. 11x12, 12x11

1943, Aug. 25 Typo. Unwmk.

339 A92 35p carmine 18.00 6.00
340 A93 1.25af dark blue 3.00 1.75

25th year of Independence.

Tomb of Gohar Shad, Herat — A94

Ruins of Qalai Bist — A95

1944, May 1 *Perf. 12, 11x12*

341 A94 35p orange .50 .32
342 A95 70p violet 1.00 .60
a. 70p rose lilac 3.50 .75

A96

A97

1944, Aug. *Perf. 12*

343 A96 35p crimson .80 .60
344 A97 1.25af ultra 1.40 1.10

26th year of Independence.

A98

A99

1945, July

345 A98 35p dp red lil .75 .65
346 A99 1.25af blue 1.75 1.50

27th year of Independence.

Mohammed Zahir Shah A100

Independence Monument A101

Mohammed Nadir Shah — A102

1946, July

347 A100 15p emerald .45 .35
348 A101 20p dp red lilac .70 .55
349 A102 125p blue 1.75 1.75
Nos. 347-349 (3) 2.90 2.65

28th year of Independence.

Zahir Shah and Ruins of Qalai Bist — A103

A104

A105

1947, Aug.
350 A103 15p yellow green .30 .15
351 A104 35p plum .38 .22
352 A105 125p deep blue 1.40 1.40
Nos. 350-352 (3) 2.08 1.77

29th year of Independence.

Begging Child — A106

A107

1948, May Unwmk. Typo. *Perf. 12*
353 A106 35p yel green 3.00 2.00
354 A107 125p gray blue 3.00 2.25

Children's Day, May 29, 1948, and valid only on that day. Proceeds were used for Child Welfare.

A108

A109

A110

1948, Aug.
355 A108 15p green .22 .15
356 A109 20p magenta .38 .18
357 A110 125p dark blue .75 .70
Nos. 355-357 (3) 1.35 1.03

30th year of Independence.

United Nations Emblem A111

1948, Oct. 24
358 A111 125p dk vio bl 6.00 6.00

3rd anniv. of the UN. Valid one day only. Sheets of 9.

Maiwand Victory Column, Kandahar — A112

Zahir Shah and Ruins of Qalai Bist — A113

Independence Monument and Nadir Shah — A114

1949, Aug. Typo. *Perf. 12*
359 A112 25p green .25 .16
360 A113 35p magenta .35 .25
361 A114 1.25af blue .90 .75
Nos. 359-361 (3) 1.50 1.16

31st year of Independence.

Catalogue values for unused stamps in this section, from this point to the end of the section, are for Never Hinged items.

Nadir Shah — A117

1950, Aug.
364 A117 35p red brown .28 .28
365 A117 125p blue .65 .65

32nd year of Independence.

Medical School and Nadir Shah A119

1950, Dec. 22 Typo. *Perf. 12*
Size: 38x25mm
367 A119 35p emerald .60 .60
Size: 46x30mm
368 A119 1.25af deep blue 1.90 1.90
a. 1.25af black (error) 6.00

19th anniv. of the founding of Afghanistan's Faculty of Medicine. On sale and valid for use on Dec. 22-28, 1950.

Minaret, Herat — A120

Zahir Shah — A121

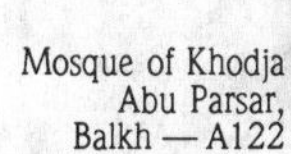

Mosque of Khodja Abu Parsar, Balkh — A122

A123

A124

Designs: 20p, Buddha at Bamian. 40p, Ruined arch. 45p, Maiwand Victory Monument. 50p, View of Kandahar. 60p, Ancient tower. 70p, Afghanistan flag. 80p, 1af, Profile of Zahir Shah in uniform.

Photogravure, Engraved, Engraved and Lithographed
Perf. 12, 12½, 13x12½, 13½
1951, Mar. 21 Unwmk.
Imprint: "Waterlow & Sons Limited, London"
369 A120 10p yel & brn .15 .15
370 A120 15p bl & brn .15 .15
371 A120 20p black 5.00 2.75
372 A121 25p green .15 .15
373 A122 30p cerise .18 .15
374 A121 35p violet .18 .15
375 A120 40p chnt brn .22 .15
376 A120 45p dp bl .18 .15
377 A122 50p ol blk .45 .15
378 A120 60p black 1.50 .75
379 A122 70p dk grn, blk, red & grn .25 .15
380 A123 75p cerise .75 .35
381 A123 80p car & blk .65 .38
382 A123 1af dp grn & vio .45 .38
383 A124 1.25af rose lil & blk 5.00 .38
384 A124 2af ultra 1.10 .38
385 A124 3af ultra & blk 2.50 .90
Nos. 369-385 (17) 18.86 7.62

Nos. 372, 374 and 381 to 385 are engraved, No. 379 is engraved and lithographed.
Imperfs. exist of the photogravure stamps.
See Nos. 445-451, 453, 552A-552D. For surcharges see Nos. B1-B2.

Arch of Paghman — A125

Nadir Shah and Independence Monument A126

Overprint in Violet سال ۳۳ استقلال

Perf. 13½x13, 13
1951, Aug. 25 Engr.
386 A125 35p dk grn & blk .60 .35
387 A126 1.25af deep blue 1.40 .85

Overprint reads "Sol 33 Istiqlal" or "33rd Year of Independence." Overprint measures about 11mm wide.
See Nos. 398-399B, 441-442.

Proposed Flag of Pashtunistan — A127

Design: 125p, Flag and Pashtunistan warrior.

1951, Sept. 2 Litho. *Perf. 11½*
388 A127 35p dl choc .80 .65
389 A127 125p blue 2.00 1.75

Issued to publicize "Free Pashtunistan" Day.

Imperforates

From 1951 to 1958, quantities of nearly all locally-printed stamps were left imperforate and sold by the government at double face. From 1959 until March, 1964, many of the imperforates were sold for more than face value.

Avicenna — A128

1951, Nov. 4 Typo. *Perf. 11½*
390 A128 35p dp claret .50 .35
391 A128 125p blue 1.40 1.10

20th anniv. of the founding of the natl. Graduate School of Medicine.

A129

Dove and UN Symbols — A130

1951, Oct. 24
392 A129 35p magenta 1.40 1.00
393 A130 125p blue 3.50 2.75

7th anniv. of the UN.

Amir Sher Ali Khan and Tiger Head Stamp — A131

Design: Nos. 395 and 397, Zahir Shah and stamp.

1951, Dec. 23 Litho.
394 A131 35p chocolate .35 .35
395 A131 35p rose lil .35 .35
396 A131 125p ultra .65 .60
a. Cliche of 35p in plate of 125p 80.00 80.00
397 A131 125p aqua .65 .60
Nos. 394-397 (4) 2.00 1.90

76th anniv. of the UPU.

Stamps of 1951 Without Overprint
Perf. 13½x13, 13
1952, Aug. 24 Engr.
398 A125 35p dk grn & blk 1.25 1.25
399 A126 1.25af deep blue 1.25 1.25

For overprints see #399A-399B, 441-442.

Same Overprinted in Violet ۳۴ استقلال

399A A125 35p dk grn & blk .60 .40
399B A126 1.25af deep blue 1.60 1.00

#398-399B issued for 34th Independence Day.

Globe — A132

Perf. 11½
1952, Oct. 25 Unwmk. Litho.
400 A132 35p rose .55 .45
401 A132 125p aqua 1.10 1.00

Issued to honor the United Nations.

Symbol of Medicine — A134

Tribal Warrior, Natl. Flag — A135

1952, Nov. *Perf. 11½*
403 A134 35p chocolate .40 .35
404 A134 125p vio bl 1.10 1.10

21st anniv. of the natl. Graduate School of Medicine.
No. 404 is inscribed in French with white letters on a colored background.

1952, Sept. 1 *Perf. 11*
405 A135 35p red .28 .28
406 A135 125p dark blue .60 .60

No. 406 is inscribed in French "Pashtunistan Day, 1952."

Flags of Afghanistan & Pashtunistan A139

Badge of Pashtunistan A140

Perf. 10¹/₂x11, 11

1953, Sept. 1 **Unwmk.**

411 A139 35p vermilion .20 .16
412 A140 125p blue .60 .42

Issued to publicize "Free Pashtunistan" Day.

Nadir Shah and Flag Bearer — A141

A142

1953, Aug. 24 *Perf. 11*

413 A141 35p green .18 .15
414 A142 125p violet .75 .60

35th anniv. of Independence.

United Nations Emblem — A143

1953, Oct. 24

415 A143 35p lilac .60 .60
416 A143 125p vio blue 1.50 1.20

United Nations Day, 1953.

Nadir Shah

A144 A145

1953, Nov. 29

417 A144 35p orange .65 .65
418 A145 125p chalky blue 1.50 1.50

22nd anniv. of the founding of the natl. Graduate School of Medicine.

Redrawn

35p. Original- Right character in second line of Persian inscription: ٣

Redrawn- Persian character: ٢

125p: Original- Inscribed "XXIII," "MADECINE" and "ANNIVERAIRE"
Redrawn- Inscribed "XXII," "MEDECINE" and "ANNIVERSAIRE"

1953

419 A144 35p deep orange 3.50
420 A145 125p chalky blue 4.25

Nadir Shah and Symbols of Independence A146

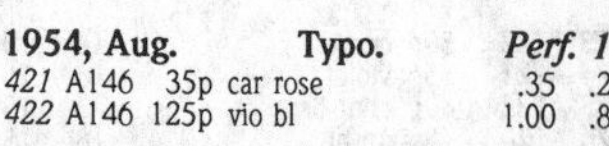

1954, Aug. **Typo.** *Perf. 11*

421 A146 35p car rose .35 .28
422 A146 125p vio bl 1.00 .80

36th year of Independence.

Raising Flag of Pashtunistan A147

1954, Sept. *Perf. 11¹/₂*

423 A147 35p chocolate .35 .28
424 A147 125p blue 1.00 .80

Issued to publicize "Free Pashtunistan" Day.

UN Flag and Map — A148

1954, Oct. 24 *Perf. 11*

425 A148 35p car rose .65 .65
426 A148 125p dk vio bl 2.00 2.00

9th anniv. of the United Nations.

UN Symbols — A149

Design: 125p, UN emblem & flags.

1955, June 26 **Litho.** *Perf. 11*

Size: 26¹/₂x36mm

427 A149 35p dark green .45 .38

Size: 28¹/₂x36mm

428 A149 125p aqua 1.10 .90

10th anniv. of the UN charter.

Nadir Shah (center) and Brothers — A150

1929 Civil War Scene and Zahir Shah — A151

Tribal Elders' Council and Pashtun Flag — A152

1955, Aug. **Unwmk.** *Perf. 11*

429 A150 35p brt pink .30 .30
430 A150 35p vio blue .30 .30
431 A151 125p rose lilac .90 .75
432 A151 125p light vio .90 .75
Nos. 429-432 (4) 2.40 2.10

37th anniv. of Independence.

1955, Sept. 5

433 A152 35p org brn .22 .22
434 A152 125p yel grn .90 .65

Issued for "Free Pashtunistan" Day.

UN Flag — A153

A154

1955, Oct. 24 **Unwmk.** *Perf. 11*

435 A153 35p org brn .75 .60
436 A153 125p brt ultra 1.40 1.10

10th anniv. of the United Nations.

1956, Aug. **Litho.**

437 A154 35p lt grn .25 .20
438 A154 140p lt vio bl .90 .75

38th year of Independence.

Jesh'n Exhibition Hall — A155

1956, Aug. 25

439 A155 50p chocolate .25 .18
440 A155 50p lt vio bl .25 .18

International Exposition at Kabul.
Of the 50p face value, only 35p paid postage. The remaining 15p went to the Exposition.

Nos. 398-399 Handstamped in Violet

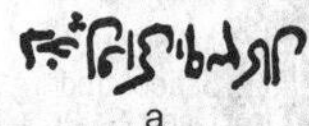

a b

1957, Aug. **Engr.** *Perf. 13¹/₂x13, 13*

441 A125 (a) 35p dk grn & blk .40 .20
442 A126 (b) 1.25af deep blue .60 .50

Arabic overprint measures 19mm.
39th year of independence.

Pashtunistan Flag — A156

1957, Sept. 1 **Litho.** *Perf. 11*

443 A156 50p pale lil rose .60 .38
444 A156 155p lt vio .90 .75

Issued for "Free Pashtunistan" Day. French inscription on No. 444. 15p of each stamp went to the Pashtunistan Fund.

Types of 1951 and

Game of Buzkashi A157

Perf. 12, 12¹/₂, 12¹/₂x13, 13, 13x12, 13x12¹/₂, 13¹/₂x14

Photo., Engr., Engr.& Litho.

1957, Nov. 23 **Unwmk.**

Imprint: "Waterlow & Sons Limited, London"

445 A122 30p brown .15 .15
446 A122 40p rose red .22 .15
447 A122 50p yellow .32 .15
448 A120 60p ultra .40 .15
449 A123 75p brt vio .50 .15
450 A123 80p vio & brn .50 .15
451 A123 1af car & ultra 1.00 .15
452 A157 140p ol & dp cl 2.00 .50
453 A124 3af org & blk 2.50 .50
Nos. 445-453 (9) 7.59 2.05

No. 452 lacks imprint.

Nadir Shah and Flag-bearer A158

1958, Aug. 25 *Perf. 13¹/₂x14*

454 A158 35p dp yel grn .16 .15
455 A158 140p brown .40 .35

40th year of Independence.

Exposition Buildings — A159

1958, Aug. 23 **Litho.** *Perf. 11*

456 A159 35p brt bl grn .16 .15
457 A159 140p vermilion .50 .40

International Exposition at Kabul.

Pres. Celal Bayar of Turkey A160

Flags of UN and Afghanistan A161

1958, Sept. 13 **Unwmk.**

458 A160 50p lt bl .20 .15
459 A160 100p brown .35 .28

Visit of President Celal Bayar of Turkey.

1958, Oct. 24 **Photo.** *Perf. 14x13¹/₂*

Flags in Original Colors

460 A161 50p dark gray .60 .60
461 A161 100p green 1.10 .90

United Nations Day, Oct. 24.

Atomic Energy Encircling the Hemispheres A162

1958, Oct. 20 *Perf. 13¹/₂x14*

462 A162 50p blue .35 .35
463 A162 100p dp red lil .55 .55

Issued to promote Atoms for Peace.

UNESCO Building, Paris — A163

1958, Nov. 3

464 A163 50p dp yel grn .50 .40
465 A163 100p brn olive .75 .60

UNESCO Headquarters in Paris opening, Nov. 3.

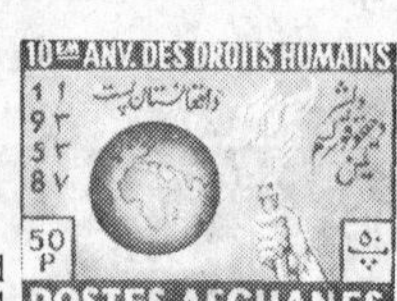

Globe and Torch — A164

Perf. 13¹/₂x14

1958, Dec. 10 **Unwmk.**

466 A164 50p lilac rose .35 .35
467 A164 100p maroon .65 .65

10th anniv. of the signing of the Universal Declaration of Human Rights.

Nadir Shah and Flags — A165

1959, Aug. Litho. *Perf. 11 Rough*

468 A165 35p light vermilion .20 .20
469 A165 165p light violet .65 .40

41st year of Independence.

Uprooted Oak Emblem — A166

1960, Apr. 7 *Perf. 11*

470 A166 50p dp org .15 .15
471 A166 165p blue .35 .28

Issued to publicize World Refugee Year, July 1, 1959-June 30, 1960.

Two imperf. souvenir sheets exist. Both contain a 50p and a 165p, type A166, with marginal inscriptions and WRY emblem in maroon. On one sheet the stamps are in the colors of Nos. 470-471 (size 108x81mm). On the other, the 50p is blue and the 165p is deep orange (size 107x80mm). Value $4 each.

For surcharges see Nos. B35-B36.

Buzkashi A167

1960, May 4 *Perf. 11, Imperf.*

472 A167 25p rose red .22 .15
473 A167 50p bluish green .50 .35
a. Cliche of 25p in plate of 50p 20.00 20.00

See Nos. 549-550A.

Independence Monument — A168

1960, Aug. *Perf. 11, 12*

474 A168 50p light blue .15 .15
475 A168 175p bright pink .38 .38

42nd Independence Day.

Globe and Flags — A169

1960, Oct. 24 Litho. *Perf. 11, 12*

476 A169 50p rose lilac .22 .18
477 A169 175p ultra .75 .65

UN Day.

An imperf. souvenir sheet contains one each of Nos. 476-477 with marginal inscriptions ("La Journée des Nations Unies 1960" in French and Persian) and UN emblem in light blue. Size: 127x85½mm. Value $4.

This sheet was surcharged "+20ps" in 1962. Value $8.50.

Teacher Pointing to Globe — A170

1960, Oct. 23 *Perf. 11*

478 A170 50p brt pink .18 .15
479 A170 100p brt grn .70 .45

Issued to publicize Teacher's Day.

Mohammed Zahir Shah — A171

1960, Oct. 15

480 A171 50p red brn .30 .15
481 A171 150p dk car rose .90 .30

Honoring the King on his 46th birthday.

Buzkashi A172

1960, Nov. 9 *Perf. 11*

482 A172 175p lt red brn 1.00 .40

See Nos. 551-552.

No. 482 Overprinted "1960" and Olympic Rings in Bright Green.

1960, Dec. 24

483 A172 175p red brn 2.00 1.75
a. Souv. sheet of 1, imperf. 7.00

17th Olympic Games, Rome, Aug. 25-Sept. 11.

Mir Wais — A173

1961, Jan. 5 Unwmk. *Perf. 10½*

484 A173 50p brt rose lil .22 .15
485 A173 175p ultra .60 .38
a. Souv. sheet of 2, #484-485, imperf. 2.00 2.00

Mir Wais (1665-1708), national leader.

No Postal Need

existed for the 1p-15p denominations issued with sets of 1961-63 (between Nos. 486 and 649, B37 and B65).

The lowest denomination actually used for non-philatelic postage in that period was 25p (except for the 2p newspaper rate for which separate stamps were provided).

Horse, Sheep and Camel — A174

Designs: No. 487, 175p, Rock partridge. 10p, 100p, Afghan hound. 15p, 150p, Grain and grasshopper, vert.

1961, Mar. 29 Photo. *Perf. 13½x14*

486 A174 2p maroon & buff
487 A174 2p ultra & org
488 A174 5p brn & yel
489 A174 10p blk & salmon
490 A174 15p bl grn & yel
491 A174 25p blk & pink
492 A174 50p blk & citron
493 A174 100p blk & pink
494 A174 150p grn & yel
495 A174 175p ultra & pink
Nos. 486-495 (10) 2.00

Two souvenir sheets, perf. and imperf., contain 2 stamps, 1 each of #492-493. Value $2 each.

Afghan Fencing A175

Designs: No. 497, 5p, 25p, 50p, Wrestlers. 10p, 100p, Man with Indian clubs. 15p, 150p, Afghan fencing. 175p, Children skating.

1961, July 6 *Perf. 13½x14*

496 A175 2p grn & rose lil
497 A175 2p brn & citron
498 A175 5p gray & rose
499 A175 10p bl & bis
500 A175 15p sl bl & dl lil
501 A175 25p blk & dl bl
502 A175 50p sl grn & bis brn
503 A175 100p brn & bl grn
504 A175 150p brn & org yel
505 A175 175p blk & bl
Nos. 496-505 (10) 1.50

Issued for Children's Day.

A souvenir sheet exists, perf. and imperf., containing one each of Nos. 502-503. Value $3.50 each.

For surcharges see Nos. B37-B41.

Bande Amir Lakes — A176

1961, Aug. 7 Photo. *Perf. 13½x14*

506 A176 3af brt bl .35 .28
507 A176 10af rose claret 1.10 1.00

Nadir Shah — A177

Girl Scout — A178

1961, Aug. 23 *Perf. 14x13½*

508 A177 50p rose red & blk .50 .40
509 A177 175p brt grn & org brn 1.00 .80

43rd Independence Day.

Two souvenir sheets, perf. and imperf., contain one each of Nos. 508-509. Value, each $2.50.

Perf. 14x13½

1961, July 23 Unwmk.

510 A178 50p dp car & dk gray .28 .15
511 A178 175p dp grn & rose brn .60 .40

Issued for Women's Day.

Two souvenir sheets exist, perf. and imperf., containing one each of Nos. 510-511. Value $3 each.

Exhibition Hall, Kabul — A179

1961, Aug. 23 *Perf. 13½x14*

512 A179 50p yel brn & yel grn .16 .15
513 A179 175p blue & brn .40 .28

International Exhibition at Kabul.

Pathan with Pashtunistan Flag — A180

1961, Aug. 31 Photo. *Perf. 14x13½*

514 A180 50p blk, lil & red .15 .15
515 A180 175p brn, grnsh bl & red .35 .28

Issued for "Free Pashtunistan Day."

Souvenir sheets exist perf. and imperf. containing one each of Nos. 514-515. Value $2 each.

Assembly Building A181

1961, Sept. 10 *Perf. 12*

516 A181 50p dk gray & brt grn .16 .15
517 A181 175p ultra & brn .45 .30

Anniv. of the founding of the Natl. Assembly.

Souvenir sheets exist, perf. and imperf., containing one each of Nos. 516-517. Value $1 each.

Exterminating Anopheles Mosquito A182

1961, Oct. 5 *Perf. 13½x14*

518 A182 50p blk & brn lil .50 .28
519 A182 175p mar & brt grn 1.10 .50

Anti-Malaria campaign. Souvenir sheets exist, perf. and imperf., containing one each of Nos. 518-519. Value $4 each.

Zahir Shah — A183

1961, Oct. 15 *Perf. 13½*

520 A183 50p lil & bl .16 .15
521 A183 175p emer & red brn .40 .35

Issued to honor King Mohammed Zahir Shah on his 47th birthday.

See Nos. 609-612.

Pomegranates A184

Fruit: No. 523, 5p, 25p, 50p, Grapes. 10p, 150p, Apples. 15p, 175p, Pomegranates. 100p, Melons.

1961, Oct. 16 *Perf. 13½x14*

Fruit in Natural Colors

522 A184 2p black
523 A184 2p green
524 A184 5p lil rose
525 A184 10p lilac
526 A184 15p dk bl
527 A184 25p dl red
528 A184 50p purple
529 A184 100p brt bl
530 A184 150p brown
531 A184 175p ol gray
Nos. 522-531 (10) 1.75

For Afghan Red Crescent Society.

Souvenir sheets exist, perf. and imperf., containing one each of Nos. 528-529. Value $1.50 each.

For surcharges see Nos. B42-B46.

UN Headquarters, NY — A185

1961, Oct. 24 *Perf. 13½x14*

Vertical Borders in Emerald, Red and Black

532 A185 1p rose lil
533 A185 2p slate
534 A185 3p brown
535 A185 4p ultra
536 A185 50p rose red

537 A185 75p gray
538 A185 175p brt grn
Nos. 532-538 (7) 1.25

16th anniv. of the UN. Souvenir sheets exist, perf. and imperf., containing one each of Nos. 536-538. Value $2 each.

Children Giving Flowers to Teacher — A186

People Raising UNESCO Symbol — A187

Designs: No. 540, 5p, 25p, 50p, Tulips. 10p, 100p, Narcissus. 15p, 150p, Children giving flowers to teacher. 175p, Teacher with children in front of school.

1961, Oct. 26 Photo. *Perf. 12*

539 A186 2p multi
540 A186 2p multi
541 A186 5p multi
542 A186 10p multi
543 A186 15p multi
544 A186 25p multi
545 A186 50p multi
546 A186 100p multi
547 A186 150p multi
548 A186 175p multi
Nos. 539-548 (10) 1.75

Issued for Teacher's Day.
Souvenir sheets exist, perf. and imperf. containing one each of Nos. 545-546. Value, 2 sheets, $4.
For surcharges see Nos. B47-B51.

Buzkashi Types of 1960

1961-72 Litho. *Perf. 10½, 11*

549 A167 25p violet .15 .15
b. 25p brt vio, typo. ('72) .15 .15
549A A167 25p citron ('63) .18 .15
550 A167 50p blue .32 .15
550A A167 50p yel org ('69) .15 .15
551 A172 100p citron .45 .15
551A A172 150p org ('64) .32 .15
552 A172 2af lt grn 1.10 .45
Nos. 549-552 (7) 2.67
Set value .85

Zahir Shah Types of 1951

Photo., Engr., Engr. & Litho.

1962 *Perf. 13x12, 13*

Imprint: "Thomas De La Rue & Co. Ltd."

552A A123 75p brt pur 1.10 .25
552B A123 1af car & ultra 1.40 .32
552C A124 2af blue 1.75 .75
552D A124 3af org & blk 4.00 1.10
Nos. 552A-552D (4) 8.25 2.42

1962, July 2 Photo. *Perf. 14x13½*

553 A187 2p rose lil & brn
554 A187 2p ol bis & brn
555 A187 5p dp org & dk grn
556 A187 10p gray & mag
557 A187 15p bl & brn
558 A187 25p org yel & pur
559 A187 50p lt grn & pur
560 A187 75p brt cit & brn
561 A187 100p dp org & brn
Nos. 553-561 (9) 1.25

15th anniv. of UNESCO. Souvenir sheets exist, perf. and imperf. One contains Nos. 558-559; the other contains one Value, $3 each.
For surcharges see Nos. B52-B60.

Ahmad Shah — A188

Afghan Hound — A189

1962, Feb. 24 Photo. *Perf. 13½*

562 A188 50p red brn & gray .15 .15
563 A188 75p grn & salmon .25 .20
564 A188 100p claret & bis .40 .30
Nos. 562-564 (3) .80 .65

Ahmad Shah (1724-73), founded the Afghan kingdom in 1747 and ruled until 1773.

1962, Apr. 21 *Perf. 14x13½*

Designs: 5p, 75p, Afghan cock. 10p, 100p, Kondjid plant. 15p, 125p, Astrakhan skins.

565 A189 2p rose & brn
566 A189 2p lt grn & brn
567 A189 5p dp rose & claret
568 A189 10p lt grn & sl grn
569 A189 15p bl grn & blk
570 A189 25p bl & brn
571 A189 50p gray & brn
572 A189 75p rose lil & lil
573 A189 100p gray & dl grn
574 A189 125p rose brn & blk
Nos. 565-574 (10) 2.00

Agriculture Day. Perf. and imperf. souvenir sheets exist. Set of 4 sheets, value $4.

Athletes with Flag and Nadir Shah A190

Woman in National Costume A191

1962, Aug. 23 *Perf. 12*

575 A190 25p multi .15 .15
576 A190 50p multi .18 .15
577 A190 150p multi .25 .15
Nos. 575-577 (3) .58
Set value .19

44th Independence Day.

1962, Aug. 30 *Perf. 11½x12*

578 A191 25p lil & brn .15 .15
579 A191 50p grn & brn .25 .15
Set value .21

Issued for Women's Day. For souvenir sheet see note after No. C16.

Man and Woman with Flag — A192

Malaria Eradication Emblem and Swamp — A193

1962, Aug. 31 Photo.

580 A192 25p blk, pale bl & red .15 .15
581 A192 50p blk, grn & red .18 .15
582 A192 150p blk, pink & red .45 .15
Nos. 580-582 (3) .78
Set value .29

Issued for "Free Pashtunistan Day."

1962, Sept. 5 *Perf. 14x13½*

583 A193 2p dk grn & ol gray
584 A193 2p dk grn & sal
585 A193 5p red brn & ol
586 A193 10p red brn & brt grn
587 A193 15p red brn & gray
588 A193 25p brt bl & bluish grn
589 A193 50p brt bl & rose lil
590 A193 75p blk & bl
591 A193 100p blk & brt pink
592 A193 150p blk & bis brn
593 A193 175p blk & org
Nos. 583-593 (11) 2.00

WHO drive to eradicate malaria. Perf. and imperf. souvenir sheets exist. Set of 4 sheets, value $6.50.
For surcharges see Nos. B61-B71.

National Assembly Building A194

Perf. 10½, 11 (100p)

1962, Sept. 10 Unwmk. Litho.

594 A194 25p lt grn .35 .25
595 A194 50p blue .55 .35
596 A194 75p rose .70 .55
597 A194 100p violet 1.10 .90
598 A194 125p ultra 1.20 1.10
Nos. 594-598 (5) 3.90 3.15

Establishment of the National Assembly.

Horse Racing — A195

Designs: 2p, Pole vaulting. 3p, Wrestling. 4p, Weight lifting. 5p, Soccer.

1962, Sept. 22 Photo. *Perf. 12*

Black Inscriptions

599 A195 1p lt ol & red brn
600 A195 2p lt grn & red brn
601 A195 3p yel & dk pur
602 A195 4p pale bl & grn
603 A195 5p bluish grn & dk brn
Nos. 599-603, C17-C22 (11) 2.50

4th Asian Games, Djakarta, Indonesia. Two souvenir sheets exist. A perforated one contains a 125p blue, dark blue and brown stamp in horse racing design. An imperf. one contains a 2af buff, purple and black stamp in soccer design. Value, $3.50 each.

Runners A196

Designs: 1p, 2p, Diver, vert. 4p, Peaches. 5p, Iris, vert.

Perf. 11½x12, 12x11½

1962, Oct. 2 Unwmk.

604 A196 1p rose lil & brn
605 A196 2p bl & brn
606 A196 3p brt bl & lil
607 A196 4p ol gray & multi
608 A196 5p gray & multi
Nos. 604-608, C23-C25 (8) 2.00

Issued for Children's Day.

King Type of 1961, Dated "1962"

1962, Oct. 15 *Perf. 13½*

Various Frames

609 A183 25p lil rose & brn .15 .15
610 A183 50p org brn & grn .15 .15
611 A183 75p bl & lake .15 .15
612 A183 100p grn & red brn .20 .20
Set value .50 .50

Issued to honor King Mohammed Zahir Shah on his 48th birthday.

Grapes A197

1962, Oct. 16 *Perf. 12*

613 A197 1p shown
614 A197 2p Grapes
615 A197 3p Pears
616 A197 4p Wistaria
617 A197 5p Blossoms
Nos. 613-617, C26-C28 (8) 1.00

For the Afghan Red Crescent Society.

UN Headquarters, NY and Flags of UN and Afghanistan A198

1962, Oct. 24 Unwmk.

618 A198 1p multi
619 A198 2p multi
620 A198 3p multi
621 A198 4p multi
622 A198 5p multi
Nos. 618-622, C29-C31 (8) 1.50

UN Day. Souvenir sheets exist. One contains a single 4af ultramarine stamp, perforated; the other, a 4af ocher stamp, imperf. Value, 2 sheets, $5.

Boy Scout — A199 Pole Vault — A200

1962 Oct. 18 Photo. *Perf. 12*

623 A199 1p yel, dk grn & sal
624 A199 2p dl yel, sl & sal
625 A199 3p rose, blk & sal
626 A199 4p multi
Nos. 623-626, C32-C35 (8) 1.50

Issued to honor the Boy Scouts.

1962, Oct. 25 Unwmk. *Perf. 12*

Designs: 3p, High jump. 4p, 5p, Different blossoms.

627 A200 1p lil & dk grn
628 A200 2p yel grn & brn
629 A200 3p bister & vio
630 A200 4p sal pink, grn & ultra
631 A200 5p yel, grn & bl
Nos. 627-631, C36-C37 (7) 1.25

Issued for Teacher's Day.

Rockets A201

1962, Nov. 29

632 A201 50p pale lil & dk bl .40
633 A201 100p lt bl & red brn .80

UN World Meteorological Day. A souvenir sheet contains one 5af pink and green stamp. Value $6.

Ansari Mausoleum, Herat — A202

Perf. 13½

1963, Jan. 3 Unwmk. Photo.

634 A202 50p pur & grn .15 .15
635 A202 75p gray & mag .18 .18
636 A202 100p org brn & brn .30 .30
Nos. 634-636 (3) .63 .63

Khwaja Abdullah Ansari, Sufi, religious leader and poet, on the 900th anniv. of his death.

Sheep — A203

Silkworm, Cocoons, Moth and Mulberry Branch A204

1963, Mar. 1 *Perf. 12*
637 A203 1p grnsh bl & blk
638 A203 2p yel grn & blk
639 A203 3p lil rose & blk
640 A204 4p gray, grn & brn
641 A204 5p red lil, grn & brn
Nos. 637-641, C42-C44 (8) 1.50

Issued for the Day of Agriculture.

Rice — A205

Designs: 3p, Corn. 300p, Wheat emblem.

1963, Mar. 27 Unwmk. *Perf. 14*
642 A205 2p gray, claret & grn .15 .15
643 A205 3p grn, yel & ocher .15 .15
644 A205 300p dk bl & yel .30 .30
Set value .44 .44

FAO "Freedom from Hunger" campaign.

Meteorological Measuring Instrument A206

Designs: 3p, 10p, Weather station. 4p, 5p, Rockets in space.

1963, May 23 Photo. *Perf. 13½x14*
645 A206 1p dp mag & brn
646 A206 2p brt bl & brn
647 A206 3p red & brn
648 A206 4p org & lil
649 A206 5p grn & dl vio

Imperf

650 A206 10p red brn & grn
Nos. 645-650, C46-C50 (11) 7.50

3rd UN World Meteorological Day, Mar. 23.

Independence Monument — A207

1963, Aug. 23 Litho. *Perf. 10½*
651 A207 25p lt grn .15 .15
652 A207 50p orange .15 .15
653 A207 150p rose car .35 .22
Set value .56 .37

45th Independence Day.

Pathans in Forest — A208

1963, Aug. 31 Unwmk. *Perf. 10½*
654 A208 25p pale vio .15 .15
655 A208 50p sky blue .15 .15
655A A208 150p dl red brn .40 .35
Nos. 654-655A (3) .70
Set value .52

Issued for "Free Pashtunistan Day."

4th Asian Games, Djakarta A208a

Designs: 2p, 250p, 300p, Wrestling. 3p, 10p, Tennis. 4p, 500p, Javelin. 5p, 9af, Shot put.

1963, Sept. 3 Litho. *Perf. 12*
656 A208a 2p rose vio & brn
656A A208a 3p olive grn & brn
656B A208a 4p blue & brn
656C A208a 5p yel grn & brn
656D A208a 10p lt bl grn & brn
656E A208a 300p yellow & vio
656F A208a 500p lt yel bis & brn
656G A208a 9af pale grn & vio

Souvenir Sheets

656H A208a 250p lilac & vio
656I A208a 300p blue & blk

Nos. 656-656F are airmail. Nos. 656-656I exist imperf.

National Assembly Building A209

1963, Sept. 10 *Perf. 11*
657 A209 25p gray .15 .15
658 A209 50p dull red .15 .15
659 A209 75p brown .20 .15
660 A209 100p olive .30 .15
661 A209 125p lilac .40 .20
Nos. 657-661 (5) 1.20
Set value .64

Issued to honor the National Assembly.

Balkh Gate A210

1963, Oct. 8
662 A210 3af choc (screened margins) .40 .28
a. White margins 1.00 .35

In the original printing a halftone screen extended across the plate, covering the space between the stamps. A retouch removed the screen between the stamps (No. 662a).

Intl. Red Cross, Cent. A210a

Designs: 4p, 5p, 200p, 3af, Nurse holding patient, vert. 10p, 4af, 6af, Crown Prince Ahmed Shah.

1963, Oct. 9 *Perf. 13½*
662B A210a 2p olive, blk & red
662C A210a 3p blue, blk & red
662D A210a 4p lt grn, blk & red
662E A210a 5p lt vio, blk & red
662F A210a 10p gray grn, red & blk
662G A210a 100p dull bl grn, red & blk
662H A210a 200p lt brn, blk & red
662I A210a 4af brt bl grn, red & blk
m. Souv. sheet of 1
662J A210a 6af lt brn, red & blk

Souvenir Sheet

662K A210a 3af dl blue, blk & red

Nos. 662G-662K are airmail. Nos. 662B-662K exist imperf.

Zahir Shah — A211

Kemal Ataturk — A212

1963, Oct. 15 *Perf. 10½*
663 A211 25p green .15 .15
663A A211 50p gray .15 .15
663B A211 75p car rose .22 .15
663C A211 100p dl redsh brn .30 .15
Nos. 663-663C (4) .82
Set value .37

King Mohammed Zahir Shah, 49th birthday.

1963, Oct. 10 *Perf. 10½*
664 A212 1af blue .15 .15
665 A212 3af rose lilac .40 .35

25th anniv. of the death of Kemal Ataturk, president of Turkey.

Protection of Nubian Monuments A213

Designs: 5af, 7.50af, 10af, Ruins, vert.

Perf. 12, Imperf. (150p, 250p, 10af)
1963, Nov. 16 Photo.
666 A213 100p lil rose & blk
666A A213 150p rose lil & blk
666B A213 200p brn & blk
666C A213 250p ultra & blk
666D A213 500p grn & blk
666E A213 5af greenish blue & gray bl
666F A213 7.50af red brn & gray bl
666G A213 10af ver & gray bl

#666E-666G are airmail. #666D exists imperf.

Women's Day — A213a

Boy and Girl Scouts — A213c

A213b

1964, Jan. 5 *Perf. 14x13½*
667 A213a 2p multicolored
667A A213a 3p multicolored
667B A213a 4p multicolored
667C A213a 5p multicolored
667D A213a 10p multicolored

Exist imperf.

1964, Jan. 5 *Perf. 13½x14, 14x13½*

Designs: Nos. 668F-668G, 668K-668M, Girl with flag.

668 A213b 2p multi
668A A213b 3p multi
668B A213b 4p multi
668C A213b 5p multi
668D A213b 10p multi
668E A213c 2af multi
668F A213c 2af multi
668G A213c 2.50af multi
668H A213c 3af multi
668I A213c 4af multi
668J A213c 5af multi
668K A213c 12af multi

Souvenir Sheets

668L A213c 5af multi
668M A213c 6af multi
668N A213c 6af multi
668O A213c 10af multi

Nos. 668E-668O are airmail. Nos 668-668K, 668N-668O exist imperf.

Children — A213d

1964, Jan. 22 *Perf. 12*
669 A213d 2p Playing ball
669A A213d 3p like #669
669B A213d 4p Swinging, jump-ing rope, vert.
669C A213d 5p Skiing, vert.
669D A213d 10p like #669
669E A213d 200p like #669C
669F A213d 300p like #669B

Nos. 669E-669F are airmail. All exist imperf.

Red Crescent Society — A213e

Designs: 100p, 200p, Pierre and Marie Curie, physicists. 2.50af, 7.50af Nurse examining child. 3.50af, 5af, Nurse and patients.

Perf. 14, Imperf. (#670A, 670C-670D)
1964, Feb. 8
670 A213e 100p multi
670A A213e 100p multi
670B A213e 200p multi
670C A213e 2.50af multi
670D A213e 3.50af multi
670E A213e 5af multi
670F A213e 7.50af multi

Nos. 670B-670D are airmail.

Teachers' Day — A213f

Flowers: 2p, 3p, 3af, 4af, Tulips. 4p, 5p, 3.50af, 6af, Flax. 10p, 1.50af, 2af, Iris.

Perf. 12, Imperf. (1.50af, 2af)
1964, Mar. 3
671 A213f 2p multicolored
671A A213f 3p multicolored
671B A213f 4p multicolored
671C A213f 5p multicolored
671D A213f 10p multicolored
671E A213f 1.50af multicolored
671F A213f 2af multicolored
671G A213f 3af multicolored
671H A213f 3.50af multicolored

Souvenir Sheets

671I A213f 4af multicolored
671J A213f 6af multi, imperf

#671E-671J are airmail. #671-671D exist imperf.

A213g

UN Day: 5p, 10p, 2af, 3af, 4af, Doctor and nurse, vert.

1964, Mar. 9 *Perf. 14*

672 A213g 2p multicolored
672A A213g 3p multicolored
672B A213g 4p multicolored
672C A213g 5p multicolored
672D A213g 10p multicolored
672E A213g 100p multicolored
672F A213g 2af multicolored
672G A213g 3af multicolored

Souvenir Sheets

672H A213g 4af multi, imperf.
672I A213g 5af multicolored

Nos. 672E-672G are airmail. Nos. 672-672G exist imperf.

For surcharges see Nos. B71A-B71J.

UNICEF A213h

Design: 5af, 7.50af, 10af, Children eating.

Perf. 14x13¹/₂, Imperf. (150p, 250p, 10af)

1964, Mar. 15

673 A213h 100p multicolored
673A A213h 150p multicolored
673B A213h 200p multicolored
673C A213h 250p multicolored
673D A213h 5af multicolored
673E A213h 7.50af multicolored
673F A213h 10af multicolored

Nos. 673D-673F are airmail.

Eradication of Malaria A213i

Designs: 4p, 5p, 5af, 10af Spraying mosquitoes.

1964, Mar. 15 *Perf. 13¹/₂*

674 A213i 2p lt red brn & yel grn
674A A213i 3p olive grn & buff
674B A213i 4p dk vio & bl grn
674C A213i 5p brn & grn
674D A213i 2af Prus bl & ver
h. Souv. sheet of 1
674E A213i 5af dk grn & lt red brn, imperf.
i. Souv. sheet of 1, imperf.
674F A213i 10af red brn & grnsh bl

X X

674G A213i 10p on 4p Prus bl & rose

No. 674G not issued without surcharge. Nos. 674-674C, 674G exist imperf. Nos. 674D-674F are airmail.

Exists imperf.

"Tiger's Head" of 1878 — A214

1964, Mar. 22 **Photo.** *Perf. 12*

675 A214 1.25af gold, grn & blk .20 .15
676 A214 5af gold, rose car & blk .50 .35

Issued to honor philately.

Unisphere and Flags — A215

1964, May 3 *Perf. 13¹/₂x14*

677 A215 6af crimson, gray & grn .30 .22

New York World's Fair, 1964-65.

Hand Holding Torch — A216

1964, May 12 **Photo.** *Perf. 14x13¹/₂*

678 A216 3.75af multi .18 .18

1st UN Seminar on Human Rights in Kabul, May 1964. The denomination in Persian at right erroneously reads "3.25" but the stamp was sold and used as 3.75af.

Kandahar Airport A217

1964, Apr. **Litho.** *Perf. 10¹/₂, 11*

679 A217 7.75af dk red brn .40 .20
680 A217 9.25af lt grn .50 .22
681 A217 10.50af lt grn .50 .28
682 A217 13.75af car rose .70 .38
Nos. 679-682 (4) 2.10 1.08

Inauguration of Kandahar Airport.

Snow Leopard A218

Designs: 50p, Ibex, vert. 75p, Head of argali. 5af, Yak.

1964, June 25 **Photo.** *Perf. 12*

683 A218 25p yel & bl .15 .15
684 A218 50p dl red & grn .15 .15
685 A218 75p Prus bl & lil .15 .15
686 A218 5af brt grn & dk brn .30 .30
Set value .54 .54

View of Herat — A219

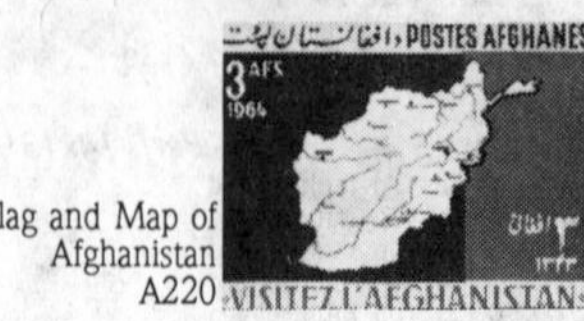

Flag and Map of Afghanistan A220

Yourist publicity: 75p, Tomb of Queen Gowhar Shad, vert.

Perf. 13¹/₂x14, 14x13¹/₂

1964, July 12

687 A219 25p sepia & bl .15 .15
688 A219 75p dp bl & buff .15 .15
689 A220 3af red, blk & grn .30 .15
Set value .40 .20

Wrestling A221

Designs: 25p, Hurdling, vert. 1af, Diving, vert. 5af, Soccer.

1964, July 26 *Perf. 12*

690 A221 25p ol bis, blk & car .15 .15
691 A221 1af bl grn, blk & car .15 .15
692 A221 3.75af yel grn, blk & car .22 .22
693 A221 5af brn, blk & car .30 .30
a. Souv. sheet of 4, #690-693, imperf. .90 .90
Nos. 690-693 (4) .82 .82

18th Olympic Games, Tokyo, Oct. 10-25, 1964. No. 693a sold for 15af. The additional 5af went to the Afghanistan Olympic Committee.

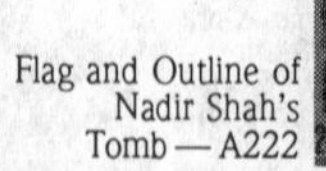

Flag and Outline of Nadir Shah's Tomb — A222

1964, Aug. 24 **Photo.**

695 A222 25p multi .15 .15
696 A222 75p multi .15 .15
Set value .17 .17

Independence Day. The stamps were printed with an erroneous inscription in upper left corner: "33rd year of independence." This was locally obliterated with a typographed gold bar.

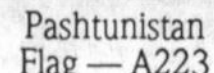

Pashtunistan Flag — A223

Zahir Shah — A225

1964, Sept. 1 **Unwmk.**

697 A223 100p gold, blk, red, bl & grn .15 .15

Issued for "Free Pashtunistan Day."

1964, Oct. 17 *Perf. 14x13¹/₂*

699 A225 1.25af gold & yel grn .15 .15
700 A225 3.75af gold & rose .20 .15
701 A225 50af gold & gray 2.00 1.75
Nos. 699-701 (3) 2.35 2.05

King Mohammed Zahir Shah, 50th birthday.

Coat of Arms of Afghanistan and UN Emblem — A226

1964, Oct. 24 *Perf. 13¹/₂x14*

702 A226 5af gold, blk & dl bl .20 .15

Issued for United Nations Day.

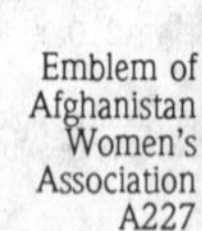

Emblem of Afghanistan Women's Association A227

1964, Nov. 9 **Photo.** **Unwmk.**

703 A227 25p pink, dk bl & emer .50 .25
704 A227 75p aqua, dk bl & emer .75 .35
705 A227 1af sil, dk bl & emer 1.00 .50
Nos. 703-705 (3) 2.25 1.10

Issued for Women's Day.

Poet Mowlana Nooruddin Abdul Rahman Jami (1414-1492) — A228

1964, Nov. 23 **Litho.** ***Perf. 11 Rough***

706 A228 1.50af blk, emer & yel .85 .85

Woodpecker A229

Birds: 3.75af, Black-throated jay, vert. 5af, Impeyan pheasant, vert.

Perf. 13¹/₂x14, 14x13¹/₂

1965, Apr. 20 **Photo.** **Unwmk.**

707 A229 1.25af multi 1.00 .50
708 A229 3.75af multi 1.75 .75
709 A229 5af multi 2.50 1.00
Nos. 707-709 (3) 5.25 2.25

ITU Emblem, Old and New Communication Equipment A230

1965, May 17 *Perf. 13¹/₂x14*

710 A230 5af lt bl, blk & red .35 .35

Cent. of the ITU.

"Red City," Bamian — A231

Designs: 3.75af, Ruins of ancient Bamian city. 5af, Bande Amir, mountain lakes.

1965, May 30 *Perf. 13x13¹/₂*

711 A231 1.25af pink & multi .15 .15
712 A231 3.75af lt bl & multi .18 .18
713 A231 5af yel & multi .30 .30
Nos. 711-713 (3) .63 .63

Issued for tourist publicity.

ICY Emblem A232

1965, June 25 *Perf. 13¹/₂x13*

714 A232 5af multi .25 .25

International Cooperation Year, 1965.

ARIANA Air Lines Emblem and DC-3 — A233

Designs: 5af, DC-6 at right. 10af, DC-3 on top.

Perf. 13¹/₂x14

1965, July 15 **Photo.** **Unwmk.**

715 A233 1.25af brt bl, gray & blk .15 .15
716 A233 5af red lil, blk & bl .30 .30
717 A233 10af bis, blk, bl gray & grn .75 .75
a. Souv. sheet of 3, #715-717, imperf. 1.00 1.00
Nos. 715-717 (3) 1.20 1.20

10th anniv. of Afghan Air Lines, ARIANA.

Nadir Shah — A234

1965, Aug. 23 *Perf. 14x13½*
718 A234 1af dl grn, blk & red brn .25 .15

For the 47th Independence Day.

Flag of Pashtunistan A235

Perf. 13½x14
1965, Aug. 31 Photo. Unwmk.
719 A235 1af multi .25 .15

Issued for "Free Pashtunistan Day."

Zahir Shah Signing Constitution — A236

1965, Sept. 11 *Perf. 13x13½*
720 A236 1.50af brt grn & blk .25 .25

Promulgation of the new Constitution.

Zahir Shah and Oak Leaves — A237

1965, Oct. 14 *Perf. 14x13½*
721 A237 1.25af blk, ultra & salmon .15 .15
722 A237 6af blk, lt bl & rose lil .40 .35

King Mohammed Zahir Shah, 51st birthday.

Flags of UN and Afghanistan A238

1965, Oct. 24 *Perf. 13½x14*
723 A238 5af multi .20 .20

Issued for United Nations Day.

Dappled Ground Gecko — A239

Designs: 4af, Caucasian agamid (lizard). 8af, Horsfield's tortoise.

Perf. 13½x14
1966, May 10 Photo. Unwmk.
724 A239 3af tan & multi .75 .35
725 A239 4af brt grn & multi .85 .40
726 A239 8af vio & multi 1.50 .75
Nos. 724-726 (3) 3.10 1.50

Soccer Player and Globe — A240

1966, July 31 Litho. *Perf. 14x13½*
727 A240 2af rose red & blk .60 .18
728 A240 6af vio bl & blk 1.10 .25
729 A240 12af bis brn & blk 2.25 .60
Nos. 727-729 (3) 3.95 1.03

World Cup Soccer Championship, Wembley, England, July 11-30.

Cotton Flower and Boll — A241

Designs: 5af, Silkworm. 7af, Farmer plowing with oxen.

1966, July 31 *Perf. 13½x14*
730 A241 1af multi .50 .15
731 A241 5af multi 1.00 .30
732 A241 7af multi 1.40 .40
Nos. 730-732 (3) 2.90 .85

Issued for the Day of Agriculture.

Independence Monument A242

1966, Aug. 23 Photo. *Perf. 13½x14*
733 A242 1af multi .25 .15
734 A242 3af multi .75 .25

Issued to commemorate Independence Day.

Flag of Pashtunistan A243

1966, Aug. 31 Litho. *Perf. 11 Rough*
735 A243 1af bright blue .50 .15

"Free Pashtunistan Day."

Bagh-i-Bala Park Casino — A244

Tourist publicity: 2af, Map of Afghanistan. 8af, Tomb of Abd-er-Rahman. The casino on 4af is the former summer palace of Abd-er-Rahman near Kabul.

1966, Oct. 3 Photo. *Perf. 13½x14*
736 A244 2af red & multi .18 .15
737 A244 4af multi .40 .30
738 A244 8af multi .65 .60
a. Souvenir sheet of 3, #736-738, imperf. 3.50 3.50
Nos. 736-738 (3) 1.23 1.05

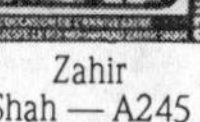
Zahir Shah — A245

UNESCO Emblem — A246

1966, Oct. 14 *Perf. 14x13½*
739 A245 1af dk slate grn .20 .15
740 A245 5af red brn .50 .25

King Mohammed Zahir Shah, 52nd birthday. See Nos. 760-761.

1967, Mar. 6 Litho. *Perf. 12*
741 A246 2af multi .60 .15
742 A246 6af multi .75 .15
743 A246 12af multi 1.50 .30
Nos. 741-743 (3) 2.85 .60

20th anniv. of UNESCO.

Zahir Shah and UN Emblem A247

1967 Photo.
744 A247 5af multi .38 .15
745 A247 10af multi .75 .30

UN Intl. Org. for Refugees, 20th anniv..

New Power Station — A248

Designs: 5af, Carpet, vert. 8af, Cement factory.

1967, Jan. 7 Photo. *Perf. 13½x14*
746 A248 2af red lil & ol grn .15 .15
747 A248 5af multi .22 .18
748 A248 8af blk, dk bl & tan .38 .25
Nos. 746-748 (3) .75 .58

Issued to publicize industrial development.

International Tourist Year Emblem — A249

Designs: 6af, International Tourist Year emblem and map of Afghanistan.

1967, May 11 Photo. *Perf. 12*
749 A249 2af yel, blk & lt bl .15 .15
750 A249 6af bis brn, blk & lt bl .38 .22
a. Souvenir sheet of 2, #749-750, imperf. 1.00 1.00
Set value .30

Intl. Tourist Year, 1967. No. 750a sold for 10af.

Power Dam, Doruntа A250

Macaque A251

Designs: 6af, Sirobi Dam, vert. 8af, Reservoir at Jalalabad.

1967, July 2 Photo. *Perf. 12*
751 A250 1af dk grn & lil .15 .15
752 A250 6af red brn & grnsh bl .35 .35
753 A250 8af plum & dk bl .50 .50
Nos. 751-753 (3) 1.00 1.00

Progress in agriculture through electricity.

1967, July 28 Photo. *Perf. 12*

Designs: 6af, Striped hyena, horiz. 12af, Persian gazelles, horiz.

754 A251 2af dl yel & indigo .25 .15
755 A251 6af lt grn & sepia .70 .35
756 A251 12af lt bl & red brn 1.50 .75
Nos. 754-756 (3) 2.45 1.25

Pashtun Dancers — A252

1967, Sept. 1 Photo. *Perf. 12*
757 A252 2af magenta & vio .50 .15

Issued for "Free Pashtunistan Day."

Retreat of British at Maiwand A253

Fireworks and UN Emblem A254

1967, Aug. 24
758 A253 1af dk brn & org ver .25 .15
759 A253 2af dk brn & brt pink .50 .15
Set value .19

Issued to commemorate Independence Day.

King Type of 1966

1967, Oct. 15 Photo. *Perf. 14x13½*
760 A245 2af brown red .15 .15
761 A245 8af dark blue .50 .25

Issued to honor King Mohammed Zahir Shah on his 53rd birthday.

1967, Oct. 24 Litho. *Perf. 12*
762 A254 10af vio bl & multi .65 .35

Issued for United Nations Day.

Greco-Roman Wrestlers A255

Said Jamalluddin Afghan A256

Design: 6af, Wrestlers (free style).

1967, Nov. 20 Photo.
763 A255 4af ol grn & rose lil .50 .15
764 A255 6af dp car & brn .80 .20
a. Souvenir sheet of 2, #763-764, imperf. 5.00 5.00

1968 Olympic Games.

1967, Nov. 27
765 A256 1af magenta .15 .15
766 A256 5af brown .35 .20
Set value .27

Said Jamalluddin Afghan, politician (1839-97).

Bronze Vase, 11th-12th Centuries A257

WHO Emblem A258

Design: 7af, Bronze vase, Ghasnavide era, 11th-12th centuries.

1967, Dec. 23 Photo. *Perf. 12*
767 A257 3af lt grn & brn .18 .15
768 A257 7af yel & slate grn .42 .30
a. Souvenir sheet of 2, #767-768, imperf. 2.50 2.50

1968, Apr. 7 **Photo.** ***Perf. 12***
769 A258 2af citron & brt bl .15 .15
770 A258 7af rose & brt bl .28 .22
Set value .30

20th anniv. of the WHO.

Karakul — A259

1968, May 20 **Photo.** ***Perf. 12***
771 A259 1af yel & blk .25 .15
772 A259 6af lt bl & blk .70 .20
773 A259 12af ultra & dk brn 1.25 .40
Nos. 771-773 (3) 2.20 .75

Issued for the Day of Agriculture.

Map of Afghanistan A260

Victory Tower, Ghazni A261

Design: 16af, Mausoleum, Ghazni.

1968, June 3 ***Perf. 13½x14, 12***
774 A260 2af red, blk, lt bl & grn .15 .15
775 A261 3af yel, dk brn & lt bl .18 .15
776 A261 16af pink & multi .95 .50
Nos. 774-776 (3) 1.28
Set value .68

Issued for tourist publicity.

Cinereous Vulture — A262

Birds: 6af, Eagle owl. 7af, Greater flamingoes.

1968, July 3 ***Perf. 12***
777 A262 1af sky bl & multi .75 .15
778 A262 6af yel & multi 1.50 .20
779 A262 7af multi 1.75 .30
Nos. 777-779 (3) 4.00 .65

Game of "Pegsticking" A263

Designs: 2af, Olympic flame and rings, vert. 12af, Buzkashi.

1968, July 20 **Photo.** ***Perf. 12***
780 A263 2af multi .16 .15
781 A263 8af org & multi .65 .30
782 A263 12af multi 1.00 .45
Nos. 780-782 (3) 1.81 .90

19th Olympic Games, Mexico City, Oct. 12-27.

Flower-decked Armored Car — A264

1968, Aug. 23
783 A264 6af multi .40 .20

Issued to commemorate Independence Day.

Flag of Pashtunistan A265

1968 Aug. 31 **Photo.** ***Perf. 12***
784 A265 3af multi .25 .15

Issued for "Free Pashtunistan Day."

Zahir Shah — A266

Human Rights Flame — A267

1968, Oct. 14 **Photo.** ***Perf. 12***
785 A266 2af ultra .15 .15
786 A266 8af brown .45 .28
Set value .34

King Mohammed Zahir Shah, 54th birthday.

1968, Oct. 24
787 A267 1af multi .15 .15
788 A267 2af vio, bis & blk .18 .15
789 A267 6af vio blk, bis & vio .38 .15
Nos. 787-789 (3) .71
Set value .25

Souvenir Sheet

Imperf

790 A267 10af plum, bis & red org 1.50 1.50

International Human Rights Year.

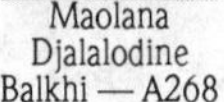

Maolana Djalalodine Balkhi — A268

Kushan Mural — A269

1968, Nov. 26 **Photo.** ***Perf. 12***
791 A268 4af dk grn & mag .27 .15

Balkhi (1207-73), historian.

1969, Jan. 2 ***Perf. 12***

Design: 3af, Jug shaped like female torso.

792 A269 1af dk grn, mar & yel .25 .15
793 A269 3af vio, gray & mar .75 .15
a. Souv. sheet of 2, #792-793, imperf. 1.50 1.50

Archaeological finds at Bagram, 1st cent. B.C. to 2nd cent. A.D.

ILO Emblem A270

1969, Mar. 23 **Photo.** ***Perf. 12***
794 A270 5af lt yel, lemon & blk .30 .18
795 A270 8af lt bl, grnsh bl & blk .50 .30

50th anniv. of the ILO.

Arms Type of 1939

1969, May (?) **Typo.**
795A A79 100p dk grn .15 .15
795B A79 150p dp brn .25 .15
Set value .15

Nos. 795A-795B were normally used as newspaper stamps.

Badakhshan Scene — A271

Tourist Publicity: 2af, Map of Afghanistan. 7af, Three men on mules ascending the Pamir Mountains.

1969, July 6 **Photo.** ***Perf. 13½x14***
796 A271 2af ocher & multi .20 .15
797 A271 4af multi .32 .15
798 A271 7af multi .75 .22
a. Souvenir sheet of 3, #796-798, imperf. 1.75 1.75
Nos. 796-798 (3) 1.27 .52

No. 798a sold for 15af.

Bust, from Hadda Treasure, 3rd-5th Centuries — A272

Zahir Shah and Queen Humeira — A273

Designs: 5af, Vase and jug. 10af, Statue of crowned woman. 5af and 10af from Bagram treasure, 1st-2nd centuries.

1969, Aug. 3 **Photo.** ***Perf. 14x13½***
799 A272 1af ol grn & gold .15 .15
800 A272 5af purple & gold .20 .16
801 A272 10af dp bl & gold .40 .32
Nos. 799-801 (3) .75
Set value .52

1969, Aug. 23 ***Perf. 12***
802 A273 5af gold, dk bl & red brn .35 .20
803 A273 10af gold, dp lil & bl grn .65 .35

Issued to commemorate Independence Day.

Map of Pashtunistan and Rising Sun — A274

1969, Aug. 31 **Typo.** ***Perf. 10½***
804 A274 2af lt bl & red .15 .15

Issued for "Free Pashtunistan Day."

Zahir Shah — A275

1969, Oct. 14 **Photo.** ***Perf. 12***

Portrait in Natural Colors

805 A275 2af dk brn & gold .15 .15
806 A275 6af brn & gold .45 .20
Set value .26

King Mohammed Zahir Shah, 55th birthday.

UN Emblem and Flag of Afghanistan A276

1969, Oct. 24 **Litho.** ***Perf. 13½***
807 A276 5af bl & multi .27 .16

Issued for United Nations Day.

ITU Emblem — A277

Wild Boar — A278

1969, Nov. 12
808 A277 6af ultra & multi .30 .20
809 A277 12af rose & multi .60 .35

Issued for World Telecommunications Day.

1969, Dec. 7 **Photo.** ***Perf. 12***

Designs: 1af, Long-tailed porcupine. 8af, Red deer.

810 A278 1af yel & multi .25 .20
811 A278 3af bl & multi .75 .50
812 A278 8af pink & multi 2.00 1.00
Nos. 810-812 (3) 3.00 1.70

Man's First Footprints on Moon, and Earth — A279

1969, Dec. 28 ***Perf. 13½x14***
813 A279 1af yel grn & multi .15 .15
814 A279 3af yel & multi .24 .15
815 A279 6af blue & multi .40 .20
816 A279 10af rose & multi .65 .32
Nos. 813-816 (4) 1.44
Set value .67

Moon landing. See note after Algeria #427.

Anti-cancer Symbol — A280

Mirza Abdul Quader Bedel — A281

1970, Apr. 7 **Photo.** ***Perf. 14***
817 A280 2af dk grn & rose car .15 .15
818 A280 6af dk bl & rose claret .40 .20
Set value .26

Issued to publicize the fight against cancer.

1970, May 6 ***Perf. 14x13½***
819 A281 5af multi .27 .15

Mirza Abdul Quader Bedel (1643-1720), poet.

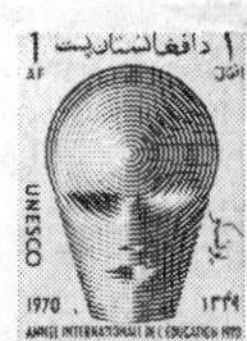

Education Year Emblem A282

Mother and Child A283

1970, June 7 Photo. *Perf. 12*

820 A282 1af black .15 .15
821 A282 6af dp rose .35 .20
822 A282 12af green .75 .35
Nos. 820-822 (3) 1.25
Set value .60

International Education Year 1970.

1970, June 15 *Perf. 13½*

823 A283 6af yel & multi .27 .20

Issued for Mother's Day.

UN Emblem, Scales of Justice, Spacecraft A284

1970, June 26

824 A284 4af yel, dk bl & dp bl .20 .15
825 A284 6af pink, dk bl & brt bl .35 .20

25th anniversary of United Nations.

Mosque of the Amir of the two Swords, Kabul — A285

Designs: 2af, Map of Afghanistan. 7af, Arch of Paghman.

1970, July 6 *Perf. 12*

Size: 30½x30½mm

826 A285 2af lt bl, blk & cit .15 .15

Size: 36x26mm

827 A285 3af pink & multi .18 .15
828 A285 7af yel & multi .42 .22
Nos. 826-828 (3) .75
Set value .38

Issued for tourist publicity.

Zahir Shah Reviewing Troops A286

1970, Aug. 23 Photo. *Perf. 13½*

829 A286 8af multi .60 .25

Issued to commemorate Independence Day.

Pathans — A287

1970, Aug. 31 Typo. *Perf. 10½*

830 A287 2af ultra & red .15 .15

Issued for "Free Pashtunistan Day."

Quail — A288

Designs: 4af, Golden eagle. 6af, Ringnecked pheasant.

1970, Sept. Photo. *Perf. 12*

831 A288 2af multi .50 .25
832 A288 4af multi 1.00 .50
833 A288 6af multi 1.50 .75
Nos. 831-833 (3) 3.00 1.50

Zahir Shah A289

Red Crescents A290

1970, Oct. 14 Photo. *Perf. 14x13½*

834 A289 3af grn & vio .20 .15
835 A289 7af dk bl & vio brn .60 .22

King Mohammed Zahir Shah, 56th birthday.

1970, Oct. 16 Typo. *Perf. 10½*

836 A290 2af blk, gold & red .15 .15

Issued for the Red Crescent Society.

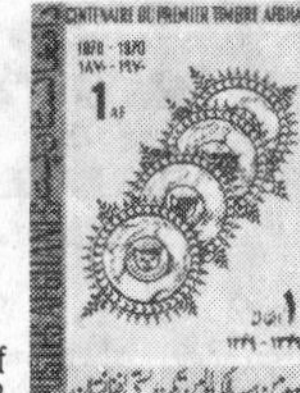

UN Emblem and Charter A291

1970, Oct. 24 Photo. *Perf. 14*

837 A291 1af gold & multi .15 .15
838 A291 5af gold & multi .20 .16
Set value .30 .20

United Nations Day.

Tiger Heads of 1871 — A292

1970, Nov. 10 *Perf. 12*

839 A292 1af sal, lt grnsh bl & blk .25 .15
840 A292 4af lt ultra, yel & blk .50 .15
841 A292 12af lil, lt bl & blk .85 .35
Nos. 839-841 (3) 1.60
Set value .52

Cent. of the 1st Afghan postage stamps. The postal service was established in 1870, but the 1st stamps were issued in May, 1871.

Globe and Waves A293

1971, May 17 Photo. *Perf. 13½*

842 A293 12af grn, blk & bl .60 .35

3rd World Telecommunications Day.

Callimorpha Principalis A294

Designs: 3af, Epizygaenella species. 5af, Parnassius autocrator.

1971, May 30 *Perf. 13½x14*

843 A294 1af ver & multi 1.00 .50
844 A294 3af yel & multi 2.25 1.00
845 A294 5af ultra & multi 3.00 1.50
Nos. 843-845 (3) 6.25 3.00

"UNESCO" and Half of Ancient Kushan Statue — A295

1971, June 26 Photo. *Perf. 13½*

846 A295 6af ocher & vio .40 .20
847 A295 10af lt bl & mar .65 .30

UNESCO-sponsored Intl. Kushani Seminar.

Tughra and Independence Monument — A296

1971, Aug. 23

848 A296 7af rose red & multi .40 .22
849 A296 9af red org & multi .65 .28

Independence Day.

Pashtunistan Square, Kabul — A297

1971, Aug. 31 Typo. *Perf. 10½*

850 A297 5af deep rose lilac .27 .15

"Free Pashtunistan Day."

Zahir Shah — A298

A299

1971, Oct. 14 Photo. *Perf. 12½x12*

851 A298 9af lt grn & multi .40 .28
852 A298 17af yel & multi .75 .55

King Mohammed Zahir Shah, 57th birthday.

1971, Oct. 16 *Perf. 14x13½*

Design: Map of Afghanistan, red crescent, various activities.

853 A299 8af lt bl, red, grn & blk .45 .25

For Afghan Red Crescent Society.

Equality Year Emblem A300

1971, Oct. 24 *Perf. 12*

854 A300 24af brt bl 1.25 .70

International Year Against Racial Discrimination and United Nations Day.

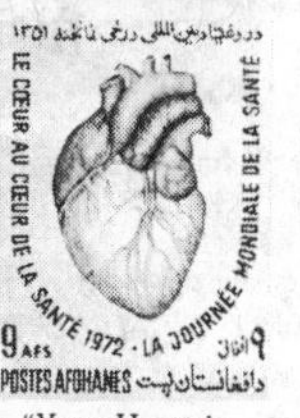

"Your Heart is your Health" — A301

Tulip — A302

1972, Apr. 7 Photo. *Perf. 14*

855 A301 9af pale yel & multi .75 .28
856 A301 12af gray & multi 1.50 .35

World Health Day.

1972, June 5 Photo. *Perf. 14*

Designs: 10af, Rock partridge, horiz. 12af, Lynx, horiz. 18af, Allium stipitatum (flower).

857 A302 7af grn & multi .50 .22
858 A302 10af bl & multi .75 .32
859 A302 12af lt grn & multi 1.00 .35
860 A302 18af bl grn & multi 1.25 .60
Nos. 857-860 (4) 3.50 1.49

Buddhist Shrine, Hadda A302a

Designs: 7af, Greco-Bactrian animal seal, 250 B.C. 9af, Greco-Oriental temple, Ai-Khanoum, 3rd-2nd centuries B.C.

1972, July 16 Photo. *Perf. 12*

861 A302a 3af brn & dl bl .50 .15
862 A302a 7af rose claret & dl grn .80 .22
863 A302a 9af grn & lilac 1.10 .30
Nos. 861-863 (3) 2.40 .67

Tourist publicity.

King and Queen Reviewing Parade — A303

1972, Aug. 23 Photo. *Perf. 13½*

864 A303 25af gold & multi 4.00 1.00

Independence Day.

Used as a provisional in 1978 with king and queen portion removed.

Wrestling A304

Designs: 10af, 19af, 21af, Wrestling, different hold.

1972, Aug. 26

865 A304 4af ol bis & multi .28 .15
866 A304 8af lt bl & multi .52 .25
867 A304 10af yel grn & multi .65 .32
868 A304 19af multi 1.20 .40

869 A304 21af lil & multi 1.40 .45
a. Souv. sheet of 5, #865-869, imperf. 3.00 3.00
Nos. 865-869 (5) 4.05 1.57

20th Olympic Games, Munich, Aug. 26-Sept. 11. No. 869a sold for 60af.

Pathan and View of Tribal Territory — A305

Zahir Shah — A306

1972, Aug. 31 *Perf. 12½x12*
870 A305 5af ultra & multi .27 .15

Pashtunistan day.

1972, Oct. 14 Photo. *Perf. 14x13½*
871 A306 7af gold, blk & Prus bl 1.50 .30
872 A306 14af gold, blk & lt brn 2.50 .50

58th birthday of King Mohammed Zahir Shah.

City Destroyed by Earthquake, Refugees — A307

1972, Oct. 16 *Perf. 13½*
873 A307 7af lt bl, red & blk .40 .22

For Afghan Red Crescent Society.

UN Emblem A308

1972, Oct. 24
874 A308 12af lt ultra & blk .65 .35

UN Economic Commission for Asia and the Far East (ECAFE), 25th anniv.

Ceramics A309

Designs: 9af, Leather coat, vert. 12af, Metal ware, vert. 16af, Inlaid artifacts.

1972, Dec. 10 Photo. *Perf. 12*
875 A309 7af gold & multi .42 .22
876 A309 9af gold & multi .55 .28
877 A309 12af gold & multi .70 .35
878 A309 16af gold & multi 1.00 .50
a. Souv. sheet of 4, #875-878, imperf. 2.25 2.25
Nos. 875-878 (4) 2.67 1.35

Handicraft industries. No. 878a sold for 45af.

WMO and National Emblems — A310

1973, Apr. 3 Photo. *Perf. 14*
879 A310 7af lt lil & dk grn .42 .22
880 A310 14af lt bl & dp claret .85 .45

Cent. of intl. meteorological cooperation.

Abu Rayhan al-Biruni — A311

Family — A312

1973, June 16 Photo. *Perf. 13½*
881 A311 10af multi .55 .32

Millennium of birth (973-1048), philosopher and mathematician.

1973, June 30 Photo. *Perf. 13½*
882 A312 9af org & red lil .50 .30

Intl. Family Planning Fed., 21st anniv.

Republic

Impeyan Pheasant A313

Birds: 9af, Great crested grebe. 12af, Himalayan snow cock.

1973, July 29 Photo. *Perf. 12x12½*
883 A313 8af yel & multi 1.25 .25
884 A313 9af bl & multi 1.75 .30
885 A313 12af multi 2.00 .35
Nos. 883-885 (3) 5.00 .90

Stylized Buzkashi Horseman A314

1973, Aug. *Perf. 13½*
886 A314 8af black .32 .25

Tourist publicity.

Fireworks A315

1973, Aug. 23 Photo. *Perf. 12*
887 A315 12af multi .48 .35

55th Independence Day.

Lake Abassine, Pashtunistan Flag — A316

1973, Aug. 31 *Perf. 14x13½*
888 A316 9af multi .50 .30

Pashtunistan Day.

Red Crescent — A317

1973, Oct. 16 *Perf. 13½*
889 A317 10af red, blk & gold .60 .32

Red Crescent Society.

Kemal Ataturk — A318

1973, Oct. 28 Litho. *Perf. 10½*
890 A318 1af blue .15 .15
891 A318 7af reddish brn .42 .22
Set value .27

50th anniversary of the Turkish Republic.

Human Rights Flame, Arms of Afghanistan A319

1973, Dec. 10 Photo. *Perf. 12*
892 A319 12af sil, blk & lt bl .45 .35

25th anniversary of the Universal Declaration of Human Rights.

Asiatic Black Bears — A320

1974, Mar. 26 Litho. *Perf. 12*
893 A320 5af shown .35 .15
894 A320 7af Afghan hound .50 .22
895 A320 10af Persian goat .70 .28
896 A320 12af Leopard .90 .35
a. Souv. sheet of 4, #893-896, imperf. 5.00 5.00
Nos. 893-896 (4) 2.45 1.00

Worker and Farmer A321

1974, May 1 Photo. *Perf. 13½x12½*
897 A321 9af rose red & multi .40 .25

International Labor Day, May 1.

Independence Monument and Arch — A322

1974, May 27 Photo. *Perf. 12*
898 A322 4af bl & multi .15 .15
899 A322 11af gold & multi .35 .30

56th Independence Day.

Arms of Afghanistan and Symbol of Cooperation A323

Pres. Mohammad Daoud Khan — A324

Designs: 5af, Flag of Republic of Afghanistan. 15af, Soldiers and coat of arms of the Republic.

1974, July 25 *Perf. 13½x12½, 14*
Sizes: 4af, 15af, 36x22mm; 5af, 7af, 36x26, 26x36mm

900 A323 4af multi .18 .15
901 A323 5af multi .22 .15
902 A324 7af grn, brn & blk .32 .18
a. Souv. sheet of 2, #901-902, imperf. .70 .70
903 A323 15af multi .65 .40
a. Souv. sheet of 2, #900, 903, imperf. 1.00 1.00
Nos. 900-903 (4) 1.37 .88

1st anniv. of the Republic of Afghanistan.

Lesser Spotted Eagle — A325

Birds: 6af, White-fronted goose, ruddy shelduck and gray-lag goose. 11af, European coots and European crane.

1974, Aug. 6 Photo. *Perf. 13½x13*
904 A325 1af car rose & multi .25 .15
905 A325 6af bl & multi .75 .18
906 A325 11af yel & multi 1.50 .40
a. Strip of 3, #904-906 1.00 1.00
Nos. 904-906 (3) 2.50
Set value .63

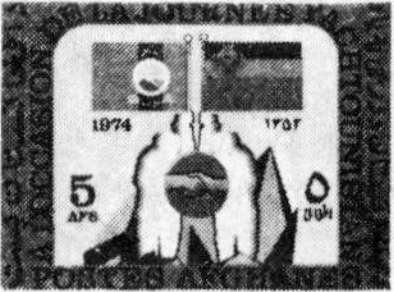

Flags of Pashtunistan and Afghanistan A326

1974, Aug. 31 Photo. *Perf. 14*
907 A326 5af multi .27 .15

Pashtunistan Day.

Natl. Arms A326a

1974, Aug. Typo. *Rough Perf. 11*
907A A326a 100p green

Coat of Arms — A327

1974, Oct. 9
908 A327 7af gold, grn & blk .22 .18

Centenary of Universal Postal Union.

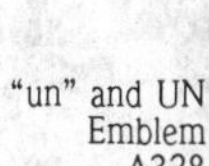

"un" and UN Emblem
A328

1974, Oct. 24 **Photo.** ***Perf. 14***
909 A328 5af lt ultra & dk bl .27 .15

United Nations Day.

Minaret of Jam — A329 Buddha, Hadda — A330

Design: 14af, Lady riding griffin, 2nd century, Bagram.

1975, May 5 **Photo.** ***Perf. 13½***

910	A329	7af multi	.28	.15
911	A330	14af multi	.60	.30
912	A330	15af multi	.65	.30
a.		Souvenir sheet of 3, #910-912, imperf.	3.50	3.50
		Nos. 910-912 (3)	1.53	.75

South Asia Tourism Year 1975.

New Flag of Afghanistan
A331

1975, May 27 **Photo.** ***Perf. 12***
913 A331 16af multi .75 .35

57th Independence Day.

Celebrating Crowd
A332

1975, July 17 **Photo.** ***Perf. 13½***

914	A332	9af bl & multi	.42	.20
915	A332	12af car & multi	.55	.28

Second anniversary of the Republic.

Women's Year Emblems — A333

1975, Aug. 24 **Photo.** ***Perf. 12***
916 A333 9af car, lt bl & blk .28 .22

International Women's Year 1975.

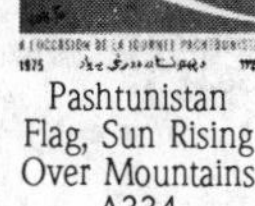

Pashtunistan Flag, Sun Rising Over Mountains
A334

Mohammed Akbar Khan
A335

1975, Aug. 31 ***Perf. 13½***
917 A334 10af multi .30 .25

Pashtunistan Day.

1976, Feb. 4 **Photo.** ***Perf. 14***
918 A335 15af lt brn & multi .45 .35

Mohammed Akbar Khan (1816-1846), warrior son of Amir Dost Mohammed Khan.

Pres. Mohammad Daoud Khan
A336 A337

1974-78 **Photo.** ***Perf. 14***

919	A336	10af multi	.55	.20
920	A336	16af multi ('78)	2.00	*.75*
921	A336	19af multi	.75	.40
922	A336	21af multi	1.10	.45
923	A336	22af multi ('78)	3.00	*1.60*
924	A336	30af multi ('78)	4.00	*2.25*
925	A337	50af multi ('75)	2.25	1.10
926	A337	100af multi ('75)	4.50	2.00
		Nos. 919-926 (8)	18.15	*8.75*

Arms of Republic, Independence Monument — A338

1976, June 1 **Photo.** ***Perf. 14***
927 A338 22af bl & multi .65 .45

58th Independence Day.

Flag Raising — A339

1976, July 17 **Photo.** ***Perf. 14***
928 A339 30af multi .90 .75

Republic Day.

Mountain Peaks and Flag of Pashtunistan
A340

1976, Aug. 31 **Photo.** ***Perf. 14***
929 A340 16af multi .48 .38

Pashtunistan Day.

Coat of Arms — A340a

1976, Sept. **Litho.** ***Perf. 11 Rough***

930	A340a	25p salmon	.25	.15
931	A340a	50p lt grn	.25	.15
932	A340a	1af ultra	.25	.15
		Nos. 930-932 (3)	.75	.45

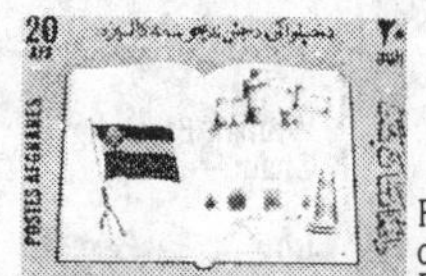

Flag and Views on Open Book — A341

1977, May 27 **Photo.** ***Perf. 14***
937 A341 20af grn & multi .60 .50

59th Independence Day.

Pres. Daoud and National Assembly — A342

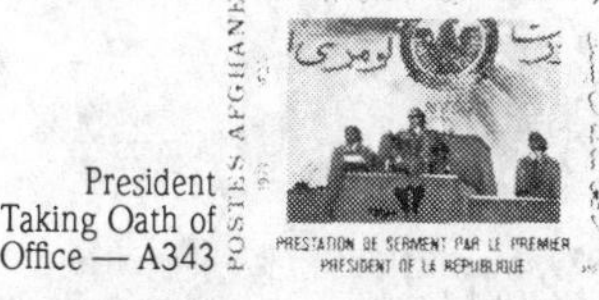

President Taking Oath of Office — A343

Designs: 10af, Inaugural address. 18af, Promulgation of Constitution.

1977, June 22

938	A342	7af multi	.65	.45
939	A343	8af multi	.70	.60
940	A343	10af multi	.90	.75
941	A342	18af multi	1.65	1.25
a.		Souvenir sheet of 4	3.00	3.00
		Nos. 938-941 (4)	3.90	3.05

Election of 1st Pres. and promulgation of Constitution. No. 941a contains 4 imperf. stamps similar to Nos. 938-941.

Jamalluddin Medal
A344

1977, July 6 **Photo.** ***Perf. 14***
942 A344 12af bl, blk & gold .35 .30

Sajo Jamalluddin Afghani, reformer, 80th death anniversary.

Afghanistan Flag over Crowd — A345

1977, July 17
943 A345 22af multi .65 .55

Dancers, Fountain, Pashtunistan Flag — A346

1977, Aug. 31
944 A346 30af multi .90 .75

Pashtunistan Day.

Arms and Carrier Pigeon
A346a

1977, Oct. 30 **Litho.** ***Perf. 11***
944A A346a 1af black & blue .15 .15

Members of Parliament Congratulating Pres. Daoud — A347

1978, Feb. 5 **Litho.** ***Perf. 14***
945 A347 20af multi 1.75

Election of first president, first anniversary.

Map of Afghanistan, UPU Emblem
A348

1978, Apr. 1 **Photo.** ***Perf. 14***
946 A348 10af grn, blk & gold .30 .25

Afghanistan's UPU membership, 50th anniv.

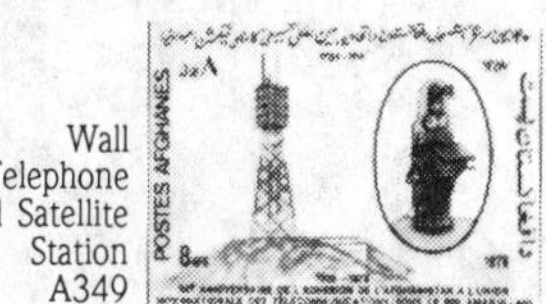

Wall Telephone and Satellite Station
A349

1978, Apr. 12
947 A349 8af multi .24 .20

Afghanistan's ITU membership, 50th anniv.

Democratic Republic

Arrows Pointing to Crescent, Cross and Lion — A350

1978, July 6 Litho. ***Perf. 11 Rough***
948 A350 3af black 1.00 .50

50th anniv. of Afghani Red Crescent Soc.

Khalq Party Emblem A350a

1978, Aug. Litho. ***Perf. 11***
948A A350a 1af rose red & gold 1.25 .50
948B A350a 4af rose red & gold 1.75 .75

Qalai Bist Arch A351

1978, Aug. 19 ***Perf. 14***

949	A351	16af Bamian Buddha	1.00	.40
949A	A351	22af shown	1.25	.55
949B	A351	30af Hazara Women	1.75	.90
		Nos. 949-949B (3)	4.00	1.85

Men with Pashtunistan Flag — A352

Coat of Arms and Emblems — A353

1978, Aug. 31 ***Perf. 11 Rough***
950 A352 7af ultra & red .22 .16

Pashtunistan Day.

1978, Sept. 8 ***Perf. 11***
951 A353 20af rose red .60 .50

World Literacy Day.

A354

Perf. 11½ Rough
1978, Oct. 25 Litho.
952 A354 18af light green .55 .45

Hero of Afghanistan.

Khalq Party Flag — A355

1978, Oct. 19 Photo. ***Perf. 11½***
953 A355 8af blk, red & gold .24 .20
954 A355 9af blk, red & gold .30 .22

"The mail serving the people."

Nour Mohammad Taraki — A356

1979, Jan. 1 Litho. ***Perf. 12***
955 A356 12af multi .35 .15

Nour Mohammad Taraki, founder of People's Democratic Party of Afghanistan, installation as president.

Woman Breaking Chain — A357

1979, Mar. 8 Litho. ***Perf. 11***
956 A357 14af red & ultra *1.50 .50*

Women's Day. Inscribed "POSSTES."

Map of Afghanistan, Census Emblem A358

1979, Mar. 25 Litho. ***Perf. 12***
957 A358 3af multi .75 .50

First comprehensive population census.

Farmers A359

1979, Mar. 21
958 A359 1af multi .50 .25

Agricultural advances.

Pres. Taraki Reading First Issue of Khalq — A360

1979, Apr. 11 ***Perf. 12½x12***
959 A360 2af multi .25 .15

Khalq, newspaper of People's Democratic Republic of Afghanistan.

Pres. Noor Mohammad Taraki — A361

Plaza with Tank Monument and Fountain — A362

House where Revolution Started — A363

Designs: 50p, Taraki, tank. 12af, House where 1st Khalq Party Congress was held.

Perf. 12, 12½x12 (A362)
1979, Apr. 27 Litho.

959A	A363	50p multi	.15	.15
960	A361	4af multi	.16	.15
961	A362	5af multi	.24	.16
962	A363	6af multi	.28	.24
963	A363	12af multi	.52	.45
		Nos. 959A-963 (5)	1.35	1.15

1st anniversary of revolution.

Carpenter and Blacksmith A364

1979, May 1 ***Perf. 12***
964 A364 10af multi .30 .25

Int'l Labor Day.

Children, Flag and Map of Afghanistan — A366

1979, June 1 Litho. ***Perf. 12½x12***
966 A366 16af multi 1.50 .75

International Year of the Child.

Doves Circling Asia in Globe A366a

1979 Litho. ***Perf. 11x10½***
966A A366a 2af red & blue 1.00 .20

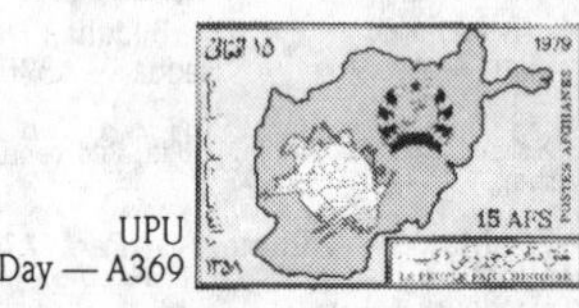

Armed Afghans, Kabul Memorial and Arch — A367

Pashtunistan Citizens, Flag — A368

1979, Aug. 19 Litho. ***Perf. 12***
967 A367 30af multi 1.25 .75

60th independence day.

1979, Aug. 31
968 A368 9 af multi .28 .22

Pashtunistan Day.

UPU Day — A369

1979, Oct. 9 Litho. ***Perf. 12***
969 A369 15af multi .45 .38

Tombstone — A369a

1979, Oct. 25 Litho. ***Perf. 12½x12***
969A A369a 22af multi 2.00 1.00

International Women's Day — A370

1980, Mar. 8 Litho. ***Perf. 12***
970 A370 8af multi *3.00 3.00*

Farmers' Day — A371

1980, Mar. 21 Litho. ***Perf. 11½x12***
971 A371 2af multi .50 .25

Non-smoker and Smoker — A372

1980, Apr. 7 ***Perf. 11½***
972 A372 5af multi .25 .15

Anti-smoking campaign; World Health Day.

Lenin, 110th Birth Anniversary A373

1980, Apr. 22 *Perf. 12x12½*
973 A373 12af multi .35 .30

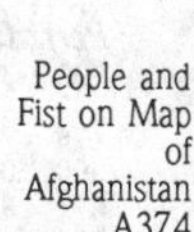

People and Fist on Map of Afghanistan A374

1980, Apr. 27 Litho. *Perf. 12½x12*
974 A374 1af multi .25 .25

Saur Revolution, 2nd anniversary.

International Workers' Solidarity Day — A375

1980, May 1
975 A375 9af multi .28 .22

Wrestling, Moscow '80 Emblem A376

Perf. 12x12½, 12½x12
1980, July 19
976 A376 3af Soccer, vert. .60 .25
977 A376 6af shown 1.00 .45
978 A376 9af Buzkashi 1.65 .60
979 A376 10af Pegsticking 1.75 .75
Nos. 976-979 (4) 5.00 2.05

22nd Summer Olympic Games, Moscow, July 19-Aug. 3.

61st Anniversary of Independence — A377

1980, Aug. 19 Litho. *Perf. 12½x12*
980 A377 3af multi .25 .15

Pashtunistan Day — A378

1980, Aug. 30
981 A378 25af multi .80 .65

Intl. UPU Day — A379

1980, Oct. 9 Litho. *Perf. 12½x12*
982 A379 20af multi .60 .50

International Women's Day — A381

1981, Mar. 9 Litho. *Perf. 12½x12*
984 A381 15af multi .45 .38

Farmers' Day — A382

1981, Mar. 20 Litho. *Perf. 12½x12*
985 A382 1af multi .25 .25

Bighorn Mountain Sheep (Protected Species) — A383

1981, Apr. 4 *Perf. 12x12½*
986 A383 12af multi 1.00 .75

Saur Revolution, 3rd Anniversary A384

Intl. Workers' Solidarity Day A385

1981, Apr. 27 *Perf. 11*
987 A384 50p brown .15 .15

1981, May 1 *Perf. 12½x12*
988 A385 10af multi .30 .25

13th World Telecommunications Day — A387

1981, May 17 Litho. *Perf. 12½x12*
990 A387 9af multi .28 .22

Intl. Children's Day — A388

1981, June 1 *Perf. 12x12½*
991 A388 15af multi .45 .38

People's Independence Monument 62nd Anniv. of Independence A389

1981, Aug. 19
992 A389 4af multi .15 .15

Pashtunistan Day — A390

1981, Aug. 31 Litho. *Perf. 12*
992A A390 2af multi .25 .15

Intl. Tourism Day — A391

1981, Sept. 27 *Perf. 12½x12*
993 A391 5af multi .25 .15

World Food Day — A392

1981, Oct. 16
995 A392 7af multi .35 .15

Asia-Africa Solidarity Meeting A393

1981, Nov. 18 Litho. *Perf. 11*
996 A393 8af blue .24 .20

Struggle Against Apartheid A394

1300th Anniv. of Bulgaria A395

1981, Dec. 1 *Perf. 12½x12*
997 A394 4af multi .30 .20

1981, Dec. 9 *Perf. 12x12½*
998 A395 20af multi 1.25 1.00

Buzkashi Game A395a

1980 Photo. *Perf. 14*
998A A395a 50af multi 3.00 1.00
998B A395a 100af multi 6.00 2.00

Intl. Women's Day — A396

1982, Mar. 8 Litho. *Perf. 12*
999 A396 6af multi .50 .25

Farmers' Day — A397

1982, Mar. 21
1000 A397 4af multi .25 .15

Rhubarb Plant — A398

Saur Revolution, 4th Anniv. — A399

Designs: Various local plants.

1982, Apr. 9 Litho. *Perf. 12*
1001 A398 3af Judas trees .25 .15
1002 A398 4af Rose of Sharon .35 .15
1003 A398 16af shown 1.00 .40
Nos. 1001-1003 (3) 1.60
Set value .58

1982, Apr. 27
1004 A399 1af multi .25 .15

George Dimitrov (1882-1947), First Prime Minister of Bulgaria — A400

Intl. Workers' Solidarity Day — A401

1982, Apr. 30
1005 A400 30af multi .90 .75

1982, May 1
1006 A401 10af multi .30 .25

Storks — A402

1982, May 31

1007 A402 6af shown .50 .25
1008 A402 11af Nightingales 1.00 .45

Hedgehogs A403

1982, July 6 Litho. *Perf. 12*

1009 A403 3af shown .25 .15
1010 A403 14af Cobra .75 .50

See Nos. 1020-1022.

63rd Anniv. of Independence A404

1982, Aug. 19

1011 A404 20af multi .60 .50

Pashtunistan Day — A405

1982, Aug. 31

1012 A405 32af multi 1.00 .80

World Tourism Day — A406

1982, Sept. 27 Litho. *Perf. 12*

1013 A406 9af multi .75 .50

UPU Day — A407

1982, Oct. 9

1014 A407 4af multi .50 .25

World Food Day — A408

1982, Oct. 16

1015 A408 9af multi .30 .22

37th Anniv. of UN — A409

1982, Oct. 24

1016 A409 15af multi .45 .38

ITU Plenipotentiaries Conference, Nairobi, Sept. — A410

1982, Oct. 26

1017 A410 8af multi .25 .20

TB Bacillus Centenary A411

Human Rights Declaration, 34th Anniv. A412

1982, Nov. 24 Litho. *Perf. 12*

1018 A411 7af multi .22 .18

1982, Dec. 10

1019 A412 5af multi .25 .15

Animal Type of 1982

1982, Dec. 16

1020 A403 2af Lions .25 .15
1021 A403 7af Donkeys .75 .18
1022 A403 12af Marmots, vert. 1.00 .28
Nos. 1020-1022 (3) 2.00
Set value .50

Intl. Women's Day — A413

Mir Alicher Nawai Research Decade — A414

1983, Mar. 8

1023 A413 3af multi .25 .15

1983, Mar. 19

1024 A414 22af multi .70 .50

Farmers' Day — A415

1983, Mar. 21 Litho. *Perf. 12*

1025 A415 10af multi .30 .25

5th Anniv. of Saur Revolution A416

1983, Apr. 27 Litho. *Perf. 12*

1026 A416 15af multi 1.00 .50

Intl. Workers' Solidarity Day — A417

1983, May 1

1027 A417 2af multi .60 .50

World Communications Year — A418

1983, May 17

1028 A418 4af Modes of communication .25 .15
1029 A418 11af Building .75 .28

Intl. Children's Day — A419

1983, June 1 Litho. *Perf. 12*

1030 A419 25af multi 1.50 1.50

2nd Anniv. of National Front — A420

1983, June 15

1031 A420 1af multi .15 .15

Local Butterflies A421

Various butterflies. 9af, 13af vert.

1983, July 6

1032 A421 9af multi .55 .55
1033 A421 13af multi .80 .80
1034 A421 21af multi 1.25 1.25
Nos. 1032-1034 (3) 2.60 2.60

Struggle Against Apartheid — A422

1983, Aug. 1 Litho. *Perf. 12*

1035 A422 10af multi .60 .60

64th Anniv of Independence A423

1983, Aug. 19

1036 A423 6af multi .35 .35

Parliament House A423a

1983, Sept. Litho. *Perf. 12*

1036A A423a 50af shown 3.00 3.00
1036B A423a 100af Afghan Woman, Camel 6.00 6.00

A424

World Tourism Day — A425

1983, Sept. 27 Litho. *Perf. 12*

1037 A424 5af shown .30 .30
1038 A425 7af shown .42 .42
1039 A424 12af Golden statues .75 .75
1040 A425 16af Stone carving 1.00 1.00
Nos. 1037-1040 (4) 2.47 2.47

World Communications Year — A426

1983, Oct. 9 Litho. *Perf. 12*

1041 A426 14af Dish antenna, dove .85 .85
1042 A426 15af shown .90 .90

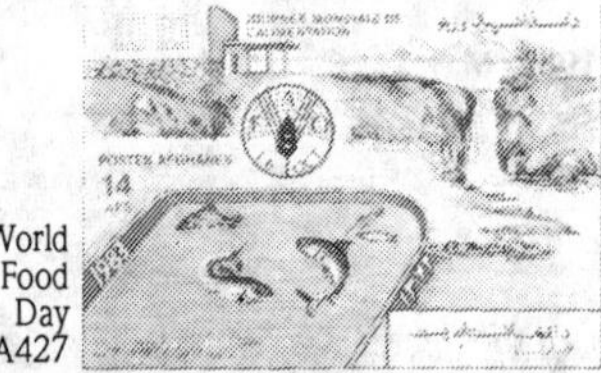

World Food Day A427

1983, Oct. 16 Litho. *Perf. 12*

1043 A427 14af multi .85 .85

Boxing A428

1983, Nov. 1 Litho. *Perf. 12*

1044 A428 1af Running .15 .15
1045 A428 18af shown 1.10 1.10
1046 A428 21af Wrestling 1.25 1.25
Nos. 1044-1046 (3) 2.50 2.50

Pashtunistan Day — A428a

1983,Nov. Litho. *Perf. 12*

1046A A428a 3af Pathans Waving Flag .18 .18

Handicrafts A429

1983, Nov. 22

1047 A429 2af Jewelry .15 .15
1048 A429 8af Stone ashtrays, dishes .50 .50
1049 A429 19af Furniture 1.10 1.10
1050 A429 30af Leather goods 1.90 1.90
Nos. 1047-1050 (4) 3.65 3.65

UN Declaration of Human Rights, 35th Anniv. A430

1983, Dec. 10 Litho. *Perf. 12*
1051 A430 20af multi 1.25 1.25

Kabul Polytechnical Institute, 20th Anniv. — A431

1983, Dec. 28 *Perf. 12½x12*
1052 A431 30af multi 1.90 1.90

1984 Winter Olympics A432

1984, Jan. *Perf. 12*
1053 A432 5af Figure skating .30 .30
1054 A432 9af Skiing .55 .55
1055 A432 11af Speed skating .65 .65
1056 A432 15af Hockey .90 .90
1057 A432 18af Biathlon 1.10 1.10
1058 A432 20af Ski jumping 1.25 1.25
1059 A432 22af Bobsledding 1.40 1.40
Nos. 1053-1059 (7) 6.15 6.15

Intl. Women's Day — A433

1984, Mar. 8
1060 A433 4af multi .25 .25

Farmers' Day — A434

Various agricultural scenes.

1984, Mar. 21 Litho. *Perf. 12*
1061 A434 2af multi .15 .15
1062 A434 4af multi .25 .25
1063 A434 7af multi .42 .42
1064 A434 9af multi .55 .55
1065 A434 15af multi .95 .95
1066 A434 18af multi 1.10 1.10
1067 A434 20af multi 1.25 1.25
Nos. 1061-1067 (7) 4.67 4.67

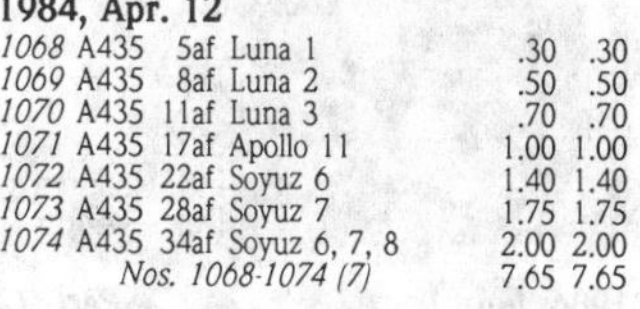
World Aviation Day — A435

1984, Apr. 12
1068 A435 5af Luna 1 .30 .30
1069 A435 8af Luna 2 .50 .50
1070 A435 11af Luna 3 .70 .70
1071 A435 17af Apollo 11 1.00 1.00
1072 A435 22af Soyuz 6 1.40 1.40
1073 A435 28af Soyuz 7 1.75 1.75
1074 A435 34af Soyuz 6, 7, 8 2.00 2.00
Nos. 1068-1074 (7) 7.65 7.65

Souvenir Sheet
Perf. 12x12½
1075 A435 25af S. Koroliov 1.50 1.50

No. 1075 contains one 30x41mm stamp.

Saur Revolution, 6th Anniv. A436

1984, Apr. 27 *Perf. 12*
1076 A436 3af multi .25 .25

65th Anniv. of Independence A437

1984, Aug. 19 Litho. *Perf. 12*
1077 A437 6af multi .38 .38

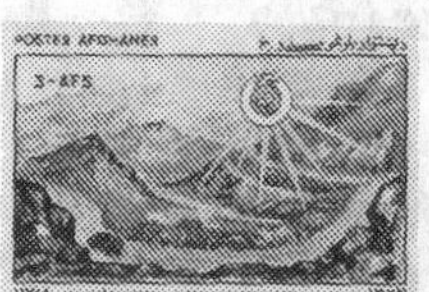
Pashto's and Baluchi's Day — A438

1984, Aug. 31
1078 A438 3af Symbolic sun, tribal terr. .25 .25

Wildlife A439

Perf. 12½x12, 12x12½
1984, May 5 Litho.
1079 A439 1af Cape hunting dog, vert. .15 .15
1080 A439 2af Argali sheep, vert. .15 .15
1081 A439 6af Przewalski's horse .38 .38
1082 A439 8af Wild boar, vert. .50 .50
1083 A439 17af Snow leopard 1.00 1.00
1084 A439 19af Tiger 1.25 1.25
1085 A439 22af Indian elephant, vert. 1.40 1.40
Nos. 1079-1085 (7) 4.83 4.83

19th UPU Congress, Hamburg A440

1984, June 18 *Perf. 12x12½*
1086 A440 25af German postman, 17th cent. 1.50 1.50
1087 A440 35af Postrider, 16th cent. 2.00 2.00
1088 A440 40af Carrier pigeon, letter 2.50 2.50
Nos. 1086-1088 (3) 6.00 6.00

Souvenir Sheet
1089 A440 50af Hamburg No. 3 in black 4.00 4.00

No. 1089 contains one 30x40mm stamp.

Natl. Aviation, 40th Anniv. A441

Soviet civil aircraft.

1984, June 29
1090 A441 1af Antonov AN-2 .15 .15
1091 A441 4af Ilyushin IL-12 .25 .25
1092 A441 9af Tupolev TU-104 .55 .55
1093 A441 10af Ilyushin IL-18 .60 .60
1094 A441 13af Tupolev TU-134 .80 .80
1095 A441 17af Ilyushin IL-62 1.00 1.00
1096 A441 21af Ilyushin IL-28 1.25 1.25
Nos. 1090-1096 (7) 4.60 4.60

Ettore Bugatti (1881-1947), Type 43, Italy — A442

Classic automobiles and their designers: 5af, Henry Ford, 1903 Model A, US. 8af, Rene Panhard (1841-1908), 1899 Landau, France. 11af, Gottlieb Daimler (1834-1900), 1935 Daimler-Benz, Germany. 12af, Carl Benz (1844-1929), 1893 Victoria, Germany. 15af, Armand Peugeot (1848-1915), 1892 Vis-a-Vis, France. 22af, Louis Chevrolet (1879-1941), 1925 Sedan, US.

1984, June 30
1097 A442 2af multi .15 .15
1098 A442 5af multi .30 .30
1099 A442 8af multi .50 .50
1100 A442 11af multi .70 .70
1101 A442 12af multi .75 .75
1102 A442 15af multi .90 .90
1103 A442 22af multi 1.40 1.40
Nos. 1097-1103 (7) 4.70 4.70

Qalai Bist Arch — A443

World Tourism Day: 2af, Ornamental buckled harness. 5af, Victory Monument and Memorial Arch, Kabul. 9af, Standing sculpture of Afghani ruler and attendants. 15af, Buffalo riders in snow. 19af, Camel driver, tent, camel in caparison. 21af, Horsemen playing buzkashi.

1984, Sept. 27
1104 A443 1af multi .15 .15
1105 A443 2af multi .15 .15
1106 A443 5af multi .30 .30
1107 A443 9af multi .55 .55
1108 A443 15af multi .60 .60
1109 A443 19af multi 1.10 1.10
1110 A443 21af multi 1.25 1.25
Nos. 1104-1110 (7) 4.10 4.10

UN World Food Day — A444

Fruit-bearing trees.

1984, Oct. 16
1111 A444 2af multi .15 .15
1112 A444 4af multi .25 .25
1113 A444 6af multi .38 .38
1114 A444 9af multi .55 .55
1115 A444 13af multi .80 .80
1116 A444 15af multi .90 .90
1117 A444 26af multi 1.65 1.65
Nos. 1111-1117 (7) 4.68 4.68

People's Democratic Party, 20th Anniv. A445

1985, Jan. 1
1118 A445 25af multi 1.50 1.50

Farmer's Day — A446

1985, Mar. 2
1119 A446 1af Oxen .15 .15
1120 A446 3af Mare, foal .18 .18
1121 A446 7af Brown horse .40 .40
1122 A446 8af White horse, vert. .50 .50
1123 A446 15af Sheep, sheepskins .90 .90
1124 A446 16af Shepherd, cattle, sheep 1.00 1.00
1125 A446 25af Family, camels 1.50 1.50
Nos. 1119-1125 (7) 4.63 4.63

Geologist's Day — A447

1985, Apr. 5
1126 A447 4af multi .25 .25

Lenin Leading Red Army, 1917 — A448

Lenin and: 10af, Soviet Workers' Party deputies, Smolny. 15af, Revolutionaries, 1917, Leningrad. 50af, Portrait.

1985, Apr. 21 *Perf. 12x12½*
1127 A448 10af multi .60 .60
1128 A448 15af multi .90 .90
1129 A448 25af multi 1.50 1.50
Nos. 1127-1129 (3) 3.00 3.00

Souvenir Sheet
1130 A448 50af multi 4.00 4.00

Saur Revolution, 7th Anniv. — A449

1985, Apr. 27
1131 A449 21af multi 1.25 1.25

Berlin-Treptow Soviet War Memorial, Red Army at Siege of Berlin, 1945 — A450

Designs: 9af, Victorious Motherland monument, fireworks over Kremlin. 10af, Caecilienhof, site of Potsdam Treaty signing, flags of Great Britain, USSR and US.

1985, May 9 *Perf. 12½x12*
1132 A450 6af multi .38 .38
1133 A450 9af multi .55 .55
1134 A450 10af multi .65 .65
Nos. 1132-1134 (3) 1.58 1.58

End of World War II, defeat of Nazi Germany, 40th anniv.

INTELSAT, 20th Anniv. A451

Designs: 6af, INTELSAT satellite orbiting Earth. 9af, INTELSAT III. 10af, Rocket launch, Baikanur Space Center, vert.

Perf. 12x12½, 12½x12

1985, Apr. 6 **Litho.**

1135 A451 6af multi .38 .38
1136 A451 9af multi .55 .55
1137 A451 10af multi .60 .60
Nos. 1135-1137 (3) 1.53 1.53

12th World Youth Festival, Moscow — A452

1985, May 5

1138 A452 7af Olympic stadium, Moscow .50 .50
1139 A452 12af Festival emblem .75 .75
1140 A452 13af Kremlin .80 .80
1141 A452 18af Folk doll, emblem 1.10 1.10
Nos. 1138-1141 (4) 3.15 3.15

Intl. Child Survival Campaign A453

1985, June 1

1142 A453 1af Weighing child .15 .15
1143 A453 2af Immunization .15 .15
1144 A453 4af Breastfeeding .25 .25
1145 A453 5af Mother, child .30 .30
Nos. 1142-1145 (4) .85 .85

Flowers A454

1985, July 5

1146 A454 2af Oenothera affinis .15 .15
1147 A454 4af Erythrina crista-galli .25 .25
1148 A454 8af Tillandsia aeranthos .50 .50
1149 A454 13af Vinca major .80 .80
1150 A454 18af Mirabilis jalapa 1.10 1.10
1151 A454 25af Cypella herbertii 1.50 1.50
1152 A454 30af Clytostoma callistegioides 1.90 1.90
Nos. 1146-1152 (7) 6.20 6.20

Souvenir Sheet

Perf. 12½x11½

1153 A454 75af Sesbania punicea, horiz. 6.00 6.00

ARGENTINA '85.

Independence, 66th Anniv. A455

1985, Aug. 19 *Perf. 12x12½*

1154 A455 33af Mosque 2.00 2.00

Pashto's and Balutchi's Day — A456

1985, Aug. 30

1155 A456 25af multi 1.50 1.50

UN Decade for Women A457

1985, Sept. 22

1156 A457 10af Emblems .60 .60

World Tourism Day, 10th Anniv. A457a

1985, Sept. 27 **Litho.** *Perf. 12*

1156A A457a 1af Guldara Stupa .15 .15
1156B A457a 2af Mirwais Tomb, vert. .15 .15
1156C A457a 10af Statue of Bamyan, vert. .60 .60
1156D A457a 13af No Gumbad Mosque, vert. .80 .80
1156E A457a 14af Pule Kheshti Mosque .85 .85
1156F A457a 15af Bost Citadel .90 .90
1156G A457a 20af Ghazni Minaret, vert. 1.25 1.25
Nos. 1156A-1156G (7) 4.70 4.70

Sports A457b

Perf. 12x12½, 12½x12

1985, Oct. 3 **Litho.**

1156H A457b 1af Boxing .15 .15
1156I A457b 2af Volleyball .15 .15
1156J A457b 3af Soccer, vert. .22 .22
1156K A457b 12af Buzkashi .88 .88
1156L A457b 14af Weight lifting 1.00 1.00
1156M A457b 18af Wrestling 1.30 1.30
1156N A457b 25af Peg sticking 1.85 1.85
Nos. 1156H-1156N (7) 5.55 5.55

World Food Day — A457c

1985, Oct. 16

1156O A457c 25af multi 1.50 1.50

UN 40th Anniv. — A458

Birds — A459

1985, Oct. 24 *Perf. 12½x12*

1157 A458 22af multi 1.40 1.40

Perf. 12½x12, 12x12½

1985, Oct. 25

1158 A459 2af Jay .15 .15
1159 A459 4af Plover, hummingbird .25 .25
1160 A459 8af Pheasant .50 .50
1161 A459 13af Hoopoe .80 .80
1162 A459 18af Falcon 1.10 1.10
1163 A459 25af Partridge 1.50 1.50
1164 A459 30af Pelicans, horiz. 1.90 1.90
Nos. 1158-1164 (7) 6.20 6.20

Souvenir Sheet

Perf. 12x12½

1165 A459 75af Parakeets 6.00 6.00

Mushrooms — A460

1985, June 10 **Litho.** *Perf. 12½x12*

1165A A460 3af Tricholomopsis rutilans .20 .20
1166 A460 4af Boletus miniatoporus .25 .25
1167 A460 7af Amanita rubescens .45 .45
1168 A460 11af Boletus scaber .65 .65
1169 A460 12af Coprinus atramentarius .75 .75
1170 A460 18af Hypholoma 1.10 1.10
1171 A460 20af Boletus aurantiacus 1.25 1.25
Nos. 1165A-1171 (7) 4.65 4.65

World Wildlife Fund — A461

1985, Nov. 25

1172 A461 2af Leopard, cubs .15 .15
1173 A461 9af Adult's head .55 .55
1174 A461 11af Adult .70 .70
1175 A461 15af Cub .90 .90
Nos. 1172-1175 (4) 2.30 2.30

Motorcycle, Cent. — A462

Designs: Different makes and landmarks.

1985, Dec. 16

1176 A462 2af multi .15 .15
1177 A462 4af multi .24 .24
1178 A462 8af multi .48 .48
1179 A462 13af multi .75 .75
1180 A462 18af multi 1.00 1.00
1181 A462 25af multi 1.50 1.50
1182 A462 30af multi 1.75 1.75
Nos. 1176-1182 (7) 5.87 5.87

Souvenir Sheet

Perf. 11½x12½

1183 A462 75af multi 6.00 6.00

People's Democratic Party, 21st Anniv. — A463

1986, Jan. 1 *Perf. 12½x12*

1184 A463 2af multi .25 .25

27th Soviet Communist Party Congress — A464

1986, Mar. 31

1185 A464 25af Lenin 1.50 1.50

First Man in Space, 25th Anniv. — A465

Designs: 3af, Spacecraft. 7af, Soviet space achievement medal, vert. 9af, Rocket lift-off, vert. 11af, Yuri Gagarin, military decorations, vert. 13af, Gagarin, cosmonaut. 15af, Gagarin, politician. 17af, Gagarin wearing flight suit, vert.

Perf. 12½x12, 12x12½

1986, Apr. 12 **Litho.**

1186 A465 3af multi
1187 A465 7af multi
1188 A465 9af multi
1189 A465 11af multi
1190 A465 13af multi
1191 A465 15af multi
1192 A465 17af multi
Nos. 1186-1192 (7) 4.50 4.50

Loya Jirgah (Grand Assembly) of the People's Democratic Republic, 1st Anniv. A465a

1986, Apr. 23 **Litho.** *Perf. 12x12½*

1192A A465a 3af multi .25 .25

Intl. Day of Labor Solidarity — A465b

1986, May 1 *Perf. 12½x12*

1192B A465b 5af multi .30 .30

Intl. Red Crescent Day A465c

1986, May 8 *Perf. 12x12½*

1192C A465c 7af multi .45 .45

Intl. Children's Day — A466

1986, June 1 *Perf. 12*

1193 A466 1af Mother, children, vert. .15 .15
1194 A466 3af Mother, child, vert. .25 .25
1195 A466 9af Children, map .40 .40
Nos. 1193-1195 (3) .80 .80

World Youth Day — A466a

1986, July 31 *Perf. 12x12½*
1195A A466a 15af multi .90 .90

Pashtos' and Baluchis' Day — A467

1986, Aug. 31 *Perf. 12x12½*
1196 A467 4af multi .25 .25

Intl. Peace Year — A468

1986, Sept. 30 Photo. *Perf. 12½x12*
1197 A468 12af blk & Prus bl .75 .75

A469

1986 World Cup Soccer Championships, Mexico — A470

Various soccer plays.

1986, Apr. 15 Litho. *Perf. 12*
1198 A469 3af multi, vert.
1199 A469 4af multi
1200 A469 7af multi
1201 A469 11af multi, vert.
1202 A469 12af multi
1203 A469 18af multi, vert.
1204 A469 20af multi, vert.
Nos. 1198-1204 (7) 4.50 4.50

Souvenir Sheet

Perf. 12½x12

1205 A470 75af multi 6.00 6.00

A471 A472

1986, Apr. 21 *Perf. 12½x12*
1206 A471 16af Lenin 1.00 1.00

1986, Apr. 27 Litho. *Perf. 12½x12*
1207 A472 8af multi .50 .50

Saur revolution, 8th anniv.

Natl. Independence, 67th Anniv. — A473

1986, Aug. 19 Litho. *Perf. 12½x12*
1208 A473 10af multi .65 .65

Literacy Day — A474

1986, Sept. 18 *Perf. 12x12½*
1209 A474 2af multi .25 .25

Dogs — A475 Lizards — A476

1986, May 19 Litho. *Perf. 12x12½*
1210 A475 5af St. Bernard
1211 A475 7af Collie
1212 A475 8af Pointer
1213 A475 9af Golden retriever
1214 A475 11af German shepherd
1215 A475 15af Bulldog
1216 A475 20af Afghan hound
Nos. 1210-1216 (7) 4.50 4.50

1986, July 7 *Perf. 12x12½, 12½x12*
1217 A476 3af Cobra
1218 A476 4af shown
1219 A476 5af Praying mantis
1220 A476 8af Beetle
1221 A476 9af Tarantula
1222 A476 10af Python
1223 A476 11af Scorpions
Nos. 1217-1223 (7) 3.00 3.00

Nos. 1217, 1219, 1221-1223 horiz.

STOCKHOLMIA '86 — A477

Ships.

1986, Aug. 28 *Perf. 12½x12*
1224 A477 4af multi
1225 A477 5af multi
1226 A477 6af multi
1227 A477 7af multi
1228 A477 8af multi
1229 A477 9af multi
1230 A477 11af multi
Nos. 1224-1230 (7) 3.00 3.00

Souvenir Sheet

1231 A477 50af Galley 4.00 4.00

A479 A480

1986, Sept. 14 *Perf. 12*
1232 A479 3af lt blue, blk & olive gray .25 .25

Reunion of Afghan tribes under the Supreme Girgah.

1986, Oct. 25 *Perf. 12½x12*
1233 A480 3af blk & brt ver .25 .25

Natl. youth solidarity.

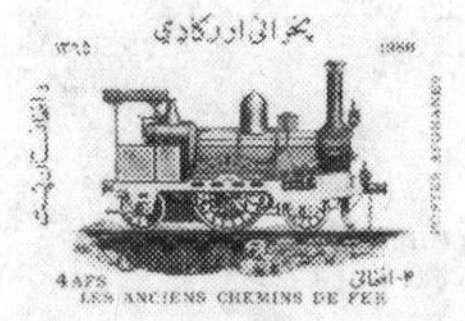

Locomotives — A481

1986, June 21 *Perf. 12½x12*
1234 A481 4af multi
1235 A481 5af multi
1236 A481 6af multi
1237 A481 7af multi
1238 A481 8af multi
1239 A481 9af multi
1240 A481 11af multi
Nos. 1234-1240 (7) 3.00 3.00

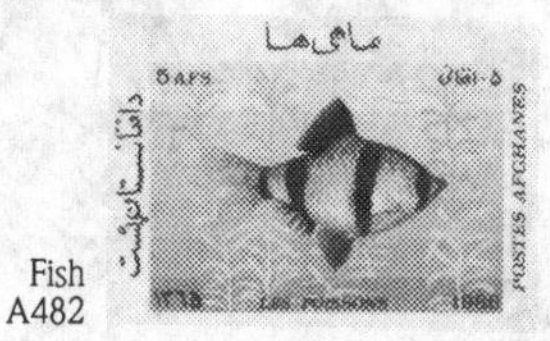

Fish A482

Various fish.

1986, May 25
1241 A482 5af multi
1242 A482 7af multi
1243 A482 8af multi
1244 A482 9af multi
1245 A482 11af multi
1246 A482 15af multi
1247 A482 20af multi
Nos. 1241-1247 (7) 4.50 4.50

Saur Revolution, 9th Anniv. A483

1987, Apr. 27 *Perf. 12*
1248 A483 3af multi .25 .25

Natl. Reconciliation A484

1987, May 27 *Perf. 12x12½*
1249 A484 3af multi .25 .25

A485 A486

UN Child Survival Campaign — A487

1987, June 1 *Perf. 12*
1250 A485 1af multi .15 .15
1251 A486 5af multi .30 .30
1252 A487 9af multi .55 .55
Nos. 1250-1252 (3) 1.00 1.00

Conference of Clergymen and Ulema, 1st Anniv. A488

1987, June 30
1253 A488 5af multi .30 .30

Butterflies — A489 A490

1987, July 3
1254 A489 7af multi
1255 A489 9af multi, diff.
1256 A489 10af multi, diff.
1257 A489 12af multi, diff.
1258 A489 15af multi, diff.
1259 A489 22af multi, diff.
1260 A489 25af multi, diff.
Nos. 1254-1260 (7) 6.00 6.00

10af, 15af and 22af horiz.

1987, Aug. 11
1261 A490 1af multi .25 .25

1st election of local representatives for State Power and Administration.

Natl. Independence, 68th Anniv. — A490a

1987, Aug. 19
1261A A490a 3af multi .25 .25

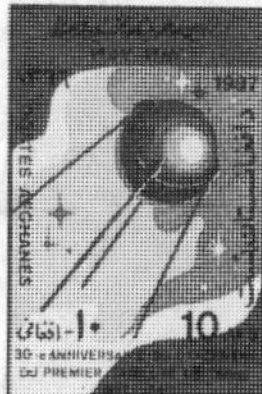

1st Artificial Satellite (Sputnik), 30th Anniv. — A491

1987, Oct. 4 Litho. *Perf. 12½x12*
1262 A491 10af Sputnik
1263 A491 15af Rocket launch
1264 A491 25af Soyuz
Nos. 1262-1264 (3) 3.00 3.00

World Post Day — A492

1987, Oct. 9 *Perf. 12x12½*
1265 A492 22af multi 1.40 1.40

Intl. Communications and Transport Day — A493

1987, Oct. 24 *Perf. 12½x12*
1266 A493 42af multi 2.50 2.50

October Revolution in Russia, 70th Anniv. — A494

Mice — A495

1987, Nov. 7
1267 A494 25af Lenin 1.50 1.50

1987, Dec. 6 *Perf. 12½x12, 12x12½*

Various mice. Nos. 1269-1272 horiz.

1268 A495 2af multi
1269 A495 4af multi, diff.
1270 A495 8af multi, diff.
1271 A495 16af multi, diff.
1272 A495 20af multi, diff.
Nos. 1268-1272 (5) 3.00 3.00

Medicinal Plants — A496

Pashto's and Baluchis' Day — A497

1987, Nov. 11 **Litho.** *Perf. 12*
1273 A496 3af Castor bean .18 .18
1274 A496 6af Licorice .35 .35
1275 A496 9af Chamomile .55 .55
1276 A496 14af Datura .80 .80
1277 A496 18af Dandelion 1.00 1.00
Nos. 1273-1277 (5) 2.88 2.88

1987, Aug. 30
1278 A497 4af multi .25 .25

Dinosaurs A498

Pashtos' and Baluchis' Day A499

Perf. 12½x12, 12x12½

1988, June 6 **Litho.**
1279 A498 3af Mesosaurus .18 .18
1280 A498 5af Styracosaurus .30 .30
1281 A498 10af Uinatherium .60 .60
1282 A498 15af Protoceratops .90 .90
1283 A498 20af Stegosaurus 1.25 1.25
1284 A498 25af Ceratosaurus 1.50 1.50
1285 A498 30af Dinornis maximus 1.90 1.90
Nos. 1279-1285 (7) 6.63 6.63

Nos. 1280-1283 horiz.

1988, Aug. 30 *Perf. 12½x12*
1286 A499 23af multi 1.40 1.40

Afghan-Soviet Joint Space Flight — A500

Valentina Tereshkova, 1st Woman in Space, 25th Anniv. — A501

1988, Aug. 30
1287 A500 32af multi 2.00 2.00

Perf. 12x12½, 12½x12

1988, Oct. 16
1288 A501 10af Portrait, rocket, horiz. .60 .60
1289 A501 15af Lift-off, dove .90 .90
1290 A501 25af Spacecraft, Earth, horiz. 1.50 1.50
Nos. 1288-1290 (3) 3.00 3.00

Traditional Crafts — A502

Precious and Semiprecious Gems — A503

Perf. 12x12½, 12½x12

1988, Nov. 9 **Litho.**
1291 A502 2af Pitcher, bowls .15 .15
1292 A502 4af Vases .25 .25
1293 A502 5af Dress .30 .30
1294 A502 9af Mats, napkins .55 .55
1295 A502 15af Pocketbooks .90 .90
1296 A502 23af Jewelry 1.40 1.40
1297 A502 50af Furniture 3.00 3.00
Nos. 1291-1297 (7) 6.55 6.55

Nos. 1291-1292, 1294-1297 horiz.

1988, Dec. 5 *Perf. 12½x12*
1298 A503 13af Emeralds .80 .80
1299 A503 37af Lapiz lazuli 2.25 2.25
1300 A503 40af Rubies 2.50 2.50
Nos. 1298-1300 (3) 5.55 5.55

1988 Winter Olympics, Calgary — A504

1988, Dec. 25
1301 A504 2af Women's figure skating .15 .15
1301A A504 5af Skiing .30 .30
1301B A504 9af Bobsledding .55 .55
1301C A504 22af Biathlon 1.40 1.40
1301D A504 37af Speed skating 2.25 2.25

Size: 80x60mm

1302 A504 75af Ice hockey 4.50 4.50
Nos. 1301-1302 (6) 9.15 9.15

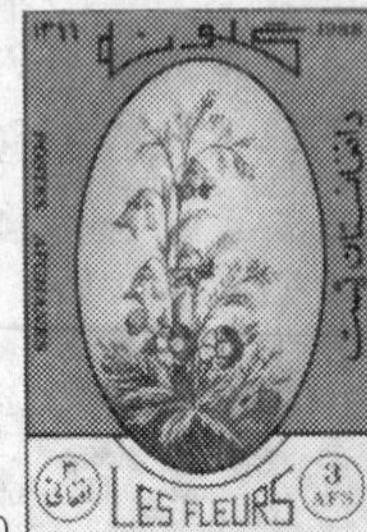
A510

A511

A512

A513

A513a

Flowers — A514

Various flowering plants.

Perf. 12x12½, 12½x12

1988, Jan. 27 **Litho.**
1303 A510 3af multi .18 .18
1304 A511 5af multi .30 .30
1305 A511 7af multi, vert. .42 .42
1306 A512 9af multi .52 .52
1307 A513 12af multi .75 .75
1308 A513a 15af multi .90 .90
1309 A514 24af multi 1.50 1.50
Nos. 1303-1309 (7) 4.57 4.57

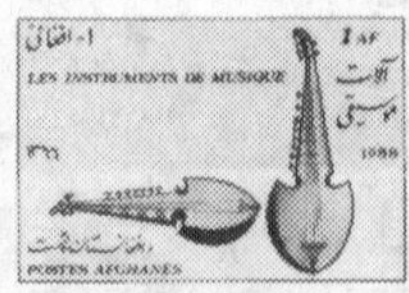
Traditional Musical Instruments A515

String and percussion instruments.

1988, Jan. 15 **Litho.** *Perf. 12*
1310 A515 1af shown .15 .15
1311 A515 3af drums .18 .18
1312 A515 5af multi, diff. .30 .30
1313 A515 15af multi, diff. .90 .90
1314 A515 18af multi, diff. 1.10 1.10
1315 A515 25af multi, diff. 1.50 1.50
1316 A515 33af multi, diff. 2.00 2.00
Nos. 1310-1316 (7) 6.13 6.13

Admission of Afghanistan to the ITU and UPU, 60th Anniv. — A516

1988, Apr. 13 **Litho.** *Perf. 12*
1317 A516 20af multi 1.25 1.25

Saur Revolution, 10th Anniv. A517

1988, Apr. 23
1318 A517 10af multi .65 .65

Fruit — A518

1988, July 18 **Litho.** *Perf. 12*
1319 A518 2af Baskets, compote .15 .15
1320 A518 4af Four baskets .25 .25
1321 A518 7af Basket .42 .42
1322 A518 8af Grapes, vert. .50 .50
1323 A518 16af Market 1.00 1.00
1324 A518 22af Market, diff. 1.40 1.40
1325 A518 25af Vendor, vert. 1.50 1.50
Nos. 1319-1325 (7) 5.22 5.22

Jawaharlal Nehru (1889-1964), 1st Prime Minister of Independent India — A519

1988, Nov. 14
1326 A519 40af multi 2.50 2.50

Natl. Independence, 69th Anniv. A520

1988, Aug. 1
1327 A520 24af multi 1.50 1.50

Intl. Red Cross and Red Crescent Organizations, 125th Annivs. — A521

1988, Sept. 26
1328 A521 10af multi .60 .60

Natl. Reconciliation Institute, 2nd Anniv. — A522

1989, Jan. 4

1329 A522 4af multi .25 .25

Chess A523

Boards, early matches and hand-made chessmen.

1989, Feb. 2 Litho. *Perf. 12x12½*

1330 A523 2af Bishop .15 .15
1331 A523 3af Queen .18 .18
1332 A523 4af King (bust) .25 .25
1333 A523 7af King, diff. .42 .42
1334 A523 16af Knight 1.00 1.00
1335 A523 24af Pawn 1.50 1.50
1336 A523 45af Bishop, diff. 2.75 2.75
Nos. 1330-1336 (7) 6.25 6.25

Paintings by Picasso — A524

Fauna — A525

Designs: 4af, *The Old Jew*. 6af, *The Two Mountebanks*. 8af, *Portrait of Ambrouse Vollar*. 22af, *Woman of Majorca*. 35af, *Acrobat on the Ball*. 75af, *Usine a Horta de Ebro*.

1989, Feb. 13 Litho. *Perf. 12½x12*

1341 A524 4af multi .25 .25
1342 A524 6af multi .35 .35
1343 A524 8af multi .50 .50
1344 A524 22af multi 1.40 1.40
1345 A524 35af multi 2.25 2.25

Size: 71x90mm

Imperf

1346 A524 75af multi 4.50 4.50
Nos. 1341-1346 (6) 9.25 9.25

1989, Feb. 20 Litho. *Perf. 12½x12*

1347 A525 3af *Allactaga euphratica* .18 .18
1348 A525 4af *Equus hemionus* .25 .25
1349 A525 14af *Felis lynx* .85 .85
1350 A525 35af *Gypaetus barbatus* 2.25 2.25
1351 A525 44af *Capra falconeri* 2.75 2.75

Size: 71x91mm

Imperf

1352 A525 100af *Naja oxiana* 6.00 6.00
Nos. 1347-1352 (6) 12.28 12.28

Intl. Women's Day — A526

1989, Mar. 8 *Perf. 12½x12*

1353 A526 8af multi .50 .50

Restoration and Development of San'a, Yemen A527

1988, Dec. 27 Litho. *Perf. 12*

1354 A527 32af multi 2.00 2.00

Agriculture Day — A528

1989, Mar. 21

1355 A528 1af Cattle .15 .15
1356 A528 2af Old and new plows .15 .15
1357 A528 3af Field workers .18 .18
Set value .36 .36

World Meteorology Day — A529

1989, Mar. 23

1358 A529 27af shown 1.65 1.65
1359 A529 32af Emblems 2.00 2.00
1360 A529 40af Weather station, balloon, vert. 2.50 2.50
Nos. 1358-1360 (3) 6.15 6.15

Saur Revolution, 11th Anniv. A530

1989, Apr. 27

1361 A530 20af multi 1.25 1.25

Classic Automobiles — A531

1989 Litho. *Perf. 12½x12*

1362 A531 5af 1910 Duchs, Germany
1363 A531 10af 1911 Ford, US
1364 A531 20af 1911 Renault, France
1365 A531 25af 1911, Russo-Balte, Russia
1366 A531 30af 1926 Fiat, Italy

Asia-Pacific Telecommunity, 10th Anniv. — A532

1989 *Perf. 12*

1367 A532 3af shown
1368 A532 27af Emblem, satellite dish

Teacher's Day — A533

1989 Litho. *Perf. 12*

1369 A533 42af multicolored 1.30

French Revolution, Bicent. — A534

1989 Litho. *Perf. 12*

1370 A534 25af multicolored .78

Natl. Independence, 70th Anniv. A535

1989 Litho. *Perf. 12*

1371 A535 25af multicolored .78

Pashtos' and Baluchis' Day — A536

1989

1372 A536 3af multicolored .15

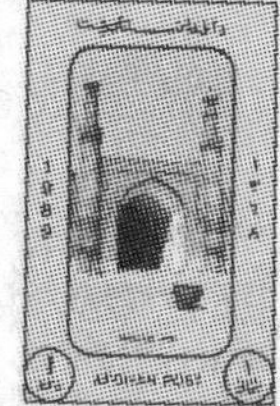

Birds — A537 Tourism — A538

1989 Litho. *Perf. 12*

1373 A537 3af Platalea leucorodia .15
1374 A537 5af Porphyrio porhyrio .15
1375 A537 10af Botaurus stellaris, horiz. .30
1376 A537 15af Pelecanus onocrotalus .45
1377 A537 20af Netta rufina .60
1378 A537 25af Cygnus olor .75
1379 A537 30af Phalacrocorax carbo, horiz. .90
Nos. 1373-1379 (7) 3.30

1989

1380 A538 1af Mosque .15
1381 A538 2af Minaret .15
1382 A538 3af Buzkashi, horiz. .15
1383 A538 4af Jet over Hendo Kush, horiz. .15
Set value .28

SEMI-POSTAL STAMPS

Catalogue values for unused stamps in this section are for Never Hinged items.

No. 373 Surcharged in Violet

MILLIEME ANNIVERSAIRE
DE BOALI SINAI BALKI
125 POULS

40 POULS

1952, July 12 Unwmk. *Perf. 12½*

B1 A122 40p + 30p cerise 10.00 1.50
B2 A122 125p + 30p cerise 12.50 2.00

1000th anniv. of the birth of Avicenna.

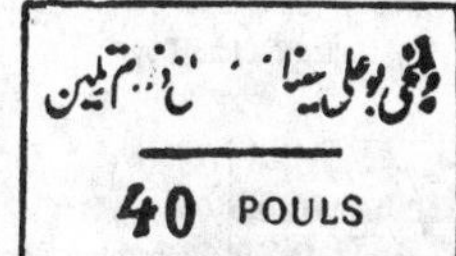

Children at Play — SP1

1955, July 3 Typo. *Perf. 11*

B3 SP1 35p + 15p dk grn .50 .35
B4 SP1 125p + 25p purple 1.00 .85

The surtax was for child welfare.

Amir Sher Ali Khan, Tiger Head Stamp and Zahir Shah — SP2

Children at Play — SP3

1955, July 2 Litho.

B5 SP2 35p + 15p carmine .40 .30
B6 SP2 125p + 25p pale vio bl .85 .55

85th anniv. of the Afghan post.

1956, June 20 Typo.

B7 SP3 35p + 15p brt vio bl .75 .25
B8 SP3 140p + 15p dk org brn 1.25 .75

Issued for Children's Day. The surtax was for child welfare. No. B8 inscribed in French.

Pashtunistan Monument, Kabul — SP4

1956, Sept. 1 Litho.

B9 SP4 35p + 15p dp vio .18 .18
B10 SP4 140p + 15p dk brn .60 .60

"Free Pashtunistan" Day. The surtax aided the "Free Pashtunistan" movement.

No. B9 measures 30½x19½mm; No. B10, 29x19mm. On sale and valid for use only on Sept. 1-2.

Globe and Sun — SP5

Children on Seesaw — SP6

1956, Oct. 24 *Perf. 11*

B11 SP5 35p + 15p ultra .65 .60
B12 SP5 140p + 15p red brn 1.25 1.00

Afghanistan's UN admission, 10th anniv.

1957, June 20 Unwmk.

B13 SP6 35p + 15p brt rose .75 .25
B14 SP6 140p + 15p ultra 1.50 .90

Children's Day. Surtax for child welfare.

UN Headquarters and Emblems — SP7

1957, Oct. 24 *Perf. 11 Rough*

B15 SP7	35p + 15p red brn	.35 .20
B16 SP7	140p + 15p lt ultra	.65 .55

United Nations Day.

Swimming Pool and Children — SP8

1958, June 22 *Perf. 11*

B17 SP8	35p + 15p rose	.25 .20
B18 SP8	140p + 15p dl red brn	.75 .60

Children's Day. Surtax for child welfare.

Pashtunistan Flag — SP9

1958, Aug. 31

B19 SP9	35p + 15p lt blue	.18 .18
B20 SP9	140p + 15p red brn	.60 .60

Issued for "Free Pashtunistan Day."

Children Playing Tug of War — SP10

1959, June 23 **Litho.** *Perf. 11*

B21 SP10	35p + 15p brn vio	.50 .20
B22 SP10	165p + 15p brt pink	1.00 .60

Children's Day. Surtax for child welfare.

Pathans in Tribal Dance — SP11

1959, Sept. **Unwmk.** *Perf. 11 Rough*

B23 SP11	35p + 15p green	.50 .18
B24 SP11	165p + 15p orange	1.00 .60

Issued for "Free Pashtunistan Day."

Afghan Cavalryman with UN Flag — SP12

1959, Oct. 24 *Perf. 11 Rough*

B25 SP12	35p + 15p orange	.20 .16
B26 SP12	165p + 15p lt bl grn	.45 .40

Issued for United Nations Day.

Children SP13

1960, Oct. 23 **Litho.**

B27 SP13	75p + 25p lt ultra	.75 .20
B28 SP13	175p + 25p lt grn	1.50 .35

Children's Day. Surtax for child welfare.

Man with Spray Gun — SP14

1960, Sept. 6 *Perf. 11 Rough*

B29 SP14	50p + 50p orange	.80 1.00
B30 SP14	175p + 50p red brn	2.25 2.25

11th anniversary of the WHO malaria control program in Afghanistan.

SP15

1960, Sept. 1 **Unwmk.**

B31 SP15	50p + 50p rose	.25 .22
B32 SP15	175p + 50p dk bl	.55 .45

Issued for "Free Pashtunistan Day."

Ambulance — SP16

1960, Oct. 16 *Perf. 11*

Crescent in Red

B33 SP16	50p + 50p violet	.40 .30
B34 SP16	175p + 50p blue	.90 .75

Issued for the Red Crescent Society.

Nos. 470-471 Surcharged in Blue or Orange

1960, Dec. 31 **Litho.** *Perf. 11*

B35 A166	50p + 25p dp org (Bl)	1.50 1.50
B36 A166	165p + 25p bl (O)	1.50 1.50

The souvenir sheets described after No. 471 were surcharged in carmine "+25 Ps" on each stamp. Value $5 each.

See general note after No. 485.

Nos. 496-500 Surcharged

UNICEF
یونیسف
+25PS

1961 **Unwmk.** **Photo.** *Perf. 13½x14*

B37 A175	2p + 25p grn & rose lil	
B38 A175	2p + 25p brn & cit	
B39 A175	5p + 25p gray & rose	
B40 A175	10p + 25p bl & bis	
B41 A175	15p + 25p sl bl & dl lil	
	Nos. B37-B41 (5)	1.50

UNICEF. The same surcharge was applied to an imperf. souvenir sheet like that noted after No. 505. Value $4.50.

Nos. 522-526 Surcharged "+25PS" and Crescent in Red

1961, Oct. 16 *Perf. 13½x14*

B42 A184	2p + 25p blk	
B43 A184	2p + 25p grn	
B44 A184	5p + 25p lil rose	
B45 A184	10p + 25p lilac	
B46 A184	15p + 25p dk bl	
	Nos. B42-B46 (5)	2.00

Issued for the Red Crescent Society.

Nos. 539-543 Surcharged in Red: "UNESCO + 25PS"

1962 *Perf. 12*

B47 A186	2p + 25p multi	
B48 A186	2p + 25p multi	
B49 A186	5p + 25p multi	
B50 A186	10p + 25p multi	
B51 A186	15p + 25p multi	
	Nos. B47-B51 (5)	1.50

UNESCO. The same surcharge was applied to the souvenir sheets mentioned after No. 548. Value, 2 sheets, $3.50.

Nos. 553-561 Surcharged: "Dag Hammarskjöld +20PS"

1962, Sept. 17 *Perf. 14x13½*

B52 A187	2p + 20p	
B53 A187	2p + 20p	
B54 A187	5p + 20p	
B55 A187	10p + 20p	
B56 A187	15p + 20p	
B57 A187	25p + 20p	
B58 A187	50p + 20p	
B59 A187	75p + 20p	
B60 A187	100p + 20p	
	Nos. B52-B60 (9)	2.00

In memory of Dag Hammarskjold, Sec. Gen. of the UN, 1953-61. Perf. and imperf. souvenir sheets exist. Value, 2 sheets, $3.

Nos. 583-593 Surcharged "+15PS"

1963, Mar. 15 *Perf. 14x13½*

B61 A193	2p + 15p	
B62 A193	2p + 15p	
B63 A193	5p + 15p	
B64 A193	10p + 15p	
B65 A193	15p + 15p	
B66 A193	25p + 15p	
B67 A193	50p + 15p	
B68 A193	75p + 15p	
B69 A193	100p + 15p	
B70 A193	150p + 15p	
B71 A193	175p + 15p	
	Nos. B61-B71 (11)	7.50

WHO drive to eradicate malaria.

Postally used copies of Nos. B37-B71 are uncommon and command a considerable premium over the values for unused copies.

Nos. 672-672G, 672I Surcharged in Various Positions

15e ANNIVERSAIRE DES DROITS HUMAINS

+
50
POULS

1964, Mar. 9

B71A A213g	2p + 50p	
B71B A213g	3p + 50p	
B71C A213g	4p + 50p	
B71D A213g	5p + 50p	
B71E A213g	10p + 50p	
B71F A213g	100p + 50p	
B71G A213g	2af + 50p	
B71H A213g	3af + 50p	

Souvenir Sheet

B71J A213g	5af + 50p	

Nos. B71E-B71G are airmail semi-postals.

Blood Transfusion Kit — SP17

1964, Oct. 18 **Litho.** *Perf. 10½*

B72 SP17	1af + 50p blk & rose	.50 .15

Issued for the Red Crescent Society and Red Crescent Week, Oct. 18-24.

First Aid Station — SP18

1965, Oct. **Photo.** *Perf. 13½x14*

B73 SP18	1.50af + 50p multi	1.00 .50

Issued for the Red Crescent Society.

Children Playing — SP19

1966, Nov. 28 **Photo.** *Perf. 13½x14*

B74 SP19	1af + 1af yel grn & cl	.35 .15
B75 SP19	3af + 2af yel & brn	.75 .20
B76 SP19	7af + 3af rose lil & grn	1.25 .40
	Nos. B74-B76 (3)	2.35 .75

Children's Day.

Nadir Shah Presenting Society Charter — SP20

1967 **Photo.** *Perf. 13x14*

B77 SP20	2af + 1af red & dk grn	.25 .15
B78 SP20	5af + 1af lil rose & brn	.50 .25

Issued for the Red Crescent Society.

Vaccination SP21

Red Crescent SP22

1967, June 6 **Photo.** *Perf. 12*

B79 SP21	2af + 1af yel & blk	.75 .15
B80 SP21	5af + 2af pink & brn	1.00 .25

The surtax was for anti-tuberculosis work.

1967, Oct. 18 **Photo.** *Perf. 12*

Crescent in Red

B81 SP22	3af + 1af gray ol & blk	.50 .15
B82 SP22	5af + 1af dl bl & blk	.75 .20

Issued for the Red Crescent Society.

Queen Humeira SP23

Red Crescent SP24

1968, June 14 **Photo.** *Perf. 12*

B83 SP23	2af + 2af red brn	.25 .20
B84 SP23	7af + 2af dl grn	.75 .50

Issued for Mother's Day.

1968, Oct. 16 **Photo.** *Perf. 12*

B85 SP24	4af + 1af yel, blk & red	.45 .27

Issued for the Red Crescent Society.

Red Cross, Crescent, Lion and Sun Emblems — SP25

Mother and Child — SP26

1969, May 5 **Litho.** *Perf. 14x13½*

B86 SP25	3af + 1af multi	.75 .18
B87 SP25	5af + 1af multi	1.25 .30

Issued to commemorate the 50th anniversary of the League of Red Cross Societies.

1969, June 14 **Photo.** *Perf. 12*

B88 SP26	1af + 1af yel org & brn	.25 .15
B89 SP26	4af + 1af rose lil & pur	.40 .27
a.	Souv. sheet of 2	1.00 1.00

Mother's Day. No. B89a contains 2 imperf. stamps similar to Nos. B88-B89. Sold for 10af.

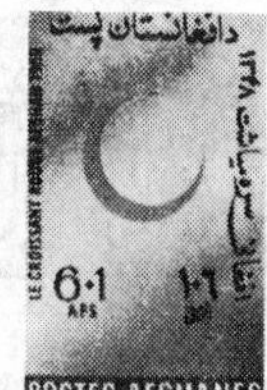

Red Crescent — SP27

1969, Oct. 16 Photo. *Perf. 12*
B90 SP27 6af + 1af multi .75 .30

Issued for the Red Crescent Society.

UN and FAO Emblems, Farmer SP28

1973, May 24 Photo. *Perf. 13½*
B91 SP28 14af + 7af grnsh bl & lil 1.10 .75

World Food Program, 10th anniversary.

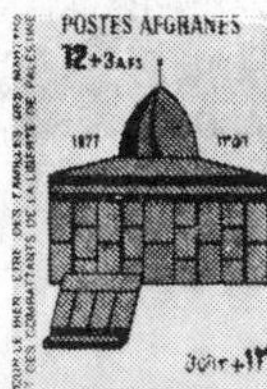

Dome of the Rock, Jerusalem — SP29

1977, Sept. 11 Photo. *Perf. 14*
B92 SP29 12af + 3af multi 1.50 .36

Surtax for Palestinian families and soldiers.

15 Cent. (lunar) of Islamic Pilgrimage (Hegira) — SP30

1981, Jan. 17 Litho. *Perf. 12½x12*
B93 SP30 13af + 2af multi .45 .38

Red Crescent Aid Programs — SP31

1981, May 8 *Perf. 12x12½*
B94 SP31 1af + 4af multi 1.00 1.00

Intl. Year of the Disabled — SP32

1981, Oct. 12 *Perf. 12x12½*
B95 SP32 6af + 1af multi .35 .25

AIR POST STAMPS

Plane over Kabul — AP1

Perf. 12, 12x11, 11

1939, Oct. 1 Typo. Unwmk.
C1 AP1 5af orange 3.75 2.25
a. Imperf., pair ('47) 22.50 22.50
b. Horiz. pair, imperf. vert. 20.00
C2 AP1 10af blue 3.75 1.75
a. 10af lt bl 5.00 5.00
b. Imperf., pair ('47) 22.50
c. Horiz. pair, imperf. vert. 20.00
C3 AP1 20af emerald 7.50 5.00
a. Imperf., pair ('47) 22.50
b. Horiz. pair, imperf. vert. 20.00
c. Vert. pair, imperf. horiz. 22.50
Nos. C1-C3 (3) 15.00 9.00

These stamps come with clean-cut or rough perforations. Counterfeits exist.

1948, June 14 *Perf. 12x11½*
C4 AP1 5af emerald 15.00 15.00
C5 AP1 10af red orange 15.00 15.00
C6 AP1 20af blue 15.00 15.00
Nos. C4-C6 (3) 45.00 45.00

Imperforates exist.

Catalogue values for unused stamps in this section, from this point to the end of the section, are for Never Hinged items.

Plane over Palace Grounds, Kabul — AP2

1951-54 Engr. *Perf. 13½*
Imprint: "Waterlow & Sons, Limited, London"
C7 AP2 5af henna brn 2.50 .55
C8 AP2 5af dp grn ('54) 3.50 .50
C9 AP2 10af gray 4.00 1.40
C10 AP2 20af dark blue 6.50 2.25

1957
C11 AP2 5af ultra .90 .35
C12 AP2 10af dark vio 1.75 .75
Nos. C7-C12 (6) 19.15 5.80

See No. C38.

Ariana Plane over Hindu Kush — AP3

Perf. 11, Imperf.
1960-63 Litho. Unwmk.
C13 AP3 75p light vio .30 .30
C14 AP3 125p blue .40 .45

Perf. 10½, 11
C14A AP3 5af citron ('63) 1.10 1.10
Nos. C13-C14A (3) 1.80 1.85

Girl Scout — AP4

1962, Aug. 30 Photo. *Perf. 11½x12*
C15 AP4 100p ocher & brn .60 .60
C16 AP4 175p brt yel grn & brn .85 .85

Women's Day. A souvenir sheet exists containing one each of #578-579, C15-C16. Value $3.

Sports Type of Regular Issue, 1962

Designs: 25p, 50p, Horse racing. 75p, 100p, Wrestling. 150p, Weight lifting. 175p, Soccer.

1962, Sept. 25 Unwmk. *Perf. 12*
Black Inscriptions
C17 A195 25p rose & red brn
C18 A195 50p gray & red brn
C19 A195 75p pale vio & dk grn
C20 A195 100p gray ol & dk pur
C21 A195 150p rose lil & grn
C22 A195 175p sal & brn
Nos. C17-C22 2.25

Children's Day Type of Regular Issue

Perf. 11½x12, 12x11½
1962, Oct. 14 Unwmk.
C23 A196 75p Runners
C24 A196 150p Peaches
C25 A196 200p Iris, vert.

A souvenir sheet contains one each of Nos. C23-C25. Value $2.50.

Red Crescent Type of Regular Issue

1962, Oct. 16 *Perf. 12*
Fruit and Flowers in Natural Colors; Carmine Crescent
C26 A197 25p Grapes
C27 A197 50p Pears
C28 A197 100p Wistaria

Two souvenir sheets exist. One contains a 150p gray brown stamp in blossom design, the other a 200p gray stamp in wistaria design, imperf. Value, each $5.

UN Type of Regular Issue

1962, Oct. 24 Photo.
Flags in Original Colors, Black Inscriptions
C29 A198 75p blue
C30 A198 100p lt brn
C31 A198 125p brt grn

Boy Scout Type of Regular Issue

1962, Oct. 25 Unwmk. *Perf. 12*
C32 A199 25p gray, blk, dl grn & sal
C33 A199 50p grn, brn & sal
C34 A199 75p bl grn, red brn & sal
C35 A199 100p bl, slate & sal

Teacher's Day Type of Regular Issue

1962, Oct. 25
C36 A200 100p Pole vault
C37 A200 150p High jump

A souvenir sheet contains one 250p pink and slate green stamp in design of 150p. Value $2.50.

Type of 1951-54

1962 Engr. *Perf. 13½*
Imprint: "Thomas De La Rue & Co. Ltd."
C38 AP2 5af ultra 6.00 1.00

Agriculture Types of Regular Issue

Unwmk.
1963, Mar. 1 Photo. *Perf. 12*
C42 A204 100p dk car, grn & brn
C43 A203 150p ocher & blk
C44 A204 200p ultra, grn & brn

Hands Holding Wheat Emblem AP5

1963, Mar. 27 Photo. *Perf. 14*
C45 AP5 500p lil, lt brn & brn 1.75 .60

FAO "Freedom from Hunger" campaign.
Two souvenir sheets exist. One contains a 1000p blue green, light brown and brown, type AP5, imperf. The other contains a 200p brown and green and 300p ultramarine, yellow and ocher in rice and corn designs, type A205. Values $6 and $2.50.

Meteorological Day Type of Regular Issue

Designs: 100p, 500p, Meteorological measuring instrument. 200p, 400p, Weather station. 300p, Rockets in space.

1963, May 23 *Imperf.*
C46 A206 100p brn & bl

Perf. 13½x14
C47 A206 200p brt grn & lil
C48 A206 300p dk bl & rose
C49 A206 400p bl & dl red brn
C50 A206 500p car rose & gray grn

Nos. C47 and C50 printed se-tenant.
Two souvenir sheets exist. One contains a 125p red and brown stamp in rocket design. The other contains a 100p blue and dull red brown in "rockets in space" design. Values $5 and $7.50.

Kabul International Airport — AP8

Perf. 12x11½
1964, Apr. Unwmk. Photo.
C57 AP8 10af red lil & grn .55 .22
C58 AP8 20af dk grn & red lil .80 .40
a. Perf. 12 ('68) 5.00 3.00
C59 AP8 50af dk bl & grnsh bl 2.25 1.00
a. Perf. 12 ('68) 8.00 5.00
Nos. C57-C59 (3) 3.60 1.62

Inauguration of Kabul Airport Terminal.
Nos. C58a-C59a are 36mm wide. Nos. C58-C59 are 35½mm wide.

Zahir Shah and Kabul Airport — AP9

Design: 100af, Zahir Shah and Ariana Plane.

1971 Photo. *Perf. 12½x13½*
C60 AP9 50af multi 10.00 8.00
C61 AP9 100af blk, red & grn 5.00 3.00

Remainders of No C60 were used, starting in 1978, with king's portrait removed.

REGISTRATION STAMPS

R1

Dated "1309"

1891 Unwmk. Litho. *Imperf.*
Pelure Paper
F1 R1 1r slate blue 2.00
a. Tete beche pair 12.50

Genuinely used copies of No. F1 are rare. Counterfeit cancellations exist.

R2

Dated "1311"

1893 Thin Wove Paper
F2 R2 1r black, *green* 1.60

Genuinely used copies of No. F2 are rare. Counterfeit cancellations exist.

R3

Undated

1894
F3 R3 2ab black, *green* 8.00 10.00

12 varieties. See note below Nos. 189-190.

R4

Undated

1898-1900

F4	R4	2ab black, *deep rose*	4.00	4.00
F5	R4	2ab black, *lilac rose*	4.00	4.00
F6	R4	2ab black, *magenta*	6.00	4.00
F7	R4	2ab black, *salmon*	2.50	4.00
F8	R4	2ab black, *orange*	6.00	4.00
F9	R4	2ab black, *yellow*	2.50	4.00
F10	R4	2ab black, *green*	6.00	4.00
		Nos. F4-F10 (7)	31.00	28.00

Many shades of paper.

Nos. F4-F10 come in two sizes, measured between outer frame lines: 52x36mm, 1st printing; 46x33mm, 2nd printing. The outer frame line (not pictured) is 3-6mm from inner frame line.

Used on P.O. receipts.

OFFICIAL STAMPS

(Used only on interior mail.)

Coat of Arms — O1

1909 Unwmk. Typo. *Perf. 12*

Wove Paper

O1	O1	red	.75	1.00
a.		Carmine ('19?)	1.25	1.25

Later printings of No. O1 in scarlet, vermilion, claret, etc., on various types of paper, were issued until 1927.

Coat of Arms — O2

1939-68? Typo. *Perf. 11, 12*

O3	O2	15p emerald	.35	.16
O4	O2	30p ocher ('40)	.50	.50
O5	O2	45p dark carmine	.40	.35
O6	O2	50p brt car ('68)	.28	.28
a.		50p carmine rose ('55)	.50	.40
O7	O2	1af brt red violet	.80	.80
		Nos. O3-O7 (5)	2.33	2.09

Size of 50p, 24x31mm, others 22½x28mm.

Catalogue values for unused stamps in this section, from this point to the end of the section, are for Never Hinged items.

1964-65 Litho. *Perf. 11*

O8	O2	50p rose	.75	.75
a.		50p salmon ('65)	1.50	1.50

Stamps of this type are revenues.

PARCEL POST STAMPS

Coat of Arms — PP1

PP2

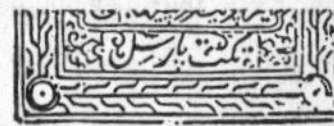
PP3

PP4

1909 Unwmk. Typo. *Perf. 12*

Q1	PP1	3sh bister	.85	1.00
a.		Imperf., pair	1.00	
Q2	PP2	1kr olive gray	1.10	1.25
a.		Imperf., pair	1.40	
Q3	PP3	1r orange	5.00	3.75
Q4	PP3	1r olive green	2.00	4.00
Q5	PP4	2r red	6.00	4.00
		Nos. Q1-Q5 (5)	14.95	14.00

1916-18

Q6	PP1	3sh green	5.00	2.50
Q7	PP2	1kr pale red	2.50	1.25
a.		1kr rose red ('18)	3.25	3.25
Q8	PP3	1r brown org	2.00	1.25
a.		1r deep brown ('18)	2.50	2.50
Q9	PP4	2r blue	5.00	3.00
		Nos. Q6-Q9 (4)	14.50	8.00

Nos. Q1-Q9 sometimes show letters of the papermaker's watermark "HOWARD & JONES LONDON."

Ungummed copies are remainders. They sell for one-third the price of mint examples.

Old Habibia College, Near Kabul — PP5

1921

Wove Paper

Q10	PP5	10pa chocolate	3.00	1.75
a.		Tete beche pair	6.25	
Q11	PP5	15pa light brn	4.50	2.50
a.		Tete beche pair	6.25	
Q12	PP5	30pa red violet	5.75	2.75
a.		Tete beche pair	8.75	
b.		Laid paper	*15.00*	*7.50*
Q13	PP5	1r brt blue	7.25	5.50
a.		Tete beche pair	20.00	
		Nos. Q10-Q13 (4)	20.50	12.50

Stamps of this issue are usually perforated on one or two sides only.

The laid paper of No. Q12b has a papermaker's watermark in the sheet.

PP6

1924-26

Wove Paper

Q15	PP6	5kr ultra ('26)	35.00	15.00
Q16	PP6	5r lilac	8.75	8.75

A 15r rose exists, but is not known to have been placed in use.

PP7

PP8

1928-29 *Perf. 11, 11xImperf.*

Q17	PP7	2r yellow orange	10.00	3.00
Q18	PP7	2r green ('29)	3.00	3.00
Q19	PP8	3r deep green	7.50	4.00
Q20	PP8	3r brown ('29)	5.00	5.00
		Nos. Q17-Q20 (4)	25.50	15.00

POSTAL TAX STAMPS

Aliabad Hospital near Kabul — PT1

Pierre and Marie Curie PT2

Perf. 12x11½, 12

1938, Dec. 22 Typo. Unwmk.

RA1	PT1	10p peacock grn	1.50	2.75
RA2	PT2	15p dull blue	1.50	2.75

Obligatory on all mail Dec. 22-28, 1938. The money was used for the Aliabad Hospital. See note with CD80.

Begging Child

PT3 PT4

1949, May 28 Typo. *Perf. 12*

RA3	PT3	35p red orange	1.60	1.60
RA4	PT4	125p ultra	2.50	2.00

United Nations Children's Day, May 28.

Obligatory on all foreign mail on that date. Proceeds were used for child welfare.

Paghman Arch and UN Emblem PT5

1949, Oct. 24

RA5	PT5	125p dk bl grn	10.00	6.00

4th anniv. of the UN. Valid one day only. Issued in sheets of 9 (3x3).

Catalogue values for unused stamps in this section, from this point to the end of the section, are for Never Hinged items.

Zahir Shah and Map of Afghanistan — PT6

1950, Mar. 30 Typo.

RA6	PT6	125p blue green	2.00	1.25

Return of Zahir Shah from a trip to Europe for his health. Valid for two weeks. The tax was used for public health purposes.

Hazara Youth — PT7

1950, May 28 Typo. *Perf. 11½*

RA7	PT7	125p dk bl grn	2.00	1.50

Tax for Child Welfare. Obligatory and valid only on May 28, 1950, on foreign mail.

Ruins of Qalai Bist and Globe PT8

1950, Oct. 24

RA8	PT8	1.25af ultramarine	7.50	4.00

5th anniv. of the UN. Proceeds went to Afghanistan's UN Projects Committee.

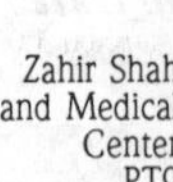

Zahir Shah and Medical Center PT9

1950, Dec. 22 Typo. *Perf. 11½*

Size: 38x25mm

RA9	PT9	35p carmine	1.00	1.00
RA10	PT9	1.25af black	4.50	2.25

The tax was for the national Graduate School of Medicine.

Koochi Girl with Lamb — PT10

Kohistani Boy and Sheep — PT11

1951, May 28

RA11	PT10	35p	emerald	.75	.65
RA12	PT11	1.25af	ultramarine	.75	.65

The tax was for Child Welfare.

Distributing Gifts to Children — PT12

Qandahari Boys Dancing the "Attan" — PT13

1952, May 28 **Litho.**

RA13	PT12	35p	chocolate	.25	.25
RA14	PT13	125p	violet	.75	.75

The tax was for Child Welfare.

Soldier Receiving First Aid — PT14

1952, Oct.

RA15	PT14	10p	light green	.50	.35

Stretcher-bearers and Wounded — PT15

Soldier Assisting Wounded PT16

1953, Oct.

RA16	PT15	10p	yel grn & org red	.50	.40
RA17	PT16	10p	vio brn & org red	.50	.40

Prince Mohammed Nadir — PT17

Map and Young Musicians — PT18

1953, May 28

RA18	PT17	35p	orange yellow	.18	.15
RA19	PT17	125p	chalky blue	.55	.55

No. RA19 is inscribed in French "Children's Day." The tax was for child welfare.

1954, May 28 **Unwmk.** ***Perf. 11***

RA20	PT18	35p	purple	.30	.15
RA21	PT18	125p	ultra	1.10	1.10

No. RA21 is inscribed in French. The tax was for child welfare.

Red Crescent

PT19 PT20

1954, Oct. 17 ***Perf. 11½***

RA22	PT19	20p	blue & red	.25	.22

1955, Oct. 18 ***Perf. 11***

RA23	PT20	20p	dl grn & car	.50	.25

Zahir Shah and Red Crescent — PT21

1956, Oct. 18

RA24	PT21	20p	lt grn & rose car	.25	.18

Red Crescent Headquarters, Kabul — PT22

1957, Oct. 17

RA25	PT22	20p	lt ultra & car	.75	.50

Map and Crescent — PT23

1958, Oct. **Unwmk.** ***Perf. 11***

RA26	PT23	25p	yel grn & red	.30	.30

PT24

1959, Oct. 17 **Litho.** ***Perf. 11***

RA27	PT24	25p	lt vio & red	.18	.15

The tax on Nos. RA15-RA17, RA22-RA27 was for the Red Crescent Society. Use of these stamps was required for one week.

AGUERA, LA

LOCATION — An administrative district in southern Rio de Oro on the northwest coast of Africa.

GOVT. — Spanish possession

AREA — Because of indefinite political boundaries, figures for area and population are not available.

100 Centimos = 1 Peseta

Type of 1920 Issue of Rio de Oro Overprinted **LA AGÜERA**

1920, June **Unwmk.** ***Perf. 13***

1	A8	1c	blue green	1.40	1.40
2	A8	2c	olive brown	1.40	1.40
3	A8	5c	deep green	1.40	1.40
4	A8	10c	light red	1.40	1.40
5	A8	15c	yellow	1.40	1.40
6	A8	20c	lilac	1.40	1.40
7	A8	25c	deep blue	1.40	1.40
8	A8	30c	dark brown	1.40	1.40
9	A8	40c	pink	1.40	1.40
10	A8	50c	bright blue	4.00	3.50
11	A8	1p	red brown	7.00	5.75
12	A8	4p	dark violet	22.50	17.50
13	A8	10p	orange	45.00	40.00
			Nos. 1-13 (13)	91.10	79.35

King Alfonso XIII — A2

1922, June **Typo.**

14	A2	1c	turquoise blue	.65	.65
15	A2	2c	dark green	.65	.65
16	A2	5c	blue green	.65	.65
17	A2	10c	red	.65	.65
18	A2	15c	red brown	.65	.65
19	A2	20c	yellow	.65	.65
20	A2	25c	deep blue	.65	.65
21	A2	30c	dark brown	.65	.65
22	A2	40c	rose red	.85	.85
23	A2	50c	red violet	3.25	2.25
24	A2	1p	rose	6.00	4.75
25	A2	4p	violet	13.00	10.00
26	A2	10p	orange	20.00	15.00
			Nos. 14-26 (13)	48.30	38.05

For later issues see Spanish Sahara.

AJMAN

äj-'man

LOCATION — Oman Peninsula, Arabia, on Persian Gulf

GOVT. — Sheikdom under British Protection

AREA — 100 sq. mi.

POP. — 4,400

CAPITAL — Ajman

Ajman is one of six Persian Gulf sheikdoms to join the United Arab Emirates, which proclaimed its independence Dec. 2, 1971. See United Arab Emirates.

100 Naye Paise = 1 Rupee

Catalogue values for all unused stamps in this country are for Never Hinged items.

Sheik Rashid bin Humaid al Naimi and Arab Stallion — A1

Designs: 2np, 50np, Regal angelfish. 3np, 70np, Camel. 4np, 1r, Angelfish. 5np, 1.50r, Green turtle. 10np, 2r, Jewelfish. 15np, 3r, White storks. 20np, 5r, White-eyed gulls. 30np, 10r, Lanner falcon. 40np as 1np.

1964 **Photo. & Litho. Unwmk.** ***Perf. 14***

Size: 35x22mm

1	A1	1np	gold & multi	.15	.15
2	A1	2np	gold & multi	.15	.15
3	A1	3np	gold & multi	.15	.15
4	A1	4np	gold & multi	.15	.15
5	A1	5np	gold & multi	.15	.15
6	A1	10np	gold & multi	.15	.15
7	A1	15np	gold & multi	.15	.15
8	A1	20np	gold & multi	.15	.15
9	A1	30np	gold & multi	.15	.15

Size: 42x27mm

10	A1	40np	gold & multi	.15	.15
11	A1	50np	gold & multi	.15	.15
12	A1	70np	gold & multi	.15	.15
13	A1	1r	gold & multi	.20	.15
14	A1	1.50r	gold & multi	.25	.15
15	A1	2r	gold & multi	.35	.15

Size: 53x33½mm

16	A1	3r	gold & multi	.60	.15
17	A1	5r	gold & multi	.90	.25
18	A1	10r	gold & multi	2.25	.55
			Set value	5.00	1.75

Issued: #1-9, 6/20; #10-15, 9/7; #16-18, 11/4.

Pres. and Mrs. John F. Kennedy with Caroline — A2

Pres. Kennedy: 10np, As a boy in football uniform. 15np, Diving. 50np, As navy lieutenant, receiving Navy and Marine Corps Medal from Capt. Frederic L. Conklin. 1r, Sailing with Jacqueline Kennedy. 2r, With Eleanor Roosevelt. 5r, With Lyndon B. Johnson and Hubert H. Humphrey. 10r, Portrait.

1964, Dec. 15 **Photo.** ***Perf. 13½x14***

19	A2	10np	grn & red lil	.15	.15
20	A2	15np	Prus bl & vio	.15	.15
21	A2	50np	org brn & dk bl	.15	.15
22	A2	1r	brn & Prus grn	.30	.15
23	A2	2r	red lil & dp ol	.55	.15
24	A2	3r	grn & red brn	.80	.20
25	A2	5r	vio & brn	1.40	.30
26	A2	10r	dk bl & red brn	2.75	.70
			Nos. 19-26 (8)	6.25	
			Set value		1.50

John F. Kennedy (1917-63). A souvenir sheet contains one each of Nos. 23-26.

Runners at Start — A3

Designs: 10np, 1.50r, Boxing. 25np, 2r, Judo. 50np, 5r, Gymnast on vaulting horse. 1r, 3r, Sailing yacht.

1965, Jan. 12 **Photo.** ***Perf. 13½x14***

27	A3	5np	red brn, brt pink & Prus grn	.15	.15
28	A3	10np	dk ol grn, bl gray & red brn	.15	.15
29	A3	15np	dk vio, grn & sep	.15	.15
30	A3	25np	bl sal pink & blk	.15	.15
31	A3	50np	mar, bl & ind	.15	.15
32	A3	1r	dk grn, lil & ultra	.30	.15
33	A3	1.50r	lil, grn & brn	.45	.15
34	A3	2r	red org, bis & dk bl	.55	.20
35	A3	3r	dk brn, grnsh bl & lil	.80	.25
36	A3	5r	grn, yel & red brn	1.40	.40
			Nos. 27-36 (10)	4.25	
			Set value		1.35

18th Olympic Games, Tokyo, Oct. 10-25, 1964. A souvenir sheet contains four stamps similar to Nos. 33-36 in changed colors.

Stanley Gibbons Catalogue, 1865, US No. 1X2 — A4

Designs: 10np, Austria, Scarlet Mercury 1856. 15np, British Guiana 1c, 1856. 25np, Canada 12p, 1851. 50np, Hawaii 2c, 1851. 1r, Mauritius 2p, 1847. 3r, Switzerland, Geneva 10c, 1843. 5r, Tuscany 31, 1860. 5np, 15np, 50np and 3r show first edition of Stanley Gibbons Catalogue; 10np, 25np, 1r and 5r show 1965 Elizabethan Catalogue.

1965, May 6 Unwmk. *Perf. 13*

37 A4 5np multi .15 .15
38 A4 10np multi .15 .15
39 A4 15np multi .15 .15
40 A4 25np multi .15 .15
41 A4 50np multi .15 .15
42 A4 1r multi .20 .15
43 A4 3r multi .60 .20
a. Souv. sheet of 4, #38-39, 42-43 1.00
44 A4 5r multi 1.00 .30
a. Souv. sheet of 4, #37, 40-41, 44 1.25
Set value 2.00 .75

Gibbons Catalogue Cent. Exhib., London, Feb. 17-20. Nos. 43a and 44a for 125th anniv. of 1st postage stamp. Sheets exist imperf.

Stamps of Ajman were replaced in 1972 by those of United Arab Emirates.

AIR POST STAMPS

Type of Regular Issue, 1964

Designs: 15np, Arab stallion. 25np, Regal angelfish. 35np, Camel. 50np, Angelfish. 75np, Green turtle. 1r, Jewelfish. 2r, White storks. 3r, White-eyed gulls. 5r, Lanner falcon.

Photo. & Litho.

1965 Unwmk. *Perf. 14*

Size: 42x25½mm

C1 A1 15np silver & multi .15 .15
C2 A1 25np silver & multi .15 .15
C3 A1 35np silver & multi .15 .15
C4 A1 50np silver & multi .15 .15
C5 A1 75np silver & multi .15 .15
C6 A1 1r silver & multi .25 .15

Size: 53x33½mm

C7 A1 2r silver & multi .45 .15
C8 A1 3r silver & multi .70 .20
C9 A1 5r silver & multi 1.10 .30
Nos. C1-C9 (9) 3.25
Set value .95

Issue dates: #C1-C6, Nov. 15, C7-C9, Dec 18.

AIR POST OFFICIAL STAMPS

Type of Regular Issue, 1964

Designs: 75np, Jewelfish. 2r, White storks. 3r, White-eyed gulls. 5r, Lanner falcon.

Photo. & Litho.

1965, Dec. 18 Unwmk. *Perf. 14*

Size: 42x25½mm

CO1 A1 75np gold & multi .20 .15

Size: 53x33½mm

CO2 A1 2r gold & multi .55 .15
CO3 A1 3r gold & multi .75 .20
CO4 A1 5r gold & multi 1.25 .35
Nos. CO1-CO4 (4) 2.75 .85

OFFICIAL STAMPS

Type of Regular Issue, 1964

Designs: 25np, Arab stallion. 40np, Regal angelfish. 50np, Camel. 75np, Angelfish. 1r, Green turtle.

Photo. & Litho.

1965, Dec. 1 Unwmk. *Perf. 14*

Size: 42x25½mm

O1 A1 25np gold & multi .15 .15
O2 A1 40np gold & multi .15 .15
O3 A1 50np gold & multi .15 .15
O4 A1 75np gold & multi .20 .15
O5 A1 1r gold & multi .25 .15
Set value .75 .25

ALAOUITES

'al-aú-,wītz

LOCATION — A division of Syria, in Western Asia
GOVT. — Under French Mandate
AREA — 2,500 sq. mi.
POP. — 278,000 (approx. 1930)
CAPITAL — Latakia

This territory became an independent state in 1924, although still administered under the French Mandate. In 1930 it was renamed Latakia and Syrian stamps overprinted "Lattaquie" superseded the stamps of Alaouites. For these and subsequent issues see Latakia and Syria.

100 Centimes = 1 Piaster

Issued under French Mandate

Stamps of France Surcharged:

ALAOUITES 0 P. 25 الملوين ١/٤ الغرش — Nos. 1-6, 16-18

ALAOUITES 2 PIASTRES الملوين غروش ٢ — Nos. 7-15, 19-21

1925 Unwmk. *Perf. 14x13½*

1 A16 10c on 2c vio brn 1.00 1.00
2 A22 25c on 5c orange .75 .75
3 A20 75c on 15c gray grn 1.25 1.25
4 A22 1p on 20c red brn .90 .90
5 A22 1.25p on 25c blue 1.10 1.10
6 A22 1.50p on 30c red 3.50 3.50
7 A22 2p on 35c violet .90 .90
8 A18 2p on 40c red & pale bl 1.60 1.60
9 A18 2p on 45c grn & bl 3.50 3.50
10 A18 3p on 60c vio & ultra 2.00 2.00
11 A20 3p on 60c lt vio 3.50 3.50
12 A20 4p on 85c vermilion .75 .75
13 A18 5p on 1fr cl & ol grn 2.50 2.50
14 A18 10p on 2fr org & pale bl 3.25 3.25
15 A18 25p on 5fr bl & buff 4.50 4.50
Nos. 1-15 (15) 31.00 31.00

For overprints see Nos. C1-C4.

Same Surcharges on Pasteur Stamps of France

16 A23 50c on 10c green .80 .80
17 A23 75c on 15c green .80 .80
18 A23 1.50p on 30c red 1.00 1.00
19 A23 2p on 45c red 1.25 1.25
20 A23 2.50p on 50c blue 1.25 1.25
21 A23 4p on 75c blue 1.90 1.90
Nos. 16-21 (6) 7.00 7.00

Stamps of Syria, 1925, Overprinted in Red, Black or Blue:

ALAOUITES الملوين — On A3, A5

ALAOUITES العلويين — On A4

1925, Mar. 1 *Perf. 12½, 13½*

25 A3 10c dk violet (R) .30 .30
a. Double overprint 12.00 12.00
26 A4 25c olive black (R) .55 .55
a. Inverted overprint 6.50 6.50
b. Blue overprint 12.00 12.00
27 A4 50c yellow green .45 .45
a. Inverted overprint 6.00 6.00
b. Blue overprint 12.00 12.00
c. Red overprint 12.00 12.00
28 A4 75c brown orange .50 .50
a. Inverted overprint 6.50 6.50
29 A5 1p magenta .75 .75
30 A4 1.25p deep green .55 .55
a. Red overprint 10.00 10.00
31 A4 1.50p rose red (Bl) .50 .50
a. Inverted overprint 6.50 6.50
b. Black overprint 12.00 12.00
32 A4 2p dk brown (R) .55 .55
a. Blue overprint 6.50 6.50
33 A4 2.50p pck blue (R) .65 .65
a. Black overprint 6.50 6.50
34 A4 3p orange brown .55 .55
a. Inverted overprint 6.50 6.50
b. Blue overprint 14.00 14.00
35 A4 5p violet .65 .65
a. Red overprint 14.00 14.00
36 A4 10p violet brown 1.00 1.00
37 A4 25p ultra (R) 2.00 2.00
Nos. 25-37 (13) 9.00 9.00

For overprints see Nos. C5-C19.

Stamps of Syria, 1925, Surcharged in Black or Red:

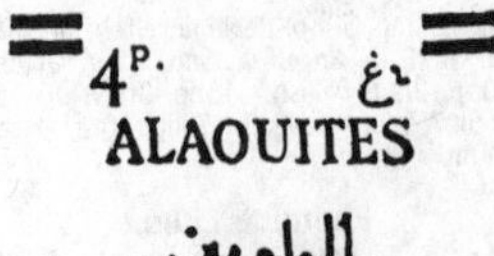

Nos. 38-42

=4P.50 ٤غ ١/٢= Alaouites العلوين

Nos. 43-45

1926

38 A4 3.50p on 75c brn org .75 .60
a. Surcharged on face and back 4.50 4.50
39 A4 4p on 25c ol blk (R) .75 .60
40 A4 6p on 2.50p pck bl (R) .70 .60
41 A4 12p on 1.25p dp grn .70 .60
a. Inverted surcharge 6.25 6.25
42 A4 20p on 1.25p dp grn 1.10 .90
43 A4 4.50p on 75c brn org 2.25 1.25
a. Inverted surcharge 6.50
44 A4 7.50p on 2.50p pck bl 1.75 .90
45 A4 15p on 25p ultra 3.25 2.25
Nos. 38-45 (8) 11.25 7.70

For overprint see No. C21.

Syria #199 Ovptd. like #25 in Red

1928

46 A3 5c on 10c dk violet .25 .25
a. Double surcharge 9.00

Syria Nos. 178 and 174 Surcharged like Nos. 43-45 in Red

47 A4 2p on 1.25p dp green 6.00 3.50
48 A4 4p on 25c olive black 3.75 2.50

For overprint see No. C20.

=4P ٤غ= ALAOUITES العلويين

49 A4 4p on 25c olive black 35.00 30.00
a. Double impression
Nos. 46-49 (4) 45.00 36.25

AIR POST STAMPS

Nos. 8, 10, 13 & 14 with Additional Overprint in Black — طيارة Avion

1925, Jan. 1 Unwmk. *Perf. 14x13½*

C1 A18 2p on 40c 3.50 3.50
a. Overprint reversed 42.50
C2 A18 3p on 60c 5.25 5.25
a. Overprint reversed 42.50 42.50
C3 A18 5p on 1fr 3.50 3.50
C4 A18 10p on 2fr 3.50 3.50
Nos. C1-C4 (4) 15.75 15.75

Nos. 32, 34, 35 & 36 With Additional Overprint in Green

AVION طيارة

1925, Mar. 1 *Perf. 13½*

C5 A4 2p dark brown 1.00 1.00
C6 A4 3p orange brown 1.00 1.00
C7 A4 5p violet 1.00 1.00
C8 A4 10p violet brown 1.00 1.00
Nos. C5-C8 (4) 4.00 4.00

Nos. 32, 34, 35 & 36 With Additional Overprint in Red

1926, May 1

C9 A4 2p dark brown 1.40 1.40
C10 A4 3p orange brown 1.40 1.40
C11 A4 5p violet 1.40 1.40
C12 A4 10p violet brown 1.40 1.40
Nos. C9-C12 (4) 5.60 5.60

No. C9 has the original overprint in black.

Double or inverted overprints, original or plane, are known on most of Nos. C9-C12. Value, $8-$10.

The red plane overprint was also applied to Nos. C5-C8. These are believed to have been essays, and were not regularly issued.

Nos. 27, 29, and 37 With Additional Overprint of Airplane in Red or Black

1929, June-July

C17 A4 50c yel grn (R) .75 .75
a. Plane overprint double 12.00
b. Plane ovpt. on face and back 9.00
c. Pair with plane overprint tete beche 27.50
C18 A5 1p magenta (Bk) 2.75 2.75
C19 A4 25p ultra (R) 17.50 10.00
a. Plane overprint inverted 42.50 42.50
Nos. C17-C19 (3) 21.00 13.50

Nos. 47 and 45 With Additional Overprint of Airplane in Red

1929-30

C20 A4 2p on 1.25p ('30) 1.20 1.20
a. Surcharge inverted 4.00
b. Double surcharge 3.50
C21 A4 15p on 25p (Bk + R) 17.50 14.00
a. Plane overprint inverted 35.00 35.00

POSTAGE DUE STAMPS

Postage Due Stamps of France, 1893-1920, Surcharged Like No. 1 (Nos. J1-J2) or No. 7 (Nos. J3-J5)

1925 Unwmk. *Perf. 14x13½*

J1 D2 50c on 10c choc 1.90 1.90
J2 D2 1p on 20c ol grn 1.90 1.90
J3 D2 2p on 30c red 1.90 1.90
J4 D2 3p on 50c vio brn 1.90 1.90
J5 D2 5p on 1fr red brn, *straw* 1.90 1.90
Nos. J1-J5 (5) 9.50 9.50

Postage Due Stamps of Syria, 1925, Overprinted Like No. 26 (Type D5) or No. 25 (Type D6) in Black, Blue or Red

1925 *Perf. 13½*

J6 D5 50c brown, *yel* .55 .55
J7 D6 1p vio, *rose* (Bl) .55 .55
a. Black overprint 9.00 9.00
b. Double overprint (Bk + Bl) 14.00 14.00
J8 D5 2p blk, *blue* (R) .90 .90
J9 D5 3p blk, *red org* 1.25 1.25
J10 D5 5p blk, *bl grn* (R) 1.75 1.75
Nos. J6-J10 (5) 5.00 5.00

The stamps of Alaouites were superseded in 1930 by those of Latakia.

ALBANIA

al-'bā-nē-ə

LOCATION — Southeastern Europe
GOVT. — Republic
AREA — 11,101 sq. mi.
POP. — 2,750,000 (1982 est.)
CAPITAL — Tirana

After the outbreak of World War I, the country fell into a state of anarchy when the Prince and all members of the International Commission left Albania. Subsequently General Ferrero in command of Italian troops declared Albania an independent country. A constitution was adopted and a republican form of government was instituted which continued until 1928 when, by constitutional amendment, Albania was declared to be a monarchy. The President of the republic, Ahmed Zogu, became king of the new state. Many unlisted varieties or surcharges and lithographed labels are said to have done postal duty in Albania and Epirus during this unsettled period.

In March 1939, Italy invaded Albania. King Zog fled but did not abdicate. The King of Italy acquired the crown.

Germany occupied Albania from September, 1943, until late 1944 when it became an independent state. The People's Republic began in January, 1946.

40 Paras = 1 Piaster = 1 Grossion
100 Centimes = 1 Franc (1917)
100 Qintar = 1 Franc
100 Qintar (Qindarka) = 1 Lek (1947)

Catalogue values for unused stamps in this country are for Never Hinged items, beginning with Scott 458 in the regular postage section, Scott B34 in the semi-postal section, and Scott C67 in the airpost section.

Watermarks

Wmk. 125- Lozenges

Wmk. 220- Double Headed Eagle

Stamps of Turkey Handstamped

Handstamped on Issue of 1908

Perf. 12, 13½ and Compound

1913, June **Unwmk.**

1 A19 2½pi violet brown 225.00 200.00

With Additional Overprint in Carmine ب

2 A19 10pa blue green 200.00 175.00

The eagle handstamp was applied to other Turkish stamps of 1908: 25pi green and 50 pi red brown. The 5pa ocher, Albania No. 4, was surcharged "2 paras." These three stamps were retained by officials. Values, $2,250, $5,500, $375.

Handstamped on Issue of 1909

4 A21 5pa ocher 95.00 95.00
5 A21 10pa blue green 75.00 75.00
6 A21 20pa car rose 57.50 45.00
7 A21 1pi ultra 65.00 57.50
8 A21 2pi blue black 110.00 82.50
10 A21 5pi dark violet 350.00 250.00
11 A21 10pi dull red 1,050. 900.00

For surcharge see No. 19.

With Additional Overprint in Blue or Carmine ب

14 A21 20pa car rose (Bl) 175.00 130.00
15 A21 1pi brt blue (C) 500.00 425.00

Handstamped on Newspaper Stamp of 1911

17 A21 2pa olive green 100.00 90.00

Handstamped on Postage Due Stamp of 1908

18 A19 1pi black, *dp rose* 650.00 475.00

No. 18 was used for regular postage.

No. 6 Surcharged With New Value

19 A21 10pa on 20pa car rose 225.00 210.00

The overprint on #1-19 was handstamped and is found inverted, double, etc.

Nos. 6, 7 and 8 exist with the handstamp in red, blue or violet, but these varieties are not known to have been regularly issued.

Excellent counterfeits exist of Nos. 1 to 19.

A1

1913, July ***Imperf.***

Handstamped on White Laid Paper Without Eagle and Value

20 A1 (1pi) black 100.00 *150.00*
Cut to shape 45.00 45.00
a. Sewing machine perf. 150.00 130.00

1913, Aug.

Value Typewritten in Violet With Eagle

21 A1 10pa violet 3.25 2.00
22 A1 20pa red & black 3.25 2.25
23 A1 1gr black 3.25 2.00
24 A1 2gr blue & violet 4.25 3.25
25 A1 5gr violet & blue 5.50 4.25
26 A1 10gr blue 5.50 4.25
Nos. 21-26 (6) 25.00 18.00

Nos. 21-26 exist with the eagle inverted or omitted and with numerous errors in the figures of value and the spelling of the word "grosh."

A2

Skanderbeg (George Castriota) — A3

1913, Nov. ***Perf. 11½***

Handstamped on White Laid Paper Eagle and Value in Black

27 A2 10pa green 2.75 1.75
b. Eagle and value in green 18.00
c. 10pa red (error) 13.50 13.50
d. 10pa violet (error) 13.50 13.50
29 A2 20pa red 2.75 1.75
b. 20pa green (error) 13.50 13.50
30 A2 30pa violet 3.00 2.25
a. 30pa ultramarine (error) 13.50 13.50
b. 30pa red (error) 13.50 13.50
31 A2 1gr ultramarine 4.50 3.00
a. 1gr green (error) 13.50 13.50
b. 1gr black (error) 13.50 13.50
c. 1gr violet (error) 13.50 13.50
33 A2 2gr black 7.00 6.25
a. 2gr violet (error) 13.50 13.50
b. 2gr blue (error) 13.50 13.50
Nos. 27-33 (5) 20.00 15.00

The stamps of this issue are known with eagle or value inverted or omitted.

1st anniv. of Albanian independence.

1913, Dec. **Typo.** ***Perf. 14***

35 A3 2q orange brn & buff .60 .60
36 A3 5q green & blue grn .60 .60
37 A3 10q rose red .60 .50
38 A3 25q dark blue .70 .80
39 A3 50q violet & red 1.10 1.10
40 A3 1fr deep brown 5.50 *8.00*
Nos. 35-40 (6) 9.10 *11.60*

For overprints and surcharges, see Nos. 41-52, 105, J1-J9.

Nos. 35-40 Handstamped in Black or Violet

1914, Mar. 7

41 A3 2q orange brn & buff 10.00 *15.00*
42 A3 5q grn & bl grn (V) 10.00 *15.00*
43 A3 10q rose red 10.00 *15.00*
44 A3 25q dark blue (V) 10.00 *15.00*
45 A3 50q violet & red 10.00 *15.00*
46 A3 1fr deep brown 10.00 *15.00*
Nos. 41-46 (6) 60.00 *90.00*

Issued to celebrate the arrival of Prince Wilhelm zu Wied on Mar. 7, 1914.

Nos. 35-40 Surcharged in Black:

5 ▪ PARA ▪
a

1 GROSH
b

1914, Apr. 2

47 A3 (a) 5pa on 2q .85 .70
48 A3 (a) 10pa on 5q .85 .70
49 A3 (a) 20pa on 10q 1.50 1.10
50 A3 (b) 1gr on 25q 1.50 1.10
51 A3 (b) 2gr on 50q 2.25 1.50
52 A3 (b) 5gr on 1fr 12.00 10.00
Nos. 47-52 (6) 18.95 15.10

For overprints, see Nos. 105, J6-J9.

Inverted Surcharge

47a A3 (a) 5pa on 2q 4.50 4.50
48a A3 (a) 10pa on 5q 4.50 4.50
49a A3 (a) 20pa on 10q 4.50 4.50
50a A3 (b) 1gr on 25q 5.50 5.50
51a A3 (b) 2gr on 50q 6.75 6.75
52b A3 (b) 5gr on 1fr 18.00 18.00
Nos. 47a-52b (6) 43.75 43.75

Korce (Korytsa) Issues

A4

1914 **Handstamped** ***Imperf.***

52A A4 10pa violet & red 55.00 45.00
c. 10pa black & red 77.50 62.50
53 A4 25pa violet & red 55.00 45.00
a. 25pa black & red 100.00 90.00

Nos. 52A-53a originally were handstamped directly on the cover, so the paper varies. Later they were also produced in sheets; these are rarely found. Nos. 52A-53a were issued by Albanian military authorities.

A5

A6

1917 **Typo. & Litho.** ***Perf. 11½***

54 A5 1c dk brown & grn 7.50 5.75
55 A5 2c red & green 7.50 5.75
56 A5 3c gray grn & grn 7.50 5.75
57 A5 5c green & black 5.50 3.00
58 A5 10c rose red & black 5.50 3.00
59 A5 25c blue & black 5.50 3.00
60 A5 50c violet & black 5.50 3.00
61 A5 1fr brown & black 7.50 5.75
Nos. 54-61 (8) 52.00 35.00

1917-18

62 A6 1c dk brown & grn 2.50 1.65
63 A6 2c red brown & grn 2.50 1.65
a. "CTM" for "CTS" 11.00 11.00
64 A6 3c black & green 2.50 1.65
a. "CTM" for "CTS" 11.00 11.00
65 A6 5c green & black 2.75 2.25
66 A6 10c dull red & black 2.75 2.25
67 A6 50c violet & black 5.25 4.50
68 A6 1fr red brn & black 9.00 5.00
Nos. 62-68 (7) 27.25 18.95

Counterfeits abound of Nos. 54-68, 80-81.

No. 65 Surcharged in Red

QARKU
I
KORÇËS

25 CTS

1918

80 A6 25c on 5c green & blk 45.00 37.50

A7

1918

81 A7 25c blue & black 27.50 22.50

General Issue

A8

A9

Handstamped in Rose or Blue XVI MCMXIX

1919 ***Perf. 12½***

84 A8 (2)q on 2h brown 4.00 3.75
85 A8 5q on 16h green 4.00 3.75
86 A8 10q on 8h rose (Bl) 4.00 3.75
87 A8 25q on 64h blue 4.00 3.75
88 A9 25q on 64h blue *165.00* *150.00*
89 A8 50q on 32h violet 4.00 3.75
90 A8 1fr on 1.28k org, *bl* 4.00 3.75
Nos. 84-90 (7) *189.00* *172.50*

See Nos. J10-J13. Compare with types A10-A14. For overprints see Nos 91-104.

Handstamped in Rose or Blue

1919, Jan. 16

91 A8 (2)q on 2h brown 4.25 4.25
92 A8 5q on 16h green 4.25 4.25
93 A8 10q on 8h rose (Bl) 4.25 4.25
94 A8 25q on 64h blue 25.00 25.00
95 A9 25q on 64h blue 20.00 20.00
96 A8 50q on 32h violet 4.25 4.25
97 A8 1fr on 1.28k org, *bl* 4.25 4.25
Nos. 91-97 (7) 66.25 66.25

Handstamped in Violet

1919

98 A8 (2)q on 2h brown 6.50 6.50
99 A8 5q on 16h green 6.50 6.50
100 A8 10q on 8h rose 6.50 6.50
101 A8 25q on 64h blue 6.50 6.50
102 A9 25q on 64h blue 25.00 25.00
103 A8 50q on 32h violet 6.50 6.50
104 A8 1fr on 1.28k org, *bl* 6.50 6.50
Nos. 98-104 (7) 64.00 64.00

No. 50 Overprinted in Violet

1919 ***Perf. 14***

105 A3 1gr on 25q blue 3.00 *3.00*

A10

A11

1919, June 5 ***Perf. 11½, 12½***

106 A10 10q on 2h brown 2.75 2.75
107 A11 15q on 8h rose 2.75 2.75
108 A11 20q on 16h green 2.75 2.75
109 A10 25q on 64h blue 2.75 2.75
110 A11 50q on 32h violet 2.75 2.75
111 A11 1fr on 96h orange 2.75 2.75
112 A10 2fr on 1.60k vio, *buff* 5.50 5.50
Nos. 106-112 (7) 22.00 22.00

Nos. 106-108, 110 exist with inverted surcharge.

A12

A13

Black or Violet Surcharge

1919

113 A12 10q on 8h car 2.75 2.75
114 A12 15q on 8h car (V) 2.75 2.75
115 A13 20q on 16h green 2.75 2.75
116 A13 25q on 35h violet 2.75 2.75
117 A13 50q on 64h blue 5.75 5.75
118 A13 1fr on 96h orange 3.50 3.50
119 A12 2fr on 1.60k vio, *buff* 3.50 3.50
Nos. 113-119 (7) 23.75 23.75

A14

A15

Overprinted in Blue or Black Without New Value

1920 *Perf. 12½*

120 A14 1q gray (Bl) 20.00 21.00
121 A14 10q rose (Bk) 1.65 2.50
a. Double overprint 21.00 *24.00*
122 A14 20q brown (Bl) 10.00 10.00
123 A14 25q blue (Bk) 100.00 *100.00*
124 A14 50q brown vio (Bk) 13.00 15.00
Nos. 120-124 (5) 144.65 *148.50*

Counterfeit overprints exist of Nos. 120-128.

Surcharged with New Value

125 A14 2q on 10q rose (R) 3.75 3.50
126 A14 5q on 10q rose (G) 3.75 3.50
127 A14 25q on 10q rose (Bl) 3.75 3.50
128 A14 50q on 10q rose (Br) 3.75 3.50
Nos. 125-128 (4) 15.00 14.00

Stamps of type A14 (Portrait of the Prince zu Wied) were not placed in use without overprint or surcharge.

Post Horn Overprinted in Black

1920 *Perf. 14x13*

129 A15 2q orange 1.25 1.25
130 A15 5q deep green 1.65 1.35
131 A15 10q red 4.25 3.25
132 A15 25q light blue 7.50 4.25
133 A15 50q gray green 1.25 1.25
134 A15 1fr claret 1.25 1.25
Nos. 129-134 (6) 17.15 12.60

Type A15 was never placed in use without post horn or "Besa" overprint.

Stamps of Type A15 (No Post Horn) Overprinted

1921

135 A15 2q orange 3.00 3.00
136 A15 5q deep green 4.25 4.25
137 A15 10q red 7.25 7.25
138 A15 25q light blue 16.00 12.50
139 A15 50q gray green 5.25 5.25
140 A15 1fr claret 4.25 4.25
Nos. 135-140 (6) 40.00 36.50

For surcharge & overprints see #154, 156-157.

Stamps of these types, and with "TAKSE" overprint, were unauthorized and never placed in use. They are common.

Gjirokaster A18

Korcha — A19

Designs: 5q, Kanina. 10q, Berati. 25q, Bridge at Vezirit. 50q, Rozafat. 2fr, Dursit.

1923 **Typo.** *Perf. 12½, 11½*

147 A18 2q orange .55 .55
148 A18 5q yellow green .48 .48
149 A18 10q carmine .48 .48
150 A18 25q dark blue .48 .48
151 A18 50q dark green .48 .48
152 A19 1fr dark violet .65 .65
153 A19 2fr olive green 1.75 1.75
Nos. 147-153 (7) 4.87 4.87

For overprints & surcharges see #158-185, B1-B8.

No. 135 Surcharged Q 1

1922 *Perf. 14x13*

154 A15 1q on 2q orange 3.00 3.00

Stamps of Type A15 (No Post Horn) Overprinted BESA

1922

156 A15 5q deep green 3.00 2.50
157 A15 10q red 3.00 2.50

Nos. 147-151 Overprinted (top line in Black; diamond in Violet)

Mbledhje Kushtetuese
TIRANE KALLNUER 1924

1924, Jan. *Perf. 12½*

158 A18 2q red orange 3.50 3.25
159 A18 5q yellow green 3.50 3.25
160 A18 10q carmine 3.50 3.25
161 A18 25q dark blue 3.50 3.25
162 A18 50q dark green 3.50 3.25
Nos. 158-162 (5) 17.50 16.25

The words "Mbledhje Kushtetuese" are in taller letters on the 25q than on the other values. Opening of the Constituent Assembly.

No. 147 Surcharged

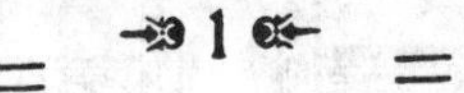

1924

163 A18 1q on 2q red orange 2.25 2.25

Nos. 163, 147-152 Overprinted

Triumf' i legalitetit
24 Dhetuer 1924

1924

164 A18 1q on 2q orange 1.40 1.40
165 A18 2q orange 1.40 1.40
166 A18 5q yellow green 1.40 1.40
167 A18 10q carmine 1.40 1.40
168 A18 25q dark blue 1.40 1.40
169 A18 50q dark green 1.40 1.40
170 A19 1fr dark violet 1.40 1.40
Nos. 164-170 (7) 9.80 9.80

Issued to celebrate the return of the Government to the Capital after a revolution.

Nos. 163, 147-152 Overprinted

Republika Shqiptare
21 Kallnduer 1925

1925

171 A18 1q on 2q orange 1.40 1.40
172 A18 2q orange 1.40 1.40
173 A18 5q yellow green 1.40 1.40
174 A18 10q carmine 1.40 1.40
175 A18 25q dark blue 1.40 1.40
176 A18 50q dark green 1.40 1.40
177 A19 1fr dark violet 1.40 1.40
Nos. 171-177 (7) 9.80 9.80

Proclamation of the Republic, Jan. 21, 1925. The date "1921" instead of "1925" occurs once in each sheet of 50.

Nos. 163, 147-153 Overprinted

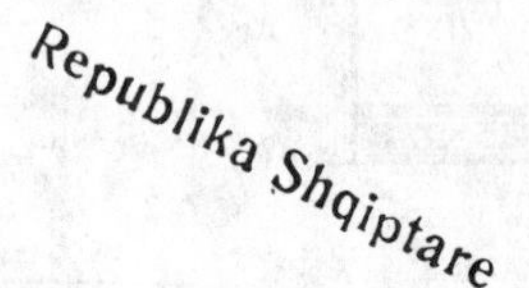

1925

178 A18 1q on 2q orange .55 .55
a. Inverted overprint 7.00 7.00
179 A18 2q orange .55 .55
180 A18 5q yellow green .55 .55
a. Inverted overprint 7.00 7.00
181 A18 10q carmine .55 .55
182 A18 25q dark blue .55 .55
183 A18 50q dark green .55 .55
184 A19 1fr dark violet .65 .65
185 A19 2fr olive green .65 .65
Nos. 178-185 (8) 4.60 4.60

President Ahmed Zogu
A25 A26

1925 *Perf. 13½, 13½x13*

186 A25 1q orange .15 .15
187 A25 2q red brown .15 .15
188 A25 5q green .15 .15
189 A25 10q rose red .15 .15
190 A25 15q gray brown 1.40 1.40
191 A25 25q dark blue .15 .15
192 A25 50q blue green .48 .48
193 A26 1fr red & ultra .85 .85
194 A26 2fr green & orange .85 .85
195 A26 3fr brown & violet 1.40 1.40
196 A26 5fr violet & black 3.50 3.50
Nos. 186-196 (11) 9.23 9.23

No. 193 in ultramarine and brown, and No. 194 in gray and brown were not regularly issued. Value, both $15.

For overprints & surcharges see #197-209, 238-248.

Nos. 186-196 Overprinted in Various Colors

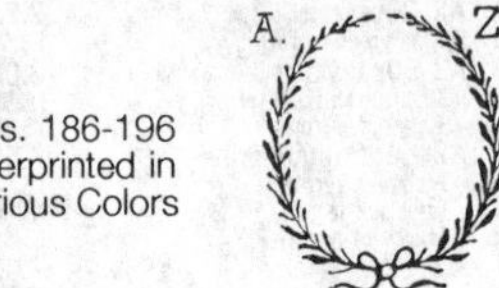

1927

197 A25 1q orange (V) .38 .38
198 A25 2q red brn (G) .15 .15
199 A25 5q green (R) .75 .75
200 A25 10q rose red (Bl) .15 .15
201 A25 15q gray brn (G) 7.50 7.50
202 A25 25q dk blue (R) .15 .15
203 A25 50q blue grn (Bl) .15 .15
204 A26 1fr red & ultra (Bk) .15 .15
205 A26 2fr green & org (Bk) .15 .15
206 A26 3fr brown & vio (Bk) .55 .55
207 A26 5fr violet & blk (Bk) .95 .95
Nos. 197-207 (11) 11.03 10.43

No. 200 exists perf. 11.
For surcharges see Nos. 208-209, 238-240.

Nos. 200, 202 Surcharged in Black or Red = 5 =

1928

208 A25 1q on 10q rose red .35 .22
a. Inverted surcharge 3.75 3.75
209 A25 5q on 25q dk blue (R) .35 .22
a. Inverted surcharge 3.75 3.75

King Zog I
A27 A28

Black Overprint

1928 *Perf. 14x13½*

210 A27 1q orange brown 2.00 2.00
211 A27 2q slate 2.00 2.00
212 A27 5q blue green 2.00 2.00
213 A27 10q rose red 2.00 2.00
214 A27 15q bister 11.00 11.00
215 A27 25q deep blue 1.65 1.65
216 A27 50q lilac rose 2.00 2.00

Red Overprint

Perf. 13½x14

217 A28 1fr blue & slate 2.25 2.25
Nos. 210-217 (8) 24.90 24.90

Compare with types A29-A32.

A29

A30

Black or Red Overprint

1928 *Perf. 14x13½*

218 A29 1q orange brown 6.00 6.00
219 A29 2q slate (R) 6.00 6.00
220 A29 5q blue green 5.00 5.00
221 A29 10q rose red 3.25 3.25
222 A29 15q bister 3.50 3.50
223 A29 25q deep blue (R) 3.50 3.50
224 A29 50q lilac rose 3.75 3.75

Perf. 13½x14

225 A30 1fr blue & slate (R) 5.50 5.50
226 A30 2fr green & slate (R) 6.75 6.75
Nos. 218-226 (9) 43.25 43.25

Proclamation of Ahmed Zogu as King of Albania.

A31

A32

Black Overprint

1928 *Perf. 14x13½*

227 A31 1q orange brown .35 .35
228 A31 2q slate .18 .18
229 A31 5q blue green 1.65 .18
230 A31 10q rose red .18 .15
231 A31 15q bister 11.00 7.25
232 A31 25q deep blue .22 .15
233 A31 50q lilac rose .22 .15

Perf. 13½x14

234 A32 1fr blue & slate .45 .65
235 A32 2fr green & slate .55 .65
236 A32 3fr dk red & ol bis 1.10 1.10
237 A32 5fr dull vio & gray 2.25 2.00
Nos. 227-237 (11) 18.15 12.81

The overprint reads "Kingdom of Albania."

Mbr. Shqiptare

Nos. 203, 202, 200 Surcharged in Black

■ 5 ■

1929 *Perf. 13½x13, 11½*

238 A25 1q on 50q blue green .35 .35
239 A25 5q on 25q dark blue .35 .35
240 A25 15q on 10q rose red .55 .50
Nos. 238-240 (3) 1.25 1.20

RROFT-MBRETI

Nos. 186-189, 191-194 Overprinted in Black or Red

8X1929.

1929 *Perf. 11½, 13½*

241 A25 1q orange 3.00 3.00
242 A25 2q red brown 3.00 3.00
243 A25 5q green 3.00 3.00
244 A25 10q rose red 3.00 3.00
245 A25 25q dark blue 3.00 3.00
246 A25 50q blue green (R) 3.50 3.50
247 A26 1fr red & ultra 5.25 5.25
248 A26 2fr green & orange 6.50 6.50
Nos. 241-248 (8) 30.25 30.25

34th birthday of King Zog. The overprint reads "Long live the King."

Lake Butrinto — A33

King Zog I — A34

Zog Bridge — A35

Ruin at Zog Manor — A36

Perf. 14, 14½

1930, Sept. 1 Photo. Wmk. 220

No.	Type	Description	Unused	Used
250	A33	1q slate	.15	.15
251	A33	2q orange red	.15	.15
252	A34	5q yellow green	.15	.15
253	A34	10q carmine	.15	.15
254	A34	15q dark brown	.16	.16
255	A34	25q dark ultra	.20	.16
256	A33	50q slate green	.30	.25
257	A35	1fr violet	.75	.75
258	A35	2fr indigo	.85	.85
259	A36	3fr gray green	1.90	1.90
260	A36	5fr orange brown	3.25	3.25
		Nos. 250-260 (11)	8.01	7.92

2nd anniversary of accession of King Zog I.
For overprints see Nos. 261-270, 299-309, J39.
For surcharges see Nos. 354-360.

Nos. 250-259 Overprinted in Black

1 1
9 9
2 3
4–24Dhetuer–4

1934, Dec. 24

No.	Type	Description	Unused	Used
261	A33	1q slate	1.50	1.50
262	A33	2q orange red	1.50	1.50
263	A34	5q yellow green	1.50	1.50
264	A34	10q carmine	1.50	1.50
265	A34	15q dark brown	1.50	1.50
266	A34	25q dark ultra	1.50	1.50
267	A33	50q slate green	1.50	1.50
268	A35	1fr violet	3.50	3.50
269	A35	2fr indigo	6.75	6.75
270	A36	3fr gray green	9.50	9.50
		Nos. 261-270 (10)	30.25	30.25

Tenth anniversary of the Constitution.

Allegory of Death of Skanderbeg A37

Albanian Eagle in Turkish Shackles A38

Designs: 5q, 25q, 40q, 2fr, Eagle with wings spread.

1937 Unwmk. *Perf. 14*

No.	Type	Description	Unused	Used
271	A37	1q brown violet	.15	.15
272	A38	2q brown	.15	.15
273	A38	5q lt green	.22	.22
274	A37	10q olive brown	.30	.30
275	A38	15q rose red	.38	.38
276	A38	25q blue	.70	.70
277	A37	50q deep green	.95	.95
278	A38	1fr violet	1.65	1.65
279	A38	2fr orange brown	4.25	4.25
		Nos. 271-279 (9)	8.75	8.75

Souvenir Sheet

No.	Type	Description	Unused	Used
280		Sheet of 3	11.50	12.00
a.	A37	20q red violet	2.10	2.50
b.	A38	30q olive brown	2.10	2.50
c.	A38	40q red	2.10	2.50

25th anniv. of independence from Turkey, proclaimed Nov. 26, 1912.

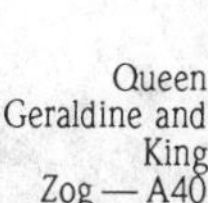

Queen Geraldine and King Zog — A40

1938 *Perf. 14*

No.	Type	Description	Unused	Used
281	A40	1q slate violet	.15	.15
282	A40	2q red brown	.15	.15
283	A40	5q green	.15	.15
284	A40	10q olive brown	.20	.24
285	A40	15q rose red	.28	.40
286	A40	25q blue	.48	.60
287	A40	50q Prus green	1.40	1.65
288	A40	1fr purple	3.00	3.25
		Nos. 281-288 (8)	5.81	6.59

Souvenir Sheet

No.	Type	Description	Unused	Used
289		Sheet of 4	14.00	16.00
a.	A40	20q dark red violet	1.40	1.40
b.	A40	30q brown olive	1.40	1.40

Wedding of King Zog and Countess Geraldine Apponyi, Apr. 27, 1938.
No. 289 contains 2 each of Nos. 289a, 289b.

Queen Geraldine — A42

National Emblems — A43

Designs: 10q, 25q, 30q, 1fr, King Zog.

1938

No.	Type	Description	Unused	Used
290	A42	1q dp red violet	.15	.15
291	A43	2q red orange	.15	.15
292	A42	5q deep green	.15	.15
293	A42	10q red brown	.15	.15
294	A42	15q deep rose	.32	.32
295	A42	25q deep blue	.42	.52
296	A43	50q gray black	1.05	1.25
297	A42	1fr slate green	3.50	3.75
		Nos. 290-297 (8)	5.89	6.44

Souvenir Sheet

No.	Type	Description	Unused	Used
298		Sheet of 3	12.50	14.00
b.	A43	20q Prussian green	1.50	1.50
c.	A42	30q deep violet	1.50	1.50

10th anniv. of royal rule. They were on sale for 3 days (Aug. 30-31, Sept. 1) only, during which their use was required on all mail.
No. 298 contains Nos. 294, 298b, 298c.

Issued under Italian Dominion

Nos. 250-260 Overprinted in Black

Mbledhja Kushtetuëse 12-IV-1939 XVII

1939 Wmk. 220 *Perf. 14*

No.	Type	Description	Unused	Used
299	A33	1q slate	.15	.15
300	A33	2q orange red	.15	.15
301	A34	5q yellow green	.15	.15
302	A34	10q carmine	.16	.16
303	A34	15q dark brown	.16	.16
304	A34	25q dark ultra	.22	.22
305	A33	50q slate grn	.32	.32
306	A35	1fr violet	.60	.60
307	A35	2fr indigo	.85	.85
308	A36	3fr gray green	1.75	1.75
309	A36	5fr orange brown	2.50	2.50
		Nos. 299-309 (11)	7.01	7.01

Resolution adopted by the Natl. Assembly, Apr. 12, 1939, offering the Albanian Crown to Italy.

Native Costumes

A46 A47 A48

King Victor Emmanuel III

A49 A50

Native Costume A51

Monastery A52

Designs: 2fr, Bridge at Vezirit. 3fr, Ancient Columns. 5fr, Amphitheater.

1939 Unwmk. Photo. *Perf. 14*

No.	Type	Description	Unused	Used
310	A46	1q blue gray	.15	.15
311	A47	2q olive green	.15	.15
312	A48	3q golden brown	.15	.15
313	A49	5q green	.15	.15
314	A50	10q brown	.15	.15
315	A50	15q crimson	.18	.15
316	A50	25q sapphire	.25	.18
317	A50	30q brt violet	.35	.22
318	A51	50q dull purple	.44	.22
319	A49	65q red brown	.65	.65
320	A52	1fr myrtle green	.85	.85
321	A52	2fr brown lake	1.90	1.90
322	A52	3fr brown black	3.75	3.75
323	A52	5fr gray violet	7.50	7.50
		Nos. 310-323 (14)	16.62	16.17

For overprints and surcharges see Nos. 331-353.

King Victor Emmanuel III — A56

1942 Photo.

No.	Type	Description	Unused	Used
324	A56	5q green	.15	.15
325	A56	10q brown	.15	.15
326	A56	15q rose red	.15	.15
327	A56	25q blue	.24	.24
328	A56	65q red brown	.35	.35
329	A56	1fr myrtle green	.70	.70
330	A56	2fr gray violet	1.50	1.50
		Nos. 324-330 (7)	3.24	3.24

Conquest of Albania by Italy, 3rd anniv..

No. 311 Surcharged in Black **1 QIND**

No.	Type	Description	Unused	Used
331	A47	1q on 2q olive green	.48	.48

Issued under German Administration

Stamps of 1939 Overprinted in Carmine or Brown

14 Shtator 1943

1943

No.	Type	Description	Unused	Used
332	A47	2q olive green	.85	1.40
333	A48	3q golden brown	.85	1.40
334	A49	5q green	.85	1.40
335	A50	10q brown	.85	1.40
336	A50	15q crimson (Br)	.85	1.40
337	A50	25q sapphire	.85	1.40
338	A50	30q brt violet	.85	1.40
339	A49	65q red brown	1.00	2.25
340	A52	1fr myrtle green	6.00	10.00
341	A52	2fr brown lake	8.00	*20.00*
342	A52	3fr brown black	35.00	*52.50*

Surcharged with New Values

No.	Type	Description	Unused	Used
343	A48	1q on 3q gldn brn	.85	1.40
344	A49	50q on 65q red brn	1.00	2.25
		Nos. 332-344 (13)	57.80	*98.20*

Proclamation of Albanian independence.
The overprint "14 Shtator 1943" on Nos. 324 to 328 is private and fraudulent.

Independent State

Nos. 312 to 317 and 319 to 321 Surcharged with New Value and Bars in Black or Carmine, and:

QEVERIJA DEMOKRAT. E SHQIPERISE 22-X-1944

1945

No.	Type	Description	Unused	Used
345	A48	30q on 3q gldn brn	2.25	2.25
346	A49	40q on 5q green	2.25	2.25
347	A50	50q on 10q brown	2.25	2.25
348	A50	60q on 15q crimson	2.25	2.25
349	A50	80q on 25q saph (C)	2.25	2.25
350	A50	1fr on 30q brt vio	2.25	2.25
351	A49	2fr on 65q red brn	2.25	2.25
352	A52	3fr on 1fr myr grn	2.25	2.25
353	A52	5fr on 2fr brn lake	2.25	2.25
		Nos. 345-353 (9)	20.25	20.25

"DEMOKRATIKE" is not abbreviated on Nos. 352 and 353.

Nos. 250, 251, 256 and 258 Surcharged in Black or Carmine, and

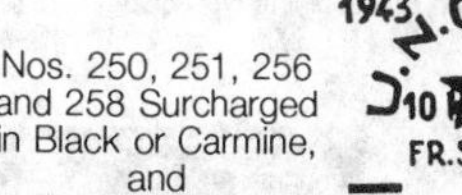

1945 Wmk. 220

No.	Type	Description	Unused	Used
354	A33	30q on 1q slate	.80	.80
355	A33	60q on 1q slate	.95	.95
356	A33	80q on 1q slate	1.10	1.10
357	A33	1fr on 1q slate	1.65	1.65
358	A33	2fr on 2q org red	2.25	2.25
359	A33	3fr on 50q sl grn	5.75	5.75
360	A35	5fr on 2fr indigo	7.50	7.50
		Nos. 354-360 (7)	20.00	20.00

Albanian Natl. Army of Liberation, 2nd anniv.
The surcharge on No. 360 is condensed to fit the size of the stamp.

Country House, Labinot — A57

Designs: 40q, 60q, Bridge at Berat. 1fr, 3fr, Permet.

Unwmk.

1945, Nov. 28 Typo. *Perf. 11*

No.	Type	Description	Unused	Used
361	A57	20q bluish green	.18	.18
362	A57	30q deep orange	.38	.38
363	A57	40q brown	.38	.38
364	A57	60q red violet	.55	.55
365	A57	1fr rose red	1.10	1.10
366	A57	3fr dark blue	5.50	5.50
		Nos. 361-366 (6)	8.09	8.09

Counterfeits exist. See note after No. B33.
For overprints and surcharges see Nos. 367-378, 418-423, B28-B33.

Nos. 361 to 366 Overprinted in Black

ASAMBLEJA KUSHTETUESE

10 KALLHUER 1946

1946

No.	Type	Description	Unused	Used
367	A57	20q bluish green	.52	.52
368	A57	30q deep orange	.52	.52
369	A57	40q brown	.85	.85
370	A57	60q red violet	1.50	1.50
371	A57	1fr rose red	4.25	4.25
372	A57	3fr dark blue	6.75	6.75
		Nos. 367-372 (6)	14.39	14.39

Convocation of the Constitutional Assembly, Jan. 10, 1946.

People's Republic

Nos. 361 to 366 Overprinted in Black

REPUBLIKA POPULLORE E SHQIPERISE

1946

No.	Type	Description	Unused	Used
373	A57	20q bluish green	.55	.55
374	A57	30q deep orange	.95	.95
375	A57	40q brown	1.25	1.25
376	A57	60q red violet	2.10	2.10
377	A57	1fr rose red	3.75	3.75
378	A57	3fr dark blue	6.25	6.25
		Nos. 373-378 (6)	14.85	14.85

Proclamation of the Albanian People's Republic.
For surcharges see Nos. 418-423.

Globe, Dove and Olive Branch — A60

Perf. 11½, Imperf.

1946, Mar. 8 Typo.

Denomination in Black

No.	Type	Description	Unused	Used
379	A60	20q lilac & dull red	.15	.15
380	A60	40q dp lilac & dull red	.25	.25
381	A60	50q violet & dull red	.40	.40
382	A60	1fr lt blue & red	.60	.60
383	A60	2fr dk blue & red	1.25	1.25
		Nos. 379-383 (5)	2.65	2.65

International Women's Congress.

Athletes with Shot and Indian Club — A61

Perf. 11½

1946, Oct. 6 Litho. Unwmk.

No.	Type	Description	Unused	Used
384	A61	1q grnsh black	5.75	5.75
385	A61	2q green	5.75	5.75
386	A61	5q brown	5.75	5.75
387	A61	10q crimson	5.75	5.75
388	A61	20q ultra	5.75	5.75
389	A61	40q rose violet	5.75	5.75
390	A61	1fr deep orange	9.25	9.25
		Nos. 384-390 (7)	43.75	43.75

Balkan Games, Tirana, Oct. 6-13.

Qemal Stafa — A62

1947, May 5 *Perf. 12½x11½*

391	A62	20q brn & yel brn	1.75	1.75
392	A62	28q dk blue & blue	1.75	1.75
393	A62	40q brn blk & gray brn	3.00	3.00
a.		Souvenir sheet, #391-393	6.50	6.50
		Nos. 391-393 (3)	6.50	6.50

5th anniv. of the death of Qemal Stafa.

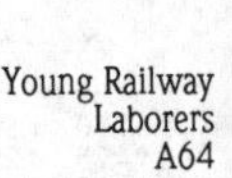

Young Railway Laborers A64

1947, May 16 *Perf. 11½*

395	A64	1q brn blk & gray brn	1.00	.50
396	A64	4q dk green & green	1.00	.50
397	A64	10q blk brn & bis brn	1.00	.50
398	A64	15q dk red & red	1.25	.50
399	A64	20q indigo & bl gray	1.75	.75
400	A64	28q dk blue & blue	2.50	.75
401	A64	40q brn vio & rose vio	6.50	3.50
402	A64	68q dk brn & org brn	10.00	6.50
		Nos. 395-402 (8)	25.00	13.50

Issued to publicize the construction of the Durres Elbasan Railway by Albanian youths.

Citizens Led by Hasim Zeneli — A65

Enver Hoxha and Vasil Shanto — A66

Vojo Kushi — A68

Inauguration of Vithkuq Brigade — A67

1947, July 10 **Litho.**

403	A65	16q brn org & red brn	1.65	1.65
404	A66	20q org brn & dk brn	1.65	1.65
405	A67	28q blue & dk blue	1.75	1.75
406	A68	40q lilac & dk brn	2.50	2.50
		Nos. 403-406 (4)	7.55	7.55

4th anniv. of the formation of Albania's army, July 10, 1943.

Conference Building Ruins, Peza — A69

Disabled Soldiers — A70

1947, Sept. 16

407	A69	2 l red violet	2.00	1.65
408	A69	2.50 l deep blue	2.00	1.65

Peza Conf., Sept. 16, 1942, 5th anniv.

1947, Nov. 17 *Perf. 12½x11½*

408A	A70	1 l red	2.75	2.75

Disabled War Veterans Cong., Nov. 14-20, 1947.

A71

A73

Designs: 2 l, Banquet. 2.50 l, Peasants rejoicing.

Perf. 11½x12½, 12½x11½

1947, Nov. 17 **Unwmk.**

409	A71	1.50 l dull violet	2.25	2.25
410	A71	2 l brown	2.25	2.25
411	A71	2.50 l blue	2.25	2.25
412	A73	3 l rose red	2.25	2.25
		Nos. 409-412 (4)	9.00	9.00

Agrarian reform law of Nov. 17, 1946, 1st anniv.

Burning Farm Buildings A74

Designs: 2.50 l, Trench scene. 5 l, Firing line. 8 l, Winter advance. 12 l, Infantry column.

1947, Nov. 29 *Perf. 11½x12½*

413	A74	1.50 l red	1.65	1.65
414	A74	2.50 l rose brown	2.00	2.00
415	A74	5 l blue	2.50	2.50
416	A74	8 l purple	4.00	4.00
417	A74	12 l brown	6.00	6.00
		Nos. 413-417 (5)	16.15	16.15

3rd anniv. of Albania's liberation.

Nos. 373 to 378 Surcharged with New Value and Bars in Black

1948, Feb. 22 *Perf. 11*

418	A57	50q on 30q deep org	.24	.24
419	A57	1 l on 20q bluish grn	.48	.48
420	A57	2.50 l on 60q red vio	1.00	1.00
421	A57	3 l on 1fr rose red	1.40	1.40
422	A57	5 l on 3fr dark blue	2.25	2.25
423	A57	12 l on 40q brown	4.75	4.75
		Nos. 418-423 (6)	10.12	10.12

The two bars consist of four type squares each set close together.

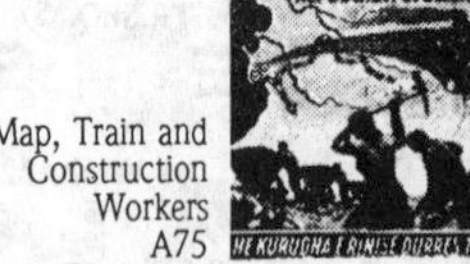

Map, Train and Construction Workers A75

1948, June 1 **Litho.** *Perf. 11½*

424	A75	50q dk car rose	1.05	.52
425	A75	1 l lt green & blk	1.25	.52
426	A75	1.50 l deep rose	1.25	.52
427	A75	2.50 l org brn & dk brn	1.25	.52
428	A75	5 l dull blue	2.10	1.05
429	A75	8 l salmon & dk brn	4.75	2.10
430	A75	12 l red vio & dk vio	6.50	2.25
431	A75	20 l olive gray	12.50	5.00
		Nos. 424-431 (8)	30.65	12.48

Issued to publicize the construction of the Durres-Tirana Railway.

Marching Soldiers A76

Design: 8 l, Battle scene.

1948, July 10

432	A76	2.50 l yellow brown	.75	.75
433	A76	5 l dark blue	1.00	1.00
434	A76	8 l violet gray	2.00	2.00
		Nos. 432-434 (3)	3.75	3.75

5th anniv. of the formation of Albania's army.

Bricklayer, Flag, Globe and "Industry" A77

Map and Soldier A78

1949, May 1 **Photo.** *Perf. 12½x12*

435	A77	2.50 l olive brown	.25	.25
436	A77	5 l blue	.65	.65
437	A77	8 l violet brown	1.00	1.00
		Nos. 435-437 (3)	1.90	1.90

Issued to publicize Labor Day, May 1, 1949.

1949, July 10 **Unwmk.**

438	A78	2.50 l brown	.35	.35
439	A78	5 l light ultra	.50	.50
440	A78	8 l brown orange	1.25	1.25
		Nos. 438-440 (3)	2.10	2.10

6th anniv. of the formation of Albania's army.

Enver Hoxha A79

Albanian Citizen and Spasski Tower, Kremlin A80

1949, Oct. 16 **Engr.** *Perf. 12½*

441	A79	50q purple	.15	.15
442	A79	1 l dull green	.15	.15
443	A79	1.50 l car lake	.15	.15
444	A79	2.50 l brown	.25	.15
445	A79	5 l violet blue	.50	.15
446	A79	8 l sepia	.85	.65
447	A79	12 l rose lilac	1.90	1.05
448	A79	20 l gray blue	3.75	1.75
		Nos. 441-448 (8)	7.70	4.20

1949, Sept. 10 **Photo.** *Perf. 12½x12*

449	A80	2.50 l orange brown	.45	.45
450	A80	5 l deep ultra	.90	.90

Albanian-Soviet friendship.

Albanian Soldier and Flag — A81

Battle Scene — A82

1949, Nov. 29 **Unwmk.** *Perf. 12*

451	A81	2.50 l brown	.22	.22
452	A82	3 l dark red	.45	.45
453	A81	5 l violet	.60	.60
454	A82	8 l black	1.65	1.65
		Nos. 451-454 (4)	2.92	2.92

Fifth anniversary of Albania's liberation.

Joseph V. Stalin — A83

Symbols of UPU and Postal Transport — A84

1949, Dec. 21

455	A83	2.50 l dark brown	.44	.52
456	A83	5 l violet blue	1.10	1.25
457	A83	8 l rose brown	1.90	2.25
		Nos. 455-457 (3)	3.44	4.02

70th anniv. of the birth of Joseph V. Stalin.

Canceled to Order

Beginning in 1950, Albania sold some issues in sheets canceled to order. Values in second column when much less than unused are for "CTO" copies. Postally used stamps are valued at slightly less than, or the same as, unused.

Catalogue values for unused stamps in this section, from this point to the end of the section, are for Never Hinged items.

1950, July 1 **Photo.** *Perf. 12x12½*

458	A84	5 l blue	1.75	1.25
459	A84	8 l rose brown	2.50	1.75
460	A84	12 l sepia	3.25	2.25
		Nos. 458-460 (3)	7.50	5.25

75th anniv. (in 1949) of the UPU.

Sami Frasheri — A85

Arms and Albanian Flags — A86

Authors: 2.50 l, Andon Zako. 3 l, Naim Frasheri. 5 l, Kostandin Kristoforidhi.

1950, Nov. 5 *Perf. 14*

461	A85	2 l dark green	.48	.15
462	A85	2.50 l red brown	.65	.20
463	A85	3 l brown carmine	.95	.25
464	A85	5 l deep blue	1.40	.60
		Nos. 461-464 (4)	3.48	1.20

"Jubilee of the Writers of the Renaissance."

1951, Jan. 11 **Engr.** *Perf. 14x13½*

465	A86	2.50 l brown carmine	.85	.25
466	A86	5 l deep blue	1.65	.50
467	A86	8 l sepia	2.50	1.00
		Nos. 465-467 (3)	5.00	1.75

5th anniv. of the formation of the Albanian People's Republic.

Skanderbeg A87

Enver Hoxha and Congress of Permet A88

1951, Mar. 1

468	A87	2.50 l brown	.60	.25
469	A87	5 l violet	1.25	.50
470	A87	8 l olive bister	2.25	1.00
		Nos. 468-470 (3)	4.10	1.75

483rd anniv. of the death of George Castriota (Skanderbeg).

1951, May 24 Photo. *Perf. 12*

471 A88 2.50 l dark brown .32 .20
472 A88 3 l rose brown .50 .30
473 A88 5 l violet blue .85 .50
474 A88 8 l rose lilac 1.40 .80
Nos. 471-474 (4) 3.07 1.80

Congress of Permet, 7th anniversary.

Child and Globe — A89

Weighing Baby — A90

1951, July 16

475 A89 2 l green .52 .30
476 A90 2.50 l brown .70 .40
477 A90 3 l red 1.00 .50
478 A89 5 l blue 1.50 .80
Nos. 475-478 (4) 3.72 2.00

Intl. Children's Day, June 1, 1951.

Enver Hoxha and Birthplace of Albanian Communist Party — A91

1951, Nov. 8 Photo. *Perf. 14*

479 A91 2.50 l olive brown .30 .25
480 A91 3 l rose brown .42 .35
481 A91 5 l dark slate blue .70 .60
482 A91 8 l black 1.00 .85
Nos. 479-482 (4) 2.42 2.05

10th anniv. of the founding of Albania's Communist Party.

Battle Scene — A92

Designs: 5 l, Schoolgirl, "Agriculture and Industry." 8 l, Four portraits.

1951, Nov. 28 *Perf. 12x12½*

483 A92 2.50 l brown .32 .15
484 A92 5 l blue .55 .40
485 A92 8 l brown carmine 1.10 .75
Nos. 483-485 (3) 1.97 1.30

Albanian Communist Youth Org., 10th anniv.

Albanian Heroes (Haxhija, Lezhe, Giyebegej, Mezi and Dedej) — A93

Nos. 486-489 each show five "Heroes of the People"; No. 490 shows two (Stafa and Shanto).

1950, Dec. 25 Unwmk. *Perf. 14*

486 A93 2 l dark green .60 .15
487 A93 2.50 l purple .75 .16
488 A93 3 l scarlet .85 .22
489 A93 5 l brt blue 1.40 .35
490 A93 8 l olive brown 3.50 1.00
Nos. 486-490 (5) 7.10 1.88

6th anniv. of Albania's liberation.

Tobacco Factory, Shkoder — A94

Composite, Lenin Hydroelectric Plant — A95

Designs: 1 l, Canal. 2.50 l, Textile factory. 3 l, "8 November" Cannery. 5 l, Motion Picture Studio, Tirana. 8 l, Stalin Textile Mill, Tirana. 20 l, Central Hydroelectric Dam.

1953, Aug. 1 *Perf. 12x12½, 12½x12*

491 A94 50q red brown .15 .15
492 A94 1 l dull green .16 .15
493 A94 2.50 l brown .60 .15
494 A94 3 l rose brown .85 .15
495 A94 5 l blue 1.25 .15
496 A94 8 l brown olive 2.25 .16
497 A95 12 l deep plum 3.50 .35
498 A94 20 l slate blue 6.25 .50
Nos. 491-498 (8) 15.01
Set value 1.30

Liberation Scene — A96

1954, Nov. 29 *Perf. 12x12½*

499 A96 50q brown violet .15 .15
500 A96 1 l olive green .24 .15
501 A96 2.50 l yellow brown .55 .15
502 A96 3 l car rose .70 .16
503 A96 5 l gray blue .90 .16
504 A96 8 l rose brown 1.75 .55
Nos. 499-504 (6) 4.29
Set value 1.00

10th anniversary of Albania's liberation.

School — A97

Pandeli Sotiri, Petro Nini Luarasi, Nuci Naci — A98

1956, Feb. 23 Unwmk.

505 A97 2 l rose violet .25 .15
506 A98 2.50 l lt green .35 .15
507 A98 5 l ultra .80 .20
508 A97 10 l brt grnsh blue 1.65 .35
Nos. 505-508 (4) 3.05
Set value .68

Opening of the 1st Albanian school, 70th anniv.

Flags — A99

Designs: 5 l, Labor Party headquarters, Tirana. 8 l, Marx and Lenin.

1957, June 1 Engr. *Perf. 11½x11*

509 A99 2.50 l brown .32 .15
510 A99 5 l lt violet blue .65 .15
511 A99 8 l rose lilac 1.50 .20
Nos. 509-511 (3) 2.47
Set value .40

Albania's Labor Party, 15th anniv.

Congress Emblem A100

1957, Oct. 4 Unwmk. *Perf. 11½*

512 A100 2.50 l gray brown .28 .15
513 A100 3 l rose red .42 .15
514 A100 5 l dark blue .52 .15
515 A100 8 l green 1.00 .30
Nos. 512-515 (4) 2.22
Set value .63

4th Intl. Trade Union Cong., Leipzig, Oct. 4-15.

Lenin and Cruiser "Aurora" — A101

1957, Nov. 7 Litho. *Perf. 10½*

516 A101 2.50 l violet brown .32 .15
517 A101 5 l violet blue .70 .16
518 A101 8 l gray .95 .30
Nos. 516-518 (3) 1.97 .61

40th anniv. of the Russian Revolution.

Albanian Fighter Holding Flag A102

Naum Veqilharxhj A103

1957, Nov. 28 *Perf. 10½*

519 A102 1.50 l magenta .24 .15
520 A102 2.50 l brown .38 .15
521 A102 5 l blue .70 .18
522 A102 8 l green 1.25 .30
Nos. 519-522 (4) 2.57
Set value .60

Proclamation of independence, 45th anniv.

1958, Feb. 1 Unwmk.

523 A103 2.50 l dark brown .30 .15
524 A103 5 l violet blue .60 .15
525 A103 8 l rose lilac 1.10 .30
Nos. 523-525 (3) 2.00 .60

160th anniv. of the birth of Naum Veqilharxhj, patriot and writer.

Luigi Gurakuqi A104

Soldiers A105

1958, Apr. 15 Photo. *Perf. 10½*

526 A104 1.50 l dark green .18 .15
527 A104 2.50 l brown .25 .15
528 A104 5 l blue .52 .15
529 A104 8 l sepia 1.00 .22
Nos. 526-529 (4) 1.95
Set value .50

Transfer of the ashes of Luigi Gurakuqi.

1958, July 10 Litho.

Design: 2.50 l, 11 l, Airman, sailor, soldier and tank.

530 A105 1.50 l blue green .16 .15
531 A105 2.50 l dark red brown .20 .15
532 A105 8 l rose red .65 .16
533 A105 11 l bright blue 1.00 .25
Nos. 530-533 (4) 2.01
Set value .50

15th anniversary of Albanian army.

Cerciz Topulli and Mihal Grameno — A106

Buildings and Tree — A107

1958, July 1

534 A106 2.50 l dk olive bister .22 .15
535 A107 3 l green .32 .15
536 A106 5 l blue .55 .15
537 A107 8 l red brown .90 .22
Nos. 534-537 (4) 1.99
Set value .50

50th anniversary, Battle of Mashkullore.

Ancient Amphitheater and Goddess of Butrinto — A108

1959, Jan. 25 Litho. *Perf. 10½*

538 A108 2.50 l redsh brown .38 .15
539 A108 6.50 l lt blue green 1.00 .18
540 A108 11 l dark blue 1.65 .38
Nos. 538-540 (3) 3.03
Set value .60

Cultural Monuments Week.

Frederic Joliot-Curie and World Peace Congress Emblem A109

Basketball A110

1959, July 1 Unwmk.

541 A109 1.50 l carmine rose .65 .20
542 A109 2.50 l rose violet 1.10 .30
543 A109 11 l blue 3.25 1.50
Nos. 541-543 (3) 5.00 2.00

10th anniv. of the World Peace Movement.

1959, Nov. 20 *Perf. 10½*

Sports: 2.50 l, Soccer, 5 l, Runner. 11 l, Man and woman runners with torch and flags.

544 A110 1.50 l bright violet .25 .15
545 A110 2.50 l emerald .32 .15
546 A110 5 l carmine rose .80 .25
547 A110 11 l ultra 2.25 1.75
Nos. 544-547 (4) 3.62 2.30

1st Albanian Spartacist Games.

Fighter and Flags A111

Mother and Child, UN Emblem A112

Designs: 2.50 l, Miner with drill standing guard. 3 l, Farm woman with sheaf of grain. 6.50 l, Man and woman in laboratory.

1959, Nov. 29

548 A111 1.50 l brt carmine .25 .15
549 A111 2.50 l red brown .35 .15
550 A111 3 l brt blue green .45 .15
551 A111 6.50 l bright red .90 .25
a. Souvenir sheet 6.00 6.00
Nos. 548-551 (4) 1.95
Set value .42

15th anniversary of Albania's liberation.

No. 551a contains one each of Nos. 548-551, imperf. and all in bright carmine. Inscribed ribbon frame of sheet and frame lines for each stamp are blue green.

1959, Dec. 5 Unwmk.

552 A112 5 l lt grnsh blue 2.50 .55
a. Miniature sheet 3.00 3.00

10th anniv. (in 1958) of the signing of the Universal Declaration of Human Rights.

No. 552a contains one imperf. stamp similar to No. 552; ornamental border.

Woman with Olive Branch A113

Alexander Moissi A114

1960, Mar. 8 Litho. *Perf. 10½*
553 A113 2.50 l chocolate .32 .15
554 A113 11 l rose carmine 1.40 .32

50th anniv. of Intl. Women's Day, Mar. 8.

1960, Apr. 20
555 A114 3 l deep brown .22 .15
556 A114 11 l Prus green .85 .25

80th anniversary of the birth of Alexander Moissi (Moisiu) (1880-1935), German actor.

Lenin
A115

School Building
A116

1960, Apr. 22
557 A115 4 l Prus blue .80 .15
558 A115 11 l lake 1.75 .18
Set value .25

90th anniversary of birth of Lenin.

1960, May 30 Litho. *Perf. 10½*
559 A116 5 l green .85 .20
560 A116 6.50 l plum .85 .20

1st Albanian secondary school, 50th anniv.

Soldier on Guard Duty — A117

Liberation Monument, Tirana, Family and Policeman — A118

1960, May 12 Unwmk. *Perf. 10½*
561 A117 1.50 l carmine rose .20 .15
562 A117 11 l Prus blue 1.10 .20
Set value .26

15th anniversary of the Frontier Guards.

1960, May 14
563 A118 1.50 l green .20 .15
564 A118 8.50 l brown 1.10 .25
Set value .30

15th anniversary of the People's Police.

Congress Site — A119

Pashko Vasa — A120

1960, Mar. 25
565 A119 2.50 l sepia .18 .15
566 A119 7.50 l dull blue .70 .25

40th anniversary, Congress of Louchnia.

1960, May 5

Designs: 1.50 l, Jani Vreto. 6.50 l, Sami Frasheri. 11 l, Page of statutes of association.

567 A120 1 l gray olive .18 .15
568 A120 1.50 l brown .25 .15
569 A120 6.50 l blue .55 .15
570 A120 11 l rose red 1.10 .18
Nos. 567-570 (4) 2.08
Set value .36

80th anniv. (in 1959) of the Association of Albanian Authors.

The only foreign revenue stamps listed in this catalogue are those also authorized for prepayment of postage.

Albanian Fighter and Cannon
A121

TU-104 Plane, Clock Tower, Tirana, and Kremlin, Moscow
A122

1960, Aug. 2 Litho. *Perf. 10½*
571 A121 1.50 l olive brown .28 .15
572 A121 2.50 l maroon .35 .15
573 A121 5 l dark blue .85 .20
Nos. 571-573 (3) 1.48
Set value .35

Battle of Viona (against Italian troops), 40th anniv.

1960, Aug. 18
574 A122 1 l redsh brown .32 .15
575 A122 7.50 l brt grnsh blue 1.25 .32
576 A122 11.50 l gray 2.25 .60
Nos. 574-576 (3) 3.82 1.07

TU-104 flights, Moscow-Tirana, 2nd anniv.

Rising Sun and Federation Emblem
A123

Ali Kelmendi
A124

1960, Nov. 10 Unwmk. *Perf. 10½*
577 A123 1.50 l ultra .18 .15
578 A123 8.50 l red .70 .20
Set value .26

Intl. Youth Federation, 15th anniv.

1960, Dec. 5 Litho. *Perf. 10½*
579 A124 1.50 l pale gray grn .25 .15
580 A124 11 l dull rose lake .65 .20
Set value .26

Ali Kelmendi, communist leader, 60th birthday.

Flags of Russia and Albania and Clasped Hands
A125

Marx and Lenin
A126

1961, Jan. 10 Unwmk. *Perf. 10½*
581 A125 2 l violet .25 .15
582 A125 8 l dull red brown .65 .20
Set value .26

15th anniv. of the Albanian-Soviet Friendship Society.

1961, Feb. 13 Litho.
583 A126 2 l rose red .20 .15
584 A126 8 l violet blue .70 .20
Set value .26

Fourth Communist Party Congress.

Man from Shkoder
A127

Otter
A128

Costumes: 1.50 l, Woman from Shkoder. 6.50 l, Man from Lume. 11 l, Woman from Mirdite.

1961, Apr. 28 *Perf. 10½*
585 A127 1 l slate .22 .15
586 A127 1.50 l dull claret .35 .15
587 A127 6.50 l ultra 1.10 .18
588 A127 11 l red 1.90 .38
Nos. 585-588 (4) 3.57
Set value .66

1961, June 25 Unwmk. *Perf. 10½*

Designs: 6.50 l, Badger. 11 l, Brown bear.

589 A128 2.50 l grayish blue 1.00 .22
590 A128 6.50 l blue green 2.25 .50
591 A128 11 l dark red brown 4.00 .85
Nos. 589-591 (3) 7.25 1.57

Dalmatian Pelicans
A129

Cyclamen
A130

1961, Sept. 30 *Perf. 14*
592 A129 1.50 l shown .90 .20
593 A129 7.50 l Gray herons 1.75 .40
594 A129 11 l Little egret 2.50 .60
Nos. 592-594 (3) 5.15 1.20

1961, Oct. 27 Litho.
595 A130 1.50 l shown .85 .15
596 A130 8 l Forsythia 1.50 .22
597 A130 11 l Lily 2.00 .40
Nos. 595-597 (3) 4.35 .77

Milosh G. Nikolla — A131

Flag with Marx and Lenin — A132

1961, Oct. 30 *Perf. 14*
598 A131 50q violet brown .18 .15
599 A131 8.50 l Prus green .70 .25
Set value .31

50th anniv. of the birth of Milosh Gjergi Nikolla, poet.

1961, Nov. 8
600 A132 2.50 l vermilion .30 .15
601 A132 7.50 l dull red brn .60 .25
Set value .31

20th anniv. of the founding of Albania's Communist Party.

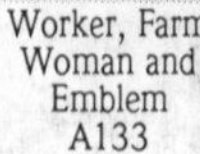
Worker, Farm Woman and Emblem
A133

Yuri Gagarin and Vostok 1
A134

1961, Nov. 23 Unwmk. *Perf. 14*
602 A133 2.50 l violet blue .38 .15
603 A133 7.50 l rose claret .75 .30

20th anniv. of the Albanian Workers' Party.

1962, Feb. 15 Unwmk. *Perf. 14*
604 A134 50q blue .30 .15
605 A134 4 l red lilac 1.40 .15
606 A134 11 l dk slate grn 2.75 .65
Nos. 604-606 (3) 4.45 .95

1st manned space flight, made by Yuri A. Gagarin, Soviet astronaut, Apr. 12, 1961.

Nos. 604-606 were overprinted with an over-all yellow tint and with "POSTA AJRORE" (Air Mail) in maroon in 1962. Value, set $50.

Petro Nini Luarasi — A135

Malaria Eradication Emblem — A136

1962, Feb. 28 Litho.
607 A135 50q Prus blue .22 .15
608 A135 8.50 l olive gray 1.25 .25
Set value .30

50th anniv. (in 1961) of the death of Petro Nini Luarasi, Albanian patriot.

1962, Apr. 30 Unwmk. *Perf. 14*
609 A136 1.50 l brt green .16 .15
610 A136 2.50 l brown red .16 .15
611 A136 10 l red lilac .55 .25
612 A136 11 l blue .85 .35
Nos. 609-612 (4) 1.72
Set value .74

WHO drive to eradicate malaria.

Souvenir sheets, perf. and imperf., contain one each of Nos. 609-612. Value $12.50 each. Nos. 609-612 imperf., value, set $12.50.

Camomile
A137

Woman Diver
A138

Medicinal plants.

1962, May 10
613 A137 50q shown .20 .15
614 A137 8 l Linden .75 .25
615 A137 11.50 l Garden sage 1.75 .50
Nos. 613-615 (3) 2.70 .90

Value, imperf. set $10.

1962, May 31 *Perf. 14*

Designs: 2.50 l, Pole vault. 3 l, Mt. Fuji and torch, horiz. 9 l, Woman javelin thrower. 10 l, Shot putting.

616 A138 50q brt grnsh bl & blk .15 .15
617 A138 2.50 l gldn brn & sepia .20 .15
618 A138 3 l blue & gray .40 .15
619 A138 9 l rose car & dk brn 1.10 .25
620 A138 10 l olive & blk 1.25 .30
Nos. 616-620 (5) 3.10
Set value .75

1964 Olympic Games, Tokyo. Value, imperf. set $25. A 15 l (like 3 l) exists in souv. sheet, perf. and imperf.

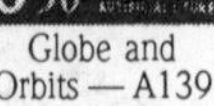
Globe and Orbits — A139

Dog Laika and Sputnik 2 — A140

Designs: 1.50 l, Rocket to the sun. 20 l, Lunik 3 photographing far side of the moon.

1962, June Unwmk. *Perf. 14*
621 A139 50q violet & org .16 .15
622 A140 1 l blue grn & brn .28 .15
623 A140 1.50 l yellow & ver .40 .15
624 A139 20 l magenta & bl 2.75 .80
Nos. 621-624 (4) 3.59
Set value 1.05

Russian space explorations.

#621-624 exist imperforate in changed colors.

Two miniature sheets exist, containing one 14-lek picturing Sputnik 1. The perforated 14-lek is yellow and brown; the imperf. red and brown.

Soccer Game, Map of South America — A141

Design: 2.50 l, 15 l, Soccer game and globe as ball.

1962, July **Litho.**

625 A141 1 l org & dk pur .15 .15
626 A141 2.50 l emer & bluish grn .22 .15
627 A141 6.50 l lt brn & pink .70 .15
628 A141 15 l bluish grn & mar 1.25 .35
Nos. 625-628 (4) 2.32
Set value .54

Issued to commemorate the World Soccer Championships, Chile, May 30-June 17.

Exist imperforate in changed colors.

Two miniature sheets exist, each containing a single 20-lek in design similar to A141. The perf. sheet is brown and green; the imperf., brown and orange.

Map of Europe and Albania — A142

Woman of Dardhe — A143

Designs: 1 l, 2.50 l, Map of Adriatic Sea and Albania and Roman statue.

1962, Aug.

630 A142 50q multicolored .32 .32
631 A142 1 l ultra & red .80 .80
632 A142 2.50 l blue & red 2.50 2.50
633 A142 11 l multicolored 5.00 5.00
Nos. 630-633 (4) 8.62 8.62

Tourist propaganda. Imperforates in changed colors exist.

Miniature sheets containing a 7 l and 8 l stamp, perf. and imperf., exist.

1962, Sept.

Regional Costumes: 1 l, Man from Devoll. 2.50 l, Woman from Lunxheri. 14 l, Man from Gjirokaster.

635 A143 50q car, bl & pur .15 .15
636 A143 1 l red brn & ocher .15 .15
637 A143 2.50 l vio, yel grn & blk .45 .15
638 A143 14 l red brn & pale grn 1.65 .50
Nos. 635-638 (4) 2.40
Set value .75

Value, imperf. set $15.

Chamois A144

Ismail Qemali A145

Animals: 1 l, Lynx, horiz. 1.50 l, Wild boar, horiz. 15 l, 20 l, Roe deer.

1962, Oct. 24 **Unwmk.** ***Perf. 14***

639 A144 50q sl grn & dk pur .50 .15
640 A144 1 l orange & blk .90 .15
641 A144 1.50 l red brn & blk 1.25 .15
642 A144 15 l yel ol & red brn 6.25 1.00
Nos. 639-642 (4) 8.90 1.45

Miniature Sheet

643 A144 20 l yel ol & red brn 15.00 15.00

Imperfs. in changed colors, value #639-642 $20, #643 $20.

1962, Dec. 28 **Litho.**

Designs: 1 l, Albania eagle. 16 l, Eagle over fortress formed by "RPSH."

644 A145 1 l red & red brn .18 .15
645 A145 3 l org brn & blk .32 .15
646 A145 16 l dk car rose & blk 2.00 .52
Nos. 644-646 (3) 2.50
Set value .65

50th anniv. of independence. Imperfs. in changed colors, value, set $12.50.

Monument of October Revolution A146

Henri Dunant, Cross, Globe and Nurse A147

Design: 10 l, Lenin statue.

1963, Jan. 5 **Unwmk.** ***Perf. 14***

647 A146 5 l yel & dull vio .42 .15
648 A146 10 l red orange & blk 1.10 .22
Set value .30

October Revolution (Russia, 1917), 45th anniv.

1963, Jan 25 **Unwmk.** ***Perf. 14***

649 A147 1.50 l rose lake, red & blk .18 .15
650 A147 2.50 l lt bl, red & blk .25 .15
651 A147 6 l emerald, red & blk .60 .22
652 A147 10 l dull yel, red & blk 1.10 .35
Nos. 649-652 (4) 2.13
Set value .72

Cent. of the Geneva Conf., which led to the establishment of the Intl. Red Cross in 1864. Imperfs. in changed colors, value, set $15.

Stalin and Battle of Stalingrad A148

Andrian G. Nikolayev A149

1963, Feb. 2

653 A148 8 l dk green & slate 2.50 .50

Battle of Stalingrad, 20th anniv. See #C67.

1963, Feb. 28 **Litho.**

Designs: 7.50 l, Vostoks 3 and 4 and globe, horiz. 20 l, Pavel R. Popovich. 25 l, Nikolayev, Popovich and globe with trajectories.

654 A149 2.50 l vio bl & sepia .35 .15
655 A149 7.50 l lt blue & blk .70 .15
656 A149 20 l violet & sepia 2.00 .70
Nos. 654-656 (3) 3.05 1.00

Miniature Sheet

657 A149 25 l vio bl & sepia 12.00 12.00

1st group space flight of Vostoks 3 and 4, Aug. 11-15, 1962. Imperfs. in changed colors, value #654-656 $10, #657 $12.

"Albania" Decorating Police Officer — A150

Polyphylla Fullo — A151

1963, Mar. 20 **Unwmk.** ***Perf. 14***

658 A150 2.50 l crim, mag & blk .38 .15
659 A150 7.50 l org ver, dk red & blk 1.40 .25

20th anniversary of the security police.

1963, Mar. 20

Beetles: 1.50 l, Lucanus cervus. 8 l, Procerus gigas. 10 l, Cicindela Albanica.

660 A151 50q ol grn & brn .25 .15
661 A151 1.50 l blue & brn .55 .15
662 A151 8 l dl rose & blk vio 2.75 1.05
663 A151 10 l brt citron & blk 3.00 1.25
Nos. 660-663 (4) 6.55 2.60

1913 Stamp and Postmark — A152

Design: 10 l, Stamps of 1913, 1937 and 1962.

1963, May 5

664 A152 5 l yel, buff, bl & blk .70 .25
665 A152 10 l car rose, grn & blk 1.35 .45

50th anniversary of Albanian stamps.

Boxer — A153

Crested Grebe — A154

Designs: 3 l, Basketball baskets. 5 l, Volleyball. 6 l, Bicyclists. 9 l, Gymnast. 15 l, Hands holding torch, and map of Japan.

1963, May 25 ***Perf. 13½***

666 A153 2 l yel, blk & red brn .22 .15
667 A153 3 l ocher, brn & bl .32 .15
668 A153 5 l gray bl, red brn & brn .55 .15
669 A153 6 l gray, dk gray & grn .75 .25
670 A153 9 l rose, red brn & bl 1.50 .30
Nos. 666-670 (5) 3.34 1.00

Miniature Sheet

671 A153 15 l lt bl, car, blk & brn 7.50 7.50

1964 Olympic Games in Tokyo. Value, imperfs. #666-670 $7.50, #671 $8.

1963, Apr. 20 **Litho.** ***Perf. 14***

Birds: 3 l, Golden eagle. 6.50 l, Gray partridges. 11 l, Capercaillie.

672 A154 50q multi .15 .15
673 A154 3 l multi .60 .20
674 A154 6.50 l multi 1.40 .45
675 A154 11 l multi 2.25 .70
Nos. 672-675 (4) 4.40 1.50

Soldier and Building A155

Designs: 2.50 l, Soldier with pack, ship and plane. 5 l, Soldier in battle. 6 l, Soldier and bulldozer.

1963, July 10 **Unwmk.** ***Perf. 12***

676 A155 1.50 l brick red, yel & blk .20 .15
677 A155 2.50 l bl, ocher & brn .28 .15
678 A155 5 l bluish grn, gray & blk .65 .15
679 A155 6 l red brn, buff & bl .85 .25
Nos. 676-679 (4) 1.98
Set value .48

Albanian army, 20th anniversary.

Maj. Yuri A. Gagarin A156

Designs: 5 l, Maj. Gherman Titov. 7 l, Maj. Andrian G. Nikolayev. 11 l, Lt. Col. Pavel R. Popovich. 14 l, Lt. Col. Valeri Bykovski. 20 l, Lt. Valentina Tereshkova.

1963, July 30

Portraits in Yellow and Black

680 A156 3 l brt purple .35 .15
681 A156 5 l dull blue .50 .15
682 A156 7 l gray .70 .15
683 A156 11 l deep claret 1.20 .35
684 A156 14 l blue green 1.75 .55
685 A156 20 l ultra 2.50 1.00
Nos. 680-685 (6) 7.00 2.35

Man's conquest of space. Value, imperf. set $15.

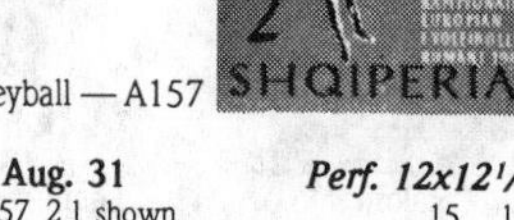

Volleyball — A157

1963, Aug. 31 ***Perf. 12x12½***

686 A157 2 l shown .15 .15
687 A157 3 l Weight lifting .25 .15
688 A157 5 l Soccer .45 .15
689 A157 7 l Boxing .55 .25
690 A157 8 l Rowing 1.05 .30
Nos. 686-690 (5) 2.45 1.00

European championships. Imperfs. in changed colors, value set $10.

Papilio Podalirius A158

1963, Sept. 29 **Litho.**

Various Butterflies and Moths in Natural Colors

691 A158 1 l red .15 .15
692 A158 2 l blue .30 .15
693 A158 4 l dull lilac .50 .25
694 A158 5 l pale green .90 .40
695 A158 8 l bister 1.10 .55
696 A158 10 l light blue 1.65 .70
Nos. 691-696 (6) 4.60 2.20

Oil Refinery, Cerrik — A159

Flag and Shield — A160

Designs: 2.50 l, Food processing plant, Tirana, horiz. 30 l, Fruit canning plant. 50 l, Tannery, horiz.

1963, Nov. 15 **Unwmk.** ***Perf. 14***

697 A159 2.50 l rose red, *pnksh* .25 .15
698 A159 20 l slate grn, *grnsh* .85 .20
699 A159 30 l dull pur, *grysh* 2.00 .50
700 A159 50 l ocher, *yel* 2.25 .75
Nos. 697-700 (4) 5.35 1.60

Industrial development in Albania.

1963, Nov. 24 ***Perf. 12½x12***

701 A160 2 l grnsh bl, blk, ocher & red .25 .15
702 A160 8 l blue, blk, ocher & red .75 .48
Set value .53

1st Congress of Army Aid Assn.

Chinese, Caucasian and Negro Men — A161

1963, Dec. 10 ***Perf. 12x11½***

703 A161 3 l bister & blk .28 .15
704 A161 5 l bister & ultra .52 .18
705 A161 7 l bister & vio .85 .30
Nos. 703-705 (3) 1.65 .63

15th anniv. of the Universal Declaration of Human Rights.

Slalom Ascent — A162

Lenin — A163

Designs: 50q, Bobsled, horiz. 6.50 l, Ice hockey, horiz. 12.50 l, Women's figure skating. No. 709A, Ski jumper.

1963, Dec. 25 *Perf. 14*

706 A162 50q grnsh bl & blk .15 .15
707 A162 2.50 l red, gray & blk .25 .15
708 A162 6.50 l yel, blk & gray .65 .20
709 A162 12.50 l red, blk & yel grn 1.50 .50
Nos. 706-709 (4) 2.55
Set value .80

Miniature Sheet

709A A162 12.50 l multi 3.75 3.75

9th Winter Olympic Games, Innsbruck, Jan. 29-Feb. 9, 1964. Imperfs. in changed colors, value #706-709 $20, #709A $25.

1964, Jan. 21 *Perf. 12½x12*

710 A163 5 l gray & bister .30 .15
711 A163 10 l gray & ocher .60 .30

40th anniversary, death of Lenin.

Hurdling A164

Fish A165

Designs: 3 l, Track, horiz. 6.50 l, Rifle shooting, horiz. 8 l, Basketball.

Perf. 12½x12, 12x12½

1964, Jan. 30 **Litho.**

712 A164 2.50 l pale vio & ultra .25 .15
713 A164 3 l lt grn & red brn .38 .15
714 A164 6.50 l blue & claret .75 .18
715 A164 8 l lt blue & ocher 1.10 .22
Nos. 712-715 (4) 2.48
Set value .60

1st Games of the New Emerging Forces, GANEFO, Jakarta, Indonesia, Nov. 10-22, 1963.

1964, Feb. 26 **Unwmk.** *Perf. 14*

716 A165 50q Sturgeon .15 .15
717 A165 1 l Gilthead .15 .15
718 A165 1.50 l Striped mullet .32 .15
719 A165 2.50 l Carp .52 .15
720 A165 6.50 l Mackerel 1.40 .40
721 A165 10 l Lake Ohrid trout 2.50 .50
Nos. 716-721 (6) 5.04
Set value 1.25

Wild Animals A166

1964, Mar. 28 *Perf. 12½x12*

722 A166 1 l Red Squirrel .15 .15
723 A166 1.50 l Beech marten .15 .15
724 A166 2 l Red fox .40 .15
725 A166 2.50 l Hedgehog .45 .15
726 A166 3 l Hare .52 .15
727 A166 5 l Jackal .90 .25
728 A166 7 l Wildcat 1.25 .35
729 A166 8 l Wolf 1.65 .50
Nos. 722-729 (8) 5.47
Set value 1.50

Lighting Olympic Torch — A167

Designs: 5 l, Torch and globes. 7 l, 15 l, Olympic flag and Mt. Fuji. 10 l, National Stadium, Tokyo.

1964, May 18 *Perf. 12x12½*

730 A167 3 l lt yel grn, yel & buff .18 .15
731 A167 5 l red & vio blue .30 .15
732 A167 7 l lt bl, ultra & yel .42 .18
733 A167 10 l orange, bl & vio .60 .25
Nos. 730-733 (4) 1.50
Set value .55

Miniature Sheet

734 A167 15 l lt bl, ultra & org 8.50 8.50

18th Olympic Games, Tokyo, Oct. 10-25, 1964. No. 734 contains one 49x62mm stamp. Imperfs. in changed colors, value #730-733 $9.50, #734 $12.50.

See No. 745.

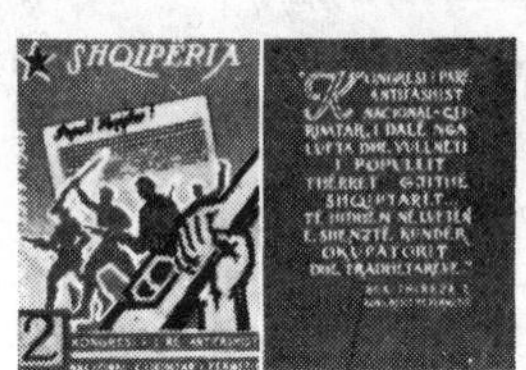

Partisans — A168

Designs: 5 l, Arms of Albania. 8 l, Enver Hoxha.

Perf. 12½x12

1964, May 24 **Litho.** **Unwmk.**

735 A168 2 l orange, red & blk .15 .15
736 A168 5 l multicolored .35 .15
737 A168 8 l red brn, blk & red .70 .20
Nos. 735-737 (3) 1.20
Set value .36

20th anniv. of the Natl. Anti-Fascist Cong. of Liberation, Permet, May 24, 1944. The label attached to each stamp, without perforations between, carries a quotation from the 1944 Congress.

Albanian Flag and Revolutionists A169

Full Moon A170

Perf. 12½x12

1964, June 10 **Litho.** **Unwmk.**

738 A169 2.50 l red & gray .15 .15
739 A169 7.50 l lilac rose & gray .35 .20

Albanian revolution of 1924, 40th anniv.

1964, June 27 *Perf. 12x12½*

Designs: 5 l, New moon. 8 l, Half moon. 11 l, Waning moon. 15 l, Far side of moon.

740 A170 1 l purple & yel .18 .15
741 A170 5 l violet & yel .45 .15
742 A170 8 l blue & yel .80 .30
743 A170 11 l green & yel 1.25 .45
Nos. 740-743 (4) 2.68 1.05

Miniature Sheet

Perf. 12 on 2 sides

744 A170 15 l ultra & yel 8.50 8.50

No. 744 contains one stamp, size: 35x36mm, perforated at top and bottom. Imperfs. in changed colors, value #740-743 $9, #744 $9.

No. 733 with Added Inscription: "Rimini 25-VI-64"

1964 *Perf. 12x12½*

745 A167 10 l orange, bl & vio 3.25 3.00

"Toward Tokyo 1964" Phil. Exhib. at Rimini, Italy, June 25-July 6.

Wren — A171

Birds: 1 l, Penduline titmouse. 2.50 l, Green woodpecker. 3 l, Tree creeper. 4 l, Nuthatch. 5 l, Great titmouse. 6 l, Goldfinch. 18 l, Oriole.

1964, July 31 *Perf. 12x12½*

746 A171 50q multi .15 .15
747 A171 1 l orange & multi .15 .15
748 A171 2.50 l multi .20 .15
749 A171 3 l blue & multi .30 .15
750 A171 4 l yellow & multi .40 .15
751 A171 5 l blue & multi .50 .15
752 A171 6 l lt vio & multi .70 .30
753 A171 18 l pink & multi 2.10 .85
Nos. 746-753 (8) 4.50
Set value 1.60

Running and Gymnastics A172

Sport: 2 l, Weight lifting, judo. 3 l, Equestrian, bicycling. 4 l, Soccer, water polo. 5 l, Wrestling, boxing. 6 l, Pentathlon, hockey. 7 l, Swimming, sailing. 8 l, Basketball, volleyball. 9 l, Rowing, canoeing. 10 l, Fencing, pistol shooting. 20 l, Three winners.

Perf. 12x12½

1964, Sept. 25 **Litho.** **Unwmk.**

754 A172 1 l lt bl, rose & emer .15 .15
755 A172 2 l bis brn, bluish grn & vio .15 .15
756 A172 3 l vio, red org & ol bis .18 .15
757 A172 4 l grnsh bl, ol & ultra .18 .15
758 A172 5 l grnsh bl, car & pale lil .30 .15
759 A172 6 l dk bl, org & lt bl .35 .15
760 A172 7 l dk bl, lt ol & org .38 .15
761 A172 8 l emerald, gray & yel .52 .22
762 A172 9 l bl, yel & lil rose .65 .30
763 A172 10 l brt grn, org brn & yel grn 1.65 .48
Nos. 754-763 (10) 4.51
Set value 1.60

Miniature Sheet

Perf. 12

764 A172 20 l violet & lemon 8.00 5.00

18th Olympic Games, Tokyo, Oct. 10-25. No. 764 contains one stamp, size: 41x68mm. Imperfs. in changed colors, value #754-763 $12.50, #764 $12.50.

Arms of People's Republic of China — A173

Mao Tse-tung and Flag A174

1964, Oct. 1 *Perf. 11½x12, 12x11½*

765 A173 7 l black, red & yellow .80 .30
766 A174 8 l black, red & yellow 1.25 .40

People's Republic of China, 15th anniv.

Karl Marx A175

Jeronim de Rada A176

Designs: 5 l, St. Martin's Hall, London. 8 l, Friedrich Engels.

1964, Nov. 5 *Perf. 12x11½*

767 A175 2 l red, lt vio & blk .45 .15
768 A175 5 l gray blue 1.00 .18
769 A175 8 l ocher, blk & red 2.00 .30
Nos. 767-769 (3) 3.45 .63

Centenary of First Socialist International.

1964, Nov. 15 *Perf. 12½x11½*

770 A176 7 l slate green .75 .30
771 A176 8 l dull violet 1.00 .35

Birth of Jeronim de Rada, poet, 150th anniv.

Arms of Albania — A177

Factories A178

Designs: 3 l, Combine harvester. 4 l, Woman chemist. 10 l, Hands holding Constitution, hammer and sickle.

Perf. 11½x12, 12x11½

1964, Nov. 29

772 A177 1 l multicolored .20 .15
773 A178 2 l red, yel & vio bl .28 .15
774 A178 3 l red, yel & brn .50 .15
775 A178 4 l red, yel & gray grn .60 .15
776 A177 10 l red, bl & blk 1.00 .45
Nos. 772-776 (5) 2.58
Set value .78

20th anniversary of liberation.

Planet Mercury — A179

Planets: 2 l, Venus and rocket. 3 l, Earth, moon and rocket. 4 l, Mars and rocket. 5 l, Jupiter. 6 l, Saturn. 7 l, Uranus. 8 l, Neptune. 9 l, Pluto. 15 l, Solar system and rocket.

1964, Dec. 15 *Perf. 12x12½*

777 A179 1 l yellow & pur .15 .15
778 A179 2 l multicolored .15 .15
779 A179 3 l multicolored .22 .15
780 A179 4 l multicolored .25 .15
781 A179 5 l yel, dk pur & brn .42 .15
782 A179 6 l lt grn, vio brn & yel .60 .15
783 A179 7 l yellow & grn .70 .18
784 A179 8 l yellow & vio .85 .22
785 A179 9 l lt grn, yel & blk 1.25 .38
Nos. 777-785 (9) 4.59
Set value 1.30

Miniature Sheet

Perf. 12 on 2 sides

786 A179 15 l car, bl, yel & grn 7.50 7.50

No. 786 contains one stamp, size: 62x51mm, perforated at top and bottom. Imperfs. in changed colors, value #777-785 $10, #786 $10.

European Chestnut A180

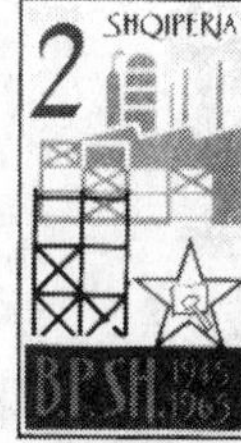

Symbols of Industry A181

1965, Jan. 25 *Perf. 11½x12*

787 A180 1 l shown .15 .15
788 A180 2 l Medlars .18 .15
789 A180 3 l Persimmon .38 .15
790 A180 4 l Pomegranate .42 .15
791 A180 5 l Quince .60 .20
792 A180 10 l Orange 1.25 .35
Nos. 787-792 (6) 2.98
Set value .90

1965, Feb. 20

Designs: 5 l, Books, triangle and compass. 8 l, Beach, trees and hotel.

793 A181 2 l blk, car rose & pink *1.40* .40
794 A181 5 l yel, gray & blk *2.75* .85
795 A181 8 l blk, vio bl & lt bl *4.75* 1.60
Nos. 793-795 (3) *8.90* 2.85

Professional trade associations, 20th anniv.

Water Buffalo A182

Various designs: Water buffalo.

1965, Mar. *Perf. 12x11½*

796 A182 1 l lt yel grn, yel & brn blk .30 .15
797 A182 2 l lt bl, dk gray & blk .70 .15
798 A182 3 l yellow, brn & grn .95 .15
799 A182 7 l brt grn, yel & brn blk 2.25 .35
800 A182 12 l pale lil, dk brn & ind 3.25 .65
Nos. 796-800 (5) 7.45 1.45

Mountain View, Valbona — A183

Views: 1.50 l, Seashore. 3 l, Glacier and peak, vert. 4 l, Gorge, vert. 5 l, Mountain peaks. 9 l, Lake and hills.

1965, Mar. **Litho.** *Perf. 12*

801 A183 1.50 l multi .75 .15
802 A183 2.50 l multi 1.00 .22
803 A183 3 l multi 1.40 .25
804 A183 4 l multi 1.65 .38
805 A183 5 l multi 2.50 .50
806 A183 9 l multi 4.00 .75
Nos. 801-806 (6) 11.30 2.25

Frontier Guard — A184

Small-bore Rifle Shooting, Prone — A185

1965, Apr. 25 **Unwmk.**

807 A184 2.50 l lt bl & multi .75 .15
808 A184 12.50 l lt ultra & multi 3.25 .90

20th anniversary of the Frontier Guards.

1965, May 10

Designs: 2 l, Rifle shooting, standing. 3 l, Target over map of Europe, showing Bucharest. 4 l, Pistol shooting. 15 l, Rifle shooting, kneeling.

809 A185 1 l lil, car rose, blk & brn .15 .15
810 A185 2 l bl, blk, brn & vio bl .30 .15
811 A185 3 l pink & car rose .35 .15
812 A185 4 l bis, blk & vio brn .48 .15
813 A185 15 l brt grn, brn & vio brn 1.75 .50
Nos. 809-813 (5) 3.03
Set value .90

European Shooting Championships, Bucharest.

ITU Emblem, Old and New Communications Equipment — A186

Col. Pavel Belyayev — A187

1965, May 17 *Perf. 12½x12*

814 A186 2.50 l brt grn, blk & lil rose .42 .15
815 A186 12.50 l vio, blk & brt bl 2.50 .28
Set value .34

Cent. of the ITU.

1965, June 15 *Perf. 12*

Designs: 2 l, Voskhod II. 6.50 l, Lt. Col. Alexei Leonov. 20 l, Leonov floating in space.

816 A187 1.50 l lt blue & brn .15 .15
817 A187 2 l dk bl, lt vio & lt ultra .15 .15
818 A187 6.50 l lilac & brn .55 .15
819 A187 20 l chlky bl, yel & blk 1.50 .35
Nos. 816-819 (4) 2.35
Set value .60

Miniature Sheet

Perf. 12 on 2 sides

820 A187 20 l brt bl, org & blk 5.25 5.25

Space flight of Voskhod II and 1st man walking in space, Lt. Col. Alexei Leonov. No. 820 contains one stamp, size: 51x59½mm, perforated at top and bottom. Imperf., brt grn background, value $5.25.

Marx and Lenin — A188

Mother and Child — A189

1965, June 21 *Perf. 12*

821 A188 2.50 l dk brn, red & yel .70 .15
822 A188 7.50 l sl grn, org ver & buff 1.75 .25

6th Conf. of Postal Ministers of Communist Countries, Peking, June 21-July 15.

Perf. 12½x12, 12x12½

1965, June 29 **Litho.** **Unwmk.**

Designs: 2 l, Pioneers. 3 l, Boy and girl at play, horiz. 4 l, Child on beach. 15 l, Girl with book.

823 A189 1 l brt bl, rose lil & blk .15 .15
824 A189 2 l salmon, vio & blk .22 .15
825 A189 3 l green, org & vio .32 .15
826 A189 4 l multicolored .45 .15
827 A189 15 l lil rose, brn & ocher 1.40 .38
Nos. 823-827 (5) 2.54
Set value .70

Issued for International Children's Day.

Statue of Magistrate A190

Fuchsia A191

Designs: 1 l, Amphora. 2 l, Illyrian armor. 3 l, Mosaic, horiz. 15 l, Torso, Apollo statue.

1965, July 20 *Perf. 12*

828 A190 1 l lt ol, org & brn .15 .15
829 A190 2 l gray grn, grn & brn .20 .15
830 A190 3 l tan, brn, car & lil .35 .15
831 A190 4 l green, bis & brn .50 .20
832 A190 15 l gray & pale cl 1.25 .65
Nos. 828-832 (5) 2.45
Set value 1.00

1965, Aug. 11 *Perf. 12½x12*

Flowers: 2 l, Cyclamen. 3 l, Tiger lily. 3.50 l, Iris. 4 l, Dahlia. 4.50 l, Hydrangea. 5 l, Rose. 7 l, Tulips.

833 A191 1 l multi .15 .15
834 A191 2 l multi .20 .15
835 A191 3 l multi .32 .15
836 A191 3.50 l multi .40 .15
837 A191 4 l multi .45 .15
838 A191 4.50 l multi .52 .15
839 A191 5 l multi .65 .20
840 A191 7 l multi 1.25 .30
Nos. 833-840 (8) 3.94
Set value 1.10

Nos. 698-700 Surcharged New Value and Two Bars

1965, Aug. 16 *Perf. 14*

841 A159 5q on 30 l .15 .15
842 A159 15q on 30 l .25 .15
843 A159 25q on 50 l .35 .15
844 A159 80q on 50 l .70 .20
845 A159 1.10 l on 20 l 1.10 .30
846 A159 2 l on 20 l 2.00 .60
Nos. 841-846 (6) 4.55
Set value 1.32

White Stork — A192

"Homecoming," by Bukurosh Sejdini — A193

Migratory Birds: 20q, Cuckoo. 30q, Hoopoe. 40q, European bee-eater. 50q, European nightjar. 1.50 l, Quail.

1965, Aug. 31 *Perf. 12*

847 A192 10q yellow, blk & gray .15 .15
848 A192 20q brt pink, blk & dk bl .18 .15
849 A192 30q violet, blk & bis .32 .15
850 A192 40q emer, blk yel & org .70 .15
851 A192 50q ultra, brn & red brn .85 .22
852 A192 1.50 l bis, red brn & dp org 2.25 .75
Nos. 847-852 (6) 4.45
Set value 1.35

1965, Sept. 26 **Litho.** *Perf. 12x12½*

853 A193 25q olive black 1.00 .16
854 A193 65q blue black 2.50 .32
855 A193 1.10 l black 3.75 .60
Nos. 853-855 (3) 7.25 1.08

Second war veterans' meeting.

Hunting — A194

Oleander — A195

1965, Oct. 6 **Litho.** **Unwmk.**

856 A194 10q Capercaillie .15 .15
857 A194 20q Deer .22 .15
858 A194 30q Pheasant .42 .18
859 A194 40q Mallards .65 .20
860 A194 50q Boar .75 .25
861 A194 1 l Rabbit 2.25 .55
Nos. 856-861 (6) 4.44 1.48

1965, Oct. 26 *Perf. 12½x12*

Flowers: 20q, Forget-me-nots. 30q, Pink. 40q, White water lily. 50q, Bird's foot. 1 l, Corn poppy.

862 A195 10q brt bl, grn & car rose .24 .15
863 A195 20q org red, bl, brn & grn .28 .15
864 A195 30q vio, car rose & grn .60 .15
865 A195 40q emerald, yel & blk .85 .18
866 A195 50q org brn, yel & grn .95 .20
867 A195 1 l yel grn, blk & rose red 2.15 .70
Nos. 862-867 (6) 5.07 1.53

Hotel Turizmi, Fier — A196

Freighter "Teuta" — A197

Buildings: 10q, Hotel, Peshkopi. 15q, Sanatorium, Tirana. 25q, Rest home, Pogradec. 65q, Partisan Sports Arena, Tirana. 80q, Rest home, Mali Dajt. 1.10 l, Culture House, Tirana. 1.60 l, Hotel Adriatik, Durres. 2 l, Migjeni Theater, Shkoder. 3 l, Alexander Moissi House of Culture, Durres.

1965, Oct. *Perf. 12x12½*

868 A196 5q blue & blk .15 .15
869 A196 10q ocher & blk .15 .15
870 A196 15q dull grn & blk .15 .15
871 A196 25q violet & blk .15 .15
872 A196 65q lt brn & blk .55 .15
873 A196 80q yel grn & blk .70 .15
874 A196 1.10 l lilac & blk 1.00 .20
875 A196 1.60 l lt vio bl & blk 1.40 .35
876 A196 2 l dull rose & blk 1.90 .50
877 A196 3 l gray & blk 3.00 .70
Nos. 868-877 (10) 9.15
Set value 2.15

1965, Nov. 16

Ships: 20q, Raft. 30q, Sailing ship, 19th cent. 40q, Sailing ship, 18th cent. 50q, Freighter "Vlora." 1 l, Illyric galleys.

878 A197 10q brt grn & dk grn .15 .15
879 A197 20q ol bis & dk grn .20 .15
880 A197 30q lt & dp ultra .35 .15
881 A197 40q vio & dp vio .60 .18
882 A197 50q pink & dk red .75 .20
883 A197 1 l bister & brn 1.50 .45
Nos. 878-883 (6) 3.55 1.28

Brown Bear — A198

Basketball and Players — A199

Designs: Various Albanian bears. 50q, 55q, 60q, horizontal.

1965, Dec. 7 *Perf. 11½x12*

884 A198 10q bister & dk brn .30 .15
885 A198 20q pale brn & dk brn .42 .15
886 A198 30q bis, dk brn & car .65 .15
887 A198 35q pale brn & dk brn .80 .15
888 A198 40q bister & dk brn 1.25 .18
889 A198 50q bister & dk brn 1.50 .20
890 A198 55q bister & dk brn 1.50 .30
891 A198 60q pale brn, dk brn & car 1.65 .45
Nos. 884-891 (8) 8.07 1.73

1965, Dec. 15 **Litho.** *Perf. 12½x12*

Designs: 10q, Games' emblem (map of Albania and basket). 30q, 50q, Players with ball (diff. designs). 1.40 l, Basketball medal on ribbon.

892 A199 10q blue, yel & car .15 .15
893 A199 20q rose lil, lt brn & blk .28 .15
894 A199 30q bis, lt brn, red & blk .35 .15
895 A199 50q lt grn, lt brn & blk .80 .15
896 A199 1.40 l rose, blk, brn & yel 1.50 .50
Nos. 892-896 (5) 3.08
Set value .80

7th Balkan Basketball Championships, Tirana, Dec. 15-19.

Arms of Republic and Smokestacks — A200

Designs (Arms and): 10q, Book. 30q, Wheat. 60q, Book, hammer and sickle. 80q, Factories.

1966, Jan. 11 Litho. *Perf. 11½x12*
Coat of Arms in Gold

897 A200 10q crimson & brn .15 .15
898 A200 20q blue & vio bl .15 .15
899 A200 30q org yel & brn .32 .15
900 A200 60q yel grn & brt grn .50 .20
901 A200 80q crimson & brn 1.10 .25
Nos. 897-901 (5) 2.22
Set value .60

Albanian People's Republic, 20th anniv.

Cow — A201

Perf. 12½x12, 12x12½
1966, Feb. 25

902 A201 10q shown .20 .15
903 A201 20q Pig .32 .15
904 A201 30q Ewe & lamb .45 .15
905 A201 35q Ram .65 .15
906 A201 40q Dog .95 .16
907 A201 50q Cat, vert. 1.00 .16
908 A201 55q Horse, vert. 1.25 .25
909 A201 60q Ass, vert. 1.50 .28
Nos. 902-909 (8) 6.32
Set value 1.22

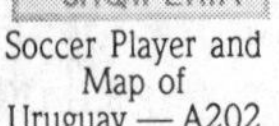

Soccer Player and Map of Uruguay — A202

Andon Zako Cajupi — A203

Designs: 5q, Globe in form of soccer ball. 15q, Player, map of Italy. 20q, Goalkeeper, map of France. 25q, Player, map of Brazil. 30q, Player, map of Switzerland. 35q, Player, map of Sweden. 40q, Player, map of Chile. 50q, Player, map of Great Britain. 70q, World Championship cup and ball.

1966, Mar. 20 Litho. *Perf. 12*

910 A202 5q gray & dp org .15 .15
911 A202 10q lt brn, bl & vio .15 .15
912 A202 15q cit, dk bl & brt bl .15 .15
913 A202 20q org, vio bl & brt bl .22 .15
914 A202 25q salmon & sepia .25 .15
915 A202 30q lt yel grn & brn .28 .15
916 A202 35q lt ultra & emer .32 .15
917 A202 40q pink & brown .50 .15
918 A202 50q pale grn, mag & rose red .50 .15
919 A202 70q gray, brn, yel & blk .65 .24
Nos. 910-919 (10) 3.17
Set value 1.00

World Cup Soccer Championship, Wembley, England, July 11-30.

1966, Mar. 27 Unwmk.

920 A203 40q bluish blk .28 .15
921 A203 1.10 l dark green .80 .15
Set value .22

Andon Zako Cajupi, poet, birth centenary .

The Scott Catalogue value is a retail value; that is, what you could expect to pay for the stamp in a grade of Very Fine. The value listed reflects recent actual dealer selling prices.

Painted Lady — A204

WHO Headquarters, Geneva, and Emblem — A205

Designs: 20q, Blue dragonfly. 30q, Cloudless sulphur butterfly. 35q, 40q, Splendid dragonfly. 50q, Machaon swallow-tail. 55q, Sulphur butterfly. 60q, Whitemarbled butterfly.

1966, Apr. 21 Litho. *Perf. 11½x12*

922 A204 10q multicolored .15 .15
923 A204 20q yellow & multi .20 .15
924 A204 30q yellow & multi .35 .15
925 A204 35q sky blue & multi .42 .15
926 A204 40q multicolored .45 .15
927 A204 50q rose & multi .60 .15
928 A204 55q multicolored .65 .15
929 A204 60q multicolored 1.10 .15
Nos. 922-929 (8) 3.92
Set value .70

Perf. 12x12½, 12½x12
1966, May 3 Litho.

Designs (WHO Emblem and): 35q, Ambulance and stretcher bearers, vert. 60q, Albanian mother and nurse weighing infant, vert. 80q, X-ray machine and hospital.

930 A205 25q lt blue & blk .26 .15
931 A205 35q salmon & ultra .52 .15
932 A205 60q lt grn, bl & red .80 .15
933 A205 80q yel, bl, grn & lt brn 1.10 .22
Nos. 930-933 (4) 2.68
Set value .42

Inauguration of the WHO Headquarters, Geneva.

Bird's Foot Starfish — A206

Designs: 25q, Starfish. 35q, Brittle star. 45q, Butthorn starfish. 50q, Starfish. 60q, Sea cucumber. 70q, Sea urchin.

1966, May 10 *Perf. 12x12½*

934 A206 15q multicolored .20 .15
935 A206 25q multicolored .35 .15
936 A206 35q multicolored .50 .15
937 A206 45q multicolored .70 .15
938 A206 50q multicolored .85 .18
939 A206 60q multicolored 1.00 .20
940 A206 70q multicolored 1.40 .35
Nos. 934-940 (7) 5.00
Set value 1.10

Luna 10 — A207

Designs: 30q, 80q, Trajectory of Luna 10, earth and moon.

1966, June 10 *Perf. 12x12½*

941 A207 20q blue, yel & blk .32 .15
942 A207 30q yel grn, blk & bl .45 .15
943 A207 70q vio, yel & blk .90 .20
944 A207 80q yel, vio, grn & blk 1.25 .20
Nos. 941-944 (4) 2.92 .70

Launching of the 1st artificial moon satellite, Luna 10, Apr. 3, 1966.

Jules Rimet Cup and Soccer A208

Designs: Various scenes of soccer play.

1966, July 12 Litho. *Perf. 12x12½*
Black Inscriptions

945 A208 10q ocher & lilac .15 .15
946 A208 20q lt blue & cit .15 .15
947 A208 30q brick red & Prus bl .20 .15
948 A208 35q lt ultra & rose .25 .15
949 A208 40q yel grn & lt red brn .30 .15
950 A208 50q lt red brn & yel grn .48 .15
951 A208 55q rose lil & yel grn .52 .15
952 A208 60q dp rose & ocher 1.00 .22
Nos. 945-952 (8) 3.05
Set value .80

World Cup Soccer Championship, Wembley, England, July 11-30.

Water Level Map of Albania — A209

Designs: 30q, Water measure and fields. 70q, Turbine and pylon. 80q, Hydrological decade emblem.

1966, July *Perf. 12½x12*

953 A209 20q brick red, blk & org .32 .15
954 A209 30q emer, blk & lt brn .48 .15
955 A209 70q brt violet & blk 1.10 .25
956 A209 80q brt bl, org, yel & blk .52 .30
Nos. 953-956 (4) 2.42 .85

Hydrological Decade (UNESCO), 1965-74.

Greek Turtle — A210

Designs: 15q, Grass snake. 25q, European pond turtle. 30q, Wall lizard. 35q, Wall gecko. 45q, Emerald lizard. 50q, Slowworm. 90q, Horned viper (or sand viper).

1966, Aug. 10 Litho. *Perf. 12½x12*

957 A210 10q gray & multi .15 .15
958 A210 15q yellow & multi .20 .15
959 A210 25q ultra & multi .30 .15
960 A210 30q multicolored .40 .18
961 A210 35q multicolored .55 .20
962 A210 45q multicolored .65 .25
963 A210 50q orange & multi .75 .30
964 A210 90q lilac & multi 1.65 .55
Nos. 957-964 (8) 4.65 1.93

Persian Cat A211

Cats: 10q, Siamese, vert. 15q, European tabby, vert. 25q, Black kitten. 60q, 65q, 80q, Various Persians.

Perf. 12x12½, 12½x12
1966, Sept. 20 Litho.

965 A211 10q multicolored .15 .15
966 A211 15q blk, sepia & car .20 .15
967 A211 25q blk, dk & lt brn .28 .15
968 A211 45q blk, org & yel .55 .16
969 A211 60q blk, brn & yel .70 .20
970 A211 65q multicolored .80 .20
971 A211 80q blk, gray & yel 1.40 .28
Nos. 965-971 (7) 4.08
Set value 1.00

Pjeter Budi, Writer — A212

1966, Oct. 5 *Perf. 12x12½*

972 A212 25q buff & slate grn .16 .15
973 A212 1.75 l gray & dull claret 1.10 .45

UNESCO Emblem A213

Designs (UNESCO Emblem and): 15q, Open book, rose and school. 25q, Male folk dancers. 1.55 l, Jug, column and old building.

1966, Oct. 20 Litho. *Perf. 12*

974 A213 5q lt gray & multi .15 .15
975 A213 15q dp blue & multi .20 .15
976 A213 25q gray & multi .40 .15
977 A213 1.55 l multi 1.75 .48
Nos. 974-977 (4) 2.50
Set value .75

20th anniv. of UNESCO.

Hand Holding Book with Pictures of Marx, Engels, Lenin and Stalin A214

Hammer and Sickle, Party Emblem in Sunburst A215

Designs: 25q, Map of Albania, hammer and sickle, symbols of agriculture and industry. 65q, Symbolic grain and factories. 95q, Fists holding rifle, spade, axe, sickle and book.

1966, Nov. 1 Litho. *Perf. 11½x12*

978 A214 15q vermilion & gold .22 .15
979 A214 25q multicolored .32 .15
980 A214 65q brn, brn org & gold .75 .15
981 A214 95q yellow & multi 1.10 .35
Nos. 978-981 (4) 2.39
Set value .60

Albanian Communist Party, 5th Cong.

1966, Nov. 8

Designs: 25q, Partisan and sunburst. 65q, Steel worker and blast furnace. 95q, Combine harvester, factories, and pylon.

982 A215 15q orange & multi .22 .15
983 A215 25q red & multi .30 .15
984 A215 65q multicolored .80 .15
985 A215 95q blue & multi 1.10 .35
Nos. 982-985 (4) 2.42
Set value .60

25th anniv. of the founding of the Albanian Workers Party.

Russian Wolfhound — A216

Dogs: 15q, Sheep dog. 25q, English setter. 45q, English springer spaniel. 60q, Bulldog. 65q, Saint Bernard. 80q, Dachshund.

1966 Litho. *Perf. 12½x12*

986 A216 10q green & multi .18 .15
987 A216 15q multicolored .25 .15
988 A216 25q lilac & multi .35 .15
989 A216 45q rose & multi .70 .35
990 A216 60q brown & multi .90 .40
991 A216 65q ultra & multi 1.00 .45
992 A216 80q blue grn & multi 1.40 .52
Nos. 986-992 (7) 4.78 2.17

Ndre Mjeda
A217

Proclamation
A218

1966 *Perf. 12½x12*

993 A217 25q brt bl & dk brn .52 .15
994 A217 1.75 l brt grn & dk brn 2.00 .65

Birth Centenary of the priest Ndre Mjeda.

1966 *Perf. 11½x12, 12x11½*

Designs: 10q, Banner, man and woman holding gun and axe, horiz. 1.85 l, man with axe and banner and partisan with gun.

995 A218 5q lt brn, red & blk .15 .15
996 A218 10q red, blk, gray & bl .18 .15
997 A218 1.85 l red, blk & salmon 1.25 .28
Nos. 995-997 (3) 1.58
Set value .38

25th anniv. of the Albanian Communist Party.

Golden Eagle — A219

Birds of Prey: 15q, European sea eagle. 25q, Griffon vulture. 40q, Common sparrowhawk. 50q, Osprey. 70q, Egyptian vulture. 90q, Kestrel.

1966, Dec. 20 Litho. *Perf. 11½x12*

998 A219 10q gray & multi .15 .15
999 A219 15q multicolored .20 .15
1000 A219 25q citron & multi .35 .15
1001 A219 40q multicolored .60 .18
1002 A219 50q multicolored .70 .22
1003 A219 70q yellow & multi 1.00 .35
1004 A219 90q multicolored 1.40 .48
Nos. 998-1004 (7) 4.40 1.68

Hake
A220

Fish: 15q, Red mullet. 25q, Opah. 40q, Atlantic wolf fish. 65q, Lumpfish. 80q, Swordfish. 1.15 l, Shorthorn sculpin.

1967, Jan. Photo. *Perf. 12x11½*
Fish in Natural Colors

1005 A220 10q blue .15 .15
1006 A220 15q lt yellow grn .24 .15
1007 A220 25q Prus blue .30 .15
1008 A220 40q emerald .75 .18
1009 A220 65q brt blue grn .85 .25
1010 A220 80q blue 1.25 .35
1011 A220 1.15 l brt green 1.65 .60
Nos. 1005-1011 (7) 5.19 1.83

White
Pelican — A221

Designs: Various groups of pelicans.

1967, Feb. 22 Litho. *Perf. 12*

1012 A221 10q pink & multi .15 .15
1013 A221 15q pink & multi .24 .15
1014 A221 25q pink & multi .48 .15
1015 A221 50q pink & multi .85 .15
1016 A221 2 l pink & multi 3.25 .75
Nos. 1012-1016 (5) 4.97
Set value 1.05

Camellia — A222

Flowers: 10q, Chrysanthemum. 15q, Hollyhock. 25q, Flowering Maple. 35q, Peony. 65q, Gladiolus. 80q, Freesia. 1.15 l, Carnation.

Unwmk.

1967, Apr. 12 Litho. *Perf. 12*
Flowers in Natural Colors

1017 A222 5q pale brown .15 .15
1018 A222 10q lt lilac .15 .15
1019 A222 15q gray .18 .15
1020 A222 25q ultra .30 .15
1021 A222 35q lt blue .55 .15
1022 A222 65q lt blue grn .85 .15
1023 A222 80q lt bluish gray 1.25 .22
1024 A222 1.15 l dull yellow 1.65 .40
Nos. 1017-1024 (8) 5.08
Set value 1.00

A223

Rose — A224

Design: Congress emblem and power station.

1967, Apr. 24 Litho. *Perf. 12*

1025 A223 25q multi .22 .15
1026 A223 1.75 l multi 1.75 .42

Cong. of the Union of Professional Workers, Tirana, Apr. 24.

1967, May 15 *Perf. 12x12½*

Various Roses in Natural Colors.

1027 A224 5q blue gray .15 .15
1028 A224 10q brt blue .15 .15
1029 A224 15q rose violet .15 .15
1030 A224 25q lemon .32 .15
1031 A224 35q brt grnsh blue .42 .15
1032 A224 65q gray .75 .16
1033 A224 80q brown .95 .25
1034 A224 1.65 l gray green 2.25 .45
Nos. 1027-1034 (8) 5.14
Set value 1.10

Seashore, Bregdet Borsh — A225

Views: 15q, Buthrotum, vert. 25q, Shore, Fshati Piqeras. 45q, Shore, Bregdet. 50q, Shore, Bregdet Himare. 65q, Ship, Sarande (Santi Quaranta). 80q, Shore, Dhermi. 1 l, Sunset, Bregdet, vert.

Perf. 12x12½, 12½x12
1967, June 10

1035 A225 15q multicolored .16 .15
1036 A225 20q multicolored .24 .15
1037 A225 25q multicolored .25 .15
1038 A225 45q multicolored .70 .15
1039 A225 50q multicolored .80 .16
1040 A225 65q multicolored 1.10 .20
1041 A225 80q multicolored 1.25 .24
1042 A225 1 l multicolored 1.65 .35
Nos. 1035-1042 (8) 6.15
Set value 1.25

Fawn
A226

Roe Deer: 20q, Stag, vert. 25q, Doe, vert. 30q, Young stag and doe. 35q, Doe and fawn. 40q, Young stag, vert. 65q, Stag and doe, vert. 70q, Running stag and does.

Perf. 12½x12, 12x12½
1967, July 20 Litho.

1043 A226 15q multicolored .25 .15
1044 A226 20q multicolored .25 .15
1045 A226 25q multicolored .38 .15
1046 A226 30q multicolored .45 .15
1047 A226 35q multicolored .55 .15
1048 A226 40q multicolored .70 .15
1049 A226 65q multicolored 1.10 .30
1050 A226 70q multicolored 1.10 .35
Nos. 1043-1050 (8) 4.78
Set value 1.15

Man and
Woman from
Madhe
A227

Regional Costumes: 20q, Woman from Zadrimes. 25q, Dancer and drummer, Kukesit. 45q, Woman spinner, Dardhes. 50q, Farm couple, Myseqese. 65q, Dancer with tambourine, Tirana. 80q, Man and woman, Dropullit. 1 l, Piper, Laberise.

1967, Aug. 25 *Perf. 12*

1051 A227 15q tan & multi .15 .15
1052 A227 20q lt yellow grn .16 .15
1053 A227 25q multicolored .16 .15
1054 A227 45q sky blue & multi .32 .20
1055 A227 50q lemon & multi .48 .24
1056 A227 65q pink & multi .55 .35
1057 A227 80q multicolored .70 .40
1058 A227 1 l gray & multi 1.00 .52
Nos. 1051-1058 (8) 3.52 2.16

Fighters and
Newspaper — A228

Designs: 75q, Printing plant, newspapers and microphone. 2 l, People holding newspaper.

1967, Aug. 25 *Perf. 12½x12*

1059 A228 25q multicolored .25 .15
1060 A228 75q pink & multi .55 .15
1061 A228 2 l multicolored 1.40 .32
Nos. 1059-1061 (3) 2.20
Set value .48

Issued for the Day of the Press.

Street
Scene, by
Kolé
Idromeno
A229

Hakmarrja Battalion, by Sali
Shijaku — A230

Designs: 20q, David, fresco by Onufri, 16th century, vert. 45q, Woman's head, ancient mosaic, vert. 50q, Men on horseback from 16th century icon, vert. 65q, Farm Women, by Zef Shoshi. 80q, Street Scene, by Vangjush Mio. 1 l, Bride, by Kolé Idromeno, vert.

Perf. 12, 12x12½, (A230)
1967, Oct. 25 Litho.

1062 A229 15q multicolored .35 .15
1063 A229 20q multicolored .40 .15
1064 A230 25q multicolored .50 .15
1065 A229 45q multicolored 1.00 .15
1066 A229 50q multicolored 1.25 .15
1067 A230 65q multicolored 1.50 .15
1068 A230 80q multicolored 1.75 .22
1069 A230 1 l multicolored 2.25 .28
Nos. 1062-1069 (8) 9.00
Set value 1.00

Lenin at
Storming of
Winter
Palace — A231

Rabbit — A232

Designs: 15q, Lenin and Stalin, horiz. 50q, Lenin and Stalin addressing meeting. 1.10 l, Storming of the Winter Palace, horiz.

1967, Nov. 7 *Perf. 12*

1070 A231 15q red & multi .15 .15
1071 A231 25q slate grn & blk .20 .15
1072 A231 50q brn, blk & brn vio .32 .15
1073 A231 1.10 l lilac, gray & blk 1.00 .22
Nos. 1070-1073 (4) 1.67
Set value .44

50th anniv. of the Russian October Revolution.

1967, Nov. 25

Designs: Various hares and rabbits. The 15q, 25q, 35q, 40q and 1 l are horizontal.

1074 A232 15q orange & multi .18 .15
1075 A232 20q brt yel & multi .18 .15
1076 A232 25q lt brn & multi .22 .15
1077 A232 35q multicolored .32 .15
1078 A232 40q yellow & multi .55 .15
1079 A232 50q pink & multi .65 .15
1080 A232 65q multicolored 1.10 .30
1081 A232 1 l lilac & multi 1.75 .45
Nos. 1074-1081 (8) 4.95
Set value 1.20

University, Torch and
Book — A233

1967 Litho. *Perf. 12*

1082 A233 25q multi .18 .15
1083 A233 1.75 l multi 1.10 .28
Set value .32

10th anniv. of the founding of the State University, Tirana.

Coat of Arms
and Soldiers
A234

Designs: 65q, Arms, Factory, grain, flag, gun and radio tower. 1.20 l, Arms and hand holding torch.

1967 *Perf. 12x11½*

1084 A234 15q multi .15 .15
1085 A234 65q multi .40 .15
1086 A234 1.20 l multi .70 .15
Nos. 1084-1086 (3) 1.25
Set value .36

25th anniversary of the Democratic Front.

Turkey — A235

Designs: 20q, Duck. 25q, Hen. 45q, Rooster. 50q, Guinea fowl. 65q, Goose, horiz. 80q, Mallard, horiz. 1 l, Chicks, horiz.

Perf. 12x12½, 12½x12

1967, Nov. 25 **Photo.**

1087 A235 15q gold & multi .18 .15
1088 A235 20q gold & multi .18 .15
1089 A235 25q gold & multi .22 .15
1090 A235 45q gold & multi .35 .15
1091 A235 50q gold & multi .52 .15
1092 A235 65q gold & multi .70 .20
1093 A235 80q gold & multi 1.25 .30
1094 A235 1 l gold & multi 1.65 .40
Nos. 1087-1094 (8) 5.05
Set value 1.25

Skanderbeg A236

Designs: 10q, Arms of Skanderbeg. 25q, Helmet and sword. 30q, Kruje Castle. 35q, Petreles Castle. 65q, Berati Castle. 80q, Skanderbeg addressing national chiefs. 90q, Battle of Albulenes.

1967, Dec. 10 **Litho.** ***Perf. 12x12½***

Medallion in Bister and Dark Brown

1095 A236 10q gold & violet .15 .15
1096 A236 15q gold & rose car .15 .15
1097 A236 25q gold & vio bl .15 .15
1098 A236 30q gold & dk blue .16 .15
1099 A236 35q gold & maroon .22 .15
1100 A236 65q gold & green .38 .15
1101 A236 80q gold & gray brn .60 .15
1102 A236 90q gold & ultra 1.10 .18
Nos. 1095-1102 (8) 2.91
Set value .70

500th anniv. of the death of Skanderbeg (George Castriota), national hero.

Ice Hockey — A237

Designs: 15q, 2 l, Winter Olympics emblem. 30q, Women's figure skating. 50q, Slalom. 80q, Downhill skiing. 1 l, Ski jump.

1967-68

1103 A237 15q multicolored .15 .15
1104 A237 25q multicolored .15 .15
1105 A237 30q multicolored .15 .15
1106 A237 50q multicolored .25 .15
1107 A237 80q multicolored .52 .18
1108 A237 1 l multicolored .75 .25
Nos. 1103-1108 (6) 1.97
Set value .65

Miniature Sheet

Imperf

1109 A237 2 l red, gray & brt bl ('68) 5.00 5.00

10th Winter Olympic Games, Grenoble, France, Feb. 6-18.

Nos. 1103-1108 issued Dec. 29, 1967.

Skanderbeg Monument, Kruje — A238

Designs: 10q, Skanderbeg monument, Tirana. 15q, Skanderbeg portrait, Uffizi Galleries, Florence. 25q, engraved portrait of Gen. Tanush Topia. 35q, Portrait of Gen. Gjergj Arianti, horiz. 65q, Portrait bust of Skanderbeg by O. Paskali. 80q, Title page of "The Life of Skanderbeg." 90q, Skanderbeg battling the Turks, painting by S. Rrota, horiz.

Perf. 12x12½, 12½x12

1968, Jan. 17 **Litho.**

1110 A238 10q multicolored .15 .15
1111 A238 15q multicolored .22 .15
1112 A238 25q blk, yel & lt bl .30 .15
1113 A238 30q multicolored .35 .15
1114 A238 35q lt vio, pink & blk .52 .15
1115 A238 65q multicolored .85 .15
1116 A238 80q pink, blk & yel 1.10 .18
1117 A238 90q beige & multi 1.50 .22
Nos. 1110-1117 (8) 4.99
Set value .82

500th anniv. of the death of Skanderbeg (George Castriota), national hero.

Carnation A239

1968, Feb. 15 ***Perf. 12***

Various Carnations in Natural Colors

1118 A239 15q green .15 .15
1119 A239 20q dk brown .15 .15
1120 A239 25q brt blue .16 .15
1121 A239 50q gray olice .28 .15
1122 A239 80q bluish gray .75 .16
1123 A239 1.10 l violet gray 1.00 .24
Nos. 1118-1123 (6) 2.49
Set value .62

"Electrification" A240

Designs: 65q, Farm tractor, horiz. 1.10 l, Cow and herd.

1968, Mar. 5 **Litho.** ***Perf. 12***

1124 A240 25q multi .16 .15
1125 A240 65q multi .48 .15
1126 A240 1.10 l multi .70 .20
Nos. 1124-1126 (3) 1.34
Set value .32

Fifth Farm Cooperatives Congress.

Goat A241

Designs: Various goats. 15q, 20q and 25q are vertical.

Perf. 12x12½, 12½x12

1968, Mar. 25

1127 A241 15q multi .15 .15
1128 A241 20q multi .15 .15
1129 A241 25q multi .15 .15
1130 A241 30q multi .22 .15
1131 A241 40q multi .30 .15
1132 A241 50q multi .35 .15
1133 A241 80q multi .60 .18
1134 A241 1.40 l multi 1.50 .35
Nos. 1127-1134 (8) 3.42
Set value .88

Zef N. Jubani — A242

Physician and Hospital — A243

1968, Mar. 30 ***Perf. 12***

1135 A242 25q yellow & choc .18 .15
1136 A242 1.75 l lt violet & blk .80 .28
Set value .36

Sesquicentennial of the birth of Zef N. Jubani, writer and scholar.

Perf. 12½x12, 12x12½

1968, Apr. 7 **Litho.**

Designs (World Health Organization Emblem and): 65q, Hospital and microscope, horiz. 1.10 l, Mother feeding child.

1137 A243 25q green & claret .16 .15
1138 A243 65q black, yel & bl .48 .15
1139 A243 1.10 l black & dp org .70 .20
Nos. 1137-1139 (3) 1.34
Set value .36

20th anniv. of WHO.

Scientist A244

Women: 15q, Militia member. 60q, Farm worker. 1 l, Factory worker.

1968, Apr. 14 ***Perf. 12***

1140 A244 15q ver & dk red .15 .15
1141 A244 25q blue grn & grn .20 .15
1142 A244 60q dull yel & brn .32 .15
1143 A244 1 l lt vio & vio .85 .28
Nos. 1140-1143 (4) 1.52
Set value .55

Albanian Women's Organization, 25th anniv.

Karl Marx — A245

Designs: 25q, Marx lecturing to students. 65q, "Das Kapital," "Communist Manifesto" and marching crowd. 95q, Full-face portrait.

1968, May 5 **Litho.** ***Perf. 12***

1144 A245 15q gray, dk bl & bis .16 .15
1145 A245 25q brn vio, dk brn & dl yel .35 .15
1146 A245 65q gray, blk, brn & car .85 .18
1147 A245 95q gray, ocher & blk 1.40 .35
Nos. 1144-1147 (4) 2.76
Set value .65

Karl Marx, 150th birth anniversary.

Heliopsis — A246

Flowers: 20q, Red flax. 25q, Orchid. 30q, Gloxinia. 40q, Turk's-cap lily. 80q, Amaryllis. 1.40 l, Red magnolia.

1968, May 10 ***Perf. 12x12½***

1148 A246 15q gold & multi .15 .15
1149 A246 20q gold & multi .15 .15
1150 A246 25q gold & multi .15 .15
1151 A246 30q gold & multi .15 .15
1152 A246 40q gold & multi .40 .15
1153 A246 80q gold & multi .50 .15
1154 A246 1.40 l gold & multi .75 .30
Nos. 1148-1154 (7) 2.25
Set value .70

Proclamation of Prizren A247

Designs: 25q, Abdyl Frasheri. 40q, House in Prizren.

1968, June 10 **Litho.** ***Perf. 12***

1155 A247 25q emerald & blk .20 .15
1156 A247 40q multicolored .45 .15
1157 A247 85q yellow & multi .85 .25
Nos. 1155-1157 (3) 1.50
Set value .40

League of Prizren against the Turks, 90th anniv.

Shepherd, by A. Kushi — A248

Paintings from Tirana Art Gallery: 20q, View of Tirana, by V. Mio, horiz. 25q, Mountaineer, by G. Madhi. 40q, Refugees, by A. Buza. 80q, Guerrillas of Shahin Matrakut, by S. Xega. 1.50 l, Portrait of an Old Man, by S. Papadhimitri. 1.70 l, View of Scutari, by S. Rrota. 2.50 l, Woman in Scutari Costume, by Z. Colombi.

1968, June 20 ***Perf. 12x12½***

1158 A248 15q gold & multi .15 .15
1159 A248 20q gold & multi .15 .15
1160 A248 25q gold & multi .20 .15
1161 A248 40q gold & multi .38 .15
1162 A248 80q gold & multi .65 .15
1163 A248 1.50 l gold & multi 1.10 .25
1164 A248 1.70 l gold & multi 1.25 .50
Nos. 1158-1164 (7) 3.88
Set value 1.10

Miniature Sheet

Perf. 12½xImperf.

1165 A248 2.50 l multi 2.00 .90

No. 1165 contains one stamp, size: 50x71mm.

Soldier and Guns — A249

Designs: 25q, Sailor and warships. 65q, Aviator and planes, vert. 95q, Militiamen and woman.

1968, July 10 **Litho.** ***Perf. 12***

1166 A249 15q multicolored .20 .15
1167 A249 25q multicolored .32 .15
1168 A249 65q multicolored .85 .15
1169 A249 95q multicolored 1.65 .20
Nos. 1166-1169 (4) 3.02
Set value .45

25th anniversary of the People's Army.

Squid — A250

Designs: 20q, Crayfish. 25q, Whelk. 50q, Crab. 70q, Spiny lobster. 80q, Shore crab. 90q, Norway lobster.

1968, Aug. 20

1170 A250 15q multicolored .16 .15
1171 A250 20q multicolored .16 .15
1172 A250 25q multicolored .22 .15
1173 A250 50q multicolored .38 .15
1174 A250 70q multicolored .60 .25
1175 A250 80q multicolored .75 .30
1176 A250 90q multicolored 1.10 .35
Nos. 1170-1176 (7) 3.37
Set value 1.10

Women's Relay Race — A251

Sport: 20q, Running. 25q, Women's discus. 30q, Equestrian. 40q, High jump. 50q, Women's hurdling. 80q, Soccer. 1.40 l, Woman diver. 2 l, Olympic stadium.

1968, Sept. 23 Photo. *Perf. 12*

1177 A251 15q multicolored .15 .15
1178 A251 20q multicolored .15 .15
1179 A251 25q multicolored .15 .15
1180 A251 30q multicolored .20 .15
1181 A251 40q multicolored .22 .15
1182 A251 50q multicolored .35 .15
1183 A251 80q multicolored .52 .15
1184 A251 1.40 l multicolored .95 .35
Nos. 1177-1184 (8) 2.69
Set value .85

Souvenir Sheet

Perf. 12 1/2 Horizontally

1185 A251 2 l multicolored 2.25 .75

19th Olympic Games, Mexico City, Oct. 12-27. No. 1185 contains one rectangular stamp, size: 64x54mm. Value of imperfs., #1177-1184 $7, #1185 $5.

Enver Hoxha — A252

1968, Oct. 16 Litho. *Perf. 12*

1186 A252 25q blue gray .28 .15
1187 A252 35q rose brown .45 .18
1188 A252 80q violet .75 .35
1189 A252 1.10 l brown 1.00 .50
Nos. 1186-1189 (4) 2.48 1.18

Souvenir Sheet

Imperf

1190 A252 1.50 l rose red, bl vio & gold 50.00 40.00

60th birthday of Enver Hoxha, First Secretary of the Central Committee of the Communist Party of Albania.

Book and Pupils — A253

1968, Nov. 14 Photo.

1191 A253 15q maroon & slate grn .20 .15
1192 A253 85q gray olive & sepia 1.25 .18
Set value .25

60th anniv. of the Congress of Monastir, Nov. 14-22, 1908, which adopted a unified Albanian alphabet.

Waxwing — A254

Birds: 20q, Rose-colored starling. 25q, Kingfishers. 50q, Long-tailed tits. 80q, Wallcreeper. 1.10 l, Bearded tit.

1968, Nov. 15 Litho.

Birds in Natural Colors

1193 A254 15q lt blue & blk .15 .15
1194 A254 20q bister & blk .15 .15
1195 A254 25q pink & blk .28 .15
1196 A254 50q lt yel grn & blk .32 .15
1197 A254 80q bis brn & blk .70 .22
1198 A254 1.10 l pale green & blk .90 .25
Nos. 1193-1198 (6) 2.50
Set value .75

Mao Tse-tung — A255

1968, Dec. 26 Litho. *Perf. 12 1/2x12*

1199 A255 25q gold, red & blk .25 .15
1200 A255 1.75 l gold, red & blk 1.25 .30

75th birthday of Mao Tse-tung, Chairman of the Communist Party of the People's Republic of China.

Adem Reka and Crane — A256

Portraits: 10q, Pjeter Lleshi and power lines. 15q, Mohammed Shehu and Myrteza Kepi. 25q, Shkurte Vata and women railroad workers. 65q, Agron Elezi, frontier guard. 80q, Ismet Bruç aj and mountain road. 1.30 l, Fuat Cela, blind revolutionary.

1969, Feb. 10 Litho. *Perf. 12x12 1/2*

1201 A256 5q multicolored .15 .15
1202 A256 10q multicolored .15 .15
1203 A256 15q multicolored .15 .15
1204 A256 25q multicolored .15 .15
1205 A256 65q multicolored .35 .15
1206 A256 80q multicolored .60 .15
1207 A256 1.30 l multicolored .95 .20
Set value 2.25 .55

Issued to honor a contemporary heroine and heroes.

Meteorological Instruments A257

Designs: 25q, Water gauge. 1.60 l, Radar, balloon and isobars.

1969, Feb. 25 *Perf. 12*

1208 A257 15q multi .20 .15
1209 A257 25q ultra, org & blk .35 .15
1210 A257 1.60 l rose vio, yel & blk 1.90 .25
Nos. 1208-1210 (3) 2.45
Set value .36

20th anniv. of Albanian hydrometeorology.

Partisans, 1944, by F. Haxmiu — A258

Paintings: 5q, Student Revolutionists, by P. Mele, vert. 65q, Steel Mill, by C. Ceka. 80q, Reconstruction, by V. Kilica. 1.10 l, Harvest, by N. Jonuzi. 1.15 l, Terraced Landscape, by S. Kaceli. 2 l, Partisans' Meeting.

Perf. 12x12 1/2, 12 1/2x12

1969, Apr. 25 Litho.

Size: 31 1/2x41 1/2mm

1211 A258 5q buff & multi .15 .15

Size: 51 1/2x30 1/2mm

1212 A258 25q buff & multi .15 .15

Size: 40 1/2x32mm

1213 A258 65q buff & multi .32 .15

Size: 51 1/2x30 1/2mm

1214 A258 80q buff & multi .60 .15
1215 A258 1.10 l buff & multi .65 .15
1216 A258 1.15 l buff & multi .90 .20
Nos. 1211-1216 (6) 2.77
Set value .65

Miniature Sheet

Imperf

Size: 111x90mm

1217 A258 2 l ocher & multi 1.50 1.50

Leonardo da Vinci, Self-portrait A259

Designs (after Leonardo da Vinci): 35q, Lilies. 40q, Design for a flying machine, horiz. 1 l, Portrait of Beatrice. No. 1222, Portrait of a Noblewoman. No. 1223, Mona Lisa.

Perf. 12x12 1/2, 12 1/2x12

1969, May 2 Litho.

1218 A259 25q gold & sepia .18 .15
1219 A259 35q gold & sepia .30 .15
1220 A259 40q gold & sepia .35 .15
1221 A259 1 l gold & multi .95 .20
1222 A259 2 l gold & sepia 1.75 .55
Nos. 1218-1222 (5) 3.53
Set value 1.00

Miniature Sheet

Imperf

1223 A259 2 l gold & multi 3.25 2.25

Leonardo da Vinci (1452-1519), painter, sculptor, architect and engineer.

First Congress Meeting Place — A260

Designs: 1 l, Albanian coat of arms. 2.25 l, Two partisans with guns and flag.

1969, May 24 *Perf. 12*

1224 A260 25q lt grn, blk & red .25 .15
1225 A260 2.25 l multi 1.75 .85

Souvenir Sheet

1226 A260 1 l gold, bl, blk & red 22.50 12.50

25th anniversary of the First Anti-Fascist Congress of Permet, May 24, 1944.

Albanian Violet — A261

Designs: Violets and Pansies.

1969, June 30 Litho. *Perf. 12x12 1/2*

1227 A261 5q gold & multi .15 .15
1228 A261 10q gold & multi .15 .15
1229 A261 15q gold & multi .15 .15
1230 A261 20q gold & multi .18 .15
1231 A261 25q gold & multi .30 .15
1232 A261 80q gold & multi .48 .30
1233 A261 1.95 l gold & multi 1.25 .65
Nos. 1227-1233 (7) 2.66
Set value 1.25

Plum, Fruit and Blossoms — A262

Designs: Blossoms and Fruits.

1969, Aug. 10 Litho. *Perf. 12*

1234 A262 10q shown .15 .15
1235 A262 15q Lemon .15 .15
1236 A262 25q Pomegranate .18 .15
1237 A262 50q Cherry .38 .15
1238 A262 80q Peach .60 .20
1239 A262 1.20 l Apple 1.10 .35
Nos. 1234-1239 (6) 2.56
Set value .75

Basketball — A263

Designs: 10q, 80q, 2.20 l, Various views of basketball game. 25q, Hand aiming ball at basket and map of Europe, horiz.

1969, Sept. 15 Litho. *Perf. 12*

1240 A263 10q multi .15 .15
1241 A263 15q buff & multi .15 .15
1242 A263 25q blue & multi .28 .15
1243 A263 80q multi .65 .16
1244 A263 2.20 l multi 1.65 .50
Nos. 1240-1244 (5) 2.88
Set value .80

16th European Basketball Championships, Naples, Italy, Sept. 27-Oct. 5.

Runner — A264

Designs: 5q, Games' emblem. 10q, Woman gymnast. 20q, Pistol shooting. 25q, Swimmer at start. 80q, Bicyclist. 95q, Soccer.

1969, Sept. 30

1245 A264 5q multicolored .15 .15
1246 A264 10q multicolored .15 .15
1247 A264 15q multicolored .15 .15
1248 A264 20q multicolored .15 .15
1249 A264 25q multicolored .18 .15

1250	A264	80q multicolored	.38	.15
1251	A264	95q multicolored	.60	.18
		Set value	1.40	.50

Second National Spartakiad.

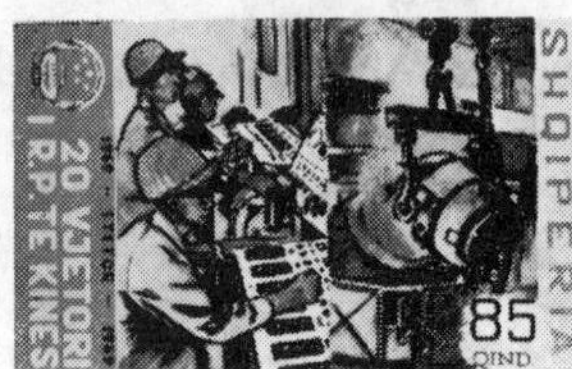

Electronic Technicians, Steel Ladle — A265

Designs: 25q, Mao Tse-tung with microphones, vert. 1.40 l, Children holding Mao's red book, vert.

1969, Oct. 1 Litho. *Perf. 12*

1252	A265	25q multi	.20	.15
1253	A265	85q multi	.50	.15
1254	A265	1.40 l multi	.80	.30
		Nos. 1252-1254 (3)	1.50	.60

People's Republic of China, 20th anniv.

Enver Hoxha — A266

Designs: 80q, Pages from Berat resolution. 1.45 l, Partisans with flag.

1969, Oct. 20 Litho. *Perf. 12*

1255	A266	25q multicolored	.20	.15
1256	A266	80q gray & multi	.50	.15
1257	A266	1.45 l ocher & multi	.80	.30
		Nos. 1255-1257 (3)	1.50	.60

25th anniv. of the 2nd reunion of the Natl. Antifascist Liberation Council, Berat.

Soldiers — A267

Designs: 30q, Oil refinery. 35q, Combine harvester. 45q, Hydroelectric station and dam. 55q, Militia woman, man and soldier. 1.10 l, Dancers and musicians.

1969, Nov. 29

1258	A267	25q multi	.22	.15
1259	A267	30q multi	.22	.15
1260	A267	35q multi	.22	.15
1261	A267	45q multi	.32	.15
1262	A267	55q multi	.80	.15
1263	A267	1.10 l multi	1.65	.15
		Nos. 1258-1263 (6)	3.43	
		Set value		.38

25th anniv. of the socialist republic.

Joseph V. Stalin, (1879-1953), Russian Political Leader — A268

1969, Dec. 21 Litho. *Perf. 12*

1264	A268	15q lilac	.15	.15
1265	A268	25q slate blue	.15	.15
1266	A268	1 l brown	.48	.15
1267	A268	1.10 l violet blue	.85	.20
		Nos. 1264-1267 (4)	1.63	
		Set value		.45

Head of Woman — A269

Greco-Roman Mosaics: 25q, Geometrical floor design, horiz. 80q, Bird and tree, horiz. 1.10 l, Floor with birds and grapes, horiz. 1.20 l, Fragment with corn within oval design.

1969, Dec. 25 *Perf. 12½x12*

1268	A269	15q gold & multi	.15	.15
1269	A269	25q gold & multi	.15	.15
1270	A269	80q gold & multi	.38	.15
1271	A269	1.10 l gold & multi	.55	.16
1272	A269	1.20 l gold & multi	.75	.28
		Nos. 1268-1272 (5)	1.98	
		Set value		.60

Cancellation of 1920 — A270

Design: 25q, Proclamation and congress site.

1970, Jan. 21 Litho. *Perf. 12*

1273	A270	25q red, gray & blk	.15	.15
1274	A270	1.25 l dk grn, yel & blk	.85	.15
		Set value		.17

Congress of Louchnia, 50th anniversary.

Worker, Student and Flag A271

1970, Feb. 11 *Perf. 12½x12*

1275	A271	25q red & multi	.15	.15
1276	A271	1.75 l red & multi	.85	.24
		Set value		.29

Vocational organizations in Albania, 25th anniv.

Turk's-cap Lily — A272

Lilies: 5q, Cernum, vert. 15q, Madonna, vert. 25q, Royal, vert. 1.10 l, Tiger. 1.15 l, Albanian.

Perf. 11½x12, 12x11½

1970, Mar. 10 Litho.

1277	A272	5q multi	.15	.15
1278	A272	15q multi	.15	.15
1279	A272	25q multi	.20	.15
1280	A272	80q multi	.52	.15
1281	A272	1.10 l multi	.75	.16
1282	A272	1.15 l multi	.95	.24
		Nos. 1277-1282 (6)	2.72	
		Set value		.65

Lenin A273

Designs (Lenin): 5q, Portrait, vert. 25q, As volunteer construction worker. 95q, Addressing crowd. 1.10 l, Saluting, vert.

1970, Apr. 22 Litho. *Perf. 12*

1283	A273	5q multi	.15	.15
1284	A273	15q multi	.15	.15
1285	A273	25q multi	.15	.15
1286	A273	95q multi	.32	.15
1287	A273	1.10 l multi	.52	.16
		Set value	1.05	.38

Centenary of birth of Lenin (1870-1924).

Frontier Guard A274

1970, Apr. 25

1288	A274	25q multi	.15	.15
1289	A274	1.25 l multi	.75	.20
		Set value		.25

25th anniversary of Frontier Guards.

Soccer Players — A275

Designs: 5q, Jules Rimet Cup and globes. 10q, Aztec Stadium, Mexico City. 25q, Defending goal. 65q, 80q, No. 1296, Two soccer players in various plays. No. 1297, Mexican horseman and volcano Popocatepetl.

1970, May 15 Litho. *Perf. 12½x12*

1290	A275	5q multicolored	.15	.15
1291	A275	10q multicolored	.15	.15
1292	A275	15q multicolored	.15	.15
1293	A275	25q lt green & multi	.15	.15
1294	A275	65q pink & multi	.28	.15
1295	A275	80q lt blue & multi	.45	.15
1296	A275	2 l yellow & multi	1.25	.24
		Set value	2.25	.65

Souvenir Sheet

Perf 12 x Imperf

1297	A275	2 l multicolored	2.00	.80

World Soccer Championships for the Jules Rimet Cup, Mexico City, May 31-June 21, 1970. No. 1297 contains one large horizontal stamp. Nos. 1290-1297 exist imperf.

UPU Headquarters and Monument, Bern — A276

1970, May 30 Litho. *Perf. 12½x12*

1298	A276	25q ultra, gray & blk	.15	.15
1299	A276	1.10 l orange, buff & blk	.48	.20
1300	A276	1.15 l green, gray & blk	.65	.24
		Nos. 1298-1300 (3)	1.28	.59

Inauguration of the new UPU Headquarters in Bern.

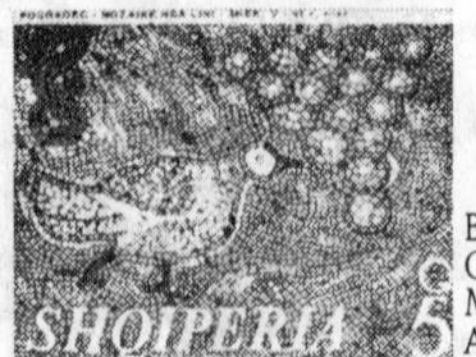

Bird and Grapes Mosaic A277

Mosaics, 5th-6th centuries, excavated near Pogradec: 10q, Waterfowl and grapes. 20q, Bird and tree stump. 25q, Bird and leaves. 65q, Fish. 2.25 l, Peacock, vert.

Perf. 12½x12, 12x12½

1970, July 10

1301	A277	5q multi	.15	.15
1302	A277	10q multi	.15	.15
1303	A277	20q multi	.16	.15
1304	A277	25q multi	.22	.15
1305	A277	65q multi	.38	.15
1306	A277	2.25 l multi	1.25	.32
		Nos. 1301-1306 (6)	2.31	
		Set value		.65

Fruit Harvest and Dancers A278

Designs: 25q, Contour-plowed fields and conference table. 80q, Cattle and newspapers. 1.30 l, Wheat harvest.

1970, Aug. 28 Litho. *Perf. 12x11½*

1307	A278	15q brt vio & blk	.15	.15
1308	A278	25q dp blue & blk	.15	.15
1309	A278	80q dp brown & blk	.40	.15
1310	A278	1.30 l org brn & blk	.60	.16
		Nos. 1307-1310 (4)	1.30	
		Set value		.34

25th anniv. of the agrarian reform law.

Attacking Partisans — A279

Designs: 25q, Partisans with horses and flag. 1.60 l, Partisans.

1970, Sept. 3 *Perf. 12*

1311	A279	15q org brn & blk	.15	.15
1312	A279	25q brn, yel & blk	.15	.15
1313	A279	1.60 l dp grn & blk	.85	.28
		Set value	1.00	.38

50th anniversary of liberation of Vlona.

Miners, by Nexhmedin Zajmi — A280

Paintings from the National Gallery, Tirana: 5q, Bringing in the Harvest, by Isuf Sulovari, vert. 15q, The Activists, by Dhimitraq Trebicka, vert. 65q, Instruction of Partisans, by Hasan Nallbani. 95q, Architectural Planning, by Vilson Kilica. No. 1319, Woman Machinist, by Zef Shoshi, vert. No. 1320, Partisan Destroying Tank, by Sali Shijaku, vert.

Perf. 12½x12, 12x12½

1970, Sept. 25 Litho.

1314	A280	5q multicolored	.15	.15
1315	A280	15q multicolored	.15	.15
1316	A280	25q multicolored	.16	.15
1317	A280	65q multicolored	.20	.15
1318	A280	95q multicolored	.32	.15
1319	A280	2 l multicolored	1.25	.30
		Set value	2.00	.60

Miniature Sheet

Imperf

1320	A280	2 l multicolored	1.50	.95

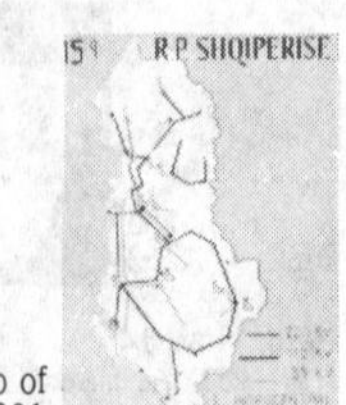

Electrification Map of Albania — A281

Designs: 25q, Light bulb, hammer and sickle emblem, map of Albania and power graph. 80q, Linemen at work. 1.10 l, Use of electricity on the farm, in home and business.

1970, Oct. 25 Litho. *Perf. 12*

1321 A281 15q multi .15 .15
1322 A281 25q multi .15 .15
1323 A281 80q multi .45 .15
1324 A281 1.10 l multi .65 .15
Nos. 1321-1324 (4) 1.40
Set value .32

Albanian village electrification completion.

Friedrich Engels — A282

Designs: 1.10 l, Engels as young man. 1.15 l, Engels addressing crowd.

1970, Nov. 28 Litho. *Perf. 12x12½*

1325 A282 25q bister & dk bl .20 .15
1326 A282 1.10 l bister & dp claret .60 .20
1327 A282 1.15 l bister & dk ol grn .70 .25
Nos. 1325-1327 (3) 1.50
Set value .50

150th anniv. of the birth of Friedrich Engels (1820-95), German socialist, collaborator with Karl Marx.

Ludwig van Beethoven — A283

Designs: 5q, Birthplace, Bonn. 25q, 65q, 1.10 l, various portraits. 1.80 l, Scene from Fidelio, horiz.

1970, Dec. 16 Litho. *Perf. 12*

1328 A283 5q dp plum & gold .15 .15
1329 A283 15q brt rose lil & sil .15 .15
1330 A283 25q green & gold .15 .15
1331 A283 65q magenta & sil .30 .15
1332 A283 1.10 l dk blue & gold .60 .22
1333 A283 1.80 l black & sil 1.25 .45
Nos. 1328-1333 (6) 2.60
Set value .90

Bicentenary of the birth of Ludwig van Beethoven (1770-1827), composer.

Coat of Arms A284

Designs: 25q, Proclamation. 80q, Enver Hoxha reading proclamation. 1.30 l, Young people and proclamation.

1971, Jan. 11 Litho. *Perf. 12*

1334 A284 15q lt bl, gold, blk & red .15 .15
1335 A284 25q rose lil, blk, gold & gray .15 .15
1336 A284 80q emerald, blk & gold .45 .15
1337 A284 1.30 l yel org, blk & gold .70 .25
Nos. 1334-1337 (4) 1.45
Set value .45

Declaration of the Republic, 25th anniv.

"Liberty" A285

Black Men A286

Designs: 50q, Women's brigade. 65q, Street battle, horiz. 1.10 l, Execution, horiz.

Perf. 12x11½, 11½x12

1971, Mar. 18 Litho.

1338 A285 25q dk bl & bl .15 .15
1339 A285 50q slate green .20 .15
1340 A285 65q dk brn & chestnut .28 .15
1341 A285 1.10 l purple .42 .16
Nos. 1338-1341 (4) 1.05
Set value .38

Centenary of the Paris Commune.

1971, Mar. 21 *Perf. 12x12½*

Designs: 1.10 l, Men of 3 races. 1.15 l, Black protest.

1342 A286 25q blk & bis brn .15 .15
1343 A286 1.10 l blk & rose car .35 .15
1344 A286 1.15 l blk & ver .42 .15
Nos. 1342-1344 (3) .92
Set value .32

Intl. year against racial discrimination.

Tulip — A287

Horseman, by Dürer — A288

Designs: Various tulips.

1971, Mar. 25

1345 A287 5q multi .15 .15
1346 A287 10q yellow & multi .15 .15
1347 A287 15q pink & multi .15 .15
1348 A287 20q lt blue & multi .15 .15
1349 A287 25q multi .22 .15
1350 A287 80q multi .42 .15
1351 A287 1 l multi .60 .18
1352 A287 1.45 l citron & multi .95 .25
Set value 2.50 .75

Perf. 11½x12, 12x11½

1971, May 15 Litho.

Art Works by Dürer: 15q, Three peasants. 25q, Dancing peasant couple. 45q, The bagpiper. 65q, View of Kalkrebut, horiz. 2.40 l, View of Trent, horiz. 2.50 l, Self-portrait.

1353 A288 10q black & pale grn .15 .15
1354 A288 15q black & pale lil .15 .15
1355 A288 25q black & pale bl .18 .15
1356 A288 45q black & pale rose .25 .15
1357 A288 65q black & multi .38 .15
1358 A288 2.40 l black & multi 1.50 .32
Nos. 1353-1358 (6) 2.61
Set value .65

Miniature Sheet

Imperf

1359 A288 2.50 l multi 2.25 .80

Albrecht Dürer (1471-1528), German painter and engraver.

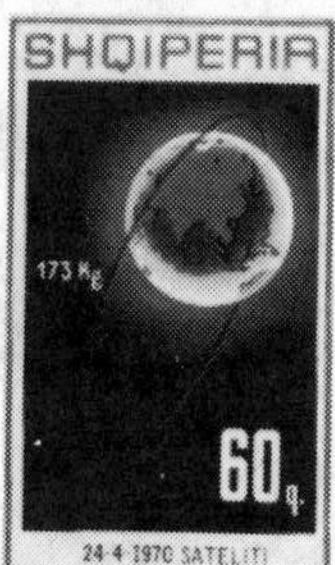

Satellite Orbiting Globe — A289

Designs: 1.20 l, Government Building, Tirana, and Red Star emblem. 2.20 l, like 60q. 2.50 l, Flag of People's Republic of China forming trajectory around globe.

1971, June 10 Litho. *Perf. 12x12½*

1360 A289 60q purple & multi .40 .15
1361 A289 1.20 l ver & multi 1.00 .25
1362 A289 2.20 l grn & multi 1.60 .45

Imperf

1363 A289 2.50 l vio blk & multi 2.50 .90
Nos. 1360-1363 (4) 5.50 1.75

Space developments of People's Republic of China.

Mao Tse-tung — A290

Designs: 1.05 l, House where Communist Party was founded, horiz. 1.20 l, Peking crowd with placards, horiz.

1971, July 1 *Perf. 12x12½, 12½x12*

1364 A290 25q sil & multi .18 .15
1365 A290 1.05 l sil & multi .55 .15
1366 A290 1.20 l sil & multi .70 .25
Nos. 1364-1366 (3) 1.43
Set value .45

50th anniv. of Chinese Communist Party.

Crested Titmouse — A291

1971, Aug. 15 Litho. *Perf. 12½x12*

1367 A291 5q shown .15 .15
1368 A291 10q European serin .15 .15
1369 A291 15q Linnet .15 .15
1370 A291 25q Firecrest .15 .15
1371 A291 45q Rock thrush .30 .15
1372 A291 60q Blue tit .45 .25
1373 A291 2.40 l Chaffinch 1.50 .60
Nos. 1367-1373 (7) 2.85
Set value 1.15

Printed se-tenant in blocks of 8 (2x4) including a label showing bird's nest. The label is se-tenant horizontally with the 5q, and vertically with the 10q.

Olympic Rings and Running — A292

Designs (Olympic Rings and): 10q, Hurdles. 15q, Canoeing. 25q, Gymnastics. 80q, Fencing. 1.05 l, Soccer. 2 l, Runner at finish line. 3.60 l, Diving, women's.

1971, Sept. 15

1374 A292 5q green & multi .15 .15
1375 A292 10q multicolored .15 .15
1376 A292 15q blue & multi .15 .15
1377 A292 25q violet & multi .15 .15
1378 A292 80q lilac & multi .28 .15
1379 A292 1.05 l multicolored .38 .15
1380 A292 3.60 l multicolored 1.90 .50
Nos. 1374-1380 (7) 3.16
Set value 1.00

Souvenir Sheet

Imperf

1381 A292 2 l brt blue & multi 1.25 .75

20th Olympic Games, Munich, Aug. 26-Sept. 10, 1972.

Workers with Flags — A293

Designs: 1.05 l, Party Headquarters, Tirana, and Red Star. 1.20 l, Rifle, star, flag and "VI," vert.

1971, Nov. 1 *Perf. 12*

1382 A293 25q gold, sil, red & bl .16 .15
1383 A293 1.05 l gold, sil, red & bl .50 .15
1384 A293 1.20 l gold, sil, red & blk .60 .22
Nos. 1382-1384 (3) 1.26
Set value .38

6th Congress of Workers' Party.

Factories and Workers A294

Designs: 80q, "XXX" and flag, vert. 1.55 l, Enver Hoxha and flags.

1971, Nov. 8

1385 A294 15q gold, sil, lil & yel .18 .15
1386 A294 80q gold, sil & red .70 .15
1387 A294 1.55 l gold, sil, red & brn 1.25 .25
Nos. 1385-1387 (3) 2.13
Set value .40

30th anniversary of Workers' Party.

Construction Work, by M. Fushekati — A295

Contemporary Albanian Paintings: 5q, Young Man, by R. Kuci, vert. 25q, Partisan, by D. Jukniu, vert. 80q, Fliers, by S. Kristo. 1.20 l, Girl in Forest, by A. Sadikaj. 1.55 l, Warriors with Spears and Shields, by S. Kamberi. 2 l, Freedom Fighter, by I. Lulani.

Perf. 12x12½, 12½x12

1971, Nov. 20

1388 A295 5q gold & multi .15 .15
1389 A295 15q gold & multi .15 .15
1390 A295 25q gold & multi .15 .15
1391 A295 80q gold & multi .35 .15
1392 A295 1.20 l gold & multi .80 .18
1393 A295 1.55 l gold & multi 1.00 .24
Nos. 1388-1393 (6) 2.60
Set value .65

Miniature Sheet

Imperf

1394 A295 2 l gold & multi 1.40 .70

Young Workers' Emblem — A296

1971, Nov. 23 *Perf. 12x12½*

1395 A296 15q lt blue & multi .15 .15
1396 A296 1.35 l grnsh gray & multi .75 .22
Set value .27

Albanian Young Workers' Union, 30th anniv.

"Halili and Hajria" Ballet — A297

Scenes from "Halili and Hajria" Ballet: 10q, Brother and sister. 15q, Hajria before Sultan Suleiman. 50q, Hajria and husband. 80q, Execution of Halili. 1.40 l, Hajria killing her husband.

1971, Dec. 27 *Perf. 12½x12*

1397 A297	5q	silver & multi	.15	.15
1398 A297	10q	silver & multi	.15	.15
1399 A297	15q	silver & multi	.15	.15
1400 A297	50q	silver & multi	.42	.15
1401 A297	80q	silver & multi	.70	.15
1402 A297	1.40 l	silver & multi	1.10	.35
Nos. 1397-1402 (6)			2.67	
Set value				.72

Albanian ballet Halili and Hajria after drama by Kol Jakova.

Biathlon and Olympic Rings — A298

Designs (Olympic Rings and): 10q, Sledding. 15q, Ice hockey. 20q, Bobsledding. 50q, Speed skating. 1 l, Slalom. 2 l, Ski jump. 2.50 l, Figure skating, pairs.

1972, Feb. 10

1403 A298	5q	lt olive & multi	.15	.15
1404 A298	10q	lt violet & multi	.15	.15
1405 A298	15q	multicolored	.15	.15
1406 A298	20q	pink & multi	.15	.15
1407 A298	50q	lt blue & multi	.20	.15
1408 A298	1 l	ocher & multi	.50	.18
1409 A298	2 l	lilac & multi	1.00	.35
Set value			2.00	.75

Souvenir Sheet

Imperf

1410 A298	2.50 l	blue & multi	1.50	.50

11th Winter Olympic Games, Sapporo, Japan, Feb. 3-13.

Wild Strawberries A299

Wild Fruits and Nuts: 10q, Blackberries. 15q, Hazelnuts. 20q, Walnuts. 25q, Strawberry-tree fruit. 30q, Dogwood berries. 2.40 l, Rowan berries.

1972, Mar. 20 **Litho.** *Perf. 12*

1411 A299	5q	lt grn & multi	.15	.15
1412 A299	10q	yellow & multi	.15	.15
1413 A299	15q	lt vio & multi	.15	.15
1414 A299	20q	pink & multi	.15	.15
1415 A299	25q	multi	.20	.15
1416 A299	30q	multi	.28	.15
1417 A299	2.40 l	multi	1.40	.42
Nos. 1411-1417 (7)			2.48	
Set value				.85

"Your Heart is your Health" — A300 Worker and Student — A301

World Health Day: 1.20 l, Cardiac patient and electrocardiogram.

1972, Apr. 7 *Perf. 12x12½*

1418 A300	1.10 l	multi	.48	.16
1419 A300	1.20 l	rose & multi	.60	.24

Perf. 11½x12½

1972, Apr. 24 **Litho.**

7th Trade Union Cong., May 8: 2.05 l, Assembly Hall, dancers and emblem.

1420 A301	25q	multi	.15	.15
1421 A301	2.05 l	blue & multi	.90	.40
Set value				.45

Qemal Stafa A302

Designs: 15q, Memorial flame. 25q, Monument "Spirit of Defiance," vert.

1972, May 5 *Perf. 12½x12, 12x12½*

1422 A302	15q	gray & multi	.15	.15
1423 A302	25q	sal rose, blk & gray	.15	.15
1424 A302	1.90 l	dull yel & blk	1.10	.30
Nos. 1422-1424 (3)			1.40	
Set value				.42

30th anniversary of the murder of Qemal Stafa and of Martyrs' Day.

Camellia — A303

Designs: Various camellias.

1972, May 10 *Perf. 12x12½*

Flowers in Natural Colors

1425 A303	5q	lt blue & blk	.15	.15
1426 A303	10q	citron & blk	.15	.15
1427 A303	15q	grnsh gray & blk	.15	.15
1428 A303	25q	pale sal & blk	.15	.15
1429 A303	45q	gray & blk	.28	.15
1430 A303	50q	sal pink & blk	.45	.15
1431 A303	2.50 l	bluish gray & blk	1.90	.75
Nos. 1425-1431 (7)			3.23	
Set value				1.10

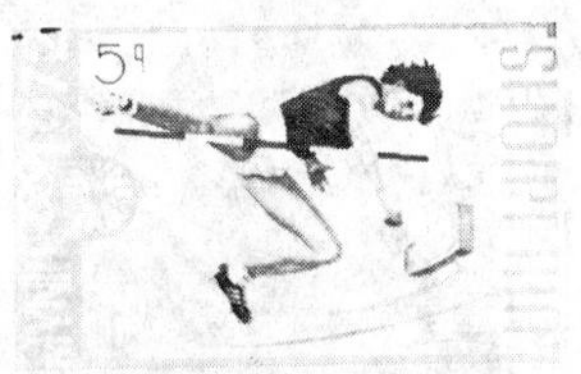

High Jump — A304

Designs (Olympic and Motion Emblems and): 10q, Running. 15q, Shot put. 20q, Bicycling. 25q, Pole vault. 50q, Hurdles, women's. 5q, Hockey. 2 l, Swimming. 2.50 l, Diving, women's.

1972, June 30 **Litho.** *Perf. 12½x12*

1432 A304	5q	multicolored	.15	.15
1433 A304	10q	lt brn & multi	.15	.15
1434 A304	15q	lt lil & multi	.15	.15
1435 A304	20q	multicolored	.15	.15
1436 A304	25q	lt vio & multi	.15	.15
1437 A304	50q	lt grn & multi	.25	.15
1438 A304	75q	multicolored	.50	.15
1439 A304	2 l	multicolored	.95	.30
Set value			2.00	.75

Miniature Sheet

Imperf

1440 A304	2.50 l	multi	1.50	.85

20th Olympic Games, Munich, Aug. 26-Sept. 11. Nos. 1432-1439 each issued in sheets of 8 stamps and one label (3x3) showing Olympic rings in gold.

Autobus A305

Designs: 25q, Electric train. 80q, Ocean liner Tirana. 1.05 l, Automobile. 1.20 l, Trailer truck.

1972, July 25 **Litho.** *Perf. 12*

1441 A305	15q	org brn & multi	.15	.15
1442 A305	25q	gray & multi	.15	.15
1443 A305	80q	dp grn & multi	.32	.15
1444 A305	1.05 l	multi	.45	.15
1445 A305	1.20 l	multi	.55	.15
Nos. 1441-1445 (5)			1.62	
Set value				.42

Arm Wrestling A306

Folk Games: 10q, Piggyback ball game. 15q, Women's jumping. 25q, Rope game (srum). 90q, Leapfrog. 2 l, Women throwing pitchers.

1972, Aug. 18

1446 A306	5q	multi	.15	.15
1447 A306	10q	lt bl & multi	.15	.15
1448 A306	15q	rose & multi	.15	.15
1449 A306	25q	lt bl & multi	.15	.15
1450 A306	90q	ocher & multi	.42	.15
1451 A306	2 l	lt grn & multi	.80	.25
Set value			1.50	.55

1st National Festival of People's Games.

Mastheads — A307

30th Press Day: 25q, Printing press. 1.90 l, Workers reading paper.

1972, Aug. 25

1452 A307	15q	lt bl & blk	.15	.15
1453 A307	25q	red, grn & blk	.15	.15
1454 A307	1.90 l	lt vio & blk	1.00	.35
Nos. 1452-1454 (3)			1.30	
Set value				.45

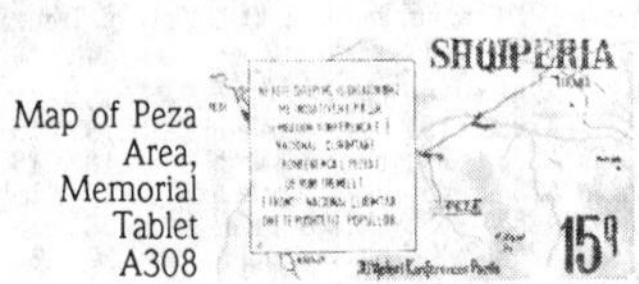

Map of Peza Area, Memorial Tablet A308

1972, Sept. 16

1455 A308	15q	shown	.15	.15
1456 A308	25q	Guerrillas with flag	.15	.15
1457 A308	1.90 l	Peza Conference memorial	1.00	.35
Nos. 1455-1457 (3)			1.30	
Set value				.45

30th anniversary, Conference of Peza.

Partisans, by Sotir Capo — A309

Paintings: 10q, Woman, by Ismail Lulani, vert. 15q, "Communists," by Lec Shkreli, vert. 20q, View of Nendorit, 1941, by Sali Shijaku, vert. 50q, Woman with Sheaf, by Zef Shoshi, vert. 1 l, Landscape with Children, by Dhimitraq Trebicka. 2 l, Women on Bicycles, by Vilson Kilica. 2.30 l, Folk Dance, by Abdurrahim Buza.

Perf. 12½x12, 12x12½

1972, Sept. 25 **Litho.**

1458 A309	5q	gold & multi	.15	.15
1459 A309	10q	gold & multi	.15	.15
1460 A309	15q	gold & multi	.15	.15
1461 A309	20q	gold & multi	.15	.15
1462 A309	50q	gold & multi	.30	.15
1463 A309	1 l	gold & multi	.60	.15
1464 A309	2 l	gold & multi	1.25	.35
Set value			2.50	.75

Miniature Sheet

Imperf

1465 A309	2.30 l	gold & multi	1.25	.80

No. 1465 contains one 41x68mm stamp.

Congress Emblem — A310

Design: 2.05 l, Young worker with banner.

1972, Oct. 23 **Litho.** *Perf. 12*

1466 A310	25q	silver, red & gold	.15	.15
1467 A310	2.05 l	silver & multi	1.00	.45
Set value				.50

Union of Working Youth, 6th Congress.

Hammer and Sickle — A311 Ismail Qemali — A312

Design: 1.20 l, Lenin as orator.

1972, Nov. 7 **Litho.** *Perf. 11½x12*

1468 A311	1.10 l	multi	.48	.20
1469 A311	1.20 l	multi	.50	.24

55th anniv. of the Russian October Revolution.

Perf. 12x11½, 11½x12

1972, Nov. 29

Designs: 15q, Albanian fighters, horiz. 65q, Rally, horiz. 1.25 l, Coat of arms.

1470 A312	15q	red, brt bl & blk	.15	.15
1471 A312	25q	yel, blk & red	.15	.15
1472 A312	65q	red, sal & blk	.35	.15
1473 A312	1.25 l	dl red & blk	.70	.25
Nos. 1470-1473 (4)			1.35	
Set value				.45

60th anniv. of independence.

Cock, Mosaic A313

Mosaics, 2nd-5th centuries, excavated near Buthrotium and Apollonia: 10q, Bird, vert. 15q, Partridges, vert. 25q, Warrior's legs. 45q, Nymph riding dolphin, vert. 50q, Fish, vert. 2.50 l, Warrior with helmet.

Perf. 12½x12, 12x12½

1972, Dec. 10

1474 A313	5q	silver & multi	.15	.15
1475 A313	10q	silver & multi	.15	.15
1476 A313	15q	silver & multi	.15	.15
1477 A313	25q	silver & multi	.15	.15
1478 A313	45q	silver & multi	.20	.15
1479 A313	50q	silver & multi	.25	.15
1480 A313	2.50 l	silver & multi	1.25	.38
Set value			1.95	.70

Nicolaus Copernicus — A314

Designs: 10q, 25q, 80q, 1.20 l, Various portraits of Copernicus. 1.60 l, Heliocentric solar system.

1973, Feb. 19 Litho. *Perf. 12x12½*

1481 A314	5q lil rose & multi	.15	.15
1482 A314	10q dl ol & multi	.15	.15
1483 A314	25q multicolored	.15	.15
1484 A314	80q lt vio & multi	.45	.15
1485 A314	1.20 l bl & multi	.65	.24
1486 A314	1.60 l gray & multi	.90	.32
Nos. 1481-1486 (6)		2.45	
Set value			.82

500th anniversary of the birth of Nicolaus Copernicus (1473-1543), Polish astronomer.

Flowering Cactus — A315

Designs: Various flowering cacti.

1973, Mar. 25 Litho. *Perf. 12*

1487 A315	10q multi	.15	.15
1488 A315	15q multi	.15	.15
1489 A315	20q beige & multi	.15	.15
1490 A315	25q gray & multi	.20	.15
1491 A315	30q beige & multi	.30	.15
1492 A315	65q gray & multi	.75	.15
1493 A315	80q multi	.95	.15
1494 A315	2 l multi	2.50	.28
a.	Block of 8, #1487-1494	5.00	3.00
Nos. 1487-1494 (8)		5.15	
Set value			.70

Nos. 1487-1494 printed se-tenant.

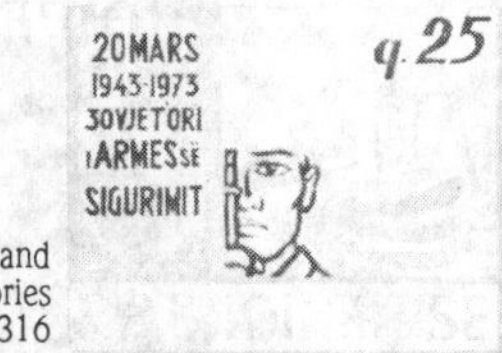

Guard and Factories A316

Design: 1.80 l, Guard and guards with prisoner.

1973, Mar. 20 Litho. *Perf. 12½x12*

1495 A316	25q ultra & blk	.16	.15
1496 A316	1.80 l dk red & multi	.75	.38
Set value			.44

30th anniv. of the State Security Branch.

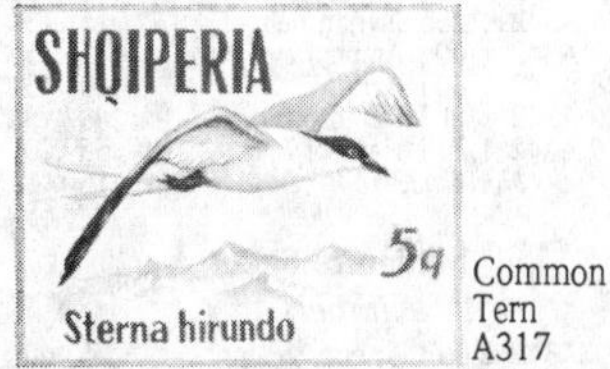

Common Tern A317

Sea Birds: 15q, White-winged black terns, vert. 25q, Black-headed gull, vert. 45q, Great black-headed gull. 80q, Slender-billed gull, vert. 2.40 l, Sandwich terns.

Perf. 12½x12, 12x12½

1973, Apr. 30

1497 A317	5q gold & multi	.15	.15
1498 A317	15q gold & multi	.15	.15
1499 A317	25q gold & multi	.20	.15
1500 A317	45q gold & multi	.25	.15
1501 A317	80q gold & multi	.55	.22
1502 A317	2.40 l gold & multi	1.75	.48
Nos. 1497-1502 (6)		3.05	
Set value			.90

Letters, 1913 Cancellation and Post Horn A318

Design: 1.80 l, Mailman, 1913 cancel.

1973, May, 5 Litho. *Perf. 12x11½*

1503 A318	25q red & multi	.28	.15
1504 A318	1.80 l red & multi	1.65	.50

60th anniversary of Albanian stamps.

Farmer, Worker, Soldier A319

Design: 25q, Woman and factory, vert.

1973, June 4 *Perf. 12*

1505 A319	25q car rose	.16	.15
1506 A319	1.80 l yel, dp org & blk	.85	.42

7th Congress of Albanian Women's Union.

Creation of General Staff, by G. Madhi — A320

Designs: 40q, "August 1949," sculpture by Sh. Haderi, vert. 60q, "Generation after Generation," sculpture by H. Dule, vert. 80q, "Defend Revolutionary Victories," by M. Fushekati.

1973, July 10 Litho. *Perf. 12½x12*

1507 A320	25q gold & multi	*2.50*	.15
1508 A320	40q gold & multi	*4.00*	.15
1509 A320	60q gold & multi	*6.00*	.22
1510 A320	80q gold & multi	*7.50*	.25
Nos. 1507-1510 (4)		*20.00*	.77

30th anniversary of the People's Army.

"Electrification," by S. Hysa — A321

Albanian Paintings: 10q, Woman Textile Worker, by N. Nallbani. 15q, Gymnasts, by M. Fushekati. 50q, Aviator, by F. Stamo. 80q, Fascist Prisoner, by A. Lakuriqi. 1.20 l, Workers with Banner, by P. Mele. 1.30 l, Farm Woman, by Zef Shoshi. 2.05 l, Battle of Tenda, by F. Haxhiu. 10q, 50q, 80q, 1.20 l, 1.30 l, vertical.

Perf. 12½x12, 12x12½

1973, Aug. 10

1511 A321	5q gold & multi	.15	.15
1512 A321	10q gold & multi	.15	.15
1513 A321	15q gold & multi	.15	.15
1514 A321	50q gold & multi	.22	.15
1515 A321	80q gold & multi	.45	.15
1516 A321	1.20 l gold & multi	.70	.15
1517 A321	1.30 l gold & multi	.75	.18
Nos. 1511-1517 (7)		2.57	
Set value			.60

Souvenir Sheet

Imperf

1518 A321	2.05 l multi	1.50	.65

Mary Magdalene, by Caravaggio A322

Paintings by Michelangelo da Caravaggio: 10q, The Lute Player, horiz. 15q, Self-portrait. 50q, Boy Carrying Fruit and Flowers. 80q, Still Life, horiz. 1.20 l, Narcissus. 1.30 l, Boy Peeling Apple. 2.05 l, Man with Feathered Hat.

Perf. 12x12½, 12½x12

1973, Sept. 28

1519 A322	5q gold & multi	.15	.15
1520 A322	10q gold & multi	.15	.15
1521 A322	15q gold, blk & gray	.15	.15
1522 A322	50q gold & multi	.22	.15
1523 A322	80q gold & multi	.55	.15
1524 A322	1.20 l gold & multi	.80	.25
1525 A322	1.30 l gold & multi	.90	.25
Nos. 1519-1525 (7)		2.92	
Set value			.75

Souvenir Sheet

Imperf

1526 A322	2.05 l multi	1.50	.60

Michelangelo da Caravaggio (Merisi; 1573?-1609), Italian painter. No. 1526 contains one stamp, size: 63x73mm.

Soccer — A323

Designs: 5q-1.25 l, Various soccer scenes. 2.05 l, Ball in goal and list of cities where championships were held.

1973, Oct. 30 Litho. *Perf. 12½x12*

1527 A323	5q multi	.15	.15
1528 A323	10q multi	.15	.15
1529 A323	15q multi	.15	.15
1530 A323	20q multi	.15	.15
1531 A323	25q multi	.15	.15
1532 A323	90q multi	.52	.15
1533 A323	1.20 l multi	.75	.15
1534 A323	1.25 l multi	.90	.18
Set value		2.50	.65

Minature Sheet

Imperf

1535 A323	2.05 l multi	2.00	.60

World Soccer Cup, Munich 1974.

Weight Lifter — A324

Designs: Various stages of weight lifting. 1.20 l, 1.60 l, horiz.

1973, Oct. 30 Litho. *Perf. 12*

1536 A324	5q multi	.15	.15
1537 A324	10q multi	.15	.15
1538 A324	25q multi	.16	.15
1539 A324	90q multi	.48	.18
1540 A324	1.20 l multi	.38	.15
1541 A324	1.60 l multi	.80	.15
Nos. 1536-1541 (6)		2.12	
Set value			.55

Weight Lifting Championships, Havana, Cuba.

Ballet — A325

Harvester Combine — A326

Designs: 5q, Cement factory, Kavaje. 10q, Ali Kelmendi truck factory and tank cars, horiz. 25q, "Communication." 35q, Skiers and hotel, horiz. 60q, Resort, horiz. 80q, Mountain lake. 1 l, Mao Tse-tung textile mill. 1.20 l, Steel workers. 2.40 l, Welder and pipe. 3 l, Skanderbeg Monument, Tirana. 5 l, Roman arches, Durres.

Perf. 12½x12, 12x12½

1973-74 Litho.

1543 A325	5q gold & multi	.15	.15
1544 A325	10q gold & multi	.15	.15
1545 A325	15q gold & multi	.15	.15
1545A A326	20q gold & multi	.15	.15
1546 A326	25q gold & multi	.18	.15
1547 A326	35q gold & multi	.18	.15
1548 A326	60q gold & multi	.28	.15
1549 A326	80q gold & multi	.40	.15
1549A A326	1 l gold & multi	.35	.15
1549B A326	1.20 l gold & multi	.60	.15
1549C A326	2.40 l gold & multi	1.25	.32
1550 A326	3 l gold & multi	1.40	.32
1551 A326	5 l gold & multi	2.25	.60
Nos. 1543-1551 (13)		7.49	
Set value			1.95

Issue dates: Nos. 1545-1546, 1549-1550, Dec. 5, 1973; others, 1974.

Mao Tse-tung — A327

80th birthday of Mao Tse-tung: 1.20 l, Mao Tse-tung addressing crowd.

1973, Dec. 26 *Perf. 12*

1552 A327	85q gold, red & sepia	.60	.15
1553 A327	1.20 l gold, red & sepia	.90	.20

Old Man and Dog, by Gericault — A328

Paintings by Jean Louis André Theodore Gericault: 10q, Horse's Head. 15q, Male Model. 25q, Head of Black Man. 1.20 l, Self-portrait. 2.05 l, Raft of the Medusa, horiz. 2.20 l, Battle of the Giants.

Perf. 12x12½, 12½x12

1974, Jan. 18 Litho.

1554 A328	10q gold & multi	.15	.15
1555 A328	15q gold & multi	.15	.15
1556 A328	20q gold & multi	.15	.15
1557 A328	25q gold & blk	.22	.15
1558 A328	1.20 l gold & multi	.75	.15
1559 A328	2.20 l gold & multi	1.50	.35
Nos. 1554-1559 (6)		2.92	
Set value			.65

Souvenir Sheet

Imperf

1560 A328	2.05 l gold & multi	1.25	.45

No. 1560 contains one 87x78mm stamp.

Lenin, by Pandi Mele — A329

Designs: 25q, Lenin with Sailors on Cruiser Aurora, by Dhimitraq Trebicka, horiz. 1.20 l, Lenin, by Vilson Kilica.

Perf. 12½x12, 12x12½

1974, Jan. 21

1561 A329 25q gold & multi .15 .15
1562 A329 60q gold & multi .35 .15
1563 A329 1.20 l gold & multi .75 .25
Nos. 1561-1563 (3) 1.25
Set value .40

50th anniv. of the death of Lenin.

Swimming Duck, Mosaic — A330

Designs: Mosaics from the 5th-6th Centuries A.D., excavated near Buthrotium, Pogradec and Apollonia.

1974, Feb. 20 Litho. *Perf. 12½x12*

1564 A330 5q shown .15 .15
1565 A330 10q Bird and flower .15 .15
1566 A330 15q Vase and grapes .15 .15
1567 A330 25q Duck .15 .15
1568 A330 40q Donkey and bird .25 .15
1569 A330 2.50 l Sea horse 1.25 .35
Nos. 1564-1569 (6) 2.10
Set value .60

Soccer — A331

Designs: Various scenes from soccer. 2.05 l, World Soccer Cup and names of participating countries.

1974, Apr. 25 Litho. *Perf. 12½x12*

1570 A331 10q gold & multi .15 .15
1571 A331 15q gold & multi .15 .15
1572 A331 20q gold & multi .15 .15
1573 A331 25q gold & multi .15 .15
1574 A331 40q gold & multi .25 .15
1575 A331 80q gold & multi .50 .15
1576 A331 1 l gold & multi .75 .25
1577 A331 1.20 l gold & multi 1.00 .35
Nos. 1570-1577 (8) 3.10
Set value 1.00

Souvenir Sheet

Imperf

1578 A331 2.05 l gold & multi 2.25 .90

World Cup Soccer Championship, Munich, June 13-July 7. No. 1578 contains one stamp (60x60mm) with simulated perforations. Nos. 1570-1577 exist imperf, No. 1578 with simulated perfs omitted.

Arms of Albania, Soldier — A332

Design: 1.80 l, Soldier and front page of 1944 Congress Book.

1974, May 24 Litho. *Perf. 12*

1579 A332 25q multi .15 .15
1580 A332 1.80 l multi .75 .25
Set value .30

30th anniversary of the First Anti-Fascist Liberation Congress of Permet.

Medicinal Plants — A333

40q, 80q, 2.20 l, horiz.

1974, May 5 *Perf. 12x12½*

1581 A333 10q Bittersweet .15 .15
1582 A333 15q Arbutus .15 .15
1583 A333 20q Lilies of the valley .15 .15
1584 A333 25q Autumn crocus .18 .15
1585 A333 40q Borage .22 .15
1586 A333 80q Soapwort .70 .15
1587 A333 2.20 l Gentian 1.50 .40
Nos. 1581-1587 (7) 3.05
Set value .80

Revolutionaries with Albanian Flag — A334

Design: 1.80 l, Portraits of 5 revolutionaries, vert.

Perf. 12½x12, 12x12½

1974, June 10

1588 A334 25q red, blk & lil .15 .15
1589 A334 1.80 l yel, red & blk .70 .25
Set value .30

50th anniversary Albanian Bourgeois Democratic Revolution.

European Redwing — A335

Designs: Songbirds; Nos. 1597-1600 vert.

Perf. 12½x12, 12x12½

1974, July 15 Litho.

1594 A335 10q shown .15 .15
1595 A335 15q European robin .15 .15
1596 A335 20q Greenfinch .15 .15
1597 A335 25q Bullfinch .15 .15
1598 A335 40q Hawfinch .35 .15
1599 A335 80q Blackcap .85 .20
1600 A335 2.20 l Nightingale 1.90 .45
Nos. 1594-1600 (7) 3.70
Set value .90

Globe — A336

Cent. of UPU: 1.20 l, UPU emblem. 2.05 l, Jet over globe.

1974, Aug. 25 Litho. *Perf. 12x12½*

1601 A336 85q green & multi .45 .15
1602 A336 1.20 l vio & ol grn .65 .20

Miniature Sheet

Imperf

1603 A336 2.05 l blue & multi 12.00 12.00

Widows, by Sali Shijaku — A337

Albanian Paintings: 15q, Drillers, by Danish Jukniu, vert. 20q, Workers with Blueprints, by Clirim Ceka. 25q, Call to Action, by Spiro Kristo, vert. 40q, Winter Battle, by Sabaudin Xhaferi. 80q, Comrades, by Clirim Ceka, vert. 1 l, Aiding the Partisans, by Guri Madhi. 1.20 l, Teacher with Pupils, by Kleo Nini Brezat. 2.05 l, Comrades in Arms, by Guri Madhi.

Perf. 12½x12, 12x12½

1974, Sept. 25

1604 A337 10q silver & multi .15 .15
1605 A337 15q silver & multi .15 .15
1606 A337 20q silver & multi .15 .15
1607 A337 25q silver & multi .15 .15
1608 A337 40q silver & multi .16 .15
1609 A337 80q silver & multi .30 .15
1610 A337 1 l silver & multi .38 .15
1611 A337 1.20 l silver & multi .42 .20
Set value 1.50 .65

Miniature Sheet

Imperf

1612 A337 2.05 l silver & multi 1.05 .42

Crowd on Tien An Men Square A338

Design: 1.20 l, Mao Tse-tung, vert.

1974, Oct. 1 *Perf. 12*

1613 A338 85q gold & multi .32 .15
1614 A338 1.20 l gold & multi .48 .15
Set value .24

25th anniversary of the proclamation of the People's Republic of China.

Women's Volleyball A339

Designs (Spartakiad Medal and): 15q, Women hurdlers. 20q, Women gymnasts. 25q, Mass exercises in Stadium. 40q, Weight lifter. 80q, Wrestlers. 1 l, Military rifle drill. 1.20 l, Soccer.

1974, Oct. 9 *Perf. 12x12½*

1615 A339 10q multi .15 .15
1616 A339 15q multi .15 .15
1617 A339 20q multi .15 .15
1618 A339 25q gray & multi .15 .15
1619 A339 40q multi .15 .15
1620 A339 80q multi .40 .15
1621 A339 1 l multi .45 .15
1622 A339 1.20 l tan & multi .50 .20
Nos. 1615-1622 (8) 2.10
Set value .70

National Spartakiad, Oct. 9-17.

View of Berat — A340

Designs: 80q, Enver Hoxha addressing Congress, bas-relief, horiz. 1 l, Hoxha and leaders leaving Congress Hall.

Perf. 12x12½, 12½x12

1974, Oct. 20 Litho.

1623 A340 25q rose car & blk .16 .15
1624 A340 80q yel, brn & blk .32 .15
1625 A340 1 l dp lilac & blk .50 .15
Nos. 1623-1625 (3) .98
Set value .32

30th anniversary of 2nd Congress of Berat.

Anniversary Emblem, Factory Guards A341

Designs (Anniversary Emblem and): 35q, Chemical industry. 50q, Agriculture. 80q, Arts. 1 l, Atomic diagram and computer. 1.20 l, Youth education. 2.05 l, Anniversary emblem: Crowd and History Book.

1974, Nov. 29 Litho. *Perf. 12½x12*

1626 A341 25q green & multi .15 .15
1627 A341 35q ultra & multi .15 .15
1628 A341 50q brown & multi .22 .15
1629 A341 80q multicolored .40 .15
1630 A341 1 l violet & multi .45 .15
1631 A341 1.20 l multicolored .50 .20
Nos. 1626-1631 (6) 1.87
Set value .68

Miniature Sheet

Imperf

1632 A341 2.05 l gold & multi 1.25 .50

30th anniv. of liberation from Fascism.

Artemis, from Apolloni — A342

1974, Dec. 25 Photo. *Perf. 12x12½*

1633 A342 10q shown .15 .15
1634 A342 15q Zeus statue .15 .15
1635 A342 20q Poseidon statue .15 .15
1636 A342 25q Illyrian helmet .15 .15
1637 A342 40q Amphora .15 .15
1638 A342 80q Agrippa .40 .15
1639 A342 1 l Demosthenes .45 .15
1640 A342 1.20 l Head of Bilia .55 .20
Nos. 1633-1640 (8) 2.15
Set value .65

Miniature Sheet

Imperf

1641 A342 2.05 l Artemis & amphora 1.75 .60

Archaeological discoveries in Albania.

Workers and Factories A343

Design: 25q, Handshake, tools and book, vert.

1975, Feb. 11 Litho. *Perf. 12*
1642 A343 25q brown & multi .15 .15
1643 A343 1.80 l yellow & multi .75 .30
Set value .35

Albanian Trade Unions, 30th anniversary.

Chicory
A344

1975, Feb. 15
1644 A344 5q shown .15 .15
1645 A344 10q Houseleek .15 .15
1646 A344 15q Columbine .15 .15
1647 A344 20q Anemone .15 .15
1648 A344 25q Hibiscus .15 .15
1649 A344 30q Gentian .15 .15
1650 A344 35q Hollyhock .15 .15
1651 A344 2.70 l Iris 1.20 .40
Set value 1.75 .75

Protected flowers.

Jesus, from Doni Madonna — A345

Works by Michelangelo: 10q, Slave, sculpture. 15q, Head of Dawn, sculpture. 20q, Awakening Giant, sculpture. 25q, Cumaenian Sybil, Sistine Chapel. 30q, Lorenzo di Medici, sculpture. 1.20 l, David, sculpture. 2.05 l, Self-portrait. 3.90 l, Delphic Sybil, Sistine Chapel.

1975, Mar. 20 Litho. *Perf. 12x12½*
1652 A345 5q gold & multi .15 .15
1653 A345 10q gold & multi .15 .15
1654 A345 15q gold & multi .15 .15
1655 A345 20q gold & multi .15 .15
1656 A345 25q gold & multi .15 .15
1657 A345 30q gold & multi .15 .15
1658 A345 1.20 l gold & multi .35 .18
1659 A345 3.90 l gold & multi 1.50 .52
Set value 2.25 .90

Miniature Sheet

Imperf

1660 A345 2.05 l gold & multi 1.10 .52

Michelangelo Buonarroti (1475-1564), Italian sculptor, painter and architect.

Two-wheeled Cart — A346

Albanian Transportation of the Past: 5q, Horseback rider. 15q, Lake ferry. 20q, Coastal three-master. 25q, Phaeton. 3.35 l, Early automobile on bridge.

1975, Apr. 15 Litho. *Perf. 12½x12*
1661 A346 5q bl grn & multi .15 .15
1662 A346 10q ol & multi .15 .15
1663 A346 15q lil & multi .15 .15
1664 A346 20q multi .15 .15
1665 A346 25q multi .15 .15
1666 A346 3.35 l ocher & multi 1.40 .50
Set value 1.75 .75

Guard at Frontier Stone — A347 Guardsman and Militia — A348

1975, Apr. 25 *Perf. 12*
1667 A347 25q multi .15 .15
1668 A348 1.80 l multi .85 .22
Set value .26

30th anniversary of Frontier Guards.

Posting Illegal Poster — A349

Designs: 60q, Partisans in battle. 1.20 l, Partisan killing German soldier, and Albanian coat of arms.

1975, May 9 *Perf. 12½x12*
1669 A349 25q multi .15 .15
1670 A349 60q multi .22 .15
1671 A349 1.20 l red & multi .60 .25
Nos. 1669-1671 (3) .97
Set value .40

30th anniversary of victory over Fascism.

European Widgeons — A350

Waterfowl: 10q, Red-crested pochards. 15q, White-fronted goose. 20q, Northern pintails. 25q, Red-breasted merganser. 30q, Eider ducks. 35q, Whooper swan. 2.70 l, Shovelers.

1975, June 15 Litho. *Perf. 12*
1672 A350 5q brt bl & multi .15 .15
1673 A350 10q yel grn & multi .15 .15
1674 A350 15q brt rose lil & multi .15 .15
1675 A350 20q bl grn & multi .15 .15
1676 A350 25q multi .15 .15
1677 A350 30q multi .15 .15
1678 A350 35q org & multi .15 .15
1679 A350 2.70 l multi 1.10 .32
Set value 1.55 .60

Shyqyri Kanapari, by Musa Qarri — A351

Albanian Paintings: 10q, Woman Saving Children in Sea, by Agim Faja. 15q, "November 28, 1912" (revolution), by Petrit Ceno, horiz. 20q, "Workers Unite," by Sali Shijaku. 25q, The Partisan Shota Galica, by Ismail Lulani. 30q, Victorious Resistance Fighters, 1943, by Nestor Jonuzi. 80q, Partisan Couple in Front of Red Flag, by Vilson Halimi. 2.05 l, Dancing Procession, by Abdurahim Buza. 2.25 l, Republic Day Celebration, by Fatmir Haxhiu, horiz.

Perf. 12x12½, 12½x12

1975, July 15 Litho.
1680 A351 5q gold & multi .15 .15
1681 A351 10q gold & multi .15 .15
1682 A351 15q gold & multi .15 .15
1683 A351 20q gold & multi .15 .15
1684 A351 25q gold & multi .15 .15
1685 A351 30q gold & multi .15 .15
1686 A351 80q gold & multi .24 .15
1687 A351 2.25 l gold & multi .80 .28
Set value 1.50 .60

Miniature Sheet

Imperf

1688 A351 2.05 l gold & multi 1.25 .48

Nos. 1680-1687 issued in sheets of 8 stamps and gold center label showing palette and easel.

Farmer Holding Reform Law — A352

Design: 2 l, Produce and farm machinery.

1975, Aug. 28 *Perf. 12*
1689 A352 15q multicolored .15 .15
1690 A352 2 l multicolored .75 .35
Set value .40

Agrarian reform, 30th anniversary.

Alcynonium Palmatum — A353

Corals: 10q, Paramuricea chamaeleon. 20q, Coralium rubrum. 25q, Eunicella covalini. 3.70 l, Cladocora cespitosa.

1975, Sept. 25 Litho. *Perf. 12*
1691 A353 5q blue, ol & blk .15 .15
1692 A353 10q blue & multi .15 .15
1693 A353 20q blue & multi .15 .15
1694 A353 25q blue & blk .15 .15
1695 A353 3.70 l blue & blk 1.75 .48
Nos. 1691-1695 (5) 2.35
Set value .65

Bicycling — A354

Designs (Montreal Olympic Games Emblem and): 10q, Canoeing. 15q, Fieldball. 20q, Basketball. 25q, Water polo. 30q, Hockey. 1.20 l, Pole vault. 2.05 l, Fencing. 2.15 l, Montreal Olympic Games emblem and various sports.

1975, Oct. 20 Litho. *Perf. 12½*
1696 A354 5q multi .15 .15
1697 A354 10q multi .15 .15
1698 A354 15q multi .15 .15
1699 A354 20q multi .15 .15
1700 A354 25q multi .15 .15
1701 A354 30q multi .15 .15
1702 A354 1.20 l multi .35 .16
1703 A354 2.05 l multi .75 .24
Set value 1.50 .65

Miniature Sheet

Imperf

1704 A354 2.15 l org & multi 2.25 1.75

21st Olympic Games, Montreal, July 18-Aug. 8, 1976. Nos. 1696-1703 exist imperf.

Power Lines Leading to Village — A355

Designs: 25q, Transformers and insulators. 80q, Dam and power station. 85q, Television set, power lines, grain and cogwheel.

1975, Oct. 25 *Perf. 12x12½*
1705 A355 15q ultra & yel .15 .15
1706 A355 25q brt vio & pink .15 .15
1707 A355 80q lt grn & gray .35 .15
1708 A355 85q ocher & brn .35 .15
Nos. 1705-1708 (4) 1.00
Set value .35

General electrification, 5th anniversary.

Child, Rabbit and Teddy Bear Planting Tree — A356

Fairy Tales: 10q, Mother fox. 15q, Ducks in school. 20q, Little pigs building house. 25q, Animals watching television. 30q, Rabbit and bear at work. 35q, Working and playing ants. 2.70 l, Wolf in sheep's clothes.

1975, Dec. 25 Litho. *Perf. 12½x12*
1709 A356 5q black & multi .15 .15
1710 A356 10q black & multi .15 .15
1711 A356 15q black & multi .15 .15
1712 A356 20q black & multi .15 .15
1713 A356 25q black & multi .15 .15
1714 A356 30q black & multi .15 .15
1715 A356 35q black & multi .16 .15
1716 A356 2.70 l black & multi 1.00 .28
Set value 1.50 .60

Arms, People, Factories A357

Design: 1.90 l, Arms, government building, celebrating crowd.

1976, Jan. 11 Litho. *Perf. 12*
1717 A357 25q gold & multi .15 .15
1718 A357 1.90 l gold & multi .55 .24
Set value .30

30th anniversary of proclamation of Albanian People's Republic.

Ice Hockey, Olympic Games' Emblem — A358

Designs: 10q, Speed skating. 15q, Biathlon. 50q, Ski jump. 1.20 l, Slalom. 2.15 l, Figure skating, pairs. 2.30 l, One-man bobsled.

1976, Feb. 4
1719 A358 5q silver & multi .15 .15
1720 A358 10q silver & multi .15 .15
1721 A358 15q silver & multi .15 .15
1722 A358 50q silver & multi .16 .15

1723 A358 1.20 l silver & multi .38 .15
1724 A358 2.30 l silver & multi .90 .35
Set value 1.60 .65

Miniature Sheet

Perf.* 12 on 2 sides x *Imperf.

1725 A358 2.15 l silver & multi 1.25 .80

12th Winter Olympic Games, Innsbruck, Austria, Feb. 4-15.

Meadow Saffron — A359

Medicinal Plants: 10q, Deadly night-shade. 15q, Yellow gentian. 20q, Horse chestnut. 70q, Shield fern. 80q, Marshmallow. 2.30 l, Thorn apple.

1976, Apr. 10 Litho. *Perf.* 12x12½

1726 A359 5q black & multi .15 .15
1727 A359 10q black & multi .15 .15
1728 A359 15q black & multi .15 .15
1729 A359 20q black & multi .15 .15
1730 A359 70q black & multi .20 .15
1731 A359 80q black & multi .40 .15
1732 A359 2.30 l black & multi 1.10 .35
Set value 1.90 .70

Bowl and Spoon — A360

Designs: 15q, Flask, vert. 20q, Carved handles, vert. 25q, Pistol and dagger. 80q, Wall hanging, vert. 1.20 l, Earrings and belt buckle. 1.40 l, Jugs, vert.

1976 Litho. *Perf.* 12½x12, 12x12½

1733 A360 10q lilac & multi .15 .15
1734 A360 15q gray & multi .15 .15
1735 A360 20q multi .15 .15
1736 A360 25q car & multi .15 .15
1737 A360 80q yellow & multi .35 .15
1738 A360 1.20 l multi .50 .15
1739 A360 1.40 l tan & multi .65 .25
Nos. 1733-1739 (7) 2.10
Set value .70

Natl. Ethnographic Conf., Tirana, June 28.
For surcharge see No. 1873.

Founding of Cooperatives, by Zef Shoshi — A361

Paintings: 10q, Going to Work, by Agim Zajmi, vert. 25q, Crowd Listening to Loudspeaker, by Vilson Kilica. 40q, Woman Welder, by Sabaudin Xhaferi, vert. 50q, Factory, by Isuf Sulovari, vert. 1.20 l, 1942 Revolt, by Lec Shkreli, vert. 1.60 l, Coming Home from Work, by Agron Dine. 2.05 l, Honoring a Young Pioneer, by Andon Lakuriqi.

***Perf.* 12½x12, 12x12½**

1976, Aug. 8 Litho.

1740 A361 5q gold & multi .15 .15
1741 A361 10q gold & multi .15 .15
1742 A361 25q gold & multi .15 .15
1743 A361 40q gold & multi .15 .15
1744 A361 50q gold & multi .15 .15
1745 A361 1.20 l gold & multi .48 .15
1746 A361 1.60 l gold & multi .70 .28
Nos. 1740-1746 (7) 1.93
Set value .70

Miniature Sheet

Perf.* 12 on 2 sides x *Imperf.

1747 A361 2.05 l gold & multi .90 .45

Red Flag, Agricultural Symbols — A362
Enver Hoxha, Partisans and Albanian Flag — A363

Design: 1.20 l, Red flag and raised pickax.

1976, Nov. 1

1748 A362 25q multi .15 .15
1749 A362 1.20 l multi .50 .20
Set value .25

7th Workers Party Congress.

1976, Oct. 28 *Perf.* 12x12½

Design: 1.90 l, Demonstrators with Albanian flag.

1750 A363 25q multi .15 .15
1751 A363 1.90 l multi .80 .30
Set value .35

Anti-Fascist demonstrations, 35th anniv.

Attacking Partisans, Meeting House — A364

Designs (Red Flag and): 25q, Partisans, pickax and gun. 80q, Workers, soldiers, pickax and gun. 1.20 l, Agriculture and industry. 1.70 l, Dancers, symbols of science and art.

1976, Nov. 8 Litho. *Perf.* 12x12½

1752 A364 15q gold & multi .15 .15
1753 A364 25q gold & multi .15 .15
1754 A364 80q gold & multi .22 .15
1755 A364 1.20 l gold & multi .40 .15
1756 A364 1.70 l gold & multi .80 .18
Nos. 1752-1756 (5) 1.72
Set value .50

35th anniv. of 1st Workers Party Cong.

Young Workers and Track A365

Design: 1.25 l, Young soldiers and Albanian flag.

1976, Nov. 23 *Perf.* 12

1757 A365 80q yellow & multi .28 .15
1758 A365 1.25 l carmine & multi .38 .20

Union of Young Communists, 35th anniv.

"Cuca e Maleve" Ballet A366

Designs: Scenes from ballet "Mountain Girl."

1976, Dec. 14 *Perf.* 12

1759 A366 10q gold & multi .15 .15
1760 A366 15q gold & multi .15 .15
1761 A366 20q gold & multi .15 .15
1762 A366 25q gold & multi .15 .15
1763 A366 80q gold & multi .40 .15
1764 A366 1.20 l gold & multi .55 .18
1765 A366 1.40 l gold & multi .70 .22
Nos. 1759-1765 (7) 2.25
Set value .65

Miniature Sheet

Perf.* 12 on 2 sides x *Imperf.

1766 A366 2.05 l gold & multi 1.25 .45

Bashtoves Castle A367

Albanian Castles: 15q, Gjirokastres. 20q, Ali Pash Tepelenes. 25q, Petreles. 80q, Beratit. 1.20 l, Durresit. 1.40 l, Krujes.

1976, Dec. 30 Litho. *Perf.* 12

1767 A367 10q black & dull bl .15 .15
1768 A367 15q black & grn .15 .15
1769 A367 20q black & gray .15 .15
1770 A367 25q black & brn .15 .15
1771 A367 80q black & rose .24 .15
1772 A367 1.20 l black & vio .28 .16
1773 A367 1.40 l black & brn red .55 .16
Set value 1.35 .60

Skanderbeg's Shield and Spear — A368

Skanderbeg's Weapons: 80q, Helmet, sword and scabbard. 1 l, Halberd, quiver with arrows, crossbow and spear.

1977, Jan. 28 Litho. *Perf.* 12

1774 A368 15q silver & multi .25 .15
1775 A368 80q silver & multi 1.00 .20
1776 A368 1 l silver & multi 1.50 .25
Nos. 1774-1776 (3) 2.75
Set value .50

Skanderbeg (1403-1468), national hero.

Ilia Oiqi, Messenger in Storm — A369

Modern Heroes: 10q, Ilia Dashi, sailor in battle. 25q, Fran Ndue Ivanaj, fisherman in storm. 80q, Zeliha Allmetaj, woman rescuing child. 1 l, Ylli Zaimi, rescuing goats from flood. 1.90 l, Isuf Plloci, fighting forest fire.

1977, Feb. 28 Litho. *Perf.* 12x12½

1777 A369 5q brown & multi .15 .15
1778 A369 10q ultra & multi .15 .15
1779 A369 25q blue & multi .15 .15
1780 A369 80q ocher & multi .35 .15
1781 A369 1 l brown & multi .52 .15
1782 A369 1.90 l brown & multi .90 .18
Set value 2.00 .50

Polyvinylchloride Plant, Vlore — A370

6th Five-year plan: 25q, Naphtha fractioning plant, Ballsh. 65q, Hydroelectric station and dam, Fjerzes. 1 l, Metallurgical plant and blast furance, Elbasan.

1977, Mar. 29 Litho. *Perf.* 12½x12

1783 A370 15q silver & multi .15 .15
1784 A370 25q silver & multi .15 .15
1785 A370 65q silver & multi .28 .15
1786 A370 1 l silver & multi .45 .16
Nos. 1783-1786 (4) 1.03
Set value .36

Qerime Halil Galica — A371

Victory Monument, Tirana — A372

Design: 1.25 l, Qerime Halil Galica "Shota" and father Azem Galica.

1977, Apr. 20 Litho. *Perf.* 12

1787 A371 80q dark red .22 .15
1788 A371 1.25 l gray blue .35 .15
Set value .22

"Shota" Galica, communist fighter.

1977, May 5 Litho. *Perf.* 12

Designs (Red Star and): 80q, Clenched fist, Albanian flag. 1.20 l, Bust of Qemal Stafa and poppies.

1789 A372 25q multi .15 .15
1790 A372 80q multi .35 .15
1791 A372 1.20 l multi .55 .20
Nos. 1789-1791 (3) 1.05
Set value .36

35th anniversary of Martyrs' Day.

Physician Visiting Farm, Mobile Clinic — A373

Designs: 10q, Cowherd and cattle ranch. 20q, Militia woman helping with harvest, rifle and combine. 80q, Modern village, highway and power lines. 2.95 l, Tractor and greenhouses.

1977, June 18

1792 A373 5q multi .15 .15
1793 A373 10q multi .15 .15
1794 A373 20q multi .15 .15
1795 A373 80q multi .22 .15
1796 A373 2.95 l multi 1.40 .38
Nos. 1792-1796 (5) 2.07
Set value .60

"Socialist transformation of the villages."

Armed Workers, Flag and Factory — A374

Design: 1.80 l, Workers with proclamation and flags.

1977, June 20

1797 A374 25q multi .15 .15
1798 A374 1.80 l multi .65 .22
Set value .26

9th Labor Unions Congress.

Kerchief Dance — A375

Designs: Various folk dances.

1977, Aug. 20 Litho. *Perf.* 12

1799 A375 5q multi .15 .15
1800 A375 10q multi .15 .15
1801 A375 15q multi .15 .15
1802 A375 25q multi .15 .15
1803 A375 80q multi .30 .15
1804 A375 1.20 l multi .60 .20
1805 A375 1.55 l multi .75 .25
Set value 1.90 .75

Miniature Sheet

Perf.* 12 on 2 sides x *Imperf.

1806 A375 2.05 l multi .85 .40

See Nos. 1836-1840, 1884-1888.

Attack A376

Designs: 25q, Enver Hoxha addressing Army. 80q, Volunteers and riflemen. 1 l, Volunteers, hydrofoil patrolboat and MiG planes. 1.90 l, Volunteers and Albanian flag.

1977, July 10 Litho. *Perf. 12*

1807	A376	15q gold & multi	.15	.15
1808	A376	25q gold & multi	.15	.15
1809	A376	80q gold & multi	.25	.15
1810	A376	1 l gold & multi	.38	.15
1811	A376	1.90 l gold & multi	.75	.22
		Nos. 1807-1811 (5)	1.68	
		Set value		.50

"One People-One Army."

Armed Workers, Article 3 of Constitution A377

Design: 1.20 l, Symbols of farming and fertilizer industry, Article 25 of Constitution.

1977, Oct.

1812	A377	25q red, gold & blk	.15	.15
1813	A377	1.20 l red, gold & blk	.48	.18
		Set value		.22

New Constitution.

Picnic — A378

Film Frames: 15q, Telephone lineman in winter. 25q, Two men and a woman. 80q, Workers. 1.20 l, Boys playing in street. 1.60 l, Harvest.

1977, Oct. 25 Litho. *Perf. 12½x12*

1814	A378	10q blue green	.15	.15
1815	A378	15q multi	.15	.15
1816	A378	25q black	.15	.15
1817	A378	80q multi	.28	.15
1818	A378	1.20 l deep claret	.48	.15
1819	A378	1.60 l multi	.60	.20
		Set value	1.50	.55

Albanian films.

Farm Workers in Field, by V. Mio A379

Paintings by V. Mio: 10q, Landscape in Snow. 15q, Grazing Sheep under Walnut Tree in Spring. 25q, Street in Korce. 80q, Horseback Riders on Mountain Pass. 1 l, Boats on Shore. 1.75 l, Tractors Plowing Fields. 2.05 l, Self-portrait.

1977, Dec. 25 Litho. *Perf. 12½x12*

1820	A379	5q gold & multi	.15	.15
1821	A379	10q gold & multi	.15	.15
1822	A379	15q gold & multi	.15	.15
1823	A379	25q gold & multi	.15	.15
1824	A379	80q gold & multi	.28	.15
1825	A379	1 l gold & multi	.32	.15
1826	A379	1.75 l gold & multi	.55	.16
		Set value	1.35	.55

Miniature Sheet

Imperf.; Perf. 12 Horiz. between Vignette and Value Panel

1827	A379	2.05 l gold & multi	.70	.32

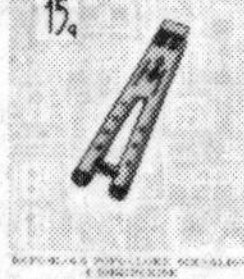
Pan Flute — A380

Albanian Flag, Monument and People — A381

Folk Musical Instruments: 25q, Single-string goat's-head fiddle. 80q, Woodwind. 1.20 l, Drum. 1.70 l, Bagpipe. Background shows various woven folk patterns.

1978, Jan. 20 *Perf. 12x12½*

1828	A380	15q multi	.15	.15
1829	A380	25q multi	.15	.15
1830	A380	80q multi	.35	.15
1831	A380	1.20 l multi	.55	.15
1832	A380	1.70 l multi	.75	.20
		Nos. 1828-1832 (5)	1.95	
		Set value		.55

1978 *Perf. 12½x12, 12x12½*

Designs: 25q, Ismail Qemali and fighters, horiz. 1.65 l, People dancing around Albanian flag, horiz.

1833	A381	15q multi	.15	.15
1834	A381	25q multi	.15	.15
1835	A381	1.65 l multi	.60	.20
		Nos. 1833-1835 (3)	.90	
		Set value		.30

65th anniversary of independence.

Folk Dancing Type of 1977

Designs: Various dances.

1978, Feb. 15 Litho. *Perf. 12*

1836	A375	5q multi	.15	.15
1837	A375	25q multi	.15	.15
1838	A375	80q multi	.32	.15
1839	A375	1 l multi	.50	.15
1840	A375	2.30 l multi	1.00	.24
		Nos. 1836-1840 (5)	2.12	
		Set value		.55

Nos. 1836-1840 have white background around dancers, Nos. 1799-1805 have pinkish shadows.

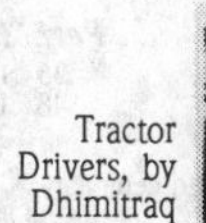

Tractor Drivers, by Dhimitraq Trebicka A382

Working Class Paintings: 80q, Steeplejack, by Spiro Kristo. 85q, "A Point in the Discussion," by Skender Milori. 90q, Oil rig crew, by Anesti Cini, vert. 1.60 l, Metal workers, by Ramadan Karanxha. 2.20 l, Political discussion, by Sotiraq Sholla.

1978, Mar. 25 Litho. *Perf. 12*

1841	A382	25q multi	.15	.15
1842	A382	80q multi	.30	.15
1843	A382	85q multi	.30	.15
1844	A382	90q multi	.35	.16
1845	A382	1.60 l multi	.75	.25
		Nos. 1841-1845 (5)	1.85	
		Set value		.70

Miniature Sheet

Perf. 12 on 2 sides x Imperf.

1846	A382	2.20 l multi	1.25	.40

Woman with Rifle and Pickax A383

Design: 1.95 l, Farm and Militia women, industrial plant.

1978, June 1 Litho. *Perf. 12*

1847	A383	25q gold & red	.15	.15
1848	A383	1.95 l gold & red	.75	.25
		Set value		.30

8th Congress of Women's Union.

Children and Flowers — A384

Designs: 10q, Children with rifle, ax, book and flags. 25q, Dancing children in folk costume. 1.80 l, Children in school.

1978, June 1 Litho.

1849	A384	5q multi	.15	.15
1850	A384	10q multi	.15	.15
1851	A384	25q multi	.15	.15
1852	A384	1.80 l multi	.60	.20
		Set value	.80	.35

International Children's Day.

Spirit of Skanderbeg as Conqueror — A385

Designs: 10q, Battle at Mostar Bridge. 80q, Marchers and Albanian flag. 1.20 l, Riflemen in winter battle. 1.65 l, Abdyl Frasheri (1839-1892). 2.20 l, Rifles, scroll and pen, League building. 2.60 l, League headquarters, Prizren.

1978, June 10 Litho. *Perf. 12*

1853	A385	10q multi	.15	.15
1854	A385	25q multi	.15	.15
1855	A385	80q multi	.22	.15
1856	A385	1.20 l multi	.45	.15
1857	A385	1.65 l multi	.70	.18
1858	A385	2.60 l multi	.80	.32
		Nos. 1853-1858 (6)	2.47	
		Set value		.82

Miniature Sheet

Perf. 12 on 2 sides x Imperf.

1859	A385	2.20 l multi	.90	.35

Centenary of League of Prizren.

Guerrillas and Flag, 1943 — A386

Designs: 25q, Soldier, sailor, airman, militiaman, horiz. 1.90 l, Members of armed forces, civil guards, and Young Pioneers.

1978, July 10 *Perf. 11½x12½*

1860	A386	5q multi	.15	.15
1861	A386	25q multi	.15	.15
1862	A386	1.90 l multi	.80	.20
		Nos. 1860-1862 (3)	1.10	
		Set value		.30

35th anniversary of People's Army.

Woman with Machine Carbine — A387

Kerchief Dance — A388

Designs: 25q, Man with target rifle, horiz. 95q, Man shooting with telescopic sights, horiz. 2.40 l, Woman target shooting with pistol.

Perf. 12½x12, 12x12½

1978, Sept. 20 Litho.

1863	A387	25q blk & yel	.15	.15
1864	A387	80q org & blk	.30	.15
1865	A387	95q red & blk	.42	.15
1866	A387	2.40 l car & blk	1.00	.30
		Nos. 1863-1866 (4)	1.87	.75

32nd National Rifle-shooting Championships, Sept. 20.

1978, Oct. 6 *Perf. 12*

Designs: 15q, Musicians. 25q, Fiddler with single-stringed instrument. 80q, Dancers, men. 1.20 l, Saber dance. 1.90 l, Singers, women.

1867	A388	10q multi	.15	.15
1868	A388	15q multi	.15	.15
1869	A388	25q multi	.15	.15
1870	A388	80q multi	.25	.15
1871	A388	1.20 l multi	.50	.15
1872	A388	1.90 l multi	.80	.25
		Nos. 1867-1872 (6)	2.00	
		Set value		.65

National Folklore Festival.

See Nos. 2082-2085, 2289-2290.

No. 1736 Surcharged with New Value, 2 Bars and "RICCIONE 78"

1978 Litho. *Perf. 12½x12*

1873	A360	3.30 l on 25q multi	5.00	1.10

Riccione 78 Philatelic Exhibition.

Enver Hoxha — A389

1978, Oct. 16 Litho. *Perf. 12x12½*

1874	A389	80q red & multi	.30	.15
1875	A389	1.20 l red & multi	.45	.15
1876	A389	2.40 l red & multi	.90	.25
		Nos. 1874-1876 (3)	1.65	.55

Miniature Sheet

Perf. 12½ on 2 sides x Imperf.

1877	A389	2.20 l red & multi	.85	.40

70th birthday of Enver Hoxha, First Secretary of Central Committee of the Communist Party of Albania.

Woman and Wheat — A390

Designs: 25q, Woman with egg crates. 80q, Shepherd and sheep. 2.60 l, Milkmaid and cows.

1978, Dec. 15 *Perf. 12x12½*

1878	A390	15q multi	.15	.15
1879	A390	25q multi	.15	.15
1880	A390	80q multi	.40	.15
1881	A390	2.60 l multi	1.10	.50
		Nos. 1878-1881 (4)	1.80	
		Set value		.70

Dora d'Istria — A391

Tower House — A392

Design: 1.10 l, Full portrait of Dora d'Istria, author; birth sesquicentennial.

1979, Jan. 22 Litho. *Perf. 12*

1882	A391	80q lt grn & blk	.42	.15
1883	A391	1.10 l vio brn & blk	.48	.15
		Set value		.20

Costume Type of 1977

Designs: Various folk dances.

1979, Feb. 25

1884 A375 15q multi .15 .15
1885 A375 25q multi .15 .15
1886 A375 80q multi .32 .15
1887 A375 1.20 l multi .42 .15
1888 A375 1.40 l multi .60 .22
Nos. 1884-1888 (5) 1.64
Set value .50

Nos. 1884-1888 have white background. Denomination in upper left on No. 1885, in upper right on No. 1802; lower left on No. 1886, upper left on No. 1803.

1979, Mar. 20

Traditional Houses: 15q, Stone gallery house, horiz. 80q, House with wooden galleries, horiz. 1.20 l, Galleried tower house. 1.40 l, 1.90 l, Tower houses, diff.

1889 A392 15q multi .15 .15
1890 A392 25q multi .15 .15
1891 A392 80q multi .32 .15
1892 A392 1.20 l multi .42 .15
1893 A392 1.40 l multi .60 .22
Nos. 1889-1893 (5) 1.64
Set value .50

Miniature Sheet

Perf. 12 on 2 sides x Imperf.

1894 A392 1.90 l multi .80 .40

See Nos. 2015-2018.

Soldier, Factories, Wheat A393

Design: 1.65 l, Soldiers, workers and coat of arms.

1979, May 14 Litho. *Perf. 12*

1895 A393 25q multi .15 .15
1896 A393 1.65 l multi .55 .18
Set value .23

Congress of Permet, 35th anniversary.

Albanian Flag — A394 RPS E SHQIPERISE

1979, June 4

1897 A394 25q multi .15 .15
1898 A394 1.65 l multi .55 .18
Set value .23

5th Congress of Albanian Democratic Front.

RPS E SHQIPERISE Vasil Shanto, (1913-44) A395

Alexander Moissi, (1880-1935), Actor — A396 RPS E SHQIPERISE

Design: 25q, 90q, Qemal Stafa (1921-42).

1979

1899 A395 15q multi .15 .15
1900 A395 25q multi .15 .15
1901 A395 60q multi .35 .15
1902 A396 80q multi .45 .15
1903 A395 90q multi .45 .15
1904 A396 1.10 l multi, diff. .60 .18
Nos. 1899-1904 (6) 2.15
Set value .68

Shanto and Stafa, anti-Fascist fighters.
Issued: type A396, Apr. 2, type A395, May 5.
For similar design see A410.

Winter Campaign, by Arben Basha — A397

Paintings of Military Scenes by: 25q, Ismail Lulani. 80q, Myrteza Fushekati. 1.20 l, Muhamet Deliu. 1.40 l, Jorgji Gjikopulli. 1.90 l, Fatmir Haxhiu.

1979, July 15 Litho. *Perf. 12½x12*

1905 A397 15q multi .15 .15
1906 A397 25q multi .15 .15
1907 A397 80q multi .35 .15
1908 A397 1.20 l multi .60 .15
1909 A397 1.40 l multi .65 .22
Nos. 1905-1909 (5) 1.90
Set value .52

Miniature Sheet

Perf. 12 on 2 sides x Imperf.

1910 A397 1.90 l multi 1.00 .40

Athletes Surrounding Flag A398

Literary Society Headquarters A399

1979, Oct. 1 Litho. *Perf. 12*

1911 A398 15q shown .15 .15
1912 A398 25q Shooting .15 .15
1913 A398 80q Dancing .25 .15
1914 A398 1.20 l Soccer .45 .15
1915 A398 1.40 l High jump .60 .22
Nos. 1911-1915 (5) 1.60
Set value .50

Liberation Spartakiad, 35th anniversary.

1979, Oct. 12

Albanian Literary Society Centenary: 25q, Seal and charter. 80q, Founder. 1.55 l, 1879 Headquarters. 1.90 l, Founders.

1916 A399 25q multi .15 .15
1917 A399 80q multi .30 .15
1918 A399 1.20 l multi .42 .15
1919 A399 1.55 l multi .55 .18
Nos. 1916-1919 (4) 1.42
Set value .46

Miniature Sheet

Perf. 12½ on 2 sides x Imperf.

1920 A399 1.90 l multi .80 .40

Congress Statute, Coat of Arms — A400

1979, Oct. 20 Photo. *Perf. 12x12½*

1921 A400 25q multi .16 .15
1922 A400 1.65 l multi .70 .25
Set value .30

2nd Congress of Berat, 35th anniversary.

Children Entering School, Books — A401

1979 Litho. *Perf. 12½x12*

1923 A401 5q shown .15 .15
1924 A401 10q Communications .15 .15
1925 A401 15q Steel workers .15 .15
1926 A401 20q Dancers, instruments .15 .15
1927 A401 25q Newspapers, radio, television .15 .15
1928 A401 60q Textile worker .22 .15
1929 A401 80q Armed forces .30 .15
1930 A401 1.20 l Industry .42 .18
1931 A401 1.60 l Transportation .55 .28
1932 A401 2.40 l Agriculture .80 .35
1932A A401 3 l Medicine 1.00 .52
Nos. 1923-1932A (11) 4.04
Set value 1.75

Workers and Factory A402

Worker, Red Flag and: 80q, Hand holding sickle and rifle. 1.20 l, Red star and open book. 1.55 l, Open book and cogwheel.

1979, Nov. 29

1933 A402 25q multi .15 .15
1934 A402 80q multi .18 .15
1935 A402 1.20 l multi .42 .15
1936 A402 1.55 l multi .48 .15
Nos. 1933-1936 (4) 1.23
Set value .42

35th anniversary of independence.

Joseph Stalin — A403

Design: 1.10 l, Stalin on dais, horiz.

1979, Dec. 21 Litho. *Perf. 12*

1937 A403 80q red & dk bl .35 .15
1938 A403 1.10 l red & dk bl .48 .18
Set value .28

Joseph Stalin (1879-1953), birth centenary.

Fireplace and Pottery, Korcar A404

Home Furnishings: 80q, Cupboard bed, dagger, pistol, ammunition pouch, Shkodar. 1.20 l, Stool, pot, chair, Mirdit. 1.35 l, Chimney, dagger, jacket, Gjirokaster.

1980, Feb. 27 Litho. *Perf. 12*

1939 A404 25q multi .15 .15
1940 A404 80q multi .35 .15
1941 A404 1.20 l multi .55 .20
1942 A404 1.35 l multi .60 .30
Nos. 1939-1942 (4) 1.65
Set value .66

See Nos. 1985-1988.

Pipe, Painted Flask — A405

1980, Mar. 4

1943 A405 25q shown .15 .15
1944 A405 80q Leather handbags .35 .15
1945 A405 1.20 l Carved eagle, embroidered rug .55 .20
1946 A405 1.35 l Lace .60 .30
Nos. 1943-1946 (4) 1.65
Set value .66

Prof. Aleksander Xhuvanit Birth Centenary — A406

1980, Mar. 14

1947 A406 80q multi .42 .15
1948 A406 1 l multi .52 .18

Revolutionaries on Horseback — A407

Insurrection at Kosove, 70th Anniversary: 1 l, Battle scene.

1980, Apr. 4

1949 A407 80q red & black .42 .15
1950 A407 1 l red & black .52 .18

Soldiers and Workers Laboring to Aid the Stricken Populations, by D. Jukinui and I. Lulani — A408

1980, Apr. 15 Litho. *Perf. 12½*

1951 A408 80q lt blue & multi .42 .15
1952 A408 1 l lt blue grn & multi .52 .18

Lenin, 110th Birth Anniversary — A409 RPS E SHQIPERISE

1980, Apr. 22

1953 A409 80q multi .42 .15
1954 A409 1 l multi .52 .18

Misto Mame and Ali Demi, War Martyrs A410

War Martyrs: 80q, Sadik Staveleci, Vojo Kusji, Hoxhi Martini. 1.20 l, Bule Naipi, Persefoni Kokedhima. 1.35 l, Ndoc Deda, Hydajet Lezha, Naim Gyylbegu, Ndoc Mazi, Ahmed Haxha.

1980, May 5

1955 A410 25q multi .15 .15
1956 A410 80q multi .35 .15
1957 A410 1.20 l multi .50 .20
1958 A410 1.35 l multi .60 .30
Nos. 1955-1958 (4) 1.60
Set value .66

See Nos. 2012A-2012D, 2025-2028, 2064-2067, 2122-2125, 2171-2174, 2207-2209.

Scene from "Mirela" A411

1980, June 7

1959 A411 15q shown .15 .15
1960 A411 25q The Scribbler .15 .15
1961 A411 80q Circus Bears .28 .15
1962 A411 2.40 l Waterdrops .80 .35
Nos. 1959-1962 (4) 1.38
Set value .55

Carrying Iron Castings in the Enver Hoxha Tractor Combine, by S. Shijaku and M. Fushekati — A412

Paintings (Gallery of Figurative Paintings, Tirana): 80q, The Welder, by Harilla Dhima. 1.20 l, Steel Erectors, by Petro Kokushta. 1.35 l, Pandeli Lena, 1.80 l Communists, by Vilson Kilica.

1980, July 22

1963 A412 25q multi .15 .15
1964 A412 80q multi .28 .15
1965 A412 1.20 l multi .40 .16
1966 A412 1.35 l multi .52 .24
Nos. 1963-1966 (4) 1.35
Set value .55

Souvenir Sheet

1967 A412 1.80 l multi .70 .48

Gate, Parchment Miniature, 11th Cent. — A413

Bas reliefs of the Middle Ages: 80q, Eagle, 13th cent. 1.20 l, Heraldic lion, 14th cent. 1.35 l, Pheasant, 14th cent.

1980, Sept. 27 **Litho.** ***Perf. 12***

1968 A413 25q gold & blk .15 .15
1969 A413 80q gold & blk .25 .15
1970 A413 1.20 l gold & blk .42 .15
1971 A413 1.35 l gold & blk .52 .22
Nos. 1968-1971 (4) 1.34
Set value .54

Divjaka National Park — A414

1980, Nov. 6 **Photo.**

1972 A414 80q shown .25 .15
1973 A414 1.20 l Lura .42 .22
1974 A414 1.60 l Thethi .55 .25
Nos. 1972-1974 (3) 1.22 .62

Souvenir Sheet

Perf. 12½

1975 A414 1.80 l Llogara Park .75 .75

Citizens, Flag and Arms of Albania A415

1981, Jan. 11 **Litho.** ***Perf. 12***

1976 A415 80q shown .35 .15
1977 A415 1 l People's Party Head-quarters, Tirana .50 .25

35th anniversary of the Republic.

Child's Bed — A416

1981, Mar. 20 **Litho.** ***Perf. 12***

1978 A416 25q shown .15 .15
1979 A416 80q Wooden bucket, brass bottle .35 .22
1980 A416 1.20 l Shoes .52 .25
1981 A416 1.35 l Jugs .55 .30
Nos. 1978-1981 (4) 1.57 .92

A417

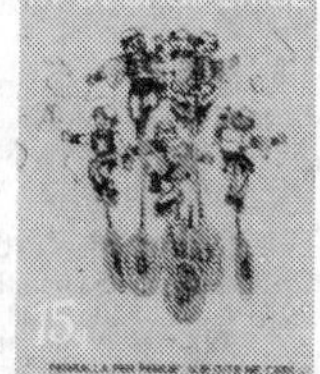

A419

1981, Apr. 20

1982 A417 80q Soldiers .35 .22
1983 A417 1 l Sword combat .48 .25

Souvenir Sheet

Perf. 12½ Vert.

1984 A417 1.80 l Soldier with pistol .80 .80

Battle of Shtimje centenary.

Home Furnishings Type of 1980

1981, Feb. 25 **Litho.** ***Perf. 12***

1985 A404 25q House interior, Labara .15 .15
1986 A404 80q Labara, diff. .35 .22
1987 A404 1.20 l Mat .52 .25
1988 A404 1.35 l Dibres .55 .30
Nos. 1985-1988 (4) 1.57 .92

1981, June ***Perf. 12***

Designs: Children's circus.

1989 A419 15q multi .15 .15
1990 A419 25q multi .15 .15
1991 A419 80q multi .35 .22
1992 A419 2.40 l multi 1.00 .60
Nos. 1989-1992 (4) 1.65
Set value .66

Soccer Players A420

1982 World Cup Soccer Elimination Games: Various soccer players.

1981, Mar. 31 **Litho.** ***Perf. 12***

1993 A420 25q multi .25 .16
1994 A420 80q multi 1.90 .40
1995 A420 1.20 l multi 2.75 .65
1996 A420 1.35 l multi 3.50 .80
Nos. 1993-1996 (4) 8.40 2.01

Allies, by S. Hysa A421

Paintings: 80q, Warriors, by A. Buza. 1.20 l, Rallying to the Flag, Dec. 1911, by A. Zajmi, vert. 1.35 l, My Flag is My Heart, by L. Cefa, vert. 1.80 l, Circling the Flag in a Common Cause, by N. Vasia.

1981, July 10 ***Perf. 12½x12***

1997 A421 25q multi .15 .15
1998 A421 80q multi .35 .18
1999 A421 1.20 l multi .50 .25
2000 A421 1.35 l multi .52 .28
Nos. 1997-2000 (4) 1.52 .86

Souvenir Sheet

2001 A421 1.80 l multi .95 .85

No. 2001 contains one stamp, size: 55x55mm.

Rifleman A422

1981, Aug. 30 ***Perf. 12***

2002 A422 25q shown .15 .15
2003 A422 80q Weight lifting .40 .20
2004 A422 1.20 l Volleyball .55 .28
2005 A422 1.35 l Soccer .65 .32
Nos. 2002-2005 (4) 1.75 .95

Albanian Workers' Party, 8th Congress A423

1981, Nov. 1

2006 A423 80q Flag, star .28 .18
2007 A423 1 l Flag, hammer and sickle .38 .22

Albanian Workers' Party, 40th Anniv. — A424

Communist Youth Org., 40th Anniv. — A425

1981, Nov. 8

2008 A424 80q Symbols of industrialization .35 .22
2009 A424 2.80 l Fist, emblem 1.25 .70

Souvenir Sheet

2010 A424 1.80 l Enver Hoxha, Memoirs .85 .85

1981, Nov. 23

2011 A425 80q Star, ax, map .28 .18
2012 A425 1 l Flags, star .38 .22

War Martyrs Type of 1980

Portraits: 25q, Perlat Rexhepi (1919-42) and Branko Kadia (1921-42). 80q, Xheladin Beqiri (1908-44) and Hajdar Dushi (1916-44). 1.20 l, Koci Bako (1905-41), Vasil Laci (1923-41) and Mujo Ulqinaku (1898-1939). 1.35 l, Mine Peza (1875-1942) and Zoja Cure (1920-44).

1981, May 5 **Litho.** ***Perf. 12***

2012A A410 25q sil & multi .25 .15
2012B A410 80q gold & multi .80 .40
2012C A410 1.20 l sil & multi 1.15 .55
2012D A410 1.35 l gold & multi 1.25 .62
Nos. 2012A-2012D (4) 3.45 1.72

Fan S. Noli, Writer, Birth Centenary A426

Traditional House, Bulqize A427

1982, Jan. 6 **Litho.** ***Perf. 12***

2013 A426 80q lt ol grn & gold .28 .18
2014 A426 1.10 l lt red brn & gold .38 .22

Traditional Houses Type of 1979

1982, Feb. ***Perf. 12½x12***

2015 A392 25q Bulqize .30 .20
2016 A392 80q Lebush .30 .20
2017 A392 1.20 l Bicaj .50 .28
2018 A392 1.55 l Klos .70 .42
Nos. 2015-2018 (4) 1.80 1.10

TB Bacillus Centenary A428

1982, Mar. 24 ***Perf. 12***

2019 A428 80q Globe .50 .25
2020 A428 1.10 l Koch .70 .35

Albanian League House, Prizren, by K. Buza A429

Kosova Landscapes: 25q, Castle at Prizrenit, by G. Madhi. 1.20 l, Mountain Gorge at Rogove, by K. Buza. 1.55 l, Street of the Hadhji at Zekes, by G. Madhi. 25q, 1.20 l, 1.55 l vert.

Perf. 12x12½, 12½x12

1982, Apr. 15 **Litho.**

2021 A429 25q multi .15 .15
2022 A429 80q multi .32 .15
2023 A429 1.20 l multi .48 .20
2024 A429 1.55 l multi .65 .28
Nos. 2021-2024 (4) 1.60
Set value .66

War Martyr Type of 1980

Designs: 25q, Hibe Palikuqi, Liri Gero. 80q, Mihal Duri, Kajo Karafili. 1.20 l, Fato Dudumi, Margarita Tutulani, Shejnaze Juka. 1.55 l, Memo Meto, Gjok Doci.

1982, May ***Perf. 12***

2025 A410 25q multi .15 .15
2026 A410 80q multi .32 .20
2027 A410 1.20 l multi .52 .28
2028 A410 1.55 l multi .70 .45
Nos. 2025-2028 (4) 1.69 1.08

Loading Freighter A430

Children's Paintings.

1982, June 15 ***Perf. 12½x12***

2029 A430 15q shown .15 .15
2030 A430 80q Forest .32 .20
2031 A430 1.20 l City .52 .28
2032 A430 1.65 l Park .75 .45
Nos. 2029-2032 (4) 1.74 1.08

9th Congress of Trade Unions A431

1982, June 6 **Litho.** ***Perf. 12***

2033 A431 80q Workers, factories .40 .18
2034 A431 1.10 l Emblem, flag .55 .22

Alpine Village Festival, by Danish Jukniu A432

Industrial Development Paintings: 80q, Hydroelectric Station Builders, by Ali Miruku. 1.20 l, Steel Workers, by Clirim Ceka. 1.55 l, Oil drillers, by Pandeli Lena. 1.90 l, Trapping the Furnace, by Jorgji Gjikopulli.

1982, July ***Perf. 12½***

2035 A432 25q multi .15 .15
2036 A432 80q multi .32 .15
2037 A432 1.20 l multi .48 .20
2038 A432 1.55 l multi .65 .28
Nos. 2035-2038 (4) 1.60 .78

Souvenir Sheet

Perf. 12

2039 A432 1.90 l multi 1.00 .40

No. 2039 contains one 54x48mm stamp.

Communist Party Newspaper "Voice of the People," 40th Anniv. — A432a

1982, Aug. 25 Litho. *Perf. 12*
2039A A432a 80q Newspapers
2039B A432a 1.10 l Paper, press

40th Anniv. of Democratic Front — A433

1982, Sept. 16 *Perf. 12*
2040 A433 80q Glory to the Heroes of Peza Monument .40 .18
2041 A433 1.10 l Marchers .55 .22

8th Youth Congress — A434

Handmade Shoulder Bags — A435

1982, Oct. 4
2042 A434 80q multi .40 .18
2043 A434 1.10 l multi .55 .22

1982, Nov.
2044 A435 25q Rug, horiz. .15 .15
2045 A435 80q shown .32 .15
2046 A435 1.20 l Wooden pots, bowls, horiz. .48 .20
2047 A435 1.55 l Jug .65 .28
Nos. 2044-2047 (4) 1.60
Set value .66

70th Anniv. of Independence A436

1982, Nov. 28
2048 A436 20q Ishamil Qemali .15 .15
2049 A436 1.20 l Partisans .48 .20
2050 A436 2.40 l Partisans, diff. .95 .40
Nos. 2048-2050 (3) 1.58 .75

Souvenir Sheet
2051 A436 1.90 l Independence Monument, Tirana 1.00 .40

Dhermi Beach A437

1982, Dec. 20
2052 A437 25q shown .15 .15
2053 A437 80q Sarande .40 .18
2054 A437 1.20 l Ksamil .60 .25
2055 A437 1.55 l Lukove .80 .35
Nos. 2052-2055 (4) 1.95 .93

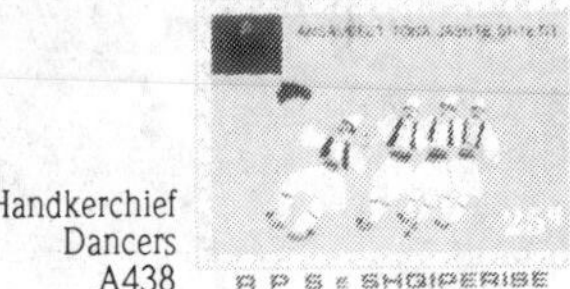
Handkerchief Dancers A438

Folkdancers.

1983, Feb. 20 Litho. *Perf. 12*
2056 A438 25q shown .15 .15
2057 A438 80q With kerchief, drum .40 .18
2058 A438 1.20 l With guitar, flute, tambourine .60 .25
2059 A438 1.55 l Women .80 .35
Nos. 2056-2059 (4) 1.95 .93

A439

A440

1983, Mar. 14 Litho. *Perf. 12*
2060 A439 80q multi .40 .18
2061 A439 1.10 l multi .55 .22

Karl Marx (1818-83).

1983, Apr. 20
2062 A440 80q Electricity generation .40 .18
2063 A440 1.10 l Gas & oil production .55 .22

Energy development.

War Martyr Type of 1980

Designs: 25q, Asim Zeneli (1916-43), Nazmi Rushiti (1919-42). 80q, Shyqyri Ishmi (1922-42), Shyqyri Alimerko (1923-43), Myzafer Asqeriu (1918-42). 1.20 l, Qybra Sokoli (1924-44), Qeriba Derri (1905-44), Ylbere Bilibashi (1928-44). 1.55 l, Themo Vasi (1915-43), Abaz Shehu (1905-42).

1983, May 5 Litho. *Perf. 12*
2064 A410 25q multi .15 .15
2065 A410 80q multi .40 .18
2066 A410 1.20 l multi .60 .25
2067 A410 1.55 l multi .80 .35
Nos. 2064-2067 (4) 1.95 .93

Women's Union, 9th Congress — A441

1983, June 1 Litho. *Perf. 12x12½*
2068 A441 80q red & gold .40 .18
2069 A441 1.10 l bl & gold .55 .22

Bicycling A442

1983, June 20 *Perf. 12*
2070 A442 25q shown .15 .15
2071 A442 80q Chess .40 .18
2072 A442 1.20 l Gymnastics .60 .25
2073 A442 1.55 l Wrestling .80 .35
Nos. 2070-2073 (4) 1.95 .93

40th Anniv. of People's Army — A443

1983, July 10
2074 A443 20q Armed services .15 .15
2075 A443 1.20 l Soldier, gun barrels .60 .25
2076 A443 2.40 l Factory guard, crowd 1.20 .50
Nos. 2074-2076 (3) 1.95 .90

Sunny Day, by Myrteza Fushekati A444

Paintings: 80q, Messenger of the Grasp, by Niko Progi. 1.20 l, 29 November 1944, by Harilla Dhimo. 1.55 l, Fireworks, by Pandi Mele. 1.90 l, Partisan Assault, by Sali Shijaku and M. Fushekati.

1983, Aug. 28 Litho. *Perf. 12½x12*
2077 A444 25q multi .15 .15
2078 A444 80q multi .40 .18
2079 A444 1.20 l multi .60 .25
2080 A444 1.55 l multi .80 .35
Nos. 2077-2080 (4) 1.95 .93

Souvenir Sheet
Perf. 12
2081 A444 1.90 l multi 4.00 .50

Folklore Festival Type of 1978

Gjirokaster Folklore Festival: folkdances.

1983, Oct. 6 Litho. *Perf. 12*
2082 A388 25q Sword dance .15 .15
2083 A388 80q Kerchief dance .40 .18
2084 A388 1.20 l Shepherd flautists .60 .25
2085 A388 1.55 l Garland dance .80 .35
Nos. 2082-2085 (4) 1.95 .93

World Communications Year — A446

1983, Nov. 10
2086 A446 60q multi .30 .15
2087 A446 1.20 l multi .60 .25

75th Birthday of Enver Hoxha — A447

1983, Oct. 16 Litho. *Perf. 12½*
2088 A447 80q multi .40 .18
2089 A447 1.20 l multi .60 .25
2090 A447 1.80 l multi .90 .38
Nos. 2088-2090 (3) 1.90 .81

Souvenir Sheet
Perf. 12
2091 A447 1.90 l multi 1.00 .50

The Right to a Joint Triumph, by J. Keraj A448

Era of Skanderbeg in Figurative Art: 80q, The Heroic Center of the Battle of Krujes, by N. Bakalli. 1.20 l, The Rights of the Enemy after our Triumph, by N. Progri. 1.55 l, The Discussion at Lezhes, by B. Ahmeti. 1.90 l, Victory over the Turks, by G. Madhi.

1983, Dec. 10 *Perf. 12½x12*
2092 A448 25q multi .15 .15
2093 A448 80q multi .40 .18
2094 A448 1.20 l multi .60 .25
2095 A448 1.55 l multi .80 .35
Nos. 2092-2095 (4) 1.95 .93

Souvenir Sheet
Perf. 12
2096 A448 1.90 l multi 1.25 .50

Greco-Roman Ruins of Illyria — A449

1983, Dec. 28 *Perf. 12*
2097 A449 80q Amphitheater, Buthroxtum .40 .18
2098 A449 1.20 l Colonnade, Apollonium .60 .25
2099 A449 1.80 l Vaulted gallery, amphitheater at Epidamnus .90 .38
Nos. 2097-2099 (3) 1.90 .81

Archeological Discoveries A450

Designs: Apollo, 3rd cent. 25q, Tombstone, Korce, 3rd cent. 80q, Apollo, diff. 1st cent. 1.10 l, Earthenware pot (child's head), Tren, 1st cent. 1.20 l, Man's head, Dyrrah, 2.20 l, Eros with Dolphin, statue Bronze Dyrrah, 3rd cent.

1984, Feb. 25 *Perf. 12x12½*
2100 A450 15q multi .15 .15
2101 A450 25q multi .15 .15
2102 A450 80q multi .40 .18
2103 A450 1.10 l multi .55 .22
2104 A450 1.20 l multi .60 .25
2105 A450 2.20 l multi 1.10 .50
Nos. 2100-2105 (6) 2.95
Set value 1.25

Clock Towers — A451

1984, Mar. 30 Litho. *Perf. 12*
2106 A451 15q Gjirokaster .15 .15
2107 A451 25q Kavaje .15 .15
2108 A451 80q Elbasan .40 .18
2109 A451 1.10 l Tirana .55 .22
2110 A451 1.20 l Peqin .60 .25
2111 A451 2.20 l Kruje 1.10 .50
Nos. 2106-2111 (6) 2.95
Set value 1.25

40th Anniv. of Liberation A452

1984, Apr. 20 Litho. *Perf. 12*
2112 A452 15q Student & microscope .15 .15
2113 A452 25q Guerrilla with flag .15 .15
2114 A452 80q Children with flag .40 .18
2115 A452 1.10 l Soldier .55 .22
2116 A452 1.20 l Workers with flag .60 .25
2117 A452 2.20 l Militia at dam 1.10 .50
Nos. 2112-2117 (6) 2.95
Set value 1.25

Children — A453

1984, May **Litho.** ***Perf. 12***

2118 A453 15q Children reading .15 .15
2119 A453 25q Young pioneers .15 .15
2120 A453 60q Gardening .30 .15
2121 A453 2.80 l Kite flying 1.40 .60
Nos. 2118-2121 (4) 2.00
Set value .84

War Martyr Type of 1980

Designs: 15q, Manush Almani, Mustafa Matohiti, Kastriot Muco. 25q, Zaho Koka, Reshit Collaku, Maliq Muco. 1.20 l, Lefter Talo, Tom Kola, Fuat Babani. 2.20 l, Myslysm Shyri, Dervish Hexali, Skender Caci.

1984, May 5 **Litho.** ***Perf. 12***

2122 A410 15q multi .15 .15
2123 A410 25q multi .15 .15
2124 A410 1.20 l multi .65 .30
2125 A410 2.20 l multi 1.25 .60
Nos. 2122-2125 (4) 2.20
Set value 1.00

A454 A455

1984, May 24 **Litho.** ***Perf. 12***

2126 A454 80q Enver Hoxha .45 .20
2127 A454 1.10 l Resistance fighter .65 .30

40th anniv. of Permet Congress.

1984, June 12 **Litho.** ***Perf. 12***

2128 A455 15q Goalkeeper .15 .15
2129 A455 25q Referee .20 .15
2130 A455 1.20 l Map of Europe .90 .45
2131 A455 2.20 l Field diagram 1.75 .90
Nos. 2128-2131 (4) 3.00 1.65

European soccer championships.

Freedom Came, by Myrteza Fushekati A456

Paintings, Tirana Gallery of Figurative Art: 25q, Morning, by Zamir Mati, vert. 80q, My Darling, by Agim Zajmi, vert. 2.60 l, For the Partisans, by Arben Basha. 1.90 l, Eagle, by Zamir Mati, vert.

1984, June 12 ***Perf. 12½***

2132 A456 15q multi .15 .15
2133 A456 25q multi .16 .15
2134 A456 80q multi .48 .25
2135 A456 2.60 l multi 1.65 .80
Nos. 2132-2135 (4) 2.44 1.35

Souvenir Sheet

Perf. 12 Horiz.

2136 A456 1.90 l multi 1.25 .60

Flora — A457

1984, Aug. 20 **Litho.** ***Perf. 12***

2137 A457 15q Moraceae L. .15 .15
2138 A457 25q Plantaginaceae L. .25 .15
2139 A457 1.20 l Hypericaceae L. 1.15 .58
2140 A457 2.20 l Leontopodium alpinum 2.10 1.05
Nos. 2137-2140 (4) 3.65 1.93

AUSIPEX '84, Melbourne, Sept. 21-30 — A458

1984, Sept. 21 **Litho.** ***Perf. 12 Horiz.***

2141 A458 1.90 l Sword dancers, emblem 1.50 .75

A459 A460

Forestry, logging, UNFAO emblem.

1984, Sept. 25 ***Perf. 12***

2142 A459 15q Beech trees, transport .15 .15
2143 A459 25q Pine forest, logging cable .20 .15
2144 A459 1.20 l Firs, sawmill .90 .45
2145 A459 2.20 l Forester clearing woods 1.75 .90
Nos. 2142-2145 (4) 3.00 1.65

1984, Oct. 13 ***Perf. 12½***

2146 A460 1.20 l View of Gjirokaster .90 .45

EURPHILA '84, Rome.

5th National Spartakiad — A461

1984, Oct. 19 ***Perf. 12***

2147 A461 15q Soccer .15 .15
2148 A461 25q Women's track & field .20 .15
2149 A461 80q Weight lifting .60 .30
2150 A461 2.20 l Pistol shooting 1.75 .90
Nos. 2147-2150 (4) 2.70 1.50

Souvenir Sheet

Perf. 12 Horiz.

2151 A461 1.90 l Opening ceremony, red flags 1.50 .75

November 29 Revolution, 40th Anniv. A462

1984, Nov. 29 ***Perf. 12***

2152 A462 80q Industrial reconstruction .60 .30
2153 A462 1.10 l Natl. flag, partisans .80 .40

Souvenir Sheet

Perf. 12 Horiz.

2154 A462 1.90 l Gen. Enver Hoxha reading 1944 declaration 1.50 .75

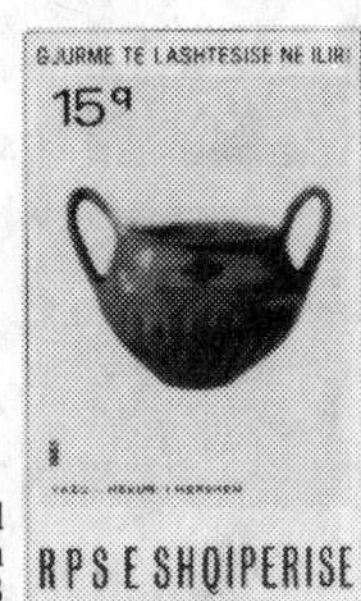

Archaeological Discoveries from Illyria — A463

Designs: 15q, Iron Age water container. 80q, Terra-cotta woman's head, 6th-7th cent. B.C. 1.20 l, Aphrodite, bust, 3rd cent. B.C. 1.70 l, Nike, A.D. 1st-2nd cent. bronze statue.

1985, Feb. 25 ***Perf. 12x12½***

2155 A463 15q multi .16 .15
2156 A463 80q multi .78 .40
2157 A463 1.20 l multi 1.15 .55
2158 A463 1.70 l multi 1.75 .85
Nos. 2155-2158 (4) 3.84 1.95

Hysni Kapo (1915-1980), Natl. Labor Party Leader — A464

1985, Mar. 4 ***Perf. 12***

2159 A464 90q red & blk .85 .42
2160 A464 1.10 l chlky bl & blk 1.10 .55

OLYMPHILEX '85, Lausanne A465

1985, Mar. 18

2161 A465 25q Women's track & field .25 .15
2162 A465 60q Weight lifting .58 .30
2163 A465 1.20 l Soccer 1.15 .55
2164 A465 1.50 l Women's pistol shooting 1.25 .65
Nos. 2161-2164 (4) 3.23 1.65

Johann Sebastian Bach — A466

1985, Mar. 31

2165 A466 80q Portrait, manuscript .78 .40
2166 A466 1.20 l Eisenach, birthplace 1.15 .55

Gen. Enver Hoxha (1908-1985) A467

1985, Apr. 11 ***Perf. 12½***

2167 A467 80q multi .78 .40

Souvenir Sheet

Imperf

2168 A467 1.90 l multi 2.00 1.00

Natl. Frontier Guards, 40th Anniv. A468

1985, Apr. 25 ***Perf. 12***

2169 A468 25q Guardsman, family .25 .15
2170 A468 80q At frontier post .78 .40

War Martyrs Type of 1980

Cameo portraits: 25q, Mitro Xhani (1916-44), Nimete Progonati (1929-44), Kozma Nushi (1909-44). 40q, Ajet Xhindoli (1922-43), Mustafa Kacaci (1903-44), Estref Caka Osaja (1919-44). 60q, Celo Sinani (1929-44), Lt. Ambro Andoni (1920-44), Meleq Gosnishti (1913-44). 1.20 l, Thodhori Mastora (1920-44), Fejzi Micoli (1919-45), Hysen Cino (1920-44).

1985, May 5

2171 A410 25q multi .25 .15
2172 A410 40q multi .40 .20
2173 A410 60q multi .58 .30
2174 A410 1.20 l multi 1.15 .55
Nos. 2171-2174 (4) 2.38 1.20

Victory over Fascism A469

Designs: 25q, Rifle, red flag, inscribed May 9. 80q, Hand holding rifle, globe, broken swastika.

1985, May 9

2175 A469 25q multi .25 .15
2176 A469 80q multi .78 .40

End of World War II, 40th anniv.

Primary School, by Thoma Malo A470

Paintings, Tirana Gallery of Figurative Art: 80q, The Heroes, by Hysen Devolli, vert. 90q, In Our Days, by Angjelin Dodmasej, vert. 1.20 l, Going Off to Sow, by Ksenofon Dilo. 1.90 l, Foundry Workers, by Mikel Gurashi.

1985, June 25 ***Perf. 12½***

2177 A470 25q multi .25 .15
2178 A470 80q multi .78 .40
2179 A470 90q multi .85 .42
2180 A470 1.20 l multi 1.15 .55
Nos. 2177-2180 (4) 3.03 1.52

Souvenir Sheet

Perf. 12 Horiz.

2181 A470 1.90 l multi 2.00 1.00

Basketball Championships, Spain — A471

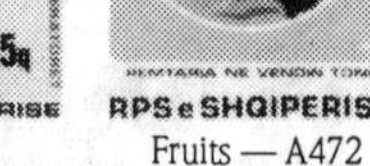

Fruits — A472

Various plays.

1985, July 20 **Litho.** ***Perf. 12***

2182 A471 25q dl bl & blk .22 .15
2183 A471 80q dl grn & blk .78 .40
2184 A471 1.20 l dl vio & blk 1.15 .58
2185 A471 1.60 l dl rose & blk 1.50 .75
Nos. 2182-2185 (4) 3.65 1.88

1985, Aug. 20

No.	Type	Value	Description	Unused	Used
2186	A472	25q	Oranges	.22	.15
2187	A472	80q	Plums	.78	.40
2188	A472	1.20 l	Apples	1.15	.58
2189	A472	1.60 l	Cherries	1.50	.75
			Nos. 2186-2189 (4)	3.65	1.88

Architecture A473

1985, Sept. 20

No.	Type	Value	Description	Unused	Used
2190	A473	25q	Kruja	.22	.15
2191	A473	80q	Gjirokastra	.78	.40
2192	A473	1.20 l	Berati	1.15	.58
2193	A473	1.60 l	Shkodera	1.50	.75
			Nos. 2190-2193 (4)	3.65	1.88

Natl. Folk Theater Festival — A474

Various scenes from folk plays.

1985, Oct. 6

No.	Type	Value	Description	Unused	Used
2194	A474	25q	multi	.22	.15
2195	A474	80q	multi	.78	.40
2196	A474	1.20 l	multi	1.15	.58
2197	A474	1.60 l	multi	1.50	.75

Size: 56x82mm

Imperf

No.	Type	Value	Description	Unused	Used
2198	A474	1.90 l	multi	3.50	1.90
			Nos. 2194-2198 (5)	7.15	3.78

Socialist People's Republic, 40th Anniv. A475

1986, Jan. 11 Litho. *Perf. 12½*

No.	Type	Value	Description	Unused	Used
2199	A475	25q	Natl. crest, vert.	.25	.15
2200	A475	80q	Proclamation, 1946	.78	.40

A476

A477

Designs: 25q, Dam, River Drin, Melgun. 80q, Bust of Enver Hoxha, dam power house.

1986, Feb. 20 *Perf. 12*

No.	Type	Value	Description	Unused	Used
2201	A476	25q	multi	.25	.15
2202	A476	80q	multi	.78	.40

Enver Hoxha hydro-electric power station, Koman.

1986, Mar. 20 Litho. *Perf. 12*

Flowers.

No.	Type	Value	Description	Unused	Used
2203	A477	25q	Gymnospermium shqipetarum	.22	.15
2204	A477	1.20 l	Leucojum valentinum	1.15	.58

Nos. 2203-2204 printed se-tenant. Sold only in booklets of 2; exist imperf.

A478

Famous Men — A479

Designs: 25q, Maxim Gorky, Russian author. 80q, Andre Marie Ampere, French physicist. 1.20 l, James Watt, English inventor of modern steam engine. 2.40 l, Franz Liszt, Hungarian composer.

1986, Apr. 20

No.	Type	Value	Description	Unused	Used
2205			Strip of 4	4.40	2.20
a.	A478	25q	dull red brown	.25	.15
b.	A478	80q	dull violet	.78	.40
c.	A478	1.20 l	blue green	1.15	.58
d.	A478	2.40 l	dull lilac rose	2.20	1.10

Size: 88x72mm

Imperf

No.	Type	Value	Description	Unused	Used
2206	A479	1.90 l	multi	1.75	.88

No. 2206 has central area picturing Gorky, Ampere, Watt and Liszt, perf. 12½.

War Martyrs Type of 1980

Portraits: 25q, Ramiz Aranitasi (1923-43), Inajete Dumi (1924-44) and Laze Nuro Ferraj (1897-1944). 80q, Dine Kalenja (1919-44), Kozma Naska (1921-44), Met Hasa (1929-44) and Fahri Ramadani (1920-44). 1.20 l, Hiqmet Buzi (1927-44), Bajram Tusha (1922-42), Mumin Selami (1923-42) and Hajrfdin Bylyshi (1923-42).

1986, May 5 *Perf. 12*

No.	Type	Value	Description	Unused	Used
2207	A410	25q	multi	.25	.15
2208	A410	80q	multi	.78	.40
2209	A410	1.20 l	multi	1.15	.55
			Nos. 2207-2209 (3)	2.18	1.10

A480

1986 World Cup Soccer Championships, Mexico — A481

1986, May 31 Litho. *Perf. 12*

No.	Type	Value	Description	Unused	Used
2210	A480	25q	Globe, world cup	.22	.15
2211	A480	1.20 l	Player, soccer ball	1.15	.58

Size: 97x64mm

Imperf

No.	Type	Value	Description	Unused	Used
2212	A481	1.90 l	multi	1.75	.88
			Nos. 2210-2212 (3)	3.12	1.61

No. 2212 has central label, perf. 12½.

Transportation Workers' Day, 40th Anniv. — A482

1986, Aug. 10 Litho. *Perf. 12*

No.	Type	Value	Description	Unused	Used
2213	A482	1.20 l	multi	1.15	.58

Prominent Albanians A483

Designs: 30q, Naim Frasheri (1846-1900), poet. 60q, Ndre Mjeda (1866-1937), poet. 90q, Petro Nini Luarasi (1865-1911), poet, journalist. 1 l, Andon Zako Cajupi (1866-1930), poet. 1.20 l, Millosh Gjergj Nikolla Migjeni (1911-1938), novelist. 2.60 l, Urani Rumbo (1884-1936), educator.

1986, Sept. 20 Litho. *Perf. 12*

No.	Type	Value	Description	Unused	Used
2214	A483	30q	multi	.30	.15
2215	A483	60q	multi	.58	.30
2216	A483	90q	multi	.88	.45
2217	A483	1 l	multi	.95	.48
2218	A483	1.20 l	multi	1.15	.58
2219	A483	2.60 l	multi	2.50	1.25
			Nos. 2214-2219 (6)	6.36	3.21

Albanian Workers' Party, 9th Congress, Tirana A484

1986, Nov. 3 Litho. *Perf. 12*

No.	Type	Value	Description	Unused	Used
2220	A484	30q	multi	.30	.25

A485

A486

Albanian Workers' Party, 45th Anniv.: 30q, Handstamp, signature of Hoxha. 1.20 l, Marx, Engels, Lenin and Stalin, party building.

1986, Nov. 8

No.	Type	Value	Description	Unused	Used
2221	A485	30q	multi	.30	.15
2222	A485	1.20 l	multi	1.15	.58

1986, Nov. 29 *Perf. 12x12½*

Statue of Mother Albania.

No.	Type	Value	Description	Unused	Used
2223	A486	10q	peacock blue	.15	.15
2224	A486	20q	henna brn	.20	.15
2225	A486	30q	vermilion	.30	.15
2226	A486	50q	dk olive bis	.50	.25
2227	A486	60q	lt olive grn	.58	.30
2228	A486	80q	rose	.78	.40
2229	A486	90q	ultra	.88	.45
2230	A486	1.20 l	green	1.15	.58
2231	A486	1.60 l	red vio	1.50	.75
2232	A486	2.20 l	myrtle grn	2.10	1.05
2233	A486	3 l	brn org	2.75	1.40
2234	A486	6 l	yel bister	5.50	2.25
			Nos. 2223-2234 (12)	16.39	7.88

For surcharges see Nos. 2435-2439.

Artifacts A487

Designs: 30q, Head of Aesoulapius, 5th cent. B.C. Byllis, marble. 80q, Aphrodite, 3rd cent. B.C., Fier, terracotta. 1 l, Pan, 3rd-2nd cent, B.C., Byllis, bronze. 1.20 l, Jupiter, A.D. 2nd cent., Tirana, limestone.

1987, Feb. 20

No.	Type	Value	Description	Unused	Used
2235	A487	30q	multi	.30	.15
2236	A487	80q	multi	.78	.40
2237	A487	1 l	multi	.95	.48
2238	A487	1.20 l	multi	1.15	.58
			Nos. 2235-2238 (4)	3.18	1.61

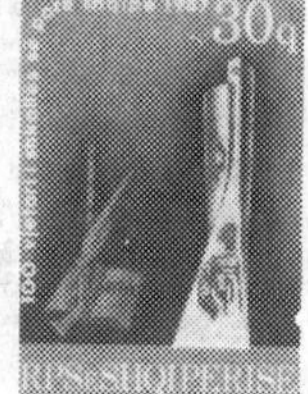

1st Albanian School, Cent. — A488

Famous Men — A489

Gun, quill pen, book of the alphabet and: 30q, Monument, vert. 80q, School, Korca. 1.20 l, Students.

1987, Mar. 7 *Perf. 12*

No.	Type	Value	Description	Unused	Used
2239	A488	30q	multi	.30	.15
2240	A488	80q	multi	.75	.38
2241	A488	1.20 l	multi	1.15	.58
			Nos. 2239-2241 (3)	2.20	1.11

1987, Apr. 20

Designs: 30q, Victor Hugo, French author. 80q, Galileo Galilei, Italian mathematician, philosopher. 90q, Charles Darwin, British biologist. 1.30 l, Miguel Cervantes, Spanish novelist.

No.	Type	Value	Description	Unused	Used
2242	A489	30q	multi	.30	.15
2243	A489	80q	multi	.75	.38
2244	A489	90q	multi	.88	.45
2245	A489	1.30 l	multi	1.25	.80
			Nos. 2242-2245 (4)	3.18	1.78

World Food Day — A490

10th Trade Unions Cong. — A491

1987, May 20

No.	Type	Value	Description	Unused	Used
2246	A490	30q	Forsythia europaea	.30	.15
2247	A490	90q	Moltkia doerfleri	.88	.45
2248	A490	2.10 l	Wulfenia baldacii	2.00	1.00
			Nos. 2246-2248 (3)	3.18	1.60

1987, June 25

No.	Type	Value	Description	Unused	Used
2249	A491	1.20 l	multi	1.15	.58

Sowing, by Bujar Asllani — A492

Paintings in the Eponymous Museum, Tirana: 30q, The Sustenance of Industry, by Myrteza Fushekati, vert. 80q, The Gifted Partisan, by

Skender Kokobobo, vert. 1.20 l, At the Forging Block, by Clirim Ceka.

Perf. 12x12½, 12½x12

1987, July 20 **Litho.**
2250 A492 30q multi .30 .15
2251 A492 80q multi .80 .40
2252 A492 1 l shown 1.00 .50
2253 A492 1.20 l multi 1.20 .60
Nos. 2250-2253 (4) 3.30 1.65

A493

OLYMPHILEX '87, Rome, Aug. 29-Sept. 6 — A494

Illustration A494 reduced.

1987, Aug. 29 **Litho.** *Perf. 12½*
2254 A493 30q Hammer throw .30 .15
2255 A493 90q Running .90 .45
2256 A493 1.10 l Shot put 1.15 .58

Size: 85x60mm

2257 A494 1.90 l Runner, globe 2.00 1.00
Nos. 2254-2257 (4) 4.35 2.18

Famous Men — A495

Designs: 30q, Themistokli Germenji (1871-1917), author, politician. 80q, Bajram Curri (1862-1925), founder of the Albanian League. 90q, Aleks Stavre Drenova (1872-1947), poet. 1.30 l, Gjerasim D. Qiriazi (1861-1894), teacher, journalist.

1987, Sept. 30 *Perf. 12*
2258 A495 30q multi .30 .15
2259 A495 80q multi .80 .40
2260 A495 90q multi .90 .45
2261 A495 1.30 l multi 1.30 .65
Nos. 2258-2261 (4) 3.30 1.65

Albanian Labor Party Congress, Tirana A496

1987, Oct. 22 **Litho.** *Perf. 12*
2262 A496 1.20 l multi 1.20 .60

Natl. Independence, 75th Anniv. — A497

Postal Administration, 75th Anniv. — A498

1987, Nov. 27
2263 A497 1.20 l State flag 1.20 .60

1987, Dec. 5
2264 A498 90q P.O. emblem .90 .45
2265 A498 1.20 l State seal 1.20 .60

Art & Literature — A499

WHO, 40th Anniv. — A500

Portraits: 30q, Lord Byron (1788-1824), English Poet. 1.20 l, Eugene Delacroix (1798-1863), French painter.

1988, Mar. 10
2266 A499 30q org brn & blk .30 .15
2267 A499 1.20 l pale vio & blk 1.20 .60

1988, Apr. 7
2268 A500 90q multi .90 .45
2269 A500 1.20 l multi 1.20 .60

Flowers — A501

1988, May 20
2270 A501 30q *Sideritis raeseri* .30 .15
2271 A501 90q *Lunaria telekiana* .90 .45
2272 A501 2.10 l *Sanguisorba albanica* 2.10 1.05
a. Bklt. pane of 3, plus label 3.50
Nos. 2270-2272 (3) 3.30 1.65

Nos. 2270-2272 issued in No. 2272a only.

10th Women's Federation Congress A502

1988, June 6
2273 A502 90q blk, red & dark org .90 .45

European Soccer Championships — A503

Various athletes. 1.90 l, Goalie designs of Nos. 2274-2276.

1988, June 10
2274 A503 30q multicolored .30 .15
2275 A503 80q multicolored .80 .40
2276 A503 1.20 l multicolored 1.20 .60

Size: 79x68mm

Imperf

2277 A503 1.90 l multicolored 1.90 .95
Nos. 2274-2277 (4) 4.20 2.10

Migjeni (1911-1938), Poet — A507

1988, Aug. 26 **Litho.** *Perf. 12*
2285 A507 90q sil & brn .95 .48

Ballads — A508

1988, Sept. 5
2286 A508 30q Dede Skurra .32 .16
2287 A508 90q Omeri Iri 1.00 .50
2288 A508 1.20 l Gjergj Elez Alia 1.30 .65
Nos. 2286-2288 (3) 2.62 1.31

Folklore Festival Type of 1978

1988, Oct. 6
2289 A388 30q Kerchief Dance .32 .16
2290 A388 1.20 l Dancers with raised arm 1.30 .65

Enver Hoxha Museum A510

Perf. 12x12½, 12½x12

1988, Oct. 16 **Litho.**
2291 A510 90q Portrait, vert. .72 .36
2292 A510 1.20 l shown .95 .48

Enver Hoxha (1908-1985), Communist leader.

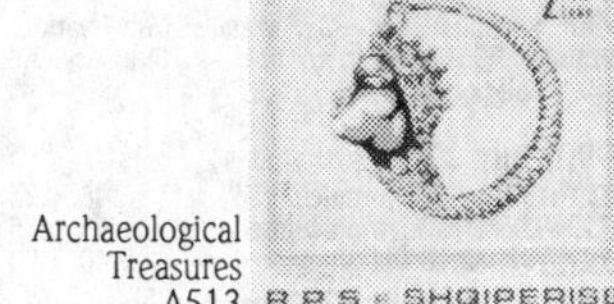

Locomotives, Map Showing Rail Network — A512

1989, Feb. 28 **Litho.** *Perf. 12½x12*
2295 A512 30q 1947 .22 .15
2296 A512 90q 1949 .65 .32
2297 A512 1.20 l 1978 .85 .42
2298 A512 1.80 l 1985 1.25 .65
2299 A512 2.40 l 1988 1.70 .85
Nos. 2295-2299 (5) 4.67 2.39

Archaeological Treasures A513

Designs: 30q, Illyrian grave. 90q, Warrior on horseback.

1989, Mar. 10 **Litho.** *Perf. 12*
2300 A513 30q blk & tan .22 .15
2301 A513 90q blk & dl grn .65 .34
2302 A513 2.10 l shown 1.50 .75
Nos. 2300-2302 (3) 2.37 1.24

Folklore — A514

1989, Apr. 5 **Litho.** *Perf. 12x12½*
2303 A514 30q multicolored .22 .15
2304 A514 80q multi, diff. .58 .30
2305 A514 1 l multi, diff. .72 .36
2306 A514 1.20 l multi, diff. .86 .44
Nos. 2303-2306 (4) 2.38 1.25

Flowers — A515

Famous People — A516

Designs: 30q, *Aster albanicus.* 90q, *Orchis x paparisti.* 2.10 l, *Orchis albanica.*

1989, May 10 *Perf. 12*
2307 A515 30q multicolored .22 .15
2308 A515 90q multicolored .65 .32
2309 A515 2.10 l multicolored 1.50 .75
Nos. 2307-2309 (3) 2.37 1.22

1989, June 3

Designs: 30q, Johann Strauss the Younger (1825-1899), composer. 80q, Marie Curie (1867-1834), chemist. 1 l, Federico Garcia Lorca (1898-1936), poet. 1.20 l, Albert Einstein (1879-1955), physicist.

2310 A516 30q gold & blk brn .22 .15
2311 A516 80q gold & blk brn .58 .30
2312 A516 1 l gold & blk brn .75 .38
2313 A516 1.20 l gold & blk brn .85 .42
Nos. 2310-2313 (4) 2.40 1.25

6th Congress of Albanian Democratic Front A517

1989, June 26
2314 A517 1.20 l multicolored 1.30 .65

French Revolution, Bicent. — A518

Designs: 90q, Storming of the Bastille. 1.20 l, Statue.

1989, July 7 **Litho.** *Perf. 12½*
2315 A518 90q multicolored .75 .38
2316 A518 1.20 l shown 1.00 .50

Illyrian Ship — A519

1989, July 25 *Perf. 12*
2317 A519 30q shown .22 .15
2318 A519 80q Caravel .58 .30
2319 A519 90q 3-masted schooner .65 .34
2320 A519 1.30 l Modern cargo ship .95 .48
Nos. 2317-2320 (4) 2.40 1.27

A520

A521

Famous Men: 30q, Pjeter Bogdani (1625-1689), writer. 80q, Gavril Dara (1826-1889), poet. 90q, Thimi Mitko (1820-1890), writer. 1.30 l, Kole Idromeno (1860-1939), painter.

1989, Aug. 30 Litho. ***Perf. 12***

2321 A520	30q multicolored		.30	.15
2322 A520	80q multicolored		.80	.40
2323 A520	90q multicolored		.90	.45
2324 A520	1.30 l multicolored		1.30	.65
		Nos. 2321-2324 (4)	3.30	1.65

1989, Sept. 29

2325 A521	90q shown	.72	.35
2326 A521	1.20 l Workers	.95	.48

First Communist International, 125th anniv.

Spartakiad Games — A522

1989, Oct. 27 ***Perf. 12x12½***

2327 A522	30q Gymasnastics		.22	.15
2328 A522	80q Soccer		.58	.30
2329 A522	1 l Cycling		.72	.36
2330 A522	1.20 l Running		.86	.44
		Nos. 2327-2330 (4)	2.38	1.25

Miniature Sheet

45th Anniv. of Liberation — A523

1989, Nov. 29 ***Perf. 12x12½***

2331	Sheet of 4	2.50	1.25
a.	A523 30q Revolutionary	.22	.15
b.	A523 80q "45"	.58	.30
c.	A523 1 l Coat of arms	.72	.36
d.	A523 1.20 l Workers	.86	.44

Rupicapra Rupicapra — A524

1990, Mar. 15 ***Perf. 12***

2332 A524	10q Two adults	.15	.15
2333 A524	30q Adult, kid	.32	.16
2334 A524	80q Adult	.82	.42
2335 A524	90q Adult head	.92	.45
a.	Block of 4, #2332-2335	2.16	1.08

World Wildlife Fund.

Tribal Masks — A525

1990, Apr. 4 ***Perf. 12x12½***

2336 A525	30q shown		.32	.16
2337 A525	90q multi, diff.		.95	.48
2338 A525	1.20 l multi, diff.		1.25	.65
2339 A525	1.80 l multi, diff.		1.90	.95
		Nos. 2336-2339 (4)	4.42	2.24

Mushrooms A526

1990, Apr. 28 Litho. ***Perf. 12***

2340 A526	30q Amanita caesarea		.25	.15
2341 A526	90q Lepiota procera		.75	.40
2342 A526	1.20 l Boletus edulis		1.00	.50
2343 A526	1.80 l Clathrus cancelatus		1.50	.75
		Nos. 2340-2343 (4)	3.50	1.80

First Postage Stamp, 150th Anniv. A527

1990, May 6 ***Perf. 12***

2344 A527	90q shown		.95	.48
2345 A527	1.20 l Post rider		1.25	.62
2346 A527	1.80 l Carriage		1.85	.95
a.	Bklt. pane of 3, #2344-2346 + label		4.25	
		Nos. 2344-2346 (3)	4.05	2.05

World Cup Soccer, Italy — A528

1990, June Litho. ***Perf. 12***

2347 A528	30q multicolored		.48	.24
2348 A528	90q multi, diff.		1.45	.75
2349 A528	1.20 l multi, diff.		1.95	1.00

Size: 80x63mm

Imperf

2350 A528	3.30 l multi, diff.		5.30	2.65
		Nos. 2347-2350 (4)	9.18	4.64

Vincent Van Gogh, Death Cent. A529

Self portraits and: 30q, Details from various paintings. 90q, Woman in field. 2.10 l, Asylum. 2.40 l, Self-portrait.

1990, July 27

2351 A529	30q multicolored		.48	.24
2352 A529	90q multicolored		1.45	.75
2353 A529	2.10 l multicolored		3.40	1.70

Size: 87x73mm

Imperf

2354 A529	2.40 l multicolored		1.85	.95
		Nos. 2351-2354 (4)	7.18	3.64

Albanian Folklore — A530

Scenes from medieval folktale of "Gjergj Elez Alia": 30q, Alia lying wounded. 90q, Alia being helped onto horse. 1.20 l, Alia fighting Bajloz. 1.80 l, Alia on horseback over severed head of Bajloz.

1990, Aug. 30 ***Perf. 12½x12***

2355 A530	30q multicolored		.48	.24
2356 A530	90q multicolored		1.45	.72
2357 A530	1.20 l multicolored		1.95	.95
2358 A530	1.80 l multicolored		2.90	1.45
		Nos. 2355-2358 (4)	6.78	3.36

Founding of Berat, 2400th Anniv. A531

Designs: 30q, Xhamia E Plumbit. 90q, Kisha E Shen Triadhes. 1.20 l, Ura E Beratit. 1.80 l, Onufri-Piktor Mesjetar. 2.40 l, Nikolla-Piktor Mesjetar.

1990, Sept. 20 ***Perf. 12½***

2359	Block of 5 + 4 labels	4.20	2.10
a.	A531 30q multi	.20	.15
b.	A531 90q multi	.65	.32
c.	A531 1.20 l multi	.70	.35
d.	A531 1.80 l multi	1.25	.65
e.	A531 2.40 l multi	1.40	.70

No. 2359 was sold in souvenir folders for 9.90 l.

Illyrian Heroes — A532

1990, Oct. 20 ***Perf. 12***

2360 A532	30q Pirroja		.48	.24
2361 A532	90q Teuta		1.45	.72
2362 A532	1.20 l Bato		1.95	.95
2363 A532	1.80 l Bardhyli		2.90	1.45
		Nos. 2360-2363 (4)	6.78	3.36

Intl. Literacy Year — A533

1990, Oct. 30

2364 A533	90q lt bl & multi	1.45	.72
2365 A533	1.20 l pink & multi	1.95	.95

Albanian Horseman by Eugene Delacroix A534

Designs: 1.20 l, Albanian Woman by Camille Corot. 1.80 l, Skanderbeg by unknown artist.

1990, Nov. 30 ***Perf. 12x12½***

2366 A534	30q multicolored		.48	.24
2367 A534	1.20 l multicolored		1.95	.95
2368 A534	1.80 l multicolored		2.90	1.45
		Nos. 2366-2368 (3)	5.33	2.64

Isa Boletini (1864-1916), Freedom Fighter — A535

1991, Jan. 23 Litho. ***Perf. 12x12½***

2369 A535	90q Portrait	.65	.32
2370 A535	1.20 l shown	.90	.45

Pierre Auguste Renoir (1841-1919), Painter — A537

Paintings: 30q, Girl Reading, 1876, vert. 90q, The Swing, 1876, vert. 1.20 l, Boating Party, 1868-1869. 1.80 l, Flowers and grapes, 1878. 3 l, Self-portrait.

1991, Feb. 25 ***Perf. 12½x12***

2373 A537	30q multicolored		.20	.15
2374 A537	90q multicolored		.65	.32
2375 A537	1.20 l multicolored		.90	.45
2376 A537	1.80 l multicolored		1.30	.65

Size: 95x75mm

Imperf

2377 A537	3 l multicolored		4.80	2.40
		Nos. 2373-2377 (5)	7.85	3.97

Flowers — A538

1991, Mar. 30 ***Perf. 12***

2378 A538	30q Cistus albanicus		.48	.24
2379 A538	90q Trifolium pilczii		1.45	.72
2380 A538	1.80 l Lilium albanicum		2.90	1.45
		Nos. 2378-2380 (3)	4.83	2.41

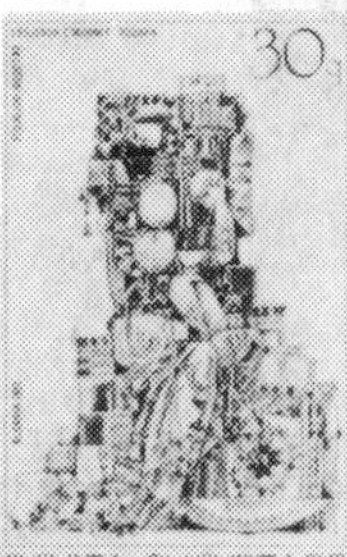

Legend of Rozafa — A539

Various scenes from legend.

1991, Sept. 30 Litho. ***Perf. 12x12½***

2381 A539	30q multicolored		.48	.24
2382 A539	90q multicolored		1.45	.72
2383 A539	1.20 l multicolored		1.95	.95
2384 A539	1.80 l multicolored		2.90	1.45
		Nos. 2381-2384 (4)	6.78	3.36

Wolfgang Amadeus Mozart, Death Bicent. — A540

1991, Oct. 5 Litho. ***Perf. 12***

2385 A540	90q Conducting		.70	.35
2386 A540	1.20 l Portrait		.90	.45
2387 A540	1.80 l Playing piano		1.40	.70

Size: 89x70mm

Imperf

2388 A540	3 l Medal, score		4.00	4.00
		Nos. 2385-2388 (4)	7.00	5.50

Airplanes A541

Designs: 30q, Glider, Otto Lilienthal, 1896. 80q, Avion III, Clement Ader, 1897. 90q, Flyer, Wright Brothers, 1903. 1.20 l, Concorde. 1.80 l, Tupolev 114. 2.40 l, Dornier 31 E.

1992, Jan. 27 Litho. *Perf. 12½x12*

2389	A541	30q	multicolored	.48	.24
2390	A541	80q	multicolored	1.30	.65
2391	A541	90q	multicolored	1.45	.72
2392	A541	1.20 l	multicolored	1.95	.95
2393	A541	1.80 l	multicolored	2.90	1.45
2394	A541	2.40 l	multicolored	4.00	2.00
			Nos. 2389-2394 (6)	12.08	6.01

No. 2393 misidentifies a Tupolev 144.

Explorers A542

1992, Jan. 10

2395	A542	30q	Bering	.48	.24
2396	A542	90q	Columbus	1.45	.72
2397	A542	1.80 l	Magellan	2.90	1.45
			Nos. 2395-2397 (3)	4.83	2.41

1992 Winter Olympics, Albertville A543

1992, Feb. 15 Litho. *Perf. 12½*

2398	A543	30q	Ski jumping	.24	.15
2399	A543	90q	Cross country skiing	.70	.35
2400	A543	1.20 l	Pairs figure skating	.95	.48
2401	A543	1.80 l	Luge	1.45	.70
			Nos. 2398-2401 (4)	3.34	1.68

Participation of Albania in Conference on Security and Cooperation in Europe, Berlin (1991) — A544

1992, Mar. 31 Litho. *Perf. 12½x12*

2402	A544	90q	shown	*.95*	*.95*
2403	A544	1.20 l	Flags, map	*1.25*	*1.25*
a.			Pair, #2402-2403	*2.25*	*2.25*

Dated 1991. Issued in sheets containing 2 #2403a, 3 each #2402-2403 + 2 labels.

Albanian Admission to CEPT A545

1992, Apr. 25 Litho. *Perf. 12½*

2404	A545	90q	Envelopes, CEPT emblem	.90	.90
2405	A545	1.20 l	shown	1.20	1.20
a.			Pair, #2404-2405	2.25	2.25

Issued in sheets containing 2 #2405a, 3 each #2404-2405 and 2 labels.

Martyrs' Day — A546

1992, May 5 *Perf. 12x12½*

2406	A546	90q	Freedom flame, vert.	*1.00*	*1.00*

Perf. 12½x12

2407	A546	4.10 l	Flowers	*4.50*	*4.50*

European Soccer Championships, Sweden'92 — A547

Various stylized designs of soccer plays.

1992, June 10 Litho. *Perf. 12*

2408	A547	30q	green & lt grn	.15	.15
2409	A547	90q	blue & pink	.25	.25
2410	A547	10.80 l	henna & tan	3.00	3.00

Size: 90x70mm

Imperf

2411	A547	5 l	tan, lt green & pink	1.40	1.40
			Nos. 2408-2411 (4)	4.80	4.80

1992 Summer Olympics, Barcelona A548

1992, June 14 Litho. *Perf. 12*

2412	A548	30q	Tennis	*.35*	*.35*
2413	A548	90q	Baseball	*1.00*	*1.00*
2414	A548	1.80 l	Table tennis	*2.00*	*2.00*

Size: 90x70mm

Imperf

2415	A548	5 l	Torch bearer	*1.45*	*1.45*
			Nos. 2412-2415 (4)	*4.80*	*4.80*

United Europe A549

1992, July 10 Litho. *Perf. 12*

2416	A549	1.20 l	multicolored	.90	.45

Horses A550

1992, Aug. 10 Litho. *Perf. 12*

2417	A550	30q	Native	*.15*	*.15*
2418	A550	90q	Nonius	*.24*	*.24*
2419	A550	1.20 l	Arabian, vert.	*.32*	*.32*
2420	A550	10.60 l	Haflinger, vert.	*2.75*	*2.75*
			Nos. 2417-2420 (4)	*3.46*	*3.46*

Discovery of America, 500th Anniv. A551

Map of North and South America and: 60q, Columbus, sailing ships. 3.20 l, Columbus meeting natives.

1992, Aug. 20

2421	A551	60q	blk, bl & gray	*.24*	*.24*
2422	A551	3.20 l	blk, brn & gray	*1.25*	*1.25*

Size: 90x70mm

Imperf

2423	A551	5 l	Map, Columbus		

A552 A553

Mother Theresa, infant.

1992, Oct. 4 Litho. *Perf. 12x12½*

2424	A552	40q	fawn	*.15*	*.15*
2425	A552	60q	brown	*.15*	*.15*
2426	A552	1 l	violet	*.15*	*.15*
2427	A552	1.80 l	gray	*.28*	*.28*
2428	A552	2 l	red	*.30*	*.30*
2429	A552	2.40 l	green	*.35*	*.35*
2430	A552	3.20 l	blue	*.48*	*.48*
2431	A552	5.60 l	rose violet	*.85*	*.85*
2432	A552	7.20 l	olive	*1.05*	*1.05*
2433	A552	10 l	orange brown	*1.50*	*1.50*
			Nos. 2424-2433 (10)	*5.26*	*5.26*

See Nos. 2472-2476.

1993, Apr. 25 Litho. *Perf. 12*

2434	A553	16 l	multicolored	*2.50*	*2.50*

Visit of Pope John Paul II.

POSTA SHQIPTARE

Nos. 2223-2226, 2229 Surcharged

1993, May 2 Litho. *Perf. 12x12½*

2435	A486	3 l	on 10q	*.58*	*.58*
2436	A486	6.50 l	on 20q	*1.25*	*1.25*
2437	A486	13 l	on 30q	*2.55*	*2.55*
2438	A486	20 l	on 90q	*3.90*	*3.90*
2439	A486	30 l	on 50q	*5.85*	*5.85*
			Nos. 2435-2439 (5)	*14.13*	*14.13*

Lef Nosi (1873-1945), Minister of Posts — A554

1993, May 5 Litho. *Perf. 12*

2440	A554	6.50 l	olive brown & bister	*.90*	*.90*

First Albanian postage stamps, 80th anniv.

Europa A555

Contemporary paintings by: 3 l, A. Zajmi, vert. 7 l, E. Hila. 20 l, B. Ahmeti-Peizazh.

1993, May 28 Litho. *Perf. 12*

2441	A555	3 l	multicolored	*.55*	*.55*
2442	A555	7 l	multicolored	*1.25*	*1.25*

Size: 116x122mm

2443	A555	20 l	multicolored	*3.75*	*3.75*
			Nos. 2441-2443 (3)	*5.55*	*5.55*

1993 Mediterranean Games, France A556

1993, June 20 Litho. *Perf. 12*

2444	A556	3 l	Running	.55	.55
2445	A556	16 l	Kayaking	3.00	3.00
2446	A556	21 l	Cycling	3.75	3.75

Size: 111x78mm

Imperf

2447	A556	20 l	Mediterranean map	3.50	3.50
			Nos. 2444-2447 (4)	10.80	10.80

Frang Bardhi, Author, 350th Death Anniv. — A557

1993, Aug. 20 Litho. *Perf. 12x12½*

2448	A557	6.50 l	shown	1.10	1.10

Size: 89x101mm

Imperf

2449	A557	20 l	Writing at desk	3.50	3.50

A558 A559

1994, July 17 Litho. *Perf. 12*

2450	A558	42 l	shown	1.50	1.50
2451	A558	68 l	Mascot, ball, US map	2.50	2.50

1994 World Cup Soccer Championships, US.

1994, Dec. 31 Litho. *Perf. 14*

European Inventors, Discoveries: 50 l, Gjovalin Gjadri, engineer. 100 l, Karl von Ghega, Austrian engineer. 150 l, Sketch of road project.

2452	A559	50 l	multicolored	2.00	2.00
2453	A559	100 l	multicolored	4.00	4.00

Size: 50x70mm

Imperf

2454	A559	150 l	multicolored	6.00	6.00
			Nos. 2452-2454 (3)	12.00	12.00

Europa (#2454).

Ali Pasa of Tepelene (Lion of Janina) (1744-1822) A560

1995, Jan. 28 *Perf. 14*

2455	A560	60 l	shown	2.50	2.50

Size: 70x50mm

Imperf

2456	A560	100 l	Tepelene Palace	4.00	4.00

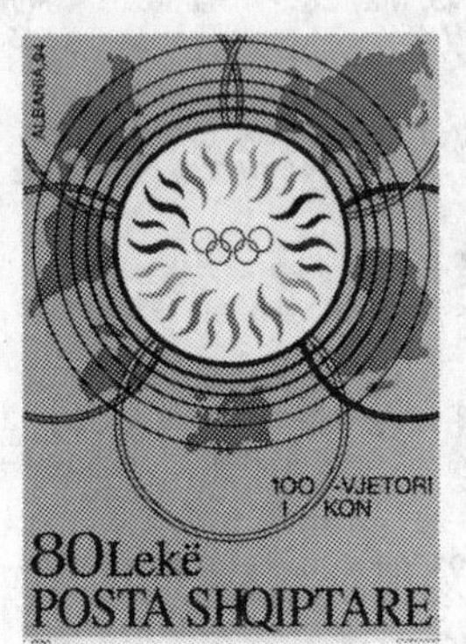

Intl. Olympic Committee, Cent. — A561

1995, Feb. 2 *Imperf.*
2457 A561 80 l multicolored 3.25 3.25

Karl Benz (1844-1929), Automobile Pioneer — A562

Designs: 5 l, Automobile company emblem, Benz. 10 l, Modern Mercedes Benz automobile. 60 l, First four-wheel Benz 1886 motor car. 125 l, Pre-war Mercedes touring car.

1995, Jan. 21 Litho. *Perf. 14*
2458 A562 5 l multicolored .15 .15
2459 A562 10 l multicolored .30 .30
2460 A562 60 l multicolored 1.65 1.65
2461 A562 125 l multicolored 3.50 3.50
Nos. 2458-2461 (4) 5.60 5.60

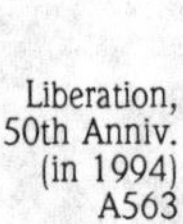

Liberation, 50th Anniv. (in 1994) A563

1995, Jan. 28 Litho. *Perf. 14*
2462 A563 50 l black, gray & red 2.00 2.00
Dated 1994.

Miniature Sheet

Albania '93 — A564

Composers: a, 3 l, Wagner. b, 6.50 l, Grieg. c, 11 l, Gounod. d, 20 l, Tchaikovsky.

1995, Jan. 26 *Perf. 12*
2463 A564 Sheet of 4, #a.-d. 2.00 2.00

Veskopoja Academy, 250th Anniv. — A565

Buildings of Veskopoja.

1995, Feb. 2
2464 A565 42 l multicolored 1.50 1.50
2465 A565 68 l multicolored 2.50 2.50
a. Pair, #2464-2465 4.00 4.00

Bleta Apricula — A566 Peace & Freedom — A567

1995, Aug. 20 Litho. *Perf. 12*
2466 A566 5 l On flower .20 .20
2467 A566 10 l Honeycomb, bee .40 .40
2468 A566 25 l Emerging from cell of honeycomb 1.00 1.00
Nos. 2466-2468 (3) 1.60 1.60

1995, Aug. 10 *Perf. 13½x14*

Stylized hands reaching for: 50 l, Olive branch. 100 l, Peace dove.
150 l, Stylized person.

2469 A567 50 l multicolored 1.50 1.50
2470 A567 100 l multicolored 3.25 3.25

Size: 80x60mm
Imperf
2471 A567 150 l multicolored 4.75 4.75
Europa.

Mother Teresa Type of 1992

1994-95 Litho. *Perf. 12x12½*
2472 A552 5 l violet .25 .25
2473 A552 18 l orange .85 .85
2474 A552 20 l rose lilac .95 .95
2475 A552 25 l green 1.10 1.10
2476 A552 60 l olive 2.75 2.75
Nos. 2472-2476 (5) 5.90 5.90

Issued: 20 l, 1994; 60 l, 1995; others, 7/94.

Arctic Explorers — A568

Designs: a, Fridiof Nansen (1861-1930), Norway. b, James Cook (1728-79), England. c, Roald Amundsen (1872-1928), Norway. d, Robert F. Scott (1872-1928), Great Britain.

1995, Sept. 14 Litho. *Perf. 13½x14*
2477 A568 25 l Block of 4, #a.-d. 4.25 4.25

UN, 50th Anniv. A569

1995, Sept. 14 Litho. *Perf. 14x13½*
2478 A569 2 l shown .15 .15
2479 A569 100 l like #2478, flags streaming to right 4.25 4.25

Poets — A570

1995 *Perf. 13½x14*
2480 A570 25 l Pol Elyar 1.10 1.10
2481 A570 50 l Sergej Esnin 2.25 2.25
a. Pair, #2480-2481 3.50 3.50

Entry into Council of Europe A571

Designs: 25 l, Doves flying from headquarters, Strasbourg. 85 l, Albanian eagle over map of Europe.

1995 *Perf. 14x13½*
2482 A571 25 l multicolored 1.10 1.10
2483 A571 85 l multicolored 3.75 3.75

Jan Kukuzeli, Composer A572

Stylized figure: 18 l, Writing. 20 l, Holding hand to head. 100 l, Holding up scroll of paper.

1995 *Perf. 13½x14*
2484 A572 18 l multicolored .85 .85
2485 A572 20 l multicolored .95 .95

Size: 74x74mm
2486 A572 100 l multicolored 4.50 4.50
Nos. 2484-2486 (3) 6.30 6.30

World Tourism Organization, 20th Anniv. — A573

Stylized designs: 18 l, Church, saint holding scroll. 20 l, City, older buildings. 42 l, City, modern buildings.

1995
2487 A573 18 l multicolored 1.00 1.00
2488 A573 20 l multicolored 1.10 1.10
2489 A573 42 l multicolored 2.50 2.50
Nos. 2487-2489 (3) 4.60 4.60

SEMI-POSTAL STAMPS

Nos. 148-151 Surcharged in Red and Black

+ 5 qind.

1924, Nov. 1
B1 A18 5q + 5q yel grn 2.75 3.50
B2 A18 10q + 5q carmine 2.75 3.50
B3 A18 25q + 5q dark blue 2.75 3.50
B4 A18 50q + 5q dark grn 2.75 3.50
Nos. B1-B4 (4) 11.00 14.00

Nos. B1 to B4 with Additional Surcharge in Red and Black

1924
B5 A18 5q + 5q + 5q yel grn 2.75 3.50
B6 A18 10q + 5q + 5q car 2.75 3.50
B7 A18 25q + 5q + 5q dk bl 2.75 3.50
B8 A18 50q + 5q + 5q dk grn 2.75 3.50
Nos. B5-B8 (4) 11.00 14.00

Issued under Italian Dominion

Nurse and Child — SP1

Unwmk.
1943, Apr. 1 Photo. *Perf. 14*
B9 SP1 5q + 5q dark grn .15 .15
B10 SP1 10q + 10q olive brn .15 .15
B11 SP1 15q + 10q rose red .15 .15
B12 SP1 25q + 15q saphire .15 .18
B13 SP1 30q + 20q violet .18 .22
B14 SP1 50q + 25q dk org .22 .25
B15 SP1 65q + 30q grnsh blk .32 .35
B16 SP1 1fr + 40q chestnut .70 .75
Nos. B9-B16 (8) 2.02 2.20

The surtax was for the control of tuberculosis. For surcharges see Nos. B24-B27.

Issued under German Administration

War Victims — SP2

1944, Sept. 22
B17 SP2 5q + 5(q) dp grn 2.10 2.75
B18 SP2 10q + 5(q) dp brn 2.10 2.75
B19 SP2 15q + 5(q) car lake 2.10 2.75
B20 SP2 25q + 10(q) dp blue 2.10 2.75
B21 SP2 1fr + 50q dk olive 2.10 2.75
B22 SP2 2fr + 1(fr) purple 2.10 2.75
B23 SP2 3fr + 1.50(fr) dk org 2.10 2.75
Nos. B17-B23 (7) 14.70 19.25

Surtax for victims of World War II.

Independent State

Nos. B9 to B12 Surcharged in Carmine

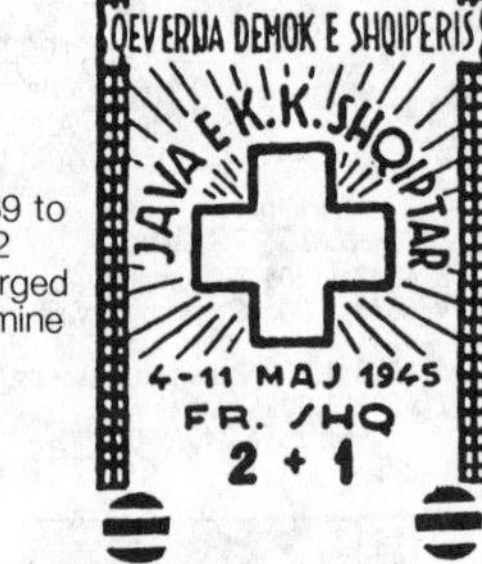

1945, May 4 Unwmk. *Perf. 14*
B24 SP1 30q +15q on 5q+5q 1.40 1.40
B25 SP1 50q +25q on 10q+10q 1.40 1.40
B26 SP1 1fr +50q on 15q+10q 4.00 4.00
B27 SP1 2fr +1fr on 25q+15q 7.00 7.00
Nos. B24-B27 (4) 13.80 13.80

The surtax was for the Albanian Red Cross.

People's Republic

Nos. 361 to 366 Overprinted in Red (cross) and Surcharged in Black

1946, July 16 *Perf. 11*
B28 A57 20q + 10q bluish grn 4.50 4.50
B29 A57 30q + 15q dp org 4.50 4.50
B30 A57 40q + 20q brown 4.50 4.50
B31 A57 60q + 30q red vio 4.50 4.50
B32 A57 1fr + 50q rose red 4.50 4.50
B33 A57 3fr + 1.50fr dk bl 4.50 4.50
Nos. B28-B33 (6) 27.00 27.00

To honor and benefit the Congress of the Albanian Red Cross.

Counterfeits: lithographed, dull gum. Genuine: typographed, shiny gum.

Catalogue values for unused stamps in this section, from this point to the end of the section, are for Never Hinged items.

First Aid and Red Cross — SP3

Designs: 25q+5q, Nurse carrying child on stretcher. 65q+25q, Symbolic blood transfusion. 80q+40q, Mother and child.

1967, Dec. 1 Litho. *Perf. 11½x12*

No.	Type	Description	Unused	Used
B34	SP3	15q + 5q blk, red & brn	.60	.45
B35	SP3	25q + 5q multi	.65	.60
B36	SP3	65q + 25q multi	2.00	.65
B37	SP3	80q + 40q multi	3.25	1.50
		Nos. B34-B37 (4)	6.50	3.20

6th congress of the Albanian Red Cross.

AIR POST STAMPS

Airplane Crossing Mountains AP1

Wmk. 125

1925, May 30 Typo. *Perf. 14*

No.	Type	Description	Unused	Used
C1	AP1	5q green	.50	.50
C2	AP1	10q rose red	.50	.50
C3	AP1	25q deep blue	.450	.50
C4	AP1	50q dark green	1.00	1.00
C5	AP1	1fr dk vio & blk	1.90	1.90
C6	AP1	2fr ol grn & vio	3.00	3.00
C7	AP1	3fr brn org & dk grn	5.25	5.25
		Nos. C1-C7 (7)	16.65	12.65

Nos. C1-C7 exist imperf.
For overprint see Nos. C8-C28.

Nos. C1-C7 Overprinted

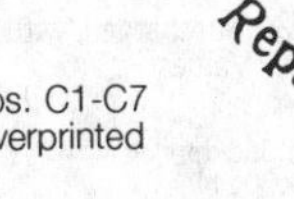

1927, Jan. 18

No.	Type	Description	Unused	Used
C8	AP1	5q green	3.00	3.00
a.		Dbl. overprint, one invtd.	35.00	
C9	AP1	10q rose red	3.00	3.00
a.		Inverted overprint	30.00	
b.		Dbl. overprint, one invtd.	35.00	
C10	AP1	25q deep blue	1.60	1.60
C11	AP1	50q dark grn	1.60	1.60
a.		Inverted overprint	30.00	
C12	AP1	1fr dk vio & blk	1.60	1.60
a.		Inverted overprint	30.00	
b.		Double overprint	30.00	
C13	AP1	2fr ol grn & vio	1.60	1.60
C14	AP1	3fr brn org & dk grn	2.75	2.75
		Nos. C8-C14 (7)	15.15	15.15

Nos. C1-C7 Overprinted

REP. SHQYPTARE
Fluturim' i I-ar
Vlonë--Brindisi
21. IV. 1928

1928, Apr. 21

No.	Type	Description	Unused	Used
C15	AP1	5q green	.90	.90
a.		Inverted overprint	20.00	
C16	AP1	10q rose red	.90	.90
C17	AP1	25q deep blue	.90	.90
C18	AP1	50q dark grn	.90	.90
C19	AP1	1fr dk vio & blk	14.00	14.00
C20	AP1	2fr ol grn & vio	14.00	14.00
C21	AP1	3fr brn org & dk grn	14.00	14.00
		Nos. C15-C21 (7)	45.60	45.60

First flight across the Adriatic, Valona to Brindisi, Apr. 21, 1928.

The variety "SHQYRTARE" occurs once in the sheet for each value. Value 3 times normal.

Nos. C1-C7 Overprinted in Red Brown

Mbr. Shqiptare

1929, Dec. 1

No.	Type	Description	Unused	Used
C22	AP1	5q green	3.25	3.25
C23	AP1	10q rose red	3.25	3.25
C24	AP1	25q deep blue	3.50	3.50
C25	AP1	50q dk grn	15.00	17.50
C26	AP1	1fr dk vio & blk	150.00	165.00
C27	AP1	2fr ol grn	150.00	165.00
C28	AP1	3fr brn org & dk grn	150.00	165.00
		Nos. C22-C28 (7)	475.00	522.50

Excellent counterfeits exist.

King Zog and Airplane over Tirana — AP2

AP3

1930, Oct. 8 Photo. Unwmk.

No.	Type	Description	Unused	Used
C29	AP2	5q yel grn	.25	.25
C30	AP2	15q rose red	.35	.35
C31	AP2	20q slate bl	.50	.50
C32	AP2	50q olive grn	.65	.65
C33	AP3	1fr dark blue	1.50	1.50
C34	AP3	2fr olive brn	4.75	4.75
C35	AP3	3fr purple	6.00	6.00
		Nos. C29-C35 (7)	14.00	14.00

For overprints and surcharges see Nos. C36-C45.

Nos. C29-C35 Overprinted

6 KORRIK 1931

1931, July 6

No.	Type	Description	Unused	Used
C36	AP2	5q yel grn	1.25	1.25
a.		Double overprint	*65.00*	
C37	AP2	15q rose red	1.25	1.25
C38	AP2	20q slate blue	1.25	1.25
C39	AP2	50q olive grn	1.25	1.25
C40	AP3	1fr dark blue	10.00	10.00
C41	AP3	2fr olive brn	10.00	10.00
C42	AP3	3fr purple	10.00	10.00
a.		Inverted overprint	*175.00*	
		Nos. C36-C42 (7)	35.00	35.00

1st air post flight from Tirana to Rome.

Only a very small part of this issue was sold to the public. Most of the stamps were given to the Aviation Company to help provide funds for conducting the service.

Issued under Italian Dominion

Nos. C29-C30 Overprinted in Black

Mbledhja
Kushtetuëse
12-IV-1939
XVII

1939, Apr. 19 Unwmk. *Perf. 14*

No.	Type	Description	Unused	Used
C43	AP2	5q yel green	.50	.50
C44	AP2	15q rose red	.50	.50

No. C32 With Additional Surcharge

No.	Type	Description	Unused	Used
C45	AP2	20q on 50q ol grn	1.00	1.00
a.		Inverted overprint		
		Nos. C43-C45 (3)	2.00	2.00

See note after No. 309.

King Victor Emmanuel III and Plane over Mountains AP4

1939, Aug. 4 Photo.

No.	Type	Description	Unused	Used
C46	AP4	20q brown	5.25	2.75

Shepherds AP5

Map of Albania Showing Air Routes — AP6

Designs: 20q, Victor Emmanuel III and harbor view. 50q, Woman and river valley. 1fr, Bridge at Vezirit. 2fr, Ruins. 3fr, Women waving to plane.

1940, Mar. 20 Unwmk.

No.	Type	Description	Unused	Used
C47	AP5	5q green	.16	.16
C48	AP6	15q rose red	.16	.16
C49	AP5	20q deep blue	.16	.16
C50	AP6	50q brown	.42	.42
C51	AP5	1fr myrtle grn	.85	.90
C52	AP6	2fr brn blk	2.50	3.00
C53	AP6	3fr rose vio	7.50	8.50
		Nos. C47-C53 (7)	11.75	13.30

People's Republic

Vuno-Himare AP12

Albanian Towns: 1 l, 10 l, Rozafat-Shkoder. 2 l, 20 l, Keshtjelle-Butrinto.

1950, Dec. 15 Engr. *Perf. 12½x12*

No.	Type	Description	Unused	Used
C54	AP12	50q gray blk	.15	.15
C55	AP12	1 l red brn	.15	.15
C56	AP12	2 l ultra	.30	.15
C57	AP12	5 l dp grn	.65	.20
C58	AP12	10 l dp bl	1.50	.85
C59	AP12	20 l purple	4.25	1.75
		Nos. C54-C59 (6)	7.00	3.25

Nos. C56-C58 Surcharged with New Value and Bars in Red or Black

1952-53

No.	Type	Description	Unused	Used
C60	AP12	50q on 2 l (R)	30.00	30.00
C61	AP12	50q on 5 l	5.00	2.75
C62	AP12	2.50 l on 5 l (R)	60.00	60.00
C63	AP12	2.50 l on 10 l	5.00	2.75
		Nos. C60-C63 (4)	100.00	95.50

Issued: #C60, C62, 12/26/52; #C61, C63, 3/14/53.

Catalogue values for unused stamps in this section, from this point to the end of the section, are for Never Hinged items.

Banner with Lenin, Map of Stalingrad and Tanks — AP13

1963, Feb. 2 Litho. *Perf. 14*

No.	Type	Description	Unused	Used
C67	AP13	7 l grn & dp car	1.50	.60

20th anniversary, Battle of Stalingrad.

Sputnik and Sun — AP14

Designs: 3 l, Lunik 4. 5 l, Lunik 3 photographing far side of the Moon. 8 l, Venus space probe. 12 l, Mars 1.

1963, Oct. 31 Unwmk. *Perf. 12*

No.	Type	Description	Unused	Used
C68	AP14	2 l org, yel & blk	.22	.15
C69	AP14	3 l multi	.28	.15
C70	AP14	5 l rose lil, yel & blk	.65	.30
C71	AP14	8 l multi	1.10	.45
C72	AP14	12 l blue & org	2.50	.95
		Nos. C68-C72 (5)	4.75	2.00

Russian interplanetary explorations.

Nos. C68 and C71 Overprinted: "Riccione 23-8-1964"

1964, Aug. 23

No.	Type	Description	Unused	Used
C73	AP14	2 l org, yel & blk	7.00	3.50
C74	AP14	8 l multicolored	10.50	5.25

Intl. Space Exhib. in Riccione, Italy.

Plane over Berat AP15

1975, Nov. 25 Litho. *Perf. 12*

No.	Type	Description	Unused	Used
C75	AP15	20q multi	.15	.15
C76	AP15	40q Gjirokaster	.15	.15
C77	AP15	60q Sarande	.15	.15
C78	AP15	90q Durres	.25	.15
C79	AP15	1.20 l Kruje	.40	.15
C80	AP15	2.40 l Boga	.90	.35
C81	AP15	4.05 l Tirana	1.40	.70
		Nos. C75-C81 (7)	3.40	
		Set value		1.50

SPECIAL DELIVERY STAMPS

Issued under Italian Dominion

King Victor Emmanuel III — SD1

1940 Unwmk. Photo. *Perf. 14*

No.	Type	Description	Unused	Used
E1	SD1	25q bright violet	.38	.38
E2	SD1	50q red orange	1.25	1.50

Issued under German Administration

No. E1 Overprinted in Carmine

14
Shtator
1943

1943

No.	Type	Description	Unused	Used
E3	SD1	25q bright violet	15.00	17.50

Proclamation of Albanian independence.

POSTAGE DUE STAMPS

Nos. 35-39 Handstamped in Various Colors

1914, Feb. 23 Unwmk. *Perf. 14*

No.	Type	Description	Unused	Used
J1	A3	2q org brn & buff (Bl)	1.00	.75
J2	A3	5q green (R)	1.00	.90
J3	A3	10q rose red (Bl)	1.40	.90
J4	A3	25q dark blue (R)	1.75	1.10
J5	A3	50q vio & red (Bk)	2.00	1.50
		Nos. J1-J5 (5)	7.15	5.15

The two parts of the overprint are handstamped separately. Stamps exist with one or both handstamps inverted, double, omitted or in wrong color.

Nos. 48-51 Overprinted in Black

TAKSË

1914, Apr. 16

No.	Type	Description	Unused	Used
J6	A3 (a)	10pa on 5q green	2.25	2.25
J7	A3 (a)	20pa on 10q rose red	2.25	2.25
J8	A3 (b)	1gr on 25q blue	2.25	2.25
J9	A3 (b)	2gr on 50q vio & red	2.25	2.25
		Nos. J6-J9 (4)	9.00	9.00

Same Design as Regular Issue of 1919, Overprinted

1919, Feb. 10 *Perf. 11½, 12½*

No.	Type	Description	Unused	Used
J10	A8	(4)q on 4h rose	3.75	3.75
J11	A8	(10)q on 10k red, *grn*	3.75	3.75
J12	A8	20q on 2k org, *gray*	3.75	3.75
J13	A8	50q on 5k brn, *yel*	3.75	3.75
		Nos. J10-J13 (4)	15.00	15.00

Fortress at Scutari — D3

D5

Post Horn Overprinted in Black

1920, Apr. 1 *Perf. 14x13*

J14 D3 4q olive green .25 .32
J15 D3 10q rose red .25 .32
J16 D3 20q bister brn .25 .32
J17 D3 50q black .45 .52
Nos. J14-J17 (4) 1.20 1.48

1922 *Perf. 12½, 11½*

Background of Red Wavy Lines

J23 D5 4q black, *red* 1.00 1.00
J24 D5 10q black, *red* 1.00 1.00
J25 D5 20q black, *red* 1.00 1.00
J26 D5 50q black, *red* 1.00 1.00
Nos. J23-J26 (4) 4.00 4.00

Same Overprinted in White

1925

J27 D5 4q black, *red* 1.00 1.00
J28 D5 10q black, *red* 1.00 1.00
J29 D5 20q black, *red* 1.00 1.00
J30 D5 50q black, *red* 1.00 1.00
Nos. J27-J30 (4) 4.00 4.00

The 10q with overprint in gold was a trial printing. It was not put in use.

D7

Coat of Arms — D8

Overprinted "QINDAR" in Red

1926, Dec. 24 *Perf. 13½x13*

J31 D7 10q dark blue .25 .20
J32 D7 20q green .50 .40
J33 D7 30q red brown .80 .60
J34 D7 50q dark brown 1.25 1.00
Nos. J31-J34 (4) 2.80 2.20

Wmk. Double Headed Eagle (220)

1930, Sept. 1 Photo. *Perf. 14, 14½*

J35 D8 10q dark blue 4.00 4.00
J36 D8 20q rose red 1.00 1.00
J37 D8 30q violet 1.00 1.00
J38 D8 50q dark green 1.25 1.25
Nos. J35-J38 (4) 7.25 7.25

Nos. J36-J38 exist with overprint "14 Shtator 1943" (see Nos. 332-344) which is private and fraudulent on these stamps.

No. 253 Overprinted **Taksë**

1936 *Perf. 14*

J39 A34 10q carmine 3.50 4.75

Issued under Italian Dominion

Coat of Arms — D9

1940 Unwmk. Photo. *Perf. 14*

J40 D9 4q red orange 5.50 5.50
J41 D9 10q bright violet 1.75 1.75
J42 D9 20q brown 1.75 1.75
J43 D9 30q dark blue 2.00 2.00
J44 D9 50q carmine rose 4.00 4.00
Nos. J40-J44 (5) 15.00 15.00

ALEXANDRETTA

ˌa-lig-(ˌ)zan-ˈdre-tə

LOCATION — A political territory in northern Syria, bordering on Turkey
GOVT. — A former French mandate
AREA — 10,000 sq. mi. (approx.)
POP. — 270,000 (approx.)

Included in the Syrian territory mandated to France under the Versailles Treaty, the name was changed to Hatay in 1938. The following year France returned the territory to Turkey in exchange for certain concessions. See Hatay.

100 Centimes = 1 Piaster

Stamps of Syria, 1930-36, Overprinted or Surcharged in Black or Red:

Sandjak d'Alexandrette a — SANDJAK D'ALEXANDRETTE b

c — *Sandjak d'Alexandrette*

d — *Sandjak d'Alexandrette* 2P.50

e — POSTES *Sandjak d'Alexandrette* 12P.50

1938 Unwmk. *Perf. 12x12½*

1 A6 (a) 10c vio brn .35 .35
2 A6 (a) 20c brn org .35 .35

Perf. 13½

3 A9 (b) 50c vio (R) .35 .35
4 A10 (b) 1p bis brn .50 .50
5 A9 (b) 2p dk vio (R) .60 .60
6 A13 (b) 3p yel grn (R) 1.75 1.75
7 A10 (b) 4p yel org 1.75 1.75
8 A16 (b) 6p grnsh blk (R) 2.00 2.00
9 A18 (b) 25p vio brn 4.75 4.75
10 A15 (c) 75c org red .50 .50
11 A10 (d) 2.50p on 4p yel org .90 .90
12 AP2 (e) 12.50p on 15p org red 2.50 2.50
Nos. 1-12 (12) 16.30 16.30

Issue dates: #1-9, Apr. 14, #10-12, Sept. 2.

Nos. 4, 7, 10-12 Overprinted in Black

10-11-1938

1938, Nov. 10

13 A15 75c 30.00 30.00
14 A10 1p 20.00 18.00
15 A10 2.50p on 4p 12.50 11.00
16 A10 4p 15.00 13.50
17 AP2 12.50p on 15p 30.00 30.00
Nos. 13-17 (5) 107.50 102.50

Death of Kemal Ataturk, pres. of Turkey.

AIR POST STAMPS

Air Post Stamps of Syria, 1937, Overprinted Type "b" in Red or Black

1938, Apr. 14 Unwmk. *Perf. 13*

C1 AP14 ½p dark vio (R) .75 .75
C2 AP15 1p black (R) .35 .35
C3 AP14 2p blue grn (R) 1.50 1.50
C4 AP15 3p deep ultra 1.75 1.75
C5 AP14 5p rose lake 4.50 4.50
C6 AP15 10p red brown 5.00 5.00
C7 AP14 15p lake brown 5.75 5.75
C8 AP15 25p dk blue (R) 7.50 7.50
Nos. C1-C8 (8) 27.10 27.10

POSTAGE DUE STAMPS

Postage Due Stamps of Syria, 1925-31, Ovptd. Type "b" in Black or Red

1938, Apr. 14 Unwmk. *Perf. 13½*

J1 D5 50c brown, *yel* 1.00 .80
J2 D6 1p violet, *rose* 1.25 1.10
J3 D5 2p blk, *blue* (R) 1.75 1.60
J4 D5 3p blk, *red org* 3.50 3.25
J5 D5 5p blk, *bl grn* (R) 5.50 5.00
J6 D7 8p blk, *gray bl* (R) 6.00 5.00
Nos. J1-J6 (6) 19.00 16.75

On No. J2, the overprint is vertical, reading up, other denominations, horizontal.

Stamps of Alexandretta were discontinued in 1938 and replaced by those of Hatay.

ALGERIA

al-ˈjir-ē-ə

LOCATION — North Africa
GOVT. — Republic
AREA — 919,595 sq. mi.
POP. — 21,463,000 (1984 est.)
CAPITAL — Algiers

The former French colony of Algeria became an integral part of France on Sept. 1, 1958, when French stamps replaced Algerian stamps. Algeria became an independent country July 3, 1962.

100 Centimes = 1 Franc
100 Centimes = 1 Dinar (1964)

Catalogue values for unused stamps in this country are for Never Hinged items, beginning with Scott 109 in the regular postage section, Scott B27 in the semi-postal section, Scott C1 in the airpost section, Scott CB1 in the airpost semi-postal section, and Scott J25 in the postage due section.

Stamps of France Overprinted in Red, Blue or Black:

ALGÉRIE a — ALGÉRIE b — ALGÉRIE c — ALGÉRIE d

1924-26 Unwmk. *Perf. 14x13½*

1 A16(a) 1c dk gray (R) .15 .15
2 A16(a) 2c violet brn .15 .15
3 A16(a) 3c orange .15 .15
4 A16(a) 4c yel brn (Bl) .15 .15
5 A22(a) 5c orange (Bl) .15 .15
6 A16(a) 5c green ('25) .15 .15
7 A23(a) 10c green .15 .15
b. Booklet pane of 10 1.50
8 A22(a) 10c green ('25) .50 .15
9 A20(a) 15c slate grn .15 .15
10 A23(a) 15c green ('25) .15 .15
11 A22(a) 15c red brn (Bl) ('26) .15 .15
12 A22(a) 20c red brn (Bl) .15 .15
13 A22(a) 25c blue (R) .15 .15
a. Booklet pane of 10 3.00
14 A23(a) 30c red (Bl) .15 .15
15 A22(a) 30c cerise ('25) .50 .15
16 A22(a) 30c lt bl (R) ('25) .15 .15
a. Booklet pane of 10 2.00
17 A22(a) 35c violet .15 .15
18 A18(b) 40c red & pale bl .15 .15
19 A22(a) 40c ol brn (R) ('25) .75 .20
20 A18(b) 45c grn & bl (R) .25 .15
21 A23(a) 45c red (Bl) ('25) .30 .15
22 A23(a) 50c blue (R) .15 .15
23 A20(a) 60c lt violet .15 .15
a. Inverted overprint 250.00
24 A20(a) 65c rose (Bl) .15 .15
25 A23(a) 75c blue (R) .25 .15
a. Double overprint 65.00
26 A20(a) 80c ver ('26) .40 .15
27 A20(a) 85c ver (Bl) .25 .15
28 A18(b) 1fr cl & ol grn 1.00 .15
29 A22(a) 1.05fr ver ('26) .55 .25
30 A18(c) 2fr org & pale bl .40 .30
31 A18(b) 3fr vio & bl ('26) 3.00 .55
32 A18(d) 5fr bl & buff (R) 7.00 4.00
Nos. 1-32 (32) 18.00
Set value 7.50

No. 15 was issued precanceled only. Values for precanceled stamps in first column are for those which have not been through the post and have original gum. Values in second column are for postally used, gumless stamps.

For surcharges see Nos. 75, P1.

Street in Kasbah, Algiers A1

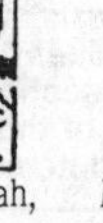

Mosque of Sidi Abd-er-Rahman A2

La Pêcherie Mosque A3

Marabout of Sidi Yacoub A4

1926-39 Typo. *Perf. 14x13½*

33 A1 1c olive .15 .15
34 A1 2c red brown .15 .15
35 A1 3c orange .15 .15
36 A1 5c blue green .15 .15
37 A1 10c brt violet .15 .15
a. Booklet pane of 10 3.25
38 A2 15c orange brn .15 .15
39 A2 20c green .15 .15
40 A2 20c deep rose .15 .15
41 A2 25c blue grn .15 .15
42 A2 25c blue ('27) .40 .15
43 A2 25c vio bl ('39) .15 .15
44 A2 30c blue .25 .15
45 A2 30c bl grn ('27) .85 .30
46 A2 35c dp violet 1.00 .65
47 A2 40c olive green .15 .15
a. Booklet pane of 10 2.25
48 A3 45c violet brn .25 .20
49 A3 50c blue .25 .15
a. Booklet pane of 10 3.50
50 A3 50c dk red ('30) .15 .15
a. Booklet pane of 10 4.75
51 A3 60c yellow grn .15 .15
52 A3 65c blk brn ('27) 1.25 .85
53 A1 65c ultra ('38) .25 .15
a. Booklet pane of 10 1.75
54 A3 75c carmine .30 .25
55 A3 75c blue ('29) 2.50 .15
56 A3 80c orange red .45 .25
57 A3 90c red ('27) 3.50 2.75
58 A4 1fr gray grn & red brn .65 .20
59 A3 1.05fr lt brown .55 .30
60 A3 1.10fr mag ('27) 4.75 1.75
61 A4 1.25fr dk bl & ultra 1.00 .80
62 A4 1.50fr dk bl & ultra ('27) 1.75 .15
63 A4 2fr Prus bl & blk brn 1.90 .20
64 A4 3fr violet & org 2.75 .65
65 A4 5fr red & violet 5.00 2.00
66 A4 10fr ol brn & rose ('27) 35.00 20.00
67 A4 20fr vio & grn ('27) 6.00 4.00
Nos. 33-67 (35) 72.55 38.00

Type A4, 50c blue and rose red, inscribed "CENTENAIRE-ALGERIE" is France No. 255.

For stamps and types surcharged see Nos. 68-74, 131, 136, 187, B1-B13, J27, P2.

Stamps of 1926 Surcharged with New Values

1927

68 A2 10c on 35c dp violet .15 .15
69 A2 25c on 30c blue .15 .15
70 A2 30c on 25c blue grn .15 .15
71 A3 65c on 60c yel grn .60 .35
72 A3 90c on 80c org red .30 .20
73 A3 1.10fr on 1.05fr lt brn .30 .16
74 A4 1.50fr on 1.25fr dk bl & ultra 1.25 .45
Nos. 68-74 (7) 2.90 1.61

Bars cancel the old value on #68, 69, 73, 74.

No. 4 Surcharged **5c**

1927

75 A16 5c on 4c yellow brown .75 .25

Bay of Algiers — A5

1930, May 4 Engr. *Perf. 11, 12½*

78 A5 10fr red brown 8.25 7.50
a. Imperf., pair 25.00

Cent. of Algeria and for Intl. Phil. Exhib. of North Africa, May, 1930.

One copy of No. 78 was sold with each 10fr admission.

Travel across the Sahara — A6

Arch of Triumph, Lambese — A7

Admiralty Building, Algiers — A8

Kings' Tombs near Touggourt — A9

El-Kebir Mosque, Algiers — A10

Oued River at Colomb-Bechar A11

Sidi Bon Medine Cemetery at Tlemcen A13

View of Ghardaia A12

1936-41 Engr. *Perf. 13*

79 A6 1c ultra .15 .15
80 A11 2c dk violet .15 .15
81 A7 3c dk blue grn .15 .15
82 A12 5c red violet .15 .15
83 A8 10c emerald .15 .15
84 A9 15c red .15 .15
85 A13 20c dk blue grn .15 .15
86 A10 25c rose vio .32 .15
87 A12 30c yellow grn .28 .15
88 A9 40c brown vio .15 .15
89 A13 45c deep ultra .65 .40
90 A8 50c red .40 .15
91 A6 65c red brn 2.50 1.75
92 A6 65c rose car ('37) .35 .15
93 A6 70c red brn ('39) .15 .15
94 A11 75c slate bl .18 .15
95 A7 90c henna brn .65 .45
96 A10 1fr brown .18 .15
97 A8 1.25fr lt violet .35 .18
98 A8 1.25fr car rose ('39) .30 .15
99 A11 1.50fr turq blue .90 .18
99A A11 1.50fr rose ('40) .35 .15
100 A12 1.75fr henna brn .15 .15
101 A7 2fr dk brown .15 .15
102 A6 2.25fr yellow grn 8.00 6.50
103 A12 2.50fr dk ultra ('41) .28 .26
104 A13 3fr magenta .26 .15
105 A10 3.50fr pck blue 1.90 1.40
106 A8 5fr slate blue .28 .15
107 A11 10fr henna brn .32 .20
108 A9 20fr turq blue .60 .35
Nos. 79-108 (31) 20.70
Set value 13.00

See Nos. 124-125, 162.

Nos. 82 and 100 with surcharge "E. F. M. 30frs" (Emergency Field Message) were used in 1943 to pay cable tolls for US and Canadian servicemen.

For other surcharges see Nos. 122, B27.

Catalogue values for unused stamps in this section, from this point to the end of the section, are for Never Hinged items.

Algerian Pavilion — A14

1937 *Perf. 13*

109 A14 40c brt green .40 .35
110 A14 50c rose carmine .25 .15
111 A14 1.50fr blue .60 .25
112 A14 1.75fr brown black .65 .50
Nos. 109-112 (4) 1.90 1.25

Paris International Exposition.

Constantine in 1837 — A15

1937

113 A15 65c deep rose .30 .15
114 A15 1fr brown 3.25 .50
115 A15 1.75fr blue green .25 .20
116 A15 2.15fr red violet .20 .15
Nos. 113-116 (4) 4.00 1.00

Taking of Constantine by the French, cent.

Ruins of a Roman Villa — A16

1938

117 A16 30c green .50 .32
118 A16 65c ultra .15 .15
119 A16 75c rose violet .55 .38
120 A16 3fr carmine rose 1.40 1.40
121 A16 5fr yellow brown 2.25 2.25
Nos. 117-121 (5) 4.85 4.50

Centenary of Philippeville.

No. 90 Surcharged in Black

0,25

1938

122 A8 25c on 50c red .15 .15
a. Double surcharge 27.50 22.50
b. Inverted surcharge 17.50 15.00

Types of 1936

1939

Numerals of Value on Colorless Background

124 A7 90c henna brown .15 .15
125 A10 2.25fr blue green .18 .20
Set value .24 .25

For surcharge, see No. B38.

American Export Liner Unloading Cargo — A17

1939

126 A17 20c green .65 .65
127 A17 40c red violet .65 .50
128 A17 90c brown black .35 .22
129 A17 1.25fr rose 2.25 .80
130 A17 2.25fr ultra .65 .60
Nos. 126-130 (5) 4.55 2.77

New York World's Fair.

Type of 1926, Surcharged in Black

Two types of surcharge:
I - Bars 6mm
II - Bars 7mm

1939-40 *Perf. 14x13½*

131 A1 1fr on 90c crimson (I) .15 .15
a. Booklet pane of 10
b. Double surcharge (I) 35.00
c. Inverted surcharge (I) 22.50
d. Pair, one without surch. (I) *800.00*
e. Type II ('40) 1.50 .15
f. Inverted surcharge (II) 27.50
g. Pair, one without surch. (II) *800.00*

View of Algiers — A18

1941 Typo.

132 A18 30c ultra .15 .15
133 A18 70c sepia .15 .15
134 A18 1fr carmine rose .15 .15
Nos. 132-134 (3) .45
Set value .15

See No. 163.

Marshal Pétain
A19 A20

1941 Engr. *Perf. 13*

135 A19 1fr dark blue .30 .16

For stamp and type surcharged see #B36-B37.

No. 53 Surcharged in Black with New Value and Bars

1941 *Perf. 14x13½*

136 A1 50c on 65c ultra .28 .15
a. Booklet pane of 10
b. Inverted surcharge 21.00
c. Pair, one without surch. 52.50

1942 *Perf. 14x13*

137 A20 1.50fr orange red .15 .15

Four other denominations of type A20 exist (4, 5, 10, 20fr), but were not placed in use.

Constantine A21

Oran A22

Arms of Algiers — A23

Engraver's Name at Lower Left

1942-43 Photo. *Perf. 12*

138 A21 40c dark vio ('43) .15 .15
139 A22 60c rose ('43) .15 .15
140 A21 1.20fr yel grn ('43) .15 .15
141 A23 1.50fr car rose .15 .15
142 A22 2fr sapphire .20 .15
143 A21 2.40fr rose ('43) .15 .15
144 A23 3fr sapphire .20 .15
145 A21 4fr blue ('43) .15 .15
146 A22 5fr yel grn ('43) .15 .15
Set value .92 .58

For type surcharged see No. 166.

Imperforates

Nearly all of Algeria Nos. 138-285, B39-B96, C1-C12 and CB1-CB3 exist imperforate. See note after France No. 395.

Without Engraver's Name

1942-45 Typo. *Perf. 14x13½*

147 A23 10c dull brn vio ('45) .15 .15
148 A22 30c dp bl grn ('45) .15 .15
149 A21 40c dull brn vio ('45) .15 .15
150 A22 60c rose ('45) .15 .15
151 A21 70c deep bl ('45) .15 .15
152 A23 80c dk bl grn ('43) .22 .22
153 A21 1.20fr dp bl grn ('45) .20 .15
154 A23 1.50fr brt rose ('43) .15 .15
155 A22 2fr dp blue ('45) .20 .15
156 A21 2.40fr rose ('45) .30 .22
157 A23 3fr dp blue ('45) .15 .15
158 A22 4.50fr brown vio .20 .15
Set value 1.50 1.00

For surcharge see No. 190.

La Pêcherie Mosque — A24

1942 Typo.

159 A24 50c dull red .15 .15
a. Booklet pane of 10 2.75

1942 Photo. *Perf. 12*

160 A24 40c gray green .15 .15
161 A24 50c red .15 .15
Set value .20 .15

Types of 1936-41, Without "RF"

1942 Engr. *Perf. 13*

162 A11 1.50fr rose .30 .15

Typo. *Perf. 14x13½*

163 A18 30c ultra .15 .15

"One Aim Alone - Victory"
A25 A26

1943 Litho. *Perf. 12*

164 A25 1.50fr deep rose .15 .15
165 A26 1.50fr dark blue .15 .15
Set value .20 .15

Type of 1942-3 Surcharged with New Value in Black

1943 Photo.

166 A22 2fr on 5fr red orange .15 .15
a. Surcharge omitted 140.00

Summer Palace, Algiers — A27

1944, Dec. 1 Litho.

167 A27 15fr slate .85 .65
168 A27 20fr lt blue grn .80 .30
169 A27 50fr dk carmine .75 .35
170 A27 100fr deep blue 1.10 1.00
171 A27 200fr dull bis brn 1.75 1.10
Nos. 167-171 (5) 5.25 3.40

Marianne A28

Gallic Cock A29

1944-45

172 A28 10c gray .15 .15
173 A28 30c red violet .15 .15
174 A29 40c rose car ('45) .15 .15
175 A28 50c red .15 .15
176 A28 80c emerald .15 .15
177 A29 1fr green ('45) .15 .15
178 A28 1.20fr rose lilac .15 .15
179 A28 1.50fr dark blue .15 .15
a. Double impression 20.00
180 A29 2fr red .15 .15
a. Double impression 22.50
181 A29 2fr dk brown ('45) .15 .15
182 A28 2.40fr rose red .15 .15
183 A28 3fr purple .15 .15
184 A29 4fr ultra ('45) .15 .15
185 A28 4.50fr olive blk .22 .22
186 A29 10fr grnsh blk ('45) .38 .28
Set value 1.50 1.20

No. 38 Surcharged in Black **0f.30**

1944 *Perf. 14x13½*

187 A2 30c on 15c orange brn .15 .15
a. Inverted surcharge 10.00 4.00

This stamp exists precanceled only. See note below No. 32.

No. 154 Surcharged "RF" and New Value

1945

190 A23 50c on 1.50fr brt rose .15 .15
a. Inverted surcharge 15.00

Stamps of France, 1944, Overprinted Type "a" of 1924 in Black

1945-46

191 A99 80c yellow grn .15 .15
192 A99 1fr grnsh blue .15 .15
193 A99 1.20fr violet .15 .15
194 A99 2fr violet brown .22 .15
195 A99 2.40fr carmine rose .22 .15
196 A99 3fr orange .22 .15
Set value .85 .75

Same Overprint on Stamps of France, 1945-47, in Black, Red or Carmine

1945-47

197 A145 40c lilac rose .15 .15
198 A145 50c violet bl (R) .15 .15
199 A146 60c brt ultra (R) .22 .15
200 A146 1fr rose red ('47) .20 .15
201 A146 1.50fr rose lilac ('47) .15 .15
202 A147 2fr myr grn (R) ('46) .15 .15
203 A147 3fr deep rose .15 .15
204 A147 4.50fr ultra (C) ('47) .55 .15
205 A147 5fr lt green ('46) .15 .15
206 A147 10fr ultra .50 .25
Set value 1.75 .75

Same Overprint on France No. 383 and New Value Surcharged in Black

1946

207 A99 2fr on 1.50fr henna brn .15 .15
a. Without "2F" 110.00

Same Overprint on France Nos. 562 and 564, in Carmine or Blue

1947

208 A153 10c dp ultra & blk (C) .15 .15
209 A155 50c brown, yel & red (Bl) .22 .22
Set value .27 .27

Constantine A30

Algiers A31

Arms of Oran — A32

Perf. 14x13½

1947-49 **Unwmk.** **Typo.**

210 A30 10c dk grn & brt red .15 .15
211 A31 50c black & orange .15 .15
212 A32 1fr ultra & yellow .15 .15
213 A30 1.30fr blk & grnsh bl .55 .35
214 A31 1.50fr pur & org yel .15 .15
215 A32 2fr blk & brt grn .15 .15
216 A30 2.50fr blk & brt red .35 .28
217 A31 3fr vio brn & grn .15 .15
218 A32 3.50fr lt grn & rose lil .15 .15
219 A30 4fr dk brn & brt grn .15 .15
220 A31 4.50fr ultra & scar .15 .15
221 A31 5fr blk & grnsh bl .16 .15
222 A32 6fr brown & scarlet .22 .15
223 A32 8fr choc & ultra ('48) .18 .15
224 A30 10fr car & choc ('48) .32 .15
225 A31 15fr black & red ('49) .35 .15
Set value 2.70 1.35

See Nos. 274-280, 285.

Peoples of the World — A33

1949, Oct. 24 **Engr.** *Perf. 13*

226 A33 5fr green 1.10 .90
227 A33 15fr scarlet 1.10 .90
228 A33 25fr ultra 2.50 2.50
Nos. 226-228 (3) 4.70 4.30

75th anniv. of the UPU.

Grapes A34

Apollo of Cherchell A35

Designs: 25fr, Dates. 40fr, Oranges and lemons.

1950, Feb. 25

229 A34 20fr multicolored 1.00 .22
230 A34 25fr multicolored 1.25 .50
231 A34 40fr multicolored 2.50 .65
Nos. 229-231 (3) 4.75 1.37

1952 **Unwmk.** *Perf. 13*

Designs: 12fr, 18fr, Isis statue, Cherchell. 15fr, 20fr, Child with eagle.

240 A35 10fr gray black .22 .15
241 A35 12fr orange brn .35 .15
242 A35 15fr deep blue .22 .15
243 A35 18fr rose red .35 .22
244 A35 20fr deep green .35 .15
245 A35 30fr deep blue .65 .35
Nos. 240-245 (6) 2.14
Set value .84

War Memorial, Algiers — A38

Fossilized Nautilus — A39

Phonolite Dike — A40

1952, Apr. 11

246 A38 12fr dark green .48 .35

Issued to honor the French Africa Army.

1952, Aug. 11

247 A39 15fr brt crimson .85 .60
248 A40 30fr deep ultra .90 .65

19th Intl. Geological Cong., Algiers, Sept. 8-15.

French and Algerian Soldiers and Camel — A41

1952, Nov. 30

249 A41 12fr chestnut brown .65 .60

50th anniv. of the establishment of the Sahara Companies.

Eugène Millon — A42

Franç ois C. Maillot — A43

Oranges — A44

Portrait: 50fr, Alphonse Laveran.

1954, Jan. 4 **Unwmk.** **Engr.** *Perf. 13*

250 A42 25fr dk grn & choc 1.10 .18
251 A43 40fr org brn & brn car 1.75 .60
252 A42 50fr ultra & indigo 1.75 .22
Nos. 250-252 (3) 4.60 1.00

Military Health Service.

1954, May 8

253 A44 15fr indigo & blue .60 .40

3rd Intl. Cong. on Agronomy, Algiers, 1954.

Type of France, 1954 Overprinted type "a" in Black

Unwmk.

1954, June 6 **Engr.** *Perf. 13*

254 A240 15fr rose carmine .45 .45

Liberation of France, 10th anniversary.

Darguinah Hydroelectric Works A45

Patio of Bardo Museum A46

1954, June 19

255 A45 15fr lilac rose .55 .45

Opening of Darguinah hydroelectric works.

1954 **Typo.** *Perf. 14x13½*

257 A46 12fr red brn & brn org .50 .25
258 A46 15fr dk blue & blue .50 .25

See Nos. 267-271.

Type of France, 1954, Overprinted type "a" in Carmine

1954 **Engr.** *Perf. 13*

260 A247 12fr dark green .50 .45

150th anniv. of the 1st Legion of Honor awards at Camp de Boulogne.

St. Augustine — A47

1954, Nov. 11

261 A47 15fr chocolate .75 .65

1600th anniv. of the birth of St. Augustine.

Aesculapius Statue and El Kattar Hospital, Algiers — A48

1955, Apr. 3 **Unwmk.** *Perf. 13*

262 A48 15fr red .50 .35

Issued to publicize the 30th French Congress of Medicine, Algiers, April 3-6, 1955.

Chenua Mountain and View of Tipasa — A49

1955, May 31

263 A49 50fr brown carmine .50 .18

2000th anniv. of the founding of Tipasa.

Type of France, 1955 Overprinted type "a" in Red

1955, June 13

264 A251 30fr deep ultra .60 .45

Rotary Intl., 50th anniv.

Marianne A50

Great Kabylia Mountains A51

Perf. 14x13½

1955, Oct. 3 **Typo.** **Unwmk.**

265 A50 15fr carmine .50 .25

See No. 284.

1955, Dec. 17 **Engr.** *Perf. 13*

266 A51 100fr indigo & ultra 2.00 .22

Bardo Type of 1954, "Postes" and "Algerie" in White

Perf. 14x13½

1955-57 **Unwmk.** **Typo.**

267 A46 10fr dk brown & lt brown .25 .15
268 A46 12fr red brn & brn org ('56) .20 .15
269 A46 18fr crimson & ver ('57) .45 .18
270 A46 20fr grn & yel grn ('57) .35 .28
271 A46 25fr purple & brt purple .50 .15
Nos. 267-271 (5) 1.75
Set value .60

Marshal Franchet d'Esperey A52

1956, May 25 **Engr.** *Perf. 13*

272 A52 15fr sapphire & indigo .60 .60

Birth cent. of Marshal Franchet d'Esperey.

Marshal Jacques Leclerc — A53

1956, Nov. 29

273 A53 15fr red brown & sepia .48 .48

Death of Marshal Leclerc.
For type surcharged, see No. B90.

Type of 1947-49 and

Arms of Bône — A54

Arms: 2fr, Tizi-Ouzou. 3fr, Mostaganem. 5fr, Tlemcen. 10fr, Setif. 12fr, Orleansville.

1956-58 **Typo.** *Perf. 14x13½*

274 A54 1fr green & ver .15 .15
275 A54 2fr ver & ultra ('58) .25 .20
276 A54 3fr ultra & emer ('58) .30 .15
277 A54 5fr ultra & yellow .15 .15
278 A31 6fr red & grn ('57) .35 .25
279 A54 10fr dp cl & emer ('58) .35 .25
280 A54 12fr ultra & red ('58) .35 .25
Nos. 274-280 (7) 1.90 1.40

Nos. 275 and 279 are inscribed "Republique Francaise." See No. 285.

View of Oran — A55

1956-58 Engr. *Perf. 13*

281 A55 30fr dull purple .45 .18
282 A55 35fr car rose ('58) .75 .45

Electric Train Crossing Bridge — A56

1957, Mar. 25

283 A56 40fr dk blue grn & emer .60 .18

Marianne Type of 1955
Inscribed "Algerie" Vertically
Perf. 14x13½

1957, Dec. 2 Typo. Unwmk.

284 A50 20fr ultra .40 .15

Arms Type of 1947-49 Inscribed "Republique Francaise"

1958, July

285 A31 6fr red & green 10.00 10.00

Independent State

France Nos. 939, 968, 945-946 and 1013 Overprinted "EA" and Bars, Handstamped or Typographed, in Black or Red

1962, July 2

286 A336 10c brt green .25 .20
a. Typographed overprint .30 .20
287 A349 25c lake & gray .20 .15
a. Handstamped overprint .25 .15
288 A339 45c brt vio & ol gray 3.50 3.00
a. Handstamped overprint *15.00 10.00*
289 A339 50c sl grn & lt claret 5.00 3.00
a. Handstamped overprint *15.00 12.00*
290 A372 1fr dk bl, sl & bis 2.75 1.00
a. Handstamped overprint *4.00 1.50*
Nos. 286-290 (5) 11.70 7.35

Post offices were authorized to overprint their stock of these 5 French stamps. The size of the letters was specified as 3x6mm each, but various sizes were used. The post offices had permission to make their own rubber stamps. Typography, pen or pencil were also used. Many types exist. Colors of handstamped overprints include black, red, blue, violet. "EA" stands for Etat Algérien.

Mosque, Tlemcen — A57

Roman Gates of Lodi, Médéa — A58

Designs: 5c, Kerrata Gorge. 10c, Dam at Foum el Gherza. 95c, Oil field, Hassi Messaoud.

1962, Nov. 1 Engr. *Perf. 13*

291 A57 5c Prus grn, grn & choc .15 .15
292 A58 10c ol blk & dk bl .15 .15
293 A57 25c sl grn, brn & ver .40 .15
294 A57 95c dk bl, blk & bis 1.50 .55
295 A58 1fr green & blk 1.50 1.10
Nos. 291-295 (5) 3.70
Set value 1.75

The designs of Nos. 291-295 are similar to French issues of 1959-61 with "Republique Algerienne" replacing "Republique Francaise."

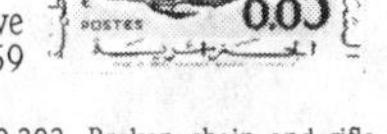

Flag, Rifle, Olive Branch — A59

Design: Nos. 300-303, Broken chain and rifle added to design A59.

1963, Jan. 6 Litho. *Perf. 12½*
Flag in Green and Red

296 A59 5c bister brown .15 .15
297 A59 10c blue .15 .15
298 A59 25c vermilion 1.00 .15
299 A59 95c violet .90 .45
300 A59 1fr green .75 .15
301 A59 2fr brown 2.00 .45
302 A59 5fr lilac 3.00 1.25
303 A59 10fr gray 11.50 7.00
Nos. 296-303 (8) 19.45 9.75

Nos. 296-299 for the successful revolution and Nos. 300-303 the return of peace.

Men of Various Races, Wheat Emblem and Globe — A60

1963, Mar. 21 Engr. *Perf. 13*

304 A60 25c maroon, dl grn & yel .28 .22

FAO "Freedom from Hunger" campaign.

Map of Algeria and Emblems — A61

Physicians from 13th Century Manuscript — A62

1963, July 5 Unwmk. *Perf. 13*

305 A61 25c bl, dk brn, grn & red .40 .22

1st anniv. of Algeria's independence.

1963, July 29 Engr.

306 A62 25c brn red, grn & bis 1.00 .35

2nd Congress of the Union of Arab physicians.

Orange and Blossom A63

Scales and Scroll A64

1963 *Perf. 14x13*

307 A63 8c gray grn & org .65 .65
308 A63 20c slate & org red .75 .75
309 A63 40c grnsh bl & org 1.00 1.00
310 A63 55c ol grn & org red 2.00 2.00
Nos. 307-310 (4) 4.40 4.40

Nos. 307-310 issued precanceled only. See note below No. 32.

1963, Oct. 13 Unwmk. *Perf. 13*

311 A64 25c blk, grn & rose red .42 .28

Issued to honor the new constitution.

Guerrillas A65

Centenary Emblem A66

1963, Nov. 1

312 A65 25c dk brn, yel grn & car .55 .25

9th anniversary of Algerian revolution.

1963, Dec. 8 Photo. *Perf. 12*

313 A66 25c lt vio bl, yel & dk red .55 .28

Centenary of International Red Cross.

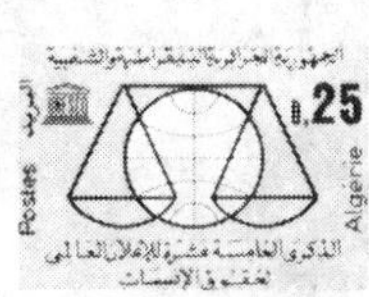

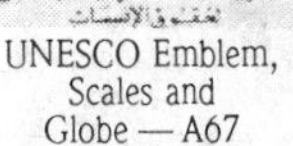

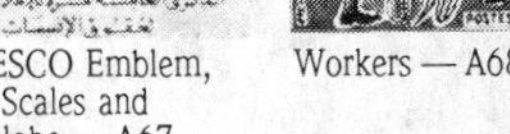

UNESCO Emblem, Scales and Globe — A67

Workers — A68

1963, Dec. 16 Unwmk. *Perf. 12*

314 A67 25c lt blue & blk .55 .25

15th anniv. of the Universal Declaration of Human Rights.

1964, May 1 Engr. *Perf. 13*

315 A68 50c dull red, red org & bl .90 .50

Issued for the Labor Festival.

Map of Africa and Flags — A69

1964, May 25 Unwmk. *Perf. 13*

316 A69 45c blue, orange & car .55 .28

Africa Day on the 1st anniv. of the Addis Ababa charter on African unity.

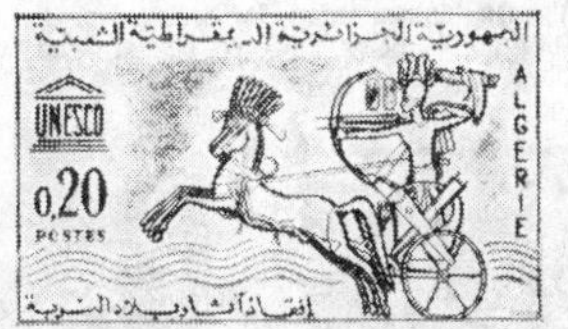

Ramses II Battling the Hittites (from Abu Simbel) — A70

Design: 30c, Two statues of Ramses II.

1964, June 28 Engr. *Perf. 13*

317 A70 20c choc, red & vio bl .55 .32
318 A70 30c brn, red & grnsh bl .65 .40

UNESCO world campaign to save historic monuments in Nubia.

A71 A72

Designs: 5c, 25c, 85c, Tractors. 10c, 30c, 65c, Men working with lathe. 12c, 15c, 45c, Electronics center and atom symbol. 20c, 50c, 95c, Draftsman and bricklayer.

1964-65 Typo. *Perf. 14x13½*

319 A71 5c red lilac .15 .15
320 A71 10c brown .15 .15
321 A71 12c emerald ('65) .38 .15
322 A71 15c dk blue ('65) .25 .15
323 A71 20c yellow .42 .15
324 A71 25c red .50 .15
325 A71 30c purple ('65) .42 .15
326 A71 45c rose car .50 .18
327 A71 50c ultra .62 .15
328 A71 65c orange .80 .18
329 A71 85c green 1.40 .22
330 A71 95c car rose 1.75 .26
Nos. 319-330 (12) 7.34
Set value 1.40

For surcharges see Nos. 389, 424.

1964, Aug. 30 Engr. *Perf. 13*

331 A72 85c Communications tower 1.50 .75

Inauguration of the Hertzian cable telephone line Algiers-Annaba.

Industrial & Agricultural Symbols — A73

Gas Flames and Pipes — A74

1964, Sept. 26 Typo. *Perf. 13½x14*

332 A73 25c lt ultra, yel & red .60 .45

1st Intl. Fair at Algiers, Sept. 26-Oct. 11.

1964, Sept. 27

333 A74 30c violet, blue & yel .45 .35

Arzew natural gas liquification plant opening.

Planting Trees A75

Children and UNICEF Emblem A76

1964, Nov. 29 Unwmk.

334 A75 25c slate grn, yel & car .28 .20

National reforestation campaign.

1964, Dec. 13 *Perf. 13½x14*

335 A76 15c pink, vio bl & lt grn .25 .20

Issued for Children's Day.

Decorated Camel Saddle — A77

1965, May 29 Typo. *Perf. 13½x14*

336 A77 20c blk, red, emer & brn .22 .15

Handicrafts of Sahara.

ICY Emblem A78

1965, Aug. 29 Engr. *Perf. 13*

337 A78 30c blk, mar & bl grn .45 .32
338 A78 60c blk, brt bl & bl grn .85 .38

International Cooperation Year, 1965.

ITU Emblem A79

1965, Sept. 19

339 A79 60c purple, emer & buff .45 .30
340 A79 95c dk brn, mar & buff .65 .35

Cent. of the ITU.

Musicians A80

Miniatures by Mohammed Racim: 60c, Two female musicians. 5d, Algerian princess and antelope.

1965, Dec. 27 Photo. *Perf. 11½*

341 A80 30c multicolored .70 .55
342 A80 60c multicolored 1.10 .70
343 A80 5d multicolored 8.00 5.25
Nos. 341-343 (3) 9.80 6.50

Bulls, Painted in 6000 B.C. A81

Wall Paintings from Tassili-N-Ajjer, c. 6000 B.C.: No. 345, Shepherd, vert. 2d, Fleeing ostriches. 3d, Two girls, vert.

1966, Jan. 29 Photo. *Perf. 11½*

344 A81 1d brn, bis & red brn 2.75 1.90
345 A81 1d gray, blk, ocher & dk brn 2.75 1.90
346 A81 2d brn, ocher & red brn 6.50 3.00
347 A81 3d buff, blk, ocher & brn red 8.00 4.25
Nos. 344-347 (4) 20.00 11.05

See Nos. 365-368.

Pottery — A82

Handicrafts from Great Kabylia: 50c, Weaving, woman at loom, horiz. 70c, Jewelry.

1966, Feb. 26 Engr. *Perf. 13*

348 A82 40c Prus bl, brn red & blk .28 .22
349 A82 50c dk red, ol & ocher .38 .28
350 A82 70c vio bl, blk & red .65 .40
Nos. 348-350 (3) 1.31 .90

Weather Balloon, Compass Rose and Anemometer A83

1966, Mar. 23 Engr. Unwmk.

351 A83 1d claret, brt bl & grn .85 .38

World Meteorological Day.

Book, Grain, Cogwheel and UNESCO Emblem — A84

Design: 60c, Grain, cogwheel, book and UNESCO emblem.

1966, May 2 Typo. *Perf. 13x14*

352 A84 30c yellow bis & blk .22 .20
353 A84 60c dk red, gray & blk .40 .22

Literacy as basis for development.

WHO Headquarters, Geneva A85

1966, May 30 Engr. *Perf. 13*

354 A85 30c multicolored .35 .30
355 A85 60c multicolored .70 .40

Inauguration of the WHO Headquarters, Geneva.

Algerian Scout Emblem — A86

Arab Jamboree Emblem — A87

1966, July 23 Photo. *Perf. 12x12½*

356 A86 30c multicolored .65 .50
357 A87 1d multicolored 1.75 1.25

No. 356 commemorates the 30th anniv. of the Algerian Mohammedan Boy Scouts. No. 357, the 7th Arab Boy Scout Jamboree, held at Good Daim, Libya, Aug. 12.

Map of Palestine and Victims A88

Abd-el-Kader A89

1966, Sept. 26 Typo. *Perf. 10½*

358 A88 30c red & black .80 .40

Deir Yassin Massacre, Apr. 9, 1948.

1966, Nov. 2 Photo. *Perf. 11½*

359 A89 30c multicolored .38 .15
360 A89 95c multicolored 1.10 .35

Transfer from Damascus to Algiers of the ashes of Abd-el-Kader (1807?-1883), Emir of Mascara. See Nos. 382-387.

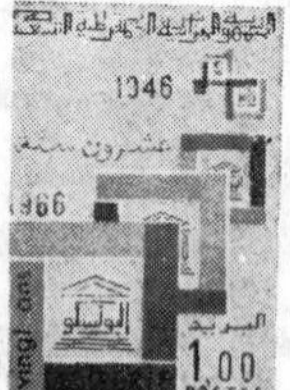

UNESCO Emblem — A90

1966, Nov. 19 Typo. *Perf. 10½*

361 A90 1d multicolored 1.00 .35

20th anniv. of UNESCO.

The Scott International album provides spaces for an extensive representative collection of the world's postage stamps.

Horseman A91

Miniatures by Mohammed Racim: 1.50d, Woman at her toilette. 2d, The pirate Barbarossa in front of the Admiralty.

1966, Dec. 17 Photo. *Perf. 11½*

Granite Paper

362 A91 1d multicolored 3.25 1.40
363 A91 1.50d multicolored 4.25 2.00
364 A91 2d multicolored 7.00 3.50
Nos. 362-364 (3) 14.50 6.90

Wall Paintings Type of 1966

Wall Paintings from Tassili-N-Ajjer, c. 6000 B.C.: 1d, Cow. No. 366, Antelope. No. 367, Archers. 3d, Warrior, vert.

1967, Jan. 28 Photo. *Perf. 11½*

365 A81 1d brn, bis & dl vio 2.75 1.90
366 A81 2d brn, ocher & red brn 5.00 3.25
367 A81 2d brn, yel & red brn 5.00 3.25
368 A81 3d blk, gray, yel & red brn 7.75 5.00
Nos. 365-368 (4) 20.50 13.40

Bardo Museum A92

La Kalaa Minaret — A93

Design: 1.30d, Ruins at Sedrata.

1967, Feb. 27 Photo. *Perf. 13*

369 A92 35c multicolored .20 .15
370 A93 95c multicolored .45 .28
371 A92 1.30d multicolored .75 .40
Nos. 369-371 (3) 1.40 .83

Moretti and International Tourist Year Emblem — A94

Design: 70c, Tuareg riding camel, Tassili, and Tourist Year Emblem, vert.

1967, Apr. 29 Litho. *Perf. 14*

372 A94 40c multi .50 .22
373 A94 70c multi 1.00 .35

International Tourist Year, 1967.

Spiny-tailed Agamid — A95

Designs: 20c, Ostrich, vert. 40c, Slender-horned gazelle, vert. 70c, Fennec.

1967, June 24 Photo. *Perf. 11½*

374 A95 5c bister & blk .60 .50
375 A95 20c ocher, blk & pink 1.25 .80
376 A95 40c ol bis, blk & red brn 2.00 1.00
377 A95 70c gray, blk & dp org 3.50 2.00
Nos. 374-377 (4) 7.35 4.30

Dancers — A96

Typographed and Engraved

1967, July 4 *Perf. 10½*

378 A96 50c gray vio, yel & blk .45 .32

National Youth Festival.

Map of the Mediterranean and Sport Scenes — A97

1967, Sept. 2 Typo. *Perf. 10½*

379 A97 30c black, red & blue .25 .20

Issued to publicize the 5th Mediterranean Games, Tunis, Sept. 8-17.

Skiers — A98

Olympic Emblem and Sports — A99

1967, Oct. 21 Engr. *Perf. 13*

380 A98 30c brt blue & ultra .32 .20
381 A99 95c brn org, pur & brt grn .80 .52

Issued to publicize the 10th Winter Olympic Games, Grenoble, Feb. 6-18, 1968.

Abd-el-Kader Type of 1966

Lithographed, Photogravure

1967-71 *Perf. 13½, 11½*

382 A89 5c dull pur ('68) .15 .15
383 A89 10c green .85 .35
383A A89 10c sl grn (litho., '69) .15 .15
383B A89 25c orange ('71) .18 .15
384 A89 30c black ('68) .50 .20
385 A89 30c lt violet ('68) .75 .30
386 A89 50c rose claret .65 .18
387 A89 70c violet blue .85 .22
Nos. 382-387 (8) 4.08
Set value 1.40

No. 383, 50c and 70c, issued Nov. 13, 1967, are on granite paper, photo. The 5c, No.383A, 25c and 30c are litho., perf. 13½; others, perf. 11½.

The three 1967 stamps (No. 383, 50c, 70c) have numerals thin, narrow and close together; the Arabic inscription at lower right is 2mm high. The 5 litho. stamps are redrawn, with numerals thicker and spaced more widely; Arabic at lower right 3mm high.

Boy Scouts Holding Jamboree Emblem A100

1967, Dec. 23 Engr. *Perf. 13*

388 A100 1d multicolored 1.00 .80

12th Boy Scout World Jamboree, Farragut State Park, Idaho, Aug. 1-9.

No. 324 Surcharged

1967 Typo. *Perf. 14x13½*

389 A71 30c on 25c red .50 .20

Mandolin — A101

1968, Feb. 17 Photo. *Perf. 12½x13*

390 A101 30c shown .35 .22
391 A101 40c Lute .40 .25
392 A101 1.30d Rebec 1.40 .65
Nos. 390-392 (3) 2.15 1.12

Nememcha Rug — A102

Algerian Rugs: 70c, Guergour. 95c, Djebel-Amour. 1.30d, Kalaa.

1968, Apr. 13 Photo. *Perf. 11½*

393 A102 30c multi .75 .75
394 A102 70c multi 1.50 1.50
395 A102 95c multi 2.00 2.00
396 A102 1.30d multi 2.50 2.50
Nos. 393-396 (4) 6.75 6.75

Human Rights Flame A103

1968, May 18 Typo. *Perf. 10½*

397 A103 40c blue, red & yel .40 .28

International Human Rights Year, 1968.

WHO Emblem A104

1968, May 18

398 A104 70c blk, lt bl & yel .55 .28

20th anniv. of the WHO.

Welder — A105

Athletes, Olympic Flame and Rings — A106

1968, June 15 Engr. *Perf. 13*

399 A105 30c gray, brn & ultra .25 .18

Algerian emigration to Europe.

Perf. 12½x13, 13x12½

1968, July 4 Photo.

Designs: 50c, Soccer player. 1d, Mexican pyramid, emblem, Olympic flame, rings and athletes, horiz.

400 A106 30c green, red & yel .35 .28
401 A106 50c rose car & multi .60 .32
402 A106 1d dk grn, org, brn & red 1.10 .65
Nos. 400-402 (3) 2.05 1.25

19th Olympic Games, Mexico City, Oct. 12-27.

Scouts and Emblem A107

Barbary Sheep A108

1968, July 4 *Perf. 13*

403 A107 30c multicolored .50 .18

8th Arab Boy Scout Jamboree, Algiers, 1968.

1968, Oct. 19 Photo. *Perf. 11½*

404 A108 40c shown .48 .25
405 A108 1d Red deer 1.25 .60

Hunting Scenes, Djemila A109

"Industry" A110

Design: 95c, Neptune's chariot, Timgad, horiz. Both designs are from Roman mosaics.

Perf. 12½x13, 13x12½

1968, Nov. 23 Photo.

406 A109 40c gray & multi .35 .22
407 A109 95c gray & multi .85 .50

1968, Dec. 14 *Perf. 11½*

Designs: No. 409, Miner with drill. 95c, "Energy" (circle and rays).

408 A110 30c dp orange & sil .25 .18
409 A110 30c brown & multi .25 .18
410 A110 95c silver, red & blk .75 .35
Nos. 408-410 (3) 1.25 .71

Issued to publicize industrial development.

Opuntia Ficus Indica — A111

Flowers: 40c, Carnations. 70c, Roses. 95c, Bird-of-paradise flower.

1969, Jan. Photo. *Perf. 11½*

Flowers in Natural Colors

411 A111 25c pink & blk .52 .25
412 A111 40c yellow & blk .65 .32
413 A111 70c gray & blk 1.25 .45
414 A111 95c brt blue & blk 2.00 .80
Nos. 411-414 (4) 4.42 1.82

See Nos. 496-499.

Irrigation Dam at Djorf Torba-Oued Guir A112

Design: 1.50d, Truck on Highway No. 51 and camel caravan.

1969, Feb. 22 Photo. *Perf. 11½*

415 A112 30c multi .24 .18
416 A112 1.50d multi 1.25 .65

Public works in the Sahara.

Mail Coach A113

1969, Mar. 22 Photo. *Perf. 11½*

417 A113 1d multicolored 1.10 .60

Issued for Stamp Day, 1969.

Capitol, Timgad — A114

Design: 1d, Septimius Temple, Djemila, horiz.

1969, Apr. 5 Photo. *Perf. 13x12½*

418 A114 30c gray & multi .35 .18
419 A114 1d gray & multi .85 .35

Second Timgad Festival, Apr. 4-8.

ILO Emblem — A115

Arabian Saddle — A116

1969, May 24 Photo. *Perf. 11½*

420 A115 95c dp car, yel & blk 1.00 .38

50th anniv. of the ILO.

1969, June 28 Photo. *Perf. 12x12½*

Algerian Handicrafts: 30c, Bookcase. 60c, Decorated copper plate.

Granite Paper

421 A116 30c multicolored .28 .20
422 A116 60c multicolored .55 .25
423 A116 1d multicolored 1.00 .45
Nos. 421-423 (3) 1.83 .90

No. 321 Surcharged **0,20**

1969 Typo. *Perf. 14x13½*

424 A71 20c on 12c emerald .22 .15

Pan-African Culture Festival Emblem — A117

African Development Bank Emblem — A118

1969, July 19 Photo. *Perf. 12½*

425 A117 30c multicolored .32 .18

Issued to commemorate the First Pan-African Culture Festival, Algiers, July 21-Aug. 1.

1969, Aug. 23 Typo. *Perf. 10½*

426 A118 30c dull blue, yel & blk .32 .20

5th anniversary of the African Development Bank.

Astronauts and Landing Module on Moon — A119

Perf. 12½x11½

1969, Aug. 23 Photo.

427 A119 50c gold & multi .60 .35

Man's 1st landing on the moon, July 20, 1969. US astronauts Neil A. Armstrong and Col. Edwin E. Aldrin, Jr., with Lieut. Col. Michael Collins piloting Apollo 11.

Algerian Women, by Dinet — A120

Design: 1.50d, The Watchmen, by Etienne Dinet.

1969, Nov. 29 Photo. *Perf. 14½*

428 A120 1d multi 1.75 .90
429 A120 1.50d multi 2.75 1.40

Mother and Child — A121

1969, Dec. 27 Photo. *Perf. 11½*

430 A121 30c multicolored .32 .24

Issued to promote mother and child protection.

Agricultural Growth Chart, Tractor and Dam — A122

Designs: 30c, Transportation and development. 50c, Abstract symbols of industrialization.

1970, Jan. 31 Photo. *Perf. 12½*
Size: 37x23mm

431 A122 25c dk brn, yel & org .16 .15

Litho. *Perf. 14*
Size: 49x23mm

432 A122 30c blue & multi .24 .18

Photo. *Perf. 12½*
Size: 37x23mm

433 A122 50c rose lilac & blk .28 .20
Nos. 431-433 (3) .68 .53

Four-Year Development Plan.

Old and New Mail Delivery A123

Spiny Lobster A124

1970, Feb. 28 Photo. *Perf. 11½*
Granite Paper

434 A123 30c multicolored .28 .18

Issued for Stamp Day.

1970, Mar. 28

Designs: 40c, Mollusks. 75c, Retepora cellulosa. 1d, Red coral.

435 A124 30c ocher & multi .35 .18
436 A124 40c multicolored .50 .22
437 A124 75c ultra & multi .90 .35
438 A124 1d lt blue & multi 1.25 .48
Nos. 435-438 (4) 3.00 1.23

Oranges, EXPO '70 Emblem — A125

Designs (EXPO '70 Emblem and): 60c, Algerian pavilion. 70c, Grapes.

1970, Apr. 25 Photo. *Perf. 12½x12*

439 A125 30c lt blue, grn & org .50 .15
440 A125 60c multicolored .65 .18
441 A125 70c multicolored 1.00 .32
Nos. 439-441 (3) 2.15 .65

EXPO '70 International Exhibition, Osaka, Japan, Mar. 15-Sept. 13, 1970.

Olives, Oil Bottle — A126

Saber — A127

1970, May 16 Photo. *Perf. 12½x12*

442 A126 1d yellow & multi 1.00 .65

Olive Year, 1969-1970.

UPU Headquarters Issue
Common Design Type

1970, May 30 *Perf. 13*
Size: 36x26mm

443 CD133 75c multicolored .50 .40

1970, June 27 Photo. *Perf. 12½*

Designs: 40c, Guns, 18th century, horiz. 1d, Pistol, 18th century, horiz.

444 A127 40c yellow & multi .65 .22
445 A127 75c red & multi .80 .40
446 A127 1d multicolored 1.25 .50
Nos. 444-446 (3) 2.70 1.12

Common Design Types pictured in section at front of book.

Map of Arab Countries and Arab League Flag — A128

Typographed and Engraved

1970, July 25 *Perf. 10½*

447 A128 30c grn, ocher & lt bl .30 .20

25th anniversary of the Arab League.

Lenin — A129

1970, Aug. 29 Litho. *Perf. 11½x12*

448 A129 30c brown & buff .25 .20

Lenin (1870-1924), Russian communist leader.

Exhibition Hall and Algiers Fair Emblem — A130

1970, Sept. 11 Engr. *Perf. 14x13½*

449 A130 60c lt olive green .40 .30

New Exhibition Hall for Algiers International Fair.

Education Year Emblem, Blackboard, Atom Symbol A131

Koran Page — A132

1970, Oct. 24 Photo. *Perf. 14*

450 A131 30c pink, blk, gold & lt bl .22 .18
451 A132 3d multicolored 2.50 1.50

Issued for International Education Year.

Great Mosque, Tlemcen — A133

Design: 40c, Ketchaoua Mosque, Algiers, vert. 1d, Mosque, Sidi-Okba, vert.

1970-71 Litho. *Perf. 14*

456 A133 30c multicolored .22 .15
457 A133 40c sepia & lemon ('71) .25 .15
458 A133 1d multicolored .65 .28
Nos. 456-458 (3) 1.12 .58

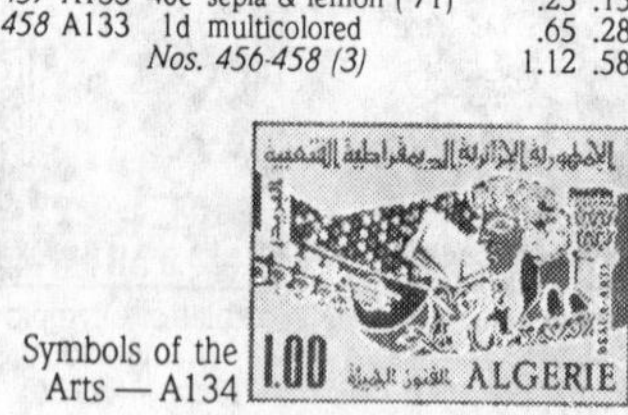

Symbols of the Arts — A134

1970, Dec. 26 Photo. *Perf. 13x12½*

459 A134 1d grn, lt grn & org .80 .45

Main Post Office, Algiers A135

1971, Jan. 23 *Perf. 11½*

460 A135 30c multicolored .32 .20

Stamp Day, 1971.

Hurdling A136

Designs: 40c, Vaulting, vert. 75c, Basketball, vert.

1971, Mar. 7 Photo. *Perf. 11½*

461 A136 20c lt blue & slate .25 .20
462 A136 40c lt ol grn & slate .35 .35
463 A136 75c salmon pink & slate .65 .50
Nos. 461-463 (3) 1.25 1.05

Mediterranean Games, Izmir, Turkey, Oct. 1971.

Symbolic Head — A137

1971, Mar. 27 *Perf. 12½*

464 A137 60c car rose, blk & sil .32 .20

Intl. year against racial discrimination.

Emblem and Technicians A138

1971, Apr. 24 Photo. *Perf. 12½x12*

465 A138 70c claret, org & bluish blk .40 .30

Founding of the Institute of Technology.

Woman from Aurès — A139

Regional Costumes: 70c, Man from Oran. 80c, Man from Algiers. 90c, Woman from Amour Mountains.

1971, Oct. 16 *Perf. 11½*

466 A139 50c gold & multi 1.50 .65
467 A139 70c gold & multi 1.65 1.00
468 A139 80c gold & multi 2.25 1.10
469 A139 90c gold & multi 2.50 1.25
Nos. 466-469 (4) 7.90 4.00

See Nos. 485-488, 534-537.

UNICEF Emblem, Birds and Plants — A140

1971, Dec. 6 *Perf. 11½*

470 A140 60c multicolored .55 .32

25th anniv. of UNICEF.

Lion of St. Mark A141

Design: 1.15d, Bridge of Sighs, Venice, vert.

1972, Jan. 24 Litho. *Perf. 12*

471 A141 80c multi .60 .32
472 A141 1.15d multi .90 .52

UNESCO campaign to save Venice.

Javelin A142

Book and Book Year Emblem A143

Designs: 25c, Bicycling, horiz. 60c, Wrestling. 1d, Gymnast on rings.

1972, Mar. 25 Photo. *Perf. 11½*

473 A142 25c maroon & multi .30 .20
474 A142 40c ocher & multi .35 .25
475 A142 60c ultra & multi .40 .40
476 A142 1d rose & multi 1.00 .50
Nos. 473-476 (4) 2.05 1.35

20th Olympic Games, Munich, Aug. 26-Sept. 11.

1972, Apr. 15

477 A143 1.15d bister, brn & red .65 .48

International Book Year 1972.

Mailmen A144

Flowers A145

1972, Apr. 22

478 A144 40c gray & multi .25 .15

Stamp Day 1972.

1972, May 27

479 A145 50c Jasmine .65 .28
480 A145 60c Violets .75 .35
481 A145 1.15d Tuberose 1.50 .55
Nos. 479-481 (3) 2.90 1.18

Olympic Stadium, Chéraga — A146

1972, June 10

482 A146 50c gray, choc & grn .60 .32

New Day, Algerian Flag — A147

1972, July 5

483 A147 1d green & multi .65 .42

10th anniversary of independence.

Festival Emblem — A148

Mailing a Letter — A149

1972, July 5 Litho. *Perf. 10½*

484 A148 40c grn, dk brn & org .22 .15

1st Arab Youth Festival, Algiers, July 5-11.

Costume Type of 1971

Regional Costumes: 50c, Woman from Hoggar. 60c, Kabyle woman. 70c, Man from Mzab. 90c, Woman from Tlemcen.

1972, Nov. 18 Photo. *Perf. 11½*

485 A139 50c gold & multi .80 .70
486 A139 60c gold & multi 1.10 .90
487 A139 70c gold & multi 1.25 1.10
488 A139 90c gold & multi 1.75 1.25
Nos. 485-488 (4) 4.90 3.95

1973, Jan. 20 Photo. *Perf. 11*

489 A149 40c orange & multi .40 .20

Stamp Day.

Ho Chi Minh, Map of Viet Nam — A150

1973, Feb. 17 Photo. *Perf. 11½*

490 A150 40c multicolored .75 .50

To honor the people of Viet Nam.

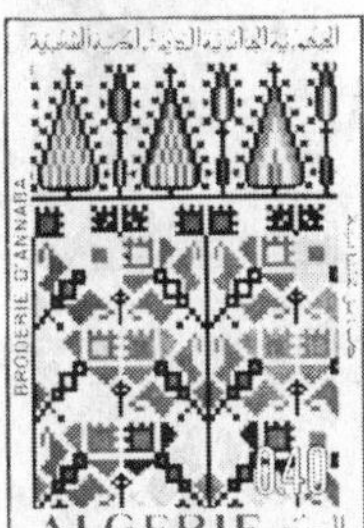

Embroidery from Annaba — A151

Designs: 60c, Tree of Life pattern from Algiers. 80c, Constantine embroidery.

1973, Feb. 24

491 A151 40c gray & multi .75 .40
492 A151 60c blue and multi 1.00 .60
493 A151 80c dk red, gold & blk 1.50 .80
Nos. 491-493 (3) 3.25 1.80

Stylized Globe and Wheat — A152

1973, Mar. 26 Photo. *Perf. 11½*

494 A152 1.15d brt rose lil, org & grn .75 .40

World Food Program, 10th anniversary.

Soldier and Flag A153

1973, Apr. 23 Photo. *Perf. 14x13½*

495 A153 40c multicolored .25 .18

Honoring the National Service.

Flower Type of 1969

Flowers: 30c, Opuntia ficus indica. 40c, Roses. 1d, Carnations. 1.15d, Bird-of-paradise flower.

1973, May 21 Photo. *Perf. 11½*
Flowers in Natural Colors

496 A111 30c pink & blk .40 .18
497 A111 40c gray & blk .50 .20
498 A111 1d yellow & multi .90 .40
499 A111 1.15d multi 1.25 .50
Nos. 496-499 (4) 3.05 1.28

For overprints and surcharges see #518-519, 531.

OAU Emblem — A154

1973, May 28 Photo. *Perf. 12½x13*

500 A154 40c multicolored .40 .20

Org. for African Unity, 10th anniv.

Desert and Fruitful Land, Farmer and Family A155

1973, June 18 *Perf. 11½*

501 A155 40c gold & multi .50 .40

Agricultural revolution.

Map of Africa, Scout Emblem — A156

1973, July 16 Litho. *Perf. 10½*

502 A156 80c purple 1.00 .50

24th Boy Scout World Conference (1st in Africa), Nairobi, Kenya, July 16-21.

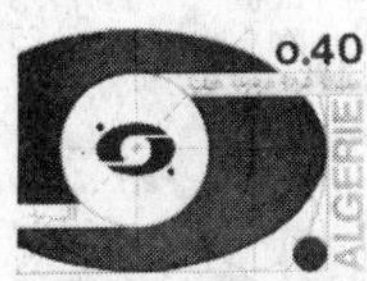

Algerian PTT Emblem — A157

1973, Aug. 6 *Perf. 14*

503 A157 40c blue & orange .22 .15

Adoption of new emblem for Post, Telegraph and Telephone System.

Conference Emblem — A158

Perf. 13½x12½
1973, Sept. 5 Photo.

504 A158 40c dp rose & multi .18 .15
505 A158 80c blue grn & multi .52 .26

4th Summit Conference of Non-aligned Nations, Algiers, Sept. 5-9.

Port of Skikda A159

1973, Sept. 29 Photo. *Perf. 11½*

506 A159 80c ocher, blk & ultra .48 .25

New port of Skikda.

Young Workers — A160

1973, Oct. 22 Photo. *Perf. 13*

507 A160 40c multicolored .22 .15

Voluntary work service.

Arms of Algiers A161

1973, Dec. 22 Photo. *Perf. 13*

508 A161 2d gold & multi 1.60 1.10

Millennium of Algiers.

Infant — A162

1974, Jan. 7 Litho. *Perf. 10½x11*

509 A162 80c orange & multi .60 .35

Fight against tuberculosis.

Man and Woman, Industry and Transportation A163

1974, Feb. 18 Photo. *Perf. 11½*

510 A163 80c multicolored .48 .20

Four-year plan.

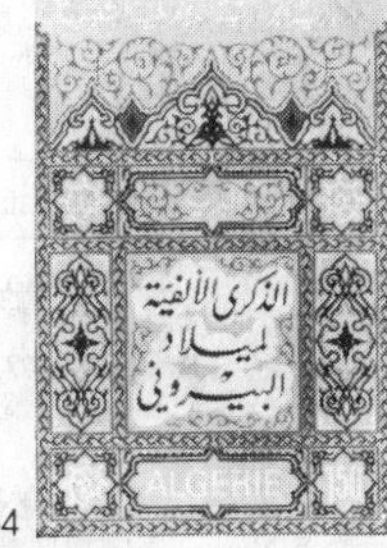

A164

1974, Feb. 25 Photo. *Perf. 11½*

511 A164 1.50d multi 1.10 .65

Millennium of the birth of abu-al-Rayhan al-Biruni (973-1048), philosopher and mathematician.

Map and Colors of Algeria, Tunisia, Morocco A165

1974, Mar. 4 Photo. *Perf. 13*

512 A165 40c gold & multi .28 .20

Maghreb Committee for Coordination of Posts and Telecommunications.

Hand Holding Rifle A166

Mother and Children A167

1974, Mar. 25 *Perf. 11½*

513 A166 80c red & black .30 .20

Solidarity with the struggle of the people of South Africa.

1974, Apr. 8 *Perf. 13½*

514 A167 85c multicolored .35 .22

Honoring Algerian mothers.

Village A168

Designs: 80c, Harvest. 90c, Tractor and sun. Designs after children's drawings.

1974, June 15

Size: 45x26mm

515 A168 70c multicolored .40 .18

Size: 48x33mm

516 A168 80c multicolored .48 .28
517 A168 90c multicolored .60 .42
Nos. 515-517 (3) 1.48 .88

Nos. 498-499 Overprinted "FLORALIES/1974"

1974, June 22 Photo. *Perf. 11½*

518 A111 1d multi .65 .35
519 A111 1.15d multi .70 .40

1974 Flower Show.

Stamp Vending Machine — A169

1974, Oct. 7 Photo. *Perf. 13*

520 A169 80c multicolored .42 .20

Stamp Day 1974.

UPU Emblem and Globe — A170

1974, Oct. 14 *Perf. 14*

521 A170 80c multicolored .50 .28

Centenary of Universal Postal Union.

"Revolution" — A171

Soldiers and Mountains — A172

Raising New Flag — A173

Design: 1d, Algerian struggle for independence (people, sun and fields).

1974, Nov. 4 Photo. *Perf. 14*

522 A171 40c multicolored .28 .18
523 A172 70c multicolored .40 .22
524 A173 95c multicolored .48 .22
525 A171 1d multicolored .60 .28
Nos. 522-525 (4) 1.76 .90

20th anniv. of the start of the revolution.

"Horizon 1980" — A174

Ewer and Basin — A175

1974, Nov. 23 Photo. *Perf. 13*

526 A174 95c ocher, dk red & blk .55 .25

10-year development plan, 1971-1980.

1974, Dec. 21 *Perf. 11½*

527 A175 50c shown .22 .15
528 A175 60c Coffee pot .28 .20
529 A175 95c Sugar bowl .45 .28
530 A175 1d Bath tub .50 .35
Nos. 527-530 (4) 1.45 .98

17th century Algerian copperware.

No. 497 Surcharged with New Value and Heavy Bar

1975, Jan. 4

531 A111 50c on 40c multi .50 .40

Mediterranean Games' Emblem — A176

1975, Jan. 27 *Perf. 13½*

532 A176 50c purple, yel & grn .28 .18
533 A176 1d orange, bl & mar .60 .22

Mediterranean Games, Algiers, 1975.

Costume Type of 1971

Regional Costumes: No. 534, Woman from Hoggar. No. 535, Woman from Algiers. No. 536, Woman from Oran. No. 537, Man from Tlemcen.

1975, Feb. 22 Photo. *Perf. 11½*

534 A139 1d gold & multi 1.00 .80
535 A139 1d gold & multi 1.00 .80
536 A139 1d gold & multi 1.00 .80
537 A139 1d gold & multi 1.00 .80
Nos. 534-537 (4) 4.00 3.20

Map of Arab Countries, ALO Emblem A177

1975, Mar. 10 Litho. *Perf. 10½x11*

538 A177 50c red brown .25 .15

Arab Labor Organization, 10th anniversary.

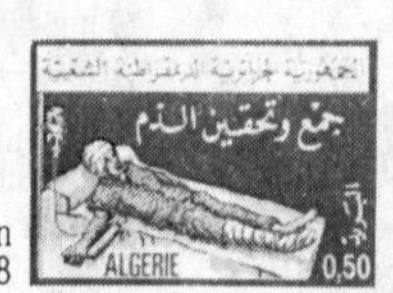
Blood Transfusion A178

1975, Mar. 15 *Perf. 14*

539 A178 50c car rose & multi .32 .18

Blood donation and transfusions.

Post Office, Al-Kantara A179

Policeman and Map of Algeria A180

1975, May 10 Photo. *Perf. 11½*

Granite Paper

540 A179 50c multicolored .25 .15

Stamp Day 1975.

1975, June 1 Photo. *Perf. 13*

541 A180 50c multicolored .75 .40

Natl. Security and 10th Natl. Police Day.

Ground Receiving Station A181

Designs: 1d, Map of Algeria with locations of radar sites, transmission mast and satellite. 1.20d, Main and subsidiary stations.

1975, June 28 Photo. *Perf. 13*

542 A181 50c blue & multi .28 .15
543 A181 1d blue & multi .55 .20
544 A181 1.20d blue & multi .60 .22
Nos. 542-544 (3) 1.43 .57

National satellite telecommunications network.

Revolutionary with Flag — A182

1975, Aug. 20 Photo. *Perf. 11½*

545 A182 1d multicolored .50 .25

August 20th Revolutionary Movement (Skikda), 20th anniversary.

Swimming and Games' Emblem A183

Perf. 13x13½, 13½x13

1975, Aug. 23 Photo.

546 A183 25c shown .15 .15
547 A183 50c Judo, map .25 .18
548 A183 70c Soccer, vert. .48 .22
549 A183 1d Running, vert. .55 .25
550 A183 1.20d Handball, vert. .70 .38
a. Souv. sheet of 5, #546-550, perf 13 4.50 4.50
Nos. 546-550 (5) 2.13 1.18

7th Mediterranean Games, Algiers, 8/23-9/46.
No. 550a sold for 4.50d. Exists imperf., same value.

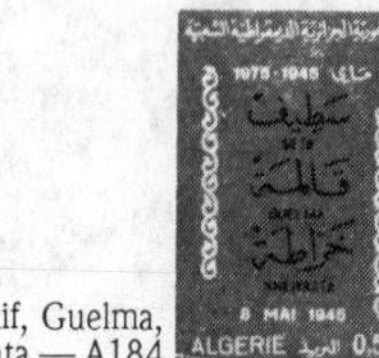
Setif, Guelma, Kherrata — A184

1975 Litho. *Perf. 13½x14*

551 A184 5c orange & blk .15 .15
552 A184 10c emerald & brn .15 .15
553 A184 25c dl blue & blk .15 .15
554 A184 30c lemon & blk .15 .15
555 A184 50c brt grn & blk .22 .15
556 A184 70c fawn & blk .35 .15
557 A184 1d vermilion & blk .50 .25
Nos. 551-557 (7) 1.67
Set value .60

30th anniv. of victory in World War II.
Issue dates: 50c, 1d, Nov. 3; others, Dec. 17.
For surcharge see No. 611.

Map of Maghreb and APU Emblem A185

1975, Nov. 20 Photo. *Perf. 11½*

558 A185 1d multicolored .55 .28

10th Cong. of Arab Postal Union, Algiers.

Mosaic, Bey Constantine's Palace — A186

Dey-Alger Palace — A187

Famous buildings: 2d, Prayer niche, Medersa Sidi-Boumediene, Tlemcen.

1975, Dec. 22

559 A186 1d lt blue & multi .60 .22
560 A186 2d buff & multi 1.10 .60
561 A187 2.50d buff & blk 1.60 .90
Nos. 559-561 (3) 3.30 1.72

Al-Azhar University A188

Perf. 11½x12½

1975, Dec. 29 Litho.

562 A188 2d multicolored 1.10 .60

Millennium of Al-Azhar University.

Red-billed Firefinch — A189

Birds: 1.40d, Black-headed bush shrike, horiz. 2d, Blue tit. 2.50d, Blackbellied sandgrouse, horiz.

1976, Jan. 24 Photo. *Perf. 11½*

563 A189 50c multi .35 .18
564 A189 1.40d multi .85 .55
565 A189 2d multi 1.10 .65
566 A189 2.50d multi 1.50 .90
Nos. 563-566 (4) 3.80 2.28

See Nos. 595-598.

Telephones 1876 and 1976 — A190

Map of Africa with Angola and its Flag — A191

1976, Feb. 23 Photo. *Perf. 13½x13*

567 A190 1.40d rose, dk & lt bl .65 .38

Centenary of first telephone call by Alexander Graham Bell, Mar. 10, 1876.

1976, Feb. 23 *Perf. 11½*

568 A191 50c brown & multi .25 .15

Algeria's solidarity with the People's Republic of Angola.

A192

A193

Sahraoui flag and child, map of former Spanish Sahara.

1976, Mar. 15 Photo. *Perf. 11½*

569 A192 50c multicolored .25 .15

Algeria's solidarity with Sahraoui Arab Democratic Republic, former Spanish Sahara.

1976, Mar. 22

570 A193 1.40d Mailman .60 .32

Stamp Day 1976.

Microscope, Slide with TB Bacilli, Patients A194

1976, Apr. 26 *Perf. 13x13½*

571 A194 50c multicolored .40 .20

Fight against tuberculosis.

"Setif, Guelma, Kherrata" — A195

1976, May 24 Photo. *Perf. 13½x13*

572 A195 50c blue & yellow .35 .15
a. Booklet pane of 6 4.75
b. Booklet pane of 10 4.00

No. 572 was issued in booklets only.

Ram's Head over Landscape — A196

People Holding Torch, Map of Algeria — A197

1976, June 17 Photo. *Perf. 11½*

573 A196 50c multicolored .40 .20

Livestock breeding.

1976, June 29 Photo. *Perf. 14x13½*

574 A197 50c multicolored .25 .15

National Charter.

Palestine Map and Flag — A198

Map of Africa — A199

1976, July 12 *Perf. 11½*

Granite Paper

575 A198 50c multicolored 2.00 1.00

Solidarity with the Palestinians.

1976, Oct. 3 Litho. *Perf. 10½x11*

576 A199 2d dk blue & multi 1.00 .50

2nd Pan-African Commercial Fair, Algiers.

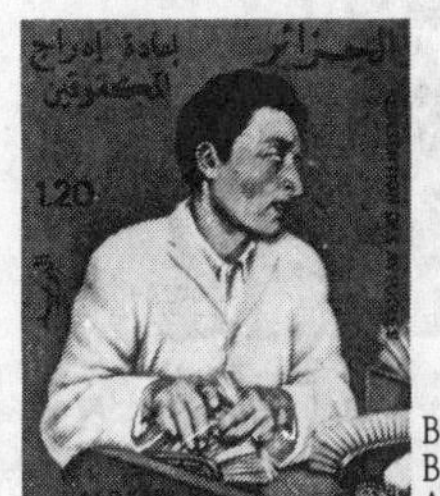

Blind Brushmaker A200

The Blind, by Dinet A201

1976, Oct. 23 Photo. *Perf. 14½*

577 A200 1.20d blue & multi .65 .35
578 A201 1.40d gold & multi 1.50 .75

Rehabilitation of the blind.

The first value column gives the catalogue value of an unused stamp, the second that of a used stamp.

"Constitution 1976" — A202

1976, Nov. 19 Photo. *Perf. 11½*

579 A202 2d multicolored 1.00 .55

New Constitution.

Soldiers Planting Seedlings — A203

1976, Nov. 25 Litho. *Perf. 12*

580 A203 1.40d multicolored .75 .35

Green barrier against the Sahara.

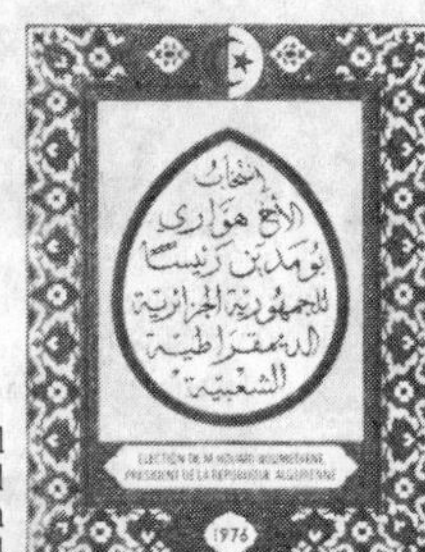

Ornamental Border and Inscription A204

1976, Dec. 18 Photo. *Perf. 11½*

Granite Paper

581 A204 2d multicolored 1.25 .75

Re-election of Pres. Houari Boumediene.

See No. 627.

Map with Charge Zones and Dials A205

People and Buildings A206

1977, Jan. 22 *Perf. 13*

582 A205 40c silver & multi .28 .15

Inauguration of automatic national and international telephone service.

1977, Jan. 29 Photo. *Perf. 11½*

583 A206 60c on 50c multi .35 .18

2nd General Population and Buildings Census. No. 583 was not issued without the typographed red brown surcharge, date, and bars.

Sahara Museum, Uargla — A207

1977, Feb. 12 Litho. *Perf. 14*

584 A207 60c multicolored .35 .20

El-Kantara Gorge — A208

Perf. 12½x13½

1977, Feb. 19 Photo.

585 A208 20c green & yellow .15 .15
a. Bklt. pane, 3 #585, 4 #586 + label 8.00
b. Bklt. pane, 5 #585, 2 #587 + label 6.50
586 A208 60c brt lilac & yel .18 .15
587 A208 1d brown & yellow .40 .15
Set value .63 .30

National Assembly — A209

1977, Feb. 27 *Perf. 11½*

588 A209 2d multicolored 1.00 .60

People and Flag — A210

Soldier and Flag — A211

Perf. 13½, 11½ (3d)

1977, Mar. 12 Photo.

589 A210 2d multicolored 1.25 .40
590 A211 3d multicolored 1.75 .65

Solidarity with the peoples of Zimbabwe (Rhodesia), 2d; Namibia, 3d.

Winter, Roman Mosaic — A212

The Seasons from Roman Villa, 2nd century A.D.: 1.40d, Fall. 2d, Summer. 3d, Spring.

1977, Apr. 21 Photo. *Perf. 11½*

Granite Paper

591 A212 1.20d multi .95 .52
592 A212 1.40d multi 1.25 .52
593 A212 2d multi 1.65 .95
594 A212 3d multi 2.50 1.65
a. Souv. sheet of 4, #591-594, perf., imperf. 10.00 10.00
Nos. 591-594 (4) 6.35 3.64

No. 594a sold for 8d.

Bird Type of 1976

Birds: 60c, Tristram's warbler. 1.40d, Moussier's redstart, horiz. 2d, Temminck's horned lark, horiz. 3d, Eurasian hoopoe.

1977, May 21 Photo. *Perf. 11½*

595 A189 60c multi .75 .22
596 A189 1.40d multi 1.25 .40
597 A189 2d multi 1.75 .65
598 A189 3d multi 2.50 1.10
Nos. 595-598 (4) 6.25 2.37

Horseman — A213

Design: 5d, Attacking horsemen, horiz.

1977, June 25 Photo. *Perf. 11½*

599 A213 2d multicolored 1.65 .75
600 A213 5d multicolored 3.50 2.00

Flag Colors, Games Emblem — A214

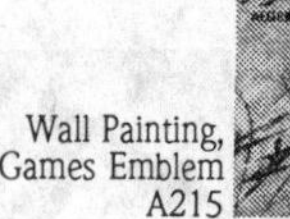

Wall Painting, Games Emblem A215

1977, Sept. 24 Photo. *Perf. 11½*

601 A214 60c multi .35 .22
602 A215 1.40d multi .80 .45

3rd African Games, Algiers 1978.

Village and Tractor A216

1977, Nov. 12 *Perf. 14x13*

603 A216 1.40d multi .90 .65

Socialist agricultural village.

Almohades Dirham, 12th Century — A217

Ancient Coins: 1.40d, Almohades coin, 12th century. 2d, Almoravides dinar, 11th century.

1977, Dec. 17 Photo. *Perf. 11½*

604 A217 60c ultra, sil & blk .50 .35
605 A217 1.40d green, gold & brn 1.10 .50
606 A217 2d red brn, gold & brn 1.50 .90
Nos. 604-606 (3) 3.10 1.75

Flowering Trees — A218

1978, Feb. 11 Photo. *Perf. 11½*

607 A218 60c Cherry .35 .24
608 A218 1.20d Peach .85 .50
609 A218 1.30d Almond .85 .50
610 A218 1.40d Apple .90 .55
Nos. 607-610 (4) 2.95 1.79

No. 555 Surcharged with New Value and Bar

1978, Feb. 11 Litho. *Perf. 13½x14*

611 A184 60c on 50c .50 .16

Children with Traffic Signs and Car — A219

1978, Apr. 29 Photo. *Perf. 11½*

612 A219 60c multicolored .28 .15

Road safety and protection of children.

Sports and Games Emblems A220

Designs (Games Emblem and): 60c, Rower, vert. 1.20d, Flag colors. 1.30d, Fireworks, vert. 1.40d, Map of Africa and dancers, vert.

1978, July 13 Photo. *Perf. 11½*

613 A220 40c multi .18 .15
614 A220 60c multi .28 .18
615 A220 1.20d multi .60 .28
616 A220 1.30d multi .60 .35
617 A220 1.40d multi .65 .35
Nos. 613-617 (5) 2.31 1.31

3rd African Games, Algiers, July 13-28.

TB Patient Returning to Family A221

1978, Oct. 5 Photo. *Perf. 13½x14*

618 A221 60c multicolored .35 .16

Anti-tuberculosis campaign.

Holy Kaaba — A222

1978, Oct. 28 Photo. *Perf. 11½*

619 A222 60c multicolored .28 .15

Pilgrimage to Mecca.

National Servicemen Building Road — A223

1978, Nov. 4

620 A223 60c multicolored .28 .15

African Unity Road from El Goleah to In Salah, inauguration.

Fibula A224 Pres. Boumediene A225

Jewelry: 1.35d, Pendant. 1.40d, Ankle ring.

1978, Dec. 21 Photo. *Perf. 12x11½*

621 A224 1.20d multi .65 .28
622 A224 1.35d multi .70 .28
623 A224 1.40d multi 1.10 1.10
Nos. 621-623 (3) 2.45 1.66

1979, Jan. 7 Photo. *Perf. 12x11½*

624 A225 60c green, red & brown .28 .15

Houari Boumediene, pres. of Algeria 1965-1978.

Torch and Books A226

1979, Jan. 27 Photo. *Perf. 11½*

625 A226 60c multicolored .28 .18

Natl. Front of Liberation Party Cong.

Pres. Boumediene A227

1979, Feb. 4 Photo. *Perf. 11½*

626 A227 1.40d multi .65 .28

40 days after death of Pres. Houari Boumediène.

Ornamental Type of 1976

Proclamation of new President.

1979, Feb. 10

627 A204 2d multicolored 1.00 .35

Election of Pres. Chadli Bendjedid.

A229 A230

1979, Apr. 18 Photo. *Perf. 11½*

628 A229 60c multicolored .28 .15

Sheik Abdul-Hamid Ben Badis (1889-1940).

1979, May 19 Photo. *Perf. 13½x14*

Designs: 1.20d, Telephone dial, map of Africa. 1.40d, Symbolic Morse key and waves.

629 A230 1.20d multi .55 .22
630 A230 1.40d multi .60 .22

Telecom '79 Exhib., Geneva, Sept. 20-26.

Harvest, IYC Emblem — A231

Design: 1.40d, Dancers and IYC emblem, vert.

Perf. 11½x11, 11x11½

1979, June 21

631 A231 60c multi .40 .20
632 A231 1.40d multi .60 .45

International Year of the Child.

A232 A233

1979, Oct. 20 Photo. *Perf. 11½*

633 A232 1.40d Nuthatch .90 .40

1979, Nov. 1 Photo. *Perf. 12½*

Designs: 1.40d, Flag, soldiers and workers. 3d, Revolutionaries and emblem.

634 A233 1.40d multi .90 .22

Size: 37x48mm

Perf. 11½

635 A233 3d multi 2.25 .65

November 1 revolution, 25th anniversary.

Hegira, 1500 Anniv. A234

1979, Dec. 2 Photo. *Perf. 11½*

636 A234 3d multicolored 1.25 .65

Camels, Lion, Men and Slave — A235

Dionysian Procession (Setif Mosaic): 1.35d, Elephants, tigers and women. Men in tiger-drawn cart. No. 639a has continuous design.

1980, Feb. 16 Photo. *Perf. 11½*

Granite Paper

637 A235 1.20d multi .55 .22
638 A235 1.35d multi .60 .35
639 A235 1.40d multi .65 .55
a. Strip of 3, #637-639 1.80 1.25
Nos. 637-639 (3) 1.80 1.12

Science Day — A236

1980, Apr. 19 Photo. *Perf. 12*
640 A236 60c multicolored .28 .20

Dam and Workers — A237

1980, June 17 Photo. *Perf. 11½*
641 A237 60c multicolored .28 .15

Extraordinary Congress of the National Liberation Front Party.

Olympic Sports, Moscow '80 Emblem A238

1980, June 28
642 A238 50c Flame, rings, vert. .22 .15
643 A238 1.40d shown .65 .35

22nd Summer Olympic Games, Moscow, July 19-Aug. 3.

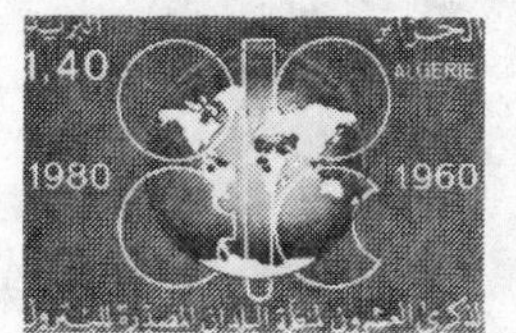
20th Anniversary of OPEC — A239

Perf. 11x10½, 10½x11
1980, Sept. 15 Engr.
644 A239 60c Men holding OPEC emblem, vert. .28 .15
645 A239 1.40d shown .65 .35

Aures Valley A240

1980, Sept. 25 Litho. *Perf. 13½x14*
646 A240 50c shown .22 .15
647 A240 1d El Oued Oasis .40 .18
648 A240 1.40d Tassili Rocks .60 .22
649 A240 2d View of Algiers .90 .40
Nos. 646-649 (4) 2.12 .95

World Tourism Conf., Manila, Sept. 27.

Avicenna (980-1037), Philosopher and Physician A241

1980, Oct. 25 Photo. *Perf. 12*
650 A241 2d multicolored 1.50 .75

Ruins of El Asnam A242

1980, Nov. 13 Photo. *Perf. 12*
651 A242 3d multicolored 1.25 .45

Earthquake relief.

Crown A243

1980, Dec. 20 Photo. *Perf. 12*
Granite Paper
652 A243 60c Necklace, vert. .28 .18
653 A243 1.40d Earrings, bracelet, vert. .60 .28
654 A243 2d shown .80 .45
Nos. 652-654 (3) 1.68 .91

See Nos. 705-707.

1980-1984 Five-Year Plan — A244

1981, Jan. 29 Litho. *Perf. 14*
655 A244 60c multicolored .25 .15

Basket Weaving — A245

1981, Feb. 19 Photo. *Perf. 12½*
Granite Paper
656 A245 40c shown .20 .15
657 A245 60c Rug weaving .28 .15
658 A245 1d Coppersmith .40 .18
659 A245 1.40d Jeweler .60 .32
Nos. 656-659 (4) 1.48 .80

Cedar Tree — A246

Arbor Day: 1.40d, Cypress tree, vert.

1981, Mar. 19 Photo. *Perf. 12*
Granite Paper
660 A246 60c multi .30 .15
661 A246 1.40d multi .60 .32

Mohamed Bachir el Ibrahimi (1869-1965) A247

Children Going to School — A248

1981, Apr. 16
Granite Paper
662 A247 60c multicolored .25 .15
663 A248 60c multicolored .25 .15
Set value .17

Science Day.

12th International Hydatidological Congress, Algiers — A249

1981, Apr. 23 *Perf. 14x13½*
664 A249 2d multicolored .80 .32

13th World Telecommunications Day — A250

1981, May 14 Photo. *Perf. 14x13½*
665 A250 1.40d multi .60 .20

Disabled People and Hand Offering Flower A251

Perf. 12½x13, 13x12½
1981, June 20 Litho.
666 A251 1.20d Symbolic globe, vert. .55 .18
667 A251 1.40d shown .60 .18

Intl. Year of the Disabled.

Papilio Machaon A252

1981, Aug. 20 Photo. *Perf. 11½*
Granite Paper
668 A252 60c shown .25 .15
669 A252 1.20d Rhodocera rhamni .55 .20
670 A252 1.40d Charaxes jasius .60 .25
671 A252 2d Papilio podalirius .80 .38
Nos. 668-671 (4) 2.20 .98

Monk Seal — A253

1981, Sept. 17 *Perf. 14x13½*
672 A253 60c shown .25 .15
673 A253 1.40d Macaque .60 .35

World Food Day — A254

Cave Drawings of Tassili — A255

1981, Oct. 16 Photo. *Perf. 14x14½*
674 A254 2d multicolored .65 .35

1981, Nov. 21 *Perf. 11½*

Designs: Various cave drawings. 1.60d, 2d horiz.

675 A255 60c multi .30 .15
676 A255 1d multi .50 .18
677 A255 1.60d multi .75 .32
678 A255 2d multi .90 .40
Nos. 675-678 (4) 2.45 1.05

Galley, 17-18th Cent. A256

1981, Dec. 17 Photo. *Perf. 11½*
679 A256 60c shown .40 .18
680 A256 1.60d Ship, diff. .90 .35

1982 World Cup Soccer A257

Designs: Various soccer players.

Perf. 13x12½x 12½x13
1982, Feb. 25 Litho.
681 A257 80c multi, vert. .35 .15
682 A257 2.80d multi 1.10 .50

TB Bacillus Centenary — A258

1982, Mar. 20 Photo. *Perf. 14½x14*
683 A258 80c multi .35 .15

Painted Stand A259

1982, Apr. 24 Photo. *Perf. 11½*
Granite Paper
684 A259 80c Mirror, vert. .35 .18
685 A259 2d shown .80 .40

Size: 48x33mm

686 A259 2.40d Chest 1.00 .55
Nos. 684-686 (3) 2.15 1.13

Djamaael Djadid Mosque, Algiers — A260

1982, May 15 Litho. *Perf. 14*

687 A260 80c shown .35 .15
688 A260 2.40d Sidi Boumediene Mosque, Tlemcen 1.00 .50
689 A260 3d Garden of Dey, Algiers 1.25 .55
Nos. 687-689 (3) 2.60 1.20

See Nos. 731-734, 745-747, 774, 778-783.

Callitris Articulata A261

Independence, 20th Anniv. A262

Designs: Medicinal plants.

1982, May 27 Photo. *Perf. 11½*

Granite Paper

690 A261 50c shown .20 .15
691 A261 80c Artemisia herba-alba .25 .15
692 A261 1d Ricinus communis .50 .20
693 A261 2.40d Thymus fontanesii .90 .45
Nos. 690-693 (4) 1.85 .95

1982, July 5

Granite Paper

694 A262 50c Riflemen .20 .15
695 A262 80c Soldiers, horiz. .32 .18
696 A262 2d Symbols, citizens, horiz. .80 .45
Nos. 694-696 (3) 1.32 .78

Souvenir Sheet

697 A262 5d Emblem 2.00 2.00

No. 697 contains one 32x39mm stamp.

Soummam Congress A263

1982, Aug. 20 Litho.

698 A263 80c Congress building .35 .15

Scouting Year — A264

1982, Oct. 21 Photo.

Granite Paper

699 A264 2.80d multi 1.10 .45

Palestinian Child — A265

Chlamydotis Undulata — A266

1982, Nov. 25 Litho. *Perf. 10½*

700 A265 1.60d multi 2.00 .75

Perf. 15x14, 14x15

1982, Dec. 23 Photo.

Protected birds. 50c, 2d horiz.

701 A266 50c Geronticus eremita .40 .15
702 A266 80c shown .65 .18
703 A266 2d Aguila rapax 1.25 .40
704 A266 2.40d Gypaetus barbatus 1.75 .45
Nos. 701-704 (4) 4.05 1.18

Jewelry Type of 1980

1983, Feb. 10 *Perf. 11½*

Granite Paper

705 A243 50c Picture frame .18 .15
706 A243 1d Flaska .38 .28
707 A243 2d Brooch, horiz. .75 .45
Nos. 705-707 (3) 1.31 .88

A267

A268

1983, Mar. 17 Photo.

Granite Paper

708 A267 80c Abies numidica, vert. .32 .15
709 A267 2.80d Acacia raddiana 1.10 .60

Intl. Arbor Day.

Perf. 12x12½, 12½x12

1983, Apr. 21 Photo.

Various minerals. 1.20d, 2.40d horiz.

Granite Paper

710 A268 70c multi .28 .15
711 A268 80c multi .32 .18
712 A268 1.20d multi .50 .28
713 A268 2.40d multi 1.00 .60
Nos. 710-713 (4) 2.10 1.21

30th Anniv. of Intl. Customs Cooperation Council A269

1983, May 14 Photo. *Perf. 11½*

Granite Paper

714 A269 80c multi .35 .18

Emir Abdelkader Death Centenary — A270

1983, May 22 Photo. *Perf. 12*

Granite Paper

715 A270 4d multi 1.60 .75

A271

A272

Local mushrooms.

1983, July 21 *Perf. 14x15*

716 A271 50c Amanita muscaria .20 .15
717 A271 80c Amanita phalloides .32 .18
718 A271 1.40d Pleurotus eryngii .55 .35
719 A271 2.80d Tefezia leonis 1.00 .60
Nos. 716-719 (4) 2.07 1.28

1983, Sept. 1 Photo. *Perf. 11½*

720 A272 80c multi .35 .15

ibn-Khaldun, historian, philosopher.

World Communications Year — A273

Perf. 11½x12½

1983, Sept. 22 Litho.

721 A273 80c Post Office, Algiers .35 .15
722 A273 2.40d Telephone, circuit box 1.00 .38

Goat and Tassili Mountains A274

1983, Oct. 20 Litho. *Perf. 12½x13*

723 A274 50c shown .20 .15
724 A274 80c Tuaregs in native costume .32 .18
725 A274 2.40d Animals, rock painting 1.00 .40
726 A274 2.80d Rock formation 1.00 .60
Nos. 723-726 (4) 2.52 1.33

Sloughi Dog — A275

Perf. 14x14½, 14½x14

1983, Nov. 24 Photo.

727 A275 80c shown .60 .40
728 A275 2.40d Sloughi, horiz. 1.50 .75

Natl. Liberation Party, 5th Congress — A276

1983, Dec. 19 Photo. *Perf. 11½*

729 A276 80c Symbols of development .35 .22

Souvenir Sheet

730 A276 5d Emblem 3.00 2.50

No. 730 contains one 32x38mm stamp.

View Type of 1982

1984, Jan. 26 Litho. *Perf. 14*

731 A260 10c View of Oran, 1830 .15 .15
732 A260 1d Sidi Abderahman and Taalibi Mosques .40 .18
733 A260 2d Bejaia, 1830 .80 .35
734 A260 4d Constantine, 1830 1.75 .60
Nos. 731-734 (4) 3.10 1.28

See Nos. 745-747, 781, 783.

Pottery A278

Perf. 11½x12, 12x11½

1984, Feb. 23 Photo.

Granite Paper

735 A278 80c Jug, vert. .35 .22
736 A278 1d Platter .40 .22
737 A278 2d Oil lamp, vert. .80 .45
738 A278 2.40d Pitcher 1.00 .60
Nos. 735-738 (4) 2.55 1.49

Fountains of Old Algiers — A279

1984 Summer Olympics — A280

Various fountains.

1984, Mar. 22 Photo. *Perf. 11½*

Granite Paper

739 A279 50c multi .20 .15
740 A279 80c multi .38 .20
741 A279 2.40d multi 1.00 .60
Nos. 739-741 (3) 1.58 .95

1984, May 19 Photo. *Perf. 11½*

Granite Paper

742 A280 1d multi .45 .28

Brown Stallion — A281

1984, June 14 Photo. *Perf. 11½*

Granite Paper

743 A281 80c shown .35 .18
744 A281 2.40d White mare 1.00 .60

View Type of 1982

1984 Litho. *Perf. 14*

745 A260 5c Mustapha Pacha .15 .15
746 A260 20c Bab Azzoun .15 .15
746A A260 30c Algiers .15 .15
746B A260 40c Kolea .15 .15
746C A260 50c Algiers .15 .15
747 A260 70c Mostaganem .32 .15
Set value .84 .40

Issue dates: Nos. 745, 746, 747, July 19. Nos. 746A-746C, Oct. 20.

Lute — A282

Native musical instruments.

1984, Sept. 22 Litho. *Perf. 15x14*

748 A282 80c shown .22 .15
749 A282 1d Drum .28 .15
750 A282 2.40d Fiddle .65 .35
751 A282 2.80d Bagpipe .70 .40
Nos. 748-751 (4) 1.85 1.05

30th Anniv. of Algerian Revolution — A284

1984, Nov. 3 Photo. *Perf. 11½x12*

757 A284 80c Partisans .22 .15

Souvenir Sheet

758 A284 5d Algerian flags, vert. 2.00 1.00

M'Zab Valley A285

1984, Dec. 15 *Perf. 15x14, 14x15*
759 A285 80c Map of valley .22 .15
760 A285 2.40d Town of M'Zab, vert. .65 .32

18th and 19th Century Metalware — A286

1985, Jan. 26 **Photo.** *Perf. 11½*
761 A286 80c Coffee pot .22 .15
762 A286 2d Bowl, horiz. .50 .25
763 A286 2.40d Covered bowl .65 .32
Nos. 761-763 (3) 1.37 .72

Fish — A287

1985, Feb. 23 **Photo.** *Perf. 15x14*
764 A287 50c Thunnus thynnus .15 .15
765 A287 80c Sparus aurata .20 .15
766 A287 2.40d Epinephelus guaza .60 .30
767 A287 2.80d Mustelus mustelus .65 .35
Nos. 764-767 (4) 1.60
Set value .82

National Games — A288

1985, Mar. 28 *Perf. 11½x12*
Granite Paper
768 A288 80c Doves, emblem .20 .15

Environmental Conservation A289

1985, Apr. 25 *Perf. 13½*
769 A289 80c Stylized trees .20 .15
770 A289 1.40d Stylized waves .38 .20

View Type of 1982 and

The Casbah — A290

View of Constantine — A290a

Street Scene in Algiers — A290b

Designs: 2.50d, Djamaael Djadid Mosque, Algiers. 2.90d, like #746. 5d, like #746A. 1.50d, like #746B. 4.20d, like #764.

Perf. 13½x12½, 13 (#774, 4.20d),
Perf. 13½x14 (#775)
Perf. 14½x14 (2d)

Photo., Litho. (2d, 6,20d, 7.50d, #775)
1985-94
771 A290 20c dk blue & buff .15 .15
772 A290 80c sage grn & buff .20 .15
773 A290a 1d dk olive grn .50 .25
a. Bklt. pane of 5 + label 2.50
774 A260 1.50d dull red .55 .30
775 A290b 1.50d red brown & brn .25 .15
a. Booklet pane of 6 1.50
776 A290b 2d dk blue & lt blue .15 .15
a. Booklet pane of 5 + label .95
777 A290 2.40d chestnut & buff .60 .30
a. Bklt. pane of 5 (20c, 3 80c, 2.40d) + label 1.40
778 A260 2.50d bluish green .98 .50
779 A260 2.90d slate 1.15 .58
780 A260 4.20d gray green 1.60 .85
781 A260 5d deep bister & black 1.95 .98

Perf. 14
782 A260 6.20d like #731 1.05 .52
783 A260 7.50d like #745 1.30 .65
Nos. 771-783 (13) 10.43 5.53

Nos. 771-772, 777 issued only in booklet panes.
Issued: 20c, 80c, 2.40d, 6/1/85; 1d, 1/26/89; 2.50d, 2.90d, 5d, 2/23/89; #774, 4.20d, 3/21/91; #775, 5/20/92; 6.20d, 7.50d, 4/22/92; 2d, 10/21/93; #776a, 10/21/94.
See No. 1010.

UN, 40th Anniv. — A291

Natl. Youth Festival — A292

1985, June 26 **Photo.** *Perf. 14*
784 A291 1d Dove, emblem, 40 .25 .15

1985, July 5 **Litho.** *Perf. 13½*
785 A292 80c multicolored .20 .15

Intl. Youth Year — A293

1985, July 5
786 A293 80c Silhouette, globe, emblem, vert. .20 .15
787 A293 1.40d Doves, globe .38 .20

World Map, OPEC — A294

1985, Sept. 14 **Photo.** *Perf. 12½x13*
788 A294 80c multicolored .20 .15

Organization of Petroleum Exporting Countries, 25th anniv.

Family Planning A295

El-Meniaa Township A296

1985, Oct. 3 **Litho.** *Perf. 14*
789 A295 80c Mother and sons .20 .15
790 A295 1.40d Weighing infant .38 .18
791 A295 1.70d Breast-feeding .45 .22
Nos. 789-791 (3) 1.03 .55

1985, Oct. 24 **Engr.** *Perf. 13*
792 A296 80c Chetaibi Bay, horiz. .20 .15
793 A296 2d shown .50 .25
794 A296 2.40d Bou Noura Town, horiz. .65 .32
Nos. 792-794 (3) 1.35 .72

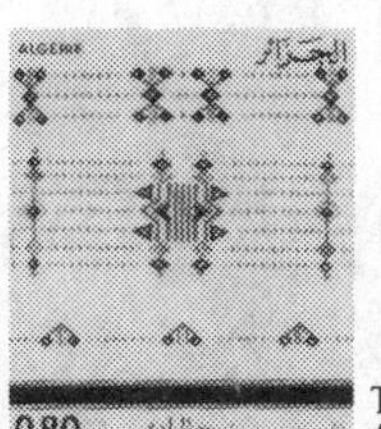
The Palm Grove, by N. Dinet — A297

1985, Nov. 21 **Photo.** *Perf. 11½x12*
Granite Paper
795 A297 2d multi .50 .25
796 A297 3d multi, diff. .70 .40

Tapestries A298

Various designs.

1985, Dec. 19
Granite Paper
797 A298 80c multi .20 .15
798 A298 1.40d multi .38 .20
799 A298 2.40d multi .60 .32
800 A298 2.80d multi .70 .40
Nos. 797-800 (4) 1.88 1.07

Wildcats A299

Perf. 12x11½, 11½x12
1986, Jan. 23
Granite Paper
801 A299 80c Felis margarita .60 .15
802 A299 1d Felis caracal .80 .15
803 A299 2d Felis sylvestris 1.50 .80
804 A299 2.40d Felis serval, vert. 2.00 .95
Nos. 801-804 (4) 4.90 2.05

UN Child Survival Campaign — A300

Algerian General Worker's Union, 30th Anniv. — A301

1986, Feb. 13 **Litho.** *Perf. 13½*
805 A300 80c Oral vaccine .20 .15
806 A300 1.40d Mother, child, sun .40 .18
807 A300 1.70d Three children .45 .22
Nos. 805-807 (3) 1.05 .55

1986, Feb. 24 *Perf. 12½*
Granite Paper
808 A301 2d multi .50 .25

National Charter — A302

Natl. Day of the Disabled — A303

1986, Mar. 6 **Photo.** *Perf. 11½*
Granite Paper
809 A302 4d multi 1.50 .55

1986, Mar. 15 *Perf. 12½x13*
810 A303 80c multi .20 .15

A304

A305

1986, Apr. 17 **Litho.** *Perf. 14x15*
811 A304 80c multi .20 .15

Anti-Tuberculosis campaign.

1986, Apr. 24 *Perf. 14*
812 A305 2d Soccer ball, sombrero .50 .25
813 A305 2.40d Soccer players .65 .32

1986 World Cup Soccer Championships, Mexico.

Inner Courtyards — A306

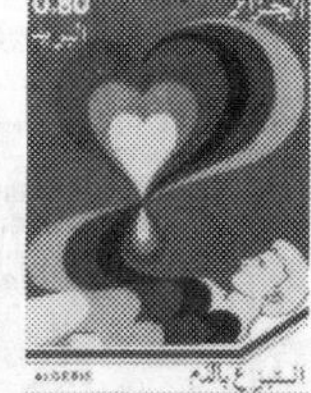
Blood Donation Campaign — A307

1986, May 15 **Photo.** *Perf. 11½*
Granite Paper
814 A306 80c multi .20 .15
815 A306 2.40d multi, diff. .65 .32
816 A306 3d multi, diff. .80 .40
Nos. 814-816 (3) 1.65 .87

1986, June 26 **Litho.** *Perf. 13½*
817 A307 80c multi .22 .15

Southern District Radio Communication Inauguration — A308

1986, July *Perf. 13*
818 A308 60c multi .16 .15

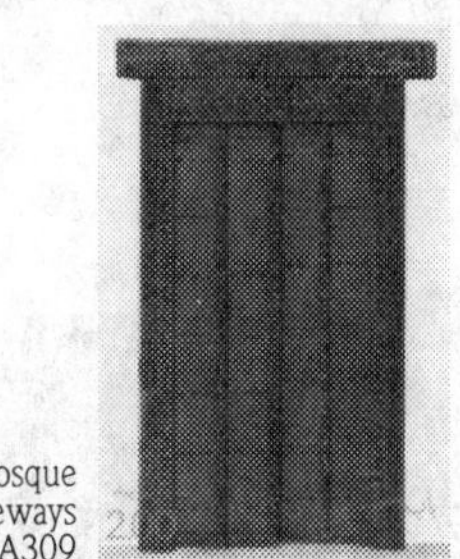
Mosque Gateways A309

1986, Sept. 27 **Photo.** *Perf. 12x11½*
Granite Paper
819 A309 2d Door .50 .25
820 A309 2.40d Ornamental arch .65 .32

Intl. Peace Year — A310

Perf. 13½x14½

1986, Oct. 16 **Photo.**

821 A310 2.40d multi .65 .32

Folk Dancing A311

1986, Nov. 22 **Litho.** *Perf. 14x13½*

822 A311	80c	Woman, scarf	.22	.15
823 A311	2.40d	Woman, diff.	.65	.32
824 A311	2.80d	Man, sword	.70	.40
		Nos. 822-824 (3)	1.57	.87

Flowers — A312

1986, Dec. 18 **Photo.** *Perf. 14*

825 A312	80c	Narcissus tazetta	.22	.15
826 A312	1.40d	Iris unguicularis	.40	.20
827 A312	2.40d	Capparis spinosa	.65	.32
828 A312	2.80d	Gladiolus segetum	.70	.40
		Nos. 825-828 (4)	1.97	1.07

See Nos. 936-938.

Abstract Paintings by Mohammed Issia Khem A313

Perf. 11½x12, 12x11½

1987, Jan. 29 **Litho.**

829 A313	2d	Man and woman, vert.	.65	.35
830 A313	5d	Man and books	1.60	.80

Jewelry from Aures A314

1987, Feb. 27 **Photo.** *Perf. 12*

Granite Paper

831 A314	1d	Earrings	.35	.16
832 A314	1.80d	Bracelets	.60	.30
833 A314	2.90d	Nose rings	1.00	.50
834 A314	3.30d	Necklace	1.10	.55
		Nos. 831-834 (4)	3.05	1.51

Nos. 831-833 vert.

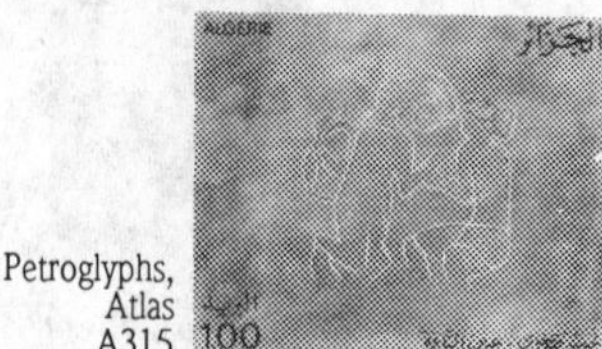

Petroglyphs, Atlas A315

1987, Mar. 26 **Litho.** *Perf. 12x11½*

Granite Paper

835 A315	1d	Man and woman	.35	.16
836 A315	2.90d	Goat	1.00	.50
837 A315	3.30d	Horse, bull	1.10	.60
		Nos. 835-837 (3)	2.45	1.26

Syringe as an Umbrella — A316

1987, Apr. 7 *Perf. 11½*

Granite Paper

838 A316 1d multi .35 .16

Child Immunization Campaign, World Health Day.

Volunteers — A317

Third General Census — A318

1987, Apr. 23 *Perf. 10½*

839 A317 1d multi .35 .16

1987, May 21 *Perf. 13½*

840 A318 1d multi .35 .16

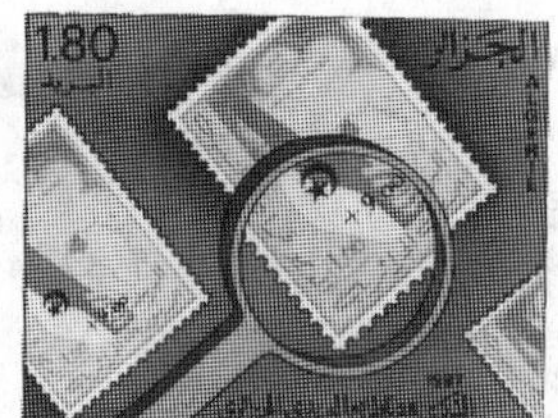

Algerian Postage, 25th Anniv. — A319

Design: War Orphans' Fund label (1fr + 9fr) of 1962.

1987, July 5 **Photo.** *Perf. 11½x12*

Granite Paper

841 A319 1.80d multi .60 .32

A320 A321

1987, July 5

Granite Paper

842 A320 1d multi .35 .16

Souvenir Sheet

843 A321 5d multi 1.60 1.60

Natl. independence, 25th anniv.

Amateur Theater Festival, Mostaganem A322

1987, July 20 *Perf. 12x11½*

Granite Paper

844 A322	1d	Actors on stage	.35	.16
845 A322	1.80d	Theater	.60	.32
a.		Pair, #844-845	1.00	.50

No. 845a has continuous design.

Mediterranean Games, Latakia A323

1987, Aug. 6 *Perf. 13x12½, 12½x13*

846 A323	1d	Discus	.35	.16
847 A323	2.90d	Tennis, vert.	1.00	.50
848 A323	3.30d	Team handball	1.10	.55
		Nos. 846-848 (3)	2.45	1.21

Birds — A324

1987 **Litho.** *Perf. 13½*

849 A324	1d	Phoenicopterus ruber roseus	.55	.24
850 A324	1.80d	Porphyrio porphyrio	1.00	.50
851 A324	2.50d	Elanus caeruleus	1.40	.65
852 A324	2.90d	Milvus milvus	1.65	.75
		Nos. 849-852 (4)	4.60	2.14

Agriculture A325

Perf. 10½x11, 11x10½

1987, Nov. 26 **Litho.**

853 A325	1d	Planting	.35	.16
854 A325	1d	Reservoir	.35	.16
855 A325	1d	Harvesting crop, vert.	.35	.16
856 A325	1d	Produce, vert.	.35	.16
		Nos. 853-856 (4)	1.40	.64

African Telecommunications Day — A326

1987, Dec. 7 *Perf. 10½*

857 A326 1d multi .35 .16

Transportation A327

1987, Dec. 18 **Litho.** *Perf. 10½x11*

858 A327	2.90d	shown	1.00	.50
859 A327	3.30d	Diesel train	1.10	.55

Algerian Universities A328

Various campuses.

Perf. 10½x11, 11x10½

1987, Dec. 26

860 A328	1d	shown	.35	.16
861 A328	2.50d	multi, diff.	.80	.40
862 A328	2.90d	multi, diff.	1.00	.50
863 A328	3.30d	multi, diff., vert.	1.10	.55
		Nos. 860-863 (4)	3.25	1.61

Intl. Rural Development Fund, 10th Anniv. A329

1988, Jan. 27 *Perf. 10½x11*

864 A329 1d multi .50 .25

Autonomy of State-owned Utilities — A330

1988, Feb. 27 **Litho.** *Perf. 11x10½*

865 A330 1d multi .50 .25

Intl. Women's Day — A331

Arab Scouts, 75th Anniv. — A332

1988, Mar. 10 **Litho.** *Perf. 11x10½*

866 A331 1d multi .50 .25

1988, Apr. 7 **Litho.** *Perf. 10½*

867 A332 2d multi .95 .48

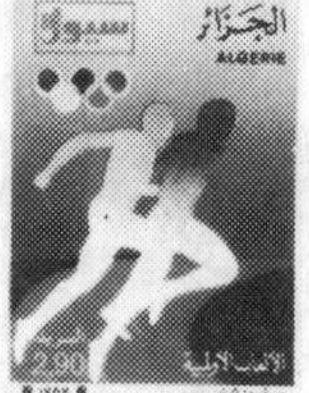

1988 Summer Olympics, Seoul — A333

Hot Springs — A334

1988, July 23 **Litho.** *Perf. 10½*

868 A333 2.90d multi 1.40 .70

1988, July 16

869 A334	1d	shown	.50	.25
870 A334	2.90d	Caverns, horiz.	1.40	.70
871 A334	3.30d	Gazebo, fountain, horiz.	1.60	.80
		Nos. 869-871 (3)	3.50	1.75

World Wildlife Fund — A335

Barbary apes, *Macaca sylvanus*.

1988, Sept. 17 **Litho.** *Perf. 10½*

872 A335	50c	Adult	.25	.15
873 A335	90c	Family	.45	.22
874 A335	1d	Close-up, vert.	.50	.25
875 A335	1.80d	Seated on branch, vert.	.90	.45
		Nos. 872-875 (4)	2.10	1.07

Intl. Literacy Day — A336

WHO, 40th Anniv. — A337

1988, Sept. 10 Photo. *Perf. 10½*
876 A336 2.90d multi 1.40 .70

1988, Oct. 15
877 A337 2.90d multi 1.40 .70

Fight Apartheid A338

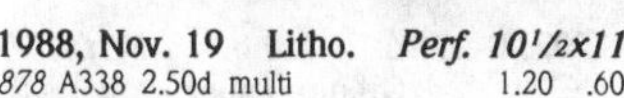

1988, Nov. 19 Litho. *Perf. 10½x11*
878 A338 2.50d multi 1.20 .60

Natl. Front Congress — A339

1988, Nov. 29 *Perf. 11x10½*
879 A339 1d multi .50 .25

Agriculture A340

1988, Dec. 24 *Perf. 10½*
880 A340 1d Irrigation .50 .25
881 A340 1d Orchard, fields, livestock .50 .25

Natl. Goals — A342

Airports — A343

1989, Mar. 9 Litho. *Perf. 11½*
Granite Paper
886 A342 1d shown .50 .25
887 A342 1d Ancient fort .50 .25
888 A342 1d Telecommunications .50 .25
889 A342 1d Modern buildings .50 .25
Nos. 886-889 (4) 2.00 1.00

Nos. 887-889 horiz.

Perf. 10½x11, 11x10½
1989, Mar. 23
890 A343 2.90d Oran Es Senia, horiz. 1.45 .72
891 A343 3.30d Tebessa, horiz. 1.65 .82
892 A343 5d shown 2.50 1.25
Nos. 890-892 (3) 5.60 2.79

Development of the South A344

1989, Apr. 24 Litho. *Perf. 13½*
893 A344 1d Irrigation .48 .25
894 A344 1.80d Building .88 .45
895 A344 2.50d Fossil fuel extraction, vert. 1.20 .60
Nos. 893-895 (3) 2.56 1.30

Eradicate Locusts A345

1989, May 25 *Perf. 10½*
896 A345 1d multi .50 .25

National Service — A346

1989, May 11 Litho. *Perf. 13½*
897 A346 2d multicolored .78 .40

1st Moon Landing, 20th Anniv. A347

Designs: 4d, Astronaut, lunar module, Moon's surface, vert.

1989, July 23 Litho. *Perf. 13½*
898 A347 2.90d shown 1.10 .55
899 A347 4d multi 1.50 .75

Interparliamentary Union, Cent. — A348

1989, Sept. 4 *Perf. 10½*
900 A348 2.90d gold, brt rose lil & blk 1.10 .55

Produce A349

1989, Sept. 23 Litho. *Perf. 11½*
Granite Paper
901 Strip of 3 4.00
a. A349 2d multi, diff. .78 .40
b. A349 3d multi, diff. 1.15 .58
c. A349 5d shown 1.95 .98

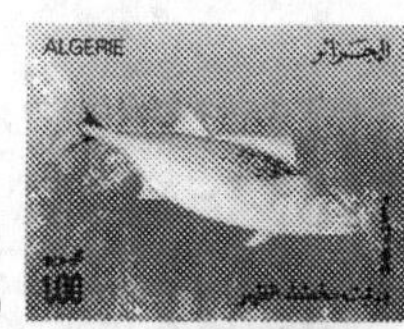

Fish — A350

1989, Oct. 27 Litho. *Perf. 13½*
902 A350 1d *Sarda sarda* .40 .20
903 A350 1.80d *Zeus faber* .70 .35
904 A350 2.90d *Pagellus bogaraveo* 1.15 .58
905 A350 3.30d *Xiphias gladius* 1.30 .65
Nos. 902-905 (4) 3.55 1.78

Algerian Revolution, 35th Anniv. — A351

1989, Nov. 4 Litho. *Perf. 13½*
906 A351 1d multicolored .40 .20

African Development Bank, 25th Anniv. A352

Mushrooms A353

1989, Nov. 18 *Perf. 10½*
907 A352 1d multicolored .40 .20

1989, Dec. 16 *Perf. 13½*
908 A353 1d *Boletus satanas* .40 .20
909 A353 1.80d *Psalliota xanthoderma* .70 .35
910 A353 2.90d *Lepiota procera* 1.15 .58
911 A353 3.30d *Lactarius deliciosus* 1.30 .65
Nos. 908-911 (4) 3.55 1.78

A354

A355

1990, Jan. 18 Litho. *Perf. 10½*
912 A354 1d multicolored .40 .20

Pan-African Postal Union, 10th anniv.

1990, Feb. 22 Litho. *Perf. 14*
913 A355 1d Energy conservation .25 .15

A356

A357

1990, Mar. 2 Photo. *Perf. 11½*
914 A356 3d multicolored .65 .32

African Soccer Championships.

1990, May 17 Litho. *Perf. 13½*
917 A357 2.90d shown .75 .38
918 A357 5d Trophy 1.25 .65

World Cup Soccer Championships, Italy.

Rural Electrification A358

1990, June 21
919 A358 2d multicolored .50 .25

Youth A359

Youth Holding Rainbow — A360

1990, July 6 *Perf. 13½*
920 A359 2d multicolored .50 .25
921 A360 3d multicolored .75 .36

Maghreb Arab Union — A361

1990 *Perf. 14x13½*
922 A361 1d multicolored .38 .20

Vocations — A362

1990, Apr. 26 Litho. *Perf. 12½*
923 A362 2d Craftsmen .75 .40
924 A362 2.90d Auto mechanics 1.15 .60
925 A362 3.30d Deep sea fishing 1.25 .65
Nos. 923-925 (3) 3.15 1.65

Organization of Petroleum Exporting Countries (OPEC), 30th Anniv. A363

1990 *Perf. 13½*
926 A363 2d multicolored .75 .40

Savings Promotion — A364

1990, Oct. 31 Litho. *Perf. 14*

927 A364 1d multicolored .38 .20

Namibian Independence A365

1990, Nov. 8

928 A365 3d multicolored 1.15 .60

A366

A367

Farm animals.

1990, Nov. 29 *Perf. 13½*

929	A366	1d	Duck	.38	.20
930	A366	2d	Rabbit, horiz.	.75	.40
931	A366	2.90d	Turkey	1.10	.60
932	A366	3d	Rooster, horiz.	1.15	.60
			Nos. 929-932 (4)	3.38	1.80

1990, Dec. 11

933 A367 1d multicolored .38 .20

Anti-French Riots, 30th anniv.

A368

A369

1990, Dec. 20 *Perf. 14*

934 A368 1d multicolored .38 .20

Fight against respiratory diseases.

1991, Feb. 24 Litho. *Perf. 13½*

935 A369 1d multicolored .36 .18

Constitution, 2nd anniv.

Flower Type of 1986

1991, May 23 Litho. *Perf. 13½*

Size: 26x36mm

936	A312	2d	Jasminum fruticans	.65	.32
937	A312	4d	Dianthus crinitus	1.30	.65
938	A312	5d	Cyclamen africanum	1.65	.85
			Nos. 936-938 (3)	3.60	1.82

Children's Drawings A370

1991, June 3 Litho. *Perf. 13½*

939	A370	3d	shown	1.00	.50
940	A370	4d	Children playing	1.30	.65

Maghreb Arab Union Summit — A371

1991, June 10

941 A371 1d multicolored .32 .16

Geneva Convention on Refugees, 40th Anniv. A372

Perf. 14½x13½

1991, July 28 Litho.

942 A372 3d multicolored 1.05 .52

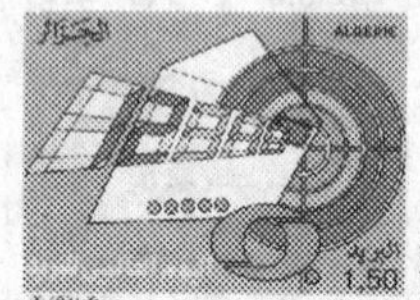

Postal Service A373

1991, Oct. 12 *Perf. 14*

943	A373	1.50d	shown	.55	.28
944	A373	4.20d	Expo emblem, vert.	1.50	.75

Telecom '91, 6th World Forum and Exposition on Telecommunications, Geneva, Switzerland (No. 944).

Butterflies A374

1991, Nov. 21 Litho. *Perf. 11½*

Granite Paper

945	A374	2d	Zerynthia rumina	.32	.16
946	A374	4d	Melitaea didyma	.65	.32
947	A374	6d	Vanessa atalanta	1.00	.50
948	A374	7d	Nymphalis polychloros	1.15	.58
			Nos. 945-948 (4)	3.12	1.56

A375

A376

1991, Dec. 21 *Perf. 12*

Granite Paper

949	A375	3d	Necklace	.50	.25
950	A375	4d	Jewelry of Southern Tuaregs	.65	.32
951	A375	5d	Brooch	.85	.42
952	A375	7d	Rings, horiz.	1.15	.58
			Nos. 949-952 (4)	3.15	1.57

1992, Mar. 8 Litho. *Perf. 14*

953 A376 1.50d Algerian Women .22 .15

Gazelles A377

Designs: 1.50d, Gazella dorcas. 6.20d, Gazella cuvieri. 8.60d, Gazella dama.

1992, May 13 *Perf. 14½x13*

954	A377	1.50d	multicolored	.25	.15
955	A377	6.20d	multicolored	1.05	.52
956	A377	8.60d	multicolored	1.45	.75
			Nos. 954-956 (3)	2.75	1.42

1992 Summer Olympics, Barcelona A379

1992, June 24 Litho. *Perf. 14*

958 A379 6.20d Runners 1.10 .55

A381

A382

1992, July 7 Litho. *Perf. 14*

960 A381 5d multicolored .90 .45

Independence, 30th anniv.

1992, Sept. 23 Litho. *Perf. 14*

Designs: Medicinal plants.

961	A382	1.50d	Ajuga iva	.20	.15
962	A382	5.10d	Rhamnus alaternus	.70	.35
963	A382	6.20d	Silybum marianum	.85	.42
964	A382	8.60d	Lavandula stoechas	1.15	.58
			Nos. 961-964 (4)	2.90	1.50

Post Office Modernization A383

1992, Oct. 10 Litho. *Perf. 14*

965 A383 1.50d multicolored .22 .15

Marine Life — A384

Designs: 1.50d, Hippocampus hippocampus. 2.70d, Caretta caretta. 6.20d, Muraena helena. 7.50d, Palinurus elephas.

1992, Dec. 23

966	A384	1.50d	multicolored	.20	.15
967	A384	2.70d	multicolored	.35	.18
968	A384	6.20d	multicolored	.85	.42
969	A384	7.50d	multicolored	1.00	.50
			Nos. 966-969 (4)	2.40	1.25

Pres. Mohammad Boudiaf (1919-92) A385

1992, Nov. 3 Litho. *Perf. 11½*

Granite Paper

970	A385	2d	green & multi	.28	.15
971	A385	8.60d	blue & multi	1.15	.58

Coins A386

1992, Dec. 16 Litho. *Perf. 11½*

Granite Paper

972	A386	1.50d	Numidia, 2nd cent. BC	.20	.15
973	A386	2d	Dinar, 14th cent.	.28	.15
974	A386	5.10d	Dinar, 11th cent.	.68	.35
975	A386	6.20d	Abdelkader, 19th cent.	.85	.40
			Nos. 972-975 (4)	2.01	1.05

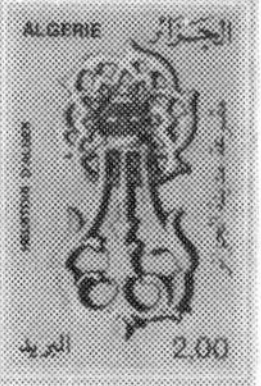

Door Knockers — A387

Flowering Trees — A388

1993, Feb. 17 Litho. *Perf. 14*

976	A387	2d	Algiers	.28	.15
977	A387	5.60d	Constantine	.75	.38
978	A387	8.60d	Tlemcen	1.15	.58
			Nos. 976-978 (3)	2.18	1.11

Perf. 12x11½, 11½x12

1993, Mar. 17

Granite Paper

979	A388	4.50d	Neflier (medlar), horiz.	.60	.30
980	A388	8.60d	Cognassier (quince)	1.20	.60
981	A388	11d	Abricotier (apricot)	1.50	.75
			Nos. 979-981 (3)	3.30	1.65

Natl. Coast Guard Service, 20th Anniv. A389

1993, Apr. 3 Litho. *Perf. 14*

982 A389 2d multicolored .28 .15

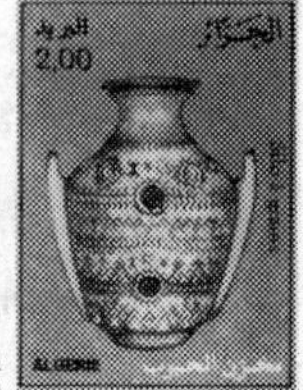

Traditional Grain Processing — A390

1993, May 19 Litho. *Perf. 14*

983	A390	2d	Container	.26	.15
984	A390	5.60d	Millstone	.75	.38
985	A390	8.60d	Press	1.15	.58
			Nos. 983-985 (3)	2.16	1.11

Royal Mausoleums A391

1993, June 16 Litho. *Perf. 14*

986 A391	8.60d	Mauretania	1.15	.58
987 A391	12d	El Khroub	1.60	.80

Ports — A392

1993, Oct. 20 Litho. *Perf. 14x13½*

988 A392	2d	Annaba	.25	.15
989 A392	8.60d	Arzew	1.10	.55

Varanus Griseus A393

Design: 2d, Chamaeleo vulgaris, vert.

Perf. 13½x14, 14x13½

1993, Nov. 20

990 A393	2d	multicolored	.25	.15
991 A393	8.60d	multicolored	1.10	.55

Tourism A394

1993, Dec. 18 Litho. *Perf. 14x13½*

992 A394	2d	Tipaza	.22	.15
993 A394	8.60d	Kerzaz	.80	.40

A395

Chahid Day — A396

1994, Jan. 2 *Perf. 13½x14*

994 A395 2d	multicolored	.22	.15

SONATRACH (Natl. Society for Research, Transformation, and Commercialization of Hydrocarbons), 30th anniv.

1994, Feb. 18 Litho. *Perf. 13½x14*

995 A396 2d	multicolored	.22	.15

1994 World Cup Soccer Championships, US — A397

1994, Mar. 16 *Perf. 14x13½*

996 A397 8.60d	multicolored	.80	.40

A398

Ancient Petroglyphs — A399

Orchids: 5.60d, Orchis simia lam. 8.60d, Ophrys lutea cavan. 11d, Ophrys apifera huds.

1994, Apr. 20 Litho. *Perf. 11½*

Granite Paper

997 A398	5.60d	multicolored	.55	.28
998 A398	8.60d	multicolored	.85	.42
999 A398	11d	multicolored	1.10	.55
		Nos. 997-999 (3)	2.50	1.25

1994, May 21 Litho. *Perf. 13x14*

1000 A399	3d	Inscriptions	.35	.18
1001 A399	10d	Man on horse	1.25	.60

A400

A401

1994, June 25

1002 A400 12d	multicolored	1.25	.65

Intl. Olympic Committee, cent.

1994, July 13

1003 A401 3d	multicolored	.35	.18

World Population Day.

Views of Algiers Type of 1992

Design: 3d, like #775.

1994 Litho. *Perf. 14*

1010 A290b 3d	dk blue & lt blue	.35	.18

This is an expanding set. Number may change.

Jewelry from Saharan Atlas Region A402

Perf. 13½x14, 14x13½

1994, Oct. 18 Litho.

1019 A402	3d	Fibules, vert.	.15	.15
1020 A402	5d	Belt	.25	.15
1021 A402	12d	Bracelets	.55	.28
		Nos. 1019-1021 (3)	.95	.58

A403

A404

1994, Nov. 3 Litho. *Perf. 13½x14*

1022 A403 3d	multicolored	.38	.18

Algerian Revolution, 40th anniv.

1994, Nov. 16 Litho. *Perf. 13½x14*

1023 A404	3d	Ladybugs	.15	.15
1024 A404	12d	Beetles	.55	.28

Fight Against AIDS — A405

1994, Dec. 1 Litho. *Perf. 14x13½*

1025 A405 3d	multicolored	.38	.18

Folk Dances — A406

Minerals — A407

1994, Dec. 17 Litho. *Perf. 13½x14*

1026 A406	3d	Algeroise	.15	.15
1027 A406	10d	Constantinoise	.50	.25
1028 A406	12d	Alaoui	.55	.28
		Nos. 1026-1028 (3)	1.20	.68

1994, Sept. 21

1029 A407	3d	Gres lite-erode	.15	.15
1030 A407	5d	Cipolin	.25	.15
1031 A407	10d	Marne a turitella	.50	.25
		Nos. 1029-1031 (3)	.90	.55

World Tourism Organization, 20th Anniv. A408

1995, Jan. 28 Litho. *Perf. 14x13½*

1032 A408 3d	multicolored	.35	.20

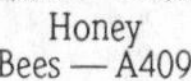
Honey Bees — A409

Flowers — A410

Perf. 13½x14, 14x13½

1995, Feb. 22

1033 A409	3d	shown	.35	.20
1034 A409	13d	On flower, horiz.	1.50	.75

1995, Mar. 29 Photo. *Perf. 11½*

Granite Paper

1035 A410	3d	Dahlias	.35	.20
1036 A410	10d	Zinnias	1.10	.55
1037 A410	13d	Lilacs	1.50	.75
		Nos. 1035-1037 (3)	2.95	1.50

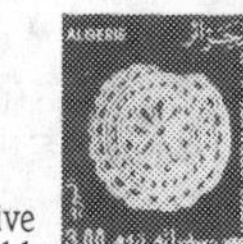
Decorative Stonework — A411

Various patterns.

1995, Apr. 19 *Perf. 14*

1039 A411	3d	brown	.35	.20
1040 A411	4d	green	.45	.25
1041 A411	5d	deep claret	.55	.30
		Nos. 1039-1041 (3)	1.35	.75

This is an expanding set. Numbers may change.

End of World War II, 50th Anniv. A413

1995, May 3 *Perf. 14x13½*

1048 A413 3d	multicolored	.35	.20

Souvenir Sheet

VE Day, 50th Anniv. — A414

Illustration reduced.

1995, May 10 Litho. *Perf. 13½x14*

1049 A414 13d	multicolored	1.65	.85

Volleyball, Cent. — A415

Environmental Protection — A416

1995, June 14

1050 A415 3d	multicolored	.40	.20

1995, June 5

1051 A416	3d	Air, water pollution	.40	.20
1052 A416	13d	Air pollution	1.65	.85

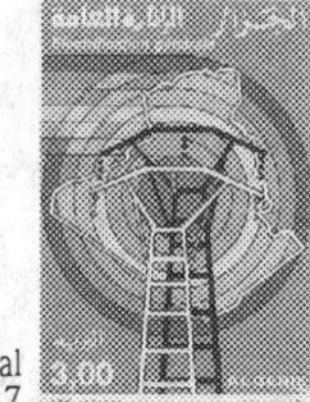
General Electrification — A417

1995, July 5 Litho. *Perf. 13½x14*

1053 A417 3d	multicolored	.45	.20

UN, 50th Anniv. A418

1995, Oct. 24 *Perf. 14x13½*

1054 A418 13d	multicolored	2.00	1.00

Pottery — A419

Designs: 10d, Pot, Lakhdaria. 20d, Pitcher, Aokas. 21d, Jar, Larbaa Nath Iraten. 30d, Vase, Ouadhia.

1995, Nov. 14 Litho. *Perf. 14*

No.	Description	Unused	Used
1055	A419 10d dark brown	1.50	.75
1056	A419 20d dull maroon	3.00	1.50
1057	A419 21d golden brown	3.25	1.65
1058	A419 30d dark rose brown	4.50	2.25
	Nos. 1055-1058 (4)	12.25	6.15

Aquatic Birds — A420

1995, Dec. 20 Litho. *Perf. 14x13½*

No.	Description	Unused	Used
1059	A420 3d Tadorna tadorna	.45	.20
1060	A420 5d Gallinago gallinago	.75	.35

1996 Summer Olympics, Atlanta A421

1996, Jan. 24 Litho. *Perf. 14x13½*

No.	Description	Unused	Used
1061	A421 20d multicolored	3.00	1.50

SEMI-POSTAL STAMPS

Regular Issue of 1926 Surcharged in Black or Red

+10c

1927 Unwmk. *Perf. 14x13½*

No.	Description	Unused	Used
B1	A1 5c +5c bl grn	.40	.50
B2	A1 10c +10c lilac	.40	.50
B3	A2 15c +15c org brn	.40	.50
B4	A2 20c +20c car rose	.40	.50
B5	A2 25c +25c bl grn	.40	.50
B6	A2 30c +30c lt bl	.40	.50
B7	A2 35c +35c dp vio	.40	.50
B8	A2 40c +40c ol grn	.40	.50
B9	A3 50c +50c dp bl (R)	.40	.50
a.	Double surcharge	110.00	110.00
B10	A3 80c +80c red org	.40	.50
B11	A4 1fr +1fr gray grn & red brn	.45	.60
B12	A4 2fr +2fr Prus bl & blk brn	12.00	12.50
B13	A4 5fr +5fr red & vio	17.50	19.00
	Nos. B1-B13 (13)	33.95	37.10

The surtax was for the benefit of wounded soldiers. Government officials speculated in this issue.

Railroad Terminal, Oran — SP1

Ruins at Djemila SP2

Mosque of Sidi Abd-er-Rahman SP3

Designs: 10c+10c, Rummel Gorge, Constantine. 15c+15c, Admiralty Buildings, Algiers. 25c+25c, View of Algiers. 30c+30c, Trajan's Arch, Timgad. 40c+40c, Temple of the North, Djemila. 75c+75c Mansourah Minaret, Tlemcen. 1f+1f, View of Ghardaia. 1.50f+1.50f, View of Tolga. 2f+2f, Tuareg warriors. 3f+3f, Kasbah, Algiers.

1930 Engr. *Perf. 12½*

No.	Description	Unused	Used
B14	SP1 5c +5c orange	4.50	4.50
B15	SP1 10c +10c ol grn	4.50	4.50
B16	SP1 15c +15c dk brn	4.50	4.50
B17	SP1 25c +25c black	4.50	4.50
B18	SP1 30c +30c dk red	4.50	4.50
B19	SP1 40c +40c ap grn	4.50	4.50
B20	SP2 50c +50c ultra	4.50	4.50
B21	SP2 75c +75c red pur	4.50	4.50
B22	SP2 1fr +1fr org red	4.50	4.50
B23	SP2 1.50fr +1.50fr deep ultra	4.50	4.50
B24	SP2 2fr +2fr dk car	4.50	4.50
B25	SP2 3fr +3fr dk grn	4.50	4.50
B26	SP3 5fr +5fr grn & car	9.00	9.00
a.	Center inverted	325.00	
	Nos. B14-B26 (13)	63.00	63.00

Centenary of the French occupation of Algeria. The surtax on the stamps was given to the funds for the celebration.

Nos. B14-B26 exist imperf. Value, set in pairs, $350.

Catalogue values for unused stamps in this section, from this point to the end of the section, are for Never Hinged items.

No. 102 Surcharged in Red

1918-11 Nov.-1938
0.65 + 0.35

1938 *Perf. 13*

No.	Description	Unused	Used
B27	A6 65c +35c on 2.25fr yel grn	.40	.40

20th anniversary of Armistice.

René Caillié, Charles Lavigerie and Henri Duveyrier SP14

1939 Engr.

No.	Description	Unused	Used
B28	SP14 30c +20c dk bl grn	1.00	.60
B29	SP14 90c +60c car rose	1.25	.65
B30	SP14 2.25fr +75c ultra	6.75	6.25
B31	SP14 5fr +5fr brn blk	12.00	12.00
	Nos. B28-B31 (4)	21.00	19.50

Pioneers of the Sahara.

French and Algerian Soldiers SP15

1940 Photo. *Perf. 12*

No.	Description	Unused	Used
B32	SP15 1fr +1fr bl & car	.40	.40
B33	SP15 1fr +2fr brn rose & blk	.40	.40
B34	SP15 1fr +4fr dp grn & red	.60	.60
B35	SP15 1fr +9fr brn & car	1.00	1.00
	Nos. B32-B35 (4)	2.40	2.40

The surtax was used to assist the families of mobilized men.

Type of Regular Issue, 1941 Surcharged in Carmine

+ 4f

1941 Engr. *Perf. 13*

No.	Description	Unused	Used
B36	A19 1fr +4fr black	.20	.20

No. 135 Surcharged in Carmine

SECOURS NATIONAL + 4f

No.	Description	Unused	Used
B37	A19 1fr +4fr dark blue	.20	.20

The surtax was for National Relief.

No. 124 Surcharged in Black "+60c"

1942

No.	Description	Unused	Used
B38	A7 90c +60c henna brn	.15	.15
a.	Double surcharge	55.00	

The surtax was used for National Relief. The stamp could also be used as 1.50 francs for postage.

Mother and Child — SP16

1943, Dec. 1 Litho. *Perf. 12*

No.	Description	Unused	Used
B39	SP16 50c +4.50fr brt pink	.30	.25
B40	SP16 1.50fr +8.50fr lt grn	.30	.25
B41	SP16 3fr +12fr dp bl	.30	.25
B42	SP16 5fr +15fr vio brn	.30	.25
	Nos. B39-B42 (4)	1.20	1.00

The surtax was for the benefit of soldiers and prisoners of war.

Planes over Fields — SP17

1945, July 2 Unwmk. Engr. *Perf. 13*

No.	Description	Unused	Used
B43	SP17 1.50fr +3.50fr lt ultra, red org & blk	.20	.20

The surtax was for the benefit of Algerian airmen and their families.

France No. B192 Overprinted Type "a" of 1924 in Black

1945

No.	Description	Unused	Used
B44	SP146 4fr +6fr dk vio brn	.20	.20

The surtax was for war victims of the P.T.T.

Overprinted in Blue on Type of France, 1945

1945, Oct. 15

No.	Description	Unused	Used
B45	SP150 2fr +3fr dk brn	.35	.35

For Stamp Day.

Overprinted in Blue on Type of France, 1946

1946, June 29

No.	Description	Unused	Used
B46	SP160 3fr +2fr red	.45	.45

For Stamp Day.

Children Playing by Stream SP18

Girl — SP19

Athlete — SP20

Repatriated Prisoner and Bay of Algiers SP21

1946, Oct. 2 Engr. *Perf. 13*

No.	Description	Unused	Used
B47	SP18 3fr +17fr dark grn	.65	.65
B48	SP19 4fr +21fr red	.65	.65
B49	SP20 8fr +27fr rose lilac	2.75	2.75
B50	SP21 10fr +35fr dark blue	.70	.70
	Nos. B47-B50 (4)	4.75	4.75

Type of France, 1947, Overprinted type "a" of 1924 in Carmine

1947, Mar. 15

No.	Description	Unused	Used
B51	SP172 4.50fr +5.50fr dp ultra	.35	.35

For Stamp Day.

Same on Type of France, 1947, Surcharged Like No. B36 in Carmine

1947, Nov. 13

No.	Description	Unused	Used
B52	A173 5fr +10fr dk Prus grn	.50	.40

Type of France, 1948, Overprinted in Dark Green — f

ALGERIE

1948, Mar. 6

No.	Description	Unused	Used
B53	SP176 6fr +4fr dk grn	.40	.40

For Stamp Day.

Type of France, 1948, Overprinted type "a" of 1924 in Blue and New Value

1948, May

No.	Description	Unused	Used
B54	A176 6fr +4fr red	.30	.30

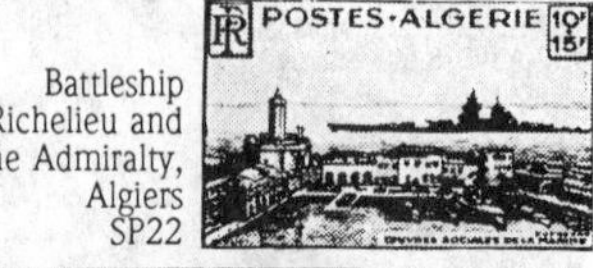

Battleship Richelieu and the Admiralty, Algiers SP22

Aircraft Carrier Arromanches SP23

Unwmk.

1949, Jan. 15 Engr. *Perf. 13*

No.	Description	Unused	Used
B55	SP22 10fr +15fr dp blue	4.00	4.00
B56	SP23 18fr +22fr red	4.00	4.00

The surtax was for naval charities.

Type of France, 1949, Overprinted in Blue — g

ALGÉRIE

1949, Mar. 26

No.	Description	Unused	Used
B57	SP180 15fr +5fr lilac rose	.80	.80

For Stamp Day, Mar. 26-27.

Type of France, 1950, Overprinted type "f" in Green

1950, Mar. 11

No.	Description	Unused	Used
B58	SP183 12fr +3fr blk brn	1.00	1.00

For Stamp Day, Mar. 11-12.

Foreign Legionary — SP24

1950, Apr. 30

No.	Description	Unused	Used
B59	SP24 15fr +5fr dk grn	1.25	1.25

Charles de Foucauld and Gen. J. F. H. Laperrine SP25

1950, Aug. 21 Unwmk. *Perf. 13*

No.	Description	Unused	Used
B60	SP25 25fr +5fr brn ol & brn blk	3.00	3.00

50th anniversary of the presence of the French in the Sahara.

Emir Abd-el-Kader and Marshal T. R. Bugeaud SP26

1950, Aug. 21
B61 SP26 40fr +10fr dk brn & blk brn 2.50 2.50

Unveiling of a monument to Emir Abd-el-Kader at Cacheron.

Col. Colonna d'Ornano and Fine Arts Museum, Algiers SP27

1951, Jan. 11
B62 SP27 15fr +5fr blk brn, vio brn & red brn .60 .60

Death of Col. Colonna d'Ornano, 10th anniv.

Type of France, 1951, Overprinted type "a" of 1924 in Black

1951, Mar. 10
B63 SP186 12fr +3fr brown .80 .80

For Stamp Day.

Type of France, 1952, Overprinted type "g" in Dark Blue

1952, Mar. 8 Unwmk. *Perf. 13*
B64 SP190 12fr +3fr dk bl 1.25 1.25

For Stamp Day.

French Military Medal — SP28

1952, July 5 Unwmk. Engr. *Perf. 13*
B65 SP28 15fr +5fr grn, yel & brn 1.25 1.25

Centenary of the creation of the French Military Medal.

Type of France 1952, Surcharged type "g" and Surtax in Black

1952, Sept. 15
B66 A222 30fr +5fr dp ultra 1.10 1.10

10th anniv. of the defense of Bir-Hakeim.

View of El Oued — SP29

Design: 12fr+3fr, View of Bou-Noura.

1952, Nov. 15 Engr.
B67 SP29 8fr +2fr ultra & red .90 .90
B68 SP29 12fr +3fr red 1.25 1.25

The surtax was for the Red Cross.

Type of France, 1953, Overprinted type "a" of 1924 in Black

1953, Mar. 14 Engr.
B69 SP193 12fr +3fr purple 1.00 .90

For Stamp Day. Surtax for Red Cross.

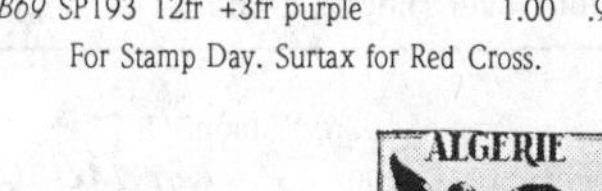

Victory of Cythera — SP30

Unwmk.

1953, Dec. 18 Engr. *Perf. 13*
B70 SP30 15fr +5fr blk brn & brn .60 .60

The surtax was for army welfare work.

Type of France, 1954, Overprinted type "a" of 1924 in Black

1954, Mar. 20 Unwmk. *Perf. 13*
B71 SP196 12fr +3fr scarlet .65 .65

For Stamp Day.

Soldiers and Flags SP31

Foreign Legionary SP32

1954, Mar. 27
B72 SP31 15fr +5fr dk brn .50 .50

The surtax was for old soldiers.

1954, Apr. 30
B73 SP32 15fr +5fr dk grn 1.00 1.00

The surtax was for the welfare fund of the Foreign Legion.

Nurses and Verdun Hospital, Algiers — SP33

Design: 15fr+5fr, J. H. Dunant & ruins at Djemila.

1954, Oct. 30
B74 SP33 12fr +3fr indigo & red 1.50 1.50
B75 SP33 15fr +5fr pur & red 1.75 1.75

The surtax was for the Red Cross.

Earthquake Victims and Ruins — SP34

First Aid — SP35

Design: #B80-B81, Removing wounded.

1954, Dec. 5
B76 SP34 12fr +4fr dk vio brn 1.00 1.00
B77 SP34 15fr +5fr dp bl 1.00 1.00
B78 SP35 18fr +6fr lil rose 1.25 1.25
B79 SP35 20fr +7fr violet 1.25 1.25
B80 SP35 25fr +8fr rose brn 1.50 1.50
B81 SP35 30fr +10fr brt bl grn 1.50 1.50
Nos. B76-B81 (6) 7.50 7.50

The surtax was for victims of the Orleansville earthquake disaster of September 1954.

Type of France, 1955, Overprinted type "a" of 1924 in Black

1955, Mar. 19
B82 SP199 12fr +3fr dp ultra .80 .80

For Stamp Day, Mar. 19-20.

Women and Children SP36

Cancer Victim SP37

1955, Nov. 5
B83 SP36 15fr +5fr blue & indigo .60 .60

The tax was for war victims.

1956, Mar. 3 Unwmk. *Perf. 13*
B84 SP37 15fr +5fr dk brn .45 .45

The surtax was for the Algerian Cancer Society. The male figure in the design is Rodin's "Age of Bronze."

Type of France, 1956, Overprinted type "a" of 1924 in Black

1956, Mar.
B85 SP202 12fr +3fr red .45 .45

For Stamp Day, Mar. 17-18.

Foreign Legion Rest Home — SP38

1956, Apr. 29
B86 SP38 15fr +5fr dk bl grn 1.00 1.00

Honoring the French Foreign Legion.

Type of France, 1957, Overprinted type "f" in Black

1957, Mar. 16 Engr. *Perf. 13*
B87 SP204 12fr +3fr dull purple .65 .65

For Stamp Day and to honor the Maritime Postal Service.

Fennec SP39

Design: 15fr+5fr, Stork flying over roofs.

1957, Apr. 6
B88 SP39 12fr +3fr red brn & red 3.00 3.00
B89 SP39 15fr +5fr sepia & red 3.00 3.00

The surtax was for the Red Cross.

Type of Regular Issue, 1956 Surcharged in Dark Blue

18 JUIN 1940
+ 5F

1957, June 18
B90 A53 15fr +5fr scar & rose red .75 .75

17th anniv. of General de Gaulle's appeal for a Free France.

The Giaour, by Delacroix — SP40

On the Banks of the Oued, by Fromentin SP41

Design: 35fr+10fr, Dancer, by Chasseriau.

Unwmk.

1957, Nov. 30 Engr. *Perf. 13*
B91 SP40 15fr +5fr dk car 3.75 3.75
B92 SP41 20fr +5fr grn 3.75 3.75
B93 SP40 35fr +10fr dk bl 3.75 3.75
Nos. B91-B93 (3) 11.25 11.25

Surtax for army welfare organizations.

Type of France Overprinted type "f" in Blue

1958, Mar. 15 Unwmk. *Perf. 13*
B94 SP206 15fr +5fr org brn .65 .65

For Stamp Day.

Bird-of-Paradise Flower — SP42

Arms & Marshal's Baton — SP43

1958, June 14 Engr. *Perf. 13*
B95 SP42 20fr +5fr grn, org & vio 2.00 2.00

The surtax was for Child Welfare.

1958, July 20
B96 SP43 20fr +5fr ultra, car & grn 1.00 1.00

Marshal de Lattre Foundation.

Independent State

Clasped Hands, Wheat, Olive Branch — SP44

Burning Books — SP45

1963, May 27 Unwmk. *Perf. 13*
B97 SP44 50c +20c sl grn, brt grn & car .80 .60

Surtax for the Natl. Solidarity Fund.

1965, June 7 Engr. *Perf. 13*
B98 SP45 20c +5c ol grn, red & blk .50 .40

Issued to commemorate the burning of the Library of Algiers, June 7, 1962.

Soldiers and Woman Comforting Wounded Soldier — SP46

1966, Aug. 20 Photo. *Perf. 11½*
B99 SP46 30c +10c multi 1.25 .70
B100 SP46 95c +10c multi 1.75 1.10

Day of the Moudjahid (Moslem volunteers).

Red Crescent, Boy and Girl — SP47

1967, May 27 Litho. *Perf. 14*
B101 SP47 30c +10c brt grn, brn & car .45 .35

Algerian Red Crescent Society.

Flood Victims — SP48

Design: 95c+25c, Rescuing flood victims.

1969, Nov. 15 Typo. *Perf. 10½*
B102 SP48 30c +10c dl bl, sal & blk .45 .35

Litho.
B103 SP48 95c +25c multi 1.00 .65

Red Crescent Flag — SP49

1971, May 17 Engr. *Perf. 10½*
B104 SP49 30c +10c slate grn & car .35 .28

Algerian Red Crescent Society.

Intl. Children's Day — SP50

1989, June 1 Litho. *Perf. 10½x11*
B105 SP50 1d +30c multi .65 .48

Surtax for child welfare.

Solidarity with Palestinians SP51

1990, Dec. 9 Litho. *Perf. 10½x11*
B106 SP51 1d +30c multi .50 .30

Natl. Solidarity with Education — SP52

1995, Sept. 20 Litho. *Perf. 13x14*
B107 SP52 3d +50c multi .50 .25

AIR POST STAMPS

> Catalogue values for unused stamps in this section are for Never Hinged items.

Plane over Algiers Harbor — AP1

Two types of 20fr:
Type I - Monogram "F" without serifs. "POSTE" indented 3mm.
Type II - Monogram "F" with serifs. "POSTE" indented 4½mm.

Unwmk.

1946, June 20 Engr. *Perf. 13*

C1	AP1	5fr red	.15	.15
C2	AP1	10fr deep blue	.15	.15
C3	AP1	15fr deep green	.35	.15
C4	AP1	20fr brown (II)	.18	.15
C4A	AP1	20fr brown (I)	72.50	45.00
C5	AP1	25fr violet	.40	.15
C6	AP1	40fr gray black	.45	.15
		Set value, #C1-C4, C5-C6	1.45	.40

For surcharges see Nos. C7, CB1-CB2.

No. C1 Surcharged in Black **— 10 %**

1947, Jan. 18
C7 AP1 (4.50fr) on 5fr red .15 .15

Storks over Mosque — AP2

Plane over Village — AP3

1949-53

C8	AP2	50fr green	2.00	.25
C9	AP3	100fr brown	1.75	.25
C10	AP2	200fr bright red	4.00	3.00
C11	AP3	500fr ultra ('53)	14.00	10.00
		Nos. C8-C11 (4)	21.75	13.50

Beni Bahdel Dam — AP4

1957, July 1 Unwmk. *Perf. 13*
C12 AP4 200fr dark red 3.25 .75

Caravelle over Ghardaia — AP5

Designs: 2d, Caravelle over El Oued. 5d, Caravelle over Tipasa.

1967-68 Engr. *Perf. 13*

C13	AP5	1d lil, org brn & emer	1.00	.50
C14	AP5	2d brt bl, org brn & emer	2.50	1.25
C15	AP5	5d brt bl, grn & org brn ('68)	6.00	2.75
		Nos. C13-C15 (3)	9.50	4.50

Plane over Casbah, Algiers — AP6

Designs: 3d, Plane over Oran. 4d, Plane over Rhumel Gorge.

1971-72 Photo. *Perf. 12½*

C16	AP6	2d grysh blk & multi	1.65	.80
C17	AP6	3d violet & blk	2.50	1.40
C18	AP6	4d blk & multi	3.25	1.75
		Nos. C16-C18 (3)	7.40	3.95

Issued: 2d, 6/12/71; 3d, 4d, 2/28/72.

Storks and Plane — AP7

1979, Mar. 24 Photo. *Perf. 11½*
C19 AP7 10d multi 4.00 1.60

Plane Approaching Coastal City — AP8

1991, Apr. 26 Litho. *Perf. 13½*
C20 AP8 10d shown 3.60 1.80
C21 AP8 20d Plane over city 7.20 3.60

Plane Over Djidjelli Corniche — AP9

1993, Sept. 25 Engr. *Perf. 13½x14*
C22 AP9 50d blue, green & brown 6.25 3.25

AIR POST SEMI-POSTAL STAMPS

> Catalogue values for unused stamps in this section are for Never Hinged items.

No. C2 Surcharged in Carmine

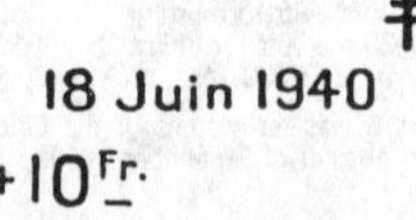

1947, June 18 *Perf. 13*
CB1 AP1 10fr +10fr deep blue .70 .60

7th anniv. of Gen. Charles de Gaulle's speech in London, June 18, 1940.

No. C1 Surcharged in Blue

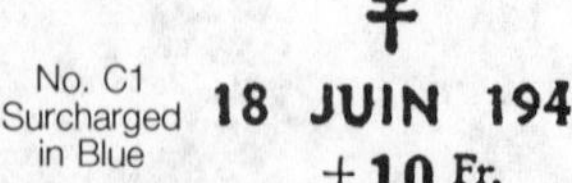

1948, June 18
CB2 AP1 5fr +10fr red .70 .60

8th anniv. of Gen. Charles de Gaulle's speech in London, June 18, 1940.

Monument, Clock Tower and Plane — SPAP1

1949, Nov. 10 Engr. Unwmk.
CB3 SPAP1 15fr +20fr dk brn 3.75 3.75

25th anniv. of Algeria's 1st postage stamps.

POSTAGE DUE STAMPS

D1

D2

Perf. 14x13½

1926-27 Typo. Unwmk.

J1	D1	5c light blue	.15	.15
J2	D1	10c dk brn	.15	.15
J3	D1	20c olive grn	.15	.15
J4	D1	25c car rose	.28	.28
J5	D1	30c rose red	.15	.15
J6	D1	45c blue grn	.40	.40
J7	D1	50c brn vio	.15	.15
J8	D1	60c green ('27)	1.00	.30
J9	D1	1fr red brn, *straw*	.15	.15
J10	D1	2fr lil rose ('27)	.15	.15
J11	D1	3fr deep blue ('27)	.15	.15
		Set value	2.50	1.74

See Nos. J25-J26, J28-J32. For surcharges, see Nos. J18-J20.

1926-27

J12	D2	1c olive grn	.15	.15
J13	D2	10c violet	.40	.18
J14	D2	30c bister	.28	.20
J15	D2	60c dull red	.22	.20
J16	D2	1fr brt vio ('27)	10.00	1.75
J17	D2	2fr lt bl ('27)	6.50	.65
		Nos. J12-J17 (6)	17.55	3.13

See note below France No. J51.
For surcharges, see Nos. J21-J24.

Stamps of 1926 Surcharged

1927

J18	D1	60c on 20c olive grn	.80	.28
J19	D1	2fr on 45c blue grn	1.00	.65
J20	D1	3fr on 25c car rose	.45	.28
		Nos. J18-J20 (3)	2.25	1.21

Recouvrement Stamps of 1926 Surcharged **= 10c**

1927-32

J21	D2	10c on 30c bis ('32)	2.25	1.50
J22	D2	1fr on 1c olive grn	.65	.60
J23	D2	1fr on 60c dl red ('32)	11.00	.22
J24	D2	2fr on 10c violet	6.25	6.25
		Nos. J21-J24 (4)	20.15	8.57

> Catalogue values for unused stamps in this section, from this point to the end of the section, are for Never Hinged items.

Type of 1926, Without "R F"

1942 Typo. *Perf. 14x13½*

J25	D1	30c dark red	.15	.15
J26	D1	2fr magenta	.18	.18
		Set value	.23	.23

Type of 1926 Surcharged in Red **T 0.50**

1944 *Perf. 14x13½*

J27	A2	50c on 20c yel grn	.15	.15
a.		Inverted surcharge	3.50	
b.		Double surcharge	9.50	

No. J27 was issued precanceled only. See note after No. 32.

Type of 1926

1944 Litho. *Perf. 12*

J28	D1	1.50fr	brt rose lilac	.28	.22
J29	D1	2fr	greenish blue	.28	.22
J30	D1	5fr	rose carmine	.28	.22
			Nos. J28-J30 (3)	.84	.66

Type of 1926

1947 Typo. *Perf. 14x13½*

J32	D1	5fr	green	.60	.45

France Nos. J80-J81 Overprinted Type "a" of 1925 in Carmine or Black

1947

J33	D5	10c	sepia (C)	.15	.15
J34	D5	30c	bright red violet	.15	.15
			Set value	.24	.20

D3

1947-55 Unwmk. Engr. *Perf. 14x13*

J35	D3	20c	red	.15	.15
J36	D3	60c	ultra	.22	.20
J37	D3	1fr	dk org brn	.15	.15
J38	D3	1.50fr	dull green	.40	.38
J39	D3	2fr	red	.15	.15
J40	D3	3fr	violet	.15	.15
J41	D3	5fr	ultra ('49)	.15	.15
J42	D3	6fr	black	.20	.18
J43	D3	10fr	lil rose	.20	.15
J44	D3	15fr	ol grn ('55)	.45	.45
J45	D3	20fr	brt grn	.22	.15
J46	D3	30fr	red org ('55)	.40	.38
J47	D3	50fr	indigo ('51)	.95	.95
J48	D3	100fr	brt bl ('53)	4.00	3.50
			Nos. J35-J48 (14)	7.79	7.09

Independent State

France Nos. J93-J97 Overprinted "EA" in Black like Nos. 286-290

Perf. 14x13½

1962, July 2 Typo. Unwmk.

Handstamped Overprint

J49	D6	5c	bright pink	2.25	1.60
J50	D6	10c	red orange	2.25	1.40
J51	D6	20c	olive bister	2.25	1.40
J52	D6	50c	dark green	3.00	2.75
J53	D6	1fr	deep green	4.25	4.00
			Nos. J49-J53 (5)	14.00	11.15

Typographed Overprint

J49a	D6	5c	bright pink	6.00	6.00
J50a	D6	10c	red orange	6.00	6.00
J51a	D6	20c	olive bister	5.50	5.50
J52a	D6	50c	dark green	14.00	14.00
J53a	D6	1fr	deep green	25.00	25.00
			Nos. J49a-J53a (5)	56.50	56.50

See note after No. 290.

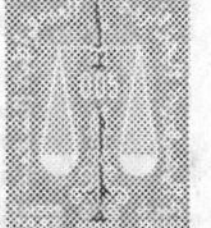
Scales — D4

Grain — D5

1963, June 25 *Perf. 14x13½*

J54	D4	5c	car rose & blk	.15	.15
J55	D4	10c	olive & car	.15	.15
J56	D4	20c	ultra & blk	.18	.15
J57	D4	50c	bister brn & grn	.50	.28
J58	D4	1fr	lilac & org	.85	.50
			Nos. J54-J58 (5)	1.83	
			Set value		.95

#J58 Surcharged with New Value & 3 Bars

1968, Mar. 28 Typo. *Perf. 14x13½*

J59	D4	60c	on 1fr lilac & org	.40	.28

1972-93 Litho. *Perf. 13½x14*

J60	D5	10c	bister	.15	.15
J61	D5	20c	deep brown	.15	.15
J62	D5	40c	orange	.20	.15
J63	D5	50c	dk vio blue	.22	.15
J64	D5	80c	dk olive gray	.38	.15
J65	D5	1d	green	.42	.25
J66	D5	2d	blue	.95	.42
J67	D5	3d	violet	.45	.22
J68	D5	4d	lilac rose	.58	.28
			Nos. J60-J68 (9)	3.50	
			Set value		1.50

Issued: 3d, 4d, 1/21/93; others, 10/21/72.

NEWSPAPER STAMPS

Nos. 1 and 33 Surcharged in Red

1/2 centime

1924-26 Unwmk. *Perf. 14x13½*

P1	A16	½c	on 1c dk gray	.15	.15
a.			Triple surcharge	87.50	
P2	A1	½c	on 1c olive ('26)	.15	.15
			Set value	.19	.19

ALLENSTEIN

'a-lən-,shtin

LOCATION — In East Prussia
AREA — 4,457 sq. mi.
POP. — 540,000 (estimated 1920)
CAPITAL — Allenstein

Allenstein, a district of East Prussia, held a plebiscite in 1920 under the Versailles Treaty, voting to join Germany rather than Poland. Later that year, Allenstein became part of the German Republic.

100 Pfennig = 1 Mark

Stamps of Germany, 1906-20, Overprinted

PLÉBISCITE OLSZTYN ALLENSTEIN

Perf. 14, 14½, 14x14½, 14½x14

1920 Wmk. 125

1	A16	5pf	green	.15	.15
2	A16	10pf	carmine	.15	.15
3	A22	15pf	dk vio	.15	.15
4	A22	15pf	vio brn	6.50	6.50
5	A16	20pf	bl vio	.15	.15
6	A16	30pf	org & blk, *buff*	.40	.25
7	A16	40pf	lake & blk	.30	.20
8	A16	50pf	pur & blk, *buff*	.30	.20
9	A16	75pf	grn & blk	.30	.20
10	A17	1m	car rose	.85	.65
a.			Double overprint	*375.00*	*600.00*
11	A17	1.25m	green	.70	.55
a.			Double overprint	*475.00*	*1,000.*
12	A17	1.50m	yel brn	.70	.55
13	A21	2.50m	lilac rose	.85	1.40
14	A19	3m	blk vio	1.75	1.75
a.			Double overprint	350.00	*925.00*
b.			Inverted overprint	*375.00*	*600.00*
			Nos. 1-14 (14)	13.25	12.85

Overprinted

15	A16	5pf	green	.15	.25
16	A16	10pf	carmine	.15	.25
17	A22	15pf	dark vio	.15	.15
18	A22	15pf	vio brn	30.00	30.00
19	A16	20pf	blue vio	.15	.15
20	A16	30pf	org & blk, *buff*	.30	.25
21	A16	40pf	lake & blk	.30	.25
22	A16	50pf	pur & blk, *buff*	.15	.15
23	A16	75pf	grn & blk	.15	.15
24	A17	1m	car rose	.55	.55
a.			Inverted overprint	550.00	750.00
25	A17	1.25m	green	.55	.55
26	A17	1.50m	yel brn	.55	.55
27	A21	2.50m	lilac rose	.85	1.50
28	A19	3m	blk vio	1.00	1.00
a.			Inverted overprint	350.00	*550.00*
b.			Double overprint	275.00	*450.00*
			Nos. 15-28 (14)	35.00	35.75

The 40pf carmine rose (Germany No. 124) exists with this oval overprint, but it is doubtful whether it was regularly issued. Value $250.

ANDORRA

an-'dȯr-ə

LOCATION — On the southern slope of the Pyrenees Mountains between France and Spain.
GOVT. — Co-principality
AREA — 179 sq. mi.
POP. — 26,500 (1976)
CAPITAL — Andorre-la-Vieille

Andorra is subject to the joint control of France and the Spanish Bishop of Urgel and pays annual tribute to both. The country has no monetary unit of its own, the peseta and franc both being in general use.

100 Centimos = 1 Peseta
100 Centimes = 1 Franc

Catalogue values for unused stamps in the Spanish Administration for this country are for Never Hinged items, beginning with Scott 50 in the regular postage section and Scott C2 in the airpost section; for the French Administration of this country, Never Hinged items begin at Scott 78 for regular postage, Scott B1 for the semi-postal section, Scott C1 for the airpost section, and Scott J21 for the postage due section.

SPANISH ADMINISTRATION

Stamps of Spain, 1922-26, Overprinted in Red or Black

:-: CORREOS :-:
ANDORRA

Perf. 14, 13½x12½, 12½x11½

1928 Unwmk.

1	A49	2c	olive green	.35	.20

Control Numbers on Back

2	A49	5c	car rose (Bk)	.45	.25
3	A49	10c	green	.45	.30
4	A49	15c	slate blue	2.25	2.00
5	A49	20c	violet	2.25	2.00
6	A49	25c	rose red (Bk)	2.25	2.00
7	A49	30c	black brown	10.00	6.75
8	A49	40c	deep blue	10.00	4.75
9	A49	50c	orange (Bk)	10.00	6.75
10	A49a	1p	blue blk	12.00	10.00
11	A49a	4p	lake (Bk)	85.00	70.00
12	A49a	10p	brown (Bk)	140.00	100.00
			Nos. 1-12 (12)	275.00	205.00

Counterfeit overprints exist.

La Vall
A1

St. Juan de Caselles
A2

St. Julia de Loria — A3

St. Coloma — A4

General Council — A5

1929, Nov. 25 Engr. *Perf. 14*

13	A1	2c	olive green	.60	.25

Control Numbers on Back

14	A2	5c	carmine lake	1.20	.30
15	A3	10c	yellow green	1.20	.90
16	A4	15c	slate green	1.25	.90
17	A3	20c	violet	1.25	.90
18	A4	25c	carmine rose	2.75	1.25
19	A1	30c	olive brown	50.00	32.50
20	A2	40c	dark blue	2.25	.60
21	A3	50c	deep orange	2.25	.90
22	A5	1p	slate	4.75	3.00
23	A5	4p	deep rose	32.50	17.50
24	A5	10p	bister brown	35.00	26.00
			Nos. 13-24 (12)	135.00	85.00

Nos. 13-24, 26, 28, 32 exist imperforate.

1931-38

Perf. 11½

13a	A1	2c		3.00	.30

Control Numbers on Back

14a	A2	5c		4.00	.90
15a	A3	10c		6.00	1.10
16a	A4	15c		20.00	14.00
17a	A3	20c		6.00	3.50
18a	A4	25c		6.00	3.50
19a	A1	30c	('33)	50.00	37.50
20a	A2	40c	('35)	10.00	7.50
22a	A5	1p	('38)	25.00	14.00
b.			Control number omitted	1,400.	

Without Control Numbers

1936-43 *Perf. 11½x11*

25	A1	2c	red brown ('37)	2.00	1.00
26	A2	5c	dark brown	2.00	1.00
27	A3	10c	blue green	9.00	1.75
a.			10c yellow green	80.00	30.00
28	A4	15c	green ('37)	6.25	2.00
29	A3	20c	violet	6.25	2.25
30	A4	25c	deep rose ('37)	2.25	2.00
31	A1	30c	carmine	4.00	2.00
31A	A2	40c	dark blue	*600.00*	37.50
32	A1	45c	rose red ('37)	2.00	1.00
33	A3	50c	deep orange	8.75	3.50
34	A1	60c	deep blue ('37)	5.00	2.00
35	A5	4p	deep rose ('43)	32.50	30.00
36	A5	10p	bister brn ('43)	45.00	30.00
			Nos. 25-36 (13)	*725.00*	116.00

Edelweiss — A6

Provost — A7

Coat of Arms — A8

Plaza of Ordino — A9

Chapel of Meritxell
A10

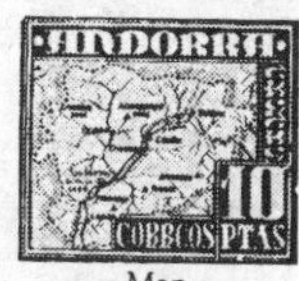
Map
A11

1948-53 Unwmk. Photo. *Perf. 12½*

37	A6	2c	dark olive grn ('51)	.40	.25
38	A6	5c	deep orange ('53)	.40	.25
39	A6	10c	deep blue ('53)	.45	.25

Engr. *Perf. 9½x10*

40	A7	20c	brown vio	6.50	.75
41	A7	25c	org, perf. 12½ ('53)	4.75	.50
42	A8	30c	dk slate grn	8.50	1.50
43	A9	50c	deep green	10.00	1.75
44	A10	75c	dark blue	15.00	1.75
45	A9	90c	dp car rose	6.50	1.75
46	A10	1p	brt orange ver	10.00	1.75
47	A8	1.35p	dk blue vio	6.50	2.00

Perf. 10

48	A11	4p	ultra ('53)	10.00	4.00
49	A11	10p	dk violet brn ('51)	21.00	8.50
			Nos. 37-49 (13)	100.00	25.00

Catalogue values for unused stamps in this section, from this point to the end of the section, are for Never Hinged items.

Bridge of St. Anthony — A12

Madonna of Meritxell, 8th Century — A13

Designs: 70c, Aynos pasture. 1p, View of Canillo. 2p, St. Coloma. 2.50p, Arms of Andorra. 3p, Old Andorra, horiz. 5p, View of Ordino, horiz.

1963-64 Unwmk. Engr. *Perf. 13*

No.	Type	Value	Description	Unused	Used
50	A12	25c	dk gray & sepia	.25	.15
51	A12	70c	dk sl grn & brn blk	.25	.15
52	A12	1p	slate & dull pur	.35	.15
53	A12	2p	violet & dull pur	.40	.15
54	A12	2.50p	rose claret	1.00	.60
55	A12	3p	blk & grnsh gray	1.75	.60
56	A12	5p	dk brn & choc	2.00	1.10
57	A13	6p	sepia & car	3.00	1.10
			Nos. 50-57 (8)	9.00	4.00

Issued: 25c-2p, 7/20/63; 2.50p-6p, 2/29/64.

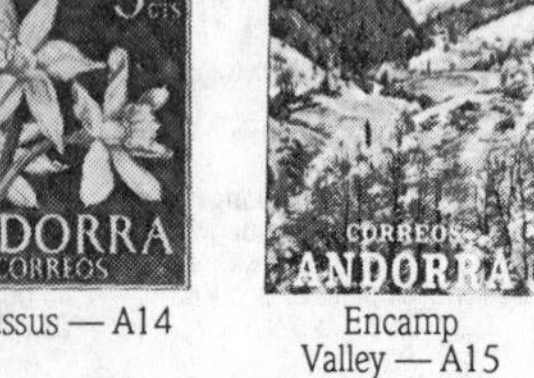

Narcissus — A14 Encamp Valley — A15

1966, June 10 Engr. *Perf. 13*

No.	Type	Value	Description	Unused	Used
58	A14	50c	shown	.20	.15
59	A14	1p	Pinks	.30	.15
60	A14	5p	Jonquils	1.50	.55
61	A14	10p	Hellebore	3.00	.65
			Nos. 58-61 (4)	5.00	1.50

Europa Issue 1972

Common Design Type

1972, May 2 Photo. *Perf. 13*

Size: 25½x38mm

No.	Type	Value	Description	Unused	Used
62	CD15	8p	multicolored	125.00	80.00

1972, July 4 Photo. *Perf. 13*

Tourist publicity: 1.50p, Massana (village). 2p, Skiing on De La Casa Pass. 5p, Pessons Lake, horiz.

No.	Type	Value	Description	Unused	Used
63	A15	1p	multicolored	.30	.15
64	A15	1.50p	multicolored	.90	.55
65	A15	2p	multicolored	2.25	.55
66	A15	5p	multicolored	3.00	.90
			Nos. 63-66 (4)	6.45	2.15

Butterfly Stroke — A16

Design: 2p, Volleyball, vert.

1972, Oct. Photo. *Perf. 13*

No.	Type	Value	Description	Unused	Used
67	A16	2p	lt blue & multi	.30	.15
68	A16	5p	multicolored	.35	.20

20th Olympic Games, Munich, Aug. 26-Sept. 11.

St. Anthony Singers A17

1972, Dec. 5 Photo. *Perf. 13*

No.	Type	Value	Description	Unused	Used
69	A17	1p	shown	.15	.15
70	A17	1.50p	Les Caramelles (boys' choir)	.15	.15
71	A17	2p	Nativity scene	.15	.15
72	A17	5p	Man holding giant cigar, vert	.70	.15
73	A17	8p	Hermit of Meritxell, vert	.85	.35
74	A17	15p	Marratxa dancers	2.00	.50
			Nos. 69-74 (6)	4.00	
			Set value		1.10

Andorran customs. No. 71 is for Christmas.

Common Design Types pictured in section at front of book.

Europa Issue 1973

Common Design Type and

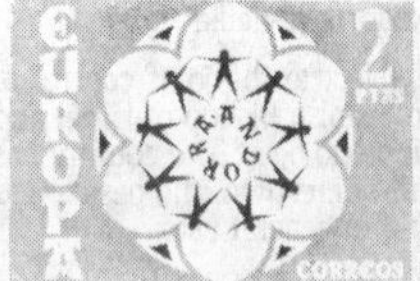

Symbol of Unity — A18

1973, Apr. 30 Photo. *Perf. 13*

No.	Type	Value	Description	Unused	Used
75	A18	2p	ultra, red & blk	.20	.15

Size: 37x25mm

No.	Type	Value	Description	Unused	Used
76	CD16	8p	tan, red & blk	.85	.30

Nativity — A19 Virgin of Ordino — A20

Christmas: 5p, Adoration of the Kings. Designs are from altar panels of Meritxell Parish Church.

1973, Dec. 14 Photo. *Perf. 13*

No.	Type	Value	Description	Unused	Used
77	A19	2p	multicolored	.22	.15
78	A19	5p	multicolored	.90	.38

1974, Apr. 29 Photo. *Perf. 13*

Europa: 8p, Les Banyes Cross.

No.	Type	Value	Description	Unused	Used
79	A20	2p	multicolored	1.50	.38
80	A20	8p	slate & brt blue	4.50	1.25

Cupboard — A21 Crowns of Virgin and Child of Roser — A22

1974, July 30 Photo. *Perf. 13*

No.	Type	Value	Description	Unused	Used
81	A21	10p	multicolored	2.25	.85
82	A22	25p	dark red & multi	5.00	1.90

UPU Monument, Bern — A23

1974, Oct. 9 Photo. *Perf. 13*

No.	Type	Value	Description	Unused	Used
83	A23	15p	multicolored	1.40	.55

Centenary of Universal Postal Union.

Nativity A24

Christmas: 5p, Adoration of the Kings.

1974, Dec. 4 Photo. *Perf. 13*

No.	Type	Value	Description	Unused	Used
84	A24	2p	multicolored	.60	.20
85	A24	5p	multicolored	2.25	.45

Mail Delivery, Andorra, 19th Century — A25 12th Century Painting, Ordino Church — A26

1975, Apr. 4 Photo. *Perf. 13*

No.	Type	Value	Description	Unused	Used
86	A25	3p	multicolored	.30	.15

Espana 75 International Philatelic Exhibition, Madrid, Apr. 4-13.

1975, Apr. 28 Photo. *Perf. 13*

Design: 12p, Christ in Glory, 12th century Romanesque painting, Ordino church.

No.	Type	Value	Description	Unused	Used
87	A26	3p	multicolored	1.65	.35
88	A26	12p	multicolored	3.00	.60

Urgel Cathedral and Document — A27

1975, Oct. 4 Photo. *Perf. 13*

No.	Type	Value	Description	Unused	Used
89	A27	7p	multicolored	1.00	.50

Millennium of consecration of Urgel Cathedral, and Literary Festival 1975.

Nativity, Ordino A28

Christmas: 7p, Adoration of the Kings, Ordino.

1975, Dec. 3 Photo. *Perf. 13*

No.	Type	Value	Description	Unused	Used
90	A28	3p	multicolored	.30	.15
91	A28	7p	multicolored	.40	.22

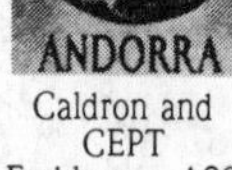

Caldron and CEPT Emblem — A29 Slalom and Montreal Olympic Emblem — A30

Europa: 12p, Chest and CEPT emblem, horiz.

1976, May 3 Photo. *Perf. 13*

No.	Type	Value	Description	Unused	Used
92	A29	3p	bister & multi	.20	.15
93	A29	12p	yellow & multi	.60	.16

1976, July 9 Photo. *Perf. 13*

Design: 15p, One-man canoe and Montreal Olympic emblem, horiz.

No.	Type	Value	Description	Unused	Used
94	A30	7p	multicolored	.18	.15
95	A30	15p	multicolored	.42	.25

21st Olympic Games, Montreal, Canada, July 17-Aug. 1.

Nativity A31

Christmas: 25p, Adoration of the Kings. Wall paintings in La Massana Church.

1976, Dec. 7 Photo. *Perf. 13*

No.	Type	Value	Description	Unused	Used
96	A31	3p	multicolored	.15	.15
97	A31	25p	multicolored	.55	.25

View of Ansalonge A32

Europa: 12p, Xuclar, valley, mountains.

1977, May 2 Litho. *Perf. 13*

No.	Type	Value	Description	Unused	Used
98	A32	3p	multicolored	.16	.15
99	A32	12p	multicolored	.55	.22

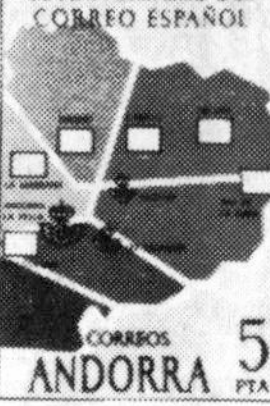

Cross of Terme — A33 Map of Post Offices — A34

Christmas: 12p, Church of St. Miguel d'Engolasters.

1977, Dec. 2 Photo. *Perf. 13x12½*

No.	Type	Value	Description	Unused	Used
100	A33	5p	multicolored	.35	.22
101	A33	12p	multicolored	.90	.50

Souvenir Sheet

Designs: 10p, Mail delivery. 20p, Post Office, 1928. 25p, Andorran coat of arms.

1978, Mar. 31 Photo. *Perf. 13x13½*

No.	Type	Value	Description	Unused	Used
102			Sheet of 4	1.00	1.00
a.	A34	5p	multicolored	.15	.15
b.	A34	10p	multicolored	.20	.15
c.	A34	20p	multicolored	.30	.30
d.	A34	25p	multicolored	.35	.35

Spanish postal service in Andorra, 50th anniversary.

La Vall — A35

Europa: 12p, St. Juan de Caselles.

1978, May 2 *Perf. 13*

No.	Type	Value	Description	Unused	Used
103	A35	5p	multicolored	.15	.15
104	A35	12p	multicolored	.30	.15
			Set value		.21

Crown, Bishop's Mitre and Staff — A36

1978, Sept. 24 Photo. *Perf. 13*

No.	Type	Value	Description	Unused	Used
105	A36	5p	brown, car & yel	.45	.15

700th anniversary of the signing of treaty establishing Co-Principality of Andorra.

Holy Family — A37

Young Woman — A38

Christmas: 25p, Adoration of the Kings. Both designs after frescoes in the Church of St. Mary d'Encamp.

1978, Dec. 5 Photo. *Perf. 13*

106 A37	5p multicolored	.15	.15
107 A37	25p multicolored	.42	.20
	Set value		.26

1979, Feb. 14 Photo. *Perf. 13*

Designs: 5p, Young man. 12p, Bridegroom and bride riding mule.

108 A38	3p multicolored	.15	.15
109 A38	5p multicolored	.15	.15
110 A38	12p multicolored	.25	.15
	Set value	.45	.24

Old Mail Truck A39

Europa: 12p, Stampless covers of 1846 and 1854.

1979, Apr. 30 Engr. *Perf. 13*

111 A39	5p yel grn & dk blue	.15	.15
112 A39	12p dk red & violet	.35	.15
	Set value		.21

Children Holding Hands A40

1979, Oct. 18 Photo. *Perf. 13*

113 A40	19p multicolored	.40	.20

International Year of the Child.

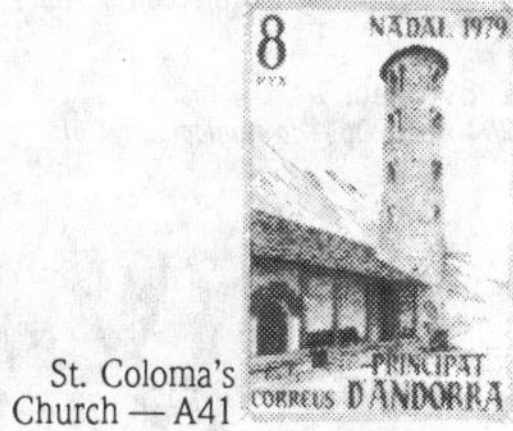
St. Coloma's Church — A41

Christmas: 25p, Agnus Dei roundel, St. Coloma's Church.

1979, Nov. 28 Photo. *Perf. 13½*

114 A41	8p multicolored	.16	.15
115 A41	25p multicolored	.45	.24
	Set value		.29

Bishop Pere d'Arg A42

Bishops of Urgel: 5p, Josep Caixal. 13p, Joan Benlloch.

1979, Dec. 27 Engr.

116 A42	1p dk blue & brown	.15	.15
117 A42	5p rose lake & purple	.15	.15
118 A42	13p brown & dk green	.25	.15
	Set value	.40	.26

See Nos. 132-133, 159, 175, C4.

Antoni Fiter, Magistrate — A43

Europa: 19p, Francesc Cairat, magistrate.

1980, Apr. 28 Photo. *Perf. 13x13½*

119 A43	8p bister, blk & brn	.15	.15
120 A43	19p lt green & blk	.40	.18

Boxing, Moscow '80 Emblem A44

1980, July 23 Photo. *Perf. 13½x13*

121 A44	5p Downhill skiing	.15	.15
122 A44	8p shown	.15	.15
123 A44	50p Target shooting	.85	.50
	Nos. 121-123 (3)	1.15	
	Set value		.69

12th Winter Olympic Games, Lake Placid, NY, Feb. 12-24 (5p); 22nd Summer Olympic Games, Moscow, July 19-Aug. 3.

Nativity A45

1980, Dec. 12 Litho. *Perf. 13*

124 A45	10p Nativity, vert.	.15	.15
125 A45	22p shown	.40	.20

Christmas 1980.

Children Dancing at Santa Anna Feast — A46

Europa: 30p, Going to church on Aplec de la Verge de Canolich Day.

1981, May 7 Photo. *Perf. 13*

126 A46	12p multicolored	.20	.15
127 A46	30p multicolored	.45	.25

50th Anniv. of Police Force — A47

1981, July 2 Photo. *Perf. 13½x13*

128 A47	30p multicolored	.45	.20

Intl. Year of the Disabled A48

1981, Oct. 8 Photo. *Perf. 13½*

129 A48	50p multicolored	.75	.30

Christmas 1981 — A49

Designs: Encamp Church retable.

1981, Dec. 3 Photo. *Perf. 13½*

130 A49	12p Nativity	.20	.15
131 A49	30p Adoration	.50	.20

Bishops of Urgel Type of 1979

1981, Dec. 12 Engr. *Perf. 13½*

132 A42	7p Salvador Casanas	.15	.15
133 A42	20p Josep de Boltas	.38	.15
	Set value		.22

Natl. Arms — A51

1982, Feb. 17 Photo. *Perf. 13x13½*

134 A51	1p bright pink	.15	.15
135 A51	3p bister brown	.15	.15
136 A51	7p red orange	.15	.15
137 A51	12p lake	.15	.15
138 A51	15p ultra	.18	.15
139 A51	20p blue green	.22	.15
140 A51	30p crimson rose	.35	.15

Perf. 13½x12½

1982, Sept. 30 Engr.

Size: 25½x30½mm

141 A51	50p dark green	.80	.18
142 A51	100p dark blue	1.65	.52
	Set value, #134-142	1.85	.70

For type A51 without "PTA" see #192-198.

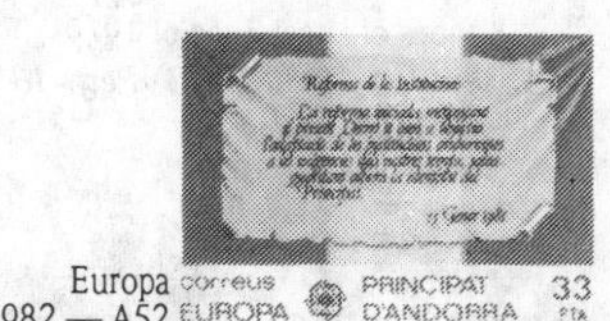
Europa 1982 — A52

1982, May 12 Photo. *Perf. 13*

143 A52	14p New Reforms, 1866, vert.	.18	.15
144 A52	33p Reform of Institutions, 1981	.48	.25

1982 World Cup — A53

Designs: Various soccer players.

1982, June 13 Photo. *Perf. 13x13½*

145 A53	14p multicolored	.60	.60
146 A53	33p multicolored	1.25	1.25
a.	Pair, #145-146 + label	1.85	1.85

A54 A55

Anniversaries: 9p, Permanent Spanish and French delegations, cent. 14p, 50th anniv. of Andorran stamps. 23p, St. Francis of Assisi (1182-1226). 33p, Anyos Pro-Vicarial District membership centenary (Relacio sobre la Vall de Andorra titlepage).

1982, Sept. 7 Engr. *Perf. 13*

147 A54	9p dk blue & brown	.15	.15
148 A54	14p black & green	.48	.20
149 A54	23p dk blue & brown	.30	.15
150 A54	33p black & olive grn	.90	.45
	Nos. 147-150 (4)	1.83	
	Set value		.80

Perf. 13x13½, 13½x13

1982, Dec. 9 Photo.

Christmas: 14p, Madonna and Child, Andorra la Vieille Church, vert. 33p, El Tio de Nadal (children in traditional costumes striking hollow tree).

151 A55	14p multicolored	.20	.15
152 A55	33p multicolored	.50	.25

Europa 1983 A56

1983, June 7 Photo. *Perf. 13*

153 A56	16p La Cortinada Church, architect, 12th cent.	.30	.15
154 A56	38p Water mill, 16th cent.	.75	.40

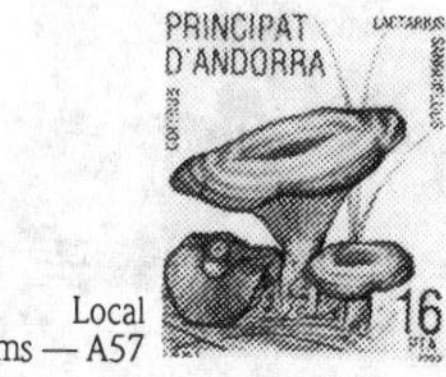
Local Mushrooms — A57

1983, July 20 Photo. *Perf. 13x12½*

155 A57	16p Lactarius sanguifluus	1.65	.50

See Nos. 165, 169, 172.

Universal Suffrage, 50th Anniv. A58

Photogravure and Engraved

1983, Sept. 6 *Perf. 13*

156 A58	10p multicolored	.25	.15

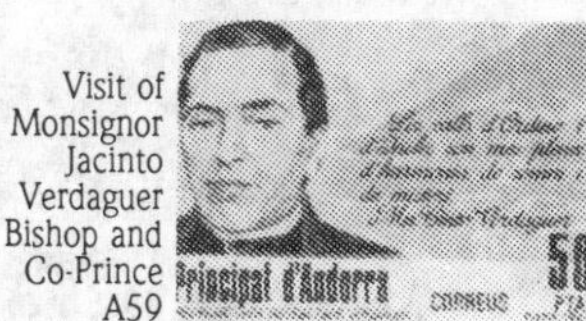
Visit of Monsignor Jacinto Verdaguer Bishop and Co-Prince A59

1983, Sept. 6

157 A59	50p multicolored	.95	.45

Christmas 1983 — A60

Saint Cerni de Nagol, Romanesque fresco, Church of San Cerni de Nagol.

1983, Nov. 24 Photo. *Perf. 13½*

158 A60	16p multicolored	.30	.15

Bishops of Urgel Type of 1979

1983, Dec. 7 Engr. *Perf. 13*

159 A42	26p Joan J. Laguarda Fenollera	.40	.18

1984 Winter Olympics A62

1984, Feb. 17 Litho. *Perf. 13½x14*

160 A62	16p Ski jumping	.40	.15

ESPANA '84 — A63

1984, Apr. 27 Photo. *Perf. 13*
161 A63 26p Emblems .40 .15

Europa (1959-84) A64

1984, May 5 Engr.
162 A64 16p brown .30 .15
163 A64 38p blue .75 .38

1984 Summer Olympics A65

1984, Aug. 9 Litho. *Perf. 13½x14*
164 A65 40p Running .70 .38

Mushroom Type of 1983

1984, Sept. 27 Photo. *Perf. 13x12½*
165 A57 11p Morchella esculenta *13.00* 1.50

Christmas 1984 — A66

1984, Dec. 6 Photo. *Perf. 13½*
166 A66 17p Nativity carving .35 .15

Europa 1985 A67

Designs: 18p, Mossen Enric Arfany, composer, natl. hymn score. 45p, Musician Playing Viol, Romanesque fresco detail, La Cortinada Church, vert.

1985, May 3 Engr. *Perf. 13½*
167 A67 18p dk vio, grn & choc .38 .15
168 A67 45p green & choc .90 .25

Mushroom Type of 1983

Perf. 13½x12½

1985, Sept. 19 Photo.
169 A57 30p Gyromitra esculenta .65 .25

Pal Village — A68

1985, Nov. 7 Engr. *Perf. 13½*
170 A68 17p brt ultra & dk blue .35 .15

Andorra, Spanish Administration, stamps can be mounted in the Scott annual Spain and Spanish Andorra supplement.

Christmas 1985 — A69

Fresco: Angels Playing Trumpet and Psaltery, St. Bartholomew Chapel.

1985, Dec. 11 Photo. *Perf. 13½x13*
171 A69 17p multicolored .35 .15

Mushroom Type of 1983

Perf. 13½x12½

1986, Apr. 10 Photo.
172 A57 30p Marasmius oreades .60 .25

Europa 1986 — A70

1986, May 5 Engr. *Perf. 13*
173 A70 17p Water .30 .15
174 A70 45p Soil and air .85 .25

Bishops of Urgel Type of 1979

1986, Sept. 11 Engr. *Perf. 13½*
175 A42 35p Justi Guitart .60 .20

A72 A73

Santa Roma de Les Bons Church bell.

1986, Dec. 11 Litho. *Perf. 14*
176 A72 19p multicolored .30 .15

Christmas.

1987, Mar. 27 Photo. *Perf. 14*

Contemporary Natl. Coat of Arms.

177 A73 48p multicolored .78 .40

Visit of the co-princes: the Bishop of Urgel and president of France, September 26, 1986.

Europa 1987 A74

Modern architecture: 19p, Meritxell Sanctuary interior. 48p, Sanctuary exterior, vert.

1987, May 15 Engr. *Perf. 14x13½*
178 A74 19p dark blue & brown .30 .15
179 A74 48p dark blue & brown .78 .28

Souvenir Sheet

1992 Summer Olympics, Barcelona A75

Designs: 20p, House of the Valleys. 50p, Bell tower, Chapel of the Archangel Michael, and torch-bearer.

1987, July 20 Photo. *Perf. 14*
180 Sheet of 2 5.00 5.00
a. A75 20p multicolored 1.40 1.40
b. A75 50p multicolored 3.50 3.50

Local Mushrooms — A76

1987, Sept. 11 *Perf. 13½x12½*
181 A76 100p Boletus edulis 1.65 .60

Christmas A77

Design: Detail from a Catalan manuscript, De Nativitat, by R. Llull.

1987, Nov. 18 Litho. *Perf. 14*
182 A77 20p multicolored .38 .15

Lance and Arrowhead (Bronze Age) — A78

1988, Mar. 25 Photo. *Perf. 14*
183 A78 50p multicolored .90 .30

Europa 1988 — A79 Pyrenean Mastiff — A80

Transport and communications: 20p, Les Bons, a medieval road. 45p, Trader and pack mules, early 20th cent.

1988, May 5 Engr. *Perf. 14x13½*
184 A79 20p dark blue & dark red .32 .15
185 A79 45p dark blue & dark red .70 .25

1988, July 26 Litho. *Perf. 14x13½*
186 A80 20p multicolored .35 .15

Bishop of Urgel and Seigneur of Caboet Confirming Co-Principality, 700th Anniv. — A81

1988, Oct. 24 Litho. *Perf. 14x13½*
187 A81 20p gold, blk & int blue .35 .15

Christmas 1988 A82

1988, Nov. 30 Litho. *Perf. 14x13½*
188 A82 20p multicolored .35 .15

Arms Type of 1982 Without "PTA"

1988, Dec. 2 Photo. *Perf. 13x13½*
192 A51 20p brt blue green .35 .15

Size: 25x30½mm

Perf. 13½x12½

Engr.

194 A51 50p grnsh black .90 .30
196 A51 100p dark blue 1.80 .60
198 A51 500p dark brown 9.00 3.00
Nos. 192-198 (4) 12.05 4.05

This is an expanding set. Numbers will change if necessary.

Europa 1989 A83

Perf. 14x13½, 13½x14

1989, May 8 Litho. & Engr.
200 A83 20p Leapfrog, vert. .32 .15
201 A83 45p Tug of war .72 .24

Santa Roma Church, Les Bons — A84

Perf. 13½x14

1989, June 20 Litho. & Engr.
202 A84 50p blk, dp blue & grn blue .90 .28

Anniv. Emblem — A85 Christmas — A86

1989, Oct. 26 Litho. *Perf. 14x13½*
203 A85 20p multicolored .35 .15

Intl. Red Cross and Red Crescent societies, 125th annivs.; Year for the Protection of Human Life.

1989, Dec. 1
204 A86 20p *The Immaculate Conception* .35 .15

Europa 1990 A87

Post offices.

Perf. 13½x14, 14x13½

1990, May 17 Photo.
205 A87 20p shown .38 .15
206 A87 50p Post office, vert. .95 .32

Gomphidius Rutilus — A88

1990, June 21 Litho. *Perf. 13x13½*
207 A88 45p multicolored .95 .35

Plandolit House — A89

Christmas — A90

Perf. 13x12½

1990, Oct. 17 Litho. & Engr.

208 A89 20p brown & org yel .45 .16

1990, Nov. 26 Litho. *Perf. 14x13½*

209 A90 25p lake, brn & bister .55 .20

4th Games of the Small European States A91

1991, Apr. 29 Photo. *Perf. 13½x14*

210 A91 25p Discus .55 .20
211 A91 45p High jump, runner .95 .35

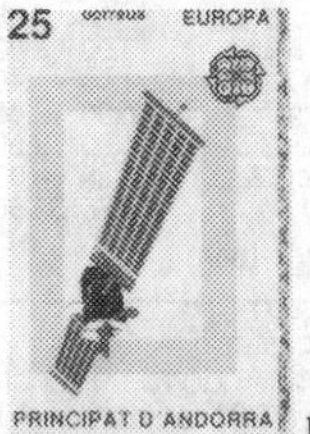

Europa — A92

Perf. 14x13½, 13½x14

1991, May 10 Litho.

212 A92 25p Olympus-1 satellite .55 .20
213 A92 55p Olympus-1, horiz. 1.25 .45

A93

Christmas — A94

1991, Sept. 20 Litho. *Perf. 13x12½*

214 A93 45p Macrolepiota Procera .95 .35

1991, Nov. 29 Photo. *Perf. 14x13½*

215 A94 25p multicolored .55 .20

Woman Carrying Water Pails — A95

1992, Feb. 14 Photo. *Perf. 13½x14*

216 A95 25p multicolored .55 .20

Discovery of America, 500th Anniv. A96

Perf. 14x13½, 13½x14

1992, May 8 Photo.

217 A96 27p Santa Maria, vert. .65 .22
218 A96 45p King Ferdinand 1.00 .38

Europa.

1992 Summer Olympics, Barcelona A97

1992, July 22 Photo. *Perf. 13½x14*

219 A97 27p Kayak .85 .30

Nativity Scene, by Fra Angelico — A98

1992, Nov. 18 Photo. *Perf. 14*

220 A98 27p multicolored .65 .22

Natl. Automobile Museum A99

Perf. 13½x14

1992, Sept. 10 Litho. & Engr.

221 A99 27p 1894 Benz .85 .30

Cantharellus Cibarius A100

1993, Mar. 25 Photo. *Perf. 13½x14*

222 A100 28p multicolored .90 .32

Contemporary Paintings — A101

Europa: 28p, Upatream, by John Alan Morrison. 45p, Rhythm, by Angel Calvente, vert.

Perf. 13½x14, 14x13½

1993, May 20 Litho.

223 A101 28p multicolored .90 .32
224 A101 45p multicolored 1.40 .50

A102

A103

1993, Sept. 23 Litho. *Perf. 14*

225 A102 28p multicolored .90 .32

Art and Literature Society, 25th anniv.

Perf. 14x13½

1993, Nov. 25 Litho. & Engr.

226 A103 28p Christmas .90 .32

Souvenir Sheet

Constitution, 1st Anniv. — A104

1994, Mar. 14 Photo. *Perf. 14*

227 A104 29p multicolored .95 .95

Sir Alexander Fleming (1881-1955), Co-discoverer of Penicillin A105

1994, May 6 Photo. *Perf. 13½x14*

228 A105 29p Portrait .95 .95
229 A105 55p AIDS virus 1.75 1.75

Europa.

Hygrophorus Gliocyclus A106

1994, Sept. 27 Photo. *Perf. 14*

230 A106 29p multicolored .95 .95

Christmas — A107

1994, Nov. 29 Photo. *Perf. 14x13½*

231 A107 29p multicolored .95 .95

Nature Conservation in Europe A108

1995, Mar. 23 Photo. *Perf. 14*

232 A108 30p Farm in valley 1.00 1.00
233 A108 60p Stone fence, valley 2.00 2.00

Europa A109

1995, May 8 Photo. *Perf. 14*

234 A109 60p multicolored 2.00 2.00

Christmas — A110

1995, Nov. 8 Photo. *Perf. 14*

235 A110 30p Flight to Egypt 1.00 1.00

Entrance Into Council of Europe A111

1995, Nov. 10

236 A111 30p multicolored 1.00 1.00

AIR POST STAMPS

AP1

Unwmk.

1951, June 27 Engr. *Perf. 11*

C1 AP1 1p dk violet brn 25.00 2.25

Catalogue values for unused stamps in this section, from this point to the end of the section, are for Never Hinged items.

AP2

AP3

Litho. & Engr.

1983, Oct. 20 *Perf. 13*

C2 AP2 20p brown & bis brn .30 .20

Jaime Sansa Nequi, Episcopal Church official.

1984, Oct. 25 Photo. *Perf. 13*

C3 AP3 20p multicolored .40 .25

Pyrenees Art Center.

Bishops of Urgel Type of 1979

1985, June 13 Engr. *Perf. 13½*

C4 A42 20p Ramon Iglesias .35 .18

SPECIAL DELIVERY STAMPS

Special Delivery Stamp of Spain, 1905 Overprinted

CORREOS

ANDORRA

1928 Unwmk. *Perf. 14*

Without Control Number on Back

E1 SD1 20c red 62.50 42.50

With Control Number on Back

E2 SD1 20c pale red 32.50 17.50

Eagle over Mountain Pass — SD2

Arms and Squirrel — SD3

1929 *Perf. 14*

With Control Number on Back

E3	SD2	20c scarlet	13.50	5.00
a.		Perf. 11½	300.00	

1937 *Perf. 11½x11*

Without Control Number on Back

E4	SD2	20c red	7.50	4.00

1949 Unwmk. Engr. *Perf. 10x9½*

E5	SD3	25c red	4.00	2.50

FRENCH ADMINISTRATION

Stamps and Types of France, 1900-1929, Overprinted **ANDORRE**

Perf. 14x13½

1931, June 16 **Unwmk.**

1	A16	1c gray	.55	.55
a.		Double overprint	950.00	950.00
2	A16	2c red brown	.60	.60
3	A16	3c orange	.60	.60
4	A16	5c green	1.00	1.00
5	A16	10c lilac	1.50	1.50
6	A22	15c red brown	3.00	3.00
7	A20	20c red violet	4.00	4.00
8	A22	25c yellow brn	4.00	4.00
9	A22	30c green	4.00	4.00
10	A22	40c ultra	6.75	6.75
11	A20	45c lt violet	7.25	7.25
12	A20	50c vermilion	6.25	6.25
13	A20	65c gray green	9.00	9.00
14	A20	75c rose lilac	12.50	12.50
15	A22	90c red	16.00	16.00
16	A20	1fr dull blue	17.00	17.00
17	A22	1.50fr light blue	22.50	22.50

Overprinted **ANDORRE**

18	A18	2fr org & pale bl	16.00	16.00
19	A18	3fr brt vio & rose	57.50	57.50
20	A18	5fr dk bl & buff	90.00	90.00
21	A18	10fr grn & red	175.00	175.00
22	A18	20fr mag & grn	225.00	225.00
		Nos. 1-22 (22)	680.00	680.00

See No. P1 for ½c on 1c gray.

Nos. 9, 15 and 17 were not issued in France without overprint.

Chapel of Meritxell A50

Bridge of St. Anthony A51

St. Miguel d'Engolasters A52

Gorge of St. Julia A53

Old Andorra — A54

1932-43 Engr. *Perf. 13*

23	A50	1c gray blk	.30	.25
24	A50	2c violet	.40	.40
25	A50	3c brown	.30	.30
26	A50	5c blue green	.40	.40
27	A51	10c dull lilac	.65	.60
28	A50	15c deep red	1.00	1.00
29	A51	20c lt rose	6.25	4.50
30	A52	25c brown	2.25	2.25
31	A51	25c brn car ('37)	4.50	6.50
32	A51	30c emerald	1.75	1.50
33	A51	40c ultra	5.00	4.25
34	A51	40c brn blk ('39)	.65	.60
35	A51	45c lt red	6.00	5.00
36	A51	45c bl grn ('39)	3.00	2.50
37	A52	50c lilac rose	6.50	5.00
38	A51	50c lt vio ('39)	3.00	2.50
38A	A51	50c grn ('40)	1.40	1.40
39	A51	55c lt vio ('38)	9.50	6.00
40	A51	60c yel brn ('38)	.60	.50
41	A52	65c yel grn	25.00	25.00
42	A51	65c blue ('38)	6.50	5.50
43	A51	70c red ('39)	1.30	1.00
44	A52	75c violet	3.25	2.50
45	A51	75c ultra ('39)	2.50	2.25
46	A51	80c green ('38)	13.00	9.50
46A	A53	80c bl grn ('40)	.25	.30
47	A53	90c deep rose	3.25	2.25
48	A53	90c dk grn ('39)	2.25	2.25
49	A53	1fr blue grn	9.50	6.00
50	A53	1fr scarlet ('38)	12.50	9.50
51	A53	1fr dp ultra ('39)	.25	.25
51A	A53	1.20fr brt vio ('42)	.25	.25
52	A50	1.25fr rose car ('33)	22.50	14.00
52A	A50	1.25fr rose ('38)	3.00	1.40
52B	A53	1.30fr sepia ('40)	.25	.25
53	A54	1.50fr ultra	8.25	7.50
53A	A53	1.50fr crim ('40)	.25	.25
54	A53	1.75fr violet ('33)	65.00	50.00
55	A53	1.75fr dk bl ('38)	22.50	16.00
56	A53	2fr red violet	3.75	3.50
56A	A50	2fr rose red ('40)	1.00	.65
56B	A50	2fr dk bl grn ('42)	.25	.20
57	A50	2.15fr dk vio ('38)	27.50	20.00
58	A50	2.25fr ultra ('39)	4.00	3.00
58A	A50	2.40fr red ('42)	.25	.20
59	A50	2.50fr gray blk ('39)	4.00	3.00
59A	A50	2.50fr dp ultra ('40)	1.30	1.25
60	A53	3fr orange brn	3.75	3.50
60A	A50	3fr red brn ('40)	.30	.25
60B	A50	4fr sl bl ('42)	.30	.25
60C	A50	4.50fr dp vio ('42)	.75	.75
61	A54	5fr brown	.40	.35
62	A54	10fr violet	.45	.40
62B	A54	15fr dp ultra ('42)	.50	.40
63	A54	20fr rose lake	.50	.40
63A	A51	50fr turq bl ('43)	1.00	.50
		Nos. 23-63A (56)	305.00	240.00

A 20c ultra exists. Value $12,500.

No. 37 Surcharged with Bars and New Value in Black

1935, Sept. 25

64	A52	20c on 50c lil rose	10.00	8.00
a.		Double surcharge	650.00	

Coat of Arms A55 A56

1936-42 *Perf. 14x13*

65	A55	1c black ('37)	.15	.15
66	A55	2c blue	.15	.15
67	A55	3c brown	.15	.15
68	A55	5c rose lilac	.15	.15
69	A55	10c ultra ('37)	.15	.15
70	A55	15c red violet	.55	.55
71	A55	20c emerald ('37)	.15	.15
72	A55	30c cop red ('38)	.30	.30
72A	A55	30c blk brn ('42)	.15	.15
73	A55	35c Prus grn ('38)	25.00	25.00
74	A55	40c cop red ('42)	.15	.15
75	A55	50c Prus grn ('42)	.15	.15
76	A55	60c turq bl ('42)	.15	.15
77	A55	70c vio ('42)	.15	.15
		Nos. 65-77 (14)	27.50	27.50

Catalogue values for unused stamps in this section, from this point to the end of the section, are for Never Hinged items.

1944

78	A56	10c violet	.15	.15
79	A56	30c deep magenta	.15	.15
80	A56	40c dull blue	.15	.15
81	A56	50c orange red	.15	.15
82	A56	60c black	.15	.15
83	A56	70c brt red violet	.15	.15
84	A56	80c blue green	.15	.15
		Set value	.60	.60

See No. 114.

St. Jean de Caselles A57

La Maison des Vallees — A58

Old Andorra A59

Provost A60

1944-47 *Perf. 13*

85	A57	1fr brown violet	.18	.15
86	A57	1.20fr blue	.15	.15
87	A57	1.50fr red	.18	.15
88	A57	2fr dk blue grn	.15	.15
89	A58	2.40fr rose red	.20	.20
90	A58	2.50fr rose red ('46)	1.25	.50
91	A58	3fr sepia	.15	.15
92	A58	4fr ultra	.18	.15
93	A59	4.50fr brown blk	.18	.15
94	A58	4.50fr dk bl grn ('47)	4.00	3.50
95	A59	5fr ultra	.22	.20
96	A59	5fr Prus grn ('46)	.40	.30
97	A59	6fr rose car ('45)	.30	.15
98	A59	10fr Prus green	.15	.15
99	A59	10fr ultra ('46)	.18	.15
100	A60	15fr rose lilac	.38	.25
101	A60	20fr deep blue	.55	.45
102	A60	25fr lt rose red ('46)	1.40	1.10
103	A60	40fr dk green ('46)	1.40	1.10
104	A60	50fr sepia	1.40	1.10
		Nos. 85-104 (20)	13.00	10.20

1948-49

105	A58	4fr lt blue grn	.70	.70
106	A59	6fr violet brn	.35	.35
107	A59	8fr indigo	1.00	1.00
108	A59	12fr bright red	.75	.75
109	A59	12fr blue grn ('49)	.85	.75
110	A59	15fr crimson ('49)	.45	.45
111	A60	18fr deep blue	2.50	1.50
112	A60	20fr dark violet	2.00	1.65
113	A60	25fr ultra ('49)	1.40	1.10
		Nos. 105-113 (9)	10.00	8.25

1949-51 *Perf. 14x13, 13*

114	A56	1fr deep blue	.75	.55
115	A57	3fr red ('51)	4.50	3.25
116	A57	4fr sepia	2.00	2.00
117	A58	5fr emerald	2.25	1.65
118	A58	5fr purple ('51)	2.25	1.40
119	A58	6fr blue grn ('51)	2.00	1.65
120	A58	8fr brown	.75	.60
121	A59	15fr blk brn ('51)	2.00	1.65
122	A59	18fr rose red ('51)	11.00	7.25
123	A60	30fr ultra ('51)	17.50	7.50
		Nos. 114-123 (10)	45.00	27.50

Les Escaldres Spa — A61

St. Coloma Belfry — A62

Designs: 15fr, 18fr, 20fr, 25fr, Gothic cross. 30fr, 35fr, 40fr, 50fr, 65fr, 70fr, 75fr, Village of Les Bons.

1955-58 Unwmk. Engr. *Perf. 13*

124	A61	1fr dk gray bl	.18	.15
125	A61	2fr dp green	.18	.15
126	A61	3fr red	.18	.15
127	A61	5fr chocolate	.18	.15
128	A62	6fr dk bl grn	.45	.38
129	A62	8fr rose brown	.45	.45
130	A62	10fr brt violet	.70	.55
131	A62	12fr indigo	.75	.60
132	A61	15fr red	1.00	.85
133	A61	18fr blue grn	1.00	.85
134	A61	20fr dp purple	1.65	1.50
135	A61	25fr sepia	2.00	1.50
136	A62	30fr deep blue	24.00	16.00
137	A62	35fr Prus bl ('57)	9.00	6.75
138	A62	40fr dk green	25.00	18.00
139	A62	50fr cerise	3.00	2.25
140	A62	65fr purple ('58)	8.50	5.75
141	A62	70fr chestnut ('57)	6.00	5.75
142	A62	75fr violet blue	40.00	32.50
		Nos. 124-142 (19)	124.22	94.28

Issued: 35fr, 70fr, 8/19; 65fr, 2/10; others, 2/15.

Coat of Arms — A63

Gothic Cross, Meritxell — A64

Designs: 65c, 85c, 1fr, Pond of Engolasters.

1961, June 19 Typo. *Perf. 14x13*

143	A63	5c brt green & blk	.15	.15
144	A63	10c red, pink & blk	.15	.15
145	A63	15c blue & black	.15	.15
146	A63	20c yellow & brown	.15	.15

Engr. *Perf. 13*

147	A64	25c violet, bl & grn	.22	.22
148	A64	30c mar, ol grn & brn	.38	.38
149	A64	45c indigo, bl & grn	13.00	8.00
150	A64	50c pur, lt brn & ol grn	1.40	1.40
151	A64	65c bl, ol & brn	16.00	12.00
152	A64	85c rose lil, vio bl & brn	16.00	12.00
153	A64	1fr grnsh bl, ind & brn	1.25	.90
		Nos. 143-153 (11)	48.85	35.50

See Nos. 161-166A.

Imperforates

Most stamps of Andorra, French Administration, from 1961 onward exist imperforate in issued and trial colors, and also in small presentation sheets in issued colors.

Telstar and Globe Showing Andover and Pleumeur-Bodou — A65

1962, Sept. 29 **Engr.**

154	A65	50c ultra & purple	1.35	1.35

1st television connection of the US and Europe through the Telstar satellite, July 11-12.

"La Sardane" A66

Charlemagne Crossing Andorra — A67

Design: 1fr, Louis le Debonnaire giving founding charter.

1963, June 22 Unwmk. *Perf. 13*

155	A66	20c lil rose, cl & ol grn	3.50	3.50
156	A67	50c sl grn & dk car rose	6.00	6.00
157	A67	1fr red brn, ultra & dk grn	9.50	9.50
		Nos. 155-157 (3)	19.00	19.00

Old Andorra Church and Champs-Elysées Palace — A68

1964, Jan. 20 **Engr.**

158 A68 25c blk, grn & vio brn 1.20 .75

"PHILATEC," Intl. Philatelic and Postal Techniques Exhib., Paris, June 5-21, 1964.

Bishop of Urgel and Seigneur of Caboet Confirming Co-Principality, 1288 — A69

Design: 60c, Napoleon re-establishing Co-principality, 1806.

1964, Apr. 25 **Engr.** ***Perf. 13***

159 A69 60c dk brn, red brn & sl grn 11.50 11.50

160 A69 1fr brt bl, org brn & blk 11.50 11.50

Arms Type of 1961

1964, May 16 **Typo.** ***Perf. 14x13***

161 A63 1c dk blue & gray .15 .15

162 A63 2c black & orange .15 .15

163 A63 12c purple, emer & yel .30 .30

164 A63 18c black, lil & pink .30 .30

Set value .75 .75

Scenic Type of 1961

Designs: 40c, 45c, Gothic Cross, Meritxell. 60c, 90c, Pond of Engolasters.

1965-71 **Engr.** ***Perf. 13***

165 A64 40c dk brn, org brn & sl grn .50 .50

165A A64 45c vio bl, ol bis & slate 1.00 .75

166 A64 60c org brn & dk brn .60 .60

166A A64 90c ultra, bl grn & bister .50 .50

Nos. 165-166A (4) 2.60 2.35

Issued: 40c, 60c, Apr. 24, 1965. 45c, June 13, 1970. 90c, Aug. 28, 1971.

Syncom Satellite over Pleumeur-Bodou Station — A70

Andorra House, Paris — A71

1965, May 17 **Unwmk.**

167 A70 60c dp car, lil & bl 4.00 3.25

Cent. of the ITU.

1965, June 5

168 A71 25c dk bl, org brn & ol gray .90 .75

Ski Lift — A72

Design: 25c, Chair lift, vert.

1966, Apr. 2 **Engr.** ***Perf. 13***

169 A72 25c brt bl, grn & dk brn 1.00 .80

170 A72 40c mag, brt ultra & sep 1.40 1.25

Winter sports in Andorra.

FR-1 Satellite — A73

1966, May 7 ***Perf. 13***

171 A73 60c brt bl, grn & dk grn 1.50 1.50

Issued to commemorate the launching of the scientific satellite FR-1, Dec. 6, 1965.

Europa Issue, 1966

Common Design Type

1966, Sept. 24 **Engr.** ***Perf. 13***

Size: 21½x35½mm

172 CD9 60c brown 3.00 2.25

Folk Dancers, Sculpture by Josep Viladomat A74

Telephone Encircling the Globe A75

1967, Apr. 29 **Engr.** ***Perf. 13***

173 A74 30c ol grn, dp grn & slate .60 .45

Cent. (in 1966) of the New Reform, which reaffirmed and strengthened political freedom in Andorra.

Europa Issue, 1967

Common Design Type

1967, Apr. 29

Size: 22x36mm

174 CD10 30c bluish blk & lt bl 1.75 1.50

175 CD10 60c dk red & brt pink 2.75 2.00

1967, Apr. 29

176 A75 60c dk car, vio & blk 1.25 1.00

Automatic telephone service.

Injured Father at Home — A76

1967, Sept. 23 **Engr.** ***Perf. 13***

177 A76 2.30fr ocher, dk red brn & brn red 6.50 4.25

Introduction of Social Security System.

Jesus in Garden of Gethsemane A77

Designs (from 16th century frescoes in La Maison des Vallees): 30c, The Kiss of Judas. 60c, The Descent from the Cross (Pieta).

1967, Sept. 23

178 A77 25c black & red brn .50 .40

179 A77 30c purple & red lilac .75 .50

180 A77 60c indigo & Prus blue 1.40 .90

Nos. 178-180 (3) 2.65 1.80

See Nos. 185-187.

Downhill Skier — A78

1968, Jan. 27 **Engr.** ***Perf. 13***

181 A78 40c org, ver & red lil .75 .60

10th Winter Olympic Games, Grenoble, France, Feb. 6-18.

Europa Issue, 1968

Common Design Type

1968, Apr. 27 **Engr.** ***Perf. 13***

Size: 36x22mm

182 CD11 30c gray & brt bl 4.00 3.00

183 CD11 60c brown & lilac 5.00 3.75

High Jump — A79

1968, Oct. 12 **Engr.** ***Perf. 13***

184 A79 40c brt blue & brn 1.20 1.00

19th Olympic Games, Mexico City, Oct. 12-27.

Fresco Type of 1967

Designs (from 16th century frescoes in La Maison des Vallees): 25c, The Scourging of Christ. 30c, Christ Carrying the Cross. 60c, The Crucifixion. (All horiz.)

1968, Oct. 12

185 A77 25c dk grn & gray grn .60 .60

186 A77 30c dk brown & lilac 1.00 1.00

187 A77 60c dk car & vio brn 1.40 1.40

Nos. 185-187 (3) 3.00 3.00

Europa Issue, 1969

Common Design Type

1969, Apr. 26 **Engr.** ***Perf. 13***

188 CD12 40c rose car, gray & dl bl 3.75 3.00

189 CD12 70c indigo, dl red & ol 5.75 4.25

10th anniv. of the Conf. of European Postal and Telecommunications Administrations.

Kayak on Isère River A80

Drops of Water and Diamond A80a

1969, Aug. 2 **Engr.** ***Perf. 13***

190 A80 70c dk sl grn, ultra & ind 1.75 1.75

Intl. Canoe & Kayak Championships, Bourg-Saint-Maurice, Savoy, July 31-Aug. 6.

1969, Sept. 27 **Engr.** ***Perf. 13***

191 A80a 70c blk, dp ultra & grnsh bl 3.25 3.25

European Water Charter.

St. John, the Woman and the Dragon — A81

The Revelation (From the Altar of St. John, Caselles): 40c, St. John Hearing Voice from Heaven on Patmos. 70c, St. John and the Seven Candlesticks.

1969, Oct. 18

192 A81 30c brn, dp pur & brn red .65 .65

193 A81 40c gray, dk brn & brn ol 1.00 1.00

194 A81 70c dk red, maroon & brt rose lilac 1.75 1.75

Nos. 192-194 (3) 3.40 3.40

See Nos. 199-201, 207-209, 214-216.

Field Ball — A82

Shot Put — A83

1970, Feb. 21 **Engr.** ***Perf. 13***

195 A82 80c multi 1.75 1.25

Issued to publicize the 7th International Field Ball Games, France, Feb. 26-Mar. 8.

Europa Issue, 1970

Common Design Type

1970, May 2 **Engr.** ***Perf. 13***

Size: 36x22mm

196 CD13 40c orange 2.50 1.90

197 CD13 80c violet blue 3.50 2.75

1970, Sept. 11 **Engr.** ***Perf. 13***

198 A83 80c bl & dk brn 1.25 1.00

1st European Junior Athletic Championships, Colombes, France, Sept. 11-13.

Altar Type of 1969

The Revelation (from the Altar of St. John, Caselles): 30c, St. John recording angel's message. 40c, Angel erecting column symbolizing faithful in heaven. 80c, St. John's trial in kettle of boiling oil.

1970, Oct. 24

199 A81 30c dp car, dk brn & brt pur .75 .75

200 A81 40c violet & slate grn .90 .90

201 A81 80c ol, dk bl & car rose 1.75 1.75

Nos. 199-201 (3) 3.40 3.40

Ice Skating A84

1971, Feb. 20 **Engr.** ***Perf. 13***

202 A84 80c dk red, red lil & pur 2.25 1.50

World Figure Skating Championships, Lyons, France, Feb. 23-28.

Capercaillie — A85

Nature protection: No. 204, Brown bear.

1971, Apr. 24 **Photo.** ***Perf. 13***

203 A85 80c multicolored 2.25 1.40

Engr.

204 A85 80c blue, grn & brn 2.25 1.40

Europa Issue, 1971

Common Design Type

1971, May 8 **Engr.** ***Perf. 13***

Size: 35½x22mm

205 CD14 50c rose red 3.00 2.25

206 CD14 80c lt blue green 4.25 3.00

Altar Type of 1969

The Revelation (from the Altar of St. John, Caselles): 30c, St. John preaching, Rev. 1:3. 50c, "The Sign of the Beast . . ." Rev. 16:1-2. 90c, The Woman, Rev. 17:1.

1971, Sept. 18

207 A81 30c dl grn, ol & brt grn	.75	.75
208 A81 50c rose car, org & ol brn	1.00	1.00
209 A81 90c blk, dk pur & bl	1.60	1.60
Nos. 207-209 (3)	3.35	3.35

Europa Issue 1972

Common Design Type

1972, Apr. 29 Photo. *Perf. 13*

Size: 21½x37mm

210 CD15 50c brt mag & multi	3.00	2.75
211 CD15 90c multicolored	4.00	3.25

Golden Eagle — A86

1972, May 27 Engr.

212 A86 60c dk grn, ol & plum	2.00	1.65

Nature protection.

Shooting A87

1972, July 8

213 A87 1fr dk purple	1.75	1.40

20th Olympic Games, Munich, Aug. 26-Sept. 11.

Altar Type of 1969

The Revelation (from the Altar of St. John, Caselles): 30c, St. John, bishop and servant. 50c, Resurrection of Lazarus. 90c, Angel with lance and nails.

1972, Sept. 16 Engr. *Perf. 13*

214 A81 30c dk ol, gray & red lil	.75	.75
215 A81 50c vio blue & slate	1.10	1.10
216 A81 90c dk Prus bl & sl grn	1.75	1.75
Nos. 214-216 (3)	3.60	3.60

De Gaulle as Coprince of Andorra — A88

Design: 90c, De Gaulle in front of Maison des Vallées.

1972, Oct. 23 Engr. *Perf. 13*

217 A88 50c violet blue	1.25	1.25
218 A88 90c dk carmine	1.75	1.75
a. Pair, #217-218 + label	3.00	3.00

Visit of Charles de Gaulle to Andorra, 5th anniv. See Nos. 399-400.

Europa Issue 1973

Common Design Type

1973, Apr. 28 Photo. *Perf. 13*

Size: 36x22mm

219 CD16 50c violet & multi	3.00	2.75
220 CD16 90c dk red & multi	4.00	3.00

Andorra, French Administration, stamps can be mounted in the Scott annual Monaco and French Andorra supplement.

Virgin of Canolich A89

1973, June 16 Engr. *Perf. 13*

221 A89 1fr ol, Prus bl & vio	1.65	1.65

Lily — A90

Blue Titmouse — A91

Designs: 45c, Iris. 50c, Columbine. 65c, Tobacco. No. 226, Pinks. No. 227, Narcissuses.

1973-74 Photo. *Perf. 13*

222 A90 30c car rose & multi	.35	.35
223 A90 45c yel grn & multi	.20	.20
224 A90 50c buff & multi	1.10	1.10
225 A90 65c gray & multi	.30	.30
226 A90 90c ultra & multi	.70	.70
227 A90 90c grnsh bl & multi	.60	.60
Nos. 222-227 (6)	3.25	3.25

See Nos. 238-240.

1973-74 Photo. *Perf. 13*

Nature protection: 60c, Citril finch and mistletoe. 80c, Eurasian bullfinch. 1fr, Lesser spotted woodpecker.

228 A91 60c buff & multi	1.40	1.10
229 A91 80c gray & multi	1.40	1.10
230 A91 90c gray & multi	1.10	.90
231 A91 1fr yel grn & multi	1.65	1.20
Nos. 228-231 (4)	5.55	4.30

Europa Issue 1974

Virgin of Pal — A92

Design: 90c, Virgin of Santa Coloma. Statues are polychrome 12th century carvings by rural artists.

1974, Apr. 27 Engr. *Perf. 13*

232 A92 50c multicolored	5.00	3.75
233 A92 90c multicolored	7.00	5.00

Arms of Andorra and Cahors Bridge — A93

Mail Box, Chutes and Globe — A94

1974, Aug. 24 Engr. *Perf. 13*

234 A93 1fr blue, vio & org	1.00	.60

First anniversary of meeting of the co-princes of Andorra: Pres. Georges Pompidou of France and Msgr. Juan Marti Alanis, Bishop of Urgel.

1974, Oct. 5 Engr. *Perf. 13*

235 A94 1.20fr multi	1.25	1.10

Centenary of Universal Postal Union.

Coronation of St. Marti, 16th Century — A95

Europa: 80c, Crucifixion, 16th cent., vert.

Perf. 11½x13, 13x11½

1975, Apr. 26 Photo.

236 A95 80c gold & multi	5.00	4.00
237 A95 1.20fr gold & multi	5.75	4.00

Flower Type of 1973

Designs: 60c, Gentian. 80c, Anemone. 1.20fr, Autumn crocus.

1975, May 10 Photo. *Perf. 13*

238 A90 60c olive & multi	.32	.32
239 A90 80c brt rose & multi	.75	.75
240 A90 1.20fr green & multi	.80	.80
Nos. 238-240 (3)	1.87	1.87

Abstract Design — A96

1975, June 7 Engr. *Perf. 13*

241 A96 2fr bl, magenta & emer	2.00	2.00

ARPHILA 75 International Philatelic Exhibition, Paris, June 6-16.

Pres. Georges Pompidou — A97

1975, Aug. 23 Engr. *Perf. 13*

242 A97 80c violet bl & blk	.80	.80

Georges Pompidou (1911-74), pres. of France and co-prince of Andorra (1969-74).

Costume and IWY Emblem — A98

1975, Nov. 8 Engr. *Perf. 13*

243 A98 1.20fr multicolored	1.20	1.00

International Women's Year.

Skier and Snowflake A99

1976, Jan. 31 Engr. *Perf. 13*

244 A99 1.20fr multicolored	1.20	1.00

12th Winter Olympic Games, Innsbruck, Austria, Feb. 4-15.

Telephone and Satellite — A100

1976, Mar. 20 Engr. *Perf. 13*

245 A100 1fr multicolored	.80	.80

Centenary of first telephone call by Alexander Graham Bell, Mar. 10, 1976.

Catalan Forge — A101

Europa: 1.20fr, Lacemaker.

1976, May 8 Engr. *Perf. 13*

246 A101 80c multi	1.25	1.10
247 A101 1.20fr multi	1.75	1.65

Thomas Jefferson A102

Trapshooting A103

1976, July 3 Engr. *Perf. 13*

248 A102 1.20fr multi	1.10	.90

American Bicentennial.

1976, July 17 Engr. *Perf. 13*

249 A103 2fr multi	1.40	1.00

21st Olympic Games, Montreal, Canada, July 17-Aug. 1.

Meritxell Sanctuary and Old Chapel — A104

1976, Sept. 4 **Engr.** ***Perf. 13***
250 A104 1fr multi 1.00 .80

Dedication of rebuilt Meritxell Church, Sept. 8, 1976.

Apollo — A105

Ermine — A106

Design: 1.40fr, Morio butterfly.

1976, Oct. 16 **Photo.** ***Perf. 13***
251 A105 80c black & multi 1.00 .90
252 A105 1.40fr salmon & multi 1.50 1.25

Nature protection.

1977, Apr. 2 **Photo.** ***Perf. 13***
253 A106 1fr vio bl, gray & blk 1.40 1.10

Nature protection.

St. Jean de Caselles A107

Manual Digest, 1748, Arms of Andorra A108

Europa: 1.40fr, Sant Vicens Castle.

1977, Apr. 30 **Engr.** ***Perf. 13***
254 A107 1fr multi 1.25 .90
255 A107 1.40fr multi 1.65 1.40

1977, June 11 **Engr.** ***Perf. 13***
256 A108 80c grn, bl & brn .80 .70

Establishment of Institute of Andorran Studies.

St. Romanus of Caesarea A109

1977, July 23 **Engr.** ***Perf. 12½x13***
257 A109 2fr multi 1.25 1.00

Design from altarpiece in Church of St. Roma de les Bons.

General Council Chamber A110

Guillem d'Arény Plandolit — A111

1977, Sept. 24 **Engr.** ***Perf. 13***
258 A110 1.10fr multi 1.10 .90
259 A111 2fr car & dk brn 1.25 .90

Andorran heritage. Guillem d'Arény Plandolit started Andorran reform movement in 1866.

Squirrel A112

Flag and Valira River Bridge A113

1978, Mar. 18 **Engr.** ***Perf. 13***
260 A112 1fr multi .75 .55

1978, Apr. 8
261 A113 80c multi .60 .55

Signing of the treaty establishing the Co-Principality of Andorra, 700th anniv.

Pal Church A114

Europa: 1.40fr, Charlemagne's Castle, Charlemagne on horseback, vert.

1978, Apr. 29 **Engr.** ***Perf. 13***
262 A114 1fr multi 1.25 1.00
263 A114 1.40fr multi 1.75 1.50

Virgin of Sispony A115

1978, May 20 **Engr.** ***Perf. 12x13***
264 A115 2fr multi 1.25 1.00

Visura Tribunal A116

1978, June 24 **Engr.** ***Perf. 13***
265 A116 1.20fr multi .75 .50

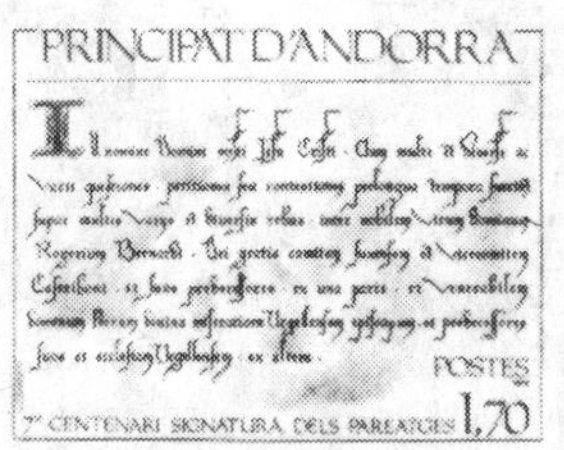

Preamble of 1278 Treaty — A117

1978, Sept. 2 **Engr.** ***Perf. 13x12½***
266 A117 1.70fr multi .75 .50

700th anniversary of the signing of treaty establishing Co-Principality of Andorra.

Pyrenean Chamois A118

White Partridges A119

1979, Mar. 26 **Engr.** ***Perf. 13***
267 A118 1fr multi .50 .35

1979, Apr. 9 **Photo.** ***Perf. 13***
268 A119 1.20fr multi .75 .60

Nature protection. See Nos. 288-289.

French Mailman, 1900 — A120

Europa: 1.70fr, 1st French p.o. in Andorra.

1979, Apr. 28 **Engr.** ***Perf. 13***
269 A120 1.20fr multi 1.10 .90
270 A120 1.70fr multi 1.50 1.10

Falcon, Pre-Roman Painting A121

1979, June 2 **Engr.** ***Perf. 12½x13***
271 A121 2fr multi 1.00 .75

A122 A123

Child with Lambs, Church, IYC emblem.

1979, July 7 **Photo.** ***Perf. 13***
272 A122 1.70fr multi .75 .50

International Year of the Child.

1979, Sept. 29 **Engr.** ***Perf. 13***

Bas-relief, Trobada monument.

273 A123 2fr multi 1.00 .75

700th anniversary of Co-Principality of Andorra

Judo Hold — A124

Farm House, Cortinada — A125

1979, Nov. 24 **Engr.** ***Perf. 13***
274 A124 1.30fr multi .65 .45

World Judo Championships, Paris, Dec. 1979.

1980, Jan. 26 **Engr.** ***Perf. 13***
275 A125 1.10fr multi .50 .45

Cross-Country Skiing — A126

1980, Feb. 9
276 A126 1.80fr ultra & lil rose 1.50 .90

13th Winter Olympic Games, Lake Placid, NY, Feb. 12-24.

A128

A129

1980, Aug. 30 **Engr.** ***Perf. 13***
278 A128 1.20fr multi .45 .38

World Bicycling championships.

1980, Apr. 26 **Engr.** ***Perf. 13***

Europa: 1.30fr, Charlemagne (742-814). 1.80fr, Napoleon I (1769-1821).

279 A129 1.30fr multi .45 .35
280 A129 1.80fr gray grn & brn .75 .55

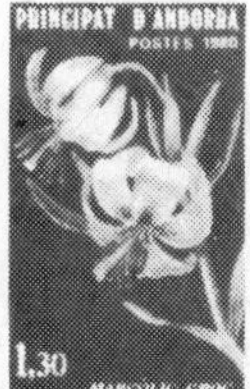

Pyrenees Lily — A130

1980 **Photo.**
281 A130 1.10fr Dog-toothed violet .45 .28
282 A130 1.30fr shown .50 .35

Nature protection. Issue dates: 1.10fr, June 21, 1.30fr, May 17.

De La Vall House, 400th Anniversary of Restoration
A131

1980, Sept. 6 **Engr.**
283 A131 1.40fr multi .50 .38

Angel, Church of St. Cerni de Nagol, Pre-Romanesque Fresco — A132

1980, Oct. 27 ***Perf. 13x12½***
284 A132 2fr multi 1.00 .70

Bordes de Mereig Mountain Village
A133

1981, Mar. 21 **Engr.** ***Perf. 13***
285 A133 1.40fr bl gray & dk brn .50 .40

Europa Issue 1981

Ball de l'Ossa, Winter Game
A134

1981, May 16 **Engr.**
286 A134 1.40fr shown .65 .45
287 A134 2fr El Contrapas dance .80 .60

Bird Type of 1979

1981, June 20 **Photo.**
288 A119 1.20fr Phylloscopus bonelli .45 .30
289 A119 1.40fr Tichodroma muraria .55 .38

World Fencing Championship, Clermont-Ferrand, July 2-13 — A135

1981, July 4 **Engr.**
290 A135 2fr bl & blk .60 .40

St. Martin, 12th Cent. Tapestry — A136

1981, Sept. 5 **Engr.** ***Perf. 12x13***
291 A136 3fr multi 1.10 .80

Intl. Drinking Water Decade
A137

Intl. Year of the Disabled
A138

1981, Oct. 17 ***Perf. 13***
292 A137 1.60fr multi .55 .40

1981, Nov. 7
293 A138 2.30fr multi .80 .70

Europa 1982 — A139

1982, May 8 **Engr.** ***Perf. 13***
294 A139 1.60fr Creation of Andorran govt., 1982 .55 .40
295 A139 2.30fr Land Council, 1419 .80 .55

1982 World Cup — A140

Designs: Various soccer players. Nos. 296-297 se-tenant with label showing natl. arms.

1982, June 12 **Engr.** ***Perf. 13***
296 A140 1.60fr red & dk brn .60 .45
297 A140 2.60fr red & dk brn .90 .65

Souvenir Sheet

No. 52 — A141

1982, Aug. 21 **Engr.**
298 A141 5fr blk & rose car 1.60 1.60

1st Andorran Stamp Exhib., Aug. 21-Sept. 19.

Horse, Roman Wall Painting — A142

1982, Sept. 4 **Photo.** ***Perf. 13x12½***
299 A142 3fr multi 1.10 .90

Wild Cat — A143

1982, Oct. 9 **Engr.** ***Perf. 13***
300 A143 1.80fr shown .75 .50
301 A143 2.60fr Pine trees 1.10 .65

TB Bacillus Centenary
A144

St. Thomas Aquinas (1225-74)
A145

1982, Nov. 13
302 A144 2.10fr Koch, lungs .75 .60

1982, Dec. 4
303 A145 2fr multi .75 .60

Manned Flight Bicentenary
A146

1983, Feb. 26 **Engr.**
304 A146 2fr multi .75 .60

Nature Protection
A147

1983, Apr. 16 **Engr.** ***Perf. 13***
305 A147 1fr Birch trees .40 .22
306 A147 1.50fr Trout .55 .38

See Nos. 325-326.

Europa 1983 — A148

Catalane Gold Works.

1983, May 7 **Engr.** ***Perf. 13***
307 A148 1.80fr Exterior .60 .45
308 A148 2.60fr Interior .80 .60

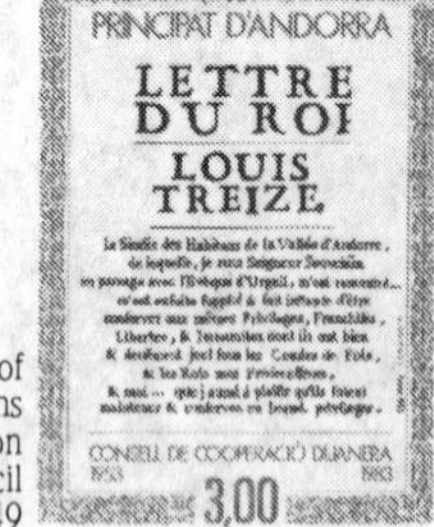

30th Anniv. of Customs Cooperation Council
A149

1983, May 14
309 A149 3fr Letter of King Louis XIII 1.10 .80

First Arms of Valleys of Andorra
A150

1983, Sept. 3 **Engr.** ***Perf. 13***
310 A150 5c olive grn & red .15 .15
311 A150 10c grn & olive grn .15 .15
312 A150 20c brt pur & red .15 .15
313 A150 30c brn vio & red .15 .15
314 A150 40c dk bl & ultra .15 .15
315 A150 50c gray & red .15 .15
316 A150 1fr deep magenta .30 .18
317 A150 2fr org red & red brn .55 .35
318 A150 5fr dk brn & red 1.40 .85
Set value 2.65 1.65

See Nos. 329-335, 380-383.

Painting, Cortinada Church
A151

1983, Sept. 24 ***Perf. 12x13***
319 A151 4fr multi 1.40 1.00

Plandolit House — A152

1983, Oct. 15 **Photo.** ***Perf. 13***
320 A152 1.60fr dp ultra & brn .50 .38

1984 Winter Olympics
A153

1984, Feb. 18 **Engr.**
321 A153 2.80fr multi .90 .70

Pyrenees Region Work Community (Labor Org.) — A154

1984, Apr. 28 **Engr.** ***Perf. 13***
322 A154 3fr brt bl & sepia .90 .65

Europa (1959-84)
A155

1984, May 5 **Engr.**
323 A155 2fr brt grn .70 .50
324 A155 2.80fr rose car 1.00 .75

Nature Protection Type of 1983

1984, July 7 **Engr.** ***Perf. 13***
325 A147 1.70fr Chestnut tree .65 .40
326 A147 2.10fr Walnut tree .80 .50

Pyrenees Art Center
A155a

1984, Sept. 7 **Engr.**
327 A155a 3fr multi 1.10 .80

Romanesque Fresco, Church of St. Cerni de Nagol
A156

1984, Nov. 17 *Perf. 12x13*
328 A156 5fr multi 1.75 1.25

First Arms Type of 1983

1984-87 Engr. *Perf. 13*
329 A150 1.90fr emerald .65 .15
330 A150 2.20fr red orange .75 .15
a. Bklt. pane, 2 #329, 6 #330 6.25
331 A150 3fr bl grn & red brn .75 .45
332 A150 4fr brt org & brn 1.15 .85
333 A150 10fr brn org & blk 2.50 1.50
334 A150 15fr grn & dk grn 4.25 3.25
335 A150 20fr brt bl & red brn 5.25 3.00
Nos. 329-335 (7) 15.30 9.35

Nos. 329-330 issued in booklets only.
Issued: 3fr, 20fr, 12/1/84; 10fr, 2/9/85; 4fr, 15fr, 4/19/86; 1.90fr, 2.20fr, 3/28/87.

Saint Julia Valley
A157

1985, Apr. 13 **Engr.**
336 A157 2fr multi .55 .45

Europa 1985 — A158

Intl. Youth Year — A159

1985, May 4 **Engr.**
337 A158 2.10fr Le Val D'Andorre .70 .52
338 A158 3fr Instruments .90 .75

1985, June 8 **Engr.**
339 A159 3fr multi .80 .60

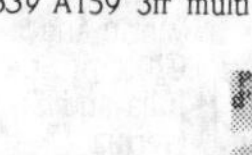

Wildlife Conservation
A160

1985, Aug. 3 **Photo.**
340 A160 1.80fr Anas platyrhynchos .50 .38
341 A160 2.20fr Carduelis carduelis .60 .45

Two Saints, Medieval Fresco in St. Cerni de Nagol Church
A161

1985, Sept. 14 **Engr.** *Perf. 12½x13*
342 A161 5fr multi 1.40 1.10

Postal Museum Inauguration — A162

1986, Mar. 22 **Engr.** *Perf. 13*
343 A162 2.20fr like No. 269 .62 .15

Europa 1986
A163

1986, May 3 **Engr.** *Perf. 13*
344 A163 2.20fr Ansalonga .62 .15
345 A163 3.20fr Isard .80 .16

1986 World Cup Soccer Championships, Mexico — A164

1986, June 14
346 A164 3fr multi .75 .15

Angonella Lake — A165

1986, June 28
347 A165 2.20fr multi .62 .15

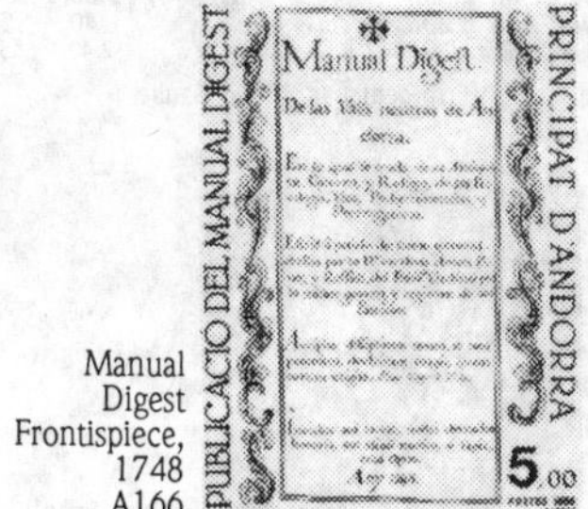
Manual Digest Frontispiece, 1748
A166

1986, Sept. 6 **Engr.**
348 A166 5fr chnt brn, gray ol & blk 1.55 .30

Intl. Peace Year — A167

1986, Sept. 29
349 A167 1.90fr bl gray & grnsh bl .58 .15

A168

A169

1986, Oct. 18 **Engr.** *Perf. 13½x13*
350 A168 1.90fr St. Vicenc D'Enclar .60 .15

1987, Mar. 27 **Litho.** *Perf. 12½x13*
351 A169 2.20fr Contemporary natl. coat of arms .75 .15

Visit of the French co-prince.

Europa 1987 — A170

1987, May 2 **Engr.** *Perf. 13*
352 A170 2.20fr Meritxell Sanctuary .75 .15
353 A170 3.40fr Pleta D'Ordino 1.15 .24

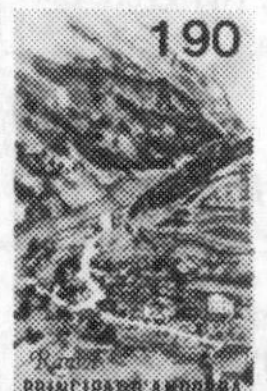
Ransol Village — A171

1987, June 13 **Photo.**
354 A171 1.90fr multi .62 .15

Nature
A172

1987, July 4
355 A172 1.90fr Cavall rogenc .62 .15
356 A172 2.20fr Graellsia isabellae .72 .15

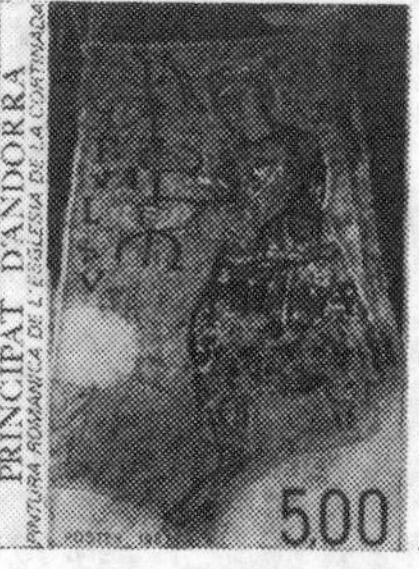
Aryalsu, Romanesque Painting, La Cortinada Church
A173

Perf. 12½x13

1987, Sept. 5 **Litho. & Engr.**
357 A173 5fr multi 1.70 .35

Hiker Looking at Map — A174

1987, Sept. 19 **Engr.** *Perf. 13*
358 A174 2fr olive, grn & dark brn vio .68 .15

Medieval Iron Key, La Cortinada
A175

1987, Oct. 17 **Litho.**
359 A175 3fr multi 1.00 .20

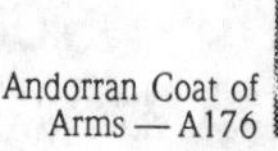
Andorran Coat of Arms — A176

Booklet Stamp

1988, Feb. 6 **Engr.** *Perf. 13*
360 A176 2.20fr red .80 .16
a. Bklt. pane of 10 8.00

See Nos. 388-389B.

Shoemaker's Last from Roc de l'Oral — A177

1988, Feb. 13 **Photo.**
361 A177 3fr multi 1.10 .22

Rugby — A178

1988, Mar. 19 **Engr.** *Perf. 13½x13*
362 A178 2.20fr emer grn, Prus grn & brn .80 .16

Europa 1988 — A179

Hot Springs, Escaldes — A180

Transport and communication: 2.20fr, Broadcast tower. 3.60fr, Computer graphics.

1988, May 2 **Engr.** *Perf. 13*
363 A179 2.20fr multicolored .78 .16
364 A179 3.60fr multicolored 1.30 .25

1988, May 14 **Engr.**
365 A180 2.20fr Prus bl, org brn & emer .80 .16

Tor D'Ansalonga Farmhouse, Ansalonga Pass — A181

1988, June 13 **Engr.**
366 A181 2fr multi .70 .15

Sheepdog — A182

1988, July 2 **Photo.**
367 A182 2fr shown .70 .15
368 A182 2.20fr Hare .78 .16

Roman Fresco, 8th Cent., St. Steven's Church, Andorre-La-Vieille — A183

1988, Sept. 3 **Engr.** ***Perf. 13x12½***
369 A183 5fr multicolored 1.60 .32

French Revolution, Bicent. — A184

1989, Jan. 1 **Litho.** ***Perf. 13***
370 A184 2.20fr red & vio bl .75 .15

Poble de Pal Village A185

1989, Mar. 4 **Engr.** ***Perf. 13***
371 A185 2.20fr .70 .15

Europa 1989 — A186

Children's games.

1989, June 9 **Engr.** ***Perf. 13***
372 A186 2.20fr Human tower .72 .15
373 A186 3.60fr The handkerchief 1.20 .24

Red Cross — A187

1989, May 6
374 A187 3.60fr multi 1.20 .24

Visigothic- Merovingian Age Cincture from a Column, St. Vicenc D'Anclar — A188

1989, June 3 **Photo.**
375 A188 3fr multi 1.00 .20

Wildlife A189

1989, Sept. 18 **Engr.** ***Perf. 13***
376 A189 2.20fr Wild boar .68 .15
377 A189 3.60fr Newt 1.10 .22

Scene of Salome from the Retable of St. Michael of Mosquera, Encamp — A190

1989, Oct. 16 ***Perf. 13x13½***
378 A190 5fr multi 1.50 .30

La Margineda Bridge A191

1990, Feb. 26 **Engr.** ***Perf. 13***
379 A191 2.30fr multi .82 .16

Tourism.

Arms Types of 1983 and 1988

1990-93 **Engr.** ***Perf. 13***
380 A150 2.10fr green .78 .16
381 A150 2.20fr green 1.50 .50
382 A150 2.30fr vermilion .85 .18
383 A150 2.40fr green .90 .30
384 A150 2.50fr vermilion 1.70 .55
385 A150 2.80fr vermilion 1.00 .32
Nos. 380-385 (6) 6.73 2.01

Booklet Stamps

Perf. 13
386 A176 2.30fr red .85 .18
a. Booklet pane of 5 4.25
387 A176 2.50fr vermilion 1.70 .55
a. Booklet pane of 5 8.50
388 A176 2.80fr red 1.00 .32
c. Booklet pane of 5 5.00
Nos. 386-388 (3) 3.55 1.05

Issued: 2.20fr, #384, 10/28/91; #387, 10/21/91; 2.40fr, 2.80fr, 8/9/93; 2.10fr, 2.30fr, 1990.

Llorts Mines A193

1990, Apr. 21 **Engr.** ***Perf. 12½x13***
390 A193 3.20fr multicolored 1.20 .25

Europa A194

Designs: 2.30fr, Early post office. 3.20fr, Modern post office.

1990, May 5 ***Perf. 13***
391 A194 2.30fr blk & scar .85 .18
392 A194 3.20fr scar & vio 1.20 .25

Otter A195

1990, May 25 ***Perf. 12x13***
393 A195 2.30fr Roses, vert. .85 .18
394 A195 3.20fr shown 1.20 .25

Censer of St. Roma of Les Bons A196

1990, June 25 ***Perf. 12½x13***
395 A196 3fr multicolored 1.15 .30

Tobacco Drying Sheds, Les Bons A197

1990, Sept. 15 **Engr.** ***Perf. 12½x13***
396 A197 2.30fr multi .85 .18

St. Coloma (Detail) A198

1990, Oct. 8 ***Perf. 12½x13***
397 A198 5fr multi 2.00 .72

Coin from Church of St. Eulalia d'Encamp A199

1990, Oct. 27 **Litho.** ***Perf. 13***
398 A199 3.20fr multi 1.15 .38

De Gaulle Type of 1972 Dated 1990

1990, Oct. 23 **Engr.** ***Perf. 13***
399 A88 2.30fr vio bl 1.00 .35
400 A88 3.20fr dk car 1.40 .55
a. Pair, #399-400 + label 2.40 .85

Birth centenary of De Gaulle.

4th Games of the Small European States — A200

1991, Apr. 8 **Photo.** ***Perf. 13***
401 A200 2.50fr multicolored .90 .30

Chapel of St. Roma Dels Vilars — A201

1991, Mar. 9 **Engr.** ***Perf. 13***
402 A201 2.50fr multicolored .90 .30

Europa — A202

Perf. 13x12½, 12½x13

1991, Apr. 27
403 A202 2.50fr TV satellite .90 .30
404 A202 3.50fr Telescope, horiz. 1.30 .45

Bottles from Tombs of St. Vincenc d'Enclar A203

1991, May 11 **Photo.** ***Perf. 13***
405 A203 3.20fr multicolored 1.20 .40

Farm Animals A204

1991, June 22 **Engr.** ***Perf. 13***
406 A204 2.50fr Sheep .90 .30
407 A204 3.50fr Cow 1.25 .42

Petanque World Championships — A205

1991, Sept. 14 **Engr.** ***Perf. 13***
408 A205 2.50fr multicolored .90 .30

Wolfgang Amadeus Mozart, Death Bicent. A206

1991, Oct. 5
409 A206 3.40fr multicolored 1.35 .45

Virgin and Child of St. Julia and St. Germa A207

1991, Nov. 16 **Engr.** ***Perf. 12½x13***
410 A207 5fr multicolored 2.00 .65

1992 Winter Olympics, Albertville — A208

1992, Feb. 10 **Litho.** ***Perf. 13***
411 A208 2.50fr Slalom skiing .90 .30
412 A208 3.40fr Figure skating 1.20 .40
a. Pair, #411-412 + label 2.10 .70

Church of St. Andrew of Arinsal A209

1992, Mar. 21 **Engr.** ***Perf. 12x13***
413 A209 2.50fr black & tan .90 .30

Discovery of America, 500th Anniv. A210

1992, Apr. 25 *Perf. 13*

414 A210 2.50fr	Columbus' fleet	.90	.30
415 A210 3.40fr	Landing in New World	1.25	.40

Europa.

1992 Summer Olympics, Barcelona A211

European Globeflower A212

1992, June 8 **Litho.** *Perf. 13*

416 A211 2.50fr	Kayaking	1.00	.35
417 A211 3.40fr	Shooting	1.40	.45
a.	Pair, #416-417 + label	2.40	.80

1992, July 6

Design: 3.40fr, Vulture, horiz.

418 A212 2.50fr	multicolored	1.00	.35
419 A212 3.40fr	multicolored	1.40	.45

Martyrdom of St. Eulalia A213

1992, Sept. 14 **Photo.** *Perf. 13*

420 A213 4fr	multicolored	1.65	.55

Sculpture by Mauro Staccioli A214

1992, Oct. 5 **Engr.** *Perf. 12½x13*

421 A214 5fr	multicolored	2.05	.68

Ordino Arcalis '91.

Tempest in a Tea Cup, by Dennis Oppenheim — A215

1992, Nov. 14 **Engr.** *Perf. 13x12½*

422 A215 5fr	multicolored	2.00	.68

Skiing in Andorra — A216

Ski resorts: No. 423a, 2.50fr, Soldeu El Tarter. b, 3.40fr, Arinsal.

No. 424a, 2.50fr, Pas de la Casa-Grau Roig. b, 2.50fr, Ordino Arcalis. c, 3.40fr, Pal.

1993, Mar. 13 **Litho.** *Perf. 13*

423 A216	Pair, #a.-b. + label	2.20	.75
424 A216	Strip of 3, #a.-c.	3.25	1.05

Sculptures — A217

Europa: 2.50fr, "Estructures Autogeneradores," by Jorge du Bon, vert. 3.40fr, Sculpture, "Fisicromia per Andorra," by Carlos Cruz-Diez.

1993, May 15 **Engr.** *Perf. 12½x13*

425 A217 2.50fr	multicolored	1.00	.35

Litho.

Perf. 14x13½

426 A217 3.40fr	multicolored	1.35	.45

Butterflies A218

1993, June 28 **Litho.** *Perf. 13*

427 A218 2.50fr	Polymmatus icarus	.95	.32
428 A218 4.20fr	Nymphalidae	1.55	.52

Tour de France Bicycle Race — A219

1993, July 20 **Litho.** *Perf. 13*

429 A219 2.50fr	multicolored	.90	.30

Andorra School, 10th Anniv. A220

1993, Sept. 20 **Litho.** *Perf. 13*

430 A220 2.80fr	multicolored	1.00	.35

Un Lloc Paga, by Michael Warren A221

1993, Oct. 18 **Engr.** *Perf. 12½x13*

431 A221 5fr	blue & black	1.75	.60

Sculpture, by Erik Dietman A222

1993, Nov. 8 **Engr.** *Perf. 12½x13*

432 A222 5fr	multicolored	1.75	.60

1994 Winter Olympics, Lillehammer A223

1994, Feb. 21 **Litho.** *Perf. 13*

433 A223 3.70fr	multicolored	1.25	.45

1st Anniversary of the Constitution — A224

Designs: 2.80fr, Monument, by Emili Armengol. 3.70fr, Stone tablet with inscription.

1994, Mar. 15 **Litho.** *Perf. 13*

434 A224 2.80fr	multicolored	1.00	.35
435 A224 3.70fr	multicolored	1.40	.48
a.	Pair, #434-435 + label	2.40	.85

European Discoveries A225

Europa: 2.80fr, Discovery of AIDS virus. 3.70fr, Radio diffusion.

1994, May 9 **Litho.** *Perf. 13*

436 A225 2.80fr	multicolored	1.10	.35
437 A225 3.70fr	multicolored	1.50	.50

1994 World Cup Soccer Championships, US — A226

1994, June 20

438 A226 3.70fr	multicolored	1.50	.50

Tourist Sports — A227

Designs: No. 439, Mountain climbing. No. 440, Fishing. No. 441, Horseback riding. No. 442, Mountain biking.

1994, July 11

439 A227 2.80fr	multicolored	1.10	.35
440 A227 2.80fr	multicolored	1.10	.35
a.	Pair, #439-440 + label	2.20	.70
441 A227 2.80fr	multicolored	1.10	.35
442 A227 2.80fr	multicolored	1.10	.35
a.	Pair, #441-442 + label	2.20	.70
	Nos. 439-442 (4)	4.40	1.40

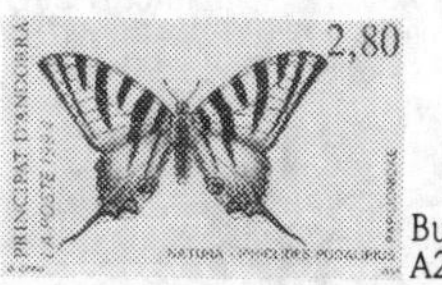

Butterflies A228

1994, Sept. 5 **Litho.** *Perf. 13*

443 A228 2.80fr	Iphiclides podalirus	1.10	.35
444 A228 4.40fr	Aglais urticae	1.75	.60

A229

A230

1994, Oct. 22 **Litho.** *Perf. 13*

445 A229 2.80fr	multicolored	1.25	.42

Meeting of the Co-Princes, 1st anniv.

1995, Feb. 27 **Litho.** *Perf. 13*

446 A230 2.80fr	multicolored	1.25	.40

European Nature Conservation Year

1995 World Cup Rugby Championships — A231

1995, Apr. 24 **Litho.** *Perf. 13*

447 A231 2.80fr	multicolored	1.25	.40

Peace & Freedom A232

Europa: 2.80fr, Dove with olive branch. 3.70fr, Flock of doves.

1995, May 2

448 A232 2.80fr	multicolored	1.25	.40
449 A232 3.70fr	multicolored	1.65	.50

Caritas in Andorra, 15th Anniv. A233

1995, May 15 **Litho.** *Perf. 13*

450 A233 2.80fr	multicolored	1.25	1.25

Caldea Health Spa — A234

1995, June 26 Litho. *Perf. 13*

451 A234 2.80fr multicolored 1.25 1.25

Ordino Natl. Auditorium A235

1995, July 10 Litho. & Engr.

452 A235 3.70fr black & buff 1.65 1.65

Virgin of Meritxell — A236

1995, Sept. 11 Litho. *Perf. 14*

453 A236 4.40fr multicolored 1.90 1.90

Protection of Nature A237

Butterflies: 2.80fr, Papallona llimonera, vert. 3.70fr, Papallona melanargia galathea.

1995, Sept. 25 *Perf. 13*

454 A237 2.80fr multicolored 1.25 1.25
455 A237 3.70fr multicolored 1.65 1.65

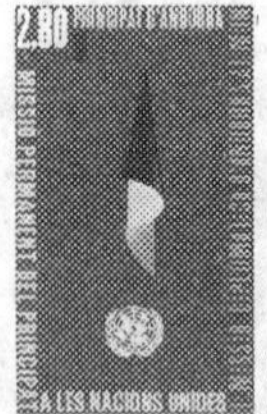

UN, 50th Anniv. — A238

1995, Oct. 21 Litho. *Perf. 13*

456 A238 2.80fr Flag, emblem 1.25 1.25
457 A238 3.70fr Emblem, "50," flag 1.65 1.65
a. Pair, #456-457 + label 3.00 3.00

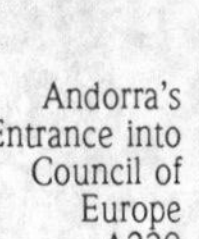

Andorra's Entrance into Council of Europe A239

1995, Nov. 4

458 A239 2.80fr multicolored 1.25 1.25

SEMI-POSTAL STAMP

Catalogue values for unused stamps in this section are for Never Hinged items.

Virgin of St. Coloma — SP1

Unwmk.

1964, July 25 Engr. *Perf. 13*

B1 SP1 25c + 10c multi 22.00 22.00

The surtax was for the Red Cross.

AIR POST STAMPS

Catalogue values for unused stamps in this section are for Never Hinged items.

Chamois AP1

Unwmk.

1950, Feb. 20 Engr. *Perf. 13*

C1 AP1 100fr indigo 60.00 45.00

East Branch of Valira River — AP2

1955-57

C2 AP2 100fr dark green 8.50 6.50
C3 AP2 200fr cerise 17.50 14.00
C4 AP2 500fr deep blue ('57) 90.00 65.00
Nos. C2-C4 (3) 116.00 85.50

D'Inclès Valley — AP3

1961-64 Unwmk. *Perf. 13*

C5 AP3 2fr red, ol gray & claret 1.00 .65
C6 AP3 3fr bl, mar & slate grn 1.25 1.25
C7 AP3 5fr rose lil & red org 2.00 1.75
C8 AP3 10fr bl grn & slate grn 3.75 3.50
Nos. C5-C8 (4) 8.00 7.15

Issued: 10fr, 4/25/64; others, 6/19/61.

POSTAGE DUE STAMPS

Postage Due Stamps of France, 1893-1931, Overprinted

ANDORRE

On Stamps of 1893-1926

1931-33 Unwmk. *Perf. 14x13½*

J1 D2 5c blue 1.00 1.00
J2 D2 10c brown 1.00 1.00
J3 D2 30c rose red .40 .40
J4 D2 50c violet brn 1.00 1.00
J5 D2 60c green 10.00 10.00
J6 D2 1fr red brn, *straw* .50 .50
J7 D2 2fr brt violet 6.00 6.00
J8 D2 3fr magenta 1.10 1.10
Nos. J1-J8 (8) 21.00 21.00

On Stamps of 1927-31

J9 D4 1c olive grn 1.25 1.25
J10 D4 10c rose 2.25 2.25
J11 D4 60c red 14.00 14.00
J12 D4 1fr Prus grn ('32) 65.00 65.00
J13 D4 1.20fr on 2fr bl 47.50 47.50
J14 D4 2fr ol brn ('33) 110.00 110.00
J15 D4 5fr on 1fr vio 60.00 60.00
Nos. J9-J15 (7) 300.00 300.00

D5

D6

1935-41 Typo.

J16 D5 1c gray grn 1.65 1.25
J17 D6 5c lt bl ('37) 4.75 4.50
J18 D6 10c brn ('41) 3.75 4.50
J19 D6 2fr vio ('41) 5.50 3.25
J20 D6 5fr red org ('41) 7.00 3.25
Nos. J16-J20 (5) 22.65 16.75

Catalogue values for unused stamps in this section, from this point to the end of the section, are for Never Hinged items.

Wheat Sheaves — D7

1943-46 *Perf. 14x13½*

J21 D7 10c sepia 1.00 1.00
J22 D7 30c brt red vio 1.50 1.50
J23 D7 50c blue grn 1.75 1.75
J24 D7 1fr brt ultra .80 .80
J25 D7 1.50fr rose red 5.75 5.75
J26 D7 2fr turq blue 1.50 1.50
J27 D7 3fr brown org 2.75 2.75
J28 D7 4fr dp vio ('45) 4.50 4.50
J29 D7 5fr brt pink 4.50 4.50
J30 D7 10fr red org ('45) 5.75 5.75
J31 D7 20fr olive brn ('46) 6.00 6.00
Nos. J21-J31 (11) 35.80 35.80

Inscribed: "Timbre Taxe"

1946-53

J32 D7 10c sepia ('46) 1.10 1.10
J33 D7 1fr ultra .75 .75
J34 D7 2fr turq blue 1.00 1.00
J35 D7 3fr orange brn 2.00 2.00
J36 D7 4fr violet 2.75 2.75
J37 D7 5fr brt pink 1.75 1.75
J38 D7 10fr red orange 2.75 2.75
J39 D7 20fr olive brn 6.25 6.25
J40 D7 50fr dk green ('50) 16.50 16.50
J41 D7 100fr dp green ('53) 87.50 87.50
Nos. J32-J41 (10) 122.35 122.35

Inscribed: "Timbre Taxe"

1961, June 19 *Perf. 14x13½*

J42 D7 5c rose pink 2.75 2.75
J43 D7 10c red orange 5.50 5.50
J44 D7 20c olive 8.25 8.25
J45 D7 50c dark slate green 13.00 13.00
Nos. J42-J45 (4) 29.50 29.50

D8 D9

1964-71 Typo. *Perf. 14x13½*

J46 D8 5c Centaury ('65) .15 .15
J47 D8 10c Gentian ('65) .15 .15
J48 D8 15c Corn poppy .15 .15
J49 D8 20c Violets ('71) .15 .15
J50 D8 30c Forget-me-not .15 .15
J51 D8 40c Columbine ('71) .15 .15
J52 D8 50c Clover ('65) .22 .22
Set value .75 .75

1985, Oct. 21 Engr. *Perf. 13*

J53 D9 10c Holly .15 .15
J54 D9 20c Blueberries .15 .15
J55 D9 30c Raspberries .15 .15
J56 D9 40c Bilberries .15 .15
J57 D9 50c Blackberries .15 .15
J58 D9 1fr Broom .30 .30
J59 D9 2fr Rosehips .60 .35
J60 D9 3fr Nightshade .90 .60
J61 D9 4fr Nabiu 1.25 .75
J62 D9 5fr Strawberries 1.50 .95
Nos. J53-J62 (10) 5.30 3.70

NEWSPAPER STAMP

France No. P7 Overprinted **ANDORRE**

1931 Unwmk. *Perf. 14x13½*

P1 A16 ½c on 1c gray .75 .75

ANGOLA

aŋ-'gō-lə

LOCATION — Southwestern Africa between Zaire and Namibia.
GOVT. — Republic
AREA — 481,351 sq. mi.
POP. — 7,108,000 (1983 est.)
CAPITAL — Luanda

Angola was a Portuguese overseas territory until it became independent November 11, 1975, as the People's Republic of Angola.

1000 Reis = 1 Milreis
100 Centavos = 1 Escudo (1913, 1954)
100 Centavos = 1 Angolar (1932)
10 Lweys = 1 Kwanza (1977)

Catalogue values for unused stamps in this country are for Never Hinged items, beginning with Scott 328 in the regular postage section, Scott C26 in the airpost section, Scott J31 in the postage due section, Scott RA7 in the postal tax section, and Scott RAJ4 in the postal tax postage due section.

Watermark

Wmk. 232- Maltese Cross

Portuguese Crown — A1

Perf. 12½, 13½

1870-77 Typo. Unwmk.

1 A1 5r black 3.00 1.10
a. Perf. 13½ 9.00 3.25
2 A1 10r yellow 22.50 10.00
3 A1 20r bister 3.50 2.00
a. Perf. 13½ 65.00 50.00
4 A1 25r red 10.00 3.00
a. 25r rose 10.00 2.00
c. 25r rose, perf. 14 225.00 75.00
d. Perf. 13½ 20.00 8.00
5 A1 40r blue ('77) 150.00 75.00
6 A1 50r green 50.00 15.00
a. Perf. 13½ 225.00 65.00
7 A1 100r lilac 3.00 2.00
a. Perf. 12½ 8.00 4.00
8 A1 200r orange ('77) 3.00 2.00
a. Perf. 12½ 4.00 1.65
9 A1 300r choc ('77) 3.00 3.00
a. Perf. 12½ 10.00 4.75

1881-85

10 A1 10r green ('83) 4.00 1.50
a. Perf. 12½ 20.00 2.25
11 A1 20r carmine rose ('85) 9.00 5.00
12 A1 25r violet ('85) 4.00 2.00
a. Perf. 13½ 6.00 2.75
13 A1 40r buff ('82) 5.00 2.00
a. Perf. 12½ 6.00 2.00

15 A1 50r blue 14.00 1.65
a. Perf. 13½ 20.00 1.65
Nos. 10-15 (5) 36.00 12.15

Two types of numerals are found on #2, 11, 13, 15.

The cliche of 40r in plate of 20r error, was discovered before the stamps were issued. All copies were defaced by a blue pencil mark.

In perf. 12½, Nos. 1-4, 4a and 6, as well as 7a, were printed in 1870 on thicker paper and 1875 on normal paper. Stamps of the earlier printing sell for 2 to 5 times more than those of the 1875 printing.

Some reprints of the 1870-85 issues are on a smooth white chalky paper, ungummed and perf. 13½.

Other reprints of these issues are on thin ivory paper with shiny white gum and clear-cut perf. 13½.

King Luiz — A2

King Carlos — A3

1886 Embossed *Perf. 12½*

16 A2 5r black 3.50 3.25
a. Perf. 13½ 11.50 8.50
17 A2 10r green 3.50 3.00
a. Perf. 13½ 13.00 7.25
18 A2 20r rose 10.00 6.25
a. Perf. 13½ 12.50 6.50
19 A2 25r red violet 7.50 1.50
20 A2 40r chocolate 8.00 5.00
21 A2 50r blue 10.50 2.00
22 A2 100r yellow brn 14.00 6.00
23 A2 200r gray violet 18.00 9.00
24 A2 300r orange 20.00 11.00
Nos. 16-24 (9) 95.00 47.00

For surcharges see #61-69, 172-174, 208-210.

Reprints of 5r, 20r & 100r have cleancut perf. 13½.

Perf. 11½, 12½, 13½

1893-94 Typo.

25 A3 5r yellow 1.00 .85
26 A3 10r redsh violet 2.00 .90
27 A3 15r chocolate 2.75 1.25
28 A3 20r lavender 2.75 1.25
29 A3 25r green 1.25 1.00
a. Perf. 12½ 4.00 2.00
30 A3 50r light blue 3.25 1.25
a. Perf. 13½ 5.00 2.75
31 A3 75r carmine 6.00 3.50
a. Perf. 11½ 8.00 6.25
32 A3 80r lt green 6.75 3.50
33 A3 100r brown, *buff* 6.75 3.50
a. Perf. 11½ 50.00 32.50
34 A3 150r car, *rose* 12.00 9.00
35 A3 200r dk blue, *lt bl* 14.00 11.00
36 A3 300r dk blue, *sal* 14.00 11.00
Nos. 25-36 (12) 72.50 48.00

For surcharges see Nos. 70-81, 175-179, 213-216, 234.

No. P1 Surcharged in Blue

CORREIOS DE ANGOLA 25 REIS

1894, Aug.

37 N1 25r on 2½r brown 80.00 22.50

King Carlos — A5

1898-1903 *Perf. 11½*

Name and Value in Black except 500r

38 A5 2½r gray .15 .15
39 A5 5r orange .15 .15
40 A5 10r yellow grn .15 .15
41 A5 15r violet brn 1.50 .70
42 A5 15r gray green ('03) .65 .50
43 A5 20r gray violet .25 .20
44 A5 25r sea green 1.00 .40
45 A5 25r car ('03) .50 .15
46 A5 50r blue 1.65 .35
47 A5 50r brown ('03) 3.00 2.00
48 A5 65r dull blue ('03) 9.00 7.00
49 A5 75r rose 4.50 1.65
50 A5 75r red violet ('03) 1.25 .90
51 A5 80r violet 5.25 1.75
52 A5 100r dk blue, *blue* .90 .65
53 A5 115r org brn, *pink* ('03) 8.00 6.00
54 A5 130r brn, *straw* ('03) 8.00 6.00
55 A5 150r brn, *straw* 8.00 5.00
56 A5 200r red vio, *pink* 2.25 1.00
57 A5 300r dk blue, *rose* 3.25 3.25
58 A5 400r dull bl, *straw* ('03) 2.50 2.25
59 A5 500r blk & red, *bl* ('01) 2.75 2.75
60 A5 700r vio, *yelsh* ('01) 14.00 10.00
Nos. 38-60 (23) 78.65 52.95

For surcharges and overprints see Nos. 83-102, 113-117, 159-171, 181-183, 217-218, 221-225.

Stamps of 1886-94 Surcharged in Black or Red

65 RÉIS

Two types of surcharge:
I - 3mm between numeral and REIS.
II - 4½mm spacing.

1902 *Perf. 12½*

61 A2 65r on 40r choc 4.50 3.50
62 A2 65r on 300r org, I 4.50 3.50
a. Type II 32.50 25.00
63 A2 115r on 10r green 3.75 3.25
a. Inverted surcharge
b. Perf. 13½ 18.00 17.00
64 A2 115r on 200r gray vio 3.50 2.75
65 A2 130r on 50r blue 5.75 4.75
66 A2 130r on 100r brown 4.00 3.00
67 A2 400r on 20r rose 60.00 30.00
a. Perf. 13½ 60.00 45.00
68 A2 400r on 25r violet 8.50 6.00
69 A2 400r on 5r black (R) 6.75 6.25
a. Double surcharge
Nos. 61-69 (9) 101.25 63.00

For surcharges see Nos. 172-174, 208-210.

Perf. 11½, 12½, 13½

70 A3 65r on 5r yel, I 4.00 2.75
a. Type II 10.00 10.00
71 A3 65r on 10r red vio, I 3.25 2.25
a. Type II 13.00 5.25
b. Perf. 11½, type I 8.75 5.25
c. Perf. 11½, type II 3.50 2.50
72 A3 65r on 20r lav 4.00 2.75
a. Type II 6.50 6.00
73 65r on 25r green 3.00 2.25
a. Perf. 11½ 9.25 7.25
74 A3 115r on 80r lt grn 5.25 4.00
75 A3 115r on 100r brn, *buff* 5.25 3.25
a. Perf. 13½ 9.25 6.50
76 A3 115r on 150r car, *rose* 8.00 5.25
a. Perf. 13½ 10.00 6.00
77 A3 130r on 15r choc 2.75 2.00
78 A3 130r on 75r carmine 3.00 2.25
a. Perf. 13½ 14.00 11.50
79 A3 130r on 300r dk bl, *sal* 8.25 6.00
80 A3 400r on 50r lt bl 3.25 2.75
81 A3 400r on 200r bl, *bl* 3.25 3.25
a. Perf. 13½ 21.00 8.75
82 N1 400r on 2½r brn 1.10 1.10
a. Type II 2.50 2.25
Nos. 70-82 (13) 54.35 39.85

For surcharges see #175-180, 211-216, 234-235.

Reprints of Nos. 65, 67, 68 and 69 have clean-cut perforation 13½.

Stamps of 1898 Overprinted — a

PROVISORIO

1902 *Perf. 11½*

83 A5 15r brown 1.00 .60
84 A5 25r sea green .85 .35
85 A5 50r blue 1.50 .85
86 A5 75r rose 2.75 2.00
Nos. 83-86 (4) 6.10 3.80

For surcharge see No. 116.

No. 48 Surcharged in Black

50 RÉIS

1905

87 A5 50r on 65r dull blue 2.75 1.25

For surcharge see No. 183.

Stamps of 1898-1903 Overprinted in Carmine or Green — b

REPUBLICA

1911

88 A5 2½r gray .15 .15
89 A5 5r orange yel .15 .15
90 A5 10r light green .22 .20
91 A5 15r gray green .25 .20
92 A5 20r gray violet .25 .20
93 A5 25r car (G) .25 .15
94 A5 50r brown 1.50 .90
95 A5 75r lilac 2.50 2.50
96 A5 100r dk blue, *bl* 2.50 2.50
97 A5 115r org brn, *pink* .90 .60
98 A5 130r brn, *straw* .90 .60
99 A5 200r red lil, *pnksh* .90 .60
100 A5 400r dull bl, *straw* 1.25 .65
101 A5 500r blk & red, *bl* 1.10 .65
102 A5 700r violet, *yelsh* 1.25 .70
Nos. 88-102 (15) 14.07 10.75

Inverted and double overprints of Nos. 88-102 were made intentionally.

For surcharges see Nos. 217-218, 221-222, 224.

King Manuel II — A6

Ceres — A7

Overprinted in Carmine or Green

1912 *Perf. 11½x12*

103 A6 2½r violet .22 .32
104 A6 5r black .25 .40
105 A6 10r gray green .35 .30
106 A6 20r carmine (G) .35 .30
107 A6 25r violet brown .35 .30
108 A6 50r dk blue .60 .50
109 A6 75r bister brown .65 .65
110 A6 100r brown, *lt green* 1.65 .70
111 A6 200r dk green, *salmon* 1.10 .70
112 A6 300r black, *azure* 1.10 .70
Nos. 103-112 (10) 6.62 4.87

For surcharges see Nos. 219-220, 226-227.

No. 91 Surcharged with New Values as 5

1912, June *Perf. 11½*

113 A5 2½r on 15r gray green 2.25 2.25
114 A5 5r on 15r gray green 1.75 1.50
115 A5 10r on 15r gray green 1.75 1.50
Nos. 113-115 (3) 5.75 5.25

Inverted and double surcharges of Nos. 113-115 were made intentionally.

Nos. 86 and 50 Surcharged "25" in Black and Overprinted in Violet — c

REPUBLICA

1912

116 A5 25r on 75r rose 65.00 50.00
117 A5 25r on 75r red violet 2.75 1.50
a. "REUPBLICA" 27.50 25.00
b. "25" omitted 27.50 25.00
c. "REPUBLICA" omitted 27.50 25.00

1914-26 Typo. *Perf. 12x11½, 15x14*

Name and Value in Black

118 A7 ¼c olive brown .15 .15
a. Inscriptions inverted 6.00
119 A7 ½c black .15 .15
120 A7 1c blue green .15 .15
121 A7 1c yel grn ('22) .15 .15
122 A7 1½c lilac brown .15 .15
123 A7 2c carmine .15 .15
124 A7 2c gray ('25) .30 1.00
125 A7 2½c lt violet .15 .15
126 A7 3c orange ('21) .15 .60
127 A7 4c dull rose ('21) .15 .15
128 A7 4½c gray ('21) .15 .80
130 A7 5c blue .15 .15
131 A7 6c lilac ('21) .15 .15
132 A7 7c ultra ('21) .15 .15
133 A7 7½c yellow brn .15 .15
134 A7 8c slate .15 .15
135 A7 10c orange brn .20 .15
136 A7 12c olive brn ('21) .35 .22
137 A7 12c dp green ('25) .20 .15
138 A7 15c plum .40 .15
139 A7 15c brown rose ('21) .15 .15
140 A7 20c yel green .25 .15
141 A7 24c ultra ('25) 1.10 .75
142 A7 25c choc ('25) 1.10 .75
143 A7 30c brown, *green* 1.25 2.00
144 A7 30c gray grn ('21) .65 .15
145 A7 40c brown, *pink* 3.00 2.00
146 A7 40c turq blue ('21) .60 .15
147 A7 50c orange, *sal* 6.00 4.25
148 A7 50c lt violet ('25) 1.00 .15
149 A7 60c dk blue ('22) .55 .15
150 A7 60c dp rose ('26) 40.00 40.00
151 A7 80c pink ('22) 1.25 .15
152 A7 1e green, *blue* 3.00 2.25
153 A7 1e rose ('22) 1.50 .15
154 A7 1e dp blue ('25) 3.00 3.00
155 A7 2e dk violet ('22) 1.25 .50
156 A7 5e buff ('25) 15.00 2.25
157 A7 10e pink ('25) 22.50 10.00
158 A7 20e pale turq ('25) 50.00 35.00
Nos. 118-158 (40) 156.85 108.97

Two kinds of paper, chalky-surfaced paper and ordinary, were used for Nos. 118-120, 122-123, 125, 130, 133-135, 138 and 140. Those on coated paper sell unused for 10 to 40 times the values listed; used for about 5 to 20 times.

All but #143, 145, 147 come perf 12x11½. All but #124, 137, 141-142, 146, 148, 151, 153-154, 156-158 come perf 15x14.

For surcharges see Nos. 228-229, 236-239.

Stamps of 1898-1903 Overprinted type "c" in Red or Green

On Stamps of 1898-1903

1914 *Perf. 11½, 12*

159 A5 10r yel green (R) 3.25 2.50
160 A5 15r gray green (R) 3.25 2.50
161 A5 20r gray violet (G) .80 .80
163 A5 75r red violet (G) .80 .80
164 A5 100r blue, *blue* (R) 1.25 1.25
165 A5 115r org brn, *pink* (R) 60.00
167 A5 200r red vio, *pnksh* (G) .90 .50
169 A5 400r dl bl, *straw* (R) 40.00 30.00
170 A5 500r blk & red, *bl* (R) 5.00 3.00
171 A5 700r vio, *yelsh* (G) 15.00 12.00

Inverted and double overprints were made intentionally. No. 165 was not regularly issued. Red overprints on the 20r, 75r, 200r were not regularly issued. The 130r was not regularly issued without surcharge (No. 225).

On Nos. 63-65, 74-76, 78-79, 82

Perf. 11½, 12½, 13½

172 A2 115r on 10r (R) 30.00 20.00
a. Perf. 13½ 30.00 20.00
173 A2 115r on 200r (R) 35.00 20.00
174 A2 130r on 50r (R) 35.00 20.00
175 A3 115r on 80r (R) 100.00 75.00
176 A3 115r on 100r (R) 250.00 150.00
177 A3 115r on 150r (G) 165.00 125.00
178 A3 130r on 75r (G) 1.75 1.65
179 A3 130r on 300r (R) 4.00 3.25
a. Perf. 12½ 7.00 4.50
180 N1 400r on 2½r (R) .40 .40
a. Perf. 11½ 1.65 1.25
Nos. 172-180 (9) 621.15 415.30

Overprinted PROVISORIO

On Stamps of 1902

Perf. 11½, 12

181 A5 50r blue (R) .90 .60
182 A5 75r rose (G) 2.75 2.00

On No. 87

183 A5 50r on 65r dull blue (R) 2.50 2.50
Nos. 181-183 (3) 6.15 5.10

Inverted and double surcharges of Nos. 181-183 were made intentionally.

Vasco da Gama Issue of Various Portuguese Colonies

Common Design Types CD20-CD27 Surcharged

REPUBLICA
ANGOLA
¼ C.

On Stamps of Macao

1913 *Perf. 12½ to 16*

184 ¼c on ½a blue grn 4.00 4.00
185 ½c on 1a red 3.00 3.00
186 1c on 2a red violet 3.00 3.00
187 2½c on 4a yel green 2.00 2.00
188 5c on 8a dk blue 2.00 2.00
189 7½c on 12a vio brn 5.50 5.50
190 10c on 16a bister brn 4.00 4.00
191 15c on 24a bister 4.00 4.00
Nos. 184-191 (8) 27.50 27.50

On Stamps of Portuguese Africa

Perf. 14 to 15

192 ¼c on 2½r blue grn .75 .75
193 ½c on 5r red .75 .75
194 1c on 10r red violet .75 .75
195 2½c on 25r yel grn .75 .75
196 5c on 50r dk blue .75 .75
197 7½c on 75r vio brn 2.50 2.50
198 10c on 100r bister brn 1.25 1.25
199 15c on 150r bister 1.75 1.75
Nos. 192-199 (8) 9.25 9.25

On Stamps of Timor

200 ¼c on ½a blue grn 2.00 2.00
201 ½c on 1a red 2.00 2.00
202 1c on 2a red vio 2.00 2.00
203 2½c on 4a yel grn 2.00 2.00
204 5c on 8a dk blue 2.00 2.00
205 7½c on 12a vio brn 3.00 3.00

206 10c on 16a bis brn 2.00 2.00
207 15c on 24a bister 2.00 2.00
Nos. 200-207 (8) 17.00 17.00
Nos. 184-207 (24) 53.75 53.75

Provisional Issue of 1902 Overprinted in Carmine

1915 *Perf. 11½, 12½, 13½*
208 A2 115r on 10r green 1.00 *2.00*
209 A2 115r on 200r gray vio .90 *2.00*
210 A2 130r on 100r brown .70 *2.00*
211 A3 115r on 80r lt green 1.10 *2.00*
212 A3 115r on 100r brn, *buff* .90 *2.00*
a. Perf. 11½ 17.00 *17.00*
213 A3 115r on 150r car, *rose* 1.75 *2.00*
214 A3 130r on 15r choc .65 *2.00*
a. Perf. 12½ 7.00 7.00
215 A3 130r on 75r carmine 1.50 *1.75*
216 A3 130r on 300r dk bl, *sal* 1.10 *1.75*
Nos. 208-216 (9) 9.60 *17.50*

Stamps of 1911-14 Surcharged in Black:

½ C.

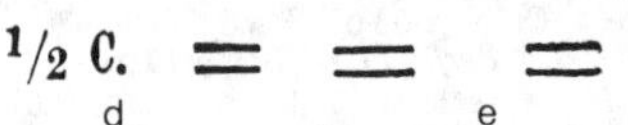

On Stamps of 1911

1919 *Perf. 11½*
217 A5 (d) ½c on 75r red lilac 1.50 *2.00*
218 A5 (d) 2½c on 100r blue, *grysh* 1.75 *2.00*

On Stamps of 1912
Perf. 11½x12
219 A6 (e) ½c on 75r bis brn .65 *.65*
220 A6 (e) 2½c on 100r brn, *lt grn* .85 .40

On Stamps of 1914
221 A5 (d) ½c on 75r red lil .65 .40
222 A5 (d) 2½c on 100r bl, *grysh* .70 .60
Nos. 217-222 (6) 6.10 *6.05*

Inverted and double surcharges were made for sale to collectors.

Nos. 163, 98 and Type of 1914 Surcharged with New Values and Bars in Black

1921
223 A5 (c) 00.5c on 75r *350.00 350.00*
224 A5 (b) 4c on 130r (#98) .70 *.70*
225 A5 (c) 4c on 130r brn, *straw* 2.75 2.50

Nos. 109 and 108 Surcharged with New Values and Bars in Black
226 A6 00.5c on 75c .85 .85
227 A6 1c on 50r .75 .65

Nos. 133 and 138 Surcharged with New Values and Bars in Black
228 A7 00.5c on 7½c .70 .60
229 A7 04c on 15c 1.10 1.10

The 04c surcharge exists on the 15c brown rose, perf 12x11½, No. 139.

República

Nos. 81-82 Surcharged

40 C.

1925 *Perf. 12½*
234 A3 40c on 400r on 200r bl, *bl* .80 .65
a. Perf. 13½ 3.25 2.25
235 N1 40c on 400c on 2½r brn .60 .60
a. Perf. 13½ .60 .60

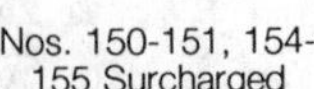

Nos. 150-151, 154-155 Surcharged

70 C.

1931 *Perf. 11½*
236 A7 50c on 60c deep rose 1.10 .80
237 A7 70c on 80c pink 2.25 1.00
238 A7 70c on 1e deep blue 2.00 1.10
239 A7 1.40e on 2e dark violet 2.00 1.10
Nos. 236-239 (4) 7.35 4.00

Ceres — A14

Perf. 12x11½
1932-46 Typo. Wmk. 232
243 A14 1c bister brn .15 .15
244 A14 5c dk brown .15 .15
245 A14 10c dp violet .15 .15
246 A14 15c black .15 .15
247 A14 20c gray .25 .15
248 A14 30c myrtle grn .25 .15
249 A14 35c yel grn ('46) 4.50 2.00
250 A14 40c dp orange .25 .15
251 A14 45c lt blue .85 .65
252 A14 50c lt brown .15 .15
253 A14 60c olive grn .30 .15
254 A14 70c orange brn .65 .15
255 A14 80c emerald .25 .15
256 A14 85c rose 2.00 2.00
257 A14 1a claret .65 .18
258 A14 1.40a dk blue 4.50 1.10
258A A14 1.75a dk blue ('46) 6.00 1.10
259 A14 2a dull vio 2.25 .35
260 A14 5a pale yel grn 3.00 .50
261 A14 10a olive bis 10.00 .90
262 A14 20a orange 17.50 2.00
Nos. 243-262 (21) 53.95 12.43

For surcharges see Nos. 263-267, 271-273, 294A-300, J31-J36.

Surcharged with New Value and Bars
5½mm between bars and new value.

1934
263 A14 10c on 45c lt bl 1.25 .70
264 A14 20c on 85c rose 1.10 .70
265 A14 30c on 1.40a dk bl 1.10 .70
266 A14 70c on 2a dl vio 1.50 1.10
267 A14 80c on 5a pale yel grn 2.25 1.00
Nos. 263-267 (5) 7.20 4.20

See Nos. 294A-300.

CORREIOS
5
CENTAVOS

Nos. J26, J30 Surcharged in Black

1935 Unwmk. *Perf. 11½*
268 D2 5c on 6c lt brown .90 .60
269 D2 30c on 50c gray .90 .60
270 D2 40c on 50c gray .90 .60
Nos. 268-270 (3) 2.70 1.80

No. 255 Surcharged in Black

0,15 Cent.

1938 Wmk. 232 *Perf. 12x11½*
271 A14 5c on 80c emerald .40 *1.00*
272 A14 10c on 80c emerald .50 *1.75*
273 A14 15c on 80c emerald .65 *2.50*
Nos. 271-273 (3) 1.55 *5.25*

Vasco da Gama Issue
Common Design Types
Engr.; Name & Value Typo. in Black
Perf. 13½x13
1938, July 26 Unwmk.
274 CD34 1c gray green .15 .15
275 CD34 5c orange brn .15 .15
276 CD34 10c dk carmine .15 .15
277 CD34 15c dk violet brn .15 .15
278 CD34 20c slate .20 .15
279 CD35 30c rose violet .25 .15
280 CD35 35c brt green .35 .20
281 CD35 40c brown .25 .15
282 CD35 50c brt red vio .25 .15
283 CD36 60c gray black .35 .15
284 CD36 70c brown vio .30 .15
285 CD36 80c orange .30 .15
286 CD36 1a red .30 .15
287 CD37 1.75a blue .85 .30
288 CD37 2a brown car 1.50 .30
289 CD37 5a olive grn 3.00 .30
290 CD38 10a blue vio 6.50 .60
291 CD38 20a red brown 15.00 1.10
Nos. 274-291 (18) 30.00 4.60

For surcharges see Nos. 301-304.

Marble Column and Portuguese Arms with Cross — A20

1938, July 29 *Perf. 12½*
292 A20 80c blue green 1.00 .95
293 A20 1.75a deep blue 5.00 1.00
294 A20 20a dk red brown 14.00 11.00
Nos. 292-294 (3) 20.00 12.95

Visit of the President of Portugal to this colony in 1938.

Common Design Types pictured in section at front of book.

Stamps of 1932 Surcharged with New Value and Bars
8mm between bars and new value.

1941-45 Wmk. 232 *Perf. 12x11½*
294A A14 5c on 80c emer ('45) .22 .20
295 A14 10c on 45c lt blue .65 .55
296 A14 15c on 45c lt blue 1.00 .70
297 A14 20c on 85c rose .65 .55
298 A14 35c on 85c rose .65 .55
299 A14 50c on 1.40a dk blue .65 .55
300 A14 60c on 1a claret 5.75 4.00
Nos. 294A-300 (7) 9.57 7.10

Nos. 285 to 287 Surcharged with New Values and Bars in Black or Red

1945 Unwmk. *Perf. 13½x13*
301 CD36 5c on 80c org .28 .20
302 CD36 50c on 1a red .60 .20
303 CD37 50c on 1.75a bl (R) .42 .20
304 CD37 50c on 1.75a bl .60 .20
Nos. 301-304 (4) 1.90 .80

Sao Miguel Fort, Luanda — A21

John IV — A22

Designs: 10c, Our Lady of Nazareth Church, Luanda. 50c, Salvador Correia de Sa e Bene vides. 1a, Surrender of Luanda. 1.75a, Diogo Cao. 2a, Manuel Cerveira Pereira. 5a, Stone Cliffs, Yelala. 10a, Paulo Dias de Novais. 20a, Massangano Fort.

Perf. 14½
1948, May Unwmk. Litho.
305 A21 5c dk violet .15 .15
306 A21 10c dk brown .25 .20
307 A22 30c blue grn .15 .15
308 A22 50c vio brown .15 .15
309 A21 1a carmine .32 .15
310 A22 1.75a slate blue .65 .20
311 A22 2a green .65 .20
312 A21 5a gray black 1.00 .32
313 A22 10a rose lilac 2.00 .35
314 A21 20a gray blue 5.00 1.10
a. Sheet of 10, #305-314 40.00 40.00
Nos. 305-314 (10) 10.32 2.97

300th anniv. of the restoration of Angola to Portugal. No. 314a sold for 42.50a.

Lady of Fatima Issue
Common Design Type

1948, Dec.
315 CD40 50c carmine .65 .50
316 CD40 3a ultra 2.00 1.00
317 CD40 6a red orange 7.00 2.50
318 CD40 9a dp claret 17.00 3.00
Nos. 315-318 (4) 26.65 7.00

Our Lady of the Rosary at Fatima, Portugal.

Chiumbe River — A24

Black Rocks — A25

Designs: 50c, View of Luanda. 2.50a, Sa da Bandeira. 3.50a, Mocamedes. 15a, Cubal River. 50a, Duke of Braganç a Falls.

1949 Unwmk. *Perf. 13½*
319 A24 20c dk slate blue .15 .15
320 A25 40c black brown .15 .15
321 A24 50c rose brown .15 .15
322 A24 2.50a blue violet 1.10 .25
323 A24 3.50a slate gray 1.10 .25
323A A24 15a dk green 8.25 1.50
324 A24 50a dp green 22.50 3.75
Nos. 319-324 (7) 33.40 6.20

Sailing Vessel — A26

UPU Symbols — A27

1949, Aug. *Perf. 14*
325 A26 1a chocolate 4.00 .32
326 A26 4a dk Prus green 10.00 .85

Centenary of founding of Mocamedes.

1949, Oct.
327 A27 4a dk grn & lt grn 3.50 1.50

75th anniv. of the UPU.

Catalogue values for unused stamps in this section, from this point to the end of the section, are for Never Hinged items.

Stamp of 1870 — A28

1950, Apr. 2 *Perf. 11½x12*
328 A28 50c yellow green .65 .22
329 A28 1a fawn .65 .25
330 A28 4a black 2.75 .70
a. Sheet of 3, #328-330 5.00 5.00
Nos. 328-330 (3) 4.05 1.17

Angola's first philatelic exhibition, marking the 80th anniversary of Angola's first stamps.

No. 330a contains Nos. 328, 329 (inverted), 330, perf. 11½ and sold for 6.50a. Size: 119x80mm. All copies carry an oval exhibition cancellation in the margin but the stamps were valid for postage.

Holy Year Issue
Common Design Types
1950, May *Perf. 13x13½*
331 CD41 1a dull rose vio .32 .15
332 CD42 4a black 3.00 .32

Dark Chanting Goshawk A31

European Bee Eater A32

Designs: 10c, Racquet-tailed roller. 15c, Bataleur eagle. 50c, Giant kingfisher. 1a, Yellow-fronted barbet. 1.50a, Openbill (stork). 2a, Southern ground hornbill. 2.50a, African skimmer. 3a, Shikra. 3.50a, Denham's bustard. 4a, African golden oriole. 4.50a, Long-tailed shrike. 5a, Red-shouldered glossy starling. 6a, Sharp-tailed glossy starling. 7a, Red-shouldered widow bird. 10a, Half-colored kingfisher. 12.50a, White-crowned shrike. 15a, White-winged babbling starling. 20a, Yellow-billed hornbill. 25a, Amethyst starling. 30a, Orange-breasted shrike. 40a, Secretary bird. 50a, Rosy-faced lovebird.

Photogravure and Lithographed

1951 Unwmk. *Perf. 11½*

Birds in Natural Colors

333	A31	5c	lt blue	.15	.50
334	A32	10c	aqua	.15	.15
335	A32	15c	salmon pink	.22	1.00
336	A32	20c	pale yellow	.38	.22
337	A31	50c	gray blue	.22	.15
338	A31	1a	lilac	.22	.15
339	A31	1.50a	gray buff	.32	.15
340	A31	2a	cream	.32	.15
341	A32	2.50a	gray	.32	.15
342	A32	3a	lemon yel	.28	.18
343	A31	3.50a	lt gray	.28	.18
344	A31	4a	rose buff	1.00	.18
345	A32	4.50a	rose lilac	1.00	.20
346	A31	5a	green	5.00	.20
347	A31	6a	blue	5.00	.55
348	A31	7a	orange	5.00	.75
349	A31	10a	lilac rose	32.50	1.10
350	A32	12.50a	slate gray	7.00	1.75
351	A31	15a	pale olive	7.00	1.75
352	A31	20a	pale bis brn	37.50	4.50
353	A31	25a	lilac rose	20.00	2.50
354	A32	30a	pale salmon	20.00	3.00
355	A31	40a	yellow	40.00	3.75
356	A31	50a	turquoise	90.00	14.00
			Nos. 333-356 (24)	273.86	37.21

Holy Year Extension Issue

Common Design Type

1951, Oct. Litho. *Perf. 14*

357 CD43 4a orange 1.25 .50

Sheets contain alternate vertical rows of stamps and labels bearing quotations from Pope Pius XII or the Patriarch Cardinal of Lisbon.

Medical Congress Issue

Common Design Type

Design: Medical examination

1952, June *Perf. 13½*

358 CD44 1a vio blue & brn blk .40 .20

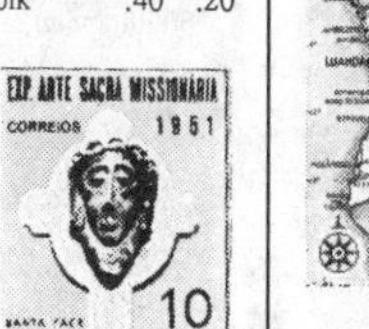

Head of Christ — A35

1952, Oct. Unwmk. *Perf. 13*

359	A35	10c	dk blue & buff	.15	.15
360	A35	50c	dk ol grn & ol gray	.20	.15
361	A35	2a	rose vio & cream	1.25	.15
			Nos. 359-361 (3)	1.60	
			Set value		.26

Issued to commemorate the Exhibition of Sacred Missionary Art held at Lisbon in 1951.

Leopard A36

Sable Antelope A37

Animals: 20c, Elephant. 30c, Eland. 40c, African crocodile. 50c, Impala. 1a, Mountain zebra. 1.50a, Sitatunga. 2a, Black rhinoceros. 2.30a, Gemsbok. 2.50a, Lion. 3a, Buffalo. 3.50a, Springbok. 4a, Brindled gnu. 5a, Hartebeest. 7a, Wart hog. 10a, Defassa waterbuck. 12.50a, Hippopotamus. 15a, Greater kudu. 20a, Giraffe.

1953, Aug. 15 *Perf. 12½*

362	A36	5c	multicolored	.15	.15
363	A37	10c	multicolored	.15	.15
364	A37	20c	multicolored	.15	.15
365	A37	30c	multicolored	.15	.15
366	A36	40c	multicolored	.15	.15
367	A37	50c	multicolored	.15	.15
368	A37	1a	multicolored	.20	.15
369	A37	1.50a	multicolored	.15	.15
370	A36	2a	multicolored	.18	.15
371	A37	2.30a	multicolored	.24	.15
372	A37	2.50a	multicolored	.30	.15
373	A36	3a	multicolored	.30	.15
374	A37	3.50a	multicolored	.18	.15
375	A37	4a	multicolored	6.00	.24
376	A37	5a	multicolored	.32	.15
377	A37	7a	multicolored	.75	.24
378	A37	10a	multicolored	1.25	.20
379	A37	12.50a	multicolored	4.00	1.65
380	A37	15a	multicolored	4.00	1.25
381	A37	20a	multicolored	5.00	.35
			Nos. 362-381 (20)	23.77	6.03

Stamp of Portugal and Arms of Colonies — A38

1953, Nov. Photo. *Perf. 13*

Stamp and Arms Multicolored

382 A38 50c gray & dark gray .55 .32

Cent. of Portugal's 1st postage stamps.

Map and Plane — A39

Typographed and Lithographed

1954, May 27 *Perf. 13½*

383	A39	35c	multicolored	.15	.15
384	A39	4.50e	multicolored	.70	.30

Visit of Pres. Francisco H C. Lopes.

Sao Paulo Issue

Common Design Type

1954 Litho.

385 CD46 1e bister & gray .32 .20

Map of Angola — A41

Artur de Paiva — A42

1955, Aug. Unwmk. *Perf. 13½*

386	A41	5c	multicolored	.15	.15
387	A41	20c	multicolored	.15	.15
388	A41	50c	multicolored	.15	.15
389	A41	1e	multicolored	.15	.15
390	A41	2.30e	multicolored	.28	.15
391	A41	4e	multicolored	.50	.15
392	A41	10e	multicolored	.50	.15
393	A41	20e	multicolored	1.00	.20
			Nos. 386-393 (8)	2.88	
			Set value		.78

For overprints see Nos. 593, 598, 604.

1956, Oct. 9 *Perf. 13½x12½*

394 A42 1e blk, dk bl & ocher .20 .15

Cent. of the birth of Col. Artur de Paiva.

Man of Malange — A43

Jose M. Antunes — A44

Various Costumes in Multicolor; Inscriptions in Black Brown

1957, Jan. 1 Photo. *Perf. 11½*

Granite Paper

395	A43	5c	gray	.15	.15
396	A43	10c	orange yel	.15	.15
397	A43	15c	lt blue grn	.15	.15
398	A43	20c	pale rose vio	.15	.15
399	A43	30c	brt rose	.15	.15
400	A43	40c	blue gray	.15	.15
401	A43	50c	pale olive	.15	.15
402	A43	80c	lt violet	.15	.15
403	A43	1.50e	buff	1.00	.15
404	A43	2.50e	lt yel grn	1.00	.15
405	A43	4e	salmon	.50	.15
406	A43	10e	salmon pink	1.00	.25
			Nos. 395-406 (12)	4.70	
			Set value		1.25

1957, Apr. *Perf. 13½*

407 A44 1e aqua & brown .65 .20

Birth cent. of Father Jose Maria Antunes.

Fair Emblem, Globe and Arms — A45

1958, July Litho. *Perf. 12x11½*

408 A45 1.50e multicolored .25 .15

World's Fair, Brussels, Apr. 17-Oct. 19.

Tropical Medicine Congress Issue

Common Design Type

Design: Securidaca longipedunculata.

1958, Dec. 15 *Perf. 13½*

409 CD47 2.50e multicolored 1.10 .70

Medicine Man — A47

Welwitschia Mirabilis — A48

Designs: 1.50e, Early government doctor. 2.50e, Modern medical team.

1958, Dec. 18 *Perf. 11½x12*

410	A47	1e	blue blk & brown	.20	.15
411	A47	1.50e	gray, blk & brown	.50	.20
412	A47	2.50e	multicolored	.75	.40
			Nos. 410-412 (3)	1.45	.75

75th anniversary of the Maria Pia Hospital, Luanda.

1959, Oct. 1 Litho. *Perf. 14½*

Various Views of Plant and Various Frames

413	A48	1.50e	lt brown, grn & blk	.55	.45
414	A48	2.50e	multicolored	.85	.50
415	A48	5e	multicolored	1.10	.75
416	A48	10e	multicolored	2.75	1.00
			Nos. 413-416 (4)	5.25	2.70

Centenary of discovery of Welwitschia mirabilis, desert plant.

Map of West Africa, c. 1540, by Jorge Reinel — A49

1960, June 25 *Perf. 13½*

417 A49 2.50e multicolored .20 .15

500th anniv. of the death of Prince Henry the Navigator.

Distributing Medicines — A50

Girl of Angola — A51

1960, Oct. Litho. *Perf. 14½*

418 A50 2.50e multicolored .30 .15

10th anniv. of the Commission for Technical Co-operation in Africa South of the Sahara (C.C.T.A.).

1961, Nov. 30 Unwmk. *Perf. 13*

419	A51	10c	multicolored	.15	.15
420	A51	15c	multicolored	.15	.15
421	A51	30c	multicolored	.15	.15
422	A51	40c	multicolored	.15	.15
423	A51	60c	multicolored	.15	.15
424	A51	1.50e	multicolored	.15	.15
425	A51	2e	multicolored	.60	.15
426	A51	2.50e	multicolored	.85	.15
427	A51	3e	multicolored	2.00	.20
428	A51	4e	multicolored	.90	.20
429	A51	5e	multicolored	.70	.20
430	A51	7.50e	multicolored	.90	.45
431	A51	10e	multicolored	.70	.25
432	A51	15e	multicolored	.65	.40
432A	A51	25e	multicolored	1.90	.65
432B	A51	50e	multicolored	3.25	1.00
			Nos. 419-432B (16)	13.35	4.55

Sports Issue

Common Design Type

Sports: 50c, Flying. 1e, Rowing. 1.50e, Water polo. 2.50e, Hammer throwing. 4.50e, High jump. 15e, Weight lifting.

1962, Jan. 18 *Perf. 13½*

Multicolored Design

433	CD48	50c	lt blue	.15	.15
434	CD48	1e	olive bister	.70	.15
435	CD48	1.50e	salmon	.32	.15
436	CD48	2.50e	lt green	.40	.15
437	CD48	4.50e	pale blue	.32	.25
438	CD48	15e	yellow	1.50	.65
			Nos. 433-438 (6)	3.39	1.50

For overprint see No. 608.

Anti-Malaria Issue

Common Design Type

Design: Anopheles funestus.

1962, April Litho. *Perf. 13½*

439 CD49 2.50e multicolored .60 .32

Gen. Norton de Matos — A54

Locusts — A56

1962, Aug. 8 Unwmk. *Perf. 14½*

440 A54 2.50e multicolored .30 .15

50th anniv. of the founding of Nova Lisboa.

1963, June 2 Litho. *Perf. 14*

447 A56 2.50e multicolored .40 .20

15th anniv. of the Intl. Anti-Locust Organ.

Arms of Luanda A57

Vila de Santo Antonio do Zaire — A58

Coats of Arms (Provinces and Cities): 10c, Massangano. 15c, Sanza-Pombo. 25c, Ambriz. 30c, Muxima. 40c, Ambrizete. 50c, Carmona. 60c, Catete. 70c, Quibaxe. No. 458, Maquelo do Zombo. 1e, Salazar. 1.20e, Bembe. No. 461, Caxito. 1.50e, Malanje. 1.80e, Dondo. 2e, Henrique de Carvalho. No. 465, Moçamedes. No. 466, Damba. 3e, Novo Redondo. 3.50e, S. Salvador do Congo. 4e, Cuimba. 5e, Luso. 6.50e, Negage. 7e, Quitexe. 7.50e, S. Filipe de Benguela. 8e, Mucaba. 9e, 31 de Janeiro. 10e, Lobito. 11e, Nova Caipemba. 12.50e, Gabela. 14e, Songo. 15e Sa da Bandeira. 17e, Quimbele. 17.50e, Silva Porto. 20e, Nova Lisboa. 22.50e, Cabinda. 25e, Noqui. 30e, Serpa Pinto. 35e, Santa Cruz. 50e, General Freire.

1963 *Perf. 13½*

Arms in Original Colors; Red and Violet Blue Inscriptions

448 A57 5c tan .15 .15
449 A57 10c lt blue .15 .15
450 A58 15c salmon .15 .15
451 A58 20c olive .15 .15
452 A58 25c lt blue .15 .15
453 A57 30c buff .15 .15
454 A58 40c gray .15 .15
455 A57 50c lt green .15 .15
456 A58 60c brt yellow .15 .15
457 A58 70c dull rose .15 .15
458 A57 1e pale lilac .30 .15
459 A58 1e dull yellow .20 .15
460 A58 1.20e rose .15 .15
461 A57 1.50e pale salmon .60 .15
462 A58 1.50e lt green .40 .15
463 A58 1.80e yel olive .22 .15
464 A57 2e lt yel green .30 .15
465 A57 2.50e lt gray 1.50 .15
466 A58 2.50e dull blue 1.25 .15
467 A57 3e yel olive .42 .15
468 A57 3.50e gray .50 .15
469 A58 4e citron .35 .15
470 A57 5e citron .40 .22
471 A58 6.50e tan .40 .25
472 A58 7e rose lilac .42 .25
473 A57 7.50e pale lilac .55 .30
474 A58 8e lt aqua .45 .30
475 A58 9e yellow .60 .30
476 A57 10e dp salmon .70 .35
477 A58 11e dull yel grn .70 .55
478 A57 12.50e pale blue .90 .45
479 A58 14e lt gray .90 .45
480 A57 15e lt blue 1.00 .45
481 A58 17e pale blue 1.10 .70
482 A57 17.50e dull yellow 1.50 1.00
483 A57 20e lt aqua 1.50 .70
484 A57 22.50e gray 1.50 1.00
485 A58 25e citron 1.50 .70
486 A57 30e yellow 2.00 1.25
487 A58 35e grysh blue 2.00 1.50
488 A58 50e dp yellow 3.00 1.25
Nos. 448-488 (41) 28.81 15.27

Pres. Américo Rodrigues Thomaz — A59

1963, Sept. 16 **Litho.**

489 A59 2.50e multicolored .50 .30

Visit of the President of Portugal.

Airline Anniversary Issue

Common Design Type

1963, Oct. 5 **Unwmk.** *Perf. 14½*

490 CD50 1e lt blue & multi .25 .15

Cathedral of Sá da Bandeira A61

Malange Cathedral A62

Churches: 20c, Landana. 30c, Luanda Cathedral. 40c, Gabela. 50c, St. Martin's Chapel, Baia dos Tigres. 1.50e, St. Peter, Chibia. 2e, Church of Our Lady, Benguela. 2.50e, Church of Jesus, Luanda. 3e, Camabatela. 3.50e, Mission, Cabinda. 4e, Vila Folgares. 4.50e, Church of Our Lady, Lobito. 5e, Church of Cabinda. 7.50e, Cacuso Church, Malange. 10e, Lubango Mission. 12.50e, Huila Mission. 15e, Church of Our Lady, Luanda Island.

1963, Nov. 1 **Litho.**

Multicolored Design and Inscription

491 A61 10c gray blue .15 .15
492 A61 20c pink .15 .15
493 A61 30c lt blue .15 .15
494 A61 40c tan .15 .15
495 A61 50c lt green .15 .15
496 A62 1e buff .15 .15
497 A61 1.50e lt vio blue .15 .15
498 A62 2e pale rose .15 .15
499 A61 2.50e gray .15 .15
500 A62 3e buff .18 .15
501 A61 3.50e olive .22 .15
502 A62 4e buff .22 .20
503 A62 4.50e pale blue .40 .22
504 A61 5e tan .50 .22
505 A62 7.50e gray .60 .32
506 A61 10e dull yellow .75 .40
507 A62 12.50e bister 1.00 .80
508 A62 15e pale gray vio 2.50 .70
Nos. 491-508 (18) 7.72
Set value 3.65

National Overseas Bank Issue

Common Design Type

Design: Antonio Teixeira de Sousa.

1964, May 16 *Perf. 13½*

509 CD51 2.50e multicolored .40 .22

Commerce Building and Arms of Chamber of Commerce A64

1964, Nov. **Litho.** *Perf. 12*

510 A64 1e multicolored .15 .15

Luanda Chamber of Commerce centenary.

ITU Issue

Common Design Type

1965, May 17 **Unwmk.** *Perf. 14½*

511 CD52 2.50e gray & multi .70 .25

Plane over Luanda Airport — A65

Harquebusier, 1539 — A66

1965, Dec. 3 **Litho.** *Perf. 13*

512 A65 2.50e multicolored .22 .15

25th anniv. of DTA, Direccao dos Transportes Aereos.

1966, Feb. 25 **Litho.** *Perf. 14½*

Designs: 50c, Harquebusier, 1539. 1e, Harquebusier, 1640. 1.50e, Infantry officer, 1777. 2e, Standard bearer, infantry, 1777. 2.50e, Infantry soldier, 1777. 3e, Cavalry officer, 1783. 4e, Cavalry soldier, 1783. 4.50e, Infantry officer, 1807. 5e, Infantry soldier, 1807. 6e, Cavalry officer, 1807. 8e, Cavalry soldier, 1807. 9e, Infantry soldier, 1873.

513 A66 50c multicolored .15 .15
514 A66 1e multicolored .15 .15
515 A66 1.50e multicolored .15 .15
516 A66 2e multicolored .15 .15
517 A66 2.50e multicolored .20 .15
518 A66 3e multicolored .20 .15
519 A66 4e multicolored .40 .25
520 A66 4.50e multicolored .40 .25
521 A66 5e multicolored .60 .18
522 A66 6e multicolored .75 .50
523 A66 8e multicolored 1.25 .85
524 A66 9e multicolored 1.50 1.00
Nos. 513-524 (12) 5.90 3.93

National Revolution Issue

Common Design Type

Design: St. Paul's Hospital and Commercial and Industrial School.

1966, May 28 **Litho.** *Perf. 12*

525 CD53 1e multicolored .20 .15

Emblem of Holy Ghost Society — A68

1966 **Litho.** *Perf. 13*

526 A68 1e blue & multi .15 .15

Centenary of the Holy Ghost Society.

Navy Club Issue

Common Design Type

Designs: 1e, Mendes Barata and cruiser Dom Carlos I. 2.50e, Capt. Augusto de Castilho and corvette Mindelo.

1967, Jan. 31 **Litho.** *Perf. 13*

527 CD54 1e multicolored .38 .15
528 CD54 2.50e multicolored .65 .18

Fatima Basilica — A70

Angola Map, Manuel Cerveira Pereira — A71

1967, May 13 **Litho.** *Perf. 12½x13*

529 A70 50c multicolored .15 .15

50th anniv. of the apparition of the Virgin Mary to 3 shepherd children at Fatima.

1967, Aug. 15 **Litho.** *Perf. 12½x13*

530 A71 50c multicolored .15 .15

350th anniv. of the founding of Benguela.

Administration Building, Carmona — A72

1967 **Litho.** *Perf. 12*

531 A72 1e multicolored .15 .15

50th anniv. of the founding of Carmona.

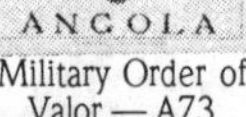

Military Order of Valor — A73

Our Lady of Hope — A74

Designs: 50c, Ribbon of the Three Orders. 1.50e, Military Order of Avis. 2e, Military Order of Christ. 2.50e, Military Order of St. John of Espada. 3e, Order of the Empire. 4e, Order of Prince Henry. 5e, Order of Benemerencia. 10e, Order of Public Instruction. 20e, Order for Industrial and Agricultural Merit.

1967, Oct. 31 *Perf. 14*

532 A73 50c lt gray & multi .15 .15
533 A73 1e lt green & multi .15 .15
534 A73 1.50e yellow & multi .15 .15
535 A73 2e multicolored .15 .15
536 A73 2.50e multicolored .15 .15
537 A73 3e lt olive & multi .18 .15
538 A73 4e gray & multi .20 .15
539 A73 5e multicolored .25 .15
540 A73 10e lilac & multi .40 .25
541 A73 20e lt blue & multi 1.00 .52
Nos. 532-541 (10) 2.78
Set value 1.28

1968, Apr. 22 **Litho.** *Perf. 14*

Designs: 1e, Belmonte Castle, horiz. 1.50e, St. Jerome's Convent. 2.50e, Cabral's Armada.

542 A74 50c yellow & multi .15 .15
543 A74 1e gray & multi .25 .15
544 A74 1.50e lt blue & multi .40 .15
545 A74 2.50e buff & multi .60 .15
Nos. 542-545 (4) 1.40
Set value .32

500th anniv. of the birth of Pedro Alvares Cabral, navigator who took possession of Brazil for Portugal.

Francisco Inocencio de Souza Coutinho — A75

1969, Jan. 7 **Litho.** *Perf. 14*

546 A75 2e multicolored .25 .20

200th anniversary of the founding of Novo Redondo.

Admiral Coutinho Issue

Common Design Type

Design: Adm. Gago Coutinho and his first ship.

1969, Feb. 17 **Litho.** *Perf. 14*

547 CD55 2.50e multicolored .30 .15

Compass Rose A77

Portal of St. Jeronimo's Monastery A79

1969, Aug. 29 **Litho.** *Perf. 14*

548 A77 1e multicolored .15 .15

500th anniv. of the birth of Vasco da Gama (1469-1524), navigator.

Administration Reform Issue

Common Design Type

1969, Sept. 25 **Litho.** *Perf. 14*

549 CD56 1.50e multicolored .15 .15

1969, Dec. 1 **Litho.** *Perf. 14*

550 A79 3e multicolored .20 .15

500th anniv. of the birth of King Manuel I.

Angolasaurus Bocagei — A80

Fossils and Minerals: 1e, Ferrometeorite. 1.50e, Dioptase crystals. 2e, Gondwanidium. 2.50e, Diamonds. 3e, Estromatolite. 3.50e, Procarcharodon megalodon. 4e, Microceratodus angolensis. 4.50e, Moscovite. 5e, Barite. 6e, Nostoceras. 10e, Rotula orbiculus angolensis.

1970, Oct. 31 **Litho.** *Perf. 13*

551 A80 50c tan & multi .15 .15
552 A80 1e multicolored .15 .15
553 A80 1.50e multicolored .15 .15
554 A80 2e multicolored .20 .15
555 A80 2.50e lt gray & multi .20 .15
556 A80 3e multicolored .20 .15
557 A80 3.50e blue & multi .30 .15
558 A80 4e lt gray & multi .30 .15
559 A80 4.50e gray & multi .30 .15
560 A80 5e gray & multi .30 .15
561 A80 6e pink & multi .60 .20
562 A80 10e lt blue & multi .75 .32
Nos. 551-562 (12) 3.60
Set value 1.40

Marshal Carmona Issue

Common Design Type

1970, Nov. 15 *Perf. 14*

563 CD57 2.50e multicolored .22 .15

Arms of Malanje, Cotton Boll and Field — A82

1970, Nov. 20 *Perf. 13*

564	A82	2.50e	multicolored	.22	.15

Centenary of the municipality of Malanje.

Mail Ships and Angola No. 1 — A83

Designs: 4.50e, Steam locomotive and Angola No. 4.

1970, Dec. 1 *Perf. 13½*

565	A83	1.50e	multicolored	.30	.15
566	A83	4.50e	multicolored	.65	.22

Cent. of stamps of Angola. See No. C36. For overprint see No. 616B.

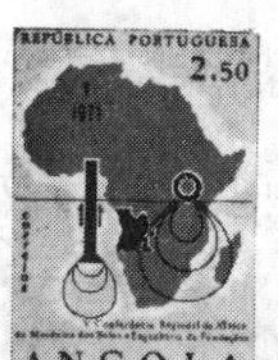

Map of Africa, Diagram of Seismic Tests — A84

Galleon on Congo River — A85

1971, Aug. 22 Litho. *Perf. 13*

567	A84	2.50e	multicolored	.15	.15

5th Regional Conference of Soil and Foundation Engineers, Luanda, Aug. 22-Sept. 5.

1972, May 25 Litho. *Perf. 13*

568	A85	1e	emerald & multi	.15	.15

4th centenary of the publication of The Lusiads by Luiz Camoens.

Olympic Games Issue

Common Design Type

1972, June 20 *Perf. 14x13½*

569	CD59	50c	multicolored	.15	.15

Lisbon-Rio de Janeiro Flight Issue

Common Design Type

1972, Sept. 20 Litho. *Perf. 13½*

570	CD60	1e	multicolored	.15	.15

WMO Centenary Issue

Common Design Type

1973, Dec. 15 Litho. *Perf. 13*

571	CD61	1e	dk gray & multi	.15	.15

Radar Station A89

1974, June 25 Litho. *Perf. 13*

572	A89	2e	multicolored	.22	.15

Establishment of satellite communications network via Intelsat among Portugal, Angola and Mozambique.

For overprint see No. 616A

Harpa Doris — A90

Designs: Sea shells.

1974, Oct. 25 Litho. *Perf. 12x12½*

573	A90	25c	shown	.15	.15
574	A90	30c	Murex melanamathos	.15	.15
575	A90	50c	Venus foliaceo lamellosa	.15	.15
576	A90	70c	Lathyrus filosus	.15	.15
577	A90	1e	Cymbium cisium	.18	.15
578	A90	1.50e	Cassis tesselata	.18	.15
579	A90	2e	Cypraea stercoraria	.18	.15
580	A90	2.50e	Conus prometheus	.18	.18
581	A90	3e	Strombus latus	.18	.18
582	A90	3.50e	Tympanotonus fuscatus	.18	.18
583	A90	4e	Cardium costatum	.25	.20
584	A90	5e	Natica fulminea	.25	.20
585	A90	6e	Lyropecten nodosus	.30	.20
586	A90	7e	Tonna galea	.75	.25
587	A90	10e	Donax rugosus	.90	.30
588	A90	25e	Cymatium trigonum	1.50	.40
589	A90	30e	Olivancilaria acuminata	2.50	.75
590	A90	35e	Semifusus morio	2.50	.75
591	A90	40e	Clavatula lineata	3.00	1.00
592	A90	50e	Solarium granulatum	4.00	1.50
			Nos. 573-592 (20)	17.63	
			Set value		4.00

For overprints see Nos. 605-607, 617-630.

No. 386 Overprinted in Blue: "1974 / FILATELIA / JUVENIL"

1974, Dec. 21 Litho. *Perf. 13½*

593	A41	5c	multicolored	.15	.15

Youth philately.

Republic

Star and Hand Holding Rifle — A91

1975, Nov. 11 Litho. *Perf. 13x13½*

594	A91	1.50e	red & multi	.15	.15

Independence in 1975.

Diquiche Mask — A92

Design: 3e, Bui ou Congolo mask.

1976, Feb. 6 *Perf. 13½*

595	A92	50c	lt blue & multi	.15	.15
596	A92	3e	multicolored	.20	.15
			Set value	.27	.15

Workers — A93

President Agostinho Neto — A94

1976, May 1 Litho. *Perf. 12*

597	A93	1e	red & multi	.15	.15

International Workers' Day.

No. 392 Overprinted Bar and: "DIA DO SELO / 15 Junho 1976 / REP. POPULAR / DE"

1976, June 15 Litho. *Perf. 13½*

598	A41	10e	multicolored	.40	.25

Stamp Day.

1976, Nov. 11 Litho. *Perf. 13*

599	A94	50c	yel & dk brown	.15	.15
600	A94	2e	lt gray & plum	.15	.15
601	A94	3e	gray & indigo	.15	.15
602	A94	5e	buff & brown	.20	.15
603	A94	10e	tan & sepia	.40	.15
a.			Souv. sheet of 1, imperf.	2.00	1.25
			Nos. 599-603 (5)	1.05	
			Set value		.40

First anniversary of independence.

Nos. 393, 588-589, 592 Overprinted with Bar over Republica Portuguesa and: "REPUBLICA POPULAR DE"

1977, Feb. 9 *Perf. 13½, 12x12½*

604	A41	20e	multicolored	1.25	.25
605	A90	25e	multicolored	1.75	.35
606	A90	30e	multicolored	2.50	.50
607	A90	50e	multicolored	4.00	.75
			Nos. 604-607 (4)	9.50	1.85

Overprint in 3 lines on No. 604, in 2 lines on others.

No. 438 Overprinted with Bar over Republica Portuguesa and: "S. Silvestre / 1976 / Rep. Popular / de"

1976, Dec. 31 *Perf. 13½*

608	CD48	15e	multicolored	3.50	.25

Child and WHO Emblem — A95

Map of Africa, Flag of Angola — A96

1977 Litho. *Perf. 10½*

609	A95	2.50k	blk & lt blue	.15	.15

Campaign for vaccination against poliomyelitis.

1977 Photo.

610	A96	6k	blk, red & bl	.20	.15

First congress of Popular Movement for the Liberation of Angola.

Anti-Apartheid Emblem — A97

1979, June 20 Litho. *Perf. 13½*

611	A97	1k	multicolored	.15	.15

Anti-Apartheid Year.

Human Rights Emblem — A98

Child Flowers, Globe, IYC Emblem — A99

1979, June 15 Litho. *Perf. 13½*

612	A98	2.50k	multicolored	.15	.15

Declaration of Human Rights, 30th anniv. (in 1975).

1980, May 1 Litho. *Perf. 14x14½*

613	A99	3.50k	multicolored	.15	.15

International Year of the Child (1979).

Running, Moscow '80 Emblem A100

5th Anniv. of Independence A101

1980, Dec. 15 Litho. *Perf. 13½*

614	A100	9k	shown	.32	.15
615	A100	12k	Swimming, horiz.	.40	.20

22nd Summer Olympic Games, Moscow, July 19-Aug. 3.

1980, Nov. 11

616	A101	5.50k	multicolored	.15	.15

Nos. 572, 566 Overprinted with Bar and: "REPUBLICA POPULAR / DE"

1980-81 Litho. *Perf. 13½x13*

616A	A89	2e	multi (bar only)	.50	
616B	A83	4.50e	multicolored	1.00	

Issue dates: 2e, May 17, 1981, 4.50e, June 15. See No. C37.

Nos. 577-580, 582-591 Overprinted with Black Bar over "Republica Portuguesa"

1981, June 15 Litho. *Perf. 12x12½*

617	A90	1e	multicolored		
618	A90	1.50e	multicolored		
619	A90	2e	multicolored		
620	A90	2.50e	multicolored		
621	A90	3.50e	multicolored		
622	A90	4e	multicolored		
623	A90	5e	multicolored		
624	A90	6e	multicolored		
625	A90	7e	multicolored		
626	A90	10e	multicolored		
627	A90	25e	multicolored		
628	A90	30e	multicolored		
629	A90	35e	multicolored		
630	A90	40e	multicolored		
			Nos. 617-630 (14)	15.00	8.00

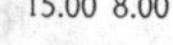

Man Walking with Canes, Tchibinda Ilunga Statue — A102

1981, Sept. 5 Litho. *Perf. 13½*

631	A102	9k	multicolored	.32	.20

Turipex '81 tourism exhibition.

M.P.L.A. Workers' Party Congress — A103

1980, Dec. 23 Litho. *Perf. 14*

632	A103	50 l	Millet	.15	.15
633	A103	5k	Coffee	.20	.15
634	A103	7.50k	Sunflowers	.25	.15
635	A103	13.50k	Cotton	.40	.20
636	A103	14k	Oil	.45	.25
637	A103	16k	Diamonds	.45	.25
			Nos. 632-637 (6)	1.90	1.15

People's Power — A104

Natl. Heroes' Day — A105

1980, Nov. 11

638	A104	40k	lt blue & blk	1.25	.40

1980, Sept. 17 *Perf. 14x13½*

639	A105	4.50k	Former Pres. Neto	.15	.15
640	A105	50k	Neto, diff.	1.50	.65

Soweto Uprising, 5th Anniv. A106

1981

641	A106	4.50k	multicolored	.20	.15

2nd Central African Games A107

1981, Sept. 3 Litho. *Perf. 13½*

642 A107 50 l Bicycling, tennis .15 .15
643 A107 5k Judo, boxing .20 .15
644 A107 6k Basketball, volleyball .22 .15
645 A107 10k Handball, soccer .40 .25
Nos. 642-645 (4) .97
Set value .52

Souvenir Sheet

Imperf

646 A107 15k multicolored *2.00*

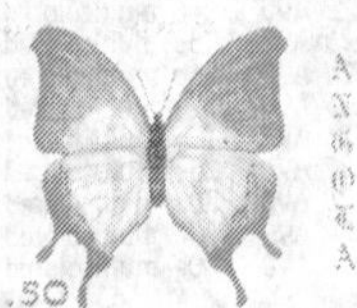

Charaxes Kahldeni A108

1982, Feb. 26 Litho. *Perf. 13½*

647 A108 50 l shown .15 .15
648 A108 1k Abantis zambesiaca .15 .15
649 A108 5k Catacroptera cloanthe .20 .15
650 A108 9k Myrina ficedula, vert. .40 .15
651 A108 10k Colotis danae .40 .15
652 A108 15k Acraea acrita .52 .25
653 A108 100k Precis hierta 2.75 1.25
a. Souvenir sheet 2.00 1.00
Nos. 647-653 (7) 4.57 2.25

No. 653a contains Nos. 647-653, imperf., and sold for 30k (stamps probably not valid individually).

5th Anniv. of UN Membership A109

Designs: 5.50k, The Silence of the Night, by Musseque Catambor. 7.50k, Cotton picking, Catete.

1982, Sept. 22 Litho.

654 A109 5.50k multicolored .20 .15
655 A109 7.50k multicolored .25 .15

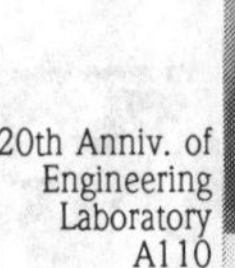

20th Anniv. of Engineering Laboratory A110

1982, Dec. 21 Litho. *Perf. 14*

656 A110 9k Lab .25 .15
657 A110 13k Worker, vert. .40 .20
658 A110 100k Equipment, vert. 3.25 1.25
Nos. 656-658 (3) 3.90 1.60

Local Flowers A111

1983, Feb. 18 *Perf. 13½*

659 A111 5k Dichrostachys glomerata .15 .15
660 A111 12k Amblygonocarpus obtusangulus .40 .15
661 A111 50k Albizzia versicolor 2.00 .65
Nos. 659-661 (3) 2.55 .95

Women's Org., First Congress — A112

Africa Day — A113

1983 Litho. *Perf. 13½*

662 A112 20k multicolored .80 .80

1983, June 30 *Perf. 13*

663 A113 6.5k multi .25 .25

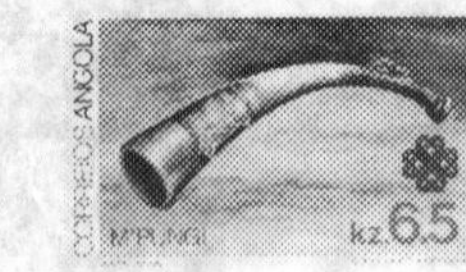

World Communications Year — A114

1983, June 30 Litho. *Perf. 13½*

664 A114 6.5k M'pungi .25 .25
665 A114 12k Mondu .40 .40

BRASILIANA '83 Stamp Exhibition, Rio de Janeiro, July 29-Aug. 7 — A115

Crop-eating insects.

1983, July 29 Litho. *Perf. 13*

666 A115 4.5k Antestiopsis lineaticollis .18 .18
667 A115 6.5k Stephanoderes hampei ferr. .25 .25
668 A115 10k Zonocerus variegatus .40 .40
Nos. 666-668 (3) .83 .83

25th Anniv. of Economic Commission for Africa A116

1983, Aug. 2

669 A116 10k Map, emblem .40 .40

185th Anniv. of Post Office A117

1983, Dec. 7 Litho. *Perf. 13½*

670 A117 50 l Mail collection, vert. .15 .15
671 A117 3.5k Unloading mail plane .15 .15
672 A117 5k Sorting mail .20 .20
673 A117 15k Mailing letter, vert. .60 .60
674 A117 30k Post office box delivery 1.25 1.25
a. Min. sheet of 3, #671-672, 674 4.00 4.00
Nos. 670-674 (5) 2.35 2.35

No. 674a sold for 100k.

Local Butterflies A118

1984, Jan. 20 Litho. *Perf. 13½*

675 A118 50 l Parasa karschi .15 .15
676 A118 1k Diaphone angolensis .15 .15
677 A118 3.5k Choeropasis jucunda .15 .15
678 A118 6.5k Hespagarista rendalli .25 .25
679 A118 15k Euchromia guineensis .60 .60
680 A118 17.5k Mazuca roseistriga .70 .70
681 A118 20k Utetheisa callima .85 .85
Nos. 675-681 (7) 2.85 2.85

A119 A120

1984, Apr. 11 Litho. *Perf. 13½*

682 A119 30k multicolored 1.25 1.25

First Natl. Worker's Union Congress, Apr. 11-16.

1984, Oct. 24 Litho. *Perf. 13½*

Local birds.

683 A120 10.50k Bucorvos leadbeateri .45 .40
684 A120 14k Gypohicax angolensis .55 .50
685 A120 16k Ardea goliath .60 .50
686 A120 19.50k Pelicanus onocrotalus .80 .75
687 A120 22k Platelea alba .90 .90
688 A120 26k Balearica pavonnia 1.00 1.00
Nos. 683-688 (6) 4.30 4.05

Local Animals A121

1984, Nov. 12

689 A121 1k Tragelephus strepsicerus .15 .15
690 A121 4k Antidorcos marsupialis angolerusis .15 .15
691 A121 5k Pan troglodytes .20 .20
692 A121 10k Sycerus caffer .40 .40
693 A121 15k Hippotragus niger variani .60 .60
694 A121 20k Orycteropus afer .80 .80
695 A121 25k Crocuta crocuta 1.00 1.00
Nos. 689-695 (7) 3.30 3.30

Angolese Monuments A122

1985, Feb. 21 Litho. *Perf. 13½*

696 A122 5k San Pedro da Barra .22 .22
697 A122 12.5k Nova Oeiras .55 .55
698 A122 18k M'Banza Kongo .80 .80
699 A122 26k Massangano 1.10 1.10
700 A122 39k Escravatura Museum 1.65 1.65
Nos. 696-700 (5) 4.32 4.32

United Workers' Party, 25th Anniv. A123

1985, May Litho. *Perf. 12*

701 A123 77k XXV, red flags 1.50 1.50

Printed in sheets of 5.

A124 A125

1985, May

702 A124 1k Flags .15 .15
703 A124 11k Oil drilling platform, Cabinda .22 .22
704 A124 57k Conference 1.10 1.10
a. Strip of 3, #702-704 1.40 1.40

Southern African Development Council, 5th anniv.

Lithographed and Typographed

1985, July 5 *Perf. 11*

Medicinal plants.

705 A125 1k Lonchocarpus sericeus .15 .15
706 A125 4k Gossypium .15 .15
707 A125 11k Cassia occidentalis .22 .22
708 A125 25.50k Gloriosa superba .50 .50
709 A125 55k Cochlospermum angolensis 1.10 1.10
Nos. 705-709 (5) 2.12 2.12

ARGENTINA '85 exhibition.

5th Natl. Heroes Day — A126

Natl. flag and: 10.50k, Portrait of Agostinho Neto, party leader. 36.50k, Neto working.

1985 Litho. *Perf. 13½*

710 A126 10.50k multicolored .20 .20
711 A126 36.50k multicolored .70 .70

Ministerial Conference of Non-Aligned Countries, Luanda A127

1985, Sept. 4 Photo. *Perf. 11*

712 A127 35k multicolored 1.50 1.50

UN, 40th Anniv. A128

1985, Oct. 29 Litho. *Perf. 11*

713 A128 12.50k multicolored .55 .55

Industry and Natural Resources A129

1985, Nov. 11

714 A129 50 l Cement Factory .15 .15
715 A129 5k Logging .22 .22
716 A129 7k Quartz .30 .30
717 A129 10k Iron mine .42 .42
a. Souvenir sheet of 4, #714-717, imperf. 1.00 1.00
Nos. 714-717 (4) 1.09 1.09

Natl. independence, 10th anniv.

2nd Natl. Workers' Party Congress (MPLA) A130

1985, Nov. 28 *Perf. 13½*

718 A130 20k multicolored .85 .85

Demostenes de Almeida Clington Races, 30th Anniv. — A131

Various runners.

1985, Dec. 13

719 A131 50 l multicolored .15 .15
720 A131 5k multicolored .22 .22
721 A131 6.50k multicolored .28 .28
722 A131 10k multicolored .42 .42
Nos. 719-722 (4) 1.07 1.07

1986 World Cup Soccer Championships, Mexico — A132

Map, soccer field and various plays.

1986, May 6 Litho. *Perf. 11½x11*

723 A132 50 l multi .15 .15
724 A132 3.50k multi .15 .15
725 A132 5k multi .22 .22
726 A132 7k multi .30 .30
727 A132 10k multi .42 .42
728 A132 18k multi .85 .85
Nos. 723-728 (6) 2.09 2.09

Struggle Against Portugal, 25th Anniv. A133

1986, May 6 *Perf. 11x11½*

729 A133 15k multicolored .65 .65

First Man in Space, 25th Anniv. A134

1986, Aug. 21 Litho. *Perf. 11x11½*

730 A134 50 l Skylab, US .15 .15
731 A134 1k Spacecraft .15 .15
732 A134 5k A. Leonov space-walking .22 .22
733 A134 10k Lunokhod on Moon .42 .42
734 A134 13k Apollo-Soyuz link-up .60 .60
Nos. 730-734 (5) 1.54 1.54

Admission of Angola to UN, 10th Anniv. — A135

1986, Dec. 1 Litho. *Perf. 11x11½*

735 A135 22k multi .90 .90

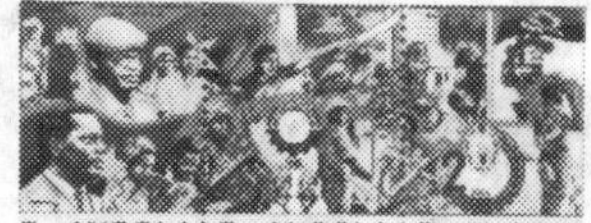

Liberation Movement, 30th Anniv. — A136

Angolese at work, fighting and: No. 736a, "1956." No. 736b, Congress emblem, "1980." No. 736c, Labor Party emblem, "1985."

1986, Dec. 3 *Perf. 11½x11*

736 A136 Strip of 3 .65 .65
a.-c. 5k any single .20 .20

Agostinho Neto University, 10th Anniv. A137

1986, Dec. 30 Litho. *Perf. 11x11½*

737 A137 50 l Mathematics .15 .15
738 A137 1k Law .15 .15
739 A137 10k Medicine .45 .45
Nos. 737-739 (3) .75 .75

Tribal Hairstyles — A138

1987, Apr. 15 Litho. *Perf. 11½x11*

740 A138 1k Ouioca .15 .15
741 A138 1.50k Luanda .15 .15
742 A138 5k Humbe .15 .15
743 A138 7k Muila .15 .15
744 A138 20k Muila, diff. .45 .45
745 A138 30k Dilolo .70 .70
Nos. 740-745 (6) 1.75 1.75

Landscapes — A139 Lenin — A140

Perf. 11½x12, 12x11½

1987, July 7 Litho.

746 A139 50 l Pambala Shore .15 .15
747 A139 1.50k Dala Waterfalls .15 .15
748 A139 3.50k Black Stones .15 .15
749 A139 5k Cuango River .15 .15
750 A139 10k Launda coast .22 .22
751 A139 20k Hills of Leba .50 .50
Set value 1.00 1.00

Nos. 746-747, 749 and 751 horiz.

1987, Nov. 25 *Perf. 12x12½*

752 A140 15k multi .58 .58

October Revolution, Russia, 70th anniv.

2nd Congress of the Organization of Angolan Women (OMA) — A141

1988, May 30 Litho. *Perf. 13x13½*

753 A141 2k shown .15 .15
754 A141 10k Soldier, nurse, technician, student .35 .35

Victory Carnival, 10th Anniv. — A142

Various carnival scenes.

1988, June 15 Litho. *Perf. 13½x13*

755 A142 5k shown .16 .16
756 A142 10k multi, diff. .32 .32

Augusto N'Gangula (1956-1968), Youth Pioneer Killed by Portuguese Colonial Army — A143

Agostinho Neto Pioneers' Organization (OPA), 25th Anniv. — A144

1989, Oct. 2 Litho. *Perf. 12x11½*

757 A143 12k multicolored .40 .40
758 A144 15k multicolored .48 .48

Pioneer Day.

10th Natl. Soccer Championships, Benguela, May 1 — A145

1989, Oct. 16

759 A145 5k shown .16 .16
760 A145 5k Luanda, 3 years .16 .16
761 A145 5k Luanda, 5 years .16 .16
Nos. 759-761 (3) .48 .48

Intl. Fund for Agricultural Development, 10th Anniv. — A146

1990, Feb. 15 Litho. *Perf. 11½x12*

762 A146 10k multicolored .70 .70

Ingombotas' Houses A147

Architecture: 2k, Alta Train Station. 5k, National Museum of Anthropology. 15k, Ana Joaquina Palace. 23k, Iron Palace. 36k, Meteorological observatory, vert. 50k, People's Palace.

Perf. 12x11½, 11½x12

1990, Feb. 20

763 A147 1k shown .15 .15
764 A147 2k multicolored .15 .15
765 A147 5k multicolored .32 .32
766 A147 15k multicolored .98 .98
767 A147 23k multicolored 1.50 1.50
768 A147 36k multicolored 2.30 2.30
769 A147 50k multicolored 3.25 3.25
Nos. 763-769 (7) 8.65 8.65

Luanda and Benguela Railways A148

Various maps and locomotives.

1990, Mar. 1 *Perf. 12x11½*

770 A148 5k shown .35 .35
771 A148 12k Garrat T (left) .80 .80
772 A148 12k Garrat T (right) .80 .80
a. Pair, #771-772 1.60 1.60
773 A148 14k Mikado .95 .95
Nos. 770-773 (4) 2.90 2.90

Souvenir Sheet

774 A148 25k Diesel electric 2.35 2.35

No. 772a has a continuous design.

Southern Africa Development Coordinating Conf. (SADCC), 10th Anniv. A149

1990, Apr. 1 Litho. *Perf. 14*

775 A149 5k shown *1.25 1.25*
776 A149 9k Floating oil rig *2.50 2.50*

Pan-African Postal Union (PAPU), 10th Anniv. A150

1990, Apr. 6

777 A150 4k shown .75 .75
778 A150 10k Simulated stamp, map 1.50 1.50

Paintings by Raul Indipwo A151

1990, Apr. 24

779 A151 6k *Tres Gracas* .42 .42
780 A151 9k *Muxima,* vert. .65 .65

Stamp World London 90.

Hippotragus Niger Variani, Adult Male and Female — A152

1990, May 9 *Perf. 14x13½*

781 A152 5k Adult male .35 .35
782 A152 5k shown .35 .35
783 A152 5k Adult female .35 .35
784 A152 5k Female, calf .35 .35
Nos. 781-784 (4) 1.40 1.40

World Wildlife Fund. Various combinations available in blocks or strips of four.

Rosa de Porcelana — A153

1990, June 2 Litho. *Perf. 14*

785 A153 5k shown .35 .35
786 A153 8k Cravo burro .56 .56
787 A153 10k Alamandra .70 .70
Nos. 785-787 (3) 1.61 1.61

Souvenir Sheet

788 A153 40k Hibiscus 2.70 2.70

Belgica '90.

Miniature Sheet

Intl. Literacy Year — A154

Various animals and forest scenes.

1990, July 26 Litho. *Perf. 14*
789 Sheet of 30 2.25 2.25
a. A154 1k any single .15 .15
790 A154 5k Zebra .35 .35
791 A154 5k Butterfly .35 .35
792 A154 5k Horse .35 .35
a. Block of 3, #790-792 + label 1.05 1.05

People's Assembly, 10th Anniv. A155

1990, Nov. 11 *Perf. 14*
793 A155 10k multicolored .70 .70

3rd Natl. Labor Congress — A156

1990 Litho. *Perf. 13½*
794 A156 14k multicolored 1.35 1.35

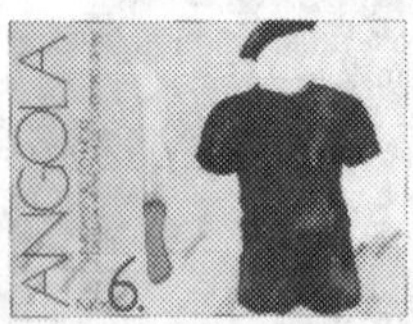

War of Independence, 30th Anniv. A157

Uniforms.

1991, Feb. 28 Litho. *Perf. 14*
795 A157 6k Machete, 1961 .42 .42
a. Perf. 13½ vert. .42 .42
796 A157 6k Rifle, 1962-63 .42 .42
a. Perf. 13½ vert. .42 .42
797 A157 6k Rifle, 1968 .42 .42
a. Perf. 13½ vert. .42 .42
798 A157 6k Automatic rifle, 1972 .42 .42
a. Perf. 13½ vert. .42 .42
b. Bklt. pane of 4, #795a-798a 1.70
Nos. 795-798 (4) 1.68 1.68

Musical Instruments A158

Designs: a, Marimba. b, Mucupela. c, Ngoma la Txina. d, Kissange.

1991, Apr. 5 Litho. *Perf. 14*
799 A158 6k Block or strip of 4, #799a-799d 1.70 1.70

Tourism A159

Designs: 3k, Iona National Park. 7k, Kalandula Waterfalls. 35k, Lobito Bay. 60k, Weltwitschia Mirabilis plant.

1991, June 25 Litho. *Perf. 14*
800 A159 3k multi .15 .15
801 A159 7k multi .24 .24
802 A159 35k multi 1.15 1.15
803 A159 60k multi 2.00 2.00
Nos. 800-803 (4) 3.54 3.54

Dogs — A160

1991, July 5 Litho. *Perf. 14*
804 A160 5k Kabir of dembos .16 .16
805 A160 7k Ombua .24 .24
806 A160 11k Kabir massongo .38 .38
807 A160 12k Kawa tchowe .40 .40
Nos. 804-807 (4) 1.18 1.18

1992 Summer Olympics, Barcelona A161

1991, July 26 *Perf. 13*
808 A161 4k Judo .15 .15
809 A161 6k Sailing .20 .20
810 A161 10k Running .35 .35
811 A161 100k Swimming 3.35 3.35
Nos. 808-811 (4) 4.05 4.05

Navigation Aids — A162

1991, Nov. 8 Litho. *Perf. 12*
812 A162 5k Quadrant .16 .16
813 A162 15k Astrolabe .52 .52
814 A162 20k Cross-staff .70 .70
815 A162 50k Portolano 1.75 1.75
Nos. 812-815 (4) 3.13 3.13

Iberex '91.

Rays — A163

1992, Mar. 30 Litho. *Perf. 14*
816 A163 40k Myliobatis aquila .15 .15
817 A163 50k Aetobatus narinari .18 .18
818 A163 66k Manta birostris .24 .24
819 A163 80k Raja miraletus .30 .30
Nos. 816-819 (4) .87 .87

Souvenir Sheet

Perf. 13½
820 A163 25k Manta birostris, diff. .15 .15

Quioca Masks — A164

1992, Apr. 30 Litho. *Perf. 13½*
821 A164 60k Kalelwa .22 .22
822 A164 100k Mukixe Wa Kino .38 .38
823 A164 150k Cikunza .55 .55
824 A164 250k Mukixi Wa Mbwesu .92 .92
Nos. 821-824 (4) 2.07 2.07

See Nos. 854-857, 868-871, 883-886, 895-898.

Medicinal Plants — A165

Designs: 200k, Ptaeroxylon obliquum. 300k, Spondias mombin. 500k, Parinari curatellifolia. 600k, Cochlospermum angolense.

1992, May 8 *Perf. 14*
825 A165 200k brown & pale yel .75 .75
826 A165 300k brown & pale yel 1.10 1.10
827 A165 500k brown & pale yel 1.85 1.85
828 A165 600k brown & pale yel 2.20 2.20
a. Block or strip of 4, #825-828 5.90 5.90

Evangelization of Angola, 500th Anniv. — A166

1992, May 10 *Perf. 13½*
829 A166 150k King, missionaries .55 .55
830 A166 420k Ruins of M'banza Congo 1.55 1.55
831 A166 470k Maxima Church 1.75 1.75
832 A166 500k Faces of people 1.90 1.90
Nos. 829-832 (4) 5.75 5.75

Traditional Houses — A167

Perf. 14, 13½ Vert. (#832A)

1992, May 22
832A A167 150k Dimbas 1.25 1.25
b. Bklt. pane of 4, #832A, 833a-835a 5.00
833 A167 330k Cokwe 1.25 1.25
a. Perf. 13½ vert. 1.25 1.25
834 A167 360k Mbali 1.35 1.35
a. Perf. 13½ vert. 1.35 1.35
835 A167 420k Ambwelas 1.55 1.55
a. Perf. 13½ vert. 1.55 1.55
836 A167 500k Upper Zambezi 1.90 1.90
Nos. 832A-836 (5) 7.30 7.30

Expo '92, Seville.

Agapornis Roseicollis A168

1992, June 2 *Perf. 12x11½*
837 A168 150k Two birds on branch .55 .55
838 A168 200k Birds feeding .75 .75
839 A168 250k Hand holding bird .92 .92
840 A168 300k Bird on perch 1.10 1.10
a. Strip of 4, #837-840 3.35 3.35

Expo '92, Seville.

Souvenir Sheet

Visit of Pope John Paul II to Angola — A169

Abstract paintings: a, 340k, The Crucifixion. b, 370k, The Resurrection.

1992, June 4 Litho. *Perf. 13½*
841 A169 Sheet of 2, #a.-b. + 2 labels 1.80 1.80

1992 Summer Olympics, Barcelona A170

1992, July 30 *Perf. 14*
842 A170 120k Hurdles .32 .32
843 A170 180k Cycling .50 .50
844 A170 240k Roller hockey .65 .65
845 A170 360k Basketball 1.00 1.00
Nos. 842-845 (4) 2.47 2.47

Native Fishing — A171

1992, Aug. 5 *Perf. 11½x12*
846 A171 65k Building traps .18 .18
847 A171 90k Using nets .25 .25
848 A171 100k Laying traps .28 .28
849 A171 120k Fisherman in boats .32 .32
Nos. 846-849 (4) 1.03 1.03

Souvenir Sheet

Discovery of America, 500th Anniv. — A172

1992, Sept. 18 Litho. *Perf. 12*
850 A172 500k multicolored 1.35 1.35

Genoa '92.

First Free Elections in Angola — A173

Designs: 120k, People voting. 150k, Map, ballot box, peace doves. 200k, People, dove, hand dropping ballot into ballot box.

1992, Oct. 27 Litho. *Perf. 11½x12*

851 A173 120k multicolored .32 .32
852 A173 150k multicolored .42 .42
853 A173 200k multicolored .55 .55
Nos. 851-853 (3) 1.29 1.29

Quioca Mask Type of 1992

1992, Nov. 6 *Perf. 13½*

854 A164 72k Cihongo .28 .28
855 A164 80k Mbwasu .30 .30
856 A164 120k Cinhanga .45 .45
857 A164 210k Kalewa .80 .80
Nos. 854-857 (4) 1.83 1.83

Inauguration of Express Mail Service A174

1992, Dec. 14 Litho. *Perf. 12x11½*

858 A174 450k Truck 1.05 1.05
859 A174 550k Airplane 1.25 1.25

Meteorological Instruments — A175

1993, Mar. 23 Litho. *Perf. 11½x12*

860 A175 250k Weather balloon .58 .58
861 A175 470k Actinometer 1.10 1.10
862 A175 500k Rain gauge 1.15 1.15
Nos. 860-862 (3) 2.83 2.83

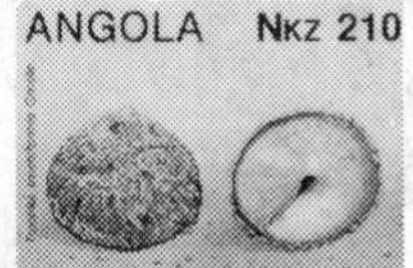

Seashells A176

1993, Apr. 6 *Perf. 12x11½*

863 A176 210k Trochita trochiformis .48 .48
864 A176 330k Strombus latus .75 .75
865 A176 400k Aporrhais pesgallinae .95 .95
866 A176 500k Fusos aff. albinus 1.15 1.15
Nos. 863-866 (4) 3.33 3.33

Souvenir Sheet

867 A176 1000k Pusionella nifat 2.30 2.30

Quioca Art Type of 1992

1993, June 7 Litho. *Perf. 12*

868 A164 72k Men with vehicles .15 .15
869 A164 210k Cavalier .45 .45
870 A164 420k Airplane .90 .90
871 A164 600k Men carrying stretcher 1.25 1.25
Nos. 868-871 (4) 2.75 2.75

Flowering Plants — A177

1993, June 28 *Perf. 11½x12*

872 A177 360k Sansevieria cylindrica .75 .75
873 A177 400k Euphorbia tirucalli .85 .85
874 A177 500k Opuntia ficus-indica 1.05 1.05
875 A177 600k Dracaena aubryana 1.25 1.25
Nos. 872-875 (4) 3.90 3.90

Souvenir Sheet

Africa Day — A178

1993, May 31 *Perf. 12*

876 A178 1500k Leopard 3.15 3.15

Tribal Pipes — A179

1993, Aug. 16 Litho. *Perf. 11½x12*

877 A179 72k Vimbundi .15 .15
878 A179 200k Vimbundi, diff. .42 .42
879 A179 420k Mutopa .88 .88
880 A179 600k Pexi 1.25 1.25
Nos. 877-880 (4) 2.70 2.70

Souvenir Sheet

Union of Portuguese Speaking Capitals — A180

1993, July 30 *Perf. 12x11½*

881 A180 1500k multicolored 3.15 3.15

Turtles — A181

Designs: a, 180k, Chelonia mydas (b). b, 450k, Eretmochelys imbricata. c, 550k, Dermochelys coriacea. d, 630k, Caretta caretta.

1993, July 9 Litho. *Perf. 12½x12*

882 A181 Block of 4, #a.-d. 3.50 3.50

Quioca Art Type of 1992

1993, Sept. 1 Litho. *Perf. 12*

883 A164 300k Leopard .65 .65
884 A164 600k Malhado 1.25 1.25
885 A164 800k Birds 1.65 1.65
886 A164 1000k Chickens 2.00 2.00
Nos. 883-886 (4) 5.55 5.55

Mushrooms — A182

A183

1993 Litho. *Perf. 12*

887 A182 300k Tricholoma georgii .55 .55
a. Perf. 11½ vert. .55 .55
888 A182 500k Amanita phalloides .95 .95
a. Perf. 11½ vert. .95 .95
889 A182 600k Amanita vaginata 1.10 1.10
a. Perf. 11½ vert. 1.10 1.10
890 A182 1000k Macrolepiota procera 1.90 1.90
a. Perf. 11½ vert. 1.90 1.90
b. Booklet pane of 4, #887a-890a 4.50
Nos. 887-890 (4) 4.50 4.50

1994, Jan. 10 Litho. *Perf. 12*

Natl. Culture Day: 500k, Cinganji, wood carving of dancer. 1000k, Ohunya yo soma, staff with woman's face. 1200k, Ongende, sculpture of man on donkey. 2200k, Upi, corn pestle.

891 A183 500k multicolored .45 .45
892 A183 1000k multicolored .90 .90
893 A183 1200k multicolored 1.10 1.10
894 A183 2200k multicolored 2.00 2.00
Nos. 891-894 (4) 4.45 4.45

Hong Kong '94.

Quioca Art Type of 1992

1994, Feb. 21 Litho. *Perf. 12*

895 A164 500k Bird on flower .32 .32
896 A164 2000k Plant with roots 1.30 1.30
897 A164 2500k Feto 1.65 1.65
898 A164 3000k Plant 2.00 2.00
Nos. 895-898 (4) 5.27 5.27

Social Responsibilities of AIDS — A184

Designs: 500k, Mass of people. 1000k, Witchdoctor receiving AIDS through needle, people being educated. 3000k, Stylized man, woman.

1994, May 5 Litho. *Perf. 12*

899 A184 500k multicolored .32 .32
900 A184 1000k multicolored .65 .65
901 A184 3000k multicolored 2.00 2.00
Nos. 899-901 (3) 2.97 2.97

1994 World Cup Soccer Championships, US — A185

1994, June 17 *Perf. 14*

902 A185 500k Large arrows, small ball .32 .32
903 A185 700k Small arrows, large ball .45 .45
904 A185 2200k Ball in goal 1.50 1.50
905 A185 2500k Ball, foot 1.65 1.65
Nos. 902-905 (4) 3.92 3.92

Dinosaurs A186

1994, Aug. 16 Litho. *Perf. 12*

906 A186 1000k Brachiosaurus .15 .15
907 A186 3000k Spinosaurus .55 .55
908 A186 5000k Ouranosaurus .90 .90
909 A186 10,000k Lesothosaurus 1.90 1.90
Nos. 906-909 (4) 3.50 3.50

Souvenir Sheet

910 A186 19,000k Lesothosaurus, map of Africa 3.50 3.50

PHILAKOREA '94, SINGPEX '94. No. 910 contains one 44x34mm stamp.

Tourism A187

1994, Sept. 27 Litho. *Perf. 12x11½*

911 A187 2000k Birds .18 .18
912 A187 4000k Wild animals .35 .35
913 A187 8000k Native women .75 .75
914 A187 10,000k Native men .90 .90
Nos. 911-914 (4) 2.18 2.18

Post Boxes — A188

Designs: 5000k, Letters, bundled mail wall box. 7500k, Wall box for letters. 10,000k, Pillar box. 21,000k, Multi-function units.

1994, Oct. 7 *Perf. 14½*

915 A188 5000k multicolored .45 .45
916 A188 7500k multicolored .70 .70
917 A188 10,000k multicolored .90 .90
918 A188 21,000k multicolored 1.90 1.90
Nos. 915-918 (4) 3.95 3.95

Cotton Pests — A189

Insects: 5000k, Heliothis armigera. 6000k, Bemisia tabasi. 10,000k, Dysdercus. 27,000k, Spodoptera exigua.

1994, Nov. 11 Litho. *Perf. 14*

919 A189 5000k multicolored .45 .45
920 A189 6000k multicolored .55 .55
921 A189 10,000k multicolored .95 .95
922 A189 27,000k multicolored 2.50 2.50
Nos. 919-922 (4) 4.45 4.45

Intl. Olympic Committee, Cent. — A190

1994, Dec. 15

923 A190 27,000k multicolored 2.75 2.75

Tribal Culture A191

Designs: 10,000k, Rubbing sticks to start fire. 15,000k, Extracting sap from tree. 20,000k, Smoking tribal pipe. 25,000k, Shooting bow & arrow. 28,000k, Mothers, children. 30,000k, Cave art.

1995, Jan. 6 Litho. *Perf. 14*

924 A191 10,000k multicolored .42 .42
925 A191 15,000k multicolored .65 .65
926 A191 20,000k multicolored .85 .85
927 A191 25,000k multicolored 1.00 1.00
928 A191 28,000k multicolored 1.10 1.10
929 A191 30,000k multicolored 1.25 1.25
Nos. 924-929 (6) 5.27 5.27

Traditional Ceramics
A192

Designs: No. 930, Pitcher with bust of a woman as stopper. No. 931, Cone-shaped vase. No. 932, Bird-shaped vase. No. 932, Pitcher with bust of a man as stopper.

1995, Jan. 2 Litho. *Perf. 14½*

930 A192 (2) 2nd class natl.
931 A192 (1) 1st class natl.
932 A192 (2) 2nd class intl.
933 A192 (1) 1st class intl.
Set value 3.36 3.36

Rotary Intl., 90th Anniv.
A193

Designs: a, Immunizing boy against polio. b, Medical examination. c, Immunizing girl against polio.
No. 936, Dove over map.

1995, Feb. 23 Litho. *Perf. 14*

934 Strip of 3 2.25 2.25
a.-c. A193 27,000k any single .75 .75
935 Strip of 3 2.25 2.25
a.-c. A193 27,000k any single .75 .75

Souvenir Sheet

936 A193 81,000k multicolored 4.00 4.00
a. English inscription 4.00 4.00

No. 934 has Portuguese inscriptions. No. 935 has English inscriptions. Both were issued in sheets of 9 stamps.
No. 936 contains Portuguese inscription in sheet margin.

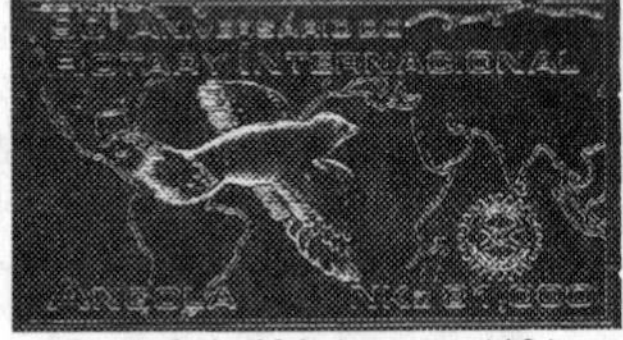

Rotary Intl., 90th Anniv. — A194

Illustration reduced.

Litho. & Embossed

1995, Feb. 23 *Perf. 11½x12*

937 A194 81,000k gold

World Telecommunications Day — A195

Designs: No. 938, 1957 Sputnik 1. No. 939, Shuttle, Intelsat satellite.

1995 Litho. *Perf. 14*

938 A195 27,000k multicolored 1.50 1.50
939 A195 27,000k multicolored 1.50 1.50
a. Souvenir sheet, #938-939 3.00 3.00

Independence, 20th Anniv. — A196

1995, Nov. Litho. *Perf. 14*

940 A196 2900k multicolored 1.50 1.50

4th World Conference on Women, Beijing — A197

Designs: 375k, Women working in fields. 1106k, Woman teaching, girls with book. 1265k, Woman in industry, career woman. 2900k, Woman in native headdress, vert.
1500k, Native mother, children, vert.

1996, Jan. 29 Litho. *Perf. 14*

941 A197 375k multicolored .15 .15
942 A197 1106k multicolored .40 .40
943 A197 1265k multicolored .45 .45
944 A197 2900k multicolored 1.00 1.00
Nos. 941-944 (4) 2.00 2.00

Souvenir Sheet

945 A197 1500k multicolored .50 .50

SEMI-POSTAL STAMPS

Angolan Red Cross — SP1

1991, Sept. 19 Litho. *Perf. 14*

B1 SP1 20k +5k Mother and child .85 .85
B2 SP1 40k +5k Zebra and foal 1.50 1.50

AIR POST STAMPS

Common Design Type
Perf. 13½x13

1938, July 26 Engr. Unwmk.

Name and Value in Black

C1 CD39 10c scarlet .15 .15
C2 CD39 20c purple .25 .15
C3 CD39 50c orange .15 .15
C4 CD39 1a ultra .38 .15
C5 CD39 2a lilac brn .85 .15
C6 CD39 3a dk green 2.25 .25
C7 CD39 5a red brown 3.25 .35
C8 CD39 9a rose carmine 4.25 1.10
C9 CD39 10a magenta 5.50 1.10
Nos. C1-C9 (9) 17.03 3.55

No. C7 exists with overprint "Exposicao Internacional de Nova York, 1939-1940" and Trylon and Perisphere.

AP2

Planes Circling Globe — AP3

1947, Aug. Litho. *Perf. 10½*

C10 AP2 1a red brown 6.25 1.65
C11 AP2 2a yellow grn 6.25 1.65
C12 AP2 3a orange 8.00 1.65
C13 AP2 3.50a orange 10.00 4.00
C14 AP2 5a olive grn 90.00 15.00
C15 AP2 6a rose 90.00 17.50
C16 AP2 9a red 275.00 200.00
C17 AP2 10a green 175.00 60.00
C18 AP2 20a blue 175.00 60.00
C19 AP2 50a black 400.00 200.00
C20 AP2 100a yellow 750.00 600.00
Nos. C10-C20 (11) 1,985. 1,161.

1949, May 1 Photo. *Perf. 11½*

C21 AP3 1a henna brown .15 .15
C22 AP3 2a red brown .40 .15
C23 AP3 3a plum .65 .15
C24 AP3 6a dull green 2.00 .40
C25 AP3 9a violet brown 3.00 1.00
Nos. C21-C25 (5) 6.20 1.85

Catalogue values for unused stamps in this section, from this point to the end of the section, are for Never Hinged items.

Cambambe Dam — AP4

Designs: 1.50e, Oil refinery, vert. 3e, Salazar Dam. 4e, Capt. Teófilo Duarte Dam. 4.50e, Craveiro Lopes Dam. 5e, Cuango Dam. 6e, Quanza River Bridge. 7e, Capt. Teófilo Duarte Bridge. 8.50e, Oliveira Salazar Bridge. 12.50e, Capt. Silva Carvalho Bridge.

Perf. 11½x12, 12x11½

1965, July 12 Litho. Unwmk.

C26 AP4 1.50e multicolored 1.00 .15
C27 AP4 2.50e multicolored .60 .15
C28 AP4 3e multicolored 1.00 .15
C29 AP4 4e multicolored .40 .15
C30 AP4 4.50e multicolored .40 .15
C31 AP4 5e multicolored .65 .20
C32 AP4 6e multicolored .65 .20
C33 AP4 7e multicolored 1.00 .20
C34 AP4 8.50e multicolored 1.25 .55
C35 AP4 12.50e multicolored 1.50 .65
Nos. C26-C35 (10) 8.45 2.55

Stamp Centenary Type

Design: 2.50e, Boeing 707 jet & Angola #2.

1970, Dec. 1 Litho. *Perf. 13½*

C36 A83 2.50e multicolored .45 .15
a. Souv. sheet of 3, #565-566, C36 2.50 2.50

No. C36a sold for 15e.

No. C36 Overprinted with Bar and: "REPUBLICA POPULAR / DE"

1980, June 15 Litho. *Perf. 13½*

C37 A83 2.50e multicolored .15

POSTAGE DUE STAMPS

D1

D2

1904 Unwmk. Typo. *Perf. 11½x12*

J1 D1 5r yellow grn .25 .15
J2 D1 10r slate .25 .15
J3 D1 20r yellow brn .35 .32
J4 D1 30r orange .60 .60
J5 D1 50r gray brown .60 .60
J6 D1 60r red brown 4.00 2.50
J7 D1 100r lilac 1.75 1.65
J8 D1 130r dull blue 1.75 1.65
J9 D1 200r carmine 4.00 3.00
J10 D1 500r gray violet 4.00 3.00
Nos. J1-J10 (10) 17.55 13.62

Postage Due Stamps of 1904 Overprinted in Carmine or Green

1911

J11 D1 5r yellow grn .20 .20
J12 D1 10r slate .20 .20
J13 D1 20r yellow brn .20 .20
J14 D1 30r orange .30 .30
J15 D1 50r gray brown .30 .30
J16 D1 60r red brown .60 .60
J17 D1 100r lilac .60 .60
J18 D1 130r dull blue .60 .60
J19 D1 200r carmine (G) .60 .60
J20 D1 500r gray violet .70 .70
Nos. J11-J20 (10) 4.30 4.30

1921 *Perf. 11½*

J21 D2 ½c yellow green .15 .15
J22 D2 1c slate .15 .15
J23 D2 2c orange brown .15 .15
J24 D2 3c orange .15 .15
J25 D2 5c gray brown .15 .15
J26 D2 6c lt brown .15 .15
J27 D2 10c red violet .15 .15
J28 D2 13c dull blue .20 .20
J29 D2 20c carmine .20 .20
J30 D2 50c gray .20 .20
Set value 1.15 1.15

For surcharges see Nos. 268-270.

Catalogue values for unused stamps in this section, from this point to the end of the section, are for Never Hinged items.

Stamps of 1932 Surcharged in Black

= =
PORTEADO
10
Centavos

1948 Wmk. 232 *Perf. 12x11½*

J31 A14 10c on 20c gray .20 .20
J32 A14 20c on 30c myrtle grn .20 .20
J33 A14 30c on 50c lt brown .45 .45
J34 A14 40c on 1a claret .45 .45
J35 A14 50c on 2a dull vio .90 .45
J36 A14 1a on 5a pale yel grn 1.25 1.00
Nos. J31-J36 (6) 3.45 2.75

Common Design Type

Photogravure and Typographed

1952 Unwmk. *Perf. 14*

Numeral in Red, Frame Multicolored

J37 CD45 10c red brown .15 .15
J38 CD45 30c olive green .15 .15
J39 CD45 50c chocolate .15 .15
J40 CD45 1a dk vio blue .15 .15
J41 CD45 2a red brown .20 .20
J42 CD45 5a black brown .32 .32
Set value .92 .92

NEWSPAPER STAMP

N1

Perf. 11½, 12½, 13½

1893 Typo. Unwmk.

P1 N1 2½r brown 1.00 .70

No. P1 was also used for ordinary postage.
For surcharges see Nos. 37, 82, 180, 235.

POSTAL TAX STAMPS

Pombal Issue

Common Design Types

1925, May 8 Unwmk. *Perf. 12½*

RA1 CD28 15c lilac & black .32 .25
RA2 CD29 15c lilac & black .32 .25
RA3 CD30 15c lilac & black .32 .25
Nos. RA1-RA3 (3) .96 .75

"Charity"
PT1

Coat of Arms
PT2

1929 Litho. *Perf. 11*

Without Gum

RA4 PT1 50c dark blue 2.00 .70

1939 Without Gum *Perf. 10½*

RA5 PT2 50c turq green 1.75 .15
RA6 PT2 1a red 3.25 1.50

A 1.50a, type PT2, was issued for fiscal use.

Catalogue values for unused stamps in this section, from this point to the end of the section, are for Never Hinged items.

Old Man — PT3

Mother and Child — PT4

Designs: 1e, Boy. 1.50e, Girl.

Imprint: "Foto-Lito-E.G.A.-Luanda"

1955 Unwmk. *Perf. 13*

Heads in dark brown

RA7 PT3 50c dk ocher .15 .15
RA8 PT3 1e orange ver .75 .40
RA9 PT3 1.50e brt yel grn .50 .25
Nos. RA7-RA9 (3) 1.40 .80

A 2.50e, type PT3 showing an old woman, was issued for revenue use.
See Nos. RA16, RA19-RA21, RA25-RA27.

No. RA7 Surcharged with New Values and two Bars in Red or Black

1957-58

Head in dark brown

RA11 PT3 10c on 50c dk ocher (R) .25 .25
RA12 PT3 10c on 50c dk ocher ('58) .20 .20
RA13 PT3 30c on 50c dk ocher .22 .22
Nos. RA11-RA13 (3) .67 .67

1959 Litho. *Perf. 13*

Design: 30c, Boy and girl.

RA14 PT4 10c orange & blk .15 .15
RA15 PT4 30c slate & blk .15 .15
Set value .24 .24

Type of 1955 Redrawn

Design: 1e, Boy.

1961, Nov. *Perf. 13*

RA16 PT3 1e sal pink & dk brn .20 .20

Denomination in italics.

Yellow, White and Black Men — PT5

1962, July 1 Typo. *Perf. 10½*

Without Gum

RA17 PT5 50c multicolored .65 .65
RA18 PT5 1e multicolored .32 .32

Issued for the Provincial Settlement Committee (Junta Provincial do Povoamento). The tax was used to promote Portuguese settlement in Angola, and to raise educational and living standards of recent immigrants.
Denominations higher than 1e were used for revenue purposes.

Head Type of 1955
Without Imprint

Designs: 50c, Old man. 1e, Boy. 1.50e, Girl.

1964-65 Litho. *Perf. 11½*

Heads in dark brown

RA19 PT3 50c orange .15 .15
RA20 PT3 1e dull red org ('65) .20 .20
RA21 PT3 1.50e yel grn ('65) .25 .25
Nos. RA19-RA21 (3) .60 .60

No. RA20 is second redrawing of 1e, with bolder lettering and denomination in gothic. Space between "Assistencia" and denomination on RA19-RA21 is ½mm; on 1955 issue space is 2mm.

Map of Angola, Industrial and Farm Workers — PT6

1965, Sept. 1 Litho. *Perf. 13*

RA22 PT6 50c multicolored .35 .15
RA23 PT6 1e multicolored .35 .25

The 2e was used for revenue purposes.

Head Type of 1955
Imprint: "I.N.A." or "INA" (1e)

Designs: 50c, Old man. 1e, Boy. 1.50e, Girl.

1966

Heads in dark brown

RA25 PT3 50c dull orange .15 .15
RA26 PT3 1e dull brick red .15 .15
RA27 PT3 1.50e lt yel grn .32 .15
Nos. RA25-RA27 (3) .62
Set value .32

Woman Planting Tree — PT7

1972 Litho. *Perf. 13*

RA28 PT7 50c shown .15 .15
RA29 PT7 1e Workers .15 .15
RA30 PT7 2e Produce .20 .20
Set value .39 .39

POSTAL TAX DUE STAMPS

Pombal Issue
Common Design Types

1925, May 8 Unwmk. *Perf. 12½*

RAJ1 CD31 30c lilac & black .50 *1.25*
RAJ2 CD32 30c lilac & black .50 *1.25*
RAJ3 CD33 30c lilac & black .50 *1.25*
Nos. RAJ1-RAJ3 (3) 1.50

See note after Portugal No. RAJ4.

ANGRA

'aŋ–grə

LOCATION — An administrative district of the Azores, consisting of the islands of Terceira, Sao Jorge and Graciosa.
GOVT. — A district of Portugal
AREA — 275 sq. mi.
POP. — 70,000 (approx.)
CAPITAL — Angra do Heroismo

1000 Reis = 1 Milreis

King Carlos
A1 A2

Perf. 11½, 12½, 13½

1892-93 Typo. Unwmk.

1 A1 5r yellow 1.25 .85
a. Perf. 11½ 4.00 2.00
2 A1 10r redsh violet 1.75 1.10
3 A1 15r chocolate 2.50 1.50
4 A1 20r lavender 3.50 1.50
a. Perf. 13½ 5.50 1.65
5 A1 25r green 2.25 .15
a. Perf. 12½ 7.00 .50
7 A1 50r blue 7.00 1.50
a. Perf. 13½ 7.00 3.25
8 A1 75r carmine 9.00 2.75
9 A1 80r yellow green 7.00 4.00
10 A1 100r brown, *yel,* perf. 13½ ('93) 22.50 10.00
a. Perf. 12½ 82.50 65.00
11 A1 150r car, *rose* ('93) 25.00 15.00
12 A1 200r dk blue, *bl* ('93) 27.50 22.50
13 A1 300r dk blue, *sal* ('93) 27.50 22.50

Reprints of 50r, 150r, 200r and 300r, made in 1900, are perf. 11½ and ungummed. Value, each $7.50. Reprints of all values, made in 1905, have shiny white gum and clean-cut perf. 13½.

1897-1905 *Perf. 11½*

Name and Value in Black except Nos. 26 and 35

14 A2 2½r gray .25 .15
15 A2 5r orange .25 .15
a. Diagonal half used as 2½r on cover 12.50
16 A2 10r yellow grn .25 .15
17 A2 15r brown 5.50 1.75
18 A2 15r gray grn ('99) .90 .45
19 A2 20r gray violet 1.50 .35
20 A2 25r sea green 1.00 .30
21 A2 25r car rose ('99) .70 .20
22 A2 50r dark blue 3.50 .60
23 A2 50r ultra ('05) 12.50 8.00
24 A2 65r slate bl ('98) .40 .25
25 A2 75r rose 1.25 .55
26 A2 75r gray brn & car, *straw* ('05) 16.00 19.00
27 A2 80r violet .50 .35
28 A2 100r dk blue, *bl* 1.50 .45
29 A2 115r org brn, *pink* ('98) 1.00 .65
30 A2 130r gray brn, *straw* ('98) 1.00 .65
31 A2 150r lt brn, *straw* 1.00 .60
32 A2 180r sl, *pnksh* ('98) 1.50 .90
33 A2 200r red vio, *pnksh* 3.00 1.50
34 A2 300r blue, *rose* 5.50 2.75
35 A2 500r blk & red, *bl* 11.00 5.25
a. Perf. 12½ 14.00 9.25
Nos. 14-35 (22) 70.00 45.00

Azores stamps were used in Angra from 1906 to 1931, when they were superseded by those of Portugal.

ANJOUAN

'an–jü–wän

LOCATION — One of the Comoro Islands in the Mozambique Channel between Madagascar and Mozambique.
GOVT. — Former French colony.
AREA — 89 sq. mi.
POP. — 20,000 (approx. 1912)
CAPITAL — Mossamondu

See Comoro Islands.

100 Centimes = 1 Franc

Navigation and Commerce — A1

Perf. 14x13½

1892-1907 Typo. Unwmk.

Name of Colony in Blue or Carmine

1 A1 1c black, *blue* .85 .80
2 A1 2c brown, *buff* 1.25 1.10
3 A1 4c claret, *lav* 1.40 1.10
4 A1 5c green, *grnsh* 3.25 2.00
5 A1 10c blk, *lavender* 4.00 2.50
6 A1 10c red ('00) 15.00 7.50
7 A1 15c blue, quadrille paper 4.00 3.00
8 A1 15c gray, *lt gray* ('00) 6.00 4.50
9 A1 20c red, *green* 4.00 2.75
10 A1 25c black, *rose* 4.25 3.50
11 A1 25c blue ('00) 7.50 6.25
12 A1 30c brn, *bister* 11.00 10.00
13 A1 35c blk, *yel* ('06) 5.00 3.50
14 A1 40c red, *straw* 20.00 12.50
15 A1 45c blk, *gray grn* ('07) 80.00 55.00
16 A1 50c car, *rose* 25.00 12.50
17 A1 50c brn, *az* ('00) 15.00 9.00
18 A1 75c vio, *orange* 25.00 12.50
19 A1 1fr brnz grn, *straw* 42.50 35.00
Nos. 1-19 (19) 275.00 185.00

Perf. 13½x14 stamps are counterfeits.

Issues of 1892-1907 Surcharged in Black or Carmine **05** **10**

1912

20 A1 5c on 2c brn, *buff* .40 .40
21 A1 5c on 4c cl, *lav* (C) .40 .40
22 A1 5c on 15c blue (C) .40 .40
23 A1 5c on 20c red, *green* .40 .40
24 A1 5c on 25c blk, *rose* (C) .40 .40
25 A1 5c on 30c brn, *bis* (C) .40 .40
26 A1 10c on 40c red, *straw* .60 .60
27 A1 10c on 45c black, *gray green* (C) .85 .85
28 A1 10c on 50c car, *rose* 1.90 1.90
29 A1 10c on 75c vio, *org* 1.00 1.00
30 A1 10c on 1fr brnz grn, *straw* 1.25 1.25
Nos. 20-30 (11) 8.00 8.00

Nos. 21-23, 30 exist in pairs, one without surcharge. Value, $225 each.
Two spacings between the surcharged numerals are found on Nos. 20-30.
Nos. 20-30 were available for use in Madagascar and the Comoro archipelago.

The stamps of Anjouan were superseded by those of Madagascar, and in 1950 by those of Comoro Islands.

ANNAM AND TONKIN

a-'nam and 'tän-'kin

LOCATION — In French Indo-China bordering on the China Sea on the east and Siam on the west.
GOVT. — French Protectorate
AREA — 97,503 sq. mi.
POP. — 14,124,000 (approx. 1890)
CAPITAL — Annam: Hue; Tonkin: Hanoi

For administrative purposes, the Protectorates of Annam, Tonkin, Cambodia, Laos and the Colony of Cochin-China were grouped together and were known as French Indo-China.

100 Centimes = 1 Franc

Stamps of French Colonies, 1881-86 Handstamped Surcharged in Black:

A & T 1 **A & T 5**

Perf. 14x13½

1888, Jan. 21 Unwmk.

1 A9 1c on 2c brn, *buff* 22.50 20.00
a. Inverted surcharge 100.00 100.00
2 A9 1c on 4c claret, *lav* 17.50 14.00
a. Inverted surcharge 100.00 100.00
b. Double surcharge 125.00 125.00
3 A9 5c on 10c blk, *lav* 17.50 15.00
a. Inverted surcharge 100.00 100.00
b. Double surcharge 125.00 125.00

Hyphen between "A" and "T"

7 A9 1c on 2c brn, *buff* 220.00 200.00
a. Inverted surcharge 450.00
8 A9 1c on 4c claret, *lav* 325.00 325.00
9 A9 5c on 10c blk, *lav* 160.00 160.00

A 5c on 2c was prepared but not issued. Value $6,500.
In these surcharges there are different types of numerals and letters.
There are numerous other errors in the placing of the surcharges, including double one inverted, double both inverted, sideways, double one sideways, pair #1, 3, and pair one without surcharge. Such varieties command substantial premiums.
These stamps were superseded in 1892 by those of Indo-China.

Angola stamps can be mounted in the Scott annual Portugal supplement.

ARGENTINA

,är–jən–'tē–nə

LOCATION — In South America
GOVT. — Republic
AREA — 1,084,120 sq. mi.
POP. — 27,949,480 (1980)
CAPITAL — Buenos Aires

100 Centavos = 1 Peso

Watermarks

Wmk. 84- Italic RA

Wmk. 85- Small Sun, 4½mm

Wmk. 86- Large Sun, 6mm

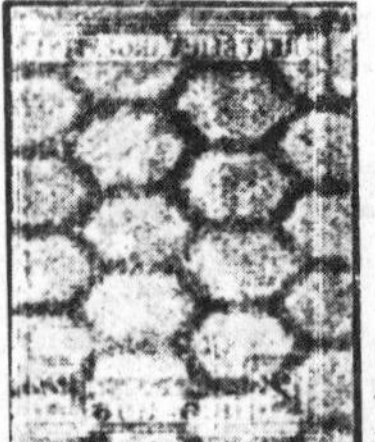

Wmk. 87- Honeycomb

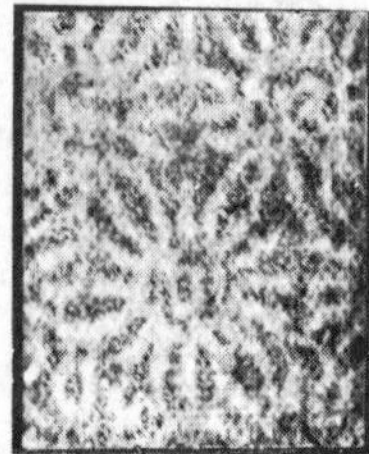

Wmk. 88- Multiple Suns

Wmk. 89- Large Sun

In this watermark the face of the sun is 7mm in diameter, the rays are heavier than in the large sun watermark of 1896-1911 and the watermarks are placed close together, so that parts of several frequently appear on one stamp. This paper was intended to be used for fiscal stamps and is usually referred to as "fiscal sun paper."

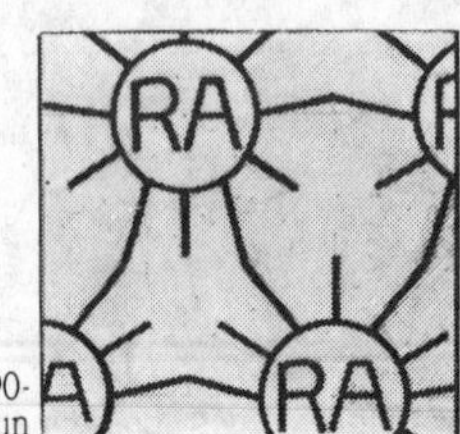

Wmk. 90- RA in Sun

In 1928 watermark 90 was slightly modified, making the diameter of the Sun 9mm instead of 10mm. Several types of this watermark exist.

Wmk. 205- AP in Oval

The letters "AP" are the initials of "AHORRO POSTAL." This paper was formerly used exclusively for Postal Savings stamps.

Wmk. 287- Double Circle and Letters in Sheet

Wmk. 288- RA in Sun with Straight Rays

Wmk. 365- Argentine Arms, "Casa de Moneda de la Nacion" & "RA" Multiple

Argentine Confederation

Symbolical of the Argentine Confederation

A1 A2

1858, May 1 Unwmk. Litho. *Imperf.*

1	A1	5c red	1.50	*9.00*
a.		Colon after "5"	1.10	*11.00*
b.		Colon after "V"	1.10	*11.00*
2	A1	10c green	2.50	*50.00*
a.		Half used as 5c on cover		*190.00*
3	A1	15c blue	16.00	*125.00*
a.		One-third used as 5c on cover		*3,500.*
		Nos. 1-3 (3)	20.00	*184.00*

1860, Jan.

4	A2	5c red	3.25	*62.50*
4A	A2	10c green	7.00	
4B	A2	15c blue	25.00	
		Nos. 4-4B (3)	35.25	

Nos. 4A and 4B were never placed in use. There are nine varieties of Nos. 1, 2 and 3, sixteen of No. 4 and eight of Nos. 4A and 4B. Counterfeits and forged cancellations of Nos. 1-4B are plentiful.

Values for Unused

Unused values for Nos. 5-15, 17-67 are for copies without gum. Copies with original gum command higher prices. From No. 68 onward, unused values are for stamps with original gum as defined in the catalogue introduction.

Argentine Republic

Seal of the Republic — A3

Broad "C" in "CENTAVOS," Accent on "U" of "REPUBLICA"

1862, Jan. 11

5	A3	5c rose	40.00	37.50
a.		5c rose lilac	87.50	35.00
6	A3	10c green	140.00	65.00
b.		Diagonal half used as 5c on cover		*4,250.*
7	A3	15c blue	275.00	225.00
a.		Without accent on "U"	*5,500.*	*2,400.*
b.		Tete beche pair	*45,000.*	*27,500.*
i.		15c ultramarine	425.00	325.00

Broad "C" in "CENTAVOS," No Accent on "U"

1863

7C	A3	5c rose	18.00	21.00
d.		5c rose lilac	100.00	110.00
e.		Worn plate	200.00	52.50
7F	A3	10c yellow green	350.00	140.00
g.		10c olive green	*500.00*	250.00

Narrow "C" in "CENTAVOS," No Accent on "U"

1864

7H	A3	5c rose red	160.00	32.50

The so-called reprints of 10c and 15c are counterfeits. They have narrow "C" and straight lines in shield. Nos. 7C and 7H have been extensively counterfeited.

Rivadavia Issue

Bernardino Rivadavia
A4 A5

Rivadavia — A6

1864-67 Engr. Wmk. 84 *Imperf.*

Clear Impressions

8	A4	5c brown rose	*1,300.*	*160.*
a.		5c orange red ('67)	*1,500.*	*110.*
9	A5	10c green	*1,500.*	*1,000.*
10	A6	15c blue	*7,250.*	*3,000.*

Perf. 11½

Dull to Worn Impressions

11	A4	5c brown rose ('65)	30.00	12.00
11B	A4	5c lake	77.50	17.50
12	A5	10c green	70.00	30.00
a.		Diagonal half used as 5c on cover		*750.00*
13	A6	15c blue	140.00	60.00

1867-72 Unwmk. *Imperf.*

14	A4	5c carmine ('72)	225.	55.
15	A4	5c rose	200.	100.
15A	A5	10c green	*4,000.*	*4,000.*
16	A6	15c blue	*1,750.*	*1,750.*

Nos. 15A-16 issued without gum.

1867 *Perf. 11½*

17	A4	5c carmine	350.00	150.00

Nos. 14, 15 and 17 exist with part of papermaker's wmk. "LACROIX FRERES."

Rivadavia
A7

Manuel Belgrano
A8

Jose de San Martin — A9

Groundwork of Horizontal Lines

1867-68 *Perf. 12*

18	A7	5c vermilion	200.00	9.00
18A	A8	10c green	30.00	4.50
b.		Diag. half used as 5c on cover		*525.00*
19	A9	15c blue	45.00	13.00

Groundwork of Crossed Lines

20	A7	5c vermilion	10.50	.65
21	A9	15c blue	92.50	10.50

See Nos. 27, 33-34, 39 and types A19, A33, A34, A37. For surcharges and overprints see Nos. 30-32, 41-42, 47-51, O6-O7, O26.

Gen. Antonio G. Balcarce
A10

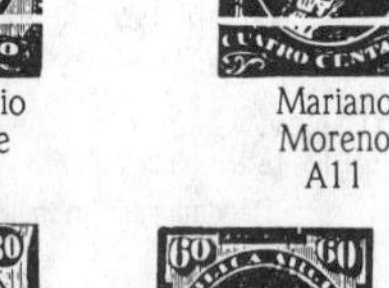

Mariano Moreno
A11

Carlos Maria de Alvear — A12

Gervasio Antonio Posadas — A13

Cornelio Saavedra — A14

1873

22	A10	1c purple	3.50	2.00
a.		1c gray violet	6.25	2.00
23	A11	4c brown	4.75	.40
a.		4c red brown	17.00	2.00
24	A12	30c orange	100.00	15.00
25	A13	60c black	100.00	4.75
26	A14	90c blue	25.00	2.25
		Nos. 22-26 (5)	233.25	23.40

For overprints see Nos. O5, O12-O14, O19-O21, O25, O29.

1873

Laid Paper

27	A8	10c green	150.00	16.00

Nos.18, 18A Surcharged in Black

Nos. 30-31

No. 32

1877, Feb.

Wove Paper

30	A7	1c on 5c vermilion	47.50	15.00
a.		Inverted surcharge	350.00	200.00
31	A7	2c on 5c vermilion	92.50	60.00
a.		Inverted surcharge	700.00	500.00
32	A8	8c on 10c green	125.00	30.00
b.		Inverted surcharge	500.00	425.00
		Nos. 30-32 (3)	265.00	105.00

Forgeries of these surcharges include the inverted and double varieties.

1876-77 ***Rouletted***

33	A7	5c vermilion	150.00	60.00
34	A7	8c lake ('77)	25.00	.35

Belgrano
A17

Dalmacio Vélez Sarsfield
A18

San Martín — A19

1878 ***Rouletted***

35	A17	16c green	8.00	1.10
36	A18	20c blue	8.50	3.00
37	A19	24c blue	17.00	3.00
		Nos. 35-37 (3)	33.50	7.10

See No. 56. For overprints see Nos. O9-O10, O15-O17, O22, O28.

Vicente
Lopez — A20

Alvear — A21

1877-80 ***Perf. 12***

38	A20	2c yellow green	4.25	.90
39	A7	8c lake ('80)	4.25	.35
a.		8c brown lake	*27.50*	.35
40	A21	25c lake ('78)	22.50	6.00
		Nos. 38-40 (3)	31.00	7.25

For overprints see Nos. O4, O11, O18, O24.

No. 18 Surcharged in Black

½
(PROVISORIO

1882

41	A7	½c on 5c ver	.90	.80
a.		Double surcharge	25.00	14.00
b.		Inverted surcharge	17.50	14.00
c.		"PROVISORIO" omitted	35.00	35.00
d.		Fraction omitted	25.00	
e.		"PROVISOBIO"	8.75	8.75
f.		Pair, one without surcharge	87.50	

Perforated across Middle of Stamp

42	A7	½c on 5c ver	2.00	2.00
a.		"PROVISORIO"	12.00	12.00

The "½ (PROVISORIO)" surcharge on Nos. 41-42 is found in two types: I - Small "P" and narrow "V." II - Large "P" and wider "V."

A23

1882 **Typo.** ***Perf. 12***

43	A23	½c brown	1.40	.80
a.		Imperf., pair	25.00	25.00
44	A23	1c red, perf. 14	3.50	1.00
a.		Perf. 12	9.00	4.25
45	A23	12c ultra	55.00	8.75
a.		Perf. 14	45.00	8.75
46	A23	12c grnsh blue, perf. 14	125.00	11.00
		Nos. 43-46 (4)	184.90	21.55

See type A29. For overprints see Nos. O2, O8, O23, O27.

No. 21 Surcharged in Red:

1884 ½ (a) — 1 C 1884 (b) — CUATRO Centavos 1884 (c)

1884 **Engr.** ***Perf. 12***

47	A9 (a)	½c on 15c blue	1.90	1.50
a.		Groundwork of horiz. lines	62.50	50.00
b.		Inverted surcharge	15.00	10.50
48	A9 (b)	1c on 15c blue	9.50	8.50
a.		Groundwork of horiz. lines	6.25	5.00
b.		Inverted surcharge	42.50	35.00
c.		Double surcharge	16.00	14.00
d.		Triple surcharge	325.00	

Nos. 20-21 Surcharged in Black

49	A7 (a)	½c on 5c ver	2.50	2.25
a.		Inverted surcharge	87.50	70.00
b.		Date omitted	32.50	
c.		Pair, one without surch.	110.00	
50	A9 (a)	½c on 15c blue	7.00	6.50
a.		Groundwork of horiz. lines	22.50	17.50
b.		Inverted surcharge	22.50	21.00
51	A7 (c)	4c on 5c ver	8.75	5.00
a.		Inverted surcharge	14.00	10.50
b.		Double surcharge	250.00	150.00
c.		Pair, one without surcharge but with "4" in manuscript	190.00	100.00
		Nos. 47-51 (5)	29.65	23.75

A29

1884-85 **Engr.** ***Perf. 12***

52	A29	½c red brown	.90	.42
a.		Imperf., pair	45.00	
53	A29	1c rose red	5.25	.42
a.		Imperf., pair	45.00	
54	A29	12c grnsh blue ('85)	25.00	1.25
a.		12c deep blue	25.00	1.25
b.		Imperf., pair	45.00	
		Nos. 52-54 (3)	31.15	2.09

For overprints see Nos. O1, O3, O9.

San Martin Type of 1878

1887 **Engr.**

56	A19	24c blue	17.50	1.40

Justo Jose de
Urquiza
A30

Lopez
A31

Miguel Juarez
Celman — A32

Rivadavia (Large
head) — A33

Rivadavia (Small
head)
A34

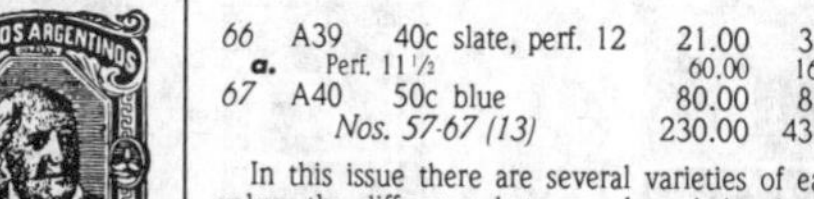
Domingo F.
Sarmiento
A35

Nicolas
Avellaneda
A36

San Martin
A37

Julio A. Roca
A37a

Belgrano
A37b

Manuel
Dorrego — A38

Moreno — A39

Bartolome
Mitre — A40

CINCO CENTAVOS.
A33 - Shows collar on left side only.
A34 - Shows collar on both sides. Lozenges in background larger and clearer than in A33.

1888-90 **Litho.** ***Perf. 11½***

57	A30	½c blue	.50	.45
58	A31	2c yellow green	9.25	6.00
59	A32	3c blue green	1.75	.60
b.		Horiz. pair, imperf. vert.	25.00	
c.		Horiz. pair, imperf. btwn.	27.50	
d.		Vert. pair, imperf. btwn.	10.50	
60	A33	5c carmine	10.50	1.90
61	A34	5c carmine	8.00	.60
b.		Vert. pair, imperf. btwn.	*35.00*	
62	A35	6c red	21.00	15.00
b.		Vert. pair, imperf. btwn.	*35.00*	
c.		Perf. 12	52.50	42.50
63	A36	10c brown	15.00	1.10
64	A37	15c orange	15.00	1.65
64A	A37a	20c green	12.00	1.25
64B	A37b	25c purple	15.00	1.65
65	A38	30c chocolate	21.00	2.50
66	A39	40c slate, perf. 12	21.00	3.00
a.		Perf. 11½	60.00	16.00
67	A40	50c blue	80.00	8.25
		Nos. 57-67 (13)	230.00	43.95

In this issue there are several varieties of each value, the difference between them being in the relative position of the head to the frame.

Imperf., Pairs

57a	A30	½c	35.00	25.00
58a	A31	2c	27.50	
59a	A32	3c	17.50	12.50
61a	A34	5c		*52.50*
62a	A35	6c	*27.50*	
63a	A36	10c	*27.50*	
64c	A37	15c		*110.00*
65a	A38	30c	*140.00*	*110.00*

Urquiza
A41

Velez Sarsfield
A42

Miguel Juarez
Celman
A43

Rivadavia
(Large head)
A44

Sarmiento
A45

Juan Bautista Alberdi
A46

1888-89 **Engr.** ***Perf. 11½, 11½x12***

68	A41	½c ultra	.30	.15
a.		Vert. pair, imperf. horiz.	16.00	10.00
b.		Imperf., pair	16.00	10.00
69	A42	1c brown	.85	.15
a.		Vert. pair, imperf. horiz.	16.00	
b.		Vert. pair, imperf. btwn.	16.00	
c.		Imperf., pair	16.00	
70	A43	3c blue green	2.00	.40
71	A44	5c rose	2.75	.15
a.		Imperf., pair	22.50	16.00
72	A45	6c blue black	1.40	.55
b.		Perf. 11½x12	10.00	2.50
73	A46	12c blue	4.25	1.10
a.		Imperf., pair	13.00	
b.		bluish paper	2.75	.80
c.		Perf. 11½	8.25	3.25
		Nos. 68-73 (6)	11.55	2.50

#69-70 exist with papermakers' watermarks.

See No. 77, types A50, A61. For surcharges see Nos. 83-84.

Jose Maria Paz
A48

Santiago
Derqui
A49

Rivadavia (Small head) A50

Avellaneda A51

Moreno A53

Mitre A54

Posadas — A55

1890 Engr. *Perf. 11½*

75 A48 ¼c green .15 .15
76 A49 2c violet .85 .15
 a. 2c purple .85 .16
 b. 2c slate 1.25 .28
 c. Horiz. pair, imperf. btwn. 15.00
 d. Imperf., pair 18.00
 e. Perf. 11½x12 3.50 .25
77 A50 5c carmine 1.90 .15
 a. Imperf., pair 40.00 20.00
 b. Perf. 11½x12 1.90 .30
78 A51 10c brown 1.65 .25
 b. Imperf., pair 100.00
80 A53 40c olive green 4.00 .80
 a. Imperf., pair 20.00
81 A54 50c orange 4.00 .80
 a. Imperf., pair 30.00
 b. Perf. 11½x12 4.25 1.10
82 A55 60c black 15.00 2.75
 a. Imperf., pair 35.00 35.00
 Nos. 75-82 (7) 27.55 5.05

Type A50 differs from type A44 in having the head smaller, the letters of "Cinco Centavos" not as tall, and the curved ornaments at sides close to the first and last letters of "Republica Argentina."

Lithographed Surcharge on No. 73 in Black or Red

1890 *Perf. 11½x12*

83 A46 ¼c on 12c blue .38 .32
 a. Perf. 11½ 35.00 21.00
84 A46 ¼c on 12c blue (R) .38 .32
 a. Double surcharge 52.50 52.50
 b. Perf. 11½ 7.00 2.00

Surcharge is different on #83 and 84.

Rivadavia A57

Jose de San Martin A58

Gregorio Araoz de Lamadrid — A59

Admiral Guillermo Brown — A60

1891 Engr. *Perf. 11½*

85 A57 8c carmine rose 1.25 .22
 a. Imperf., pair 52.50
86 A58 1p deep blue 40.00 5.50
87 A59 5p ultra 200.00 21.00
88 A60 20p green 275.00 60.00
 Nos. 85-88 (4) 516.25 86.72

A 10p brown and a 50p red were prepared but not issued. Values $1,500 and $1,000.

Velez Sarsfield — A61

"Santa Maria," "Nina" and "Pinta" — A62

1890 *Perf. 11½*

89 A61 1c brown .80 .25

Type A61 is a re-engraving of A42. The figure "1" in each upper corner has a short horizontal serif instead of a long one pointing downward. In type A61 the first and last letters of "Correos y Telegrafos" are closer to the curved ornaments below than in type A42. Background is of horizontal lines (crosshatching on No. 69).

1892, Oct. 12 Wmk. 85 *Perf. 11½*

90 A62 2c light blue 6.00 3.00
 a. Double impression 190.00
91 A62 5c dark blue 8.50 5.00

Discovery of America, 400th anniv. Counterfeits of Nos. 90-91 are litho.

Rivadavia A63

Belgrano A64

San Martin — A65

Perf. 11½, 12 and Compound

1892-95 Wmk. 85

92 A63 ½c dull blue .18 .15
 a. ½c bright ultra 25.00 7.00
93 A63 1c brown .35 .15
94 A63 2c green .35 .15
95 A63 3c orange ('95) 1.00 .15
96 A63 5c carmine 1.50 .15
 b. 5c green (error) 190.00 140.00
98 A64 10c carmine rose 5.50 .15
99 A64 12c deep blue ('93) 5.50 .22
100 A64 16c gray 10.00 .55
101 A64 24c gray brown 10.00 .55
 b. Perf. 12 25.00 7.00
102 A64 50c blue green 15.00 .55
 b. Perf. 12 25.00 2.75
103 A65 1p lake ('93) 9.00 .70
 a. 1p red brown 17.50 5.00
104 A65 2p dark green 21.00 2.25
 a. Perf. 12 77.50 27.50
105 A65 5p dark blue 38.00 2.75
 Nos. 92-105 (13) 117.38 8.47

Part-perforate varieties of Nos. 92-98 include vert. or horiz. pairs imperf. between and pairs imperf. vert. or horiz. Value $6-$35.

The high values of this and succeeding issues are frequently punched with the word "INUTILIZADO," parts of the letters showing on each stamp. These punched stamps sell for only a small fraction of the catalogue values.

Reprints of No. 96b have white gum. The original stamp has yellowish gum. Value $125.

Imperf., Pairs

92b A63 ½c 27.50
93a A63 1c 27.50
94a A63 2c 12.50
96a A63 5c 12.50 12.50
98a A64 10c 32.50
99a A64 12c 32.50
100a A64 16c 32.50
101a A64 24c 32.50
102a A64 50c 25.00
103b A65 1p 35.00
105a A65 5p 70.00

1896-97 Wmk. 86

106 A63 ½c slate .35 .15
 a. ½c gray blue .35 .15
 b. ½c indigo .35 .15
107 A63 1c brown .35 .15
108 A63 2c yellow green .60 .15
109 A63 3c orange .60 .15
110 A63 5c carmine .60 .15
 a. Imperf., pair 18.00
111 A64 10c carmine rose 5.00 .15
112 A64 12c deep blue 2.50 .15
 a. Imperf., pair *27.50*
113 A64 16c gray 6.00 .52
114 A64 24c gray brown 10.50 1.25
 a. Imperf., pair 15.00
115 A64 30c orange ('97) 7.50 .45
116 A64 50c blue green 9.50 .45
117 A64 80c dull violet 11.00 .60
118 A65 1p lake 16.00 .75
119 A65 1p20c black ('97) 8.50 3.50
120 A65 2p dark green 15.00 7.00
121 A65 5p dark blue 75.00 7.00
 a. Perf. 12 165.00 42.50
 Nos. 106-121 (16) 169.00 22.57

Allegory, Liberty Seated
A66 A67

Perf. 11½, 12 and Compound

1899-1903

122 A66 ½c yellow brown .15 .15
123 A66 1c green .20 .15
124 A66 2c slate .20 .15
125 A66 3c orange ('01) .85 .15
126 A66 4c yellow ('03) 1.50 .16
127 A66 5c carmine rose .20 .15
128 A66 6c black ('03) 1.00 .18
129 A66 10c dark green 1.50 .15
130 A66 12c dull blue 1.00 .28
131 A66 12c olive grn ('01) 1.00 .24
132 A66 15c sea green ('01) 2.75 .15
132B A66 15c dull blue ('01) 3.00 .25
133 A66 16c orange 7.50 3.75
134 A66 20c claret 2.00 .15
135 A66 24c violet 3.50 .70
136 A66 30c rose 7.50 .40
137 A66 30c vermilion ('01) 3.75 .15
 a. 30c scarlet 50.00 2.50
138 A66 50c brt blue 4.75 .16
139 A67 1p bl & blk, perf. 11½ 14.00 .70
 a. Center inverted *1,500.* *475.00*
 b. Perf. 12 190.00 47.50
140 A67 5p orange & blk 57.50 9.25
 Punch cancellation .75
 a. Center inverted *1,700.*
141 A67 10p green & blk 50.00 9.25
 Punch cancellation .75
 a. Center inverted *2,400.*
 Punch cancellation 675.00
142 A67 20p red & black 200.00 27.50
 Punch cancellation .35
 a. Center invtd.(punch cancel) *2,000.*
 Nos. 122-142 (22) 363.85 54.17

Part-perforate varieties of Nos. 122-129 include vert. or horiz. pairs imperf. between and pairs imperf. vert. or horiz. Value 35 cents to $7.

Imperf., Pairs

122a A66 ½c 17.00
123a A66 1c 24.00
124a A66 2c 6.00 3.00
125a A66 3c 95.00 50.00
127a A66 5c 5.00 3.50
128a A66 6c 30.00
129a A66 10c 30.00
132a A66 15c 30.00

River Port of Rosario A68

1902, Oct. 26 *Perf. 11½, 11½x12*

143 A68 5c deep blue 4.50 2.50
 a. Imperf., pair 95.00

Completion of port facilities at Rosario.

San Martin
A69 A70

Perf. 13½, 13½x12½

1908-09 Typo.

144 A69 ½c violet .15 .15
145 A69 1c brnsh buff .18 .15
146 A69 2c chocolate .55 .15
147 A69 3c green .70 .32
148 A69 4c redsh violet 1.40 .32
149 A69 5c carmine .32 .15
150 A69 6c olive bister .80 .25
151 A69 10c gray green 1.50 .15
152 A69 12c yellow buff .40 .38
153 A69 12c dk blue ('09) 1.25 .15
154 A69 15c apple green 1.75 .85
155 A69 20c ultra 1.25 .15
156 A69 24c red brown 3.25 .60
157 A69 30c dull rose 5.00 .60
158 A69 50c black 4.75 .42
159 A70 1p sl bl & pink 11.00 1.75
 Nos. 144-159 (16) 34.25 6.54

The 1c blue was not issued. Value $250.

Wmk. 86 appears on ½, 1, 6, 20, 24 and 50c. Other values have similar wmk. with wavy rays.

Stamps lacking wmk. are from outer rows printed on sheet margin.

Pyramid of May — A71

Nicolas Rodriguez Pena and Hipolito Vieytes — A72

Meeting at Pena's Home — A73

Designs: 3c, Miguel de Azcuenaga (1754-1833) and Father Manuel M. Alberti (1763-1811). 4c, Viceroy's house and Fort Buenos Aires. 5c, Cornelio Saavedra (1759-1829). 10c, Antonio Luis Beruti (1772-1842) and French distributing badges. 12c, Congress building. 20c, Juan Jose Castelli (1764-1812) and Domingo Matheu (1765-1831). 24c, First council. 30c, Manuel Belgrano (1770-1820) and Juan Larrea (1782-1847). 50c, First meeting of republican government, May 25, 1810. 1p, Mariano Moreno (1778-1811) and Juan Jose Paso (1758-1833). 5p, Oath of the Junta. 10p, Centenary Monument. 20p, Jose Francisco de San Martin (1778-1850).

Inscribed "1810 1910"
Various Frames

1910, May 1 Engr. *Perf. 11½*

160 A71 ½c bl & gray bl .32 .15
161 A72 1c blue grn & blk .32 .15
 b. Horiz. pair, imperf. btwn. *65.00*
162 A73 2c olive & gray .22 .15
163 A72 3c green .70 .15
164 A73 4c dk blue & grn .70 .24
165 A71 5c carmine .45 .15
166 A73 10c yel brn & blk 1.75 .22
167 A73 12c brt blue 1.40 .24
168 A72 20c gray brn & blk 3.25 .35
169 A73 24c org brn & bl 1.75 .90
170 A72 30c lilac & blk 1.75 .65
171 A71 50c carmine & blk 4.50 .90
172 A72 1p brt blue 10.00 3.50
173 A73 5p orange & vio 70.00 30.00
 Punch cancel 2.50
174 A71 10p orange & blk 90.00 65.00
 Punch cancel 3.00
175 A71 20p dp blue & ind 150.00 90.00
 Punch cancel 4.50
 Nos. 160-175 (16) 337.11 192.75

Centenary of the republic.

Center Inverted

160a A71 ½c *650.00*
161a A72 1c *650.00*
162a A73 2c *800.00*
164a A73 4c *375.00*
167a A73 12c *650.00*
171a A71 50c *650.00*
173a A73 5p *650.00*

Domingo F. Sarmiento A87

Agriculture A88

1911, May 15 Typo. *Perf. 13½*

176 A87 5c gray brn & blk .75 .50

Domingo Faustino Sarmiento (1811-88), pres. of Argentina, 1868-74.

Wmk. 86, without Face

1911 Engr. *Perf. 12*

Size: 19x25mm

177 A88 5c vermilion .30 .15
178 A88 12c deep blue 4.00 .18
 Set value .24

Wmk. 86, with Face

1911 Typo. *Perf. 13½x12½*

Size: 18x23mm

179 A88 ½c violet .15 .15
180 A88 1c brown ocher .15 .15
181 A88 2c chocolate .18 .15
 a. Perf. 13½ 4.25 1.75
 b. Imperf., pair 26.00
182 A88 3c green .42 .15
183 A88 4c brown violet .35 .25
184 A88 10c gray green .52 .15

185 A88 20c ultra 4.25 1.00
186 A88 24c red brown 5.25 3.50
187 A88 30c claret 1.75 .48
188 A88 50c black 8.00 .85
Nos. 179-188 (10) 21.02 6.83

The 5c dull red is a proof. In this issue Wmk. 86 comes: straight rays (4c, 20c, 24c) and wavy rays (2c). All other values exist with both forms.

Wmk. 87 (Horiz. or Vert.)

1912-14 ***Perf. 13½x12½***

189 A88 ½c violet .16 .15
190 A88 1c ocher .16 .15
191 A88 2c chocolate .32 .15
192 A88 3c green .60 .16
193 A88 4c brown violet .60 .16
194 A88 5c red .16 .15
195 A88 10c deep green 1.40 .15
196 A88 12c deep blue 1.40 .15
197 A88 20c ultra 8.00 .70
198 A88 24c red brown 3.25 1.65
199 A88 30c claret 8.00 .60
200 A88 50c black 5.00 .60
Nos. 189-200 (12) 29.05 4.77

See Nos. 208-212. For overprints see Nos. OD1-OD8, OD47-OD54, OD102-OD108, OD146-OD152, OD183-OD190, OD235-OD241, OD281-OD284, OD318-OD323.

Perf. 13½

189a A88 ½c .80 .28
190a A88 1c .80 .28
191a A88 2c .80 .16
192a A88 3c 35.00 16.00
193a A88 4c 1.65 .70
194a A88 5c .32 .15
196a A88 12c 3.25 .80
197a A88 20c 5.00 .70
Nos. 189a-197a (8) 47.62 19.07

A89

1912-13 ***Perf. 13½***

201 A89 1p dull bl & rose 6.00 1.00
Punch cancel .28
202 A89 5p slate & ol grn 19.00 6.00
Punch cancel .60
203 A89 10p violet & blue 75.00 9.00
Punch cancel 1.40
204 A89 20p blue & claret 175.00 60.00
Punch cancel 2.00
Nos. 201-204 (4) 275.00 76.00

1915 Unwmk. ***Perf. 13½x12½***

208 A88 1c ocher .50 .15
209 A88 2c chocolate .50 .15
212 A88 5c red .50 .15
Nos. 208-212 (3) 1.50
Set value .20

Only these denominations were printed on paper without watermark.

Other stamps of the series are known unwatermarked but they are from the outer rows of sheets the other parts of which are watermarked.

Francisco Narciso de Laprida
A90

Declaration of Independence
A91

Jose de San Martin
A92 A92a

Perf. 13½, 13½x12½

1916, July 9 Litho. Wmk. 87

215 A90 ½c violet .18 .15
216 A90 1c buff .24 .15

Perf. 13½x12½

217 A90 2c chocolate .18 .15
218 A90 3c green .45 .15
219 A90 4c red violet .68 .15

Perf. 13½

220 A91 5c red .30 .15
a. Imperf., pair 40.00
221 A91 10c gray green 1.50 .15
222 A92 12c blue .65 .15
223 A92 20c ultra 1.00 .25
224 A92 24c red brown 1.65 .75
225 A92 30c claret 1.65 .32
226 A92 50c gray black 3.25 .42
227 A92a 1p sl bl & red 9.25 4.00
Punch cancel .50
a. Imperf., pair 325.00
228 A92a 5p blk & gray grn 110.00 40.00
Punch cancel 3.25
229 A92a 10p violet & blue 110.00 75.00
Punch cancel 2.50
230 A92a 20p dull blue & cl 165.00 67.50
Punch cancel 1.00
a. Imperf., pair 650.00
Nos. 215-230 (16) 405.98 189.44

Cent. of Argentina's declaration of independence of Spain, July 9, 1816.

The watermark is either vert. or horiz. on Nos. 215-220, 222; only vert. on No. 221, and only horiz. on Nos. 223-230.

For overprints see #OD9, OD55-OD56, OD109, OD153, OD191-OD192, OD285, OD324.

A93

A94

A94a

Juan Gregorio Pujol — A95

1917 ***Perf. 13½, 13½x12½***

231 A93 ½c violet .20 .15
232 A93 1c buff .25 .15
233 A93 2c brown .25 .15
234 A93 3c lt green .75 .15
235 A93 4c red violet .75 .40
236 A93 5c red .25 .15
a. Imperf., pair 14.00
237 A93 10c gray green 1.50 .15

Perf. 13½

238 A94 12c blue 1.00 .15
239 A94 20c ultra 1.50 .18
240 A94 24c red brown 4.50 2.00
241 A94 30c claret 4.50 .60
242 A94 50c gray black 4.00 .60
243 A94a 1p slate bl & red 4.00 .35
244 A94a 5p black & gray grn 17.00 3.00
Punch cancel 1.50
245 A94a 10p violet & blue 40.00 9.25
Punch cancel 1.00
246 A94a 20p dull blue & cl 77.50 15.00
Punch cancel .80
a. Center inverted 1,200. 875.00
Nos. 231-246 (16) 157.95 32.43

The watermark is either vert. or horiz. on Nos. 231-236, 238; only vert. on No. 237, and only horiz. on Nos. 239-246.

1918, June 15 Litho. ***Perf. 13½***

247 A95 5c bister & gray .70 .25

Cent. of the birth of Juan G. Pujol (1817-61), lawyer and legislator.

Perf. 13½, 13½x12½

1918-19 Unwmk.

248 A93 ½c violet .15 .15
249 A93 1c buff .15 .15
a. Imperf., pair 14.00
250 A93 2c brown .15 .15
251 A93 3c lt green .25 .15
252 A93 4c red violet .25 .15
253 A93 5c red .15 .15
254 A93 10c gray green 1.10 .15

Perf. 13½

255 A94 12c blue 1.25 .15
256 A94 20c ultra 1.65 .15
257 A94 24c red brown 2.00 .50
258 A94 30c claret 2.50 .30
259 A94 50c gray black 5.50 .26
Nos. 248-259 (12) 15.10
Set value 1.50

The stamps of this issue sometimes show letters of papermakers' watermarks.

There were two printings, in 1918 and 1923, using different ink and paper.

Perf. 13½, 13½x12½

1920 Wmk. 88

264 A93 ½c violet .20 .15
265 A93 1c buff .26 .15
266 A93 2c brown .26 .15
267 A93 3c green 1.50 .32
268 A93 4c red violet 2.00 1.25
269 A93 5c red .40 .15
270 A93 10c gray green 3.25 .15

Perf. 13½

271 A94 12c blue 1.75 .15
272 A94 20c ultra 2.50 .15
274 A94 30c claret 8.25 .70
275 A94 50c gray black 5.00 .90
Nos. 264-275 (11) 25.37
Set value 3.50

See #292-300, 304-307A, 310-314, 318, 322.

For overprints see Nos. OD10-OD20, OD57-OD71, OD74, OD110-OD121, OD154-OD159, OD161-OD162, OD193-OD207, OD209-OD211, OD242-OD252, OD254-OD255, OD286-OD290, OD325-OD328, OD330.

Belgrano's Mausoleum
A96

Creation of Argentine Flag
A97

Gen. Manuel Belgrano — A98

1920, June 18 ***Perf. 13½***

280 A96 2c red .38 .20
a. Perf. 13½x12½ .38 .20
281 A97 5c rose & blue .38 .15
282 A98 12c green & blue .75 .75
Nos. 280-282 (3) 1.51 1.10

Belgrano (1770-1820), Argentine general, patriot and diplomat.

Gen. Justo Jose de Urquiza — A99

Bartolome Mitre — A100

1920, Nov. 11

283 A99 5c gray blue .24 .15

Gen. Justo Jose de Urquiza (1801-70), pres. of Argentina, 1854-60. See No. 303.

1921, June 26 Unwmk.

284 A100 2c violet brown .26 .20
285 A100 5c light blue .26 .15
Set value .29

Bartolome Mitre (1821-1906), pres. of Argentina, 1862-65.

Allegory, Pan-America — A101

1921, Aug. 25 ***Perf. 13½***

286 A101 3c violet .55 .30
287 A101 5c blue .80 .15
288 A101 10c vio brown 1.40 .35
289 A101 12c rose 2.00 .75
Nos. 286-289 (4) 4.75 1.55

Inscribed "Buenos Aires-Agosto de 1921"
A102

Inscribed "Republica Argentina"
A103

1921, Oct. ***Perf. 13½x12½***

290 A102 5c rose .28 .15
a. Perf. 13½ 1.25 .15
291 A103 5c rose 1.50 .15
a. Perf. 13½ 2.50 .15
Set value .15

1st Pan-American Postal Cong., Buenos Aires, Aug., 1921.

See Nos. 308-309, 319. For overprints see Nos. OD72, OD160, OD208, OD253, OD329.

Perf. 13½, 13½x12½

1920 Wmk. 89

292 A93 ½c violet 2.00 .75
293 A93 1c buff 5.00 .75
294 A93 2c brown 3.00 .75
297 A93 5c red 4.00 .50
298 A93 10c gray green 4.00 .38

Perf. 13½

299 A94 12c blue 3,000. 125.00
300 A94 20c ultra 12.00 .75
Nos. 292-298,300 (6) 30.00 3.88

1920

303 A99 5c gray blue 275.00 190.00

Perf. 13½, 13½x12½

1922-23 Wmk. 90

304 A93 ½c violet .15 .15
305 A93 1c buff .15 .15
306 A93 2c brown .15 .15
307 A93 3c green .45 .28
307A A93 4c red violet 3.75 1.00
308 A102 5c rose 2.25 .15
309 A103 5c red 1.50 .15
310 A93 10c gray green 4.75 .28

Perf. 13½

311 A94 12c blue .85 .15
312 A94 20c ultra 1.25 .15
313 A94 24c red brown 9.25 4.50
314 A94 30c claret 5.50 .50
Nos. 304-314 (12) 30.00 7.61

Paper with Gray Overprint RA in Sun

Perf. 13½, 13½x12½

1922-23 Unwmk.

318 A93 2c brown 3.00 1.00
319 A103 5c red 2.00 .30

Perf. 13½

322 A94 20c ultra 15.00 1.50
Nos. 318-322 (3) 20.00 2.80

San Martín
A104 A105
With Period after Value

1923, May Litho. Wmk. 90

323 A104 ½c red violet .20 .18
324 A104 1c buff .32 .15
325 A104 2c dark brown .32 .15
326 A104 3c lt green .32 .22
327 A104 4c red brown .32 .18
328 A104 5c red .32 .15
329 A104 10c dull green 2.50 .15
330 A104 12c deep blue .40 .15
331 A104 20c ultra 1.00 .15
332 A104 24c lt brown 2.50 1.50
333 A104 30c claret 7.75 .60
334 A104 50c black 4.00 .35

Without Period after Value

Wmk. 87 ***Perf. 13½***

335 A105 1p blue & red 4.00 .15
336 A105 5p gray lilac & grn 16.00 1.75
Punch cancel .60
337 A105 10p claret & blue 55.00 10.50
Punch cancel 1.00
338 A105 20p slate & brn lake 90.00 30.00
Punch cancel .60
a. Center inverted
Nos. 323-338 (16) 184.95 46.33

Nos. 335-338 and 353-356 canceled with round or oval killers in purple (revenue cancellations) sell for one-fifth to one-half as much as postally used copies.

For overprints see Nos. 399-404.

Design of 1923
Without Period after Value

Perf. 13½, 13½x12½

1923-24 Litho. Wmk. 90

340 A104 ½c red violet .15 .15
341 A104 1c buff .15 .15
342 A104 2c dk brown .15 .15
343 A104 3c green .15 .15
a. Imperf., pair 8.00
344 A104 4c red brown .40 .15
345 A104 5c red .15 .15

346 A104 10c dull green .28 .15
347 A104 12c deep blue .48 .15
348 A104 20c ultra .65 .15
349 A104 24c lt brown 1.65 .70
350 A104 25c purple .80 .15
351 A104 30c claret 1.65 .15
352 A104 50c black 1.65 .15
353 A105 1p blue & red 2.00 .15
354 A105 5p dk violet & grn 15.00 .75
Punch cancel .20
355 A105 10p claret & blue 32.50 3.25
Punch cancel .22
356 A105 20p slate & lake 47.50 7.50
Punch cancel .22
Nos. 340-356 (17) 105.31 14.15

1931-33

Typographed

343b A104 3c 1.40 .26
345a A104 5c 2.50 .15
346a A104 10c 4.00 .20
347a A104 12c 8.50 1.50
348a A104 20c 32.50 1.65
350a A104 25c 20.00 .75
351a A104 30c 15.00 .40
Nos. 343b-351a (7) 83.90 4.91

The typographed stamps were issued only in coils and have a rough impression with heavy shading about the eyes and nose. Nos. 343 and 346 are known without watermark.

Nos. 341-345, 347-349, 351a may be found in pairs, one with period.

See note after No. 338. See Nos. 362-368. For overprints see Nos. OD21-OD33, OD75-OD87, OD122-OD133, OD163-OD175, OD212-OD226, OD256-OD268, OD291-OD304, OD331-OD345.

Rivadavia — A106

1926, Feb. 8 *Perf. 13½*
357 A106 5c rose .42 .15

Presidency of Bernardino Rivadavia, cent.

Rivadavia A108

San Martin A109

General Post Office, 1926 — A110

General Post Office, 1826 — A111

1926, July 1 *Perf. 13½x12½*
358 A108 3c gray green .15 .15
359 A109 5c red .15 .15

Perf. 13½

360 A110 12c deep blue .90 .18
361 A111 25c chocolate 1.65 .15
a. "1326" for "1826" 6.00 .75
Nos. 358-361 (4) 2.85
Set value .38

Centenary of the Post Office.

For overprints see Nos. OD34, OD88, OD134, OD227-OD228, OD269, OD305, OD346.

Type of 1923-31 Issue
Without Period after Value

1927 Wmk. 205 *Perf. 13½x12½*
362 A104 ½c red violet .24 .24
a. Pelure paper 1.75 1.50
363 A104 1c buff .24 .24
364 A104 2c dark brown .24 .15
a. Pelure paper .35 .18
365 A104 5c red .30 .15
a. Period after value 3.50 1.90
b. Pelure paper .45 .22
366 A104 10c dull green 4.50 2.25
367 A104 20c ultra 18.00 2.25

Perf. 13½

368 A105 1p blue & red 35.00 7.00
Nos. 362-368 (7) 58.52 12.28

Arms of Argentina and Brazil — A112

Wmk. RA in Sun (90)

1928, Aug. 27 *Perf. 12½x13*
369 A112 5c rose red 1.00 .25
370 A112 12c deep blue 1.50 .50

Cent. of peace between the Empire of Brazil and the United Provinces of the Rio de la Plata.

Allegory, Discovery of the New World A113

"Spain" and "Argentina" A114

"America" Offering Laurels to Columbus — A115

1929, Oct. 12 Litho. *Perf. 13½*
371 A113 2c lilac brown .85 .25
372 A114 5c light red .85 .15
373 A115 12c dull blue 2.00 .75
Nos. 371-373 (3) 3.70 1.15

Discovery of America by Columbus, 437th anniv.

Spirit of Victory Attending Insurgents A116

March of the Victorious Insurgents A117

Perf. 13½x12½ (A116), 12½x13 (A117)

1930
374 A116 ½c violet gray .15 .15
375 A116 1c myrtle green .18 .18
376 A117 2c dull violet .24 .15
377 A116 3c green .32 .25
378 A116 4c violet .25 .25
379 A116 5c rose red .15 .15
380 A116 10c gray black .75 .35
381 A117 12c dull blue .55 .25
382 A117 20c ocher .55 .25
383 A117 24c red brown 2.25 1.50
384 A117 25c green 2.50 1.50
385 A117 30c deep violet 4.50 2.00
386 A117 50c black 6.25 2.50
387 A117 1p sl bl & red 11.00 10.00
388 A117 2p black & org 22.50 10.00
389 A117 5p dull grn & blk 65.00 40.00
390 A117 10p dp red brn & dull blue 90.00 42.50
391 A117 20p yel grn & dl bl 225.00 100.00
392 A117 50p dk grn & vio 600.00 450.00
Nos. 374-390 (17) 207.14 111.98

Revolution of 1930.

Nos. 387-392 with oval (parcel post) cancellation sell for less.

For overprint see No. 405.

1931 *Perf. 12½x13*
393 A117 ½c red violet .15 .15
394 A117 1c gray black 1.25 .50
395 A117 3c green .60 .30
396 A117 4c red brown .35 .25
397 A117 5c red .18 .15
a. Plane omitted, top left corner 3.00 1.65
398 A117 10c dl grn 1.25 .28
Nos. 393-398 (6) 3.78 1.63

Revolution of 1930.

Stamps of 1924-25 Overprinted in Red or Green

-6-
Septiembre
1930 - 1931

1931, Sept. 6 *Perf. 13½, 13½x12½*
399 A104 3c green .20 .20
400 A104 10c dull green .60 .60
401 A104 30c claret (G) 3.25 3.25
402 A104 50c black 3.25 3.25

Overprinted in Blue

1930
Septiembre
6
1931

403 A105 1p blue & red 3.75 3.25
404 A105 5p dk violet & grn 70.00 20.00

No. 388 Overprinted in Blue

6 Septiembre 1931

Perf. 12½x13

405 A117 2p black & orange 13.00 9.00
Nos. 399-405 (7) 94.05 39.55

1st anniv. of the Revolution of 1930.
See Nos. C30-C34.

Refrigeration Compressor — A118

Perf. 13½x12½

1932, Aug. 29 **Litho.**
406 A118 3c green .40 .24
407 A118 10c scarlet 1.25 .15
408 A118 12c gray blue 3.25 1.25
Nos. 406-408 (3) 4.90 1.64

6th Intl. Refrigeration Congress.

Port of La Plata — A119

Pres. Julio A. Roca — A120

Municipal Palace — A121

Cathedral of La Plata — A122

Dardo Rocha — A123

Perf. 13½x13, 13x13½ (10c)

1933, Jan.
409 A119 3c green & dk brn .32 .30
410 A120 10c orange & dk vio .50 .20
411 A121 15c dk blue & dp blue 3.50 1.75
412 A122 20c violet & yel brn 1.65 1.00
413 A123 30c dk grn & vio brn 14.00 5.50
Nos. 409-413 (5) 19.97 8.75

50th anniv. of the founding of the city of La Plata, Nov. 19th, 1882.

Christ of the Andes — A124

Buenos Aires Cathedral A125

1934, Oct. 1 *Perf. 13x13½, 13½x13*
414 A124 10c rose & brown .70 .18
415 A125 15c dark blue 1.40 .45

32nd Intl. Eucharistic Cong., Oct. 10-14.

"Liberty" with Arms of Brazil and Argentina A126

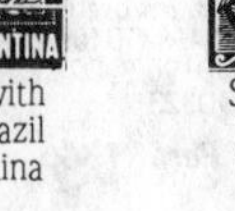

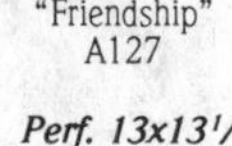

Symbolical of "Peace" and "Friendship" A127

1935, May 15 *Perf. 13x13½*
416 A126 10c red .85 .24
417 A127 15c blue 1.65 .48

Visit of Pres. Getulio Vargas of Brazil.

Belgrano A128

Sarmiento A129

Urquiza A130

Louis Braille A131

San Martin A132

Brown A133

Moreno A134

Alberdi A135

Nicolas Avellaneda A136

Rivadavia A137

Mitre
A138

Bull (Cattle Breeding)
A139

Martin Güemes
A140

Agriculture
A141

Merino Sheep (Wool) — A142

Sugar Cane
A143

Oil Well (Petroleum)
A144

Map of South America
A145 A146

Fruit
A147

Iguacu Falls (Scenic Wonders)
A148

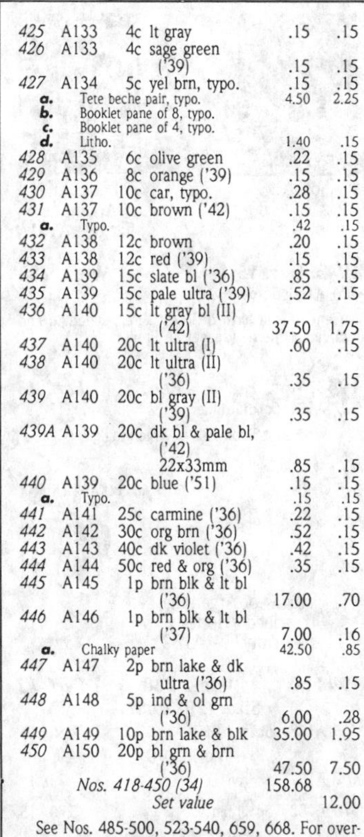

Grapes (Vineyards)
A149

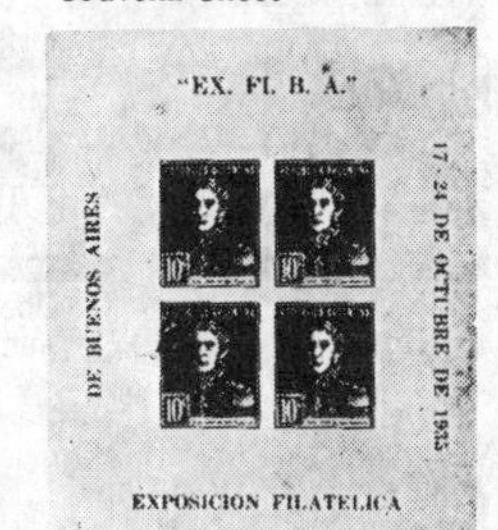

Cotton
A150

Two types of A140:
Type I - Inscribed Juan Martin Guemes.
Type II - Inscribed Martin Güemes.

Perf. 13, 13½x13, 13x13½

1935-51 Litho. Wmk. 90

418	A128	½c red violet	.15	.15
419	A129	1c buff	.15	.15
a.		Typo.	.15	.15
420	A130	2c dark brown	.15	.15
421	A131	2½c black ('39)	.15	.15
422	A132	3c green	.15	.15
423	A132	3c lt gray ('39)	.15	.15
424	A134	3c lt gray ('46)	.15	.15
425	A133	4c lt gray	.15	.15
426	A133	4c sage green ('39)	.15	.15
427	A134	5c yel brn, typo.	.15	.15
a.		Tete beche pair, typo.	4.50	2.25
b.		Booklet pane of 8, typo.		
c.		Booklet pane of 4, typo.		
d.		Litho.	1.40	.15
428	A135	6c olive green	.22	.15
429	A136	8c orange ('39)	.15	.15
430	A137	10c car, typo.	.28	.15
431	A137	10c brown ('42)	.15	.15
a.		Typo.	.42	.15
432	A138	12c brown	.20	.15
433	A138	12c red ('39)	.15	.15
434	A139	15c slate bl ('36)	.85	.15
435	A139	15c pale ultra ('39)	.52	.15
436	A140	15c lt gray bl (II) ('42)	37.50	1.75
437	A140	20c lt ultra (I)	.60	.15
438	A140	20c lt ultra (II) ('36)	.35	.15
439	A140	20c bl gray (II) ('39)	.35	.15
439A	A139	20c dk bl & pale bl, ('42) 22x33mm	.85	.15
440	A139	20c blue ('51)	.15	.15
a.		Typo.	.15	.15
441	A141	25c carmine ('36)	.22	.15
442	A142	30c org brn ('36)	.52	.15
443	A143	40c dk violet ('36)	.42	.15
444	A144	50c red & org ('36)	.35	.15
445	A145	1p brn blk & lt bl ('36)	17.00	.70
446	A146	1p brn blk & lt bl ('37)	7.00	.16
a.		Chalky paper	42.50	.85
447	A147	2p brn lake & dk ultra ('36)	.85	.15
448	A148	5p ind & ol grn ('36)	6.00	.28
449	A149	10p brn lake & blk	35.00	1.95
450	A150	20p bl grn & brn ('36)	47.50	7.50
		Nos. 418-450 (34)	158.68	
		Set value		12.00

See Nos. 485-500, 523-540, 659, 668. For overprints see Nos. O37-O41, O43-O51, O53-O56, O58-O78, O108, O112, OD35-OD46, OD89-OD101, OD135-OD145, OD176-OD182C, OD229-OD234F, OD270-OD280, OD306-OD317, OD347-OD357.

No. 439A exists with attached label showing medallion. Value $42.50 unused, $22.50 used.

Souvenir Sheet

A151

Without Period after Value

1935, Oct. 17 Litho. *Imperf.*

452	A151	Sheet of 4	52.50	30.00
a.		10c dull green	7.00	4.00

Phil. Exhib. at Buenos Aires, Oct. 17-24, 1935. The stamps were on sale during the 8 days of the exhibition only. Sheets measure 83x101mm.

Plaque — A152

1936, Dec. 1 *Perf. 13x13½*

453	A152	10c rose	.52	.25

Inter-American Conference for Peace.

Domingo Faustino Sarmiento
A153

"Presidente Sarmiento"
A154

1938, Sept. 5

454	A153	3c sage green	.18	.15
455	A153	5c red	.18	.15
456	A153	15c deep blue	.60	.15
457	A153	50c orange	1.75	1.00
		Nos. 454-457 (4)	2.71	
		Set value		1.20

50th anniv. of the death of Domingo Faustino Sarmiento, pres., educator and author.

1939, Mar. 16

458	A154	5c greenish blue	.35	.15

Final voyage of the training ship "Presidente Sarmiento."

Allegory of the UPU — A155

Coat of Arms — A157

Post Office, Buenos Aires — A156

Iguacu Falls — A158

Bonete Hill, Nahuel Huapi Park — A159

Allegory of Modern Communications
A160

Argentina, Land of Promise
A161

Lake Frias, Nahuel Huapi Park — A162

Perf. 13x13½, 13½x13

1939, Apr. 1 Photo.

459	A155	5c rose carmine	.16	.15
460	A156	15c grnsh black	.42	.26
461	A157	20c brt blue	.42	.15
462	A158	25c dp blue grn	.85	.40
463	A159	50c brown	1.65	.65
464	A160	1p brown violet	1.90	.80
465	A161	2p magenta	8.75	5.25
466	A162	5p purple	35.00	16.00
		Nos. 459-466 (8)	49.15	23.66

Universal Postal Union, 11th Congress.

Souvenir Sheets

A163

A164

1939, May 12 Wmk. 90 *Imperf.*

467	A163	Sheet of 4	6.00	4.25
a.		5c rose carmine (A155)	1.25	.75
b.		20c bright blue (A157)	1.25	.75
c.		25c deep blue green (A158)	1.25	.75
d.		50c brown (A159)	1.25	.75
468	A164	Sheet of 4	6.00	4.28

Issued in four forms:

a.	Unsevered horizontal pair of sheets, type A163 at left, A164 at right	15.00	15.00
b.	Unsevered vertical pair of sheets, type A163 at top, A164 at bottom	15.00	15.00
c.	Unsevered block of 4 sheets, type A163 at left, A164 at right	52.50	52.50
d.	Unsevered block of 4 sheets, type A163 at top, A164 at bottom	52.50	52.50

11th Cong. of the UPU and the Argentina Intl. Phil. Exposition (C.Y.T.R.A.).

No. 468 contains Nos. 467a-467d.

Family and New House — A165

Perf. 13½x13

1939, Oct. 2 Litho. Wmk. 90

469	A165	5c bluish green	.25	.15

1st Pan-American Housing Congress.

Bird Carrying Record — A166

Head of Liberty and Arms of Argentina — A167

Record and Winged Letter — A168

1939, Dec. 11 Photo. *Perf. 13*

470	A166	1.18p indigo	15.00	7.00
471	A167	1.32p brt blue	15.00	7.00
472	A168	1.50p dark brown	50.00	27.50
		Nos. 470-472 (3)	80.00	41.50

These stamps were issued for the recording and mailing of flexible phonograph records.

Map of the Americas — A169

1940, Apr. 14 *Perf. 13x13½*
473 A169 15c ultra .42 .15

50th anniv. of the Pan American Union.

Souvenir Sheet

Reproductions of Early Argentine Stamps — A170

Wmk. RA in Sun (90)

1940, May 25 **Litho.** ***Imperf.***
474 A170 Sheet of 5 9.50 5.50
- ***a.*** 5c dark blue (Corrientes A2) 1.10 .70
- ***b.*** 5c red (Argentina A1) 1.10 .70
- ***c.*** 5c dark blue (Cordoba #1) 1.10 .70
- ***d.*** 5c red (Argentina A3) 1.10 .70
- ***e.*** 10c dark blue (Buenos Aires A1) 1.10 .70

100th anniv. of the first postage stamp.

General Domingo French and Colonel Antonio Beruti — A171

1941, Feb. 20 *Perf. 13½x13*
475 A171 5c dk gray blue & lt blue .32 .15

Issued in honor of General French and Colonel Beruti, patriots.

Marco M. de Avellaneda A172

Statue of Gen. Julio Roca A173

1941, Oct. 3 *Perf. 13x13½*
476 A172 5c dull slate blue .32 .15

Marco M. de Avellaneda, (1814-41), Army leader and martyr.

1941, Oct. 19 **Photo.** **Wmk. 90**
477 A173 5c dark olive green .32 .15

Dedication of a monument to Lt. Gen. Julio Argentino Roca (1843-1914).

Carlos Pellegrini and Bank of the Nation — A174

1941, Oct. 26 *Perf. 13½x13*
478 A174 5c brown carmine .32 .15

Founding of the Bank of the Nation, 50th anniv.

Gen. Juan Lavalle — A175

1941, Dec. 5 *Perf. 13x13½*
479 A175 5c bright blue .32 .15

Gen. Juan Galo de Lavalle (1797-1841).

National Postal Savings Bank — A176

1942, Apr. 5 **Litho.** *Perf. 13½x13*
480 A176 1c pale olive .20 .15

Jose Manuel Estrada — A177

1942, July 13 *Perf. 13x13½*
481 A177 5c brown violet .32 .15

Jose Estrada (1842-1894), writer and diplomat.

No. 481 exists with label, showing medallion, attached. Value, pair $10.

Types of 1935-51

Perf. 13, 13x13½, 13½x13

1942-50 **Litho.** **Wmk. 288**
485 A128 ½c brown violet 4.75 1.00
486 A129 1c buff ('50) .15 .15
487 A130 2c dk brown ('50) .15 .15
488 A132 3c lt gray 16.00 1.25
489 A134 3c lt gray ('49) .16 .15
490 A137 10c red brown ('49) .20 .15
491 A138 12c red .20 .15
492 A140 15c lt gray blue (II) .28 .15
493 A139 20c dk sl bl & pale bl 1.25 .15
494 A141 25c dull rose ('49) .60 .15
495 A142 30c orange brn ('49) 1.25 .15
496 A143 40c violet ('49) 8.00 .15
497 A144 50c red & org ('49) 8.00 .18
498 A146 1p brn blk & lt bl 6.50 .18
499 A147 2p brn lake & bl ('49) 13.00 .75
500 A148 5p ind & ol grn ('49) 50.00 4.50
Nos. 485-500 (16) 110.49 9.36

No. 493 measures 22x33mm.

Post Office, Buenos Aires — A178

Proposed Columbus Lighthouse — A179

Inscribed: "Correos y Telegrafos."

1942, Oct. 5 **Litho.** *Perf. 13*
503 A178 35c lt ultra 2.75 .15

See Nos. 541-543.

1942, Oct. 12 **Wmk. 288**
504 A179 15c dull blue 3.00 .15

Wmk. 90

505 A179 15c dull blue 60.00 5.00

450th anniv. of the discovery of America by Columbus.

Jose C. Paz — A180

Books and Argentine Flag — A181

1942, Dec. 15 **Wmk. 288**
506 A180 5c dark gray .35 .15

Cent. of the birth of Jose C. Paz, stateman and founder of the newspaper La Prensa.

1943, Apr. 1 **Litho.** *Perf. 13*
507 A181 5c dull blue .18 .15

1st Book Fair of Argentina.

Arms of Argentina Inscribed "Honesty, Justice, Duty" — A182

1943-50 **Wmk. 288** *Perf. 13*

Size: 20x26mm

508 A182 5c red ('50) 2.50 .15

Wmk. 90

509 A182 5c red .22 .15
- ***a.*** 5c dull red, unsurfaced paper 3.00 .15

510 A182 15c green .70 .15

Perf. 13x13½

Size: 22x33mm

511 A182 20c dark blue 1.10 .15
Nos. 508-511 (4) 4.52
Set value .30

Change of political organization, June 4, 1943.

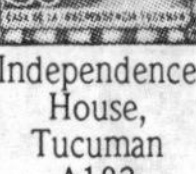

Independence House, Tucuman A183

Liberty Head and Savings Bank A184

1943-51 **Wmk. 90** *Perf. 13*
512 A183 5c blue green .90 .15

Wmk. 288

513 A183 5c blue green ('51) .35 .15
Set value .15

Restoration of Independence House.

1943, Oct. 25 **Wmk. 90**
514 A184 5c violet brown .15 .15

Wmk. 288

515 A184 5c violet brown 37.50 3.00

1st conference of National Postal Savings.

Port of Buenos Aires in 1800 — A185

1943, Dec. 11 **Wmk. 90**
516 A185 5c gray black .15 .15

Day of Exports.

Warship, Merchant Ship and Sailboat A186

Arms of Argentine Republic A187

1944, Jan. 31 *Perf. 13*
517 A186 5c blue .18 .15

Issued to commemorate Sea Week.

1944, June 4
518 A187 5c dull blue .15 .15

1st anniv. of the change of political organization in Argentina.

St. Gabriel A188

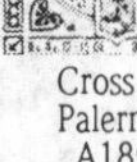

Cross at Palermo A189

1944, Oct. 11
519 A188 3c yellow green .15 .15
520 A189 5c deep rose .15 .15
Set value .15

Fourth national Eucharistic Congress.

Allegory of Savings A190

Reservists A191

1944, Oct. 24
521 A190 5c gray .15 .15

20th anniv. of the National Savings Bank.

1944, Dec. 1
522 A191 5c blue .15 .15

Day of the Reservists.

Types of 1935-51

Perf. 13x13½, 13½x13

1945-47 **Litho.** **Unwmk.**
523 A128 ½c brown vio ('46) .15 .15
524 A129 1c yellow brown .15 .15
525 A130 2c sepia .15 .15
526 A132 3c lt gray (San Martin) .42 .15
527 A134 3c lt gray (Moreno) ('46) .15 .15
528 A135 6c olive grn ('47) .18 .15
529 A137 10c brown ('46) 1.25 .15
530 A140 15c lt gray bl (II) .75 .15
531 A139 20c dk sl bl & pale bl 1.25 .15
532 A141 25c dull rose .45 .15
533 A142 30c orange brown .35 .15
534 A143 40c violet 1.25 .15
535 A144 50c red & orange 1.25 .15
536 A146 1p brown blk & lt bl 1.65 .15
537 A147 2p brown lake & bl 8.00 .22
538 A148 5p ind & ol grn ('46) 45.00 2.50
539 A149 10p dp cl & int blk 5.50 .90
540 A150 20p bl grn & brn ('46) 5.75 .90
Nos. 523-540 (18) 73.65
Set value 5.25

No. 531 measures 22x33mm.

Post Office Type Inscribed: "Correos y Telecommunicaciones"

1945 **Unwmk.** *Perf. 13x13½*
541 A178 35c lt ultra 1.25 .15

Wmk. 90

542 A178 35c lt ultra 1.25 .15

Wmk. 288

543 A178 35c lt ultra .35 .15
Nos. 541-543 (3) 2.85
Set value .15

Bernardino Rivadavia
A192 A193

Mausoleum of Rivadavia
A194

Perf. 13½x13

1945, Sept. 1 Litho. Unwmk.

544 A192 3c blue green .15 .15
545 A193 5c rose .15 .15
546 A194 20c blue .28 .15
Nos. 544-546 (3) .58
Set value .15

Cent. of the death of Bernardino Rivadavia, Argentina's first president.

No. 546 exists with mute label attached. The pair sells for four times the price of the single stamp.

San Martin
A195

Monument to Army of the Andes, Mendoza
A196

1945-46 Wmk. 90 Typo. or Litho.

547 A195 5c carmine .15 .15
a. Litho. ('46) .15 .15

Wmk. 288

548 A195 5c carmine, litho. 120.00 20.00

Unwmk.

549 A195 5c carmine ('46) .52 .15
a. Litho. ('46) .20 .15

For overprints see Nos. O42, O57.

1946, Jan. 14 Litho. *Perf. 13½x13*

550 A196 5c violet brown .15 .15

Issued to honor the Unknown Soldier of the War for Independence.

A197 A198

1946, Apr. 12

551 A197 5c Franklin D. Roosevelt .15 .15

1946, June 4 *Perf. 13x13½*

Liberty Administering Presidential Oath.

552 A198 5c blue .15 .15

Inauguration of Pres. Juan D. Perón, 6/4/46.

Argentina Receiving Popular Acclaim
A199

1946, Oct. 17 *Perf. 13½x13*

553 A199 5c rose violet .16 .15
554 A199 10c blue green .24 .15
555 A199 15c dark blue .48 .18
556 A199 50c red brown .70 .30
557 A199 1p carmine rose 1.40 .70
Nos. 553-557 (5) 2.98
Set value 1.25

First anniversary of the political organization change of Oct. 17, 1945.

Coin Bank and World Map — A200

1946, Oct. 31 Unwmk.

558 A200 30c dk rose car & pink .60 .15

Universal Day of Savings, October 31, 1946.

Argentine Industry
A201

International Bridge Connecting Argentina and Brazil
A202

1946, Dec. 6 *Perf. 13x13½*

559 A201 5c violet brown .15 .15

Day of Argentine Industry, Dec. 6.

1947, May 21 Litho. *Perf. 13½x13*

560 A202 5c green .15 .15

Opening of the Argentina-Brazil International Bridge, May 21, 1947.

Map of Argentine Antarctic Claims — A203

Justice — A204

1947-49 Unwmk. *Perf. 13x13½*

561 A203 5c violet & lilac .35 .15
562 A203 20c dk car rose & rose .70 .15

Wmk. 90

563 A203 20c dk car rose & rose 2.00 .20

Wmk. 288

564 A203 20c dk car rose & rose ('49) 2.00 .15
Nos. 561-564 (4) 5.05
Set value .35

1st Argentine Antarctic mail, 43rd anniv.

1947, June 4 Unwmk.

565 A204 5c brn vio & pale yel .15 .15

1st anniversary of the Peron government.

Icarus Falling — A205

1947, Sept. 25 *Perf. 13½x13*

566 A205 15c red violet .15 .15

Aviation Week.

Training Ship Presidente Sarmiento — A206

1947, Oct. 5 *Perf. 13x13½*

567 A206 5c blue .18 .15

50th anniv. of the launching of the Argentine training frigate "Presidente Sarmiento."

Cervantes and Characters from Don Quixote — A207

Perf. 13½x13

1947, Oct. 12 Photo. Wmk. 90

568 A207 5c olive green .15 .15

400th anniv. of the birth of Miguel de Cervantes Saavedra, playwright and poet.

Gen. Jose de San Martin — A208

Perf. 13½x13

1947-49 Unwmk. Litho.

569 A208 5c dull green .15 .15

Wmk. 288

570 A208 5c dull green ('49) .15 .15
Set value .15

Transfer of the remains of Gen. Jose de San Martin's parents.

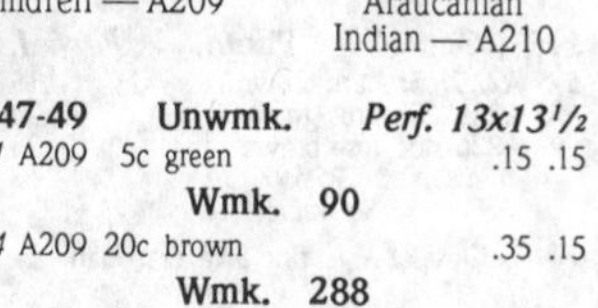

School Children — A209

Statue of Araucanian Indian — A210

1947-49 Unwmk. *Perf. 13x13½*

571 A209 5c green .15 .15

Wmk. 90

574 A209 20c brown .35 .15

Wmk. 288

575 A209 5c green ('49) .35 .15
Nos. 571-575 (3) .85
Set value .22

Argentine School Crusade for World Peace.

1948, May 21 Wmk. 90

576 A210 25c yellow brown .30 .15

American Indian Day, Apr. 19.

Cap of Liberty — A211

Manual Stop Signal — A212

1948, July 16

577 A211 5c ultra .15 .15

Revolution of June 4, 1943, 5th anniv.

1948, July 22

578 A212 5c chocolate & yellow .15 .15

Traffic Safety Day, June 10.

Post Horn and Oak Leaves — A213

Argentine Farmers — A214

1948, July 22 Unwmk.

579 A213 5c lilac rose .15 .15

200th anniversary of the establishment of regular postal service on the Plata River.

Perf. 13x13½

1948, Sept. 20 Wmk. 288

580 A214 10c red brown .15 .15

Agriculture Day, Sept. 8, 1948.

Liberty and Symbols of Progress — A215

Perf. 13x13½

1948, Nov. 23 Photo. Wmk. 287

581 A215 25c red brown .18 .15

3rd anniversary of President Juan D. Peron's return to power, October 17, 1945.

Souvenir Sheets

A216

Designs: 15c, Mail coach. 45c, Buenos Aires in 18th century. 55c, First train, 1857. 85c, Sailing ship, 1767.

1948, Dec. 21 Unwmk. *Imperf.*

582 A216 Sheet of 4 3.00 3.00
a. 15c dark green .45 .45
b. 45c orange brown .45 .45
c. 55c lilac brown .45 .45
d. 85c ultramarine .45 .45

A217

Designs: 85c, Domingo de Basavilibaso (1709-75). 1.05p, Postrider. 1.20p, Sailing ship, 1798. 1.90p, Courier in the Andes, 1772.

583 A217 Sheet of 4 14.00 11.00
a. 85c brown 3.00 2.50
b. 1.05p dark green 3.00 2.50
c. 1.20p dark blue 3.00 2.50
d. 1.90p red brown 3.00 2.50

200th anniversary of the establishment of regular postal service on the Plata River.

Winged Wheel — A218

Perf. 13½x13

1949, Mar. 1 **Wmk. 288**
584 A218 10c blue .22 .15

Railroad nationalization, 1st anniv.

Liberty A219

1949, June 20 **Engr.** **Wmk. 90**
585 A219 1p red & red violet .42 .15

Ratification of the Constitution of 1949.

Allegory of the UPU A220

1949, Nov. 19
586 A220 25c dk grn & yel grn .22 .15

75th anniv. of the UPU.

Catalogue values for unused stamps in this section, from this point to the end of the section, are for Never Hinged items.

Gen. Jose de San Martin — A221

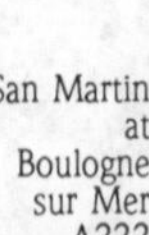

San Martin at Boulogne sur Mer A222

Mausoleum of San Martin — A223

Designs: 20c, 50c, 75c, Different Portraits of San Martin. 1p, House where San Martin died.

Engr., Photo. (25c, 1p, 2p)

1950, Aug. 17 **Wmk. 90** *Perf. 13½*
587 A221 10c indigo & dk pur .15 .15
588 A221 20c red brn & dk brn .15 .15
589 A222 25c brown .15 .15
590 A221 50c dk green & ind .42 .15
591 A221 75c choc & dk grn .42 .15
a. Souv. sheet of 4, #587, 588, 590, 591, imperf. 1.25 .80

592 A222 1p dark green .85 .25
593 A223 2p dp red lilac .70 .35
Nos. 587-593 (7) 2.84
Set value .90

Death cent. of General Jose de San Martin.

Map Showing Antarctic Claims — A224

1951, May 21 **Litho.** *Perf. 13x13½*
594 A224 1p choc & lt blue .70 .15

For overprint see No. O52.

Pegasus and Train A225

Communications Symbols — A226

Design: 25c, Ship and dolphin.

1951, Oct. 17 **Photo.** *Perf. 13½*
595 A225 5c dark brown .15 .15
596 A225 25c Prus green .24 .15
597 A226 40c rose brown .28 .15
Nos. 595-597 (3) .67
Set value .32

Close of Argentine Five Year Plan.

Woman Voter and "Argentina" A227

1951, Dec. 14 *Perf. 13½x13*
598 A227 10c brown violet .15 .15

Granting of women's suffrage.

Eva Peron
A228 A229

Litho. or Engraved (#605)

1952, Aug. 26 **Wmk. 90** *Perf. 13*
599 A228 1c orange brown .15 .15
600 A228 5c gray .15 .15
601 A228 10c rose lilac .15 .15
602 A228 20c rose pink .15 .15
603 A228 25c dull green .15 .15
604 A228 40c dull violet .15 .15
605 A228 45c deep blue .15 .15
606 A228 50c dull brown .15 .15

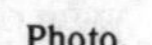

Photo.
607 A229 1p dark brown .26 .15
608 A229 1.50p deep green 1.50 .15
609 A229 2p brt carmine .45 .15
610 A229 3p indigo .75 .15
Nos. 599-610 (12) 4.16
Set value .75

For overprints see Nos. O79-O85.

Inscribed: "Eva Peron"

1952-53 *Perf. 13x13½*
611 A229 1p dark brown .50 .15
612 A229 1.50p deep green .50 .15
613 A229 2p brt car ('53) 1.10 .15
614 A229 3p indigo 1.50 .15

Engr.
Perf. 13½x13
Size: 30x40mm
615 A229 5p red brown 1.50 .35
616 A228 10p red 4.25 1.40
617 A229 20p green 11.00 4.00
618 A228 50p ultra 17.00 10.00
Nos. 611-618 (8) 37.35 16.35

For overprints see Nos. O86-O93.

Indian Funeral Urn — A230

1953, Aug. 28 **Photo.** *Perf. 13x13½*
619 A230 50c blue green .18 .15

Founding of Santiago del Estero, 400th anniv.

Rescue Ship "Uruguay" A231

1953, Oct. 8 *Perf. 13½*
620 A231 50c ultra .85 .15

50th anniv. of the rescue of the Antarctic expedition of Otto C. Nordenskjold.

Planting Argentine Flag in the Antarctic — A232

1954, Jan. 20 **Engr.** *Perf. 13½x13*
621 A232 1.45p blue 1.25 .15

50th anniv. of Argentina's 1st antarctic p.o. and the establishing of the La Hoy radio p.o. in the South Orkneys.

Wired Communications A233

Television A234

Perf. 13x13½, 13½x13

1954, Apr. **Photo.** **Wmk. 90**
622 A233 1.50p shown .35 .25
623 A233 3p Radio 1.10 .28
624 A234 5p shown 1.40 .55
Nos. 622-624 (3) 2.85 1.08

Intl. Plenipotentiary Conf. of Telecommunications, Buenos Aires, 1952.

Pediment, Buenos Aires Stock Exchange A235

1954, July 13 *Perf. 13½x13*
625 A235 1p dark green .28 .15

Cent. of the establishment of the Buenos Aires Stock Exchange.

Eva Peron — A236

1954 **Wmk. 90**
626 A236 3p dp car rose 1.25 .25

Wmk. 288
627 A236 3p dp car rose 175.00 32.50

2nd anniv. of the death of Eva Peron.

Jose de San Martin A237

Wheat A238

Industry A238a

Eva Peron Foundation Building A239

Cliffs of Humahuaca A240

Gen. Jose de San Martin — A241

Designs: 50c, Buenos Aires harbor. 1p, Cattle ranch (Ganaderia). 3p, Nihuil Dam. 5p, Iguacu Falls, vert. 20p, Mt. Fitz Roy, vert.

Perf. 13½, 13x13½ (80c), 13½x13 (#639, 641-642)
Engraved (#632, 638-642), Photogravure (#634-637)

1954-59 **Wmk. 90**

628 A237 20c brt red, typo. .15 .15
629 A237 20c red, litho. ('55) .60 .15
630 A237 40c red, litho. ('56) .16 .15
631 A237 40c brt red, typo. ('55) .25 .15
632 A239 50c blue ('56) .15 .15
633 A239 50c bl, litho. ('59) .16 .15
634 A238 80c brown .22 .15
635 A239 1p brown ('58) .26 .15
636 A238a 1.50p ultra ('58) .20 .15
637 A239 2p dk rose lake .32 .15
638 A239 3p violet brn ('56) .32 .15
639 A240 5p gray grn ('55) 5.25 .15
a. Perf. 13½ 6.50 .15
640 A240 10p yel grn ('55) 3.75 .15
641 A240 20p dull vio ('55) 7.75 .15
a. Perf. 13½ 9.50 .15
642 A241 50p ultra & ind ('55) 7.75 .15
a. Perf. 13½ 7.75 .15
Nos. 628-642 (15) 27.29
Set value .80

See Nos. 699-700. For similar designs inscribed "Republica Argentina" see Nos. 823-827, 890, 935, 937, 940, 990, 995, 1039, 1044, 1048.
For overprints see Nos. O94-O106, O142, O153-O157.

Allegory — A242

1954, Aug. 26 **Typo.** *Perf. 13½*
643 A242 1.50p slate black .65 .15

Cent. of the establishment of the Buenos Aires Grain Exchange.

Clasped Hands and Congress Medal — A243

1955, Mar. 21 **Photo.** *Perf. 13½x13*
644 A243 3p red brown .80 .15

Issued to publicize the National Productivity and Social Welfare Congress.

Allegory of Aviation — A244

Argentina Breaking Chains — A245

1955, June 18 **Wmk. 90** *Perf. 13½*
645 A244 1.50p olive gray .65 .15

Commercial aviation in Argentina, 25th anniv.

1955, Oct. 16 **Litho.**
647 A245 1.50p olive green .32 .15

Liberation Revolution of Sept. 16, 1955.

Army Navy and Air Force Emblems A246

Perf. 13½x13
1955, Dec. 31 **Photo.** **Wmk. 90**
648 A246 3p blue .42 .15

"Brotherhood of the Armed Forces."

A247

A248

1956, Feb. 3 *Perf. 13½*
649 A247 1.50p Justo Jose de Urquiza .28 .15

Battle of Caseros, 104th anniversary.

1956, July 28 **Engr.** *Perf. 13½x13*
650 A248 2p Coin and die .28 .15

75th anniversary of the Argentine Mint.

1856 Stamp of Corrientes A249

Juan G. Pujol — A250

Design: 2.40p, Stamp of 1860-78.

1956, Aug. 21
651 A249 40c dk grn & blue .15 .15
652 A249 2.40p brn & lil rose .30 .15

Photo.

653 A250 4.40p brt blue .65 .18
a. Souv. sheet of 3, #651-653, imperf. 2.25 2.00
Nos. 651-653 (3) 1.10 .48

Centenary of Argentine postage stamps.
No. 653a for the Argentine stamp cent. and Philatelic Exhib. for the Cent. of Corrientes Stamps, Oct. 12-21. The 4.40p is photo., the other two stamps and border litho. Colors of 40c and 2.40p differ slightly from engraved stamps.

Felling Trees, La Pampa A251

Maté Herb and Gourd, Misiones A252

Design: 1p, Cotton plant and harvest, Chaco.

1956, Sept. 1 *Perf. 13½*
654 A251 50c ultra .15 .15
655 A251 1p magenta .18 .15
656 A252 1.50p green .22 .15
Nos. 654-656 (3) .55
Set value .15

Elevation of the territories of La Pampa, Chaco and Misiones to provinces.

"Liberty" A253

Florentino Ameghino A254

Perf. 13½
1956, Sept. 15 **Wmk. 90** **Photo.**
657 A253 2.40p lilac rose .30 .15

1st anniv. of the Revolution of Liberation.

1956, Nov. 30
658 A254 2.40p brown .30 .15

Issued to honor Florentino Ameghino (1854-1911), anthropologist.
For overprint see No. O110.

Adm. Brown Type of 1935-51

1956 **Litho.** *Perf. 13*

Two types:
I. Bust touches upper frame line of name panel at bottom.
II. White line separates bust from frame line.

Size: 19½-20½x26-27mm

659 A133 20c dull purple (I) .18 .15
a. Type II .18 .15
b. Size 19½x25¼mm (I) .15 .15

For overprint see No. O108.

Benjamin Franklin A255

1956, Dec. 22 **Photo.** *Perf. 13½*
660 A255 40c intense blue .30 .15

250th anniv. of the birth of Benjamin Franklin.

Frigate "Hercules" A256

Guillermo Brown A257

1957, Mar. 2
661 A256 40c brt blue .15 .15
662 A257 2.40p gray black .35 .15
Nos. 661-662,C63-C65 (5) 1.00
Set value .42

Admiral Guillermo (William) Brown (1777-1857), founder of the Argentine navy.

Roque Saenz Pena (1851-1914) A258

Church of Santo Domingo, 1807 A259

1957, Apr. 1
663 A258 4.40p grnsh gray .45 .15

Roque Saenz Pena, pres. 1910-14.
For overprint see No. O111.

1957, July 6 **Wmk. 90**
664 A259 40c brt blue green .15 .15

150th anniv. of the defense of Buenos Aires.

"La Portena" — A260

1957, Aug. 31 **Wmk. 90** *Perf. 13½*
665 A260 40c pale brown .18 .15

Centenary of Argentine railroads.

Esteban Echeverria A261

"Liberty" A262

1957, Sept. 2 *Perf. 13x13½*
666 A261 2p claret .22 .15

Esteban Echeverria (1805-1851), poet.
For overprint see No. O109.

1957, Sept. 28 *Perf. 13½*
667 A262 40c carmine rose .15 .15

Constitutional reform convention.

Portrait Type of 1935-51

1957, Oct. 28 **Litho.** *Perf. 13½*
Size: 16½x22mm

668 A128 5c Jose Hernandez .15 .15

For overprint see No. O112.

Oil Derrick and Hands Holding Oil — A263

Perf. 13½
1957, Dec. 21 **Wmk. 90** **Photo.**
669 A263 40c bright blue .18 .15

50th anniv. of the national oil industry.

Museum, La Plata — A264

1958, Jan. 11
670 A264 40c dark gray .15 .15

City of La Plata, 75th anniversary.

A265

A266

Designs: 40c, Locomotive and arms of Argentina and Bolivia. 1p, Map of Argentine-Bolivian boundary and plane.

1958, Apr. 19 **Wmk. 90** *Perf. 13½*
671 A265 40c slate & dp car .28 .15
672 A266 1p dark brown .28 .15
Set value .25

Argentine-Bolivian friendship. No. 671 for the opening of the Jacuiba-Santa Cruz railroad; No. 672, the exchange of presidential visits.

Symbols of the Republic A267

Flag Monument A268

1958, Apr. 30 Photo. & Engr.
673 A267 40c multicolored .15 .15
674 A267 1p multicolored .16 .15
675 A267 2p multicolored .25 .15
Nos. 673-675 (3) .56
Set value .25

Transmission of Presidential power.

1958, June 21 Litho. Wmk. 90
676 A268 40c blue & violet bl .15 .15

1st anniv. of the Flag Monument of Rosario.

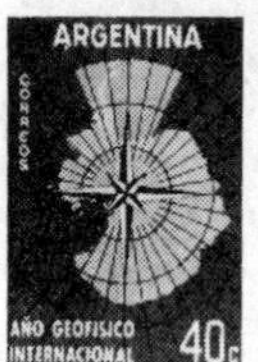

Map of Antarctica A269

Stamp of Cordoba and Mail Coach A270

1958, July 12 ***Perf. 13½***
677 A269 40c car rose & blk .48 .18

International Geophysical Year, 1957-58.

1958, Oct. 18
678 A270 40c pale blue & slate .15 .15
Nos. 678,C72-C73 (3) .60
Set value .25

Contenary of Cordoba postage stamps.

"Slave" by Michelangelo and UN Emblem — A271

Engraved and Lithographed
1959, Mar. 14 Wmk. 90 ***Perf. 13½***
679 A271 40c violet brn & gray .15 .15

10th anniv. (in 1958) of the signing of the Universal Declaration of Human Rights.

Orchids and Globe — A272

1959, May 23 Photo. ***Perf. 13½***
680 A272 1p dull claret .22 .15

1st International Horticulture Exposition.

Pope Pius XII — A273

William Harvey — A274

1959, June 20 Engr. ***Perf. 13½***
681 A273 1p yellow & black .18 .15

Pope Pius XII, 1876-1958.

1959, Aug. 8 Litho. Wmk. 90

Portraits: 1p, Claude Bernard. 1.50p, Ivan P. Pavlov.

682 A274 50c green .15 .15
683 A274 1p dark red .15 .15
684 A274 1.50p brown .22 .15
Nos. 682-684 (3) .52
Set value .18

21st International Congress of Physiological Sciences, Buenos Aires.

Type of 1958 and

Domestic Horse A275

Jose de San Martin A276

Tierra del Fuego — A277

Inca Bridge, Mendoza A278

Ski Jumper A279

Mar del Plata A280

Designs: 10c, Cayman. 20c, Llama. 50c, Puma. No. 690, Sunflower. 3p, Zapata Slope, Catamarca. 12p, 23p, 25p, Red Quebracho tree. 20p, Nahuel Huapi Lake. 22p, "Industry" (cogwheel and factory).

Two overall paper sizes for 1p, 5p:
I - 27x37½mm or 37½x27mm.
II - 27x39mm or 39x27mm.

Perf. 13x13½
1959-70 Litho. Wmk. 90
685 A275 10c slate green .15 .15
686 A275 20c dl red brn ('61) .15 .15
687 A275 50c bister ('60) .15 .15
688 A275 50c bis, typo. ('60) .18 .15
689 A275 1p rose red .15 .15

Perf. 13½
690 A278 1p brn, photo., I ('61) .15 .15
a. Paper II ('69) .18 .15
690B A278 1p brown, I .65 .15
691 A276 2p rose red ('61) .25 .15
692 A276 2p red, typo. (19½ x 26mm) ('61) .32 .15
a. Redrawn (19½ x 25mm) 4.75 .15
693 A277 3p dk bl, photo. ('60) .16 .15
694 A276 4p red, typo ('62) .18 .15
694A A276 4p red ('62) .38 .15
695 A277 5p gray brn, photo., I .38 .15
e. 5p dark brown, paper II ('70) 6.25 .15
695A A276 8p ver ('65) 1.25 .15
695B A276 8p red, typo. ('65) .32 .15
695C A276 10p ver ('66) .65 .15
695D A276 10p red, typo. ('66) .48 .15

Photo.
696 A278 10p lt red brn ('60) .48 .15
697 A278 12p dk brn vio ('62) .80 .15
697A A278 12p dk brn, litho. ('64) 8.00 .15
698 A278 20p Prus grn ('60) 2.75 .15
698A A276 20p red, typo. ('67) .25 .15
699 A238a 22p ultra ('62) 1.50 .15
700 A238a 22p ultra, litho. ('62) 24.00 .15
701 A278 23p green ('65) 4.75 .15
702 A278 25p dp vio ('66) 1.25 .15
703 A278 25p pur, litho. ('66) 6.25 .15
704 A279 100p blue ('61) 5.00 .15
705 A280 300p dp vio ('62) 2.75 .15
Nos. 685-705 (29) 63.73
Set value 1.50

See Nos. 882-887, 889, 892, 923-925, 928-930, 938, 987-989, 991.

For overprints and surcharges see Nos. 1076, C82-C83, O113-O118, O122-O124, O126-O141, O143-O145, O163.

The 300p remained on sale as a 3p stamp after the 1970 currency exchange.

Symbolic Sailboat — A281

Child Playing with Doll — A282

1959, Oct. 3 Litho. ***Perf. 13½***
706 A281 1p blk, red & bl .15 .15

Red Cross sanitary education campaign.

1959, Oct. 17
707 A282 1p red & blk .15 .15

Issued for Mother's Day, 1959.

Buenos Aires 1p Stamp of 1859 — A283

1959, Nov. 21 Wmk. 90 ***Perf. 13½***
708 A283 1p gray & dk bl .15 .15

Issued for the Day of Philately.

Bartolomé Mitre and Justo José de Urquiza A284

1959, Dec. 12 Photo. ***Perf. 13½***
709 A284 1p purple .15 .15

Treaty of San Jose de Flores, centenary.

WRY Emblem A285

Abraham Lincoln A286

1960, Apr. 7 Litho. Wmk. 90
710 A285 1p bister & car .15 .15
711 A285 4.20p apple grn & dp claret .32 .20
Set value .27

World Refugee Year, July 1, 1959-June 30, 1960. See No. B25.

1960, Apr. 14 Photo. ***Perf. 13½***
712 A286 5p ultra .42 .18

Sesquicentennial (in 1959) of the birth of Abraham Lincoln.

Cornelio Saavedra and Cabildo, Buenos Aires — A287

"Cabildo" and: 2p, Juan José Paso. 4.20p, Manuel Alberti and Miguel Azcuénaga. 10.70p, Juan Larrea and Domingo Matheu.

Perf. 13½
1960, May 28 Wmk. 90 Photo.
713 A287 1p rose lilac .15 .15
714 A287 2p bluish grn .15 .15
715 A287 4.20p gray & grn .24 .15
716 A287 10.70p gray & ultra .45 .20
Nos. 713-716,C75-C76 (6) 1.49
Set value .55

150th anniversary of the May Revolution. Souvenir sheets are Nos. C75a and C76a.

Luis Maria Drago — A288

Juan Bautista Alberdi — A289

1960, July 8
717 A288 4.20p brown .22 .15

Ccentenary of the birth of Dr. Luis Maria Drago, statesman and jurist.

1960, Sept. 10 Wmk. 90 ***Perf. 13½***
718 A289 1p green .15 .15

150th anniversary of the birth of Juan Bautista Alberdi, statesman and philosopher.

Map of Argentina and Antarctic Sector — A290

Caravel and Emblem — A291

1960, Sept. 24 Litho. ***Perf. 13½***
719 A290 5p violet .85 .22

National census of 1960.

1960, Oct. 1 Photo.
720 A291 1p dk olive grn .15 .15
721 A291 5p brown .45 .15
Nos. 720-721,C78-C79 (4) 1.15
Set value .15

8th Congress of the Postal Union of the Americas and Spain.

Footnotes near stamp listings often refer to other stamps of the same design.

Virgin of Luján, Patroness of Argentina A292

Argentine Boy Scout Emblem A293

1960, Nov. 12 Wmk. 90 *Perf. 13½*
722 A292 1p dark blue .15 .15

First Inter-American Marian Congress.

1961, Jan. 17 Litho.
723 A293 1p car rose & blk .28 .15

International Patrol Encampment of the Boy Scouts, Buenos Aires.

"Shipment of Cereals," by Quinquela Martin A294

1961, Feb. 11 Photo. *Perf. 13½*
724 A294 1p red brown .28 .15

Export drive: "To export is to advance."

Naval Battle of San Nicolás — A295

Mariano Moreno by Juan de Dios Rivera — A296

1961, Mar. 2 *Perf. 13½*
725 A295 2p gray .28 .15

Naval battle of San Nicolas, 150th anniv.

1961, Mar. 25 *Perf. 13½*
726 A296 2p blue .15 .15

Mariano Moreno (1778-1811), writer, politician, member of the 1810 Junta.

Emperor Trajan Statue — A297

Rabindranath Tagore — A298

1961, Apr. 11
727 A297 2p slate green .15 .15

Visit of Pres. Giovanni Gronchi of Italy to Argentina, April 1961.

1961, May 13 Photo. *Perf. 13½*
728 A298 2p purple, *grysh* .15 .15

Centenary of the birth of Rabindranath Tagore, Indian poet.

San Martin Statue, Madrid — A299

1961, May 24 Wmk. 90
729 A299 1p olive gray .15 .15

Unveiling of a statue of General José de San Martin in Madrid.

Manuel Belgrano — A300

1961, June 17 *Perf. 13½*
730 A300 2p violet blue .15 .15

Erection of a monument by Hector Rocha, to General Manuel Belgrano in Buenos Aires.

Explorers, Sledge and Dog Team — A301

1961, Aug. 19 Photo. Wmk. 90
731 A301 2p black .70 .22

10th anniversary of the General San Martin Base, Argentine Antarctic.

Spanish Conquistador and Sword — A302

Sarmiento Statue by Rodin, Buenos Aires — A303

1961, Aug. 19 Litho.
732 A302 2p red & blk .15 .15

First city of Jujuy, 400th anniversary.

1961, Sept. 9 Photo.
733 A303 2p violet .15 .15

Domingo Faustino Sarmiento (1811-88), political leader and writer.

Symbol of World Town Planning A304

1961, Nov. 25 Litho. *Perf. 13½*
734 A304 2p ultra & yel .15 .15

World Town Planning Day, Nov. 8.

Manuel Belgrano Statue, Buenos Aires A305

Grenadier, Flag and Regimental Emblem A306

1962, Feb. 24 Photo.
735 A305 2p Prus blue .15 .15

150th anniversary of the Argentine flag.

1962, Mar. 31 Wmk. 90 *Perf. 13½*
736 A306 2p carmine rose .15 .15

150th anniversary of the San Martin Grenadier Guards regiment.

Mosquito and Malaria Eradication Emblem — A307

1962, Apr. 7 Litho.
737 A307 2p vermilion & blk .15 .15

WHO drive to eradicate malaria.

Church of the Virgin of Lujàn — A308

Bust of Juan Jufrè — A309

1962, May 12 *Perf. 13½*
738 A308 2p org brn & blk .15 .15

75th anniversary of the pontifical coronation of the Virgin of Lujan.

1962, June 23 Photo.
739 A309 2p Prus blue .15 .15

Founding of San Juan, 4th cent.

"Soaring into Space" A310

Juan Vucetich A311

1962, Aug. 18 Litho. *Perf. 13½*
740 A310 2p maroon, blk & bl .15 .15

Argentine Air Force, 50th anniversary.

1962, Oct. 6 Photo. Wmk. 90
741 A311 2p green .15 .15

Juan Vucetich (1864-1925), inventor of the Argentine system of fingerprinting.

Domingo F. Sarmiento A312

February 20th Monument, Salta A313

Design: 4p, Jose Hernandez.

1962-66 Photo. *Perf. 13½*
742 A312 2p deep green .65 .15

Litho.
742A A312 2p lt green ('64) .55 .15

Photo.
742B A312 4p dull red ('65) .45 .15

Litho.
742C A312 4p rose red ('66) .60 .15
Nos. 742-742C (4) 2.25
Set value .20

See No. 817-819. For overprints see Nos. O119-O121, O125, O149.

1963, Feb. 23 Photo. Wmk. 90
743 A313 2p dark green .15 .15

150th anniversary of the Battle of Salta, War of Independence.

Gear Wheels — A314

1963, Mar. 16 Litho. *Perf. 13½*
744 A314 4p gray, blk & brt rose .15 .15

Argentine Industrial Union, 75th anniv.

National College, Buenos Aires — A315

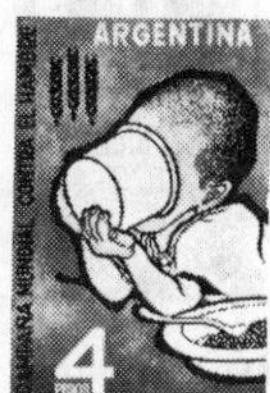

Child Draining Cup — A316

1963, Mar. 16 Wmk. 90
745 A315 4p dull org & blk .18 .15

National College of Buenos Aires, cent.

1963, Apr. 6
746 A316 4p multicolored .15 .15

FAO "Freedom from Hunger" campaign.

Frigate "La Argentina," 1817, by Emilio Biggeri — A317

1963, May 18 Photo.
747 A317 4p bluish green .28 .15

Issued for Navy Day, May 17.

Seat of 1813 Assembly and Official Seal — A318

1963, July 13 Litho. *Perf. 13½*
748 A318 4p lt blue & blk .15 .15

150th anniversary of the 1813 Assembly.

Battle of San Lorenzo, 1813
A319

1963, Aug. 24
749 A319 4p grn & blk, *grnsh* .20 .15

Sesquicentennial of the Battle of San Lorenzo.

Queen Nefertari Offering Papyrus Flowers, Abu Simbel — A320

1963, Sept. 14 *Perf. 13½*
750 A320 4p ocher, blk & bl grn .28 .15

Campaign to save the historic monuments in Nubia.

Government House, Buenos Aires
A321

1963, Oct. 12 Wmk. 90 *Perf. 13½*
751 A321 5p rose & brown .16 .15

Inauguration of President Arturo Illia.

"Science"
A322

Francisco de las Carreras, Supreme Court Justice
A323

1963, Oct. 16 Litho.
752 A322 4p org brn, bl & blk .15 .15

10th Latin-American Neurosurgery Congress.

1963, Nov. 23 Photo. *Perf. 13½*
753 A323 5p bluish green .15 .15

Centenary of judicial power.

Blackboards
A324

1963, Nov. 23 Litho.
754 A324 5p red, blk & bl .15 .15

Issued to publicize "Teachers for America" through the Alliance for Progress program.

Kemal Atatürk
A325

"Payador" by Juan Carlos Castagnino
A326

1963, Dec. 28 Photo. *Perf. 13½*
755 A325 12p dark gray .28 .15

25th anniversary of the death of Kemal Atatürk, president of Turkey.

1964, Jan. 25 Litho.
756 A326 4p ultra, blk & lt bl .32 .15

Fourth National Folklore Festival.

Maps of South Georgia, South Orkney and South Sandwich Islands — A327

Design: 4p, Map of Argentina and Antarctic claims, vert.

1964, Feb. 22 Wmk. 90 *Perf. 13½*

Size: 33x22mm

757 A327 2p lt & dk bl & bister 1.25 .24

Size: 30x40mm

758 A327 4p lt & dk bl & ol grn 1.75 .30
Nos. 757-758,C92 (3) 4.75 1.24

60th anniversary of Argentina's claim to Antarctic territories.

Jorge Newbery in Cockpit — A328

1964, Feb. 23 Photo.
759 A328 4p deep green .16 .15

Newbery, aviator, 50th death anniv.

John F. Kennedy — A329

José Brochero by José Cuello — A330

1964, Apr. 14 Engr. Wmk. 90
760 A329 4p claret & dk bl .35 .15

President John F. Kennedy (1917-63).

1964, May 9 Photo. *Perf. 13½*
761 A330 4p light sepia .16 .15

50th anniversary of the death of Father Jose Gabriel Brochero.

Soldier of Patricios Regiment — A331

1964, May 29 Litho. Wmk. 90
762 A331 4p blk, ultra & red .38 .20

Issued for Army Day. Later Army Day stamps, inscribed "Republica Argentina," are of type A340a.

Pope John XXIII — A332

1964, June 27 Engr.
763 A332 4p orange & blk .22 .15

Issued in memory of Pope John XXIII.

University of Cordoba Arms — A333

Pigeons and UN Building, NYC — A334

1964, Aug. 22 Litho. Wmk. 90
764 A333 4p blk, ultra & yel .15 .15

350th anniv. of the University of Cordoba.

1964, Oct. 24 *Perf. 13½*
765 A334 4p dk blue & lt blue .15 .15

Issued for United Nations Day.

Joaquin V. Gonzalez — A335

Julio Argentino Roca — A336

1964, Nov. 14 Photo.
766 A335 4p dk rose carmine .15 .15

Centenary (in 1963) of the birth of Joaquin V. Gonzalez, writer.

1964, Dec. 12 *Perf. 13½*
767 A336 4p violet blue .15 .15

General Julio A. Roca, (1843-1914), president of Argentina, (1880-86, 1898-1904).

Market at Montserrat Square, by Carlos Morel — A337

1964, Dec. 19 Photo.
768 A337 4p sepia .30 .18

19th century Argentine painter Carlos Morel.

Icebreaker General San Martin — A338

Girl with Piggy Bank — A339

Design: 2p, General Belgrano Base, Antarctica.

1965 *Perf. 13½*
769 A338 2p dull purple .42 .15
770 A338 4p ultra .48 .15

Issued to publicize the national territory of Tierra del Fuego, Antarctic and South Atlantic Isles.
Issue dates: 4p, Feb. 27; 2p, June 5.

1965, Apr. 3 Litho.
771 A339 4p red org & blk .15 .15

National Postal Savings Bank, 50th anniv.

Sun and Globe — A340

1965, May 29
772 A340 4p blk, org & dl bl .24 .15
Nos. 772,C98-C99 (3) 1.66 .85

International Quiet Sun Year, 1964-65.

Hussar of Pueyrredon Regiment
A340a

Ricardo Rojas (1882-1957)
A341

1965, June 5 Wmk. 90 *Perf. 13½*
773 A340a 8p dp ultra, blk & red .48 .18

Issued for Army Day. See Nos. 796, 838, 857, 893, 944, 958, 974, 1145.

1965, June 26 Photo.

Portraits: No. 775, Ricardo Guiraldes (1886-1927). No. 776, Enrique Larreta (1873-1961). No. 777, Leopoldo Lugones (1874-1938). No. 778, Roberto J. Payro (1867-1928).

774 A341 8p brown .35 .16
775 A341 8p brown .35 .16
776 A341 8p brown .35 .16
777 A341 8p brown .35 .16
778 A341 8p brown .35 .16
Nos. 774-778 (5) 1.75 .80

Issued to honor Argentine writers. Printed se-tenant in sheets of 100 (10x10); 2 horizontal rows of each design with Guiraldes in top rows and Rojas in bottom rows.

Set Values
A 15-cent minimum now applies to individual stamps and sets. Where the 15-cent minimum per stamp would increase the value of a set beyond retail, there is a "Set Value" notation giving the retail value of the set.

Hipolito Yrigoyen — A342

1965, July 3 **Litho.**
779 A342 8p pink & black .20 .15

Hipolito Yrigoyen (1852-1933), president of Argentina 1916-22, 1928-30.

Children Looking Through Window A343

1965, July 24 **Photo.**
780 A343 8p salmon & blk .24 .15

International Seminar on Mental Health.

Child's Funerary Urn and 16th Century Map A344

1965, Aug. 7 **Litho.**
781 A344 8p lt grn, dk red, brn & ocher .32 .15

City of San Miguel de Tucuman, 400th anniv.

Cardinal Cagliero A345

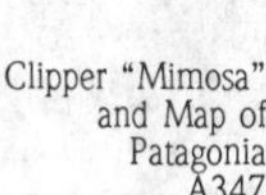

Dante Alighieri A346

1965, Aug. 21 **Photo.**
782 A345 8p violet .20 .15

Juan Cardinal Cagliero (1839-1926), missionary to Argentina and Bishop of Magida.

1965, Sept. 16 Wmk. 90 ***Perf. 13½***
783 A346 8p light ultra .28 .15

Dante Alighieri (1265-1321), Italian poet.

Clipper "Mimosa" and Map of Patagonia A347

1965, Sept. 25 **Litho.**
784 A347 8p red & black .28 .15

Centenary of Welsh colonization of Chubut, and the founding of the city of Rawson.

Map of Buenos Aires, Cock and Compass Emblem of Federal Police — A348

1965, Oct. 30 Photo. ***Perf. 13½***
785 A348 8p carmine rose .32 .15

Issued for Federal Police Day.

Child's Drawing of Children — A349

1965, Nov. 6 Litho. Wmk. 90
786 A349 8p lt yel grn & blk .28 .15

Public education law, 81st anniversary.

Church of St. Francis, Catamarca A350

Ruben Dario A351

1965, Dec. 8
787 A350 8p org yel & red brn .20 .15

Brother Mamerto de la Asuncion Esquiu, preacher, teacher and official of 1885 Provincial Constitutional Convention.

Litho. and Photo.

1965, Dec. 22 ***Perf. 13½***
788 A351 15p bl vio, *gray* .20 .15

Ruben Dario (pen name of Felix Ruben Garcia Sarmiento, 1867-1916), Nicaraguan poet, newspaper correspondent and diplomat.

"The Orange Seller" A352

Pueyrredon Paintings: No. 790, "Stop at the Grocery Store." No. 791, "Landscape at San Fernando" (sailboats). No. 792, "Bathing Horses at River Plata."

1966, Jan. 29 Photo. ***Perf. 13½***
789 A352 8p bluish green .70 .40
790 A352 8p bluish green .70 .40
791 A352 8p bluish green .70 .40
792 A352 8p bluish green .70 .40
Nos. 789-792 (4) 2.80 1.60

Prilidiano Pueyrredon (1823-1870), painter. Nos. 789-792 are printed in one sheet of 40 stamps and 20 labels.

Sun Yat-sen, Flags of Argentina and China — A353

1966, Mar. 12 Wmk. 90 ***Perf. 13½***
793 A353 8p dk red brown .70 .22

Dr. Sun Yat-sen (1866-1925), founder of the Republic of China.

Souvenir Sheet

Rivadavia Issue of 1864 — A354

Wmk. 90

1966, Apr. 20 Litho. ***Imperf.***
794 A354 Sheet of 3 .95 .95
a. 4p gray & red brown .15 .15
b. 5p gray & green .15 .15
c. 8p gray & dark blue .16 .16

2nd Rio de la Plata Stamp Show, Buenos Aires, Mar. 16-24.

People of Various Races and WHO Emblem A355

1966, Apr. 23 ***Perf. 13½***
795 A355 8p brown & blk .28 .15

Opening of the WHO Headquarters, Geneva.

Soldier Type of 1965

Army Day: 8p, Cavalryman, Guemes Infernal Regiment.

1966, May 28 **Litho.**
796 A340a 8p multicolored .55 .30

Coat of Arms — A356

Arms: a, Buenos Aires. b, Federal Capital. c, Catamarca. d, Cordoba. e, Corrientes. f, Chaco. g, Chubut. h, Entre Rios. i, Formosa. j, Jujuy. k, La Pampa. l, La Rioja. m, Mendoza. n, Misiones. o, Neuquen. p, Salta. q, San Juan. r, San Luis. s, Santa Cruz. t, Santa Fe. u, Santiago del Estero. v, Tucuman. w, map of Rio Negro. x, map of Tierra del Fuego, Antarctica. y, South Atlantic Islands.

1966, July 30 Wmk. 90 ***Perf. 13½***
797 Sheet of 25 40.00
a.-y. A356 10p black & multi 1.00 .65

150th anniv. of Argentina's Declaration of Independence.

Three Crosses, Caritas Emblem — A357

1966, Sept. 10 Litho. ***Perf. 13½***
798 A357 10p ol grn, blk & lt bl .22 .15

Caritas, charity organization.

Hilario Ascasubi (1807-75) — A358

Portraits: #800, Estanislao del Campo (1834-80). #801, Miguel Cane (1851-1905). #802, Lucio V. Lopez (1848-94). #803, Rafael Obligado (1851-1920). #804, Luis Agote (1868-1954), M.D. #805, Juan B. Ambrosetti (1865-1917), naturalist and archaeologist. #806, Miguel Lillo (1862-1931), botanist and chemist. #807, Francisco P. Moreno (1852-1919), naturalist and paleontologist. #808, Francisco J. Muñiz (1795-1871), physician.

1966 Photo. Wmk. 90
799 A358 10p dk blue green .42 .35
800 A358 10p dk blue green .42 .35
801 A358 10p dk blue green .42 .35
802 A358 10p dk blue green .42 .35
803 A358 10p dk blue green .42 .35
804 A358 10p deep violet .42 .35
805 A358 10p deep violet .42 .35
806 A358 10p deep violet .42 .35
807 A358 10p deep violet .42 .35
808 A358 10p deep violet .42 .35
Nos. 799-808 (10) 4.20 3.50

Nos. 799-803 issued Sept. 17 to honor Argentine writers. Printed se-tenant in sheets of 100 (10x10); 2 horizontal rows of each portrait. Nos. 804-808 issued Oct. 22 to honor Argentine scientists; 2 horizontal rows of each portrait. Scientists set has value at upper left, frame line with rounded corners.

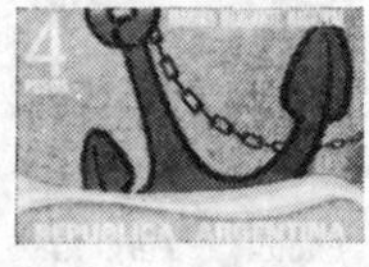

Anchor — A359

1966, Oct. 8 **Litho.**
809 A359 4p multicolored .22 .15

Argentine merchant marine.

Flags and Map of the Americas — A360

Argentine National Bank — A361

1966, Oct. 29 ***Perf. 13½***
810 A360 10p gray & multi .24 .15

7th Conference of American Armies.

1966, Nov. 5 **Photo.**
811 A361 10p brt blue green .20 .15

75th anniv. of the Argentine National Bank.

La Salle Monument and College, Buenos Aires — A362

1966, Nov. 26 Litho. ***Perf. 13½***
812 A362 10p brown org & blk .20 .15

75th anniv. of the Colegio de la Salle, Buenos Aires, and to honor Saint Jean Baptiste de la Salle (1551-1719), educator.

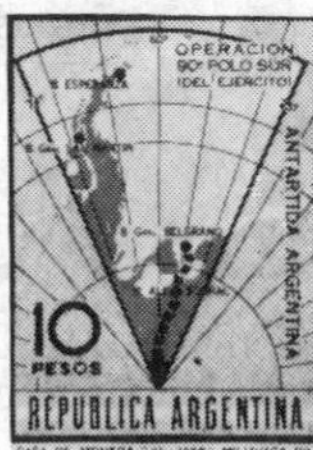

Map of Argentine Antarctica and Expedition Route — A363

1966, Dec. 10 **Wmk. 90**
813 A363 10p multicolored .70 .45

1965 Argentine Antarctic expedition, which planted the Argentine flag on the South Pole. See No. 851.

Juan Martin de Pueyrredon
A364

Gen. Juan de Las Heras
A365

1966, Dec. 17 Photo. *Perf. 13½*
814 A364 10p dull red brn .18 .15

Issued to honor Juan Martin de Pueyrredon (1777-1850), Governor of Cordoba and of the United Provinces of the River Plata.

1966, Dec. 17 Engr.
815 A365 10p black .18 .15

Issued to honor Gen. Juan Gregorio de Las Heras (1780-1866), Peruvian field marshal and aide-de-camp to San Martin.

Inscribed "Republica Argentina"
Types of 1955-61 and

Guillermo Brown — A366

Trout Leaping in National Park — A366a

Designs: 6p, Jose Hernandez. 50p, Gen. Jose de San Martin. 500p, Red deer in forest.

Two overall paper sizes for 6p, 50p (No. 827) and 90p:
I - 27x37½mm
II - 27x39mm

1965-68 Wmk. 90 Photo. *Perf. 13½*

817 A366	6p rose red, litho, I ('67)	1.25	.15
818 A366	6p rose red ('67)	2.25	.15
819 A366	6p brn, 15x22mm ('68)	.15	.15
823 A238a	43p dk car rose	6.25	.15
824 A238a	45p brn ('66)	4.25	.15
825 A238a	45p brn, litho ('67)	7.00	.15
826 A241	50p dk bl, 29x40mm	7.00	.15
827 A241	50p dk bl, 22x31½mm, I ('67)	4.75	.15
a.	Paper II	2.75	.15
828 A366	90p ol bis, I ('67)	3.00	.15
a.	Paper II	12.00	.15

Engr.

829 A495	500p yel grn ('66)	1.40	.28
829A A366a	1,000p vio bl ('68)	5.50	1.25
	Nos. 817-829A (11)	42.80	
	Set value		2.25

The 500p and 1,000p remained on sale as 5p and 10p stamps after the 1970 currency exchange.
See Nos. 888, 891, 939, 941, 992, 1031, 1040, 1045-1047. For surcharge and overprints see Nos. 1077, O153-O158, O162.

Pre-Columbian Pottery — A367

1967, Feb. 18 Litho. *Perf. 13½*
830 A367 10p multi .28 .15

20th anniv. of UNESCO.

"The Meal" by Fernando Fader
A368

1967, Feb. 25 Photo. Wmk. 90
831 A368 10p red brn .28 .15

Issued in memory of the Argentine painter Fernando Fader (1882-1935).

Col. Juana Azurduy de Padilla (1781-1862), Soldier — A369

Schooner "Invencible," 1811 — A370

Famous Argentine Women: #833, Juana Manuela Gorriti, writer. #834, Cecilia Grierson (1858-1934), physician. #835, Juana Paula Manso (1819-75), writer and educator. #836, Alfonsina Storni (1892-1938), writer and educator.

1967, May 13 Photo. *Perf. 13½*

832 A369	6p dark brown	.32	.20
833 A369	6p dark brown	.32	.20
834 A369	6p dark brown	.32	.20
835 A369	6p dark brown	.32	.20
836 A369	6p dark brown	.32	.20
	Nos. 832-836 (5)	1.60	1.00

Printed se-tenant in sheets of 100 (10x10); 2 horizontal rows of each portrait.

1967, May 20 Litho.
837 A370 20p multi .85 .35

Issued for Navy Day.

Soldier Type of 1965

Army Day: 20p, Highlander (Arribeños Corps).

1967, May 27
838 A340a 20p multi .70 .28

Souvenir Sheet

Manuel Belgrano and José Artigas — A371

1967, June 22 *Imperf.*

839 A371	Sheet of 2	.40	.40
a.	6p gray & brown	.15	.15
b.	22p brown & gray	.24	.24

Third Rio de la Plata Stamp Show, Montevideo, Uruguay, June 18-25.

Peace Dove and Valise
A372

PADELAI Emblem
A373

1967, Aug. 5 Litho. *Perf. 13½*
840 A372 20p multi .22 .15

Issued for International Tourist Year 1967.

1967, Aug. 12 Litho.
841 A373 20p multi .22 .15

75th anniv. of the Children's Welfare Association (Patronato de la Infancia-PADELAI).

Stagecoach and Modern City — A374

1967, Sept. 23 Wmk. 90 *Perf. 13½*
842 A374 20p rose, yel & blk .26 .15

Centenary of Villa Maria, Cordoba.

San Martin by Ibarra — A375

"Battle of Chacabuco" by P. Subercaseaux — A376

1967, Sept. 30 Litho.
843 A375 20p blk brn & pale yel .55 .15

Engr.
844 A376 40p bl blk .85 .20
Set value .27

Battle of Chacabuco, 150th anniversary.

Exhibition Rooms — A377

1967, Oct. 11 Photo.
845 A377 20p bl gray .20 .15

Government House Museum, 10th anniv.

Pedro L. Zanni, Fokker and 1924 Flight Route — A378

1967, Oct. 21 Litho. *Perf. 13½*
846 A378 20p multi .28 .15

Issued for Aviation Week and to commemorate the 1924 flight of the Fokker seaplane "Province of Buenos Aires" from Amsterdam, Netherlands, to Osaka, Japan.

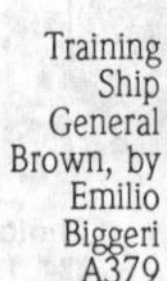

Training Ship General Brown, by Emilio Biggeri
A379

1967, Oct. 28 Wmk. 90
847 A379 20p multi .85 .35

Issued to honor the Military Naval School.

Ovidio Lagos and Front Page — A380

St. Barbara — A381

1967, Nov. 11 Photo.
848 A380 20p sepia .15 .15

Centenary of La Capital, Rosario newspaper.

1967, Dec. 2 *Perf. 13½*
849 A381 20p rose red .28 .15

St. Barbara, patron saint of artillerymen.

Portrait of his Wife, by Eduardo Sivori — A382

1968, Jan. 27 Photo. *Perf. 13½*
850 A382 20p bl grn .28 .15

Eduardo Sivori (1847-1918), painter.

Antarctic Type of 1966 and

Admiral Brown Scientific Station
A383

Planes over Map of Antarctica
A384

Design: 6p, Map showing radio-postal stations 1966-67.

1968, Feb. 17 Litho. Wmk. 90

851 A363 6p multi .45 .18
852 A383 20p multi .60 .24
853 A384 40p multi 1.00 .30
Nos. 851-853 (3) 2.05 .72

Issued to publicize Argentine research projects in Argentine Antarctica.

The Annunciation, by Leonardo da Vinci — A385

Man in Wheelchair and Factory — A386

1968, Mar. 23 Photo. *Perf. 13½*

854 A385 20p lilac rose .20 .15

Issued for the Day of the Army Communications System and its patron saint, Gabriel.

1968, Mar. 23 Litho.

855 A386 20p green & black .20 .15

Day of Rehabilitation of the Handicapped.

Children and WHO Emblem — A387

1968, May 11 Wmk. 90 *Perf. 13½*

856 A387 20p dk vio bl & ver .20 .15

20th anniv. of WHO.

Soldier Type of 1965

Army Day: 20p, Uniform of First Artillery Regiment "General Iriarte."

1968, June 8 Litho.

857 A340a 20p multi .75 .24

Frigate "Libertad," Painting by Emilio Biggeri A388

1968, June 15 Wmk. 90

858 A388 20p multi .75 .24

Issued for Navy Day.

Guillermo Rawson and Old Hospital — A389

1968, July 20 Photo. *Perf. 13½*

859 A389 6p olive bister .16 .15

Cent. of Rawson Hospital, Buenos Aires.

Student Directing Traffic for Schoolmates A390

1968, Aug. 10 Litho. *Perf. 13½*

860 A390 20p lt bl, blk, buff & car .15 .15

Traffic safety and education.

O'Higgins Joining San Martin at Battle of Maipu, by P. Subercaseaux — A391

1968, Aug. 15 Engr.

861 A391 40p bluish blk .65 .30

Sesquicentennial of the Battle of Maipu.

Osvaldo Magnasco (1864-1920), Lawyer, Professor of Law and Minister of Justice — A392

1968, Sept. 7 Photo. *Perf. 13½*

862 A392 20p brown .22 .15

Grandmother's Birthday, by Patricia Lynch — A393

The Sea, by Edgardo Gomez — A394

1968, Sept. 21 Litho.

863 A393 20p multicolored .24 .15
864 A394 20p multicolored .24 .15
Set value .16

The designs were chosen in a competition among kindergarten and elementary school children.

Mar del Plata at Night — A395

1968, Oct. 19 Litho. *Perf. 13½*

865 A395 20p blk, ocher & bl .22 .15
Nos. 865,C113-C114 (3) 1.27 .61

4th Plenary Assembly of the Intl. Telegraph and Telephone Consultative Committee, Mar del Plata, Sept. 23-Oct. 25.

Frontier Gendarme A396

Patrol Boat A397

1968, Oct. 26

866 A396 20p multi .30 .15
867 A397 20p bl, vio bl & blk .30 .15

No. 866 honors the Gendarmery; No. 867 the Coast Guard.

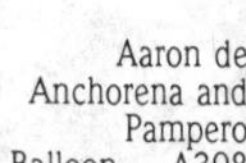

Aaron de Anchorena and Pampero Balloon — A398

1968, Nov. 2 Photo.

868 A398 20p bl & multi .32 .15

22nd Aeronautics and Space Week.

St. Martin of Tours, by Alfredo Guido — A399

1968, Nov. 9 Litho.

869 A399 20p lil & dk brn .20 .15

St. Martin of Tours, patron saint of Buenos Aires.

Municipal Bank Emblem — A400

1968, Nov. 16

870 A400 20p multi .20 .15

90th anniv. of the Buenos Aires Municipal Bank.

Anniversary Emblem A401

1968, Dec. 14 Wmk. 90 *Perf. 13½*

871 A401 20p car rose & dk grn .20 .15

25th anniversary of ALPI (Fight Against Polio Association).

Shovel and State Coal Fields Emblem A402

Pouring Ladle and Army Manufacturing Emblem A403

1968, Dec. 21 Litho.

872 A402 20p org, bl & blk .26 .15
873 A403 20p dl vio, dl yel & blk .26 .15
Set value .18

Issued to publicize the National Coal and Steel industry at the Rio Turbio coal fields and the Zapla blast furnaces.

Woman Potter, by Ramon Gomez Cornet — A404

1968, Dec. 21 Photo. *Perf. 13½*

874 A404 20p car rose .48 .40

Centenary of the Witcomb Gallery.

View of Buenos Aires and Rio de la Plata by Ulrico Schmidl A405

1969, Feb. 8 Litho. Wmk. 90

875 A405 20p yel, blk & ver .48 .35

Ulrico Schmidl (c. 1462-1554) who wrote "Journey to the Rio de la Plata and Paraguay."

Types of 1955-67

Designs: 50c, Puma. 1p, Sunflower. 3p, Zapata Slope, Catamarca. 5p, Tierra del Fuego. 6p, José Hernandez. 10p, Inca Bridge, Mendoza. 50p, José de San Martin. 90p, Guillermo Brown. 100p, Ski jumper.

Photo.; Litho. (50c, 3p, 10p)

1969-70 Wmk. 365 *Perf. 13½*

882 A275 50c bister ('70) .70 .15
883 A277 5p brown 1.25 .15
884 A279 100p blue 26.00 .70

Unwmk.

885 A278 1p brown ('70) .65 .15
886 A277 3p dk blue ('70) .65 .15
a. Wmk. 90 5.25 .35
887 A277 5p brown ('70) .75 .15
888 A366 6p red brn, 15x22mm ('70) 1.25 .15
889 A278 10p dl red ('70) .52 .15
a. Wmk. 90 425.00 32.50
890 A241 50p dk bl, 22x31½mm ('70) 1.75 .15
891 A366 90p ol brn, 22x32mm ('70) 3.50 .18
892 A279 100p blue ('70) 9.00 .30
Nos. 882-892 (11) 46.02
Set value 1.78

For surcharges see Nos. 1076-1077.

Soldier Type of 1965

Army Day: 20p, Sapper (gastador) of Buenos Aires Province, 1856.

Perf. 13½

1969, May 31 Wmk. 365 Litho.

893 A340a 20p multicolored .85 .35

Frigate Hercules, by Emilio Biggeri — A406

1969, May 31

894 A406 20p multicolored 1.00 .28

Issued for Navy Day.

"All Men are Equal" A407

ILO Emblem A408

1969, June 28 Wmk. 90

895 A407 20p black & ocher .20 .15

International Human Rights Year.

1969, June 28 Litho. Wmk. 365

896 A408 20p lt green & multi .20 .15

50th anniv. of the ILO.

Pedro N. Arata (1849-1922), Chemist — A409

Radar Antenna, Balcarce Station and Satellite — A410

Portraits: No. 898, Miguel Fernandez (1883-1950), zoologist. No. 899, Angel P. Gallardo (1867-1934), biologist. No. 900, Cristobal M. Hicken (1875-1933), botanist. No. 901, Eduardo Ladislao Holmberg, M.D. (1852-1937), natural scientist.

1969, Aug. 9 Wmk. 365 *Perf. 13½*

897 A409	6p	Arata	.42	.15
898 A409	6p	Fernandez	.42	.15
899 A409	6p	Gallardo	.42	.15
900 A409	6p	Hicken	.42	.15
901 A409	6p	Holmberg	.42	.15
		Nos. 897-901 (5)	2.10	
		Set value		.50

Argentine scientists. See No. 778 note.

1969, Aug. 23 Wmk. 99

902 A410 20p yellow & blk .28 .15

Communications by satellite through Intl. Telecommunications Satellite Consortium (INTELSAT). See No. C115.

Nieuport 28, Flight Route and Map of Buenos Aires Province A411

1969, Sept. 13 Litho. Wmk. 90

903 A411 20p multicolored .28 .15

50th anniv. of the first Argentine airmail service from El Palomar to Mar del Plata, flown Feb. 23-24, 1919, by Capt. Pedro L. Zanni.

Military College Gate and Emblem A412

1969, Oct. 4 Wmk. 365 *Perf. 13½*

904 A412 20p multicolored .28 .15

Cent. of the National Military College, El Palomar (Greater Buenos Aires).

Gen. Angel Pacheco A413

La Farola, Logotype of La Prensa A414

1969, Nov. 8 Photo. Wmk. 365

905 A413 20p deep green .22 .15

Gen. Angel Pacheco (1795-1869).

1969, Nov. 8 Litho. *Perf. 13½*

Design: No. 907, Bartolomé Mitre and La Nacion logotype.

906 A414	20p	org, yel & blk	.70	.22
907 A414	20p	brt green & blk	.70	.22

Cent. of newspapers La Prensa and La Nacion.

Julian Aguirre — A415

Musicians: No. 909, Felipe Boero. No. 910, Constantino Gaito. No. 911, Carlos Lopez Buchardo. No. 912, Alberto Williams.

Perf. 13½

1969, Dec. 6 Wmk. 365 Photo.

908 A415	6p	Aguirre	.55	.30
909 A415	6p	Boero	.55	.30
910 A415	6p	Gaito	.55	.30
911 A415	6p	Buchardo	.55	.30
912 A415	6p	Williams	.55	.30
		Nos. 908-912 (5)	2.75	1.50

Argentine musicians. See No. 778 note.

Lt. Benjamin Matienzo and Nieuport Plane A416

1969, Dec. 13 Litho.

913 A416 20p multicolored .55 .35

23rd Aeronautics and Space Week.

High Power Lines and Map A417

Design: 20p, Map of Santa Fe Province and schematic view of tunnel.

1969, Dec. 13

914 A417	6p	multicolored	.50	.15
915 A417	20p	multicolored	1.00	.15
		Set value		.18

Completion of development projects: 6p for the hydroelectric dams on the Limay and Neuquen Rivers, the 20p the tunnel under Rio Grance from Sante Fe to Parana.

Lions Emblem A418

1969, Dec. 20 Wmk. 365 *Perf. 13½*

916 A418 20p blk, emer & org .60 .24

Argentine Lions Intl. Club, 50th anniv.

Madonna and Child, by Raul Soldi — A419

1969, Dec. 27 Litho.

917 A419 20p multicolored .70 .28

Christmas 1969.

Manuel Belgrano, by Jean Gericault — A420

The Creation of the Flag, Bas-relief by Jose Fioravanti — A421

Perf. 13½

1970, July 4 Unwmk. Photo.

918 A420 20c deep brown .35 .15

Litho. *Perf. 12½*

919 A421 50c bis, blk & bl .85 .50

Gen. Manuel Belgrano (1770-1820), Argentine patriot.

San Jose Palace A422

1970, Aug. 9 Litho. *Perf. 13½*

920 A422 20c yel grn & multi .22 .15

Cent. of the death of Gen. Justo Jose de Urquiza (1801-70), pres. of Argentina, 1854-60.

Schooner "Juliet" A423

1970, Aug. 8 Unwmk.

921 A423 20c multi 1.00 .40

Issued for Navy Day.

Belgrano A425

Lujan Basilica A426

Receiver of 1920 and Waves A424

1970, Aug. 29

922 A424 20c lt bl & multi .30 .15

50th anniv. of Argentine broadcasting.

Types of 1955-67 Inscribed "Republica Argentina" and Types A425, A426

Designs: 1c, Sunflower. 3c, Zapata Slope, Catamarca. 5c, Tierra del Fuego. 8c, No. 931, Belgrano. 10c, Inca Bridge, Mendoza. 25c, 50c, 70c, Jose de San Martin. 65c, 90c, 1.20p, San Martin. 1p, Ski jumper. 1.15p, 1.80p, Adm. Brown.

1970-73 Photo. Unwmk. *Perf. 13½*

923 A278	1c	dk grn ('71)	.15	.15
924 A277	3c	car rose ('71)	.15	.15
925 A277	5c	blue ('71)	.15	.15
926 A425	6c	dp bl	.15	.15
927 A425	8c	grn ('72)	.15	.15
928 A278	10c	dl red ('71)	.38	.15
929 A278	10c	brn, litho. ('71)	.52	.15
930 A278	10c	org brn ('72)	.45	.15
931 A425	10c	brown ('73)	.20	.15
932 A426	18c	yel & dk brn, litho ('73)	.20	.15
933 A425	25c	brown ('71)	.32	.15
934 A425	50c	scar ('72)	1.25	.15
935 A241	65c	brn, 22x31½mm, paper II ('71)	.65	.15
936 A425	70c	dk bl ('73)	.32	.15
937 A241	90c	emer, 22x31½ mm ('72)	3.25	.15
938 A279	1p	brn, 22½x29½ mm ('71)	1.90	.15
939 A366	1.15p	dk bl, 22½x32 mm ('71)	1.10	.15
940 A241	1.20p	org, 22x31½ mm ('73)	1.10	.15
941 A366	1.80p	brn ('73)	1.10	.15
		Nos. 923-941 (19)	13.49	
		Set value		1.00

The imprint "Casa de Moneda de la Nacion" (in capitals) appears on 3c, 5c, Nos. 928-929; 65c, 90c, 1p, 1.20p.

On type A425 only the 6c is inscribed "Ley 18.188" below denomination.

Fluorescent paper was used in printing the 25c, 50c, and 70c. The 3c, 5c, 8c, No. 931 and 65c were issued on both ordinary and fluorescent paper.

See Nos. 987-996, 1032-1038, 1042-1043, 1089-1107. For overprint and surcharge see Nos. 1010, 1078.

Soldier Type of 1965

Design: 20c, Galloping messenger of Field Army, 1879.

1970, Oct. 17 Litho. *Perf. 13½*

944 A340a 20c multi .80 .26

Dome of Cathedral of Cordoba — A430

1970, Nov. 7 Unwmk.

945 A430 50c gray & blk .80 .15

Bishopric of Tucuman, 400th anniv. See #C131.

People Around UN Emblem — A431

1970, Nov. 7

946 A431 20c tan & multi .20 .15

25th anniversary of the United Nations.

State Mint and Medal A432

1970, Nov. 28 Unwmk. *Perf. 13½*

947 A432 20c gold, grn & blk .20 .15

Inauguration of the State Mint Building, 25th anniversary.

St. John Bosco and Dean Funes College
A433

1970, Dec. 19 **Litho.**
948 A433 20c olive & blk .20 .15

Honoring the work of the Salesian Order in Patagonia.

Nativity, by Horacio Gramajo Gutierrez — A434

1970, Dec. 19
949 A434 20c multi .55 .35

Christmas 1970.

Argentine Flag, Map of Argentine Antarctica — A435

1971, Feb. 20 **Litho.** ***Perf. 13½***
950 A435 20c multi 1.25 .50

Argentine South Pole Expedition, 5th anniv.

Phosphorescent Sorting Code and Albert Einstein — A436

1971, Apr. 30 **Unwmk.** ***Perf. 13½***
951 A436 25c multi .48 .30

Electronics in postal development.

Symbolic Road Crossing
A437

1971, May 29 **Litho.**
952 A437 25c bl & blk .25 .18

Inter-American Regional Meeting of the Intl. Federation of Roads, Buenos Aires, Mar. 28-31.

Elias Alippi — A438

Actors: No. 954, Juan Aurelio Casacuberta. No. 955, Angelina Pagano. No. 956, Roberto Casaux. No. 957, Florencio Parravicini. See No. 778 note.

1971, May 29 **Litho.**
953 A438 15c Alippi .35 .20
954 A438 15c Casacuberta .35 .20
955 A438 15c Pagano .35 .20
956 A438 15c Casaux .35 .20
957 A438 15c Parravicini .35 .20
Nos. 953-957 (5) 1.75 1.00

Soldier Type of 1965

Army Day, May 29: Artilleryman, 1826.

1971, July 3 **Unwmk.** ***Perf. 13½***
958 A340a 25c multi 1.25 .50

Bilander "Carmen," by Emilio Biggeri
A439

1971, July 3
959 A439 25c multi 1.25 .25

Navy Day

Peruvian Order of the Sun
A440

1971, Aug. 28
960 A440 31c multi .32 .15

Sesquicentennial of Peru's independence.

Güemes in Battle, by Lorenzo Gigli
A441

Design: No. 962, Death of Güemes, by Antonio Alice.

1971, Aug. 28
Size: 39x29mm
961 A441 25c multi .48 .30
Size: 84x29mm
962 A441 25c multi .48 .30

Sesquicentennial of the death of Martin Miguel de Güemes, leader in Gaucho War, Governor and Captain General of Salta Province.

Stylized Tulip — A442

1971, Sept. 18
963 A442 25c tan & multi .26 .15

3rd Intl. and 8th Natl. Horticultural Exhib.

Father Antonio Saenz, by Juan Gut — A443

1971, Sept. 18
964 A433 25c gray & multi .26 .15

Sesquicentennial of University of Buenos Aires, and to honor Father Antonio Saenz, first Chancellor and Rector.

Fabricaciones Militares Emblem — A444

1971, Oct. 16 **Unwmk.** ***Perf. 13½***
965 A444 25c brn, gold, bl & blk .26 .15

30th anniv. of military armament works.

Cars and Trucks
A445

Design: 65c, Tree converted into paper.

1971, Oct. 16
966 A445 25c dl bl & multi .52 .20
967 A445 65c grn & multi 1.25 .50
Nos. 966-967,C134 (3) 2.37 .94

Nationalized industries.

Luis C. Candelaria and his Plane, 1918
A446

1971, Nov. 27
968 A446 25c multi .25 .18

25th Aeronautics and Space Week.

Observatory and Nebula of Magellan
A447

1971, Nov. 27
969 A447 25c multi .25 .15

Cordoba Astronomical Observatory, cent.

Christ in Majesty — A448

1971, Dec. 18 **Litho.**
970 A448 25c blk & multi .25 .15

Christmas 1971. Design is from a tapestry by Horacio Butler in Basilica of St. Francis, Buenos Aires.

Mother and Child, by J. C. Castagnino — A449

1972, May 6 **Unwmk.** ***Perf. 13½***
971 A449 25c fawn & black .25 .18

25th anniv. (in 1971) of UNICEF.

Mailman's Bag
A450

1972, Sept. 2 **Litho.** ***Perf. 13½***
972 A450 25c lemon & multi .16 .15

Bicentenary of appointment of first Argentine mailman.

Adm. Brown Station, Map of Antarctica
A451

1972, Sept. 2
973 A451 25c blue & multi .70 .35

10th anniv. (in 1971) of Antarctic Treaty.

Soldier Type of 1965

Army Day: 25c, Sergeant, Negro and Mulatto Corps, 1806-1807.

1972, Sept. 23
974 A340a 25c multi .75 .35

Brigantine "Santisima Trinidad"
A452

1972, Sept. 23
975 A452 25c multi .75 .35

Navy Day. See No. 1006.

A453 A454

1972, Sept. 30 **Litho.** ***Perf. 13½***
976 A453 45c Oil pump .90 .20

50th anniv. of the organ. of the state oil fields (Yacimientos Petroliferos Fiscales).

1972, Sept. 30
977 A454 25c Sounding balloon .25 .15

Cent. of Natl. Meteorological Service.

Trees and Globe — A455

1972, Oct. 14 ***Perf. 13x13½***
978 A455 25c bl, blk & lt bl .70 .20

7th World Forestry Congress, Buenos Aires, Oct. 4-18.

Arms of Naval School, Frigate "Presidente Sarmiento" — A456

1972, Oct. 14
979 A456 25c gold & multi .65 .35

Centenary of Military Naval School.

Early Balloon and Plane, Antonio de Marchi — A457

Bartolomé Mitre — A458

1972, Nov. 4 ***Perf. 13½***
980 A457 25c multi .26 .20

Aeronautics and Space Week, and in honor of Baron Antonio de Marchi (1875-1934), aviation pioneer.

1972, Nov. 4 **Engr.**
981 A458 25c dark blue .16 .15

Pres. Bartolome Mitre (1821-1906), writer, historian, soldier.

Flower and Heart — A459

1972, Dec. 2 **Litho.** ***Perf. 13½***
982 A459 90c lt bl, ultra & blk .60 .35

"Your heart is your health," World Health Day.

"Martin Fierro," by Juan C. Castignano — A460

"Spirit of the Gaucho," by Vicente Forte — A461

1972, Dec. 2 **Litho.** ***Perf. 13½***
983 A460 50c multi .32 .20
984 A461 90c multi .65 .35

Intl. Book Year 1972, and cent. of publication of the poem, Martin Fierro, by Jose Hernandez (1834-86).

Iguacu Falls and Tourist Year Emblem — A462

1972, Dec. 16 ***Perf. 13x13½***
985 A462 45c multi .28 .15

Tourism Year of the Americas.

King, Wood Carving, 18th Century — A463

1972, Dec. 16 ***Perf. 13½***
986 A463 50c multi .50 .25

Christmas 1972.

Types of 1955-73 Inscribed "Republica Argentina" and

Moon Valley, San Juan Province — A463a

Designs: 1c, Sunflower. 5c, Tierra del Fuego. 10c, Inca Bridge, Mendoza. 50c, Lujan Basilica. 65c, 22.50p, San Martin. 1p, Ski jumper. 1.15p, 4.50p, Guillermo Brown. 1.80p, Manuel Belgrano.

Litho.; Photo. (1c, 65c, 1p)
Perf. 13½, 12½ (1.80p)

1972-75 **Wmk. 365**

987	A278	1c	dk grn	.16	.15
988	A277	5c	dark blue	.16	.15
989	A278	10c	bis brn	.16	.15
989A	A426	50c	dl pur ('75)	.16	.15
990	A241	65c	gray brn	3.25	.15
991	A279	1p	brown	1.40	.15
992	A366	1.15p	dk gray bl	1.40	.15
993	A425	1.80p	bl ('75)	.16	.15
994	A366	4.50p	grn ('75)	.65	.15
995	A241	22.50p	vio bl ('75)	1.40	.15
996	A463a	50p	multi ('75)	2.75	.32
		Nos. 987-996 (11)		11.65	
			Set value		1.05

Paper size of 1c is 27½x39mm; others of 1972, 37x27, 27x37mm.
Size of 22.50p, 50p: 26½x38½mm.
See Nos. 1050, 1108.

Cock (Symbolic of Police) — A464

First Coin of Bank of Buenos Aires — A465

1973, Feb. 3 **Litho.** **Unwmk.**
997 A464 50c lt grn & multi .30 .15

Sesqui. of Federal Police of Argentina.

1973, Feb. 3 ***Perf. 13½***
998 A465 50c pur, yel & brn .15 .15

Sesquicentennial of the Bank of Buenos Aires Province.

DC-3 Planes Over Antarctica A466

1973, Apr. 28 **Litho.** ***Perf. 13½***
999 A466 50c lt bl & multi 1.50 .60

10th anniversary of Argentina's first flight to the South Pole.

Rivadavia's Chair, Argentine Arms and Colors — A467

1973, May 19 **Litho.** ***Perf. 13½***
1000 A467 50c multi .25 .15

Inauguration of Pres. Hector J. Campora, May 25, 1973.

San Martin, by Gil de Castro — A468

San Martin and Bolivar A469

1973, July 7 **Litho.** ***Perf. 13½***
1001 A468 50c lt grn & multi .35 .15
1002 A469 50c yel & multi .35 .15

Gen. San Martin's farewell to the people of Peru and his meeting with Simon Bolivar at Guayaquil July 26-27, 1822.

Eva Peron A470

1973, July 26 **Litho.** ***Perf. 13½***
1003 A470 70c blk, org & bl .20 .15

Maria Eva Duarte de Peron (1919-1952), political leader.

House of Viceroy Sobremonte, by Hortensia de Virgilion — A471

1973, July 28 ***Perf. 13x13½***
1004 A471 50c bl & multi .20 .15

400th anniversary of the city of Cordoba.

Woman, by Lino Spilimbergo A472

New and Old Telephones A473

1973, Aug. 28 **Litho.** ***Perf. 13½***
1005 A472 70c multi .70 .15

Philatelists' Day. See Nos. B60-B61.

Ship Type of 1972

Navy Day: 70c, Frigate "La Argentina."

1973, Oct. 27 **Litho.** ***Perf. 13½***
1006 A452 70c multi .60 .35

1973, Oct. 27
1007 A473 70c brt bl & multi .40 .20

25th anniv. of natl. telecommunications system.

Plume Made of Flags of Participants A474

1973, Nov. 3 ***Perf. 13½***
1008 A474 70c yel bis & multi .25 .15

12th Cong. of Latin Notaries, Buenos Aires.

No. 940 Overprinted TRANSMISION DEL MANDO PRESIDENCIAL 12 OCTUBRE 1973

1973, Nov. 30 **Photo.**
1010 A241 1.20p orange .85 .20

Assumption of presidency by Juan Peron, Oct. 12.

Virgin and Child, Window, La Plata Cathedral — A476

Christmas: 1.20p, Nativity, by Bruno Venier, b. 1914.

1973, Dec. 15 **Litho.** ***Perf. 13½***
1011 A476 70c gray & multi .35 .18
1012 A476 1.20p black & multi .70 .35

The Lama, by Juan Batlle Planas — A477

Paintings: 50c, Houses in Boca District, by Eugenio Daneri, horiz. 90c, The Blue Grotto, by Emilio Pettoruti, horiz.

1974, Feb. 9 **Litho.** ***Perf. 13½***
1013 A477 50c multicolored .28 .15
1014 A477 70c multicolored .35 .20
1015 A477 90c multicolored .60 .28
Nos. 1013-1015,B64 (4) 1.51 .85

Argentine painters.

Mar del Plata A478

1974, Feb. 9
1016 A478 70c multicolored .28 .15

Centenary of Mar del Plata.

Weather Symbols A479 — Justo Santa Maria de Oro A480

1974, Mar. 23 Litho. *Perf. 13½*
1017 A479 1.20p multi .35 .20

Cent. of intl. meteorological cooperation.

1974, Mar. 23
1018 A480 70c multi .20 .15

Bicentenary of the birth of Brother Justo Santa Maria de Oro (1772-1836), theologian, patriot, first Argentine bishop.

Belisario Roldan (1873-1922), Writer — A481

1974, June 29 Photo. Unwmk.
1019 A481 70c bl & brn .20 .15

Poster with Names of OAS Members A482

1974, June 29 Litho.
1020 A482 1.38p multi .18 .15

Organization of American States, 25th anniv.

ENCOTEL Emblem — A483

1974, Aug. 10 Litho. *Perf. 13*
1021 A483 1.20p bl, gold & blk .42 .15

ENCOTEL, Natl. Post and Telegraph Press.

Flags of Argentina, Bolivia, Brazil, Paraguay, Uruguay — A484

1974, Aug. 16 *Perf. 13½*
1022 A484 1.38p multi .22 .15

6th Meeting of Foreign Ministers of Rio de la Plata Basin Countries.

El Chocon Hydroelectric Complex, Limay River — A485 — Somisa Steel Mill, San Nicolas — A486

Gen. Belgrano Bridge, Chaco-Corrientes — A487

Perf. 13½, 13x13½ (4.50p)
1974, Sept. 14

1023 A485	70c multi	.40	.18
1024 A486	1.20p multi	.60	.35
1025 A487	4.50p multi	2.00	.52
	Nos. 1023-1025 (3)	3.00	1.05

Development projects.

Brigantine Belgrano, by Emilio Biggeri A488

1974, Oct. 26 Litho. *Perf. 13½*
1026 A488 1.20p multi .60 .30

Departure into exile in Chile of General San Martin, Sept. 22, 1822.

Alberto R. Mascias and Bleriot Plane — A489

1974, Oct. 26 Unwmk.
1027 A489 1.20p multi .50 .25

Air Force Day, Aug. 10, and to honor Alberto Roque Garcias (1878-1951), aviation pioneer.
Exists with wmk. 365.

Hussar, 1812, by Eleodoro Marenco — A490

1974, Oct. 26
1028 A490 1.20p multi .50 .25

Army Day.

Post Horn and Flags A491

1974, Nov. 23 Unwmk. *Perf. 13½*
1029 A491 2.65p multi .85 .20

Centenary of Universal Postal Union.
Exists with wmk. 365.

Franciscan Monastery A492

1974, Nov. 23 Litho.
1030 A492 1.20p multi .40 .15

400th anniversary, city of Santa Fe.

Trout Type of 1968

1974 Engr. Unwmk.
1031 A366a 1000p vio bl 3.25 .80

Due to a shortage of 10p stamps a quantity of this 1,000p was released for use as 10p.

Types of 1954-73 Inscribed "Republica Argentina" and

Red Deer in Forest — A495

Congress Building A497

Designs: 30c, 60c, 1.80p, Manuel Belgrano. 50c, Lujan Basilica. No. 1036, 2p, 6p, San Martin (16x22½mm). 2.70p, 7.50p, 22.50p, San Martin (22x31½mm). 4.50p, 13.50p, Guillermo Brown. 10p, Leaping trout.

1974-76 Unwmk. Photo. *Perf. 13½*

1032 A425	30c brn vio	.15	.15
1033 A426	50c blk & brn red	.15	.15
1034 A426	50c bis & bl	.15	.15
1035 A425	60c ocher	.15	.15
1036 A425	1.20p red	.30	.15
1037 A425	1.80p dp bl	.15	.15
1038 A425	2p dk pur	.20	.15
1039 A241	2.70p dk bl, 22 x 31½mm	.24	.15
1040 A366	4.50p green	.85	.15
1041 A495	5p yel grn	.40	.15
1042 A425	6p red org	.20	.15
1043 A425	6p emer	.20	.15
1044 A241	7.50p grn, 22 x 31½mm	.85	.15
1045 A366a	10p vio bl	1.00	.15
1046 A366	13.50p scar, 16 x 22½mm	.85	.15
1047 A366	13.50p scar, 22 x 31½mm	.85	.15
1048 A241	22.50p dp bl, 22 x 31½mm	.75	.15
1049 A497	30p yel & dk red brn	1.10	.15
1050 A463a	50p multi	1.50	.15
	Nos. 1032-1050 (19)	10.04	
	Set value		1.50

Nos. 1033-1035, 1037-1038, 1042-1044, 1046-1048 issued in 1976, No. 1050 in 1976.

Fluorescent paper was used in printing No. 1036, 2p, Nos. 1044 and 1047. The 30p was issued on both ordinary and fluorescent paper.

See No. 829. For type of A495 overprinted see No. 1144.

Miniature Sheet

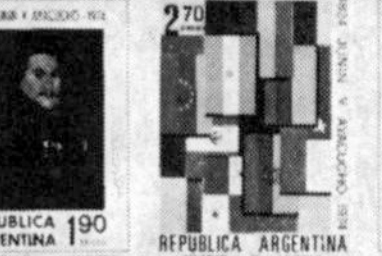

A498

1974, Dec. 7 Litho. *Perf. 13½*
1052 A498 Sheet of 6 3.50 2.75

a.	1p Mariano Necochea	.25
b.	1.20p Jose de San Martin	.25
c.	1.70p Manuel Isidoro Suarez	.35
d.	1.90p Juan Pascual Pringles	.42
e.	2.70p Latin American flags	.65
f.	4.50p Jose Felix Bogado	1.10

Sesqui. of Battles of Junin and Ayacucho.

Dove, by Vito Campanella A499

St. Anne, by Raul Soldi — A500

1974, Dec. 21 Litho. *Perf. 13½*
1053 A499 1.20p multi .48 .18
1054 A500 2.65p multi .75 .30

Christmas 1974.

Boy Looking at Stamp — A501

1974, Dec. 21
1055 A501 1.70p blk & yel .38 .15

World Youth Philately Year.

Space Monsters, by Raquel Forner A502

Argentine modern art: 4.50p, Dream, by Emilio Centurion.

1975, Feb. 22 Litho. *Perf. 13½*
1056 A502 2.70p multi .90 .26
1057 A502 4.50p multi 1.75 .40

Indian Woman and Cathedral, Catamarca — A503

Tourist Publicity: #1059, Carved chancel and street scene. #1060, Grazing cattleand monastery yard. #1061, Painted pottery and power station. #1062, Farm cart and colonial mansion. #1063, Perito Moreno glacier and spinning mill. #1064, Lake Lapataia and scientific surveyor. #1065, Los Alerces National Park and oil derrick.

1975 Litho. Unwmk. *Perf. 13½*

1058 A503	1.20p	shown	.25	.15
1059 A503	1.20p	Jujuy	.25	.15
1060 A503	1.20p	Salta	.25	.15
1061 A503	1.20p	Santiago del Estero	.25	.15
1062 A503	1.20p	Tucuman	.25	.15
1063 A503	6p	Santa Cruz	.50	.15
1064 A503	6p	Tierra del Fuego	.50	.15
1065 A503	6p	Chubut	.50	.15
		Nos. 1058-1065 (8)	2.75	1.20

Issue dates: 1.20p, Mar. 8; 6p, Dec. 20.

"We Have Been Inoculated" A504

1975, Apr. 26 Unwmk. *Perf. 13½*
1066 A504 2p multi .45 .22

Children's inoculation campaign (child's painting).

Hugo A. Acuña and South Orkney Station — A505

Designs: No. 1068, Francisco P. Moreno and Lake Nahuel Huapi. No. 1069, Lt. Col. Luis Piedra Buena and cutter, Luisito. No. 1070, Ensign José M. Sobral and Snow Hill House. No. 1071, Capt. Carlos M. Moyano and Cerro del Toro (mountain).

1975, June 28 Litho. *Perf. 13*

1067 A505	2p	grnsh bl & multi	.26	.15
1068 A505	2p	yel grn & multi	.26	.15
1069 A505	2p	lt vio & multi	.26	.15
1070 A505	2p	gray bl & multi	.26	.15
1071 A505	2p	pale grn & multi	.26	.15
		Nos. 1067-1071 (5)	1.30	.75

Pioneers of Antarctica.

Frigate "25 de Mayo" A506

1975, Sept. 27 Unwmk. *Perf. 13½*
1072 A506 6p multi .42 .22

Navy Day 1975.

Eduardo Bradley and Balloon — A507

1975, Sept. 27 Wmk. 365
1073 A507 6p multi .42 .22

Air Force Day.

Declaration of Independence, by Juan M. Blanes — A508

1975, Oct. 25
1074 A508 6p multi .32 .15

Sesquicentennial of Uruguay's declaration of independence.

Flame A509

1975, Oct. 17 Unwmk.
1075 A509 6p gray & multi .32 .15

Loyalty Day, 30th anniversary of Pres. Peron's accession to power.

Nos. 886, 891 and 932 Surcharged

REVALORIZADO
6 c.

REVALORIZADO **30 c**

REVALORIZADO
5 pesos

1975 Lithographed, Photogravure

1076 A277	6c on 3p	.15	.15
1077 A366	30c on 90p	.15	.15
1078 A426	5p on 18c	.35	.18
	Nos. 1076-1078 (3)	.65	
	Set value		.38

Issue dates: 6c, Oct. 30; 30c, Nov. 20; 5p, Oct. 24. The 6c also exists on No. 886a.

International Bridge, Flags of Argentina and Uruguay A510

1975, Oct. 25 Litho. Wmk. 365
1081 A510 6p multi .35 .18

Opening of bridge connecting Colon, Argentina, and Paysandu, Uruguay.

Post Horn, Surcharged A511

1975, Nov. 8
1082 A511 10p on 20c multi .45 .15

Introduction of postal code. Not issued without surcharge.

Nurse Holding Infant A512

1975, Dec. 13 Litho. *Perf. 13½*
1083 A512 6p multi .45 .15

Children's Hospital, centenary.

Nativity, Nueva Pompeya Church — A513

1975, Dec. 13 Litho. Unwmk.
1084 A513 6p multi .30 .18

Christmas 1975.

Types of 1970-75 and

1000 PESOS
REPUBLICA ARGENTINA

Church of St. Francis, Salta — A515

Designs: 3p, No. 1099, 60p, 90p, Manuel Belgrano. 12p, 15p, 20p, 30p, No. 1100, 100p, 110p, 120p, 130p, San Martin. 15p, 70p, Guillermo Brown. 300p, Moon Valley (lower inscriptions italic). 500p, Adm. Brown Station, Antarctica.

1976-78 Photo. Unwmk. *Perf. 13½*

1089 A425	3p slate	.15	.15
1090 A425	12p rose red	.25	.15

Perf. 12½x13
Litho. Wmk. 365

1091 A425	12p rose red	.20	.15
1092 A425	12p emerald	.20	.15

Perf. 13½
Photo. Unwmk.

1093 A425	12p emer ('77)	.20	.15
1094 A425	15p rose red	.20	.15
1095 A425	15p vio bl ('77)	.20	.15
1097 A425	20p rose red ('77)	.35	.15
1098 A425	30p rose red ('77)	.35	.15
1099 A425	40p dp grn	.52	.15
1100 A425	40p rose red ('77)	.35	.15
1101 A425	60p dk bl ('77)	.70	.20
1102 A425	70p dk bl ('77)	.85	.20
1103 A425	90p emer ('77)	1.00	.28
1104 A425	100p red	.75	.24
1105 A425	110p rose red ('78)	.52	.18
1106 A425	120p rose red ('78)	.60	.20
1107 A425	130p rose red ('78)	.70	.24

Litho.

1108 A463a	300p multi	3.50	1.50
1109 A515	500p multi ('77)	8.25	1.40
1110 A515	1000p multi ('77)	10.00	2.00
	Nos. 1089-1110 (21)	29.84	8.09

Fluorescent paper was used in printing both 12p rose red, 15p rose red, 20p, 30p, 40p rose red, 100p, 110p, 120p, 130p. No. 1099 and the 300p were issued on both ordinary and fluorescent paper.

300p and 500p exist with wmk. 365.

See Nos. B73-B74.

A516

1976 Photo. Unwmk. *Perf. 13½*

1112 A516	12c	gray & blk	.15	.15
1113 A516	50c	gray & grn	.15	.15
1114 A516	1p	red & blk	.15	.15
1115 A516	4p	bl & blk	.15	.15
1116 A516	5p	org & blk	.15	.15
1117 A516	6p	dp brn & blk	.15	.15
1118 A516	10p	gray & vio bl	.22	.15
1119 A516	27p	lt grn & blk	.52	.15
1120 A516	30p	lt bl & blk	.90	.15
1121 A516	45p	yel & blk	.90	.15
1122 A516	50p	dl grn & blk	1.25	.15
1123 A516	100p	brt grn & red	1.65	.25

Perf. 13x12½
1976 Litho. Wmk. 365

1124 A516	5p	org & blk	.20	.15
1125 A516	27p	lt grn & blk	.52	.15
1126 A516	45p	yel & blk	1.25	.15
		Nos. 1112-1126 (15)	8.31	
		Set value		1.35

The 1p, 6p, 10p, 50p and No. 1116 were issued on both ordinary and fluorescent paper.

Jet and Airlines Emblem — A517

Perf. 13x13½
1976, Apr. 24 Litho. Unwmk.
1130 A517 30p bl, lt bl & dk bl 1.00 .20

Argentine Airlines, 25th anniversary.

Frigate Heroina and Map of Falkland Islands — A518

1976, Apr. 26
1131 A518 6p multi 1.00 .40

Argentina's claim to Falkland Islands.

Louis Braille — A519

Perf. 13½
1976, May 22 Engr. Wmk. 365
1132 A519 19.70 dp bl .28 .15

Sesquicentennial of the invention of the Braille system of writing for the blind by Louis Braille (1809-1852).

Private, 7th Infantry Regiment — A520

1976, May 29 Litho. Unwmk.
1133 A520 12p multi .38 .18

Army Day.

Schooner Rio de la Plata, by Emilio Biggeri A521

1976, June 19
1134 A521 12p multi .38 .18

Navy Day.

Dr. Bernardo Houssay A522

Argentine Nobel Prize Winners: 15p, Luis F. Leloir, chemistry, 1970. 20p, Carlos Saavedra Lamas, peace, 1936. Bernardo Houssay, medicine and physiology, 1947.

1976, Aug. 14 Litho. *Perf. 13½*

1135	A522	10p org & blk	.22	.15
1136	A522	15p yel & blk	.32	.16
1137	A522	20p ocher & blk	.45	.22
		Nos. 1135-1137 (3)	.99	.53

Rio de la Plata International Bridge A523

1976, Sept. 18 Litho. *Perf. 13½*

1138	A523	12p multi	.28	.15

Inauguration of International Bridge connecting Puerte Unzue, Argentina, and Fray Bentos, Uruguay.

Pipelines and Cooling Tower, Gen. Mosconi Plant A524

1976, Nov. 20 Litho. *Perf. 13½*

1139	A524	28p multi	.42	.20

Pablo Teodoro Fels and Bleriot Monoplane, 1910 A525

1976, Nov. 20

1140	A525	15p multi	.32	.15

Air Force Day.

Nativity A526

1976, Dec. 18 Litho. *Perf. 13½*

1141	A526	20p multi	.65	.28

Christmas. Painting by Edith Chiapetto.

Water Conference Emblem — A527

1977, Mar. 19 Litho. *Perf. 13½*

1142	A527	70p multi	.70	.25

UN Water Conf., Mar del Plata, Mar. 14-25.

Dalmacio Velez Sarsfield A528

1977, Mar. 19 Engr.

1143	A528	50p blk & red brn	.70	.28

Dalmacio Velez Sarsfield (1800-1875), author of Argentine civil code.

Red Deer Type of 1974 Surcharged

1977, July 30 Photo. *Perf. 13½*

1144	A495	100p on 5p brn	1.40	.35

Sesquicentennial of Uruguayan postal service. Not issued without surcharge.

Soldier, 16th Lancers — A529

1977, July 30

1145	A529	30p multi	.40	.20

Army Day.

Schooner Sarandi, by Emilio Biggeri A530

1977, July 30

1146	A530	30p multi	.42	.22

Navy Day.

CAMPEONATO MUNDIAL DE FUTBOL 1978
Argentina'78
30 PESOS REPUBLICA ARGENTINA

Soccer Games' Emblem — A531

Design: 70p, Argentina '78 emblem, flags and soccer field.

1977, May 14

1147	A531	30p multi	.40	.18
1148	A531	70p multi	.85	.42

11th World Cup Soccer Championship, Argentina, June 1-25, 1978.

The Visit, by Horacio Butler A532

Consecration, by Miguel P. Caride — A533

1977, Mar. 26 Litho.

1149	A532	50p multi	.52	.25
1150	A533	70p multi	.65	.38

Argentine artists.

Sierra de la Ventana — A534

Views: No. 1152, Civic Center, Santa Rosa. No. 1153, Skiers, San Martin de los Andes. No. 1154, Boat on Lake Fonck, Rio Negro.

1977, Oct. 8 Litho. *Perf. 13x13½*

1151	A534	30p multi	.32	.16
1152	A534	30p multi	.32	.16
1153	A534	30p multi	.32	.16
1154	A534	30p multi	.32	.16
		Nos. 1151-1154 (4)	1.28	.64

Guillermo Brown, by R. del Villar — A535

1977, Oct. 8 *Perf. 13½*

1155	A535	30p multi	.38	.22

Adm. Guillermo Brown (1777-1857), leader in fight for independence, bicentenary of birth.

Jet — A536

Double-decker, 1926 — A537

1977 Litho. *Perf. 13½*

1156	A536	30p multi	.24	.15
1157	A537	40p multi	.32	.20

50th anniversary of military plane production (30p); Air Force Day (40p).

Issue dates: 30p, Dec. 3; 40p, Nov. 26.

Adoration of the Kings — A538

1977, Dec. 17

1158	A538	100p multi	1.00	.28

Christmas 1977.

Historic City Hall, Buenos Aires — A539

Chapel of Rio Grande Museum, Tierra del Fuego — A540

Designs: 5p, 20p, La Plata Museum. 10p, Independence Hall, Tucuman. 40p, City Hall, Salta, vert. No. 1165, City Hall, Buenos Aires. 100p, Columbus Theater, Buenos Aires. 200p, flag Monument, Rosario. 280p, 300p, Chapel of Rio Grande Museum, Tierra del Fuego. 480p, 520p, 800, Ruins of Jesuit Mission Church of San Ignacio, Misiones. 500p, Candonga Chapel, Cordoba. 1000p, G.P.O., Buenos Aires. 2000p, Civic Center, Bariloche, Rio Negro.

Three types of 10p: I. Nine vertical window bars; small imprint "E. MILIAVACA Dib." II. Nine bars; large imprint "E. MILIAVACA DIB." III. Redrawn; 5 bars; large imprint.

1977-81 Photo. Unwmk. *Perf. 13½*
Size: 32x21mm, 21x32mm

1159	A540	5p	gray & blk	.15	.15
1160	A540	10p	lt ultra & blk, I	.15	.15
a.			Type II	.15	.15
1161	A540	10p	lt bl & blk, III	.15	.15
1162	A540	20p	citron & blk, litho.	.15	.15
1163	A540	40p	gray bl & blk	.24	.15
1164	A539	50p	yel & blk	.28	.15
1165	A540	50p	citron & blk	.16	.15
1166	A540	100p	org & blk, litho.	.35	.15
a.			Wmk. 365	92.50	24.00
1167	A540	100p	red org & blk	.15	.15
1168	A540	100p	turq & blk	.15	.15
1169	A539	200p	lt bl & blk	.48	.24
1170	A540	280p	rose & blk	14.00	.20
1171	A540	300p	lemon & blk	.95	.15
1172	A540	480p	org & blk	1.75	.24
1173	A540	500p	yel grn & blk	1.75	.20
1174	A540	520p	org & blk	1.75	.30
1175	A540	800p	rose lil & blk	2.25	.32
1176	A540	1000p	lem bis & blk	2.50	.38
1177	A540	1000p	gold & blk, 40x29mm	3.75	.38
1178	A540	2000p	multi	2.25	.38
			Nos. 1159-1178 (20)	33.36	
			Set value		3.35

#1161, 1163, 1165, 1167, 1169, 1171, 1173, 1176, 1177 were issued on both ordinary and fluorescent paper. No. 1174 was issued only on fluorescent paper. All others were issued only on ordinary paper.

Issued: #1164, 5/30/77; 280p, 12/15/77; #1160, 3/14/78; 480p, 5/22/78; 5p, 7/25/78; 20p, 500p, 9/8/78; #1166, 9/20/78; #1177, 9/28/78; 520p, 9/30/78; 300p, 10/5/78; 40p, 12/1/78; #1161/79; #1165, 1/8/79; 800p, 3/20/79; #1167, 4/25/79; 200p, 6/23/79; #1176, 12/15/79; 2000p, 6/25/80; #1168, 5/26/81.

For overprints see Nos. 1253, 1315.

Soccer Games' Emblem A544

1978, Feb. 10 Photo. *Perf. 13½*

1179	A544	200p yel grn & bl	.85	.28

11th World Cup Soccer Championship, Argentina, June 1-25. Exists with wmk. 365.

View of El Rio, Rosario — A545

Designs (Argentina '78 Emblem and): 100p, Rio Tercero Dam, Cordoba. 150p, Cordillera Mountains, Mendoza. 200p, City Center, Mar del Plata. 300p, View of Buenos Aires.

1978, May 6 Litho. *Perf. 13*

1180 A545 50p multi	.16	.15
1181 A545 100p multi	.32	.15
1182 A545 150p multi	.50	.16
1183 A545 200p multi	.50	.24
1184 A545 300p multi	1.10	.32
Nos. 1180-1184 (5)	2.58	1.02

Sites of 11th World Cup Soccer Championship, June 1-25.

Children — A546

1978, May 20

1185 A546 100p multi .35 .15

50th anniversary of Children's Institute.

Labor Day, by B. Quinquela Martin — A547

Design: No. 1187, Woman's torso, sculpture by Orlando Pierri.

1978, May 20 *Perf. 13½*

1186 A547 100p multi	.35	.15
1187 A547 100p multi	.35	.15

Argentina, Hungary, France, Italy and Emblem — A548

Stadium A549

Teams and Argentina '78 Emblem: 200p, Poland, Fed. Rep. of Germany, Tunisia, Mexico. 300p, Austria, Spain, Sweden, Brazil. 400p, Netherlands, Iran, Peru, Scotland.

1978 Litho. *Perf. 13*

1188 A548 100p multi	.32	.15
1189 A548 200p multi	.65	.15
1190 A548 300p multi	.95	.25
1191 A548 400p multi	1.25	.30
Nos. 1188-1191 (4)	3.17	.85

Souvenir Sheet

Lithographed and Engraved

Perf. 13½

1192 A549 700p buff & blk 2.50 1.40

11th World Cup Soccer Championship, Argentina, June 1-25. Issued: Nos. 1188-1191, June 6, No. 1192, June 3.

Stadium Type of 1978 Inscribed in Red: "ARGENTINA / CAMPEON"

Lithographed and Engraved

1978, Sept. 2 *Perf. 13½*

1193 A549 1000p bulf, blk & red 3.25 1.40

Argentina's victory in 1978 Soccer Championship. No. 1193 has margin similar to No. 1192 with Rimet Cup emblem added in red.

Young Tree Nourished by Old Trunk, UN Emblem A550

1978 Sept. 2 Litho.

1194 A550 100p multi .35 .22

Technical Cooperation among Developing Countries Conf., Buenos Aires, Sept. 1978.

Emblems of Buenos Aires and Bank A551

1978, Sept. 16

1195 A551 100p multi .35 .22

Bank of City of Buenos Aires, centenary.

General Savio and Steel Production A552

1978, Sept. 16

1196 A552 100p multi .35 .22

Gen. Manuel N. Savio (1892-1948), general manager of military heavy industry.

San Martin — A553

1978, Oct. Engr.

1197 A553 2000p grnsh blk 6.25 1.10

1979 Wmk. 365

1198 A553 2000p grnsh blk 4.75 .35

Gen Jose de San Martin (1778-1850), soldier and statesman. See No. 1292.

Globe and Argentine Flag — A554

1978, Oct. 7 Litho. *Perf. 13½*

1199 A554 200p multi .70 .28

12th International Cancer Congress, Buenos Aires, Oct. 5-11.

Chessboard, Queen and Pawn — A555

1978, Oct. 7

1200 A555 200p multi 2.00 .65

23rd National Chess Olympics, Buenos Aires, Oct. 25-Nov. 12.

Correct Positioning of Stamps — A557

Design: 50p, Use correct postal code number.

1978 Photo. *Perf. 13½*

1201 A557 20p ultra	.15	.15
1203 A557 50p carmine	.22	.15
Set value		.15

No. 1201 issued on both ordinary and fluorescent paper.

A558

A559

1978-82 Photo. *Perf. 13½*

1204 A558 150p bl & ultra	.35	.15
1205 A558 180p bl & ultra	.45	.15
1206 A558 200p bl & ultra	.32	.15
1207 A559 240p ol bis & bl ('79)	.38	.15
1208 A559 260p blk & lt bl ('79)	.42	.15
1209 A559 290p blk & lt bl ('79)	.45	.15
1210 A559 310p mag & bl ('79)	.50	.18
1211 A559 350p ver & bl ('79)	.65	.20
1212 A559 450p ultra & bl	.52	.18
1213 A559 600p grn & bl ('80)	.70	.24
1214 A559 700p blk & bl ('80)	.70	.24
1215 A559 800p red & bl ('81)	.65	.15
1216 A559 1100p gray & bl ('81)	.90	.15
1217 A559 1500p blk & bl ('81)	.35	.15
1218 A559 1700p grn & bl ('82)	.45	.15
Nos. 1204-1218 (15)	7.79	
Set value		2.00

No. 1204 issued on fluorescent and ordinary paper. No. 1206 issued only on fluorescent paper.

For overprint see No. 1338.

Balsa "24" A561

Ships: 200p, Tug Legador. 300p, River Parana tug No. 34. 400p, Passenger ship Ciudad de Parana.

1978, Nov. 4 Litho. *Perf. 13½*

1220 A561 100p multi	.24	.15
1221 A561 200p multi	.48	.20
1222 A561 300p multi	.70	.30
a. Pair, #1221-1222	1.20	
1223 A561 400p multi	.95	.40
a. Pair, #1220, 1223	1.20	
Nos. 1220-1223 (4)	2.37	1.05

20th anniversary of national river fleet. Issued on fluorescent paper.

View and Arms of Bahia Blanca A562

1978, Nov. 25 Litho. *Perf. 13½*

1224 A562 20p multi .48 .15

Sesquicentennial of Bahia Blanca.

"Spain," (Queen Isabella and Columbus) by Arturo Dresco A563

1978, Nov. 25

1225 A563 300p multi 2.75 .30

Visit of King Juan Carlos and Queen Sofia of Spain to Argentina, Nov. 26.

Virgin and Child, San Isidro Cathedral — A564

1978, Dec. 16

1226 A564 200p gold & multi .55 .28

Christmas 1978.

Slope at Chacabuco, by Pedro Subercaseaux — A565

Painting: 1000p, The Embrace of Maipu (San Martin and O'Higgins), by Pedro Subercaseaux, vert.

1978, Dec. 16 Litho. *Perf. 13½*

1227 A565 500p multi	1.00	.26
1228 A565 1000p multi	2.00	.40

José de San Martin, 200th birth anniversary.

Adolfo Alsina A566

Design: No. 1230, Mariano Moreno.

1979, Jan. 20

1229 A566 200p lt bl & blk	.30	.15
1230 A566 200p yel red & blk	.30	.15
Set value		.16

Adolfo Alsina (1828-1877), political leader, vice-president; Mariano Moreno (1778-1811), lawyer, educator, political leader.

Argentina No. 37 and UPU Emblem A567

1979, Jan. 20
1231 A567 200p multi .22 .15

Centenary of Argentina's UPU membership.

Still-life, by Carcova A568

Painting: 300p, The Laundresses, by Faustino Brughetti.

1979, Mar. 3
1232 A568 200p multi .45 .15
1233 A568 300p multi .60 .20

Ernesto de la Carcova (1866-1927) and Faustino Brughetti (1877-1956), Argentine painters.

A569

A570

1979, Mar. 3
1234 A569 200p Balcarce Earth station .55 .25

Third Inter-American Telecommunications Conference, Buenos Aires, March 5-9.

1979
1235 A570 30p Stamp collecting .15 .15

Printed on ordinary and fluorescent paper.

European Olive — A571

Laurel and Regimental Emblem — A572

1979, June 2 Litho. *Perf. 13½*
1236 A571 100p shown .26 .15
1237 A571 200p Tea .55 .26
1238 A571 300p Sorghum .85 .40
1239 A571 400p Common flax 1.10 .55
Nos. 1236-1239 (4) 2.76 1.36

1979, June 9
1240 A572 200p gold & multi .42 .22

Founding of Subteniente Berdina Village in memory of Sub-lieutenant Rodolfo Hernan Berdina, killed by terrorists in 1975.

"75" and Automobile Club Emblem A573

1979, June 9
1241 A573 200p gold & multi .40 .20

Argentine Automobile Club, 75th anniv.

Exchange Building and Emblem A574

1979, June 9
1242 A574 200p bl, blk & gold .40 .20

Grain Exchange, 125th anniversary.

Cavalry Officer, 1817 — A575

1979, July 7 Litho. *Perf. 13½*
1243 A575 200p multi 1.00 .30

Army Day.

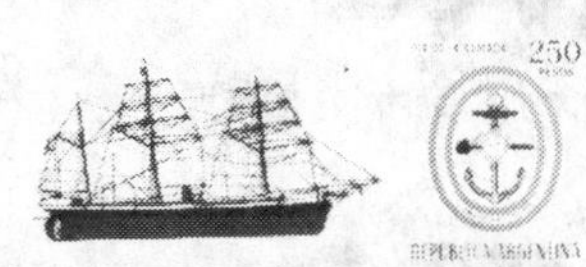
Corvette Uruguay and Navy Emblem — A576

Design: No. 1245, Hydrographic service ship and emblem.

1979 *Perf. 13*
1244 A576 250p multi .85 .35
1245 A576 250p multi .85 .35

Navy Day; Cent. of Naval Hydrographic Service. Issued: #1244, July 28; #1245, July 7.

Tree and Man — A577

1979, July 28 *Perf. 13½*
1246 A577 250p multi .60 .22

Protection of the Environment Day, June 5.

"Spad" Flying over Andes, and Vicente Almandos Almonacid A578

1979, Aug. 4
1247 A578 250p multi .70 .22

Air Force Day.

Gen. Julio A. Roca Occupying Rio Negro, by Juan M. Blanes A579

1979, Aug. 4
1248 A579 250p multi .70 .22

Conquest of Rio Negro Desert, centenary.

Rowland Hill — A580

1979, Sept. 29 Litho. *Perf. 13½*
1249 A580 300p gray red & blk .55 .22

Sir Rowland Hill (1795-1879), originator of penny postage.

Viedma Navarez Monument A581

1979, Sept. 29
1250 A581 300p multi .60 .22

Viedma and Carmen de Patagones towns, bicentenary.

Pope Paul VI — A582

Design: No. 1252, Pope John Paul I.

1979, Oct. 27 Engr. *Perf. 13½*
1251 A582 500p black 1.00 .28
1252 A582 500p sepia 1.00 .28

No. 1169 Overprinted in Red: "75 ANIV. / SOCIEDAD/ FILATELICA / DE ROSARIO"

1979, Nov. 10 Photo. *Perf. 13½*
1253 A539 200p lt bl & blk .60 .20

Rosario Philatelic Society, 75th anniversary.

A583

A584

1979, Nov. 10 Litho.
1254 A583 300p multi .70 .28

Frontier resettlement.

1979, Dec. 1 Litho. *Perf. 13½*
1255 A584 300p multi .70 .28

Military Geographic Institute centenary.

Christmas 1979 A585

1979, Dec. 1
1256 A585 300p multi .55 .22

General Mosconi Birth Centenary — A586

1979, Dec. 15 Engr. *Perf. 13½*
1257 A586 1000p blk & bl 1.50 .24

Rotary Emblem and Globe A587

1979, Dec. 29 Litho.
1258 A587 300p multi 1.75 .35

Rotary International, 75th anniversary.

Child and IYC Emblem — A588

Family, by Pablo Menicucci A589

1979, Dec. 29
1259 A588 500p lt bl & sep .75 .15
1260 A589 1000p multi 1.50 .22

International Year of the Child.

Microphone, Waves, ITU Emblem — A590

1980, Mar. 22 Litho. *Perf. 13x13½*
1261 A590 500p multi .95 .26

Regional Administrative Conference on Broadcasting by Hectometric Waves for Area 2, Buenos Aires, Mar. 10-29.

Guillermo Brown — A591

1980 Engr. *Perf. 13½*
1262 A591 5000p black 4.50 .15

See No. 1372.

Argentine Red Cross Centenary A592

1980, Apr. 19 Litho. *Perf. 13½*
1263 A592 500p multi .52 .20

OAS Emblem — A593

1980, Apr. 19
1264 A593 500p multi .55 .22

Day of the Americas, Apr. 14.

Dish Antennae, Balcarce A594

1980, Apr. 26 Litho. & Engr.
1265 A594 300p shown .38 .20
1266 A594 300p Hydroelectric Station, Salto Grande .38 .20
1267 A594 300p Bridge, Zarate-Brazo Largo .38 .20
Nos. 1265-1267 (3) 1.14 .60

Capt. Hipolito Bouchard, Frigate "Argentina" — A595

1980, May 31 Litho. *Perf. 13x13½*
1268 A595 500p multi .70 .28

Navy Day.

"Villarino," San Martin, by Theodore Gericault — A596

1980, May 31
1269 A596 500p multi .70 .28

Return of the remains of Gen. Jose de San Martin to Argentina, centenary.

Buenos Aires Gazette, 1810, Signature A597

1980, June 7 *Perf. 13½*
1270 A597 500p multi .55 .22

Journalism Day.

Coaches in Victoria Square — A598

1980 June 14
1271 Block of 14 9.00 3.25
a. A598 500p any single .60 .22

Buenos Aires, 400th anniv. No. 1271 shows ceramic mural of Victoria Square by Rodolfo Franco in continuous design. See No. 1285.

Gen. Pedro Aramburu — A599

1980, July 12 Litho. *Perf. 13½*
1272 A599 500p yel & blk .55 .22

Gen. Pedro Eugenio Aramburu (1903-1970), provisional president, 1955.

Army Day A600

1980, July 12
1273 A600 500p multicolored .85 .28

Gen. Juan Gregorio de Las Heras (1780-1866), Hero of 1817 War of Independence — A601

Grandees of Argentina Bicentenary: No. 1275, Rivadavia. No. 1276, Brig. Gen Jose Matias Zapiola (1780-1874), naval commander and statesman.

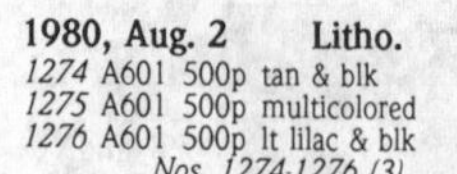

1980, Aug. 2 Litho. *Perf. 13½*
1274 A601 500p tan & blk .55 .22
1275 A601 500p multicolored .55 .22
1276 A601 500p lt lilac & blk .55 .22
Nos. 1274-1276 (3) 1.65 .66

Avro "Gosport" Biplane, Maj. Francisco de Artega — A602

1980, Aug. 16 *Perf. 13*
1277 A602 500p multicolored .70 .22

Air Force Day. Artega (1882-1930) was first director of Military Aircraft Factory where Avro "Gosport" was built (1927).

University of La Plata, 75th Anniversary A603

1980, Aug. 16 *Perf. 13½*
1278 A603 500p multi .55 .22

Souvenir Sheets

Emperor Penguin — A604

South Orkneys Argentine Base A605 A606

No. 1279 (A604): a, shown. b, Bearded penguin. c, Adelie penguins. d, Papua penguins. e, Sea elephants. f, A605 shown. g, A606 shown. h, Fur seals. i, Giant petrels. j, Blue-eyed cororants. k, Stormy petrels. m, Anarctic doves.

1980, Sept. 27 Litho. *Perf. 13½*
1279 Sheet of 12 11.00 11.00
a.-m. A604 500p, any single .75 .60
1280 Sheet of 12 11.00 11.00
a. A605 500p Puerto Soledad .75 .60
b. A606 500p Different view .75 .60

75th anniv. of Argentina's presence in the South Orkneys and 150th anniv. of political and military command in the Falkland Islands. Nos. 1279-1280 each contain 12 stamps (4x3) with landscape designs in center of sheets. Silhouettes of Argentine exploration ships in margins. #1280 contains #1279a-1279e, 1279h-1279m, 1280a-1280b.

Anti-smoking Campaign — A608

1980, Oct. 11
1282 A608 700p multi .90 .22

National Census — A609

1980, Sept.
1283 A609 500p blk & bl 1.00 .20

Madonna and Child (Congress Emblem) A610

1980, Oct. 1 Litho.
1284 A610 700p multi .85 .15

National Marian Cong., Mendoza, Oct. 8-12

Mural Type of 1980

1980, Oct. 25
1285 Block of 14 7.75 7.75
a. A598 500p, any single .52 .40

Buenos Aires, 400th anniv./Buenos Aires '80 Stamp Exhib., Oct. 24-Nov. 2. No. 1285 shows ceramic mural Arte bajo la Ciudad by Alfredo Guido in continuous design.

Technical Military Academy, 50th Anniversary A611

Amateur Radio Operation A612

1980, Nov. 1
1286 A611 700p multi .75 .15

1980, Nov. 1
1287 A612 700p multi .75 .15

Medal — A613

Lujan Cathedral Floor Plan — A614

1980, Nov. 29 Litho. *Perf. 13½*
1288 A613 700p multi .75 .25
1289 A614 700p olive & brn .75 .25

Christmas 1980. 150th anniv. of apparition of Holy Virgin to St. Catherine Laboure, Paris (No. 1288), 350th anniv. of apparition at Lujan.

150th Death Anniversary of Simon Bolivar — A615

1980, Dec. 13
1290 A615 700p multi .75 .25

Soccer Gold Cup Championship, Montevideo, 1980 — A616

1981, Jan. 3 **Litho.**
1291 A616 1000p multi 1.10 .25

San Martin Type of 1978

1981, Jan. 20 **Engr.** ***Perf. 13½***
1292 A553 10,000p dark blue 7.25 .16

Landscape in Lujan, by Marcos Tiglio A617

Paintings: No. 1304, Expansion of Light along a Straight Line, by Miguel Angel Vidal, vert.

1981, Apr. 11 **Litho.**
1303 A617 1000p multi .85 .30
1304 A617 1000p multi .85 .30

Intl. Sports Medicine Congress, June 7-12 — A618

1981, June 6 **Litho.** ***Perf. 13½***
1305 A618 1000p bl & dk brn .75 .20

Esperanza Base, Antarctica A619

Cargo Plane, Map of Vice-Commodore Marambio Island — A620

Perf. 13½, 13x13½ (No. 1308)

1981, June 13
1306 A619 1000p shown 1.40 .42
1307 A619 2000p Almirante Irizar 2.50 .55
1308 A620 2000p shown 2.50 .85
Nos. 1306-1308 (3) 6.40 1.82

Antarctic Treaty 20th anniv.

Antique Pistols (Military Club Centenary) A621

1981, June 27 ***Perf. 13½***
1309 A621 1000p Club building .80 .15
1310 A621 2000p shown .80 .15

Gen. Juan A. Alvarez de Arenales (1770-1831) A622

Famous Men: No. 1312, Felix G. Frias (1816-1881), writer. No. 1313, Jose E. Uriburu (1831-1914), statesman.

1981, Aug. 8 **Litho.** ***Perf. 13½***
1311 A622 1000p multi .70 .15
1312 A622 1000p multi .70 .15
1313 A622 1000p multi .70 .15
Nos. 1311-1313 (3) 2.10 .45

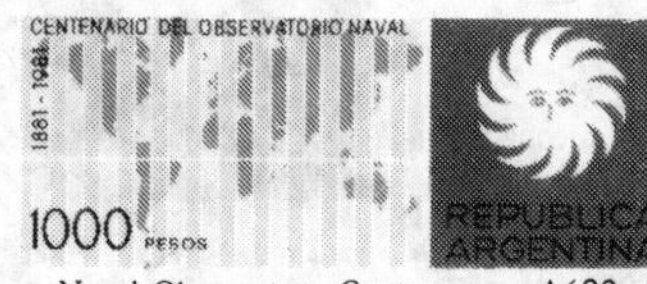

Naval Observatory Centenary — A623

1981, Aug. 15 **Litho.** ***Perf. 13x13½***
1314 A623 1000p multi .75 .24

No. 1176 Overprinted in Red: "50 ANIV. DE LA ASOCIACION / FILATELICA Y NUMISMATICA / DE BAHIA BLANCA"

1981, Aug. 15 **Photo.** ***Perf. 13½***
1315 A540 1000p lem & blk 1.90 .25

50th anniv. of Bahia Blanca Philatelic and Numismatic Society.

St. Cayetano, Stained-glass Window, Buenos Aires — A624

1981, Sept. 5 **Litho.** ***Perf. 13½***
1316 A624 1000p multi .70 .15

St. Cayetano, founder of Teatino Order, 500th birth anniv.

Pablo Castaibert (1883-1909) and his Monoplane (Air Force Day) — A625

1981, Sept. 5 ***Perf. 13x13½***
1317 A625 1000p multi .65 .15

Intl. Year of the Disabled A626

1981, Sept. 10 ***Perf. 13½***
1318 A626 1000p multi .65 .15

22nd Latin-American Steelmakers' Congress, Buenos Aires, Sept. 21-23 — A627

1981, Sept. 19
1319 A627 1000p multi .65 .15

Army Regiment No. 1 (Patricios), 175th Anniv. — A628

1981, Oct. 10 **Litho.** ***Perf. 13½***
1320 A628 1500p Natl. arms .45 .15
1321 A628 1500p shown .45 .15
a. Pair, #1320-1321 .90 .30

A629 A630

San Martin as artillery Captain in Battle of Bailen, 1808.

1981, Oct. 5
1322 Sheet of 8 + 4 labels 4.75 1.75
a. A629 1000p multi .35 .18
b. A629 1500p multi .52 .18

Espamer '81 Intl. Stamp Exhib. (Americas, Spain, Portugal), Buenos Aires, Nov. 13-22.
No. 1322 contains 4 se-tenant pairs.

1981, Oct. 5
1323 A630 1000p multi 2.25 .32

Anti-indiscriminate whaling.

Espamer '81 Emblem and Ship — A631

1981
1324 A631 1300p multi .55 .16

No. 1324 Overprinted in Blue: "CURSO SUPERIOR DE ORGANIZACIONES DE FILATELICOS-UPAE-BUENOS AIRES-1981"

1981, Nov. 7 **Photo.** ***Perf. 13½***
1325 A631 1300p multi 1.25 .18

Postal Administration philatelic training course.

Soccer Players — A632

Designs: Soccer players.

1981, Nov. 13 **Litho.**
1326 Sheet of 4 + 2 labels 7.25 4.50
a. A632 1000p multi .22 .15
b. A632 3000p multi .65 .22
c. A632 5000p multi 1.10 .38
d. A632 15,000p multi 3.25 1.10

Espamer '81.

"Peso" Coin Centenary A633

1981, Nov. 21
1327 A633 2000p Patacon, 1881 .38 .15
1328 A633 3000p Argentine Oro, 1881 .60 .15
Set value .20

Christmas 1981 — A634

1981, Dec. 12
1329 A634 1500p multi .85 .24

Traffic Safety A635

1981, Dec. 19 **Litho.**
1330 A635 1000p Observe traffic lights, vert. .75 .38
1331 A635 2000p Drive carefully, vert. .75 .38
1332 A635 3000p Cross at white lines .75 .38
1333 A635 4000p Don't shine head-lights 1.50 .38
Nos. 1330-1333 (4) 3.75 1.52

Francisco Luis Bernardez, Ciuda Laura — A636

Writers and title pages from their works: 2000p, Lucio V. Mansilla, Excursion a los indios ranqueles. 3000p, Conrado Nale Roxlo, El Grillo. 4000p, Victoria Ocampo, Sur.

1982, Mar. 20 **Litho.**
1334 A636 1000p shown .60 .20
1335 A636 2000p multi .85 .20
1336 A636 3000p multi 1.25 .28
1337 A636 4000p multi 1.75 .28
Nos. 1334-1337 (4) 4.45 .96

No. 1218 Overprinted: "LAS / MALVINAS / SON/ ARGENTINAS"

1982, Apr. 17 **Photo.** ***Perf. 13½***
1338 A559 1700p grn & bl .48 .20

Argentina's claim on Falkland Islds.

Robert Koch — A637

American Airforces Commanders' 22nd Conf. — A638

1982, Apr. 17 Litho. Wmk. 365
1339 A637 2000p multi .48 .25

TB bacillus centenary and 25th Intl. Tuberculosis Conference.

1982, Apr. 17
1340 A638 2000p multi .70 .28

Stone Carving, City Founder's Signature (Don Hernando de Lerma) A639

1982, Apr. 17
1341 A639 2000p multi .70 .28

Souvenir Sheet

1342 A639 5000p multi 2.00 2.00

City of Salta, 400th anniv. No. 1342 contains one 43x30mm stamp.

Naval Center Centenary — A640

1982, Apr. 24 ***Perf. 13x13½***
1343 A640 2000p multi .70 .28

Chorisia Speciosa — A641

1982 Unwmk. Photo. ***Perf. 13½***

1344	A641	200p	Zinnia peruviana	.15	.15
1345	A641	300p	Ipomoea purpurea	.15	.15
1346	A641	400p	Tillandsia aeranthos	.15	.15
1347	A641	500p	shown	.15	.15
1348	A641	800p	Oncidium bifolium	.15	.15
1349	A641	1000p	Erythrina crista-galli	.15	.15
1350	A641	2000p	Jacaranda mimosi-folia	.22	.15
1351	A641	3000p	Bauhinia candicans	.32	.15
1352	A641	5000p	Tecoma stans	.52	.15
1353	A641	10,000p	Tabebuia ipe	1.10	.22
1354	A641	20,000p	Passiflora coerulea	2.25	.35
1355	A641	30,000p	Aristolochia littoralis	3.25	.52
1356	A641	50,000p	Oxalis enneaphylla	5.25	.70
	Nos. 1344-1356 (13)			13.81	
	Set value				2.35

Nos. 1344-1346, 1348-1350 issued on fluorescent paper. Nos. 1353-1356 issued on ordinary paper. Others issued on both fluorescent and ordinary paper.

Issue dates: 500p, 2000p, 5000p, 10,000p, May 22. 200p, 300p, 1000p, 20,000p, Sept. 25. 400p, 800p, 30,000p, 50,000p, Dec. 4. 3000p, Dec. 18.

See Nos. 1429-1443A, 1515-1527, 1683-1691. For overprint see No. 1382.

10th Death Anniv. of Gen. Juan C. Sanchez A641a

1982, May 29 Litho. Wmk. 365
1364 A641a 5000p grn & blk .90 .28

Luis Venet, First Commander — A641b

1982, June 12
1365 A641b 5000p org & blk 1.10 .45

Size: 83x28mm

1366 A641b 5000p Map .75 .30

153rd Anniv. of Malvinas Political and Military Command District.

Visit of Pope John Paul II — A641c

1982, June 12
1367 A641c 5000p multi 1.75 .55

Organ Grinder, by Aldo Severi (b. 1928) — A641d

Design: 3000p, Still Life, by Santiago Cogorno (b. 1915).

1982, July 3 Wmk. 365
1368 A641d 2000p shown .26 .20
1369 A641d 3000p multi .40 .20

Guillermo Brown Type of 1980 and:

Jose de San Martin — A641e

Litho. and Engr.

1982 Unwmk. ***Perf. 13½***
1372 A591 30,000p blk & bl 3.25 .65
1376 A641e 50,000p sepia & car 6.50 .85

Issue dates: 30,000p, June; 50,000p, July.

Scouting Year A641f

Perf. 13½

1982, Aug. 7 Litho. Wmk. 365
1380 A641f 5000p multi 1.25 .15

Alconafta Fuel Campaign A641g

1982, Aug. 7 Wmk. 365
1381 A641g 2000p multi .32 .15

No. 1352 Overprinted: "50 ANIVERSARIO SOCIEDAD FILATELICA DE TUCUMAN"

1982, Aug. 7 Photo. Unwmk.
1382 A641 5000p multi 1.25 .95

Rio III Central Nuclear Power Plant, Cordoba A642

Perf. 13½

1982, Sept. 4 Litho. Wmk. 365
1383 A642 2000p shown .30 .15
1384 A642 2000p Control room .30 .15
Set value .15

Namibia Day — A643

1982, Sept. 4
1385 A643 5000p Map .75 .15

Formosa Cathedral A644

Churches and Cathedrals of the Northeast: 2000p, Our Lady of Itati, Corrientes, vert. 3000p, Resistencia Cathedral, Chaco, vert. 10,000p, St. Ignatius Church ruins, Misiones.

1982, Sept. 18 Litho. & Engr.
1386 A644 2000p dk grn & blk .24 .15
1387 A644 3000p dk brn & brn .35 .15
1388 A644 5000p dk bl & brn .60 .20
1389 A644 10,000p dp org & blk 1.10 .35
Nos. 1386-1389 (4) 2.29 .85

Tension Sideral, by Mario Alberto Agatiello — A645

Sculpture (Espamer '81 and Juvenex '82 Exhibitions): 3000p, Sugerencia II, by Eduardo Mac Entyre. 5000p, Storm, by Carlos Silva.

1982, Oct. 2 Litho. ***Perf. 13½***
1390 A645 2000p multi .24 .15
1391 A645 3000p multi .45 .15
1392 A645 5000p multi .60 .18
Nos. 1390-1392 (3) 1.29
Set value .39

Sante Fe Bridge A646

1982, Oct. 16 Litho. & Engr.
1393 A646 2000p bl & blk .38 .15

2nd Southern Cross Games, Santa Fe and Rosario, Nov. 26-Dec. 5.

10th World Men's Volleyball Championship — A647

1982, Oct. 16 Litho. Wmk. 365
1394 A647 2000p multi .24 .15
1395 A647 5000p multi .48 .18

Los Andes Newspaper Centenary A648

Design: Army of the Andes Monument, Hill of Glory, Mendoza.

1982, Oct. 30
1396 A648 5000p multi .50 .18

A649

A650

1982, Oct. 30 Wmk. 365
1397 A649 5000p Signs .55 .22

50th Anniv. of Natl. Roads, Administration.

1982, Nov. 20 Litho.

La Plata City Cent.: No. 1400: a, Cathedral, diff. b, Head, top. c, Observatory. d, City Hall, diff. e, Head, bottom. f, University.

1398 A650 5000p Cathedral .75 .15
1399 A650 5000p City Hall .75 .15
1400 Sheet of 6 2.25 1.00
a.-f. A650 2500p any single .28 .15

Well, Natl. Hydrocarbon Congress Emblem — A651

1982, Nov. 20

1401 A651 5000p multi .50 .20

75th Anniv. of Oil Discovery, Comodoro Rivadavia.

Jockey Club of Buenos Aires Centenary — A652

Christmas 1982 — A653

Design: No. 1403, Carlos Pellegrini, first president.

1982, Dec. 4 **Litho.**

1402 A652 5000p Emblem .52 .15
1403 A652 5000p multi .52 .15
Set value .20

1982, Dec. 18 ***Perf. 13½***

1404 A653 3000p St. Vincent de Paul 1.50 .15

Size: 29x38mm

1405 A653 5000p St. Francis of Assisi 1.25 .15
Set value .15

Pedro B. Palacios (1854-1917), Writer — A654

Writers: 2000p, Leopoldo Marechal (1900-1970). 3000p, Delfina Bunge de Galvez (1881-1952). 4000p, Manuel Galvez (1882-1962). 5000p, Evaristo Carriego (1883-1912).

1983, Mar. 26 **Litho.** ***Perf. 13½***

1406 A654 1000p multi .15 .15
1407 A654 2000p multi .22 .15
1408 A654 3000p multi .32 .15
1409 A654 4000p multi .42 .15
1410 A654 5000p multi .55 .18
a. Strip of 5, #1406-1410 1.75 1.00
Nos. 1406-1410 (5) 1.66
Set value .57

Recovery of the Malvinas (Falkland Islands) — A655

1983, Apr. 9 **Litho.** ***Perf. 13½***

1411 A655 20,000p Map, flag .60 .30

Telecommunications Systems — A656

1983, Apr. 16 **Wmk. 365**

1412 A656 5000p SITRAM .75 .15
1413 A656 5000p RED ARPAC .75 .15
Set value .15

Naval League Emblem — A657

1983, May 14 **Litho.** ***Perf. 13½***

1414 A657 5000p multi .35 .15

Navy Day and 50th anniv. of Naval League.

Allegory, by Victor Rebuffo — A658

1983, May 14

1415 A658 5000p multi .35 .15

Natl. Arts Fund, 25th Anniv.

75th Anniv. of Colon Opera House, Buenos Aires — A659

1983, May 28 **Wmk. 365**

1416 A659 5000p Main hall .70 .15
1417 A659 10000p Stage 1.00 .15
Set value .17

Protected Species A660

1983, July 2 **Litho.** ***Perf. 13½***

1418 A660 1p Chrysocyon brachyurus .32 .15
1419 A660 1.50p Ozotocerus bezoarticus .48 .15
1420 A660 2p Myrmecophaga tridactyla .55 .15
1421 A660 2.50p Leo onca .65 .16
Nos. 1418-1421 (4) 2.00
Set value .42

City of Catamarca, 300th Anniv. — A661

Foundation of the City of Catamarca, by Luis Varela Lezana (1900-1982).

1983, July 16 **Litho.** ***Perf. 13½***

1422 A661 1p multi .32 .15

Mamerto Esquiu (1826-1883) A662

1983, July 16

1423 A662 1p multi .32 .15

Bolivar, by Herrera Toro — A663

Bolivar, Engraving by Kepper — A664

Perf. 13 (A663), 13½ (A664)

1983 **Unwmk.**

1424 A663 1p multi .30 .15
1425 A664 2p black .60 .15
1426 A664 10p San Martin 3.00 1.50
Nos. 1424-1426 (3) 3.90 1.80

Issue dates: 1p, 2p, July 23. 10p, Aug. 20.
See Nos. 1457-1462B.

Gen. Toribio de Luzuriaga (1782-1842) A665

1983, Aug. 20 **Litho.** ***Perf. 13½***

1427 A665 1p multi .30 .15

50th Anniv. of San Martin National Institute A666

1983, Aug. 20 **Engr.** **Unwmk.**

1428 A666 2p sepia .60 .16

Flower Type of 1982 in New Currency

1983-85 **Photo.** ***Perf. 13½***

1429 A641 5c like #1347 .15 .15
1430 A641 10c like #1349 .15 .15
1431 A641 20c like #1350 .15 .15
1432 A641 30c like #1351 .15 .15
1433 A641 40c Eichhornia crassipes .15 .15
1434 A641 50c like #1352 .15 .15
1435 A641 1p like #1353 .15 .15
1435A A641 1.80p Mutisia retusa .15 .15
1436 A641 2p like #1354 .22 .15
1437 A641 3p like #1355 .32 .15
1438 A641 5p like #1356 .55 .20
1439 A641 10p Alstroemeria aurantiaca 1.10 .80
1440 A641 20p like #1345 .55 .16
1441 A641 30p Embothrium coccineum 3.50 2.50
1442 A641 50p like #1346 1.10 .40
1443 A641 100p like #1348 1.65 .48
1443A A641 300p Cassia carnaval .80 .24
Nos. 1429-1443A (17) 10.99
Set value 5.25

Issue Dates: 20p, Aug. 27, 1984. 50p, Oct. 19, 1984. 100p, Dec. 1984. 300p, June 15, 1985.

Nos. 1429, 1433, 1435A issued on fluorescent paper. Nos. 1443, 1443A issued on ordinary paper. Others issued on both ordinary and fluorescent paper.

For overprint and surcharge see #1489, 1530.

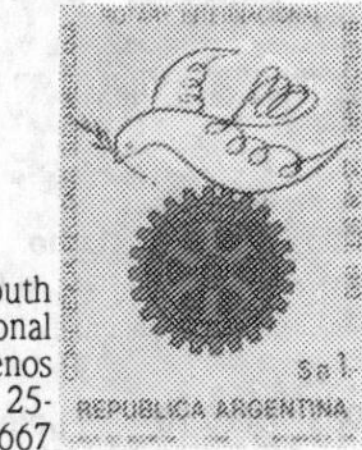

Intl. Rotary South American Regional Conference, Buenos Aires, Sept. 25-28 — A667

1983, Sept. 24 **Litho.**

1444 A667 1p multi .55 .24

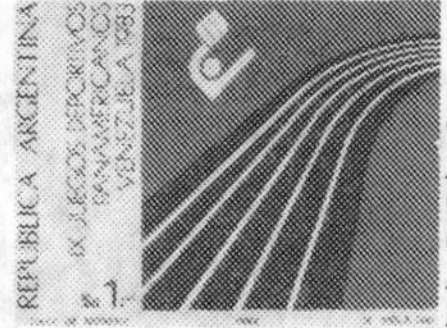

9th Pan American Games, Caracas, Aug. 13-28 A668

1983, Sept. 24

1445 A668 1p Track .32 .15
1446 A668 2p Emblem .65 .28

World Communications Year — A669

1983, Oct. 8 ***Perf. 13½***

1447 A669 2p multi .60 .24

Squash Peddler by Antonio Berni (1905-1981) A670

Designs: 2p, Figure in Yellow by Luis Seoane (1910-1979).

1983, Oct. 15 ***Perf. 13½***

1448 A670 1p multi .32 .15
1449 A670 2p multi .52 .22

World Communications Year — A671

Designs: 1p, Wagon, 18th cent. 2p, Post chaise, 19th cent. 4p, Steam locomotive, 1857. 5p, Tramway, 1910.

1983, Nov. 19 Litho. *Perf. 13½*

1450 A671 1p multi .15 .15
1451 A671 2p multi .24 .15
1452 A671 4p multi .50 .20
1453 A671 5p multi .65 .26
Nos. 1450-1453 (4) 1.54 .76

A672

A673

1983, Nov. 26 Litho. *Perf. 12½x12*

1454 A672 2p General Post Office .42 .18

World Communications Year.

1983, Dec. 10 Photo. *Perf. 13½*

1455 A673 2p Coin, 1813 .30 .18

Return to elected government.

Eudyptes Crestatus A674

Designs: b, Diomedea exulans. c, Diomedea melanophris. d, Eudyptes chrysolophus. e, Luis Piedra Buena. f, Carlos Maria Moyano. g, Luis Py. h, Augusto Lasserre. i, Phoebetria palpebrata. j, Hydrurga leptonyx. k, Lobodon carcinophagus. l, Leptonychotes weddelli.

1983, Dec. 10 Litho.

1456 Sheet of 12 4.50 2.25
a.-l. A674 2p any single .35 .15

Southern pioneers and fauna. Margin depicts various airplanes and emblems.

Bolivar Type of 1983

Famous men: 10p, Angel J. Carranza (1834-99), historian. No. 1458, 500p, Guillermo Brown. No. 1459, Estanislao del Campo (1834-80), poet. 30p, Jose Hernandez (1834-86), author. 40p, Vicente Lopez y Planes (1784-1856), poet and patriot. 50p, San Martin. 200p, Belgrano.

1983-85 Litho. & Engr. *Perf. 13½*

1457 A664 10p pale bl & dk bl .15 .15
1458 A664 20p dk bl & blk 2.75 1.40
1459 A664 20p dl brn ol & ol blk .15 .15
1460 A664 30p pale bl & bluish blk .15 .15
1461 A664 40p lt bl grn & blk .18 .15
1462 A664 50p Prus & choc 1.10 .24
1462A A664 200p int bl & blk 3.00 .95
1462B A664 500p brn & int bl 1.50 .32
Nos. 1457-1462B (8) 8.98 3.51

Issue dates: #1458, Oct. 6, 1983. 10p, #1459, 30p, 40p, Mar. 23, 1985. 50p, Apr. 23, 1985. 200p, Nov. 2, 1985. 500p, May 2, 1985.

Christmas 1983 A675

Nativity Scenes: 2p, Tapestry, by Silke. 3p, Stained-glass window, San Carlos de Bariloche's Wayn Church, vert.

1983, Dec. 17 Litho. *Perf. 13½*

1463 A675 2p multi .30 .15
1464 A675 3p multi .55 .28

Centenary of El Dia Newspaper — A676

1984, Mar. 24 Litho.

1465 A676 4p Masthead, printing roll .38 .20

Alejandro Carbo Teachers' College Centenary A677

1984, June 2 Litho. *Perf. 13½*

1466 A677 10p Building .42 .22

1984 Olympics A678

Designs: #1468, Weightlifting, discus, shot put. #1469, Javelin, fencing. #1470, Bicycling, swimming.

1984, July 28 Litho. *Perf. 13½*

1467 A678 5p shown .22 .15
1468 A678 5p multicolored .22 .15
1469 A678 10p multicolored .45 .22
1470 A678 10p multicolored .45 .22
Nos. 1467-1470 (4) 1.34 .74

Rosario Stock Exchange Centenary A679

1984, Aug. 11

1471 A679 10p multicolored .45 .22

Wheat A680

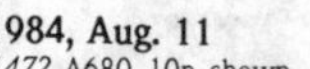

1984, Aug. 11

1472 A680 10p shown .48 .24
1473 A680 10p Corn .48 .24
1474 A680 10p Sunflower .48 .24
Nos. 1472-1474 (3) 1.44 .72

18th FAO Regional Conference for Latin America and Caribbean (No. 1472); 3rd Natl. Corn Congress (No. 1473); World Food Day (No. 1474).

Wildlife Protection A681

1984, Sept. 22 Litho. *Perf. 13½*

1475 A681 20p Hippocamelus bisulcus .40 .15
1476 A681 20p Vicugna vicugna .40 .15
1477 A681 20p Aburria jacutinga .40 .15
1478 A681 20p Mergus octosetaceus .40 .15
1479 A681 20p Podiceps gallardoi .40 .15
Nos. 1475-1479 (5) 2.00 .75

First Latin American Theater Festival, Cordoba, Oct. — A682

1984, Oct. 13 Litho. *Perf. 13½*

1480 A682 20p Mask .25 .15

Intl. Eucharistic Congress, 50th Anniv. A683

Design: Apostles' Communion, by Fra Angelico.

1984, Oct. 13

1481 A683 20p multicolored .30 .15

Glaciares Natl. Park (UNESCO World Heritage List) A684

1984, Nov. 17 Litho.

1482 A684 20p Sea .25 .15
1483 A684 30p Glacier .42 .15
Set value .25

City of Puerto Deseado Centenary A685

1984, Nov. 17 *Perf. 13½*

1484 A685 20p shown .30 .15
1485 A685 20p Ushuaia centenary .30 .15
Set value .15

Childrens' Paintings, Christmas 1984 A686

1984, Dec. 1 Litho. *Perf. 13½*

1486 A686 20p Diego Aguero .32 .15
1487 A686 30p Leandro Ruiz .60 .15
1488 A686 50p Maria Castillo, vert. .60 .15
Nos. 1486-1488 (3) 1.52 .45

No. 1439 Overprinted

1934 - 50° ANIVERSARIO - 1984 CENTRO FILATELICO BUENOS AIRES

1984, Dec. 1 Photo. *Perf. 13½*

1489 A641 10p multicolored .26 .22

Buenos Aires Philatelic Center, 50th anniv.

Vista Del Jardin Zoologico, by Fermin Eguia — A687

Paintings: No. 1491, El Congreso Iluminado, by Francisco Travieso. No. 1492, Galpones (La Boca), by Marcos Borio.

1984, Dec. 15 *Perf. 13½*

1490 A687 20p multi .28 .15
1491 A687 20p multi, vert. .28 .15
1492 A687 20p multi, vert. .28 .15
Nos. 1490-1492 (3) .84 .45

Gen. Martin Miguel de Guemes (1785-1821) — A688

1985, Mar. 23 Litho. *Perf. 13½*

1493 A688 30p multicolored .26 .15

ARGENTINA '85 Exhibition — A689

First airmail service from: 20p, Buenos Aires to Montevideo, 1917. 40p, Cordoba to Villa Dolores, 1925. 60p, Bahia Blanca to Comodoro Rivadavia, 1929. 80p, Argentina to Germany, 1934. 100p, naval service to the Antarctic, 1952.

1985, Apr. 27

1494 A689 20p Bleriot Gnome .16 .15
1495 A689 40p Junker F-13L .32 .15
1496 A689 60p Latte 25 .50 .20
1497 A689 80p L.Z. 127 Graf Zeppelin .65 .30
1498 A689 100p Consolidated PBY Catalina .85 .40
Nos. 1494-1498 (5) 2.48 1.20

Central Bank, 50th Anniv. A690

1985, June 1

1499 A690 80p Bank Bldg., Buenos Aires .55 .18

Jose A. Ferreyra (1889-1943), Director of Munequitas Portenas A691

Famous directors and their films: No. 1501, Leopoldo Torre Nilsson (1924-1978), scene from Martin Fierro.

1985, June 1

1500 A691 100p shown .60 .18
1501 A691 100p multi .60 .18

Carlos Gardel (1890-1935), Entertainer — A692

Paintings: No. 1502, Gardel playing the guitar on stage, by Carlos Alonso (b. 1929). No. 1503, Gardel in a wide-brimmed hat, by Hermegildo Sabat (b. 1933). No. 1504, Portrait of Gardel in an ornamental frame, by Aldo Severi (b. 1928) and Martiniano Arce (b. 1939).

1985, June 15

1502 A692 200p multi .95 .45
1503 A692 200p multi .95 .45
1504 A692 200p multi .95 .45
Nos. 1502-1504 (3) 2.85 1.35

The Arrival, by Pedro Figari A693

A Halt on the Plains, by Prilidiano Pueyrredon — A693a

Oil paintings (details): 30c, The Wagon Square, by C. B. de Quiros. Illustration A693a is reduced.

1985, July 6 Litho. *Perf. 13½*

1505 A693 20c multi 1.00 .24
1506 A693 30c multi 1.25 .24

Souvenir Sheet

Perf. 12

1507 A693a Sheet of 2 2.50
a. 20c Pilgrims, vert. .26
b. 30c Wagon .40

ARGENTINA '85. No. 1507 contains 2 30x40mm stamps. See No. 1542.

Buenos Aires to Montevideo, 1917 Teodoro Fels Flight A694

Historic flight covers: No. 1508, Shown. No. 1509, Villa Dolores to Cordoba, 1925. No. 1510, Buenos Aires to France, 1929 St. Exupery flight. No. 1511, Buenos Aires to Bremerhaven, 1934 Graf Zeppelin flight. No. 1512, First Antarctic flight, 1952.

1985, July 13 *Perf. 12x12½*

1508 A694 10c emer & multi .40 .15
1509 A694 10c ultra & multi .40 .15
1510 A694 10c lt choc & multi .40 .15
1511 A694 10c chnt & multi .40 .15
1512 A694 10c ap grn & multi .40 .15
Nos. 1508-1512 (5) 2.00
Set value .60

ARGENTINA '85.

Illuminated Fruit, by Fortunato Lacamera (1887-1951) — A695

Paintings: 20c, Woman with Bird, by Juan del Prete, vert.

1985, Sept. 7 *Perf. 13½*

1513 A695 20c multi .85 .30
1514 A695 30c multi 1.00 .30

Flower Types of 1982-85

Designs: 1a, Begonia micranthera var. hieronymi. 5a, Gymnocalycium bruchii.

1985-88 Photo. *Perf. 13½*

1515 A641 ½c like #1356 .15 .15
1516 A641 1c like #1439 .15 .15
1517 A641 2c like #1345 .15 .15
1518 A641 3c like #1441 .15 .15
1519 A641 5c like #1346 .22 .15
1520 A641 10c like #1348 .35 .15
1521 A641 20c like #1347 .70 .16
1522 A641 30c like #1443A 1.10 .25
1523 A641 50c like #1344 1.75 .35
1524 A641 1a multi 3.50 .65
1525 A641 2a like #1351 .38 .15
1526 A641 5a multi 6.75 3.00

Size: 15x23mm

1527 A641 8½c like #1349 .32 .15
Nos. 1515-1527 (13) 15.67 5.61

Issue dates: ½c, 1c, Dec. 16. 2c, 8½c, 30c, Sept. 18. 3c, 5c, 10c, 50c, 1a, Sept. 7. 20c, Oct. 17. 5a, Mar. 21, 1987. 2a, Dec. 5, 1988.

No. 1435 Surcharged

1986, Nov. 4 Photo. *Perf. 13½*

1530 A641 10c on 1p No. 1435 .15 .15

Folk Musical Instruments A699

1985, Sept. 14 Litho. *Perf. 13½*

1531 A699 20c Frame drum .55 .22
1532 A699 20c Long flute .55 .22
1533 A699 20c Jew's harp .55 .22
1534 A699 20c Pan flutes .55 .22
1535 A699 20c Musical bow .55 .22
Nos. 1531-1535 (5) 2.75 1.10

Juan Bautista Alberdi (1810-1884), Historian, Politician A700

Famous men: Nicolas Avellaneda (1836-1885), President in 1874. 30c, Fr. Luis Beltran (1784-1827), military and naval engineer. 40c, Ricardo Levene (1885-1959), historian, author.

1985, Oct. 5

1536 A700 10c multi .22 .15
1537 A700 20c multi .45 .22
1538 A700 30c multi .65 .32
1539 A700 40c multi 1.10 .45
Nos. 1536-1539 (4) 2.42 1.14

Type of 1985 and

Skaters A701

Deception, by J. H. Rivoira A702

1985, Oct. 19 Litho. *Perf. 13½*

1540 A701 20c multi .35 .32
1541 A702 30c multi .50 .48

Size: 147x75mm

Imperf

1542 A693a 1a multi 1.90

IYY. No. 1542 is inscribed in silver with the UN 40th anniversary and IYY emblems.

Provincial Views — A703

Designs: No. 1543, Rock Window, Buenos Aires. No. 1544, Forclaz Windmill, Entre Rios. No. 1545, Lake Potrero de los Funes, San Luis. No. 1546, Mission church, north-east province. No. 1547, Penguin colony, Punta Tombo, Chubut. No. 1548, Water Mirrors, Cordoba.

1985, Nov. 23 *Perf. 13½*

1543 A703 10c multi .26 .25
1544 A703 10c multi .26 .25
1545 A703 10c multi .26 .25
1546 A703 10c multi .26 .25
1547 A703 10c multi .26 .25
1548 A703 10c multi .26 .25
Nos. 1543-1548 (6) 1.56 1.50

Christmas 1985 — A704

Designs: 10c, Birth of Our Lord, by Carlos Cortes. 20c, Christmas, by Hector Viola.

1985, Dec. 7

1549 A704 10c multi .24 .18
1550 A704 20c multi .48 .45

Natl. Campaign for the Prevention of Blindness A705

1985, Dec. 7

1551 A705 10c multi .24 .18

Rio Gallegos City, Cent. — A716

1985, Dec. 21 Litho. *Perf. 13½*

1552 A716 10c Church .24 .18

Natl. Grape Harvest Festival, 50th Anniv. A717

1986, Mar. 15

1553 A717 10c multi .24 .18

Historical Architecture in Buenos Aires — A718

Designs: No. 1554, Valentin Alsina House, Italian Period, 1860-70. No. 1555, House on Cerrito Street, French influence, 1880-1900. No. 1556, House on the Avenida de Mayo y Santiago del Estero, Art Nouveau, 1900-10. No. 1557, Customs Building, academic architecture, 1900-15. No. 1558, Isaac Fernandez Blanco Museum, house of architect Martin Noel, natl. restoration, 1910-30. Nos. 1554-1556 vert.

1986, Apr. 19

1554 A718 20c multi .40 .30
1555 A718 20c multi .40 .30
1556 A718 20c multi .40 .30
1557 A718 20c multi .40 .30
1558 A718 20c multi .40 .30
Nos. 1554-1558 (5) 2.00 1.50

Antarctic Bases, Pioneers and Fauna — A719

Designs: a, Base, Jubany. b, Arctocephalus gazella. c, Otaria byronia. d, Gen. Belgrano Base. e, Daption capensis. f, Diomedia melanophris. g, Apterodytes patagonica. h, Macronectes giganteus. i, Hugo Alberto Acuna (1885-1953). j, Spheniscus magellanicus. k, Gallinago gallinage. l, Capt. Agustin del Castillo (1855-89).

1986, May 31

1559 Sheet of 12 2.50 3.50
a.-l. A719 10c any single .20 .25

Famous People — A720

Statuary, Buenos Aires — A721

Designs: No. 1560, Dr. Alicia Moreau de Justo, human rights activist. No. 1561, Dr. Emilio

Ravignani (1886-1954), historian. No. 1562, Indira Gandhi.

1986, July 5 Litho. *Perf. 13½*

1560 A720 10c multi .40 .22
1561 A720 10c multi .40 .22
1562 A720 30c multi 1.25 .65
Nos. 1560-1562 (3) 2.05 1.09

1986, July 5

Designs: 20c, Fountain of the Nereids, by Dolores Lola Mora (1866-1936). 30c, Lamenting at Work, by Rogelio Yrurtia (1879-1950), horiz.

1563 A721 20c multi .52 .45
1564 A721 30c multi .80 .65

Famous Men — A722

Designs: No. 1565, Francisco N. Laprida (1786-1829), politician. No. 1566, Estanislao Lopez (1786-1838), brigadier general. No. 1567, Francisco Ramirez (1786-1821), general.

1986, Aug. 9 Litho. *Perf. 13*

1565 A722 20c dl yel, brn & blk .42 .38
1566 A722 20c dl yel, brn & blk .42 .38
1567 A722 20c dl yel, brn & blk .42 .38
Nos. 1565-1567 (3) 1.26 1.14

Fr. Ceferino Namuncura (1886-1905) A723

1986, Aug. 30 *Perf. 13½*

1568 A723 20c multi .60 .40

Miniature Sheets

Natl. Team Victory, 1986 World Cup Soccer Championships, Mexico — A724

Designs: No. 1569a-1569d, Team. Nos. 1569e-1569h, Shot on goal. Nos. 1570a-1570d, Action close-up. Nos. 1570e-1570h, Diego Maradona holding soccer cup.

1986, Nov. 8 Litho. *Perf. 13½*

1569 A724 Sheet of 8 9.25 12.00
a.-h. 75c any single 1.15 1.50
1570 A724 Sheet of 8 9.25 12.00
a.-h. 75c any single 1.15 1.50

San Francisco (Cordoba), Cent. A725

1986, Nov. 8

1571 A725 20c Municipal Building .50 .45

Trelew City (Chubut), Cent. A726

1986, Nov. 22 Litho. *Perf. 13½*

1572 A726 20c Old railroad station, 1865 .50 .45

Mutualism Day A727

1986, Nov. 22

1573 A727 20c multi .60 .45

Christmas A728

Designs: 20c, Naif retable, by Aniko Szabo (b. 1945). 30c, Everyone's Tree, by Franca Delacqua (b. 1947).

1986, Dec. 13 Litho. *Perf. 13½*

1574 A728 20c multicolored .35
1575 A728 30c multicolored .60

Santa Rosa de Lima, 400th Birth Anniv. — A729

Rio Cuarto Municipal Building — A730

1986, Dec. 13

1576 A729 50c multicolored 1.75

1986, Dec. 20

1577 A730 20c shown .40
1578 A730 20c Court Building, Cordoba .40

Rio Cuarto City, bicent. Court Building, Cordoba, 50th anniv.

Antarctic Treaty, 25th Anniv. — A731

1987, Mar. 7 Litho. *Perf. 13½*

1579 A731 20c Marine biologist .35
1580 A731 30c Ornithologist .60

Souvenir Sheet

Perf. 12

1581 Sheet of 2 1.00
a. A731 20c like No. 1579 .40
b. A731 30c like No. 1580 .55

No. 1581 contains 2 stamps, size: 40x50mm.

Natl. Mortgage Bank, Cent. A732

1987, Mar. 21 *Perf. 13½*

1582 A732 20c multi .65

Natl. Cooperative Associations Movement — A733

1987, Mar. 21

1583 A733 20c multi .65

Second State Visit of Pope John Paul II — A734

Engr., Litho. (No. 1585)

1987, Apr. 4 *Perf. 13½*

1584 A734 20c shown .35
1585 A734 80c Papal blessing 1.40

Souvenir Sheet

Perf. 12

1586 A734 1a like 20c 1.90

No. 1586 contains one 40x50mm stamp.

Intl. Peace Year A735

Designs: 30c, Pigeon, abstract sculpture by Victor Kaniuka.

1987, Apr. 11 Litho.

1587 A735 20c multi .35
1588 A735 30c multi .52

Low Handicap World Polo Championships A736

Design: Polo Players, painting by Alejandro Moy.

1987, Apr. 11

1589 A736 20c multi .35

Miniature Sheet

ICOM '86 — A737

Designs: a, Emblem. b, Family crest, National History Museum, Buenos Aires. c, St. Bartholomew, Enrique Larreta Museum of Spanish Art, Buenos Aires. d, Zoomorphic club, Patagonian Museum, San Carlos de Bariloche. e, Supplication, anthropomorphic sculpture, Natural Sciences Museum, La Plata. f, Wrought iron lattice from the house of J. Urquiza, president of the Confederation of Argentina, Entre Rios History Museum, Parana. g, St. Joseph, 18th cent. wood figurine, Northern History Museum, Salta. h, Funerary urn, Provincial Archaeological Museum, Santiago del Estero.

1987, May 30

1590 Sheet of 8 3.50
a.-h. A737 25c any single .40

Intl. Council of Museums, 14th general conf.

Natl. College of Monserrat, Cordoba, 300th Anniv. — A738

1987, July 4 *Imperf.*

1591 A738 1a multi 1.10

Monserrat '87 Philatelic Exposition.

Fight Drug Abuse A739

Design: The Proportions of Man, by da Vinci.

1987, Aug. 15 *Perf. 13½*

1592 A739 30c multi .40

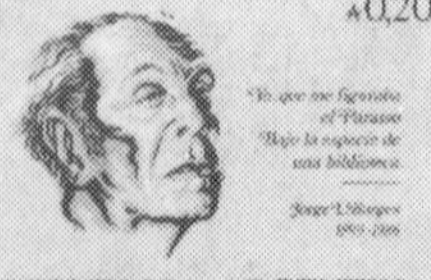

Famous Men A740

Portraits and quotations: 20c, Jorge Luis Borges (1899-1986), writer. 30c, Armando Discepolo (1887-1971), playwright. 50c, Carlos A. Pueyrredon (1887-1962), professor, Legion of Honor laureate.

1987, Aug. 15

1593 A740 20c multi .30
1594 A740 30c multi .50
1595 A740 50c multi .75
Nos. 1593-1595 (3) 1.55

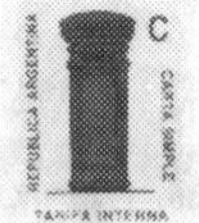

Pillar Boxes
A741 A742

1987 Photo. *Perf. 13½*

1596 A741 (30c) yel, blk & dark red .80
1597 A742 (33c) lt blue grn, blk & yel .85

Issue dates: (30c), June 8; (33c), July 13.

The Sower, by Julio Vanzo A743

1987, Sept. 12

1598 A743 30c multi .35

Argentine Agrarian Federation, 75th anniv.

10th Pan American Games, Indianapolis, Aug. 7-25 — A744

1987, Sept. 26

1599 A744 20c Basketball .25
1600 A744 30c Rowing .35
1601 A744 50c Yachting .55
Nos. 1599-1601 (3) 1.15

Children Playing Doctor, WHO Emblem A745

1987, Oct. 7

1602 A745 30c multi .35

Vaccinate every child campaign.

Heroes of the Revolution A746

Signing of the San Nicolas Accord, 1852, by Rafael del Villar A747

Independence anniversaries and historic events: No. 1603, Maj.-Col. Ignacio Alvarez Thomas (1787-1857). No. 1604, Col. Manuel Crispulo Bernabe Dorrego (1787-1829). No. 1606, 18th cent. Spanish map of the Falkland Isls., administered by Jacinto de Altolaguirre.

1987, Oct. 17

1603 A746 25c shown .30
1604 A746 25c multi .30
1605 A747 50c shown .55
1606 A747 50c multi .55
Nos. 1603-1606 (4) 1.70

Museum established in the House of the San Nicholas Accord, 50th anniv. (#1605); Jacinto de Altolaguirre (1754-1787), governor the Malvinas Isls. for the King of Spain (#1606).

Celedonio Galvan Moreno, 1st Director A748

1987, Nov. 21

1607 A748 50c multi .55

Postas Argentinas magazine, 50th anniv.

LRA National Radio, Buenos Aires, 50th Anniv. — A749

1987, Nov. 21

1608 A749 50c multi .55

Natl. Philatelic Society, Cent. A750

1987, Nov. 21

1609 A750 1a Jose Marco del Pont 1.10

Christmas A751

Tapestries: 50c, *Navidad,* by Alisia Frega. 1a, *Vitral,* by Silvina Trigos.

1987, Dec. 5

1610 A751 50c multi .55
1611 A751 1a multi 1.10

Natl. Parks — A752

1987, Dec. 19 *Perf. 13x13½*

1612 A752 50c Baritu .55
1613 A752 50c Nahuel Huapi .55
1614 A752 50c Rio Pilcomayo .55
1615 A752 50c Tierra del Fuego .55
1616 A752 50c Iguacu .55
Nos. 1612-1616 (5) 2.75

See Nos. 1647-1651, 1715-1719, 1742-1746.

Landscapes in Buenos Aires Painted by Jose Cannella A753

1988-89 Litho. *Perf. 13½*

1617 A753 5a Caminito 2.00
1618 A753 10a Viejo Almacen 4.00
1618A A753 10a like No. 1618 1.05
1618B A753 50a like No. 1617 1.05
Nos. 1617-1618B (4) 8.10

No. 1618 inscribed "Viejo Almacen"; No. 1618A inscribed "El Viejo Almacen."

Issue dates: 5a, #1618, Mar. 15; 50a, 1989.

For overprint see No. 1635.

Minstrel in a Tavern, by Carlos Morel A754

Paintings: No. 1620, Interior of Curuzu, by Candido Lopez.

1988, Mar. 19 Litho. *Perf. 13½*

1619 A754 1a shown .60
1620 A754 1a multi .60

See Nos. 1640-1641.

Argentine-Brazilian Economic Cooperation and Integration Program for Mutual Growth — A755

1988, Mar. 19

1621 A755 1a multi .50

Cities of Alta Gracia and Corrientes, 400th Annivs. A756

1988, Apr. 9 Litho. *Perf. 13½*

1622 A756 1a Alta Gracia Church .75
1623 A756 1a Chapel of St. Anne, Corrientes .75

Labor Day — A757

Grain Carriers, a tile mosaic by Alfredo Guido, Line D of Nueve de Julio station, Buenos Aires subway: a, (UL). b, (UR). c, (LL). d, (LR).

1988, May 21

1624 A757 Block of 4 1.25
a.-d. 50c any single .25

1988 Summer Olympics, Seoul — A758

1988, July 16 Litho. *Perf. 13½*

1625 A758 1a Running .25
1626 A758 2a Soccer .60
1627 A758 3a Field hockey .90
1628 A758 4a Tennis 1.10
Nos. 1625-1628 (4) 2.85

Mendoza Bank, Cent. A759

Natl. Gendarmerie, Cent. — A760

1988, Aug. 13

1629 A759 2a multi .35
1630 A760 2a multi .35

Sarmiento and Cathedral School to the North, Buenos Aires A761

1988, Sept. 10 Litho. *Perf. 13½*

1631 A761 3a multi .50

Domingo Faustino Sarmiento (1811-1888), educator, politician.

St. Cayetano, Patron of Workers — A762

El Amor, by Antonio Berni, Pacific Gallery, Buenos Aires — A763

1988, Sept. 10 Litho.

1632 A762 2a multi .45
1633 A762 3a Our Lady of Carmen, Cuyo .70

Souvenir Sheet

Perf. 12

1634 A763 5a multi 1.00

Liniers Philatelic Circle and the Argentine Western Philatelic Institution (IFADO), 50th annivs.

No. 1634 contains one 40x30mm stamp.

No. 1617 Ovptd. with Congress Emblem and:
"XXI CONGRESO
DE LA SOCIEDAD
INTERNACIONAL
DE UROLOGIA"

1988, Oct. 29 Litho. *Perf. 13½*
1635 A753 5a multi .85

21st Congress of the Intl. Urology Soc.

Tourism A763a

1988, Nov. 1 Litho. *Perf. 13½*
1635A A763a 3a Purmamarca, Jujuy .50

Size: 28½x38mm

1635B A763a 20a Ushuaia 3.35

Buenos Aires Subway, 75th Anniv. A764

1988, Dec. 17 Litho. *Perf. 13½*
1636 A764 5a Train, c. 1913 .85

Christmas A765

Frescoes in Ucrania Cathedral, Buenos Aires: No. 1637, *Virgin Patron.* No. 1638, *Virgin of Tenderness.*

1988, Dec. 17
1637 A765 5a multi .85
1638 A765 5a multi .85

St. John Bosco (1815-1888), Educator, and Church in Ushuaia — A766

1989, Apr. 8 Litho. *Perf. 13½*
1639 A766 5a multi .30

Dated 1988.

Art Type of 1988

Paintings: No. 1640, *Blancos,* by Fernando Fader (1882-1935). No. 1641, *Rincon de los Areneros,* by Justo Lynch (1870-1953).

1989, Apr. 8
1640 A754 5a multi .30
1641 A754 5a multi .30

Holy Week A767

Sculpture and churches: No. 1642, *The Crown of Thorns,* Calvary of Tandil, and Church of Our Lady Carmelite, Tandil. No. 1643, *Jesus the Nazarene* and Metropolitan Cathedral, Buenos Aires. No. 1644, *Jesus Encounters His Mother* (scene of the crucifixion), La Quebrada Village, San Luis. No. 1645, *Our Lady of Sorrow* and Church of Humahuaca, Jujuy.

1989, Apr. 22 Litho. *Perf. 13½*
1642 A767 2a multi .20
1643 A767 2a multi .20
1644 A767 3a multi .30
1645 A767 3a multi .30
Nos. 1642-1645 (4) 1.00

Printed in sheets of 16+4 labels containing blocks of 4 of each design. Labels picture Jesus's arrival in Jerusalem (Palm Sunday).

Prevent Alcoholism A768

1989, Apr. 22
1646 A768 5a multi .30

Natl. Park Type of 1987

1989, May 6 *Perf. 13x13½*
1647 A752 5a Lihue Calel .30
1648 A752 5a El Palmar .30
1649 A752 5a Calilegua .30
1650 A752 5a Chaco .30
1651 A752 5a Los Glaciares .30
Nos. 1647-1651 (5) 1.50

Admission of Argentina to the ITU, Cent. A769

1989, May 6 *Perf. 13½*
1652 A769 10a multi .45

World Model Aircraft Championships — A770

1989, May 27 Litho. *Perf. 13½*
1653 A770 5a F1A glider .20
1654 A770 5a F1B rubber band motor .20
1655 A770 10a F1C gas motor .35
Nos. 1653-1655 (3) .75

French Revolution, Bicent. — A771

Designs: 10a, "All men are born free and equal." 15a, French flag and *La Marianne,* by Gandon. 25a, *Liberty Guiding the People,* by Delacroix.

1989, July 1 Litho. *Perf. 13½*
1656 A771 10a shown .15
1657 A771 15a multi .15
Set value .20

Souvenir Sheet
Perf. 12

1658 A771 25a multi .25

No. 1658 contains one 40x30mm stamp.

The Republic, a Bronze Bust in the Congreso de la Nacion, Buenos Aires — A772

1989, Aug. 12 Litho. *Perf. 13½*
1659 A772 300a on 50a multi

Peaceful transition of power (presidential office). Not issued without surcharge.

Immigration to Argentina — A773

1989, Aug. 19 *Perf. 13½*
1660 A773 150a S.S. *Weser,* 1889
1661 A773 200a Immigrant hotel, 1889

Souvenir Sheet
Perf. 12

1662 Sheet of 2
a. A773 150a like No. 1660
b. A773 200a like No. 1661

No. 1662 contains 40c30mm stamps.

Famous Men A774

Designs: No. 1663, Fr. Guillermo Furlong (1889-1974), historian, and title page of *The Jesuits.* No. 1664, Dr. Gregorio Alvarez (1889-1986), physician, and title page of *Canto a Chos Malal.* 200a, Brig.-Gen. Enrique Martinez (1789-1870) and lithograph *La Batalla de Maipu,* by Teodoro Gericault.

1989, Oct. 7 Litho. *Perf. 13½*
1663 A774 150a multi
1664 A774 150a multi
1665 A774 200a multi

America Issue — A775

Emblem of the Postal Union of the Americas and Spain (PUAS) and pre-Columbian art from Catamarca Province: 200a, Wooden mask from Atajo, Loma Morada. 300a, Urn of the Santa Maria Culture (Phase 3) from Punta de Balastro, Santa Maria Department.

1989, Oct. 14
1666 A775 200a multi
1667 A775 300a multi

Federal Police Week — A776

Children's drawings: No. 1668, Diego Molinari, age 13. No. 1669, Carlos Alberto Sarago, age 8. No. 1670, Roxana Andrea Osuna, age 7. No. 1671, Pablo Javier Quaglia, age 9.

1989, Oct. 28 Litho. *Perf. 13½*
1668 A776 100a multi
1669 A776 100a multi
1670 A776 150a multi
1671 A776 150a multi

Battle of Vuelta de Obligado, 1845 — A777

(Illustration reduced.)

1989, Dec. 2 Litho. *Perf. 13x13½*
1672 A777 300a multicolored

Paintings A778

Cristo de los Cerros, Sculpture by Chipo Cespedes — A779

1989, Dec. 2 *Perf. 13½*
1673 A778 200a Gato Frias
1674 A778 200a Maria Carballido
1675 A779 300a shown

Christmas.

Buenos Aires Port, Cent. — A780

(Illustration reduced.)

1990, Mar. 3 Litho. *Perf. 13½*
1676 A780 Strip of 4
a.-d. 200a any single

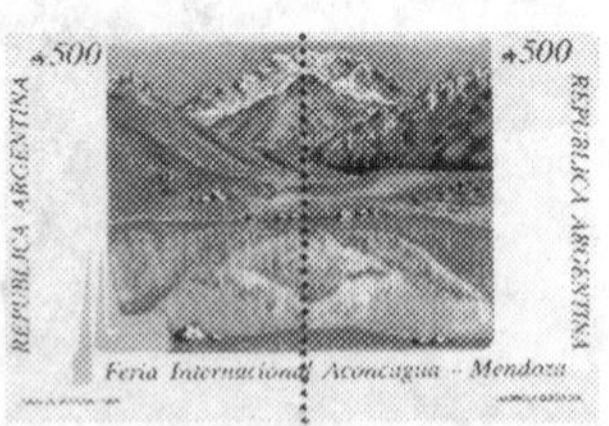

Aconcagua Intl. Fair, Mendoza — A781

Design: Aconcagua mountain, Los Horcones Lagoon and fair emblem.
(Illustration reduced.)

1990, Mar. 3
1677 A781 Pair
a.-b. 500a any single

Natl. Savings and Insurance Fund, 75th Anniv. A782

1990, May 5 Litho. *Perf. 13½*
1678 A782 1000a multicolored

Miniature Sheet

1990 World Cup Soccer Championships, Italy — A783

Designs: a, Athlete's torso (striped jersey). b, Athlete's torso (solid jersey). c, Players' feet, soccer ball. d, Player (knee to waist).

1990, May 5
1679 Sheet of 4
a.-d. A783 2500a multicolored

Carlos Pellegrini, Commercial High School Founder, Cent. — A784

1990, June 2 Litho. *Perf. 13½*
1680 A784 2000a multicolored

Youth Against Drugs A785

1990, June 2
1681 A785 2000a multicolored

Intl. Literacy Year A786

1990, July 14 Litho. *Perf. 13½*
1682 A786 2000a multicolored

Flower Type of 1982 in New Currency

1989-90 Photo. *Perf. 13½*
1683 A641 10a like #1433
1684 A641 20a like #1435A
1685 A641 50a like #1354
1686 A641 100a like #1439
1687 A641 300a like #1345
1688 A641 500a like #1441
1689 A641 1000a like #1355
1690 A641 5000a like #1349
1691 A641 10,000a like #1350

Issue dates: 20a, 100a, 300a, 500a, Aug. 1, 1989. 10a, Aug. 24, 1989. 50a, Aug. 30, 1989. 1000, Mar. 8, 1990. 5000a, Apr. 6, 1990. 10,000a, July 2, 1990.

World Basketball Championships A787

1990, Aug. 11 Litho. *Perf. 13½*
1703 A787 2000a multicolored .95

Souvenir Sheet
Perf. 12
1704 A787 5000a Jump ball 2.40

Postal Union of the Americas and Spain, 14th Congress A788

1990, Sept. 15 Litho. *Perf. 13½*
1705 A788 3000a Arms, seal 1.50
1706 A788 3000a Sailing ships 1.50
1707 A788 3000a Modern freighter 1.50
1708 A788 3000a Van, cargo plane 1.50
Nos. 1705-1708 (4) 6.00

America Issue A789

1990, Oct. 13
1709 A789 3000a Iguacu Falls, hamelia erecta 2.00
1710 A789 3000a Puerto Deseado, elephant seal 2.00

Natl. Parks Type of 1987

1990, Oct. 27 *Perf. 13x13½*
1715 A752 3000a Lanin 1.50
1716 A752 3000a Laguna Blanca 1.50
1717 A752 3000a Perito Moreno 1.50
1718 A752 3000a Puelo 1.50
1719 A752 3000a El Rey 1.50
Nos. 1715-1719 (5) 7.50

Stamp Day A790

1990, Oct. 27 *Perf. 13½*
1720 A790 3000a multicolored 1.50

Salvation Army, Cent. A793

Designs: No. 1722, Natl. University of the Littoral, Santa Fe, cent.

1990, Dec. 1 Litho. *Perf. 13½*
1721 A793 3000a multicolored
1722 A793 3000a multicolored
a. Pair, #1721-1722 + label

Miniature Sheets

Christmas — A794

Stained glass windows: No. 1723, The Immaculate Conception. No. 1724, The Nativity. No. 1725, Presentation of Jesus at the Temple.

1990, Dec. 1 *Perf. 13½x13*
Sheets of 4
1723 A794 3000a #a.-d.
1724 A794 3000a #a.-d.
1725 A794 3000a #a.-d.

Landscapes A795

Paintings: No. 1726, Los Sauces, by Atilio Malinverno. No. 1727, Paisaje, by Pio Collivadino, vert.

1991, May 4 Litho. *Perf. 13½*
1726 A795 4000a multicolored 1.00
1727 A795 4000a multicolored 1.00

Return of Remains of Juan Manuel de Rosas (1793-1877) A796

1991, June 1 Litho. *Perf. 13½*
1728 A796 4000a multicolored 1.00

Swiss Confederation, 700th Anniv. — A797

1991, Aug. 3 Litho. *Perf. 13½*
1729 A797 4000a multicolored .95

Miniature Sheet

Cartoons — A798

Designs: a, Hernan, the Corsair by Jose Luis Salinas. b, Don Fulgencio by Lino Palacio. c, Medical Rules of Salerno by Oscar Esteban Conti. d, Buenos Aires Undershirt by Alejandro del Prado. e, Girls! by Jose A.G. Divito. f, Langostino by Eduardo Carlos Ferro. g, Mafalda by Joaquin Salvador Lavoro. h, Mort Cinder by Alberto Breccia.

1991, Aug. 3
1730 A798 4000a Sheet of 8, #a.-h. 7.75

City of La Rioja, 400th Anniv. — A799

1991, Sept. 14 Litho. *Perf. 13½*
1731 A799 4000a multicolored 1.00

First Balloon Flight over the Andes, 75th Anniv. — A800

Illustration reduced.

1991, Sept. 14
1732 A800 4000a multicolored 1.00

America Issue A801

Designs: No. 1733, Magellan's caravel, Our Lady of Victory. No. 1734, Ships of Juan Diaz de Solis.

1991, Nov. 9 Litho. *Perf. 13½*
1733 A801 4000a multicolored 1.00
1734 A801 4000a multicolored 1.00

Anniversaries — A802

Designs: a, J. Enrique Pestalozzi, founder of newspaper, Daily Argentinian. b, Leandro N. Alem, founder of Radical People's Party. c, Man with rifle, emblem of Argentine Federal Shooting Club. d, Dr. Nicasio Etchepareborda, emblem of College of Odontology. e, Dalmiro Huergo, emblem of Graduate School of Economics.

1991, Nov. 30
1735 A802 4000a Strip of 5, #a.-e. 5.00

Christmas — A803

Stained glass windows from Our Lady of Lourdes Basilica, Buenos Aires: Nos. 1736a-1736b, Top and bottom portions of Virgin of the Valley, Catamarca. Nos. 1736c-1736d, Top and bottom portions of Virgin of the Rosary of the Miracle, Cordoba.

1991, Nov. 30
1736 A803 4000a Block of 4, #a.-d. 4.00

Famous Men A804

Designs: a, Gen. Juan de Lavalle (1797-1841), Peruvian medal of honor. b, Brig. Gen. Jose Maria del Rosario Siriaco Paz (1791-1854), medal. c, Marco Manuel de Avellaneda (1813-1841), lawyer. d, Guillermo Enrique Hudson (1841-1922), author.

1991, Dec. 14 Litho. *Perf. 13½*
1737 A804 4000a Block of 4, #a.-d. 4.00

Birds — A805

1991, Dec. 28
1738 A805 4000a Pterocnemia pennata 1.00
1739 A805 4000a Morphnu guianensis 1.00
1740 A805 4000a Ara chloroptera 1.00
Nos. 1738-1740 (3) 3.00

Miniature Sheet

Arbrafex '92, Argentina-Brazil Philatelic Exhibition — A806

Traditional costumes: a, Gaucho, woman. b, Gaucho, horse. c, Gaucho in store. d, Gaucho holding lariat.

1992 Litho. *Perf. 13½*
1741 A806 38c Sheet of 4, #a.-d. 4.10

Natl. Parks Type of 1987

1992, Apr. 4 Litho. *Perf. 13x13½*
1742 A752 38c Alerces .90
1743 A752 38c Formosa Nature Reserve .90
1744 A752 38c Petrified Forest .90
1745 A752 38c Arrayanes .90
1746 A752 38c Laguna de los Pozuelos .90
Nos. 1742-1746 (5) 4.50

Mushrooms — A807

1992-94 Photo. *Perf. 13½*
1748 A807 10c Psilocybe cubensis .25 .15
1749 A807 25c Coprinus atramentarius .60
1750 A807 38c Psilocybe cubensis .90
1751 A807 48c Coprinus atramentarius 1.20
1752 A807 50c Suillus granulatus 1.25
1753 A807 51c Morchella esculenta 1.30
1754 A807 61c Amanita muscaria 1.55
1755 A807 68c Coprinus comatus 1.75
1756 A807 1p like #1756 2.50
1757 A807 1.25p like #1753 3.25
1758 A807 1.77p Stropharia oerugi-nosa 4.25
1759 A807 2p like #1754 5.00
Nos. 1748-1759 (12) 23.80

No. 1763 not issued without overprint "Centro Filatelico de Neuquen y Rio Negro 50th Aniversario."
Issued: 38c, 4/4/92; 48c, 51c, 61c, 8/1/92; 1.77p, 11/7/92; 25c, 50c, 8/17/93; 1p, 2p, 8/26/93; 10c, 1/11/94; 68c, 1.25p, 10/10/92.

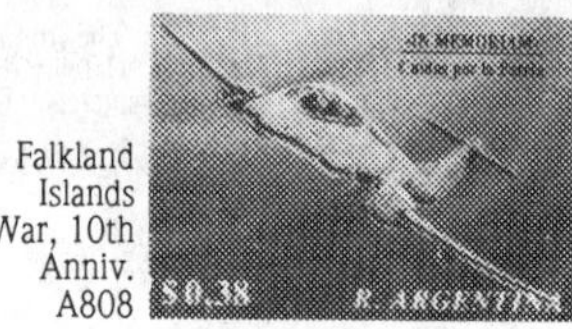
Falkland Islands War, 10th Anniv. A808

1992, May 2 Litho. *Perf. 13½*
1767 A808 38c Pucara 1A-58 .95
1768 A808 38c Cruiser Gen. Belgrano .95
1769 A808 38c Soldier and truck .95
Nos. 1767-1769 (3) 2.85

Miniature Sheet

Preserve the Environment A809

Designs: a, Deer. b, Geese. c, Butterflies. d, Whale.

1992, June 6 Litho. *Perf. 12*
1770 A809 38c Sheet of 4, #a.-d. 3.70

Paintings by Florencio Molina Campos A810

1992, June 6 *Perf. 13½*
1771 A810 38c A La Sombra .95
1772 A810 38c Tileforo Areco, vert. .95

Famous Men A811

Designs: No. 1773, Gen. Lucio N. Mansilla (1792-1871). No. 1774, Jose Manuel Estrada (1842-1894), writer. No. 1775, Brig. Gen. Jose I. Garmendia (1842-1915).

1992, July 4 Litho. *Perf. 13½*
1773 A811 38c multicolored .95
1774 A811 38c multicolored .95
1775 A811 38c multicolored .95
Nos. 1773-1775 (3) 2.85

Fight Against Drugs — A812

1992, Aug. 1 *Perf. 13½x13*
1776 A812 38c multicolored .95

Col. Jose M. Calaza, 140th Birth Anniv. A813

1992, Sept. 5 Litho. *Perf. 13½*
1777 A813 38c multicolored .95

Discovery of America, 500th Anniv. — A814

Designs: a, Columbus, castle, ship. b, Native drawings, Columbus.

1992, Oct. 10 Litho. *Perf. 13½*
1778 A814 38c Pair, #a.-b. 1.90

Argentine Film Posters — A815

1992, Nov. 7 Litho. *Perf. 13½*
1779 A815 38c Dios Se Lo Pague, 1948 .90
1780 A815 38c Las Aguas Bajan Turbias, 1952 .90
1781 A815 38c Un Guapo Del 900, 1960 .90
1782 A815 38c La Tregua, 1974 .90
1783 A815 38c La Historia Oficial, 1984 .90
Nos. 1779-1783 (5) 4.50

Christmas — A816

1992, Nov. 28
1784 A816 38c multicolored .90

Miniature Sheet

Iberoprenfil '92 — A817

Lighthouses: a, Punta Mogotes. b, Rio Negro. c, San Antonio. d, Cabo Blanco.

1992, Dec. 5
1785 A817 38c Sheet of 4, #a.-d. 3.60

Fight Against AIDS
A818 A819

1992, Dec. 12 Litho. *Perf. 13½*
1786 A818 10c multicolored .22
1787 A819 26c multicolored .65

Intl. Space Year A820

1992, Dec. 19
1788 A820 38c multicolored .90

Souvenir Sheet

Miraculous Lord Crucifix, 400th Anniv. of Arrival in America — A821

1992, Dec. 26 *Perf. 12*
1789 A821 76c multicolored 2.00

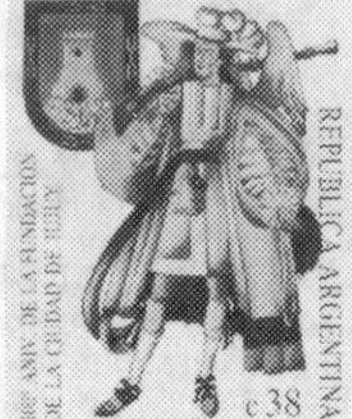
Jujuy City, 400th Anniv. — A822

1993, Apr. 24 Litho. *Perf. 13½*
1790 A822 38c multicolored .90

Argentina Soccer Assoc., Cent. A823

1993, Mar. 27
1791 A823 38c multicolored 1.00

Souvenir Sheet

Intl. Philatelic Exhibitions — A824

Designs: a, 38c, City Hall, Poznan, Poland. b, 48c, Statue of Christ the Redeemer, Rio de Janeiro, Brazil. c, 76c, Royal Palace, Bangkok, Thailand.

1993, May 8 Litho. *Perf. 12*
1792 A824 Sheet of 3, #a.-c. 3.85

Polska '93 (#1792a), Brasiliana '93 (#1792b), Bangkok '92 (#1792c).

Luis C. Candelaria's Flight Over Andes Mountains, 75th Anniv. — A825

1993, June 26 Litho. *Perf. 13x13½*
1793 A825 38c multicolored .95

Illustration reduced.

Order of San Martin, 50th Anniv. — A826

National History Academy, Cent. — A827

1993, May 29 *Perf. 13½*
1794 A826 38c multicolored .95
1795 A827 38c multicolored .95

Armed Forces Memorial Day — A828

1993, June 12
1796 A828 38c National Gendarmerie .95
1797 A828 38c Coast Guard .95

Paintings A829

Designs: No. 1798, Old House, by Norberto Russo. No. 1799, Pa'las Casas, by Adriana Zaefferer.

1993, Aug. 14 Litho. *Perf. 13½*
1798 A829 38c multicolored .90
1799 A829 38c multicolored .90

Pato — A830

1993, Aug. 28 Litho. *Perf. 12*
1800 A830 1p multicolored 2.50

Nut-Bearing Trees — A831

Designs: No. 1801, Enterolobium contortisiliquum. No. 1802, Prosopis alba. No. 1803, Magnolia grandiflora. No. 1804, Erythrina falcata. Illustration reduced.

1993, Sept. 25 Litho. *Perf. 13x13½*
1801 A831 75c multicolored 1.75
1802 A831 75c multicolored 1.75
1803 A831 1.50p multicolored 3.50
1804 A831 1.50p multicolored 3.50
Nos. 1801-1804 (4) 10.50

America Issue A832

Whales: 50c, Eubalaena australis. 75c, Cephalorhynchus commersonii.

1993, Oct. 9 *Perf. 13½*
1805 A832 50c multicolored 1.10
1806 A832 75c multicolored 1.75

Miniature Sheet

Christmas, New Year — A833

Denomination at: a, UL. b, UR. c, LL. d, LR.

1993, Dec. 4 Litho. *Perf. 13½*
1807 A833 75c Sheet of 4, #a.-d. 7.00

Cave of the Hands, Santa Cruz — A834

1993, Dec. 18
1808 A834 1p multicolored 2.00

New Emblem, Argentine Postal Service — A835

Illustration reduced.

1994, Jan. 8 *Perf. 11½*
1809 A835 75c multicolored 1.75

A836

1994 World Cup Soccer Championships, US — A837

Players from: 25c, Germany, 1990. 50c, Brazil, 1970. 75c, 1.50p, Argentina, 1986. 1p, Italy, 1982.

1994, June 11 Litho. *Perf. 13½*
1810 A836 25c multicolored .50
1811 A836 50c multicolored 1.00
1812 A836 75c multicolored 1.50
1813 A836 1p multicolored 2.00
Nos. 1810-1813 (4) 5.00

Souvenir Sheet
Perf. 12
1814 A836 1.50p multicolored 3.00

No. 1814 contains one 40x50mm stamp with continuous design.
Nos. 1810-1813 issued in sheets containing a block of 4 of each stamp + 4 labels.

/ftnote

1994, July 23 *Perf. 13½*

Drawings of championships by: No. 1815, Julian Lisenberg. No. 1816, Matias Taylor, vert. No. 1817, Torcuato S. Gonzalez Agote, vert. No. 1818, Maria Paula Palma.

1815 A837 75c multicolored 1.50
1816 A837 75c multicolored 1.50
1817 A837 75c multicolored 1.50
1818 A837 75c multicolored 1.50
Nos. 1815-1818 (4) 6.00

A838

Molothrus Badius — A838a

1994-95 Litho. *Perf. 13½*
1819 A838 10c like #1748 .20
1820 A838 25c like #1749 .50
1823 A838 50c like #1753 1.00
1828 A838 1p like #1760 2.00
1832 A838 2p like #1764 4.00
1835 A838a 9.40p multicolored 19.00
Nos. 1819-1835 (6) 26.70

Issued: 10c, 25c, 50c, 1p, 2p, 6/14/94; 9.40p, 4/12/95.
This is an expanding set. Numbers may change.

Wildlife of Falkland Islands A839

Designs: 25c, Melanodera melanodera. 50c, Pygoscelis papua. 75c, Tachyeres brachypterus. 1p, Mirounga leonina.

1994, Aug 6
1839 A839 25c multicolored .50
1840 A839 50c multicolored 1.00
1841 A839 75c multicolored 1.50
1842 A839 1p multicolored 2.00
Nos. 1839-1842 (4) 5.00

City of San Luis, 400th Anniv. — A840

1994, Aug. 20
1843 A840 75c multicolored 1.50

Province of Tierra del Fuego, Antarctica and South Atlantic Islands — A841

1994, Aug. 20
1844 A841 75c multicolored 1.50

Argentine Inventors — A842

Designs: No. 1845, Ladislao Jose Biro (1899-1985), ball point pen. No. 1846, Raul Pateras de Pescara (1890-1966), helicopter. No. 1847, Quirino Cristiani (1896-1984), animated drawings. No. 1848, Enrique Finochietto (1881-1948), surgical instruments.

1994, Oct. 1

1845 A842 75c multicolored 1.50
1846 A842 75c multicolored 1.50
1847 A842 75c multicolored 1.50
1848 A842 75c multicolored 1.50
a. Block of 4, #1845-1848 6.00
Nos. 1845-1848 (4) 6.00

Issued in sheets containing 4 #1848a + 4 labels.

UNICEF Christmas A843

1994, Nov. 26 Litho. *Perf. 11½*

1849 A843 50c shown 1.00
1850 A843 75c Bell, bulb, star, diff. 1.50

Take Care of Our Planet A844

Children's paintings: No. 1851, Boy, girl holding earth, vert. No. 1852, Children outdoors, vert. No. 1853, World as house. No. 1854, People around "world" table.

1994, Dec. 3 *Perf. 13½*

1851 A844 25c multicolored .50
1852 A844 25c multicolored .50
1853 A844 50c multicolored 1.00
1854 A844 50c multicolored 1.00
Nos. 1851-1854 (4) 3.00

Christmas — A845

1994, Dec. 10

1855 A845 50c Annunciation 1.00
1856 A845 75c Madonna & Child 1.50

Nos. 1855-1856 each issued in sheets of 20 + 5 labels.

12th Pan American Games, Mar del Plata A846

1995 Litho. *Perf. 13½*

1857 A846 75c Running 1.50
1858 A846 75c Cycling 1.50
1859 A846 75c Diving 1.50
1860 A846 1.25p Gymnastics, vert. 3.25
1861 A846 1.25p Soccer, vert. 3.25
Nos. 1857-1861 (5) 11.00

Issued: No. 1857, 2/18; others, 3/11.

Natl. Constitution — A847

Design: 75c, Natl. Congress Dome, woman from statue The Republic Triumphant.

1995, Apr. 8

1862 A847 75c multicolored 1.50

21st Intl. Book Fair — A848

Illustration reduced.

1995, Apr. 8

1863 A848 75c multicolored 1.50

Birds A849

1995 Litho. *Perf. 13½*

1876 A849 5p Carduelis magellanica 10.00
1880 A849 10p Zonotrichia capensis 20.00

Issued: 5p, 10p, 5/23/95. This is an expanding set. Numbers may change.

75c CORREO ARGENTINO REPUBLICA ARGENTINA A850

1995, Mar. 25 Litho. *Die Cut*

Self-Adhesive

1883A A850 25c multicolored .50
1884 A850 75c multicolored 1.50
a. Booklet pane, 2 #1883A, 6 #1884 12.50
Complete booklet, #1884a 12.50
b. Booklet pane, 4 #1883A, 12 #1884 25.00
Complete booklet, #1884b 25.00

Argentine Engineers' Center, Cent. A851

1995, June 3 *Perf. 13½*

1885 A851 75c multicolored 1.50

Jose Marti (1853-95) — A852

Design: No. 1887, Antonio Jose de Sucre (1795-1830).

1995, Aug. 12 Litho. *Perf. 13½*

1886 A852 1p multicolored 2.00
1887 A852 1p multicolored 2.00

Fauna — A853

1995, Sept. 1 Litho. *Perf. 13½*

1888 A853 5c Ostrich .15
1889 A853 25c Penguin .50
1890 A853 50c Toucan 1.00
1891 A853 75c Condor 1.50
1892 A853 1p Owl 2.00
1893 A853 2p Bigua 4.00
1894 A853 2.75p Tero 5.50

Booklet Stamps

1895 A853 25c Alligator .50
1896 A853 50c Fox 1.00
1897 A853 75c Anteater 1.50
1898 A853 75c Deer 1.50
1899 A853 75c Whale 1.50
a. Booklet pane, 1 each Nos. 1889-1891, 1895-1899 9.00
Complete booklet, #1899a 9.00
Nos. 1888-1899 (12) 20.65

Native Heritage — A854

Designs: a, Cave drawings, shifting sands. b, Stone mask. c, Anthropomorphous vessel. d, Woven textile.

1995, Sept. 9

1900 A854 75c Block of 4, #a.-d. 6.00

Sunflower, Postal Service Emblem — A855

1995, Oct. 7

1901 A855 75c multicolored 1.50

Juan D. Peron (1895-1974) — A856

1995, Oct. 7

1902 A856 75c lt ol bis & dk bl 1.50

Miniature Sheet

Anniversaries — A857

Designs: a, UN, 50th anniv. b, ICAO, 50th anniv. (in 1994). c, FAO, 50th anniv. d, ILO, 75th anniv. (in 1994).

1995, Oct. 14 *Perf. 12*

1903 A857 75c Sheet of 4, #a.-d. 6.00

Christmas and New Year — A858

Designs: Nos. 1904, 1908, Christmas tree, presents. No. 1905, "1996." No. 1906, Champagne glasses. No. 1907, Present.

1995, Nov. 25 Litho. *Perf. 13½*

1904 A858 75c multicolored 1.50

Booklet Stamps

Perf. 13½ on 1 or 2 Sides

1905 A858 75c multicolored 1.50
1906 A858 75c multicolored 1.50
1907 A858 75c multicolored 1.50
1908 A858 75c multicolored 1.50
a. Booklet pane, #1905-1908 + label 6.00
Complete booklet, #1908a 6.00
Nos. 1904-1908 (5) 7.50

No. 1908a is a continuous design. Ribbon extends from edge to edge on #1908 and stops at edge of package on #1904.

Miniature Sheet

Motion Pictures, Cent. — A859

Black and white film clips, director: a, The Battleship Potemkin, Sergei Eisenstein (Soviet Union). b, Casablanca, Michael Curtiz (US). c, Bicycle Thief, Vittorio De Sica (Italy). d, Limelights, Charles Chaplin (England). e, The 400 Blows, Francois Truffaut (France). f, Chronicle of the Lonely Child, Leonardo Favio (Argentina).

1995, Dec. 2 *Perf. 13½*

1909 A859 75c Sheet of 6, #a.-f. 9.00

The Sky — A860

1995, Dec. 16 *Perf. 13½ on 3 Sides*

Booklet Stamps

1910	A860	25c	Dirigible	.50
1911	A860	25c	Kite	.50
1912	A860	25c	Hot air balloon	.50
1913	A860	50c	Balloons	1.00
1914	A860	50c	Paper airplane	1.00
1915	A860	75c	Airplane	1.50
1916	A860	75c	Helicopter	1.50
1917	A860	75c	Parachute	1.50
a.			Booklet pane, #1910-1917 + label	8.00
			Complete booklet, No. 1917a	8.00
			Nos. 1910-1917 (8)	8.00

Nos. 1910-1917 do not appear in Scott number order in No. 1917a, which has a continuous design.

America Issue A861

Postal vehicles from Postal and Telegraph Museum: No. 1918, Horse and carriage. No. 1919, Truck.

1995, Dec. 16 *Perf. 13½*

1918	A861	75c	multicolored	1.50
1919	A861	75c	multicolored	1.50

SEMI-POSTAL STAMPS

Samuel F. B. Morse — SP1

Globe — SP2

Landing of Columbus — SP5

Map of Argentina — SP6

Designs: 10c+5c, Alexander Graham Bell. 25c+15c, Rowland Hill.

Wmk. RA in Sun (90)

1944, Jan. 5 **Litho.** *Perf. 13*

B1	SP1	3c +2c lt vio & sl bl	.35	.25
B2	SP2	5c +5c dl red & sl bl	.65	.20
B3	SP1	10c +5c org & slate bl	1.25	.70
B4	SP1	25c +15c red brn & sl bl	1.75	1.10
B5	SP5	1p +50c lt grn & sl bl	8.00	7.25
		Nos. B1-B5 (5)	12.00	9.50

The surtax was for the Postal Employees Benefit Association.

1944, Feb. 17 **Wmk. 90** *Perf. 13*

B6	SP6	5c +10c ol yel & slate	.75	.50
B7	SP6	5c +50c vio brn & slate	3.25	2.00
B8	SP6	5c +1p dl org & slate	9.00	6.50
B9	SP6	5c +20p dp bl & slate	22.50	15.00
		Nos. B6-B9 (4)	35.50	24.00

The surtax was for the victims of the San Juan earthquake.

Souvenir Sheets

National Anthem and Flag — SP7

Illustration reduced.

1944, July 17 *Imperf.*

B10	SP7	5c +1p vio brn & lt bl	1.90	1.90
B11	SP7	5c +50p bl blk & lt bl	350.00	250.00

Surtax for the needy in the provinces of La Rioja and Catamarca.

> Catalogue values for unused stamps in this section, from this point to the end of the section, are for Never Hinged items.

Stamp Designing — SP8

1950, Aug. 26 **Photo.** *Perf. 13½*

B12	SP8	10c +10c violet	.24	.24
		Nos. B12,CB1-CB5 (6)	20.42	15.61

Argentine Intl. Philatelic Exhibition, 1950.

Poliomyelitis Victim — SP9

1956, Apr. 14 *Perf. 13½x13*

B13	SP9	20c +30c slate	.30	.15

The surtax was for the poliomyelitis fund. Head in design is from Correggio's "Antiope," Louvre.

Stamp of 1858 and Mail Coach on Raft — SP10

Designs: 2.40p+1.20p, Album, magnifying glass and stamp of 1858. 4.40p+2.20p, Government seat of Confederation, Parana.

1958, Mar. 29 **Litho.** *Perf. 13½*

B14	SP10	40c +20c brt grn & dl pur	.32	.24
B15	SP10	2.40p +1.20p ol gray & bl	.40	.26
B16	SP10	4.40p +2.20p lt bl & dp claret	.60	.40
		Nos. B14-B16,CB8-CB12 (8)	5.84	4.66

Surtax for Intl. Centennial Philatelic Exhibition, Paraná, Entre Rios, Apr. 19-27.

View of Flooded Land — SP11

1958, Oct. 4 **Photo.** *Perf. 13½*

B17	SP11	40c +20c brown	.15	.15
		Nos. B17,CB13-CB14 (3)	1.20	1.10

The surtax was for flood victims in the Buenos Aires district.

Child Receiving Blood — SP12

Runner — SP13

1958, Dec. 20 **Litho.** **Wmk. 90**

B18	SP12	1p +50c blk & rose red	.20	.15

The surtax went to the Anti-Leukemia Foundation.

1959, Sept. 5 *Perf. 13½*

Designs: 50c+20c, Basketball players, vert. 1p+50c, Boxers, vert.

B19	SP13	20c +10c emer & blk	.20	.16
B20	SP13	50c +20c yel & blk	.15	.15
B21	SP13	1p +50c mar & blk	.20	.16
		Nos. B19-B21,CB15-CB16 (5)	1.55	1.21

3rd Pan American Games, Chicago, Aug. 27-Sept. 7, 1959.

Condor — SP14

Birds: 50c+20c, Fork-tailed flycatchers. 1p+50c, Magellanic woodpecker.

1960, Feb. 6

B22	SP14	20c +10c dk bl	.15	.15
B23	SP14	50c +20c dp vio bl	.15	.15
B24	SP14	1p +50c brn & buff	.20	.15
		Nos. B22-B24,CB17-CB18 (5)	1.25	
		Set value		.72

The surtax was for child welfare work. See Nos. B30, CB29.

Souvenir Sheet

Uprooted Oak Emblem — SP15

1960, Apr. 7 **Wmk. 90** *Imperf.*

B25	SP15	Sheet of 2	1.25	1.25
a.		1p + 50c bister & carmine	.55	.55
b.		4.20p + 2.10p apple grn & dp claret	.55	.55

WRY, July 1, 1959-June 30, 1960.
The surtax was for aid to refugees.

Jacaranda — SP16

Flowers: 1p+1p, Passionflower. 3p+3p, Orchid. 5p+5p, Tabebuia.

1960, Dec. 3 **Photo.** *Perf. 13½*

B26	SP16	50c +50c deep blue	.15	.15
B27	SP16	1p +1p bluish grn	.15	.15
B28	SP16	3p +3p henna brn	.32	.22
B29	SP16	5p +5p dark brn	.52	.35
		Nos. B26-B29 (4)	1.14	
		Set value		.70

"TEMEX 61" (Intl. Thematic Exposition).
For overprints see Nos. B31-B34.

Type of 1960

Bird: 4.20p+2.10p, Blue-eyed shag.

1961, Feb. 25 **Wmk. 90** *Perf. 13½*

B30	SP14	4.20p +2.10p chestnut brn	.48	.32

Surtax for child welfare work. See #CB29.

Nos. B26-B29 Overprinted in Black, Brown, Blue or Red: "14 DE ABRIL DIA DE LAS AMERICAS"

1961, Apr. 15

B31	SP16	50c +50c deep blue	.15	.15
B32	SP16	1p +1p bluish grn (Brn)	.15	.15
B33	SP16	3p +3p henna brn (Bl)	.32	.25
B34	SP16	5p +5p dk brn (R)	.52	.42
		Nos. B31-B34 (4)	1.14	.97

Day of the Americas, Apr. 14.

Cathedral, Cordoba — SP17

Stamp of 1862 — SP18

Flight into Egypt, by Ana Maria Moncalvo — SP19

Design: 10p+10p, Cathedral, Buenos Aires.

Perf. 13½

1961, Oct. 21 **Wmk. 90** **Photo.**

B35	SP17	2p +2p rose claret	.22	.15
B36	SP18	3p +3p green	.32	.18
B37	SP17	10p +10p brt blue	.90	.52
a.		Souvenir sheet of 3	1.75	1.10
		Nos. B35-B37 (3)	1.44	.85

1962 International Stamp Exhibition.
No. B37a contains three imperf. stamps similar to Nos. B35-B37 in dark blue.

1961, Dec. 16 **Litho.**

B38	SP19	2p +1p lilac & blk brn	.15	.15
B39	SP19	10p +5p light & deep claret	.52	.15
		Set value		.22

The surtax was for child welfare.

Chalk-browed Mockingbird — SP20

Soccer — SP21

Design: 12p+6p, Rufous-collared sparrow.

1962, Dec. 29 *Perf. 13½*

B40	SP20	4p +2p bis, brn & bl grn	.90	.60
B41	SP20	12p +6p gray, yel, grn & brn	1.50	1.10

The surtax was for child welfare. See Nos. B44, B47, B48-B50, CB32, CB35-CB36.

1963, May 18 *Perf. 13½*

B42 SP21 4p +2p multi .22 .15
B43 SP21 12p +6p Horsemanship .45 .35
a. Dark carmine (jacket) omitted
Nos. B42-B43,CB31 (3) 1.22 1.00

4th Pan American Games, Sao Paulo.

Bird Type of 1962

Design: Vermilion flycatcher.

1963, Dec. 21 **Litho.**

B44 SP20 4p +2p blk, red, org & grn .60 .28

The surtax was for child welfare. See No. CB32.

Fencers — SP22

Design: 4p+2p, National Stadium, Tokyo, horiz.

1964, July 18 **Wmk. 90** *Perf. 13½*

B45 SP22 4p +2p red, ocher & brn .16 .15
B46 SP22 12p +6p bl grn & blk .40 .32
Nos. B45-B46,CB33 (3) 1.06 .97

18th Olympic Games, Tokyo, Oct. 10-25, 1964. See No. CB33.

Bird Type of 1962

Design: Red-crested cardinal.

1964, Dec. 23 **Litho.**

B47 SP20 4p +2p dk bl, red & grn .60 .30

The surtax was for child welfare. See #CB35.

Bird Type of 1962
Inscribed "R. ARGENTINA"

Designs: 8p+4p, Lapwing. 10p+5p, Scarlet-headed marshbird, horiz. 20p+10p, Amazon kingfisher.

1966-67 *Perf. 13½*

B48 SP20 8p +4p blk, ol, brt grn & red .80 .35
B49 SP20 10p +5p blk, bl, org & grn .80 .55
B50 SP20 20p +10p blk, yel, bl & pink .40 .35
Nos. B48-B50,CB36,CB38-CB39 (6) 4.30 3.25

The surtax was for child welfare.
Issue dates: 8p+4p, Mar. 26, 1966. 10p+5p, Jan. 14, 1967. 20p+10p, Dec. 23, 1967.

Grandmother's Birthday, by Patricia Lynch; Lions Emblem — SP23

Perf. 12½x13½

1968, Dec. 14 **Litho.** **Wmk. 90**

B51 SP23 40p + 20p multi .45 .38

1st Lions Intl. Benevolent Phil. Exhib. Surtax for the Children's Hospital Benevolent Fund.

White-faced Tree Duck — SP24

1969, Sept. 20 **Wmk. 365** *Perf. 13½*

B52 SP24 20p + 10p multi .48 .35

Surtax for child welfare. See No. CB40.

Slender-tailed Woodstar (Hummingbird) SP25

1970, May 9 **Wmk. 365** *Perf. 13½*

B53 SP25 20c + 10c multi .45 .40

The surtax was for child welfare. See Nos. CB41, B56-B59, B62-B63.

Dolphinfish — SP26

1971, Feb. 20 **Unwmk.** *Perf. 12½*
Size: 75x15mm

B54 SP26 20c + 10c multi .52 .45

Surtax for child welfare. See No. CB42.

Children with Stamps, by Mariette Lydis — SP27

1971, Dec. 18 **Litho.** *Perf. 13½*

B55 SP27 1p + 50p multi .48 .32

2nd Lions Intl. Solidarity Stamp Exhib.

Bird Type of 1970

Birds: 25c+10c, Saffron finch. 65c+30c, Rufous-bellied thrush, horiz.

1972, May 6 **Unwmk.** *Perf. 13½*

B56 SP25 25c + 10c multi .32 .20
B57 SP25 65c + 30c multi .45 .32

Surtax was for child welfare.

Bird Type of 1970

Birds: 50c+25c, Southern screamer (chaja). 90c+45c, Saffron-cowled blackbird, horiz.

1973, Apr. 28

B58 SP25 50c + 25c multi .48 .32
B59 SP25 90c + 45c multi .70 .48

Surtax was for child welfare.

Painting Type of Regular Issue

Designs: 15c+15c, Still Life, by Alfredo Guttero, horiz. 90c+90c, Nude, by Miguel C. Victorica, horiz.

1973, Aug. 28 **Litho.** *Perf. 13½*

B60 A472 15c + 15c multi .28 .18
B61 A472 90c + 90c multi 1.00 .70

Bird Type of 1970

Birds: 70c+30c, Blue seed-eater. 1.20p+60c, Hooded siskin.

1974, May 11 **Litho.** *Perf. 13½*

B62 SP25 70c + 30c multi .50 .35
B63 SP25 1.20p + 60c multi .75 .42

Surtax was for child welfare.

Painting Type of 1974

Design: 70c+30c, The Lama, by Juan Batlle Planas.

1974, May 11 **Litho.** *Perf. 13½*

B64 A477 70c + 30c multi .28 .22

PRENFIL-74 UPU, Intl. Exhib. of Phil. Periodicals, Buenos Aires, Oct. 1-12.

Plushcrested Jay — SP28

Designs: 13p+6.50p, Golden-collared macaw. 20p+10p, Begonia. 40p+20p, Teasel.

1976, June 12 **Litho.** *Perf. 13½*

B65 SP28 7p + 3.50p multi .20 .15
B66 SP28 13p + 6.50p multi .32 .20
B67 SP28 20p + 10p multi .48 .32
B68 SP28 40p + 20p multi .95 .48
Nos. B65-B68 (4) 1.95 1.15

Argentine philately.

Telegraph, Communications Satellite — SP29

Designs: 20p+10p, Old and new mail trucks. 60p+30p, Old, new packet boats. 70p+35p, Biplane and jet.

1977, July 16 **Litho.** *Perf. 13½*

B69 SP29 10p + 5p multi .30 .20
B70 SP29 20p + 10p multi .50 .60
B71 SP29 60p + 30p multi 1.00 .85
B72 SP29 70p + 35p multi 1.25 .85
Nos. B69-B72 (4) 3.05 2.50

Surtax was for Argentine philately.
No. B70 exists with wmk. 365.

Church of St. Francis Type, 1977,
Inscribed: "EXPOSICION ARGENTINA '77"

1977, Aug. 27

B73 A515 160p + 80p multi 2.50 2.00

Surtax was for Argentina '77 Philatelic Exhibition. Issued in sheets of 4.

No. B73 Overprinted with Soccer Cup Emblem

1978, Feb. 4 **Litho.** *Perf. 13½*

B74 A515 160p + 80p multi 4.50 4.25
a. Souvenir sheet of 4 20.00 19.00

11th World Cup Soccer Championship, Argentina, June 1-25.

Spinus Magellanicus SP30

Birds: 100p+100p, Variable seedeater. 150p+150p, Yellow thrush. 200p+200p, Pyrocephalus rubineus. 500p+500p, Great kiskadee.

1978, Aug. 5 **Litho.** *Perf. 13½*

B75 SP30 50p + 50p multi .90 .60
B76 SP30 100p + 100p multi 1.10 .90
B77 SP30 150p + 150p multi 1.40 1.25
B78 SP30 200p + 200p multi 1.75 1.75
B79 SP30 500p + 500p multi 8.50 7.25
Nos. B75-B79 (5) 13.65 11.75

ARGENTINA '78, Inter-American Philatelic Exhibition, Buenos Aires, Oct. 27-Nov. 5. Nos. B75-B79 issued in sheets of 4 with marginal inscriptions commemorating Exhibition and 1978 Soccer Championship.

Caravel "Magdalena," 16th Century — SP31

Sailing Ships: 500+500p, 3 master "Rio de la Plata," 17th cent. 600+600p, Corvette "Descubierta," 18th cent. 1500+1500p, Naval Academy yacht "A.R.A. Fortuna," 1979.

1979, Sept. 8 **Litho.** *Perf. 13½*

B80 SP31 400p +400p multi 4.00 2.25
B81 SP31 500p +500p multi 4.75 2.50
B82 SP31 600p +600p multi 6.00 3.25
B83 SP31 1500p +1500p multi 15.00 8.00
Nos. B80-B83 (4) 29.75 16.00

Buenos Aires '80, International Philatelic Exhibition, Oct. 24-Nov. 2, 1980. Issued in sheets of 4.

Purmamarca Church — SP32

Churches: 200p + 100p, Molinos. 300p + 150p, Animana. 400p + 200p, San Jose de Lules.

1979, Nov. 3 **Litho.** *Perf. 13½*

B84 SP32 100p + 50p multi .25 .15
B85 SP32 200p + 100p multi .45 .15
B86 SP32 300p + 150p multi .60 .18
B87 SP32 400p + 200p multi .90 .24
Nos. B84-B87 (4) 2.20
Set value .62

Buenos Aires No. 3, Exhibition and Society Emblems — SP33

Argentine Stamps: 750p+750p, type A580. 1000p+1000p, No. 91. 2000p+2000p, type A588.

1979, Dec. 15 **Litho.** *Perf. 13½*

B88 SP33 250p + 250p multi .90 .70
B89 SP33 750p + 750p multi 2.25 1.75
B90 SP33 1000p + 1000p multi 3.00 2.50
B91 SP33 2000p + 2000p multi 6.00 5.00
Nos. B88-B91 (4) 12.15 9.95

PRENFIL '80, Intl. Philatelic Literature and Publications Exhib., Buenos Aires, Nov. 7-16, 1980.

Minuet, by Carlos E. Pellegrini SP34

Paintings: 700p+350p, Media Cana, by Carlos Morel. 800p+400p, Cielito, by Pellegrini. 1000p+500p, El Gato, by Juan Leon Palliere.

1981, July 11 **Litho.** *Perf. 13½*

B92 SP34 500p + 250p multi .70 .35
B93 SP34 700p + 350p multi 1.00 .70
B94 SP34 800p + 400p multi 1.10 .90
B95 SP34 1000p + 500p multi 1.40 1.25
Nos. B92-B95 (4) 4.20 3.20

Espamer '81 Intl. Stamp Exhib. (Americas, Spain, Portugal), Buenos Aires, Nov. 13-22.

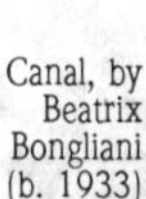

Canal, by Beatrix Bongliani (b. 1933) SP35

Tapestries: 1000p+500p, Shadows, by Silvia Sieburger, vert. 2000p+1000p, Interpretation of a Rectangle, by Silke R. de Haupt, vert. 4000p+2000p, Tilcara, by Tana Sachs.

1982, July 31 Litho. Perf. 13½

B96 SP35 1000p + 500p multi	.20	.20
B97 SP35 2000p + 1000p multi	.40	.40
B98 SP35 3000p + 1500p multi	.60	.60
B99 SP35 4000p + 2000p multi	.80	.80
Nos. B96-B99 (4)	2.00	2.00

Boy Playing Marbles — SP36

1983, July 2 Litho. Perf. 13½

B100 SP36 20c + 10c shown	.20	.15
B101 SP36 30c + 15c Jumping rope	.45	.16
B102 SP36 50c + 25c Hopscotch	.85	.20
B103 SP36 1p + 50c Flying kites	1.10	.48
B104 SP36 2p + 1p Spinning top	1.65	.65
Nos. B100-B104 (5)	4.25	1.64

Surtax was for natl. philatelic associations.
See Nos. B106-B110.

Compass, 15th Cent. SP37

ARGENTINA '85 Intl. Stamp Show: b, Arms of Spain, Argentina. c, Columbus' arms. d-f, Columbus' arrival at San Salvador Island. Nos. B105d-B105f in continuous design; ships shown on singles range in size, left to right, from small to large. Surtax was for exhibition.

1984, Apr. 28 Litho. Perf. 13½

B105 Block of 6	3.75	3.75
a.-f. SP37 5p + 2.50p, any single	.52	.26

Children's Game Type of 1983

1984, July 7 Litho. Perf. 13½

B106 SP36 2p + 1p Blind Man's Buff	.15	.15
B107 SP36 3p + 1.50p The Loop	.30	.24
B108 SP36 4p + 2p Leap Frog	.35	.30
B109 SP36 5p + 2.50p Rolling the loop	.45	.35
B110 SP36 6p + 3p Ball Mold	.55	.45
Nos. B106-B110 (5)	1.80	1.49

Butterflies SP38

1985, Nov. 9 Litho. Perf. 13½

B111 SP38 5c + 2c Rothschildia jacobaeae	.20	.15
B112 SP38 10c + 5c Heliconius erato phyllis	.45	.30
B113 SP38 20c + 10c Precis evarete hilaris	.85	.60
B114 SP38 25c + 13c Cyanopepla pretiosa	1.10	.75
B115 SP38 40c + 20c Papilio androgeus	1.65	1.10
Nos. B111-B115 (5)	4.25	2.90

Children's Drawings SP39

1986, Aug. 30 Litho.

B116 SP39 5c + 2c N. Pastor	.15	.15
B117 SP39 10c + 5c T. Valleistein	.30	.30
B118 SP39 20c + 10c J.M. Flores	.60	.60
B119 SP39 25c + 13c M.E. Pezzuto	.75	.75
B120 SP39 40c + 20c E. Diehl	1.10	1.10
Nos. B116-B120 (5)	2.90	2.90

Surtax for natl. philatelic associations.

Miniature Sheets

Fresh-water Fish — SP40

No. B121: a, Metynnis maculatus. b, Cynolebias nigripinnis. c, Leporinus solarii. d, Aphyocharax rathbuni. e, Corydoras aeneus. f, Thoracocharax securis. g, Cynolebias melanotaenia. h, Cichlasoma facetum.

No. B122: a, Tetragonopterus argenteus. b, Hemigrammus caudovittatus. c, Astyanax bimaculatus. d, Gymnocorymbus ternetzi. e, Hoplias malabaricus. f, Aphyocharax rubripinnis. g, Apistogramma agassizi. h, Pyrrhulina rachoviana.

1987, June 27

B121 Sheet of 8	2.00	
a.-h. SP40 10c +5c, any single	.25	
B122 Sheet of 8	4.00	
a.-h. SP40 20c +10c, any single	.50	

PRENFIL '88, Intl. Philatelic Literature and Media Exhibition, Buenos Aires, Nov. 25-Dec. 2 — SP41

Locomotives and railroad car: No. B123, Yatay locomotive, 1888. No. B124, FCCA electric passenger car, 1914. No. B125, B-15 locomotive, 1942. No. B126, GT-22 No. 200 locomotive, 1988.

1988, June 4 Litho. Perf. 13½

B123 SP41 1a +50c multi	.65
B124 SP41 1a +50c multi	.65
B125 SP41 1a +50c multi	.65
B126 SP41 1a +50c multi	.65
Nos. B123-B126 (4)	2.60

Nos. B123-B125 each issued in sheets of 4.

Horses SP42

Paintings: No. B127, *The Waiting*, by Gustavo Solari. No. B128, *Mare and Foal*, by E. Castro. No. B129, *Saint Isidor*, by Castro. No. B130, *At Lagoon's Edge*, by F. Romero Carranza. No. B131, *Under the Tail*, by Castro.

1988, Oct. 29 Litho. Perf. 13½

B127 SP42 2a +1a multi	.70
B128 SP42 2a +1a multi	.70
B129 SP42 2a +1a multi	.70
B130 SP42 2a +1a multi	.70
B131 SP42 2a +1a multi	.70
Nos. B127-B131 (5)	3.50

PRENFIL '88 — SP43

Covers of philatelic magazines.

1988, Nov. 26 Litho. Perf. 13½

B132 SP43 1a +1a *Cronaca Filatelica*, Italy	.32
B133 SP43 1a +1a *CO-FI*, Brazil	.32
B134 SP43 1a +1a *References de la Poste*, France	.32
B135 SP43 2a +2a *Postas Argentinas*	.65
Nos. B132-B135 (4)	1.61

Souvenir Sheet

ARBRAPEX '88 — SP44

Designs: No. B136a, *Candel Delivery at San Ignacio*, by Leonie Matthis, Cornelio Saavedra Museum, Buenos Aires. No. B136b, *Immaculate Conception*, a statue in the Isaac Fernandez Blanco Museum, Buenos Aires.

1988, Nov. 26 Perf. 12

B136 SP44 Sheet of 2	1.60
a. 2a +2a multi	.65
b. 3a +3a multi	.95

Fish SP45

Designs: No. B137, *Diplomystes viedmensis*. No. B138, *Haplochiton taeniatus*. No. B139, *Percichthys trucha*. No. B140, *Galaxias platei*. No. B141, *Salmo fario*.

1989, June 24 Litho. Perf. 13½

B137 SP45 10a +5a multi	.15
B138 SP45 10a +5a multi	.15
B139 SP45 10a +5a multi	.15
B140 SP45 10a +5a multi	.15
B141 SP45 10a +5a multi	.15
Set value	.50

Printed in sheets of 4.

Discovery of America 500th Anniv. (in 1992) and ESPAMER '90 — SP46

Documents and chronicles: No. B142, Columbus's coat of arms, *Book of Privileges* title page. No. B143, Illustration from *New Chronicle and Good Government*, by Guaman Poma de Ayala. No. B144, Illustration from *Discovery and Conquest of Peru*, by Pedro de Cieza de Leon. No. B145, Illustration from *Travel to the River Plate*, by Ulrico Schmidl.

1989, Sept. 16 Litho. Perf. 13½
Yellow, Rose Violet & Black

B142 SP46 100a +50a
B143 SP46 150a +50a
B144 SP46 200a +100a
B145 SP46 250a +100a

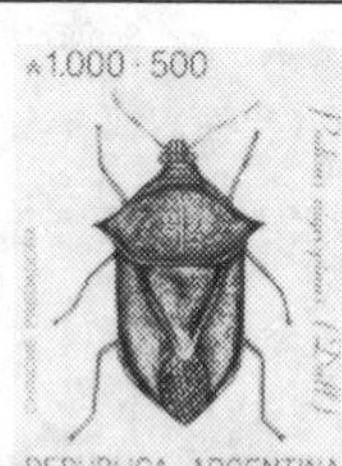

Insects — SP47

Designs: No. B146, *Podisus nigrispinus*. No. B147, *Adalia bipunctata*. No. B148, *Nabis punctipennis*. No. B149, *Hippodamia convergens*. No. B150, *Calleida suturalis*.

1990, June 30 Litho. Perf. 13½

B146 SP47 1000a +500a multi
B147 SP47 1000a +500a multi
B148 SP47 1000a +500a multi
B149 SP47 1000a +500a multi
B150 SP47 1000a +500a multi

Souvenir Sheet

First Natl. Exposition of Aerophilately — SP48

Designs: a, Lieut. Marcos A. Zar, Macchi seaplane. b, Capt. Antonio Parodi, Ansaldo SVA biplane. (Illustration reduced).

1990, July 14 Litho. Perf. 12

B151 Sheet of 2
a. SP48 2000a +2000a multi
b. SP48 3000a +3000a multi

Souvenir Sheet

1992 Summer Olympics, Barcelona SP49

Designs: a, Shot put. b, High jump. c, Hurdles. d, Pole vault.

1990, Dec. 15 Litho. Perf. 13½

B152 Sheet of 4
a.-d. SP49 2000a +2000a multi

Espamer '91 Philatelic Exhibition.
See No. B155.

Souvenir Sheet

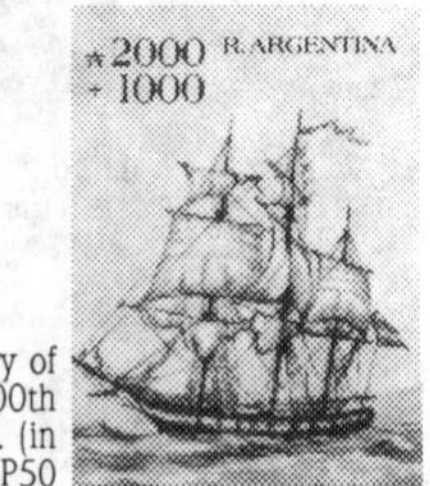

Discovery of America, 500th Anniv. (in 1992) — SP50

Voyage of Alesandro Malaspina, 1789-1794: a, Sailing ship. b, Malaspina. c, Indian, hut. d, Indian, horse, artist drawing.

1990, Oct. 13 Litho. Perf. 13½

B153 Sheet of 4	6.00
a.-d. SP50 2000a +1000a, any single	1.50

Espamer '91, Buenos Aires.

Souvenir Sheet

Race Cars and Drivers — SP51

Designs: a, Juan Manuel Fangio. b, Juan Manuel Bordeu. c, Carlos Alberto Reutemann. d, Oscar and Juan Galvez.

1991 Litho. *Perf. 13½*
B154 SP51 Sheet of 4 4.80
a.-d. 2500a +2500a, any single 1.20

Espamer '91.

Souvenir Sheet
1992 Summer Olympics Type of 1990

Women's gymnastics routines: a, Floor exercise. b, Uneven parallel bars. c, Balance beam. d, Rhythmic gymnastics.

1991, June 29 Litho. *Perf. 13½*
B155 Sheet of 4 4.80
a.-d. SP49 2500a +2500a, any single 1.20

Espamer '91.

Iberoprenfil '92
SP52

Designs: No. B156, Castor missile. No. B157, Satellite LUSAT 1.

1991, Dec. 28 Litho. *Perf. 13½*
B156 SP52 4000a +4000a multi 2.00
B157 SP52 4000a +4000a multi 2.00

Dinosaurs — SP53

1992, May 2 Litho. *Perf. 13½*
B158 SP53 38c +38c Carnotaurus 1.90
B159 SP53 38c +38c Amargasaurus 1.90

Iberoprenfil '92, Buenos Aires
SP54

Paintings by Raul Soldi (b. 1905): No. B160, The Fiesta. No. B161, Church of St. Anne of Glew.

1992, Sept. 5 Litho. *Perf. 13½*
B160 SP54 76c +76c multi 3.75
B161 SP54 76c +76c multi 3.75

Parafil '92 — SP55

1992, Nov. 21 Litho. *Perf. 13½*
B162 SP55 76c +76c multi 3.60

2nd Argentine-Paraguayan Philatelic Exhibition, Buenos Aires.

Souvenir Sheet

Birds — SP56

Designs: a, Egretta thula. b, Amblyramphus holosericeus. c, Paroaria coronata. d, Chloroceryle amazona.

1993, July 17 Litho. *Perf. 13½*
B163 SP56 38c +38c Sheet of 4 7.25

Souvenir Sheet

Latin American Air Post Philatelic Exhibition — SP57

Designs: a, 25c+25c, Antoine de Saint-Exupery (1940-44), pilot, author. b, 75c+75c, "The Little Prince," vert. Illustration reduced.

1995, June 3 Litho. *Perf. 12*
B164 SP57 Sheet of 2, #a.-b. 4.00

Souvenir Sheet

Exploration of Antarctica
SP58

Designs: 75c+25c, Transport ship ARA Bahia Aguirre. 1.25p+75c, Argentine Air Force Hercules C-130.

1995, July 8
B165 SP58 Sheet of 2, #a.-b. 6.00

AIR POST STAMPS

Airplane Circles the Globe — AP1

Eagle — AP2

Wings Cross the Sea — AP3

Condor on Mountain Crag — AP4

Perforations of Nos. C1-C37 vary from clean-cut to rough and uneven, with many skipped perfs.

Perf. 13x13½, 13½x13

1928, Mar. 1 Litho. Wmk. 90

C1	AP1	5c	lt red	1.25	.50
C2	AP1	10c	Prus blue	2.25	1.00
C3	AP2	15c	lt brown	2.25	.80
C4	AP1	18c	lilac gray	3.00	2.75
a.			18c brown lilac	3.25	2.75
b.			Double impression	375.00	
C5	AP2	20c	ultra	2.25	.80
C6	AP2	24c	deep blue	3.50	2.75
C7	AP3	25c	brt violet	3.50	1.50
C8	AP3	30c	rose red	5.25	1.00
C9	AP4	35c	rose	3.50	1.00
C10	AP1	36c	bister brn	2.50	1.50
C11	AP4	50c	gray black	4.00	.50
C12	AP2	54c	chocolate	3.50	2.00
C13	AP2	72c	yellow grn	4.75	2.00
a.			Double impression	300.00	
C14	AP3	90c	dk brown	9.00	1.75
C15	AP3	1p	slate bl & red	11.00	.65
C16	AP3	1.08p	rose & dk bl	16.00	4.50
C17	AP4	1.26p	dull vio & grn	20.00	8.00
C18	AP4	1.80p	blue & lil rose	20.00	8.00
C19	AP4	3.60p	gray & blue	42.50	19.00
			Nos. C1-C19 (19)	160.00	60.00

The watermark on No. C4a is larger than on the other stamps of this set, measuring 10mm across Sun.

Zeppelin First Flight

Air Post Stamps of 1928 Overprinted in Blue

1930, May

C20	AP2	20c	ultra	10.00	5.00
C21	AP4	50c	gray black	20.00	10.00
a.			Inverted overprint	475.00	
C22	AP3	1p	slate bl & red	21.00	10.00
a.			Inverted overprint	550.00	
C23	AP4	1.80p	blue & lil rose	55.00	25.00
C24	AP4	3.60p	gray & blue	150.00	70.00
			Nos. C20-C24 (5)	256.00	120.00

Overprinted in Green

C25	AP2	20c	ultra	10.00	6.00
C26	AP4	50c	gray black	12.50	9.00
C27	AP3	90c	dark brown	10.00	6.00
C28	AP3	1p	slate bl & red	20.00	12.50
C29	AP4	1.80p	blue & lil rose	600.00	400.00
a.			Thick paper	750.00	
			Nos. C25-C29 (5)	652.50	433.50

Air Post Stamps of 1928 Overprinted in Red or Blue

1930
6
Septiembre
-1931-
On AP1-AP2

6 de Septiembre
1930 — 1931
On AP3-AP4

1931

C30	AP1	18c	lilac gray	2.00	1.50
C31	AP2	72c	yellow green	14.00	10.50
C32	AP3	90c	dark brown	14.00	10.50
C33	AP4	1.80p	bl & lil rose (Bl)	30.00	22.50
C34	AP4	3.60p	gray & blue	57.50	40.00
			Nos. C30-C34 (5)	117.50	85.00

1st anniv. of the Revolution of 1930.

Zeppelin Issue

Nos. C1, C4, C4a, C14 Overprinted in Blue or Red

GRAF
ZEPPELIN
1932
On AP1

GRAF ZEPPELIN
1932
On AP3

1932, Aug. 4

C35	AP1	5c	lt red (Bl)	3.00	2.00
C36	AP1	18c	lilac gray (R)	12.50	9.00
a.			18c brown lilac (R)	100.00	60.00
C37	AP3	90c	dark brown (R)	32.50	26.00
			Nos. C35-C37 (3)	48.00	37.00

Plane and Letter — AP5

Mercury — AP6

Plane in Flight — AP7

Perf. 13½x13, 13x13½

1940, Oct. 23 Photo. Wmk. 90

C38	AP5	30c	deep orange	5.00	.15
C39	AP6	50c	dark brown	7.50	.20
C40	AP5	1p	carmine	1.75	.15
C41	AP7	1.25p	deep green	.50	.15
C42	AP5	2.50p	bright blue	1.25	.20
			Nos. C38-C42 (5)	16.00	
			Set value		.70

Plane and Letter — AP8

Mercury and Plane — AP9

Perf. 13½x13, 13x13½

1942, Oct. 6 Litho. Wmk. 90

C43	AP8	30c	orange	.15	.15
C44	AP9	50c	dull brn & buff	.40	.15
			Set value		.15

See Nos. C49-C52, C57, C61.

Plane over Iguaç u Falls — AP10

Plane over the Andes — AP11

Perf. 13½x13

1946, June 10 Unwmk.

C45	AP10	15c	dull red brn	.25	.15
C46	AP11	25c	gray green	.15	.15
			Set value		.15

See Nos. C53-C54.

Allegory of Flight — AP12

Astrolabe — AP13

Perf. 13½x13, 13x13½

1946, Sept. 25 Litho. Unwmk.

Surface-Tinted Paper

C47	AP12	15c	sl grn, *pale grn*	.55	.15
C48	AP13	60c	vio brn, *ocher*	.55	.35

Types of 1942

1946-48 Unwmk. Perf. 13½x13

C49 AP8 30c orange 1.40 .15
C50 AP9 50c dull brn & buff 2.50 .15
C51 AP8 1p carmine ('47) 1.25 .15
C52 AP8 2.50p brt blue ('48) 5.50 .75
Nos. C49-C52 (4) 10.65 1.20

Types of 1946

1948 Wmk. 90

C53 AP10 15c dull red brn .15 .15
C54 AP11 25c gray green .25 .15
Set value .15

Atlas (National Museum, Naples) — AP14

Map of Argentine Republic, Globe and Caliper AP15

Perf. 13½x13, 13x13½

1948-49 Photo. Wmk. 288

C55 AP14 45c dk brown ('49) .35 .20
C56 AP15 70c dark green .50 .25

4th Pan-American Reunion of Cartographers, Buenos Aires, Oct.-Nov., 1948.

Mercury Type of 1942

1949 Litho. Perf. 13x13½

C57 AP9 50c dull brn & buff .40 .15

Marksmanship Trophy — AP16

1949, Nov. 4 Photo.

C58 AP16 75c brown .75 .20

World Rifle Championship, 1949.

Catalogue values for unused stamps in this section, from this point to the end of the section, are for Never Hinged items.

Douglas DC-3 and Condor AP17

Perf. 13x13½

1951, June 20 Wmk. 90

C59 AP17 20c dk olive grn .20 .15

10th anniversary of the State air lines.

Douglas DC-6 and Condor — AP18

1951, Oct. 17 Perf. 13½

C60 AP18 20c blue .20 .15

End of Argentine 5-year Plan.

Plane-Letter Type of 1942

1951 Litho. Perf. 13½x13

C61 AP8 1p carmine .40 .15

Jesus by Leonardo da Vinci (detail, "Virgin of the Rocks") — AP19

Perf. 13½x13

1956, Sept. 29 Photo. Wmk. 90

C62 AP19 1p dull purple .35 .15

Issued to express the gratitude of the children of Argentina to the people of the world for their help against poliomyelitis.

Battle of Montevideo AP20

Leonardo Rosales and Tomas Espora — AP21

Guillermo Brown — AP22

AP23

1957, Mar. 2 Perf. 13½

C63 AP20 60c blue gray .15 .15
C64 AP21 1p brt pink .15 .15
C65 AP22 2p brown .25 .15
Set value .45 .25

Cent. of the death of Admiral Guillermo Brown, founder of the Argentine navy.

1957, Aug. 16

Map of Americas and Arms of Buenos Aires.

C66 AP23 2p rose violet .42 .20

Issued to publicize the Inter-American Economic Conference in Buenos Aires.

AP24

AP25

1957, Aug. 31 Wmk. 90 Perf. 13½

C67 AP24 60c Modern jlcomotive .15 .15

Centenary of Argentine railroads.

1957, Sept. 14

C68 AP25 1p Globe, Flag,Compass Rose .20 .15
C69 AP25 2p Key .30 .15
Set value .15

1957 International Congress for Tourism.

Birds Carrying Letters — AP26

1957, Nov. 6

C70 AP26 1p bright blue .15 .15

Issued for Letter Writing Week, Oct. 6-12.

Early Plane — AP27

1958, May 31 Perf. 13½

C71 AP27 2p maroon .20 .15

50th anniversary of the Argentine Aviation Club.

Stamp Anniv. Type

Designs: 80c, Stamp of Buenos Aires and view of the Plaza de la Aduana. 1p, Stamp of 1858 and "The Post of Santa Fe."

1958 Litho. Perf. 13½

C72 A270 80c pale bis & sl bl .20 .15
C73 A270 1p red org & dk bl .25 .15

Centenary of the first postage stamps of Buenos Aires and the Argentine Confederation.
Issue dates: 80c, Oct. 18; 1p, Aug. 23.

Comet Jet over World Map AP29

1959, May 16 Perf. 13½

C74 AP29 5p black & olive .35 .15

Inauguration of jet flights by Argentine Airlines.

Type of Regular Issue, 1960.

"Cabildo" and: 1.80p, Mariano Moreno. 5p, Manuel Belgrano and Juan Jose Castelli.

Perf. 13½

1960, May 28 Wmk. 90 Photo.

C75 A287 1.80p red brown .15 .15
a. Souvenir sheet of 3 .65 .40
C76 A287 5p buff & purple .35 .15
a. Souvenir sheet of 3 1.25 .80
Set value .20

Souvenir sheets are imperf. No. C75a contains one No. C75 and 1p and 2p resembling Nos. 713-714; stamps in reddish brown. No. C76a contains one No. C76 and 4.20p and 10.70p resembling Nos. 715-716; stamps are in green.

Symbolic of New Provinces — AP30

1960, July 8 Litho.

C77 AP30 1.80p dp car & blue .15 .15

Elevation of the territories of Chubut, Formosa, Neuquen, Rio Negro and Santa Cruz to provinces.

Type of Regular Issue, 1960

1960, Oct. 1 Photo. Perf. 13½

C78 A291 1.80p rose lilac .15 .15
C79 A291 10.70p brt grnsh blue .40 .15

UNESCO Emblem AP31

1962, July 14 Litho.

C80 AP31 13p ocher & brown .40 .25

15th anniv. of UNESCO.

Mail Coach — AP32

1962, Oct. 6 Wmk. 90 Perf. 13½

C81 AP32 5.60p gray brn & blk .20 .15

Mailman's Day, Sept. 14, 1962.

No. 695 and Type of 1959 Surcharged in Green

AEREO 5.60 PESOS

1962, Oct. 31 Photo.

C82 A277 5.60p on 5p brown .30 .15
C83 A277 18p on 5p brn, *grnsh* 1.00 .20

UPAE Emblem AP33

Skylark AP34

1962, Nov. 24 Photo. Perf. 13½

C84 AP33 5.60p dark blue .20 .15

50th anniv. of the founding of the Postal Union of the Americas and Spain, UPAE.

1963, Feb. 9 Litho.

Design: 11p, Super Albatros.

C85 AP34 5.60p blue & black .20 .15
C86 AP34 11p blue, blk & red .30 .15

9th World Gliding Championships.

Symbolic Plane — AP35

1963-65 Wmk. 90 Perf. 13½

C87 AP35 5.60p dk pur, car & brt grn .40 .15
C88 AP35 7p black & bis ('64) .55 .15
C88A AP35 7p black & bis ('65) 4.00 .55

C89 AP35 11p blk, dk pur & grn .55 .25
C90 AP35 18p dk pur, red & vio bl 1.10 .35
C91 AP35 21p brown, red & gray 1.40 .55
Nos. C87-C91 (6) 8.00 2.00

"Argentina" reads down on No. C88, up on No. C88A. See Nos. C101-C104, C108-C111, C123-C126, C135-C141. For overprint and surcharges see Nos. C96, C146-C150.

Type of Regular Issue, 1964

Design: 18p, Map of Falkland Islands (Islas Malvinas).

1964, Feb. 22 ***Perf. 13½***

Size: 33x22mm

C92 A327 18p lt & dk bl & ol grn 1.75 .70

UPU Monument, Bern, and UN Emblem — AP36

1964, May 23 **Engr.** ***Perf. 13½***

C93 AP36 18p red & dk brown .52 .25

15th UPU Cong., Vienna, Austria, May-June 1964.

Discovery of America, Florentine Woodcut — AP37

1964, Oct. 10 **Litho.**

C94 AP37 13p tan & black .35 .30

Day of the Race, Columbus Day.

Lt. Matienzo Base, Antarctica AP38

1965, Feb. 27 **Photo.** ***Perf. 13½***

C95 AP38 11p salmon pink .52 .15

Issued to publicize the national territory of Tierra del Fuego, Antarctic and South Atlantic Isles.

No. C88A Overprinted in Silver: "PRIMERS / JORNADAS FILATELICAS / RIOPLATENSES"

1965, Mar. 17 **Litho.**

C96 AP35 7p black & bister .24 .15

1st Rio de la Plata Stamp Show, sponsored jointly by the Argentine and Uruguayan Philatelic Associations, Montevideo, Mar. 19-28.

ITU Emblem — AP39

Ascending Rocket — AP40

1965, May 11 **Wmk. 90** ***Perf. 13½***

C97 AP39 18p slate, blk & red .42 .22

Centenary of the ITU.

1965, May 29 **Photo.** ***Perf. 13½***

Design: 50p, Earth with trajectories and magnetic field, horiz.

C98 AP40 18p vermilion .42 .20
C99 AP40 50p dp violet blue 1.00 .50

6th Symposium on Space Research, held in Buenos Aires, and to honor the Natl. Commission of Space Research.

Type of 1963-65 Inscribed "Republica Argentina" Reading Down

1965, Oct. 13 **Litho.** **Wmk. 90**

C101 AP35 12p dk car rose & brn 1.40 .20
C102 AP35 15p vio blue & dk red .85 .26
C103 AP35 27.50p dk bl grn & gray 1.40 .40
C104 AP35 30.50p dk brown & dk bl 2.00 .60
Nos. C101-C104 (4) 5.65 1.46

Argentine Antarctica Map and Centaur Rocket — AP41

1966, Feb. 19 ***Perf. 13½***

C105 AP41 27.50p blue, blk & dp org 1.00 .75

Launchings of sounding balloons and of a Gamma Centaur rocket in Antarctica during February, 1965.

Sea Gull and Southern Cross AP42

1966, May 14 ***Perf. 13½***

C106 AP42 12p Prus blue, blk & red .32 .15

50th anniv. of the Naval Aviation School.

Blériot Plane Flown by Fels, 1917 — AP43

1967, Sept. 2 **Litho.** ***Perf. 13½***

C107 AP43 26p olive, bl & blk .26 .15

Flight by Theodore Fels from Buenos Aires to Montevideo, Sept. 2, 1917, allegedly the 1st intl. airmail flight.

Type of 1963-65 Inscribed "Republica Argentina" Reading Down

1967, Dec. 20 ***Perf. 13½***

C108 AP35 26p brown .60 .22
C109 AP35 40p violet 4.50 .30
C110 AP35 68p blue green 3.00 .45
C111 AP35 78p ultra 1.25 .60
Nos. C108-C111 (4) 9.35 1.57

Vito Dumas and Ketch "Legh II" AP44

1968, July 27 **Litho.** **Wmk. 90**

C112 AP44 68p bl, blk, red & vio bl .65 .40

Issued to commemorate Vito Dumas's one-man voyage around the world in 1943.

Type of Regular Issue and

Assembly Emblem AP45

Design: 40p, Globe and map of South America.

1968, Oct. 19 **Litho.** ***Perf. 13½***

C113 A395 40p brt pink, lt bl & blk .40 .16
C114 AP45 68p bl, lt bl, gold & blk .65 .30

4th Plenary Assembly of the Intl. Telegraph and Telephone Consultative Committee, Mar del Plata, Sept. 23-Oct. 25.

Radar Antenna, Balcarce Station — AP46

Perf. 13½

1969, Aug. 23 **Wmk. 90** **Photo.**

C115 AP46 40p blue gray .70 .22

Communications by satellite through Intl. Telecommunications Consortium (INTELSAT).

Atucha Nuclear Center AP47

1969, Dec. 13 **Litho.** **Wmk. 365**

C116 AP47 26p blue & multi 1.40 .80

Completion of Atucha Nuclear Center.

Type of 1963-65 Inscribed "Republica Argentina" Reading Down

1969-71 ***Perf. 13½***

C123 AP35 40p violet 5.00 .32
C124 AP35 68p dk blue grn ('70) 2.00 .60

Unwmk.

C125 AP35 26p yellow brn ('71) .32 .20
C126 AP35 40p violet ('71) 2.75 .40
Nos. C123-C126 (4) 10.07 1.52

Old Fire Engine and Fire Brigade Emblem AP48

1970, Aug. 8 **Litho.** **Unwmk.**

C128 AP48 40c green & multi .55 .28

Centenary of the Fire Brigade.

Education Year Emblem — AP49

1970, Aug. 29 ***Perf. 13½***

C129 AP49 68c blue & blk .42 .25

Issued for International Education Year.

Fleet Leaving Valparaiso, by Antonio Abel AP50

1970, Oct. 17 **Litho.** ***Perf. 13½***

C130 AP50 26c multicolored 1.00 .35

150th anniv. of the departure for Peru of the liberation fleet from Valparaiso, Chile.

Sumampa Chapel AP51

1970, Nov. 7 **Photo.**

C131 AP51 40c multicolored .95 .35

Bishopric of Tucuman, 400th anniversary.

Buenos Aires Planetarium AP52

1970, Nov. 28 **Litho.** ***Perf. 13½***

C132 AP52 40c multicolored .60 .26

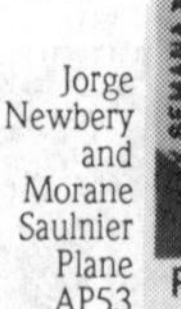

Jorge Newbery and Morane Saulnier Plane AP53

1970, Dec. 19

C133 AP53 26c bl, blk, yel & grn .38 .25

24th Aeronautics and Space Week.

Industries Type of Regular Issue

Design: 31c, Refinery.

1971, Oct. 16 **Litho.** ***Perf. 13½***

C134 A445 31c red, blk & yel .60 .24

Type of 1963-65 Inscribed "Republica Argentina" Reading Down

1971-74 **Unwmk.**

C135 AP35 45c brown 3.25 .15
C136 AP35 68c red .48 .15
C137 AP35 70c vio blue ('73) .80 .15
C138 AP35 90c emerald ('73) 1.90 .15
C139 AP35 1.70p blue ('74) .48 .25
C140 AP35 1.95p emerald ('74) .48 .30
C141 AP35 2.65p dp claret ('74) .48 .40
Nos. C135-C141 (7) 7.87
Set value 1.30

Fluorescent paper was used for Nos. C135-C136, C138-C141. The 70c was issued on both papers.

Don Quixote, Drawing by Ignacio Zuloaga — AP54

1975, Apr. 26 **Photo.** ***Perf. 13½***

C145 AP54 2.75p yellow, blk & red .60 .35

Day of the Race and for Espana 75 Intl. Philatelic Exhibition, Madrid, Apr. 4-13.

No. C87 Surcharged **100 PESOS**

1975, Sept. 15 Litho. Wmk. 90

C146	AP35	9.20p on 5.60p	.90	.18
C147	AP35	19.70p on 5.60p	1.25	.45
C148	AP35	100p on 5.60p	5.50	2.25
		Nos. C146-C148 (3)	7.65	2.88

REVALORIZADO

No. C87 Surcharged **920 PESOS**

1975, Oct. 15

C149	AP35	9.20p on 5.60p	.70	.30
C150	AP35	19.70p on 5.60p	1.25	.60

Argentine State Airline, 50th Anniv. AP55

1990, Sept. 15 Litho. *Perf. 13½*

C151	AP55	2500a Junkers JU52-3M	1.25
C152	AP55	2500a Grumman SA-16	1.25
C153	AP55	2500a Fokker F-27	1.25
C154	AP55	2500a Fokker F-28	1.25
		Nos. C151-C154 (4)	5.00

AIR POST SEMI-POSTAL STAMPS

Catalogue values for unused stamps in this section are for Never Hinged items.

Philatelic Exhibition Type

Designs: 45c+45c, Stamp engraving. 70c+70c, Proofing stamp die. 1p+1p, Sheet of stamps. 2.50p+2.50p, The letter. 5p+5p, Gen. San Martin.

Perf. 13½

1950, Aug. 26 Wmk. 90 Photo.

CB1	SP8	45c + 45c violet bl	.38	.24
CB2	SP8	70c + 70c dark brown	.55	.38
a.		Souv. sheet of 3, #B12, CB1, CB2, imperf.	3.00	3.00
CB3	SP8	1p + 1p cerise	1.50	1.50
CB4	SP8	2.50p + 2.50p ol gray	8.50	6.00
CB5	SP8	5p + 5p dull green	9.25	7.25
		Nos. CB1-CB5 (5)	20.18	15.37

Argentine Intl. Philatelic Exhib., 1950.

Pieta by Michelangelo SPAP2

1951, Dec. 22 *Perf. 13½x13*

CB6	SPAP2	2.45p +7.55p grnsh blk	21.00	14.00

Surtax as for the Eva Peron Foundation.

Flower and Child's Head — SPAP3

Stamp of 1858 — SPAP4

1958, Mar. 15 *Perf. 13½*

CB7	SPAP3	1p +50c deep claret	.28	.28

Surtax for National Council for Children.

1958, Mar. 29 Litho. Wmk. 90

CB8	SPAP4	1p + 50c gray ol & bl	.40	.32
CB9	SPAP4	2p + 1p rose lilac & vio	.52	.42
CB10	SPAP4	3p + 1.50p green & brown	.60	.52
CB11	SPAP4	5p + 2.50p gray ol & car rose	1.00	.85
CB12	SPAP4	10p + 5p gray ol & brn	2.00	1.65
		Nos. CB8-CB12 (5)	4.52	3.76

The surtax was for the Intl. Centennial Philatelic Exhibition, Buenos Aires, Apr. 19-27.

Type of Semi-Postal Issue, 1958

Designs: 1p+50c, Flooded area. 5p+2.50p, House and truck under water.

1958, Oct. 4 Photo. *Perf. 13½*

CB13	SP11	1p + 50c dull purple	.25	.20
CB14	SP11	5p + 2.50p grnsh blue	.80	.75

The surtax was for victims of a flood in the Buenos Aires district.

Type of Semi-Postal Issue, 1959

1959, Sept. 5 Litho. *Perf. 13½*

CB15	SP13	2p + 1p Rowing	.40	.26
CB16	SP13	3p + 1.50p Woman diver	.60	.48

Type of Semi-Postal Issue, 1960

Birds: 2p+1p, Rufous tinamou. 3p+1.50p, Rhea.

1960, Feb. 6 *Perf. 13½*

CB17	SP14	2p + 1p rose car & sal	.30	.20
CB18	SP14	3p + 1.50p slate green	.45	.35

The surtax was for child welfare work.
See No. CB29.

Buenos Aires Market Place, 1810 — SPAP5

Seibo, National Flower — SPAP6

Designs: 6p+3p, Oxcart water carrier. 10.70p+5.30p, Settlers landing. 20p+10p, The Fort.

1960, Aug. 20 Photo. Wmk. 90

CB19	SPAP5	2 + 1p rose brown	.16	.15
CB20	SPAP5	6 + 3p gray	.35	.24
CB21	SPAP5	10.70 + 5.30p blue	.60	.35
CB22	SPAP5	20 + 10p bluish grn	1.00	.85
		Nos. CB19-CB22 (4)	2.11	1.59

Inter-American Philatelic Exhibition EFIMAYO 1960, Buenos Aires, Oct. 12-24, held to for the sesquicentennial of the May Revolution of 1910.
For overprints see Nos. CB25-CB28.

1960, Sept. 10 *Perf. 13½*

Design: 10.70p+5.30p, Copihue, Chile's national flower.

CB23	SPAP6	6 + 3p lilac rose	.35	.28
CB24	SPAP6	10.70 + 5.30p vermilion	.52	.42

The surtax was for earthquake victims in Chile.

Nos. CB19-CB22 Overprinted: "DIA DE LAS NACIONES UNIDAS 24 DE OCTUBRE"

1960, Oct. 8

CB25	SPAP5	2 + 1p rose brown	.20	.15
CB26	SPAP5	6 + 3p gray	.32	.28
CB27	SPAP5	10.70 + 5.30p blue	.48	.42
CB28	SPAP5	20 + 10p bluish green	.85	.75
		Nos. CB25-CB28 (4)	1.85	1.60

United Nations Day, Oct. 24, 1960.

Type of Semi-Postal Issue, 1960

Design: Emperor penguins.

1961, Feb. 25 Photo. Wmk. 90

CB29	SP14	1.80p + 90c gray	.32	.20

The surtax was for child welfare work.

Stamp of 1862 — SPAP7

Crutch, Olympic Torch and Rings — SPAP8

1962, May 19 Litho.

CB30	SPAP7	6.50p + 6.50p Prus bl & grnsh bl	.70	.65

Opening of the "Argentina 62" Philatelic Exhibition, Buenos Aires, May 19-29.

Type of Semi-Postal Issue, 1963

1963, May 18 Wmk. 90 *Perf. 13½*

CB31	SP21	11p + 5p Bicycling	.55	.50

Type of Semi-Postal Issue, 1962

1963, Dec. 21 *Perf. 13½*

CB32	SP20	11p + 5p Great kiskadee	.70	.60

The surtax was for child welfare.

Type of Semi-Postal Issue, 1964

1964, July 18 Litho.

CB33	SP22	11p + 5p Sailboat	.50	.50

1964, Sept. 19 Litho. *Perf. 13½*

CB34	SPAP8	18p + 9p bluish grn, blk, red & yel	.60	.60

13th "Olympic" games for the handicapped, Tokyo, 1964.

Bird Type of Semi-Postal Issue, 1962

1964, Dec. 23 Litho. Wmk. 90

CB35	SP20	18p + 9p Chilean swallow	.90	.75

The surtax was for child welfare.

Bird Type of Semi-Postal Issue, 1962, Inscribed "R. ARGENTINA"

Design: Rufous ovenbird.

1966, Mar. 26 *Perf. 13½*

CB36	SP20	27.50p + 12.50p bl, ocher, yel & grn	.80	.70

The surtax was for child welfare.

Coat of Arms — SPAP9

1966, June 25 Litho. *Perf. 13½*

CB37	SPAP9	10p + 10p yellow & multi	1.75	1.40

ARGENTINA '66 Philatelic Exhibition held in connection with the sesquicentennial celebration of the Declaration of Independence, Buenos Aires, July 16-23. The surtax was for the Exhibition. Issued in sheets of 4.

Bird Type of Semi-Postal Issue, 1962, Inscribed "R. ARGENTINA"

Designs: 15p+7p, Blue and yellow tanager. 26p+13p, Toco toucan.

1967 Litho. Wmk. 90

CB38	SP20	15p + 7p blk, bl, grn & yel	1.00	.90
CB39	SP20	26p + 13p blk, org, yel & bl	.50	.40

The surtax was for child welfare.
Issue dates: 15p+7p, Jan. 14. 26p+13p, Dec. 23.

Bird Type of Semi-Postal Issue, 1969

Design: 26p+13p, Lineated woodpecker.

1969, Sept. 20 Wmk. 365 *Perf. 13½*

CB40	SP24	26p + 13p multi	.48	.40

The surtax was for child welfare.

Bird Type of Semi-Postal Issue, 1970

Design: 40c+20c, Chilean flamingo.

1970, May 9 Litho. Wmk. 365

CB41	SP25	40c + 20c multi	.45	.40

The surtax was for child welfare.

Fish Type of Semi-Postal Issue, 1971

Design: Pejerrey (atherinidae family).

1971, Feb. 20 Unwmk. *Perf. 12½*
Size: 75x15mm

CB42	SP26	40c + 20c lt blue & multi	.40	.40

The surtax was for child welfare.

OFFICIAL STAMPS

Regular Issues Overprinted in Black

1884-87 Unwmk. *Perf. 12, 14*

O1	A29	½c brown	7.00	5.00
O2	A23	1c red	4.50	3.25
b.		Perf. 12	37.50	27.50
O3	A29	1c red	.40	.26
b.		Double overprint	20.00	20.00
O4	A20	2c green	.40	.26
b.		Double overprint	20.00	20.00
O5	A11	4c brown	.38	.26
O6	A7	8c lake	.38	.26
O7	A8	10c green	37.50	19.00
O8	A23	12c ultra (#45)	3.50	2.50
a.		Perf. 14	37.50	37.50
O9	A29	12c grnsh bl	.60	.50
O10	A19	24c blue	1.00	.60
O11	A21	25c lake	8.50	5.50
O12	A12	30c orange	15.00	10.00
O13	A13	60c black	10.00	6.50
O14	A14	90c blue	7.50	5.50
b.		Double overprint	30.00	
		Nos. O1-O14 (14)	96.66	59.39

Inverted Overprint

O1a	A29	½c	10.00	10.00
O2a	A23	1c perf. 14	32.50	25.00
c.		perf. 12	24.00	24.00
O3a	A29	1c	.85	.55
O4a	A20	2c	37.50	18.00
O5a	A11	4c	27.50	18.00
O6a	A7	8c	37.50	37.50
O9a	A29	12c	72.50	67.50
O10a	A19	24c	2.75	1.65
O13a	A13	60c	37.50	24.00
O14a	A14	90c	30.00	24.00

1884 *Rouletted*

O15	A17	16c green	1.75	.65
a.		Double overprint	10.00	10.00
b.		Inverted overprint	72.50	
O16	A18	20c blue	7.00	5.00
a.		Inverted overprint	37.50	25.00
O17	A19	24c blue	1.25	.75
a.		Inverted overprint	3.00	2.25
b.		Double ovpt., one inverted	18.00	
		Nos. O15-O17 (3)	10.00	6.40

Overprinted Diagonally in Red

1885 *Perf. 12*

O18	A20	2c green	1.75	1.00
a.		Inverted overprint	30.00	18.00
O19	A11	4c brown	1.75	.85
a.		Inverted overprint	30.00	18.00
b.		Double overprint	30.00	30.00
O20	A13	60c black	17.00	10.00
O21	A14	90c blue	185.00	125.00

1885 *Rouletted*

O22	A19	24c blue	13.00	7.50

On all of these stamps, the overprint is found reading both upwards and downwards.
Counterfeits exist of No. O21 overprint and others.

Regular Issues Handstamped Horizontally in Black **OFICIAL**

1884 *Perf. 12, 14*

O23	A23	1c red	47.50	17.00
a.		Perf. 12	150.00	85.00
O24	A20	2c green, diagonal overprint	24.00	14.00
a.		Horizontal overprint	150.00	125.00
O25	A11	4c brown	10.00	7.50
O26	A7	8c lake	10.00	7.50

O27 A23 12c ultra 27.50 17.00

Overprinted Diagonally

O28 A19 24c bl, rouletted 20.00 14.00
O29 A13 60c black 14.00 6.75

Counterfeit overprints exist.

Liberty Head — O1

1901, Dec. 1 Engr. *Perf. 11½*

O31 O1 1c gray .20 .15
O32 O1 2c org brn .30 .18
O33 O1 5c red .40 .18
O34 O1 10c dk grn .45 .20
O35 O1 30c dk bl 3.00 .75
O36 O1 50c orange 1.65 .52
Nos. O31-O36 (6) 6.00 1.98

Regular Stamps of 1935-51 Overprinted in Black

SERVICIO OFICIAL
c

Perf. 13x13½, 13½x13, 13

1938-54 Wmk. RA in Sun (90)

O37 A129 1c buff ('40) .15 .15
O38 A130 2c dk brn ('40) .15 .15
O39 A132 3c grn ('39) .15 .15
O40 A132 3c lt gray ('39) .15 .15
O41 A134 5c yel brn .15 .15
O42 A195 5c car ('53) .15 .15
O43 A137 10c carmine .15 .15
O44 A137 10c brn ('39) .15 .15
O45 A140 15c lt gray bl, type II ('47) .15 .15
O46 A139 15c slate blue .50 .15
O47 A139 15c pale ultra ('39) .15 .15
O48 A139 20c blue ('53) .28 .15
O49 A141 25c carmine .15 .15
a. Overprint 11mm .18 .15
O49B A143 40c dk vio .90 .15
O50 A144 50c red & org .15 .15
a. Overprint 11mm .24 .15
O51 A146 1p brn blk & lt bl ('40) .18 .15
a. Overprint 11mm
O52 A224 1p choc & lt bl ('51) .18 .15
a. Overprint 11mm .18 .15
O53 A147 2p brn lake & dk ultra (ovpt. 11mm) ('54) .70 .15
Nos. O37-O53 (18) 4.54
Set value 1.05

Overprinted in Black on Stamps and Types of 1945-47

Perf. 13x13½, 13½x13

1945-46 Unwmk.

O54 A130 2c sepia 1.50 .40
O55 A134 3c lt gray 1.25 .30
O56 A134 5c yel brn .35 .15
O57 A195 5c dp car .15 .15
O58 A137 10c brown .15 .15
a. Double overprint
O59 A140 15c lt gray bl, type II .15 .15
O61 A141 25c dl rose .16 .15
O62 A144 50c red & org .28 .15
O63 A146 1p brn blk & lt bl .15 .15
O64 A147 2p brn lake & bl .20 .15
O65 A148 5p ind & ol grn .15 .15
O66 A149 10p dp cl & int blk .24 .15
O67 A150 20p bl grn & brn .48 .30
Nos. O54-O67 (13) 5.21
Set value 1.50

Overprinted in Black on Stamps and Types of 1942-50

Perf. 13, 13x13½

1944-51 Wmk. 288

O73 A134 3c lt gray 1.10 .50
O74 A134 5c yel brn .25 .15
O75 A137 10c red brn .15 .15
O76 A140 15c lt gray bl, type II .25 .15
O77 A144 50c red & org (overprint 11 mm) 1.50 .50
O78 A146 1p brn blk & lt bl (overprint 11mm) 1.75 .35
Nos. O73-O78 (6) 5.00
Set value 1.50

Catalogue values for unused stamps in this section, from this point to the end of the section, are for Never Hinged items.

Nos. 600-606 Overprinted in Black

SERVICIO OFICIAL
d

1953 Wmk. 90 *Perf. 13*

O79 A228 5c gray .15 .15
O80 A228 10c rose lil .15 .15
O81 A228 20c rose pink .15 .15
O82 A228 25c dl grn .15 .15
O83 A228 40c dl vio .15 .15
O84 A228 45c dp bl .18 .15
O85 A228 50c dl brn .15 .15

SERVICIO OFICIAL
e

SERVICIO OFICIAL
f

Nos. 611-617 Overprinted Type "e" in Blue

Perf. 13x13½, 13½x13

O86 A229 1p dk brn .15 .15
O87 A229 1.50p dp grn .28 .15
O88 A229 2p brt car .18 .15
O89 A229 3p indigo .55 .25

Size: 30x40mm

O90 A229 5p red brn .55 .45
O91 A228 10p red 2.75 1.75
O92 A229 20p green 30.00 20.00
Nos. O79-O92 (14) 35.54 23.95

No. 612 Overprinted Type "f" in Blue

O93 A229 1.50p dp grn 1.00 .30

Regular Issues of 1954-59 Variously Overprinted in Black or Blue

S. OFICIAL
g

SERVICIO OFICIAL
h

Perf. 13½, 13x13½, 13½x13

1955-61 Litho. Wmk. 90

O94 A237(c) 20c red (#629) .15 .15
O95 A237(d) 20c red (#629) .15 .15
O96 A237(d) 40c red, ovpt. 15mm (#630) .15 .15

Engr.

O97 A239(g) 50c bl (#632) .15 .15

Photo.

O98 A239(h) 1p brn (#635) .15 .15
O99 A239(e) 1p brn (Bl, #635) .15 .15
O100 A239(e) 1p brn (Bk, #635) .15 .15

Engr.

O101 A239(h) 3p vio brn (#638) .15 .15
O102 A240(h) 5p gray grn (#639) .28 .15
O103 A240(e) 10p yel grn (#640) .42 .15
O104 A240(f) 20p dl vio (#641) .75 .30
O105 A240(h) 20p dl vio (#641) .75 .25
O106 A241(e) 50p ultra & ind (#642) 1.10 .20
Nos. O94-O106 (13) 4.50
Set value 1.30

The overprints on Nos. O99-O100 and O103-O104 are horizontal; that on No. O109 is vertical. On No. O106 overprint measures 23mm.

Issue dates: No. O102, 1957. Nos. O97, O101, O103, O105, 1958. Nos. O98-O99, O104, 1959. No. O100, 1960. No. O106, 1961.

No. 659 Overprinted Type "d"

1957 Wmk. 90 Litho. *Perf. 13*

O108 A133 20c dl pur (ovpt. 15mm) .15 .15

Nos. 666, 658 and 663 Variously Overprinted

1957 Photo. *Perf. 13x13½, 13½*

O109 A261(g) 2p claret .22 .15
O110 A254(e) 2.40p brown .22 .15
O111 A258(c) 4.40p grnsh gray .26 .15
Nos. O109-O111 (3) .70
Set value .18

Nos. 668, 685-687, 690-691, 693-705, 742, 742C and Types of 1959-65 Overprinted in black, Blue or Red Types "e," "g," or

S. OFICIAL
i

S. OFICIAL
j

S. OFICIAL
k

S. OFICIAL
m

S. OFICIAL
n

Lithographed; Photogravure

1960-68 *Perf. 13x13½, 13½*

O112 A128(g) 5c buff (vert. ovpt.) .15 .15
O113 A275(j) 10c sl grn .15 .15
O114 A275(j) 20c dl red brn .15 .15
O115 A275(i) 50c bister .15 .15
O116 A278(k) 1p brn .15 .15
O117 A278(j) 1p brn, photo. (vert. ovpt.) .18 .15
O117A A278(j) 1p brn, litho., (down) .18 .15
O118 A276(j) 2p rose red .15 .15
O119 A312(m) 2p dp grn (down) .22 .15
O120 A312(j) 2p brt grn (up) .15 .15
O121 A312(j) 2p grn litho. (down) .22 .15
O122 A277(e) 3p dk bl (horiz.) .18 .15
O123 A277(j) 3p dk bl .18 .15
O124 A276(j) 4p red, litho. .18 .15
O125 A312(j) 4p rose red, litho. (down) .18 .15
O126 A277(e) 5p brn (Bl) (horiz.) .22 .15
O127 A277(e) 5p brn (Bk) (horiz.) .22 .15
O128 A277(j) 5p sep .15 .15
O129 A277(e) 5p sep (horiz. ovpt.) .15 .15
O130 A276(j) 8p red .18 .15
O131 A278(i) 10p lt red brn .45 .15
O132 A276(j) 10p ver .18 .15
O133 A278(j) 10p brn car (up) .18 .15
O134 A278(m) 12p dk brn vio .35 .15
O135 A278(k) 20p Prus grn .52 .15
O136 A278(j) 20p Prus grn (up) .40 .15
O137 A276(j) 20p red, litho. .35 .15
O138 A276(m) 20p red, litho. .22 .15
O139 A278(j) 23p grn (vert. ovpt.) .52 .15
O140 A278(j) 25p dp vio, photo. (R) (up) .52 .15
O141 A278(j) 25p pur, litho. (R) (down) .52 .15
O142 A241(n) 50p dk bl 1.10 .15
O143 A279(m) 100p bl (horiz. ovpt.) 1.10 .35
O144 A279(m) 100p bl (up) 1.10 .35
O145 A280(m) 300p dp vio 2.25 .60
Nos. O112-O145 (35) 13.25
Set value 3.20

The "m" overprint measures 15½mm on 2p; 14½mm on 12p, 100p and 300p; 13mm on 20p.

Issue dates: Nos. O122, O127, O135, 1961. Nos. O122-O114, O116, O118, 1962. No. O124, 1963. Nos. O119, O134, O143, 1964. Nos. O117, O125, O130, O139, O144, 1965. Nos. O120, O128, O132-O133, O136, O140, O142, O145, 1966. Nos. O121, O129, O137-O138, O141, 1967. No. O117A, 1968.

Nos. 699, 823-825, 827-829, and Type of 1962 Overprinted in Black or Red Types "j," "m," or "o"

SERVICIO OFICIAL
o

Inscribed: "Republica Argentina"

Litho., Photo., Engr.

1964-67 Wmk. 90 *Perf. 13½*

O149 A312(j) 6p rose red (down) .26 .15
O153 A238a(m) 22p ultra .52 .15
O154 A238a(j) 43p dk car rose (down) .75 .15
O155 A238a(j) 45p brn, photo. (up) .75 .15
O156 A238a(j) 45p brn, litho. (up) 1.10 .20
O157 A241(j) 50p dk bl (up) (R) 2.25 .15
O158 A366(j) 90p ol bis (up) 2.75 .20
O162 A495(o) 500p yel grn 3.50 .80
Nos. O149-O162 (8) 11.88
Set value 1.50

Issued: No. O153, 1964; No. O155, 1966; Nos. O149, O156-O162, 1967.

Type of 1959-67 Ovptd. Type "j"

1969 Litho. Wmk. 365 *Perf. 13½*

O163 A276 20p vermilion .22 .15

OFFICIAL DEPARTMENT STAMPS

Regular Issues of 1911-37 Overprinted in Black

M. A.
Type I

M. A.
Type II

Ministry of Agriculture (M. A.)

Type I

1913-37

On Stamp of 1911

OD1 A88 2c #181 .15 .15

On Stamps of 1912-14

OD2 A88 1c #190 .15 .15
OD3 A88 2c #191 .15 .15
OD4 A88 5c #194 .30 .15
OD5 A88 12c #196 .15 .15
Set value .65 .25

On Stamps of 1915-16

OD6 A88 1c #208 .15 .15
OD7 A88 2c #209 .15 .15
OD8 A88 5c #212 .15 .15
OD9 A91 5c #220 .15 .15
Set value .45 .32

On Stamp of 1917

OD10 A94 12c #238 .30 .15

On Stamps of 1918-19

OD11 A93 1c #249 .15 .15
OD12 A93 2c #250 .15 .15
OD13 A93 5c #253 .15 .15
OD14 A94 12c #255 .15 .15
OD15 A94 20c #256 .15 .15
Set value .55 .35

On Stamps of 1920

OD16 A93 1c #265 .30 .25
OD17 A93 2c #266 .50 .25
OD18 A93 5c #269 .20 .15
Nos. OD16-OD18 (3) 1.00
Set value .55

On Stamps of 1922-23

OD19 A94 12c #311 1.00 .40
OD20 A94 20c #312 25.00

On Stamps of 1923

OD21 A104 1c #324 .15 .15
OD22 A104 2c #325 .25 .15
OD23 A104 5c #328 .15 .15
OD24 A104 12c #330 .15 .15
OD25 A104 20c #331 .15 .15
Set value .45 .30

On Stamps of 1923-31

OD26 A104 1c #341 .15 .15
OD27 A104 2c #342, I .15 .15
a. Type II 1.50 .75
OD28 A104 3c #343 .15 .15
OD29 A104 5c #345, II .15 .15
a. Type I .15 .15
OD30 A104 10c #346, II .15 .15
a. Type I .15 .15
OD31 A104 12c #347 .15 .15
OD32 A104 20c #348, I .15 .15
a. Type II .15 .15
OD33 A104 30c #351 .15 .15
Set value .70 .40

On Stamp of 1926

OD34 A110 12c #360 .15 .15

Type II

On Stamps of 1935-37

OD35 A129 1c #419 .15 .15
OD36 A130 2c #420 .15 .15
OD37 A132 3c #422 .15 .15
OD38 A134 5c #427 .15 .15
OD39 A137 10c #430 .15 .15
OD40 A139 15c #434 .50 .15
OD41 A140 20c #437 .30 .15
OD42 A140 20c #438 .20 .15
OD43 A141 25c #441 .25 .15
OD44 A142 30c #442 .15 .15
OD45 A145 1p #445 2.50 1.50
OD46 A146 1p #446 .50 .25
Nos. OD35-OD46 (12) 5.15
Set value 2.00

Ministry of War (M. G.)

Type I

On Stamp of 1911

OD47 A88 2c #181 .15 .15

On Stamps of 1912-14

OD48 A88 1c #190 .15 .15
OD49 A88 2c #191 .75 .15
OD50 A88 5c #194 .15 .15
OD51 A88 12c #196 .15 .15
Set value 1.05 .20

On Stamps of 1915-16

OD52 A88 1c #208 6.00 .75
OD53 A88 2c #209 .60 .15
OD54 A88 5c #212 .75 .15
OD55 A91 5c #220 1.00 .25
OD56 A92 12c #222 1.00 .35
Nos. OD52-OD56 (5) 9.35 1.65

On Stamps of 1917

OD57 A93 1c #232 .30 .15
OD58 A93 2c #233 .40 .15
OD59 A93 5c #236 .30 .15
OD60 A94 12c #238 .60 .15
Nos. OD57-OD60 (4) 1.60
Set value .20

On Stamps of 1918-19
OD61 A93 1c #249 .15 .15
OD62 A93 2c #250 .15 .15
OD63 A93 5c #253 .15 .15
OD64 A94 12c #255 .40 .15
OD65 A94 20c #256 1.25 .15
Nos. OD61-OD65 (5) 2.10
Set value .25

On Stamps of 1920
OD66 A93 2c #266 .40 .15
OD67 A93 5c #269 .40 .15
OD68 A94 12c #271 .35 .15
Nos. OD66-OD68 (3) 1.15
Set value .15

On Stamp of 1920
OD69 A94 12c #299 2.00 .25

On Stamps of 1922-23
OD70 A93 1c #305 .75 .15
OD71 A93 2c #306 1.50 .45
OD72 A103 5c #309 .75 .15
OD73 A94 20c #312 .30 .15
Nos. OD70-OD73 (4) 3.30
Set value .70

On Stamp of 1922-23
OD74 A93 2c #318 5.00 .50

On Stamps of 1923
OD75 A104 1c #324 .15 .15
OD76 A104 2c #325 .15 .15
OD77 A104 5c #328 .15 .15
OD78 A104 12c #330 .15 .15
OD79 A104 20c #331 1.00 .15
Nos. OD75-OD79 (5) 1.60
Set value .25

On Stamps of 1923-31
OD80 A104 1c #341 1.25 .45
OD81 A104 2c #342 .20 .15
OD82 A104 3c #343, I .15 .15
a. Type II .40 .15
OD83 A104 5c #345, I .15 .15
a. Type II .20 .15
OD84 A104 10c #346, II .15 .15
a. Type I .60 .15
OD85 A104 20c #348, I .15 .15
a. Type II .40 .15
OD86 A104 30c #351, II .20 .15
a. Type I 1.00 .15
OD87 A105 1p #353 2.00 .30
Nos. OD80-OD87 (8) 4.25
Set value .75

On Stamp of 1926
OD88 A109 5c #359 .60 .15

Type II
On Stamps of 1935-37
OD89 A129 1c #419 .15 .15
OD90 A130 2c #420 .15 .15
OD91 A132 3c #422 .15 .15
OD92 A134 5c #427 .15 .15
OD93 A137 10c #430 .15 .15
OD94 A139 15c #434 .25 .15
OD95 A140 20c #437 1.00 .15
OD96 A140 20c #438 .25 .15
OD97 A141 25c #441 .15 .15
OD98 A142 30c #442 .15 .15
OD99 A144 50c #444 .25 .15
OD100 A145 1p #445 1.25 .50
OD101 A146 1p #446 .50 .25
Set value 4.00 1.30

Ministry of Finance (M. H.)
Type I
On Stamp of 1911
OD102 A88 2c #181 .15 .15

On Stamps of 1912-14
OD103 A88 1c #190 .15 .15
OD104 A88 2c #191 .15 .15
OD105 A88 5c #194 .20 .15
OD106 A88 12c #196 .15 .15
Set value .40 .20

On Stamps of 1915-16
OD107 A88 2c #209 .15 .15
OD108 A88 5c #212 .15 .15
OD109 A91 5c #220 .15 .15
Set value .30 .16

On Stamps of 1917
OD110 A93 2c #233 .15 .15
OD111 A93 5c #236 1.25 .15
OD112 A94 12c #238 .15 .15
Nos. OD110-OD112 (3) 1.55
Set value .25

On Stamps of 1918-19
OD113 A93 2c #250 25.00
OD114 A93 5c #253 .20 .15
OD115 A94 12c #255 .45 .15
OD116 A94 20c #256 .45 .15

On Stamps of 1920
OD117 A93 1c #265 .75 .45
OD118 A93 2c #266 1.25 .45
OD119 A93 5c #269 .30 .15
OD120 A94 12c #271 .60 .20
Nos. OD117-OD120 (4) 2.90 1.25

On Stamp of 1922-23
OD121 A94 20c #312 12.50 2.50

On Stamps of 1923
OD122 A104 1c #324 .75 .40
OD123 A104 2c #325 .15 .15
OD124 A104 5c #328 .15 .15
OD125 A104 12c #330 .15 .15
OD126 A104 20c #331 .15 .15
Set value .90 .60

On Stamps of 1923-31
OD127 A104 3c #343 7.00 1.50
OD128 A104 5c #345 .15 .15
OD129 A104 10c #346 .15 .15
OD130 A104 12c #347 7.00 3.75
OD131 A104 20c #348, I .15 .15
a. Type II .35 .15
OD132 A104 30c #351 .25 .15
OD133 A105 1p #353 .40 .15
Nos. OD127-OD133 (7) 15.10 6.00

On Stamp of 1926
OD134 A110 12c #360 12.50 12.50

Type II
On Stamps of 1935-37
OD135 A129 1c #419 .15 .15
OD136 A130 2c #420 .15 .15
OD137 A132 3c #422 .15 .15
OD138 A134 5c #427 .15 .15
OD139 A137 10c #430 .15 .15
OD140 A139 15c #434 .45 .15
OD141 A140 20c #437 .15 .15
OD142 A140 20c #438 .15 .15
OD143 A142 30c #442 .15 .15
OD144 A145 1p #445 2.00 1.00
OD145 A146 1p #446 .50 .25
Set value 3.50 1.70

Ministry of the Interior (M. I.)
Type I
On Stamp of 1911
OD146 A88 2c #181 .25 .15

On Stamps of 1912-14
OD147 A88 1c #190 .15 .15
OD148 A88 2c #191 .15 .15
OD149 A88 5c #194 .15 .15
OD150 A88 12c #196 .15 .15
Set value .40 .30

On Stamps of 1915-17
OD151 A88 2c #209 .80 .30
OD152 A88 5c #212 .75 .15
OD153 A91 5c #220 .60 .15
OD154 A93 5c #236 1.50 .15
Nos. OD151-OD154 (4) 3.65
Set value .65

On Stamps of 1918-19
OD155 A93 2c #250 .15 .15
OD156 A93 5c #253 .15 .15
Set value .20 .15

On Stamps of 1920
OD157 A93 1c #265 3.75 1.25
OD158 A93 5c #269 .75 .35

On Stamps of 1922-23
OD159 A93 2c #306 12.50 12.50
OD160 A103 5c #309 3.50 1.25
OD161 A94 12c #311 1.25 .40
OD162 A94 20c #312 1.25 .40
Nos. OD159-OD162 (4) 18.50 14.55

On Stamps of 1923
OD163 A104 1c #324 .15 .15
OD164 A104 2c #325 .15 .15
OD165 A104 5c #328 .15 .15
OD166 A104 12c #330 2.00 2.00
OD167 A104 20c #331 .75 .15
Nos. OD163-OD167 (5) 3.20
Set value 2.10

On Stamps of 1923-31
OD168 A104 1c #341 .15 .15
OD169 A104 2c #342 .15 .15
OD170 A104 3c #343, II .15 .15
a. Type I 1.25 .30
OD171 A104 5c #345, I .15 .15
a. Type II .15 .15
OD172 A104 10c #346, II .15 .15
OD173 A104 12c #347 .30 .15
OD174 A104 20c #348, II .15 .15
a. Type I .75 .15
OD175 A104 30c #351 .15 .15
Set value .60 .45

Type II
On Stamps of 1935-37
OD176 A129 1c #419 .15 .15
OD177 A130 2c #420 .15 .15
OD178 A132 3c #422 .15 .15
OD178A A134 5c #427 .15 .15
OD179 A137 10c #430 .15 .15
OD180 A139 15c #434 .30 .15
OD181 A140 20c #437 .75 .15
OD182 A140 20c #438 .20 .15
OD182A A142 30c #442 .15 .15
OD182B A145 1p #445 2.00 1.00
OD182C A146 1p #446 .50 .25
Set value 4.00 1.65

Ministry of Justice and Instruction (M. J. I.)
Type I
On Stamp of 1911
OD183 A88 2c #181 1.25 .15

On Stamps of 1912-14
OD184 A88 1c #190 1.50 .15
OD185 A88 2c #191 1.00 .15
OD186 A88 5c #194 .45 .15
OD187 A88 12c #196 .45 .15
Nos. OD184-OD187 (4) 3.40
Set value .30

On Stamps of 1915-17
OD188 A88 1c #208 .30 .15
OD189 A88 2c #209 .30 .15
OD190 A88 5c #212 1.00 .15
OD191 A91 5c #220 .25 .15
OD192 A92 12c #222 .75 .15
Nos. OD188-OD192 (5) 2.60
Set value .45

On Stamps of 1917
OD193 A93 1c #232 .25 .15
OD194 A93 2c #233 .75 .15
OD195 A93 5c #236 .25 .15
OD196 A94 12c #238 17.50 5.00
Nos. OD193-OD196 (4) 18.75 5.45

On Stamps of 1918-19
OD197 A93 1c #249 .15 .15
OD198 A93 2c #250 .15 .15
OD199 A93 5c #253 .15 .15
OD200 A94 12c #255 .20 .15
OD201 A94 20c #256 .50 .15
Set value 1.00 .35

On Stamps of 1920
OD202 A93 1c #265 .25 .15
OD203 A93 2c #266 .20 .15
OD204 A93 5c #269 .20 .15
OD205 A94 12c #271 .40 .15
Nos. OD202-OD205 (4) 1.05
Set value .30

On Stamps of 1922-23
OD206 A93 1c #305 .25 .15
OD207 A93 2c #306 1.50 .50
OD208 A103 5c #309 .25 .15
OD209 A94 12c #311 10.00 1.75
OD210 A94 20c #312 1.50 .30
Nos. OD206-OD210 (5) 13.50 2.85

On Stamp of 1922-23
OD211 A93 2c #318 2.50 2.50

On Stamps of 1923
OD212 A104 1c #324 .15 .15
OD213 A104 2c #325 .15 .15
OD214 A104 5c #328 .15 .15
OD215 A104 12c #330 .15 .15
OD216 A104 20c #331 .50 .15
Set value 1.00 .30

On Stamps of 1923-31
OD217 A104 ½c #340 2.00 .75
OD218 A104 1c #341, I .15 .15
a. Type II .15 .15
OD219 A104 2c #342 .15 .15
OD220 A104 3c #343, I .15 .15
a. Type II .15 .15
OD221 A104 5c #345, I .15 .15
a. Type II .15 .15
OD222 A104 10c #346, II .15 .15
a. Type I .30 .15
OD223 A104 12c #347, I .15 .15
a. Type II .30 .15
OD224 A104 20c #348, I .15 .15
a. Type II .15 .15
OD225 A104 30c #351 .15 .15
OD226 A105 1p #353 .40 .50
Set value 2.10 1.30

On Stamps of 1926
OD227 A109 5c #359 .15 .15
OD228 A110 12c #360 .20 .15
Set value .30 .15

Type II
On Stamps of 1935-37
OD229 A129 1c #419 .15 .15
OD230 A130 2c #420 .15 .15
OD231 A132 3c #422 .15 .15
OD232 A134 5c #427 .15 .15
OD233 A137 10c #430 .15 .15
OD234 A139 15c #434 .45 .15
OD234A A140 20c #437 .15 .15
OD234B A140 20c #438 .20 .15
OD234C A141 25c #441 .15 .15
OD234D A142 30c #442 .15 .15
OD234E A145 1p #445 1.00 .60
OD234F A146 1p #446 .30 .20
Set value 2.60 1.20

Ministry of Marine (M. M.)
Type I
On Stamp of 1911
OD235 A88 2c #181 .20 .15

On Stamps of 1912-14
OD236 A88 1c #190 .15 .15
OD237 A88 2c #191 .15 .15
OD238 A88 5c #194 2.00 .15
OD239 A88 12c #196 .15 .15
Nos. OD236-OD239 (4) 2.45
Set value .25

On Stamps of 1915-16
OD240 A88 2c #209 .60 .15
OD241 A88 5c #212 .40 .15
Set value .15

On Stamps of 1917
OD242 A93 1c #232 .15 .15
OD243 A93 2c #233 .15 .15
OD244 A93 5c #236 .15 .15
Nos. OD242-OD244 (3) .45
Set value .15

On Stamps of 1918-19
OD245 A93 1c #249 .15 .15
OD246 A93 2c #250 .15 .15
OD247 A93 5c #253 .25 .15
OD248 A94 12c #255 .25 .15
OD249 A94 20c #256 3.00 .35
Nos. OD245-OD249 (5) 3.80
Set value .60

On Stamps of 1920
OD250 A93 1c #265 .15 .15
OD251 A93 2c #266 .20 .15
OD252 A93 5c #269 .25 .15
Nos. OD250-OD252 (3) .60
Set value .20

On Stamps of 1922-23
OD253 A103 5c #309 1.00 .15
OD254 A94 12c #311 7.00 7.00
OD255 A94 20c #312 7.00 1.50
Nos. OD253-OD254 (2) 8.00 7.15

On Stamps of 1923
OD256 A104 1c #324 .15 .15
OD257 A104 2c #325 .15 .15
OD258 A104 5c #328 .35 .15
OD259 A104 12c #330 .65 .15
OD260 A104 20c #331 .65 .15
Nos. OD256-OD260 (5) 1.95
Set value .35

On Stamps of 1923-31
OD261 A104 1c #341 .75 .25
OD262 A104 2c #342 .15 .15
OD263 A104 3c #343 .60 .20
OD264 A104 5c #345, I .15 .15
a. Type II .60 .15
OD265 A104 10c #346 .60 .15
OD266 A104 20c #348, II .60 .15
a. Type I .75 .15
OD267 A104 30c #351 1.00 .15
OD268 A105 1p #353 11.00 3.00
Nos. OD261-OD268 (8) 14.85
Set value 3.60

On Stamp of 1926
OD269 A109 5c #359 .50 .15

Type II
On Stamps of 1935-37
OD270 A129 1c #419 .15 .15
OD271 A130 2c #420 .15 .15
OD272 A132 3c #422 .15 .15
OD273 A134 5c #427 .15 .15
OD274 A137 10c #430 .25 .15
OD275 A139 15c #434 .30 .15
OD276 A140 20c #437 .40 .15
OD277 A140 20c #438 .30 .15
OD278 A142 30c #442 .25 .15
OD279 A145 1p #445 3.25 1.00
OD280 A146 1p #446 .75 .25
Nos. OD270-OD280 (11) 6.10
Set value 1.65

Ministry of Public Works (M. O. P.)
Type I
On Stamp of 1911
OD281 A88 2c #181 .30 .15

On Stamps of 1912-14
OD282 A88 1c #190 .30 .15
OD283 A88 5c #194 .15 .15
OD284 A88 12c #196 1.50 .35
Nos. OD282-OD284 (3) 1.95
Set value .45

On Stamps of 1916-19
OD285 A91 5c #220 10.00 1.00
OD286 A94 12c #238 25.00
OD287 A94 20c #256 25.00

On Stamps of 1920
OD288 A93 2c #266 6.00 2.50
OD289 A93 5c #269 2.00 .15
OD290 A94 12c #271 20.00 6.00
Nos. OD288-OD290 (3) 28.00 8.65

On Stamps of 1923
OD291 A104 1c #324 .40 .15
OD292 A104 2c #325 .30 .15
OD293 A104 5c #328 .40 .15
OD294 A104 12c #330 .60 .15
OD295 A104 20c #331 1.00 .15
Nos. OD291-OD295 (5) 2.70
Set value .50

On Stamps of 1923-31
OD296 A104 1c #341 .15 .15
OD297 A104 2c #342 .15 .15
OD298 A104 3c #343 .15 .15
OD299 A104 5c #345, I .15 .15
a. Type II .15 .15
OD300 A104 10c #346 .15 .15
OD301 A104 12c #347 9.00 1.25
OD302 A104 20c #348, I .15 .15
a. Type II 2.50 .50

OD303 A104 30c #351 .40 .15
OD304 A105 1p #353 20.00 6.00
Nos. OD296-OD304 (9) 30.30 8.30

On Stamp of 1926

OD305 A109 5c #359 .60 .15

Type II

On Stamps of 1935-37

OD306 A129 1c #419 .15 .15
OD307 A130 2c #420 .15 .15
OD308 A132 3c #422 .15 .15
OD309 A134 5c #427 .15 .15
OD310 A137 10c #430 .30 .15
OD311 A139 15c #434 .60 .15
OD312 A140 20c #437 .75 .15
OD313 A140 20c #438 .15 .15
OD314 A142 30c #442 .15 .15
OD315 A144 50c #444 .15 .15
OD316 A145 1p #445 2.00 1.00
OD317 A146 1p #446 .50 .25
Set value 4.75 1.70

Ministry of Foreign Affairs and Religion (M. R. C.)

Type I

On Stamp of 1911

OD318 A88 2c #181 5.00 1.25

On Stamps of 1912-14

OD319 A88 1c #190 .15 .15
OD320 A88 2c #191 .15 .15
OD321 A88 5c #194 .40 .15
OD322 A88 12c #196 1.50 .25
Nos. OD319-OD322 (4) 2.20
Set value .40

On Stamps of 1915-19

OD323 A88 5c #212 .40 .15
OD324 A91 5c #220 .15 .15
OD325 A94 20c #256 2.00 .75
Nos. OD323-OD325 (3) 2.55
Set value .90

On Stamps of 1920

OD326 A93 1c #265 .40 .15
OD327 A93 5c #269 .15 .15
Set value .15

On Stamps of 1922-23

OD328 A93 2c #306 9.00 3.50
OD329 A103 5c #309 27.50
OD330 A93 10c #311 22.50
Nos. OD328-OD330 (3) 59.00

On Stamps of 1923

OD331 A104 1c #324 .15 .15
OD332 A104 2c #325 .15 .15
OD333 A104 5c #328 .15 .15
OD334 A104 12c #330 .15 .15
OD335 A104 20c #331 .15 .15
Set value .40 .30

On Stamps of 1923-31

OD336 A104 ½c #340 1.00 .50
OD337 A104 1c #341 .15 .15
OD338 A104 2c #342 .15 .15
OD339 A104 3c #343 .15 .15
OD340 A104 5c #345 .15 .15
OD341 A104 10c #346, II .15 .15
a. Type I 1.50 .15
OD342 A104 12c #347 .15 .15
OD343 A104 20c #348, I .15 .15
a. Type II .15 .15
OD344 A104 30c #351, I .15 .15
a. Type II .15 .15
OD345 A105 1p #353 .40 .20
Set value 2.00 1.10

On Stamp of 1926

OD346 A110 12c #360 .15 .15

Type II

On Stamps of 1935-37

OD347 A129 1c #419 .15 .15
OD348 A130 2c #420 .15 .15
OD349 A132 3c #422 .15 .15
OD350 A134 5c #427 .15 .15
OD351 A137 10c #430 .15 .15
OD352 A139 15c #434 .15 .15
OD353 A140 20c #437 .15 .15
OD354 A140 20c #438 .15 .15
OD355 A142 30c #442 .15 .15
OD356 A145 1p #445 2.50 1.25
OD357 A146 1p #446 1.00 .50
Set value 4.25 2.25

BUENOS AIRES

The central point of the Argentine struggle for independence. At intervals Buenos Aires maintained an independent government but after 1862 became a province of the Argentine Republic.

8 Reales = 1 Peso

Values of Buenos Aires Nos. 1-8 vary according to condition. Quotations are for fine copies. Very fine to superb specimens sell at much higher prices, and inferior or poor copies sell at reduced values, depending on the condition of the individual specimen.

Steamship — A1

1858 Unwmk. Typo. *Imperf.*

1 A1 1 (in) pesos lt brn *350.* *250.*
2 A1 2 (dos) pesos blue 175. 140.
3 A1 3 (tres) pesos grn 1,400. *750.*
a. 3p dark green 1,700. *825.*
4 A1 4 (cuatro) pesos ver 4,750. *1,500.*
5 A1 5 (cinco) pesos org 4,250. *1,400.*
a. 5p ocher 4,250. *1,400.*
b. 5p olive yellow 4,250. *1,400.*

Issued: #2-5, Apr. 29; #1, Oct. 26.

1858, Oct. 26

6 A1 4 (cuatro) reales brown 250. 200.
a. 4r gray brown 250. 200.
b. 4r yellow brown 250. 200.

1859, Jan. 1

7 A1 1 (in) pesos blue 165. 225.
a. 1p indigo 200. 250.
b. Impression on reverse of stamp in blue *2,100.*
c. Double impression 200. 165.
d. Tete beche pair *45,000.*
8 A1 1 (to) pesos blue 350. 225.

Nos. 1, 2, 3 and 7 have been reprinted on very thick, hand-made paper. The same four stamps and No. 8 have been reprinted on thin, hard, white wove paper.

Counterfeits of Nos. 1-8 are plentiful.

Liberty Head — A2

1859, Sept. 3

9 A2 4r green, *bluish* 190.00 90.00
10 A2 1p blue 35.00 17.50
11 A2 2p vermilion 350.00 150.00
a. 2p red 350.00 150.00

Both clear and rough impressions of these stamps may be found. They have generally been called Paris and Local prints, respectively, but the opinion now obtains that the differences are due to the impression and that they do not represent separate issues.

Many shades exist of Nos. 1-11.

1862, Oct. 4

12 A2 1p rose 125.00 60.00
13 A2 2p blue 350.00 75.00

All three values have been reprinted in black, brownish black, blue and red brown on thin hard white paper. The 4r has also been reprinted in green on bluish paper.

CORDOBA

A province in the central part of the Argentine Republic.

100 Centavos = 1 Peso

Arms of Cordoba — A1

Unwmk.

1858, Oct. 28 Litho. *Imperf.*

Laid Paper

1 A1 5c blue 125.
2 A1 10c black *2,500.*

Cordoba stamps were printed on laid paper, but stamps from edges of the sheets sometimes do not show any laid lines and appear to be on wove paper. Counterfeits are plentiful.

CORRIENTES

The northeast province of the Argentine Republic.

1 Real M(oneda) C(orriente) =
12½ Centavos M.C. = 50 Centavos
100 Centavos Fuertes = 1 Peso Fuerte

Ceres
A1 A2

1856, Aug. 21 Unwmk. *Imperf.*

1 A1 1r black, *blue* 85.00 *275.00*

Pen Stroke Through "Un Real"

1860, Feb. 8

2 A1 (3c) black, *blue* 350.00 *525.00*

1860-78

3 A2 (3c) black, *blue* 9.50 *30.00*
4 A2 (2c) blk, *yel grn* ('64) 37.50 37.50
a. (2c) black, *blue green* 92.50 110.00
5 A2 (2c) blk, *yel* ('67) 7.50 *19.00*
6 A2 (3c) blk, *dk bl* ('71) 3.00 *19.00*
7 A2 (3c) blk, *lil rose* ('75)
a. (3c) black, *rose red* ('76)
8 A2 (3c) blk, *red vio* ('78) 60.00 35.00

Pen canceled copies sell for much less.

Printed from settings of 8 varieties, 3 or 4 impressions constituting a sheet. Some impressions were printed inverted and tete beche pairs may be cut from adjacent impressions.

From Jan. 1 to Feb. 24, 1864, No. 4 was used as a 5 centavos stamp but copies so used can only be distinguished when they bear dated cancellations.

The reprints show numerous spots and small defects which are not found on the originals. They are printed on gray blue, dull blue, gray green, dull orange and light magenta papers.

ARMENIA

är-'mē-nē-ə

LOCATION — South of Russia bounded by Georgia, Azerbaijan, Iran and Turkey
GOVT. — Republic
AREA — 11,306 sq. mi.
POP. — 3,300,000 (1989)
CAPITAL — Yerevan

With Azerbaijan and Georgia, Armenia made up the Transcaucasian Federation of Soviet Republics.

Stamps of Armenia were replaced in 1923 by those of Transcaucasian Federated Republics.

With the breakup of the Soviet Union on Dec. 26, 1991, Armenia and ten former Soviet republics established the Commonwealth of Independent States.

100 Kopecks = 1 Ruble
100 Luma = 1 Dram (1993)

Catalogue values for unused stamps in this country are for Never Hinged items, beginning with Scott 430 in the regular postage section.

Counterfeits abound of all overprinted and surcharged stamps.

Watermark

Diamonds — Wmk. 171

Perforations
Perforations are the same as the basic Russian stamps.

National Republic

Russian Stamps of 1902-19 Handstamped

Thirteen types exist of both framed and unframed overprints. The device is the Armenian "H," initial of Hayasdan (Armenia). Inverted and double overprints are found.

Surcharged K 60 K

Type I - Without periods.
Type II - Periods after 1st "K" and "60."

Black Surcharge

1919 Unwmk. *Perf. 14x14½*

1 A14 60k on 1k orange (II) 2.50 .40
a. Imperf. (I) 1.00 .24
b. Imperf. (II) 1.00 .24

Violet Surcharge

2 A14 60k on 1k orange (II) .50 .50

Handstamped in Violet — a 

Perf.

6 A15 4k carmine 2.00 2.00
7 A14 5k claret, imperf. 7.50 7.50
a. Perf. 5.00 5.00
9 A14 10k on 7k lt blue 5.00 1.25
10 A11 15k red brn & bl 3.00 .25
11 A8 20k blue & car 2.00 1.00
13 A11 35k red brn & grn 3.50 3.50
14 A8 50k violet & green 3.50 3.50
15 A14 60k on 1k orange (II) 2.00 2.00
a. Imperf. (I) 1.90 2.00
b. Imperf. (II) 8.50 9.00
18 A13 5r dk bl, grn & pale bl 3.50 4.25
a. Imperf. 1.00 1.00
19 A12 7r dk green & pink 1.75 2.00
20 A13 10r scarlet, yel & gray 1.75 2.00

Handstamped in Black

31 A14 2k green, imperf. 1.00 .15
a. Perf. 5.00 4.25
32 A14 3k red, imperf. 1.00 .20
a. Perf. 5.00 2.00
33 A15 4k carmine .15 .20
34 A14 5k claret 1.00 .20
a. Imperf. 5.00 5.00
36 A15 10k dark blue 2.00 .65
37 A14 10k on 7k lt blue .50 .15
38 A11 15k red brn & bl .50 .15
a. Imperf. 3.00 3.00
39 A8 20k blue & car 1.00 .20
40 A11 25k green & gray vio 1.00 .20
41 A11 35k red brn & grn 1.00 .15
42 A8 50k violet & green 1.00 .15
43 A14 60k on 1k orange (II) 2.50 2.50
43A A11 70k brown & org 1.00 .30
b. Imperf. .50 .30
44 A9 1r pale brn, dk brn & org 1.50 .30
a. Imperf. .50 .50
45 A12 3½r mar & lt grn, imperf. 5.00 .65
a. Perf. 5.00 .85
46 A13 5r dk bl, grn & pale bl .60 .65
a. Imperf. 6.00 1.00
47 A12 7r dk green & pink 6.00 1.10
48 A13 10r scar, yel & gray *50.00* 1.00

Wmk. Wavy Lines (168)

1920 *Imperf.*

Vertically Laid Paper

60 A13 5r dk bl, grn & pale bl 20.00

Handstamped in Violet — c 

Unwmk. *Perf.*

Wove Paper

62 A14 2k green, imperf. .40 .40
a. Perf. 4.50 4.50
63 A14 3k red, imperf. .25 .25
a. Perf. 3.00 2.75
64 A15 4k carmine .50 .50
65 A14 5k claret 3.00 .40
a. Imperf. 3.00 .60

67 A15 10k dark blue 1.00 .85
68 A14 10k on 7k lt bl 1.00 .65
69 A11 15k red brn & bl 2.50 2.50
70 A8 20k blue & car .40 .40
71 A11 25k grn & gray vio 1.00 1.00
72 A11 35k red brn & grn 1.50 1.50
73 A8 50k violet & grn .50 .50
74 A14 60k on 1k org (II) 2.50 2.00
a. Imperf. (I) 1.65 1.65
b. Imperf. (II) 2.00 2.00
75 A9 1r pale brn, dk brn & org .60 .60
a. Imperf. 1.50 1.50
76 A12 3½r mar & lt grn, imperf. .75 .75
a. Perf. 1.00 1.00
77 A13 5r dk bl, grn & pale bl, imperf. 5.00 5.00
a. Perf. 4.00 4.00
78 A12 7r dk green & pink 7.50 7.50
79 A13 10r scar, yel & gray 2.25 1.90

Imperf

85 A11 70k brown & org 5.00 2.00

Handstamped in Black

Perf.

90 A14 1k orange 10.00 4.50
a. Imperf. 10.00 6.00
91 A14 2k green, imperf. 1.00 .15
a. Perf. 7.50 2.50
92 A14 3k red, imperf. 1.00 .20
a. Perf. 10.00 2.75
93 A15 4k carmine .50 .50
94 A14 5k claret 1.00 .15
a. Imperf. 3.00 .60
95 A14 7k light blue 15.00 15.00
96 A15 10k dark blue 12.00 12.00
97 A14 10k on 7k lt bl .15 .15
98 A11 15k red brn & bl .20 .15
99 A8 20k blue & car .15 .15
100 A11 25k grn & gray vio .50 .20
101 A11 35k red brn & grn .20 .15
102 A8 50k violet & grn .20 .15
102A A14 60k on 1k org, imperf. (I) .30 .30
b. Imperf. (II) .50 .50
c. Perf. (II) 2.50 1.25
103 A9 1r pale brn, dk brn & org 1.00 1.00
a. Imperf. .75 .75
104 A12 3½r maroon & lt grn 4.00 .50
a. Imperf. 5.00 .30
105 A13 5r dk bl, grn & pale bl 2.50 2.50
a. Imperf. 2.50 2.50
106 A12 7r dk green & pink 3.00 2.50
107 A13 10r scar, yel & gray 7.00 3.50

Imperf

113 A11 70k brown & org 1.00 .25

Handstamped in Violet or Black:

5r
f

10r
g

Violet Surcharge, Type f

1920 **Perf.**

120 A14 3r on 3k red, imperf. .85 .85
a. Perf. 2.50 2.50
121 A14 5r on 3k red 3.75 3.25
122 A15 5r on 4k car 10.00 8.00
123 A14 5r on 5k claret, imperf. 10.00 10.00
a. Perf. 10.00 8.00
124 A15 5r on 10k dk blue 10.00 8.00
125 A14 5r on 10k on 7k lt bl 10.00 8.00
126 A8 5r on 20k bl & car

Imperf

127 A14 5r on 2k green 7.00 7.00
128 A11 5r on 35k red brn & grn 7.00 7.00

Black Surcharge, Type f or Type g (#130)

Perf.

130 A14 1r on 1k orange .50 .50
a. Imperf. .75 .75
131 A14 3r on 3k red .15 .15
a. Imperf. .15 .15
132 A15 3r on 4k carmine 3.00 3.00
133 A14 5r on 2k green, imperf. .15 .15
a. Perf. 2.00 2.00
134 A14 5r on 3k red 5.00 5.00
a. Imperf. 2.50 2.50
135 A15 5r on 4k carmine .40 .40
a. Imperf. 4.75 4.75
136 A14 5r on 5k claret .50 .50
a. Imperf. .50 .50
137 A14 5r on 7k lt blue 2.00 2.00
138 A15 5r on 10k dk blue .50 .50
139 A14 5r on 10k on 7k lt bl .50 .50
140 A11 5r on 14k bl & rose 2.00 2.00
141 A11 5r on 15k red brn & blue .50 .50
a. Imperf. 2.00 2.00
142 A8 5r on 20k bl & car .50 .50
a. Imperf. 10.00 10.00
143 A11 5r on 20k on 14k bl & rose 12.00 12.00
144 A11 5r on 25k grn & gray vio 12.00 12.00

Black Surcharge, Type g or Type f (#148A, 151)

145 A14 10r on 1k org, imperf. .90 .90
a. Perf. 225.00 225.00
146 A14 10r on 3k red 175.00 175.00
147 A14 10r on 5k claret 15.00 15.00
a. Imperf. 6.00
148 A8 10r on 20k bl & car 15.00 15.00
148A A11 10r on 25k grn & gray vio 8.00 8.00
149 A11 10r on 25k grn & gray vio 5.00 5.00
a. Imperf. 8.00 8.00
150 A11 10r on 35k red brn & grn .50 .50
151 A8 10r on 50k brn vio & grn 1.75 1.75
152 A8 10r on 50k brn vio & grn .45 .45
152A A11 10r on 70k brn & org, imperf. 3.00 3.00
b. Perf. 200.00 200.00
152C A8 25r on 20k bl & car 4.00 4.00
153 A11 25r on 25k grn & gray vio 2.00 2.00
154 A11 25r on 35k red brn & grn 2.00 2.00
a. Imperf. 3.50 3.50
155 A8 25r on 50k vio & grn 4.00 4.00
a. Imperf. 5.00 5.00
156 A11 25r on 70k brn & org 8.00 8.00
a. Imperf. 5.00 5.00
157 A9 50r on 1r pale brn, dk brn & org, imperf. 1.00 1.00
a. Perf. 5.00 5.00
158 A13 50r on 5r dk bl, grn & lt bl 10.00 10.00
a. Imperf. 10.00 10.00
159 A12 100r on 3½r mar & lt grn 7.00 7.00
a. Imperf. 7.00 7.00
160 A13 100r on 5r dk bl, grn & pale bl 10.00 10.00
a. Imperf. 7.00 7.00
161 A12 100r on 7r dk grn & pink 10.00 10.00
a. Imperf. 35.00 35.00
162 A13 100r on 10r scar, yel & gray 10.00 10.00

Wmk. Wavy Lines (168)
Perf. 11½
Vertically Laid Paper

163 A12 100r on 3½r blk & gray 50.00 50.00
164 A12 100r on 7r blk & yel 35.00 35.00

1920 **Unwmk.** *Imperf.*
Wove Paper

166 A14 (g) 1r on 60k on 1k org (I) 12.00 12.00
168 A14 (f) 5r on 1k orange 9.00 9.00
173 A11 (f) 5r on 35k red brn & grn 2.50 2.50
177 A11 (g) 50r on 70k brn & org 5.00 5.00
179 A12 (g) 50r on 3½r mar & lt grn 2.00 2.00
181 A9 (g) 100r on 1r pale brn, dk brn & org 4.00 4.00

Romanov Issues Surcharged Type g or Type f (#185-187, 190)
On Stamps of 1913

1920 *Perf. 13½*

184 A16 1r on 1k brn org 10.00 10.00
185 A18 3r on 3k rose red 15.00 15.00
186 A19 5r on 4k dull red 10.00 10.00
187 A22 5r on 14k blue grn 60.00 60.00
187A A19 10r on 4k dull red 30.00
187B A26 10r on 35k gray vio & dk grn
187C A19 25r on 4k dull red 10.00 10.00
188 A26 25r on 35k gray vio & dk grn 2.75 2.75
189 A28 25r on 70k yel grn & brn 2.75 2.75
190 A31 50r on 3r dk violet 2.00 2.00
190A A16 100r on 1k brn org 100.00 100.00
190B A17 100r on 2k green 100.00 100.00
191 A30 100r on 2r brown 10.50 10.50
192 A31 100r on 3r dk vio 10.50 10.50

On Stamps of 1915, Type g
Thin Cardboard
Inscriptions on Back
Perf. 12

193 A21 100r on 10k blue 3.00
194 A23 100r on 15k brown 3.00
195 A24 100r on 20k ol grn 3.00

On Stamps of 1916, Type f
Perf. 13½

196 A20 5r on 10k on 7k brown 5.00 5.00
197 A22 5r on 20k on 14k bl grn 8.00 8.00

Surch. Type f or Type g (#204-205A, 207-207C, 210-211) over Type c
Type c in Violet
Perf.

200 A15 5r on 4k carmine 1.00 1.00
201 A15 5r on 10k dk blue 1.00 1.00
202 A11 5r on 15k red brn & bl 2.00 2.00
203 A8 5r on 20k blue & car 1.75 1.75
204 A11 10r on 25k grn & gray vio 1.50 1.50
205 A11 10r on 35k red brn & grn 3.00 3.00
205A A8 10r on 50k brn vio & grn 3.50 3.50
206 A8 25r on 50k brn vio & grn 150.00 150.00
207 A9 50r on 1r pale brn, dk brn & org, imperf. 3.50 3.50
a. Perf. 25.00 25.00
207B A12 100r on 3½r mar & lt grn 30.00
207C A12 100r on 7r dk grn & pink 9.00

Imperf

208 A14 5r on 2k green 25.00 25.00
209 A14 5r on 5k claret 25.00 25.00
210 A11 25r on 70k brn & org 5.50 5.50
211 A13 100r on 5r dk bl, grn & pale bl 1.00 1.00

Surcharged Type g or Type f (212-213, 215, 219-219A, 221-222) over Type c
Type c in Black
Perf.

212 A14 5r on 7k lt bl 150.00 150.00
213 A14 5r on 10k on 7k lt bl 5.00 5.00
214 A11 5r on 15k red brn & bl .50 .50
215 A8 5r on 20k blue & car 3.00 3.00
215A A11 10r on 5r on 25k grn & gray vio 5.00 5.00
216 A11 10r on 35k red brn & grn .50 .50
217 A8 10r on 50k brn vio & grn 1.00 1.00
217A A9 50r on 1r pale brn, dk brn & org 1.00 1.00
b. Imperf. 1.10 1.10
217C A12 100r on 3½r mar & lt grn 1.50 1.50
218 A13 100r on 5r dk bl, grn & pale bl 10.00 10.00
a. Imperf. 1.75 1.75
219 A12 100r on 7r dk grn & pink 15.00 15.00
219A A13 100r on 10r scar, yel & gray 10.00 10.00

Imperf

220 A14 1r on 60k on 1k org (I) 20.00 20.00
221 A14 5r on 2k green .80 .80
222 A14 5r on 5k claret 3.00 3.00
223 A11 10r on 70k brn & org 2.00 2.00
224 A11 25r on 70k brn & org 2.00 2.00

Surcharged Type g or Type f (#233) over Type a
Type a in Violet
Imperf

231 A9 50r on 1r pale brn, dk brn & org 140.00 140.00
232 A13 100r on 5r dk bl, grn & pale bl 10.50

Type a in Black
Perf.

233 A8 5r on 20k blue & car .80 .80
233A A11 10r on 25k grn & gray vio 55.00 55.00
234 A11 10r on 35k red brn & grn .90 .90
235 A12 100r on 3½r mar & lt grn 1.25 1.25
a. Imperf. 1.50 1.50

Imperf

237 A14 5r on 2k green 125.00 125.00
237A A11 10r on 70k brn & org

Surcharged Type a and New Value
Type a in Violet
Perf.

238 A11 10r on 15k red brn & blue .80 .80

Type a in Black

239 A8 5r on 20k blue & car 3.00 3.00
239A A8 10r on 20k blue & car 3.00 3.00
239B A8 10r on 50k brn red & grn 7.50

Imperf

240 A12 100r on 3½r mar & lt grn 1.90 1.90

Surcharged Type c and New Value
Type c in Black

1920 *Perf.*

241 A15 5r on 4k red 1.75 1.75
242 A11 5r on 15k red brn & bl 1.00 1.00
243 A8 10r on 20k blue & car 1.75 1.75
243A A11 10r on 25k grn & gray vio 1.00 1.00
244 A11 10r on 35k red brn & grn 1.00 1.00
a. With additional surch. "5r" 1.50 1.50
245 A12 100r on 3½r mar & lt grn 1.50 1.50

Imperf

247 A14 3r on 3k red 4.75 4.75
248 A14 5r on 2k green .30 .30
249 A9 50r on 1r pale brn, dk brn & org .90 .90

Type c in Violet

249A A14 5r on 2k green 6.50

Postal Savings Stamps Surcharged

A1 A2 A3

Perf. 14½x15
Wmk. 171

250 A1 60k on 1k red & buff 50.00 50.00
251 A2 1r on 1k red & buff 5.00 5.00
252 A3 5r on 5k green & buff 7.25 7.25
253 A3 5r on 10k brown & buff 30.00 3.00

Russian Semi-Postal Stamps of 1914-18 Surcharged with Armenian Monogram and New Values like Regular Issues
On Stamps of 1914

Unwmk. *Perf.*

255 SP5 25r on 1k red brn & dk grn, *straw* 60.00 60.00
256 SP6 25r on 3k mar & gray grn, *pink* 60.00 60.00
257 SP7 50r on 7 dk brn & dk grn, *buff* 20.00 20.00
258 SP5 100r on 1k red brn & dk grn, *straw* 3.25 3.50
259 SP6 100r on 3k mar & gray grn, *pink* 3.25 3.50
260 SP7 100r on 7k dk brn & dk grn, *buff* 3.25 3.50

On Stamps of 1915-19

261 SP5 25r on 1k org brn & gray 75.00 75.00
262 SP6 25r on 3k car & gray 30.00 30.00
263 SP8 50r on 10k dk bl & brn 25.00 25.00
264 SP5 100r on 1k org brn & gray 3.25 3.50
265 SP8 100r on 10k dk bl & brn 3.25 3.50

These surcharged semi-postal stamps were used for ordinary postage.

A set of 10 stamps in the above designs, and in a third design showing a woman quilling, was prepared in 1920, but not issued. Value of set, $4. Exist with "SPECIMEN" overprint and imperf. Reprints exist.

Armenia stamps can be mounted in the Scott annually supplemented Russia album part 1.

Soviet Socialist Republic

Hammer and Sickle — A7

Mythological Monster — A8

Symbols of Soviet Republics on Designs from old Armenian Manuscripts — A9

Ruined City of Ani — A10

Mythological Monster — A11

Armenian Soldier — A12

Soviet Symbols, Armenian Designs — A14

Mythological Monster — A13

Mt. Alagöz and Plain of Shirak A15

Fisherman on River Aras — A16

Post Office in Erevan and Mt. Ararat A17

Ruin in City of Ani — A18

Street in Erevan — A19

Lake Sevan and Sevan Monastery A20

Mythological Subject from old Armenian Monument — A21

Mt. Ararat A22

1921 Unwmk. ***Perf. 11½, Imperf.***

278 A7	1r gray green	.30	
279 A8	2r slate gray	.30	
280 A9	3r carmine	.30	
281 A10	5r dark brown	.30	
282 A11	25r gray	.30	.20
283 A12	50r red	.15	
284 A13	100r orange	.15	
285 A14	250r dark blue	.15	
286 A15	500r brown vio	.15	
287 A16	1000r sea green	.25	
288 A17	2000r bister	.30	
289 A18	5000r dark brown	.30	
290 A19	10,000r dull red	.30	
291 A20	15,000r slate blue	.30	
292 A21	20,000r lake	.30	
293 A22	25,000r gray blue	.65	
294 A22	25,000r brown olive	5.50	
	Nos. 278-294 (17)	10.00	

Except the 25r, Nos. 278-294 were not regularly issued and used. Counterfeits exist.

For surcharges see Nos. 347-390.

Russian Stamps of 1909-17 Surcharged

Wove Paper
Lozenges of Varnish on Face

1921, Aug. ***Perf. 13½***

295 A9	5000r on 1r	2.00
296 A12	5000r on 3½r	2.00
297 A13	5000r on 5r	2.00
298 A12	5000r on 7r	2.00
299 A13	5000r on 10r	2.00
	Nos. 295-299 (5)	10.00

Nos. 295-299 were not officially issued. Counterfeits abound.

Mt. Ararat and Soviet Star
A23 A24

Soviet Symbols — A25

Crane — A26

Peasant — A27

Harpy — A28

Peasant Sowing — A29

Soviet Symbols — A30

Forging — A31

Plowing A32

1922 ***Perf. 11½***

300 A23	50r green & red	.35
301 A24	300r slate bl & buff	.40
302 A25	400r blue & pink	.40
303 A26	500r vio & pale lil	.40
304 A27	1000r dull bl & pale bl	.40
305 A28	2000r black & gray	.65
306 A29	3000r black & grn	.65
307 A30	4000r black & lt brn	.65
308 A31	5000r black & dull red	.55
309 A32	10,000r black & pale rose	.55
a.	Tête bêche pair	11.00
	Nos. 300-309 (10)	5.00

Nos. 300 to 309 were not placed in use without surcharge.

Stamps of types A23 to A32, printed in other colors than Nos. 300 to 309, are essays.

Nos. 300-309 with Handstamped Surcharge of New Values in Rose, Violet or Black

1922

310 10,000 on 50r (R)	4.75	4.75
311 10,000 on 50r (V)	5.00	5.00
312 10,000 on 50r	2.00	2.00
313 15,000 on 300r (R)	25.00	25.00
314 15,000 on 300r (V)	5.00	5.00
315 15,000 on 300r	5.00	5.00
316 25,000 on 400r (V)	5.00	5.00
317 25,000 on 400r	2.00	2.00
318 30,000 on 500r (R)	9.00	9.00
319 30,000 on 500r (V)	.75	.75
320 30,000 on 500r	5.00	5.00
321 50,000 on 1000r (R)	7.25	7.25
322 50,000 on 1000r (V)	5.00	5.00
323 50,000 on 1000r	5.00	5.00
324 75,000 on 3000r	4.00	4.00
325 100,000 on 2000r (R)	70.00	70.00
326 100,000 on 2000r (V)	10.00	10.00
327 100,000 on 2000r	5.00	5.00
328 200,000 on 4000r (V)	5.00	5.00
329 200,000 on 4000r	10.00	10.00
330 300,000 on 5000r (V)	20.00	20.00
331 300,000 on 5000r	5.00	5.00
332 500,000 on 10,000r (V)	10.00	10.00
333 500,000 on 10,000r	10.00	10.00
Nos. 310-333 (24)	234.75	234.75

Goose — A33

Armenian Woman at Well — A35

Armenian Village Scene — A34

Mt. Ararat — A36

Mt. Ararat A37

New Values in Gold Kopecks, Handstamped Surcharge in Black

1922 ***Imperf.***

334 A33	1(k) on 250r rose	8.00	8.00
335 A33	1(k) on 250r gray	14.00	14.00
336 A34	2(k) on 500r rose	5.50	5.50
337 A34	3(k) on 500r gray	5.50	5.50
338 A35	4(k) on 1000r rose	5.50	5.50
339 A35	4(k) on 1000r gray	10.00	10.00
340 A36	5(k) on 2000r gray	5.50	5.50
341 A36	10(k) on 2000r rose	5.50	5.50
342 A37	15(k) on 5000r rose	35.00	35.00
343 A37	20(k) on 5000r gray	5.50	5.50
	Nos. 334-343 (10)	100.00	100.00

Nos. 334-343 were issued for postal tax purposes.

Nos. 334-343 exist without surcharge but are not known to have been issued in that condition. Counterfeits exist of both sets.

Regular Issue of 1921 Handstamped with New Values in Black or Red
Short, Thick Numerals

1922 ***Imperf.***

347 A8	2(k) on 2r (R)	25.00	25.00
350 A11	4(k) on 25r (R)	10.00	10.00
353 A13	10(k) on 100r (R)	7.50	7.50
354 A14	15(k) on 250r	3.00	3.00
355 A15	20(k) on 500r	15.00	15.00
a.	With "k" written in red	10.00	10.00
357 A22	50(k) on 25,000r bl (R)	12.00	12.00
358 A22	50(k) on 25,000r brn ol (R)	9.00	9.00
359 A22	50(k) on 25,000r brn ol		
	Nos. 347-358 (7)	81.50	81.50

Perf. 11½

360 A7	1(k) on 1r, imperf.	*25.00*	*25.00*
a.	Perf.	*15.00*	*15.00*
361 A7	1(k) on 1r (R)	*35.00*	*35.00*
a.	Imperf.	*40.00*	*40.00*
362 A8	2(k) on 2r, imperf.	*40.00*	*40.00*
a.	Perf.	*40.00*	*40.00*
363 A15	2(k) on 500r	*35.00*	*35.00*
a.	Imperf.	*50.00*	*50.00*
364 A15	2(k) on 500r (R)	9.00	9.00
365 A11	4(k) on 25r, imperf.	*25.00*	*25.00*
a.	Perf.	*25.00*	*25.00*
366 A12	5(k) on 50r, imperf.	1.75	1.75
a.	Perf.	*2.50*	*2.50*
367 A13	10(k) on 100r	*20.00*	*20.00*
a.	Imperf.	*20.00*	*20.00*
368 A21	35(k) on 20,000r, imperf.	*50.00*	*50.00*
a.	With "k" written in violet	*50.00*	*50.00*
b.	Perf.	*65.00*	*65.00*
c.	As "a," perf.	*65.00*	*65.00*
d.	With "kop" written in violet, imperf.		
	Nos. 360-368 (9)	240.75	240.75

Manuscript Surcharge in Red

Perf. 11½

371 A14	1k on 250r dk bl	*40.00*	*40.00*

Handstamped in Black or Red

Tall, Thin Numerals

Imperf

377 A11	4(k) on 25r (R)	4.25	4.25
379 A13	10(k) on 100r	10.00	10.00
380 A15	20(k) on 500r	6.00	6.00
381 A22	50k on 25,000r bl	*75.00*	*75.00*
a.	Surcharged "50" only	50.00	50.00
382 A22	50k on 25,000r bl (R)	12.00	12.00
382A A22	50k on 25,000r brn ol	24.00	24.00
	Nos. 377-382A (6)	131.25	131.25

On Nos. 381, 382 and 382A the letter "k" forms part of the surcharge.

Perf. 11½

383 A7	1(k) on 1r (R)	3.00	3.00
a.	Imperf.		

384 A14 1(k) on 250r 1.75 1.75
385 A15 2(k) on 500r 8.00 8.00
a. Imperf. 12.00 12.00
386 A15 2(k) on 500r (R) 4.75 4.75
387 A9 3(k) on 3r 20.00 20.00
a. Imperf. 20.00 20.00
388 A21 3(k) on 20,000r, imperf. 10.00 10.00
a. Perf. 50.00 50.00
389 A11 4(k) on 25r 2.50 2.50
a. Imperf. 4.25 4.25
390 A12 5(k) on 50r, imperf. *10.00 10.00*
a. Perf. *15.00 15.00*
Nos. 383-390 (8) 60.00 60.00

Catalogue values for unused stamps in this section, from this point to the end of the section, are for Never Hinged items.

Mt. Ararat — A45

Designs: a, 20k. b, 2r. c, 5r. 7r, Eagle and Mt. Ararat.

1992, Apr. 28 Litho. *Perf. 14*
430 A45 Strip of 3, #a.-c. *3.75*

Souvenir Sheet

431 A45 7r multicolored *35.00*

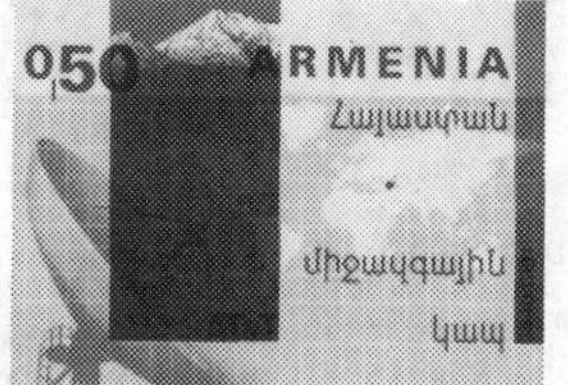

AT & T Communications System in Armenia — A45a

1992 Litho. *Perf. 13x13½*
431A A45a 50k multicolored *5.00*

A46

A47

1992 Summer Olympics, Barcelona: a, 40k, Ancient Greek wrestlers. b, 3.60r, Boxing. c, 5r, Weight lifting. d, 12r, Gymnastics.

1992 Litho. *Perf. 14*
432 A46 Strip of 4, #a.-d. *7.50*

1992-93 Litho. *Perf. 14½, 15x14½*

Designs: 20k, Natl. flag. 2r, Yerevan Airport. 1r, Goddess Waroubini, Orgov radio telescope. No. 435, Goddess Anahit. No. 436, Runic message, 7th cent B.C. 5r, UPU emblem. 20r, Silver cup.

433 A47 20k multicolored *.15*
434 A47 1r black *.15*
435 A47 2r blue *1.00*
436 A47 3r brown *1.65*
437 A47 3r brown *.15*
438 A47 5r brown black *2.75*
439 A47 20r gray *.15*
Nos. 433-439 (7) *6.00*

No. 435 is airmail. See Nos. 464-471.
Issued: #436, 20k, 2r, 5r, 8/25/92; others, 7/93.

David of Sassoun, by Hakop Kojoian — A50a

Religious Artifacts — A50

Yerevan '93 — A52

Scenic Views — A51

1993, May 23 Litho. *Perf. 14*
448 A50 40k Marker *.15*
449 A50 80k Gospel page *.30*
450 A50 3.60r Bas-relief, 13th cent. *1.25*
451 A50 5r Icon of the Madonna *1.90*
Nos. 448-451 (4) *3.60*

Souvenir Sheet
Perf. 14x13½

451A A50a 12r multicolored *4.50*

1993, May 24 *Perf. 14*

Designs (illustration reduced): 40k, Garni Canyon, vert. 80k, Shaki Waterfall, Zangezur, vert. 3.60r, Arpa River Canyon, vert. 5r, Lake Sevan. 12r, Mount Aragats.

452 A51 40k multicolored *.15*
453 A51 80k multicolored *.15*
454 A51 3.60r multicolored *.60*
455 A51 5r multicolored *.80*
456 A51 12r multicolored *2.00*
Nos. 452-456 (5) *3.70*

1993, May 25 *Perf. 14½*
457 A52 10r multicolored *.70*
a. Min. sheet of 6 + 2 labels *7.50*

For surcharges see Nos. 485-486.

Souvenir Sheet

Noah's Descent from Mt. Ararat, by Hovhannes Aivazovsky — A52

1993, May 24 Litho. *Perf. 14½*
458 A52 7r multicolored *1.10*

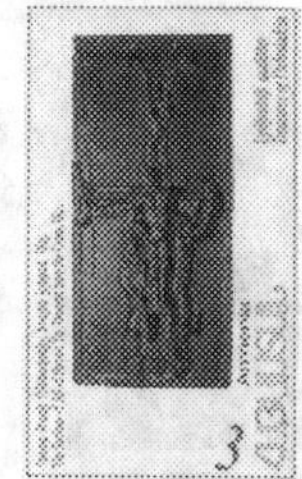

Religious Relics, Echmiadzin — A53

Designs: 3r, Wooden panel, descent from cross, 9th cent. 5r, Gilded silver reliquary for Holy Cross of Khotakerats. 12r, Cross depicting right hand of St. Karapet, 14th cent. 30r, Reliquary for arm of St. Thaddeus the Apostle, 17th cent. 50r, Gilded silver vessel for consecrated ointment, 1815.

1994, Aug. 4 Litho. *Perf. 14x14½*
459 A53 3d multicolored *.15*
460 A53 5d multicolored *.20*
461 A53 12d multicolored *.45*
462 A53 30d multicolored *1.25*
463 A53 50d multicolored *2.00*
Nos. 459-463 (5) *4.05*

Artifacts and Landmarks Type of 1993

Gods of Van (Urartu): 10 l, Shivini, god of the sun. 50 l, Tayshaba, god of elements. 10d, Khaldi, supreme god.
25d, Natl. arms.

1994 *Perf. 14½*
464 A47 10 l black & brown *.15*
465 A47 50 l black & red brown *.15*
469 A47 10d black & gray *.55*
471 A47 25d red & bister *1.40*
Nos. 464-471 (4) *2.25*

Issued: 10 l, 50 l, 10d, 25d, 8/4/94.
This is an expanding set. Numbers may change.

Anniversaries & Events — A54

Designs: 16d, #1a. No. 480, Early printing press, vert. No. 481, Natl. arms, stadium, vert. 40d, Olympic rings, vert. No. 483, Ervand Otian (1869-1926), vert. No. 484, Levon Shant (1869-1951).

Perf. 14½x14, 14x14½

1994, Dec. 31 Litho.
479 A54 16d multi *.45*
480 A54 30d multi *.85*
481 A54 30d multi *.85*
482 A54 40d multi *1.10*
483 A54 50d multi + label *1.40*
484 A54 50d multi + label *1.40*
Nos. 479-484 (6) *6.05*

First Armenian postage stamp, 75th anniv. (#479). First Armenian periodical, 170th anniv. (#480). Natl. Olympic Committee (#481). Intl. Olympic Committee, Cent. (#482).

No. 457 Surcharged in Blue or Red Brown

40
a

40
b

1994, Sept. 10 Litho. *Perf. 14*
485 A52(a) 40d on 10r (Bl) *2.50 2.50*
486 A52(b) 40d on 10r (RB) *2.50 2.50*

Yerevan '94.

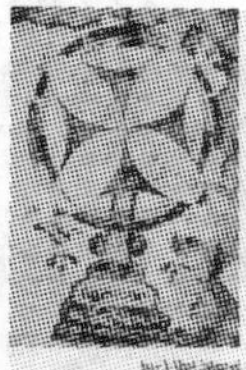

A55

A56

Christianity in Armenia: 60d, Cross, 10th-11th cent. No. 488, Kings Abgar & Trdat, 1836. No. 489, St. Bartholomew, St. Thaddeus. 80d, St. Gregory, the Illuminator. 90d, Baptism of the Armenian people, 1892. 400d, Plan of Echmiadzin, c. 1660, engr. by Jakob Peeters.

1995, Apr. 3 Litho. *Perf. 14x15*
487 A55 60d multicolored *2.00 2.00*
488 A55 70d multicolored *2.25 2.25*
489 A55 70d multicolored *2.25 2.25*
490 A55 80d multicolored *2.50 2.50*
491 A55 90d multicolored *3.00 3.00*
Nos. 487-491 (5) *12.00 12.00*

Souvenir Sheet

492 A55 400d multicolored *13.00 13.00*

Nos. 488-489 are 45x44mm.

1995, Apr. 3
493 A56 150d gray & black *2.75 2.75*

Vazgen I (1908-94), Patriarch, Armenian Orthodox Church.

Armenian Fund — A57

1995 *Perf. 15x14*
494 A57 90d multicolored *1.90 1.90*

UN, 50th Anniv. A58

1995
495 A58 90d multicolored *1.90 1.90*

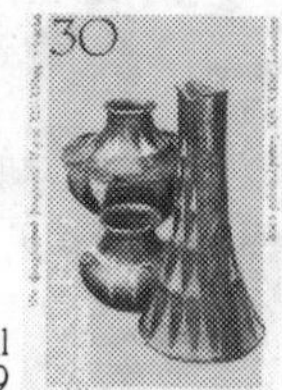

Cultural Artifacts — A59

Designs: 30d, Black polished pottery, 14th-13th cent. B.C. 60d, Silver cup, 5th cent. B.C. 130d, Gohar carpet, 1700 A.D.

1995 *Perf. 15x14*
496 A59 30d multicolored *.55 .55*
497 A59 60d multicolored *1.10 1.10*
498 A59 130d multicolored *2.50 2.50*
Nos. 496-498 (3) *4.15 4.15*

Birds — A60

1995 *Perf. 14*
499 A60 40d Milvus milvus *1.00 1.00*
500 A60 60d Aquila chrysaetos *1.50 1.50*

End of World War II, 50th Anniv. A61

Designs: No. 501, P. Kitsook, 408th Armenian Rifle Division. No. 502, A. Sargissin, N. Safarian, 89th Taman Armenian Triple Order-Bearer Division. No. 503, B. Chernikov, N. Tavartkeladze, V. Penkovsky, 76th Armenian Alpine Rifle Red Banner (51st Guards) Division. No. 504, S. Zakian, H. Babayan, I. Lyudnikov, 390th Armenian Rifle Division. No. 505, A. Vasillian, M. Dobrovolsky, Y. Grechany, G. Sorokin, 409th Armenian Rifle Division.

No. 506, vert.: a, Marshal Hovhannes Baghramian. b, Adm. Hovhannes Issakov. c, Marshal Hamazasp Babajanian. d, Marshal Sergey Khoudyakov.

No. 507: Return of the Hero, by Mariam Aslamazian.

1995 Litho. *Perf. 15x14*

501 A61 60d multicolored	.80	.80
502 A61 60d multicolored	.80	.80
503 A61 60d multicolored	.80	.80
504 A61 60d multicolored	.80	.80
505 A61 60d multicolored	.80	.80
Nos. 501-505 (5)	*4.00*	*4.00*

Miniature Sheet

Perf. 15x14½

506 A61 60d Sheet of 4, #a.-d.	*3.25*	*3.25*

Souvenir Sheet

Perf. 15x14

507 A61 300d multicolored	*4.00*	*4.00*

Authors A62

Designs: No. 508, Ghevond Alishan (1820-1901). No. 509, Gregor Artsruni (1845-92), vert. No. 510, Franz Werfel (1890-1945).

1995 Litho. *Perf. 15x14*

508 A62 90d blue & black	*1.00*	*1.00*
509 A62 90d multicolored	*1.00*	*1.00*
510 A62 90d blue & maroon	*1.00*	*1.00*
Nos. 508-510 (3)	*3.00*	*3.00*

Nos. 508-510 issued with se-tenant label.

A63

A64

Design: 90d, Artiom Katsian (1886-1943), world record holding pilot on range and altitude in 1909.

1995, Dec. 5 Litho. *Perf. 14x15*

511 A63 90d multicolored	*1.50*	*1.50*

1995, Dec. 5 *Perf. 14½x15, 15x14½*

Prehistoric artifacts: 40d, Four-wheeled carriages, 15th cent. BC, horiz. 60d, Bronze model of geocentric solar system, 11-10th cent. BC. 90d, Tombstone, Red Tufa, 7-6th cent. BC.

512 A64 40d multicolored	.65	.65
513 A64 60d multicolored	*1.00*	*1.00*
514 A64 90d multicolored	*1.50*	*1.50*
Nos. 512-514 (3)	*3.15*	*3.15*

A65

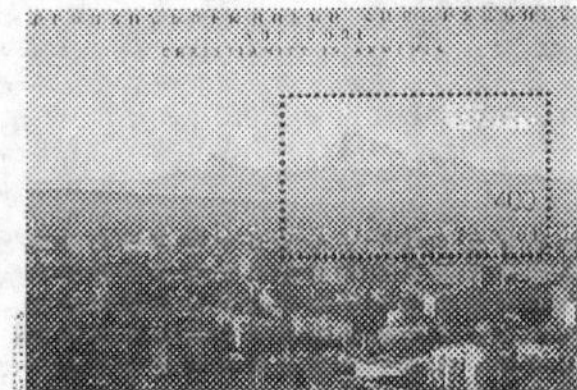

Christianity in Armenia — A66

Views of Yerevan: 60d, Brandy distillery, wine cellars. 80d, Abovian Street. 90d, Sports and concert complex. 100d, Baghramian Avenue. 120d, Republic Square.

400d, Panoramic photograph of Yerevan.

1995, Dec. 5 *Perf. 15x14*

515 A65 60d salmon & black	*1.00*	*1.00*
516 A65 80d pale orange & black	*1.30*	*1.30*
517 A65 90d buff & black	*1.50*	*1.50*

Size: 61x24mm

518 A65 100d pale yellow bis & blk	*1.65*	*1.65*
519 A65 120d dull orange & black	*2.00*	*2.00*
Nos. 515-519 (5)	*7.45*	*7.45*

Souvenir Sheet

520 A66 400d multicolored	*6.50*	*6.50*

ARUBA

ə-'rü-bə

LOCATION — West Indies, north of Venezuela
AREA — 78 sq. mi.
POP. — 67,014

On Jan. 1, 1986 Aruba, formerly part of Netherlands Antilles, achieved a separate status within the Kingdom.

100 Cents = 1 Gulden

Catalogue values for all unused stamps in this country are for Never Hinged items.

Traditional House — A1

1986-87 Litho. *Perf. 14x13*

1 A1 5c shown	.15	.15
2 A1 15c King William III Tower	.15	.15
3 A1 20c Loading crane	.15	.15
4 A1 25c Lighthouse	.20	.20
5 A1 30c Snake	.25	.25
6 A1 35c Owl	.30	.30
7 A1 45c Shell	.40	.40
8 A1 55c Frog	.50	.50
9 A1 60c Water skier	.55	.55
10 A1 65c Net fishing	.60	.60
11 A1 75c Music box	.70	.70
12 A1 85c Pre-Columbian bisque pot	.75	.75
13 A1 90c Bulb cactus	.80	.80
14 A1 100c Grain	.85	.85
15 A1 150c Watapana tree	1.40	1.40
16 A1 250c Aloe plant	2.25	2.25
Nos. 1-16 (16)	10.00	10.00

Issue dates: 5c, 30c, 60c, 150c, Jan. 1. 15c, 35c, 65c, 250c, Feb. 5. 20c, 45c, 75c, 100c, Apr. 7, 1987. 25c, 55c, 85c, 90c, July 17, 1987.

Independence A2

1986, Jan. 1 *Perf. 14x13, 13x14*

18 A2 25c Map	.20	.20
19 A2 45c Coat of arms, vert.	.35	.35
20 A2 55c Natl. anthem, vert.	.45	.45
21 A2 100c Flag	.75	.75
Nos. 18-21 (4)	1.75	1.75

Intl. Peace Year — A3

1986, Aug. 29 Litho. *Perf. 14x13*

22 A3 60c shown	.45	.45
23 A3 100c Barbed wire	.75	.75

Princess Juliana and Prince Bernhard, 50th Wedding Anniv. — A4

1987, Jan. 7 Photo. *Perf. 13x14*

24 A4 135c multicolored	1.25	1.25

State Visit of Queen Beatrix and Prince Claus of the Netherlands A5

1987, Feb. 16 Litho. *Perf. 14x13*

25 A5 55c shown	.50	.50
26 A5 60c Prince William-Alexander	.50	.50

Tourism — A6

1987, June 5 Litho.

27 A6 60c Beach and sea	.90	.90
28 A6 100c Rock and cacti	1.50	1.50

Aloe Vera Plant — A7 Coins — A8

1988, Jan. 27 Litho. *Perf. 13x14*

29 A7 45c Field	.50	.50
30 A7 60c Plant	.65	.65
31 A7 100c Harvest	1.10	1.10
Nos. 29-31 (3)	2.25	2.25

1988, Mar. 16 Litho. *Perf. 13x14*

32 A8 25c 25-cent	.35	.35
33 A8 55c 50-cent	.70	.70
34 A8 65c 5 and 10-cent	.85	.85
35 A8 150c 1-florin	2.00	2.00
Nos. 32-35 (4)	3.90	3.90

Love Issue — A9 A10

1988, May 4

36 A9 70c shown	.75	.75
37 A9 135c Seashells, coastal scenery	1.45	1.45

1988, Aug. 24

38 A10 35c shown	.40	.40
39 A10 100c Emblems	1.10	1.10

Aruba, the 162nd member of the Intl. Olympic Committee (35c), 1988 Summer Olympics, Seoul (100c).

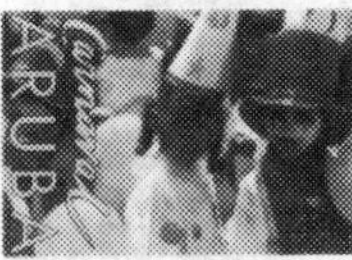

Carnival — A11

1989, Jan. 5 *Perf. 14x13*

40 A11 45c Two children	.45	.45
41 A11 60c Girl	.60	.60
42 A11 100c Entertainer	1.00	1.00
Nos. 40-42 (3)	2.05	2.05

Maripampun, *Omphalophalmum zumbrum* — A12

1989, Mar. 16 Litho. *Perf. 14x13*

43 A12 35c Leaves	.35	.35
44 A12 55c Pods	.55	.55
45 A12 200c Blossom	1.95	1.95
Nos. 43-45 (3)	2.85	2.85

New Year 1990 — A13

UPU — A14

Dande band members playing instruments or singing: 25c, Violin, tambor, cuatro, marimba. 70c, Lead singer, guitar. 150c, Accordion, urri, guitar.

1989, Nov. 16 Litho. *Perf. 13x14*

46 A13 25c multicolored	.25	.25
47 A13 70c multicolored	.70	.70
48 A13 150c multicolored	1.50	1.50
Nos. 46-48 (3)	2.45	2.45

1989, June 8 Litho. *Perf. 13x14*

49 A14 250c multicolored	2.50	2.50

Crotalus durissus unicolor — A15

1989, Aug. 24 *Perf. 14x13*

50 A15 45c shown	.50	.50
51 A15 55c multi, diff.	.60	.60
52 A15 60c multi, diff.	.70	.70
Nos. 50-52 (3)	1.80	1.80

Species in danger of extinction.

Man Living in Harmony with Nature — A16

1990, Feb. 7 *Perf. 13x14, 14x13*

53 A16 45c The land	.50	.50
54 A16 55c shown	.60	.60
55 A16 100c The sea	1.15	1.15
Nos. 53-55 (3)	2.25	2.25

Environmental protection. #53, 55 horiz.

Marine Life — A17

Designs: 60c, Giant caribbean anemone, Pederson's cleaning shrimp. 70c, Queen angelfish, red and orange coral. 100c, Banded coral shrimp, fire sponge, yellow boring sponge.

1990, Apr. 4 Litho. *Perf. 14x13*

56 A17 60c multicolored .70 .70
57 A17 70c multicolored .80 .80
58 A17 100c multicolored 1.15 1.15
Nos. 56-58 (3) 2.65 2.65

A18

A19

1990, May 30 Litho. *Perf. 13x14*

59 A18 35c multicolored .30 .30
60 A18 200c Character trademark 1.75 1.75

World Cup Soccer Championships, Italy.

1990, Sept. 12

61 A19 45c Tools .50 .50
62 A19 60c Stone figure .65 .65
63 A19 100c Jar 1.05 1.05
Nos. 61-63 (3) 2.20 2.20

Archeological discoveries.

Landscapes A20

1991, Jan. 31 Litho. *Perf. 14x13*

64 A20 55c Seashore .60 .60
65 A20 65c Desert .70 .70
66 A20 100c Cactus, ocean view 1.10 1.10
Nos. 64-66 (3) 2.40 2.40

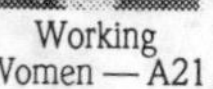

Working Women — A21

Medicinal Plants — A22

Designs: 35c, Taking care of others. 70c, Housewife. 100c, Women in society.

1991, Mar. 28 Litho. *Perf. 13x14*

67 A21 35c multicolored .40 .40
68 A21 70c multicolored .85 .85
69 A21 100c multicolored 1.25 1.25
Nos. 67-69 (3) 2.50 2.50

Style of inscriptions varies.

1991, May 29

70 A22 65c Ocimum sanctum .70 .70
71 A22 75c Jatropha gossypifolia .80 .80
72 A22 95c Croton flavens 1.05 1.05
Nos. 70-72 (3) 2.55 2.55

A23

A24

Aruban Handicrafts: 35c, Fish net, wood float, wooden needle. 250c, Straw hat, hat block.

1991, July 31 Litho. *Perf. 13x14*

73 A23 35c lt bl, dk bl & blk .40 .40
74 A23 250c pink, lil rose & blk 2.75 2.75

1991, Nov. 29 Litho. *Perf. 13x14*

75 A24 35c Toucan .40 .40
76 A24 70c People shaking hands .75 .75
77 A24 100c Windmill 1.10 1.10
Nos. 75-77 (3) 2.25 2.25

Welcome to Aruba.

Aruba Postal Service, Cent. — A25

Designs: 60c, Government decree, 1892, vert. 75c, First post office. 80c, Current post office.

Perf. 13x14, 14x13

1992, Jan. 31 Litho.

78 A25 60c multicolored .65 .65
79 A25 75c multicolored .85 .85
80 A25 80c multicolored .90 .90
Nos. 78-80 (3) 2.40 2.40

Equality Day — A26

1992, Mar. 25 Litho. *Perf. 14x13*

81 A26 100c People of five races 1.00 1.00
82 A26 100c Woman, man, scales 1.00 1.00

Discovery of America, 500th Anniv. — A27

1992, July 30 Litho. *Perf. 13x14*

83 A27 30c Columbus .35 .35
84 A27 40c Sailing ship .45 .45
85 A27 50c Natives, map .55 .55
Nos. 83-85 (3) 1.35 1.35

Natural Bridges in Aruba — A28

Designs: 70c, Seroe Colorado Bridge, south coast. 80c, Natural Bridge, north coast.

1992, Nov. 30 Litho. *Perf. 14x13*

86 A28 70c multicolored .85 .85
87 A28 80c multicolored .90 .90

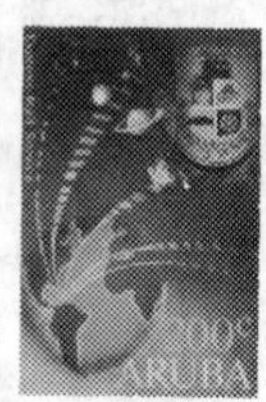

A29

A30

1993, Jan. 29 Litho. *Perf. 13x14*

88 A29 200c multicolored 2.50 2.50

Express mail service.

1993, Mar. 31 Litho. *Perf. 13x14*

Various rock formations found in Districts of Ayo and Casibari.

89 A30 50c multicolored .65 .65
90 A30 60c multicolored .75 .75
91 A30 100c multicolored 1.25 1.25
Nos. 89-91 (3) 2.65 2.65

Folklore — A31

Sailing Sports — A32

Designs: 40c, String instruments, drum. 70c, Traditional music and games. 80c, Dera Gai song lyrics.

1993, May 28 Litho. *Perf. 13x14*

92 A31 40c multicolored .50 .50
93 A31 70c multicolored .85 .85
94 A31 80c multicolored 1.00 1.00
Nos. 92-94 (3) 2.35 2.35

1993, July 30 Litho. *Perf. 13x14*

95 A32 50c Sailboating .60 .60
96 A32 65c Land sailing .80 .80
97 A32 75c Wind surfing .95 .95
Nos. 95-97 (3) 2.35 2.35

Iguana Iguana — A33

Perf. 14x13, 13x14

1993, Sept. 1 Litho.

98 A33 35c Young .45 .45
99 A33 60c Almost grown .75 .75
100 A33 100c Mature, vert. 1.25 1.25
Nos. 98-100 (3) 2.45 2.45

Burrowing Owl — A34

Perf. 14x13, 13x14

1994, Jan. 28 Litho.

101 A34 5c Two adults .15 .15
102 A34 10c Two adults, young .15 .15
103 A34 35c Adult with prey, vert. .45 .45
104 A34 40c Adult, vert. .50 .50
Nos. 101-104 (4) 1.25 1.25

World Wildlife Fund.

A35

A36

Intl. Olympic Committee, Cent.: 90c, Baron Pierre de Coubertin (1863-1937), founder of modern Olympics.

1994, Mar. 29 Litho. *Perf. 13x14*

105 A35 50c multicolored .65 .65
106 A35 90c multicolored 1.10 1.10

1994, July 7 Litho. *Perf. 13x14*

107 A36 65c shown .80 .80
108 A36 150c Mascot, soccer ball 1.90 1.90

1994 World Cup Soccer Championships, US.

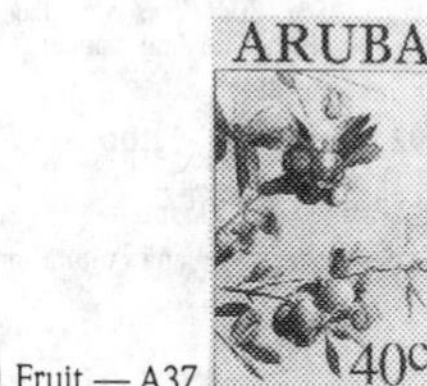

Wild Fruit — A37

Designs: 40c, Malpighia punicifolia. 70c, Cordia sebestena. 85c, Pithecellobium unguis-cati. 150c, Coccoloba uvifera.

1994, Sept. 28 Litho. *Perf. 13x14*

109 A37 40c multicolored .50 .50
110 A37 70c multicolored .90 .90
111 A37 85c multicolored 1.10 1.10
112 A37 150c multicolored 1.90 1.90
Nos. 109-112 (4) 4.40 4.40

Architectural Landmarks A38

Designs: 35c, Government building, 1888. 60c, Ecury residence, 1929, vert. 100c, Protestant Church, 1846, vert.

1995, Jan. 27 Litho. *Perf. 14x13*

113 A38 35c multicolored .45 .45

Perf. 13x14

114 A38 60c multicolored .75 .75
115 A38 100c multicolored 1.25 1.25
Nos. 113-115 (3) 2.45 2.45

UN, 50th Anniv. — A39

Interpaso Horses — A40

Designs: 30c, Flags, sea, UN emblem, dove, text from UN charter. 200c, World with flags, doves, UN emblem.

1995, Mar. 29 Litho. *Perf. 13x14*

116 A39 30c multicolored .35 .35
117 A39 200c multicolored 2.25 2.25

1995, May 26 *Perf. 14x13, 13x14*

Designs: 25c, 10-time champion Casanova II, ribbons, horiz. 75c, Paso Fino, horiz. 80c, Horse doing figure 8. 90c, Girl on horse.

118 A40 25c multicolored .28 .28
119 A40 75c multicolored .85 .85
120 A40 80c multicolored .90 .90
121 A40 90c multicolored 1.00 1.00
Nos. 118-121 (4) 3.03 3.03

Vegetables — A41

1995, July 28 Litho. *Perf. 13x14*

122 A41 25c Vigna sinensis .30 .30
123 A41 50c Cucumis anguria .55 .55
124 A41 70c Hibiscus esculentus .80 .80
125 A41 85c Cucurbita moschata .95 .95
Nos. 122-125 (4) 2.60 2.60

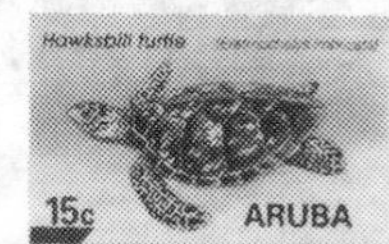

Turtles — A42

1995, Sept. 27 Litho. *Perf. 14x13*

126 A42 15c Hawksbill .15 .15
127 A42 50c Green .55 .55
128 A42 95c Loggerhead 1.00 1.00
129 A42 100c Leatherback 1.10 1.10
Nos. 126-129 (4) 2.80 2.80

Separate Status, 10th Anniv. — A43

Statesmen and politicians: No. 130, Jan Hendrik Albert Eman (1887-1957). No. 131, Juan Enrique Irausquin (1904-62). No. 132, Cornelis Albert Eman (1916-67). No. 133, Gilberto Francois Croes (1938-86).

1996, Jan. 1 Litho. *Perf. 13x14*

130 A43	100c multicolored	1.10	1.10
131 A43	100c multicolored	1.10	1.10
132 A43	100c multicolored	1.10	1.10
133 A43	100c multicolored	1.10	1.10
	Nos. 130-133 (4)	4.40	4.40

SEMI-POSTAL STAMPS

Solidarity SP1

1986, May 7 Litho. *Perf. 14x13*

B1 SP1	30c + 10c shown	.30	.30
B2 SP1	35c + 15c Three ropes	.40	.40
B3 SP1	60c + 25c One rope	.60	.60
	Nos. B1-B3 (3)	1.30	1.30

Surtax for social and cultural projects.

Child Welfare — SP2

1986, Oct. 29 Litho. *Perf. 14x13*

B4 SP2	45c + 20c Boy, caterpillar	.70	.70
B5 SP2	70c + 25c Boy, cocoon	1.00	1.00
B6 SP2	100c + 40c Girl, butterfly	1.50	1.50
	Nos. B4-B6 (3)	3.20	3.20

Surtax for child welfare organizations.

Christmas SP3

1987, Oct. 27 Litho. *Perf. 14x13*

B7 SP3	25c +10c Boy on beach	.35	.35
B8 SP3	45c +20c Drawing Christmas tree	.70	.70
B9 SP3	70c +30c Child, creche figures	1.10	1.10
	Nos. B7-B9 (3)	2.15	2.15

Surtax for child welfare organizations.

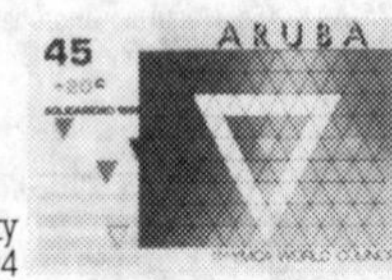
Solidarity SP4

YMCA emblem in various geometric designs.

1988, Aug. 3 Litho. *Perf. 14x13*

B10 SP4	45c +20c shown	.70	.70
B11 SP4	60c +25c multi, diff.	.90	.90
B12 SP4	100c +50c multi, diff.	1.60	1.60
	Nos. B10-B12 (3)	3.20	3.20

11th YMCA world council.
Surtax for social and cultural projects.

Aruba stamps can be mounted in the Scott annual Netherlands supplement.

Children's Toys — SP5

1988, Oct. 26 *Perf. 13x14*

B13 SP5	45c +20c Jacks	.70	.70
B14 SP5	70c +30c Top	1.10	1.10
B15 SP5	100c +50c Kite	1.60	1.60
	Nos. B13-B15 (3)	3.40	3.40

Surtax for child welfare organizations.

Children — SP6

1989, Oct. 26 *Perf. 14x13*

B16 SP6	45c +20c Baby spoon	.65	.65
B17 SP6	60c +30c Chasing a ball	.85	.85
B18 SP6	100c +50c Adult & child holding hands	1.50	1.50
	Nos. B16-B18 (3)	3.00	3.00

Surtax for child welfare organizations.

Solidarity — SP7

1990, July 25

B19 SP7	55c +25c shown	1.10	1.10
B20 SP7	100c +50c Family, house	2.00	2.00

Surtax for social and cultural projects.

SP8 SP9

Christmas song.

1990, Oct. 24 Litho. *Perf. 13x14*

B21 SP8	45c +20c Wind surfboards	.75	.75
B22 SP8	60c +30c shown	1.05	1.05
B23 SP8	100c +50c Kites, lizard	1.70	1.70
	Nos. B21-B23 (3)	3.50	3.50

Surtax for child welfare organizations.

1991, Oct. 25 Litho. *Perf. 13x14*

Literacy: 45c+25c, Discovery of reading. 60c+35c, Pointing to letter. 100c+50c, Child reading.

B24 SP9	45c +25c multi	.75	.75
B25 SP9	60c +35c multi	1.00	1.00
B26 SP9	100c +50c multi	1.65	1.65
	Nos. B24-B26 (3)	3.40	3.40

Surtax for child welfare organizations.

Solidarity SP10

Designs: 55c+30c, Girl scouts, flag and emblem. 100c+50c, Hand holding cancer fund emblem, people.

1992, May 27 Litho. *Perf. 14x13*

B27 SP10	55c +30c multi	.90	.90
B28 SP10	100c +50c multi	1.65	1.65

Surtax for social and cultural projects.

Postal Services of Aruba, Cent. — SP11

Designs: 50c+30c, Heart. 70c+35c, Airplane, letters. 100c+55c, Pigeon with letter in beak, vert.

1992, Oct. 30 Litho. *Perf. 14x13*

B29 SP11	50c +30c multi	1.00	1.00
B30 SP11	70c +35c multi	1.40	1.40

Perf. 13x14

B31 SP11	100c +50c multi	2.00	2.00
	Nos. B29-B31 (3)	4.40	4.40

Surtax for child welfare organizations.

Youth Foreign Study Programs SP12

Abstract designs of: 50c+30c, Landscapes. 75c+40c, Young man, scenes of other countries, vert. 100c+50c, Integrating cultures.

Perf. 14x13, 13x14

1993, Oct. 27 Litho.

B32 SP12	50c +30c multi	1.00	1.00
B33 SP12	75c +40c multi	1.40	1.40
B34 SP12	100c +50c multi	1.90	1.90
	Nos. B32-B34 (3)	4.30	4.30

Surtax for child welfare organizations.

Intl. Year of the Family — SP13

Designs: 50c+35c, Family seated, reading, studying. 100c+50c, Family playing in front of house.

1994, May 30 Litho. *Perf. 14x13*

B35 SP13	50c +35c multi	1.10	1.10
B36 SP13	100c +50c multi	1.90	1.90

Surtax for social and cultural projects.

Child Welfare — SP14

Designs: 50c+30c, Children on anchor with umbrella. 80c+35c, Children inside Sun. 100c+50c, Child riding owl.

1994, Oct. 27 Litho. *Perf. 14x13*

B37 SP14	50c +30c multi	1.00	1.00
B38 SP14	80c +35c multi	1.40	1.40
B39 SP14	100c +50c multi	1.90	1.90
	Nos. B37-B39 (3)	4.30	4.30

Surtax for child welfare organizations.

SP15

Children's drawings: 50c+25c, Children with balloons, house. 70c+35c, Three people with picnic basket on sunny day. 100c+50c, People gardening on sunny day.

1995, Oct. 26 Litho. *Perf. 13x14*

B40 SP15	50c +25c multi	.85	.85
B41 SP15	70c +35c multi	1.25	1.25
B42 SP15	100c +50c multi	1.65	1.65
	Nos. B40-B42 (3)	3.75	3.75

Surtax for child welfare organizations.

AUSTRIA

'ós–trē–ə

LOCATION — Central Europe
GOVT. — Republic
AREA — 32,376 sq. mi.
POP. — 7,555,338 (1981)
CAPITAL — Vienna

Before 1867 Austria was an absolute monarchy, which included Hungary and Lombardy-Venetia. In 1867 the Austro-Hungarian Monarchy was established, with Austria and Hungary as equal partners. After World War I, in 1918, the different nationalities established their own states and only the German-speaking parts remained, forming a republic under the name "Deutschosterreich" (German Austria), which name was shortly again changed to "Austria." In 1938 German forces occupied Austria, which became part of the German Reich. After the liberation by Allied troops in 1945, an independent republic was re-established.

60 Kreuzer = 1 Gulden
100 Neu-Kreuzer = 1 Gulden (1858)
100 Heller = 1 Krone (1899)
100 Groschen = 1 Schilling (1925)

Catalogue values for unused stamps in this country are for Never Hinged items, beginning with Scott 432 in the regular postage section, Scott B165 in the semi-postal section, Scott C47 in the airpost section, Scott J175 in the postage due section, and Scott 4N1 in the AMG section.

Watermarks

Wmk. 91 - "BRIEF-MARKEN" In Double-lined Capitals Across the Middle of the Sheet

Wmk. 140 - Crown

Issues of the Austrian Monarchy (including Hungary)

Coat of Arms — A1

NINE KREUZER

Type I. One heavy line around coat of arms center. On the 9kr the top of "9" is about on a level with "Kreuzer" and not near the top of the label. Each cliche has the "9" in a different position.

Type IA. As type I, but with 1 1/4mm between "9" and "K."

Type II. One heavy line around coat of arms center. On the 9kr the top of "9" is much higher than the top of the word "Kreuzer" and nearly touches the top of the label.

Type III. As type II, but with two, thinner, lines around the center.

Wmk. K.K.H.M. in Sheet or Unwmk.
1850 Typo. *Imperf.*

The stamps of this issue were at first printed on a rough hand-made paper, varying in thickness and having a watermark in script letters K.K.H.M., the initials of Kaiserlich Königliches Handels-Ministerium (Imperial and Royal Ministry of Commerce), vertically in the gutter between the panes. Parts of these letters show on margin stamps in the sheet.

From 1854 a thick, smooth machine-made paper without watermark was used.

Thin to Thick Paper

1 A1 1kr yellow 900.00 70.00
a. Printed on both sides 1,900. 130.00
b. 1kr orange 1,100. 100.00
c. 1kr brown orange 1,900. 350.00
2 A1 2kr black 775.00 60.00
a. Ribbed paper 1,350.
b. 2kr gray black 1,100. 70.00
d. Half used as 1kr on cover 23,500.
3 A1 3kr red 300.00 3.00
a. Ribbed paper 1,600. 72.50
b. Laid paper 8,000.
c. Printed on both sides 7,500.
4 A1 6kr brown 475.00 4.00
a. Ribbed paper 1,150.
c. Diagonal half used as 3kr on cover 10,000.
5 A1 9kr blue, type II 650.00 3.00
a. 9kr blue, type I 1,150. 7.50
b. 9kr blue, type IA 13,500. 1,000.
c. Laid paper, type III 6,750.
d. Printed on both sides, type II 7,500.

1854 Machine-made Paper, Type III

1d A1 1kr yellow 800.00 67.50
2c A1 2kr black 675.00 47.50
3e A1 3kr red 250.00 2.00
f. 3kr red, type I 1,900. 25.00
4b A1 6kr brown 375.00 3.25
5e A1 9kr blue 500.00 2.25

In 1852-54, Nos. 1 to 5, rouletted 14, were used in Tokay and Homonna. A 12kr blue exists, but was not issued.

The reprints are type III in brighter colors, some on paper watermarked "Briefmarken" in the sheet.

For similar design see Lombardy-Venetia A1.

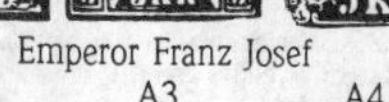

Emperor Franz Josef
A2 A3 A4

A5 A6

1858-59 Embossed *Perf. 14½*

Two Types of Each Value.

Type I. Loops of the bow at the back of the head broken, except the 2kr. In the 2kr, the "2" has a flat foot, thinning to the right. The frame line in the UR corner is thicker than the line below. In the 5kr the top frame line is unbroken.

Type II. Loops complete. Wreath projects further at top of head. In the 2kr, the "2" has a more curved foot of uniform thickness, with a shading line in the upper and lower curves. The frame line UR is thicker than the line below. In the 5kr the top frame line is broken.

6 A2 2kr yellow, type II 675.00 42.50
a. 2kr yellow, type I 1,600. 350.00
b. 2kr orange, type II 1,800. 250.00
c. Half used as 1kr on cover 25,000.
7 A3 3kr black, type II 1,900. 175.00
a. 3kr black, type I 1,100. 250.00
8 A3 3kr green, type II ('59) 925.00 125.00
9 A4 5kr red, type II 250.00 .85
a. 5kr red, type I 350.00 11.00
b. 5kr red, type II with type I frame 425.00 22.50
10 A5 10kr brown, type II 550.00 2.50
a. 10kr brown, type I 625.00 25.00
b. Half used as 5kr on cover 10,000.
11 A6 15kr blue, type II 550.00 2.00
a. Type I 1,050. 12.50

The reprints are of type II and are perforated 10½, 11, 12, 12½ and 13. There are also imperforate reprints of Nos. 6 to 8.

For similar designs see Lombardy-Venetia A2-A6.

Franz Josef — A7 Coat of Arms — A8

1860-61 Embossed *Perf. 14*

12 A7 2kr yellow 300.00 25.00
a. Half used as 1kr on cover 12,500.
13 A7 3kr green 275.00 22.50
14 A7 5kr red 175.00 .75
15 A7 10kr brown 250.00 1.75
16 A7 15kr blue 225.00 1.00

The reprints are perforated 9, 9½, 10, 10½, 11, 11½, 12, 12½, 13 and 13½. There are also imperforate reprints of the 2 and 3kr.

For similar design see Lombardy-Venetia A7. For overprints see Poland Nos. J11-J12.

1863

17 A8 2kr yellow 425.00 80.00
a. Half used as 1kr on cover 12,500.
18 A8 3kr green 350.00 75.00
19 A8 5kr rose 275.00 6.50
20 A8 10kr blue 750.00 8.00
21 A8 15kr yellow brown 950.00 10.00

For similar design see Lombardy-Venetia A1.

Wmk. 91, or, before July 1864, Unwmkd.

1863-64 *Perf. 9½*

22 A8 2kr yellow ('64) 125.00 10.00
23 A8 3kr green ('64) 125.00 10.00
24 A8 5kr rose 45.00 .40
25 A8 10kr blue 125.00 2.50
a. Half used as 5kr on cover 10,500.
26 A8 15kr yellow brown 125.00 1.50
Nos. 22-26 (5) 545.00 24.40

The reprints are perforated 10½, 11½, 13 and 13½. There are also imperforate reprints of the 2 and 3kr.

Issues of Austro-Hungarian Monarchy

From 1867 to 1871 the independent postal administrations of Austria and Hungary used the same stamps.

A9 A10

5 kr:

Type I. In arabesques in lower left corner, the small ornament at left of the curve nearest the figure "5" is short and has three points at bottom.

Type II. The ornament is prolonged within the curve and has two points at bottom. The corresponding ornament at top of the lower left corner does not touch the curve (1872).

Type III. Similar to type II but the top ornament is joined to the curve (1881). Two different printing methods were used for the 1867-74 issues. The first produced stamps on which the hair and whiskers were coarse and thick, from the second they were fine and clear.

1867-72 Wmk. 91 Typo. *Perf. 9½*

Coarse Print

27 A9 2kr yellow 85.00 1.75
a. Half used as 1kr on cover 12,500.
28 A9 3kr green 80.00 2.00
29 A9 5kr rose, type I 55.00 .15
a. 5kr rose, type II 50.00 .15
b. Perf. 10½, type II 125.00
c. Cliché of 3kr in plate of 5kr 30,000.
30 A9 10kr blue 165.00 1.50
a. Half used as 5kr on cover 15,000.
31 A9 15kr brown 140.00 4.00
32 A9 25kr lilac 20.00 12.50
a. 25kr gray lilac 20.00 15.00
b. 25kr brown violet 125.00 30.00

Perf. 12

33 A10 50kr light brown 27.50 80.00
a. 50kr pale red brown 250.00 95.00
b. 50kr brownish rose 325.00 175.00
c. Pair, imperf. btwn., vert. or horizontal 700.00 1,000.

Issues for Austria only

1874-80 *Perf. 9½*

Fine Print

34 A9 2kr yellow ('76) 7.50 .75
35 A9 3kr green ('76) 24.00 .50
36 A9 5kr rose, type III 12.50 .20
37 A9 10kr blue ('75) 65.00 .40
38 A9 15kr brown ('77) 5.00 3.50
39 A9 25kr gray lil ('78) 1.25 100.00

Perf. 9

34a A9 2kr 140.00 40.00
35a A9 3kr 125.00 20.00
36a A9 5kr 50.00 2.00
37a A9 10kr 250.00 22.50
38a A9 15kr 325.00 67.50

Perf. 10½

34b A9 2kr 35.00 2.75
35b A9 3kr 55.00 1.75
36b A9 5kr 8.00 .50
37b A9 10kr 110.00 1.75
38b A9 15kr 150.00 16.00

Perf. 12

34c A9 2kr 165.00 87.50
35c A9 3kr 140.00 12.50
36c A9 5kr 35.00 3.25
37c A9 10kr 300.00 90.00
38c A9 15kr 425.00 110.00
40 A10 50kr brown ('80) 10.00 100.00
b. perf. 10½x12 250.00 —

Perf. 13

34d A9 2kr 200.00 200.00
35d A9 3kr 125.00 20.00
36d A9 5kr 70.00 12.50
37d A9 10kr 165.00 55.00
38d A9 15kr 375.00 275.00
40a A10 50kr 20.00 110.00

Various compound perforations exist.

For similar designs see Offices in the Turkish Empire A1-A2.

A11

Perf. 9, 9½, 10, 10½, 11½, 12, 12½

1883

Inscriptions in Black

41 A11 2kr brown 5.50 .50
42 A11 3kr green 4.75 .30
43 A11 5kr rose 10.00 .25
a. Vert. pair, imperf. btwn. 250.00 350.00
44 A11 10kr blue 4.75 .25
45 A11 20kr gray 55.00 3.25
46 A11 50kr red lilac 300.00 50.00

The last printings of Nos. 41 to 46 are watermarked "ZEITUNGS-MARKEN" instead of "BRIEF-MARKEN."

The 5kr has been reprinted in a dull red rose, perforated 10½.

For similar design see Offices in the Turkish Empire A3.

For surchargess see Offices in the Turkish Empire Nos. 15-19.

A12 A13

Perf. 9 to 13½, also Compound

1890-96 **Unwmk.**

Granite Paper

Numerals in black, Nos. 51 to 61

51 A12 1kr dark gray 1.25 .20
a. Pair, imperf. between 190.00 350.00
52 A12 2kr light brown .25 .20
53 A12 3kr gray green .40 .25
a. Pair, imperf. between 200.00 425.00
54 A12 5kr rose .40 .25
a. Pair, imperf. between 180.00 325.00
55 A12 10kr ultramarine .60 .20
a. Pair, imperf. between 225.00 425.00
56 A12 12kr claret 2.00 .25
a. Pair, imperf. between — —
57 A12 15kr lilac 1.00 .25
a. Pair, imperf. between 225.00 425.00
58 A12 20kr olive green 30.00 2.00
59 A12 24kr gray blue 2.00 1.25
a. Pair, imperf. between 240.00 425.00
60 A12 30kr dark brown 2.50 .60
61 A12 50kr violet 5.00 7.00

Engr.

62 A13 1gld dark blue 1.25 2.00
63 A13 1gld pale lilac ('96) 35.00 3.50
64 A13 2gld carmine 3.50 10.00
65 A13 2gld gray green ('96) 15.00 25.00
Nos. 51-65 (15) 100.15 52.95

Nearly all values of the 1890-1907 issues are found with numerals missing in one or more corners, some with numerals printed on the back.

For surcharges see Offices in the Turkish Empire Nos. 20-25, 28-31.

A14

Perf. 9 to 13½, also Compound

1891 **Typo.**

Numerals in black

66 A14 20kr olive green 2.25 .25
67 A14 24kr gray blue 5.00 .75
68 A14 30kr brown 2.25 .25
a. Pair, imperf. between 250.00 350.00
b. Perf. 9 100.00 32.50
69 A14 50kr violet 3.00 .35
Nos. 66-69 (4) 12.50 1.60

For surcharges see Offices in the Turkish Empire Nos. 26-27.

A15 A16

A17

A18

Perf. 10½ to 13½ and Compound

1899

Without Varnish Bars

Numerals in black, Nos. 70-82

70	A15	1h lilac	.60	.15
b.		Imperf.	55.00	110.00
c.		Perf. 10½	15.00	4.50
d.		Numerals inverted	375.00	950.00
71	A15	2h dark gray	2.50	.50
72	A15	3h bister brown	5.00	.35
b.		"3" in lower right corner sideways		*1,100.*
73	A15	5h blue green	8.00	.15
c.		Perf. 10½	10.50	3.00
74	A15	6h orange	.40	.15
75	A16	10h rose	8.00	.15
b.		Perf. 10½	275.00	125.00
76	A16	20h brown	.55	.20
77	A16	25h ultramarine	50.00	.30
78	A16	30h red violet	16.00	2.25
b.		Horiz. pair, imperf. btwn.	275.00	
80	A17	40h green	27.50	2.50
81	A17	50h gray blue	17.50	3.50
b.		All four "50's" parallel		*1,600.*
82	A17	60h brown	35.00	.90
b.		Horiz. pair, imperf. btwn.	275.00	
c.		Perf. 10½	50.00	1.50

Engr.

83	A18	1k carmine rose	2.00	.20
a.		1k carmine	5.00	.20
b.		Vert. pair, imperf. btwn.	275.00	300.00
84	A18	2k gray lilac	45.00	.35
a.		Vert. pair, imperf. btwn.	300.00	500.00
85	A18	4k gray green	4.00	8.00
		Nos. 70-85 (15)	222.05	19.65

For surcharges see Offices in Crete Nos. 1-7, Offices in the Turkish Empire Nos. 32-45.

1901 **With Varnish Bars**

70a	A15	1h lilac	1.75	.40
71a	A15	2h dark gray	1.75	.35
72a	A15	3h bister brown	.35	.15
73a	A15	5h blue green	.20	.15
74a	A15	6h orange	.20	.15
75a	A16	10h rose	.25	.15
76a	A16	20h brown	.75	.15
77a	A16	25h ultra	.85	.20
78a	A16	30h red violet	1.75	.90
79	A17	35h green	.85	.35
80a	A17	40h green	1.65	3.25
81a	A17	50h gray blue	4.00	6.75
82a	A17	60h brown	2.00	.65
		Nos. 70a-78a,79,80a-82a (13)	16.35	13.60

The diagonal yellow bars of varnish were printed across the face to prevent cleaning.

A19

A20

A21

Perf. 12½ to 13½ and Compound

1905-07 **Typo.**

Colored Numerals

Without Varnish Bars

86	A19	1h lilac	.20	.15
87	A19	2h dark gray	.20	.15
88	A19	3h bister brown	.20	.15
89	A19	5h dk blue green	8.50	.15
90	A19	5h yellow grn ('06)	.35	.15
91	A19	6h deep orange	.35	.15
92	A20	10h carmine ('06)	.50	.15
93	A20	12h violet ('07)	1.00	.30
94	A20	20h brown ('06)	2.00	.15
95	A20	25h ultra ('06)	3.50	.20
96	A20	30h red violet ('06)	6.00	.15

Black Numerals

97	A20	10h carmine	7.50	.15
98	A20	20h brown	35.00	.75
99	A20	25h ultra	35.00	1.75
100	A20	30h red violet	35.00	1.75

White Numerals

101	A21	35h green	2.25	.20
102	A21	40h deep violet	2.25	.55
103	A21	50h dull blue	3.00	2.50
104	A21	60h yellow brown	3.00	.30
105	A21	72h rose	3.00	.95
		Nos. 86-105 (20)	148.80	10.75

For surcharges see Offices in Crete #8-14.

1904

With Varnish Bars

86a	A19	1h lilac	.50	.30
87a	A19	2h dark gray	1.75	.30
88a	A19	3h bister brown	1.75	.15
89a	A19	5h dk blue green	4.00	.15
91a	A19	6h deep orange	6.00	.20
97a	A20	10h carmine	2.50	.15
98a	A20	20h brown	32.50	.40
99a	A20	25h ultra	37.50	.40
100a	A20	30h red violet	40.00	.75
101a	A21	35h green	35.00	.30
102a	A21	40h deep violet	32.50	2.75
103a	A21	50h dull blue	32.50	4.00
104a	A21	60h yellow brown	32.50	.65
105a	A21	72h rose	1.00	.50
		Nos. 86a-105a (14)	260.00	11.00

Stamps of the 1901, 1904 and 1905 issues perf. 9 or 10½, also compound with 12½, were not sold at any post office, but were supplied only to some high-ranking officials. This applies also to the contemporary issues of Austrian Offices Abroad.

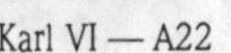

Karl VI — A22

Franz Josef — A23

Schönbrunn Castle — A24

Franz Josef — A25

Designs: 2h, Maria Theresa. 3h, Joseph II. 5h, 10h, 25h, Franz Josef. 6h, Leopold II. 12h, Franz I. 20h, Ferdinand I. 30h, Franz Josef as youth. 35h, Franz Josef in middle age. 60h, Franz Josef on horseback. 1k, Franz Josef in royal robes. 5k, Hofburg, Vienna.

1908-13 **Typo.** *Perf. 12½*

110	A22	1h gray black	.35	.20
111	A22	2h blue violet ('13)	.25	.20
a.		2h violet	.30	.15
112	A22	3h magenta	.20	.20
113	A22	5h yellow green	.20	.20
a.		Booklet pane of 6	20.00	
114	A22	6h buff	.60	.40
b.		6h orange brown ('13)	1.00	1.00
115	A22	10h rose	.20	.20
a.		Booklet pane of 6	70.00	
116	A22	12h scarlet	1.25	.30
117	A22	20h chocolate	1.75	.20
118	A22	25h ultra ('13)	1.10	.20
a.		25h deep blue	1.75	.20
119	A22	30h olive green	3.75	.25
120	A22	35h slate	3.00	.25

Engr.

121	A23	50h dark green	.70	.25
a.		Pair, imperf. btwn., vert. or horiz.	210.00	225.00
122	A23	60h deep carmine	.40	.20
a.		Pair, imperf. btwn., vert. or horiz.	300.00	325.00
123	A23	72h dk brown ('13)	1.75	.25
124	A23	1k purple	12.00	.25
a.		Pair, imperf. btwn., vert. or horiz.	210.00	225.00
125	A24	2k lake & olive grn	20.00	.35
126	A24	5k bister & dk vio	37.50	3.50
127	A25	10k blue, bis & dp brn	165.00	42.50
		Nos. 110-127 (18)	250.00	49.90

Definitive set issued for the 60th year of the reign of Emperor Franz Josef.

The 1h-35h exist on both ordinary (1913) and chalk-surfaced (1908) paper.

All values exist imperforate. They were not sold at any post office, but presented to a number of high government officials. This applies also to all imperforate stamps of later issues, including semi-postals, etc., and those of the Austrian Offices Abroad.

Litho. forgeries of No. 127 exist.

For overprint and surcharge see #J47-J48. For similar designs see Offices in Crete A5-A6, Offices in the Turkish Empire A16-A17.

Birthday Jubilee Issue

Similar to 1908 Issue, but designs enlarged by labels at top and bottom bearing dates "1830" and "1910"

1910 **Typo.**

128	A22	1h gray black	3.75	4.00
129	A22	2h violet	5.00	5.75
130	A22	3h magenta	5.00	5.75
131	A22	5h yellow green	.20	.25
132	A22	6h buff	2.25	2.00
133	A22	10h rose	.20	.25
134	A22	12h scarlet	3.00	3.00
135	A22	20h chocolate	3.75	4.50
136	A22	25h deep blue	.85	1.00
137	A22	30h olive green	3.75	4.50
138	A22	35h slate	3.75	4.50

Engr.

139	A23	50h dark green	4.50	5.75
140	A23	60h deep carmine	4.50	5.75
141	A23	1k purple	4.50	8.00
142	A24	2k lake & ol grn	112.50	140.00
143	A24	5k bister & dk vio	92.50	160.00
144	A25	10k blue, bis & dp brn	175.00	225.00
		Nos. 128-144 (17)	425.00	580.00

80th birthday of Emperor Franz Josef.

All values exist imperforate.

Litho. forgeries of Nos. 142 to 144 exist.

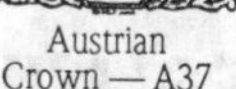
Austrian Crown — A37

Franz Josef — A38

Coat of Arms
A39 A40

1916-18 **Typo.**

145 A37 3h brt violet .15 .15
146 A37 5h lt green .15 .15
a. Booklet pane of 6 14.00
b. Booklet pane of 4 + 2 labels 27.50
147 A37 6h deep orange .20 .40
148 A37 10h magenta .15 .15
a. Booklet pane of 6 27.50
149 A37 12h light blue .35 1.00
150 A38 15h rose red .45 .15
a. Booklet pane of 6 15.00
151 A38 20h chocolate 3.75 .15
152 A38 25h blue 5.50 .40
153 A38 30h slate 5.00 .65
154 A39 40h olive green .15 .15
155 A39 50h blue green .25 .15
156 A39 60h deep blue .20 .15
157 A39 80h orange brown .20 .15
158 A39 90h red violet .20 .15
159 A39 1k car, *yel* ('18) .35 .20

Engr.

160 A40 2k dark blue .45 .20
161 A40 3k claret 5.00 .90
162 A40 4k deep green 1.00 1.75
163 A40 10k deep violet 17.50 30.00
Nos. 145-163 (19) 41.00 37.00

Stamps of type A38 have two varieties of the frame. Stamps of type A40 have various decorations about the shield.

Nos. 145-163 exist imperf. Value, set $400.

1917 **Ordinary Paper**

164 A40 2k light blue .75 .50
165 A40 3k carmine rose 10.00 .75
166 A40 4k yellow green 1.25 1.25
167 A40 10k violet 100.00 60.00
Nos. 164-167 (4) 112.00 62.50

Nos. 164-167 exist imperf. Value, set $250.

See Nos. 172-175 (granite paper). For overprints and surcharges see Nos. 181-199, C1-C3, J60-J63, N1-N5, N10-N19, N33-N37, N42-N51. Western Ukraine 2-7, 11-15, 19-28, 57-58, 85-89, 94-103, N3-N14, NJ13.

Emperor Karl I — A42

1917-18 **Typo.**

168 A42 15h dull red .15 .15
a. Booklet pane of 6 14.00
169 A42 20h dk green ('18) .15 .15
a. 20h green ('17) .40 .15
170 A42 25h blue .15 .15
171 A42 30h dull violet .15 .15
Set value .45 .20

Nos. 168-171 exist imperf. Value, set $40.

For overprints and surcharges see Nos. N6-N9, N20, N38-N41, N52, N64. Western Ukraine 1, 8, 16-18, 90-93, N15-N18.

1918-19 **Engr.**

Granite Paper

172 A40 2k light blue .20 *.50*
a. Perf. 11½ 425.00 350.00
173 A40 3k carmine rose .25 *1.25*
174 A40 4k yellow green ('19) 3.50 *9.50*
175 A40 10k lt violet ('19) 4.25 *8.00*
Nos. 172-175 (4) 8.20 19.25

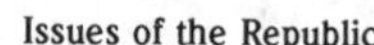

Issues of the Republic

Austrian Stamps of 1916-18 Overprinted

Deutschösterreich

1918-19 **Unwmk.** ***Perf. 12½***

181 A37 3h bright violet .15 .15
182 A37 5h light green .15 .15
183 A37 6h deep orange .15 .20
184 A37 10h magenta .15 .20
185 A37 12h light blue .15 .35
186 A42 15h dull red .15 .35
187 A42 20h deep green .15 .15
188 A42 25h blue .15 .15
189 A42 30h dull violet .15 .15
190 A39 40h olive green .15 .15
191 A39 50h deep green .35 .35
192 A39 60h deep blue .25 .35
193 A39 80h orange brown .15 .15
a. Inverted overprint 175.00 175.00
194 A39 90h red violet .15 .15
195 A39 1k carmine, *yel* .20 .15

Granite Paper

196 A40 2k light blue .20 .15
a. Pair, imperf. between 175.00 175.00
b. Perf. 11½ 10.00 5.00
197 A40 3k carmine rose .20 .35
198 A40 4k yellow green 1.00 1.25
a. Perf. 11½ 17.50 10.00
199 A40 10k deep violet 8.00 *12.50*
Nos. 181-199 (19) 12.00 17.40
Set, never hinged 22.50

Nos. 181, 182, 184, 187-191, 194, 197 and 199 exist imperforate.

Post Horn — A43

Coat of Arms — A44

Allegory of New Republic — A45

1919-20 **Typo.** ***Perf. 12½***

Ordinary Paper

200 A43 3h gray .15 .15
201 A44 5h yellow green .15 .15
202 A44 5h gray ('20) .15 .15
203 A43 6h orange .15 .30
204 A44 10h deep rose .15 .15
205 A44 10h red ('20) .15 .15
a. Thick grayish paper ('20) .15 .15
206 A43 12h grnsh blue .15 .40
207 A43 15h bister ('20) .20 .65
a. Thick grayish paper ('20) .15 .15
208 A45 20h dark green .15 .15
a. 20h yellow green .15 .15
b. As "a," thick grysh paper ('20) .45 1.25
209 A44 25h blue .15 .15
210 A43 25h violet ('20) .15 .15
211 A45 30h dark brown .15 .15
212 A45 40h violet .15 .15
213 A45 40h lake ('20) .15 .15
214 A44 45h olive green .20 .45
215 A45 50h dark blue .15 .15
a. Thick grayish paper ('20) .15 .15
216 A43 60h olive green ('20) .15 .15
217 A44 1k carmine, *yel* .15 .15
218 A44 1k light blue ('20) .15 .15
Set value 1.25 2.50
Set, never hinged 2.50

All values exist imperf. (For regularly issued imperfs, see Nos. 227-235).

For overprints and surcharge see Nos. B11-B19, B30-B38, J102, N21, N27, N53, N58, N65, N71.

Parliament Building — A46

1919-20 **Engr.** ***Perf. 12½, 11½***

Granite Paper

219 A46 2k vermilion & blk .25 .45
a. Center inverted *3,250.*
220 A46 2½k olive bis ('20) .15 .20
221 A46 3k blue & blk brn .15 .15
222 A46 4k carmine & blk .15 .15
a. Center inverted *1,600. 1,200.*
223 A46 5k black ('20) .15 .15
a. Perf. 11½x12½ 45.00 60.00
224 A46 7½k plum .15 .35
a. Perf. 11½ 75.00 100.00
b. Perf. 11½x12½ 75.00 125.00
225 A46 10k olive grn & blk brn .20 .45
a. Perf. 11½x12½ 100.00 110.00
b. Perf. 11½ 16.00 20.00
226 A46 20k lilac & red ('20) .15 .55
a. Center inverted *6,500. 5,750.*
b. Perf. 11½ 40.00 70.00
Set value 1.00
Set, never hinged 2.50

A number of values exist imperforate between. Values, $300 to $400 a pair.

See No. 248. For overprints and surcharge see Nos. B43-B49, N30, N60, N74.

1920 **Typo.** ***Imperf.***

Ordinary Paper

227 A44 5h yellow green .15 .30
228 A44 5h gray .15 .15
229 A44 10h deep rose .15 .15
230 A44 10h red .15 .15
231 A43 15h bister .15 .15
232 A43 25h violet .15 .15
233 A45 30h dark brown .15 .15
234 A45 40h violet .15 .15
235 A43 60h olive green .15 .15
Set value .60 .90
Set, never hinged 1.25

Arms
A47 A48

1920-21 **Typo.** ***Perf. 12½***

Ordinary Paper

238 A47 80h rose .15 .15
239 A47 1k black brown .15 .15
241 A47 1½k green ('21) .15 .15
242 A47 2k blue .15 .15
243 A48 3k yel grn & dk grn ('21) .15 .15
244 A48 4k red & claret ('21) .15 .15
245 A48 5k vio & claret ('21) .15 .15
246 A48 7½k yellow & brown ('21) .15 .15
247 A48 10k ultra & blue ('21) .15 .15
Set value .60 .65
Set, never hinged 1.25

Nos. 238-245, 247 exist on white paper of good quality and on thick grayish paper of inferior quality; No. 246 only on white paper.

For overprints and surcharges see Nos. N22-N23, N31, N54-N55, N61-N62, N66-N67.

1921 **Engr.**

248 A46 50k dk violet, *yel* .35 .80
a. Perf. 11½ 30.00 47.50
Never hinged .65

Symbols of Agriculture
A49

Symbols of Labor and Industry
A50

1922-24 **Typo.** ***Perf. 12½***

250 A49 ½k olive bister .15 .35
251 A50 1k brown .15 .15
252 A50 2k cobalt blue .15 .15
253 A49 2½k orange brown .15 .15
254 A50 4k dull violet .15 .45
255 A50 5k gray green .15 .15
256 A49 7½k gray violet .15 .15
257 A50 10k claret .15 .15
258 A49 12½k gray green .15 .15
259 A49 15k bluish green .15 .15
260 A49 20k dark blue .15 .15
261 A49 25k claret .15 .15
262 A50 30k pale gray .15 .15
263 A50 45k pale red .15 .15
264 A50 50k orange brown .15 .15
265 A50 60k yellow green .15 .15
266 A50 75k ultramarine .15 .15
267 A50 80k yellow .15 .15
268 A49 100k gray .15 .15
269 A49 120k brown .15 .15
270 A49 150k orange .15 .15
271 A49 160k light green .15 .15
272 A49 180k red .15 .15
273 A49 200k pink .15 .15
274 A49 240k dark violet .15 .15
275 A49 300k light blue .20 .15
276 A49 400k deep green .90 .15
a. 400k gray green .90 .15
277 A49 500k yellow .20 .15
278 A49 600k slate .20 .15
279 A49 700k brown ('24) .45 .15
280 A49 800k violet ('24) .90 *2.00*
281 A50 1000k violet ('23) .45 .15
282 A50 1200k car rose ('23) .25 .30
283 A50 1500k orange ('24) 1.50 .15
284 A50 1600k slate ('23) 2.00 1.75
285 A50 2000k deep blue ('23) 4.00 .30
286 A50 3000k lt blue ('23) 12.50 .65
287 A50 4000k dk bl, *bl* ('24) 5.25 1.75
Nos. 250-287 (38) 32.55
Set value 10.00
Set, never hinged 75.00

Nos. 250-287 exist imperf. Value, set $500.

For overprints & surcharges see #N24-N26, N28-N29, N32, N56, N59, N63, N68-N70, N72-N73.

Symbols of Art and Science — A51

1922-24 **Engr.** ***Perf. 12½***

288 A51 20k dark brown .15 .15
a. Perf. 11½ 1.10 1.25
a. Never hinged 1.65
289 A51 25k blue .15 .15
a. Perf. 11½ 1.10 1.25
a. Never hinged 1.65
290 A51 50k brown red .15 .15
a. Perf. 11½ 2.50 3.50
a. Never hinged 4.25
291 A51 100k deep green .15 .15
a. Perf. 11½ 6.00 7.00
a. Never hinged 9.00
292 A51 200k dark violet .15 .15
a. Perf. 11½ 9.00 15.00
a. Never hinged 12.00
293 A51 500k dp orange .15 1.00
294 A51 1000k blk vio, *yel* .15 .15
a. Perf. 11½ 125.00 190.00
a. Never hinged 325.00
295 A51 2000k olive grn, *yel* .15 .15
296 A51 3000k claret brn ('23) 8.00 .35
297 A51 5000k gray black ('23) 2.00 .95

Granite Paper

298 A51 10,000k red brown ('24) 3.00 2.50
Nos. 288-298 (11) 14.20 5.85
Set, never hinged 32.50

On Nos. 281-287, 291-298 "kronen" is abbreviated to "k" and transposed with the numerals.

Nos. 288-298 exist imperf. Value, set $300.

Numeral
A52

Fields Crossed by Telegraph Wires
A53

White-Shouldered Eagle — A54

Church of Minorite Friars — A55

1925-27 **Typo.** ***Perf. 12***

303 A52 1g dark gray .15 .15
304 A52 2g claret .20 .15
305 A52 3g scarlet .25 .15
306 A52 4g grnsh blue ('27) .70 .15
307 A52 5g brown orange 1.40 .15
308 A52 6g ultramarine .85 .15
309 A52 7g chocolate 1.50 .15
310 A52 8g yellow green 6.25 .15
311 A53 10g orange .15 .15
313 A53 15g red lilac .15 .15
314 A53 16g dark blue .15 .15
315 A53 18g olive green .90 .20
316 A54 20g dark violet .30 .15
317 A54 24g carmine .40 .20
318 A54 30g dark brown .35 .15
319 A54 40g ultramarine .50 .15
320 A54 45g yellow brown .70 .15
321 A54 50g gray .85 .15
322 A54 80g turquoise blue 3.00 2.00

Perf. 12½

Engr.

323 A55 1s deep green 15.00 .20
a. 1s light green 125.00 1.25
324 A55 2s brown rose 6.25 5.00
Nos. 303-324 (21) 40.00
Set value 8.50
Set, never hinged 130.00

#303-305, 307-324 exist imperf. Value, set $275.
For type A52 surcharged see Nos. B118.

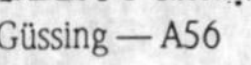

Güssing — A56

National Library, Vienna — A57

Designs: 15g, Hochosterwitz. 16g, 20g, Durnstein. 18g, Traunsee. 24g, Salzburg. 30g, Seewiesen. 40g, Innsbruck. 50g, Worthersee. 60g, Hohenems. 2s, St. Stephen's Cathedral, Vienna.

1929-30 Typo. *Perf. 12½*

Size: 25½x21½mm

326 A56 10g brown orange .80 .15
327 A56 10g bister ('30) .80 .15
328 A56 15g violet brown .55 *.90*
329 A56 16g dark gray .15 .15
330 A56 18g blue green .40 .30
331 A56 20g dark gray ('30) .40 .15
332 A56 24g maroon 4.25 4.00
333 A56 24g lake ('30) 7.25 .30
334 A56 30g dark violet 4.25 .15
335 A56 40g dark blue 8.00 .15
336 A56 50g gray violet ('30) 30.00 .20
337 A56 60g olive green 22.50 .20

Engr.

Size: 21x26mm

338 A57 1s black brown 5.00 .20
339 A57 2s dark green 9.25 4.50
Nos. 326-339 (14) 93.60 11.50
Set, never hinged 300.00

Type of 1929-30 Issue

Designs: 12g, Traunsee. 64g, Hohenems.

1932 *Perf. 12*

Size: 21x16½mm

340 A56 10g olive brown .90 .15
341 A56 12g blue green 1.50 .15
342 A56 18g blue green .85 *1.90*
343 A56 20g dark gray 1.25 .15
344 A56 24g carmine rose 5.00 .15
345 A56 24g dull violet 4.00 .15
346 A56 30g dark violet 16.00 .15
347 A56 30g carmine rose 3.75 .15
348 A56 40g dark blue 19.00 .60
349 A56 40g dark violet 5.50 .20
350 A56 50g gray violet 21.00 .20
351 A56 50g dull blue 6.25 .20
352 A56 60g gray green 47.50 1.50
353 A56 64g gray green 7.50 .15
Nos. 340-353 (14) 140.00
Set value *5.00*
Set, never hinged 500.00

For overprints and surcharges see Nos. B87-B92, B119-B121.

Burgenland A67

Tyrol A68

Designs (costumes of various districts): 3g, Burgenland. 4g, 5g, Carinthia. 6g, 8g, Lower Austria. 12g, 20g, Upper Austria. 24g, 25g, Salzburg. 30g, 35g, Styria. 45g, Tyrol. 60g, Vorarlberg bridal couple. 64g, Vorarlberg. 1s, Viennese family. 2s, Military.

1934-35 Typo. *Perf. 12*

354 A67 1g dark violet .15 .15
355 A67 3g scarlet .15 .15
356 A67 4g olive green .15 .15
357 A67 5g red violet .15 .15
358 A67 6g ultramarine .20 .15
359 A67 8g green .15 .15
360 A67 12g dark brown .15 .15
361 A67 20g yellow brown .15 .15
362 A67 24g grnsh blue .15 .15
363 A67 25g violet .20 .15
364 A67 30g maroon .15 .15
365 A67 35g rose carmine .35 .25

Perf. 12½

366 A68 40g slate gray .40 .15
367 A68 45g brown red .35 .15
368 A68 60g ultramarine .60 .15
369 A68 64g brown .75 .15
370 A68 1s deep violet .65 .35
371 A68 2s dull green 37.50 45.00

Designs Redrawn

Perf. 12 (6g), 12½ (2s)

372 A67 6g ultra ('35) .15 .15
373 A68 2s emerald ('35) 2.50 4.50
Nos. 354-373 (20) 45.00 52.50
Set, never hinged 90.00

The design of No. 358 looks as though the man's ears were on backwards, while No. 372 appears correctly.

On No. 373 there are seven feathers on each side of the eagle instead of five.

Nos. 354-373 exist imperf. Value, set $375.

For surcharges see Nos. B128-B131.

Dollfuss Mourning Issue

Engelbert Dollfuss — A85

1934-35 Engr. *Perf. 12½*

374 A85 24g greenish black .45 .20
Never hinged .80
375 A85 24g indigo ('35) .75 .55
Never hinged 1.40

"Mother and Child," by Joseph Danhauser — A86

"Madonna and Child," after Painting by Dürer — A87

1935, May 1

376 A86 24g dark blue .40 .20
Never hinged .80

Mother's Day. Nos. 376-377 exist imperf. Value, each $165.

1936, May 5 Photo.

377 A87 24g violet blue .15 .20
Never hinged .30

Mother's Day.

Farm Workers — A88

Design: 5s, Factory workers.

1936, June Engr. *Perf. 12½*

378 A88 3s red orange 15.00 17.50
Never hinged 27.50
379 A88 5s brown black 30.00 45.50
Never hinged 52.50

Nos. 378-379 exist imperf. Value, set $250.

Engelbert Dollfuss — A90

Mother and Child — A91

1936, July 25

380 A90 10s dark blue 650.00 800.00
Never hinged 900.00

Second anniv. of death of Engelbert Dollfuss, chancellor. Exists imperf. Value, $1,750.

1937, May 5 Photo. *Perf. 12*

381 A91 24g henna brown .20 .15
Never hinged .40

Mother's Day. Exists imperf. Value, $175.

S.S. Maria Anna — A92

Steamships: 24g, Uranus, 64g, Oesterreich.

1937, June 9

382 A92 12g red brown .55 .25
383 A92 24g deep blue .55 .25
384 A92 64g dark green .55 .65
Nos. 382-384 (3) 1.65 1.15
Set, never hinged 3.50

Cent. of steamship service on Danube River. Exist imperf. Value, set $135.

First Locomotive, "Austria" — A95

Designs: 25g, Modern steam locomotive. 35g, Modern electric train.

1937, Nov. 22

385 A95 12g black brown .25 .15
386 A95 25g dark violet .50 .65
387 A95 35g brown red 1.00 1.00
Nos. 385-387 (3) 1.75 1.80
Set, never hinged 3.75

Centenary of Austrian railways. Exist imperf. Value, set $135.

Rose and Zodiac Signs — A98

1937 Engr. *Perf. 13x12½*

388 A98 12g dark green .15 .15
389 A98 24g dark carmine .15 .15
Set value .25 .25
Set, never hinged .35

For Use in Vienna, Lower Austria and Burgenland

Germany Nos. 509-511 and 511B Overprinted in Black

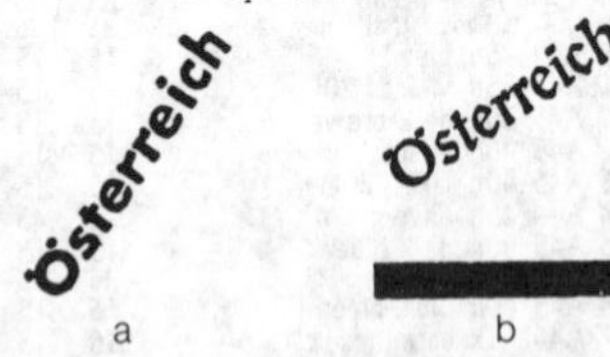

a b

1945 Unwmk. *Perf. 14*

390 A115(a) 5pf dp yellow green .15 .20
391 A115(b) 6pf purple .15 .20
392 A115(a) 8pf red .15 .20
393 A115(b) 12pf carmine .15 .20
Nos. 390-393 (4) .80
Set value .25
Set, never hinged .40

Nos. 390-393 exist with overprint inverted or double.

Germany No. 507, the 3pf, with overprint "a" was prepared, not issued, but sold to collectors after the definitive Republic issue had been placed in use. Value $30, hinged, $60, never hinged.

German Semi-Postal Stamps, #B207, B209, B210, B283 Surcharged in Black

ÖSTERREICH
5 Pf.

c

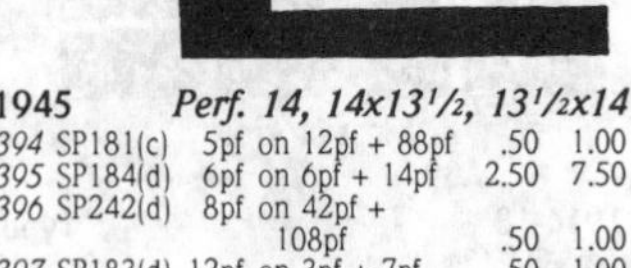

d

1945 *Perf. 14, 14x13½, 13½x14*

394 SP181(c) 5pf on 12pf + 88pf .50 1.00
395 SP184(d) 6pf on 6pf + 14pf 2.50 7.50
396 SP242(d) 8pf on 42pf + 108pf .50 1.00
397 SP183(d) 12pf on 3pf + 7pf .50 1.00
Nos. 394-397 (4) 4.00 10.50
Set, never hinged 10.00

The surcharges are spaced to fit the stamps.

Stamps of Germany, Nos. 509 to 511, 511B, 519 and 529 Overprinted

e f

1945 Typo. *Perf. 14*

Size: 18½x22½mm

398 A115(e) 5pf dp yellow green .25 .45
399 A115(f) 5pf dp yellow green 4.00 *7.75*
400 A115(e) 6pf purple .15 *.30*
401 A115(e) 8pf red .15 *.30*
402 A115(e) 12pf carmine .20 *.35*

Engr.

Size: 21½x26mm

403 A115(e) 30pf olive green 6.00 *10.00*
a. Thin bar at bottom 15.00 *17.50*
a. Never hinged 25.00
404 A118(e) 42pf brt green 15.00 *32.50*
a. Thin bar at bottom 15.00 27.50
a. Never hinged 25.00
Nos. 398-404 (7) 25.75 *51.65*
Set, never hinged 55.00

On Nos. 403a and 404a, the bottom bar of the overprint is 2½mm wide, and, as the overprint was applied in two operations, "Osterreich" is usually not exactly centered in its diagonal slot. On Nos. 403 and 404, the bottom bar is 3mm wide, and "Osterreich" is always well centered.

Germany Nos. 524-527 (the 1m, 2m, 3m and 5m), overprinted with vertical bars and "Osterreich" similar to "e" and "f," were prepared, not issued, but sold to collectors after the definitive Republic issue had been placed in use. Value for set, $70 hinged, $150 ever hinged.

Counterfeits exist of Nos. 403-404, 403a-404a and 1m-5m overprints.

For Use in Styria

Stamps of Germany Nos. 506 to 511, 511A, 511B, 514 to 523 and 529 Overprinted in Black

1945 Unwmk. Typo. *Perf. 14*

Size: 18½x22½mm

405 A115 1pf gray black 1.50 3.00
406 A115 3pf lt brown 1.50 3.00
407 A115 4pf slate 5.00 10.00
408 A115 5pf dp yellow grn 1.00 2.00
409 A115 6pf purple .20 .30
410 A115 8pf red .75 1.65
411 A115 10pf dark brown 1.50 3.25
412 A115 12pf carmine .15 .30

Engr.

413	A115	15pf brown lake	.75	1.75
414	A115	16pf pck green	14.00	18.00
415	A115	20pf blue	2.75	5.25
416	A115	24pf orange brown	10.00	18.00

Size: 22½x26mm

417	A115	25pf brt ultra	1.00	2.75
418	A115	30pf olive green	1.00	2.00
419	A115	40pf brt red violet	1.25	2.25
420	A118	42pf brt green	2.00	3.50
421	A115	50pf myrtle green	1.40	3.50
422	A115	60pf dk red brown	2.25	4.75
423	A115	80pf indigo	2.00	3.75
		Nos. 405-423 (19)	50.00	89.00
		Set, never hinged	110.00	

Overprinted on Nos. 524-527

Perf. 12½, 14

424	A116	1m dk slate grn	7.25	*20.00*
a.		Perf. 12½	100.00	
425	A116	2m violet	7.50	*25.00*
a.		Perf. 14	12.00	*45.00*
426	A116	3m copper red	25.00	*55.00*
a.		Perf. 14	125.00	
427	A116	5m dark blue	225.00	*525.00*
a.		Perf. 14	*575.00*	
		Nos. 424-427 (4)	264.75	
		Set, never hinged	450.00	

On the preceding four stamps the innermost vertical lines are 10½mm apart; on the pfennig values 6½mm apart.

Counterfeits exist of Nos. 405-427 overprints.

Germany Nos. 524 to 527 Overprinted in Black

Perf. 14

428	A116	1m dk slate grn	10.50	*22.50*
429	A116	2m violet	10.50	*27.50*

Perf. 12½

430	A116	3m copper red	21.00	*60.00*
431	A116	5m dark blue	140.00	*450.00*
a.		Perf. 14	*600.00*	
		Nos. 428-431 (4)	182.00	
		Set, never hinged	375.00	

On the preceding four stamps, "Osterreich" is thinner, measuring 16mm. On the previous set of 23 values it measures 18mm.

Counterfeits exist of Nos. 428-431 overprints.

Catalogue values for unused stamps in this section, from this point to the end of the section, are for Never Hinged items.

For Use in Vienna, Lower Austria and Burgenland

Coat of Arms

A99 A100

Typographed or Lithographed

1945, July 3 Unwmk. *Perf. 14x13½*

Size: 21x25mm

432	A99	3pf brown	.15	.15
433	A99	4pf slate	.15	.15
434	A99	5pf dark green	.15	.15
435	A99	6pf deep violet	.15	.15
436	A99	8pf orange brown	.15	.15
437	A99	10pf deep brown	.15	.15
438	A99	12pf rose carmine	.15	.15
439	A99	15pf orange red	.15	.15
440	A99	16pf dull blue green	.15	.35

Perf. 14

Size: 24x28½mm

441	A99	20pf light blue	.15	.15
442	A99	24pf orange	.15	.20
443	A99	25pf dark blue	.15	.15
444	A99	30pf deep gray grn	.15	.15
445	A99	38pf ultramarine	.15	.15
446	A99	40pf brt red vio	.15	.15
447	A99	42pf sage green	.15	.15
448	A99	50pf blue green	.15	.60
449	A99	60pf maroon	.15	.15
450	A99	80pf dull lilac	.15	.15

Engr. *Perf. 14x13½*

451	A100	1m dark green	.15	*.60*
452	A100	2m dark purple	.15	*.60*
453	A100	3m dark violet	.15	*.60*
454	A100	5m brown red	.15	*.60*
		Set value	1.75	*6.00*

Nos. 432, 433, 437, 439, 440, 443, 446, 448, 449 are typographed. Nos. 434, 435, 441. 442 are lithographed; the other values exist both ways.

For overprint see No. 604.

For General Use

Lermoos, Winter Scene — A101

The Prater Woods, Vienna — A105

Hochosterwitz, Carinthia A106

Lake Constance A110

Dürnstein, Lower Austria A124

Designs: 4g, Eisenerz surface mine. 5g, Leopoldsberg, near Vienna. 6g, Hohensalzburg, Salzburg Province. 12g, Wolfgang See, near Salzburg. 15g, Forchtenstein Castle, Burgenland. 16g, Gesäuse Valley. 24g, Höldrichs Mill, Lower Austria. 25g, Oetz Valley Outlet, Tyrol. 30g, Neusiedler Lake, Burgenland. 35g, Belvedere Palace, Vienna. 38g, Langbath Lake. 40g, Mariazell, Styria. 42g, Traunkirchen. 45g, Hartenstein Castle. 50g, Silvretta Mountains, Vorarlberg. 60g, Railroad viaducts near Semmering. 70g, Waterfall of Bad-Gastein, Salzburg. 80g, Kaiser Mountains, Tyrol. 90g, Wayside Shrine, Tragöss, Styria. 2s, St. Christof am Arlberg, Tyrol. 3s, Heiligenblut, Carinthia. 5s, Schönbrunn, Vienna.

Perf. 14x13½

1945-46 Photo. Unwmk.

455	A101	3g sapphire	.15	.15
456	A101	4g dp orange ('46)	.15	.15
457	A101	5g dk carmine rose	.15	.15
458	A101	6g dk slate green	.15	.15
459	A105	8g golden brown	.15	.15
460	A106	10g dark green	.15	.15
461	A106	12g dark brown	.15	.15
462	A106	15g dk slate bl ('46)	.15	.15
463	A106	16g chnt brn ('46)	.15	.15

Perf. 13½x14

464	A110	20g dp ultra ('46)	.15	.15
465	A110	24g dp yellow grn ('46)	.15	.15
466	A110	25g gray black ('46)	.15	.15
467	A110	30g dark red	.15	.15
468	A110	35g brown red ('46)	.15	.15
469	A110	38g brown olive ('46)	.15	.15
470	A110	40g gray	.15	.15
471	A110	42g brown orange ('46)	.15	.15
472	A110	45g dark blue ('46)	.15	.25
473	A110	50g dark blue	.15	.15
474	A110	60g dark violet	.15	.15
a.		Imperf., pair	50.00	60.00
475	A110	70g Prus blue ('46)	.15	.25
476	A110	80g brown	.15	.40
477	A110	90g Prussian green	1.10	1.10
478	A124	1s dk red brn ('46)	.75	.75
479	A124	2s blue gray ('46)	2.75	2.75
480	A124	3s dk slate grn ('46)	.75	.80
481	A124	5s dark red ('46)	1.50	1.75
		Set value	8.00	7.00

See Nos. 486-488, 496-515. For overprints and surcharges see Nos. 492-493, B166, B280, B287.

No. 461 Overprinted in Carmine

1946, Sept. 26

482	A106	12g dark brown	.15	.20

Meeting of the Soc. for Cultural and Economic Relations with the USSR, Vienna, Sept. 26-29.

City Hall Park, Vienna A128

Hochosterwitz, Carinthia A129

Perf. 14x13½

1946-47 Photo. Unwmk.

483	A128	8g deep plum	.15	.15
484	A128	8g olive brown	.15	.15
a.		8g dark olive green	.15	.15
485	A129	10g dk brn vio ('47)	.15	.15

Perf. 13½x14

486	A110	30g blue gray ('47)	.15	.15
487	A110	50g brown violet ('47)	.25	.25
488	A110	60g violet blue ('47)	2.00	1.10
		Set value	2.45	1.60

See No. 502.

Franz Grillparzer — A130

Franz Schubert — A131

1947 Engr. *Perf. 14x13½*

489	A130	18g chocolate	.15	.15

Photo.

490	A130	18g dk violet brn	.15	.15
		Set value	.15	.20

Death of Grillparzer, dramatic poet, 75th anniv.

A second printing of No. 490 on thicker paper has a darker frame and clearer delineation of the portrait.

Issue dates: #489, Feb. 10; #490, Mar. 31.

1947, Mar. 31 Engr.

491	A131	12g dark green	.15	.15

150th birth anniv. of Franz Schubert, musician and composer.

Nos. 469 and 463 Surcharged in Brown

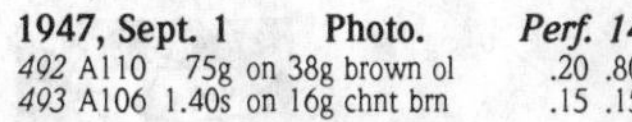

1947, Sept. 1 Photo. *Perf. 14*

492	A110	75g on 38g brown ol	.20	.80
493	A106	1.40s on 16g chnt brn	.15	.15

The surcharge on No. 493 varies from brown to black brown.

Symbols of Global Telegraphic Communication A132

1947, Nov. 5 Engr. *Perf. 14x13½*

495	A132	40g dark violet	.15	.15

Centenary of the telegraph in Austria.

Scenic Type of 1946

1946, Aug. Photo. *Perf. 13½x14*

496	A124	1s dark brown	1.25	.50
497	A124	2s dark blue	7.00	2.75
498	A124	3s dark slate green	2.25	.75
499	A124	5s dark red	32.50	8.00
		Nos. 496-499 (4)	43.00	12.00

On Nos. 478 to 481 the upper and lower panels show a screen effect. On Nos. 496 to 499 the panels appear to be solid color.

Scenic Types of 1945-46

1947-48 Photo. *Perf. 14x13½*

500	A101	3g bright red	.15	.15
501	A101	5g bright red	.15	.15
502	A129	10g bright red	.15	.15
503	A106	15g brt red ('48)	1.40	1.25

Perf. 13½x14

504	A110	20g bright red	.50	.15
505	A110	30g bright red	.75	.15
506	A110	40g bright red	.75	.15
507	A110	50g bright red	1.00	.15
508	A110	60g brt red ('48)	6.50	1.25
509	A110	70g brt red ('48)	3.50	.15
510	A110	80g brt red ('48)	3.50	.15
511	A110	90g brt red ('48)	3.75	.25
512	A124	1s dark violet	.80	.15
513	A124	2s dark violet	1.10	.20
514	A124	3s dk violet ('48)	9.00	1.00
515	A124	5s dk violet ('48)	11.00	1.50
		Nos. 500-515 (16)	44.00	
		Set value		6.00

Carl Michael Ziehrer (1843-1922), Composer — A133

Designs: No. 517, Adalbert Stifter (1805-68), novelist. No. 518, Anton Bruckner (1824-96), composer. 60g, Friedrich von Amerling (1803-87), painter.

1948-49 Engr.

516	A133	20g dull green	.35	.20
517	A133	40g chocolate	5.00	2.50
518	A133	40g dark green	5.00	4.00
519	A133	60g rose brown	.65	.30
		Nos. 516-519 (4)	11.00	7.00

Issue dates: 20g, Jan. 21, No. 517, Sept. 6, No. 518, Sept. 3, 1949, 60g, Jan. 26.

Vorarlberg, Montafon Valley — A134

Costume of Vienna, 1850 — A135

Designs (Austrian Costumes): 3g, Tyrol, Inn Valley. 5g, Salzburg, Pinzgau. 10g, Styria, Salzkammergut. 15g, Burgenland, Lutzmannsburg. 25g, Vienna, 1850. 30g, Salzburg, Pongau. 40g, Vienna, 1840. 45g, Carinthia, Lesach Valley. 50g, Vorarlberg, Bregenzer Forest. 60g, Carinthia, Lavant Valley. 70g, Lower Austria, Wachau. 75g, Styria, Salzkammergut. 80g, Styria, Enns Valley. 90g, Central Styria. 1s, Tyrol, Puster Valley. 1.20s, Lower Austria, Vienna Woods. 1.40s, Upper Austria, Inn District. 1.45s, Wilten. 1.50s, Vienna, 1853. 1.60s, Vienna, 1830. 1.70s, East Tyrol, Kals. 2s, Upper Austria. 2.20s, Ischl, 1820. 2.40s, Kitzbuhel. 2.50s, Upper Steiermark, 1850. 2.70s, Little Walser Valley. 3s, Burgenland. 3.50s, Lower Austria, 1850. 4.50s, Gail Valley. 5s, Ziller Valley. 7s, Steiermark, Sulm Valley.

Perf. 14x13½

1948-52 Unwmk. Photo.

520 A134 3g gray ('50) .60 .50
521 A134 5g dark green ('49) .25 .15
522 A134 10g deep blue .25 .15
523 A134 15g brown .60 .15
524 A134 20g yellow green .20 .15
525 A134 25g brown ('49) .20 .15
526 A134 30g dk car rose 2.50 .15
527 A134 30g dk violet ('50) .60 .15
528 A134 40g violet 2.50 .15
529 A134 40g green ('49) .20 .15
530 A134 45g violet blue 2.25 .40
531 A134 50g orange brn ('49) .60 .15
532 A134 60g scarlet .20 .15
533 A134 70g brt blue grn ('49) .20 .15
534 A134 75g blue 3.75 .40
535 A134 80g carmine rose ('49) .35 .15
536 A134 90g brown vio ('49) 22.50 .30
537 A134 1s ultramarine 4.00 .15
538 A134 1s rose red ('50) 62.50 .15
539 A134 1s dk green ('51) .20 .15
540 A134 1.20s violet ('49) .40 .15
541 A134 1.40s brown 2.50 .15
542 A134 1.45s dk carmine ('51) 1.10 .15
543 A134 1.50s ultra ('51) .60 .15
544 A134 1.60s orange red ('49) .20 .15
545 A134 1.70s violet blue ('50) 2.50 .55
546 A134 2s blue green .40 .15
547 A134 2.20s slate ('52) 4.75 .15
548 A134 2.40s blue ('51) 1.00 .15
549 A134 2.50s brown ('52) 4.50 .15
550 A134 2.70s dk brown ('51) .45 .45
551 A134 3s brown car ('49) 1.90 .15
552 A134 3.50s dull grn ('51) 9.75 .15
553 A134 4.50s brown vio ('51) .60 .40
554 A134 5s dark red vio 1.00 .15
555 A134 7s olive ('52) 1.50 .15

Engr.

556 A135 10s gray ('50) 27.50 5.00
Nos. 520-556 (37) 165.10
Set value 9.00

In 1958-59, 21 denominations of this set were printed on white paper, differing from the previous grayish paper with yellowish gum.

Pres. Karl Renner — A136

1948, Nov. 12 ***Perf. 14x13½***
557 A136 1s deep blue 1.90 1.10

Founding of the Austrian Republic, 30th anniv. See Nos. 573, 636.

Franz Gruber and Josef Mohr — A137

1948, Dec. 18 ***Perf. 13½x14***
558 A137 60g red brown 4.25 4.00

130th anniv. of the hymn "Silent Night, Holy Night".

Symbolical of Child Welfare — A138

Johann Strauss, the Younger — A139

1949, May 14 Photo. ***Perf. 14x13½***
559 A138 1s bright blue 11.50 1.25

1st year of activity of UNICEF in Austria.

1949 Engr.

Designs: 30g, Johann Strauss, the elder. No. 561, Johann Strauss, the younger. No. 562, Karl Millöcker.

560 A139 30g violet brown 2.25 1.65
561 A139 1s dark blue 3.00 1.10
562 A139 1s dark blue 12.00 6.25
Nos. 560-562 (3) 17.25 9.00

Johann Strauss, the elder (1804-49), Johann Strauss, the younger (1825-99), and Karl Millöcker (1842-1899), composers. See #574.

Esperanto Star, Olive Branches — A140

St. Gebhard — A141

1949, June 25 Photo.
563 A140 20g blue green 1.00 .50

Austrian Esperanto Congress at Graz.

1949, Aug. 6 Engr.
564 A141 30g dark violet 1.50 1.25

St. Gebhard (949-995), Bishop of Vorarlberg.

Letter, Roses and Post Horn — A142

UPU, 75th Anniv.: 60g, Plaque. 1s, "Austria," wings and monogram.

1949, Oct. 8 ***Perf. 13½x14***
565 A142 40g dark green 3.75 1.65
566 A142 60g dk carmine 3.75 1.65
567 A142 1s dk violet blue 6.50 4.75
Nos. 565-567 (3) 14.00 8.05

Moritz Michael Daffinger — A143

Andreas Hofer — A144

Designs: 30g, Alexander Girardi. No. 569, Daffinger. No. 570, Hofer. No. 571, Josef Madersperger.

1950 Unwmk. ***Perf. 14x13½***
568 A144 30g dark blue 1.50 .85
569 A143 60g red brown 6.00 3.25
570 A144 60g dark violet 10.50 6.50
571 A144 60g purple 4.50 2.25
Nos. 568-571 (4) 22.50 12.85

Alexander Girardi (1850-1918), actor; Moritz Michael Daffinger (1790-1849), painter; Andreas Hofer (1767-1810), patriot; Josef Madersperger (1768-1850), inventor.

Issue dates: 30g, Dec. 5; No. 569, Jan. 25; No. 570, Feb. 20; No. 571, Oct. 2.

Austrian Stamp of 1850 — A146

1950, May 20 ***Perf. 14½***
572 A146 1s black, *straw* 1.50 .90

Centenary of Austrian postage stamps.

Renner Type of 1948, Frame and Inscriptions Altered

1951, Mar. 3
573 A136 1s black, *straw* 1.40 .20

In memory of Pres. Karl Renner, 1870-1950.

Strauss Type of 1949

Portrait: 60g, Joseph Lanner.

1951, Apr. 12
574 A139 60g dk blue green 3.50 1.10

150th birth anniv. of Joseph Lanner, composer.

Martin Johann Schmidt — A147

Boy Scout Emblem — A148

1951, June 28 Engr. ***Perf. 14x13½***
575 A147 1sh brown red 4.50 2.00

150th death anniv. of Martin Johann Schmidt, painter.

1951, Aug. 3 Engr. and Litho.
576 A148 1sh dk grn, ocher & pink 3.50 2.75

7th World Scout Jamboree, Bad Ischl-St. Wolfgang, Aug. 3-13, 1951.

Wilhelm Kienzl A149

Josef Schrammel A150

Design: 1s, Karl von Ghega.

1951-52 Engr. Unwmk.
577 A149 1s deep green ('52) 6.50 1.10
578 A149 1.50s indigo 3.00 .90
579 A150 1.50s violet blue ('52) 6.50 1.10
Nos. 577-579 (3) 16.00 3.10

Ghega (1802-60), civil engineer; Kienzl (1857-1941), composer; Schrammel (1852-95), composer. See #582.

Issued: 1s, Mar. 2; #578, Oct. 3; #579, Mar. 3.

Breakfast Pavilion, Schönbrunn A151

1952, May 24 ***Perf. 13½x14***
580 A151 1.50s dark green 5.75 1.00

Vienna Zoological Gardens, 200th anniv.

Globe as Dot Over "i" — A152

School Girl — A153

1952, July 1 ***Perf. 14x13½***
581 A152 1.50s dark blue 6.00 .65

Formation of the Intl. Union of Socialist Youth Camp, Vienna, July 1-10, 1952.

Type Similar to A150

Portrait: 1s, Nikolaus Lenau.

1952, Aug. 13
582 A150 1s deep green 6.50 1.10

Nikolaus Lenau, pseudonym of Nikolaus Franz Niembsch von Strehlenau (1802-50), poet.

1952, Sept. 6
583 A153 2.40s dp violet blue 10.00 1.75

Issued to stimulate letter-writing between Austrian and foreign school children.

Hugo Wolf — A154

Pres. Theodor Körner — A155

1953, Feb. 21 Engr. ***Perf. 14x13½***
587 A154 1.50s dark blue 6.75 .70

Hugo Wolf, composer, 50th death anniv.

1953, Apr. 24
588 A155 1.50s dk violet blue 6.75 .70

80th birthday of Pres. Theodor Körner. See Nos. 591, 614.

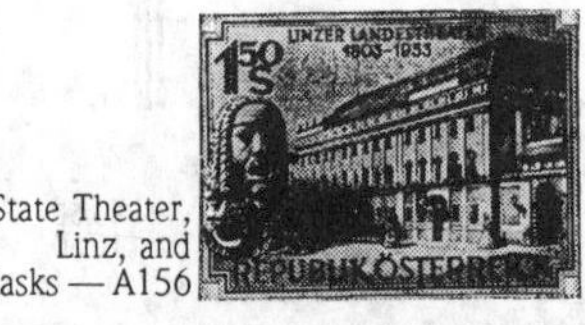

State Theater, Linz, and Masks — A156

1953, Oct. 17 ***Perf. 13½x14***
589 A156 1.50s dark gray 15.00 1.50

State Theater at Linz, 150th anniv.

Child and Christmas Tree — A157

Karl von Rokitansky — A158

1953, Nov. 30 ***Perf. 14x13½***
590 A157 1s dark green 1.40 .20

See No. 597.

Type Similar to A155

Portrait: 1.50s, Moritz von Schwind.

1954, Jan. 21 ***Perf. 14x13½***
591 A155 1.50s purple 12.00 1.10

Moritz von Schwind, painter, 150th birth anniv.

1954, Feb. 19
592 A158 1.50s purple 14.00 1.40

Karl von Rokitansky, physician, 150th birth anniv. See No. 595.

Esperanto Star and Wreath A159

Engr. and Photo.

1954, June 5 ***Perf. 13½x14***
593 A159 1s dk brown & emer 4.25 .20

Esperanto movement in Austria, 50th anniv.

A160

A161

1954, Aug. 4 Engr. *Perf. 14x13½*

594 A160 1s dark blue green 11.00 1.65

300th birth anniv. of Johann Michael Rottmayr von Rosenbrunn, painter.

Type Similar to A158

Portrait: 1.50s, Carl Auer von Welsbach.

1954, Aug. 4

595 A158 1.50s violet blue 30.00 1.50

25th death anniv. of Carl Auer von Welsbach (1858-1929), chemist.

1954, Oct. 2 Unwmk.

Organ, St. Florian Monastery and Cherub.

596 A161 1s brown 2.25 .18

2nd Intl. Congress for Catholic Church Music, Vienna, Oct. 4-10, 1954.

Christmas Type of 1953

1954, Nov. 30

597 A157 1s dark blue 2.75 .25

Arms of Austria and Official Publication A162

1954, Dec. 18 Engr.

598 A162 1s salmon & black 2.25 .20

Austria's State Printing Plant, 150th anniv., and Wiener Zeitung, government newspaper, 250th year of publication.

Parliament Building A163

Designs: 1s, Western railroad station, Vienna. 1.45s, Letters forming flag. 1.50s, Public housing, Vienna. 2.40s, Limberg dam.

1955, Apr. 27 *Perf. 13½x14*

599 A163 70g rose violet 1.40 .20
600 A163 1s deep ultra 5.00 .20
601 A163 1.45s scarlet 7.75 1.50
602 A163 1.50s brown 17.00 .20
603 A163 2.40s dk blue green 7.75 3.00
Nos. 599-603 (5) 38.90 5.10

10th anniv. of Austria's liberation.

Type of 1945 Overprinted in Blue **STAATSVERTRAG 1955**

1955, May 15 *Perf. 14x13½*

604 A100 2s blue gray 1.90 .20

Signing of the state treaty with the US, France, Great Britain and Russia, May 15, 1955.

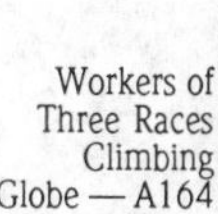

Workers of Three Races Climbing Globe — A164

1955, May 20 *Perf. 13½x14*

605 A164 1s indigo 2.00 1.65

4th congress of the Intl. Confederation of Free Trade Unions, Vienna, May.

Burgtheater, Vienna — A165

Design: 2.40s, Opera House, Vienna.

1955, July 25

606 A165 1.50s light sepia 3.00 .20
607 A165 2.40s dark blue 4.00 1.25

Re-opening of the Burgtheater and Opera House in Vienna.

Symbolic of Austria's Desire to Join the UN — A166

1955, Oct. 24 Unwmk.

608 A166 2.40s green 14.00 1.40

Tenth anniversary of UN.

Wolfgang Amadeus Mozart — A167

Symbolic of Austria's Joining the UN — A168

1956, Jan. 21 *Perf. 14x13½*

609 A167 2.40s slate blue 3.75 .50

200th birth anniv. of Wolfgang Amadeus Mozart, composer.

1956, Feb. 20

610 A168 2.40s chocolate 11.00 1.10

Austria's admission to the UN.

Globe Showing Energy of the Earth — A169

1956, May 8 *Perf. 13½x14*

611 A169 2.40s deep blue 10.00 1.40

Fifth Intl. Power Conf., Vienna, June 17-23.

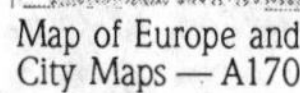

Map of Europe and City Maps — A170

J.B. Fischer von Erlach — A171

Photo. and Typo.

1956, June 8 *Perf. 14x13½*

612 A170 1.45s lt grn blk & red 2.50 .50

23rd Intl. Housing and Town Planning Congress, Vienna, July 22-28.

1956, July 20 Engr.

613 A171 1.50s brown 1.25 1.10

300th birth anniv. of Johann Bernhard Fischer von Erlach, architect.

Körner Type of 1953

1957, Jan. 11

614 A155 1.50s gray black 1.50 1.25

Death of Pres. Theodor Körner.

Dr. Julius Wagner-Jauregg A172

Anton Wildgans A173

1957, Mar. 7 *Perf. 14x13½*

615 A172 2.40s brn violet 3.50 1.25

Birth cent. of Dr. Julius Wagner-Jauregg, psychiatrist.

1957, May 3 Unwmk.

616 A173 1s violet blue .35 .15

Anton Wildgans, poet, 25th death anniv.

Old and New Postal Motor Coach — A174

1957, June 14 *Perf. 13½x14*

617 A174 1s black, *yellow* .35 .15

Austrian Postal Motor Coach Service, 50th anniv.

Gasherbrum II and Glacier A175

1957, July 27

618 A175 1.50s gray blue .42 .15

Austrian Karakorum Expedition, which climbed Mount Gasherbrum II on July 7, 1956.

A176

A177

Designs: 20g, Farmhouse at Mörbisch. 50g, Heiligenstadt, Vienna. 1s, Mariazell. 1.40s, County seat, Klagenfurt. 1.50s, Rabenhof Building, Erdberg, Vienna. 1.80s, The Mint, Hall, Tyrol. 2s, Christkindl Church. 3.40s, Steiner Gate, Krems. 4s, Vienna Gate, Hainburg. 4.50s, Schwechat Airport, Vienna. 5.50s, Chur Gate, Feldkirch. 6s, County seat, Graz. 6.40s, "Golden Roof," Innsbruck. 10s, Heidenreichstein Castle.

1957-61 Litho. *Perf. 14x13½*

Size: 20x25mm

618A A176 20g violet blk ('61) .15 .15
619 A176 50g bluish black ('59) .15 .15

Engr.

620 A176 1s chocolate 1.25 .15

Typo.

621 A176 1s chocolate 1.75 .15

Litho.

622 A176 1s choc ('59) .90 .15
622A A176 1.40s brt greenish bl ('60) .30 .15
623 A176 1.50s rose lake ('58) .50 .15
624 A176 1.80s brt ultra ('60) .30 .15
625 A176 2s dull blue ('58) 6.00 .15
626 A176 3.40s yel grn ('60) .90 .80
627 A176 4s brt red lil ('60) .75 .15
627A A176 4.50s dl green ('60) 1.00 .50
628 A176 5.50s grnsh gray ('60) .55 .20
629 A176 6s brt vio ('60) 1.00 .15
629A A176 6.40s brt blue ('60) .95 .90

Engr.

Size: 22x28mm

630 A177 10s dk bl grn 3.00 .45
Nos. 618A-630 (16) 19.45
Set value 3.50

Of the three 1s stamps above, Nos. 620 and 621 have two names in imprint (designer H. Strohofer, engraver G. Wimmer). No. 622 has only Strohofer's name.

Values for Nos. 618A-624, 626-630 are for stamps on white paper. Most denominations also come on grayish paper with yellowish gum.

See Nos. 688-702.

1960-65 Photo. *Perf. 14½x14*

Size: 17x21mm

630A A176 50g slate ('64) .15 .15

Size: 18x21½mm

630B A176 1s chocolate .15 .15

Size: 17x21mm

630C A176 1.50s dk car ('65) .20 .15
Set value .35 .25

Nos. 630A-630C issued in sheets and coils.

Graukogel, Badgastein — A180

1958, Feb. 1 Engr. *Perf. 14x13½*

631 A180 1.50s dark blue .25 .15

Intl. Ski Federation Alpine championships, Badgastein; Feb. 2-7.

Plane over Map of Austria — A181

1958, Mar. 27 *Perf. 13½x14*

632 A181 4s red .45 .15

Re-opening of Austrian Airlines.

Mother and Daughter A182

Walther von der Vogelweide A183

1958, May 8 Unwmk. *Perf. 14x13½*

633 A182 1.50s dark blue .25 .15

Issued for Mother's Day.

1958, July 17 Litho. and Engr.

634 A183 1.50s multicolored .25 .15

3rd Austrian Song Festival, Vienna, July 17-20.

Oswald Redlich — A184

Giant "E" on Map — A185

1958, Sept. 17 Engr.

635 A184 2.40s ultramarine .55 .15

Prof. Oswald Redlich (1858-1944), historian, birth cent.

Renner Type of 1948

1958, Nov. 12
636 A136 1.50s deep green .45 .25

Austrian Republic, 40th anniv.

1959, Mar. 9
637 A185 2.40s emerald .35 .20

Idea of a United Europe.

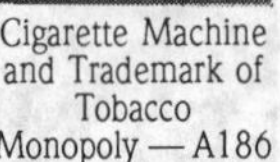

Cigarette Machine and Trademark of Tobacco Monopoly — A186

Archduke Johann — A187

1959, May 8 Unwmk. *Perf. 13½*
638 A186 2.40s dark olive bister .25 .15

Austrian tobacco monopoly, 175th anniv.

1959, May 11 *Perf. 14x13½*
639 A187 1.50s deep green .25 .20

Archduke Johann of Austria, military leader and humanitarian, death cent.

Capercaillie A188

Joseph Haydn A189

Animals: 1.50s, Roe buck. 2.40s, Wild boar. 3.50s, Red deer, doe and fawn.

1959, May 20 Engr.
640 A188 1s rose violet .25 .15
641 A188 1.50s blue violet .55 .15
642 A188 2.40s dk bl green .40 .35
643 A188 3.50s dark brown .30 .20
Nos. 640-643 (4) 1.50 .85

Congress of the Intl. Hunting Council, Vienna, May 20-24.

1959, May 30 Unwmk.
644 A189 1.50s violet brown .45 .20

Joseph Haydn, composer, 150th death anniv.

Coat of Arms, Tyrol A190

Antenna, Zugspitze A191

1959, June 13 *Perf. 14x13½*
645 A190 1.50s rose red .25 .15

Fight for liberation of Tyrol, 150th anniv.

1959, June 19 *Perf. 13½*
646 A191 2.40s dk bl grn .30 .15

Inauguration of Austria's relay system.

Field Ball Player A192

Orchestral Instruments A193

Designs: 1s, Runner. 1.80s, Gymnast on vaulting horse. 2s, Woman hurdler. 2.20s, Hammer thrower.

1959-70 Engr. *Perf. 14x13½*
647 A192 1s lilac .18 .15
648 A192 1.50s blue green .50 .20
648A A192 1.80s carmine ('62) .45 .35
648B A192 2s rose lake ('70) .25 .15
648C A192 2.20s bluish blk ('67) .25 .15
Nos. 647-648C (5) 1.63 1.00

Litho. and Engr.

1959, Aug. 19 *Perf. 14x13½*
649 A193 2.40s dull bl & blk .30 .15

World tour of the Vienna Philharmonic Orchestra.

Family Fleeing over Mountains A194

1960, Apr. 7 Engr. *Perf. 13½x14*
650 A194 3s Prussian green .65 .25

WRY, July 1, 1959-June 30, 1960.

President Adolf Schärf — A195

1960, Apr. 20 *Perf. 14x13½*
651 A195 1.50s gray olive .65 .15

Pres. Adolf Scharf, 70th birthday.

Young Hikers and Hostel — A196

1960, May 20 *Perf. 13½x14*
652 A196 1s carmine rose .20 .15

Youth hiking; youth hostel movement.

Anton Eiselsberg — A197

Gustav Mahler — A198

Litho. and Engr.

1960, June 20 *Perf. 14x13½*
653 A197 1.50s buff & dk brn .70 .15

Dr. Anton Eiselsberg, surgeon, birth cent.

1960, July 7 Engr.
654 A198 1.50s chocolate .70 .15

Gustav Mahler, composer, birth cent.

Jakob Prandtauer, Melk Abbey — A199

Gross Glockner Mountain Road — A200

1960, July 16 Unwmk.
655 A199 1.50s red brown .70 .15

Jakob Prandtauer, architect, 300th birth anniv.

1960, Aug. 3
656 A200 1.80s dark blue .75 .50

Gross Glockner Mountain Road, 25th anniv.

Ionic Capital — A201

1960, Aug. 29 *Perf. 14x13½*
657 A201 3s black 1.40 .75

Europa: Idea of a United Europe.

Griffen, Carinthia A202

1960, Oct. 10 Engr. *Perf. 13½x14*
658 A202 1.50s slate green .30 .15

40th anniv. of the plebiscite which kept Carinthia with Austria.

Flame and Broken Chain — A203

1961, May 8 Unwmk. *Perf. 14x13½*
659 A203 1.50s scarlet .30 .15

Victims in Austria's fight for freedom.

First Austrian Mail Plane, 1918 — A204

1961, May 15 *Perf. 13½x14*
660 A204 5s violet blue .70 .30

Airmail Phil. Exhib., LUPOSTA 1961, Vienna, May.

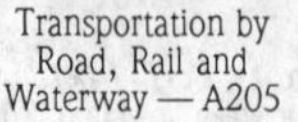

Transportation by Road, Rail and Waterway — A205

Mountain Mower, by Albin Egger-Lienz — A206

Engraved and Typographed

1961, May 29 *Perf. 13½*
661 A205 3s rose red & olive .45 .30

13th European Conference of Transportation ministers, Vienna, May 29-31.

1961, June 12 Engr. *Perf. 13½x14*

Designs: 1.50s, The Kiss, by August von Pettenkofen. 3s, Girl, by Anton Romako. 5s, Ariadne's Triumph, by Hans Makart.

Inscriptions in Red Brown

662 A206 1s rose lake .15 .15
663 A206 1.50s dull violet .25 .25
664 A206 3s olive green .75 .70
665 A206 5s blue violet .45 .40
Nos. 662-665 (4) 1.60 1.50

Society of Creative Artists, Künstlerhaus, Vienna, cent.

Sonnblick Mountain and Observatory A207

Mercury and Globe A208

1961, Sept. 1 *Perf. 14x13½*
666 A207 1.80s violet blue .40 .30

Sonnblick meteorological observatory, 75th anniv.

1961, Sept. 18
667 A208 3s black .65 .40

Intl. Banking Congress, Vienna, Sept. 1961. English inscription listing UN financial groups.

Coal Mine Shaft — A209

Designs: 1.50s, Generator. 1.80s, Iron blast furnace. 3s, Pouring steel. 5s, Oil refinery.

1961, Sept. 15 Engr. *Perf. 14x13½*
668 A209 1s black .20 .15
669 A209 1.50s green .25 .20
670 A209 1.80s dark car rose .55 .40
671 A209 3s bright lilac .70 .55
672 A209 5s blue .90 .70
Nos. 668-672 (5) 2.60 2.00

15th anniversary of nationalized industry.

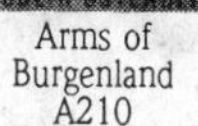
Arms of Burgenland A210

Franz Liszt A211

1961, Oct. 9 **Engr. and Litho.**

673	A210	1.50s	blk, yel & dk red	.35	.15

Burgenland as part of the Austrian Republic, 40th anniv.

1961, Oct. 20 **Engr.**

674	A211	3s	dark brown	.55	.40

Franz Liszt, composer, 150th birth anniv.

Parliament A212

1961, Dec. 18 ***Perf. 13¹/₂x14***

675	A212	1s	brown	.20	.15

Austrian Bureau of Budget, 200th anniv.

Kaprun-Mooserboden Reservoir — A213

Hydroelectric Power Plants: 1.50s, Ybbs-Persenbeug dam and locks. 1.80s, Lünersee dam and reservoir. 3s, Grossraming dam. 4s, Bisamberg transformer plant. 6.40s, St. Andrä power plant.

1962, Mar. 26 **Unwmk.**

676	A213	1s	violet blue	.15	.15
677	A213	1.50s	red lilac	.24	.20
678	A213	1.80s	green	.40	.35
679	A213	3s	brown	.40	.35
680	A213	4s	rose red	.40	.35
681	A213	6.40s	gray	1.25	1.10
			Nos. 676-681 (6)	2.84	2.50

Nationalization of the electric power industry, 15th anniv.

Johann Nestroy A214

Friedrich Gauermann A215

1962, May 25 ***Perf. 14x13¹/₂***

682	A214	1s	violet	.20	.15

Johann Nepomuk Nestroy, Viennese playwright, author and actor, death cent.

1962, July 6 **Engr.**

683	A215	1.50s	intense blue	.20	.15

Friedrich Gauermann (1807-1862), landscape painter, death cent.

Scout Emblem and Handshake — A216

1962, Oct. 5

684	A216	1.50s	dark green	.35	.20

Austria's Boy Scouts, 50th anniv.

Lowlands Forest A217

Designs: 1.50s, Deciduous forest. 3s, Fir and larch forest.

1962, Oct. 12 ***Perf. 13¹/₂x14***

685	A217	1s	greenish gray	.20	.15
686	A217	1.50s	reddish brown	.25	.25
687	A217	3s	dk slate green	.90	.70
			Nos. 685-687 (3)	1.35	1.10

Buildings Types of 1957-61

Designs: 30g, City Hall, Vienna. 40g, Porcia Castle, Spittal on the Drau. 60g, Tanners' Tower, Wels. 70g, Residenz Fountain, Salzburg. 80g, Old farmhouse, Pinzgau. 1s, Romanesque columns, Millstatt Abbey. 1.20s, Kornmesser House, Bruck on the Mur. 1.30s, Schatten Castle, Feldkirch, Vorarlberg. 2s, Dragon Fountain, Klagenfurt. 2.20s, Beethoven House, Vienna. 2.50s, Danube Bridge, Linz. 3s, Swiss Gate, Vienna. 3.50s, Esterhazy Palace, Eisenstadt. 8s, City Hall, Steyr. 20s, Melk Abbey.

1962-70 **Litho.** ***Perf. 14x13¹/₂***

Size: 20x25mm

688	A176	30g	greenish gray	.50	.15
689	A176	40g	rose red	.15	.15
690	A176	60g	violet brown	.35	.15
691	A176	70g	dark blue	.25	.15
692	A176	80g	yellow brown	.35	.15
693	A176	1s	brown ('70)	.20	.15
694	A176	1.20s	red lilac	.40	.15
695	A176	1.30s	green ('67)	.15	.15
696	A176	2s	dk blue ('68)	.25	.15
697	A176	2.20s	green	1.40	.15
698	A176	2.50s	violet	.80	.15
699	A176	3s	bright blue	.70	.15
700	A176	3.50s	rose carmine	.80	.15
701	A176	8s	claret ('65)	1.00	.15

Perf. 13¹/₂

Engr.

Size: 28x36¹/₂mm

702	A177	20s	rose claret ('63)	2.40	.35
			Nos. 688-702 (15)	9.70	
			Set value		1.15

Values for Nos. 688-702 are for stamps on white paper. Some denominations also come on grayish paper with yellowish gum.

Electric Locomotive and Train of 1837 A218

Lithographed and Engraved

1962, Nov. 9 ***Perf. 13¹/₂x14***

703	A218	3s	buff & black	1.00	.40

125th anniversary of Austrian railroads.

Postilions and Postal Clerk, 1863 — A219

Hermann Bahr — A220

1963, May 7 **Photo.** ***Perf. 14x13¹/₂***

704	A219	3s	dk brn & citron	.70	.40

First Intl. Postal Conference, Paris, cent.

Lithographed and Envraved

1963, July 19 ***Perf. 14x13¹/₂***

705	A220	1.50s	blue & black	.25	.15

Centenary of birth of Hermann Bahr, poet.

St. Florian Statue, Kefermarkt, Contemporary and Old Fire Engines — A221

1963, Aug. 30 **Unwmk.**

706	A221	1.50s	brt rose & blk	.25	.15

Austrian volunteer fire brigades, cent.

Factory, Flag and "ÖGB" on Map of Austria A222

1963, Sept. 23 **Litho.** ***Perf. 13¹/₂x14***

707	A222	1.50s	gray, red & dk brn	.25	.15

5th Congress of the Austrian Trade Union Federation (ÖGB), Sept. 23-28.

Arms of Austria and Tyrol — A223

1963, Sept. 27 **Unwmk.**

708	A223	1.50s	tan, blk, red & yel	.25	.15

Tyrol's union with Austria, 600th anniv.

Prince Eugene of Savoy — A224

Centenary Emblem — A225

1963, Oct. 18 **Engr.** ***Perf. 14x13¹/₂***

709	A224	1.50s	violet	.25	.15

Prince Eugene of Savoy (1663-1736), Austrian general, 300th birth anniv.

1963, Oct. 25 **Engr. and Photo.**

710	A225	3s	blk, sil & red	.50	.20

Intl. Red Cross, cent.

Slalom A226

Sports: 1.20s, Biathlon (skier with rifle). 1.50s, Ski jump. 1.80s, Women's figure skating. 2.20s, Ice hockey. 3s, Tobogganing. 4s, Bobsledding.

Photo. and Engr.

1963, Nov. 11 ***Perf. 13¹/₂x14***

711	A226	1s	multi	.15	.15
712	A226	1.20s	multi	.15	.15
713	A226	1.50s	multi	.20	.15
714	A226	1.80s	multi	.25	.15
715	A226	2.20s	multi	.40	.25
716	A226	3s	multi	.30	.20
717	A226	4s	multi	.60	.40
			Nos. 711-717 (7)	2.05	1.45

9th Winter Olympic Games, Innsbruck, Jan. 29-Feb. 9, 1964.

Baroque Creche by Josef Thaddäus Stammel — A227

1963, Nov. 29 **Engr.** ***Perf. 14x13¹/₂***

718	A227	2s	dark Prus green	.25	.15

Flowers A228

1964, Apr. 17 **Litho.** ***Perf. 14***

719	A228	1s	Nasturtium	.15	.15
720	A228	1.50s	Peony	.20	.15
721	A228	1.80s	Clematis	.25	.15
722	A228	2.20s	Dahlia	.35	.20
723	A228	3s	Morning glory	.40	.25
724	A228	4s	Hollyhock	.50	.35
			Nos. 719-724 (6)	1.85	1.25

Vienna Intl. Garden Show, Apr. 16-Oct. 11.

St. Mary Magdalene and Apostle — A229

Pallas Athena and National Council Chamber — A230

1964, May 21 **Engr.** ***Perf. 13¹/₂***

725	A229	1.50s	bluish black	.25	.15

Romanesque art in Austria. The 12th century stained-glass window is from the Weitensfeld Church, the bust of the Apostle from the portal of St. Stephen's Cathedral, Vienna.

Engr. and Litho.

1964, May 25 ***Perf. 14x13¹/₂***

726	A230	1.80s	black & emer	.30	.15

2nd Parliamentary and Scientific Conf., Vienna.

The Kiss, by Gustav Klimt
A231

1964, June 5 Litho. Perf. 13½

727 A231 3s multicolored .35 .25

Re-opening of the Vienna Secession, a museum devoted to early 20th century art (art nouveau).

Brother of Mercy and Patient — A232

1964, June 11 Engr. Perf. 14x13½

728 A232 1.50s dark blue .25 .15

Brothers of Mercy in Austria, 350th anniv.

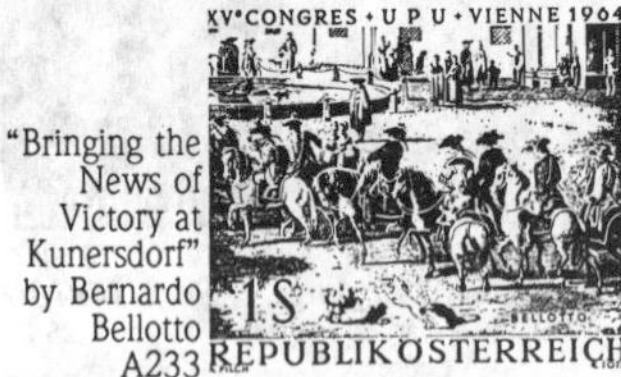

"Bringing the News of Victory at Kunersdorf" by Bernardo Bellotto
A233

"The Post in Art": 1.20s, Changing Horses at Relay Station, by Julius Hörmann. 1.50s, The Honeymoon Trip, by Moritz von Schwind. 1.80s, After the Rain, by Ignaz Raffalt. 2.20s, Mailcoach in the Mountains, by Adam Klein. 3s, Changing Horses at Bavarian Border, by Friedrich Gauermann. 4s, Postal Sleigh (Truck) in the Mountains, by Adalbert Pilch. 6.40s, Saalbach Post Office, by Adalbert Pilch.

1964, June 15 Perf. 13½x14

729 A233	1s	rose claret	.15	.15
730 A233	1.20s	sepia	.15	.15
731 A233	1.50s	violet blue	.15	.15
732 A233	1.80s	brt violet	.15	.15
733 A233	2.20s	black	.20	.15
734 A233	3s	dl car rose	.30	.20
735 A233	4s	slate green	.35	.20
736 A233	6.40s	dull claret	.80	.45
		Nos. 729-736 (8)	2.25	
		Set value		1.22

15th UPU Cong., Vienna, May-June 1964.

Workers — A234

1964, Sept. 4 Perf. 14x13½

737 A234 1s black .15 .15

Centenary of Austrian Labor Movement.

Europa Issue, 1964
Common Design Type

1964, Sept. 14 Litho. Perf. 12
Size: 21x36mm

738 CD7 3s dark blue .50 .15

Emblem of Radio Austria and Transistor Radio Panel
A235

1964, Oct. 1 Photo. Perf. 13½

739 A235 1s black brn & red .15 .15

Forty years of Radio Austria.

A236

A237

Litho. and Engr.

1964, Oct. 12 Perf. 14x13½

740 A236 1.50s Old printing press .15 .15

6th Congress of the Intl. Graphic Federation, Vienna, Oct. 12-17.

Typo. and Engr.

1965, Apr. 20 Perf. 12

Pres. Adolf Schärf and Scharf Student Center.

741 A237 1.50s bluish black .20 .15

Dr. Adolf Schärf (1890-1965), Pres. of Austria (1957-65).

Ruins and New Buildings — A238

1965, Apr. 27 Engr. Perf. 14x13½

742 A238 1.80s carmine lake .20 .15

Twenty years of reconstruction.

Oldest Seal of Vienna University — A239

St. George, 16th Century Wood Sculpture — A240

Photo. and Engr.

1965, May 10 Perf. 14x13½

743 A239 3s gold & red .35 .20

University of Vienna, 600th anniv.

1965, May 17 Engr.

744 A240 1.80s bluish black .25 .15

Art of the Danube Art School, 1490-1540, exhibition, May-Oct. 1965. The stamp background shows an engraving by Albrecht Altdorfer.

ITU Emblem, Telegraph Key and TV Antenna — A241

Ferdinand Raimund — A242

1965, May 17 Unwmk.

745 A241 3s violet blue .35 .20

ITU, cent.

1965 Engr. Perf. 14x13½

Portraits: No. 746, Dr. Ignaz Philipp Semmelweis. No. 747, Bertha von Suttner. No. 749, Ferdinand Georg Waldmüller.

746 A242	1.50s	violet	.30	.15
747 A242	1.50s	bluish black	.30	.15
748 A242	3s	dark brown	.55	.15
749 A242	3s	greenish blk	.55	.20
		Nos. 746-749 (4)	1.70	
		Set value		.53

Semmelweis (1818-65), who discovered the cause of puerperal fever and introduced antisepsis into obstetrics (#746). 60th anniv. of the awarding of the Nobel Prize for Peace to von Suttner (1843-1914), pacifist and author (#747). Raimund (1790-1836), actor and playwright (#748). Waldmüller (1793-1865), painter (#749).

Issue dates: No. 746, Aug. 13; No. 747, Dec. 1; No. 748, June 1; No. 749, Aug. 23.

Dancers with Tambourines
A243

Red Cross and Strip of Gauze
A244

Design: 1.50s, Male gymnasts with practice bars.

1965, July 20 Photo. and Engr.

750 A243 1.50s gray & black .20 .15
751 A243 3s bister & blk .35 .25

4th Gymnaestrada, intl. athletic meet, Vienna, July 20-24.

1965, Oct. 1 Litho. Perf. 14x13½

752 A244 3s black & red .35 .15

20th Intl. Red Cross Conference, Vienna.

Austrian Flag and Eagle with Mural Crown — A245

Austrian Flag, UN Headquarters and Emblem — A246

1965, Oct. 7 Photo. and Engr.

753 A245 1.50s gold, red & blk .15 .15

50th anniv. of the Union of Austrian Towns.

Lithographed and Engraved

1965, Oct. 25 Unwmk. Perf. 12

754 A246 3s blk, brt bl & red .45 .15

Austria's admission to the UN, 10th anniv.

University of Technology, Vienna — A247

1965, Nov. 8 Engr. Perf. 13½x14

755 A247 1.50s violet .15 .15

Vienna University of Technology, 150th anniv.

Map of Austria with Postal Zone Numbers — A248

1966, Jan. 14 Photo. Perf. 12

756 A248 1.50s yel, red & blk .15 .15

Introduction of postal zone numbers, Jan. 1, 1966.

PTT Building, Emblem and Churches of Sts. Maria Rotunda and Barbara
A249

Maria von Ebner Eschenbach
A250

Lithographed and Engraved

1966, Mar. 4 Perf. 14x13½

757 A249 1.50s blk, *dull yellow* .15 .15

Headquarters of the Post and Telegraph Administration, cent.

1966, Mar. 11 Engr.

758 A250 3s plum .35 .15

50th death anniv. of Maria von Ebner Eschenbach (1830-1916), novelist and poet.

Ferris Wheel, Prater — A251

1966, Apr. 19 Engr. Perf. 14x13½

759 A251 1.50s slate green .15 .15

Opening of the Prater (park), Vienna, to the public by Emperor Joseph II, 200th anniv.

A252

A253

1966, May 6 Unwmk. Perf. 12

760 A252 3s dark brown .35 .15

Josef Hoffmann (1870-1956), architect, 10th death anniv.

Photo. and Engr.

1966, May 27 Perf. 14

761 A253 1.50s Wiener Neustadt Arms .15 .15

Wiener Neustadt Art Exhib., centered around the time and person of Frederick III (1440-93).

Austrian Eagle and Emblem of National Bank
A254

1966, May 27 *Perf. 14*
762 A254 3s gray grn, dk brn & dk green .35 .15

Austrian National Bank, 150th anniv.

Puppy — A255 A256

Litho. and Engr.

1966, June 16 *Perf. 12*
763 A255 1.80s yellow & black .25 .15

120th anniv. of the Vienna Humane Society.

1966, Aug. 17 Litho. *Perf. 13½*

Alpine Flowers: 1.50s, Columbine. 1.80s, Turk's cap. 2.20s, Wulfenia carinthiaca. 3s, Globeflowers. 4s, Fire lily. 5s, Pasqueflower.

Flowers in Natural Colors

764 A256 1.50s dark blue .15 .15
765 A256 1.80s dark blue .20 .15
766 A256 2.20s dark blue .30 .20
767 A256 3s dark blue .45 .30
768 A256 4s dark blue .45 .35
769 A256 5s dark blue .45 .35
Nos. 764-769 (6) 2.00 1.50

Fair Building A257

1966, Aug. 26 Engr. *Perf. 13½x13*
770 A257 3s violet blue .35 .15

First International Fair at Wels.

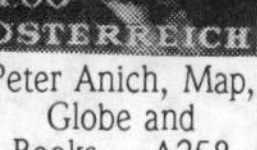

Peter Anich, Map, Globe and Books — A258

Sick Worker and Health Emblem — A259

1966, Sept. 1 *Perf. 14x13½*
771 A258 1.80s black .20 .15

Peter Anich (1723-1766), Tirolean cartographer and farmer, 200th death anniv.

1966, Sept. 19 Engr. and Litho.
772 A259 3s black & vermilion .35 .15

15th Occupational Medicine Congress, Vienna, Sept. 19-24.

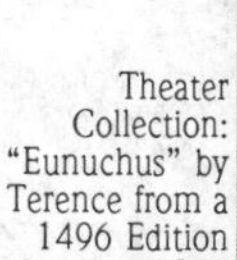

Theater Collection: "Eunuchus" by Terence from a 1496 Edition A260

Designs: 1.80s, Map Collection: Title page of Geographia Blavania (Cronus, Hercules and celestial sphere). 2.20s, Picture Archive and Portrait Collection: View of Old Vienna after a watercolor by Anton Stutzinger. 3s, Manuscript Collection: Illustration from the 15th century "Livre du Cuer d'Amours Espris" of the Duke René d'Anjou.

Photogravure and Engraved

1966, Sept. 28 *Perf. 13½x14*
773 A260 1.50s multicolored .15 .15
774 A260 1.80s multicolored .20 .15
775 A260 2.20s multicolored .25 .20
776 A260 3s multicolored .30 .20
Nos. 773-776 (4) .90 .70

Austrian National Library.

Young Girl A261

Strawberries A262

Litho. and Engr.

1966, Oct. 3 *Perf. 14x13½*
777 A261 3s light blue & black .35 .15

"Save the Child" society, 10th anniv.

1966, Nov. 25 Photo. *Perf. 13½x13*
778 A262 50g shown .20 .15
779 A262 1s Grapes .20 .15
780 A262 1.50s Apple .20 .15
781 A262 1.80s Blackberries .25 .20
782 A262 2.20s Apricots .25 .20
783 A262 3s Cherries .35 .25
Nos. 778-783 (6) 1.45 1.10

Coat of Arms of University of Linz — A263

Ice Skater, 1866 — A264

Photo. and Engr.

1966, Dec. 9 *Perf. 14x13½*
784 A263 3s multi .35 .15

Inauguration of the Universary of Linz, Oct. 8, 1966.

Photo. and Engr.

1967, Feb. 3 *Perf. 14x13½*
785 A264 3s pale bl & dk bl .35 .15

Centenary of Vienna Ice Skating Club.

Ballet Dancer — A265

Karl Schönherr — A266

1967, Feb. 15 Engr. *Perf. 11½x12*
786 A265 3s deep claret .35 .15
a. Perf. 12 1.25 1.10

"Blue Danube" waltz by Johann Strauss, cent.

1967, Feb. 24 Engr. *Perf. 14x13½*
787 A266 3s gray brown .35 .15

Dr. Karl Schönherr (1867-1943), poet, playwright and physician.

Ice Hockey Goalkeeper A267

Photogravure and Engraved

1967, Mar. 17 *Perf. 13½x14*
788 A267 3s pale grn & dk bl .35 .15

Ice Hockey Championships, Vienna, Mar. 18-29.

Violin, Organ and Laurel — A268

1967, Mar. 28 Engr. *Perf. 13½*
789 A268 3.50s indigo .40 .15

Vienna Philharmonic Orchestra, 125th anniv.

Motherhood, Watercolor by Peter Fendi A269

1967, Apr. 28 Litho. *Perf. 14*
790 A269 2s multicolored .25 .15

Mother's Day.

Gothic Mantle Madonna — A270

1967, May 19 Engr. *Perf. 13½x14*
791 A270 3s slate .35 .15

"Austrian Gothic," art exhibition, Krems, 1967. The Gothic wood carving is from Frauenstein in Upper Austria.

Medieval Gold Cross — A271

Swan, Tapestry by Oscar Kokoschka — A272

Litho. and Engr.

1967, June 9 *Perf. 13½*
792 A271 3.50s Prus grn & multi .40 .15

Salzburg Treasure Chamber; exhibition at Salzburg Cathedral, June 12-Sept. 15.

1967, June 9 Photo.
793 A272 2s multicolored .25 .15

Nibelungen District Art Exhibition, Pöchlarn, celebrating the 700th anniversary of Pöchlarn as a city. The design is from the border of the Amor and Psyche tapestry at the Salzburg Festival Theater.

View and Arms of Vienna A273

Engraved and Photogravure

1967, June 12 *Perf. 13x13½*
794 A273 3s black & red .35 .15

10th Europa Talks, "Science and Society in Europe," Vienna, June 13-17.

Prize Bull "Mucki" A274

1967, Aug. 28 Engr. *Perf. 13½*
795 A274 2s deep claret .35 .15

Centenary of the Ried Festival and the Agricultural Fair.

Potato Beetle — A275

Engraved and Photogravure

1967, Aug. 29 *Perf. 13½x14*
796 A275 3s black & multi .35 .15

6th Intl. Congress for Plant Protection, Vienna.

First Locomotive Used on Brenner Pass — A276

1967, Sept. 23 Photo. *Perf. 12*
797 A276 3.50s tan & slate grn .40 .15

Centenary of railroad over Brenner Pass.

Christ in Glory — A277

1967, Oct. 9 *Perf. 13½*
798 A277 2s multicolored .25 .15

Restoration of the Romanesque (11th century) frescoes in the Lambach monastery church.

Main Gate to Fair, Prater, Vienna — A278

1967, Oct. 24 Photo. *Perf. 13½x14*
799 A278 2s choc & buff .25 .15

Congress of Intl. Trade Fairs, Vienna, Oct., 1967.

Medal Showing Minerva and Art Symbols A279

Frankfurt Medal for Reformation, 1717 A280

Litho. & Engr.

1967, Oct. 25 *Perf. 13½*
800 A279 2s dk brn, dk bl & yel .25 .15

Vienna Academy of Fine Arts, 275th anniv. The medal was designed by Georg Raphael Donner (1693-1741) and is awarded as an artist's prize.

1967, Oct. 31 Engr. *Perf. 14x13½*
801 A280 3.50s blue black .40 .15

450th anniversary of the Reformation.

Mountain Range and Stone Pines A281

1967, Nov. 7 *Perf. 13½*
802 A281 3.50s green .40 .15

Centenary of academic study of forestry.

Land Survey Monument, 1770 — A282

St. Leopold, Window, Heiligenkreuz Abbey — A283

1967, Nov. 7 **Photo.**
803 A282 2s olive black .25 .15

150th anniversary of official land records.

1967, Nov. 15 **Engr. & Photo.**
804 A283 1.80s multicolored .25 .15

Margrave Leopold III (1075-1136), patron saint of Austria.

Tragic Mask and Violin — A284

Nativity from 15th Century Altar — A285

1967, Nov. 17 *Perf. 13½*
805 A284 3.50s bluish lil & blk .40 .15

Academy of Music and Dramatic Art, 150th anniv.

1967, Nov. 27 Engr. *Perf. 14x13½*
806 A285 2s green .25 .15

Christmas.

The design shows the late Gothic carved center panel of the altar in St. John's Chapel in Nonnberg Convent, Salzburg.

Buying Sets
It is often less expensive to purchase complete sets than individual stamps that make up the set. Set values are provided for many such sets.

Innsbruck Stadium, Alps and FISU Emblem — A286

Camillo Sitte — A287

1968, Jan. 22 Engr. *Perf. 13½*
807 A286 2s dark blue .25 .15

Winter University Games under the auspices of FISU (Fédération Internationale du Sport Universitaire), Innsbruck, Jan. 21-28.

1968, Apr. 17 *Perf. 13½*
808 A287 2s black brown .25 .15

125th birth anniv. of Camillo Sitte (1843-1903), architect and city planner.

Mother and Child — A288

1968, May 7
809 A288 2s slate green .25 .15

Mother's Day.

Cup and Serpent Emblem — A289

1968, May 7 **Photo.**
810 A289 3.50s dp plum, gray & gold .40 .15

Bicentenary of the Veterinary College.

Bride with Lace Veil — A290

1968, May 24 Engr. *Perf. 12*
811 A290 3.50s blue black .40 .15

Embroidery industry of Vorarlberg, cent.

Horse Race A291

1968, June 4 *Perf. 13½*
812 A291 3.50s sepia .40 .20

Centenary of horse racing at Freudenau, Vienna.

Dr. Karl Landsteiner A292

Peter Rosegger A293

1968, June 14 *Perf. 14x13½*
813 A292 3.50s dark blue .40 .20

Birth cent. of Dr. Karl Landsteiner (1868-1943), pathologist, discoverer of the four main human blood types.

1968, June 26
814 A293 2s slate green .25 .15

50th death anniv. of Peter Rosegger (1843-1918), poet and writer.

Angelica Kauffmann, Self-portrait A294

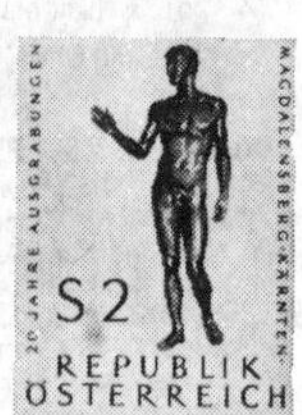

Bronze Statue of Young Man, 1st Century B.C. A295

1968, July 15 Engr. *Perf. 14x13½*
815 A294 2s intense black .25 .15

"Angelica Kauffmann and her Contemporaries," art exhibitions, Bregenz, July 28-Oct. 13, and Vienna, Oct. 22, 1968-Jan. 6, 1969.

1968, July 15 **Litho. & Engr.**
816 A295 2s grnsh gray & blk .25 .15

20 years of excavations on Magdalene Mountain, Carinthia.

Bishop, Romanesque Bas-relief — A296

1968, Sept. 20 Engr. *Perf. 14x13½*
817 A296 2s blue gray .25 .15

Graz-Seckau Bishopric, 750th anniv.

Koloman Moser — A297

Human Rights Flame — A298

Engr. & Photo.

1968, Oct. 18 *Perf. 12*
818 A297 2s black brn & ver .25 .15

50th death anniv. of Koloman Moser (1868-1918), stamp designer and painter.

1968, Oct. 18 Photo. *Perf. 14x13½*
819 A298 1.50s gray, dp car & dk green .30 .15

International Human Rights Year.

A299

A300

Designs: No. 820, Pres. Karl Renner and States' arms. No. 821, Coats of arms of Austria and Austrian states. No. 822, Article I of Austrian Constitution and States' coats of arms.

Engr. & Photo.

1968, Nov. 11 *Perf. 13½*
820 A299 2s black & multi .35 .30
821 A299 2s black & multi .35 .30
822 A299 2s black & multi .35 .30
Nos. 820-822 (3) 1.05 .90

50th anniversary of Republic of Austria.

1968, Nov. 29 Engr. *Perf. 14x13½*

Crèche, Memorial Chapel, Oberndorf-Salzburg.

823 A300 2s slate green .25 .15

Christmas; 150th anniv. of "Silent Night, Holy Night" hymn.

Angels, from Last Judgment by Troger (Röhrenbach-Greillenstein Chapel) — A301

Baroque Frescoes: No. 825, Vanquished Demons, by Paul Troger, Altenburg Abbey. No. 826, Sts. Peter and Paul, by Troger, Melk Abbey. No. 827, The Glorification of Mary, by Franz Anton Maulpertsch, Maria Treu Church, Vienna. No. 828, St. Leopold Carried into Heaven, by Maulpertsch, Ebenfurth Castle Chapel. No. 829, Symbolic figures from The Triumph of Apollo, by Maulpertsch, Halbthurn Castle.

Engr. & Photo.

1968, Dec. 11 *Perf. 13½x14*
824 A301 2s multicolored .30 .30
825 A301 2s multicolored .30 .30
826 A301 2s multicolored .30 .30
827 A301 2s multicolored .30 .30
828 A301 2s multicolored .30 .30
829 A301 2s multicolored .30 .30
Nos. 824-829 (6) 1.80 1.80

St. Stephen — A302

Statues in St. Stephen's Cathedral, Vienna: No. 831, St. Paul. No. 832, Mantle Madonna. No. 833, St. Christopher. No. 834, St. George and the Dragon. No. 835, St. Sebastian.

1969, Jan. 28 Engr. *Perf. 13½*
830 A302 2s black .30 .30
831 A302 2s rose claret .30 .30
832 A302 2s gray violet .30 .30
833 A302 2s slate blue .30 .30
834 A302 2s slate green .30 .30
835 A302 2s dk red brn .30 .30
Nos. 830-835 (6) 1.80 1.80

500th anniversary of Diocese of Vienna.

Parliament and Pallas Athena Fountain, Vienna A303

1969, Apr. 8 Engr. *Perf. 13½*
836 A303 2s greenish black .25 .15

Interparliamentary Union Conf., Vienna, 4/7-13.

Europa Issue, 1969
Common Design Type

1969, Apr. 28 Photo. *Perf. 12*
837 CD12 2s gray grn, brick red & blue .25 .15

Council of Europe Emblem — A304

1969, May 5
838 A304 3.50s gray, ultra, blk & yel .45 .25

20th anniversary of Council of Europe.

Frontier Guards — A305

Engr. & Photo.

1969, May 14 *Perf. 12*
839 A305 2s sepia & red .25 .15

Austrian Federal Army.

Don Giovanni, by Mozart — A306

Cent. of Vienna Opera House: a, Don Giovanni, Mozart. b, Magic Flute, Mozart. c, Fidelio, Beethoven. d, Lohengrin, Wagner. e, Don Carlos, Verdi. f, Carmen, Bizet. g, Rosencavalier, Richard Strauss. h, Swan Lake, Ballet by Tchaikovsky.

1969, May 23 *Perf. 13½*
840 A306 Sheet of 8 4.00 4.00
a.-h. 2s, any single .32 .32

Centenary of Vienna Opera House.
No. 840 contains 8 stamps arranged around gold and red center label showing Opera House. Printed in sheets containing 4 Nos. 840 with wide gutters between.

A307

A308

Gothic armor of Maximilian I.

1969, June 4 Engr.
841 A307 2s bluish black .25 .15

Emperor Maximilian I Exhibition, Innsbruck, May 30-Oct. 5.

1969, June 16 Photo. *Perf. 13½*

Oldest Municipal Seal of Vienna.

842 A308 2s tan, red & black .25 .15

19th Cong. of the Intl. Org. of Municipalities, Vienna, June 1969.

A309

A310

Girl's head and village house.

Engraved and Photogravure

1969, June 16 *Perf. 13½x14*
843 A309 2s yel grn & sepia .25 .15

20th anniv. of the Children's Village Movement in Austria (SOS Villages).

1969, Aug. 22 Photo. *Perf. 13x13½*

Hands holding wrench, and UN emblem.

844 A310 2s deep green .25 .15

ILO, 50th anniv.

A311

A312

Austria's flag and shield circling the world.

Engraved and Lithographed

1969, Aug. 22 *Perf. 14x13½*
845 A311 3.50s slate & red .40 .20

Year of Austrians Living Abroad, 1969.

Engraved and Photogravure

1969, Sept. 26 *Perf. 13½*

Etchings: No. 846, Young Hare, by Dürer. No. 847, El Cid Killing a Bull, by Francisco de Goya. No. 848, Madonna with the Pomegranate, by Raphael. No. 849, The Painter, by Peter Brueghel. No. 850, Rubens' Son Nicolas, by Rubens. No. 851, Self-portrait, by Rembrandt. No. 852, Lady Reading, by Francois Guerin. No. 853, Wife of the Artist, by Egon Schiele.

Gray Frame, Buff Background

846 A312 2s black & brown .25 .25
847 A312 2s black .25 .25
848 A312 2s black .25 .25
849 A312 2s black .25 .25
850 A312 2s black & salmon .25 .25
851 A312 2s black .25 .25
852 A312 2s black & salmon .25 .25
853 A312 2s black .25 .25
Nos. 846-853 (8) 2.00 2.00

Etching collection in the Albertina, Vienna, 200th anniv.

President Franz Jonas — A313

1969, Oct. 3
854 A313 2s gray & vio blue .25 .15

70th birthday of Franz Jonas, Austrian Pres.

Post Horn, Globe and Lightning A314

1969, Oct. 17 *Perf. 13½x14*
855 A314 2s multicolored .25 .15

Union of Postal and Telegraph employees, 50th anniv.

Savings Box, about 1450 A315

Madonna, by Albin Egger-Lienz A316

1969, Oct. 31 Photo. *Perf. 13x13½*
856 A315 2s silver & slate green .25 .15

The importance of savings.

Engr. & Photo.

1969, Nov. 24 *Perf. 12*
857 A316 2s dp cl & pale yel .25 .15

Christmas.

Josef Schöffel — A317

St. Klemens M. Hofbauer — A318

1970, Feb. 6 Engr. *Perf. 14x13½*
858 A317 2s dull purple .25 .15

60th death anniv. of Josef Schöffel, (1832-1910), who saved the Vienna Woods.

Engraved and Photogravure

1970, Mar. 13 *Perf. 14x13½*
859 A318 2s dk brn & lt tan .25 .15

150th death anniv. St. Klemens Maria Hofbauer (1751-1820); Redemptorist preacher in Poland and Austria, canonized in 1909.

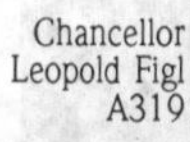

Chancellor Leopold Figl A319

Belvedere Palace, Vienna A320

1970, Apr. 27 Engr. *Perf. 13½*
860 A319 2s dark olive gray .25 .15
861 A320 2s dark rose brown .25 .15
Set value .20

25th anniversary of Second Republic.

A321

A322

1970, May 19 Engr. *Perf. 13½*
862 A321 2s Krimml waterfalls .25 .15

European Nature Conservation Year, 1970.

Litho. & Engr.

1970, June 5 *Perf. 13½*

St. Leopold on oldest seal of Innsbruck University.

863 A322 2s red & black .25 .15

Leopold Franzens University, Innsbruck, 300th anniv.

Organ, Great Hall, Music Academy — A323

Photo. & Engr.

1970, June 5 *Perf. 14*
864 A323 2s gold & deep claret .25 .15

Vienna Music Academy Building, cent.

Tower Clock, 1450-1550 A324

The Beggar Student, by Carl Millöcker A325

Old Clocks from Vienna Horological Museum: #866, Lyre clock, 1790-1815. #867, Pendant clock 1600-50. #868, Pendant watch, 1800-30. #869, Bracket clock, 1720-60. #870, French column clock, 1820-50.

1970

865 A324 1.50s buff & sepia .25 .25
866 A324 1.50s greenish & grn .25 .25
867 A324 2s pale bl & dk bl .30 .30
868 A324 2s pale rose & lake .30 .30
869 A324 3.50s buff & brown .50 .50
870 A324 3.50s pale lil & brn vio .50 .50
Nos. 865-870 (6) 2.10 2.10

Issued: #865, 867, 869, 6/22; others, 10/23.

1970 Photo & Engr. *Perf. 13½*

Operettas: No. 872, Fledermaus, by Johann Strauss. No. 873, The Dream Waltz, by Oscar Strauss. No. 874, The Bird Seller, by Carl Zeller. No. 875, The Merry Widow, by Franz Lehar. No. 876, Two Hearts in Three-quarter Time, by Robert Stolz.

871 A325 1.50s pale grn & grn .25 .25
872 A325 1.50s yel & vio blue .25 .25
873 A325 2s pale rose & vio brn .30 .30
874 A325 2s pale grn & sep .30 .30
875 A325 3.50s pale bl & ind .50 .50
876 A325 3.50s beige & slate .50 .50
Nos. 871-876 (6) 2.10 2.10

Issued: #871, 873, 875, 7/3; others 9/11.

Bregenz Festival Stage — A326

1970, July 23 **Photo.**
877 A326 3.50s dark blue & buff .40 .20

25th anniversary of Bregenz Festival.

Salzburg Festival Emblem — A327

1970, July 27 ***Perf. 14***
878 A327 3.50s blk, red, gold & gray .40 .20

50th anniversary of Salzburg Festival.

A328 A329

1970, Aug. 31 **Engr.**
879 A328 3.50s dark gray .40 .20

13th General Assembly of the World Veterans Federation, Aug. 28-Sept. 4. The head of St. John is from a sculpture showing the Agony in the Garden in the chapel of the Parish Church in Ried. It is attributed to Thomas Schwanthaler (1634-1702).

1970, Sept. 16 ***Perf. 14x13½***
880 A329 2s chocolate .25 .15

Thomas Koschat (1845-1914), Carinthian composer of songs.

Mountain Scene A330

1970, Sept. 16 **Photo.** ***Perf. 14x13½***
881 A330 2s vio bl & pink .25 .15

Hiking and mountaineering in Austria.

Alfred Cossmann A331 Arms of Carinthia A332

1970, Oct. 2 **Engr.** ***Perf. 14x13½***
882 A331 2s dark brown .25 .15

Birth cent. of Alfred Cossmann (1870-1951), engraver.

1970, Oct. 2 **Photo. & Engr.** ***Perf. 14***
883 A332 2s ol, red, gold, blk & sil .25 .15

Carinthian plebiscite, 50th anniversary.

UN Emblem — A333

1970, Oct. 23 **Litho.** ***Perf. 14x13½***
884 A333 3.50s lt blue & blk .50 .20

25th anniversary of the United Nations.

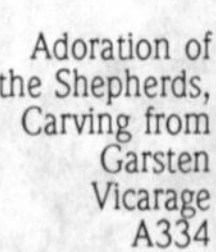

Adoration of the Shepherds, Carving from Garsten Vicarage A334

1970, Nov. 27 **Engr.** ***Perf. 13½x14***
885 A334 2s dk violet blue .25 .15

Christmas.

Karl Renner — A335 Beethoven, by Georg Waldmüller — A336

1970, Dec. 14 **Engr.** ***Perf. 14x13½***
886 A335 2s deep claret .25 .15

Karl Renner (1870-1950), Austrian Pres., birth cent.

Photo. & Engr.

1970, Dec. 16 ***Perf. 13½***
887 A336 3.50s black & buff .40 .20

Ludwig van Beethoven (1770-1827), composer, birth bicentenary.

Enrica Handel-Mazzetti A337

1971, Jan. 11 **Engr.** ***Perf. 14x13½***
888 A337 2s sepia .25 .15

Birth cent. of Enrica von Handel-Mazzetti (1871-1955), novelist and poet.

"Watch Out for Children!" A338

1971, Feb. 18 **Photo.** ***Perf. 13½***
889 A338 2s blk, red brn & brt grn .25 .15

Traffic safety.

Saltcellar, by Benvenuto Cellini A339

Art Treasures: 1.50s, Covered vessel, made of prase, gold and precious stones, Florentine, 1580. 2s, Emperor Joseph I, ivory statue by Matthias Steinle, 1693.

Photo. & Engr.

1971, Mar. 22 ***Perf. 14***
890 A339 1.50s gray & slate grn .20 .15
891 A339 2s gray & deep plum .25 .20
892 A339 3.50s gray, blk & bister .50 .35
Nos. 890-892 (3) .95 .70

Emblem of Austrian Wholesalers' Organization A340

1971, Apr. 16 **Photo.** ***Perf. 13½***
893 A340 3.50s multicolored .40 .20

Intl. Chamber of Commerce, 23rd Congress, Vienna, Apr. 17-23.

Jacopo de Strada, by Titian — A341

Paintings in Vienna Museum: 2s, Village Feast, by Peter Brueghel, the Elder. 3.50s, Young Venetian Woman, by Albrecht Dürer.

1971, May 6 **Engr.** ***Perf. 13½***
894 A341 1.50s rose lake .25 .15
895 A341 2s greenish black .25 .20
896 A341 3.50s deep brown .50 .35
Nos. 894-896 (3) 1.00 .70

Seal of Paulus of Franchenfordia, 1380 — A342

Photo. & Engr.

1971, May 6 ***Perf. 13½x14***
897 A342 3.50s dk brn & bister .40 .20

Congress commemorating the centenary of the Austrian Notaries' Statute, May 5-8.

St. Matthew A343 August Neilreich A344

1971, May 27 ***Perf. 12½x13½***
898 A343 2s brt rose lil & brn .25 .15

Exhibition of "1000 Years of Art in Krems." The statue of St. Matthew is from the Lentl Altar, created about 1520 by the Master of the Pulkau Altar.

1971, June 1 **Engr.** ***Perf. 14x13½***
899 A344 2s brown .25 .15

August Neilreich (1803-71), botanist.

Singer with Lyre — A345

Photo. & Engr.

1971, July 1 ***Perf. 13½x14***
900 A345 4s lt bl, vio bl & gold .50 .30

Intl. Choir Festival, Vienna, July 1-4.

Coat of Arms of Kitzbuhel — A346

1971, Aug. 23 ***Perf. 14***
901 A346 2.50s gold & multi .30 .15

700th anniversary of the town of Kitzbuhel.

Vienna Stock Exchange — A347

1971, Sept. 1 **Engr.** ***Perf. 13½x14***
902 A347 4s reddish brown .45 .20

Bicentenary of the Vienna Stock Exchange.

First and Latest Exhibition Halls — A348

1971, Sept. 6 **Photo.** ***Perf. 13½x13***
903 A348 2.50s dp rose lilac .35 .15

Vienna Intl. Fair, 50th anniv.

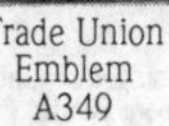

Trade Union Emblem A349 Arms of Burgenland A350

1971, Sept. 20 ***Perf. 14x13½***
904 A349 2s gray, buff & red .25 .15

Austrian Trade Union Assoc., 25th anniv.

1971, Oct. 1
905 A350 2s dk bl, gold, red & blk .25 .15

50th anniv. of Burgenland joining Austria.

Marcus Car — A351

1971, Oct. 1 **Photo. & Engr.** ***Perf. 14***
906 A351 4s pale green & blk .50 .25

Austrian Automobile, Motorcycle and Touring Club, 75th anniv.

Europa Bridge — A352

1971, Oct. 8 Engr. *Perf. 14x13½*

907 A352 4s violet blue	.50	.25

Opening of highway over Brenner Pass.

Styria's Iron Mountain A353

Designs: 2s, Austrian Nitrogen Products, Ltd., Linz. 4s, United Austrian Iron and Steel Works, Ltd. (VÖEST), Linz Harbor.

1971, Oct. 15 *Perf. 13½*

908 A353 1.50s reddish brown	.20	.15
909 A353 2s bluish black	.25	.20
910 A353 4s dk slate grn	.40	.35
Nos. 908-910 (3)	.85	.70

25 years of nationalized industry.

High-speed Train on Semmering A354

Trout Fisherman A355

1971, Oct. 21 *Perf. 14*

911 A354 2s claret	.25	.15

Inter-city rapid train service.

1971, Nov. 15 *Perf. 13½*

912 A355 2s dark red brn	.25	.15

Erich Tschermak-Seysenegg A356

Infant Jesus as Savior, by Dürer A357

Photo. & Engr.

1971, Nov. 15 *Perf. 14x13½*

913 A356 2s pale ol & dk pur	.25	.15

Birth cent. of Dr. Erich Tschermak-Seysenegg (1871-1962), botanist.

1971, Nov. 26 *Perf. 13½*

914 A357 2s gold & multi	.25	.15

Christmas.

Franz Grillparzer, by Moritz Daffinger — A358

Fountain, Main Square, Friesach — A359

Perf. 14x13½

1972, Jan. 21 Litho. & Engr.

915 A358 2s buff, gold & blk	.25	.15

Death cent. of Franz Grillparzer (1791-1872), dramatic poet.

1972, Feb. 23 Engr. *Perf. 14x13½*

Designs: 2s, Fountain, Heiligenkreuz Abbey. 2.50s, Leopold Fountain, Innsbruck.

916 A359 1.50s rose lilac	.25	.15
917 A359 2s brown	.30	.20
918 A359 2.50s olive	.35	.25
Nos. 916-918 (3)	.90	.60

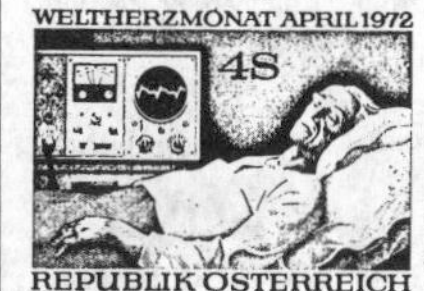

Cardiac Patient and Monitor A360

1972, Apr. 11 *Perf. 13½x14*

919 A360 4s violet brown	.45	.25

World Health Day.

A361

A362

Design: St. Michael's Gate, Royal Palace, Vienna.

1972, Apr. 11 *Perf. 14x13½*

920 A361 4s violet blue	.45	.25

Conference of European Post and Telecommunications Ministers, Vienna, Apr. 11-14.

1972, May 5 Photo. & Engr. *Perf. 14*

921 A362 2s Sculpture, Gurk Cathedral	.25	.15

900th anniv. of Gurk (Carinthia) Diocese. The design is after the central column supporting the sarcophagus of St. Hemma in Gurk Cathedral.

City Hall, Congress Emblem — A363

1972, May 23 Litho. & Engr.

922 A363 4s red, blk & yel	.45	.20

9th Intl. Congress of Public and Cooperative Economy, Vienna, May 23-25.

Power Line in Carnic Alps — A364

Designs: 2.50s, Power Station, Simmering. 4s, Zemm Power Station (lake in Zillertaler Alps).

1972, June 28 *Perf. 13½x14*

923 A364 70g gray & violet	.15	.15
924 A364 2.50s gray & red brn	.30	.30
925 A364 4s gray & slate	.45	.45
Nos. 923-925 (3)	.90	.90

Nationalization of the power industry, 25th anniv.

Runner with Olympic Torch — A365

St. Hermes, by Conrad Laib — A366

Engr. & Photo.

1972, Aug. 21 *Perf. 14x13½*

926 A365 2s sepia & red	.25	.15

Olympic torch relay from Olympia, Greece, to Munich, Germany, passing through Austria.

1972, Aug. 21 Engr.

927 A366 2s violet brown	.25	.15

Exhibition of Late Gothic Art, Salzburg.

Pears — A367

1972, Sept. *Perf. 14*

928 A367 2.50s dk blue & multi	.30	.15

World Congress of small plot Gardeners, Vienna, Sept. 7-10.

Souvenir Sheet

Spanish Walk — A368

1972, Sept. 12 *Perf. 13½*

929 A368 Sheet of 6	2.75	2.75
a. 2s Spanish walk	.25	.25
b. 2s Piaffe	.25	.25
c. 2.50s Levade	.32	.32
d. 2.50s On long rein	.32	.32
e. 4s Capriole	.52	.52
f. 4s Courbette	.52	.52

400th anniv. of the Spanish Riding School in Vienna.

Arms of University of Agriculture A369

Church and Old University A370

Photo. & Engr.

1972, Oct. 17 *Perf. 14x13½*

930 A369 2s black & multi	.25	.15

University of Agriculture, Vienna, cent.

1972, Nov. 7 Engr.

931 A370 4s red brown	.45	.20

Paris Lodron University, Salzburg, 350th anniv.

Carl Michael Ziehrer — A371

1972, Nov. 14

932 A371 2s rose claret	.25	.15

50th death anniv. of Carl Michael Ziehrer (1843-1922), composer.

Virgin and Child, Wood, 1420-30 A372

Photo. & Engr.

1972, Dec. 1 *Perf. 13½*

933 A372 2s olive & choc	.25	.15

Christmas.

Racing Sleigh, 1750 A373

Designs: 2s, Coronation landau, 1824. 2.50s, Imperial state coach, 1763.

1972, Dec. 12

934 A373 1.50s pale gray & brn	.22	.15
935 A373 2s pale gray & sl grn	.30	.15
936 A373 2.50s pale gray & plum	.35	.25
Nos. 934-936 (3)	.87	.55

Collection of historic state coaches and carriages in Schönbrunn Palace.

Map of Austrian Telephone System — A374

1972, Dec. 14 Photo. *Perf. 14*

937 A374 2s yellow & blk	.25	.15

Completion of automation of Austrian telephone system.

"Drugs are Death" — A375

1973, Jan. 26 Photo. *Perf. 13½x14*

938 A375 2s scarlet & multi	1.50	.45

Fight against drug abuse.

Alfons Petzold — A376

Theodor Körner — A377

1973, Jan. 26 Engr. *Perf. 14x13½*

939 A376 2s reddish brn	.25	.15

50th death anniv. of Alfons Petzold (1882-1923), poet.

Photo. & Engr.

1973, Apr. 24 *Perf. 14x13½*

940 A377 2s gray & dp cl .25 .15

Theodor Korner (1873-1957), Austrian Pres., birth cent.

Douglas DC-9 — A378

1973, May 14 *Perf. 13½x14*

941 A378 2s vio bl & rose red .25 .15

First intl. airmail service, Vienna to Kiev, Mar. 31, 1918, 55th anniv.; Austrian Aviation Corporation, 50th anniv.; Austrian Airlines, 15th anniv.

Otto Loewi — A379

"Support" — A380

1973, June 4 Engr. *Perf. 14x13½*

942 A379 4s deep violet .50 .20

Birth cent. of Otto Loewi (1873-1961), pharmacologist, winner of 1936 Nobel prize.

1973, June 25

943 A380 2s dark blue .25 .15

Federation of Austrian Social Insurance Institutes, 25th anniv.

Europa Issue 1973

Post Horn and Telephone — A381

1973, July 9 Photo. *Perf. 14*

944 A381 2.50s ocher, blk & yel .30 .15

Dornbirn Fair Emblem A382

1973, July 27 *Perf. 13½x14*

945 A382 2s multicolored .25 .15

Dornbirn Trade Fair, 25th anniversary.

Hurdles — A383

Leo Slezak — A384

1973, Aug. 13 Engr. *Perf. 14x13½*

946 A383 4s gray olive .50 .20

23rd Intl. Military Pentathlon Championships, Wiener Neustadt, Aug. 13-18.

1973, Aug. 17 *Perf. 14*

947 A384 4s dark brown .50 .20

Leo Slezak (1873-1946), operatic tenor.

Gate, Vienna Hofburg, and ISI Emblem — A385

Photogravure and Engraved

1973, Aug. 20 *Perf. 14x13½*

948 A385 2s gray, dk brn & ver .25 .15

39th Congress of Intl. Statistical Institute, Vienna, Aug. 20-30.

Tegetthoff off Franz Josef Land, by Julius Prayer — A386

1973, Aug. 30 Engr. *Perf. 13½x14*

949 A386 2.50s Prussian grn .30 .15

Discovery of Franz Josef Land by an Austrian North Pole expedition, cent.

Academy of Science, by Canaletto A387

1973, Sept. 4

950 A387 2.50s violet .30 .15

Intl. meteorological cooperation, cent.

Arms of Viennese Tanners A388

Max Reinhardt A389

Photo. & Engr.

1973, Sept. 4 *Perf. 14*

951 A388 4s red & multi .40 .20

13th Congress of the Intl. Union of Leather Chemists' Societies, Vienna, Sept. 1-7.

1973, Sept. 7 Engr. *Perf. 13x13½*

952 A389 2s rose magenta .25 .15

Max Reinhardt (1873-1943), theatrical director and stage manager.

Trotter A390

1973, Sept. 28 *Perf. 13½*

953 A390 2s green .30 .15

Centenary of Vienna Trotting Association.

Ferdinand Hanusch — A391

1973, Sept. 28 *Perf. 14x13½*

954 A391 2s rose brown .25 .15

50th death anniv. of Ferdinand Hanusch (1866-1923), secretary of state.

Police Radio Operator A392

1973, Oct. 2 *Perf. 13½x14*

955 A392 4s violet blue .50 .20

50th anniv. of Intl. Criminal Police Org. (INTERPOL).

Josef Petzval's Photographic Lens — A393

1973, Oct. 8 Litho. & Engr. *Perf. 14*

956 A393 2.50s blue & multi .30 .15

EUROPHOT Photographic Cong., Vienna.

Emperor's Spring, Hell Valley — A394

Photo. & Engr.

1973, Oct. 23 *Perf. 13½x14*

957 A394 2s sepia, bl & red .25 .15

Vienna's first mountain spring water supply system, cent.

Almsee, Upper Austria — A395

Hofburg and Prince Eugene Statue, Vienna — A395a

Designs: 50g, Farmhouses, Zillertal, Tirol. 1s, Kahlenbergerdorf. 1.50s, Bludenz, Vorarlberg. 2s, Inn Bridge, Alt Finstermunz. 2.50s, Murau, Styria. 3s, Bischofsmütze, Salzburg. 3.50s, Easter Church, Oberwart. 4.50s, Windmill, Retz. 5s, Aggstein Castle, Lower Austria. 6s, Lindauer Hut, Vorarlberg. 6.50s, Holy Cross Church, Villach, Carinthia. 7s, Falkenstein Castle, Carinthia. 7.50s, Hohensalzburg. 8s, Votive column, Reiteregg, Styria. 10s, Lake Neusiedl, Burgenland. 11s, Old Town, Enns. 16s, Openair Museum, Bad Tatzmannsdorf. 20s, Myra waterfalls.

Photo. & Engr.

1973-78 *Perf. 13½x14*

Size: 23x29mm

Type A395

No.	Value	Color	Unused	Used
958	50g	gray & sl green	.15	.15
959	1s	brn & dk brown	.15	.15
960	1.50s	rose & brown	.25	.15
961	2s	gray bl & dk blue	.30	.15
962	2.50s	vio & dp violet	.35	.15
963	3s	lt ultra & vio blue	.45	.15
963A	3.50s	dl org & brown	.50	.15
964	4s	brt lil & pur	.55	.15
965	4.50s	brt grn & bl green	.60	.15
966	5s	lilac & vio	.65	.15
967	6s	dp rose & dk violet	.80	.15
968	6.50s	bl grn & indigo	.90	.15
969	7s	sage grn & sl green	.95	.15
970	7.50s	lil rose & claret	1.00	.25
971	8s	dl red & dp brown	1.10	.20
972	10s	gray grn & dk green	1.40	.20
973	11s	ver & dk carmine	1.65	.15
974	16s	ocher & black	2.25	.60
975	20s	ol bis & ol grn	2.75	1.25

Type A395a

No.	Value	Color	Unused	Used
976	50s	gray vio & vio bl	6.75	2.50
		Nos. 958-976 (20)	23.50	
		Set value		5.75

Issue dates: 1974, Nos. 960-963. 1975, Nos. 958-959, 967, 976. 1976, Nos. 965, 971, 973. 1977, Nos. 968, 970, 974-975. 1978, No. 963A. See Nos. 1100-1109.

Nativity — A396

Pregl — A397

1973, Nov. 30 *Perf. 14*

977 A396 2s multicolored .25 .15

Christmas. Design from 14th century stained-glass window.

1973, Dec. 12 Engr. *Perf. 14x13½*

978 A397 4s deep blue .50 .20

50th anniv. of the awarding of the Nobel prize for chemistry to Fritz Pregl (1869-1930).

Telex Machine A398

Hofmannsthal A399

1974, Jan. 14 Photo. *Perf. 14x13½*

979 A398 2.50s ultramarine .30 .15

50th anniversary of Radio Austria.

1974, Feb. 1 Engr. *Perf. 14*

980 A399 4s violet blue .50 .20

Birth cent. of Hugo Hofmannsthal (1874-1929), poet and playwright.

Anton Bruckner and Bruckner House A400

1974, Mar. 22 Engr. *Perf. 14*

981 A400 4s brown .50 .20

Founding of Anton Bruckner House (concert hall), Linz, and birth of Anton Bruckner (1824-1896), composer, 150th anniv.

Vegetables A401

Photo. & Engr.

1974, Apr. 18 *Perf. 14*

982 A401 2s shown .30 .20
983 A401 2.50s Fruits .35 .30
984 A401 4s Flowers .50 .50
Nos. 982-984 (3) 1.15 1.00

Intl. Garden Show, Vienna, Apr. 18-Oct. 14.

Seal of Judenburg A402

Karl Kraus A403

1974, Apr. 24 Photo. *Perf. 14x13½*

985 A402 2s plum & multi .25 .15

750th anniversary of Judenburg.

1974, Apr. 6 **Engr.**

986 A403 4s dark red .50 .20

Karl Kraus (1874-1936), poet and satirist, birth cent.

St. Michael, by Thomas Schwanthaler — A404

1974, May 3

987 A404 2.50s slate green .30 .15

Exhibition of the works by the Schwanthaler Family of sculptors, (1633-1848), Reichersberg am Inn, May 3-Oct. 13.

A405

A406

Europa: King Arthur, from tomb of Maximilian I

1974, May 8 *Perf. 13½*

988 A405 2.50s ocher & slate blue .30 .15

Photo. & Engr.

1974, May 17 *Perf. 14x13½*

De Dion Bouton motor tricycle.

989 A406 2s gray & vio brn .25 .15

Austrian Automobile Assoc., 75th anniv.

Satyr's Head, Terracotta A407

1974, May 22 *Perf. 13½x14*

990 A407 2s org brn, gold & blk .25 .15

Exhibition, "Renaissance in Austria," Schallaburg Castle, May 22-Nov. 14.

Road Transport Union Emblem A408

Maulbertsch, Self-portrait A409

1974, May 24 Photo. *Perf. 14x13½*

991 A408 4s deep orange & blk .50 .20

14th Congress of the Intl. Road Transport Union, Innsbruck.

1974, June 7 Engr. *Perf. 14x13½*

992 A409 2s violet brown .25 .15

Franz Anton Maulbertsch (1724-96), painter, 250th birth anniv.

Gendarmes, 1824 and 1974 — A410

1974, June 7 Photo. *Perf. 13½x14*

993 A410 2s red & multi .25 .15

125th anniversary of Austrian gendarmery.

Fencing A411

Photo. & Engr.

1974, June 14 *Perf. 13½*

994 A411 2.50s red org & blk .30 .15

Transportation Symbols — A412

St. Virgil, Sculpture from Nonntal Church — A413

1974, June 18 Photo. *Perf. 14x13½*

995 A412 4s lt ultra & multi .50 .20

European Conference of Transportation Ministers, Vienna, June 18-21.

1974, June 28 Engr. *Perf. 13½x14*

996 A413 2s violet blue .25 .15

Consecration of the Cathedral of Salzburg by Scotch-Irish Bishop Feirgil (St. Virgil), 1200th anniv. Salzburg was a center of Christianization in the 8th century.

Franz Jonas and Austrian Eagle — A414

1974, June 28

997 A414 2s black .25 .15

Jonas (1899-1974), Austrian Pres., 1965-1974.

Franz Stelzhamer — A415

Diver — A416

1974, July 12 Engr. *Perf. 14x13½*

998 A415 2s indigo .25 .15

Franz Stelzhamer (1802-1874), poet who wrote in Upper Austrian vernacular, death cent.

Photo. & Engr.

1974, Aug. 16 *Perf. 13x13½*

999 A416 4s blue & sepia .50 .20

13th European Swimming, Diving and Water Polo Championships, Vienna, Aug. 18-25.

Ferdinand Ritter von Hebra — A417

1974, Sept. 10 Engr. *Perf. 14x13½*

1000 A417 4s brown .50 .20

30th Meeting of the Assoc. of German-speaking Dermatologists, Graz, Sept. 10-14. Dr. von Hebra (1816-1880) was a founder of modern dermatology.

Arnold Schonberg A418

1974, Sept. 13 *Perf. 13½x14*

1001 A418 2.50s purple .30 .15

Schönberg (1874-1951), composer.

Radio Station, Salzburg A419

1974, Oct. 1 Photo. *Perf. 13½x14*

1002 A419 2s multicolored .25 .15

50th anniversary of Austrian broadcasting.

Edmund Eysler (1874-1949), Composer — A420

1974, Oct. 4 Engr. *Perf. 14x13½*

1003 A420 2s dark olive .25 .15

Mailman, Mail Coach and Train, UPU Emblem A421

Design: 4s, Mailman, jet, truck, 1974, and UPU emblem.

1974, Oct. 9 Photo. *Perf. 13½*

1004 A421 2s deep claret & lil .25 .15
1005 A421 4s dark blue & gray .50 .20

Centenary of Universal Postal Union.

Gauntlet Protecting Rose — A422

1974, Oct. 23 Photo. *Perf. 13½x14*

1006 A422 2s multicolored .25 .15

Environment protection.

Austrian Sports Pool Emblem A423

1974, Oct. 23 Photo. *Perf. 13½x14*

1007 A423 70g multicolored .15 .15

Austrian Sports Pool (lottery), 25th anniv.

Carl Ditters von Dittersdorf A424

Virgin and Child, Wood, c. 1600 A425

1974, Oct. 24 Engr. *Perf. 14x13½*

1008 A424 2s Prussian green .20 .15

Von Dittersdorf (1739-1799), composer.

1974, Nov. 29 **Photo. & Engr.**

1009 A425 2s brown & gold .30 .15

Christmas.

A426

A427

1974, Dec. 18

1010 A426 4s gray & black .50 .20

Franz Schmidt (1874-1939), composer.

Photo. & Engr.

1975, Jan. 24 *Perf. 13½*

1011 A427 2.50s St. Christopher .40 .15

European Architectural Heritage Year. The design shows part of a wooden figure from central panel of the retable in the Kefermarkt Church, 1490-1497.

Safety Belt and Skeleton Arms — A428

Stained Glass Window, Vienna City Hall — A429

1975, Apr. 1 Photo. ***Perf. 14x13½***
1012 A428 70g violet & multi .15 .15

Introduction of obligatory use of automobile safety belts.

1975, Apr. 2 ***Perf. 14***
1013 A429 2.50s multicolored .30 .15

11th meeting of the Council of European Municipalities, Vienna, Apr. 2-5.

Austria as Mediator — A430

Forest — A431

1975, May 2 Litho. ***Perf. 14***
1014 A430 2s blk & bister .25 .15

2nd Republic of Austria, 30th anniv.

1975, May 6 **Engr.**
1015 A431 2s green .25 .15

National forests, 50th anniversary.

High Priest, by Michael Pacher — A432

Gosaukamm Funicular — A433

Europa Issue 1975

Photo. & Engr.

1975, May 27 ***Perf. 14x13½***
1016 A432 2.50s black & multi .40 .15

Design is detail from painting "The Marriage of Joseph and Mary," by Michael Pacher (c. 1450-1500).

1975, June 23 ***Perf. 14x13½***
1017 A433 2s slate & red .30 .15

4th Intl. Funicular Cong., Vienna, June 23-27.

Josef Misson and Mühlbach am Manhartsberg A434

1975, June 27 ***Perf. 13½x14***
1018 A434 2s choc & redsh brn .25 .15

Josef Misson (1803-1875), poet who wrote in Lower Austrian vernacular, death cent.

Setting Sun and "P" — A435

1975, Aug. 27 Litho. ***Perf. 14x13½***
1019 A435 1.50s org, blk & bl .20 .15

Austrian Assoc. of Pensioners 25th anniv. meeting, Vienna, Aug. 1975.

Ferdinand Porsche A436

Photo. & Engr.

1975, Sept. 3 ***Perf. 13½x14***
1020 A436 1.50s gray & purple .20 .15

Ferdinand Porsche (1875-1951), engineer, developer of Porsche and Volkswagen cars, birth cent.

Leo Fall (1873-1925), Composer — A437

1975, Sept. 16 Engr. ***Perf. 14x13½***
1021 A437 2s violet .25 .15

Judo Throw — A438

Heinrich Angeli — A439

1975, Oct. 20 Photo. ***Perf. 14x13½***
1022 A438 2.50s gold & multi .30 .15

10th World Judo Championships, Vienna, Oct. 20-26.

1975, Oct. 21 Engr. ***Perf. 14x13½***
1023 A439 2s rose lake .25 .15

Heinrich Angeli (1840-1925), painter, 50th death anniv.

Johann Strauss and Dancers A440

Photo. & Engr.

1975, Oct. 24 ***Perf. 13½x14***
1024 A440 4s ocher & sepia .50 .20

Johann Strauss (1825-1899), composer.

Stylized Musician Playing a Viol — A441

Symbolic House — A442

1975, Oct. 30 ***Perf. 14x13½***
1025 A441 2.50s silver & vio bl .30 .15

Vienna Symphony Orchestra, 75th anniv.

1975, Oct. 31 **Photo.**
1026 A442 2s multicolored .25 .15

Austrian building savings societies, 50th anniv.

Fan with "Hanswurst" Scene, 18th Century A443

1975, Nov. 14 Photo. ***Perf. 13½x14***
1027 A443 1.50s green & multi .20 .15

Salzburg Theater bicentenary.

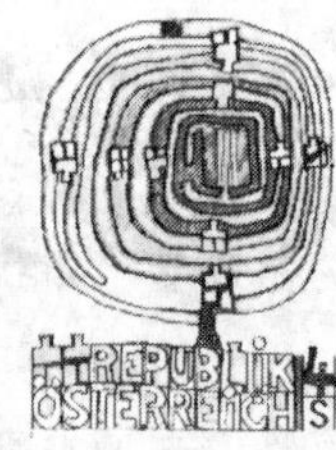

Virgin and Child, from 15th Century Altar A444

"The Spiral Tree," by Hundertwasser A445

Photo. & Engr.

1975, Nov. 28 ***Perf. 13x13½***
1028 A444 2s gold & dull purple .25 .15

Christmas.

Photo., Engr. & Typo.

1975, Dec. 11 ***Perf. 13½x14***
1029 A445 4s multicolored .60 .25

Austrian modern art. Friedenstreich Hundertwasser is the pseudonym of Friedrich Stowasser (b. 1928).

Old Burgtheater A446

Design: No. 1030b, Grand staircase, new Burgtheater.

Perf. 14 (pane), 13½x14 (stamps)

1976, Apr. 8 **Engr.**

1030		Pane of 2 + label	.85	.85
a.	A446	3s violet blue	.28	.28
b.	A446	3s deep brown	.28	.28

Bicentenary of Vienna Burgtheater. Label (head of Pan) and inscription in vermilion.

Dr. Robert Barany (1876-1936), Winner of Nobel Prize for Medicine, 1914 — A447

Photo. & Engr.

1976, Apr. 22 ***Perf. 14x13½***
1031 A447 3s blue & brown .35 .15

Ammonite A448

1976, Apr. 30 Photo. ***Perf. 13½x14***
1032 A448 3s red & multi .35 .15

Vienna Museum of Natural History, Centenary Exhibition.

Carinthian Dukes' Coronation Chair — A449

Siege of Linz, 17th Century Etching — A450

Photo. & Engr.

1976, May 6 ***Perf. 14x13½***
1033 A449 3s grnsh blk & org .35 .15

Millennium of Carinthia.

1976, May 14
1034 A450 4s blk & gray grn .50 .20

Upper Austrian Peasants' War, 350th anniv.

Skittles — A451

1976, May 14 ***Perf. 13½x14***
1035 A451 4s black & org .50 .20

11th World Skittles Championships, Vienna.

Duke Heinrich II, Stained-glass Window — A452

1976, May 14 ***Perf. 14***
1036 A452 3s multicolored .35 .15

Babenberg Exhibition, Lilienfeld.

St. Wolfgang, from Pacher Altar — A453

1976, May 26 Engr. ***Perf. 13½***
1037 A453 6s bright violet .75 .40

Intl. Art Exhibition at St. Wolfgang.

Europa Issue 1976

Tassilo Cup, Kremsmunster, 777 — A454

Photo. & Engr.

1976, Aug. 13 ***Perf. 14x13½***
1038 A454 4s ultra & multi .60 .20

Timber Fair Emblem — A455

Constantin Economo, M.D. — A456

1976, Aug. 13 **Photo.**
1039 A455 3s green & multi .35 .15

Austrian Timber Fair, Klagenfurt, 25th anniv.

1976, Aug. 23 **Engr.**
1040 A456 3s dark red brown .35 .15

Dr. Economo (1876-1931), neurologist.

Administrative Court, by Salomon Klein — A457

1976, Oct. 25 **Engr.** ***Perf. 13½x14***
1041 A457 6s deep brown .75 .30

Austrian Central Administrative Court, cent.

Souvenir Sheet

Coats of Arms of Austrian Provinces — A458

Millennium of Austria: a, Lower Austria. b, Upper Austria. c, Styria. d, Carinthia. e, Tyrol. f, Voralberg. g, Salzburg. h, Burgenland. i, Vienna.

Photo. & Engr.

1976, Oct. 25 ***Perf. 14***
1042 Sheet of 9 2.75 2.75
a.-i. A458 2s any single .30 .30

"Cancer" A459

1976, Nov. 17 **Photo.** ***Perf. 14x13½***
1043 A459 2.50s multicolored .35 .15

Fight against cancer.

UN Emblem and Bridge — A460

1976, Nov. 17
1044 A460 3s blue & gold .40 .15

UN Industrial Development Org. (UNIDO), 10th anniv.

Punched Tape, Map of Europe — A461

1976, Nov. 17 ***Perf. 14***
1045 A461 1.50s multicolored .15 .15

Austrian Press Agency (APA), 30th anniv.

Viktor Kaplan, Kaplan Turbine — A462

Photo. & Engr.

1976, Nov. 26 ***Perf. 13½x14***
1046 A462 2.50s multicolored .30 .15

Viktor Kaplan (1876-1934), inventor of Kaplan turbine, birth centenary.

Nativity, by Konrad von Friesach, c. 1450 A463

1976, Nov. 26 ***Perf. 13½***
1047 A463 3s multicolored .30 .15

Christmas.

Augustin, the Piper — A464

Photo. & Engr.

1976, Dec. 29 ***Perf. 13½***
1048 A464 6s multicolored .75 .25

Modern Austrian art.

Rainer Maria Rilke (1875-1926), Poet A465

Vienna City Synagogue A466

1976, Dec. 29 **Engr.** ***Perf. 14x13½***
1049 A465 3s deep violet .30 .15

1976, Dec. 29 **Photo.** ***Perf. 13½***
1050 A466 1.50s multicolored .15 .15

Sesquicentennial of Vienna City Synagogue.

Nikolaus Joseph von Jacquin (1727-1817), Botanist — A467

1977, Feb. 16 **Engr.** ***Perf. 14x13½***
1051 A467 4s chocolate .45 .20

Oswald von Wolkenstein (1377-1445), Poet — A468

Photo. & Engr.

1977, Feb. 16 ***Perf. 14***
1052 A468 3s multicolored .35 .15

Handball A469

1977, Feb. 25 **Photo.** ***Perf. 13½x14***
1053 A469 1.50s multicolored .15 .15

World Indoor Handball Championships, Austria, Feb. 5-Mar. 6.

A470

A471

1977, Apr. 12 **Engr.** ***Perf. 14x13½***
1054 A470 6s dk violet blue .70 .25

Alfred Kubin (1877-1959), illustrator and writer.

1977, Apr. 22 **Engr.** ***Perf. 13½***

Designs: 2.50s, Great Spire, St. Stephen's Cathedral. 3s, Heathen Tower and Frederick's Gable. 4s, Interior view with Albertinian Choir.

1055 A471 2.50s dark brown .35 .15
1056 A471 3s dark blue .40 .25
1057 A471 4s rose lake .50 .35
Nos. 1055-1057 (3) 1.25 .75

Restoration and re-opening of St. Stephen's Cathedral, Vienna, 25th anniversary.

Fritz Hermanovsky-Orlando (1877-1954), Poet and Artist — A472

Photo. & Engr.

1977, Apr. 29 ***Perf. 13½x14***
1058 A472 6s Prus green & gold .70 .25

IAEA Emblem A473

Arms of Schwanenstadt A474

1977, May 2 **Photo.** ***Perf. 14***
1059 A473 3s brt bl, lt bl & gold .35 .15

Intl. Atomic Energy Agency (IAEA), 20th anniv.

1977, June 10 **Photo.** ***Perf. 14x13½***
1060 A474 3s dk brown & multi .35 .15

Town of Schwanenstadt, 350th anniv.

Europa Issue 1977

Attersee, Upper Austria — A475

1977, June 10 **Engr.** ***Perf. 14***
1061 A475 6s olive green .90 .30

Globe, by Vincenzo Coronelli, 1688 — A476

Photo. & Engr.

1977, June 29 ***Perf. 14***
1062 A476 3s black & buff .35 .15

5th Intl. Symposium of the Coronelli World Fed. of Friends of the Globe, Austria, June 29-July 3.

Kayak Race — A477

1977, July 15 **Photo.** ***Perf. 13½x14***
1063 A477 4s multicolored .50 .20

3rd Kayak Slalom White Water Race on Lieser River, Spittal.

The values of stamps in extremely fine to superb condition are greater than catalogue value.

The Good Samaritan, by Francesco Bassano — A478

1977, Sept. 16 **Photo. & Engr.**
1064 A478 1.50s brown & red .20 .15

Workers' Good Samaritan Org., 50th anniv.

Papermakers' Coat of Arms — A479

Man with Austrian Flag Lifting Barbed Wire — A480

1977, Oct. 10 ***Perf. 14x13½***
1065 A479 3s multicolored .35 .15

17th Conf. of the European Committee of Pulp and Paper Technology (EUCEPA), Vienna.

1977, Nov. 3 ***Perf. 14***
1066 A480 2.50s slate & red .30 .15

Honoring the martyrs for Austria's freedom.

"Austria," First Steam Locomotive in Austria — A481

Designs: 2.50s, Steam locomotive 214. 3s, Electric locomotive 1044.

Photo. & Engr.

1977, Nov. 17 ***Perf. 13½***
1067 A481 1.50s multicolored .20 .15
1068 A481 2.50s multicolored .40 .15
1069 A481 3s multicolored .45 .20
Nos. 1067-1069 (3) 1.05
Set value .40

140th anniversary of Austrian railroads.

A482

A483

Virgin and Child, wood statue, Mariastein, Tyrol.

1977, Nov. 25 ***Perf. 14x13½***
1070 A482 3s multicolored .30 .15

Christmas.

1977, Dec. 2 ***Perf. 13½x14***

The Danube Maiden, by Wolfgang Hutter.

1071 A483 6s multicolored .75 .20

Modern Austrian art.

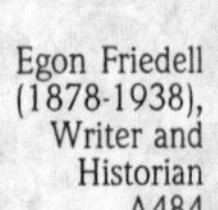

Egon Friedell (1878-1938), Writer and Historian A484

1978, Jan. 23 **Photo. & Engr.**
1072 A484 3s lt blue & blk .35 .15

Subway Train — A485

1978, Feb. 24 **Photo.** ***Perf. 13½x14***
1073 A485 3s multicolored .50 .15

New Vienna subway system.

Biathlon Competition A486

1978, Feb. 28 **Photo. & Engr.**
1074 A486 4s multicolored .45 .20

Biathlon World Championships, Hochfilzen, Tyrol, Feb. 28-Mar. 5.

Leopold Kunschak (1871-1953), Political Leader — A487

1978, Mar. 13 **Engr.** ***Perf. 14x13½***
1075 A487 3s violet blue .30 .15

Coyote, Aztec Feather Shield — A488

1978, Mar. 13 **Photo.** ***Perf. 13½x14***
1076 A488 3s multicolored .30 .15

Ethnographical Museum, 50th anniv. exhibition.

Alpine Farm, Woodcut by Suitbert Lobisser — A489

1978, Mar. 23 **Engr.** ***Perf. 13½***
1077 A489 3s dark brown, *buff* .30 .15

Lobisser (1878-1943), graphic artist.

Capercaillie, Hunting Bag, 1730, and Rifle, 1655 — A490

Photo. & Engr.

1978, Apr. 28 ***Perf. 13½***
1078 A490 6s multicolored .75 .35

Intl. Hunting Exhibition, Marchegg.

Europa Issue 1978

Riegersburg, Styria — A491

1978, May 3 **Engr.**
1079 A491 6s deep rose lilac .75 .35

Parliament, Vienna, and Map of Europe — A492

Admont Pietà, c. 1410 — A493

1978, May 3 **Photo.** ***Perf. 14x13½***
1080 A492 4s multicolored .45 .20

3rd Interparliamentary Conference for European Cooperation and Security, Vienna.

1978, May 26 **Photo. & Engr.**
1081 A493 2.50s ocher & black .25 .15

Gothic Art in Styria Exhibition, St. Lambrecht, 1978.

Ort Castle, Gmunden — A494

1978, June 9
1082 A494 3s multicolored .30 .15

700th anniversary of Gmunden City.

Child with Flowers and Fruit — A495

Lehar and his Home, Bad Ischl — A496

Photo. & Engr.

1978, June 30 ***Perf. 14x13½***
1083 A495 6s gold & multi .75 .35

25 years of Social Tourism.

1978, July 14 **Engr.** ***Perf. 14x13½***
1084 A496 6s slate .75 .30

International Lehar Congress, Bad Ischl. Franz Lehar (1870-1948), operetta composer.

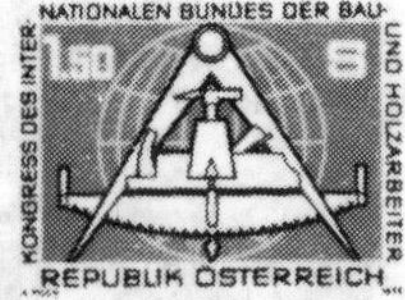

Congress Emblem A497

1978, Aug. 21 **Photo.** ***Perf. 13½x14***
1085 A497 1.50s black, red & yel .20 .15

Cong. of Intl. Fed. of Building Construction and Wood Workers, Vienna, Aug. 20-24.

Ottokar of Bohemia and Rudolf of Hapsburg A498

1978, Aug. 25 **Photo. & Engr.**
1086 A498 3s multicolored .35 .15

Battle of Durnkrut and Jedenspeigen (Marchfeld), which established Hapsburg rule in Austria, 700th anniversary.

First Documentary Reference to Villach, "ad pontem uillah" A499

1978, Sept. 8 **Litho.** ***Perf. 13½x14***
1087 A499 3s multicolored .35 .15

1100th anniversary of Villach, Carinthia.

Seal of Graz, 1440 — A500

Emperor Maximilian Fishing — A501

Photo. & Engr.

1978, Sept. 13 ***Perf. 14x13½***
1088 A500 4s multicolored .50 .25

850th anniversary of Graz.

1978, Sept. 15 ***Perf. 14x13½***
1089 A501 4s multicolored .50 .20

World Fishing Championships, Vienna, Sept. 1978.

"Aid to the Handicapped" A502

1978, Oct. 2 **Photo.** ***Perf. 13½x14***
1090 A502 6s orange brn & blk .75 .30

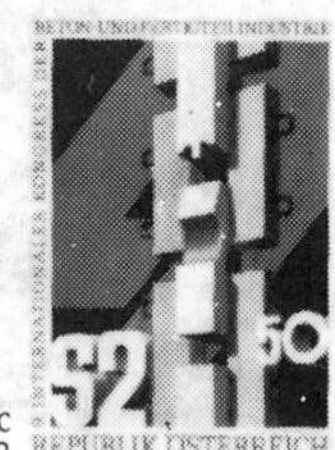

Symbolic Column — A503

1978, Oct. 9 Photo. *Perf. 13½*

1091 A503 2.50s orange, blk & gray .30 .15

9th Intl. Congress of Concrete and Prefabrication Industries, Vienna, Oct. 8-13.

Grace, by Albin Egger-Lienz A504

1978, Oct. 27 *Perf. 13½x14*

1092 A504 6s multicolored .75 .30

European Family Congress, Vienna, Oct. 26-29.

Lise Meitner (1878-1968), Physicist, and Atom Symbol — A505

1978, Nov. 7 Engr. *Perf. 14x13½*

1093 A505 6s dark violet .75 .30

Viktor Adler, by Anton Hanak A506

Photo. & Engr.

1978, Nov. 10 *Perf. 13½x14*

1094 A506 3s vermilion & black .35 .15

Viktor Adler (1852-1918), leader of Social Democratic Party, 60th death anniversary.

Franz Schubert, by Josef Kriehuber — A507

Virgin and Child, Wilhering Church — A508

1978, Nov. 17 Engr. *Perf. 14*

1095 A507 6s reddish brown .75 .35

Franz Schubert (1797-1828), composer.

Perf. 12½x13½

1978, Dec. 1 Photo. & Engr.

1096 A508 3s multicolored .35 .15

Christmas.

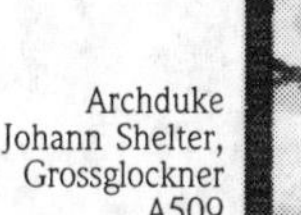

Archduke Johann Shelter, Grossglockner A509

1978, Dec. 6 *Perf. 13½x14*

1097 A509 1.50s gold & dk vio bl .20 .15

Austrian Alpine Club, centenary.

A510 A511

Adam, by Rudolf Hausner.

1978, Dec. 6 Photo. *Perf. 13½x14*

1098 A510 6s multicolored .75 .35

Modern Austrian art.

1978, Dec. 6 *Perf. 14x13½*

1099 A511 6s Bound Hands .75 .30

Universal Declaration of Human Rights, 30th anniv.

Type of 1973

Designs: 20g, Freistadt, Upper Austria. 3s, Bishofsmutze, Salzburg. 4.20s, Hirschegg, Kleinwalsertal. 5.50s, Peace Chapel, Stoderzinken. 5.60s, Riezlern, Kleinwalsertal. 9s, Asten Carinthia. 12s, Kufstein Fortress. 14s, Weiszsee, Salzburg.

Photo. & Engr.

1978-83 *Perf. 13½x14*

Size: 23x29mm

1100 A395 20g vio bl & dk bl .15 .15

Size: 17x21mm

1102 A395 3s lt ultra & vio bl .45 .15

Size: 23x29mm

1104 A395 4.20s blk & grysh bl .55 .15
1105 A395 5.50s lilac & pur .75 .20
1106 A395 5.60s yel grn & ol grn .75 .20
1107 A395 9s red 1.25 .45
1108 A395 12s ocher & vio brn 1.75 .15
1109 A395 14s lt green & green 2.00 .20
Nos. 1100-1109 (8) 7.65 1.65

Issued: 3s, 12/7/78; 4.20s, 6/22/79; 20g, 6/27/80; 12s, 10/3/80; 14s, 1/27/82; 5.50s, 5.60s, 7/1/82; 9s, 2/9/83.

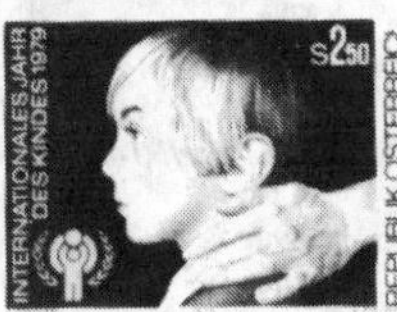

Child and IYC Emblem A512

Photo. & Engr.

1979, Jan. 16 *Perf. 14*

1110 A512 2.50s dk blue, blk & brn .25 .15

International Year of the Child.

CCIR Emblem A513

1979, Jan. 16 Photo. *Perf. 13½x14*

1111 A513 6s multicolored .75 .30

Intl. Radio Consultative Committee (CCIR) of the ITU, 50th anniv.

Air Rifle, Air Pistol and Club Emblem A514

Photo. & Engr.

1979, Mar. 7 *Perf. 13½*

1112 A514 6s multicolored .75 .30

Austrian Shooting Club, cent., and European Air Rifle and Air Pistol Championships, Graz.

Figure Skater — A515

1979, Mar. 7 Photo. *Perf. 14x13½*

1113 A515 4s multicolored .45 .25

World Ice Skating Championships, Vienna.

Steamer Franz I A516

Designs: 2.50s, Tugboat Linz. 3s, Passenger ship Theodor Körner.

1979, Mar. 13 Engr. *Perf. 13½*

1114 A516 1.50s violet blue .20 .15
1115 A516 2.50s sepia .30 .15
1116 A516 3s magenta .35 .20
Nos. 1114-1116 (3) .85
Set value .40

1st Danube Steamship Company, 150th anniv.

Fashion Design, by Theo Zasche, 1900 — A517

Photo. & Engr.

1979, Mar. 26 *Perf. 13x13½*

1117 A517 2.50s multicolored .30 .15

50th Intl. Fashion Week, Vienna.

Wiener Neustadt Cathedral A518

1979, Mar. 27 Engr. *Perf. 13½*

1118 A518 4s violet blue .50 .25

Cathedral of Wiener Neustadt, 700th anniv.

Teacher and Pupils, by Franz A. Zauner — A519

Population Chart and Barock Angel — A520

Photo. & Engr.

1979, Mar. 30 *Perf. 14x13½*

1119 A519 2.50s multicolored .30 .15

Education of the deaf in Austria, 200th anniv.

1979, Apr. 6

1120 A520 2.50s multicolored .30 .15

Austrian Central Statistical Bureau, 150th anniv.

Laurenz Koschier — A521

Diesel Motor — A522

Europa Issue, 1979

1979, May 4

1121 A521 6s ocher & purple .80 .30

1979, May 4 Photo.

1122 A522 4s multicolored .45 .20

13th CIMAC Congress (Intl. Org. for Internal Combustion Machines).

Arms of Ried, Schärding and Braunau — A523

Photo. & Engr.

1979, June 1 *Perf. 14x13½*

1123 A523 3s multicolored .30 .15

200th anniversary of Innviertel District.

Flood and City — A524

1979, June 1 *Perf. 13½x14*

1124 A524 2.50s multicolored .30 .15

Control and eliminate water pollution.

Arms of Rottenmann A525

Jodok Fink A526

Photo. & Engr.

1979, June 22 *Perf. 14x13½*

1125 A525 3s multicolored .30 .15

700th anniversary of Rottenmann.

1979, June 29 Engr. *Perf. 14*

1126 A526 3s brown carmine .30 .15

Jodok Fink (1853-1929), governor of Vorarlberg.

Arms of Wels, Returnees' Emblem, "Europa Sail" — A527

1979, July 6 Photo. ***Perf. 14x13½***
1127 A527 4s yellow grn & blk .45 .20

5th European Meeting of the Intl. Confederation of Former Prisoners of War, Wels, July 6-8.

Symbolic Flower, Conference Emblem — A528

1979, Aug. 20 Litho. ***Perf. 14x13½***
1128 A528 4s turq blue .45 .20

UN Conf. for Science and Technology, Vienna, Aug. 20-31.

Donaupark, UNIDO and IAEA Emblems A529

1979, Aug. 24 Engr. ***Perf. 13½x14***
1129 A529 6s grayish blue .75 .30

Opening of the Donaupark Intl. Center in Vienna, seat of the UN Industrial Development Org. (UNIDO) and the Intl. Atomic Energy Agency (IAEA).

Diseased Eye and Blood Vessels A530

1979, Sept. 10 Photo. ***Perf. 14***
1130 A530 2.50s multicolored .35 .15

10th World Congress of Intl. Diabetes Federation, Vienna, Sept. 9-14.

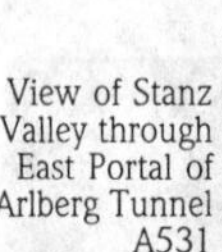

View of Stanz Valley through East Portal of Arlberg Tunnel A531

1979, Sept. 14 Photo. & Engr.
1131 A531 4s multicolored .45 .20

16th World Road Cong., Vienna, Sept. 16-21.

Steam Printing Press A532

Photo. & Engr.

1979, Sept. 18 ***Perf. 13½x14***
1132 A532 3s multicolored .30 .15

Austrian Government Printing Office, 175th anniv.

Richard Zsigmondy (1865-1929), Chemist — A533

1979, Sept. 21 Engr. ***Perf. 14x13½***
1133 A533 6s multicolored .75 .30

"Save Energy" A534

1979, Oct. 1 Photo. ***Perf. 14x13½***
1134 A534 2.50s multicolored .30 .15

Festival and Convention Center, Bregenz (Model) A535

1979, Oct. 1 Engr. ***Perf. 14***
1135 A535 2.50s purple .30 .15

Lions International Emblem — A536

1979, Oct. 11 Photo. & Engr.
1136 A536 4s multicolored .45 .25

25th Lions Europa Forum, Vienna, Oct. 11-13.

A537

A538

Photo. & Engr.

1979, Oct. 19 ***Perf. 13½x14***
1137 A537 2.50s Wilhelm Exner .30 .15

Centenary of Technological Handicraft Museum, founded by Wilhelm Exner.

1979, Oct. 23 Litho. ***Perf. 13½x14***

The Compassionate Christ, by Hans Fronius.

1138 A538 4s olive & ol blk .50 .25

Modern Austrian art.

Locomotive and Arms A539

1979, Oct. 24 Photo. ***Perf. 13½x14***
1139 A539 2.50s multicolored .30 .15

Raab-Odenburg-Ebenfurt railroad, cent.

August Musger — A540

Photo. & Engr.

1979, Oct. 30 ***Perf. 14x13½***
1140 A540 2.50s bl gray & blk .30 .15

August Musger (1868-1929), developer of slow-motion film technique.

Nativity, St. Barbara's Church A541

1979, Nov. 30 ***Perf. 13½x14***
1141 A541 4s multicolored .45 .25

Christmas.

Arms of Baden — A542

1980, Jan. 25 ***Perf. 14***
1142 A542 4s multicolored .45 .25

Baden, 500th anniversary.

A543 A544

1980, Feb. 21 ***Perf. 13½***
1143 A543 2.50s red & aqua .30 .15

Fight rheumatism.

1980, Feb. 21 Photo. ***Perf. 14x13½***
1144 A544 4s dark blue & red .45 .25

Austrian exports.

Austrian Red Cross Centenary A545

1980, Mar. 14 Photo. ***Perf. 13½x14***
1145 A545 2.50s multicolored .30 .15

Rudolph Kirchschlager — A546

Photo. & Engr.

1980, Mar. 20 ***Perf. 14x13½***
1146 A546 4s sepia & red .45 .25

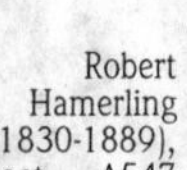

Robert Hamerling (1830-1889), Poet — A547

1980, Mar. 24 Engr. ***Perf. 13½x14***
1147 A547 2.50s olive green .30 .15

Seal of Hallein — A548

Maria Theresa, by Andreas Moller — A549

Photo. & Engr.

1980, Apr. 30 ***Perf. 14x13½***
1148 A548 4s red & black .45 .25

Hallein, 750th anniversary.

1980, May 13 Engr. ***Perf. 13½***

Empress Maria Theresa (1717-1780) Paintings by: 4s, Martin van Meytens. 6s, Josef Ducreux.

1149 A549 2.50s violet brown .30 .25
1150 A549 4s dark blue .45 .40
1151 A549 6s rose lake .65 .75
Nos. 1149-1151 (3) 1.40 1.40

Flags of Austria and Four Powers — A550

1980, May 14 Photo. ***Perf. 13½x14***
1152 A550 4s multicolored .45 .25

State Treaty, 25th anniversary.

St. Benedict, by Meinrad Guggenbichler A551

1980, May 16 Engr. ***Perf. 14½***
1153 A551 2.50s olive green .30 .15

Congress of Benedictine Order of Austria.

Hygeia by Gustav Klimt — A552

1980, May 20 Photo. ***Perf. 14***
1154 A552 4s multicolored .45 .25

Academic teaching of hygiene, 175th anniv.

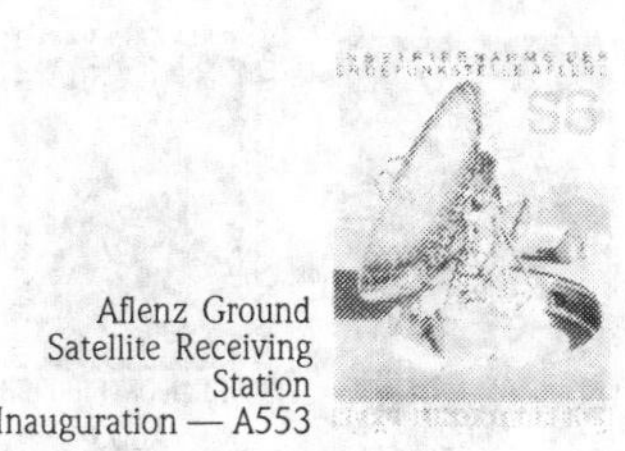
Aflenz Ground Satellite Receiving Station Inauguration — A553

1980, May 30 Photo. *Perf. 14*
1155 A553 6s multicolored .75 .30

Steyr, Etching, 1693 A554

Photo. & Engr.

1980, June 4 *Perf. 13½*
1156 A554 4s multicolored .45 .25

Millennium of Steyr.

Worker, Oil Drill Head — A555

1980, June 12
1157 A555 2.50s multicolored .30 .15

Austrian oil production, 25th anniversary.

Seal of Innsbruck, 1267 — A556

1980, June 23 *Perf. 13½x14½*
1158 A556 2.50s multicolored .30 .15

Innsbruck, 800th anniversary.

Duke's Hat — A557

Bible Illustration, Book of Genesis — A559

Leo Ascher (1880-1942), Composer A558

Perf. 14½x13½

1980, June 23 Photo.
1159 A557 4s multicolored .45 .20

800th anniversary of Styria as a Duchy.

1980, Aug. 18 Engr. *Perf. 14*
1160 A558 3s dark purple .40 .20

1980, Aug. 25 *Perf. 13½*
1161 A559 4s multicolored .45 .25

10th Intl. Cong. of the Org. for Old Testament Studies.

Europa Issue 1980

Robert Stolz (1880-1975), Composer — A560

1980, Aug. 25 Engr. *Perf. 14x13½*
1162 A560 6s red brown .85 .30

Old and Modern Bridges A561

1980, Sept. 1 Photo. *Perf. 13½*
1163 A561 4s multicolored .45 .25

11th Congress of the Intl. Assoc. for Bridge and Structural Engineering, Vienna.

Moon Figure, by Karl Brandstätter A562

Customs Service, Sesquicentennial A563

Photo. & Engr.

1980, Oct. 10 *Perf. 14x13½*
1164 A562 4s multicolored .45 .25

1980, Oct. 13 Photo.
1165 A563 2.50s multicolored .30 .15

Gazette Masthead, 1810 A564

1980, Oct. 23 Photo. *Perf. 13½*
1166 A564 2.50s multicolored .30 .15

Official Gazette of Linz, 350th anniversary.

Waidhofen Town Book Title Page, 14th Century — A565

Photo. & Engr.

1980, Oct. 24 *Perf. 14*
1167 A565 2.50s multicolored .30 .15

Waidhofen on Thaya, 750th anniversary.

Federal Austrian Army, 25th Anniversary A566

1980, Oct. 24 Photo. *Perf. 13½x14*
1168 A566 2.50s grnsh black & red .30 .15

Alfred Wegener A567

1980, Oct. 31 Engr.
1169 A567 4s violet blue .45 .25

Alfred Wegener (1880-1930), scientist, formulated theory of continental drift.

A568

A569

1980, Nov. 6 *Perf. 14x13½*
1170 A568 4s dark red brown .45 .25

Robert Musil (1880-1942), poet.

Photo. & Engr.

1980, Nov. 28 *Perf. 13½*

Nativity, stained glass window, Klagenfurt.

1171 A569 4s multicolored .45 .25

Christmas.

25th Anniversary of Social Security A570

1981, Jan. 19 Litho. *Perf. 13½x14*
1172 A570 2.50s multicolored .30 .15

Niebelungen Saga, 1926, by Dachauer A571

Machinist in Wheelchair A572

1981, Apr. 6 Engr. *Perf. 14x13½*
1173 A571 3s sepia .40 .15

Wilhelm Dachauer (1881-1951), artist and engraver.

1981, Apr. 6 Photo. & Engr.
1174 A572 6s multicolored .75 .35

Rehabilitation Intl., 3rd European Regional Conf.

Sigmund Freud — A573

Congress, Vienna — A574

1981, May 6 Engr.
1175 A573 3s rose violet .35 .15

Sigmund Freud (1856-1939), psychoanalyst.

1981, May 11 Photo.
1176 A574 4s multicolored .45 .25

A575

Europa — A576

Azzo (founder of House of Kuenringer) and his followers, bear-skin manuscript.

1981, May 15 Photo. & Engr.
1177 A575 3s multicolored .35 .15

Kuenringer Exhibition, Zwettl Monastery.

1981, May 22 Photo.
1178 A576 6s Maypole .80 .35

Telephone Service Centenary A577

Photo. and Engr.

1981 May 29 *Perf. 13½x14*
1179 A577 4s multicolored .45 .25

Seibersdorf Research Center, 25th Anniv. A578

1981, June 29 Photo. *Perf. 13½*
1180 A578 4s multicolored .45 .25

The Frog King (Child's Drawing) A579

1981, June 29 *Perf. 13½x14*
1181 A579 3s multicolored .35 .15

Town Hall and Town Seal of 1250 — A580

Photo. & Engr.

1981, July 17 *Perf. 13½x14*
1182 A580 4s multicolored .45 .25

St. Veit an der Glan, 800th anniv.

Johann Florian Heller (1813-1871), Pioneer of Urinalysis — A581

1981, Aug. 31 *Perf. 14x13½*
1183 A581 6s red brown .75 .35

11th Intl. Clinical Chemistry Congress.

Ludwig Boltzmann (1844-1906), Physicist — A582

Scale — A583

1981, Sept. 4 Engr. ***Perf. 14x13½***
1184 A582 3s dark green .35 .15

Photo. & Engr.

1981, Sept. 7 ***Perf. 14***
1185 A583 6s multicolored .75 .35

Intl. Pharmaceutical Federation World Congress, Vienna, Sept. 6-11.

Otto Bauer, Politician, Birth Centenary A584

Escher's Impossible Cube A585

1981, Sept. 7 Photo. ***Perf. 14x13½***
1186 A584 4s multicolored .45 .25

1981, Sept. 14
1187 A585 4s dk blue & brt blue .45 .25

10th Intl. Mathematicians' Cong., Innsbruck.

Kneeling Virgin, Detail of Coronation of Mary Altarpiece, St. Wolfgang, 500th Anniv. — A586

1981, Sept. 25 Engr. ***Perf. 14x13½***
1188 A586 3s dark blue .35 .15

South-East Fair, Graz, 75th Anniv. — A587

1981, Sept. 25 Photo. ***Perf. 13½x14***
1189 A587 4s multicolored .45 .25

Holy Trinity, 12th Cent. Byzantine Miniature A588

1981, Oct. 5
1190 A588 6s multicolored .75 .35

16th Intl. Byzantine Congress.

Hans Kelsen (1881-1973), Co-author of Federal Constitution A589

1981, Oct. 9 **Engr.**
1191 A589 3s dark carmine .35 .15

Edict of Tolerance Bicen. — A590

1981, Oct. 9 Photo. & Engr. ***Perf. 14***
1192 A590 4s Joseph II .45 .25

World Food Day — A591

1981, Oct. 16 Photo. ***Perf. 13½***
1193 A591 6s multicolored .75 .35

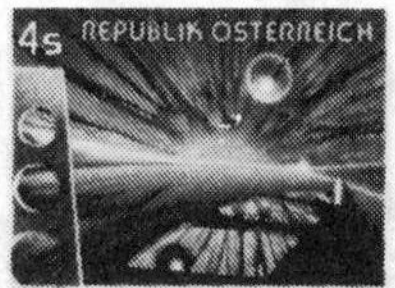

Between the Times, by Oscar Asboth A592

1981, Oct. 22 Litho. ***Perf. 13½x14***
1194 A592 4s multicolored .45 .25

Intl. Catholic Workers' Day — A593

Photo. & Engr.

1981, Oct. 23 ***Perf. 14x13½***
1195 A593 3s multicolored .35 .15

Baron Josef Hammer-Purgstall, Founder of Oriental Studies, 125th Death Anniv. — A594

Photo. & Engr.

1981, Nov. 23 ***Perf. 14***
1196 A594 3s multicolored .35 .15

Julius Raab (1891-1964), Politician — A595

1981, Nov. 27 Engr. ***Perf. 13½***
1197 A595 6s rose lake .75 .35

Nativity, Corn Straw Figures A596

1981, Nov. 27 **Photo. & Engr.**
1198 A596 4s multicolored .50 .20

Christmas.

Stefan Zweig (1881-1942), Poet — A597

1981, Nov. 27 Engr. ***Perf. 14x13½***
1199 A597 4s dull violet .50 .20

800th Anniv. of St. Nikola on the Danube — A598

1981, Dec. 4 **Photo. & Engr.**
1200 A598 4s multicolored .45 .20

Vienna Emergency Medical Service Centenary A599

1981, Dec. 9 Photo. ***Perf. 13½x14***
1201 A599 3s multicolored .35 .15

Schladming-Haus Alpine World Skiing Championship A600

1982, Jan. 27 ***Perf. 14***
1202 A600 4s multicolored .45 .20

Dorotheum (State Auction Gallery), 275th Anniv. — A601

Photo. & Engr.

1982, Mar. 12 ***Perf. 14***
1203 A601 4s multicolored .45 .20

A602 A603

1982, Mar. 19 Photo. ***Perf. 14x13½***
1204 A602 5s multicolored .60 .30

Water Rescue Service, 25th anniv.

Photo. & Engr.

1982, Apr. 23 ***Perf. 14x13½***
1205 A603 3s St. Severin .35 .15

St. Severin and the End of the Roman Era exhibition.

A604 A605

1982, May 4 ***Perf. 14***
1206 A604 4s multicolored .45 .20

Intl. Kneipp Hydropathy Congress, Vienna.

1982, May 7
1207 A605 4s Printers' guild arms .45 .20

Printing in Austria, 500th anniv.

A606 A607

Design: Urine analysis, Canone di Avicenna manuscript.

1982, May 12 **Photo.**
1208 A606 6s multicolored .75 .35

5th European Urology Soc. Cong., Vienna.

1982, May 14 **Photo. & Engr.**
1209 A607 3s multicolored .35 .15

800th birth anniv. of St. Francis of Assisi.

A608 A609

1982, May 19 Engr. ***Perf. 13½***
1210 A608 3s olive green .35 .15

Haydn and His Time Exhibition, Rohrau.

1982, May 25 Photo. ***Perf. 14x13½***
1211 A609 7s multicolored .85 .40

25th World Milk Day.

800th Anniv of Gfohl (Market Town) — A610

Photo. & Engr.

1982, May 28 *Perf. 14*
1212 A610 4s multicolored .45 .20

Tennis Player and Austrian Tennis Federation Emblem — A611

1982, June 11
1213 A611 3s multicolored .35 .15

900th Anniv. of City of Langenlois A612

Photo. & Engr.

1982, June 11 *Perf. 13½x14*
1214 A612 4s multicolored .45 .20

800th Anniv. of City of Weiz — A613

Ignaz Seipel (1876-1932), Statesman — A614

1982, June 18 Photo. *Perf. 14x13½*
1215 A613 4s Arms .45 .20

1982, July 30 Engr. *Perf. 14x13½*
1216 A614 3s brown violet .35 .15

Europa Issue 1982

Sesquicentennial of Linz-Freistadt-Budweis Horse-drawn Railroad — A615

1982, July 30 *Perf. 13½*
1217 A615 6s brown .90 .35

Mail Bus Service, 75th Anniv. — A616

Rocket Lift-off — A617

1982, Aug. 6 Photo. *Perf. 14x13½*
1218 A616 4s multicolored .45 .20

1982, Aug. 9 *Perf. 14*
1219 A617 4s multicolored .45 .20

2nd UN Conference on Peaceful Uses of Outer Space, Vienna, Aug. 9-21.

Geodesists' Day — A618

Photo. & Engr.

1982, Sept. 1 *Perf. 13½x14*
1220 A618 3s Tower, Office of Standards .35 .15

Protection of Endangered Species — A619

1982, Sept. 9 *Perf. 14*
1221 A619 3s Bustard .45 .25
1222 A619 4s Beaver .60 .30
1223 A619 6s Capercaillie .90 .45
Nos. 1221-1223 (3) 1.95 1.00

10th Anniv. of Intl. Institute for Applied Systems Anaysis, Vienna A620

1982, Oct. 4 **Photo.**
1224 A620 3s Laxenburg Castle .35 .15

St. Apollonia (Patron Saint of Dentists) A621

1982, Oct. 11 **Photo. & Engr.**
1225 A621 4s multicolored .45 .20

70th Annual World Congress of Dentists.

Emmerich Kalman (1882-1953), Composer A622

1982, Oct. 22 Engr. *Perf. 13½*
1226 A622 3s dark blue .35 .15

Max Mell (1882-1971), Poet — A623

Christmas — A624

1982, Nov. 10 Photo. *Perf. 14x13½*
1227 A623 3s multicolored .35 .15

Photo. & Engr.

1982, Nov. 25 *Perf. 13½*

Design: Christmas crib, Damuls Church, Vorarlberg, 1630.

1228 A624 4s multicolored .45 .20

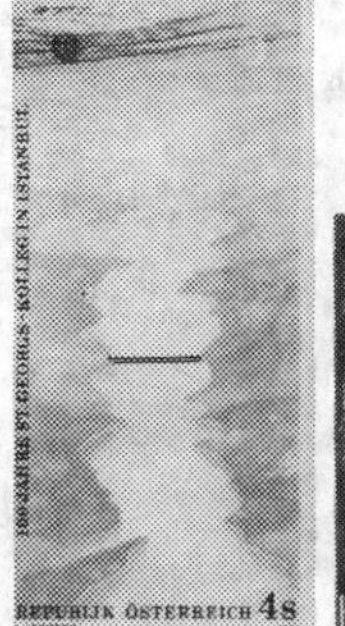

Centenary of St. George's College, Istanbul — A625

Portrait of a Girl, by Ernst Fuchs — A626

1982, Nov. 26 Litho. *Perf. 14*
1229 A625 4s Bosporus .45 .20

1982, Dec. 10 **Photo. & Engr.**
1230 A626 4s multicolored .45 .20

Postal Savings Bank Centenary A627

Photo. & Engr.

1983, Jan. 12 *Perf. 14*
1231 A627 4s Bank .55 .20

Hildegard Burjan (1883-1933), Founder of Caritas Socialis — A628

1983, Jan. 28 **Engr.**
1232 A628 4s rose lake .55 .20

World Communications Year — A629

1983, Feb. 18 Photo. *Perf. 13½x14*
1233 A629 7s multicolored .95 .40

75th Anniv. Children's Friends Org. — A630

Photo. & Engr.

1983, Feb. 23 *Perf. 14x13½*
1234 A630 4s multicolored .55 .20

Josef Matthias Hauer (1883-1959), Composer A631

1983, Mar. 18 Engr. *Perf. 14*
1235 A631 3s deep lilac rose .40 .15

25th Anniv. of Austrian Airlines A632

1983, Mar. 31 Photo. *Perf. 13½x14*
1236 A632 6s multicolored .85 .35

Work Inspection Centenary A633

1983, Apr. 8 Photo. *Perf. 13½*
1237 A633 4s multicolored .55 .20

Upper Austria Millennium Provincial Exhibition A634

1983, Apr. 28 Photo. *Perf. 13½*
1238 A634 3s Wels Castle, by Matthaus Merian .40 .15

Gottweig Monastery, 900th Anniv. A635

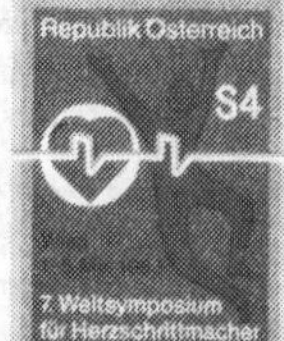

7th World Pacemakers Symposium A636

Photo. & Engr.

1983, Apr. 29 *Perf. 13½*
1239 A635 3s multicolored .40 .15

1983, Apr. 29 Photo. *Perf. 14x13½*
1240 A636 4s multicolored .55 .20

Catholic Students' Org. — A637

1983, May 20 **Photo.** ***Perf. 14***
1241 A637 4s multicolored .55 .20

Weitra, 800th Anniv. A638

Photo. & Engr.

1983, May 20 ***Perf. 13½***
1242 A638 4s multicolored .55 .20

Granting of Town Rights to Hohenems, 650th Anniv. — A639

1983, May 27 **Photo.** ***Perf. 14***
1243 A639 4s multicolored .55 .20

25th Anniv. of Stadthall, Vienna A640

1983, June 24 **Photo.** ***Perf. 14***
1244 A640 4s multicolored .55 .20

Europa Issue 1983

A641 A642

1983, June 24 **Engr.** ***Perf. 14x13½***
1245 A641 6s dark green .95 .35

Europa: Viktor Franz Hess (1883-1964), 1936 Nobel Prize winner in physics.

1983, July 1 **Photo.** ***Perf. 13½***
1246 A642 5s multicolored .70 .30

Kiwanis Intl. Convention, Vienna, July 3-6.

7th World Congress of Psychiatry, Vienna — A643

1983, July 11 **Photo.** ***Perf. 14***
1247 A643 4s Emblem, St. Stephen's Cathedral .55 .20

Baron Carl von Hasenauer (1833-1894), Architect A644

1983, July 20 **Engr.** ***Perf. 13½x14***
1248 A644 3s Natural History Museum, Vienna .45 .15

27th Intl. Chamber of Commerce Professional Competition, Linz — A645

1983, Aug. 16 **Photo.**
1249 A645 4s Chamber building .55 .20

13th Intl. Chemotherapy Congress, Vienna, Aug. 28-Sept. 2 — A646

1983, Aug. 26
1250 A646 5s Penicillin test on cancer .70 .30

Catholics' Day — A647 Visit of Pope John Paul II — A648

1983, Sept. 9 **Photo.** ***Perf. 14x13½***
1251 A647 3s multicolored .40 .15

Photo. & Engr.

1983, Sept. 9 ***Perf. 13½***
1252 A648 6s multicolored .90 .35

Souvenir Sheet

Battle of 1683 to Relieve Vienna, by Frans Geffel A649

1983, Sept. 9 ***Perf. 14***
1253 A649 6s multicolored .95 .50

300th anniv. of Vienna's rescue from Turkey.

Vienna Rathaus Centenary — A650

1983, Sept. 23 ***Perf. 13½x14***
1254 A650 4s multicolored .55 .20

Karl von Terzaghi (1883-1963), Founder of Scientific Subterranean Engineering A651

1983, Oct. 3 **Engr.**
1255 A651 3s dark blue .40 .15

10th Trade Unions Federal Congress, Oct. 3-8 — A652

1983, Oct. 3 **Photo.** ***Perf. 13½***
1256 A652 3s black & red .40 .15

Evening Sun in Burgenland, by Gottfried Kumpf — A653

Photo. & Engr.

1983, Oct. 7 ***Perf. 13½x14***
1257 A653 4s multicolored .55 .20

Modling-Hinterbruhl Electric Railroad Centenary — A654

1983, Oct. 21 **Photo.**
1258 A654 3s multicolored .40 .15

Provincial Museum of Upper Austria Sesquicentennial — A655

1983, Nov. 4 **Photo. & Engr.**
1259 A655 4s Francisco-Carolinum Museum .55 .20

Creche, St. Andreas Parish Church, Kitzbuhel A656

1983, Nov. 25 ***Perf. 14***
1260 A656 4s multicolored .55 .20

Christmas.

Parliament Bldg. Vienna, 100th Anniv. — A657

1983, Dec. 2 **Engr.**
1261 A657 4s slate blue .55 .20

A658 A659

Altar picture, St. Nikola/Pram Church.

1983, Dec. 6 **Photo.** ***Perf. 14x13½***
1262 A658 3s multicolored .40 .15

Perf. 14½x13½

1983, Dec. 15 **Engr.**
1263 A659 6s dark red brn .90 .35

Wolfgang Pauli (1900-58), physicist, Nobel Prize winner.

Gregor Mendel (1822-1884), Genetics Founder — A660

Photo. & Engr.

1984, Jan. 5 ***Perf. 13½***
1264 A660 4s multicolored .55 .20

Anton Hanak (1875-1934), Sculptor — A661

1984, Jan. 5
1265 A661 3s red brown & blk .40 .15

50th Anniv. of 1934 Uprising — A662

1984, Feb. 10 **Photo.** ***Perf. 14***
1266 A662 4.50s Memorial, Woellersdorf .65 .30

Wernher von Reichersberg Family, Bas-relief, 15th Cent. — A663

Photo. & Engr.

1984, Apr. 25 ***Perf. 14x13½***
1267 A663 3.50s brown & blue .50 .25

900th anniv. of Reichersberg Monastery.

Tobacco Monopoly Bicentenary A665

1984, May 4 *Perf. 13½*

1269 A665 4.50s Cigar wrapper, tobacco plant .65 .30

1200th Anniv. of Kostendorf Municipality — A666

1984, May 4

1270 A666 4.50s View, arms .65 .30

Automobile Engineers World Congress A667

1984, May 4 **Photo.** *Perf. 13½x14*

1271 A667 5s Wheel bearing cross-section .70 .30

Europa (1959-1984) A668

1984, May 4 *Perf. 13½*

1272 A668 6s multicolored .90 .35

A669 Aragonite — A670

Archduke Johann (1782-1859) by S. von Carolsfeld.

Photo. & Engr.

1984, May 11 *Perf. 14*

1273 A669 4.50s multicolored .65 .30

1984, May 11 *Perf. 13½*

1274 A670 3.50s multicolored .50 .20

Ore and Iron Provincial Exhibition.

Era of Emperor Francis Joseph Exhibition — A671

Design: Cover of Viribus Unitis, publ. by Max Herzig, 1898.

1984, May 18

1275 A671 3.50s red & gold .50 .20

A672 A673

Photo. & Engr.

1984, May 30 *Perf. 14x13½*

1276 A672 4.50s Tower, arms .65 .30

City of Vocklabruck, 850th anniv.

1984, June 1 *Perf. 13½*

Dionysius, Virinum mosaic.

1277 A673 3.50s multicolored .50 .20

Museum of Carinthia, centenary.

Erosion Prevention Systems Centenary A674

1984, June 5 **Engr.** *Perf. 14*

1278 A674 4.50s Stone reinforcement wall .65 .30

Tyrol Provincial Celebration, 1809-1984 — A675

Art Exhibition: Meeting of Imperial Troops with South Tyrolean Reserves under Andreas Hofer near Sterzing in April 1809, by Ludwig Schnorr von Carolsfeld, 1830.

Photo. & Engr.

1984, June 5 *Perf. 14x13½*

1279 A675 3.50s multicolored .50 .20

A676 A677

1984, June 5 **Engr.**

1280 A676 4s violet brown .55 .25

Ralph Benatzky (1884-1957), composer.

1984, June 22 **Photo.** *Perf. 14*

1281 A677 3.50s multicolored .50 .20

Christian von Ehrenfels (1859-1932), philosopher.

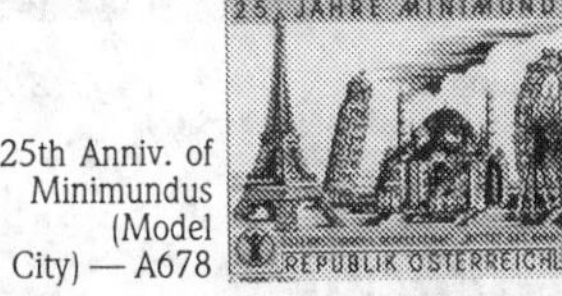

25th Anniv. of Minimundus (Model City) — A678

1984, June 22 *Perf. 13½x14*

1282 A678 4s Eiffel Tower, Tower of Pisa, ferris wheel .55 .25

Blockheide Eibenstein Nature Park — A679

1984 **Photo. & Engr.**

1283 A679 4s shown .55 .25

1284 A679 4s Lake Neusiedl .55 .25

Issued: #1283, June 29; #1284, Aug. 13.

See Nos. 1349-1354, 1492-1496.

Monasteries and Abbeys — A679a

Designs: 3.50s, Geras Monastery, Lower Austria. 4s, Stams. 4.50s, Schlagl. 5s, Benedictine Abbey of St. Paul Levanttal. 6s, Rein-Hohenfurth.

1984-85 *Perf. 14*

1285	A679a	3.50s	multicolored	.50	.20
1286	A679a	4s	multicolored	.50	.20
1287	A679a	4.50s	multicolored	.65	.30
1288	A679a	5s	multicolored	.65	.30
1288A	A679a	6s	multicolored	.90	.35
			Nos. 1285-1288A (5)	3.20	1.35

Issued: 3.50s, 4/27/84; 4s, 9/28/84; 4.50s, 5/18/84; 5s, 9/27/85; 6s, 10/4/84.

See Nos. 1361-1365, 1464A-1468.

Schanatobel Railroad Bridge A680

Railroad Anniversaries: 3.50s, Arlberg centenary. 4.50s, Tauern, 75th.

1984, July 6 *Perf. 14*

1289 A680 3.50s shown .50 .20

1290 A680 4.50s Falkenstein Bridge .65 .20

A681 A682

1984, July 6 **Photo.**

1291 A681 6s Johan Stuwer's balloon .90 .35

Balloon flight in Austria bicentenary.

1984, Aug. 31 **Photo. & Engr.**

1292 A682 7s Vienna Palace of Justice, emblem .95 .45

Intl. Lawyers' Congress, Vienna.

A683 A684

1984, Sept. 3 **Photo.**

1293 A683 6s Josef Hyrtl, anatomist .90 .35

7th European Anatomy Congress, Innsbruck, Sept. 3-7.

1984, Oct. 12

1294 A684 4s Window, by Karl Korab .55 .20

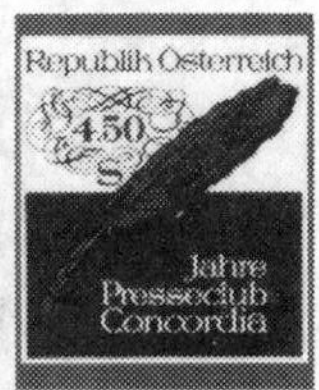

A685 A686

1984, Oct. 18

1295 A685 3.50s Clock (Immset Uhr), 1555 .50 .20

Johannes of Gmunden, mathematician, 600th birth anniv.

1984, Nov. 9 **Photo.** *Perf. 13½*

1296 A686 4.50s Quill .65 .30

Concordia Press Club, 125th anniv.

Fanny Eissler, Dancer, Birth Centenary — A687

1984, Nov. 23 **Photo. & Engr.**

1297 A687 4s multicolored .55 .30

Christmas A688

Design: Christ is Born, Aggsbacher Altar, Herzogenburg Monastery.

1984, Nov. 30 *Perf. 14*

1298 A688 4.50s multicolored .65 .20

A689 A690

1985, Jan. 4 *Perf. 14x13½*

1299 A689 3.50s Seal .50 .15

Karl Franzens University, Graz, 400th anniv.

1985, Jan. 15 **Engr.**

1300 A690 4.50s dk rose lake .60 .20

Dr. Lorenz Bohler, Surgeon, birth cent.

Nordic Events, Ski Championships, Seefeld — A691

1985, Jan. 17 **Photo.** *Perf. 13½*

1301 A691 4s Ski jumper, cross country racer .55 .15

Linz Diocese Bicentenary A692

1985, Jan. 25
1302 A692 4.50s Linz Cathedral interior .60 .20

Alban Berg (1885-1935), Composer — A693

1985, Feb. 8 **Engr.**
1303 A693 6s bluish black .80 .25

Vocational Training Inst., 25th Anniv. — A694

1985, Feb. 15 **Photo.** ***Perf. 13½x14***
1304 A694 4.50s multicolored .60 .20

City of Bregenz, Bimillennium — A695

1985, Feb. 22 ***Perf. 14x13½***
1305 A695 4s multicolored .55 .15

Austrian Registration Labels Cent. — A696

1985, Mar. 15 ***Perf. 13½x14***
1306 A696 4.50s Label, 1885 .60 .20

Josef Stefan (1835-1893), Physicist — A697

Photo. & Engr.

1985, Mar. 22 ***Perf. 14x13½***
1307 A697 6s buff, dl red brn & dk brn .80 .25

A698 A699

St. Leopold 16th-17th cent. embroidery.

1985, Mar. 29
1308 A698 3.50s multicolored .50 .15

St. Leopold Exhibition, Klosterneuberg.

1985, Apr. 26 **Photo.**
1309 A699 4.50s multicolored .60 .20

Liberation from German occupation forces, 40th anniv.

Painter Franz von Defregger (1835-1921) A700

1985, Apr. 26
1310 A700 3.50s Fairy tale teller .50 .15

Europa Issue 1985

Johann Joseph Fux (1660-1741), Composer, Violin and Trombone A701

Photo. & Engr.

1985, May 3 ***Perf. 13½***
1311 A701 6s lil gray & dk brn .90 .25

Boheimkirchen (Market Town) Millennium — A702

1985, May 10 ***Perf. 14***
1312 A702 4.50s View, coat of arms .60 .20

A703

A704

Mercury staff, flags of member and affiliate nations.

1985, May 10 **Photo.** ***Perf. 13½***
1313 A703 4s multicolored .55 .15

European Free Trade Assoc., 25th anniv.

1985, May 15 **Photo. & Engr.**

Episcopal residence gate, St. Polten diocese arms.

1314 A704 4.50s multicolored .60 .20

St. Polten Diocese, bicentenary.

The Gumpp Family of Builders, Innsbruck — A705

Perf. 14½x13½

1985, May 17 **Photo.**
1315 A705 3.50s multicolored .50 .15

Garsten Market Town Millennium A706

Design: 17th century engraving by George Mathaus Fischer (1628-1696).

Photo. & Engr.

1985, June 7 ***Perf. 13½x14***
1316 A706 4.50s multicolored .60 .20

UN, 40th Anniv. A707

Perf. 13½x14½

1985, June 26 **Photo.**
1317 A707 4s multicolored .55 .20

Austrian membership, 30th anniv.

Intl. Assoc. for the Prevention of Suicide, 13th Congress — A708

Photo. & Engr.

1985, June 28 ***Perf. 14***
1318 A708 5s brn, lt ap grn & yel .70 .30

Souvenir Sheet

Year of the Forest A709

1985, June 28 ***Perf. 13½***
1319 A709 6s Healthy and damaged woodland 1.00 .35

Kurhaus, Bad Ischl Operetta Activities Emblem A710

1985, July 5 ***Perf. 14***
1320 A710 3.50s multicolored .50 .15

Bad Ischl Festival, 25th anniv.

Intl. Competition of Fire Brigades, Vocklabruck — A711

1985, July 18 **Photo.** ***Perf. 14x13½***
1321 A711 4.50s Fireman, emblem .60 .20

Grossglockner Alpine Motorway, 50th Anniv. — A712

Photo. & Engr.

1985, Aug. 2 ***Perf. 13½***
1322 A712 4s View of Fuschertorl .55 .20

World Chess Federation Congress, Graz — A713

1985, Aug. 28 **Photo.** ***Perf. 13½***
1323 A713 4s Checkered globe, emblem .55 .20

The Legendary Foundation of Konigstetten by Charlemagne, by Auguste Stephan, c. 1870 — A714

Photo. & Engr.

1985, Aug. 30 ***Perf. 14***
1324 A714 4.50s multicolored .60 .20

Konigstetten millennium.

Hofkirchen-Taufkirchen-Weibern Municipalities, 1200th Anniv. — A715

1985, Aug. 30 ***Perf. 13½x14***
1325 A715 4.50s View of Weiburn, municipal arms .60 .20

Dr. Adam Politzer (1835-1923), Physician — A716

1985, Sept. 12 **Engr.** ***Perf. 14***
1326 A716 3.50s blue violet .50 .15

Politzer pioneered aural therapy for auditory disorders.

Intl. Assoc. of Forwarding Agents, World Congress, Vienna — A717

1985, Oct. 7 **Photo.** *Perf. 13½*
1327 A717 6s multicolored .85 .35

Carnival Figures Riding High Bicycles, By Paul Flora A718

Photo. & Engr.

1985, Oct. 25 *Perf. 14*
1328 A718 4s multicolored .55 .20

St. Martin on Horseback A719

1985, Nov. 8 **Photo.**
1329 A719 4.50s multicolored .60 .30

Eisenstadt Diocese, 25th anniv.

Creche, Marble Bas-relief, Salzburg — A720

Photo. & Engr.

1985, Nov. 29 *Perf. 13½*
1330 A720 4.50s gold, dl vio & buff .60 .30

Christmas.

Hanns Horbiger (1860-1931), Inventor — A721

1985, Nov. 29 *Perf. 14*
1331 A721 3.50s gold & sepia .50 .20

Aqueduct, Hundsau Brook, Near Gostling A722

1985, Nov. 29 *Perf. 13½x14½*
1332 A722 3.50s red, bluish blk & brt ultra .50 .20

Vienna Aqueduct, 75th anniv.

Chateau de la Muette, Paris Headquarters A723

1985, Dec. 13
1333 A723 4s sep, rose lil & gold .55 .25

Org. for Economic Cooperation and Development, 25th anniv.

Johann Bohm (1886-1959), Pres. Austrian Trade Fed. — A724

1986, Jan. 24 **Photo.** *Perf. 14*
1334 A724 4.50s blk, ver & grayish black .65 .30

Intl. Peace Year — A725

Perf. 13½x14½

1986, Jan. 24 **Photo.**
1335 A725 6s multicolored .85 .35

Digital Telephone Service Introduction A726

1986, Jan. 29 **Photo.**
1336 A726 5s Push-button keyboard .75 .30

Johann Georg Albrechtsberger (b. 1736), Composer — A727

Perf. 13½x14½

1986, Jan. 31 **Photo. & Engr.**
1337 A727 3.50s Klosterneuberg organ .50 .20

Korneuberg, 850th Anniv. A728

1986, Feb. 7 **Photo.** *Perf. 14*
1338 A728 5s multicolored .75 .30

A729

A730

Self-portrait, by Oskar Kokoschka (b.1886).

Perf. 14½x13½

1986, Feb. 28 **Photo.**
1339 A729 4s multicolored .60 .30

1986, Feb. 28 **Photo.** *Perf. 13x13½*
1340 A730 6s multicolored .85 .35

Admission to Council of Europe, 30th anniv.

Clemens Holzmeister (b. 1886), Architect, Salzburg Festival Theater, 1926 — A731

Photo. & Engr.

1986, Mar. 27 *Perf. 13½*
1341 A731 4s sepia & redsh brn .60 .30

3rd Intl. Geotextile Congress, Vienna A732

Perf. 13½x14½

1986, Apr. 7 **Photo.**
1342 A732 5s multicolored .75 .30

Prince Eugen and Schlosshof Castle — A733

Photo. & Engr.

1986, Apr. 21 *Perf. 14*
1343 A733 4s multicolored .60 .30

Prince Eugen Exhibition, Schlosshof and Niederweiden.

St. Florian Monastery, Upper Austria A734

1986, Apr. 24
1344 A734 4s multicolored .60 .30

The World of Baroque provincial exhibition, St. Florian.

Herberstein Castle, Arms of Styria — A735

1986, May 2 *Perf. 13½x14½*
1345 A735 4s multicolored .60 .30

Europa 1986 — A736

1986, May 2 *Perf. 13½*
1346 A736 6s Pasque flower .85 .45

Wagner, Scene from Opera Lohengrin A737

1986, May 21
1347 A737 4s multicolored .60 .30

Intl. Richard Wagner Congress, Vienna.

Antimonite A738

1986, May 23 *Perf. 13½x14½*
1348 A738 4s multicolored .60 .30

Burgenland Provincial Minerals Exhibition.

Scenery Type of 1984

1986-89 **Photo. & Engr.** *Perf. 14*

1349	A679	5s	Martinswall, Tyrol	.65	.35
1350	A679	5s	Tschauko Falls, Carinthia	.65	.35
1351	A679	5s	Dachstein Ice Caves	.80	.45
1352	A679	5s	Gauertal, Montafon	.80	.45
1353	A679	5s	Krimmler Waterfalls	.80	.60
1354	A679	5s	Lusthauswasser	.80	.60
			Nos. 1349-1354 (6)	4.50	2.80

Issued: #1351, 6/11/87; #1352, 8/21/87; #1353, 8/19/88; #1354, 9/1/89.

Waidhofen on Ybbs Township, 800th Anniv. A739

1986, June 20 **Photo.** *Perf. 13½*
1355 A739 4s multicolored .50 .30

Salzburg Local Railway, Cent. A740

1986, Aug. 8 **Photo.** *Perf. 14*
1356 A740 4s multicolored .55 .30

Seals of Dukes Leopold Of Austria, Otakar of Styria, and Georgenberg Church A741

1986, Aug. 14 **Photo. & Engr.**
1357 A741 5s multicolored .70 .30

Georgenberg Treaty, 800th anniv.

Julius Tandler (1869-1936), Social Reformer — A742

1986, Aug. 22
1358 A742 4s multicolored .60 .30

Sonnblick Observatory, Cent. — A743

Perf. 13½x14½
1986, Aug. 27 **Photo. & Engr.**
1359 A743 4s Observatory, 1886 .60 .30

Discovery of Mandrake Root — A744

1986, Aug. 27 ***Perf. 14½x13½***
1360 A744 5s multicolored .75 .30

European Assoc. for Anesthesiology, 7th cong.

Monasteries and Abbeys Type of 1984

Designs: 5.50s, St. Gerold's Provostry, Vorarlberg. 7s, Loretto Monastery, Burgenland. 7.50s, Dominican Convent, Vienna. 8s, Zwettl Monastery. 10s, Wilten Monastery.

1986-88 **Photo. & Engr.** ***Perf. 14***

1361	A679a	5.50s	multicolored	.80	.60
1362	A679a	7s	multicolored	1.10	.90
1363	A679a	7.50s	multicolored	1.10	.85
1364	A679a	8s	multicolored	1.40	1.00
1365	A679a	10s	multicolored	1.75	1.25
			Nos. 1361-1365 (5)	6.15	4.60

Issued: 5.50s, 9/12/86; 7.50s, 10/3; 7s, 8/14/87; 8s, 5/27/88; 10s, 3/18/88.

A745 A746

Photo. & Engr.
1986, Sept. 3 ***Perf. 14***
1366 A745 4s multicolored .60 .30

Otto Stoessl (d. 1936), writer.

1986, Sept. 3 **Photo.**
1367 A746 4s Fireman, 1686 .60 .30

Vienna fire brigade, 300th anniv.

Silk Viennese Hunting Tapestry — A747

Photo. & Engr.
1986, Sept. 3 ***Perf. 14***
1368 A747 5s multicolored .75 .40

Intl. conf. on Oriental Carpets, Vienna, Budapest.

A748 A749

Photo. & Engr.
1986, Oct. 10 ***Perf. 14***
1369 A748 5s Minister at pulpit .70 .40

Protestant Act, 25th anniv., and Protestant Patent of Franz Josef I ensuring religious equality, 125th anniv.

1986, Oct. 17 ***Perf. 13½x14***

Disintegration, by Walter Schmogner.

1370 A749 4s multicolored .60 .30

Franz Liszt, Composer, and Birthplace, Burgenland A750

1986, Oct. 17 ***Perf. 13½***
1371 A750 5s green & sepia .70 .40

Souvenir Sheet

European Security Conference, Vienna — A751

Illustration reduced.

1986, Nov. 4 ***Perf. 13½x14***
1372 A751 6s Vienna .95 .65

Strettweg Cart, 7th Cent. B.C. — A752

Photo. & Engr.
1986, Nov. 26 ***Perf. 14***
1373 A752 4s multicolored .65 .30

Joanneum Styrian Land Museum, 175th anniv.

Christmas A753

Design: The Little Crib, bas-relief by Schwanthaler (1740-1810), Schlierbach Monastery.

1986, Nov. 28
1374 A753 5s gold & rose lake .80 .40

Federal Chamber of Commerce, 40th Anniv. — A754

1986, Dec. 2 **Photo.**
1375 A754 5s multicolored .80 .40

Industry A755

1986-91 ***Perf. 14x13½***

1376	A755	4s	Steel workers	.80	.30
1377	A755	4s	Office worker, computer	.80	.35
1378	A755	4s	Lab assistant	.80	.30
1378A	A755	4.50s	Textile worker	.75	.60
1379	A755	5s	Bricklayer	.80	.60
			Nos. 1376-1379 (5)	3.95	2.15

Issued: #1376, 12/4/86; #1377, 10/5/87; #1378, 10/21/88; 5s, 10/10/89; 4.50s, 10/11/91.

This is an expanding set. Numbers will change if necessary.

The Educated Eye, by Arnulf Rainer — A756

1987, Jan. 13 **Photo.** ***Perf. 13½x14***
1386 A756 5s multicolored .80 .40

Adult education in Vienna, cent.

The Large Blue Madonna, by Anton Faistauer (1887-1970) A757

Paintings: 6s, Self-portrait, 1922, by A. Paris Gutersloh (1887-1973).

1987, Jan. 29 ***Perf. 14***
1387 A757 4s multicolored .55 .20
1388 A757 6s multicolored .90 .40

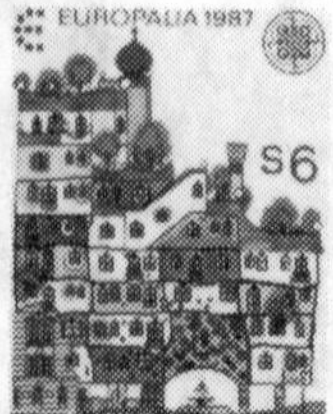

Europa 1987 — A758

Photo. & Engr.
1987, Apr. 6 ***Perf. 13½x14***
1389 A758 6s Hundertwasser House .95 .55

World Ice Hockey Championships, Vienna — A759

Perf. 13½x14½
1987, Apr. 17 **Photo.**
1390 A759 5s multicolored .80 .60

Opening of the Austria Center, Vienna A760

1987, Apr. 22
1391 A760 5s multicolored .80 .60

Salzburg City Charter, 700th Anniv. A761

1987, Apr. 24
1392 A761 5s multicolored .80 .60

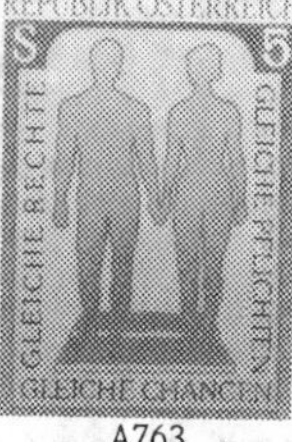

A762 A763

Photo. & Engr.
1987, Apr. 29 ***Perf. 14***
1393 A762 4s Factory, 1920 .65 .50

Work-Men-Machines, provincial exhibition, Upper Austria.

1987, Apr. 29 **Photo.** ***Perf. 13½***
1394 A763 5s multicolored .80 .60

Equal rights for men and women.

A764 A765

Adele Block-Bauer I, abstract by Gustav Klimt.

Photo. & Engr.
1987, May 8 ***Perf. 13½***
1395 A764 4s multicolored .65 .50

The Era of Emperor Franz Joseph, provincial exhibition, Lower Austria.

1987, May 15 ***Perf. 14½x13½***
1396 A765 6s multicolored 1.00 .75

Arthur Schnitzler (1862-1931), poet.

Von Raitenau, View of Salzburg A766

1987, May 15 ***Perf. 14***
1397 A766 4s multicolored .65 .50

Prince Archbishop Wolf Dietrich von Raitenau, patron of baroque architecture in Salzburg, provincial exhibition.

Lace, Lustenau Municipal Arms — A767

1987, May 22
1398 A767 5s multicolored .80 .60

Lustenau, 1100th anniv.

Souvenir Sheet

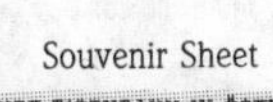
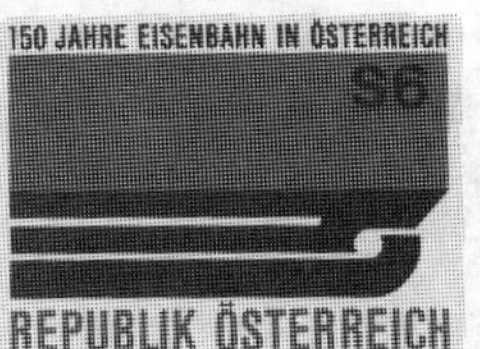

Austrian Railways Sesquicentenary — A768

1987, June 5 **Photo.** ***Perf.*** $13^1/_2$
1399 A768 6s multicolored 1.00 .75

8th Intl. Congress of Engravers, Vienna A769

Photo. & Engr.

1987, June 17 ***Perf. 14***
1400 A769 5s gray, gray brn & dull rose .80 .60

Dr. Karl Josef Bayer (1847-1904), Chemist — A770

Shipping on Achensee, Cent. — A771

1987, June 22 ***Perf.*** $14x13^1/_2$
1401 A770 5s multicolored .80 .60

Eighth Intl. Light Metals Congress, June 22-26, Leoben and Vienna; Bayer Technique for producing aluminum oxide from bauxite, cent.

1987, June 26 **Photo.**
1402 A771 4s multicolored .65 .50

A772 A773

1987, July 1
1403 A772 5s Palais Rottal, Vienna .80 .60

Ombudsmen's office, 10th anniv.

1987, Aug. 11 **Photo. & Engr.**
1404 A773 5s dull olive bister, choc & buff .80 .60

Dr. Erwin Schrodinger (1887-1961), 1933 Nobel laureate in physics.

Freistadt Exhibitions, 125th Anniv. A774

1987, Aug. 11 ***Perf.*** $14x14^1/_2$
1405 A774 5s multicolored .80 .60

Arbing, 850th Anniv. — A775

1987, Aug. 21 ***Perf.*** $13^1/_2$
1406 A775 5s multicolored .80 .60

1987 World Cycling Championships, Villach to Vienna — A776

1987, Aug. 25 ***Perf. 14***
1407 A776 5s multicolored .80 .60

World Congress of Savings Banks, Vienna A777

Perf. $13^1/_2x14^1/_2$

1987, Sept. 9 **Photo.**
1408 A777 5s multicolored .80 .60

Johann Michael Haydn (1737-1806), Composer A778

Perf. $13^1/_2x14^1/_2$

1987, Sept. 14 **Engr.**
1409 A778 4s dull violet .65 .50

Paul Hofhaymer (1459-1537), Composer A779

Photo. & Engr.

1987, Sept. 11 ***Perf. 14***
1410 A779 4s gold, blk & ultra .65 .50

Bearded Vulture — A780

1987, Sept. 25
1411 A780 4s multicolored .65 .50

Innsbruck Zoo, 25th anniv.

Baumgottinnen, by Arnulf Neuwirth — A781

1987, Oct. 9 ***Perf.*** $14x13^1/_2$
1412 A781 5s multicolored .80 .60

Modern Art.

Gambling Monopoly, 200th Anniv. — A782

Perf. $14^1/_2x13^1/_2$

1987, Oct. 30 **Photo.**
1413 A782 5s Lottery drum .80 .60

Christoph Willibald Gluck (1714-1787), Composer A784

Photo. & Engr.

1987, Nov. 13 ***Perf. 14***
1415 A784 5s cream & blk .88 .65

Oskar Helmer (b. 1887), Politician — A785

1987, Nov. 13
1416 A785 4s multicolored .70 .50

Joseph Mohr (1792-1848) and Franz Gruber (1787-1863), Opening Bars of "Silent Night, Holy Night" — A786

1987, Nov. 27
1417 A786 5s multicolored .90 .65

Christmas.

A787 A788

Photo. & Engr.

1988, Jan. 12 ***Perf.*** $13^1/_2$
1418 A787 5s St. John Bosco, children .90 .65

Intl. Education Congress of Salesian Fathers.

Perf. $14^1/_2x13^1/_2$

1988, Feb. 19 **Photo. & Engr.**
1419 A788 6s multicolored 1.05 .80

Ernst Mach (1838-1916), physicist.

Village with Bridge (1904), by Franz von Zulow (1883-1963), Painter — A789

1988, Feb. 25 **Photo.** ***Perf.*** $14^1/_2x14$
1420 A789 4s multicolored .70 .50

Biedermeier Provincial Exhibition, Vormarz in Vienna A790

Painting: Confiscation, by Ferdinand Georg Waldmuller (1793-1865).

Photo. & Engr.

1988, Mar. 11 ***Perf. 14***
1421 A790 4s multicolored .70 .50

Anschluss of March 11, 1938 A791

1988, Mar. 11 **Photo.** ***Perf.*** $13^1/_2$
1422 A791 5s gray olive, brn blk & ver .85 .65

No. 2 Aigen Steam Locomotive, 1887 — A792

1988, Mar. 22 ***Perf.*** $13^1/_2x14^1/_2$
1423 A792 4s shown .70 .50
1424 A792 5s Electric train, Josepsplatz .85 .65

Muhlkreis Railway, cent. (4s); Vienna Local Railway, cent. (5s).

World Wildlife Fund — A793

Photo. & Engr.

1988, Apr. 15 ***Perf.*** $13^1/_2x14$
1425 A793 5s Bee eater .90 .65

Styrian Provincial Exhibition on Glass and Coal, Barnbach A794

1988, Apr. 29 *Perf. $13^1/_2$*
1426 A794 4s Frosted glass .70 .50

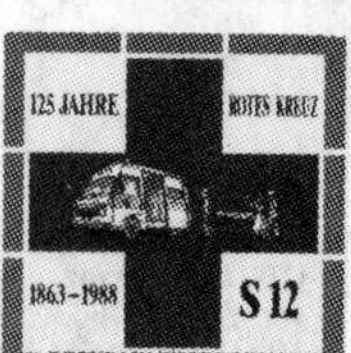

Intl. Red Cross, 125th Anniv. — A795

1988, May 6 **Photo.** *Perf. 14*
1427 A795 12s grn, brt red & blk 2.25 1.65

Gothic Silver Censer — A796

1988, May 6 **Photo. & Engr.**
1428 A796 4s multicolored .70 .50

Art and Monasticism at the Birth of Austria, lower Austrian provincial exhibition, Seitenstetten.

Europa 1988 A797

Communication and transportation.

1988, May 13 **Photo.**
1429 A797 6s multicolored 1.10 .80

Mattsee Monastery and Lion of Alz — A798

1988, May 18 **Photo. & Engr.**
1430 A798 4s multicolored .70 .50

Provincial exhibition at Mattsee Monastery: Bavarian Tribes in Salzburg.

Weinberg Castle — A799

Perf. $13^1/_2x14^1/_2$

1988, May 20 **Photo.**
1431 A799 4s multicolored .70 .50

Upper Austrian provincial exhibition: Weinberg Castle.

Odon von Horwath (1901-1938), Dramatist — A800

Perf. $14^1/_2x13^1/_2$

1988, June 1 **Photo. & Engr.**
1432 A800 6s olive bis & slate grn 1.10 .80

Stockerau Festival, 25th Anniv. — A801

1988, June 17 *Perf. 14*
1433 A801 5s Stockerau Town Hall .80 .60

Tauern Motorway Opening — A802

1988, June 24 **Photo.** *Perf. $13^1/_2x14$*
1434 A802 4s multicolored .65 .50

Brixlegg, 1200th Anniv. A803

Perf. $13^1/_2x14^1/_2$

1988, July 1 **Photo. & Engr.**
1435 A803 5s multicolored .80 .60

View of Klagenfurt, Engraving by Matthaus Merian (1593-1650) A804

Photo. & Engr.

1988, Aug. 12 *Perf. 14*
1436 A804 5s multicolored .80 .60

Carinthian Postal Service, 400th Anniv.

Brixen-im-Thale, 1200th Anniv. — A805

1988, Aug. 12
1437 A805 5s multicolored .80 .60

Feldkirchen, 1100th Anniv. — A806

1988, Sept. 2 *Perf. $13^1/_2$*
1438 A806 5s multicolored .80 .60

Feldbach, 800th Anniv. A807

1988, Sept. 15 **Photo. & Engr.**
1439 A807 5s multicolored .80 .60

Ansfelden, 1200th Anniv. — A808

1988, Sept. 23 *Perf. 14*
1440 A808 5s multicolored .80 .60

Exports — A809

1988, Oct. 18 **Photo.** *Perf. $14x13^1/_2$*
1441 A809 8s multicolored 1.50 1.25

No. 1441 has a holographic image. Soaking in water may affect the hologram.

Vienna Concert Hall, 75th Anniv. A810

Photo. & Engr.

1988, Oct. 19 *Perf. $13^1/_2$*
1442 A810 5s multicolored .80 .60

The Watchmen, by Giselbert Hoke — A811

1988, Oct. 21 *Perf. 14*
1443 A811 5s multicolored .80 .60

Social Democrats Unification Party Congress, Cent. — A812

1988, Nov. 11 **Photo.** *Perf. $14^1/_2x14$*
1444 A812 4s multicolored .65 .50

Leopold Schonbauer (1888-1963), Physician — A813

Perf. $14^1/_2x13^1/_2$

1988, Nov. 11 **Photo. & Engr.**
1445 A813 4s multicolored .65 .50

Christmas A814

Design: Nativity painting from St. Barbara's Church.

1988, Nov. 25 *Perf. 14*
1446 A814 5s multicolored .80 .60

Benedictine Monastery, Melk, 900th Anniv. A815

Design: Fresco by Paul Troger.

1989, Mar. 17 **Photo. & Engr.**
1447 A815 5s multicolored .80 .60

Madonna and Child, by Lucas Cranach (1472-1553) A816

Marianne Hainisch (1839-1936), Women's Rights Activist A817

1989, Mar. 17 *Perf. $14^1/_2x13^1/_2$*
1448 A816 4s multicolored .60 .50

Diocese of Innsbruck, 25th anniv.

1989, Mar. 24 *Perf. $14x13^1/_2$*
1449 A817 6s multicolored .95 .70

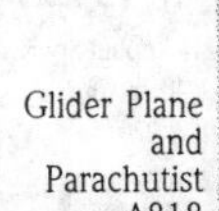

Glider Plane and Parachutist
A818

1989, Mar. 31 **Photo.** ***Perf. 14***
1450 A818 6s multicolored 1.00 .75

World Gliding Championships, Wiener Neustadt, and World Parachuting Championships, Damuls.

Bruck an der Leitha Commune, 750th Anniv.
A819

Painting by Georg Matthaus Vischer (1628-1696).

1989, Apr. 21
1451 A819 5s multicolored .85 .60

A820

A821

Die Malerei, 1904, by Rudolf Jettmar (1869-1939).

Perf. 14½x13½

1989, Apr. 21 **Photo.**
1452 A820 5s multicolored .85 .60

1989, Apr. 26 **Photo. & Engr.**

Holy Trinity Church, Stadl-Paura.

1453 A821 5s multicolored .85 .60

Michael Prunner (1669-1739), baroque architect.

A822

A823

Eduard Suess (1831-1914, structural geologist) portrait by J. Krieher (1800-1876) and map.

1989, Apr. 26
1454 A822 6s multicolored 1.00 .75

1989, Apr. 26
1455 A823 5s multicolored .85 .60

Ludwig Wittgenstein (1889-1951), philosopher.

Styrian Provincial Exhibition, Judenburg
A824

Design: Judenberg, 17th cent., an engraving by Georg Matthaus Vischer.

1989, Apr. 28 ***Perf. 14x13½***
1456 A824 4s multicolored .70 .50

Industrial Technology Exhibition, Pottenstein — A825

1989, Apr. 28 **Photo.** ***Perf. 13½***
1457 A825 4s Steam engine .70 .50

Radstadt Township, 700th Anniv.
A826

1989, May 3 **Photo.** ***Perf. 13½x14½***
1458 A826 5s multicolored .85 .60

Europa 1989 — A827

1989, May 5
1459 A827 6s Toy boat 1.00 .75

Monastery Church at Lambach, 900th Anniv. — A828

Photo. & Engr.

1989, May 19 ***Perf. 14***
1460 A828 4s multicolored .70 .50

Paddle Steamer *Gisela*— A829

1989, May 19 **Photo.** ***Perf. 13½***
1461 A829 5s multicolored .85 .60

Shipping on the Traunsee, 150th anniv.

St. Andra im Lavanttal, 650th Anniv.
A830

Period cityscape by Matthaus Merian.

1989, May 26 **Photo. & Engr.**
1462 A830 5s multicolored .85 .60

Richard Strauss (1864-1949), Composer — A831

Perf. 14½x13½

1989, June 1 **Photo. & Engr.**
1463 A831 6s dark brn, gold & red brn 1.00 .75

Achensee Railway, Cent. — A832

1989, June 8 **Photo.** ***Perf. 13½***
1464 A832 5s multicolored .85 .60

Monastery Type of 1984

Design: 50g, Vorau Abbey, Styria. 1s, Monastery of Mehrerau, Vorarlberg. 1.50s, Monastery of the German Order in Vienna. 2s, Bendictine Monastery, Michaelbeuern. 11s, Engelszell Abbey. 12s, Monastery of the Hospitalers, Eisenstadt. 17s, St. Peter, Salzburg. 20s, Wernberg Monastery.

1989-92 **Photo. & Engr.** ***Perf. 14***

1464A	A679a	50g multicolored	.15	.15
1465	A679a	1s multicolored	.15	.15
1465A	A679a	1.50s multicolored	.30	.25
1466	A679a	2s multicolored	.35	.25
1467	A679a	11s multicolored	1.90	1.40
1467A	A679a	12s multicolored	2.25	1.75
1468	A679a	17s multicolored	2.75	2.00
1469	A679a	20s multicolored	2.75	2.00
		Nos. 1464A-1469 (8)	10.60	7.95

Issued: 1s, 9/1/89; 17s, 6/29/89; 11s, 3/9/90; 50g, 10/12/90; 20s, 5/3/91; 2s, 9/27/91; 1.50s, 10/23/92; 12s, 6/17/92.

This is an expanding set. Numbers will change if necessary.

Interparliamentary Union, Cent. — A833

Photo. & Engr.

1989, June 30 ***Perf. 14***
1475 A833 6s Parliament, Vienna 1.00 .75

Social Security in Austria, Cent. — A834

1989, Aug. 1 **Photo.**
1476 A834 5s multicolored .70 .50

UN Offices in Vienna, 10th Anniv.
A835

1989, Aug. 23
1477 A835 8s multicolored 1.10 .85

Wildalpen, 850th Anniv.
A836

Photo. & Engr.

1989, Sept. 15 ***Perf. 13½x14***
1478 A836 5s Foundry, coat of arms .80 .60

33rd Congress of the Association for Quality Assurance (EOQC) — A837

1989, Sept. 18 **Photo.** ***Perf. 14x13½***
1479 A837 6s multicolored .90 .70

14th World Congress of the Soc. for Criminal Law (AIDP)
A838

Photo. & Engr.

1989, Oct. 2 ***Perf. 13½***
1480 A838 6s Justice Palace, Vienna .90 .70

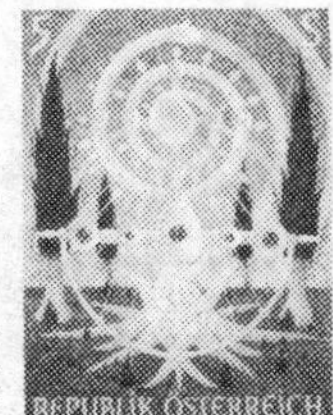

Lebensbaum, by Ernst Steiner — A839

1989, Oct. 10 ***Perf. 13½x14***
1481 A839 5s multicolored .80 .60

A840

A841

Perf. 14½x13½

1989, Nov. 6 **Photo.**
1482 A840 4s Trakl .60 .45
1483 A840 4s Anzengruber .60 .45

Georg Trakl (1887-1914), expressionist poet; Ludwig Anzengruber (1839-1889), playwright and novelist.

1989, Nov. 10 **Photo. & Engr.**
1484 A841 6s multicolored .90 .70

Alfred Fried (1864-1921), pacifist and publisher awarded the Nobel peace prize for 1911 with Tobias Asser.

Parish Church Christ Child, by Johann Carl Reslfeld
A842

1989, Dec. 1 ***Perf. 13½x14½***
1485 A842 5s multicolored .75 .60

Christmas.

A843

A844

The Young Post Rider, an Engraving by Albrecht Durer

1990, Jan. 12 Photo. & Engr. *Perf. 14*
1486 A843 5s multicolored .80 .60

Postal communications in Europe, 500th anniv.
See Belgium No. 1332, Germany No. 1592, Berlin No. 9N584 and German Democratic Republic No. 2791.

Perf. 13½x14½
1990, Jan. 12 Photo.
1487 A844 5s multicolored .80 .60

Hahnenkamm alpine competition, Kitzbuhel, 50th anniv.

A845 A846

Perf. 14½x13½
1990, Jan. 17 Photo.
1488 A845 4.50s multicolored .70 .55

Salomon Sulzer (1804-90), cantor and composer.

1990, Jan. 22 Photo. & Engr.
1489 A846 6s claret & pale green .95 .70

Friedrich Emich (1860-1940), chemist.

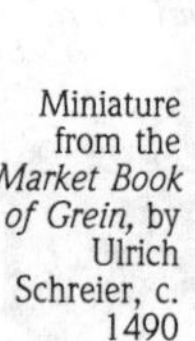

Miniature from the *Market Book of Grein,* by Ulrich Schreier, c. 1490
A847

1990, Mar. 9 *Perf. 14*
1490 A847 5s sepia, buff & gray .80 .60

City of Linz, 500th anniv.

University Seals — A848

1990, Apr. 6
1491 A848 5s multicolored .85 .65

625th Anniv. of Vienna University and 175th anniv. of Vienna Technical University.

Scenery Type of 1984

1990-95 *Perf. 14*

1492 A679	5s Styrian Vineyards	.85	.65
1493 A679	5s Obir Caverns	.95	.70
1494 A679	5s Natural Bridge, Vorarlberg	.90	.75
1495 A679	6s Wilder Kaiser Mountain, Tyrol	1.25	.95
1496 A679	6s Peggau Cave, Styria	1.00	.80
1497 A679	6s Moorland, swamp, Heidenreichstein	1.25	1.00
	Nos. 1492-1497 (6)	6.20	4.85

Issued: #1492, 4/27; #1493, 3/26/91; #1494, 2/5/92; #1495, 2/19/93; #1496, 4/29/94; #1497, 5/19/95.
This is an expanding set. Numbers will change if necessary.

A849 A850

Church and municipal arms.

1990, Apr. 27 Photo. *Perf. 14x13½*
1500 A849 7s multicolored 1.25 .25

1200th anniv. of Anthering.

1990, Apr. 30 Photo. *Perf. 13½*
1501 A850 4.50s multicolored .80 .60

Labor Day, cent.

Seckau Abbey, 850th Anniv. — A851

Ebene Reichenau Post Office — A852

1990, May 4 Engr. *Perf. 14x13½*
1502 A851 4.50s bluish black .80 .60

1990, May 4 Photo. *Perf. 13½x14*
1503 A852 7s multicolored 1.25 .25

A853 A854

Self Portraits: 4.50s, Hans Makart (1840-84). 5s, Egon Schiele (1890-1918).

Photo. & Engr.
1990, May 29 *Perf. 14*
1504 A853 4.50s multicolored .80 .60
1505 A853 5s multicolored .85 .65

1990, June 1 Photo. *Perf. 14x13½*
1506 A854 4.50s multicolored .80 .60

Ferdinand Raimund (1790-1836), actor.

Christ Healing the Sick by Rembrandt A855

1990, June 5 Photo. & Engr. *Perf. 14*
1507 A855 7s multicolored 1.25 1.00

Second Intl. Christus Medicus Congress, Bad Ischl.

Hardegg, 700th Anniv. — A856

Photo. & Engr.
1990, June 8 *Perf. 13½x14*
1508 A856 4.50s multicolored .80 .60

Oberdrauburg, 750th Anniv. A857

1990, June 8 Photo.
1509 A857 5s multicolored .85 .65

Gumpoldskirchen, 850th Anniv. — A858

Photo. & Engr.
1990, June 15 *Perf. 13½*
1510 A858 5s multicolored .85 .65

Mathias Zdarsky (1856-1940), Alpine Skier — A859

1990, June 20 *Perf. 14x13½*
1511 A859 5s multicolored .85 .65

Telegraph, 1880, Anton Tschechow, 1978 — A860

1990, June 28 Photo. *Perf. 14*
1512 A860 9s multicolored 1.50 1.10

Modern shipbuilding in Austria, 150th anniv.

A861 A862

Photo. & Engr.
1990, Aug. 3 *Perf. 14x13½*
1513 A861 5s gold & brown .85 .65

Joseph Friedrich Perkonig (1890-1959), poet.

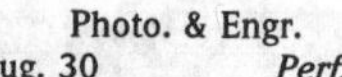

Photo. & Engr.
1990, Aug. 30 *Perf. 13½x14*

Herr des Regenbogens, by Robert Zeppel-Sperl.
1514 A862 5s gold & brown .85 .65

European Dialysis and Transplantation Society, 27th Congress — A863

1990, Sept. 4 Photo. *Perf. 14*
1515 A863 7s multicolored 1.25 1.00

Franz Werfel (1890-1945), Writer — A864

Photo. & Engr.
1990, Sept. 11 *Perf. 14x13½*
1516 A864 5s multicolored .95 .70

Austrian Forces in UN Peace Keeping Forces, 30th Anniv. A865

1990, Sept. 20 Photo. *Perf. 13½*
1517 A865 7s multicolored 1.25 1.00

Federal and State Arms A866

1990, Sept. 24 Photo. & Engr.
1518 A866 5s multicolored .95 .70

Federalism in Austria.

A867 A868

1990, Oct. 22 Photo & Engr. *Perf. 14*
1519 A867 4.50s blk, bl grn & red .85 .65

Mining Univ., Leoben, 150th anniv.

Photo. & Engr.
1990, Nov. 8 *Perf. 14x13½*
1520 A868 4.50s multicolored .85 .65

Karl Freiherr von Vogelsang (1818-90), politician.

Metalworkers and Miners Trade Union, Cent. — A869

1990, Nov. 16 *Perf. 14*
1521 A869 5s multicolored .95 .70

3rd World Curling Championships A870

1990, Nov. 23 Photo. *Perf. 14x13½*
1522 A870 7s multicolored 1.40 1.00

Palmhouse at Schonbrunn A871

1990, Nov. 30 *Perf. 14*
1523 A871 5s multicolored .95 .70

A872 A873

Christmas: Altar in Klosterneuburg Abbey by the Master from Verdun.

Photo. & Engr.

1990, Nov. 23 *Perf. 13½*
1524 A872 5s multicolored .95 .70

Photo. & Engr.

1991, Jan. 15 *Perf. 14x13½*
1525 A873 4.50s multicolored .85 .65

Franz Grillparzer (1791-1872), dramatic poet.

A874 A875

1991, Jan. 21 *Perf. 13½*
1526 A874 5s multicolored .95 .70

Alpine Skiing World Championship, Saalbach-Hinterglemm.

1991, Jan. 21 Photo. *Perf. 14x13½*
1527 A875 5s multicolored .95 .70

Bruno Kreisky (1911-90), chancellor.

Friedrich Freiherr von Schmidt (1825-1891), Architect A876

1991, Jan. 21 *Perf. 14*
1528 A876 7s multicolored 1.35 1.00

Visual Arts — A877

Designs: 4.50s, Donner Fountain, Vienna, by Raphael Donner (1693-1741), sculptor. 5s, Kitzbuhel in Winter, by Alfons Walde (1891-1958), painter. 7s, Vienna Stock Exchange, Theophil Hansen (1813-1891), architect.

1991, Feb. 8
1529 A877 4.50s multicolored .85 .65
1530 A877 5s multicolored .95 .70
1531 A877 7s multicolored 1.40 1.00
Nos. 1529-1531 (3) 3.20 2.35

See No. 1543.

Marie von Ebner Eschenbach (1830-1916), Poet — A878

Perf. 13½x14½

1991, Mar. 12 **Engr.**
1532 A878 4.50s rose violet .85 .65

Miniature Sheet

Wolfgang Amadeus Mozart (1756-1791), Composer — A879

Design: b, Magic Flute Fountain, Vienna.

1991, Mar. 22 *Perf. 13½*
1533 Sheet of 2 + label 1.65 1.25
a.-b. A879 5s any single .80 .60

Spittal an der Drau, 800th Anniv. A880

1991, Apr. 11 *Perf. 14*
1534 A880 4.50s multicolored .75 .60

Europa A881

1991, May 3 Photo. *Perf. 14*
1535 A881 7s ERS-1 satellite 1.10 .80

Garden Banquet by Anthony Bays A882

1991, May 10 Photo. *Perf. 13½*
1536 A882 5s multicolored .75 .60

Vorarlberg Provincial Exhibition, Hohenems.

Museum of Military History, Cent. A883

Design: 7s, Interior of Museum of Art History.

Photo. & Engr.

1991, May 24 *Perf. 13½*
1537 A883 5s multicolored .95 .80
1538 A883 7s multicolored 1.25 1.00

Museum of Art History, Cent. (#1538).

Grein, 500th Anniv. A884

1991, May 24 Photo. *Perf. 14*
1539 A884 4.50s multicolored .90 .45

Tulln, 1200th Anniv. A885

1991, May 24 *Perf. 13½x14*
1540 A885 5s multicolored .95 .80

Completion of Karawanken Tunnels — A886

1991, May 31 *Perf. 14x13½*
1541 A886 7s multicolored 1.25 1.00

5th Anniv. of St. Polten as Provincial Capital of Lower Austria A887

1991, July 5 Photo. *Perf. 14*
1542 A887 5s multicolored .80 .65

Visual Arts Type of 1991

Design: 4.50s, Karlsplatz Station of Vienna Subway by Otto Wagner (1841-1918), Architect.

1991, July 12 Photo. & Engr.
1543 A877 4.50s multicolored .75 .60

Rowing and Junior Canoeing World Championships, Vienna — A888

1991, Aug. 20 Photo. *Perf. 13½x14*
1544 A888 5s multicolored .85 .70

European Congress of Radiologists A889

1991, Sept. 13 *Perf. 14*
1545 A889 7s multicolored 1.10 .95

Paracelsus (1493-1541), Physician — A890

1991, Sept. 27 *Perf. 14x13½*
1546 A890 4.50s multicolored .75 .60

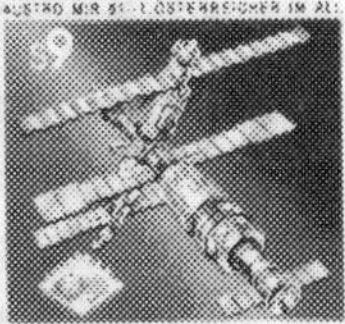

Joint Austrian-Soviet Space Mission — A891

1991, Oct. 2 *Perf. 14*
1547 A891 9s multicolored 1.50 1.25

Austrian Folk Festivals — A892

Designs: 4.50s, Almabtrieb, Tyrol. 5s, Winzerkrone, Vienna. 7s, Ernte-Monstranz, Styria.

1991, Oct. 4 Photo. & Engr.
1548 A892 4.50s multicolored .75 .60
1549 A892 5s multicolored .85 .70
1550 A892 7s multicolored 1.10 .95
Nos. 1548-1550 (3) 2.70 2.25

See Nos. 1577-1579, 1619-1621, 1671-1673, 1694.

The General by Rudolph Pointner — A893

Photo. & Engr.

1991, Oct. 11 *Perf. 13½x14*
1551 A893 5s multicolored .85 .70

Birth of Christ, Baumgartenberg Church — A894

1991, Nov. 29

1552 A894 5s multicolored .85 .70

Christmas.

Julius Raab, Politician, Birth Cent. — A895

1991, Nov. 29 ***Perf. 14x13½***

1553 A895 4.50s red brn & brn .75 .60

1992 Winter and Summer Olympic Games A897

1992, Jan. 14 **Photo.** ***Perf. 14***

1555 A897 7s multicolored 1.25 1.00

Trade Union of Clerks in Private Enterprises, Cent. — A898

1992, Jan. 14

1556 A898 5.50s multicolored .95 .80

A899

A900

1992, Jan. 29 ***Perf. 14x13½***

1557 A899 5s multicolored .90 .75

8th Natural Run Toboggan World Championships.

1992, Feb. 5 **Engr.** ***Perf. 14x13½***

1558 A900 5.50s brown .95 .80

George Saiko, Poet, nirth cent.

Worker's Sports, Cent. — A901

1992, Feb. 5 **Photo.** ***Perf. 14***

1559 A901 5.50s multicolored .95 .80

Souvenir Sheet

Vienna Philharmonic Orchestra, 150th Anniv. — A902

Photo. & Engr.

1992, Mar. 27 ***Perf. 14***

1560 A902 5.50s multicolored .95 .80

Scientists — A903

Designs: 5s, Franz Joseph Muller von Reichenstein (1742-1825), discoverer of tellurium. 5.50s, Dr. Paul Kitaibel (1757-1817), botanist. 6s, Christian Johann Doppler (1803-1853), physicist. 7s, Richard Kuhn (1900-1967), chemist.

1992, Mar. 27 **Photo.**

1561 A903 5s multicolored .85 .70
1562 A903 5.50s multicolored .95 .80
1563 A903 6s multicolored 1.00 .85
1564 A903 7s multicolored 1.25 .95
Nos. 1561-1564 (4) 4.05 3.30

Railway Workers Union, Cent. A904

1992, Apr. 2 ***Perf. 14x13½***

1565 A904 5.50s black & red .95 .80

Norbert Hanrieder (1842-1913), Poet — A905

Photo. & Engr.

1992, Apr. 30 ***Perf. 14x13½***

1566 A905 5.50s purple & buff .95 .80

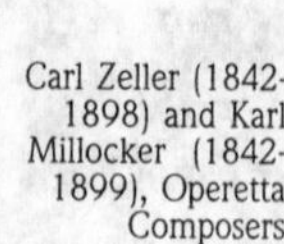

Carl Zeller (1842-1898) and Karl Millocker (1842-1899), Operetta Composers A906

Photo. & Engr.

1992, Apr. 30 ***Perf. 14***

1567 A906 6s multicolored 1.00 .85

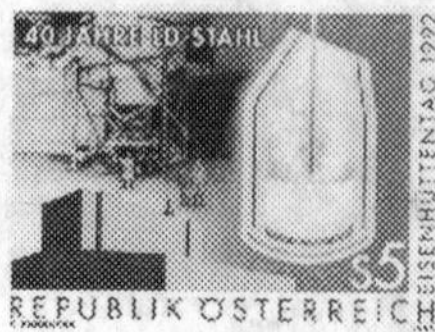

LD Steel Mill, 40th Anniv. A907

1992, May 8 **Photo.** ***Perf. 14x13½***

1568 A907 5s multicolored .85 .70

Discovery of America, 500th Anniv. A908

1992, May 8 **Photo. & Engr.** ***Perf. 14***

1569 A908 7s multicolored 1.25 .95

Europa.

Austro-Swiss Treaty on Regulation of Rhine River, Cent. — A909

1992, May 8 **Photo.** ***Perf. 13½x14***

1570 A909 7s multicolored 1.25 .95

Protection of the Alps — A910

1992, May 22 ***Perf. 14x13½***

1571 A910 5.50s multicolored .95 .80

Dr. Anna Dengel (1892-1980), Physician — A911

Sebastian Rieger (1867-1953), Poet — A912

1992, May 22 **Photo. & Engr.**

1572 A911 5.50s multicolored .95 .80

1992, May 22 **Engr.**

1573 A912 5s red brown .85 .70

Lienz, 750th Anniv. A913

1992, June 17 **Photo.** ***Perf. 14x13½***

1574 A913 5s Town Hall .90 .70

Intl. Congress of Austrian Society of Surgeons — A914

Photo. & Engr.

1992, June 17 ***Perf. 14***

1575 A914 6s multicolored 1.10 .90

Dr. Kurt Waldheim, President of Austria, 1986-92 — A915

1992, June 22 ***Perf. 14x13½***

1576 A915 5.50s multicolored .95 .75

Folk Festivals Type of 1991

Designs: 5s, Marksman's target, Lower Austria. 5.50s, Peasant's chest, Carinthia. 7s, Votive icon, Vorarlberg.

Photo. & Engr.

1992, Sept. 18 ***Perf. 14***

1577 A892 5s multicolored .90 .70
1578 A892 5.50s multicolored .95 .75
1579 A892 7s multicolored 1.25 1.00
Nos. 1577-1579 (3) 3.10 2.45

Marchfeld Canal — A917

1992, Oct. 9 **Photo.** ***Perf. 13½x14***

1580 A917 5s multicolored .90 .70

5th Intl. Ombudsman Conference, Vienna A918

1992, Oct. 9 **Photo & Engr.** ***Perf. 14***

1581 A918 5.50s multicolored .95 .75

The Clearance of Seawater, by Peter Pongratz A919

1992, Oct. 9

1582 A919 5.50s multicolored .95 .75

Academy of Fine Arts, 300th Anniv. — A920

Photo. & Engr.

1992, Oct. 23 *Perf. 14*
1583 A920 5s red & blue 1.00 .85

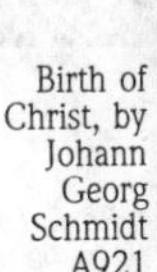

Birth of Christ, by Johann Georg Schmidt A921

1992, Nov. 27 *Perf. 14x13½*
1584 A921 5.50s multicolored 1.10 .90

Christmas.

Veit Koniger, Sculptor, Death Bicent. — A922

Photo. & Engr.

1992, Nov. 27 *Perf. 14*
1585 A922 5s multicolored 1.00 .80

Herman Potocnik, Theoretician of Geosynchronous Satellite Orbit, Birth Cent. — A923

1992, Nov. 27 **Photo.**
1586 A923 10s multicolored 2.00 1.65

Famous Buildings A924

Designs: 5s, Statues and dome of Imperial Palace, Vienna, designed by Joseph Emanuel Fischer von Erlach. 5.50s, Kinsky Palace, designed by Lukas von Hildebrandt. 7s, Vienna State Opera, designed by Eduard van der Null and August Siccard von Siccardsburg.

1993, Jan. 22 **Photo. & Engr.**
1587 A924 5s multicolored 1.00 .80
1588 A924 5.50s multicolored 1.10 .90
1589 A924 7s multicolored 1.40 1.10
Nos. 1587-1589 (3) 3.50 2.80

Joseph Emanuel Fischer von Erlach, 300th birth anniv. (#1587). Johann Lukas von Hildebrandt, 325th birth anniv. (#1588). Eduard van der Null, August Siccard von Siccardsburg, 125th death anniv. (#1589).

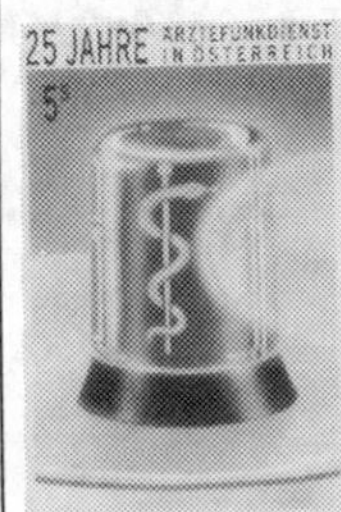

Radio Dispatched Medical Service, 25th Anniv. — A925

1993, Feb. 19 **Photo.**
1590 A925 5s multicolored 1.00 .80

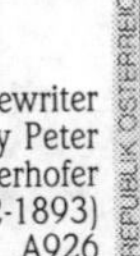

Typewriter Made by Peter Mitterhofer (1822-1893) A926

1993, Feb. 19 *Perf. 13½x14*
1591 A926 17s multicolored 3.50 2.75

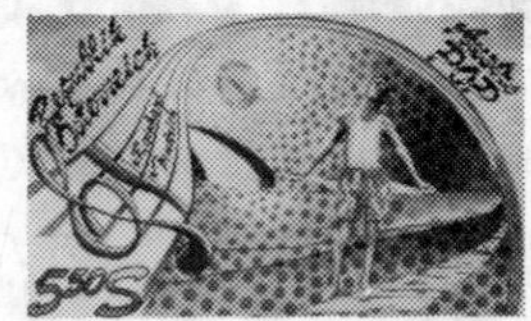

Popular Entertainers — A927

Design: 5.50s, Strada del Sole, by Rainhard Fendrich.

1993, Mar. 19 **Photo.** *Perf. 14*
1592 A927 5.50s multicolored 1.00 .80

See Nos. 1626, 1639.

Charles Sealsfield (1793-1864), Writer A928

Photo. & Engr.

1993, Mar. 19 *Perf. 13½x14*
1593 A928 10s multicolored 1.75 1.40

Rights of the Child — A930

1993, Apr. 16 **Photo.** *Perf. 13½x14*
1595 A930 7s multicolored 1.25 1.00

Flying Harlequin, by Paul Flora — A931

1993, Apr. 16 **Photo. & Engr.**
1596 A931 7s multicolored 1.25 1.00

Europa.

Monastery of Admont — A932

Designs: 1s, Detail of abbesse's crosier, St. Gabriel Abbey, Styria. 5.50s, Death, wooden statue by Josef Stammel (1695-1765). 6s, Stained glass, Mariastern-Gwiggen Monastery. 7s, Marble lion, Franciscan Monastery, Salzburg. 8s, Gothic entry, Wilhering Monastery, Upper Austria. 7.50s, Cupola fresco, by Paul Troger, Monastery of Altenburg. 10s, Altarpiece, St. Peregrinus praying, Maria Luggau Monastery. 20s, Crosier, Fiecht Monastery. 26s, Sculpture of Mater Dolorosa, Franciscan Monastery, Schwaz, Tirol. 30s, Madonna of Scottish Order, Schottenstift Monastery, Vienna.

Perf. 14x13½, 13½x14 (8s, 26s), 14 (1s, 30s)

1993-95 **Photo. & Engr.**
1599 A932 1s multicolored .20 .16
1603 A932 5.50s green, black & yel 1.00 .80

Perf. 14

1606 A932 6s multicolored 1.10 .85
1606A A932 7s gray, blk & yel 1.25 1.00
1607 A932 7.50s brown, blk & bl 1.25 1.00
1608 A932 8s multicolored 1.60 1.25
1609 A932 10s multicolored 1.75 1.40
1613 A932 20s multicolored 3.50 1.75
1613A A932 26s multicolored 5.25 4.25
1614 A932 30s multicolored 5.50 4.50
Nos. 1599-1614 (10) 22.40 16.96

Issued: 5.50s, 4/16; 6s, 9/17; 20s, 10/8; 7.50s, 4/4/94; 10s, 8/26/94; 30s, 10/7/94; 7s, 11/18/94; 8s, 9/15/95; 26s, 10/6/95; 1s, 4/28/95.

This is an expanding set. Numbers may change.

Peter Rosegger (1843-1918), Writer — A933

1993, May 5 **Photo.** *Perf. 14x13½*
1617 A933 5.50s green & black 1.00 .80

Lake Constance Steamer Hohentwiel A934

1993, May 5 **Photo.** *Perf. 14*
1618 A934 6s multicolored 1.05 .85

See Germany No. 1786, Switzerland No. 931.

Folk Festivals Type of 1991

Designs: 5s, Corpus Christi Day Procession, Upper Austria. 5.50s, Blockdrawing, Burgenland. 7s, Cracking whip when snow is melting, Salzburg.

Photo. & Engr.

1993, June 11 *Perf. 14*
1619 A892 5s multicolored .90 .70
1620 A892 5.50s multicolored 1.00 .80
1621 A892 7s multicolored 1.25 1.00
Nos. 1619-1621 (3) 3.15 2.50

UN Conference on Human Rights, Vienna — A935

1993, June 11 **Photo.**
1622 A935 10s multicolored 1.75 1.40

Franz Jagerstatter (1907-1943), Resistance Fighter — A936

1993, Aug. 6 **Photo.** *Perf. 14x13½*
1623 A936 5.50s multicolored 1.00 .80

Schafberg Railway, Cent. — A937

1993, Aug. 6 *Perf. 13½x14*
1624 A937 6s multicolored 1.10 .90

Self-portrait with Puppet, by Rudolf Wacker (1893-1939) A938

1993, Aug. 6 **Photo. & Engr.** *Perf. 14*
1625 A938 6s multicolored 1.10 .90

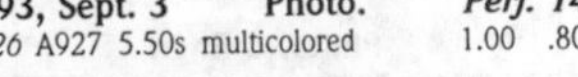

Popular Entertainers Type of 1993

Design: 5.50s, Granny, by Ludwig Hirsch.

1993, Sept. 3 **Photo.** *Perf. 14*
1626 A927 5.50s multicolored 1.00 .80

Vienna Mens' Choral Society, 150th Anniv. A940

1993, Sept. 17 **Photo.** *Perf. 14*
1627 A940 5s multicolored .90 .75

Easter, by Max Weiler A941

99 Heads, by Hundertwasser A942

Photo. & Engr.

1993, Oct. 8 *Perf. 13½x14*
1628 A941 5.50s multicolored 1.00 .80

1993, Oct. 8
1629 A942 7s multicolored 1.25 1.00

Council of Europe Conference, Vienna.

Austrian Republic, 75th Anniv. — A943

Design: 5.50s, Statue of Pallas Athena.

Photo. & Engr.

1993, Nov. 12 ***Perf. 13½x14***

1630 A943 5.50s multicolored 1.00 .80

Trade Unions in Austria, Cent. A944

1993, Nov. 12 **Photo.** ***Perf. 14***

1631 A944 5.50s multicolored 1.00 .80

Birth of Christ, by Master of the Krainburger Altar — A945

Photo. & Engr.

1993, Nov. 26 ***Perf. 13½x14***

1632 A945 5.50s multicolored 1.00 .80

Christmas.

Folklore and Customs Type of 1991

Antiques: 5.50s, Dolls, cradle, Vorarlberg. 6s, Sled, Steiermark. 7s, Godparent's bowl, Upper Austria.

1994, Jan. 28 **Photo. & Engr.** ***Perf. 14***

1633 A892 5.50s multicolored 1.00 .80
1634 A892 6s multicolored 1.10 .90
1635 A892 7s multicolored 1.25 1.00
Nos. 1633-1635 (3) 3.35 2.70

1994 Winter Olympics, Lillehammer, Norway — A946

1994, Feb. 9

1636 A946 7s multicolored 1.25 1.00

Vienna Mint, 800th Anniv. A947

1994, Feb. 18

1637 A947 6s multicolored 1.10 .90

Lying Lady, by Herbert Boeckl (1894-1966) A948

1994, Mar. 18 **Photo.** ***Perf. 14x13½***

1638 A948 5.50s multicolored .95 .70

Popular Entertainers Type of 1993

Design: 6s, Rock Me Amadeus, by Falco.

1994, Mar. 18 ***Perf. 14***

1639 A927 6s multicolored 1.00 .80

Wiener Neustadt, 800th Anniv. — A949

1994, Mar. 18

1640 A949 6s multicolored 1.00 .80

Lake Rudolph, Teleki-Hohnel Expedition — A950

Photo. & Engr.

1994, May 27 ***Perf. 14x13½***

1641 A950 7s multicolored 1.25 1.00

Europa.

Daniel Gran, 300th Birth Anniv. A951

Fresco: 20s, Allegory of Theology, Jurisprudence and Medicine.

1994, May 27

1642 A951 20s multicolored 3.50 2.75

Carinthian Summer Festival, 25th Anniv. — A952

Design: 5.50s, Scene from The Prodigal Son.

Photo. & Engr.

1994, June 17 ***Perf. 14***

1643 A952 5.50s lake & gold .95 .75

Railway Centennials — A953

1994 **Photo. & Engr.** ***Perf. 14***

1647 A953 5.50s Gailtal .95 .75
1648 A953 6s Murtal 1.00 .80

Issued: 5.50s, 6s, 6/17/94.

Hermann Gmeiner, 75th Birth Anniv. — A954

1994, June 17 ***Perf. 14x13½***

1656 A954 7s multicolored 1.25 1.00

Karl Seitz (1869-1950) Politician — A955

Karl Bohm (1894-1981), Conductor — A956

1994, Aug. 12 **Photo.** ***Perf. 14***

1657 A955 5.50s multicolored 1.00 .80

Photo. & Engr.

1994, Aug. 26 ***Perf. 14x13½***

1658 A956 7s gold & dk blue 1.25 1.00

Ethnic Minorities in Austria A957

1994, Sept. 9 **Photo.** ***Perf. 13½***

1659 A957 5.50s multicolored 1.00 .80

Franz Theodor Csokor (1885-1969), Writer — A958

Design: 7s, Joseph Roth (1894-1939), writer.

1994, Sept. 9 ***Perf. 14x13½***

1660 A958 6s multicolored 1.00 .80
1661 A958 7s multicolored 1.25 1.00

Coin Bank — A959 Modern Art — A960

Photo. & Engr.

1994, Oct. 7 ***Perf. 14x13½***

1662 A959 7s multicolored 1.25 1.00

Savings banks in Austria, 175th anniv.

1994, Oct. 7 ***Perf. 13½x14***

Design: 6s, "Head," by Franz Ringel.

1663 A960 6s multicolored 1.10 .90

Austrian Working Environment — A961

1994, Nov. 18 **Photo.** ***Perf. 14***

1664 A961 6s Stewardess, child 1.10 .90

See No. 1690.

Richard Coudenhove Kalergi, Founder of PanEuropean Union, Birth Cent. — A962

Photo. & Engr.

1994, Nov. 18 ***Perf. 13½***

1665 A962 10s multicolored 1.90 1.50

Birth of Christ, by Anton Wollenek A963

1994, Nov. 25 ***Perf. 14***

1666 A963 6s multicolored 1.10 .90

Christmas.

Membership in European Union — A964

1995, Jan. 13 **Photo.** ***Perf. 14***

1667 A964 7s multicolored 1.25 1.00

Adolf Loos (1870-1933), Architect — A965

1995, Jan. 13

1668 A965 10s House, Vienna 1.90 1.50

Official Representation for Workers, 75th Anniv. — A966

1995, Feb. 24 ***Perf. 14x13½***

1669 A966 6s multicolored 1.10 .90

Austrian Gymnastics and Sports Assoc., 50th Anniv. A967

1995, Feb. 24
1670 A967 6s multicolored 1.10 .90

Folklore and Customs Type of 1991

Designs: 5.50s, Belt, Gailtal, Carinthia. 6s, Vineyard watchman's costume, Vienna. 7s, Bonnet, Wachau, Lower Austria.

Photo. & Engr.

1995, Mar. 24 *Perf. 14*
1671 A892 5.50s multicolored 1.10 .90
1672 A892 6s multicolored 1.25 1.00
1673 A892 7s multicolored 1.40 1.10
Nos. 1671-1673 (3) 3.75 3.00

Second Republic, 50th Anniv. — A968

1995, Apr. 27
1674 A968 6s State seal 1.25 1.00

History of Mining & Industry A969

Design: Blast furnaces, old Heft ironworks.

1995, Apr. 28 *Perf. $13^1/_2$x14*
1675 A969 5.50s multicolored 1.10 .90

Carinthian Provincial Exhibition.

Nature Lovers Club, Cent. — A970

1995, Apr. 28 *Perf. 14*
1676 A970 5.50s multicolored 1.10 .90

Europa — A971

1995, May 19 *Perf. 14*
1677 A971 7s multicolored 1.50 1.25

1995 Conference of Ministers of Transportation, Vienna — A972

1995, May 26 **Photo.** *Perf. 14*
1678 A972 7s multicolored 1.40 1.25

Bregenz Festival, 50th Anniv. A973

1995, June 9
1679 A973 6s multicolored 1.25 1.00

St. Gebhard (949-995) — A974

Design: Stained glass window, by Martin Hausle.

1995, June 9
1680 A974 7.50s multicolored 1.50 1.25

UN, 50th Anniv. — A975

1995, June 26 **Photo.** *Perf. 14*
1681 A975 10s multicolored 2.00 2.00

Josef Loschmidt (1821-95), Chemist — A976

Photo. & Engr.

1995, June 26 *Perf. $14x13^1/_2$*
1682 A976 20s multicolored 4.00 4.00

A977

A978

Photo. & Engr.

1995, Aug. 18 *Perf. $13^1/_2$x14*
1683 A977 6s multicolored 1.25 1.00

Salzburg Festival, 75th anniv.

1995, Aug. 18 *Perf. $14x13^1/_2$*
1684 A978 6s buff, black & red 1.25 1.00

Kathe Leichter, resistance member, birth cent.

Europaisches Landschaftsbild, by Adolf Frohner — A979

1995, Aug. 18
1685 A979 6s multicolored 1.25 1.00

Operetta Composers A980

Designs: 6s, Franz von Suppe (1819-95), scene from "The Beautiful Galathea." 7s, Nico Dostal (b. 1895), scene from "The Hungarian Wedding."

1995, Sept. 15 *Perf. 14*
1686 A980 6s multicolored 1.25 1.00
1687 A980 7s multicolored 1.40 1.10

University of Klagenfurt, 25th Anniv. — A981

1995, Oct. 6 **Photo.** *Perf. 14*
1688 A981 5.50s multicolored 1.10 .90

Carinthian Referendum, 75th Anniv. A982

1995, Oct. 6 **Photo. & Engr.**
1689 A982 6s multicolored 1.25 1.00

Austria Working Environment Type of 1994

1995, Oct. 20
1690 A961 6s Post office official 1.25 1.00

Composers — A983

Designs: 6s, Anton von Webern (1883-1945). 7s, Ludwig van Beethoven (1770-1827).

1995, Oct. 20 *Perf. $13^1/_2$x14*
1691 A983 6s orange & blue 1.25 1.00
1692 A983 7s orange & red 1.40 1.10

Christmas — A984

Photo. & Engr.

1995, Dec. 1 *Perf. $13^1/_2$*
1693 A984 6s Christ Child 1.25 1.00

Folklore and Customs Type of 1991

Design: Roller and Scheller in "Procession of Masked Groups in Imst," Tyrol.

1996, Feb. 9 **Photo. & Engr.** *Perf. 14*
1694 A892 6s multicolored 1.25 1.00

Maria Theresa Academy, 250th Anniv. — A985

1996, Feb. 9
1695 A985 6s multicolored 1.25 1.00

1996 World Ski Jumping Championships A986

1996, Feb. 9 **Photo.**
1696 A986 7s multicolored 1.40 1.10

SEMI-POSTAL STAMPS

Issues of the Monarchy

Emperor Franz Josef — SP1

The Firing Step — SP2

Perf. $12^1/_2$

1914, Oct. 4 **Typo.** **Unwmk.**
B1 SP1 5h green .15 .15
B2 SP1 10h rose .15 .15
Set value .20 .15
Set, never hinged .40

Nos. B1-B2 were sold at an advance of 2h each over face value. Exist imperf.; value, set $60.

1915, May 1

Designs: 5h+2h, Cavalry. 10h+2h, Siege gun. 20h+3h, Battleship. 35h+3h, Airplane.

B3 SP2 3h + 1h violet brn .15 .30
B4 SP2 5h + 2h green .15 .15
B5 SP2 10h + 2h deep rose .15 .15
B6 SP2 20h + 3h Prus blue .15 .70
B7 SP2 35h + 3h ultra 1.75 1.10
Nos. B3-B7 (5) 2.35 2.40
Set, never hinged 5.00

Exist imperf. Value, set $110.

Issues of the Republic

Kärnten

Types of Austria, 1919-20, Overprinted in Black

Abstimmung

1920, Sept. 16 — *Perf. 12 1/2*

No.	Type	Description	Unused	Used
B11	A44	5h gray, *yellow*	.25	.55
B12	A44	10h red, *pink*	.45	.85
B13	A43	15h bister, *yel*	.25	.55
B14	A45	20h dark grn, *bl*	.25	.55
B15	A43	25h violet, *pink*	.25	.55
B16	A45	30h brown, *buff*	.55	1.75
B17	A45	40h carmine, *yel*	.35	.75
B18	A45	50h dark bl, *blue*	.35	.75
B19	A43	60h ol grn, *azure*	.95	1.90
B20	A47	80h red	.25	.55
B21	A47	1k orange brown	.30	.60
B22	A47	2k pale blue	.25	.55

Granite Paper

Imperf

No.	Type	Description	Unused	Used
B23	A46	2 1/2k brown red	.30	.70
B24	A46	3k dk blue & green	.30	.70
B25	A46	4k carmine & violet	.45	1.10
B26	A46	5k blue	.60	1.25
B27	A46	7 1/2k yellow green	.60	1.25
B28	A46	10k gray grn & red	.60	1.25
B29	A46	20k lilac & orange	.60	1.25
		Nos. B11-B29 (19)	7.90	17.40
		Set, never hinged	20.00	

Carinthia Plebiscite. Sold at three times face value for the benefit of the Plebiscite Propaganda Fund.

Nos. B11-B19 exist imperf. Value, set $125.

Hochwasser

Types of Regular Issues of 1919-21 Overprinted

1920

1921, Mar. 1 — *Perf. 12 1/2*

No.	Type	Description	Unused	Used
B30	A44	5h gray, *yellow*	.20	.35
B31	A44	10h orange brown	.20	.35
B32	A43	15h gray	.20	.35
B33	A45	20h green, *yellow*	.20	.35
B34	A43	25h blue, *yellow*	.20	.35
B35	A45	30h violet, *bl*	.20	.35
B36	A45	40h org brn, *pink*	.25	.65
B37	A45	50h green, *blue*	.75	2.25
B38	A43	60h lilac, *yellow*	.20	.35
B39	A47	80h pale blue	.20	.35
B40	A47	1k red org, *blue*	.50	1.50
B41	A47	1 1/2k green, *yellow*	.25	.35
B42	A47	2k lilac brown	.25	.35

Hochwasser

Overprinted

1920

No.	Type	Description	Unused	Used
B43	A46	2 1/2k light blue	.25	.35
B44	A46	3k ol grn & brn red	.25	.35
B45	A46	4k lilac & orange	.55	1.75
B46	A46	5k olive green	.30	.85
B47	A46	7 1/2k brown red	.30	.85
B48	A46	10k blue & olive grn	.45	1.25
B49	A46	20k car rose & vio	.80	1.50
		Nos. B30-B49 (20)	6.50	14.80
		Set, never hinged	15.00	

Nos. B30-B49 were sold at three times face value, the excess going to help flood victims. Exists imperf. Value, set $175.

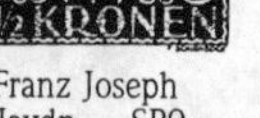

Franz Joseph Haydn — SP9

View of Bregenz — SP16

Musicians: 5k, Mozart. 7 1/2k, Beethoven. 10k, Schubert. 25k, Anton Bruckner. 50k, Johann Strauss (son). 100k, Hugo Wolf.

1922, Apr. 24 — Engr. — *Perf. 12 1/2*

No.	Type	Description	Unused	Used
B50	SP9	2 1/2k brown	5.00	6.00
a.		Perf. 11 1/2	4.25	4.50
B51	SP9	5k dark blue	1.10	1.50
B52	SP9	7 1/2k black	1.25	2.25
a.		Perf. 11 1/2	65.00	110.00
B53	SP9	10k dark violet	1.90	2.50
a.		Perf. 11 1/2	2.00	2.50
B54	SP9	25k dark green	2.50	3.75
a.		Perf. 11 1/2	3.25	4.00
B55	SP9	50k claret	1.75	3.50
B56	SP9	100k brown olive	6.00	7.50
a.		Perf. 11 1/2	6.00	8.75
		Nos. B50-B56 (7)	19.50	27.00
		Set, never hinged	47.50	

These stamps were sold at 10 times face value, the excess being given to needy musicians.

All values exist imperf. on both regular and hand-made papers. Value, set $425.

A 1969 souvenir sheet without postal validity contains reprints of the 5k in black, 7 1/2k in claret and 50k in dark blue, each overprinted "NEUDRUCK" in black at top. It was issued for the Vienna State Opera Centenary Exhibition.

1923, May 22 — *Perf. 12 1/2*

Designs: 120k, Mirabelle Gardens, Salzburg. 160k, Church at Eisenstadt. 180k, Assembly House, Klagenfurt. 200k, "Golden Roof," Innsbruck. 240k, Main Square, Linz. 400k, Castle Hill, Graz. 600k, Abbey at Melk. 1000k, Upper Belvedere, Vienna.

Various Frames

No.	Type	Description	Unused	Used
B57	SP16	100k dk green	2.50	5.00
B58	SP16	120k deep blue	2.50	5.00
B59	SP16	160k dk violet	2.50	5.00
B60	SP16	180k red violet	2.50	5.00
B61	SP16	200k lake	2.50	5.00
B62	SP16	240k red brown	2.50	5.00
B63	SP16	400k dark brown	2.50	5.00
B64	SP16	600k olive brn	2.50	5.00
B65	SP16	1000k black	2.50	5.00
		Nos. B57-B65 (9)	22.50	45.00
		Set, never hinged	52.50	

Nos. B57-B65 were sold at five times face value, the excess going to needy artists.

All values exist imperf. on both regular and hand-made papers. Value, set $350.

Feebleness SP25

Siegfried Slays the Dragon SP30

Designs: 300k+900k, Aid to industry. 500k+1500k, Orphans and widow. 600k+1800k, Indigent old man. 1000k+3000k, Alleviation of hunger.

1924, Sept. 6 — Photo.

No.	Type	Description	Unused	Used
B66	SP25	100k + 300k yel green	3.25	3.25
B67	SP25	300k + 900k red brn	4.50	9.00
B68	SP25	500k + 1500k brn vio	4.50	9.00
B69	SP25	600k + 1800k pck bl	4.50	9.00
B70	SP25	1000k + 3000k brn org	7.50	12.50
		Nos. B66-B70 (5)	24.25	42.75
		Set, never hinged	52.50	

The surtax was for child welfare and anti-tuberculosis work. Set exists imperf. Value, $300.

1926, Mar. 8 — Engr.

Designs: 8g+2g, Gunther's voyage to Iceland. 15g+5g, Brunhild accusing Kriemhild. 20g+5g, Nymphs telling Hagen the future. 24g+6g, Rudiger von Bechelaren welcomes the Nibelungen. 40g+10g, Dietrich von Bern vanquishes Hagen.

No.	Type	Description	Unused	Used
B71	SP30	3g + 2g olive blk	1.00	.35
B72	SP30	8g + 2g indigo	.25	.35
B73	SP30	15g + 5g dk claret	.25	.35
B74	SP30	20g + 5g olive grn	.40	.75
B75	SP30	24g + 6g dk violet	.40	.75
B76	SP30	40g + 10g red brn	3.00	2.75
		Nos. B71-B76 (6)	5.30	5.30
		Set, never hinged	12.50	

Nibelungen issue.

The surtax was for child welfare. Set exists imperf. Value, $225.

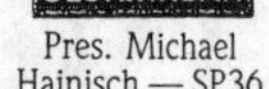

Pres. Michael Hainisch — SP36

Pres. Wilhelm Miklas — SP37

1928, Nov. 5

No.	Type	Description	Unused	Used
B77	SP36	10g dark brown	5.00	9.00
B78	SP36	15g red brown	5.00	9.00
B79	SP36	30g black	5.00	9.00
B80	SP36	40g indigo	5.00	9.00
		Nos. B77-B80 (4)	20.00	36.00
		Set, never hinged	35.00	

Tenth anniversary of Austrian Republic. Sold at double face value, the premium aiding war orphans and children of war invalids.

Set exists imperf. Value $300.

1930, Oct. 4

No.	Type	Description	Unused	Used
B81	SP37	10g light brown	7.50	12.50
B82	SP37	20g red	7.50	12.50
B83	SP37	30g brown violet	7.50	12.50
B84	SP37	40g indigo	7.50	12.50
B85	SP37	50g dark green	7.50	12.50
B86	SP37	1s black brown	7.50	12.50
		Nos. B81-B86 (6)	45.00	75.00
		Set, never hinged	85.00	

Nos. B81-B86 were sold at double face value. The excess aided the anti-tuberculosis campaign and the building of sanatoria in Carinthia.

Set exists imperf. Value, $325.

Regular Issue of 1929-30 Overprinted in Various Colors

1931, June 20

No.	Type	Description	Unused	Used
B87	A56	10g bister (Bl)	30.00	35.00
B88	A56	20g dk gray (R)	30.00	35.00
B89	A56	30g dk violet (Gl)	30.00	35.00
B90	A56	40g dk blue (Gl)	30.00	35.00
B91	A56	50g gray vio (O)	30.00	35.00
B92	A57	1s black brn (Bk)	30.00	35.00
		Nos. B87-B92 (6)	180.00	210.00
		Set, never hinged	350.00	

Rotary convention, Vienna.

Nos. B87 to B92 were sold at double their face values. The excess was added to the beneficent funds of Rotary International.

Exists imperf.

Ferdinand Raimund — SP38

Poets: 20g, Franz Grillparzer. 30g, Johann Nestroy. 40g, Adalbert Stifter. 50g, Ludwig Anzengruber. 1s, Peter Rosegger.

1931, Sept. 12

No.	Type	Description	Unused	Used
B93	SP38	10g dark violet	12.00	17.50
B94	SP38	20g gray black	12.00	17.50
B95	SP38	30g orange red	12.00	17.50
B96	SP38	40g dull blue	12.00	17.50
B97	SP38	50g gray green	12.00	17.50
B98	SP38	1s yellow brown	12.00	17.50
		Nos. B93-B98 (6)	72.00	105.00
		Set, never hinged	130.00	

Nos. B93-B98 were sold at double face value. The surtax aided unemployed young people.

Set exists imperf. Value, $500.

Chancellor Ignaz Seipel SP44

Ferdinand Georg Waldmüller SP45

1932, Oct. 12 — *Perf. 13*

No.	Type	Description	Unused	Used
B99	SP44	50g ultra	10.00	17.50
		Never hinged	18.00	

Msgr. Ignaz Seipel, Chancellor of Austria, 1922-29. Sold at double face value, the excess aiding wounded veterans of World War I.

Exists imperf. Value, $150.

1932, Nov. 21

Artists: 24g, Moritz von Schwind. 30g, Rudolf von Alt. 40g, Hans Makart. 64g, Gustav Klimt. 1s, Albin Egger-Lienz.

No.	Type	Description	Unused	Used
B100	SP45	12g slate green	17.50	30.00
B101	SP45	24g dp violet	17.50	30.00
B102	SP45	30g dark red	17.50	30.00
B103	SP45	40g dark gray	17.50	30.00
B104	SP45	64g dark brown	17.50	30.00
B105	SP45	1s claret	17.50	30.00
		Nos. B100-B105 (6)	105.00	180.00
		Set, never hinged	180.00	

Nos. B100 to B105 were sold at double their face values. The surtax was for the assistance of charitable institutions.

Set exists imperf. Value, $600.

Mountain Climbing SP51

Designs: 24g, Ski gliding. 30g, Walking on skis. 50g, Ski jumping.

1933, Jan. 9 — Photo. — *Perf. 12 1/2*

No.	Type	Description	Unused	Used
B106	SP51	12g dark green	6.50	12.50
B107	SP51	24g dark violet	55.00	85.00
B108	SP51	30g brown red	12.50	17.50
B109	SP51	50g dark blue	55.00	85.00
		Nos. B106-B109 (4)	129.00	200.00
		Set, never hinged	325.00	

Meeting of the Intl. Ski Federation, Innsbruck, Feb. 8-13.

These stamps were sold at double their face value. The surtax was for the benefit of "Youth in Distress."

#B106-B109 exist imperf. Value $1,500.

Stagecoach, after Painting by Moritz von Schwind SP55

1933, June 23 — Engr. — *Perf. 12 1/2*

Ordinary Paper

No.	Type	Description	Unused	Used
B110	SP55	50g deep ultra	150.00	190.00
		Never hinged	225.00	
a.		Granite paper	275.00	350.00
a.		Never hinged	425.00	

Sheets of 25.

Nos. B110 and B110a exist imperf. Values $750 and $1,500.

Souvenir Sheet

Perf. 12

Granite Paper

No.	Type	Description	Unused	Used
B111		Sheet of 4	2,000.	2,750.
		Never hinged	2,500.	
a.		SP55 50g deep ultra	350.	550.
a.		Never hinged	525.	

Intl. Phil. Exhib., Vienna, 1933. In addition to the postal value of 50g the stamp was sold at a premium of 50g for charity and of 1.60s for the admission fee to the exhibition.

Size of No. B111: 126x103mm.

A 50g dark red in souvenir sheet, with dark blue overprint ("NEUDRUCK WIPA 1965"), had no postal validity.

Even though the margins No. B111 have no gum, the sheet sells for a premium when definitely never hinged.

St. Stephen's Cathedral in 1683 — SP56

Marco d'Aviano, Papal Legate — SP57

Designs: 30g, Count Ernst Rudiger von Starhemberg. 40g, John III Sobieski, King of Poland. 50g, Karl V, Duke of Lorraine. 64g, Burgomaster Johann Andreas von Liebenberg.

1933, Sept. 6 — Photo. — *Perf. 12 1/2*

No.	Type	Description	Unused	Used
B112	SP56	12g dark green	20.00	25.00
B113	SP57	24g dark violet	19.00	22.50
B114	SP57	30g brown red	19.00	22.50
B115	SP57	40g blue black	22.50	37.50

B116 SP57 50g dark blue 19.00 22.50
B117 SP57 64g olive brown 22.50 35.00
Nos. B112-B117 (6) 122.00 165.00
Set, never hinged 240.00

Deliverance of Vienna from the Turks, 250th anniv., and Pan-German Catholic Congress, Sept. 6, 1933.

The stamps were sold at double their face value, the excess being for the aid of Catholic works of charity.

Set exists imperf. Value, $750.

Types of Regular Issue of 1925-30 Surcharged:

+2g Winterhilfe a

WINTERHILFE +6g b

+50g WINTERHILFE c

1933, Dec. 15

B118 A52(a) 5g + 2g olive grn .30 .65
B119 A56(b) 12g + 3g lt blue .30 .70
B120 A56(b) 24g + 6g brn orange .30 .65
B121 A57(c) 1s + 50g orange red 27.50 40.00
Nos. B118-B121 (4) 28.40 42.00
Set, never hinged 50.00

Winterhelp. Exists imperf. Value, set $175.

Anton Pilgram — SP62

Architects: 24g, J. B. Fischer von Erlach. 30g, Jakob Prandtauer. 40g, A. von Siccardsburg & E. van der Null. 60g, Heinrich von Ferstel. 64g, Otto Wagner.

1934, Dec. 2 Engr. *Perf. 12½*
Thick Yellowish Paper

B122 SP62 12g black 9.00 15.00
B123 SP62 24g dull violet 9.00 15.00
B124 SP62 30g carmine 9.00 15.00
B125 SP62 40g brown 9.00 15.00
B126 SP62 60g blue 9.00 15.00
B127 SP62 64g dull green 9.00 15.00
Nos. B122-B127 (6) 54.00 90.00
Set, never hinged 100.00

Exist imperf. Value, set $500.

Nos. B124-B127 exist in horiz. pairs imperf. between. Value, $175 to $225.

These stamps were sold at double their face value. The surtax on this and the following issues was devoted to general charity.

Types of Regular Issue of 1934 Surcharged in Black:

Winterhilfe +2g a

+50g WINTERHILFE b

1935, Nov. 11 *Perf. 12, 12½*

B128 A67(a) 5g + 2g emerald .45 1.00
B129 A67(a) 12g + 3g blue .75 1.00
B130 A67(a) 24g + 6g lt brown .45 1.00
B131 A68(b) 1s + 50g ver 19.00 35.00
Nos. B128-B131 (4) 20.65 38.00
Set, never hinged 47.50

Winterhelp. Set exists imperf. Value, $140.

Prince Eugene of Savoy — SP68

Slalom Turn — SP74

Military Leaders: 24g, Field Marshal Laudon. 30g, Archduke Karl. 40g, Field Marshal Josef Radetzky. 60g, Admiral Wilhelm Tegetthoff. 64g, Field Marshal Franz Conrad Hotzendorff.

1935, Dec. 1 *Perf. 12½*

B132 SP68 12g brown 9.00 14.00
B133 SP68 24g dark green 9.00 14.00
B134 SP68 30g claret 9.00 14.00
B135 SP68 40g slate 9.00 14.00
B136 SP68 60g deep ultra 9.00 14.00
B137 SP68 64g dark violet 9.00 14.00
Nos. B132-B137 (6) 54.00 84.00
Set, never hinged 100.00

These stamps were sold at double their face value. Set exists imperf. Value, $500.

1936, Feb. 20 Photo.

Designs: 24g, Jumper taking off. 35g, Slalom turn. 60g, Innsbruck view.

B138 SP74 12g Prus green 2.50 3.00
B139 SP74 24g dp violet 4.50 4.50
B140 SP74 35g rose car 22.50 32.50
B141 SP74 60g sapphire 22.50 35.00
Nos. B138-B141 (4) 52.00 75.00
Set, never hinged 100.00

Ski concourse issue. These stamps were sold at twice face value. Set exists imperf. Value, $475.

St. Martin of Tours — SP78

Designs: 12g+3g, Medical clinic. 24g+6g, St. Elizabeth of Hungary. 1s+1s, "Flame of Charity."

1936, Nov. 2 Unwmk.

B142 SP78 5g + 2g dp green .25 .40
B143 SP78 12g + 3g dp violet .25 .40
B144 SP78 24g + 6g dp blue .25 .40
B145 SP78 1s + 1s dk carmine 5.50 10.00
Nos. B142-B145 (4) 6.25 11.20
Set, never hinged 12.00

Winterhelp. Set exists imperf. Value, $175.

Josef Ressel — SP82

Nurse and Infant — SP88

Inventors: 24g, Karl von Ghega. 30g, Josef Werndl. 40g, Carl Auer von Welsbach. 60g, Robert von Lieben. 64g, Viktor Kaplan.

1936, Dec. 6 Engr.

B146 SP82 12g dk brown 2.00 5.00
B147 SP82 24g dk violet 2.00 5.00
B148 SP82 30g dp claret 2.00 5.00
B149 SP82 40g gray violet 2.00 5.00
B150 SP82 60g vio blue 2.00 5.00
B151 SP82 64g dk slate green 2.00 5.00
Nos. B146-B151 (6) 12.00 30.00
Set, never hinged 25.00

These stamps were sold at double their face value. Exists imperf. Value, set $325.

1937, Oct. 18 Photo.

Designs: 12g+3g, Mother and child. 24g+6g, Nursing the aged. 1s+1s, Sister of Mercy with patient.

B152 SP88 5g + 2g dk green .20 .25
B153 SP88 12g + 3g dk brown .20 .25
B154 SP88 24g + 6g dk blue .20 .25
B155 SP88 1s + 1s dk carmine 3.00 6.00
Nos. B152-B155 (4) 3.60 6.75
Set, never hinged 7.50

Winterhelp. Set exists imperf. Value, $85.

Gerhard van Swieten — SP92

The Dawn of Peace — SP101

Physicians: 8g, Leopold Auenbrugger von Auenbrugg. 12g, Karl von Rokitansky. 20g, Joseph Skoda. 24g, Ferdinand von Hebra. 30g, Ferdinand von Arlt. 40g, Joseph Hyrtl. 60g, Theodor Billroth. 64g, Theodor Meynert.

1937, Dec. 5 Engr. *Perf. 12½*

B156 SP92 5g choc 1.75 4.00
B157 SP92 8g dk red 1.75 4.00
B158 SP92 12g brown blk 1.75 4.00
B159 SP92 20g dk green 1.75 4.00
B160 SP92 24g dk violet 1.75 4.00
B161 SP92 30g brown car 1.75 4.00
B162 SP92 40g dp olive grn 1.75 4.00
B163 SP92 60g indigo 1.75 4.00
B164 SP92 64g brown vio 1.75 4.00
Nos. B156-B164 (9) 15.75 36.00
Set, never hinged 30.00

These stamps were sold at double their face value. Set exists imperf. Value, $450.

Catalogue values for unused stamps in this section, from this point to the end of the section, are for Never Hinged items.

1945, Sept. 10 Photo. *Perf. 14*

B165 SP101 1s + 10s dk green .80 1.40

No. 467 Surcharged in Black

1946, June 25

B166 A110 30g + 20g dk red 3.00 5.00

First anniversary of United Nations.

Pres. Karl Renner SP102

1946 Engr. *Perf. 13½x14*

B167 SP102 1s + 1s dk slate grn 2.00 4.00
B168 SP102 2s + 2s dk blue vio 2.00 4.00
B169 SP102 3s + 3s dk purple 2.00 4.00
B170 SP102 5s + 5s dk violet brn 2.00 4.00
Nos. B167-B170 (4) 8.00 16.00

See Nos. B185-B188.

Nazi Sword Piercing Austria — SP103

Sweeping Away Fascist Symbols — SP104

Designs: 8g+6g, St. Stephen's Cathedral in Flames. 12g+12g, Pleading hand in concentration camp. 30g+30g, Hand choking Nazi serpent. 42g+42g, Hammer breaking Nazi pillar. 1s+1s, Oath of allegiance. 2s+2s, Austrian eagle and burning swastika.

Unwmk.

1946, Sept. 16 Photo. *Perf. 14*

B171 SP103 5g + (3g) dk brown .45 .65
B172 SP104 6g + (4g) dk slate grn .30 .55
B173 SP104 8g + (6g) orange red .30 .55
B174 SP104 12g + (12g) slate blk .30 .55
B175 SP104 30g + (30g) violet .30 .55
B176 SP104 42g + (42g) dull brn .30 .55
B177 SP104 1s + 1s dk red .45 .65
B178 SP104 2s + 2s dk car rose .60 .65
Nos. B171-B178 (8) 3.00 4.70

Anti-fascist propaganda.

Race Horse with Foal — SP111

Various Race Horses.

1946, Oct. 20 Engr. *Perf. 13½x14*

B179 SP111 16g + 16g rose brown 2.00 3.00
B180 SP111 24g + 24g dk purple 2.00 3.00
B181 SP111 60g + 60g dk green 2.00 3.00
B182 SP111 1s + 1s dk blue gray 2.00 3.00
B183 SP111 2s + 2s yel brown 2.00 3.00
Nos. B179-B183 (5) 10.00 15.00

Austria Prize race, Vienna.

St. Ruprecht's Church, Vienna — SP116

1946, Oct. 30 *Perf. 14x13½*

B184 SP116 30g + 70g dark red .35 .70

Founding of Austria, 950th anniv. The surtax aided the Stamp Day celebration.

Renner Type of 1946
Souvenir Sheets

1946, Sept. 5 *Imperf.*

B185 Sheet of 8 500.00 *900.00*
a. SP102 1s+1s dk slate grn 55.00 *100.00*
B186 Sheet of 8 500.00 *900.00*
a. SP102 2s+2s dk blue vio 55.00 *100.00*
B187 Sheet of 8 500.00 *900.00*
a. SP102 3s+3s dark purple 55.00 *100.00*
B188 Sheet of 8 500.00 *900.00*
a. SP102 5s+5s dk vio brown 55.00 *100.00*

1st anniv. of Austria's liberation. Sheets of 8 plus center label showing arms.

Statue of Rudolf IV the Founder — SP118

Reaping Wheat — SP128

Designs: 5g+20g, Tomb of Frederick III. 6g+24g, Main pulpit. 8g+32g, Statue of St. Stephen. 10g+40g, Madonna of the Domestics statue. 12g+48g, High altar. 30g+1.20s, Organ, destroyed in 1945. 50g+1.80s, Anton Pilgram statue. 1s+5s, Cathedral from northeast. 2s+10s, Southwest corner of cathedral.

1946, Dec. 12 Engr. *Perf. 14x13½*

B189 SP118 3g + 12g brown .25 .50
B190 SP118 5g + 20g dk vio brown .25 .50
B191 SP118 6g + 24g dk blue .25 .50
B192 SP118 8g + 32g dk green .25 .50
B193 SP118 10g + 40g dp blue .40 .75
B194 SP118 12g + 48g dk vio .45 .80
B195 SP118 30g + 1.20s car 1.10 1.90
B196 SP118 50g + 1.80s dk bl 1.25 2.00

B197 SP118 1s + 5s brn vio 1.75 3.25
B198 SP118 2s + 10s vio brn 3.50 7.50
Nos. B189-B198 (10) 9.45 18.20

The surtax aided reconstruction of St. Stephen's Cathedral, Vienna.

1947, Mar. 23 *Perf. 14x13½*

Designs: 8g+2g, Log raft. 10g+5g, Cement factory. 12g+8g, Coal mine. 18g+12g, Oil derricks. 30g+10g, Textile machinery. 35g+15g, Iron furnace. 60g+20g, Electric power lines.

B199 SP128 3g + 2g yel brown .40 .50
B200 SP128 8g + 2g dk bl grn .40 .50
B201 SP128 10g + 5g slate blk .40 .50
B202 SP128 12g + 8g dark pur .40 .50
B203 SP128 18g + 12g ol green .40 .50
B204 SP128 30g + 10g deep cl .40 .50
B205 SP128 35g + 15g crimson .40 .50
B206 SP128 60g + 20g dk blue .40 .50
Nos. B199-B206 (8) 3.20 4.00

Vienna International Sample Fair, 1947.

Race Horse and Jockey SP136

1947, June 29 *Perf. 13½x14*

B207 SP136 60g + 20g deep blue, *pale pink* .15 .20

Cup of Corvinus — SP137

Prisoner of War — SP147

Designs: 8g+2g, Statue of Providence, Vienna. 10g+5g, Abbey at Melk. 12g+8g, Picture of a Woman, by Kriehuber. 18g+12g, Children at the Window, by Waldmuller. 20g+10g, Entrance, Upper Belvedere Palace. 30g+10g, Nymph Egeria, Schönbrunn Castle. 35g+15g, National Library, Vienna. 48g+12g, "Workshop of a Printer of Engravings," by Schmutzer. 60g+20g, Girl with Straw Hat, by Amerling.

1947, June 20 *Perf. 14x13½*

B208 SP137 3g + 2g brown .30 .40
B209 SP137 8g + 2g dk blue grn .30 .40
B210 SP137 10g + 5g dp claret .30 .40
B211 SP137 12g + 8g dk purple .30 .40
B212 SP137 18g + 12g golden brn .30 .40
B213 SP137 20g + 10g sepia .30 .40
B214 SP137 30g + 10g dk yel grn .30 .40
B215 SP137 35g + 15g deep car .30 .40
B216 SP137 48g + 12g dk brn vio .30 .40
B217 SP137 60g + 20g dp blue .30 .40
Nos. B208-B217 (10) 3.00 4.00

1947, Aug. 30

Designs: 12g+8g, Prisoners' Mail, 18g+12g, Prison camp visitor. 35g+15g, Family reunion. 60g+20g, "Industry" beckoning. 1s+40g, Sower.

B218 SP147 8g + 2g dk green .20 .30
B219 SP147 12g + 8g dk vio brn .20 .30
B220 SP147 18g + 12g black brn .20 .30
B221 SP147 35g + 15g rose brn .20 .30
B222 SP147 60g + 20g dp blue .20 .30
B223 SP147 1s + 40g redsh brn .20 .30
Nos. B218-B223 (6) 1.20 1.80

Olympic Flame and Emblem SP153

Laabenbach Bridge Neulengbach SP154

1948, Jan. 16 **Engr.**

B224 SP153 1s + 50g dark blue .35 .35

The surtax was used to help defray expenses of Austria's 1948 Olympics team.

1948, Feb. 18 *Perf. 14x13½*

Designs: 20g+10g, Dam, Vermunt Lake. 30g+10g, Danube Port, Vienna. 40g+20g, Mining, Erzberg. 45g+20g, Tracks, Southern Railway Station, Vienna. 60g+30g, Communal housing project, Vienna. 75g+35g, Gas Works, Vienna. 80g+40g, Oil refinery. 1s+50g, Gesäuse Highway, Styria. 1.40s+70g, Parliament Building, Vienna.

B225 SP154 10g + 5g slate blk .20 .20
B226 SP154 20g + 10g lilac .20 .20
B227 SP154 30g + 10g dull grn .50 .50
B228 SP154 40g + 20g ol brn .20 .20
B229 SP154 45g + 20g dk blue .20 .20
B230 SP154 60g + 30g dk red .20 .20
B231 SP154 75g + 35g dk vio brn .15 .15
B232 SP154 80g + 40g vio brn .20 .20
B233 SP154 1s + 50g dp blue .20 .20
B234 SP154 1.40s + 70g dp car .50 .50
Set value 1.60 1.55

The surtax was for the Reconstruction Fund.

Violet — SP155

Designs: 20g+10g, Anemone. 30g+10g, Crocus. 40g+20g, Yellow primrose. 45g+20g, Pasqueflower. 60g+30g, Rhododendron. 75g+35g, Dog-rose. 80g+40g, Cyclamen. 1s+50g, Alpine Gentian. 1.40s+70g, Edelweiss.

1948, May 14 **Engr. & Typo.**

B235 SP155 10g + 5g multi .35 .25
B236 SP155 20g + 10g multi .15 .20
B237 SP155 30g + 10g multi 2.50 2.00
B238 SP155 40g + 20g multi .50 .25
B239 SP155 45g + 20g multi .15 .20
B240 SP155 60g + 30g multi .15 .20
B241 SP155 75g + 35g multi .15 .20
B242 SP155 80g + 40g multi .30 .20
B243 SP155 1s + 50g multi .40 .30
B244 SP155 1.40s + 70g multi .65 .55
Nos. B235-B244 (10) 5.30 4.35

Hans Makart — SP156

St. Rupert — SP157

Designs: 20g+10g, Künstlerhaus, Vienna. 40g+20g, Carl Kundmann. 50g+25g, A. S. von Siccardsburg. 60g+30g, Hans Cannon. 1s+50g, William Unger. 1.40s+70g, Friedrich von Schmidt.

1948, June 15 **Unwmk.** **Engr.**

B245 SP156 20g + 10g dp yel green 6.25 5.00
B246 SP156 30g + 15g dark brown 3.00 1.90
B247 SP156 40g + 20g indigo 3.00 1.90
B248 SP156 50g + 25g dk vio 3.50 2.75
B249 SP156 60g + 30g dk red 3.50 2.75
B250 SP156 1s + 50g dk blue 6.25 5.00
B251 SP156 1.40s + 70g red brown 8.50 7.50
Nos. B245-B251 (7) 34.00 26.80

Kunstlerhaus, home of the leading Austrian Artists Association, 80th anniv.

1948, Aug. 6 *Perf. 14x13½*

Designs: 30g+15g, Cathedral and Fountain. 40g+20g, Facade of Cathedral. 50g+25g, Cathedral from South. 60g+30g, Abbey of St. Peter. 80g+40g, Inside Cathedral. 1s+50g, Salzburg Cathedral and Castle. 1.40s+70g, Madonna by Michael Pacher.

B252 SP157 20g + 10g dp grn 6.00 5.50
B253 SP157 30g + 15g red brn 2.50 2.50
B254 SP157 40g + 20g sl blk 1.90 1.75
B255 SP157 50g + 25g choc .40 .40
B256 SP157 60g + 30g dk red .40 .40
B257 SP157 80g + 40g dk brn vio .40 .40
B258 SP157 1s + 50g dp blue .75 .50
B259 SP157 1.40s + 70g dk grn 1.50 1.25
Nos. B252-B259 (8) 13.85 12.70

The surtax was to aid in the reconstruction of Salzburg Cathedral.

Easter — SP158

Arms of Austria, 1230 — SP159

Designs: 60g+20g, St. Nicholas Day. 1s+25g, Birthday. 1.40s+35g, Christmas.

1949, Apr. 13 **Unwmk.**

Inscribed: "Gluckliche Kindheit"

B260 SP158 40g + 10g brn vio 17.00 12.50
B261 SP158 60g + 20g brn red 17.00 12.50
B262 SP158 1s + 25g dp ultra 17.00 12.50
B263 SP158 1.40s + 35g dk grn 17.00 12.50
Nos. B260-B263 (4) 68.00 50.00

The surtax was for Child Welfare.

1949, Aug. 17 **Engr. & Photo.**

B264 SP159 40g + 10g 1230 7.00 6.00

Engraved and Typographed

B265 SP159 60g + 15g 1450 7.00 6.00
B266 SP159 1s + 25g 1600 7.00 6.00
B267 SP159 1.60s + 40g 1945 7.00 6.00
Nos. B264-B267 (4) 28.00 24.00

Surtax was for returned prisoners of war.

Laurel Branch, Stamps and Magnifier — SP160

1949, Dec. 3 **Engr.**

B268 SP160 60g + 15g dk red 2.25 1.50

Stamp Day, Dec. 3-4.

Arms of Austria and Carinthia — SP161

Carinthian with Austrian Flag — SP162

Design: 1.70s+40g, Casting ballot.

1950, Oct. 10 **Photo.** *Perf. 14x13½*

B269 SP161 60g + 15g 26.00 18.00
B270 SP162 1s + 25g 35.00 20.00
B271 SP162 1.70s + 40g 40.00 29.00
Nos. B269-B271 (3) 101.00 67.00

Plebiscite in Carinthia, 30th anniv.

Collector Examining Cover — SP163

Miner and Mine — SP164

1950, Dec. 2 **Engr.**

B272 SP163 60g + 15g blue grn 9.00 6.00

Stamp Day.

1951, Mar. 10 **Unwmk.**

Designs: 60g+15g, Mason holding brick and trowel. 1s+25g, Bridge builder with hook and chain. 1.70s+40g, Electrician, pole and insulators.

B273 SP164 40g + 10g dark brown 13.00 11.00
B274 SP164 60g + 15g dk grn 13.00 11.00
B275 SP164 1s + 25g red brown 13.00 11.00
B276 SP164 1.70s + 40g vio bl 13.00 11.00
Nos. B273-B276 (4) 52.00 44.00

Issued to publicize Austrian reconstruction.

Laurel Branch and Olympic Circles SP165

1952, Jan. 26 *Perf. 13½x14*

B277 SP165 2.40s + 60g grnsh black 16.00 14.00

The surtax was used to help defray expenses of Austria's athletes in the 1952 Olympic Games.

Cupid as Postman — SP166

1952, Mar. 10 *Perf. 14x13½*

B278 SP166 1.50s + 35g dark brn car 17.50 16.00

Stamp Day.

Sculpture, "Christ, The Almighty" SP167

1952, Sept. 6 *Perf. 13½x14*

B279 SP167 1s + 25g grnsh gray 11.00 9.00

Austrian Catholic Conv., Vienna, Sept. 11-14.

Type of 1945-46 Overprinted in Gold

1953, Aug. 29 **Unwmk.**

B280 A124 1s + 25g on 5s dl bl 2.50 2.00

60th anniv. of labor unions in Austria.

Bummerlhaus Steyr SP168

Globe and Philatelic Accessories SP169

Designs: 1s+25g, Johannes Kepler. 1.50s+40g, Lutheran Bible, 1st edition. 2.40s+60g, Theophil von Hansen. 3s+75g, Reconstructed Lutheran School, Vienna.

1953, Nov. 5 Engr. *Perf. 14x13½*

B281 SP168 70g + 15g vio brn .30 .30
B282 SP168 1s + 25g dk gray blue .30 .30
B283 SP168 1.50s + 40g choc .90 .90
B284 SP168 2.40s + 60g dk grn 2.75 2.25
B285 SP168 3s + 75g dk pur 6.25 5.75
Nos. B281-B285 (5) 10.50 9.50

The surtax was used toward reconstruction of the Lutheran School, Vienna.

1953, Dec. 5

B286 SP169 1s + 25g choc 5.00 3.75

Stamp Day.

Type of 1945-46 with Denomination Replaced by Asterisks

Overprinted in Brown

LAWINENOPFER
1954

1s + 20g

1954, Feb. 19 *Perf. 13½x14*

B287 A124 1s + 20g blue gray .15 .15

Surtax for aid to avalanche victims.

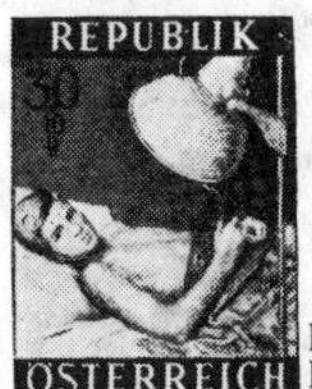

Patient Under Sun Lamp — SP170

Designs: 70g+15g, Physician using microscope. 1s+25g, Mother and children. 1.45s+35g, Operating room. 1.50s+35g, Baby on scale. 2.40s+60g, Nurse.

1954 Engr. *Perf. 14x13½*

B288 SP170 30g + 10g purple 1.50 1.10
B289 SP170 70g + 15g dk brn .25 .20
B290 SP170 1s + 25g dk bl .30 .25
B291 SP170 1.45s + 35g dk bl green .40 .35
B292 SP170 1.50s + 35g dk red 5.00 4.50
B293 SP170 2.40s + 60g dk red brown 6.00 5.50
Nos. B288-B293 (6) 13.45 11.90

The surtax was for social welfare.

Early Vienna-Ulm Ferryboat SP171

1954, Dec. 4 *Perf. 13½x14*

B294 SP171 1s + 25g dk gray grn 4.25 4.00

Stamp Day.

"Industry" Welcoming Returned Prisoner of War — SP172

1955, June 29

B295 SP172 1s + 25g red brn 2.00 1.50

Surtax for returned prisoners of war and relatives of prisoners not yet released.

Collector Looking at Album — SP173

Ornamental Shield and Letter — SP174

1955, Dec. 3 *Perf. 14x13½*

B296 SP173 1s + 25g vio brn 3.00 2.75

Stamp Day. The surtax was for the promotion of Austrian philately.

1956, Dec. 1 Engr.

B297 SP174 1s + 25g scarlet 2.75 2.50

Stamp Day. See note after No. B296.

Arms of Austria, 1945 — SP175

Perf. 14x13½

1956, Dec. 21 Engr. & Typo.

B298 SP175 1.50s + 50g on 1.60s + 40g gray & red .25 .20

The surtax was for Hungarian refugees.

New Post Office, Linz 2 — SP176

Design: 2.40s+60g, Post office, Kitzbuhel.

1957-58 Engr. *Perf. 13½x14*

B299 SP176 1s + 25g dk sl grn 2.75 2.50
B300 SP176 2.40s + 60g blue .65 .60

Stamp Day. See note after B296. Issue dates: 1s, Nov. 30, 1957. 2.40s, Dec. 6, 1957. See No. B303.

Roman Carriage from Tomb at Maria Saal — SP177

Perf. 13½x14

1959, Dec. 5 Litho. & Engr.

B301 SP177 2.40s + 60g pale lil & blk .55 .50

Stamp Day.

Progressive Die Proof under Magnifying Glass — SP178

1960, Dec. 2 Engr. *Perf. 13½x14*

B302 SP178 3s + 70g vio brn .85 .70

Stamp Day.

Post Office Type of 1957

Design: 3s+70g, Post Office, Rust.

1961, Dec. 1 Unwmk. *Perf. 13½*

B303 SP176 3s + 70g dk bl grn .90 .70

Stamp Day. See note after No. B296.

Hands of Stamp Engraver at Work — SP179

1962, Nov. 30 *Perf. 13½x14*

B304 SP179 3s + 70g dull pur 1.25 .90

Stamp Day.

Railroad Exit, Post Office Vienna 101 — SP180

1963, Nov. 29 Litho. & Engr.

B305 SP180 3s + 70g tan & blk .80 .80

Stamp Day.

View of Vienna, North SP181

Designs: Various view of Vienna with compass indicating direction.

1964, July 20 Litho. *Perf. 13½x14*

B306 SP181 1.50s + 30g ("N") .20 .15
B307 SP181 1.50s + 30g ("NO") .20 .15
B308 SP181 1.50s + 30g ("O") .20 .15
B309 SP181 1.50s + 30g ("SO") .20 .15
B310 SP181 1.50s + 30g ("S") .20 .15
B311 SP181 1.50s + 30g ("SW") .20 .15
B312 SP181 1.50s + 30g ("W") .20 .15
B313 SP181 1.50s + 30g ("NW") .20 .15
Nos. B306-B313 (8) 1.60 1.20

Vienna Intl. Phil. Exhib. (WIPA 1965).

Post Bus Terminal, St. Gilgen, Wolfgangsee SP182

1964, Dec. 4 Unwmk. *Perf. 13½*

B314 SP182 3s + 70g multi .45 .45

Stamp Day.

Wall Painting, Tomb at Thebes — SP183

Development of Writing: 1.80s+50g, Cuneiform writing on stone tablet and man's head from Assyrian palace. 2.20s+60g, Wax tablet with Latin writing, Corinthian column. 3s+80g, Gothic writing on sealed letter, Gothic window from Munster Cathedral. 4s+1s, Letter with seal and postmark and upright desk. 5s+1.20s, Typewriter.

Perf. 14x13½

1965, June 4 Litho. & Engr.

B315 SP183 1.50s + 40g multi .15 .15
B316 SP183 1.80s + 50g multi .15 .15
B317 SP183 2.20s + 60g multi .35 .35
B318 SP183 3s + 80g multi .20 .20
B319 SP183 4s + 1s multi .45 .45
B320 SP183 5s + 1.20s multi .60 .60
Nos. B315-B320 (6) 1.90 1.90

Vienna Intl. Phil. Exhib., WIPA, June 4-13.

Mailman Distributing Mail — SP184

1965, Dec. 3 Engr. *Perf. 13½x14*

B321 SP184 3s + 70g blue grn .40 .35

Stamp Day.

Letter Carrier, 16th Century SP185

Letter Carrier, 16th Century Playing Card SP186

Litho. & Engr.

1966, Dec. 2 *Perf. 13½*

B322 SP185 3s + 70g multi .40 .35

Stamp Day. Design is from Ambras Heroes' Book, Austrian National Library.

Engr. & Photo.

1967, Dec. 1 *Perf. 13x13½*

B323 SP186 3.50s + 80g multi .40 .35

Stamp Day.

Mercury, Bas-relief from Purkersdorf SP187

Unken Post Station Sign, 1710 SP188

1968, Nov. 29 Engr. *Perf. 13½*

B324 SP187 3.50s + 80g slate green .40 .35

Stamp Day.

Engr. & Photo.

1969, Dec. 5 *Perf. 12*

B325 SP188 3.50s + 80g tan, red & blk .40 .35

Stamp Day. Design is from a watercolor by Friedrich Zeller.

Saddle, Bag, Harness and Post Horn — SP189

Perf. 13½x14

1970, Dec. 4 Engr. & Litho.

B326 SP189 3.50s + 80g gray blk & yel .40 .35

Stamp Day.

"50 Years" SP190

Engr. & Photo.

1971, Dec. 3 *Perf. 13½*
B327 SP190 4s + 1.50s gold & red brn .60 .45

50th anniversary of the Federation of Austrian Philatelic Societies.

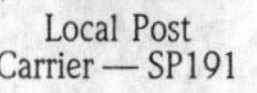

Local Post Carrier — SP191

Gabriel, by Lorenz Luchsperger, 15th Century — SP192

1972, Dec. 1 Engr. *Perf. 14x13½*
B328 SP191 4s + 1s olive green .60 .45

Stamp Day.

1973, Nov. 30
B329 SP192 4s + 1s maroon .60 .45

Stamp Day.

Mail Coach Leaving Old PTT Building — SP193

1974, Nov. 29 Engr. *Perf. 14x13½*
B330 SP193 4s + 2s violet blue .70 .70

Stamp Day.

Alpine Skiing, Women's SP194

Designs: 1.50s+70g, Ice hockey. 2s+90g, Ski jump. 4s+1.90s, Bobsledding.

1975, Mar. 14 Photo. *Perf. 13½x14*
B331 SP194 1s + 50g multi .20 .20
B332 SP194 1.50s + 70g multi .25 .25
B333 SP194 2s + 90g multi .30 .30
B334 SP194 4s + 1.90s multi .65 .65
Nos. B331-B334 (4) 1.40 1.40

1975, Nov. 14

Designs: 70g+30g, Figure skating, pair. 2s+1s, Cross-country skiing. 2.50s+1s, Luge. 4s+2s, Biathlon.

B335 SP194 70g + 30g multi .15 .15
B336 SP194 2s + 1s multi .25 .25
B337 SP194 2.50s + 1s multi .35 .35
B338 SP194 4s + 2s multi .60 .60
Nos. B335-B338 (4) 1.35 1.35

12th Winter Olympic Games, Innsbruck, Feb. 4-15, 1976.

Austria Nos. 5, 250, 455 — SP195

Photo. & Engr.

1975, Nov. 28 *Perf. 14*
B339 SP195 4s + 2s multi .65 .65

Stamp Day; 125th anniv. of Austrian stamps.

Postilion's Gala Hat and Horn — SP196

1976, Dec. 3 *Perf. 13½x14*
B340 SP196 6s + 2s blk & lt vio .80 .80

Stamp Day.

Emanuel Herrmann — SP197

1977, Dec. 2 *Perf. 14x13½*
B341 SP197 6s + 2s multi .80 .80

Stamp Day. Emanuel Herrmann (1839-1902), economist, invented postal card. Austria issued first postal card in 1869.

Post Bus, 1913 — SP198

1978, Dec. 1 Photo. *Perf. 13½x14*
B342 SP198 10s + 5s multi 1.40 1.40

Stamp Day.

Heroes' Square, Vienna SP199

Photo. & Engr.

1979, Nov. 30 *Perf. 13½*
B343 SP199 16s + 8s multi 3.00 2.50

No. B343 Inscribed "2. Phase"

1980, Nov. 21
B344 SP199 16s + 8s multi 2.90 2.50

Souvenir Sheet

1981, Feb. 20
B345 SP199 16s + 8s multi 3.00 2.50

WIPA 1981 Phil. Exhib., Vienna, May 22-31. No. B345 contains one stamp without inscription.

Mainz-Weber Mailbox, 1870 — SP200

1982, Nov. 26 Photo. & Engr.
B346 SP200 6s + 3s multi 1.00 1.00

Stamp Day.

Boy Examining Cover — SP201

Photo. & Engr.

1983, Oct. 21 *Perf. 14*
B347 SP201 6s + 3s multi 1.25 1.25

Stamp Day. See Nos. B349-B352, B354-B355.

World Winter Games for the Handicapped SP202

1984, Jan. 5 Photo. *Perf. 13½x13*
B348 SP202 4s + 2s Downhill skier .75 .75

Stamp Day Type of 1983

Designs: No. B349, Seschemnofer III burial chamber detail, pyramid of Cheops, Gizeh. No. B350, Roman messenger on horseback. No. B351, Nuremberg messenger, 16th cent. No. B352, *The Postmaster* (detail), 1841, lithograph by Carl Schuster.

1984-87 Photo. & Engr. *Perf. 14*
B349 SP201 6s + 3s multi 1.25 1.25
B350 SP201 6s + 3s multi 1.25 1.25
B351 SP201 6s + 3s multi 1.30 1.30
B352 SP201 6s + 3s multi 1.50 1.50
Nos. B349-B352 (4) 5.30 5.30

Issue: #B349, 11/30/84; #B350, 11/28/85; #B351, 11/28/86; #B352, 11/19/87.

4th World Winter Sports Championships for the Disabled, Innsbruck — SP203

1988, Jan. 15 Photo. *Perf. 13½*
B353 SP203 5s + 2.50s multi 1.25 1.25

Stamp Day Type of 1983

Designs: No. B354, Railway mail car. No. B355, Hansa-Brandenburg CI mail plane.

1988-89 Photo. & Engr. *Perf. 14*
B354 SP201 6s +3s multi 1.50 1.50
B355 SP201 6s +3s multi 1.50 1.10

Issued: #B354, Nov. 17; #B355, May 24, 1989.

Stamp Day — SP204

1990, May 25 Photo. *Perf. 13½*
B356 SP204 7s +3s multi 1.75 1.25

SP205

Stamp Day — SP205a

1991, May 29 Photo. & Engr.
B357 SP205 7s +3s "B" and "P" 1.90 1.25

1992, May 22
B358 SP205 7s +3s "R" and "H" 1.75 1.40

1993, May 5
B359 SP205 7s +3s "I" and "I" 1.75 1.40

1994, May 27
B360 SP205 7s +3s "E" and "L" 1.75 1.40

1995, May 26
B361 SP205a 10s +5s "F" & "A" 3.25 2.75
Nos. B357-B361 (5) 10.40 8.20

The first letters will spell "Briefmarke," the second "Philatelie."

Special Olympics Winter Games SP206

1993, Mar. 19 Photo. *Perf. 13½x14*
B367 SP206 6s +3s multi 1.65 1.25

AIR POST STAMPS

Issues of the Monarchy

Types of Regular Issue of 1916 Surcharged

FLUGPOST

2·50 K 2·50

1918, Mar. 30 Unwmk. *Perf. 12½*
C1 A40 1.50k on 2k lilac 2.25 3.00
C2 A40 2.50k on 3k ocher 8.00 16.00
a. Inverted surcharge *1,250.*
b. Perf. 11½ 325.00 240.00
c. Perf. 12½x11½ 27.50 37.50

Overprinted FLUGPOST

C3 A40 4k gray 5.00 10.00
Set, never hinged 30.00

Set exists imperf. Value, $325.

Nos. C1-C3 also exist without surcharge or overprint. Value, set perf., $625; imperf., $625.

Nos. C1-C3 were printed on grayish and on white paper.

A 7k on 10k red brown was prepared but not regularly issued. Value, perf. or imperf., $400.

Issues of the Republic

Hawk — AP1

Wilhelm Kress — AP2

1922-24 Typo. *Perf. 12½*
C4 AP1 300k claret .35 1.25
C5 AP1 400k green ('24) 4.50 12.50
C6 AP1 600k bister .15 .55
C7 AP1 900k brn orange .15 .55

Engr.

C8 AP2 1200k brn violet .15 .55
C9 AP2 2400k slate .15 .55
C10 AP2 3000k dp brn ('23) 1.75 3.50
C11 AP2 4800k dark bl ('23) 2.25 3.75
Nos. C4-C11 (8) 9.45 23.20
Set, never hinged 20.00

Set exists imperf. Value, $300.

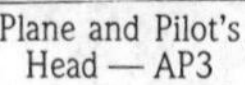
Plane and Pilot's Head — AP3

Airplane Passing Crane — AP4

1925-30 Typo. *Perf. 12½*

C12 AP3 2g gray brown .40 1.00
C13 AP3 5g red .25 .25
a. Horiz. pair, imperf. btwn. 205.00
C14 AP3 6g dark blue .90 1.50
C15 AP3 8g yel green 1.00 1.75
C16 AP3 10g dp org ('26) 1.00 1.75
a. Horiz. pair, imperf. btwn. 275.00
C17 AP3 15g red vio ('26) .40 .90
a. Horiz. pair, imperf. btwn. 300.00
C18 AP3 20g org brn ('30) 10.00 4.25
C19 AP3 25g blk vio ('30) 2.25 6.50
C20 AP3 30g bister ('26) 6.50 6.50
C21 AP3 50g bl gray ('26) 12.50 10.00
C22 AP3 80g dk grn ('30) 1.25 4.50

Photo.

C23 AP4 10g orange red .90 2.75
a. Horiz. pair, imperf. btwn. 275.00
C24 AP4 15g claret .60 1.50
C25 AP4 30g brn violet .80 2.75
C26 AP4 50g gray black .75 2.75
C27 AP4 1s deep blue 1.75 4.00
C28 AP4 2s dark green 1.50 4.00
a. Vertical pair, imperf. btwn. 275.00
C29 AP4 3s red brn ('26) 40.0 37.50
C30 AP4 5s indigo ('26) 12.50 22.50

Size: 25½x32mm

C31 AP4 10s blk brown, *gray* ('26) 10.00 17.50
Nos. C12-C31 (20) 105.25 134.15
Set, never hinged 225.00

Exists imperf. Value, set $900.

Airplane over Güssing Castle — AP5

Airplane over the Danube — AP6

Designs (each includes plane): 10g, Maria-Worth. 15g, Durnstein. 20g, Hallstatt. 25g, Salzburg. 30g, Upper Dachstein and Schladminger Glacier. 40g, Lake Wetter. 50g, Arlberg. 60g, St. Stephen's Cathedral. 80g, Church of the Minorites. 2s, Railroad viaduct, Carinthia. 3s, Gross Glockner mountain. 5s, Aerial railway. 10s, Seaplane and yachts.

1935, Aug. 16 Engr. *Perf. 12½*

C32 AP5 5g rose violet .15 .15
C33 AP5 10g red orange .15 .15
C34 AP5 15g yel green .55 .30
C35 AP5 20g gray blue .15 .20
C36 AP5 25g violet brn .15 .20
C37 AP5 30g brn orange .15 .25
C38 AP5 40g gray green .15 .25
C39 AP5 50g light sl bl .15 .25
C40 AP5 60g black brn .30 .40
C41 AP5 80g light brown .30 .40
C42 AP6 1s rose red .30 .55
C43 AP6 2s olive green 1.75 *4.00*
C44 AP6 3s yellow brn 7.50 *12.50*
C45 AP6 5s dark green 5.00 *12.50*
C46 AP6 10s slate blue 37.50 *75.00*
Nos. C32-C46 (15) 54.25 *107.10*
Set, never hinged 90.00

Set exists imperf. Value, $275.

Catalogue values for unused stamps in this section, from this point to the end of the section, are for Never Hinged items.

Windmill, Neusiedler Lake Shore — AP20

Designs: 1s, Roman arch, Carnuntum. 2s, Town Hall, Gmund. 3s, Schieder Lake, Hinterstoder. 4s, Praegraten, Eastern Tyrol. 5s, Torsäule, Salzburg. 10s, St. Charles Church, Vienna.

1947 Unwmk. *Perf. 14x13½*

C47 AP20 50g black brown .15 .20
C48 AP20 1s dark brn vio .30 .25
C49 AP20 2s dark green .35 .40
C50 AP20 3s chocolate 2.25 2.75
C51 AP20 4s dark green 1.40 2.00
C52 AP20 5s dark blue 1.40 2.00
C53 AP20 10s dark blue .75 1.50
Nos. C47-C53 (7) 6.60 9.10

Rooks — AP27

Birds: 1s, Barn swallows. 2s, Blackheaded gulls. 3s, Great cormorants. 5s, Buzzard. 10s, Gray heron. 20s, Golden eagle.

1950-53 *Perf. 13½x14*

C54 AP27 60g dark bl vio 2.50 1.10
C55 AP27 1s dark vio blue ('53) 17.50 15.00
C56 AP27 2s dark blue 15.00 6.00
C57 AP27 3s dk slate green ('53) 100.00 65.00
C58 AP27 5s red brn ('53) 100.00 65.00
C59 AP27 10s gray vio ('53) 45.00 30.00
C60 AP27 20s brn blk ('52) 10.00 4.00
Nos. C54-C60 (7) 290.00 186.10
Set, hinged 180.00

Value at lower left on Nos. C59 and C60. No. C60 exists imperf.

Etrich "Dove" AP28

Designs: 3.50s, Twin-engine jet airliner. 5s, Four-engine jet airliner.

1968, May 31 Engr. *Perf. 13½x14*

C61 AP28 2s olive bister .30 .25
C62 AP28 3.50s slate green .50 .40
C63 AP28 5s dark blue .75 .60
Nos. C61-C63 (3) 1.55 1.25

IFA WIEN 1968 (International Air Post Exhibition), Vienna, May 30-June 4.

POSTAGE DUE STAMPS

Issues of the Monarchy

D1

D2

Perf. 10 to 13½

1894-95 Typo. Wmk. 91

J1 D1 1kr brown 1.75 1.40
a. Perf. 13½ 25.00 30.00
J2 D1 2kr brown ('95) 3.75 2.00
a. Pair, imperf. btwn. 150.00 200.00
J3 D1 3kr brown 3.00 1.00
J4 D1 5kr brown 2.75 1.50
a. Perf. 13½ 16.00 15.00
b. Pair, imperf. btwn. 160.00 175.00
J5 D1 6kr brown ('95) 2.75 5.00
J6 D1 7kr brown ('95) .80 4.00
a. Vert. pair, imperf. btwn. 250.00 300.00
b. Horiz. pair, imperf. btwn. 275.00 —
J7 D1 10kr brown 4.50 .50
J8 D1 20kr brown .80 4.50
J9 D1 50kr brown 35.00 55.00
Nos. J1-J9 (9) 55.10 74.90

See Nos. J204-J231.

1899-1900 *Imperf.*

J10 D2 1h brown .20 .40
J11 D2 2h brown .25 .50
J12 D2 3h brown ('00) .20 .40
J13 D2 4h brown 2.00 1.50
J14 D2 5h brown ('00) 3.00 1.25
J15 D2 6h brown .30 .95
J16 D2 10h brown .25 .40
J17 D2 12h brown .40 1.75
J18 D2 15h brown .40 .95
J19 D2 20h brown 18.50 3.00
J20 D2 40h brown .80 2.50
J21 D2 100h brown 4.25 2.50
Nos. J10-J21 (12) 30.55 16.10

Perf. 10½, 12½, 13½ and Compound

J22 D2 1h brown .55 .20
J23 D2 2h brown .45 .20
J24 D2 3h brown ('00) .40 .15
J25 D2 4h brown .40 .15
J26 D2 5h brown ('00) .40 .15
J27 D2 6h brown .40 .15
J28 D2 10h brown .45 .15
J29 D2 12h brown .45 .60
J30 D2 15h brown .75 .80
J31 D2 20h brown .60 .30
J32 D2 40h brown 1.00 .75
J33 D2 100h brown 22.50 .40
Nos. J22-J33 (12) 28.35 4.00

Nos. J10-J33 exist on unwmkd. paper.
For surcharges see Offices in the Turkish Empire Nos. J1-J5.

D3

1908-13 Unwmk. *Perf. 12½*

J34 D3 1h carmine 1.10 .60
J35 D3 2h carmine .40 .25
J36 D3 4h carmine .40 .15
J37 D3 6h carmine .40 .15
J38 D3 10h carmine .40 .15
J39 D3 14h carmine ('13) 3.75 .70
J40 D3 20h carmine 5.25 .15
J41 D3 25h carmine ('10) 9.50 1.25
J42 D3 30h carmine 5.50 .15
J43 D3 50h carmine 7.50 .15
J44 D3 100h carmine 15.00 .20
Nos. J34-J44 (11) 49.20 3.90

All values exist on ordinary paper, #J34-J38, J40, J42-J44 on chalky paper and #J34-J38, J40, J44 on thin ordinary paper. Thin paper copies sell for 5-10 times the listed values. All values exist imperf.
See Offices in the Turkish Empire type D2.

1911, July 16

J45 D3 5k violet 40.00 6.00
J46 D3 10k violet 200.00 3.00

Regular Issue of 1908 Overprinted or Surcharged in Carmine or Black:

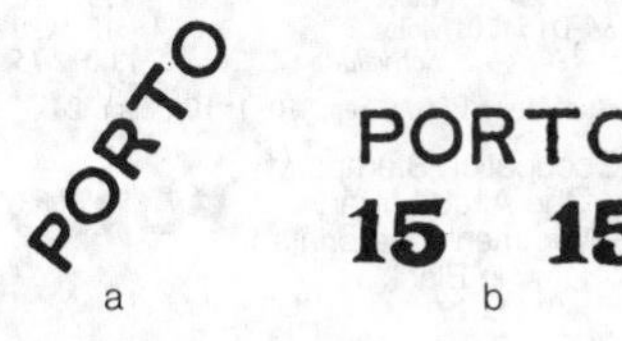

a b

1916, Oct. 21

J47 A22 1h gray (C) .15 .15
a. Pair, one without overprint 125.00
J48 A22 15h on 2h vio (Bk) .20 .25
Set value .30 .35
Set, never hinged .90

D4

D5

1916, Oct. 1

J49 D4 5h rose red .15 .15
J50 D4 10h rose red .15 .15
J51 D4 15h rose red .15 .15
J52 D4 20h rose red .15 .15
J53 D4 25h rose red .35 .30
J54 D4 30h rose red .15 .15
J55 D4 40h rose red .20 .15
J56 D4 50h rose red .90 .90
J57 D5 1k ultramarine .30 .15
a. Horiz. pair, imperf. btwn. 350.00 350.00
J58 D5 5k ultramarine 1.25 1.40
J59 D5 10k ultramarine 1.25 .90
Nos. J49-J59 (11) 5.00 4.55
Set, never hinged 16.00

Exists imperf. Value, set $80.
For overprints see Western Ukraine Nos. 54-55, NJ1-NJ6, Poland Nos. J1-J10.

Type of Regular Issue of 1916 Surcharged

PORTO

1917

J60 A38 10h on 24h blue 1.25 .20
J61 A38 15h on 36h violet .20 .15
J62 A38 20h on 54h orange .20 .20
J63 A38 50h on 42h chocolate .20 .15
Nos. J60-J63 (4) 1.85 .70
Set, never hinged 5.00

All values of this issue are known imperforate, also without surcharge, perforated and imperforate.
For overprints see Western Ukraine Nos. 57-58.

Issues of the Republic

Postage Due Stamps of 1916 Overprinted

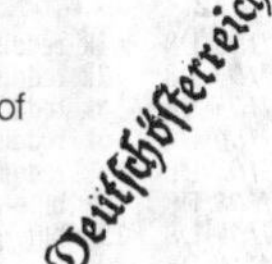

1919

J64 D4 5h rose red .15 .15
a. Inverted overprint 200.00 225.00
J65 D4 10h rose red .15 .15
J66 D4 15h rose red .15 .30
J67 D4 20h rose red .25 .25
J68 D4 25h rose red 4.75 12.00
J69 D4 30h rose red .15 .15
J70 D4 40h rose red .15 .25
J71 D4 50h rose red .30 .80
J72 D5 1k ultramarine 8.00 7.00
J73 D5 5k ultramarine 9.00 8.00
J74 D5 10k ultramarine 8.00 3.00
Nos. J64-J74 (11) 31.05 32.05
Set, never hinged 70.00

Nos. J64, J65, J67 and J70 exist imperforate.

D6

D7

1920-21 *Perf. 12½*

J75 D6 5h bright red .15 .15
J76 D6 10h bright red .15 .15
J77 D6 15h bright red .15 .30
J78 D6 20h bright red .15 .15
J79 D6 25h bright red .15 .30
J80 D6 30h bright red .15 .15
J81 D6 40h bright red .15 .15
J82 D6 50h bright red .15 .15
J83 D6 80h bright red .15 .15
J84 D7 1k ultramarine .15 .15
J85 D7 1½k ultra ('21) .15 .15
J86 D7 2k ultra ('21) .15 .15
J87 D7 3k ultra ('21) .15 .15
J88 D7 4k ultra ('21) .15 .15
J89 D7 5k ultramarine .15 .15
J90 D7 8k ultra ('21) .15 .15
J91 D7 10k ultramarine .15 .15
J92 D7 20k ultra ('21) .15 .35
Set value .95 2.18
Set, never hinged 3.00

Nos. J84 to J92 exist on white paper and on grayish white paper. They also exist imperf.; value, set $65.

Imperf

J93 D6 5h bright red .15 .15
J94 D6 10h bright red .15 .15
J95 D6 15h bright red .15 .25
J96 D6 20h bright red .15 .15
J97 D6 25h bright red .15 .30

J98 D6 30h bright red .15 .15
J99 D6 40h bright red .15 .15
J100 D6 50h bright red .15 .20
J101 D6 80h bright red .15 .15
Set value .50 1.30
Set, never hinged 1.25

Nachmarke

No. 207a Surcharged in Dark Blue

7½ K

1921, Dec. *Perf. 12½*
J102 A43 7½k on 15h bister .15 .20
Never hinged .15
a. Inverted surcharge 185.00 185.00

D8

D9

D10

1922
J103 D8 1k reddish buff .15 .15
J104 D8 2k reddish buff .15 .15
J105 D8 4k reddish buff .15 .15
J106 D8 5k reddish buff .15 .15
J107 D8 7½k reddish buff .15 .15
J108 D8 10k blue green .15 .15
J109 D8 15k blue green .15 .15
J110 D8 20k blue green .15 .15
J111 D8 25k blue green .15 .15
J112 D8 40k blue green .15 .15
J113 D8 50k blue green .15 .25
Set value .60 1.50
Set, never hinged 1.00

Issue date: Nos. J108-J113, June 2.

1922-24
J114 D9 10k cobalt blue .15 .15
J115 D9 15k cobalt blue .15 .15
J116 D9 20k cobalt blue .15 .15
J117 D9 50k cobalt blue .15 .20
J118 D10 100k plum .15 .15
J119 D10 150k plum .15 .15
J120 D10 200k plum .15 .15
J121 D10 400k plum .15 .15
J122 D10 600k plum ('23) .15 .15
J123 D10 800k plum .15 .15
J124 D10 1,000k plum ('23) .15 .15
J125 D10 1,200k plum ('23) .50 1.50
J126 D10 1,500k plum ('24) .15 .15
J127 D10 1,800k plum ('24) 1.50 4.25
J128 D10 2,000k plum ('23) .20 .50
J129 D10 3,000k plum ('24) 5.75 7.50
J130 D10 4,000k plum ('24) 3.75 9.75
J131 D10 6,000k plum ('24) 3.75 15.00
Nos. J114-J131 (18) 17.25 40.35
Set, never hinged 40.00

Value, Nos. J103-J131 imperf, $200.

D11

D12

1925-34 *Perf. 12½*
J132 D11 1g red .15 .15
J133 D11 2g red .15 .15
J134 D11 3g red .15 .15
J135 D11 4g red .15 .15
J136 D11 5g red ('27) .15 .15
J137 D11 6g red .15 .30
J138 D11 8g red .15 .15
J139 D11 10g dark blue .15 .15
J140 D11 12g dark blue .15 .15
J141 D11 14g dark blue ('27) .15 .15
J142 D11 15g dark blue .15 .15
J143 D11 16g dark blue ('29) .25 .15
J144 D11 18g dark blue ('34) .95 3.00
J145 D11 20g dark blue .15 .15
J146 D11 23g dark blue .55 .15
J147 D11 24g dark blue ('32) .85 .15
J148 D11 28g dark blue ('27) .35 .25
J149 D11 30g dark blue .15 .15
J150 D11 31g dark blue ('29) .70 .15
J151 D11 35g dark blue ('30) .45 .15
J152 D11 39g dark blue ('32) .75 .15
J153 D11 40g dark blue .75 1.50
J154 D11 60g dark blue .55 .85
J155 D12 1s dark green 6.00 .85
J156 D12 2s dark green 30.00 3.00
J157 D12 5s dark green 75.00 24.00
J158 D12 10s dark green 50.00 3.50
Nos. J132-J158 (27) 169.10 39.95
Set, never hinged 300.00

Issues of 1925-27 (21 values) imperf, value, set $400.

Issue dates: 3g, 2s-10s, Dec. 5g, 28g, Jan. 1. 14g, June. 31g, Feb. 1. 35g, Jan. 24g, 39g, Sept. 16g, May. 18g, June 25. Others, June 1.

Coat of Arms
D13 D14

1935, June 1
J159 D13 1g red .15 .15
J160 D13 2g red .15 .15
J161 D13 3g red .15 .15
J162 D13 5g red .15 .15
J163 D13 10g blue .15 .15
J164 D13 12g blue .15 .15
J165 D13 15g blue .15 .40
J166 D13 20g blue .15 .15
J167 D13 24g blue .15 .15
J168 D13 30g blue .15 .15
J169 D13 39g blue .20 .15
J170 D13 60g blue .40 1.10
J171 D14 1s green .65 .40
J172 D14 2s green 1.00 .50
J173 D14 5s green 2.50 1.10
J174 D14 10s green 3.75 .60
Nos. J159-J174 (16) 10.00
Set value 5.00
Set, never hinged 40.00

On Nos. J163-J170, background lines are horizontal.

Nos. J159-J174 exist imperf. Value, set $125.

Catalogue values for unused stamps in this section, from this point to the end of the section, are for Never Hinged items.

D15

1945 Unwmk. Typo. *Perf. 10½*
J175 D15 1g vermilion .15 .15
J176 D15 2g vermilion .15 .15
J177 D15 3g vermilion .15 .15
J178 D15 5g vermilion .15 .15
J179 D15 10g vermilion .15 .15
J180 D15 12g vermilion .15 .15
J181 D15 20g vermilion .15 .15
J182 D15 24g vermilion .15 .15
J183 D15 30g vermilion .15 .15
J184 D15 60g vermilion .15 .20
J185 D15 1s violet .15 .35
J186 D15 2s violet .15 .45
J187 D15 5s violet .15 .20
J188 D15 10s violet .15 .20
Set value 1.00 2.15

Issue dates: 1g-60g, Sept. 10, 1s-10s, Sept. 24.

Occupation Stamps of the Allied Military Government Overprinted in Black

PORTO

1946 *Perf. 11*
J189 OS1 3g deep orange .15 .15
J190 OS1 5g bright green .15 .15
J191 OS1 6g red violet .15 .15
J192 OS1 8g rose pink .15 .15
J193 OS1 10g light gray .15 .20
J194 OS1 12g pale buff brown .15 .15
J195 OS1 15g rose red .15 .20
J196 OS1 20g copper brown .15 .15
J197 OS1 25g deep blue .15 .15
J198 OS1 30g bright violet .15 .15
J199 OS1 40g light ultra .15 .15
J200 OS1 60g light olive grn .15 .15
J201 OS1 1s dark violet .15 .20
J202 OS1 2s yellow .25 .30
J203 OS1 5s deep ultra .25 .30
Set value 1.42 1.88

Nos. J189-J203 were issued by the Renner Government. Inverted overprints exist on about half of the denominations.

Issue dates: 3g-60g, Apr. 23, 1s-5s, May 20.

Type of 1894-95
Inscribed "Republik Osterreich"

1947 Typo. *Perf. 14*
J204 D1 1g chocolate .15 .15
J205 D1 2g chocolate .15 .15
J206 D1 3g chocolate .15 .15
J207 D1 5g chocolate .15 .15
J208 D1 8g chocolate .15 .15
J209 D1 10g chocolate .15 .15
J210 D1 12g chocolate .15 .15
J211 D1 15g chocolate .15 .15
J212 D1 16g chocolate .20 .40
J213 D1 17g chocolate .20 .40
J214 D1 18g chocolate .20 .40
J215 D1 20g chocolate .50 .15
J216 D1 24g chocolate .30 .30
J217 D1 30g chocolate .20 .25
J218 D1 36g chocolate .50 .60
J219 D1 40g chocolate .15 .15
J220 D1 42g chocolate .50 .60
J221 D1 48g chocolate .50 .60
J222 D1 50g chocolate .60 .15
J223 D1 60g chocolate .20 .15
J224 D1 70g chocolate .15 .15
J225 D1 80g chocolate 3.75 1.65
J226 D1 1s blue .20 .15
J227 D1 1.15s blue 2.50 .30
J228 D1 1.20s blue 3.00 1.00
J229 D1 2s blue .40 .40
J230 D1 5s blue .40 .40
J231 D1 10s blue .45 .40
Nos. J204-J231 (28) 16.10 9.80

Issue dates: 1g, 20g, 50g, 80g, 1.15s, 1.20s, Sept. 25, others, Aug. 14.

D16

D17

1949-57
J232 D16 1g carmine .20 .15
J233 D16 2g carmine .20 .15
J234 D16 4g carmine ('51) 1.00 .15
J235 D16 5g carmine 2.25 .25
J236 D16 8g carmine ('51) 2.75 1.20
J237 D16 10g carmine .15 .15
J238 D16 20g carmine .15 .15
J239 D16 30g carmine .15 .15
J240 D16 40g carmine .15 .15
J241 D16 50g carmine .15 .15
J242 D16 60g carmine ('50) 7.75 .15
J243 D16 63g carmine ('57) 4.75 3.25
J244 D16 70g carmine .15 .15
J245 D16 80g carmine .15 .15
J246 D16 90g carmine ('50) .20 .15
J247 D16 1s purple .20 .15
J248 D16 1.20s purple .35 .15
J249 D16 1.35s purple .30 .15
J250 D16 1.40s purple ('51) .50 .20
J251 D16 1.50s purple ('53) .20 .15
J252 D16 1.65s purple ('50) .40 .15
J253 D16 1.70s purple .40 .15
J254 D16 2s purple .35 .15
J255 D16 2.50s purple ('51) .50 .15
J256 D16 3s purple ('51) 1.00 .15
J257 D16 4s purple ('51) 1.00 .40
J258 D16 5s purple 1.75 .20
J259 D16 10s purple 2.75 .20
Nos. J232-J259 (28) 29.85
Set value 7.20

Issue dates: 60g, 90g, 1.65s, Aug. 7. 4g, 8g, 1.40s, 2.50s-4s, Dec. 4. 1.50s, Feb. 18. 63g, Apr. 30. Others, Nov. 17.

1985-89 Photo. *Perf. 14*
Background Color
J260 D17 10g brt yel ('86) .15 .15
J261 D17 20g pink ('86) .15 .15
J262 D17 50g orange ('86) .15 .15
J263 D17 1s lt blue ('86) .15 .15
J264 D17 2s pale brn ('86) .30 .20
J265 D17 3s violet ('86) .40 .30
J266 D17 5s ocher .60 .40
J267 D17 10s pale grn ('89) 1.55 1.15
Nos. J260-J267 (8) 3.45 2.65

Issue dates: 5s, Dec. 12. 20g, 1s, 3s, Mar. 19. 10g, 50g, 2s, Oct. 3. 10s, June 30.

This is an expanding set. Numbers will change if necessary.

MILITARY STAMPS

Issues of the Austro-Hungarian Military Authorities for the Occupied Territories in World War I

See Bosnia and Herzegovina for similar designs inscribed "MILITARPOST" instead of "FELDPOST."

Stamps of Bosnia of 1912-14 Overprinted

1915 Unwmk. *Perf. 12½*
M1 A23 1h olive green .15 .20
M2 A23 2h bright blue .15 .20
M3 A23 3h claret .15 .20
M4 A23 5h green .15 .15
M5 A23 6h dark gray .15 .20
M6 A23 10h rose carmine .15 .15
M7 A23 12h deep ol grn .20 .35
M8 A23 20h orange brn .30 .40
M9 A23 25h ultramarine .30 .35
M10 A23 30h orange red 2.75 5.00
M11 A24 35h myrtle grn 2.50 4.00
M12 A24 40h dark violet 2.50 4.00
M13 A24 45h olive brown 2.75 4.50
M14 A24 50h slate blue 2.50 4.00
M15 A24 60h brn violet .35 .50
M16 A24 72h dark blue 2.50 4.00
M17 A25 1k brn vio, *straw* 2.75 5.00
M18 A25 2k dk gray, *blue* 2.75 4.00
M19 A26 3k car, *green* 20.00 24.00
M20 A26 5k dk vio, *gray* 20.00 24.00
M21 A25 10k dk ultra, *gray* 175.00 150.00
Nos. M1-M21 (21) 238.05 235.20

Exists imperf. Value, set $300.

Nos. M1-M21 also exist with overprint double, inverted and in red. These varieties were made by order of an official but were not regularly issued.

Emperor Franz Josef
M1 M2

Perf. 11½, 12½ and Compound

1915-17 **Engr.**
M22 M1 1h olive green .15 .15
M23 M1 2h dull blue .15 .15
M24 M1 3h claret .15 .15
M25 M1 5h green .15 .15
a. Perf. 11½ 35.00 40.00
b. Perf. 11½x12½ 47.50 70.00
c. Perf. 12½x11½ 75.00 100.00
M26 M1 6h dark gray .15 .15
M27 M1 10h rose carmine .15 .15
M28 M1 10h gray bl ('17) .15 .15
M29 M1 12h dp olive grn .15 .15
M30 M1 15h car rose ('17) .15 .15
a. Perf. 11½ 7.50 7.50
M31 M1 20h orange brn .35 .15
M32 M1 20h ol green ('17) .35 .15
M33 M1 25h ultramarine .15 .15
M34 M1 30h vermilion .15 .15
M35 M1 35h dark green .30 .35
M36 M1 40h dark violet .30 .35
M37 M1 45h olive brown .25 .35
M38 M1 50h myrtle green .25 .20
M39 M1 60h brown violet .25 .35
M40 M1 72h dark blue .25 .35
M41 M1 80h org brn ('17) .15 .15
M42 M1 90h magenta ('17) .70 .75
M43 M2 1k brn vio, *straw* 1.25 1.75
M44 M2 2k dk gray, *blue* 1.10 .65
M45 M2 3k car, *green* .80 .90
M46 M2 4k dark violet, *gray* ('17) .70 .90
M47 M2 5k dk vio, *gray* 18.00 20.00
M48 M2 10k dk ultra, *gray* 2.75 5.25
Nos. M22-M48 (27) 29.40 34.25

Nos. M22-M48 exist imperf. Value, set $75.

Emperor Karl I
M3 M4

1917-18 *Perf. 12½*
M49 M3 1h grnsh blue ('18) .15 .15
a. Perf. 11½ 3.50 4.00
M50 M3 2h red org ('18) .15 .15
M51 M3 3h olive gray .15 .15
a. Perf. 11½ 12.00 15.00
b. Perf. 11½x12½ 18.00 27.50
M52 M3 5h olive green .15 .15
M53 M3 6h violet .15 .15
M54 M3 10h orange brn .15 .15
M55 M3 12h blue .15 .15
a. Perf. 11½ 2.75 3.50

No.	Type	Description	Unused	Used
M56	M3	15h bright rose	.15	.15
M57	M3	20h red brown	.15	.15
M58	M3	25h ultramarine	.35	.35
M59	M3	30h slate	.15	.15
M60	M3	40h olive bister	.15	.15
a.		Perf. 11½	1.40	1.50
M61	M3	50h deep green	.15	.15
a.		Perf. 11½	4.25	6.00
M62	M3	60h car rose	.15	.15
M63	M3	80h dull blue	.15	.15
M64	M3	90h dk violet	.40	.45
M65	M4	2k rose, *straw*	.15	.15
a.		Perf. 11½	2.25	3.50
M66	M4	3k green, *blue*	.95	.95
M67	M4	4k rose, *green*	15.00	12.00
a.		Perf. 11½	27.50	35.00
M68	M4	10k dl vio, *gray*	2.25	3.50
a.		Perf. 11½	11.00	17.50
		Nos. M49-M68 (20)	21.20	19.50

Nos. M49-M68 exist imperf. Value, set $36.

See No. M82. For overprints see Western Ukraine Nos. 34-53, 75-81.

Emperor Karl I — M5

1918 Typo. *Perf. 12½*

No.	Type	Description	Unused	Used
M69	M5	1h grnsh blue	20.00	
M70	M5	2h orange	10.00	
M71	M5	3h olive gray	8.00	
M72	M5	5h yellow green	.30	
M73	M5	10h dark brown	.30	
M74	M5	20h red	.70	
M75	M5	25h blue	.70	
M76	M5	30h bister	75.00	
M77	M5	45h dark slate	75.00	
M78	M5	50h deep green	50.00	
M79	M5	60h violet	100.00	
M80	M5	80h rose	50.00	
M81	M5	90h brown violet	2.00	

Engr.

No.	Type	Description	Unused	Used
M82	M4	1k ol bister, *blue*	.30	
		Nos. M69-M82 (14)	392.30	

Nos. M69-M82 were on sale at the Vienna post office for a few days before the Armistice signing. They were never issued at the Army Post Offices. They exist imperf.; value, set $400.

MILITARY SEMI-POSTAL STAMPS

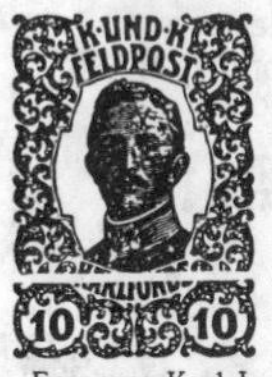

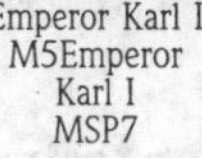

Emperor Karl I M5Emperor Karl I MSP7

Empress Zita MSP8

Perf. 12½x13

1918, July 20 Unwmk. Typo.

No.	Type	Description	Unused	Used
MB1	MSP7	10h gray green	.20	.20
MB2	MSP8	20h magenta	.20	.20
MB3	MSP7	45h blue	.20	.20
		Nos. MB1-MB3 (3)	.60	.60
		Set, never hinged	1.25	

These stamps were sold at a premium of 10h each over face value. The surtax was for "Karl's Fund."

For overprints see Western Ukraine Nos. 31-33.

Exist imperf. Value, set $8.

MILITARY NEWSPAPER STAMPS

Mercury — MN1

1916 Unwmk. Typo. *Perf. 12½*

No.	Type	Description	Unused	Used
MP1	MN1	2h blue	.15	.15
a.		Perf. 11½	1.50	1.00
b.		Perf. 12½x11½	125.00	*125.00*
MP2	MN1	6h orange	.55	.50
MP3	MN1	10h carmine	.70	.50
MP4	MN1	20h brown	.40	.45
a.		Perf. 11½	1.90	1.25
		Nos. MP1-MP4 (4)	1.80	1.60
		Set, never hinged	4.50	

Exist imperf. Values, Nos. MP2-MP3, $1 each, Nos. MP1, MP4, $18 each.

NEWSPAPER STAMPS

From 1851 to 1866, the Austrian Newspaper Stamps were also used in Lombardy-Venetia.

> Values for unused stamps 1851-67 are for fine copies with original gum. Specimens without gum sell for about a third or less of the figures quoted.

Issues of the Monarchy

Mercury — N1

Three Types

Type I - The "G" has no crossbar.

Type II - The "G" has a crossbar.

Type IIa - as type II but the rosette is deformed. Two spots of color in the "G."

1851-56 Unwmk. Typo. *Imperf.*

Machine-made Paper

No.	Type	Description	Unused	Used
P1	N1	(0.6kr) bl, type IIa	130.00	70.00
a.		Blue, type I	175.00	85.00
b.		Ribbed paper	400.00	145.00
c.		Blue, type II	375.00	165.00
P2	N1	(6kr) yel, type I	*12,500.*	*7,500.*
P3	N1	(30kr) rose, type I	*17,500.*	*10,000.*
P4	N1	(6kr) scar, type II ('56)	*37,500.*	*40,000.*

From 1852 No. P3 and from 1856 No. P2 were used as 0.6 kreuzer values.

Pale shades of Nos. P2 and P3 sell at considerably lower values.

Originals of Nos. P2 and P3 are usually in pale colors and poorly printed. Values are for stamps clearly printed and in bright colors. Numerous reprints of Nos. P1 to P4 were made between 1866 and 1904. Those of Nos. P2 and P3 are always well printed and in much deeper colors. All reprints are in type I, but occasionally show faint traces of a crossbar on "G" of "ZEITUNGS."

N2 N3

Two Types of the 1858-59 Issue

Type I - Loops of the bow at the back of the head broken.

Type II - Loops complete. Wreath projects further at top of head.

1858-59 Embossed

No.	Type	Description	Unused	Used
P5	N2	(1kr) blue, type I	500.00	550.00
P6	N2	(1kr) lilac, type II ('59)	700.00	275.00

1861

No.	Type	Description	Unused	Used
P7	N3	(1kr) gray	140.00	140.00
a.		(1kr) gray lilac	350.00	200.00
b.		(1kr) deep lilac	1,500.	575.00

The embossing on the reprints of the 1858-59 and 1861 issues is not as sharp as on the originals.

N4

Wmk. 91, or, before July 1864, Unwmkd.

1863

No.	Type	Description	Unused	Used
P8	N4	(1.05kr) gray	35.00	13.00
a.		Tete beche pair	*20,000.*	
b.		(1.05kr) gray lilac	60.00	17.50

The embossing of the reprints is not as sharp as on the originals.

Mercury

N5 N6

Three Types

Type I - Helmet not defined at back, more or less blurred. Two thick short lines in front of wing of helmet. Shadow on front of face not separated from hair.

Type II - Helmet distinctly defined. Four thin short lines in front of wing. Shadow on front of face clearly defined from hair.

Type III - Outer white circle around head is open at top (closed on types I and II). Greek border at top and bottom is wider than on types I and II.

1867-73 Typo. Wmk. 91

Coarse Print

No.	Type	Description	Unused	Used
P9	N5	(1kr) vio, type I	37.50	4.00
a.		(1kr) violet, type II ('73)	120.00	18.00

1874-76

Fine Print

No.	Type	Description	Unused	Used
P9B	N5	(1kr) violet, type III ('76)	.50	.20
c.		(1kr) gray lilac, type I ('76)	100.00	25.00
d.		(1kr) violet, type II	30.00	5.00
e.		Double impression, type III		175.00

Stamps of this issue, except No. P9c, exist in many shades, from gray to lilac brown and deep violet. Stamps in type III exist also privately perforated or rouletted.

1880

No.	Type	Description	Unused	Used
P10	N6	½kr green	5.00	.90

Nos. P9B and P10 also exist on thicker paper without sheet watermark and No. P10 exists with unofficial perforation.

N7

1899 Unwmk. *Imperf.*

Without Varnish Bars

No.	Type	Description	Unused	Used
P11	N7	2h dark blue	2.00	.15
P12	N7	6h orange	2.00	1.75
P13	N7	10h brown	.90	.75
P14	N7	20h rose	1.75	1.75
		Nos. P11-P14 (4)	6.65	4.40

1901

With Varnish Bars

No.	Type	Description	Unused	Used
P11a	N7	2h dark blue	.70	.20
P12a	N7	6h orange	9.50	12.50
P13a	N7	10h brown	10.00	7.50
P14a	N7	20h rose	20.00	25.00
		Nos. P11a-P14a (4)	40.20	45.20

Nos. P11 to P14 were re-issued in 1905.

Mercury

N8 N9

1908 *Imperf.*

No.	Type	Description	Unused	Used
P15	N8	2h dark blue	1.50	.15
a.		Tete beche pair	190.00	275.00
P16	N8	6h orange	2.25	.30
P17	N8	10h carmine	2.25	.30
P18	N8	20h brown	2.25	.25
		Nos. P15-P18 (4)	8.25	1.00

All values are found on chalky, regular and thin ordinary paper. They exist privately perforated.

1916 *Imperf.*

No.	Type	Description	Unused	Used
P19	N9	2h brown	.15	.15
P20	N9	4h green	.20	.30
P21	N9	6h dark blue	.20	.60
P22	N9	10h orange	.20	.30
P23	N9	30h claret	.25	.30
		Nos. P19-P23 (5)	1.00	1.65
		Set, never hinged	2.00	

Issues of the Republic

Newspaper Stamps of 1916 Overprinted

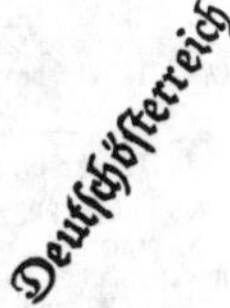

1919

No.	Type	Description	Unused	Used
P24	N9	2h brown	.15	.15
P25	N9	4h green	.15	*.45*
P26	N9	6h dark blue	.15	*.70*
P27	N9	10h orange	.25	*.45*
P28	N9	30h claret	.15	*.70*
		Set value	.60	
		Set, never hinged	1.65	

Mercury

N10 N11

1920-21 *Imperf.*

No.	Type	Description	Unused	Used
P29	N10	2h violet	.15	.15
P30	N10	4h brown	.15	.15
P31	N10	5h slate	.15	.15
P32	N10	6h turq blue	.15	.15
P33	N10	8h green	.15	.15
P34	N10	9h yellow ('21)	.15	.15
P35	N10	10h red	.15	.15
P36	N10	12h blue	.15	.15
P37	N10	15h lilac ('21)	.15	.15
P38	N10	18h blue grn ('21)	.15	.15
P39	N10	20h orange	.15	.15
P40	N10	30h yellow brn ('21)	.15	.15
P41	N10	45h green ('21)	.15	.15
P42	N10	60h claret	.15	.20
P43	N10	72h chocolate ('21)	.15	.35
P44	N10	90h violet ('21)	.15	.35
P45	N10	1.20k red ('21)	.15	.35
P46	N10	2.40k yellow grn ('21)	.15	.35
P47	N10	3k gray ('21)	.15	.35
		Set value	1.10	3.00
		Set, never hinged	1.75	

Nos. P37-P40, P42, P44 and P47 exist also on thick gray paper.

1921-22

No.	Type	Description	Unused	Used
P48	N11	45h gray	.15	.15
P49	N11	75h brown org ('22)	.15	.15
P50	N11	1.50k ol bister ('22)	.15	.15
P51	N11	1.80k gray blue ('22)	.15	.15
P52	N11	2.25k light brown	.15	.15
P53	N11	3k dull green ('22)	.15	.35
P54	N11	6k claret ('22)	.15	.35
P55	N11	7.50k bister	.18	.35
		Set value	.60	
		Set, never hinged	1.25	

Nos. P24-P55 exist privately perforated.

NEWSPAPER TAX STAMPS

> Values for unused stamps 1853-59 are for copies in fine condition with gum. Specimens without gum sell for about one-third or less of the figures quoted.

Issues of the Monarchy

NT1 NT2

Unwmk.

1853, Mar. 1 Typo. *Imperf.*

No.	Type	Description	Unused	Used
PR1	NT1	2kr green	1,500.	50.00

The reprints are in finer print than the more coarsely printed originals, and on a smooth toned paper.

Wmk. 91, or, before July 1864, Unwmkd.

1858-59

Two Types.

Type I - The banderol on the Crown of the left eagle touches the beak of the eagle.

Type II - The banderol does not touch the beak.

PR2 NT2 1kr blue, type II ('59) 32.50 6.00
a. 1kr blue, type I 650.00 150.00
b. Printed on both sides, type II —
PR3 NT2 2kr brown, type II ('59) 20.00 7.50
a. 2kr red brown, type II 400.00 150.00
PR4 NT2 4kr brn, type I 400.00 *1,000.*

Nos. PR2a, PR3a, and PR4 were printed only on unwatermarked paper. Nos. PR2 and PR3 exist on unwatermarked and watermarked paper.

Nos. PR2 and PR3 exist in coarse and (after 1874) in fine print, like the contemporary postage stamps.

The reprints of the 4kr brown are of type II and on a smooth toned paper.

Issue date: 4kr, Nov. 1.

See Lombardy-Venetia for the 1kr in black and the 2kr, 4fk in red.

NT3

NT4

1877 **Redrawn**

PR5 NT3 1kr blue 12.50 1.50
a. 1kr pale ultramarine *1,500.*
PR6 NT3 2kr brown 14.00 1.25

In the redrawn stamps the shield is larger and the vertical bar has eight lines above the white square and nine below, instead of five.

Nos. PR5 and PR6 exist also watermarked "WECHSEL" instead of "ZEITUNGS-MARKEN."

1890, June 1

PR7 NT4 1kr brown 10.00 1.20
PR8 NT4 2kr green 11.00 1.50

#PR5-PR8 exist with private perforation.

NT5

Perf. 13, 12½

1890, June 1 **Wmk. 91**

PR9 NT5 25kr carmine 100.00 400.00

Nos. PR1-PR9 did not pay postage, but were a fiscal tax, collected by the postal authorities on newspapers.

SPECIAL HANDLING STAMPS

(For Printed Matter Only)
Issues of the Monarchy

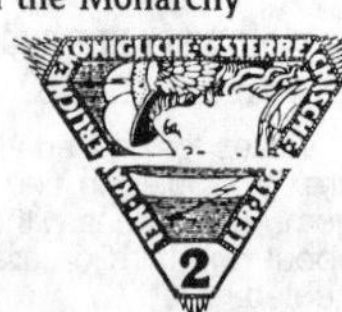
Mercury — SH1

1916 **Unwmk.** ***Perf. 12½***

QE1 SH1 2h claret, *yel* .30 .40
QE2 SH1 5h dp green, *yel* .30 .40
Set, never hinged 1.75

SH2

1917 ***Perf. 12½***

QE3 SH2 2h claret, *yel* .15 .15
a. Pair, imperf. between 200.00 200.00
b. Perf. 11½x12½ 45.00 60.00
c. Perf. 12½x11½ 60.00 90.00
d. Perf. 11½ .95 1.40
QE4 SH2 5h dp green, *yel* .15 .15
a. Pair, imperf. between 175.00 175.00
b. Perf. 11½x12½ 45.00 60.00
c. Perf. 12½x11½ 60.00 90.00
d. Perf. 11½ .95 1.40
Set value .20 .20
Set, never hinged .35

Nos. QE1-QE4 exist imperforate.

Issues of the Republic

Nos. QE3 and QE4 Overprinted

1919

QE5 SH2 2h claret, *yel* .15 .15
a. Inverted overprint 175.00
b. Perf. 11½x12½ 5.00 8.00
c. Perf. 12½x11½ 65.00 85.00
d. Perf. 11½ .22 .70
QE6 SH2 5h deep green, *yel* .15 .20
a. Perf. 11½x12½ 2.25 3.75
b. Perf. 12½x11½ 25.00 35.00
c. Perf. 11½ .18 .48
Set value .15
Set, never hinged .20

Nos. QE5 and QE6 exist imperforate.

SH3

Dark Blue Surcharge

1921

QE7 SH3 50h on 2h claret, *yel* .15 .15
Never hinged .15

SH4

1922 ***Perf. 12½***

QE8 SH4 50h lilac, *yel* .15 .20
Never hinged .15

#QE5-QE8 exist in vertical pairs, imperf between. No. QE8 exists imperf.

OCCUPATION STAMPS

Issued under Italian Occupation

Issued in Trieste

Austrian Stamps of 1916-18 Overprinted

Regno d'Italia
Venezia Giulia
3. XI. 18.

1918 **Unwmk.** ***Perf. 12½***

N1 A37 3h bright vio .20 .20
a. Double overprint 7.00 9.00
b. Inverted overprint 7.00 9.00
N2 A37 5h light grn .20 .20
a. Inverted overprint 7.00 9.00
b. "3.XI." omitted 7.00 7.00
c. Double overprint 9.00
N3 A37 6h dp orange .25 .30
N4 A37 10h magenta .20 .25
a. Inverted overprint 5.00 6.00
N5 A37 12h light bl .55 .70
a. Double overprint 7.00 9.00
N6 A42 15h dull red .20 .25
a. Inverted overprint 6.00 8.25
b. Double overprint 7.00 9.00
c. "3.XI." omitted 7.00 7.00
N7 A42 20h dark green .20 .25
a. Inverted overprint 5.00 6.00
b. "3.XI." omitted 7.00 8.25
c. Double overprint 14.00
N8 A42 25h deep blue 1.40 1.75
a. Inverted overprint 20.00 25.00
b. "3.XI." omitted 40.00 40.00
N9 A42 30h dl violet .40 .55
N10 A39 40h olive grn 14.00 17.50
N11 A39 50h dark green .60 .80
N12 A39 60h deep blue 1.00 1.40
N13 A39 80h orange brn .70 .80
a. Inverted overprint
N14 A39 1k car, *yel* .60 .80
a. Double overprint 14.00 14.00
N15 A40 2k light bl 25.00 27.50
N16 A40 4k yellow grn 55.00 72.50

Handstamped

N17 A40 10k dp violet *8,000. 10,000.*

Granite Paper

N18 A40 2k light blue
N19 A40 3k car rose 40.00 72.50
Nos. N1-N16,N19 (17) 140.50 198.25

Some authorities question the authenticity of No. N18. Counterfeits of Nos. N10, N15-N19 are plentiful.

Italian Stamps of 1901-18 Overprinted

Venezia
Giulia

Wmk. 140 ***Perf. 14***

N20 A42 1c brown .20 .40
a. Inverted overprint 3.25 5.00
N21 A43 2c orange brn .20 .40
a. Inverted overprint 2.50 *3.75*
N22 A48 5c green .15 .30
a. Inverted overprint 5.00 *7.00*
b. Double overprint 14.00
N23 A48 10c claret .15 .30
a. Inverted overprint 7.00 *10.00*
b. Double overprint 14.00
N24 A50 20c brn orange .15 .30
a. Inverted overprint 10.00 *15.00*
b. Double overprint 14.00 *20.00*
N25 A49 25c blue .15 .30
a. Double overprint *40.00*
b. Inverted overprint 14.00 *20.00*
N26 A49 40c brown .80 *2.00*
a. Inverted overprint *35.00*
N27 A45 45c olive grn .25 .50
a. Inverted overprint 14.00 *20.00*
N28 A49 50c violet .30 *.75*
N29 A49 60c brown car 3.25 *8.25*
N30 A46 1 l brn & green 1.40 *3.50*
Nos. N20-N30 (11) 7.00 *17.00*

Italian Stamps of 1901-18 Surcharged

Venezia
Giulia
5 Heller

N31 A48 5h on 5c green .15 .30
a. "5" omitted 10.00 *15.00*
b. Inverted surcharge 12.50 *17.50*
N32 A50 20h on 20c brn org .15 .30
a. Double surcharge 12.50 *17.50*

Issued in the Trentino

Austrian Stamps of 1916-18 Overprinted

Regno d Italia
Trentino
3 nov 1918

1918 **Unwmk.** ***Perf. 12½***

N33 A37 3h bright vio .50 .70
a. Double overprint 14.00 *20.00*
b. Inverted overprint 12.50 *16.00*
N34 A37 5h light grn .30 .45
a. "8 nov. 1918" *750.00*
b. Inverted overprint 12.50 *16.00*
N35 A37 6h dp orange 13.00 17.50
N36 A37 10h magenta .40 .60
a. "8 nov. 1918" 16.00 22.50
N37 A37 12h light blue 40.00 60.00
N38 A42 15h dull red 1.10 1.65
N39 A42 20h dark green .20 .30
a. "8 nov. 1918" 20.00 *32.50*
b. Double overprint 14.00 20.00
c. Inverted overprint 5.00 6.00
N40 A42 25h deep blue 9.00 13.00
N41 A42 30h dl violet 2.00 3.00
N42 A39 40h olive grn 13.00 17.50
N43 A39 50h dark green 5.00 7.25
a. Inverted overprint 20.00 26.00
N44 A39 60h deep blue 9.00 13.00
a. Double overprint 25.00 *32.50*
N45 A39 80h orange brn 14.00 20.00
N46 A39 90h red violet 200.00 300.00
N47 A39 1k car, *yel* 14.00 20.00
N48 A40 2k light blue 62.50 92.50
N49 A40 4k yel green *375.00 700.00*
N50 A40 10k dp violet *25,000.*

Granite Paper

N51 A40 2k light blue *100.00*

Counterfeits of Nos. N33-N51 are plentiful.

Italian Stamps of 1901-18 Overprinted

Venezia
Tridentina

Wmk. 140 ***Perf. 14***

N52 A42 1c brown .20 .50
a. Inverted overprint 6.00 9.00
N53 A43 2c orange brn .20 .50
a. Inverted overprint 6.00 9.00
N54 A48 5c green .20 .50
a. Inverted overprint 6.00 9.00
b. Double overprint 8.25 12.50
N55 A48 10c claret .20 .50
a. Inverted overprint 8.25 12.50
b. Double overprint 8.25 12.50
N56 A50 20c brn orange .20 .50
a. Inverted overprint 8.25 12.50
N57 A49 40c brown 4.00 10.50
N58 A45 45c olive grn 2.50 6.00
a. Double overprint 26.00 *40.00*
N59 A49 50c violet 2.50 6.00
N60 A46 1 l brn & green 2.50 6.00
a. Double overprint 26.00 *40.00*
Nos. N52-N60 (9) 12.50 31.00

Italian Stamps of 1906-18 Surcharged

Venezia
Tridentina
5 Heller

N61 A48 5h on 5c green .15 .25
N62 A48 10h on 10c claret .15 .25
a. Inverted overprint 9.50 *13.00*
N63 A50 20h on 20c brn org .15 .25
a. Double surcharge 9.50 *13.00*
Set value .25

General Issue

Italian Stamps of 1901-18 Surcharged

5
centesimi
di corona

1919

N64 A42 1c on 1c brown .15 .15
a. Inverted surcharge 1.80 2.75
N65 A43 2c on 2c org brn .15 .15
a. Double surcharge 32.50
b. Inverted surcharge .95 1.50
N66 A48 5c on 5c green .15 .15
a. Inverted surcharge 4.50 6.50
b. Double surcharge 9.00 9.00
N67 A48 10c on 10c claret .15 .15
a. Inverted surcharge 4.50 6.50
b. Double surcharge 9.00 *13.00*
N68 A50 20c on 20c brn org .15 .15
a. Double surcharge 13.00 *19.00*
N69 A49 25c on 25c blue .15 .15
a. Double surcharge 13.00 13.00
N70 A49 40c on 40c brown .15 .15
a. "ccrona" 15.00 *22.50*
N71 A45 45c on 45c ol grn .15 .15
a. Inverted surcharge 13.00 19.00
N72 A49 50c on 50c violet .15 .15
N73 A49 60c on 60c brn car .15 .15
a. "00" for "60" 15.00 *22.50*

Surcharged

1
corona

N74 A46 1cor on 1 l brn & grn .15 .15
Set value, N64-N74 .90 .90

Surcharges similar to these but differing in style or arrangement of type were used in Dalmatia.

OCCUPATION SPECIAL DELIVERY STAMPS

Issued in Trieste

Special Delivery Stamp of Italy of 1903 Overprinted

Venezia Giulia

1918 **Wmk. 140** ***Perf. 14***

NE1 SD1 25c rose red 2.50 6.00
a. Inverted overprint 16.00 25.00

General Issue

Special Delivery Stamps of Italy of 1903-09 Surcharged

25 centesimi
di corona

1919

NE2 SD1 25c on 25c rose .15 .20
a. Double surcharge 8.25 *12.50*
NE3 SD2 30c on 30c bl & rose .15 .40
Set value .25

OCCUPATION POSTAGE DUE STAMPS

Issued in Trieste

Postage Due Stamps of Italy, 1870-94, Overprinted

Venezia
Giulia

1918 **Wmk. 140** ***Perf. 14***

NJ1 D3 5c buff & mag .15 .30
a. Inverted overprint 3.75 3.00
b. Double overprint 25.00
NJ2 D3 10c buff & mag .15 .30
a. Inverted overprint 7.25 *10.50*
NJ3 D3 20c buff & mag .15 .30
a. Double overprint 25.00
b. Inverted overprint 7.25 *10.50*

NJ4 D3 30c buff & mag .25 .50
NJ5 D3 40c buff & mag 2.00 5.00
a. Inverted overprint 37.50 *55.00*
NJ6 D3 50c buff & mag 5.00 12.50
a. Inverted overprint 37.50 *55.00*
NJ7 D3 1 l bl & mag 13.00 32.50
Nos. NJ1-NJ7 (7) 20.70 51.40

General Issue

Postage Due Stamps of Italy, 1870-1903 Surcharged **5 centesimi di corona**

1919

Buff & Magenta

NJ8 D3 5c on 5c .15 .30
a. Inverted overprint 2.00 3.00
NJ9 D3 10c on 10c .15 .30
a. Center and surcharge invtd. 10.00 *15.00*
NJ10 D3 20c on 20c .15 .30
a. Double overprint 20.00 *30.00*
NJ11 D3 30c on 30c .15 .30
NJ12 D3 40c on 40c .15 .30
NJ13 D3 50c on 50c .15 .30

Surcharged **una corona**

NJ14 D3 1cor on 1 l bl & mag .15 .30
NJ15 D3 2cor on 2 l bl & mag 4.50 11.00
NJ16 D3 5cor on 5 l bl & mag 4.50 11.00
Nos. NJ8-NJ16 (9) 10.05 24.10

A. M. G. ISSUE FOR AUSTRIA

> Catalogue values for unused stamps in this section are for Never Hinged items.

Issued jointly by the Allied Military Government of the US and Great Britain, for civilian use in areas under American, British and French occupation. (Upper Austria, Salzburg, Tyrol, Vorarlberg, Styria and Carinthia).

OS1

1945 Unwmk. Litho. *Perf. 11*

4N1 OS1 1g aquamarine .15 .15
4N2 OS1 3g deep orange .15 .15
4N3 OS1 4g buff .15 .15
4N4 OS1 5g bright green .15 .15
4N5 OS1 6g red violet .15 .15
4N6 OS1 8g rose pink .15 .15
4N7 OS1 10g light gray .15 .15
4N8 OS1 12g pale buff brown .15 .15
4N9 OS1 15g rose red .15 .15
4N10 OS1 20g copper brown .15 .15
4N11 OS1 25g deep blue .15 .15
4N12 OS1 30g bright violet .15 .15
4N13 OS1 40g light ultra .15 .15
4N14 OS1 60g light olive grn .15 .18
4N15 OS1 1s dark violet .15 .30
4N16 OS1 2s yellow .20 .30
4N17 OS1 5s deep ultra .40 .45
Set value 1.40 1.90

For Nos. 4N2, 4N4-4N17 overprinted "PORTO" see Nos. J189-J203.

AUSTRIAN OFFICES ABROAD

These stamps were on sale and usable at all Austrian post-offices in Crete and in the Turkish Empire.

100 Centimes = 1 Franc

OFFICES IN CRETE

> Used values are italicized for stamps often found with false cancellations.

Stamps of Austria of 1899-1901 Issue, Surcharged in Black:

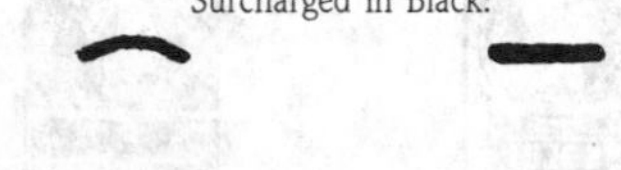

CENTIMES a

CENTIMES b

CENTIMES c

FRANC d

1903-04 Unwmk. *Perf. 12½, 13½*

On Nos. 73a, 75a, 77a, 81a

Granite Paper

With Varnish Bars

1 A15(a) 5c on 5h blue green 1.50 3.50
2 A16(b) 10c on 10h rose .70 *3.75*
3 A16(b) 25c on 25h ultra 30.00 22.50
4 A17(c) 50c on 50h gray blue 6.75 *110.00*

On Nos. 83, 83a, 84, 85

Without Varnish Bars

5 A18(d) 1fr on 1k car rose 2.25 *90.00*
a. 1fr on 1k carmine 4.00
b. Horiz. or vert. pair, imperf. between 175.00
6 A18(d) 2fr on 2k ('04) 10.00 *225.00*
7 A18(d) 4fr on 4k ('04) 10.50 *400.00*
Nos. 1-7 (7) 61.70

Surcharged on Austrian Stamps of 1904-05

1905

On Nos. 89, 97

Without Varnish Bars

8 A19(a) 5c on 5h bl grn 40.00 18.00
9 A20(b) 10c on 10h car .80 *6.00*

On Nos. 89a, 97a, 99a, 103a

With Varnish Bars

8a A19(a) 5c on 5h blue green 4.00 5.00
9a A20(b) 10c on 10h carmine 20.00 14.00
10 A20(b) 25c on 25h ultra .65 *35.00*
11 A21(b) 50c on 50h dl bl 1.00 *150.00*

Surcharged on Austrian Stamps and Type of 1906-07

1907 *Perf. 12½, 13½*

Without Varnish Bars

12 A19(a) 5c on 5h yel green (#90) .80 *3.25*
13 A20(b) 10c on 10h car (#92) 1.10 *15.00*
14 A20(b) 15c on 15h vio 1.25 *15.00*
Nos. 12-14 (3) 3.15

A5

A6

1908 Typo. *Perf. 12½*

15 A5 5c green, *yellow* .35 .20
16 A5 10c scarlet, *rose* .40 .30
17 A5 15c brown, *buff* .45 *2.75*
18 A5 25c dp blue, *blue* 11.50 2.75

Engr.

19 A6 50c lake, *yellow* 1.75 *18.00*
20 A6 1fr brown, *gray* 2.50 *25.00*
a. Vert pair, imperf. btwn. 175.00
Nos. 15-20 (6) 16.95 *49.00*

Nos. 15 to 18 are on paper colored on the surface only. All values exist imperforate.

60th year of the reign of Emperor Franz Josef, for permanent use.

Paper Colored Through

1914 Typo.

21 A5 10c rose, *rose* 1.65 *575.00*
22 A5 25c ultra, *blue* .65 *65.00*

Nos. 21 and 22 exist imperforate.

OFFICES IN THE TURKISH EMPIRE

From 1863 to 1867 the stamps of Lombardy-Venetia (Nos. 15 to 24) were used at the Austrian Offices in the Turkish Empire.

100 Soldi = 1 Florin
40 Paras = 1 Piaster

> Values for unused stamps are for copies with gum. Specimens without gum sell for about one-third or less of the figures quoted.
> Used values are italicized for stamps often found with false cancellations.

For similar designs in Kreuzers, see early Austria.

A1

A2

Two different printing methods were used, as in the 1867-74 issues of Austria. They may be distinguished by the coarse or fine lines of the hair and whiskers and by the paper, which is more transparent on the later issue.

1867 Typo. Wmk. 91 *Perf. 9½*

Coarse Print

1 A1 2sld orange 1.75 *22.50*
a. 2sld yellow 55.00 30.00
2 A1 3sld green 100.00 40.00
a. 3sld dark green 125.00 40.00
3 A1 5sld red 100.00 11.00
a. 5sld carmine 110.00 16.00
4 A1 10sld blue 100.00 1.75
a. 10sld light blue 110.00 2.50
b. 10sld dark blue 110.00 3.00
5 A1 15sld brown 16.00 6.00
a. 15sld dark brown 45.00 20.00
b. 15sld reddish brown 16.00 10.00
6 A1 25sld gray lilac 50.00 *40.00*
a. 25sld brown violet 16.00 *40.00*
7 A2 50sld brn, perf. 10½ 1.00 *45.00*
a. Perf. 12 90.00 *70.00*
b. Perf. 13 250.00
k. Perf. 9 25.00 *50.00*
l. 50sld pale red brn, perf. 12 55.00 60.00
m. Vert. pair, imperf. btwn. 325.00 *650.00*
n. Horiz. pair, imperf. btwn. 325.00 *750.00*
o. Perf. 10½x9 65.00 100.00

Perf. 9, 9½, 10½ and Compound

1876-83

Fine Print

7C A1 2sld yellow ('83) .20 *1,375.*
7D A1 3sld green ('78) 1.00 *20.00*
7E A1 5sld red ('78) .40 *15.00*
7F A1 10sld blue 55.00 1.00
7I A1 15sld org brn ('81) 9.00 *125.00*
7J A1 25sld gray lilac ('83) .50 *275.00*
Nos. 7C-7J (6) 66.10

The 10 soldi has been reprinted in deep dull blue, perforated 10½.

A3

1883 *Perf. 9½, 10, 10½*

8 A3 2sld brown .20 *115.00*
9 A3 3sld green 1.00 *27.50*
10 A3 5sld rose .20 *16.00*
11 A3 10sld blue .75 .50
12 A3 20sld gray 5.50 *7.50*
13 A3 50sld red lilac 1.50 *17.50*
Nos. 8-13 (6) 9.15

A4

A5

10 PARAS ON 3 SOLDI:

Type I - Surcharge 16½mm across. "PARA" about ½mm above bottom of "10." 2mm space between "10" and "P"; 1½mm between "A" and "10." Perf. 9½ only.

Type II - Surcharge 15¼ to 16mm across. "PARA" on same line with figures or slightly higher or lower. 1½mm space between "10" and "P"; 1mm between "A" and "10." Perf. 9½ and 10.

1886 *Perf. 9½ and 10*

14 A4 10pa on 3sld green, type II .30 *6.00*
a. 10pa on 3sld green, type I 185.00 350.00
b. Inverted surcharge, type I *1,850.*

1888

15 A5 10pa on 3kr grn 3.00 7.50
a. "01 PARA 10" *400.00*
16 A5 20pa on 5kr rose .60 *8.00*
17 A5 1pi on 10kr blue 45.00 1.10
a. Perf. 13½ 225.00
b. Double surcharge 275.00
18 A5 2pi on 20kr gray 1.50 4.50
19 A5 5pi on 50kr vio 2.25 *15.00*
Nos. 15-19 (5) 52.35

A6

1890-92 Unwmk. *Perf. 9 to 13½*

Granite Paper

20 A6 8pa on 2kr brn ('92) .15 .15
a. Perf. 9½ 10.00 15.00
21 A6 10pa on 3kr green .65 .15
a. Pair, imperf. between
22 A6 20pa on 5kr rose .15 .15
23 A6 1pi on 10kr ultra .35 .15
24 A6 2pi on 20kr ol grn 5.50 *25.00*
25 A6 5pi on 50kr violet 11.00 *60.00*
Nos. 20-25 (6) 17.80

See note after Austria No. 65 on missing numerals, etc.

Austria Nos. 66, 69 Surcharged **2 PIASTER 2**

1891 *Perf. 9 to 13½*

26 A14 2pi on 20kr 4.75 1.25
a. Perf. 9½ 80.00 20.00
27 A14 5pi on 50kr 2.75 2.50

Two types of the surcharge on No. 26 exist.

A8

1892 *Perf. 10½, 11½*

28 A8 10pi on 1gld blue 11.00 25.00
29 A8 20pi on 2gld car 13.00 35.00
a. Double surcharge

1896 *Perf. 10½, 11½, 12½*

30 A8 10pi on 1gld pale lilac 13.00 20.00
31 A8 20pi on 2gld gray grn 42.50 65.00

A9

A10

A11

A12

Perf. 10½, 12½, 13½ and Compound

1900

Without Varnish Bars

32 A9 10pa on 5h bl grn 4.50 .75
33 A10 20pa on 10h rose 5.00 .75
b. Perf. 12½x10½ 250.00 85.00
34 A10 1pi on 25h ultra 3.50 .25
35 A11 2pi on 50h gray bl 7.25 3.00
36 A12 5pi on 1k car rose 1.10 .30
a. 5pi on 1k carmine 1.25 1.00
b. Horiz. or vert. pair, imperf. btwn. 115.00

37	A12	10pi on 2k gray lil	3.00	2.25
a.		Horiz. pair, imperf. btwn.		
38	A12	20pi on 4k gray grn	2.50	6.00
		Nos. 32-38 (7)	26.85	13.30

In the surcharge on Nos. 37 and 38 "piaster" is printed "PIAST."

1901

With Varnish Bars

32a	A9	10pa on 5h blue green	2.00	2.50
33a	A10	20pa on 10h rose	2.50	175.00
34a	A10	1pi on 25h ultra	1.65	.40
35a	A11	2pi on 50h gray blue	3.75	3.50
		Nos. 32a-35a (4)	9.90	

A13

A14

A15

1906 ***Perf. 12½ to 13½***

Without Varnish Bars

39	A13	10pa dark green	12.00	1.00
40	A14	20pa rose	.80	.35
41	A14	1pi ultra	.35	.15
42	A15	2pi gray blue	.90	.40
		Nos. 39-42 (4)	14.05	1.90

1903 **With Varnish Bars**

39a	A13	10pa dark green	4.75	.75
40a	A14	20pa rose	2.25	.35
41a	A14	1pi ultra	1.75	.20
42a	A15	2pi gray blue	105.00	1.10

1907

Without Varnish Bars

43	A13	10pa yellow green	.35	1.25
45	A14	30pa violet	.50	2.25

A16

A17

1908 **Typo.** ***Perf. 12½***

46	A16	10pa green, *yellow*	.15	.15
47	A16	20pa scarlet, *rose*	.20	.15
48	A16	30pa brown, *buff*	.30	.40
49	A16	1pi deep bl, *blue*	12.00	.15
50	A16	60pa vio, *bluish*	.60	2.25

Engr.

51	A17	2pi lake, *yellow*	.40	.15
52	A17	5pi brown, *gray*	.60	.40
53	A17	10pi green, *yellow*	.90	1.10
54	A17	20pi blue, *gray*	1.50	2.25
		Nos. 46-54 (9)	16.65	7.00

Nos. 46 to 50 are on paper colored on the surface only. 60th year of the reign of Emperor Franz Josef I, for permanent use. All values exist imperforate.

1913-14 **Typo.**

Paper Colored Through

57	A16	20pa rose, *rose* ('14)	.80	175.00
58	A16	1pi ultra, *blue*	.35	.30

Nos. 57 and 58 exist imperforate.

POSTAGE DUE STAMPS

D1

D2

Black Surcharge

1902 **Unwmk.** ***Perf. 12½, 13½***

J1	D1	10pa on 5h green	1.25	2.75
J2	D1	20pa on 10h green	1.25	2.50
J3	D1	1pi on 20h green	2.00	3.50
J4	D1	2pi on 40h green	2.00	2.75
J5	D1	5pi on 100h green	3.00	1.65
		Nos. J1-J5 (5)	9.50	13.15

Shades of Nos. J1 to J5 exist, varying from yellowish green to dark green.

1908 **Typo.** ***Perf. 12½***

J6	D2	¼pi green	3.25	5.00
J7	D2	½pi green	1.50	3.50
J8	D2	1pi green	2.00	5.00
J9	D2	1½pi green	.75	6.50
J10	D2	2pi green	2.25	8.00
J11	D2	5pi green	2.25	5.00
J12	D2	10pi green	18.00	85.00
J13	D2	20pi green	17.50	110.00
J14	D2	30pi green	12.50	7.00
		Nos. J6-J14 (9)	60.00	235.00

Nos. J6 to J14 exist in distinct shades of green and on thick chalky, regular and thin ordinary paper. Values are for the least expensive variety. No. J6-J14 exist imperforate.

Forgeries exist.

LOMBARDY-VENETIA

Formerly a kingdom in the north of Italy forming part of the Austrian Empire. Milan and Venice were the two principal cities. Lombardy was annexed to Sardinia in 1859, and Venetia to the kingdom of Italy in 1866.

100 Centesimi = 1 Lira
100 Soldi = 1 Florin (1858)

For similar designs in Kreuzers, see early Austria.

Coat of Arms — A1

15 CENTESIMI:

Type I- "5" is on a level with the "1." One heavy line around coat of arms center.

Type II- As type I, but "5" is a trifle sideways and is higher than the "1."

Type III- As type II, but two, thinner, lines around center.

45 CENTESIMI:

Type I- Lower part of "45" is lower than "Centes." One heavy line around coat of arms center. "45" varies in height and distance from "Centes."

Type II- One heavy line around coat of arms center. Lower part of "45" is on a level with lower part of "Centes."

Type III- As type II, but two, thinner, lines around center.

Wmk. K.K.H.M. in Sheet or Unwmkd.

1850 **Typo.** ***Imperf.***

Thick to Thin Paper

1	A1	5c buff	1,425.	90.00
a.		Printed on both sides	6,250.	125.00
b.		5c yellow	3,500.	325.00
c.		5c orange	1,750.	175.00
d.		5c lemon yellow		1,250.
3	A1	10c black	1,600.	85.00
a.		10c gray black	1,600.	100.00
4	A1	15c red, type III	675.00	5.00
b.		15c red, type I	1,900.	20.00
c.		Ribbed paper, type II	17,500.	550.00
d.		Ribbed paper, type I	7,500.	125.00
f.		15c red, type II	875.00	8.00
5	A1	30c brown	2,000.	5.00
a.		Ribbed paper	3,500.	65.00
6	A1	45c blue, type III	6,000.	15.00
a.		45c blue, type I	7,000.	27.50
b.		Ribbed paper, type I	14,000.	225.00
c.		45c blue, type II	12,500.	42.50

1854 **Machine-made Paper, Type III**

3c	A1	10c black	4,000.	175.00
4g	A1	15c pale red	500.00	2.25
5b	A1	30c brown	1,900.	4.50
6d	A1	45c blue	6,000.	22.50

See note about the paper of the 1850 issue of Austria. *The reprints are type III, in brighter colors.*

A2

A3

A4

A5

A6

Two Types of Each Value.

Type I- Loops of the bow at the back of the head broken.

Type II- Loops complete. Wreath projects further at top of head.

1858-62 **Embossed** ***Perf. 14½***

7	A2	2s yel, type II	440.00	95.00
a.		2s yellow, type I	2,000.	425.00
8	A3	3s black, type II	3,000.	125.00
a.		3s black, type I	1,900.	200.00
b.		Perf. 16, type I		875.00
c.		Perf. 15x16 or 16x15, type I	3,500.	325.00
9	A3	3s grn, type II ('62)	350.00	65.00
10	A4	5s red, type II	200.00	5.00
a.		5s red, type I	525.00	8.50
b.		Printed on both sides, type II		4,750.
11	A5	10s brown, type II	1,250.	8.00
a.		10s brown, type I	350.00	30.00
12	A6	15s blue, type II	1,500.	15.00
a.		15s blue, type I	2,500.	80.00
b.		Printed on both sides, type II		13,500.

The reprints are of type II and are perforated 10½, 11, 11½, 12, 12½ and 13. There are also imperforate reprints of Nos. 7-9.

A7

A8

1861-62 ***Perf. 14***

13	A7	5s red	1,400.	3.00
14	A7	10s brown ('62)	2,100.	25.00

The reprints are perforated 9, 9 ½, 10½, 11, 12, 12½ and 13. There are also imperforate reprints of the 2 and 3s.

The 2, 3 and 15s of this type exist only as reprints.

1863

15	A8	2s yellow	110.00	150.00
16	A8	3s green	1,200.	85.00
17	A8	5s rose	1,300.	10.00
18	A8	10s blue	2,750.	85.00
19	A8	15s yellow brown	1,900.	125.00

1864-65 **Wmk. 91** ***Perf. 9½***

20	A8	2s yellow ('65)	165.00	375.00
21	A8	3s green	25.00	18.00
22	A8	5s rose	3.50	2.00
23	A8	10s blue	21.00	6.00
24	A8	15s yellow brown	190.00	80.00

Nos. 15-24 reprints are perforated 10½ and 13. There are also imperforate reprints of the 2s and 3s.

NEWSPAPER TAX STAMPS

From 1853 to 1858 the Austrian Newspaper Tax Stamp 2kr green (No. PR1) was also used in Lombardy-Venetia, at the value of 10 centesimi.

NT1

Type I - The banderol of the left eagle touches the beak of the eagle.

Type II - The banderol does not touch the beak.

1858-59 **Unwmk.** **Typo.** ***Imperf.***

PR1	NT1	1kr black, type I ('59)	2,000.	2,750.
PR2	NT1	2kr red, type II ('59)	250.00	50.00
PR3	NT1	4kr red, type I	85,000.	3,250.

No. PR2 exists with watermark 91.

The reprints are on a smooth toned paper and are all of type II.

AZERBAIJAN

ˌa–zər–ˌbī–ˈjän

(Azerbaidjan)

LOCATION — Southernmost part of Russia in Eastern Europe, bounded by Georgia, Dagestan, Caspian Sea, Persia and Armenia

GOVT. — A Soviet Socialist Republic

AREA — 32,686 sq. mi.

POP. — 2,096,973 (1923)

CAPITAL — Baku

100 Kopecks = 1 Ruble

Catalogue values for unused stamps in this country are for Never Hinged items, beginning with Scott 350 in the regular postage section.

National Republic

Standard Bearer — A1

Farmer at Sunset — A2

Baku — A3

Temple of Eternal Fires — A4

1919 **Unwmk.** **Litho.** ***Imperf.***

1	A1	10k multicolored	.15	.30
2	A1	20k multicolored	.15	.30
3	A2	40k green, yellow & blk	.15	.30
4	A2	60k red, yellow & blk	.25	.30
5	A2	1r blue, yellow & blk	.35	.50
6	A3	2r red, bister & blk	.35	.50
7	A3	5r blue, bister & blk	.45	.85
8	A3	10r olive grn, bis & blk	.65	.95
9	A4	25r blue, red & black	1.10	1.50
10	A4	50r ol grn, red & black	1.40	1.75
		Nos. 1-10 (10)	5.00	7.25

The two printings of Nos. 1-10 are distinguished by the grayish or thin white paper. Both have yellowish gum. White paper copies are worth five times the above values.

For surcharges see Nos. 57-64, 75-80.

Soviet Socialist Republic

Symbols of Labor — A5

Oil Well — A6

Bibi Eibatt Oil Field — A7

Khan's Palace, Baku — A8

Globe and Workers — A9

Maiden's Tower, Baku — A10

Goukasoff House A11

Blacksmiths A12

Hall of Judgment, Baku — A13

1922

15	A5	1r gray green	.20	.35
16	A6	2r olive black	.50	.50
17	A7	5r gray brown	.20	.35
18	A8	10r gray	.50	.65
19	A9	25r orange brown	.20	.40
20	A10	50r violet	.20	.40
21	A11	100r dull red	.35	.50
22	A12	150r blue	.35	.50
23	A9	250r violet & buff	.35	.50
24	A13	400r dark blue	.35	.50
25	A12	500r gray vio & blk	.35	.50
26	A13	1000r dk blue & rose	.35	.60
27	A8	2000r blue & black	.35	.50
28	A7	3000r brown & blue	.35	.50
a.		Tete beche pair	13.00	14.00
29	A11	5000r black, *ol grn*	.60	.75
		Nos. 15-29 (15)	5.20	7.50

Counterfeits exist of Nos. 1-29. They generally sell for more than genuine copies.

For overprints and surcharges see Nos. 32-41, 43, 45-55, 65-72, 300-304, 307-333.

Nos. 15, 17, 23, 28, 27 Handstamped from Metal Dies in a Numbering Machine

15000

1922

32	A5	10,000r on 1r	8.00	8.00
33	A7	15,000r on 5r	9.50	10.00
34	A9	33,000r on 250r	5.00	5.00
35	A7	50,000r on 3000r	5.00	5.00
36	A8	66,000r on 2000r	11.00	10.00
		Nos. 32-36 (5)	38.50	38.00

Same Surcharges on Regular Issue and Semi-Postal Stamps of 1922

1922-23

36A	A7	500r on 5r	60.00	67.50
37	A6	1000r on 2r	15.00	15.00
38	A8	2000r on 10r	5.00	4.00
39	A8	5000r on 2000r	5.00	3.00
40	A11	15,000r on 5000r	12.00	10.00
41	A5	20,000r on 1r	10.00	9.00
42	SP1	25,000r on 500r	35.00	
43	A7	50,000r on 5r	12.50	12.50
44	SP2	50,000r on 1000r	26.00	
45	A11	50,000r on 5000r	5.00	4.50
45A	A8	60,000r on 2000r	12.50	14.00
46	A11	70,000r on 5000r	20.00	20.00
47	A6	100,000r on 2r	15.00	15.00
48	A8	200,000r on 10r	10.00	10.00
49	A9	200,000r on 25r	15.00	15.00
50	A7	300,000r on 3000r	5.00	5.00
51	A8	500,000r on 2000r	15.00	10.00

Revalued

52	A7	500r on #33	30.00	*52.50*
53	A11	15,000r on #46	30.00	*52.50*
54	A7	300,000r on #35	45.00	*55.00*
55	A8	500,000r on #36	50.00	*75.00*

The surcharged semi-postal stamps were used for regular postage.

Same Surcharges on Stamps of 1919

57	A1	25,000r on 10k	.70	1.00
58	A1	50,000r on 20k	.70	1.00
59	A2	75,000r on 40k	1.75	2.50
60	A2	100,000r on 60k	.70	.95
61	A2	200,000r on 1r	.70	.95
62	A3	300,000r on 2r	.88	1.10
63	A3	500,000r on 5r	1.00	1.10
64	A2	750,000r on 40k	3.50	2.75
		Nos. 57-64 (8)	9.93	11.35

Handstamped from Settings of Rubber Type in Black or Violet

100000 **200.000**

Nos. 65-66, 71-80 Nos. 67-70

On Stamps of 1922

65	A6	100,000r on 2r	12.00	12.00
66	A8	200,000r on 10r	13.00	14.00
67	A8	200,000r on 10r (V)	17.50	15.00
68	A9	200,000r on 25r (V)	15.00	11.00
a.		Black surcharge	26.00	27.50
69	A7	300,000r on 3000r (V)	25.00	25.00
70	A8	500,000r on 2000r (V)	20.00	20.00
a.		Black surcharge	27.50	29.00
72	A11	1,500,000r on 5000r (V)	16.00	15.00
a.		Black surcharge	16.00	15.00

On Stamps of 1919

75	A1	50,000r on 20k	1.00	
76	A2	75,000r on 40k	.65	
77	A2	100,000r on 60k	1.25	
78	A2	200,000r on 1r	.15	.15
79	A3	300,000r on 2r	1.00	
80	A3	500,000r on 5r	1.25	

Inverted and double surcharges of Nos. 32-80 sell for twice the normal price.

Counterfeits exist of Nos. 32-80.

Baku Province

Regular and Semi-Postal Stamps of 1922 Handstamped in Violet or Black

БАКИНСКОИ П. К.

The overprint reads "Bakinskoi P(ochtovoy) K(ontory)," meaning Baku Post Office.

1922 Unwmk. *Imperf.*

300	A5	1r gray green	*13.00*
301	A7	5r gray brown	*13.00*
302	A12	150r blue	*4.00*
303	A9	250r violet & buff	*6.00*
304	A13	400r dark blue	*5.25*
305	SP1	500r blue & pale blue	*6.00*
306	SP2	1000r brown & bister	*8.00*
307	A8	2000r blue & black	*8.00*
308	A7	3000r brown & blue	*13.00*
309	A11	5000r black, *ol grn*	*13.00*
		Nos. 300-309 (10)	*89.25*

Stamps of 1922 Handstamped in Violet

Бакинскаго Г-П-Т.О.№1

Ovpt. reads: Baku Post, Telegraph Office No. 1.

1924

Overprint 24x2mm

312	A12	150r blue	*6.00*
313	A9	250r violet & buff	*6.00*
314	A13	400r dark blue	*6.00*
317	A8	2000r blue & black	*6.50*
318	A7	3000r brown & blue	*6.50*
319	A11	5000r black, *ol grn*	*6.50*

Overprint 30x3½mm

323	A12	150r blue	*6.00*
324	A9	250r violet & buff	*6.00*
325	A13	400r dark blue	*6.00*
328	A8	2000r blue & black	*6.00*
329	A7	3000r brown & blue	*6.50*
330	A11	5000r black, *ol grn*	*6.00*

Overprinted on Nos. 32-33, 35

331	A5	10,000r on 1r	*22.50*
332	A7	15,000r on 5r	*22.50*
333	A7	50,000r on 3000r	*27.50*
		Nos. 312-333 (15)	*146.50*

The overprinted semipostal stamps were used for regular postage.

A 24x2mm handstamp on #17, B1-B2, and 30x3½mm on #15, 17, B1-B2, was of private origin.

With the breakup of the Soviet Union on Dec. 26, 1991, Azerbaijan and ten former Soviet republics established the Commonwealth of Independent States.

100 Kopecks = 1 Ruble

100 Giapiks = 1 Manat (1992)

Catalogue values for unused stamps in this section, from this point to the end of the section, are for Never Hinged items.

Flag, Map — A20

Unwmk.

1992, Mar. 26 Litho. *Perf. 14*

350	A20	35k multicolored	*3.00*

Park — A21

1992, May 7 *Perf. 12*

351	A21	25g on 15k multicolored	*.35*
352	A21	35g on 15k multicolored	*.50*
353	A21	50g on 15k multicolored	*.70*
354	A21	1.50m on 15k multicolored	*2.10*
355	A21	2.50m on 15k multicolored	*3.50*
		Nos. 351-355 (5)	*7.15*

Nos. 351-355 are overprintsuecharged on a National Park series prepared for the Soviet Union with one stamp for each republic. Not issued without surcharges.

For surcharges see Nos. 435, 501-504.

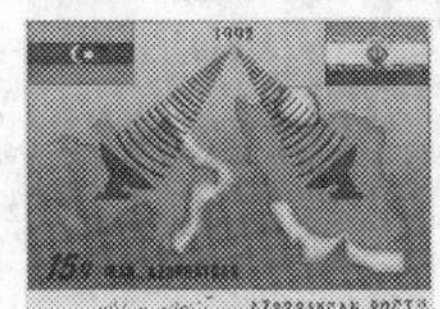

Iran-Azerbaijan Telecommunications — A21a

1992 Photo. *Perf. 13x13½*

355A	A21a	15g multicolored	*5.00*

See Iran No. 2544.

For surcharges see Nos. 403-406.

Horses — A22

1993, Feb. 1 Litho. *Perf. 13*

356	A22	20g shown	*.30*
357	A22	30g Kabarda	*.40*
358	A22	50g Qarabair	*.70*
359	A22	1m Don	*1.40*
360	A22	2.50m Yakut	*3.50*
361	A22	5m Orlov	*7.00*
362	A22	10m Diliboz	*14.00*
		Nos. 356-362 (7)	*27.30*

Perf. 12½

Souvenir Sheet

362A	A22	8m Qarabag	*5.25*

Ruins — A23

Government Building — A24

1992-93 Litho. *Perf. 12½x12*

363	A23	10g blk & blue grn	*.15*
365	A23	20g black & red	*.20*
367	A23	50g black & green	*.15*
368	A23	50g black & yellow	*.50*
370	A23	1m black & rose lilac	*.25*
372	A23	1.50m black & blue	*1.50*
373	A23	2.50m black & yellow	*.50*
374	A23	5m black & green	*1.00*
		Nos. 363-374 (8)	*4.25*

Issued: 10g, 20g, 1.50m, #367, Dec. 20; #368, 1m, 2.50m, 5m, June 20, 1993.

This is an expanding set. Numbers may change.

1993, Oct. 12 Litho. *Perf. 12½*

375	A24	25g yellow & black	*.15*
376	A24	30g green & black	*.20*
377	A24	50g blue & black	*.30*
378	A24	1m red & black	*.55*
		Nos. 375-378 (4)	*1.20*

For surcharges see No. 407-414.

Flowers — A25

1993, Aug. 12 Litho. *Perf. 12½*

379	A25	25g Tulipa eichleri	*.15*
380	A25	50g Puschkinia scilloides	*.15*
381	A25	1m Iris elegantissima	*.30*
382	A25	1.50m Iris acutiloba	*.40*
383	A25	5m Tulipa florenskyii	*1.50*
384	A25	10m Iris reticulata	*2.75*
		Nos. 379-384 (6)	*5.25*

Souvenir Sheet

Perf. 13

385	A25	10m Muscari elecostomum	*2.75*

No. 385 contains one 32x40mm stamp.

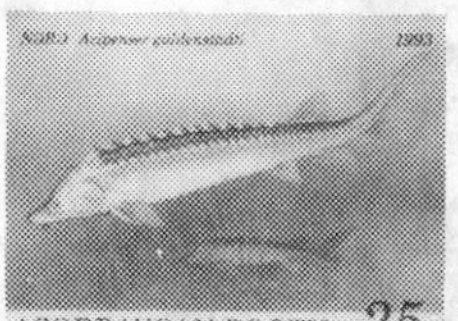

Fish A26

Designs: 25g, Acipenser guldenstadti. 50g, Acipenser stellatus. 1m, Rutilus frisii kutum. 1.50m, Rutilus rutilus caspicus. 5m, Salmo trutta caspius. No. 391, Alosa kessleri. No. 392, Huso huso.

1993, Aug. 27 *Perf. 12½*

386	A26	25g multicolored	*.15*
387	A26	50g multicolored	*.15*
388	A26	1m multicolored	*.30*
389	A26	1.50m multicolored	*.40*
390	A26	5m multicolored	*1.50*
391	A26	10m multicolored	*2.75*
		Nos. 386-391 (6)	*5.25*

Souvenir Sheet

Perf. 13

392	A26	10m multicolored	*2.75*

No. 392 contains one 40x32mm stamp.

Pres. Geidar A. Aliyev — A27

Design: No. 394, Map of Nakhichevan.

1993, Sept. 12 Litho. *Perf. 12½x13*

393	A27	25m multicolored	*2.00*	
394	A27	25m multicolored	*2.00*	
a.		Pair, #393-394	*4.00*	
b.		Souv. sheet, #393-394, perf. 12	*4.00*	
c.		Souv. sheet, #393-394, perf. 12	*4.00*	

Name on map spelled "Naxcivan" on #394c. It is spelled "Haxcivan" on #394-394b.

No. 394c issued Sept. 20, 1993.

Historic Buildings, Baku — A28

Style of tombs: 2m, Fortress, 13th-14th cent. 4m, Moorish gate, 15th cent. 8m, Oriental-style columns, 15th cent.

1994, Jan. 17 Litho. *Perf. 11*

395 A28 2m red, silver & black *.20*
396 A28 4m green, silver & black *.35*
397 A28 8m blue, silver & black *.75*
Nos. 395-397 (3) 1.30

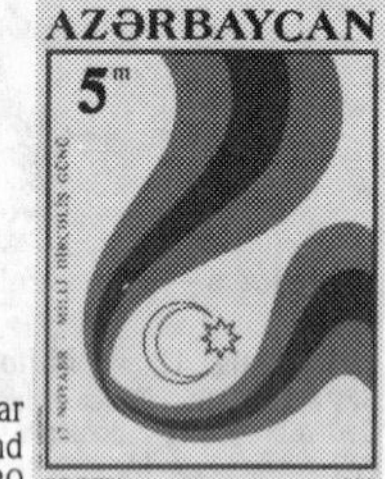

Natl. Colors, Star and Crescent — A29

1994, Jan. 17 *Perf. 12½*

398 A29 5m shown *.60*
399 A29 8m Natl. coat of arms *1.00*

Mohammed Fizuli (1494-1556), Poet — A30

1994, Jan. 17 *Perf. 12½*

400 A30 10m multicolored *1.40*

No. 400 printed se-tenant with label.

Mammed Amin Rasulzade (1884-1955), Politician A31

AZƏRBAYCAN
POÇTU 1994 20m
CƏLİL MƏMMƏDQULUZADƏ

Jalil Mamedkulizade, Politician, 125th Birth Anniv. — A32

1994, May 21 *Perf. 12½, 13 (#402)*

401 A31 15m black, yellow & brown *1.65*
402 A32 20m black, blue & gold *1.90*

No. 402 printed se-tenant with label.

No. 355A Surchaged

2 m.

1994, Jan. 18 Photo. *Perf. 13x13½*

403 A21a 2m on 15g *.15*
404 A21a 20m on 15g *.80*
405 A21a 25m on 15g *1.00*
406 A21a 50m on 15g *2.00*
Nos. 403-406 (4) 3.95

5 m.

Nos. 375-378 Surcharged

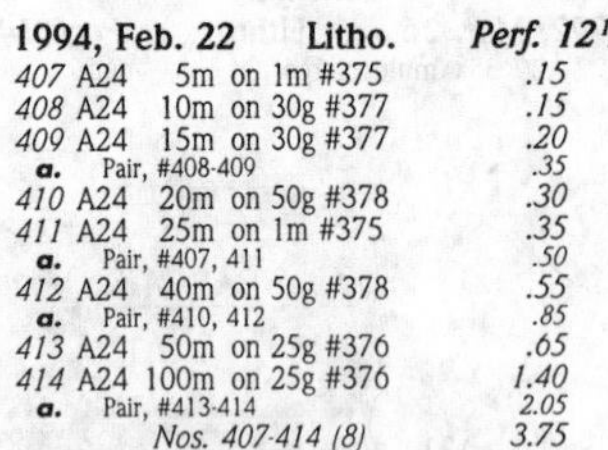

1994, Feb. 22 Litho. *Perf. 12½*

407 A24 5m on 1m #375 *.15*
408 A24 10m on 30g #377 *.15*
409 A24 15m on 30g #377 *.20*
a. Pair, #408-409 *.35*
410 A24 20m on 50g #378 *.30*
411 A24 25m on 1m #375 *.35*
a. Pair, #407, 411 *.50*
412 A24 40m on 50g #378 *.55*
a. Pair, #410, 412 *.85*
413 A24 50m on 25g #376 *.65*
414 A24 100m on 25g #376 *1.40*
a. Pair, #413-414 *2.05*
Nos. 407-414 (8) 3.75

Baku Oil Fields — A33

Designs: 15m, Temple of Eternal Fires. 20m, Oil derricks. 25m, Early tanker. 50m, Ludwig Nobel, Robert Nobel, Petr Bilderling, Alfred Nobel.

1994, June 10 Photo. *Perf. 13*

415 A33 15m multicolored *.70*
416 A33 20m multicolored *.90*
417 A33 25m multicolored *1.10*
418 A33 50m multicolored *2.25*
a. Souvenir sheet of 1 *2.25*
Nos. 415-418 (4) 4.95

See Turkmenistan Nos. 39-43.

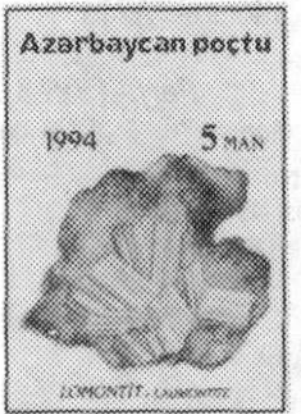

Minerals — A34

Posthorn — A35

1994, June 15 Litho. *Perf. 13*

419 A34 5m Laumontite *.45*
420 A34 10m Epidot calcite *.85*
421 A34 15m Andradite *1.25*
422 A34 20m Amethyst *1.65*
a. Souvenir sheet, #420-423 + 2 labels, perf. 12 *4.75*
Nos. 419-422 (4) 4.20

1994 Litho. *Perf. 12½*

426 A35 5m black & red *.15*
427 A35 10m black & green *.15*
428 A35 20m black & blue *.20*
429 A35 25m black & yellow *.30*
431 A35 40m black & brown *.45*
Nos. 426-431 (5) 1.25

For surcharges see Nos. 487-489A.

400 м.

No. 351 Surcharged

Unwmk.

1994, Oct. 17 Litho. *Perf. 12*

435 A21 400m on 25g multi *.85*

Souvenir Sheet

Pres. Geidar A. Aliyev — A36

Illustration reduced.

1994, Oct. 28 Litho. *Perf. 14*

436 A36 150m multicolored *3.50*

Ships of the Caspian Sea A37

Designs: a, Tugboat, "Captain Racebov." b, "Azerbaijan." c, Balt Ro Ro line, "Merkuri I." d, Tanker, "Tovuz." e, Tanker.

1994, Oct. 28

437 A37 50m Strip of 5, #a.-e. *3.00*
f. Min. sheet of 3, #437 *9.00*

The background of #437f shows a nautical chart, giving each stamp a different background.

1994 World Cup Soccer Championships, US — A38

Various soccer plays. Denominations: 5m, 10m, 20m, 25m, 30m, 50m, 80m.

1994, June 17 Litho. *Perf. 13*

438-444 A38 Set of 7 *5.25*

Souvenir Sheet

445 A38 100m multicolored *2.25*

No. 445 contains one 32x40mm stamp and is a continuous design.

Dinosaurs A39

Designs: 5m, Coelophysis, segisaurus. 10m, Pentaceratops, tyrannosaurids. 20m, Segnosaurus, oviraptor. 25m, Albertosaurus, corythosaurus. 30m, Iguanodons. 50m, Stegosaurus, allosaurus. 80m, Tyrannosaurus, saurolophus.
100m, Phobetor.

1994, Sept. 15

446-452 A39 Set of 7 *5.25*

Souvenir Sheet

Perf. 12½

453 A39 100m multicolored *2.25*

No. 453 contains one 40x32mm stamp and is a continuous design.

Lyrurus Mlokosiewickzi — A40

Designs: a, 50m, Female on nest. b, 80m, Female on mountain cliff. c, 100m, Two males. d, 120m, Male.

1994, Dec. 15 Litho. *Perf. 12½*

454 A40 Block of 4, #a.-d. *3.25*

World Wildlife Fund.

Nos. 455-457 are unassigned.

Raptors A41

Designs: 10m, Haliaeetus albicilla. 15m, Aguila heliaca. 20m, Aguila rapax. 25m, Gypaetus barbatus, vert. 50m, Falco cherrug, vert.
100m, Aguila chrysaetos.

1994, Nov. 15 Litho. *Perf. 13*

458-462 A41 Set of 5 *5.25*

Souvenir Sheet

Perf. 12½

463 A41 100m multicolored *2.25*

No. 463 contains one 40x32mm stamp and is a continuous design.

Cats A42

Designs: 10m, Felis libica, vert. 15m, Felis otocolobus, vert. 20m, Felis lyns, vert. 25m, Felis pardus. 50m, Panthera tigrus.
100m, Panthera tigrus adult and cub, vert.

1994, Dec. 14 *Perf. 13*

464-468 A42 Set of 5 *5.25*

Souvenir Sheet

469 A42 100m multicolored *2.25*

No. 469 contains one 32x40mm stamp and is a continuous design.

Butterflies A43

Designs: 10m, Parnassius apollo. 25m, Zegris menestho. 50m, Manduca atropos. 60m, Pararge adrastoides.

1995, Jan. 23 Litho. *Perf. 14*

470 A43 10m multicolored *.42*
471 A43 25m multicolored *1.00*
472 A43 50m multicolored *2.00*
473 A43 60m multicolored *2.50*
a. Souvenir sheet of 4, #470-473 *6.00*
Nos. 470-473 (4) 5.92

Intl. Olympic Committee, Cent. — A44

Designs: No. 474, Pierre de Coubertin. No. 475, Discus. No. 476, Javelin.

1994, Dec. 15 Litho. *Perf. 12*

474-476 A44 100m Set of 3 *3.30*

A45

A46

1994 Winter Olympic medalists, Lillehammer: 10m, Aleksei Urnamov, Russia, figure skating, 25, Nancy Kerrigan, US, figure skating. 40m Bonnie Blair, US, speed skating, horiz. 50m, Takanori Kano, Japan, ski jumping, horiz. 80m, Philip Laros, Canada, freestyle skiing. 100m, Four-man bobsled, Germany.

200m, Katja Seizinger, skiing, Germany, vert.

1995, Feb. 10 Litho. *Perf. 14*

478-483 A45 Set of 6 5.00

Souvenir Sheet

484 A45 200m multicolored 4.50

1995, Feb. 21

Women in space: No. 485a, Mary Kliv, US. b, Valentina Tereshkova, Russia. c, Tamara Cernigan, US. d, Wendy Lourens, US.

No. 486a, Meg Jamison, US. b, Kitty Coleman, US. c, Ellen Sulman, US. d, M.I. Weber, US.

Miniature Sheets of 4

485-486 A46 100m each, #a.-d. 7.00

First manned moon landing, 25th anniv. (in 1994).

Nos. 426-428 Surcharged

100 M.

1995 Litho. *Perf. 12½*

487	A35 100m on 5m #426	.20
488	A35 250m on 10m #427	.55
488A	A35 400m on 25m No. 429	.75
489	A35 500m on 20m #428	1.10
489A	A35 900m on 40m No. 431	1.65
	Nos. 487-489A (5)	4.25

Issued: #488A, 7/7; #487-488, 489, 2/28.

Mushrooms — A47

Designs: 100m, Gymnopilus spectabilis. 250m, Fly agaris. 300m, Lepiota procera. 400m, Hygrophorus spectosus.

500m, Fly agaris, diff.

1995, Sept. 1 Litho. *Perf. 14*

490-493 A47 Set of 4 4.50

Souvenir Sheet

494 A47 500m multicolored 4.50

Singapore '95 A48

Orchids: 100m, Paphiopedilum argus, paphiopedilum barbatum. 250m, Maxillaria picta. 300m, Laeliocattleya. 400m, Dendrobium nobile.

500m, Cattleya gloriette.

1995, Sept. 1

495-498 A48 Set of 4 4.50

Souvenir Sheet

499 A48 500m multicolored 4.50

UN, 50th Anniv. A49

Design: 250m, Azerbaijan Pres. Geidar A. Aliyev, UN Sec. Gen. Boutros Boutros-Ghali.

1995, Sept. 15

500 A49 250m multicolored 2.25

200 M.

Nos. 352-355 Surcharged

1995 Litho. *Perf. 12*

501	A21	200m on 2.50m #355	.30
502	A21	600m on 35g #352	.85
503	A21	800m on 50q #353	1.10
504	A21	1000m on 1.50m #354	1.40
		Nos. 501-504 (4)	3.65

Uzeyir Hacibeyov (1885-1948) — A50

Design: 400m, Oglu Iskenderov (1895-1965).

1995, June 30 Litho. *Perf. 12x12½*

505 A50 250m silver gray & black .45

506 A50 400m gold bister & brown .75

Balloons and Airships A51

Designs: 100m, First hydrogen balloon, 1784, vert. 150m, First motorized balloon, 1883, vert. 250m, First elliptical balloon, 1784. 300m, First Scott Baldwin dirigible, 1904. 400m, US Marine balloon, 1917. 500m, Pedal-powered dirigible, 1909.

800m, First rigid dirigible designed by Hugo Eckener, 1924.

1995, July 20 Litho. *Perf. 13*

507	A51	100m multicolored	.20
508	A51	150m multicolored	.30
509	A51	250m multicolored	.45
510	A51	300m multicolored	.55
511	A51	400m multicolored	.75
512	A51	500m multicolored	.90
		Nos. 507-512 (6)	3.15

Souvenir Sheet

513 A51 800m multicolored 1.50

1998 World Cup Soccer Championships, France — A52

Various soccer plays.

1995, Sept. 30 Litho. *Perf. 12½*

526	A54	100m orange & multi	.20
527	A54	150m green & multi	.30
528	A54	250m yellow orange & multi	.45
529	A54	300m yellow & multi	.55
530	A54	400m blue & multi	.75
		Nos. 526-530 (5)	2.25

Souvenir Sheet

Perf. 13

531 A54 600m multicolored 1.10

Domestic Cats — A55

1995, Oct. 30 *Perf. 12½*

532	A55	100m Persian	.20
533	A55	150m Chartreux	.30
534	A55	250m Somali	.45
535	A55	300m Longhair Scottish fold	.55
536	A55	400m Cumric	.75
537	A55	500m Turkish angora	.90
		Nos. 532-537 (6)	3.15

Souvenir Sheet

538 A55 800m Birman 1.50

No. 538 contains one 32x40mm stamp.

Fauna and Flora — A56

Designs: 100m, Horse. 200m, Muscari elecostomum, vert. 250m, Huso huso. 300m, Aquila chrysaetos. 400m, Panthera tigrus. 500m, Lyrurus miokosiewickzi, facing right. 1000m, Lyrurus miokosiewickzi, facing left.

1995, Nov. 30

539	A56	100m multicolored	.20
540	A56	200m multicolored	.40
541	A56	250m multicolored	.45
542	A56	300m multicolored	.55
543	A56	400m multicolored	.75
544	A56	500m multicolored	.90
545	A56	1000m multicolored	2.00
		Nos. 539-545 (7)	5.25

John Lennon (1940-80) A57

1995, Dec. 8 *Perf. 14½*

546 A57 500m multicolored .90

Miniature Sheet

Locomotives — A58

Designs: No. 547a, 4-4-0, America. b, J3 Hudson, US. c, 2-8-2. d, 2-6-2, Germany. e, 2-8-2, Germany. f, 2-6-2, Italy. g, G-C5, Japan. h, 2-10-2 QJ, China. i, 0-10-0, China.

500m, Electric passenger train, vert.

1995 *Perf. 14*

547 A58 100m Sheet of 9, #a.-i. 12.00

Souvenir Sheet

548 A58 500m multicolored 6.00

Azerbaijan stamps can be mounted in the Scott annually supplemented Russia album part 1.

Dr. M. Topcubasov, Surgeon — A59

1995

549 A59 300m multicolored 4.00

SEMI-POSTAL STAMPS

Carrying Food to Sufferers — SP1

1922 Unwmk. *Imperf.*

B1 SP1 500r blue & pale blue .40 .75

For overprint and surcharge see Nos. 42, 305.

Widow and Orphans — SP2

1922

B2 SP2 1000r brown & bister .50 1.25

Counterfeits exist.

For overprint and surcharge see Nos. 44, 306.

Russian stamps of 1909-18 were privately overprinted as above in red, blue or black by a group of Entente officers working with Russian soldiers returning from Persia. Azerbaijan was not occupied by the Allies. There is evidence that existing covers (some seemingly postmarked at Baku, dated Oct. 19, 1917, and at Tabriz, Russian Consulate, Apr. 25, 1917) are fakes.

AIR POST STAMP

Catalogue values for all stamps in this section are for never hinged items.

Eagle — AP1

1995, Oct. 16 Litho. *Perf. 14*

C1 AP1 2200m multicolored 6.00

AZORES

'ā-,zōrz

LOCATION — Group of islands in the North Atlantic Ocean, due west of Portugal
GOVT. — Integral part of Portugal, former colony
AREA — 922 sq. mi.
POP. — 253,935 (1930)
CAPITAL — Ponta Delgada

Azores stamps were supplanted by those of Portugal in 1931.

1000 Reis = 1 Milreis
100 Centavos = 1 Escudo (1912)

See Portugal for other recent issues.

Stamps of Portugal Overprinted in Black or Carmine

AÇORES
a

A second type of this overprint has a broad "O" and open "S."

1868 Unwmk. *Imperf.*
1 A14 5r black 3,000. 2,000.
2 A14 10r yellow 7,500. 4,000.
3 A14 20r bister 250.00 100.00
4 A14 50r green 250.00 100.00
5 A14 80r orange 250.00 100.00
6 A14 100r lilac 250.00 100.00

The reprints are on thick chalky white wove paper, ungummed, and on thin ivory paper with shiny white gum. Value $20 each.

1868-70 *Perf. 12½*
5 REIS:
Type I - The "5" at the right is 1mm from end of label.
Type II - The "5" is 1½mm from end of label.
7 A14 5r black (C) 30.00 20.00
8 A14 10r yellow 65.00 50.00
a. Inverted overprint 200.00 110.00
9 A14 20r bister 60.00 40.00
10 A14 25r rose 50.00 4.25
a. Inverted overprint 80.00 80.00
11 A14 50r green 200.00 75.00
12 A14 80r orange 200.00 75.00
13 A14 100r lilac 200.00 75.00
14 A14 120r blue 75.00 42.50
15 A14 240r violet 500.00 300.00

The reprints are on thick chalky white paper ungummed, perf 13½, and on thin ivory paper with shiny white gum, perf 13½. Value $10 each.

1871-75 *Perf. 12½, 13½*
21 A15 5r black (C) 10.00 6.00
a. Inverted overprint 60.00 60.00
23 A15 10r yellow 15.00 10.00
a. Inverted overprint 60.00 60.00
24 A15 20r bister 15.00 10.00
25 A15 25r rose 12.00 1.75
a. Inverted overprint 60.00 60.00
b. Double overprint 60.00
c. Perf. 14 125.00 37.50
d. Dbl. impression of stamp
26 A15 50r green 60.00 20.00
27 A15 80r orange 75.00 35.00
28 A15 100r lilac 60.00 25.00
a. Perf. 14 125.00 72.50
29 A15 120r blue 125.00 50.00
a. Inverted overprint 165.00 165.00
30 A15 240r violet 750.00 400.00

Nos. 21-29 exist with overprint "b."

The reprints are of type "b." They are on thick chalky white paper ungummed, perf 13½, and also on thin white paper with shiny white gum and perforated 13½.

Overprinted in Black

AÇORES
b

1875-80
15 REIS:
Type I - The figures of value, 1 and 5, at the right in upper label are close together.
Type II - The figures of value at the right in upper label are spaced.
31 A15 10r blue green 175.00 100.00
32 A15 10r yellow green 75.00 40.00
33 A15 15r lilac brown 10.00 8.00
a. Inverted overprint 60.00 60.00
34 A15 50r blue 100.00 40.00
35 A15 150r blue 150.00 100.00
36 A15 150r yellow 200.00 175.00
37 A15 300r violet 75.00 50.00

The reprints have the same papers, gum and perforations as those of the preceding issue.

Black Overprint

1880 *Perf. 11½, 12½ and 13½*
38 A17 25r gray 50.00 10.00
39 A18 25r red lilac 30.00 6.00
a. 25r gray 20.00 6.00
b. Double overprint

Overprinted in Carmine or Black

1881-82
40 A16 5r black (C) 8.00 3.50
41 A23 25r brown ('82) 15.00 2.25
a. Double overprint
42 A19 50r blue 100.00 12.00
Nos. 40-42 (3) 123.00 17.75

Reprints of Nos. 38, 39, 39a, 40 and 42 have the same papers, gum and perforations as those of preceding issues.

Overprinted in Red or Black

AÇORES
c

1882-85
15, 20 REIS
Type I - The figures of value are some distance apart and close to the end of the label.
Type II - The figures are closer together and farther from the end of the label. On the 15 reis this is particularly apparent in the upper right figures.
43 A16 5r black (R) 7.50 4.50
44 A21 5r slate 3.50 1.00
a. Double overprint
c. Inverted overprint
45 A15 10r green 45.00 24.00
a. Inverted overprint
46 A22 10r green 7.25 3.25
a. Double overprint
47 A15 15r lilac brn 30.00 10.50
b. Inverted overprint
48 A15 20r bister 45.00 27.50
a. Inverted overprint
49 A15 20r carmine 110.00 35.00
a. Double overprint
50 A23 25r brown 10.00 1.75
51 A15 50r blue 1,200. 1,000.
52 A24 50r blue 10.50 1.75
a. Double overprint
53 A15 80r yellow 30.00 10.00
a. 80r orange 40.00 24.00
b. Double overprint
54 A15 100r lilac 25.00 12.00
55 A15 150r blue 1,000. 750.00
56 A15 150r yellow 40.00 20.00
57 A15 300r violet 50.00 40.00

Reprints of the 1882-85 issues have the same papers, gum and perforations as those of preceding issues.

Red Overprint
58 A21 5r slate 7.50 1.75
59 A24a 500r black 150.00 100.00
60 A15 1000r black 75.00 50.00

1887 Black Overprint
61 A25 20r pink 9.50 4.75
a. Inverted overprint
b. Double overprint
62 A26 25r lilac rose 9.50 1.00
a. Inverted overprint
b. Double ovpt., one invtd.
63 A26 25r red violet 9.50 1.00
a. Double overprint
64 A24a 500r red violet 125.00 75.00
a. Perf. 13½ 400.00 200.00
Nos. 61-64 (4) 153.50 81.75

Nos. 58-64 inclusive have been reprinted on thin white paper with shiny white gum and perforated 13½.

Prince Henry the Navigator Issue

Portugal Nos. 97-109 Overprinted AÇORES

1894, Mar. 4 *Perf. 14*
65 A46 5r orange yel 1.75 1.25
a. Inverted overprint 20.00 13.00
66 A46 10r violet rose 1.75 1.25
a. Double overprint 25.00
b. Inverted overprint 20.00 13.00
67 A46 15r brown 2.25 1.25
68 A46 20r violet 2.25 1.25
a. Double overprint 20.00
69 A47 25r green 2.25 1.25
a. Double overprint 20.00 20.00
b. Inverted overprint 20.00 20.00
70 A47 50r blue 4.75 2.50
71 A47 75r dp carmine 10.00 4.75
72 A47 80r yellow grn 12.00 4.75
73 A47 100r lt brn, *pale buff* 10.00 3.50
a. Double overprint 35.00
74 A48 150r lt car, *pale rose* 18.00 8.75
75 A48 300r dk bl, *sal buff* 40.00 17.00
76 A48 500r brn vio, *pale lil* 60.00 20.00
77 A48 1000r gray blk, *yelsh* 100.00 40.00
a. Double overprint
Nos. 65-77 (13) 265.00 107.50

St. Anthony of Padua Issue

Portugal Nos. 132-146 Overprinted in Red or Black AÇORES

1895, June 13 *Perf. 12*
78 A50 2½r black (R) 1.75 1.50
79 A51 5r brown yel 3.50 1.50
80 A51 10r red lilac 3.50 2.50
81 A51 15r red brown 4.25 2.50
82 A51 20r gray lilac 4.25 2.50
83 A51 25r green & vio 3.50 2.75
84 A52 50r blue & brn 20.00 14.00
85 A52 75r rose & brn 30.00 20.00
86 A52 80r lt green & brn 40.00 25.00
87 A52 100r choc & blk 50.00 20.00
88 A53 150r vio rose & bis 75.00 60.00
89 A53 200r blue & bis 100.00 50.00
90 A53 300r slate & bis 125.00 65.00
91 A53 500r vio brn & grn 200.00 100.00
92 A53 1000r violet & grn 400.00 200.00
Nos. 78-92 (15) 1,060. 567.25

7th cent. of the birth of Saint Anthony of Padua.

Vasco da Gama Issue
Common Design Types

1898, Apr. 1 *Perf. 14, 15*
93 CD20 2½r blue green 1.00 .60
94 CD21 5r red 1.10 .70
95 CD22 10r gray lilac 2.00 1.25
96 CD23 25r yellow green 1.75 .70
97 CD24 50r dark blue 3.50 2.75
98 CD25 75r violet brown 8.00 4.75
99 CD26 100r bister brown 8.00 4.50
100 CD27 150r bister 12.00 6.25
Nos. 93-100 (8) 37.35 21.50

For overprints and surcharges see Nos. 141-148.

King Carlos — A28

King Manuel II — A29

1906 Typo. *Perf. 11½x12*
101 A28 2½r gray .20 .15
a. Inverted overprint 15.00 15.00
102 A28 5r orange yel .20 .15
a. Inverted overprint 15.00 15.00
103 A28 10r yellow grn .20 .15
104 A28 20r gray vio .40 .20
105 A28 25r carmine .20 .15
106 A28 50r ultra 3.00 2.00
107 A28 75r brown, *straw* .65 .60
108 A28 100r dk blue, *bl* .65 .80
109 A28 200r red lilac, *pnksh* 1.25 1.00
110 A28 300r dk blue, *rose* 2.00 1.65
111 A28 500r black, *blue* 2.75 1.25
Nos. 101-111 (11) 11.50 8.10

"Acores" and letters and figures in the corners are in red on the 2½, 10, 20, 75 and 500r and in black on the other values.

1910, Apr. 1 *Perf. 14x15*
112 A29 2½r violet .25 .20
113 A29 5r black .25 .20
114 A29 10r dk green .30 .25
115 A29 15r lilac brn .40 .50
116 A29 20r carmine .45 .45
117 A29 25r violet brn .25 .20
a. Perf. 11½ 1.25 .80
118 A29 50r blue 1.00 .70
119 A29 75r bister brn 1.75 1.25
120 A29 80r slate 1.75 1.25
121 A29 100r brown, *lt grn* 2.25 1.75
122 A29 200r green, *sal* 2.25 1.75
123 A29 300r black, *blue* 3.50 2.50
124 A29 500r olive & brown 7.00 7.00
125 A29 1000r blue & black 12.00 12.00
Nos. 112-125 (14) 33.40 30.00

The errors of color 10r black, 15r dark green, 25r black and 50r carmine are considered to be proofs.

Stamps of 1910 Overprinted in Carmine or Green

1910
126 A29 2½r violet .15 .15
a. Inverted overprint 9.00 9.00
127 A29 5r black .20 .15
a. Inverted overprint 9.00 9.00
128 A29 10r dk green .20 .20
a. Inverted overprint 9.00 9.00
129 A29 15r lilac brn .80 .65
a. Inverted overprint 9.00 9.00
130 A29 20r carmine (G) 1.00 .80
a. Inverted overprint 16.00 16.00
b. Double overprint 16.00 16.00
131 A29 25r violet brn .25 .15
a. Perf. 11½ 40.00 30.00
132 A29 50r blue .60 .50
133 A29 75r bister brn .35 .20
a. Double overprint 9.00 9.00
134 A29 80r slate .45 .35
135 A29 100r brown, *grn* .40 .25
136 A29 200r green, *sal* .60 .60
137 A29 300r black, *blue* 1.25 1.25
138 A29 500r olive & brn 1.25 1.75
139 A29 1000r blue & blk 3.50 4.00
Nos. 126-139 (14) 11.00 11.00

Vasco da Gama Issue Overprinted or Surcharged in Black:

REPUBLICA
d

REPUBLICA **REPUBLICA**

REIS 15 REIS **1$000**
e f

1911 *Perf. 14, 15*
141 CD20(d) 2½r blue green .35 .30
142 CD21(e) 15r on 5r red .20 .20
143 CD23(d) 25r yellow grn .40 .25
144 CD24(d) 50r dk blue 1.00 .70
145 CD25(d) 75r violet brn .60 .60
146 CD27(e) 80r on 150r bister .60 .60
147 CD26(d) 100r yellow brn .60 .60
a. Double surcharge 35.00 35.00
148 CD22(f) 1000r on 10r lilac 8.50 6.50
Nos. 141-148 (8) 12.25 9.75

Postage Due Stamps of Portugal Overprinted or Surcharged in Black "ACORES" and

REPUBLICA

REPUBLICA **R^s 300 R^s**

1911 *Perf. 12*
149 D1 5r black .75 .35
150 D1 10r magenta 1.75 1.25
a. "Acores" double 20.00 20.00
151 D1 20r orange 2.00 2.00
152 D1 200r brn, *buff* 7.25 6.00
a. "Acores" inverted
153 D1 300r on 50r slate 7.25 6.00
154 D1 500r on 100r car, *pink* 7.25 6.00
Nos. 149-154 (6) 26.25 21.60

Ceres — A30

Ceres Issue of Portugal Overprinted "ACORES" in Black or Carmine With Imprint

1912-31 *Perf. 12x11½, 15x14*
155 A30 ¼c olive brown .15 .15
a. Inverted overprint 9.00
156 A30 ½c black (C) .15 .15
157 A30 1c deep green .55 .35
a. Inverted overprint 9.00
158 A30 1c deep brown ('18) .15 .15
a. Inverted overprint
159 A30 1½c choc ('13) .50 .40
a. Inverted overprint 9.00
160 A30 1½c deep green ('18) .35 .15
a. Inverted overprint
161 A30 2c carmine .30 .20
a. Inverted overprint 14.00
162 A30 2c orange ('18) .20 .15
a. Inverted overprint 18.00
163 A30 2½c violet .25 .15
164 A30 3c rose ('18) .20 .15
165 A30 3c dull ultra ('25) .20 .15
166 A30 3½c lt green ('18) .30 .15
167 A30 4c lt green ('19) .15 .15
168 A30 4c orange ('30) .25 .20
169 A30 5c dp blue .25 .15
170 A30 5c yellow brn ('18) .25 .20
171 A30 5c olive brn ('23) .15 .15

172 A30 5c black brn ('30) 2.75 2.50
173 A30 6c dull rose ('20) .20 .15
174 A30 6c choc ('25) .20 .15
175 A30 6c red brn ('31) .35 .80
176 A30 7½c yel brn 4.75 1.25
177 A30 7½c deep blue ('18) .60 .40
178 A30 8c slate ('13) .55 .20
179 A30 8c blue grn ('22) .25 .20
180 A30 8c orange ('25) .50 .25
181 A30 10c orange brown .30 .15
182 A30 12c blue gray ('20) 1.00 .70
183 A30 12c deep green ('22) .45 .35
184 A30 13½c chlky bl ('20) 1.00 3.25
185 A30 14c dk bl, *yel* ('20) 3.25 6.00
186 A30 15c plum ('13) .60 .60
187 A30 15c blk (R) ('23) .40 .40
188 A30 16c brt ultra ('24) .80 .40
189 A30 16c dp bl ('30) 1.25 1.50
190 A30 20c vio brn, *grn* ('13) 8.00 3.25
191 A30 20c choc ('20) .60 .20
192 A30 20c deep green ('23) .80 .80
a. Double overprint
193 A30 20c gray ('24) .55 .20
194 A30 24c grnsh bl ('21) .55 .40
195 A30 25c salmon ('23) .30 .20
196 A30 30c brn, *pink* ('13) 40.00 22.50
197 A30 30c brn, *yel* ('19) 2.25 2.25
198 A30 30c gray brn ('21) .80 .65
199 A30 32c dp green ('25) 4.00 1.00
200 A30 36c red ('21) .40 .20
201 A30 40c dp blue ('23) .40 .40
202 A30 40c black brn ('24) .20 .15
203 A30 40c brt green ('30) 1.40 .40
204 A30 48c brt rose ('24) 1.40 1.00
205 A30 48c dull pink ('31) 6.00 6.00
206 A30 50c org, *sal* ('13) 5.00 1.00
207 A30 50c yellow ('23) 1.25 1.00
208 A30 50c bister ('30) 2.50 1.75
209 A30 50c red brn ('31) 2.00 1.40
210 A30 60c blue ('21) .90 .70
211 A30 64c pale ultra ('24) 1.40 1.00
212 A30 64c brown rose ('31) 45.00 45.00
213 A30 75c dull rose ('23) 4.00 4.00
214 A30 75c car rose ('30) 1.50 1.25
215 A30 80c dull rose ('21) 1.25 .60
216 A30 80c violet ('24) 1.25 .80
217 A30 80c dk green ('31) 1.50 1.25
218 A30 90c chlky bl ('21) 1.25 .65
219 A30 96c dp rose ('26) 8.00 4.50
220 A30 1e dp grn, *bl* 4.50 1.50
221 A30 1e violet ('21) 1.25 .65
222 A30 1e gray vio ('24) 1.50 1.00
223 A30 1e brn lake ('30) 12.00 10.00
224 A30 1.10e yel brn ('21) 1.25 1.25
225 A30 1.20e yel grn ('21) 1.40 1.00
226 A30 1.20e buff ('24) 3.50 1.75
227 A30 1.25e dk blue ('30) 1.40 .65
228 A30 1.50e blk vio ('23) 2.75 1.75
229 A30 1.50e lilac ('25) 2.75 1.75
230 A30 1.60e dp bl ('25) 2.75 1.75
231 A30 2e slate grn ('21) 4.00 2.00
232 A30 2.40e apple grn ('26) 60.00 50.00
233 A30 3e lilac pink ('26) 60.00 55.00
234 A30 3.20e gray grn ('25) 10.00 4.50
235 A30 5e emerald ('24) 20.00 12.00
236 A30 10e pink ('24) 40.00 20.00
237 A30 20e pale turq ('25) 125.00 75.00
Nos. 155-237 (83) 522.05 368.45

For same overprint on surcharged stamps see Nos. 300-306. For same design without imprint see Nos. 307-313.

Castello-Branco Issue

Stamps of Portugal, 1925, Overprinted in Black or Red **AÇORES**

1925, Mar. 29 *Perf. 12½*
238 A73 2c orange .20 .50
239 A73 3c green .20 .50
240 A73 4c ultra (R) .20 .50
241 A73 5c scarlet .20 .50
242 A74 10c pale blue .20 .45
243 A74 16c red orange .25 .75
244 A75 25c car rose .25 .75
245 A74 32c green .55 .80
246 A75 40c grn & blk (R) .25 .75
247 A74 48c red brn 1.25 2.25
248 A76 50c blue green .80 2.25
249 A76 64c orange brn 1.40 2.25
250 A76 75c gray blk (R) 1.00 3.00
251 A75 80c brown 1.00 3.00
252 A76 96c car rose 1.25 3.00
253 A77 1.50e dk bl, *bl* (R) 1.25 2.25
254 A75 1.60e indigo (R) 1.25 2.25
255 A77 2e dk grn, *grn* (R) 1.50 3.00
256 A77 2.40e red, *org* 2.00 3.25
257 A77 3.20e blk, *grn* (R) 3.00 5.00
Nos. 238-257 (20) 18.00 37.00

First Independence Issue

Stamps of Portugal, 1926, Overprinted in Red **AÇÔRES**

1926, Aug. 13 *Perf. 14, 14½*
Center in Black
258 A79 2c orange .25 .70
259 A80 3c ultra .25 .70
260 A79 4c yellow grn .25 .70
261 A80 5c black brn .25 .70
262 A79 6c ocher .25 .70
263 A80 15c dk green .50 .90
264 A81 20c dull violet .50 .90
265 A82 25c scarlet .50 .90
266 A81 32c deep green .50 .90
267 A82 40c yellow brn .50 .90
268 A82 50c olive bis 1.25 2.00
269 A82 75c red brown 1.25 2.00
270 A83 1e black violet 1.75 3.25
271 A84 4.50e olive green 2.00 6.75
Nos. 258-271 (14) 10.00 22.00

The use of these stamps instead of those of the regular issue was obligatory on Aug. 13th and 14th, Nov. 30th and Dec. 1st, 1926.

Second Independence Issue

Same Overprint on Stamps of Portugal, 1927, in Red

1927, Nov. 29
Center in Black
272 A86 2c lt brown .25 .70
273 A87 3c ultra .25 .70
274 A86 4c orange .25 .70
275 A88 5c dk brown .25 .70
276 A89 6c orange brn .25 .70
277 A87 15c black brn .25 .70
278 A86 25c gray 1.00 3.00
279 A89 32c blue grn 1.00 3.00
280 A90 40c yellow grn 1.00 3.00
281 A90 96c red 2.50 5.75
282 A88 1.60e myrtle grn 2.50 5.75
283 A91 4.50e bister 4.50 8.00
Nos. 272-283 (12) 14.00 32.70

Third Independence Issue

Same Overprint on Stamps of Portugal, 1928, in Red

1928, Nov. 27
Center in Black
284 A93 2c lt blue .25 .70
285 A94 3c lt green .25 .70
286 A95 4c lake .25 .70
287 A96 5c olive grn .25 .70
288 A97 6c orange brn .25 .70
289 A94 15c slate .40 1.25
290 A95 16c dk violet .65 2.25
291 A93 25c ultra .65 2.00
292 A97 32c dk green .65 2.00
293 A96 40c olive brn .65 2.00
294 A95 50c red orange 1.25 3.00
295 A94 80c lt gray 1.25 3.00
296 A97 96c carmine 1.75 6.00
297 A96 1e claret 1.75 6.00
298 A93 1.60e dk blue 1.75 6.00
299 A98 4.50e yellow 4.00 8.50
Nos. 284-299 (16) 16.00 45.50

A31

A32

1929-30 *Perf. 12x11½, 15x14*
300 A31 4c on 25c pink ('30) .35 .35
301 A31 4c on 60c dp blue .35 .35
302 A31 10c on 25c pink .80 .40
303 A31 12c on 25c pink .80 .40
304 A31 15c on 25c pink .65 .60
305 A31 20c on 25c pink .80 .65
306 A31 40c on 1.10e yel brn 2.75 2.25
Nos. 300-306 (7) 6.50 5.00

Black or Red Overprint

1930 *Perf. 14*
Without Imprint at Foot
307 A32 4c orange .35 .40
308 A32 5c dp brown 1.50 1.00
309 A32 10c vermilion .80 .55
310 A32 15c black (R) .80 .55
311 A32 40c brt green .80 .55
312 A32 80c violet 11.00 8.75
313 A32 1.60e dk blue 1.75 1.00
Nos. 307-313 (7) 17.00 12.80

POSTAGE DUE STAMPS

D2

D3

Portugal Nos. J7-J13 Overprinted in Black

1904 **Unwmk.** *Perf. 12*
J1 D2 5r brown .45 .65
J2 D2 10r orange .45 .65
J3 D2 20r lilac .85 1.10
J4 D2 30r gray green 1.00 1.10
a. Double overprint
J5 D2 40r gray violet 1.75 1.75
J6 D2 50r carmine 2.75 3.00
J7 D2 100r dull blue 4.25 4.50
Nos. J1-J7 (7) 11.50 12.75

Same Overprinted in Carmine or Green (Portugal Nos. J14-J20)

1911
J8 D2 5r brown .20 .20
J9 D2 10r orange .20 .20
J10 D2 20r lilac .20 .20
J11 D2 30r gray green .20 .20
J12 D2 40r gray violet .45 .45
J13 D2 50r carmine (G) 2.00 2.00
J14 D2 100r dull blue 1.25 1.25
Nos. J8-J14 (7) 4.50 4.50

Portugal Nos. J21-J27 Overprinted in Black

1918
J15 D3 ½c brown .15 .15
a. Inverted overprint 4.00 4.00
b. Double overprint 4.00 4.00
J16 D3 1c orange .15 .15
a. Inverted overprint 4.00 4.00
b. Double overprint 4.00 4.00
J17 D3 2c red lilac .15 .15
a. Inverted overprint 4.00 4.00
b. Double overprint 4.00 4.00
J18 D3 3c green .15 .15
a. Inverted overprint 4.00 4.00
b. Double overprint 4.00 4.00
J19 D3 4c gray .15 .15
a. Inverted overprint 4.00 4.00
b. Double overprint 4.00 4.00
J20 D3 5c rose .15 .15
b. Double overprint 4.00 4.00
J21 D3 10c dark blue .20 .20
Nos. J15-J21 (7) 1.10 1.10

Stamps and Type of Portugal Postage Dues, 1921-27, Overprinted in Black

1922-24 *Perf. 11½x12*
J30 D3 ½c gray green ('23) .15 .15
J31 D3 1c gray green ('23) .15 .15
J32 D3 2c gray green ('23) .15 .15
J33 D3 3c gray green ('24) .35 .35
J34 D3 8c gray green ('24) .20 .20
J35 D3 10c gray green ('24) .20 .20
J36 D3 12c gray green ('24) .20 .20
J37 D3 16c gray green ('24) .20 .20
J38 D3 20c gray green .60 .50
J39 D3 24c gray green .20 .20
J40 D3 32c gray green ('24) .20 .20
J41 D3 36c gray green .20 .20
J42 D3 40c gray green ('24) .50 .50
J43 D3 48c gray green ('24) .50 .30
J44 D3 50c gray green .60 .50
J45 D3 60c gray green .65 .35
J46 D3 72c gray green .65 .35
J47 D3 80c gray green ('24) 1.75 1.40
J48 D3 1.20e gray green 1.75 1.40
Nos. J30-J48 (19) 9.00 7.50

NEWSPAPER STAMPS

Newspaper Stamps of Portugal, Nos. P1, P1a, Overprinted Types b & c in Black or Red and:

N3

Perf. 11½, 12½ and 13½
1876-88 **Unwmk.**
P1 N1 2½r (a) olive 4.50 1.75
a. Inverted overprint
P2 N1 2½r (b) olive ('82) 3.25 1.00
a. Inverted overprint
b. Double overprint
P3 N3 2r black ('85) 1.50 1.00
a. Inverted overprint
b. Double overprint, one inverted
P4 N1 2½r (b) bister ('82) 3.25 1.00
a. Double overprint
P5 N3 2r black (R) ('88) 5.50 3.50
Nos. P1-P5 (5) 18.00 8.25

Reprints of the newspaper stamps have the same papers, gum and perforations as reprints of the regular issues. Value $2 each.

PARCEL POST STAMPS

Portugal Nos. Q1-Q17 Overprinted Like Nos. 155-237 in Black or Red

1921-22 **Unwmk.** *Perf. 12*
Q1 PP1 1c lilac brown .15 .15
a. Inverted overprint 4.00 4.00
Q2 PP1 2c orange .15 .15
a. Inverted overprint 4.00 4.00
Q3 PP1 5c light brown .15 .15
a. Inverted overprint 5.00 5.00
b. Double overprint 5.00 5.00
Q4 PP1 10c red brown .15 .25
a. Inverted overprint 5.00 5.00
b. Double overprint 5.00 5.00
Q5 PP1 20c gray blue .30 .25
a. Inverted overprint 5.00 5.00
b. Double overprint 5.00 5.00
Q6 PP1 40c carmine .30 .30
a. Double overprint 6.50 6.50
Q7 PP1 50c black (R) .55 .55
Q8 PP1 60c dark blue (R) .55 .55
Q9 PP1 70c gray brown 2.50 1.25
a. Double overprint
Q10 PP1 80c ultra 2.50 1.25
Q11 PP1 90c light violet 2.50 1.25
Q12 PP1 1e light green 3.00 1.25
Q13 PP1 2e pale lilac 4.00 2.50
Q14 PP1 3e olive 6.00 3.25
Q15 PP1 4e ultra 7.00 5.00
Q16 PP1 5e gray 7.00 5.00
Q17 PP1 10e chocolate 20.00 13.00
Nos. Q1-Q17 (17) 56.80 36.10

POSTAL TAX STAMPS

These stamps represent a special fee for the delivery of postal matter on certain days in the year. The money derived from their sale is applied to works of public charity.

Nos. 114 and 157 Overprinted in Carmine **ASSISTENCIA**

1911-13 **Unwmk.** *Perf. 14x15*
RA1 A29 10r dark green .55 .40

The 20r of this type was for use on telegrams.

Perf. 15x14
RA2 A30 1c deep green 1.25 1.25

The 2c of this type was for use on telegrams.

Postal Tax Stamp of Portugal, No. RA4, Overprinted Like Nos. 155-237 in Black

1915 *Perf. 12*
RA3 PT2 1c carmine .15 .15

The 2c of this type was for use on telegrams.

Postal Tax Stamp of 1915 Surcharged **15 ctvs.**

1924
RA4 PT1 15c on 1c rose .75 1.25

Comrades of the Great War Issue

Postal Tax Stamps of Portugal, 1925, Overprinted **AÇORES**

1925, Apr. 8 *Perf. 11*
RA5 PT3 10c brown .40 .30
RA6 PT3 10c green .40 .30
RA7 PT3 10c rose .40 .30
RA8 PT3 10c ultra .40 .30
Nos. RA5-RA8 (4) 1.60 1.20

The use of Nos. RA5-RA11 in addition to the regular postage was compulsory on certain days. If the tax represented by these stamps was not prepaid, it was collected by means of Postal Tax Due Stamps.

In 1934-45, #RA5-RA11, RAJ1-RAJ4 were used for regular postage in Portugal.

Pombal Issue

Common Design Types

1925 *Perf. 12½*
RA9 CD28 20c dp green & black .35 .30
RA10 CD29 20c dp green & black .35 .30
RA11 CD30 20c dp green & black .35 .30
Nos. RA9-RA11 (3) 1.05 .90

POSTAL TAX DUE STAMPS

Postal Tax Due Stamp of Portugal Overprinted like Nos. RA5-RA8

1925, Apr. 8 Unwmk. ***Perf.* 11x11½**
RAJ1 PTD1 20c brown orange .40 .40

See note after No. RA8.

Pombal Issue
Common Design Types

1925, May 8 ***Perf.* 12½**
RAJ2 CD31 40c dp green & black .60 *4.00*
RAJ3 CD32 40c dp green & black .60 *4.00*
RAJ4 CD33 40c dp green & black .60 *4.00*
Nos. RAJ2-RAJ4 (3) 1.80

See note after No. RA8.
See Portugal for later issues.

BELARUS

ˌbē–lə–ˈrüs

(Byelorussia)

(White Russia)

LOCATION — Eastern Europe, bounded by Russia, Latvia, Lithuania and Poland
GOVT. — Independent republic, member of the Commonwealth of Independent States
AREA — 80,200 sq. mi.
POP. — 10,200,000 (1989)
CAPITAL — Minsk

With the breakup of the Soviet Union on Dec. 26, 1991, Belarus and ten former Soviet republics established the Commonwealth of Independent States.

100 Kopecks = 1 Ruble

Catalogue values for all unused stamps in this country are for Never Hinged items.

Five denominations, perf and imperf, of this design produced in 1920 were not put in use and were probably propaganda labels. They are common.

Cross of Ephrosinia of Polotsk — A1

1992, Mar. 20 Litho. ***Perf.* 12x12½**
1 A1 1r multicolored .40

R.R. Schurma (1892-1978), Composer — A2

1992, Apr. 10 Photo. ***Perf.* 12x11½**
2 A2 20k blue & black .60

Arms of Polotsk — A3

Designs: No. 13, Stag jumping fence. No. 14, Man's head, sword.

1992-94 Photo. ***Perf.* 12x11½**
11 A3 2r shown .60

***Perf.* 12x12½**
12 A3 25r Minsk .15
13 A3 700r Grodno .25
14 A3 700r Vitebsk .25
Nos. 11-14 (4) 1.25

Issued: 2r, 6/9/92; 25r, 11/11/93; #13, 14, 10/17/94.
This is an expanding set. Numbers will change if necessary.

National Symbols — A4

Designs: No. 15, Natl. arms. No. 16, Map, flag.

1992, Aug. 31 Litho. ***Perf.* 12x12½**
15 A4 5r black, red & yellow .40
16 A4 5r multicolored .40

For surcharges see Nos. 55-58, 61-64.

No. 1 Overprinted

1000 — ГОДДЗЕ БЕЛАРУСКАЙ ПРАВАСЛАЎНАЙ ЦАРКВЫ

Cross of Ephrosinia of Polotsk — A5

A5 illustration reduced.

1992, Sept. 25 Litho. ***Perf.* 12x12½**
17 A1 1r on #1 multi .25

Souvenir Sheet
***Perf.* 12**
18 A5 5r multicolored .40

Orthodox Church in Belarus, 1000th anniv. No. 18, imperf, was issued Feb. 15, 1993.

Orthodox Church in Belarus, 1000th anniv. For surcharges see Nos. 59-60, 65-66.

Buildings A6

Designs: No. 19, Church of Boris Gleb, Grodno, 12th cent. No. 20, World Castle, 16th cent. No. 21, Nyasvizh Castle, 16th-19th cent. No. 22, Kamyanets Tower, 12th-13th cent, vert. No. 23, Church of Ephrosinia of Polotsk, 12th cent., vert. No. 24, Calvinist Church, Zaslaw, 16th cent., vert.

1992, Oct. 15 Litho. ***Perf.* 12**
19 A6 2r multicolored .20
20 A6 2r multicolored .20
21 A6 2r multicolored .20
22 A6 2r multicolored .20
23 A6 2r multicolored .20
24 A6 2r multicolored .20
Nos. 19-24 (6) 1.20

Centuries of construction are in Roman numerals.

Natl. Arms — A7

1992-94 Litho. ***Perf.* 12x12½**
25 A7 30k light blue .15
26 A7 45k olive green .15
27 A7 50k green .15
28 A7 1r brown .15
29 A7 2r green .15
30 A7 3r green .25
31 A7 5r blue .15
32 A7 10r green .80
33 A7 15r violet .25
34 A7 25r yellow green .40
35 A7 50r bright pink .30
36 A7 100r henna brown .55
37 A7 150r plum .85
38 A7 200r blue green .15
39 A7 300r salmon pink .15
40 A7 600r light lilac .20
40A A7 1000r rose carmine .32
40B A7 3000r gray blue 1.00
Nos. 25-40B (18) 6.12

Issued: 30k, 45k, 50k, 11/10; 50r, 100r, 150r, 6/16/93; 200r-3,000r, 12/28/94; others, 1992.
This is an expanding set. Numbers may change.

Ceramics — A8

Designs: No. 41, Pitcher and bowl. No. 42, Four pieces on tree branches. No. 43, Two large pitchers. No. 44, One large pitcher.

1992 Litho. ***Perf.* 11½**
41 A8 1r multicolored .15
42 A8 1r multicolored .15
43 A8 1r multicolored .15
44 A8 1r multicolored .15
Set value .50

M. I. Garetzky (1893-1938), Writer — A9

1993, June 22 Photo. ***Perf.* 12x11½**
45 A9 50r magenta .30

Straw Figures — A10

Designs: 5r, Chickens. 10r, Child, mother, vert. 15r, Woman, vert. 25r, Man with scythe, woman with rake, vert.

***Perf.* 12x11½, 11½x12**
1993, Apr. 22 Litho.
47 A10 5r multicolored .20
48 A10 10r multicolored .35
49 A10 15r multicolored .55
50 A10 25r multicolored .90
Nos. 47-50 (4) 2.00

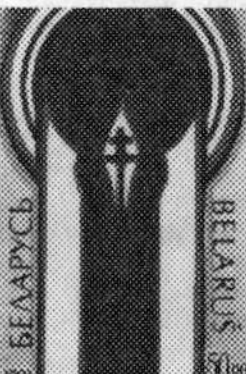

First World Congress of White Russians — A11

1993, July 8 Litho. ***Perf.* 12**
51 A11 50r multicolored 3.50

Europa — A12

Paintings by Chagall: No. 52, Promenade, vert. No. 53, Man Over Vitebsk. 2500r, Allegory.

1993, Oct. 12 Litho. ***Perf.* 14**
52 A12 1500r multicolored 3.00
53 A12 1500r multicolored 3.00
a. Pair, #52-53 6.00

Souvenir Sheet
54 A12 2500r multicolored 17.50

Nos. 15-16, 18 Surcharged

a

WINTER
PRE-OLYMPICS
GAMES
LILLEHAMMER,
NORWAY

b

Size and location of surcharge varies.

1993, Oct. 15 Litho. ***Perf.* 12x12½**
55 A4(a) 1500r on 5r #15 3.50
56 A4(b) 1500r on 5r #15 3.50
a. Pair, #55-56 7.00
57 A4(a) 1500r on 5r #16 3.50
58 A4(b) 1500r on 5r #16 3.50
a. Pair, #57-58 7.00
Nos. 55-58 (4) 14.00

Souvenir Sheets
***Perf.* 12**
59 A5(a) 1500r on 5r #18 3.50
60 A5(b) 1500r on 5r #18 3.50

No. 59 exists imperf.

Belarus stamps can be mounted in the Scott annually supplemented Russia album part 1.

Abkhazia and Batum

Available from your favorite dealer, in case of difficulty - From

International Stampdile Stamp Dealers

ABKHAZIA

The Autonomous Region of Abkhazia is contained within the Republic of Georgia. It has a population of over 500,000, the Official Capital is Sukhumi and the language spoken is Abkhazian, which is a form of Georgian, but the writing is with Russian letters.

March 1995	Mint	Used
Ab-01 Abkhazia-Birds 4v mint set	$3.50	$3.50
Abkhazia-Birds Souvenir Sheet	5.00	5.00
Ab-02 Abkhazia-Butterflies/Scouts 4v mint set	6.00	6.00
Abkhazia-Butterflies/Scouts S/S	4.00	4.00
Ab-03 Abkhazia-Animals 4 mint set (composite design)	6.00	6.00
Abkhazia-Animals Souvenir Sheet	6.00	6.00

April 1995		
Ab-04 Abkhazia-Dinosaurs 6v set	4.00	4.00
Abkhazia-Dinosaurs Souvenir Sheet	6.00	6.00
Ab-05 Abkhazia-Jackson/Elvis set	8.00	8.00
Abkhazia-Jackson/Elvis Souvenir Sheet	4.00	4.00

July 1995		
Ab-06 Abkhazia-Fish 4v mint set	5.00	5.00
Abkhazia-Fish Souvenir Sheet	3.50	3.50
Ab-07 Abkhazia-"Anyone for Dinner" 10v mint set (Entertainer series)	9.00	9.00

September 1995		
Ab-08 Abkhazia-Dogs 2 mint sheets x 4v each	16.00	16.00

November 1995		
Ab-09 Abkhazia-Fighter Aircraft	5.00	5.00
Ab-10 Abkhazia-Euro-Tunnel Trains	8.00	8.00
Ab-11 Abkhazia-Rain Forest/animals	9.00	9.00
Ab-12 Abkhazia "Rock Legends"	12.00	12.00

January 1996		
Ab-9601 Abkhazia Cats 6v set	8.00	8.00
Abkhazia Cats Souvenir Sheet 2v	4.00	4.00
Ab-9602 Abkhazia-Garden Animals/ Mushrooms 6v set	7.00	7.00
Abkhazia-Garden Animals/ Mushrooms Souvenir Sheet 2v p	3.00	3.00
Ab-9603 Abkhazia-Bhuda II 4v set	4.00	4.00
Ab-9604 Abkhazia-Year of the Rat 3v set	2.00	2.00
printed sheet of 4v sets of 3 stamps, with gutter design	8.00	8.00
Ab-9605 Abkhazia-Butterflies & Flowers set of 6v in strip	7.00	7.00
Ab-9606 Abkhazia-Marilyn Monroe set of 6v plus 1 label	6.00	6.00
Ab-9607 Abkhazia-Gerry Garcia-sheet of 12v with one picture and one label repeated with gutter design	14.00	14.00

BATUM

Batum is situated on the Black Sea, and is an autonomous region in Georgia. After the 1st World War it was occupied by British forces in December 1918 until it was handed back to the Republic of Georgia.

Today the population of Batum stands at 347,000, and while the language spoken is Georgian, and Georgia is still a major influence in the region they strive for full independence, and it will not be too long before we see the Republic of Batum featured on the stamps.

The first stamps were issued from Batum in 1919. The new Region of Batum issued its first sets on the 27th Jan. 1994, following the break-up of the former U.S.S.R.

Batum 1994	Mint	Used
Mushrooms/Scouts 6v set	$2.00	$2.00
Mushrooms/Scouts Souvenir Sheet	2.00	2.00
1v Gold & Silver both stamps	20.00	20.00
Souvenir Sheet perf Gold & Silver	30.00	30.00
W.W.F. 4v set	2.00	2.00
W.W.F. Souvenir Sheet	2.00	2.00
W.W.F. Perf 4v Silver	20.00	20.00
W.W.F. Perf 4v Gold	25.00	25.00
W.W.F. Souvenir Sheet Silver	44.00	44.00
W.W.F. Souvenir Sheet Gold	54.00	54.00
Cats 4v set	2.00	2.00
Cats Souvenir Sheet	2.00	2.00
Cats 2v Silver	16.00	16.00
Cats 2v Gold	20.00	20.00
Cats 2 Souvenir Sheet Silver	30.00	30.00
Cats 2 Souvenir Sheet Gold	40.00	40.00
Dogs 4v set	2.00	2.00
Dogs Souvenir Sheet	2.00	2.00
Dogs Silver set of 2 stamps	16.00	16.00
Dogs Gold set of 2 stamps	20.00	20.00
Dogs Silver Souvenir Sheet (2)	30.00	30.00
Dogs Gold Souvenir Sheet (2)	36.00	36.00
Whales 4v set	2.00	2.00
Whales Souvenir Sheet	2.00	2.00
Whales Silver set of 2 stamps	10.00	10.00
Whales Gold set of 2 stamps	13.00	13.00
Whales Silver Souvenir Sheet (2)	20.00	20.00
Whales Gold Souvenir Sheet (2)	24.00	24.00
Birds 6v set	2.00	2.00
Birds Souvenir Sheet	2.00	2.00
Birds Silver set of 2 stamps	10.00	10.00
Birds gold set of 2 stamps	13.00	13.00
Birds Silver Souvenir Sheet (2)	20.00	20.00
Birds Gold Souvenir Sheet (2)	24.00	24.00

March 1995		
BA-01 Batum-Pre-historic Animals 6v set	4.00	4.00
Batum-Pre-historic Animals S/S	6.00	6.00
BA-02 Batum-Sports 4v mint set (rugby cricket etc.)	7.00	7.00
Batum-Sports Souvenir Sheet	4.00	4.00
BA-03 Batum-Film Stars of the Past 4v mint set (Presley, Monroe, Chaplin, Bruce Lee)	6.00	6.00
Batum-Film Stars of the Past S/S	4.00	4.00

April 1995		
BA-04 Batum-Beatles set of 2 sheetlets	8.00	8.00
BA-05 Batum-Sea birds/Dolphins set	3.50	3.50

July & August 1995		
BA-06 Batum-Animals 8v mint set (composite design)	7.00	7.00
BA-07 Batum-Sea World 8v mint set	7.00	7.00
**Sea World 8v mint set with Scout Jamboree '95 in the Netherlands o/p	7.00	7.00
BA-08 Batum "Dessert"-4v mint set (Entertainer Series)	6.00	6.00

November 1995		
BA-09 Batum Lions & Tigers 4v mint set	5.50	5.50
BA-10 Batum "Hall of Fame" O.J. Simpson 2v Souvenir Sheet	6.00	6.00
BA-11 Batum Dinosaurs	9.00	9.00
BA-12 Batum Bhuda Images	6.00	6.00
BA-13 Batum Ayrton Senn	5.00	5.00
BA-14 Batum "The Kiss" (Elvis/Monroe)	8.00	8.00

January 1996		
BA-9601 Dogs set of 6v	8.00	8.00
Dogs Souvenir Sheet 2v	4.00	4.00
BA-9602 Teddy Bears set of 6v	6.00	6.00
Teddy Bears Souvenir Sheet 2v	3.00	3.00
BA-9603 Arctic Animals set of 6v	8.00	8.00
Arctic Animals Souvenir Sheet 2v	4.00	4.00
BA-9604 Horses set of 6v	6.00	6.00
Horses Souvenir Sheet 2v	3.00	3.00
BA-9605 Year of the Rat sheet of 4v	4.00	4.00
BA-9606 Year of the Rat animal dial set of 4v	4.00	4.00
BA-9607 Elvis set of 6v	8.00	8.00
Elvis Souvenir Sheet	3.00	3.00
BA-9608 Teng set of 4v	4.00	4.00
BA-9609 Chess/Hongpex/Taiwan set of 8v	9.00	9.00
Chess/Hongpex/Taiwan S/S	5.00	5.00
BA-9512 o/p Bhuda I-Overprint for: International Stamp Exhibition Bangkok-with Exhibition logo in GOLD on the stamps + Ex.details	4.00	4.00

STAMPDILE
LIMITED

P.O. Box 72 • Harrow • Middx HA2 OLQ • Great Britain
Telephone: 44-181-864 3517 Facsimile: 44-181-864 6190

Nos. 15-16, 18 Surcharged

ЧЭМПІЯНАТ СВЕТУ
ПА ФУТБОЛУ.
ЗША. 1994

1500
c

WORLD CUP
USA 94

1500
d

Size and location of surcharge varies.

1993, Oct. 15 Litho. *Perf. 12x12½*

61	A4(c) 1500r on 5r #15	3.50	
62	A4(d) 1500r on 5r #15	3.50	
a.	Pair, #61-62	7.00	
63	A4(c) 1500r on 5r #16	3.50	
64	A4(d) 1500r on 5r #16	3.50	
a.	Pair, #63-64	7.00	
	Nos. 61-64 (4)	14.00	

Souvenir Sheets

Perf. 12

65	A5(c) 1500r on 5r #18	3.50
66	A5(d) 1500r on 5r #18	3.50

Stansilavski Church A13

1993, Nov. 24 Litho. *Perf. 12*

67 A13 150r multicolored .50

Famous People — A14

Designs: 50r, Kastus Kalinovsky, led 1863 independence movement. No. 69, Prince Rogvold of Polotsk, map of Polotsk. No. 70, Princess Rogneda, daughter of Rogvold, fortress. 100r, Statue of Simon Budny (1530-93), writer and printer, vert.

1993 *Perf. 12x12½, 12½x12*

68	A14 50r multicolored	.15
69	A14 75r multicolored	.25
70	A14 75r multicolored	.25
71	A14 100r multicolored	.35
	Nos. 68-71 (4)	1.00

Issued: 50r, 12/29; 75r, 12/30; 100r, 12/31.

Nos. 27, 29, 30 Surcharged

15.00

1994, Feb. 1 Photo. *Perf. 12x12½*

72	A7 15r on 30k light green	.15
73	A7 25r on 45k olive green	.15
74	A7 50r on 50k green	.15
	Set value	.20

Birds A15

1994, Jan. 19 Litho. *Perf. 11½*

75	A15 20r Aguila chrysaetos	.15
76	A15 40r Cygnus olor	.15
77	A15 40r Alcedo atthis	.15
a.	Block of 3, #75-77 + label	.40

See Nos. 87-89.

Liberation of Russian Areas, 50th Anniv. A16

Battle maps and: a, Katyusha rockets, liberation of Russia. b, Russian fighter planes, liberation of Ukraine. c, Combined offensive, liberation of Belarus.

1994, July 3 Litho. *Perf. 12*

78 A16 500r Block of 3 + label .45

See Russia No. 6213, Ukraine No. 195.

1994 Winter Olympics, Lillehammer — A17

1994, Aug. 30 Litho. *Perf. 12x12½*

79	A17 1000r Speed skating	.15
80	A17 1000r Women's figure skating	.15
81	A17 1000r Hockey	.15
82	A17 1000r Cross-country skiing	.15
83	A17 1000r Biathlon	.15
	Set value	.65

Painters — A18

Designs: No. 84, Farmer, oxen in field, by Ferdinand Rushchyts. No. 85, Knight on horseback, by Jasev Drazdovich. No. 86, Couple walking up path, by Petra Sergievich. Illustration reduced

1994, July 18 Litho. *Perf. 12*

84	A18 300r multicolored	.15
85	A18 300r multicolored	.15
86	A18 300r multicolored	.15
	Set value	.30

Bird Type of 1994

1994, Sept. 30 *Perf. 11½*

87	A15 300r like #75	.15
88	A15 400r like #76	.15
89	A15 400r like #77	.15
	Set value	.25

Ilya Yefimovich Repin (1844-1930), Ukrainian Painter — A19

Designs: #90, Self-portrait. #91, Repin Museum.

1994, Oct. 31 Litho. *Perf. 12x12½*

90	A19 1000r multicolored	.48
91	A19 1000r multicolored	.48
a.	Pair, #90-91	.95

Churches A20

Designs: No. 92, Sacred Consolidated Church, Sinkavitsch, 16th cent. No. 93, Sts. Peter and Paul Cathedral, Gomel, 19th cent.

1994, Oct. 20 Litho. *Perf. 12*

92	A20 700r multicolored	.20
93	A20 700r multicolored	.20

Kosciuszko Uprising, Bicent. (in 1994) A21

Battle scene and: No. 94, Tomasz Vaishetcki (1754-1816). No. 95, Jakov Jasinski (1761-94). No. 96, Tadeusz Kosziuszko (1746-1817). No. 97, Mikhail K. Aginski (1765-1833).

1995, Jan. 11 *Perf. 12½x12*

94	A21 600r multicolored	.18
95	A21 600r multicolored	.18
96	A21 1000r multicolored	.32
97	A21 1000r multicolored	.32
	Nos. 94-97 (4)	1.00

End of World War II, 50th Anniv. — A22

1995, May 4 Litho. *Perf. 13½*

98	A22 180r multicolored	.15
99	A22 600r multicolored	.20
	Set value	.28

Radio, Cent. — A23

1995, May 7 *Perf. 14*

100 A23 600r multicolored .20

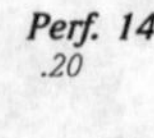

Monument — A24

1995 Litho. *Perf. 13x14*

102	A24 180r olive brown & red	.18
105	A24 280r green & blue	.22
109	A24 600r plum & bister	.20
	Nos. 102-109 (3)	.60

Issued: 180r, 5/10/95; 280r, 5/18/95; 600r, 8/29/95.

This is an expanding set. Numbers may change.

Ivan Chersky (1845-92), Geographer A25

1995, May 15 Litho. *Perf. 13½x14*

113 A25 600r multicolored .22

A26 A27

Traditional Costumes: 600r, Woman wearing shawl, coat, ankle length skirt, man with long coat. 1200r, Woman wearing shawl & apron holding child, man wearing vest, knickers.

1995, July 13 Litho. *Perf. 14½x14*

114	A26 180r multicolored	.15
115	A26 600r multicolored	.20
116	A26 1200r multicolored	.40
	Nos. 114-116 (3)	.75

1995, July 20 *Perf. 12*

World Wildlife Fund: Various pictures of a beaver.

117	A27 300r multicolored	.15
118	A27 450r multicolored	.15
119	A27 450r multi, horiz.	.15
120	A27 800r multi, horiz.	.20
	Set value	.48

A28 A29

1995 Litho. *Perf. 14*

121 A28 600r Book Fair .20

1995, Oct. 3 Litho. *Perf. 14*

122	A29 600r Natl. arms	.20
123	A29 600r Flag	.20

New national symbols.

UN, 50th Anniv. — A30

1995, Oct. 24 Litho. *Perf. 13½x14*

124 A30 600r bister, black & blue .20

Churches A31

Designs: No. 125, Mstislav, 17th-19th cent. No. 126, Kamai, 17th cent.

1995, Nov. 21 *Perf. 14*

125	A31	600r multicolored	.20	
126	A31	600r multicolored	.20	

BELGIAN CONGO

'bel-jən 'käŋ-(,)gō

LOCATION — Central Africa
GOVT. — Belgian colony
AREA — 902,082 sq. mi. (estimated)
POP. — 12,660,000 (1956)
CAPITAL — Léopoldville

Congo was an independent state, founded by Leopold II of Belgium, until 1908 when it was annexed to Belgium as a colony. In 1960 it became the independent Republic of the Congo. See Congo Democratic Republic and Zaire.

100 Centimes = 1 Franc

Catalogue values for unused stamps in this country are for Never Hinged items, beginning with Scott 187 in the regular postage section, Scott B32 in the semi-postal section, Scott C17 in the airpost section, and Scott J8 in the postage due section.

Independent State

King Leopold II
A1 A2 A3

1886 **Unwmk.** **Typo.** *Perf. 15*

1	A1	5c green	8.00	20.00
2	A1	10c rose	4.00	3.00
3	A2	25c blue	40.00	32.50
4	A3	50c olive green	6.00	6.00
5	A1	5fr lilac	325.00	250.00
a.		Perf. 14	600.00	
b.		5fr deep lilac	600.00	475.00

Counterfeits exist.
For surcharge see No. Q1.

King Leopold II — A4

1887-94

6	A4	5c grn ('89)	.75	.75
7	A4	10c rose ('89)	1.25	1.25
8	A4	25c blue ('89)	1.25	1.25
9	A4	50c brown	45.00	20.00
10	A4	50c gray ('94)	2.50	*15.00*
11	A4	5fr violet	800.00	325.00
12	A4	5fr gray ('92)	95.00	95.00
13	A4	10fr buff ('91)	400.00	225.00

The 25fr and 50fr in gray were not issued. Values, each $20.
Counterfeits exist of Nos. 10-13, 25fr and 50fr, unused, used, genuine stamps with faked cancels and counterfeit stamps with genuine cancels.
For surcharges see Nos. Q3-Q6.

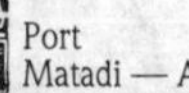

Port Matadi — A5

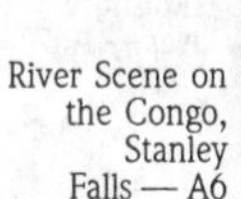

River Scene on the Congo, Stanley Falls — A6

Inkissi Falls — A7

Railroad Bridge on M'pozo River — A8

Hunting Elephants A9

Bangala Chief and Wife — A10

1894-1901 **Engr.** ***Perf. 12½ to 15***

14	A5	5c pale bl & blk	12.50	12.50
15	A5	5c red brn & blk ('95)	3.25	1.35
16	A5	5c grn & blk ('00)	1.75	.50
17	A6	10c red brn & blk	12.50	12.50
18	A6	10c grnsh bl & blk ('95)	1.50	1.25
a.		Center inverted	*1,850.*	*2,000.*
19	A6	10c car & blk ('00)	2.50	1.25
20	A7	25c yel org & blk	3.25	2.25
21	A7	25c lt bl & blk ('00)	2.50	1.25
22	A8	50c grn & blk	1.25	1.25
23	A8	50c ol & blk ('00)	2.50	.65
24	A9	1fr lilac & blk	17.50	10.00
a.		1fr rose lilac & black	210.00	20.00
25	A9	1fr car & blk ('01)	190.00	4.00
26	A10	5fr lake & blk	35.00	20.00
a.		5fr carmine rose & black	80.00	35.00
		Nos. 14-26 (13)	286.00	68.75

For overprints see Nos. 31-32, 34, 36-37, 39.

Climbing Oil Palms — A11

Congo Canoe — A12

1896

27	A11	15c ocher & blk	3.25	.50
28	A12	40c bluish grn & blk	3.25	2.50

For overprints see Nos. 33, 35.

Congo Village — A13

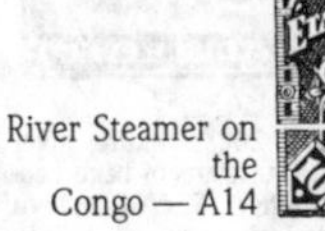

River Steamer on the Congo — A14

1898

29	A13	3.50fr red & blk	125.00	70.00
a.		Perf. 14x12	325.00	—
30	A14	10fr yel grn & blk	80.00	20.00
a.		Center inverted	*25,000.*	
b.		Perf. 12	475.00	22.50
c.		Perf. 12x14	275.00	—
		As "c," pen canceled		12.50

For overprints see Nos. 38, 40.

Belgian Congo

Overprinted CONGO BELGE

1908

31	A5	5c green & blk	5.75	5.50
a.		Handstamped	2.00	1.50
32	A6	10c carmine & blk	11.00	10.00
a.		Handstamped	2.00	1.50
33	A11	15c ocher & blk	5.75	2.75
a.		Handstamped	4.00	2.50
34	A7	25c lt blue & blk	4.75	4.00
a.		Handstamped	6.00	3.00
35	A12	40c bluish grn & blk	2.25	2.25
a.		Handstamped	6.00	4.75
36	A8	50c olive & blk	4.00	2.25
a.		Handstamped	3.75	3.00
37	A9	1fr carmine & blk	19.00	2.25
a.		Handstamped	22.50	6.00
38	A13	3.50fr red & blk	17.50	12.50
a.		Handstamped	140.00	85.00
39	A10	5fr carmine & blk	35.00	20.00
a.		Handstamped	52.50	32.50
40	A14	10fr yel grn & blk	75.00	16.00
a.		Perf. 14	200.00	—
b.		Handstamped	100.00	32.50
c.		Handstamped, perf. 14	225.00	200.00
		Nos. 31-40 (10)	180.00	77.50

Most of the above handstamps are also found inverted and double.
Values for handstamped overprints are for those applied locally.
Counterfeits of the handstamped overprints exist.

Port Matadi — A15

River Scene on the Congo, Stanley Falls — A16

Climbing Oil Palms — A17

Railroad Bridge on M'pozo River — A18

1909 *Perf. 14*

41	A15	5c green & blk	.65	.65
42	A16	10c carmine & blk	.55	.45
43	A17	15c ocher & blk	17.50	10.00
44	A18	50c olive & blk	2.50	2.00
		Nos. 41-44 (4)	21.20	13.10

Port Matadi — A19

River Scene on the Congo, Stanley Falls — A20

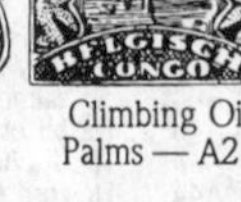

Climbing Oil Palms — A21

Inkissi Falls — A22

Congo Canoe — A23

Railroad Bridge on M'pozo River — A24

Hunting Elephants A25

Congo Village — A26

Bangala Chief and Wife — A27

River Steamer on the Congo — A28

1910-15 Engr. *Perf. 14, 15*

45 A19 5c green & blk .75 .15
46 A20 10c carmine & blk .40 .15
47 A21 15c ocher & blk .40 .15
48 A21 15c grn & blk ('15) .20 .15
a. Booklet pane of 10 14.00
49 A22 25c blue & blk 1.50 .30
50 A23 40c bluish grn & blk 2.00 1.75
51 A23 40c brn red & blk ('15) 3.75 1.75
52 A24 50c olive & blk 3.00 1.50
53 A24 50c brn lake & blk ('15) 6.00 1.75
54 A25 1fr carmine & blk 2.75 2.10
55 A25 1fr ol bis & blk ('15) 2.00 .65
56 A26 3fr red & blk 15.00 10.00
57 A27 5fr carmine & blk 17.00 14.00
58 A27 5fr ocher & blk ('15) 1.50 .65
59 A28 10fr green & blk 16.00 12.50
Nos. 45-59 (15) 72.25 47.55

Nos. 48, 51, 53, 55 and 58 exist imperforate.
For overprints and surcharges see Nos. 64-76, 81-86, B5-B9.

Port Matadi — A29

Stanley Falls, Congo River — A30

Inkissi Falls — A31

TEN CENTIMES.
Type I - Large white space at top of picture and two small white spots at lower edge. Vignette does not fill frame.
Type II - Vignette completely fills frame.

1915

60 A29 5c green & blk .15 .15
a. Booklet pane of 10 7.50
61 A30 10c car & blk (II) .20 .15
a. 10c carmine & black (I) .20 .15
d. Booklet pane of 10 (II) 14.00
62 A31 25c blue & blk .85 .25
a. Booklet pane of 10 65.00
Nos. 60-62 (3) 1.20 .55

Nos. 60 to 62 exist imperforate.
For surcharges see Nos. 77-80, 87, B1-B4.

Stamps of 1910 Issue Surcharged in Red or Black

10c 10c

1921

64 A23 5c on 40c bluish grn & blk (R) .25 .25
65 A19 10c on 5c grn & blk (R) .25 .25
66 A24 15c on 50c ol & blk (R) .25 .25
67 A21 25c on 15c ocher & blk (R) 1.50 1.00
68 A20 30c on 10c car & blk .35 .35
69 A22 50c on 25c bl & blk (R) 1.40 .90
Nos. 64-69 (6) 4.00 3.00

The position of the new value and the bars varies on Nos. 64 to 69.

Overprinted **1921**

1921

70 A25 1fr carmine & blk .75 .75
a. Double overprint 20.00
71 A26 3fr red & blk 2.50 2.50
72 A27 5fr carmine & blk 4.75 4.75
73 A28 10fr green & blk (R) 4.25 2.50
Nos. 70-73 (4) 12.25 10.50

Belgian Surcharges

Nos. 51, 53, 60-62 Surcharged in Black or Red **·10c**

1922

74 A24 5c on 50c .35 .30
75 A29 10c on 5c (R) .35 .25
76 A23 25c on 40c (R) 2.00 .30
77 A30 30c on 10c (II) .15 .15
a. 30c on 10c (I) .15 .15
b. Double surcharge 4.75 4.75
78 A31 50c on 25c (R) .40 .25
Nos. 74-78 (5) 3.25 1.25

No. 74 has the surcharge at each side.

Congo Surcharges
Nos. 60, 51 Surcharged in Red or Black:

10 c.
a

25 c.
b

1922

80 A29 10c on 5c (R) .55 .55
a. Inverted surcharge 17.50 17.50
b. Double surcharge 4.75
c. Double surch., one invtd. 40.00
d. Pair, one without surcharge 42.50
e. On No. 45 125.00 125.00
81 A23 25c on 40c .70 .35
a. Inverted surcharge 17.50 17.50
b. Double surcharge 5.50
c. "25c" double
d. 25c on 5c, No. 60 100.00 100.00

Nos. 55, 58 Surcharged with vertical bars over original values **10 c.**

1922

84 A25 10c on 1fr (R) .55 .55
a. Double surcharge 14.00
b. Inverted surcharge 17.50 17.50
85 A27 25c on 5fr 1.50 1.50

Nos. 68, 77 Handstamped **0,25**

86 A20 25c on 30c on 10c 7.00 8.50
87 A30 25c on 30c on 10c (II) 7.00 8.50

Nos. 86-87 exist with handstamp surcharge inverted.
Counterfeit handstamped surcharges exist.

Ubangi Woman — A32

Watusi Cattle — A44

Designs: 10c, Baluba woman. 15c, Babuende woman. No. 90, 40c, 1.25fr, 1.50fr, 1.75fr, Ubangi man. 25c, Basketmaking. 30c, 35c, Nos. 101, 102, Carving wood. 50c, Archer. Nos. 92, 100, Weaving. 1fr, Making pottery. 3fr, Working rubber. 5fr, Making palm oil. 10fr, African elephant.

1923-27 Engr. *Perf. 12*

88 A32 5c yellow .15 .15
89 A32 10c green .15 .15
90 A32 15c olive brn .15 .15
91 A32 20c olive grn ('24) .15 .15
92 A44 20c green ('26) .15 .15
93 A44 25c red brown .25 .15
94 A44 30c rose red ('24) .50 .70
95 A44 30c olive grn ('25) .15 .15
96 A44 35c green ('27) .35 .35
97 A32 40c violet ('25) .15 .15
98 A44 50c gray blue .25 .15
99 A44 50c buff ('25) .30 .15
100 A44 75c red orange .35 .35
101 A44 75c gray bl ('25) .40 .25
102 A44 75c salmon red ('26) .15 .15
103 A44 1fr bister brn .40 .15
104 A44 1fr dl blue ('25) .35 .15
105 A44 1fr rose red ('27) .50 .15
106 A32 1.25fr dl blue ('26) .30 .20
107 A32 1.50fr dl blue ('26) .30 .15
108 A32 1.75fr dl blue ('27) 2.75 3.00
109 A44 3fr gray brn ('24) 3.25 1.25
110 A44 5fr gray ('24) 7.00 3.75
111 A44 10fr gray blk ('24) 15.00 5.75

1925-26

112 A44 45c dk vio ('26) .35 .25
113 A44 60c carmine rose .35 .15
Nos. 88-113 (26) 34.15 18.25

For surcharges see Nos. 114, 136-138, 157.

No. 107 Surcharged **1.75**

1927, June 14

114 A32 1.75fr on 1.50fr dl bl .30 .20

Sir Henry Morton Stanley — A45

1928, June 30 *Perf. 14*

115 A45 5c gray blk .15 .15
116 A45 10c dp violet .15 .15
117 A45 20c orange red .20 .20
118 A45 35c green .60 .60
119 A45 40c red brown .25 .15
120 A45 60c black brn .25 .15
121 A45 1fr carmine .25 .15
122 A45 1.60fr dk gray 2.50 2.50
123 A45 1.75fr dp blue 1.00 .70
124 A45 2fr dk brown .70 .25
125 A45 2.75fr red violet 2.75 .35
126 A45 3.50fr rose lake .85 .60
127 A45 5fr slate grn .70 .25
128 A45 10fr violet blue 1.00 .60
129 A45 20fr claret 4.25 1.90
Nos. 115-129 (15) 15.60 8.70

Sir Henry M. Stanley (1841-1904), explorer.

Nos. 118, 121-123, 125-126 Surcharged in Red, Blue or Black **1F25**

1931, Jan. 15

130 A45 40c on 35c .50 .40
131 A45 1.25fr on 1fr (Bl) .40 .15
132 A45 2fr on 1.60fr .80 .30
133 A45 2fr on 1.75fr .75 .30
134 A45 3.25fr on 2.75fr (Bk) 2.25 2.00
135 A45 3.25fr on 3.25fr (Bk) 3.00 2.10

Nos. 96, 108, 112 Surcharged in Red **50c**

Perf. 12½, 12

136 A44 40c on 35c grn 3.25 3.00
137 A44 50c on 45c dk vio 2.00 1.10

Surcharged **2**

138 A32 2(fr) on 1.75fr dl bl 8.50 7.50
Nos. 130-138 (9) 21.45 16.85

View of Sankuru River — A46

Flute Players — A50

Designs: 15c, Kivu Kraal. 20c, Sankuru River rapids. 25c, Uele hut. 50c, Musicians of Lake Leopold II. 60c, Batetelas drummers. 75c, Mangbetu woman. 1fr, Domesticated elephant of Api. 1.25fr, Mangbetu chief. 1.50fr, 2fr, Village of Mondimbi. 2.50fr, 3.25fr, Okapi. 4fr, Canoes at Stanleyville. 5fr, Woman preparing cassava. 10fr, Baluba chief. 20fr, Young woman of Irumu.

1931-37 Engr. *Perf. 11½*

139 A46 10c gray brn ('32) .15 .15
140 A46 15c gray ('32) .15 .15
141 A46 20c brn lil ('32) .15 .15

142 A46 25c dp blue ('32) .15 .15
143 A50 40c dp grn ('32) .20 .20
144 A46 50c violet ('32) .15 .15
b. Booklet pane of 8 6.25
145 A50 60c vio brn ('32) .15 .15
146 A50 75c rose ('32) .15 .15
b. Booklet pane of 8 1.25
147 A50 1fr rose red ('32) .15 .15
148 A50 1.25fr red brown .15 .15
b. Booklet pane of 8 1.25
149 A46 1.50fr dk ol gray ('37) .15 .15
b. Booklet pane of 8 6.00
150 A46 2fr ultra ('32) .20 .15
151 A46 2.50fr dp blue ('37) .30 .15
b. Booklet pane of 8 8.50
152 A46 3.25fr gray blk ('32) .45 .30
153 A46 4fr dl vio ('32) .20 .15
154 A50 5fr dp vio ('32) .50 .25
155 A50 10fr red ('32) .50 .40
156 A50 20fr blk brn ('32) 1.50 1.25
Set value 5.00 3.75

No. 109 Surcharged in Red **3F25**

1932, Mar. 15 *Perf. 12*

157 A44 3.25fr on 3fr gray brn 2.75 2.25

King Albert Memorial Issue

King Albert — A62

1934, May 7 Photo. *Perf. 11½*

158 A62 1.50fr black .65 .35

Leopold I, Leopold II, Albert I, Leopold III — A63

1935, Aug. 15 Engr. *Perf. 12½x12*

159 A63 50c green .65 .50
160 A63 1.25fr dk carmine .65 .15
161 A63 1.50fr brown vio .65 .15
162 A63 2.40fr brown org 2.00 2.00
163 A63 2.50fr lt blue 2.00 .90
164 A63 4fr brt violet 2.00 1.25
165 A63 5fr black brn 2.00 1.50
Nos. 159-165 (7) 9.95 6.45

Founding of Congo Free State, 50th anniv.
For surcharges see Nos. B21-B22.

Molindi River — A64

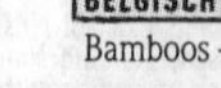
Bamboos — A65

Suza River — A66

Rutshuru River — A67

Karisimbi — A68

Mitumba Forest — A69

1937-38 Photo. *Perf. 11½*

166 A64 5c purple & blk .15 .15
167 A65 90c car & brn .40 .30
168 A66 1.50fr dp red brn & blk .15 .15
169 A67 2.40fr ol blk & brn .15 .15
170 A68 2.50fr dp ultra & blk .30 .15
171 A69 4.50fr dk grn & brn .30 .15
172 A69 4.50fr car & sep .20 .20
Nos. 166-172 (7) 1.65
Set value 1.00

National Parks.

No. 172 was issued in sheets of four measuring 140x111mm. It was sold by subscription, the subscription closing Oct. 20, 1937. Value, $1.60.

Nos. 166-171 were issued Mar. 1, 1938.

See No. B26. For surcharges see Nos. 184, 186.

King Albert Memorial, Leopoldville — A70

1941, Feb. 7 Litho. *Perf. 11*

173 A70 10c lt gray .15 .15
174 A70 15c brown vio .15 .15
175 A70 25c lt blue .25 .15
176 A70 50c lt violet .15 .15
177 A70 75c rose pink .75 .30
178 A70 1.25fr gray .15 .15
179 A70 1.75fr orange .60 .45
180 A70 2.50fr carmine .35 .15
181 A70 2.75fr vio blue .75 .60
182 A70 5fr lt olive grn 1.50 1.50
183 A70 10fr rose red 1.75 1.75
Nos. 173-183 (11) 6.55 5.50

Exist imperforate.

For surcharge see No. 185.

Nos. 168, 179, 169 Surcharged in Blue or Black

5 c.

75 c.

Nos. 184, 186 No. 185

1941-42 *Perf. 11½, 11*

184 A66 5c on 1.50fr (Bl) .15 .15
a. Inverted surcharge 14.00 14.00
185 A70 75c on 1.75fr ('42) .35 .35
a. Inverted surcharge 14.00 14.00
186 A67 2.50(fr) on 2.40fr ('42) .85 .70
a. Double surcharge 27.50 27.50
b. Inverted surcharge 14.00 14.00
Nos. 184-186 (3) 1.35 1.20

Catalogue values for unused stamps in this section, from this point to the end of the section, are for Never Hinged items.

Oil Palms
A71 A72

Congo Woman — A73

Askari — A75

Leopard A74

Okapi — A76

Inscribed "Congo Belge Belgisch Congo"

1942, May 23 Engr. *Perf. 12½*

187 A71 5c red .15 .15
188 A72 10c olive grn .15 .15
189 A72 15c brown car .15 .15
190 A72 20c dp ultra .15 .15
191 A72 25c brown vio .15 .15
192 A72 30c blue .15 .15
193 A72 50c dp green .15 .15
194 A72 60c chestnut .15 .15
195 A73 75c dl lil & blk .15 .15
196 A73 1fr dk brn & blk .20 .15
197 A73 1.25fr rose red & blk .20 .15
198 A74 1.75fr dk gray brn .85 .35
199 A74 2fr ocher .85 .15
200 A74 2.50fr carmine .85 .15
201 A75 3.50fr dk ol grn .30 .15
202 A75 5fr orange .60 .15
203 A75 6fr brt ultra .55 .15
204 A75 7fr black .55 .15
205 A75 10fr dp brown .70 .15
206 A76 20fr plum & blk 4.50 .65
Nos. 187-206 (20) 11.50
Set value 2.50

Same Inscribed "Belgisch Congo Congo Belge"

207 A72 10c olive grn .15 .15
208 A72 15c brown car .15 .15
209 A72 20c dp ultra .15 .15
210 A72 25c brown vio .15 .15
211 A72 30c blue .15 .15
212 A72 50c dp green .15 .15
213 A72 60c chestnut .15 .15
214 A73 75c dl lil & blk .15 .15
215 A73 1fr dk brn & blk .20 .15
216 A73 1.25fr rose red & blk .20 .15
217 A74 1.75fr dk gray brn .85 .35
218 A74 2fr ocher .85 .15
219 A74 2.50fr carmine .85 .15
220 A75 3.50fr dk ol grn .30 .15
221 A75 5fr orange .60 .15
222 A75 6fr brt ultra .55 .15
223 A75 7fr black .55 .15
224 A75 10fr dp brown .70 .15
225 A76 20fr plum & blk 4.50 .65
Nos. 207-225 (19) 11.35
Set value 2.35

Miniature sheets of Nos. 193, 194, 197, 200, 211, 214, 217 and 219 were printed in 1944 by the Belgian Government in London and given to the Belgian political review, Message, which distributed them to its subscribers, one a month. Value per sheet, about $12.50.

Remainders of these eight miniature sheets received marginal overprints in various colors in 1950, specifying a surtax of 100fr per sheet and paying tribute to the UPU. These sheets, together with four of Ruanda-Urundi, were sold by the Committee of Cultural Works (and not at post offices) in sets of 12 for 1,217.15 francs. Set value, about $150.

Nos. 187-227 imperforate had no franking value.

For surcharges see Nos. B34-B37.

Congo Woman — A77

Askari — A78

1943, Jan. 1

226 A77 50fr ultra & blk 5.00 .40
227 A78 100fr car & blk 6.50 .60

Slaves and Arab Guards A79

Auguste Lambermont A80

Design: 10fr, Leopold II.

Perf. 13x11½, 12½x12

1947 Engr. Unwmk.

228 A79 1.25fr black brown .25 .15
229 A80 3.50fr dark blue .38 .15
230 A80 10fr red orange .75 .15
Nos. 228-230 (3) 1.38
Set value .30

50th anniv. of the abolition of slavery in Belgian Congo. See Nos. 261-262.

Baluba Carving of Former King — A82

Carved Figures and Masks of Baluba Tribe: 10c, 50c, 2fr, "Ndoha," figure of tribal king. 15c, 70c, 1.20fr, 2.50fr, "Tshimanyi," an idol. 20c, 75c, 1.60fr, 3.50fr, "Buangakokoma," statue of kneeling beggar. 25c, 1fr, 2.40fr, 5fr, "Mbuta," sacred double cup, carved with two faces, Man and Woman. 40c, 1.25fr, 6fr, 8fr, "Ngadimuashi," female mask. 1.50fr, 3fr, 10fr, 50fr, "Buadi-Muadi," mask with squared features. 6.50fr, 20fr, 100fr, "Mbowa," executioner's mask with buffalo horns.

1947-50 *Perf. 12½*

231 A82 10c dp org ('48) .15 .15
232 A82 15c ultra ('48) .15 .15
233 A82 20c brt bl ('48) .15 .15
234 A82 25c rose car ('48) .25 .15
235 A82 40c violet ('48) .15 .15
236 A82 50c olive brn .15 .15
237 A82 70c yel grn ('48) .15 .15
238 A82 75c magenta ('48) .15 .15
239 A82 1fr yel org & dk vio 1.25 .15
240 A82 1.20fr gray & brn ('50) .15 .15
241 A82 1.25fr lt bl grn & mag ('48) .25 .15
242 A82 1.50fr ol & mag ('50) 8.00 1.10
243 A82 1.60fr bl gray & brt bl ('50) .20 .15
244 A82 2fr org & mag ('48) .20 .15
245 A82 2.40fr bl grn & dk grn ('50) .25 .15
246 A82 2.50fr brn red & bl grn .15 .15
247 A82 3fr lt ultra & ind ('49) 3.75 .15
248 A82 3.50fr lt bl & blk ('48) 2.75 .15
249 A82 5fr bis & mag ('48) .50 .15
250 A82 6fr brn org & ind ('48) .65 .15
251 A82 6.50fr red org & red brn ('49) 1.25 .15
252 A82 8fr gray bl & dk grn ('50) .65 .15
253 A82 10fr pale vio & red brn ('48) 2.00 .15
254 A82 20fr red org & vio brn ('48) 1.00 .15
255 A82 50fr dp org & blk ('48) 2.50 .15
256 A82 100fr crim & blk brn ('48) 3.75 .30
Nos. 231-256 (26) 30.55
Set value 3.75

Railroad Train and Map — A83

1948, July 1 Unwmk. *Perf. 13½*

257 A83 2.50fr dp bl & grn 1.00 .15

50th anniv. of railway service in the Congo.

Globe and Ship — A84

1949, Nov. 21 *Perf. 11½*

Granite Paper

258 A84 4fr violet blue .85 .15

75th anniv. of the UPU.

Allegorical Figure and Map — A85

1950, Aug. 12 *Perf. 12x12½*

259 A85 3fr blue & indigo 1.75 .15
260 A85 6.50fr car rose & blk brn 2.00 .25

Establishment of Katanga Province, 50th anniv.

Portrait Type of 1947

Designs: 1.50fr, Cardinal Lavigerie. 3fr, Baron Dhanis.

Perf. 12½x12

1951, June 25 Unwmk.

261 A80 1.50fr purple 2.00 .25
262 A80 3fr black brown 2.00 .15

Littonia — A86

St. Francis Xavier — A86a

1952-53 Photo. *Perf. 11½*

Granite Paper

Flowers in Natural Colors

Size: 21x25½mm

263 A86 10c Dissotis .15 .15
264 A86 15c Protea .15 .15
265 A86 20c Vellozia .15 .15
266 A86 25c shown .15 .15
267 A86 40c Ipomoea .20 .15
268 A86 50c Angraecum .15 .15
269 A86 60c Euphorbia .15 .15
270 A86 75c Ochna .15 .15
271 A86 1fr Hibiscus .15 .15
272 A86 1.25fr Protea ('53) .65 .45
273 A86 1.50fr Schrizoglossum .15 .15
274 A86 2fr Ansellia .25 .15
275 A86 3fr Costus .25 .15
276 A86 4fr Nymphaea .30 .15
277 A86 5fr Thunbergia .45 .15
278 A86 6.50fr Thonningia .55 .15
279 A86 7fr Gerbera .55 .15
280 A86 8fr Gloriosa ('53) .90 .15
281 A86 10fr Silene ('53) 1.65 .15
282 A86 20fr Aristolochia 1.40 .15

Size: 22x32mm

283 A86 50fr Eulophia ('53) 7.00 .45
284 A86 100fr Crytosepalum ('53) 11.00 1.00
Nos. 263-284 (22) 26.50
Set value 2.90

Nos. 264, 269 and 270 with additional surcharges are varieties of Congo Democratic Republic Nos. 324, 327 and 328.

1953, Jan. 5 Engr. *Perf. 12½x13*

285 A86a 1.50fr ultra & gray blk .75 .30

400th death anniv. of St. Francis Xavier.

Canoe on Lake Kivu — A87

1953, Jan. 5 *Perf. 14*

286 A87 3fr car & blk 1.25 .20
287 A87 7fr dp bl & brn org 1.25 .25

Issued to publicize the Kivu Festival, 1953.

Royal Colonial Institute Jubilee Medal A88

Design: 6.50fr, Same with altered background and transposed inscriptions.

1954, Dec. 27 Photo. *Perf. 13½*

288 A88 4.50fr indigo & gray 1.10 .28
289 A88 6.50fr dk grn & brn .90 .15

25th anniv. of the founding of the Belgian Royal Colonial Institute.

King Baudouin and Tropical Scene — A89

Designs: King and various views.

Inscribed "Congo Belge-Belgisch Congo"

Engr.; Portrait Photo.

1955, Feb. 15 Unwmk. *Perf. 11½*

Portrait in Black

290 A89 1.50fr rose car .70 .25
291 A89 3fr green .25 .15
292 A89 4.50fr ultra .30 .15
293 A89 6.50fr dp claret .55 .15

Inscribed "Belgisch Congo-Congo Belge"

294 A89 1.50fr rose car .30 .16
295 A89 3fr green .25 .15
296 A89 4.50fr ultra .30 .15
297 A89 6.50fr deep claret .55 .15
Nos. 290-297 (8) 3.20
Set value .90

Map of Africa and Emblem of Royal Touring Club — A90

1955, July 26 Engr. *Perf. 11½*

Inscription in French

298 A90 6.50fr vio blue 3.25 .25

Inscription in Flemish

299 A90 6.50fr vio blue 3.25 .25

5th International Congress of African Tourism, Elisabethville, July 26-Aug. 4. Nos. 298-299 printed in alternate rows.

Kings of Belgium A91

1958, July 1 Unwmk. *Perf. 12½*

300 A91 1fr rose vio .22 .15
301 A91 1.50fr ultra .22 .15
302 A91 3fr rose car .22 .15
303 A91 5fr green .70 .32
304 A91 6.50fr brn red .45 .15
305 A91 10fr dl vio .65 .15
Nos. 300-305 (6) 2.46
Set value .73

Belgium's annexation of Congo, 50th anniv.

Roan Antelope — A92 Black Buffaloes — A93

Animals: 20c, White rhinoceros. 40c, Giraffe. 50c, Thick-tailed bushbaby. 1fr, Gorilla. 2fr, Black-and-white colobus (monkey). 3fr, Elephants. 5fr, Okapis. 6.50fr, Impala. 8fr, Giant pangolin. 10fr, Eland and zebras.

1959, Oct. 15 Photo. *Perf. 11½*

Granite Paper

306 A92 10c bl & brn .15 .15
307 A93 20c red org & slate .15 .15
308 A92 40c brn & bl .15 .15
309 A93 50c brt ultra, red & sep .15 .15
310 A92 1fr brn, grn & blk .15 .15
311 A93 1.50fr blk & org yel .15 .15
312 A92 2fr crim, blk & brn .15 .15
313 A93 3fr blk, gray & lil rose .25 .15
314 A92 5fr brn, dk brn & brt grn .40 .20
315 A93 6.50fr bl, brn & org yel .45 .15
316 A92 8fr org brn, ol bis & lil .50 .30
317 A93 10fr multi .60 .15
Set value 2.80 1.30

Madonna and Child — A94

1959, Dec. 1 Unwmk. *Perf. 11½*

318 A94 50c golden brn, ocher & red brn .15 .15
319 A94 1fr dk bl, pur & red brn .15 .15
320 A94 2fr gray, brt bl & red brn .20 .15
Set value .40 .25

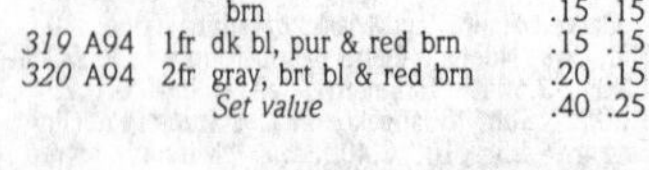

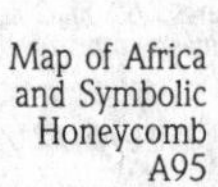

Map of Africa and Symbolic Honeycomb A95

1960, Feb. 19 Unwmk. *Perf. 11½*

Inscription in French

321 A95 3fr gray & red .25 .15

Inscription in Flemish

322 A95 3fr gray & red .25 .15

10th anniv. of the Commission for Technical Co-operation in Africa South of the Sahara (C. C. T. A.).

Succeeding issues are listed under Congo Democratic Republic.

SEMI-POSTAL STAMPS

Types of 1910-15 Issues Surcharged in Red **+ 10c**

1918, May 15 Unwmk. *Perf. 14, 15*

B1 A29 5c + 10c grn & bl .15 .20
B2 A30 10c + 15c car & bl (I) .15 .20
B3 A21 15c + 20c bl grn & bl .15 .20
B4 A31 25c + 25c dp bl & pale bl .20 .20
B5 A23 40c + 40c brn red & bl .40 .40
B6 A24 50c + 50c brn lake & bl .40 .40
B7 A25 1fr + 1fr ol bis & bl 2.00 2.00
B8 A27 5fr + 5fr ocher & bl 11.00 11.00
B9 A28 10fr + 10fr grn & bl 85.00 85.00
Nos. B1-B9 (9) 99.45 99.60

The position of the cross and the added value varies on the different stamps.

Nos. B1-B9 exist imperforate.

SP1

Design: #B11 inscribed "Belgisch Congo."

1925, July 8 *Perf. 12½*

B10 SP1 25c + 25c carmine & blk .20 .25
B11 SP1 25c + 25c carmine & blk .20 .25
a. Pair, Nos. B10-B11 .35 .35

Colonial campaigns in 1914-1918.

The surtax helped erect at Kinshasa a monument to those who died in World War I.

Nurse Weighing Child — SP3

First Aid Station — SP5

Designs: 20c+10c, Missionary and Child. 60c+30c, Congo hospital. 1fr+50c, Dispensary service. 1.75fr+75c, Convalescent area. 3.50fr+1.50fr, Instruction on bathing infant. 5fr+2.50fr, Operating room. 10fr+5fr, Students.

1930, Jan. 16 Engr. *Perf. 11½*

B12 SP3 10c + 5c ver .35 .35
B13 SP3 20c + 10c dp brn .45 .45
B14 SP5 35c + 15c dp grn .85 .85
B15 SP5 60c + 30c dl vio 1.00 1.00
B16 SP3 1fr + 50c dk car 1.50 1.50
B17 SP5 1.75fr + 75c dp bl 2.75 3.00
B18 SP5 3.50fr + 1.50fr rose lake 5.50 6.00
B19 SP5 5fr + 2.50fr red brn 5.00 5.50
B20 SP5 10fr + 5fr gray blk 5.50 6.00
Nos. B12-B20 (9) 22.90 24.65

The surtax on these stamps was intended to aid welfare work among the natives, especially the children.

Nos. 161, 163 Surcharged "+50c" in Blue or Red

1936, May 15 *Perf. 12½x12*

B21 A63 1.50fr + 50c (Bl) 2.50 3.00
B22 A63 2.50fr + 50c (R) 2.00 2.00

The surtax was for the benefit of the King Albert Memorial Fund.

Queen Astrid with Congolese Children — SP12

1936, Aug. 29 Photo. *Perf. 12½*

B23 SP12 1.25fr + 5c dark brown .40 .35
B24 SP12 1.50fr + 10c dull rose .40 .35
B25 SP12 2.50fr + 25c dark blue .60 .60
Nos. B23-B25 (3) 1.40 1.30

Issued in memory of Queen Astrid. The surtax was for the aid of the National League for Protection of Native Children.

Souvenir Sheet

SP13

1938, Oct. 3 *Perf. 11½*

B26 SP13 Sheet of 9 9.00 9.00
a. A64 5c ultra & light brown 1.50 1.50
b. A65 90c ultra & light brown 1.50 1.50
c. A66 1.50fr ultra & light brown 1.50 1.50
d. A67 2.40fr ultra & light brown 1.50 1.50
e. A68 2.50fr ultra & light brown 1.50 1.50
f. A69 4.50fr ultra & light brown 1.50 1.50

Intl. Tourist Cong. The star is printed in yellow. A surtax of 3.15fr was for the benefit of the Congo Tourist Service.

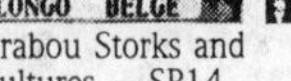

Marabou Storks and Vultures — SP14 Buffon's Kob — SP15

Designs: 1.50fr+1.50fr, Pygmy chimpanzees. 4.50fr+4.50fr, Dwarf crocodiles. 5fr+5fr, Lioness.

1939 Photo. *Perf. 14*

B27 SP14 1fr + 1fr dp claret 3.75 3.75
B28 SP15 1.25fr + 1.25fr car 3.75 3.75
B29 SP15 1.50fr + 1.50fr brt pur 5.00 5.00
B30 SP14 4.50fr + 4.50fr sl grn 3.75 3.75
B31 SP15 5fr + 5fr brown 4.00 4.00
Nos. B27-B31 (5) 20.25 20.25

Surtax for the Leopoldville Zoological Gardens. Sold in full sets by subscription.

Catalogue values for unused stamps in this section, from this point to the end of the section, are for Never Hinged items.

Lion of Belgium and Inscription "Belgium Shall Rise Again" — SP19

1942, Feb. 17 Engr. *Perf. 12½*

B32 SP19 10fr + 40fr brt grn 1.50 1.00
B33 SP19 10fr + 40fr vio bl 1.50 1.00

Nos. 193, 216, 198 and 220 Surcharged in Red

Au profit de la Croix Rouge + 50 Fr. Ten voordeele van het Roode Kruis
a

Ten voordeele van het Roode Kruis + 100 Fr. Au profit de la Croix Rouge
b

c **Au profit de la Croix Rouge + 100 Fr. Ten voordeele van het Roode Kruis**

1945

B34 A72 (a) 50c + 50fr 2.00 2.00
B35 A73 (b) 1.25fr + 100fr 2.00 2.00
B36 A74 (c) 1.75fr + 100fr 2.00 2.25
B37 A75 (b) 3.50fr + 100fr 2.00 2.25
Nos. B34-B37 (4) 8.00 8.50

The surtax was for the Red Cross. Sold in full sets by subscription.

Mozart at Age 7 — SP20

Queen Elisabeth and Sonata by Mozart — SP21

Perf. 11½

1956, Oct. 10 Unwmk. Engr.

B38 SP20 4.50fr + 1.50fr brt lil 2.00 1.50
B39 SP21 6.50fr + 2.50fr ultra 3.00 2.50

200th anniv. of the birth of Wolfgang Amadeus Mozart.
The surtax was for the Pro-Mozart Committee.

Nurse and Children — SP22

Designs: 4.50fr+50c, Patient receiving injection. 6.50fr+40c, Patient being bandaged.

1957, Dec. 10 Photo. *Perf. 13x10½*
Cross in Carmine

B40 SP22 3fr + 50c dk bl .90 .65
B41 SP22 4.50fr + 50c dk grn .80 .60
B42 SP22 6.50fr + 50c red brn 1.00 .75
Nos. B40-B42 (3) 2.70 2.00

The surtax was for the Red Cross.

High Jump — SP23

1960, May 2 Unwmk. *Perf. 13½*

B43 SP23 50c + 25c shown .15 .15
B44 SP23 1.50fr + 50c Hurdles .20 .15
B45 SP23 2fr + 1fr Soccer .20 .15
B46 SP23 3fr + 1.25fr Javelin .75 .55
B47 SP23 6.50fr + 3.50fr Discus 1.00 .75
Nos. B43-B47 (5) 2.30 1.75

17th Olympic Games, Rome, Aug. 25-Sept. 11. The surtax was for the youth of Congo.

AIR POST STAMPS

Wharf on Congo River AP1

Congo "Country Store" AP2

View of Congo River AP3

Stronghold in the Interior — AP4

1920, July 1 Unwmk. Engr. *Perf. 12*

C1 AP1 50c orange & blk .15 .15
C2 AP2 1fr dull vio & blk .15 .15
C3 AP3 2fr blue & blk .50 .20
C4 AP4 5fr green & blk .90 .40
Nos. C1-C4 (4) 1.70 .90

Kraal — AP5

Porters on Safari AP6

1930, Apr. 2

C5 AP5 15fr dk brn & blk 1.90 .75
C6 AP6 30fr brn vio & blk 2.25 .75

Fokker F VII over Congo — AP7

1934, Jan. 22 *Perf. 13½x14*

C7 AP7 50c gray black .15 .15
C8 AP7 1fr dk carmine .20 .15
a. Booklet pane of 8 5.25
C9 AP7 1.50fr green .15 .15
C10 AP7 3fr brown .20 .15
C11 AP7 4.50fr brt ultra .25 .15
a. Booklet pane of 8 10.00
C12 AP7 5fr red brown .20 .15
C13 AP7 15fr brown vio .40 .25
C14 AP7 30fr red orange .70 .60
C15 AP7 50fr violet 2.00 .95
Nos. C7-C15 (9) 4.25 2.70

The 1fr, 3fr, 4.50fr, 5fr, 15fr exist imperf.

No. C10 Surcharged in Blue with New Value and Bars

1936, Mar. 25

C16 AP7 3.50fr on 3fr brown .20 .15

Catalogue values for unused stamps in this section, from this point to the end of the section, are for Never Hinged items.

No. C9 Surcharged in Black

50 c.

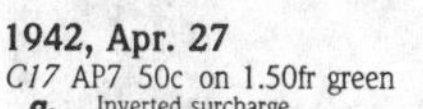

1942, Apr. 27

C17 AP7 50c on 1.50fr green .35 .15
a. Inverted surcharge 6.50 6.50

POSTAGE DUE STAMPS

In 1908-23 regular postage stamps handstamped "TAXES" or "TAXE," usually boxed, were used in lieu of postage due stamps.

D1

D2

1923-29(?) Typo. Unwmk. *Perf. 14*

J1 D1 5c black brown .15 .15
J2 D1 10c rose red .15 .15
J3 D1 15c violet .15 .15
J4 D1 30c green .25 .20
J5 D1 50c ultramarine .30 .30
J6 D1 50c blue ('29) .30 .30
J7 D1 1fr gray .45 .25
Nos. J1-J7 (7) 1.75 1.50

Catalogue values for unused stamps in this section, from this point to the end of the section, are for Never Hinged items.

1943 *Perf. 14x14½*

J8 D2 10c olive green .15 .15
J9 D2 20c dark ultra .15 .15
J10 D2 50c green .15 .15
J11 D2 1fr dark brown .20 .20
J12 D2 2fr yellow orange .25 .25
Set value .75 .75

1943 *Perf. 12½*

J8a D2 10c olive green .30 .30
J9a D2 20c dark ultramarine .30 .30
J10a D2 50c green .30 .30
J11a D2 1fr dark brown .45 .45
J12a D2 2fr yellow orange .45 .45
Nos. J8a-J12a (5) 1.80 1.80

D3

1957 Engr. *Perf. 11½*

J13 D3 10c olive brown .15 .15
J14 D3 20c claret .15 .15
J15 D3 50c green .15 .15
J16 D3 1fr light blue .30 .25
J17 D3 2fr vermilion .40 .25
J18 D3 4fr purple .60 .35
J19 D3 6fr violet blue .75 .45
Nos. J13-J19 (7) 2.50 1.75

PARCEL POST STAMPS

PP1

PP2

PP3

Handstamped Surcharges on Nos. 5, 11-12

1887-93 Unwmk. *Perf. 15*

Blue-Black Surcharge

Q1 PP1 3.50fr on 5fr lil 650.00 450.00

Black Surcharge

Q3 PP2 3.50fr on 5fr vio 600.00 325.00
Q4 PP3 3.50fr on 5fr vio ('88) 525.00 300.00
a. Blue surcharge 600.00 350.00
Q6 PP3 3.50fr on 5fr gray ('93) 82.50 52.50

Nos. Q1, Q3-Q4, Q4a and Q6 are known with inverted surcharge, No. Q1 with double surcharge and No. Q6 in pair with unsurcharged stamp. These varieties sell for somewhat more than the normal surcharges.
Genuine stamps with counterfeit surcharges, counterfeit stamps with counterfeit surcharges, and both with counterfeit cancels exist.

BELGIUM

'bel-jəm

LOCATION — Western Europe, bordering the North Sea
GOVT. — Constitutional Monarchy
AREA — 11,778 sq. mi.
POP. — 9,853,000 (est. 1983)
CAPITAL — Brussels

100 Centimes = 1 Franc

Catalogue values for unused stamps in this country are for Never Hinged items, beginning with Scott 322 in the regular postage section, Scott B370 in the semi-postal section, Scott C8 in the airpost section, Scott CB1 in the airpost semi-postal section, Scott J40 in the postage due section, Scott M1 in the military stamp section, Scott O36 in the officials section, and Scott Q267 in the parcel post section.

Watermark

Wmk. 96 (No Frame)

King Leopold I
A1 A2

Wmk. Two "L's" Framed (96)

1849 Engr. *Imperf.*

1 A1 10c brown *2,300.* 75.00
a. 10c red brown *3,250.* 400.00
2 A1 20c blue *2,850.* 57.50
a. 20c milky blue *3,250.* 150.00

The reprints are on thick and thin wove and thick laid paper unwatermarked.
A souvenir sheet containing reproductions of the 10c, 20c and 40c of 1849-51 with black burelage on back was issued Oct. 17, 1949, for the cent. of the 1st Belgian stamps. It was sold at BEPITEC 1949, an intl. stamp exhib. at Brussels, and was not valid.

1849-50

3 A2 10c brown ('50) *1,500.* 67.50
4 A2 20c blue ('50) *1,250.* 55.00
5 A2 40c carmine rose *1,200.* 300.00

Nos. 3-5 on thin paper are as valued. Copies on thick paper generally sell for 15 to 25 percent more.

Wmk. Two "L's" Without Frame (96)

1851-54

6 A2 10c brown 550.00 8.50
a. Ribbed paper ('54) 750.00 47.50
7 A2 20c blue 550.00 8.50
a. Ribbed paper ('54) 750.00 47.50
8 A2 40c car rose *2,100.* 80.00
a. Ribbed paper ('54) *1,750.* 240.00

Nos. 6-8 were printed on thin and thick paper and sell for about the same prices.
Nos. 6a, 7a, 8a must have regular and parallel ribs covering the whole stamp.

1858-61 Unwmk.

9 A2 1c green ('61) *225.00* 120.00
10 A2 10c brown 300.00 7.50
11 A2 20c blue 375.00 7.50
12 A2 40c carmine rose *2,100.* 75.00

Nos. 9 and 13 were valid for postage on newspapers and printed matter only.
Reprints of Nos. 9 to 12 are on thin wove paper. The colors are brighter than those of the originals. They were made from the dies and show lines outside the stamps.

Perf. 12½, 12½x13, 12½x13½, 14½

1863

13 A2 1c green 90.00 72.50
14 A2 10c brown 110.00 3.25
15 A2 20c blue 110.00 3.25
16 A2 40c carmine rose 725.00 35.00

Values for Nos. 13-16 are for copies with perfs cutting into design.

King Leopold I
A3 A3a

A4

A4a

A5

London Print

1865 **Typo.** ***Perf. 14***
17 A5 1fr pale violet 1,150. 100.00

Brussels Print
Thick or Thin Paper

1865-66 ***Perf. 15, 14½x14***
18 A3 10c slate ('66) 125.00 1.50
 a. Pair, imperf. between *200.00*
19 A3a 20c blue ('66) 175.00 1.50
 a. 20c lilac blue 175.00 1.75
20 A4 30c brown 400.00 11.00
 a. Pair, imperf. between *1,000.*
21 A4a 40c rose ('66) 500.00 20.00
22 A5 1fr violet 900.00 90.00

Nos. 18 to 22 on thin paper are perf. 14½x14; on thick paper, perf. 15.

The reprints are on thin paper, imperforate and ungummed.

Coat of Arms — A6

1866-67 ***Imperf.***
23 A6 1c gray 250.00 150.00

Perf. 15, 14½x14
24 A6 1c gray 45.00 16.00
25 A6 2c blue ('67) 135.00 90.00
 a. 2c ultramarine 150.00 110.00
26 A6 5c brown 135.00 90.00

Nos. 23-26 were valid for postage on newspapers and printed matter only.

Nos. 24 to 26 on thin paper are perf. 14½ x 14; on thick paper, perf. 15.

Counterfeits exist.

Reprints of Nos. 24 to 26 are on thin paper, imperforate and ungummed.

Imperf. varieties of 1869-1912 (between Nos. 28-105) are without gum.

A7 A8 A9

A10 A11 A12

King Leopold II
A13 A14 A15

1869-70 ***Perf. 15***
28 A7 1c green 6.00 .30
29 A7 2c ultra ('70) 17.50 1.25
30 A7 5c buff ('70) 40.00 .70
31 A7 8c lilac ('70) 80.00 50.00
32 A8 10c green 17.50 .40
33 A9 20c lt ultra ('70) 120.00 .70
34 A10 30c buff ('70) 75.00 4.00
35 A11 40c brt rose ('70) 100.00 6.00
36 A12 1fr dull lilac ('70) 325.00 17.00
 a. 1fr rose lilac 325.00 19.00

The frames and inscriptions of Nos. 30, 31 and 42 differ slightly from the illustration.

Minor "broken letter" varieties exist on several values.

Nos. 28-36, 40 also were printed in aniline colors. These are not valued separately.

See Nos. 40-43, 49-51, 55.

1875-78
37 A13 25c olive bister 135.00 1.25
 a. 25c ocher 135.00 1.50
38 A14 50c gray 200.00 8.50
 Roller cancel 12.50
 a. 50c gray black 325.00 55.00
 b. 50c deep black 1,750. 175.00
39 A15 5fr dp red brown *1,500.* 1,150.
 Roller cancel 525.00
 a. 5fr pale brown ('78) *3,750.* 1,250.
 Roller cancel 500.00

Dangerous counterfeits of No. 39 exist.

Printed in Aniline Colors

1881 ***Perf. 14***
40 A7 1c gray green 17.50 .55
41 A7 2c lt ultra 12.00 2.25
42 A7 5c orange buff 57.50 1.10
 a. 5c red orange 57.50 1.10
43 A8 10c gray green 30.00 .75
44 A13 25c olive bister 75.00 1.40
 Nos. 40-44 (5) 192.00 6.05

See note following No. 36.

A16

A17

A18

A19

1883
45 A16 10c carmine 27.50 2.00
46 A17 20c gray 115.00 5.00
47 A18 25c blue 250.00 27.50
 Roller cancel 15.00
48 A19 50c violet 250.00 35.00
 Roller cancel 15.00

A20

A21

A22

1884-85 ***Perf. 14***
49 A7 1c olive green 7.50 .85
50 A7 1c gray 2.75 .15
51 A7 5c green 20.00 .20
52 A20 10c rose, *bluish* 5.00 .35
 a. Grayish paper 5.00 .35
 c. Yellowish paper 175.00 20.00
53 A21 25c blue, *pink* ('85) 8.00 .55
54 A22 1fr brown, *grnsh* *550.00* 17.50

The frame and inscription of No. 51 differ slightly from the illustration.

See note after No. 36.

A23

A24

A25

A26

1886-91
55 A7 2c purple brn ('88) 12.00 .90
56 A23 20c olive, *grnsh* 115.00 .90
57 A24 35c vio brn, *brnsh* ('91) 18.00 2.75
58 A25 50c bister, *yelsh* 9.50 2.00
59 A26 2fr violet, *pale lil* 90.00 40.00
 Roller cancel 6.00

Coat of Arms
A27

King Leopold
A28

1893-1900
60 A27 1c gray 1.10 .20
61 A27 2c yellow 1.25 1.10
 a. Wmkd. coat of arms in sheet ('95) — —
62 A27 2c violet brn ('94) 1.65 .25
63 A27 2c red brown ('98) 3.25 .35
64 A27 5c yellow grn 5.00 .25
65 A28 10c orange brn 5.00 .25
66 A28 10c brt rose ('00) 3.50 .25
67 A28 20c olive green 22.50 .55
68 A28 25c ultra 20.00 .45
 a. No ball to "5" in upper left corner 32.50 12.00
69 A28 35c violet brn 37.50 1.25
 a. 35c red brown 42.50 1.65
70 A28 50c bister 62.50 17.50
71 A28 50c gray ('97) 57.50 2.25
72 A28 1fr car, *lt grn* 75.00 17.50
73 A28 1fr orange ('00) 105.00 5.00
74 A28 2fr lilac, *rose* 110.00 82.50
75 A28 2fr lilac ('00) 150.00 13.50

Values quoted for Nos. 60-107 are for stamps with label attached. Stamps without label sell for much less.

Antwerp Exhibition Issue

Arms of Antwerp — A29

1894
76 A29 5c green, *rose* 4.75 3.25
77 A29 10c carmine, *bluish* 3.75 2.25
78 A29 25c blue, *rose* .90 .90
 Nos. 76-78 (3) 9.40 6.40

Brussels Exhibition Issue

St. Michael and Satan
A30 A31

1896-97 ***Perf. 14x14½***
79 A30 5c dp violet .90 .45
80 A31 10c orange brown 8.50 3.00
81 A31 10c lilac brown .50 .35
 Nos. 79-81 (3) 9.90 3.80

A32

A33

A34

A35

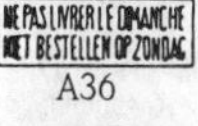
A36

A37

A38

A39

Two types of 1c:
I - Periods after "Dimanche" and "Zondag" in label.
II - No period after "Dimanche." Period often missing after "Zondag."

1905-07 ***Perf. 14***

No.	Type	Description	Unused	Used
82	A32	1c gray (I) ('07)	.75	.20
a.		Type II ('08)	.75	.25
83	A32	2c red brown ('07)	4.75	2.25
84	A32	5c green ('07)	4.75	.20
85	A33	10c dull rose	1.75	.20
86	A34	20c olive grn	12.50	.90
87	A35	25c ultra	10.00	.75
a.		25c dull blue	10.00	.75
88	A36	35c purple brn	20.00	1.90
89	A37	50c bluish gray	50.00	2.50
90	A38	1fr yellow	65.00	8.00
91	A39	2fr violet	65.00	22.50
		Bar cancellation		4.00
		Nos. 82-91 (10)	234.50	39.40

A40

A41

Lion of Belgium — A42

A43

King Albert I — A44

1912

No.	Type	Description	Unused	Used
92	A40	1c orange	.20	.15
93	A41	2c orange brn	.45	.50
94	A42	5c green	.35	.15

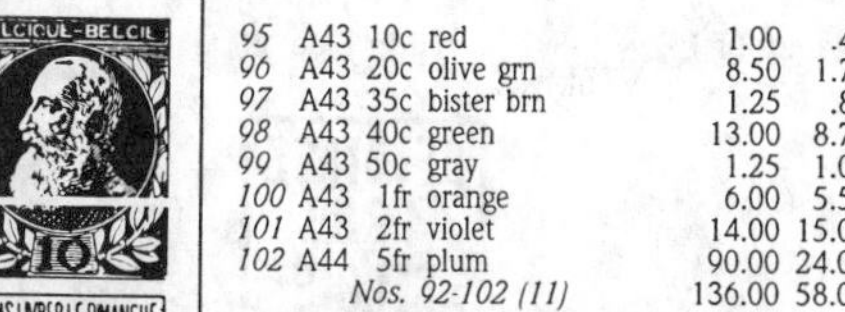

No.	Type	Description	Unused	Used
95	A43	10c red	1.00	.40
96	A43	20c olive grn	8.50	1.75
97	A43	35c bister brn	1.25	.80
98	A43	40c green	13.00	8.75
99	A43	50c gray	1.25	1.00
100	A43	1fr orange	6.00	5.50
101	A43	2fr violet	14.00	15.00
102	A44	5fr plum	90.00	24.00
		Nos. 92-102 (11)	136.00	58.00

Counterfeits exist of Nos. 97-102. Those of No. 102 are common.

For overprints see Nos. Q49-Q50, Q52, Q55-Q55A, Q57-Q60.

A45

1912-13

Larger Head

No.	Type	Description	Unused	Used
103	A45	10c red	.35	.20
a.		Without engraver's name	.25	.15
104	A45	20c olive grn ('13)	.50	.50
a.		Without engraver's name	1.10	1.10
105	A45	25c ultra	.35	.45
a.		With engraver's name	2.75	1.90
107	A45	40c green ('13)	.60	.75
		Nos. 103-107 (4)	1.80	1.90

For overprints see #Q51, Q53-Q54, Q56.

Albert I
A46

Cloth Hall of Ypres
A47

Bridge of Dinant — A48

Library of Louvain — A49

Scheldt River at Antwerp
A50

Anti-slavery Campaign in the Congo — A51

King Albert I at Furnes — A52

Kings of Belgium Leopold I, Albert I, Leopold II
A53

1915-20 **Typo.** ***Perf. 14, 14½***

No.	Type	Description	Unused	Used
108	A46	1c orange	.15	.15
109	A46	2c chocolate	.15	.15
110	A46	3c gray blk ('20)	.20	.15
111	A46	5c green	.40	.15
112	A46	10c carmine	.75	.15
113	A46	15c purple	.90	.15
114	A46	20c red violet	.90	.15
115	A46	25c blue	1.10	.20

Engr.

No.	Type	Description	Unused	Used
116	A47	35c brown org & blk	.75	.20
117	A48	40c green & black	1.25	.20
a.		Vert. pair, imperf. btwn.		
118	A49	50c car rose & blk	4.00	.25
119	A50	1fr violet	15.00	.40
120	A51	2fr slate	20.00	1.50
121	A52	5fr dp blue	200.00	80.00
		Telegraph or railroad cancel		55.00
122	A53	10fr brown	20.00	17.50
		Nos. 108-122 (15)	265.55	101.30

Two types each of the 1c, 10c and 20c; three of the 2c and 15c; four of the 5c, differing in the top left corner.

Nos. 108-120, 122 exist imperforate. See No. 138. For surcharges see Nos. B34-B47.

Perron of Liege (Fountain)
A54

King Albert in Trench Helmet
A55

1919 ***Perf. 11½***

No.	Type	Description	Unused	Used
123	A54	25c deep blue	1.75	.30
a.		Sheet of 10	*5,750.*	*5,750.*

Perf. 11, 11½, 11½x11, 11x11½

1919

Size: 18½x22mm

No.	Type	Description	Unused	Used
124	A55	1c lilac brn	.15	.15
125	A55	2c olive	.15	.15

Size: 23x26mm

No.	Type	Description	Unused	Used
126	A55	5c green	.20	.15
127	A55	10c carmine	.15	.15
128	A55	15c gray vio	.25	.20
129	A55	20c olive blk	.80	.95
130	A55	25c deep blue	.80	.65
131	A55	35c bister brn	1.50	1.50
132	A55	40c red	2.50	3.50
133	A55	50c red brn	8.50	10.00
134	A55	1fr lt orange	30.00	40.00
135	A55	2fr violet	375.00	375.00

Size: 28x33½mm

No.	Type	Description	Unused	Used
136	A55	5fr car lake	100.00	100.00
137	A55	10fr claret	110.00	110.00
		Nos. 124-137 (14)	630.00	642.40

Type of 1915 Inscribed: "FRANK" instead of "FRANKEN"

1919, Dec. ***Perf. 14, 15***

No.	Type	Description	Unused	Used
138	A52	5fr deep blue	1.75	1.25

Town Hall at Termonde
A56 A57

1920 ***Perf. 11½***

No.	Type	Description	Unused	Used
139	A56	65c claret & black	1.10	.20
a.		Center inverted	*25,000.*	

For surcharge see No. 143.

Semi-Postal Stamps of 1920 Surcharged in Red or Black

20c X 20c X

1921 ***Perf. 12***

No.	Type	Description	Unused	Used
140	SP6	20c on 5c (R)	.60	.22
a.		Inverted surcharge	185.00	185.00
141	SP7	20c on 10c	.42	.22
b.		Inverted surcharge	185.00	185.00
142	SP8	20c on 15c (R)	.45	.22
a.		Inverted surcharge	185.00	185.00

Red Surcharge

No.	Type	Description	Unused	Used
143	A57	55c on 65c claret & blk	1.10	.35
a.		Pair, one without surcharge	1.75	.85
		Nos. 140-143 (4)	2.57	1.01

A58

A59

1922-27 **Typo.** ***Perf. 14***

No.	Type	Description	Unused	Used
144	A58	1c orange	.15	.15
145	A58	2c olive ('26)	.15	.15
146	A58	3c fawn	.15	.15
147	A58	5c gray	.15	.15
148	A58	10c blue grn	.15	.15
149	A58	15c plum ('23)	.15	.15
150	A58	20c black brn	.20	.15
151	A58	25c dull violet	.15	.15
152	A58	30c vermilion	.55	.15
153	A58	30c rose ('25)	.40	.15
154	A58	35c red brown	.35	.15
155	A58	35c blue grn ('27)	.60	.30
156	A58	40c rose	.55	.15
157	A58	50c bister ('25)	.55	.15
158	A58	60c olive brn ('27)	2.25	.15
159	A58	1.25fr dp blue ('26)	.65	.85
160	A58	1.50fr brt blue ('26)	1.60	.40
161	A58	1.75fr ultra ('27)	1.10	.15
a.		Tete beche pair	8.00	5.00
c.		Bklt. pane of 4 + 2 labels	40.00	
		Nos. 144-161 (18)	9.85	
		Set value		3.00

See Nos. 185-190. For overprints and surcharges see Nos. 191-195, 197, B56, O1-O6.

Perf. 11½, 11½x11, 11½x12, 11½x12½

1921-25 **Engr.**

No.	Type	Description	Unused	Used
162	A59	50c dull blue	.35	.15
163	A59	75c scarlet ('22)	.15	.15
164	A59	75c ultra ('24)	.50	.15
165	A59	1fr black brn ('22)	.90	.15
166	A59	1fr dk blue ('25)	.70	.15
167	A59	2fr dk green ('22)	.90	.30
168	A59	5fr brown vio ('23)	15.00	15.00
169	A59	10fr magenta ('22)	9.00	6.50
		Nos. 162-169 (8)	27.50	22.55

No. 162 measures 18x20¾mm and was printed in sheets of 100.

Philatelic Exhibition Issues

1921, May 26 ***Perf. 11½***

No.	Type	Description	Unused	Used
170	A59	50c dark blue	3.50	3.50
a.		Sheet of 25	225.00	200.00

No. 170 measures 17½x21¼mm, was printed in sheets of 25 and sold at the Philatelic Exhibition at Brussels.

The sheet normally has pin holes and a cancellation-like marking in the margin. These are considered unused and the condition valued here.

Souvenir Sheet

1924, May 24 ***Perf. 11½***

No.	Type	Description	Unused	Used
171		Sheet of 4	140.00	125.00
a.		A59 5fr red brown	12.00	12.00

Sold only at the Intl. Phil. Exhib., Brussels. Sheet size: 130x145mm.

The sheet normally has pin holes and a cancellation-like marking in the margin. These are considered unused and the condition valued here.

Kings Leopold I and Albert I — A60

1925 ***Perf. 14***

No.	Type	Description	Unused	Used
172	A60	10c dp green	5.75	6.25
173	A60	15c dull vio	3.75	4.50
174	A60	20c red brown	3.75	4.50
175	A60	25c grnsh black	3.75	4.50
176	A60	30c vermilion	3.75	4.50
177	A60	35c lt blue	3.75	4.50
178	A60	40c brnsh blk	3.75	4.50
179	A60	50c yellow brn	3.75	4.50
180	A60	75c dk blue	3.75	4.50
181	A60	1fr dk violet	5.75	6.75
182	A60	2fr ultra	3.75	4.50
183	A60	5fr blue blk	3.75	4.50
184	A60	10fr dp rose	6.00	8.00
		Nos. 172-184 (13)	55.00	66.00

75th anniv. of Belgian postage stamps.

Nos. 172-184 were sold only in sets and only by The Administration of Posts, not at post offices.

A61

1926-27 **Typo.**

185 A61 75c dk violet .75 .70
186 A61 1fr pale yellow .65 .25
187 A61 1fr rose red ('27) .85 .15
a. Tete beche pair 8.25 5.00
c. Bklt. pane 4 + 2 labels 25.00
188 A61 2fr Prus blue 2.25 .15
189 A61 5fr emerald ('27) 15.00 1.00
190 A61 10fr dk brown ('27) 27.50 4.50
Nos. 185-190 (6) 47.00 6.75

For overprints and surcharge see Nos. 196, Q174-Q175.

Stamps of 1921-27 Surcharged in Carmine, Red or Blue ≡ 1F75 ≡

1927

191 A58 3c on 2c olive (C) .15 .15
192 A58 10c on 15c plum (R) .15 .15
193 A58 35c on 40c rose (Bl) .50 .15
194 A58 1.75fr on 1.50fr brt bl (C) 2.50 .80
Nos. 191-194 (4) 3.30 1.25

Nos. 153, 185 and 159 Surcharged in Black

BRUXELLES
1929
BRUSSEL
=5c=

1929, Jan. 1

195 A58 5c on 30c rose .15 .15
196 A61 5c on 75c dk violet .30 .30
197 A58 5c on 1.25fr dp blue .15 .15
Nos. 195-197 (3) .60 .60

The surcharge on Nos. 195 to 197 is a precancelation which alters the value of the stamp to which it is applied.

Values for precanceled stamps in unused column are for those which have not been through the post and have original gum. Values in second column are for postally used, gumless stamps.

A63

A64

1929-32 **Typo.** *Perf. 14*

198 A63 1c orange .15 .15
199 A63 2c emerald ('31) .20 .35
200 A63 3c red brown .15 .15
201 A63 5c slate .15 .15
c. Bklt. pane of 4 + 2 labels 8.25
202 A63 10c olive grn .15 .15
c. Bklt. pane of 4 + 2 labels 4.50
203 A63 20c brt violet 1.00 .15
204 A63 25c rose red .45 .15
c. Bklt. pane of 4 + 2 labels 8.25
205 A63 35c green .65 .15
c. Bklt. pane of 4 + 2 labels 9.75
206 A63 40c red vio ('30) .30 .15
c. Bklt. pane of 4 + 2 labels 9.75
207 A63 50c dp blue .50 .15
c. Bklt. pane of 4 + 2 labels 8.25
208 A63 60c rose ('30) 1.10 .20
c. Bklt. pane of 4 + 2 labels 30.00
209 A63 70c org brn ('30) .70 .15
c. Bklt. pane of 4 + 2 labels 22.50
210 A63 75c dk blue ('30) 1.75 .15
211 A63 75c dp brown ('32) 6.00 .15
b. Bklt. pane of 4 + 2 labels 100.00
Nos. 198-211 (14) 13.25
Set value 1.75

For overprints and surcharges see Nos. 225-226, 240-241, 254-256, 309, O7-O15.

Tete Beche Pairs

201a	A63	5c	1.00	.90
202a	A63	10c	.65	.60
204a	A63	25c	2.00	2.00
205a	A63	35c	3.00	3.00
206a	A63	40c	3.00	3.00
207a	A63	50c	2.50	2.50
208a	A63	60c	9.00	8.50
209a	A63	70c	6.50	5.50
210a	A63	75c	10.00	9.50
211a	A63	75c	32.50	27.50
Nos. 201a-211a (10)			70.15	63.00

1929, Jan. 25 **Engr.** *Perf. 14½, 14*

212 A64 10fr dk brown 15.00 4.50
213 A64 20fr dk green 85.00 16.00
214 A64 50fr red violet 7.50 9.00
a. Perf. 14½ 37.50 40.00
215 A64 100fr rose lake 14.00 15.00
a. Perf. 14½ 37.50 40.00
Nos. 212-215 (4) 121.50 44.50

Peter Paul Rubens — A65

Zenobe Gramme — A66

1930, Apr. 26 **Photo.** *Perf. 12½x12*

216 A65 35c blue green .45 .25
217 A66 35c blue green .45 .25

No. 216 issued for the Antwerp Exhibition, No. 217 the Liege Exhibition.

Leopold I, by Jacques de Winne — A67

Leopold II, by Joseph Lempoels — A68

Design: 1.75fr, Albert I.

1930, July 1 **Engr.** *Perf. 11½*

218 A67 60c brown violet .25 .15
219 A68 1fr carmine 1.25 1.25
220 A68 1.75fr dk blue 3.00 .95
Nos. 218-220 (3) 4.50 2.35

Centenary of Belgian independence.
For overprints see Nos. 222-224.

Antwerp Exhibition Issue

Souvenir Sheet

Arms of Antwerp — A70

1930, Aug. 9 *Perf. 11½*

221 A70 4fr Sheet of 1 175.00 175.00

Size: 142x141mm. Inscription in lower margin "ATELIER DU TIMBRE-1930-ZEGELFABRIEK." Each purchaser of a ticket to the Antwerp Phil. Exhib., Aug. 9-15, was allowed to purchase one stamps. The ticket cost 6 francs.

The sheet normally has pin holes and a cancellation-like marking in the margin. These are considered unused and the condition valued here.

Nos. 218-220 Overprinted in Blue or Red

B.I.T.
OCT. 1930

1930, Oct.

222 A67 60c brown vio (Bl) 1.75 1.50
223 A68 1fr carmine (Bl) 8.25 7.50
224 A68 1.75fr dk blue (R) 14.00 14.00
Nos. 222-224 (3) 24.00 23.00

50th meeting of the administrative council of the Intl. Labor Bureau at Brussels.

The names of the painters and the initials of the engraver have been added at the foot of these stamps.

Stamps of 1929-30 Surcharged in Blue or Black:

≡2c≡

1931, Feb. 20 *Perf. 14*

225 A63 2c on 3c red brown (Bl) .15 .15
226 A63 10c on 60c rose (Bk) .50 .20

The surcharge on No. 226 is a precancelation which alters the denomination. See note after No. 197.

A71

A71a

King Albert

1931, June 15 **Photo.**

227 A71 1fr brown carmine .85 .15

1932, June 1

228 A71a 75c bister brown .65 .15
a. Tete beche pair 11.00 11.00
c. Bklt. pane 4 + 2 labels 27.50

See No. 257. For overprint see No. O18.

A72

1931-32 **Engr.**

229 A72 1.25fr gray black .85 .35
230 A72 1.50fr brown vio 1.25 .30
231 A72 1.75fr dp blue .90 .15
232 A72 2fr red brown 1.25 .15
233 A72 2.45fr dp violet 1.75 .30
234 A72 2.50fr black brn ('32) 11.50 .35
235 A72 5fr dp green 12.50 .90
236 A72 10fr claret 30.00 11.00
Nos. 229-236 (8) 60.00 13.50

Nos. 206 and 209 Surcharged as No. 226, but dated "1932"

1932, Jan. 1

240 A63 10c on 40c red vio 2.75 .30
241 A63 10c on 70c org brn 2.25 .20

See note after No. 197.

Gleaner A73

Mercury A74

1932, June 1 **Typo.** *Perf. 13½x14*

245 A73 2c pale green .15 .45
246 A74 5c dp orange .15 .15
247 A73 10c olive grn .25 .15
a. Tete beche pair 4.50 4.50
c. Bklt. pane 4 + 2 labels 15.00
248 A74 20c brt violet .45 .15
249 A73 25c deep red .45 .15
a. Tete beche pair 4.00 4.00
c. Bklt. pane 4 + 2 labels 15.00
250 A74 35c dp green 1.75 .15
Nos. 245-250 (6) 3.20
Set value .95

For overprints see Nos. O16-O17.

Auguste Piccard's Balloon — A75

1932, Nov. 26 **Engr.** *Perf. 11½*

251 A75 75c red brown 3.50 .30
252 A75 1.75fr dk blue 8.00 1.75
253 A75 2.50fr dk violet 10.00 8.50
Nos. 251-253 (3) 21.50 10.55

Issued in commemoration of Prof. Auguste Piccard's two ascents to the stratosphere.

Nos. 206 and 209 Surcharged as No. 226, but dated "1933"

1933, Nov. *Perf. 14*

254 A63 10c on 40c red vio 14.00 4.00
255 A63 10c on 70c org brn 11.00 1.50

No. 206 Surcharged as No. 226, but dated "1934"

1934, Feb.

256 A63 10c on 40c red vio 11.00 1.50

For Nos. 254 to 256 see note after No. 197. Regummed copies of Nos. 254-256 abound.

King Albert Memorial Issue

Type of 1932 with Black Margins

1934, Mar. 10 **Photo.**

257 A71a 75c black .30 .15

Congo Pavilion — A76

Designs: 1fr, Brussels pavilion. 1.50fr, "Old Brussels." 1.75fr, Belgian pavilion.

1934, July 1 *Perf. 14x13½*

258 A76 35c green .50 .15
259 A76 1fr dk carmine .65 .20
260 A76 1.50fr brown 1.75 .75
261 A76 1.75fr blue 4.00 .15
Nos. 258-261 (4) 6.90 1.25

Brussels Intl. Exhib. of 1935.

A80

A81

King Leopold III

1934-35 *Perf. 13½x14*

262 A80 70c ol blk ('35) .35 .15
a. Tete beche pair 1.75 1.00
c. Bklt. pane 4 + 2 labels 6.25
263 A80 75c brown .70 .15

Perf. 14x13½

264 A81 1fr rose car ('35) 3.50 .35
Nos. 262-264 (3) 4.55
Set value .55

For overprint see No. O19.

Coat of Arms — A82

1935-48 **Typo.** *Perf. 14*

265 A82 2c green ('37) .15 .15
266 A82 5c orange .15 .15
267 A82 10c olive bister .15 .15
a. Tete beche pair .35 .30
b. Bklt. pane 4 + 2 labels 4.50
268 A82 15c dk violet .15 .15
269 A82 20c lilac .15 .15
270 A82 25c carmine rose .15 .15
a. Tete beche pair .59 .45
c. Bklt. pane 4 + 2 labels 4.50

271 A82 25c yel org ('46) .15 .15
272 A82 30c brown .15 .15
273 A82 35c green .15 .15
a. Tete beche pair .30 .20
c. Bklt. pane 4 + 2 labels 3.00
274 A82 40c red vio ('38) .20 .15
275 A82 50c blue .25 .15
276 A82 60c slate ('41) .15 .15
277 A82 65c red lilac ('46) .30 .15
278 A82 70c lt blue grn ('45) .15 .15
279 A82 75c lilac rose ('45) .25 .15
280 A82 80c green ('48) 3.50 .45
281 A82 90c dull vio ('46) .20 .15
282 A82 1fr red brown ('45) .15 .15
Nos. 265-282 (18) 6.50
Set value 1.25

Several stamps of type A82 exist in various shades.

Nos. 265, 361 were privately overprinted and surcharged "+10FR." by the Association Belgo-Americaine for the dedication of the Bastogne Memorial, July 16, 1950. The overprint is in six types.

See design O1. For overprints and surcharges see Nos. 312-313, 361-364, 390-394, O20-O22, O24, O26-O28, O33.

A83

A83a

Perf. 14, 14x13½, 11½

1936-51 **Photo.**

Size: 17½x21¾mm

283 A83 70c brown .35 .15
a. Tete beche pair .75 .65
c. Bklt. pane 4 + 2 labels 7.50

Size: 20¾x24mm

284 A83a 1fr rose car .30 .15
285 A83a 1.20fr dk brown ('51) .90 .15
286 A83a 1.50fr brt red vio ('43) .25 .15
287 A83a 1.75fr dp ultra ('43) .15 .20
288 A83a 1.75fr dk car ('50) .15 .15
289 A83a 2fr dk pur ('43) .90 .85
290 A83a 2.25fr grnsh blk ('43) .25 .15
291 A83a 2.50fr org red ('51) 1.90 .15
292 A83a 3.25fr chestnut ('43) .15 .15
293 A83a 5fr dp green ('43) .90 .40
Nos. 283-293 (11) 6.20
Set value 2.00

Nos. 287-288, 290-291, 293 inscribed "Belgie-Belgique."

See designs A85, A91. For overprints and surcharges see #314, O23, O25, O29, O31, O34.

A84

A85

1936-51 **Engr.** *Perf. 14x13½*

294 A84 1.50fr rose lilac .30 .15
295 A84 1.75fr dull blue .20 .15
296 A84 2fr dull vio .30 .15
297 A84 2.25fr gray vio ('41) .25 .15
298 A84 2.45fr black 22.50 .45
299 A84 2.50fr ol blk ('40) 2.00 .25
300 A84 3.25fr org brn ('41) .30 .15
301 A84 5fr dull green 1.50 .35
302 A84 10fr dk vio brn .60 .15
a. 10fr light brown 22.50 .35
303 A84 20fr vermilion 1.00 .15

Perf. 11½

304 A84 3fr yel brn ('51) .60 .15
305 A84 4fr bl, *bluish* ('50) 1.50 .15
a. White paper 5.50 .15
306 A84 6fr brt rose car ('51) 3.00 .15
307 A84 10fr brn vio ('51) .60 .15
308 A84 20fr red ('51) 1.25 .15
Nos. 294-308 (15) 35.90
Set value 2.00

See No. 1159. For overprint and surcharges see Nos. 316-317, O32.

No. 206 Surcharged as No. 226, but dated "1937"

1937 **Unwmk.** *Perf. 14*

309 A63 10c on 40c red vio .15 .20

See note after No. 197.

1938-41 **Photo.** *Perf. 13½x14*

310 A85 75c olive gray .30 .15
a. Tete beche pair 1.50 1.25
c. Bklt. pane 4 + 2 labels 6.75

311 A85 1fr rose pink ('41) .15 .15
a. Tete beche pair .35 .25
b. Booklet pane of 6 2.25
c. Bklt. pane 4 + 2 labels 2.25
Set value .15

For overprints and surcharges see Nos. 315, O25, O30, O35.

Nos. 272, 274, 283, 310, 299, 298 Surcharged in Blue, Black, Carmine or Red

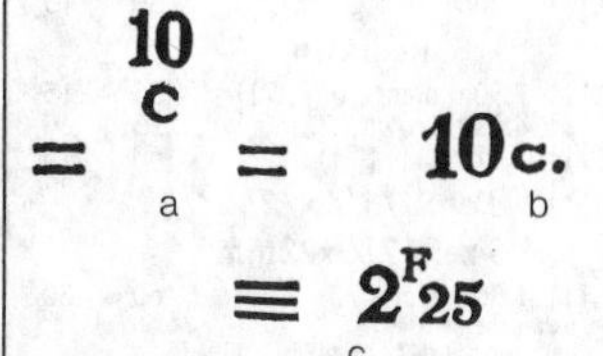

a b c

1938-42

312 A82 (a) 10c on 30c (Bl) .15 .15
313 A82 (a) 10c on 40c (Bl) .15 .15
314 A83 (b) 10c on 70c (Bk) .15 .15
315 A85 (b) 50c on 75c (C) .15 .15
316 A84 (c) 2.25fr on 2.50fr (C) .40 .60
317 A84 (c) 2.50fr on 2.45fr (R) 12.00 .15
Nos. 312-317 (6) 13.00 1.35

Issue date: No. 317, Oct. 31, 1938.

Basilica and Bell Tower — A86

Water Exhibition Buildings — A87

Designs: 1.50fr, Albert Canal and Park. 1.75fr, Eygenbilsen Cut in Albert Canal.

Perf. 14x13½, 13½x14

1938, Oct. 31

318 A86 35c dk blue grn .15 .15
319 A87 1fr rose red .50 .20
320 A87 1.50fr vio brn 1.25 .70
321 A87 1.75fr ultra 1.40 .20
Nos. 318-321 (4) 3.30 1.25

Intl. Water Exhibition, Liège, 1939.

Catalogue values for unused stamps in this section, from this point to the end of the section, are for Never Hinged items.

Lion Rampant A90

Leopold III, Crown and V A91

1944 **Unwmk.** **Photo.** *Perf. 12½*

Inscribed: "Belgique-Belgie"

322 A90 5c chocolate .15 .15
323 A90 10c green .15 .15
324 A90 25c lt blue .15 .15
325 A90 35c brown .15 .15
326 A90 50c lt bl grn .15 .15
327 A90 75c purple .15 .15
328 A90 1fr vermilion .15 .15
329 A90 1.25fr chestnut .18 .16
330 A90 1.50fr orange .45 .38
331 A90 1.75fr brt ultra .15 .15
332 A90 2fr aqua 3.75 1.90
333 A90 2.75fr dp mag .20 .15
334 A90 3fr claret .75 .60
335 A90 3.50fr sl blk .75 .60
336 A90 5fr dk olive 6.75 4.75
337 A90 10fr black 1.25 1.10
Nos. 322-337 (16) 15.28 10.84

Inscribed: "Belgie-Belgique"

338 A90 5c chocolate .15 .15
339 A90 10c green .15 .15
340 A90 25c lt bl .15 .15
341 A90 35c brown .15 .15
342 A90 50c lt bl grn .15 .15
343 A90 75c purple .15 .15
344 A90 1fr vermilion .15 .15
345 A90 1.25fr chestnut .15 .20
346 A90 1.50fr orange .32 .45
347 A90 1.75fr brt ultra .15 .15
348 A90 2fr aqua 2.00 2.00
349 A90 2.75fr dp magenta .18 .15
350 A90 3fr claret .65 .75
351 A90 3.50fr slate blk .65 .75
352 A90 5fr dark olive 5.75 5.00
353 A90 10fr black 1.00 1.25
Nos. 338-353 (16) 11.90 11.75

1944-57 *Perf. 14x13½*

354 A91 1fr brt rose red .35 .15
355 A91 1.50fr magenta .50 .15
356 A91 1.75fr dp ultra .50 .55
357 A91 2fr dp vio 1.50 .15
358 A91 2.25fr grnsh blk .55 .65
359 A91 3.25fr chnt brn .75 .15
360 A91 5fr dk bl grn 3.00 .15
a. Perf. 11½ ('57) 75.00 .15
Nos. 354-360 (7) 7.15
Set value 1.50

Nos. 355, 357, 359 inscribed "Belgique-Belgie."

For surcharges see Nos. 365-367 and footnote following No. 367.

Stamps of 1935-41 Overprinted in Red **V**

1944 *Perf. 14*

361 A82 2c pale green .15 .15
362 A82 15c indigo .15 .15
363 A82 20c brt violet .15 .15
364 A82 60c slate .24 .15
Set value .48 .32

See note following No. 282.

Nos. 355, 357, and 360 Surcharged Typographically in Black or Carmine **-10%**

1946 *Perf. 14x13½*

365 A91 On 1.50fr magenta .52 .15
366 A91 On 2fr dp vio (C) 1.90 .45
367 A91 On 5fr dk bl grn (C) 2.50 .28
Nos. 365-367 (3) 4.92 .88

To provide denominations created by a reduction in postal rates, the Government produced Nos. 365-367 by surcharging typographically. Also, each post office was authorized on May 20, 1946, to surcharge its stock of 1.50fr, 2fr and 5fr stamps "-10 percent." Hundreds of types and sizes of this surcharge exist, both hand-stamped and typographed. These include the "1,35," "1,80" and "4,50" applied at Ghislenghien.

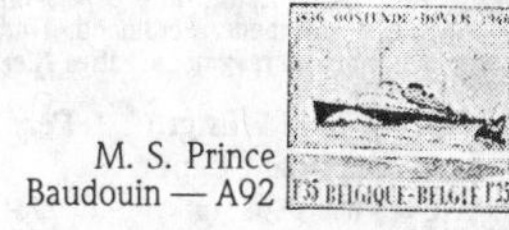
M. S. Prince Baudouin — A92

Designs: 2.25fr, S.S. Marie Henriette. 3.15fr, S.S. Diamant.

Perf. 14x13½, 13½x14

1946, June 15 **Photo.** **Unwmk.**

368 A92 1.35fr brt bluish grn .15 .15
369 A92 2.25fr slate green .30 .15
370 A92 3.15fr slate black .30 .15
Nos. 368-370 (3) .75
Set value .31

Centenary of the steamship line between Ostend and Dover.

#368 exists in two sizes: 21¼x18¼mm and 21x17mm. #369-370 are 24½x20mm.

Capt. Adrien de Gerlache A95

Belgica and Explorers A96

1947, June *Perf. 14x13½, 11½*

371 A95 1.35fr crimson rose .38 .15
372 A96 2.25fr gray black 2.25 2.00

50th anniv. of Capt. Adrien de Gerlache's Antarctic Expedition.

Joseph A. F. Plateau — A97

1947, June *Perf. 14x13½*

373 A97 3.15fr deep blue .80 .15

Issued to mark the World Film and Fine Arts Festival, Brussels, June, 1947.

Chemical Industry — A98

Industrial Arts — A99

Agriculture — A100

Textile Industry — A102

Communications Center — A101

Iron Manufacture A103

Photogravure (#374-376, 378), Typographed (#377, 380), Engraved

1948 **Unwmk.** *Perf. 11½*

374 A98 60c blue grn .85 .22
375 A98 1.20fr brown 2.25 .16
376 A99 1.35fr red brown .85 .15
377 A100 1.75fr brt red 1.65 .15
378 A99 1.75fr dk gray grn 1.10 .15
379 A101 2.25fr gray blue 2.00 1.75
380 A100 2.50fr dk car rose 6.75 .18
381 A101 3fr brt red vio 9.00 .28
382 A102 3.15fr deep blue 2.00 .22
383 A102 4fr brt ultra 8.25 .18
384 A103 6fr blue green 13.00 .18
385 A103 6.30fr brt red vio 4.00 3.75
Nos. 374-385 (12) 51.70 7.37

See Nos. O42-O46.

Leopold I — A104

1949, July 1 **Engr.** *Perf. 14x13½*

386 A104 90c dk green 1.10 .65
387 A104 1.75fr brown .90 .15
388 A104 3fr red 3.50 3.25
389 A104 4fr deep blue 5.00 1.40
Nos. 386-389 (4) 10.50 5.45

Cent. of Belgium's 1st postage stamps.

See note on souvenir sheet below No. 2.

Stamps of 1935-45 Precanceled and Surcharged in Black

1949 *Perf. 14*

390	A82	5c on 15c dk vio	.15	.15
391	A82	5c on 30c brown	.15	.15
392	A82	5c on 40c red vio	.15	.15
393	A82	20c on 70c lt bl grn	.35	.45
394	A82	20c on 75c lil rose	.20	.18

Similar Surcharge and Precancellation in Black on Nos. B455-B458

Perf. 14x13½

395	SP251	10c on #B455	4.00	4.00
396	SP251	40c on #B456	1.25	1.10
397	SP251	80c on #B457	.70	.65
398	SP251	1.20fr on #B458	2.50	2.00
		Nos. 390-398 (9)	9.45	8.83

See note after No. 197.

St. Mary Magdalene, from Painting by Gerard David — A105

1949, July 15 **Photo.** *Perf. 11*

399 A105 1.75fr dk brown .65 .35

Gerard David Exhibition at Bruges, 1949.

Allegory of UPU — A106

1949, Oct. 1 **Engr.** *Perf. 11½*

400 A106 4fr deep blue 4.50 2.50

75th anniv. of the UPU.

Symbolical of Pension Fund A107

Lion Rampant A108

Perf. 11½

1950, May 1 **Unwmk.** **Photo.**

401 A107 1.75fr dark brown .50 .25

General Pension Fund founding, cent.

1951, Feb. 15 **Engr.** *Perf. 11½*

402 A108 20c blue .25 .15

1951-75 **Typo.** *Perf. 13½x14*

Size: 17½x21mm

403	A108	2c org brn ('60)	.15	.15
404	A108	3c brt lil ('60)	.15	.15
405	A108	5c pale violet	.15	.15
406	A108	5c brt pink ('74)	.15	.15
407	A108	10c red orange	.15	.15
408	A108	15c brt pink ('59)	.15	.15
409	A108	20c claret	.15	.15
410	A108	25c green	1.50	.22
411	A108	25c lt bl grn ('66)	.15	.15
412	A108	30c gray grn ('57)	.15	.15
413	A108	40c brown olive	.15	.15
414	A108	50c ultra	.15	.15
a.		50c light blue	.15	.15
415	A108	60c lilac rose	.15	.15
416	A108	65c violet brn	12.50	.55
417	A108	75c bluish lilac	.30	.15
418	A108	80c emerald	1.00	.15
419	A108	90c deep blue	1.25	.15
420	A108	1fr rose	.15	.15
421	A108	2fr emerald ('73)	.30	.15
422	A108	2.50fr brown ('70)	.30	.15

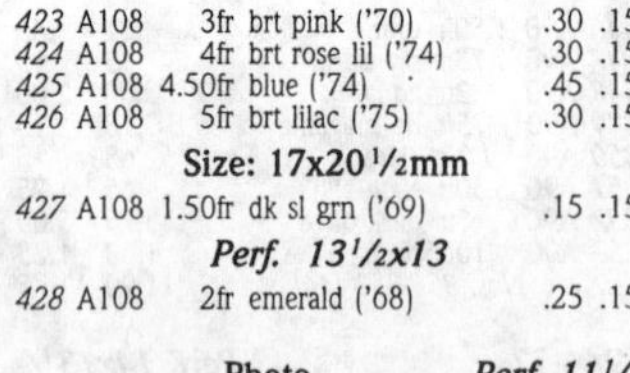

423	A108	3fr brt pink ('70)	.30	.15
424	A108	4fr brt rose lil ('74)	.30	.15
425	A108	4.50fr blue ('74)	.45	.15
426	A108	5fr brt lilac ('75)	.30	.15

Size: 17x20½mm

427 A108 1.50fr dk sl grn ('69) .15 .15

Perf. 13½x13

428 A108 2fr emerald ('68) .25 .15

Photo. *Perf. 11½*

Size: 20½x24mm

429	A108	50c lt blue ('61)	1.00	.15
430	A108	60c lil rose ('66)	2.25	2.00
431	A108	1fr car rose ('59)	.15	.15

Perf. 13½x12½

Size: 17½x22mm

432	A108	50c lt blue ('75)	.15	.15
a.		Booklet pane of 4 (#432, 784 and 2 #785) + labels	1.00	
b.		Booklet pane of 4 (#432 and 3 #787) + labels	1.35	
433	A108	1fr rose ('69)	4.00	1.00
434	A108	2fr emerald ('72)	.60	.30
e.		Booklet pane of 6 (4 #434 + 2 #475)	5.50	
f.		Booklet pane of 5 (#434, 4 #476 + label)	8.00	
		Nos. 403-434 (32)	29.00	
		Set value		6.00

Counterfeits exist of No. 416. Nos. 429, 431 also issued in coils with black control number on back of every fifth stamp. Nos. 432-434 issued in booklet panes only. No. 432 has one straightedge, and stamps in the pane are tete-beche. Each pane has 2 labels showing Belgian postal emblem and a large selvage with postal code instructions.

Nos. 433-434 have 1 or 2 straight-edges. Panes have a large selvage with inscription or map of Belgium showing postal zones.

See designs A386, O5. For surcharges see Nos. 477-478, 563-567.

Francois de Tassis (Franz von Taxis) — A109

Portraits: 1.75fr, Jean-Baptiste of Thurn & Taxis. 2fr, Baron Leonard I. 2.50fr, Count Lamoral I. 3fr, Count Leonard II. 4fr, Count Lamoral II. 5fr, Prince Eugene Alexander. 5.75fr, Prince Anselme François. 8fr, Prince Alexander Ferdinand. 10fr, Prince Charles Anselme. 20fr, Prince Charles Alexander.

1952, May 14 **Engr.** *Perf. 11½*

Laid Paper

435	A109	80c olive grn	.75	.30
436	A109	1.75fr red org	.75	.30
437	A109	2fr violet brn	1.50	.40
438	A109	2.50fr carmine	2.25	1.65
439	A109	3fr olive bis	2.00	1.00
440	A109	4fr ultra	3.00	.85
441	A109	5fr red brn	4.00	1.75
442	A109	5.75fr blue vio	6.75	2.25
443	A109	8fr gray	12.50	2.75
444	A109	10fr rose vio	22.50	4.50
445	A109	20fr brown	60.00	22.50
		Nos. 435-445,B514 (12)	291.00	213.25

13th UPU Cong., Brussels, 1952.

King Baudouin
A110 A111

1952-58 **Engr.** *Perf. 11½*

Size: 21x24mm

446	A110	1.50fr gray	.55	.15
447	A110	2fr crimson	.40	.15
448	A110	4fr ultra	3.50	.20

Size: 24½x35mm

449	A110	50fr gray brn	1.75	.20
a.		50fr violet brown	20.00	.60
450	A110	100fr rose red ('58)	5.00	.25

1953-72 **Photo.** *Perf. 11½*

451	A111	1.50fr gray	.25	.15
452	A111	2fr rose carmine	6.75	.15
453	A111	2fr green	.25	.15
454	A111	2.50fr red brn ('57)	.60	.15
a.		2.50fr orange brown ('70)	.45	.15
455	A111	3fr rose lilac ('58)	.40	.15
456	A111	3.50fr brt yel grn ('58)	.75	.15
457	A111	4fr brt ultra	.50	.15
458	A111	4.50fr dk red brn ('62)	3.00	.15
459	A111	5fr violet ('57)	1.25	.15
460	A111	6fr dp pink ('58)	.75	.15
461	A111	6.50fr gray ('60)	62.50	12.00
462	A111	7fr blue ('60)	.90	.15
463	A111	7.50fr grysh brn ('58)	47.50	14.00
464	A111	8fr bluish gray ('58)	1.25	.15
465	A111	8.50fr claret ('58)	15.00	.30
466	A111	9fr gray ('58)	47.50	.75
467	A111	12fr lt bl grn ('66)	.90	.15
468	A111	30fr red org ('58)	5.50	.15

Redrawn

469	A111	2.50fr orange brn ('71)	.35	.15
470	A111	4.50fr brown ('72)	2.25	.60
471	A111	7fr blue ('71)	.60	.15

Perf. 13½x12½

Size: 17½x22mm

472	A111	1.50fr gray ('70)	.60	.30
b.		Bklt. pane of 10	6.50	
c.		Bklt. pane, 3 #472, 3 #475	15.00	
473	A111	2.50fr org brn ('70)	9.00	6.25
h.		Bklt. pane, 1 #473, 5 #475	16.00	
474	A111	3fr lilac rose ('69)	.60	.15
a.		Bklt. pane of 5 + label	25.00	
b.		Bklt. pane, 2 #433, 6 #474	18.00	
475	A111	3.50fr brt yel grn ('70)	.60	.25
476	A111	4.50fr dull red brn ('72)	.75	.45
		Nos. 446-476 (31)	221.50	38.40

Nos. 451, 453, 454a, 455, 456, 458 also issued in coils with black control number on back of every fifth stamp. These coils, except for No. 451, are on luminescent paper.

On Nos. 469-471, the 2, 4 and 7 are 3mm high. The background around the head is white. On Nos. 454, 458, 462 the 2, 4 and 7 are 2½mm high and the background is tinted.

Nos. 472-476 issued in booklets only and have 1 or 2 straight-edges. All panes have a large selvage with inscription or map.

See designs M1, O3.

Luminescent Paper

Stamps issued on both ordinary and luminescent paper include: Nos. 307-308, 430-431, 449-451, 453-460, 462, 464, 467-468, 472, 643-644, 650-651, 837, Q385, Q410.

Stamps issued only on luminescent paper include: Nos. 433, 454a, 472b, 473-474, 649, 652-658, 664-670, 679-682, 688-690, 694-696, 698-703, 705-711, 713-726, 729-747, 751-754, 756-757, 759, 761-762, 764, 766, 769, 772, 774, 778, 789, 791-793, 795, 797-799, 801-807, 809-811, 814-818, 820-834, 836, 838-848.

See note after No. 857.

Nos. 416 and 419 Surcharged and Precanceled in Black

20c
I-I-54
31-XII-54

1954, Jan. 1 **Unwmk.** *Perf. 13½x14*

477	A108	20c on 65c vio brn	1.75	.65
478	A108	20c on 90c dp blue	1.75	.45

See note after No. 197.

Map and Rotary Emblem A112

Designs: 80c, Mermaid and Mercury holding emblem. 4fr, Rotary emblem and two globes.

1954, Sept. 10 **Engr.** *Perf. 11½*

479	A112	20c red	.25	.25
480	A112	80c dark green	.65	.50
481	A112	4fr ultra	1.40	.75
		Nos. 479-481 (3)	2.30	1.50

5th regional conf. of Rotary Intl. at Ostend. No. 481 for Rotary 50th Anniv. (in 1955).

A souv. sheet containing one each, imperf., was sold for 500 francs. It was not valid for postage.

The Rabot and Begonia — A113

Designs: 2.50fr, The Oudeburg and azalea. 4fr, "Three Towers" and orchid.

1955, Feb. 15 **Photo.**

482	A113	80c brt carmine	.85	.38
483	A113	2.50fr black brn	5.25	3.75
484	A113	4fr dk rose brn	5.00	1.25
		Nos. 482-484 (3)	11.10	5.38

Ghent Intl. Flower Exhibition, 1955.

Homage to Charles V as a Child, by Albrecht de Vriendt — A114

Charles V, by Titian — A115

Design: 4fr, Abdication of Charles V, by Louis Gallait.

1955, Mar. 25 **Unwmk.** *Perf. 11½*

485	A114	20c rose red	.25	.18
486	A115	2fr dk gray green	1.90	.15
487	A114	4fr blue	5.00	1.25
		Nos. 485-487 (3)	7.15	1.58

Charles V Exhibition, Ghent, 1955.

Emile Verhaeren, by Montald Constant — A116

1955, May 11 **Engr.**

488 A116 20c dark gray .15 .15

Birth cent. of Verhaeren, poet.

Allegory of Textile Manufacture A117

1955, May 11

489 A117 2fr violet brown 1.00 .18

2nd Intl. Textile Exhibition, Brussels, June 1955.

"The Foolish Virgin" by Rik Wouters — A118

"Departure of Volunteers from Liege, 1830" by Charles Soubre — A119

1955, June 10

490	A118	1.20fr olive green	1.00	1.10
491	A118	2fr violet	1.50	.15

3rd biennial exhibition of sculpture, Antwerp, June 11-Sept. 10, 1955.

1955, Sept. 10 **Photo.**
492 A119 20c grnsh slate .18 .18
493 A119 2fr chocolate .90 .22

Exhibition "The Romantic Movement in Liege Province," Sept. 10-Oct. 31, 1955; and 125th anniv. of Belgium's independence from the Netherlands.

Pelican Giving Blood to Young — A120

Buildings of Tournai, Ghent and Antwerp — A121

1956, Jan. 14 **Engr.**
494 A120 2fr brt carmine .42 .18

Blood donor service of the Belgian Red Cross.

1956, July 14 **Photo.**
495 A121 2fr brt ultra .28 .18

The Scheldt exhibition (Scaldis) at Tournai, Ghent and Antwerp, July-Sept. 1956.

Europa Issue

"Rebuilding Europe" — A122

1956, Sept. 15 **Engr.**
496 A122 2fr lt green 2.00 .15
497 A122 4fr purple 9.00 .70

Issued to symbolize the cooperation among the six countries comprising the Coal and Steel Community.

Train on Map of Belgium and Luxembourg A123

1956, Sept. 29
498 A123 2fr dark blue .55 .18

Issued to mark the electrification of the Brussels-Luxembourg railroad.

Edouard Anseele — A124

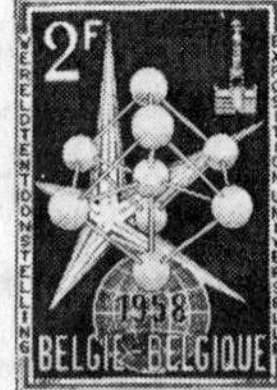

"The Atom" and Exposition Emblem — A125

1956, Oct. 27
499 A124 20c violet brown .15 .15

Cent. of the birth of Edouard Anseele, statesman, and in connection with an exhibition held in his honor at Ghent.

1957-58 **Unwmk.**
500 A125 2fr car rose .22 .15
501 A125 2.50fr green ('58) .30 .15
502 A125 4fr brt vio bl .75 .18
503 A125 5fr claret ('58) .65 .50
Nos. 500-503 (4) 1.92 .98

1958 World's Fair at Brussels.

Emperor Maximilian I Receiving Letter — A126

1957, May 19
504 A126 2fr claret .40 .15

Day of the Stamp, May 19, 1957.

Sikorsky S-58 Helicopter A127

1957, June 15
505 A127 4fr gray grn & brt bl .90 .80

100,000th passenger carried by Sabena helicopter service, June 15, 1957.

Zeebrugge Harbor A128

1957, July 6
506 A128 2fr dark blue .38 .15

50th anniv. of the completion of the port of Zeebrugge-Bruges.

Leopold I Entering Brussels, 1831 — A129

Leopold I Arriving at Belgian Border — A130

1957, July 17 **Photo.**
507 A129 20c dk gray grn .15 .15
508 A130 2fr lilac .52 .20

126th anniv. of the arrival in Belgium of King Leopold I.

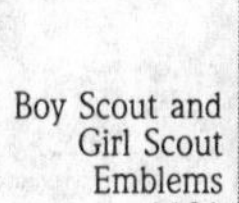

Boy Scout and Girl Scout Emblems A131

Design: 4fr, Robert Lord Baden-Powell, painted by David Jaggers, vert.

Perf. 11½

1957, July 29 **Unwmk.** **Engr.**
509 A131 80c gray .24 .15
510 A131 4fr light green 1.00 .45

Cent. of the birth of Lord Baden-Powell, founder of the Boy Scout movement.

"Kneeling Woman" by Lehmbruck A132

"United Europe" A133

1957, Aug. 20 **Photo.**
511 A132 2.50fr dk blue grn 1.10 1.50

4th Biennial Exposition of Sculpture, Antwerp, May 25-Sept. 15.

1957, Sept. 16 **Engr.** *Perf. 11½*
512 A133 2fr dk violet brn 1.00 .15
513 A133 4fr dark blue 1.90 .45

Europa: United Europe for peace and prosperity.

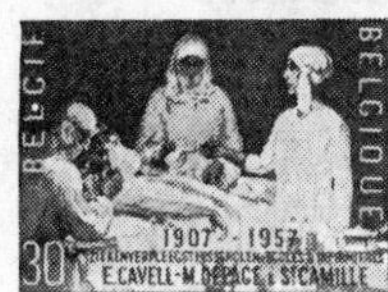

Queen Elisabeth Assisting at Operation, by Allard L'Olivier A134

Perf. 11½

1957, Nov. 23 **Unwmk.** **Engr.**
514 A134 30c rose lilac .15 .15

50th anniv. of the founding of the Edith Cavell-Marie Depage and St. Camille schools of nursing.

Post Horn and Historic Postal Insignia A135

1958, Mar. 16 **Photo.** *Perf. 11½*
515 A135 2.50fr gray .24 .15

Postal Museum Day.

United Nations Issue

International Labor Organization A136

Allegory of UN — A137

Designs: 1fr, FAO. 2fr, World Bank. 2.50fr, UNESCO. 3fr, UN Pavilion. 5fr, ITU. 8fr, Intl. Monetary Fund. 11fr, WHO. 20fr, UPU.

Perf. 11½

1958, Apr. 17 **Unwmk.** **Engr.**
516 A136 50c gray .90 1.40
517 A136 1fr claret .28 .45
518 A137 1.50fr dp ultra .28 .45
519 A137 2fr gray brown .85 1.25
520 A136 2.50fr olive grn .28 .45
521 A136 3fr grnsh blue .85 1.25
522 A137 5fr rose lilac .55 .90
523 A136 8fr red brown 1.00 1.65
524 A136 11fr dull lilac 1.25 2.00
525 A136 20fr car rose 1.65 2.50
Nos. 516-525,C15-C20 (16) 10.19 14.75

World's Fair, Brussels, Apr. 17-Oct. 19.
Postally valid only from the UN pavilion at the Brussels Fair. Proceeds went toward financing the UN exhibits.

Eugène Ysaye — A138

1958, Sept. 1
526 A138 30c dk blue & plum .15 .15

Ysaye (1858-1931), violinist, composer.

Europa Issue, 1958
Common Design Type

1958, Sept. 13 **Photo.**
Size: 24½x35mm
527 CD1 2.50fr brt red & blue .22 .15
528 CD1 5fr brt blue & red .38 .45

Issued to show the European Postal Union at the service of European integration.

Infant and UN Emblem — A140

Charles V and Jean-Baptiste of Thurn and Taxis — A141

1958, Dec. 10 **Engr.**
529 A140 2.50fr blue gray .28 .15

10th anniv. of the signing of the Universal Declaration of Human Rights.

1959, Mar. 15 **Unwmk.**
530 A141 2.50fr green .35 .15

Issued for the Day of the Stamp. Design from painting by J.-E. van den Bussche.

NATO Emblem A142

City Hall, Audenarde A143

1959, Apr. 3 **Photo.** *Perf. 11½*
531 A142 2.50fr dp red & dk bl .45 .15
532 A142 5fr emerald & dk bl 1.25 1.40

10th anniv. of NATO. See No. 720.

1959, Aug. 17 **Engr.**
533 A143 2.50fr deep claret .28 .15

Pope Adrian VI, by Jan van Scorel — A144

1959, Aug. 31 *Perf. 11½*
534 A144 2.50fr dark red .20 .15
535 A144 5fr Prus blue .55 .55

500th anniv. of the birth of Pope Adrian VI.

Europa Issue, 1959
Common Design Type

1959, Sept. 19 **Photo.**
Size: 24x35½mm
536 CD2 2.50fr dark red .18 .15
537 CD2 5fr brt grnsh blue .40 .50

Boeing 707
A146

Engraved and Photogravure

1959, Dec. 1 *Perf. 11½*
538 A146 6fr dk bl gray & car 1.75 1.00

Inauguration of jet flights by Sabena Airlines.

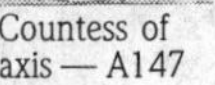

Countess of Taxis — A147 Indian Azalea — A148

1960, Mar. 21 **Engr.** *Perf. 11½*
539 A147 3fr dark blue .85 .15

Alexandrine de Rye, Countess of Taxis, Grand Mistress of the Netherlands Posts, 1628-1645, and day of the stamp, Mar. 21, 1960. The painting of the Countess is by Nicholas van der Eggermans.

1960, Mar. 28 **Unwmk.**
540 A148 40c shown .22 .15
541 A148 3fr Begonia .90 .15
542 A148 6fr Anthurium, bromelia 1.00 .90
Nos. 540-542 (3) 2.12 1.20

24th Ghent Intl. Flower Exhibition, Apr. 23-May 2, 1960.

Steel Workers, by Constantin Meunier — A149

Design: 3fr, The sower, field and dock workers, from "Monument to Labor," Brussels, by Constantin Meunier, horiz.

Engraved and Photogravure

1960, Apr. 30 *Perf. 11½*
543 A149 40c claret & brt red .15 .15
544 A149 3fr brown & brt red .85 .28

Socialist Party of Belgium, 75th anniv.

Congo River Boat Pilot — A150

Designs: 40c, Medical team. 1fr, Planting tree. 2fr, Sculptors. 2.50fr, Shot put. 3fr, Congolese officials. 6fr, Congolese and Belgian girls playing with doll. 8fr, Boy pointing on globe to independent Congo.

1960, June 30 **Photo.** *Perf. 11½*

Size: 35x24mm

545 A150 10c bright red .30 .15
546 A150 40c rose claret .45 .15
547 A150 1fr brt lilac .85 .75
548 A150 2fr gray green .95 .85
549 A150 2.50fr blue .85 .75
550 A150 3fr dk bl gray 1.00 .45

Size: 51x35mm

551 A150 6fr violet bl 3.00 1.90
552 A150 8fr dk brown 5.00 4.00
Nos. 545-552 (8) 12.40 9.00

Independence of Congo.

Europa Issue, 1960
Common Design Type

1960, Sept. 17

Size: 35x24½mm

553 CD3 3fr claret .60 .15
554 CD3 6fr gray 1.25 .40

Children Examining Stamp and Globe A152 H. J. W. Frère-Orban A153

1960, Oct. 1 **Photo.** *Perf. 11½*
555 A152 40c bister & blk + label .15 .15

Promoting stamp collecting among children.

Common Design Types pictured in section at front of book.

Engraved and Photogravure

1960, Oct. 17 **Unwmk.**

Portrait in Brown

556 A153 10c orange yel .15 .15
557 A153 40c blue grn .15 .15
558 A153 1.50fr brt violet .70 .70
559 A153 3fr red 1.10 .15
Nos. 556-559 (4) 2.10 1.15

Centenary of Communal Credit Society.

King Baudouin and Queen Fabiola A154

1960, Dec. 13 **Photo.** *Perf. 11½*

Portraits in Dark Brown

560 A154 40c green .15 .15
561 A154 3fr red lilac .28 .15
562 A154 6fr dull blue 1.25 .60
Nos. 560-562 (3) 1.68 .90

Wedding of King Baudouin and Dona Fabiola de Mora y Aragon, Dec. 15, 1960.

Nos. 412, 414 Surcharged — 15c

1961-68 **Typo.** *Perf. 13½x14*
563 A108 15c on 30c gray grn .24 .15
564 A108 15c on 50c blue ('68) .15 .15
565 A108 20c on 30c gray grn .24 .15
Nos. 563-565 (3) .63
Set value .28

No. 412 Surcharged and Precanceled

1961
566 A108 15c on 30c gray grn .90 .15
567 A108 20c on 30c gray grn 1.90 1.40

See note after No. 197.

Nicolaus Rockox, by Anthony Van Dyck — A155 Seal of Jan Bode, Alderman of Antwerp, 1264 — A156

Engraved and Photogravure

1961, Mar. 18 *Perf. 11½*
568 A155 3fr bister, blk & brn .32 .15

400th anniv. of the birth of Nicolaus Rockox, mayor of Antwerp.

1961, Apr. 16 **Photo.**
569 A156 3fr buff & brown .32 .15

Issued for Stamp Day, April 16.

Senate Building, Brussels, Laurel and Sword — A157

Engraved and Photogravure

1961, Sept. 14 **Unwmk.** *Perf. 11½*
570 A157 3fr brn & Prus grn .30 .15
571 A157 6fr dk brn & dk car 2.75 1.00

50th Conference of the Interparliamentary Union, Brussels, Sept. 14-22.

Europa Issue, 1961
Common Design Type

1961, Sept. 16 **Photo.**

Size: 35x25½mm

572 CD4 3fr yel grn & dk grn .20 .15
573 CD4 6fr org brn & blk .30 .25

Atomic Reactor Plant, BR2, Mol — A159

Designs: 3fr, Atomic Reactor BR3, vert. 6fr, Atomic Reactor plant BR3.

1961, Nov. 8 **Unwmk.** *Perf. 11½*
574 A159 40c dk bl grn .15 .15
575 A159 3fr red lilac .15 .15
576 A159 6fr bright blue .30 .22
Nos. 574-576 (3) .60
Set value .36

Aatomic nuclear research center at Mol.

Horta Museum — A160

1962, Feb. 15 **Engr.**
577 A160 3fr red brown .25 .15

Baron Victor Horta (1861-1947), architect.

Postrider, 16th Century A161

Engraved and Photogravure

1962, Mar. 25 *Perf. 11½*

Chalky Paper

578 A161 3fr brn & slate grn .30 .15

Stamp Day. See No. 677.

Gerard Mercator — A162 Bro. Alexis-Marie Gochet — A163

Engraved and Photogravure

1962, Apr. 14 **Unwmk.**
579 A162 3fr sepia & gray .30 .15

Mercator (Gerhard Kremer, 1512-1594), geographer and map maker.

1962, May 19 **Engr.** *Perf. 11½*

Portrait: 3fr, Canon Pierre-Joseph Triest.

580 A163 2fr dark blue .30 .18
581 A163 3fr golden brown .30 .15

Brother Alexis-Marie Gochet (1835-1910), geographer and educator, and Canon Pierre-Joseph Triest (1760-1836), educator and founder of hospitals and orphanages.

Europa Issue, 1962
Common Design Type

1962, Sept. 15 **Photo.**

Size: 35x24mm

582 CD5 3fr dp car, citron & blk .24 .15
583 CD5 6fr olive, citron & blk .35 .35

Hand with Barbed Wire and Freed Hand — A165

1962, Sept. 16 **Engr. & Photo.**
584 A165 40c lt bl & blk .15 .15

Issued in memory of concentration camp victims.

Adam, by Michelangelo, Broken Chain and UN Emblem A166

1962, Nov. 24 *Perf. 11½*
585 A166 3fr gray & blk .20 .15
586 A166 6fr lt redsh brn & dk brn .35 .30

UN Declaration of Human Rights.

Henri Pirenne (1862-1935), Historian — A167

1963, Jan. 15 **Engr.**
587 A167 3fr ultra .30 .15

Swordsmen and Ghent Belfry — A168

Designs: 3fr, Modern fencers. 6fr, Arms of the Royal and Knightly Guild of St. Michael, vert.

Engraved and Photogravure

1963, Mar. 23 **Unwmk.** *Perf. 11½*
588 A168 1fr brn red & pale bl .15 .15
589 A168 3fr dk vio & yel grn .15 .15
590 A168 6fr gray, blk, red, bl & gold .28 .28
Nos. 588-590 (3) .58
Set value .43

350th anniv. of the granting of a charter to the Ghent guild of fencers.

Stagecoach A169

1963, Apr. 7
591 A169 3fr gray & ocher .25 .15

Stamp Day. See No. 678.

Hotel des Postes, Paris, Stagecoach and Stamp, 1863 A170

Perf. 11½

1963, May 7 Unwmk. Engr.
592 A170 6fr dk brn, gray & yel grn .38 .38

Cent. of the 1st Intl. Postal Conf., Paris, 1863.

"Peace," Child in Rye Field — A171

1963, May 8 Engr. & Photo.
593 A171 3fr grn, blk, yel & brn .16 .15
594 A171 6fr buff, blk, brn & org .32 .28

May 8th Movement for Peace. (On May 8, 1945, World War II ended in Europe).

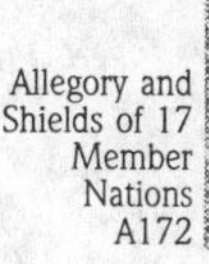

Allegory and Shields of 17 Member Nations A172

1963, June 13 Unwmk. *Perf. 11½*
595 A172 6fr bl & blk .38 .30

10th anniversary of the Conference of European Transport Ministers.

Seal of Union of Belgian Towns — A173

1963, June 17
596 A173 6fr grn, red, blk & gold .38 .38

Intl. Union of Municipalities, 50th anniv.

Caravelle over Brussels National Airport A174

Photogravure and Engraved

1963, Sept. 1 Unwmk. *Perf. 11½*
597 A174 3fr green & gray .22 .15

40th anniversary of SABENA airline.

Europa Issue, 1963
Common Design Type

1963, Sept. 14 Photo.
Size: 35x24mm
598 CD6 3fr blk, dl red & lt brn .60 .15
599 CD6 6fr blk, lt bl & lt brn 1.65 .32

Jules Destrée A176

Design: No. 601, Henry Van de Velde.

Perf. 11½

1963, Nov. 16 Unwmk. Engr.
600 A176 1fr rose lilac .15 .15
601 A176 1fr green .15 .15
Set value .18 .16

Jules Destrée (1863-1936), statesman and founder of the Royal Academy of French Language and Literature, and of Henry Van de Velde (1863-1957), architect.
No. 600 incorrectly inscribed "1864."

Development of the Mail, Bas-relief A177

1963, Nov. 23 Engr. & Photo.
602 A177 50c dl red, slate & blk .15 .15

50th anniversary of the establishment of postal checking service.

Dr. Armauer G. Hansen A178

Fight Against Leprosy: 2fr, Leprosarium. 5fr, Father Joseph Damien.

1964, Jan. 25 Unwmk. *Perf. 11½*
603 A178 1fr brn org & blk .15 .15
604 A178 2fr brn org & blk .18 .15
605 A178 5fr brn org & blk .25 .20
a. Souvenir sheet of 3, #603-605 1.75 1.75
Nos. 603-605 (3) .58
Set value .36

No. 605a sold for 12fr.

Andreas Vesalius (1514-64), Anatomist — A179

Jules Boulvin (1855-1920), Mechanical Engineer A180

Design: 2fr, Henri Jaspar (1870-1939), statesman and lawyer.

Engraved and Photogravure

1964, Mar. 2 Unwmk. *Perf. 11½*
606 A179 50c pale grn & blk .15 .15
607 A180 1fr pale grn & blk .15 .15
608 A180 2fr pale grn & blk .16 .15
Set value .36 .27

Postilion of Liege, 1830-40 — A181

1964, Apr. 5 Engr. *Perf. 11½*
609 A181 3fr black .22 .15

Issued for Stamp Day 1964.

Arms of Ostend A182

1964, May 16 Photo.
610 A182 3fr ultra, ver, gold & blk .22 .15

Millennium of Ostend.

Flame, Hammer and Globe — A183

Designs: 1fr, "SI" and globe. 2fr, Flame over wavy lines.

1964, July 18 Unwmk. *Perf. 11½*
611 A183 50c dark blue & red .15 .15
612 A183 1fr dark blue & red .15 .15
613 A183 2fr dark blue & red .15 .15
Set value .27 .23

Centenary of the First Socialist International, founded in London, Sept. 28, 1864.

Europa Issue, 1964
Common Design Type

1964, Sept. 12 Photo. *Perf. 11½*
Size: 24x35½mm
614 CD7 3fr yel grn, dk car & gray .25 .15
615 CD7 6fr car rose, yel grn & bl .38 .38

Benelux Issue

King Baudouin, Queen Juliana and Grand Duchess Charlotte — A185

1964, Oct. 12
616 A185 3fr ol, lt grn & mar .15 .15

20th anniv. of the customs union of Belgium, Netherlands and Luxembourg.

Hand, Round & Pear-shaped Diamonds A186

Symbols of Textile Industry A187

1965, Jan. 23 Unwmk. *Perf. 11½*
617 A186 2fr ultra, dp car & blk .15 .15

Diamond Exhibition "Diamantexpo," Antwerp, July 10-28, 1965.

1965, Jan. 25 Photo.
618 A187 1fr bl, red & blk .15 .15

Eighth textile industry exhibition "Textirama," Ghent, Jan. 29-Feb. 2, 1965.

Vriesia — A188

Paul Hymans — A189

Designs: 2fr, Echinocactus. 3fr, Stapelia.

1965, Feb. 13 Engr. & Photo.
619 A188 1fr multi .15 .15
620 A188 2fr multi .15 .15
621 A188 3fr multi .15 .15
a. Souvenir sheet of 3, #619-621 1.75 1.75
Set value .30 .30

25th Ghent International Flower Exhibition, Apr. 24-May 3, 1965.
No. 621a was issued Apr. 26 and sold for 20fr.

1965, Feb. 24 Engr. *Perf. 11½*
622 A189 1fr dl pur .15 .15

Paul Hymans (1865-1941), Belgian Foreign Minister and first president of the League of Nations.

Peter Paul Rubens A190

Sir Rowland Hill as Philatelist A191

Portraits: 2fr, Frans Snyders. 3fr, Adam van Noort. 6fr, Anthony Van Dyck. 8fr, Jacob Jordaens.

1965, Mar. 15 Photo. & Engr.
Portraits in Sepia
623 A190 1fr car rose .15 .15
624 A190 2fr bl grn .15 .15
625 A190 3fr plum .15 .15
626 A190 6fr dp car .24 .15
627 A190 8fr dk bl .35 .35
Nos. 623-627 (5) 1.04 .95

Issued to commemorate the founding of the General Savings and Pensions Bank.

1965, Mar. 27 Engr. *Perf. 11½*
628 A191 50c blue green .15 .15

Issued to publicize youth philately. The design is from a mural by J. E. Van den Bussche in the General Post Office, Brussels.

Postmaster, c. 1833 — A192

Staircase, Affligem Abbey — A194

15-Cent Minimum Value
The minimum catalogue value is 15 cents. Separating se-tenant pieces into individual stamps does not increase the value of the stamps since demand for the separated stamps may be small.

Telephone, Globe and Teletype Paper — A193

1965, Apr. 26 Unwmk. *Perf. 11½*
629 A192 3fr emerald .15 .15

Issued for Stamp Day.

1965, May 8 Photo.
630 A193 2fr dl pur & blk .15 .15

Cent. of the ITU.

1965, May 27 Engr.
631 A194 1fr gray blue .15 .15

St. Jean Berchmans and his Birthplace A195

1965, May 27 Engr. & Photo.
632 A195 2fr dk brn & red brn .15 .15

Issued to honor St. Jean Berchmans (1599-1621), Jesuit "Saint of the Daily Life."

TOC H Lamp and Arms of Poperinge A196

Farmer with Tractor A197

1965, June 19 Photo. *Perf. 11½*
633 A196 3fr ol bis, blk & car .15 .15

50th anniv. of the founding of Talbot House in Poperinge, which served British soldiers in World War I, and where the TOC H Movement began (Christian Social Service; TOC H is army code for Poperinge Center).

Engraved and Photogravure

1965, July 17 Unwmk. *Perf. 11½*

Design: 3fr, Farmer with horse-drawn roller.

634 A197 50c bl, ol, bis brn & blk .15 .15
635 A197 3fr bl, ol grn, ol & blk .15 .15
Set value .20 .15

75th anniv. of the Belgian Farmers' Association (Boerenbond).

Europa Issue, 1965

Common Design Type

1965, Sept. 25 *Perf. 11½*

Size: 35½x24mm

636 CD8 1fr dl rose & blk .15 .15
637 CD8 3fr grnsh gray & blk .15 .15
Set value .22 .16

Leopold I A199

Joseph Lebeau A200

1965, Nov. 13 Engr.
638 A199 3fr sepia .18 .15
639 A199 6fr bright violet .25 .25
Set value .31

King Leopold I (1790-1865). The designs of the vignettes are similar to A4 and A5.

1965, Nov. 13 Photo.
640 A200 1fr multi .15 .15

Joseph Lebeau (1794-1865), Foreign Minister.

Tourist Issue

Grapes and Houses, Hoeilaart A201

Bridge and Castle, Huy A202

Designs: No. 643, British War Memorial, Ypres. No. 644, Castle Spontin. No. 645, City Hall, Louvain. No. 646, Ourthe Valley. No. 647, Romanesque Cathedral, gothic fountain, Nivalles. No. 648, Water mill, Kasterlee. No. 649, City Hall, Cloth Guild and Statue of Margarethe of Austria, Malines. No. 650, Town Hall, Lier. No. 651, Castle Bouillon. No. 652, Fountain and Kursaal Spa. No. 653, Windmill, Bokrijk. No. 654, Mountain road, Vielsalm. No. 655, View of Furnes. No. 656, City Hall and Belfry, Mons. No. 657, St. Martin's Church, Aalst. No. 658, Abbey and fountain, St. Hubert.

1965-71 Engr. *Perf. 11½*
641 A201 50c vio bl, lt bl & yel grn .15 .15
642 A202 50c sl grn, lt bl & red brn .15 .15
643 A202 1fr grn, lt bl, sal & brn .15 .15
644 A202 1fr ind, lt bl & ol .15 .15
645 A201 1fr brt rose lil, lt bl & blk .15 .15
646 A202 1fr blk, grnsh bl & ol .15 .15
647 A201 1.50fr sl, sky bl & bis .15 .15
648 A202 1.50fr blk, bl & ol .15 .15
649 A202 1.50fr dk bl & buff .18 .15
650 A201 2fr brn, lt bl & ind .18 .15
651 A202 2fr dk brn, grn & ocher .18 .15
652 A202 2fr bl, brt grn & blk .15 .15
653 A202 2fr blk, lt bl & yel .15 .15
654 A202 2fr blk, lt bl & yel grn .15 .15
655 A202 2fr car, lt bl & dk brn .15 .15
656 A201 2.50fr vio, buff & blk .18 .15
657 A201 2.50fr vio, lt bl, blk & ol .25 .15
658 A201 2.50fr vio bl & yel .25 .15
Nos. 641-658 (18) 3.02
Set value 1.50

Issued: #641-642, 11/13/65; #643-644, 7/15/67; #645-646, 12/16/68; #647-648, 7/6/70; #649, 656, 12/11/71; #650-651, 11/11/66; #652-653, 6/24/68; #654-655, 9/6/69; #657-658, 9/11/71.

Queen Elisabeth Type of Semi-Postal Issue, 1956

1965, Dec. 23 Photo. *Perf. 11½*
659 SP305 3fr dark gray .22 .15

Queen Elisabeth (1876-1965).

A dark frame has been added in design of No. 659; 1956 date has been changed to 1965; inscription in bottom panel is Koningin Elisabeth Reine Elisabeth 3F.

"Peace on Earth" — A203

Arms of Pope Paul VI — A204

Rural Mailman, 19th Century — A205

Design: 1fr, "Looking toward a Better Future" (family, new buildings, sun and landscape).

1966, Feb. 12 Photo. *Perf. 11½*
660 A203 50c multi .15 .15
661 A203 1fr ocher, blk & bl .15 .15
662 A204 3fr gray, gold, car & blk .15 .15
Set value .25 .19

75th anniv. of the encyclical by Pope Leo XIII "Rerum Novarum," which proclaimed the general principles for the organization of modern industrial society.

1966, Apr. 17 Photo. Unwmk.
663 A205 3fr blk, dl yel & pale lil .18 .15

Stamp Day. For overprint see No. 673.

Iguanodon, Natural Science Institute A206

Arend-Roland Comet, Observatory — A207

Designs: No. 665, Ancestral head and spiral pattern, Kasai; Central Africa Museum. No. 666, Snowflakes, Meteorological Institute. No. 667, Seal of Charles V, Royal Archives. No. 668, Medieval scholar, Royal Library. 8fr, Satellite and rocket, Space Aeronautics Institute.

1966, May 28 Engr. & Photo.
664 A206 1fr grn & blk .15 .15
665 A206 2fr gray, blk & brn org .15 .15
666 A206 2fr bl, blk & yel .15 .15
667 A207 3fr dp rose, blk & gold .15 .15
668 A207 3fr multi .15 .15
669 A207 6fr ultra, yel & blk .22 .15
670 A207 8fr multi .30 .30
Set value 1.00 .78

National scientific heritage.

Atom Symbol and Retort — A208

August Kekulé, Benzene Ring — A209

Engraved and Photogravure

1966, July 9 Unwmk. *Perf. 11½*
671 A208 6fr gray, blk & red .30 .18

Issued to publicize the European chemical plant, EUROCHEMIC, at Mol.

1966, July 9
672 A209 3fr brt bl & blk .18 .15

August Friedrich Kekule (1829-96), chemistry professor at University of Ghent (1858-67).

No. 663 Overprinted with Red and Blue Emblem

1966, July 11 Photo.
673 A205 3fr multi .18 .15

19th Intl. P.T.T. Cong., Brussels, July 11-15.

Rik Wouters (1882-1916), Self-portrait — A210

1966, Sept. 6 Photo. *Perf. 11½*
674 A210 60c multi .15 .15

Europa Issue, 1966

Common Design Type

1966, Sept. 24 Engr. *Perf. 11½*

Size: 24x34mm

675 CD9 3fr brt grn .15 .15
676 CD9 6fr brt rose lil .32 .28

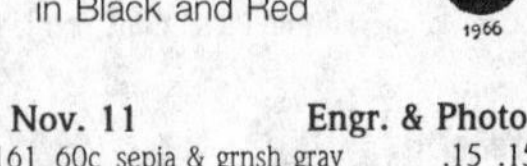
Types of 1962-1963 Overprinted in Black and Red

1966, Nov. 11 Engr. & Photo.
677 A161 60c sepia & grnsh gray .15 .15
678 A169 3fr sepia & pale bister .15 .15
Set value .19 .16

75th anniv., Royal Fed. of Phil. Circles of Belgium. Overprint shows emblem of F.I.P.

Lions Emblem — A214

1967, Jan. 14 *Perf. 11½*
679 A214 3fr gray, blk & bl .15 .15
680 A214 6fr lt grn, blk & vio .28 .15
Set value .23

Lions Club Intl., 50th anniv.

Pistol by Leonhard Cleuter A215

1967, Feb. 11 Photo.
681 A215 2fr dp car, blk & cream .15 .15

Fire Arms Museum in Liege.

International Tourist Year Emblem A216

1967, Feb. 11
682 A216 6fr ver, ultra & blk .28 .15

International Tourist Year, 1967.

Birches and Trientalis A217

Design: No. 684, Dunes, beach grass, privet and blue thistles.

1967, Mar. 11 Photo. *Perf. 11½*
683 A217 1fr multi .15 .15
684 A217 1fr multi .15 .15
Set value .16 .16

Issued to publicize the nature preserves at Hautes Fagnes and Westhoek.

Paul E. Janson — A218

1967, Apr. 15 Engr. *Perf. 11½*

685 A218 10fr blue .35 .18

Issued in memory of Paul Emile Janson (1872-1944), lawyer and statesman.

Postilion A219

1967, Apr. 16 Photo. & Engr.

686 A219 3fr rose red & claret .18 .15

Issued for Stamp Day, 1967.

Inscribed: "FITCE"

1967, June 24 *Perf. 11½*

687 A219 10fr ultra, sep & emer .42 .30

Issued to commemorate the meeting of the Federation of Common Market Telecommunications Engineers, Brussels, July 3-8.

Europa Issue, 1967

Common Design Type

1967, May 2 Photo.

Size: 24x35mm

688 CD10 3fr blk, lt bl & red .18 .15
689 CD10 6fr blk, grnsh gray & yel .30 .28

Flax, Shuttle and Mills — A221

1967, June 3 Photo. *Perf. 11½*

690 A221 6fr tan & multi .28 .20

Belgian linen industry.

Old Kursaal, Ostend — A222

1967, June 3 Engr. & Photo.

691 A222 2fr dk brn, lt bl & yel .15 .15

700th anniversary of Ostend as a city.

A223

A224

Designs: #692, Caesar Crossing Rubicon, 15th Century Tapestry. #693, Emperor Maximilian Killing a Boar, 16th cent. tapestry.

1967, Sept. 2 Photo. *Perf. 11½*

692 A223 1fr multi .15 .15
693 A223 1fr multi .15 .15
Set value .20 .16

Issued for the Charles Plisnier and Lodewijk de Raet Foundations.

Engraved and Photogravure

1967, Sept. 30 *Perf. 11½*

Arms of Universities: #694, Ghent. #695, Liege.

694 A224 3fr gray & multi .15 .15
695 A224 3fr gray & multi .15 .15
Set value .20

Universities of Ghent and Liège, 150th anniv.

Princess Margaret of York — A225

"Virga Jesse," Hasselt — A226

1967, Sept. 30 Photo.

696 A225 6fr multi .28 .24

British Week, Sept. 28-Oct. 2.

1967, Nov. 11 Engr. *Perf. 11½*

697 A226 1fr slate blue .15 .15

Christmas, 1967.

Hand Guarding Worker — A227

Military Mailman, 1916, by James Thiriar — A228

1968, Feb. 3 Photo. *Perf. 11½*

698 A227 3fr multi .18 .15

Issued to publicize industrial safety.

Engraved and Photogravure

1968, Mar. 17 *Perf. 11½*

699 A228 3fr sepia, lt bl & brn .18 .15

Issued for Stamp Day, 1968.

View of Grammont and Seal of Baudouin VI — A229

Stamp of 1866, No. 23 — A230

Historic Sites: 3fr, Theux-Franchimont tortress, sword and seal. 6fr, Neolithic cave and artifacts, Spiennes. 10fr, Roman oil lamp and St. Medard's Church, Wervik.

1968, Apr. 13 Photo. *Perf. 11½*

700 A229 2fr bl, blk, lil & rose .15 .15
701 A229 3fr org, blk & car .15 .15
702 A229 6fr ultra, ind & bis .25 .15
703 A229 10fr tan, blk, yel & gray .40 .28
Nos. 700-703 (4) .95 .73

1968, Apr. 13 Engr. *Perf. 13*

704 A230 1fr black .15 .15

Centenary of the Malines Stamp Printery.

Europa Issue, 1968

Common Design Type

1968, Apr. 27 Photo. *Perf. 11½*

Size: 35x24mm

705 CD11 3fr dl grn, gold & blk .15 .15
706 CD11 6fr car, sil & blk .35 .25

St. Laurent Abbey, Liège A232

Designs: 3fr, Gothic Church, Lisseweghe. No. 709. Barges in Zandvliet locks. No. 710, Ship in Neuzen lock, Ghent Canal. 10fr, Ronquieres canal ship lift.

Engraved and Photogravure

1968, Sept. 7 *Perf. 11½*

707 A232 2fr ultra, gray ol & sep .15 .15
708 A232 3fr ol bis, gray & sep .15 .15
709 A232 6fr ind, brt bl & sep .30 .15
710 A232 6fr blk, grnsh bl & ol .22 .15
711 A232 10fr bis, brt bl & sep .50 .32
Nos. 707-711 (5) 1.32 .92

No. 710 issued Dec. 14 for opening of lock at Neuzen, Netherlands.

Christmas Candle — A233

1968, Dec. 7 *Perf. 11½*

712 A233 1fr multi .15 .15

Christmas, 1968.

St. Albertus Magnus — A234

1969, Feb. 15 Engr. *Perf. 11½*

713 A234 2fr sepia .15 .15

The Church of St. Paul in Antwerp (16th century) was destroyed by fire in Apr. 1968.

Ruins of Aulne Abbey, Gozee A235

1969, Feb. 15 Engr. & Photo.

714 A235 3fr brt pink & blk .15 .15

Aulne Abbey was destroyed in 1794 during the French Revolution.

The Travelers, Roman Sculpture — A236

Broodjes Chapel, Antwerp — A237

1969, Mar. 15 Engr. *Perf. 11½*

715 A236 2fr vio brn .15 .15

2,000th anniversary of city of Arlon.

1969, Mar. 15 Engr. & Photo.

716 A237 3fr gray & blk .15 .15

150th anniv. of public education in Antwerp.

Post Office Train — A238

1969, Apr. 13 Photo. *Perf. 11½*

717 A238 3fr multi .15 .15

Issued for Stamp Day.

Europa Issue, 1969

Common Design Type

1969, Apr. 26

Size: 35x24mm

718 CD12 3fr lt grn, brn & blk .20 .15
719 CD12 6fr sal, rose car & blk .30 .30

NATO Type of 1959 Redrawn and Dated "1949-1969"

1969, May 31 Photo. *Perf. 11½*

720 A142 6fr org brn & ultra .28 .28

20th anniv. of NATO. No. 720 inscribed Belgique-Belgie and OTAN-NAVO.

Construction Workers, by F. Leger A240

Bicyclist A241

1969, May 31

721 A240 3fr multi .15 .15

50th anniversary of the ILO.

1969, July 5 Photo. *Perf. 11½*

722 A241 6fr rose & multi .28 .24

World Bicycling Road Championships, Terlaemen to Zolder, Aug. 10.

Ribbon in Benelux Colors — A242

1969, Sept. 6 Photo. *Perf. 11½*

723 A242 3fr blk, red, ultra & yel .20 .15

25th anniv. of the signing of the customs union of Belgium, Netherlands and Luxembourg.

Annevoie Garden and Pascali Rose — A243

Design: No. 725, Lochristi Garden and begonia.

1969, Sept. 6
724 A243 2fr multi .15 .15
725 A243 2fr multi .15 .15
Set value .20 .16

Armstrong, Collins, Aldrin and Map Showing Tranquillity Base — A245

1969, Sept. 20 **Photo.**
726 A245 6fr black .28 .24

See note after Algeria #427. See #B846.

Wounded Veteran — A246

Mailman — A247

1969, Oct. 11 **Engr.** ***Perf. 11½***
727 A246 1fr blue gray .15 .15

Natl. war veterans' aid organization (O.N.I.G.). The design is similar to type SP10.

1969, Oct. 18 **Photo.**
728 A247 1fr deep rose & multi .15 .15

Issued to publicize youth philately. Design by Danielle Saintenoy, 14.

Kennedy Tunnel Under the Schelde, Antwerp A248

Design: 6fr, Three highways crossing near Loncin.

1969, Nov. 8 **Engr.** ***Perf. 11½***
729 A248 3fr multi .22 .15
730 A248 6fr multi .28 .28

Issued to publicize the John F. Kennedy Tunnel under the Schelde and the Walloon auto route and interchange near Loncin.

Henry Carton de Wiart, by Gaston Geleyn — A249

1969, Nov. 8
731 A249 6fr sepia .28 .20

Count de Wiart (1869-1951), statesman.

The Census at Bethlehem (detail), by Peter Brueghel A250

1969, Dec. 13 **Photo.**
732 A250 1.50fr multi .15 .15

Christmas, 1969.

Symbols of Bank's Activity, 100fr Coin — A251

1969, Dec. 13 **Engr. & Photo.**
733 A251 3.50fr lt ultra, blk & sil .15 .15

50th anniv. of the Industrial Credit Bank (Societe nationale de credit a l'industrie).

Camellia — A252

Beeches in Botanical Garden — A253

1970, Jan. 31 **Photo.** ***Perf. 11½***
734 A252 1.50fr shown .15 .15
735 A252 2.50fr Water lily .15 .15
736 A252 3.50fr Azalea .15 .15
a. Souvenir sheet of 3, #734-736 2.00 2.00
Nos. 734-736 (3) .45
Set value .26

Ghent Int'l Flower Exhibition. No. 736a was issued Apr. 25 and sold for 25fr.

1970, Mar. 7 **Engr. & Photo.**
737 A253 3.50fr shown .20 .15
738 A253 7fr Birches .30 .30

European Nature Conservation Year.

Mailman A254

1970, Apr. 4 **Photo.**
739 A254 1.50fr multi .15 .15

Issued for Youth Stamp Day.

New UPU Headquarters and Monument, Bern — A255

1970, Apr. 12 **Engr. & Photo.**
740 A255 3.50fr grn & lt grn .30 .15

Opening of the new UPU Headquarters, Bern.

Europa Issue, 1970
Common Design Type

1970, May 1 **Photo.** ***Perf. 11½***
Size: 35x24mm
741 CD13 3.50fr rose cl, yel & blk .20 .15
742 CD13 7fr ultra, pink & blk .40 .30

Cooperative Alliance Emblem — A257

1970, June 27 **Photo.** ***Perf. 11½***
743 A257 7fr blk & org .30 .15

Intl. Cooperative Alliance, 75th anniv.

Ship in Ghent Terneuzen Lock, Zelzate A258

Design: No. 745, Clock Tower, Virton, vert.

1970, June 27 **Engr. & Photo.**
744 A258 2.50fr ind & lt bl .15 .15
745 A258 2.50fr dk pur & ocher .15 .15

King Baudouin — A259

1970-80 **Engr.** ***Perf. 11½***
746 A259 1.75fr green ('71) .24 .15
747 A259 2.25fr gray grn ('72) .35 .15
748 A259 2.50fr gray grn ('74) .16 .15
749 A259 3fr emer ('73) 3.00 2.00
750 A259 3.25fr vio brn ('75) .20 .15
751 A259 3.50fr org brn .24 .15
752 A259 3.50fr brown ('71) .24 .15
753 A259 4fr blue ('72) .35 .15
754 A259 4.50fr brown ('72) .24 .15
755 A259 4.50fr grnsh bl ('74) .24 .15
756 A259 5fr lilac ('72) .24 .15
757 A259 6fr rose car ('72) .28 .15
758 A259 6.50fr vio blk ('74) .35 .15
759 A259 7fr ver ('71) .35 .15
760 A259 7.50fr brt pink ('75) .35 .15
761 A259 8fr black ('72) .35 .15
762 A259 9fr ol bis ('71) .60 .15
763 A259 9fr red brn ('80) .45 .15
764 A259 10fr rose car ('71) .48 .15
765 A259 11fr gray ('76) .52 .15
766 A259 12fr Prus bl ('72) .60 .15
767 A259 13fr slate ('75) .70 .15
768 A259 14fr gray grn ('76) .65 .15
769 A259 15fr lt vio ('71) .70 .15
770 A259 16fr green ('77) .70 .15
771 A259 17fr dl mag ('75) .80 .15
772 A259 18fr steel bl ('71) 1.00 .20
773 A259 18fr grnsh bl ('80) .90 .15
774 A259 20fr vio bl ('71) 1.00 .15
775 A259 22fr black ('74) 1.40 1.25
776 A259 22fr lt grn ('79) 1.10 .15
777 A259 25fr lilac ('75) 1.25 .15
778 A259 30fr ocher ('72) 1.50 .15
779 A259 35fr emer ('80) 1.50 .20
780 A259 40fr dk bl ('77) 2.00 .15
781 A259 45fr brown ('80) 2.25 .20

Perf. 12½x13½
Photo.
Size: 22x17mm
782 A259 3fr emer ('73) 3.00 2.50
a. Booklet pane of 4 (#782 and 3 #783) + labels 10.00
783 A259 4fr blue ('73) .70 .60
784 A259 4.50fr grnsh bl ('75) .40 .30
785 A259 5fr lilac ('73) .24 .15
a. Booklet pane of 4 + labels 2.75
786 A259 6fr car ('78) .28 .16
787 A259 6.50fr dl pur ('75) .45 .20
788 A259 8fr gray ('78) .35 .15
Nos. 746-788 (43) 32.70
Set value 10.75

No. 751 issued Sept. 7, 1970, King Baudouin's 40th birthday, and is inscribed "1930-1970." Dates are omitted on other stamps of type A259.

Nos. 754, 756 also issued in coils in 1973 and Nos. 757, 761 in 1978, with black control number on back of every fifth stamp.

Nos. 782-788 issued in booklets only. Nos. 782, 784 have one straight-edge, Nos. 786, 788 have two. The rest have one or two. Stamps in the panes are tete-beche. Each pane has two labels showing Belgian Postal emblem with a large selvage with postal code instructions. Nos. 786, 788 not luminescent.

See designs M2, O4. See Nos. 432a, 432b, 977a, 977b.

UN Headquarters, NY — A260

Fair Emblem — A261

1970, Sept. 12 **Engr. & Photo.**
789 A260 7fr dk brn & Prus bl .30 .15

25th anniversary of the United Nations.

1970, Sept. 19
790 A261 1.50fr bis, org & brn .15 .15

Issued to publicize the 25th International Fair at Ghent, Sept. 12-27.

Queen Fabiola — A262

The Mason, by Georges Minne — A263

1970, Sept. 19
791 A262 3.50fr lt bl & blk .15 .15

Issued to publicize the Queen Fabiola Foundation for Mental Health.

1970, Oct. 17 ***Perf. 11½***
792 A263 3.50fr dl yel & sep .15 .15

50th anniv. of the National Housing Society.

Man, Woman and City — A264

1970, Oct. 17 **Photo.**
793 A264 2.50fr blk & multi .15 .15

Social Security System, 25th anniv.

Madonna with the Grapes, by Jean Gossaert — A265

1970, Nov. 14 **Engr.** ***Perf. 11½***
794 A265 1.50fr dk brn .15 .15

Christmas 1970.

Arms of Eupen, Malmédy and Saint-Vith A266

Engraved and Photogravure
1970, Dec. 12 ***Perf. 11½***
795 A266 7fr sepia & dk brn .30 .15

The 50th anniversary of the return of the districts of Eupen, Malmédy and Saint-Vith.

Automatic Telephone — A267

Touring Club Emblem — A269

"Auto" A268

1971, Jan. 16 **Photo.** *Perf. 11½*
796 A267 1.50fr multi .15 .15

Automatization of Belgian telephone system.

1971, Jan. 16
797 A268 2.50fr car & blk .15 .15

50th Automobile Show, Brussels, Jan. 19-31.

1971, Feb. 13
798 A269 3.50fr ultra & multi .18 .15

Belgian Touring Club, 75th anniversary.

Tournai Cathedral A270

1971, Feb. 13 **Engr.**
799 A270 7fr brt bl .30 .20

Cathedral of Tournai, 8th centenary.

"The Letter Box," by T. Lobrichon — A271

1971, Mar. 13 **Engr.** *Perf. 11½*
800 A271 1.50fr dk brn .15 .15

Youth philately.

Albert I, Jules Destrée and Academy — A272

Engraved and Photogravure

1971, Apr. 17 *Perf. 11½*
801 A272 7fr gray & blk .30 .20

50th anniversary of the founding of the Royal Academy of Language and French Literature.

Stamp Day — A273

1971, Apr. 25
802 A273 3.50fr Mailman .15 .15

Europa Issue, 1971
Common Design Type

1971, May 1 **Photo.**
Size: 35x24mm

803 CD14 3.50fr olive & blk .24 .15
804 CD14 7fr dk ol grn & blk .35 .15
Set value .20

Radar Ground Station A275

1971, May 15 **Photo.** *Perf. 11½*
805 A275 7fr multi .30 .15

3rd World Telecommunications Day.

Antarctic Explorer, Ship and Penguins — A276

1971, June 19 **Photo.** *Perf. 11½*
806 A276 10fr multi .50 .50

Tenth anniversary of the Antarctic Treaty pledging peaceful uses of and scientific cooperation in Antarctica.

A277

A278

1971, June 26 **Engr.** *Perf. 11½*
807 A277 2.50fr Orval Abbey .15 .15

9th cent. of the Abbey of Notre Dame, Orval.

1971, June 26 **Engr. & Photo.**
808 A278 1.50fr vio bl & blk .15 .15

Georges Hubin (1863-1947), socialist leader and Minister of State.

Mr. and Mrs. Goliath, the Giants of Ath — A279

View of Ghent A280

1971, Aug. 7 **Photo.**
809 A279 2.50fr multi .15 .15

Engr.

810 A280 2.50fr gray brn .15 .15

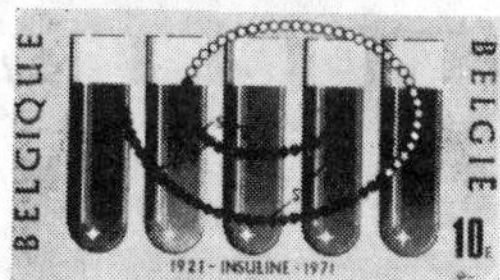

Test Tubes and Insulin Molecular Diagram — A281

1971, Aug. 7 **Photo.**
811 A281 10fr lt gray & multi .40 .30

50th anniversary of the discovery of insulin.

Family and "50" — A283

1971, Sept. 11 **Photo.**
812 A283 1.50fr grn & multi .15 .15

Belgian Large Families League, 50th anniv.

Achaemenidaen Tomb, Buzpar, and Persian Coat of Arms — A284

Engraved and Photogravure

1971, Oct. 2 *Perf. 11½*
813 A284 7fr multi .30 .15

2500th anniversary of the founding of the Persian empire by Cyrus the Great.

Dr. Jules Bordet A285

Flight into Egypt, Anonymous A286

Portrait: No. 815, Stijn Streuvels.

1971, Oct. 2 **Engr.**
814 A285 3.50fr slate green .15 .15
815 A285 3.50fr dark brown .15 .15
Set value .16

No. 814 honors Dr. Jules Bordet (1870-1945), serologist and immunologist; No. 815, Stijn Streuvels (1871-1945), novelist whose pen name was Frank Lateur.

1971, Nov. 13 **Photo.**
816 A286 1.50fr multi .15 .15

Christmas 1971.

Federation Emblem — A287

Book Year Emblem — A288

1971, Nov. 13
817 A287 3.50fr blk, ultra & gold .18 .15

25th anniversary of the Federation of Belgian Industries (FIB).

1972, Feb. 19
818 A288 7fr bis, blk & bl .30 .20

International Book Year 1972.

Coins of Belgium and Luxembourg — A289

Traffic Signal and Road Signs — A290

1972, Feb. 19 **Engr. & Photo.**
819 A289 1.50fr org blk & sil .15 .15

Economic Union of Belgium and Luxembourg, 50th anniversary.

1972, Feb. 19 **Photo.**
820 A290 3.50fr bl & multi .15 .15

Via Secura (road safety), 25th anniversary.

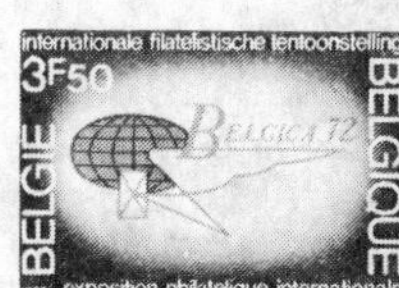

Belgica '72 Emblem A291

1972, Mar. 27
821 A291 3.50fr choc, bl & lil .15 .15

International Philatelic Exhibition, Brussels, June 24-July 9.

"Your Heart is your Health" A292

Auguste Vermeylen A293

1972, Mar. 27
822 A292 7fr blk, gray, red & bl .25 .18

World Health Day.

1972, Mar. 27
823 A293 2.50fr multi .15 .15

Centenary of the birth of Auguste Vermeylen (1872-1945), Flemish writer and educator. Portrait by Isidore Opsomer.

A294

A296

1972, Apr. 23
824 A294 3.50fr Astronaut on Moon .15 .15

Stamp Day 1972.

Europa Issue 1972
Common Design Type

1972, Apr. 29
Size: 24x35mm

825 CD15 3.50fr light blue & multi .20 .15
826 CD15 7fr rose & multi .40 .30

1972, May 13 Photo. ***Perf.*** ***11½***
827 A296 2.50fr "Freedom of the Press" .15 .15

50th anniv. of the BELGA news information agency and 25th Congress of the Intl. Federation of Newspaper Editors (F.I.E.J.), Brussels, May 15-19.

Freight Cars with Automatic Coupling A297

1972, June 3
828 A297 7fr bl & multi .30 .20

Intl. Railroad Union, 50th anniv.

View of Couvin — A298

Design: No. 830, Aldeneik Church, Maaseik, vert.

1972, June 24 Engr. ***Perf. 13½x14***
829 A298 2.50fr bl, vio brn & sl grn .20 .20
830 A298 2.50fr dk brn & bl .20 .20

Beatrice, by Gustave de Smet — A299

Radar Station, Intelsat 4 — A300

1972, Sept. 9 Photo. ***Perf. 11½***
831 A299 3fr multi .18 .15

Youth philately.

1972, Sept. 16
832 A300 3.50fr lt bl, sil & blk .18 .15

Opening of the Lessive satellite earth station.

Frans Masereel, Self-portrait A301

Adoration of the Kings, by Felix Timmermans A302

1972, Oct. 21
833 A301 4.50fr lt ol & blk .18 .15

Frans Masereel (1889-1972), wood engraver.

1972, Nov. 11 Photo. ***Perf. 11½***
834 A302 3.50fr blk & multi .18 .15

Christmas 1972.

Maria Theresa, Anonymous A303

1972, Dec. 16 Photo. ***Perf. 11½***
835 A303 2fr multi .15 .15

200th anniversary of the Belgian Academy of Science, Literature and Art, founded by Empress Maria Theresa.

WMO Emblem, Meteorological Institute, Ukkel — A304

1973, Mar. 24 Photo. ***Perf. 11½***
836 A304 9fr bl & multi .38 .18

Cent. of intl. meteorological cooperation.

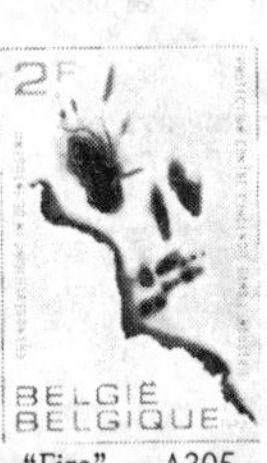

"Fire" — A305

Man and WHO Emblem — A306

1973, Mar. 24
837 A305 2fr multi .15 .15

Natl. industrial fire prevention campaign.

1973, Apr. 7
838 A306 8fr dk red, ocher & blk .32 .24

25th anniv. of WHO.

Europa Issue 1973
Common Design Type

1973, Apr. 28
Size: 35x24mm

839 CD16 4.50fr org brn, vio bl & yel .22 .15
840 CD16 8fr ol, dk bl & yel .55 .45

Thurn and Taxis Courier — A308

Arrows Circling Globe — A309

Engraved and Photogravure

1973, Apr. 28 ***Perf. 11½***
841 A308 4.50fr blk & red brn .20 .15

Stamp Day.

1973, May 12 Photo.
842 A309 3.50fr dp ocher & multi .16 .15

5th International Telecommunications Day.

Workers' Sports Exhibition Poster, Ghent, 1913 — A310

1973, May 12
843 A310 4.50fr multi .20 .15

60th anniversary of the International Workers' Sports Movement.

Fair Emblem A311

1973, May 12 Photo. ***Perf. 11½***
844 A311 4.50fr multi .18 .15

25th International Fair, Liege, May 12-27.

DC-10 and 1923 Biplane over Brussels Airport A312

Design: 10fr, Tips biplane, 1908.

1973, May 19 Engr. & Photo.
845 A312 8fr gray bl, blk & ultra .28 .20
846 A312 10fr grn, lt bl & blk .45 .35

50th anniv. of SABENA, Belgian airline (8fr) and 25th anniv. of the "Vieilles Tiges" Belgian flying pioneers' society (10fr).

Adolphe Sax and Tenor Saxophone A313

Fresco from Bathhouse, Ostend A314

1973, Sept. 15 Photo.
847 A313 9fr grn, blk & bl .40 .20

Adolphe Sax (1814-1894), inventor of saxophone.

1973, Sept. 15
848 A314 4.50fr multi .22 .15

Year of the Spa.

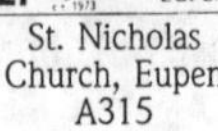

St. Nicholas Church, Eupen A315

Charley, by Henri Evenepoel A316

Designs: No. 850, Town Hall, Leau. No. 851, Aarshot Church. No. 852, Chiman Castle. No. 853, Gemmenich Border: Belgium, Germany, Netherlands. No. 854, St. Monan and church, Nassogne. No. 855, Church tower, Dottignes. No. 856, Grand-Place, Sint-Truiden.

1973-75 Engr. ***Perf. 13***
849 A315 2fr plum, sep & lt vio .20 .15
850 A315 3fr blk, lt bl & mar .50 .15
851 A315 3fr brn blk & yel .32 .15
852 A315 4fr grnsh blk & grnsh bl .35 .15
853 A315 4fr grnsh blk & bl .40 .18
854 A315 4fr grnsh blk & bl .40 .18
855 A315 4.50fr multi .50 .20
856 A315 5fr multi .50 .18
Nos. 849-856 (8) 3.17 1.34

Nos. 851, 855 not luminescent. Nos. 850, 852-854, 856 horiz.

1973, Oct. 13 Photo. ***Perf. 11½***
857 A316 3fr multi .18 .15

Youth philately.

Luminescent Paper

Starting with No. 858, all stamps are on luminescent paper unless otherwise noted.

Jean-Baptiste Moens A317

1973, Oct. 13 Engr. & Photo.
858 A317 10fr gray & multi .42 .20

50th anniversary of the Belgian Stamp Dealers' Association. Printed in sheets of 12 stamps and 12 labels showing association emblem.

Adoration of the Shepherds, by Hugo van der Goes
A318

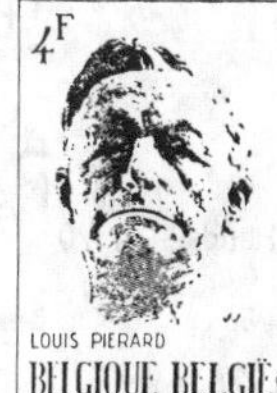

Louis Pierard, by M. I. Ianchelevici
A319

1973, Nov. 17 Engr. *Perf. 11½*
859 A318 4fr blue .18 .15

Christmas 1973.

1973, Nov. 17 Engr. & Photo.
860 A319 4fr ver & buff .25 .15

Louis Pierard (1886-1952), journalist, member of Parliament.

Highway, Automobile Club Emblem
A320

1973, Nov. 17 Photo.
861 A320 5fr yellow & multi .25 .15

Flemish Automobile Club, 50th anniv.

Early Microphone, Emblem of Radio Belgium — A321

1973, Nov. 24 Engr. & Photo.
862 A321 4fr blue & black .18 .15

50th anniversary of Radio Belgium.

Felicien Rops, Self-portrait
A323

Engraved and Photogravure

1973, Dec. 8 *Perf. 11½*
863 A323 7fr tan & black .32 .15

Felicien Rops (1833-1898), painter and engraver.

King Albert, (1875-1934) — A324

Sun, Bird, Flowers and Girl — A325

1974, Feb. 16 Photo. *Perf. 11½*
864 A324 4fr Prus grn & blk .22 .15

1974, Mar. 25 Photo. *Perf. 11½*
865 A325 3fr vio & multi .15 .15

Protection of the environment.

NATO Emblem
A326

1974, Apr. 20 Photo. *Perf. 11½*
866 A326 10fr dp to lt bl .45 .25

25th anniversary of the signing of the North Atlantic Treaty.

Hubert Krains — A327

"Destroyed City," by Ossip Zadkine — A328

1974, Apr. 27 Engr. & Photo.
867 A327 5fr blk & gray .20 .15

Stamp Day.

Europa Issue 1974

1974, May 4

Design: 10fr, Solidarity, by Georges Minne.

868 A328 5fr blk & red .24 .15
869 A328 10fr blk & ultra .60 .30

Children
A329

1974, May 18 Photo. *Perf. 11½*
870 A329 4fr lt bl & multi .20 .15

10th Lay Youth Festival.

Planetarium, Brussels
A330

Soleilmont Abbey Ruins — A331

Designs: 4fr, Pillory, Braine-le-Chateau. 7fr, Fountain, Ghent (procession symbolic of Chamber of Rhetoric). 10fr, Belfry, Bruges, vert.

Engr. and Photo.

1974, June 22 *Perf. 11½*
871 A330 3fr sky bl & blk .15 .15
872 A330 4fr lil rose & blk .18 .15
873 A331 5fr lt grn & blk .28 .15
874 A331 7fr dl yel & blk .35 .20
875 A330 10fr blk, bl & brn .45 .15
Nos. 871-875 (5) 1.41
Set value .55

Historic buildings and monuments.

"BENELUX"
A332

1974, Sept. 7 Photo. *Perf. 11½*
876 A332 5fr bl grn, dk grn & lt bl .25 .15

30th anniversary of the signing of the customs union of Belgium, Netherlands and Luxembourg.

Jan Vekemans, by Cornelis de Vos — A333

1974, Sept. 14
877 A333 3fr multi .18 .15

Youth philately.

Leon Tresignies, Willebroek Canal Bridge
A334

1974, Sept. 28 Engr. & Photo.
878 A334 4fr brn & ol grn .18 .15

60th death anniversary of Corporal Leon Tresignies (1886-1914), hero of World War I.

Montgomery Blair, UPU Emblem
A335

Design: 10fr, Heinrich von Stephan and UPU emblem.

1974, Oct. 5 *Perf. 11½*
879 A335 5fr grn & blk .20 .15
880 A335 10fr brick red & blk .40 .28

Centenary of Universal Postal Union.

Symbolic Chart — A336

1974, Oct. 12 Photo. *Perf. 11½*
881 A336 7fr multi .30 .20

Central Economic Council, 25th anniv.

Rotary Emblem
A337

1974, Oct. 19
882 A337 10fr multi .42 .20

Rotary International of Belgium.

A338

A341

Wild boar (regiment's emblem).

1974, Oct. 26
883 A338 3fr multi .18 .15

Granting of the colors to the Ardennes Chasseurs Regiment, 40th anniversary.

1974, Nov. 16 *Perf. 11½*

Angel, by Van Eyck brothers.

884 A341 4fr rose lilac .20 .15

Christmas 1974. The Angel shown is from the triptyque "The Mystical Lamb" in the Saint-Bavon Cathedral, Ghent.

A342

A343

Adolphe Quetelet, by J. Odevaere.

1974, Dec. 14 Engr. & Photo.
885 A342 10fr blk & buff .42 .20

Death centenary of Adolphe Quetelet (1796-1874), statistician, astronomer and Secretary of Royal Academy of Brussels.

1975, Feb. 15 Photo. *Perf. 11½*
912 A343 6.50fr Themabelga emblem .30 .15

Themabelga, International Thematic Stamp Exhibition, Brussels, Dec. 13-21, 1975.

A344

A345

1975, Feb. 22
913 A344 4.50fr Neoregelia carolinae .22 .15

Photogravure and Engraved

914 A344 5fr Coltsfoot .25 .16
915 A344 6.50fr Azalea .30 .15
Nos. 913-915 (3) .77 .46

Ghent Intl. Flower Exhib., Apr. 26-May 5.

1975, Mar. 15 *Perf. 11½*

School emblem, man Leading boy.

916 A345 4.50fr blk & multi .20 .15

Centenary of the founding of the Charles Buls Normal School for Boys, Brussels.

Davids Foundation Emblem
A346

1975, Mar. 22 Photo.
917 A346 5fr yel & multi .25 .15

Centenary of the Davids Foundation, a Catholic organization for the promotion of Flemish through education and books.

King Albert (1875-1934) A347

Mailman, 1840, by James Thiriar A348

1975, Apr. 5 **Engr. & Photo.**
918 A347 10fr blk & mar .45 .25

1975, Apr. 19 **Engr.** ***Perf. 11½***
919 A348 6.50fr dl mag .30 .15

Stamp Day 1975.

St. John, from Last Supper, by Bouts — A349

Concentration Camp Symbols — A350

Europa: 10fr, Woman's Head, detail from "Trial by Fire," by Dirk Bouts.

1975, Apr. 26 **Engr. & Photo.**
920 A349 6.50fr blk, grn & bl .35 .15
921 A349 10fr blk, ocher & red .60 .32

1975, May 3 **Photo.**

Design: "B" denoted political prisoners, "KG" prisoners of war.

922 A350 4.50fr multi .20 .15

Liberation of concentration camps, 30th anniversary.

Hospice of St. John, Bruges A351

Church of St. Loup, Namur — A352

Design: 10fr, Martyrs' Square, Brussels.

1975, May 12 **Engr.** ***Perf. 11½***
926 A351 4.50fr deep rose lilac .22 .20
927 A352 5fr slate grn .22 .15
928 A351 10fr brt blue .45 .32
Nos. 926-928 (3) .89 .67

European Architectural Heritage Year.

Library, Louvain University, Ryckmans and Cerfaux A355

1975, June 7 **Photo.** ***Perf. 11½***
931 A355 10fr dl bl & sepia .40 .20

25th anniversary of Louvain Bible Colloquium, founded by Professors Gonzague Ryckmans (1887-1969) and Lucien Cerfaux (1883-1968).

"Metamorphose" by Pol Mara — A356

Marie Popelin, Palace of Justice, Brussels — A357

1975, June 14
932 A356 7fr multi .30 .20

Queen Fabiola Mental Health Foundation.

1975, June 21 **Engr. & Photo.**
933 A357 6.50fr grn & claret .30 .15

International Women's Year 1975. Marie Popelin (1846-1913), first Belgian woman doctor of law.

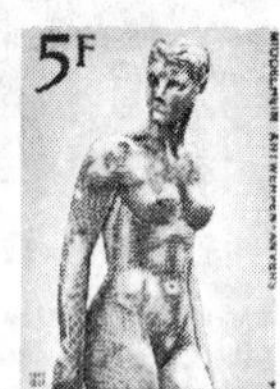
Assia, by Charles Despiau — A358

Cornelia Vekemans, by Cornelis de Vos — A359

1975, Sept. 6 ***Perf. 11½***
934 A358 5fr yel grn & blk .24 .15

Middelheim Outdoor Museum, 25th anniv.

1975, Sept. 20 **Photo.**
935 A359 4.50fr multi .20 .15

Youth philately.

Map of Schelde-Rhine Canal — A360

1975, Sept. 20
936 A360 10fr multi .45 .22

Opening of connection between the Schelde and Rhine, Sept. 23, 1975.

National Bank, W. F. Orban, Founder A361

Photogravure and Engraved

1975, Oct. 11 ***Perf. 12½x13***
937 A361 25fr multi 1.00 .30

Natl. Bank of Belgium, 125th anniv.

Edmond Thieffry and Plane, 1925 — A362

1975, Oct. 18 ***Perf. 11½***
938 A362 7fr blk & lil .30 .20

First flight Brussels to Kinshasa, Congo, 50th anniversary.

"Seat of Wisdom" St. Peter's, Louvain — A363

1975, Nov. 8 ***Perf. 11½***
939 A363 6.50fr bl, blk & grn .28 .15

University of Louvain, 550th anniversary.

Angels, by Rogier van der Weyden A364

1975, Nov. 15
940 A364 5fr multi .24 .15

Christmas 1975.

Willemsfonds Emblem — A365

American Bicentennial Emblem — A366

1976, Feb. 21 **Photo.** ***Perf. 11½***
941 A365 5fr multi .24 .15

125th anniversary of the Willems Foundation, which supports Flemish language and literature.

1976, Mar. 13 **Photo.** ***Perf. 11½***
942 A366 14fr gold, red, bl & blk .60 .30

American Bicentennial. No. 942 printed checkerwise in sheets of 30 stamps and 30 gold and black labels which show medal with 1626 seal of New York. Black engraved inscription on labels commemorates arrival of first Walloon settlers in Nieu Nederland.

Cardinal Mercier — A367

Symbolic of V.E.V. — A368

1976, Mar. 20 **Engr.**
943 A367 4.50fr brt rose lil .20 .15

Desire Joseph Cardinal Mercier (1851-1926), professor at Louvain University, spiritual and patriotic leader during World War I, 50th death anniversary.

1976, Apr. 3 **Photo.** ***Perf. 11½***
944 A368 6.50fr multi .28 .15

Flemish Economic Organization (Vlaams Ekonomisch Verbond), 50th anniversary.

General Post Office, Brussels A369

1976, Apr. 24 **Engr.** ***Perf. 11½***
945 A369 6.50fr sepia .28 .15

Stamp Day.

Potter's Hands — A370

Europa: 6.50fr, Basket maker, vert.

1976, May 8 **Photo.**
946 A370 6.50fr multi .45 .15
947 A370 14fr multi .65 .38

Truck on Road — A371

1976, May 8
948 A371 14fr blk, yel & red .65 .35

15th International Road Union Congress, Brussels, May 9-13.

Queen Elisabeth (1876-1965) — A372

1976, May 24 ***Perf. 11½***
949 A372 14fr green .60 .30

Ardennes Draft Horses — A373

1976, June 19
950 A373 5fr multicolored .22 .15

Ardennes Draft Horses Association, 50th anniversary.

Souvenir Sheets

King Baudouin — A374

1976, June 26
951 A374 Sheet of 3 2.50 .50
a. 4.50fr gray .70 .70
b. 6.50fr ocher .70 .70
c. 10fr brick red .70 .70
952 A374 Sheet of 2 3.50 3.50
a. 20fr yellow green .85 .85
b. 30fr Prussian blue .85 .85

25th anniv. of the reign of King Baudouin. No. 951 sold for 30fr, No. 952 for 70fr. The surtax went to a new foundation for the improvement of living conditions in honor of the King.

Electric Train and Society Emblem A375

1976, Sept. 11 **Photo.** ***Perf. 11½***
953 A375 6.50fr multi .30 .15

Natl. Belgian Railroad Soc., 50th anniv.

William of Nassau, Prince of Orange — A376

1976, Sept. 11 **Engr.**
954 A376 10fr slate green .42 .20

400th anniv. of the pacification of Ghent.

New Subway Train — A377

1976, Sept. 18 **Photo.**
955 A377 6.50fr multi .30 .15

Opening of first line of Brussels subway.

Young Musician, by W. C. Duyster — A378

1976, Oct. 2 **Photo.** ***Perf. 11½***
956 A378 4.50fr multi .20 .15

Young musicians and youth philately.

Charles Bernard — A379

St. Jerome in the Mountains, by Le Patinier — A380

Blind Leading the Blind, by Breughel the Elder — A381

Design: No. 958, Fernand Victor Toussaint van Boelaere.

1976, Oct. 16 **Engr.**
957 A379 5fr violet .16 .16
958 A379 5fr red brn & sepia .16 .16
959 A380 6.50fr dark brown .28 .15
960 A381 6.50fr slate green .28 .15
Nos. 957-960 (4) .88
Set value .48

Charles Bernard (1875-1961), Frenchspeaking journalist; Toussaint van Boelaere (1875-1947), Flemish journalist; No. 959, Charles Plisnier Belgian-French Cultural Society. No. 960, Assoc. for Language Promotion.

Remouchamps Caves — A382

Hunnegem Priory, Gramont, and Madonna — A383

Designs: No. 963, River Lys and St. Martin's Church. No. 964, Ham-sur-Heure Castle.

1976, Oct. 23 **Engr.** ***Perf. 13***
961 A382 4.50fr multi .15 .15
962 A383 4.50fr multi .15 .15
963 A383 5fr multi .22 .15
964 A383 5fr multi .22 .15
Nos. 961-964 (4) .74
Set value .48

Tourism. #961-962 are not luminescent.

Nativity, by Master of Flemalle — A384

1976, Nov. 20 ***Perf. 11½***
965 A384 5fr violet .22 .18

Christmas 1976.

Rubens' Monogram — A385

1977, Feb. 12 **Photo. & Engr.**
966 A385 6.50fr lilac & blk .30 .15

Peter Paul Rubens (1577-1640), painter.

Heraldic Lion — A386

1977-85 **Typo.** ***Perf. 13½x14***
Size: 17x20mm

967 A386 50c brn ('80) .15 .15
a. 50c orange brown ('85) .15 .15
968 A386 1fr brt lil .15 .15
a. 1fr bright rose lilac ('84) .15 .15
969 A386 1.50fr gray ('78) .15 .15
970 A386 2fr yel ('78) .15 .15
970A A386 2.50fr yel grn ('81) .15 .15
971 A386 2.75fr Prus bl ('80) .30 .15
972 A386 3fr vio ('78) .30 .15
a. 3fr dull violet ('84) .18 .15
973 A386 4fr red brn ('80) .25 .15
a. 4fr rose brown ('85) .25 .15
974 A386 4.50fr lt ultra .30 .15
975 A386 5fr grn ('80) .30 .15
a. 5fr emerald green ('84) .20 .15
976 A386 6fr dl red brn .35 .15
a. 6fr light red brown ('85) .35 .15
Nos. 967-976 (11) 2.55
Set value .60

Perf. 13½x12½, 12½x13½
1978, Aug. **Photo.**
Size: 17x22mm, 22x17mm
Booklet Stamps

977 A386 1fr brt lilac .15 .15
a. Bklt. pane, #977-978, 2 #786 1.50
b. Bklt. pane, #977, 979, 2 #788 2.00
978 A386 2fr yellow .30 .30
979 A386 3fr violet .45 .45
Nos. 977-979 (3) .90 .90

See Nos. 1084-1088. Each pane has 2 labels showing Belgian Postal emblem, also a large selvage with zip code instructions. No. 977-979 not luminescent.

See design O5.

Anniversary Emblem A387

1977, Mar. 14 **Photo.** ***Perf. 11½***
982 A387 6.50fr sil & multi .30 .15

Royal Belgian Association of Civil and Agricultural Engineers, 50th anniversary.

Birds and Lions Emblem A388

1977, Mar. 28
983 A388 14fr multi .60 .30

Belgian District No. 112 of Lions International, 25th anniversary.

Pillar Box, 1852 — A389

1977, Apr. 23 **Engr.**
984 A389 6.50fr slate green .45 .15

Stamp Day 1977.

Gileppe Dam, Jalhay — A390

Europa: 14fr, War Memorial, Yser at Nieuport.

1977, May 7 **Photo.** ***Perf. 11½***
985 A390 6.50fr multi .40 .15
986 A390 14fr multi .90 .15
Set value .20

Mars and Mercury Association Emblem — A391

1977, May 14
987 A391 5fr multi .25 .15

Mars and Mercury Association of Reserve and Retired Officers, 50th anniversary.

Prince de Hornes Coat of Arms — A392

Conversion of St. Hubertus — A394

Battle of the Golden Spur, from Oxford Chest A393

Design: 6.50fr, Froissart writing book.

1977, June 11 **Engr.** ***Perf. 11½***
988 A392 4.50fr violet .30 .15
989 A393 5fr red .35 .16
990 A394 6.50fr dark brown .40 .15
991 A394 14fr slate green .75 .35
Nos. 988-991 (4) 1.80
Set value .66

300th anniv. of the Principality of Overijse (4.50fr); 675th anniv. of the Battle of the Golden Spur (5f); 600th anniv. of publication of 1st volume of the Chronicles of Jehan Froissart (6.50fr); 1250th anniv. of the death of St. Hubertus (14fr).

Rubens, Self-portrait — A395

1977, June 25 **Photo.**
992 A395 5fr multi .25 .15
a. Souvenir sheet of 3 1.25 .90

Peter Paul Rubens (1577-1640), painter. No. 992a sold for 20fr.

Open Book, from The Lamb of God, by Van Eyck Brothers A396

1977, Sept. 3 **Photo.** ***Perf. 11½***
993 A396 10fr multi .45 .25

Intl. Federation of Library Associations (IFLA), 50th Anniv. Congress, Brussels, Sept. 5-10.

Gymnast and Soccer Player — A397

Designs: 6.50fr, Fencers in wheelchairs, horiz. 10fr, Basketball players. 14fr, Hockey players.

1977, Sept. 10
994 A397 4.50fr multi .25 .15
995 A397 6.50fr multi .40 .15
996 A397 10fr multi .60 .20
997 A397 14fr multi .80 .30
Nos. 994-997 (4) 2.05
Set value .65

Workers' Gymnastics and Sports Center, 50th anniversary (4.50fr); sport for the Handicapped (6.50fr); 20th European Basketball Championships (10fr); First World Hockey Cup (14fr).

Europalia 77 Emblem — A398

1977, Sept. 17
998 A398 5fr gray & multi .22 .15

5th Europalia Arts Festival, featuring German Federal Republic, Belgium, Oct.-Nov. 1977.

The Egg Farmer, by Gustave De Smet — A399

1977, Oct. 8 **Engr. & Photo.**
999 A399 4.50fr bister & blk .22 .15

Publicity for Belgian eggs.

Mother and Daughter with Album, by Constant Cap — A400

1977, Oct. 15 **Engr.**
1000 A400 4.50fr dark brown .22 .15

Youth Philately.

Bailiff's House, Gembloux — A401

Market Square, St. Nicholas A402

Designs: No. 1002, St. Aldegonde Church and Cultural Center. No. 1004, Statue and bridge, Liège.

1977, Oct. 22

1001 A401	4.50fr multi		.22	.15
1002 A401	4.50fr multi		.22	.15
1003 A402	5fr multi		.22	.18
1004 A402	5fr multi		.22	.18
	Nos. 1001-1004 (4)		.88	
	Set value			.56

Tourism. Nos. 1001-1004 not luminescent. See Nos. 1017-1018, 1037-1040.

Nativity, by Rogier van der Weyden — A403

1977, Nov. 11 **Engr.**
1005 A403 5fr rose red .30 .15

Christmas 1977.

Symbols of Transportation and Map — A404

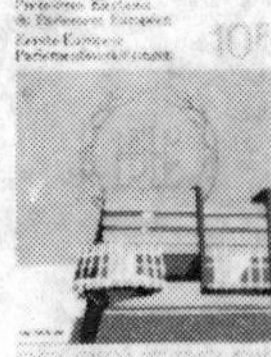
Parliament of Europe, Strasbourg, and Emblem — A405

Campidoglio Palace, Rome, and Map — A406

Design: No. 1009, Paul-Henri Spaak and map of 19 European member countries.

1978, Mar. 18 **Photo.** ***Perf.*** ***11½***

1006 A404	10fr blue & multi	.55	.20
1007 A405	10fr blue & multi	1.10	.20
1008 A406	14fr blue & multi	.65	.55
1009 A406	14fr blue & multi	.65	.55
	Nos. 1006-1009 (4)	2.95	1.50

European Action: 25th anniversary of the European Transport Ministers' Conference; 1st general elections for European Parliament; 20th anniversary of the signing of the Treaty of Rome; Paul Henri Spaak (1899-1972), Belgian statesman who worked for the establishment of European Community.

Grimbergen Abbey — A407

1978, Apr. 1 **Engr.**
1010 A407 4.50fr red brown .22 .15

850th anniversary of the Premonstratensian Abbey at Grimbergen.

Emblem — A408

No. 39 with First Day Cancel — A409

1978, Apr. 8 **Photo.**
1011 A408 8fr multicolored .50 .15

Ostend Chamber of Commerce and Industry, 175th anniversary.

1978, Apr. 15
1012 A409 8fr multicolored .35 .15

Stamp Day.

Europa Issue

Pont des Trous, Tournai A410

Design: 8fr, Antwerp Cathedral, by Vaclav Hollar, vert.

Photogravure and Engraved

1978, May 6 ***Perf.*** ***11½***
1013 A410 8fr multicolored .50 .15
1014 A410 14fr multicolored .75 .30

Virgin of Ghent, Porcelain Plaque — A411

Paul Pastur Workers' University, Charleroi — A412

1978, Sept. 16 **Photo.** ***Perf.*** ***11½***

1015 A411	6fr multicolored	.42	.15
1016 A412	8fr multicolored	.55	.15
	Set value		.21

Municipal education in Ghent, 150th anniversary; Paul Pastur Workers' University, Charleroi, 75th anniv. #1015-1016 are not luminescent.

Types of 1977 and

Tourist Guide, Brussels A413

Designs: No. 1017, Jonathas House, Enghien. No. 1018, View of Wetteren and couple in local costume. No. 1020, Prince Carnival, Eupen-St. Vith.

1978, Sept. 25 **Photo. & Engr.**

1017 A401	4.50fr multi	.16	.15
1018 A402	4.50fr multi	.16	.15
1019 A413	6fr multi	.25	.15
1020 A413	6fr multi	.25	.15
	Nos. 1017-1020 (4)	.82	
	Set value		.48

Tourism. #1017-1020 are not luminescent.

Emblem A414

1978, Oct. 7 **Photo.**
1021 A414 8fr red & blk .35 .15

Royal Flemish Engineer's Organization, 50th anniversary.

Young Philatelist A415

1978, Oct. 14 **Engr.** ***Perf.*** ***11½***
1022 A415 4.50fr dk violet .22 .15

Youth philately.

Nativity, Notre Dame, Huy — A416

1978, Nov. 18 **Engr.** ***Perf.*** ***11½***
1023 A416 6fr black .28 .15

Christmas 1978.

Tyll Eulenspiegel, Lay Action Emblem — A417

European Parliament Emblem — A418

1979, Mar. 3 **Photo.** ***Perf.*** ***11½***
1024 A417 4.50fr multi .28 .15

10th anniversary of Lay Action Centers.

1979, Mar. 3
1025 A418 8fr multicolored .50 .15

European Parliament, first direct elections, June 7-10.

St. Michael Banishing Lucifer — A419

1979, Mar. 17 **Photo. & Engr.**

1026 A419	4.50fr rose red & blk	.20	.15
1027 A419	8fr brt green & blk	.30	.15
	Set value		.19

Millennium of Brussels.

NATO Emblem and Monument A420

1979, Mar. 31 **Photo.**
1028 A420 3fr multicolored 1.75 .45

NATO, 30th anniv.

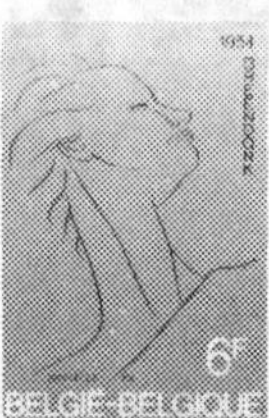
Prisoner's Head — A421

1979, Apr. 7 **Photo. & Engr.**
1029 A421 6fr orange & blk .25 .15

25th anniversary of the National Political Prisoners' Monument at Breendonk.

Belgium No. Q2 — A422

1979, Apr. 21 **Photo.** ***Perf.*** ***11½***
1030 A422 8fr multicolored .50 .15

Stamp Day 1979.

Mail Coach and Truck A423

Europa: 14fr, Chappe's heliograph, Intelsat satellite and dish antenna.

1979, Apr. 28 **Photo. & Engr.**
1031 A423 8fr multicolored .45 .15
1032 A423 14fr multicolored .90 .40

Chamber of Commerce Emblem — A424

1979, May 19 **Photo.** ***Perf. 11½***
1033 A424 8fr multicolored .35 .15

Verviers Chamber of Commerce and Industry, 175th anniversary.

"50" Emblem A425

1979, June 9 **Photo.** ***Perf. 11½***
1034 A425 4.50fr gold & ultra .30 .15

Natl. Fund for Professional Credit, 50th anniv.

Merchants, Roman Bas-relief A426

1979, June 9
1035 A426 10fr multicolored .60 .16

Belgian Chamber of Trade and Commerce, 50th anniversary.

"Tintin" as Philatelist A427

1979, Sept. 29 **Photo.** ***Perf. 11½***
1036 A427 8fr multicolored 1.10 .15

Youth philately.

Tourism Types of 1977

Designs: No. 1037, Belfry, Thuin. No. 1038, Royal Museum of Central Africa, Tervuren. No. 1039, St. Nicholas Church and cattle, Ciney. No. 1040, St. John's Church and statue of Our Lady, Poperinge.

Perf. 11½ (A401), 13 (A402)

1979, Oct. 22 **Photo. & Engr.**
1037 A401 5fr multicolored .20 .15
1038 A402 5fr multicolored .20 .15
1039 A401 6fr multicolored .35 .15
1040 A402 6fr multicolored .35 .15
Nos. 1037-1040 (4) 1.10
Set value .44

Francois Auguste Gevaert A429

Piano, String Instruments A430

Design: 6fr, Emmanuel Durlet.

1979, Nov. 3 ***Perf. 11½***
1041 A429 5fr brown .35 .15
1042 A429 6fr brown .42 .15
1043 A430 14fr brown .90 .35
Nos. 1041-1043 (3) 1.67
Set value .53

Francois Auguste Gevaert (1828-1908), musicologist and composer; Emmanuel Durlet (1893-1977), pianist; Queen Elisabeth Musical Chapel Foundation, 40th anniv.

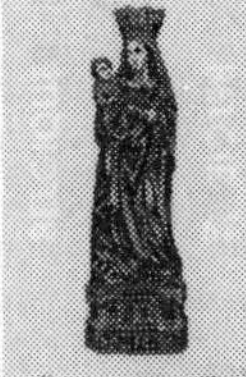
Virgin and Child, Notre Dame, Foy — A431

1979, Nov. 24 **Photo. & Engr.**
1044 A431 6fr lt grnsh blue .30 .15

Christmas 1979.

Independence, 150th Anniversary A432

1980, Jan. 26 **Photo.** ***Perf. 11½***
1045 A432 9fr purple .40 .15

Frans van Cauwelaert A433

Spring Flowers A434

1980, Feb. 25 **Engr.**
1046 A433 5fr gray .22 .15

Frans van Cauwelaert (1880-1961), Minister of State.

1980, Mar. 10 **Photo.**
1047 A434 5fr shown .24 .15
1048 A434 6.50fr Summer flowers .32 .15
1049 A434 9fr Autumn flowers .45 .15
Nos. 1047-1049 (3) 1.01
Set value .28

Ghent Flower Show, Apr. 19-27.

P.T.T., 50th Anniv. A435

1980, Apr. 14 **Photo.** ***Perf. 11½***
1050 A435 10fr multicolored .45 .22

Belgium No. C4 — A436

1980, Apr. 21
1051 A436 9fr multicolored .50 .15

Stamp Day.

A437 A438

Europa: 9fr, St. Benedict, by Hans Memling. 14fr, Margaret of Austria (1480-1530).

1980, Apr. 28
1052 A437 9fr multicolored .45 .15
1053 A437 14fr multicolored .70 .24

1980, May 10 **Photo.** ***Perf. 11½***
1054 A438 5fr Palais des Nations, Brussels .25 .15

4th Interparliamentary Conference for European Cooperation and Security, Brussels, May 12-18.

Golden Carriage, 1780, Mons — A439

Tourism: #1056, Canal landscape, Damme.

1980, May 17
1055 A439 6.50fr multi .32 .20
1056 A439 6.50fr multi .32 .20

Souvenir Sheet

Royal Mint Theater, Brussels — A440

Photo. & Engr.

1980, May 31 ***Perf. 11½***
1057 A440 50fr black 3.25 3.25

150th anniv. of independence. Sold for 75fr.

King Baudouin, 50th Birthday — A441

1980, Sept. 6 **Photo.** ***Perf. 11½***
1058 A441 9fr rose claret .42 .15

View of Chiny A442

Portal and Court, Diest — A443

1980 **Engr.** ***Perf. 13***
1059 A442 5fr multicolored .25 .15
1060 A443 5fr multicolored .25 .15
Set value .20

Tourism. Nos. 1059-1060 are not luminescent. Issue dates: No. 1059, Sept. 27; No. 1060, Dec. 13. See Nos. 1072-1075, 1120-1125.

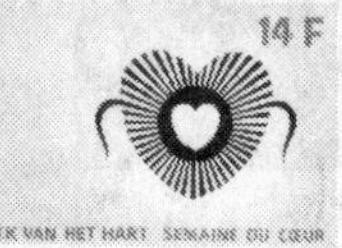

Emblem of Belgian Heart League A444

1980, Oct. 4 **Photo.** ***Perf. 11½***
1061 A444 14fr blue & magenta .55 .25

Heart Week, Oct. 20-25.

Rodenbach Statue, Roulers — A445

1980, Oct. 11
1062 A445 9fr multicolored .40 .15

Albrecht Rodenbach (1856-1880), poet.

Youth Philately — A446

1980, Oct. 27 **Photo.** ***Perf. 11½***
1063 A446 5fr multicolored .22 .15

National Broadcasting Service, 50th Anniversary — A447

1980, Nov. 10
1064 A447 10fr gray & blk .45 .22

Garland and Nativity, by Daniel Seghers, 17th Century A448

1980, Nov. 17
1065 A448 6.50fr multicolored .40 .15

Christmas 1980.

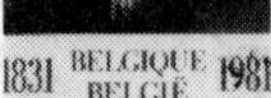

Baron de Gerlache, by F.J. Navez — A449

Leopold I, By Geefs — A450

Design: 9fr, Baron de Stassart, by F.J. Navez.

1981, Mar. 16 Photo. *Perf. 11½*

1066 A449 6fr multicolored .35 .15
1067 A449 9fr multicolored .55 .15

Photogravure and Engraved

1068 A450 50fr multicolored 3.00 .55

Sesquicentennial of Chamber of Deputies, Senate and Dynasty.

Europa Issue 1981

Tchantchès and Op-Signoorke, Puppets — A451

Photogravure and Engraved

1981, May 4 *Perf. 11½*

1069 A451 9fr shown .40 .15
1070 A451 14fr d'Artagnan and Woltje .65 .35

Impression of M.A. de Cock (Founder of Post Museum) — A452

1981, May 18 Photo.

1071 A452 9fr multicolored .40 .15

Stamp Day.

Tourism Types of 1980

Designs: No. 1072, Virgin and Child statue, Our Lady's Church, Tongre-Notre Dame. No. 1073, Egmont Castle, Zottegem. No. 1074, Eau d'Heure River. No. 1075, Tongerlo Abbey, Antwerp.

1981, June 15 Engr. *Perf. 11½*

1072 A442 6fr multi .35 .15
1073 A442 6fr multi .35 .20
1074 A443 6.50fr multi .35 .20
1075 A443 6.50fr multi .35 .20
Nos. 1072-1075 (4) 1.40 .75

Soccer Player — A453

E. Remouchamps, Founder — A454

1981, Sept. 5 Photo. *Perf. 11½*

1076 A453 6fr multicolored .35 .15

Soccer in Belgium centenary; Royal Antwerp Soccer Club.

1981, Sept. 5 Photo. & Engr.

1077 A454 6.50fr multi .40 .15

Walloon Language and Literature Club 125th anniv.

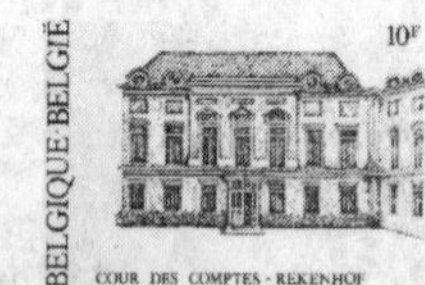

Audit Office Sesquicentennial — A455

1981, Sept. 12 Engr.

1078 A455 10fr tan & dk brn .60 .24

French Horn — A456

1981, Sept. 12 Photo.

1079 A456 6.50fr multi .40 .15

Vredekring (Peace Circle) Band of Antwerp centenary.

Souvenir Sheet

Pieta, by Ben Genaux — A457

1981, Sept. 19 Photo. *Perf. 11½*

1080 A457 20fr multicolored 1.75 1.40

Mining disaster at Marcinelle, 25th anniv. Sold for 30fr.

Mausoleum of Marie of Burgundy and Charles the Bold, Bruges — A458

1981, Oct. 10 Photo. & Engr.

1081 A458 50fr multi 2.75 .60

Youth Philately — A459

1981, Oct. 24 Photo.

1082 A459 6fr multi .28 .15

Type of 1977 and

A459a A460

King Baudouin A460a

Photo. and Engr.; Photo.

1980-86 *Perf. 13½x14, 11½*

1084 A386 65c brt rose .20 .15
1085 A386 1fr on 5fr grn ('82) .20 .15
1086 A386 7fr brt rose ('82) .55 .15
1087 A386 8fr grnsh bl ('83) .60 .15
1088 A386 9fr dl org ('85) .55 .15
1089 A459a 10fr blue ('82) .85 .15
1090 A459a 11fr dl red ('83) .90 .15
1091 A459a 12fr grn ('84) .90 .15
1092 A459a 13fr scar ('86) .85 .15
1093 A459a 15fr red org ('84) 1.25 .20
1094 A459a 20fr dk bl ('84) 1.50 .28
1095 A459a 22fr lilac ('84) 1.65 .30
1096 A459a 23fr gray grn ('85) 1.00 .55
1097 A459a 30fr brown ('84) 2.25 .40
1098 A459a 40fr red org ('84) 2.50 .55
1099 A460 50fr lt grnsh bl & bl 3.25 .30
1100 A460a 50fr tan & dk brn ('84) 3.25 .60
1101 A460 65fr pale lil & blk ('81) 4.50 .90
1102 A460 100fr lt bis brn & dk bl ('81) 6.75 1.25
1103 A460a 100fr lt bl & dk bl ('84) 6.75 1.25
Nos. 1084-1103 (20) 40.25 7.93

See Nos. 1231-1234.

Max Waller, Movement Founder A461

The Spirit Drinkers, by Gustave van de Woestyne A462

Fernand Severin, Poet, 50th Death Anniv. — A463

Jan van Ruusbroec, Flemish Mystic, 500th Birth Anniv. — A464

Thought and Man TV Series, 25th Anniv. A465

Nativity, 16th Cent. Engraving A466

1981, Nov. 7

1104 A461 6fr multi .30 .15
1105 A462 6.50fr multi .35 .18
1106 A463 9fr multi .50 .15
1107 A464 10fr multi .80 .22
1108 A465 14fr multi .75 .35
Nos. 1104-1108 (5) 2.70 1.05

La Jeune Belgique cultural movement cent. (6fr).

1981, Nov. 21

1109 A466 6.50fr multi .30 .15

Christmas 1981.

Royal Conservatory of Music Sesquicentennial — A467

Design: 9fr, Judiciary sesquicentennial.

1982, Jan. 25 Photo. *Perf. 11½*

1110 A467 6.50fr multi .30 .15
1111 A467 9fr multi .40 .15
Set value .22

A468

A469

1982, Mar. 1

1112 A468 6fr Cyclotron .35 .15
1113 A468 14fr Galaxy, telescope .85 .35
1114 A468 50fr Koch 3.00 .65
Nos. 1112-1114 (3) 4.20 1.15

Radio-isotope production, Natl. Radio-elements Institute, Fleurus (6fr); Royal Belgian Observatory (14fr); centenary of TB bacillus discovery (50fr).

1982, Apr. 17 Photo. *Perf. 11½*

1115 A469 6.50fr multi .32 .15

Joseph Lemaire (1882-1966), Minister of State.

Europa 1982 — A470

1982, May 1

1116 A470 10fr Universal suffrage .48 .15
1117 A470 17fr Edict of Tolerance, 1781 .80 .40

Stamp Day — A471

1982, May 22 Photo. & Engr.

1118 A471 10fr multi .50 .15

67th World Esperanto Congress, Anvers A472

1982, June 7 Photo. *Perf. 11½*

1119 A472 12fr Tower of Babel .60 .30

Tourism Type of 1980

Designs: No. 1120, Tower of Gosselies. No. 1121, Zwijveke Abbey, Dendermonde. No. 1122, Stavelot Abbey. No. 1123, Villers-la-Ville Abbey ruins. No. 1124, Geraardsbergen Abbey entrance. No. 1125, Beveren Pillory.

1982, June 21 Photo. & Engr.

1120 A443 7fr lt bl & blk .50 .15
1121 A443 7fr lt grn & blk .50 .15
1122 A442 7.50fr tan & dk brn .55 .25
1123 A442 7.50fr lt vio & pur .55 .25
1124 A443 7.50fr slate & blk .55 .25
1125 A443 7.50fr beige & blk .55 .25
Nos. 1120-1125 (6) 3.20 1.30

Self Portrait, by L.P. Boon (b. 1912) A473

Abraham Hans, Writer (1882-1932) A474

Designs: 10fr, Adoration of the Shepherds, by Hugo van der Goes (1440-1482). 12fr, The King on His Throne, carving by M. de Ghelderode (1898-1962). 17fr, Madonna and Child, by Pieter Paulus (1881-1959).

1982, Sept. 13 Photo. Perf. 11½
1126 A473 7fr multicolored .50 .15
1127 A473 10fr multicolored .60 .15
1128 A473 12fr multicolored .70 .35
1129 A473 17fr multicolored 1.00 .35
Nos. 1126-1129 (4) 2.80
Set value .82

1982, Sept. 27
1130 A474 17fr multicolored 1.10 .35

Youth Philately and Scouting A475

1982, Oct. 2 Photo. Perf. 11½
1131 A475 7fr multicolored .50 .15

Grand Orient Lodge of Belgium Sesquicentennial A476

1982, Oct. 16 Photo. & Engr.
1132 A476 10fr Man taking oath .60 .15

Cardinal Joseph Cardijn (1882-1967) A477

1982, Nov. 13 Photo.
1133 A477 10fr multicolored .48 .15

St. Francis of Assisi (1182-1226) — A478

1982, Nov. 27
1134 A478 20fr multicolored .90 .30

Horse-drawn Trolley A479

1983, Feb. 12 Photo. Perf. 11½
1135 A479 7.50fr shown .38 .22
1136 A479 10fr Electric trolley .50 .15
1137 A479 50fr Trolley, diff. 2.50 .50
Nos. 1135-1137 (3) 3.38 .87

Intl. Fed. for Periodical Press, 24th World Congress, Brussels, May 11-13 — A480

1983, Mar. 19 Photo. Perf. 11½
1138 A480 20fr multicolored 1.00 .25

Homage to Women A481

1983, Apr. 16
1139 A481 8fr Operator .45 .15
1140 A481 11fr Homemaker .55 .15
1141 A481 20fr Executive .95 .25
Nos. 1139-1141 (3) 1.95
Set value .38

Stamp Day — A482

1983, Apr. 23
1142 A482 11fr multicolored .60 .15

Procession of the Precious Blood, Bruges A483

1983, Apr. 30 Photo. Perf. 11½
1143 A483 8fr multi .60 .15

Europa 1983 A484

Paintings by P. Delvaux. 11fr vert.

1983, May 14
1144 A484 11fr Common Man .65 .15
1145 A484 20fr Night Train 1.25 .45

Manned Flight Bicentenary A485

1983, June 11 Photo. Perf. 11½
1146 A485 11fr Balloon over city .65 .15
1147 A485 22fr Country 1.40 .45

Our Lady's Church, Hastiere A486

1983, June 25
1148 A486 8fr shown .40 .18
1149 A486 8fr Landen .40 .18
1150 A486 8fr Park, Mouscron .40 .18
1151 A486 8fr Wijnendale Castle, Torhout .40 .18
Nos. 1148-1151 (4) 1.60 .72

Tineke Festival, Heule — A487

1983, Sept. 10 Photo.
1152 A487 8fr multi .40 .15

Enterprise Year Emblem A488

1983, Sept. 24
1153 A488 11fr multicolored .55 .15

European year for small and medium-sized enterprises and craft industry.

Youth Philately — A489

1983, Oct. 10 Photo. Perf. 11½
1154 A489 8fr multicolored .40 .15

Belgian Exports — A490

1983, Oct. 24 Perf. 11½
1155 A490 10fr Diamond industry .55 .15
1156 A490 10fr Metallurgy .55 .15
1157 A490 10fr Textile industry .55 .15
Nos. 1155-1157 (3) 1.65
Set value .30

See Nos. 1161-1164.

A491 A492

1983, Nov. 7
1158 A491 20fr multicolored 1.00 .25

Hendrik Conscience, novelist (1812-1883).

Leopold III Type of 1936

1983, Dec. 12 Engr. Perf. 12x11½
1159 A84 11fr black .55 .15

Leopold III memorial (1901-1983), King 1934-1951.

Photogravure and Engraved

1984, Jan. 14 Perf. 11½
1160 A492 11fr multicolored .55 .15

Free University of Brussels, sesquicentennial.

Exports Type of 1983

1984, Jan. 28 Photo.
1161 A490 11fr Chemicals .55 .15
1162 A490 11fr Food .55 .15
1163 A490 11fr Transportation equipment .55 .15
1164 A490 11fr Technology .55 .15
Nos. 1161-1164 (4) 2.20
Set value .48

A494 A495

1984, Feb. 11 Photo. & Engr.
1165 A494 8fr tan & dk brn .40 .15

50th death anniv. of King Albert I.

1984, Mar. 3 Photo.
Souvenir Sheet
1166 Sheet of 2 2.00 2.00
a. A495 10fr Archery .55 .55
b. A495 24fr Dressage 1.40 1.40

1984 Olympics. See Nos. B1029-B1030.

Family, Globe, Birds A496

St. John Bosco Canonization A497

1984, Mar. 24 Photo. Perf. 11½
1167 A496 12fr multicolored .60 .15

"Movement without a Name" peace org.

1984, Apr. 7
1168 A497 8fr multicolored .40 .15

Europa (1959-84) A498

1984, May 5 Photo. Perf. 11½
1169 A498 12fr black & red .75 .15
1170 A498 22fr black & ultra 1.40 .30

Stamp Day — A499

1984, May 19
1171 A499 12fr No. 52 .60 .15

2nd European Parliament Elections A500

1984, May 26
1172 A500 12fr multicolored .60 .15

Royal Military School, 150th Anniv. — A501

1984, June 9 Photo. Perf. 11½
1173 A501 22fr Hat 1.10 .25

Notre-Dame de la Chappelle, Brussels A502

Churches: No. 1175, St. Martin's, Montignyle-Tilleul. No. 1176, Tielt, vert.

Perf. 11½x12, 12x11½

1984, June 23 **Photo. & Engr.**
1174 A502 10fr multicolored .55 .15
1175 A502 10fr multicolored .55 .15
1176 A502 10fr multicolored .55 .15
Nos. 1174-1176 (3) 1.65 .45

50th Anniv. of Chirojeugd (Christian Youth Movement) A503

1984, Sept. 15 **Photo.** ***Perf. 11½***
1177 A503 10fr Emblem .50 .15

Affligem Abbey A504

1984, Oct. 6 **Photo. & Engr.**
1178 A504 8fr Averbode, vert. .40 .25
1179 A504 22fr Chimay, vert. 1.25 .25
1180 A504 24fr Rochefort, vert. 1.25 .38
1181 A504 50fr shown 2.50 .50
Nos. 1178-1181 (4) 5.40 1.38

Youth Philately A505

1984, Oct. 20 **Photo.**
1182 A505 8fr Postman smurf .45 .15

Arthur Meulemans (1884-1966), Composer — A506

1984, Nov. 17 **Photo. & Engr.**
1183 A506 12fr multi .60 .15

St. Norbert, 850th Death Anniv. — A507

Europalia '85 — A508

1985, Jan. 14 **Photo. & Engr.**
1184 A507 22fr sepia & beige 1.10 .30

1985, Jan. 21 **Photo.**
1185 A508 12fr Virgin with Lion .65 .15

Belgian Assoc. of Professional Journalists, Cent. — A509

1985, Feb. 11 **Photo.**
1186 A509 9fr multicolored .42 .15

Ghent Flower Festival, Orchids A510

Visit of Pope John Paul II A511

Photogravure and Engraved

1985, Mar. 18 ***Perf. 11½***
1187 A510 12fr Vanda coerules .70 .15
1188 A510 12fr Phalaenopsis .70 .15
1189 A510 12fr Suphrolaelio cattlea riffe .70 .15
Nos. 1187-1189 (3) 2.10 .45

1985, Apr. 1 **Photo.**
1190 A511 12fr multicolored .60 .15

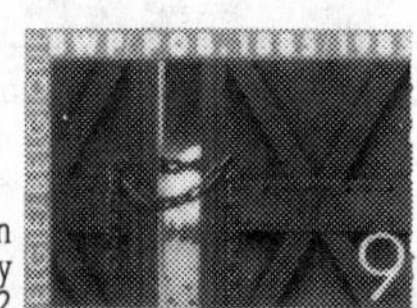

Belgian Worker's Party Cent. — A512

1985, Apr. 15 **Photo.**
1191 A512 9fr Chained factory gate .42 .15
1192 A512 12fr Broken wall, red flag .60 .15
Set value .24

Jean de Bast (1883-1975), Engraver A513

1985, Apr. 22 **Engr.**
1193 A513 12fr blue black .60 .15

Stamp Day.

Public Transportation Year — A514

Design: 9fr, Steam tram locomotive Type 18, 1896. 12fr, Locomotive Elephant and tender, 1835. 23fr, Type 23 tank engine, 1904. 24fr, Type 1 Pacific locomotive, 1935. 50fr, Type 27 electric locomotive, 1975.

1985, May 6 **Photo.**
1194 A514 9fr multicolored .65 .20
1195 A514 12fr multicolored .85 .20
1196 A514 23fr multicolored 1.50 .35
1197 A514 24fr multicolored 1.90 .40
Nos. 1194-1197 (4) 4.90 1.15

Souvenir Sheet

1198 A514 50fr multicolored 4.50 3.75

Europa 1985 — A515

1985, May 13 **Photo.**
1199 A515 12fr Cesar Franck at organ, 1887 .80 .15
1200 A515 23fr Folk figures 1.50 .25

26th Navigation Congress, Brussels A516

1985, June 10 **Photo.** ***Perf. 11½***
1201 A516 23fr Zeebruge Harbor 1.25 .25
1202 A516 23fr Projected lock at Strepy-Thieu 1.25 .25

St. Martin's Church, Marcinelle A517

Tourism: No. 1203, Church of the Assumption of Our Lady, Avernas-le-Baudouin, vert. No. 1204, Church of the Old Beguinage, Tongres, vert. No. 1206, Private residence, Puyenbroeck.

1985, June 24 ***Perf. 11½***
1203 A517 12fr multicolored .60 .15
1204 A517 12fr multicolored .60 .15
1205 A517 12fr multicolored .60 .15
1206 A517 12fr multicolored .60 .15
Nos. 1203-1206 (4) 2.40
Set value .48

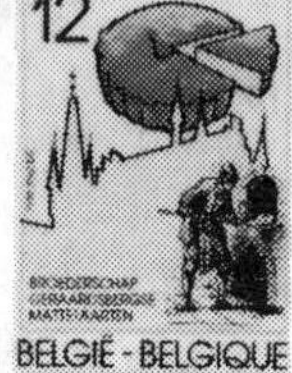

Queen Astrid (1905-1935) A518

Baking Pies for the Mattetart of Geraardsbergen A519

1985, Sept. 2 ***Perf. 11½***
1207 A518 12fr brown .60 .15

1985, Sept. 16

Folk events: 24fr, Children dancing, centenary of the St. Lambert de Hermalle-Argenteau Le Rouges youth organization.

1208 A519 12fr multicolored .60 .15
1209 A519 24fr multicolored .95 .28

Liberation from German Occupation, 40th Anniv. — A520

Allegories: 9fr, Dove, liberation of concentration camps. 23fr, Battle of Ardennes. 24fr, Destroyer, liberation of the River Scheldt estuary.

1985, Sept. 30 **Photo.** ***Perf. 11½***
1210 A520 9fr multicolored .50 .25
1211 A520 23fr multicolored 1.25 .65
1212 A520 24fr multicolored 1.25 .68
Nos. 1210-1212 (3) 3.00 1.58

Ernest Claes (1885-1968), Author A521

1985, Oct. 7
1213 A521 9fr Portrait, book character .48 .25

Intl. Youth Year — A522

1985, Oct. 21
1214 A522 9fr Nude in repose, angel .50 .25

King Baudouin & Queen Fabiola, 25th Wedding Anniv. — A523

1985, Dec. 9
1215 A523 12fr multicolored .52 .38

Birds — A524

Photo. (50c-2fr, No. 1220, 4.50fr-6fr, No. 1229, 10fr), Typo. (Others)

1985-91 ***Perf. 11½***
1216 A524 50c Crested wren .15 .15
1217 A524 1fr Lesser spotted woodpecker .15 .15
1218 A524 2fr Tree sparrow .15 .15
1219 A524 3fr Hawkfinch .15 .15
1220 A524 3fr Reed bunting (Rietgors) .25 .15
1221 A524 3.50fr Robin .20 .15
1222 A524 4fr Blue throat .25 .15
1223 A524 4.50fr Stone chat .35 .15
1224 A524 5fr Nuthatch .35 .15
1225 A524 6fr Bullfinch .40 .15
1226 A524 7fr Blue tit .45 .15
1227 A524 8fr Kingfisher .45 .15
1228 A524 9fr Goldfinch .35 .15
1229 A524 9fr Song thrush (Zanglijster) .65 .15
1230 A524 10fr Chaffinch .65 .15
Nos. 1216-1230 (15) 4.95
Set value 2.00

Issue dates: 7fr, Sept. 7, 1987. 5fr, 6fr, Sept. 12, 1988. 4fr, Apr. 17, 1989. 2fr, Dec. 4, 1989. 1fr, Jan. 8, 1990. 10fr, Jan. 15, 1990. 50c, Nos. 1220, 1229, Sept. 30, 1991. Others, Sept. 30, 1985.
See Nos. 1432-1447.

King Type of 1981

1986-90 **Photo.** ***Perf. 11½***
1231 A459a 14fr black .80 .20
1232 A459a 24fr dk grysh green 1.10 .85
1233 A459a 25fr blue black 1.45 .38
1234 A460a 200fr sage grn & dl gray grn 11.00 2.00
Nos. 1231-1234 (4) 14.35 3.43

Issued: 14fr, Jan. 15, 1990; 25fr, Feb. 19, 1990.

Congo Stamp Cent. — A525

1986, Jan. 27 **Photo.** ***Perf. 11½***
1236 A525 10fr Belgian Congo #3 .42 .15

See Zaire No. 1230.

Carnival Cities of Aalst and Binche A526

Folklore: masks, giants.

1986, Feb. 3

1237 A526 9fr Aalst Belfry	.48	.15
1238 A526 12fr Binche Gilles	.60	.18

Intl. Peace Year — A527

1986, Mar. 10

1239 A527 23fr Emblem, dove	1.25	.35

Stamp Day — A528

1986, Apr. 21 Photo. *Perf. 11½*

1240 A528 13fr Artifacts	.65	.42

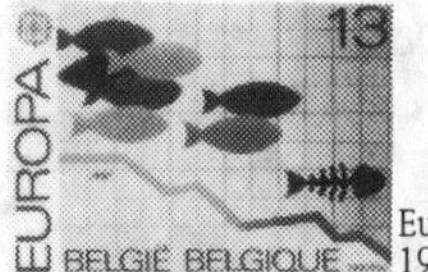

Europa 1986 — A529

1986, May 5

1241 A529 13fr Fish	.65	.42
1242 A529 24fr Flora	1.40	.85

Dogs — A530

St. Ludger's Church, Zele — A531

1986, May 26 Photo. *Perf. 11½*

1243 A530 9fr Malines sheepdog	.65	.30
1244 A530 13fr Tervueren sheepdog	.85	.45
1245 A530 24fr Groenendael sheepdog	1.65	.82
1246 A530 26fr Flemish cattle dog	1.65	.85
Nos. 1243-1246 (4)	4.80	2.42

1986, June 30 Photo. & Engr.

Designs: No. 1248, Waver Town Hall. No. 1249, Nederzwalm Canal, horiz. No. 1250, Chapel of Our Lady of the Dunes, Bredene. No. 1251, Licot Castle, Viroinval, horiz. No. 1252, Eynenbourg Castle, La Calamine, horiz.

1247 A531 9fr multicolored	.60	.30
1248 A531 9fr multicolored	.60	.30
1249 A531 13fr multicolored	.80	.45
1250 A531 13fr multicolored	.80	.45
1251 A531 13fr multicolored	.80	.45
1252 A531 13fr multicolored	.80	.45
Nos. 1247-1252 (6)	4.40	2.40

Youth Philately A532

1986, Sept. 1 Photo. *Perf. 11½*

1253 A532 9fr dl ol grn, blk & dk red	.50	.32

Cartoon Exhibition, Knokke.

Famous Men — A533

Designs: 9fr, Constant Permeke, painter, sculptor. 13fr, Baron Michel-Edmond de Selys Longchamps, scientist. 24fr, Felix Timmermans, writer. 26fr, Maurice Careme, poet.

1986, Sept. 29

1254 A533 9fr multicolored	.52	.32
1255 A533 13fr multicolored	.75	.45
1256 A533 24fr multicolored	1.40	.82
1257 A533 26fr multicolored	1.50	.90
Nos. 1254-1257 (4)	4.17	2.49

Royal Academy for Dutch Language and Literature, Cent. — A534

1986, Oct. 6 Engr.

1258 A534 9fr dark blue	.52	.32

Natl. Beer Industry A535

Perf. 12½x11½

1986, Oct. 13 Photo.

1259 A535 13fr Glass, barley, hops	.70	.50

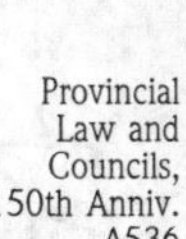

Provincial Law and Councils, 150th Anniv. A536

1986, Oct. 27 *Perf. 11½*

1260 A536 13fr Stylized map	.70	.50

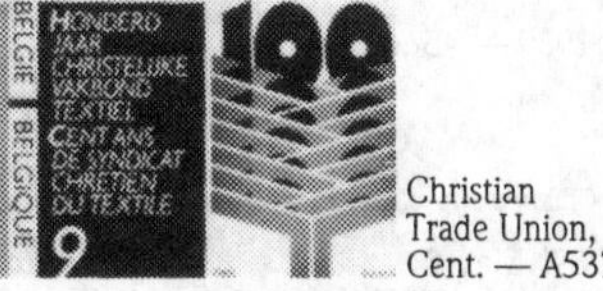

Christian Trade Union, Cent. — A537

1986, Dec. 13 Photo. *Perf. 11½*

1261 A537 9fr shown	.45	.35
1262 A537 13fr design reversed	.65	.50

Flanders Technology Intl. — A538

1987, Mar. 2 Photo.

1263 A538 13fr multi	.70	.50

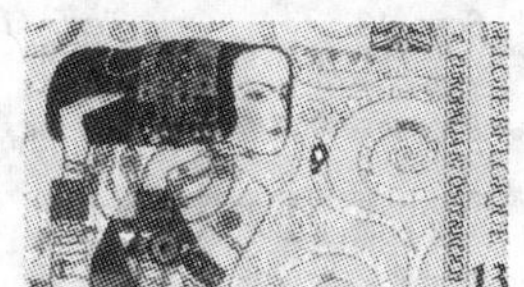

EUROPALIA '87, Austrian Cultural Events — A539

Design: Woman, detail of a fresco by Gustav Klimt, Palais Stoclet, Brussels.

1987, Apr. 4 Photo. *Perf. 11½*

1264 A539 13fr multicolored	.70	.50

Stamp Day 1987 — A540

Portrait: Jakob Wiener (1815-1899), 1st engraver of Belgian stamps.

1987, Apr. 11 Photo. & Engr.

1265 A540 13fr lt greenish blue & sage grn	.70	.50

Folklore A541

1987, Apr. 25 Photo.

1266 A541 9fr Penitents procession, Veurne	.45	.35
1267 A541 13fr Play of John and Alice, Wavre	.65	.50

Europa 1987 — A542

Modern architecture: 13fr, Louvain-la-Neuve Church. 24fr, Regional Housing Assoc. Tower, St. Maartensdal at Louvain.

1987, May 9 Photo.

1268 A542 13fr multicolored	.85	.55
1269 A542 24fr multicolored	1.50	1.00

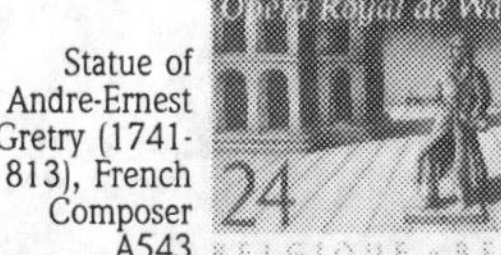

Statue of Andre-Ernest Gretry (1741-1813), French Composer A543

1987, May 23

1270 A543 24fr multicolored	1.50	1.00

Wallonie Royal Opera, Liege, 20th anniv.

Tourism — A544

Designs: No. 1271, Statues of Jan Breydel and Pieter de Conin, Bruges. No. 1272, Boondael Chapel, Brussels. No. 1273, Windmill, Keerbergen. No. 1274, St. Christopher's Church, Racour. No. 1275, Virelles Lake, Chimay.

1987, June 13

1271 A544 13fr multicolored	1.00	.55
1272 A544 13fr multicolored	1.00	.55
1273 A544 13fr multicolored	1.00	.55
1274 A544 13fr multicolored	1.00	.55
1275 A544 13fr multicolored	1.00	.55
Nos. 1271-1275 (5)	5.00	2.75

Royal Belgian Rowing Assoc., Cent. — A545

European Volleyball Championships A546

1987, Sept. 5

1276 A545 9fr multicolored	.50	.38
1277 A546 13fr multicolored	.75	.55

Foreign Trade Year — A547

1987, Sept. 12

1278 A547 13fr multi	.75	.55

Belgian Social Reform, Cent. — A548

1987, Sept. 19

1279 A548 26fr Leisure, by P. Paulus	1.45	1.10

Youth Philately A549

1987, Oct. 3

1280 A549 9fr multi	.50	.38

Newspaper Centennials A550

1987, Dec. 12

1281 A550 9fr Le Soir .55 .42
1282 A550 9fr Hett Lattste Nieuws, vert. .55 .42

The Sea — A551

Designs: a, Lighthouse, trawler, rider and mount. b, Trawler, youths playing volleyball on beach. c, Cruise ship, sailboat, beach and cabana. d, Shore, birds.

1988, Feb. 6 Photo. *Perf. 11½*

1283 Strip of 4 + label 2.50 1.80
a.-d. A551 10fr any single .62 .45

No. 1283 has a continuous design.

Dynamism of the Regions A552

1988, Mar. 5 Photo. *Perf. 11½*

1284 A552 13fr Operation Athena .80 .58
1285 A552 13fr Flanders Alive Campaign .80 .58

Stamp Day — A553

Europa 1988 — A554

Painting: 19th Cent. Postman, by James Thiriar.

1988, Apr. 16 Photo. & Engr.

1286 A553 13fr buff & sepia .80 .58

1988, May 9 Photo. *Perf. 11½*

Transport and communication.

1287 A554 13fr Satellite dish 1.10 .58
1288 A554 24fr Non-polluting combustion engine 1.90 1.10

Tourism A555

Designs: No. 1289, Romanesque watchtower, ca. 12th-13th cent., Amay, vert. No. 1290, Our Lady of Hanswijk Basilica, 988, Mechelen, vert. No. 1291, St. Sernin's Church, 16th cent., Waimes. No. 1292, Old Town Hall, 1637, and village water pump, 1761, Peer, vert. No. 1293, Our Lady of Bon-Secours Basilica, 1892, Peruwelz.

Photo. & Engr.

1988, June 20 *Perf. 11½*

1289 A555 9fr beige & blk .50 .38
1290 A555 9fr lt blue & blk .50 .38
1291 A555 9fr pale blue grn & blk .50 .38
1292 A555 13fr pale pink & blk .75 .55
1293 A555 13fr pale gray & blk .75 .55
Nos. 1289-1293 (5) 3.00 2.24

Our Lady of Hanswijk Basilica millennium (No. 1290); Waimes village, 1100th anniv. (No. 1291).

Jean Monnet (1888-1979), French Economist — A556

Tapestry in the Hall of the Royal Academy of Medicine — A557

1988, Sept. 12 *Perf. 11½*

1294 A556 13fr black .70 .52

1988, Sept. 17 Photo.

Academies building and: No. 1296, Lyre, quill pen, open book and atomic symbols.

1295 A557 9fr shown .50 .38
1296 A557 9fr multi .50 .38

Royal Academy of Medicine (#1295); Royal Academy of Science, Literature and Fine Arts (#1296).

Cultural Heritage A558

Artifacts: 9fr, Statue and mask in the Antwerp Ethnographical Museum. 13fr, Sarcophagus, St. Martin's Church, Trazegnies. 24fr, Church organ, Geraardsbergen. 26fr, Shrine, St. Hadelin's Church, Vise.

1988, Sept. 24

1297 A558 9fr multi .50 .38
1298 A558 13fr multi .70 .52
1299 A558 24fr multi 1.30 1.00
1300 A558 26fr multi 1.40 1.05
Nos. 1297-1300 (4) 3.90 2.95

Youth Philately A559

1988, Oct. 10

1301 A559 9fr multi .50 .38

Natl. Postal Savings Bank, 75th Anniv. A560

1988, Nov. 7

1302 A560 13fr multi .70 .52

Christmas 1988 and New Year 1989 — A561

1988, Nov. 21

1303 A561 9fr Winter landscape .50 .38

Royal Mounted Guard, 50th Anniv. A562

1988, Dec. 12

1304 A562 13fr multi .75 .55

Printing Presses A563

Designs: 9fr, J. Moretus I, Antwerp Museum, vert. 24fr, Stanhope, Printing Museum, Brussels, vert. 26fr, Litho Krause, Royal Museum, Mariemont.

1988, Dec. 19 Engr.

1305 A563 9fr bl blk & blk .52 .40
1306 A563 24fr dark red brn 1.40 1.05
1307 A563 26fr grn & slate grn 1.50 1.15
Nos. 1305-1307 (3) 3.42 2.60

Lace — A564

1989, Mar. 20 Photo.

1308 A564 9fr Marche-en-Famenne .50 .38
1309 A564 13fr Brussels .70 .52
1310 A564 13fr Brugge .70 .52
Nos. 1308-1310 (3) 1.90 1.42

Stamp Day — A565

1989, Apr. 24 Photo. & Engr.

1311 A565 13fr Mail coach, post chaise .75 .55

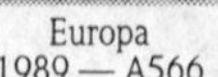

Europa 1989 — A566

Royal Academy of Fine Arts, Antwerp, 325th Anniv. — A567

Children's toys.

1989, May 8 Photo.

1312 A566 13fr Marbles, horiz. .75 .52
1313 A566 24fr Jumping-jack 1.35 1.00

1989, May 22 *Perf. 11½*

1314 A567 13fr multi .75 .52

European Parliament 3rd Elections — A568

Illustration reduced.

1989, June 5 Photo.

1315 A568 13fr Brussels .75 .52

Declaration of Rights of Man and the Citizen, Bicent. — A569

1989, June 12 *Perf. 11½*

1316 A569 13fr multi + label .75 .52

Tourism A570

Designs: No. 1317, St. Tillo's Church, Izegem. No. 1318, Logne Castle, Ferrieres. No. 1319, St. Laurentius's Church, Lokeren. No. 1320, Antoing Castle, Antoing. Nos. 1318-1320 vert.

1989, June 26 Photo. & Engr.

1317 A570 9fr shown .50 .38
1318 A570 9fr multi .50 .38
1319 A570 13fr multi .75 .52
1320 A570 13fr multi .75 .52
Nos. 1317-1320 (4) 2.50 1.80

Ducks — A571

1989, Sept. 4 Photo. *Perf. 12*

Booklet Stamps

1321 A571 13fr Mallard (8a) 1.25 .50
1322 A571 13fr Winter teal (8b) 1.25 .50
1323 A571 13fr Shoveller (8c) 1.25 .50
1324 A571 13fr Pintail (8d) 1.25 .50
a. Bklt. pane of 4, #1321-1324 5.00

Shigefusa Uesugi, a Seated Japanese Warrior, 13th Cent. A572

1989, Sept. 18 *Perf. 11½*

1325 A572 24fr multicolored 1.50 .50

Europalia.

Education League, 125th Anniv. — A573

1989, Sept. 25

1326 A573 13fr multicolored .80 .20

Treaty of London, 150th Anniv. — A574

Mr. Nibbs — A575

1989, Oct. 2 **Photo.**
1327 A574 13fr Map of Limburg Provinces .80 .20

See Netherlands No. 750.

1989, Oct. 9 ***Perf. 11½***
1328 A575 9fr multicolored .60 .20

Youth philately promotion.

Christmas, New Year 1990 A576

1989, Nov. 20 **Photo.**
1329 A576 9fr Salvation Army band .60 .15

Fr. Damien (1840-89), Missionary, Molokai Is. Leper Colony, Hawaii A577

1989, Nov. 27 **Photo.**
1330 A577 24fr multicolored 1.50 .50

Father Adolf Daens — A578

1989, Dec. 11 **Photo. & Engr.**
1331 A578 9fr pale & dk grn .55 .15

The Young Post Rider, an Engraving by Albrecht Durer A579

Ghent Flower Festival A580

1990, Jan. 12 **Photo. & Engr.**
1332 A579 14fr buff & red blk .75 .55

Postal communications in Europe, 500th anniv.
See Austria No. 1486, Germany No. 1592, Berlin No. 9N584 and German Democratic Republic No. 2791.

1990, Mar. 3 **Photo.**
1333 A580 10fr *Iris florentina* .55 .40
1334 A580 14fr *Cattleya harrisoniana* .75 .55
1335 A580 14fr *Lilium bulbiferum* .75 .55
Nos. 1333-1335 (3) 2.05 1.50

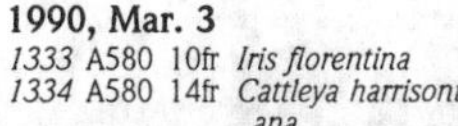

Intl. Women's Day — A581

1990, Mar. 12 **Photo.** ***Perf. 11½***
1336 A581 25fr Emilienne Brunfaut 1.45 1.05

Wheelchair Basketball — A582

Sports.

1990, Mar. 19
1337 A582 10fr multicolored .58 .42
1338 A582 14fr multicolored .80 .60
1339 A582 25fr shown 1.45 1.05
Nos. 1337-1339 (3) 2.83 2.07

Special Olympics (10fr); and 1990 World Cup Soccer Championships, Italy (14fr).

Natl. Water Supply Soc., 75th Anniv. A583

1990, Apr. 2
1340 A583 14fr Water means life .80 .60

Postman Roulin, by Van Gogh — A584

1990, Apr. 9
1341 A584 14fr multicolored .80 .60

Stamp Day.

Labor Day, Cent. A585

1990, Apr. 30
1342 A585 25fr multicolored 1.45 1.05

Europa 1990 A586

Post offices.

1990, May 7 **Photo. & Engr.**
1343 A586 14fr Ostend 1 .80 .60
1344 A586 25fr Liege 1, vert. 1.45 1.05

18-Day Campaign, 1940 — A587

1990, May 14 **Photo.** ***Perf. 11½***
1345 A587 14fr Lys Monument, Courtrai .80 .60

Resistance of German occupation.

Stamp Collecting Promotion Type of 1988
Souvenir Sheet

Various flowers from *Sixty Roses for a Queen,* by P.J. Redoute (1759-1840): a, *Rose tricolore.* b, Belle Rubaree. c, *Mycrophylla.* d, Amelie rose. e, Adelaide rose. f, Helene rose.

1990, June 2 **Photo. & Engr.**
1346 Sheet of 6 22.50 22.50
a.-c. SP487 14fr any single .80 .60
d.-f. SP487 25fr any single 1.45 1.05

BELGICA '90, Brussels, June 2-10. sold for 220fr.

Battle of Waterloo, 1815 — A588

Design: Marshal Ney leading the French cavalry. (Illustration reduced).

1990, June 18 **Photo.**
1352 A588 25fr multi + label 1.60 1.15

Tourism A589

1990, July 9
1353 A589 10fr Antwerp .58 .45
1354 A589 10fr Dendermonde .58 .45
1355 A589 14fr Gerpinnes, vert. .80 .60
1356 A589 14fr Lommel .80 .60
1357 A589 14fr Watermael .80 .60
Nos. 1353-1357 (5) 3.56 2.70

A590

A590a

King Baudouin A590b

1990-92 **Photo.** ***Perf. 11½***
1364 A590 14fr multicolored .80 .60
1365 A590a 15fr rose car .85 .65
1366 A590a 28fr blue green 1.75 1.30
1367 A590b 100fr slate green 6.00 1.50
Nos. 1364-1367 (4) 9.40 4.05

Issue dates: 14fr, Sept. 7; 15fr, Apr. 1; 28fr, Aug. 3, 1992; 100fr, Sept. 14, 1992.

Fish — A591

Designs: No. 1383, Perch (Perche). No. 1384, Minnow (Vairon). No. 1385, Bitterling (Bouviere). No. 1386, Stickleback (Epinoche).

1990, Sept. 8 ***Perf. 12***
1383 A591 14fr multicolored 1.25 .60
1384 A591 14fr multicolored 1.25 .60
1385 A591 14fr multicolored 1.25 .60
1386 A591 14fr multicolored 1.25 .60
a. Bklt. pane of 4, #1383-1386 5.00

Youth Philately A592

1990, Oct. 13 ***Perf. 11½***
1387 A592 10fr multicolored .58 .45

St. Bernard, 900th Birth Anniv. — A593

1990, Nov. 5 **Photo & Engr.**
1388 A593 25fr black & buff 1.45 1.10

Winter Scene by Jozef Lucas A594

1990, Nov. 12 **Photo.**
1389 A594 10fr .58 .42

Christmas.

Self-Portrait A595

Paintings by David Teniers (1610-1690).

1990, Dec. 3
1390 A595 10fr shown .58 .42
1391 A595 14fr Dancers .82 .62
1392 A595 25fr Bowlers 1.45 1.10
Nos. 1390-1392 (3) 2.85 2.14

15-Cent Minimum Value
The minimum value for a single stamp is 15 cents. This value reflects the costs of handling inexpensive stamps.

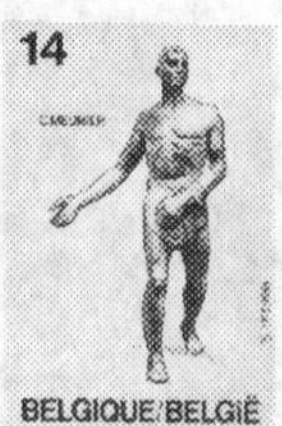

A596

A597

Designs: 14fr, The Sower by Constantin Meunier (1831-1905). 25fr, Brabo Fountain by Jef Lambeaux (1852-1908).

Photo. & Engr.

1991, Mar. 18 *Perf.* $11^1/_2$

1393	A596	14fr buff & blk	.82	.62
1394	A596	25fr lt bl & dk bl	1.45	1.10

1991, Apr. 8 **Photo.** *Perf.* $11^1/_2$

1395	A597	10fr Rhythmic gymnastics	.65	.50
1396	A597	10fr Korfball	.65	.50

No. 1395, European Youth Olympics. No. 1396, Korfball World Championships.

Stamp Printing Office, Mechlin — A598

1991, Apr. 22

1397	A598	14fr multicolored	.90	.65

Stamp Day.

Liberal Trade Union, Cent. A599

1991, Apr. 29

1398	A599	25fr blue & lt blue	1.50	1.15

Europa A600

1991, May 6

1399	A600	14fr Olympus-1 satellite	.90	.65
1400	A600	25fr Hermes space shuttle	1.50	1.15

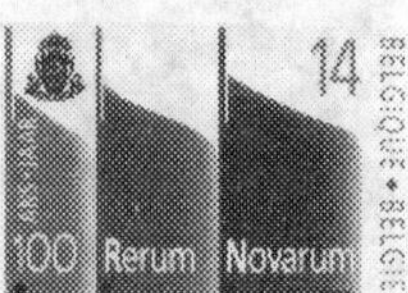

Rerum Novarum Encyclical, Cent. A601

1991, May 13 **Photo.** *Perf.* $11^1/_2$

1401	A601	14fr multicolored	.85	.65

Princess Isabel & Philip le Bon — A602

1991, May 27 **Photo.** *Perf.* $11^1/_2$

1402	A602	14fr multicolored	.85	.65

Europalia '91. See Portugal No. 1861.

Tourism A603

Designs: No. 1403, Neptune's Grotto, Couvin. No. 1404, Dieleghem Abbey, Jette. No. 1405, Town Hall, Niel, vert. No. 1406, Nature Reserve, Hautes Fagnes. No. 1407, Legend of giant Rolarius, Roeselare, vert.

1991, June 17 **Photo. & Engr.**

1403	A603	14fr multicolored	.85	.65
1404	A603	14fr multicolored	.85	.65
1405	A603	14fr multicolored	.85	.65
1406	A603	14fr multicolored	.85	.65
1407	A603	14fr multicolored	.85	.65
		Nos. 1403-1407 (5)	4.25	3.25

King Baudouin, Coronation, 40th Anniv. and 60th Birthday A604

1991, June 24 **Photo.**

1408	A604	14fr multicolored	.85	.65

Royal Academy of Medicine, 150th Anniv. — A605

Photo. & Engr.

1991, Sept. 2 *Perf.* $11^1/_2$

1409	A605	10fr multicolored	.65	.50

The English Coast at Dover by Alfred W. Finch (1854-1930) — A606

1991, Sept. 9 **Photo.**

1410	A606	25fr multicolored	1.50	1.15

See Finland Nos. 868-869.

Mushrooms — A607

1991, Sept. 16 **Photo.** *Perf. 12*

Booklet Stamps

1411	A607	14fr Amanita phalloides (13A)	1.25	.65
1412	A607	14fr Amanita rubescens (13B)	1.25	.65
1413	A607	14fr Boletus erythropus (13C)	1.25	.65
1414	A607	14fr Hygrocybe persistens (13D)	1.25	.65
a.		Bklt. pane of 4, #1411-1414	5.00	

Doctors Without Borders A608

Design: No. 1415, Amnesty Intl.

1991, Sept. 23 *Perf.* $11^1/_2$

1415	A608	25fr multicolored	1.50	1.15
1416	A608	25fr multicolored	1.50	1.15

Telecom '91 — A609

1991, Oct. 7 **Photo.** *Perf.* $11^1/_2$

1417	A609	14fr multicolored	.90	.70

6th World Forum and Exposition on Telecommunications, Geneva, Switzerland.

Youth Philately — A610

Cartoon characters: No. 1418, Blake and Mortimer, by Edgar P. Jacobs (16a). No. 1419, Cori the ship boy, by Bob De Moor (16b). No. 1420, Cities of the Fantastic, by Francois Schuiten (16c). No. 1421, Boule and Bill, by Jean Roba (16d).

1991, Oct. 14 *Perf. 12*

Booklet Stamps

1418	A610	14fr multicolored	.90	.70
1419	A610	14fr multicolored	.90	.70
1420	A610	14fr multicolored	.90	.70
1421	A610	14fr multicolored	.90	.70
a.		Bklt. pane of 4, #1418-1421	3.60	

Belgian Newspapers, Cent. A611

1991, Nov. 4 **Photo.** *Perf.* $11^1/_2$

1422	A611	10fr Gazet Van Antwerpen	.65	.50
1423	A611	10fr Het Volk	.65	.50

Icon of Madonna and Child, Chevetogne Abbey — A612

1991, Nov. 25 **Photo.** *Perf.* $11^1/_2$

1424	A612	10fr multicolored	.65	.50

Christmas.

Wolfgang Amadeus Mozart, Death Bicent. — A613

1991, Dec. 2 **Photo.** *Perf.* $11^1/_2$

1425	A613	25fr multicolored	1.70	1.30

A614

A615

1992, Feb. 10 **Photo.** *Perf.* $11^1/_2$

1426	A614	14fr Fire fighting	.80	.60

1992, Feb. 24

1427	A615	14fr multicolored	.80	.60

Belgian resistance in WWII.

Belgian Carpet Industry — A616

Antwerp Diamond Club, Cent. A617

Design: 14fr, Chef's hat, cutlery.

1992, Mar. 9

1428	A616	10fr multicolored	.55	.42
1429	A616	14fr multicolored	.80	.60
1430	A617	27fr multicolored	1.50	1.15
		Nos. 1428-1430 (3)	2.85	2.17

Belgian Association of Master Chefs.

Expo '92, Seville A618

1992, Mar. 23

1431	A618	14fr multicolored	.80	.60

Bird Type of 1985

1992-94 **Photo.** *Perf.* $11^1/_2$

1432	A524	1fr	Sizerin flamme	.15	.15
1433	A524	2fr	Merle noir	.15	.15
1435	A524	4fr	Bergeronette grise	.25	.15
1436	A524	5fr	Hirondelle de cheminee	.32	.15
1436A	A524	5.50fr	Geai des chenes	.30	.22
1437	A524	6fr	Cincle flongeur	.35	.15
1437A	A524	6.50fr	Phragmite des jongs	.45	.30
1438	A524	7fr	Loriot	.45	.15
1439	A524	8fr	Mesange charbonniere	.45	.15
1442	A524	10fr	Verdier	.58	.15
1444	A524	11fr	Troglodyte mignon	.65	.15

1446 A524 13fr Moineau domestique .70 .18
1447 A524 16fr Jaseur boreal .90 .22
Nos. 1432-1447 (13) 5.70
Set value .70

Issued: 11fr, 4/1/92; 1fr, 2fr, 6fr, 8fr, 10fr, 6/92; 4fr, 5fr, 7fr, 9/7/92; 5.50fr, 9/27/93; 13fr, 16fr, 1/3/94; 6.50fr, 10/3/94.
This is an expanding set. Numbers may change.

Jean Van Noten (1903-1982), Stamp Designer — A619

Photo. & Engr.

1992, Apr. 13 ***Perf. 11½***
1448 A619 15fr ver & black .90 .70

Stamp Day.

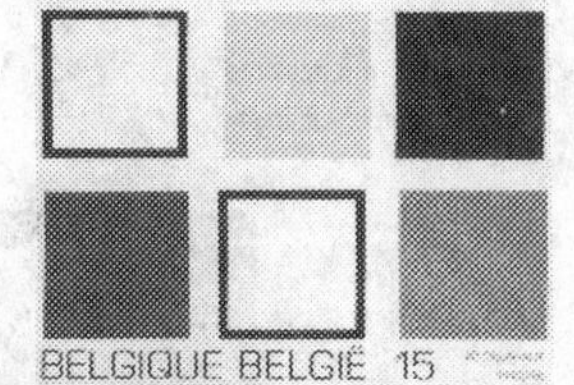

Abstract Painting by Jo Delahaut — A620

Design: No. 1449, Witte Magie No. 6, by Roger Raveel, vert.

1992, Apr. 27 **Photo.** ***Perf. 11½***
1449 A620 15fr multicolored .85 .65
1450 A620 15fr multicolored .85 .65

Discovery of America, 500th Anniv. — A621

1992, May 4
1451 A621 15fr shown .85 .65
1452 A621 28fr 500, globe, astrolabe 1.60 1.20

Europa.

Fight Racism — A622

1992, May 18 **Photo.** ***Perf. 11½***
1453 A622 15fr black, gray & pink .90 .70

Paintings from Orsay Museum, Paris — A623

Paintings by Belgian artists: 11fr, The Hamlet, by Jacob Smits. 15fr, The Bath, by Alfred Stevens. 30fr, The Man at the Helm, by Theo Van Rysselberghe.

1992, June 15 **Photo.** ***Perf. 11½***
1454 A623 11fr multicolored .65 .48
1455 A623 15fr multicolored .90 .70
1456 A623 30fr multicolored 1.75 1.35
Nos. 1454-1456 (3) 3.30 2.53

Tourism — A624

Designs: No. 1457, Manneken Pis Fountain, Brussels. No. 1458, Landcommander Castle Alden Biesen, Bilzen, horiz. No. 1459, Building facade, Andenne. No. 1460, Fools' Monday Carnival, Renaix, horiz. No. 1461, Great Procession, Tournai, horiz.

Photo. & Engr.

1992, July 6 ***Perf. 11½***
1457 A624 15fr multicolored .90 .70
1458 A624 15fr multicolored .90 .70
1459 A624 15fr multicolored .90 .70
1460 A624 15fr multicolored .90 .70
1461 A624 15fr multicolored .90 .70
Nos. 1457-1461 (5) 4.50 3.50

Village of Andenne, 1300th anniv. (#1459). Grand Procession of Tournai, 900th anniv. (#1461).

Animals — A625

1992, Sept. 7 **Photo.** ***Perf. 12***

Booklet Stamps

1462 A625 15fr Polecat (13a) 1.05 .80
1463 A625 15fr Squirrel (13b) 1.05 .80
1464 A625 15fr Hedgehog (13c) 1.05 .80
1465 A625 15fr Dormouse (13d) 1.05 .80
a. Bklt. pane of 4, #1462-1465 4.25

Brabant Revolution — A626

Design: 15fr, Troops fighting and Henri Van der Noot, Jean Andre Van der Meersch, and Jean Francois Vonck, rebel leaders.

Photo. & Engr.

1992, Sept. 21 ***Perf. 11½***
1466 A626 15fr multicolored .90 .70

Arms of Thurn and Taxis — A627

1992, Oct. 5 **Photo.** ***Perf. 11½***
1467 A627 15fr multicolored .90 .70

Gaston Lagaffe, by Andre Franquin — A628

1992, Oct. 12
1468 A628 15fr multicolored .90 .70

Youth philately.

Single European Market — A629

1992, Oct. 26
1469 A629 15fr multicolored .90 .70

Antwerp Zoo, 150th Anniv. — A630

1992, Nov. 16
1470 A630 15fr Okapi .90 .70
1471 A630 30fr Tamarin 1.80 1.40

The Brussels Place Royale in Winter, by Luc De Decker — A631

1992, Nov. 23
1472 A631 11fr multicolored .70 .52

Christmas.

History — A632

Designs: 11fr, Council of Leptines, 1250th anniv.. 15fr, 28fr, Missale Romanum of Matthias Corvinus (Matyas Hunyadi, King of Hungary) (diff. details). 30fr, Battles of Neerwinden (1693, 1793).

1993, Mar. 15 **Photo.** ***Perf. 11½***
1473 A632 11fr multicolored .65 .48
1474 A632 15fr multicolored .90 .70
1475 A632 30fr multicolored 1.80 1.35
Nos. 1473-1475 (3) 3.35 2.53

Souvenir Sheet

1476 A632 28fr multicolored 1.75 1.30

Size of No. 1474, 80x28mm. No. 1476 contains one 55x40mm stamp.
See Hungary No. 3385-3386.

A633

A634

Antwerp, Cultural City of Europe — A635

Designs: No. 1477, Panoramic view of Antwerp (illustration reduced). No. 1478, Antwerp Town Hall, designed by Cornelis Floris. No. 1479, Woman's Head and Warrior's Torso, by Jacob Jordaens. No. 1480, St. Job's Altar (detail), Schoonbroek. No. 1481, Angels on stained glass window, Mater Dei Chapel of Institut Marie-Josee, by Eugeen Yoors, vert.

1993, Mar. 22
1477 A633 15fr multicolored .90 .70
1478 A634 15fr multicolored .90 .70
1479 A635 15fr gray & multi .90 .70
1480 A635 15fr green & multi .90 .70
1481 A635 15fr blue & multi .90 .70
Nos. 1477-1481 (5) 4.50 3.50

Antwerp '93.

Stamp Day — A636

1993, Apr. 5
1482 A636 15fr No. 74 .90 .70

Contemporary Paintings — A637

Europa: 15fr, Florence 1960, by Gaston Bertrand. 28fr, De Sjees, by Constant Permeke.

1993, Apr. 26 **Photo.** ***Perf. 11½***
1483 A637 15fr multicolored .90 .70
1484 A637 28fr multicolored 1.70 1.35

Butterflies — A638

1993, May 10
1485 A638 15fr Vanessa atalanta .90 .70
1486 A638 15fr Apatura iris .90 .70
1487 A638 15fr Inachis io .90 .70
1488 A638 15fr Aglais urticae .90 .70
Nos. 1485-1488 (4) 3.60 2.80

Alumni Assoc. (UAE), Free University of Brussels, 150th Anniv. A639

1993, May 17

1489 A639 15fr blue & black .90 .70

Europalia '93 — A640

1993, May 24

1490 A640 15fr Mayan statuette .90 .70

Folklore A641

Designs: 11fr, Ommegang Procession, Brussels. 15fr, Royal Moncrabeau Folk Group, Namur. 28fr, Stilt walkers of Merchtem, vert.

1993, June 7 Photo. *Perf. 11½*

1491 A641 11fr multicolored .65 .48
1492 A641 15fr multicolored .90 .70
1493 A641 28fr multicolored 1.65 1.30
Nos. 1491-1493 (3) 3.20 2.48

Tourism A642

Castles: No. 1494, La Hulpe. No. 1495, Cortewalle (Beveren). No. 1496, Jehay. No. 1497, Arenberg (Heverlee), vert. No. 1498, Raeren.

Photo. & Engr.

1993, June 21 *Perf. 11½*

1494 A642 15fr pale green & black .90 .70
1495 A642 15fr pale lilac & black .90 .70
1496 A642 15fr pale blue & black .90 .70
1497 A642 15fr pale brown & black .90 .70
1498 A642 15fr pale olive & black .90 .70
Nos. 1494-1498 (5) 4.50 3.50

Intl. Triennial Exhibition of Tournai A643

1993, July 5 Photo. *Perf. 11½*

1499 A643 15fr black, blue & red .90 .70

Belgian Presidency of European Community Council A644

1993, Aug. 9 Photo. *Perf. 11½*

1500 A644 15fr multicolored .90 .70

Rene Magritte (1898-1967), Artist A645

1993, Aug. 9

1501 A645 30fr multicolored 1.75 1.40

King Baudouin (1930-1993) — A646

1993, Aug. 17 Photo. *Perf. 11½*

1502 A646 15fr black & gray .90 .70

European House Cats — A647

1993, Sept. 6 Photo. *Perf. 12*

Booklet Stamps

1503 A647 15fr Brown & white (10a) .90 .70
1504 A647 15fr Black & white (10b) .90 .70
1505 A647 15fr Gray tabby (10c) .90 .70
1506 A647 15fr Calico (10d) .90 .70
a. Booklet pane of 4, #1503-1506 3.75

Publication of De Humani Corporis Fabrica, by Andreas Vesalius, 1543 — A648

1993, Oct. 4 Photo. *Perf. 11½*

1507 A648 15fr multicolored .90 .70

Air Hostess Natacha, by Francois Walthery — A649

1993, Oct. 18

1508 A649 15fr multicolored .85 .65

Youth philately.

Publication of "Faux Soir," 50th Anniv. — A650

1993, Nov. 8 Photo. *Perf. 11½*

1509 A650 11fr multicolored .60 .45

Notre-Dame de la Chapelle, Brussels A651

1993, Nov. 22 Photo. *Perf. 11½*

1510 A651 11fr multicolored .65 .48

Christmas, New Year.

Children, Future Decisionmakers — A652

1993, Dec. 13 Photo. *Perf. 11½*

1511 A652 15fr multicolored .90 .70

King Albert II

A653 A654

1993-95 Photo. *Perf. 11½*

1519 A653 16fr lt gray & multi .95 .25
1520 A653 16fr lt & dk blue green 1.00 .75
1522 A653 20fr cream & brown 1.25 .32
1526 A653 30fr red lilac 1.65 .40
1527 A653 32fr cream & org brn 1.90 .48
1528 A653 40fr pink & carmine 2.50 .60
1529 A653 50fr green 3.00 .75
1533 A654 100fr multicolored 6.25 4.75
1535 A654 200fr multicolored 14.00 3.50
Nos. 1519-1535 (9) 32.50 11.80

Issued: No. 1519, 12/15/93; No. 1520, 1/17/94; 30fr, 2/4/94; 32fr, 3/7/94; 50fr, 4/18/94; 20fr, 6/6/94; 40fr, 6/20/94; 100fr, 10/3/94; 200fr, 5/2/95.

This is part of an expanding set. Numbers may change.

Paintings A656

Designs: No. 1537, The Malleable Darkness, by Octave Landuyt. No. 1538, Ma Toute Belle, by Serge Vandercam, vert.

1994, Jan. 31 Photo. *Perf. 11½*

1537 A656 16fr multicolored .90 .70
1538 A656 16fr multicolored .90 .70

Airplanes A657

Designs: 13fr, Hanriot-Dupont HD-1. 15fr, Spad XIII. 30fr, Schreck FBA-H. 32fr, Stampe-Vertongen SV-4B.

1994, Feb. 28

1539 A657 13fr multicolored .70 .52
1540 A657 15fr multicolored .85 .65
1541 A657 30fr multicolored 1.65 1.25
1542 A657 32fr multicolored 1.75 1.40
Nos. 1539-1542 (4) 4.95 3.82

Daily Newspapers A658

Designs: No. 1543, "Le Jour-Le Courier," cent., vert. No. 1544, "La Wallonie," 75th anniv.

1994, Mar. 21 Photo. *Perf. 11½*

1543 A658 16fr multicolored .95 .70
1544 A658 16fr multicolored .95 .70

Fall of the Golden Calf (Detail), by Fernand Allard l'Olivier — A659

1994, Mar. 28

1545 A659 16fr multicolored .95 .70

Charter of Quaregnon, cent.

Stamp Day — A660

1994, Apr. 11 Photo. *Perf. 11½*

1546 A660 16fr No. 102 .95 .70

History A661

Scenes from Brabantse Yeesten, 15th cent. illuminated manuscript: 13fr, Reconciliation between John I and Arnold, squire of Wezemaal. 16fr, Tournament at wedding of John II and Margaret of York. 30fr, Battle of Woeringen.

1994, Apr. 25

1547 A661 13fr multicolored .75 .55
1548 A661 16fr multicolored .95 .70
1549 A661 30fr multicolored 1.75 1.25
Nos. 1547-1549 (3) 3.45 2.50

No. 1549 is 81x28mm.

Europa — A662

Designs: 16fr, Abbe Georges Lemaitre (1894-1966), proposed "big-bang" theory of origins of universe. 30fr, Gerardus Mercator (1512-94), cartographer, astronomer.

1994, May 9 Photo. *Perf. 11½*

1550 A662 16fr multicolored .95 .70
1551 A662 30fr multicolored 1.75 1.25

Papal Visit A663

Designs: No. 1552, Father Damien (1840-89). No. 1553, St. Mutien-Marie (1841-1917), Christian educator.

1994, May 16 *Perf. 11½x12*

1552	A663	16fr multicolored	.95	.70
1553	A663	16fr multicolored	.95	.70

Tourism
A664

Churches: No. 1554, St. Peter's, Bertem. No. 1555, St. Bavo's, Kanegem, vert. No. 1556, Royal St. Mary's, Schaarbeek. No. 1557, St. Gery's, Aubechies. No. 1558, Sts. Peter and Paul, Saint-Severin, Condroz, vert.

1994, June 13 **Photo.** *Perf. 11½*

1554	A664	16fr multicolored	.95	.70
1555	A664	16fr multicolored	.95	.70
1556	A664	16fr multicolored	.95	.70
1557	A664	16fr multicolored	.95	.70
1558	A664	16fr multicolored	.95	.70
		Nos. 1554-1558 (5)	4.75	3.50

Guillaume Lekeu (1870-94), Composer
A665

Design: No. 1560, Detail of painting by Hans Memling (c.1430-94).

1994, Aug. 16 **Photo.** *Perf. 11½*

1559	A665	16fr multicolored	1.10	.75
1560	A665	16fr multicolored	1.10	.75

Liberation of Belgium, 50th Anniv. — A666

Design: 16fr, General Crerar, Field Marshal Montgomery, Gen. Bradley, Belgium landscape. Illustration reduced.

1994, Sept. 5 **Photo.** *Perf. 11x11½*

1561	A666	16fr multicolored	.95	.70

Wildflowers — A667

Designs: No. 1562, Caltha palustris. No. 1563, Cephalanthera damasonium. No. 1564, Calystegia soldanella. No. 1565, Epipactis helleborine.

1994, Sept. 26 **Photo.** *Perf. 12*

Booklet Stamps

1562	A667	16fr multi (14a)	1.10	.75
1563	A667	16fr multi (14b)	1.10	.75
1564	A667	16fr multi (14c)	1.10	.75
1565	A667	16fr multi (14d)	1.10	.75
a.		Booklet pane of 4, #1562-1565	4.50	

Cubitus the Dog, by Luc Dupanloup — A668

1994, Oct. 10 *Perf. 11½*

1566	A668	16fr multicolored	1.10	.75

Youth philately.

Georges Simenon (1903-89), Writer
A669

Photo. & Engr.

1994, Oct. 17 *Perf. 11½*

1567	A669	16fr multicolored	1.10	.75

See France No. 2443, Switzerland No. 948.

Christmas
A670

1994, Dec. 5 **Photo.** *Perf. 11½*

1568	A670	13fr multicolored	.85	.65

Anniversaries and Events
A671

Designs: No. 1569, August Vermeylen Fund, 50th anniv. No. 1560, Belgian Touring Club, cent. No. 1561, Assoc. of Belgian Enterprises, cent. No. 1562, Dept. of Social Security, 50th anniv.

1995, Feb. 13 **Photo.** *Perf. 11½*

1569	A671	16fr multicolored	1.10	.75
1570	A671	16fr multicolored	1.10	.75
1571	A671	16fr multicolored	1.10	.75
1572	A671	16fr multicolored	1.10	.75
		Nos. 1569-1572 (4)	4.40	3.00

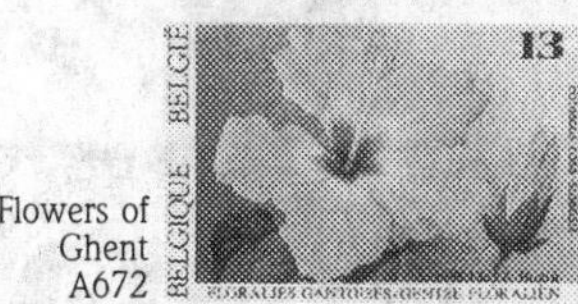

Flowers of Ghent
A672

1995, Mar. 6

1573	A672	13fr Hibiscus rosa-sinensis	.95	.70
1574	A672	16fr Rhododendron simsii	1.10	.75
1575	A672	30fr Fuchsia hybrida	2.25	1.65
		Nos. 1573-1575 (3)	4.30	3.10

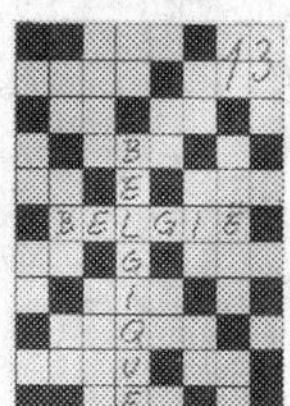

Games — A673

Stamp Day — A674

1995, Mar. 20

1576	A673	13fr Crossword puzzles	.95	.70
1577	A673	16fr Chess	1.10	.75
1578	A673	30fr Scrabble	2.25	1.65
1579	A673	34fr Cards	2.50	1.75
		Nos. 1576-1579 (4)	6.80	4.85

1995, Apr. 10 **Photo. & Engr.**

1580	A674	16fr Frans de Troyer	1.10	.75

Peace & Freedom
A675

Europa: 16fr, Broken barbed wire, prison guard tower. 30fr, Mushroom cloud, "Never again."

1995, Apr. 24 **Photo.** *Perf. 11½*

1581	A675	16fr multicolored	1.10	.75
1582	A675	30fr multicolored	2.25	1.75

Liberation of concentration camps, 50th anniv. (#1581). Nuclear Non-Proliferation Treaty, 25th anniv. (#1582).

Battle of Fontenoy, 250th Anniv. — A676

Design: 16fr, Irish soldiers, Cross of Fontenoy.

1995, May 15 **Photo.** *Perf. 11½*

1583	A676	16fr multicolored	1.10	.75

See Ireland No. 967.

UN, 50th Anniv.
A677

1995, May 22 **Photo.** *Perf. 11½*

1584	A677	16fr multicolored	1.10	.75

"Sauvagemont, Maransart," by Pierre Alechinsky — A678

Design: No. 1586: "Telegram-style," by Pol Mara.

1995, June 6

1585	A678	16fr multicolored	1.10	.75
1586	A678	16fr multicolored	1.10	.75

Tourism
A679

Architectural designs: No. 1587, Cauchie house, Brussels, by Paul Cauchie (1875-1952). No. 1588, De Viif Werelddelen, corner building, Antwerp, by Frans Smet-Verhas (1851-1925). No. 1589, House, Liege, by Paul Jaspar (1859-1945).

1995, June 26

1587 A679 16fr multicolored 1.10 .75
1588 A679 16fr multicolored 1.10 .75
1589 A679 16fr multicolored 1.10 .75
Nos. 1587-1589 (3) 3.30 2.25

Sailing Ships — A680

1995, Aug. 21 Photo. *Perf. 12*

Booklet Stamps

1590 A680 16fr Mercator 1.10 .80
1591 A680 16fr Kruzenstern 1.10 .80
1592 A680 16fr Sagres II 1.10 .80
1593 A680 16fr Amerigo Vespucci 1.10 .80
a. Booklet pane of 4, #1590-1593 4.50
Complete booklet, #1593a 4.50

Classic Motorcycles A681

1995, Sept. 25 Photo. *Perf. 11½*

1594 A681 13fr 1908 Minerva .90 .65
1595 A681 16fr 1913 FN, vert. 1.10 .80
1596 A681 30fr 1929 La Mondiale 2.00 1.50
1597 A681 32fr 1937 Gillet, vert. 2.25 1.65
Nos. 1594-1597 (4) 6.25 4.60

Comic Character, Sammy, by Arthur Berckmans A682

1995, Oct. 9 Photo. *Perf. 11½*

1598 A682 16fr multicolored 1.10 .80

Youth philately.

King's Day A683

Design: 16fr, King Albert II and Queen Paola.

1995, Nov. 15 Photo. *Perf. 11½*

1599 A683 16fr multicolored 1.10 .80

Christmas — A684

Design: 13fr, Nativity scene from "Breviary," book of devotions, c. 1500.

1995, Nov. 20

1600 A684 13fr multicolored .90 .70

SEMI-POSTAL STAMPS

Values quoted for Nos. B1-B24 are for stamps with label attached. Copies without label sell for one-tenth or less.

St. Martin of Tours Dividing His Cloak with a Beggar
SP1 SP2

Unwmk.

1910, June 1 Typo. *Perf. 14*

B1 SP1 1c gray 1.65 1.25
B2 SP1 2c purple brn 13.00 9.25
B3 SP1 5c peacock blue 3.50 2.50
B4 SP1 10c brown red 3.50 2.50
B5 SP2 1c gray green 3.50 2.50
B6 SP2 2c violet brn 10.00 7.25
B7 SP2 5c peacock blue 3.50 2.50
B8 SP2 10c carmine 3.50 2.50
Nos. B1-B8 (8) 42.15 30.25

Overprinted "1911" in Black

1911, Apr. 1

B9 SP1 1c gray 18.00 14.00
a. Inverted overprint
B10 SP1 2c purple brn 42.50 45.00
B11 SP1 5c peacock blue 5.00 4.00
B12 SP1 10c brown red 5.00 4.00
B13 SP2 1c gray green 35.00 35.00
B14 SP2 2c violet brn 32.50 27.50
B15 SP2 5c peacock blue 5.00 4.00
B16 SP2 10c carmine 5.00 4.00
Nos. B9-B16 (8) 148.00 137.50

Overprinted "CHARLEROI-1911"

1911, June

B17 SP1 1c gray 4.00 4.00
B18 SP1 2c purple brn 14.00 14.00
B19 SP1 5c peacock blue 6.50 6.50
B20 SP1 10c brown red 6.00 6.00
B21 SP2 1c gray green 4.00 4.00
B22 SP2 2c violet brn 13.00 13.00
B23 SP2 5c peacock blue 5.50 5.50
B24 SP2 10c carmine 4.00 4.00
Nos. B17-B24 (8) 57.00 57.00

Nos. B1-B24 were sold at double face value, except the 10c denominations which were sold for 15c. The surtax benefited the national anti-tuberculosis organization.

SP3

Merode Monument — SP4 King Albert I — SP5

1914, Oct. 3 Litho.

B25 SP3 5c green & red *1.65 2.00*
B26 SP3 10c red *.45 .50*
B27 SP3 20c violet & red *10.50 13.00*
Nos. B25-B27 (3) *12.60 15.50*

Counterfeits of Nos. B25-B27 abound. Probably as many as 90% of the stamps on the market are counterfeits. Competently certified copies sell for much more.

1914, Oct. 3

B28 SP4 5c green & red 4.50 5.00
B29 SP4 10c red 4.50 5.00
B30 SP4 20c violet & red 42.50 47.50
Nos. B28-B30 (3) 51.50 57.50

Counterfeits of Nos. B28-B30 abound. Probably as many as 90% of the stamps on the market are counterfeits. Competently certified copies sell for much more.

1915, Jan. 1 *Perf. 12, 14*

B31 SP5 5c green & red 5.00 3.00
a. Perf. 12x14 16.00 12.00
B32 SP5 10c rose & red 20.00 6.00
B33 SP5 20c violet & red 25.00 14.00
a. Perf. 14x12 500.00 250.00
b. Perf. 12 50.00 32.50
Nos. B31-B33 (3) 50.00 23.00

Nos. B25-B33 were sold at double face value. The surtax benefited the Red Cross.

Types of Regular Issue of 1915 Surcharged in Red:

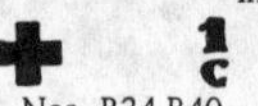

Nos. B34-B40 Nos. B41-B43

+ 1F

Nos. B44-B47

1918, Jan. 15 Typo. *Perf. 14*

B34 A46 1c + 1c dp orange .50 .50
B35 A46 2c + 2c brown .60 .60
B36 A46 5c + 5c blue grn 1.25 1.25
B37 A46 10c + 10c red 2.25 2.25
B38 A46 15c + 15c brt violet 3.25 3.25
B39 A46 20c + 20c plum 7.50 7.50
B40 A46 25c + 25c ultra 7.50 7.50

Engr.

B41 A47 35c + 35c lt vio & blk 10.00 10.00
B42 A48 40c + 40c dull red & blk 10.00 10.00
B43 A49 50c + 50c turq blue & blk 12.00 12.00
B44 A50 1fr + 1fr bluish slate 35.00 35.00
B45 A51 2fr + 2fr dp gray grn 100.00 100.00
B46 A52 5fr + 5fr brown 250.00 250.00
B47 A53 10fr + 10fr dp blue 500.00 500.00
Nos. B34-B47 (14) 939.85 939.85

Discus Thrower — SP6

Racing Chariot — SP7

Runner — SP8

1920, May 20 Engr. *Perf. 12*

B48 SP6 5c + 5c dp green 1.40 1.40
B49 SP7 10c + 5c carmine 1.40 1.40
B50 SP8 15c + 15c dk brown 3.00 3.00
Nos. B48-B50 (3) 5.80 5.80

7th Olympic Games, 1920. Surtax benefited wounded soldiers. Exists imperf.

For surcharges see Nos. 140-142.

Allegory: Asking Alms from the Crown — SP9

Wounded Veteran — SP10

1922, May 20

B51 SP9 20c + 20c brown 1.40 1.40

1923, July 5

B52 SP10 20c + 20c slate gray 1.75 1.75

Surtax on #B51-B52 was to aid wounded veterans.

SP11

SP12

St. Martin, by Van Dyck
SP13 SP14

1925, Dec. 15 Typo. *Perf. 14*

B53 SP11 15c + 15c dull vio & red .50 .20
B54 SP11 30c + 5c gray & red .25 .20
B55 SP11 1fr + 10c chalky blue & red 1.25 1.40
Nos. B53-B55 (3) 2.00 1.80

Surtax for the Natl. Anti-Tuberculosis League.

1926, Feb. 10

B56 SP12 30c + 30c bluish grn (red surch.) .50 .55
B57 SP13 1fr + 1fr lt blue 7.25 7.25
B58 SP14 1fr + 1fr lt blue 1.10 1.25
Nos. B56-B58 (3) 8.85 9.05

The surtax aided victims of the Meuse flood.

Lion and Cross of Lorraine
SP15

Queen Elisabeth and King Albert
SP16

1926, Dec. 6 Typo. *Perf. 14*

B59 SP15 5c + 5c dk brown .25 .20
B60 SP15 20c + 5c red brown .45 .40
B61 SP15 50c + 5c dull violet .30 .20

Engr. *Perf. 11½*

B62 SP16 1.50fr + 25c dk blue .75 .70
B63 SP16 5fr + 1fr rose red 6.50 6.00
Nos. B59-B63 (5) 8.25 7.50

Surtax was used to benefit tubercular war veterans.

Boat Adrift — SP17

1927, Dec. 15 Engr. *Perf. 11½, 14*

B64 SP17 25c + 10c dk brown .70 .70
B65 SP17 35c + 10c yel grn .70 .70
B66 SP17 60c + 10c dp violet .60 .40
B67 SP17 1.75fr + 25c dk blue 1.50 2.00
B68 SP17 5fr + 1fr plum 4.50 4.75
Nos. B64-B68 (5) 8.00 8.55

The surtax on these stamps was divided among several charitable associations.

Ogives of Orval Abbey — SP18

Monk Carving Capital of Column — SP19

Ruins of Orval Abbey — SP20

Design: 60c+15c, 1.75fr+25c, 3fr+1fr, Countess Matilda recovering her ring.

1928, Sept. 15 Photo. *Perf. 11½*

B69 SP18 5c + 5c red & gold .25 .30
B70 SP18 25c + 5c dk vio & gold .45 .50

Engr.

B71 SP19 35c + 10c dp green 1.10 1.10
B72 SP19 60c + 15c red brown 1.65 1.65
B73 SP19 1.75fr + 25c dk blue 3.50 3.50
B74 SP19 2fr + 40c dp violet 13.00 13.00
B75 SP19 3fr + 1fr red 15.00 15.00

Perf. 14

B76 SP20 5fr + 5fr rose lake 15.00 15.00
B77 SP20 10fr + 10fr ol green 15.00 15.00
Nos. B69-B77 (9) 64.95 65.05

Surtax for the restoration of the ruined Orval Abbey.

For overprints see Nos. B84-B92.

St. Waudru, Mons — SP22

St. Rombaut, Malines — SP23

Designs: 25c + 15c, Cathedral of Tournai. 60c + 15c, St. Bavon, Ghent. 1.75fr + 25c, St. Gudule, Brussels. 5fr + 5fr, Louvain Library.

1928, Dec. 1 Photo. *Perf. 14, 11½*

B78 SP22 5c + 5c carmine .20 .20
B79 SP22 25c + 15c ol brn .35 .38

Engr.

B80 SP23 35c + 10c dp green 1.25 1.25
B81 SP23 60c + 15c red brn .50 .25
B82 SP23 1.75fr + 25c vio blue 8.50 7.00
B83 SP23 5fr + 5fr red vio 16.00 15.00
Nos. B78-B83 (6) 26.80 24.08

The surtax was for anti-tuberculosis work.

Nos. B69-B77 with this overprint in blue or red was privately produced. They are for the laying of the 1st stone toward the restoration of the ruined Abbey of Orval. Forgeries of the overprint exist. Value, set, $650.

Waterfall at Coo — SP28

Bayard Rock, Dinant — SP29

Designs: 35c+10c, Menin Gate, Ypres. 60c+15c, Promenade d'Orleans, Spa. 1.75fr+25c, Antwerp Harbor. 5fr+5fr, Quai Vert, Bruges.

1929, Dec. 2 Engr. *Perf. 11½*

B93 SP28 5c + 5c red brown .20 .25
B94 SP29 25c + 15c gray blk .65 .60
B95 SP28 35c + 10c green .80 .95
B96 SP28 60c + 15c rose lake .55 .50
B97 SP28 1.75fr + 25c dp blue 4.50 4.50

Perf. 14

B98 SP29 5fr + 5fr dl vio 27.50 27.50
Nos. B93-B98 (6) 34.20 34.30

Bornhem — SP34

Beloeil — SP35

Gaesbeek
SP36

Designs: 25c + 15c, Wynendaele. 70c + 15c, Oydonck. 1fr + 25c, Ghent. 1.75fr + 25c, Bouillon.

1930, Dec. 1 Photo. *Perf. 14*

B99 SP34 10c + 5c violet .25 .30
B100 SP34 25c + 15c olive brn .60 .60

Engr.

B101 SP35 40c + 10c brown vio .80 1.00
B102 SP35 70c + 15c gray blk .55 .55
B103 SP35 1fr + 25c rose lake 3.50 3.50
B104 SP35 1.75fr + 25c dp blue 4.50 2.75
B105 SP36 5fr + 5fr gray grn 27.50 32.50
Nos. B99-B105 (7) 37.70 41.20

Prince Leopold
SP41

Queen Elisabeth
SP42

Philatelic Exhibition Issue

Souvenir Sheet

1931, July 18 Photo. *Perf. 14*

B106 SP41 2.45fr + 55c car brown 140.00 140.00

Sold exclusively at the Brussels Phil. Exhib., July 18-21, 1931. Size: 122x159mm. Surtax for the Veterans' Relief Fund.

The sheet normally has pin holes and a cancellation-like marking in the margin. These are considered unused and the condition valued here.

1931, Dec. 1 Engr.

B107 SP42 10c + 5c red brown .30 .52
B108 SP42 25c + 15c dk violet 1.10 1.25
B109 SP42 50c + 10c dk green .95 1.00
B110 SP42 75c + 15c black brn .90 .65
B111 SP42 1fr + 25c rose lake 6.75 6.00
B112 SP42 1.75fr + 25c ultra 4.75 4.00
B113 SP42 5fr + 5fr brown vio 55.00 55.00
Nos. B107-B113 (7) 69.75 68.42

The surtax was for the National Anti-Tuberculosis League.

Désiré Cardinal Mercier
SP43

Mercier Protecting Children and Aged at Malines
SP44

Mercier as Professor at Louvain University — SP45

Mercier in Full Canonicals, Giving His Blessing
SP46

1932, June 10 Photo. *Perf. 14½x14*

B114 SP43 10c + 10c dk violet .40 .60
B115 SP43 50c + 30c brt violet 2.25 2.50
B116 SP43 75c + 25c olive brn 2.25 2.25
B117 SP43 1fr + 2fr brown red 6.00 6.00

Engr. *Perf. 11½*

B118 SP44 1.75fr + 75c dp blue 70.00 82.50
B119 SP45 2.50fr + 2.50fr dk brn 70.00 70.00
B120 SP44 3fr + 4.50fr dull grn 70.00 70.00
B121 SP45 5fr + 20fr vio brn 80.00 82.50
B122 SP46 10fr + 40fr brn lake 175.00 210.00
Nos. B114-B122 (9) 475.90 526.35

Issued in commemoration of Cardinal Mercier and to obtain funds to erect a monument to his memory.

Belgian Infantryman
SP47

Sanatorium at Waterloo
SP48

1932, Aug. 4 *Perf. 14½x14*

B123 SP47 75c + 3.25fr red brn 55.00 55.00
B124 SP47 1.75fr + 4.25fr dk blue 55.00 55.00

Honoring Belgian soldiers who fought in WWI and to obtain funds to erect a natl. monument to their glory.

1932, Dec. 1 Photo. *Perf. 13½x14*

B125 SP48 10c + 5c dk vio .30 .90
B126 SP48 25c + 15c red vio 1.00 1.25
B127 SP48 50c + 10c red brn 1.00 1.25
B128 SP48 75c + 15c ol brn 1.00 .80
B129 SP48 1fr + 25c dp red 13.00 10.50
B130 SP48 1.75fr + 25c dp blue 10.50 9.25
B131 SP48 5fr + 5fr gray grn 85.00 90.00
Nos. B125-B131 (7) 111.80 113.95

Surtax for the assistance of the Natl. Anti-Tuberculosis Society at Waterloo.

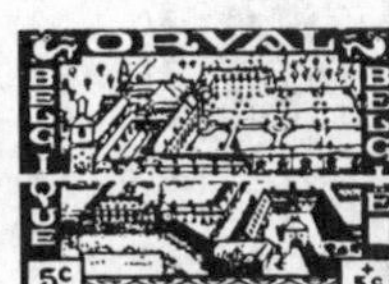

View of Old Abbey — SP49

Ruins of Old Abbey — SP50

Count de Chiny Presenting First Abbey to Countess Matilda
SP56

Restoration of Abbey in XVI and XVII Centuries SP57

Abbey in XVIII Century, Maria Theresa and Charles V — SP58

Madonna and Arms of Seven Abbeys — SP60

Designs: 25c+15c, Guests, courtyard, 50c+25c, Transept. 75c+50c, Bell Tower. 1fr+1.25fr, Fountain. 1.25fr+1.75fr, Cloisters. 5fr+20fr, Duke of Brabant placing 1st stone of new abbey.

1933, Oct. 15 *Perf. 14*

B132 SP49	5c + 5c dull grn		35.00	40.00
B133 SP50	10c + 15c ol grn		32.50	35.00
B134 SP49	25c + 15c dk brn		32.50	35.00
B135 SP50	50c + 25c red brn		32.50	35.00
B136 SP50	75c + 50c dp grn		32.50	35.00
B137 SP50	1fr + 1.25fr cop red		32.50	35.00
B138 SP49	1.25fr + 1.75fr gray blk		32.50	35.00
B139 SP56	1.75fr + 2.75fr blue		37.50	40.00
B140 SP57	2fr + 3fr mag		37.50	40.00
B141 SP58	2.50fr + 5fr dull brn		37.50	40.00
B142 SP56	5fr + 20fr vio		40.00	40.00

Perf. 11½

B143 SP60	10fr + 40fr blue		225.00	225.00
	Nos. B132-B143 (12)		607.50	635.00

The surtax was for a fund to aid in the restoration of Orval Abbey. Counterfeits exist.

"Tuberculosis Society" SP61

Peter Benoit SP62

1933, Dec. 1 **Engr.** *Perf. 14x13½*

B144 SP61	10c + 5c black	.85	.85
B145 SP61	25c + 15c violet	3.00	3.00
B146 SP61	50c + 10c red brn	2.25	2.25
B147 SP61	75c + 15c blk brn	9.25	9.00
B148 SP61	1fr + 25c claret	10.50	10.50
B149 SP61	1.75fr + 25c vio bl	12.50	12.50
B150 SP61	5fr + 5fr lilac	115.00	115.00
	Nos. B144-B150 (7)	153.35	153.10

The surtax was for anti-tuberculosis work.

1934, June 1 **Photo.**

B151 SP62	75c + 25c olive brn	5.50	5.50

The surtax was to raise funds for the Peter Benoit Memorial.

King Leopold III
SP63 SP64

1934, Sept. 15

B152 SP63	75c + 25c ol blk	18.00	17.00
a.	Sheet of 20	750.00	750.00
B153 SP64	1fr + 25c red vio	17.00	16.00
a.	Sheet of 20	750.00	750.00

The surtax aided the National War Veterans' Fund. Sold for 4.50fr a set at the Exhibition of War Postmarks 1914-18, held at Brussels by the Royal Philatelic Club of Veterans. The price included an exhibition ticket. Sold at Brussels post office Sept. 18-22. No. B152 printed in sheets of 20 (4x5) and 100 (10x10). No. B153 printed in sheets of 20 (4x5) and 150 (10x15).

1934, Sept. 24

B154 SP63	75c + 25c violet	1.25	1.25
B155 SP64	1fr + 25c red brn	7.00	7.00

The surtax aided the National War Veterans' Fund. No. B154 printed in sheets of 100 (10x10); No. B155 in sheets of 150 (10x15). These stamps remained in use one year.

Crusader — SP65

1934, Nov. 17 **Engr.** *Perf. 13½x14*

Cross in Red

B156 SP65	10c + 5c black	1.25	1.25
B157 SP65	25c + 15c brown	1.75	1.75
B158 SP65	50c + 10c dull grn	1.75	1.75
B159 SP65	75c + 15c vio brn	.85	.85
B160 SP65	1fr + 25c rose	8.50	8.50
B161 SP65	1.75fr + 25c ultra	7.50	7.50
B162 SP65	5fr + 5fr brn vio	105.00	105.00
	Nos. B156-B162 (7)	126.60	126.60

The surtax was for anti-tuberculosis work.

Prince Baudouin, Princess Josephine and Prince Albert SP66

1935, Apr. 10 **Photo.**

B163 SP66	35c + 15c dk green	.85	.75
B164 SP66	70c + 30c red brn	.85	.60
B165 SP66	1.75fr + 50c dk blue	3.00	3.50
	Nos. B163-B165 (3)	4.70	4.85

Surtax was for Child Welfare Society.

Stagecoach SP67

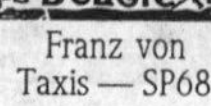
Franz von Taxis — SP68

Queen Astrid — SP69

1935, Apr. 27

B166 SP67	10c + 10c ol blk	.55	.65
B167 SP67	25c + 25c bis brn	1.90	1.75
B168 SP67	35c + 25c dk green	2.50	2.25
	Nos. B166-B168 (3)	4.95	4.65

Printed in sheets of 10. Value, set of 3, $175.

Souvenir Sheet

1935, May 25 **Engr.** *Perf. 14*

B169 SP68	5fr + 5fr grnsh blk	125.00	125.00

Sheets measure 91½x117mm.

Nos. B166-B169 were issued for the Brussels Philatelic Exhibition (SITEB).

The sheet normally has pin holes and a cancellation-like marking in the margin. These are considered unused and the condition valued here.

1935, Dec. 1 **Photo.** *Perf. 11½*

Borders in Black

B170 SP69	10c + 5c ol blk	.15	.15
B171 SP69	25c + 15c brown	.15	.30
B172 SP69	35c + 5c dk green	.20	.25
B173 SP69	50c + 10c rose lil	.65	.55
B174 SP69	70c + 5c gray blk	.15	.15
B175 SP69	1fr + 25c red	.90	.70
B176 SP69	1.75fr + 25c blue	2.00	1.50
B177 SP69	2.45fr + 55c dk vio	2.50	2.75
	Nos. B170-B177 (8)	6.70	6.35

Queen Astrid Memorial issue. The surtax was divided among several charitable organizations.

Borgerhout Philatelic Exhibition Issue

Souvenir Sheet

Town Hall, Borgerhout — SP70

1936, Oct. 3

B178 SP70	70c + 30c pur brn	50.00	35.00

Sheet measures 115x126mm.

The sheet normally has pin holes and a cancellation-like marking in the margin. These are considered unused and the condition valued here.

Town Hall and Belfry of Charleroi SP71

Prince Baudouin SP72

Charleroi Youth Exhibition

Souvenir Sheet

1936, Oct. 18 **Engr.**

B179 SP71	2.45fr + 55c gray blue	42.50	40.00

Sheet measures 95x120mm.

The sheet normally has pin holes and a cancellation-like marking in the margin. These are considered unused and the condition valued here.

1936, Dec. 1 **Photo.** *Perf. 14x13½*

B180 SP72	10c + 5c dk brown	.15	.20
B181 SP72	25c + 5c violet	.20	.25
B182 SP72	35c + 5c dk green	.20	.25
B183 SP72	50c + 5c vio brn	.30	.35
B184 SP72	70c + 5c ol grn	.20	.20
B185 SP72	1fr + 25c cerise	.65	.45
B186 SP72	1.75fr + 25c ultra	1.10	.65
B187 SP72	2.45fr + 2.55fr vio rose	3.00	4.00
	Nos. B180-B187 (8)	5.80	6.35

The surtax was for the assistance of the National Anti-Tuberculosis Society.

1937, Jan. 10

B188 SP72	2.45fr + 2.55fr slate	1.50	1.50

Intl. Stamp Day. Surtax for the benefit of the Brussels Postal Museum, the Royal Belgian Phil. Fed. and the Anti-Tuberculosis Soc.

Queen Astrid and Prince Baudouin SP73

Queen Mother Elisabeth SP74

1937, Apr. 15 *Perf. 11½*

B189 SP73	10c + 5c magenta	.15	.15
B190 SP73	25c + 5c ol blk	.20	.25
B191 SP73	35c + 5c dk grn	.20	.25
B192 SP73	50c + 5c violet	.50	.55
B193 SP73	70c + 5c slate	.20	.30
B194 SP73	1fr + 25c dk car	.65	.65
B195 SP73	1.75fr + 25c dp ultra	1.10	1.10
B196 SP73	2.45fr + 1.55fr dk brn	2.75	2.75
	Nos. B189-B196 (8)	5.75	6.00

The surtax was to raise funds for Public Utility Works.

1937, Sept. 15 *Perf. 14x13½*

B197 SP74	70c + 5c int black	.30	.30
B198 SP74	1.75fr + 25c brt ultra	.70	.70

Souvenir Sheet

Perf. 11½

B199	Sheet of 4	26.00	15.00
a.	SP74 1.50fr+2.50fr red brown	3.75	3.25
b.	SP74 2.45fr+3.55fr red violet	3.25	2.00

Issued for the benefit of the Queen Elisabeth Music Foundation in connection with the Eugene Ysaye intl. competition.

No. B199 contains two se-tenant pairs of Nos. B199a and B199b. Size: 111x145mm. On sale one day, Sept. 15, at Brussels.

The sheet normally has pin holes and a cancellation-like marking in the margin. These are considered unused and the condition valued here.

Princess Josephine-Charlotte SP75

1937, Dec. 1 *Perf. 14x13½*

B200 SP75	10c + 5c sl grn	.15	.20
B201 SP75	25c + 5c lt brn	.20	.20
B202 SP75	35c + 5c yel grn	.20	.20
B203 SP75	50c + 5c ol gray	.40	.35
B204 SP75	70c + 5c brn red	.15	.20
B205 SP75	1fr + 25c red	.70	.55
B206 SP75	1.75fr + 25c vio bl	.80	.70
B207 SP75	2.45fr + 2.55fr mag	3.25	3.50
	Nos. B200-B207 (8)	5.85	5.90

King Albert Memorial Issue

Souvenir Sheet

King Albert Memorial — SP76

1938, Feb. 17 *Perf. 11½*

B208 SP76	2.45fr + 7.55fr brn vio	13.00	11.00

Dedication of the monument to King Albert.

The sheet normally has pin holes and a cancellation-like marking in the margin. These are considered unused and the condition valued here.

King Leopold III in Military Plane — SP77

1938, Mar. 15

B209 SP77	10c + 5c car brn	.20	.30
B210 SP77	35c + 5c dp grn	.35	.90
B211 SP77	70c + 5c gray blk	.65	.50
B212 SP77	1.75fr + 25c ultra	1.50	1.40
B213 SP77	2.45fr + 2.55fr pur	3.50	3.00
	Nos. B209-B213 (5)	6.20	6.10

The surtax was for the benefit of the National Fund for Aeronautical Propaganda.

Basilica of Koekelberg SP78

Interior View of the Basilica of Koekelberg — SP79

1938, June 1 **Photo.**

B214	SP78	10c + 5c lt brn	.15	.20
B215	SP78	35c + 5c grn	.20	.20
B216	SP78	70c + 5c gray grn	.20	.20
B217	SP78	1fr + 25c car	.65	.55
B218	SP78	1.75fr + 25c ultra	.65	.65
B219	SP78	2.45fr + 2.55fr brn vio	2.75	3.50

Engr.

B220	SP79	5fr + 5fr dl grn	11.00	10.50
		Nos. B214-B220 (7)	15.60	15.80

Souvenir Sheet

1938, July 21 **Engr.** ***Perf. 14***

B221	SP79	5fr + 5fr lt vio	14.00	14.00

The surtax was for a fund to aid in completing the National Basilica of the Sacred Heart at Koekelberg.

Nos. B214, B216 and B218 are different views of the exterior of the Basilica.

The sheet normally has pin holes and a cancellation-like marking in the margin. These are considered unused and the condition valued here.

Stamps of 1938 Surcharged in Black:

Nos. B222-B223

2.50Fr 2.50Fr

No. B224

1938, Nov. 10 ***Perf. 11½***

B222	SP78	40c on 35c+5c grn	.35	.40
B223	SP78	75c on 70c+5c gray grn	.50	.65
B224	SP78	2.50 +2.50fr on 2.45+2.55fr	4.50	5.00
		Nos. B222-B224 (3)	5.35	6.05

Prince Albert of Liege — SP81

1938, Dec. 10 **Photo.** ***Perf. 14x13½***

B225	SP81	10c + 5c brown	.15	.20
B226	SP81	30c + 5c magenta	.20	.30
B227	SP81	40c + 5c olive gray	.20	.30
B228	SP81	75c + 5c slate grn	.15	.20
B229	SP81	1fr + 25c dk car	.55	.75
B230	SP81	1.75fr + 25c ultra	.55	.75
B231	SP81	2.50fr + 2.50fr dp grn	3.50	5.50
B232	SP81	5fr + 5fr brn lake	11.00	8.50
		Nos. B225-B232 (8)	16.30	16.50

Henri Dunant SP82

Florence Nightingale SP83

Queen Mother Elisabeth and Royal Children — SP84

Queen Astrid — SP86

King Leopold and Royal Children SP85

Queen Mother Elisabeth and Wounded Soldier — SP87

1939, Apr. 1 **Photo.** ***Perf. 11½***

Cross in Carmine

B233	SP82	10c + 5c brn	.15	.20
B234	SP83	30c + 5c brn car	.30	.30
B235	SP84	40c + 5c ol gray	.20	.30
B236	SP85	75c + 5c slate blk	.40	.20
B237	SP84	1fr + 25c brt rose	1.90	1.10
B238	SP85	1.75fr + 25c brt ultra	.60	.85
B239	SP86	2.50fr + 2.50fr dl vio	1.25	1.65
B240	SP87	5fr + 5fr gray grn	4.25	5.50
		Nos. B233-B240 (8)	9.05	10.10

75th anniversary of the founding of the International Red Cross Society.

Rubens' House, Antwerp SP88

"Albert and Nicolas Rubens" — SP89

Arcade, Rubens' House SP90

"Helena Fourment and Her Children" — SP91

Rubens and Isabelle Brandt — SP92

Peter Paul Rubens — SP93

"The Velvet Hat" — SP94

"Descent from the Cross" SP95

1939, July 1

B241	SP88	10c + 5c brn	.15	.20
B242	SP89	40c + 5c brn car	.30	.30
B243	SP90	75c + 5c ol blk	.60	.50
B244	SP91	1fr + 25c rose	1.65	1.50
B245	SP92	1.50fr + 25c sep	1.65	1.50
B246	SP93	1.75fr + 25c dp ultra	2.25	1.65
B247	SP94	2.50fr + 2.50fr brt red vio	9.25	10.50
B248	SP95	5fr + 5fr slate gray	14.00	14.00
		Nos. B241-B248 (8)	29.85	30.15

Issued to honor Peter Paul Rubens. The surtax was used to restore Rubens' home in Antwerp.

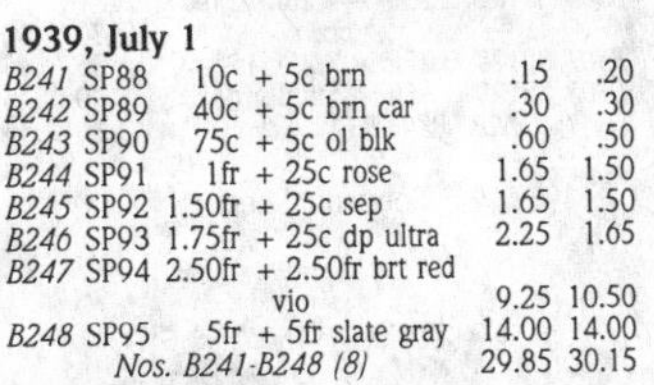

"Martin van Nieuwenhove" by Hans Memling (1430?-1495), Flemish Painter — SP96

1939, July 1

B249	SP96	75c + 75c olive blk	2.75	2.75

Twelfth Century Monks at Work — SP97

Reconstructed Tower Seen through Cloister — SP98

Monks Laboring in the Fields — SP99

Orval Abbey, Aerial View — SP100

Bishop Heylen of Namur, Madonna and Abbot General Smets of the Trappists — SP101

King Albert I and King Leopold III and Shrine — SP102

1939, July 20

B250	SP97	75c + 75c ol blk	2.50	2.75
B251	SP98	1fr + 1fr rose red	1.65	1.65
B252	SP99	1.50fr + 1.50fr dl brn	1.65	1.65
B253	SP100	1.75fr + 1.75fr saph	1.65	1.65
B254	SP101	2.50fr + 2.50fr brt red vio	7.25	6.50
B255	SP102	5fr + 5fr brn car	7.25	7.25
		Nos. B250-B255 (6)	21.95	21.45

The surtax was used for the restoration of the Abbey of Orval.

Bruges SP103

Furnes SP104

Belfries: 30c+5c, Thuin. 40c+5c, Lierre. 75c+5c, Mons. 1.75fr+25c, Namur. 2.50fr+2.50fr, Alost. 5fr+5fr, Tournai.

1939, Dec. 1 **Photo.** ***Perf. 14x13½***

B256	SP103	10c + 5c ol gray	.15	.25
B257	SP103	30c + 5c brn org	.25	.35
B258	SP103	40c + 5c brt red vio	.40	.45
B259	SP103	75c + 5c olive blk	.15	.25

Engr.

B260	SP104	1fr + 25c rose car	1.00	1.25
B261	SP104	1.75fr + 25c dk blue	1.00	1.25
B262	SP104	2.50fr + 2.50fr dp red brn	7.25	8.00
B263	SP104	5fr + 5fr purple	10.00	11.00
		Nos. B256-B263 (8)	20.20	22.80

Mons SP111

Ghent SP112

Coats of Arms: 40c+10c, Arel. 50c+10c, Bruges. 75c+15c, Namur. 1fr+25c, Hasselt. 1.75fr+50c, Brussels. 2.50fr+2.50fr, Antwerp. 5fr+5fr, Liege.

1940-41 **Typo.** ***Perf. 14x13½***

B264	SP111	10c + 5c multi	.15	.15
B265	SP112	30c + 5c multi	.20	.15
B266	SP111	40c + 10c multi	.20	.15
B267	SP112	50c + 10c multi	.20	.15
B268	SP111	75c + 15c multi	.15	.15
B269	SP112	1fr + 25c multi	.30	.30
B270	SP111	1.75fr + 50c multi	.45	.40
B271	SP112	2.50fr + 2.50fr multi	1.25	1.25
B272	SP111	5fr + 5fr multi	1.50	1.50
		Nos. B264-B272 (9)	4.40	4.20

Nos. B264, B269-B272 issued in 1941. Surtax for winter relief. See No. B279.

Queen Elisabeth Music Chapel
SP120

Bust of Prince Albert of Liege — SP121

1940, Nov. Photo. *Perf. 11½*

B273	SP120	75c + 75c slate	1.25	1.25
B274	SP120	1fr + 1fr rose red	1.25	1.25
B275	SP121	1.50fr + 1.50fr Prus grn	1.25	1.25
B276	SP121	1.75fr + 1.75fr ultra	1.25	1.25
B277	SP120	2.50fr + 2.50fr brn org	2.50	2.50
B278	SP121	5fr + 5fr red vio	3.00	3.00
		Nos. B273-B278 (6)	10.50	10.50

The surtax was for the Queen Elisabeth Music Foundation. Nos. B273-B278 were not authorized for postal use, but were sold to advance subscribers either mint or canceled to order. See Nos. B317-B318.

Arms Types of 1940-41
Souvenir Sheets

Perf. 14x13½, Imperf.

1941, May Typo.

Cross and City Name in Carmine
Arms in Color of Stamp

B279		Sheet of 9	13.00	13.00
a.	SP111	10c + 5c slate	1.10	1.25
b.	SP112	30c + 5c emerald	1.10	1.25
c.	SP111	40c + 10c chocolate	1.10	1.25
d.	SP112	50c + 10c light violet	1.10	1.25
e.	SP111	75c + 15c dull purple	1.10	1.25
f.	SP112	1fr + 25c carmine	1.10	1.25
g.	SP111	1.75fr + 50c dull blue	1.10	1.25
h.	SP112	2.50fr + 2.50fr olive gray	1.10	1.25
i.	SP111	5fr + 5fr dull violet	4.00	4.25

The sheets measure 106x148mm. The surtax was used for relief work.

Painting
SP123

Sculpture
SP124

Monks Studying Plans of Orval Abbey — SP128

Designs: 40c+60c, 2fr+3.50fr, Monk carrying candle. 50c+65c, 1.75fr+2.50fr, Monk praying. 75c+1fr, 3fr+5fr, Two monks singing.

1941, June Photo. *Perf. 11½*

B281	SP123	10c + 15c brn org	.35	.40
B282	SP124	30c + 30c ol gray	.35	.40
B283	SP124	40c + 60c dp brn	.35	.40
B284	SP124	50c + 65c vio	.35	.40
B285	SP124	75c + 1fr brt red vio	.35	.40
B286	SP124	1fr + 1.50fr rose red	.35	.40
B287	SP123	1.25fr + 1.75fr dp yel grn	.35	.40
B288	SP123	1.75fr + 2.50fr dp ultra	.35	.40
B289	SP123	2fr + 3.50fr red vio	.35	.40
B290	SP124	2.50fr + 4.50fr dl red brn	.35	.40
B291	SP124	3fr + 5fr dk ol grn	.35	.40
B292	SP128	5fr + 10fr grnsh blk	1.25	1.25
		Nos. B281-B292 (12)	5.10	5.65

The surtax was used for the restoration of the Abbey of Orval.

Maria Theresa — SP129

Charles the Bold — SP130

Portraits (in various frames): 35c+5c, Charles of Lorraine. 50c+10c, Margaret of Parma. 60c+10c, Charles V. 1fr+15c, Johanna of Castile. 1.50fr+1fr, Philip the Good. 1.75fr+1.75fr, Margaret of Austria. 3.25fr+3.25fr, Archduke Albert. 5fr+5fr, Archduchess Isabella.

1941-42 Photo.

B293	SP129	10c + 5c ol blk	.15	.15
B294	SP129	35c + 5c dl grn	.15	.15
B295	SP129	50c + 10c brn	.15	.15
B296	SP129	60c + 10c pur	.15	.15
B297	SP129	1fr + 15c brt car rose	.15	.15
B298	SP129	1.50fr + 1fr red vio	.20	.20
B299	SP129	1.75fr + 1.75fr ryl bl	.20	.20
B300	SP130	2.25fr + 2.25fr dl red brn	.30	.30
B301	SP129	3.25fr + 3.25fr lt brn	.35	.45
B302	SP129	5fr + 5fr sl grn	.40	.45
		Nos. B293-B302 (10)	2.20	2.35

Souvenir Sheet

Archduke Albert and Archduchess Isabella — SP139

B302A	SP139	Sheet of 2 ('42)	6.00	6.00
b.		3.25fr+6.75fr turquoise blue	2.25	2.25
c.		5fr+10fr dark carmine	2.25	2.25

The surtax was for the benefit of National Social Service Work among soldiers' families.

Souvenir Sheets

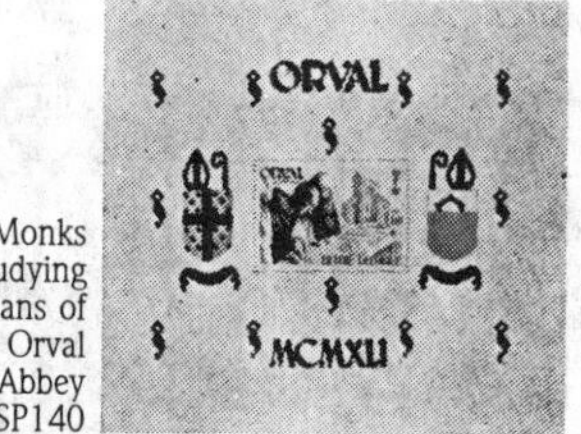

Monks Studying Plans of Orval Abbey
SP140

1941, Oct. Photo. *Perf. 11½*

Inscribed "Belgie-Belgique"

B303	SP140	5fr + 15fr ultra	6.25	6.25

Inscribed "Belgique-Belgie"

B304	SP140	5fr + 15fr ultra	6.25	6.25

Surtax for the restoration of Orval Abbey.
No. B304 exists perforated.
In 1942 these sheets were privately trimmed and overprinted "1142 1942" and ornament.

St. Martin Statue, Church of Dinant
SP141

Lennik, Saint-Quentin
SP142

St. Martin's Church, Saint-Trond
SP146

Designs (Statues of St. Martin): 50c+10c, 3.25fr+3.25fr, Beck, Limburg. 60c+10c, 2.25fr+2.25fr, Dave on the Meuse. 1.75fr+50c, Hal, Brabant.

1941-42 Photo. *Perf. 11½*

B305	SP141	10c + 5c chestnut	.15	.15
B306	SP142	35c + 5c dk bl grn	.15	.15
B307	SP142	50c + 10c violet	.15	.15
B308	SP142	60c + 10c dp brn	.15	.15
B309	SP142	1fr + 15c carmine	.15	.15
B310	SP141	1.50fr + 25c sl grn	.20	.20
B311	SP142	1.75fr + 50c dk ultra	.30	.30
B312	SP142	2.25fr + 2.25fr red vio	.30	.30
B313	SP142	3.25fr + 3.25fr brn vio	.30	.30
B314	SP146	5fr + 5fr dk ol grn	.45	.45
		Nos. B305-B314 (10)	2.30	2.30

Souvenir Sheets

Inscribed "Belgie-Belgique"

B315	SP146	5fr + 20fr vio brn ('42)	12.50	12.50

Inscribed "Belgique-Belgie"

B316	SP146	5fr + 20fr vio brn ('42)	12.50	12.50

In 1956, the Bureau Europeen de la Jeunesse et de l'Enfance privately overprinted Nos. B315-B316: "Congres Europeen de l'education 7-12 Mai 1956," in dark red and dark green respectively. A black bar obliterates "Winterhulp-Secours d'Hiver."

Souvenir Sheets

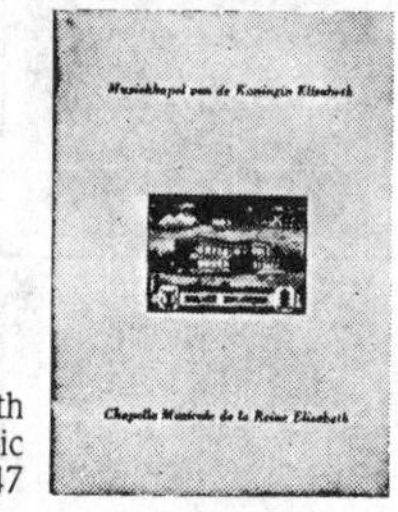

Queen Elisabeth Music Chapel — SP147

1941, Dec. 1 Photo. *Perf. 11½*

Inscribed "Belgique-Belgie"

B317	SP147	10fr + 15fr ol blk	4.50	4.00

Inscribed "Belgie-Belique"

B318	SP147	10fr + 15fr ol blk	4.50	4.00

The surtax was for the Queen Elisabeth Music Foundation. These sheets were perforated with the monogram of Queen Elisabeth in 1942.

In 1954 Nos. B317-B318 were overprinted to for the birth cent. of Edgar Tinel, composer. These overprinted sheets were not postally valid.

Jean Bollandus
SP148

Christophe Plantin
SP156

Designs: 35c+5c, Andreas Vesalius. 50c+10c, Simon Stevinus. 60c+10c, Jean Van Helmont. 1fr+15c, Rembert Dodoens. 1.75fr+50c, Gerardus Mercator. 3.25fr+3.25fr, Abraham Ortelius. 5fr+5fr, Justus Lipsius.

1942, May 15 Photo. *Perf. 14x13½*

B319	SP148	10c + 5c dl brn	.15	.15
B320	SP148	35c + 5c gray grn	.15	.15
B321	SP148	50c + 10c fawn	.15	.15
B322	SP148	60c + 10c grnsh blk	.15	.15

Engr.

B323	SP148	1fr + 15c brt rose	.15	.15
B324	SP148	1.75fr + 50c dl bl	.20	.20
B325	SP148	3.25fr + 3.25fr lil rose	.20	.20
B326	SP148	5fr + 5fr vio	.25	.25

Perf. 13½x14

B327	SP156	10fr + 30fr red org	.95	1.00
		Nos. B319-B327 (9)	2.35	2.40

The surtax was used to help fight tuberculosis.
No. B327 was sold by subscription at the Brussels Post Office, July 1-10, 1942.

Belgian Prisoner — SP158

1942, Oct. 1 *Perf. 11½*

B331	SP158	5fr + 45fr olive gray	5.50	5.50

The surtax was for prisoners of war. Value includes a brown label, inscribed "1942 POUR NOS PRISONNIERS/VOOR ONZE GEVANGENEN," which alternates with the stamps in the sheet.

SP159 SP164

SP162

SP168

Various Statues of St. Martin.

1942-43

B332	SP159	10c + 5c org	.15	.15
B333	SP159	35c + 5c dk bl grn	.15	.15
B334	SP159	50c + 10c dp brn	.15	.15
B335	SP162	60c + 10c blk	.15	.15
B336	SP159	1fr + 15c brt rose	.15	.15
B337	SP164	1.50fr + 25c grnsh blk	.20	.20
B338	SP164	1.75fr + 50c dk bl	.20	.20
B339	SP162	2.25fr + 2.25fr brn	.30	.25
B340	SP162	3.25fr + 3.25fr brt red vio	.35	.30
B341	SP168	5fr + 10fr hn brn	.50	.45
B342	SP168	10fr + 20fr rose brn & vio brn ('43)	.65	.65

Inscribed "Belgique-Belgie"

B343	SP168	10fr + 20fr gldn brn & vio brn ('43)	.65	.65
		Nos. B332-B343 (12)	3.60	3.45

The surtax was for winter relief.
Issue dates: Nos. B332-B341, Nov. 12, 1942. Nos. B342-B343, Apr. 3, 1943.

Prisoners of War — SP170

Design: No. B345, Two prisoners with package from home.

1943, May Photo. Perf. 11½

B344	SP170	1fr + 30fr ver	2.50	2.50
B345	SP170	1fr + 30fr brn rose	2.50	2.50

The surtax was used for prisoners of war.

Roof Tiler
SP172

Coppersmith
SP173

Statues in Petit Sablon Park, Brussels: 35c+5c, Blacksmith. 60c+10c, Gunsmith. 1fr+15c, Armsmith. 1.75fr+75c, Goldsmith. 3.25fr+3.25fr, Fishdealer. 5fr+25fr, Watchmaker.

1943, June 1

B346	SP172	10c + 5c chnt brn	.15	.15
B347	SP172	35c + 5c grn	.15	.15
B348	SP173	50c + 10c dk brn	.15	.15
B349	SP173	60c + 10c slate	.15	.15
B350	SP173	1fr + 15c dl rose brn	.15	.15
B351	SP173	1.75fr + 75c ultra	.20	.20
B352	SP173	3.25fr + 3.25fr brt red vio	.30	.40
B353	SP173	5fr + 25fr dk pur	.50	.55
		Set value	1.45	1.75

Surtax for the control of tuberculosis.

"O" — SP180

"ORVAL" — SP185

1943, Oct. 9

B354	SP180	50c + 1fr "O"	.50	.50
B355	SP180	60c + 1.90fr "R"	.30	.25
B356	SP180	1fr + 3fr "V"	.30	.25
B357	SP180	1.75fr + 5.25fr "A"	.30	.25
B358	SP180	3.25fr + 16.75fr "L"	.40	.40
B359	SP185	5fr + 30fr dp brn	.75	.75
		Nos. B354-B359 (6)	2.55	2.40

Surtax aided restoration of Orval Abbey.

St. Leonard Church, Leau — SP186

St. Martin Church, Courtrai
SP190

Basilica of St. Martin, Angre
SP191

Notre Dame, Hal — SP193

St. Martin
SP194

Designs: 35c+5c, St. Martin Church, Dion-le-Val. 50c+15c, St. Martin Church, Alost. 60c+20c, St. Martin Church, Liege. 3.25fr+11.75fr, St. Martin Church, Loppem. No. B369, St. Martin, beggar and Meuse landscape.

1943-44

B360	SP186	10c + 5c dp brn	.15	.15
B361	SP186	35c + 5c dk bl grn	.20	.20
B362	SP186	50c + 15c ol blk	.30	.30
B363	SP186	60c + 20c brt red vio	.30	.40
B364	SP190	1fr + 1fr rose brn	.40	.40
B365	SP191	1.75fr + 4.25fr dp ultra	.90	.60
B366	SP186	3.25fr + 11.75fr red lil	.90	.65
B367	SP193	5fr + 25fr dk bl	1.25	1.25
B368	SP194	10fr + 30fr gray grn ('44)	.90	.90
B369	SP194	10fr + 30fr blk brn ('44)	.90	.90
		Nos. B360-B369 (10)	6.20	5.75

Surtax for winter relief.

Catalogue values for unused stamps in this section, from this point to the end of the section, are for Never Hinged items.

"Daedalus and Icarus"
SP196

Sir Anthony Van Dyck, Self-portrait
SP200

Paintings by Van Dyck: 50c+2.50fr. "The Good Samaritan." 60c+3.40fr, Detail of "Christ Healing the Paralytic." 1fr+5fr, "Madonna and Child." 5fr+30fr, "St. Sebastian."

1944, Apr. 16 Photo. Perf. 11½
Crosses in Carmine

B370	SP196	35c + 1.65fr dk sl grn	.42	.30
B371	SP196	50c + 2.50fr grnsh blk	.42	.30
B372	SP196	60c + 3.40fr blk brn	.42	.30
B373	SP196	1fr + 5fr dk car	.60	.45
B374	SP200	1.75fr + 8.25fr int bl	.75	.60
B375	SP196	5fr + 30fr cop brn	.75	.60
		Nos. B370-B375 (6)	3.36	2.55

The surtax was for the Belgian Red Cross.

Jan van Eyck
SP202

Godfrey of Bouillon
SP203

Designs: 50c+25c, Jacob van Maerlant. 60c+40c, Jean Joses de Dinant. 1fr+50c, Jacob van Artevelde. 1.75fr+4.25fr, Charles Joseph de Ligne. 2.25fr+8.25fr, Andre Gretry. 3.25fr+11.25fr, Jan Moretus-Plantin. 5fr+35fr, Jan van Ruysbroeck.

1944, May 31

B376	SP202	10c + 15c dk pur	.32	.30
B377	SP203	35c + 15c green	.32	.30
B378	SP203	50c + 25c chnt brn	.32	.30
B379	SP203	60c + 40c ol blk	.32	.30
B380	SP203	1fr + 50c rose brn	.32	.30
B381	SP203	1.75fr + 4.25fr ultra	.32	.30
B382	SP203	2.25fr + 8.25fr grnsh blk	.85	.75
B383	SP203	3.25fr + 11.25fr dk brn	.32	.30
B384	SP203	5fr + 35fr sl bl	.65	.90
		Nos. B376-B384 (9)	3.74	3.75

The surtax was for prisoners of war.

Sons of Aymon Astride Bayard
SP211

Brabo Slaying the Giant Antigoon
SP212

Till Eulenspiegel Singing to Nele
SP214

Designs: 50c+10c, St. Hubert converted by stag with crucifix. 1fr+15fr, St. George slaying the dragon. 1.75fr+5.25fr, Genevieve of Brabant with son and roe-deer. 3.25fr+11.75fr, Tchantches wrestling with the Saracen. 5fr+25fr, St. Gertrude rescuing the knight with the cards.

1944, June 25

B385	SP211	10c + 5c choc	.15	.20
B386	SP212	35c + 5c dk bl grn	.15	.20
B387	SP211	50c + 10c dl vio	.15	.20
B388	SP214	60c + 10c blk brn	.15	.20
B389	SP214	1fr + 15c rose brn	.15	.20
B390	SP214	1.75fr + 5.25fr ultra	.22	.40
B391	SP211	3.25fr + 11.75fr grnsh blk	.32	.60
B392	SP211	5fr + 25fr dk bl	.45	.80
		Nos. B385-B392 (8)	1.74	2.80

The surtax was for the control of tuberculosis.

Nos. B385-B389 were overprinted "Breendonk+10fr." in 1946 by the Union Royale Philatelique for an exhibition at Brussels. They had no postal validity.

Union of the Flemish and Walloon Peoples in their Sorrow — SP219

Union in Reconstruction — SP220

Perf. 11½
1945, May 1 Unwmk. Photo.

B395	SP219	1fr + 30fr carmine	1.40	1.00
B396	SP220	1¾fr + 30fr brt ultra	1.40	1.00

1945, July 21
Size: 34½x23½mm

B397	SP219	1fr + 9fr scarlet	.30	.22
B398	SP220	1fr + 9fr car rose	.30	.22
		Nos. B395-B398 (4)	3.40	2.44

Surtax for the postal employees' relief fund.

Prisoner of War — SP221

Reunion
SP222

Awaiting Execution
SP223

Symbolical Figures "Recovery of Freedom"
SP225

Design: 70c+30c, 3.50fr+3.50fr, Member of Resistance Movement.

1945, Sept. 10

B399	SP221	10c + 15c orange	.15	.15
B400	SP222	20c + 20c dp purple	.15	.15
B401	SP223	60c + 25c sepia	.15	.15
B402	SP221	70c + 30c dp yel grn	.15	.15
B403	SP221	75c + 50c org brn	.15	.18
B404	SP222	1fr + 75c brt bl grn	.22	.22
B405	SP223	1.50fr + 1fr brt red	.22	.22
B406	SP221	3.50fr + 3.50fr brt bl	1.00	1.10
B407	SP225	5fr + 40fr brown	.85	1.00
		Nos. B399-B407 (9)	3.04	3.32

The surtax was for the benefit of prisoners of war, displaced persons, families of executed victims and members of the Resistance Movement.

Arms of West Flanders — SP226

Arms of Provinces: 20c+20c, Luxembourg. 60c+25c, East Flanders. 70c+30c, Namur. 75c+50c, Limburg. 1fr+75c, Hainaut. 1.50fr+1fr, Antwerp. 3.50fr+1.50fr, Liege. 5fr+45fr, Brabant.

1945, Dec. 1
B408 SP226 10c + 15c sl blk & sl gray .15 .15
B409 SP226 20c + 20c rose car & rose .15 .15
B410 SP226 60c + 25c dk brn & pale brn .15 .15
B411 SP226 70c + 30c dk grn & lt grn .15 .15
B412 SP226 75c + 50c org brn & pale org brn .20 .20
B413 SP226 1fr + 75c pur & lt pur .15 .15
B414 SP226 1.50fr + 1fr car & rose .15 .15
B415 SP226 3.50fr + 1.50fr dp bl & gray bl .24 .24
B416 SP226 5fr + 45fr dp mag & cerise 1.75 1.90
Nos. B408-B416 (9) 3.09 3.24

The surtax was for tuberculosis prevention.

Father Joseph Damien — SP227

Father Damien Comforting Leper — SP229

Leper Colony, Molokai Island, Hawaii SP228

Symbols of Wisdom and Patriotism SP230

"In Memoriam" SP232

Franç ois Bovesse SP231

Sower SP235

Emile Vandervelde SP233

Vandervelde, Laborer and Family SP234

Perf. 11½
1946, July 15 Unwmk. Photo.
B417 SP227 65c + 75c dk blue 1.00 .60
B418 SP228 1.35fr + 2fr brown 1.00 .60
B419 SP229 1.75fr + 18fr rose brn 1.50 1.00

The surtax was for the erection of a museum in Louvain.

1946, July 15
B420 SP230 65c + 75c violet 1.00 .60
B421 SP231 1.35fr + 2fr dk org brn 1.25 .75
B422 SP232 1.75fr + 18fr car rose 1.75 1.00

The surtax was for the erection of a "House of the Fine Arts" at Namur.

1946, July 15
B423 SP233 65c + 75c dk sl grn 1.10 .60
B424 SP234 1.35fr + 2fr dk vio bl 1.25 .75
B425 SP235 1.75fr + 18fr dp car 1.75 1.00
Nos. B417-B425 (9) 11.60 6.90

The surtax was for the Emile Vandervelde Institute, to promote social, economic and cultural activities.

For surcharges see Nos. CB4-CB12.

Pepin of Herstal — SP236

Malines — SP241

Designs: 1fr+50c, Charlemagne. 1.50fr+1fr, Godfrey of Bouillon. 3.50fr+1.50fr, Robert of Jerusalem. Nos. B430-B431, Baldwin of Constantinople.

1946, Sept. 15 Engr. *Perf. 11½x11*
B426 SP236 75c + 25c green .60 .35
B427 SP236 1fr + 50c violet 1.00 .50
B428 SP236 1.50fr + 1fr plum 1.25 .60
B429 SP236 3.50fr + 1.50fr brt bl 1.50 .75
B430 SP236 5fr + 45fr red vio 12.00 7.00
B431 SP236 5fr + 45fr red org 15.00 7.75
Nos. B426-B431 (6) 31.35 16.95

The surtax on Nos. B426-B429 was for the benefit of former prisoners of war, displaced persons, the families of executed patriots, and former members of the Resistance Movement.

The surtax on Nos. B430-B431 was divided among several welfare, national celebration and educational organizations.

Issue dates: Nos. B426-B429, Apr. 15; No. B430, Sept. 15; No. B431, Nov. 15.

See Nos. B437-B441, B465-B466, B472-B476.

1946, Dec. 2 *Perf. 11½*

Coats of Arms: 90c+60c, Dinant. 1.35fr+1.15fr, Ostend. 3.15fr+1.85fr, Verviers. 4.50fr+45.50fr, Louvain.

B432 SP241 65c + 35c rose car .55 .55
B433 SP241 90c + 60c lemon .55 .55
B434 SP241 1.35fr + 1.15fr dp grn .55 .55
B435 SP241 3.15fr + 1.85fr blue 1.40 1.40
B436 SP241 4.50fr + 45.50fr dk vio brn 13.00 13.00
Nos. B432-B436 (5) 16.05 16.05

The surtax was for anti-tuberculosis work. See Nos. B442-B446.

Type of 1946

Designs: 65c+35c, John II, Duke of Brabant. 90c+60c, Count Philip of Alsace. 1.35fr+1.15fr, William the Good. 3.15fr+1.85fr, Bishop Notger of Liege. 20fr+20fr, Philip the Noble.

1947, Sept. 25 Engr. *Perf. 11½x11*
B437 SP236 65c + 35c Prus grn .60 .60
B438 SP236 90c + 60c yel grn 1.00 1.00
B439 SP236 1.35fr + 1.15fr car 1.40 1.40
B440 SP236 3.15fr + 1.85fr ultra 2.00 2.00
B441 SP236 20fr + 20fr red vio 52.50 52.50
Nos. B437-B441 (5) 57.50 57.50

The surtax was for victims of World War II.

Arms Type of 1946 Dated "1947"

Coats of Arms: 65c+35c, Nivelles. 90c+60c, St. Trond. 1.35fr+1.15fr, Charleroi. 3.15fr+1.85fr, St. Nicolas. 20fr+20fr, Bouillon.

1947, Dec. 15 *Perf. 11½*
B442 SP241 65c + 35c orange .85 .65
B443 SP241 90c + 60c dp cl .70 .65
B444 SP241 1.35fr + 1.15fr dk brn 1.10 .70
B445 SP241 3.15fr + 1.85fr dp bl 2.50 1.75
B446 SP241 20fr + 20fr dk grn 20.00 12.50
Nos. B442-B446 (5) 25.15 16.25

The surtax was for anti-tuberculosis work.

St. Benedict and King Totila — SP247

Achel Abbey SP248

Designs: 3.15fr+2.85fr, St. Benedict, legislator and builder. 10fr+10fr, Death of St. Benedict.

1948, Apr. 5 Photo.
B447 SP247 65c + 65c red brn 1.25 .55
B448 SP248 1.35fr + 1.35fr gray 1.75 .55
B449 SP247 3.15fr + 2.85fr dp ultra 2.50 1.90
B450 SP247 10fr + 10fr brt red vio 12.50 10.00
Nos. B447-B450 (4) 18.00 13.00

The surtax was to aid the Abbey of the Trappist Fathers at Achel.

St. Begga and Chevremont Castle — SP249

Chevremont Basilica and Convent SP250

Designs: 3.15fr+2.85fr, Madonna of Chevremont and Chapel. 10fr+10fr, Madonna of Mt. Carmel.

1948, Apr. 5 Unwmk.
B451 SP249 65c + 65c bl grn 1.25 .55
B452 SP250 1.35fr + 1.35fr dk car rose 1.65 .55
B453 SP249 3.15fr + 2.85fr dp bl 2.50 1.75
B454 SP249 10fr + 10fr dp brn 12.00 10.00
Nos. B451-B454 (4) 17.40 12.85

The surtax was to aid the Basilica of the Carmelite Fathers of Chèvremont.

Anseele Monument Showing French Inscription — SP251

Designs: 90c+60c, View of Ghent. 1.35fr+1.15fr, Van Artevelde monument, Ghent. 3.15fr+1.85fr. Anseele Monument, Flemish inscription.

1948, June 21 *Perf. 14x13½*
B455 SP251 65c + 35c rose red 2.75 1.40
B456 SP251 90c + 60c gray 3.50 2.25
B457 SP251 1.35fr + 1.15fr hn brn 2.25 1.75
B458 SP251 3.15fr + 1.85fr brt bl 8.50 6.00
a. Souv. sheet of 4, #B455-B458 140.00 55.00
Nos. B455-B458 (4) 17.00 11.40

Issued to honor Edouard Anseele, statesman, founder of the Belgian Socialist Party.

No. B458a sold for 50fr.

For surcharges see Nos. 395-398.

Statue "The Unloader" SP252

Underground Fighter SP253

1948, Sept. 4 *Perf. 11½x11*
B460 SP252 10fr + 10fr gray grn 35.00 21.00
B461 SP253 10fr + 10fr red brn 20.00 13.00

The surtax was used toward erection of monuments at Antwerp and Liege.

Portrait Type of 1946 and

Double Barred Cross — SP254

Designs: 4fr+3.25fr, Isabella of Austria. 20fr+20fr, Archduke Albert of Austria.

1948, Dec. 15 Photo. *Perf. 13½x14*
B462 SP254 20c + 5c dk sl grn .50 .15
B463 SP254 1.20fr + 30c magenta 1.25 .70
B464 SP254 1.75fr + 25c red 1.75 .60

Engr. *Perf. 11½x11*
B465 SP236 4fr + 3.25fr ultra 9.75 6.50
B466 SP236 20fr + 20fr Prus grn 42.50 30.00
Nos. B462-B466 (5) 55.75 37.95

The surtax was divided among several charities.

Souvenir Sheets

Rogier van der Weyden Paintings — SP255

Paintings by van der Weyden (No. B466A): 90c, Virgin and Child. 1.75fr, Christ on the Cross. 4fr, Mary Magdalene.

Paintings by Jordaens (No. B466B): 90c, Woman Reading. 1.75fr, The Flutist. 4fr, Old Woman Reading Letter.

1949, Apr. 1 Photo. *Perf. 11½*
B466A SP255 Sheet of 3 125.00 110.00
c. 90c deep brown 37.50 32.50
d. 1.75fr deep rose lilac 37.50 32.50
e. 4fr dark violet blue 37.50 32.50
B466B SP255 Sheet of 3 125.00 110.00
f. 90c dark violet 37.50 32.50
g. 1.75fr red 37.50 32.50
h. 4fr blue 37.50 32.50

The surtax went to various cultural and philanthropic organizations. Sheets sold for 50fr each.

Gum on Nos. B466A-B466B is irregularly applied.

Guido Gezelle — SP256

1949, Nov. 15 Photo. *Perf. 14x13½*
B467 SP256 1.75fr + 75c dk Prus grn 2.50 1.75

50th anniversary of the death of Guido Gezelle, poet. The surtax was for the Guido Gezelle Museum, Bruges.

Portrait Type of 1946 and

Arnica — SP257

Designs: 65c+10c, Sand grass. 90c+10c, Wood myrtle. 1.20fr+30c, Field poppy. 1.75fr+25c, Philip the Good. 3fr+1.50fr, Charles V. 4fr+2fr, Maria-Christina. 6fr+3fr, Charles of Lorraine. 8fr+4fr, Maria-Theresa.

1949, Dec. 20 Typo. *Perf. 13½x14*

B468	SP257	20c + 5c multi	.50	.50
B469	SP257	65c + 10c multi	1.25	1.10
B470	SP257	90c + 10c multi	2.00	1.50
B471	SP257	1.20fr + 30c multi	2.50	1.75

Engr. *Perf. 11½x11*

B472	SP236	1.75fr + 25c red org	1.40	.80
B473	SP236	3fr + 1.50fr dp claret	10.00	6.75
B474	SP236	4fr + 2fr ultra	10.00	8.00
B475	SP236	6fr + 3fr choc	16.00	11.00
B476	SP236	8fr + 4fr dl grn	16.00	8.75
		Nos. B468-B476 (9)	59.65	40.15

The surtax was apportioned among several welfare organizations.

Arms of Belgium and Great Britain SP258

British Memorial SP260

Design: 2.50fr+50c, British tanks at Hertain.

Perf. 13½x14, 11½

1950, Mar. 15 Engr.

B477	SP258	80c + 20c green	1.50	1.10
B478	SP258	2.50fr + 50c red	5.00	4.50
B479	SP260	4fr + 2fr dp bl	9.25	7.50
		Nos. B477-B479 (3)	15.75	13.10

6th anniv. of the liberation of Belgian territory by the British army.

Hurdling SP261

Relay Race SP262

Designs: 90c+10c, Javelin throwing. 4fr+2fr, Pole vault. 8fr+4fr, Foot race.

Perf. 14x13½, 13½x14

1950, July 1 Engr. Unwmk.

B480	SP261	20c + 5c brt grn	.90	.75
B481	SP261	90c + 10c vio brn	3.75	1.90
B482	SP262	1.75fr + 25c car	4.50	1.90
a.		Souvenir sheet of 1	55.00	40.00
B483	SP261	4fr + 2fr lt bl	35.00	19.00
B484	SP261	8fr + 4fr dp grn	40.00	24.00
		Nos. B480-B484 (5)	84.15	47.55

Issued to publicize the European Athletic Games, Brussels, August 1950.

The margins of No. B482a were trimmed in April, 1951, and an overprint ("25 Francs pour le Fonds Sportif-25e Fofre Internationale Bruxelles") was added in red in French and in black in Flemish by a private committee. These pairs of altered sheets were sold at the Brussels Fair.

Gentian SP263

Sijsele Sanatorium SP264

Tombeek Sanatorium — SP265

Designs: 65c+10c, Cotton Grass. 90c+10c, Foxglove. 1.20fr+30c, Limonia. 4fr+2fr, Jauche Sanatorium.

1950, Dec. 20 Typo. *Perf. 14x13½*

B485	SP263	20c + 5c multi	.80	.40
B486	SP263	65c + 10c multi	1.50	.80
B487	SP263	90c + 10c multi	1.65	1.10
B488	SP263	1.20fr + 30c multi	2.75	2.25

Perf. 11½

Engr.

Cross in Red

B489	SP264	1.75fr + 25c car	2.50	1.40
B490	SP264	4fr + 2fr blue	13.00	7.00
B491	SP265	8fr + 4fr bl grn	21.00	15.00
		Nos. B485-B491 (7)	43.20	27.95

The surtax was for tuberculosis prevention and other charitable purposes.

Chemist — SP266

Allegory of Peace — SP268

Colonial Instructor and Class — SP267

1951, Mar. 27 Unwmk.

B492	SP266	80c + 20c grn	1.40	1.00
B493	SP267	2.50fr + 50c vio brn	9.50	5.00
B494	SP268	4fr + 2fr dp bl	10.25	6.00
		Nos. B492-B494 (3)	21.15	12.00

Surtax for the reconstruction fund of the UNESCO.

Monument to Political Prisoners SP269

Fort of Breendonk SP270

Design: 8fr+4fr, Monument: profile of figure on pedestal.

1951, Aug. 20 Photo. *Perf. 11½*

B495	SP269	1.75fr + 25c blk brn	2.50	1.75
B496	SP270	4fr + 2fr bl & sl gray	17.00	14.00
B497	SP269	8fr + 4fr dk bl grn	22.50	17.00
		Nos. B495-B497 (3)	42.00	32.75

The surtax was for the erection of a national monument.

Queen Elisabeth — SP271

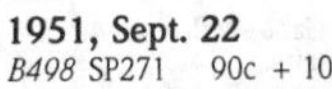

1951, Sept. 22

B498	SP271	90c + 10c grnsh gray	1.50	.80
B499	SP271	1.75fr + 25c plum	1.90	1.40
B500	SP271	3fr + 1fr green	17.50	8.75
B501	SP271	4fr + 2fr gray bl	19.00	11.50
B502	SP271	8fr + 4fr sepia	24.00	13.00
		Nos. B498-B502 (5)	63.90	35.45

The surtax was for the Queen Elisabeth Medical Foundation.

Cross, Sun Rays and Dragon SP272

Beersel Castle SP273

Horst Castle — SP274

Castles: 4fr+2fr, Lavaux St. Anne. 8fr+4fr, Veves.

1951, Dec. 17 Engr. Unwmk.

B503	SP272	20c + 5c red	.25	.20
B504	SP272	65c + 10c dp ultra	.80	.60
B505	SP272	90c + 10c sepia	.85	.80
B506	SP272	1.20fr + 30c rose vio	1.10	.85
B507	SP273	1.75fr + 75c red brn	1.75	1.40
B508	SP274	3fr + 1fr yel grn	11.50	7.25
B509	SP273	4fr + 2fr bl	14.00	8.50
B510	SP274	8fr + 4fr gray	19.00	11.00
		Nos. B503-B510 (8)	49.25	30.60

The surtax was for anti-tuberculosis work.

See Nos. B523-B526, B547-B550.

Main Altar SP275

Basilica of the Sacred Heart Koekelberg SP276

Procession Bearing Relics of St. Albert of Louvain — SP277

1952, Mar. 1 Photo. *Perf. 11½*

B511	SP275	1.75fr + 25c blk brn	1.50	1.25
B512	SP276	4fr + 2fr indigo	12.00	8.00

Engr.

B513	SP277	8fr + 4fr vio brn	16.00	10.00
a.		Souv. sheet, #B511-B513	210.00	125.00
		Nos. B511-B513 (3)	29.50	19.25

25th anniv. of the Cardinalate of J. E. Van Roey, Primate of Belgium. The surtax was for the Basilica. No. B513a sold for 30fr.

Beaulieu Castle, Malines SP278

August Vermeylen SP279

1952, May 14 Engr.

Laid Paper

B514	SP278	40fr + 10fr lt grnsh bl	175.00	175.00

Issued on the occasion of the 13th Universal Postal Union Congress, Brussels, 1952.

Perf. 11½

1952, Oct. 24 Unwmk. Photo.

Portraits: 80c+40c, Karel Van de Woestijne. 90c+45c, Charles de Coster. 1.75fr+75c, M. Maeterlinck. 4fr+2fr, Emile Verhaeren. 8fr+4fr, Hendrik Conscience.

B515	SP279	65c + 30c pur	1.75	.95
B516	SP279	80c + 40c dk grn	3.75	1.25
B517	SP279	90c + 45c sep	2.75	1.40
B518	SP279	1.75fr + 75c cer	3.75	1.75
B519	SP279	4fr + 2fr bl vio	30.00	19.00
B520	SP279	8fr + 4fr dk brn	30.00	21.00
		Nos. B515-B520 (6)	72.00	45.35

1952, Nov. 15

Portraits: 4fr, Emile Verhaeren. 8fr, Hendrik Conscience.

B521	SP279	4fr (+ 9fr) blue	100.00	70.00
B522	SP279	8fr (+ 9fr) dk car rose	100.00	70.00

On Nos. B521-B522, the denomination is repeated at either side of the stamp. The surtax is expressed on se-tenant labels bearing quotations of Verhaeren (in French) and Conscience (in Flemish). Value is for stamp with label.

A 9-line black overprint was privately applied to these labels: "Conference Internationale de la Musique Bruxelles UNESCO International Music Conference Brussels 1953*"

Type of 1951 Dated "1952," and

Arms of Malmédy — SP281

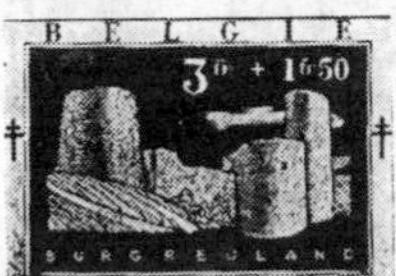
Castle Ruins, Burgreuland SP282

Designs: 4fr+2fr, Vesdre Dam, Eupen. 8fr+4fr, St. Vitus, patron saint of Saint-Vith.

1952, Dec. 15 Engr.

B523	SP272	20c + 5c red brn	.45	.35
B524	SP272	80c + 20c green	.90	.55
B525	SP272	1.20fr + 30c lil rose	1.75	.85
B526	SP272	1.50fr + 50c ol brn	1.75	.85
B527	SP281	2fr + 75c carmine	3.00	2.00
B528	SP282	3fr + 1.50fr choc	14.00	7.75
B529	SP281	4fr + 2fr blue	12.00	7.00
B530	SP281	8fr + 4fr vio brn	21.00	10.00
		Nos. B523-B530 (8)	54.85	29.35

The surtax on Nos. B523-B530 was for anti-tuberculosis and other charitable works.

The Scott Catalogue value is a retail value; that is, what you could expect to pay for the stamp in a grade of Very Fine. The value listed reflects recent actual dealer selling prices.

Walthère Dewé
SP283

Princess Josephine-Charlotte
SP284

1953, Feb. 16 **Photo.**

B531	SP283	2fr + 1fr brn car	3.25	2.00

The surtax was for the construction of a memorial to Walthère Dewé, Underground leader in World War II.

1953, Mar. 14 **Cross in Red**

B532	SP284	80c + 20c ol grn	1.10	.65
B533	SP284	1.20fr + 30c brown	1.65	.80
B534	SP284	2fr + 50c rose lake	1.10	1.10
a.		Booklet pane of 8	80.00	65.00
B535	SP284	2.50fr + 50c crimson	13.00	6.00
B536	SP284	4fr + 1fr brt blue	8.50	4.75
B537	SP284	5fr + 2fr sl grn	10.50	6.00
		Nos. B532-B537 (6)	35.85	19.30

The surtax was for the Belgian Red Cross.
The selvage of No. B534a is inscribed in French or Dutch. The value is for the French.

Boats at Dock — SP285

Bridge and Citadel, Namur — SP286

Allegory — SP287

Designs: 1.20fr+30c, Bridge at Bouillon. 2fr+50c, Antwerp waterfront. 4fr+2fr, Wharf at Ghent. 8fr+4fr, Meuse River at Freyr.

1953, June 22 **Unwmk.** ***Perf. 11½***

B538	SP285	80c + 20c green	.90	.85
B539	SP285	1.20fr + 30c redsh brn	1.75	1.50
B540	SP285	2fr + 50c sepia	2.25	2.00
B541	SP286	2.50fr + 50c dp mag	11.00	8.50
B542	SP286	4fr + 2fr vio bl	16.00	8.50
B543	SP286	8fr + 4fr gray blk	20.00	8.50
		Nos. B538-B543 (6)	51.90	29.85

The surtax was used to promote tourism in the Ardenne-Meuse region and for various cultural works.

1953, Oct. 26 **Engr.**

B544	SP287	80c + 20c green	3.50	2.75
B545	SP287	2.50fr + 1fr rose car	32.50	27.50
B546	SP287	4fr + 1.50fr blue	37.50	35.00
		Nos. B544-B546 (3)	73.50	65.25

The surtax was for the European Bureau of Childhood and Youth.

Type of 1951 Dated "1953," and

Ernest Malvoz — SP288

Robert Koch — SP289

Portraits: 3fr+1.50fr, Carlo Forlanini. 4fr+2fr, Leon Charles Albert Calmette.

1953, Dec. 15

B547	SP272	20c + 5c blue	.40	.45
B548	SP272	80c + 20c rose vio	.90	.60
B549	SP272	1.20fr + 30c choc	1.10	.85
B550	SP272	1.50fr + 50c dk gray	1.65	1.00
B551	SP288	2fr + 75c dk grn	2.75	1.65
B552	SP288	3fr + 1.50fr dk red	12.00	8.50
B553	SP288	4fr + 2fr ultra	10.00	7.00
B554	SP289	8fr + 4fr choc	16.00	10.00
		Nos. B547-B554 (8)	44.80	30.05

The surtax was for anti-tuberculosis and other charitable works.

King Albert I Statue — SP290

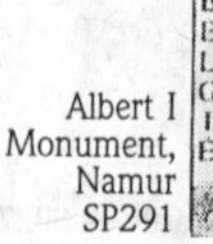

Albert I Monument, Namur
SP291

Design: 9fr+4.50fr, Cliffs of Marche-les-Dames.

1954, Feb. 17 **Photo.**

B555	SP290	2fr + 50c chnt brn	1.90	1.25
B556	SP291	4fr + 2fr blue	11.00	7.75
B557	SP290	9fr + 4.50fr ol blk	15.00	8.25
		Nos. B555-B557 (3)	27.90	17.25

20th anniv. of the death of King Albert I. The surtax aided in the erection of the monument pictured on #B556.

Political Prisoners' Monument — SP292

Camp and Fort, Breendonk
SP293

Design: 9fr+4.50fr, Political prisoners' monument (profile).

1954, Apr. 1 **Unwmk.** ***Perf. 11½***

B558	SP292	2fr + 1fr red	12.00	5.50
B559	SP293	4fr + 2fr dk brn	27.50	13.00
B560	SP292	9fr + 4.50fr ol grn	30.00	13.00
		Nos. B558-B560 (3)	69.50	31.50

The surtax was used toward the creation of a monument to political prisoners.

Gatehouse and Gateway
SP294

Nuns in Courtyard — SP295

Our Lady of the Vine — SP296

Designs: 2fr+1fr, Swans in stream. 7fr+3.50fr Nuns at well. 8fr+4fr, Statue above door.

1954, May 15

B561	SP294	80c + 20c dk bl grn	1.10	.85
B562	SP294	2fr + 1fr crimson	11.00	1.50
B563	SP295	4fr + 2fr violet	16.00	9.25
B564	SP295	7fr + 3.50fr lil rose	35.00	22.50
B565	SP295	8fr + 4fr brown	32.50	19.00
B566	SP296	9fr + 4.50fr gray bl	55.00	30.00
		Nos. B561-B566 (6)	150.60	83.10

The surtax was for the Friends of the Beguinage of Bruges.

Child's Head
SP297

"The Blind Man and the Paralytic," by Antoine Carte
SP298

1954, Dec. 1 **Engr.**

B567	SP297	20c + 5c dk grn	.45	.38
B568	SP297	80c + 20c dk gray	.80	.60
B569	SP297	1.20fr + 30c org brn	1.25	.75
B570	SP297	1.50fr + 50c purple	1.50	1.25
B571	SP298	2fr + 75c rose car	6.00	2.75
B572	SP298	4fr + 1fr brt blue	13.00	7.00
		Nos. B567-B572 (6)	23.00	12.73

The surtax was for anti-tuberculosis work.

Ernest Solvay
SP299

Jean-Jacques Dony — SP300

Portraits: 1.20fr+30c, Egide Walschaerts. 25fr+50c, Leo H. Baekeland. 3fr+1fr, Jean-Etienne Lenoir. 4fr+2fr, Emile Fourcault and Emile Gobbe.

Perf. 11½

1955, Oct. 22 **Unwmk.** **Photo.**

B573	SP299	20c + 5c brn & dk brn	.35	.30
B574	SP300	80c + 20c violet	.90	.45
B575	SP299	1.20fr + 30c indigo	1.00	.60
B576	SP300	2fr + 50c dp car	3.50	2.00
B577	SP300	3fr + 1fr dk grn	10.50	5.00
B578	SP299	4fr + 2fr brown	10.50	5.00
		Nos. B573-B578 (6)	26.75	13.35

Issued in honor of Belgian scientists.
The surtax was for the benefit of various cultural organizations.

"The Joys of Spring" by E. Canneel — SP301

Einar Holböll — SP302

Portraits: 4fr+2fr, John D. Rockefeller. 8fr+4fr, Sir Robert W. Philip.

1955, Dec. 5 **Unwmk.** ***Perf. 11½***

B579	SP301	20c + 5c red lilac	.65	.25
B580	SP301	80c + 20c green	.90	.55
B581	SP301	1.20fr + 30c redsh brn	1.25	.70
B582	SP301	1.50fr + 50c vio bl	1.25	.90
B583	SP302	2fr + 50c carmine	8.25	4.00
B584	SP302	4fr + 2fr ultra	17.00	9.00
B585	SP302	8fr + 4fr ol gray	20.00	11.00
		Nos. B579-B585 (7)	49.30	26.40

The surtax was for anti-tuberculosis work.

Palace of Charles of Lorraine — SP303

Queen Elisabeth and Sonata by Mozart — SP304

Design: 2fr+1fr, Mozart at age 7.

1956, Mar. 5 **Engr.**

B586	SP303	80c + 20c steel bl	1.00	1.00
B587	SP303	2fr + 1fr rose lake	4.00	3.00
B588	SP304	4fr + 2fr dull pur	6.50	3.75
		Nos. B586-B588 (3)	11.50	7.75

200th anniversary of the birth of Wolfgang Amadeus Mozart, composer.
The surtax was for the benefit of the Pro-Mozart Committee in Belgium.

Queen Elisabeth — SP305

1956, Aug. 16 **Photo.**

B589	SP305	80c + 20c slate grn	.90	1.00
B590	SP305	2fr + 1fr deep plum	2.50	1.50
B591	SP305	4fr + 2fr brown	3.50	2.50
		Nos. B589-B591 (3)	6.90	5.00

Issued in honor of the 80th birthday of Queen Elisabeth. The surtax went to the Queen Elisabeth Foundation. See No. 659.

Ship with Cross
SP306

Infant on Scales
SP307

Rehabilitation — SP308

Design: 4fr+2fr, X-Ray examination.

1956, Dec. 17 **Engr.**

B592 SP306	20c + 5c redsh brn	.35	.30
B593 SP306	80c + 20c green	.75	.60
B594 SP306	1.20fr + 30c dl lil	.90	.60
B595 SP306	1.5fr + 50c lt sl bl	.95	.90
B596 SP307	2fr + 50c ol grn	2.25	1.65
B597 SP307	4fr + 2fr dl pur	11.00	6.25
B598 SP308	8fr + 4fr dp car	11.00	7.25
	Nos. B592-B598 (7)	27.20	17.55

The surtax was for anti-tuberculosis work.

Charles Plisnier and Albrecht Rodenbach SP309

Portraits: 80c+20c, Emiel Vliebergh and Maurice Wilmotte. 1.20fr+30c, Paul Pastur and Julius Hoste. 2fr+50c, Lodewijk de Raet and Jules Destree. 3fr+1fr, Constantin Meunier and Constant Permeke. 4fr+2fr, Lieven Gevaert and Edouard Empain.

Perf. 11½

1957, June 8 **Unwmk.** **Photo.**

B599 SP309	20c + 5c brt vio	.35	.30
B600 SP309	80c + 20c lt red brn	.55	.30
B601 SP309	1.20f + 30c blk brn	.65	.50
B602 SP309	2fr + 50c claret	1.65	.85
B603 SP309	3fr + 1fr dk ol grn	2.25	1.65
B604 SP309	4fr + 2fr vio bl	3.25	2.50
	Nos. B599-B604 (6)	8.70	6.10

The surtax was for the benefit of various cultural organizations.

Dogs and Antarctic Camp SP310

1957, Oct. 18 **Engr.** *Perf. 11½*

B605 SP310	5fr + 2.50fr gray, org & vio brn	3.00	2.50
a.	Sheet of 4, #B605b	120.00	130.00
b.	Blue, slate & red brown	25.00	40.00

Surtax for Belgian Antarctic Expedition, 1957-58.

Gen. Patton's Grave and Flag — SP311

Gen. George S. Patton, Jr. — SP312

Designs: 2.50fr+50c, Memorial, Bastogne. 3fr+1fr, Gen. Patton decorating Brig. Gen. Anthony C. McAuliffe. 6fr+3fr, Tanks of 1918 and 1944.

1957, Oct. 28 **Photo.**

Size: 36x25mm, 25x36mm

B606 SP311	1fr + 50c dk gray	1.25	.85
B607 SP311	2.50fr + 50c ol grn	1.75	1.50
B608 SP311	3fr + 1fr red brn	2.75	1.65
B609 SP312	5fr + 2.50fr grysh bl	6.50	4.75

Size: 53x35mm

B610 SP311	6fr + 3fr pale brn car	10.00	6.00
	Nos. B606-B610 (5)	22.25	14.75

The surtax was for the General Patton Memorial Committee and Patriotic Societies.

Adolphe Max — SP313

1957, Nov. 10 **Engr.**

B611 SP313	2.50fr + 1fr ultra	1.40	1.00

18th anniversary of the death of Adolphe Max, mayor of Brussels. The surtax was for the national "Adolphe Max" fund.

"Chinels," Fosses SP314

"Op Signoorken," Malines SP315

Infanta Isabella Shooting Crossbow SP316

Legends: 1.50fr+50c, St. Remacle and the wolf. 2fr+1fr, Longman and the pea soup. 5fr+2fr, The Virgin with Inkwell, vert. 6fr+2.50fr, "Gilles" (clowns), Binche.

1957, Dec. 14 **Engr. & Photo.**

B612 SP314	30c + 20c pur & org yel	.20	.30
B613 SP315	1fr + 50c brn & lt bl	.40	.30
B614 SP314	1.50fr + 50c gray & red	.85	.50
B615 SP315	2fr + 1fr gray & brt grn	1.00	1.00
B616 SP316	2.50fr + 1fr bl grn & lil	1.10	.90
B617 SP316	5fr + 2fr bl & dk gray	3.00	2.25
B618 SP316	6fr + 2.50fr vio brn & red org	4.00	3.25
	Nos. B612-B618 (7)	10.55	8.50

The surtax was for anti-tuberculosis work. See Nos. B631-B637.

Benelux Gate — SP317

Designs: 1fr+50c, Civil Engineering Pavilion. 1.50fr+50c, Ruanda-Urundi Pavilion. 2.50fr+1fr, Belgium 1900. 3fr+1.50fr, Atomium. 5fr+3fr, Telexpo Pavilion.

Perf. 11½

1958, Apr. 15 **Unwmk.** **Engr.**

Size: 35½x24½mm

B619 SP317	30c + 20c multi	.15	.15
B620 SP317	1fr + 50c multi	.15	.15
B621 SP317	1.50fr + 50c multi	.25	.25
B622 SP317	2.50fr + 1fr multi	.40	.45
B623 SP317	3fr + 1.50fr multi	.85	.50

Size: 49x33mm

B624 SP317	5fr + 3fr multi	1.00	.50
	Nos. B619-B624 (6)	2.80	2.00

World's Fair, Brussels, Apr. 17-Oct. 19.

Marguerite van Eyck by Jan van Eyck — SP318

Christ Carrying Cross, by Hieronymus Bosch — SP319

Paintings: 1.50fr+50c, St. Donatien, Jan Gossart. 2.50fr+1fr, Self-portrait, Lambert Lombard. 3fr+1.50fr, The Rower, James Ensor. 5fr+3fr, Henriette, Henri Evenepoel.

1958, Oct. 30 **Photo.** *Perf. 11½*

Various Frames in Ocher and Brown

B625 SP318	30c + 20c dk ol grn	.25	.30
B626 SP319	1fr + 50c mar	.75	.70
B627 SP318	1.50fr + 50c vio bl	1.00	.75
B628 SP318	2.50fr + 1fr dk brn	2.00	1.40
B629 SP319	3fr + 1.50fr dl red	2.50	2.00
B630 SP318	5fr + 3fr brt bl	4.75	5.00
	Nos. B625-B630 (6)	11.25	10.15

The surtax was for the benefit of various cultural organizations.

Type of 1957

Legends: 40c+10c, Elizabeth, Countess of Hoogstraten. 1fr+50c, Jean de Nivelles. 1.50fr+50c, St. Evermare play, Russon. 2fr+1fr, The Penitents of Furnes. 2.50fr+1fr, Manger and "Pax." 5fr+2fr, Sambre-Meuse procession. 6fr+2.50fr, Our Lady of Peace and "Pax," vert.

Engraved and Photogravure

1958, Dec. 6 **Unwmk.** *Perf. 11½*

B631 SP314	40c + 10c ultra & brt grn	.30	.20
B632 SP315	1fr + 50c gray brn & org	.40	.30
B633 SP315	1.50fr + 50c cl & brt grn	.60	.35
B634 SP314	2fr + 1fr brn & red	.75	.50
B635 SP316	2.50fr + 1fr vio brn & bl grn	2.50	1.90
B636 SP316	5fr + 2fr cl & bl	3.75	3.00
B637 SP316	6fr + 2.50fr bl & rose red	4.75	4.50
	Nos. B631-B637 (7)	13.05	10.75

The surtax was for anti-tuberculosis work.

"Europe of the Heart" SP320

1959, Feb. 25 **Photo.** **Unwmk.**

B638 SP320	1fr + 50c red lilac	.90	.45
B639 SP320	2.50fr + 1fr dk green	1.50	1.25
B640 SP320	5fr + 2.50fr dp brn	2.00	1.50
	Nos. B638-B640 (3)	4.40	3.20

The surtax was for aid for displaced persons.

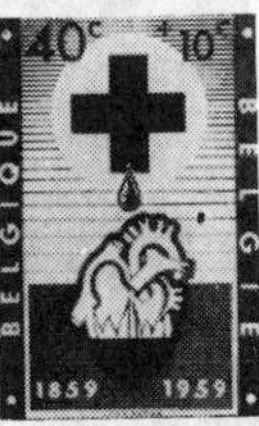

Allegory of Blood Transfusion — SP321

Henri Dunant and Battlefield at Solferino — SP322

Design: 2.50fr+1fr, 3fr+1.50fr, Red Cross, broken sword and drop of blood, horiz.

1959, June 10 **Photo.** *Perf. 11½*

B641 SP321	40c + 10c bl gray & car	.55	.30
B642 SP321	1fr + 50c brn & car	.95	.45
B643 SP321	1.50fr + 50c dl vio & car	1.15	.60
B644 SP321	2.50fr + 1fr sl grn & car	1.65	1.10
B645 SP321	3fr + 1.50fr vio bl & car	4.00	2.50
B646 SP322	5fr + 3fr dk brn & car	6.25	3.25
	Nos. B641-B646 (6)	14.55	8.20

Cent. of the Intl. Red Cross idea. Surtax for the Red Cross and patriotic organizations.

Philip the Good — SP323

Arms of Philip the Good SP324

Designs: 1fr+50c, Charles the Bold. 1.50fr+50c, Emperor Maximilian of Austria. 2.50fr+1fr, Philip the Fair. 3fr+1.50fr, Charles V. Portraits from miniatures by Simon Bening (c. 1483-1561).

1959, July 4 **Engr.**

B647 SP323	40c + 10c multi	.45	.30
B648 SP323	1fr + 50c multi	.75	.45
B649 SP323	1.50fr + 50c multi	.90	.60
B650 SP323	2.50fr + 1fr multi	1.25	1.10
B651 SP323	3fr + 1.50fr multi	3.00	2.50
B652 SP324	5fr + 3fr multi	5.00	3.25
	Nos. B647-B652 (6)	11.35	8.20

The surtax was for the Royal Library, Brussels. Portraits show Grand Masters of the Order of the Golden Fleece.

Whale, Antwerp SP325

Carnival, Stavelot SP326

Designs: 1fr+50c, Dragon, Mons. 2fr+50c, Prince Carnival, Eupen. 3fr+1fr, Jester and cats, Ypres. 6fr+2fr, Holy Family, horiz. 7fr+3fr, Madonna, Liége, horiz.

Engraved and Photogravure

1959, Dec. 5 *Perf. 11½*

B653 SP325	40c + 10c cit, Prus bl & red	.45	.40
B654 SP325	1fr + 50c ol & grn	.70	.55
B655 SP325	2fr + 50c lt brn, org & cl	.50	.40
B656 SP326	2.50fr + 1fr gray, pur & ultra	.75	.55
B657 SP326	3fr + 1fr gray, mar & yel	1.75	1.25
B658 SP326	6fr + 2fr ol, brt bl & hn brn	3.25	2.50
B659 SP326	7fr + 3fr chlky bl & org yel	4.75	4.00
	Nos. B653-B659 (7)	12.15	9.65

The surtax was for anti-tuberculosis work.

Child Refugee — SP327

Designs: 3fr+1.50fr, Man. 6fr+3fr, Woman.

1960, Apr. 7 Engr.

B660 SP327 40c + 10c rose claret .20 .15
B661 SP327 3fr + 1.50fr gray brn .70 .45
B662 SP327 6fr + 3fr dk bl 1.90 1.00
a. Souvenir sheet of 3 50.00 50.00
Nos. B660-B662 (3) 2.80 1.60

Issued to publicize World Refugee Year, July 1, 1959-June 30, 1960.

No. B662a contains Nos. B660-B662 with colors changed: 40c+10c, dull purple; 3fr+1.50fr, red brown; 6fr+3fr, henna brown.

Parachutists and Plane SP328

Designs: 2fr+50c, 2.50fr+1fr, Parachutists coming in for landing, vert 3fr+1fr, 6fr+2fr, Parachutist walking with parachute.

Photogravure and Engraved

1960, June 13 *Perf. 11½*

B663 SP328 40c + 10c lt ultra & blk .15 .15
B664 SP328 1fr + 50c bl & blk .80 .60
B665 SP328 2fr + 50c bl, blk & ol 2.50 1.25
B666 SP328 2.50fr + 1fr grnsh bl, blk & gray ol 2.75 2.00
B667 SP328 3fr + 1fr bl, blk & sl grn 2.75 2.00
B668 SP328 6fr + 2fr lt vio bl, blk & ol 5.25 3.75
Nos. B663-B668 (6) 14.20 9.75

The surtax was for various patriotic and cultural organizations.

Mother and Child, Planes and Rainbow SP329

Designs: 40c+10c, Brussels Airport, planes and rainbow. 6fr+3fr, Rainbow connecting Congo and Belgium, and planes, vert

Perf. 11½

1960, Aug. 3 Unwmk. Photo.

Size: 35x24mm

B669 SP329 40c + 10c grnsh blue .15 .15
B670 SP329 3fr + 1.50fr brt red 2.75 2.25

Size: 35x52mm

B671 SP329 6fr + 3fr violet 4.25 3.00
Nos. B669-B671 (3) 7.15 5.40

The surtax was for refugees from Congo.

Infant, Milk Bottle and Mug — SP330

UNICEF: 1fr+50c, Nurse and children of 3 races. 2fr+50c, Refugee woman carrying gift clothes. 2.50fr+1fr, Negro nurse weighing infant. 3fr+1fr, Children of various races dancing. 6fr+2fr, Refugee boys.

Photogravure and Engraved

1960, Oct. 8 *Perf. 11½*

B672 SP330 40c + 10c gldn brn, yel & bl grn .15 .15
B673 SP330 1fr + 50c ol gray, mar & slate 1.25 .70
B674 SP330 2fr + 50c vio, pale brn & brt grn 1.40 .95
B675 SP330 2.50fr + 1fr dk red, sep & lt bl 1.65 1.25
B676 SP330 3fr + 1fr bl grn, red org & dl vio .90 .80
B677 SP330 6fr + 2fr ultra, emer & brn 3.50 2.75
Nos. B672-B677 (6) 8.85 6.60

Tapestry SP331

Belgian handicrafts: 1fr+50c, Cut crystal vases, vert. 2fr+50c, Lace, vert. 2.50fr+1fr, Metal plate & jug. 3fr+1fr, Diamonds. 6fr+2fr, Ceramics.

1960, Dec. 5 *Perf. 11½*

B678 SP331 40c + 10c bl, bis & brn .15 .15
B679 SP331 1fr + 50c ind & org brn 1.10 1.10
B680 SP331 2fr + 50c dk red brn, blk & cit 2.00 1.65
B681 SP331 2.50fr + 1fr choc & yel 2.50 2.50
B682 SP331 3fr + 1fr org brn, blk & ultra 1.25 1.25
B683 SP331 6fr + 2fr dp blk & yel 5.00 4.00
Nos. B678-B683 (6) 12.00 10.65

The surtax was for anti-tuberculosis work.

Jacob Kats and Abbe Nicolas Pietkin SP332

Portraits: 1fr+50c, Albert Mockel and J. F. Willems. 2fr+50c, Jan van Rijswijck and Xavier M. Neujean. 2.50fr+1fr, Joseph Demarteau and A. Van de Perre. 3fr+1fr, Canon Jan-Baptist David and Albert du Bois. 6fr+2fr, Henri Vieuxtemps and Willem de Mol.

1961, Apr. 22 Unwmk. *Perf. 11½*

Portraits in Gray Brown

B684 SP332 40c + 10c ver & mar .15 .15
B685 SP332 1fr + 50c bis brn & mar 1.50 1.00
B686 SP332 2fr + 50c yel & crim 1.75 1.40
B687 SP332 2.50fr + 1fr pale cit & dk grn 2.75 1.50
B688 SP332 3fr + 1fr lt & dk bl 2.75 2.25
B689 SP332 6fr + 2fr lil & ultra 5.00 4.00
Nos. B684-B689 (6) 13.90 10.30

The surtax was for the benefit of various cultural organizations.

White Rhinoceros SP333

Antonius Cardinal Perrenot de Granvelle SP334

Animals: 1fr+50c, Przewalski horses. 2fr+50c, Okapi. 2.50fr+1fr, Giraffe, horiz. 3fr+1fr, Lesser panda, horiz. 6fr+2fr, European elk, horiz.

Perf. 11½

1961, June 5 Unwmk. Photo.

B690 SP333 40c + 10c bis brn & dk brn .15 .15
B691 SP333 1fr + 50c gray & brn .90 .90
B692 SP333 2fr + 50c dp rose & blk 1.25 1.10
B693 SP333 2.50fr + 1fr red org & brn 1.00 .90
B694 SP333 3fr + 1fr org & brn .90 .90
B695 SP333 6fr + 2fr bl & bis brn 2.25 1.40
Nos. B690-B695 (6) 6.45 5.35

The surtax was for various philanthropic organizations.

1961, July 29 Engr.

Designs: 3fr+1.50fr, Arms of Cardinal de Granvelle. 6fr+3fr, Tower and crosier, symbolic of collaboration between Malines and the Archbishopric.

B696 SP334 40c + 10c magenta, car & brn .15 .15
B697 SP334 3fr + 1.50fr multi .90 .60
B698 SP334 6fr + 3fr mag pur & bis 1.75 1.50
Nos. B696-B698 (3) 2.80 2.25

400th anniv. of Malines as an Archbishopric.

Mother and Child by Pierre Paulus — SP335

Castle of the Counts of Male — SP336

Paintings: 1fr+50c, Mother Love, Francois-Joseph Navez. 2fr+50c, Motherhood, Constant Permeke. 2.50fr+1fr, Madonna and Child, Rogier van der Weyden. 3fr+1fr, Madonna with Apple, Hans Memling. 6fr+2fr, Madonna of the Forget-me-not, Peter Paul Rubens.

1961, Dec. 2 Photo. *Perf. 11½*

Gold Frame

B699 SP335 40c + 10c dp brn .15 .15
B700 SP335 1fr + 50c brt bl .40 .30
B701 SP335 2fr + 50c rose red .60 .45
B702 SP335 2.50fr + 1fr magenta .90 .70
B703 SP335 3fr + 1fr vio bl 1.00 .85
B704 SP335 6fr + 2fr dk sl grn 1.75 1.50
Nos. B699-B704 (6) 4.80 3.95

The surtax was for anti-tuberculosis work.

1962, Mar. 12 Engr. *Perf. 11½*

Designs: 90c+10c, Royal library, horiz. 1fr+50c, Church of Our Lady, Tongres. 2fr+50c, Collegiate Church, Soignies (horiz.). 2.50fr+1fr, Church of Our Lady, Malines. 3fr+1fr, St. Denis Abbey, Broqueroi. 6fr+2fr, Cloth Hall, Ypres, horiz.

B705 SP336 40c + 10c brt grn .15 .15
B706 SP336 90c + 10c lil rose .22 .22
B707 SP336 1fr + 50c dl vio .45 .45
B708 SP336 2fr + 50c violet .65 .65
B709 SP336 2.50fr + 1fr red brn .95 .95
B710 SP336 3fr + 1fr bl grn .95 .95
B711 SP336 6fr + 2fr car rose 1.50 1.40
Nos. B705-B711 (7) 4.87 4.77

The surtax was for various cultural and philanthropic organizations.

Andean Cock of the Rock — SP337

Handicapped Child — SP338

Birds: 1fr+50c, Red lory. 2fr+50c, Guinea touraco. 2.50fr+1fr, Keel-billed toucan. 3fr+1fr, Great bird of paradise. 6fr+2fr, Congolese peacock.

Engraved and Photogravure

1962, June 23 Unwmk. *Perf. 11½*

B712 SP337 40c + 10c multi .15 .15
B713 SP337 1fr + 50c multi .45 .38
B714 SP337 2fr + 50c multi .52 .45
B715 SP337 2.50fr + 1fr multi .60 .52
B716 SP337 3fr + 1fr multi 1.25 1.10
B717 SP337 6fr + 2fr multi 2.25 2.00
Nos. B712-B717 (6) 5.22 4.60

The surtax was for various philanthropic organizations.

1962, Sept. 22 Photo.

Handicapped Children: 40c+10c, Reading Braille. 2fr+50c, Deaf-mute girl with earphones and electronic equipment, horiz. 2.50fr+1fr, Child with ball (cerebral palsy). 3fr+1fr, Girl with crutches (polio). 6fr+2fr, Sitting boys playing ball, horiz.

B718 SP338 40c + 10c choc .15 .15
B719 SP338 1fr + 50c rose red .32 .30
B720 SP338 2fr + 50c brt lil .65 .55
B721 SP338 2.50fr + 1fr dl grn .70 .65
B722 SP338 3fr + 1fr dk bl .90 .85
B723 SP338 6fr + 2fr dk brn 1.65 1.25
Nos. B718-B723 (6) 4.37 3.75

The surtax was for various institutions for handicapped children.

Queen Louise-Marie — SP339

Belgian Queens: No. B725, like No. B724 with "ML" initials. 1fr+50c, Marie-Henriette. 2fr+1fr, Elisabeth. 3fr+1.50fr, Astrid. 8fr+2.50fr, Fabiola.

1962, Dec. 8 Photo. & Engr.

Gray, Black & Gold

B724 SP339 40c + 10c ("L") .15 .15
B725 SP339 40c + 10c ("ML") .15 .15
B726 SP339 1fr + 50c .52 .52
B727 SP339 2fr + 1fr .90 .90
B728 SP339 3fr + 1.50fr 1.00 .90
B729 SP339 8fr + 2.50fr 1.50 1.10
Nos. B724-B729 (6) 4.22 3.72

The surtax was for anti-tuberculosis work.

British War Memorial (Porte de Menin), Ypres — SP340

1962, Dec. 26 Engr. *Perf. 11½*

B730 SP340 1fr + 50c multi .65 .65

Millennium of the city of Ypres. Issued in sheets of eight.

Peace Bell Ringing over Globe SP341

The Sower by Brueghel SP342

Engraved and Photogravure

1963, Feb. 18 Unwmk. *Perf. 11½*

B731 SP341 3fr + 1.50fr blk, bl, org & grn 1.75 1.75
a. Sheet of 4 8.00 8.00
B732 SP341 6fr + 3fr blk, brn & org 1.10 1.10

The surtax was for the installation of the Peace Bell (Bourdon de la Paix) at Koekelberg Basilica and for the benefit of various cultural organizations.

No. B731 was issued in sheets of 4. No. B732 was issued in sheets of 30.

1963, Mar. 21 *Perf. 11½*

Designs: 3fr+1fr, The Harvest, by Brueghel, horiz. 6fr+2fr, "Bread," by Anton Carte, horiz.

B733 SP342 2fr + 1fr grn, ocher & blk .20 .20
B734 SP342 3fr + 1fr red lil, ocher & blk .52 .45
B735 SP342 6fr + 2fr red brn, cit & blk .75 .60
Nos. B733-B735 (3) 1.47 1.25

FAO "Freedom from Hunger" campaign.

Speed Racing — SP343

Designs: 2fr+1fr, Bicyclists at check point, horiz. 3fr+1.50fr, Team racing, horiz. 6fr+3fr, Pace setters.

Perf. 11½

1963, July 13 Unwmk. Engr.

B736 SP343 1fr + 50c multi .15 .15
B737 SP343 2fr + 1fr bl, car, blk & ol gray .25 .25
B738 SP343 3fr + 1.50fr multi .42 .42
B739 SP343 6fr + 3fr multi .60 .60
Nos. B736-B739 (4) 1.42 1.42

80th anniversary of the founding of the Belgian Bicycle League. The surtax was for athletes at the 1964 Olympic Games.

Princess Paola with Princess Astrid — SP344

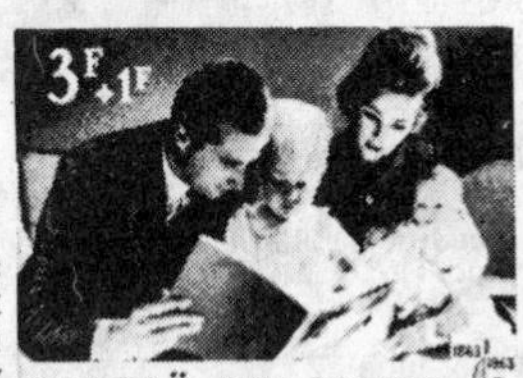

Prince Albert and Family SP345

Designs: 40c+10c, Prince Philippe. 2fr+50c, Princess Astrid. 2.50fr+1fr, Princess Paola. 6fr+2fr, Prince Albert.

1963, Sept. 28 Photo.

B740 SP344 40c + 10c .15 .15
B741 SP344 1fr + 50c .30 .30
B742 SP344 2fr + 50c .38 .38
B743 SP344 2.50fr + 1fr .45 .45
B744 SP345 3fr + 1fr .45 .45
B745 SP345 3fr + 1fr 1.40 1.40
a. Booklet pane of 8 17.00 17.00
B746 SP344 6fr + 2fr .80 .80
Nos. B740-B746 (7) 3.93 3.93

Cent. of the Intl. Red Cross. No. B745 issued in booklet panes of 8, which are in two forms: French and Flemish inscriptions in top and bottom margins transposed.

Daughter of Balthazar Gerbier, Painted by Rubens — SP346

Jesus, St. John and Cherubs by Rubens — SP347

Portraits (Rubens' sons): 1fr+40c, Nicolas, 2 yrs. old. 2fr+50c, Franz. 2.50fr+1fr, Nicolas, 6 yrs. old. 3fr+1fr, Albert.

Photogravure and Engraved

1963, Dec. 7 Unwmk. *Perf. 11½*

B747 SP346 50c + 10c .15 .15
B748 SP346 1fr + 40c .15 .15
B749 SP346 2fr + 50c .28 .28
B750 SP346 2.50fr + 1fr .55 .55
B751 SP346 3fr + 1fr .45 .45
B752 SP347 6fr + 2fr .60 .60
Nos. B747-B752 (6) 2.18 2.18

The surtax was for anti-tuberculosis work. See No. B771.

John Quincy Adams and Lord Gambier Signing Treaty of Ghent, by Amédée Forestier — SP348

1964, May 16 Photo. *Perf. 11½*

B753 SP348 6fr + 3fr dk blue .75 .75

Signing of the Treaty of Ghent between the US and Great Britain, Dec. 24, 1814.

Philip van Marnix — SP349

Portraits: 3fr+1.50fr, Ida de Bure Calvin. 6fr+3fr, Jacob Jordaens.

1964, May 30 Engr.

B754 SP349 1fr + 50c blue gray .15 .15
B755 SP349 3fr + 1.50fr rose pink .25 .25
B756 SP349 6fr + 3fr redsh brn .45 .45
Nos. B754-B756 (3) .85 .85

Issued to honor Protestantism in Belgium. The surtax was for the erection of a Protestant church.

Foot Soldier, 1918 — SP350

Battle of Bastogne — SP351

Designs: 2fr+1fr, Flag bearer, Guides Regiment, 1914. 3fr+1.50fr, Trumpeter of the Grenadiers and drummers, 1914.

1964, Aug. 1 Photo. *Perf. 11½*

B757 SP350 1fr + 50c multi .15 .15
B758 SP350 2fr + 1fr multi .24 .24
B759 SP350 3fr + 1.50fr multi .24 .24
Nos. B757-B759 (3) .63 .63

50th anniversary of the German aggression against Belgium in 1914. The surtax aided patriotic undertakings.

1964, Aug. 1 Unwmk.

Design: 6fr+3fr, Liberation of the estuary of the Escaut.

B760 SP351 3fr + 1fr multi .18 .18
B761 SP351 6fr + 3fr multi .28 .28

Belgium's Resistance and liberation of World War II. The surtax was to help found an International Student Center at Antwerp and to aid cultural undertakings.

Souvenir Sheets

Rogier van der Weyden Paintings — SP352

Descent From the Cross — SP353

1964, Sept. 19 Photo. *Perf. 11½*

B762 SP352 Sheet of 3 2.25 2.25
a. 1fr Philip the Good .52 .52
b. 2fr Portrait of a Lady .52 .52
c. 3fr Man with Arrow .52 .52

Engr.

B763 SP353 8fr red brown 2.25 2.25

Rogier van der Weyden (Roger de La Pasture, 1400-64). The surtax went to various cultural organizations. #B762 sold for 14fr, #B763 for 16fr.

Ancient View of the Pand SP354

Design: 3fr+1fr, Present view of the Pand from Lys River.

1964, Oct. 10 Photo.

B764 SP354 2fr + 1fr blk, grnsh bl & ultra .40 .40
B765 SP354 3fr + 1fr lil rose, bl & dk brn .40 .40

The surtax was for the restoration of the Pand Dominican Abbey in Ghent.

Type of 1963 and

Child of Charles I, Painted by Van Dyck — SP355

Designs: 1fr+40c, William of Orange with his bride, by Van Dyck. 2fr+1fr, Portrait of a small boy with dogs by Erasmus Quellin and Jan Fyt. 3fr+1fr, Alexander Farnese by Antonio Moro. 4fr+2fr, William II, Prince of Orange by Van Dyck. 6fr+3fr, Artist's children by Cornelis De Vos.

1964, Dec. 5 Engr. *Perf. 11½*

B766 SP355 50c + 10c rose cl .15 .15
B767 SP355 1fr + 40c car rose .15 .15
B768 SP355 2fr + 1fr vio brn .15 .15
B769 SP355 3fr + 1fr gray .15 .15
B770 SP355 4fr + 2fr vio bl .24 .24
B771 SP347 6fr + 3fr brt pur .24 .24
Nos. B766-B771 (6) 1.08 1.08

The surtax was for anti-tuberculosis work.

Liberator, Shaking Prisoner's Hand, Concentration Camp — SP356

Designs: 1fr+50c, Prisoner's hand reaching for the sun. 3fr+1.50fr, Searchlights and tank breaking down barbed wire, horiz. 8fr+5fr, Rose growing amid the ruins, horiz.

Engraved and Photogravure

1965, May 8 Unwmk. *Perf. 11½*

B772 SP356 50c + 50c tan, blk & buff .15 .15
B773 SP356 1fr + 50c multi .15 .15
B774 SP356 3fr + 1.50fr dl lil & blk .18 .18
B775 SP356 8fr + 5fr multi .35 .35
Nos. B772-B775 (4) .83 .83

20th anniv. of the liberation of the concentration camps for political prisoners and prisoners of war.

Stoclet House, Brussels SP357

Stoclet House: 6fr+3fr, Hall with marble foundation, vert. 8fr+4fr, View of house from garden.

1965, June 21

B776 SP357 3fr + 1fr slate & tan .22 .22
B777 SP357 6fr + 3fr sepia .32 .32
B778 SP357 8fr + 4fr vio brn & tan .42 .42
Nos. B776-B778 (3) .96 .96

Austrian architect Josef Hoffmann (1870-1956), builder of the art nouveau residence of Adolphe Stoclet, engineer and financier.

Jackson's Chameleon SP358

Animals from Antwerp Zoo: 2fr+1fr, Common iguanas. 3fr+1.50fr, African monitor. 6fr+3fr, Komodo monitor. 8fr+4fr, Nile softshell turtle.

1965, Oct. 16 Photo. *Perf. 11½*

B779 SP358 1fr + 50c multi .15 .15
B780 SP358 2fr + 1fr multi .16 .16
B781 SP358 3fr + 1.50fr multi .22 .22
B782 SP358 6fr + 3fr multi .45 .45
Nos. B779-B782 (4) .98 .98

Miniature Sheet

B783 SP358 8fr + 4fr multi 1.75 1.75

The surtax was for various cultural and philanthropic organizations. No. B783 contains one stamp, size: 52x35mm.

Boatmen's and Archers' Guild Halls — SP359

Buildings on Grand-Place, Brussels: 1fr+40c, Brewers' Hall. 2fr+1fr, "King of Spain." 3fr+1.50fr, "Dukes of Brabant." 10fr+4.50fr, Tower of City Hall and St. Michael.

1965, Dec. 4 Engr. *Perf. 11½*

Size: 35x24mm

B784 SP359 50c + 10c ultra .15 .15
B785 SP359 1fr + 40c bl grn .15 .15
B786 SP359 2fr + 1fr rose claret .18 .18
B787 SP359 3fr + 1.50fr vio .20 .20

Size: 24x44mm

B788 SP359 10fr + 4.50fr sep & gray .32 .32
Nos. B784-B788 (5) 1.00 1.00

The surtax was for anti-tuberculosis work.

Souvenir Sheets

Queen Elisabeth — SP360

Design: No. B790, Types of 1931 and 1956.

1966, Apr. 16 Photo. *Perf. 11½*

B789 SP360 Sheet of 2 + label 1.50 1.50
a. SP74 3fr dk brn & gray grn .60 .60
b. SP87 3fr dk brn, yel grn & gold .60 .60
B790 SP360 Sheet of 2 + label 1.50 1.50
a. SP42 3fr dk brn & dl bl .60 .60
b. SP304 3fr dk brn & gray .60 .60

The surtax went to various cultural organizations. Each sheet sold for 20fr.

Luminescent Paper was used in printing Nos. B789-B790, B801-B806, B808-B809, B811-B823, B825-B831, B833-B835, B837-B840, B842-B846, B848-B850, B852-B854, B856-B863, and from B865 onward unless otherwise noted.

Diver — SP361

Design: 10fr+4fr, Swimmer at start.

1966, May 9 Engr.

B791 SP361 60c + 40c Prus grn, ol & org brn .15 .15
B792 SP361 10fr + 4fr ol grn, org brn & mag .38 .38

Issued to publicize the importance of swimming instruction.

Minorites' Convent, Liège — SP362

Designs: 1fr+50c, Val-Dieu Abbey, Aubel. 2fr+1fr, View and seal of Huy. 10fr+4.50fr, Statue of Ambiorix by Jules Bertin, and tower, Tongeren.

1966, Aug. 27 Engr. *Perf. 11½*

B793 SP362 60c + 40c multi .15 .15
B794 SP362 1fr + 50c multi .15 .15
B795 SP362 2fr + 1fr multi .15 .15
B796 SP362 10fr + 4.50fr multi .42 .42
Set value .69 .69

The surtax was for various patriotic and cultural organizations.

Surveyor and Dog Team — SP363

Designs: 3fr+1.50fr, Adrien de Gerlache and "Belgica." 6fr+3fr, Surveyor, weather balloon and ship. 10fr+5fr, Penguins and "Magga Dan" (ship used for 1964, 1965 and 1966 expeditions).

1966, Oct. 8 Engr. *Perf. 11½*

B797 SP363 1fr + 50c bl grn .15 .15
B798 SP363 3fr + 1.50fr pale vio .20 .20
B799 SP363 6fr + 3fr dk car .35 .35
Nos. B797-B799 (3) .70 .70

Souvenir Sheet

Engraved and Photogravure

B800 SP363 10fr + 5fr dk gray, sky bl & dk red .70 .70

Belgian Antarctic expeditions. #B800 contains one 52x35mm stamp.

Boy with Ball and Dog — SP364

Designs: 2fr+1fr, Girl skipping rope. 3fr+1.50fr, Girl and boy blowing soap bubbles. 6fr+3fr, Girl and boy rolling hoops, horiz. 8fr+3.50fr, Four children at play and cat, horiz.

1966, Dec. 3 *Perf. 11½*

B801 SP364 1fr + 1fr pink & blk .15 .15
B802 SP364 2fr + 1fr lt bluish grn & blk .15 .15
B803 SP364 3fr + 1.50fr lt vio & blk .15 .15
B804 SP364 6fr + 3fr pale sal & dk brn .24 .24
B805 SP364 8fr + 3.50fr lt yel grn & dk brn .28 .28
Nos. B801-B805 (5) .97 .97

The surtax was for anti-tuberculosis work.

Souvenir Sheet

Refugees — SP365

Designs: 1fr, Boy receiving clothes. 2fr, Tibetan children. 3fr, African mother and children.

1967, Mar. 11 Photo. *Perf. 11½*

B806 SP365 Sheet of 3 1.25 1.25
a. 1fr black & yellow .28 .28
b. 2fr black & blue .28 .28
c. 3fr black & orange .40 .40

Issued to help refugees around the world. Sheet has black border with Belgian P.T.T. and UN Refugee emblems. Sold for 20fr.

Robert Schuman — SP366

Colonial Brotherhood Emblem — SP368

Kongolo Memorial, Gentinnes SP367

1967, June 24 Engr. *Perf. 11½*

B807 SP366 2fr + 1fr gray blue .24 .24

Engraved and Photogravure

B808 SP367 5fr + 2fr brn & olive .28 .28
B809 SP368 10fr + 5fr multi .45 .35

Robert Schuman (1886-1963), French statesman, one of the founders of European Steel and Coal Community, 1st pres. of European Parliament (2fr+1fr); Kongolo Memorial, erected in memory of missionary and civilian victims in the Congo (5fr+2fr); a memorial for African Troops, Brussels (10fr+5fr).

Preaching Fool from "Praise of Folly" by Erasmus — SP369

Erasmus, by Quentin Massys — SP370

Designs: 2fr+1fr, Exhorting Fool from Praise of Folly. 5fr+2fr, Thomas More's Family, by Hans Holbein, horiz. 6fr+3fr, Pierre Gilles (Aegidius), by Quentin Massys.

Photogravure and Engraved (SP369); Photogravure (SP370)

1967, Sept. 2 Unwmk. *Perf. 11*

B810 SP369 1fr + 50c tan, blk, bl & car .15 .15
B811 SP369 2fr + 1fr tan, blk & car .15 .15
B812 SP370 3fr + 1.50fr multi .15 .15
B813 SP369 5fr + 2fr tan, blk & car .18 .18
B814 SP370 6fr + 3fr multi .24 .24
Nos. B810-B814 (5) .87 .87

Issued to commemorate Erasmus (1466(?)-1536), Dutch scholar and his era.

Souvenir Sheet

Pro-Post Association Emblem — SP371

Engraved and Photogravure

1967, Oct. 21 *Perf. 11½*

B815 SP371 10fr + 5fr multi .75 .75

Issued to publicize the POSTPHILA Philatelic Exhibition, Brussels, Oct. 21-29.

Detail from Brueghel's "Children's Games" — SP372

Designs: Various Children's Games. Singles of Nos. B816-B821 arranged in 2 rows of 3 show complete painting by Pieter Brueghel.

1967, Dec. 9 Photo. *Perf. 11½*

B816 SP372 1fr + 50c multi .15 .15
B817 SP372 2fr + 50c multi .18 .18
B818 SP372 3fr + 1fr multi .18 .18
B819 SP372 6fr + 3fr multi .30 .30
B820 SP372 10fr + 4fr multi .40 .40
B821 SP372 13fr + 6fr multi .60 .60
Nos. B816-B821 (6) 1.81 1.81

Queen Fabiola Holding Refugee Child from Congo — SP373

Design: 6fr+3fr, Queen Elisabeth and Dr. Depage.

1968, Apr. 27 Photo. *Perf. 11½*

Cross in Red

B822 SP373 6fr + 3fr sepia & gray .25 .25
B823 SP373 10fr + 5fr sepia & gray .45 .45

The surtax was for the Red Cross.

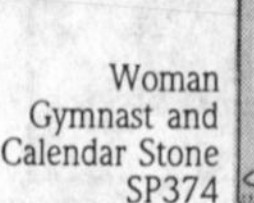

Woman Gymnast and Calendar Stone SP374

Yachting and "The Swimmer" by Andrien SP375

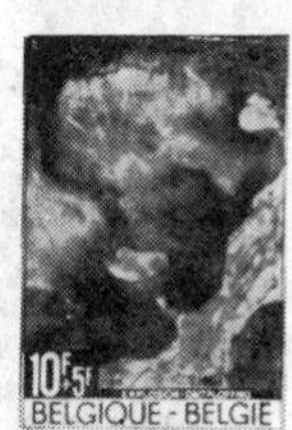

"Explosion" SP376

Designs: 2fr+1fr, Weight lifter and Mayan motif. 3fr+1.50fr, Hurdler, colossus of Tula and animal head from Kukulkan. 6fr+2fr, Bicyclists and Chichen Itza Temple.

Engraved and Photogravure

1968, May 27 *Perf. 11½*

B824 SP374 1fr + 50c multi .15 .15
B825 SP374 2fr + 1fr multi .15 .15
B826 SP374 3fr + 1.50fr multi .15 .15
B827 SP374 6fr + 2fr multi .24 .24

Photo.

B828 SP375 13fr + 5fr multi .52 .52
Nos. B824-B828 (5) 1.21 1.21

Issued to publicize the 19th Olympic Games, Mexico City, Oct. 12-27.

1968, June 22 Photo.

Designs (Paintings by Pol Mara): 12fr+5fr, "Fire." 13fr+5fr, "Tornado."

B829 SP376 10fr + 5fr multi .40 .40
B830 SP376 12fr + 5fr multi .65 .65
B831 SP376 13fr + 5fr multi .70 .70
Nos. B829-B831 (3) 1.75 1.75

The surtax was for disaster victims.

Undulate Triggerfish SP377

Tropical Fish: 3fr+1.50fr, Angelfish. 6fr+3fr, Turkeyfish (Pterois volitans). 10fr+5fr, Orange butterflyfish.

1968, Oct. 19 Engr. & Photo.

B832 SP377 1fr + 50c multi .15 .15
B833 SP377 3fr + 1.50fr multi .15 .15
B834 SP377 6fr + 3fr multi .30 .30
B835 SP377 10fr + 5fr multi .42 .42
Nos. B832-B835 (4) 1.02 1.02

King Albert and Queen Elisabeth Entering Brussels SP378

Tomb of the Unknown Soldier and Eternal Flame, Brussels — SP379

Designs: 1fr+50c, King Albert, Queen Elisabeth and Crown Prince Leopold on balcony, Bruges, vert. 6fr+3fr, King and Queen entering Liège.

1968, Nov. 9 Photo. *Perf. 11½*

B836 SP378 1fr + 50c multi .15 .15
B837 SP378 3fr + 1.50fr multi .15 .15
B838 SP378 6fr + 3fr multi .30 .30

Engraved and Photogravure

B839 SP379 10fr + 5fr multi .40 .40
Nos. B836-B839 (4) 1.00 1.00

50th anniv. of the victory in World War I.

Souvenir Sheet

The Painter and the Amateur, by Peter Brueghel — SP380

1969, May 10 Engr. *Perf. 11½*

B840 SP380 10fr + 5fr sepia 1.10 1.10

Issued to publicize the POSTPHILA 1969 Philatelic Exhibition, Brussels, May 10-18.

Huts, by Ivanka D. Pancheva, Bulgaria SP381

Msgr. Victor Scheppers SP382

Children's Drawings and UNICEF Emblem: 3fr+1.50fr, "My Art" (Santa Claus), by Claes Patric, Belgium. 6fr+3fr, "In the Sun" (young boy), by Helena Rejchlova, Czechoslovakia. 10fr+5fr, "Out for a Walk" by Phillis Sporn, US, horiz.

1969, May 31 Photo. *Perf. 11½*

B841 SP381 1fr + 50c multi .15 .15
B842 SP381 3fr + 1.50fr multi .16 .16
B843 SP381 6fr + 3fr multi .35 .35
B844 SP381 10fr + 5fr multi .52 .52
Nos. B841-B844 (4) 1.18 1.18

The surtax was for philanthropic purposes.

1969, July 5 Engr.

B845 SP382 6fr + 3fr rose claret .45 .45

Msgr. Victor Scheppers (1802-77), prison reformer and founder of the Brothers of Mechlin (Scheppers).

Moon Landing Type of 1969
Souvenir Sheet

Design: 20fr+10fr, Armstrong, Collins and Aldrin and moon with Tranquillity Base, vert.

1969, Sept. 20 Photo. *Perf. 11½*

B846 A245 20fr + 10fr indigo 3.00 3.00

See note after No. 726.

Heads from Alexander the Great Tapestry, 15th Century — SP383

Designs from Tapestries: 3fr+1.50fr, Fiddler from "The Feast," c. 1700. 10fr+4fr, Head of beggar from "The Healing of the Paralytic," 16th century.

1969, Sept. 20

B847 SP383 1fr + 50c multi .15 .15
B848 SP383 3fr + 1.50fr multi .18 .18
B849 SP383 10fr + 4fr multi .45 .45
Nos. B847-B849 (3) .78 .78

The surtax was for philanthropic purposes.

Bearded Antwerp Bantam SP384

1969, Nov. 8 Engr. & Photo.

B850 SP384 10fr + 5fr multi .70 .70

Angel Playing Lute — SP385

Designs from Stained Glass Windows: 1.50fr+50c, Angel with trumpet, St. Waudru's, Mons. 7fr+3fr, Angel with viol, St. Jacques', Liege. 9fr+4fr, King with bagpipes, Royal Art Museum, Brussels.

1969, Dec. 13 Photo.

Size: 24x35mm

B851 SP385 1.50fr + 50c multi .15 .15
B852 SP385 3.50fr + 1.50fr multi .18 .18
B853 SP385 7fr + 3fr multi .35 .35

Size: 35x52mm

B854 SP386 9fr + 4fr multi .52 .52
Nos. B851-B854 (4) 1.20 1.20

The surtax was for philanthropic purposes.

Farm and Windmill, Open-air Museum, Bokrijk SP386

Belgian Museums: 3.50fr+1.50fr, Stage Coach Inn, Courcelles. 7fr+3fr, "The Thresher of Trevires," Gallo-Roman sculpture, Gaumais Museum, Virton. 9fr+4fr, "The Sovereigns," by Henry Moore, Middelheim Museum, Antwerp.

Engraved and Photogravure

1970, May 30 *Perf. 11½*

B855 SP386 1.50fr + 50c multi .15 .15
B856 SP386 3.50fr + 1.50fr multi .25 .25
B857 SP386 7fr + 3fr multi .35 .35
B858 SP386 9fr + 4fr multi .40 .40
Nos. B855-B858 (4) 1.15 1.15

The surtax went to various culture organizations.

"Resistance" — SP387

Design: 7fr+3fr, "Liberation of Camps." The designs were originally used as book covers.

1970, July 4 Photo. *Perf. 11½*

B859 SP387 3.50fr + 1.50fr blk, gray grn & dp car .20 .20
B860 SP387 7fr + 3fr blk, lil & dp car .40 .40

Honoring the Resistance Movement and 25th anniv. of the liberation of concentration camps.

Fishing Rod and Reel — SP388

Design: 9fr+4fr, Hockey stick and puck, vert.

1970, Sept. 19 Engr. & Photo.

B861 SP388 3.50fr + 1.50fr multi .28 .28
B862 SP388 9fr + 4fr multi .48 .48

Souvenir Sheet

Belgium Nos. 31, 36, 39 — SP389

1970, Oct. 10 *Perf. 11½*

B863 SP389 Sheet of 3 4.75 4.75
a. 1.50fr + 50c black & dull lilac 1.40 1.40
b. 3.50fr + 1.50fr black & lilac 1.40 1.40
c. 9fr + 4fr black & red brown 1.40 1.40

BELGICA 72 International Philatelic Exhibition, Brussels, June 24-July 9.

Camille Huysmans (1871-1968) SP390

"Anxious City" (Detail) by Paul Delvaux SP391

Portraits: 3.50fr+1.50fr, Joseph Cardinal Cardijn (1882-1967). 7fr+3fr, Maria Baers (1883-1959). 9fr+4fr, Paul Pastur (1866-1938).

1970, Nov. 14 *Perf. 11½*

Portraits in Sepia

B864 SP390 1.50fr + 50c car rose .15 .15
B865 SP390 3.50fr + 1.50fr lilac .20 .20
B866 SP390 7fr + 3fr green .40 .40
B867 SP390 9fr + 4fr blue .48 .48
Nos. B864-B867 (4) 1.23 1.23

1970, Dec. 12 Photo.

Design: 7fr+3fr, "The Memory," by Rene Magritte.

B868 SP391 3.50fr + 1.50fr multi .18 .18
B869 SP391 7fr + 3fr multi .38 .38

Notre Dame du Vivier, Marche-les-Dames — SP392

Design: 7fr+3fr, Turnhout Beguinage and Beguine.

1971, Mar. 13 *Perf. 11½*

B870 SP392 3.50fr + 1.50fr multi .20 .20
B871 SP392 7fr + 3fr multi .40 .40

The surtax was for philanthropic purposes.

Red Cross — SP393

1971, May 22 Photo. *Perf. 11½*

B872 SP393 10fr + 5fr crim & blk .75 .75

Belgian Red Cross.

Discobolus and Munich Cathedral SP394

Festival of Flanders SP395

1971, June 19 Engr. & Photo.

B873 SP394 7fr + 3fr bl & blk .42 .42

Publicity for the 20th Summer Olympic Games, Munich 1972.

1971, Sept. 11 Photo. *Perf. 11½*

Design: 7fr+3fr, Wallonia Festival.

B874 SP395 3.50fr + 1.50fr multi .18 .18
B875 SP395 7fr + 3fr multi .38 .38

Attre Palace — SP396

Steen Palace, Elewijt — SP397

Design: 10fr+5fr, Royal Palace, Brussels.

1971, Oct. 23 Engr.

B876 SP396 3.50fr + 1.50fr sl grn .30 .30
B877 SP397 7fr + 3fr red brn .50 .50
B878 SP396 10fr + 5fr vio bl .70 .70
Nos. B876-B878 (3) 1.50 1.50

Surtax was for BELGICA 72, International Philatelic Exposition.

Ox Fly — SP398

Insects: 1.50fr+50c, Luna moth, vert. 7fr+3fr, Wasp, polistes gallicus. 9fr+4fr, Tiger beetle, vert.

1971, Dec. 11 Photo. *Perf. 11½*

B879 SP398 1.50fr + 50c multi .20 .20
B880 SP398 3.50fr + 1.50fr multi .20 .20
B881 SP398 7fr + 3fr multi .40 .40
B882 SP398 9fr + 4fr multi .60 .60
Nos. B879-B882 (4) 1.40 1.40

Surtax was for philanthropic purposes.

Leopold I on #1 — SP399

Epilepsy Emblem — SP400

Designs: 2fr+1fr, Leopold I on No. 5. 2.50fr+1fr, Leopold II on No. 45. 3.50fr+1.50fr, Leopold II on No. 48. 6fr+3fr, Albert I on No. 135. 7fr+3fr, Albert I on No. 214. 10fr+5fr, Albert I on No. 231. 15fr+7.50fr, Leopold III on No. 290. 20fr+10fr, King Baudouin on No. 718.

Engraved and Photogravure

1972, June 24 *Perf. 11½*

B883 SP399 1.50fr + 50c .16 .16
B884 SP399 2fr + 1fr .16 .16
B885 SP399 2.50 + 1fr .20 .20
B886 SP399 3.50fr + 1.50fr .32 .32
B887 SP399 6fr + 3fr .52 .52
B888 SP399 7fr + 3fr .70 .70
B889 SP399 10fr + 5fr .90 .90
B890 SP399 15fr + 7fr 1.10 1.10
B891 SP399 20fr + 10fr 2.00 2.00
Nos. B883-B891 (9) 6.06 6.06

Belgica 72, Intl. Philatelic Exhibition, Brussels, June 24-July 9. Nos. B883-B891 issued in sheets of 10 and of 20 (2 tete beche sheets with gutter between). Sold in complete sets.

1972, Sept. 9 **Photo.** *Perf. 11½*

B892 SP400 10fr + 5fr multi .55 .55

The surtax was for the William Lennox Center for epilepsy research and treatment.

Gray Lag Goose — SP401

Designs: 4.50fr+2fr, Lapwing. 8fr+4fr, Stork. 9fr+4.50fr, Kestrel, horiz.

1972, Dec. 16 **Photo.** *Perf. 11½*

B893 SP401 2fr + 1fr multi .22 .22
B894 SP401 4.50fr + 2fr multi .32 .32
B895 SP401 8fr + 4fr multi .60 .60
B896 SP401 9fr + 4.50fr multi .60 .60
Nos. B893-B896 (4) 1.74 1.74

Bijloke Abbey, Ghent — SP402

Designs: 4.50fr+2fr, St. Ursmer Collegiate Church, Lobbes. 8fr+4fr, Park Abbey, Heverle. 9fr+4.50fr, Abbey, Floreffe.

1973, Mar. 24 **Engr.** *Perf. 11½*

B897 SP402 2fr + 1fr slate grn .16 .16
B898 SP402 4.50fr + 2fr brown .24 .24
B899 SP402 8fr + 4fr rose lil .48 .48
B900 SP402 9fr + 4.50fr brt bl .60 .60
Nos. B897-B900 (4) 1.48 1.48

Basketball SP403

1973, Apr. 7 **Photo. & Engr.**

B901 SP403 10fr + 5fr multi .60 .60

First World Basketball Championships of the Handicapped, Bruges, Apr. 16-21.

Dirk Martens' Printing Press — SP404

Lady Talbot, by Petrus Christus — SP405

Hadrian and Marcus Aurelius Coins — SP406

Council of Malines, by Coussaert — SP407

Designs: 3.50fr+1.50fr, Head of Amon and Tutankhamen's cartouche. 10fr+5fr, Three-master of Ostend Merchant Company.

Photogravure and Engraved; Photogravure (#B906)

1973, June 23 *Perf. 11½*

B902 SP404 2fr + 1fr multi .15 .15
B903 SP404 3.50fr + 1.50fr multi .15 .15
B904 SP405 4.50fr + 2fr multi .20 .20
B905 SP406 8fr + 4fr multi .60 .60
B906 SP407 9fr + 4.50fr multi .85 .85
B907 SP407 10fr + 5fr multi 1.50 1.50
Nos. B902-B907 (6) 3.45 3.45

500th anniv. of 1st book printed in Belgium (#B902); 50th anniv. of Queen Elisabeth Egyptological Foundation (#B903); 500th anniv. of death of painter Petrus Christus (#B904); Discovery of Roman treasure at Luttre-Liberchies (#B905); 500th anniv. of Great Council of Malines (#B906); 250th anniv. of the Ostend Merchant Company (#B907).

No. B902 is not luminescent.

Queen of Hearts SP408

Symbol of Blood Donations SP409

Old Playing Cards: #B909, King of Clubs. #B910, Jack of Diamonds. #B911, King of Spades.

1973, Dec. 8 **Photo.** *Perf. 11½*

B908 SP408 5fr + 2.50fr multi .38 .38
B909 SP408 5fr + 2.50fr multi .38 .38
B910 SP408 5fr + 2.50fr multi .38 .38
B911 SP408 5fr + 2.50fr multi .38 .38
a. Block of 4, #B908-B911 1.60 1.60

Surtax was for philanthropic purposes.

1974, Feb. 23 **Photo.** *Perf. 11½*

Design: 10fr+5fr, Traffic lights, Red Cross (symbolic of road accidents).

B912 SP409 4fr + 2fr multi .24 .24
B913 SP409 10fr + 5fr multi .55 .55

The Red Cross as blood collector and aid to accident victims.

Armand Jamar, Self-portrait SP410

Van Gogh, Self-portrait and House at Cuesmes SP411

Designs: 5fr+2.50fr, Anton Bergmann and view of Lierre. 7fr+3.50fr, Henri Vieuxtemps and view of Verviers. 10fr+5fr, James Ensor, self-portrait, and masks.

1974, Apr. 6 **Photo.** *Perf. 11½*

Size: 24x35mm

B914 SP410 4fr + 2fr multi .24 .24
B915 SP410 5fr + 2.50fr multi .32 .32
B916 SP410 7fr + 3.50fr multi .40 .40

Size: 35x52mm

B917 SP410 10fr + 5fr multi .65 .65
Nos. B914-B917 (4) 1.61 1.61

1974, Sept. 21 **Photo.** *Perf. 11½*

B918 SP411 10fr + 5fr multi .55 .55

Opening of Vincent van Gogh House at Cuesmes, where he worked as teacher.

Gentian — SP412

Spotted Cat's Ear — SP414

Badger SP413

Design: 7fr+3.50fr, Beetle.

1974, Dec. 8 **Photo.** *Perf. 11½*

B919 SP412 4fr + 2fr multi .25 .25
B920 SP413 5fr + 2.50fr multi .30 .30
B921 SP413 7fr + 3.50fr multi .40 .40
B922 SP414 10fr + 5fr multi .60 .60
Nos. B919-B922 (4) 1.55 1.55

Pesaro Palace, Venice SP415

St. Bavon Abbey, Ghent SP416

Virgin and Child, by Michelangelo — SP417

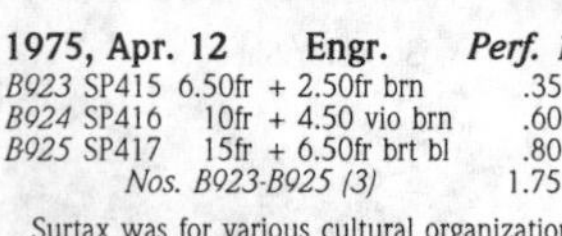

1975, Apr. 12 **Engr.** *Perf. 11½*

B923 SP415 6.50fr + 2.50fr brn .35 .35
B924 SP416 10fr + 4.50 vio brn .60 .60
B925 SP417 15fr + 6.50fr brt bl .80 .80
Nos. B923-B925 (3) 1.75 1.75

Surtax was for various cultural organizations.

Frans Hemerijckx and Leprosarium, Kasai — SP418

1975, Sept. 13 **Photo.** *Perf. 11½*

B926 SP418 20fr + 10fr multi 1.40 1.40

Dr. Frans Hemerijckx (1902-1969), tropical medicine and leprosy expert.

Emile Moyson — SP419

Beheading of St. Dympna — SP420a

Hand Reading Braille SP420

Design: 6.50fr+3fr, Dr. Ferdinand Augustin Snellaert.

1975, Nov. 22 **Engr.** *Perf. 11½*

B927 SP419 4.50fr + 2fr lilac .24 .24
B928 SP419 6.50fr + 3fr green .35 .35

Engraved and Photogravure

B929 SP420 10fr + 5fr multi .50 .50

Photo.

B930 SP420a 13fr + 6fr multi .70 .70
Nos. B927-B930 (4) 1.79 1.79

Emile Moyson (1838-1868), freedom fighter for the rights of Flemings and Walloons; Dr. Snellaert (1809-1872), physician and Flemish patriot; Louis Braille (1809-1852), sesquicentennial of invention of Braille system of writing for the blind; St. Dympna, patron saint of Geel, famous for treatment of mentally ill.

The Cheese Vendor — SP421

Designs (THEMABELGA Emblem and): No. B932, Potato vendor. No. B933, Basket carrier. No. B934, Shrimp fisherman with horse, horiz. No. B935, Knife grinder, horiz. No. B936, Milk vendor with dog cart, horiz.

1975, Dec. 13 **Engr. & Photo.**

B931 SP421 4.50fr + 1.50fr multi .15 .15
B932 SP421 6.50fr + 3fr multi .32 .32
B933 SP421 6.50fr + 3fr multi .32 .32
B934 SP421 10fr + 5fr multi .45 .45
B935 SP421 10fr + 5fr multi .45 .45
B936 SP421 30fr + 15fr multi 1.50 1.50
Nos. B931-B936 (6) 3.19 3.19

THEMABELGA International Topical Philatelic Exhibition, Brussels, Dec. 13-21. Issued in sheets of 10 (5x2).

Blackface Fund Collector — SP422

1976, Feb. 14 Photo. *Perf. 11½*

B937 SP422 10fr + 5fr multi .55 .55

Centenary of the "Conservatoire Africain" philanthropic society, and to publicize the Princess Paola creches.

Swimming and Olympic Emblem SP423

Designs (Montreal Olympic Games Emblem and): 5fr+2fr, Running, vert. 6.50fr+2.50fr, Equestrian.

1976, Apr. 10 Photo. *Perf. 11½*

B938 SP423 4.50fr + 1.50fr multi .18 .18
B939 SP423 5fr + 2fr multi .25 .25
B940 SP423 6.50fr + 2.50fr multi .45 .45
Nos. B938-B940 (3) .88 .88

21st Olympic Games, Montreal, Canada, July 17-Aug. 1.

Queen Elisabeth Playing Violin SP424

Perf. 11½

1976, May 1 Engr. Photo.

B941 SP424 14fr + 6fr blk & claret .95 .95

Queen Elisabeth International Music Competition, 25th anniversary.

Souvenir Sheet

Jan Olieslagers, Bleriot Monoplane, Aero Club Emblem SP425

Engraved and Photogravure

1976, June 12 *Perf. 11½*

B942 SP425 25fr + 10fr multi 2.25 2.25

Royal Belgian Aero Club, 75th anniversary, and Jan Olieslagers (1883-1942), aviation pioneer.

Adoration of the Shepherds (detail), by Rubens SP426

Dwarf, by Velazquez SP427

Rubens Paintings (Details): 4.50fr, Descent from the Cross. No. B945, The Virgin with the Parrot. No. B946, Adoration of the Kings. No. B947, Last Communion of St. Francis. 30fr+15fr, Virgin and Child.

1976, Sept. 4 Photo. *Perf. 11½*

Size: 35x52mm

B943 SP426 4.50fr + 1.50fr multi .35 .35

Size: 24x35mm

B944 SP426 6.50fr + 3fr multi .55 .55
B945 SP426 6.50fr + 3fr multi .55 .55
B946 SP426 10fr + 5fr multi .85 .85
B947 SP426 10fr + 5fr multi .85 .85

Size: 35x52mm

B948 SP426 30fr + 15fr multi 1.75 1.75
Nos. B943-B948 (6) 4.90 4.90

Peter Paul Rubens (1577-1640), Flemish painter, 400th birth anniversary.

1976, Nov. 6 Photo. *Perf. 11½*

B949 SP427 14fr + 6fr multi .80 .80

Surtax was for the National Association for the Mentally Handicapped.

Dr. Albert Hustin — SP428

Red Cross and Rheumatism Year Emblem — SP429

1977, Feb. 19 Photo. *Perf. 11½*

B950 SP428 6.50fr + 2.50 multi .38 .38
B951 SP429 14fr + 7fr multi .75 .75

Belgian Red Cross.

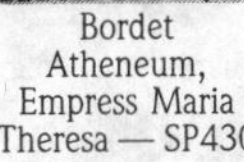

Bordet Atheneum, Empress Maria Theresa — SP430

Conductor and Orchestra, by E. Tytgat — SP431

Lucien Van Obbergh, Stage — SP432

Humanistic Society Emblem SP433

Camille Lemonnier SP434

Design: No. B953, Marie-Therese College, Herve, and coat of arms.

1977, Mar. 21 Photo. *Perf. 11½*

B952 SP430 4.50fr + 1fr multi .20 .20
B953 SP430 4.50fr + 1fr multi .20 .20
B954 SP431 5fr + 2fr multi .24 .24
B955 SP432 6.50fr + 2fr multi .32 .32
B956 SP433 6.50fr + 2fr blk & red .32 .32

Engr.

B957 SP434 10fr + 5fr slate bl .48 .48
Nos. B952-B957 (6) 1.76 1.76

Bicentenaries of the Jules Bordet Atheneum, Brussels, and the Marie-Therese College, Herve (#B952-B953); 50th anniv. of the Brussels Philharmonic Soc., and Artists' Union (#B954-B955); 25th anniv. of the Flemish Humanistic Organization (#B956); 75th anniv. of the French-speaking Belgian writers' organization (#957).

Young Soccer Players — SP435

Albert-Edouard Janssen, Financier — SP436

1977, Apr. 18 Photo.

B958 SP435 10fr + 5fr multi .55 .55

30th Intl. Junior Soccer Tournament.

1977, Dec. 3 Engr. *Perf. 11½*

Famous Men: No. B960, Joseph Wauters (1875-1929), editor of Le Peuple, and newspaper. No. B961, Jean Capart (1877-1947), Egyptologist, and hieroglyph. No. B962, August de Boeck (1865-1937), composer, and score.

B959 SP436 5fr + 2.50fr brown .28 .28
B960 SP436 5fr + 2.50fr red .28 .28
B961 SP436 10fr + 5fr magenta .55 .55
B962 SP436 10fr + 5fr blue gray .55 .55
Nos. B959-B962 (4) 1.66 1.66

Abandoned Child — SP437

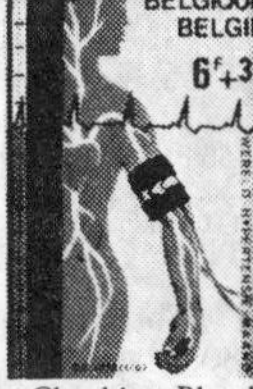

Checking Blood Pressure — SP438

De Mick Sanatorium, Brasschaat — SP439

1978, Feb. 18 Photo. *Perf. 11½*

B963 SP437 4.50fr + 1.50fr multi .15 .15
B964 SP438 6fr + 3fr multi .38 .38
B965 SP439 10fr + 5fr multi .60 .60
Nos. B963-B965 (3) 1.13 1.13

Help for abandoned children (No. B963); fight against hypertension (No. B964); fight against tuberculosis (No. B965).

Actors and Theater SP440

Karel van de Woestijne SP441

Designs: No. B967, Harquebusier, Harquebusier Palace and coat of arms. 10fr+5fr, John of Austria and his signature.

Engraved and Photogravure

1978, June 17 *Perf. 11½*

B966 SP440 6fr + 3fr multi .38 .38
B967 SP440 6fr + 3fr multi .38 .38

Engr.

B968 SP441 8fr + 4fr black .45 .45
B969 SP441 10fr + 5fr black .55 .55
Nos. B966-B969 (4) 1.76 1.76

Cent. of Royal Flemish Theater, Brussels (#B966); 400th anniv. of Harquebusiers' Guild of Vise, Liege (#967); Karel van de Woestijne (1878-1929), poet (#B968); 400th anniv. of signing of Perpetual Edict by John of Austria (#969).

Lake Placid '80 and Belgian Olympic Emblems — SP442

Designs (Moscow '80 Emblem and): 8fr+3.50fr, Kremlin Towers and Belgian Olympic Committee emblem. 7fr+3fr, Runners from Greek vase, Lake Placid '80 emblem and Olympic rings. 14fr+6fr, Olympic flame, Lake Placid '80 and Belgian emblems, Olympic rings.

1978, Nov. 4 Photo. *Perf. 11½*

B970 SP442 6fr + 2.50fr multi .30 .30
B971 SP442 8fr + 3.50fr multi .45 .45

Souvenir Sheet

B972 Sheet of 2 1.40 1.40
a. SP442 7fr + 3fr multi .55 .55
b. SP442 14fr + 6fr multi .90 .90

Surtax was for 1980 Olympic Games.

Great Synagogue, Brussels — SP443

Dancers SP444

Father Pire, African Village SP445

1978, Dec. 2 Engr. *Perf. 11½*

B973 SP443 6fr + 2fr sepia .45 .45

Photo.

B974 SP444 8fr + 3fr multi .35 .35
B975 SP445 14fr + 7fr multi .65 .65
Nos. B973-B975 (3) 1.45 1.45

Centenary of Great Synagogue of Brussels; Flemish Catholic Youth Action Organization, 50th anniversary; Nobel Peace Prize awarded to Father Dominique Pire for his "Heart Open to the World" movement, 20th anniversary.

Young People Giving First Aid — SP446

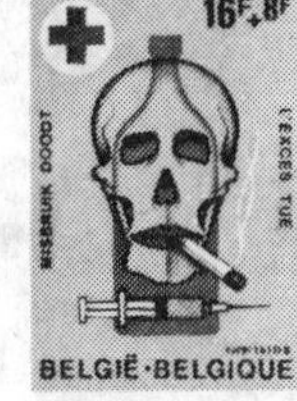

Skull with Bottle, Cigarette, Syringe — SP447

1979, Feb. 10 Photo. *Perf. 11½*

B976 SP446 8fr + 3fr multi .35 .35
B977 SP447 16fr + 8fr multi .85 .85

Belgian Red Cross.

Beatrice Soetkens with Statue of Virgin Mary — SP448

Details from Tapestries, 1516-1518, Showing Legend of Our Lady of Sand: 8fr+3fr, Francois de Tassis accepting letter from Emperor Frederick III (beginning of postal service). 14fr+7fr, Arrival of statue, Francois de Tassis and Philip the Fair. No. B981, Statue carried in procession by future Emperor Charles V and his brother Ferdinand. No. B982, Ship carrying Beatrice Soetkens with statue to Brussels, horiz.

1979, May 5 Photo. *Perf. 11½*

B978 SP448 6fr + 2fr multi .25 .25
B979 SP448 8fr + 3fr multi .40 .40
B980 SP448 14fr + 7fr multi .65 .65
B981 SP448 20fr + 10fr multi 1.10 1.10
Nos. B978-B981 (4) 2.40 2.40

Souvenir Sheet

B982 SP448 20fr + 10fr multi .90 .90

The surtax was for festivities in connection with the millennium of Brussels.

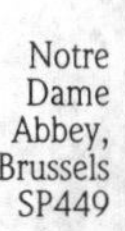

Notre Dame Abbey, Brussels SP449

Designs: 8fr+3fr, Beauvoorde Castle. 14fr+7fr, 1st issue of "Courrier de L'Escaut" and Barthelemy Dumortier, founder. 20fr+10fr, Shrine of St. Hermes, Renaix.

Engraved and Photogravure

1979, Sept. 15 *Perf. 11½*

B983 SP449 6fr + 2fr multi .35 .35
B984 SP449 8fr + 3fr multi .50 .50
B985 SP449 14fr + 7fr multi .60 .60
B986 SP449 20fr + 10fr multi 1.10 1.10
Nos. B983-B986 (4) 2.55 2.55

50th anniv. of restoration of Notre Dame de la Cambre Abbey; historic Beauvoorde Castle, 15th cent. sesquicentennial of the regional newspaper "Le Courrier de L'Escaut"; 850th anniv. of the consecration of the Collegiate Church of St. Hermes, Renaix.

Grand-Hornu Coal Mine — SP450

1979, Oct. 22 Engr. *Perf. 11½*

B987 SP450 10fr + 5fr blk .55 .55

Henry Heyman — SP451

Veterans Organization Medal — SP452

Boy and IYC Emblem SP453

1979, Dec. 8 Photo. *Perf. 11½*

B988 SP451 8fr + 3fr multi .45 .45
B989 SP452 10fr + 5fr multi .55 .55
B990 SP453 16fr + 8fr multi .75 .75
Nos. B988-B990 (3) 1.75 1.75

Henri Heyman (1879-1958), Minister of State; Disabled Veterans' Organization, 50th anniv.; Intl. Year of the Child.

Ivo Van Damme, Olympic Rings — SP454

1980, May 3 Photo. *Perf. 11½*

B991 SP454 20fr + 10fr multi 1.10 1.10

Ivo Van Damme (1954-1976), silver medalist, 800-meter race, Montreal Olympics, 1976. Surtax was for Van Damme Memorial Foundation.

Queen Louis, King Leopold I SP455

150th Anniversary of Independence (Queens and Kings): 9fr+3fr, Marie Henriette. Leopold II. 14fr+6fr, Elisabeth, Albert I. 17fr+8fr, Astrid, Leopold III. 25fr+10fr, Fabiola, Baudouin.

Photogravure and Engraved

1980, May 31 *Perf. 11½*

B992 SP455 6.50 + 1.50fr multi .28 .28
B993 SP455 9 + 3fr multi .50 .50
B994 SP455 14 + 6fr multi .70 .70
B995 SP455 17 + 8fr multi 1.00 1.00
B996 SP455 25 + 10fr multi 1.25 1.25
Nos. B992-B996 (5) 3.73 3.73

Miner, by Constantine Meunier SP456

Seal of Bishop Notger, First Prince-Bishop — SP457

Designs: 9fr+3fr, Brewer, 16th century, from St. Lambert's reliquary, vert. 25fr+10fr, Virgin and Child, 13th century, St. John's Collegiate Church, Liege.

1980, Sept. 13 Photo. *Perf. 11½*

B997 SP456 9 + 3fr multi .35 .35
B998 SP456 17 + 6fr multi .70 .70
B999 SP456 25 + 10fr multi 1.10 1.10
Nos. B997-B999 (3) 2.15 2.15

Souvenir Sheet

B1000 SP457 20 + 10fr multi 1.25 1.25

Millennium of the Principality of Liege.

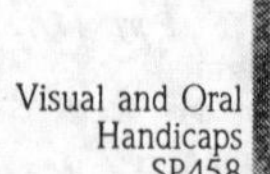

Visual and Oral Handicaps SP458

Intl. Year of the Disabled: 10fr+5fr, Cerebral handicap, vert.

1981, Feb. 9 Photo. *Perf. 11½*

B1001 SP458 10 + 5fr multi .70 .70
B1002 SP458 25 + 10fr multi 1.65 1.65

Dove with Red Cross Carrying Globe SP459

Design: 10fr+5fr, Atomic model, vert.

1981, Apr. 6 Photo. *Perf. 11½*

B1003 SP459 10 + 5fr multi .70 .70
B1004 SP459 25 + 10fr multi 1.65 1.65

Red Cross and: 15th Intl. Radiology Congress, Brussels, June 24-July 1 (#B1003); intl. disaster relief (#B1004).

Ovide Decroly SP460

1981, June 1 Photo. *Perf. 11½*

B1005 SP460 35 + 15fr multi 2.00 2.00

Ovide Decroly (1871-1932), developer of educational psychology.

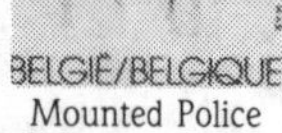

Mounted Police Officer — SP461

Billiards — SP462

Anniversaries: 9fr+4fr, Gendarmerie (State Police Force), 150th. 20fr+7fr, Carabineers Regiment, 150th. 40fr+20fr, Guides Regiment.

1981, Dec. 7 Photo. *Perf. 11½*

B1006 SP461 9 + 4fr multi .60 .60
B1007 SP461 20 + 7fr multi 1.25 1.25
B1008 SP461 40 + 20fr multi 2.75 2.75
Nos. B1006-B1008 (3) 4.60 4.60

1982, Mar. 29 Photo. *Perf. 11½*

B1009 SP462 6 + 2fr shown .38 .38
B1010 SP462 9 + 4fr Cycling .60 .60
B1011 SP462 10 + 5fr Soccer .70 .70
B1012 SP462 50 + 14fr Yachting 3.00 3.00
Nos. B1009-B1012 (4) 4.68 4.68

Souvenir Sheet

B1013 Sheet of 4 5.00 5.00
a. SP462 25fr like #B1009 1.40 1.40
b. SP462 25fr like #B1010 1.40 1.40
c. SP462 25fr like #B1011 1.40 1.40
d. SP462 25fr like #B1012 1.40 1.40

#B1013 shows designs in changed colors.

Christmas SP463

1982, Nov. 6

B1014 SP463 10 + 1fr multi .60 .45

Surtax was for tuberculosis research.

Belgica '82 Intl. Stamp Exhibition, Brussels, Dec. 11-19 SP464

Messengers (Prints). Nos. B1016-B1018 vert.

Photogravure and Engraved

1982, Dec. 11 *Perf. 11½*

B1015 SP464 7 + 2fr multi .38 .38
B1016 SP464 7.50 + 2.50fr multi .45 .45
B1017 SP464 10 + 3fr multi .55 .55
B1018 SP464 17 + 7fr multi 1.10 1.10
B1019 SP464 20 + 9fr multi 1.25 1.25
B1020 SP464 25 + 10fr multi 1.50 1.50
Nos. B1015-B1020 (6) 5.23 5.23

Souvenir Sheet

B1021 SP464 50 + 25fr multi 6.00 6.00

No. B1021 contains one 48x37mm stamp.

50th Anniv. of Catholic Charities SP465

Mountain Climbing SP466

1983, Jan. 22 Photo. *Perf. 11½*

B1022 SP465 10 + 2fr multi .65 .65

1983, Mar. 7 Photo.

B1023 SP466 12 + 3fr shown .80 .80
B1024 SP466 20 + 5fr Hiking 1.25 1.25

Surtax was for Red Cross.

Madonna by Jef Wauters — SP467

Rifles Uniform — SP468

1983, Nov. 21 Photo. *Perf. 11½*

B1025 SP467 11 + 1fr multi .60 .60

1983, Dec. 5 Photo. *Perf. 11½*

B1026 SP468 8 + 2fr shown .50 .50
B1027 SP468 11 + 2fr Lancers uniform .75 .75
B1028 SP468 50 + 12fr Grenadiers uniform 3.50 3.50
Nos. B1026-B1028 (3) 4.75 4.75

Type of 1984

1984, Mar. 3 Photo. *Perf. 11½*

B1029 A495 8 + 2fr Judo, horiz. .55 .55
B1030 A495 12 + 3fr Wind surfing .85 .85

50th Anniv. of Natl. Lottery SP469

1984, Mar. 31 Photo. *Perf. 11½*

B1031 SP469 12 + 3fr multi .75 .75

Brussels Modern Art Museum Opening SP470

Paintings: 8fr+2fr, Les Masques Singuliers, by James Ensor. 12fr+3fr, Empire des Lumieres, by Rene Magritte. 22fr+5fr, The End, by Jan Cox. 50fr+13fr, Rhythm No. 6, by Jo Delahaut.

1984, Sept. 1 **Photo.**

B1032	SP470	8 + 2fr multi	.60	.60
B1033	SP470	12 + 3fr multi	.90	.90
B1034	SP470	22 + 5fr multi	1.65	1.65
B1035	SP470	50 + 13fr multi	3.75	3.75
		Nos. B1032-B1035 (4)	6.90	6.90

Child with Parents — SP471

1984, Nov. 3 **Photo.**

B1036	SP471	10 + 2fr shown	.60	.60
B1037	SP471	12 + 3fr Siblings	.75	.75
B1038	SP471	15 + 3fr Merry-go-round	.85	.85
		Nos. B1036-B1038 (3)	2.20	2.20

Surtax was for children's programs.

Christmas 1984 SP472

1984, Dec. 1

B1039	SP472	12 + 1fr Three Kings	.75	.75

Belgian Red Cross Blood Transfusion Service, 50th Anniv. — SP473

1985, Mar. 4 **Photo.** ***Perf. 11½***

B1040	SP473	9 + 2fr Tree	.60	.60
B1041	SP473	23 + 5fr Hearts	1.40	1.40

Surtax was for the Belgian Red Cross.

Solidarity SP474

Castles.

1985, Nov. 4 **Photo. & Engr.**

B1042	SP474	9 + 2fr Trazegnies	.60	.60
B1043	SP474	12 + 3fr Laarne	.80	.80
B1044	SP474	23 + 5fr Turnhout	1.40	1.40
B1045	SP474	50 + 12fr Colonster	3.50	3.50
		Nos. B1042-B1045 (4)	6.30	6.30

Christmas 1985, New Year 1986 — SP475

Painting: Miniature from the Book of Hours, by Jean duc de Berry.

1985, Nov. 25 **Photo.**

B1046	SP475	12 + 1fr multi	.70	.70

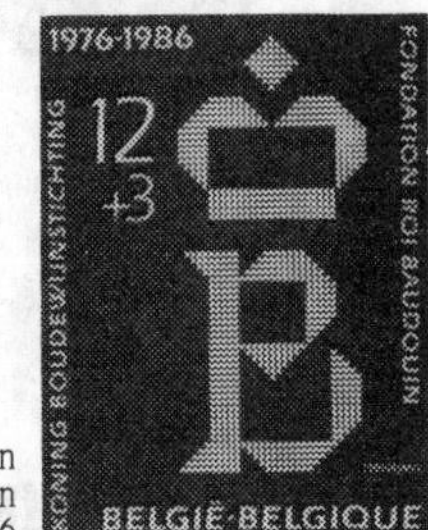

King Baudouin Foundation SP476

1986, Mar. 24 **Photo.**

B1047	SP476	12 + 3fr Emblem	.80	.80

Surtax for the foundation.

Madonna SP477

Adoration of the Mystic Lamb, St. Bavon Cathedral Altarpiece, Ghent — SP478

Paintings by Hubert van Eyck (c. 1370-1426).

1986, Apr. 5 **Photo.** ***Perf. 11½***

B1048	SP477	9 + 2fr shown	.65	.65
B1049	SP477	13 + 3fr Christ in Majesty	.95	.95
B1050	SP477	24 + 6fr St. John the Baptist	1.75	1.75
		Nos. B1048-B1050 (3)	3.35	3.35

Souvenir Sheet

B1051	SP478	50 + 12fr multi	5.25	5.25

Surtax for cultural organizations.

Antique Automobiles SP479

1986, Nov. 3 **Photo.**

B1052	SP479	9 + 2fr Lenoir, 1863	.65	.65
B1053	SP479	13 + 3fr Pipe de Tourisme, 1911	.90	.90
B1054	SP479	24 + 6fr Minerva 22 HP, 1930	1.75	1.75
B1055	SP479	26 + 6fr FN 8 Cylinder, 1931	1.90	1.90
		Nos. B1052-B1055 (4)	5.20	5.20

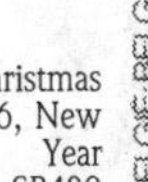

Christmas 1986, New Year 1987 — SP480

1986, Nov. 24 **Photo.**

B1056	SP480	13 + 1fr Village in winter	.75	.75

Natl. Red Cross — SP482

European Conservation Year — SP483

Nobel Prize winners for physiology (1938) and medicine (1974): No. B1058, Corneille Heymans (1892-1968). No. B1059, A. Claude (1899-1983).

Photogravure and Engraved

1987, Feb. 16 ***Perf. 11½***

B1058	SP482	13 + 3fr dk brn & red	.90	.90
B1059	SP482	24 + 6fr dk brn & red	1.65	1.65

1987, Mar. 16 **Photo.**

B1060	SP483	9 + 2fr Bee orchid	.60	.60
B1061	SP483	24 + 6fr Horseshoe bat	1.65	1.65
B1062	SP483	26 + 6fr Peregrine falcon	1.75	1.75
		Nos. B1060-B1062 (3)	4.00	4.00

Castles — SP484

1987, Oct. 17 **Photo. & Engr.**

B1063	SP484	9 + 2fr Rixensart	.60	.60
B1064	SP484	13 + 3fr Westerlo	.90	.90
B1065	SP484	26 + 5fr Fallais	1.75	1.75
B1066	SP484	50 + 12fr Gaasbeek	3.50	3.50
		Nos. B1063-B1066 (4)	6.75	6.75

Christmas 1987 — SP485

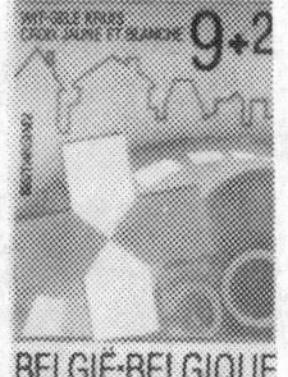

White and Yellow Cross of Belgium, 50th Anniv. — SP486

Painting: Holy Family, by Rev. Father Lens.

1987, Nov. 14 **Photo.**

B1067	SP485	13 + 1fr multi	.85	.85

1987, Dec. 5

B1068	SP486	9 + 2fr multi	.70	.70

Promote Philately — SP487

Various flowers from Sixty Roses for a Queen, by P. J. Redoute (1759-1840).

1988, Apr. 25 **Photo.** ***Perf. 11½***

B1069	SP487	13 + 3fr shown	.98	.98
B1070	SP487	24 + 6fr multi, diff.	1.80	1.80

Souvenir Sheet

B1071	SP487	50 + 12fr multi, diff.	3.75	3.75

See Nos. B1081-B1083, B1089-B1091, 1346.

1988 Summer Olympics, Seoul — SP488

1988, June 6 **Photo.** ***Perf. 11½***

B1072	SP488	9fr + 2fr Table tennis	.65	.65
B1073	SP488	13fr + 3fr Cycling	.95	.95

Souvenir Sheet

B1074	SP488	50fr + 12fr Marathon runners	3.70	3.70

Solidarity — SP489

1988, Oct. 24 **Photo.** ***Perf. 12x11½***

B1075	SP489	9fr + 2fr Jacques Brel	.60	.60
B1076	SP489	13fr + 3fr Jef Denyn	.88	.88
B1077	SP489	26fr + 6fr Fr. Ferdinand Verbiest	1.75	1.75
		Nos. B1075-B1077 (3)	3.23	3.23

Belgian Red Cross SP490

Paintings: No. B1078, *Crucifixion of Christ*, by Rogier van der Weyden (c. 1399-1464). No. B1079, *Virgin and Child*, by David (c. 1460-1523). B1089, *The Good Samaritan*, by Denis van Alsloot.

1989, Feb. 20 **Photo.** ***Perf. 11½***

B1078	SP490	9fr + 2fr multi	.60	.60
B1079	SP490	13fr + 3fr multi	.88	.88
B1080	SP490	24fr + 6fr multi	1.65	1.65
		Nos. B1078-B1080 (3)	3.13	3.13

Stamp Collecting Promotion Type of 1988

Various flowers from *Sixty Roses for a Queen*, by P.J. Redoute (1759-1840) and inscriptions: No. B1081, "Centfeuille unique melee de rouge." No. B1082, "Bengale a grandes feuilles." No. B1083, Aeme vibere (tea roses).

1989, Apr. 17

B1081	SP487	13fr + 5fr multi	1.00	1.00
B1082	SP487	24fr + 6fr multi	1.65	1.65

Souvenir Sheet

B1083	SP487	50fr + 17fr multi	3.75	3.75

Solidarity SP491

Royal Greenhouses of Laeken.

1989, Oct. 23

B1084	SP491	9fr + 3fr Exterior	.60	.60
B1085	SP491	13fr + 4fr Interior, vert.	.82	.82
B1086	SP491	24fr + 5fr Dome exterior, vert.	1.40	1.40
B1087	SP491	26fr + 6fr Dome interior, vert.	1.55	1.55
		Nos. B1084-B1087 (4)	4.37	4.37

Queen Elisabeth Chapelle Musicale, 50th Anniv. — SP492

1989, Nov. 6

B1088 SP492 24fr + 6fr G clef 1.45 1.45

Stamp Collecting Promotion Type of 1988

Various flowers from *Sixty Roses for a Queen*, by P.J. Redoute (1759-1840): No. B1089, *Bengale desprez.* No. B1090, *Bengale philippe.* No. B1091, *Maria leonida.*

1990, Feb. 5

B1089 SP487 14fr + 7fr multi 1.15 1.15
B1090 SP487 25fr + 12fr multi 2.00 2.00

Souvenir Sheet

B1091 SP487 50fr + 20fr multi 3.75 3.75

Youth and Music — SP493

Designs: 14fr+3fr, Beethoven and Lamoraal, Count of Egmont (1522-1568). 25fr+6fr, Joseph Cantre (1890-1957), drawing and sculpture.

1990, Oct. 6

B1092 SP493 10fr + 2fr multi .70 .70
B1093 SP493 14fr + 3fr multi 1.00 1.00
B1094 SP493 25fr + 6fr multi 1.80 1.80
Nos. B1092-B1094 (3) 3.50 3.50

King Baudouin & Queen Fabiola, 30th Wedding Anniv. — SP494

1990, Dec. 10

B1095 SP494 50fr +15fr multi 4.25 4.25

Belgian Red Cross SP495

Details from paintings: No. B1096, The Temptation of St. Anthony by Hieronymus Bosch. No. B1097, The Annunciation by Dirk Bouts.

1991, Feb. 25, Photo. *Perf. 11½*

B1096 SP495 14fr +3fr multi 1.10 1.10
B1097 SP495 25fr +6fr multi 2.00 2.00

Belgian Film Personalities — SP496

Designs: 10fr+2fr, Charles Dekeukeleire (1905-1971), producer. 14fr+3fr, Jacques Ledoux (1921-1988), film conservationist. 25fr+6fr, Jacques Feyder (1899-1948), director.

1991, Oct. 28 Photo. *Perf. 11½*

B1098 SP496 10fr +2fr multi .75 .75
B1099 SP496 14fr +3fr multi 1.05 1.05
B1100 SP496 25fr +6fr multi 1.90 1.90
Nos. B1098-B1100 (3) 3.70 3.70

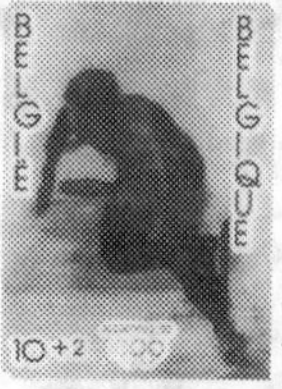

1992 Winter and Summer Olympics, Albertville and Barcelona — SP497

1992, Jan. 20 Photo. *Perf. 11½*

B1101 SP497 10fr +2fr Speed skating .75 .75
B1102 SP497 10fr +2fr Baseball .75 .75
B1103 SP497 14fr +3fr Women's tennis, horiz. 1.05 1.05
B1104 SP497 25fr +6fr Skeet shooting 1.90 1.90
Nos. B1101-B1104 (4) 4.45 4.45

Folk Legends SP498

Designs: 11fr + 2fr, Proud Margaret. 15fr + 3fr, Gustine Maca and the Witches. 28fr + 6fr, Reynard the Fox.

1992, June 22 Photo. *Perf. 11½*

B1105 SP498 11fr +2fr multi .78 .78
B1106 SP498 15fr +3fr multi 1.10 1.10
B1107 SP498 28fr +6fr multi 2.00 2.00
Nos. B1105-B1107 (3) 3.88 3.88

Belgian Red Cross SP499

Paintings: 15fr + 3fr, Man with the Pointed Hat, by Adriaen Brouwer (1605-1638). 28fr + 7fr, Nereid and Triton, by Peter Paul Rubens, horiz.

1993, Feb. 15 Photo. *Perf. 11½*

B1108 SP499 15fr +3fr multi 1.10 1.10
B1109 SP499 28fr +7fr multi 2.10 2.10

Fight Against Cancer SP500

1993, Sept. 20 Photo. *Perf. 11½*

B1110 SP500 15fr +3fr multicolored 1.10 1.10

Intl. Olympic Committee, Cent. — SP501

Designs: No. B1112, Soccer players. No. B1113, Figure skater.

1994, Feb. 14 Photo. *Perf. 11½*

B1111 SP501 16fr +3fr multi 1.00 1.00
B1112 SP501 16fr +3fr multi 1.00 1.00
B1113 SP501 16fr +3fr multi 1.00 1.00
Nos. B1111-B1113 (3) 3.00 3.00

1994 World Cup Soccer Championships, Los Angeles (#B1112). 1994 Winter Olympics, Lillehammer, Norway (#B1113).

Porcelain — SP502

Designs: No. B1114, Tournai plate, Museum of Mariemont-Morlanweiz. No. B1115, Etterbeek cup, saucer, Municipal Museum, Louvain. 50fr+11fr, Delft earthenware jars, Pharmacy Museum of Maaseik.

1994, June 27 Photo. *Perf. 11½*

B1114 SP502 16fr +3fr multi 1.10 1.10
B1115 SP502 16fr +3fr multi 1.10 1.10

Souvenir Sheet

B1116 SP502 50fr +11fr multi 3.50 3.50

No. B1116 contains one 49x38mm stamp.

Solidarity SP503

Design: 16fr+3fr, Hearing-impaired person.

1994, Nov. 14 Photo. *Perf. 11½*

B1117 SP503 16fr +3fr multi 1.25 1.25

Museums — SP504

Designs: No. B1118, Natl. Flax Museum, Kortrijk. No. B1119, Natl. Water and Fountain Museum, Genval.
34fr+6fr, Intl. Carnival and Mask Museum, Binche.

1995, Jan. 30 Photo. *Perf. 11½*

B1118 SP504 16fr +3fr multi 1.25 1.25
B1119 SP504 16fr +3fr multi 1.25 1.25

Souvenir Sheet

B1120 SP504 34fr +6fr multi 2.75 2.75

Surtax for promotion of philately.

Royal Belgian Soccer Assoc., Cent. SP505

1995, Aug. 21 Photo. *Perf. 11½*

B1121 SP505 16fr +4fr multi 1.40 1.40

Belgian Red Cross SP506

Designs: No. B1122, Princess Astrid, chairwoman of Belgian Red Cross. No. B1123, Wilhelm C. Röntgen (1845-1923), discoverer of the X-ray. No. B1124, Louis Pasteur (1822-95), scientist.

1995, Sept. 11

B1122 SP506 16fr +3fr multi 1.25 1.25
B1123 SP506 16fr +3fr multi 1.25 1.25
B1124 SP506 16fr +3fr multi 1.25 1.25
Nos. B1122-B1124 (3) 3.75 3.75

Solidarity — SP507

1995, Nov. 6 Photo. *Perf. 11½*

B1125 SP507 16fr +4fr multi 1.30 1.30

Surtax for fight against AIDS.

AIR POST STAMPS

Fokker FVII/3m over Ostend — AP1

Designs: 1.50fr, Plane over St. Hubert. 2fr, over Namur. 5fr, over Brussels.

Perf. 11½

1930, Apr. 30 Unwmk. Photo.

C1 AP1 50c blue .40 .40
C2 AP1 1.50fr black brn 2.25 2.50
C3 AP1 2fr deep green 2.00 .55
C4 AP1 5fr brown lake 1.75 .95
Nos. C1-C4 (4) 6.40 4.40

Exist imperf.

1930, Dec. 5

C5 AP1 5fr dark violet 30.00 30.00

Issued for use on a mail carrying flight from Brussels to Leopoldville, Belgian Congo, starting Dec. 7.
Exists imperf.

Nos. C2 and C4 Surcharged in Carmine or Blue

1935, May 23

C6 AP1 1fr on 1.50fr (C) .55 .40
C7 AP1 4fr on 5fr (Bl) 7.50 7.00

Catalogue values for unused stamps in this section, from this point to the end of the section, are for Never Hinged items.

DC-4 Skymaster, Sabena Airline AP5

1946, Apr. 20 Engr. *Perf. 11½*

C8 AP5 6fr blue .80 .25
C9 AP5 8.50fr violet brn 1.00 .35
C10 AP5 50fr yellow grn 5.00 .55
a. Perf. 12x11½ ('54) 325.00 1.00
C11 AP5 100fr gray 8.00 .75
a. Perf. 12x11½ ('54) 75.00 1.10
Nos. C8-C11 (4) 14.80 1.90

Evolution of Postal Transportation — AP6

1949, July 1

C12 AP6 50fr dark brown 40.00 15.00

Centenary of Belgian postage stamps.

Glider — AP7

Design: 7fr, "Tipsy" plane.

1951, June 18 Photo. *Perf. 13½*

C12A Strip of 2 + label 70.00 60.00
b. AP7 6fr dark blue 25.00 17.50
c. AP7 7fr carmine rose 25.00 17.50

For the 50th anniv. of the Aero Club of Belgium. The strip sold for 50fr.

1951, July 25 *Perf. 13½*

C13 AP7 6fr sepia 4.50 .15
C14 AP7 7fr Prus green 3.50 .95

UN Types of Regular Issue, 1958

Designs: 5fr, ICAO. 6fr, World Meteorological Organization. 7.50fr, Protection of Refugees. 8fr, General Agreement on Tariffs and Trade. 9fr, UNICEF. 10fr, Atomic Energy Agency.

Perf. 11½

1958, Apr. 17 Unwmk. Engr.

C15 A137 5fr dull blue .25 .30
C16 A136 6fr yellow grn .30 .45
C17 A137 7.50fr lilac .30 .30
C18 A136 8fr sepia .30 .30
C19 A137 9fr carmine .40 .50
C20 A136 10fr redsh brown .75 .60
Nos. C15-C20 (6) 2.30 2.45

World's Fair, Brussels, Apr. 17-Oct. 19. See note after No. 476.

AIR POST SEMI-POSTAL STAMPS

Catalogue values for unused stamps in this section are for Never Hinged items.

American Soldier in Combat — SPAP1

Perf. 11x11½

1946, June 15 Unwmk. Engr.

CB1 SPAP1 17.50fr + 62.50fr dl brn .90 1.40
CB2 SPAP1 17.50fr + 62.50fr dl gray grn .90 1.40

Surtax for an American memorial at Bastogne.

An overprint, "Hommage a Roosevelt," was privately applied to Nos. CB1-CB2 in 1947 by the Association Belgo-Americaine.

In 1950 another private overprint was applied, in red, to Nos. CB1-CB2. It consists of "16-12-1944, 25-1-1945, Dedication July 16, 1950" and outlines of the American eagle emblem and the Bastogne Memorial. Similar overprints were applied to Nos. 265 and 345.

Flight Allegory SPAP2

1946, Sept. 7 *Perf. 11½*

CB3 SPAP2 2fr + 8fr brt vio .60 1.00

The surtax was for the benefit of aviation.

Nos. B417-B425 Surcharged in Various Arrangements in Red or Dark Blue

POSTE AERIENNE LUCHTPOST 1F
LUCHTPOST + POSTE AERIENNE 2F 1F +2F

Type I- Top line "POSTE AERIENNE"
Type II- Top line "LUCHTPOST"

1947, May 18 Photo. *Perf. 11½*

Type I

CB4 1fr + 2fr on #B417 (R) .60 .90
CB5 1.50fr + 2.50fr on #B418 .60 .90
CB6 2fr + 45fr on #B419 .60 .90
CB7 1fr + 2fr on #B420 (R) .60 .90
CB8 1.50fr + 2.50fr on #B421 .60 .90
CB9 2fr + 45fr on #B422 .60 .90
CB10 1fr + 2fr on #B423 (R) .60 .90
CB11 1.50fr + 2.50fr on #B424 (R) .60 .90
CB12 2fr + 45fr on #B425 .60 .90

Type II

CB4a 1fr + 2fr on #B417 (R) .60 .90
CB5a 1.50fr + 2.50fr on #B418 .60 .90
CB6a 2fr + 45fr on #B419 .60 .90
CB7a 1fr + 2fr on #B420 (R) .60 .90
CB8a 1.50fr + 2.50fr on #B421 .60 .90
CB9a 2fr + 45fr on #B422 .60 .90
CB10a 1fr + 2fr on #B423 (R) .60 .90
CB11a 1.50fr + 2.50fr on #B424 (R) .60 .90
CB12a 2fr + 45fr on #B425 .60 .90
Nos. CB4-CB12 (9) 5.40 8.10
Nos. CB4a-CB12a (9) 5.40 8.10

In 1948 Nos. CB4-CB12 and CB4a-CB12a were punched with the letters "IMABA," and the inscription "Imaba du 21 au 29 aout 1948" was applied to the backs. Value $20.

Helicopter Leaving Airport SPAP3

1950, Aug. 7

CB13 SPAP3 7fr + 3fr blue 9.00 5.25

Surtax for the Natl. Aeronautical Committee.

SPECIAL DELIVERY STAMPS

From 1874 to 1903 certain hexagonal telegraph stamps were used as special delivery stamps.

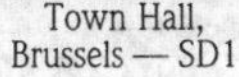

Town Hall, Brussels — SD1

Eupen — SD2

Designs: 2.35fr, Street in Ghent. 3.50fr, Bishop's Palace, Liege. 5.25fr, Notre Dame Cathedral, Antwerp.

1929 Unwmk. Photo. *Perf. 11½*

E1 SD1 1.75fr dark blue .80 .32
E2 SD1 2.35fr carmine 1.50 .45
E3 SD1 3.50fr dark violet 10.00 9.00
E4 SD1 5.25fr olive green 5.50 5.25

1931

E5 SD2 2.45fr dark green 11.00 2.50
Nos. E1-E5 (5) 28.80 17.52

No. E5 Surcharged in Red

1932

E6 SD2 2.50fr on 2.45fr dk grn 8.00 1.25

POSTAGE DUE STAMPS

D1

D2

1870 Unwmk. Typo. *Perf. 15*

J1 D1 10c green 4.50 1.75
J2 D1 20c ultra 30.00 3.50

In 1909 many bisects of Nos. J1-J2 were created. The 10c bisect used as 5c on piece sells for $3.50.

1895-09 *Perf. 14*

J3 D2 5c yellow grn .15 .15
J4 D2 10c orange brn 4.50 1.10
J5 D2 10c carmine ('00) .15 .15
J6 D2 20c olive green .15 .15
J7 D2 30c pale blue ('09) .30 .25
J8 D2 50c yellow brn 12.50 4.50
J9 D2 50c gray ('00) .75 .45
J10 D2 1fr carmine 20.00 13.00
J11 D2 1fr ocher ('00) 6.50 6.00
Nos. J3-J11 (9) 45.00 25.75

1916 Redrawn

J12 D2 5c blue grn 10.00 7.00
J13 D2 10c carmine 12.00 6.00
J14 D2 20c dp gray grn 25.00 15.00
J15 D2 30c brt blue 6.00 5.00
J16 D2 50c gray 60.00 45.00
Nos. J12-J16 (5) 113.00 78.00

In the redrawn stamps the lions have a heavy, colored outline. There is a thick vertical line at the outer edge of the design on each side.

D3

D4

1919 *Perf. 14*

J17 D3 5c green .40 .50
J18 D3 10c carmine .95 .40
J19 D3 20c gray green 7.25 1.25
J20 D3 30c bright blue 1.40 .40
J21 D3 50c gray 2.75 .50
Nos. J17-J21 (5) 12.75 3.05

1922-32

J22 D4 5c dk gray .15 .15
J23 D4 10c green .15 .15
J24 D4 20c deep brown .15 .15
J25 D4 30c ver ('24) .65 .15
a. 30c rose red 1.00 .45
J26 D4 40c red brn ('25) .25 .15
J27 D4 50c ultra 1.90 .15
J28 D4 70c red brn ('29) .30 .15
J29 D4 1fr violet ('25) .45 .15
J30 D4 1fr rose lilac ('32) .55 .15
J31 D4 1.20fr ol grn ('29) .65 .45
J32 D4 1.50fr ol grn ('32) .65 .45
J33 D4 2fr violet ('29) .75 .20
J34 D4 3.50fr dp blue ('29) 1.00 .25
Nos. J22-J34 (13) 7.60
Set value 2.25

1934-46 *Perf. 14x13½*

J35 D4 35c green ('35) .40 .45
J36 D4 50c slate .20 .15
J37 D4 60c carmine ('38) .40 .30
J38 D4 80c slate ('38) .30 .15
J39 D4 1.40fr gray ('35) .65 .45
J39A D4 3fr org brn ('46) 1.50 .60
J39B D4 7fr brt red vio ('46) 2.25 3.25
Nos. J35-J39B (7) 5.70 5.35

See Nos. J54-J61.

Catalogue values for unused stamps in this section, from this point to the end of the section, are for Never Hinged items.

D5

D6

1945 Typo. *Perf. 12½*

Inscribed "TE BETALEN" at Top

J40 D5 10c gray olive .15 .15
J41 D5 20c ultramarine .15 .15
J42 D5 30c carmine .15 .15
J43 D5 40c black violet .15 .15
J44 D5 50c dl bl grn .15 .15
J45 D5 1fr sepia .15 .15
J46 D5 2fr red orange .15 .15

Inscribed "A PAYER" at Top

J47 D5 10c gray olive .15 .15
J48 D5 20c ultramarine .15 .15
J49 D5 30c carmine .15 .15
J50 D5 40c black vio .15 .15
J51 D5 50c dl bl grn .15 .15
J52 D5 1fr sepia .15 .15
J53 D5 2fr red orange .15 .15
Set value 1.40 1.25

Type of 1922-32

1949-53 Typo. *Perf. 14x13½*

J54 D4 65c emerald 7.00 3.75
J55 D4 1.60fr lilac rose ('53) 14.00 6.50
J56 D4 1.80fr red 15.00 6.50
J57 D4 2.40fr gray lilac ('53) 9.00 4.00
J58 D4 4fr deep blue ('53) 11.00 .50
J59 D4 5fr red brown 3.75 .40
J60 D4 8fr lilac rose 7.25 3.75
J61 D4 10fr dark violet 7.25 3.75
Nos. J54-J61 (8) 74.25 29.15

Numerals 6½mm or More High

1966-70 Photo.

J62 D6 1fr brt pink .15 .15
J63 D6 2fr blue green .15 .15
J64 D6 3fr blue .15 .15
J65 D6 5fr purple .25 .25
J66 D6 6fr bister brn .35 .35
J67 D6 7fr red org ('70) .40 .40
J68 D6 20fr slate grn 1.40 1.40
Nos. J62-J68 (7) 2.85 2.85

Printed on various papers.

Numerals 4½-5½mm High

1985-87 Photo. *Perf. 14x13½*

J69 D6 1fr lilac rose .15 .15
J70 D6 2fr dull blue grn .15 .15
J71 D6 3fr greenish blue .15 .15
J72 D6 4fr green .20 .15
J73 D6 5fr lt violet .25 .20
J74 D6 7fr brt orange .35 .30
J75 D6 8fr pale gray .40 .30
J76 D6 9fr rose lake .45 .35
J77 D6 10fr lt red brown .50 .40
J78 D6 20fr lt olive grn 1.10 1.10
Nos. J69-J78 (10) 3.70 3.25

Printed on various papers.

Issue dates: 3fr, 4fr, 8fr-10fr, Mar. 25, 1985. 2fr, 20fr, 1986. 1fr, 5fr, 7fr, 1987.

This is an expanding set. Numbers will change again if necessary.

MILITARY STAMPS

Catalogue values for unused stamps in this section are for Never Hinged items.

King Baudouin
M1 M2

Unwmk.

1967, July 17 Photo. *Perf. 11*

M1 M1 1.50fr greenish gray .55 .45

1971-75 Engr. *Perf. 11½*

M2 M2 1.75fr green 1.10 .55
M3 M2 2.25fr gray green ('72) 1.00 .40
M4 M2 2.50fr gray green ('74) .40 .30
M5 M2 3.25fr vio brown ('75) .30 .15
Nos. M2-M5 (4) 2.80 1.40

#M1-M3 are luminescent, #M4-M5 are not.

MILITARY PARCEL POST STAMP

Type of Parcel Post Stamp of 1938 Surcharged with New Value and "M" in Blue.

1939 Unwmk. *Perf. 13½*

MQ1 PP19 3fr on 5.50fr copper red .30 .20

OFFICIAL STAMPS

For franking the official correspondence of the Administration of the Belgian National Railways.

Counterfeits exist of Nos. O1-O25.

Regular Issue of 1921-27 Overprinted in Black

1929-30 Unwmk. *Perf. 14*

O1 A58 5c gray .20 .20
O2 A58 10c blue green .30 .40
O3 A58 35c blue green .40 .30
O4 A58 60c olive green .45 .30
O5 A58 1.50fr brt blue 8.00 6.25
O6 A58 1.75fr ultra ('30) 1.75 2.00
Nos. O1-O6 (6) 11.10 9.45

Same Overprint, in Red or Black, on Regular Issues of 1929-30

1929-31

O7 A63 5c slate (R) .25 .35
O8 A63 10c olive grn (R) .50 .40
O9 A63 25c rose red (Bk) 1.50 .85
O10 A63 35c dp green (R) 1.75 .50
O11 A63 40c red vio (Bk) 1.25 .45
O12 A63 50c dp blue (R) ('31) .80 .35
O13 A63 60c rose (Bk) 6.00 6.00
O14 A63 70c orange brn (Bk) 4.25 1.25
O15 A63 75c black vio (R) ('31) 4.00 .85
Nos. O7-O15 (9) 20.30 11.00

Overprinted on Regular Issue of 1932

1932

O16 A73 10c olive grn (R) .55 .60
O17 A74 35c dp green 9.00 .75
O18 A71a 75c bister brn (R) 1.50 .30
Nos. O16-O18 (3) 11.05 1.65

Overprinted on No. 262 in Red

1935 *Perf. 13½x14*

O19 A80 70c olive black 2.75 .25

Regular Stamps of 1935-36 Overprinted in Red

1936-38 *Perf. 13½, 13½x14, 14*

O20 A82 10c olive bister .15 .35
O21 A82 35c green .25 .40
O22 A82 50c dark blue .45 .35
O23 A83 70c brown 1.50 .65

Overprinted in Black or Red on Regular Issue of 1938

Perf. 13½x14

O24 A82 40c red violet (Bk) .30 .35
O25 A85 75c olive gray (R) .65 .30
Nos. O20-O25 (6) 3.30 2.40

Regular Issues of 1935-41 Overprinted in Red or Dark Blue

1941-44 *Perf. 14, 14x13½, 13½x14*

O26 A82 10c olive bister .15 .15
a. Inverted overprint 40.00
O27 A82 40c red violet .55 .75
O28 A82 50c dark blue .15 .15
a. Inverted overprint
O29 A83a 1fr rose car (Bl) .45 .35
O30 A85 1fr rose pink (Bl) .15 .15
O31 A83a 2.25fr grnsh blk ('44) .30 .50
O32 A84 2.25fr gray violet .45 .70
Nos. O26-O32 (7) 2.20 2.75

Nos. O21, O23 and O25 Surcharged with New Values in Black or Red

1942

O33 A82 10c on 35c green .20 .35
O34 A83 50c on 70c brown .15 .20
O35 A85 50c on 75c ol gray (R) .15 .20
Nos. O33-O35 (3) .50 .75

Catalogue values for unused stamps in this section, from this point to the end of the section, are for Never Hinged items.

O1

O2

1946-48 Unwmk. *Perf. 14*

O36 O1 10c olive bister .20 .20
O37 O1 20c brt violet 1.75 .75
O38 O1 50c dk blue .25 .20
O39 O1 65c red lilac ('48) 2.75 1.10
O40 O1 75c lilac rose .20 .30
O41 O1 90c brown violet 3.50 .50
Nos. O36-O41 (6) 8.65 3.05

Types A99, A101 and A102 with "B" Emblem Added to Design

1948 *Perf. 11½*

O42 A99 1.35fr red brown 4.00 .80
O43 A99 1.75fr dk gray green 4.75 .30
O44 A101 3fr brt red violet 25.00 4.00
O45 A102 3.15fr deep blue 11.00 8.00
O46 A102 4fr brt ultra 20.00 15.00
Nos. O42-O46 (5) 64.75 28.10

1953-66 Typo. *Perf. 13½x14*

O47 O2 10c orange .65 .85
O48 O2 20c red lilac .75 .60
O49 O2 30c gray green ('58) .75 1.00
O50 O2 40c olive gray .50 .40
O51 O2 50c light blue .70 .50
O51A O2 60c lilac rose ('66) 1.10 .90
O52 O2 65c red lilac 25.00 21.00
O53 O2 80c emerald 4.00 .85
O54 O2 90c deep blue 5.50 1.25
O55 O2 1fr rose .40 .40
Nos. O47-O55 (10) 39.35 27.75

See Nos. O66, O68.

King Baudouin

O3 O4

1954-70 Photo. *Perf. 11½*

O56 O3 1.50fr gray .65 .40
O57 O3 2fr rose red 25.00 .75
O58 O3 2fr blue grn ('59) .50 .30
O59 O3 2.50fr red brown ('58) 16.00 .75
O60 O3 3fr red lilac ('58) 1.25 .60
O61 O3 3.50fr yel green ('70) .70 .60
O62 O3 4fr brt blue 1.50 1.00
O63 O3 6fr car rose ('58) 3.25 1.65
Nos. O56-O63 (8) 48.85 6.05

Type of 1953-66 Redrawn

1970-75 Typo. *Perf. 13½x14*

O66 O2 1.50fr grnsh gray ('75) .20 .15
O68 O2 2.50fr brown .20 .15
Set value .20

1971-73 Engr. *Perf. 11½*

O71 O4 3.50fr org brn ('73) 1.75 1.25
O72 O4 4.50fr brown ('73) 1.10 .90
O73 O4 7fr red .45 .40
O74 O4 15fr violet .90 .90
Nos. O71-O74 (4) 4.20 3.45

Nos. O71-O74 are on luminescent paper.

1974-80

O75 O4 3fr yellow grn 4.00 1.25
O76 O4 4fr blue 1.50 .75
O77 O4 4.50fr grnsh bl ('75) .45 .25
O78 O4 5fr lilac .20 .20
O79 O4 6fr carmine ('78) .30 .30
O80 O4 6.50fr black ('76) .45 .45
O81 O4 8fr bluish blk ('78) .35 .30
O82 O4 9fr lt red brn ('80) .35 .30
O83 O4 10fr rose carmine .40 .35
O84 O4 25fr lilac ('76) 1.00 1.00
O85 O4 30fr org brn ('78) 1.40 1.25
Nos. O75-O85 (11) 10.40 6.40

Heraldic Lion — O5

1977-82 Typo. *Perf. 13½x14*

O87 O5 50c brown ('82) .15 .15
O92 O5 1fr lilac ('82) .15 .15
O94 O5 2fr orange ('82) .15 .15
O95 O5 4fr red brown .30 .25
O96 O5 5fr green ('80) .35 .30
Set value .90 .75

NEWSPAPER STAMPS

Counterfeits exist of Nos. P1-P40.

Parcel Post Stamps of 1923-27 Overprinted **JOURNAUX DAGBLADEN 1928**

Perf. 14½x14, 14x14½

1928 Unwmk.

P1 PP12 10c vermilion .25 .40
P2 PP12 20c turq blue .25 .40
P3 PP12 40c olive grn .25 .40
P4 PP12 60c orange .70 .90
P5 PP12 70c dk brown .45 .40
P6 PP12 80c violet .60 .70
P7 PP12 90c slate 2.25 2.00
P8 PP13 1fr brt blue .90 .60
a. 1fr ultramarine 12.00 5.00
P10 PP13 2fr olive grn 1.50 .60
P11 PP13 3fr orange red 1.65 .90
P12 PP13 4fr rose 2.25 1.10
P13 PP13 5fr violet 2.25 1.00
P14 PP13 6fr bister brn 4.50 1.75
P15 PP13 7fr orange 5.00 2.25
P16 PP13 8fr dk brown 6.00 2.75
P17 PP13 9fr red violet 10.00 3.00
P18 PP13 10fr blue green 9.00 2.75
P19 PP13 20fr magenta 15.00 7.00
Nos. P1-P8,P10-P19 (18) 62.80 28.90

Parcel Post Stamps of 1923-28 Overprinted **JOURNAUX DAGBLADEN**

1929-31

P20 PP12 10c vermilion .25 .20
P21 PP12 20c turq blue .25 .20
P22 PP12 40c olive green .30 .20
a. Inverted overprint
P23 PP12 60c orange .55 .35
P24 PP12 70c dk brown .55 .20
P25 PP12 80c violet .60 .25
P26 PP12 90c gray 2.00 1.00
P27 PP13 1fr ultra .60 .25
a. 1fr bright blue 4.00 2.50
P28 PP13 1.10fr org brn ('31) 6.25 1.40
P29 PP13 1.50fr gray vio ('31) 6.25 1.90
P30 PP13 2fr olive green 2.00 .25
P31 PP13 2.10fr sl gray ('31) 17.00 12.00
P32 PP13 3fr orange red 2.25 .45
P33 PP13 4fr rose 2.25 .70
P34 PP13 5fr violet 3.00 .55
P35 PP13 6fr bister brn 3.75 1.00
P36 PP13 7fr orange 3.75 1.00
P37 PP13 8fr dk brown 3.75 1.10
P38 PP13 9fr red violet 5.25 1.50
P39 PP13 10fr blue green 3.75 1.10
P40 PP13 20fr magenta 13.00 4.50
Nos. P20-P40 (21) 77.35 30.10

PARCEL POST AND RAILWAY STAMPS

Values for used Railway Stamps (Chemins de Fer) stamps are for copies with railway cancellations. Railway Stamps with postal cancellations sell for twice as much.

Coat of Arms — PP1

1879-82 Unwmk. Typo. *Perf. 14*

Q1 PP1 10c violet brown 40.00 5.00
Q2 PP1 20c blue 125.00 16.00
Q3 PP1 25c green ('81) 165.00 9.00
Q4 PP1 50c carmine 1,250. 9.00
Q5 PP1 80c yellow 1,300. 50.00
Q6 PP1 1fr gray ('82) 125.00 15.00

Used copies of Nos. Q1-Q6 with pinholes, a normal state, sell for half price.

Most of the stamps of 1882-1902 (Nos. Q7 to Q28) are without watermark. Twice in each sheet of 100 stamps they have one of three watermarks: (1) A winged wheel and "Chemins de Fer de l'Etat Belge," (2) Coat of Arms of Belgium and "Royaume de Belgique," (3) Larger Coat of Arms, without inscription.

PP2

1882-94 *Perf. 15½x14½*

Q7 PP2 10c brown ('86) 17.50 1.25
Q8 PP2 15c gray ('94) 8.00 6.50
Q9 PP2 20c blue ('86) 60.00 2.50
a. 20c ultra ('90) 65.00 3.00
Q10 PP2 25c yel grn ('91) 60.00 3.75
a. 25c blue green ('87) 60.00 3.50
Q11 PP2 50c carmine 60.00 .65
Q12 PP2 80c brnsh buff 60.00 .65
Q13 PP2 80c lemon 65.00 1.75
Q14 PP2 1fr lavender 325.00 2.25
Q15 PP2 2fr yel buff ('94) 195.00 60.00

Counterfeits exist.

PP3

Name of engraver below frame

1895-97

Numerals in Black, except 1fr, 2fr

Q16 PP3 10c red brown ('96) 10.00 .55
Q17 PP3 15c gray 10.00 6.50
Q18 PP3 20c blue 16.00 .90
Q19 PP3 25c green 16.00 1.25
Q20 PP3 50c carmine 20.00 .55
Q21 PP3 60c violet ('96) 32.50 .55
Q22 PP3 80c ol yel ('96) 25.00 .55
Q23 PP3 1fr lilac brown 125.00 1.10
Q24 PP3 2fr yel buff ('97) 125.00 3.50

Counterfeits exist.

1902

Numerals in Black

Q25 PP3 30c orange 21.00 1.25
Q26 PP3 40c green 26.00 1.25
Q27 PP3 70c blue 45.00 .45
a. Numerals omitted 750.00
Q28 PP3 90c red 62.50 .75
Nos. Q25-Q28 (4) 154.50 3.70

Winged Wheel — PP4

Without engraver's name

1902-14 *Perf. 15*

Q29 PP3 10c yel brn & slate .15 .15
Q30 PP3 15c slate & vio .20 .15
Q31 PP3 20c ultra & yel brn .15 .15
Q32 PP3 25c yel grn & red .20 .15
Q33 PP3 30c orange & bl grn .20 .15
Q34 PP3 35c bister & bl grn ('12) .35 .20
Q35 PP3 40c blue grn & vio .20 .15
Q36 PP3 50c pale rose & vio .15 .15
Q37 PP3 55c lilac brn & ultra ('14) .35 .20
Q38 PP3 60c violet & red .20 .15
Q39 PP3 70c blue & red .15 .15
Q40 PP3 80c lemon & vio brn .15 .15
Q41 PP3 90c red & yel grn .20 .15
Q42 PP4 1fr vio brn & org .20 .15
Q43 PP4 1.10fr rose & blk ('06) .20 .15
Q44 PP4 2fr ocher & bl grn .20 .15
Q45 PP4 3fr black & ultra .35 .20
Q46 PP4 4fr yel grn & red ('13) 1.25 .70
Q47 PP4 5fr org & bl grn ('13) .55 .55
Q48 PP4 10fr ol yel & brn vio ('13) .90 .55
Nos. Q29-Q48 (20) 6.30
Set value 3.70

Exist imperforate.

Regular Issues of 1912-13 Handstamped in Violet

1915 *Perf. 14*

Q49 A42 5c green 165.00 165.00
Q50 A43 10c red 800.00 800.00
Q51 A45 10c red 175.00 175.00
a. With engraver's name 750.00 750.00

Q52 A43 20c olive grn 1,200. 1,200.
Q53 A45 20c olive grn 200.00 200.00
a. With engraver's name 750.00 750.00
Q54 A45 25c ultra 200.00 200.00
a. With engraver's name 750.00 750.00
Q55 A43 35c bister brn 250.00 250.00
Q55A A43 40c green 1,750. 1,750.
Q56 A45 40c green 250.00 250.00
Q57 A43 50c gray 250.00 250.00
Q58 A43 1fr orange 200.00 200.00
Q59 A43 2fr violet 1,650. 1,650.
Q60 A44 5fr plum 3,500. 3,500.

Excellent forgeries of this overprint exist.

PP5 PP6

1916 **Litho.** *Perf. 13½*
Q61 PP5 10c pale blue 1.10 .20
Q62 PP5 15c olive grn 1.40 .50
Q63 PP5 20c red 2.25 .50
Q64 PP5 25c lt brown 2.25 .50
Q65 PP5 30c lilac 1.40 .45
Q66 PP5 35c gray 1.40 .45
Q67 PP5 40c orange yel 3.00 1.50
Q68 PP5 50c bister 2.25 .45
Q69 PP5 55c brown 3.00 2.25
Q70 PP5 60c gray vio 2.25 .45
Q71 PP5 70c green 2.25 .45
Q72 PP5 80c red brown 2.25 .45
Q73 PP5 90c blue 2.25 .45
Q74 PP6 1fr gray 2.25 .45
Q75 PP6 1.10fr ultra *(Franken)* 27.50 21.00
Q76 PP6 2fr red 25.00 .45
Q77 PP6 3fr violet 25.00 .45
Q78 PP6 4fr emerald 45.00 1.50
Q79 PP6 5fr brown 45.00 3.00
Q80 PP6 10fr orange 45.00 1.50
Nos. Q61-Q80 (20) 241.80 36.95

Type of 1916 Inscribed "FRANK" instead of "FRANKEN"

1920
Q81 PP6 1.10fr ultra 2.00 .45

PP7 PP8

1920 *Perf. 14*
Q82 PP7 10c blue grn 1.75 .75
Q83 PP7 15c olive grn 1.75 1.10
Q84 PP7 20c red 1.75 .75
Q85 PP7 25c gray brn 2.50 .75
Q86 PP7 30c red vio 27.00 22.50
Q87 PP7 40c pale org 11.00 .75
Q88 PP7 50c bister 9.00 .75
Q89 PP7 55c pale brown 5.50 4.50
Q90 PP7 60c dk violet 10.00 .75
Q91 PP7 70c green 18.00 1.10
Q92 PP7 80c red brown 40.00 1.50
Q93 PP7 90c dull blue 10.00 .75
Q94 PP8 1fr gray 85.00 1.50
Q95 PP8 1.10fr ultra 26.00 2.00
Q96 PP8 1.20fr dk green 11.00 .75
Q97 PP8 1.40fr black brn 11.00 .75
Q98 PP8 2fr vermilion 110.00 1.25
Q99 PP8 3fr red vio 120.00 .85
Q100 PP8 4fr yel grn 120.00 .75
Q101 PP8 5fr bister brn 120.00 .75
Q102 PP8 10fr brown org 120.00 .75
Nos. Q82-Q102 (21) 861.25 45.30

PP9 PP10

Types PP7 and PP9 differ in the position of the wheel and the tablet above it.

Types PP8 and PP10 differ in the bars below "FR".

There are many other variations in the designs.

1920-21 **Typo.**
Q103 PP9 10c carmine .30 .15
Q104 PP9 15c yel grn .30 .15
Q105 PP9 20c blue grn .70 .20
Q106 PP9 25c ultra .65 .20
Q107 PP9 30c chocolate .85 .20
Q108 PP9 35c orange brn .90 .30
Q109 PP9 40c orange 1.10 .15
Q110 PP9 50c rose 1.10 .15
Q111 PP9 55c yel ('21) 4.50 3.25
Q112 PP9 60c dull rose 1.10 .20
Q113 PP9 70c emerald 3.00 .40
Q114 PP9 80c violet 2.25 .15
Q115 PP9 90c lemon 37.50 21.00
Q116 PP9 90c claret 4.50 .40
Q117 PP10 1fr buff 4.50 .35
Q118 PP10 1fr red brown 4.00 .30
Q119 PP10 1.10fr ultra 1.65 .45
Q120 PP10 1.20fr orange 6.25 .30
Q121 PP10 1.40fr yellow 10.00 1.75
Q122 PP10 1.60fr turq blue 18.00 .70
Q123 PP10 1.60fr emerald 40.00 .70
Q124 PP10 2fr pale rose 26.00 .30
Q125 PP10 3fr dp rose 24.00 .30
Q126 PP10 4fr emerald 24.00 .30
Q127 PP10 5fr lt violet 17.50 .30
Q128 PP10 10fr lemon 110.00 9.00
Q129 PP10 10fr dk brown 22.50 .30
Q130 PP10 15fr dp rose ('21) 22.50 .30
Q131 PP10 20fr dk blue ('21) 325.00 3.00
Nos. Q103-Q131 (29) 714.65 45.25

PP11

1922 **Engr.** *Perf. 11½*
Q132 PP11 2fr black 4.00 .15
Q133 PP11 3fr brown 37.50 .20
Q134 PP11 4fr green 9.00 .15
Q135 PP11 5r claret 9.00 .15
Q136 PP11 10fr yel brown 10.00 .15
Q137 PP11 15fr rose red 10.00 .25
Q138 PP11 20fr blue 67.50 .25
Nos. Q132-Q138 (7) 147.00 1.30

PP12

PP13

Perf. 14x13½, 13½x14

1923-40 **Typo.**
Q139 PP12 5c red brown .20 .25
Q140 PP12 10c vermilion .15 .15
Q141 PP12 15c ultra .20 .30
Q142 PP12 20c turq blue .15 .15
Q143 PP12 30c brn vio ('27) .20 .15
Q144 PP12 40c olive grn .20 .15
Q145 PP12 50c magenta ('27) .20 .15
Q146 PP12 60c orange .25 .15
Q147 PP12 70c dk brown ('24) .15 .15
Q148 PP12 80c violet .20 .15
Q149 PP12 90c slate ('27) 1.25 .15
Q150 PP13 1fr ultra .35 .15
Q151 PP13 1fr brt blue ('28) .55 .15
Q152 PP13 1.10fr orange 3.00 .30
Q153 PP13 1.50fr turq blue 3.25 .30
Q154 PP13 1.70fr dp brown ('31) .75 .60
Q155 PP13 1.80fr claret 4.25 .60
Q156 PP13 2fr olive grn ('24) .35 .20
Q157 PP13 2.10fr gray grn 7.50 .85
Q158 PP13 2.40fr dp violet 4.00 .85
Q159 PP13 2.70fr gray ('24) 12.00 .75
Q160 PP13 3fr orange red .45 .15
Q161 PP13 3.30fr brown ('24) 12.50 .75
Q162 PP13 4fr rose ('24) .55 .15
Q163 PP13 5fr violet ('24) .90 .15
Q163A PP13 5fr brn vio ('40) .45 .30
Q164 PP13 6fr bis brn ('27) .50 .15
Q165 PP13 7fr orange ('27) .90 .15
Q166 PP13 8fr dp brown ('27) .75 .15
Q167 PP13 9fr red vio ('27) 2.50 .15
Q168 PP13 10fr blue grn ('27) 1.10 .15
Q168A PP13 10fr black ('40) 4.00 3.75
Q169 PP13 20fr magenta ('27) 1.90 .15
Q170 PP13 30fr turq green ('31) 6.00 .40
Q171 PP13 40fr gray ('31) 55.00 .75
Q172 PP13 50fr bister ('27) 9.00 .30
Nos. Q139-Q172 (36) 135.65
Set value 7.75

See Nos. Q239-Q262. For overprints see Nos. Q216-Q238. Stamps overprinted "Bagages Reisgoed" are revenues.

No. Q158 Surcharged

2R30

1924

Green Surcharge
Q173 PP34 2.30fr on 2.40fr violet 3.00 .50
a. Inverted surcharge 57.50

Type of Regular Issue of 1926-27 Overprinted

1928 *Perf. 14*
Q174 A61 4fr buff 6.50 .90
Q175 A61 5fr bister 6.50 1.10

Central P.O., Brussels PP15

1929-30 **Engr.** *Perf. 11½*
Q176 PP15 3fr black brn 1.40 .20
Q177 PP15 4fr gray 1.40 .20
Q178 PP15 5fr carmine 1.40 .20
Q179 PP15 6fr vio brn ('30) 22.50 25.00
Nos. Q176-Q179 (4) 26.70 25.60

No. Q179 Surcharged in Blue

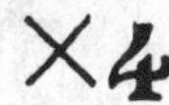

1933
Q180 PP15 4(fr) on 6fr vio brn 25.00 .25

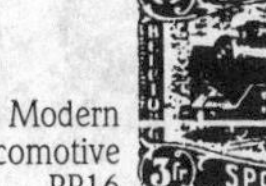

Modern Locomotive PP16

1934 **Photo.** *Perf. 13½x14*
Q181 PP16 3fr dk green 15.00 2.25
Q182 PP16 4fr red violet 4.00 .20
Q183 PP16 5fr dp rose 14.00 .20
Nos. Q181-Q183 (3) 33.00 2.65

Modern Railroad Train — PP17

Old Railroad Train — PP18

1935 **Engr.** *Perf. 14x13½, 13½x14*
Q184 PP17 10c rose car .30 .15
Q185 PP17 20c violet .35 .15
Q186 PP17 30c black brn .45 .30
Q187 PP17 40c dk blue .55 .15
Q188 PP17 50c orange red .55 .15
Q189 PP17 60c green .65 .15
Q190 PP17 70c ultra .70 .15
Q191 PP17 80c olive blk .65 .15
Q192 PP17 90c rose lake .85 .45
Q193 PP18 1fr brown vio .85 .15
Q194 PP18 2fr gray blk 2.00 .15
Q195 PP18 3fr red org 2.50 .15
Q196 PP18 4fr violet brn 3.00 .15
Q197 PP18 5fr plum 3.25 .15
Q198 PP18 6fr dp green 3.50 .15
Q199 PP18 7fr dp violet 17.00 .15
Q200 PP18 8fr olive blk 17.00 .20
Q201 PP18 9fr dk blue 17.00 .15
Q202 PP18 10fr car lake 17.00 .15
Q203 PP18 20fr green 90.00 .20
Q204 PP18 30fr violet 90.00 2.00
Q205 PP18 40fr black brn 90.00 2.50
Q206 PP18 50fr rose car 100.00 2.00
Q207 PP18 100fr ultra 250.00 45.00
Nos. Q184-Q207 (24) 708.15 55.05

Centenary of Belgian State Railway.

Winged Wheel — PP19

Surcharge in Red or Blue

1938 **Photo.** *Perf. 13½*
Q208 PP19 5fr on 3.50fr dk grn 6.50 .45
Q209 PP19 5fr on 4.50fr rose vio (Bl) .15 .15
Q210 PP19 6fr on 5.50fr cop red (Bl) .35 .15
a. Half used as 3fr on piece 1.50
Nos. Q208-Q210 (3) 7.00
Set value .60

See Nos. MQ1, Q297-Q299.

Symbolizing Unity Achieved Through Railroads PP20

1939 **Engr.** *Perf. 13½x14*
Q211 PP20 20c redsh brn 3.50 3.75
Q212 PP20 50c vio bl 3.50 3.75
Q213 PP20 2fr rose red 3.50 3.75
Q214 PP20 9fr sl grn 3.50 3.75
Q215 PP20 10fr dk vio 3.50 3.75
Nos. Q211-Q215 (5) 17.50 18.75

Issued in commemoration of the Railroad Exposition and Congress held at Brussels.

Parcel Post Stamps of 1925-27 Overprinted in Blue or Carmine

Perf. 14½x14, 14x14½

1940 **Unwmk.**
Q216 PP12 10c vermilion .15 .15
Q217 PP12 20c turq bl (C) .15 .15
Q218 PP12 30c brn vio .15 .15
Q219 PP12 40c ol grn (C) .15 .15
Q220 PP12 50c magenta .15 .15
Q221 PP12 60c orange .15 .25
Q222 PP12 70c dk brn .15 .15
Q223 PP12 80c vio (C) .15 .15
Q224 PP12 90c slate (C) .25 .25
Q225 PP13 1fr ultra (C) .25 .15
Q226 PP13 2fr ol grn (C) .25 .15
Q227 PP13 3fr org red .25 .15
Q228 PP13 4fr rose .25 .15
Q229 PP13 5fr vio (C) .25 .15
Q230 PP13 6fr bis brn .35 .25
Q231 PP13 7fr orange .35 .15
Q232 PP13 8fr dp brn .35 .15
Q233 PP13 9fr red vio .35 .15
Q234 PP13 10fr bl grn (C) .35 .25
Q235 PP13 20fr magenta .60 .25
Q236 PP13 30fr turq grn (C) 1.10 .75
Q237 PP13 40fr gray (C) 1.40 2.00
Q238 PP13 50fr bister 1.65 1.10
Nos. Q216-Q238 (23) 9.20 7.35

Types of 1923-40

1941
Q239 PP12 10c dl olive .15 .15
Q240 PP12 20c lt vio .15 .15
Q241 PP12 30c fawn .15 .15
Q242 PP12 40c dull blue .15 .15
Q243 PP12 50c lt grn .15 .15
Q244 PP12 60c gray .15 .15
Q245 PP12 70c chalky grn .15 .15
Q246 PP12 80c orange .15 .15
Q247 PP12 90c rose lilac .15 .15
Q248 PP13 1fr lt yel grn .15 .15
Q249 PP13 2fr vio brn .40 .15
Q250 PP13 3fr slate .45 .15
Q251 PP13 4fr dl olive .50 .15
Q252 PP13 5fr rose lilac .50 .15
Q253 PP13 5fr black .80 .30
Q254 PP13 6fr org ver .75 .30
Q255 PP13 7fr lilac .75 .15
Q256 PP13 8fr chalky grn .75 .15
Q257 PP13 9fr blue .90 .15
Q258 PP13 10fr rose lilac .90 .15
Q259 PP13 20fr milky blue 2.00 .15
Q260 PP13 30fr orange 4.50 .35
Q261 PP13 40fr rose 5.00 .35
Q262 PP13 50fr brt red vio 6.75 .15
Nos. Q239-Q262 (24) 26.45 4.30

Adjusting Tie Plates — PP21

Engineer at Throttle — PP22

Freight Station Interior — PP23

Signal and Electric Train — PP24

1942 **Engr.** ***Perf. 14x13½***
Q263 PP21 9.20fr red org .60 .80
Q264 PP22 12.30fr dp grn .60 .85
Q265 PP23 14.30fr dk car .85 1.25

Perf. 11½
Q266 PP24 100fr ultra 20.00 17.00
Nos. Q263-Q266 (4) 22.05 19.90

Catalogue values for unused stamps in this section, from this point to the end of the section, are for Never Hinged items.

PP25

PP26

PP27

1945-46 **Photo.** **Unwmk.**
Q267 PP25 10c ol blk ('46) .30 .15
Q268 PP25 20c dp vio .30 .15
Q269 PP25 30c chnt brn ('46) .30 .15
Q270 PP25 40c dp bl ('46) .30 .15
Q271 PP25 50c peacock grn .30 .15
Q272 PP25 60c blk ('46) .30 .15
Q273 PP25 70c emer ('46) .45 .25
Q274 PP25 80c orange .75 .20
Q275 PP25 90c brn vio ('46) .30 .25
Q276 PP26 1fr bl grn ('46) .30 .15
Q277 PP26 2fr blk brn .30 .15
Q278 PP26 3fr grnsh blk ('46) 2.00 .20
Q279 PP26 4fr dark blue .45 .20
Q280 PP26 5fr sepia .45 .15
Q281 PP26 6fr dk ol grn ('46) 2.25 .15
Q282 PP26 7fr dk vio ('46) .75 .25
Q283 PP26 8fr red org .75 .15
Q284 PP26 9fr dp bl ('46) .90 .15
Q285 PP27 10fr dk red ('46) 3.25 .15
Q286 PP27 10fr sepia ('46) 1.65 .25
Q287 PP27 20fr dk yel grn ('46) .75 .15
Q288 PP27 30fr dp vio 1.10 .15
Q289 PP27 40fr rose pink .95 .15
Q290 PP27 50fr brt bl ('46) 12.00 .15
Nos. Q267-Q290 (24) 31.15
Set value 3.00

Mercury — PP28

1945-46 ***Perf. 13½x13***
Q291 PP28 3fr emer ('46) .35 .25
Q292 PP28 5fr ultra .15 .20
Q293 PP28 6fr red .20 .15

Inscribed "Belgique-Belgie"
Q294 PP28 3fr emer ('46) .35 .25
Q295 PP28 5fr ultra .15 .20
Q296 PP28 6fr red .20 .15
Nos. Q291-Q296 (6) 1.40 1.20

Winged Wheel Type of 1938
Carmine Surcharge

1946 ***Perf. 13½x14***
Q297 PP19 8fr on 5.50fr brn .65 .15
Q298 PP19 10fr on 5.50fr dk bl .75 .25
Q299 PP19 12fr on 5.50fr vio 1.10 .25
Nos. Q297-Q299 (3) 2.50 .65

Railway Crossing PP29

1947 **Engr.** ***Perf. 12½***
Q300 PP29 100fr dark green 7.50 .25

Crossbowman with Train — PP30

1947 **Photo.** ***Perf. 11½***
Q301 PP30 8fr dk ol brn 1.00 .25
Q302 PP30 10fr gray & bl 1.10 .30
Q303 PP30 12fr dk vio 1.75 .50
Nos. Q301-Q303 (3) 3.85 1.05

Surcharged with New Value and Bars in Carmine

1948
Q304 PP30 9fr on 8fr 1.00 .25
Q305 PP30 11fr on 10fr 1.10 .40
Q306 PP30 13.50fr on 12fr 1.75 .40
Nos. Q304-Q306 (3) 3.85 1.05

Delivery of Parcel — PP31

1948
Q307 PP31 9fr chocolate 6.25 .15
Q308 PP31 11fr brn car 6.50 .15
Q309 PP31 13.50fr gray 10.00 .35
Nos. Q307-Q309 (3) 22.75 .65

Locomotive of 1835 — PP32

Various Locomotives.

Lathe Work in Frame Differs

1949 **Engr.** ***Perf. 12½***
Q310 PP32 ½fr dk brn .60 .15
Q311 PP32 1fr car rose .70 .15
Q312 PP32 2fr dp ultra .90 .15
Q313 PP32 3fr dp mag 2.00 .15
Q314 PP32 4fr bl grn 2.75 .15
Q315 PP32 5fr org red 2.75 .15
Q316 PP32 6fr brn vio 3.00 .20
Q317 PP32 7fr yel grn 4.00 .15
Q318 PP32 8fr grnsh bl 5.00 .15
Q319 PP32 9fr yel brn 6.00 .20
Q320 PP32 10fr citron 7.00 .15
Q321 PP32 20fr orange 11.00 .15
Q322 PP32 30fr blue 15.00 .15
Q323 PP32 40fr lil rose 21.00 .20
Q324 PP32 50fr violet 21.00 .25
Q325 PP32 100fr red 65.00 .20

Engraved; Center Typographed
Q326 PP32 10fr car rose & blk 9.00 .70
Nos. Q310-Q326 (17) 176.70 3.40

See No. Q337.

1949 **Engr.**

Design: Electric locomotive.

Q327 PP32 60fr blk brn 20.00 .25

Opening of Charleroi-Brussels electric railway line, Oct. 15, 1949.

Mailing Parcel Post — PP33

Sorting PP34

Loading PP35

1950-52 ***Perf. 12, 12½***
Q328 PP33 11fr red org 6.50 .40
Q329 PP33 12fr red vio ('51) 20.00 1.10
Q330 PP34 13fr dk bl grn 6.50 .20
Q331 PP34 15fr ultra ('51) 15.00 .30
Q332 PP35 16fr gray 6.50 .20
Q333 PP33 17fr brn ('52) 8.00 .40
Q334 PP35 18fr brt car ('51) 16.00 .40
Q335 PP35 20fr brn org ('52) 8.00 .45
Nos. Q328-Q335 (8) 86.50 3.45

For surcharges see Nos. Q338-Q340.

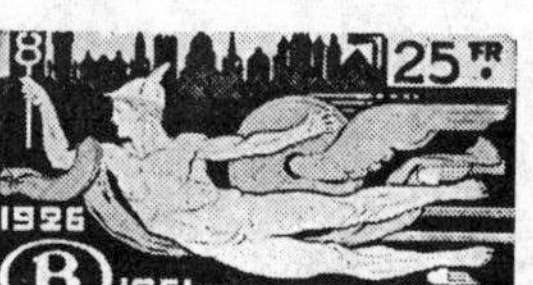

Mercury and Winged Wheel — PP36

1951
Q336 PP36 25fr dark blue 9.00 8.00

25th anniv. of the founding of the Natl. Soc. of Belgian Railroads.

Type of 1949

Design: Electric locomotive.

1952 **Unwmk.** ***Perf. 11½***
Q337 PP32 300fr red violet 150.00 .65

Nos. Q331, Q328 and Q334 Surcharged with New Value and "X" in Red, Blue or Green

1953 ***Perf. 12***
Q338 PP34 13fr on 15fr (R) 60.00 3.00
Q339 PP33 17fr on 11fr (Bl) 37.50 2.25
Q340 PP35 20fr on 18fr (G) 30.00 2.50
Nos. Q338-Q340 (3) 127.50 7.75

Electric Train, 1952 — PP37

1953 **Engr.**
Q341 PP37 200fr dk yel grn & vio brn 250.00 4.00
Q342 PP37 200fr dk green 225.00 1.00

No. Q341 was issued to commemorate the opening of the railway link connecting Brussels North and South Stations, Oct. 4, 1952.

New North Station, Brussels — PP38

Chapelle Station, Brussels PP39

Designs: No. Q348, 15fr, Congress Station. 10fr, 20fr, 30fr, 40fr, 50fr, South Station. 100fr, 200fr, 300fr, Central Station.

1953-57 **Unwmk.** ***Perf. 11½***
Q343 PP38 1fr bister .75 .15
Q344 PP38 2fr slate .90 .15
Q345 PP38 3fr blue grn 1.75 .15
Q346 PP38 4fr orange 2.00 .15
Q347 PP38 5fr red brn 2.00 .15
Q348 PP38 5fr dk red brn 13.00 .25
Q349 PP38 6fr rose vio 2.25 .15
Q350 PP38 7fr brt green 2.25 .15
Q351 PP38 8fr rose red 2.25 .15
Q352 PP38 9fr brt grnsh bl 4.25 .15
Q353 PP38 10fr lt grn 4.25 .15
Q354 PP38 15fr dl red 17.00 .15
Q355 PP38 20fr blue 6.25 .15
Q356 PP38 30fr purple 10.00 .15
Q357 PP38 40fr brt purple 12.50 .15
Q358 PP38 50fr lilac rose 15.00 .15
Q359 PP39 60fr brt purple 30.00 .15
Q360 PP39 80fr brown vio 35.00 .15
Q361 PP39 100fr emerald 32.50 .15
Q361A PP39 200fr brt vio bl 75.00 1.65
Q361B PP39 300fr lilac rose 125.00 2.25
Nos. Q343-Q361B (21) 393.90
Set value 5.25

Issue dates: No. Q347, 20fr and 30fr, 1953; 80fr, 1955; 200fr, 1956; 300fr, 1957. Rest of set, 1954.

See Nos. Q407, Q431-Q432.

Electric Train — PP40

Mercury and Winged Wheel — PP41

1954
Q362 PP40 13fr chocolate 13.00 .15
Q363 PP40 18fr dark blue 16.00 .15
Q364 PP40 21fr lilac rose 17.00 .50
Nos. Q362-Q364 (3) 46.00 .80

Nos. Q362-Q364 Surcharged with New Value and "X" in Blue, Red or Green

1956
Q365 PP40 14fr on 13fr (B) 8.00 .15
Q366 PP40 19fr on 18fr (R) 8.50 .25
Q367 PP40 22fr on 21fr (G) 8.75 .45
Nos. Q365-Q367 (3) 25.25 .85

1957 **Engr.** ***Perf. 11½***
Q368 PP41 14fr brt green 7.75 .25
Q369 PP41 19fr olive gray 8.00 .35
Q370 PP41 22fr carmine rose 8.75 .60
Nos. Q368-Q370 (3) 24.50 1.20

Nos. Q369-Q370 Surcharged with New Value and "X" in Pink or Green

1959
Q371 PP41 20fr on 19fr (P) 22.50 .40
Q372 PP41 20fr on 22fr (G) 27.50 .60

Old North Station, Brussels PP42

1959 **Engr.** ***Perf. 11½***
Q373 PP42 20fr olive green 14.00 .40

See Nos. Q381, Q383. For surcharges see Nos. Q378, Q382, Q384.

Diesel and Electric Locomotives and Association Emblem PP43

1960 Unwmk. *Perf. 11½*
Q374 PP43 20fr red 40.00 30.00
Q375 PP43 50fr dark blue 40.00 27.50
Q376 PP43 60fr red lilac 40.00 27.50
Q377 PP43 70fr emerald 40.00 27.50
Nos. Q374-Q377 (4) 160.00 112.50

Intl. Assoc. of Railway Congresses, 75th anniv.

No. Q373 Surcharged with New Value and "X" in Red

1961
Q378 PP42 24fr on 20fr ol grn 65.00 .40

South Station, Brussels — PP44

1962 Unwmk. *Perf. 11½*
Q379 PP44 24fr dull red 6.00 .40

No. Q379 Surcharged with New Value and "X" in Light Green

1963
Q380 PP44 26fr on 24fr dl red 5.00 .40

Type of 1959

Design: 26fr, Central Station, Antwerp.

1963 Engr. *Perf. 11½*
Q381 PP42 26fr blue 5.25 .75

No. Q381 Surcharged in Red

1964, Apr. 20
Q382 PP42 28fr on 26fr blue 5.50 .50

Type of 1959

Design: 28fr, St. Peter's Station, Ghent.

1965 Engr. *Perf. 11½*
Q383 PP42 28fr red lilac 5.25 1.25

Nos. Q383 Surcharged with New Value and "X" in Green

1966
Q384 PP42 35fr on 28fr red lil 5.25 1.00

Arlon Railroad Station — PP45

Perf. 11½
1967, Aug. Unwmk. Engr.
Q385 PP45 25fr bister 10.00 .30
Q386 PP45 30fr blue green 5.00 .40
Q387 PP45 35fr deep blue 7.00 .65
Nos. Q385-Q387 (3) 22.00 1.35

See #Q408. For surcharges see #Q410-Q412.

Electric Train — PP46

Designs: 2fr, 3fr, 4fr, 5fr, 6fr, 7fr, 8fr, 9fr, like 1fr. 10fr, 20fr, 30fr, 40fr, Train going right. 50fr, 60fr, 70fr, 80fr, 90fr, Train going left. 100fr, 200fr, 300fr, Diesel train.

1968-73 Engr. *Perf. 11½*
Q388 PP46 1fr olive bis .15 .15
Q389 PP46 2fr slate .15 .15
Q390 PP46 3fr bl grn .15 .15
Q391 PP46 4fr orange .15 .15
Q392 PP46 5fr brown .20 .15
Q393 PP46 6fr plum .30 .15
Q394 PP46 7fr brt grn .30 .15
Q395 PP46 8fr carmine .35 .15
Q396 PP46 9fr blue .40 .15
Q397 PP46 10fr green .45 .15
Q398 PP46 20fr dk bl .75 .15
Q399 PP46 30fr dk pur 1.10 .15
Q400 PP46 40fr brt lil 1.40 .15
Q401 PP46 50fr brt pink 1.75 .15
Q402 PP46 60fr brt vio 2.00 .15
Q402A PP46 70fr dp bis ('73) 2.75 1.00
Q403 PP46 80fr dk brn 2.75 .25
Q403A PP46 90fr yel grn ('73) 3.75 1.25
Q404 PP46 100fr emerald 4.00 .45
Q405 PP46 200fr vio bl 8.75 .80
Q406 PP46 300fr lil rose 19.00 1.25
Nos. Q388-Q406 (21) 50.60
Set value 5.90

See No. Q409.

Types of 1953-68

Designs: 10fr, Congress Station, Brussels. 40fr, Arlon Station. 500fr, Electric train going left.

1968, June Engr. *Perf. 11½*
Q407 PP38 10fr gray 1.00 .15
Q408 PP45 40fr vermilion 20.00 .40
Q409 PP46 500fr yellow 25.00 2.25
Nos. Q407-Q409 (3) 46.00 2.80

Nos. Q385, Q387 and Q408 Surcharged with New Value and "X"

1970, Dec.
Q410 PP45 37fr on 25fr bister 45.00 3.50
Q411 PP45 48fr on 35fr dp bl 13.00 5.50
Q412 PP45 53fr on 40fr ver 15.00 6.75
Nos. Q410-Q412 (3) 73.00 15.75

Ostend Station PP47

1971, Mar. Engr. *Perf. 11½*
Q413 PP47 32fr bis & blk 2.50 2.25
Q414 PP47 37fr gray & blk 2.50 2.50
Q415 PP47 42fr bl & blk 4.00 2.75
Q416 PP47 44fr brt rose & blk 4.50 3.00
Q417 PP47 46fr vio & blk 4.50 3.00
Q418 PP47 50fr brick red & blk 5.50 3.25
Q419 PP47 52fr sep & blk 5.50 3.25
Q420 PP47 54fr yel grn & blk 6.00 3.25
Q421 PP47 61fr grnsh bl & blk 6.00 4.00
Nos. Q413-Q421 (9) 41.00 27.25

Nos. Q413-Q416, Q419-Q421 Surcharged with New Value and "X"

1971, Dec. 15
Denomination in Black
Q422 PP47 34fr on 32fr bister 2.25 .50
Q423 PP47 40fr on 37fr gray 2.75 .60
Q424 PP47 47fr on 44fr brt rose 3.00 .65
Q425 PP47 53fr on 42fr blue 3.50 .75
Q426 PP47 56fr on 52fr sepia 3.50 .85
Q427 PP47 59fr on 54fr yel grn 3.50 .85
Q428 PP47 66fr on 61fr grnsh blue 4.25 1.00
Nos. Q422-Q428 (7) 22.75 5.20

Track, Underpinning of Railroad Car and Emblems PP48

1972, Mar. Photo.
Q429 PP48 100fr emer, red & blk 10.00 1.75

Centenary of International Railroad Union.

100F Congress Emblem — PP49

1974, Apr. Photo. *Perf. 11½*
Q430 PP49 100fr yel, blk & red 8.50 1.25

4th International Symposium on Railroad Cybernetics, Washington, DC, Apr. 1974.

Type of 1953-1957

1975, June 1 Engr. *Perf. 11½*
Q431 PP38 20fr emerald .90 .50
Q432 PP38 50fr blue 2.00 1.25

Railroad Tracks — PP50

1976, June 10 Photo. *Perf. 11½*
Q433 PP50 20fr ultra & multi 3.00 .60
Q434 PP50 50fr brt grn & multi 1.75 1.40
Q435 PP50 100fr dp org & multi 4.00 2.75
Q436 PP50 150fr brt lil & multi 6.00 4.75
Nos. Q433-Q436 (4) 14.75 9.50

1000F Railroad Station — PP51

1977 Photo. *Perf. 11½*
Q437 PP51 1000fr multi 45.00 *10.00*

Freight Car — PP52

Designs: 1fr-9fr, Freight car. 10fr-40fr, Hopper car. 50fr-90fr, Maintenance car. 100fr-500fr, Liquid fuel car.

1980, Dec. 16 Engr. *Perf. 11½*
Q438 PP52 1fr bis brn & blk .15 .15
Q439 PP52 2fr cl & blk .15 .15
Q440 PP52 3fr brt bl & blk .15 .15
Q441 PP52 4fr grnsh blk & blk .15 .15
Q442 PP52 5fr sep & blk .25 .15
Q443 PP52 6fr dp org & blk .35 .15
Q444 PP52 7fr pur & blk .40 .15
Q445 PP52 8fr black .40 .15
Q446 PP52 9fr grn & blk .45 .15
Q447 PP52 10fr yel bis & blk .50 .15
Q448 PP52 20fr grnsh bl & blk 1.10 .30
Q449 PP52 30fr bis & blk 2.25 .45
Q450 PP52 40fr lt lil & blk 2.50 .55
Q451 PP52 50fr dk brn & blk 2.75 .70
Q452 PP52 60fr ol & blk 2.75 .90
Q453 PP52 70fr vio bl & blk 3.50 1.00
Q454 PP52 80fr vio brn & blk 4.00 1.10
Q455 PP52 90fr lil rose & blk 5.00 1.25
Q456 PP52 100fr crim rose & blk 5.25 1.40
Q457 PP52 200fr brn & blk 10.00 2.75
Q458 PP52 300fr ol gray & blk 14.00 4.25
Q459 PP52 500fr dl pur & blk 25.00 7.00
Nos. Q438-Q459 (22) 81.05 23.15

Train in Station PP53

Electric Locomotives PP54

1982 Engr. *Perf. 11½*
Q460 PP53 10fr red & blk .85 .25
Q461 PP53 20fr green & blk 1.50 .50
Q462 PP53 50fr sepia & blk 4.00 1.40
Q463 PP53 100fr blue & blk 8.00 2.75
Nos. Q460-Q463 (4) 14.35 4.90

1985, May 3 Photo. *Perf. 11½*
Q464 PP54 250fr BB-150 11.00 2.00
Q465 PP54 500fr BB-120 24.00 10.00

Stylized Castle, Gabled Station and Electric Rail Car — PP55

1987, Oct. 12 Engr. *Perf. 11½*
Q466 PP55 10fr dk red & blk .50 .40
Q467 PP55 20fr dk grn & blk 1.00 .75
Q468 PP55 50fr dk brn & blk 2.50 1.90
Q469 PP55 100fr dk lil & blk 5.00 3.75
Q470 PP55 150fr dark olive bister & blk 7.50 5.65
Nos. Q466-Q470 (5) 16.50 12.45

ISSUED UNDER GERMAN OCCUPATION

German Stamps of 1906-11 Surcharged

Belgien
3 Centimes
Nos. N1-N6

✻ 1Fr.25C. ✻

Belgien
Nos. N7-N9

Wmk. Lozenges (125)

1914-15 *Perf. 14, 14½*
N1 A16 3c on 3pf brown .45 .25
N2 A16 5c on 5pf green .40 .25
N3 A16 10c on 10pf car .50 .25
N4 A16 25c on 20pf ultra .55 .35
N5 A16 50c on 40pf lake & blk 2.25 1.65
N6 A16 75c on 60pf mag .90 1.25
N7 A16 1fr on 80pf lake & blk, *rose* 2.50 2.00
N8 A17 1fr25c on 1m car 22.50 18.00
N9 A21 2fr50c on 2m gray bl 20.00 22.50
Nos. N1-N9 (9) 50.05 46.50

German Stamps of 1906-18 Surcharged

Belgien
3 Cent.
Nos. N10-N21

Belgien
1F.
No. N22

✻ 1F.25Cent. ✻

Belgien
Nos. N23-N25

1916-18
N10 A22 2c on 2pf drab .25 .25
N11 A16 3c on 3pf brn .35 .25
N12 A16 5c on 5pf grn .35 .25
N13 A22 8c on 7½pf org .65 .35
N14 A16 10c on 10pf car .25 .25
N15 A22 15c on 15pf yel brn .65 .25
N16 A22 15c on 15pf dk vio .65 .45
N17 A16 20c on 25pf org & blk, *yel* .35 .35
N18 A16 25c on 20pf ultra .35 .25
a. 25c on 20pf blue .40 .25
N19 A16 40c on 30pf org & blk, *buff* .40 .35
N20 A16 50c on 40pf lake & blk .35 .35
N21 A16 75c on 60pf mag .65 *8.50*
N22 A16 1fr on 80pf lake & blk, *rose* 2.00 *2.50*
N23 A17 1fr25c on 1m car 3.25 3.25
N24 A21 2fr50c on 2m gray bl 30.00 30.00
a. 2fr50c on 1m car (error) *3,500.*
N25 A20 6fr25c on 5m sl & car 40.00 37.50
Nos. N10-N25 (16) 80.50 85.10

A similar series of stamps without "Belgien" was used in parts of Belgium and France while occupied by German forces. See France Nos. N15-N26.

BENIN

bə-'nin

French Colony

LOCATION — West Coast of Africa
GOVT. — French Possession
AREA — 8,627 sq. mi.
POP. — 493,000 (approx.)
CAPITAL — Benin

In 1895 the French possessions known as Benin were incorporated into the colony of Dahomey and postage stamps of Dahomey superseded those of Benin. Dahomey took the name Benin when it became a republic in 1975.

100 Centimes = 1 Franc

Catalogue values for unused stamps in this country are for Never Hinged items, beginning with Scott 342 in the regular postage section, Scott C240 in the airpost section, Scott J44 in the postage due section, and Scott Q8 in the parcel post section.

Handstamped on Stamps of French Colonies **BÉNIN**

1892 Unwmk. Perf. 14x13½

Black Overprint

No.	Type	Description	Unused	Used
1	A9	1c blk, *bluish*	100.00	75.00
2	A9	2c brn, *buff*	75.00	67.50
3	A9	4c claret, *lav*	32.50	30.00
4	A9	5c grn, *grnsh*	13.00	12.00
5	A9	10c blk, *lavender*	42.50	35.00
6	A9	15c blue	20.00	8.00
7	A9	20c red, *grn*	150.00	150.00
8	A9	25c blk, *rose*	50.00	27.50
9	A9	30c brn, *yelsh*	125.00	90.00
10	A9	35c blk, *orange*	125.00	90.00
11	A9	40c red, *straw*	90.00	75.00
12	A9	75c car, *rose*	250.00	175.00
13	A9	1fr brnz grn, *straw*	300.00	200.00

Red Overprint

No.	Type	Description	Unused	Used
14	A9	15c blue	55.00	45.00

Blue Overprint

No.	Type	Description	Unused	Used
15	A9	5c grn, *grnsh*	1,400.	350.00
15A	A9	15c blue	1,400.	350.00

Nos. 1-13 all exist with overprint inverted, and several with it double. These sell for slightly more than normal stamps. The overprints of Nos. 1-15A are of four types, three without accent mark on "E." They exist diagonal.
Counterfeits exist of Nos. 1-19.

Additional Surcharge in Red or Black **40**

1892

No.	Type	Description	Unused	Used
16	A9	01c on 5c grn, *grnsh*	190.	125.
17	A9	40c on 15c blue	125.	40.
18	A9	75c on 15c blue	625.	425.
19	A9	75c on 15c bl (Bk)	2,500.	1,900.

Counterfeits exist.

Navigation and Commerce
A3 A4

1893 Typo. Perf. 14x13½

Name of Colony in Blue or Carmine

No.	Type	Description	Unused	Used
20	A3	1c blk, *bluish*	1.75	1.40
21	A3	2c brn, *buff*	2.25	1.75
22	A3	4c claret, *lav*	2.50	1.75
23	A3	5c grn, *grnsh*	3.25	2.00
24	A3	10c blk, *lavender*	3.25	2.25
25	A3	15c blue, quadrille paper	16.00	9.50
26	A3	20c red, *grn*	9.50	4.75
27	A3	25c blk, *rose*	22.50	9.50
28	A3	30c brn, *bis*	10.50	7.50
29	A3	40c red, *straw*	3.00	1.75
30	A3	50c car, *rose*	2.00	1.75
31	A3	75c vio, *org*	6.25	4.25
32	A3	1fr brnz grn, *straw*	40.00	25.00
		Nos. 20-32 (13)	122.75	73.15

Perf. 13½x14 stamps are counterfeits.

1894 Perf. 14x13½

No.	Type	Description	Unused	Used
33	A4	1c blk, *bluish*	2.00	1.40
34	A4	2c brn, *buff*	2.00	1.40
35	A4	4c claret, *lav*	2.00	1.40
36	A4	5c grn, *grnsh*	2.50	1.40
37	A4	10c blk, *lavender*	3.00	2.25
38	A4	15c bl, quadrille paper	4.50	2.25
39	A4	20c red, *grn*	4.50	3.50
40	A4	25c blk, *rose*	4.75	2.50
41	A4	30c brn, *bis*	3.50	2.50
42	A4	40c red, *straw*	11.00	7.00
43	A4	50c car, *rose*	13.00	7.50
44	A4	75c vio, *org*	8.50	8.00
45	A4	1fr brnz grn, *straw*	2.00	2.00
		Nos. 33-45 (13)	63.25	43.10

Perf. 13½x14 stamps are counterfeits.

PEOPLE'S REPUBLIC OF BENIN

LOCATION — West Coast of Africa
GOVT. — Republic.
AREA — 43,483 sq. mi.
POP. — 3,832,000 (est. 1984)
CAPITAL — Porto Novo

The Republic of Dahomey proclaimed itself the People's Republic of Benin on Nov. 30, 1975. See Dahomey for stamps issued before then.

Catalogue values for unused stamps in this section are for Never Hinged items.

Allamanda Cathartica — A83

Flag Bearers, Arms of Benin — A84

Flowers: 35fr, Ixora coccinea. 45fr, Hibiscus, 60fr, Phaemeria magnifica.

Unwmk.

1975, Dec. 8 Photo. Perf. 13

No.	Type	Description	Unused	Used
342	A83	10fr lilac & multi	.15	.15
343	A83	35fr gray & multi	.22	.15
344	A83	45fr multi	.35	.22
345	A83	60fr blue & multi	.40	.30
		Nos. 342-345 (4)	1.12	.82

For surcharge see No. 788.

1976, Apr. 30 Litho. Perf. 12

Design: 60fr, Speaker, wall with "PRPB," flag and arms of Benin. 100fr, Flag and arms of Benin.

No.	Type	Description	Unused	Used
346	A84	50fr ocher & multi	.28	.20
347	A84	60fr ocher & multi	.30	.20
348	A84	100fr multi	.55	.40
		Nos. 346-348 (3)	1.13	.80

Proclamation of the People's Republic of Benin. Nov. 30, 1975.

A.G. Bell, Satellite and 1876 Telephone — A85

1976, July 9 Litho. Perf. 13

No.	Type	Description	Unused	Used
349	A985	200fr lilac, red & brn	1.10	.45

Centenary of first telephone call by Alexander Graham Bell, Mar. 10, 1876.

Dahomey Nos. 277-278 Surcharged

1976, July 19 Photo. Perf. 12½x13

No.	Type	Description	Unused	Used
350	A57	50fr on 1fr multi	.32	.15
351	A57	60fr on 2fr multi	.42	.15

For overprint see No. 711.

African Jamboree, Nigeria 1976 — A86

1976, Aug. 16 Litho. Perf. 12½x13

No.	Type	Description	Unused	Used
352	A86	50fr Scouts Cooking	.28	.20
353	A86	70fr Three scouts	.38	.28

Blood Bank, Cotonou — A87

Designs: 50fr, Accident and first aid station. 60fr, Blood donation.

1976, Sept. 24 Litho. Perf. 13

No.	Type	Description	Unused	Used
354	A87	5fr multicolored	.15	.15
355	A87	50fr multicolored	.28	.20
356	A87	60fr multicolored	.35	.22
		Nos. 354-356 (3)	.78	
		Set value		.47

National Blood Donors Day.

A88 A89

1976, Oct. 4 Litho. Perf. 13x12½

No.	Type	Description	Unused	Used
357	A88	20fr Manioc	.15	.15
358	A88	50fr Corn	.28	.20
359	A88	60fr Cacao	.30	.20
360	A88	150fr Cotton	.80	.60
		Nos. 357-360 (4)	1.53	1.15

Natl. agricultural production campaign. For surcharge see No. 565.

1976, Oct. 25

No.	Type	Description	Unused	Used
361	A89	50fr Classroom	.28	.20

Third anniversary of KPARO newspaper, used in local language studies.

Roan Antelope — A90

Flags, Wall, Broken Chains — A91

Penhari National Park: 30fr, Buffalo. 50fr, Hippopotamus, horiz. 70fr, Lion.

1976, Nov. 8 Photo.

No.	Type	Description	Unused	Used
362	A90	10fr multicolored	.15	.15
363	A90	30fr multicolored	.16	.15
364	A90	50fr multicolored	.28	.20
365	A90	70fr multicolored	.38	.22
		Nos. 362-365 (4)	.97	
		Set value		.59

1976, Nov. 30 Litho. Perf. 12½

Design: 150fr, Corn, raised hands with weapons.

No.	Type	Description	Unused	Used
366	A91	40fr multicolored	.20	.15
367	A91	150fr multicolored	.80	.60

First anniversary of proclamation of the People's Republic of Benin.

Table Tennis, Map of Africa (Games' Emblem) — A92

Design: 50fr, Stadium, Cotonou.

1976, Dec. 26 Litho. Perf. 13

No.	Type	Description	Unused	Used
368	A92	10fr multi	.15	.15
369	A92	50fr multi	.28	.20
		Set value	.35	.25

West African University Games, Cotonou, Dec. 26-31.

Europafrica Issue

Planes over Africa and Europe — A93

1977, May 13 Litho. Perf. 13

No.	Type	Description	Unused	Used
370	A93	200fr multi	.70	.55

For surcharge see No. 590.

Snake — A94

1977, June 13 Litho. Perf. 13x13½

No.	Type	Description	Unused	Used
371	A94	2fr shown	.15	.15
372	A94	3fr Tortoise	.15	.15
373	A94	5fr Zebus	.15	.15
374	A94	10fr Cats	.16	.15
		Set value	.37	.20

Patients at Clinic — A95

1977, Aug. 2 Litho. Perf. 12½

No.	Type	Description	Unused	Used
375	A95	100fr multi	.60	.40

World Rheumatism Year.

Karate, Map of Africa — A96

Designs: 100fr, Javelin, map of Africa, Benin Flag, horiz. 150fr, Hurdles.

1977, Aug. 30 Litho. *Perf. 12½*

376 A96 90fr multi		.35	.25
377 A96 100fr multi		.45	.35
378 A96 150fr multi		.60	.45
a.	Souvenir sheet of 3, #376-378	2.00	2.00
	Nos. 376-378 (3)	1.40	1.05

2nd West African Games, Lagos, Nigeria.

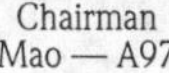

Chairman Mao — A97

Lister and Vaporizer — A98

1977, Sept. 9 Litho. *Perf. 13x12½*

379 A97 100fr multicolored	.50	.40

Mao Tse-tung (1893-1976), Chinese communist leader.

1977, Sept. 20 Engr. *Perf. 13*

Designs: 150fr, Scalpels and flames, symbols of antisepsis, and Red Cross.

380 A98 150fr multi	.80	.60
381 A98 210fr multi	1.20	.80

Joseph Lister (1827-1912), surgeon, founder of antiseptic surgery.

For surcharges see Nos. 560, 566.

Guelege Mask, Ethnographic Museum, Porto Novo — A99

Designs: 50fr, Jar, symbol of unity, emblem of King Ghezo, Historical Museum, Abomey, vert. 210fr, Abomey Museum.

1977, Oct. 17 *Perf. 13*

382 A99 50fr red & multi	.28	.20
383 A99 60fr blk, bl & bister	.35	.22
384 A99 210fr multi	1.20	.80
Nos. 382-384 (3)	1.83	1.22

For surcharge see No. 562.

Atacora Falls — A100

Mother and Child, Owl of Wisdom — A101

Tourist Publicity: 60fr, Pile houses, Ganvie, horiz. 150fr, Round huts, Savalou.

1977, Oct. 24 Litho. *Perf. 12½*

385 A100 50fr multi		.32	.24
386 A100 60fr multi		.42	.25
387 A100 150fr multi		1.00	.70
a.	Souvenir sheet of 3, #385-387	2.00	2.00
	Nos. 385-387 (3)	1.74	1.19

Perf. 12½x13, 13x12½

1977, Dec. 3 Photo.

Design: 150fr, Chopping down magical tree, horiz.

388 A101 60fr multi	.35	.22
389 A101 150fr multi	.80	.60

Campaign against witchcraft.

For surcharge see No. 576.

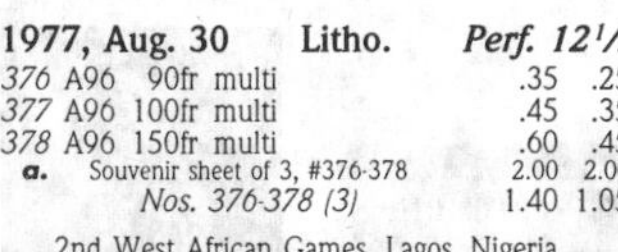

Battle Scene A102

1978, Jan. 16 Litho. *Perf. 12½*

390 A102 50fr multi	.35	.20

Victory of people of Benin over imperialist forces.

Map, People and Houses of Benin — A103

1978, Feb. 1

391 A103 50fr multi	.35	.20

General population and dwelling census.

Alexander Fleming, Microscope and Penicillin — A104

1978, Mar. 12 Litho. *Perf. 13*

392 A104 300fr multi	2.00	1.10

Alexnader Fleming (1881-1955), 50th anniversary of discovery of penicillin.

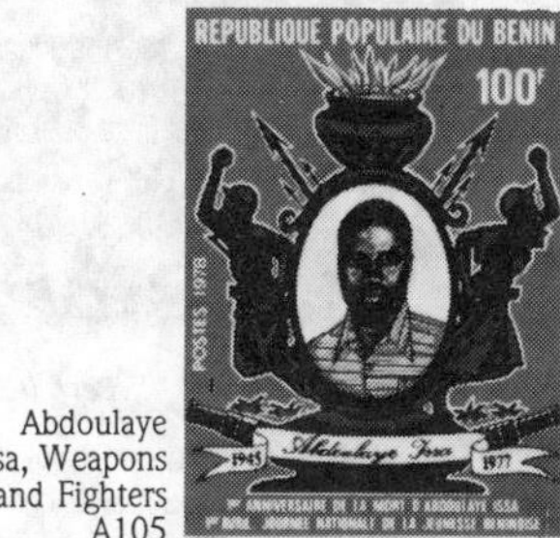

Abdoulaye Issa, Weapons and Fighters A105

1978, Apr. 1 *Perf. 12½x13*

393 A105 100fr red, blk & gold	.65	.38

First anniversary of death of Abdoulaye Issa and National Day of Benin's Youth.

Ed Hadj Omar and Horseback Rider — A106

Design: 90fr, L'Almamy Samory Toure (1830-1900) and horseback riders.

1976, Apr. 10 *Perf. 13x12½*

394 A106 90fr red & multi	.60	.35
395 A106 100fr multi	.65	.38

African heroes of resistance against colonialism.

ITU Emblem, Satellite, Landscape — A107

1978, May 17 Litho. *Perf. 13*

396 A107 100fr multi	.65	.38

10th World Telecommunications Day.

Soccer Player, Stadium, Argentina '78 Emblem — A108

Designs (Argentina '78 Emblem and): 300fr, Soccer players and ball, vert. 500fr, Soccer player, globe with ball on map.

1978, June 1 Litho. *Perf. 12½*

397 A108 200fr multi		1.40	.70
398 A108 300fr multi		2.00	1.10
399 A108 500fr multi		3.50	1.75
a.	Souvenir sheet of 3	7.00	7.00
	Nos. 397-399 (3)	6.90	3.55

11th World Cup Soccer Championship, Argentina, June 1-25. No. 399a contains 3 stamps similar to Nos. 397-399 in changed colors.

For surcharges see Nos. 591, 593, 595-596.

Nos. 397-399a Overprinted in Red Brown:
a. FINALE / ARGENTINE: 3 / HOLLANDE: 1
b. CHAMPION / 1978 / ARGENTINE
c. 3e BRESIL / 4e ITALIE

1978, June 25 Litho. *Perf. 12½*

400 A108 (a) 200fr multi		1.40	.75
401 A108 (b) 300fr multi		2.00	1.10
402 A108 (c) 500fr multi		3.50	1.75
a.	Souvenir sheet of 3	7.00	7.00
	Nos. 400-402 (3)	6.90	3.60

Argentina's victory in 1978 Soccer Championship.

Games' Flag over Africa, Basketball Players — A109

Designs: 60fr, Map of Africa, volleyball players. 80fr, Map of Benin, bicyclists.

1978, July 13 *Perf. 13x12½*

403 A109 50fr lt bl & multi		.35	.20
404 A109 60fr ultra & multi		.40	.22
405 A109 80fr multi		.55	.35
a.	Souvenir sheet of 3	1.40	1.40
	Nos. 403-405 (3)	1.30	.77

3rd African Games, Algiers, July 13-28. No. 405a contains 3 stamps in changed colors similar to Nos. 403-405.

Martin Luther King, Jr. — A110

1978, July 30 *Perf. 12½*

406 A110 300fr multi	2.00	1.10

Martin Luther King, Jr. (1929-1968), American civil rights leader.

For surcharge see No. 592.

Kanna Taxi, Oueme A111

Designs: 60fr Leatherworker and goods. 70fr, Drummer and tom-toms. 100fr, Metalworker and calabashes.

1978, Aug. 26

407 A111 50fr multi	.35	.20
408 A111 60fr multi	.40	.22
409 A111 70fr multi	.45	.28
410 A111 100fr multi	.65	.40
Nos. 407-410 (4)	1.85	1.10

Getting to know Benin through its provinces.

Map of Italy and Exhibition Poster — A112

1978, Aug. 26 Litho. *Perf. 13*

411 A112 200fr multi	1.40	.70

Riccione 1978 Philatelic Exhibition.

For overprint see No. 537.

Poultry Breeding — A113

1978 Oct. 5 Photo. *Perf. 12½x13*

412 A113 10fr Turkeys	.15	.15
413 A113 20fr Ducks	.15	.15
414 A113 50fr Chicken	.35	.35
415 A113 60fr Guinea fowl	.40	.40
Nos. 412-415 (4)	1.05	1.05

Royal Messenger, UPU Emblem A114

Designs (UPU Emblem and): 60fr, Boatsman, ship and car, vert. 90fr, Special messenger and plane, vert.

Perf. 13x12½, 12½x13

1978, Oct. 16

416 A114 50fr multi	.35	.35
417 A114 60fr multi	.40	.40
418 A114 90fr multi	.60	.60
Nos. 416-418 (3)	1.35	1.35

Centenary of change of "General Postal Union" to "Universal Postal Union."

Raoul Follereau A115

1978, Dec. 17 Litho. *Perf. 12½*

419 A115 200fr multi 1.75 1.75

Raoul Follereau (1903-1977), apostle to the lepers and educator of the blind.

IYC Emblem A116

Intl. Year of the Child: 20fr, Glove as balloon carrying childern. 50fr, Children of various races surrounding globe.

1979, Feb. 20 Litho. *Perf. 12x13*

420 A116 10fr multi .15 .15
421 A116 20fr multi .15 .15
422 A116 50fr multi .35 .35
Nos. 420-422 (3) .65 .65

Hydrangea — A117

Flowers: 25fr, Assangokan. 30fr, Geranium. 40fr, Water lilies, horiz.

Perf. 13x12½, 12½x13

1979, Feb. 28 Litho.

423 A117 20fr multi .15 .15
424 A117 25fr multi .16 .16
425 A117 30fr multi .20 .20
426 A117 40fr mutli .25 .25
Nos. 423-426 (4) .76 .76

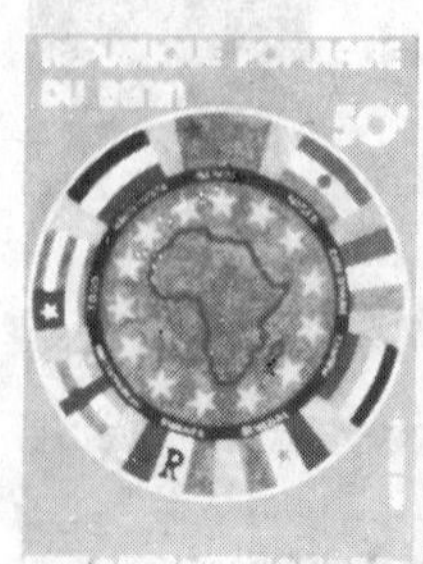

Emblem: Map of Africa and Members' Flags — A118

Designs: 60fr, Map of Benin and flags. 80fr, OCAM flag and map of Africa showing member states.

1979, Mar. 20 Litho. *Perf. 12x13*

427 A118 50fr multi .40 .40
428 A118 60fr multi .45 .45
429 A118 80fr multi .65 .65
Nos. 427-429 (3) 1.50 1.50

OCAM Summit Conf., Cotonou, Mar. 20-28.
For overprints see Nos. 434-436.

Tower, Waves, Satellite, ITU Emblem A119

1979, May 17 Litho. *Perf. 12½*

430 A119 50fr multi .40 .40

World Telecommunications Day.

Bank Building and Sculpture — A120

1979, May 26 Litho.

431 A120 50fr multi .35 .35

Opening of Headquarters of West African Savings Bank in Dakar.

Guelede Mask, Abomey Tapestry, Malaconotus Bird — A121

Design: 50fr, Jet, canoe, satellite, UPU and exhibition emblems.

1979, June 8 Litho. *Perf. 13*

432 A121 15fr multi .15 .15

Engr.

433 A121 50fr multi .35 .35

Philexafrique II, Libreville, Gabon, June 8-17. Nos. 432, 433 each printed in sheets of 10 with 5 labels showing exhibition emblem.

Nos. 427-429 Overprinted: "26 au 28 juin 1979" and Dots

1979, June 26

434 A118 50fr multi .35 .35
435 A118 60fr multi .40 .40
436 A118 80fr multi .55 .55
Nos. 434-436 (3) 1.30 1.30

2nd OCAM Summit Conf., June 26-28.

Olympic Flame, and Emblems A122

Pre-Olympic Year: 50fr, High jump.

1979, July 1 Litho.

437 A122 10fr multi .15 .15
438 A122 50fr multi .35 .35

Antelope A123

Animals: 10fr, Giraffes, map of Benin, vert 20fr, Chimpanzee. 50fr, Elephants, map of Benin, vert.

1979, Oct. 1 Litho. *Perf. 13*

439 A123 5fr multi .15 .15
440 A123 10fr multi .15 .15
441 A123 20fr multi .15 .15
442 A123 50fr multi .35 .35
Set value .60 .60

Map of Africa, Emblem and Jet — A124

1979, Dec. 12 Litho. *Perf. 12½*

443 A124 50fr multi .35 .35
444 A124 60fr multi .40 .40

ASECNA (Air Safety Board), 20th anniv.

Mail Services — A125

Design: 50fr, Post Office and headquarters, vert.

1979, Dec. 19 Litho. *Perf. 13*

445 A125 50fr multi .35 .35
446 A125 60fr multi .40 .40

Office of Posts and Telecommunications, 20th anniversary.

Lenin and Globe A126

1980, Apr. 22 Litho. *Perf. 12½*

447 A126 50fr shown .25 .25
448 A126 150fr Lenin in library .80 .80

Lenin, 110th birth anniversary.

Monument to King Behanzin A126a

Litho. & Embossed

1980, May 31 *Perf. 12½*

448A A126a 1000fr gold & multi 5.50 5.50

For overprint see No. Q10A.

Cotonou Club Emlem — A127

Galileo, Astrolabe — A128

1980, Feb. 23 Litho. *Perf. 12½*

449 A127 90fr shown .60 .60
450 A127 200fr Rotary emblem on globe, horiz. 1.40 1.40

Rotary International, 75th anniversary.

1980, Apr. 2

451 A128 100fr shown .45 .45
452 A128 100fr Copernicus, solar system .65 .65

Discovery of Pluto, 50th anniversary.

Abu Simbel, UNESCO Emblem — A129

1980, Apr. 15 *Perf. 13*

453 A129 50fr Column, vert. .35 .35
454 A129 60fr Ramses II, vert. .40 .40
455 A129 150fr shown 1.00 1.00
Nos. 453-455 (3) 1.75 1.75

UNESCO campaign to save Nubian monuments, 20h anniversary.

Monument, Martyrs' Square, Cotonou A130

Designs: Various monuments in Martyrs' Square. Cotonou. 60fr, 70fr, 100fr, horiz.

1980, May 2 *Perf. 12½x13, 13x12½*

456 A130 50fr multi .35 .35
457 A130 60fr multi .40 .40
458 A130 70fr multi .45 .45
459 A130 100fr multi .65 .65
Nos. 456-459 (4) 1.85 1.85

For surcharge see No. 539.

Musical Instruments A131

1980, May 20 *Perf. 12½*

460 A131 5fr Assan, vert. .15 .15
461 A131 10fr Tinbo .15 .15
462 A131 15fr Tam-tam sato, vert. .15 .15
463 A131 20fr Kora .15 .15
464 A131 30fr Gangan .20 .20
465 A131 50fr Sinhoun .35 .35
Set value .90 .90

First Non-stop Flight, Paris-New York — A132

1980, June 2 **Litho.** ***Perf. 12½***

466 A132 90fr shown .60 .60

467 A132 100fr Dieudonne Coste, Maurice Bellonte .65 .65

For surcharge see No. 564.

Lunokhod I on the Moon — A133

1980, June 15 **Engr.** ***Perf. 13***

468 A133 90fr multi .60 .60

Lunokhod I Soviet unmanned moon mission, 10th anniv. See #C290. For surcharge see #C305.

Olympic Flame and Mischa, Moscow '80 Emblem — A134

1980, July 16 **Litho.** ***Perf. 12½***

469 A134 50fr shown .35 .35

470 A134 60fr Equestrian, vert. .40 .40

471 A134 70fr Judo .50 .50

472 A134 200fr Flag, sports, globe, vert. 1.40 1.40

473 A134 300fr Weight lifting, vert. 2.25 2.25

Nos. 469-473 (5) 4.90 4.90

22nd Summer Olympic Games, Moscow, July 19-Aug. 3.
For surcharges see Nos. 559, 561.

Telephone and Rising Sun — A135

World Telecommunications Day: 50fr, Farmer on telephone, vert.

1980, May 17 **Litho.** ***Perf. 12½***

474 A135 50fr multi .35 .35

475 A135 60fr multi .40 .40

Cotonou West African Community Village A136

Designs: View of Cotonou.

1980, July 26 ***Perf. 13x13½***

476 A136 50fr multi .35 .35

477 A136 60fr multi .40 .40

478 A136 70fr multi .45 .45

Nos. 476-478 (3) 1.20 1.20

For surcharge see No. 540.

Agbadja Dancers — A137

Designs: Dancers and muscians.

1980, Aug. 1 ***Perf. 12½***

479 A137 30fr multi .20 .20

480 A137 50fr multi .35 .35

481 A137 66fr multi .40 .40

Nos. 479-481 (3) .95 .95

Fisherman A138

Philippines under Magnifier A139

Designs: 5fr, Throwing net. 15fr, Canoe and shore fishing. 20fr, Basket traps. 50fr, Hauling net. 60fr, River fishing. All horiz.

1980, Sept. 1

482 A138 5fr multi .15 .15

483 A138 10fr multi .15 .15

484 A138 15fr multi .15 .15

485 A138 20fr multi .15 .15

486 A138 50fr multi .35 .35

487 A138 60fr multi .40 .40

Set value 1.10 1.10

For surcharge see No. 535.

Perf. 13x13½, 13½x13

1980, Sept. 27

World Tourism Conference, Manila, Sept. 27: 60fr, Emblem on flag, hand pointing to Manila on globe, horiz.

488 A139 50fr multi .35 .35

489 A139 60fr multi .40 .40

For surcharge see No. 557.

A140

A141

1980, Oct. 1 ***Perf. 12½***

490 A140 40fr Othreis materna .25 .25

491 A140 50fr Othreis fullonia .35 .35

492 A140 200fr Oryctes sp. 1.40 1.40

Nos. 490-492 (3) 2.00 2.00

1980, Oct. 24 **Photo.** ***Perf. 13½***

493 A141 75fr multi .50 .50

African Postal Union, 5th Anniv.

A142

A143

1980, Nov. 4 ***Perf. 12½x13***

494 A142 30fr shown .20 .20

495 A142 50fr Freed prisoner .35 .35

496 A142 60fr Man holding torch .40 .40

Nos. 494-496 (3) .95 .95

Declaration of human rights, 30th anniv.

1980, Dec. 1 **Litho.** ***Perf. 13***

Self-portrait, by Vincent van Gogh, 1888.

497 A143 100fr shown .75 .75

498 A143 300fr Facteur Roulin 2.25 2.25

Vincent van Gogh (1853-1890), artist.
For surcharge see No. 579.

Offenbach and Scene from Orpheus in the Underworld — A144

1980, Dec. 15 **Engr.**

499 A144 50fr shown .40 .40

500 A144 60fr Paris Life .45 .45

Jacques Offenbach (1819-1880), composer.

Kepler and Satellites — A145

1980, Dec. 20

501 A145 50fr Kepler, diagram, vert. .35 .35

502 A145 60fr shown .40 .40

Johannes Kepler (1571-1630), astronomer.

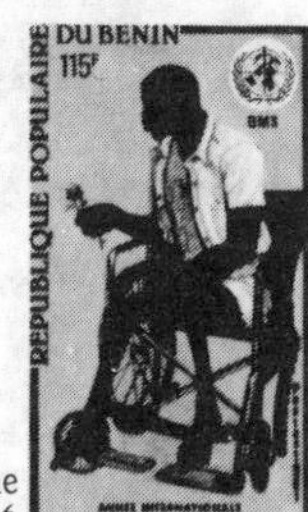

Intl. Year of the Disabled — A146

1981, Apr. 10 **Litho.** ***Perf. 12½***

503 A146 115fr multi .75 .75

For surcharge see No. 582.

20th Anniv. of Manned Space Flight — A147

1981, May 30 ***Perf. 13***

504 A147 500fr multi 3.50 3.50

For surcharges see Nos. 580, 790.

13th World Telecommunications Day — A148

1981, May 30 **Litho.** ***Perf. 12½***

505 A148 115fr multi .75 .75

For surcharge see No. 583.

Amaryllis A149

1981, June 20 ***Perf. 12½***

506 A149 10fr shown .15 .15

507 A149 20fr Eischornia crassipes, vert. .15 .15

508 A149 80fr Parkia biglobosa, vert. .55 .55

Nos. 506-508 (3) .85 .85

For surcharge see No. 542.

Benin Sheraton Hotel — A150

1981, July

509 A150 100fr multi .65 .65

For surcharge see No. 541.

Guinea Pig — A151

1981, July 31 ***Perf. 13x13½***

510 A151 5fr shown .15 .15

511 A151 60fr Cat .40 .40

512 A151 80fr Dogs .55 .55

Nos. 510-512 (3) 1.10 1.10

For surcharges see Nos. 536, 543, 563.

World UPU Day — A152

1981, Oct. 9 **Engr.** ***Perf. 13***

513 A152 100fr red brn & blk .65 .65

25th Intl. Letter Writing Week, Oct. 6-12 — A153

1981, Oct. 15

514 A153 100fr dk bl & pur .65 .65

For surcharge see No. 558.

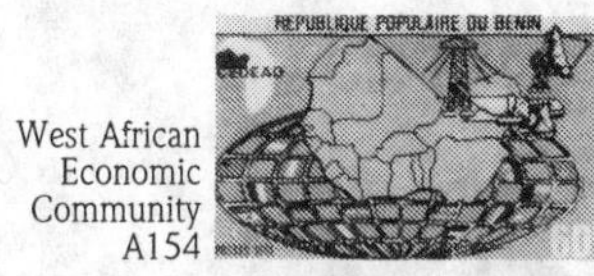

West African Economic Community A154

1981, Nov. 20 Litho. *Perf. 12½*

515 A154 60fr multi .40 .40

West African Rice Development Assoc. 10th Anniv. A155

1981, Dec. 10 *Perf. 13x13½*

516 A155 60fr multi .40 .40

TB Bacillus Centenary A156

1982, Mar. 1 Litho. *Perf. 13*

517 A156 115fr multi 1.20 1.20

For surcharge see No. 584.

West African Economic Community, 5th Summit Conference — A157

1982, May 27 *Perf. 12½*

518 A157 60fr multi .40 .40

1982 World Cup A158

1982, June 1 *Perf. 13*

519 A158 90fr Players .65 .65
520 A158 300fr Flags on leg 2.25 2.25

For overprints and surcharges see #523-524, 594, 789.

France No. B349 Magnified, Map of France — A159

1982, June 11

521 A159 90fr multi .60 .60

PHILEXFRANCE '82 Stamp Exhibition, Paris, June 11-21.

George Washington A160

1982, Mar. 10 Litho. *Perf. 14*

522 A160 200fr Washington, flag, map 1.00 1.00

For surcharge see No. 577.

Nos. 519-520 Overprinted with Finalists Names

1982, Aug. 16 *Perf. 12½*

523 A158 90fr multi .60 .60
524 A158 300fr multi 2.00 2.00

Italy's victory in 1982 World Cup.

Bluethroat A161

Perf. 14x14½, 14½x14

1982, Sept. 1

525 A161 5fr Daoelo gigas, vert. .15 .15
526 A161 10fr shown .15 .15
527 A161 15fr Swallow, vert. .15 .15
528 A161 20fr Kingfisher, weaver bird, vert. .16 .16
529 A161 30fr Great sedge warbler .25 .25
530 A161 60fr Common warbler .50 .50
531 A161 80fr Owl, vert. .65 .65
532 A161 100fr Cockatoo, vert. .80 .80
Nos. 525-532 (8) 2.81 2.81

ITU Plenipotentiaries Conference, Nairobi, Sept. — A162

1982, Sept. 26 *Perf. 13*

533 A162 200fr Map 1.00 1.00

For surcharge see No. 585.

13th World UPU Day A163

1982, Oct. 9 Engr. *Perf. 13*

534 A163 100fr Monument .65 .65

Nos. 482, 510, 411 Overprinted in Red or Blue:
#535 "Croix Rouge / 8 Mai 1982"
#536 "UAPT 1982"
#537 "RICCONE 1982"

Perf. 13, 12½, 13x13½

1982, Nov. Litho.

535 A138 60fr on 5fr multi .40 .40
536 A151 60fr on 5fr multi .40 .40
537 A112 200fr multi (Bl) 1.40 1.40
Nos. 535-537 (3) 2.20 2.20

Visit of French Pres. Francois Mitterand A164

1983, Jan. 15 Litho. *Perf. 12½x13*

538 A164 90fr multi .60 .60

Nos. 458, 476, 508-509, 512 Surcharged

Perf. 13x12½, 13x13½, 12½

1983 Litho.

539 A130 60fr on 70fr multi .40 .40
540 A136 60fr on 50fr multi .40 .40
541 A150 60fr on 100fr multi .40 .40
542 A149 75fr on 80fr multi .50 .50
543 A151 75fr on 80fr multi .50 .50
Nos. 539-543 (5) 2.20 2.20

Seme Oil Rig — A165

1983, Apr. 28 Litho. *Perf. 13x12½*

544 A165 125fr multi .80 .80

World Communications Year — A166

1983, May 17 Litho. *Perf. 13*

545 A166 185fr multi 1.00 1.00

Riccione '83, Stamp Show — A167

1983, Aug. 27 Litho. *Perf. 13*

546 A167 500fr multi 3.25 3.25

Benin Red Cross, 20th Anniv. A168

1983, Sept. 5 Photo. *Perf. 13*

547 A168 105fr multi .70 .70

For surcharge see No. 581.

Handicrafts A169

Designs: 75fr, Handcarved lion chairs and table. 90fr, Natural tree table and stools. 200fr, Monkeys holding jar.

1983, Sept. 18 Litho. *Perf. 13*

548 A169 75fr multi .40 .40
549 A169 90fr multi .50 .50
550 A169 200fr multi 1.10 1.10
Nos. 548-550 (3) 2.00 2.00

For surcharge see No. 578.

14th UPU Day — A170

1983, Oct. 9 Engr. *Perf. 13*

551 A170 125fr multi .80 .80

For surcharge see No. 575.

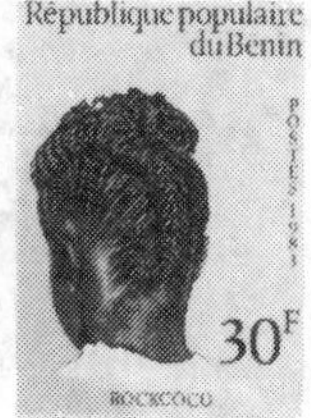

Religious Movements A171

Plaited Hair Styles A172

1983, Oct. 31 Litho. *Perf. 14x15*

552 A171 75fr Zangbeto .35 .35
553 A171 75fr Egoun .35 .35

1983, Nov. 14

554 A172 30fr Rockcoco .15 .15
555 A172 75fr Serpent .35 .35
556 A172 90fr Songas .40 .40
Nos. 554-556 (3) .90 .90

Stamps of 1976-81 Surcharged

1983, Nov.

557 A139 5fr on 50fr #488 .15 .15
558 A153 10fr on 100fr #514 .15 .15
559 A134 15fr on 200fr #472 .15 .15
560 A98 15fr on 210fr #381 .15 .15
561 A134 25fr on 70fr #471 .15 .15
562 A99 25fr on 210fr #384 .15 .15
563 A151 75fr on 5fr #510 .35 .35
564 A132 75fr on 100fr #467 .35 .35
565 A88 75fr on 150fr #360 .35 .35
566 A98 75fr on 150fr #380 .35 .35
Set value 1.85 1.85

Alfred Nobel (1833-96) A173

1983, Dec. 19 Litho. *Perf. 15x14*

567 A173 300fr multi 1.40 1.40

Council of Unity — A174

1984, May 29 Litho. *Perf. 12*

568 A174 75fr multi .35 .35
569 A174 90fr multi .40 .40

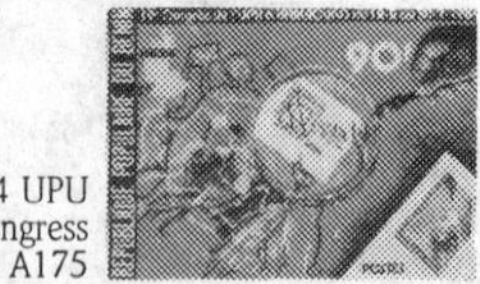

1984 UPU Congress A175

1984, June 18 Litho. *Perf. 13*

570 A175 90fr multi .40 .40

Abomey Calavi Earth Station A176

1984, June 29 Litho. *Perf. 12½x13*

571 A176 75fr Satellite dish .35 .35

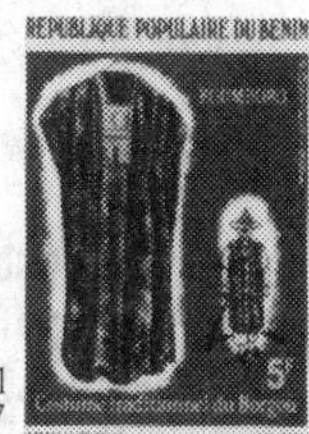

Traditional Costumes — A177

1984, July 2 Litho. *Perf. 13½x13*

572 A177 5fr Koumboro .15 .15
573 A177 10fr Taka .15 .15
574 A177 20fr Toko .15 .15
Set value .17 .17

Nos. 389, 498, 503-505, 517, 522, 533, 547, 550 and 551 Surcharged

1984, Sept.

575 A170 5fr on 125fr #551 .15 .15
576 A101 5fr on 150fr #389 .15 .15
577 A160 10fr on 200fr #522 .15 .15
578 A169 10fr on 200fr #550 .15 .15
579 A143 15fr on 300fr #498 .15 .15
580 A147 40fr on 500fr #504 .15 .15
581 A168 75fr on 105fr #547 .35 .35
582 A146 75fr on 115fr #503 .35 .35
583 A148 75fr on 115fr #505 .35 .35
584 A156 75fr on 115fr #517 .35 .35
585 A162 75fr on 200fr #533 .35 .35
Set value 2.15 2.15

World Food Day — A178

Dinosaurs — A179

1984, Oct. 16 Litho. *Perf. 12½*

586 A178 100fr Malnourished child .30 .30

1984, Dec. 14 Litho. *Perf. 13½*

587 A179 75fr Anatosaurus .22 .22
588 A179 90fr Brontosaurus .25 .25

Cultural & Technical Cooperation Agency, 15th Anniv. A180

1985, Mar 20 Litho. *Perf. 13*

589 A180 300fr Emblem, globe, hands, book .90 .90

Stamps of 1977-82 Surcharged

1985, Mar.

590 A93 75fr on 200fr No. 370 .20 .20
591 A108 75fr on 200fr No. 397 .20 .20
592 A110 75fr on 300fr No. 406 .20 .20
593 A108 75fr on 300fr No. 398 .20 .20
594 A158 90fr on 300fr No. 520 .25 .25
595 A108 90fr on 500fr No. 399 .25 .25
596 A108 90fr on 500fr No. 402 .25 .25
Nos. 590-596 (7) 1.55 1.55

End of World War II, 40th Anniv. — A180a

1985, May Litho. *Perf. 12*

596A A180a 100fr multicolored

Traditional Dances A181

1985, June 1 Litho. *Perf. 15x14½*

597 A181 75fr Teke, Borgou Tribe .20 .20
598 A181 100fr Tipen'ti, L'Atacora Tribe .28 .28

Intl. Youth Year — A182

1985, July 16 *Perf. 13½*

599 A182 150fr multi .45 .45

1986 World Cup Soccer Championships, Mexico — A183

1985, July 22 *Perf. 13x12½*

600 A183 200fr multi .60 .60

Dahomey No. 336 Ovptd. "REPUBLIQUE POPULAIRE DU BENIN" and Surcharged with Black Bars and New Value

1985, Aug. *Perf. 12½*

601 A78 15fr on 40fr multi .18 .18

ASECNA Airlines, 25th Anniv. — A184

1985, Sept. 16 *Perf. 13*

602 A184 150fr multi .45 .45

UN 40th Anniv. A185

1985, Oct. 24 *Perf. 12½*

603 A185 250fr multi .90 .90

Benin UN membership, 25th anniv.

ITALIA'85, Rome — A186

1985, Oct. 25 *Perf. 13½*

604 A186 200fr multi .75 .75

PHILEXAFRICA '85, Lome — A187

1985, Nov. 16 *Perf. 13*

605 A187 250fr #569, labor emblem .90 .90
606 A187 250fr #C252, Gabon #365, magnified stamp .90 .90

Nos. 605-606 printed se-tenant with center label picturing map of Africa or UAPT emblem.

Audubon Birth Bicent. — A188

Mushrooms and Toadstools — A189

1985, Oct. 17 Litho. *Perf. 14x15*

607 A188 150fr Skua gull .55 .55
608 A188 300fr Oyster catcher 1.10 1.10

1985, Oct. 17

609 A189 35fr Boletus edible .15 .15
610 A189 40fr Amanite phalloide .15 .15
611 A189 100fr Brown chanterelle .38 .38
Nos. 609-611 (3) .68 .68

Dahomey Nos. 282, 292, 343 Surcharged and Ovptd. with 2 Black Bars and "Populaire Republique du Benin" in 3 lines

1986, Mar. Photo.

612 A83 75fr on 35fr #343 .25 .25
613 A57 90fr on 75fr #282 .35 .35
614 A60 90fr on 140fr #292 .35 .35
Nos. 612-614 (3) .95 .95

African Parliamentary Union, 10th Anniv. — A190

1986, May 8 Litho. *Perf. 13x12½*

615 A190 100fr multi .38 .38

9th Conference, Cotonou, May 8-10.

Halley's Comet — A191

1986, May 30 *Perf. 12½x12*

616 A191 250fr multi .75 .75

Dahomey Nos. 283, 344 Surcharged with Bar, "Republique/Populaire/du Benin" and New Value

Engraved, Photogravure

1986, June *Perf. 13*

617 A58 100fr on 40fr #283 .38 .38
618 A83 150fr on 45fr #344 .55 .55

1986 World Cup Soccer Championships, Mexico — A192

1986, June 29 Litho.

619 A192 500fr multi 1.75 1.75

For surcharge see No. 792.

Fight against Desert Encroachment A193

1986, July 16 *Perf. 13½*

620 A193 150fr multi .55 .55

King Behanzin A194

Amazon A194a

1986-88 Engr. *Perf. 13*

621 A194 40fr black .20 .20
622 A194a 100fr brt blue .40 .40
623 A194 125fr maroon .60 .60
624 A194a 150fr violet .60 .60
625 A194 190fr dark ultra .90 .90
627 A194 220fr dark grn 1.00 1.00
Nos. 621-627 (6) 3.70 3.70

Issued: 100fr, 150fr, 8/1; others, 10/1/88.
See No. 636. For surcharge see No. 787.

Flowers — A195

Butterflies — A196

Perf. 13x12½, 12½x13

1986, Sept. 1 Litho.

631 A195 100fr Haemanthus .42 .42
632 A195 205fr Hemerocalle, horiz. .90 .90

1986, Sept. 15

Designs: No. 633, Day peacock, little tortoise-shell, morio. No. 634, Aurora, machaon and fair lady.

633 A196 150fr multi .60 .60
634 A196 150fr multi .60 .60

Dahomey Nos. 290, 307 Overprinted "Republique / Populaire / du Benin"

1985, Oct. 15

Perfs. & Printing Methods as Before

634A A67 50fr on #307
634B A60 150fr on 100fr #290

Statue of Liberty, Cent. — A197

King Behanzin — A198

1986, Oct. 28 Litho. *Perf. 12½*
635 A197 250fr multi .90 .90

1986, Oct. 30 *Perf. 13½*
636 A198 440fr multi 1.60 1.60

Behanzin, leader of resistance movement against French occupation (1886-1894).

Brazilian Cultural Week, Cotonou — A200

1987, Jan. 17 *Perf. 12½*
638 A200 150fr multi .88 .88

Rotary Intl. District 910 Conference, Cotonou, Apr. 23-25 — A201

1987, Apr. 23 Litho. *Perf. 13½*
639 A201 300fr Center for the Blind, Cotonou 1.75 1.75

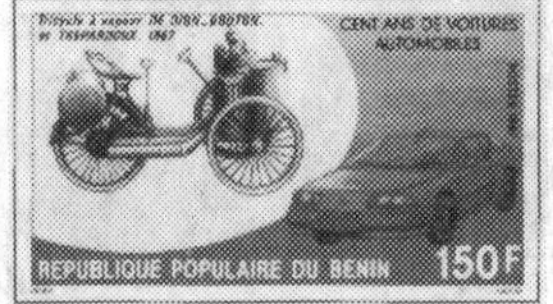

Automobile Cent. — A202

Modern car and: 150fr, Steam tricycle, by De Dion-Bouton and Trepardoux, 1887. 300fr, Gas-driven Victoria, by Daimler, 1886.

1987, July 1 *Perf. 12½*
640 A202 150fr multi .88 .88
641 A202 300fr multi 1.75 1.75

Snake Temple Baptism — A203

1987, July 20 *Perf. 13½*
642 A203 100fr multi .55 .55

Shellfish A204

1987, July 24 *Perf. 12½*
643 A204 100fr crayfish .55 .55
644 A204 150fr crab .90 .90

Cure Leprosy — A205

1987, Sept. 4 *Perf. 13*
645 A205 200fr G. Hansen, R. Follereau 1.10 1.10

Locust Control A206

1987, Dec. 7 Litho. *Perf. 12½x13*
646 A206 100fr multi .72 .72

Christmas 1987 — A207

1987, Dec. 21 *Perf. 13*
647 A207 150fr multi 1.10 1.10

Dahomey Nos. 268, 328 Ovptd. or Surchd.

Republique Populaire du Bénin

1987 Engr. *Perf. 13*
647B A53 40fr on #268

See Nos. C362, C369. Eleven other stamps exist in this set. The editors need to see these stamps before listings can be created.

Intl. Red Cross and Red Crescent Organizations, 125th Anniv. — A208

1988, May 25 Litho. *Perf. 13½*
648 A208 200fr multi 1.30 1.30

A209

A210

1988, July 11 *Perf. 12½*
649 A209 200fr multi 1.30 1.30

Martin Luther King, Jr. (1929-68), American civil rights leader.

1988, May 25 Litho. *Perf. 13½*
650 A210 125fr multi .88 .88

Organization of African Unity, 25th anniv.

WHO, 40th Anniv. — A211

1988, Sept. 1 Litho. *Perf. 13x12½*
651 A211 175fr multi 1.15 1.15

Alma Ata Declaration, 10th anniv.; Health Care for All on Earth by the Year 2000.
For surcharge see No. 786.

Ganvie Lake Village A212

1988, Sept. 4 *Perf. 13½*
652 A212 125fr shown .85 .85
653 A212 190fr Boatman, village, diff. 1.25 1.25

A213

A214

1988, Aug. 14 *Perf. 12½*
654 A213 125fr multi .88 .88

1st Benin Scout Jamboree, Aug. 12-19.

Dahomey No. 328 Surch. "Republique / Populaire / du Benin"

1988
Printing Method & Perfs as Before
654E A74 150fr on 200fr #328

1988, Dec. 30 Litho. *Perf. 13*

Ritual Offering to Hebiesso, God of Thunder and Lightning.

655 A214 125fr multicolored .82 .82

Dahomey No. 247 Surcharged

50 f
République
Populaire
du Bénin

1988 Photo. *Perf. 12½x13*
655E A45 50fr on 45fr #247

This is one stamp from a set of 13 known to exist. Another set of 19 surcharges also is known to exist. The editors need to see these stamps before listings can be created.

World Wildlife Fund — A216

Roseate terns, *Sterna dougalli.*

1989, Jan. 30 Litho. *Perf. 13*
657 A216 10fr Three terns .15 .15
658 A216 15fr Feeding on fish .15 .15
659 A216 50fr Perched .32 .32
660 A216 125fr In flight .82 .82
Nos. 657-660 (4) 1.44 1.44

Eiffel Tower Cent. — A217

1989, Apr. 24 Litho. *Perf. 13x12½*
661 A217 190fr multi 1.10 1.10

PHILEXFRANCE '89, French Revolution Bicent. — A218

Design: Bastille, emblems, Declaration of Human Rights and Citizenship, France No. B252-B253.

1989, July 7 *Perf. 13*
662 A218 190fr multicolored 1.10 1.10

Electric Corp. of Benin, 20th Anniv. A219

1989, Oct. Litho. *Perf. 12½x13*
663 A219 125fr multicolored .80 .80

Fish — A220

1989, Sept. 22 *Perf. 13½*
664 A220 125fr Lote .80 .80
665 A220 190fr Pike, salmon 1.20 1.20

Death of King Glele, Cent. — A221

1989, Dec. 16 **Litho.** *Perf. 13½*
666 A221 190fr multicolored 1.25 1.25

Christmas A222

1989, Dec. 25 *Perf. 13*
667 A222 200fr Holy family 1.30 1.30

Benin Posts & Telecommunications, Cent. — A223

1990, Jan. 1 *Perf. 13½*
668 A223 125fr multicolored .82 .82

Fruits and Flora A224

1990, Jan. 23 **Litho.** *Perf. 11½*
669 A224 60fr Oranges .42 .42
670 A224 190fr Kaufmann Tulips, vert. 1.40 1.40
671 A224 250fr Cashews, vert. 1.75 1.75
Nos. 669-671 (3) 3.57 3.57

Dated 1989.

Moon Landing, 20th Anniv. A225

1990, Jan. 23
672 A225 190fr multicolored 1.40 1.40

Dated 1989.

World Cup Soccer Championships, Italy — A226

1990, June 8 **Litho.** *Perf. 12½*
673 A226 125fr shown 1.00 1.00
674 A226 190fr Character trademark, vert. 1.50 1.50

For overprint see No. 676.

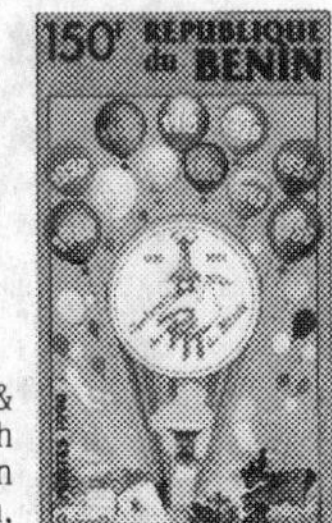

Post, Telephone & Telegraph Administration in Benin, Cent. — A227

1990, July 1 *Perf. 13*
675 A227 150fr multicolored 1.25 1.25

No. 673 Ovptd. **FINALE R.F.A. - ARGENTINE 1 - 0**

1990 **Litho.** *Perf. 12½*
676 A226 125fr multicolored 1.00 1.00

Charles de Gaulle (1890-1970) A228

1990, Nov. 22 **Litho.** *Perf. 13*
677 A228 190fr multicolored 1.50 1.50

See No. 689.

Galileo Probe and Jupiter A229

1990, Dec. 1
678 A229 100fr multicolored .75 .75

For overprint see No. 681.

A230 A231

1990, Dec. 25 **Litho.** *Perf. 12½x13*
679 A230 200fr multicolored 1.75 1.75

Christmas.

1991, Sept. 3 **Litho.** *Perf. 13½*
680 A231 125fr multicolored 1.05 1.05

Independence, 31st anniv.

No. 678 Ovptd. in Red

1991 *Perf. 13*
681 A229 100fr multicolored .85 .85

French Open Tennis Championships, Cent. — A232

1991 *Perf. 13½*
682 A232 125fr multicolored 1.05 1.05

African Tourism Year — A233

1991
683 A233 190fr multicolored 1.65 1.65

Christmas A234

1991, Dec. 2 **Litho.** *Perf. 13½*
684 A234 125fr multicolored 1.05 1.05

Dancer of Guelede — A235

Wolfgang Amadeus Mozart, Death Bicent. — A236

1991, Dec. 2
685 A235 190fr multicolored 1.65 1.65

1991, Dec. 2
686 A236 1000fr multicolored 8.50 8.50

For surcharge see No. 793.

Discovery of America, 500th Anniv. A237

Design: 1000fr, Columbus coming ashore, horiz.

1992, Apr. 24 **Litho.** *Perf. 13*
687 A237 500fr blk, blue & brn 3.75 3.75
688 A237 1000fr multicolored 7.50 7.50
a. Souvenir sheet of 2, #687-688 11.25 11.25

De Gaulle Type of 1990

1992 **Litho.** *Perf. 13*
689 A228 300fr like #677 2.25 2.25

Intl. Conference on Nutrition, Rome — A238

1992, Dec. 5 **Litho.** *Perf. 13*
690 A238 190fr multicolored 1.60 1.60

Dahomey Nos. 160, 266 Surcharged "REPUBLIQUE / DU BENIN" (a) or "DU BENIN" (b)

1992

Perfs. & Printing Methods as Before
690F A19(a) 125fr on 2fr #160
690J A52(b) 190fr on 45fr #266

Visit of Pope John Paul II, Feb. 3-5 — A239

Ouidah 92, First Festival of Voodoo Culture — A240

1993, Feb. 3 **Litho.** *Perf. 13x12½*
691 A239 190fr multicolored 1.50 1.50

1993, Feb. 8 *Perf. 13½*
692 A240 125fr multicolored 1.00 1.00

Well of Possotome, Eurystome A241

1993, May 25 Litho. *Perf. 12½*
693 A241 125fr multicolored 1.00 1.00

OAU, 30th Anniv. A242

1993, June 7 Litho. *Perf. 13½*
694 A242 125fr multicolored 1.00 1.00

John F. Kennedy — A243

1993, June 24 *Perf. 13*
695 A243 190fr shown 1.50 1.50
696 A243 190fr Martin Luther King, vert. 1.50 1.50

Assassinations of Kennedy, 30th anniv. (#695), and King, 25th anniv. (#696).

Dahomey Nos. 161, 175 Overprinted With Types a or b

1993
Perfs. & Printing Methods as Before
697 A21(a) 5fr on #175
700 A19(b) 10fr on 3fr #161

Benin No. 350, Dahomey Nos. 226, 249 Surch. "REPUBLIQUE / DU BENIN" (a), "DU BENIN" (b)

1994-95
707 A38(b) 5fr on 1fr #226
711 A57 50fr on 1fr #350
725 A45(a) 200fr on 100fr #249

UNESCO Conference on The Slave Route — A244

1994 Litho. *Perf. 13x13½*
730 A244 300fr multicolored

The editors would like to see the 135fr and 200fr values in this set, for which numbers have been reserved.

Intl. Year of the Family A246

1994 Litho. *Perf. 12½*
732 A246 200fr multicolored

1996 Summer Olympics, Atlanta A248

Perf. 12½x13, 13x12½
1995, Apr. 30 Litho.
734 A248 45fr Water polo .45 .45
735 A248 50fr Javelin .50 .50
736 A248 75fr Weight lifting .75 .75
737 A248 100fr Tennis 1.00 1.00
738 A248 135fr Baseball 1.40 1.40
739 A248 200fr Synchronized swimming 2.00 2.00
Nos. 734-739 (6) 6.10 6.10

Souvenir Sheet
740 A248 300fr Diving 4.50 4.50

Nos. 735-740 are vert. No. 740 contains one 32x40mm stamp.

Dogs — A249

1995 Litho. *Perf. 12½*
741 A249 40fr German shepherd .40 .40
742 A249 50fr Beagle .50 .50
743 A249 75fr Great dane .75 .75
744 A249 100fr Boxer 1.00 1.00
745 A249 135fr Pointer 1.40 1.40
746 A249 200fr Fox terrier 2.00 2.00
Nos. 741-746 (6) 6.05 6.05

Souvenir Sheet
747 A249 300fr Schnauzer 6.50 6.50

Ships A250

Designs: 40fr, Steam driven paddle boat, 1788. 50fr, Paddle steamer Charlotte, 1802. 75fr, Transatlantic steamship, Citta de Catania. 100fr, Hovercraft Mountbatten SR-N4. 135fr, QE II. 200fr, Japanese experimental atomic energy ship, Mutsu-NEF. 300fr, Paddle-steamer Savannah, 1819.

1995
748 A250 40fr multicolored .40 .40
749 A250 50fr multicolored .50 .50
750 A250 75fr multicolored .75 .75
751 A250 100fr multicolored 1.00 1.00
752 A250 135fr multicolored 1.40 1.40
753 A250 200fr multicolored 2.00 2.00
Nos. 748-753 (6) 6.05 6.05

Souvenir Sheet
754 A250 300fr multicolored 4.50 4.50

No. 754 contains one 40x32mm stamp.

Primates — A251

1995
755 A251 50fr Pan troglodytes .50 .50
756 A251 75fr Mandrillus sphinx .75 .75
757 A251 100fr Colobus 1.00 1.00
758 A251 135fr Macaca sylvanus 1.40 1.40
759 A251 200fr Comopithecus hamadryas 2.00 2.00
Nos. 755-759 (5) 5.65 5.65

Souvenir Sheet
760 A251 300fr Papio cynocephalus 4.50 4.50

No. 760 contains one 32x40mm stamp.

Domestic Cats A252

1995 Litho. *Perf. 12½x13*
761 A252 40fr Shorthair tabby .40 .40
762 A252 50fr Ruddy red .50 .50
763 A252 75fr White longhair .75 .75
764 A252 100fr Seal color point 1.00 1.00
765 A252 135fr Tabby point 1.40 1.40
766 A252 200fr Black shorthair 2.00 2.00
Nos. 761-766 (6) 6.05 6.05

Souvenir Sheet
767 A252 300fr Cat in basket 4.50 4.50

No. 767 contains one 40x32mm stamp.

Flowers — A253

Designs: 40fr, Dracunculus vulgaris. 50fr, Narcissus watieri. 75fr, Amaryllis belladonna. 100fr, Nymphaea capensis. 135fr, Chrysanthemum carinatum. 200fr, Iris tingitana.

1995 Litho. *Perf. 12½*
768 A253 40fr multicolored .40 .40
769 A253 50fr multicolored .55 .55
770 A253 75fr multicolored .80 .80
771 A253 100fr multicolored 1.10 1.10
772 A253 135fr multicolored 1.40 1.40
773 A253 200fr multicolored 2.25 2.25
Nos. 768-773 (6) 6.50 6.50

Wild Animals A254

Designs: 50fr, Panthera leo. 75fr, Syncerus caffer. 100fr, Pan troglodytes. 135fr, Aepyceros melampus. 200fr, Geosciurus inaurus.
300fr, Loxodonta, vert.

1995 *Perf. 13x12½, 12½x13*
774 A254 50fr multicolored .55 .55
775 A254 75fr multicolored .80 .80
776 A254 100fr multicolored 1.10 1.10
777 A254 135fr multicolored 1.50 1.50
778 A254 200fr multicolored 2.25 2.25
Nos. 774-778 (5) 6.20 6.20

Souvenir Sheet
779 A254 300fr multicolored 4.75 4.75

Nos. 774-777 are vert. No. 779 contains one 32x40mm stamp.

Birds Feeding Their Chicks — A255

Designs: 40fr, Cocothraustes cocothraustes. 50fr, Streptopelia chinensis. 75fr, Falco peregrinus. 100fr, Dendroica fusca. 135fr, Larus ridibundus. 200fr, Pelecanus onocrotalus.

1995 *Perf. 12½x13*
780 A255 40fr multicolored .40 .40
781 A255 50fr multicolored .55 .55
782 A255 75fr multicolored .80 .80
783 A255 100fr multicolored 1.10 1.10
784 A255 135fr multicolored 1.40 1.40
785 A255 200fr multicolored 2.25 2.25
Nos. 780-785 (6) 6.50 6.50

Benin No. 344 Surch. "Republique / Populaire / du Benin"
Benin Nos. 504, 520, 619, 627, 651, 686 and Dahomey No. 291 Surch. "du BENIN"

1994-95
Printing Method and Perfs as Before
786 A211 25fr on 175fr #651
787 A194 50fr on 220fr #627
788 A83 150fr on 45fr #344
789 A158 150fr on 90fr #520
790 A147 150fr on 500fr #504
791 A60 200fr on 135fr #291
792 A192 200fr on 500fr #619
793 A236 250fr on 1000fr #686

Natl. Arms — A256

1995 Litho. *Perf. 12½*
794 A256 200fr multicolored

AIR POST STAMPS

PEOPLE'S REPUBLIC

Catalogue values for unused stamps in this section are for Never Hinged items.

Nativity, by Aert van Leyden — AP84

Christmas: 85fr, Adoration of the Kings, by Rubens, vert. 140fr, Adoration of the Shepherds, by Charles Lebrun. 300fr, The Virgin with the Blue Diadem, by Raphael, vert.

1975, Dec. 19 Litho. *Perf. 13*
C240 AP84 40fr gold & multi .20 .15
C241 AP84 85fr gold & multi .42 .15
C242 AP84 140fr gold & multi .60 .25
C243 AP84 300fr gold & multi 1.40 .65
Nos. C240-C243 (4) 2.62 1.20

For surcharges see Nos. C362, C367, C407.

Slalom, Innsbruck Olympic Emblem — AP85

Designs (Innsbruck Olympic Games Emblem and): 150fr, Bobsledding, vert. 300fr, Figure skating, pairs.

1976, June 28 Litho. *Perf. 12½*
C244 AP85 60fr multi .25 .15
C245 AP85 150fr multi .65 .25
C246 AP85 300fr multi 1.25 .55
Nos. C244-C246 (3) 2.15 .95

12th Winter Olympic Games, Innsbruck, Austria, Feb. 4-15.

Dahomey Nos. C235-C237 Overprinted or Surcharged: "POPULAIRE / DU BENIN" and Bars

1976, July 4 Engr. *Perf. 13*
C247 AP82 135fr multi .55 .25
C248 AP82 210fr on 300fr multi .90 .35
C249 AP82 380fr on 500fr multi 1.50 .65
Nos. C247-C249 (3) 2.95 1.25

The overprint includes a bar covering "DU DAHOMEY" in shades of brown; "POPULAIRE DU BENIN" is blue on Nos. C247-C248, red on No. C249. The surcharge and bars over old value are blue on No. C248, red, brown on No. C249.

Long Jump AP86

Designs (Olympic Rings and): 150fr, Basketball, vert. 200fr, Hurdles.

1976, July 16 Photo. *Perf. 13*

C250 AP86 60fr multi .32 .15
C251 AP86 150fr multi .85 .30
C252 AP86 200fr multi 1.25 .45
a. Souv. sheet of 3, #C250-C252 3.00 3.00
Nos. C250-C252 (3) 2.42 .90

21st Olympic Games, Montreal, Canada, July 17-Aug 1.

Konrad Adenauer and Cologne Cathedral — AP87

Design: 90fr, Konrad Adenauer, vert.

1976, Aug. 27 Engr. *Perf. 13*

C253 AP87 90fr multi .60 .25
C254 AP87 250fr multi 1.75 .70

Konrad Adenauer (1876-1967), German Chancellor, birth centenary.
For surcharge see No. C289B.

Children's Heads and Flying Fish (Dahomey Type A32) — AP88

Design: 210fr, Lion cub's head and Benin type A3, vert.

1976, Sept. 13

C255 AP88 60fr Prus bl & vio bl .35 .15
C256 AP88 210fr multi 1.10 .45

JUVAROUEN 76, Intl. Youth Phil. Exhib., Rouen, France, Apr. 25-May 2.
For surcharge see No. C300.

Apollo 14 Emblem and Blast-off — AP89

Design: 270fr, Landing craft and man on moon.

1976, Oct. 18 Engr. *Perf. 13*

C257 AP89 130fr multi .45 .30
C258 AP89 270fr multi 1.00 .65

Apollo 14 Moon Mission, 5th anniversary.
For surcharge see No. C312.

Annunciation, by Master of Jativa — AP90

Christmas: 60fr, Nativity, by Gerard David. 270fr, Adoration of the Kings, Dutch School. 300fr, Flight into Egypt, by Gentile Fabriano, horiz.

1976, Dec. 20 Litho. *Perf. 12½*

C259 AP90 50fr gold & multi .25 .16
C260 AP90 60fr gold & multi .35 .22
C261 AP90 270fr gold & multi 1.50 .60
C262 AP90 300fr gold & multi 1.60 1.00
Nos. C259-C262 (4) 3.70 1.98

For surcharges see Nos. C310, C321.

Gamblers and Lottery Emblem — AP91

1977, Mar. 13 Litho. *Perf. 13*

C263 AP91 50fr multi .25 .20

National lottery, 10th anniversary.

Sassenage Castle, Grenoble — AP92

1977, May 16 *Perf. 12½*

C264 AP92 200fr multi .80 .60

10th anniv. of Intl. French Language Council.
For surcharge see No. C334.

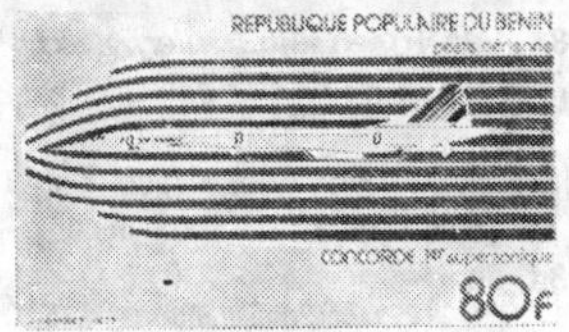

Concorde, Supersonic Plane — AP93

Designs: 150fr, Zeppelin. 300fr, Charles A. Lindbergh and Spirit of St. Louis. 500fr, Charles Nungesser and Franç ois Coli, French aviators lost over Atlantic, 1927.

1977, July 25 Engr. *Perf. 13*

C265 AP93 80fr ultra & red .40 .35
C266 AP93 150fr multi .80 .60
C267 AP93 300fr multi 1.60 1.20
C268 AP93 500fr multi 2.50 2.00
Nos. C265-C268 (4) 5.30 4.15

Aviation history.
For overprint and surcharges see Nos. C274, C316, C336.

Soccer Player — AP94

Design: 200fr, Soccer players and Games' emblem.

1977, July 28 Litho. *Perf. 12½x12*

C269 AP94 60fr multi .35 .20
C270 AP94 200fr multi 1.10 .80

World Soccer Cup elimination games.
For surcharge see No. C308.

Miss Haverfield, by Gainsborough AP95

Designs: 150fr, Self-portrait, by Rubens. 200fr, Anguish, man's head by Da Vinci.

1977, Oct. 3 Engr. *Perf. 13*

C271 AP95 100fr sl grn & mar .55 .40
C272 AP95 150fr red brn & dk brn .80 .60
C273 AP95 200fr brn & red 1.10 .80
Nos. C271-C273 (3) 2.45 1.80

For surcharges see Nos. C309, C317.

No. C265 Overprinted: "1er VOL COMMERCIAL / 22.11.77 PARIS NEW-YORK"

1977, Nov. 22 Engr. *Perf. 13*

C274 AP93 80fr ultra & red .42 .35

Concorde, 1st commercial flight, Paris to NY.

Viking on Mars AP96

Designs: 150fr, Isaac Newton, apple globe, stars. 200fr, Vladimir M. Komarov, spacecraft and earth. 500fr, Dog Laika, rocket and space.

1977, Nov. 28 Engr. *Perf. 13*

C275 AP96 100fr multi .55 .40
C276 AP96 150fr multi .80 .60
C277 AP96 200fr multi 1.10 .80
C278 AP96 500fr multi 2.75 2.00
Nos. C275-C278 (4) 5.20 3.80

Operation Viking on Mars; Isaac Newton (1642-1727); 10th death anniv. of Russian cosmonaut Vladimir M. Komarov; 20th anniv. of 1st living creature in space.
For surcharges see Nos. C301, C314.

Monument, Red Star Place, Cotonou AP97

Lithographed; Gold Embossed

1977 Nov. 30 *Perf. 12½*

C279 AP97 500fr multi 1.75 1.10

Suzanne Fourment, by Rubens — AP98

Design: 380fr, Nicholas Rubens, By Rubens.

1977, Dec. 12 Engr. *Perf. 13*

C280 AP98 200fr multi 1.10 .80
C281 AP98 380fr claret & ocher 2.00 1.40

For surcharges see Nos. C311, C313.

Parthenon and UNESCO Emblem — AP99

Designs: 70fr, Acropolis and frieze showing Pan-Athenaic procession, vert. 250fr, Parthenon and frieze showing horsemen, vert.

1978, Sept. 22 Litho. *Perf. 12½x12*

C282 AP99 70fr multi .35 .20
C283 AP99 250fr multi 1.25 .80
C284 AP99 500fr multi 2.75 1.50
Nos. C282-C284 (3) 4.35 2.50

Save the Parthenon in Athens campaign.
For surcharge see No. C338.

Philexafrique II—Essen Issue

Common Design Types

Designs: No. C285, Buffalo and Dahomey #C33. No. C286, Wild ducks and Baden #1.

1978, Nov. 1 Litho. *Perf. 12½*

C285 CD138 100fr multi .65 .40
C286 CD139 100fr multi .65 .40
a. Pair, #C285-C286 1.30 1.00

Wilbur and Orville Wright and Flyer — AP100

1978, Dec. 28 Engr. *Perf. 13*

C287 AP100 500fr multi 3.50 2.00

75th anniversary of 1st powered flight.
For surcharge see No. C339.

Cook's Ships, Hawaii, World Map — AP101

Design: 50fr, Battle at Kowrowa.

1979, June 1 Engr. *Perf. 13*

C288 AP101 20fr multi .20 .20
C289 AP101 50fr multi .45 .45

Capt. James Cook (1728-1779), explorer.

No. C253 Surcharged

1979 **Engr.** ***Perf. 13***

C289B AP87 50fr on 90fr multi

Lunokhod Type of 1980

1980, June 15 **Engr.** ***Perf. 13***

Size: 27x48mm

C290 A133 210fr multi 1.40 1.40

For surcharge see No. C305.

Soccer Players — AP102

1981, Mar. 31 **Litho.** ***Perf. 13***

C291 AP102 200fr Ball, globe .90 .90
C292 AP102 500fr shown 2.50 2.50

ESPANA '82 World Soccer Cup eliminations.
For surcharges see Nos. C335, Q10B.

Prince Charles and Lady Diana, London Bridge — AP103

1981, July 29 **Litho.** ***Perf. 12½***

C293 AP103 500fr multi 3.00 3.00

Royal wedding.
For surcharge see No. C323.

Three Musicians, by Pablo Picasso (1881-1973) — AP104

Perf. 12½x13, 13x12½

1981, Nov. 2 **Litho.**

C294 AP104 300fr Dance, vert. 2.00 2.00
C295 AP104 500fr shown 3.50 3.50

For surcharges see Nos. C320, C340.

1300th Anniv. of Bulgaria — AP105

1981, Dec. 2 **Litho.** ***Perf. 13***

C296 AP105 100fr multi .60 .60

Visit of Pope John Paul II — AP106

1982, Feb. 17 **Litho.** ***Perf. 13***

C297 AP106 80fr multi .55 .55

20th Anniv. of John Glenn's Flight — AP107

1982, Feb. 21 **Litho.** ***Perf. 13***

C298 AP107 500fr multi 3.00 3.00

For surcharge see No. C315.

Scouting Year AP108

1982, June 1 ***Perf. 12½***

C299 AP108 105fr multi .70 .70

For surcharge see No. C324.

Nos. C256, C275 Surcharged

1982, Nov. **Engr.** ***Perf. 13***

C300 AP88 50fr on 210fr multi .35 .35
C301 AP96 50fr on 100fr multi .35 .35

Monet in Boat, by Claude Monet (1832-1883) — AP109

1982, Dec. 6 **Litho.** ***Perf. 13x12½***

C302 AP109 300fr multi 2.00 2.00

For surcharge see No. C326.

Christmas 1982 AP110

Virgin and Child Paintings.

1982, Dec. 20 ***Perf. 12½x13***

C303 AP110 200fr Matthias Grunewald 1.25 1.25
C304 AP110 300fr Correggio 1.75 1.75

For surcharges see Nos. C325, C337.

No. C290 Surcharged

1983 **Engr.** ***Perf. 13***

C305 A133 75fr on 210fr multi .50 .50

Bangkok '83 Stamp Exhibition AP111

1983, Aug. 4 **Photo.** ***Perf. 13***

C306 AP111 300fr multi 1.50 1.50

For surcharge see No. C322.

Christmas 1983 AP112

1983, Dec. 26 **Litho.** ***Perf. 12½x13***

C307 AP112 200fr Loretto Madonna, by Raphael .65 .65

For surcharge see No. C319.

Types of 1976-82 Surcharged

1983, Nov.

C308	AP94	10fr on 200fr C270	.15	.15
C309	AP95	15fr on 200fr C273	.15	.15
C310	AP90	15fr on 270fr C261	.15	.15
C311	AP98	20fr on 200fr C280	.15	.15
C312	AP89	25fr on 270fr C258	.15	.15
C313	AP98	25fr on 380fr C281	.15	.15
C314	AP96	30fr on 200fr C277	.15	.15
C315	AP107	40fr on 500fr C298	.20	.20
C316	AP93	75fr on 150fr C266	.38	.38
C317	AP95	75fr on 150fr C272	.38	.38
		Set value	1.60	1.60

Summer Olympics — AP113

1984, July 16 **Litho.** ***Perf. 13x13½***

C318 AP113 300fr Sam the Eagle, mascot 1.00 1.00

Nos. C262, C293-C294, C299, C302-C303, C306-C307 Surcharged

1984, Sept.

C319	AP112	15fr on 200fr multi	.15	.15
C320	AP104	15fr on 300fr multi	.15	.15
C321	AP90	25fr on 300fr multi	.15	.15
C322	AP111	25fr on 300fr multi	.15	.15
C323	AP103	40fr on 500fr multi	.15	.15
C324	AP108	75fr on 105fr multi	.25	.25
C325	AP110	90fr on 200fr multi	.30	.30
C326	AP109	90fr on 300fr multi	.30	.30
		Set value	1.25	1.25

Christmas 1984 AP114

1984, Dec. 17 **Litho.** ***Perf. 12½x13***

C327 AP114 500fr Virgin and Child, by Murillo 1.50 1.50

Ships — AP115

1984, Dec. 28 **Litho.** ***Perf. 13***

C328 AP115 90fr Sidon merchant ship .30 .30
C329 AP115 125fr Wavertree, vert. .38 .38

Benin-S.O.M. Postal Convention AP116

1985, Apr. 15 **Litho.** ***Perf. 13½***

C330 AP116 75fr Benin arms .22 .22
C331 AP116 75fr Sovereign Order of Malta .22 .22
a. Pair, #C330-C331 .45 .45

PHILEXAFRICA III, Lome — AP117

1985, June 24 ***Perf. 13***

C332 AP117 200fr Oil platform .60 .60
C333 AP117 200fr Soccer players .60 .60
a. Pair, #C332-C333 + label 1.25 1.25

Stamps of 1977-82 Surcharged

1985, Mar.

C334	AP92	75fr on 200fr #C264	.20	.20
C335	AP102	75fr on 200fr #C291	.20	.20
C336	AP93	75fr on 300fr #C267	.20	.20
C337	AP110	75fr on 300fr #C304	.20	.20
C338	AP99	90fr on 500fr #C284	.25	.25
C339	AP100	90fr on 500fr #C287	.25	.25
C340	AP104	90fr on 500fr #C295	.25	.25
		Nos. C334-C340 (7)	1.55	1.55

Dahomey Stamps of 1971-75 Ovptd. "REPUBLIQUE POPULAIRE DU BENIN" or "POPULAIRE DU BENIN" and Surcharged with Black Bar and New Value

1985, Aug.

C341	AP83	25fr on 40fr #C238	.15	.15
C342	AP49	40fr #C142	.15	.15
C343	AP56	75fr on 85fr #C164	.20	.20
C344	AP60	75fr on 100fr #C173	.20	.20
C345	AP64	75fr on 125fr #C186	.20	.20
C346	AP56	90fr on 20fr #C163	.25	.25
C347	A61	90fr on 150fr #C153	.25	.25
C348	AP49	90fr on 200fr #C143	.25	.25
C349	AP76	90fr on 200fr #C221	.25	.25
C350	AP76	150fr #C220	.45	.45
		Nos. C341-C350 (10)	2.35	2.35

Christmas — AP118

1985, Dec. 20 **Litho.** ***Perf. 13x12½***

C351 AP118 500fr multi 1.75 1.75

For surcharge see No. C449.

Dahomey Nos. C34-C37, C84, C131 Surcharged and Overprinted with 1 or 2 Black Bars and "Republique Populaire du Benin" in 3 lines

1986 Photo. Perfs. as before

C352	AP33	75fr on 70fr #C84	.25	.25
C353	AP14	75fr on 100fr #C34	.25	.25
C354	AP15	75fr on 200fr #C35	.25	.25
C355	AP15	90fr on 250fr #C36	.35	.35
C356	AP45	100fr #C131	.38	.38
C357	AP14	150fr on 500fr #C37	.55	.55
		Nos. C352-C357 (6)	2.03	2.03

Issued: 75fr, 90fr, Mar; 100fr, 150fr, June.

Dahomey Nos. C141, C146 Surcharged "Republique / Populaire / du Benin" in Silver or Black

1986

Perfs. & Printing Methods as Before

C357B	AP48	25fr on 200fr #C141 (S)	
C357E	CD135	100fr on #C146	

Christmas — AP119

1986, Dec. 24 Litho. *Perf. 13x12½*

C358	AP119	300fr multi	1.20	1.20

Air Africa, 25th Anniv. AP120

1986, Dec. 30 *Perf. 12½*

C359	AP120	100fr multi	.40	.40

Intl. Agricultural Development Fund (FIDA), 10th Anniv. AP121

1987, Dec. 14 Litho. *Perf. 13½*

C360	AP121	500fr multi	3.50	3.50

Christmas — AP122

1988, Dec. 23 Litho. *Perf. 13x12½*

C361	AP122	500fr Adoration of the Magi, storyteller	3.25	3.25

No. C241 Surcharged

République Populaire du Bénin

15f ═

1989, Apr. 24 Litho. *Perf. 13*

C362	AP84	15fr on 85fr multi	.15	.15

Dahomey Nos. C53, C152, C156, C165, Benin No. C242 Surcharged or Overprinted

Dahomey No. Overprinted

République Populaire du Bénin

1987

Perfs. & Printing Methods as Before

C366	AP48	40fr on 100fr #C152
C367	AP84	50fr on 140fr #C242
C369	AP22	80fr multicolored
C370	AP56	80fr on 150fr #C165
C373	AP52	100fr on #C156

Dahomey Nos. C140, C177, C185, C188 C191, C195 Surcharged "Republique / Populaire / du Benin"

1988

Perfs. & Printing Methods as Before

C375	AP64	10fr on 65fr #C185
C377	AP67	25fr on 200fr #C191
C378	AP61	40fr on 35fr #C195
C381	AP48	100fr on #C140
C382	AP65	100fr on #C188
C384	AP61(b)	125fr on #C177

Dahomey Nos. C181, C208 Surcharged "Republic / Populaire / du Benin"

1988

Perfs. & Printing Methods as Before

C390	AP62	40fr on 100fr #C181
C391	AP73	40fr on 150fr #C208

Dahomey Nos. C108, C148, C162, C178, C194 Surcharged with Type b, "REPUBLIQUE / DU / BENIN" (c) or "BENIN" (d)

1992

Perfs. & Printing Methods as Before

C394	AP51(b)	70fr on #C148
C395	AP55(c)	100fr on #C162
C396	AP68(d)	100fr on #C194
C398	A52(b)	125fr on 70fr #C108
C401	AP61(b)	190fr on 140fr #C178

Dahomey Nos. C145, C149-C150, C182, C189, C198, C257, C265 Surcharged with Types b-c Benin No. C241 Surcharged with Type c

1993

Perfs. & Printing Methods as Before

C403	AP51(c)	5fr on 100fr #C149
C404	AP50(b)	10fr on 100fr #C145
C405	AP51(b)	20fr on 200fr #C150
C406	AP83(c)	20fr on 500fr #C257
C407	AP84(c)	25fr on 85fr #C241
C408	AP86(b)	25fr on 500fr #C265
C409	AP63(b)	30fr on 15fr #C182
C410	AP61(b)	30fr on 200fr #C198
C411	AP66(b)	35fr on #C189

Dahomey Nos. C101, C151, C153, C197, C234, C256, C261 Surcharged or Overprinted with Types b, d

1994-95?

Perfs. & Printing Methods as Before

C415	AP83(b)	25fr on 200fr #C256
C417	AP49(d)	50fr on #C101
C418	AP48(d)	75fr on 40fr #C151
C433	A61(b)	150fr on #C153
C434	AP61(b)	150fr on #C197
C445	AP61(a)	200fr on 250fr #C234
C447	AP85(b)	300fr on #C261

Dahomey No. C37 Surch. "Republique / Populaire / du Benin" Benin No. C351 Surcharged

1994-95

Printing Method and Perfs as Before

C448	AP14	150fr on 500fr #C37
C449	AP118	200fr on 500fr #C351

POSTAGE DUE STAMPS

French Colony

Handstamped in Black on Postage Due Stamps of French Colonies

BENIN

1894 Unwmk. *Imperf.*

J1	D1	5c black	90.00	40.00
J2	D1	10c black	90.00	40.00
J3	D1	20c black	90.00	40.00
J4	D1	30c black	90.00	40.00
		Nos. J1-J4 (4)	360.00	160.00

Nos. J1-J4 exist with overprint in various positions.

> Catalogue values for unused stamps in this section are for Never Hinged items.

People's Republic

Pineapples D6

Mail Delivery — D7

Designs: 20fr, Cashew, vert. 40fr, Oranges. 50fr, Akee. 80fr, Mail delivery by boat.

1978, Sept. 5 Photo. *Perf. 13*

J44	D6	10fr multi	.15	.15
J45	D6	20fr multi	.15	.15
J46	D6	40fr multi	.28	.16
J47	D6	50fr multi	.45	.25

Engr.

J48	D7	60fr multi	.32	.22
J49	D7	80fr multi	.45	.28
		Nos. J44-J49 (6)	1.80	1.21

PARCEL POST STAMPS

> Catalogue values for unused stamps in this section are for Never Hinged items.

Nos. 448-448A, 459, 473, C292 Overprinted or Surcharged "Colis Postaux"

Perfs. and Printing Methods as Before

1982, Nov.

Q8	A126	100fr on 150fr	.40	.20
Q9	A130	100fr multi	.40	.20
Q10	A134	300fr multi	1.20	.60
Q10A	A126a	1000fr multi	5.50	5.50
Q10B	AP102	5000fr on 500fr	27.50	27.50
		Nos. Q8-Q10B (5)	35.00	34.00

Dahomey No. C205 Surcharged

═ 500 f

République Populaire du Bénin

colis postaux

1989 Photo. *Perf. 12½x13*

Q11	AP71	500fr on 200fr multi	3.25	3.25

BHUTAN

bü-'tän

LOCATION — Eastern Himalayas
GOVT. — Kingdom
AREA — 18,000 sq. mi.
POP. — 1,250,000 (est. 1983)
CAPITAL — Thimphu

100 Chetrum = 1 Ngultrum or Rupee

> Catalogue values for all unused stamps in this country are for Never Hinged items.

Postal Runner — A1

Designs: 3ch, 70ch, Archer. 5ch, 1.30nu, Yak. 15ch, Map of Bhutan, portrait of Druk Gyalpo (Dragon King) Ugyen Wangchuk (1867-1902) and Paro Dzong (fortress-monastery). 33ch, Postal runner. All horiz. except 2ch and 33ch.

Perf. 14x14½, 14½x14

1962 Litho. Unwmk.

1	A1	2ch red & gray	.15	.15
2	A1	3ch red & ultra	.15	.15
3	A1	5ch green & brown	.40	.40
4	A1	15ch red, blk & org yel	.15	.15
5	A1	33ch blue grn & lil	.15	.15
6	A1	70ch dp ultra & lt blue	.30	.30
7	A1	1.30nu blue & black	.80	.80
		Set value	1.80	1.80

Nos. 1-7 were issued for inland use in April, 1962, and became valid for international mail on Oct. 10, 1962.

For overprint and surcharges see #42, 72-73.

Refugee Year Emblem and Arms of Bhutan — A2

1962, Oct. 10 *Perf. 14½x14*

8	A2	1nu dk blue & dk car rose	.40	.40
9	A2	2nu yel grn & red lilac	1.00	1.00

World Refugee Year. For surcharges see #68-69.

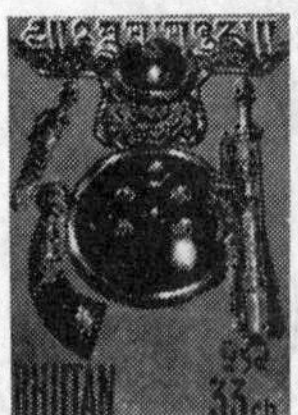

Equipment of Ancient Warrior — A3

Boy Filling Grain Box and Wheat Emblem — A4

1963 Unwmk. *Perf. 14x14½*

10	A3	33ch multicolored	.15	.15
11	A3	70ch multicolored	.28	.28
12	A3	1.30nu multicolored	.60	.60
		Nos. 10-12 (3)	1.03	1.03

Bhutan's membership in Colombo Plan.

1963, July 15 *Perf. 13½x14*

13	A4	20ch lt blue, yel & red brn	.16	.16
14	A4	1.50nu rose lil, bl & red brn	.65	.65

FAO "Freedom from Hunger" campaign.
For surcharge see No. 117M.

Masked Dancer A5

Various Bhutanese Dancers (Five Designs; 2ch, 5ch, 20ch, 1nu, 1.30nu vert.)

Perf. 14½x14, 14x14½

1964, Apr. 16

15	A5	2ch multicolored	.15	.15
16	A5	3ch multicolored	.15	.15
17	A5	5ch multicolored	.15	.15
18	A5	20ch multicolored	.15	.15
19	A5	33ch multicolored	.15	.15
20	A5	70ch multicolored	.22	.22
21	A5	1nu multicolored	.40	.40
22	A5	1.30nu multicolored	.45	.45
23	A5	2nu multicolored	.75	.75
		Set value	2.10	2.10

For surcharges see Nos. 70-71, 74-75, 129A, 129G. For overprints see Nos. C1-C3, C11-C13.

Stone Throwing — A6

Sport: 5ch, 33ch, Boxing. 1nu, 3nu, Archery. 2nu, Soccer.

1964, Oct. 10 Litho. *Perf. 14½*

24	A6	2ch emerald & multi	.15	.15
25	A6	5ch orange & multi	.15	.15
26	A6	15ch brt cit & multi	.15	.15
27	A6	33ch rose lil & multi	.15	.15
28	A6	1nu multicolored	.35	.35
29	A6	2nu rose lilac & multi	.55	.55
30	A6	3nu lt blue & multi	.80	.80
		Set value	1.95	1.95

18th Olympic Games, Tokyo, Oct. 10-25. See No. B4.
Nos. 24-30 exist imperf. Value $4.

Flags of the World at Half-mast — A7

1964, Nov. 22 Unwmk. *Perf. 14½*

Flags in Original Colors

31	A7	33ch steel gray	.15	.15
32	A7	1nu silver	.50	.50
33	A7	3nu gold	1.20	1.20
a.		Souv. sheet, perf. 13½ or imperf.	2.75	2.75
		Nos. 31-33 (3)	1.85	1.85

Issued in memory of those who died in the service of their country. Nos. 31-33 exist imperf.
No. 33a contains 2 stamps similar to Nos. 32-33.
For overprints see Nos. 44, 46.

Flowers — A8

1965, Jan. 6 Litho. *Perf. 13*

34	A8	2ch Primrose	.15	.15
35	A8	5ch Gentian	.15	.15
36	A8	15ch Primrose	.15	.15
37	A8	33ch Gentian	.15	.15
38	A8	50ch Rhododendron	.15	.15
39	A8	75ch Peony	.20	.20
40	A8	1nu Rhododendron	.22	.22
41	A8	2nu Peony	.45	.45
		Set value	1.20	1.20

For overprints see Nos. 43, 45, C4-C5, C14-C15.

Nos. 5, 40, 32, 41 and 33 Overprinted: "WINSTON CHURCHILL 1874-1965"

1965, Feb. 27

42	A1	33ch bl grn & lilac	.16	.16
43	A8	1nu pink, grn & dk gray	.42	.42
44	A7	1nu silver & multi	.42	.42
45	A8	2nu sepia, yel & grn	.75	.75
46	A7	3nu gold & multi	1.00	1.00
		Nos. 42-46 (5)	2.75	2.75

Issued in memory of Sir Winston Churchill (1874-1965), British statesman. The overprint is in three lines on Nos. 42-43 and 45; in two lines on Nos. 43 and 46.
Nos. 44 and 46 exist imperf. Value, both, $4.50.

Skyscraper, Pagoda and World's Fair Emblem — A9

Designs: 10ch, 2nu, Pieta by Michelangelo and statue of Khmer Buddha. 20ch, Skyline of NYC and Bhutanese village. 33ch, George Washington Bridge, NY, and foot bridge, Bhutan.

1965, Apr. 21 Litho. *Perf. 14½*

47	A9	1ch blue & multi	.15	.15
48	A9	10ch green & multi	.15	.15
49	A9	20ch rose lilac & multi	.15	.15
50	A9	33ch bister & multi	.15	.15
51	A9	1.50nu bister & multi	.50	.50
52	A9	2nu multicolored	.65	.65
a.		Souv. sheet, perf. 13½ or imperf.	2.00	2.00
		Set value	1.45	1.45

Nos. 47-52 exist imperf.; value $3.50.
No. 52a contains two stamps similar to Nos. 51-52.
For overprints see #87-87B, C6-C10, C16-C20.

Telstar, Short-wave Radio and ITU Emblem — A10

Designs (ITU Emblem and): 2nu, Telstar and Morse key. 3nu, Syncom and ear phones.

1966, Mar. 2 Litho. *Perf. 14½*

53	A10	35ch multicolored	.15	.15
54	A10	2nu multicolored	.60	.60
55	A10	3nu multicolored	.85	.85
		Nos. 53-55 (3)	1.60	1.60

Cent. (in 1965) of the ITU. Souvenir sheets exist containing two stamps similar to Nos. 54-55, perf. 13½ and imperf. Value, 2 sheets, $5.

Leopard — A11

Animals: 1ch, 4nu, Asiatic black bear. 4ch, 2nu, Pigmy hog. 8ch, 75ch, Tiger. 10ch, 1.50nu, Dhole (Asiatic hunting dog). 1nu, 5nu, Takin (goat).

1966, Mar. 24 Litho. *Perf. 13*

56	A11	1ch yellow & blk	.15	.15
57	A11	2ch pale grn & blk	.15	.15
58	A11	4ch lt citron & blk	.15	.15
59	A11	8ch lt blue & blk	.15	.15
60	A11	10ch lt lilac & blk	.15	.15
61	A11	75ch lt yel grn & blk	.20	.20
62	A11	1nu lt green & blk	.50	.50
63	A11	1.50nu lt bl grn & blk	.40	.40
64	A11	2nu dull org & blk	.50	.50
65	A11	3nu bluish lil & blk	.75	.75
66	A11	4nu lt green & blk	1.00	1.00
67	A11	5nu pink & black	1.40	1.40
		Nos. 56-67 (12)	5.50	5.50

For surcharges see Nos. 115C, 115E, 115I, 117N, 117P, 129B, 129J.

Nos. 6-9, 20-23 Surcharged

10 CH

1965(?) *Perf. 14½x14, 14x14½*

68	A2	5ch on 1nu	*26.00*	*26.00*
69	A2	5ch on 2nu	*26.00*	*26.00*
70	A5	10ch on 70ch	*4.25*	*4.25*
71	A5	10ch on 2nu	*4.25*	*4.25*
72	A1	15ch on 70ch	*6.25*	*6.25*
73	A1	15ch on 1.30nu	*6.25*	*6.25*
74	A5	20ch on 1nu	*8.25*	*8.25*
75	A5	20ch on 1.30nu	*8.25*	*8.25*
		Nos. 68-75 (8)	*89.50*	*89.50*

The surcharges on Nos. 68-69 contain two bars at left and right obliterating the denomination on both sides of the design. Four bars on Nos. 72-73.

Simtokha Dzong A12

Tashichho Dzong — A13

Daga Dzong — A14

Designs: 5ch, Rinpung Dzong. 50ch, Tongsa Dzong. 1nu, Lhuntsi Dzong.

Perf. 14½x14 (A12), 13½ (A13, A14)

1966-70 Photo.

76	A12	5ch orange brn ('67)	.15	.15
77	A13	10ch dk grn & rose vio ('68)	.15	.15
78	A12	15ch brown	.15	.15
79	A12	20ch green	.15	.15
80	A13	50ch blue grn ('68)	.20	.15
81	A14	75ch dk bl & ol gray ('70)	.20	.20
82	A14	1nu dk vio & vio bl ('70)	.28	.28
		Set value	1.05	.90

Sizes: 5ch, 15ch, 20ch, 37x20½mm. 10ch, 53½x28½mm. 50ch, 35½x25½mm.

King Jigme Wangchuk A14a

Coins: 1.30nu, 3nu, 5nu, reverse.

Litho. & Embossed on Gold Foil

1966, July 8 Die Cut *Imperf.*

83	A14a	10ch green	.15	.15
83A	A14a	25ch green	.22	.22
83B	A14a	50ch green	.45	.45
83C	A14a	1nu red	.90	.90
83D	A14a	1.30nu red	1.10	1.10
83E	A14a	2nu red	1.75	1.75
83F	A14a	3nu red	2.50	2.50
83G	A14a	4nu red	3.50	3.50
83H	A14a	5nu red	4.25	4.25
		Nos. 83-83H (9)	14.82	14.82

See Nos. 98-98B.

Abominable Snowman — A14b

1966 Photo. *Perf. 13½*

84	A14b	1ch multicolored	.15	.15
84A	A14b	2ch multi, diff.	.15	.15
84B	A14b	3ch multi, diff.	.15	.15
84C	A14b	4ch multi, diff.	.15	.15
84D	A14b	5ch multi, diff.	.15	.15
84E	A14b	15ch like #84	.15	.15
84F	A14b	30ch like #84A	.15	.15
84G	A14b	40ch like #84B	.15	.15
84H	A14b	50ch like #84C	.15	.15
84I	A14b	1.25nu like #84D	.30	.30
84J	A14b	2.50nu like #84	.65	.65
84K	A14b	3nu like #84A	.75	.75
84L	A14b	5nu like #84B	1.25	1.25
84M	A14b	6nu like #84C	1.50	1.50
84N	A14b	7nu like #84D	1.75	1.75
		Set value	6.50	6.50

Issue dates: 1ch, 2ch, 3ch, 4ch, 5ch, 15ch, 30ch, 40ch, 50ch, Oct. 12. Others, Nov. 15. Exist imperf.
For overprints see Nos. 93-93G. For surcharges see Nos. 115D, 115K, 115O, 115P, 117I, 117S.

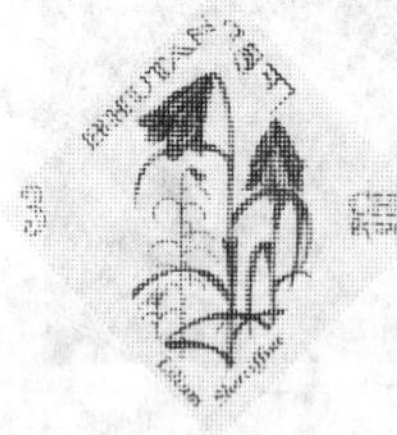

Flowers A14c

Designs: 3ch, 50ch, Lilium sherriffiae. 5ch, 1nu, Meconopsis dhwoju. 7ch, 2.50nu, Rhododendron chaetomallum. 10ch, 4nu, Pleione hookeriana. 5nu, Rhododendron giganteum.

1967, Feb. 9 Litho. *Perf. 13*

85	A14c	3ch multicolored	.15	.15
85A	A14c	5ch multicolored	.15	.15
85B	A14c	7ch multicolored	.15	.15
85C	A14c	10ch multicolored	.15	.15

Gray Background

85D	A14c	50ch multicolored	.15	.15
85E	A14c	1nu multicolored	.30	.30
85F	A14c	2.50nu multicolored	.75	.75
85G	A14c	4nu multicolored	1.20	1.20
85H	A14c	5nu multicolored	1.50	1.50
		Nos. 85-85H (9)	4.50	4.50

For surcharges see Nos. 115F, 115L.

Boy Scouts — A14d

1967, Mar. 28 Photo. *Perf. 13½*
86 A14d 5ch Planting tree .15 .15
86A A14d 10ch Cooking .15 .15
86B A14d 15ch Mountain climbing .15 .15

Emblem, Border in Gold
86C A14d 50ch like #86 .16 .16
86D A14d 1.25nu like #86A .40 .40
86E A14d 4nu like #86B 1.25 1.25
f. Souv. sheet of 2, #86D, 86E 1.75 1.75
Nos. 86-86E (6) 2.26 2.26

Exist imperf.
See Nos. 89-89E for overprints. For surcharges see Nos. 115G, 117J, 129K.

Nos. 50-52, 52a Ovptd.

expo67

1967, May 25 Litho. *Perfs. as Before*
87 A9 33ch on #50 .15 .15
87A A9 1.50nu on #51 .40 .40
87B A9 2nu on #52 .50 .50
c. Souv. sheet of 2, on #52a 1.50 1.50
Nos. 87-87B (3) 1.05 1.05

Nos. 87-87B exist imperf.

Airplanes — A14f

1967, June 26 Litho. *Perf. 13½*
88 A14f 45ch Lancaster .15 .15
88A A14f 2nu Spitfire .45 .45
88B A14f 4nu Hurricane .95 .95
c. Souv. sheet of 2, #88A, 88B 2.00 2.00
Nos. 88-88B (3) 1.55 1.55

Churchill and Battle of Britain. Exist imperf.
For surcharges see Nos. 117Q, 117T.

Nos. 86-86D, 86e Overprinted "WORLD JAMBOREE / IDAHO, U.S.A. / AUG. 1-9,/67"

1967, Aug. 8 Photo. *Perf. 13½*
89 A14d 5ch Planting tree .15 .15
89A A14d 10ch Cookout .15 .15
89B A14d 15ch Mountain climbing .15 .15
89C A14d 50ch like #89 .16 .16
89D A14d 1.25nu like #89A .45 .45
89E A14d 4nu like #89B 1.50 1.50
f. Souv. sheet of 2, #89D, 89E 2.00 2.00
Nos. 89-89E (6) 2.56 2.56

No. 89f sold for 6.25nu. Exist imperf.

Girl Scouts — A14g

1967, Sept. 28 Photo. *Perf. 13½*
90 A14g 5ch Painting .15 .15
90A A14g 10ch Making music .15 .15
90B A14g 15ch Picking fruit .15 .15

Emblem, Border in Gold
90C A14g 1.50nu like #90 .25 .25
90D A14g 2.50nu like #90A .40 .40
90E A14g 5nu like #90B .80 .80
f. Souv. sheet of 2, #90A, 90B 1.75 1.75
Set value 1.50 1.50

Exist imperf.
For surcharge see No. 266.

Astronaut, Space Capsule — A14h

Astronaut walking in space and: 5ch, 30ch, 4nu, Orbiter, Lunar modules docked. 7ch, 50ch, 5nu, Lunar module. 10ch, 1.25nu, 9nu, Other astronauts.

1967, Oct. 30 Litho. *Imperf.*
91 A14h 3ch multi .15 .15
91A A14h 5ch multi .15 .15
91B A14h 7ch multi .18 .18
91C A14h 10ch multi .25 .25
m. Souv. sheet of 4, #91-91C .75 .75
91D A14h 15ch multi .35 .35
91E A14h 30ch multi .75 .75
91F A14h 50ch multi 1.25 1.25
91G A14h 1.25nu multi 3.00 3.00
n. Souv. sheet of 4, #91D-91G 6.75 6.75
91H A14h 2.50nu multi 1.75 1.75
91I A14h 4nu multi 3.00 3.00
91J A14h 5nu multi 3.75 3.75
91K A14h 9nu multi 6.50 6.50
o. Souv. sheet of 4, #91H-91K 20.00 20.00
Nos. 91-91K (12) 21.08 21.08

Nos. 91H-91K are airmail. Simulated 3-dimensions using a plastic overlay.
For other space issues see types A15a, A15e.

Pheasants — A14i

Designs: 1ch, 2nu, Tragopan satyra. 2ch, 4nu, Lophophorus sclareti. 4ch, 5nu, Lophophorus impeyanus. 8ch, 7nu, Lophura leucomelana. 15ch, 9nu, Crossoptilon crossoptilon.

1968 Photo. *Perf. 13½*
92 A14i 1ch multicolored .15 .15
92A A14i 2ch multicolored .15 .15
92B A14i 4ch multicolored .15 .15
92C A14i 8ch multicolored .15 .15
92D A14i 15ch multicolored .15 .15

Border in Gold
92E A14i 2nu multicolored .35 .35
92F A14i 4nu multicolored .70 .70
92G A14i 5nu multicolored .90 .90
92H A14i 7nu multicolored 1.25 1.25
92I A14i 9nu multicolored 1.65 1.65
Set value 5.00 5.00

Issue dates: 1ch, 2ch, 4ch, 8ch, 15ch, 2nu, 4nu, 7nu, Jan 20. 5nu, 9nu, Apr. 23.

Unauthorized imperfs. exist.
For surcharges see Nos. 115H, 117R, 117V, 129D, 129L.

Nos. 84G, 84I, 84K, 84M Ovptd. in Black on Silver

a

b

1968, Feb. 16 Photo. *Perfs. as Before*
Overprint Type "a"
93 A14b 40ch on #84G .15 .15
93A A14b 1.25nu on #84I .20 .20
93B A14b 3nu on #84K .50 .50
93C A14b 6nu on #84M 1.00 1.00

Overprint Type "b"
93D A14b 40ch on #84G .15 .15
93E A14b 1.25nu on #84I .20 .20
93F A14b 3nu on #84K .50 .50
93G A14b 6nu on #84M 1.00 1.00
Nos. 93-93G (8) 3.70 3.70

Exist imperf.

Snow Lion — A14j

1968, Mar. 14 Photo. *Perf. 12½*
94 A14j 2ch Elephant .15 .15
94A A14j 3ch Garuda .15 .15
94B A14j 4ch Monastery Tiger .15 .15
94C A14j 5ch Wind Horse .15 .15
94D A14j 15ch Snow Lion .15 .15
94E A14j 20ch like #94 .15 .15
94F A14j 30ch like #94A .15 .15
94G A14j 50ch like #94B .15 .15
94H A14j 1.25nu like #94C .20 .20
94I A14j 1.50nu like #94 .25 .25
94J A14j 2nu like #94D .32 .32
94K A14j 2.50nu like #94A .40 .40
94L A14j 4nu like #94B .65 .65
94M A14j 5nu like #94C .80 .80
94N A14j 10nu like #94D 1.65 1.65
Set value 4.50 4.50

Nos. 94I, 94K-94N are airmail. All exist imperf.
For surcharges see Nos. 115, 115M, 115O, 117-117E, 129C, C35-C36.

Butterflies
A14k

Designs: 15ch, Catagramma sorana. 50ch, Delias hyparete. 1.25nu, Anteos maerula. 2nu, Ornithoptera priamus urvilleanus. 3nu, Euploea mulciber. 4nu, Morpho rhetenor. 5nu, Papilio androgeous. 6nu, Troides magellanus.

1968, May 20 Litho. *Imperf.*
95 A14k 15ch multi .15 .15
95A A14k 50ch multi .45 .45
95B A14k 1.25nu multi 1.10 1.10
95C A14k 2nu multi 1.75 1.75
h. Souv. sheet of 4, #95-95C 3.50 3.50
95D A14k 3nu multi 1.25 1.25
95E A14k 4nu multi 1.65 1.65
95F A14k 5nu multi 2.00 2.00
95G A14k 6nu multi 2.50 2.50
i. Souv. sheet of 4, #95D-95G 7.50 7.50
Nos. 95-95G (8) 10.85 10.85

Souv. sheets issued Oct. 23. Nos. 95D-95G, 95i are airmail. Simulated 3-dimensions using a plastic overlay.

Paintings — A14m

1968 Litho. & Embossed *Imperf.*
96 A14m 2ch Van Gogh .15 .15
96A A14m 4ch Millet .15 .15
96B A14m 5ch Monet .15 .15
96C A14m 10ch Corot .15 .15
p. Souv. sheet of 4, #96-96C .15 .15
96D A14m 45ch like #96 .20 .20
96E A14m 80ch like #96A .35 .35
96F A14m 1.05nu like #96B .45 .45
96G A14m 1.40nu like #96C .60 .60
q. Souv. sheet of 4, #96D-96G 1.65 1.65
96H A14m 1.50nu like #96 .65 .65
96I A14m 2nu like #96 .85 .85
96J A14m 2.50nu like #96A 1.10 1.10
96K A14m 3nu like #96A 1.25 1.25
96L A14m 4nu like #96B 1.10 1.10
96M A14m 5nu like #96C 1.40 1.40
r. Souv. sheet of 4, #96I, 96K-96M 4.75 4.75
96N A14m 6nu like #96B 1.75 1.75
96O A14m 8nu like #96C 2.25 2.25
s. Souv. sheet of 4, #96H, 96J, 96N-96O 6.00 6.00
Nos. 96-96O (16) 12.55 12.55

Issue dates: Nos. 96-96G, 96I, 96K-96M, July 8. Nos. 96p, 96q, 96r, Aug. 5. Others, Aug. 28. Nos. 96H, 96J, 96N-96O are airmail.
See Nos. 114-114O, 144-144G.

Summer Olympics, Mexico, 1968
A14n

1968, Oct. 1 Photo. *Perf. 13½*
97 A14n 5ch Discus .15 .15
97A A14n 45ch Basketball .15 .15
97B A14n 60ch Javelin .15 .15
97C A14n 80ch Shooting .15 .15
97D A14n 1.05nu like #97 .15 .15
97E A14n 2nu like #97B .24 .24
97F A14n 3nu like #97C .35 .35
97G A14n 5nu Soccer .60 .60
h. Souv. sheet of 2, #97D, 97G 2.25 2.25
Set value 1.50 1.50

Exist imperf.
For surcharges see Nos. 129E, B5-B7.

Coin Type of 1966 Overprinted

Embossed on Gold Foil
1968, Nov. 12 Die Cut *Imperf.*
98 A14a 15ch green .15 .15
98A A14a 33ch green .16 .16
98B A14a 9nu green 4.25 4.25
Nos. 98-98B (3) 4.56 4.56

Human Rights Year.

Birds — A14p

Designs: 2ch, 20ch, 1.50nu, Crimson-winged laughing thrush. 3ch, 30ch, 2.50nu, Ward's trogon, vert. 4ch, 50ch, 4nu, Grey peacock-pheasant. 5ch, 1.25nu, 5nu, Rufous necked hornbill, vert. 15ch, 2nu, 10nu, Myzornis.

1968-69 Photo. *Perf. 12½*

99	A14p	2ch multicolored	.15	.15
99A	A14p	3ch multicolored	.15	.15
99B	A14p	4ch multicolored	.15	.15
99C	A14p	5ch multicolored	.15	.15
99D	A14p	15ch multicolored	.15	.15
99E	A14p	20ch multicolored	.15	.15
99F	A14p	30ch multicolored	.15	.15
99G	A14p	50ch multicolored	.15	.15
99H	A14p	1.25nu multicolored	.30	.30
99I	A14p	1.50nu multicolored	.38	.38
99J	A14p	2nu multicolored	.42	.42
99K	A14p	2.50nu multicolored	.52	.52
99L	A14p	4nu multicolored	.85	.85
99M	A14p	5nu multicolored	1.10	1.10
99N	A14p	10nu multicolored	2.00	2.00
		Nos. 99-99N (15)	6.77	6.77

Issue dates: 2ch, 3ch, 4ch, 5ch, 15ch, 30ch, 50ch, Dec. 7, 1968. 20ch, 1.25nu, 2nu, Dec. 28, 1968. Others, Jan. 29, 1969.

1.50nu, 2.50nu, 4nu, 5nu, 10nu are airmail.

Exist imperf.

For surcharges see Nos. 115A-115B, 115I, 115M, 115R, 117F-117G, 117K, 117O, 129H.

Fish A14q

1969, Feb. 27 Litho. *Imperf.*

100	A14q	15ch multicolored	.80	.80
100A	A14q	20ch multi, diff.	1.00	1.00
100B	A14q	30ch multi, diff.	1.50	1.50
100C	A14q	5nu multi, diff.	2.00	2.00
100D	A14q	6nu multi, diff.	2.50	2.50
100E	A14q	7nu multi, diff.	3.00	3.00
f.		Souv. sheet of 4, #100B-100E	9.00	9.00
		Nos. 100-100E (6)	10.80	10.80

Nos. 100C-100E are airmail. Simulated 3-dimensions using a plastic overlay.

Insects — A14r

1969, Apr. 10 Litho. *Imperf.*

101	A14r	10ch multicolored	.15	.15
101A	A14r	75ch multi, diff.	.35	.35
101B	A14r	1.25nu multi, diff.	.60	.60
101C	A14r	2nu multi, diff.	1.00	1.00
h.		Souv. sheet of 4, #101-101C	3.75	3.75
101D	A14r	3nu multi, diff.	1.10	1.10
101E	A14r	4nu multi, diff.	1.50	1.50
101F	A14r	5nu multi, diff.	1.90	1.90
101G	A14r	6nu multi, diff.	2.25	2.25
i.		Souv. sheet of 4, #101D-101G	8.00	8.00
		Nos. 101-101G (8)	8.85	8.85

Nos. 101D-101G, 101i are airmail. Stamps from souvenir sheets have inscription at lower right. Simulated 3-dimensions using a plastic overlay.

Admission to UPU — A14s

Illustration reduced.

1969, May 2 Photo. *Perf. 13*

102	A14s	5ch multicolored	.15	.15
102A	A14s	10ch multicolored	.15	.15
102B	A14s	15ch multicolored	.15	.15
102C	A14s	45ch multicolored	.15	.15
102D	A14s	60ch multicolored	.16	.16
102E	A14s	1.05nu multicolored	.25	.25
102F	A14s	1.40nu multicolored	.35	.35
102G	A14s	4nu multicolored	1.00	1.00
		Set value	2.00	2.00

Exist imperf.

For surcharges see #117H, 117L, 117U, 129.

History of Steel Making — A14t

Designs: 2ch, Pre-biblical. 5ch, Damascus sword. 15ch, 3nu, Saugus Mill. 45ch, Beehive coke ovens. 75ch, 4nu, Bessemer converter. 1.50nu, 5nu, Rolling mill. 1.75nu, Steel mill. 2nu, 6nu, Future applications.

Litho. on Steel Foil

1969, June 2 *Imperf.*

Without Gum

103	A14t	2ch multicolored	.15	.15
103A	A14t	5ch multicolored	.15	.15
103B	A14t	15ch multicolored	.15	.15
m.		Souv. sheet of 2, #103A-103B	.15	.15
103C	A14t	45ch multicolored	.15	.15
n.		Souv. sheet of 2, #103, 103C	.30	.30
103D	A14t	75ch multicolored	.22	.22
103E	A14t	1.50nu multicolored	.45	.45
103F	A14t	1.75nu multicolored	.52	.52
o.		Souv. sheet of 2, #103E-103F	2.25	2.25
103G	A14t	2nu multicolored	.60	.60
p.		Souv. sheet of 2, #103D, 103G	1.90	1.90
103H	A14t	3nu multicolored	.85	.85
103I	A14t	4nu multicolored	1.10	1.10
103J	A14t	5nu multicolored	1.40	1.40
q.		Souv. sheet of 2, #103I-103J	3.75	3.75
103K	A14t	6nu multicolored	1.65	1.65
r.		Souv. sheet of 2, #103H,103K	3.75	3.75
		Nos. 103-103K (12)	7.39	7.39

Nos. 103H-103K, 103q, 103r are airmail. Souv. sheets issued June 30.

Birds A14u

1969, Aug. 5 Litho. *Imperf.*

104	A14u	15ch Owl	.15	.15
104A	A14u	50ch Red birds	.38	.38
104B	A14u	1.25nu Hawk	.95	.95
104C	A14u	2nu Penguin	1.50	1.50
h.		Souv. sheet of 4, #104-104C	3.25	3.25
104D	A14u	3nu Macaws	1.10	1.10
104E	A14u	4nu Bird of paradise	1.40	1.40
104F	A14u	5nu Duck	1.75	1.75
104G	A14u	6nu Pheasant	2.00	2.00
i.		Souv. sheet of 4, #104D-104G	6.75	6.75
		Nos. 104-104G (8)	9.23	9.23

Nos. 104D-104G, 104i are airmail. Simulated 3-dimensions using a plastic overlay. Souv. sheets issued Aug. 28.

Buddhist Prayer Banners — A14v

Litho. on Cloth

1969, Sep. 30 *Imperf.*

Self-adhesive

Sizes: 15ch, 75ch, 2nu, 57x57mm, 5nu, 6nu, 70x37mm

105	A14v	15ch multicolored	.15	.15
105A	A14v	75ch multi, diff.	.26	.26
105B	A14v	2nu multi, diff.	.70	.70
105C	A14v	5nu multi, diff.	1.75	1.75
105D	A14v	6nu multi, diff.	2.25	2.25
		Nos. 105-105D (5)	5.11	5.11

Souvenir Sheet

105E		Sheet of 3	5.00	5.00

No. 105E shows denominations of 75ch, 5nu, 6nu with design elements of Nos. 105A, 105C, 105D with gray frame. Exists perf. 13½.

Mahatma Gandhi — A15

1969, Oct. 2 Litho. *Perf. 13x13½*

106	A15	20ch light blue & brn	.15	.15
107	A15	2nu lemon & brn ol	.75	.75

Mohandas K. Gandhi (1869-1948), leader in India's struggle for independence.

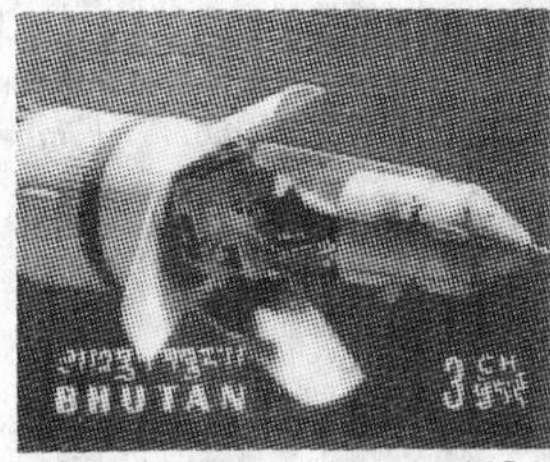

Apollo 11 Moon Landing — A15a

Designs: 3ch, Separation from third stage. 5ch, Entering lunar orbit. 15ch, Lunar module separating from orbiter. 20ch, 3nu, Astronaut standing on lunar module's foot pad. 25ch, Astronaut, lunar module on moon. 45ch, Astronaut, flag. 50ch, 4nu, Setting up experiments. 1.75nu, Lunar module docking with orbiter. 5nu, Lift-off from Cape Canaveral. 6nu, Recovery at sea.

1969 Litho. *Imperf.*

108	A15a	3ch multi	.15	.15
108A	A15a	5ch multi	.15	.15
108B	A15a	15ch multi	.16	.16
108C	A15a	20ch multi	.20	.20
m.		Souv. sheet of 4, #108-108C	.55	.55
108D	A15a	25ch multi	.25	.25
108E	A15a	45ch multi	.48	.48
108F	A15a	50ch multi	.52	.52
108G	A15a	1.75nu multi	1.75	1.75
n.		Souv. sheet of 4, #108D-108G	4.00	4.00
108H	A15a	3nu multi	1.50	1.50
108I	A15a	4nu multi	2.00	2.00
108J	A15a	5nu multi	2.50	2.50
108K	A15a	6nu multi	3.00	3.00
o.		Souv. sheet of 4, #108H-108K	21.00	21.00
		Nos. 108-108K (12)	12.66	12.66

Issue dates: Nos. 108-108G, Nov. 3. Nos. 108H-108K, Nov. 20. Souv. sheets, Dec. 20.

Nos. 108H-108K, 108o are airmail. Simulated 3-dimensions using a plastic overlay.

"Aldrin" misspelled on No. 108o.

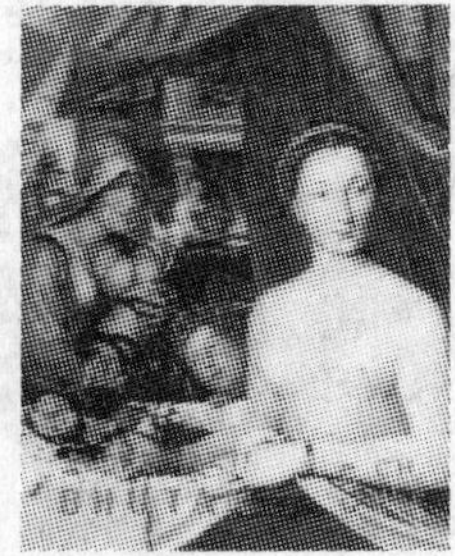

Paintings A15b

1970, Jan. 19 Litho. *Imperf.*

109	A15b	5ch Clouet	.15	.15
109A	A15b	10ch van Eyck	.15	.15
109B	A15b	15ch David	.15	.15
109C	A15b	2.75nu Rubens	1.75	1.75
h.		Souv. sheet of 4, #109-109C	2.50	2.50
109D	A15b	3nu Homer	1.10	1.10
109E	A15b	4nu Gentileschi	1.40	1.40
109F	A15b	5nu Raphael	1.75	1.75
109G	A15b	6nu Ghirlandaio	2.25	2.25
i.		Souv. sheet of 4, #109D-109G	7.50	7.50
		Nos. 109-109G (8)	8.70	8.70

Nos. 109D-109G, 109i are airmail. Simulated 3-dimensions using a plastic overlay. Souv. sheets issued Feb. 25.

Various Forms of Mail Transport, UPU Headquarters, Bern — A15c

1970, Feb. 27 Photo. *Perf. 13½*

110	A15c	3ch ol grn & gold	.15	.15
111	A15c	10ch red brn & gold	.15	.15
112	A15c	20ch Prus bl & gold	.15	.15
113	A15c	2.50nu dp mag & gold	.65	.65
		Set value	.75	.75

New Headquarters of Universal Postal Union, Bern, Switzerland.

Exist imperf. Value $5.

For surcharge see No. 129I.

Painting Type of 1968

Paintings of flowers.

Litho. & Embossed

1970, May 6 *Imperf.*

114	A14m	2ch Van Gogh	.15	.15
114A	A14m	3ch Redon	.15	.15
114B	A14m	5ch Kuroda	.15	.15
114C	A14m	10ch Renoir	.15	.15
p.		Souv. sheet of 4, #114-114C	.15	.15
114D	A14m	15ch Renoir, diff.	.15	.15
114E	A14m	75ch Monet	.32	.32
114F	A14m	80ch like #114	.20	.20
114G	A14m	90ch like #114A	.22	.22
114H	A14m	1nu La Tour	.42	.42
114I	A14m	1.10nu like #114B	.28	.28
114J	A14m	1.40nu Oudot	.60	.60
q.		Souv. sheet of 4, #114D, 114E, 114H, 114J	1.90	1.90
114K	A14m	1.40nu like #114C	.35	.35
r.		Souv. sheet of 4, #114F, 114G, 114I, 114K	1.25	1.25
114L	A14m	1.60nu like #114D	.40	.40
114M	A14m	1.70nu like #114E	.42	.42
114N	A14m	3nu like #114H	.75	.75
114O	A14m	3.50nu like #114J	.85	.85
s.		Souv. sheet of 4, #114L-114O	2.75	2.75
		Nos. 114-114O (16)	5.56	5.56

#114F-114G, 114I, 114K-114O are airmail.

Stamps of 1966-69 Surcharged

1970, June 19

115	A14j	20ch on 2nu, #94J	*2.50*	*2.50*
115A	A14p	20ch on 2nu, #99J	*2.50*	*2.50*
115B	A14p	20ch on 2.50nu, #99K	*2.50*	*2.50*
115C	A11	20ch on 3nu, #65	*2.50*	*2.50*
115D	A14b	20ch on 3nu, #84K	*2.50*	*2.50*
115E	A11	20ch on 4nu, #66	*2.50*	*2.50*
115F	A14c	20ch on 4nu, #85G	*2.50*	*2.50*
115G	A14d	20ch on 4nu, #86E	*2.50*	*2.50*
115H	A14i	20ch on 4nu, #92F	*2.50*	*2.50*
115I	A14p	20ch on 4nu, #99L	*2.50*	*2.50*
115J	A11	20ch on 5nu, #67	*2.50*	*2.50*
115K	A14b	20ch on 5nu, #84L	*2.50*	*2.50*
115L	A14c	20ch on 5nu, #85H	*2.50*	*2.50*
115M	A14j	20ch on 5nu, #94M	*2.50*	*2.50*
115N	A14p	20ch on 5nu, #99M	*2.50*	*2.50*
115O	A14b	20ch on 6nu, #84M	*2.50*	*2.50*
115P	A14b	20ch on 7nu, #84N	*2.50*	*2.50*
115Q	A14j	20ch on 10nu, #94N	*2.50*	*2.50*
115R	A14p	20ch on 10nu, #99N	*2.50*	*2.50*
		Nos. 115-115R (19)	*47.50*	*47.50*

Nos. 115B, 115I, 115M-115N, 115Q-115R are airmail.

Animals — A15d

1970, Oct. 15 Litho. *Imperf.*

116	A15d	5ch African elephant	.15	.15
116A	A15d	10ch Leopard	.15	.15
116B	A15d	20ch Ibex	.15	.15
116C	A15d	25ch Tiger	.15	.15
116D	A15d	30ch Abominable snow-man	.16	.16
116E	A15d	40ch Water buffalo	.22	.22
116F	A15d	65ch Rhinoceros	.35	.35
116G	A15d	75ch Giant pandas	.42	.42
116H	A15d	85ch Snow leopard	.48	.48
116I	A15d	2nu Young deer	.65	.65
116J	A15d	3nu Wild boar, vert.	.95	.95
116K	A15d	4nu Collared bear, vert.	1.25	1.25
116L	A15d	5nu Takin	1.65	1.65
		Nos. 116-116L (13)	6.73	6.73

Nos. 116I-116L are airmail. Simulated 3-dimensions using a plastic overlay.

Stamps of 1963-69 Surcharged

1970, Nov. 2

117	A14j	5ch on 30ch, #94F	.60	.60
117A	A14j	5ch on 50ch, #94G	.60	.60
117B	A14j	5ch on 1.25nu, #94H	.60	.60
117C	A14j	5ch on 1.50nu, #94I	.60	.60
117D	A14j	5ch on 2nu, #94J	.60	.60
117E	A14j	5ch on 2.50nu, #94K	.60	.60
117F	A14p	20ch on 30ch, #99F	2.50	2.50
117G	A14p	20ch on 50ch, #99G	2.50	2.50
117H	A14s	20ch on 1.05nu, #102E	2.50	2.50
117I	A14b	20ch on 1.25nu, #84I	2.50	2.50
117J	A14d	20ch on 1.25nu, #86D	2.50	2.50
117K	A14p	20ch on 1.25nu, #99H	2.50	2.50
117L	A14s	20ch on 1.40nu, #102F	2.50	2.50
117M	A4	20ch on 1.50nu, #14	2.50	2.50
117N	A11	20ch on 1.50nu, #63	2.50	2.50
117O	A14p	20ch on 1.50nu, #99I	2.50	2.50
117P	A11	20ch on 2nu, #64	2.50	2.50
117Q	A14f	20ch on 2nu, #88A	2.50	2.50
117R	A14i	20ch on 2nu, #92E	2.50	2.50
117S	A14b	20ch on 2.50nu, #84J	2.50	2.50
117T	A14f	20ch on 4nu, #88B	2.50	2.50
117U	A14s	20ch on 4nu, #102G	2.50	2.50
117V	A14i	20ch on 7nu, #92H	2.50	2.50
		Nos. 117-117V (23)	46.10	46.10

Nos. 117C, 117E, 117O are airmail.

Conquest of Space — A15e

Designs: 2ch, Jules Verne's "From the Earth to the Moon." 5ch, V-2 rocket. 15ch, Vostok. 25ch, Mariner 2. 30ch, Gemini 7. 50ch, Lift-off. 75ch, Edward White during space walk. 1.50nu, Apollo 13. 2nu, View of Earth from moon. 3nu, Another galaxy. 6nu, Moon, Earth, Sun, Mars, Jupiter. 7nu, Future space station.

1970 Litho. *Imperf.*

118	A15e	2ch multicolored	.15	.15
118A	A15e	5ch multicolored	.15	.15
118B	A15e	15ch multicolored	.15	.15
118C	A15e	25ch multicolored	.18	.18
m.		Souv. sheet of 4, #118-118C	.40	.40
118D	A15e	30ch multicolored	.22	.22
118E	A15e	50ch multicolored	.35	.35
118F	A15e	75ch multicolored	.55	.55
118G	A15e	1.50nu multicolored	1.10	1.10
n.		Souv. sheet of 4, #118D-118G	2.50	2.50
118H	A15e	2nu multicolored	.65	.65
118I	A15e	3nu multicolored	1.00	1.00
118J	A15e	6nu multicolored	2.00	2.00
118K	A15e	7nu multicolored	2.25	2.25
o.		Souv. sheet of 4, #118H-118K	6.50	6.50
		Nos. 118-118K (12)	8.75	8.75

Issue dates: Nos. 118-118G, Nov. 9. Nos. 118H-118K, Nov. 30. Souv. sheets, Dec. 18. Nos. 118H-118K are airmail. Simulated 3-dimensions using a plastic overlay.

See Nos. 127-127C. For surcharge see No. 129F.

Wangdiphodrang Dzong and Bridge — A15f

1971-72 Photo. *Perf. 13½*

119	A15f	2ch gray	.15	.15
120	A15f	3ch deep red lilac	.15	.15
121	A15f	4ch violet	.15	.15
122	A15f	5ch dark green	.15	.15
123	A15f	10ch orange brown	.15	.15
124	A15f	15ch deep blue	.15	.15
125	A15f	20ch deep plum	.15	.15
		Set value	.55	.55

Issued: 5ch-20ch, Feb. 22. 2ch-4ch, Apr. 1972.

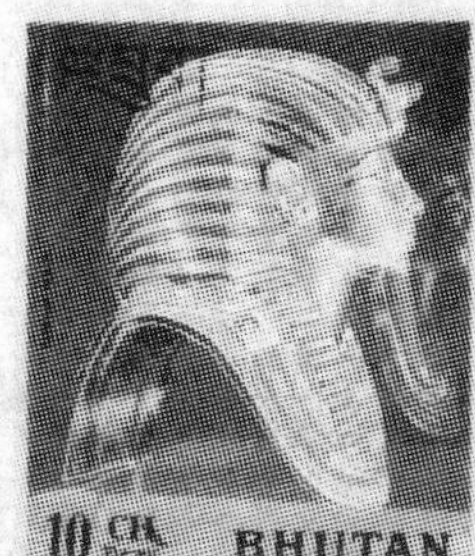
Funeral Mask of King Tutankhamen — A15g

History of Sculpture: 75ch, Winged Bull. 1.25nu, Head of Zeus. 2nu, She-wolf Suckling Romulus and Remus, horiz. 3nu, Head of Cicero. 4nu, Head of David, by Michaelangelo. 5nu, Age of Bronze, by Rodin. 6nu, Head of Woman, by Modigliani.

1971, Feb. 27 Litho. *Imperf.*
Self-adhesive

126	A15g	10ch multicolored	.15	.15
126A	A15g	75ch multicolored	.35	.35
126B	A15g	1.25nu multicolored	.60	.60
126C	A15g	2nu multicolored	1.00	1.00
h.		Souv. sheet of 4, #126-126C	2.50	2.50
126D	A15g	3nu multicolored	.80	.80
126E	A15g	4nu multicolored	1.10	1.10
126F	A15g	5nu multicolored	1.40	1.40
126G	A15g	6nu multicolored	1.65	1.65
i.		Souv. sheet of 4, #126D-126G	5.50	5.50
		Nos. 126-126G (8)	7.05	7.05

Stamps are plastic heat molded into three dimensions. Nos. 126D-126G are airmail.

Conquest of Space Type of 1970

Designs: 10ch, 2.50nu, Lunokhod 1. 1.70nu, 4nu, Apollo 15.

1971, Mar. 20 Litho. *Imperf.*

127	A15e	10ch multicolored	.15	.15
127A	A15e	1.70nu multicolored	1.00	1.00
127B	A15e	2.50nu multicolored	1.50	1.50
127C	A15e	4nu multicolored	2.25	2.25
d.		Souv. sheet of 4, #127-127C	5.00	5.00
		Nos. 127-127C (4)	4.90	4.90

Nos. 127B-127C are airmail. Simulated 3-dimensions using a plastic overlay.

Antique Automobiles — A15h

1971 Litho. *Imperf.*

128	A15h	2ch Mercedes Benz, Germany	.15	.15
128A	A15h	5ch Ford, US	.15	.15
128B	A15h	10ch Alfa Romeo, Italy	.15	.15
128C	A15h	15ch Cord, US	.15	.15
128D	A15h	20ch Hispano Suiza, Spain	.15	.15
128E	A15h	30ch Invicta, Britain	.15	.15
128F	A15h	60ch Renault, France	.20	.20
128G	A15h	75ch Talbot, Britain	.25	.25
128H	A15h	85ch Mercer, US	.30	.30
128I	A15h	1nu Sunbeam, Britain	.35	.35
128J	A15h	1.20nu Austrian Daimler	.42	.42
128K	A15h	1.55nu Bugatti, Italy	.55	.55
128L	A15h	1.80nu Simplex, US	.60	.60
128M	A15h	2nu Amilcar, France	.65	.65
128N	A15h	2.50nu Bentley, Britain	.85	.85
128O	A15h	4nu Morris Garage, Britain	.85	.85
128P	A15h	6nu Duesenberg, US	1.10	1.10
128Q	A15h	7nu Aston Martin, Britain	1.25	1.25
128R	A15h	9nu Packard, US	1.65	1.65
128S	A15h	10nu Rolls Royce, Britain	1.75	1.75
		Nos. 128-128S (20)	11.67	11.67

Issue dates: Nos. 128-128F, May 20. Nos. 128G-128N, June 10. Nos. 128O-128S, July 5. Nos. 128O-128S are airmail. Simulated 3-dimensions using a plastic overlay.

"Romeo" misspelled.

Stamps of 1964-71 Surcharged

1971, July 1

129	A14s	55ch on 60ch, #102D	.75	.75
129A	A5	55ch on 1.30nu, #22	.38	.38
129B	A11	55ch on 3nu, #65	.38	.38
129C	A14j	55ch on 4nu, #94L	.38	.38
129D	A14i	55ch on 5nu, #92G	.38	.38
129E	A14n	90ch on 1.05nu, #97D	1.90	1.90
129F	A15e	90ch on 1.70nu, #127A	4.25	4.25
129G	A5	90ch on 2nu, #23	.38	.38
129H	A14p	90ch on 2nu, #99J	.75	.75
129I	A15c	90ch on 2.50nu, #88	1.10	1.10
129J	A11	90ch on 4nu, #66	.75	.75
129K	A14d	90ch on 4nu, #86E	1.90	1.90
129L	A14i	90ch on 9nu, #92I	.75	.75
		Nos. 129-129L (13)	14.05	14.05

No. 129C is airmail. No. 129F comes with lines 8mm or 18mm long.

UN Emblem and Bhutan Flag A16

Designs (Bhutan Flag and): 10ch, UN Headquarters, NY. 20ch, Security Council Chamber and mural by Per Krohg. 3nu, General Assembly Hall.

1971, Sept. 21 Photo. *Perf. 13½*

130	A16	5ch gold, bl & multi	.15	.15
131	A16	10ch gold & multi	.15	.15
132	A16	20ch gold & multi	.15	.15
133	A16	3nu gold & multi	.45	.45
		Set value, Nos. 130-133, C21-C23	2.50	2.50

Bhutan's admission to the United Nations. Exist imperf.

For overprints see Nos. 140-143. For surcharge see No. 252.

Boy Scout Crossing Stream in Rope Sling — A17

Designs (Emblem and Boy Scouts): 20ch, 2nu, mountaineering. 50ch, 6nu, reading map. 75ch, as 10ch.

1971, Nov. 30 Litho. *Perf. 13½*

134	A17	10ch gold & multi	.15	.15
135	A17	20ch gold & multi	.15	.15
136	A17	50ch gold & multi	.15	.15
137	A17	75ch silver & multi	.16	.16
138	A17	2nu silver & multi	.40	.40
139	A17	6nu silver & multi	1.00	1.00
a.		Souv. sheet of 2, #138-139 + 2 labels	2.00	2.00
		Nos. 134-139 (6)	2.01	2.01

60th anniv. of the Boy Scouts. Exist imperf.

For overprint and surcharge see #253, 383.

Nos. 130-133 Overprinted in Gold

UNHCR
UNRWA
1971

1971, Dec. 23

140	A16	5ch gold & multi	.15	.15
141	A16	10ch gold & multi	.15	.15
142	A16	20ch gold & multi	.15	.15
143	A16	3nu gold & multi	.65	.65
		Nos. 140-143,C24-C26 (7)	4.15	4.15

World Refugee Year. Exist imperf.

The Bathing Girl by Renoir A17a

Designs: 20ch, A Bar at the Follies, by Monet, horiz. 90ch, Mona Lisa, by da Vinci. 1.70nu, Cart of Father Junier, by Rousseau, horiz. 2.50nu, The Gleaners, by Millet, horiz. 4.60nu, White Horse, by Gaugin. 5.40nu, The Dancing Lesson, by Degas. 6nu, After the Rain, by Gaillauman, horiz.

1972 Litho. & Embossed *Imperf.*

144	A17a	15ch multicolored	.15	.15
144A	A17a	20ch multicolored	.15	.15
144B	A17a	90ch multicolored	.35	.35
144C	A17a	1.70nu multicolored	.52	.52
144D	A17a	2.50nu multicolored	1.00	1.00
h.		Souv. sheet of 4, #144-144B, 144D	3.50	3.50
144E	A17a	4.60nu multicolored	1.40	1.40
144F	A17a	5.40nu multicolored	1.65	1.65
144G	A17a	6nu multicolored	1.90	1.90
i.		Souv. sheet of 4, #144C, 144E-144G	6.00	6.00
		Nos. 144-144G (8)	7.12	7.12

Issued: #144-144B, 144D, 1/29; others, 2/28.
Nos. 144C, 144E-144G are airmail.

Set Values
A 15-cent minimum now applies to individual stamps and sets. Where the 15-cent minimum per stamp would increase the value of a set beyond retail, there is a "Set Value" notation giving the retail value of the set.

Famous Men A17b

1972, Apr. 17 Litho. *Imperf.*

Self-adhesive

No.	Type	Denomination / Description	Unused	Used
145	A17b	10ch John F. Kennedy	.15	.15
145A	A17b	15ch Gandhi	.15	.15
145B	A17b	55ch Churchill	.45	.45
145C	A17b	2nu De Gaulle	.50	.50
145D	A17b	6nu Pope John XVIII	1.50	1.50
145E	A17b	8nu Eisenhower	2.00	2.00
f.		Souv. sheet of 4, #145B-145E	5.00	5.00
		Nos. 145-145E (6)	4.75	4.75

Nos. 145C-145E are airmail. Stamps are plastic heat molded into three dimensions.

Book Year Emblem A17c

1972, May 15 Photo. *Perf. 13½x13*

No.	Type	Denomination / Description	Unused	Used
146	A17c	2ch multicolored	.15	.15
146A	A17c	3ch multicolored	.15	.15
146B	A17c	5ch multicolored	.15	.15
146C	A17c	20ch multicolored	.15	.15
		Set value	.26	.26

International Book Year.

1972 Summer Olympics, Munich A17d

1972, June 6 Photo. *Perf. 13½*

No.	Type	Denomination / Description	Unused	Used
147	A17d	10ch Handball	.15	.15
147A	A17d	15ch Archery	.15	.15
147B	A17d	20ch Boxing	.15	.15
147C	A17d	30ch Discus	.15	.15
147D	A17d	35ch Javelin	.15	.15
147E	A17d	45ch Shooting	.15	.15
147F	A17d	1.35nu like #147A	.38	.38
147G	A17d	7nu like #147	1.90	1.90
h.		Souv. sheet of 3, #147D, 147F-147G	3.00	3.00
		Set value	2.75	2.75

Nos. 147D, 147F-147G are airmail and have a gold border.

Exist imperf.

For overprint see No. 384.

Apollo 11 Type of 1969

Apollo 16: 15ch, Lift-off, vert. 20ch, Achieving lunar orbit. 90ch, Astronauts Young, Mattingly, Duke, vert. 1.70nu, Lunar module. 2.50nu, Walking on moon. 4.60nu, Gathering rock samples. 5.40nu, Apollo 16 on launch pad, vert. 6nu, Looking at earth, vert.

1972, Sept. 1 Litho. *Imperf.*

No.	Type	Denomination / Description	Unused	Used
148	A15a	15ch multicolored	.15	.15
148A	A15a	20ch multicolored	.15	.15
148B	A15a	90ch multicolored	.18	.18
148C	A15a	1.70nu multicolored	.35	.35
148D	A15a	2.50nu multicolored	.50	.50
h.		Souv. sheet of 4, #148-148B, 148D	3.00	3.00
148E	A15a	4.60nu multicolored	.90	.90
148F	A15a	5.40nu multicolored	1.10	1.10
148G	A15a	6nu multicolored	1.20	1.20
i.		Souv. sheet of 4, #148C, 148E-148G	5.00	5.00
		Nos. 148-148G (8)	4.53	4.53

Nos. 148C, 148E-148G are airmail. Simulated 3-dimensions using a plastic overlay.

Dogs A17f

1972-73 Photo. *Perf. 13½*

No.	Type	Denomination / Description	Unused	Used
149	A17f	2ch Pointer	.15	.15
149A	A17f	3ch Irish Setter	.15	.15
149B	A17f	5ch Lhasa Apso, vert	.15	.15
149C	A17f	10ch Dochi	.15	.15
149D	A17f	15ch Damci	.15	.15
149E	A17f	15ch Collie	.15	.15
149F	A17f	20ch Basset hound	.15	.15
149G	A17f	25ch Damci, diff	.15	.15
149H	A17f	30ch Fox terrier	.15	.15
149I	A17f	55ch Lhasa Apso, diff.	.15	.15
149J	A17f	99ch Boxer	.22	.22
149K	A17f	2.50nu St. Bernard	.55	.55
149L	A17f	4nu Cocker Spaniel	.90	.90
o.		Souv. sheet of 3, #149J-149L, perf. 14	3.00	3.00
149M	A17f	8nu Damci, diff.	1.90	1.90
p.		Souv. sheet of 2, #149I, 149M, perf. 14	3.25	3.25
		Set value	4.00	4.00

Souvenir Sheet

Perf. 14

No.	Type	Denomination / Description	Unused	Used
149N	A17f	18nu Poodle	5.00	5.00

Issue dates: Nos. 149B-149D, 149G, 149I, 149M, 149p, Oct. 5. Nos. 149-149A, 149E-149F, 149H, 149J-149L, 149o, Jan. 1, 1973. No. 149N, Jan. 15, 1973. No. 149N is airmail. All exist imperf.

For surcharges & overprints see #268-269, 385.

Roses — A17g

1973, Jan. 30 Photo. *Perf. 13½*

Scented Paper

No.	Type	Denomination / Description	Unused	Used
150	A17g	15ch Wendy Cussons	.15	.15
150A	A17g	25ch Iceberg	.15	.15
150B	A17g	30ch Marchioness of Urquio	.15	.15
150C	A17g	3nu Pink parfait	.70	.70
150D	A17g	6nu Roslyn	1.40	1.40
150E	A17g	7nu Blue moon	1.65	1.65
f.		Souv. sheet of 2, #150D-150E	2.50	2.50
		Nos. 150-150E (6)	4.20	4.20

#150D-150E are airmail. Exist imperf.

Apollo 11 Type of 1969

Apollo 17: 10ch, Taking photographs on moon. 15ch, Setting up experiments. 55ch, Earth. 2nu, Driving lunar rover. 7nu, Satellite. 9nu, Astronauts Cernan, Evans, Schmitt.

1973, Feb. 28 Litho. *Imperf.*

Size: 50x49mm

No.	Type	Denomination / Description	Unused	Used
151	A15a	10ch multicolored	.15	.15
151A	A15a	15ch multicolored	.15	.15
151B	A15a	55ch multicolored	.20	.20
151C	A15a	2nu multicolored	.70	.70
f.		Souv. sheet of 4, #151-151C	2.50	2.50
151D	A15a	7nu multicolored	2.25	2.25
151E	A15a	9nu multicolored	3.25	3.25
g.		Souv. sheet of 2, #151D-151E	10.00	10.00
		Nos. 151-151E (6)	6.70	6.70

Simulated 3-dimensions using a plastic overlay. Nos. 151D-151E are airmail. No. 151g is circular, 160mm in diameter.

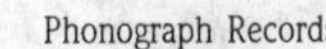

Phonograph Records

A17h

Recordings: 10ch, Bhutanese History. 25ch, Royal Bhutan Anthem. 1.25nu, Bhutanese History (English). 3nu, Bhutanese History (Bhutanese), Folk Song #1. 7nu, Folk Song #1. 8nu, Folk Song #2. 9nu, History in English, Folk Songs #1 & 2.

1973, Apr. 15

Self-adhesive

Diameter: #152-152B, 152D-152E, 69mm, #152C, 152F, 100mm

No.	Type	Denomination / Description	Unused	Used
152	A17h	10ch yel on red	*.45*	*.45*
152A	A17h	25ch gold on grn	*.65*	*.65*
152B	A17h	1.25nu sil on bl	*3.25*	*3.25*
152C	A17h	3nu sil on pur	*7.50*	*7.50*
152D	A17h	7nu sil on blk	*18.00*	*18.00*
152E	A17h	8nu red on white	*21.00*	*21.00*
152F	A17h	9nu blk on yel	*24.00*	*24.00*
		Nos. 152-152F (7)	*74.85*	*74.85*

Nos. 152C, 152F are airmail.

King Jigme Dorji Wangchuk (d. 1972) — A17i

Embossed on Gold Foil

1973, May 2 Die Cut *Imperf.*

No.	Type	Denomination / Description	Unused	Used
153	A17i	10ch orange	.15	.15
153A	A17i	25ch red	.15	.15
153B	A17i	3nu green	.70	.70
153C	A17i	6nu blue	1.40	1.40
153D	A17i	8nu purple	1.90	1.90
e.		Souv. sheet of 2, #153C-153D	2.75	2.75
		Nos. 153-153D (5)	4.30	4.30

Nos. 153C-153D are airmail.

Mushrooms — A17j

Different mushrooms.

1973, Sept. 25 Litho. *Imperf.*

No.	Type	Denomination / Description	Unused	Used
154	A17j	15ch multicolored	*.15*	*.15*
154A	A17j	25ch multicolored	*.20*	*.20*
154B	A17j	30ch multicolored	*.24*	*.24*
154C	A17j	3nu multicolored	*2.50*	*2.50*
f.		Souvenir sheet of 4, #154-154C	*15.00*	*15.00*
154D	A17j	6nu multicolored	*5.75*	*5.75*
154E	A17j	7nu multicolored	*6.75*	*6.75*
g.		Souvenir sheet of 2, #154D-154E	*35.00*	*35.00*
		Nos. 154-154E (6)	15.59	15.59

Simulated 3-dimensions using a plastic overlay. Nos. 154D-154E are airmail.

Bhutanese Mail Service — A17k

Designs: 5ch, 6nu, Letter carrier at mail box. 10ch, 5nu, Postmaster, letter carrier. 15ch, Sacking mail. 25ch, Mailtruck. 1.25nu, Sorting mail. 3nu, Hand-delivered mail.

1973, Nov. 14 Photo. *Perf. 13½*

No.	Type	Denomination / Description	Unused	Used
155	A17k	5ch multicolored	.15	.15
155A	A17k	10ch multicolored	.15	.15
155B	A17k	15ch multicolored	.15	.15
155C	A17k	25ch multicolored	.15	.15
155D	A17k	1.25nu multicolored	.28	.28
155E	A17k	3nu multicolored	.65	.65
155F	A17k	5nu multicolored	1.10	1.10
155G	A17k	6nu multicolored	1.25	1.25
h.		Souv. sheet of 2, #155F-155G	6.00	6.00
		Nos. 155-155G (8)	3.88	3.88

Indipex '73. Nos. 155F-155G are airmail. All exist imperf.

For surcharges and overprint see Nos. 267, 382, C37-C38.

A set of 15 stamps plus souvenir sheet of 3 showing paintings with reading and writing themes was not authorized.

King Jigme Singye Wangchuk and Royal Crest — A18

Designs (King and): 25ch, 90ch, Flag of Bhutan. 1.25nu, Wheel with 8 good luck signs. 2nu, 4nu, Punakha Dzong, former winter capital. 3nu, 5nu, Crown. 5ch, same as 10ch.

1974, June 2 Litho. *Perf. 13½*

No.	Type	Denomination / Description	Unused	Used
157	A18	10ch maroon & multi	.15	.15
158	A18	25ch gold & multi	.15	.15
159	A18	1.25nu multi	.35	.35
160	A18	2nu gold & multi	.55	.55
161	A18	3nu multi	.75	.75
		Nos. 157-161 (5)	1.95	1.95

Souvenir Sheets

Perf. 13½, Imperf.

No.	Type	Denomination / Description	Unused	Used
162		Sheet of 2	2.75	2.75
a.		A18 5ch maroon & multi	.15	
b.		A18 5nu red orange & multi	2.50	
163		Sheet of 2	2.75	2.75
a.		A18 90ch gold & multi	.75	
b.		A18 4nu gold & multi	2.00	

Coronation of King Jigme Singye Wangchuk, June 2, 1974.

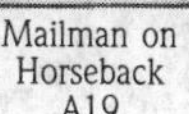

Mailman on Horseback A19

Old and New Locomotives A20

Designs (UPU Emblem, Carrier Pigeon and): 3ch, Sailing and steam ships. 4ch, Old biplane and jet. 25ch, Mail runner and jeep.

1974, Oct. 9 Litho. *Perf. 14½*

164	A19	1ch grn & multi	.15	.15
165	A20	2ch lilac & multi	.15	.15
166	A20	3ch ocher & multi	.15	.15
167	A20	4ch yel grn & multi	.15	.15
168	A20	25ch salmon & multi	.15	.15
		Set value, #164-168, C27-C29	1.25	1.25

Centenary of Universal Postal Union. Issued in sheets of 50 and sheets of 5 plus label with multicolored margin. Exist imperf.

Family and WPY Emblem — A21

1974, Dec. 17 *Perf. 13½*

169 A21	25ch bl & multi	.15	.15
170 A21	50ch org & multi	.15	.15
171 A21	90ch ver & multi	.28	.28
172 A21	2.50nu brn & multi	.75	.75
a.	Souvenir sheet, 10nu	2.25	2.25
	Nos. 169-172 (4)	1.33	1.33

For surcharge see No. 254.

Sephisa Chandra A22

Designs: Indigenous butterflies.

1975, Sept. 15 Litho. *Perf. 14½*

173 A22	1ch *shown*	.15	.15
174 A22	2ch *Lethe kansa*	.15	.15
175 A22	3ch *Neope bhadra*	.15	.15
176 A22	4ch *Euthalia duda*	.15	.15
177 A22	5ch *Vindula erota*	.15	.15
178 A22	10ch *Bhutanitis Lidderdale*	.15	.15
179 A22	3nu *Limenitis zayla*	.60	.60
180 A22	5nu *Delis thysbe*	1.40	1.40
	Set value	2.25	2.25

Souvenir Sheet

Perf. 13

181 A22	10nu *Dabasa gyas*	2.50	2.50

For surcharges see Nos. 255-256.

Apollo and Apollo-Soyuz Emblem — A23

Design: No. 183, Soyuz and emblem.

1975, Dec. 1 Litho. *Perf. 14x13½*

182 A23	10nu multicolored	2.25	2.25
183 A23	10nu multicolored	2.25	2.25
a.	Souvenir sheet of 2, 15nu	7.00	7.00

Apollo Soyuz link-up in space, July 17. Nos. 182-183 printed se-tenant in sheets of 10. No. 183a contains two 15nu stamps similar to Nos 182-183. Exist imperf.

For surcharges see Nos. 257-258.

Jewelry A24

Designs: 2ch, Coffee pot, bell and sugar cup. 3ch, Container and drinking horn. 4ch, Pendants and box cover. 5ch, Painter. 15ch, Silversmith. 20ch, Wood carver with tools. 1.50nu, Mat maker. 5nu, 10nu, Printer.

1975, Dec. 17 *Perf. 14½*

184 A24	1ch multicolored	.15	.15
185 A24	2ch multicolored	.15	.15
186 A24	3ch multicolored	.15	.15
187 A24	4ch multicolored	.15	.15
188 A24	5ch multicolored	.15	.15
189 A24	15ch multicolored	.15	.15
190 A24	20ch multicolored	.15	.15
191 A24	1.50nu multicolored	.40	.40
192 A24	10nu multicolored	2.50	2.50
	Set value	3.20	3.20

Souvenir Sheet

Perf. 13

193 A24	5nu multicolored	1.40	1.40

Handicrafts and craftsmen.

For surcharges see No. 259, 381.

King Jigme Singye Wangchuk A25

Designs: 25ch, 90ch, 1nu, 2nu, 4nu, like 15ch. 1.30nu, 3nu, 5nu, Coat of arms. Sizes (Diameter): 15ch, 1nu, 1.30nu, 38mm. 25ch, 2nu, 3nu, 49mm. 90ch, 4nu, 5nu, 63mm.

Lithographed, Embossed on Gold Foil

1975, Nov. 11 *Imperf.*

194 A25	15ch emerald	.15	.15
195 A25	25ch emerald	.15	.15
196 A25	90ch emerald	.35	.35
197 A25	1nu bright carmine	.40	.40
198 A25	1.30nu bright carmine	.45	.45
199 A25	2nu bright carmine	.65	.65
200 A25	3nu bright carmine	1.00	1.00
201 A25	4nu bright carmine	1.65	1.65
202 A25	5nu bright carmine	2.00	2.00
	Nos. 194-202 (9)	6.80	6.80

King Jigme Singye Wangchuk's 20th birthday.

Rhododendron Cinnabarinum — A28

Designs (Rhododendron): 2ch, Campanulatum. 3ch, Fortunei. 4ch, Red arboreum. 5ch, Pink arboreum. 1nu, Falconeri. 3nu, Hodgsonii. 5nu, Keysii. 10nu, Cinnabarinum.

1976, Feb. 15 Litho. *Perf. 15*

203 A28	1ch rose & multi	.15	.15
204 A28	2ch lt grn & multi	.15	.15
205 A28	3ch gray & multi	.15	.15
206 A28	4ch lil & multi	.15	.15
207 A28	5ch ol gray & multi	.15	.15
208 A28	1nu brn org & multi	.25	.20
209 A28	3nu ultra & multi	.75	.60
210 A28	5nu gray & multi	1.25	.90
	Set value	2.40	1.85

Souvenir Sheet

Perf. 13½

211 A28	10nu multicolored	2.50	2.50

For surcharge see No. 260.

Slalom and Olympic Games Emblem — A29

Designs (Olympic Games Emblem and): 2ch, 4-men bobsled. 3ch, Ice hockey. 4ch, Cross-country skiing. 5ch, Figure skating, women's. 2nu, Downhill skiing. 4nu, Speed skating. 6nu, Ski jump. 10nu, Figure skating, pairs.

1976, Mar. 29 Litho. *Perf. 13½*

212 A29	1ch multicolored	.15	.15
213 A29	2ch multicolored	.15	.15
214 A29	3ch multicolored	.15	.15
215 A29	4ch multicolored	.15	.15
216 A29	5ch multicolored	.15	.15
217 A29	2nu multicolored	.40	.35
218 A29	4nu multicolored	.90	.75
219 A29	10nu multicolored	2.50	1.75
	Nos. 212-219 (8)	4.55	
	Set value		3.00

Souvenir Sheet

220 A29	6nu multicolored	1.50	1.50

12th Winter Olympic Games, Innsbruck, Austria, Feb. 4-15.

For surcharges see Nos. 261-262.

Ceremonial Masks A29a

Various masks.

1976, Apr. 23 Litho. *Imperf.*

220A A29a	5ch multicolored	.15	.15
220B A29a	10ch multicolored	.15	.15
220C A29a	15ch multicolored	.15	.15
220D A29a	20ch multicolored	.15	.15
220E A29a	25ch multi, horiz.	.15	.15
220F A29a	30ch multi, horiz.	.15	.15
220G A29a	35ch multi, horiz.	.16	.16
220H A29a	1nu multi, horiz.	.45	.45
220I A29a	2nu multi, horiz.	.90	.90
220J A29a	2.50nu multi, horiz.	1.10	1.10
220K A29a	3nu multi, horiz.	1.40	1.40
	Nos. 220A-220K (11)	4.91	4.91

Souvenir Sheets

220L A29a	5nu like #220C	1.65	1.65
220M A29a	10nu like #220F	3.25	3.25

Simulated 3-dimensions using a plastic overlay. Nos. 220H-220M are airmail.

Sizes of stamps: No. 220L, 59x70mm, No. 220M, 69x57mm.

Orchid A30

Designs: Various flowers.

1976, May 29 Litho. *Perf. 14½*

221 A30	1ch multicolored	.15	.15
222 A30	2ch multicolored	.15	.15
223 A30	3ch multicolored	.15	.15
224 A30	4ch multicolored	.15	.15
225 A30	5ch multicolored	.15	.15
226 A30	2nu multicolored	.40	.30
227 A30	4nu multicolored	.80	.60
228 A30	6nu multicolored	1.25	1.00
	Set value	2.60	2.00

Souvenir Sheet

Perf. 13½

229 A30	10nu multicolored	2.75	2.50

For surcharges see Nos. 263-264.

Double Carp Design A31

Designs: Various symbolic designs and Colombo Plan emblem.

1976, July 1 Litho. *Perf. 14½*

230 A31	3ch red & multi	.15	.15
231 A31	4ch ver & multi	.15	.15
232 A31	5ch multicolored	.15	.15
233 A31	25ch bl & multi	.20	.15
234 A31	1.25nu multicolored	.38	.30
335 A31	2nu yel & multi	.60	.48
236 A31	2.50nu vio & multi	.75	.60
237 A31	3nu multicolored	.90	.72
	Nos. 230-237 (8)	3.28	2.70

Colombo Plan, 25th anniversary.

For surcharge see No. 265.

Bandaranaike Conference Hall — A32

1976, Aug. 16 Litho. *Perf. 13½*

238 A32	1.25nu multicolored	.35	.22
239 A32	2.50nu multicolored	.65	.45

5th Summit Conference of Non-aligned Countries, Colombo, Sri Lanka, Aug. 9-19.

Elizabeth II — A33

Liberty Bell — A34

Spirit of St. Louis — A35

Bhutanese Archer, Olympic Rings — A36

Designs: No. 242, Alexander Graham Bell. No. 245, LZ 3 Zeppelin docking, 1907. No. 246, Alfred B. Nobel.

1978, Nov. 15 Litho. *Perf. 14½*

240 A33	20nu multicolored	5.00	5.00
241 A34	20nu multicolored	5.00	5.00
242 A33	20nu multicolored	5.00	5.00
243 A35	20nu multicolored	5.00	5.00
244 A36	20nu multicolored	5.00	5.00
245 A35	20nu multicolored	5.00	5.00
246 A33	20nu multicolored	5.00	5.00
	Nos. 240-246 (7)	35.00	35.00

25th anniv. of coronation of Elizabeth II; American Bicentennial; cent. of 1st telephone call by Alexander Graham Bell; Charles A. Lindbergh crossing the Atlantic, 50th anniv.; Olympic Games; 75th anniv. of the Zeppelin; 75th anniv. of Nobel Prize. Seven souvenir sheets exist, each 25nu, commemorating same events with different designs. Size: 103x80mm.

Issues of 1967-1976 Surcharged with New Value and Bars

Perforations and Printing as Before

1978

252 A16 25ch on 3nu (#133)
253 A17 25ch on 6nu (#139)
254 A21 25ch on 2.50nu (#172)
255 A22 25ch on 3nu (#179)
256 A22 25ch on 5nu (#180)
257 A23 25ch on 10nu (#182)
258 A23 25ch on 10nu (#183)
259 A24 25ch on 10nu (#192)
260 A28 25ch on 5nu (#210)
261 A29 25ch on 4nu (#218)
262 A29 25ch on 10nu (#219)
263 A30 25ch on 4nu (#227)
264 A30 25ch on 6nu (#228)
265 A31 25ch on 2.50nu (#236)
266 A14g 25ch on 5nu (#90E)
267 A17k 25ch on 3nu (#155E)
268 A17f 25ch on 4nu (#149L)
269 A17f 25ch on 8nu (#149M)
Nos. 252-269, C31-C38 (26) *37.50 37.50*

Mother and Child, IYC Emblem — A37

IYC Emblem and: 5nu, Mother and two children. 10nu, Boys with blackboards and stylus.

1979, June Litho. *Perf. 14x13½*

289 A37 2nu multicolored .52 .40
290 A37 5nu multicolored 1.40 1.00
291 A37 10nu multicolored 2.50 2.00
a. Souv. sheet of 3, #289-291 + label, perf. 15x13½ 4.25 3.25
Nos. 289-291 (3) 4.42 3.40

International Year of the Child.
For overprints see Nos. 761-763.

Conference Emblem and Dove — A38

Design: 10nu, Emblem and Bhutanese symbols.

1979, Sept. 3 Litho. *Perf. 14x13½*

292 A38 25ch multicolored .15 .15
293 A38 10nu multicolored 3.25 2.50

6th Non-Aligned Summit Conference, Havana, August 1979.

Silver Rattle, Dorji A39

Antiques: 10ch, Silver handell, Dilbu, vert. 15ch, Cylindrical jar, Jadum, vert. 25ch, Ornamental teapot, Jamjee. 1nu, Leather container, Kem, vert. 1.25nu, Brass teapot, Jamjee. 1.70nu, Vessel with elephant-head legs, Sangphor, vert. 2nu, Teapot with ornamental spout, Jamjee, vert. 3nu, Metal pot on claw-shaped feet, Yangtho, vert. 4nu, Dish inlaid with precious stones, Battha. 5nu, Metal circular flask, Chhap, vert.

1979, Dec. 17 Photo. *Perf. 14*

294 A39 5ch multicolored .15 .15
295 A39 10ch multicolored .15 .15
296 A39 15ch multicolored .15 .15
297 A39 25ch multicolored .15 .15
298 A39 1nu multicolored .45 .38
299 A39 1.25nu multicolored .52 .52
300 A39 1.70nu multicolored .70 .70
301 A39 2nu multicolored .90 .75
302 A39 3nu multicolored 1.25 1.10
303 A39 4nu multicolored 1.65 1.50
304 A39 5nu multicolored 2.25 1.90
Nos. 294-304 (11) 8.32 7.45

Hill, Rinpiang Dzong — A40

Hill Statue, Stamps of Bhutan and: 2nu, Dzong. 5nu, Ounsti Dzong. 10nu, Lingzi Dzong, Gt. Britain Type 81. 20nu, Rope bridge, Penny Black.

1980, May 6 Litho. *Perf. 14x13½*

305 A40 1nu multicolored .30 .25
306 A40 2nu multicolored .60 .50
307 A40 5nu multicolored 1.60 1.25
308 A40 10nu multicolored 3.00 2.50
Nos. 305-308 (4) 5.50 4.50

Souvenir Sheet

309 A40 20nu multicolored 5.75 4.25

Sir Rowland Hill (1795-1879), originator of penny postage.

Kichu Lhakhang Monastery, Phari — A41

Guru Padma Sambhava's Birthday: Monasteries.

1981, July 11 Litho. *Perf. 14*

310 A41 1nu Dungtse, Phari, vert .32 .25
311 A41 2nu shown .65 .50
312 A41 2.25nu Kurjey .75 .55
313 A41 3nu Tangu, Thimphu 1.00 .75
314 A41 4nu Cheri, Thimphu 1.30 1.00
315 A41 5nu Chorten, Kora 1.65 1.25
316 A41 7nu Tak-Tsang, Phari, vert 2.30 1.75
Nos. 310-316 (7) 7.97 6.05

Prince Charles and Lady Diana — A42

Orange- bellied Chloropsis — A43

1981, Sept. 10 Litho. *Perf. 14½*

317 A42 1nu St. Paul's Cathedral .20 .15
318 A42 5nu like #317 1.00 .65
319 A42 20nu shown 4.00 2.50
320 A42 25nu like #319 4.50 3.50
Nos. 317-320 (4) 9.70 6.80

Souvenir Sheet

321 A42 20nu Wedding procession 5.00 4.00

Royal wedding. Nos. 318-319 issued in sheets of 5 plus label.
For surcharges see Nos. 471-475.

1982, Apr. 19 Litho. *Perf. 14*

322 A43 2nu shown .52 .40
323 A43 3nu Monal pheasant .80 .60
324 A43 5nu Ward's trogon 1.40 1.00
325 A43 10nu Mrs. Gould's sunbird 2.50 2.00
Nos. 322-325 (4) 5.22 4.00

Souvenir Sheet

326 A43 25nu Maroon oriole 7.00 5.00

1982 World Cup — A44

Designs: Various soccer players.

1982, June 25 Litho. *Perf. 14½x14*

327 A44 1nu multicolored .25 .20
328 A44 2nu multicolored .52 .40
329 A44 3nu multicolored .80 .60
330 A44 20nu multicolored 5.25 4.00
Nos. 327-330 (4) 6.82 5.20

Souvenir Sheets

331 A44 25nu multicolored 12.00 7.50

Nos. 331 have margins continuing design and listing finalists (Algeria, etc. or Hungary, etc.).
For surcharges see Nos. 481-485.

21st Birthday of Princess Diana — A45

1982, Aug.

332 A45 1nu St. James' Palace .25 .22
332A A45 10nu Diana, Charles 2.50 1.75
332B A45 15nu Windsor Castle 4.00 4.50
333 A45 25nu Wedding 6.50 4.50
Nos. 332-333 (4) 13.25 10.97

Souvenir Sheet

334 A45 20nu Diana 5.50 4.00

10nu-15nu issued only in sheets of 5 + label.
For overprints and surcharges see Nos. 361-363, 455-459, 476-480.

Scouting Year — A46

1982, Aug. 23 Litho. *Perf. 14*

335 A46 3nu Baden-Powell, vert. .65 .50
336 A46 5nu Eating around fire 1.10 .85
337 A46 15nu Reading map 3.50 2.50
338 A46 20nu Pitching tents 4.50 3.50
Nos. 335-338 (4) 9.75 7.35

Souvenir Sheet

339 A46 25nu Mountain climbing 6.00 4.50

For surcharges see Nos. 450-454.

Rama and Cubs with Mowgli — A47

Designs: Scenes from Walt Disney's The Jungle Book.

1982, Sept. 1 *Perf. 11*

340 A47 1ch multicolored .15 .15
341 A47 2ch multicolored .15 .15
342 A47 3ch multicolored .15 .15
343 A47 4ch multicolored .15 .15
344 A47 5ch multicolored .15 .15
345 A47 10ch multicolored .15 .15
346 A47 30ch multicolored .15 .15
347 A47 2nu multicolored .50 .40
348 A47 20nu multicolored 5.50 4.25
Nos. 340-348 (9) 7.05
Set value 5.00

Souvenir Sheets

Perf. 13½

349 A47 20nu Baloo and Mowgli in forest 5.25 4.00
350 A47 20nu Baloo and Mowgli floating 5.25 4.00

George Washington Surveying A48

1982, Nov. 15 Litho. *Perf. 15*

351 A48 50ch shown .15 .15
352 A48 1nu FDR, Harvard .16 .15
353 A48 2nu Washington at Valley Forge .32 .25
354 A48 3nu FDR, family .50 .38
355 A48 4nu Washington, Battle of Monmouth .65 .50
356 A48 5nu FDR, White House .85 .65
357 A48 15nu Washington, Mt. Vernon 2.50 2.00
358 A48 20nu FDR, Churchill, Stalin 3.25 2.50
Nos. 351-358 (8) 8.38 6.58

Souvenir Sheets

359 A48 25nu Washington, vert. 4.25 3.25
360 A48 25nu FDR, vert. 4.25 3.25

Washington and Franklin D. Roosevelt.

Nos. 332-334 Overprinted: "ROYAL BABY / 21.6.82"

1982, Nov. 19 *Perf. 14½x14*

361 A45 1nu multicolored .25 .25
361A A45 10nu multicolored 2.50 1.75
361B A45 15nu multicolored 3.75 3.00
362 A45 25nu multicolored 6.25 4.75
Nos. 361-362 (4) 12.75 9.75

Souvenir Sheet

363 A45 20nu multicolored 5.25 4.25

Birth of Prince William of Wales, June 21.

500th Birth Anniv. of Raphael — A51

Portraits.

1983, Mar. 23 *Perf. 13½*

375 A51 1nu Angelo Doni .25 .18
376 A51 4nu Maddalena Doni 1.00 .75
377 A51 5nu Baldassare Castiglione 1.25 .90
378 A51 20nu La Donna Velata 5.00 3.75
Nos. 375-378 (4) 7.50 5.58

Souvenir Sheets

379 A51 25nu Expulsion of Heliodorus 6.25 4.75
380 A51 25nu Mass of Bolsena 6.25 4.75

Nos. 184, 155F, 139, 184, 147G, 149M Surchd. or Ovptd.: "Druk Air"

1983, Feb. 11

381 A24 30ch on 1ch multi .15 .15
382 A17k 5nu multicolored 1.25 .85
383 A17 6nu multicolored 1.50 1.00
384 A17d 7nu multicolored 1.75 1.10
385 A17f 8nu multicolored 1.75 1.40
Nos. 381-385 (5) 6.40 4.50

Druk Air Service inauguration. Overprint of 8nu all caps. Nos. 382, 384 air mail.

Manned Flight Bicentenary A52

1983, Aug. 15 Litho. *Perf. 15*

386 A52 50ch Dornier Wal .15 .15
387 A52 3nu Savoia-Marchetti S-66 .75 .55
388 A52 10nu Hawker Osprey 2.50 1.75
389 A52 20nu Ville de Paris 5.00 3.75
Nos. 386-389 (4) 8.40 6.20

Souvenir Sheet

390 A52 25nu Balloon Captif 5.00 3.75

Buddhist Symbols — A53

1983, Aug. 11 Litho. *Perf. 13½*

391 A53 25ch Sacred vase .15 .15
392 A53 50ch Five Sensory Symbols .15 .15
393 A53 2nu Seven Treasures .38 .30
394 A53 3nu Five Sensory Organs .60 .45
395 A53 8nu Five Fleshes 1.50 1.10
396 A53 9nu Sacrificial cake 1.75 1.25
a. Souv. sheet of 6, #391-396 4.50 3.50
Nos. 391-396 (6) 4.53 3.40

Size of Nos. 393, 396: 45x40mm.

World Communications Year (1983) — A54

Various Disney characters and history of communications.

1984, Apr. 10 Litho. *Perf. 14½x14*

397 A54 4ch multicolored .15 .15
398 A54 5ch multicolored .15 .15
399 A54 10ch multicolored .15 .15
400 A54 20ch multicolored .15 .15
401 A54 25ch multicolored .15 .15
402 A54 50ch multicolored .16 .15
403 A54 1nu multicolored .32 .25
404 A54 5nu multicolored 1.10 .95
405 A54 20nu multicolored 4.25 3.75
Nos. 397-405 (9) 6.58 5.85

Souvenir Sheets

Perf. 14x14½

406 A54 20nu Donald Duck on phone, horiz. 4.75 4.00
407 A54 20nu Mickey Mouse on TV 4.75 4.00

1984 Winter Olympics — A55

1984, June 16 *Perf. 14*

408 A55 50ch Skiing .15 .15
409 A55 1nu Cross-country skiing .25 .20
410 A55 3nu Speed skating .60 .45
411 A55 20nu Bobsledding 3.75 3.00
Nos. 408-411 (4) 4.75 3.80

Souvenir Sheet

412 A55 25nu Hockey 5.00 3.25

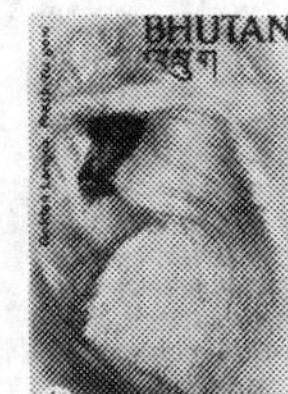

Golden Langur
A56

Locomotives
A57

1984, June 10 Litho. *Perf. 14½*

413 A56 50ch shown .15 .15
414 A56 1nu Group in tree, horiz. .20 .15
415 A56 2nu Family, horiz. .40 .30
416 A56 4nu Group walking .80 .60
Nos. 413-416 (4) 1.55 1.20

Souvenir Sheets

417 A56 20nu Snow leopard 3.00 2.00
418 A56 25nu Yak 3.00 2.00
419 A56 25nu Blue sheep, horiz. 3.00 2.00

1984, July 16

420 A57 50ch Sans Pareil, 1829 .15 .15
421 A57 1nu Planet, 1830 .20 .15
422 A57 3nu Experiment, 1832 .60 .45
423 A57 4nu Black Hawk, 1835 .80 .60
424 A57 5.50nu Jenny Lind, 1847 1.10 .85
425 A57 8nu Semmering-Bavaria, 1851 1.60 1.25
426 A57 10nu Great Northern #1, 1870 2.00 1.50
427 A57 25nu German Natl. Tinder, 1880 5.00 3.75
Nos. 420-427 (8) 11.45 8.70

Souvenir Sheets

428 A57 20nu Darjeeling Himalayan Railway, 1984 4.00 3.00
429 A57 20nu Sondermann Freight, 1896 4.00 3.00
430 A57 20nu Crampton's locomotive, 1846 4.00 3.00
431 A57 20nu Erzsebet, 1870 4.00 3.00

Nos. 424-427 horiz.

Classic Cars
A58

1984, Aug. 29 Litho. *Perf. 14*

432 A58 50ch Riley Sprite, 1936 .15 .15
433 A58 1nu Lanchester, 1919 .20 .15
434 A58 3nu Itala, 1907 .65 .45
435 A58 4nu Morris Oxford Bullnose, 1913 .90 .60
436 A58 5.50nu Lagonda LG6, 1939 1.25 .85
437 A58 6nu Wolseley, 1903 1.40 .90
438 A58 8nu Buick Super, 1952 1.75 1.20
439 A58 20nu Maybach Zeppelin, 1933 4.50 3.00
Nos. 432-439 (8) 10.80 7.30

Souvenir Sheets

440 A58 25nu Simplex, 1912 2.50 1.50
441 A58 25nu Renault, 1901 2.50 1.50

For surcharges see Nos. 537-544.

Summer Olympic Games — A59

1984, Oct. 27 Litho.

442 A59 15ch Women's archery .15 .15
443 A59 25ch Men's archery .15 .15
444 A59 2nu Table tennis .40 .30
445 A59 2.25nu Basketball .45 .35
446 A59 5.50nu Boxing 1.10 .85
447 A59 6nu Running 1.20 .90
448 A59 8nu Tennis 1.60 1.20
Nos. 442-448 (7) 5.05 3.90

Souvenir Sheet

449 A59 25nu Archery 5.00 3.50

For overprints see Nos. 537-544.

Nos. 335-339 Surcharged with New Values and Bars in Black or Silver

1985 Litho. *Perf. 14*

450 A46 10nu on 3nu multi 2.00 1.50
451 A46 10nu on 5nu multi 2.00 1.50
452 A46 10nu on 15nu multi 2.00 1.50
453 A46 10nu on 20nu multi 2.00 1.50
Nos. 450-453 (4) 8.00 6.00

Souvenir Sheet

454 A46 20nu on 25nu multi 4.00 3.00

Nos. 332, 332A, 332B, 333-334 Surcharged with New Values and Bars

1985, Feb. 28

455 A45 5nu on 1nu multi 1.00 .68
456 A45 5nu on 10nu multi 1.00 .68
457 A45 5nu on 15nu multi 1.00 .68
458 A45 40nu on 25nu multi 8.00 5.25
Nos. 455-458 (4) 11.00 7.29

Souvenir Sheet

459 A45 25nu on 20nu multi 5.00 4.00

50th Anniv. of Donald Duck — A60

1984, Dec. 10 Litho. *Perf. 13½x14*

460 A60 4ch Magician Mickey .15 .15
461 A60 5ch Slide, Donald, Slide .15 .15
462 A60 10ch Donald's Golf Game .15 .15
463 A60 20ch Mr. Duck Steps Out .15 .15
464 A60 25ch Lion Around .15 .15
465 A60 50ch Alpine Climbers .15 .15
466 A60 1nu Flying Jalopy .25 .15
467 A60 5nu Frank Duck 1.10 .75
468 A60 20nu Good Scouts 4.50 3.25
Nos. 460-468 (9) 6.75 5.05

Souvenir Sheets

469 A60 20nu Three Caballeros 4.50 3.25
470 A60 20nu Sea Scouts 4.50 3.25

Nos. 317-321 Surcharged with New Values and Bars

1985, Feb. 28 Litho. *Perf. 14½*

471 A42 10nu on 1nu multi 2.00 1.50
472 A42 10nu on 5nu multi 2.00 1.50
473 A42 10nu on 20nu multi 2.00 1.50
474 A42 10nu on 25nu multi 2.00 1.50
Nos. 471-474 (4) 8.00 6.00

Souvenir Sheet

475 A42 30nu on 20nu multi 6.00 5.00

Nos. 361, 361A, 361B, 362-363 Surcharged with New Values and Bars

1985, Feb. 28 *Perf. 14½x14*

476 A45 5nu on 1nu multi .75 .75
477 A45 5nu on 10nu multi .75 .55
478 A45 5nu on 15nu multi .75 .55
479 A45 40nu on 25nu multi 7.50 5.50
Nos. 476-479 (4) 9.75 7.35

Souvenir Sheet

480 A45 25nu on 20nu multi 5.00 3.75

Nos. 327-331 Surcharged with New Values and Bars in Black or Silver

1985, June

481 A44 5nu on 1nu multi 1.50 1.10
482 A44 5nu on 2nu multi 1.50 1.10
483 A44 5nu on 3nu multi 1.50 1.10
484 A44 5nu on 20nu multi 1.50 1.10
Nos. 481-484 (4) 6.00 4.40

Souvenir Sheets

485 A44 20nu on 25nu multi 7.50 5.50

Mask Dance of the Judgement of Death — A61

1985, Apr. 27 *Perf. 13½*

486 A61 5ch Shinje Choegyel .15 .15
487 A61 35ch Raksh Lango .15 .15
488 A61 50ch Druelgo .15 .15
489 A61 2.50nu Pago .45 .35
490 A61 3nu Telgo .55 .42
491 A61 4nu Due Nakcung .75 .58
492 A61 5nu Lha Karpo .90 .68
a. Souv. sheet of 4, #486-487, 491-492 1.90 1.50
493 A61 5.50nu Nyalbum 1.00 .75
494 A61 6nu Khimda Pelkyi 1.10 .85
Nos. 486-494 (9) 5.20 4.08

For overprints see Nos. 764-772.

Monasteries
A62

1984, Dec. 1 Litho. *Perf. 12*

495 A62 10ch Domkhar .15 .15
496 A62 25ch Shemgang .15 .15
497 A62 50ch Chapcha .15 .15
498 A62 1nu Tashigang .15 .15
499 A62 2nu Pungthang Chhug .28 .28
500 A62 5nu Dechhenphoda .70 .70
Set value 1.25 1.25

Veteran's War Memorial Building, San Francisco
A63

1985, Oct. 24 Litho. *Perf. 14*

502 A63 50ch Flags of Bhutan, UN, vert. .15 .15
503 A63 15nu Headquarters, NY, vert. 2.75 2.00
504 A63 20nu shown 3.75 2.75
Nos. 502-504 (3) 6.65 4.90

Souvenir Sheet

505 A63 25nu UN Human Rights Declaration 4.25 3.00

UN, 40th anniv.

Audubon Birth Bicentenary
A64

Illustrations of North American bird species by Audubon.

1985

506 A64 50ch Anas breweri .15 .15
507 A64 1nu Lagopus lagopus .18 .15
508 A64 2nu Charadrius montanus .35 .25
509 A64 3nu Cavia stellata .52 .40
510 A64 4nu Canachites canadensis .70 .52
511 A64 5nu Mergus cucullatus .85 .62
512 A64 15nu Olor buccinator 2.50 1.75
513 A64 20nu Bucephala clangula 3.50 2.50
Nos. 506-513 (8) 8.75 6.34

Souvenir Sheets

514 A64 25nu Accipiter striatus 3.75 2.25
515 A64 25nu Parus bicolor 3.75 2.25

Issue dates: Nos. 507, 510-511, 514 Nov. 15. Nos. 506, 508-509, 513, 515 Dec. 6.

A Tramp Abroad, by Mark Twain (1835-1910)
A65

Walt Disney animated characters.

1985, Nov. 15

516 A65 50ch multicolored .15 .15
517 A65 2nu multicolored .35 .25
518 A65 5nu multicolored .85 .62

519 A65 9nu multicolored 1.50 1.15
520 A65 20nu multicolored 3.50 2.50
Nos. 516-520 (5) 6.35 4.67

Souvenir Sheet

521 A65 25nu Goofy, Mickey Mouse 5.00 3.50

Intl. Youth Year.
For overprints see Nos. 554, 556-557.

Rapunzel, by Jacob and Wilhelm Grimm — A66

Walt Disney animated characters.

1985, Nov. 15

522 A66 1nu multicolored .18 .15
523 A66 4nu multicolored .70 .52
524 A66 7nu multicolored 1.25 .95
525 A66 8nu multicolored 1.40 1.05
526 A66 15nu multicolored 2.50 1.75
Nos. 522-526 (5) 6.03 4.42

Souvenir Sheet

527 A66 25nu multicolored 5.00 4.00

No. 525 printed in sheets of 8.
For overprints see Nos. 553, 555, 558.

First South Asian Regional Cooperation Summit, Dec. 7-8, Dacca, Bangladesh A67

1985, Dec. 8 *Perf. 14*

528 A67 50ch multicolored .15 .15
529 A67 5nu multicolored .85 .62

Seven Precious Attributes of the Universal King — A68

1986, Feb. 12 Litho. *Perf. 13x12½*

530 A68 30ch Wheel .15 .15
531 A68 50ch Gem .15 .15
532 A68 1.25nu Queen .18 .18
533 A68 2nu Minister .28 .28
534 A68 4nu Elephant .55 .55
535 A68 6nu Horse .85 .85
536 A68 8nu General 1.15 1.15
Nos. 530-536 (7) 3.31 3.31

Nos. 442-443, 445-449 Ovptd. with Medal, Winners' Names and Countries. No. 449 Ovptd. for Men's and Women's Events

1986, May 5 Litho. *Perf. 14*

537 A59 15ch Hyang Soon Seo, So. Korea .15 .15
538 A59 25ch Darrell Pace, US .15 .15
539 A59 2.25nu US .32 .32
540 A59 5.50nu Mark Breland, US .78 .78
541 A59 6nu Daley Thompson, Britain .85 .85
542 A59 8nu Stefan Edberg, Sweden 1.15 1.15
Nos. 537-542 (6) 3.40 3.40

Souvenir Sheets

543 A59 25nu Hyang Soon Seo 3.50 3.50
544 A59 25nu Darrel Pace 3.50 3.50

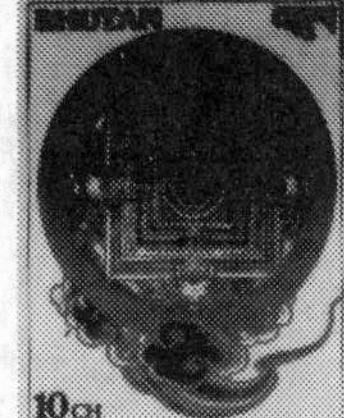

Kilkhor Mandalas, Deities — A69

Religious art: 10ch, 1nu, Phurpa, ritual dagger. 25ch, 3nu, Amitayus in wrath. 50ch, 5nu, Overpowering Deities. 75ch, 7nu, Great Wrathful One, Guru Rinpoche.

1986, June 17 *Perf. 13½*

545 A69 10ch multicolored .15 .15
546 A69 25ch multicolored .15 .15
547 A69 50ch multicolored .15 .15
548 A69 75ch multicolored .15 .15
549 A69 1nu multicolored .15 .15
550 A69 3nu multicolored .42 .42
551 A69 5nu multicolored .70 .70
552 A69 7nu multicolored 1.00 1.00
Nos. 545-552 (8) 2.87 2.87

Nos. 525, 519, 526, 520, 521 and 527 Ovptd. with AMERIPEX '86 Emblem

1986, June 16 Litho. *Perf. 14*

553 A66 8nu multi 1.40 1.05
554 A65 9nu multi 1.50 1.15
555 A66 15nu multi 2.50 1.75
556 A65 20nu multi 3.50 2.50
Nos. 553-556 (4) 8.90 6.45

Souvenir Sheets

557 A65 25nu #521 4.25 3.00
558 A66 25nu #527 4.25 3.00

A70

A71

Halley's Comet A72

Designs: 50ch, Babylonian tablet fragments, 2349 B.C. sighting. 1nu, 17th cent. print, A.D. 66 sighting. 2nu, French silhouette art, 1835 sighting. 3nu, Bayeux Tapestry, 1066 sighting. 4nu, Woodblock, 684 sighting. 5nu, Illustration from Bybel Printen, 1650. 15nu, 1456 Sighting, Cancer constellation. 20nu, Delft plate, 1910 sighting. No. 572, Comet over Himalayas. No. 573, Comet over domed temple Dug-gye Jong.

1986, Nov. 4 Litho. *Perf. 15*

564 A70 50ch multicolored .15 .15
565 A70 1nu multicolored .18 .15
566 A71 2nu multicolored .35 .28
567 A70 3nu multicolored .50 .35
568 A70 4nu multicolored .68 .52
569 A71 5nu multicolored .85 .65
570 A70 15nu multicolored 2.50 2.00
571 A70 20nu multicolored 3.50 2.50
Nos. 564-571 (8) 8.71 6.60

Souvenir Sheets

572 A72 25nu multicolored 4.25 3.00
573 A72 25nu multicolored 4.25 3.00

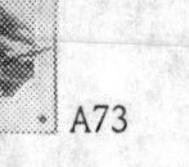

A73

Statue of Liberty, Cent. — A74

Statue and ships: 50ch, Mircea, Romania. 1nu, Shalom, Israel. 2nu, Leonardo da Vinci, Italy. 3nu, Libertad, Argentina. 4nu, France, France. 5nu, SS United States, US. 15nu, Queen Elizabeth II, England. 20nu, Europa, West Germany. No. 582, Statue. No. 583, Statue, World Trade Center.

1986, Nov. 4

574 A73 50ch multicolored .15 .15
575 A73 1nu multicolored .18 .15
576 A73 2nu multicolored .35 .28
577 A73 3nu multicolored .50 .35
578 A73 4nu multicolored .68 .52
579 A73 5nu multicolored .85 .65
580 A73 15nu multicolored 2.50 1.90
581 A73 20nu multicolored 3.40 2.50
Nos. 574-581 (8) 8.61 6.50

Souvenir Sheets

582 A74 25nu multicolored 4.25 3.00
583 A74 25nu multi, diff. 4.25 3.00

Discovery of America, 500th Anniv. A75

1987, May 25 Litho. *Perf. 14*

584 A75 20ch Santa Maria .15 .15
585 A75 25ch Queen Isabella .15 .15
586 A75 50ch Ship, flying fish .15 .15
587 A75 1nu Columbus's coat of arms .25 .18
588 A75 2nu Christopher Columbus .50 .38
589 A75 3nu Landing in the New World .75 .55
a. Miniature sheet of 6, #584-589 1.75 1.75
Nos. 584-589 (6) 1.95
Set value 1.30

Souvenir Sheets

590 A75 20ch Pineapple
591 A75 25ch Indian hammock
592 A75 50ch Tobacco plant
593 A75 1nu Flamingo
594 A75 2nu Navigator, astrolabe, 15th cent.
595 A75 3nu Lizard
596 A75 5nu Iguana 1.25 .95

All stamps are vertical except those contained in Nos. 591, 595 and 596. Stamps from No. 589a have white background.

CAPEX '87 — A76

Locomotives.

1987, June 15

597 A76 50ch Canadian Natl. U1-f .15 .15
598 A76 1nu Via Rail L.R.C. .18 .15
599 A76 2nu Canadian Natl. GM GF-30t .35 .28
600 A76 3nu Canadian Natl. 4-8-4 .50 .35
601 A76 8nu Canadian Pacific 4-6-2 1.35 1.00
602 A76 10nu Via Express passenger train 1.75 1.30
603 A76 15nu Canadian Nat. Turbotrain 2.50 1.90
604 A76 20nu Canadian Pacific Diesel-Electric Express 3.25 2.50
Nos. 597-604 (8) 10.03 7.63

Souvenir Sheet

605 A76 25nu Royal Hudson 4-6-4 4.25 3.00
606 A76 25nu Canadian Natl. 4-8-4, diff. 4.25 3.00

Two Faces, Sculpture by Marc Chagall (1887-1984) A77

Paintings: 1nu, At the Barber's. 2nu, Old Jew with Torah. 3nu, Red Maternity. 4nu, Eve of Yom Kippur. 5nu, The Old Musician. 6nu, The Rabbi of Vitebsk. 7nu, Couple at Dusk. 9nu, The Artistes. 10nu, Moses Breaking the Tablets of the Law. 12nu, Bouquet with Flying Lovers. 20nu, In the Sky of the Opera. No. 619, Romeo and Juliet. No. 620, Magician of Paris. No. 621, Maternity. No. 622, The Carnival for Aleko: Scene II. No. 623, Visit to the Grandparents. No. 624, The Smolensk Newspaper. No. 625, The Concert. No. 626, Composition with Goat. No. 627, Still Life. No. 628. The Red Gateway. No. 629, Cow with Parasol. No. 630, Russian Village.

1987, Dec. 17 Litho. *Perf. 14*

607 A77 50ch multicolored .15 .15
608 A77 1nu multicolored .16 .15
609 A77 2nu multicolored .32 .24
610 A77 3nu multicolored .48 .35
611 A77 4nu multicolored .65 .48
612 A77 5nu multicolored .80 .60
613 A77 6nu multicolored .95 .72
614 A77 7nu multicolored 1.15 .88
615 A77 9nu multicolored 1.45 1.10
616 A77 10nu multicolored 1.60 1.20
617 A77 12nu multicolored 1.90 1.45
618 A77 20nu multicolored 3.20 2.40

Size: 110x95mm

Imperf

619 A77 25nu multicolored 4.00 3.00
620 A77 25nu multicolored 4.00 3.00
621 A77 25nu multicolored 4.00 3.00
622 A77 25nu multicolored 4.00 3.00
623 A77 25nu multicolored 4.00 3.00
624 A77 25nu multicolored 4.00 3.00
625 A77 25nu multicolored 4.00 3.00
626 A77 25nu multicolored 4.00 3.00
627 A77 25nu multicolored 4.00 3.00
628 A77 25nu multicolored 4.00 3.00
629 A77 25nu multicolored 4.00 3.00
630 A77 25nu multicolored 4.00 3.00
Nos. 607-630 (24) 60.81 45.72

1988 Winter Olympics, Calgary — A78

Emblem and Disney animated characters as competitors in Olympic events.

1988, Feb. 15 Litho. *Perf. 14*

631 A78 50ch Slalom .15 .15
632 A78 1nu Downhill skiing .16 .15
633 A78 2nu Ice hockey .32 .24
634 A78 4nu Biathlon .65 .48
635 A78 7nu Speed skating 1.15 .85
636 A78 8nu Figure skating 1.30 .95
637 A78 9nu Figure skating, diff. 1.45 1.10
638 A78 20nu Bobsled 3.20 2.40
Nos. 631-638 (8) 8.38 6.32

Souvenir Sheets

639 A78 25nu Ski jumping 4.00 4.00
640 A78 25nu Ice dancing 4.00 4.00

Transportation Innovations — A79

1988, Mar. 31

641 A79 50ch Pullman Pioneer, 1865 .15 .15
642 A79 1nu Stephenson's Rocket, 1829 .16 .15
643 A79 2nu Pierre L'Allement's Velocipede, 1866 .32 .25

644 A79 3nu Benz Velocipede, 1886 .48 .35
645 A79 4nu Volkswagen Beetle, c. 1960 .65 .48
646 A79 5nu Natchez Vs. Robert E. Lee, 1870 .80 .60
647 A79 6nu American La France, 1910 1.00 .75
648 A79 7nu USS Constitution, 1787, vert. 1.15 .85
649 A79 9nu Bell Rocket Belt, 1961, vert. 1.45 1.10
650 A79 10nu Trevithick Locomotive, 1804 1.60 1.20
Nos. 641-650 (10) 7.76 5.88

Souvenir Sheets

651 A79 25nu Concorde jet 4.00 4.00
652 A79 25nu Mallard, 1938, vert. 4.00 4.00
653 A79 25nu Shinkansen 4.00 4.00
654 A79 25nu TGV, 1981 4.00 4.00

1988 Summer Olympics, Seoul A80

7nu-20nu vert.

1989, Feb. 15 **Litho.**

655 A80 50ch Women's gymnastics .15 .15
656 A80 1nu Tae kwon do .16 .15
657 A80 2nu Shot put .32 .24
658 A80 4nu Women's volleyball .65 .48
659 A80 7nu Basketball 1.15 .85
660 A80 8nu Soccer 1.30 .95
661 A80 9nu Women's high jump 1.45 1.10
662 A80 20nu Running 3.20 2.40
Nos. 655-662 (8) 8.38 6.32

Souvenir Sheets

663 A80 25nu Archery, vert. 4.00 4.00
664 A80 25nu Fencing 4.00 4.00

BHUTAN 50CH Paintings by Titian — A81

Designs: 50ch, *Gentleman with a Book.* 1nu, *Venus and Cupid, with a Lute Player.* 2nu, *Diana and Actaeon.* 3nu, *Cardinal Ippolito dei Medici.* 4nu, *Sleeping Venus.* 5nu, *Venus Risen from the Waves.* 6nu, *Worship of Venus.* 7nu, *Fete Champetre.* 10nu, *Perseus and Andromeda.* 15nu, *Danae.* 20nu, *Venus at the Mirror.* 25nu, *Venus and the Organ Player.* No. 677, *The Pardo Venus,* horiz. No. 678, *Venus and Cupid, with an Organist.* No. 679, *Miracle of the Irascible Son.* No. 680, *Diana and Callisto.* No. 681, *Saint John the Almsgiver.* No. 682, *Danae with the Shower of Gold,* horiz. No. 683, *Bacchus and Ariadne.* No. 684, *Venus Blindfolding Cupid.* No. 685, *Portrait of Laura Dianti.* No. 686, *Venus of Urbino.* No. 687, *Portrait of Johann Friedrich.* No. 688, *Mater Dolorosa with Raised Hands.*

Perf. 13½x14, 14x13½

1989, Feb. 15 **Litho.**

665 A81 50ch multicolored .15 .15
666 A81 1nu multicolored .16 .15
667 A81 2nu multicolored .32 .24
668 A81 3nu multicolored .48 .35
669 A81 4nu multicolored .65 .48
670 A81 5nu multicolored .80 .60
671 A81 6nu multicolored .95 .72
672 A81 7nu multicolored 1.15 .85
673 A81 10nu multicolored 1.60 1.20
674 A81 15nu multicolored 2.40 1.80
675 A81 20nu multicolored 3.20 2.40
676 A81 25nu multicolored 4.00 3.00
Nos. 665-676 (12) 15.86 11.94

Souvenir Sheets

677-688 A81 25nu each 4.00 4.00

Mickey Mouse, 60th Anniv. (in 1988) — A82

Movie posters.

1989, June 20 **Litho.** ***Perf. 13½x14***

689 A82 1ch Mickey Mouse, 1930s .15 .15
690 A82 2ch *Barnyard Olympics,* 1932 .15 .15
691 A82 3ch *Society Dog Show,* 1939 .15 .15
692 A82 4ch *Fantasia,* 1980s re-release .15 .15
693 A82 5ch *The Mad Dog,* 1932 .15 .15
694 A82 10ch *A Gentleman's Gentleman,* 1941 .15 .15
695 A82 50ch *Symphony hour,* 1942 .15 .15
696 A82 10nu *The Moose Hunt,* 1931 1.50 1.20
697 A82 15nu *Wild Waves,* 1929 2.25 1.80
698 A82 20nu *Mickey in Arabia,* 1932 3.00 2.40
699 A82 25nu *Tugboat Mickey,* 1940 3.75 3.00
700 A82 30nu *Building a Building,* 1933 4.25 3.50
Nos. 689-700 (12) 15.80 12.95

Souvenir Sheets

701 A82 25nu *The Mad Doctor,* 1933 4.00 4.00
702 A82 25nu *The Meller Drammer,* 1933 4.00 4.00
703 A82 25nu *Ye Olden Days,* 1933 4.00 4.00
704 A82 25nu *Mickey's Good Deed,* 1932 4.00 4.00
705 A82 25nu *Mickey's Pal Pluto,* 1933 4.00 4.00
706 A82 25nu *Trader Mickey,* 1932 4.00 4.00
707 A82 25nu *Touchdown Mickey,* 1932 4.00 4.00
708 A82 25nu *Steamboat Willie,* 1928 4.00 4.00
709 A82 25nu *The Whoopee Party,* 1932 4.00 4.00
710 A82 25nu *Mickey's Nightmare,* 1932 4.00 4.00
711 A82 25nu *The Klondike Kid,* 1932 4.00 4.00
712 A82 25nu *The Wayward Canary,* 1932 4.00 4.00

Mushrooms — A83

1989, Aug. 22 **Litho.** ***Perf. 14***

713 A83 50ch *Tricholoma pardalotum* .15 .15
714 A83 1nu *Suillus placidus* .16 .15
715 A83 2nu *Boletus regius* .32 .24
716 A83 3nu *Gomphidius glutinosus* .48 .35
717 A83 4nu *Boletus calopus* .65 .48
718 A83 5nu *Suillus grevillei* .80 .60
719 A83 6nu *Boletus appendiculatus* .95 .70
720 A83 7nu *Lactarius torminosus* 1.10 .82
721 A83 10nu *Macrolepiota rhacodes* 1.60 1.20
722 A83 15nu *Amanita rubescens* 2.40 1.80
723 A83 20nu *Amanita phalloides* 3.20 2.40
724 A83 25nu *Amanita citrina* 4.00 3.00
Nos. 713-724 (12) 15.81 11.89

Souvenir Sheets

725 A83 25nu *Russula aurata* 4.00 4.00
726 A83 25nu *Gyroporus castaneus* 4.00 4.00
727 A83 25nu *Cantharellus cibarius* 4.00 4.00
728 A83 25nu *Boletus rhodoxanthus* 4.00 4.00
729 A83 25nu *Paxillus involutus* 4.00 4.00
730 A83 25nu *Gyroporus cyanescens* 4.00 4.00
731 A83 25nu *Lepista nuda* 4.00 4.00
732 A83 25nu *Dentinum repandum* 4.00 4.00
733 A83 25nu *Lepista saeva* 4.00 4.00
734 A83 25nu *Hydnum imbricatum* 4.00 4.00
735 A83 25nu *Xerocomus subtomentosus* 4.00 4.00
736 A83 25nu *Russula olivacea* 4.00 4.00

Intl. Maritime Organization, 30th Anniv. — A84

Ships: 50ch, Spanish galleon *La Reale,* 1680. 1nu, Submersible *Turtle,* 1776. 2nu, *Charlote Dundas,* 1802. 3nu, *Great Eastern,* c. 1858. 4nu, HMS *Warrior,* 1862. 5nu, Mississippi steamer, 1884. 6nu, *Preussen,* 1902. 7nu, USS *Arizona,* 1915. 10nu, *Bluenose,* 1921. 15nu, Steam trawler, 1925. 20nu, American liberty ship, 1943. No. 748, S.S. *United States,* 1952. No. 749, Moran tug, c. 1950. No. 750, Sinking of the *Titanic,* 1912. No. 751, U-boat, c. 1942. No. 752, Japanese warship *Yamato,* 1944. No. 753, HMS *Dreadnought.* Not 754, S.S. *Normandie,* c. 1933, and a Chinese junk. No. 755, HMS *Victory,* 1805. No. 756, USS *Monitor,* 1862. No. 757, *Cutty Sark,* 1869. No. 758, USS *Constitution.* No. 759, HMS *Resolution.* No. 760, Chinese junk.

1989, Aug. 24 **Litho.** ***Perf. 14***

737 A84 50ch multicolored .15 .15
738 A84 1nu multicolored .16 .15
739 A84 2nu multicolored .32 .24
740 A84 3nu multicolored .48 .35
741 A84 4nu multicolored .65 .48
742 A84 5nu multicolored .80 .60
743 A84 6nu multicolored .95 .70
744 A84 7nu multicolored 1.10 .82
745 A84 10nu multicolored 1.60 1.20
746 A84 15nu multicolored 2.40 1.80
747 A84 20nu multicolored 3.20 2.40
748 A84 25nu multicolored 4.00 3.00
Nos. 737-748 (12) 15.81 11.89

Souvenir Sheets

749-760 A84 25nu each 4.00 4.00

Nos. 289-291 Overprinted: WORLD / AIDS DAY

1988, Dec. 1 **Litho.** ***Perf. 14x13½***

761 A37 2nu multicolored .45 .35
762 A37 5nu multicolored 1.15 .88
763 A37 10nu multicolored 2.25 1.70
Nos. 761-763 (3) 3.85 2.93

Nos. 486-494 Ovptd. in Silver: ASIA-PACIFIC EXPOSITION FUKUOKA '89

1989, Mar. 17 ***Perf. 13½***

764 A61 5ch multicolored .15 .15
765 A61 35ch multicolored .15 .15
766 A61 50ch multicolored .15 .15
767 A61 2.50nu multicolored .40 .30
768 A61 3nu multicolored .48 .35
769 A61 4nu multicolored .65 .50
770 A61 5nu multicolored .80 .60
771 A61 5.50nu multicolored .88 .65
772 A61 6nu multicolored 1.05 .80
Nos. 764-772 (9) 4.71 3.65

This set exists overprinted in Japanese.

Chhukha Hydroelectric Project — A85

1988, Oct. 21 **Litho.** ***Perf. 13½***

773 A85 50ch multicolored .15 .15

Jawaharlal Nehru (1889-1964), Indian Prime Minister — A85a

1989, Nov. 14 **Photo.** ***Perf. 14***

773A A85a 100ch olive brown .16 .16

Denomination is shown as 1.00ch in error.

Birds A86

Designs: 50ch, Larger goldenbacked woodpecker. 1nu, Black-naped monarch. 2nu, White-crested laughing thrush. 3nu, Blood-pheasant. 4nu, Blossom-headed parakeet. 5nu, Rosy minivet. 6nu, Chestnut-headed tit babbler. 7nu, Blue pitta. 10nu, Black-naped oriole. 15nu, Green magpie. 20nu, Indian three-toed kingfisher. No. 785, Ibisbill. No. 786, Great pied hornbill. No. 787, Himalayan red-breasted falconet. No. 788, Lammergeier. No. 789, Large racket-tailed drongo. No. 790, Fire-tailed sunbird. No. 791, Indian crested swift. No. 792, White-eared pheasant. No. 793, Satyr tragopan. No. 794, Wallcreeper. No. 795, Fairy bluebird. No. 796, Little spiderhunter. No. 797, Spotted forktail. Nos. 774-779 vert.

1989, Nov. 22 **Litho.** ***Perf. 14***

774 A86 50ch multicolored .15 .15
775 A86 1nu multicolored .16 .15
776 A86 2nu multicolored .32 .24
777 A86 3nu multicolored .48 .35
778 A86 4nu multicolored .65 .48
779 A86 5nu multicolored .80 .60
780 A86 6nu multicolored .95 .70
781 A86 7nu multicolored 1.10 .82
782 A86 10nu multicolored 1.60 1.20
783 A86 15nu multicolored 2.40 1.80
784 A86 20nu multicolored 3.20 2.40
785 A86 25nu multicolored 4.00 3.00
Nos. 774-785 (12) 15.81 11.89

Souvenir Sheets

786-797 A86 25nu each 4.00 4.00

Steam Locomotives A87

Designs: 50ch, *Best Friend of Charleston,* 1830, US 1nu, Class U, 1949, France. 2nu, *Consolidation,* 1866, US. 3nu, *Luggage Engine,* 1843, Great Britain. 4nu, Class 60-3 Shay, 1913, US. 5nu, *John Bull,* 1831, US. 6nu, *Hercules,* 1837, US. 7nu, Eight-wheel tank engine, 1874, Great Britain. 10nu, *The Illinois,* 1852, US. 15nu, German State 4-6-4, 1935. 20nu, American Standard, 1865. No. 809, Class Ps-4, 1926, US. No. 810, *Puffing Billy,* 1814, Great Britain. No. 811, Stephenson's *Rocket,* 1829, Great Britain. No. 812, *Cumberland,* 1845, US, vert. No. 813, *John Stevens,* 1849, US, vert. No. 814, No. 22 Baldwin Locomotive Works, 1873, US, No. 815, *Ariel,* 1877, US. No. 816, 1899 *No. 1301* Webb Compound Engine, Great Britain. No. 817, 1893 *No. 999* Empire State Express, US. No. 818, 1923 Class K-36, US. No. 819, 1935 Class A4, Great Britain. No. 820, 1935 Class A, US. No. 821, 1943 Class P-1, US.

1990, Jan. 30

798 A87 50ch multi .15 .15
799 A87 1nu multi .16 .15
800 A87 2nu multi .32 .24
801 A87 3nu multi .48 .35
802 A87 4nu multi .65 .48
803 A87 5nu multi .80 .60
804 A87 6nu multi .95 .70
805 A87 7nu multi 1.10 .82
806 A87 10nu multi 1.60 1.20
807 A87 15nu multi 2.40 1.80
808 A87 20nu multi 3.20 2.40
809 A87 25nu multi 4.00 3.00
Nos. 798-809 (12) 15.81 11.89

Souvenir Sheets

810-821 A87 25nu each 4.00 4.00

Butterflies
A88

1990, Jan. 30 Litho. *Perf. 14*

822 A88 50ch *Charaxes harmodius* .15 .15
823 A88 1nu *Prioneris thestylis* .16 .15
824 A88 2nu *Sephisa chandra* .32 .24
825 A88 3nu *Penthema usarda* .48 .35
826 A88 4nu *Troides aecus* .65 .48
827 A88 5nu *Polyura eudamippus* .80 .60
828 A88 6nu *Polyura dolon* .95 .70
829 A88 7nu *Neope bhadra* 1.10 .82
830 A88 10nu *Delias descombesi* 1.60 1.20
831 A88 15nu *Childreni childrena* 2.40 1.80
832 A88 20nu *Kallima inachus* 3.20 2.40
833 A88 25nu *Elymnias malelas* 4.00 3.00
Nos. 822-833 (12) 15.81 11.89

Souvenir Sheets

834 A88 25nu Red lacewing 4.00 4.00
835 A88 25nu Bhutan glory 4.00 4.00
836 A88 25nu Great eggfly 4.00 4.00
837 A88 25nu Kaiser-I-Hind 4.00 4.00
838 A88 25nu Chestnut tiger 4.00 4.00
839 A88 25nu Common map 4.00 4.00
840 A88 25nu Swallowtail 4.00 4.00
841 A88 25nu Jungle glory 4.00 4.00
842 A88 25nu Checkered swallowtail 4.00 4.00
843 A88 25nu Common birdwing 4.00 4.00
844 A88 25nu Blue banded peacock 4.00 4.00
845 A88 25nu Camberwell beauty 4.00 4.00

Nos. 822-824, 826-827, 830-831, 834-835, 844-845 are vert.

Paintings by Hiroshige
A89

Designs: 10ch, Plum Estate, Kameido. 20ch, Yatsumi Bridge. 50ch, Ayase River and Kanegafuchi. 75ch, View of Shiba Coast. 1nu, Grandpa's Teahouse, Meguro. 2nu, Kameido Tenjin Shrine. 6nu, Yoroi Ferry, Koami-cho. 7nu, Sakasai Ferry. 10nu, Fukagawa Lumberyards. 15nu, Suido Bridge and Surugadai. 20nu, Meguro Drum Bridge and Sunset Hill. No. 857, Atagoshita and Yabu Lane. No. 858, Towboats Along the Yotsugi-dori Canal. No. 859, Minowa, Kanasugi, Mikawashima. No. 860, Horikiri Iris Garden. No. 861, Fukagawa Susaki and Jumantsubo. No. 862, Suijin Shrine and Massaki on the Sumida River. No. 863, New Year's Eve Foxfires at the Changing Tree, Oji. No. 864, Nihonbashi, Clearing After Snow. No. 865, View to the North from Asukayama. No. 866, Komakata Hall and Azuma Bridge. No. 867, The City Flourishing, Tanabata Festival. No. 868, Suruga-cho. No. 869, Sudden Shower over Shin-Ohashi Bridge and Atake.

1990, May 21 Litho. *Perf. 13½*

846 A89 10ch multicolored .15 .15
847 A89 20ch multicolored .15 .15
848 A89 50ch multicolored .15 .15
849 A89 75ch multicolored .15 .15
850 A89 1nu multicolored .16 .15
851 A89 2nu multicolored .32 .25
852 A89 6nu multicolored .95 .70
853 A89 7nu multicolored 1.10 .85
854 A89 10nu multicolored 1.60 1.20
855 A89 15nu multicolored 2.40 1.80
856 A89 20nu multicolored 3.20 2.40
857 A89 25nu multicolored 4.00 3.00
Nos. 846-857 (12) 14.33 10.95

Souvenir Sheets

858-869 A89 25nu each 4.00 3.00

Hirohito (1901-1989) and enthronement of Akihito as emperor of Japan.

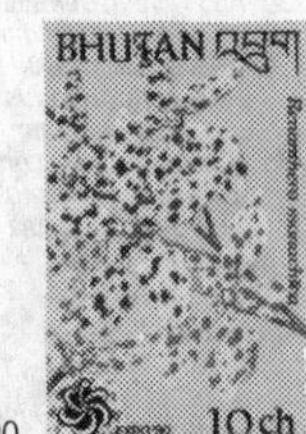

Orchids — A90

1990, Apr. 6 Litho. *Perf. 14*

870 A90 10ch *Renanthera monachica* .15 .15
871 A90 50ch *Vanda coerulea* .15 .15
872 A90 1nu *Phalaenopsis violacea* .16 .15
873 A90 2nu *Dendrobium nobile* .32 .24
874 A90 5nu *Vandopsis lissochiloides* .80 .60
875 A90 6nu *Paphiopedilum rothschildianum* .95 .70
876 A90 7nu *Phalaenopsis schilleriana* 1.10 .82
877 A90 9nu *Paphiopedilum insigne* 1.45 1.10
878 A90 10nu *Paphiopedilum bellatulum* 1.60 1.20
879 A90 20nu *Doritis pulcherrima* 3.20 2.40
880 A90 25nu *Cymbidium giganteum* 4.00 3.00
881 A90 35nu *Phalaenopsis mariae* 5.50 4.15
Nos. 870-881 (12) 19.38 14.66

Souvenir Sheets

882 A90 30nu *Vanda coerulescens* 4.75 4.75
883 A90 30nu *Vandopsis parishi* 4.75 4.75
884 A90 30nu *Dendrobium aphyllum* 4.75 4.75
885 A90 30nu *Phalaenopsis amabilis* 4.75 4.75
886 A90 30nu *Paphiopedilum haynaldianum* 4.75 4.75
887 A90 30nu *Dendrobium lodigesii* 4.75 4.75
888 A90 30nu *Vanda alpina* 4.75 4.75
889 A90 30nu *Phalaenopsis equestris* 4.75 4.75
890 A90 30nu *Vanda cristata* 4.75 4.75
891 A90 30nu *Phalaenopsis cornu cervi* 4.75 4.75
892 A90 30nu *Paphiopedilum niveum* 4.75 4.75
893 A90 30nu *Dendrobium margaritaceum* 4.75 4.75

EXPO '90 Intl. Garden and Greenery Exposition, Osaka, Apr. 1-Dec. 31.

G.P.O., Thimphu — A90a

1990, May 29 Photo. *Perf. 14*

893A A90a 1nu multicolored .16 .16

Penny Black, 150th Anniv.
A90b

Penny Black and: 50ch, Bhutan #1. 1nu, Oldenburg #1. 2nu, Bergedorf #3. 4nu, German Democratic Republic #48. 5nu, Brunswick #1. 6nu, Basel #3L1. 8nu, Geneva #2L1. 10nu, Zurich #1L1. No. 902, France #3. 20nu, Vatican City #1. 25nu, Israel #1. No. 905, Japan #1.

Penny Black and: No. 906a, Mecklenburg-Schwerin #1. b, Mecklenburg-Strelitz #1. No. 907a, Germany #5, #9. b, Prussia #2. No. 908a, Hamburg #1. b, North German Confederation #1, #7. No. 909a, Baden #1. b, Wurttemberg #1. No. 910a, Heligoland #1. b, Hanover #1. No. 911a, Thurn & Taxis #3. b, Thurn & Taxis #42. No. 912a, Schleswig-Holstein #1. b, Lubeck #5. No. 913, Saxony #1. No. 914, Berlin #9N1. No. 915, No other stamp. No. 916, US #1. No. 917, Bavaria #1.

1990, Oct. 9 *Perf. 14*

894 A90b 50ch multicolored .15 .15
895 A90b 1nu multicolored .16 .15
896 A90b 2nu multicolored .32 .24
897 A90b 4nu multicolored .65 .50
898 A90b 5nu multicolored .80 .60
899 A90b 6nu multicolored 1.00 .75
900 A90b 8nu multicolored 1.30 1.00
901 A90b 10nu multicolored 1.60 1.20
902 A90b 15nu multicolored 2.40 1.80
903 A90b 20nu multicolored 3.20 2.40
904 A90b 25nu multicolored 4.00 3.00
905 A90b 30nu multicolored 4.80 3.60
Nos. 894-905 (12) 20.38 15.39

Souvenir Sheets

Sheets of 2 (#906-912) or 1

906-912 A90b 15nu each 4.75 4.75
913-917 A90b 30nu each 4.75 4.75

Stamp World London '90.

Giant Pandas
A91

Tiger
A92

Endangered wildlife of Asia.

1990 *Perf. 14*

918 A91 50ch multi, diff. .15 .15
919 A91 1nu multi, diff. .16 .15
920 A91 2nu multi, diff. .32 .24
921 A91 3nu shown .48 .35
922 A91 4nu multi, diff. .65 .48
923 A92 5nu shown .80 .60
924 A91 6nu multi, diff. .95 .70
925 A91 7nu multi, diff. 1.10 .82
926 A92 10nu Elephant 1.60 1.20
927 A91 15nu multi, diff. 2.40 1.80
928 A92 20nu Barking deer 3.20 2.40
929 A92 25nu Snow leopard 4.00 3.00
Nos. 918-929 (12) 15.81 11.89

Souvenir Sheets

930 A92 25nu Rhinoceros 4.00 4.00
931 A92 25nu Clouded leopard 4.00 4.00
932 A92 25nu Asiatic wild dog 4.00 4.00
933 A92 25nu Himalayan shou 4.00 4.00
934 A92 25nu Golden cat 4.00 4.00
935 A92 25nu Himalayan musk deer 4.00 4.00
936 A91 25nu multi, diff. 4.00 4.00
937 A92 25nu Asiatic black bear 4.00 4.00
938 A92 25nu Gaur 4.00 4.00
939 A92 25nu Pygmy hog 4.00 4.00
940 A92 25nu Wolf 4.00 4.00
941 A92 25nu Sloth bear 4.00 4.00

Nos. 919-920 and 927 vert.

Buddhist Musical Instruments — A93

1990, Sept. 29 Litho. *Perf. 13½x13*

942 A93 10ch Dungchen .15 .15
943 A93 20ch Dungkar .15 .15
944 A93 30ch Roim .15 .15
945 A93 50ch Tinchag .15 .15
946 A93 1nu Dradu & drilbu .16 .15
947 A93 2nu Gya-ling .32 .24
948 A93 2.50nu Nga .40 .30
a. Souv. sheet of 4, #943, 945, 947-948 .85 .65
949 A93 3.50nu Kang-dung .56 .42
a. Souv. sheet of 4, #942, 944, 946, 949 .85 .65
Set value 1.65 1.25

Year of the Girl Child — A94

1990, Dec. 8

950 A94 50ch shown .15 .15
951 A94 20nu Young girl 3.20 2.40

Wonders of the World
A95

Walt Disney characters viewing: 1ch, Temple of Artemis, Ephesus. 2ch, Statue of Zeus, Olympia. 3ch, Egyptian pyramids. 4ch, Lighthouse, Alexandria. 5ch, Mausoleum at Halicarnassus. 10ch, Colossus of Rhodes. 50ch, Hanging gardens of Babylon. 5nu, Mauna Loa volcano, Hawaii. 6nu, Carlsbad Caverns, New Mexico. 10nu, Rainbow Bridge, Utah. 15nu, Grand Canyon of the Colorado, Arizona. 20nu, Old Faithful geyser, Wyoming. 25nu, Giant sequoias, California. 30nu, Crater Lake and Wizard Island, Oregon. 5nu, 6nu, 10nu, 15nu, 20nu, 25nu, 30nu are horiz.

Walt Disney characters viewing: No. 966, Great Wall of China, horiz. No. 967, Mosque of St. Sophia, Istanbul, Turkey. No. 968, The Leaning Tower of Pisa, Italy. No. 969, Colosseum, Rome. No. 970, Stonehenge, England. No. 971, Catacombs of Alexandria, Egypt. No. 972, Porcelain Tower, Nanking, China, horiz. No. 973, The Panama Canal, horiz. No. 974, Golden Gate Bridge, San Francisco, horiz. No. 975, Sears Tower, Chicago, horiz. No. 976, Gateway Arch, St. Louis. No. 977, Alcan Highway, Alaska and Canada, horiz. No. 978, Hoover Dam, Nevada. No. 979, Empire State Building, New York.

1991, Feb. 2 Litho. *Perf. 14*

952 A95 1ch multicolored .15 .15
953 A95 2ch multicolored .15 .15
954 A95 3ch multicolored .15 .15
955 A95 4ch multicolored .15 .15
956 A95 5ch multicolored .15 .15
957 A95 10ch multicolored .15 .15
958 A95 50ch multicolored .15 .15
959 A95 5nu multicolored .80 .60
960 A95 6nu multicolored .95 .70
961 A95 10nu multicolored 1.60 1.20
962 A95 15nu multicolored 2.40 1.80
963 A95 20nu multicolored 3.20 2.40
964 A95 25nu multicolored 4.00 3.00
965 A95 30nu multicolored 4.80 3.60
Nos. 952-965 (14) 18.80 14.35

Souvenir Sheets

Perf. 14x13½, 13½x14

966-979 A95 25nu each 4.00 4.00

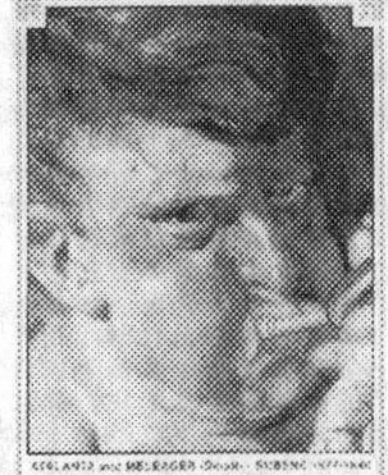

Peter Paul Rubens (1577-1640), Painter — A96

Entire paintings or different details from: 10ch, 5nu, 6nu, 10nu, No. 992, Atalanta and Meleager. 50ch, Fall of Phaethon. 1nu, No. 993, Feast of Venus Verticordia. 2nu, Achilles Slaying Hector. 3nu, No. 994, Arachne Punished by Minerva. 4nu, No. 995, Jupiter Receives Psyche on Olympus. 7nu, Venus in Vulcan's Furnace. 20nu, No. 996, Briseis Returned to Achilles. 30nu, No. 997, Mars and Rhea Sylvia. No. 998, Venus Shivering. No. 999, Ganymede and the Eagle. No. 1000, Origin of the Milky Way. No. 1001, Adonis and Venus. No. 1002, Hero and Leander. No. 1003, Fall of the Titans.

Nos. 994, 996-997, 1000-1003 are horiz.

1991, Feb. 2

980 A96 10ch multicolored .15 .15
981 A96 50ch multicolored .15 .15
982 A96 1nu multicolored .16 .15
983 A96 2nu multicolored .32 .15
984 A96 3nu multicolored .48 .15
985 A96 4nu multicolored .64 .15
986 A96 5nu multicolored .80 .60
987 A96 6nu multicolored .95 .70
988 A96 7nu multicolored 1.15 .85
989 A96 10nu multicolored 1.60 1.20
990 A96 20nu multicolored 3.20 2.40
991 A96 30nu multicolored 4.80 3.60
Nos. 980-991 (12) 14.40 10.25

Souvenir Sheets

992-1003 A96 25nu each 4.00 4.00

Vincent Van Gogh (1853-1890), Painter — A97

Paintings: 10ch, Cottages, Reminiscence of the North. 50ch, Head of a Peasant Woman with Dark Cap. 1nu, Portrait of a Woman in Blue. 2nu, The Midwife. 8nu, Vase with Hollyhocks. 10nu, Portrait of a Man with a Skull Cap. 12nu, Agostina Segatori Sitting in the Cafe du Tambourin. 15nu, Vase with Daisies and Anemones. 18nu, Fritillaries in a Copper Vase. 20nu, Woman Sitting in the Grass. 25nu, On the Outskirts of Paris, horiz. 30nu, Chrysanthemums and Wild Flowers in a Vase.

No. 1016, Le Moulin de la Galette. No. 1017, Bowl with Sunflowers, Roses and Other Flowers, horiz. No. 1018, Poppies and Butterflies. No. 1019, Trees in the Garden of Saint-Paul Hospital: No. 1020, Le Moulin de Blute Fin. No. 1021, Le Moulin de la Galette, diff. No. 1022, Vase with Peonies. No. 1023, Vase with Zinnias. No. 1024, Fishing in the Spring, Pont de Clichy, horiz. No. 1025, Village Street in Auvers, horiz. No. 1026, Vase with Zinnias and Other Flowers, horiz. No. 2027, Vase with Red Poppies.

1991, July 22 Litho. *Perf. 13½*

1004	A97	10ch multicolored	.15	.15
1005	A97	50ch multicolored	.15	.15
1006	A97	1nu multicolored	.16	.15
1007	A97	2nu multicolored	.32	.15
1008	A97	8nu multicolored	1.30	1.00
1009	A97	10nu multicolored	1.60	1.20
1010	A97	12nu multicolored	2.00	1.50
1011	A97	15nu multicolored	2.40	1.80
1012	A97	18nu multicolored	2.90	2.15
1013	A97	20nu multicolored	3.20	2.40
1014	A97	25nu multicolored	4.00	3.00
1015	A97	30nu multicolored	4.80	3.60
		Nos. 1004-1015 (12)	22.98	17.25

Size: 76x102mm, 102x76mm

Imperf

1016-1027	A97	30nu each	4.80	4.80

History of World Cup Soccer — A98

Winning team pictures, plays or possible future site: 50ch, Uruguay, 1930. 1nu, Italy, 1934. 2nu, Italy, 1938. 3nu, Uruguay, 1950. 5nu, West Germany, 1954. 10nu, Brazil, 1958. 20nu, Brazil, 1962. 25nu, England, 1966. 29nu, Brazil, 1970. 30nu, West Germany, 1974. 31nu, Argentina, 1978. 32nu, Italy, 1982. 33nu, Argentina, 1986. 34nu, West Germany, 1990. 35nu, Los Angeles Coliseum, 1994.

Players: No. 1043, Claudio Caniggia, Argentina, vert. No. 1044, Salvatore Schillaci, Italy, vert. No. 1045, Roberto Baggio, Italy, vert. No. 1046, Peter Shilton, England, vert. No. 1047, Lothar Matthaus, West Germany, vert. No. 1048, Paul Gascoigne, England, vert.

1991, Aug. 1 Litho. *Perf. 13½*

1028	A98	50ch multicolored	.15	.15
1029	A98	1nu multicolored	.16	.15
1030	A98	2nu multicolored	.32	.15
1031	A98	3nu multicolored	.48	.15
1032	A98	5nu multicolored	.80	.60
1033	A98	10nu multicolored	1.60	1.20
1034	A98	20nu multicolored	3.20	2.40
1035	A98	25nu multicolored	4.00	3.00
1036	A98	29nu multicolored	4.75	3.55
1037	A98	30nu multicolored	4.80	3.60
1038	A98	31nu multicolored	5.10	3.80
1039	A98	32nu multicolored	5.25	3.95
1040	A98	33nu multicolored	5.40	4.05
1041	A98	34nu multicolored	5.60	4.20
1042	A98	35nu multicolored	5.75	4.30
		Nos. 1028-1042 (15)	47.36	35.25

Souvenir Sheets

1043-1048	A98	30nu each	4.80	4.00

Phila Nippon '91 — A99

1991, Nov. 16 *Perf. 13*

1049	A99	15nu multicolored	2.40	1.80

Education in Bhutan A100

1992, Mar. 5 Photo. *Perf. 13½*

1050	A100	1nu multicolored	.18	.15

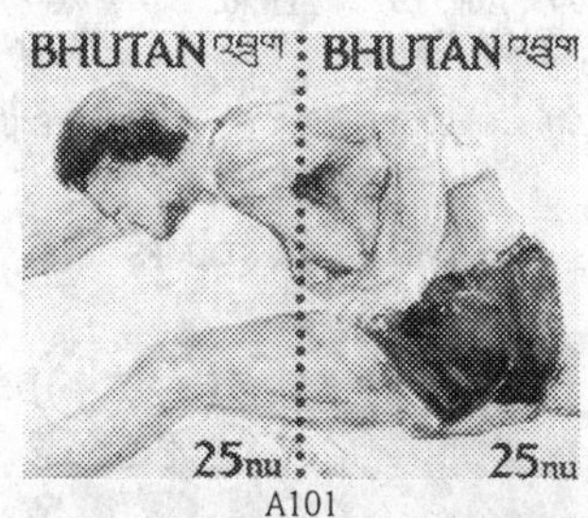

A101

1992 Summer Olympics, Barcelona — A102

1992, July 24 Litho. *Perf. 12*

1051	A101	25nu Pair, #a.-b.	8.25	8.25

Souvenir Sheet

1052	A102	25nu Archer	4.10	4.10

German Reunification — A103

1992, Oct. 3 Litho. *Perf. 12*

1053	A103	25nu multicolored	2.00	2.00

Souvenir Sheet

1054	A103	25nu multicolored	2.00	2.00

Stamp from No. 1054 does not have white inscription or border.

Bhutan Postal Service, 30th Anniv. A104

Designs: 1nu, Mail truck, plane. 3nu, Letter carrier approaching village. 5nu, Letter carrier emptying mail box.

1992, Oct. 9

1055	A104	1nu multicolored	.15	.15
1056	A104	3nu multicolored	.24	.24
1057	A104	5nu multicolored	.40	.40
		Nos. 1055-1057 (3)	.79	.79

This miniature sheet of four was never officially issued.

A106

A107

1992, Sept. 18 *Perf. 12*

1059	A106	15nu Ship	1.20	1.20
1060	A106	20nu Portrait	1.60	1.60

Souvenir Sheet

1061	A106	25nu like #1060	2.00	2.00

Discovery of America, 500th anniv.

Stamp from No. 1061 does not have silver inscription or white border.

1992, Nov. 11 Litho. *Perf. 12*

Reign of King Jigme Singye Wangchuk, 20th Anniv.: a, 1nu, Man tilling field, factory. b, 5nu, Airplane. c, 10nu, House, well. d, 15nu, King. 20nu, People, flag, King, horiz.

1062	A107	Block of 4, #a.-d.	2.50	2.50

Souvenir Sheet

1063	A107	20nu multicolored	1.70	1.70

Intl. Volunteer Day A108

Designs: a, 1.50nu, White inscription. b, 9nu, Green inscription. c, 15nu, Red inscription.

1992, Dec. 5 Litho. *Perf. 14*

1067	A108	Block of 4, #a.-c. + label	2.05	2.05

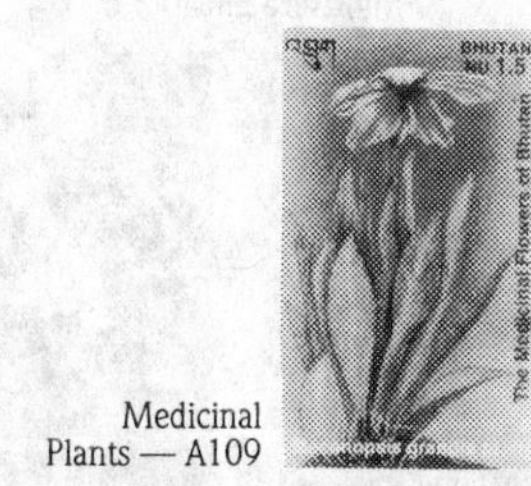

Medicinal Plants — A109

1993, Jan. 1 Litho. *Perf. 12*

1068	A109	1.50nu Meconopsis grandis prain	.15	.15
1069	A109	7nu Meconopsis sp.	.58	.58
1070	A109	10nu Meconopsis wallichii	.40	.40
1071	A109	12nu Meconopsis horridula	1.00	1.00
1072	A109	20nu Meconopsis discigera	1.70	1.70
		Nos. 1068-1072 (5)	3.83	3.83

Souvenir Sheet

1073	A109	25nu Meconopsis horridula, diff.	2.00	2.00

Miniature Sheet

Lunar New Year — A110

1993, Feb. 22 Litho. *Perf. 14*

1074	A110	25nu multicolored	2.05	2.05

No. 1074 Surcharged "TAIPEI '93" in Silver and Black

1993, Aug. 14 Litho. *Perf. 14*

1075	A110	30nu on 25nu	2.50	2.50

Door Gods — A112

Flowers — A113

1993, Dec. 17 Litho. *Perf. 12*

1091	A112	1.50nu Namtheo-Say	.15	.15
1092	A112	5nu Pha-Ke-Po	.50	.50
1093	A112	10nu Chen-Mi-Jang	1.00	1.00
1094	A112	15nu Yul-Khor-Sung	1.50	1.50
		Nos. 1091-1094 (4)	3.15	3.15

1993, Jan. 1 *Perf. 13*

Designs: No. 1095a, 1nu, Rhododendron mucronatum. b, 1.5nu. Anemone rupicola. c, 2nu, Polemonium coeruleum. d, 2.5nu, Rosa marophylla. e, 4nu, Paraquilegia microphylla. f, 5nu, Aquilegia nivalis. g, 6nu, Geranium wallichianum. h, 7nu, Rhodendron campanulatum. i, 9nu, Viola suavis. j, 10nu, Cyananthus lobatus.

13nu, Red flower, horiz.

1095	A113	Strip of 10, #a.-j.	4.75	4.75

Souvenir Sheet

1096	A113	13nu multicolored	1.40	1.40

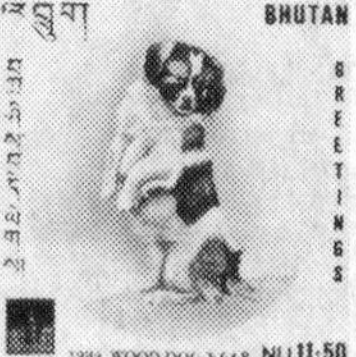

New Year 1994 (Year of the Dog) — A114

1994, Feb. 11 Litho. *Perf. 14*

1097	A114	11.50nu multicolored	.80	.80

Souvenir Sheet

1098	A114	20nu like #1097	1.40	1.40

Hong Kong '94.

Stamp Cards — A115

Designs: 16nu, Tagtshang Monastery. 20nu, Map of Bhutan. Illustration reduced.

Rouletted 26 on 2 or 3 Sides

1994, Aug. 15 Litho.

Self-Adhesive

Cards of 6 + 6 labels

1099 A115 16nu #a.-f. 6.25 6.25
1100 A115 20nu #a.-f. 7.75 7.75

Individual stamps measure 70x9mm and have a card backing. Se-tenant labels inscribed "AIR MAIL."

Souvenir Sheet

First Manned Moon Landing, 25th Anniv. — A116

Designs: a, 30nu, Astronaut on moon. b, 36nu, Space shuttle, earth, moon. Illustration reduced.

1994, Nov. 11 Litho. ***Perf. 14x14½***
1101 A116 Sheet of 2, #a.-b. 4.25 4.25

Nos. 1101a, 1101b have holographic images. Soaking in water may affect the holograms.

Souvenir Sheet

Victory Over Tibet-Mongol Army, 350th Anniv. — A117

Battle scene: a, Mounted officer. b, Hand to hand combat, soldiers in yellow or blue armor. c, Soldier on gray horse. d, Soldiers in red, drummer, horn player.

1994, Dec. 17 Litho. ***Perf. 12½***

Granite Paper

1102 A117 15nu Sheet of 4, #a.-d. 4.00 4.00

Souvenir Sheet

Bridges A118

Designs: a, 15nu, Tower Bridge, London, cent. b, 16nu, Wangdue Bridge, Bhutan, 250th anniv.

1994, Nov. 11 ***Perf. 12***
1103 A118 Sheet of 2, #a.-b. 2.00 2.00

1994 World Cup Soccer Championships, US — A119

1994, July 17 Litho. ***Perf. 12***
1104 A119 15nu multicolored 1.00 1.00

Souvenir Sheet

World Tourism Year A120

Scenes of Bhutan: a, 1.50nu, Paro Valley. b, 5nu, Chorten Kora. c, 10nu, Thimphu Tshechu. d, 15nu, Wangdue Tshechu.

1995, Apr. 2 Litho. ***Perf. 12***
1105 A120 Sheet of 4, #a.-d. 2.00 2.00

Miniature Sheet of 12

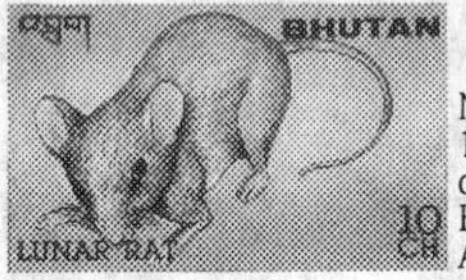
New Year 1995 (Year of the Boar) A121

Symbols of Chinese Lunar New Year: a, 10ch, Rat. b, 20ch, Ox. c, 30ch, Tiger. d, 40ch, Rabbit. e, 1nu, Dragon. f, 2nu, Snake. g, 3nu, Horse. h, 4nu, Sheep. i, 5nu, Monkey. j, 7nu, Rooster. k, 8nu, Dog. l, 9nu, Boar.
10nu, Wood Hog.

1995, Mar. 2
1106 A121 #a.-l. 2.50 2.50

Souvenir Sheet

1107 A121 10nu multicolored .65 .65

No. 1107 is a continuous design.

A122

A123

Flowers: 9nu, Pleione praecox. 10nu, Primula calderina. 16nu, Primula whitei. 18nu, Notholirion macrophyllum.

1995, May 2 Litho. ***Perf. 12***
1108-1111 A122 Set of 4 3.50 3.50

1995, June 26 ***Perf. 14***

UN, 50th Anniv.: a, 1.5nu, Human resources development. b, 9nu, Health & population. c, 10nu, Water & sanitation. d, 5nu, Transport & communications. e, 16nu, Forestry & environment. f, 18nu, Peace & security. g, 11.5nu, UN in Bhutan.

1112 A123 Strip of 7 4.75 4.75

Miniature Sheet of 6

Singapore '95 — A124

Birds: No. 1113a, 1nu, Himalayan pied kingfisher. b, 2nu, Blyth's tragopan. c, 3nu, Long-tailed minivet. d, 10nu, Red junglefowl. e, 15nu, Black-capped sibia. f, 20nu, Red-billed chough.
No. 1114, Black-neck crane.

1995, June 2 Litho. ***Perf. 12***
1113 A124 #a.-f. + 3 labels 3.50 3.50

Souvenir Sheet

1114 A124 20nu multicolored 1.40 1.40

Traditional Crafts — A125

Designs: 1nu, Drying parchment. 2nu, Making tapestry. 3nu, Restoring archaeological finds. 10nu, Weaving textiles. 15nu, Sewing garments. No. 1120, 20nu, Carving wooden vessels.
No. 1121, Mosaic.

1995, Aug. 15 Litho. ***Perf. 14***
1115-1120 A125 Set of 6 2.50 2.50

Souvenir Sheet

1121 A125 20nu multicolored 1.40 1.40

SEMI-POSTAL STAMPS

Nos. 10-12 Surcharged

Perf. 14x14½

1964, Mar. Litho. Unwmk.
B1 A3 33ch + 50ch multi 2.00 2.00
B2 A3 70ch + 50ch multi 2.00 2.00
B3 A3 1.30nu + 50ch multi 2.00 2.00
Nos. B1-B3 (3) 6.00 6.00

9th Winter Olympic Games, Innsbruck, Jan. 29-Feb. 9, 1964.

Olympic Games Type of Regular Issue, 1964

Souvenir Sheet

1964, Oct. 10 ***Perf. 13½, Imperf.***
B4 A6 Sheet of 2 7.50 7.50
a. 1nu + 50ch Archery .90 .90
b. 2nu + 50ch Soccer 2.00 2.00

18th Olympic Games, Tokyo, Oct. 10-25.

FLOOD RELIEF

+ 5Ch

1968, Dec. 7 Photo. ***Perf. 13½***
B5 A14n 5ch +5ch .15 .15
B6 A14n 80ch +25ch .35 .35
B7 A14n 2nu +50ch .85 .85
Nos. B5-B7 (3) 1.35 1.35

AIR POST STAMPS

Nos. 19-21, 38-39, 63-67 Ovptd.

a b

1967, Jan. 10 Litho. ***Perfs. as Before***

Overprint "a"

C1 A5 33ch on #19 .15 .15
C2 A5 70ch on #20 .30 .30
C3 A5 1nu on #21 .42 .42
C4 A8 50ch on #38 .22 .22
C5 A8 75ch on #39 .32 .32
C6 A11 1.50nu on #63 .65 .65
C7 A11 2nu on #64 .85 .85
C8 A11 3nu on #65 1.25 1.25
C9 A11 4nu on #66 1.75 1.75
C10 A11 5nu on #67 2.25 2.25

Overprint "b"

C11 A5 33ch on #19 .15 .15
C12 A5 70ch on #20 .30 .30
C13 A5 1nu on #21 .42 .42
C14 A8 50ch on #38 .22 .22
C15 A8 75ch on #39 .32 .32
C16 A11 1.50nu on #63 .65 .65
C17 A11 2nu on #64 .85 .85
C18 A11 3nu on #65 1.25 1.25
C19 A11 4nu on #66 1.75 1.75
C20 A11 5nu on #67 2.25 2.25
Nos. C1-C20 (20) 16.32 16.32

UN Type of Regular Issue

Bhutan Flag and: 2.50nu, UN Headquarters, NYC. 5nu, Security Council Chamber and mural by Per Krohg. 6nu, General Assembly Hall.

1971, Sept. 21 Photo. ***Perf. 13½***
C21 A16 2.50nu silver & multi .38 .38
C22 A16 5nu silver & multi .75 .75
C23 A16 6nu silver & multi .90 .90
Nos. C21-C23 (3) 2.03 2.03

Bhutan's admission to the United Nations. Exist imperf.

Nos. C21-C23 Overprinted in Gold: "UNHCR / UNRWA / 1971" like Nos. 145-145C

1971, Dec. 23 Litho. ***Perf. 13½***
C24 A16 2.50nu silver & multi .55 .55
C25 A16 5nu silver & multi 1.10 1.10
C26 A16 6nu silver & multi 1.40 1.40
Nos. C24-C26 (3) 3.05 3.05

World Refugee Year. Exist imperf.

UPU Types of 1974

UPU Emblem, Carrier Pigeon and: 1nu, Mail runner and jeep. 1.40nu, 10nu, Old and new locomotives. 2nu, Old biplane and jet.

1974, Oct. 9 Litho. ***Perf. 14½***
C27 A19 1nu salmon & multi .25 .25
C28 A20 1.40nu lilac & multi .38 .38
C29 A20 2nu multicolored .48 .48
Nos. C27-C29 (3) 1.11 1.11

Souvenir Sheet

Perf. 13

C30 A20 10nu lilac & multi 2.75 2.75

Cent. of the UPU. Nos. C27-C29 were issued in sheets of 50 and sheets of 5 plus label with multicolored margin. Exist imperf.

Issues of 1968-1974 Surcharged 25ch and Bars

1978 Perf. & Printing as Before
C31 A16 25ch on 5nu, #C22
C32 A16 25ch on 6nu, #C23
C33 A20 25ch on 1.40nu, #C28
C34 A20 25ch on 2nu, #C29
C35 A14j 25ch on 4nu, #94L
C36 A14j 25ch on 10nu, #94N
C37 A17k 25ch on 5nu, #154F
C38 A17k 25ch on 6nu, #154G

BOLIVIA

bə-'li-vē-ə

LOCATION — Central South America, separated from the Pacific Ocean by Chile and Peru.
GOVT. — Republic
AREA — 424,165 sq. mi.
POP. — 6,252,250 (est. 1984)
CAPITAL — Sucre (La Paz is the actual seat of government).

100 Centavos = 1 Boliviano
100 Centavos = 1 Peso Boliviano (1963)
100 Centavos = 1 Boliviano (1987)

Catalogue values for unused stamps in this country are for Never Hinged items, beginning with Scott 308 in the regular postage section, Scott C112 in the airpost section, Scott RA5 in the postal tax section, and Scott RAC1 in airpost postal tax section.

On Feb. 21, 1863, the Bolivian Government decreed contracts for carrying the mails should be let to the highest bidder, the service to commence on the day the bid was accepted, and stamps used for the payment of postage. On Mar. 18, the contract was awarded to Sr. Justiniano Garcia and was in effect until Apr. 29, 1863, when it was rescinded. Stamps in the form illustrated above were prepared in denominations of ½, 1, 2 and 4 reales. All values exist in black and in blue. The blue are twice as scarce as the black. Value, black, $75 each.

It is said that used copies exist on covers, but the authenticity of these covers remains to be established.

Condor — A1

A2

A3

72 varieties of each of the 5c, 78 varieties of the 10c, 30 varieties of each of the 50c and 100c.

The plate of the 5c stamps was entirely reengraved 4 times and retouched at least 6 times. Various states of the plate have distinguishing characteristics, each of which is typical of most, though not all the stamps in a sheet. These characteristics (usually termed types) are found in the shading lines at the right side of the globe. a, vertical and diagonal lines. b, diagonal lines only. c, diagonal and horizontal with traces of vertical lines. d, diagonal and horizontal lines. e, horizontal lines only. f, no lines except the curved ones forming the outlines of the globe.

1867-68 Unwmk. Engr. *Imperf.*

No.	Type	Description	Unused	Used
1	A1	5c yel grn, thin paper (a, b)	3.50	*4.50*
a.		5c blue green (a)	4.50	*14.00*
b.		5c deep green (a)	4.50	*14.00*
c.		5c ol grn, thick paper (a)	35.00	25.00
d.		5c yel grn, thick paper (a)	80.00	80.00
e.		5c yel grn, thick paper (b)	80.00	80.00
f.		5c blue green (b)	4.50	14.00
2	A1	5c green (d)	4.00	7.00
a.		5c green (c)	4.00	7.00
b.		5c green (e)	4.00	7.00
c.		5c green (f)	4.00	7.00
3	A1	5c vio ('68)	185.00	140.00
a.		5c rose lilac ('68)	185.00	140.00
		Revenue cancel		28.00
4	A3	10c brown	225.00	140.00
5	A2	50c orange	20.00	
6	A2	50c blue ('68)	*325.00*	
a.		50c dark blue ('68)	*325.00*	
		Revenue cancel		28.00
7	A3	100c blue	60.00	
		Revenue cancel		15.00
8	A3	100c green ('68)	140.00	
a.		100c pale blue grn ('68)	140.00	
		Revenue cancel		28.00

Used values are for postally canceled copies. Pen cancellations usually indicate that the stamps have been used fiscally and such stamps sell for about one-fifth as much as those with postal cancellations.

The 500c is an essay.

Reprints of Nos. 3,4, 6 and 8 are common. Value, $10 each. Reprints of Nos. 2 and 5 are scarcer. Value, $25 each.

Coat of Arms
A4 A5

1868-69 *Perf. 12*

Nine Stars

No.	Type	Description	Unused	Used
10	A4	5c green	17.50	8.75
11	A4	10c vermilion	25.00	8.75
12	A4	50c blue	45.00	25.00
13	A4	100c orange	45.00	27.50
14	A4	500c black	475.00	375.00

Eleven Stars

No.	Type	Description	Unused	Used
15	A5	5c green	10.00	6.25
16	A5	10c vermilion	14.00	10.00
a.		Half used as 5c as cover		400.00
17	A5	50c blue	37.50	17.50
18	A5	100c dp orange	35.00	17.50
19	A5	500c black	*1,750.*	*1,750.*

See Nos. 26-27, 31-34.

Arms and "The Law" — A6

1878 Various Frames *Perf. 12*

No.	Type	Description	Unused	Used
20	A6	5c ultra	9.25	4.25
21	A6	10c orange	7.50	3.25
a.		Half used as 5c on cover		50.00
22	A6	20c green	22.50	4.25
a.		Half used as 10c on cover		160.00
23	A6	50c dull carmine	110.00	12.00
		Nos. 20-23 (4)	149.25	23.75

Numerals Upright
(11 Stars)-A7 (9 Stars)-A8

1887 *Rouletted*

No.	Type	Description	Unused	Used
24	A7	1c rose	2.25	2.00
25	A7	2c violet	2.25	2.00
26	A5	5c blue	7.25	3.50
27	A5	10c orange	7.25	3.50
		Nos. 24-27 (4)	19.00	11.00

See No. 37.

1890 *Perf. 12*

No.	Type	Description	Unused	Used
28	A8	1c rose	1.65	.80
29	A8	2c violet	4.25	2.00
30	A4	5c blue	3.00	.80
31	A4	10c orange	6.25	.95
32	A4	20c dk green	12.50	1.65
33	A4	50c red	6.25	1.65
34	A4	100c yellow	12.50	3.25
		Nos. 28-34 (7)	46.40	11.10

See Nos. 35-36, 38-39.

1893 Litho. *Perf. 11*

No.	Type	Description	Unused	Used
35	A8	1c rose	3.50	2.50
a.		Imperf. pair	35.00	
b.		Horiz. pair, imperf. vert.	20.00	
c.		Horiz. pair, imperf. btwn.	35.00	
36	A8	2c violet	3.50	2.50
a.		Block of 4 imperf. vert. and horiz. through center	50.00	
b.		Horiz. pair, imperf. btwn.	27.50	
37	A7	5c blue	6.00	2.50
a.		Vert. pair, imperf. horiz.	27.50	
b.		Horiz. pair, imperf. btwn.	35.00	
38	A8	10c orange	17.00	4.00
a.		Horiz. pair, imperf. btwn.	50.00	
39	A8	20c dark green	40.00	18.00
a.		Imperf. pair, vert. or horiz.	140.00	
b.		Pair, imperf. btwn., vert. or horiz.	140.00	
		Nos. 35-39 (5)	70.00	29.50

Coat of Arms — A9

1894 Unwmk. Engr. *Perf. 14, 14½*

Thin Paper

No.	Type	Description	Unused	Used
40	A9	1c bister	1.00	.60
41	A9	2c red orange	1.00	.60
42	A9	5c green	1.00	.60
43	A9	10c yellow brn	1.00	.60
44	A9	20c dark blue	3.00	1.25
45	A9	50c claret	7.50	1.75
46	A9	100c brown rose	17.50	6.25
		Nos. 40-46 (7)	32.00	11.65

Stamps of type A9 on thick paper were surreptitiously printed in Paris on the order of an official and without government authorization. Some of these stamps were substituted for part of a shipment of stamps on thin paper, which had been printed in London on government order. When the thick paper stamps reached Bolivia they were at first repudiated but afterwards were allowed to do postal duty. A large quantity of the thick paper stamps were fraudulently canceled in Paris with a cancellation of heavy bars forming an oval.

To be legitimate, copies of the thick paper stamps must have genuine cancellations of Bolivia. Value, on cover, each $125.

The 10c blue on thick paper is not known to have been issued.

Some copies of Nos. 40-46 show part of a papermakers' watermark "1011."

For overprints see Nos. 55-59.

President Tomas Frias — A10

President Jose M. Linares — A11

Pedro Domingo Murillo A12

Bernardo Monteagudo A13

Gen. Jose Ballivian — A14

Gen. Antonio Jose de Sucre — A15

Simon Bolivar — A16

Coat of Arms — A17

1897 Litho. *Perf. 12*

No.	Type	Description	Unused	Used
47	A10	1c pale yellow grn	1.25	.80
a.		Vert. pair, imperf. horiz.	50.00	
b.		Vert. pair, imperf. btwn.	50.00	
48	A11	2c red	1.75	1.40
49	A12	5c dk green	2.50	.80
a.		Horiz. pair, imperf. btwn.	50.00	
50	A13	10c brown vio	2.50	.80
a.		Vert. pair, imperf. btwn.	50.00	
51	A14	20c lake & blk	4.75	.95
a.		Imperf., pair		150.00
52	A15	50c orange	4.75	2.50
53	A16	1b Prus blue	4.75	5.50
54	A17	2b red, yel, grn & blk	37.50	50.00
		Nos. 47-54 (8)	59.75	62.75

Excellent forgeries of No. 54, perf and imperf, exist, some postally used.

Reprint of No. 53 has dot in numeral. Same value.

Nos. 40-44 Handstamped in Violet or Blue

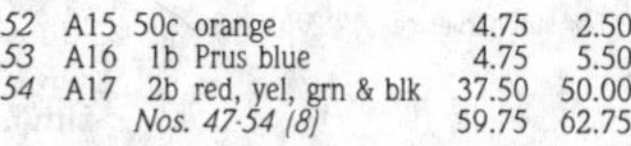

1899 *Perf. 14½*

No.	Type	Description	Unused	Used
55	A9	1c yellow bis	13.00	13.00
56	A9	2c red orange	16.00	16.00
57	A9	5c green	10.50	10.50
58	A9	10c yellow brn	13.00	10.50
59	A9	20c dark blue	21.00	21.00
		Nos. 55-59 (5)	73.50	71.00

The handstamp is found inverted, double, etc. Values twice the listed amounts. Forgeries of this handstamp are plentiful. "E.F." stands for Estado Federal.

The 50c and 100c (Nos. 45-46) were overprinted at a later date in Brazil.

Antonio José de Sucre — A18

Perf. 11½, 12

1899 Engr. Thin Paper

No.	Type	Description	Unused	Used
62	A18	1c gray blue	2.50	.75
63	A18	2c brnsh red	1.75	.75
64	A18	5c dk green	6.00	1.50
65	A18	10c yellow org	2.50	1.25
66	A18	20c rose pink	3.00	.80
67	A18	50c bister brn	6.00	2.50
68	A18	1b gray violet	1.75	1.75
		Nos. 62-68 (7)	23.50	9.30

1901

No.	Type	Description	Unused	Used
69	A18	5c dark red	1.90	.60

Col. Adolfo Ballivian A19

Eliodoro Camacho A20

President Narciso Campero A21

Jose Ballivian A22

Gen. Andres Santa Cruz — A23

Coat of Arms — A24

1901-02 Engr.

No.	Type	Description	Unused	Used
70	A19	1c claret	.55	.15
71	A20	2c green	.55	.20
73	A21	5c scarlet	.55	.20
74	A22	10c blue	1.40	.15
75	A23	20c violet & blk	.80	.15
76	A24	2b brown	3.75	2.75
		Nos. 70-71,73-76 (6)	7.60	3.60

Nos. 73, 74 exist imperf. Value, pairs, each $50.

For surcharges see #95-96, 193.

1904 **Litho.**
77 A19 1c claret 2.25 .55

In No. 70 the panel above "CENTAVO" is shaded with continuous lines. In No. 77 the shading is of dots.
See Nos. 103-105, 107, 110.

Coat of Arms of Dept. of La Paz — A25

Murillo — A26

Jose Miguel Lanza — A27

Ismael Montes — A28

1909 **Litho.** ***Perf. 11***
78 A25 5c blue & blk 9.00 5.00
79 A26 10c green & blk 9.00 5.00
80 A27 20c orange & blk 9.00 5.00
81 A28 2b red & black 9.00 5.00
Nos. 78-81 (4) 36.00 20.00

Centenary of Revolution of July, 1809.
Nos. 78-81 exist imperf. and tête bêche. Nos. 79-81 exist with center inverted.

Miguel Betanzos A29

Col. Ignacio Warnes A30

Murillo A31

Monteagudo A32

Esteban Arce — A33

Antonio Jose de Sucre — A34

Simon Bolivar A35

Manuel Belgrano A36

1909 **Dated 1809-1825** ***Perf. 11½***
82 A29 1c lt brown & blk .55 .35
83 A30 2c green & blk .55 .40
84 A31 5c red & blk .55 .30
85 A32 10c dull bl & blk .55 .30
86 A33 20c violet & blk .65 .40
87 A34 50c olive bister & blk 1.00 .55
88 A35 1b gray brn & blk 1.00 .80
89 A36 2b chocolate & blk 1.65 1.10
Nos. 82-89 (8) 6.50 4.20

War of Independence, 1809-1825.

Exist imperf. For surcharge see #97.

Warnes A37

Betanzos A38

Arce — A39

Dated 1910-1825

1910 ***Perf. 13x13½***
92 A37 5c green & black .40 .15
  a. Imperf., pair 5.00
93 A38 10c claret & indigo .40 .15
  a. Imperf., pair 5.00
94 A39 20c dull blue & indigo .65 .40
  a. Imperf., pair 5.00
Nos. 92-94 (3) 1.45 .70

War of Independence.
Nos. 92-94 may be found with parts of a papermaker's watermark: "A I & Co/EXTRA STRONG/9303."
Exist with inverted centers.

Nos. 71 and 75 Surcharged in Black

1911 ***Perf. 11½, 12***
95 A20 5c on 2c green .45 .20
  a. Inverted surcharge 5.00 5.00
  b. Double surcharge 15.00
  c. Period after "1911" 3.50 .80
  d. Blue surcharge 75.00 60.00
  e. Double dsurch., one invtd. 15.00
96 A23 5c on 20c vio & blk 16.00 16.00
  a. Inverted surcharge 30.00 30.00
  b. Double surch., one invtd. 60.00

No. 83 Handstamp Surcharged in Green

97 A30 20c on 2c grn & blk *1,100.*

This provisional was issued by local authorities at Villa Bella, a town on the Brazilian border. The 20c surcharge was applied after the stamp had been affixed to the cover. Excellent forgeries of No. 96-97 exist.

"Justice"

A40 A41

1912

Black or Dark Blue Overprint On Revenue Stamps

98 A40 2c green (Bk) .35 .25
  a. Inverted overprint 5.00
99 A41 10c ver (Bl) 1.10 .40
  a. Inverted overprint 5.00

A42

A43

Red or Black Overprint

Engr.
100 A42 5c orange (R) .55 .40
  a. Inverted overprint 5.00
  b. Pair, one without overprint 12.50
  c. Black overprint 50.00

Red or Black Surcharge
101 A43 10c on 1c bl (R) .55 .20
  a. Inverted surcharge 6.00
  b. Double surcharge 6.00
  c. Dbl. surcharge, one invtd. 7.50
  d. Black surcharge 100.00 100.00
  e. As "d," inverted
  f. As "d," double surcharge
  g. Pair, one without black surch. 200.00

Revenue Stamp Surcharged "CORREOS / 10 Cts. / - 1917 -" in Red

1917 **Litho.**
102 10c on 1c blue *6,000. 1,750.*

Design similar to type A43.
Excellent forgeries exist.

Types of 1901 and

Frias-A45

Sucre-A46

Bolivar-A47

1913 **Engr.** ***Perf. 12***
103 A19 1c car rose .40 .25
104 A20 2c vermilion .40 .15
105 A21 5c green .45 .15
106 A45 8c yellow .80 .50
107 A22 10c gray .80 .25
108 A46 50c dull violet 1.50 .55
109 A47 1b slate blue 2.25 1.40
110 A24 2b black 4.50 2.75
Nos. 103-110 (8) 11.10 6.00

No. 107, litho., was not regularly issued.

Nine values commemorating the Guiqui-La Paz railroad were printed in 1915 but never issued. Typographed forgeries exist.

Monolith of Tiahuanacu A48

Mt. Potosí A49

Lake Titicaca — A50

Mt. Illimani — A51

Legislature Building — A53

FIVE CENTAVOS.
Type I - Numerals have background of vertical lines. Clouds formed of dots.
Type II - Numerals on white background. Clouds near the mountain formed of wavy lines.

1916-17 **Litho.** ***Perf. 11½***
111 A48 ½c brown .15 .15
  a. Horiz. pair, imperf. vert. 5.00
112 A49 1c gray green .15 .15
  a. Imperf., pair 2.00
113 A50 2c car & blk .25 .15
  a. Imperf., pair 2.00
  b. Vert. pair, imperf. horiz.
  c. Center inverted 12.50 11.25
  d. Imperf., center inverted 17.50
114 A51 5c dk blue (I) .50 .18
  a. Imperf., pair 2.00
  b. Vert. pair, imperf. horiz. 3.50
  c. Horiz. pair, imperf. vert. 3.50
115 A51 5c dk blue (II) .50 .15
  a. Imperf., pair 2.50
116 A53 10c org & bl 1.00 .15
  a. Imperf., pair 3.50
  b. No period after "Legislativo" 1.00 .15
  c. Center inverted 40.00 40.00
  d. Vertical pair, imperf. between 5.00
Nos. 111-116 (6) 2.55
Set value .69

For surcharges see Nos. 194-196.

Coat of Arms
A54 A55

Printed by the American Bank Note Co.

1919-20 **Engr.** ***Perf. 12***
118 A54 1c carmine .25 .20
119 A54 2c dk violet 4.75 3.00
120 A54 5c dk green .50 .15
121 A54 10c vermilion .50 .15
122 A54 20c dk blue 1.50 .30
123 A54 22c lt blue .90 .75
124 A54 24c purple .60 .50
125 A54 50c orange 4.75 .60
126 A55 1b red brown 6.00 1.75
127 A55 2b black brn 9.00 4.50
Nos. 118-127 (10) 28.75 11.90

Printed by Perkins, Bacon & Co., Ltd.

1923-27 **Re-engraved** ***Perf. 13½***
128 A54 1c carmine ('27) .15 .15
129 A54 2c dk violet .25 .15
130 A54 5c dp green .80 .15
131 A54 10c vermilion 14.00 12.00
132 A54 20c slate blue 1.75 .20
135 A54 50c orange 2.75 .60
136 A55 1b red brown .70 .30
137 A55 2b black brown .50 .30
Nos. 128-137 (8) 20.90 13.85

There are many differences in the designs of the two issues but they are too minute to be illustrated or described.
Nos. 128-137 exist imperf.
See Nos. 144-146, 173-177. For surcharges see Nos. 138-143, 160, 162, 181-186, 236-237.

Stamps of 1919-20 Surcharged in Blue, Black or Red

Habilitada
15 cts.

1924 ***Perf. 12***
138 A54 5c on 1c car (Bl) .40 .20
  a. Inverted surcharge 5.00 5.00
  b. Double surcharge 5.00 5.00
139 A54 15c on 10c ver (Bk) .70 .50
  a. Inverted surcharge 6.00 6.00
140 A54 15c on 22c lt bl (Bk) .70 .30
  a. Inverted surcharge 5.25 5.25
  b. Double surcharge, one inverted

No. 140 surcharged in red or blue probably are trial impressions. They appear jointly, and with black in blocks.

Same Surcharge on No. 131
Perf. 13½
142 A54 15c on 10c ver (Bk) .70 .25
  a. Inverted surcharge 6.00 6.00

No. 121 Surcharged

Habilitada
15 cts.

Perf. 12
143 A54 15c on 10c ver (Bk) .90 .30
  a. Inverted surcharge 6.00 6.00
  b. Double surcharge 5.00 5.00
Nos. 138-143 (5) 3.40 1.55

Type of 1919-20 Issue
Printed by Waterlow & Sons

Second Re-engraving

1925 **Unwmk.** ***Perf. 12½***
144 A54 5c deep green .80 .25
145 A54 15c ultra .80 .15
146 A54 20c dark blue .35 .15
Nos. 144-146 (3) 1.95 .55

These stamps may be identified by the perforation.

Miner — A56

Condor Looking Toward the Sea — A57

Designs: 2c, Sower. 5c, Torch of Eternal Freedom. 10c, National flower (kantuta). 15c, Pres. Bautista Saavedra. 50c, Liberty head. 1b, Archer on horse. 2b, Mercury. 5b, Gen. A. J. de Sucre.

1925 Engr. *Perf. 14*

150	A56	1c dark green	.75	
151	A56	2c rose	.75	
152	A56	5c red, *grn*	.75	.35
153	A56	10c car, *yel*	1.25	.75
154	A56	15c red brown	.50	.25
155	A57	25c ultra	.50	.50
156	A56	50c dp violet	.50	.50
157	A56	1b red	1.25	1.25
158	A57	2b orange	1.75	1.75
159	A56	5b black brn	2.00	2.00
		Nos. 150-159 (10)	10.00	

Cent. of the Republic. The 1c and 2c were not released for general use.

Nos. 150-159 exist imperf. Value, $60 each pair.

For surcharges see Nos. C59-C62.

Stamps of 1919-27 Surcharged in Blue, Black or Red

1927
5
CENTAVOS

1927

160	A54	5c on 1c car (Bl)	2.50	.90
a.		Inverted surcharge	6.00	6.00
b.		Black surcharge	22.50	22.50

Perf. 12

162	A54	10c on 24c pur (Bk)	2.50	1.50
a.		Inverted surcharge	30.00	30.00
b.		Red surcharge	22.50	22.50

Coat of Arms — A66

Printed by Waterlow & Sons

1927 Litho. *Perf. 13½*

165	A66	2c yellow	.40	.20
166	A66	3c pink	.50	.50
167	A66	4c red brown	.40	.40
168	A66	20c lt ol grn	.65	.20
169	A66	25c deep blue	.65	.30
170	A66	30c violet	.80	.80
171	A66	40c orange	1.50	1.25
172	A66	50c dp brown	1.50	.50
173	A55	1b red	1.75	1.25
174	A55	2b plum	2.50	2.50
175	A55	3b olive grn	2.50	2.50
176	A55	4b claret	4.00	3.50
177	A55	5b bister brn	4.75	4.00
		Nos. 165-177 (13)	21.90	17.90

For overprints and surcharges see Nos. 178-180, 208, 211-212.

Type of 1927 Issue Overprinted

Octubre
1927

1927

178	A66	5c dark green	.20	.15
179	A66	10c slate	.45	.15
180	A66	15c carmine	.65	.25
		Nos. 178-180 (3)	1.30	.55

Exist with inverted overprint. Value $20 each.

Stamps of 1919-27 Surcharged

15 cts.
1928

1928 *Perf. 12, 12½, 13½*

Red Surcharge

181	A54	15c on 20c #122	9.00	9.00
182	A54	15c on 20c #132	9.00	9.00
a.		Black surcharge	30.00	
183	A54	15c on 20c #146	165.00	165.00

Black Surcharge

184	A54	15c on 24c #124	1.65	.90
a.		Inverted surcharge	5.00	5.00
b.		Blue surcharge	50.00	
185	A54	15c on 50c #125	50.00	42.50
186	A54	15c on 50c #135	1.25	.70
		Nos. 181-186 (6)	235.90	227.10

Condor — A67

Hernando Siles — A68

Map of Bolivia — A69

Printed by Perkins, Bacon & Co., Ltd.

1928 Engr. *Perf. 13½*

189	A67	5c green	1.50	.15
190	A68	10c slate	.30	.15
191	A69	15c carmine lake	.60	.15
		Nos. 189-191 (3)	2.40	
		Set value		.15

Nos. 104, 111, 113, Surcharged in Various Colors

0.03
Centavos
R. S. 21-4
1930

1930 *Perf. 12, 11½*

193	A20	1c on 2c (Bl)	.80	.80
a.		"0.10" for "0.01"	12.50	12.50
194	A50	3c on 2c (Br)	.80	.80
195	A48	25c on ½c (Bk)	.80	.80
196	A50	25c on 2c (V)	.80	.80
		Nos. 193-196 (4)	3.20	3.20

The lines of the surcharges were spaced to fit the various shapes of the stamps. The surcharges exist inverted, double, etc.

Trial printings were made of the surcharges on #193 and 194 in black and on #196 in brown.

Mt. Potosi — A70

Mt. Illimani — A71

Eduardo Abaroa — A72

Map of Bolivia — A73

Sucre — A74

Bolivar — A75

1931 Engr. *Perf. 14*

197	A70	2c green	1.40	.50
198	A71	5c light blue	1.40	.20
199	A72	10c red orange	1.40	.20
200	A73	15c violet	1.40	.20
201	A73	35c carmine	2.00	.85
202	A73	45c orange	2.00	.75
203	A74	50c gray	.55	.55
204	A75	1b brown	.55	.55
		Nos. 197-204 (8)	10.70	3.80

No. 198 exists imperf.

See #207, 241. For surcharges see #209-210.

Symbols of 1930 Revolution — A76

1931 Litho. *Perf. 11*

205	A76	15c scarlet	2.25	.40
a.		Pair, imperf. between		
206	A76	50c brt violet	.70	.70
a.		Pair, imperf. between	7.50	

Revolution of June 25, 1930.

For surcharges see Nos. 239-240.

Map Type of 1931 Without Imprint

1932 Litho.

207	A73	15c violet	1.50	.35

Stamps of 1927-31 Surcharged

Habilitada
A 15 Cts.
D. S. 13-7.1933

1933 *Perf. 13½, 14*

208	A66	5c on 1b red	.60	.35
a.		Without period after "Cts"	1.25	1.25
209	A73	15c on 35c car	.35	.35
a.		Inverted surcharge	20.00	
210	A73	15c on 45c orange	.35	.35
a.		Inverted surcharge	3.00	3.00
211	A66	15c on 50c dp brn	1.50	.30
212	A66	25c on 40c orange	.60	.25
		Nos. 208-212 (5)	3.40	1.60

The hyphens in "13-7-33" occur in three positions.

Coat of Arms — A77

1933 Engr. *Perf. 12*

213	A77	2c blue green	.25	.15
214	A77	5c blue	.25	.15
215	A77	10c red	.45	.30
216	A77	15c deep violet	.35	.15
217	A77	25c dark blue	.65	.55
		Nos. 213-217 (5)	1.95	1.30

For surcharges see Nos. 233-235, 238.

Mariano Baptista — A78

Map of Bolivia — A79

1935

218	A78	15c dull violet	.45	.20

1935

219	A79	2c dark blue	.15	.15
220	A79	3c yellow	.15	.15
221	A79	5c vermilion	.15	.15
222	A79	5c blue grn	.35	.15
223	A79	10c black brn	.35	.15
224	A79	15c deep rose	.35	.15
225	A79	15c ultra	.35	.15
226	A79	20c yellow grn	.40	.15
227	A79	25c lt blue	.40	.15
228	A79	30c deep rose	.80	.55
229	A79	40c orange	.80	.55
230	A79	50c gray violet	.80	.25
231	A79	1b yellow	.55	.35
232	A79	2b olive brown	.80	.70
		Nos. 219-232 (14)	6.40	3.75

Regular Stamps of 1925-33 Surcharged in Black

Comunicaciones
D. S.
25-2-37
0.05

1937 *Perf. 11, 12, 13½*

233	A77	5c on 2c bl grn	.25	.25
234	A77	15c on 25c dk bl	.30	.30
235	A77	30c on 25c dk bl	.50	.50
236	A55	45c on 1b red brn	.60	.60
237	A55	1b on 2b plum	.75	.75
a.		"1" missing	7.50	7.50
238	A77	2b on 25c dk bl	.75	.75

"Comunicaciones" on one line

239	A76	3b on 50c brt vio	1.25	1.25
a.		"3" of value missing	6.00	6.00
240	A76	5b on 50c brt vio	1.25	1.25
		Nos. 233-240 (8)	5.65	5.65

Exist inverted, double, etc.

President Siles — A80

1937 Unwmk. *Perf. 14*

241	A80	1c yellow brown	.30	.30

Native School — A81

Oil Wells — A82

Modern Factories A83

Torch of Knowledge A84

Map of the Sucre-Camiri R. R. — A85

Allegory of Free Education — A86

Allegorical Figure of Learning A87

Symbols of Industry A88

Modern Agriculture — A89

1938 Litho. *Perf. 10½, 11*

242	A81	2c dull red	.40	.40
243	A82	10c pink	.45	.25
244	A83	15c yellow grn	.60	.30
245	A84	30c yellow	.75	.35
246	A85	45c rose red	1.40	.75
247	A86	60c dk violet	1.10	.35
248	A87	75c dull blue	1.50	.35
249	A88	1b lt brown	2.25	.35
250	A89	2b bister	2.00	.75
		Nos. 242-250 (9)	10.45	3.85

For surcharge see No. 314.

Llamas — A90

Vicuna — A91

Coat of Arms — A92

Cocoi Herons — A93

Chinchilla — A94

Toco Toucan — A95

Condor — A96

Jaguar — A97

1939, Jan. 21 *Perf. 10½, 11½x10½*

251 A90 2c green .30 .30
252 A90 4c fawn .30 .30
253 A90 5c red violet .30 .25
254 A91 10c black .45 .30
255 A91 15c emerald .45 .35
256 A91 20c dk slate grn .45 .25
257 A92 25c lemon .45 .25
258 A92 30c dark blue .45 .30
259 A93 40c vermilion 1.10 .30
260 A93 45c gray 1.10 .30
261 A94 60c rose red 1.10 .55
262 A94 75c slate blue 2.25 .55
263 A95 90c orange 1.65 .55
264 A95 1b blue 1.65 .55
265 A96 2b rose lake 2.25 .55
266 A96 3b dark violet 2.75 .80
267 A97 4b brown org 3.25 1.10
268 A97 5b gray brown 4.00 1.40
Nos. 251-268 (18) 24.25 8.95

All but 20c exist imperf.
Imperf. counterfeits with altered designs exist of some values.
For surcharges see Nos. 315-317.

Flags of 21 American Republics A98

1940, Apr. **Litho.** *Perf. 10½*

269 A98 9b multicolored 1.10 1.10

Pan American Union, 150th anniversary.

Statue of Murillo — A99

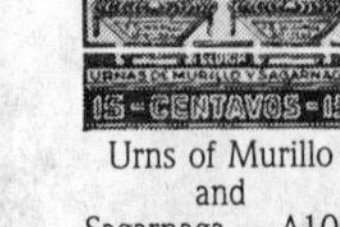
Urns of Murillo and Sagarnaga — A100

Dream of Murillo A101

Murillo A102

1941, Apr. 15

270 A99 10c dull vio brn .15 .15
271 A100 15c lt green .20 .15
a. Imperf., pair 3.50
b. Double impression 6.00
272 A101 45c carmine rose .20 .15
a. Double impression 6.00
273 A102 1.05b dk ultra .45 .15
Nos. 270-273 (4) 1.00
Set value .50

130th anniv. of the execution of Pedro Domingo Murillo (1759-1810), patriot.
For surcharge see No. 333.

First Stamp of Bolivia and 1941 Airmail Stamp — A103

1942, Oct. **Litho.** *Perf. 13½*

274 A103 5c pink .50 .50
275 A103 10c orange .50 .40
276 A103 20c yellow grn 1.00 .65
277 A103 40c carmine rose 1.25 .80
278 A103 90c ultra 2.50 1.00
279 A103 1b violet 3.00 1.65
280 A103 10b olive bister 10.00 8.25
Nos. 274-280 (7) 18.75 13.25

1st School Phil. Exposition held in La Paz, Oct., 1941.

Gen. Ballivian Leading Cavalry Charge, Battle of Ingavi — A104

1943 **Photo.** *Perf. 12½*

281 A104 2c lt blue grn .15 .15
282 A104 3c orange .15 .15
283 A104 25c deep plum .15 .15
284 A104 45c ultra .18 .15
285 A104 3b scarlet .38 .35
286 A104 4b brt rose lilac .55 .45
287 A104 5b black brown .80 .55
Nos. 281-287 (7) 2.36 1.95

Souvenir Sheets

Perf. 13, Imperf.

288 A104 Sheet of 4 1.50 1.50
289 A104 Sheet of 3 4.50 4.50

Centenary of the Battle of Ingavi, 1841. No. 288 contains 4 stamps similar to Nos. 281-284, No. 289 three stamps similar to Nos. 285-287.

Potosi A107

Quechisla A108

Miner — A109

Dam A110

Mine Interior A111

Chaquiri Dam A112

Entrance to Pulacayo Mine A113

1943 **Engr.** *Perf. 12½*

290 A107 15c red brown .20 .15
291 A108 45c vio blue .20 .15
292 A109 1.25b brt rose vio .25 .30
293 A110 1.50b emerald .25 .30
294 A111 2b brown blk .30 .35
295 A112 2.10b lt blue .40 .45
296 A113 3b red orange .50 .55
Nos. 290-296 (7) 2.10 2.25

General José Ballivián and Cathedral at Trinidad A114

1943, Nov. 18

297 A114 5c dk green & brn .15 .15
298 A114 10c dull pur & brn .15 .15
299 A114 30c rose red & brn .15 .15
300 A114 45c brt ultra & brn .20 .25
301 A114 2.10b dp org & brn .30 .35
Nos. 297-301,C91-C95 (10) 2.05 1.98

Department of Beni centenary.

"Honor, Work, Law" A115

"United for the Country" A116

1944 **Litho.** *Perf. 13½*

302 A115 20c orange .15 .15
303 A115 90c ultra .15 .15
304 A116 1b brt red vio .15 .15
305 A116 2.40b dull brown .20 .15

1945

306 A115 20c green .15 .15
307 A115 90c dp rose .15 .15
Set value, #302-307, C96-C99 1.50 1.00

Nos. 302-307 were issued to commemorate the Revolution of Dec. 20, 1943.

Catalogue values for unused stamps in this section, from this point to the end of the section, are for Never Hinged items.

Leopold Benedetto Vincenti, Joseph Ignacio de Sanjines and Bars of Anthem A117

1946, Aug. 21 **Litho.** *Perf. 10½*

308 A117 5c rose vio & blk .15 .15
309 A117 10c ultra & blk .15 .15
310 A117 15c blue grn & blk .15 .15
311 A117 30c vermilion & brn .15 .15
a. Souv. sheet of 1, imperf. .65 .65
312 A117 90c dk blue & brn .15 .15
313 A117 2b black & brn .30 .15
a. Souv. sheet of 1, imperf. 1.25 1.25
Set value .85 .60

Cent. of the adoption of Bolivia's natl. anthem.
Nos. 311a and 313a sold for 4b over face.

Nos. 248 and 262 Surcharged in Carmine, Black or Orange

1947, Mar. 12 *Perf. 10½, 11*

314 A87 1.40b on 75c (C) .15 .15
315 A94 1.40b on 75c (Bk) .15 .15
316 A94 1.40b on 75c (C) .15 .15
317 A94 1.40b on 75c (O) .15 .15
Set value, #314-317, C112 .65 .65

People Attacking Presidential Palace — A118

Arms of Bolivia and Argentina — A119

1947, Sept. **Litho.** *Perf. 13½*

318 A118 20c blue grn .15 .15
319 A118 50c lilac rose .15 .15
320 A118 1.40b grnsh bl .15 .15
321 A118 3.70b dull org .15 .15
322 A118 4b violet .18 .15
323 A118 10b olive .40 .25
Set value, #318-323, C113-C117 1.50 1.10

1st anniv. of the Revolution of July 21, 1946. Exist imperf.

1947, Oct. 23

324 A119 1.40b deep orange .20 .15

Meeting of Presidents Enrique Hertzog of Bolivia and Juan D. Peron of Argentina at Yacuiba on Oct. 23, 1947. Exist imperf.
See No. C118.

Statue of Christ above La Paz — A120

Designs: 2b, Child kneeling before cross of Golgotha. 3b, St. John Bosco. No. 328, Virgin of Copacabana. No. 329, Pope Pius XII blessing University of La Paz.

1948, Sept. 26 **Unwmk.** *Perf. 11½*

325 A120 1.40b blue & yel .30 .15
326 A120 2b yel grn & sal .40 .15
327 A120 3b green & gray .65 .20
328 A120 5b violet & sal .80 .25
329 A120 5b red brn & lt grn 1.10 .25
Nos. 325-329,C119-C123 (10) 6.05 2.51

3rd Inter-American Cong. of Catholic Education.

Map and Emblem of Bolivia Auto Club — A125

Pres. Gregorio Pacheco, Map and Post Horn — A126

1948, Oct. 20

330 A125 5b indigo & salmon 1.50 .15

Intl. Automobile Races of South America, Sept.-Oct. 1948. See No. C124.

1950, Jan. 2 **Litho.** ***Perf. 11½***
331 A126 1.40b violet blue .15 .15
332 A126 4.20b red .15 .15
Set value, #331-332, C125-C127 .60 .60

75th anniv. of the UPU.

No. 273 Surcharged in Black

Bs.2.- Habilitada
D.S.6·VII·50

1950 ***Perf. 10½***
333 A102 2b on 1.05b dk ultra .16 .15

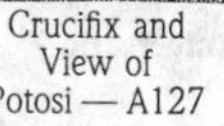

Crucifix and View of Potosi — A127

Symbols of United Nations — A128

Perf. 11½
1950, Sept. 14 **Litho.** **Unwmk.**
334 A127 20c violet .15 .15
335 A127 30c dp orange .15 .15
336 A127 50c lilac rose .15 .15
337 A127 1b carmine .15 .15
338 A127 2b blue .30 .15
339 A127 6b chocolate .25 .15
Set value .85 .35

400th anniv. of the appearance of a crucifix at Potosi. Exist imperf.

1950, Oct. 24
340 A128 60c ultra 1.00 .15
341 A128 2b green 1.40 .22

5th anniv. of the UN, Oct. 24, 1945. See Nos. C138-C139.

Gate of the Sun and Llama A129

Church of San Francisco A130

Designs: 40c, Avenue Camacho. 50c, Consistorial Palace. 1b, Legislative Palace. 1.40b, Communications Bldg. 2b, Arms. 3b, La Gasca ordering Mendoza to found La Paz. 5b, Capt. Alonso de Mendoza founding La Paz. 10b, Arms; portrait of Mendoza.

1951, Mar. **Engr.** ***Perf. 12½***
Center in Black
342 A129 20c green .15 .15
343 A130 30c dp orange .15 .15
344 A129 40c bister brn .15 .15
345 A129 50c dk red .15 .15
346 A129 1b dp purple .15 .15
347 A129 1.40b dk vio blue .15 .15
348 A129 2b dp purple .15 .15
349 A129 3b red lilac .20 .15
a. Sheet, Nos. 345, 346, 348, 349 1.10 1.10
b. As "a," imperf. 1.10 1.10
350 A129 5b dk red .22 .16
a. Sheet, Nos. 344, 347, 350 1.10 1.10
b. As "a," imperf. 1.10 1.10
351 A129 10b sepia .50 .22
a. Sheet, Nos. 342, 343, 351 1.10 1.10
b. As "a," imperf. 1.10 1.10
Nos. 342-351,C140-C149 (20) 4.97 4.58

400th anniv. of the founding of La Paz.
For surcharges see Nos. 393-402.

Boxing — A131

Perf. 12½
1951, July 1 **Unwmk.** **Engr.**
352 A131 20c shown .16 .15
353 A131 50c Tennis .16 .15
354 A131 1b Diving .20 .15
355 A131 1.40b Soccer .20 .15
356 A131 2b Skiing .38 .30
357 A131 3b Handball .80 .80
a. Sheet, Nos. 352, 353, 356, 357 2.25 1.75
b. As "a," imperf. 2.25 1.75
358 A131 4b Cycling 1.00 1.00
a. Sheet, Nos. 354, 355, 358 2.00 1.50
b. As "a," imperf. 2.00 1.50
Nos. 352-358,C150-C156 (14) 8.15 5.85

The stamps were intended to commemorate the 5th athletic championship matches held at La Paz, October 1948.

Eagle and Flag of Bolivia — A132

1951, Nov. 5 **Litho.** ***Perf. 11½***
Flag in Red, Yellow and Green.
359 A132 2b aqua .15 .15
360 A132 3.50b ultra .15 .15
361 A132 5b purple .15 .15
362 A132 7.50b gray .20 .15
363 A132 15b dp car .25 .22
364 A132 30b sepia .50 .50
Nos. 359-364 (6) 1.40 1.32

Cent. of the adoption of Bolivia's natl. flag.

Eduardo Abaroa A133

Queen Isabella I A134

1952, Mar. ***Perf. 11***
365 A133 80c dk carmine .15 .15
366 A133 1b red orange .15 .15
367 A133 2b emerald .20 .15
368 A133 5b ultra .25 .15
369 A133 10b lilac rose .50 .16
370 A133 20b dk brown .75 .65
Nos. 365-370,C157-C162 (12) 5.00 4.11

73rd anniversary of the death of Eduardo Abaroa.

1952, July 16 **Unwmk.** ***Perf. 13½***
371 A134 2b vio bl .15 .15
372 A134 6.30b carmine .20 .20
Set value .30 .30

500th anniv. of the birth of Isabella I of Spain. See Nos. C163-C164.

Columbus Lighthouse A135

1952, July 16 **Litho.**
373 A135 2b vio bl, *bl* .15 .15
374 A135 5b car, *sal* .50 .40
375 A135 9b emer, *grn* .85 .60
Nos. 373-375,C165-C168 (7) 2.50 1.90

Miner — A136

1953, Apr. 9
376 A136 2.50b vermilion .15 .15
377 A136 8b violet .15 .15
Set value .25 .20

Nationalization of the mines.

Gualberto Villarroel, Victor Paz Estenssoro and Hernan Siles Zuazo — A137

1953, Apr. 9 ***Perf. 11½***
378 A137 50c rose lil .15 .15
379 A137 1b brt rose .15 .15
380 A137 2b vio bl .15 .15
381 A137 3b lt grn .15 .15
382 A137 4b yel org .15 .15
383 A137 5b dl vio .16 .15
Set value, #378-383, C169-C175 1.90 1.50

Revolution of Apr. 9, 1952, 1st anniv.

Map of Bolivia and Cow's Head — A138

Designs: 17b, Same as 5b. 25b, 85b, Map and ear of wheat.

1954, Aug. 2 ***Perf. 12x11½***
384 A138 5b car rose .15 .15
385 A138 17b aqua .15 .15
386 A138 25b chalky blue .15 .15
387 A138 85b blk brn .25 .20
Set value, #384-387, C176-C181 2.35 1.15

Nos. 384-385 for the agrarian reform laws of 1953-54. Nos. 386-387 for the 1st National Congress of Agronomy. Exist imperf.

Oil Refinery A139

1955, Oct. 9 **Unwmk.** ***Perf. 12x11½***
388 A139 10b ultra & lt ultra .15 .15
389 A139 35b rose car & rose .15 .15
390 A139 40b dk & lt yel grn .15 .15
391 A139 50b red vio & lil rose .15 .15
392 A139 80b brn & bis brn .18 .15
Nos. 388-392,C182-C186 (10) 3.28
Set value 2.25

Exist imperf.

Nos. 342-351, Surcharged with New Values and Bars in Ultramarine

1957, Feb. 14 **Engr.** ***Perf. 12½***
Center in Black
393 A129 50b on 3b red lilac .15 .15
394 A129 100b on 2b dp pur .15 .15
395 A129 200b on 1b dp pur .15 .15
396 A129 300b on 1.40b dk vio bl .16 .15
397 A129 350b on 20c green .22 .15
398 A129 400b on 40c bis brn .22 .15
399 A130 600b on 30c dp org .35 .15
400 A129 800b on 50c dk red .40 .15
401 A129 1000b on 10b sepia .40 .15
402 A129 2000b on 5b dk red .65 .20
Nos. 393-402 (10) 2.85
Set value .75

See Nos. C187-C196.

CEPAL Building, Santiago de Chile, and Meeting Hall in La Paz — A140

1957, May 15 **Litho.** ***Perf. 13***
403 A140 150b gray & ultra .15 .15
404 A140 350b bis brn & gray .18 .18
405 A140 550b chlky bl & brn .20 .20
406 A140 750b dp rose & grn .30 .20
407 A140 900b grn & brn blk .40 .15
Nos. 403-407,C197-C201 (10) 5.03 3.48

7th session of the C. E. P. A. L. (Comision Economica para la America Latina de las Naciones Unidas), La Paz. Exist imperf.

For surcharges see Nos. 482-484.

Presidents Siles Zuazo and Aramburu A141

1957, Dec. 15 **Unwmk.** ***Perf. 11½***
408 A141 50b red org .15 .15
409 A141 350b blue .25 .15
410 A141 1000b redsh brn .50 .15
Nos. 408-410,C202-C204 (6) 1.97
Set value .48

Opening of the Santa Cruz-Yacuiba Railroad and the meeting of the Presidents of Bolivia and Argentina. Exist imperf.
For surcharge see No. 699.

Flags of Bolivia and Mexico and Presidents Hernan Siles Zuazo and Adolfo Lopez Mateos A142

1960, Jan. 30 **Litho.** ***Perf. 11½***
411 A142 350b olive .16 .16
412 A142 600b red brn .22 .22
413 A142 1500b blk brn .50 .50
Nos. 411-413,C205-C207 (6) 3.03 2.18

Issued for an expected visit of Mexico's President Adolfo Lopez Mateos. On sale Jan. 30-Feb. 1, 1960.

Indians and Mt. Illimani A143

Refugee Children A144

1960, Mar. 26 **Unwmk.**
414 A143 500b ol bis .50 .15
415 A143 1000b blue .90 .30
416 A143 2000b brown 2.00 .50
417 A143 4000b green 3.75 2.50
Nos. 414-417,C208-C211 (8) 22.15 12.90

1960, Apr. 7 ***Perf. 11½***
418 A144 50b brown .15 .15
419 A144 350b claret .15 .15
420 A144 400b steel blue .16 .16
421 A144 1000b gray brn .50 .50
422 A144 3000b slate grn 1.00 1.00
Nos. 418-422,C212-C216 (10) 4.26 4.21

Issued to publicize World Refugee Year, July 1, 1959-June 30, 1960.
For surcharges see Nos. 454-458, 529.

Jaime Laredo A145

Rotary Emblem and Nurse with Children A146

1960, Aug. 15 **Litho.** ***Perf. 11½***
423 A145 100b olive .20 .15
424 A145 350b dp rose .30 .25
425 A145 500b Prus grn .38 .20
426 A145 1000b brown .50 .50
427 A145 1500b vio bl .90 .90
428 A145 5000b gray 3.00 3.00
Nos. 423-428,C217-C222 (12) 13.03 8.70

Issued to honor violinist Jaime Laredo.
For surcharge see No. 485.

1960, Nov. 19 *Perf. 11½*

429 A146 350b multi .16 .15
430 A146 500b multi .22 .15
431 A146 600b multi .35 .35
432 A146 1000b multi .40 .20
Nos. 429-432,C223-C226 (8) 6.13 3.49

Issued for the Children's Hospital, sponsored by the Rotary Club of La Paz.
For surcharges see Nos. 486-487.

Designs from Gate of the Sun
A147 A148

Designs: Various prehistoric gods and ornaments from Tiahuanacu excavations.

1960, Dec. 16 *Perf. 13x12, 12x13*

Gold Background

Surcharge in Black or Dark Red

Sizes: 21x23mm, 23x21mm

433 A147 50b on ½c red .45 .30
434 A147 100b on 1c red .35 .15
435 A147 200b on 2c blk .75 .35
436 A147 300b on 5c grn (DR) .25 .20
437 A147 350b on 10c grn .25 .75
438 A148 400b on 15c ind .35 .15
439 A148 500b on 20c red .35 .30
440 A148 500b on 50c red .40 .15
441 A148 600b on 22½c grn .45 .45
442 A148 600b on 60c vio .60 .50
443 A148 700b on 25c vio .75 .15
444 A148 700b on 1b grn 1.00 1.00
445 A148 800b on 30c red .60 .15
446 A148 900b on 40c grn .45 .20
447 A148 1000b on 2b bl .60 .50
448 A148 1800b on 3b gray 5.00 3.50

Perf. 11

Size: 49½x23mm

449 A148 4000b on 4b gray 30.00 25.00

Perf. 11x13½

Size: 49x53mm

450 A147 5000b on 5b gray 7.50 7.00
Nos. 433-450 (18) 50.10 40.80

Nos. 433-450 were not regularly issued without surcharge. Value, set $20.
The decree for Nos. 433-450 stipulated that 7 were for air mail (500b on 50c, 600b on 60c, 700b on 1b, 1000b, 1800b, 4000b and 5000b), but the overprinting failed to include "Aereo."
The 800b surcharge also exists on the 1c red and gold. This was not listed in the decree.
For surcharges see Nos. 528, 614.

Miguel de Cervantes A149

Nuflo de Chaves A150

1961, Nov. **Photo.** *Perf. 13x12½*

451 A149 600b ocher & dl vio .38 .15

Cervantes' appointment as Chief Magistrate of La Paz. See No. C230.

1961, Nov. **Unwmk.**

452 A150 1500b dk bl, *buff* .75 .30

Founding of Santa Cruz de la Sierra, 400th anniv. See #468, C246. For surcharge see #533.

People below Eucharist Symbol — A151

Flowers — A152

1962, Mar. 19 **Litho.** *Perf. 10½*

453 A151 1000b gray grn, red & yel .65 .35

4th Natl. Eucharistic Congress, Santa Cruz, 1961. See No. C231.

Nos. 418-422 Surcharged Horizontally with New Value and Bars or Greek Key Border Segment

1962, June *Perf. 11½*

454 A144 600b on 50b brown .18 .18
455 A144 900b on 350b claret .22 .15
456 A144 1000b on 400b steel blue .32 .15
457 A144 2000b on 1000b gray brn .38 .22
458 A144 3500b on 3000b slate grn .65 .65
Nos. 454-458,C232-C236 (10) 5.15 4.45

Old value obliterated with two short bars on No. 454; four short bars on Nos. 455-456 and Greek key border on Nos. 457-458. The Greek key obliteration comes in two positions: two full "keys" on top, and one full and two half keys on top.

1962, June 28 **Litho.** *Perf. 10½*

459 A152 200b Hibiscus .30 .15
460 A152 400b Bicolored vanda .45 .15
461 A152 600b Lily .75 .15
462 A152 1000b Orchid 1.00 .18
Nos. 459-462,C237-C240 (8) 7.50 3.18

Bolivia's Armed Forces A153

Anti-Malaria Emblem A154

1962, Sept. 5 *Perf. 11½*

463 A153 400b Infantry .15 .15
464 A153 500b Cavalry .15 .15
465 A153 600b Artillery .16 .15
466 A153 2000b Engineers .50 .35
Nos. 463-466,C241-C244 (8) 3.96 2.15

1962, Oct. 4

467 A154 600b dk & lt vio & yel .25 .25

WHO drive to eradicate malaria. See #C245.

Portrait Type of 1961

Design: 600b, Alonso de Mendoza.

1962 **Photo.** *Perf. 13x12½*

468 A150 600b rose vio, *bluish* .25 .15

Soccer and Flags — A155

Design: 1b, Goalkeeper catching ball, vert.

1963, Mar. 21 **Litho.** *Perf. 11½*

Flags in National Colors

469 A155 60c gray .40 .40
470 A155 1b gray .60 .20

21st South American Soccer Championships. See Nos. C247-C248.

Globe and Wheat Emblem — A156

1963, Aug. 1 **Unwmk.** *Perf. 11½*

471 A156 60c dk bl, bl & yel .25 .25

"Freedom from Hunger" campaign of the FAO. See No. C249.

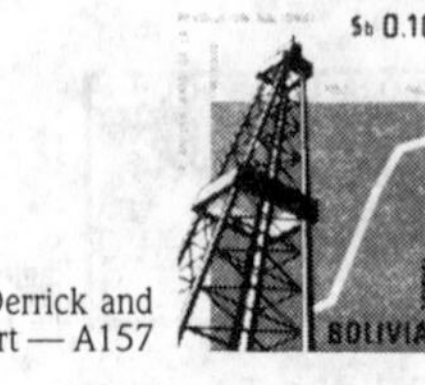

Oil Derrick and Chart — A157

Designs: 60c, Map of Bolivia. 1b, Students.

1963, Dec. 21 **Litho.** *Perf. 11½*

472 A157 10c grn & dk brn .15 .15
473 A157 60c ocher & dk brn .22 .15
474 A157 1b dk bl, grn & yel .28 .15
Nos. 472-474,C251-C253 (6) 2.55 1.80

Revolution of Apr. 9, 1952, 10th anniv.

Flags of Bolivia and Peru — A158

1966, Aug. 10 **Wmk. 90** *Perf. 13½*

Flags in National Colors

475 A158 10c blk & tan .15 .15
476 A158 60c blk & lt grn .20 .20
477 A158 1b blk & gray .35 .35
478 A158 2b blk & rose .50 .50
Nos. 475-478,C254-C257 (8) 2.85 2.85

Marshal Andrés Santa Cruz (1792-1865), president of Bolivia and of Peru-Bolivian Confederation.

Children — A159

Perf. 13½

1966, Dec. 16 **Unwmk.** **Litho.**

479 A159 30c ocher & sepia .15 .15

Issued to help poor children. See No. C258.

Map and Flag of Bolivia and Generals Ovando and Barrientos A160

1966, Dec. 16 **Litho.** *Perf. 13½*

Flag in Red, Yellow and Green

480 A160 60c vio brn & tan .30 .20
481 A160 1b dl grn & tan .45 .15

Issued to honor Generals Rene Barrientos Ortuno and Alfredo Ovando C., co-Presidents, 1965-66. See Nos. C259-C260.

Various Issues 1957-60 and Type A161 Surcharged with New Values and Bars

A161

1966, Dec. 21

On No. 403: "Centenario de la / Cruz Roja / Internacional"

482 A140 20c on 150b gray & ultra .20 .15

On Nos. 405-406: "Homenaje a la / Generala / J. Azurduy de / Padilla"

483 A140 30c on 550b chlky bl & brn .30 .15
484 A140 2.80b on 750b dp rose & grn .75 .50

On No. 424: "CL Aniversario / Heroinas Coronilla"

485 A145 60c on 350b dp rose .50 .15

Nos. 429-430 Surcharged

486 A146 1.60b on 350b multi .75 .50
487 A146 2.40b on 500b multi 1.00 .75

Revenue Stamps of 1946 surcharged with New Value, "X" and: "XXV Aniversario / Gobierno Busch"

488 A161 20c on 5b red .20 .15

Overprinted: "XX Aniversario / Gob. Villaroel"

489 A161 60c on 2b grn .30 .15

Overprinted: "Centenario do / Rurrenabaque"

490 A161 1b on 10b brn .50 .15

Overprinted: "XXV Aniversario / Dpto. Pando"

491 A161 1.60b on 50c vio .50 .16
Nos. 482-491,C261-C272 (22) 14.50 8.86

For surcharge see No. C272.

Sower A162

"Macheteros" A163

1967, Sept. 20 **Litho.** *Perf. 13½x13*

492 A162 70c multi .35 .15

50th anniv. of Lions Intl. See #C273-C273a.

1968, June 24 *Perf. 13½x13*

Designs (Folklore characters): 60c, Chunchos. 1p, Wiphala. 2p, Diablada.

493 A163 30c gray & multi .15 .15
494 A163 60c sky bl & multi .25 .25
495 A163 1b gray & multi .40 .15
496 A163 2b gray ol & multi .60 .20
Nos. 493-496,C274-C277 (8) 3.90 1.65

Issued to publicize the 9th Congress of the Postal Union of the Americas and Spain.
A souvenir sheet exists containing 4 imperf. stamps similar to #493-496. Size: 131x81½mm.

Arms of Tarija — A164

Pres. Gualberto Villaroel — A165

1968, Oct. 29 **Litho.** *Perf. 13½x13*

497 A164 20c pale sal & multi .15 .15
498 A164 30c gray & multi .15 .15
499 A164 40c dl yel & multi .15 .15
500 A164 60c lt yel grn & multi .20 .20
Nos. 497-500,C278-C281 (8) 3.15 2.40

Battle of Tablada sesquicentennial.

1968, Nov. 6 **Unwmk.**

501 A165 20c sep & org .30 .15
502 A165 30c sep & dl bl grn .30 .15
503 A165 40c sep & dl rose .30 .20
504 A165 50c sep & yel grn .30 .15
505 A165 1b sep & ol bis .30 .15
Nos. 501-505 (5) 1.50
Set value .45

4th centenary of the founding of Cochabamba. See Nos. C282-C286.

ITU Emblem — A166

1968, Dec. 3 Litho. *Perf. 13x13½*

506 A166 10c gray, blk & yel .20 .20
507 A166 60c org, blk & ol .40 .40

Cent. (in 1965) of the ITU. See Nos. C287-C288.

Polychrome Painted Clay Cup, Inca Period — A167

1968, Nov. 14 *Perf. 13½x13*

508 A167 20c dk bl grn & multi .15 .15
509 A167 60c vio bl & multi .35 .35

20th anniv. (in 1966) of UNESCO. See Nos. C289-C290.

John F. Kennedy — A168

Tennis Player — A169

1968, Nov. 22 *Perf. 13x13½*

510 A168 10c yel grn & blk .15 .15
511 A168 4b vio & blk 1.40 1.40

A souvenir sheet contains one imperf. stamp similar to No. 511. Green marginal inscription. Size: 131x81½mm.

See Nos. C291-C292.

1968, Dec. 10 *Perf. 13x13½*

512 A169 10c gray, blk & lt brn .25 .25
513 A169 20c yel, blk & lt brn .25 .25
514 A169 30c ultra, blk & lt brn .25 .25
Nos. 512-514 (3) .75 .75

32nd South American Tennis Championships, La Paz, 1965. See Nos. C293-C294.

A souvenir sheet exists containing 3 imperf. stamps similar to Nos. 512-514. Size: 131x81½mm.

Issue of 1863 — A170

1968, Dec. 23 Litho. *Perf. 13x13½*

515 A170 10c yel grn, brn & blk .35 .20
516 A170 30c lt bl, brn & blk .35 .35
517 A170 2b gray, brn & blk .35 .35
Nos. 515-517,C295-C297 (6) 3.55 3.40

Cent. of Bolivian postage stamps. See Nos. C295-C297.

A souvenir sheet exists containing 3 imperf. stamps similar to Nos. 515-517. Yellow green marginal inscription. Size: 131x81½mm.

Rifle Shooting — A171

Sports: 50c, Equestrian. 60c, Canoeing.

1969, Oct. 29 Litho. *Perf. 13x13½*

518 A171 40c red brn, org & blk .40 .40
519 A171 50c emer, red & blk .40 .40
520 A171 60c bl, emer & blk .40 .40
Nos. 518-520,C299-C301 (6) 4.20 3.85

Issued to commemorate the 19th Olympic Games, Mexico City, Oct. 12-27, 1968.

A souvenir sheet exists containing 3 imperf. stamps similar to Nos. 518-520. Size: 130½x81mm.

Temenis Laothoe Violetta A172

Butterflies: 10c, Papilio crassus. 20c, Catagramma cynosura. 30c, Eunica eurota flora. 80c, Ituna phenarete.

1970, Apr. 24 Litho. *Perf. 13x13½*

521 A172 5c pale lil & multi .50 .50
522 A172 10c pink & multi 1.00 1.00
523 A172 20c gray & multi 1.00 1.00
524 A172 30c yel & multi 1.00 1.00
525 A172 80c multicolored 1.00 1.00
Nos. 521-525,C302-C306 (10) 15.00 15.00

A souvenir sheet exists containing 3 imperf. stamps similar to Nos. 521-523. Black marginal inscription. Size: 129½x80mm.

Boy Scout — A173

Design: 10c, Girl Scout planting rose bush.

1970, June 17 *Perf. 13½x13*

526 A173 5c multicolored .20 .15
527 A173 10c multicolored .20 .15

Issued to honor the Bolivian Scout movement. See Nos. C307-C308.

No. 437 Surcharged "EXFILCA 70 / $b. 0.30" and Two Bars in Red

1970, Dec. 6 Litho. *Perf. 13x12*

528 A147 30c on 350b on 10c .25 .25

EXFILCA 70, 2nd Interamerican Philatelic Exhib., Caracas, Venezuela, Nov. 27-Dec. 6.

Nos. 455 and 452 Surcharged in Black or Red

1970, Dec. Photo. *Perf. 11½*

529 A144 60c on 900b on 350b .25 .20
533 A150 1.20b on 1500b (R) .50 .15

Amaryllis Yungacensis A174

Sica Sica Church, EXFILIMA Emblem A175

Bolivian Flowers: 30c, Amaryllis escobar uriae, horiz. 40c, Amaryllis evansae, horiz. 2b, Gymnocalycium chiquitanum.

Perf. 13x13½, 13½x13

1971, Aug. 9 Litho. Unwmk.

534 A174 30c gray & multi .30 .30
535 A174 40c multi .30 .30
536 A174 50c multi .35 .35
537 A174 2b multi 1.00 .60
Nos. 534-537,C310-C313 (8) 6.95 4.45

1971, Nov. 6 *Perf. 14x13½*

538 A175 20c red & multi .20 .15

EXFILIMA '71, 3rd Inter-American Philatelic Exhibition, Lima, Peru, Nov. 6-14.

A176 A177

Design: Pres. Hugo Banzer Suarez.

1972, Jan. 24 Litho. *Perf. 13½*

539 A176 1.20b blk & multi .50 .15

Bolivia's development, Aug. 19, 1971, to Jan. 24, 1972.

1972, Mar. 23 Litho. *Perf. 13½x13*

Folk Dances: 20c, Chiriwano de Achocalla. 40c, Rueda Chapaca. 60c, Kena-kena. 1b, Waca Thokori.

540 A177 20c red & multi .15 .15
541 A177 40c rose lil & multi .30 .25
542 A177 60c cream & multi .45 .20
543 A177 1b citron & multi .55 .22
Nos. 540-543,C314-C315 (6) 2.60 1.14

Madonna and Child by B. Bitti — A178

Tarija Cathedral, EXFILBRA Emblem — A179

Bolivian paintings: 10c, Nativity, by Melchor Perez de Holguin. 50c, Coronation of the Virgin, by G. M. Berrio. 70c, Harquebusier, anonymous. 80c, St. Peter of Alcantara, by Holguin.

1972 Litho. *Perf. 14x13½*

544 A178 10c gray & multi .15 .15
545 A178 50c sal & multi .25 .15
546 A178 70c lt grn & multi .35 .15
547 A178 80c buff & multi .40 .15
548 A178 1b multi .50 .15
Nos. 544-548,C316-C319 (9) 3.40
Set value 1.10

Issue dates: 1b, Aug. 17; others, Dec. 4.

1972, Aug. 26

549 A179 30c multi .16 .15

4th Inter-American Philatelic Exhibition, EXFILBRA, Rio de Janeiro, Brazil, Aug. 26-Sept. 2.

Echinocactus Notocactus — A180

Designs: Various cacti.

1973, Aug. 6 Litho. *Perf. 13½*

550 A180 20c crim & multi .30 .25
551 A180 40c multi .30 .25
552 A180 50c multi .30 .15
553 A180 70c multi .30 .20
Nos. 550-553,C321-C323 (7) 2.70 1.45

Power Station, Santa Isabel A181

Designs: 20c, Tin industry. 90c, Bismuth industry. 1b, Natural gas plant.

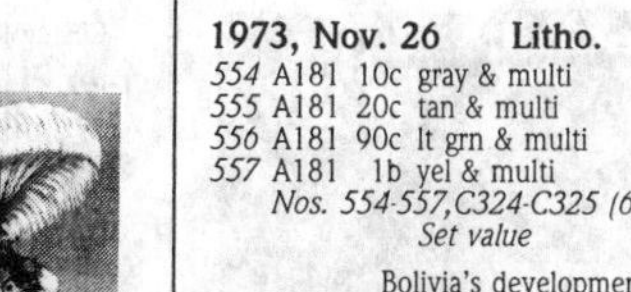

1973, Nov. 26 Litho. *Perf. 13½*

554 A181 10c gray & multi .15 .15
555 A181 20c tan & multi .15 .15
556 A181 90c lt grn & multi .25 .20
557 A181 1b yel & multi .25 .15
Nos. 554-557,C324-C325 (6) 1.80
Set value .75

Bolivia's development.

Cattleya Nobilior — A182

Orchids: 50c, Zygopetalum bolivianum. 1b, Huntleya melagris.

1974, May 15 *Perf. 13½*

558 A182 20c gray & multi .40 .15
559 A182 50c lt bl & multi .40 .15
560 A182 1b cit & multi .40 .15
Nos. 558-560,C327-C330 (7) 7.70 1.97

For surcharge see No. 704.

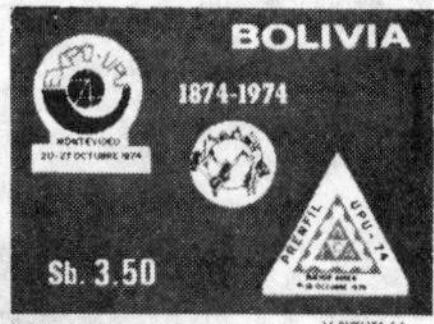

UPU and Philatelic Exposition Emblems A183

1974, Oct. 9

561 A183 3.50b grn, blk & bl 1.00 .40

Centenary of Universal Postal Union: PRENFIL-UPU Philatelic Exhibition, Buenos Aires, Oct. 1-12; EXPO-UPU Philatelic Exhibition, Montevideo, Oct. 20-27.

Gen. Sucre, by I. Wallpher — A184

1974, Dec. 9 Litho. *Perf. 13½*

562 A184 5b multicolored 1.10 .50

Sesquicentennial of the Battle of Ayacucho.

Lions Emblem and Steles A185

1975, Mar. Litho. *Perf. 13½*

563 A185 30c red & multi .35 .35

Lions Intl. in Bolivia, 25th anniv.

España 75 Emblem A186

1975, Mar.

564 A186 4.50b yel, red & blk .80 .35

Espana 75 International Philatelic Exhibition, Madrid, Apr. 4-13.

Emblem
A187

1975 Litho. *Perf. 13½*
565 A187 2.50b lil, blk & sil .65 .25

First meeting of Postal Ministers, Quito, Ecuador, March 1974, and for the Cartagena Agreement.

Pando Coat of Arms — A188

Designs: Departmental coats of arms.

1975, July 16 Litho. *Perf. 13½*
566 A188 20c shown .15 .15
567 A188 2b Chuquisaca .40 .40
568 A188 3b Cochabamba .50 .50
Nos. 566-568,C336-C341 (9) 4.10 4.10

Sesquicentennial of Republic of Bolivia.

Simón Bolívar — A189

Presidents and Statesmen of Bolivia: 30c, Victor Paz Estenssoro. 60c, Tomas Frias. 1b, Ismael Montes. 2.50b, Aniceto Arce. 7b, Bautista Saavedra. 10b, Jose Manuel Pando. 15b, Jose Maria Linares. 50b, Simon Bolivar.

1975 Litho. *Perf. 13½*
Size: 24x32mm
569 A189 30c multi .15 .15
569A A189 60c multi .20 .20
570 A189 1b multi .30 .30
571 A189 2.50b multi .50 .50
572 A189 7b multi 1.40 .50
573 A189 10b multi 2.00 .75
574 A189 15b multi 2.50 2.50
Size: 28x39mm
575 A189 50b multi 10.00 10.00
Nos. 569-575,C346-C353 (16) 36.05 31.15

Sesquicentennial of Republic of Bolivia.

"EXFIVIA 75"
A190

1975, Dec. 1 Litho. *Perf. 13½*
576 A190 3b multicolored .75 .60
a. Souvenir sheet 1.50 1.50

EXFIVIA 75, first Bolivian Philatelic Exposition. No. 576a contains one stamp similar to No. 576 with simulated perforations. Sold for 5b.

A191

A192

Chiang Kai-shek, flags of Bolivia and China.

1976, Apr. 4 Litho. *Perf. 13½*
577 A191 2.50b multi, red circle 1.00 1.00
578 A191 2.50b multi, bl circle 1.00 1.00

Pres. Chiang Kai-shek of China (1887-1975).
Erroneous red of sun's circle on Chinese flag of No. 577 was corrected on No. 578 with a dark blue overlay.

1976, Apr. Litho. *Perf. 13½*
579 A192 50c Naval insignia .40 .35

Navy anniversary.

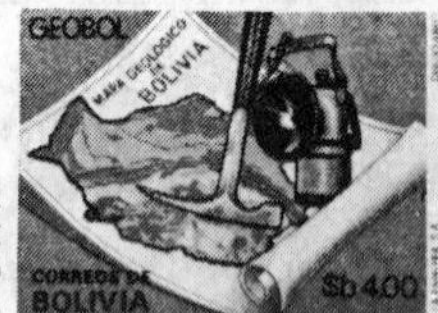

Geological Map, Pickax and Lamp
A193

1976, May
580 A193 4b multicolored .80 .60

Bolivian Geological Institute.

Lufthansa Jet, Bolivian and German Colors
A194

1976, May
581 A194 3b multicolored .80 .35

Lufthansa, 50th anniversary.

Boy Scout and Scout Emblem — A195

1976, May Litho. *Perf. 13½*
582 A195 1b multicolored .50 .50

Bolivian Boy Scouts, 60th anniversary.

Battle Scene, US Bicentennial Emblem
A196

1976, May 25
583 A196 4.50b bis & multi 1.40 .65

American Bicentennial.
A souvenir sheet contains one stamp similar to No. 583 with simulated perforations. Size: 130x80mm.

Family, Map of Bolivia — A197

Vicente Bernedo — A198

1976 *Perf. 13½*
584 A197 2.50b multicolored .50 .40

National Census 1976.

1976, Oct.
585 A198 1.50b multicolored .35 .30

Brother Vicente Bernedo de Potosi (1544-1619), missionary to the Indians.

Policeman with Dog, Rainbow over La Paz — A199

1976, Oct.
586 A199 2.50b multicolored .60 .60

Bolivian Police, 150 years of service.

Emblem, Bolivar and Sucre
A200

1976, Nov. 18 Litho. *Perf. 13½*
587 A200 1.50b multicolored .60 .60

Intl. Congress of Bolivarian Societies.

Pedro Poveda, View of La Paz — A201

1976, Dec.
588 A201 1.50b multicolored .35 .25

Pedro Poveda (1874-1936), educator.

A202

Boy and Girl — A203

1976, Dec. 17 *Perf. 10½*
594 A202 20c brown .30 .15
595 A202 1b ultra .45 .15
596 A202 1.50b green .75 .50
Nos. 594-596 (3) 1.50
Set value .62

1977, Feb. 4 Litho. *Perf. 13½*
599 A203 50c multicolored .15 .15

Christmas 1976, and for 50th anniversary of the Inter-American Children's Institute.

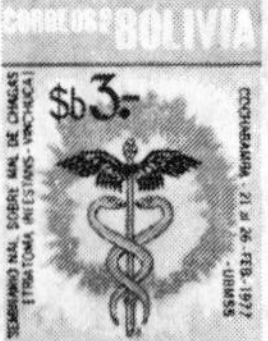

Staff of Aesculapius
A204

Supreme Court, La Paz
A205

1977, Mar. 18 Litho. *Perf. 13½x13*
600 A204 3b multicolored .75 .30

National Seminar on Chagas' disease, Cochabamba, Feb. 21-26.

1977, May 3

Designs: 4b, Manuel Maria Urcullu, first President of Supreme Court. 4.50b, Pantaleon Dalence, President 1883-1889.

601 A205 2.50b multi .30 .30
602 A205 4b multi .42 .15
603 A205 4.50b multi .50 .20
Nos. 601-603 (3) 1.22 .65

Sesquicentennial of Bolivian Supreme Court.

Newspaper Mastheads
A206

Map of Bolivia, Tower and Flag
A207

Designs: 2.50b, Alfredo Alexander and Hoy, horiz. 3b, Jose Carrasco and El Diario, horiz. 4b, Demetrio Canelas and Los Tiempos. 5.50b, Frontpage of Presencia.

1977, June Litho. *Perf. 13½*
604 A206 1.50b multi .22 .15
605 A206 2.50b multi .35 .30
606 A206 3b multi .42 .25
607 A206 4b multi .50 .35
608 A206 5.50b multi .65 .20
Nos. 604-608 (5) 2.14 1.25

Bolivian newspapers and their founders.

1977, June
609 A207 3b multi .50 .16

90th anniversary of Oruro Club.

Games' Poster — A208

Tin Miner and Emblem — A209

1977, Oct. 20 Litho. *Perf. 13½*
610 A208 5b blue & multi .75 .20

8th Bolivian Games, La Paz, Oct. 1977.

1977, Oct. 31 Litho. *Perf. 13*
611 A209 3b multicolored .60 .40

Bolivian Mining Corp., 25th anniv.

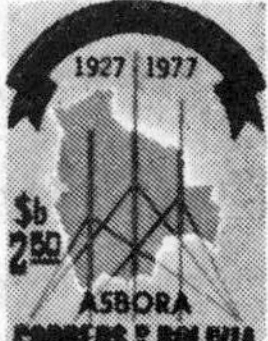

Miners, Globe, Tin Symbol — A210

Map of Bolivia, Radio Masts — A211

1977, Nov. 3

612 A210 6b silver & multi .80 .25

Intl. Tin Symposium, La Paz, Nov. 14-21.

1977, Nov. 11

613 A211 2.50b blue & multi .50 .35

Radio Bolivia, ASBORA, 50th anniversary.

No. 450 Surcharged with New Value, 3 Bars and "EXFIVIA-77"

1977, Nov. 25 Litho. ***Perf. 11x13½***

614 A147 5b on 5000b on 5b 1.00 1.25

EXFIVIA '77 Philatelic Exhibition, Cochabamba.

Eye, Compass, Book of Law — A212

1978, May 3 Litho. ***Perf. 13½x13***

615 A212 5b multi .65 .16

Audit Department, 50th anniversary.

Mt. Illimani — A213

Pre-Columbian Monolith — A214

Design: 1.50b, Mt. Cerro de Potosi.

Perf. 11x10½, 10½x11

1978, June 1 **Litho.**

616	A213	50c bl & Prus bl	.15	.15
617	A214	1b brn & lemon	.20	.15
618	A213	1.50b red & bl gray	.35	.25
		Nos. 616-618 (3)	.70	
		Set value		.35

Andean Countries, Staff of Aesculapius — A215

Map of Americas with Bolivia — A216

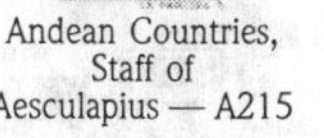

1978, June 1 ***Perf. 10½x11***

626 A215 2b org & blk .35 .15

Health Ministers of Andean Countries, 5th meeting.

1978, June 1

627 A216 2.50b dp ultra & red .35 .15

World Rheumatism Year.

For surcharge see No. 697.

Central Bank Building — A217

Jesus and Children — A218

1978, July 26 Litho. ***Perf. 13½***

628 A217 7b multi 1.00 .25

50th anniversary of Bank of Bolivia.

1979, Feb. 20 Litho. ***Perf. 13½***

629 A218 8b multicolored .90 .16

International Year of the Child.

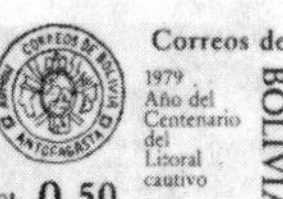

Antofagasta Cancel — A219

Eduardo Abaroa, Chain — A220

Designs: 1b, La Chimba cancel. 1.50b, Mejillones cancel. 5.50b, View of Antofagasta, horiz. 6.50b, Woman in chains, symbolizing captive province. 8b, Map of Antofagasta Province, 1876. 10b, Arms of province.

1979, Mar. 23 Litho. ***Perf. 10½***

630	A219	50c buff & blk	.30	.20
631	A219	1b pink & blk	.50	.25
632	A219	1.50b pale grn & blk	.50	.25

Perf. 13½

633	A220	5.50b multi	.60	.25
634	A220	6.50b multi	.80	.30
635	A220	7b multi	.80	.30
636	A220	8b multi	.90	.35
637	A220	10b multi	1.10	.35
		Nos. 630-637 (8)	5.50	2.25

Loss of Antofagasta coastal area to Chile, cent.

For surcharge see No. 696.

Emblem and Map of Bolivia — A221

Gymnast — A222

1979, Mar. 26 ***Perf. 13½x13***

638 A221 3b multicolored .75 .50

Radio Club of Bolivia.

Perf. 13x13½, 13½x13

1979, Mar. 27

Design: 6.50b, Runner and Games emblem, horiz.

639	A222	6.50b multi	.80	.50
640	A222	10b multi	1.10	.25

Southern Cross Sports Games, Bolivia, Nov. 3-12, 1978.

A souvenir sheet contains 1 stamp similar to No. 640 with simulated perforations. Sold for 20b. Size: 80x130mm.

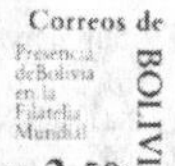

Bulgaria No. 1 — A223

EXFILMAR Emblem — A224

1979, Mar. 30 ***Perf. 10½***

641 A223 2.50b multi .35 .25

PHILASERDICA '79 International Philatelic Exhibition, Sofia, Bulgaria, May 18-27.

For surcharge see No. 694.

1979, Apr. 2

642 A224 2b multi .20 .20

Bolivian Maritime Philatelic Exhibition, La Paz, Nov. 18-28.

For surcharge see No. 698.

OAS Emblem, Map of Bolivia — A226

1979, Oct. 22 Litho. ***Perf. 14x13½***

644 A226 6b multi .75 .25

Organization of American States, 9th Congress, La Paz, Oct.-Nov.

Franz Tamayo — A227

Bolivian and Japanese Flags, Hospital — A228

UN Emblem and Meeting — A229

Radio Tower and Waves — A230

1979, Dec.

645	A227	2.80b blk & gray	.35	.25
646	A228	5b multi	.50	.35
648	A229	5b multi	.50	.35
649	A230	6b multi	.65	.25
		Nos. 645-649 (4)	2.00	1.20

Franz Tamayo, lawyer, birth centenary; Japanese-Bolivian health care cooperation; CEPAL, 18th Congress, La Paz, Sept. 18-26; Bolivian National Radio, 50th anniversary.

For surcharge see No. 695.

Puerto Suarez Iron Ore Deposits A231

1979 Litho. ***Perf. 13½x14***

650 A231 9.50b multi 1.10 .50

Bolivia No. 19, EXFILMAR Emblem, Bolivian Flag — A232

1980 Litho. ***Perf. 13½***

651 A232 4b multi .55 .30

EXFILMAR, Bolivian Maritime Philatelic Exhibition, La Paz, Nov. 18-28, 1979.

Juana Azurduy on Horseback — A233

1980 Litho. ***Perf. 14x13½***

652 A233 4b multi .55 .30

Juana Azurduy de Padilla, independence fighter, birth bicentenary.

La Salle and World Map A234

1980 ***Perf. 13½x14***

653 A234 9b multi 1.10 .60

St. Jean Baptiste de la Salle (1651-1719), educator.

"Victory" in Chariot, Madrid, Exhibition Emblem, Flags of Bolivia and Spain A235

1980, Oct. Litho. ***Perf. 13½x14***

654 A235 14b multi 1.60 .75

ESPAMER '80 Stamp Exhibition, Madrid.

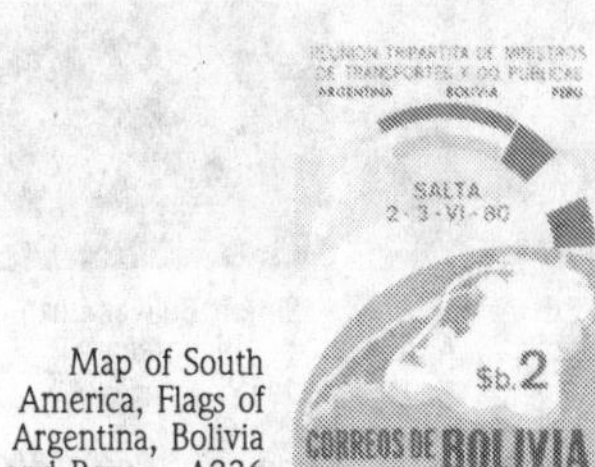

Map of South America, Flags of Argentina, Bolivia and Peru — A236

1980, Oct. ***Perf. 14x13½***

655 A236 2b multi .25 .20

Ministers of Public Works and Transport of Argentina, Bolivia and Peru meeting.

Santa Cruz-Trinidad Railroad, Inauguration of Third Section — A237

1980, Oct.

656 A237 3b multi .35 .20

Flag on Provincial Map — A238

Parrots — A239

Perf. 14x13½, 13½x14

1981, May 11 **Litho.**

657	A238	1b Soldier, flag, map	.15	.15
658	A238	3b Flag, map	.35	.15
659	A238	40b shown	5.00	1.25
660	A238	50b Soldier, civilians, horiz.	6.00	1.25
		Nos. 657-660 (4)	11.50	2.80

July 17 Revolution memorial.

1981, May 11 *Perf. 14x13½*

661	A239	4b Ara macao	.50	.30
662	A239	7b Ara chloroptera	.80	.50
663	A239	8b Ara ararauna	1.00	.60
664	A239	9b Ara rubrogenys	1.10	.65
665	A239	10b Ara auricollis	1.10	.65
666	A239	12b Anodorynchus hyacinthinus	1.50	.75
667	A239	15b Ara militaris	1.75	1.00
668	A239	20b Ara severa	2.25	1.25
		Nos. 661-668 (8)	10.00	5.70

Christmas 1981 — A240

1981, Dec. 7 **Litho.** *Perf. 10½*

669	A240	1b Virgin and Child, vert.	.15	.15
670	A240	2b Child, star	.25	.15

American Airforces Commanders' 22nd Conference, Buenos Aires — A241

1982, Apr. 12 **Litho.** *Perf. 13½*

671	A241	14b multi	1.60	.50

75th Anniv. of Cobija — A242

Simon Bolivar Birth Bicentenary (1983) — A243

1982, July 8 **Litho.** *Perf. 13½*

672	A242	28b multi	.40	.25

1982, July 12

673	A243	18b multi	.25	.20

1983 World Telecommunications Day — A244

1982 World Cup — A245

1982, July 15

674	A244	26b Receiving station	.40	.25

1982, July 21 *Perf. 11*

675	A245	4b shown	.15	.15
676	A245	100b Final Act, by Picasso	1.75	.95

For surcharge see No. 701.

Girl Playing Piano — A246

1982, July 25 *Perf. 13½*

677	A246	16b Boy playing soccer, vert.	.25	.15
678	A246	20b shown	.35	.20

Bolivian-Chinese Agricultural Cooperation, 1972-1982 — A247

1982, Aug. 12

679	A247	30b multi	.50	.25

First Bolivian-Japanese Gastroenterology Conference, La Paz, Jan. — A248

1982, Aug. 26

680	A248	22b multi	.35	.25

A249

A250

1982, Aug. 31 **Litho.** *Perf. 14x13½*

681	A249	19b Stamps	.35	.20

10th Anniv. of Bolivian Philatelic Federation.

1982, Sept. 1

682	A250	20b tan & dk brown	.30	.20

Pres. Hernando Siles, birth centenary.

Scouting Year — A251

Cochabamba Philatelic Center, 25th Anniv. — A252

1982, Sept. 3 *Perf. 11*

683	A251	5b Baden-Powell	.15	.15

For surcharge see No. 703.

1982, Sept. 14

684	A252	3b multicolored	.15	.15

For surcharge see No. 700.

Cochabamba Superior Court of Justice Sesquicentennial A253

1982 **Litho.** *Perf. 13½*

685	A253	10b multicolored	.20	.15

Enthronement of Virgin of Copacabana, 400th Anniv. — A254

Navy Day — A255

1982, Nov. 15 **Litho.** *Perf. 13½*

686	A254	13b multicolored	.25	.15

1982, Nov. 17

687	A255	14b Port Busch Naval Base	.25	.15

A256

A257

1982, Nov. 19 *Perf. 11*

688	A256	10b grn & gray	.20	.15

Christmas. For surcharge see No. 702.

1983, Feb. 13 **Litho.** *Perf. 13½*

689	A257	50b multicolored	.80	.40

10th Youth Soccer Championship, Jan. 22-Feb. 13.

EXFIVIA '83 Philatelic Exhibition A258

1983, Nov. 5 **Litho.** *Perf. 13½*

690	A258	150b brn car	1.00	.50

CORREOS DE BOLIVIA $b150

Visit of Brazilian Pres. Joao Figueiredo, Feb. A259

1984, Feb. 7 **Litho.** *Perf. 13½x14*

691	A259	150b multicolored	.40	.20

CORREOS DE BOLIVIA 200

Simon Bolivar Entering La Paz, by Carmen Baptista A260

Paintings of Bolivar: 50b, Riding Horse, by Mulato Gil de Quesada, vert.

Perf. 14x13½, 13½x14

1984, Mar. 30

692	A260	50b multi	.15	.15
693	A260	200b multi	.55	.22
		Set value		.28

Types of 1957-79 Surcharged

1984, Mar.

694	A223	40b on 2.50b #641	.15	.15
695	A227	40b on 2.80b #645	.15	.15
696	A219	60b on 1.50b #632	.18	.15
697	A216	60b on 2.50b #627	.18	.15
698	A224	100b on 2b #642	.30	.15
699	A141	200b on 350b #409	.60	.25
		Nos. 694-699 (6)	1.56	
		Set value		.80

Nos. 675, 683-684, 688, C328 Surcharged

1984, June 27 **Litho.** *Perf. 11*

700	A252	500b on 3b #684	.75	.35
701	A245	1000b on 4b #675	1.50	.75
702	A256	2000b on 10b #688	3.00	1.25
703	A251	5000b on 5b #683	7.50	3.00

Perf. 13½

704	A182	10,000b on 3.80b #C328	10.00	6.00
		Nos. 700-704 (5)	22.75	11.35

Road Safety Education A261

Jose Eustaquio Mendez, 200th Birth Anniv. A262

Cartoons.

1984, Sept. 7 **Litho.** *Perf. 11*

705	A261	80b Jaywalker	.15	.15
706	A261	120b Motorcycle policeman, ambulance	.15	.15
		Set value	.15	.15

Perf. 14x13½, 13½x14

1984, Sept. 19

Paintings: 300b, Birthplace, by Jorge Campos. 500b, Mendez Leading the Battle of La Tablada, by M. Villegas, horiz.

707	A262	300b multi	.15	.15
708	A262	500b multi	.15	.15
		Set value		.15

1983 World Cup Soccer Championships, Mexico — A263

Chasqui, Postal Runner — A264

Sponsoring shoe-manufacturers' trademarks and: 100b, 200b, Outline map of Bolivia, national colors. 600b, World map and soccer ball, horiz.

1984, Oct. 26 *Perf. 11*

709	A263	100b multi	.15	.15
710	A263	200b multi	.15	.15
711	A263	600b multi	.15	.15
		Set value	.25	.16

1985

712	A264	11000b vio bl	.25	.15

Intl. Year of Professional Education A265

Intl. Anti-Polio Campaign A266

1985, Apr. 25

713	A265	2000b Natl. Manual Crafts emblem	.15	.15

For surcharges see Nos. 721-722.

1985, May 22

714	A266	20000b lt bl & vio	.25	.15

Endangered Wildlife — A267

1985, May 22

715 A267 23000b Altiplano boliviano .20 .15
716 A267 25000b Sarcorhamphus gryphus .22 .15
717 A267 30000b Blastocaros dichotomus .30 .15
Nos. 715-717 (3) .72
Set value .30

Nos. 716-717 vert.

Dona Vicenta Juaristi Eguino (b. 1785), Independence Heroine — A268

UN, 40th Anniv. — A269

1985, Oct. Litho. *Perf. 13½*

718 A268 300000b multi .20 .15

1985, Oct. 24 *Perf. 11*

719 A269 1000000b bl & gold .65 .30

A270

A271

1985, Nov.

720 A270 200000b multi .15 .15

Natl. Soccer Team, 75th anniv.

No. 713 Surcharged

1986 Litho. *Perf. 11*

721 A265 200000b on 2000b .22 .15
722 A265 5000000b on 2000b 5.25 2.50

1986

723 A271 300000 Emblems, vert. .32 .15
724 A271 550000 Pique trademark, vert. .58 .24
725 A271 1000000 Azteca Stadium 1.05 .50
726 A271 2500000 World cup, vert. 2.65 1.25
Nos. 723-726 (4) 4.60 2.14

1986 World Cup Soccer Championships.

Intl. Youth Year

A272 A273

1986

727 A272 150000 brt car rose .16 .15
728 A272 500000 bl grn .55 .35
729 A273 3000000 multi 3.15 1.50
Nos. 727-729 (3) 3.86 2.00

Inscribed 1985.

Alfonso Sobieta Viaduct, Carretera Quillacollo, Confital — A274

1986 *Perf. 13½*

730 A274 400000 int bl & gray .42 .20

Inter-American Development Bank, 25th anniv.

Admission of Bolivia to the UPU, Cent. — A275

Postal Workers Soc., 50th Anniv. — A276

1986, Apr. 3 *Perf. 11*

731 A275 800000 multi .85 .40

1986, Sept. 5

732 A276 2000000 brn & pale brn 2.10 1.00

Founding of Trinidad, 300th Anniv. A277

1986, May 25 *Perf. 13½x14*

733 A277 1400000 Bull and Rider, by Vaca 1.50 .75

Bolivian Philatelic Federation, 15th Anniv. A278

1986, Nov. 28

734 A278 600000b No. 19 .62 .30

Death of a Priest, by Jose Antonio Zampa — A279

Intl. Peace Year — A280

1986, Nov. 21 *Perf. 14x13½*

735 A279 400000b multi .42 .20

1986, Sept. 16 *Perf. 11*

736 A280 200000 yel grn & pale grn .22 .15

Natl. Oil Corp. (YPBF), 50th Anniv. — A281

1986, Dec. 22 Litho. *Perf. 11*

737 A281 1000000b multi 1.50 .50

A282 A283

Photograph of a Devil-mask Dancer, by Jimenez Cordero.

1987, Feb. 13 Litho. *Perf. 14x13½*

738 A282 20c multi .30 .15

February 10th Society, cent. (in 1985).

1987, Mar. 20 Litho. *Perf. 14x13½*

739 A283 30c Crossed flags .45 .25

State Visit of Richard von Weizsacker, Pres. of Germany, Mar. 20.

State Visit of King Juan Carlos of Spain, May 20 — A284

1987, May 20 *Perf. 13½x14*

740 A284 60c Natl. arms .90 .40

EXFIVIA '87 — A285

Mount Potosi, 18th cent. engraving.

1987, Oct. Litho. *Perf. 13½*

741 A285 50c multi .72 .35

See No. 750.

Wildlife Conservation A286

1987, Oct.

742 A286 20c Condor .30 .15
743 A286 20c Tapir .30 .15
744 A286 30c Vicuna .45 .25
745 A286 30c Armadillo .45 .25
746 A286 40c Spectacled bears .58 .30
747 A286 60c Toucans .88 .40
Nos. 742-747 (6) 2.96 1.50

Wildlife in danger of extinction.

ESPAMER '87, La Coruna A287

1987, Oct. Litho. *Perf. 14x13½*

748 A287 20c Nina, stern of Santa Maria .30 .15
749 A287 20c Bow of Santa Maria, Pinta .30 .15
a. Pair, #748-749 .60 .25

No. 749a has a continuous design.

EXFIVIA Type of 1987

Design: Photograph of Mt. Potosi by Jimenez Cordero.

1987, Aug. 5 Litho. *Perf. 13½*

750 A285 40c multi .58 .30

Musical Instruments A288

1987, Dec. 3 *Perf. 13½x14, 14x13½*

751 A288 50c Zampona and quena (wind instruments) .72 .35
752 A288 1b Charango, vert. 1.45 .70

A289

State Visit of Pope John Paul II A290

Pontiff, religious architecture and art: No. 753, Cathedral of Kings, Beni. No. 754, Carabuco Church. No. 755, Tihuanacu Church. No. 756, St. Francis's Church, Sucre. No. 757, St. Joseph's of Chiquitos Church. 40c, Cobija Chapel, vert. No. 759, Jayu Kcota Church. No. 760, Cochabamba Cathedral, vert. 60c, St. Francis's Basilica, La Paz, vert. No. 762, Christ of Machaca Church. No. 763, St. Lawrence's Church, Potosi, vert. No. 764, *The Holy Family*, by Rubens, vert. No. 765, *The Virgin of Copacabana*, statue, vert. No. 766, Vallegrande Church. No. 767, Tarija Cathedral, vert. No. 768, Concepcion Church.

1988 Litho. *Perf. 13½x14, 14x13½*

753 A289 20c multi .25 .15
754 A289 20c multi .25 .15
755 A289 20c multi .25 .15
756 A289 30c multi .38 .20
757 A289 30c multi .38 .20
758 A289 40c multi .50 .25
759 A289 50c multi .65 .30
760 A289 50c multi .65 .30
761 A289 60c multi .75 .35
762 A289 70c multi .90 .35
763 A289 70c multi .90 .35
764 A289 80c multi 1.00 .45
765 A289 80c multi 1.00 .45
766 A289 80c multi 1.00 .45
767 A289 1.30b multi 1.65 .75
768 A289 1.30b multi 1.65 .75
769 A290 1.50b shown 1.90 .90
Nos. 753-769 (17) 14.06 6.50

Issue dates: 1.50b, May 9. Others, Mar. 3.

Visit of Pres. Jose Sarney of Brazil A291

1988, Aug. 2 Litho. *Perf. 13½x14*

770 A291 50c multi .60 .30

St. John Bosco (1815-1888) — A292

1988, Aug. 16 *Perf. 13½*

771 A292 30c multi .42 .20

Bolivian Railways, Cent. — A293

Design: 1b, Steam locomotive from the La Paz-Beni line, made by Marca Shy Ohio, Natl. Railway Museum, Sucre.

1988, Aug. 29
772 A293 1b multi 1.20 .60

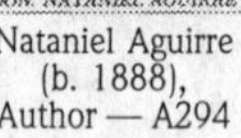

Nataniel Aguirre (b. 1888), Author — A294

Department of Pando, 50th Anniv. — A295

1988, Sept. 14 Litho. *Perf. 13½*
773 A294 1b blk & beige 1.20 .60

1988, Sept. 26 *Perf. 13½*

Designs: 40c, *Columna Porvenir,* memorial to the Battle of Bahio. 60c, Siringuero rubber production (worker sapping latex from *Hevea brasiliensis*).

774 A295 40c multi .48 .25
775 A295 60c multi .72 .35

A296 A297

1988, Sept. 27
776 A296 1.50b multi 1.85 .90

1988 Summer Olympics, Seoul.

1988

Designs: 70c, Archbishop Bernardino de Cardenas (1579-1668). 80c, Mother Rosa Gattorno (1831-1900), founder of the Sisters of Santa Ana.

777 A297 70c multi .90 .45
778 A297 80c multi 1.05 .50

Issue dates: 70c, Oct. 20, 80c, Oct. 14.

Ministry of Transportation & Communications A298

1988, Oct. 24 Litho. *Perf. 14x13½*
779 A298 2b deep car, blk & pale olive grn 2.35 1.00

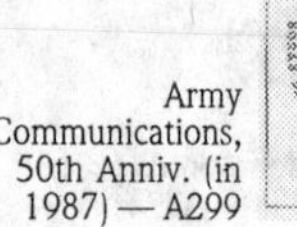

Army Communications, 50th Anniv. (in 1987) — A299

1988, Nov. 29 Litho. *Perf. 13½*
780 A299 70c multi .95 .45

Bolivian Automobile Club, 50th Anniv. — A300

1988, Dec. 29 Litho. *Perf. 13½*
781 A300 1.50b multi 1.45 .70

Flowering Plants and Emblems A301

Designs: 50c, Orchid, BULGARIA '89 emblem, vert. 60c, Kantuta blossoms, ITALIA '90 emblem. 70c, *Heliconia humilis,* Albertville '86 emblem, vert. 1b, Hoffmanseggia, Barcelona '92 Games emblem, vert. 2b, Puya raymondi, Seoul '88 Games and five-ring emblems, vert.

1989, Feb. 17 Litho. *Perf. 13½*
782 A301 50c multi .58 .24
783 A301 60c multi .70 .28
784 A301 70c multi .80 .32
785 A301 1b multi 1.15 .45
786 A301 2b multi 2.30 .92
Nos. 782-786 (5) 5.53 2.21

Radio FIDES, 50th Anniv. — A302

1989, Feb. 2
787 A302 80c multi .92 .38

Gold Quarto of 1852 A303

1989, Feb. 9 *Perf. 13½x14*
788 A303 1b multi 1.20 .48

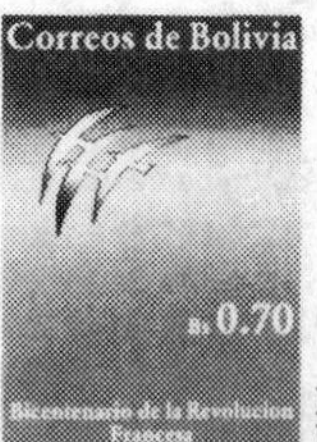

French Revolution, Bicent. — A304

1989, June 23 Litho. *Perf. 14x13½*
789 A304 70c red, blk & blue .90 .35

Uyuni Township, Cent. — A305

1989, July 9 Litho. *Perf. 14x13½*
790 A305 30c blue, black & gray .38 .15

Noel Kempff Mercado Natl. Park, Santa Cruz — A306

Designs: 1.50b, Federico Ahlfeld Falls, Pauserna River. 3b, *Ozotoceros bezcarticus* (deer).

1989, Sept. 24 Litho. *Perf. 13½x14*
791 A306 1.50b multicolored 1.70 .68
792 A306 3b multicolored 3.40 1.35

UPAEP — A306a

1989, Oct. 12 Litho. *Perf. 13½*
792A A306a 50c Metalworking .52 .20
792B A306a 1b Temple of Kalasasaya 1.05 .42

See Nos. 808-809

State Visit by Dr. Carlos Andres Perez, Pres. of Venezuela A306b

1989, Oct. 14
792C A306b 2b multi 2.05 .82

See Nos. 825-826, 832.

City of Potosi — A306c

1989, Nov. 10 Litho. *Perf. 13½*
792D A306c 60c Cobija Arch .75 .30
792E A306c 80c Mint .85 .40
f. Pair, #792D-792E 1.60 .70

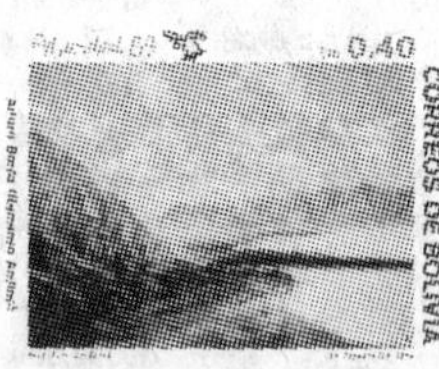

Christmas A307

Paintings: 40c, *Andean Stillwaters,* by Arturo Borda. 60c, *The Virgin of the Roses,* anonymous. 80c, *The Conquistador,* by Jorge de la Reza. 1b, *Native Harmony,* by Juan Rimsa. 1.50b, *Woman with Jug,* by Cecilio Guzman de Rojas. 2b, *Bloom of Tenderness,* by Gil Imana. Nos. 794-798 vert.

Perf. 13½x14, 14x13½

1989, Dec. 18
793 A307 40c multicolored .42 .17
794 A307 60c multicolored .62 .25
795 A307 80c multicolored .82 .32
796 A307 1b multicolored 1.05 .42
797 A307 1.50b multicolored 1.55 .62
798 A307 2b multicolored 2.05 .82
Nos. 793-798 (6) 6.51 2.60

A308 A309

1990, Jan. 23 Litho. *Perf. 13½*
799 A308 80c multicolored .85 .35

Fight against drug abuse.

1990, May 13 *Perf. 14x13½*

Design: Great Britain No. 1, Sir Rowland Hill and Bolivia No. 1

800 A309 4b multicolored 4.10 1.70

Penny Black, 150th anniv.

World Cup Soccer Championships, Italy — A310

1990, June 16 *Perf. 13½*
801 A310 2b Stadium, Milan 2.00 .80
802 A310 6b Game 6.00 2.40

Organization of American States, Cent. — A311

1990, Apr. 14
803 A311 80c dark bl & brt bl .82 .32

A312 A313

1990, Apr. 16
804 A312 1.20b multi 1.22 .62

1990 Litho. *Perf. 14x13½*
805 A313 70c Telecommunications .72 .55

National Chamber of Commerce, Cent. — A314

1990, June
806 A314 50c gold, blk & bl .58 .42

Cochabamba Social Club, Cent. — A315

1990, Sept. 14 Litho. *Perf. 13½*
807 A315 40c multicolored .42 .32

UPAEP Type of 1989
Perf. 13½x14, 14x13½

1990, Oct. 12 Litho.
808 A306a 80c Huts .75 .30
809 A306a 1b Mountains, lake, vert. .95 .38

A317 A318

1990, Oct. 19 *Perf. 14x13½*
810 A317 1.20b multicolored 1.05 .42

Magistrate's District of Larecaja, 400th Anniv.

1990, Oct. 12 *Perf. 14x13½*
811 A318 2b multicolored 1.75 .70

Discovery of America, 500th anniv. (in 1992).

German Reunification A319

1990, Nov. 19 Litho. *Perf. 14x13½*
812 A319 2b multicolored 1.70 .70

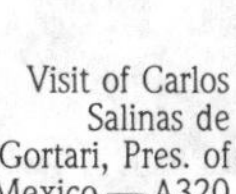

Visit of Carlos Salinas de Gortari, Pres. of Mexico — A320

Design: 80c, Visit of Rodrigo Borja Cevallos, Pres. of Ecuador.

1990, Dec. 13 Litho. *Perf. 13½*
813 A320 60c multicolored .75 .30
814 A320 80c multicolored .85 .40

4th Congress of the Andean Presidents A321

1990, Nov. 29 *Perf. 13½x14*
815 A321 1.50b multicolored 1.35 .55

Exfivia '90 A322   Christmas A323

1990, Dec. 9 *Perf. 13½*
816 A322 40c dk blue .40 .15

1990, Nov. 20 *Perf. 11*
817 A323 50c multicolored .45 .18

Express Mail Service A324

1990, Dec. 14 *Perf. 13½x14*
818 A324 1b multicolored .90 .35

Bolivian Radio Club, 50th Anniv. — A325

1991, Mar. 1 Litho. *Perf. 14x13½*
819 A325 2.40b multicolored 2.00 .80

End of Chaco War, 56th Anniv. — A326   National Museums — A327

Map of Heroes of Chaco Highway.

1991, June 14 Litho. *Perf. 14x13½*
820 A326 60c multicolored .55 .22

1991, June 13 *Perf. 13½*
821 A327 50c Archaeology .42 .18
822 A327 50c Art .42 .18
823 A327 1b Ethnology, Folklore .85 .35
a. Strip of 3, #821-823 1.70 .70

Espamer '91.

A328 A329

Our Lady of Peace, Metropolitan Cathedral.

1991, July 15 Litho. *Perf. 14x13½*
824 A328 1.20b multicolored 1.15 .45

Presidential State Visit Type of 1989

Jaime Paz Zamora, Pres. of Bolivia and: No. 825, Dr. Carlos Saul Menem, Pres. of Argentina. No. 826, Dr. Luis Alberto Lacalle, Pres. of Uruguay.

1991 *Perf. 13½x14*
825 A306b 1b multicolored .85 .35
826 A306b 1b multicolored .85 .35

Issue dates: #825, Aug. 5; #826, Aug. 12.

1991, May 31 *Perf. 13½*

Tremarctos ornatus.

827 A329 30c Adult, 2 cubs .28 .15
828 A329 30c Adult's head .28 .15
829 A329 30c Adult on tree limb .28 .15
830 A329 30c Adult, cubs on tree limb .28 .15
Nos. 827-830 (4) 1.12 .60

World Wildlife Fund.

A330 A331

1991, Aug. 21 Litho. *Perf. 14x13½*
831 A330 70c multicolored .68 .28

Bolivian Philatelic Federation, 20th anniv.

Presidential State Visit Type of 1989

Design: 50c, Jaime Paz Zamora, Pres. of Bolivia and Alberto Fujimori, Pres. of Peru.

1991, Aug. 29 *Perf. 13½x14*
832 A306b 50c multicolored .45 .18

1991, Nov. 19 Litho. *Perf. 14x13½*
833 A331 50c multicolored .45 .18

National census.

America Issue — A332

UPAEP emblem and: 60c, First Discovery of Chuquiago, 1535, by Arturo Reque M. 1.20c, Founding of the City of La Paz, 1548, by J. Rimsa, vert.

Perf. 13½x14, 14x13½

1991, Oct. 12
834 A332 60c multicolored .58 .25
835 A332 1.20b multicolored 1.15 .45

First National Grand Prix Auto and Motorcycle Race — A332a

1991, Sept. 5 Litho. *Perf. 14x13½*
835A A332a 50c multicolored .45 .18

ECOBOL, Postal Security System A333

1991, Sept. 9 *Perf. 13½x14*
836 A333 1.40b multicolored 1.35 .52

Simon Bolivar — A334

1992, Feb. 15 Litho. *Perf. 13½*
837 A334 1.20b buff, brn & org brn 1.15 .45

Exfilbo '92.

Scouting in Bolivia, 75th Anniv. (in 1990) and 1992 Andes Jamboree A335

1992, Jan. 13 *Perf. 13½x14*
838 A335 1.20b multicolored 1.15 .45

Dated 1991.

Christmas A336

Paintings: 2b, Landscape, by Daniel Pena y Sarmiento. 5b, Woman with Fruit, by Cecilio Guzman de Rojas. 15b, Native Mother, by Crespo Gastelu.

1991, Dec.19 Litho. *Perf. 13½*
839 A336 2b multicolored 1.50 .60
840 A336 5b multicolored 3.75 1.50
841 A336 15b multicolored 11.20 4.50
Nos. 839-841 (3) 16.45 6.60

Pacific Ocean Access Pact Between Bolivia and Peru A337

Designs: 1.20b, Pres. Zamora raising flag, vert. 1.50b, Pres. Jaime Paz Zamora of Bolivia and Pres. Alberto Fujimori, Peru. 1.80b, Shoreline of access zone near Ilo, Peru.

Perf. 14x13½, 13½x14

1992, Mar. 23
842 A337 1.20b multicolored .95 .40
843 A337 1.50b multicolored 1.15 .48
844 A337 1.80b multicolored 1.40 .55
Nos. 842-844 (3) 3.50 1.43

Expo '92, Seville A338

1992, Apr. 15 *Perf. 13½x14*
845 A338 30c multicolored .28 .15
846 A338 50c Columbus' ships .45 .18

Miraflores Rotary Club, District 4690, Mt. Illimani — A339

1992, Apr. 30 Litho. *Perf. 13½*
847 A339 90c multicolored .70 .45

Prof. Elizardo Perez, Founder of Ayllu of Warisata School, Birth Cent. — A340

1992, June 6 Litho. *Perf. 13½*
848 A340 60c multicolored .52 .22

Government Palace, Sucre A341

1992, July 10 Litho. *Perf. 13½x14*
849 A341 50c multicolored .42 .16

A342 A343

1992, Sept. 11 *Perf. 14x13½*
850 A342 50c multicolored .42 .16

Los Tiempos Newpaper, 25th anniv.

1992, Aug. 9 *Perf. 13½*

Design: 1.50b, Mario Martinez Guzman, tennis player.

851 A343 1.50b multicolored 1.15 .48

1992 Summer Olympics, Barcelona.

First Intl. Whitewater Canoe Regatta, Bermejo River — A343a

1992, Sept. 17 Litho. *Perf. 13½*
851A A343a 1.20b multicolored 1.10 .48

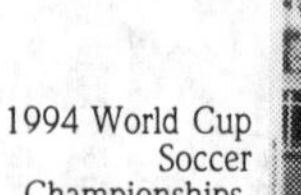

1994 World Cup Soccer Championships, US — A344

1992, Oct. 2 Litho. *Perf. 13½*
852 A344 1.20b multicolored 1.85 .75

Oruro Technical University, Cent. — A345

1992, Oct. 15 *Perf. 13½x14*
853 A345 50c multicolored .38 .15

Interamerican Institute for Agricultural Cooperation, 50th Anniv. — A346

1992, Oct. 7 *Perf. 13½*
854 A346 1.20b Chenopodium quinoa 1.15 .48

Discovery of America, 500th Anniv. A347

Paintings: 60c, Columbus departing from Palos, vert. 2b, Columbus with Caribbean natives.

1992, Oct. 1 *Perf. 14x13½, 13½x14*
855 A347 60c multicolored .42 .18
856 A347 2b multicolored 1.40 .58

Battle of Ingavi, 150th Anniv. (in 1991) A348

1992, Nov. 18 Litho. *Perf. 13½x14*
857 A348 1.20b sepia & black .95 .38

12th Bolivian Games, Cochabamba and Santa Cruz — A349

1992, Nov. 13
858 A349 2b multicolored 1.50 .60

Fauna, Events — A350

Event emblem and fauna: 20c, Beni Dept., sesquicentennial, caiman. 50c, Polska '93, paca. 1b, Bangkok '93, chinchilla. 2b, 1994 Winter Olympics, Lillehammer, Norway, anteater. 3b, Brandenburg Gate, jaguar. 4b, Brasiliana '93, hummingbird, vert. 5b, 1994 World Cup Soccer Championships, US, piranhas.

1992, Nov. 18 Litho. *Perf. 13½*
859 A350 20c multicolored .15 .15
860 A350 50c multicolored .35 .15
861 A350 1b multicolored .75 .30
862 A350 2b multicolored 1.50 .60
863 A350 3b multicolored 2.25 .90
864 A350 4b multicolored 3.00 1.25
865 A350 5b multicolored 3.75 1.50
Nos. 859-865 (7) 11.75 4.85

Christmas A350a

Designs: 1.20b, Man in canoe, star. 2.50b, Star over churches. 6b, Flowers, church, infant on hay.

1992, Dec. 1 Litho. *Perf. 13½*
865A A350a 1.20b multicolored .90 .35
865B A350a 2.50b multicolored 1.90 .75
865C A350a 6b multicolored 4.50 1.75
Nos. 865A-865C (3) 7.30 2.85

A351 A352

Nicolaus Copernicus (1473-1543), Polish Astronomer: 50c, Santa Ana Intl. astrometrical observatory, Tarija, horiz.

Perf. 13x13½, 13½x13
1993, Feb. 18 Litho.
866 A351 50c multicolored .38 .15
867 A351 2b black 1.50 .60

1993, Apr. 14 Litho. *Perf. 13½*
868 A352 60c multicolored .58 .24

Beatification of Mother Nazaria.

12th Bolivar Games A353

1993, Apr. 24 *Perf. 13½x14*
869 A353 2.30b multicolored 1.65 .65

Bolivia #C240, Brazil #3 — A354

1993, May 31
870 A354 2.30b multicolored 1.65 .65

First Brazilian Stamp, 150th anniv.

A355 A356

Eternal Father, by Gaspar de la Cueva.

1993, June 9 Litho. *Perf. 13½*
871 A355 1.80b multicolored 1.30 .52

1993, July 31 Litho. *Perf. 14x13½*
872 A356 50c Virgin of Urkupina .35 .15

City of Quillacollo, 400th anniv.

Pedro Domingo Murillo Industrial School — A357

1993, Aug. 4 *Perf. 13½*
873 A357 60c multicolored .42 .16

Butterflies A358

1993, June 4 *Perf. 13½x14*
874 A358 60c Archaeoprepona demophon .40 .16
875 A358 60c Morpho sp. .40 .16
876 A358 80c Papilio sp. .55 .22
877 A358 80c Historis odius .55 .22
878 A358 80c Euptoieta hegesia .55 .22
879 A358 1.80b Morpho deidamia 1.25 .48
880 A358 1.80b Papilio thoas 1.25 .48
881 A358 1.80b Danaus plexippus 1.25 .48
882 A358 2.30b Caligo sp. 1.50 .60
883 A358 2.30b Anaea marthesia 1.50 .60
884 A358 2.30b Rothschildia sp. 1.50 .60
885 A358 2.70b Heliconius sp. 1.75 .75
886 A358 2.70b Marpesia corinna 1.75 .75
887 A358 2.70b Prepona chromus 1.75 .75
888 A358 3.50b Heliconius sp., diff. 2.25 .95
889 A358 3.50b Siproeta epaphus 2.25 .95
a. Sheet of 16, #874-889 20.50 20.50
Nos. 874-889 (16) 20.45 8.37

Pan-American Health Organization, 90th Anniv. — A359

1993, Oct. 13 Litho. *Perf. 13½*
890 A359 80c multicolored .52 .20

Archaeological Finds — A360

Location of cave paintings: No. 891, Oruro. No. 892, Santa Cruz, vert. No. 893, Beni, vert. No. 894, Chuquisaca, vert. No. 895, Chuquisaca. No. 896, Potosi. No. 897, La Paz, vert. No. 898, Tarija, vert. No. 899, Cochabamba.

1993, Sept. 28
891 A360 80c multicolored .52 .20
892 A360 80c multicolored .52 .20
893 A360 80c multicolored .52 .20
894 A360 80c multicolored .52 .20
895 A360 80c multicolored .52 .20
896 A360 80c multicolored .52 .20
897 A360 80c multicolored .52 .20
898 A360 80c multicolored .52 .20
899 A360 80c multicolored .52 .20
Nos. 891-899 (9) 4.68 1.80

America Issue — A361

1993, Oct. 9 Litho. *Perf. 13½*
900 A361 80c Saimiri sciereus .52 .20
901 A361 2.30b Felis pordalis 1.50 .60

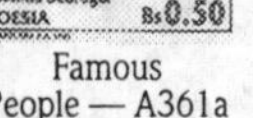

Famous People — A361a Christmas — A361b

Designs: 50c, Yolanda Bedregal, poet. 70c, Simon Martinic, President of Cochabamba Philatelic Center. 90c, Eugenio von Boeck, politician, President of Bolivian Philatelic Federation. 1b, Marina Nunez del Prado, sculptor.

1993, Nov. 17 Litho. *Perf. 11*
901A A361a 50c sepia .32 .15
901B A361a 70c sepia .45 .18
901C A361a 90c sepia .55 .22
901D A361a 1b sepia .60 .25
Nos. 901A-901D (4) 1.92 .80

1993, Dec. 8 *Perf. 14x13½*

Paintings: 2.30b, Adoration of the Shepherds, by Leonardo Flores. 3.50b, Virgin with Child and Saints, by unknown artist. 6b, Virgin of the Milk, by Melchor Perez de Holguin.

901E A361b 2.30b multicolored 1.40 .55
901F A361b 3.50b multicolored 2.25 .85
901G A361b 6b multicolored 3.75 1.50
Nos. 901E-901G (3) 7.40 2.90

Town of Riberalta, Cent. — A362

1994, Feb. 3 **Litho.** *Perf. 13½*
902 A362 2b multicolored 1.25 .60

World Population Day A363

1994, Feb. 17 **Litho.** *Perf. 13½*
903 A363 2.30b multicolored 1.50 .60

A364 A365

1994, Feb. 21 *Perf. 13½*
904 A364 2b buff & multi 1.25 .60
905 A364 2.30b multi 1.50 .60

Inauguration of Pres. Gonzalo Sanchez de Lozada.

1994, Mar. 22

1994 World Cup Soccer Championships, US: 80c, Mascot. 1.80b, Bolivia, Uruguay. 2.30b, Bolivia, Venezuela. No. 909, Part of Bolivian team, goalies in black. No. 910, Part of Bolivian team, diff. 2.70b, Bolivia, Ecuador. 3.50b, Bolivia, Brazil.

906 A365 80c multicolored .48 .20
907 A365 1.80b multicolored 1.10 .45
908 A365 2.30b multicolored 1.40 .55
909 A365 2.50b multicolored 1.50 .60
910 A365 2.50b multicolored 1.50 .60
a. Pair, #909-910 3.00 1.25
911 A365 2.70b multicolored 1.65 .65
912 A365 3.50b multicolored 2.25 .85
Nos. 906-912 (7) 9.88 3.90

SOS Children's Village, Bolivia — A366

1994, Apr. 12 **Litho.** *Perf. 13½*
913 A366 2.70b multicolored 1.65 .65

Catholic Archdiocese La Paz, 50th Anniv. — A367

Churches, priests: 1.80b, Church of San Pedro, Msgr. Jorge Manrique Hurtado. 2b, Archbishop Abel I. Antezana y Rojas, Church of the Sacred Heart of Mary, vert. 3.50b, Msgr. Luis Sainz Hinojosa, Church of Santo Domingo, vert.

1994, July 12 **Litho.** *Perf. 13½*
914 A367 1.80b multicolored 1.10 .45
915 A367 2b multicolored 1.25 .60
916 A367 3.50b multicolored 2.25 .85
Nos. 914-916 (3) 4.60 1.90

A368 A369

Design: 2b, Pres. Victor Paz Estenssoro.

1994, Oct. 2 **Litho.** *Perf. 13½*
917 A368 2b multicolored 1.25 .50

1994, Oct. 9
918 A369 1.80b No. 46 1.10 .45

Battle of Ft. Boqueron A370

Design: Col. Manuel Marzana Oroza, battle scene.

1994, Oct. 6
919 A370 80c multicolored .50 .20

San Borja, 300th Anniv. — A371

1994, Oct. 14
920 A371 1.60b Erythrina fusca 1.00 .40

America Issue — A372

Old, new methods of postal transport: 1b, Streetcar, van. 5b, Airplane, ox cart.

1994, Oct. 12
921 A372 1b multicolored .65 .25
922 A372 5b multicolored 3.25 1.25

1994 Solar Eclipse — A373 Environmental Protection — A374

1994 Oct. 21
923 A373 3.50b multicolored 2.25 .85

1994, Sept. 21

Trees: 60c, Buddleja coriacea. 1.80b, Bertholletia exelsa. 2b, Schinus molle, horiz. 2.70b, Polylepis racemosa. 3, Tabebuia chrysantha. 3.50b, Erythrina falcata, horiz.

924 A374 60c multicolored .38 .15
925 A374 1.80b multicolored 1.10 .45
926 A374 2b multicolored 1.25 .50
927 A374 2.70b multicolored 1.65 .65
928 A374 3b multicolored 1.90 .75
929 A374 3.50b multicolored 2.25 .85
Nos. 924-929 (6) 8.53 3.35

Gen. Antonio Jose de Sucre (1795-1830) A375

1995, Jan. 25 **Litho.** *Perf. 13½*
930 A375 1.80b shown .75 .30
931 A375 3.50b diff. background 1.50 .60

A377 A378

1994, Nov. 25 **Litho.** *Perf. 13½*
933 A377 2b Tarija girl .95 .38
934 A377 5b High plateau child 2.40 .95
935 A377 20b Eastern girl 9.50 3.75
Nos. 933-935 (3) 12.85 5.08

Christmas.

1994, Nov. 28 **Litho.** *Perf. 13½*
936 A378 1.80b multicolored .90 .35

Pan-American Scout Jamboree, Cochabamba

Yacuma-Beni Province, Cent. — A379

Design: 1.90b, 2.90b, Cathedral of St. Anne.

1995, Apr. 21 **Litho.** *Perf. 13½*
937 A379 1.90b black & multi 1.25 .60
938 A379 2.90b blue & multi 1.75 .90

Franciscans at Copacabana Natl. Sanctuary, Cent. — A380

1995, May 2
939 A380 60c gray & multi .40 .15
940 A380 80c bister & multi .55 .20

Peace Between Bolivia and Paraguay — A381

1995 **Litho.** *Perf. 13½*
941 A381 2b multicolored 1.00 .40

Dated 1994.

Andes Development Corporation (CAF), 25th Anniv. — A382

1995, July 25
942 A382 2.40b multicolored 1.25 .50

50th Anniv. of Publication of "Nationalism and the Colonial Age," by Carlos Montenegro (1904-53) — A383

1995, Aug. 8
943 A383 1.20b pink & black .60 .25

A384 A385

1995, Sept. 26
944 A384 1b multicolored .50 .20

FAO, 50th anniv.

1995, Oct. 24 *Perf. 14½*
945 A385 2.90b multicolored 1.50 .60

UN, 50th anniv.

America Issue — A386

1995, Nov. 21 *Perf. 14*
946 A386 5b Condor 2.50 1.00
947 A386 5b Llamas 2.50 1.00
a. Pair, #946-947 5.00 2.00

ICAO, 50th Anniv. — A387

1995, Dec. 4 *Perf. 13½x13*
948 A387 50c multicolored .25 .15

Temple of Samaipata A388

Archaeological finds and: a, 1.90b, Top of ruins. b, 1b, Top of ruins, diff. c, 2.40b, Lower excavation. d, 2b, Floor, tiers.

1995, Dec. 4 *Perf. 13x13½*
949 A388 Block of 4, #a.-d. 3.75 1.50

No. 949 is a continuous design.

Taquiña Brewery, Cent. — A389

1995, Dec. 8 *Perf. 14*
950 A389 1b multicolored .50 .20

Christmas — A390

Paintings: 1.20b, The Annunciation, by Cima da Conegliano. 3b, The Nativity, by Hans Baldung. 3.50b, Adoration of the Magi, by Rogier van der Weyden.

1995, Dec. 15 *Perf. 14x13½*
951 A390 1.20b multicolored .60 .25
952 A390 3b multicolored 1.50 .60
953 A390 3.50b multicolored 1.75 .70
Nos. 951-953 (3) 3.85 1.55

AIR POST STAMPS

Aviation School
AP1 AP2

1924, Dec. Unwmk. Engr. *Perf. 14*
C1 AP1 10c ver & blk .25 .30
a. Inverted center 800.00
C2 AP1 15c carmine & blk 1.50 .50
C3 AP1 25c dk bl & blk .60 .60
C4 AP1 50c orange & blk 1.50 1.25
C5 AP2 1b red brn & blk .95 .95
C6 AP2 2b blk brn & blk 1.75 1.75
C7 AP2 5b dk vio & blk 5.50 5.50
Nos. C1-C7 (7) 12.05 10.85

Natl. Aviation School establishment.

These stamps were available for ordinary postage. Nos. C1, C3, C5 and C6 exist imperforate. Proofs of the 2b with inverted center exist imperforate and privately perforated.

For overprints and surcharges see Nos. C11-C23, C56-C58.

Emblem of Lloyd Aéreo Boliviano — AP3

1928 Litho. *Perf. 11*
C8 AP3 15c green 1.00 1.00
a. Imperf., pair 50.00
C9 AP3 20c dark blue .25 .25
C10 AP3 35c red brown .60 .60
Nos. C8-C10 (3) 1.85 1.85

No. C8 exists imperf. between.
For surcharges see #C24-C26, C53-C55.

Graf Zeppelin Issues

Nos. C1-C5 Surcharged or Overprinted in Various Colors:

CORREO AEREO
R. S. 6-V-1930
5 Cts.

Nos. C11, C19

CORREO AEREO
R. S.
6-V- 1930

Nos. C12-C18, C20-C23

1930, May 6 *Perf. 14*
C11 AP1 5c on 10c ver & blk (G) 9.50 9.50
C12 AP1 10c ver & blk (Bl) 9.50 9.50
C13 AP1 10c ver & blk (Br) 600.00 875.00
C14 AP1 15c car & blk (V) 9.50 9.50
C15 AP1 25c dk bl & blk (R) 9.50 9.50
C16 AP1 50c org & blk (Br) 9.50 9.50
C17 AP1 50c org & blk (R) 475.00 600.00
C18 AP2 1b red brn & blk (gold) 150.00 150.00

Experts consider the 50c with gold or silver overprint and 5c with black to be a trial color proofs.

Nos. C11-C18 exist with the surcharges inverted, double, or double with one inverted, but the regularity of these varieties is questioned.

See notes following No. C23.

Surcharged or Overprinted in Bronze Inks of Various Colors

C19 AP1 5c on 10c ver & blk (G) 77.50 80.00
C20 AP1 10c ver & blk (Bl) 67.50 67.50
C21 AP1 15c car & blk (V) 77.50 80.00
C22 AP1 25c dk bl & blk (cop) 77.50 80.00
C23 AP2 1b red brn & blk (gold) 190.00 200.00
Nos. C19-C23 (5) 490.00 507.50

Flight of the airship Graf Zeppelin from Europe to Brazil and return via Lakehurst, NJ.

Nos. C19 to C23 were intended for use on postal matter forwarded by the Graf Zeppelin.

No. C18 was overprinted with light gold or gilt bronze ink. No. C23 was overprinted with deep gold bronze ink. Nos. C13 and C17 were overprinted with trial colors but were sold with the regular printings. The 5c on 10c is known surcharged in black and in blue.

No. C8-C10 Surcharged

Z 1930
Bs. 3.—

1930, May 6 *Perf. 11*
C24 AP3 1.50b on 15c 25.00 25.00
a. Inverted surcharge 57.50 57.50
b. Comma instead of period after "1" 35.00 35.00
C25 AP3 3b on 20c 25.00 25.00
a. Inverted surcharge 62.50 62.50
b. Comma instead of period after "3" 40.00 40.00
C26 AP3 6b on 35c 37.50 40.00
a. Inverted surcharge 110.00 110.00
b. Comma instead of period after "6" 62.50 62.50
Nos. C24-C26 (3) 87.50 90.00

Airplane and Bullock Cart — AP6

Airplane and River Boat — AP7

1930, July 24 Litho. *Perf. 14*
C27 AP6 5c dp violet 1.25 1.00
C28 AP7 15c red 1.25 1.00
C29 AP7 20c yellow .50 .50
C30 AP6 35c yellow grn .40 .25
C31 AP7 50c deep blue .40 .25
C32 AP6 1b lt brown .40 .25
C33 AP7 2b deep rose .40 .40
C34 AP6 3b slate 1.40 1.40
Nos. C27-C34 (8) 6.00 5.05

Nos. C27 to C34 exist imperforate.
For surcharge see No. C52.

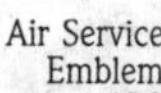

Air Service Emblem AP8

1932, Sept. 16 *Perf. 11*
C35 AP8 5c ultra .70 .55
C36 AP8 10c gray .45 .35
C37 AP8 15c dark rose .70 .55
C38 AP8 25c orange .70 .55
C39 AP8 30c green .60 .30
C40 AP8 50c violet .60 .35
C41 AP8 1b dk brown .60 .35
Nos. C35-C41 (7) 4.35 3.00

Map of Bolivia — AP9

1935, Feb. 1 Engr. *Perf. 12*
C42 AP9 5c brown red .15 .15
C43 AP9 10c dk green .15 .15
C44 AP9 20c dk violet .15 .15
C45 AP9 30c ultra .25 .15
C46 AP9 50c orange .30 .15
C47 AP9 1b bister brn .30 .25
C48 AP9 1½b yellow .60 .15
C49 AP9 2b carmine .60 .30
C50 AP9 5b green 1.10 .40
C51 AP9 10b dk brown 1.75 .75
Nos. C42-C51 (10) 5.35 2.60

Nos. C1, C4, C10, C30 Surcharged in Red (#C52-C56) or Green (#C57-C58) — c

Correo Aéreo
D. S. 25-2-37
0.05

1937, Oct. 6 *Perf. 11, 14*
C52 AP6 5c on 35c yel grn .40 .30
a. "Carreo" 12.50
b. Inverted surcharge
C53 AP3 20c on 35c red brn .50 .40
a. Inverted surcharge
C54 AP3 50c on 35c red brn 1.50 1.25
a. Inverted surcharge 17.50
C55 AP3 1b on 35c red brn 1.10 .65
a. Inverted surcharge
C56 AP1 2b on 50c org & blk 1.65 1.00
a. Inverted surcharge
C57 AP1 12b on 10c ver & blk 5.75 4.75
a. Inverted surcharge 22.50
C58 AP1 15b on 10c ver & blk 5.75 2.75
a. Inverted surcharge

Regular Postage Stamps of 1925 Surcharged in Green or Red — d

Correo
Aéreo
D. S.
25-2-37
Bs. 4.—

Perf. 14
C59 A56 (d) 3b on 50c dp vio (G) 1.10 1.00
C60 A56 (d) 4b on 1b red (G) 1.40 1.40
C61 A57 (c) 5b on 2b org (G) 1.90 1.65
a. Double surcharge 90.00
C62 A56 (d) 10b on 5b blk brn 4.50 3.25
a. Double surcharge 35.00
Nos. C52-C62 (11) 25.55 18.40

No. C59-C62 exist with inverted surcharge, No. C62 with black and black and red surcharges.

Courtyard of Potosi Mint — AP10

Miner — AP11

Emancipated Woman — AP12

Pincers, Torch and Good Will Principles — AP15

Airplane over Field — AP13

Airplanes and Liberty Monument AP14

Airplane over River — AP16

Emblem of New Government AP17

Transport Planes over Map of Bolivia AP18

1938, May Litho. *Perf. 10½*
C63 AP10 20c deep rose .25 .25
C64 AP11 30c gray .25 .25
C65 AP12 40c yellow .25 .25
C66 AP13 50c yellow grn .50 .25
C67 AP14 60c dull blue .50 .25
C68 AP15 1b dull red .75 .25
C69 AP16 2b bister 1.25 .25
C70 AP17 3b lt brown 1.25 .25
C71 AP18 5b dk violet 1.90 .25
Nos. C63-C71 (9) 6.90 2.25

40c, 1b, 2b exist imperf.

Chalice — AP19

Virgin of Copacabana AP20

Jesus Christ AP21

Church of San Francisco, La Paz — AP22

St. Anthony of Padua — AP23

Perf. 13½, 10½

1939, July 19 **Litho.**

C72 AP19 5c dull violet .35 .35
a. Pair, imperf. between 30.00
C73 AP20 30c lt bl grn .30 .20
C74 AP21 45c violet bl .60 .20
a. Vertical pair, imperf. between 42.50
C75 AP22 60c carmine .40 .35
C76 AP23 75c vermilion .65 .60
C77 AP23 90c deep blue .45 .25
C78 AP22 2b dull brown .75 .25
C79 AP21 4b deep plum 1.00 .40
C80 AP20 5b lt blue 2.50 .25
C81 AP19 10b yellow 5.00 .25
Nos. C72-C81 (10) 12.00 3.10

2nd National Eucharistic Congress.
For surcharge see No. C112.

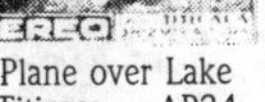

Plane over Lake Titicaca — AP24

Mt. Illimani and Condor — AP25

1941, Aug. 21 *Perf. 13½*

C82 AP24 10b dull green 3.25 .38
C83 AP24 20b light ultra 3.75 .65
C84 AP25 50b rose lilac 6.50 1.00
C85 AP25 100b olive bister 16.00 6.00
Nos. C82-C85 (4) 29.50 8.03

Counterfeits exist.

Liberty and Clasped Hands — AP26

1942, Nov. 12

C86 AP26 40c rose lake .25 .25
C87 AP26 50c ultra .25 .25
C88 AP26 1b orange brn 1.25 .75
C89 AP26 5b magenta .75 .25
a. Double impression
C90 AP26 10b dull brn vio 2.50 1.25
Nos. C86-C90 (5) 5.00 2.75

Conference of Chancellors, Jan. 15, 1942.

General José Ballivián; Old and Modern Transportation — AP27

1943, Nov. 18 **Engr.** *Perf. 12½*

C91 AP27 10c rose vio & brn .15 .15
C92 AP27 20c emerald & brn .15 .15
C93 AP27 30c rose car & brn .18 .15
C94 AP27 3b blue & brn .22 .18
C95 AP27 5b black & brn .40 .30
Nos. C91-C95 (5) 1.10 .93

Department of Beni centenary.

Condor and Sun Rising — AP28

Plane — AP29

1944, Sept. 19 **Litho.** *Perf. 13½*

C96 AP28 40c red violet .15 .15
C97 AP28 1b blue violet .15 .15
C98 AP29 1.50b yellow green .18 .15
C99 AP29 2.50b dk gray blue .38 .18
Nos. C96-C99 (4) .86
Set value .42

Revolution of Dec. 20, 1943.

Map of Natl. Airways — AP30

Map of Bolivian Air Lines — AP31

1945, May 31 *Perf. 11*

C100 AP30 10c red .15 .15
a. Imperf., pair 9.00
C101 AP30 50c yellow .15 .15
a. Imperf., pair 27.50
C102 AP30 90c lt green .20 .15
a. Imperf., pair 30.00
C103 AP30 5b lt ultra .35 .15
C104 AP30 20b deep brown 1.00 .45
Nos. C100-C104 (5) 1.85
Set value .84

10th anniversary of first flight, La Paz to Tacha, Peru, by Panagra Airways.
For surcharges see Nos. C128-C129.

1945, Sept. 15 *Perf. 13½*

Centers in Red and Blue

C105 AP31 20c violet .15 .15
C106 AP31 30c orange brn .15 .15
C107 AP31 50c brt blue grn .15 .15
C108 AP31 90c brt violet .15 .15
C109 AP31 2b blue .15 .15
C110 AP31 3b magenta .20 .15
C111 AP31 4b olive bister .35 .16
Set value 1.00 .68

Founding of Lloyd Aéreo Boliviano, 20th anniv.

Catalogue values for unused stamps in this section, from this point to the end of the section, are for Never Hinged items.

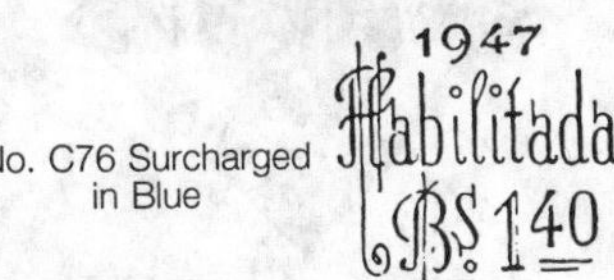

No. C76 Surcharged in Blue

1947, Mar. 23

C112 AP23 1.40b on 75c ver .18 .18

Mt. Illimani — AP32

Arms of Bolivia and Argentina — AP33

1947, Sept. 15 **Litho.** *Perf. 11½*

C113 AP32 1b rose car .15 .15
C114 AP32 1.40b emerald .15 .15
C115 AP32 2.50b blue .15 .15
C116 AP32 3b dp orange .18 .15
C117 AP32 4b rose lilac .20 .15
Set value .64 .46

1st anniv. of the Revolution of July 21, 1946. 1.40b, 2.50b exist imperf.
For surcharge see No. C137.

1947, Oct. 23 *Perf. 13½*

C118 AP33 2.90b ultra .25 .25
a. Imperf., pair 20.00
b. Perf. 10½ 5.00 4.00

Meeting of Presidents Enrique Hertzog of Bolivia and Juan D. Perón of Argentina at Yacuiba, Oct. 23, 1947.

Types of Regular Issue of 1948

Designs: 2.50b, Statue of Christ above La Paz. 3.70b, Child kneeling before cross. No. C121, St. John Bosco. No. C122, Virgin of Copacabana. 13.60b, Pope Pius XII blessing University of La Paz.

1948, Sept. 26 *Perf. 11½*

C119 A120 2.50b ver & yel .45 .35
C120 A120 3.70b rose & cream .55 .35
C121 A120 4b rose lil & gray .55 .25
C122 A120 4b lt ultra & sal .55 .16
C123 A120 13.60b ultra & lt grn .70 .40
Nos. C119-C123 (5) 2.80 1.51

Type of Regular Issue of 1948

1948, Oct.

C124 A125 10b emerald & salmon 1.60 .18

Pres. Gregorio Pacheco, Map and Post Horn — AP34

L. A. B. Plane — AP35

1950, Jan. 2 **Unwmk.**

C125 AP34 1.40b orange brown .15 .15
C126 AP34 2.50b orange .15 .15
C127 AP34 3.30b rose violet .15 .15
Nos. C125-C127 (3) .45 .45

75th anniv. of the UPU.

Nos. C100 and C104 Surcharged in Black

XV ANIVERSARIO PANAGRA Bs 4.- 1935-1950

1950, May 31 *Perf. 11*

C128 AP30 4b on 10c red .15 .15
a. Inverted surcharge 17.50 17.50
C129 AP30 10b on 20b dp brn .30 .22
a. Inverted surcharge 17.50 17.50

Panagra air services in Bolivia, 15th anniv.

1950, Sept. 15 **Litho.** *Perf. 13½*

C130 AP35 20c red orange .15 .15
C131 AP35 30c purple .15 .15
C132 AP35 50c green .15 .15
C133 AP35 1b orange .15 .15
C134 AP35 3b ultra .25 .15
C135 AP35 15b carmine .50 .15
C136 AP35 50b chocolate 1.00 .35
Nos. C130-C136 (7) 2.35
Set value 1.00

25th anniv. of the founding of Lloyd Aero Boliviano. 30c, 50c, 15b exist imperforate.
No. C132 exists without imprint at bottom of stamp.

No. C116 Surcharged in Black

Triunfo de la Democracia 24 de Sept.49 Bs. 1.40

1950, Sept. 24 *Perf. 11½*

C137 AP32 1.40b on 3b dp orange .25 .25

1st anniv. of the ending of the Civil War of Aug. 24-Sept. 24, 1949.
Exists with inverted and double surcharge.

Symbols of United Nations — AP36

1950, Oct. 24 **Unwmk.**

C138 AP36 3.60b crimson rose .50 .16
C139 AP36 4.70b black brown .65 .16

5th anniv. of the UN.

Gate of the Sun and Llama AP37

Church of San Francisco AP38

Designs: 40c, Avenue Camacho. 50c, Consistorial Palace. 1b, Legislative Palace. 2b, Communications Bldg. 3b, Arms. 4b, La Gasca ordering Mendoza to found La Paz. 5b, Capt. Alonso de Mendoza founding La Paz. 10b, Arms; portrait of Mendoza.

1951, Mar. 1 **Engr.** *Perf. 12½*

Center in Black

C140 AP37 20c carmine .15 .15
C141 AP38 30c dk vio bl .15 .15
C142 AP37 40c dark blue .15 .15
C143 AP37 50c blue green .15 .15
C144 AP37 1b red .20 .20
C145 AP37 2b red orange .35 .35
C146 AP37 3b deep blue .35 .35
C147 AP37 4b vermilion .45 .45
a. Souvenir sheet of 4 1.00 1.00
C148 AP37 5b dark green .40 .40
a. Souvenir sheet of 3 1.00 1.00
C149 AP37 10b red brown .65 .65
a. Souvenir sheet of 3 1.00 1.00
Nos. C140-C149 (10) 3.00 3.00

400th anniv. of the founding of La Paz.
No. C147a contains C143-C145, C147; No. C148a contains C142, C146, C148; No. C149a contains C140, C141, C149. Perf. and imperf., size: 150x100mm.
For surcharges see Nos. C187-C196.

Horsemanship AP39

Designs: 30c, Basketball. 50c, Fencing. 1b, Hurdling. 2.50b, Javelin throwing. 3b, Relay race. 5b, La Paz stadium.

1951, Aug. 23 **Unwmk.**

Center in Black

C150 AP39 20c purple .20 .15
C151 AP39 30c rose vio .30 .15
C152 AP39 50c dp red org .50 .15
C153 AP39 1b chocolate .50 .15
C154 AP39 2.50b orange .75 .30
C155 AP39 3b black brn 1.00 .75
a. Souvenir sheet of 3 4.00 3.50
C156 AP39 5b red 2.00 1.50
a. Souvenir sheet of 4 4.50 4.00
Nos. C150-C156 (7) 5.25 3.15

The stamps were intended to commemorate the 5th South American Games and the 2nd National Sports Congress held at La Paz, October 1948.
No. C155a contains C153-C155; No. C156a contains C150-C152, C156. Perf. and imperf., size: 150x100mm.

Eduardo Abaroa — AP40

Queen Isabella I — AP41

1952, Mar. 24 **Litho.** *Perf. 11*

C157 AP40 70c rose red .15 .15
C158 AP40 2b orange yel .25 .25
C159 AP40 3b yellow green .25 .15
C160 AP40 5b blue .25 .15
C161 AP40 50b rose lilac 1.00 .90
C162 AP40 100b gray black 1.10 1.10
a. Perf. 14 10.00
Nos. C157-C162 (6) 3.00 2.70

73rd anniv. of the death of Abaroa.

1952, July 16 *Perf. 13½*

C163 AP41 50b emerald .35 .25
C164 AP41 100b brown .65 .35

500th anniversary of the birth of Queen Isabella I of Spain. Exist imperforate.

Columbus Lighthouse AP42

1952, July 16

C165	AP42	2b rose lilac, *salmon*	.20	.20
C166	AP42	3.70b blue grn, *bl*	.20	.20
C167	AP42	4.40b orange, *salmon*	.20	.20
C168	AP42	20b dk brn, *cream*	.40	.15
		Nos. C165-C168 (4)	1.00	.75

No. C168 exists imperforate.

Soldiers — AP43

Gualberto Villarroel, Victor Paz Estenssoro and Hernan Siles Zuazo — AP44

Perf. 13½ (AP43), 11½ (AP44)

1953, Apr. 9 **Litho.**

C169	AP44	3.70b chocolate	.15	.15
C170	AP43	6b red violet	.15	.15
C171	AP44	9b brown rose	.15	.15
C172	AP44	10b aqua	.15	.15
C173	AP44	16b vermilion	.15	.15
C174	AP43	22.50b dk brown	.25	.20
C175	AP44	40b gray	.40	.15
		Nos. C169-C175 (7)	1.40	1.10

1st anniv. of the Revolution of Apr. 9, 1952.
Nos. C169-C170 and C174 exist imperf.

Pres. Victor Paz Estenssoro Embracing Indian — AP45

Map and Peasant — AP46

1954, Aug. 2 ***Perf. 12x11½***

C176	AP45	20b orange brn	.15	.15
C177	AP46	27b brt pink	.15	.16
C178	AP46	30b red org	.15	.15
C179	AP46	45b violet brn	.20	.15
C180	AP45	100b blue grn	.38	.15
C181	AP46	300b yellow grn	1.00	.28
		Nos. C176-C181 (6)	2.03	
		Set value		.77

Nos. C176, C180 for 3rd Inter-American Indian Congress. Nos. C177-C179, C181 agrarian reform laws of 1953-1954.
Nos. C176-C180 exist imperf.
For surcharge see No. C261.

Oil Derricks — AP47

Map of South America and La Paz Arms — AP48

1955, Oct. 9 ***Perf. 10½***

C182	AP47	55b dk & lt grnsh bl	.20	.15
C183	AP47	70b dk gray & gray	.20	.15
C184	AP47	90b dk & lt grn	.20	.15

Perf. 13

C185	AP47	500b red lilac	.65	.40
C186	AP47	1000b blk brn & fawn	1.25	1.25
		Nos. C182-C186 (5)	2.50	2.10

For surcharge see No. C262.

Nos. C140-C149 Surcharged with New Values and Bars in Black or Carmine

1957 **Engr.** ***Perf. 12½***

Center in Black

C187	AP37	100b on 3b (C)	.15	.15
C188	AP37	200b on 2b	.15	.15
C189	AP37	500b on 4b	.16	.15
C190	AP37	600b on 1b	.16	.15
C191	AP37	700b on 20c	.25	.15
C192	AP37	800b on 40c (C)	.35	.15
C193	AP38	900b on 30c (C)	.40	.15
C194	AP37	1800b on 50c (C)	.65	.25
C195	AP37	3000b on 5b (C)	1.00	.45
C196	AP37	5000b on 10b (C)	1.60	.75
		Nos. C187-C196 (10)	4.87	
		Set value		2.15

Unwmk.

1957, May 25 **Litho.** ***Perf. 12***

C197	AP48	700b lilac & vio	.35	.35
C198	AP48	1200b pale brn	.40	.35
C199	AP48	1350b rose car	.55	.50
C200	AP48	2700b blue grn	1.10	.65
C201	AP48	4000b violet bl	1.40	.75
		Nos. C197-C201 (5)	3.80	2.60

7th session of the C. E. P. A. L. (Comision Economica para la America Latina de las Naciones Unidas), La Paz.
Exist imperf.
For surcharges see Nos. C263-C265.

Type of Regular Issue, 1957

1957, Dec. 19 ***Perf. 11½***

C202	A141	600b magenta	.22	.15
C203	A141	700b violet bl	.35	.15
C204	A141	900b pale grn	.50	.15
		Nos. C202-C204 (3)	1.07	
		Set value		.27

Type of Regular Issue, 1960

1960, Jan. 30

C205	A142	400b rose claret	.50	.30
C206	A142	800b slate blue	.65	.40
C207	A142	2000b slate	1.00	.60
		Nos. C205-C207 (3)	2.15	1.30

Gate of the Sun, Tiahuanacu AP49

Uprooted Oak Emblem AP50

1960, Mar. 26 **Litho.** ***Perf. 11½***

C208	AP49	3000b gray	1.75	1.10
C209	AP49	5000b orange	2.75	1.10
C210	AP49	10,000b rose claret	4.25	2.75
C211	AP49	15,000b blue violet	6.25	4.50
		Nos. C208-C211 (4)	15.00	9.45

1960, Apr. 7 ***Perf. 11½***

C212	AP50	600b ultra	.35	.35
C213	AP50	700b lt red brn	.35	.35
C214	AP50	900b dk bl grn	.35	.35
C215	AP50	1800b violet	.60	.60
C216	AP50	2000b gray	.65	.60
		Nos. C212-C216 (5)	2.30	2.25

WRY, July 1, 1959-June 30, 1960.
No. C215 exists with "1961" overprint in dark carmine, but was not regularly issued in this form.

Jaime Laredo — AP51

Perf. 11½

1960, Aug. 15 **Unwmk.** **Litho.**

C217	AP51	600b rose vio	.75	.45
C218	AP51	700b ol gray	.75	.25
C219	AP51	800b vio brn	.75	.25
C220	AP51	900b dk bl	1.00	.25
C221	AP51	1800b green	1.50	1.50
C222	AP51	4000b dk gray	3.00	1.00
		Nos. C217-C222 (6)	7.75	3.70

Issued to honor the violinist Jaime Laredo.
For surcharges see Nos. C266-C267.

Children's Hospital Type of 1960

1960, Nov. 21 ***Perf. 11½***

C223	A146	600b multi	.40	.22
C224	A146	1000b multi	.60	.22
C225	A146	1800b multi	1.00	1.00
C226	A146	5000b multi	3.00	1.20
		Nos. C223-C226 (4)	5.00	2.64

For surcharges see No. C268-C269.

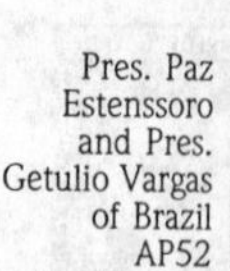

Pres. Paz Estenssoro and Pres. Getulio Vargas of Brazil AP52

1960, Dec. 14 **Litho.** ***Perf. 11½***

C227	AP52	1200b on 10b org & blk	.70	.70

Exists with surcharge inverted.
No. C227 without surcharge was not regularly issued, although a decree authorizing its circulation was published. Value, 50-cents.
Postally-used counterfeits of surcharge exist.

Pres. Paz Estenssoro and Pres. Frondizi of Argentina AP53

Design: 4000b, Flags of Bolivia and Argentina.

1961, May 23 ***Perf. 10½***

C228	AP53	4000b brn, red, yel, grn & bl	.75	.75
C229	AP53	6000b dk grn & blk	1.50	1.50

Visit of the President of Argentina, Dr. Arturo Frondizi, to Bolivia.
For surcharge see No. C309.

Miguel de Cervantes — AP54

1961, Oct. **Photo.** ***Perf. 13***

C230	AP54	1400b pale grn & dk ol grn	.58	.22

Cervantes' appointment as Chief Magistrate of La Paz.

Virgin of Cotoca and Symbol of Eucharist AP55

Planes and Parachutes AP56

1962, Mar. 19 **Litho.** ***Perf. 10½***

C231	AP55	1400b brn, pink & yel	.65	.35

4th Natl. Eucharistic Cong., Santa Cruz, 1961.

Nos. C212-C216 Surcharged Vertically with New Value and Greek Key Border

1962, June **Unwmk.** ***Perf. 11½***

C232	AP50	1200b on 600b	.55	.55
C233	AP50	1300b on 700b	.50	.50
C234	AP50	1400b on 900b	.55	.55
C235	AP50	2800b on 1,800b	.90	.75
C236	AP50	3000b on 2,000b	.90	.75
		Nos. C232-C236 (5)	3.40	3.10

The overprinted segment of Greek key border on Nos. C232-C236 comes in two positions: two full "keys" on top, and one full and two half keys on top.

Flower Type of 1962

Flowers: 100b, 1800b, Cantua buxifolia. 800b, 10,000b, Cantua bicolor.

1962, June 28 **Litho.** ***Perf. 10½***

Flowers in Natural Colors

C237	A152	100b dk bl	.25	.15
C238	A152	800b green	.50	.15
C239	A152	1800b violet	1.00	.50
a.		Souvenir sheet of 3	3.50	3.50
C240	A152	10,000b dk bl	3.25	1.75
		Nos. C237-C240 (4)	5.00	2.55

No. C239a contains 3 imperf. stamps similar to Nos. C237-C239, but with the 1,800b background color changed to dark violet blue.
For surcharges see Nos. C270-C271.

1962, Sept. 5 **Litho.** ***Perf. 11½***

Designs: 1200b, 5000b, Plane and oxcart. 2000b, Aerial photography (plane over South America).

Emblem in Red, Yellow & Green

C241	AP56	600b blk & bl	.25	.15
C242	AP56	1200b multi	.50	.20
C243	AP56	2000b multi	.75	.35
C244	AP56	5000b multi	1.50	.65
		Nos. C241-C244 (4)	3.00	1.35

Armed Forces of Bolivia.

Malaria Type of 1962

Design: Inscription around mosquito, laurel around globe.

1962, Oct. 4

C245	A154	2000b ind, grn & yel	.80	.50

Type of Regular Issue, 1961

Design: Pedro de la Gasca (1485-1567).

1962 **Unwmk.** **Photo.** ***Perf. 13x12½***

C246	A150	1200b brn, *yel*	.35	.20

Condor, Soccer Ball and Flags AP57

Alliance for Progress Emblem AP58

Design: 1.80b, Map of Bolivia, soccer ball, goal and flags.

1963, Mar. 21 **Litho.** ***Perf. 11½***

C247	AP57	1.40b multi	1.00	.65
C248	AP57	1.80b multi	1.00	1.00

Issued to publicize the 21st South American Soccer Championships.

Freedom from Hunger Type

Design: Wheat, globe and wheat emblem.

1963, Aug. 1 **Unwmk.** ***Perf. 11½***

C249	A156	1.20b dk grn, bl & yel	.75	.75

1963, Nov. 15 ***Perf. 11½***

C250	AP58	1.20b dl yel, ultra & grn	.80	.75

2nd anniv. of the Alliance for Progress, which aims to stimulate economic growth and raise living standards in Latin America.

Type of Regular Issue, 1963

Designs: 1.20b, Ballot box and voters. 1.40b, Map and farmer breaking chain. 2.80b, Miners.

1963, Dec. 21 ***Perf. 11½***

C251	A157	1.20b gray, dk brn & rose	.40	.20
C252	A157	1.40b bister & grn	.50	.25
C253	A157	2.80b slate & buff	1.00	.90
		Nos. C251-C253 (3)	1.90	1.35

Andrés Santa Cruz — AP59

Perf. 13½

1966, Aug. 10 Wmk. 90 Litho.

C254 AP59 20c dp bl .15 .15
C255 AP59 60c dp grn .20 .20
C256 AP59 1.20b red brn .50 .50
C257 AP59 2.80b black .80 .80
Nos. C254-C257 (4) 1.65 1.65

Cent. (in 1965) of the death of Marshal Andrés Santa Cruz (1792-1865), pres. of Bolivia and of Peru-Bolivia Confederation.

Children Type of 1966

Design: 1.40b, Mother and children.

1966, Dec. 16 Unwmk. *Perf. 13½*

C258 A159 1.40b gray bl & blk 1.00 .42

Co-Presidents Type of Regular Issue

1966, Dec. 16 Litho. *Perf. 12½*

Flag in Red, Yellow and Green

C259 A160 2.80b gray & tan 1.40 1.00
C260 A160 10b sep & tan 1.60 .50
a. Souvenir sheet of 4 6.50 6.50

No. C260a contains 4 imperf. stamps similar to Nos. 480-481 and C259-C260. Dark green marginal inscription. Size: 135x82mm.

Various Issues 1954-62 Surcharged with New Values and Bars

1966, Dec. 21

On No. C177: "XII Aniversario / Reforma / Agraria"

C261 AP46 10c on 27b .20 .15
a. Agraria/Agraria 10.00

On No. C182: "XXV / Aniversario Paz / del Chaco"

C262 AP47 10c on 55b .20 .15

On No. C199: "Centenario de / Tupiza"

C263 AP48 60c on 1350b .50 .20

On No. C200: "XXV / Aniversario / Automovil Club / Boliviano"

C264 AP48 2.80b on 2700b 2.00 1.60

On No. C201: "Centenario de la / Cruz Roja / Internacional"

C265 AP48 4b on 4000b 1.40 1.00

On No. C219: "CL Aniversario / Heroinas Coronilla"

C266 AP51 1.20b on 800b .75 .50

On No. C222: "Centenario Himno / Paceño"

C267 AP51 1.40b on 4,000b .75 .50

Nos. C224-C225 Surcharged

C268 A146 1.40b on 1,000b .60 .60
C269 A146 1.40b on 1,800b .60 .60

On Nos. C238-C239: "Aniversario / Centro Filatelico / Cochabamba"

C270 A152 1.20b on 800b 1.00 .25
C271 A152 1.20b on 1,800b 1.00 .25

Revenue Stamp of 1946 Surcharged with New Value "X" and: "XXV Aniversario / Dpto. Pando / Aéreo"

C272 A161 1.20b on 1b dk bl .50 .25
Nos. C261-C272 (12) 9.50 6.05

Lions Emblem and Pre-historic Sculptures AP60

1967, Sept. 20 Litho. *Perf. 13x13½*

C273 AP60 2b red & multi .80 .65
a. Souvenir sheet of 2 3.75 3.75

50th anniv. of Lions Intl. No. C273a contains 2 imperf. stamps similar to Nos. 492 and C273.

Folklore Type of Regular Issue

Designs (Folklore characters): 1.20p, Pujllay. 1.40p, Ujusiris. 2p, Morenada. 3p, Auki-aukis.

1968, June 24 *Perf. 13½x13*

C274 A163 1.20b lt yel grn & multi .35 .20
C275 A163 1.40b gray & multi .40 .20
C276 A163 2b dk ol bis & multi .75 .25
C277 A163 3b sky bl & multi 1.00 .25
Nos. C274-C277 (4) 2.50 .90

A souvenir sheet exists containing 4 imperf. stamps similar to Nos. C274-C277. Size: 131x81½mm.

Moto Mendez — AP61

1968, Oct. 29 Litho. *Perf. 13½x13*

C278 AP61 1b multi .35 .15
C279 AP61 1.20b multi .40 .35
C280 AP61 2b multi .75 .50
C281 AP61 4b multi 1.00 .75
Nos. C278-C281 (4) 2.50 1.75

Battle of Tablada sesquicentennial.

Pres. Gualberto Villaroel — AP62

1968, Nov. 6 *Perf. 13x13½*

C282 AP62 1.40b org & blk .30 .22
C283 AP62 3b lt bl & blk .55 .32
C284 AP62 4b rose & blk .70 .40
C285 AP62 5b gray grn & blk .90 .55
C286 AP62 10b pale pur & blk 1.60 1.10
Nos. C282-C286 (5) 4.05 2.59

4th centenary of Cochabamba.

ITU Type of Regular Issue

1968, Dec. 3 Litho. *Perf. 13x13½*

C287 A166 1.20b gray, blk & yel .60 .30
C288 A166 1.40b bl, blk & gray ol .60 .20

UNESCO Emblem — AP63

1968, Nov. 14 *Perf. 13½x13*

C289 AP63 1.20b pale vio & blk .35 .35
C290 AP63 2.80b yel grn & blk .65 .65

20th anniv. (in 1966) of UNESCO.

Kennedy Type of Regular Issue

1968, Nov. 22 Unwmk.

C291 A168 1b grn & blk .25 .15
C292 A168 10b scar & blk 2.75 2.75

A souvenir sheet contains one imperf. stamp similar to No. C291. Dark violet marginal inscription. Size: 131x81½mm.

Tennis Type of Regular Issue

1968, Dec. 10 *Perf. 13x13½*

C293 A169 1.40b org, blk & lt brn .35 .35
C294 A169 2.80b sky bl, blk & lt brn .65 .65

A souvenir sheet exists containing one imperf. stamp similar to No. C293. Size: 131x81½mm.

Stamp Centenary Type of Regular Issue

Design: 1.40b, 2.80b, 3b, Bolivia No. 1.

1968, Dec. 23 Litho. *Perf. 13x13½*

C295 A170 1.40b org, grn & blk .50 .50
C296 A170 2.80b pale rose, grn & blk 1.00 1.00
C297 A170 3b lt vio, grn & blk 1.00 1.00
Nos. C295-C297 (3) 2.50 2.50

A souvenir sheet exists containing 3 imperf. stamps similar to Nos. C295-C297. Size: 131x81½mm.

Franklin D. Roosevelt — AP64

1969, Oct. 29 Litho. *Perf. 13½x13*

C298 AP64 5b brn, blk & buff 1.75 1.10

Olympic Type of Regular Issue

Sports: 1.20b, Woman runner, vert. 2.80b, Discus thrower, vert. 5b, Hurdler.

Perf. 13½x13, 13x13½

1969, Oct. 29 Litho.

C299 A171 1.20b yel grn, bis & blk .50 .40
C300 A171 2.80b red, org & blk 1.00 .75
C301 A171 5b bl, lt bl, red & blk 1.50 1.50
Nos. C299-C301 (3) 3.00 2.65

A souvenir sheet exists containing 3 imperf. stamps similar to Nos. C299-C301. Size: 130½x81mm.

Butterfly Type of Regular Issue

Butterflies: 1b, Metamorpha dido wernichei. 1.80b, Heliconius felix. 2.80b, Morpho casica. 3b, Papilio yuracares. 4b, Heliconius melitus.

1970, Apr. 24 Litho. *Perf. 13x13½*

C302 A172 1b sal & multi 1.00 1.00
C303 A172 1.80b lt bl & multi 1.50 1.50
C304 A172 2.80b multi 2.50 2.50
C305 A172 3b multi 2.50 2.50
C306 A172 4b multi 3.00 3.00
Nos. C302-C306 (5) 10.50 10.50

A souvenir sheet exists containing 3 imperf. stamps similar to Nos. C302-C304. Black marginal inscription. Size: 129½x80mm.

Scout Type of Regular Issue

Designs: 50c, Boy Scout building brick wall. 1.20b, Bolivian Boy Scout emblem.

1970, June 17 Litho. *Perf. 13½x13*

C307 A173 50c yel & multi .15 .15
C308 A173 1.20b multi .40 .40

No. C228 Surcharged

1970, Dec. Litho. *Perf. 10½*

C309 AP53 1.20b on 4000b multi .25 .15

Flower Type of Regular Issue

Bolivian Flowers: 1.20b, Amaryllis pseudopardina, horiz. 1.40b, Rebutia kruegeri. 2.80b, Lobivia pentlandii, horiz. 4b, Rebutia tunariensis.

Perf. 13x13½, 13½x13

1971, Aug. 9 Litho. Unwmk.

C310 A174 1.20b multi .70 .40
C311 A174 1.40b multi .80 .50
C312 A174 2.80b multi 1.50 .75
C313 A174 4b multi 2.00 1.25
Nos. C310-C313 (4) 5.00 2.90

Two souvenir sheets of 4 exist. One contains imperf. stamps similar to Nos. 534-535 and C310, C312. The other contains imperf. stamps similar to Nos. 536-537, C311, C313. Size: 130x80mm.

Folk Dance Type of Regular Issue

1972, Mar. 23 Litho. *Perf. 13½x13*

C314 A177 1.20b Kusillo .50 .16
C315 A177 1.40b Taquirari .65 .16

Two souvenir sheets of 3 exist. One contains imperf. stamps similar to Nos. 542-543, C314. The other contains imperf. stamps similar to Nos. 540-541, C315. Size: 80x129mm.

Painting Type of Regular Issue

Bolivian Paintings: 1.40b, Portrait of Chola Paceña, by Cecilio Guzman de Rojas. 1.50b, Adoration of the Kings, by G. Gamarra. 1.60b, Adoration of Pachamama (mountain), by A. Borda. 2b, The Kiss of the Idol, by Guzman de Rojas.

1972 Litho. *Perf. 13½*

C316 A178 1.40b multi .40 .15
C317 A178 1.50b multi .40 .15
C318 A178 1.60b multi .40 .20
C319 A178 2b multi .55 .20
Nos. C316-C319 (4) 1.75 .70

Two souvenir sheets of 2 exist. One contains imperf. stamps similar to Nos. 548 and C318. The other contains imperf. stamps similar to Nos. C317 and C319. Size: 129x80mm.

Issue dates: 1.40b, Dec. 4. Others, Aug. 17.

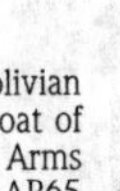

Bolivian Coat of Arms AP65

1972, Dec. 4 *Perf. 13½x14*

C320 AP65 4b lt bl & multi 1.40 .50

Cactus Type of Regular Issue

Designs: Various cacti.

1973, Aug. 6 Litho. *Perf. 13½*

C321 A180 1.20b tan & multi .35 .15
C322 A180 1.90b org & multi .50 .20
C323 A180 2b multi .65 .25
Nos. C321-C323 (3) 1.50 .60

Development Type of Regular Issue

Designs: 1.40b, Highway 1Y4. 2b, Rail car on bridge.

1973, Nov. 26 Litho. *Perf. 13½*

C324 A181 1.40b sal & multi .40 .15
C325 A181 2b multi .60 .20

Santos-Dumont and 14-Bis Plane — AP66

1973, July 20

C326 AP66 1.40b yel & blk .65 .35

Centenary of the birth of Alberto Santos-Dumont (1873-1932), Brazilian aviation pioneer.

Orchid Type of 1974

Orchids: 2.50b, Cattleya luteola, horiz. 3.80b, Stanhopaea. 4b, Catasetum, horiz. 5b, Maxillaria.

1974 Litho. *Perf. 13½*

C327 A182 2.50b multi 1.00 .22
C328 A182 3.80b rose & multi 1.50 .45
C329 A182 4b multi 1.50 .40
C330 A182 5b sal & multi 2.50 .45
Nos. C327-C330 (4) 6.50 1.52

Air Force Emblem, Plane over Map of Bolivia — AP67

Designs: 3.80b, Plane over Andes. 4.50b, Triple decker and jet. 8b, Rafael Pabon and double decker. 15b, Jet and "50."

1974 Litho. *Perf. 13x13½*

C331 AP67 3b multi .65 .25
C332 AP67 3.80b multi 1.00 .25
C333 AP67 4.50b multi 1.00 .25
C334 AP67 8b multi 1.60 .40
C335 AP67 15b multi 3.50 .50
Nos. C331-C335 (5) 7.75 1.65

Bolivian Air Force, 50th anniv. Exist imperf.

Coat of Arms Type of 1975

Designs: Departmental coats of arms.

1975, July 16 Litho. *Perf. 13½*

C336 A188 20c Beni .15 .15
C337 A188 30c Tarija .15 .15
C338 A188 50c Potosi .25 .25
C339 A188 1b Oruro .50 .50
C340 A188 2.50b Santa Cruz 1.00 1.00
C341 A188 3b La Paz 1.00 1.00
Nos. C336-C341 (6) 3.05 3.05

LAB Emblem — AP68

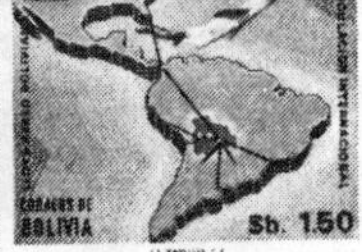

Bolivia on Map of Americas — AP69

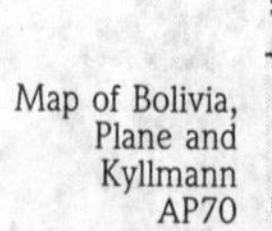

Map of Bolivia, Plane and Kyllmann
AP70

1975 Litho. *Perf. 13½*

C342 AP68 1b gold, bl & blk .40 .40
C343 AP69 1.50b multi .60 .60
C344 AP70 2b multi .75 .75
Nos. C342-C344 (3) 1.75 1.75

Lloyd Aereo Boliviano, 50th anniversary, founded by Guillermo Kyllmann.

Bolivar, Presidents Perez and Banzer, and Flags
AP71

1975, Aug. 4 Litho. *Perf. 13½*

C345 AP71 3b gold & multi .75 .65

Visit of Pres. Carlos A. Perez of Venezuela.

Bolivar Type of 1975

Presidents and Statesmen of Bolivia: 50c, Rene Barrientes O. 2b, Francisco B. O'Connor. 3.80b, Gualberto Villarroel. 4.20b, German Busch. 4.50b, Hugo Banzer Suarez. 20b, José Ballivian. 30b, Andres de Santa Cruz. 40b, Antonio Jose de Sucre.

1975 *Perf. 13½*

Size: 24x33mm

C346 A189 50c multi .25 .25
C347 A189 2b multi .50 .50
C348 A189 3.80b multi .75 .75
C349 A189 4.20b multi 1.00 .75

Size: 28x39mm

C350 A189 4.50b multi 1.00 .50

Size: 24x33mm

C351 A189 20b multi 4.00 2.00
C352 A189 30b multi 5.00 5.00
C353 A189 40b multi 6.50 6.50
Nos. C346-C353 (8) 19.00 16.25

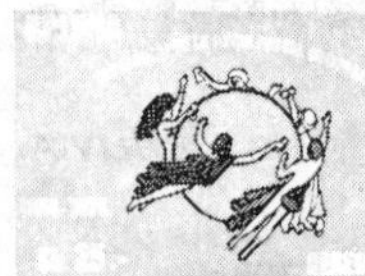

UPU Emblem
AP72

1975, Dec. 7 Litho. *Perf. 13½*

C358 AP72 25b bl & multi 3.00 3.00

Cent. of UPU (in 1974).

POSTAGE DUE STAMPS

D1

1931 Unwmk. Engr. *Perf. 14, 14½*

J1 D1 5c ultra 1.10 1.25
J2 D1 10c red 1.10 1.25
J3 D1 15c yellow 1.75 1.90
J4 D1 30c deep green 1.75 1.90
J5 D1 40c deep violet 2.75 3.00
J6 D1 50c black brown 4.00 4.25
Nos. J1-J6 (6) 12.45 13.55

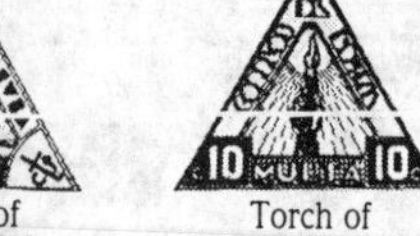

Symbol of Youth — D2
Torch of Knowledge — D3

Symbol of the Revolution of May 17, 1936 — D4

1938 Litho. *Perf. 11*

J7 D2 5c deep rose .50 .45
a. Pair, imperf. between
J8 D3 10c green .50 .45
J9 D4 30c gray blue .50 .45
Nos. J7-J9 (3) 1.50 1.35

POSTAL TAX STAMPS

Worker
PT1

Symbols of Communications
PT2

Imprint: "LITO. UNIDAS LA PAZ."

Perf. 13½x10½, 10½, 13½

1939 Litho. Unwmk.

RA1 PT1 5c dull violet .70 .15
a. Double impression

Redrawn

Imprint: "TALL. OFFSET LA PAZ."

1940 *Perf. 12x11, 11*

RA2 PT1 5c violet .60 .15
a. Horizontal pair, imperf. between 2.00
b. Imperf. horiz., pair

Tax of Nos. RA1-RA2 was for the Workers' Home Building Fund.

1944-45 Litho. *Perf. 10½*

RA3 PT2 10c salmon .40 .15
RA4 PT2 10c blue ('45) .40 .15

A 30c orange inscribed "Centenario de la Creacion del Departmento del Beni" was issued in 1946 and required to be affixed to all air and surface mail to and from the Department of Beni in addition to regular postage. Five higher denominations in the same scenic design were used for local revenue purposes.

Catalogue values for unused stamps in this section, from this point to the end of the section, are for Never Hinged items.

Type of 1944 Redrawn

1947-48 Unwmk. *Perf. 10½*

RA5 PT2 10c carmine .40 .15
RA6 PT2 10c org yel ('48) .35 .15
RA7 PT2 10c yel brn ('48) .35 .15
RA8 PT2 10c emerald ('48) .35 .15
Nos. RA5-RA8 (4) 1.45
Set value .30

Post horn and envelope reduced in size.

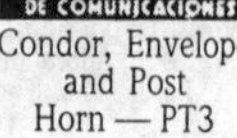

Condor, Envelope and Post Horn — PT3
Communication Symbols — PT4

1951-52

RA9 PT3 20c deep orange .40 .20
a. Imperf., pair 20.00
RA10 PT3 20c green ('52) .50 .20
a. Imperf., pair 20.00
RA11 PT3 20c blue ('52) .50 .20
a. Imperf., pair 20.00
Nos. RA9-RA11 (3) 1.40 .60

For surcharges see Nos. RA17-RA18.

1952-54 *Perf. 13½, 10½, 10½x12*

RA12 PT4 50c green .50 .15
RA13 PT4 50c carmine .50 .15
RA14 PT4 3b green .50 .15
RA15 PT4 3b olive bister .50 .50
RA16 PT4 5b violet ('54) .50 .50
Nos. RA12-RA16 (5) 2.50 1.45

For surcharges see Nos. RA21-RA22.

No. RA10 and Type of 1951-52 Surcharged with New Value in Black

1953 *Perf. 10½*

RA17 PT3 50c on 20c green .25 .15
RA18 PT3 50c on 20c red vio .25 .15

Postman Blowing Horn — PT5

1954-55 Unwmk. *Perf. 10½*

RA19 PT5 1b brown .20 .15
RA20 PT5 1b car rose ('55) .20 .15
Set value .20

Exist imperf.

Nos. RA15 and RA14 Surcharged in Black "Bs. 5.-/D. S./21-IV-55"

1955 *Perf. 10½, 10½x12*

RA21 PT4 5b on 3b olive bister .25 .15
RA22 PT4 5b on 3b green .25 .15
Set value .20

Tax of Nos. RA3-RA22 was for the Communications Employees Fund.

No. RA21 is known with surcharge in thin type of different font and with comma added after "55."

Plane over Airport — PT6
Planes — PT7

Perf. 10½, 12, 13½

1955 Unwmk. Litho.

RA23 PT6 5b dp ultra .25 .15
a. Vertical pair imperf. between

Perf. 11½

RA24 PT7 10b light green .20 .15

PT8
PT9

1955 Litho. *Perf. 10½*

RA25 PT8 5b red 7.50 7.50

Perf. 12

RA26 PT9 20b dark brown .25 .15

Tax of Nos. RA23-RA26 was for the building of new airports.

General Alfredo Ovando and Three Men — PT10

1970, Sept. 26 Litho. *Perf. 13x13½*

RA27 PT10 20c black & red .50 .15

See No. RAC1.

Pres. German Busch — PT11

1971, May 13 Litho. *Perf. 13x13½*

RA28 PT11 20c lilac & black .50 .15

AIR POST POSTAL TAX STAMPS

Catalogue values for unused stamps in this section are for Never Hinged items.

Type of Postal Tax Issue

Design: 30c, General Ovando and oil well.

1970, Sept. 26 Litho. *Perf. 13x13½*

RAC1 PT10 30c blk & grn .50 .15

Pres. Gualberto Villarroel, Refinery
PTAP1

1971, May 25 Litho. *Perf. 13x13½*

RAC2 PTAP1 30c lt bl & blk .50 .15

Type of 1971 Inscribed: "XXV ANIVERSARIO DE SU GOBIERNO"

1975 Litho. *Perf. 13x13½*

RAC3 PTAP1 30c lt bl & blk 3.00 3.00

BOSNIA AND HERZEGOVINA

'bäz–nē–ə and ,hert–sə–gō–'vē–nə

LOCATION — Dalmatia and Serbia
GOVT. — Provinces of Turkey under Austro-Hungarian occupation, 1879-1908; provinces of Austria-Hungary 1908-1918
AREA — 19,768 sq. mi.
POP. — 2,000,000 (approx. 1918)
CAPITAL — Sarajevo

Following World War I Bosnia and Herzegovina united with the kingdoms of Montenegro and Serbia, and Croatia, Dalmatia and Slovenia, to form the Kingdom of Yugoslavia (See Yugoslavia.)

100 Novcica (Neukreuzer) = 1 Florin (Gulden)

100 Heller = 1 Krone (1900)

Watermark

Wmk. 91- BRIEF-MARKEN or (from 1890) ZEITUNGS-MARKEN in Double-lined Capitals, Across the Sheet

Coat of Arms — A1

Type I - The heraldic eaglets on the right side of the escutcheon are entirely blank. The eye of the lion is indicated by a very small dot, which sometimes fails to print.

Type II - There is a colored line across the lowest eaglet. A similar line sometimes appears on the middle eaglet. The eye of the lion is formed by a large dot which touches the outline of the head above it.

Type III - The eaglets and eye of the lion are similar to type I. Each tail feather of the large eagle has two lines of shading and the lowest feather does not touch the curved line below it. In types I and II there are several shading lines in these feathers, and the lowest feather touches the curved line.

Varieties of the Numerals

2 NOVCICA:
A - The "2" has curved tail. All are type I.
B - The "2" has straight tail. All are type II.

15 NOVCICA:

C - The serif of the "1" is short and forms a wide angle with the vertical stroke.

D - The serif of the "1" forms an acute angle with the vertical stroke.

The numerals of the 5n were retouched several times and show minor differences, especially in the flag.

Other Varieties

½ NOVCICA:

There is a black dot between the curved ends of the ornaments near the lower spandrels.

G - This dot touches the curve at its right. Stamps of this (1st) printing are litho.

H - This dot stands clear of the curved lines. Stamps of this (2nd) printing are typo.

10 NOVCICA:

Ten stamps in each sheet of type II show a small cross in the upper section of the right side of the escutcheon.

Perf. 9 to 13½ and Compound

1879-94 Litho. Wmk. 91

Type I

1	A1	½n blk (type II) ('94)	7.25	*15.00*
2	A1	1n gray	4.75	1.50
c.		In gray lilac		1.50
4	A1	2n yellow	9.00	.90
5	A1	3n green	6.00	1.75
6	A1	5n rose red	10.00	.40
7	A1	10n blue	30.00	.75
8	A1	15n brown	32.50	4.50
9	A1	20n gray green ('93)	150.00	6.75
10	A1	25n violet	27.50	6.75

No. 2c was never issued. It is usually canceled by blue pencil marks and "mint" copies generally have been cleaned.

Perf. 10½ to 13 and Compound

1894-98 Typo.

Type II

1a	A1	½n black	10.00	*15.00*
2a	A1	1n gray	4.00	1.00
4a	A1	2n yellow	3.00	.55
5a	A1	3n green	4.00	1.25
6a	A1	5n rose red	55.00	.35
7a	A1	10n blue	5.50	.70
8a	A1	15n brown	4.75	3.25
9a	A1	20n gray green	6.75	3.50
10a	A1	25n violet	7.25	5.75

Type III

6b	A1	5n rose red ('98)	1.50	.35

All the preceding stamps exist in various shades.

Nos. 1a to 10a were reprinted in 1911 in lighter colors, on very white paper and perf. 12½. Value, set $25.

A2

A3

Perf. 10½, 12½ and Compound

1900 Typo.

11	A2	1h gray black	.30	.15
12	A2	2h gray	.30	.15
13	A2	3h yellow	.30	.15
14	A2	5h green	.30	.15
15	A2	6h brown	.60	.15
16	A2	10h red	.25	.15
17	A2	20h rose	100.00	4.00
18	A2	25h blue	.85	.15
19	A2	30h bister brown	110.00	4.75
20	A2	40h orange	150.00	8.00
21	A2	50h red lilac	1.00	.35
22	A3	1k dark rose	1.25	.50
23	A3	2k ultra	1.50	1.25
24	A3	5k dull blue grn	3.75	3.75
		Nos. 11-24 (14)	370.40	23.65

All values of this issue except the 3h exist on ribbed paper.

Nos. 17, 19 and 20 were reprinted in 1911. The reprints are in lighter colors and on whiter paper than the originals. Reprints of Nos. 17 and 19 are perf. 10½ and those of No. 20 are perf. 12½. Value each $1.50.

Numerals in Black

1901-04 ***Perf. 12½***

25	A2	20h pink ('02)	.55	.30
26	A2	30h bister brn ('03)	.55	.30
27	A2	35h blue	.75	.30
a.		35h ultramarine	*80.00*	4.75
28	A2	40h orange ('03)	1.00	.60
29	A2	45h grnsh blue ('04)	.65	.35
		Nos. 25-29 (5)	3.50	1.85

Nos. 11-16, 18, 21-29 exist imperf. Most of Nos. 11-29 exist perf. 6½; compound with 12½; part perf.; in pairs imperf. between. These were supplied only to some high-ranking officials and never sold at any P.O.

View of Deboj — A4

The Carsija at Sarajevo — A5

Designs: 2h, View of Mostar. 3h, Pliva Gate, Jajce. 5h, Narenta Pass and Prenj River. 6h, Rama Valley. 10h, Vrbas Valley. 20h, Old Bridge, Mostar. 25h, Bey's Mosque, Sarajevo. 30h, Donkey post. 35h, Jezero and tourists' pavilion. 40h, Mail wagon. 45h, Bazaar at Sarajevo. 50h, Postal car. 2k, St. Luke's Campanile, Jajce. 5k, Emperor Franz Josef.

Perf. 6½, 9½, 10½ and 12½, also Compounds

1906 Engr. Unwmk.

30	A4	1h black	.15	.15
31	A4	2h violet	.15	.15
32	A4	3h olive	.15	.15
33	A4	5h dark green	.15	.15
34	A4	6h brown	.15	.15
a.		Perf. 13½	15.00	18.00
35	A4	10h carmine	.15	.15
36	A4	20h dark brown	.35	.20
a.		Perf. 13½	37.50	37.50
37	A4	25h deep blue	1.00	.75
38	A4	30h green	1.10	.30
39	A4	35h myrtle green	1.25	.30
40	A4	40h orange red	1.25	.30
41	A4	45h brown red	1.25	.90
42	A4	50h dull violet	1.40	.60
43	A5	1k maroon	3.50	1.25
44	A5	2k gray green	4.25	6.00
45	A5	5k dull blue	3.75	4.50
		Nos. 30-45 (16)	20.00	16.00

Nos. 30-45 exist imperf. Value, set $50 unused, $37.50 canceled.

For overprint and surcharges see #126, B1-B4.

Birthday Jubilee Issue

Designs of 1906 Issue, with "1830-1910" in Label at Bottom

1910 ***Perf. 12½***

46	A4	1h black	.35	.15
47	A4	2h violet	.40	.15
48	A4	3h olive	.40	.20
49	A4	5h dark green	.45	.15
50	A4	6h orange brn	.45	.20
51	A4	10h carmine	.45	.15
52	A4	20h dark brown	1.00	1.10
53	A4	25h deep blue	2.00	2.25
54	A4	30h green	1.50	1.90
55	A4	35h myrtle grn	2.00	2.00
56	A4	40h orange red	2.00	2.50
57	A4	45h brown red	3.50	4.25
58	A4	50h dull violet	3.50	4.50
59	A5	1k maroon	3.50	4.50
60	A5	2k gray green	13.00	13.00
61	A5	5k dull blue	2.50	3.00
		Nos. 46-61 (16)	37.00	40.00

80th birthday of Emperor Franz Josef.

Scenic Type of 1906

Designs (Views): 12h, Jaice. 60h, Konjica. 72h, Vishegrad.

1912

62	A4	12h ultra	3.25	4.00
63	A4	60h dull blue	2.00	3.50
64	A4	72h carmine	10.00	13.00
		Nos. 62-64 (3)	15.25	20.50

Value, imperf. set, $75.

See Austria for similar designs inscribed "FELDPOST" instead of "MILITARPOST."

Emperor Franz Josef

A23 A24

A25 A26

1912-14

Various Frames

65	A23	1h olive green	.35	.15
66	A23	2h brt blue	.35	.15
67	A23	3h claret	.35	.15
68	A23	5h green	.35	.15
69	A23	6h dark gray	.35	.15
70	A23	10h rose car	.40	.15
71	A23	12h dp olive grn	1.10	.30
72	A23	20h orange brn	4.50	.15
73	A23	25h ultra	2.25	.15
74	A23	30h orange red	2.25	.15
75	A24	35h myrtle grn	2.25	.15
76	A24	40h dk violet	6.75	.15
77	A24	45h olive brn	3.00	.15
78	A24	50h slate blue	3.00	.15
79	A24	60h brown vio	2.75	.15
80	A24	72h dark blue	3.25	3.00
81	A25	1k brn vio, *straw*	12.50	.35
82	A25	2k dk gray, *bl*	7.25	.25
83	A26	3k carmine, *grn*	12.00	9.00
84	A26	5k dk vio, *gray*	22.50	20.00
85	A25	10k dk ultra, *gray* ('14)	82.50	70.00
		Nos. 65-85 (21)	170.00	105.00

Value, imperf. set, $450.

For overprint and surcharges see #127, B5-B8.

A27 A28

1916-17 ***Perf. 12½***

86	A27	3h dark gray	.15	.20
87	A27	5h olive green	.25	.35
88	A27	6h violet	.30	.35
89	A27	10h bister	1.25	1.65
90	A27	12h blue gray	.40	.45
91	A27	15h car rose	.15	.15
92	A27	20h brown	.35	.45
93	A27	25h blue	.25	.35
94	A27	30h dark green	.25	.35
95	A27	40h vermilion	.25	.35
96	A27	50h green	.25	.35
97	A27	60h lake	.25	.35
98	A27	80h orange brn	1.10	.40
a.		Perf. 11½	3.25	3.00
99	A27	90h dark violet	.65	.50
a.		Perf. 11½	450.00	*675.00*
101	A28	2k claret, *straw*	.65	.75
102	A28	3k green, *bl*	1.75	3.25
103	A28	4k carmine, *grn*	5.25	7.25
104	A28	10k dp vio, *gray*	14.00	20.00
		Nos. 86-104 (18)	27.50	37.50

Value, imperf. set, $175.

For overprints see Nos. B11-B12.

Emperor Karl I

A29 A30

1917 ***Perf. 12½***

105	A29	3h olive gray	.15	.20
a.		Perf. 11½	75.00	75.00
b.		Perf. 12½x11½	13.00	21.00
106	A29	5h olive green	.15	.15
107	A29	6h violet	.30	.55
108	A29	10h orange brn	.15	.15
a.		Perf. 11½x12½	62.50	95.00
b.		Perf. 11½		
109	A29	12h blue	.50	.75
110	A29	15h brt rose	.15	.15
111	A29	20h red brown	.15	.15
112	A29	25h ultra	1.00	.50
113	A29	30h gray green	.25	.20
114	A29	40h olive bis	.25	.15
115	A29	50h dp green	.85	.50
116	A29	60h car rose	.85	.45
a.		Perf. 11½	15.00	21.00
117	A29	80h steel blue	.25	.25
118	A29	90h dull violet	1.00	1.40
119	A30	2k carmine, *straw*	.50	.45
120	A30	3k green, *bl*	13.00	16.00
121	A30	4k carmine, *grn*	5.25	7.25
122	A30	10k dp violet, *gray*	3.25	5.75
		Nos. 105-122 (18)	28.00	35.00

Value, imperf. set, $85.

Nos. 47 and 66 Overprinted in Red **1918**

1918

126	A4	2h violet	.45	.50
b.		Inverted overprint	15.00	
d.		Double overprint	35.00	
f.		Double overprint, one inverted		
127	A23	2h bright blue	.50	.60
a.		Pair, one without overprint		
b.		Inverted overprint	15.00	
c.		Double overprint	13.00	
d.		Double overprint, one inverted		

Emperor Karl I — A31

1918 Typo. ***Perf. 12½, Imperf.***

128	A31	2h orange	9.00
129	A31	3h dark green	9.00
130	A31	5h lt green	9.00
131	A31	6h blue green	9.00
132	A31	10h brown	9.00
133	A31	20h brick red	9.00
134	A31	25h ultra	9.00
135	A31	45h dk slate	9.00
136	A31	50h lt bluish grn	9.00
137	A31	60h blue violet	9.00
138	A31	70h ocher	9.00
139	A31	80h rose	9.00
140	A31	90h violet brn	9.00

Engr.

141	A30	1k ol grn, *grnsh*	*1,900.*
		Nos. 128-140 (13)	117.00

Nos. 128-141 were prepared for use in Bosnia and Herzegovina, but were not issued there. They were sold after the Armistice at the Vienna post office for a few days.

SEMI-POSTAL STAMPS

Nos. 33 and 35 Surcharged in Red **1914. 7 Heller**

1914 Unwmk. ***Perf. 12½***

B1	A4	7h on 5h dk grn	.40	.40
B2	A4	12h on 10h car	.40	.40

Various minor varieties of the surcharge include "4" with open top, narrow "4" and wide "4."

Nos. B1-B2 exist with double and inverted surcharges. Value about $20 each.

Nos. 33 and 35 Surcharged in Red or Blue **❖ 1915. ❖ 7 Heller**

1915 ***Perf. 12½***

B3	A4	7h on 5h (R)	8.75	8.75
a.		Perf. 9½	140.00	140.00
B4	A4	12h on 10h (Bl)	.30	.30

Nos. B3-B4 exist with double and inverted surcharges. Value about $18.50 each.

Nos. 68 and 70 Surcharged in Red or Blue **❖ 1915 ❖ 7 Heller.**

1915

B5	A23	7h on 5h (R)	.75	.75
a.		"1915" at top and bottom	35.00	37.50
B6	A23	12h on 10h (Bl)	1.25	1.50
a.		Surcharged "7 Heller."	35.00	37.50

Nos. B5-B6 are found in three types differing in length of surcharge lines:

I- date 18mm, denomination 14mm.

II- date 16mm, denomination 14mm.

III- date 18mm, denomination 16mm.

Nos. B5-B6 exist with double and inverted surcharges. Value $25 each.

Nos. B5a and B6a exist double and inverted.

Bosnia and Herzegovina stamps can be mounted in the Scott Austria album.

❖ 1916. ❖

Nos. 68 and 70 Surcharged in Red or Blue

7 Heller.

1916

B7	A23	7h on 5h (R)	.50	.65
B8	A23	12h on 10h (Bl)	.50	.65

Nos. B7-B8 exist with double and inverted surcharges. Value $12.50 each.

Wounded Soldier — SP1

Blind Soldier — SP2

1916 **Engr.**

B9	SP1	5h (+ 2h) green	.60	.60
B10	SP2	10h (+ 2h) magenta	.90	.90

Nos. B9-B10 exist imperf. Value, set $27.50.

Nos. 89, 91 Overprinted

WITWEN- UND WAISENWOCHE 1917

1917

B11	A27	10h bister	.15	.15
B12	A27	15h carmine rose	.15	.15
		Set value	.20	.20

Nos. B11-B12 exist imperf. Value set, $16.
Nos. B11-B12 exist with double and inverted overprint. Value $9 each.

Design for Memorial Church at Sarajevo SP3

Archduke Francis Ferdinand — SP4

Duchess Sophia and Archduke Francis Ferdinand SP5

1917 **Typo.** ***Perf. 11½, 12½***

B13	SP3	10h violet black	.15	.25
B14	SP4	15h claret	.15	.25
B15	SP5	40h deep blue	.15	.25
		Set value	.35	

Assassination of Archduke Ferdinand and Archduchess Sophia. Sold at a premium of 2h each which helped build a memorial church at Sarajevo. Exist imperf. Value, set $2.50.

Blind Soldier — SP6

Emperor Karl I — SP8

Design: 15h, Wounded soldier.

1918 **Engr.** ***Perf. 12½***

B16	SP6	10h (+ 10h) grnsh bl	.45	.55
B17	SP6	15h (+ 10h) red brn	.45	.55

#B16-B17 exist imperf. Value, set $18.50.

1918 **Typo.** ***Perf. 12½x13***

Design: 15h, Empress Zita.

B18	SP8	10h gray green	.30	.45
B19	SP8	15h brown red	.30	.45
B20	SP8	40h violet	.30	.45
		Nos. B18-B20 (3)	.90	1.35

Sold at a premium of 10h each which went to the "Karl's Fund."
#B18-B20 exist imperf. Value, set $22.50.

POSTAGE DUE STAMPS

D1

D2

Perf. 9½, 10½, 12½ and Compound

1904 **Unwmk.**

J1	D1	1h black, red & yel	.35	.15
J2	D1	2h black, red & yel	.35	.20
J3	D1	3h black, red & yel	.40	.15
J4	D1	4h black, red & yel	.40	.15
J5	D1	5h black, red & yel	.40	.15
J6	D1	6h black, red & yel	.15	.15
J7	D1	7h black, red & yel	2.25	2.50
J8	D1	8h black, red & yel	2.25	.50
J9	D1	10h black, red & yel	.55	.15
J10	D1	15h black, red & yel	.50	.15
J11	D1	20h black, red & yel	2.75	.20
J12	D1	50h black, red & yel	1.90	.15
J13	D1	200h black, red & grn	7.75	.70
		Nos. J1-J13 (13)	20.00	5.30

Value, imperf. set, $150.
For overprints see Western Ukraine Nos. 61-72.

1916-18 ***Perf. 12½***

J14	D2	2h red ('18)	.40	.40
J15	D2	4h red ('18)	.30	.30
J16	D2	5h red	.40	.40
J17	D2	6h red ('18)	.30	.30
J18	D2	10h red	.40	.40
J19	D2	15h red	3.00	3.00
J20	D2	20h red	.45	.45
J21	D2	25h red	1.25	1.25
J22	D2	30h red	1.00	1.00
J23	D2	40h red	7.50	7.50
J24	D2	50h red	24.00	24.00
J25	D2	1k dark blue	3.00	3.00
J26	D2	3k dark blue	13.00	13.00
		Nos. J14-J26 (13)	55.00	55.00

Nos. J25-J26 have colored numerals on a white tablet.
Value, imperf. set, $110.

NEWSPAPER STAMPS

Bosnian Girl — N1

1913 **Unwmk.** ***Imperf.***

P1	N1	2h ultra	.40	.40
P2	N1	6h violet	1.50	1.50
P3	N1	10h rose	1.50	1.50
P4	N1	20h green	1.90	1.90
		Nos. P1-P4 (4)	5.30	5.30

After Bosnia and Herzegovina became part of Yugoslavia stamps of type N1 perf., and imperf. copies surcharged with new values, were used as regular postage stamps. See Yugoslavia Nos. 1L21-1L22, 1L43-1L45.

SPECIAL HANDLING STAMPS

"Lightning" — SH1

1916 **Unwmk.** **Engr.** ***Perf. 12½***

QE1	SH1	2h vermilion	.20	.20
a.		Perf. 11½x12½	250.00	250.00
QE2	SH1	5h deep green	.35	.35
a.		Perf. 11½	13.00	13.00

BRAZIL

brə-'zil

Brasil (after 1918)

LOCATION — On the north and east coasts of South America, bordering on the Atlantic Ocean.
GOVT. — Republic
AREA — 3,286,000 sq. mi.
POP. — 132,580,000 (est. 1984)
CAPITAL — Brasilia

Brazil was an independent empire from 1822 to 1889, when a constitution was adopted and the country became officially known as The United States of Brazil.

1000 Reis = 1 Milreis
100 Centavos = 1 Cruzeiro (1942)
100 Centavos = 1 Cruzado (1986)
100 Centavos = 1 Cruzeiro (1990)
100 Centavos = 1 Cruzeiro Real (Aug. 2, 1993)

Catalogue values for unused stamps in this country are for Never Hinged items, beginning with Scott 680 in the regular postage section, Scott C66 in the airpost section, Scott RA2 in the postal tax section, and Scott RAB1 in the postal tax semi-postal section.

Values for unused stamps are for examples with original gum as defined in the catalogue introduction except for Nos. 1-38 and 42-52 which are valued without gum.

Watermarks

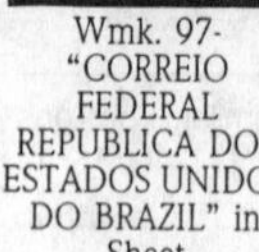

Wmk. 97- "CORREIO FEDERAL REPUBLICA DOS ESTADOS UNIDOS DO BRAZIL" in Sheet

Wmk. 98- "IMPOSTO DE CONSUMO REPUBLICA DOS ESTADOS UNIDOS DO BRAZIL" in Sheet

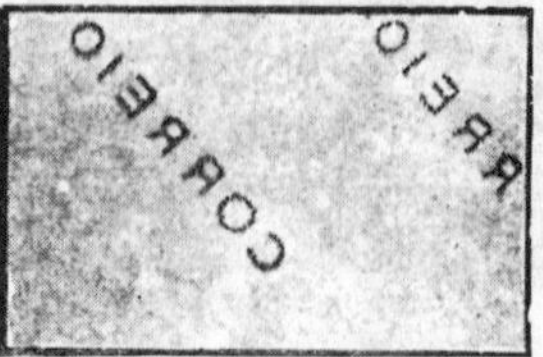

Wmk. 99- "CORREIO"

Wmk. 100- "CASA DA MOEDA" in Sheet

Because of the spacing of this watermark, a few stamps in each sheet may show no watermark.

Wmk. 101- Stars and CASA DA MOEDA

Wmk. 193- ESTADOS UNIDOS DO BRASIL

Wmk. 206- Star-framed CM, Multiple

Wmk. 218- E U BRASIL Multiple, Letters 8mm High

Wmk. 221- ESTADOS UNIDOS DO BRASIL, Multiple, Letters 6mm High

Wmk. 222- CORREIO BRASIL and 5 Stars in Squared Circle

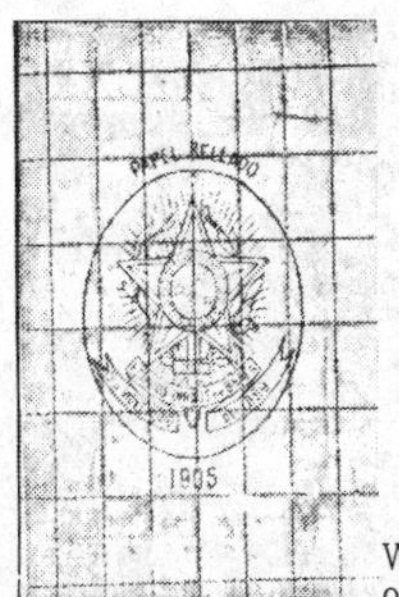

Wmk. 236- Coat of Arms in Sheet

Watermark (reduced illustration) covers 22 stamps in sheet.

Wmk. 245- Multiple "CASA DA MOEDA DO BRASIL" and Small Formee Cross

Wmk. 249- "CORREIO BRASIL" multiple

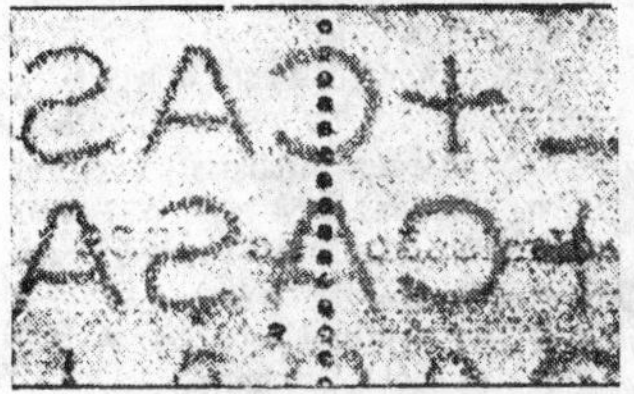

Wmk. 256- "CASA+DA+MOEDA+DO+BRAZIL" in 8mm Letters

Wmk. 264- "*CORREIO*BRASIL*" Multiple, Letters 7mm High

Wmk. 267- "*CORREIO*BRASIL*" Multiple in Small Letters 5mm High

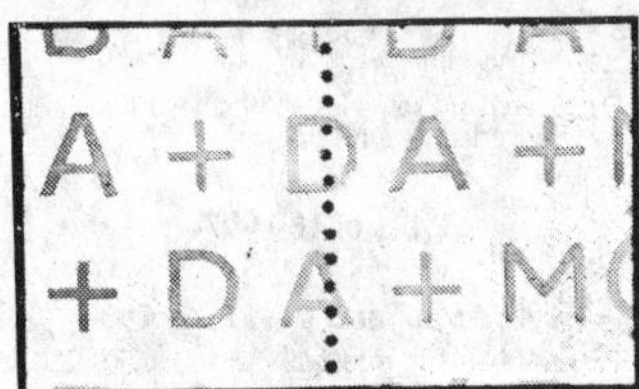

Wmk. 268- "CASA+DA+MOEDA+DO+BRASIL" in 6mm Letters

Wmk. 270- Wavy Lines and Seal

Wmk. 271- Wavy Lines

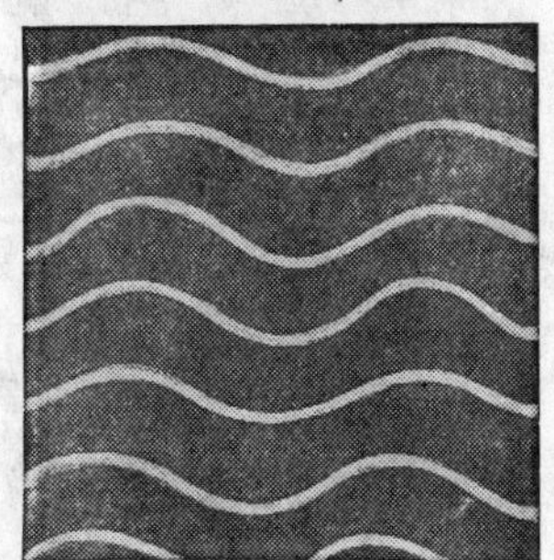

Wmk. 281- Wavy Lines

Issues of the Empire

A1

Grayish or Yellowish Paper

1843, Aug. 1 Unwmk. Engr. *Imperf.*

No.	Type	Description	Unused	Used
1	A1	30r black	2,250.	550.
a.		In pair with No. 2		*300,000.*
2	A1	60r black	600.	225.
3	A1	90r black	2,750.	1,150.

Nos. 1-3 were issued with gum, but very few unused examples retain even a trace of their original gum. Copies with original gum command substantial premiums.

Fine impressions are true black and have background lathework complete. Intermediate impressions are grayish black and have weaker lathework in the background. These sell for somewhat less than fine impressions. Worn impressions have white areas in the background surrounding the numerals due to plate wear affecting especially the lathework. These examples sell for somewhat less than intermediate impressions.

Most examples of Nos. 1-3 also exist on white paper, usually thin and somewhat translucent. Such examples are scarce and command premiums.

A2

A3

Grayish or Yellowish Paper

1844-46

No.	Type	Description	Unused	Used
7	A2	10r black	100.00	20.00
8	A2	30r black	125.00	30.00
9	A2	60r black	100.00	22.50
10	A2	90r black	750.00	100.00
11	A2	180r black	3,500.	1,300.
12	A2	300r black	5,250.	1,800.
13	A2	600r black	5,000.	2,000.

Nos. 8, 9 and 10 exist on thick paper and are considerably scarcer.

Grayish or Yellowish Paper

1850, Jan. 1

No.	Type	Description	Unused	Used
21	A3	10r black	25.00	35.00
22	A3	20r black	75.00	100.00
23	A3	30r black	10.00	3.00
24	A3	60r black	10.00	2.25
25	A3	90r black	80.00	11.50
26	A3	180r black	80.00	52.50
27	A3	300r black	325.00	60.00
28	A3	600r black	375.00	90.00

No. 22 used is generally found precanceled with a single horizontal line in pen or blue crayon. Value precanceled without gum, $75.

All values except the 90r were reprinted in 1910 on very thick paper.

1854

No.	Type	Description	Unused	Used
37	A3	10r blue	12.00	11.50
38	A3	30r blue	32.50	50.00

A4

1861

No.	Type	Description	Unused	Used
39	A4	280r red	140.00	100.00
40	A4	430r yellow	225.00	140.00

Nos. 39 and 40 have been reprinted on thick white paper with white gum. They are printed in aniline inks and the colors are brighter than those of the originals.

1866 ***Perf. 13½***

No.	Type	Description	Unused	Used
42	A3	10r blue	120.00	*150.00*
43	A3	20r black	900.00	400.00
44	A3	30r black	300.00	150.00
45	A3	30r blue	*675.00*	*750.00*
46	A3	60r black	120.00	25.00
47	A3	90r black	575.00	275.00
48	A3	180r black	600.00	275.00
49	A4	280r red	650.00	675.00
50	A3	300r black	750.00	400.00
51	A4	430r yellow	600.00	350.00
52	A3	600r black	575.00	240.00

Fraudulent perforations abound. Purchases should be accompanied by certificates of authenticity.

A 10r black is questioned.

A5

A6

A7

A8

A8a

A9

Emperor Dom Pedro — A9a

Thick or Thin White Wove Paper

1866, July 1 ***Perf. 12***

No.	Type	Description	Unused	Used
53	A5	10r vermilion	12.00	5.00
54	A6	20r red lilac	65.00	25.00
a.		20r dull violet	20.00	3.00
56	A7	50r blue	30.00	2.50
57	A8	80r slate violet	75.00	5.00
58	A8a	100r blue green	30.00	1.50
a.		100r yellow green	30.00	1.50
59	A9	200r black	100.00	8.00
a.		Half used as 100r on cover		*1,500.*
60	A9a	500r orange	200.00	35.00
		Nos. 53-60 (7)	512.00	82.00

The 10r and 20r exist imperf. on both white and bluish paper. Some authorities consider them proofs.

Nos. 58 and 65 are found in three types.

Bluish Paper

No.	Type	Description	Unused	Used
53a	A5	10r	500.00	425.00
54b	A6	20r	160.00	24.00
56a	A7	50r	200.00	25.00
57a	A8	80r	240.00	27.50
58b	A8a	100r	800.00	115.00

1876-77 ***Rouletted***

No.	Type	Description	Unused	Used
61	A5	10r vermilion ('77)	60.00	35.00
62	A6	20r red lilac ('77)	70.00	27.50
63	A7	50r blue ('77)	70.00	10.00
64	A8	80r violet ('77)	175.00	20.00
65	A8a	100r green	40.00	1.25
66	A9	200r black ('77)	80.00	7.50
a.		Half used as 100r on cover		*1,000.*
67	A9a	500r orange	190.00	40.00
		Nos. 61-67 (7)	685.00	141.25

A10

A11

A12

A13

A14

A15

A16

A17

A18

A19

A20

1878-79 *Rouletted*

68 A10 10r vermilion 12.00 3.00
69 A11 20r violet 15.00 2.50
70 A12 50r blue 24.00 2.00
71 A13 80r lake 27.50 10.00
72 A14 100r green 27.50 1.25
73 A15 200r black 140.00 17.50
  a. Half used as 100r on cover *1,200.*
74 A16 260r dk brown 80.00 22.00
75 A18 300r bister 80.00 6.00
  a. One-third used as 100r on cover *10,000.*
76 A19 700r red brown 160.00 85.00
77 A20 1000r gray lilac 190.00 37.50
  a. Half used as 500r on cover *10,000.*
  Nos. 68-77 (10) 756.00 186.75

1878, Aug. 21 *Perf. 12*

78 A17 300r orange & grn 85.00 20.00

Nos. 68-78 exist imperforate.

A21 A22 A23

Small Heads
Laid Paper

Perf. 13, 13½ and Compound

1881, July 15

79 A21 50r blue 120.00 18.00
80 A22 100r olive green 500.00 30.00
81 A23 200r pale red brn 475.00 110.00
  a. Half used as 100r on cover *1,750.*

On Nos. 79 and 80 the hair above the ear curves forward. On Nos. 83 and 88 it is drawn backward. On the stamps of the 1881 issue the beard is smaller than in the 1882-85 issues and fills less of the space between the neck and the frame at the left.

See No. 88.

A24

A26

A25 A27

Two types each of the 100 and 200 reis.

100 REIS:
Type I - Groundwork formed of diagonal crossed lines and horizontal lines.
Type II - Groundwork formed of diagonal crossed lines and vertical lines.

200 REIS:
Type I - Groundwork formed of diagonal and horizontal lines.
Type II - Groundwork formed of diagonal crossed lines.

Larger Heads
Laid Paper

Perf. 12½ to 14 and Compound

1882-84

82 A24 10r black 10.00 20.00
83 A25 100r ol grn, type I 35.00 3.00
  a. 100r dark green, type I 37.50 3.00
  b. 100r dark green, type II 200.00 12.00
84 A26 200r pale red brn, type I 85.00 22.50
  a. Half used as 100r on cover *1,100.*
85 A27 200r pale rose, type II 45.00 4.50
  a. Diag. half used as 100r on cover 800.00
  Nos. 82-85 (4) 175.00 50.00

See No. 86.

A28 A29 A30

Three types of A29

Type I - Groundwork of horizontal lines.
Type II - Groundwork of diagonal crossed lines.
Type III - Groundwork solid.

Perf. 13, 13½, 14 and Compound

1884-85

86 A24 10r orange 2.50 2.00
87 A28 20r slate green 30.00 3.00
  a. 20r olive green 30.00 3.00
  b. Half used as 10r on newspaper *3,000.*
88 A21 50r bl, head larger 30.00 3.00
90 A29 100r lilac, type I 120.00 2.50
  a. 100r lilac, type II 450.00 75.00
  b. 100r lilac, type III 325.00 55.00
91 A30 100r lilac 180.00 4.00

A31

A32

Southern Cross
A33

Crown
A34

Perf. 13, 13½, 14 and Compound

1885

92 A31 100r lilac 100.00 2.50

Compare design A31 with A35.

1887

93 A32 50r chalky blue 27.50 4.00
94 A33 300r gray blue 200.00 25.00
95 A34 500r olive 110.00 12.00

A35 A36

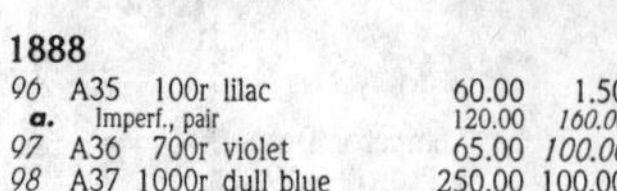
Entrance to Bay of Rio de Janeiro — A37

1888

96 A35 100r lilac 60.00 1.50
  a. Imperf., pair 120.00 *160.00*
97 A36 700r violet 65.00 *100.00*
98 A37 1000r dull blue 250.00 100.00

Issues of the Republic

Southern Cross — A38

Wove Paper, Thin to Thick

Perf. 12½ to 14, 11 to 11½, and 12½ to 14x11 to 11½, Rough or Clean-Cut

Engraved; Typographed (#102)

1890-91

99 A38 20r gray green 2.00 1.50
  a. 20r blue green 2.00 1.50
  b. 20r emerald 16.00 6.00
100 A38 50r gray green 5.00 1.50
  a. 50r olive green 12.00 6.00
  b. 50r yellow green 12.00 6.00
  c. 50r dark slate green 7.00 3.50
  d. Horiz. pair, imperf. btwn.
101 A38 100r lilac rose 360.00 4.50
102 A38 100r red lil, redrawn 25.00 1.50
  a. Tete beche pair *15,000. 16,500.*
103 A38 200r purple 8.00 1.50
  a. 200r violet 10.00 2.00
  b. 200r violet blue 22.50 3.00
104 A38 300r slate vio 150.00 25.00
  a. 300r gray 75.00 8.50
  b. 300r gray blue 85.00 8.50
  c. 300r dark violet 75.00 5.00
105 A38 500r olive bister 17.50 8.00
  a. 500r olive gray 17.50 10.00
106 A38 500r slate 17.50 12.00
107 A38 700r chocolate 20.00 22.50
  a. 700r fawn 16.00 16.00
108 A38 1000r bister 15.00 3.00
  a. 1000r yellow buff 30.00 7.50
  Nos. 99-108 (10) 620.00 81.00

The redrawn 100r may be distinguished by the absence of the curved lines of shading in the left side of the central oval. The pearls in the oval are not well aligned and there is less shading at right and left of "CORREIO" and "100 REIS."

A 100 reis stamp of type A38 but inscribed "BRAZIL" instead of "E. U. DO BRAZIL" was not placed in issue but postmarked copies are known. A reprint on thick paper was made in 1910.

No. 101 exists imperf., not regularly issued.

For surcharges see Nos. 151-158.

Liberty Head
A39 A40

Perf. 12½ to 14, 11 to 11½ and 12½ to 14x11 to 11½

1891, May 1 **Typo.**

109 A39 100r blue & red 32.50 1.50
  a. Head inverted 100.00 90.00
  b. Tete beche pair 675.00 750.00
  c. 100r ultra & red 32.50 1.50

Perf. 11, 11½, 13, 13½, 14 and Compound

1893, Jan. 18 **Litho.**

111 A40 100r rose 75.00 1.75

Sugarloaf Mountain
A41 A41a

Liberty Head
A42 A42a

Hermes — A43

Perf. 11 to 11½, 12½ to 14 and 12½ to 14x11 to 11½

1894-97 **Unwmk.**

112 A41 10r rose & blue 2.00 .75
113 A41a 10r rose & blue 2.00 .75
114 A41a 20r orange & bl 1.10 .35
115 A41a 50r dk blue & blue 8.00 1.25
116 A42 100r carmine & blk 4.00 .40
  a. Vert. pair, imperf. btwn. 100.00
118 A42a 200r orange & blk 1.00 .40
  a. Imperf. horiz., pair 80.00
  b. Vert. pair, imperf. btwn. 80.00
119 A42a 300r green & blk 15.00 .60
120 A42a 500r blue & blk 25.00 1.75
121 A42a 700r lilac & blk 16.00 2.00
122 A43 1000r green & vio 55.00 1.75
124 A43 2000r blk & gray lil 65.00 15.00
  Nos. 112-124 (11) 194.10 25.00

The head of No. 116 exists in five types. See Nos. 140-150A, 159-161, 166-171d.

Newspaper Stamps Surcharged:

100 **200**

1898 **1898**
100 **200**
a b

100
1898
100
c

Surcharged on 1889 Issue of type N1

1898 *Rouletted*

Green Surcharge

125 (b) 700r on 500r yel 6.75 10.00
126 (c) 1000r on 700r yel 32.50 27.50
  a. Surcharged "700r" 675.00 775.00
127 (c) 2000r on 1000r yel 27.50 15.00
128 (c) 2000r on 1000r brn 20.00 6.00

Violet Surcharge

129 (a) 100r on 50r brn yel 2.00 *45.00*
130 (c) 100r on 50r brn yel 65.00 45.00
131 (c) 300r on 200r blk 3.50 1.25
  a. Double surcharge 160.00 275.00

The surcharge on No. 130 is handstamped. The impression is blurred and lighter in color than on No. 129. The two surcharges differ most in the shapes and serifs of the figures "1."

Counterfeits exist of No. 126a.

Black Surcharge

132 (b) 200r on 100r violet 3.50 1.25
  a. Double surcharge 80.00 *175.00*
  b. Inverted surcharge 80.00 *175.00*
132C (b) 500r on 300r car 5.50 3.00
133 (b) 700r on 500r green 8.00 2.00

Blue Surcharge

134 (b) 500r on 300r car 6.50 5.50

Red Surcharge

135 (c) 1000r on 700r ultra 22.50 15.00
  a. Inverted surcharge 200.00 200.00

Surcharged on 1890-94 Issues:

200 **1898**
1898 **50 RÉIS 50**
d e

Black Surcharge

136 N3(e) 20r on 10r blue 3.00 6.00
137 N2(d) 200r on 100r red lilac 20.00 15.00
  a. Double surcharge 225.00 250.00

Surcharge on No. 137 comes blue to deep black.

Blue Surcharge

138 N3(e) 50r on 20r green 8.00 10.00

Red Surcharge

139 N3(e) 100r on 50r green 18.00 20.00
  a. Blue surcharge 12.50

The surcharge on Nos. 139 and 139a exists double, inverted, one missing, etc.

Types of 1894-97

1899

Perf. 5½-7 and 11-11½x5½-7

140 A41a 10r rose & bl 4.50 12.00
141 A41a 20r orange & bl 7.50 7.50
142 A41a 50r dk bl & lt bl 9.00 30.00
143 A42 100r carmine & blk 16.00 4.50
144 A42a 200r orange & blk 9.00 3.00
145 A42a 300r green & blk 60.00 7.50

Perf. 8½-9½, 8½-9½x11-11½

146 A41a 10r rose & bl 4.50 3.00
147 A41a 20r orange & bl 15.00 3.00
147A A41a 50r dk bl & bl 125.00 30.00
148 A42 100r carmine & blk 30.00 1.50
149 A42a 200r orange & blk 15.00 1.00
150 A42a 300r green & blk 60.00 5.00
150A A43 1000r green & vio 125.00 12.50

Nos. 140-150A are valued with perfs just cut into the design on one or two sides. Expect some irregularity of the perforations.

Issue of 1890-93 Surcharged in Violet or Magenta

1899
50 RÉIS

Perf. 11 to 11½, 12½ to 14 and Compound

1899, June 25

151 A38 50r on 20r gray grn 2.00 3.00
a. Double surcharge 125.00 125.00
152 A38 100r on 50r gray grn 2.00 3.00
b. Double surcharge 100.00 100.00
153 A38 300r on 200r pur 7.50 *12.00*
a. Double surcharge 250.00 250.00
b. Pair, one without surcharge 425.00 —
154 A38 500r on 300r sl vio 37.50 15.00
a. 500r on 300r gray lilac 30.00 9.00
b. Pair, one without surcharge 425.00 *500.00*
155 A38 700r on 500r ol bis 24.00 6.00
a. Pair, one without surcharge 425.00 —
156 A38 1000r on 700r choc 17.50 6.00
157 A38 1000r on 700r fawn 17.50 6.00
a. Pair, one without surcharge 425.00 *500.00*
158 A38 2000r on 1000r yel buff 60.00 4.50
a. 2000r on 1000r bister 30.00 4.50
b. Pair, one without surcharge 425.00 *500.00*
Nos. 151-158 (8) 168.00 55.50

Types of 1894-97

Perf. 11, 11½, 13 and Compound

1900

159 A41a 50r green 10.00 .60
160 A42 100r rose 20.00 .30
a. Frame around inner oval 100.00 4.00
161 A42a 200r blue 12.00 .35
Nos. 159-161 (3) 42.00 1.25

Three types exist of No. 161, all of which have the frame around inner oval.

Cabral Arrives at Brazil — A44

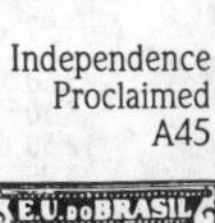

Independence Proclaimed A45

"Emancipation of Slaves" — A46

Allegory, Republic of Brazil — A47

1900, Jan. 1 **Litho.** *Perf. 12½*

162 A44 100r red 5.50 4.50
a. Imperf., pair 400.00 500.00
163 A45 200r green & yel 5.50 4.50
164 A46 500r blue 5.50 4.50
165 A47 700r emerald 5.50 4.50
Nos. 162-165 (4) 22.00 18.00

Discovery of Brazil, 400th anniversary.

Types of 1894-97
Wmk. (97? or 98?)

1905 *Perf. 11, 11½*

166 A41a 10r rose & bl 5.75 4.00
167 A41a 20r orange & bl 10.00 2.00
168 A41a 50r green 20.00 3.00
169 A42 100r rose 27.50 1.00
170 A42a 200r dark blue 16.00 1.00
171 A42a 300r green & blk 55.00 2.00
Nos. 166-171 (6) 134.25 13.00

Positive identification of Wmk. 97 or 98 places stamp in specific watermark groups below.

Wmk. 97

166b A41a 10r rose & blue 30.00 16.00
167b A41a 20r orange & blue 30.00 8.00
168b A41a 50r green 55.00 8.00
169b A42 100r rose 200.00 30.00
170b A42a 200r dark blue 120.00 4.00
171b A42a 300r green & blk 375.00 30.00
171A A43 1000r green & vio 290.00 30.00
Nos. 166b-171A (7) 1,100. 126.00

Wmk. 98

166c A41a 10r rose & blue 40.00 40.00
167c A41a 20r orange & blue 80.00 20.00
168c A41a 50r green 160.00 30.00
169c A42 100r rose 80.00 4.00
170c A42a 200r dark blue 120.00 4.00
171d A42a 300r green & blk 290.00 30.00
Nos. 166c-171d (6) 770.00 128.00

Allegory, Pan-American Congress A48

1906, July 23 **Litho.** **Unwmk.**

172 A48 100r carmine rose 30.00 30.00
173 A48 200r blue 75.00 10.00

Third Pan-American Congress.

Aristides Lobo — A48a

Benjamin Constant — A49

Pedro Alvares Cabral — A50

Eduardo Wandenkolk — A51

Manuel Deodoro da Fonseca — A52

Floriano Peixoto — A53

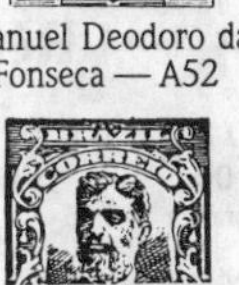

Prudente de Moraes — A54

Manuel Ferraz de Campos Salles — A55

Francisco de Paula Rodrigues Alves — A56

Liberty Head — A57

A58

A59

1906-16 **Engr.** *Perf. 12*

174 A48a 10r bluish slate .90 .20
175 A49 20r aniline vio .90 .20
176 A50 50r green .90 .20
a. Booklet pane of 6 ('08) 40.00 *120.00*
177 A51 100r anil rose 2.00 .20
a. Imperf. vert., coil ('16) 4.00 .35
b. Booklet pane of 6 ('08) 80.00 *120.00*
178 A52 200r blue 2.00 .20
a. Booklet pane of 6 ('08) 60.00 *120.00*
179 A52 200r ultra ('15) 2.00 .35
a. Imperf. vert., coil ('16) 2.00 .35
180 A53 300r gray blk 3.00 .65
181 A54 400r olive grn 30.00 2.00
182 A55 500r dk violet 6.00 .65
183 A54 600r olive grn ('10) 3.00 1.00
184 A56 700r red brown 6.00 3.00
185 A57 1000r vermilion 32.50 1.00
186 A58 2000r yellow grn 20.00 .65
187 A58 2000r Prus blue ('15) 10.00 1.00
188 A59 5000r carmine rose 8.00 2.00
Nos. 174-188 (15) 127.20 13.30

Allegorical Emblems: Liberty, Peace, Industry, etc. — A60

1908, July 14

189 A60 100r carmine 20.00 1.75

National Exhibition, Rio de Janeiro.

Emblems of Peace Between Brazil and Portugal A61

1908, July 14

190 A61 100r red 8.00 1.25

Opening of Brazilian ports to foreign commerce, cent. Medallions picture King Carlos I of Portugal and Pres. Affonso Penna of Brazil.

Bonifacio, Bolivar, Hidalgo, O'Higgins, San Martin, Washington — A62

1909

191 A62 200r deep blue 7.50 1.00

For surcharge see No. E1.

Nilo Peçanha — A63

Baron of Rio Branco — A64

1910, Nov. 15

192 A63 10,000r brown 8.00 2.00

1913-16

193 A64 1000r deep green 3.75 .35
194 A64 1000r slate ('16) 21.00 .65

Cabo Frio — A65

Perf. 11½

1915, Nov. 13 **Litho.** **Wmk. 99**

195 A65 100r dk grn, *yelsh* 4.00 3.50

Founding of the town of Cabo Frio, 300th anniversary.

Bay of Guajara — A66

1916, Jan. 5

196 A66 100r carmine 7.50 4.00

City of Belem, 300th anniversary.

Revolutionary Flag — A67

1917, Mar. 6

197 A67 100r deep blue 15.00 7.50

Revolution of Pernambuco, Mar. 6, 1817.

Rodrigues Alves — A68

Unwmk.

1917, Aug. 31 **Engr.** *Perf. 12*

198 A68 5000r red brown 60.00 10.00

Liberty Head
A69 A70

Perf. 12½, 13, 13x13½.

1918-20 **Typo.** **Unwmk.**

200 A69 10r orange brn .50 .25
201 A69 20r slate .50 .25
202 A69 25r ol gray ('20) .50 .25
203 A69 50r green 27.50 3.25
204 A70 100r rose 1.75 .25
a. Imperf., pair —
205 A70 300r red orange 19.00 3.25
206 A70 500r dull violet 19.00 3.25
Nos. 200-206 (7) 68.75 10.75

1918-20 **Wmk. 100**

207 A69 10r red brown 6.00 1.75
a. Imperf., pair —
207B A69 20r slate 1.50 1.50
c. Imperf., pair —
208 A69 25r ol gray ('20) .75 .50
209 A69 50r green 1.50 .50
210 A70 100r rose 47.50 .50
a. Imperf., pair —
211 A70 200r dull blue 6.00 .50
212 A70 300r orange 47.50 3.50
213 A70 500r dull violet 47.50 7.50
214 A70 600r orange 2.50 *7.50*
Nos. 207-214 (9) 160.75 23.75

Because of the spacing of this watermark, a few stamps in each sheet may show no watermark.

"Education" — A72

1918 **Engr.** *Perf. 11½*

215 A72 1000r blue 6.00 .25
216 A72 2000r red brown 27.50 6.00
217 A72 5000r dark violet 7.50 6.00
Nos. 215-217 (3) 41.00 12.25

Watermark note below No. 257 also applies to Nos. 215-217.

See Nos. 233-234, 283-285, 404, 406, 458, 460. For surcharge see No. C30.

Railroad A73

"Industry" A74

"Aviation" A75

Mercury A76

"Navigation" — A77

Perf. 13½x13, 13x13½

1920-22 Typo. Unwmk.

No.	Type	Description	Unused	Used
218	A73	10r red violet	.75	.40
219	A73	20r olive green	.75	.40
220	A74	25r brown violet	.50	.40
221	A74	50r blue green	.85	.40
222	A74	50r orange brn ('22)	1.40	.40
223	A75	100r rose red	2.75	.40
224	A75	100r orange ('22)	7.50	.40
225	A75	150r violet ('21)	1.40	.40
226	A75	200r blue	4.50	.40
227	A75	200r rose red ('22)	8.00	.40
228	A76	300r olive gray	12.50	.50
229	A76	400r dull blue ('22)	22.50	3.50
230	A76	500r red brown	17.50	.50
		Nos. 218-230 (13)	80.90	8.50

See Nos. 236-257, 265-266, 268-271, 273-274, 276-281, 302-311, 316-322, 326-340, 357-358, 431-434, 436-441, 461-463B, 467-470, 472-474, 488-490, 492-494. For surcharges see Nos. 356-358, 376-377.

Perf. 11, 11½

Engr. Wmk. 100

No.	Type	Description	Unused	Used
231	A77	600r red orange	2.00	.35
232	A77	1000r claret	5.00	.25
a.		Perf. 8½	37.50	7.50
233	A72	2000r dull violet	20.00	.75
234	A72	5000r brown	16.00	9.00
		Nos. 231-234 (4)	43.00	10.35

Nos. 233 and 234 are inscribed "BRASIL CORREIO." Watermark note below No. 257 also applies to Nos. 231-234.

See No. 282.

King Albert of Belgium and President Epitacio Pessoa A78

1920, Sept. 19 Engr. *Perf. 11½x11*

No.	Type	Description	Unused	Used
235	A78	100r dull red	.65	.65

Visit of the King and Queen of Belgium.

Types of 1920-22 Issue

Perf. 13x13½, 13x12½

1922-29 Typo. Wmk. 100

No.	Type	Description	Unused	Used
236	A73	10r red violet	.30	.15
237	A73	20r olive green	.30	.15
238	A75	20r gray violet ('29)	.30	.15
239	A74	25r brown violet	.35	.15
240	A74	50r blue grn	*3.25*	*35.00*
241	A74	50r org brn ('23)	.45	.35
a.		Booklet pane of 6		
242	A75	100r rose red	22.50	.40
243	A75	100r orange ('26)	.50	.15
a.		Booklet pane of 6		
244	A75	100r turq grn ('28)	.35	.15
245	A75	150r violet	2.50	.15
246	A75	200r blue	300.00	12.50
247	A75	200r rose red	.40	.15
a.		Booklet pane of 6		
248	A75	200r ol grn ('28)	2.50	3.00
249	A76	300r olive gray	1.90	.25
a.		Booklet pane of 6		
250	A76	300r rose red ('29)	.35	.25
251	A76	400r blue	1.90	.15
252	A76	400r orange ('29)	.75	.60
253	A76	500r red brown	7.50	.50
a.		Booklet pane of 6		
254	A76	500r ultra ('29)	8.50	.15
255	A76	600r brn org ('29)	7.50	3.00
256	A76	700r dull vio ('29)	7.50	1.75
257	A76	1000r turq bl ('29)	9.50	.70
		Nos. 236-257 (22)	379.10	*59.80*

Because of the spacing of the watermark, a few stamps in each sheet show no watermark.

"Agriculture" — A79

1922 Unwmk. *Perf. 13x13½*

No.	Type	Description	Unused	Used
258	A79	40r orange brown	.50	.35
259	A79	80r grnsh blue	.35	*2.50*

See Nos. 263, 267, 275.

Declaration of Ypiranga — A80

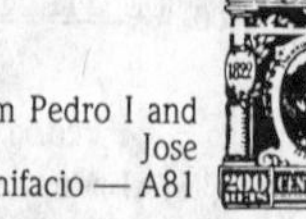

Dom Pedro I and Jose Bonifacio — A81

National Exposition and President Pessoa — A82

Unwmk.

1922, Sept. 7 Engr. *Perf. 14*

No.	Type	Description	Unused	Used
260	A80	100r ultra	5.00	.45
261	A81	200r red	6.00	.30
262	A82	300r green	6.00	.30
		Nos. 260-262 (3)	17.00	1.05

Cent. of independence and Natl. Exposition of 1922.

Agriculture Type of 1922

Perf. 13½x12

1923 Wmk. 100 Typo.

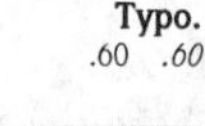

No.	Type	Description	Unused	Used
263	A79	40r orange brown	.60	*.60*

Brazilian Army Entering Bahia — A83

Unwmk.

1923, July 12 Litho. *Perf. 13*

No.	Type	Description	Unused	Used
264	A83	200r rose	7.50	5.00

Centenary of the taking of Bahia from the Portuguese.

Types of 1920-22 Issues

Perf. 13x13½

1924 Typo. Wmk. 193

No.	Type	Description	Unused	Used
265	A73	10r red violet	5.50	3.75
266	A73	20r olive green	6.00	3.75
267	A79	40r orange brown	4.25	.60
268	A74	50r orange brown	3.75	*18.00*
269	A75	100r orange	4.25	.35
270	A75	200r rose	6.00	.25
271	A76	400r blue	3.75	3.75
		Nos. 265-271 (7)	33.50	*30.45*

Arms of Equatorial Confederation, 1824 — A84

Unwmk.

1924, July 2 Litho. *Perf. 11*

No.	Type	Description	Unused	Used
272	A84	200r bl, blk, yel, & red	3.00	2.25
a.		Red omitted	275.00	275.00

Centenary of the Equatorial Confederation.

Types of 1920-22 Issues

Perf. 9½ to 13½ and Compound

1924-28 Typo. Wmk. 101

No.	Type	Description	Unused	Used
273	A73	10r red violet	.45	.30
274	A73	20r olive gray	.45	.30
275	A79	40r orange brn	.45	.30
276	A74	50r orange brn	.75	.30
277	A75	100r red orange	1.50	.30
278	A75	200r rose	.75	.30
279	A76	300r ol gray ('25)	7.00	1.00
280	A76	400r blue	4.00	.35
281	A76	500r red brown	9.00	.45
		Engr.		
282	A77	600r red orange ('26)	1.00	.30
283	A72	2000r dull vio ('26)	5.00	.30
284	A72	5000r brown ('26)	15.00	.70
285	A72	10,000r rose ('28)	17.50	.90
		Nos. 273-285 (13)	62.85	5.80

Nos. 283-285 are inscribed "BRASIL CORREIO."

Ruy Barbosa — A85

1925 Wmk. 100 *Perf. 11½*

No.	Type	Description	Unused	Used
286	A85	1000r claret	4.25	1.50

1926 Wmk. 101

No.	Type	Description	Unused	Used
287	A85	1000r claret	1.75	.35

"Justice" — A86

Scales of Justice and Map of Brazil — A87

Perf. 13½x13

1927, Aug. 11 Typo. Wmk. 206

No.	Type	Description	Unused	Used
288	A86	100r deep blue	.90	.50
289	A87	200r rose	.80	.35

Founding of the law courses, cent.

Liberty Holding Coffee Leaves — A88

1928, Mar. 5

No.	Type	Description	Unused	Used
290	A88	100r blue green	1.00	.60
291	A88	200r carmine	.65	.50
292	A88	300r olive black	5.00	.40
		Nos. 290-292 (3)	6.65	1.50

Introduction of the coffee tree in Brazil, bicent.

Official Stamps of 1919 Surcharged in Red or Black **700 Réis**

Perf. 11, 11½

1928 Wmk. 100 Engr.

No.	Type	Description	Unused	Used
293	O3	700r on 500r orange	2.25	1.50
a.		Inverted surcharge	175.00	175.00
294	O3	1000r on 100r rose red (Bk)	1.50	.30
295	O3	2000r on 200r dull bl	2.25	.45
296	O3	5000r on 50r green	2.25	.55
297	O3	10,000r on 10r ol grn	11.00	.90
		Nos. 293-297 (5)	19.25	3.70

#293-297 were used for ordinary postage.

Stamps in the outer rows of the sheets are often without watermark.

Ruy Barbosa — A89

Perf. 9, 9½x11, 11, and Compound

1929 Wmk. 101

No.	Type	Description	Unused	Used
300	A89	5000r blue violet	12.50	.75

See #405, 459. For surcharge see #C29.

Types of 1920-21 Issue

Perf. 13½x12½

1929 Typo. Wmk. 218

No.	Type	Description	Unused	Used
302	A75	20r gray violet	.25	.20
303	A75	50r red brown	.25	.20
304	A75	100r turq green	.30	.20
305	A75	200r olive green	12.50	2.25
306	A76	300r rose red	.60	.20
307	A76	400r orange	.70	.25
308	A76	500r ultra	7.00	.45
309	A76	600r brown org	8.50	.60
310	A76	700r dp violet	2.25	.20
311	A76	1000r turq blue	4.00	.20
		Nos. 302-311 (10)	36.35	4.75

Wmk. 218 exists both in vertical alignment and in echelon.

Wmk. in echelon

No.	Type	Description	Unused	Used
302a	A75	20r	.25	.35
303a	A75	50r	80.00	27.50
306a	A76	300r	.65	.30
308a	A76	500r	110.00	15.00
311a	A76	1000r	6.50	6.50

Architectural Fantasies
A90 A91

Architectural Fantasy — A92

Perf. 13x13½

1930, June 20 Wmk. 206

No.	Type	Description	Unused	Used
312	A90	100r turq blue	1.25	.80
313	A91	200r olive gray	2.00	.70
314	A92	300r rose red	3.50	.80
		Nos. 312-314 (3)	6.75	2.30

Fourth Pan-American Congress of Architects and Exposition of Architecture.

Types of 1920-21 Issues

1930 Wmk. 221 *Perf. 13x12½*

No.	Type	Description	Unused	Used
316	A75	20r gray violet	.20	.15
317	A75	50r red brown	.20	.15
318	A75	100r turq blue	.25	.15
319	A75	200r olive green	3.00	.25
320	A76	300r rose red	.60	.25
321	A76	500r ultra	1.50	.25
322	A76	1000r turq blue	25.00	.70
		Nos. 316-322 (7)	30.75	1.90

Imperforates

Since 1930, imperforate or partly perforated sheets of nearly all commemorative and some definitive issues have become obtainable.

Types of 1920-29 Issue

Perf. 11, 13½x13, 13x12½

1931-34 Typo. Wmk. 222

No.	Type	Description	Unused	Used
326	A75	10r deep brown	.15	.15
327	A75	20r gray violet	.15	.15
328	A74	25r brn vio ('34)	.15	.60
330	A75	50r blue green	.15	.15
331	A75	50r red brown	.15	.15
332	A75	100r orange	.30	.15
334	A75	200r dp carmine	.45	.15
335	A76	300r olive green	.60	.15
336	A76	400r ultra	.85	.15
337	A76	500r red brown	3.50	.15
338	A76	600r brown org	3.50	.15
339	A76	700r deep violet	3.50	.15
340	A76	1000r turq blue	12.50	.15
		Nos. 326-340 (13)	25.95	
		Set value		1.75

Getulio Vargas and Joao Pessoa — A93

Vargas and Pessoa — A94

Oswaldo Aranha
A95 A96

Antonio Carlos
A97

Pessoa
A98

Vargas — A99

Unwmk.

1931, Apr. 29 Litho. *Perf. 14*

342 A93 10r + 10r lt bl .15 *4.50*
343 A93 20r + 20r yel brn .15 *3.25*
344 A95 50r + 50r bl grn, red & yel .15 .15
a. Red missing at left .90 .90
345 A93 100r + 50r orange .30 .30
346 A93 200r + 100r green .30 .30
347 A94 300r + 150r multi .30 .30
348 A93 400r + 200r dp rose 1.00 .65
349 A93 500r + 250r dk blue .70 .55
350 A93 600r + 300r brn vio .50 *6.50*
351 A94 700r + 350r multi .90 .55
352 A96 1000r + 500r brt grn, red & yel 2.00 .25
353 A97 2000r + 1000r gray blk & red 4.00 .55
354 A98 5000r + 2500r blk & red 17.50 4.50
355 A99 10000r + 5000r brt grn & yel 42.50 10.00
Nos. 342-355 (14) 70.45 32.35

Revolution of Oct. 3, 1930. Prepared as semi-postal stamps, Nos. 342-355 were sold as ordinary postage stamps with stated surtax ignored.

Nos. 306, 320 and 250 Surcharged **1931 200 Réis**

Wmk. E U BRASIL Multiple (218)

1931, July 20 *Perf. 13½x12½*

356 A76 200r on 300r rose red .90 .90
a. Wmk. in echelon 17.50 17.50
b. Inverted surcharge 40.00

Perf. 13x12½
Wmk. 221

357 A76 200r on 300r rose red .30 .20
a. Inverted surcharge 45.00 45.00

Perf. 13½x12½
Wmk. 100

358 A76 200r on 300r rose red 60.00 60.00

Map of South America Showing Meridian of Tordesillas A100

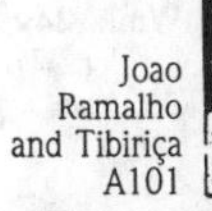

Joao Ramalho and Tibiriça A101

Martim Affonso de Souza A102

King John III of Portugal A103

Disembarkation of M. A. de Souza at Sao Vicente — A104

Wmk. 222

1932, June 3 Typo. *Perf. 13*

359 A100 20r dk violet .20 .20
360 A101 100r black .35 .35
361 A102 200r purple 1.00 .25
362 A103 600r red brown 1.65 1.25

Engr.
Wmk. 101
Perf. 9½, 11, 9½x11

363 A104 700r ultra 2.50 1.75
Nos. 359-363 (5) 5.70 3.80

1st colonization of Brazil at Sao Vicente, in 1532, under the hereditary captaincy of Martim Affonso de Souza.

Revolutionary Issue

Map of Brazil — A105

Soldier and Flag — A106

Allegory: Freedom, Justice, Equality — A107

Soldier's Head — A108

"LEX" and Sword A109

Symbolical of Law and Order A110

Symbolical of Justice A111

Perf. 11½

1932, Sept. 13 Litho. Unwmk.

364 A105 100r brown org .40 2.00
365 A106 200r dk carmine .35 .70
366 A107 300r gray green 2.00 3.50
367 A108 400r dark blue 7.25 7.25
368 A105 500r black brown 7.25 7.25
369 A107 600r red 7.25 7.25
370 A106 700r violet 3.50 *7.25*
371 A108 1000r orange 1.75 *7.25*
372 A109 2000r dark brown 14.00 20.00
373 A110 5000r yellow grn 17.50 32.50
374 A111 10000r plum 20.00 37.50
Nos. 364-374 (11) 81.25 132.45

Issued by the revolutionary forces in the state of Sao Paulo during the revolt of September, 1932. Subsequenty the stamps were recognized by the Federal Government and placed in general use.

Excellent counterfeits of Nos. 373 and 374 exist. Counterfeit cancellations abound.

City of Vassouras and Illuminated Memorial — A112

Wmk. 222

1933, Jan. 15 Typo. *Perf. 12*

375 A112 200r rose red 1.00 .90

City of Vassouras founding, cent.

Nos. 306, 320 Surcharged **200 RÉIS**

Perf. 13½x12½

1933, July 28 Wmk. 218

376 A76 200r on 300r rose red .60 .60
a. Wmk. 218 in echelon (No. 306a) 12.50 12.50
b. Wmk. 100 (No. 250) 87.50 87.50

Perf. 13x12½
Wmk. 221

377 A76 200r on 300r rose red .45 .45
a. Inverted surcharge 35.00
b. Double surcharge 35.00

Religious Symbols and Inscriptions — A113

Wmk. 222

1933, Sept. 3 Typo. *Perf. 13*

378 A113 200r dark red .90 .75

1st Natl. Eucharistic Congress in Brazil.

"Flag of the Race" A114

1933, Aug. 18

379 A114 200r deep red .90 .75

The raising of the "Flag of the Race" and the 441st anniv. of the sailing of Columbus from Palos, Spain, Aug. 3, 1492.

Republic Figure, Flags of Brazil and Argentina — A115

Perf. 11½

1933, Oct. 7 Wmk. 101 Engr.

380 A115 200r blue .35 .25

Thick Laid Paper
Perf. 11, 11½
Wmk. 236

381 A115 400r green .90 .80
382 A115 600r brt rose 3.00 3.25
383 A115 1000r lt violet 4.50 3.75
Nos. 380-383 (4) 8.75 8.05

Visit of President Justo of the Argentina to Brazil, Oct. 2-7, 1933.

Allegory: "Faith and Energy" — A116

Allegory of Flight — A117

1933 Typo. Wmk. 222

384 A116 200r dark red .25 .15
385 A116 200r dark violet .30 .15
Set value .20

See Nos. 435, 471 and 491.

Wmk. 236

1934, Apr. 15 Engr. *Perf. 12*

386 A117 200r blue .50 .50

1st Natl. Aviation Congress at Sao Paulo.

A118

Wmk. 222

1934, May 12 Typo. *Perf. 11*

387 A118 200r dark olive .30 .30
388 A118 400r carmine 1.50 1.50
389 A118 700r ultra 1.50 .90
390 A118 1000r orange 3.75 .60
Nos. 387-390 (4) 7.05 3.30

7th Intl. Fair at Rio de Janeiro.

Christ of Corcovado — A119

1934, Oct. 20

392 A119 300r dark red 1.90 1.90
a. Tete beche pair 6.00 7.25
393 A119 700r ultra 8.00 5.00
a. Tete beche pair 19.00 22.50

Visit of Eugenio Cardinal Pacelli, later Pope Pius XII, to Brazil.

The three printings of Nos. 392-393, distinguishable by shades, sell for different prices.

José de Anchieta A120

Thick Laid Paper

1934, Nov. 8 Wmk. 236 *Perf. 11, 12*

394 A120 200r yellow brown .55 .15
395 A120 300r violet .45 .25
396 A120 700r blue 1.75 1.40
397 A120 1000r lt green 3.50 .55
Nos. 394-397 (4) 6.25 2.35

Jose de Anchieta, S.J. (1534-1597), Portuguese missionary and "father of Brazilian literature."

"Brazil" and "Uruguay" A121 A122

Wmk. 222

1935, Jan. 8 Typo. *Perf. 11*

398 A121 200r orange .65 .40
399 A122 300r yellow .80 .50
400 A122 700r ultra 3.25 3.25
401 A121 1000r dk violet 8.00 4.00
Nos. 398-401 (4) 12.70 8.15

Visit of President Terra of Uruguay.

View of Town of Igarassu A123

1935, July 1

402 A123 200r maroon & brn .85 .45
403 A123 300r vio & olive brn .85 .35

Captaincy of Pernambuco founding, 400th anniv.

Types of 1918-29
Thick Laid Paper
Perf. 9½, 11, 12, 12x11

1934-36 Engr. Wmk. 236

404 A72 2000r violet 3.75 .40
405 A89 5000r blue vio ('36) 11.00 .50
406 A72 10000r claret ('36) 8.75 .75
Nos. 404-406 (3) 23.50 1.65

No. 404 is inscribed "BRASIL CORREIO."

Revolutionist — A124

Bento Gonçalves da Silva — A125

Duke of Caxias A126

1935, Sept. 20 *Perf. 11, 12*

407 A124 200r black .55 .45
408 A124 300r rose lake .55 .35
409 A125 700r dull blue 2.25 2.25
410 A126 1000r light violet 2.50 1.40
Nos. 407-410 (4) 5.85 4.45

Centenary of the "Ragged" Revolution.

Federal District Coat of Arms A127

Wmk. 222

1935, Oct. 19 **Typo.** *Perf. 11*

411 A127 200r blue 2.25 2.25

8th Intl. Sample Fair held at Rio de Janeiro.

Coutinho's Ship A128

Arms of Fernandes Coutinho — A129

1935, Oct. 25

412 A128 300r maroon 2.25 1.00
413 A129 700r turq blue 3.25 2.00

400th anniversary of the establishment of the first Portuguese colony at Espirito Santo by Vasco Fernandes Coutinho.

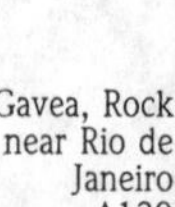

Gavea, Rock near Rio de Janeiro A130

1935, Oct. 12 **Wmk. 245** *Perf. 11*

414 A130 300r brown & vio 1.75 1.50
415 A130 300r blk & turq bl 1.75 1.50
416 A130 300r Prus bl & ultra 1.75 1.50
417 A130 300r crimson & blk 1.75 1.50
Nos. 414-417 (4) 7.00 6.00

"Child's Day," Oct. 12.

Viscount of Cairu — A131

Perf. 11, 12x11

1936, Jan. 20 **Engr.** **Wmk. 236**

418 A131 1200r violet 6.00 2.75

Jose da Silva Lisboa, Viscount of Cairu (1756-1835).

View of Cametá A132

1936, Feb. 26 *Perf. 11, 12*

419 A132 200r brown orange 1.25 1.00
420 A132 300r green 1.25 .80

300th anniversary of the founding of the city of Cameta, Dec. 24, 1635.

Coining Press A133

Thick Laid Paper

1936, Mar. 24 *Perf. 11*

421 A133 300r pur brn, *cr* 1.25 .90

1st Numismatic Cong. at Sao Paulo, Mar., 1936.

Carlos Gomes A134

"Il Guarany" A135

Thick Laid Paper

1936, July 11 *Perf. 11, 11x12*

422 A134 300r dull rose .50 .35
423 A134 300r black brown .50 .35
424 A135 700r ocher 2.00 .90
425 A135 700r blue 1.75 .90
Nos. 422-425 (4) 4.75 2.50

100th anniversary of the birth of Antonio Carlos Gomes, who composed the opera "Il Guarany."

Scales of Justice — A136

Wmk. 222

1936, July 4 **Typo.** *Perf. 11*

426 A136 300r rose 1.25 .45

First National Judicial Congress.

Federal District Coat of Arms A137

1936, Nov. 13 **Typo.** **Wmk. 249**

427 A137 200r rose red .75 .45

Ninth International Sample Fair held at Rio de Janeiro.

Eucharistic Congress Seal — A138

1936, Dec. 17 **Wmk. 245** *Perf. 11½*

428 A138 300r grn, yel, bl & blk .70 .45

2nd Natl. Eucharistic Congress in Brazil.

Botafogo Bay — A139

Thick Laid Paper

Wmk. 236

1937, Jan. 2 **Engr.** *Perf. 11*

429 A139 700r blue .75 .45
430 A139 700r black .75 .45

Birth cent. of Francisco Pereira Passos, engineer who planned the modern city of Rio de Janeiro.

Types of 1920-21, 1933

Perf. 11, 11½ and Compound

1936-37 **Typo.** **Wmk. 249**

431 A75 10r deep brown .15 .15
432 A75 20r dull violet .15 .15
433 A75 50r blue green .15 .15
434 A75 100r orange .25 .15
435 A116 200r dk violet .45 .15
436 A76 300r olive green .25 .15
437 A76 400r ultra .45 .15
438 A76 500r lt brown .70 .15
439 A76 600r brn org ('37) 1.50 .15
440 A76 700r deep violet 2.75 .15
441 A76 1000r turq blue 3.00 .15
Nos. 431-441 (11) 9.80
Set value 1.00

Massed Flags and Star of Esperanto A140

1937, Jan. 19

442 A140 300r green 1.00 .50

Ninth Brazilian Esperanto Congress.

Bay of Rio de Janeiro A141

1937, June 9 **Unwmk.** *Perf. 12½*

443 A141 300r orange red & blk .50 .50
444 A141 700r blue & dk brn 1.25 .50

2nd South American Radio Communication Conf. held in Rio, June 7-19.

Monroe Palace, Rio de Janeiro — A143

Botanical Garden, Rio de Janeiro — A144

1937, Sept. 30 **Unwmk.** *Perf. 12½*

446 A143 200r lt brn & bl .50 .35
447 A144 300r org & ol grn .50 .35
448 A143 2000r grn & cerise 3.75 5.50
449 A144 10000r lake & indigo 32.50 27.50
Nos. 446-449 (4) 37.25 33.70

Brig. Gen. Jose da Silva Paes — A145

Eagle and Shield — A146

1937, Oct. 11 **Wmk. 249** *Perf. 11½*

450 A145 300r blue .75 .30

Bicentenary of Rio Grande do Sul.

1937, Dec. 2 **Typo.** *Perf. 11*

451 A146 400r dark blue .75 .30

150th anniversary of the US Constitution.

Bags of Brazilian Coffee — A147

Frame Engraved, Center Typographed

1938, Jan. 17 **Unwmk.** *Perf. 12½*

452 A147 1200r multicolored 3.00 .40

Arms of Olinda A148

Perf. 11, 11x11½

1938, Jan. 24 **Engr.** **Wmk. 249**

453 A148 400r violet .50 .25

4th cent. of the founding of the city of Olinda.

Independence Memorial, Ypiranga — A149

1938, Jan. 24 **Typo.** *Perf. 11*

454 A149 400r brown olive .60 .25

Proclamation of Brazil's independence by Dom Pedro, Sept. 7, 1822.

Iguaçu Falls — A150

Perf. 12½

1938, Jan. 10 **Unwmk.** **Engr.**

455 A150 1000r sepia & yel brn 1.50 .75
456 A150 5000r ol blk & grn 17.00 7.50

Globe — A142

1937, Sept. 4 **Wmk. 249** *Perf. 11, 12*

445 A142 300r green .85 .50

50th anniversary of Esperanto.

Couto de Magalhaes — A151

Perf. 11, 11x11½

1938, Mar. 17 Wmk. 249

457	A151	400r dull green	.50	.25

General Couto de Magalhaes (1837-1898), statesman, soldier, explorer, writer, developer.

Types of 1918-38

Perf. 11, 12x11, 12x11½, 12

1938 Engr. Wmk. 249

458	A72	2000r blue violet	6.50	.15
459	A89	5000r violet blue	24.00	.50
a.		5000r deep blue	20.00	.50
460	A72	10000r rose lake	27.50	1.00
		Nos. 458-460 (3)	58.00	1.65

No. 458 is inscribed "BRASIL CORREIO."

Types of 1920-22

1938 Wmk. 245 Typo. *Perf. 11*

461	A75	50r blue green	.50	.75
462	A75	100r orange	.50	.75
463	A76	300r olive green	.50	.15
463A	A76	400r ultra	100.00	35.00
463B	A76	500r red brown	.50	*10.00*
		Nos. 461-463B (5)	102.00	46.65

National Archives Building A152

1938, May 20 Wmk. 249

464	A152	400r brown	.40	.25

Centenary of National Archives.

Souvenir Sheets

Sir Rowland Hill A153

1938, Oct. 22 *Imperf.*

465	A153	Sheet of 10	12.50	12.50
a.		400r dull green, single stamp	.75	.75

Brazilian Intl. Philatelic Exposition (Brapex).

Issued in sheets measuring 106x118mm. A few perforated sheets exist.

President Vargas A154

1938, Nov. 10 *Perf. 11*

Without Gum

466	A154	Sheet of 10	5.00	8.50
a.		400r slate blue, single stamp	.40	.40

Constitution of Brazil, set up by President Vargas, Nov. 10, 1937. Size: 113x135½mm.

Types of 1920-33

1939 Typo. Wmk. 256 *Perf. 11*

467	A75	10r red brown	.30	.25
468	A75	20r dull violet	.30	.15
469	A75	50r blue green	.30	.15
470	A75	100r yellow org	.45	.15
471	A116	200r dk violet	.55	.15
472	A76	400r ultra	1.00	.15
473	A76	600r dull orange	1.00	.15
474	A76	1000r turq blue	7.00	.15
		Nos. 467-474 (8)	10.90	
		Set value		.75

View of Rio de Janeiro — A155

View of Santos — A156

1939, June 14 Engr. Wmk. 249

475	A155	1200r dull violet	1.25	.25

1939, Aug. 23

476	A156	400r dull blue	.40	.20

Centenary of founding of Santos.

Chalice Vine and Blossoms — A157

Eucharistic Congress Seal — A158

1939, Aug. 23

477	A157	400r green	1.00	.25

1st South American Botanical Congress held in January, 1938.

1939, Sept. 3

478	A158	400r rose red	.40	.20

Third National Eucharistic Congress.

Duke of Caxias, Army Patron — A159

1939, Sept. 12 Photo. *Rouletted*

479	A159	400r deep ultra	.40	.25

Issued for Soldiers' Day.

A159a

A159b

A159d

A159c

Designs: 400r, George Washington. 800r, Emperor Pedro II. 1200r, Grover Cleveland. 1600r, Statue of Friendship, given by US.

1939, Oct. 7 Unwmk. Engr. *Perf. 12*

480	A159a	400r yellow orange	.40	.25
481	A159b	800r dark green	.25	.15
482	A159c	1200r rose car	.50	.15
483	A159d	1600r dark blue	.50	.25
		Nos. 480-483 (4)	1.65	.80

New York World's Fair.

Benjamin Constant A160

Fonseca on Horseback A161

Manuel Deodoro da Fonseca and President Vargas — A162

Wmk. 249

1939, Nov. 15 Photo. *Rouletted*

484	A160	400r deep green	.30	.20
485	A162	1200r chocolate	.75	.30

Engr. *Perf. 11*

486	A161	800r gray black	.45	.30
		Nos. 484-486 (3)	1.50	.80

50th anniv. of the Proclamation of the Republic.

President Roosevelt, President Vargas and Map of the Americas A163

1940, Apr. 14

487	A163	400r slate blue	.70	.40

Pan American Union, 50th anniversary.

Types of 1920-33

1940-41 Typo. Wmk. 264 *Perf. 11*

488	A75	10r red brown	.15	.25
489	A75	20r dull violet	.25	.25
489A	A75	50r blue grn ('41)	.85	*1.25*
490	A75	100r yellow org	1.00	.15
491	A116	200r violet	.75	.15
492	A76	400r ultra	4.50	.15
493	A76	600r dull orange	4.50	.15
494	A76	1000r turq blue	11.00	.15
		Nos. 488-494 (8)	23.00	
		Set value		*2.00*

Map of Brazil — A164

1940, Sept. 7 Engr.

495	A164	400r carmine	.40	.20
a.		Unwmkd.	50.00	30.00

9th Brazilian Congress of Geography held at Florianopolis.

Victoria Regia Water Lily — A165

President Vargas — A166

Relief Map of Brazil — A167

1940, Oct. 30 Wmk. 249 *Perf. 11*

Without Gum

496	A165	1000r dull violet	.85	.85
a.		Sheet of 10	8.50	*25.00*
497	A166	5000r red	6.75	5.00
a.		Sheet of 10	72.50	*110.00*
498	A167	10,000r slate blue	7.50	2.50
a.		Sheet of 10	100.00	110.00
		Nos. 496-498 (3)	15.10	8.35

New York World's Fair.

All three sheets exist unwatermarked and also with papermaker's watermark of large globe and "AMERICA BANK" in sheet. A few imperforate sheets also exist.

Joaquim Machado de Assis — A168

Pioneers and Buildings of Porto Alegre — A169

1940, Nov. 1

499	A168	400r black	.50	.20

Birth centenary of Joaquim Maria Machado de Assis, poet and novelist.

1940, Nov. 2 Wmk. 264

500	A169	400r green	.40	.15

Colonization of Porto Alegre, bicent.

Proclamation of King John IV of Portugal A173

1940, Dec. 1 Wmk. 249

501	A173	1200r blue black	1.00	.25

800th anniv. of Portuguese independence and 300th anniv. of the restoration of the monarchy.

No. 501 was also printed on paper with papermaker's watermark of large globe and "AMERICA BANK." Unwatermarked copies are from these sheets.

Brazilian Flags and Head of Liberty — A175

Wmk. 256

1940, Dec. 18 Engr. *Perf. 11*

502	A175	400r dull violet	.50	.20
b.		Unwmkd.	40.00	40.00

Wmk. 245

502A	A175	400r dull violet	40.00	40.00

10th anniv. of the inauguration of President Vargas.

Calendar Sheet and Inscription "Day of the Fifth General Census of Brazil" — A176

Wmk. 256

1941, Jan. 14 Typo. *Perf. 11*

503	A176	400r blue & red	.40	.20

Wmk. 245

504	A176	400r blue & red	3.00	.80

Fifth general census of Brazil.

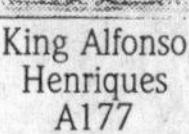

King Alfonso Henriques A177

Father Antonio Vieira A178

Salvador Corrêia de Sa e Benevides — A179

President Carmona of Portugal and President Vargas A180

Wmk. 264

1940-41 Photo. *Rouletted*

504A	A177	200r pink	.15	.15
505	A178	400r ultra	.20	.15
506	A179	800r brt violet	.25	.15
506A	A180	5400r slate grn	1.65	.70

Wmk. 249

507	A177	200r pink	5.25	3.25
507A	A178	400r ultra	25.00	8.50
508	A180	5400r slate grn	2.50	1.25
		Nos. 504A-508 (7)	35.00	14.15

Portuguese Independence, 800th anniv.
For surcharge and overprint see Nos. C45, C47.

Jose de Anchieta A181

Amador Bueno A182

Wmk. 264

1941, Aug. 1 Engr. *Perf. 11*

509	A181	1000r gray vio	1.00	.50

Society of Jesus, 400th anniversary.

1941, Oct. 20 *Perf. 11½*

510	A182	400r black	.50	.30

300th anniv. of the acclamation of Amador Bueno (1572-1648) as king of Sao Paulo.

Air Force Emblem A183

1941, Oct. 20 *Perf. 11*

511	A183	5400r slate grn	3.00	2.00

Issued in connection with Aviation Week, as propaganda for the Brazilian Air Force.

Petroleum — A184

Agriculture — A185

Steel Industry — A186

Commerce — A187

Marshal Peixoto — A188

Count of Porto Alegre — A189

Admiral J. A. C. Maurity — A190

"Armed Forces" — A191

Vargas — A192

1941-42 Wmk. 264 Typo. *Perf. 11*

512	A184	10r yellow brn	.20	.20
513	A184	20r olive grn	.15	.15
514	A184	50r olive bis	.15	.15
515	A184	100r blue grn	.20	.15
516	A185	200r brown org	.45	.15
517	A185	300r lilac rose	.25	.15
518	A185	400r grnsh blue	.65	.15
519	A185	500r salmon	.30	.15
520	A186	600r violet	.65	.15
521	A186	700r brt rose	.30	.15
522	A186	1000r gray	1.75	.15
523	A186	1200r dl blue	3.00	.15
524	A187	2000r gray vio	2.50	.15
		Engr.		
525	A188	5000r blue	5.50	.15
526	A189	10,000r rose red	7.00	.20
527	A190	20,000r dp brown	7.00	.35
528	A191	50,000r red ('42)	27.50	21.00
529	A192	100,000r blue ('42)	.60	*9.00*
		Nos. 512-529 (18)	58.15	32.70

Nos. 512 to 527 and later issues come on thick or thin paper. The stamps on both papers also exist with three vertical green lines printed on the back, a control mark.

See Nos. 541-587, 592-593, 656-670.

Bernardino de Campos A193

Prudente de Morais A194

1942, May 25

533	A193	1000r red	1.25	.40
534	A194	1200r blue	3.00	.25

100th anniversary of the birth of Bernardino de Campos and Prudente de Morais, lawyers and statesmen of Brazil.

Head of Indo-Brazilian Bull — A195

1942, May 1 Wmk. 264 *Perf. 11½*

535	A195	200r blue	.45	.25
536	A195	400r orange brn	.45	.25
a.		Wmk. 267	45.00	45.00

2nd Agriculture and Livestock Show of Central Brazil held at Uberaba.

Outline of Brazil and Torch of Knowledge A196

Map of Brazil Showing Goiania A197

Wmk. 264

1942, July 5 Typo. *Perf. 11*

537	A196	400r orange brn	.30	.25

8th Brazilian Congress of Education.

1942, July 5

538	A197	400r lt violet	.40	.30

Founding of Goiania city.

Seal of Congress — A198

1942, Sept. 20 Wmk. 264

539	A198	400r olive bister	.25	.20
a.		Wmk. 267	25.00	12.50

4th Natl. Eucharistic Cong. at Sao Paulo.

Types of 1941-42

1942-47 Wmk. 245 *Perf. 11*

541	A184	20r olive green	.15	.40
542	A184	50r olive bister	.15	.15
543	A184	100r blue grn	.40	.40
544	A185	200r brown org	.65	.50
545	A185	400r grnsh blue	.40	.15
546	A186	600r lt violet	3.00	.15
547	A186	700r brt rose	.35	.80
548	A186	1200r dl blue	1.25	.15
549	A187	2000r gray vio ('47)	9.00	9.00
		Engr.		
550	A188	5000r blue	10.00	.40
551	A189	10,000r rose red	6.00	1.50
552	A190	20,000r dp brn ('47)	4.50	.45
553	A192	100,000r blue	3.50	8.00
		Nos. 541-553 (13)	39.35	22.05

Types of 1941-42

1941-47 Typo. Wmk. 268 *Perf. 11*

554	A184	20r olive grn	.20	.15
555	A184	50r ol bis ('47)	.55	.55
556	A184	100r bl grn ('43)	.20	.15
557	A185	200r brn org ('43)	.20	.15
558	A185	300r lilac rose ('43)	.15	.15
559	A185	400r grnsh bl ('42)	.30	.15
560	A185	500r salmon ('43)	.20	.15
561	A186	600r violet	.60	.15
562	A186	700r brt rose ('45)	.35	*1.75*
563	A186	1000r gray	.65	.15
564	A186	1200r dp blue ('44)	.85	.15
565	A187	2000r gray vio ('43)	3.00	.15
		Engr.		
566	A188	5000r blue ('43)	4.25	.15
567	A189	10,000r rose red ('43)	8.50	.40
568	A190	20,000r dp brn ('42)	19.00	.45
569	A191	50,000r red ('42)	21.00	3.00
a.		50,000r dark brown red ('47)	15.00	8.50
570	A192	100,000r blue	.55	.55
		Nos. 554-570 (17)	60.55	8.35

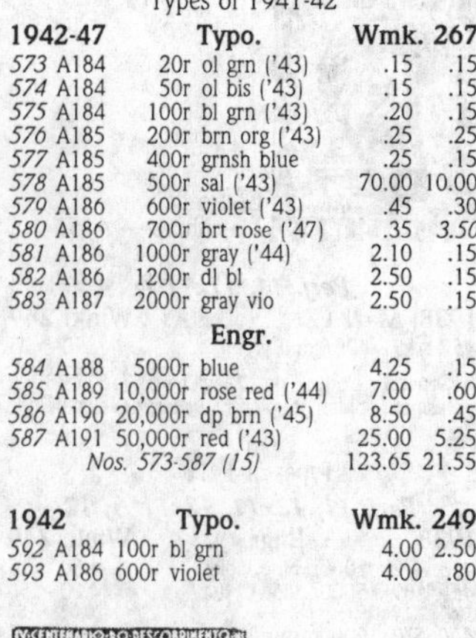

Types of 1941-42

1942-47 Typo. Wmk. 267

573	A184	20r ol grn ('43)	.15	.15
574	A184	50r ol bis ('43)	.15	.15
575	A184	100r bl grn ('43)	.20	.15
576	A185	200r brn org ('43)	.25	.25
577	A185	400r grnsh blue	.25	.15
578	A185	500r sal ('43)	70.00	10.00
579	A186	600r violet ('43)	.45	.30
580	A186	700r brt rose ('47)	.35	*3.50*
581	A186	1000r gray ('44)	2.10	.15
582	A186	1200r dl bl	2.50	.15
583	A187	2000r gray vio	2.50	.15
		Engr.		
584	A188	5000r blue	4.25	.15
585	A189	10,000r rose red ('44)	7.00	.60
586	A190	20,000r dp brn ('45)	8.50	.45
587	A191	50,000r red ('43)	25.00	5.25
		Nos. 573-587 (15)	123.65	21.55

1942 Typo. Wmk. 249

592	A184	100r bl grn	4.00	2.50
593	A186	600r violet	4.00	.80

Map Showing Amazon River — A199

1943, Mar. 19 Wmk. 267 *Perf. 11*

607	A199	40c orange brown	.35	.35

Discovery of the Amazon River, 400th anniv.

Reproduction of Brazil Stamp of 1866 — A200

1943, Mar. 28 Wmk. 267

608	A200	40c violet	.50	.25
a.		Wmk. 268	*650.00*	

Centenary of city of Petropolis.

Adaptation of 1843 "Bull's-eye" A201

1943, Aug. 1 Engr. *Imperf.*

609	A201	30c black	.45	.25
610	A201	60c black	.55	.25
611	A201	90c black	.45	.25
		Nos. 609-611 (3)	1.45	.75

Cent. of the 1st postage stamp of Brazil. The 30c and 90c exist unwatermarked; values $25 and $65.

Souvenir Sheet

A202

Wmk. 281 Horizontally or Vertically

1943 Engr. *Imperf.*

Without Gum

612	A202	Sheet of 3	7.50	6.75
a.		30c black	1.90	1.90
b.		60c black	1.90	1.90
c.		90c black	1.90	1.90

Ubaldino do Amaral A203

"Justice" A204

Perf. 11, 12

1943, Aug. 27 Typo. Wmk. 264

613 A203 40c dull slate green .40 .20
a. Wmk. 267 20.00 15.00

Birth centenary of Ubaldino do Amaral, banker and statesman.

1943, Aug. 30 Wmk. 267

614 A204 2cr bright rose .70 .40

Centenary of Institute of Brazilian Lawyers.

Indo-Brazilian Bull — A205

1943, Aug. 30 Engr.

615 A205 40c dk red brn .70 .40

9th Livestock Show at Bahia.

José Barbosa Rodrigues A206

1943, Nov. 13 Typo.

616 A206 40c bluish grn .40 .20

Birth cent. of Jose Barbosa Rodrigues, botanist.

Charity Hospital, Santos A207

1943, Nov. 7 Engr.

617 A207 1cr blue .40 .30

400th anniv. of Charity Hospital, Santos.

Pedro Americo de Figueirido e Melo (1843-1905), Artist-hero and Statesman — A208

Wmk. 267

1943, Dec. 16 Typo. *Perf. 11*

618 A208 40c brown orange .20 .20

Gen. A. E. Gomes Carneiro A209

1944, Feb. 9 Engr.

619 A209 1.20cr rose .50 .35

50th anniversary of the Lapa siege.

Statue of Baron of Rio Branco — A210

1944, May 13 Typo.

620 A210 1cr blue .40 .25

Statue of the Baron of Rio Branco unveiling.

Duke of Caxias A211

1944, May 13 Unwmk. *Perf. 12*

Granite Paper

621 A211 1.20cr bl grn & pale org .50 .30

Centenary of pacification of Sao Paulo and Minas Gerais in an independence movement in 1842.

YMCA Seal — A212

1944, June 7 Litho. *Perf. 11*

Granite Paper

622 A212 40c dp bl, car & yel .30 .20

Centenary of Young Men's Christian Assn.

Chamber of Commerce Rio Grande — A213

Wmk. 268

1944, Sept. 25 Engr. *Perf. 12*

623 A213 40c lt yellow brn .30 .25

Centenary of the Chamber of Commerce of Rio Grande.

Martim F. R. de Andrada A214

1945, Jan. 30 *Perf. 11*

624 A214 40c blue .30 .25

Ccentenary of the death of Martim F. R. de Andrada, statesman.

Meeting of Duke of Caxias and David Canabarro A215

1945, Mar. 19 Photo.

625 A215 40c ultra .30 .20

Pacification of Rio Grande do Sul, cent.

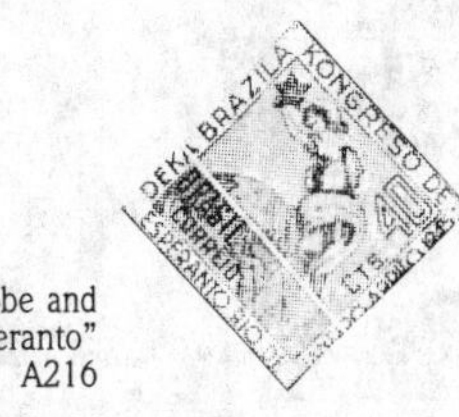

Globe and "Esperanto" A216

1945, Apr. 16

626 A216 40c lt blue grn .50 .25

10th Esperanto Congress, Rio, Apr. 14-22.

Baron of Rio Branco's Bookplate — A217

1945, Apr. 20 Wmk. 268 *Perf. 11*

627 A217 40c violet .50 .25

Cent. of the birth of Jose Maria da Silva Paranhos, Baron of Rio Branco.

Tranquility — A218 Glory — A219

Victory A220

Peace A221

Cooperation A222

Rouletted 7

1945, May 8 Engr. Wmk. 268

628 A218 20c dk rose vio .15 .15
629 A219 40c dk carmine .15 .15
630 A220 1cr dull orange .35 .30
631 A221 2cr steel blue .85 .45
632 A222 5cr green 1.65 .55
Nos. 628-632 (5) 3.15 1.60

Victory of the Allied Nations in Europe.

Nos. 628-632 exist on thin card, imperf. and unwatermarked.

Francisco Manoel da Silva (1795-1865), Composer (in 1831) of the National Anthem — A223

Wmk. 245

1945, May 30 Typo. *Perf. 12*

633 A223 40c brt rose .45 .30
a. Wmk. 268 6.75 6.75

Bahia Institute of Geography and History A224

1945, May 30 Wmk. 268 *Perf. 11*

634 A224 40c lt ultra .25 .20

50th anniv. of the founding of the Institute of Geography and History at Bahia.

Emblems of 5th Army and B.E.F. A225 A226

US Flag and Shoulder Patches A227

Brazilian Flag and Shoulder Patches A228

Victory Symbol and Shoulder Patches — A229

1945, July 18 Litho.

635 A225 20c multicolored .15 .15
636 A226 40c multicolored .15 .15
637 A227 1cr multicolored .70 .40
638 A228 2cr multicolored 1.00 .60
639 A229 5cr multicolored 3.00 .70
Nos. 635-639 (5) 5.00 2.00

Honoring the Brazilian Expeditionary Force and the US 5th Army Battle against the Axis in Italy.

Radio Tower and Map — A230

1945, Sept. 3 Engr.

640 A230 1.20cr gray .45 .25

Third Inter-American Conference on Radio Communications.

No. 640 was reproduced on a souvenir card with blue background and inscriptions. Size: 145x161mm.

A 40c lilac stamp, picturing the International Bridge between Argentina and Brazil and portraits of Presidents Justo and Vargas, was prepared late in 1945. It was not issued, but later was sold, without postal value, to collectors. Value, 15 cents.

Admiral Luiz Felipe Saldanha da Gama (1846-1895) A231

1946, Apr. 7
641 A231 40c gray black .25 .25

Princess Isabel d'Orleans-Braganca Birth Cent. — A232

1946, July 29 **Unwmk.**
642 A232 40c black .25 .25

Post Horn, V and Envelope — A233

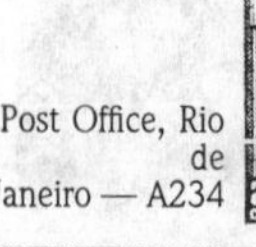

Post Office, Rio de Janeiro — A234

Bay of Rio de Janeiro and Plane A235

Wmk. 268
1946, Sept. 2 **Litho.** ***Perf. 11***
643 A233 40c blk & pale org .15 .15

Perf. 12½
Engr. **Unwmk.**
Center in Ultramarine
644 A234 2cr slate .40 .15
645 A234 5cr orange brn 2.00 .85
646 A234 10cr dk violet 2.25 .50

Center in Brown Orange
647 A235 1.30cr dk green .25 .35
648 A235 1.70cr car rose .25 .35
649 A235 2.20cr dp ultra .40 .50
Nos. 643-649 (7) 5.70 2.85

5th Postal Union Congress of the Americas and Spain.
No. 643 was reproduced on a souvenir card. Size: 188x239mm. Sold for 10cr.

Liberty — A236

Perf. 11x11½
1946, Sept. 18 **Wmk. 268**
650 A236 40c blk & gray .25 .15
a. Unwmkd. 150.00

Adoption of the Constitution of 1946.

Columbus Lighthouse, Dominican Republic A237

1946, Sept. 14 **Litho.** ***Perf. 11***
651 A237 5cr Prus grn 4.00 1.50

Orchid — A238 Gen. A. E. Gomes Carneiro — A239

1946, Nov. 8 **Wmk. 268**
652 A238 40c ultra, red & yel .40 .30
a. Unwmkd. 55.00

4th National Exhibition of Orchids, Rio de Janeiro, November, 1946.

Perf. 10½x12
1946, Dec. 6 **Engr.** **Unwmk.**
653 A239 40c deep green .20 .20

Centenary of the birth of Gen. Antonio Ernesto Gomes Carneiro.

Brazilian Academy of Letters A240

1946, Dec. 14 ***Perf. 11***
654 A240 40c blue .25 .20

50th anniv. of the foundation of the Brazilian Academy of Letters, Rio de Janeiro.

Antonio de Castro Alves (1847-1871), Poet — A241

1947, Mar. 14 **Litho.** **Wmk. 267**
655 A241 40c bluish green .20 .20

Types of 1941-42, Values in Centavos or Cruzeiros

1947-54 **Wmk. 267** **Typo.** ***Perf. 11***
656 A184 2c olive .15 .15
657 A184 5c yellow brn .15 .15
658 A184 10c green .15 .15
659 A185 20c brown org .15 .15
660 A185 30c dk lilac rose .60 .15
661 A185 40c blue .30 .15
b. Wmk. 268 800.00 60.00
661A A185 50c salmon .60 .15
662 A186 60c lt violet 1.00 .15
663 A186 70c brt rose ('54) .40 .15
664 A186 1cr gray 1.00 .15
665 A186 1.20cr dull blue 2.50 .15
a. Wmk. 268 11.00 9.00
666 A187 2cr gray violet 4.00 .15

Engr.
667 A188 5cr blue 7.50 .15
668 A189 10cr rose red 7.50 .15

Perf. 11, 13
669 A190 20cr deep brown 15.00 .75
670 A191 50cr red 30.00 .50
Nos. 656-670 (16) 71.00
Set value 2.50

The 5, 20, 50cr also exist with perf. 12-13.

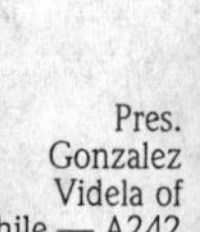

Pres. Gonzalez Videla of Chile — A242

1947, June 26 **Unwmk.** ***Perf. 12x11***
671 A242 40c dk brown orange .20 .15

Visit of President Gabriel Gonzalez Videla of Chile, June 1947.
A souvenir folder contains four impressions of No. 671, and measures 6½x8¼ inches.

"Peace" and Western Hemisphere — A243

1947, Aug. 15 ***Perf. 11x12***
672 A243 1.20cr blue .20 .15

Inter-American Defense Conference at Rio de Janeiro, August-September, 1947.

Pres. Harry S Truman, Map and Statue of Liberty A244

1947, Sept. 1 **Typo.** ***Perf. 12x11***
673 A244 40c ultra .20 .15

Visit of US President Harry S Truman to Brazil, Sept. 1947.

Pres. Eurico Gaspar Dutra — A245 Mother and Child — A246

Wmk. 268
1947, Sept. 7 **Engr.** ***Perf. 11***
674 A245 20c green .15 .15
675 A245 40c rose carmine .15 .15
676 A245 1.20cr deep blue .25 .15
Nos. 674-676 (3) .55
Set value .30

The souvenir sheet containing Nos. 674-676 is listed as No. C73A. See No. 679.

1947, Oct. 10 **Typo.** **Unwmk.**
677 A246 40c brt ultra .20 .15

Issued to mark Child Care Week, 1947.

Arms of Belo Horizonte A247 Globe A248

1947, Dec. 12 **Engr.** **Wmk. 267**
678 A247 1.20cr rose carmine .30 .15

50th anniversary of the founding of the city of Belo Horizonte.

Dutra Type of 1947
1948 **Engr.** **Wmk. 267**
679 A245 20c green 1.50 1.50

Catalogue values for unused stamps in this section, from this point to the end of the section, are for Never Hinged items.

1948, July 10 **Litho.**
680 A248 40c dl grn & pale lil .35 .15

International Exposition of Industry and Commerce, Petropolis, 1948.

Arms of Paranagua A249 Child Reading Book A250

1948, July 29
681 A249 5cr bister brown 1.75 .50

300th anniversary of the founding of the city of Paranagua, July 29, 1648.

1948, Aug. 1
682 A250 40c green .25 .20

National Education Campaign.
No. 682 was reproduced on a souvenir card. Size: 124x157mm.

Tiradentes A251 Symbolical of Cancer Eradication A252

1948, Nov. 12
683 A251 40c brown orange .25 .20

200th anniversary of the birth of Joaquim José da Silva Xavier (Tiradentes).

1948, Dec. 14
684 A252 40c claret .25 .25

Anti-cancer publicity.

Adult Student A253

1949, Jan. 3 **Wmk. 267** ***Perf. 12x11***
685 A253 60c red vio & pink .25 .15

Campaign for adult education.

"Battle of Guararapes," by Vitor Meireles — A254

1949, Feb. 15 ***Perf. 11½x12***
686 A254 60c lt blue .95 .60

2nd Battle of Guararapes, 300th anniv.

Church of Sao Francisco de Paula — A255

Manuel de Nobrega — A256

Perf. 11x12

1949, Mar. 8 Unwmk. Engr.

687 A255 60c dark brown .20 .16

a. Souvenir sheet 27.50 27.50

Bicentenary of city of Ouro Fino, state of Minas Gerais.

No. 687a contains one imperf. stamp similar to No. 687, with dates in lower margin. Size: 70x89mm.

1949, Mar. 29 ***Imperf.***

688 A256 60c violet .25 .25

Founding of the City of Salvador, 400th anniv.

Emblem of Brazilian Air Force and Plane — A257

1949, June 18

689 A257 60c blue violet .25 .25

Issued to honor the Brazilian Air Force.

Star and Angel — A258

1949 Wmk. 267 Litho. ***Perf. 11x12***

690 A258 60c pink .20 .16

1st Ecclesiastical Cong., Salvador, Bahia.

Globe — A259

1949, Oct. 31 Typo. ***Perf. 12x11***

691 A259 1.50cr blue .25 .16

75th anniv. of the UPU.

Ruy Barbosa A260

Unwmk.

1949, Dec. 14 Engr. ***Perf. 12***

692 A260 1.20cr rose carmine .65 .32

Centenary of birth of Ruy Barbosa.

Joaquim Cardinal Arcoverde A. Cavalcanti, Birth Centenary — A261

Perf. 11x12

1950, Feb. 27 Litho. Wmk. 267

693 A261 60c rose .25 .20

Grapes and Factory A262

1950, Mar. 15 ***Perf. 12x11***

694 A262 60c rose lake .25 .20

75th anniversary of Italian immigration to the state of Rio Grande do Sul.

Virgin of the Globe — A263

Globe and Soccer Players — A264

1950, May 31 ***Perf. 11x12***

695 A263 60c blk & lt bl .25 .20

Establishment in Brazil of the Daughters of Charity of St. Vincent de Paul, cent.

1950, June 24

696 A264 60c ultra, bl & gray .85 .50

4th World Soccer Championship.

Symbolical of Brazilian Population Growth A265

1950, July 10 Typo. ***Perf. 12x11***

697 A265 60c rose lake .25 .20

Issued to publicize the 6th Brazilian census.

Dr. Oswaldo Cruz — A266

1950, Aug. 23 Litho. ***Perf. 11x12***

698 A266 60c orange brown .25 .20

5th International Congress of Microbiology.

View of Blumenau and Itajai River — A267

1950, Sept. 9 Wmk. 267 ***Perf. 12x11***

699 A267 60c bright pink .25 .20

Centenary of the founding of Blumenau.

Amazonas Theater, Manaus A268

1950, Sept. 27

700 A268 60c light brn red .20 .16

Centenary of Amazonas Province.

Arms of Juiz de Fora — A269

1950, Oct. 24 ***Perf. 11x12***

701 A269 60c carmine .25 .25

Centenary of the founding of Juiz de Fora.

Post Office at Recife — A270

1951, Jan. 10 Typo. ***Perf. 12x11***

702 A270 60c carmine .20 .20

703 A270 1.20cr carmine .30 .20

Opening of the new building of the Pernambuco Post Office.

Arms of Joinville — A271

Jean-Baptiste de La Salle — A272

1951, Mar. 9 ***Perf. 11x12***

704 A271 60c orange brown .25 .20

Centenary of the founding of Joinville.

1951, Apr. 30 Litho.

705 A272 60c blue .25 .20

Birth of Jean-Baptiste de La Salle, 300th anniv.

Heart and Flowers — A273

Sylvio Romero — A274

1951, May 13 Engr.

706 A273 60c deep plum .25 .20

Mother's Day, May 14, 1951.

1951, Apr. 21 Litho.

707 A274 60c dl vio brn .20 .20

Romero (1851-1914), poet and author.

Joao Caetano, Stage and Masks — A275

1951, July 9 ***Perf. 12x11***

708 A275 60c lt gray bl .25 .20

1st Brazilian Theater Cong., Rio, July 9-13, 1951.

Orville A. Derby — A276

First Mass Celebrated in Brazil — A277

1951, July 23 ***Perf. 11x12***

709 A276 2cr slate .35 .35

Centenary of the birth (in New York State) of Orville A. Derby, geologist.

1951, July 25

710 A277 60c dl brn & buff .20 .16

4th Inter-American Congress on Catholic Education, Rio de Janeiro, 1951.

Euclides Pinto Martins A278

1951, Aug. 16 ***Perf. 12x11***

711 A278 3.80cr brn & citron 1.50 .35

1st flight from NYC to Rio, 29th anniv.

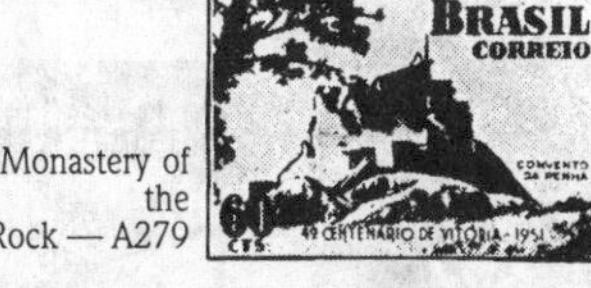

Monastery of the Rock — A279

1951, Sept. 8

712 A279 60c dl brn & cream .20 .20

Founding of Vitoria, 4th centenary.

Santos-Dumont and Model Plane Contest — A280

Dirigible and Eiffel Tower — A281

Perf. 11x12

1951, Oct. 19 Wmk. 267 Litho.

713 A280 60c salmon & dk brn .42 .35

Unwmk. Engr.

714 A281 3.80cr dk pur 1.25 .40

Week of the Wing and 50th anniv. of Santos-Dumont's flight around the Eiffel Tower.

In December 1951, Nos. 713 and 714 were privately overprinted: "Exposicao Filatelica Regional Distrito Federal 15-XII-1951 23-XII-1951." These were attached to souvenir sheets bearing engraved facsimiles of Nos. 38, 49 and 51, which were sold by Clube Filatelico do Brasil to mark its 20th anniversary. The overprinted stamps on the sheets were canceled, but 530 "unused" sets were sold by the club.

Farmers and Ear of Wheat — A282

1951, Nov. 10 Litho. Wmk. 267
715 A282 60c dp grn & gray .25 .25

Festival of Grain at Bage, 1951.

Map and Open Bible — A283

1951, Dec. 9 ***Perf. 12x11***
716 A283 1.20cr brn org .50 .35

Issued to publicize the Day of the Bible.

Queen Isabella — A284

Henrique Oswald — A285

1952, Mar. 10 ***Perf. 11x12***
717 A284 3.80cr lt bl .60 .30

500th anniversary of the birth of Queen Isabella I of Spain.

1952, Apr. 22
718 A285 60c brown .25 .20

Oswald (1852-1931), composer.

Vicente Licinio Cardoso A286

Map and Symbol of Labor A287

1952, May 2
719 A286 60c gray bl .25 .20

4th Brazilian Homeopathic Congress.

1952, Apr. 30
720 A287 1.50cr brnsh pink .25 .20

5th International Labor Organization Conference for American Countries.

Gen. Polidoro da Fonseca — A288

Luiz de Albuquerque M. P. Caceres — A289

Portraits: 5cr, Baron de Capanema. 10cr, Minister Eusebio de Queiros.

Unwmk.

1952, May 11 Engr. ***Perf. 11***
721 A288 2.40cr lt car .35 .20
722 A288 5cr blue 2.25 .28
723 A288 10cr dk bl grn 2.25 .28
Nos. 721-723 (3) 4.85 .76

Centenary of telegraph in Brazil.

Perf. 11x12

1952, June 8 Litho. Wmk. 267
724 A289 1.20cr vio bl .25 .20

200th anniversary of the founding of the city of Mato Grosso.

Symbolizing the Glory of Sports — A290

1952, July 21 ***Perf. 12x11***
725 A290 1.20cr dp bl & bl .60 .40

Fluminense Soccer Club, 50th anniversary.

José Antonio Saraiva — A291

Emperor Dom Pedro — A292

1952, Aug. 16 ***Perf. 11x12***
726 A291 60c lil rose .25 .20

Centenary of the founding of Terezina, capital of Piaui State.

1952, Sept. 3 Wmk. 267
727 A292 60c lt bl & blk .25 .20

Issued for Stamp Day and the 2nd Philatelic Exhibition of Sao Paulo.

Flag-encircled Globe — A293

1952, Oct. 24 ***Perf. 13½***
728 A293 3.80cr blue .85 .50

Issued to publicize United Nations Day.

View of Sao Paulo, Sun and Compasses A294

1952, Nov. 8 Litho. ***Perf. 12x11***
729 A294 60c dl bl, yel & gray grn .25 .20

City Planning Day.

Father Diogo Antonio Feijo — A295

1952, Nov. 9 ***Perf. 11x12***
730 A295 60c fawn .25 .20

Rodolpho Bernardelli and His "Christ and the Adultress" A297

1952, Dec. 18 ***Perf. 12x11***
732 A297 60c gray bl .25 .20

Bernardelli, sculptor and painter, birth cent.

Map of Western Hemisphere and View of Rio de Janeiro A298

1952, Sept. 20
733 A298 3.80cr vio brn & lt grn .80 .30

2nd Congress of American Industrial Medicine, Rio de Janeiro, 1952.

Arms and Head of Pioneer A299

Coffee, Cotton and Sugar Cane — A300

Designs: 2.80cr, Jesuit monk planting tree. 3.80cr and 5.80cr, Spiral, symbolizing progress.

1953, Jan. 25 Litho. ***Perf. 11***
734 A299 1.20cr ol brn & blk brn .52 .35
735 A300 2cr olive grn & yel 1.75 .35
736 A300 2.80cr red brn & dp org 1.20 .20
737 A300 3.80cr dk brn & yel grn 1.00 .20
738 A300 5.80cr int bl & yel grn .70 .20
Nos. 734-738 (5) 5.17 1.30

400th anniversary of Sao Paulo.

Used copies of No. 734 exist with design inverted.

Ledger and Winged Cap — A301

1953, Feb. 22 ***Perf. 12x11***
739 A301 1.20cr dl brn & fawn .25 .20

6th Brazilian Accounting Congress.

Joao Ramalho — A302

Perf. 11½

1953, Apr. 8 Wmk. 264 Engr.
740 A302 60c blue .25 .20

Founding of the city of Santo Andre, 4th cent.

Aarao Reis and Plan of Belo Horizonte A303

1953, May 6 Photo.
741 A303 1.20cr red brn .25 .20

Aarao Leal de Carvalho Reis (1853-1936), civil engineer.

A304

A305

1953, May 16
742 A304 1.50cr Almirante Saldanha .40 .25

4th globe-circling voyage of the training ship Almirante Saldanha.

1953, July 5 Photo.

Joaquim Jose Rodrigues Torres, Viscount of Itaborai.

743 A305 1.20cr violet .20 .16

Centenary of the Bank of Brazil.

Lamp and Rio-Petropolis Highway A306

1953, July 14
744 A306 1.20cr gray .25 .20

10th Intl. Congress of Nursing, Petropolis, 1953.

Bay of Rio de Janeiro A307

1953, July 15
745 A307 3.80cr dk bl grn .40 .20

Issued to publicize the fourth World Congress of Baptist Youth, July 1953.

Arms of Jau and Map — A308

1953, Aug. 15 Engr.
746 A308 1.20cr purple .25 .20

Centenary of the city of Jau.

Ministry of Health and Education Building, Rio — A309

Maria Quiteria de Jesus Medeiros — A310

1953, Aug. 1
747 A309 1.20cr dp grn .25 .20

Day of the Stamp and the first Philatelic Exhibition of National Education.

1953, Aug. 21 **Photo.**
748 A310 60c vio bl .25 .20

Centenary of the death of Maria Quiteria de Jesus Medeiros (1792-1848), independence heroine.

Pres. Odria of Peru — A311

Duke of Caxias Leading his Troops — A312

1953, Aug. 25
749 A311 1.40cr rose brn .25 .20

Issued to publicize the visit of Gen. Manuel A. Odria, President of Peru, Aug. 25, 1953.

Engr. (60c, 5.80cr); Photo.
1953, Aug. 25

Designs: 1.20cr, Caxias' tomb. 1.70cr, 5.80cr, Portrait of Caxias. 3.80cr, Arms of Caxias.

750 A312 60c dp grn .32 .16
751 A312 1.20cr dp claret .40 .16
752 A312 1.70cr slate grn .40 .16
753 A312 3.80cr rose brn .65 .16
754 A312 5.80cr gray vio .65 .16
Nos. 750-754 (5) 2.42 .80

150th anniversary of the birth of Luis Alves de Lima e Silva, Duke of Caxias.

Quill Pen, Map and Tree — A313

Horacio Hora — A314

1953, Sept. 12 **Photo.**
755 A313 60c ultra .25 .20

5th National Congress of Journalism.

1953, Sept. 17 **Litho.** **Wmk. 267**
756 A314 60c org & dp plum .25 .20

Horacio Pinto de Hora (1853-1890), painter.

Pres. Somoza of Nicaragua A315

Auguste de Saint-Hilaire A316

1953, Sept. 24 **Photo.** **Wmk. 264**
757 A315 1.40cr dk vio brn .25 .20

Issued to publicize the visit of Gen. Anastasio Somoza, president of Nicaragua.

1953, Sept. 30
758 A316 1.20cr dk brn car .25 .25

Centenary of the death of Auguste de Saint-Hilaire, explorer and botanist.

Jose Carlos do Patrocinio A317

Clock Tower, Crato A318

1953, Oct. 9 **Photo.**
759 A317 60c dk slate gray .25 .20

Jose Carlos do Patrocinio, (1853-1905), journalist and abolitionist.

1953, Oct. 17
760 A318 60c blue green .25 .20

Centenary of the city of Crato.

Joao Capistrano de Abreu — A319

Allegory: "Justice" — A320

1953, Oct. 23
761 A319 60c dull blue .20 .20
762 A319 5cr purple .85 .85

Joao Capistrano de Abreu (1853-1927), historian.

1953, Nov. 17
763 A320 60c indigo .25 .20
764 A320 1.20cr dp magenta .25 .20

50th anniv. of the Treaty of Petropolis.

Farm Worker in Wheat Field — A321

Teacher and Pupils — A322

1953, Nov. 29 **Photo.** ***Perf. 11½***
766 A321 60c dk green .25 .20

3rd Natl. Wheat Festival, Erechim, 1953.

1953, Dec. 14
767 A322 60c red .25 .25

First National Conference of Primary School Teachers, Salvador, 1953.

Zacarias de Gois e Vasconsellos A323

Alexandre de Gusmao A324

Design: 5cr, Porters with Trays of Coffee Beans.

1953-54 **Photo.**
768 A323 2cr org brn & blk, *buff* ('54) .65 .40
a. White paper 1.75 .40
769 A323 5cr dp org & blk 1.25 .40

Centenary of the state of Parana.

1954, Jan. 13
770 A324 1.20cr brn vio .25 .20

Gusmao (1695-1753), statesman, diplomat and writer.

Symbolical of Sao Paulo's Growth — A325

Arms and View of Sao Paulo A326

Designs: 2cr, Priest, settler and Indian. 2.80cr, José de Anchieta.

1954, Jan. 25 ***Perf. 11½x11***
771 A325 1.20cr dk vio brn .75 .50
a. Buff paper 1.75 1.00

Engr.
772 A325 2cr lilac rose 1.05 .60
773 A325 2.80cr pur gray 1.05 1.00

Perf. 11x11½
774 A326 3.80cr dl grn 1.25 .50
a. Buff paper 2.25 2.00
775 A326 5.80cr dl red 1.25 .60
a. Buff paper 5.00 .75
Nos. 771-775 (5) 5.35 3.20

400th anniversary of Sao Paulo.

J. Fernandes Vieira, A. Vidal de Negreiros, A. F. Camarao and H. Dias — A327

Perf. 11x11½
1954, Feb. 18 **Photo.** **Unwmk.**
776 A327 1.20cr ultra .25 .25

300th anniversary of the recovery of Pernambuco from the Dutch.

Sao Paulo and Minerva A328

1954, Feb. 24
777 A328 1.50cr dp plum .25 .25

10th International Congress of Scientific Organizations, Sao Paulo, 1954.

Stylized Grapes, Jug and Map A329

Monument of the Immigrants A330

1954, Feb. 27 **Photo.** ***Perf. 11½x11***
778 A329 40c dp claret .25 .20

Grape Festival, Rio Grande do Sul.

1954, Feb. 28
779 A330 60c dp vio bl .25 .20

Unveiling of the Monument to the Immigrants of Caxias do Sul.

First Brazilian Locomotive A331

Perf. 11x11½
1954, Apr. 30 **Unwmk.**
781 A331 40c carmine .25 .20

Centenary of the first railroad engine built in Brazil.

Pres. Chamoun of Lebanon — A332

1954, May 12 **Photo.** ***Perf. 11½x11***
782 A332 1.50cr maroon .25 .25

Visit of Pres. Camille Chamoun of Lebanon.

Sao Jose College, Rio de Janeiro A333

The values of stamps in less than very fine condition generally are less than catalogue value.

J. B. Champagnat Marcelin A334

Apolonia Pinto A335

1954, June 6 ***Perf. 11x11½, 11½x11***

783 A333 60c purple .18 .15
784 A334 120cr vio blue .22 .20

50th anniversary of the founding of the Marist Brothers in Brazil.

1954, June 21 **Photo.**

785 A335 1.20cr bright green .15 .15

Apolonia Pinto (1854-1937), actress.

Adm. Margues Tamandare — A336

Portraits: 2c, 5c, 10c, Admiral Margues Tamandare. 20c, 30c, 40c, Oswaldo Cruz. 50c, 60c, 90c, Joaquim Murtinho. 1cr, 1.50cr, 2cr, Duke of Caxias. 5cr, 10cr, Ruy Barbosa. 20cr, 50cr, Jose Bonifacio.

1954-60 **Wmk. 267** ***Perf. 11x11½***

786 A336 2c vio blue .15 .15
787 A336 5c org red .15 .15
788 A336 10c brt green .15 .15
789 A336 20c magenta .15 .15
790 A336 30c dk gray grn .15 .15
791 A336 40c rose red .26 .15
792 A336 50c violet .16 .15
793 A336 60c gray grn .15 .15
794 A336 90c orange ('55) .26 .15
795 A336 1cr brown .15 .15
796 A336 1.50cr blue .15 .15
a. Wmk. 264 16.00 8.00
797 A336 2cr dk bl grn ('56) .32 .15
798 A336 5cr rose lil ('56) .26 .15
799 A336 10cr lt grn ('60) .65 .15
800 A336 20cr crim rose ('59) .65 .15
801 A336 50cr ultra ('59) 4.00 .20
Nos. 786-801 (16) 7.76
Set value 1.25

See Nos. 890, 930-933.

Boy Scout Waving Flag (Statue) A337

Baltasar Fernandes, Explorer A338

1954, Aug. 2 **Unwmk.** ***Perf. 11½x11***

802 A337 1.20cr vio bl .40 .24

Intl. Boy Scout Encampment, Sao Paulo.

1954, Aug. 15

803 A338 60c dk red .25 .25

300th anniversary of city of Sorocaba.

Adeodato Giovanni Cardinal Piazza — A339

Our Lady of Aparecida, Map of Brazil — A340

1954, Sept. 2

804 A339 4.20cr red org .50 .35

Visit of Adeodato Cardinal Piazza, papal legate to Brazil.

1954

Design: 1.20cr, Virgin standing on globe.

805 A340 60c claret .32 .32
806 A340 1.20cr vio bl .42 .28

No. 805 was issued for the 1st Cong. of Brazil's Patron Saint (Our Lady of Aparecida); No. 806, the cent. of the proclamation of the dogma of the Immaculate Conception. Both stamps also for the Marian Year.

Issue dates: 60c, Sept. 6; 1.20cr, Sept. 8.

Benjamin Constant and Hand Reading Braille A341

1954, Sept. 27 **Photo.** **Unwmk.**

807 A341 60c dk grn .25 .20

Centenary of the founding of the Benjamin Constant Institute.

River Battle of Riachuelo A342

Admiral F. M. Barroso A343

Dr. Christian F. S. Hahnemann A344

1954, Oct. 6 ***Perf. 11x11½, 11½x11***

808 A342 40c redsh brown .30 .20
809 A343 60c purple .20 .20

Admiral Francisco Manoel Barroso da Silva (1804-82).

1954, Oct. 8 ***Perf. 11½x11***

810 A344 2.70cr dk green .30 .25

1st World Cong. of Homeopathic Medicine.

Nizia Floresta A345

Ears of Wheat A346

1954, Oct. 12

811 A345 60c lilac rose .25 .20

Reburial of the remains of Nizia Floresta (Dio Nizia Pinto Lisboa), writer and educator.

1954, Oct. 22

812 A346 60c olive green .20 .16

4th National Wheat Festival, Carazinho.

Basketball Player and Ball-Globe A347

Allegory of the Spring Games A348

1954, Oct. 23 **Photo.**

813 A347 1.40cr orange red .30 .30

Issued to publicize the second World Basketball Championship Matches, 1954.

Perf. 11½x11

1954, Nov. 6 **Wmk. 267**

814 A348 60c red brown .25 .20

Issued to publicize the 6th Spring Games.

San Francisco Hydroelectric Plant — A349

1955, Jan. 15 ***Perf. 11x11½***

815 A349 60c brown org .20 .15

Issued to publicize the inauguration of the San Francisco Hydroelectric Plant.

Itutinga Hydroelectric Plant — A350

1955, Feb. 3

816 A350 40c blue .20 .15

Issued to publicize the inauguration of the Itutinga Hydroelectric Plant at Lavras.

Rotary Emblem and Bay of Rio de Janeiro — A351

1955, Feb. 23 ***Perf. 12x11½***

817 A351 2.70cr slate gray & blk .85 .25

Rotary International, 50th anniversary.

Fausto Cardoso Palace A352

1955, Mar. 17 ***Perf. 11x11½***

818 A352 40c henna brown .25 .25

Centenary of Aracaju.

Aviation Symbols A353

1955, Mar. 13 **Photo.** ***Perf. 11½***

819 A353 60c dark gray green .16 .15

Issued to publicize the third National Aviation Congress at Sao Paulo, Mar. 6-13.

Arms of Botucatu A354

1955, Apr. 14

820 A354 60c orange brn .15 .15
821 A354 1.20cr brt green .25 .15

Centenary of Botucatu.

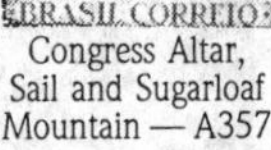

Young Racers at Starting Line — A355

Perf. 11½

1955, Apr. 30 **Photo.** **Unwmk.**

823 A355 60c orange brn .25 .20

5th Children's Games.

Marshal Hermes da Fonseca — A356

Congress Altar, Sail and Sugarloaf Mountain — A357

1955, May 12 **Wmk. 267**

824 A356 60c purple .20 .16

Centenary of the birth of Marshal Hermes da Fonseca.

Engraved; Photogravure (2.70cr)

1955, July 17 **Unwmk.** ***Perf. 11½***

Designs: 2.70cr, St. Pascoal. 4.20cr, Aloisi Benedetto Cardinal Masella.

825 A357 1.40cr green .15 .15
826 A357 2.70cr deep claret .25 .20
827 A357 4.20cr blue .30 .15
Nos. 825-827 (3) .70 .50

36th World Eucharistic Cong. in Rio de Janeiro.

Girl Gymnasts A358

1955, Nov. 12 **Engr.**

Granite Paper

828 A358 60c rose lilac .20 .20

Issued to publicize the 7th Spring Games.

José B. Monteiro Lobato, Author A359

1955, Dec. 8
Granite Paper
829 A359 40c dark green .20 .15

Adolfo Lutz — A360

Lt. Col. Vilagran Cabrita — A361

1955, Dec. 18
Granite Paper
830 A360 60c dk green .20 .15

Centenary of the birth of Adolfo Lutz, public health pioneer.

1955, Dec. 22 Photo. Wmk. 267
831 A361 60c vio bl .20 .15

First Battalion of Engineers, cent.

Salto Grande Hydroelectric Dam — A362

1956, Jan. 15 Unwmk. *Perf. 11½*
Granite Paper
832 A362 60c brick red .20 .15

Arms of Mococa — A363

"G" and Globe — A364

Perf. 11½
1956, Apr. 17 Wmk. 256 Photo.
833 A363 60c brick red .16 .15

Centenary of Mococa, Sao Paulo.

1956, Apr. 14 Unwmk.
Granite Paper
834 A364 1.20cr violet blue .16 .20

18th Intl. Geographic Cong., Rio, Aug. 1956.

Girls' Foot Race — A365

1956, Apr. 28 Photo.
Granite Paper
835 A365 2.50cr brt blue .30 .20

6th Children's Games.

Plane over Map of Brazil — A366

1956, June 12 Wmk. 267 *Perf. 11½*
836 A366 3.30cr brt vio bl .40 .20

National Airmail Service, 25th anniv.

Fireman Rescuing Child — A367

1956, July 2 Wmk. 264
837 A367 2.50cr crimson .40 .25
a. Buff paper 2.25 2.00

Centenary of the Fire Brigade.

Map of Brazil and Open Book — A368

1956, Sept. 8 Wmk. 267
838 A368 2.50cr brt vio bl .30 .20

50th anniversary of the arrival of the Marist Brothers in Northern Brazil.

Church and Monument, Franca — A369

1956, Sept. 7 Engr.
839 A369 2.50cr dk blue .30 .20

Centenary of city of Franca, Sao Paulo.

Woman Hurdler A370

1956, Sept. 22 Photo. Unwmk.
Granite Paper
840 A370 2.50cr dk car .40 .20

Issued to publicize the 8th Spring Games.

Forest and Map of Brazil — A371

1956, Sept. 30 Wmk. 267 *Perf. 11½*
841 A371 2.50cr dk green .25 .20

Issued to publicize education in forestry.

Baron da Bocaina A372

1956, Oct. 8 Engr. Wmk. 268
842 A372 2.50cr reddish brown .25 .20

Centenary of the birth of Baron da Bocaina, who introduced the special delivery mail system to Brazil.

Marbleized Paper

Paper with a distinct wavy-line or marbleized watermark (which Brazilians call *marmorizado* paper) has been found on many stamps of Brazil, 1956-68, including Nos. 843-845, 847, 851-854, 858-858A, 864, 878, 880, 882, 884, 886-887, 896, 909, 918, 920-921, 925-928, 936-939, 949, 955-958, 960, 962-964, 978-979, 983, 985-987, 997-998, 1002-1003, 1005, 1009-1012, 1017, 1024, 1026, 1055, 1075, 1078, 1082, C82, C82a, C83-C87, C96, C99, C109.

Quantities are much less than those of stamps on regular paper.

Panama Stamp Showing Pres. Juscelino Kubitschek — A373

1956, Oct. 12 Photo. Wmk. 267
843 A373 3.30cr green & blk .40 .20

Issued on America Day, Oct. 12, to commemorate the meeting of the Presidents and the Pan-American Conference at Panama City, July 21-22.

Symbolical of Steel Production A374

Perf. 11½
1957, Jan. 31 Wmk. 267 Photo.
844 A374 2.50cr chocolate .25 .15

2nd expansion of the National Steel Company at Volta Redonda.

Joaquim E. Gomes da Silva — A375

1957, Mar. 1 Photo. Unwmk.
Granite Paper
845 A375 2.50cr dk bl grn .25 .15

Centenary of the birth (in 1856) of Joaquim E. Gomes da Silva.

Allan Kardec A376

Perf. 11½
1957, Apr. 18 Wmk. 268 Engr.
846 A376 2.50cr dk brown .25 .15

Issued in honor of Allan Kardec, pen name of Leon Hippolyto Denizard Rivail, and for the centenary of the publication of his "Codification of Spiritism."

Boy Gymnast A377

1957, Apr. 27 Photo. Unwmk.
Granite Paper
847 A377 2.50cr lake .48 .25

7th Children's Games.

Pres. Craveiro Lopes — A378

Stamp of 1932 — A379

1957, June 7 Engr. Wmk. 267
848 A378 6.50cr blue .40 .20

Visit of Gen. Francisco Higino Craveiro Lopes, President of Portugal.

1957, July 9 Photo.
849 A379 2.50cr rose .25 .15

25th anniv. of the movement for a constitution.

St. Antonio Monastery, Pernambuco A380

1957, Aug. 24 Engr. Wmk. 267
850 A380 2.50cr dp magenta .25 .15

300th anniv. of the emancipation of the Franciscan province of St. Antonio in Pernambuco State.

Volleyball A381

Basketball A382

1957, Sept. 28 Photo. *Perf. 11½*
851 A381 2.50cr dull org red .45 .25

Issued for the 9th Spring Games.

1957, Oct. 12
852 A382 3.30cr org & brt grn .45 .25

2nd Women's International Basketball Championship, Rio de Janeiro.

Count of Pinhal and Sao Carlos A383

1957, Nov. 4 Wmk. 267 *Perf. 11½*
853 A383 2.50cr rose .28 .25

Centenary of the city of Sao Carlos and honoring the Count of Pinhal, its founder.

Auguste Comte — A384

1957, Nov. 15
854 A384 2.50cr dk red brn .25 .20

Centenary of the death of Auguste Comte, French mathematician and philosopher.

Radio Station A385

1957, Dec. 10 **Wmk. 268**
855 A385 2.50cr dk green .20 .15

Opening of Sarapui Central Radio Station.

Admiral Tamandare and Warship A386

Design: 3.30cr, Aircraft carrier.

1957-58 **Photo.**
856 A386 2.50cr light blue .25 .20

Engr.
857 A386 3.30cr green ('58) .28 .20

150th anniversary of the birth of Admiral Joaquin Marques de Tamandare, founder of the Brazilian navy.

Coffee Plant and Symbolic "R" — A387

Perf. 11½

1957-58 **Wmk. 267** **Photo.**
858 A387 2.50cr magenta .52 .35

Unwmk.
Granite Paper
858A A387 2.50cr magenta ('58) .45 .35

Centenary (in 1956) of the city of Ribeirao Preto in Sao Paulo state.

Dom John VI — A388

1958, Jan. 28 **Engr.** **Wmk. 268**
859 A388 2.50cr magenta .35 .25

150th anniversary of the opening of the ports of Brazil to foreign trade.

Bugler A389

1958, Mar. 18 **Wmk. 267**
860 A389 2.50cr red .35 .25

Brazilian Marine Corps, 150th anniv.

Station at Rio and Locomotive of 1858 — A390

Court House — A391

Perf. 11½

1958, Mar. 29 **Wmk. 267** **Photo.**
861 A390 2.50cr red brn .35 .25

Central Railroad of Brazil, cent.

1958, Apr. 1 **Engr.** **Wmk. 256**
862 A391 2.50cr green .25 .15

150th anniv. of the Military Superior Court.

Emblem and Brazilian Pavilion A392

1958, Apr. 17 **Wmk. 267**
863 A392 2.50cr dk blue .25 .25

World's Fair, Brussels, Apr. 17-Oct. 19.

High Jump — A393

1958, Apr. 20 **Photo.** **Unwmk.**
Granite Paper
864 A393 2.50cr crimson rose .25 .15

8th Children's Games.

Marshal Mariano da Silva Rondon A394

1958, Apr. 19 **Engr.** **Wmk. 267**
865 A394 2.50cr magenta .25 .15

Issued to honor Marshal Mariano da Silva Rondon and the "Day of the Indian."

Hydroelectric Station A395

1958, Apr. 28 **Wmk. 267** ***Perf. 11½***
866 A395 2.50cr magenta .25 .15

Opening of Sao Paulo State power plant.

National Printing Plant — A396

1958, May 22 **Photo.**
867 A396 2.50cr redsh brn .20 .15

150th anniversary of the founding of the National Printing Plant.

Marshal Osorio — A397

1958, May 24
868 A397 2.50cr brt violet .20 .15

150th anniversary of the birth of Marshal Manoel Luiz Osorio.

Pres. Ramon Villeda Morales — A398

Fountain — A399

1958, June 7 **Engr.** ***Perf. 11½***
869 A398 6.50cr dk green 1.25 .75
a. Wmk. 268 5.00 2.00

Visit of Pres. Ramon Villeda Morales of Honduras.

1958, June 13
870 A399 2.50cr dk green .25 .15

Botanical Garden, Rio de Janeiro, 150th anniv.

Symbols of Agriculture A400

Prophet Joel A401

1958, June 18 **Photo.**
871 A400 2.50cr rose carmine .25 .15

50th anniv. of Japanese immigration to Brazil.

1958, June 21 **Engr.**
872 A401 2.50cr dk blue .25 .15

Bicentenary of the Cathedral of Bom Jesus at Matosinhos.

Stylized Globe — A402

1958, July 10 **Photo.**
873 A402 2.50cr dk brown .20 .15

Issued to publicize the International Investment Conference, Belo Horizonte.

Julio Bueno Brandao — A403

1958, Aug. 1 **Wmk. 268** ***Perf. 11½***
874 A403 2.50cr red brown .25 .15

Centenary of the birth of Julio Bueno Brandao, President of Minas Gerais.

Palacio Tiradentes (House of Congress) A404

1958, July 24 **Engr.**
875 A404 2.50cr sepia .25 .15

47th Interparliamentary Conference, Rio de Janeiro, July 24-Aug. 1.

Presidential Palace, Brasilia A405

1958, Aug. 8 **Photo.** **Wmk. 267**
876 A405 2.50cr ultra .20 .15

Issued to publicize the construction of Brazil's new capital, Brasilia.

Freighters A406

1958, Aug. 22
877 A406 2.50cr blue .25 .15

Brazilian merchant marine.

Joaquim Caetano da Silva — A407

1958, Sept. 2 **Unwmk.**
Granite Paper
878 A407 2.50cr redsh brn .25 .15

Issued in honor of Joaquim Caetano da Silva, scientist and historian.

Giovanni Gronchi — A408

Archers — A409

1958, Sept. 4 **Engr.** **Wmk. 268**
879 A408 7cr dk blue .50 .15

Visit of Italy's President Giovanni Gronchi to Brazil.

Perf. 11½

1958, Sept. 21 **Photo.** **Unwmk.**
Granite Paper
880 A409 2.50cr red org .35 .20

Issued to publicize the 10th Spring Games.

Elderly Couple — A410

Machado de Assis — A411

1958, Sept. 27 **Wmk. 267**
881 A410 2.50cr magenta .25 .15

Day of the Old People, Sept. 27.

1958, Sept. 28 **Unwmk.**
882 A411 2.50cr red brn .25 .15

50th anniversary of the death of Joaquim Maria Machado de Assis, writer.

Pres. Vargas and Oil Derrick A412

1958, Oct. 6 **Wmk. 268**
883 A412 2.50cr blue .25 .15

5th anniv. of Pres. Getulio D. Vargas' oil law.

Globe — A413

Gen. Lauro Sodré — A414

Perf. 11½

1958, Nov. 14 **Photo.** **Wmk. 267**
884 A413 2.50cr blue .30 .15

7th Inter-American Congress of Municipalities.

1958, Nov. 15 **Engr.**
885 A414 3.30cr green .25 .15

Cent. of the birth of Gen. Lauro Sodré.

UN Emblem — A415

Soccer Player — A416

1958, Dec. 26 **Photo.** ***Perf. 11½***
886 A415 2.50cr brt blue .20 .15

10th anniv. of the signing of the Universal Declaration of Human Rights.

1959, Jan. 20
887 A416 3.30cr emer & red brn .40 .20

World Soccer Championships of 1958.

Railroad Track and Map A417

Pres. Sukarno of Indonesia A418

1959, Apr. **Wmk. 267** ***Perf. 11½***
888 A417 2.50cr dp orange .25 .20

Centenary of the linking of Patos and Campina Grande by railroad.

1959, May 20
889 A418 2.50cr blue .25 .15

Visit of President Sukarno of Indonesia.

Dom John VI — A419

Boy Polo Players — A420

Perf. 10½x11½

1959, June 12 **Wmk. 267**
890 A419 2.50cr crimson .25 .15

1959, June 13 ***Perf. 11½***
891 A420 2.50cr orange brn .25 .15

9th Children's Games.

Loading Freighter A421

Organ and Emblem A422

1959, July 10
892 A421 2.50cr dk green .25 .15

Issued to honor the merchant marine.

1959, July 16 **Photo.**
893 A422 3.30cr magenta .25 .15

Bicentenary of the Carmelite Order in Brazil.

Joachim Silverio de Souza — A423

Symbolic Road — A424

1959, July 20 ***Perf. 11½***
894 A423 2.50cr red brown .25 .15

Birth centenary of Joachim Silverio de Souza, first bishop of Diamantina, Minas Gerais.

1959, Sept. 27 **Wmk. 267**
895 A424 3.30cr bl grn & ultra .25 .15

11th International Roadbuilding Congress.

Woman Athlete — A425

1959, Oct. 4
896 A425 2.50cr lilac rose .25 .15

11th Spring Games.

Map of Parana A426

1959, Sept. 27
897 A426 2.50cr dk green .25 .15

Founding of Londrina, Parana, 25th anniv.

Globe and Snipes A427

Cross of Lusitania A428

1959, Oct. 22 ***Perf. 11½***
898 A427 6.50cr dull grn .20 .15

World Championship of Snipe Class Sailboats, Porto Alegre, won by Brazilian yachtsmen.

1959, Oct. 24 **Engr.**
899 A428 6.50cr dull blue .20 .15

4th Intl. Conf. on Brazilian-Portuguese Studies, University of Bahia, Aug. 10-20.

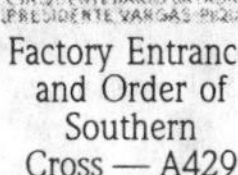

Factory Entrance and Order of Southern Cross — A429

Corcovado Christ, Globe and Southern Cross — A430

1959, Nov. 19 **Photo.**
900 A429 3.30cr orange red .20 .15

Pres. Vargas Gunpowder Factory, 50th anniv.

1959, Nov. 26 ***Perf. 11½***
901 A430 2.50cr blue .20 .15

Universal Thanksgiving Day.

Burning Bush — A431

1959, Dec. 24 **Wmk. 267**
902 A431 3.30cr lt grn .20 .15

Centenary of Presbyterian work in Brazil.

Piraja da Silva and Schistosoma Mansoni A432

1959, Dec. 28
903 A432 2.50cr rose violet .20 .15

25th anniv. of the discovery and identification of schistosoma mansoni, a parasite of the fluke family, by Dr. Piraja da Silva.

Luiz de Matos — A433

1960, Jan. 3 **Photo.**
904 A433 3.30cr red brown .16 .15

Birth centenary of Luiz de Matos.

Zamenhof A434

Adél Pinto A435

1960, Mar. 10 **Wmk. 267** ***Perf. 11½***
905 A434 6.50cr emerald .20 .15

Lazarus Ludwig Zamenhof (1859-1917), Polish oculist who invented Esperanto in 1887.

1960, Mar. 19 **Engr.** **Wmk. 268**
906 A435 11.50cr rose red .20 .15

Centenary of the birth of Adél Pinto, civil engineer and railroad expert.

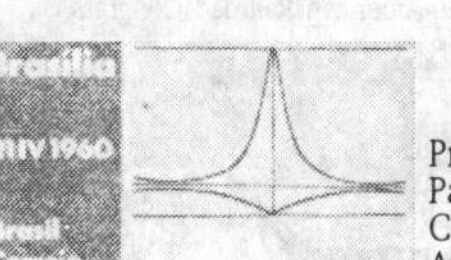

Presidential Palace, Colonnade A436

Design: 27cr, Plan of Brasilia (like #C98).

Perf. 11x11½

1960 **Photo.** **Wmk. 267**
907 A436 2.50cr brt green .22 .15
908 A436 27cr salmon .60 .60
Nos. 907-908,C95-C98 (6) 2.02 1.35

No. 907 issued Apr. 21 to commemorate the inauguration of Brazil's new capital, Brasilia, Apr. 21, 1960.

No. 908 issued Sept. 12 to commemorate the birthday of Pres. Juscelino Kubitschek. It measures 105x46½mm, carrying at center a 27cr in design of No. C98, flanked by the chief design features of Nos. 907, C95-C97, with Kubitschek signature below. Issued in sheets of 4 with wide horizontal gutter.

Grain, Coffee, Cotton and Cacao — A437

Paulo de Frontin — A438

Perf. 11½x11

1960, July 28 **Wmk. 267**
909 A437 2.50cr brown .20 .15

Centenary of Ministry of Agriculture.

1960, Oct. 12 **Wmk. 268**
910 A438 2.50cr orange red .20 .15

Cent. of the birth of Paulo de Frontin, engineer.

Woman Athlete Holding Torch — A439

1960, Oct. 18 ***Perf. 11½x11***
911 A439 2.50cr blue grn .20 .15

12th Spring Games.

Volleyball and Net A440

Locomotive Wheels A441

Perf. 11½x11

1960, Nov. 12 **Wmk. 268**
912 A440 11cr blue .20 .15

International Volleyball Championships.

1960, Oct. 15 ***Perf. 11½x11***
913 A441 2.50cr ultra .20 .15

10th Pan-American Railroad Congress.

Symbols of Flight A442

1960, Dec. 16 **Photo.** ***Perf. 11½***
914 A442 2.50cr brn & yel .16 .15

Intl. Fair of Industry and Commerce, Rio.

Emperor Haile Selassie — A443

1961, Jan. 31 ***Perf. 11½x11***
915 A443 2.50cr dk brown .16 .15

Visit of Emperor Haile Selassie of Ethiopia to Brazil, Dec. 1960.

Map of Brazil, Open Book and Sacred Heart Emblem A444

Perf. 11x11½

1961, Mar. 13 **Wmk. 268**
916 A444 2.50cr blue .20 .15

50th anniv. of the operation in Brazil of the Order of the Blessed Heart of Mary.

Map of Guanabara A445

1961, Mar. 27 **Wmk. 267**
917 A445 7.50cr org brn .20 .15

Promulgation of the constitution of the state of Guanabara.

Arms of Agulhas Negras A446

Brazil and Senegal Linked on Map A447

Design: 3.30cr, Dress helmet and sword.

Perf. 11½x11

1961, Apr. 23 **Wmk. 267**
918 A446 2.50cr green .20 .15
919 A446 3.30cr rose car .15 .15

Sesquicentennial of the Agulhas Negras Military Academy.

1961, Apr. 28 **Photo.**
920 A447 27cr ultra .25 .20

Issued to commemorate the visit of Afonso Arinos, Brazilian foreign minister, to Senegal to attend its independence ceremonies.

View of Ouro Preto, 1711 A448

1961, June 6 ***Perf. 11x11½***
921 A448 1cr orange .20 .20

250th anniversary of Ouro Preto.

War Arsenal A449

1961, June 20 **Wmk. 256**
924 A449 5cr dk red brn .25 .15

150th anniv. of the War Arsenal, Rio de Janeiro.

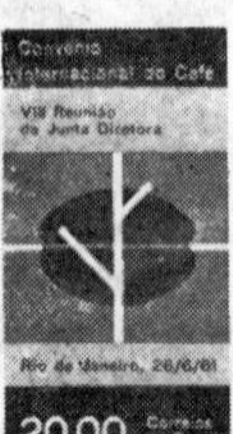

Coffee Bean and Branch A450

Rabindranath Tagore A451

Perf. 11½x11

1961, June 26 **Wmk. 267**
925 A450 20cr redsh brn .80 .25

8th Directorial Committee meeting of the Intl. Coffee Convention, Rio, June 26.

1961, July 28 **Photo.** **Wmk. 267**
926 A451 10cr rose car .20 .15

Rabindranath Tagore, Indian poet, birth cent.

Stamp of 1861 and Map of English Channel A452

Design: 20cr, 430r stamp of 1861 and map of Netherlands.

1961, Aug. 1 ***Perf. 11x11½***
927 A452 10cr rose .75 .20
928 A452 20cr salmon pink 2.00 .30

Centenary of 1861 stamp issue.

Portrait Type of 1954-60
Designs as Before

1961 **Wmk. 268** ***Perf. 11x11½***
930 A336 1cr brown .80 .50
931 A336 2cr dk bl grn 1.25 .50
932 A336 5cr red lilac 3.75 .30
933 A336 10cr emerald 7.25 .30
Nos. 930-933 (4) 13.05 1.60

1cr, 5cr and 10cr have patterned background.

Sun, Clouds, Rain and Weather Symbols — A453

Dedo de Deus Peak — A454

1962, Mar. 23 ***Perf. 11½x11***
936 A453 10cr red brown .75 .30

World Meteorological Day, Mar. 23.

1962, Apr. 14 **Photo.** **Wmk. 267**
937 A454 8cr emerald .20 .25

50th anniversary of the climbing of Dedo de Deus (Finger of God) peak.

Dr. Gaspar Vianna and Leishmania Protozoa A455

1962, Apr. 24 ***Perf. 11x11½***
938 A455 8cr blue .25 .15

Discovery by Gaspar Oliveiro Vianna (1885-1914) of a cure for leishmaniasis, 50th anniv.

Henrique Dias A456

1962, June 18 **Wmk. 267**
939 A456 10cr dk vio brn .32 .15

300th anniversary of the death of Henrique Dias, Negro military leader who fought against the Dutch and Spaniards.

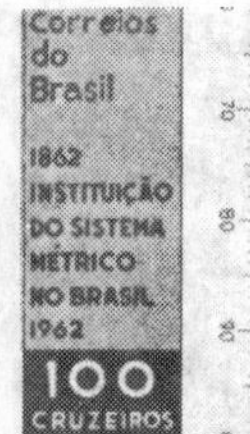

Millimeter Gauge — A457

Sailboats, Snipe Class — A458

1962, June 26 ***Perf. 11½x11***
940 A457 100cr car rose .35 .20

Centenary of the introduction of the metric system in Brazil.

1962, July 21 **Photo.** **Wmk. 267**
941 A458 8cr Prus grn .20 .15

Issued to commemorate the 13th Brazilian championships for Snipe Class sailing.

Julio Mesquita A459

1962, Aug. 18 ***Perf. 11x11½***
942 A459 8cr dull brown .20 .15

Centenary of the birth of Julio Mesquita, journalist and founder of Sao Paulo.

Empress Leopoldina — A460

1962, Sept. 7 ***Perf. 11½x11***
943 A460 8cr rose claret .20 .15

140th anniversary of independence.

Buildings, Brasilia A461

Perf. 11x11½

1962, Oct. 24 **Wmk. 267**
944 A461 10cr orange .30 .15

51st Interparliamentary Conf., Brasilia.

Pouring Ladle — A462

1962, Oct. 26 ***Perf. 11½x11***
945 A462 8cr orange .20 .15

Inauguration of the Usiminas State Iron and Steel Foundry at Belo Horizonte, Minas Gerais.

UPAE Emblem A463

1962, Nov. 19 *Perf. 11x11½*
946 A463 8cr bright magenta .20 .15

Founding of the Postal Union of the Americas and Spain, UPAE, 50th anniv.

Chimney and Cogwheel Forming "10" — A464

1962, Nov. 26 *Perf. 11½x11*
947 A464 10cr lt blue grn .20 .15

Natl. Economic and Development Bank, 10th anniv.

Quintino Bocaiuva A465

Soccer Player and Globe A466

Perf. 11½x11

1962, Dec. 27 Photo. Wmk. 267
948 A465 8cr brown org .20 .15

Bocaiuva, journalist, 50th death anniv.

1963, Jan. 14
949 A466 10cr blue grn .40 .15

World Soccer Championship of 1962.

Carrier Pigeon A467

1963, Jan. Unwmk. Litho. *Perf. 14*
950 A467 8cr yel, dk bl, red & grn .20 .15

Souvenir Sheet

Imperf

951 A467 100cr yel, dk bl, red & grn 1.25 *3.00*

300 years of Brazilian postal service. Issue dates: 8cr, Jan. 25; 100cr, Jan. 31.

Severino Neiva — A468

Perf. 10½x11½

1963, Jan. 31 Photo. Wmk. 267
952 A468 8cr brt vio .20 .15

Radar Tracking Station and Rockets — A469

"Cross of Unity" — A470

Perf. 11½x11

1963, Mar. 15 Wmk. 268
953 A469 21cr lt ultra .20 .15

Issued to publicize the International Aeronautics and Space Exhibition, Sao Paulo.

1963 Wmk. 267 *Perf. 11½x11*
954 A470 8cr red lilac .20 .15

Vatican II, the 21st Ecumenical Council of the Roman Catholic Church.

"ABC" in Geometric Form — A471

Basketball Player — A472

1963, Apr. 22 Photo. Wmk. 267
955 A471 8cr brt bl & lt bl .16 .15

Education Week, Apr. 22-27, 3-year alphabetization program.

1963, May 15
956 A472 8cr dp lilac rose .20 .15

4th International Basketball Championships, Rio de Janeiro, May 10-25, 1963.

Games Emblem A473

"OEA" and Map of the Americas A474

1963, May 22 *Perf. 11½x11*
957 A473 10cr car rose .30 .15

4th Pan American Games, Sao Paulo.

1963, June 6
958 A474 10cr org & dp org .30 .15

15th anniversary of the charter of the Organization of American States.

José Bonifacio de Andrada — A475

1963, June 13
959 A475 8cr dk brown .15 .15

Bicentenary of the birth of José Bonifacio de Andrada de Silva, statesman.

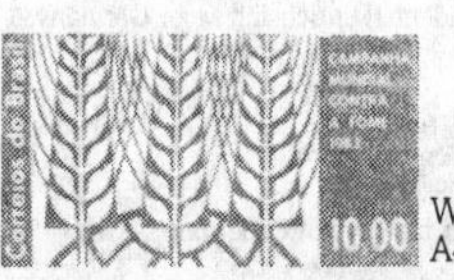
Wheat A476

Perf. 11x11½

1963, June 19 Photo. Wmk. 267
960 A476 10cr blue .30 .15

FAO "Freedom from Hunger" campaign.

Centenary Emblem A477

Joao Caetano A478

1963, Aug. 19 *Perf. 11½x11*
961 A477 8cr yel org & red .25 .15

Centenary of International Red Cross.

1963, Aug. 24 *Perf. 11½x11*
962 A478 8cr slate .20 .15

Death centenary of Joao Caetano, actor.

Symbols of Agriculture, Industry and Atomic Energy A479

Hammer Thrower A480

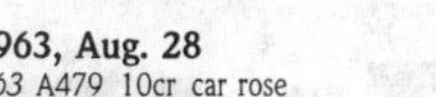

1963, Aug. 28
963 A479 10cr car rose .25 .15

Atomic Development Law, 1st anniv.

1963, Sept. 13
964 A480 10cr gray .42 .15

Intl. College Students' Games, Porto Alegre.

Marshal Tito — A481

Compass Rose, Map of Brazil and View of Rio — A482

1963, Sept. 19
965 A481 80cr sepia .35 .30

Visit of Marshal Tito of Yugoslavia.

1963, Sept. 20
966 A482 8cr lt blue grn .16 .15

8th International Leprology Congress.

Oil Derrick and Storage Tank A483

1963, Oct. 3 *Perf. 11x11½*
967 A483 8cr dk slate grn .16 .15

10th anniv. of Petrobras, the natl. oil company.

"Spring Games" A484

1963, Nov. 5 Photo. Wmk. 267
968 A484 8cr yel & org .20 .20

1963 Spring Games.

Dr. Borges de Medeiros (1863-1962), Governor of Rio Grande do Sul — A485

1963, Nov. 29 *Perf. 11½x11*
969 A485 8cr red brown .16 .15

Sao Joao del Rei — A486

1963, Dec. 8 *Perf. 11x11½*
970 A486 8cr violet blue .16 .15

250th anniversary of Sao Joao del Rei.

Dr. Alvaro Alvim A487

1963, Dec. 19
971 A487 8cr dk gray .16 .15

Alvaro Alvim (1863-1928), X-ray specialist and martyr of science.

Viscount de Mauá A488

Mandacaru Cactus and Emblem A489

1963, Dec. 28 *Perf. 11½x11*
972 A488 8cr rose car .16 .15

Sesquicentennial of the birth of Viscount de Mauá, founder of first Brazilian railroad.

1964, Jan. 23 Photo. Wmk. 267
973 A489 8cr dull green .16 .15

Bank of Northeast Brazil, 10th anniv.

Coelho Netto — A490

Lauro Müller — A491

1964, Feb. 21 *Perf. 11½x11*
974 A490 8cr brt violet .16 .15

Birth centenary of Coelho Netto, writer.

1964, Mar. 8 Wmk. 267
975 A491 8cr dp orange .16 .15

Lauro Siverino Müller, politician and member of the Brazilian Academy of Letters, birth cent.

Child Holding Spoon A492

1964, Mar. 25 *Perf. 11x11½*
976 A492 8cr yel brn & yel .16 .15

Issued for "School Meals Week."

Chalice Rock — A493

Allan Kardec — A494

1964, Apr. 9 Engr. *Perf. 11½x11*
977 A493 80cr red orange .20 .15

Issued for tourist publicity.

1964, Apr. 18 Photo.
978 A494 30cr slate green .45 .15

Cent. of "O Evangelho" (Gospel) of the codification of Spiritism.

Heinrich Lübke — A495

Pope John XXIII — A496

Perf. 11½x11

1964, May 8 Photo. Wmk. 267
979 A495 100cr red brown .60 .18

Visit of President Heinrich Lübke of Germany.

1964, June 29 Wmk. 267
980 A496 20cr dk car rose .20 .18
a. Unwmkd. .20 .18

Issued in memory of Pope John XXIII.

Pres. Senghor of Senegal — A497

1964, Sept. 19 Wmk. 267
981 A497 20cr dk brown .25 .15

Visit of Leopold Sedar Senghor, President of Senegal.

Botafogo Bay and Sugarloaf Mountain A498

Designs: 100cr, Church of Our Lady of the Rock, vert. 200cr, Copacabana beach.

Perf. 11x11½, 11½x11

1964-65 Photo.

983	A498	15cr org & bl	.30	.22
984	A498	100cr brt grn & red brn, *yel*	.18	.16
985	A498	200cr black & red	1.75	.30
a.		Souvenir sheet of 3 ('65)	4.75	4.00
		Nos. 983-985 (3)	2.23	.68

4th cent. of Rio de Janeiro.

No. 985a contains three imperf. stamps similar to Nos. 983-985, but printed in brown. Sold for 320cr. Issued Dec. 30, 1965.

A souvenir card containing one lithographed facsimile of No. 984, imperf., exists, but has no franking value. Size: 100x125mm. Sold by P.O. for 250cr.

Pres. Charles de Gaulle A499

Pres. John F. Kennedy A500

1964, Oct. 13 *Perf. 11½x11*
986 A499 100cr orange brn .35 .15

Visit of Charles de Gaulle, President of France, Oct. 13-15.

1964, Oct. 24 Photo. Wmk. 267
987 A500 100cr slate .20 .15

"Prophet" by A. F. Lisbao — A501

1964, Nov. 18 *Perf. 11½x11*
988 A501 10cr slate .16 .15

150th death anniv. of the sculptor Antonio Francisco Lisbao, "O Aleijadinho" (The Cripple).

Antonio Goncalves Dias — A502

Designs: 30cr, Euclides da Cunha. 50cr, Prof. Angelo Moreira da Costa Lima. 200cr, Tiradentes. 500cr, Dom Pedro I. 1000cr, Dom Pedro II.

1965-66 Wmk. 267 *Perf. 11x11½*

989	A502	30cr brt bluish grn ('66)	2.00	.25
989A	A502	50cr dull brn ('66)	1.50	.15
990	A502	100cr blue	.60	.15
991	A502	200cr brown org	2.00	.15
992	A502	500cr red brown	6.00	.50
992A	A502	1000cr sl bl ('66)	10.00	.50
		Nos. 989-992A (6)	22.10	1.70

Statue of St. Sebastian, Guanataro Bay — A503

The Arches A504

Design: 35cr, Estacio de Sa (1520-67), founder of Rio de Janeiro.

1965 Photo. *Perf. 11½*
Size: 24x37mm
993 A503 30cr bl & rose red .30 .15

Lithographed and Engraved
Perf. 11x11½
994 A504 30cr lt bl & blk .30 .15

Photo. *Perf. 11½*
Size: 21x39mm

995	A503	35cr blk & org	.18	.25
a.		Souvenir sheet of 3	3.25	4.00
		Nos. 993-995 (3)	.78	.55

4th cent. of Rio de Janeiro. Issue dates: No. 993, Mar. 5. No. 994, Nov. 30. No. 995, July 28. No. 995a, Dec. 30.

No. 995a contains three imperf. stamps similar to Nos. 993-995, but printed in deep orange. Size: 130x79mm. Sold for 100cr.

Sword and Cross — A505

1965, Apr. 15 Wmk. 267 *Perf. 11½*
996 A505 120cr gray .30 .15

1st anniv. of the democratic revolution.

Vital Brazil — A506

Shah of Iran — A507

1965, Apr. 28 Wmk. 267 *Perf. 11½*
997 A506 120cr dp orange .30 .15

Centenary of birth of Vital Brazil, M.D.

A souvenir card containing one impression similar to No. 997, imperf., exists, printed in dull plum. Sold by P.O. for 250cr. Size: 114x180mm.

1965, May 5 Photo.
998 A507 120cr rose claret .25 .15

Issued to commemorate the visit of Shah Mohammed Riza Pahlavi of Iran.

Marshal Mariano da Silva Rondon A508

Lions' Emblem A509

1965, May 7 Engr.
999 A508 30cr claret .25 .15

Marshal Mariano da Silva Rondon (1865-1958), explorer and expert on Indians.

1965, May 14 Photo.
1000 A509 35cr pale vio & blk .20 .15

12th convention of the Lions Clubs of Brazil, Rio de Janeiro, May 11-16.

ITU Emblem, Old and New Communication Equipment — A510

1965, May 21 *Perf. 11½*
1001 A510 120cr yellow & grn .30 .20

Centenary of the ITU.

Epitácio Pessoa — A511

Statue of Admiral Barroso — A512

1965, May 23 Photo.
1002 A511 35cr blue gray .20 .15

Epitácio da Silva Pessoa (1865-1942), jurist, president of Brazil, 1919-22.

1965, June 11
1003 A512 30cr blue .25 .15

Cent. of the naval battle of Riachuelo.

A souvenir card containing one lithographed facsimile of No. 1003, imperf., exists. Size: 100x139½mm.

José de Alencar and Indian Princess — A513

1965, June 24 *Perf. 11½x11*
1004 A513 30cr deep plum .25 .15

Centenary of the publication of "Iracema" by Joséde Alencar.

A souvenir card containing one lithographed facsimile of No. 1004, printed in rose red and imperf., exists. Size: 100x141½mm.

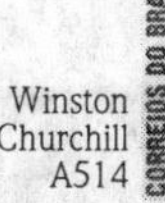

Winston Churchill A514

1965, June 25 *Perf. 11x11½*
1005 A514 200cr slate .50 .25

Scout Jamboree Emblem — A515

1965, July 17 **Photo.**
1006 A515 30cr dull bl grn .30 .15

1st Pan-American Boy Scout Jamboree, Fundao Island, Rio de Janeiro, July 15-25.

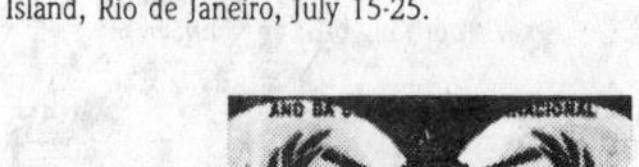

ICY Emblem A516

1965, Aug. 25 Wmk. 267 *Perf. 11½*
1007 A516 120cr dl bl & blk .25 .15

International Cooperation Year, 1965.

Leoncio Correias A517

Emblem A518

1965, Sept. 1 *Perf. 11½x11*
1008 A517 35cr slate grn .25 .15

Leoncio Correias, poet, birth cent.

1965, Sept. 4
1009 A518 30cr brt rose .20 .15

Issued to publicize the Eighth Biennial Fine Arts Exhibition, Sao Paulo, Nov.-Dec., 1965.

Pres. Saragat of Italy — A519

1965, Sept. 11 Photo. Wmk. 267
1010 A519 100cr slate grn, *pink* .25 .15

Visit of Pres. Giuseppe Saragat of Italy.

Grand Duke and Duchess of Luxembourg — A520

1965, Sept. 17 *Perf. 11x11½*
1011 A520 100cr brn olive .25 .15

Visit of Grand Duke Jean and Grand Duchess Josephine Charlotte of Luxembourg.

Biplane — A521

1965, Oct. 8 Photo. *Perf. 11½x11*
1012 A521 35cr ultra .20 .15

3rd Aviation Week Philatelic Exhibition, Rio.

A souvenir card carries one impression of this 35cr, imperf. Size: 102x140mm. Sold for 100cr.

Flags of OAS Members A522

1965, Nov. 17 *Perf. 11x11½*
1013 A522 100cr brt bl & blk .25 .20

2nd meeting of OAS Foreign Ministers, Rio.

King Baudouin and Queen Fabiola of Belgium A523

1965, Nov. 18
1014 A523 100cr gray .25 .20

Visit of King and Queen of Belgium.

"Coffee Beans" — A524

Perf. 11½x11
1965, Dec. 21 Photo. Wmk. 267
1015 A524 30cr brown .30 .15

Brazilian coffee publicity.

Conveyor and Loading Crane A525

1966, Apr. 1 *Perf. 11x11½*
1016 A525 110cr tan & dk sl grn .25 .20

Opening of the new terminal of the Rio Doce Iron Ore Company at Tubarao.

Pouring Ladle and Steel Beam — A526

Prof. de Rocha Dissecting Cadaver — A527

Perf. 11½x11
1966, Apr. 16 Photo. Wmk. 267
1017 A526 30cr blk, *dp org* .25 .15

25th anniv. of the National Steel Company (nationalization of the steel industry).

1966, Apr. 26
1018 A527 30cr brt bluish grn .40 .15

50th anniv. of the discovery and description of Rickettsia prowazeki, the cause of typhus fever, by Prof. Henrique de Rocha Lima.

Battle of Tuiuti A528

Perf. 11x11½
1966, May 24 Photo. Wmk. 267
1019 A528 30cr gray grn .30 .15

Centenary of the Battle of Tuiuti.

Symbolic Water Cycle — A529

Pres. Shazar of Israel — A530

1966, July 1 *Perf. 11½x11*
1020 A529 100cr lt brn & bl .25 .20

Hydrological Decade (UNESCO), 1965-74.

1966, July 18 Photo. Wmk. 267
1021 A530 100cr ultra .30 .20

Visit of Pres. Zalman Shazar of Israel.

Imperial Academy of Fine Arts A531

Perf. 11x11½
1966, Aug. 12 Engr. Wmk. 267
1022 A531 100cr red brown .60 .20

150th anniversary of French art mission.

Military Service Emblem A532

1966, Sept. 6 Photo. *Perf. 11x11½*
1023 A532 30cr yel, ultra & grn .25 .15
a. With commemorative border 3.50 3.00

New Military Service Law.

No. 1023a issued in sheets of 4. It carries at left a 30cr, design A532, in deeper tones of yellow and ultramarine, Wmk. 264. Without gum. Sold for 100cr.

Ruben Dario — A533

Perf. 11½x11
1966, Sept. 20 Photo. Wmk. 267
1024 A533 100cr brt rose lilac .25 .15

Ruben Dario (pen name of Felix Ruben Garcia Sarmiento (1867-1916), Nicaraguan poet, newspaper correspondent and diplomat.

Ceramic Candlestick from Santarém A534

1966, Oct. 6 *Perf. 11x11½*
1025 A534 30cr dk brn, *sal* .25 .15

Centenary of Goeldi Museum at Belem.

Arms of Santa Cruz — A535

Perf. 11½x11
1966, Oct. 15 Photo. Wmk. 267
1026 A535 30cr slate grn .25 .15

1st Natl. Tobacco Exposition, Santa Cruz.

UNESCO Emblem — A536

1966, Oct. 24 Engr. *Perf. 11½*
1027 A536 120cr black .75 .25
a. With commemorative border 6.00 6.00

20th anniv. of UNESCO. No. 1027a issued in sheets of 4. It carries at right a design similar to No. 1027. Unwatermarked granite paper, without gum. Sold for 150cr.

Captain Antonio Correia Pinto and Map of Lages — A537

Cross of Lusitania and Southern Cross — A538

Perf. 11½x11

1966, Nov. 22 Photo. Wmk. 267

1028 A537 30cr salmon pink .25 .15

Arrival of Capt. Antonio Correia Pinto, cent.

1966, Dec. 4 *Perf. 11½*

1029 A538 100cr blue green .30 .15

LUBRAPEX 1966 philatelic exhibition at the National Museum of Fine Arts, Rio.

Madonna and Child — A539

A540

Perf. 11½x11

1966, Dec. Photo. Wmk. 267

1030 A539 30cr blue green .25 .15

Perf. 11½

1031 A540 35cr salmon & ultra .20 .20
a. 150cr salmon & ultra 2.50 3.00

Christmas 1966.

No. 1031a measures 46x103mm and is printed in sheets of 4. It is inscribed "Pax Hominibus" (but not "Brasil Correio") and carries the Madonna shown on No. 1031. Issued without gum.

Issued: 30cr, Dec. 8; 35cr, Dec. 22; 150cr, Dec. 28.

Arms of Laguna A541

1967, Jan. 4 Engr. *Perf. 11x11½*

1032 A541 60cr sepia .20 .15

Centenary of the Post and Telegraph Agency of Laguna, Santa Catarina.

Railroad Bridge A542

1967, Feb. 16 Photo. Wmk. 267

1033 A542 50cr deep orange .45 .20

Centenary of the Santos-Jundiai railroad.

Black Madonna of Czestochowa, Polish Eagle and Cross — A543

1967, Mar. 12 *Perf. 11x11½*

1034 A543 50cr yel, bl & rose red .35 .20

Adoption of Christianity in Poland, 1,000th anniv.

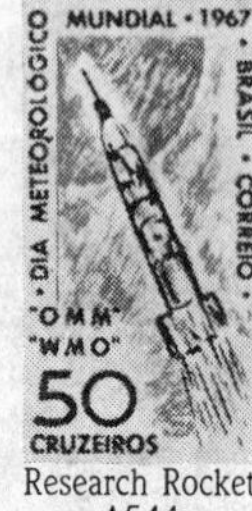

Research Rocket A544

Anita Garibaldi A545

1967, Mar. 23 *Perf. 11½x11*

1035 A544 50cr blk & brt bl .60 .30

World Meteorological Day, March 23.

Perf. 11x11½

1967-69 Photo. Wmk. 267

Portraits: 1c, Mother Joana Angelica. 2c, Marilia de Dirceu. 3c, Dr. Rita Lobato. 6c, Ana Neri. 10c, Darcy Vargas.

1036 A545 1c dp ultra .15 .15
1037 A545 2c red brn .15 .15
1038 A545 3c brt grn .18 .15
1039 A545 5c black .35 .15
1040 A545 6c brown .35 .15
1041 A545 10c dk slate grn ('69) 1.10 .30
Nos. 1036-1041 (6) 2.28
Set value .64

Issued: 1c, May 3; 2c, Aug. 14; 3c, June 7; 5c, Apr. 14; 6c, May 14, 1967; 10c, June 18, 1969.

VARIG Airlines A546

Madonna and Child, by Robert Feruzzi A548

Lions Emblem and Globes A547

1967, May 8 *Perf. 11½x11*

1046 A546 6c brt bl & blk .30 .25

40th anniversary of VARIG Airlines.

1967, May 9 Engr. *Perf. 11x11½*

1047 A547 6c green .30 .25
a. Souvenir sheet 2.50 3.00

50th anniv. of Lions Intl. No. 1047a contains one imperf. stamp similar to No. 1047. Sold for 15c.

1967, May 14 Photo. *Perf. 11½x11*

1048 A548 5c violet .25 .20
a. 15c Souvenir sheet 2.25 2.25

Mother's Day. No. 1048a contains one 15c imperf. stamp in design of No. 1048.

Prince Akihito and Princess Michiko A549

1967, May 25 *Perf. 11x11½*

1049 A549 10c black & pink .30 .20

Visit to Brazil of Crown Prince Akihito and Princess Michiko of Japan.

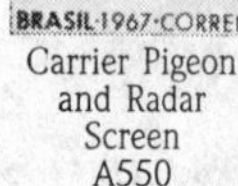

Carrier Pigeon and Radar Screen A550

Brother Vicente do Salvador A551

Perf. 11½x11

1967, June 20 Photo. Wmk. 267

1050 A550 10c sl & brt pink .25 .20

Issued to commemorate the opening of the Communications Ministry in Brasília.

1967, June 28 Engr.

1051 A551 5c brown .25 .20

400th birth anniv. of Brother Vicente do Salvador (1564-1636), founder of Franciscan convent in Rio de Janeiro, and historian.

Boy, Girl and 4-S Emblem A552

1967, July 12 Photo. *Perf. 11½*

1052 A552 5c green & blk .25 .20

National 4-S (4-H) Day.

Möbius Strip A553

1967, July 21 *Perf. 11x11½*

1053 A553 5c brt bl & blk .25 .20

6th Brazilian Mathematical Congress.

Fish — A554

1967, Aug. 1 *Perf. 11½*

1054 A554 5c slate .30 .20

Bicentenary of city of Piracicaba.

Golden Rose and Papal Arms — A555

1967, Aug. 15

1055 A555 20c mag & yel 1.00 .40

Offering of a golden rose by Pope Paul VI to the Virgin Mary of Fatima (Our Lady of Peace), Patroness of Brazil.

General Sampaio A556

King Olaf of Norway A557

1967, Aug. 25 Engr. *Perf. 11½x11*

1056 A556 5c blue .25 .20

Issued to honor General Antonio de Sampaio, hero of the Battle of Tutui.

1967, Sept. 8 Photo.

1057 A557 10c brown org .25 .20

Visit of King Olaf of Norway.

Sun over Sugar Loaf, Botafogo Bay A558

Nilo Peçanha A559

Photogravure and Embossed

1967, Sept. 25 Wmk. 267 *Perf. 11½*

1058 A558 10c blk & dp org .25 .20

22nd meeting of the Intl. Monetary Fund, Intl. Bank for Reconstruction and Development, Intl. Financial Corporation and Intl. Development Assoc.

Perf. 11½x11

1967, Oct. 1 Photo. Wmk. 267

1059 A559 5c brown violet .25 .20

Peçanha (1867-1924), Pres. of Brazil 1909-10.

Virgin of the Apparition and Basilica of Aparecida A560

Cockerel, Festival Emblem A561

1967, Oct. 11 *Perf. 11½*
1060 A560 5c ultra & dl yel .30 .20
a. Souvenir sheet of 2 3.25 *3.25*

250th anniv. of the discovery of the statue of Our Lady of the Apparition, now in the National Basilica of the Apparition at Aparecida do Norte.

No. 1060a contains imperf. 5c and 10c stamps similar to No. 1060. Issued Dec. 27, 1967, for Christmas.

Engraved and Photogravure

1967, Oct. 16 *Perf. 11½x11*
1061 A561 20c black & multi .50 .40

Second International Folksong Festival.

Balloon, Plane and Rocket A562

Perf. 11x11½

1967, Oct. 18 Photo. Unwmk.
1062 A562 10c blue .50 .30
a. 15c souvenir sheet 4.50 *4.50*

Week of the Wing, Oct. 18-23. No. 1062a contains one imperf. 15c stamp similar to No. 1062 and was issued Oct. 23.

Pres. Arthur Bernardes — A563

Portraits of Brazilian Presidents: 20c, Campos Salles. 50c, Wenceslau Pereira Gomes Braz. 1cr, Washington Pereira de Souza Luiz. 2cr, Castello Branco.

Perf. 11x11½

1967-68 Photo. Wmk. 267
1063 A563 10c blue .24 .20
1064 A563 20c dk red brn .75 .20

Engr.
1065 A563 50c black ('68) 3.75 .30
1066 A563 1cr lil rose ('68) 6.00 .30
1067 A563 2cr emerald ('68) 1.10 .30
Nos. 1063-1067 (5) 11.84 1.30

Carnival of Rio — A564

Ships, Anchor and Sailor — A565

1967, Nov. 22 *Perf. 11½x11*
1070 A564 10c lem, ultra & pink .30 .20
a. 15c souvenir sheet 3.50 *4.50*

Issued for International Tourist Year, 1967. No. 1070a contains a 15c imperf. stamp in design of No. 1070. Issued Nov. 24.

1967, Dec. 6
1071 A565 10c ultra .30 .25

Issued for Navy Week.

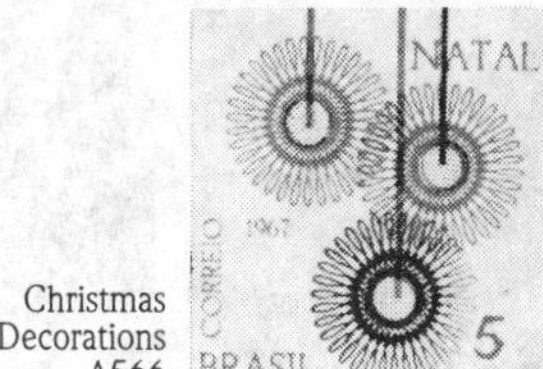

Christmas Decorations A566

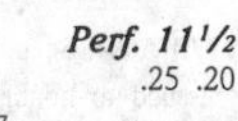

1967, Dec. 8 *Perf. 11½*
1072 A566 5c car, yel & bl .25 .20

Christmas 1967.

Olavo Bilac, Planes, Tank and Aircraft Carrier A567

Perf. 11x11½

1967, Dec. 16 Photo. Wmk. 267
1073 A567 5c brt blue & yel .30 .20

Issued for Reservists' Day and to honor Olavo Bilac, sponsor of compulsory military service.

Rodrigues de Carvalho — A568

1967, Dec. 18 Engr. *Perf. 11½x11*
1074 A568 10c green .25 .20

Cent. of the birth of Rodrigues de Carvalho, poet and lawyer.

Orlando Rangel A569

1968, Feb. 29 Photo. *Perf. 11x11½*
1075 A569 5c lt grnsh bl & blk .35 .25

Orlando de Fonseca Rangel, pioneer of pharmaceutical industry in Brazil, birth cent.

Virgin of Paranagua and Diver A570

Map of Brazil Showing Manaus A571

1968, Mar. 9 *Perf. 11½x11*
1076 A570 10c dk sl grn & brt yel grn .35 .25

250th anniversary of the first underwater explorations at Paranagua.

1968, Mar. 13 Photo. Wmk. 267
1077 A571 10c yel, grn & red .35 .25

Free port of Manaus on the Amazon River.

Human Rights Flame A572

Paul Harris and Rotary Emblem A573

1968, Mar. 21 *Perf. 11½x11*
1078 A572 10c blue & salmon .35 .25

International Human Rights Year.

1968, Apr. 19 Litho. Unwmk.
Without Gum
1079 A573 20c grn & org brn 1.25 .70

Paul Percy Harris (1868-1947), founder of Rotary International.

Pedro Alvares Cabral and his Fleet — A574

Design: 20c, First Mass celebrated in Brazil.

1968 Without Gum *Perf. 11½*
1080 A574 10c multicolored .55 .45
1081 A574 20c multicolored .80 .60

500th anniversary of the birth of Pedro Alvares Cabral, navigator, who took possession of Brazil for Portugal.

Issue dates: 10c, Apr. 22; 20c, July 11.

College Arms — A575

1968, Apr. 22 Photo. Wmk. 267
1082 A575 10c vio bl, red & gold .55 .35

Centenary of St. Luiz College, Sao Paulo.

Motherhood, by Henrique Bernardeli A576

1968, May 12 Litho. Unwmk.
Without Gum
1083 A576 5c multicolored .35 .25

Issued for Mother's Day.

Harpy Eagle — A577

Photogravure and Engraved

1968, May 28 Wmk. 267
1084 A577 20c brt bl & blk 1.50 .50

Sesquicentennial of National Museum.

Brazilian and Japanese Women — A578

1968, June 28 Litho. Unwmk.
Without Gum
1085 A578 10c yellow & multi .60 .40

Issued to commemorate the inauguration of Varig's direct Brazil-Japan airline.

Horse Race A579

Perf. 11x11½

1968, July 16 Litho. Unwmk.
Without Gum
1086 A579 10c multicolored .35 .25

Centenary of the Jockey Club of Brazil.

Musician Wren A580

Designs: 10c, Red-crested cardinal, vert. 50c, Royal flycatcher, vert.

Perf. 11½x11, 11x11½

1968-69 Engr. Wmk. in Sheet
Without Gum
1087 A580 10c multi ('69) .45 .28
1088 A580 20c multicolored .75 .28
1089 A580 50c multicolored 1.00 .55
Nos. 1087-1089 (3) 2.20 1.11

Some stamps in each sheet of Nos. 1087-1089 show parts of a two-line papermaker's watermark: "WESTERPOST / INDUSTRIA BRASILEIRA" with diamond-shaped emblem between last two words. Entire watermark appears in one sheet margin.

Issue dates: 10c, Aug. 20, 1969. 20c, July 19, 1968. 50c, Aug. 2, 1968.

Mailbox and Envelope A581

Photogravure and Engraved

1968, Aug. 1 Wmk. 267 *Perf. 11*
1091 A581 5c citron, blk & grn .20 .20

Stamp Day, 1968 and for 125th anniv. of the 1st Brazilian postage stamps.

Emilio Luiz Mallet A582

Map of South America A583

Perf. 11½x11

1968, Aug. 25 Engr. Wmk. 267

1092 A582 10c pale purple .20 .20

Issued to honor Marshal Emilio Luiz Mallet, Baron of Itapevi, patron of the marines.

1968, Sept. 5 Photo.

1093 A583 10c deep orange .20 .20

Visit of President Eduardo Frei of Chile.

Seal of Portuguese Literary School — A584

Photogravure and Engraved

1968, Sept. 10 *Perf. 11½*

1094 A584 5c pink & grn .20 .20

Centenary of Portuguese Literary School.

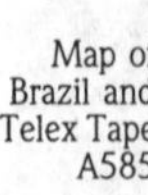

Map of Brazil and Telex Tape A585

1968, Sept. Photo. *Perf. 11x11½*

1095 A585 20c citron & brt grn .50 .25

Linking of 25 Brazilian cities by teletype.

Soldiers' Heads on Medal — A586

Perf. 11½x11

1968, Sept. 24 Litho. Unwmk.

Without Gum

1096 A586 5c blue & gray .20 .25

8th American Armed Forces Conference.

Clef, Notes and Sugarloaf Mountain A587

1968, Sept. 30 *Perf. 11½*

Without Gum

1097 A587 6c blk, yel & red .50 .30

Third International Folksong Festival.

Catalytic Cracking Plant — A588

1968, Oct. 4

Without Gum

1098 A588 6c blue & multi .50 .40

Petrobras, the natl. oil company, 15th anniv.

Child Protection A589

Whimsical Girl — A590

Design: 5c, School boy walking toward the sun.

Perf. 11½x11, 11x11½

1968, Oct. 16 Litho. Unwmk.

Without Gum

1099 A590	5c gray & lt bl		.32	.30
1100 A589	10c brt bl, dk red & blk		.40	.25
1101 A590	20c multicolored		.48	.25
	Nos. 1099-1101 (3)		1.20	.80

22nd anniv. of UNICEF.

Children with Books A591

1968, Oct. 23 *Perf. 11x11½*

Without Gum

1102 A591 5c multicolored .25 .25

Issued to publicize Book Week.

UN Emblem and Flags — A592

1968, Oct. 24 *Perf. 11½x11*

Without Gum

1103 A592 20c black & multi .45 .24

20th anniv. of WHO.

Jean Baptiste Debret, Self-portrait — A593

Perf. 11x11½

1968, Oct. 30 Litho. Unwmk.

Without Gum

1104 A593 10c dk gray & pale yel .35 .25

Jean Baptiste Debret, (1768-1848), French painter who worked in Brazil (1816-31). Design includes his "Burden Bearer."

Queen Elizabeth II A594

1968, Nov. 4 *Perf. 11½*

Without Gum

1105 A594 70c lt bl & multi 1.75 1.00

Visit of Queen Elizabeth II of Great Britain.

Francisco Braga — A595

Perf. 11½x11

1968, Nov. 19 Wmk. 267

1106 A595 5c dull red brn .40 .25

Cent. of the birth of Antonio Francisco Braga, composer of the Hymn of the Flag.

Brazilian Flag — A596

1968, Nov. 19 Unwmk. *Perf. 11½*

Without Gum

1107 A596 10c multicolored .40 .30

Issued for Flag Day.

Clasped Hands and Globe A597

Perf. 11x11½

1968, Nov. 25 Typo. Unwmk.

Without Gum

1108 A597 5c multicolored .25 .25

Issued for Voluntary Blood Donor's Day.

Old Locomotive — A598

1968, Nov. 28 Litho. *Perf. 11½*

Without Gum

1109 A598 5c multicolored 1.00 .50

Centenary of the Sao Paulo Railroad.

Bell — A599

Francisco Caldas, Jr. — A600

Design: 6c, Santa Claus and boy.

1968 Without Gum *Perf. 11½x11*

1110 A599 5c multicolored .30 .25

1111 A599 6c multicolored .30 .25

Christmas 1968.

Issue dates: 5c, Dec. 12; 6c, Dec. 20.

1968, Dec. 13

Without Gum

1112 A600 10c crimson & blk .20 .18

Cent. of the birth of Francisco Caldas, Jr., journalist and founder of Correio de Povo, newspaper.

Map of Brazil, War Memorial and Reservists' Emblem A601

Perf. 11x11½

1968, Dec. 16 Photo. Wmk. 267

1113 A601 5c bl grn & org brn .30 .22

Issued for Reservists' Day.

Radar Antenna A602

Viscount of Rio Branco A603

Perf. 11½x11

1969, Feb. 28 Litho. Unwmk.

Without Gum

1114 A602 30c ultra, lt bl & blk .70 .55

Inauguration of EMBRATEL, satellite communications ground station bringing US television to Brazil via Telstar.

1969, Mar. 16

Without Gum

1115 A603 5c black & buff .25 .25

José Maria da Silva Paranhos, Viscount of Rio Branco (1819-1880), statesman.

St. Gabriel — A604

1969, Mar. 24

Without Gum

1116 A604 5c multicolored .40 .25

Issued to honor St. Gabriel as patron saint of telecommunications.

Shoemaker's Last and Globe — A605

Perf. 11x11½

1969, Mar. 29 Litho. Unwmk.

Without Gum

1117 A605 5c multicolored .25 .25

4th Intl. Shoe Fair, Novo Hamburgo.

Allan Kardec A606

1969, Mar. 31 Photo. Wmk. 267

1118 A606 5c brt grn & org brn .25 .25

Allan Kardec (pen name of Leon Hippolyto Denizard Rivail, 1803-1869), French physician and spiritist.

Men of 3 Races and Arms of Cuiabá A607

1969, Apr. 8 Litho. Unwmk.

Without Gum

1119 A607 5c black & multi .25 .25

250th anniversary of the founding of Cuiabá, capital of Matto Grosso.

State Mint — A608

1969, Apr. 11 *Perf. 11½*

Without Gum

1120 A608 5c olive bister & org .45 .35

Opening of the state money printing plant.

Brazilian Stamps and Emblem A609

Perf. 11x11½

1969, Apr. 30 Litho. Unwmk.

Without Gum

1121 A609 5c multicolored .25 .25

Sao Paulo Philatelic Society, 50th anniv.

St. Anne, Baroque Statue — A610

1969, May 8 *Perf. 11½*

Without Gum

1122 A610 5c lemon & multi .50 .40

Issued for Mother's Day.

ILO Emblem A611

Perf. 11x11½

1969, May 13 Photo. Wmk. 267

1123 A611 5c dp rose red & gold .25 .20

50th anniv. of the ILO.

Diving Platform and Swimming Pool — A612

Mother and Child at Window — A613

Lithographed and Photogravure

Perf. 11½x11

1969, June 13 Unwmk.

Without Gum

1124 A612 20c bis brn, blk & bl grn .55 .42

40th anniversary of the Cearense Water Sports Club, Fortaleza.

1969 Litho. *Perf. 11½*

Designs: 20c, Modern sculpture by Felicia Leirner. 50c, "The Sun Sets in Brasilia," by Danilo di Prete. 1cr, Angelfish, painting by Aldemir Martins.

Size: 24x36mm

1125 A613 10c orange & multi .55 .25

Size: 33x34mm

1126 A613 20c red & multi .55 .50

Size: 33x53mm

1127 A613 50c yellow & multi 1.90 1.25

Without Gum

1128 A613 1cr gray & multi 2.50 1.25

Nos. 1125-1128 (4) 5.50 3.25

Issued to publicize the 10th Biennial Art Exhibition, Sao Paulo, Sept.-Dec. 1969.

Angelfish A614

Fish — A615

Fish: 10c, Tetra. 15c, Piranha. No. 1130c, Megalamphodus megalopterus. 30c, Black tetra.

Perf. 11½

1969, July 21 Litho. Wmk. 267

1129 A614 20c multicolored .70 .40

Souvenir Sheet

1969, July 24 Unwmk. *Imperf.*

1130 A615 Sheet of 4 4.50 *5.00*

a. 10c yellow & multi .90 .90

b. 15c bright blue & multi .90 .90

c. 20c green & multi .90 .90

d. 30c orange & multi .90 .90

Issued to publicize the work of ACAPI, an organization devoted to the preservation and development of fish in Brazil.

No. 1130 contains 4 stamps, size: 38½x21mm.

L. O. Teles de Menezes A616

Mailman A617

Perf. 11½x11

1969, July 26 Photo. Wmk. 267

1131 A616 50c dp org & bl grn 1.25 1.00

Centenary of Spiritism press in Brazil.

1969, Aug. 1

1132 A617 30c blue 1.10 .90

Issued for Stamp Day.

Map of Brazil A618

Gen. Tasso Fragoso A620

Railroad Bridge A619

Perf. 11½

1969, Aug. 25 Unwmk. Litho.

Without Gum

1133 A618 10c lt ultra, grn & yel .24 .22

Perf. 11x11½

1134 A619 20c multicolored .80 .40

Perf. 11½x11

Engr. Wmk. 267

With Gum

1135 A620 20c green .80 .50

Nos. 1133-1135 (3) 1.84 1.12

No. 1133 honors the Army as guardian of security; No. 1134, as promoter of development. No. 1135 the birth centenary of Gen. Tasso Fragoso.

Jupia Dam, Parana River — A621

Perf. 11½

1969, Sept. 10 Litho. Unwmk.

Without Gum

1136 A621 20c lt blue & multi .35 .35

Inauguration of the Jupia Dam, part of the Urubupunga hydroelectric system serving Sao Paulo.

Gandhi and Spinning Wheel A622

1969, Oct. 2 *Perf. 11x11½*

1137 A622 20c yellow & blk .40 .30

Mohandas K. Gandhi (1869-1948), leader in India's fight for independence.

Santos Dumont, Eiffel Tower and Module Landing on Moon — A623

1969, Oct. 17 *Perf. 11½*

Without Gum

1138 A623 50c dk bl & multi 1.75 1.25

Man's first landing on the moon, July 20, 1969. See note after US No. C76.

Smelting Plant — A624

1969, Oct. 26 Unwmk. *Perf. 11½*

Without Gum

1139 A624 20c multicolored .45 .40

Expansion of Brazil's steel industry.

Steel Furnace A625

1969, Oct. 31 Litho.

Without Gum

1140 A625 10c yellow & multi .45 .40

25th anniversary of Acesita Steel Works.

Water Vendor, by J. B. Debret — A626

Design: 30c, Street Scene, by Debret.

1969-70

Without Gum

1141 A626 20c multicolored 1.25 .50
1141A A626 30c multicolored 1.25 1.00

Jean Baptiste Debret (1768-1848), painter.
Issued: 20c, Nov. 5, 1969; 30c, May 19, 1970.

Exhibition Emblem — A627

1969, Nov. 15 *Perf. 11½x11*

Without Gum

1142 A627 10c multicolored .35 .22

Issued to publicize the ABUEXPO 69 Philatelic Exposition, Sao Paulo, Nov. 15-23.

Plane — A628

1969, Nov. 23

Without Gum

1143 A628 50c multicolored 2.75 1.40

Issued to publicize the year of the expansion of the national aviation industry.

Pelé Scoring — A629

1969-70

Without Gum

1144 A629 10c multicolored .38 .30

Souvenir Sheet

Imperf

1145 A629 75c multi ('70) 4.50 3.50

Issued to commemorate the 1,000th goal scored by Pele, Brazilian soccer player.
No. 1145 contains one imperf. stamp with simulated perforations.
Issued: 10c, Nov. 28, 1969; 75c, Jan. 23, 1970.

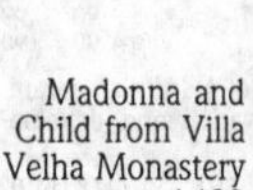

Madonna and Child from Villa Velha Monastery A630

Perf. 11½

1969, Dec. **Unwmk.** **Litho.**

Without Gum

1146 A630 10c gold & multi .35 .20

Souvenir Sheet

Imperf

1147 A630 75c gold & multi 12.00 *15.00*

Christmas 1969.
No. 1147 has simulated perforations.
Issue dates: 10c, Dec. 8; 75c, Dec. 18.

Destroyer and Submarine A631

Perf. 11x11½

1969, Dec. 9 **Engr.** **Wmk. 267**

1148 A631 5c bluish gray .40 .25

Issued for Navy Day.

Dr. Herman Blumenau A632

1969, Dec. 26 *Perf. 11½*

1149 A632 20c gray grn .85 .40

Dr. Herman Blumenau (1819-1899), founder of Blumenau, Santa Catarina State.

Carnival Scene — A633

Sugarloaf Mountain, Mask, Confetti and Streamers A634

Designs: 5c, Jumping boy and 2 women, vert. 20c, Clowns. 50c, Drummer.

1969-70 **Litho.** **Unwmk.**

Without Gum

1150 A633 5c multicolored .40 .30
1151 A633 10c multicolored .40 .30
1152 A633 20c multicolored .52 .40
1153 A634 30c multicolored 3.00 3.00
1154 A634 50c multicolored 2.75 2.50
Nos. 1150-1154 (5) 7.07 6.50

Carico Carnival, Rio de Janeiro.
Issue dates: Nos. 1150-1152, Dec. 29, 1969. Nos. 1153-1154, Feb. 5, 1970.

Opening Bars of "Il Guarani" with Antonio Carlos Gomes Conducting A635

1970, Mar. 19 **Litho.** *Perf. 11½*

Without Gum

1155 A635 20c blk, yel, gray & brn .60 .40

Centenary of the opera Il Guarani, by Antonio Carlos Gomes.

Church of Penha — A636

1970, Apr. 6 **Unwmk.** *Perf. 11½*

Without Gum

1156 A636 20c black & multi .30 .20

400th anniversary of the Church of Penha, State of Esperito Santo.

Assembly Building A637

10th anniv. of Brasilia: 50c, Reflecting Pool. 1cr, Presidential Palace.

1970, Apr. 21

Without Gum

1157 A637 20c multicolored .90 .70
1158 A637 50c multicolored 2.25 1.75
1159 A637 1cr multicolored 2.25 1.75
Nos. 1157-1159 (3) 5.40 4.20

Symbolic Water Design — A638

1970, May 5 **Unwmk.** *Perf. 11½*

Without Gum

1161 A638 50c multicolored 2.50 3.00

Issued to publicize the Rondon Project for the development of the Amazon River basin.

Marshal Manoel Luiz Osorio and Osorio Arms — A639

1970, May 8

Without Gum

1162 A639 20c multicolored 1.50 1.00

Issued to commemorate the inauguration of the Marshal Osorio Historical Park.

Madonna, from San Antonio Monastery, Rio de Janeiro A640

Detail from Brasilia Cathedral A641

1970, May 10

Without Gum

1163 A640 20c multicolored .40 .40

Issued for Mother's Day.

1970, May 27 **Engr.** **Wmk. 267**

1164 A641 20c lt yellow grn .25 .25

8th National Eucharistic Congress, Brasilia.

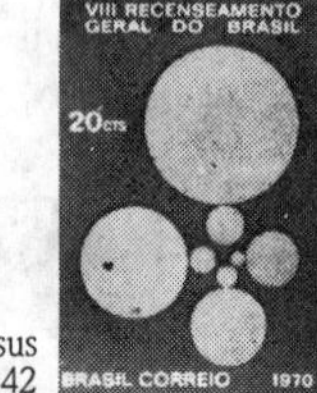

Census Symbol — A642

Perf. 11½

1970, June 22 **Unwmk.** **Litho.**

Without Gum

1165 A642 20c green & yel .60 .60

Issued to publicize the 8th general census.

Soccer Cup, Maps of Brazil and Mexico A643

Swedish Flag and Player Holding Rimet Cup — A644

Designs: 2cr, Chilean flag and soccer. 3cr, Mexican flag and soccer.

1970

Without Gum

1166 A643 50c blk, lt bl & gold .90 .90
1167 A644 1cr pink & multi 2.75 1.50
1168 A644 2cr gray & multi 5.25 1.50
1169 A644 3cr multicolored 4.50 1.00
Nos. 1166-1169 (4) 13.40 4.90

9th World Soccer Championships for the Jules Rimet Cup, Mexico City, May 30-June 21. No. 1166 honors Brazil's victory.
Issued: #1166, June 24; #1167-1169, Aug. 4.

Corcovado Christ and Map of South America A645

1970, July 18

Without Gum

1170 A645 50c brn, dk red & bl 2.50 2.50

6th World Cong. of Marist Brothers' Alumni.

Pandia Calogeras, Minister of War — A646

Perf. 11½x11

1970, Aug. 25 Photo. Unwmk.

1171 A646 20c blue green .50 .50

Brazilian Military Emblems and Map A647

Perf. 11x11½

1970, Sept. 8 Litho. Unwmk.

Without Gum

1172 A647 20c gray & multi .50 .50

25th anniv. of victory in World War II.

Annunciation (Brazilian Primitive Painting) A648

1970, Sept. 29 *Perf. 11½*

Without Gum

1173 A648 20c multicolored 1.25 1.00

Issued for St. Gabriel's (patron saint of communications) Day.

Boy in Library — A649

UN Emblem — A650

1970, Oct. 23

Without Gum

1174 A649 20c multicolored 1.25 1.00

Issued to publicize Book Week.

1970, Oct. 24

Without Gum

1175 A650 50c dk bl, lt bl & sil 1.25 1.25

25th anniversary of the United Nations.

Rio de Janeiro, 1820 — A651

Designs: 50c, LUBRAPEX 70 emblem. 1cr, Rio de Janeiro with Sugar Loaf Mountain, 1970. No. 1179, like 20c.

1970, Oct.

Without Gum

1176 A651	20c multicolored	1.75	1.00
1177 A651	50c yel brn & blk	3.50	2.00
1178 A651	1cr multicolored	3.50	3.75
	Nos. 1176-1178 (3)	8.75	6.75

Souvenir Sheet

Imperf

1179 A651 1cr multicolored 11.00 *17.00*

LUBRAPEX 70, 3rd Portuguese-Brazilian Phil. Exhib., Rio de Janeiro, Oct. 24-31.
Issued: #1176-1178, Oct. 27; #1179, Oct. 31.

Holy Family by Candido Portinari A652

1970, Dec. Litho. *Perf. 11½*

Without Gum

1180 A652 50c multicolored 1.25 1.50

Souvenir Sheet

Imperf

1181 A652 1cr multicolored 15.00 *24.00*

Christmas 1970. No. 1181 contains one stamp with simulated perforations.
Issue dates: 50c, Dec. 1; 1cr, Dec. 8.

Battleship A653

CIH Emblem A654

1970, Dec. 11 Litho. *Perf. 11½*

Without Gum

1182 A653 20c multicolored 1.25 .75

Navy Day.

1971, Mar. 28 Litho. *Perf. 11½*

Without Gum

1183 A654 50c black & red 1.50 1.75

3rd Inter-American Housing Congress, Mar. 27-Apr. 3.

Links Around Globe — A655

1971, Mar. 31 Litho. *Perf. 12½x11*

Without Gum

1184 A655 20c grn, yel, blk & red .65 .50

Intl. year against racial discrimination.

Morpho Melacheilus — A656

Design: 1cr, Papilio thoas brasiliensis.

Perf. 11x11½

1971, Apr. 28 Litho. Unwmk.

Without Gum

1185 A656 20c multicolored 1.25 .60
1186 A656 1cr multicolored 5.50 3.25

Madonna and Child — A657

1971, May 9 Litho. *Perf. 11½*

Without Gum

1187 A657 20c multicolored .85 .40

Mother's Day, 1971.

Basketball A658

1971, May 19

Without Gum

1188 A658 70c multicolored 1.50 1.00

6th World Women's Basketball Championship.

Map of Trans-Amazon Highway
A660 A659

Perf. 11½

1971, July 1 Unwmk. Litho.

Without Gum

1189 A659	40c multicolored	5.50	2.75
1190 A660	1cr multicolored	5.50	5.50
a.	Pair, #1189-1190	11.00	11.00

Trans-Amazon Highway. No. 1190a printed in sheets of 28 (4x7). Horizontal rows contain 2 No. 1190a with a label between. Each label carries different inscription.

Man's Head, by Victor Mairelles de Lima — A661

Stamp Day: 1cr, Arab Violinist, by Pedro Américo.

1971, Aug. 1

Without Gum

1191 A661 40c pink & multi 1.25 .80
1192 A661 1cr gray & multi 3.25 1.65

Duke of Caxias and Map of Brazil — A662

1971, Aug. 23 Photo.

1193 A662 20c yel grn & red brn .50 .60

Army Day.

Anita Garibaldi — A663

1971, Aug. 30 Litho.

Without Gum

1194 A663 20c multicolored .42 .42

Anita Garibaldi (1821-1849), heroine in liberation of Brazil.

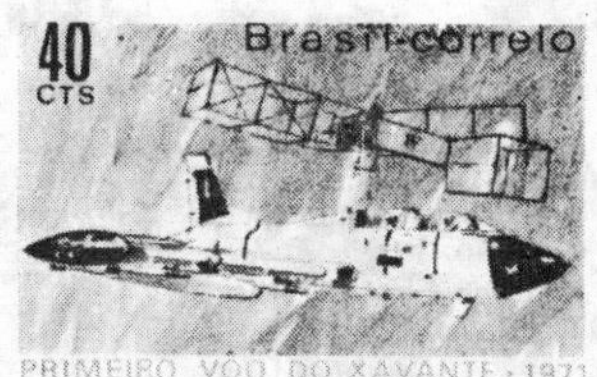

Xavante Jet and Santos Dumont's Plane, 1910 — A664

1971, Sept. 6

Without Gum

1195 A664 40c yellow & multi 1.40 .75

First flight of Xavante jet plane.

Flags and Map of Central American Nations — A665

"71" in French Flag Colors — A666

1971, Sept. 15

Without Gum

1196 A665 40c ocher & multi 1.25 .60

Sesquicentennial of the independence of Central American nations.

1971, Sept. 16

Without Gum

1197 A666 1.30cr ultra & multi 1.25 1.10

French Exhibition.

Black Mother, by Lucilio de Albuquerque A667

Archangel Gabriel A668

1971, Sept. 28
Without Gum

1198 A667 40c multicolored .60 .50

Centenary of law guaranteeing personal freedom starting at birth.

1971, Sept. 29 *Perf. 11½x11*
Without Gum

1199 A668 40c multicolored .75 .65

St. Gabriel's Day.

Bridge over River — A669

Children's Drawings: 35c, People crossing bridge. 60c, Woman with hat.

1971, Oct. 25 *Perf. 11½*
Without Gum

1200 A669 35c pink, bl & blk .55 .45
1201 A669 45c black & multi 1.40 .45
1202 A669 60c olive & multi .55 .45
Nos. 1200-1202 (3) 2.50 1.35

Children's Day.

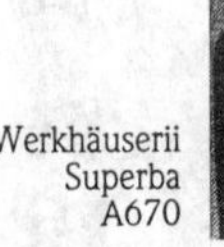

Werkhäuserii Superba A670

1971, Nov. 16
Without Gum

1203 A670 40c blue & multi 2.00 1.00

In memory of Carlos Werkhauser, botanist.

Greek Key Pattern "25" — A671

Design: 40c, like 20c but inscribed "sesc / servicio social / do comercio."

1971, Dec. 3
Without Gum

1204 A671 20c black & blue 1.25 1.00
1205 A671 40c black & org 1.25 1.00
a. Pair, #1204-1205 2.50 2.50

25th anniversary of SENAC (national apprenticeship system) and SESC (commercial social service).

Gunboat A672

1971, Dec. 8 *Perf. 11*
Without Gum

1206 A672 20c blue & multi .85 .50

Navy Day.

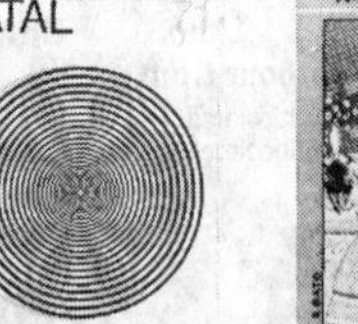

Cross and Circles — A673

Washing of Bonfim Church, Salvador, Bahia — A674

1971, Dec. 11

1207 A673 20c car & blue .40 .40
1208 A673 75c silver & gray .80 *3.00*
1209 A673 1.30cr blk, yel, grn & bl 4.75 2.50
Nos. 1207-1209 (3) 5.95 *5.90*

Christmas 1971.

1972, Feb. 18 Litho. *Perf. 11½x11*

Designs: 40c, Grape Festival, Rio Grande do Sul. 75c, Festival of the Virgin of Nazareth, Belém. 1.30cr, Winter Arts Festival, Ouro Preto.

Without Gum

1210 A674 20c silver & multi 1.50 .75
1211 A674 40c silver & multi 2.75 .75
1212 A674 75c silver & multi 2.75 3.00
1213 A674 1.30cr silver & multi 6.00 3.00
Nos. 1210-1213 (4) 13.00 7.50

Pres. Lanusse and Flag of Argentina A675

1972, Mar. 13 *Perf. 11x11½*
Without Gum

1214 A675 40c blue & multi 2.00 2.50

Visit of Lt. Gen. Alejandro Agustin Lanusse, president of Argentina.

Presidents Castello Branco, Costa e Silva and Garrastazu Medici A676

1972, Mar. 29
Without Gum

1215 A676 20c emerald & multi 1.25 .60

Anniversary of 1964 revolution.

Post Office Emblem — A677

Perf. 11½x11
1972, Apr. 10 Photo. Unwmk.

1216 A677 20c red brown 2.00 .20

No. 1216 is luminescent.

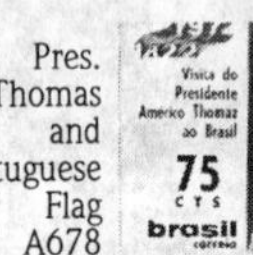

Pres. Thomas and Portuguese Flag A678

1972, Apr. 22 Litho. *Perf. 11*
Without Gum

1217 A678 75c ol brn & multi 1.75 1.75

Visit of Pres. Americo Thomas of Portugal to Brazil, Apr. 22-27.

Soil Research (CPRM) A679

1972, May 3 *Perf. 11½*
Without Gum

1218 A679 20c shown 1.50 .50
1219 A679 40c Offshore oil rig 3.50 .85
1220 A679 75c Hydroelectric dam 1.50 1.75
1221 A679 1.30cr Iron ore production 3.50 1.40
Nos. 1218-1221 (4) 10.00 4.50

Industrial development. Stamps are inscribed with names of industrial firms.

See Nos. 1228-1229.

Souvenir Sheet

Poster for Modern Art Week 1922 — A680

1972, May 5

1222 A680 1cr black & car 26.00 26.00

50th anniversary of Modern Art Week.

Mailman, Map of Brazil and Letters A681

Designs: 45c, "Telecommunications", vert. 60c, Tropospheric scatter system. 70c, Road map of Brazil and worker.

1972, May 26
Without Gum

1223 A681 35c blue & multi 1.25 .40
1224 A681 45c silver & multi 1.50 1.50
1225 A681 60c black & multi 1.50 1.25
1226 A681 70c multicolored 1.75 1.25
Nos. 1223-1226 (4) 6.00 4.40

Unification of communications in Brazil.

Development Type and

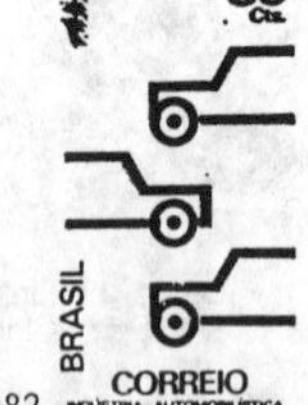

Automobiles — A682

Perf. 11x11½, 11½x11
1972, June 21 Photo.

1227 A682 35c shown 1.00 .50

Litho.

1228 A679 45c Ships 1.00 .60
1229 A679 70c Ingots 1.00 .40
Nos. 1227-1229 (3) 3.00 1.50

Industrial development. The 35c is luminescent.

Soccer — A683

Designs: 75c, Folk music. 1.30cr, Plastic arts.

Perf. 11½x11
1972, July 7 Photo. Unwmk.

1230 A683 20c black & yel 1.00 .50
1231 A683 75c black & ver 2.00 3.50
1232 A683 1.30cr black & ultra 4.00 3.50
Nos. 1230-1232 (3) 7.00 7.50

150th anniversary of independence. No. 1230 publicizes the 1972 sports tournament, a part of independence celebrations. Luminescent.

Souvenir Sheet

Shout of Independence, by Pedro Americo de Figueiredo e Melo — A684

1972, July 19 Litho. *Perf. 11½*
Without Gum

1233 A684 1cr multicolored 4.00 *9.00*

4th Interamerican Philatelic Exhibition, EXFILBRA, Rio de Janeiro, Aug 26-Sept. 2.

Figurehead A685

Brazilian folklore: 60c, Gauchos dancing fandango. 75c, Acrobats (capoeira). 1.15cr, Karajá (ceramic) doll. 1.30cr, Mock bullfight (bumba meu boi).

1972, Aug. 6
Without Gum

1234 A685 45c multicolored .85 .35
1235 A685 60c orange & multi 1.65 1.50
1236 A685 75c gray & multi .30 .30
1237 A685 1.15cr multicolored .55 .55
1238 A685 1.30cr yellow & multi 5.00 2.00
Nos. 1234-1238 (5) 8.35 4.70

Map of Brazil, by Diego Homem, 1568 — A686

Designs: 1cr, Map of Americas, by Nicholas Visscher, 1652. 2cr, Map of Americas, by Lopo Homem, 1519.

1972, Aug. 26 Litho. *Perf. 11½*
Without Gum

1239 A686 70c multicolored .50 .50
1240 A686 1cr multicolored 9.00 1.00
1241 A686 2cr multicolored 4.50 1.50
Nos. 1239-1241 (3) 14.00 3.00

4th Inter-American Philatelic Exhibition, EXFILBRA, Rio de Janeiro, Aug. 26-Sept. 2.

Dom Pedro Proclaimed Emperor, by Jean Baptiste Debret A687

Designs: 30c, Founding of Brazil (people with imperial flag; vert.). 1cr, Coronation of Emperor Dom Pedro, vert. 2cr, Dom Pedro commemorative medal. 3.50cr, Independence Monument, Ipiranga.

1972, Sept. 4 Litho. *Perf. 11½x11*
1242 A687 30c yellow & grn 1.25 1.25
1243 A687 70c pink & rose lil 1.25 .80
1244 A687 1cr buff & red brn 8.00 1.25
1245 A687 2cr pale yel & blk 4.00 1.25
1246 A687 3.50cr gray & blk 7.25 4.00
Nos. 1242-1246 (5) 21.75 8.55

Sesquicentennial of independence.

Souvenir Sheet

"Automobile Race" — A688

1972, Nov. 14 *Perf. 11½*
1247 A688 2cr multicolored 10.00 15.00

Emerson Fittipaldi, Brazilian world racing champion.

Numeral and Post Office Emblem — A689

Mö — A689a

Perf. 11½x11
1972-75 Unwmk. Photo.
1248 A689 5c orange .35 .15
a. Wmk. 267 .20 .15
1249 A689 10c brown ('73) .20 .15
a. Wmk. 267 4.00 .15
1250 A689 15c brt blue ('75) .15 .15
1251 A689 20c ultra .35 .15
1252 A689 25c sepia ('75) .25 .15
1253 A689 30c dp carmine .40 .15
1254 A689 40c dk grn ('73) .20 .15
1255 A689 50c olive .30 .15
1256 A689 70c red lilac ('75) .30 .15

Engr. *Perf. 11½*
1257 A689a 1cr lilac ('74) .45 .15
1258 A689a 2cr grnsh bl ('74) .65 .15
1259 A689a 4cr org & vio ('75) 1.40 .20
1260 A689a 5cr brn, car & buff ('74) 2.00 .20
1261 A689a 10cr grn, blk & buff ('74) 4.50 .30
Nos. 1248-1261 (14) 11.50
Set value 1.55

The 5cr and 10cr have beige lithographed multiple Post Office emblem underprint.
Nos. 1248-1261 are luminescent. Nos. 1248a and 1249a are not.

Hand Writing "Mobral" A690

Designs: 20c, Multiracial group and population growth curve. 1cr, People and hands holding house. 2cr, People, industrial scene and upward arrow.

1972, Nov. 28 Litho. *Perf. 11½*
Without Gum
1262 A690 10c black & multi .20 .50
1263 A690 20c black & multi 1.00 .75
1264 A690 1cr black & multi 8.75 .30
1265 A690 2cr black & multi 2.00 .75
Nos. 1262-1265 (4) 11.95 2.30

Publicity for: "Mobral" literacy campaign (10c); Centenary of census (20c); Housing and retirement fund (1cr); Growth of gross national product (2cr).

Congress Building, Brasilia, by Oscar Niemeyer, and "Os Guerreiros," by Bruno Giorgi A691

1972, Dec. 4
Without Gum
1266 A691 1cr blue, blk & org 10.00 6.00

Meeting of Natl. Cong., Brasilia, Dec. 4-8.

Holy Family (Clay Figurines) A692

Retirement Plan A693

1972, Dec. 13 Photo. *Perf. 11½x11*
1267 A692 20c ocher & blk .85 .50

Christmas 1972. Luminescent.

Perf. 11½x11, 11x11½
1972, Dec. 20 Litho.

Designs: No. 1269, School children and traffic lights, horiz. 70c, Dr. Oswaldo Cruz with Red Cross, caricature. 2cr, Produce, fish and cattle, horiz.

Without Gum
1268 A693 10c blk, bl & dl org .50 .50
1269 A693 10c orange & multi 1.00 1.00
1270 A693 70c blk, red & brn 9.00 3.75
1271 A693 2cr green & multi 15.00 6.50
Nos. 1268-1271 (4) 25.50 11.75

Publicity for: Agricultural workers' assistance program (No. 1268); highway and transportation development (No. 1269); centenary of the birth of Dr. Oswaldo Cruz (1872-1917), Director of Public Health Institute (70c); agricultural and cattle export (2cr). Nos. 1268-1271 are luminescent.

Sailing Ship, Navy A694

Designs: 10c, Monument, Brazilian Expeditionary Force. No. 1274, Plumed helmet, Army. No. 1275, Rocket, Air Force.

Lithographed and Engraved
1972, Dec. 28 *Perf. 11x11½*
Without Gum
1272 A694 10c brn, dk brn & blk 1.50 1.10
1273 A694 30c lt ultra, grn & blk 1.50 1.10
1274 A694 30c yel grn, bl grn & blk 1.50 1.10
1275 A694 30c lilac, mar & blk 1.50 1.10
a. Block of 4, #1272-1275 6.00 5.00

Armed Forces Day.

Rotary Emblem and Cogwheels A695

Perf. 11½
1973, Mar. 21 Litho. Unwmk.
1276 A695 1cr ultra, grnsh bl & yel 1.75 1.50

Rotary International serving Brazil 50 years.

Swimming A696

Designs: No. 1278, Gymnastics. No. 1279, Volleyball, vert.

1973 Photo. *Perf. 11x11½, 11½x11*
1277 A696 40c brt bl & red brn .35 .35
1278 A696 40c green & org brn 2.75 .70
1279 A696 40c violet & org brn .70 .70
Nos. 1277-1279 (3) 3.80 1.75

Issue dates: No. 1277, Apr. 19; No. 1278, May 22; No. 1279, Oct. 15.

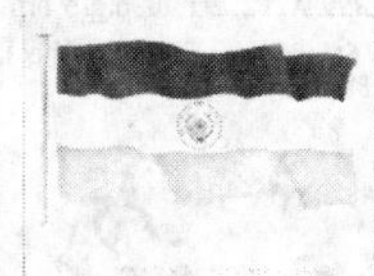

Flag of Paraguay A697

Perf. 11½
1973, Apr. 27 Litho. Unwmk.
1280 A697 70c multicolored 1.75 1.25

Visit of Pres. Alfredo Stroessner of Paraguay, Apr. 25-27.

"Communications" — A698

Design: 1cr, Neptune, map of South America and Africa.

1973, May 5 *Perf. 11x11½*
1281 A698 70c multicolored .80 .70
1282 A698 1cr multicolored 4.25 3.00

Inauguration of the Ministry of Communications Building, Brasilia (70c); and of the first underwater telephone cable between South America and Europe, Bracan 1 (1cr).

Congress Emblem — A699

1973, May 19 *Perf. 11½x11*
1283 A699 1cr orange & pur 4.00 3.00

24th Congress of the International Chamber of Commerce, Rio de Janeiro, May 19-26.

Swallowtailed Manakin — A700

Birds: No. 1285, Orange-backed oriole. No. 1286, Brazilian ruby (hummingbird).

1973 Litho. *Perf. 11x11½*
1284 A700 20c multicolored .50 .20
1285 A700 20c multicolored .50 .20
1286 A700 20c multicolored .50 .20
Nos. 1284-1286 (3) 1.50 .60

Issue dates: No. 1284, May 26; No. 1285, June 6; No. 1286, June 19.

Tourists A701

1973, June 28 Litho. *Perf. 11x11½*
1287 A701 70c multicolored .90 .85

National Tourism Year.

Conference at Itu — A702

Satellite and Multispectral Image — A703

1973 *Perf. 11½x11*
1288 A702 20c shown .52 .35
1289 A702 20c Decorated wagon .52 .35
1290 A702 20c Indian .52 .35
1291 A702 20c Graciosa Road .52 .35
Nos. 1288-1291 (4) 2.08 1.40

Centenary of the Itu Convention (1288); sesquicentennial of the July 2 episode (1289); 400th anniversary of the founding of Niteroi (1290); centenary of Graciosa Road (1291).
Issue dates: #1291, July 29; others July 2.

1973, July 11 *Perf. 11½*

Designs: 70c, Official opening of Engineering School, 1913. 1cr, Möbius strips and "IMPA."

1292 A703 20c black & multi .25 .40
1293 A703 70c dk blue & multi 2.25 1.00
1294 A703 1cr lilac & multi 3.00 1.00
Nos. 1292-1294 (3) 5.50 2.40

Institute for Space Research (20c); School of Engineering, Itajubá, 60th anniversary (70c); Institute for Pure and Applied Mathematics (1cr).

Santos-Dumont and 14-Bis Plane — A704

Designs (Santos-Dumont and): 70c, No. 6 Balloon and Eiffel Tower. 2cr Demoiselle plane.

Lithographed and Engraved
1973, July 20 *Perf. 11x11½*
1295 A704 20c lt grn, brt grn & brn .75 .25
1296 A704 70c yel, rose red & brn 1.75 1.25
1297 A704 2cr bl, vio bl & brn 1.75 1.25
Nos. 1295-1297 (3) 4.25 2.75

Centenary of the birth of Alberto Santos-Dumont (1873-1932), aviation pioneer.

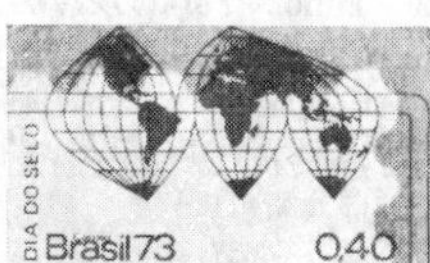

Mercator Map A705

Design: No. 1299, Same, red border on top and at left.

Photogravure and Engraved

1973, Aug. 1 **Wmk. 267**

1298 A705 40c red & black 2.50 1.50
1299 A705 40c red & black 2.10 2.10
a. Block of 4 21.00 15.00

Stamp Day. Nos. 1298-1299 are printed se-tenant horizontally and tête bêche vertically in sheets of 55. Blocks of 4 have red border all around.

Gonçalves Dias (1823-1864), Poet — A706

Perf. 11½x11

1973, Aug. 10 **Wmk. 267**

1300 A706 40c violet & blk .70 .42

Souvenir Sheet

Copernicus and Sun — A707

Perf. 11x11½

1973, Aug. 15 **Litho.** **Unwmk.**

1301 A707 1cr multicolored 4.00 5.00

500th anniversary of the birth of Nicolaus Copernicus (1473-1543), Polish astronomer.

Folklore Festival Banner — A708

1973, Aug. 22 ***Perf. 11½***

1302 A708 40c ultra & multi .75 .52

Folklore Day, Aug. 22.

Masonic Emblem A709

1973, Aug. 24 **Photo.** ***Perf. 11x11½***

1303 A709 1cr Prus blue 3.00 2.00

Free Masons of Brazil, 1822-1973.

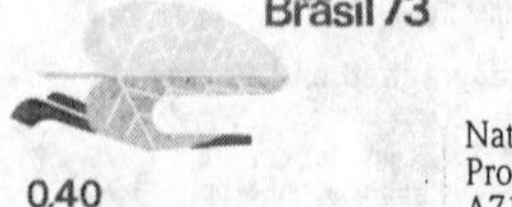

Nature Protection A710

Designs: No. 1305, Fire protection. No. 1306, Aviation safety. No. 1307, Safeguarding cultural heritage.

1973, Sept. 20 **Litho.** ***Perf. 11x11½***

1304 A710 40c brt grn & multi .75 .40
1305 A710 40c dk blue & multi .75 .40
1306 A710 40c lt blue & multi .75 .40
1307 A710 40c pink & multi .75 .40
Nos. 1304-1307 (4) 3.00 1.60

Souvenir Sheet

St. Gabriel and Proclamation of Pope Paul VI — A711

Lithographed and Engraved

1973, Sept. 29 **Unwmk.** ***Perf. 11½***

1308 A711 1cr bister & blk 7.50 10.00

1st National Exhibition of Religious Philately, Rio de Janeiro, Sept. 29-Oct. 6.

St. Teresa — A712

Photogravure and Engraved

Perf. 11½x11

1973, Sept. 30 **Wmk. 267**

1309 A712 2cr dk org & brn 3.50 2.50

St. Teresa of Lisieux, the Little Flower (1873-1897), Carmelite nun.

Monteiro Lobato and Emily A713

Perf. 11½

1973, Oct. 12 **Litho.** **Unwmk.**

1310 A713 40c shown .80 .50
1311 A713 40c Aunt Nastacia .80 .50
1312 A713 40c Snubnose, Peter and Rhino .80 .50
1313 A713 40c Viscount de Sabugosa .80 .50
1314 A713 40c Dona Benta .80 .50
a. Block of 5 + label 4.00 4.00

Monteiro Lobato, author of children's books.

Soapstone Sculpture of Isaiah (detail) — A714

Baroque Art in Brazil: No. 1316, Arabesque, gilded wood carving, horiz. 70c, Father José Mauricio Nuñes Garcia and music score. 1cr, Church door, Salvador, Bahia. 2cr, Angels, church ceiling painting by Manoel da Costa Athayde, horiz.

1973, Nov. 5

1315 A714 40c multicolored .30 .30
1316 A714 40c multicolored .30 .30
1317 A714 70c multicolored 1.50 1.40
1318 A714 1cr multicolored 9.00 3.00
1319 A714 2cr multicolored 4.00 3.00
Nos. 1315-1319 (5) 15.10 8.00

Old and New Telephones A715

1973, Nov. 28 ***Perf. 11x11½***

1320 A715 40c multicolored .35 .30

50th anniv. of Brazilian Telephone Co.

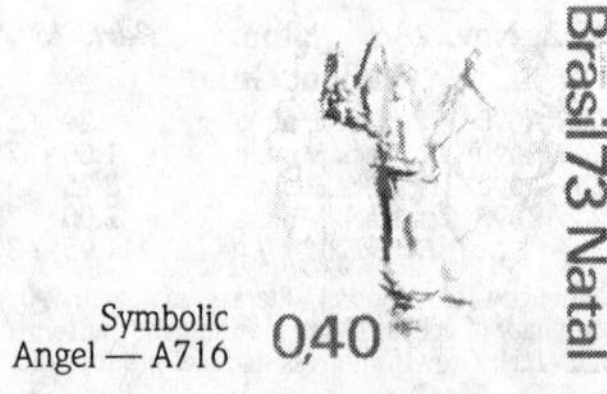

Symbolic Angel — A716

1973, Nov. 30 ***Perf. 11½***

1321 A716 40c ver & multi .35 .30

Christmas 1973.

River Boats A717

1973, Nov. 30 **Litho.** ***Perf. 11x11½***

1322 A717 40c "Gaiola" .35 .35
1323 A717 70c "Regatao" 1.05 1.05
1324 A717 1cr "Jangada" 4.50 3.00
1325 A717 2cr "Saveiro" 4.25 3.00
Nos. 1322-1325 (4) 10.15 7.40

Nos. 1322-1325 are luminescent.

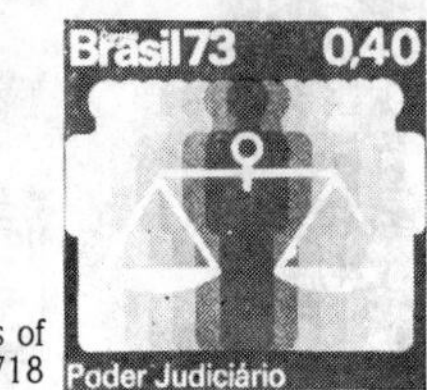

Scales of Justice — A718

1973, Dec. 5 ***Perf. 11½***

1326 A718 40c magenta & vio .50 .32

To honor the High Federal Court, created in 1891. Luminescent.

José Placido de Castro — A719

Scarlet Ibis and Victoria Regia — A720

Lithographed and Engraved

Perf. 11½x11

1973, Dec. 12 **Wmk. 267**

1327 A719 40c lilac rose & blk .60 .35

Centenary of the birth of Jose Placido de Castro, liberator of the State of Acre.

Perf. 11½x11

1973, Dec. 28 **Litho.** **Unwmk.**

Designs: 70c, Jaguar and spathodea campanulata. 1cr, Scarlet macaw and carnauba palm. 2cr, Rhea and coral tree.

1328 A720 40c brown & multi .80 .50
1329 A720 70c brown & multi 2.25 1.50
1330 A720 1cr bister & multi 3.50 .40
1331 A720 2cr bister & multi 6.25 3.50
Nos. 1328-1331 (4) 12.80 5.90

Nos. 1328-1331 are luminescent.

Saci Perere, Mocking Goblin — A721

Characters from Brazilian Legends: 80c, Zumbi, last chief of rebellious slaves. 1cr, Chico Rei, African king. 1.30cr, Little Black Boy of the Pasture. 2.50cr, Iara, Queen of the Waters.

Perf. 11½x11

1974, Feb. 28 **Litho.** **Unwmk.**

Size: 21x39mm

1332 A721 40c multicolored .32 .22
1333 A721 80c multicolored .65 .60
1334 A721 1cr multicolored 1.40 .42

Perf. 11½

Size: 32½x33mm

1335 A721 1.30cr multicolored 2.25 .85
1336 A721 2.50cr multicolored 9.25 2.50
Nos. 1332-1336 (5) 13.87 4.59

Nos. 1332-1336 are luminescent.

Pres. Costa e Silva Bridge A722

1974, Mar. 11

1337 A722 40c multicolored .60 .30

Inauguration of the Pres. Costa e Silva Bridge, Rio Niteroi, connecting Rio de Janeiro and Guanabara State.

"The Press" — A723

1974, Mar. 25 ***Perf. 11½***

1338 A723 40c shown .48 .32
1339 A723 40c "Radio" .24 .24
1340 A723 40c "Television" .40 .32
Nos. 1338-1340 (3) 1.12 .88

Communications Commemorations: No. 1338, bicentenary of first Brazilian newspaper, published in London by Hipolito da Costa; No. 1339, founding of the Radio Sociedade do Rio de Janeiro by Roquette Pinto; No. 1340, installation of first Brazilian television station by Assis Chateaubriand. Luminescent.

"Reconstruction" A724

1974, Mar. 31

1341 A724 40c multicolored .70 .45

10 years of progress. Luminescent.

Corcovado Christ, Marconi, Colors of Brazil and Italy — A725

1974, Apr. 25 **Litho.** ***Perf. 11½***

1342 A725 2.50cr multi 6.00 3.00

Guglielmo Marconi (1874-1937), Italian physicist and inventor. Luminescent.

Stamp Printing Press, Stamp Designing A726

1974, May 6
1343 A726 80c multicolored 1.00 .50

Brazilian mint.

World Map, Indian, Caucasian and Black Men — A727

Designs (World Map and): No. 1345, Brazilians. No. 1346, Cabin and German horseback rider. No. 1347, Italian farm wagon. No. 1348, Japanese woman and torii.

1974, May 3 **Unwmk.**

1344	A727	40c multicolored	.28	.28
1345	A727	40c multicolored	.18	.18
1346	A727	2.50cr multicolored	3.00	1.50
1347	A727	2.50cr multicolored	4.25	1.50
1348	A727	2.50cr multicolored	1.10	.85
		Nos. 1344-1348 (5)	8.81	4.31

Ethnic and migration influences in Brazil.

Sandstone Cliffs, Sete Cidades National Park A728

Tourist publicity: 80c, Ruins of Cathedral of Sao Miguel das Missões.

Lithographed and Engraved

1974, June 8 ***Perf. 11x11½***
1349 A728 40c multicolored .75 .50
1350 A728 80c multicolored .75 .50

Souvenir Sheet

Soccer — A729

1974, June 20 **Litho.** ***Perf. 11½***
1351 A729 2.50cr multi 3.50 *6.00*

World Cup Soccer Championship, Munich, June 13-July 7.

Church and College, Caraça A730

1974, July 6 **Litho.** ***Perf. 11x11½***
1352 A730 40c multicolored .45 .30

College (Seminary) of Caraça, bicent.

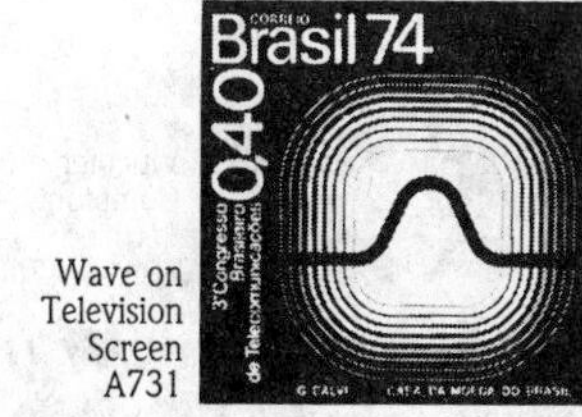

Wave on Television Screen A731

1974, July 15 ***Perf. 11½***
1353 A731 40c black & blue .30 .40

TELEBRAS, Third Brazilian Congress of Telecommunications, Brasilia, July 15-20.

Fernao Dias Paes — A732

1974, July 21 ***Perf. 11½***
1354 A732 20c green & multi .30 .30

3rd centenary of the expedition led by Fernao Dias Paes exploring Minas Gerais and the passage from South to North in Brazil.

Mexican Flag — A733

1974, July 24 **Litho.** ***Perf. 11½***
1355 A733 80c multicolored 2.25 1.10

Visit of Pres. Luis Echeverria Alvares of Mexico, July 24-29.

Flags of Brazil and Germany A734

1974, Aug. 5 ***Perf. 11x11½***
1356 A734 40c multicolored .50 .50

World Cup Soccer Championship, 1974, victory of German Federal Republic.

Souvenir Sheet

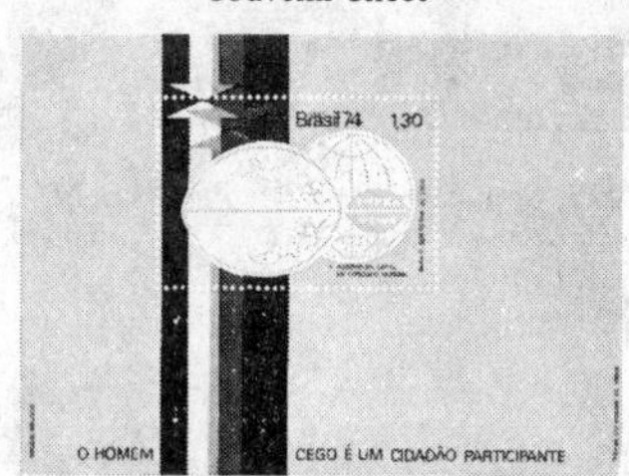

Congress Emblem — A735

1974, Aug. 7 ***Perf. 11½***
1357 A735 1.30cr multi .85 *1.75*

5th World Assembly of the World Council for the Welfare of the Blind, Sao Paulo, Aug. 7-16. Stamp and margin inscribed in Braille with name of Assembly.

Raul Pederneiras (1874-1953, Journalist, Professor of Law and Fine Arts), Caricature by J. Carlos — A736

Lithographed and Engraved

1974, Aug. 15 ***Perf. 11½x11***
1358 A736 40c buff, blk & ocher .30 .40

Society Emblem and Landscape A737

1974, Aug. 19 **Litho.** ***Perf. 11x11½***
1359 A737 1.30cr multi 1.25 .90

13th Congress of the International Union of Building and Savings Societies.

Souvenir Sheet

Five Women, by Di Cavalcanti — A738

1974, Aug. 26 **Litho.** ***Perf. 11½***
1360 A738 2cr multicolored 2.50 *6.00*

LUBRAPEX 74, 5th Portuguese-Brazilian Phil. Exhib., Sao Paulo, Nov. 26-Dec. 4.

"UPU" and World Map — A739

1974, Oct. 9 **Litho.** ***Perf. 11½***
1361 A739 2.50cr blk & brt bl 4.50 1.75

Centenary of Universal Postal Union.

Hammock (Antillean Arawak Culture) — A740

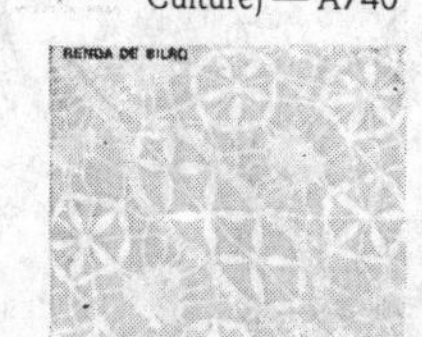

Bilro Lace — A741

Singer of "Cord" Verses — A742

Ceramic Figure by Master Vitalino — A743

1974, Oct. 16 **Litho.** ***Perf. 11½***

1362	A740	50c deep rose lilac	2.00	.40
1363	A741	50c lt & dk blue	2.50	.40
1364	A742	50c yel & red brn	.60	.40
1365	A743	50c brt yel & dk brn	.75	.40
		Nos. 1362-1365 (4)	5.85	1.60

Popular Brazilian crafts.

Branch of Coffee A744

1974, Oct. 27 **Unwmk.** ***Perf. 11***
1366 A744 50c multicolored 1.00 .60

Centenary of city of Campinas.

Hornless Tabapua A745

Animals of Brazil: 1.30cr, Creole horse. 2.50cr, Brazilian mastiff.

1974, Nov. 10 ***Perf. 11½***

1367	A745	80c multi	1.10	.75
1368	A745	1.30cr multi	1.10	.75
1369	A745	2.50cr multi	7.75	2.50
		Nos. 1367-1369 (3)	9.95	4.00

Christmas — A746

1974, Nov. 18 ***Perf. 11½x11***
1370 A746 50c Angel .70 .30

Solteira Island Hydroelectric Dam A747

1974, Nov. 11 ***Perf. 11½***
1371 A747 50c black & yel 1.40 .50

Inauguration of the Solteira Island Hydroelectric Dam over Parana River.

The Girls, by Carlos Reis — A748

1974, Nov. 26

1372 A748 1.30cr multi .70 .50

LUBRAPEX 74, 5th Portuguese-Brazilian Phil. Exhib., Sao Paulo, Nov. 26-Dec. 4.

Youths, Judge, Scales A749

1974, Dec. 20 Litho. ***Perf. 11½***

1373 A749 90c yel, red & bl .30 .35

Juvenile Court of Brazil, 50th anniversary.

Long Distance Runner — A750

1974, Dec. 23

1374 A750 3.30cr multi .75 .75

Sao Silvestre long distance running, 50th anniversary.

News Vendor, 1875, Masthead, 1975 — A751

1975, Jan. 4

1375 A751 50c multicolored 1.25 .75

Newspaper "O Estado de S. Paulo," cent.

Sao Paulo Industrial Park A752

Designs: 1.40cr, Natural rubber industry, Acre. 4.50cr, Manganese mining, Amapá.

1975, Jan. 24 Litho. ***Perf. 11x11½***

1376 A752 50c vio bl & yel 1.25 .40
1377 A752 1.40cr yellow & brn .60 .40
1378 A752 4.50cr yellow & blk 6.00 .40
Nos. 1376-1378 (3) 7.85 1.20

Economic development.

Fort of the Holy Cross A753

Colonial forts: No. 1380, Fort of the Three Kings. No. 1381, Fort of Monteserrat. 90c, Fort of Our Lady of Help.

Litho. & Engr.

1975, Mar. 14 ***Perf. 11½***

1379 A753 50c yel & red brn .24 .16
1380 A753 50c yel & red brn .40 .16
1381 A753 50c yel & red brn .80 .16
1382 A753 90c yel & red brn .24 .16
Nos. 1379-1382 (4) 1.68 .64

House on Stilts, Amazon Region A754

Designs: 50c, Modern houses and plan of Brasilia. 1.40cr, Indian hut, Rondonia. 3.30cr, German-style cottage (Enxaimel), Santa Catarina.

1975, Apr. 18 Litho. ***Perf. 11½***

1383 A754 50c yel & multi 1.25 2.25
1384 A754 50c yel & multi 8.50 6.25
a. Pair, #1383-1384 10.00 8.50
1385 A754 1cr yel & multi .85 .22
1386 A754 1.40cr yel & multi 1.75 2.50
1387 A754 1.40cr yel & multi .50 .85
a. Pair, #1386-1387 2.25 3.50
1388 A754 3.30cr yel & multi .75 1.25
1389 A754 3.30cr yel & multi 3.50 4.00
a. Pair, #1388-1380 4.25 5.25
Nos. 1383-1389 (7) 17.10 17.32

Brazilian architecture. Nos. 1383, 1386, 1388 have yellow strip at right side, others at left.

Astronotus Ocellatus A755

Designs: Brazilian fresh-water fish.

1975, May 2 Litho. ***Perf. 11½***

1390 A755 50c *shown* 1.40 .40
1391 A755 50c *Colomesus psitacus* .25 .25
1392 A755 50c *Phallocerus caudimaculatus* .25 .40
1393 A755 50c *Symphysodon discus* .48 .50
Nos. 1390-1393 (4) 2.38 1.55

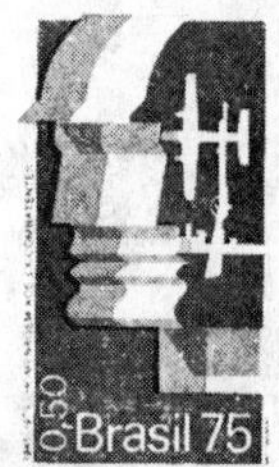

Soldier's Head in Brazil's Colors, Plane, Rifle and Ship — A756

Brasil 75 1,00

Brazilian Otter — A757

1975, May 8 ***Perf. 11½x11***

1394 A756 50c vio bl & multi .35 .30

In honor of the veterans of World War II, on the 30th anniversary of victory.

1975, June 17 Litho. ***Perf. 11½***

Nature protection: 70c, Brazilian pines, horiz. 3.30cr, Marsh cayman, horiz.

1395 A757 70c bl, grn & blk 1.05 .50
1396 A757 1cr multi 1.05 1.00
1397 A757 3.30cr multi .90 .75
Nos. 1395-1397 (3) 3.00 2.25

Petroglyphs, Stone of Ingá — A758

Brasil 75 1,00

Marjoara Vase, Pará — A759

Vinctifer Comptoni, Petrified Fish — A760

1975, July 8 Litho. ***Perf. 11½***

1398 A758 70c multicolored .55 .40
1399 A759 1cr multicolored .35 .40
1400 A760 1cr multicolored .35 .40
Nos. 1398-1400 (3) 1.25 1.20

Archaeological discoveries.

Immaculate Conception, Franciscan Monastery, Vitoria — A761

Brasil 75 0,70 dia do selo

Post and Telegraph Ministry — A762

1975, July 15

1401 A761 3.30cr blue & multi .95 .95

Holy Year 1975 and 300th anniv. of establishment of the Franciscan Province in Southern Brazil.

1975, Aug. 8 Engr. ***Perf. 11½***

1402 A762 70c dk carmine .70 .30

Stamp Day 1975.

Sword Dance, Minas Gerais — A763

Folk Dances: No. 1404, Umbrella Dance, Pernambuco. No. 1405, Warrior's Dance, Alagoas.

1975, Aug. 22 Litho. ***Perf. 11½***

1403 A763 70c gray & multi .35 .35
1404 A763 70c pink & multi .35 .35
1405 A763 70c yellow & multi .35 .35
Nos. 1403-1405 (3) 1.05 1.05

Trees A764

1975, Sept. 15 ***Perf. 11x11½***

1406 A764 70c multicolored .30 .25

Annual Tree Festival.

Globe, Radar and Satellite — A765

1975, Sept. 16 ***Perf. 11½***

1407 A765 3.30cr multi .70 .75

Inauguration of 2nd antenna of Tangua Earth Station, Rio de Janeiro State.

Woman Holding Flowers and Globe A766

1975, Sept. 23

1408 A766 3.30cr multi 1.00 1.00

International Women's Year 1975.

Tile, Railing and Column, Alcantara A767

Cross and Monastery, Sao Cristovao — A768

Historic cities: No. 1411, Jug and Clock Tower, Goiás, vert.

1975, Sept. 27 Litho. ***Perf. 11½***

1409 A767 70c multicolored .32 .45
1410 A768 70c multicolored .60 .45
1411 A768 70c multicolored .60 .45
Nos. 1409-1411 (3) 1.52 1.35

"Books teach how to live" — A769

1975, Oct. 23 Litho. ***Perf. 11½***

1412 A769 70c multicolored .25 .30

Day of the Book.

ASTA Congress Emblem A770

1975, Oct. 27 ***Perf. 11x11½***

1413 A770 70c multicolored .25 .30

American Society of Travel Agents, 45th World Congress, Rio, Oct. 27-Nov. 1.

Angels — A771

1975, Nov. 11

1414 A771 70c red & brown .25 .20

Christmas 1975.

Map of Americas, Waves — A772

Dom Pedro II — A773

1975, Nov. 19 *Perf. 11½x12*

1415 A772 5.20cr gray & multi 2.75 2.00

2nd Interamerican Conference of Telecommunications (CITEL), Rio, Nov. 19-27.

1975, Dec. 2 **Engr.** *Perf. 12*

1416 A773 70c violet brown .75 .45

Dom Pedro II (1825-1891), emperor of Brazil, birth sesquicentennial.

People and Cross A774

1975, Nov. 27 **Litho.** *Perf. 11x11½*

1417 A774 70c lt bl & dp bl .50 .65

National Day of Thanksgiving.

Guarapari Beach, Espirito Santo A775

Tourist Publicity: #1419, Salt Stone beach, Piaui. #1420, Cliffs, Rio Grande Do Sul.

1975, Dec. 19 **Litho.** *Perf. 11½*

1418 A775 70c multicolored .28 .28
1419 A775 70c multicolored .28 .28
1420 A775 70c multicolored .28 .28
Nos. 1418-1420 (3) .84 .84

Triple Jump, Games Emblem A776

1975, Dec. 22 *Perf. 11x11½*

1421 A776 1.60cr bl grn & blk .25 .35

Triple jump world record by Joao Carlos de Oliveira in 7th Pan-American Games, Mexico City, Oct. 12-26.

UN Emblem and Headquarters A777

1975, Dec. 29 *Perf. 11½*

1422 A777 1.30cr dp bl & vio bl .25 .30

United Nations, 30th anniversary.

Light Bulbs, House and Sun A778

Energy conservation: No. 1424, Gasoline drops, car and sun.

1976, Jan. 16

1423 A778 70c multicolored .30 .20
1424 A778 70c multicolored .30 .15

Concorde A779

1976, Jan. 21 **Litho.** *Perf. 11x11½*

1425 A779 5.20cr bluish blk .50 .35

First commercial flight of supersonic jet Concorde from Paris to Rio, Jan. 21.

Souvenir Sheet

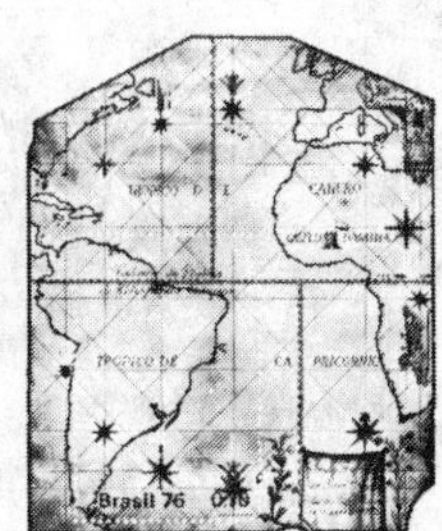

Nautical Map of South Atlantic, 1776 A780

1976, Feb. 2 *Perf. 11½*

1426 A780 70c salmon & multi .85 1.50

Centenary of the Naval Hydrographic and Navigation Institute.

Telephone Lines, 1876 Telephone A781

1976, Mar. 10 **Litho.** *Perf. 11x11½*

1427 A781 5.20cr orange & bl .65 .48

Centenary of first telephone call by Alexander Graham Bell, March 10, 1876.

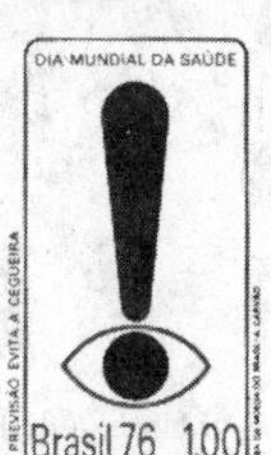
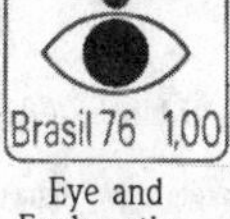

Eye and Exclamation Point — A782

Kaiapo Body Painting — A783

1976, Apr. 7 **Litho.** *Perf. 11½x11*

1428 A782 1cr vio red brn & brn .50 .75

World Health Day: "Foresight prevents blindness."

1976, Apr. 19 **Litho.** *Perf. 11½*

Designs: No. 1430, Bakairi ceremonial mask. No. 1431, Karajá feather headdress.

1429 A783 1cr lt violet & multi .16 .16
1430 A783 1cr lt violet & multi .16 .16
1431 A783 1cr lt violet & multi .16 .16
Nos. 1429-1431 (3) .48 .48

Preservation of indigenous culture.

Itamaraty Palace, Brasilia A784

1976, Apr. 20

1432 A784 1cr multicolored .60 .60

Diplomats' Day. Itamaraty Palace, designed by Oscar Niemeyer, houses the Ministry of Foreign Affairs.

Watering Can over Stones, by José Tarcisio A785

Fingers and Ribbons, by Pietrina Checcacci A786

1976, May 14 **Litho.** *Perf. 11½*

1433 A785 1cr multi .22 .20
1434 A786 1.60cr multi .28 .20

Modern Brazilian art.

Basketball — A787

Orchid — A788

Designs (Olympic Rings and): 1.40cr, Yachting. 5.20cr, Judo.

1976, May 21 **Litho.** *Perf. 11½*

1435 A787 1cr emerald & blk .16 .15
1436 A787 1.40cr dk blue & blk .20 .15
1437 A787 5.20cr orange & blk .65 .50
Nos. 1435-1437 (3) 1.01 .80

21st Olympic Games, Montreal, Canada, July 17-Aug. 1.

1976, June 4 *Perf. 11½x11*

Nature protection: No. 1439, Golden-faced lion monkey.

1438 A788 1cr multicolored .22 .20
1439 A788 1cr multicolored .22 .20

Film Camera, Brazilian Colors — A789

1976, June 19

1440 A789 1cr vio bl, brt grn & yel .20 .25

Brazilian film industry.

Bahia Woman — A790

Designs: 10c, Oxcart driver, horiz. 20c, Raft fishermen, horiz. 30c, Rubber plantation worker. 40c, Cowboy, horiz. 50c, Gaucho. 80c, Gold panner. 1cr, Banana plantation worker. 1.10cr, Grape harvester. 1.30cr, Coffee picker. 1.80cr, Farmer gathering wax palms. 2cr, Potter. 5cr, Sugar cane cutter. 7cr, Salt mine worker. 10cr, Fisherman. 15cr, Coconut seller. 20cr, Lacemaker.

Perf. 11½x11, 11x11½

1976-78 **Photo.**

1441 A790 10c red brn ('77) .15 .15
1442 A790 15c brown .24 .32
1443 A790 20c vio blue .15 .15
1444 A790 30c lilac rose .15 .15
1445 A790 40c org ('77) .15 .15
1446 A790 50c citron .15 .15
1447 A790 80c slate grn .38 .15
1448 A790 1cr black .16 .15

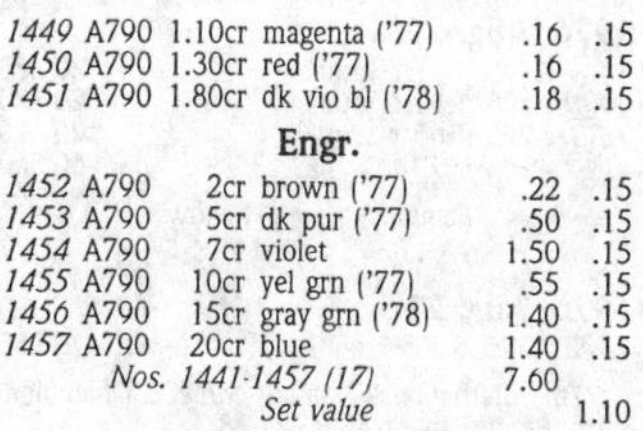
1449 A790 1.10cr magenta ('77) .16 .15
1450 A790 1.30cr red ('77) .16 .15
1451 A790 1.80cr dk vio bl ('78) .18 .15

Engr.

1452 A790 2cr brown ('77) .22 .15
1453 A790 5cr dk pur ('77) .50 .15
1454 A790 7cr violet 1.50 .15
1455 A790 10cr yel grn ('77) .55 .15
1456 A790 15cr gray grn ('78) 1.40 .15
1457 A790 20cr blue 1.40 .15
Nos. 1441-1457 (17) 7.60
Set value 1.10

See Nos. 1653-1657.

Hyphessobrycon Innesi — A791

Designs: Brazilian fresh-water fish.

1976, July 12 **Litho.** *Perf. 11x11½*

1460 A791 1cr *shown* .42 .40
1461 A791 1cr *Copeina arnoldi* .42 .40
1462 A791 1cr *Prochilodus insignis* .42 .40
1463 A791 1cr *Crenicichla lepidota* .42 .40
1464 A791 1cr *Ageneiosus* .42 .40
1465 A791 1cr *Corydoras reticulatus* .42 .40
a. Block of 6, #1460-1465 2.50 2.50

Santa Marta Lighthouse — A792

1976, July 29 **Engr.** *Perf. 12x11½*

1466 A792 1cr blue .20 .30

300th anniversary of the city of Laguna.

Children on Magic Carpet A793

1976, Aug. 1 **Litho.** *Perf. 11½x12*

1467 A793 1cr multicolored .20 .20

Stamp Day.

Nurse's Lamp and Head A794

1976, Aug. 12 **Litho.** *Perf. 11½*

1468 A794 1cr multicolored .20 .20

Brazilian Nurses' Assoc., 50th anniv.

Puppet, Soldier — A795

Winner's Medal — A796

Designs: 1.30cr, Girl's head. 1.60cr, Hand with puppet head on each finger, horiz.

1976, Aug. 20

1469 A795 1cr multi	.20	.20
1470 A795 1.30cr multi	.20	.20
1471 A795 1.60cr multi	.20	.20
Nos. 1469-1471 (3)	.60	.60

Mamulengo puppet show.

1976, Aug. 21

1472 A796 5.20cr multi	.70	.50

27th International Military Athletic Championships, Rio de Janeiro, Aug. 21-28.

Family Protection — A797

1976, Sept. 12

1473 A797 1cr lt & dk blue	.20	.20

National organizations SENAC and SESC helping commercial employees to improve their living standard, both commercially and socially.

Dying Tree — A798

1976, Sept. 20 Litho. *Perf. 11½*

1474 A798 1cr gray & multi	.20	.20

Protection of the environment.

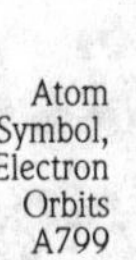

Atom Symbol, Electron Orbits A799

1976, Sept. 21

1475 A799 5.20cr multi	.70	.50

20th General Conference of the International Atomic Energy Agency, Rio de Janeiro, Sept. 21-29.

Train in Tunnel — A800

1976, Sept. 26

1476 A800 1.60cr multi	.25	.25

Sao Paulo subway, 1st in Brazil.

St. Francis and Birds A801

1976, Oct. 4

1477 A801 5.20cr multi	.60	.42

St. Francis of Assisi, 750th death anniv.

Ouro Preto School of Mining — A802

1976, Oct. 12 Engr. *Perf. 12x11½*

1478 A802 1cr dk vio	.40	.50

Ouro Preto School of Mining, centenary.

Three Kings — A803

Designs: Children's drawings.

1976, Nov. 4 Litho. *Perf. 11½*

1479 A803 80c shown	.28	.28
1480 A803 80c Santa Claus on donkey	.28	.28
1481 A803 80c Virgin and Child and Angels	.28	.28
1482 A803 80c Angels with candle	.28	.28
1483 A803 80c Nativity	.28	.28
a. Strip of 5, #1479-1483	1.40	1.40

Christmas 1976.

Souvenir Sheet

30,000 Reis Banknote — A804

1976, Nov. 5 Litho. *Perf. 11½*

1484 A804 80c multicolored	.40	*1.50*

Opening of 1000th branch of Bank of Brazil, Barra do Bugres, Mato Grosso.

Virgin of Monte Serrat, by Friar Agostinho A805

St. Joseph, 18th Century Wood Sculpture — A806

Designs: 5.60cr, The Dance, by Rodolfo Bernadelli, 19th century. 6.50cr, The Caravel, by Bruno Giorgi, 20th century abstract sculpture.

1976, Nov. 5

1485 A805 80c multi	.15	.15
1486 A806 5cr multi	.65	.40
1487 A805 5.60cr multi	.65	.40
1488 A806 6.50cr multi	.65	.40
Nos. 1485-1488 (4)	2.10	1.35

Development of Brazilian sculpture.

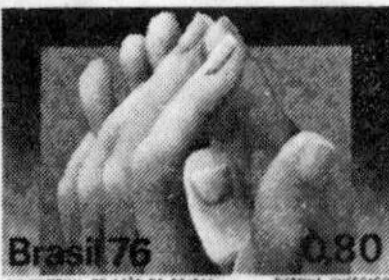

Praying Hands A807

1976, Nov. 25

1489 A807 80c multicolored	.25	.25

National Day of Thanksgiving.

Sailor, 1840 — A808

Design: 2cr, Marine's uniform, 1808.

1976, Dec. 13 Litho. *Perf. 11½x11*

1490 A808 80c multicolored	.22	.22
1491 A808 2cr multicolored	.32	.22

Brazilian Navy.

"Natural Resources and Development" — A809

1976, Dec. 17 *Perf. 11½*

1492 A809 80c multicolored	.20	.16

Brazilian Bureau of Standards, founded 1940.

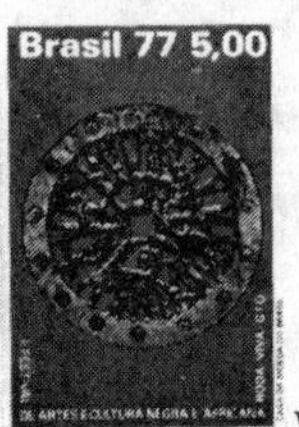

Wheel of Life — A810

Designs: 5.60cr, Beggar, sculpture by Agnaldo dos Santos. 6.50cr, Benin mask.

1977, Jan. 14

1493 A810 5cr multi	.55	.35
1494 A810 5.60cr multi	.55	.35
1495 A810 6.50cr multi	1.10	.35
Nos. 1493-1495 (3)	2.20	1.05

FESTAC '77, 2nd World Black and African Festival, Lagos, Nigeria, Jan. 15-Feb. 12.

A811

1977, Jan. 20 Litho. *Perf. 11½*

1496 A811 6.50cr bl & yel grn	.85	.65

Rio de Janeiro International Airport.

Seminar Emblem with Map of Americas A812

Salicylate, Microphoto A813

1977, Feb. 6

1497 A812 1.10cr gray, vio bl & bl	.35	.18

6th Inter-American Budget Seminar.

1977, Apr. 10 Litho. *Perf. 11½*

1498 A813 1.10cr multi	.20	.15

International Rheumatism Year.

Lions International Emblem A814

1977, Apr. 16

1499 A814 1.10cr multi	.20	.20

25th anniv. of Brazilian Lions Intl.

Heitor Villa Lobos A815

1977, Apr. 26 *Perf. 11x11½*

1500 A815 1.10cr shown	.15	.20
1501 A815 1.10cr Chiquinha Gonzaga	.15	.20
1502 A815 1.10cr Noel Rosa	.15	.20
Nos. 1500-1502 (3)	.45	.60

Brazilian composers.

Farmer and Worker — A816

Medicine Bottles and Flask — A817

1977, May 8 Litho. *Perf. 11½*

1503 A816 1.10cr grn & multi	.15	.20
1504 A817 1.10cr lt & dk grn	.15	.20

Support and security for rural and urban workers (No. 1503) and establishment in 1971 of Medicine Distribution Center (CEME) for low-cost medicines (No. 1504).

Churchyard Cross, Porto Seguro A818

Views, Porto Seguro: 5cr, Beach and boats. 5.60cr, Our Lady of Pena Chapel. 6.50cr, Town Hall.

1977, May 25 Litho. *Perf. 11½*

1505 A818 1.10cr multi .15 .15
1506 A818 5cr multi 1.40 .35
1507 A818 5.60cr multi .55 .45
1508 A818 6.50cr multi .80 .55
Nos. 1505-1508 (4) 2.90 1.50

Cent. of Brazil's membership in UPU.

Diario de Porto Alegre A819

1977, June 1

1509 A819 1.10cr multi .20 .20

Diario de Porto Alegre, newspaper, 150th anniv.

Blue Whale A820

1977, June 3

1510 A820 1.30cr multi .20 .20

Protection of marine life.

"Life and Development" — A821

1977, June 20

1511 A821 1.30cr multi .20 .20

National Development Bank, 25th anniversary.

Train Leaving Tunnel — A822

1977, July 8 Engr. *Perf. 11½*

1512 A822 1.30cr black .20 .20

Centenary of Sao Paulo-Rio de Janeiro railroad.

Vasum Cassiforme A823

Caduceus, Formulas for Water and Fluoride A824

Sea Shells: No. 1514, Strombus goliath. No. 1515, Murex tenuivaricosus.

1977, July 14 Litho.

1513 A823 1.30cr blue & multi .20 .20
1514 A823 1.30cr brown & multi .20 .20
1515 A823 1.30cr green & multi .20 .20
Nos. 1513-1515 (3) .60 .60

1977, July 15 *Perf. 11½x11*

1516 A824 1.30cr multi .20 .20

3rd Intl. Odontology Congress, Rio, July 15-21.

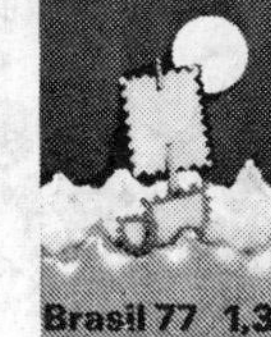

Masonic Emblem, Map of Brazil — A825

"Stamps Don't Sink or Lose their Way" — A826

1977, July 18 *Perf. 11½*

1517 A825 1.30cr bl, lt bl & blk .20 .20

50th anniversary of the founding of the Brazilian Grand Masonic Lodge.

1977, Aug. 1

1518 A826 1.30cr multi .20 .20

Stamp Day 1977.

Dom Pedro's Proclamation — A827

Horses and Bulls — A828

1977, Aug. 11 Litho. *Perf. 11½*

1519 A827 1.30cr multi .20 .20

150th anniversary of Brazilian Law School.

Perf. 11½x11, 11x11½

1977, Aug. 20 Litho.

Brazilian folklore: No. 1521, King on horseback. No. 1522, Joust, horiz.

1520 A828 1.30cr ocher & multi .20 .20
1521 A828 1.30cr blue & multi .20 .20
1522 A828 1.30cr yel & multi .20 .20
Nos. 1520-1522 (3) .60 .60

2000-reis Doubloon A829

Brazilian Colonial Coins: No. 1524, 640r pataca. No. 1525, 20r copper "vintem."

1977, Aug. 31 *Perf. 11½*

1523 A829 1.30cr vio bl & multi .20 .15
1524 A829 1.30cr dk red & multi .20 .15
1525 A829 1.30cr yel & multi .20 .15
Nos. 1523-1525 (3) .60 .45

Pinwheel A830

Neoregelia Carolinae A831

1977, Sept. 1

1526 A830 1.30cr multi .20 .15

National Week.

1977, Sept. 21 Litho. *Perf. 11½*

1527 A831 1.30cr multi .20 .15

Nature preservation.

Pen, Pencil, Letters — A832

1977, Oct. 15 Litho. *Perf. 11½*

1528 A832 1.30cr multi .20 .15

Primary education, sesquicentennial.

Dome and Telescope A833

1977, Oct. 15

1529 A833 1.30cr multi .20 .15

National Astrophysics Observatory, Brasópolis, sesquicentennial.

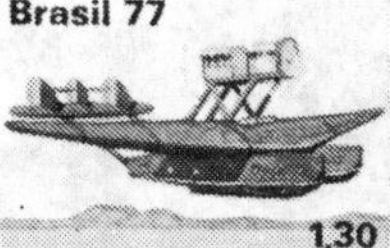

"Jahu" Hydroplane (Savoia Marchetti S-55) — A834

Design: No. 1531, PAX, dirigible.

1977, Oct. 17

1530 A834 1.30cr multi .25 .25
1531 A834 1.30cr multi .25 .25

50th anniv. of crossing of South Atlantic by Joao Ribeiro de Barros, Genoa-Sao Paulo (#1530) and 75th anniv. of the PAX airship (#1531).

A835

A836

1977, Oct. 24

1532 A835 1.30cr Il'Guarani .20 .15

Book Day and to honor Jose Martiniano de Alencar, writer, jurist.

1977, Nov. 5 Litho. *Perf. 11½*

1533 A836 1.30cr Waves .20 .15

Amateur Radio Operators' Day.

Nativity — A837

Christmas (folk art): 2cr, Annunciation. 5cr, Nativity.

1977, Nov. 10

1534 A837 1.30cr bister & multi .22 .15
1535 A837 2cr bister & multi .32 .15
1536 A837 5cr bister & multi .65 .25
Nos. 1534-1536 (3) 1.19 .55

Brasil 77 1,30

A838

A839

1977, Nov. 19

1537 A838 1.30cr Emerald .20 .20
1538 A838 1.30cr Topaz .20 .20
1539 A838 1.30cr Aquamarine .20 .20
Nos. 1537-1539 (3) .60 .60

PORTUCALE 77, 2nd International Topical Exhibition, Porto, Nov. 19-20.

1977, Nov. 24 Litho. *Perf. 11½*

1540 A839 1.30cr Angel, cornucopia .20 .20

National Thanksgiving Day.

Army's Railroad Construction Battalion A840

Civilian services of armed forces: No. 1542, Navy's Amazon flotilla. No. 1543, Air Force's postal service (plane).

1977, Dec. 5

1541 A840 1.30cr multi .20 .20
1542 A840 1.30cr multi .20 .20
1543 A840 1.30cr multi .20 .20
Nos. 1541-1543 (3) .60 .60

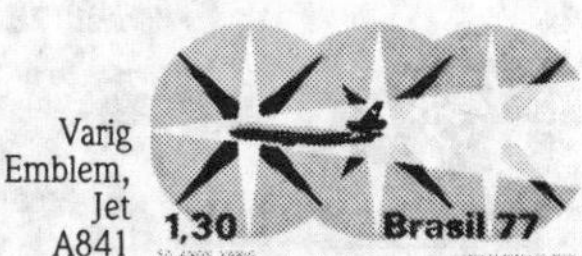

Varig Emblem, Jet A841

1977, Dec. *Perf. 11x11½*

1544 A841 1.30cr bl & blk .20 .20

50th anniversary of Varig Airline.

Sts. Cosme and Damiao Church, Igaracu — A842

Woman Holding Sheaf — A843

Brazilian Architecture: 7.50cr, St. Bento Monastery Church, Rio de Janeiro. 8.50cr, Church of St. Francis of Assisi, Ouro Preto. 9.50cr, St. Anthony Convent Church, Joao Pessoa.

1977, Dec. 8

1545 A842 2.70cr multi .30 .15
1546 A842 7.50cr multi .90 .35
1547 A842 8.50cr multi .90 .40
1548 A842 9.50cr multi 1.25 .45
Nos. 1545-1548 (4) 3.35 1.35

1977, Dec. 19 *Perf. 11½*

1549 A843 1.30cr multi .20 .20

Brazilian diplomacy.

Soccer Ball and Foot — A844

Designs: No. 1551, Soccer ball in net. No. 1552, Symbolic soccer player.

1978, Mar. 1 Litho. *Perf. 11½*

1550 A844 1.80cr multi .28 .20
1551 A844 1.80cr multi .28 .20
1552 A844 1.80cr multi .28 .20
Nos. 1550-1552 (3) .84 .60

11th World Cup Soccer Championship, Argentina, June 1-25.

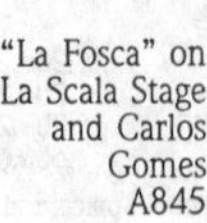

"La Fosca" on La Scala Stage and Carlos Gomes A845

1978, Feb. 9

1553 A845 1.80cr multi .20 .20

Bicentenary of La Scala in Milan, and to honor Carlos Gomes (1836-1893), Brazilian composer.

Symbols of Postal Mechanization — A846

1978, Mar. 15 Litho. *Perf. 11½*

1554 A846 1.80cr multi .20 .20

Opening of Postal Staff College.

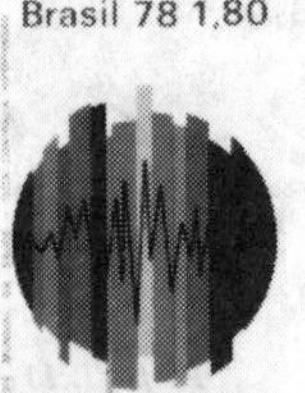

Hypertension Chart — A847

Waves from Antenna Uniting World — A848

1978, Apr. 4

1555 A847 1.80cr multi .20 .20

World Health Day, fight against hypertension.

1978, May 17 Litho. *Perf. 12x11½*

1556 A848 1.80cr multi .20 .20

10th World Telecommunications Day.

Brazilian Canary A849

Birds: 8.50cr, Cotinga. 9.50cr, Tanager fastuosa.

1978, June 5 *Perf. 11½x12*

1557 A849 7.50cr multi 1.00 .75
1558 A849 8.50cr multi 1.00 .80
1559 A849 9.50cr multi 1.00 1.00
Nos. 1557-1559 (3) 3.00 2.55

Inocencio Serzedelo Correa and Manuel Francisco Correa, 1893 A850

1978, June 20 Litho. *Perf. 11x11½*

1560 A850 1.80cr multi .20 .20

85th anniversary of Union Court of Audit.

Post and Telegraph Building A851

1978, June 22 *Perf. 11½*

1561 A851 1.80cr multi .20 .25

Souvenir Sheet

Imperf

1562 A851 7.50cr multi .75 1.50

Inauguration of Post and Telegraph Building (ECT), Brasilia, and for BRAPEX, 3rd Brazilian Philatelic Exhibition, Brasilia, June 23-28 (No. 1562).

Ernesto Geisel, President of Brazil — A852

1978, June 22 Engr. *Perf. 11½*

1563 A852 1.80cr dl grn .20 .15

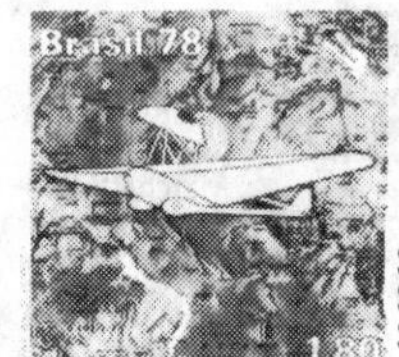

Savoia-Marchetti S-64, Map of South Atlantic A853

1978, July 3 Litho.

1564 A853 1.80cr multi .20 .20

50th anniv. of 1st crossing of South Atlantic by Carlos del Prete and Arturo Ferrarin.

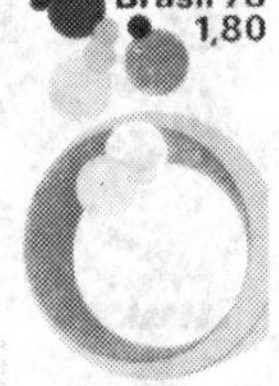

Symbolic of Smallpox Eradication A854

Brazil No. 68 A855

1978, July 25

1565 A854 1.80cr multi .20 .20

Eradication of smallpox.

1978, Aug. 1

1566 A855 1.80cr multi .20 .20

Stamp Day, centenary of the "Barba Branca" (white beard) issue.

Stormy Sea, by Seelinger A856

1978, Aug. 4

1567 A856 1.80cr multi .20 .20

Helios Seelinger, painter, birth centenary.

Guitar Players — A857

Musicians and Instruments: No. 1569, Flutes. No. 1570, Percussion instruments.

1978, Aug. 22 Litho. *Perf. 11½*

1568 A857 1.80cr multi .20 .15
1569 A857 1.80cr multi .20 .15
1570 A857 1.80cr multi .20 .20
Nos. 1568-1570 (3) .60 .50

Children at Play A858

1978, Sept. 1 Litho. *Perf. 11½*

1571 A858 1.80cr multi .20 .20

National Week.

Collegiate Church A859

1978, Sept. 6 Engr.

1572 A859 1.80cr red brn .20 .20

Restoration of patio of Collegiate Church, Sao Paulo.

Justice by A. Geschiatti A860

1978, Sept. 18 Litho.

1573 A860 1.80cr blk & olive .20 .20

Federal Supreme Court, sesquicentennial.

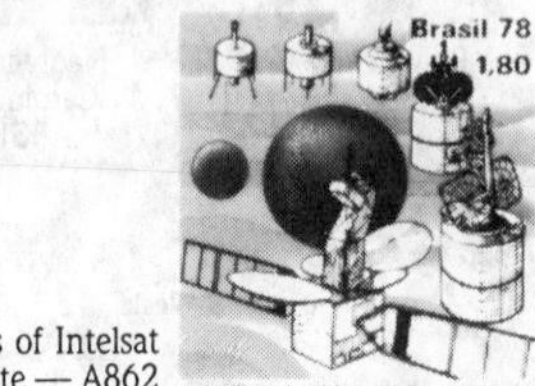

Iguacu Falls — A861

Design: No. 1575, Yellow ipecac.

1978, Sept. 21

1574 A861 1.80cr multi .20 .20
1575 A861 1.80cr multi .20 .20

Iguacu National Park.

Stages of Intelsat Satellite — A862

1978, Oct. 9 Litho. *Perf. 11½*

1576 A862 1.80cr multi .20 .20

Flag of Order of Christ A863

Brazilian Flags: No. 1578, Principality of Brazil. No. 1579, United Kingdom. No. 1580, Imperial Brazil. No. 1581, National flag (current).

1978, Oct. 13

1577 A863 1.80cr multi .65 .55
1578 A863 1.80cr multi .65 .55
1579 A863 1.80cr multi .65 .55
1580 A863 8.50cr multi .65 .55
1581 A863 8.50cr multi .65 .55
a. Block of 5, #1577-1581 + label 3.25 6.50
Nos. 1577-1581 (5) 3.25 2.75

7th LUBRAPEX Philatelic Exhibition, Porto Alegre.

Mail Street Car A864

Mail Transportation: No. 1583, Overland mail truck. No. 1584, Mail delivery truck. 7.50cr. Railroad mail car. 8.50cr, Mail coach. 9.50cr, Post riders.

1978, Oct. 21 *Perf. 11x11½*

1582 A864 1.80cr multi .50 .40
1583 A864 1.80cr multi .50 .40
1584 A864 1.80cr multi .50 .40
1585 A864 7.50cr multi .50 .40
1586 A864 8.50cr multi .50 .40
1587 A864 9.50cr multi .50 .50
a. Block of 6, #1582-1587 3.00 3.00

18th UPU Congress, Rio de Janeiro, 1979.

Gaucho Herding Cattle, and Cactus — A865

1978, Oct. 23 *Perf. 11½x11*

1588 A865 1.80cr multi .20 .20

Joao Guimaraes Rosa, poet and diplomat, 70th birthday.

St. Anthony's Hill, by Nicholas A. Taunay A866

Landscape Paintings: No. 1590, Castle Hill, by Victor Meirelles. No. 1591, View of Sabara, by Alberto da Veiga Guignard. No. 1592, View of Pernambuco, by Frans Post.

1978, Nov. 6 Litho. *Perf. 11½*

1589 A866 1.80cr multi .20 .20
1590 A866 1.80cr multi .20 .20
1591 A866 1.80cr multi .20 .20
1592 A866 1.80cr multi .20 .20
Nos. 1589-1592 (4) .80 .80

Angel with Harp — A867

Christmas: No. 1594, Angel with lute. No. 1595, Angel with oboe.

1978, Nov. 10
1593 A867 1.80cr multi .20 .20
1594 A867 1.80cr multi .20 .20
1595 A867 1.80cr multi .20 .20
Nos. 1593-1595 (3) .60 .60

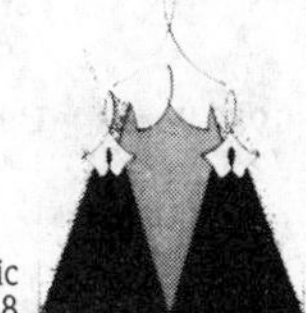

Symbolic Candles — A868

1978, Nov. 23
1596 A868 1.80cr blk, gold & car .20 .20

National Thanksgiving Day.

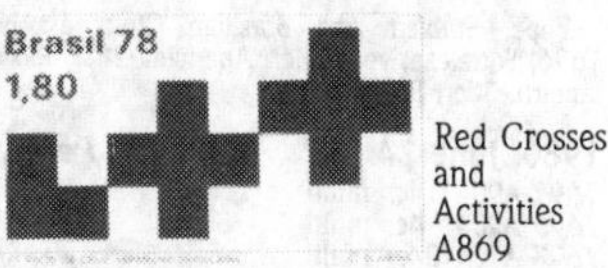

Red Crosses and Activities A869

1978, Dec. 5 Litho. ***Perf. 11x11½***
1597 A869 1.80cr blk & red .20 .20

70th anniversary of Brazilian Red Cross.

Paz Theater, Belem — A870

Designs: 12cr, José de Alencar Theater, Portaleza. 12.50cr, Municipal Theater, Rio de Janeiro.

1978, Dec. 6 ***Perf. 11½***
1598 A870 10.50cr multi .70 .25
1599 A870 12cr multi .70 .25
1600 A870 12.50cr multi .70 .25
Nos. 1598-1600 (3) 2.10 .75

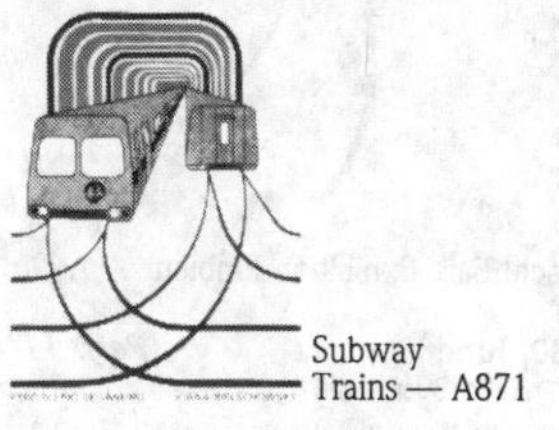

Subway Trains — A871

1979, Mar. 5 Litho. ***Perf. 11½***
1601 A871 2.50cr multi .20 .18

Inauguration of Rio subway system.

Old and New Post Offices A872

Designs: No. 1603, Old and new mail boxes. No. 1604, Manual and automatic mail sorting. No. 1605, Old and new planes. No. 1606, Telegraph and telex machine. No. 1607, Mailmen's uniforms.

1979, Mar. 20 Litho. ***Perf. 11x11½***
1602 A872 2.50cr multi .25 .20
1603 A872 2.50cr multi .25 .20
1604 A872 2.50cr multi .25 .20
1605 A872 2.50cr multi .25 .20
1606 A872 2.50cr multi .25 .20
1607 A872 2.50cr multi .25 .20
Nos. 1602-1607 (6) 1.50 1.20

10th anniv. of the new Post and Telegraph Dept., and 18th Universal Postal Union Cong., Rio de Janeiro, Sept.-Oct., 1979.

O'Day 23 Class Yacht A873

Yachts and Stamp Outlines: 10.50cr, Penguin Class. 12cr, Hobie Cat Class. 12.50cr, Snipe Class.

1979, Apr. 18 Litho. ***Perf. 11x11½***
1608 A873 2.50cr multi .28 .26
1609 A873 10.50cr multi .55 .45
1610 A873 12cr multi .55 .35
1611 A873 12.50cr multi .75 .35
Nos. 1608-1611 (4) 2.13 1.41

Brasiliana '79, 3rd World Thematic Stamp Exhibition, Sao Conrado, Sept. 15-23.

Children, IYC Emblem — A874

1979, May 30 Litho. ***Perf. 11½***
1612 A874 2.50cr multi .25 .20

Intl. Year of the Child & Children's Book Day.

Giant Water Lily — A875

Designs: 12cr, Amazon manatee. 12.50cr, Arrau (turtle).

1979, June 5 Litho. ***Perf. 11½***
1613 A875 10.50cr multi .70 .50
1614 A875 12cr multi .90 .60
1615 A875 12.50cr multi .90 .60
Nos. 1613-1615 (3) 2.50 1.70

Amazon National Park, nature conservation.

Brasil 79 2,50

Bank Emblem — A876

1979, June 7
1616 A876 2.50cr multi .20 .15

Northwest Bank of Brazil, 25th anniversary.

Physician Tending Patient 15th Cent. Woodcut A877

1979, June 30
1617 A877 2.50cr multi .20 .15

Natl. Academy of Medicine, 50th anniv.

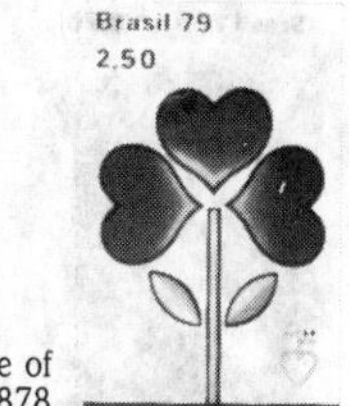

Flower made of Hearts — A878

1979, July 8 Litho. ***Perf. 11½***
1618 A878 2.50cr multi .20 .15

35th Brazilian Cardiology Congress.

Souvenir Sheet

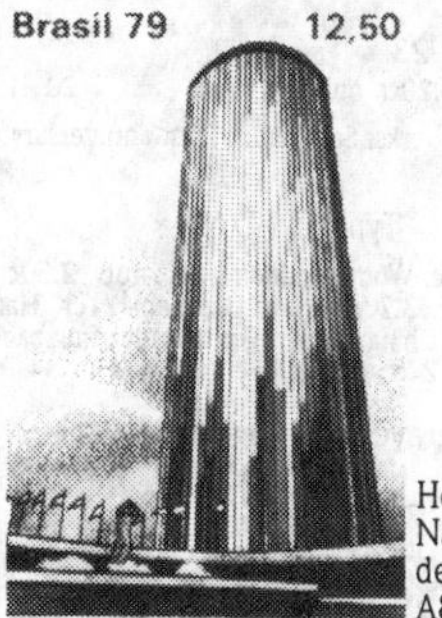

Hotel Nacional, Rio de Janeiro A879

1979, July 16
1619 A879 12.50cr multi .75 1.50

Brasiliana '79 comprising 1st Inter-American Exhibition of Classical Philately and 3rd World Topical Exhibition, Rio de Janeiro, Sept. 15-23.

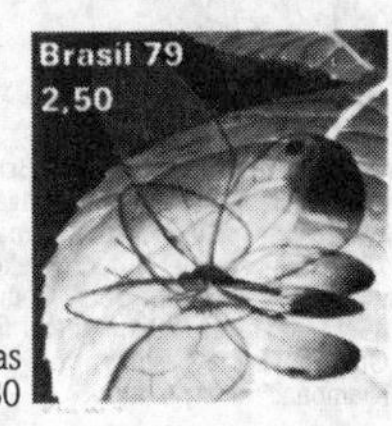

Cithaerias Aurora — A880

Moths: 10.50cr, Evenus regalis. 12cr, Caligo eurilochus. 12.50cr, Diaethria clymena janeira.

1979, Aug. 1
1620 A880 2.50cr multi .18 .15
1621 A880 10.50cr multi .60 .40
1622 A880 12cr multi .70 .52
1623 A880 12.50cr multi .70 .52
Nos. 1620-1623 (4) 2.18 1.59

Stamp Day 1979.

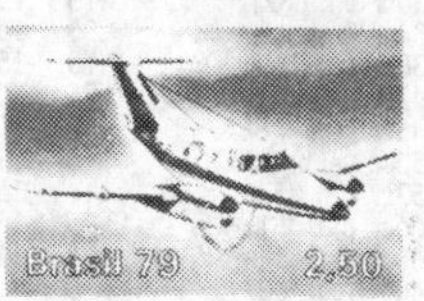

EMB-121 Xingo A881

1979, Aug. 19 Litho. ***Perf. 11½***
1624 A881 2.50cr vio blue .20 .20

Embraer, Brazilian aircraft company, 10th anniversary.

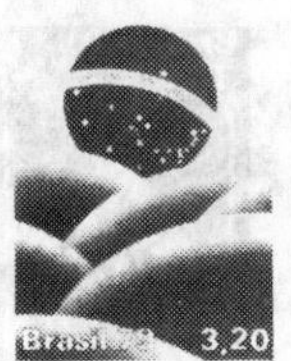

A882

Brasil 79 2,50

A883

Natl. emblem over landscape.

1979, Sept. 12
1625 A882 3.20cr multi .20 .20

National Week.

1979, Sept. 8 Litho. ***Perf. 11½***
1626 A883 2.50cr multi .20 .20

Statue of Our Lady of the Apparition, 75th anniversary of coronation.

"UPU," Envelope and Mail Transport A884

"UPU" and: No. 1628, Post Office emblems. 10.50cr, Globe. 12cr, Flags of Brazil and UN. 12.50cr, UPU emblem.

1979, Sept. 12 ***Perf. 11x11½***
1627 A884 2.50cr multi .16 .16
1628 A884 2.50cr multi .16 .16
1629 A884 10.50cr multi .52 .52
1630 A884 12cr multi .70 .70
1631 A884 12.50cr multi .70 .70
Nos. 1627-1631 (5) 2.24 2.24

18th UPU Cong., Rio, Sept.-Oct. 1979.

Pyramid Fountain, Rio de Janeiro — A885

Fountains: 10.50cr, Facade, Marilia, Ouro Preto, horiz. 12cr, Boa Vista, Recife.

Perf. 12x11½, 11½x12

1979, Sept. 15
1632 A885 2.50cr multi .16 .16
1633 A885 10.50cr multi .50 .50
1634 A885 12cr multi .60 .60
Nos. 1632-1634 (3) 1.26 1.26

Brasiliana '79, 1st Interamerican Exhibition of Classical Philately.

Church of the Glory — A886

Landscapes by Leandro Joaquim: 12cr, Fishing on Guanabara Bay. 12.50cr, Boqueirao Lake and Carioca Arches.

1979, Sept. 15 ***Perf. 11½***
1635 A886 2.50cr multi .16 .16
1636 A886 12cr multi .60 .60
1637 A886 12.50cr multi .60 .60
Nos. 1635-1637 (3) 1.36 1.36

Brasiliana '79, 3rd World Topical Exhibition, Sao Conrado, Sept. 15-23.

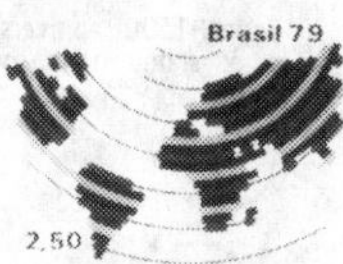

World Map — A887

1979, Sept. 20
1638 A887 2.50cr multi .20 .20

3rd World Telecommunications Exhibition, Geneva, Sept. 20-26.

"UPU" and UPU Emblem — A888

1979, Oct. 9 Litho. *Perf. 11½x11*

1639 A888	2.50cr multi		.18	.18
1640 A888	10.50cr multi		.55	.55
1641 A888	12cr multi		.65	.65
1642 A888	12.50cr multi		.65	.65
		Nos. 1639-1642 (4)	2.03	2.03

Universal Postal Union Day.

IYC Emblem, Feather Toy A889

IYC Emblem and Toys: No. 1644, Bumble bee, ragdoll. No. 1645, Flower, top. No. 1646, Wooden acrobat.

1979, Oct. 12 *Perf. 11½*

1643 A889	2.50cr multi		.25	.20
1644 A889	3.20cr multi		.25	.25
1645 A889	3.20cr multi		.25	.25
1646 A889	3.20cr multi		.25	.25
		Nos. 1643-1646 (4)	1.00	.95

International Year of the Child.

Adoration of the Kings — A890

Christmas 1979: No. 1648, Nativity. No. 1649 Jesus and the Elders in the Temple.

1979, Nov. 12 Litho. *Perf. 11½*

1647 A890	3.20cr multi		.20	.18
1648 A890	3.20cr multi		.20	.18
1649 A890	3.20cr multi		.20	.18
		Nos. 1647-1649 (3)	.60	.54

Souvenir Sheet

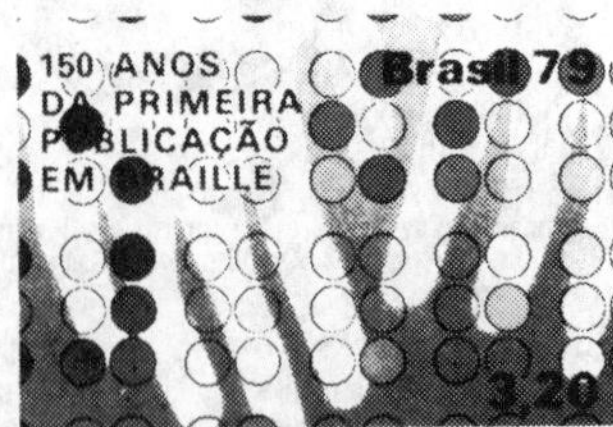

Hands Reading Braille — A891

Lithographed and Embossed

1979, Nov. 20. *Perf. 11½*

1650 A891 3.20cr multi .50 1.25

Publication of Braille script, 150th anniversary. Margin shows extension of stamp design with Braille printed and embossed.

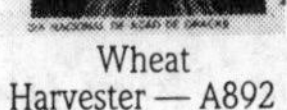

Wheat Harvester — A892

Steel Mill — A893

1979, Nov. 22

1651 A892 3.20cr multi .20 .15

Thanksgiving 1979.

1979, Nov. 23

1652 A893 3.20cr multi .20 .15

COSIPA Steelworks, Sao Paulo, 25th anniversary.

Type of 1976

Designs: 70c, Women grinding coconuts. 2.50cr, Basket weaver. 3.20cr, River boatman. 21cr, Harvesting ramie (China grass). 27cr, Man leading pack mule. 3.20cr, 27cr, horiz.

Photogravure, Engraved (21cr)

1979 *Perf. 11x11½, 11½x11*

1653 A790	70c gray grn		.15	.15
1654 A790	2.50cr sepia		.15	.15
1655 A790	3.20cr blue		.15	.15
1656 A790	21cr purple		.38	.15
1657 A790	27cr sepia		.45	.15
		Nos. 1653-1657 (5)	1.28	
		Set value		.40

A894

Designs: 2cr, Coconuts. 3cr, Mangoes. 4cr, Corn. 5cr, Onions. 7cr, Oranges. 10cr, Maracuja. 12cr, Pineapple. 15cr, Bananas. 17cr, Guarana. 20cr, Sugar cane. 24cr, Beekeeping. 30cr, Silkworm. 34cr, Cacao. 38cr, Coffee. 42cr, Soybeans. 45cr, Mandioca. 50cr, Wheat. 57cr, Peanuts. 66cr, Grapes. 100cr, Cashews. 140cr, Tomatoes. 200cr, Mamona. 500cr, Cotton.

1980-83 Photo. *Perf. 11½x11*

1658	A894	2cr yel brn ('82)		.15	.15
1659	A894	3cr red ('82)		.15	.15
1660	A894	4cr orange		.15	.15
1661	A894	5cr dk pur ('82)		.15	.15
1662	A894	7cr org ('81)		.15	.15
1663	A894	10cr bl grn ('82)		.15	.15
1664	A894	12cr dk grn ('81)		.22	.15
1665	A894	15cr gldn brn ('83)		.15	.15
1666	A894	17cr brn org ('82)		.24	.15
1667	A894	20cr olive ('82)		.22	.15
1668	A894	24cr bis ('82)		.15	.15
1669	A894	30cr blk ('82)		.15	.15
1670	A894	34cr brown		.35	.15
1671	A894	38cr red ('83)		.15	.15
1672	A894	42cr green		5.75	.50
1673	A894	45cr sepia ('83)		.55	.15
1674	A894	50cr yel org ('82)		.16	.15
1675	A894	57cr brn ('83)		.16	.15
1676	A894	66cr pur ('81)		3.75	.15
1677	A894	100cr dk red brn ('81)		2.25	.15
1678	A894	140cr red ('82)		2.75	.15

Engr.

1678A	A894	200cr grn ('82)		2.75	.15
1679	A894	500cr brn ('82)		5.75	.15
			Nos. 1658-1679 (23)	26.40	
			Set value		2.25

See Nos. 1934-1941.

Plant Inside Raindrop — A896

Light Bulb Containing: 17cr+7cr, Sun. 20cr+8cr, Windmill. 21cr+9cr, Dam.

1980, Jan. 2 Litho. *Perf. 12*

1680 A896	3.20cr multi		.15	.15
1681 A896	24cr (17 + 7)		1.25	.65
1682 A896	28cr (20 + 8)		1.50	.75
1683 A896	30cr (21 + 9)		2.25	.85
		Nos. 1680-1683 (4)	5.15	2.40

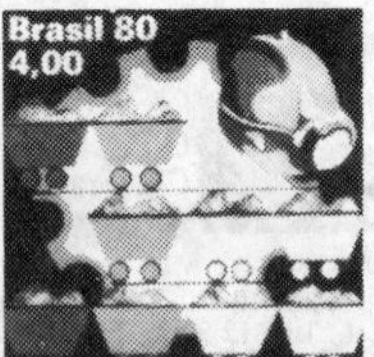

Anthracite Industry — A897

1980, Mar. 19 Litho. *Perf. 11½*

1684 A897 4cr multi .20 .15

Map of Americas, Symbols of Development — A898

1980, Apr. 14 Litho. *Perf. 11x11½*

1685 A898 4cr multi .20 .15

21st Assembly of Inter-American Development Bank Governors, Rio, Apr. 14-16.

Tapirape Mask, Mato Grosso A899

1980, Apr. 18 *Perf. 11½*

1686 A899	4cr shown		.20	.15
1687 A899	4cr Tukuna mask, Amazonas, vert.		.20	.15
1688 A899	4cr Kanela mask, Maranhao, vert.		.20	.15
		Nos. 1686-1688 (3)	.60	.45

Brazilian Television, 30th Anniversary A900

1980, May 5 Litho. *Perf. 11½*

1689 A900 4cr multicolored .18 .15

Duke of Caixas, by Miranda — A901

The Worker, by Candido Partinari — A902

1980, May 7

1690 A901 4cr multicolored .18 .15

Duke of Caixas, death centenary.

1980, May 18

Paintings: 28cr, Mademoiselle Pogany, by Constantin Brancusi. 30cr, The Glass of Water, by Francisco Aurelio de Figueiredo.

1691 A902	24cr multi		1.10	.55
1692 A902	28cr multi		1.10	.55
1693 A902	30cr multi		1.65	.55
		Nos. 1691-1693 (3)	3.85	1.65

Graf Zeppelin, 50th Anniversary of Atlantic Crossing A903

1980, June Litho. *Perf. 11x11½*

1694 A903 4cr multicolored .20 .15

Pope John Paul II, St. Peter's, Rome, Congress Emblem A904

Pope, Emblem and Brazilian Churches: No. 1696, Fortaleza, vert. 24cr, Apericida 28cr, Rio de Janeiro. 30cr, Brasilia.

1980, June 24 *Perf. 12*

1695 A904	4cr multi		.18	.15
1696 A904	4cr multi		.18	.15
1697 A904	24cr multi		.90	.40
1698 A904	28cr multi		.90	.40
1699 A904	30cr multi		1.75	.40
		Nos. 1695-1699 (5)	3.91	1.50

Visit of Pope John Paul II to Brazil, June 30-July 12; 10th National Eucharistic Congress, Fortaleza, July 9-16.

First Transatlantic Flight, 50th Anniversary — A905

1980, June Litho. *Perf. 11x11½*

1700 A905 4cr multicolored .20 .15

Souvenir Sheet

Yacht Sail, Exhibition Emblem — A906

1980, June *Perf. 11½*

1701 A906 30cr multi 1.00 1.50

Brapex IV Stamp Exhib., Fortaleza, June 13-21.

Rowing, Moscow '80 Emblem A907

1980, June 30

1702 A907	4cr shown		.20	.15
1703 A907	4cr Target shooting		.20	.15
1704 A907	4cr Bicycling		.20	.15
		Nos. 1702-1704 (3)	.60	.45

22nd Summer Olympic Games, Moscow, July 19-Aug. 3.

Rondon Community Works Project A908

1980, July 11

1705 A908 4cr multicolored .20 .15

Helen Keller and Anne Sullivan
A909

1980, July 28
1706 A909 4cr multicolored .20 .15

Helen Keller (1880-1968), blind deaf writer and lecturer taught by Anne Sullivan (1867-1936).

Souvenir Sheet

São Francisco River Canoe — A910

1980, Aug. 1 Litho. *Perf. 11½*
1707 A910 24cr multi 1.00 1.50

Stamp Day.

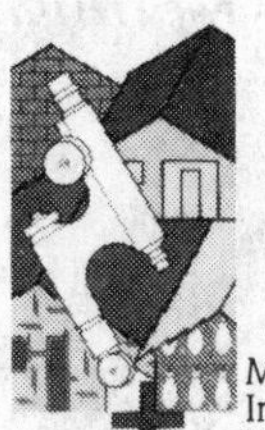

Microscope, Red Cross, Insects, Brick and Tile Houses — A911

1980, Aug. 5 *Perf. 11½x11*
1708 A911 4cr multi .25 .15

National Health Day.

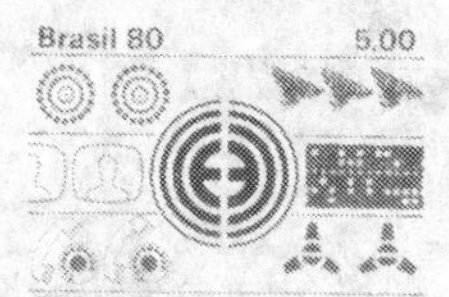

Brazilian Postal Administration, 15th Anniversary — A912

1980, Sept. 16 Litho. *Perf. 12*
1709 A912 5cr multi .25 .20

Souvenir Sheet

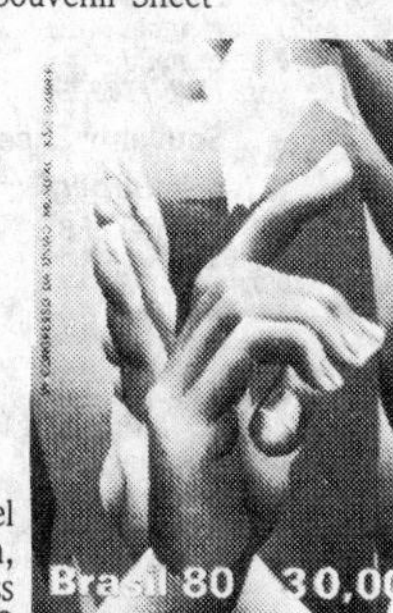

St. Gabriel World Union, 6th Congress
A913

1980, Sept. 29 *Perf. 11½x12*
1710 A913 30cr multi 1.00 1.50

Cattleya Amethystoglossa
A914

1980, Oct. 3 *Perf. 11½*
1711 A914 5cr *shown* .18 .15
1712 A914 5cr *Laelia cinnabarina* .18 .15
1713 A914 24cr *Zygopetalum crinitum* 1.10 .60
1714 A914 28cr *Laelia tenebrosa* 1.10 .60
Nos. 1711-1714 (4) 2.56 1.50

Espamer 80, American-European Philatelic Exhibition, Madrid, Oct. 3-12.

Red-tailed Amazon Parrot — A915

Capitao Rodrigo, Hero of Erico Verissimo's "O Continento" — A916

Parrots: No. 1716, Vinaceous Amazon. No. 1717, Brown-backed. No. 1718, Red-spectacled.

1980, Oct. 18 Litho. *Perf. 12*
1715 A915 5cr multi .18 .15
1716 A915 5cr multi .18 .15
1717 A915 28cr multi 1.10 .60
1718 A915 28cr multi 1.10 .60
Nos. 1715-1718 (4) 2.56 1.50

Lubrapex '80 Stamp Exhib., Lisbon, Oct. 18-26.

1980, Oct. 23
1719 A916 5cr multi .25 .20

Book Day.

Flight into Egypt — A917

1980, Nov. 5
1720 A917 5cr multi .25 .20

Christmas 1980.

Sound Waves and Oscillator Screen
A918

1980, Nov. 7
1721 A918 5cr multi .25 .20

Telebras Research Center inauguration.

Carvalho Viaduct, Paranagua-Curitiba Railroad — A919

1980, Nov. 10
1722 A919 5cr multi .25 .20

Engineering Club centenary.

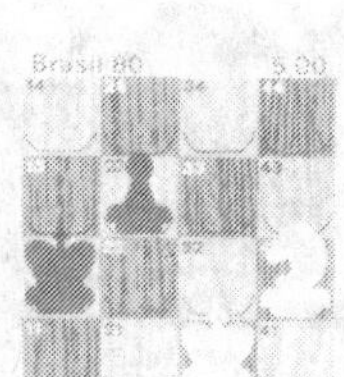

A920

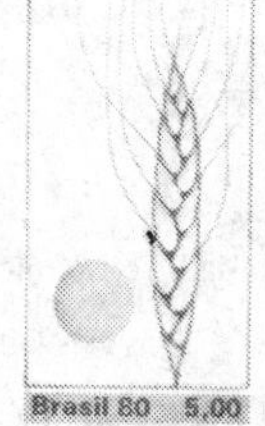

A921

1980, Nov. 18 Litho. *Perf. 11½*
1723 A920 5cr Portable chess board .25 .50

Postal chess contest.

1980, Nov. 27 *Perf. 11½x11*
1724 A921 5cr Sun, wheat .25 .40

Thanksgiving 1980

Father Anchieta Writing "Virgin Mary, Mother of God" on Sand of Iperoig Beach — A922

1980, Dec. 8 *Perf. 12*
1725 A922 5cr multi .25 .20

Christ Carrying Cross, By O Aleijadinho
A923

Antonio Francisco Lisboa (O Aleijadinho), 250th Birth Anniv.: Paintings of the life of Christ: a, Mount of Olives. b, Arrest in the Garden. c, Flagellation. d, Crown of Thorns. f, Crucifixion.

1980, Dec. 29
1726 Block of 6 1.65 1.65
a.-f. A923 5cr any single .24 .16

Agricultural Productivity
A924

1981, Jan. 2 Litho. *Perf. 11x11½*
1727 A924 30cr shown 1.25 .35
1728 A924 35cr Domestic markets 1.10 .35
1729 A924 40cr Exports 1.10 .35
Nos. 1727-1729 (3) 3.45 1.05

Boy Scout and Campfire
A925

1981, Jan. 22 Litho. *Perf. 11x11½*
1730 A925 5cr shown .25 .20
1731 A925 5cr Scouts cooking .25 .20
1732 A925 5cr Scout, tents .25 .20
Nos. 1730-1732 (3) .75 .60

4th Pan-American Scout Jamboree.

Souvenir Sheet

Mailman, 1930 — A926

1981, Mar. 11 Litho. *Perf. 11*
1733 Sheet of 3 4.00 4.00
a. A926 30cr shown 1.00 1.00
b. A926 35cr Mailman, 1981 1.00 1.00
c. A926 40cr Telegram messenger, 1930 1.00 1.00

Dept. of Posts & Telegraphs, 50th anniv.

Souvenir Sheet

The Hunter and the Jaguar, by Felix Taunay (1795-1881)
A927

1981, Apr. 10 Litho. *Perf. 11*
1734 A927 30cr multi 1.00 *2.00*

Lima Barreto and Rio de Janeiro, 1900
A928

1981, May 13 Litho. *Perf. 11½*
1735 A928 7cr multi .25 .20

Lima Barreto, writer, birth centenary.

Maraca Indian Funerary Urn — A929

1981, May 18
1736 A929 7cr shown .25 .20
1737 A929 7cr Marajoara triangular jug .25 .20
1738 A929 7cr Tupi-Guarani bowl .25 .20
Nos. 1736-1738 (3) .75 .60

Lophornis Magnifica
A930

Designs: Hummingbirds.

1981, May 22 *Perf. 11½*
1739 A930 7cr shown .30 .20
1740 A930 7cr Phaethornis pretrei .30 .20
1741 A930 7cr Chrysolampis mosquitus .30 .20
1742 A930 7cr Heliactin cornuta .30 .20
Nos. 1739-1742 (4) 1.20 .80

Rotary Emblem and Faces — A931

1981, May 31
1743 A931 7cr Emblem, hands .20 .15
1744 A931 35cr shown 1.00 .80

72nd Convention of Rotary Intl., Sao Paulo.

Environmental Protection A932

1981, June 5 *Perf. 12*
1745 A932 7cr shown .25 .20
1746 A932 7cr Forest .25 .20
1747 A932 7cr Clouds (air) .25 .20
1748 A932 7cr Village (soil) .25 .20
a. Block of 4, #1745-1748 1.00 1.00

Biplane, 1931 (Airmail Service, 50th Anniv.) A933

1981, June 10 *Perf. 11½*
1749 A933 7cr multi .25 .20

Madeira-Mamore Railroad, 50th Anniv. of Nationalization — A934

1981, July 10 Litho. *Perf. 11x11½*
1750 A934 7cr multi .25 .20

66th Intl. Esperanto Congress, Brasilia A935

1981, July 26 *Perf. 12*
1751 A935 7cr green & blk .25 .20

No. 79 A936

1981, Aug. 1
1752 A936 50cr shown 1.40 .30
1753 A936 55cr No. 80 1.40 .30
1754 A936 60cr No. 81 1.40 .30
Nos. 1752-1754 (3) 4.20 .90

Stamp Day; cent. of "small head" stamps.

Institute of Military Engineering, 50th Anniv. — A937

1981, Aug. 11 Litho. *Perf. 11½*
1755 A937 12cr multi .25 .20

Reisado Dancers — A938

1981, Aug. 22
1756 A938 50cr Dancers, diff. .80 .22
1757 A938 55cr Sailors .80 .25
1758 A938 60cr shown .80 .20
Nos. 1756-1758 (3) 2.40 .67

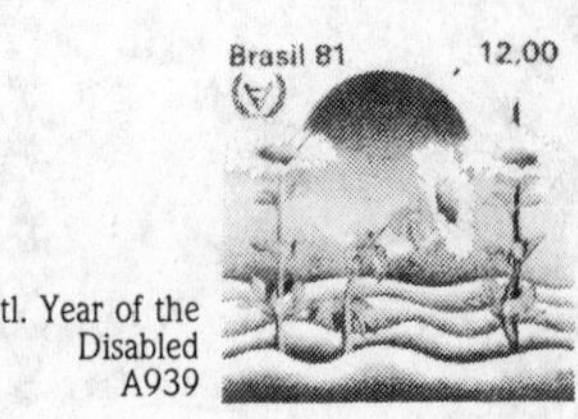

Intl. Year of the Disabled A939

1981, Sept. 17 Litho. *Perf. 11½*
1759 A939 12cr multi .25 .20

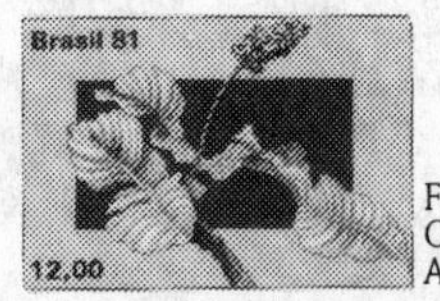

Flowers of the Central Plateau A940

1981, Sept. 21 Litho. *Perf. 12*
1760 A940 12cr Palicourea rigida .25 .20
1761 A940 12cr Dalechampia caperonioides .25 .20
1762 A940 12cr Cassia clausseni, vert. .25 .20
1763 A940 12cr Eremanthus sphaerocephalus, vert. .25 .20
Nos. 1760-1763 (4) 1.00 .80

Virgin of Nazareth Statue — A941

Christ the Redeemer Statue, Rio de Janeiro, 50th Anniv. — A942

1981, Oct. 10 Litho. *Perf. 12*
1764 A941 12cr multi .25 .20

Candle Festival of Nazareth, Belem.

1981, Oct. 12
1765 A942 12cr multi .25 .20

World Food Day — A943

1981, Oct. 16
1766 A943 12c multi .25 .20

75th Anniv. of Santos-Dumont's First Flight — A944

1981, Oct. 23 Litho. *Perf. 12*
1767 A944 60cr multi 1.00 .35

Father José de Santa Rita Durao, Titlepage of his Epic Poem Caramuru, Diego Alvares Correia (Character) A945

1981, Oct. 29
1768 A945 12cr multi .25 .20

Caramuru publication centenary; World Book Day.

Christmas 1981 — A946

Designs: Creches and figurines.

1981, Nov. 10 Litho. *Perf. 12*
1769 A946 12cr multi .15 .15
1770 A946 50cr multi 1.25 .25
1771 A946 55cr multi, vert. 1.25 .28
1772 A946 60cr multi, vert. 1.25 .30
Nos. 1769-1772 (4) 3.90 .98

State Flags — A947

Designs: a, Alagoas. b, Bahia. c, Federal District. d, Pernambuco. e, Sergipe.

1981, Nov. 19
1773 Block of 5 + label 1.25 1.25
a.-e. A947 12cr, any single .20 .20

Label shows arms of Brazil.

Thanksgiving 1981 — A948

1981, Nov. 26 Litho. *Perf. 11½*
1776 A948 12cr multi .25 .15

Ministry of Labor, 50th Anniv. A949

1981, Nov. 26
1777 A949 12cr multi .20 .15

School of Engineering, Itajuba A950

1981, Nov. 30 *Perf. 11x11½*
1778 A950 15cr lt grn & pur .35 .15

Theodomiro C. Santiago, founder, birth centenary.

Sao Paulo State Police Sesquicentennial A951

1981, Dec. 15 Litho. *Perf. 12*
1779 A951 12cr Policeman with saxophone .20 .15
1780 A951 12cr Mounted policemen .20 .15

Army Library Centenary A952

1981, Dec. 17
1781 A952 12cr multi .20 .15

Souvenir Sheet

Philatelic Club of Brazil, 50th Anniv. A953

1981, Dec. 18 *Perf. 11*
1782 A953 180cr multi 4.50 *4.50*

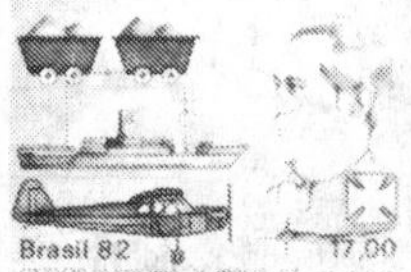

Brigadier Eduardo Gomes A954

1982, Jan. 20 Litho. *Perf. 11x11½*
1783 A954 12cr blue & blk .30 .15

Birth Centenary of Henrique Lage, Industrialist A956

1982, Mar. 14 Litho. *Perf. 11½*
1785 A956 17cr multi .50 .16

Brasil 82
75,00
1982 World Cup Soccer — A957

Brasil 82
90,00
TB Bacillus Cent. — A958

Designs: Various soccer players.

1982, Mar. 19
1786 A957 75cr multi .75 .25
1787 A957 80cr multi .75 .28
1788 A957 85cr multi .75 .28
Nos. 1786-1788 (3) 2.25 .81

Souvenir Sheet

Imperf

1789 Sheet of 3 3.00 *6.00*
a. A957 100cr like #1786 1.00
b. A957 100cr like #1787 1.00
c. A957 100cr like #1788 1.00

1982, Mar. 24 *Perf. 12*
1790 A958 90cr Microscope, lung 1.25 .80
1791 A958 100cr Lung, pills 1.25 .90
a. Pair, #1790-1791 2.50 2.00

Souvenir Sheet

A959

1982, Apr. 17 **Litho.** ***Perf. 11***
1792 Sheet of 3 3.50 3.25
a. A959 75cr Laelia Purpurata 1.00 .50
b. A959 80cr Oncidium flexuosum 1.00 .50
c. A959 85cr Cleistes revoluta 1.25 .55

BRAPEX V Stamp Exhibition, Blumenau.

Oil Drilling Centenary A960

1982, Apr. 18 ***Perf. 11½***
1793 A960 17cr multi .25 .15

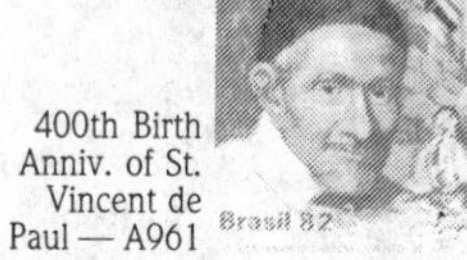

400th Birth Anniv. of St. Vincent de Paul — A961

1982, Apr. 24 **Litho.** ***Perf. 11½***
1794 A961 17cr multi .25 .15

Seven Steps of Guaira (Waterfalls) A962

1982, Apr. 29
1795 A962 17cr Fifth Fall .20 .15
1796 A962 21cr Seventh Fall .30 .20

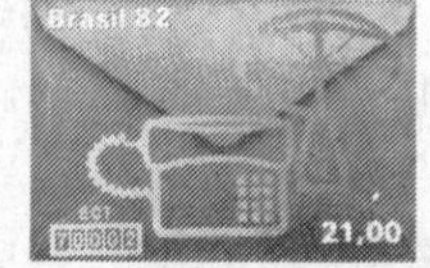

Ministry of Communications, 15th Anniv. — A963

1982, May 15
1797 A963 21cr multi .25 .20

Museology Course, Natl. Historical Museum, 50th Anniv. A964

1982, May 18
1798 A964 17cr blk & sal pink .20 .15

Vale de Rio Doce Mining Co. — A965

1982, June 1
1799 A965 17cr Gears .25 .15

Martin Afonso de Souza Reading Charter to Settlers A966

1982, June 3 **Litho.** ***Perf. 11½***
1800 A966 17cr multi .25 .15

Town of Sao Vincente, 450th anniv.

Armadillo A967

1982, June 4
1801 A967 17cr shown .55 .15
1802 A967 21cr Wolves .55 .18
1803 A967 30cr Deer 1.65 .22
Nos. 1801-1803 (3) 2.75 .55

Film Strip and Award A968

1982, June 19
1804 A968 17cr multi .25 .15

20th anniv. of Golden Palm award for The Promise Keeper, Cannes Film Festival.

Souvenir Sheet

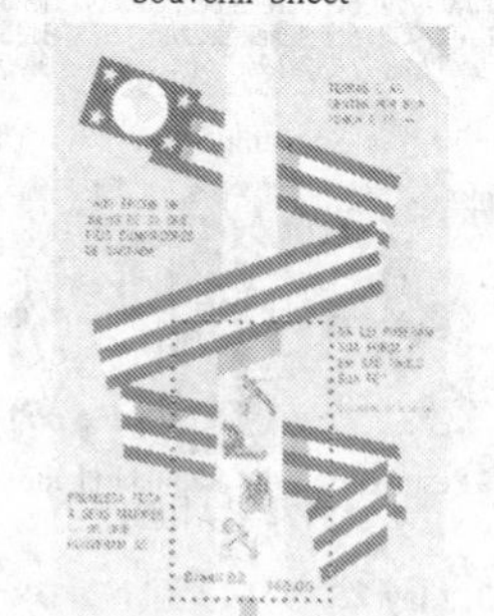

50th Anniv. of Constitutionalist Revolution — A969

1982, July 9 **Litho.** ***Perf. 11***
1805 A969 140cr multi 1.75 1.75

Church of Our Lady of O'Sabara — A970

St. Francis of Assisi, 800th Birth Anniv. — A971

Baroque Architecture, Minas Gerais State: No. 1807, Church of Our Lady of the Rosary, Diamantina, horiz. No. 1808, Town Square, Mariana, horiz.

1982, July 16 ***Perf. 11½***
1806 A970 17cr multi .25 .15
1807 A970 17cr multi .25 .15
1808 A970 17cr multi .25 .15
Nos. 1806-1808 (3) .75 .45

1982, July 24
1809 A971 21cr multi .20 .16

Stamp Day and Centenary of Pedro II "Large Head" Stamps A972

1982, Aug. 1
1810 A972 21cr No. 82 .25 .20

Port of Manaus Free Trade Zone A973

1982, Aug. 15 ***Perf. 11x11½***
1811 A973 75cr multi .65 .35

Scouting Year — A974

1982, Aug. 21 **Litho.** ***Perf. 11***
1812 Sheet of 2 2.75 *3.75*
a. A974 85cr Baden-Powell 1.00 *1.10*
b. A974 185cr Scout 1.65 *2.00*

Orixas Folk Costumes of African Origin — A975

1982, Aug. 21 ***Perf. 11½***
1813 A975 20cr Iemanja .20 .16
1814 A975 20cr Xango .20 .16
1815 A975 20cr Oxumare .20 .16
Nos. 1813-1815 (3) .60 .48

10th Anniv. of Central Bank of Brazil Currency Museum A976

1982, Aug. 31
1816 A976 25cr 12-florin coin, 1645, obverse and reverse .25 .20
1817 A976 25cr Emperor Pedro's 6.40-reis coronation coin, 1822 .25 .20

National Week — A977

1982, Sept. 1
1818 A977 25cr Don Pedro proclaiming independence .38 .25

A978 A979

1982, Oct. 4
1819 A978 85cr Portrait 1.00 .60

St. Theresa of Avila (1515-1582).

1982, Oct. 15 **Litho.** ***Perf. 11½x11***
1820 A979 75cr Instruments .65 .38
1821 A979 80cr Dancers .65 .38
1822 A979 85cr Musicians .70 .40
a. Souvenir sheet of 3, #1820-1822, perf. 11 *2.75 2.75*
Nos. 1820-1822 (3) 2.00 1.16

Lubrapex '82, 4th Portuguese-Brazilian Stamp Exhibition. Stamps in No. 1822a are without "LUBRAPEX 82."

Aviation Industry Day — A980

1982, Oct. 17 ***Perf. 12***
1823 A980 24cr Embraer EMB-312 trainer plane .25 .20

Bastos Tigre, Poet, Birth Centenary, and "Saudade" Text — A981

1982, Oct. 29
1824 A981 24cr multi .25 .20

Book Day.

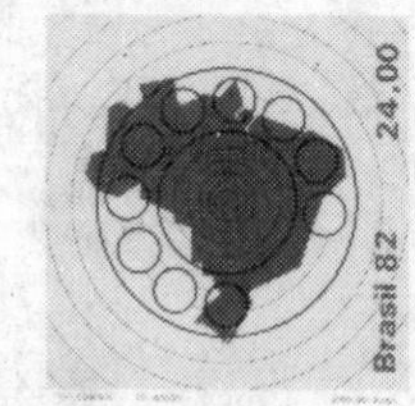

10th Anniv. of Brazilian Telecommunications Co. — A982

1982, Nov. 9 **Litho.** ***Perf. 11½***
1825 A982 24cr multi .25 .20

Christmas 1982 — A983

Children's Drawings.

1982, Nov. 10
1826 A983 24cr Nativity .25 .20
1827 A983 24cr Angels .25 .20
1828 A983 30cr Nativity, diff. .32 .45
1829 A983 30cr Flight into Egypt .32 .45
Nos. 1826-1829 (4) 1.14 1.30

State Flags — A984

Designs: a, Ceara. b, Espirito Santo. c, Paraiba. d, Grande de Norte. e, Rondonia.

1982, Nov. 19
1830 Block of 5 + label 5.25 5.25
a.-e. A984 24cr any single 1.00 .20

Thanksgiving 1982 — A985

1982, Nov. 25
1835 A985 24cr multi .25 .20

Homage to the Deaf — A986

1982, Dec. 1
1836 A986 24cr multi .25 .20

Naval Academy Bicentenary A987

Training Ships.

1982, Dec. 14
1837 A987 24cr Brazil .35 .20
1838 A987 24cr Benjamin Constant .35 .20
1839 A987 24cr Almirante Saldanha .35 .20
Nos. 1837-1839 (3) 1.05 .60

Souvenir Sheet

No. 12 — A988

1982, Dec. 18 **Litho.** ***Perf. 11***
1840 A988 200cr multi 4.00 *5.00*

BRASILIANA '83 Intl. Stamp Exhibition, Rio de Janeiro, July 29-Aug. 7.

Brasiliana '83 Carnival A989

1983, Feb. 9 **Litho.** ***Perf. 11½***
1841 A989 24cr Samba drummers .20 .15
1842 A989 130cr Street parade 1.40 .50
1843 A989 140cr Dancer 1.40 .52
1844 A989 150cr Male dancer 1.40 .55
Nos. 1841-1844 (4) 4.40 1.72

Antarctic Expedition A990

1983, Feb. 20 **Litho.** ***Perf. 11½***
1845 A990 150cr Support ship Barano de Teffe 2.00 .55

50th Anniv. of Women's Rights — A991

1983, Mar. 8
1846 A991 130cr multi 1.25 .50

Itaipu Hydroelectric Power Station Opening A992

1983, Mar. **Litho.** ***Perf. 12***
1847 A992 140cr multi 1.90 .42

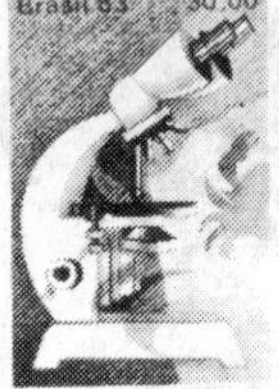

Cancer Prevention A993

Martin Luther (1483-1546) A994

Designs: 30cr, Microscope. 38cr, Antonio Prudente, Paulista Cancer Assoc. founder, Camargo Hospital.

1983, Apr. 18
1848 A993 30cr multi .30 .15
1849 A993 38cr multi .32 .15
a. Pair, #1848-1849 .65 .35
Set value .22

1983, Apr. 18
1850 A994 150cr pale grn & blk 1.25 .50

Agricultural Research A995

1983, Apr. 26 **Litho.** ***Perf. 11½***
1851 A995 30cr Chestnut tree .20 .15
1852 A995 30cr Genetic research .20 .15
1853 A995 38cr Tropical soy beans .25 .15
Nos. 1851-1853 (3) .65
Set value .20

Father Rogerio Neuhaus (1863-1934), Centenary of Ordination — A996

1983, May 3 ***Perf. 11½x11***
1854 A996 30cr multi .25 .15

30th Anniv. of Customs Cooperation Council A997

1983, May 5 ***Perf. 11x11½***
1855 A997 30cr multi .25 .15

World Communications Year — A998

1983, May 17 **Litho.** ***Perf. 11½***
1856 A998 250cr multi 1.50 .45

Toucans A999

1983, May 21
1857 A999 30cr Tucanucu .15 .15
1858 A999 185cr White-breasted 1.25 .38
1859 A999 205cr Green-beaked 1.25 .40
1860 A999 215cr Black-beaked 1.25 .45
Nos. 1857-1860 (4) 3.90 1.38

Souvenir Sheet

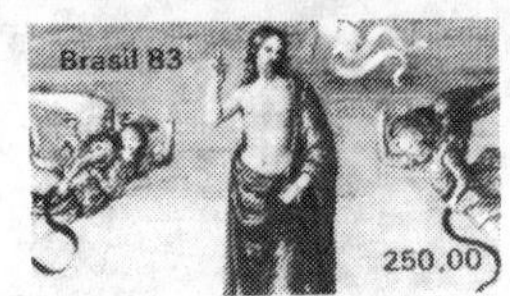

Resurrection, by Raphael (1483-1517) — A1000

1983, May 25 ***Perf. 11***
1861 A1000 250cr multi 2.50 *3.00*

Hohenzollern 980 Locomotive, 1875 A1001

Various locomotives.

1983, June 12 **Litho.** ***Perf. 11½***
1862 A1001 30cr shown .25 .15
1863 A1001 30cr Baldwin #1, 1881 .25 .15
1864 A1001 38cr Fowler #1, 1872 .30 .15
Nos. 1862-1864 (3) .80
Set value .20

9th Women's Basketball World Championship — A1002

1983, July 24 **Litho.** ***Perf. 11½x11***
1865 A1002 30cr Players, front view .20 .15
1866 A1002 30cr Players, rear view .20 .15
Set value .15

Simon Bolivar (1783-1830) A1003

1983, July 24 ***Perf. 12***
1867 A1003 30cr multi .20 .15

Children's Polio and Measles Vaccination Campaign A1004

1983, July 25
1868 A1004 30cr Girl, measles .20 .15
1869 A1004 30cr Boy, polio .20 .15
Set value .15

A1005 A1006

1983, July 28 ***Perf. 11½x11***
1870 A1005 30cr Minerva (goddess of wisdom), computer tape .20 .15

20th Anniv. of Master's program in engineering.

1983, July 29 **Engr.**

Guanabara Bay.

1871 A1006 185cr No. 1 1.50 .38
1872 A1006 205cr No. 2 1.50 .40
1873 A1006 215cr No. 3 1.50 .45
Nos. 1871-1873 (3) 4.50 1.23

Souvenir Sheet

Perf. 11

1874 Sheet of 3 8.00 *10.00*
a. A1006 185cr No. 1 2.00 *3.00*
b. A1006 205cr No. 2 2.00 *3.00*
c. A1006 215cr No. 3 2.00 *3.00*

BRASILIANA '83 Intl. Stamp Show, Rio de Janeiro, July 29-Aug. 7.

Souvenir Sheet

The First Mass in Brazil, by Vitor Meireles (1833-1903) — A1007

1983, Aug. 18 ***Perf. 11***
1875 A1007 250cr multi 3.00 1.50

EMB-120 Brasilia Passenger Plane A1008

1983, Aug. 19 ***Perf. 12***
1876 A1008 30cr multi .25 .15

Vision of Don Bosco Centenary A1009

1983, Aug. 30
1877 A1009 130cr multi .75 .25

Independence Week A1010

1983, Sept. 1 Litho. ***Perf. 11½***
1878 A1010 50cr multi .25 .15

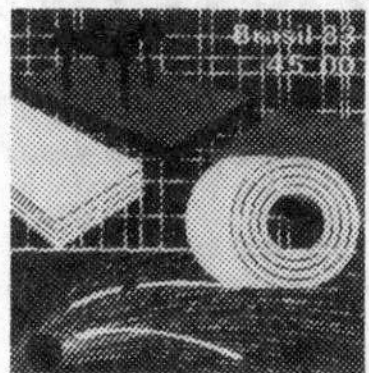

National Steel Corp., 10th Anniv. — A1011

1983, Sept. 17 Litho. ***Perf. 11½***
1879 A1011 45cr multi .25 .15

Cactus — A1012

1983, Sept. 12 Litho. ***Perf. 11½***
1880 A1012 45cr Pilosocereus gounellei .32 .15
1881 A1012 45cr Melocactus bahiensis .32 .15
1882 A1012 57cr Cereus jamacaru .40 .15
Nos. 1880-1882 (3) 1.04
Set value .32

1st National Eucharistic Congress — A1013

1983, Oct. 12 Litho. ***Perf. 11½***
1883 A1013 45cr multi .25 .15

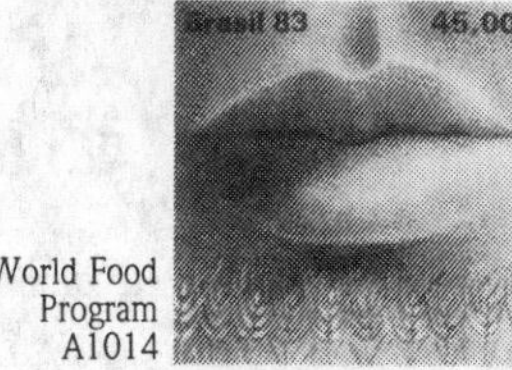

World Food Program A1014

1983, Oct. 14 Litho. ***Perf. 11½***
1884 A1014 45cr Mouth, grain .30 .15
1885 A1014 57cr Fish, sailboat .40 .15
Set value .22

Souvenir Sheet

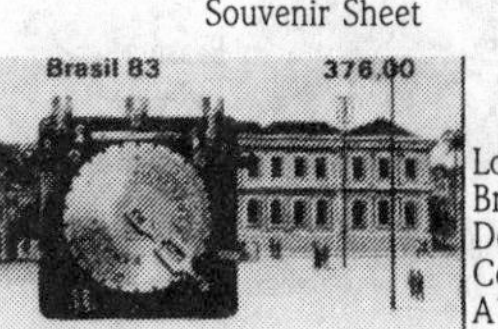

Louis Breguet, Death Centenary A1015

1983, Oct. 27 Litho. ***Perf. 11***
1886 A1015 376cr Telegraph transmitter 4.25 1.50

Christmas 1983 — A1016

17th-18th Cent. Statues: 45cr, Our Lady of the Angels. 315cr, Our Lady of the Parturition. 335cr, Our Lady of Joy. 345cr, Our Lady of the Presentation.

1983, Nov. 10 Litho. ***Perf. 11½***
1887 A1016 45cr multi .25 .15
1888 A1016 315cr multi 1.65 .60
1889 A1016 335cr multi 1.65 .65
1890 A1016 345cr multi 1.65 .70
Nos. 1887-1890 (4) 5.20 2.10

Marshal Mascarenhas Birth Centenary A1017

1983, Nov. 13 Litho. ***Perf. 11½***
1891 A1017 45cr Battle sites .20 .15

Commander of Brazilian Expeditionary Force in Italy.

State Flags A1018

Designs: a, Amazonas. b, Goias. c, Rio. d, Mato Grosso Do Sol. e, Parana.

1983, Nov. 17 Litho. ***Perf. 11½***
1892 Block of 5 + label 3.00 3.00
a.-e. A1018 45cr any single .50 .20

Thanksgiving A1018a

1983, Nov. 24 Litho. ***Perf. 12***
1896 A1018a 45cr Madonna, wheat .35 .15

Manned Flight Bicentenary — A1019

1983, Dec. 15 Litho. ***Perf. 12***
1897 A1019 345cr Montgolfiere balloon, 1783 5.00 .50

Ethnic Groups A1020

1984, Jan. 20 Litho. ***Perf. 12***
1898 A1020 45cr multi .20 .15

50th anniv. of publication of Masters and Slaves, sociological study by Gilberto Freyre.

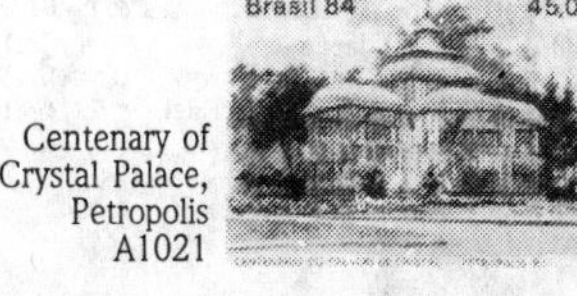

Centenary of Crystal Palace, Petropolis A1021

1984, Feb. 2
1899 A1021 45cr multi .18 .15

Souvenir Sheet

Flags (Sculpture with 40 Figures), by Victor Brecheret (b. 1894) A1022

1984, Feb. 22 Litho. ***Perf. 11***
1900 A1022 805cr multi 1.50 1.00

Naval Museum Centenary A1023

1984, Mar. 23 Litho. ***Perf. 11½***
1901 A1023 620cr Figurehead, frigate, 1847 .85 .52

Slavery Abolition Centenary A1024

1984, Mar. 25
1902 A1024 585cr Broken chain, raft .85 .55
1903 A1024 610cr Freed slave .90 .60

Souvenir Sheet

Visit of King Carl XVI Gustaf of Sweden A1025

1984, Apr. 2 ***Perf. 11***
1904 A1025 2105cr multi 3.50 2.50

1984 Summer Olympics A1026

1984, Apr. 13 ***Perf. 11½***
1905 A1026 65cr Long jump .15 .15
1906 A1026 65cr 100-meter race .15 .15
1907 A1026 65cr Relay race .15 .15
1908 A1026 585cr Pole vault .80 .65
1909 A1026 610cr High jump .85 .70
1910 A1026 620cr Hurdles .90 .80
a. Block of 6, #1905-1910 3.00 3.00
Nos. 1905-1910 (6) 3.00 2.60

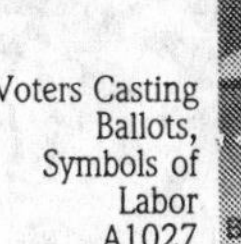

Voters Casting Ballots, Symbols of Labor A1027

Pres. Getulio Vargas Birth Centenary: Symbols of Development.

1984, Apr. 19 Litho. ***Perf. 11½***
1911 A1027 65cr shown .15 .15
1912 A1027 65cr Oil rig, blast furnace .15 .15
1913 A1027 65cr High-tension towers .15 .15
Nos. 1911-1913 (3) .45
Set value .24

Columbus, Espana '84 Emblem — A1028

1984, Apr. 27
1914 A1028 65cr Pedro Cabral .15 .15
1915 A1028 610cr shown 1.25 .70

Map of Americas, Heads — A1029

Lubrapex '84 — A1030

1984, May 7 Litho. ***Perf. 11½***
1916 A1029 65cr multi .15 .15

Pan-American Association of Finance and Guarantees, 8th Assembly.

1984, May 8 ***Perf. 11½x11***

18th Century Paintings, Mariana Cathedral.

1917 A1030 65cr Hunting scene .15 .15
1918 A1030 585cr Pastoral scene .75 .42
1919 A1030 610cr People under umbrellas .80 .50
1920 A1030 620cr Elephants .85 .50
Nos. 1917-1920 (4) 2.55 1.57

Souvenir Sheet

Intl. Fedn. of Soccer Associations, 80th Anniv. — A1031

1984, May 21 ***Perf. 11***
1921 A1031 2115cr Globe 3.50 1.75

Matto Grosso Lowland Fauna A1032

1984, June 5 Litho. ***Perf. 11½***
1922 Strip of 3 .60 .30
a. A1032 65cr Deer .20 .15
b. A1032 65cr Jaguar .20 .15
c. A1032 80cr Alligator .20 .15

First Letter Mailed in Brazil, by Guido Mondin — A1033

1984, June 8 ***Perf. 12x11½***
1923 A1033 65cr multi .15 .15

Postal Union of Americas and Spain, first anniv. of new headquarters.

Brazil-Germany Air Service, 50th Anniv.
A1034 A1035

1984, June 19

1924 A1034 610cr Dornier-Wal seaplane 1.00 .70
1925 A1035 620cr Steamer Westfalen 1.05 .72
a. Pair, #1924-1925 2.05 1.50

Woolly Spider Monkey, World Wildlife Fund Emblem — A1036

1984, July 6 *Perf. 11½*

1926 A1036 65cr Mother, baby .48 .15
1927 A1036 80cr Monkey .32 .15
Set value .18

Agriculture Type of 1980

Designs: 65cr, Rubber tree. 80cr, Brazil nuts. 120cr, Rice. 150cr, Eucalyptus. 300cr, Pinha da Parana. 800cr, Carnauba. 1000cr, Babacu. 2000cr, Sunflower.

Photogravure (65, 80, 120, 150cr), Engraved

1984-85 *Perf. 11x11½*

1934 A894 65cr lilac .20 .15
1935 A894 80cr brn red .25 .15
1936 A894 120cr dk sl bl .35 .15
1937 A894 150cr green .15 .15
1938 A894 300cr rose mag .50 .15
1939 A894 800cr grnsh bl 1.40 .15
1940 A894 1000cr lemon 1.40 .15
1941 A894 2000cr yel org ('85) .70 .25
Nos. 1934-1941 (8) 4.95
Set value 1.00

Marajo Isld. Buffalo A1037

1984, July 9 **Litho.** *Perf. 12*

1942 Strip of 3 .50 .28
a. A1037 65cr Approaching stream .15 .15
b. A1037 65cr Standing on bank .15 .15
c. A1037 80cr Drinking .18 .15

Continuous design.

Banco Economico Sesquicentenary — A1038

1984, July 13 *Perf. 11½*

1943 A1038 65cr Bank, coins .15 .15

Historic Railway Stations A1039

1984, July 23 **Litho.** *Perf. 11½*

1944 A1039 65cr Japeri .15 .15
1945 A1039 65cr Luz, vert. .15 .15
1946 A1039 80cr Sao Joao del Rei .16 .15
Nos. 1944-1946 (3) .46
Set value .26

A1040 A1041

1984, Aug. 13 *Perf. 11*

Souvenir Sheet

1947 A1040 585cr Girl scout 1.40 1.00

Girl Scouts in Brazil, 65th anniv.

1984, Aug. 21 **Litho.** *Perf. 11½*

1948 A1041 65cr Couple sheltered from rain .15 .15

Housing project bank, 20th anniv.

Independence Week A1042

Children's Drawings.

1984, Sept. 3

1949 A1042 100cr Explorer & ship .15 .15
1950 A1042 100cr Sailing ships .15 .15
1951 A1042 100cr "BRASIL" mural .15 .15
1952 A1042 100cr Children under rainbow .15 .15
Nos. 1949-1952 (4) .60
Set value .48

Rio de Janeiro Chamber of Commerce Sesquicentenary — A1043

1984, Sept. 10

1953 A1043 100cr Monument, worker silhouette .15 .15

Death Sesquicentenary of Don Pedro I (IV of Portugal) — A1044

1984, Sept. 23 *Perf. 12x11½*

1954 A1044 1000cr Portrait 1.50 1.10

Local Mushrooms — A1045 Book Day — A1046

1984, Oct. 22 *Perf. 11½*

1955 A1045 120cr Pycnoporus sanguineus .15 .15
1956 A1045 1050cr Calvatia sp 1.10 1.25
1957 A1045 1080cr Pleurotus sp, horiz. 1.20 1.30
Nos. 1955-1957 (3) 2.45 2.70

1984, Oct. 23 *Perf. 11½*

1958 A1046 120cr Girl in open book .15 .15

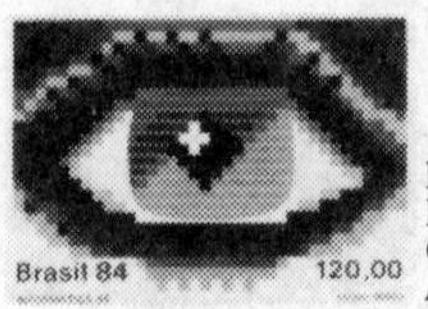

New State Mint Opening — A1047

1984, Nov. 1

1959 A1047 120cr multi .15 .15

Informatics Fair & Congress A1048

1984, Nov. 5 **Litho.** *Perf. 12*

1960 A1048 120cr Eye, computer terminal .15 .15

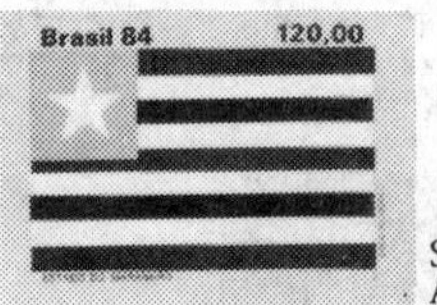

Org. of American States, 14th Assembly — A1049

1984, Nov. 14

1961 A1049 120cr Emblem, flags .15 .15

State Flags A1050

Designs: a, Maranhaio. b, Mato Grosso. c, Minas Gerais. d, Piaui. e, Santa Catarina.

1984, Nov. 19 *Perf. 11½*

1962 Block of 5 + label 1.00 1.00
a.-e. A1050 120cr, any single .20 .15

See Nos. 2037, 2249.

Thanksgiving 1984 — A1051

1984, Nov. 22

1963 A1051 120cr Bell tower, Brasilia .15 .15

Christmas 1984 A1052

Paintings: No. 1964, Nativity, by Djanira. No. 1965, Virgin and Child, by Glauco Rodrigues. No. 1966, Flight into Egypt, by Paul Garfunkel. No. 1967, Nativity, by Di Cavalcanti.

1984, Dec. 3 **Litho.** *Perf. 12*

1964 A1052 120cr multi .15 .15
1965 A1052 120cr multi .15 .15
1966 A1052 1050cr multi .85 .40
1967 A1052 1080cr multi .85 .40
Nos. 1964-1967 (4) 2.00
Set value .90

40th Anniv., International Civil Aviation Organization A1053

1984, Dec. 7 **Litho.** *Perf. 12*

1968 A1053 120cr Aircraft, Earth globe .15 .15

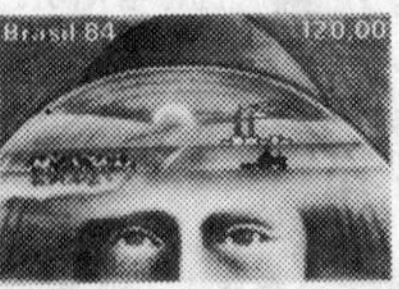

25th Anniv., North-Eastern Development A1054

1984, Dec. 14 **Litho.** *Perf. 12*

1969 A1054 120cr Farmer, field .15 .15

Emilio Rouede A1055

Painting: Church of the Virgin of Safe Travels, by Rouede.

1985, Jan. 22 **Litho.** *Perf. 12*

1970 A1055 120cr multi .15 .15

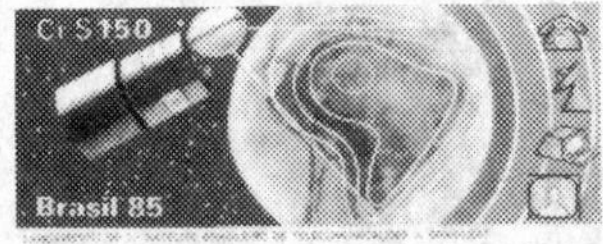

BRASILSAT — A1056

1985, Feb. 8 **Litho.** *Perf. 11½x12*

1971 A1056 150cr Satellite, Brazil .15 .15

Metropolitan Railways — A1057

1985, Mar. 2 **Litho.** *Perf. 11x11½*

1972 A1057 200cr Passenger trains .15 .15

Brasilia Botanical Gardens A1058

1985, Mar. 8 **Litho.** *Perf. 11½x12*

1973 A1058 200cr Caryocar brasiliense .15 .15

40th Anniv., Brazilian Paratroops — A1059

1985, Mar. 8 **Litho.** *Perf. 11½x12*

1974 A1059 200cr Parachute drop .15 .15

Natl. Climate Awareness Program — A1060

1985, Mar. 18 Litho. ***Perf. 11½x12***
1975 A1060 500cr multi .20 .15

Thoroughbred Horses A1061

1985, Mar. 19 Litho. ***Perf. 12***
1976 A1061 1000cr Campolina .38 .22
1977 A1061 1500cr Marajoara .70 .35
1978 A1061 1500cr Mangalarga marchador .70 .35
Nos. 1976-1978 (3) 1.78 .92

Ouro Preto — A1062

1985, Apr. 18 Litho. ***Perf. 11½x12***
1979 A1062 220cr shown .15 .15
1980 A1062 220cr St. Miguel des Missoes .15 .15
1981 A1062 220cr Olinda .15 .15
Set value .30 .18

Polivolume, by Mary Vieira — A1063

1985, Apr. 20 **Litho.**
1982 A1063 220cr multi .15 .15

Rio Branco Inst., 40th anniv.

Natl. Capital, Brasilia, 25th Anniv. — A1064

1985, Apr. 22 **Litho.**
1983 A1064 220cr Natl. Theater, acoustic shell .15 .15
1984 A1064 220cr Catetinho Palace, JK Memorial .15 .15
Set value .20 .15

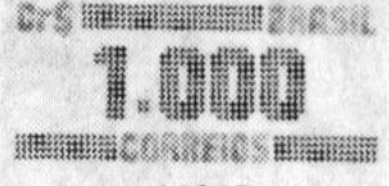

A1065 A1065a

1985-86 Photo. ***Perf. 11½***
1985 A1065 50cr lake .15 .15
1986 A1065 100cr dp vio .15 .15
1987 A1065 150cr violet .15 .15
1988 A1065 200cr ultra .15 .15
1989 A1065 220cr green .15 .15
1990 A1065 300cr royal bl .18 .15
1991 A1065 500cr olive blk .30 .22
1992 A1065a 1000cr brn ol ('86) .18 .15
1993 A1065a 2000cr brt grn ('86) .35 .22
1994 A1065a 3000cr dl vio .42 .32
1995 A1065a 5000cr brn .58 .42
Set value 2.35 1.65

Marshal Rondon, 120th Birth Anniv. A1066

1985, May 5 ***Perf. 11x11½***
1996 A1066 220cr multi .15 .15

Educator, protector of the Indians, building superintendent of telegraph lines.

Candido Fontoura (1885-1974) A1067

Brapex VI A1068

1985, May 14 ***Perf. 12x11½***
1997 A1067 220cr multi .15 .15

Pioneer of the Brazilian pharmaceutical industry.

1985, May 18 ***Perf. 11½x11***

Cave paintings: No. 1998, Deer, Cerca Grande. No. 1999, Lizards, Lapa do Caboclo. No. 2000, Running deer, Grande Abrigo de Santana do Riacho.

1998 A1068 300cr multi .15 .15
1999 A1068 300cr multi .15 .15
2000 A1068 2000cr multi .75 .50
a. Souvenir sheet of 3, #1998-2000, perf. 10½x11 1.00 1.00
Nos. 1998-2000 (3) 1.05
Set value .66

Wildlife Conservation A1069

Birds in Marinho dos Abrolhos National Park.

1985, June 5 ***Perf. 11½x12***
2001 A1069 220cr Fregata magnificens .15 .15
2002 A1069 220cr Sula dactylatra .15 .15
2003 A1069 220cr Anous stolidus .15 .15
2004 A1069 2000cr Pluvialis squatarola .60 .25
Nos. 2001-2004 (4) 1.05
Set value .40

A1070 A1071

1985, June 11 ***Perf. 12x11½***
2005 A1070 220cr Mother breastfeeding infant .15 .15
2006 A1070 220cr Hand, eyedropper, children .15 .15
a. Pair, #2005-2006 .25 .15

UN infant survival campaign.

1985, June 22 Litho. ***Perf. 11½x11***

Helicopter rescue, search ship, diver.

2007 A1071 220cr multi .15 .15

Sea Search & Rescue.

Souvenir Sheet

World Cup Soccer, Mexico, 1986 A1072

1985, June 23 ***Perf. 11***
2008 A1072 2000cr Player dribbling, World Cup 4.00 .85

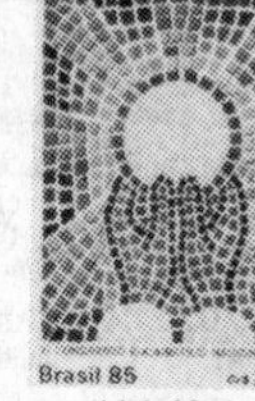

Intl. Youth Year — A1073

11th Natl. Eucharistic Congress — A1074

1985, June 28 ***Perf. 12***
2009 A1073 220cr Circle of children .15 .15

1985, July 16 ***Perf. 12x11½***
2010 A1074 2000cr Mosaic, Priest raising host .55 .38

Director Humberto Mauro, Scene from Sangue Mineiro, 1929 A1075

1985, July 27
2011 A1075 300cr multi .15 .15

Cataguases Studios, 60th anniv.

Escola e Sacro Museum, Convent St. Anthony, Joao Pessoa, Paraiba A1076

1985, Aug. 5 ***Perf. 11½x12***
2012 A1076 330cr multi .15 .15

Paraiba State 400th anniv.

Inconfidencia Museum — A1077

Cabanagem Insurrection, 150th Anniv. — A1078

1985, Aug. 11 ***Perf. 12x11½***
2013 A1077 300cr shown .15 .15
2014 A1077 300cr Museum of History & Diplomacy .15 .15
Set value .20 .16

1985, Aug. 14

Design: Revolutionary, detail from an oil painting by Guido Mondin.

2015 A1078 330cr multi .15 .15

AMX Subsonic Air Force Fighter Plane A1079

1985, Aug. 19 ***Perf. 11½x12***
2016 A1079 330cr multi .15 .15

AMX Project, joint program with Italy.

16th-17th Century Military Uniforms — A1080

1985, Aug. 26 ***Perf. 12x11½***
2017 A1080 300cr Captain, crossbowman .16 .15
2018 A1080 300cr Harquebusier, sergeant .16 .15
2019 A1080 300cr Musketeer, pikeman .16 .15
2020 A1080 300cr Fusilier, pikeman .16 .15
Nos. 2017-2020 (4) .64
Set value .48

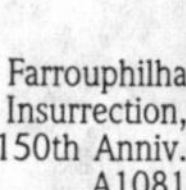

Farrouphilha Insurrection, 150th Anniv. A1081

Design: Bento Goncalves and insurrectionist cavalry on Southern battlefields, detail of an oil painting by Guido Mondin.

1985, Sept. 20 ***Perf. 11½x12***
2021 A1081 330cr multi .15 .15

Aparados da Serra National Park A1082

1985, Sept. 23
2022 A1082 3100cr Ravine .65 .52
2023 A1082 3320cr Mountains .70 .55
2024 A1082 3480cr Forest, waterfall .75 .60
Nos. 2022-2024 (3) 2.10 1.67

President-elect Tancredo Neves — A1083

Design: Portrait, Natl. Congress, Alvorada Palace, Federal Supreme Court.

1985, Oct. 10 Litho. ***Perf. 11x11½***
2025 A1083 330cr multi .15 .15

FEB, Postmark A1084

1985, Oct. 10 ***Perf. 11½x12***
2026 A1084 500cr multi .15 .15

Brazilian Expeditionary Force Postal Service, 41st anniv.

Rio de Janeiro-Niteroi Ferry Service, 150th Anniv. — A1085

1985, Oct. 14 *Perf. 11½x12*

2027 A1085 500cr Segunda .20 .15
2028 A1085 500cr Terceira .20 .15
2029 A1085 500cr Especuladora .20 .15
2030 A1085 500cr Urca .20 .15
Nos. 2027-2030 (4) .80 .60

Muniz M-7 Inaugural Flight, 50th Anniv. — A1086

1985, Oct. 22

2031 A1086 500cr multi .15 .15

UN 40th Anniv. — A1087

Natl. Press System — A1088

1985, Oct. 24 *Perf. 11½x11*

2032 A1087 500cr multi .15 .15

1985, Nov. 7

2033 A1088 500cr Newspaper masthead, reader .15 .15

Diario de Pernambuco, newspaper, 160th anniv.

Christmas 1985 A1089

1985, Nov. 11 *Perf. 11½x12*

2034 A1089 500cr Christ in Manger .20 .15
2035 A1089 500cr Adoration of the Magi .20 .15
2036 A1089 500cr Flight to Egypt .20 .15
Nos. 2034-2036 (3) .60 .45

State Flag Type

State Flags: a, Para. b, Rio Grande do Sul. c, Acre. d, Sao Paulo.

1985, Nov. 19 *Perf. 12*

2037 Block of 4 .80 .60
a.-d. A1050 500cr, any single .20 .15

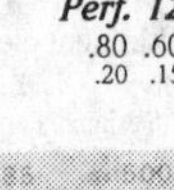

Thanksgiving Day — A1091

1985, Nov. 28 *Perf. 12x11½*

2038 A1091 500cr Child gathering wheat .20 .15

Economic Development of Serra dos Carajas Region A1092

1985, Dec. 11 Litho. *Perf. 11½x12*

2039 A1092 500cr multi .15 .15

Fr. Bartholomeu Lourenco de Gusmao (1685-1724), Inventor, the Aerostat A1093

1985, Dec. 19 Litho. *Perf. 11x11½*

2040 A1093 500cr multi .15 .15

A1094

A1095

The Trees, by Da Costa E Silva (b. 1885), poet.

1985, Dec. 20 Litho. *Perf. 12x11½*

2041 A1094 500cr multi .15 .15

1986, Mar. 3 Litho. *Perf. 11*

Souvenir Sheet

2042 A1095 10000cr multi 2.25 2.00

1986 World Cup Soccer Championships, Mexico. LUBRAPEX '86, philatelic exhibition.

Halley's Comet — A1096

1986, Apr. 11 Litho. *Perf. 11½x12*

2043 A1096 50c multi .15 .15

Commander Ferraz Antarctic Station, 2nd Anniv. A1097

1986, Apr. 25

2044 A1097 50c multi .15 .15

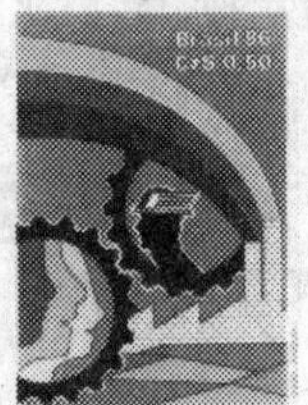

Labor Day A1098

Maternity, by Henrique Bernardelli (1858-1936) A1099

1986, May 1 Litho. *Perf. 12x11½*

2045 A1098 50c multi .15 .15

1986, May 8

2046 A1099 50c multi .15 .15

Amnesty Intl., 25th Anniv. A1100

1986, May 28 Litho. *Perf. 11½x12*

2047 A1100 50c multi .15 .15

Butterflies — A1101

1985, June 5 *Perf. 12x11½*

2048 A1101 50c Pyrrhopyge ruficauda .15 .15
2049 A1101 50c Prepona eugenes diluta .15 .15
2050 A1101 50c Pierriballia mandel molione .15 .15
Nos. 2048-2050 (3) .45
Set value .15

Score from Opera "Il Guarani" and Antonio Carlos Gomes (1836-1896), Composer A1102

1986, July 11 *Perf. 11½x12*

2051 A1102 50c multi .18 .15

Natl. Accident Prevention Campaign — A1103

Stamp Day — A1104

1986, July 30 Litho. *Perf. 11½x11*

2052 A1103 50c Lineman .15 .15

Souvenir Sheet

1986, Aug. 1 *Perf. 11*

2053 A1104 5cz No. 53 .85 .35

Brazilian Phil. Soc., 75th anniv., and Dom Pedro II issue, Nos. 53-60, 120th anniv.

Architecture A1105

Famous Men A1106

Designs: 10c, House of Garcia D'Avila, Nazare de Mata, Bahia. 20c, Church of Our Lady of the Assumption, Anchieta Village. 50c, Fort Reis Magos, Natal. 1cz, Pilgrim's Column, Alcantara Village, 1648. 2cz, Cloisters, St. Francis Convent, Olinda. 5cz, St. Anthony's Chapel, Sao Roque. 10cz, St. Lawrence of the Indians Church, Niteroi. 20cz, Principe da Beiro Fort, Mato Dentro. 50cz, Jesus of Matozinhos Church, vert. 100cz, Church of our Lady of Sorrow, Campanha. 200cz, Casa dos Contos, Ouro Preto. 500cz, Antiga Alfandega, Belem, Para.

Perf. 11½x11, 11x11½

1986-88 **Photo.**

2055 A1105 10c sage grn .15 .15
2057 A1105 20c brt blue .15 .15
2059 A1105 50c orange .15 .15
2064 A1105 1cz golden brn .15 .15
2065 A1105 2cz dull rose .25 .18
a. Litho., perf. 13 ('88) .15 .15
2067 A1105 5cz lt olive grn .60 .45
a. Litho., perf. 13 ('88) .15 .15
2068 A1105 10cz slate blue .50 .35
2069 A1105 20cz lt red brn .75 .58
2070 A1105 50cz brn org 2.25 1.75
2071 A1105 100cz dull grn 2.70 2.00
2072 A1105 200cz deep blue 2.50 1.85
2073 A1105 500cz dull red brn 1.30 1.00
Nos. 2055-2073 (12) 11.45 8.76

Issued: 10c, Aug. 11; 20c, Dec. 8; 50c, Aug. 19; 1cz, Nov. 19; 2cz, Nov. 9; 5cz, Dec. 30; 10cz, June 2, 1987; 20cz, 50cz, Sept. 18, 1987; 100cz, Dec. 21, 1987; 200cz, May 9, 1988; 500cz, Nov. 22, 1988.

This is an expanding set. Numbers will change if necessary.

1986 *Perf. 12x11½, 11½x12*

Designs: No. 2074, Juscelino Kubitschek de Oliveira, president 1956-61, and Alvorado Palace, Brasilia. No. 2075, Octavio Mangabeira, statesman, and Itamaraty Palace, Rio de Janeiro, horiz.

2074 A1106 50c multi .15 .15
2075 A1106 50c multi .15 .15
Set value .15 .15

Issue dates: #2074, Aug. 21. #2075, Aug. 27.

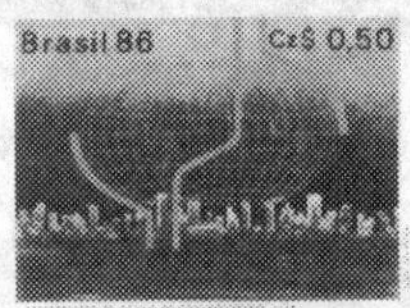

World Gastroenterology Congress, Sao Paulo — A1107

1986, Sept. 7 *Perf. 11½x12*

2076 A1107 50c multi .15 .15

Federal Broadcasting System, 50th Anniv. — A1108

Intl. Peace Year — A1109

1986, Sept. 15 *Perf. 12x11½*

2077 A1108 50c multi .15 .15

1986, Sept. 16

Painting (detail): War and Peace, by Candido Portinari.

2078 A1109 50c multi .15 .15

Ernesto Simoes Filho (b. 1886), Publisher of La Tarde A1110

1986, Oct. 4 Litho. *Perf. 11½x12*

2079 A1110 50c multi .15 .15

Famous Men — A1111

Federal Savings Bank, 125th Anniv. — A1112

Designs: No. 2080, Title page from manuscript, c. 1683-94, by Gregorio Mattose e Guerra (b. 1636), author. No. 2081, Manuel Bandeira (1886-1968), poet, text from I'll Go Back to Pasargada.

1986, Oct. 29 *Perf. 11½x11*
2080 A1111 50c lake & beige .15 .15
2081 A1111 50c lake & dl grn .15 .15
Set value .20 .15

1986, Nov. 4 *Perf. 12x11½*
2082 A1112 50c multi .15 .15

Flowering Plants A1113

Glauber Rocha, Film Industry Pioneer A1114

Perf. 12x11½, 11½x12
1986, Sept. 23
2083 A1113 50c Urera mitis .15 .15
2084 A1113 6.50cz Couroupita guyanensis .52 .40
2085 A1113 6.90cz Bauhinia variegata, horiz. .55 .42
Nos. 2083-2085 (3) 1.22 .97

1986, Nov. 20 *Perf. 12x11½*
2086 A1114 50c multi .15 .15

LUBRAPEX '86 — A1115

Cordel Folk Tales: No. 2087, Romance of the Mysterious Peacock. No. 2088, History of the Empress Porcina.

1986, Nov. 21 *Perf. 11x12*
2087 A1115 6.90cz multi .45 .35
2088 A1115 6.90cz multi .45 .35
a. Souvenir sheet of 2, #2087-2088, perf. 11 1.10 .85

Christmas A1116

Birds: 50c, And Christ child. 6.50cz, And tree. 7.30cz, Eating fruit.

1986, Nov. 10 *Perf. 11½x12*
2089 A1116 50c multi .15 .15
2090 A1116 6.50cz multi .65 .48
2091 A1116 7.30cz multi .75 .58
Nos. 2089-2091 (3) 1.55 1.21

Military Uniforms, c. 1930 — A1117

Bartolomeu de Gusmao Airport, 50th Anniv. — A1118

Designs: No. 2092, Navy lieutenant commander, dreadnought Minas Gerais. No. 2093, Army flight lieutenant, WACO S.C.O. biplane, Fortaleza Airport.

1986, Dec. 15 *Perf. 12x11½*
2092 A1117 50c multi .15 .15
2093 A1117 50c multi .15 .15
Set value .15 .15

Fortaleza Air Base, 50th anniv. (No. 2093).

1986, Dec. 26
2094 A1118 1cz multi .15 .15

Heitor Villa Lobos (1887-1959), Conductor — A1119

1987, Mar. 5 Litho. *Perf. 12x11½*
2095 A1119 1.50cz multi .15 .15

Natl. Air Force C-130 Transport Plane, Flag, the Antarctic A1120

1987, Mar. 9 *Perf. 11x11½*
2096 A1120 1cz multi .15 .15

Antarctic Project.

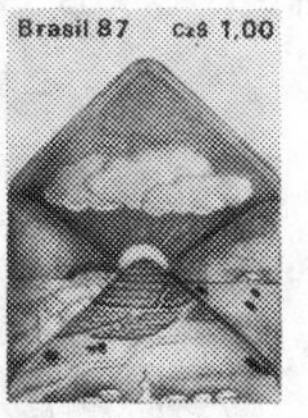
Special Mail Services — A1121

1987, Mar. 20 *Perf. 12x11½*
2097 A1121 1cz Rural delivery .15 .15
2098 A1121 1cz Intl. express .15 .15
Set value .20 .16

TELECOM '87, Geneva A1122

1987, May 5 *Perf. 11½x12*
2099 A1122 2cz Brazilsat, wave, globe .20 .15

10th Pan American Games, Indianapolis, Aug. 7-25 — A1123

1987, May 20 *Perf. 12x11½*
2100 A1123 18cz multi 1.00 .75

Natl. Fine Arts Museum, 150th Anniv A1124

1987, Jan. 13 *Perf. 11½x12*
2101 A1124 1cz multi .15 .15

Marine Conservation — A1125

1987, June 5
2102 A1125 2cz Eubalaena australis .15 .15
2103 A1125 2cz Eretmochelys imbricata .15 .15
Set value .20

Federal Court of Appeal, 40th Anniv. A1126

1987, June 15
2104 A1126 2cz multi .15 .15

Military Club, Cent. — A1127

1987, June 26 *Perf. 12x11½*
2105 A1127 3cz multi .18 .15

Agriculture Institute of Campinas, Cent. A1128

1987, June 27 *Perf. 11½x12*
2106 A1128 2cz multi .15 .15

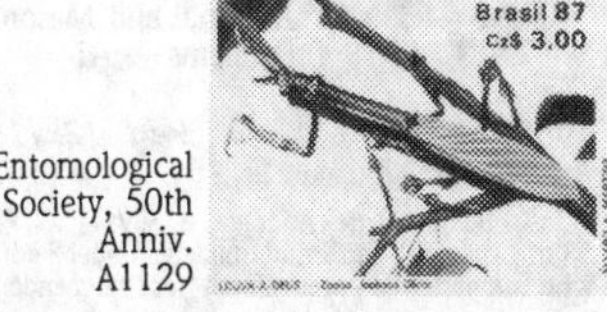
Entomological Society, 50th Anniv. A1129

1987, July 17
2107 A1129 3cz Zoolea lopiceps .15 .15
2108 A1129 3cz Fulgora servillei .15 .15
Set value .20

Natl. Tourism Year A1130

Designs: No. 2109, Monuments and Sugarloaf Mountain, Rio de Janeiro. No. 2110, Colonial church, sailboats, parrot, cashews.

1987, Aug. 4
2109 A1130 3cz multi .15 .15
2110 A1130 3cz multi .15 .15

Royal Portuguese Cabinet of Literature, 150th Anniv. — A1131

1987, Aug. 27 *Perf. 12x11½*
2111 A1131 30cz ver & brt grn 1.10 .85

Sport Club Intl. — A1132

Championship soccer clubs, Brazil's Gold Cup: b, Sao Paulo. c, Guarani. d, Regatas do Flamengo.

1987, Aug. 29 *Perf. 11½x12*
2112 Block of 4 .60 .40
a.-d. A1132 3cz any single .15 .15

St. Francis Convent, 400th Anniv. A1133

1987, Oct. 4
2113 A1133 4cz multi .20 .15

Jose Americo de Almeida, Author A1134

Design: Characters from romance novel, "A Bagaceira," 1928, and portrait of author.

1987, Oct. 23 Litho. *Perf. 11x11½*
2114 A1134 4cz multi .18 .15

Spanish Galleons Anchored in Recife Port, 1537 A1135

1987, Nov. 12 Litho. *Perf. 11½x12*
2115 A1135 5cz Harbor entrance .18 .15

Recife City, 450th anniv.

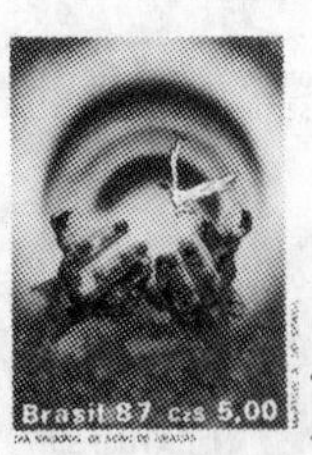

Thanksgiving A1136

1987, Nov. 26 *Perf. 12x11½*
2116 A1136 5cz multi .18 .15

Christmas 1987 A1137

1987, Nov. 30 *Perf. 11½x12*
2117 A1137 6cz Shepherd and flock .20 .15
2118 A1137 6cz Christmas pageant .20 .15
2119 A1137 6cz Six angels .20 .15
Nos. 2117-2119 (3) .60 .45

Pedro II College, 150th Anniv. — A1138

Gold pen Emperor Pedro II used to sign edict establishing the school, and Senator Bernardo Pereira de Vasconcellos, founder.

1987, Dec. 2
2120 A1138 6cz multi .18 .15

Natl. Orchid Growers' Soc., 50th Anniv. A1139

1987, Dec. 3
2121 A1139 6cz Laelia lobata veitch .20 .15
2122 A1139 6cz Cattleya guttata lindley .20 .15

Marian Year — A1140

Statue of Our Lady and Basilica at Fatima, Portugal.

1987, Dec. 20 *Perf. 12x11½*
2123 A1140 50cz multi 1.10 .85

Exhibit of the Statue of Our Lady of Fatima in Brazil.

Descriptive Treatise of Brazil, by Gabriel S. de Sousa, 400th Anniv. A1141

1987, Dec. 21 Litho. *Perf. 11x11½*
2124 A1141 7cz multi .20 .16

Natl. Archives, 150th Anniv. A1142

Design: Text from illuminated Gregorian canticle and computer terminal.

1988, Jan. 5 *Perf. 11½x12*
2125 A1142 7cz multi .20 .16

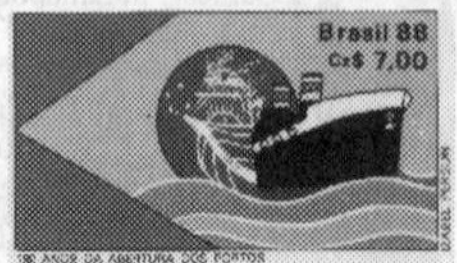

Opening of Brazilian Ports to Ships of Friendly Nations, 180th Anniv. A1143

1988, Jan. 28 *Perf. 11x11½*
2126 A1143 7cz multi .24 .18

Souvenir Sheet

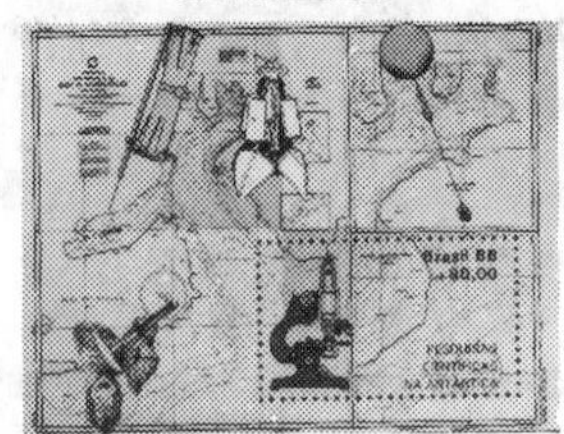
Antarctic Research — A1144

1988, Feb. 9 Litho. *Perf. 11*
2127 A1144 80cz multi 2.00 2.00

Energy Resources — A1145

1988, Mar. 15 Litho. *Perf. 12x11½*
2128 A1145 14cz Electricity .22 .16
2129 A1145 14cz Fossil fuels .22 .16

Souvenir Sheet

Brazilians as Formula 1 World Champions in 1981, 1983, 1987 — A1146

1988, Mar. 30 *Perf. 11*
2130 A1146 300cz multi 4.50 4.50

Jose Bonifacio, Armorial and Masonic Emblems — A1147

1988, Apr. 6 *Perf. 12x11½*
2131 A1147 20cz multi .30 .24

Jose Bonifacio de Andrada e Silva (c. 1763-1838), geologist and prime minister under Pedro I who supported the movement for independence from Portugal and was exiled for opposing the emperor's advisors.

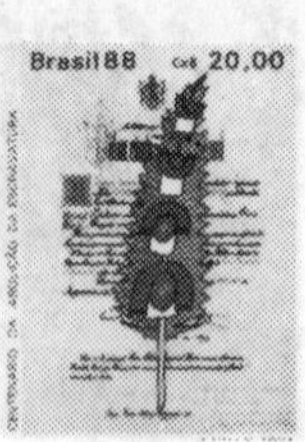

Abolition of Slavery, Cent. — A1148

Telecom '88 — A1149

Designs: 20cz, Declaration and quill pen. 50cz, Slave ship and maps of African coastline and slave trade route between Africa and South America.

1988, May 12 Litho. *Perf. 12x11½*
2132 A1148 20cz multi .25 .18
2133 A1148 50cz multi .65 .50

1988, May 16 *Perf. 11½x11*
2134 A1149 50cz multi .60 .45

Jesus of Matosinhos Sanctuary A1150

1988, May 16 *Perf. 11½x12*
2135 A1150 20cz shown .22 .16
2136 A1150 50cz Pilot plan of Brazilia .58 .45
2137 A1150 100cz Salvador historic district 1.20 .90
Nos. 2135-2137 (3) 2.00 1.51

LUBRAPEX '88. World heritage list.

Japanese Immigrants in Brazil, 80th Anniv. — A1151

1988, June 18 Litho. *Perf. 11½x11*
2138 A1151 100cz multi .75 .55

A1152

A1153

1988, July 1 Photo. *Perf. 13*
2139 A1152 (A) brt blue .22 .16

No. 2139 met the first class domestic letter postage rate (28cz).
See Nos. 2201, 2218.

1988, July 14 Litho. *Perf. 12x11½*
2140 A1153 20cz Judo .22 .16

1988 Summer Olympics, Seoul.

Wildlife Conservation A1154

1988, July 24 *Perf. 11½x12*
2141 A1154 20cz Myrmecophaga tridactyla .15 .15
2142 A1154 50cz Chaetomys subspinosus .32 .24
2143 A1154 100cz Speothos venaticus .65 .48
Nos. 2141-2143 (3) 1.12 .87

Souvenir Sheet

The Motherland, 1919 by Pedro Bruno — A1155

1988, Aug. 1 Litho. *Perf. 11*
2144 A1155 250cz multi 1.50 1.50

Stamp Day, BRASILIANA '89.

Natl. Confederation of Industries, 50th Anniv. — A1156

1988, Aug. 12 *Perf. 11½x12*
2145 A1156 50cz multi .26 .20

Soccer Clubs A1157

No. 2146, Recife, Pernambuco. No. 2147, Coritiba, Parana. 100cz, Gremio, Porto Alegre, Rio Grande do Sul. 200cz, Fluminense, Rio de Janeiro.

1988, Sept. 29 *Perf. 11½x12*
2146 A1157 50cz multi .16 .15
2147 A1157 50cz multi .16 .15
2148 A1157 100cz multi .32 .22
2149 A1157 200cz multi .60 .48
a. Block of 4, #2146-2149 1.25 .95

Brasil 88 Cz$ 50,00
Poems, 1888 A1158

Portraits and text: 50cz, *O Ateneu,* by Raul Pompeia. 100cz, *Poesias,* by Olavo Bilac.

1988, Oct. 28 *Perf. 11x11½*
2150 A1158 50cz multi .15 .15
2151 A1158 100cz multi .26 .20

Souvenir Sheet

1988 Democratic Constitution for the Union of the People and the State — A1159

1988, Oct. 5 Litho. *Perf. 11*
2152 A1159 550cz Government building 2.40 2.40

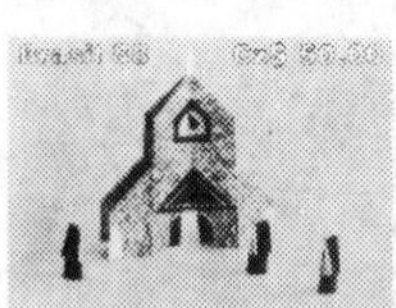

Origami Art — A1160

1988, Nov. 11 Litho. *Perf. 11½x12*

2153 A1160	50cz	Abbey, nuns	.15	.15
2154 A1160	100cz	Nativity	.25	.20
2155 A1160	200cz	Santa Claus, presents	.52	.38
		Nos. 2153-2155 (3)	.92	.73

Christmas.

ARBRAFEX Philatelic Exhibition of Argentina and Brazil A1161

1988, Nov. 26

2156 A1161 400cz multi .85 .65

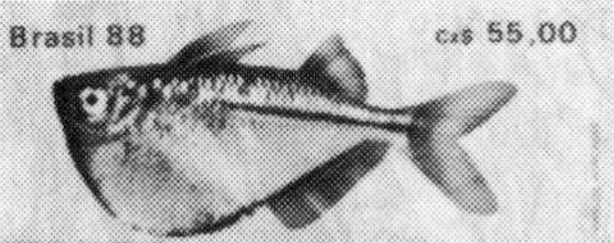

Fresh-water Fish — A1162

Designs: a, *Gasteropelecus*. b, *Osteoglossum ferreirai*. c, *Moenkhausia*. d, *Xavantei*. e, *Ancistrus hoplogenys*. f, *Brochis splendens*. Se-tenant in a continuous design.

Illustration reduced.

1988, Nov. 29 Litho. *Perf. 11½x12*

2157	Block of 6	.90	.72
a.-f.	A1162 55cz any single	.15	.15

Souvenir Sheet

BRAPEX '88, Ecological Preservation — A1163

1988, Dec. 10 *Perf. 11*

2158	Sheet of 3	1.80	1.80
a.	A1163 100cz Parrot	.25	.25
b.	A1163 250cz Plant	.60	.60
c.	A1163 400cz Pelican	.95	.95

Satellite Dishes A1164

Performing Arts A1165

1988, Dec. 20 *Perf. 12x11½*

2159 A1164 70cz multi .18 .15

Ansat 10-Earth satellite station communication.

1988, Dec. 21

2160 A1165 70cz multi .18 .15

Court of Justice, Bahia, 380th Anniv. A1166

1989, Mar. 10 Litho. *Perf. 11½x12*

2161 A1166 25c multi .42 .32

Public Library Year — A1167

1989, Mar. 13 *Perf. 11½*

2162 A1167 25c Library, Bahia, 1811 .42 .32

Brazilian Post & Telegraph Enterprise, 20th Anniv. A1168

Intl. and domestic postal services: a, Facsimile transmission (Post-Grama). b, Express mail (EMS). c, Parcel post (Sedex). d, Postal savings (CEFPostal).

1989, Mar. 20 *Perf. 11½x12*

2163	Block of 4	1.65	1.25
a.-d.	A1168 25c any single	.40	.30

Souvenir Sheet

Ayrton Senna, 1988 Formula 1 World Champion — A1169

1989, Mar. 23

2164 A1169 2cz multi 4.00 4.00

Environmental Conservation A1170

1989, Apr. 6 Litho. *Perf. 12x11½*

2165 A1170 25c multi .35 .25

Mineira Inconfidencia Independence Movement, Bicent. — A1171

Designs: a, Pyramid, hand. b, Figure of a man, houses. c, Destruction of houses.

1989, Apr. 21 *Perf. 11½x12*

2166	Strip of 3	1.30	.95
a.-b.	A1171 30c any single	.38	.28
c.	A1171 40c multi	.52	.38

First rebellion against Portuguese dominion.

Military School, Rio de Janeiro, Cent. A1172

1989, May 6 Litho. *Perf. 11½x12*

2167 A1172 50c multi .50 .38

Flowering Plants A1173

1989, June 5 *Perf. 11½x12, 12x11½*

2168 A1173	50c	*Pavonia alnifolia*	.60	.45
2169 A1173	1cz	*Worsleya rayneri*	1.25	.90
2170 A1173	1.50cz	*Heliconia farinosa*	1.75	1.40
		Nos. 2168-2170 (3)	3.60	2.75

Nos. 2169-2170 vert.

Barreto and Recife Law School, Pedro II Square A1174

1989, June 7 *Perf. 11x11½*

2171 A1174 50c multi .65 .48

Tobias Barreto (b. 1839), advocate of Germanization of Brazil.

Cultura Broadcasting System, 20th Anniv. — A1175

1989, June 27 Litho. *Perf. 11½x12*

2172 A1175 50c multi .60 .45

Aviation A1176

1989, July 7

2173 A1176	50c	Ultra-light aircraft	.52	.40
2174 A1176	1.50cz	Eiffel Tower, *Demoiselle*	1.65	1.10

Flight of Santos-Dumont's *Demoiselle*, 80th anniv (1.50cz).

Indigenous Flora — A1177

1989 Photo. *Perf. 11x11½, 11½x11*

2176 A1177	10c	*Dichorisandra*, vert.	.15	.15
2177 A1177	20c	*Quiabentia zehnteri*	.22	.16
2178 A1177	50c	*Bougainvillea glabra*	.52	.42
2179 A1177	1cz	*Impatiens specie*	1.00	.80
2180 A1177	2cz	*Chorisia crispiflora*	.25	.18
2181 A1177	5cz	*Hibiscus trilineatus*	.60	.45
		Nos. 2176-2181 (6)	2.74	2.16

Issued: 10c, July 4; 20c, June 21; 50c, June 26; 1cz, June 19; 2cz, 5cz, Dec. 4.

No. 2181 vert.

See Nos. 2259-2273.

Souvenir Sheet

Largo da Carioca, by Nicolas Antoine Taunay — A1179

1989, July 7 Litho. *Perf. 11*

2197 A1179 3cz multi 3.00 3.00

PHILEXFRANCE '89, French revolution bicent.

Cut and Uncut Gemstones — A1180

1989, July 12 Litho. *Perf. 12x11½*

2198 A1180	50c	Tourmaline	.40	.30
2199 A1180	1.50cz	Amethyst	1.20	.90

Souvenir Sheet

Paco Imperial, Rio de Janeiro, and Map — A1181

1989, July 28 *Perf. 11*

2200 A1181 5cz multi 3.75 3.75

BRASILANA '89.

Type of 1988 Redrawn

1989, July 26 Photo. *Perf. 13*

Size: 17x21mm

2201 A1152 (A) org & brt blue .18 .15

Size of type and postal emblem are smaller on No. 2201; "1e PORTE" is at lower left.

No. 2201 met the first class domestic letter postage rate (cz).

Pernambuco Commercial Assoc., 150th Anniv. A1182

1989, Aug. 1 Litho. *Perf. 11½x12*

2202 A1182 50c multi .40 .30

Photography, 150th Anniv. — A1183

1989, Aug. 14

2203 A1183 1.50cz multi 1.10 .85

1st Hydroelecric Power Station in South America, Marmelos-o, Cent. A1184

1989, Sept. 5 Litho. ***Perf. 11½x12***
2204 A1184 50c multi .35 .25

Conchs Endemic to the Brazilian Coast A1185

1989, Sept. 8
2205 A1185 50c *Voluta ebraea* .32 .22
2206 A1185 1cz *Morum matthewsi* .60 .45
2207 A1185 1.50cz *Agaronia travassosi* .90 .65
Nos. 2205-2207 (3) 1.82 1.32

Wildlife conservation.

America Issue A1186

UPAE emblem and pre-Columbian stone carvings: 1cz, Muiraquita ritual statue, vert. 4cz, Ceramic brazier under three-footed votive urn.

Perf. 12x11½, 11½x12
1989, Oct. 12 Litho.
2208 A1186 1cz multicolored .48 .35
2209 A1186 4cz shown 1.85 1.40

Discovery of America 500th anniv. (in 1992).

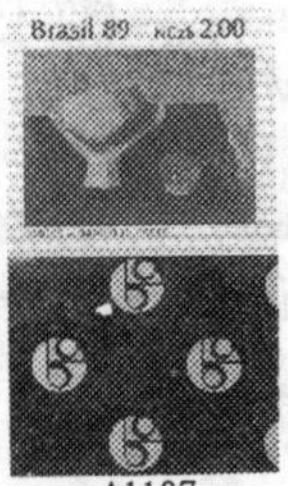
A1187

A1188

Hologram and: a. *Lemons*, by Danilo di Prete. b. *O Indio E A Suacuapara*, by sculptor Victor Brecheret. c. Francisco Matarazzo.

1989, Oct. 14 ***Perf. 11***
Souvenir Sheet
2210 Sheet of 3 3.75 3.75
a. A1187 2cz multicolored .72 .72
b. A1187 3cz multicolored 1.10 1.10
c. A1187 5cz multicolored 1.75 1.75

Sao Paulo 20th intl. art biennial.

1989, Oct. 26 ***Perf. 11½x11***

Writers, residences and quotes: No. 2211, Casimiro de Abreu (b. 1839). No. 2212, Cora Coralina (b. 1889). No. 2213, Joaquim Machado de Assis (b. 1839).

2211 A1188 1cz shown .57 .42
2212 A1188 1cz multicolored .57 .42
2213 A1188 1cz multicolored .57 .42
Nos. 2211-2213 (3) 1.71 1.26

Federal Police Department, 25th Anniv. A1189

1989, Nov. 9 ***Perf. 11½x12***
2214 A1189 1cz multicolored .27 .20

Christmas — A1190

Thanksgiving Day — A1191

1989, Nov. 10 ***Perf. 12x11½***
2215 A1190 70c Heralding angel .18 .15
2216 A1190 1cz Holy family .24 .18

1989, Nov. 23
2217 A1191 1cz multicolored .24 .18

Type of 1988 Redrawn

1989, Nov. 6 Photo. ***Perf. 13x13½***
Size: 22x26mm
2218 A1152 (B) org & dark red 2.00 1.50

Size of type and postal emblem are smaller on No. 2218; "1e PORTE" is at lower left.
No. 2218 met the first class intl. letter postage rate, initially at 9cz.

Souvenir Sheet

Proclamation of the Republic, Cent. — A1192

1989, Nov. 19 Litho. ***Perf. 11***
2225 A1192 15cz multicolored 4.50 4.50

Bahia Sports Club, 58th Anniv. A1193

1989, Nov. 30 ***Perf. 11½x12***
2226 A1193 50c Soccer .15 .15

Yellow Man, by Anita Malfatti (b. 1889) — A1194

1989, Dec. 2 ***Perf. 12x11½***
2227 A1194 1cz multicolored .26 .20

Bahia State Public Archives, Cent. — A1195

1990, Jan. 16 Litho. ***Perf. 11½x12***
2228 A1195 2cz multicolored .28 .20

Brazilian Botanical Soc., 40th Anniv. A1196

1990, Jan. 21
2229 A1196 2cz Sabia, Caatinga .22 .16
2230 A1196 13cz Pau, Brazil 1.40 1.10

Churches A1197

Designs: 2cz, St. John the Baptist Cathedral, Santa Cruz do Sul, vert. 3cz, Our Lady of Victory Church, Oeiras. 5cz, Our Lady of the Rosary Church, Ouro Preto, vert.

1990, Feb. 5 ***Perf. 12x11½, 11½x12***
2231 A1197 2cz multicolored .16 .15
2232 A1197 3cz multicolored .25 .20
2233 A1197 5cz multicolored .42 .32
Nos. 2231-2233 (3) .83 .67

Lloyd's of London in Brazil, Cent. A1198

1990, Feb. 19 Litho. ***Perf. 11½x12***
2234 A1198 3cz multicolored .15 .15

Souvenir Sheet

Antarctic Research Program — A1199

1990, Feb. 22 Litho. ***Perf. 11***
2235 A1199 20cz Fauna, map 1.55 1.55

Vasco da Gama Soccer Club A1200

1990, Mar. 5
2236 A1200 10cz multicolored .48 .38

Lindolfo Collor (b. 1890), Syndicated Columnist, and Labor Monument A1201

1990, Mar. 7
2237 A1201 20cz multicolored .95 .70

A1202

A1203

Pres. Jose Sarney.

1990, Mar. 8 ***Perf. 12x11½***
2238 A1202 20cz chalky blue .95 .70

1990, Apr. 6 ***Perf. 12x11½***
2239 A1203 20cz multicolored .70 .52

AIDS prevention.

Souvenir Sheet

Penny Black, 150th Anniv. — A1204

Designs: 20cz, Dom Pedro, Brazil No. 1. 100cz, Queen Victoria, Great Britain No. 1.

1990, May 3 Litho. ***Perf. 11***
2240 A1204 Sheet of 2 2.35 1.75
a. 20cr multicolored
b. 100cr multicolored

Central Bank, 25th Anniv. A1205

1990, Mar. 30 Litho. ***Perf. 11½x12***
2241 A1205 20cr multicolored .70 .52

Amazon River Postal Network, 21st Anniv. A1207

1990, Apr. 20 ***Perf. 11x11½***
2243 A1207 20cr multicolored .70 .52

Souvenir Sheet

World Cup Soccer Championships, Italy — A1208

1990, May 12 Litho. ***Perf. 12x11½***
2244 A1208 120cr multicolored 3.00 3.00

22nd Congress of the Intl. Union of Highway Transportation — A1209

1990. May 14 ***Perf. 11½x12***
2245 A1209 20cr multicolored .65 .48
2246 A1209 80cr multicolored 3.00 2.25
a. Pair, #2245-2246 3.75 2.75

No. 2246a has a continuous design.

Imperial Crown, 18th Cent. — A1210

Designs: No. 2248, Our Lady of Immaculate Conception, 18th cent.

1990, May 18 ***Perf. 12x11½***
2247 A1210 20cr shown .68 .52
2248 A1210 20cr multicolored .68 .52

Imperial Museum, 50th anniv.(No. 2247). Mission Museum, 50th anniv. (No. 2248).

State Flags Type

1990, May 20 ***Perf. 11½x12***
2249 A1050 20cr Tocantins .68 .52

Army Geographical Service, Cent. — A1212

1990, May 30 ***Perf. 11x11½***
2250 A1212 20cr multicolored .68 .52

Film Personalities A1213

1990, June 19 ***Perf. 11½x12***
2251 A1213 25cr Adhemar Gonzaga .80 .60
2252 A1213 25cr Carmen Miranda .80 .60
2253 A1213 25cr Carmen Santos .80 .60
2254 A1213 25cr Oscarito .80 .60
a. Block of 4, #2251-2254 3.20 2.40

France-Brazil House, Rio de Janeiro A1214

1990, July 14 Litho. ***Perf. 11½x11***
2255 A1214 50cr multicolored 1.50 1.10

See France No. 2226.

World Men's Volleyball Chmpships. A1215

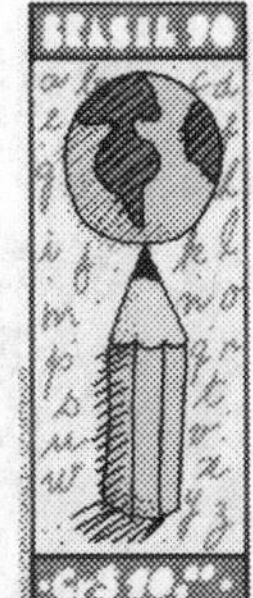

Intl. Literacy Year A1217

CBA 123 — A1216

1990, July 28 Litho. ***Perf. 12x11½***
2256 A1215 10cr multicolored .30 .24

1990, July 30 ***Perf. 11½x12***
2257 A1216 10cr multicolored .30 .24

1990, Aug. 22 ***Perf. 12x11½***
2258 A1217 10cr multicolored .30 .24

Flora Type of 1989

Perf. 11x11½, 11½x11

1989-93 Photo.

Design A1177

2259 1cr like #2179 .15 .15
2260 2cr like #2180 .15 .15
2261 5cr like #2181 .15 .15
2262 10cr Tibouchina granulosa .15 .15
2263 20cr Cassia macranthera .15 .15
2264 50cr Clitoria fairchildiana .28 .15
2265 50cr Tibouchina mutabilis .35 .35
2266 100cr Erythrina crista-galli, perf. 13 .55 .28
2267 200cr Jacaranda mimosifolia 1.10 .55
2268 500cr Caesalpinia peltophoroides 2.75 1.40
2269 1000cr Pachira aquatica .15 .15
2270 2000cr Hibiscus pernambucensis .15 .15
2271 5000cr Triplaris surinamensis .85 .85
2272 10,000cr Tabebuia heptaphylla 1.65 1.65
2273 20,000cr Erythrina speciosa 2.25 2.25
Nos. 2259-2273 (15) 10.83 8.53

Issued: 1cr, 11/8/90; 2cr, 11/12/90; 5cr, 11/16/90; #2264, 6/1/89; 10cr, 4/18/90; 20cr, 5/4/90; 100cr, 8/24/90; 200cr, 6/16/91; 500cr, 5/14/91; 1000cr, 9/2/92; 2000cr, 9/8/92; 5000cr, 10/16/92; 10,000cr, 11/16/92; 20,000cr, 4/25/93; #2265, 10/20/93.

Granbery Instutute, Cent. A1218

1990, Sept. 8 Litho. ***Perf. 11½x12***
2279 A1218 13cr multicolored .40 .28

18th Panamerican Railroad Congress A1219

1990, Sept. 9
2280 A1219 95cr multicolored 2.00 1.50

Embratel, 25th Anniv. — A1220

1990, Sept. 21
2281 A1220 13cr multicolored .40 .30

LUBRAPEX '90 — A1221

Statues by Ceschiatti and Giorgi (No. 2283).

1990, Sept. 22
2282 A1221 25cr As Banhistas .62 .45
2283 A1221 25cr Os Candangos .62 .45
2284 A1221 100cr Evangelista Sao Joao 1.25 .90
2285 A1221 100cr A Justica 1.25 .90
a. Block of 4, #2282-2285 4.00 3.00
b. Souv. sheet of 4, #2282-2285 6.00 6.00

Praia Do Sul Wildlife Reserve A1222

1990, Oct. 12
2286 A1222 15cr Flowers .45 .32
2287 A1222 105cr Shoreline 2.60 1.80
a. Pair, #2286-2287 3.05 2.12

Discovery of America, 500th anniv. (in 1992).

Natl. Library, 180th Anniv. A1223

Writers: No. 2289, Guilherme de Almeida (1890-1969). No. 2290, Oswald de Andrade (1890-1954).

1990, Oct. 29 Litho. ***Perf. 11x11½***
2288 A1223 15cr multicolored .40 .30
2289 A1223 15cr multicolored .40 .30
2290 A1223 15cr multicolored .40 .30
Nos. 2288-2290 (3) 1.20 .90

Natl. Tax Court, Cent. A1224

1990, Nov. 7 Litho. ***Perf. 11½x12***
2291 A1224 15cr multicolored .40 .30

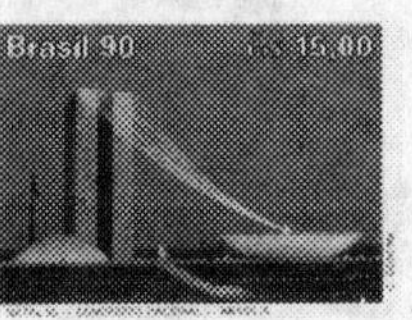

Christmas A1225

Architecture of Brasilia: No. 2292, National Congress. No. 2293, Television tower.

1990, Nov. 20
2292 A1225 15cr multicolored .40 .30
2293 A1225 15cr multicolored .40 .30

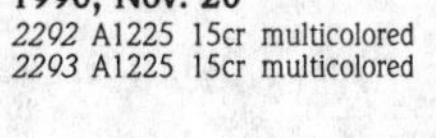

A1226 A1227

1990, Dec. 13 Litho. ***Perf. 12x11½***
2294 A1226 15cr multicolored .18 .15

Organization of American States, cent.

1990, Dec. 14
2295 A1227 15cr multicolored .18 .15

First Flight of Nike Apache Missile, 25th anniv.

Colonization of Sergipe, Founding of Sao Cristovao, 400th Anniv. A1228

1990, Dec. 18 Litho. ***Perf. 11½x12***
2296 A1228 15cr multicolored .18 .15

World Congress of Physical Education A1229

1991, Jan. 7 ***Perf. 11½x12***
2297 A1229 17cr multicolored .18 .15

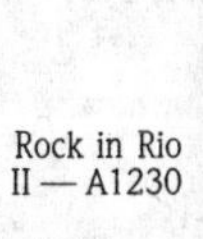

Rock in Rio II — A1230

1991, Jan. 9 ***Perf. 12x11½***
2298 A1230 25cr Cazuza .20 .15
2299 A1230 185cr Raul Seixas 1.65 1.00
a. Pair, #2298-2299 2.00 1.10

Printed in sheets of 12.

Ministry of Aviation, 50th Anniv. A1231

1991, Jan. 20 *Perf. 11x11½*

2300 A1231 17cr multicolored .20 .15

A1232 A1233

Carnivals.

1991, Feb. 8 Litho. *Perf. 12x11½*

2301 A1232 25cr Olinda .24 .16

2302 A1232 30cr Salvador .28 .20

2303 A1232 280cr Rio de Janeiro 2.50 2.00

Nos. 2301-2303 (3) 3.02 2.36

1991, Feb. 20

2304 A1233 300cr multicolored 3.00 2.25

Visit by Pres. Collor to Antarctica.

Hang Gliding World Championships — A1234

1991, Feb. 24 *Perf. 11½x12*

2305 A1234 36cr multicolored .36 .28

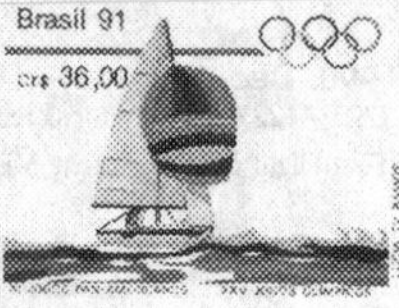

11th Pan American Games, 25th Summer Olympics A1235

1991, Mar. 30 Litho. *Perf. 11½x12*

2306 A1235 36cr Sailing .32 .24

2307 A1235 36cr Rowing .32 .24

2308 A1235 300cr Swimming 2.50 1.90

a. Block of 3, #2306-2308 + label 3.25 2.50

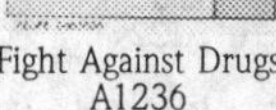

Fight Against Drugs A1236

Yanomami Indian Culture A1237

1991, Apr. 7 Litho. *Perf. 12x11½*

2309 A1236 40cr Drugs .35 .30

2310 A1236 40cr Alcohol .35 .30

2311 A1236 40cr Smoking .35 .30

Nos. 2309-2311 (3) 1.05 .90

Perf. 11½x11, 11x11½

1991, Apr. 19

2312 A1237 40cr shown .35 .28

2313 A1237 400cr Indian, horiz. 3.50 2.75

Journal of Brazil, Cent. A1238

1991, Apr. 8 Litho. *Perf. 11x11½*

2314 A1238 40cr multicolored .35 .28

Neochen Jubata (Orinoco Goose) — A1239

1991, June 5 Litho. *Perf. 12x11½*

2315 A1239 45cr multi .30 .22

UN Conference on Development.

Snakes & Dinosaurs A1240

1991, June 6 *Perf. 11½x12*

2316 A1240 45cr Bothrops jararaca .30 .22

2317 A1240 45cr Corallus caninus .30 .22

a. Pair, #2316-2317 .60 .45

2318 A1240 45cr Teropods .30 .22

2319 A1240 350cr Sauropods 2.10 1.60

a. Pair, #2318-2319 2.40 1.85

Nos. 2316-2319 (4) 3.00 2.26

Flag of Brazil — A1241

1991, June 10 Photo. *Perf. 13x13½*

2320 A1241 A multicolored .25 .20

Valued at domestic letter rate (cr) on day of issue.

Exists with inscription at lower right. Same value.

Fire Pumper A1242

1991, July 2 Litho. *Perf. 11½x12*

2321 A1242 45cr multicolored .30 .22

Tourism A1243

Map location and: 45cr, Painted stones, Roraima. 350cr, Dedo de Deus Mountain, Rio De Janeiro.

1991, July 6 *Perf. 11x11½*

2322 A1243 45cr multicolored .28 .20

2323 A1243 350cr multicolored 2.00 1.50

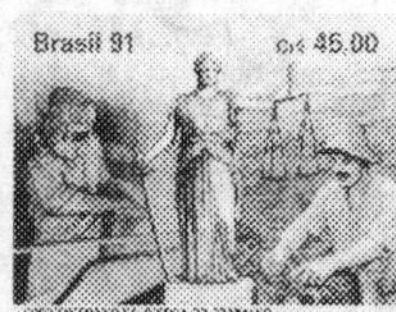

Labor Laws, 50th Anniv. A1244

1991, Aug. 11 *Perf. 11½x12*

2324 A1244 45cr multicolored .30 .22

Leonardo Mota, Birth Cent. A1245

1991, Aug. 22

2325 A1245 45cr buff, blk & red .30 .22

Folklore Festival.

Jose Basilio da Gama (1741-1795), Poet A1246

Designs: No. 2327, Fagundes Varela (b. 1841), poet. No. 2328, Jackson de Figueiredo (b. 1891), writer.

1991, Aug. 29

2326 A1246 45cr multicolored .26 .18

2327 A1246 50cr multicolored .30 .22

2328 A1246 50cr multicolored .30 .22

Nos. 2326-2328 (3) .86 .62

12th Natl. Eucharistic Congress — A1247

1991, Oct. 6 Litho. *Perf. 12x11½*

2329 A1247 50cr Pope John Paul II .18 .15

2330 A1247 400cr Map, crosses 1.40 1.05

a. Pair, #2329-2330 1.60 1.20

Visit by Pope John Paul II.

First Brazilian Constitution, Cent. A1248

1991, Oct. 7 *Perf. 11½x12*

2331 A1248 50cr multicolored .18 .15

Telecom '91 — A1249

1991, Oct. 8 *Perf. 12x11½*

2332 A1249 50cr multicolored .18 .15

Sixth World Forum and Exposition on Telecommunications, Geneva, Switzerland.

America Issue A1250

UPAEP emblem and explorers: 50cr, Ferdinand Magellan (c. 1480-1521). 400cr, Francisco de Orellana (c. 1490-c. 1546).

1991, Oct. 12 *Perf. 11½x12*

2333 A1250 50cr multicolored .18 .15

2334 A1250 400cr multicolored 1.40 1.05

Discovery of America, 500th anniv. (in 1992).

A1251 A1252

BRAPEX VIII (Orchids and Hummingbirds): 50cr, Colibri serrirostris, cattleya warneri. No. 2336, Chlorostilbon aureoventris, rodriguezia venusta. No. 2337, Clytolaema rubricauda, zygopetalum intermedium. No. 2338a, 50cr, Colibri serrirostris. b, 50cr, Chlorostilbon aureoventris. c, 500cr, Clytolaema rubricauda.

1991, Oct. 29 Litho. *Perf. 12x11½*

2335 A1251 50cr multicolored .15 .15

2336 A1251 65cr multicolored .18 .15

2337 A1251 65cr multicolored .18 .15

Nos. 2335-2337 (3) .51 .45

Souvenir Sheet

2338 A1251 Sheet of 3, #a.-c. 2.20 1.65

1991, Oct. 29 Litho. *Perf. 11½x11*

2339 A1252 400cr multicolored .90 .65

Lasar Segall, artist, birth cent.

Bureau of Agriculture and Provision of Sao Paulo, Cent. — A1253

1991, Nov. 11 *Perf. 12x11½*

2340 A1253 70cr multicolored .20 .15

First Civilian Presidents, Birth Sesquicentennials — A1254

1991, Nov. 14 *Perf. 11½x12*

2341 A1254 70cr Manuel de Campos Salles .20 .15

2342 A1254 90cr Prudente de Moraes Barros .25 .18

a. Pair, #2341-2342 .45 .35

Christmas A1255 — Thanksgiving A1256

1991, Nov. 20 — *Perf. 12x11½*

2343 A1255 70cr multicolored .20 .15

1991, Nov. 28

2344 A1256 70cr multicolored .20 .15

Military Police A1257

1991, Dec. 1 — *Perf. 11½x12*

2345 A1257 80cr multicolored .22 .16

Souvenir Sheet

Emperor Dom Pedro (1825-1891) — A1258

Designs: No. 2346a, 80cr, Older age. b, 800cr, Wearing crown.

Litho. & Engr.

1991, Nov. 29 — *Perf. 11*

2346 A1258 Sheet of 2, #a.-b. 2.50 2.50

BRASILIANA 93.

Churches — A1259

Designs: No. 2347, Presbyterian Church, Rio de Janeiro. No. 2348, First Baptist Church, Niteroi.

1992, Jan. 12 Litho. — *Perf. 12x11½*

2347 A1259 250cr multicolored .30 .22

2348 A1259 250cr multicolored .30 .22

1992 Summer Olympics, Barcelona A1260

Medalists in shooting, Antwerp, 1920: 300cr, Afranio Costa, silver. 2500cr, Guihlherme Paraense, gold.

1992, Jan. 28 — *Perf. 11½x12*

2349 A1260 300cr multicolored .32 .24

2350 A1260 2500cr multicolored 2.75 2.00

Port of Santos, Cent. — A1261

1992, Feb. 3 Litho. — *Perf. 11½*

2351 A1261 300cr multicolored .45 .35

Fauna of Fernando de Noronha Island A1262

1992, Feb. 25 Litho. — *Perf. 11½x12*

2352 A1262 400cr White-tailed tropicbirds .40 .30

2353 A1262 2500cr Dolphins 2.50 1.75

Earth Summit, Rio de Janeiro.

Yellow Amaryllis — A1263

1992, Feb. 27 Photo. — *Perf. 13½*

2354 A1263 (A) multicolored .25 .20

No. 2354 met the second class domestic letter postage rate of 265cr on date of issue.

ARBRAFEX '92, Argentina-Brazil Philatelic Exhibition — A1264

Designs: No. 2355, Gaucho throwing bola at rhea. No. 2356, Man playing accordion, couple dancing. No. 2357, Couple in horse-drawn cart, woman. 1000cr, Gaucho throwing lasso at steer.

No. 2358c, 250cr, like #2356. d, 500cr, like #2355. e, 1500cr, like #2358.

1992, Mar. 20 Litho. — *Perf. 11½x12*

2355 A1264 250cr multicolored .15 .15

2356 A1264 250cr multicolored .15 .15

2357 A1264 250cr multicolored .15 .15

2358 A1264 1000cr multicolored .60 .60

a. Block of 4, Nos. 2355-2358 1.05 1.05

Souvenir Sheet

2358B A1264 Sheet of 4, #2357, 2358c-2358e 1.05 1.05

1992 Summer Olympics, Barcelona — A1265

1992, Apr. 3 — *Perf. 12x11½*

2359 A1265 300cr multicolored .18 .18

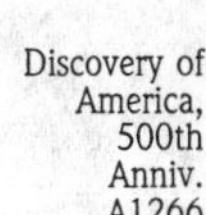

Discovery of America, 500th Anniv. A1266

1992, Apr. 24 — *Perf. 11½x12*

2360 A1266 500cr Columbus' fleet .30 .30

2361 A1266 3500cr Columbus, map 2.10 2.10

a. Pair, #2360-2361 2.40 2.40

Telebras Telecommunications System — A1267

1992, May 5 — *Perf. 11x11½*

2362 A1267 350cr multicolored .20 .20

Installation of 10 million telephones.

Langsdorff Expedition to Brazil, 170th Anniv. A1268

Designs: No. 2363, Aime-Adrien Taunay, natives. No. 2364, Johann Moritz Rugendas, monkey . No. 2365, Hercule Florence, flowering plant. 3000cr, Gregory Ivanovitch Langsdorff, map.

1992, June 2 — *Perf. 11½x12*

2363 A1268 500cr multicolored .25 .25

2364 A1268 500cr multicolored .25 .25

2365 A1268 500cr multicolored .25 .25

2366 A1268 3000cr multicolored 1.50 1.50

Nos. 2363-2366 (4) 2.25 2.25

UN Conf. on Environmental Development, Rio.

UN Conference on Environmental Development, Rio de Janeiro — A1269

Globe and: No. 2367, Flags of Sweden and Brazil. No. 2368, City, grain, mountain and tree. 3000cr, Map of Brazil, parrot, orchid.

1992, June 3 Litho. — *Perf. 11x11½*

2367 A1269 450cr multicolored .20 .20

2368 A1269 450cr multicolored .20 .20

2369 A1269 3000cr multicolored 1.50 1.50

Nos. 2367-2369 (3) 1.90 1.90

Ecology A1270

Designs: No. 2370, Flowers, waterfall, and butterflies. No. 2371, Butterflies, canoe, and hummingbirds. No. 2372, Boy taking pictures of tropical birds. No. 2373, Armadillo, girl picking fruit.

1992, June 4 — *Perf. 11½x12*

2370 A1270 500cr multicolored .25 .25

2371 A1270 500cr multicolored .25 .25

2372 A1270 500cr multicolored .25 .25

2373 A1270 500cr multicolored .25 .25

a. Strip of 4, #2370-2373 1.00 1.00

UN Conf. on Environmental Development, Rio.

Floral Paintings by Margaret Mee — A1271

1992, June 5 — *Perf. 12x11½*

2374 A1271 600cr Nidularium innocentii .35 .35

2375 A1271 600cr Canistrum exiguum .35 .35

2376 A1271 700cr Canistrum cyathiforme .42 .42

2377 A1271 700cr Nidularium rubens .42 .42

Nos. 2374-2377 (4) 1.54 1.54

UN Conf. on Environmental Development, Rio.

Souvenir Sheet

Joaquim Jose da Silva Xavier (1748-1792), Patriot — A1272

1992, Apr. 21 Litho. & Engr. — *Perf. 11*

2378 A1272 3500cr multicolored 2.10 2.10

Souvenir Sheet

Expedition of Alexandre Rodrigues Ferreira, Bicent. A1273

Designs: a, 500cr, Sailing ships, gray and green hulls. b, 1000cr, Sailing ships, red hulls. c, 2500cr, Sailing ship at shore.

1992, May 9 Litho. — *Perf. 11½x12*

2379 A1273 Sheet of 3, #a.-c. 2.40 2.40

Lubrapex '92.

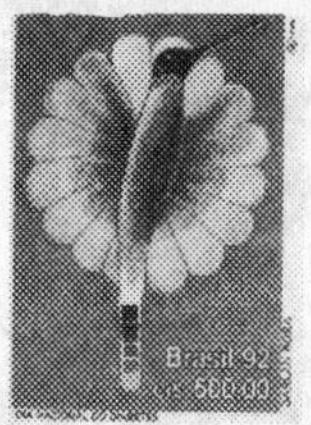

A1274 — A1275

1992, June 5 Litho. — *Perf. 12x11½*

2380 A1274 600cr Hummingbird .25 .25

Diabetes Day.

1992, July 13 Litho. — *Perf. 11½x11*

2381 A1275 550cr multicolored .25 .25

Volunteer firemen of Joinville.

A1276 — A1277

Serra da Capivara National Park: No. 2382, Leopard, animals, map of park. No. 2383, Canyon, map of Brazil.

1992, July 17 — *Perf. 12x11½*

2382 A1276 550cr multicolored .22 .22

2383 A1276 550cr multicolored .22 .22

a. Pair, #2382-2383 .45 .45

1992, July 24

2384 A1277 550cr multicolored .25 .25

Financing for studies and projects.

Natl. Service for Industrial Training, 50th Anniv. — A1278

1992, Aug. 5 *Perf. 11½x12*
2385 A1278 650cr multicolored .35 .35

Fortresses A1279

1992, Aug. 19 Litho. *Perf. 11½x12*
2386 A1279 650cr Santa Cruz .28 .28
2387 A1279 3000cr Santo Antonio 1.25 1.25

Masonic Square, Compass and Lodge A1280

1992, Aug. 20
2388 A1280 650cr multicolored .28 .28

Brazilian Assistance Legion, 50th Anniv. A1281

Hospital of Medicine and Orthopedics A1282

1992, Aug. 28 *Perf. 12x11½*
2389 A1281 650cr multicolored .28 .28

1992, Sept. 11
2390 A1282 800cr multicolored .30 .30

Merry Christmas A1283

1992, Nov. 20 *Perf. 11½*
2391 A1283 (1) multicolored .25 .25

No. 2391 met the first class domestic letter postage rate of 1090cr on day of issue.

Writers A1284

Designs: No. 2392, Graciliano Ramos (1892-1953), vert. No. 2393, Menotti del Picchia (1892-1988), vert. 1000cr, Assis Chateaubriand (1892-1968).

Perf. 12x11½, 11½x12
1992, Oct. 29 Litho.
2392 A1284 900cr multicolored .22 .22
2393 A1284 900cr multicolored .22 .22
2394 A1284 1000cr multicolored .28 .28

Expedition of Luis Cruls, Cent. A1285

1992, Nov. 11 *Perf. 11½x12*
2395 A1285 900cr multicolored .22 22

Brazillian Program for Quality and Productivity A1286

1992, Nov. 12
2396 A1286 1200cr multicolored .28 .28

Souvenir Sheet

Tourism Year in the Americas — A1287

Designs: a, 1200cr, Mountains, coastline. b, 9000cr, Sugarloaf Mt., aerial tram, Rio de Janeiro.

1992, Nov. 18 Litho. *Perf. 11½x12*
2397 A1287 Sheet of 2, #a.-b. 2.00 2.00

Brasiliana '93.

Sister Irma Dulce A1288

1993, Mar. 13 Litho. *Perf. 11½x12*
2398 A1288 3500cr multicolored .35 .35

Souvenir Sheet

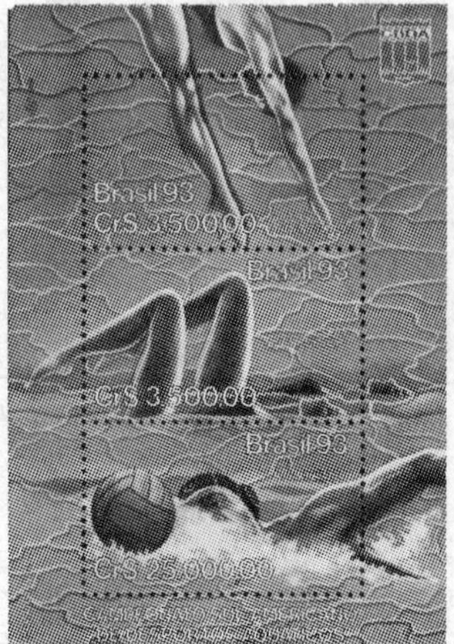

Water Sports Championships of South America — A1289

Designs: a, 3500cr, Diver. b, 3500cr, Synchronized swimmers. c, 25,000cr, Water polo.

1993, Mar. 21 Litho. *Perf. 11*
2399 A1289 Sheet of 3, #a.-c. 2.75 2.75

Curitiba, 300th Anniv. A1290

1993, Mar. 29
2400 A1290 4500cr multicolored .40 .40

Health and Preservation of Life — A1291

Pedro Americo, 150th Birth Anniv. — A1292

Red Cross emblem and: No. 2401, Bleeding heart, flowers. No. 2402, Cancer symbol, breast. No. 2403, Brain waves, rainbow emerging from head.

1993, Apr. 7 Litho. *Perf. 12x11½*
2401 A1291 4500cr multicolored .30 .30
2402 A1291 4500cr multicolored .30 .30
2403 A1291 4500cr multicolored .30 .30
a. Strip of 3, #2401-2403 .90 .90

Perf. 12x11½, 11½x12
1993, Apr. 29

Paintings: 5500cr, A Study of Love, 1883. No. 2405, David and Abizag, 1879, horiz. No. 2406, Seated Nude, 1882.

2404 A1292 5500cr multi .25 .25
2405 A1292 36,000cr multi 1.65 1.65
2406 A1292 36,000cr multi 1.65 1.65
Nos. 2404-2406 (3) 3.55 3.55

Natl. Flag — A1292a

1993, May 26 Litho. *Die Cut*
Self-adhesive
2407 A1292a A multicolored .35 .35

No. 2407 valued at first class domestic letter rate of 9570cr on day of issue.

Beetles A1293

1993, June 5 Litho. *Perf. 11½x12*
2408 A1293 8000cr Dynastes hercules .35 .35
2409 A1293 55,000cr Batus barbicornis 2.25 2.25

3rd Iberian-American Conference of Chiefs of State and Heads of Government, Salvador — A1294

1993, July 15 Litho. *Perf. 11x11½*
2410 A1294 12,000cr multi .15 .15

1st Brazilian Postage Stamps, 150th Anniv. — A1295

Perf. 12x11½
1993, July 30 Litho. & Engr.
2411 A1295 30,000cr No. 1 .30 .30
2412 A1295 60,000cr No. 2 .60 .60
2413 A1295 90,000cr No. 3 .90 .90
a. Souvenir sheet of 3, #2411-2413, wmk. 268 2.00 2.00
Nos. 2411-2413 (3) 1.80 1.80

No. 2413a sold for 200,000cr.

Union of Portuguese Speaking Capitals A1296

Designs: a, 15,000cr, Brasilia. b, 71,000cr, Rio de Janeiro.

1993, July 30 Litho. *Perf. 11½x12*
2414 A1296 Pair, #a.-b. .90 .90

No. 2414 printed in continuous design.

Monica & Friends, by Mauricio de Sousa A1297

Monica, Cebolinha, Cascao, Magali, and Bidu: a, Engraving die. b, Reading proclamation, king, No. 1. c, Writing and sending letter, No. 2. d, Receiving letter, No. 3.

1993, Aug. 1
2415 A1297 (1) Strip of 4, #a.-d. .85 .85

First Brazilian postage stamps, 150th anniv. Nos. 2415a-2415d paid the first class rate in the new currency on day of issue.

Brazilian Post, 330th Anniv. A1298

Postal buildings: a, Imperial Post Office, Rio de Janeiro. b, Petropolis. c, Central office, Rio de Janeiro. d, Niteroi.

1993, Aug. 3 Litho. *Perf. 11½x12*
2416 A1298 20,000cr Block of 4, #a.-d. .45 .45

Brazilian Engineering Schools A1299

Designs: No. 2417, School of Engineering, Federal University, Rio de Janeiro. No. 2418, Polytechnical School, University of Sao Paulo.

1993, Aug. 24 Litho. *Perf. 11x11½*

2417 A1299 17cr multicolored .30 .30
2418 A1299 17cr multicolored .30 .30

Preservation of Sambaquis Archaelogical Sites — A1300

1993, Sept. 19 *Perf. 12x11½*

2419 A1300 17cr Two artifacts .22 .22
2420 A1300 17cr Six artifacts .22 .22

Ulysses Guimaraes, Natl. Congress — A1301

1993, Oct. 6 Litho. *Perf. 11x11½*

2421 A1301 22cr multicolored .28 .28

A1302

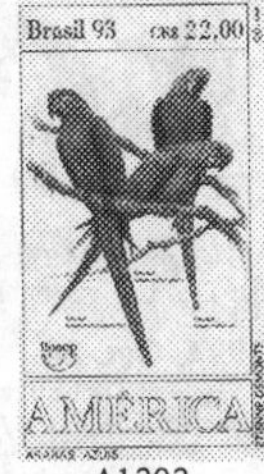

A1303

1993, Oct. 8 Litho. *Perf. 12x11½*

2422 A1302 22cr multicolored .28 .28

Virgin of Nazare Religious Festival, bicent.

1993, Oct. 13 Litho. *Perf. 11½x11*

Endangered birds (America Issue): 22cr, Anodorhynchus hyacinthinus, anodorhynchus glaucus, anodorhynchus leari. 130cr, Cyanopsitta spixii.

2423 A1303 22cr multicolored .25 .25
2424 A1303 130cr multicolored 1.40 1.40

Composers — A1304

A1307

1993, Oct. 19 Litho. *Perf. 12x11½*

2425 A1304 22cr Vinicius de Moraes .18 .18
2426 A1304 22cr Pixinguinha .18 .18

1993, Oct. 29 Litho. *Perf. 12x11½*

Poets: No. 2427, Mario de Andrade (1893-1945). No. 2428, Alceu Amoroso Lima (Tristao de Athayde) (1893-1983). No. 2429, Gilka Machado (1893-1980).

2427 A1307 30cr multicolored .28 .28
2428 A1307 30cr multicolored .28 .28
2429 A1307 30cr multicolored .28 .28
Nos. 2427-2429 (3) .84 .84

Natl. Book Day.

Brazil-Portugal Treaty of Consultation and Friendship, 40th Anniv. — A1308

1993, Nov. 3 Litho. *Perf. 11½x12*

2430 A1308 30cr multicolored .28 .28

See Portugal No. 1980.

Image of the Republic — A1309

1993, Nov. 3 Photo. & Engr. *Perf. 13*

2431 A1309 (B) multicolored 2.50 2.50

Valued at first class international letter rate (cr) on day of issue.

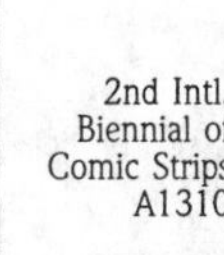

2nd Intl. Biennial of Comic Strips A1310

Cartoon drawings: No. 2432, Nho-Quim. No. 2433, Benjamin. No. 2434, Lamparina. No. 2435, Reco-Reco, Bolao, Azeitona.

1993, Nov. 11 Litho. *Perf. 11½x12*

2432 A1310 (1) multicolored .42 .42
2433 A1310 (1) multicolored .42 .42
2434 A1310 (1) multicolored .42 .42
2435 A1310 (1) multicolored .42 .42
a. Block of 4, #2432-2435 1.75 1.75

Valued at first class domestic letter rate (cr) on day of issue.

Launching of First Brazilian-Built Submarine — A1311

1993, Nov. 18 *Perf. 11½*

2436 A1311 240cr multicolored 1.75 1.75

Christmas A1312

1993, Nov. 20

2437 A1312 (1) multicolored .45 .45

Valued at first class domestic letter rate (cr) on day of issue.

First Fighter Group, 50th Anniv. A1313

1993, Dec. 18 Litho. *Perf. 11½*

2438 A1313 42cr multicolored .35 .35

Convent of Merces, 340th Anniv. A1314

1994, Jan. 31 Litho. *Perf. 11½x12*

2439 A1314 58cr multicolored .32 .32

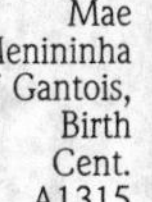

Mae Menininha of Gantois, Birth Cent. A1315

1994, Feb. 10 Litho. *Perf. 11x11½*

2440 A1315 80cr multicolored .40 .40

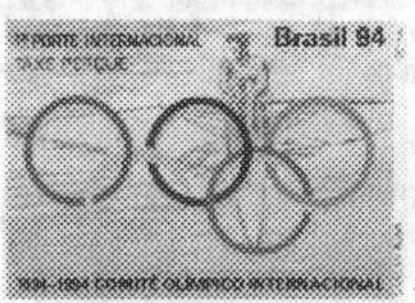

Intl. Olympic Committee, Cent. A1316

1994, Feb. 17 *Perf. 11½x12*

2441 A1316 (1) multicolored 2.25 2.25

No. 2441 valued at first class international letter rate (cr) on day of issue.

Natl. Flag — A1317

1994, Jan. 31 Litho. *Die Cut*

Self-Adhesive

2442 A1317 (1) multicolored .40 .40

No. 2442 valued at first class domestic letter rate (cr) on day of issue.

Birds — A1318

1994 Photo. *Perf. 11x11½*

2443 A1318 10cr Notiochelidon cyanoleuca .15 .15
2444 A1318 20cr Buteo magnirostris .15 .15
2445 A1318 50cr Turdus rufiventris .15 .15
2446 A1318 100cr Columbina talpacoti .15 .15
2447 A1318 200cr Vanellus chilensis .20 .20
2448 A1318 500cr Zonotrichia capensis .50 .50
Set value .90 .90

Issued: 10cr, 3/17/94. 20cr, 3/9/94. 50cr, 3/1/94. 100cr, 200cr, 4/4/94. 500cr, 4/13/94.

See Nos. 2484-2494.

Image of the Republic — A1318a

1994, May 10 Litho. *Perf. 12x11½*

Self-Adhesive

Die Cut

2449 A1318a (1) blue .22 .22
2450 A1318a (3) claret .40 .40

Size: 25x35mm

2451 A1318a (4) green .80 .80
2452 A1318a (5) henna brown 1.50 1.50
Nos. 2449-2452 (4) 2.92 2.92

Nos. 2449, 2450, 2451 valued (cr) on day of issue. No. 2452 valued at (cr) on day of issue.

Prince Henry the Navigator (1394-1460) — A1319

1994, Mar. 4 Litho. *Perf. 11½x12*

2463 A1319 635cr multicolored 2.25 2.25

See Macao No. 719, Portugal No. 1987.

America Issue A1320

Postal vehicles: 110cr, Bicycle, country scene. 635cr, Motorcycle, city scene.

1994, Mar. 18

2464 A1320 110cr multicolored .20 .20
2465 A1320 635cr multicolored 1.10 1.10

Father Cicero Romao Batista, 150th Birth Anniv. A1321

1994, Mar. 24 *Perf. 11x11½*

2466 A1321 (1) multicolored .35 .35

No. 2466 valued at first class domestic letter rate (cr) on day of issue.

Albert Sabin, Campaign Against Polio A1322

1994, Apr. 7 *Perf. 11½x12*

2467 A1322 160cr multicolored .30 .30

Carlos Castello Branco, Journalist A1323

1994, Apr. 14

2468 A1323 160cr multicolored .30 .30

Karl Friedrich Phillip von Martius, Naturalist — A1324

Flowers: No. 2469, Euterpe oleracea. No. 2470, Jacaranda paucifoliolata. No. 2471, Barbacernia tomentosa.

1994, Apr. 24 *Perf. 12x11½*

2469 A1324 (1) multicolored .35 .35
2470 A1324 (1) multicolored .35 .35
2471 A1324 (1) multicolored 2.00 2.00
Nos. 2469-2471 (3) 2.70 2.70

Nos. 2469-2470 were valued at first class domestic letter rate (cr) on day of issue. No. 2471 valued at first class intl. letter rate (cr) on day of issue.

Monkeys — A1326

Designs: No. 2474, Leontopithecus rosalia. No. 2475, Saguinus imperator. No. 2476, Saguinus bicolor.

1994, May 24

2474 A1326 (1) multicolored .35 .35
2475 A1326 (1) multicolored .35 .35
2476 A1326 (1) multicolored .35 .35
Nos. 2474-2476 (3) 1.05 1.05

Nos. 2474-2476 were valued at first class domestic letter rate (cr) on day of issue.

1994 World Cup Soccer Championships, US — A1327

1994, May 19 *Perf. 11½x12*

2477 A1327 (1) multicolored 2.00 2.00

No. 2477 was valued at first class intl. rate (cr) on day of issue.
Soccer in Brazil, cent.

Souvenir Sheet

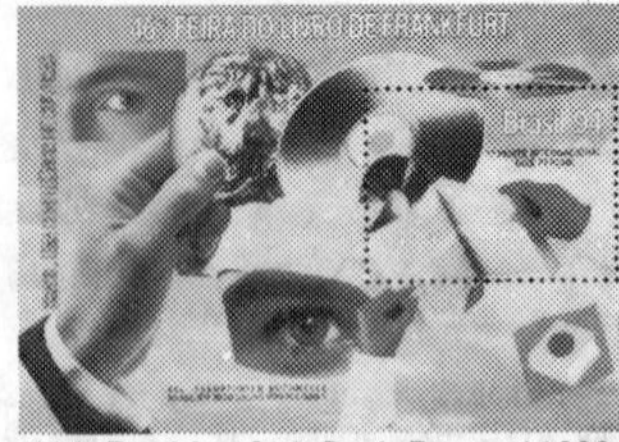

46th Frankfurt Intl. Book Fair — A1328

Illustration reduced.

1994, May 27

2478 A1328 (1) multicolored 2.00 2.00

No. 2478 was valued at first class intl. rate (cr) on day of issue.

Natl. Literacy Program — A1329

Designs: No. 2479, Pencil, buildings. No. 2480, Pencil, people on television, people watching. No. 2481, Classroom, pencil. No. 2482, Pencils crossed over fingerprint, map of Brazil.

1994, June 3 Litho. *Perf. 12x11½*

2479 A1329 (1) multicolored .32 .32
2480 A1329 (1) multicolored .32 .32
2481 A1329 (1) multicolored .32 .32
2482 A1329 (1) multicolored .32 .32
Nos. 2479-2482 (4) 1.28 1.28

Nos. 2479-2482 were valued at first class domestic letter rate (cr) on day of issue.

Souvenir Sheet

Treaty of Tordesillas, 500th Anniv. — A1330

1994, June 7

2483 A1330 (1) multicolored 2.25 2.25

No. 2483 was valued at first class intl. letter rate (cr) on day of issue.

Bird Type of 1994

1994 Photo. *Perf. 11x11½*

2484 A1318 1c like No. 2443 .15 .15
2485 A1318 2c like No. 2444 .15 .15
2486 A1318 5c like No. 2445 .15 .15
2487 A1318 10c like No. 2446 .20 .20
2489 A1318 20c like No. 2447 .42 .42
2491 A1318 50c like No. 2448 1.00 1.00
2494 A1318 1r Furnarius rufus 2.25 2.25
Nos. 2484-2494 (7) 4.32 4.32

Issued: 1c, 2c, 5c, 20c, 20c, 50c, 1r, 7/1/94.
This is an expanding set. Numbers may change.

Prominent Brazilians A1331

Designs: No. 2504, Edgard Santos (1894-1962), surgeon, educator. No. 2505, Oswaldo Aranha (1894-1960), politician. No. 2507, Otto Lara Resende (1922-92), writer, educator.

1994, July 5 Litho. *Perf. 11½x12*

2504 A1331 (1) multicolored .28 .28
2505 A1331 (1) multicolored .28 .28
2506 A1331 (1) multicolored .28 .28
Nos. 2504-2506 (3) .84 .84

Nos. 2504-2506 were valued at first class domestic letter rate (12c) on day of issue.

A1332 A1333

1994, July 15 *Perf. 12x11½*

2507 A1332 12c multicolored .28 .28

Petrobras, 40th anniv.

Litho. & Engr.

1994, July 26 *Perf. 11½*

2508 A1333 12c multicolored .28 .28

Brazilian State Mint, 300th anniv.

Campaign Against Famine & Misery A1334

1994, July 27 Litho. *Perf. 11½x12*

2509 A1334 (1) Fish .28 .28
2510 A1334 (1) Bread .28 .28

Nos. 2509-2510 were valued at first class domestic letter rate (12c) on day of issue.

Institute of Brazilian Lawyers, 150th Anniv. A1335

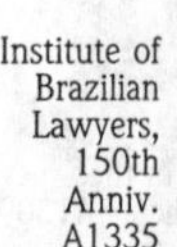

1994, Aug. 11

2511 A1335 12c multicolored .28 .28

Intl. Year of the Family A1336

1994, Aug. 16 *Perf. 11½*

2512 A1336 84c multicolored 2.00 2.00

Maternity Hospital of Sao Paulo, Cent. A1337

1994, Aug. 26 *Perf. 11½x12*

2513 A1337 12c multicolored .28 .28

Vincente Celestino (1894-1968), Singer A1338

1994, Sept. 12

2514 A1338 12c multicolored .28 .28

"Contos da Carochinha," First Brazilian Children's Book, Cent. A1339

Fairy tales: a, Joao e Maria (Hansel & Gretel). b, Dona Baratinha. c, Puss 'n Boots. d, Tom Thumb.

1994, Oct. 5 Litho. *Perf. 11½x12*

2515 Block of 4 4.75 4.75
a.-b. A1339 12c any single .28 .28
c.-d. A1339 84c any single 2.00 2.00

Brazilian Literature A1340

Portraits: No. 2516, Tomas Antonio Gonzaga (1744-1809?), poet. No. 2517, Fernando de Azevedo (1894-1974), author.

1994, Oct. 5 *Perf. 11½*

2516 A1340 12c multicolored .28 .28
2517 A1340 12c multicolored .28 .28

St. Clare of Assisi (1194-1253) A1341

1994, Oct. 19 *Perf. 12x11½*

2518 A1341 12c multicolored .28 .28

Ayrton Senna (1960-1994), Race Car Driver A1342

Designs: a, McClaren Formula 1 race car, Brazilian flag. b, Fans, Senna. c, Flags, race cars, Senna.

1994, Oct. 24 *Perf. 11½x12*

2519 Triptych 2.75 2.75
a.-b. A1342 12c any single .28 .28
c. A1342 84c multicolored 2.00 2.00

Institute of History & Geography of Sao Paulo, Cent. A1343

1994, Nov. 1

2520 A1343 12c multicolored .28 .28

Popular Music A1344

Designs: No. 2521, Music from "The Sea," by Dorival Caymmi. No. 2522, Adoniran Barbosa (1910-82), samba composer.

1994, Nov. 5 *Perf. 11½*

2521 A1344 12c multicolored .28 .28
2522 A1344 12c multicolored .28 .28

Christmas A1345

Folk characters: No. 2523a, Boy wearing Santa coat, pot on head. b, Worm in apple. c, Man, animals singing. d, Shoe on tree stump, man with pipe holding pen.

1994, Dec. 1 Litho. *Perf. 11½*

2523	Block of 4	2.75	2.75
a.	A1345 84c multicolored	1.90	1.90
b.-d.	A1345 12c any single	.28	.28
e.	Booklet pane, #2523 + 4 labels	*5.50*	
	Complete booklet, #2523a	*5.50*	

Souvenir Sheet

Brazil, 1994 World Cup Soccer Champions — A1346

Illustration reduced.

1994, Dec. 5 *Perf. 12x11½*

2524 A1346 2.14r multicolored 5.00 5.00

Louis Pasteur (1822-95) A1347

1995, Feb. 19 Litho. *Perf. 11½x12*

2525 A1347 84c multicolored 2.00 2.00

Historical Events A1348

Designs: No. 2526, Capture of Monte Castello, 50th anniv. No. 2527, End of the Farroupilha Revolution, 150th anniv.

1995, Feb. 21

2526 A1348	12c multicolored	.28	.28
2527 A1348	12c multicolored	.28	.28

Pres. Itamar Franco — A1349

FAO, 50th Anniv. — A1350

1995, Mar. 22 Litho. *Perf. 12x11½*

2528 A1349 12c multicolored .28 .28

1995, Apr. 3 *Perf. 11½x11*

2529 A1350 84c multicolored 2.00 2.00

Famous Men A1351

Designs: No. 2530, Alexandre de Gusmao (1695-1753), diplomat. No. 2531, Francisco Brandao, Viscount of Jequitinhonha (1794-1870), lawyer, abolitionist. 15c, Jose da Silva Paranhos, Jr., Baron of Rio Branco (1845-1912), politician, diplomat.

1995, Apr. 28 *Perf. 11½x12*

2530 A1351	12c multicolored	.28	.28
2531 A1351	12c multicolored	.28	.28
2532 A1351	15c multicolored	.35	.35
	Nos. 2530-2532 (3)	.91	.91

Radio, Cent. A1352

Design: Guglielmo Marconi (1874-1937), transmitting equipment.

1995, May 5 Litho. *Perf. 11½x12*

2533 A1352 84c multicolored 2.00 2.00

Friendship Between Brazil & Japan — A1353

1995, May 29

2534 A1353 84c multicolored 2.00 2.00

Endangered Birds — A1354

1995, June 5 *Perf. 12x11½*

2535 A1354	12c Tinamus solitarius	.30	.30
2536 A1354	12c Mitu mitu	.30	.30

June Festivals — A1355

Designs: No. 2537, Couples dancing at Campina Grande, "Greatest St. John's Party of the World." No. 2538, Bride, bridegroom, festivities, Caruaru.

1995, June 11 *Perf. 11½x12*

2537 A1355	12c multicolored	.30	.30
2538 A1355	12c multicolored	.30	.30

St. Anthony of Padua (1195-1231) — A1356

1995, June 13

2539 A1356 84c multicolored 2.00 2.00

See Portugal No. 2054.

Souvenir Sheet

Motion Picture, Cent. — A1357

Design: Louis and Auguste Lumiere, camera.

1995, June 21

2540 A1357 2.14r multicolored 4.75 4.75

New Currency, The Real, 1st Anniv. — A1358

Volleyball, Cent. — A1359

1995, July 1 Litho. *Perf. 12x11½*

2541 A1358 12c multicolored .30 .30

1995, July 8

2542 A1359 15c multicolored .35 .35

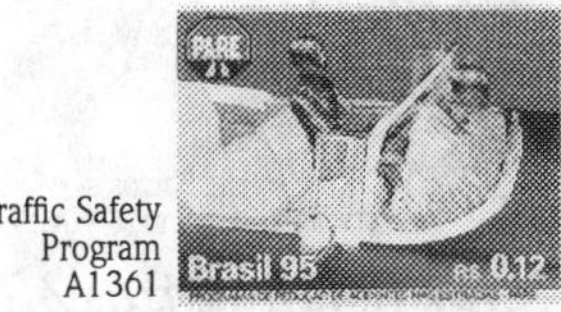

Dinosaurs A1360

1995, July 23 *Perf. 11½x12*

2543 A1360	15c Angaturama limai	.35	.35
2544 A1360	1.50r Titanosaurus	3.25	3.25

Traffic Safety Program A1361

Designs: 12c, Test dummy without seat belt hitting windshield. 71c, Auto hitting alcoholic beverage glass.

1995, July 25

2545 A1361	12c multicolored	.30	.30
2546 A1361	71c multicolored	1.65	1.65

Souvenir Sheet

Roberto Burle Marx, Botanist — A1362

Designs: a, 15c, Calathea burle-marxii. b, 15c, Vellozia burle-marxii. c, 1.50r, Heliconia aemygdiana. Illustration reduced.

1995, Aug. 4 Litho. *Perf. 12x11½*

2547 A1362 Sheet of 3, #a.-c. 4.50 4.50

Singapore '95.

Parachute Infantry Brigade, 50th Anniv. — A1363

1995, Aug. 23

2548 A1363 15c multicolored .35 .35

Paulista Museum, Cent. — A1364

1995, Sept. 5 *Perf. 11½*

2549 A1364 15c multicolored .35 .35

Lighthouses A1365

1995, Sept. 28

2550 A1365	15c Olinda	.35	.35
2551 A1365	15c Sao Joao	.35	.35
2552 A1365	15c Santo Antonio da Barra	.35	.35
	Nos. 2550-2552 (3)	1.05	1.05

Wilhelm Röntgen (1845-1923), Discovery of the X-Ray, Cent. — A1366

1995, Sept. 30

2553 A1366 84c multicolored 2.00 2.00

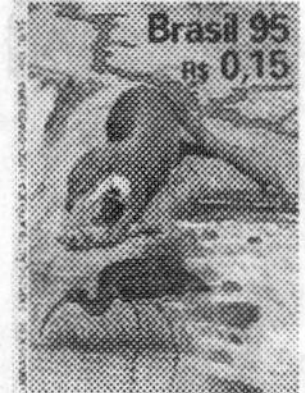

Lubrapex '95, 15th Brazilian-Portuguese Philatelic Exhibition — A1367

Wildlife scene along Tiete River: 15c, #2556a, Bird, otter with fish. 84c, #2556b, Birds, river boat.

1995, Sept. 30 *Perf. 12x11½*

2554 A1367	15c multicolored	.35	.35
2555 A1367	84c multicolored	2.00	2.00

Souvenir Sheet

2556 A1367 1.50r Sheet of 2, #a.-b. 6.50 6.50

No. 2556 is a continuous design.

Flamengo Regatta Soccer Club A1368

1995, Oct. 6 *Perf. 11x11½*

2557 A1368 15c multicolored .35 .35

SEMI-POSTAL STAMPS

National Philatelic Exhibition Issue

SP1

Wmk. Coat of Arms in Sheet (236)

1934, Sept. 16 Engr. *Imperf.*

Thick Paper

B1 SP1 200r + 100r dp claret 1.00 *2.00*
B2 SP1 300r + 100r ver 1.00 *2.00*
B3 SP1 700r + 100r brt bl 6.00 *17.50*
B4 SP1 1000r + 100r blk 6.00 *17.50*
Nos. B1-B4 (4) 14.00 39.00

The surtax was to help defray the expenses of the exhibition. Issued in sheets of 60, inscribed "EXPOSICAO FILATELICA NACIONAL."

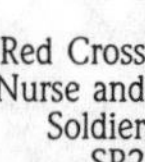

Red Cross Nurse and Soldier SP2

Wmk. 222

1935, Sept. 19 Typo. *Perf. 11*

B5 SP2 200r + 100r pur & red 1.25 1.25
B6 SP2 300r + 100r ol brn & red 1.25 .90
B7 SP2 700r + 100r turq bl & red 8.00 7.00
Nos. B5-B7 (3) 10.50 9.15

3rd Pan-American Red Cross Conf. Exist imperf.

Three Wise Men and Star of Bethlehem — SP3

Angel and Child — SP4

Southern Cross and Child — SP5

Mother and Child — SP6

Perf. 10½

1939, Dec. 20 Litho. Wmk. 249

B8 SP3 100r + 100r chlky bl & bl blk .75 .75
a. Horiz. or vert. pair, imperf. between 35.00
B9 SP4 200r + 100r brt grnsh bl 1.00 1.00
a. Horizontal pair, imperf. between 35.00
B10 SP5 400r + 200r ol grn & ol .80 .50
B11 SP6 1200r + 400r crim & brn red 3.25 1.50
a. Vertical pair, imperf. between 35.00
Nos. B8-B11 (4) 5.80 3.75

Surtax for charitable institutions. For surcharges see Nos. C55-C59.

AIR POST STAMPS

Nos. O14-O29 Surcharged **SERVIÇO AEREO 200 Rs.**

1927, Dec. 28 Unwmk. *Perf. 12*

C1 O2 50r on 10r .35 .35
a. Inverted surcharge 325.00
b. Top ornaments missing 75.00
C2 O2 200r on 1000r 2.25 2.75
a. Double surcharge 325.00
C3 O2 200r on 2000r 1.40 4.75
a. Double surcharge 750.00
b. Double surcharge, one inverted 750.00
C4 O2 200r on 5000r 1.50 1.00
a. Double surcharge 325.00 —
b. Double surcharge, one inverted 350.00
c. Triple surcharge 450.00
C5 O2 300r on 500r 1.50 2.00
C6 O2 300r on 600r .75 .90
b. Pair, one without surch. —
C6A O2 500r on 10r 325.00 375.00
C7 O2 500r on 50r 1.50 .65
a. Double surcharge 300.00 —
C8 O2 1000r on 20r 1.00 .35
a. Double surcharge 300.00 —
C9 O2 2000r on 100r 2.25 1.40
a. Pair, one without surcharge —
b. Double surcharge 300.00
C10 O2 2000r on 200r 2.75 1.40
C11 O2 2000r on 10,000r 2.25 .50
C12 O2 5000r on 20,000r 7.50 3.00
C13 O2 5000r on 50,000r 7.50 3.00

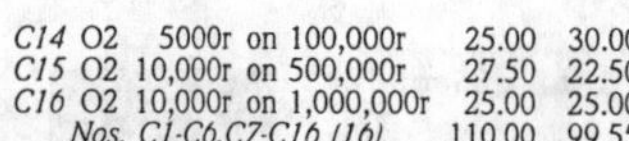

C14 O2 5000r on 100,000r 25.00 30.00
C15 O2 10,000r on 500,000r 27.50 22.50
C16 O2 10,000r on 1,000,000r 25.00 25.00
Nos. C1-C6,C7-C16 (16) 110.00 99.55

Nos. C1, C1b, C7, C8 and C9 have small diamonds printed over the numerals in the upper corners.

Monument to de Gusmao — AP1

Santos-Dumont's Airship — AP2

Augusto Severo's Airship "Pax" — AP3

Santos-Dumont's Biplane "14 Bis" — AP4

Ribeiro de Barros's Seaplane "Jahu" — AP5

Perf. 11, 12½x13, 13x13½

1929 Typo. Wmk. 206

C17 AP1 50r blue grn .35 .20
C18 AP2 200r red 1.40 .20
C19 AP3 300r brt blue 1.75 .20
C20 AP4 500r red violet 2.50 .20
C21 AP5 1000r orange brn 9.00 .40
Nos. C17-C21 (5) 15.00 1.20

See #C32-C36. For surcharges see #C26-C27.

Bartholomeu de Gusmao AP6

Augusto Severo AP7

Alberto Santos-Dumont — AP8

Perf. 9, 11 and Compound

1929-30 Engr. Wmk. 101

C22 AP6 2000r lt green ('30) 7.50 .35
C23 AP7 5000r carmine 7.50 1.25
C24 AP8 10,000r olive grn 7.50 1.40
Nos. C22-C24 (3) 22.50 3.00

Nos. C23-C24 exist imperf. See Nos. C37, C40.

Allegory: Airmail Service between Brazil and the US — AP9

1929 Typo. Wmk. 206

C25 AP9 3000r violet 10.00 1.75

Exists imperf. See Nos. C38, C41. For surcharge see No. C28.

Nos. C18-C19 Surcharged in Blue or Red **ZEPPELIN 2$500**

1931, Aug. 16 *Perf. 12½x13½*

C26 AP2 2500r on 200r (Bl) 25.00 25.00
C27 AP3 5000r on 300r (R) 30.00 30.00

No. C25 Surcharged **2.500 REIS**

1931, Sept. 2 *Perf. 11*

C28 AP9 2500r on 3000r vio 27.50 *27.50*
a. Inverted surcharge 160.00 —
b. Surch. on front and back 160.00

Regular Issues of 1928-29 Surcharged **ZEPPELIN 3$500**

1932, May Wmk. 101 *Perf. 11, 11½*

C29 A89 3500r on 5000r gray lil 20.00 20.00
C30 A72 7000r on 10,000r rose 20.00 20.00
b. Horiz. pair, imperf. between *750.00*

Imperforates

Since 1933, imperforate or partly perforated sheets of nearly all of the airmail issues have become available.

Flag and Airplane — AP10

Wmk. 222

1933, June 7 Typo. *Perf. 11*

C31 AP10 3500r grn, yel & dk bl 5.00 2.00

See Nos. C39, C42.

1934 Wmk. 222

C32 AP1 50r blue grn 1.75 1.75
C33 AP2 200r red 2.25 .65
C34 AP3 300r brt blue 5.50 1.90
C35 AP4 500r red violet 2.25 .65
C36 AP5 1000r orange brn 7.50 .65
Nos. C32-C36 (5) 19.25 5.60

1934 Wmk. 236 Engr. *Perf. 12x11*

Thick Laid Paper

C37 AP6 2000r lt green 4.50 1.50

Types of 1929, 1933

Perf. 11, 11½, 12

1937-40 Typo. Wmk. 249

C38 AP9 3000r violet 17.50 1.75
C39 AP10 3500r grn, yel & dk bl 3.00 1.50

Engr.

C40 AP7 5000r ver ('40) 4.00 .75
Nos. C38-C40 (3) 24.50 4.00

Watermark note after #501 also applies to #C40.

Types of 1929-33

Perf. 11, 11½x12

1939-40 Typo. Wmk. 256

C41 AP9 3000r violet 1.25 .60
C42 AP10 3500r bl, dl grn & yel ('40) .90 .50

Map of the Western Hemisphere Showing Brazil AP11

1941, Jan. 14 Engr. *Perf. 11*

C43 AP11 1200r dark brown 2.50 .65

5th general census of Brazil.

No. 506A Overprinted in Carmine **AÉREO "10 Nov." 937-941**

1941, Nov. 10 Wmk. 264 *Rouletted*

C45 A180 5400r slate grn 2.50 1.25
a. Overprint inverted 140.00

President Varges' new constitution, 4th anniv.

Nos. 506A and 508 Surcharged in Black **AÉREO "10 Nov." 937-942 Cr.$ 5,40**

1942, Nov. 10 Wmk. 264

C47 A180 5.40cr on 5400r sl grn 2.50 1.90
a. Wmk. 249 80.00 80.00
b. Surcharge inverted 60.00 75.00

President Vargas' new constitution, 5th anniv. The status of No. C47a is questioned.

Southern Cross and Arms of Paraguay AP12

Perf. 12½

1943, May 11 Engr. Wmk. 270

C48 AP12 1.20cr lt gray blue 1.75 1.00

Issued in commemoration of the visit of President Higinio Morinigo of Paraguay.

Map of South America — AP13

1943, June 30 Wmk. 271 *Perf. 12½*

C49 AP13 1.20cr multi 1.75 .75

Visit of President Penaranda of Bolivia.

Numeral of Value — AP14

1943, Aug. 7

C50 AP14 1cr blk & dull yel 2.00 1.50
a. Double impression 30.00
C51 AP14 2cr blk & pale grn 2.75 1.50
a. Double impression 40.00
C52 AP14 5cr blk & pink 3.25 2.00
Nos. C50-C52 (3) 8.00 5.00

Centenary of Brazil's first postage stamps.

Souvenir Sheet

AP15

Without Gum *Imperf.*

C53 AP15 Sheet of three 35.00 35.00
a. 1cr black & dull yellow 10.00 10.00
b. 2cr black & pale green 10.00 10.00
c. 5cr black & pink 10.00 10.00

100th anniv. of the 1st postage stamps of Brazil and the 2nd Phil. Exposition (Brapex). Printed in panes of 6 sheets, perforated 12½ between. Each sheet is perforated on two or three sides. Size approximately 155x155mm.

Law Book — AP16

1943, Aug. 13 *Perf. 12½*
C54 AP16 1.20cr rose & lil rose .50 .30

2nd Inter-American Conf. of Lawyers.

AÉREO

No. B10 Surcharged in Red, Carmine or Black **20 Cts.**

1944, Jan. 3 Wmk. 249 *Perf. 10½*

C55 SP5	20c on 400r+200r (R)	.85	.65
C56 SP5	40c on 400r+200r (Bk)	1.25	.65
C57 SP5	60c on 400r+200r (C)	1.25	.45
C58 SP5	1cr on 400r+200r (Bk)	1.75	.65
C59 SP5	1.20cr on 400r+200r (C)	2.25	.45
	Nos. C55-C59 (5)	7.35	2.85

No. C59 is known with surcharge in black but its status is questioned.

Bartholomeu de Gusmao and the "Aerostat" — AP17

Wmk. 268

1944, Oct. 23 Engr. *Perf. 12*
C60 AP17 1.20cr rose carmine .35 .15

Week of the Wing.

L. L. Zamenhof AP18

1945, Apr. 16 Litho. *Perf. 11*
C61 AP18 1.20cr dull brown .35 .25

Esperanto Congress held in Rio, Apr. 14-22.

Map of South America — AP19

Baron of Rio Branco — AP20

1945, Apr. 20
C62 AP19 1.20cr gray brown .35 .25
C63 AP20 5cr rose lilac .95 .40

Centenary of the birth of José Maria de Silva Paranhos, Baron of Rio Branco.

Dove and Flags of American Republics AP21

Perf. 12x11

1947, Aug. 15 Engr. Unwmk.
C64 AP21 2.20cr dk blue green .30 .25

Inter-American Defense Conference at Rio de Janeiro August-September, 1947.

Santos-Dumont Monument, St. Cloud, France — AP22

Bay of Rio de Janeiro and Rotary Emblem — AP23

1947, Nov. 15 Typo. *Perf. 11x12*
C65 AP22 1.20cr org brn & ol .30 .25

Issued to commemorate the Week of the Wing and to honor the Santos-Dumont monument which was destroyed in World War II.

Catalogue values for unused stamps in this section, from this point to the end of the section, are for Never Hinged items.

1948, May 16 Engr. *Perf. 11*
C66 AP23 1.20cr deep claret .50 .40
C67 AP23 3.80cr dull violet 1.00 .40

39th convention of Rotary Intl., Rio.

Hotel Quitandinha, Petropolis AP24

1948, July 10 Litho. Wmk. 267
C68 AP24 1.20cr org brn .25 .25
C69 AP24 3.80cr violet .50 .30

International Exposition of Industry and Commerce, Petropolis, 1948.

Musician and Singers AP25

1948, Aug. 13 Engr. Unwmk.
C70 AP25 1.20cr blue .30 .20

National School of Music, cent.

Luis Batlle Berres AP26

1948, Sept. 2 Typo.
C71 AP26 1.70cr blue .20 .20

Visit of President Luis Batlle Berres of Uruguay, September, 1948.

Merino Ram — AP27

1948, Oct. 10 Wmk. 267 *Perf. 12x11*
C72 AP27 1.20cr dp orange .50 .30

Intl. Livestock Exposition at Bagé.

Eucharistic Congress Seal — AP28

Unwmk.

1948, Oct. 23 Engr. *Perf. 11*
C73 AP28 1.20cr dk car rose .30 .30

5th Natl. Eucharistic Cong., Porto Alegre, Oct. 24-31.

Souvenir Sheet

AP28a

1948, Dec. 14 Engr. *Imperf.*
Without Gum
C73A AP28a Sheet of 3 50.00 65.00

No. C73A contains one each of Nos. 674-676. Issued in honor of President Eurico Gasper Dutra and the armed forces. Exists both with and without number on back. Measures 130x75mm.

Church of Prazeres, Guararapes — AP29

Perf. 11½x12

1949, Feb. 15 Litho. Wmk. 267
C74 AP29 1.20cr pink 1.50 .75

Second Battle of Guararapes, 300th anniv.

Thomé de Souza Meeting Indians — AP30

Perf. 11x12

1949, Mar. 29 Engr. Unwmk.
C75 AP30 1.20cr blue .20 .20

Founding of the City of Salvador, 400th anniv.

A souvenir folder, issued with No. C75, has an engraved 20cr red brown postage stamp portraying John III printed on it, and a copy of No. C75 affixed to it and postmarked. Paper is laid, and size of folder front is 100x150mm. Value, $5.

Franklin D. Roosevelt AP31

1949, May 20 Unwmk. *Imperf.*
C76 AP31 3.80cr deep blue .60 .60
 a. Souvenir sheet 12.00 15.00

No. C76a measures 85x110mm, with deep blue inscriptions in upper and lower margins. It also exists with papermaker's watermark.

Joaquim Nabuco (1849-1910), Lawyer and Writer — AP32

1949, Aug. 30 *Perf. 12*
C77 AP32 3.80cr rose lilac .40 .32
 a. Wmk. 256, imperf. 25.00

Maracaná Stadium AP33

Soccer Player and Flag — AP34

Perf. 11x12, 12x11

1950, June 24 Litho. Wmk. 267
C78 AP33 1.20cr ultra & salmon .95 .40
C79 AP34 5.80cr bl, yel grn & yel 2.75 .50

4th World Soccer Championship, Rio.

AP35

AP36

Symbolical of Brazilian population growth.

1950, July 10 *Perf. 12x11*
C80 AP35 1.20cr red brown .30 .15

Issued to publicize the 6th Brazilian census.

1956, Sept. 8 Engr. *Perf. 11½*

Design: J. B. Marcelino Champagnat.

C81 AP36 3.30cr rose lilac .30 .15

50th anniversary of the arrival of the Marist Brothers in Northern Brazil.

Santos-Dumont's 1906 Plane — AP37

1956, Oct. 16 **Photo.**

C82 AP37	3cr dk blue grn	.85	.30
a.	Souv. sheet of 4, #C82b	6.00	6.00
b.	3cr dark carmine	1.50	.90
C83 AP37	3.30cr brt ultra	.20	.15
C84 AP37	4cr dp claret	.40	.15
C85 AP37	6.50cr red brown	.15	.15
C86 AP37	11.50cr orange red	.85	.35
	Nos. C82-C86 (5)	2.45	1.10

1st flight by Santos-Dumont, 50th anniv. No. C82b issued Oct. 14, 1956.

Lord Baden-Powell — AP38

1957, Aug. 1 **Unwmk.**

Granite Paper

C87 AP38 3.30cr deep red lilac .25 .15

Centenary of the birth of Lord Baden-Powell, founder of the Boy Scouts.

UN Emblem, Soldier and Map of Suez Canal Area — AP39

Perf. 11½

1957, Oct. 24 **Wmk. 267** **Engr.**

C88 AP39 3.30cr dark blue .25 .18

Brazilian contingent of the UN Emergency Force.

Basketball Player — AP40

1959, May 30 **Photo.** ***Perf. 11½***

C89 AP40 3.30cr brt red brn & bl .25 .15

Brazil's victory in the World Basketball Championships of 1959.

Symbol of Flight — AP41

1959, Oct. 21 **Wmk. 267**

C90 AP41 3.30cr deep ultra .16 .15

Issued to publicize Week of the Wing.

Caravelle AP42

1959, Dec. 18 ***Perf. 11½***

C91 AP42 6.50cr ultra .16 .15

Inauguration of Brazilian jet flights.

Pres. Adolfo Lopez Mateos AP43

Pres. Dwight D. Eisenhower AP44

1960, Jan. 19 **Photo.** **Wmk. 267**

C92 AP43 6.50cr brown .16 .15

Issued to commemorate the visit of President Adolfo Lopez Mateos of Mexico.

1960, Feb. 23 ***Perf. 11½***

C93 AP44 6.50cr deep orange .16 .15

Visit of Pres. Dwight D. Eisenhower.

World Refugee Year Emblem — AP45

Tower at Brasilia — AP46

1960, Apr. 7 **Wmk. 268**

C94 AP45 6.50cr blue .16 .15

WRY, July 1, 1959-June 30, 1960.

Type of Regular Issue and AP46

Designs: 3.30cr, Square of the Three Entities. 4cr, Cathedral. 11.50cr, Plan of Brasilia.

Perf. 11x11½, 11½x11

1960, Apr. 21 **Photo.** **Wmk. 267**

C95 A436	3.30cr violet		.15	.15
C96 A436	4cr blue		.75	.15
C97 AP46	6.50cr rose carmine		.15	.15
C98 A436	11.50cr brown		.15	.15
	Nos. C95-C98 (4)		1.20	
	Set value			.40

Inauguration of Brazil's new capital, Brasilia, Apr. 21, 1960.

Chrismon and Oil Lamp AP47

1960, May 16 ***Perf. 11x11½***

C99 AP47 3.30cr lilac rose .15 .15

7th Natl. Eucharistic Congress at Curitiba.

Cross, Sugarloaf Mountain and Emblem AP48

1960, July 1 **Wmk. 267**

C100 AP48 6.50cr brt blue .15 .15

10th Cong. of the World Baptist Alliance, Rio.

Boy Scout — AP49

Caravel — AP50

1960, July 23 ***Perf. 11½x11***

C101 AP49 3.30cr orange ver .15 .15

Boy Scouts of Brazil, 50th anniversary.

1960, Aug. 5 **Engr.** **Wmk. 268**

C102 AP50 6.50cr black .15 .15

Prince Henry the Navigator, 500th birth anniv.

Maria E. Bueno AP51

1960, Dec. 15 **Photo.** ***Perf. 11x11½***

C103 AP51 60cr pale brown .15 .15

Victory at Wimbledon of Maria E. Bueno, women's singles tennis champion.

War Memorial, Sugarloaf Mountain and Allied Flags AP52

1960, Dec. 22 **Wmk. 268**

C104 AP52 3.30cr lilac rose .15 .15

Reburial of Brazilian servicemen of WW II.

Power Line and Map AP53

Malaria Eradication Emblem AP54

1961, Jan. 20 ***Perf. 11½x11***

C105 AP53 3.30cr lilac rose .15 .15

Inauguration of Three Marias Dam and hydroelectric station in Minas Gerais.

1962, May 24 **Wmk. 267** **Engr.**

C106 AP54 21cr blue .15 .15

WHO drive to eradicate malaria.

F. A. de Varnhagen — AP55

1966, Feb. 17 **Photo.** **Wmk. 267**

C107 AP55 45cr red brown .18 .15

Francisco Adolfo de Varnhagen, Viscount of Porto Seguro (1816-1878), historian and diplomat.

Map of the Americas and Alliance for Progress Emblem AP56

1966, Mar. 14 ***Perf. 11x11½***

C108 AP56 120cr grnsh bl & vio bl .40 .15

5th anniv. of the Alliance for Progress.

A souvenir card contains one impression of No. C108, imperf. Size: 113x160mm.

Nun and Globe — AP57

Face of Jesus from Shroud of Turin — AP58

1966, Mar. 25 **Photo.** ***Perf. 11½x11***

C109 AP57 35cr violet .18 .15

Centenary of the arrival of the teaching Sisters of St. Dorothea.

1966, June 3 **Photo.** **Wmk. 267**

C110 AP58 45cr brown org .20 .15

Issued to commemorate Vatican II, the 21st Ecumenical Council of the Roman Catholic Church, Oct. 11, 1962-Dec. 8, 1965.

A souvenir card contains one impression of No. C110, imperf. Size: 100x39mm.

Admiral Mariz e Barros AP59

"Youth" by Eliseu Visconti AP60

1966, June 13 **Photo.** **Wmk. 267**

C111 AP59 35cr red brown .16 .15

Death centenary of Admiral Antonio Carlos Mariz e Barros, who died in the Battle of Itaperu.

1966, July 31 ***Perf. 11½x11***

C112 AP60 120cr red brown .40 .20

Birth centenary of Eliseu Visconti, painter.

SPECIAL DELIVERY STAMPS

No. 191 Surcharged

1930 **Unwmk.** ***Perf. 12***

E1 A62 1000r on 200r dp blue 4.00 1.75

a. Inverted surcharge 500.00

POSTAGE DUE STAMPS

D1

D2

1889 Unwmk. Typo. *Rouletted*

J1 D1 10r carmine 2.00 1.40
J2 D1 20r carmine 2.75 2.00
J3 D1 50r carmine 5.00 4.00
J4 D1 100r carmine 2.00 1.40
J5 D1 200r carmine 55.00 15.00
J6 D1 300r carmine 6.00 8.00
J7 D1 500r carmine 6.00 8.00
J8 D1 700r carmine 10.00 14.00
J9 D1 1000r carmine 10.00 10.00
Nos. J1-J9 (9) 98.75 63.80

Counterfeits are common.

1890

J10 D1 10r orange .60 .30
J11 D1 20r ultra .60 .30
J12 D1 50r olive 1.25 .30
J13 D1 200r magenta 6.00 .60
J14 D1 300r blue green 3.00 1.50
J15 D1 500r slate 4.00 3.00
J16 D1 700r purple 4.50 7.50
J17 D1 1000r dk violet 5.50 5.00
Nos. J10-J17 (8) 25.45 18.50

Perf. 11 to 11½, 12½ to 14 and Compound

1895-1901

J18 D2 10r dk blue ('01) 2.00 1.25
J19 D2 20r yellow grn 8.00 3.00
J20 D2 50r yellow grn ('01) 10.00 5.50
J21 D2 100r brick red 6.25 1.25
J22 D2 200r violet 6.00 .60
a. 200r gray lilac ('98) 12.00 2.00
J23 D2 300r dull blue 3.50 2.25
J24 D2 2000r brown 12.00 12.00
Nos. J18-J24 (7) 47.75 25.85

1906 Wmk. 97

J25 D2 100r brick red 8.00 3.00

Wmk. (97? or 98?)

J26 D2 200r violet 7.50 1.25
a. Wmk. 97 275.00 85.00
b. Wmk. 98 12.50 50.00

D3

D4

1906-10 Unwmk. Engr. *Perf. 12*

J28 D3 10r slate .15 .15
J29 D3 20r brt violet .15 .15
J30 D3 50r dk green .25 .15
J31 D3 100r carmine 1.75 .60
J32 D3 200r dp blue 1.00 .30
J33 D3 300r gray blk .40 .60
J34 D3 400r olive grn 1.00 .90
J35 D3 500r dk violet 35.00 35.00
J36 D3 600r violet ('10) 1.25 *3.00*
J37 D3 700r red brown 30.00 30.00
J38 D3 1000r red 1.50 *3.00*
J39 D3 2000r green 4.75 5.50
J40 D3 5000r choc ('10) 1.50 *14.00*
Nos. J28-J40 (13) 78.70 93.35

Perf. 12½, 11, 11x10½

1919-23 Typo.

J41 D4 5r red brown .15 .25
J42 D4 10r violet .25 .25
J43 D4 20r olive gray .20 .15
J44 D4 50r green ('23) .20 .20
J45 D4 100r red 1.10 1.00
J46 D4 200r blue 5.25 1.50
J47 D4 400r brown ('23) 1.40 1.25
Nos. J41-J47 (7) 8.55 4.60

Perf. 12½, 12½x13½

1924-35 Wmk. 100

J48 D4 5r red brown .25 .20
J49 D4 100r red .75 .30
J50 D4 200r slate bl ('29) 1.00 .50
J51 D4 400r dp brn ('29) 1.50 1.00
J52 D4 600r dk vio ('29) 1.75 1.10
J53 D4 600r orange ('35) .75 .50
Nos. J48-J53 (6) 6.00 3.60

1924 Wmk. 193 *Perf. 11x10½*

J54 D4 100r red 45.00 45.00
J55 D4 200r slate blue 5.50 5.50

Perf. 11x10½, 13x13½

1925-27 Wmk. 101

J56 D4 20r olive gray .20 .15
J57 D4 100r red 1.05 .30
J58 D4 200r slate blue 3.25 .35
J59 D4 400r brown 1.75 1.25
J60 D4 600r dk violet 4.25 2.50
Nos. J56-J60 (5) 10.50 4.55

Wmk. E U BRASIL Multiple (218)

1929-30 *Perf. 12½x13½*

J61 D4 100r light red .25 .20
J62 D4 200r blue black .40 .25
J63 D4 400r brown .40 .25
J64 D4 1000r myrtle green .75 .50
Nos. J61-J64 (4) 1.80 1.20

Perf. 11, 12½x13, 13

1931-36 Wmk. 222

J65 D4 10r lt violet ('35) .15 .15
J66 D4 20r black ('33) .20 .15
J67 D4 50r blue grn ('35) .25 .20
J68 D4 100r rose red ('35) .25 .20
J69 D4 200r sl blue ('35) .40 .30
J70 D4 400r blk brn ('35) 2.00 2.00
J71 D4 600r dk violet .35 .20
J72 D4 1000r myrtle grn .50 .35
J73 D4 2000r brown ('36) .80 .80
J74 D4 5000r indigo ('36) 1.25 1.00
Nos. J65-J74 (10) 6.15 5.35

1938 Wmk. 249 *Perf. 11*

J75 D4 200r slate blue 2.00 .75

1940 Typo. Wmk. 256

J76 D4 10r light violet .50 .50
J77 D4 20r black .50 .50
J79 D4 100r rose red .50 .50
J80 D4 200r myrtle green .50 .50
Nos. J76-J80 (4) 2.00 2.00

1942 Wmk. 264

J81 D4 10r lt violet .15 .15
J82 D4 20r olive blk .15 .15
J83 D4 50r lt blue grn .15 .15
J84 D4 100r vermilion .40 .30
J85 D4 200r gray blue .40 .30
J86 D4 400r claret .40 .30
J87 D4 600r rose vio .30 .20
J88 D4 1000r dk bl grn .30 .20
J89 D4 2000r dp yel brn .75 .50
J90 D4 5000r indigo .40 .30
Nos. J81-J90 (10) 3.40 2.55

1949 Wmk. 268

J91 D4 10c pale rose lilac 4.00 3.25
J92 D4 20r black 25.00 25.00

No. J92 exists in shades of gray ranging to gray olive.

OFFICIAL STAMPS

Pres. Affonso Penna — O1

Pres. Hermes da Fonseca — O2

Unwmk.

1906, Nov. 15 Engr. *Perf. 12*

O1 O1 10r org & grn .75 .30
O2 O1 20r org & grn .90 .30
O3 O1 50r org & grn 1.50 .30
O4 O1 100r org & grn .75 .30
O5 O1 200r org & grn .90 .30
O6 O1 300r org & grn 2.75 .60
O7 O1 400r org & grn 6.00 1.75
O8 O1 500r org & grn 3.00 1.25
O9 O1 700r org & grn 4.50 3.00
O10 O1 1000r org & grn 4.50 1.25
O11 O1 2000r org & grn 5.00 2.25
O12 O1 5000r org & grn 10.00 .50
O13 O1 10,000r org & grn 10.00 1.25
Nos. O1-O13 (13) 50.55 13.35

The portrait is the same but the frame differs for each denomination of this issue.

1913, Nov. 15

Center in Black

O14 O2 10r gray .35 .50
O15 O2 20r ol grn .35 .50
O16 O2 50r gray .35 .50
O17 O2 100r ver 1.00 .35
O18 O2 200r blue 1.75 .35
O19 O2 500r orange 3.00 .65
O20 O2 600r violet 3.50 2.75
O21 O2 1000r blk brn 4.25 1.25
O22 O2 2000r red brn 6.50 1.25
O23 O2 5000r brown 7.50 3.00
O24 O2 10,000r black 15.00 7.50
O25 O2 20,000r blue 27.50 27.50
O26 O2 50,000r green 50.00 55.00
O27 O2 100,000r org red 175.00 200.00
O28 O2 500,000r brown 300.00 325.00
O29 O2 1,000,000r dk brn 325.00 350.00
Nos. O14-O29 (16) 921.05 976.10

The portrait is the same on all denominations of this series but there are eight types of the frame.

Pres. Wenceslau Braz — O3

Perf. 11, 11½

1919, Apr. 11 Wmk. 100

O30 O3 10r olive green .40 2.00
O31 O3 50r green 1.00 1.25
O32 O3 100r rose red 2.00 .85
O33 O3 200r dull blue 2.75 .85
O34 O3 500r orange 7.50 14.00
Nos. O30-O34 (5) 13.65 18.95

The official decree called for eleven stamps in this series but only five were issued.

For surcharges see Nos. 293-297.

NEWSPAPER STAMPS

N1

Rouletted

1889, Feb. 1 Unwmk. Litho.

P1 N1 10r yellow 3.00 3.00
a. Pair, imperf. between 125.00 145.00
P2 N1 20r yellow 6.00 7.50
P3 N1 50r yellow 10.00 6.00
P4 N1 100r yellow 3.75 3.00
P5 N1 200r yellow 3.00 1.50
P6 N1 300r yellow 3.00 1.50
P7 N1 500r yellow 20.00 8.00
P8 N1 700r yellow 3.00 10.00
P9 N1 1000r yellow 3.00 10.00
Nos. P1-P9 (9) 54.75 50.50

For surcharges see Nos. 125-127.

1889, May 1

P10 N1 10r olive 2.00 .50
P11 N1 20r green 2.00 .50
P12 N1 50r brn yel 2.75 1.00
P13 N1 100r violet 3.00 2.00
P14 N1 200r black 3.00 2.00
P15 N1 300r carmine 12.00 10.00
P16 N1 500r green 50.00 50.00
P17 N1 700r pale blue 25.00 30.00
P18 N1 1000r brown 12.00 15.00
Nos. P10-P18 (9) 111.75 111.00

For surcharges see Nos. 128-135.

N2

N3

White Wove Paper Thin to Thick

Perf. 11 to 11½, 12½ to 14 and 12½ to 14x11 to 11½

1890 Typo.

P19 N2 10r blue 14.00 10.00
a. 10r ultramarine 14.00 10.00
P20 N2 20r emerald 40.00 15.00
P21 N2 100r violet 16.00 14.00
Nos. P19-P21 (3) 70.00 39.00

For surcharge see No. 137.

1890-93

P22 N3 10r blue 7.50 4.00
a. 10r ultramarine 10.00 9.00
P23 N3 10r ultra, *buff* 10.00 4.00
P24 N3 20r green 10.00 3.00
a. 20r emerald 10.00 3.00
P25 N3 50r yel grn ('93) 17.50 10.00
Nos. P22-P25 (4) 45.00 21.00

For surcharges see Nos. 136, 138-139.

POSTAL TAX STAMPS

Icarus from the Santos-Dumont Monument at St. Cloud, France — PT1

Perf. 13½x12½, 11

1933, Oct. 1 Typo. Wmk. 222

RA1 PT1 100r deep brown .65 .25

Honoring the Brazilian aviator, Santos-Dumont. Its use was obligatory as a tax on all correspondence sent to countries in South America, the U.S. and Spain. Its use on correspondence to other countries was optional. The funds obtained were used for the construction of airports throughout Brazil.

Catalogue values for unused stamps in this section, from this point to the end of the section, are for Never Hinged items.

Father Joseph Damien and Children PT2

Perf. 12x11

1952, Nov. 24 Litho. Wmk. 267

RA2 PT2 10c yellow brown .25 .15

1953, Nov. 30

RA3 PT2 10c yellow green .25 .15

Father Bento Dias Pacheco PT3

Eunice Weaver PT4

1954, Nov. 22 Photo. *Perf. 11½*

RA4 PT3 10c violet blue .20 .15

1955-66, Nov. 24

RA5 PT3 10c dk car rose .20 .15
RA6 PT3 10c org red ('57) .20 .15
RA7 PT3 10c dp emer ('58) .15 .15
RA8 PT3 10c red lilac ('61) .15 .15
RA9 PT3 10c choc ('62) .15 .15
RA10 PT3 10c slate ('63) .15 .15
RA11 PT3 2cr dp mag ('64) .15 .15
RA12 PT3 2cr violet ('65) .15 .15
RA13 PT3 2cr orange ('66) .15 .15
Set value .95

1968, Nov. 25

RA14 PT3 5c brt yel grn 1.25 .75

1969, Nov. 28

RA15 PT3 5c deep plum .50 .25

1971, Nov. 24

RA16 PT4 10c slate green 1.00 .40

1973, Nov. 24

RA17 PT4 10c brt rose lil ('73) .20 .15

Father Nicodemos PT5

Father Vicente Borgard (1888-1977) PT6

1975, Nov. 24 Litho. Unwmk.

RA18 PT5 10c sepia .20 .15

1983, Nov. 24 Photo. *Perf. 11½*

RA19 PT6 10cr brown .60 .60

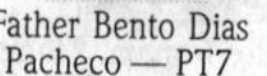

Father Bento Dias Pacheco — PT7

Father Santiago Uchoa — PT8

1984, Nov. 24 Photo. *Perf. 11½*
RA20 PT7 30cr deep blue .15 .15

1985, Nov. 24 Litho.
RA21 PT7 100cr lake .15 .15

1986, Nov. 24 Litho.
RA22 PT7 10c gray brown .15 .15

1987, Nov. 24 Photo.
RA23 PT7 30c sage green .15 .15

1988, Nov. 24 Litho.
RA24 PT8 1.30cz dull red brn .15 .15

See Nos. RA29-RA30.

Fr. Joseph Damien — PT9

1989-92 Photo. *Perf. 11½*
RA25 PT9 2c deep lilac rose .15 .15
RA26 PT9 50c blue .15 .15

Perf. 12½
RA27 PT9 3cr green .15 .15
RA28 PT9 30cr brown .15 .15
Set value .20 .20

Issued: 2c, Nov. 24; 50c, Nov. 24, 1990; 3cr, Nov. 24, 1991; 30cr, Nov. 24, 1992.

Father Santiago Uchoa Type of 1988

1993, Nov. 24 Photo. *Perf. 12½*
RA29 PT8 50c blue .15 .15

1994, Nov. 24
RA30 PT8 1c dull lake .15 .15

The tax was for the care and treatment of lepers. Use of #RA2-RA30 was required for one week.

POSTAL TAX SEMI-POSTAL STAMP

Catalogue values for unused stamps in this section are for Never Hinged items.

Icarus — PTSP1

Wmk. 267

1947, Nov. 15 Typo. *Perf. 11*
RAB1 PTSP1 40c + 10c brt red .35 .20
a. Pair, imperf. between *350.00*

Aviation Week, November 15-22, 1947, and compulsory on all domestic correspondence during that week.

BULGARIA

ˌbəl-ˈgar-ē-ə

LOCATION — Southeastern Europe bordering on the Black Sea on the east and the Danube River on the north
GOVT. — Republic
AREA — 42,823 sq. mi.
POP. — 8,929,332 (1983)
CAPITAL — Sofia

In 1885 Bulgaria, then a principality under the suzerainty of the Sultan of Turkey, was joined by Eastern Rumelia. Independence from Turkey was obtained in 1908.

100 Centimes = 1 Franc
100 Stotinki = 1 Lev (1881)

Catalogue values for unused stamps in this country are for Never Hinged items, beginning with Scott 293 in the regular postage section, Scott B1 in the semi-postal section, Scott C15 in the airpost section, Scott CB1 in the airpost semi-postal section, Scott E1 in the special delivery section, Scott J47 in the postage due section, Scott O1 in the officials section, and Scott Q1 in the parcel post section.

Watermarks

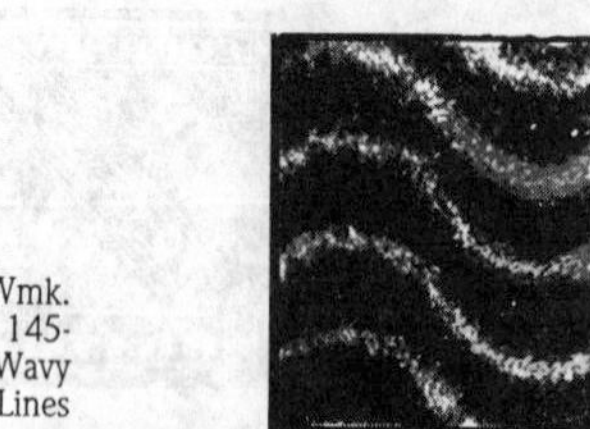

Wmk. 145- Wavy Lines

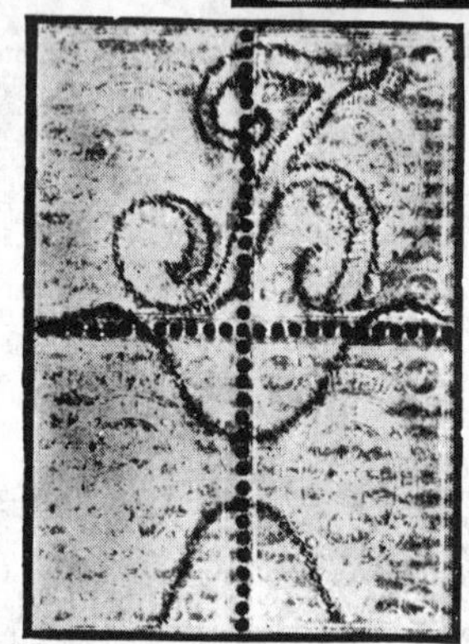

Wmk. 168- Wavy Lines and EZGV in Cyrillic

Wmk. 275- Entwined Curved Lines

Lion of Bulgaria
A1 A2 A3

Perf. 14½x15
1879, June 1 Wmk. 168 Typo.
Laid Paper
1 A1 5c black & yel 65.00 18.00
2 A1 10c black & grn 250.00 60.00
3 A1 25c black & vio 175.00 15.00
a. Imperf.
4 A1 50c black & blue 250.00 50.00
5 A2 1fr black & red 50.00 17.50

1881, June 10
6 A3 3s red & silver 12.50 2.50
7 A3 5s black & org 15.00 2.50
a. Background inverted *1,750.*
8 A3 10s black & grn 65.00 6.50
9 A3 15s red & grn 60.00 6.50
10 A3 25s black & vio 250.00 30.00
11 A3 30s blue & fawn 17.50 6.50

1882, Dec. 4
12 A3 3s orange & yel 1.00 .50
a. Background inverted *2,750. 1,400.*
13 A3 5s green & pale green 6.00 .50
a. 5s rose & pale rose (error) *1,600. 1,300.*
14 A3 10s rose & pale rose 8.00 .75
15 A3 15s red vio & pale lil 6.00 .40
16 A3 25s blue & pale blue 6.00 .50
17 A3 30s violet & grn 6.00 .75
18 A3 50s blue & pink 6.00 .75
Nos. 12-18 (7) 39.00 4.15

See Nos. 207-210, 286.

A4

A5

Surcharged in Black, Carmine or Vermilion

1884, May 1
Typo. Surcharge
19 A4 3s on 10s rose (Bk) 95.00 30.00
20 A4 5s on 30s blue & fawn (C) 95.00 45.00
20A A4 5s on 30s bl & fawn (Bk) *1,750. 1,750.*
21 A5 15s on 25s blue (C) 140.00 40.00

On some values the surcharge may be found inverted or double.

1885, June
Litho. Surcharge
21B A4 3s on 10s rose (Bk) 45.00 27.50
21C A4 5s on 30s bl & fawn (V) 50.00 35.00
21D A5 15s on 25s blue (V) 70.00 45.00
22 A5 50s on 1fr blk & red (Bk) 190.00 125.00

Forgeries of Nos. 19-22 are plentiful.

Word below left star in oval has 5 letters — A6

Third letter below left star is "A" — A7

1885, May 25
23 A6 1s gray vio & pale gray 12.00 5.00
24 A7 2s sl grn & pale gray 12.00 4.00

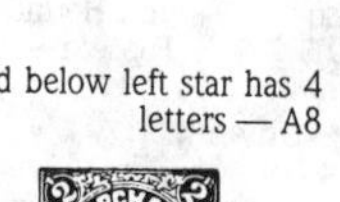

Word below left star has 4 letters — A8

Third letter below left star is "b" with cross-bar in upper half — A9

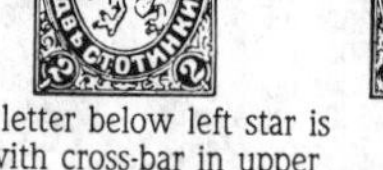

A10

1886-87
25 A8 1s gray vio & pale gray 1.00 .20
26 A9 2s sl grn & pale gray 1.00 .20
27 A10 1 l black & red ('87) 27.50 3.00
Nos. 25-27 (3) 29.50 3.40

For surcharge see No. 40.

A11

Perf. 10½, 11, 11½, 13, 13½
1889 Wove Paper Unwmk.
28 A11 1s lilac .16 .15
29 A11 2s gray .60 .15
30 A11 3s bister brown .40 .15
31 A11 5s yellow green .25 .15
a. Vert. pair, imperf. btwn.
32 A11 10s rose 1.10 .15
33 A11 15s orange .65 .15
34 A11 25s blue 1.00 .15
35 A11 30s dk brown 8.75 .15
36 A11 50s green .60 .32
37 A11 1 l orange red .52 .38
Nos. 28-37 (10) 14.03
Set value 1.50

The 10s orange is a proof.

Nos. 28-34 are known imperforate. Value, set $225.

See Nos. 39, 41-42. For overprints and surcharges see Nos. 38, 55-56, 77-81, 113.

No. 35 Surcharged in Black **15**

1892, Jan. 26
38 A11 15s on 30s brn 10.00 1.00
a. Inverted surcharge *70.00 52.50*

1894 *Perf. 10½, 11, 11½*
Pelure Paper
39 A11 10s red 7.00 .50
a. Imperf. *57.50*

No. 26 Surcharged in Red **01**

Wmk. Wavy Lines (168)
1895, Oct. 25 *Perf. 14½x15*
Laid Paper
40 A9 1s on 2s .75 .20
a. Inverted surcharge 6.00 5.00
b. Double surcharge *62.50 62.50*
c. Pair, one without surcharge *125.00 125.00*

This surcharge on No. 24 is a proof.

Wmk. Coat of Arms in the Sheet
1896, Apr. 30 *Perf. 11½, 13*
Wove Paper
41 A11 2 l rose & pale rose 2.00 1.50
42 A11 3 l black & buff 3.50 3.00

Coat of Arms — A14

Cherry Wood Cannon — A15

1896, Feb. 2 *Perf. 13*
43 A14 1s blue green .32 .15
44 A14 5s dark blue .32 .15
45 A14 15s purple .50 .18
46 A14 25s red 4.75 .85
Nos. 43-46 (4) 5.89 1.33

Baptism of Prince Boris.

Examples of Nos. 41-46 from sheet edges show no watermark.

Nos. 43, 45-46 were also printed on rough unwatermarked paper.

1901, Apr. 20 Litho. Unwmk.
53 A15 5s carmine 1.25 .90
54 A15 15s yellow green 1.25 .90

Insurrection of Independence in April, 1876, 25th anniversary.

Exist imperf. Forgeries exist.

Nos. 30 and 36 Surcharged in Black **5**

1901, Mar. 24 Typo.
55 A11 5s on 3s bister brn 1.75 .75
a. Inverted surcharge 42.50 42.50
b. Pair, one without surcharge *70.00 70.00*
56 A11 10s on 50s green 2.25 .75
a. Inverted surcharge 50.00 50.00
b. Pair, one without surcharge *70.00 70.00*

Tsar Ferdinand A17

Fighting at Shipka Pass A18

ONE LEV:

Type I - The numerals in the upper corners have, at the top, a sloping serif on the left side and a short straight serif on the right.

Type II - The numerals in the upper corners are of ordinary shape without the serif at the right.

1901-05 Typo. Perf. 12½

57 A17 1s vio & gray blk .15 .15
58 A17 2s brnz grn & ind .15 .15
a. Imperf.
59 A17 3s orange & ind .15 .15
60 A17 5s emerald & brn 2.25 .15
61 A17 10s rose & blk 1.50 .15
62 A17 15s claret & gray blk .65 .15
63 A17 25s blue & blk .65 .15
64 A17 30s bis & gray blk 15.00 .15
65 A17 50s dk blue & brn .80 .15
66 A17 1 l red org & brnz grn, type I 2.00 .15
67 A17 1 l brn red & brnz grn, II ('05) 45.00 1.75
68 A17 2 l carmine & blk 4.00 .85
69 A17 3 l slate & red brn 5.00 1.90
Nos. 57-69 (13) 77.30
Set value 4.50

For surcharges see Nos. 73, 83-85, 87-88.

1902, Aug. 29 Litho. Perf. 11½

70 A18 5s lake 1.00 .35
71 A18 10s blue green 1.00 .35
72 A18 15s blue 5.25 1.65
Nos. 70-72 (3) 7.25 2.35

Battle of Shipka Pass, 1877.

Imperf. copies are proofs.

Excellent forgeries of Nos. 70 to 72 exist.

No. 62 Surcharged in Black **10**

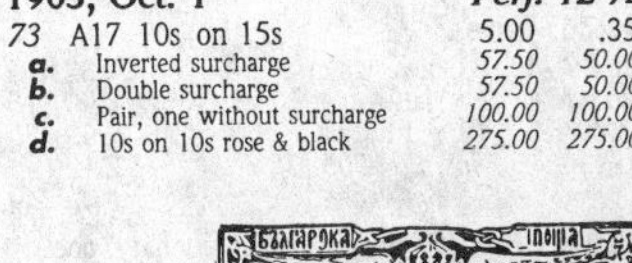

1903, Oct. 1 Perf. 12½

73 A17 10s on 15s 5.00 .35
a. Inverted surcharge 57.50 50.00
b. Double surcharge 57.50 50.00
c. Pair, one without surcharge 100.00 100.00
d. 10s on 10s rose & black 275.00 275.00

Ferdinand in 1887 and 1907 — A19

1907, Aug. 12 Litho. Perf. 11½

74 A19 5s deep green 9.00 .90
75 A19 10s red brown 16.00 .90
76 A19 25s deep blue 24.00 1.75
Nos. 74-76 (3) 49.00 3.55

Accession to the throne of Ferdinand I, 20th anniversary.

Nos. 74-76 imperf. are proofs. Nos. 74-76 exist in pairs imperforate between.

Stamps of 1889 Overprinted **1909**

1909

77 A11 1s lilac 1.00 .50
a. Inverted overprint 21.00 17.50
b. Double overprint, one inverted 25.00 25.00
78 A11 5s yellow green 1.00 .50
a. Inverted overprint 25.00 25.00
b. Double overprint 25.00 25.00

With Additional Surcharge **5** or **10**

79 A11 5s on 30s brown (Bk) 1.50 .18
a. "5" double
b. "1990" for "1909" 700.00 550.00
80 A11 10s on 15s org (Bk) 1.50 .40
a. Inverted surcharge 17.50 17.50
b. "1909" omitted 27.50 27.50
81 A11 10s on 50s dk grn (R) 1.50 .40
a. "1990" for "1909" 100.00 100.00
b. Black surcharge 52.50 52.50

Nos. 62 & 64 Surcharged with Value Only

83 A17 5s on 15s (Bl) 1.75 .60
a. Inverted surcharge 21.00 21.00
84 A17 10s on 15s (Bl) 4.50 .40
a. Inverted surcharge 21.00 21.00
85 A17 25s on 30s (R) 5.75 .90
a. Double surcharge 70.00 70.00
b. "2" of "25" omitted 87.50 87.50
c. Blue surcharge 275.00 175.00

1910

Nos. 59 and 62 Surcharged in Blue

5

1910, Oct.

87 A17 1s on 3s 3.50 .75
a. "1910" omitted 21.00
88 A17 5s on 15s 1.50 .50

Tsar Assen's Tower (Crown over lion) A20

Tsar Ferdinand A21

City of Trnovo A22

Tsar Ferdinand A23

Ferdinand A24

Isker River A25

Ferdinand A26

Rila Monastery (Crown at UR) A27

Tsar and Princes — A28

Ferdinand in Robes of Ancient Tsars — A29

Monastery of Holy Trinity — A30

View of Varna — A31

1911, Feb. 14 Engr. Perf. 12

89 A20 1s myrtle green .16 .15
90 A21 2s car & blk .16 .15
91 A22 3s lake & blk .40 .15
92 A23 5s green & blk 1.00 .15
93 A24 10s dp red & blk 1.40 .15
94 A25 15s brown bister 2.50 .15
95 A26 25s ultra & blk .50 .15
96 A27 30s blue & blk 6.75 .16
97 A28 50s ocher & blk 16.00 .22
a. Center inverted 2,250.
98 A29 1 l chocolate 6.00 .28
99 A30 2 l dull pur & blk 1.65 .90
100 A31 3 l blue vio & blk 6.75 3.00
Nos. 89-100 (12) 43.27 5.61

See Nos. 114-120, 161-162. For overprints and surcharges see Nos. 104-112, 188, B8, Greece N167-N178, N182-N187, Thrace 16-21, Romania 2N1-2N4.

Tsar Ferdinand — A32

1912, Aug. 2 Typo. Perf. 12½

101 A32 5s olive green 2.25 .70
a. 5s pale green 275.00 125.00
102 A32 10s claret 3.50 1.50
103 A32 25s slate 5.00 1.75
Nos. 101-103 (3) 10.75 3.95

25th year of reign of Tsar Ferdinand.

Nos. 89-95 Overprinted in Various Colors

ОСВОБ. ВОЙНА 1912-1913

1913, Aug. 6 Engr.

104 A20 1s myrtle grn (C) .15 .15
105 A21 2s car & blk (Bl) .15 .15
107 A22 3s lake & blk (Bl Bk) .18 .15
108 A23 5s grn & blk (R) .15 .15
109 A24 10s dp red & blk (Bk) .28 .15
110 A25 15s brown bis (G) .55 .26
111 A26 25s ultra & blk (R) 2.75 .38
Nos. 104-111 (7) 4.21
Set value 1.00

Victory over the Turks in Balkan War of 1912-1913.

No. 95 Surcharged in Red **10 ст.**

1915, July 6

112 A26 10s on 25s .50 .15

No. 28 Surcharged in Green **3 стотинки**

113 A11 3s on 1s lilac 3.50 4.50

Types of 1911 Re-engraved

1915, Nov. 7 Perf. 11½, 14

114 A20 1s dk bl grn .15 .15
115 A23 5s grn & brn vio 1.40 .15
116 A24 10s red brn & brnsh blk .22 .15
117 A25 15s olive green .22 .15
118 A26 25s indigo & blk .22 .15
119 A27 30s ol grn & red brn .22 .15
120 A29 1 l dark brown .32 .28
Nos. 114-120 (7) 2.75
Set value .55

Widths: No. 114 is 19¼mm; No. 89, 18½mm. No. 118 is 19¼mm; No. 95, 18¼mm. No. 120 is 20mm; No. 98, 19mm. The re-engraved stamps also differ from the 1911 issue in many details of design. Nos. 114-120 exist imperforate.

The 5s and 10s exist perf. 14x11½.

For Nos. 114-116 and 118 overprinted with Cyrillic characters and "1916-1917," see Romania Nos. 2N1-2N4.

Coat of Arms — A33

Peasant and Bullock — A34

Soldier and Mt. Sonichka — A35

View of Nish — A36

Town and Lake Okhrida — A37

Demir-Kapiya (Iron Gate) — A37a

View of Gevgeli — A38

Perf. 11½, 12½x13, 13x12½

1917-19 Typo.

122 A33 5s green .28 .15
123 A34 15s slate .15 .15
124 A35 25s blue .15 .15
125 A36 30s orange .15 .15
126 A37 50s violet .52 .28
126A A37a 2 l brn org ('19) .52 .35
127 A38 3 l claret .80 .75
Nos. 122-127 (7) 2.57 1.98

Liberation of Macedonia. A 1 l dark green was prepared but not issued. Value $1.65.

For surcharges see Nos. B9-B10, B12.

View of Veles — A39

Monastery of St. Clement at Okhrida — A40

1918 Perf. 13x14

128 A39 1s gray .15 .15
129 A40 5s green .15 .15
Set value .15 .15

Tsar Ferdinand A41

Plowing with Oxen A42

1918, July 1 Perf. 12½x13

130 A41 1s dark green .15 .15
131 A41 2s dark brown .15 .15
132 A41 3s indigo .30 .16
133 A41 10s brown red .30 .16
Set value .75 .50

Tsar Ferdinand's accession to the throne, 30th anniv.

1919 Perf. 13½x13

134 A42 1s gray .15 .15

Sobranye Palace — A43

Tsar Boris III — A44

1919 Perf. 11½x12, 12x11½

135 A43 1s black .15 .15
137 A43 2s olive green .15 .15
Set value .15 .15

For surcharges see Nos. 186, B1.

1919, Oct. 3

138 A44 3s orange brn .15 .15
139 A44 5s green .15 .15
140 A44 10s rose red .15 .15
141 A44 15s violet .15 .15
142 A44 25s deep blue .15 .15

143 A44 30s chocolate .18 .15
144 A44 50s yellow brn .18 .15
Set value .65 .35

1st anniv. of enthronement of Tsar Boris III.
Nos. 135-144 exist imperforate.
For surcharges see Nos. 187, B2-B7.

Birthplace of Vazov at Sopot and Cherrywood Cannon — A47

"The Bear Fighter"-a Character from "Under the Yoke" — A48

Ivan Vazov in 1870 and 1920 — A49

Vazov — A50

The Monk Paisii — A52

Homes of Vazov at Plovdiv and Sofia — A51

1920, Oct. 20 Photo. *Perf. 11½*
147 A47 30s brown red .15 .15
148 A48 50s dark green .15 .15
149 A49 1 l drab .22 .28
150 A50 2 l light brown .60 .60
151 A51 3 l black violet .95 .65
152 A52 5 l deep blue 1.10 .80
Nos. 147-152 (6) 3.17 2.63

70th birthday of Ivan Vazov (1850-1921), Bulgarian poet and novelist.
Several values of this series exist imperforate and in pairs imperforate between.

Tsar Ferdinand
A53 A54

Mt. Shar — A55

Bridge over Vardar River — A56

View of Ohrid — A57

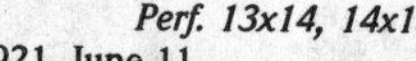

Perf. 13x14, 14x13

1921, June 11 Typo.
153 A53 10s claret .15 .15
154 A54 10s claret .15 .15
155 A55 10s claret .15 .15
156 A56 10s rose lil .15 .15
157 A57 20s blue .28 .16
Set value .55 .36

Nos. 153-157 were intended to be issued in 1915 to commemorate the liberation of Macedonia. They were not put in use until 1921. A 50s violet was prepared but never placed in use. Value $1.75.

View of Sofia — A58

"The Liberator," Monument to Alexander II A59

Monastery at Shipka Pass — A62

Tsar Boris III — A63

Harvesting Grain — A64

Tsar Assen's Tower (No crown over lion) — A65

Rila Monastery (Rosette at upper right) — A66

1921-23 Engr. *Perf. 12*
158 A58 10s blue gray .15 .15
159 A59 20s deep green .15 .15
160 A63 25s blue grn ('22) .15 .15
161 A22 50s orange .15 .15
162 A22 50s dk blue ('23) 2.50 2.50
163 A62 75s dull vio .15 .15
164 A62 75s dp blue ('23) .30 .15
165 A63 1 l carmine .30 .16
166 A63 1 l dp blue ('22) .30 .15
167 A64 2 l brown .32 .15
168 A65 3 l brown vio .38 .15
169 A66 5 l lt blue 2.50 .32
170 A63 10 l violet brn 6.75 1.10
Nos. 158-170 (13) 14.10 5.43

For surcharge see No. 189.

Bourchier in Bulgarian Costume A67

James David Bourchier A68

View of Rila Monastery A69

1921, Dec. 31
171 A67 10s red orange .15 .15
172 A67 20s orange .15 .15
173 A68 30s dp gray .15 .15
174 A68 50s bluish gray .15 .15
175 A68 1 l dull vio .18 .15
176 A69 1½ l olive grn .18 .15
177 A69 2 l deep green .18 .15
178 A69 3 l Prus blue .45 .20
179 A69 5 l red brown .85 .35
Set value 2.00 1.00

Death of James D. Bourchier, Balkan correspondent of the London Times.
For surcharges see Nos. B13-B16.

Postage Due Stamps of 1919-22 Surcharged

a **10 СТОТИНКИ**

1924
182 D6 10s on 20s yellow .15 .15
183 D6 20s on 5s gray grn .15 .15
a. 20s on 5s emerald 7.00 7.00
184 D6 20s on 10s violet .15 .15
185 D6 20s on 30s orange .15 .15
Set value .35 .35

Nos. 182 to 185 were used for ordinary postage.

Regular Issues of 1919-23 Surcharged in Blue or Red:

1 левъ b **3 ЛЕВА** c

186 A43 (a) 10s on 1s black (R) .15 .15
187 A44 (b) 1 l on 5s emer (Bl) .15 .15
188 A22 (c) 3 l on 50s dk bl (R) .20 .15
189 A63 (b) 6 l on 1 l car (Bl) .60 .20
Set value 1.10 .60

The surcharge of No. 188 comes in three types: normal, thick and thin.
Nos. 182, 184-189 exist with inverted surcharge.

Lion of Bulgaria
A70 A71

Tsar Boris III — A72

New Sofia Cathedral — A73

Harvesting — A74

1925 Typo. *Perf. 13, 11½*
191 A70 10s red & bl, *pink* .15 .15
192 A70 15s car & org, *blue* .15 .15
193 A70 30s blk & buff .15 .15
a. Cliche of 15s in plate of 30s
194 A71 50s choc, *green* .15 .15
195 A72 1 l dull green .48 .15
196 A73 2 l dk grn & buff 1.10 .15
197 A74 4 l lake & yellow 1.10 .15
Set value 2.90 .50

Several values of this series exist imperforate and in pairs imperforate between.
See #199, 201. For overprint see #C2.

Cathedral of Sveta Nedelya, Sofia, Ruined by Bomb — A75

1926 *Perf. 11½*
198 A75 50s gray black .15 .15

A76 A77

Type A72 Re-engraved. (Shoulder at left does not touch frame)

1926
199 A76 1 l gray .45 .15
a. 1 l green .45 .15
201 A76 2 l olive brown .52 .15

Center Embossed
202 A77 6 l dp bl & pale lemon 1.10 .15
203 A77 10 l brn blk & brn org 4.00 .75
Nos. 199-203 (4) 6.07
Set value 1.00

For overprints see Nos. C1, C3-C4.

Christo Botev — A78

Tsar Boris III — A79

1926, June 2
204 A78 1 l olive green .32 .15
205 A78 2 l slate violet .90 .15
206 A78 4 l red brown .90 .35
Nos. 204-206 (3) 2.12
Set value .49

Botev (1847-76), Bulgarian revolutionary, poet.

Lion Type of 1881

1927-29 *Perf. 13*
207 A3 10s dk red & drab .15 .15
208 A3 15s blk & org ('29) .15 .15
209 A3 30s dk bl & bis brn ('28) .15 .15
a. 30s indigo & buff .15 .15
210 A3 50s blk & rose red ('28) .15 .15
Set value .35 .25

1928, Oct. 3 *Perf. 11½*
211 A79 1 l olive green .90 .15
212 A79 2 l deep brown 1.00 .15
Set value .15

St. Clement — A80

Konstantin Miladinov — A81

George S. Rakovski A82

Drenovo Monastery A83

Paisii — A84

Tsar Simeon — A85

Lyuben Karavelov A86

Vassil Levski A87

Georgi Benkovski A88

Tsar Alexander II A89

1929, May 12

213	A80	10s dk violet	.15	.15
214	A81	15s violet brn	.15	.15
215	A82	30s red	.15	.15
216	A83	50s olive grn	.25	.15
217	A84	1 l orange brn	.60	.15
218	A85	2 l dk blue	.70	.15
219	A86	3 l dull green	1.50	.45
220	A87	4 l olive brown	2.50	.22
221	A88	5 l brown	1.50	.35
222	A89	6 l Prus green	2.25	.90
		Nos. 213-222 (10)	9.75	2.82

Millenary of Tsar Simeon and 50th anniv. of the liberation of Bulgaria from the Turks.

Royal Wedding Issue

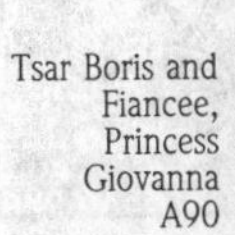

Tsar Boris and Fiancee, Princess Giovanna A90

Queen Ioanna and Tsar Boris — A91

1930, Nov. 12 *Perf. 11½*

223	A90	1 l green	.25	.24
224	A91	2 l dull violet	.22	.32
225	A90	4 l rose red	.22	.32
226	A91	6 l dark blue	.25	.38
		Nos. 223-226 (4)	.94	1.26

Fifty-five copies of a miniature sheet incorporating one each of Nos. 223-226 were printed and given to royal, governmental and diplomatic personages.

Tsar Boris III

A92 A93

Perf. 11½, 12x11½, 13

1931-37 **Unwmk.**

227	A92	1 l blue green	.25	.15
228	A92	2 l carmine	.40	.15
229	A92	4 l red org ('34)	.75	.15
230	A92	4 l yel org ('37)	.20	.15
231	A92	6 l deep blue	.70	.15
232	A92	7 l dp bl ('37)	.20	.15
233	A92	10 l slate blk	8.75	.70
234	A92	12 l lt brown	.40	.18
235	A92	14 l lt brn ('37)	.28	.22
236	A93	20 l claret & org brn	1.00	.45
		Nos. 227-236 (10)	12.93	
		Set value		2.00

Nos. 230-233 and 235 have outer bars at top and bottom as shown on cut A92; Nos. 227-229 and 234 are without outer bars.

See Nos. 251, 279-280, 287. For surcharge see No. 252.

Balkan Games Issues

Gymnast — A95

Soccer — A96

Riding — A97

Swimmer A100

"Victory" A101

Designs: 6 l, Fencing. 10 l, Bicycle race.

1931, Sept. 18 *Perf. 11½*

237	A95	1 l lt green	.85	.50
238	A96	2 l garnet	.85	.50
239	A97	4 l carmine	1.90	.75
240	A95	6 l Prus blue	4.00	1.25
241	A95	10 l red org	9.50	3.75
242	A100	12 l dk blue	32.50	7.50
243	A101	50 l olive brn	30.00	22.50
		Nos. 237-243 (7)	79.60	36.75

1933, Jan. 5

244	A95	1 l blue grn	1.10	.95
245	A96	2 l blue	1.90	.95
246	A97	4 l brn vio	2.50	1.10
247	A95	6 l brt rose	4.75	1.65
248	A95	10 l olive brn	26.00	9.00
249	A100	12 l orange	55.00	18.00
250	A101	50 l red brown	100.00	82.50
		Nos. 244-250 (7)	191.25	114.15

Nos. 244-250 were sold only at the philatelic agency.

Boris Type of 1931
Outer Bars at Top and Bottom Removed

1933 *Perf. 13*

251	A92	6 l deep blue	.80	.15

Type of 1931 Surcharged in Blue **2**

1934

252	A92	2 (l) on 3 l ol brn	4.00	.25

Soldier Defending Shipka Pass A102

Shipka Battle Memorial A103

Color-Bearer A104

Veteran of the War of Liberation, 1878 A105

Widow and Orphans — A106

Perf. 10½, 11½

1934, Aug. 26 **Wmk. 145**

253	A102	1 l green	.45	.38
254	A103	2 l pale red	.45	.24
255	A104	3 l bister brn	1.40	1.25
256	A105	4 l dk carmine	1.25	.60
257	A104	7 l dk blue	2.25	2.00
258	A106	14 l plum	6.00	5.75
		Nos. 253-258 (6)	11.80	10.22

Shipka Pass Battle memorial unveiling.

An unwatermarked miniature sheet incorporating one each of Nos. 253-258 was put on sale in 1938 in five cities at a price of 8,000 leva. Printing: 100 sheets.

1934, Sept. 21

259	A102	1 l bright green	.45	.38
260	A103	2 l dull orange	.45	.24
261	A104	3 l yellow	1.40	1.25
262	A105	4 l rose	1.25	.60
263	A104	7 l blue	2.25	2.00
264	A106	14 l olive bister	6.00	5.75
		Nos. 259-264 (6)	11.80	10.22

An unwatermarked miniature sheet incorporating one each of Nos. 259-263 was issued.

Velcho A. Djamjiyata A108

Capt. G. S. Mamarchev A109

1935, May 5 *Perf. 11½*

265	A108	1 l deep blue	.95	.25
266	A109	2 l maroon	.95	.28

Bulgarian uprising against the Turks, cent.

Soccer Game — A110

Cathedral of Alexander Nevski — A111

Soccer Team — A112

Symbolical of Victory — A113

Player and Trophy — A114

The Trophy — A115

1935, June 14

267	A110	1 l green	1.10	.90
268	A111	2 l blue gray	2.50	1.40
269	A112	4 l crimson	4.00	2.00
270	A113	7 l brt blue	7.75	2.50
271	A114	14 l orange	7.75	3.25
272	A115	50 l lilac brn	60.00	52.50
		Nos. 267-272 (6)	83.10	62.55

5th Balkan Soccer Tournament.

Gymnast on Parallel Bars — A116

Youth in "Yunak" Costume — A117

Girl in "Yunak" Costume A118

Pole Vaulting A119

Stadium, Sofia — A120

Yunak Emblem — A121

1935, July 10

273	A116	1 l green	1.90	1.10
274	A117	2 l lt blue	2.50	1.10
275	A118	4 l carmine	5.00	2.25
276	A119	7 l dk blue	5.00	3.00
277	A120	14 l dk brown	5.00	3.00
278	A121	50 l red	55.00	42.50
		Nos. 273-278 (6)	74.40	52.95

8th tournament of the Yunak Gymnastic Organization at Sofia, July 12-14.

Boris Type of 1931

1935 **Wmk. 145** *Perf. 12½, 13*

279	A92	1 l green	.30	.15
280	A92	2 l carmine	20.00	.15
		Set value		.15

Janos Hunyadi A122

King Ladislas Varnenchik A123

Varna Memorial — A124

King Ladislas III — A125

Battle of Varna, 1444 — A126

1935, Aug. 4 *Perf. 10½, 11½*

281	A122	1 l brown org	1.10	.75
282	A123	2 l maroon	1.10	.75
283	A124	4 l vermilion	5.50	3.75

284 A125 7 l dull blue 2.50 1.25
285 A126 14 l green 2.50 1.25
Nos. 281-285 (5) 12.70 7.75

Battle of Varna, and the death of the Polish King, Ladislas Varnenchik (1424-44).

Lion Type of 1881

1935 Wmk. 145 ***Perf. 13***
286 A3 10s dk red & drab .70 .15

Boris Type of 1933
Outer Bars at Top and Bottom Removed

1935
287 A92 6 l gray blue .60 .15

Dimitr Monument
A127

Haji Dimitr
A128

Haji Dimitr and Stefan Karaja — A129

Taking the Oath — A130

Birthplace of Dimitr — A131

1935, Oct. 1 Unwmk. ***Perf. 11½***
288 A127 1 l green 1.25 .35
289 A128 2 l brown 1.75 .70
290 A129 4 l car rose 3.50 2.50
291 A130 7 l blue 4.50 3.50
292 A131 14 l orange 4.50 3.50
Nos. 288-292 (5) 15.50 10.55

67th anniv. of the death of the Bulgarian patriots, Haji Dimitr and Stefan Karaja.

Catalogue values for unused stamps in this section, from this point to the end of the section, are for Never Hinged items.

A132

A133

1936-39 ***Perf. 13x12½, 13***
293 A132 10s red org ('37) .15 .15
294 A132 15s emerald .15 .15
295 A133 30s maroon .15 .15
296 A133 30s yel brn ('37) .15 .15
297 A133 30s Prus bl ('37) .15 .15
298 A133 50s ultra .15 .15
299 A133 50s dk car ('37) .20 .15
300 A133 50s sl grn ('39) .15 .15
Set value 1.00 .50

Meteorological Station, Mt. Moussalla — A134

Peasant Girl — A135

Town of Nessebr
A136

1936, Aug. 16 Photo. ***Perf. 11½***
301 A134 1 l purple 1.40 .65
302 A135 2 l ultra 1.40 .60
303 A136 7 l dark blue 3.75 1.50
Nos. 301-303 (3) 6.55 2.75

4th Geographical & Ethnographical Cong., Sofia, Aug. 1936.

Sts. Cyril and Methodius
A137

Displaying the Bible to the People
A138

1937, June 2
304 A137 1 l dk green .22 .15
305 A137 2 l dk plum .22 .15
306 A138 4 l vermilion .45 .22
307 A137 7 l dk blue 1.75 1.10
308 A138 14 l rose red 1.75 1.10
Nos. 304-308 (5) 4.39 2.72

Millennium of Cyrillic alphabet.

Princess Marie Louise — A139

Tsar Boris III — A140

1937, Oct. 3
310 A139 1 l yellow green .35 .15
311 A139 2 l brown red .26 .15
312 A139 4 l scarlet .35 .15
Nos. 310-312 (3) .96
Set value .30

Issued in honor of Princess Marie Louise.

1937, Oct. 3
313 A140 2 l brown red .35 .15

19th anniv. of the accession of Tsar Boris III to the throne. See No. B11.

National Products Issue

Peasants Bundling Wheat
A141

Sunflower
A142

Wheat — A143

Chickens and Eggs — A144

Cluster of Grapes — A145

Rose and Perfume Flask — A146

Strawberries
A147

Girl Carrying Grape Clusters
A148

Rose — A149

Tobacco Leaves — A150

1938 ***Perf. 13***
316 A141 10s orange .15 .15
317 A141 10s red org .15 .15
318 A142 15s brt rose .30 .15
319 A142 15s deep plum .30 .15
320 A143 30s golden brn .15 .15
321 A143 30s copper brn .15 .15
322 A144 50s black .15 .15
323 A144 50s indigo .15 .15
324 A145 1 l yel grn .65 .15
325 A145 1 l green .65 .15
326 A146 2 l rose pink .60 .15
327 A146 2 l rose brn .60 .15
328 A147 3 l dp red lil 1.25 .15
329 A147 3 l brn lake 1.25 .15
330 A148 4 l plum .80 .15
331 A148 4 l golden brn .80 .15
332 A149 7 l vio blue 1.50 .55
333 A149 7 l dp blue 1.50 .55
334 A150 14 l dk brown 2.25 .90
335 A150 14 l red brn 2.25 .90
Nos. 316-335 (20) 15.60
Set value 4.00

Several values of this series exist imperforate.

Crown Prince Simeon
A151 A153

Designs: 2 l, Same portrait as 1 l, value at lower left. 14 l, similar to 4 l, but no wreath.

1938, June 16
336 A151 1 l brt green .15 .15
337 A151 2 l rose pink .15 .15
338 A153 4 l dp orange .16 .15
339 A151 7 l ultra .80 .38
340 A153 14 l dp brown .80 .38
Nos. 336-340 (5) 2.06
Set value .90

First birthday of Prince Simeon.

Tsar Boris III
A155 A156

Various Portraits of Tsar.

1938, Oct. 3
341 A155 1 l lt green .15 .15
342 A156 2 l rose brown .60 .15
343 A156 4 l golden brn .15 .15
344 A156 7 l brt ultra .30 .22
345 A156 14 l deep red lilac .35 .26
Nos. 341-345 (5) 1.55
Set value .65

Reign of Tsar Boris III, 20th anniv.

Early Locomotive
A160

Designs: 2 l, Modern locomotive. 4 l, Train crossing bridge. 7 l, Tsar Boris in cab.

1939, Apr. 26
346 A160 1 l yel green .20 .15
347 A160 2 l copper brn .20 .15
348 A160 4 l red orange 1.40 .16
349 A160 7 l dark blue 3.25 .85
Nos. 346-349 (4) 5.05 1.31

50th anniv. of Bulgarian State Railways.

Post Horns and Arrows — A164

Central Post Office, Sofia — A165

1939, May 14 ***Typo.***
350 A164 1 l yellow grn .16 .15
351 A165 2 l brt carmine .24 .15
Set value .15

Establishment of the postal system, 60th anniv.

Gymnast on Bar — A166

Yunak Emblem — A167

Discus Thrower — A168

Athletic Dancer — A169

Weight Lifter — A170

1939, July 7 **Photo.**

352	A166	1 l yel grn & pale grn	.35	.15
353	A167	2 l brt rose	.35	.15
354	A168	4 l brn & gldn brn	.52	.22
355	A169	7 l dk bl & bl	1.25	.65
356	A170	14 l plum & rose vio	5.50	2.75
		Nos. 352-356 (5)	7.97	3.92

9th tournament of the Yunak Gymnastic Organization at Sofia, July 4-8.

Tsar Boris III — A171

Bulgaria's First Stamp — A172

1940-41 **Typo.**

356A	A171	1 l dl grn ('41)	.80	.15
357	A171	2 l brt crimson	.20	.15
		Set value		.15

1940, May 19 **Photo.** ***Perf. 13***

Design: 20 l, Similar design, scroll dated "1840-1940."

358	A172	10 l olive black	1.25	.85
359	A172	20 l indigo	1.25	.85

Cent. of 1st postage stamp. Exist imperf.

Peasant Couple and Tsar Boris — A174

Flags over Wheat Field and Tsar Boris — A175

Tsar Boris and Map of Dobrudja A176

1940, Sept. 20

360	A174	1 l slate green	.15	.15
361	A175	2 l rose red	.15	.15
362	A176	4 l dark brown	.15	.15
363	A176	7 l dark blue	.60	.32
		Nos. 360-363 (4)	1.05	
		Set value		.50

Return of Dobrudja from Romania.

Fruit A177

Bees and Flowers A178

Plowing A179

Shepherd and Sheep A180

Tsar Boris III — A181

Perf. 10, 10½x11½, 11½, 13

1940-44 **Typo.** **Unwmk.**

364	A177	10s red orange	.15	.15
365	A178	15s blue	.15	.15
366	A179	30s olive brn ('41)	.15	.15
367	A180	50s violet	.15	.15
368	A181	1 l brt green	.15	.15
369	A181	2 l rose car	.15	.15
370	A181	4 l red orange	.15	.15
371	A181	6 l red vio ('44)	.28	.15
372	A181	7 l blue	.28	.15
373	A181	10 l blue grn ('41)	.30	.15
		Set value	1.50	.55

See Nos. 373A-377, 440. For overprints see Nos. 455-463, C31-C32.

1940-41 **Wmk. 145** ***Perf. 13***

373A	A180	50s vio ('41)	.15	.15
374	A181	1 l brt grn	.15	.15
375	A181	2 l rose car	.18	.15
376	A181	7 l dull blue	.45	.15
377	A181	10 l blue green	.65	.15
		Nos. 373A-377 (5)	1.58	
		Set value		.35

Watermarked vertically or horizontally.

P. R. Slaveikov A182

Sofronii, Bishop of Vratza A183

Saint Ivan Rilski — A184

Martin S. Drinov — A185

Monk Khrabr — A186

Kolio Ficheto — A187

1940, Sept. 23 **Photo.** **Unwmk.**

378	A182	1 l brt bl grn	.15	.15
379	A183	2 l brt carmine	.15	.15
380	A184	3 l dp red brn	.15	.15
381	A185	4 l red orange	.15	.15
382	A186	7 l deep blue	1.00	.60
383	A187	10 l dp red brn	1.50	.85
		Nos. 378-383 (6)	3.10	
		Set value		1.65

Issued in commemoration of the liberation of Bulgaria from the Turks in 1878.

Johannes Gutenberg A188

N. Karastoyanov, 1st Bulgarian Printer A189

1940, Dec. 16

384	A188	1 l slate green	.15	.15
385	A189	2 l orange brown	.15	.15
		Set value	.25	.15

500th anniv. of the invention of the printing press and 100th anniv. of the 1st Bulgarian printing press.

Christo Botev — A190

Monument to Botev — A192

Botev with his Insurgent Band — A191

1941, May 3

386	A190	1 l dark blue green	.15	.15
387	A191	2 l crimson rose	.20	.15
388	A192	3 l dark brown	.65	.32
		Nos. 386-388 (3)	1.00	
		Set value		.42

Christo Botev, patriot and poet.

Palace of Justice, Sofia — A193

Designs: 20 l, Workers' hospital. 50 l, National Bank.

1941-43 **Engr.** ***Perf. 11½***

389	A193	14 l lt gray brn ('43)	.20	.15
390	A193	20 l gray grn ('43)	.38	.16
391	A193	50 l lt bl gray	1.90	1.25
		Nos. 389-391 (3)	2.48	1.56

Macedonian Woman — A196

City of Okhrida — A200

Outline of Macedonia and Tsar Boris III A197

View of Aegean Sea — A198

Poganovski Monastery A199

1941, Oct. 3 **Photo.** ***Perf. 13***

392	A196	1 l slate grn	.15	.15
393	A197	2 l crimson	.15	.15
394	A198	2 l red org	.15	.15
395	A199	4 l org brn	.15	.15
396	A200	7 l dp gray bl	.38	.28
		Set value	.65	.50

Issued to commemorate the acquisition of Macedonian territory from neighboring countries.

Peasant Working in a Field — A201

Designs: 15s, Plowing. 30s, Apiary. 50s, Women harvesting fruit. 3 l, Shepherd and sheep. 5 l, Inspecting cattle.

1941-44

397	A201	10s dk violet	.15	.15
398	A201	10s dk blue	.15	.15
399	A201	15s Prus blue	.15	.15
400	A201	15s dk ol brn	.15	.15
401	A201	30s red orange	.15	.15
402	A201	30s dk slate grn	.15	.15
403	A201	50s blue vio	.15	.15
404	A201	50s red lilac	.15	.15
405	A201	3 l henna brn	.42	.25
406	A201	3 l dk brn ('44)	1.40	1.10
407	A201	5 l sepia	.52	.48
408	A201	5 l vio bl ('44)	1.40	1.10
		Set value	4.00	3.25

Girls Singing — A207

Boys in Camp — A208

Raising Flag — A209

Folk Dancers — A211

Camp Scene — A210

1942, June 1 **Photo.**

409	A207	1 l dk bl grn	.15	.15
410	A208	2 l scarlet	.15	.15
411	A209	4 l olive gray	.15	.15
412	A210	7 l deep blue	.16	.15
413	A211	14 l fawn	.32	.22
		Nos. 409-413 (5)	.93	
		Set value		.45

National "Work and Joy" movement.

Wounded Soldier — A212

Soldier's Farewell — A213

Designs: 4 l, Aiding wounded soldier. 7 l, Widow and orphans at grave. 14 l, Tomb of Unknown Soldier. 20 l, Queen Ioanna visiting wounded.

1942, Sept. 7

414	A212	1 l slate grn	.15	.15
415	A213	2 l brt rose	.15	.15
416	A213	4 l yel org	.15	.15
417	A213	7 l dark blue	.15	.15
418	A213	14 l brown	.15	.15
419	A213	20 l olive blk	.22	.15
		Set value	.75	.36

Issued to aid war victims. No. 419 was printed in sheets of 50, alternating with 50 labels.

Legend of Kubrat — A218

Cavalry Charge — A219

Designs: 30s, Rider of Madara. 50s, Christening of Boris I. 1 l, School, St. Naum. 2 l, Crowning of Tsar Simeon by Boris I. 3 l, Golden era of Bulgarian literature. 4 l, Sentencing of the Bogomil Basil. 5 l, Proclamation of 2nd Bulgarian Empire. 7 l, Ivan Assen II at Trebizond. 10 l, Deporting the Patriarch Jeftimi. 14 l, Wandering minstrel. 20 l, Monk Paisii. 30 l, Monument, Shipka Pass.

1942, Oct. 12

420	A218	10s bluish blk	.15	.15
421	A219	15s Prus grn	.15	.15
422	A219	30s dk rose vio	.15	.15
423	A219	50s indigo	.15	.15
424	A219	1 l slate grn	.15	.15
425	A219	2 l crimson	.15	.15
426	A219	3 l brown	.15	.15
427	A219	4 l orange	.15	.15
428	A219	5 l grnsh blk	.15	.15
429	A219	7 l dk blue	.15	.15
430	A219	10 l brown blk	.15	.15
431	A219	14 l olive blk	.15	.15
432	A219	20 l henna brn	.42	.28
433	A219	30 l black	.70	.42
		Set value	2.00	1.25

Tsar Boris III — A234

Designs: Various portraits of Tsar.

Perf. 13, Imperf.

1944, Feb. 28 Photo. Wmk. 275

Frames in Black

434	A234	1 l olive grn	.15	.15
435	A234	2 l red brown	.16	.15
436	A234	4 l brown	.20	.15
437	A234	5 l gray vio	.28	.16
438	A234	7 l slate blue	.28	.16
		Nos. 434-438 (5)	1.07	
		Set value		.52

Tsar Boris III (1894-1943).

Tsar Simeon II — A239

Perf. 11½, 13

1944, June 12 Typo. Unwmk.

439	A239	3 l red orange	.25	.15

Shepherd Type of 1940

1944

440	A180	50s yellow green	.20	.15

Parcel Post Stamps of 1944 Overprinted in Black or Orange

ВСИЧКО
ЗА
ФРОНТА

1945, Jan. 25 *Perf. 11½*

448	PP5	1 l dk carmine	.15	.15
449	PP5	7 l rose lilac	.15	.15
450	PP5	20 l org brn	.15	.15
451	PP5	30 l dk brn car	.15	.15
452	PP5	50 l red orange	.25	.15
453	PP5	100 l blue (O)	.60	.16

Overprint reads: "Everything for the Front."

No. 448 with Additional Surcharge of New Value in Black

454	PP5	4 l on 1 l dk car	.15	.15
		Nos. 448-454 (7)	1.60	
		Set value		.45

Nos. 368 to 370 Overprinted in Black

СЪБИРАЙТЕ
СТАРО
ЖЕЛЪЗО

1945, Mar. 15 *Perf. 11½, 13*

455	A181	1 l brt green	.25	.15
456	A181	2 l rose carmine	.40	.15
457	A181	4 l red orange	.60	.15

Overprint reads: "Collect old iron."

Overprinted in Black

СЪБИРАЙТЕ
ХАРТИЕНИ
ОТПАДЪЦИ

458	A181	1 l brt green	.25	.15
459	A181	2 l rose carmine	.40	.15
460	A181	4 l red orange	.60	.15

Overprint reads: "Collect discarded paper."

Overprinted in Black

СЪБИРАЙТЕ
ВСЪКАКВИ
ПАРЦАЛИ

461	A181	1 l brt green	.25	.15
462	A181	2 l rose carmine	.40	.15
463	A181	4 l red orange	.60	.15
		Nos. 455-463 (9)	3.75	
		Set value		.40

Overprint reads: "Collect all kinds of rags."

Oak Tree — A245

Imperf., Perf. 11½.

1945 Litho. Unwmk.

464	A245	4 l vermilion	.15	.15
465	A245	10 l blue	.15	.15

Imperf

466	A245	50 l brown lake	.15	.15
		Set value	.25	.25

Slav Congress, Sofia, March, 1945.

A246

A247

A248

A249

A251

A252

A253

A254

Two types of 2 l and 4 l: Type I. Large crown close to coat of arms. Type II. Smaller crown standing high.

1945-46 Photo. *Perf. 13*

469	A246	30s yellow grn	.15	.15
470	A247	50s peacock grn	.15	.15
471	A248	1 l dk green	.15	.15
472	A249	2 l choc (I)	.15	.15
a.		Type II	.15	.15
473	A249	4 l dk blue (I)	.15	.15
a.		Type II	.15	.15
475	A251	5 l red violet	.15	.15
476	A251	9 l slate gray	.15	.15
477	A252	10 l Prus blue	.15	.15
478	A253	15 l brown	.15	.15
479	A254	20 l carmine	.20	.15
480	A254	20 l gray blk	.20	.15
		Set value	1.00	.55

Breaking Chain — A255

1 Lev Coin — A256

Water Wheel — A257

Coin and Symbols of Agriculture and Industry — A258

Unwmk.

1945, June 4 Litho. *Imperf.*

Laid Paper

481	A255	50 l brn red, *pink*	.15	.15
482	A255	50 l org, *pink*	.15	.15
483	A256	100 l gray bl, *pink*	.20	.15
484	A256	100 l brn, *pink*	.20	.15
485	A257	150 l dk ol gray, *pink*	.35	.18
486	A257	150 l dl car, *pink*	.35	.18
487	A258	200 l dp bl, *pink*	.50	.30
488	A258	200 l ol grn, *pink*	.50	.30
		Nos. 481-488 (8)	2.40	
		Set value		1.25

Souvenir Sheets

489		Sheet of 4	3.00	1.75
a.		A255 50 l violet blue	.30	.18
b.		A256 100 l violet blue	.30	.18
c.		A257 150 l violet blue	.30	.18
d.		A258 200 l violet blue	.30	.18
490		Sheet of 4	3.00	1.75
a.		A255 50 l brown orange	.30	.18
b.		A256 100 l brown orange	.30	.18
c.		A257 150 l brown orange	.30	.18
d.		A258 200 l brown orange	.30	.18

Publicizing Bulgaria's Liberty Loan.

Olive Branch — A260

1945, Sept. 1 Typo. *Perf. 13*

491	A260	10 l org brn & yel grn	.15	.15
492	A260	50 l dull red & dp grn	.25	.15
		Set value	.31	.20

Victory of Allied Nations, World War II.

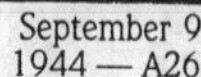
September 9, 1944 — A261

Numeral, Broken Chain — A262

1945, Sept. 7

493	A261	1 l gray green	.15	.15
494	A261	4 l deep blue	.15	.15
495	A261	5 l rose lilac	.15	.15
496	A262	10 l lt blue	.15	.15
497	A262	20 l brt car	.18	.15
498	A261	50 l brt bl grn	.42	.20
499	A261	100 l orange brn	.48	.35
		Set value	1.25	.80

1st anniv. of Bulgaria's liberation.

Old Postal Savings Emblem — A263

Child Putting Coin in Bank — A265

First Bulgarian Postal Savings Stamp — A264

Postal Savings Building, Sofia — A266

1946, Apr. 12

500	A263	4 l brown org	.15	.15
501	A264	10 l dk olive	.15	.15
502	A265	20 l ultra	.15	.15
503	A266	50 l slate gray	.52	.52
		Set value	.75	.66

50th anniv. of Bulgarian Postal Savings.

Refugee Children — A267

Nurse Assisting Wounded Soldier — A269

Wounded Soldier — A268

Design: 35 l, 100 l, Red Cross hospital train.

1946, Apr. 4

Cross in Carmine

504	A267	2 l dk olive	.15	.15
505	A268	4 l violet	.15	.15
506	A267	10 l plum	.15	.15
507	A268	20 l ultra	.15	.15
508	A269	30 l brown org	.15	.15
509	A268	35 l gray blk	.15	.15
510	A269	50 l violet brn	.22	.18
511	A268	100 l gray brn	.70	.60
		Set value	1.50	1.15

See Nos. 553 to 560.

Advancing Troops A271

Grenade Thrower A272

Attacking Planes — A274

Designs: 5 l, Horse-drawn cannon. 9 l, Engineers building pontoon bridge. 10 l, 30 l, Cavalry charge. 40 l, Horse-drawn supply column. 50 l, Motor transport column. 60 l, Infantry, tanks and planes.

1946, Aug. 9 Typo. Unwmk.

512	A271	2 l dk red vio	.15	.15
513	A272	4 l dk gray	.15	.15
514	A271	5 l dk org red	.15	.15
515	A274	6 l black brn	.15	.15
516	A271	9 l rose lilac	.15	.15
517	A271	10 l dp violet	.15	.15
518	A271	20 l dp blue	.24	.15
519	A271	30 l red org	.24	.15
520	A271	40 l dk ol bis	.30	.16
521	A271	50 l dk green	.30	.16
522	A271	60 l red brown	.42	.28
		Set value	1.85	1.10

Bulgaria's participation in World War II.

Arms of Russia and Bulgaria A279

Lion Rampant A280

1946, May 23

523	A279	4 l red orange	.15	.15
525	A279	20 l turq green	.22	.15
		Set value	.30	.21

Congress of the Bulgarian-Soviet Association, May 1946. The 4 l exists in dk car rose and 20 l in blue, value, set $7.

1946, May 25 ***Imperf.***

526	A280	20 l blue	.30	.22

Day of the Postage Stamp, May 26, 1946.

Alekandr Stamboliski A281

Flags of Albania, Romania, Bulgaria and Yugoslavia A282

1946, June 13 ***Perf. 12***

527	A281	100 l red orange	4.00	1.90

23rd anniversary of the death of Alekandr Stamboliski, agrarian leader.

1946, July 6 ***Perf. 11½***

528	A282	100 l black brown	.75	.50

1946 Balkan Games.

Sheet of 100 arranged so that all stamps are tete beche vert. and horiz., except 2 center rows in left pane which provide 10 vert. pairs that are not tete beche vert.

St. Ivan Rilski — A283

A286

A284

A285

Views of Rila Monastery A287

1946, Aug. 26

529	A283	1 l red brown	.15	.15
530	A284	4 l black brn	.15	.15
531	A285	10 l dk green	.15	.15
532	A286	20 l dp blue	.18	.15
533	A287	50 l dk red	.80	.50
		Set value	1.25	.70

Millenary of Rila Monastery.

People's Republic

A288

1946, Sept. 15 Typo.

534	A288	4 l brown lake	.15	.15
535	A288	20 l dull blue	.15	.15
536	A288	50 l olive bister	.18	.16
		Set value	.30	.26

No. 535 is inscribed "BULGARIA" in Latin characters.

Referendum of Sept. 8, 1946, resulting in the establishment of the Bulgarian People's Republic.

Partisan Army — A289

Snipers — A290

Soldiers: Past and Present — A291

Design: 30 l, Partisans advancing.

1946, Dec. 2

537	A289	1 l violet brn	.15	.15
538	A290	4 l dull grn	.15	.15
539	A291	5 l chocolate	.15	.15
540	A290	10 l crimson	.15	.15
541	A289	20 l ultra	.24	.15
542	A290	30 l olive bister	.24	.15
543	A291	50 l black	.28	.22
		Set value	1.00	.66

Relief Worker and Children — A294

Child with Gift Parcels — A295

Waiting for Food Distribution A296

Mother and Child A297

1946, Dec. 30

545	A294	1 l dk vio brn	.15	.15
546	A295	4 l brt red	.15	.15
547	A295	9 l olive bis	.15	.15
548	A294	10 l slate gray	.15	.15
549	A296	20 l ultra	.15	.15
550	A297	30 l dp brn org	.15	.15
551	A296	40 l maroon	.18	.15
552	A294	50 l peacock grn	.32	.28
		Set value	.90	.72

"Bulgaria" is in Latin characters on No. 548.

Red Cross Types of 1946

1947, Jan. 31

Cross in Carmine

553	A267	2 l olive bister	.15	.15
554	A268	4 l olive black	.15	.15
555	A267	10 l blue grn	.15	.15
556	A268	20 l brt blue	.15	.15
557	A269	30 l yellow grn	.30	.22
558	A268	35 l grnsh gray	.32	.24
559	A269	50 l henna brn	.48	.35
560	A268	100 l dark blue	.70	.50
		Nos. 553-560 (8)	2.40	1.91

Laurel Branch, Allied and Bulgarian Emblems — A298

Dove of Peace — A299

1947, Feb. 28

561	A298	4 l olive	.15	.15
562	A299	10 l brown red	.15	.15
563	A299	20 l deep blue	.18	.16
		Set value	.30	.26

Return to peace at the close of World War II. "Bulgaria" in Latin characters on No. 563.

A302

Guerrilla Fighters
A303 A304

1947, Jan. 21 ***Perf. 11½***

567	A302	10 l choc & brn org	.32	.16
568	A303	20 l dk bl & bl	.32	.16
569	A304	70 l dp claret & rose	18.00	8.00
		Nos. 567-569 (3)	18.64	8.32

Issued to honor the anti-fascists.

Hydroelectric Station — A305

Miner A306

Symbols of Industry A307

Tractor — A308

1947, Aug. 6

570	A305	4 l olive green	.15	.15
571	A306	9 l red brown	.15	.15
572	A307	20 l deep blue	.18	.18
573	A308	40 l olive brown	.42	.28
		Nos. 570-573 (4)	.90	
		Set value		.50

Exhibition Building A309

Former Home of Alphonse de Lamartine A310

Symbols of Agriculture and Horticulture — A311

Perf. 11x11½, 11½x11

1947, Aug. 31 Litho. Unwmk.

574	A309	4 l scarlet	.15	.15
575	A310	9 l brown lake	.18	.15
576	A311	20 l brt ultra	.20	.15
		Set value	.31	.18

Plovdiv Intl. Fair, 1947. See No. C54.

Basil Evstatiev Aprilov — A312

1947, Oct. 19 Photo. ***Perf. 11***

577	A312	40 l brt ultra	.35	.18

Cent. of the death of Basil Evstatiev Aprilov, educator and historian. See No. 603.

Bicycle Race — A313

Basketball
A314

Chess
A315

Balkan Games: 20 l, Soccer players. 60 l, Four flags of participating nations.

1947, Sept. 29 Typo. *Perf. 11½*

578	A313	2 l plum	.18	.15
579	A314	4 l dk olive grn	.18	.15
580	A315	9 l orange brn	.42	.15
581	A315	20 l brt ultra	.80	.18
582	A315	60 l violet brn	1.65	.75
		Nos. 578-582 (5)	3.23	1.38

People's Theater, Sofia
A316

National Assembly
A317

Central Post Office, Sofia
A318

Presidential Mansion
A319

1947-48 Typo. *Perf. 12½*

583	A316	50s yellow grn	.15	.15
584	A317	50s yellow grn	.15	.15
585	A318	1 l green	.15	.15
586	A319	1 l green	.15	.15
587	A316	2 l brown lake	.15	.15
588	A317	2 l lt brown	.15	.15
589	A316	4 l deep blue	.15	.15
590	A317	4 l deep blue	.15	.15
591	A316	9 l carmine	.35	.15
592	A317	20 l deep blue	.75	.30
		Set value	1.50	.75

On Nos. 583-592 inscription reads "Bulgarian Republic." No. 592 is inscribed in Latin characters.

Redrawn
НАРОДНА
added to inscription

593	A318	1 l green	.15	.15
594	A318	2 l brown lake	.15	.15
595	A318	4 l deep blue	.15	.15
		Set value	.25	.15

Cyrillic inscription beneath design on Nos. 593-595 reads "Bulgarian People's Republic".

Geno Kirov — A320

Actors' Portraits: 1 l, Zlatina Nedeva. 2 l, Ivan Popov. 3 l, Athanas Kirchev. 4 l, Elena Snejina. 5 l, Stoyan Bachvarov.

Perf. 10½
1947, Dec. 8 Unwmk. Litho.

596	A320	50s bister brn	.15	.15
597	A320	1 l lt blue grn	.15	.15
598	A320	2 l slate green	.15	.15
599	A320	3 l dp blue	.15	.15
600	A320	4 l scarlet	.15	.15
601	A320	5 l red brown	.15	.15
		Set value, #596-601, B22-B26	1.60	1.00

National Theater, 50th anniversary.

Merchant Ship "Fatherland" — A321

1947, Dec. 19

602	A321	50 l Prus bl, *cream*	.45	.15

B. E. Aprilov — A322

Worker — A323

1948, Feb. 19 *Perf. 11*

603	A322	4 l brn car, *cream*	.15	.15

Centenary of the death of Basil Evstatiev Aprilov, educator and historian.

1948, Feb. 29 Photo. *Perf. 11½x12*

604	A323	4 l dp blue, *cream*	.15	.15

2nd Bulgarian Workers' Congress.

Self-education — A324

Accordion Player — A325

Factory Recess
A326

Girl Throwing Basketball
A327

1948, Mar. 31 Photo.

605	A324	4 l red	.15	.15
606	A325	20 l deep blue	.15	.15
607	A326	40 l dull green	.20	.15
608	A327	60 l brown	.60	.35
		Nos. 605-608 (4)	1.10	
		Set value		.60

Nicholas Vaptzarov — A328

Portraits: 9 l, P. K. Iavorov. 15 l, Christo Smirnenski. 20 l, Ivan Vazov. 45 l, P. R. Slaveikov.

1948, May 18 Litho. *Perf. 11*
Cream Paper

611	A328	4 l brt ver	.15	.15
612	A328	9 l lt brown	.15	.15
613	A328	15 l claret	.15	.15
614	A328	20 l deep blue	.15	.15
615	A328	45 l green	.32	.32
		Set value	.60	.56

Soviet Soldier — A329

Civilians Offering Gifts to Soldiers — A330

Designs: 20 l, Soldiers, 1878 and 1944. 60 l, Stalin and Spasski Tower.

1948, July 5 Photo.
Cream Paper

616	A329	4 l brown org	.15	.15
617	A330	10 l olive grn	.15	.15
618	A330	20 l dp blue	.15	.15
619	A329	60 l olive brn	.42	.35
		Set value	.62	.52

The Soviet Army.

Demeter Blagoev — A331

Monument to Bishop Andrey — A332

Designs: 9 l, Gabriel Genov. 60 l, Marching youths.

1948, Sept. 6 Litho.
Cream Paper

620	A331	4 l dk brown	.15	.15
621	A331	9 l brown org	.15	.15
622	A332	20 l dp blue	.15	.15
623	A332	60 l brown	.52	.42
		Set value	.69	.58

No. 623 is inscribed in Cyrillic characters.
Natl. Insurrection of 1923, 25th anniv.

Christo Smirnenski
A333

Battle of Grivitza, 1877
A334

1948, Oct. 2 Photo. *Perf. 11½*
Cream Paper

624	A333	4 l blue	.15	.15
625	A333	16 l red brown	.16	.15
		Set value	.25	.15

Christo Smirnenski, poet, 1898-1923.

1948, Nov. 1

626	A334	20 l blue	.15	.15

Issued to publicize Romanian-Bulgarian friendship. See Nos. C56-C57.

Bath, Gorna Banya — A335

Bath, Bankya — A336

Mineral Bath, Sofia
A337

Maliovitza
A338

1948-49 Typo. *Perf. 12½*

627	A335	2 l red brown	.15	.15
628	A336	3 l red orange	.15	.15
629	A337	4 l deep blue	.15	.15
630	A338	5 l violet brown	.15	.15
631	A336	10 l red violet	.15	.15
632	A338	15 l olive grn ('49)	.20	.15
633	A335	20 l deep blue	.75	.16
		Nos. 627-633 (7)	1.70	
		Set value		.50

Latin characters on No. 633. See No. 653.

Emblem of the Republic — A339

1948-50

634	A339	50s red orange	.15	.15
634A	A339	50s org brn ('50)	.15	.15
635	A339	1 l green	.15	.15
636	A339	9 l black	.15	.15
		Set value	.30	.20

Botev's Birthplace, Kalofer — A340

Christo Botev — A341

Designs: 9 l, Steamer "Radetzky." 15 l, Kalofer village. 20 l, Botev in uniform. 40 l, Botev's mother. 50 l, Pen, pistol and wreath.

Perf. 11x11½, 11½
1948, Dec. 21 Photo.
Cream Paper

638	A340	1 l dk green	.15	.15
639	A341	4 l violet brn	.15	.15
640	A340	9 l violet	.15	.15
641	A340	15 l brown	.15	.15
642	A341	20 l blue	.16	.15
643	A340	40 l red brown	.25	.16
644	A341	50 l olive blk	.35	.22
		Set value	1.00	.65

Botev, Bulgarian natl. poet, birth cent.

Lenin — A342

Lenin Speaking — A343

1949, Jan. 24 Unwmk. *Perf. 11½*
Cream Paper

645	A342	4 l brown	.15	.15
646	A343	20 l brown red	.30	.18
		Set value		.23

25th anniversary of the death of Lenin.

Road Construction
A344

Designs: 5 l, Tunnel construction. 9 l, Locomotive. 10 l, Textile worker. 20 l, Female tractor driver. 40 l, Workers in truck.

1949, Apr. 6 *Perf. 10½*
Inscribed: "CHM"
Cream Paper

647	A344	4 l dark red	.15	.15
648	A344	5 l dark brown	.15	.15
649	A344	9 l dk slate grn	.22	.15
650	A344	10 l violet	.25	.15
651	A344	20 l dull blue	.60	.38
652	A344	40 l brown	.95	.55
		Nos. 647-652 (6)	2.32	
		Set value		1.28

Issued to honor the Workers' Cultural Brigade.

Type of 1948
Redrawn
Country Name and "POSTA" in Latin Characters

1949 Typo. *Perf. 12½*

653 A337	20 l deep blue		.55	.15

Miner — A345

1949 *Perf. 11x11½*

654 A345	4 l dark blue		.20	.15

A347

Prime Minister George Dimitrov, 1882-1949 — A348

1949, July 10 Photo.

656 A347	4 l red brown	.22	.15
657 A348	20 l dark blue	.52	.16
	Set value		.21

Power Station — A349

Grain Towers — A350

Farm Machinery A351

Tractor Parade A352

Agriculture and Industry — A353

1949, Aug. 5 *Perf. 11½x11, 11x11½*

658 A349	4 l olive green	.15	.15
659 A350	9 l dark red	.15	.15
660 A351	15 l purple	.18	.15
661 A352	20 l blue	.55	.38
662 A353	50 l orange brn	1.75	.85
	Nos. 658-662 (5)	2.78	1.68

Bulgaria's Five Year Plan.

Grenade and Javelin Throwers A354

Hurdlers A355

Motorcycle and Tractor — A356

Boy and Girl Athletes — A357

1949, Sept. 5

663 A354	4 l brown orange	.30	.15
664 A355	9 l olive green	.60	.22
665 A356	20 l violet blue	1.25	.65
666 A357	50 l red brown	3.00	1.25
	Nos. 663-666 (4)	5.15	2.27

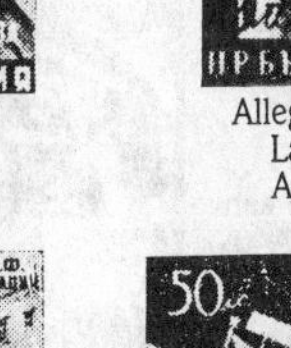

Frontier Guards
A358 A359

1949, Oct. 31

667 A358	4 l chestnut brn	.15	.15
668 A359	20 l gray blue	.60	.26
	Set value		.31

See No. C60.

George Dimitrov A360

Allegory of Labor A361

Laborers of Both Sexes — A362

Workers and Flags of Bulgaria and Russia — A363

Perf. 11½

1949, Dec. 13 Photo. Unwmk.

669 A360	4 l orange brn	.15	.15
670 A361	9 l purple	.18	.15
671 A362	20 l dull blue	.32	.22
672 A363	50 l red	.65	.45
	Nos. 669-672 (4)	1.30	
	Set value		.77

Joseph V. Stalin — A364

Stalin and Dove — A365

1949, Dec. 21

673 A364	4 l deep orange	.20	.15
674 A365	40 l rose brown	.60	.32
	Set value		.37

70th anniv. of the birth of Joseph V. Stalin.

Kharalamby Stoyanov — A366

Communications Strikers — A368

Railway Strikers — A367

1950, Feb. 15

675 A366	4 l yellow brown	.15	.15
676 A367	20 l violet blue	.22	.15
677 A368	60 l brown olive	.60	.38
	Nos. 675-677 (3)	.97	
	Set value		.50

30th anniv. (in 1949) of the General Railway and Postal Employees' Strike of 1919.

Miner — A369

Locomotive — A370

Shipbuilding A371

Tractor A372

Stalin Central Heating Plant — A374

Textile Worker — A375

Farm Machinery A373

1950-51 *Perf. 11½, 13*

678	A369	1 l olive	.15	.15
679	A370	2 l gray blk	.15	.15
680	A371	3 l gray blue	.20	.15
681	A372	4 l dk blue grn	1.75	.52
682	A373	5 l henna brn	.40	.15
682A	A373	9 l gray blk ('51)	.20	.15
683	A374	10 l dp plum ('51)	.28	.15
684	A375	15 l dk car ('51)	.40	.15
685	A375	20 l dk blue ('51)	.70	.40
		Nos. 678-685 (9)	4.23	
		Set value		1.30

No. 685 is inscribed in Latin characters. See Nos. 750-751A.

Vassil Kolarov (1877-1950) — A377

1950, Mar. 6 *Perf. 11½*

Size: 21½x31½mm

686 A377	4 l red brown	.15	.15

Size: 27x39½mm

687 A377	20 l violet blue	.26	.22
	Set value	.31	.27

No. 687 has altered frame and is inscribed in Latin characters.

Stanislav Dospevski, Self-portrait A378

King Kaloyan and Desislava A379

Plowman Resting, by Christo Stanchev A380

Statue of Dimtcho Debelianov, by Ivan Lazarov A381

"Harvest," by V. Dimitrov A382

Design: 9 l, Nikolai Pavlovich, self-portrait.

1950, Apr. 15 *Perf. 11½*

688 A378	1 l dk olive grn	.32	.15
689 A379	4 l dk red	.90	.22
690 A378	9 l chocolate	.90	.22
691 A380	15 l brown	1.50	.25
692 A380	20 l deep blue	2.00	.80
693 A381	40 l red brown	2.75	1.25
694 A382	60 l deep orange	4.00	1.65
	Nos. 688-694 (7)	12.37	4.54

Latin characters on No. 692.

Ivan Vazov (1850-1921), Poet and Birthplace A383

1950, June 26

695 A383	4 l olive green	.15	.15

Road Building — A384

Men of Three Races and "Stalin" Flag — A385

Perf. 11½x11, 11x11½

1950, Sept. 19

696	A384	4 l brown red	.15	.15
697	A385	20 l violet blue	.32	.16
		Set value	.40	.21

2nd National Peace Conference.

Molotov, Kolarov, Stalin and Dimitrov — A386

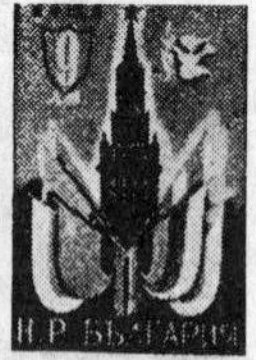
Spasski Tower and Flags — A387

Russian and Bulgarian Women — A388

Loading Russian Ship — A389

Perf. 11½

1950, Oct. 10 Unwmk. Photo.

698	A386	4 l brown	.15	.15
699	A387	9 l rose carmine	.15	.15
700	A388	20 l gray blue	.20	.15
701	A389	50 l dk grnsh blue	1.10	.45
		Nos. 698-701 (4)	1.60	
		Set value		.67

2nd anniversary of the Soviet-Bulgarian treaty of mutual assistance.

St. Constantine Sanatorium — A390

Designs: 2 l, 10 l, Children at seashore. 5 l, Rest home.

1950 Typo.

702	A390	1 l dark green	.15	.15
703	A390	2 l carmine	.15	.15
704	A390	5 l deep orange	.16	.15
705	A390	10 l deep blue	.42	.22
		Set value	.75	.42

Originally prepared in 1945 as "Sunday Delivery Stamps," this issue was released for ordinary postage in 1950.

Runners — A393

1950, Aug. 21 Photo. *Perf. 11*

706	A393	4 l shown	.15	.15
707	A393	9 l Cycling	.15	.15
708	A393	20 l Shot put	.20	.20
709	A393	40 l Volleyball	.42	.42
		Nos. 706-709 (4)	.92	.92

Marshal Fedor I. Tolbukhin A394

Natives Greeting Tolbukhin A395

Perf. 11½x11, 11x11½

1950, Dec. 10 Photo. Unwmk.

710	A394	4 l claret	.15	.15
711	A395	20 l dk blue	.35	.18
		Set value		.24

The return of Dobrich and part of the province of Dobruja from Romania to Bulgaria.

Dimitrov's Birthplace A396

George Dimitrov
A397 A398

Various Portraits, Inscribed:

Г.ДИМИТРОВ

Design: 2 l, Dimitrov Museum, Sofia.

1950, July 2 *Perf. 10½*

712	A396	50s olive grn	.15	.15
713	A397	50s brown	.15	.15
714	A397	1 l redsh brn	.22	.15
715	A396	2 l gray	.22	.15
716	A397	4 l claret	.40	.15
717	A397	9 l red brown	.60	.25
718	A398	10 l brown red	.65	.35
719	A397	15 l olive gray	.65	.35
720	A396	20 l dark blue	1.75	.55
		Nos. 712-720,C61 (10)	7.79	
		Set value		2.90

1st anniversary of the death of George Dimitrov, statesman. No. 720 is inscribed in Latin characters.

A. S. Popov — A400

1951, Feb. 10

722	A400	4 l red brown	.20	.15
723	A400	20 l dark blue	.55	.15
		Set value		.24

No. 723 is inscribed in Latin characters.

Arms of Bulgaria
A401 A402

1950 Unwmk. Typo. *Perf. 13*

724	A401	2 l dk brown	.15	.15
725	A401	3 l rose	.15	.15
726	A402	5 l carmine	.15	.15
727	A402	9 l aqua	.15	.15
		Set value	.31	.20

Nos. 724-727 were prepared in 1947 for official use but were issued as regular postage stamps Oct. 1, 1950.

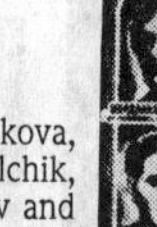

Heroes Chankova, Antonov-Malchik, Dimitrov and Dimitrova — A403

Stanke Dimitrov-Marek A404

George Kirkov A405

George Dimitrov at Leipzig — A406

Natcho Ivanov and Avr. Stoyanov — A407

Portraits: 9 l, Anton Ivanov. 15 l, Christo Michailov.

1951, Mar. 25 Photo. *Perf. 11½*

728	A403	1 l red violet	.15	.15
729	A404	2 l dk red brn	.15	.15
730	A405	4 l car rose	.15	.15
731	A405	9 l orange brn	.45	.15
732	A405	15 l olive brn	.80	.22
733	A406	20 l dark blue	1.10	.55
734	A407	50 l olive gray	2.50	.90
		Nos. 728-734 (7)	5.30	2.27

First Bulgarian Tractor A408

First Steam Roller — A409

First Truck — A410

Bulgarian Embroidery — A411

Designs: 15 l, Carpet. 20 l, Tobacco and roses. 40 l, Fruits.

Perf. 11x10½

1951, Mar. 30 Photo. Unwmk.

735	A408	1 l olive brn	.18	.15
736	A409	2 l violet	.28	.15
737	A410	4 l red brown	.50	.15
738	A411	9 l purple	.70	.15
739	A409	15 l deep plum	1.00	.28
740	A411	20 l violet blue	1.50	.32
741	A410	40 l deep green	2.50	.65

Perf. 13

Size: 23x18½mm

742	A408	1 l purple	.15	.15
743	A409	2 l Prus green	.28	.15
744	A410	4 l red brown	.28	.15
		Nos. 735-744 (10)	7.37	
		Set value		1.70

See Nos. 894, 973. For surcharge see No. 973.

Turkish Attack on Mt. Zlee Dol A412

Designs: 4 l, Georgi Benkovski speaking to rebels. 9 l, Cherrywood cannon of 1876 and Russian cavalry, 1945. 20 l, Rebel, 1876 and partisan, 1944. 40 l, Benkovski and Dimitrov.

1951, May 3 *Perf. 10½*

Cream Paper

745	A412	1 l redsh brown	.16	.15
746	A412	4 l dark green	.16	.15
747	A412	9 l violet brown	.50	.28
748	A412	20 l deep blue	.65	.48
749	A412	40 l dark red	1.00	.70
		Nos. 745-749 (5)	2.47	1.76

75th anniv. of the "April" revolution.

Industrial Types of 1950

1951 *Perf. 13*

750	A369	1 l violet	.15	.15
751	A370	2 l dk brown	.15	.15
751A	A372	4 l dk yel grn	.75	.15
		Nos. 750-751A (3)	1.05	
		Set value		.17

Demeter Blagoev Addressing 1891 Congress at Busludja — A413

1951 Photo. *Perf. 11*

752	A413	1 l purple	.24	.15
753	A413	4 l dark green	.35	.15
754	A413	9 l deep claret	.60	.32
		Nos. 752-754 (3)	1.19	
		Set value		.50

60th anniversary of the first Congress of the Bulgarian Social-Democratic Party.

See Nos. 1174-1176.

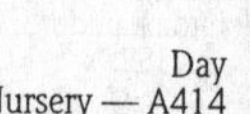

Day Nursery — A414

Designs: 4 l, Model building construction. 9 l, Playground. 20 l, Children's town.

1951, Oct. 10 Unwmk.

755	A414	1 l brown	.15	.15
756	A414	4 l deep plum	.20	.15
757	A414	9 l blue green	.60	.22
758	A414	20 l deep blue	1.00	.55
		Nos. 755-758 (4)	1.95	1.07

Children's Day, Sept. 25, 1951.

Order of Labor
A415 A416

1952, Feb. 1 *Perf. 13*

Reverse of Medal

759	A415	1 l red brown	.15	.15
760	A415	4 l blue green	.15	.15
761	A415	9 l dark blue	.28	.15

Obverse of Medal

762 A416 1 l carmine .15 .15
763 A416 4 l green .15 .15
764 A416 9 l purple .28 .15
Set value .85 .32

No. 764 has numeral at lower left and different background.

Workers and Symbols of Industry — A417

Design: 4 l, Flags, Dimitrov, Chervenkov.

1951, Dec. 29 *Perf. 11*
Inscribed: "16 XII 1951"

765 A417 1 l olive black .15 .15
766 A417 4 l chocolate .16 .15
Set value .25 .15

Third Congress of Bulgarian General Workers' Professional Union.

Dimitrov and Chemical Works — A418

George Dimitrov and V. Chervenkov A419

Portrait: 80s, Dimitrov.

Unwmk.
1952, June 18 **Photo.** *Perf. 11*

767 A418 16s brown .35 .22
768 A419 44s brown carmine .52 .25
769 A418 80s brt blue 1.10 .52
Nos. 767-769 (3) 1.97 .99

70th anniv. of the birth of George Dimitrov.

Vassil Kolarov Dam — A420

Republika Power Station — A421

1952, May 16 *Perf. 13*

770 A420 4s dark green .15 .15
771 A420 12s purple .15 .15
772 A420 16s red brown .15 .15
773 A420 44s rose brown .50 .15
774 A420 80s brt blue 1.65 .18
Nos. 770-774 (5) 2.60
Set value .40

No. 774 is inscribed in Latin characters.

1952, June 30 *Perf. 13, Pin Perf.*

775 A421 16s dark brown .20 .15
776 A421 44s magenta .75 .15
Set value .20

Nikolai I. Vapzarov — A422

Designs: Various portraits.

1952, July 23 *Perf. 10½*

777 A422 16s rose brown .16 .15
778 A422 44s dk red brn .65 .16
779 A422 80s dk olive brn 1.40 .52
Nos. 777-779 (3) 2.21 .83

10th anniversary of the death of Nikolai I. Vapzarov, poet and revolutionary.

Dimitrov and Youth Conference — A423

Designs: 16s, Resistance movement incident. 44s, Frontier guards and industrial scene. 80s, George Dimitrov and young workers.

1952, Sept. 1 *Perf. 11x11½*

780 A423 2s brown carmine .15 .15
781 A423 16s purple .20 .15
782 A423 44s dark green .52 .28
783 A423 80s dark brown 1.10 .60
Nos. 780-783 (4) 1.97 1.18

40th anniv. of the founding conference of the Union of Social Democratic Youth.

Assault on the Winter Palace — A424

Designs: 8s, Volga-Don Canal. 16s, Symbols of world peace. 44s, Lenin and Stalin. 80s, Himlay hydroelectric station.

Perf. 11½
1952, Nov. 6 **Unwmk.** **Photo.**
Dated: "1917-1952"

784 A424 4s red brown .15 .15
785 A424 8s dark green .15 .15
786 A424 16s dark blue .15 .15
787 A424 44s brown .32 .18
788 A424 80s olive brown .75 .35
Nos. 784-788 (5) 1.52
Set value .70

35th anniv. of the Russian revolution.

Vassil Levski — A425

Design: 44s, Levski and comrades.

1953, Feb. 19 **Cream Paper** *Perf. 11*

789 A425 16s brown .15 .15
790 A425 44s brown blk .25 .15
Set value .15

80th anniv. of the death of Levski, patriot.

Ferrying Artillery and Troops into Battle A426

Soldier A427

Mother and Children A428

Designs: 44s, Victorious soldiers. 80s, Soldier welcomed. 1 l, Monuments.

1953, Mar. 3 *Perf. 10½*

791 A426 8s Prus green .16 .15
792 A427 16s dp brown .22 .15
793 A426 44s dk slate grn .42 .15
794 A426 80s dull red brn .85 .20
795 A426 1 l black 1.10 .32
Nos. 791-795 (5) 2.75
Set value .70

75th anniversary of Bulgaria's independence from Turkey.

1953, Mar. 9

796 A428 16s slate green .15 .15
797 A428 16s bright blue .15 .15
Set value .25 .15

Women's Day.

Woodcarvings at Rila Monastery
A429 A430

Designs: 12s, 16s, 28s, Woodcarvings, Rila Monastery. 44s, Carved Ceilings, Trnovo. 80s, 1 l, 4 l, Carvings, Pasardjik.

1953 **Unwmk.** **Photo.** *Perf. 13*

798 A429 2s gray brown .15 .15
799 A430 8s dk slate grn .15 .15
800 A430 12s brown .15 .15
801 A430 16s rose lake .24 .15
802 A429 28s dk olive grn .32 .15
803 A430 44s dk brown .50 .15
804 A430 80s ultra .85 .15
805 A430 1 l violet blue 1.75 .22
806 A430 4 l rose lake 3.50 .90
Nos. 798-806 (9) 7.61
Set value 1.55

Karl Marx A431

"Das Kapital" A432

1953, Apr. 30 *Perf. 10½*

807 A431 16s bright blue .15 .15
808 A432 44s deep brown .32 .18
Set value .25

70th anniversary of the death of Karl Marx.

Labor Day Parade — A433

Joseph V. Stalin — A434

1953, Apr. 30 *Perf. 13*

809 A433 16s brown red .15 .15

Labor Day, May 1, 1953.

1953, May 23 *Perf. 13x13½*

810 A434 16s dark gray .20 .15
811 A434 16s dark brown .20 .15
Set value .15

Death of Joseph V. Stalin, Mar. 5, 1953.

Georgi Delchev — A435

Battle Scene — A436

Peasants Attacking Turkish Troops — A437

1953, Aug. 8 *Perf. 13*

812 A435 16s dark brown .15 .15
813 A436 44s purple .30 .15
814 A437 1 l deep claret .45 .16
Nos. 812-814 (3) .90
Set value .35

50th anniv. of the Ilinden Revolt (#812, 814) and the Preobrazhene Revolt (#813).

Soldier and Rebels — A438

Design: 44s, Soldier guarding industrial construction.

1953, Sept. 18

815 A438 16s deep claret .15 .15
816 A438 44s greenish blue .35 .15
Set value .17

Army Day.

George Dimitrov and Vassil Kolarov — A439

Demeter Blagoev — A440

Designs: 16s, Citizens in revolt. 44s, Attack.

1953, Sept. 22

817 A439 8s olive gray .15 .15
818 A439 16s dk red brn .18 .15
819 A439 44s cerise .45 .18
Nos. 817-819 (3) .78
Set value .28

September Revolution, 30th anniversary.

1953, Sept. 21

Portraits: 44s, G. Dimitrov and D. Blagoev.

820 A440 16s brown .25 .15
821 A440 44s red brown .38 .15
Set value .17

50th anniversary of the formation of the Social Democratic Party.

Railway Viaduct — A441

Pouring Molten Metal — A442

Designs: 16s, Welder and storage tanks. 80s, Harvesting machine.

1953, Oct. 17

826 A441 8s brt blue .15 .15
827 A441 16s grnsh blk .15 .15
828 A442 44s brown red .28 .15
829 A441 80s orange .45 .28
Nos. 826-829 (4) 1.03
Set value .50

Month of Bulgarian-Russian friendship.

Belladonna
A443

Kolarov Library, Sofia
A444

Medicinal Flowers: 4s, Jimson weed. 8s, Sage. 12s, Dog rose. 16s, Gentian. 20s, Poppy. 28s, Peppermint. 40s, Bear grass. 44s, Coltsfoot. 80s, Cowslip. 1 l, Dandelion. 2 l, Foxglove.

1953 Unwmk. Photo. *Perf. 13*

White or Cream Paper

830 A443 2s dull blue .15 .15
831 A443 4s brown org .15 .15
832 A443 8s blue grn .15 .15
833 A443 12s brown org .15 .15
834 A443 12s blue grn .15 .15
835 A443 16s violet blue .15 .15
836 A443 16s dp red brn .15 .15
837 A443 20s car rose .15 .15
838 A443 28s dk gray grn .30 .15
839 A443 40s dark blue .35 .18
840 A443 44s brown .35 .18
841 A443 80s yellow brn .60 .35
842 A443 1 l henna brn 2.25 .48
843 A443 2 l purple 3.75 1.25
a. Souvenir sheet 27.50 20.00
Nos. 830-843 (14) 8.80
Set value 2.95

No. 843a contains 12 stamps, one of each denomination above, printed in dark green. Size: 161x172mm. Sold for 6 leva.

1953, Dec. 16

854 A444 44s brown .25 .15

75th anniversary of the founding of the Kolarov Library, Sofia.

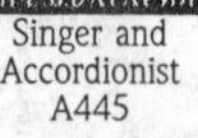

Singer and Accordionist
A445

Lenin and Stalin
A446

1953, Dec. 26

855 A445 16s shown .15 .15
856 A445 44s Dancers .18 .15
Set value .25 .17

1954, Mar. 13

Designs: 44s, Lenin statue. 80s, Lenin mausoleum, Moscow. 1 l, Lenin.

Cream Paper

857 A446 16s brown .20 .15
858 A446 44s rose brown .26 .15
859 A446 80s blue .42 .15
860 A446 1 l dp olive grn .60 .26
Nos. 857-860 (4) 1.48
Set value .50

30th anniversary of the death of Lenin.

Demeter Blagoev and Followers
A447

Design: 44s, Blagoev at desk.

1954, Apr. 28

Cream Paper

861 A447 16s dp red brn .15 .15
862 A447 44s black brn .32 .15
Set value .15

30th anniv. of the death of Demeter Blagoev.

George Dimitrov
A448

Dimitrov and Refinery
A449

1954, June 11

863 A448 44s lake, *cream* .22 .15
864 A449 80s brown, *cream* .65 .15
Set value .15

5th anniv. of the death of George Dimitrov.

Train Leaving Tunnel — A450

1954, July 30

865 A450 44s dk grn, *cream* .60 .15
866 A450 44s blk brn, *cream* .60 .15
Set value .20

Day of the Railroads, Aug. 1, 1954.

Miner at Work — A451

1954, Aug. 19

867 A451 44s grnsh blk, *cream* .20 .15

Miners' Day.

Academy of Science — A452

1954, Oct. 27

868 A452 80s black, *cream* .55 .18

85th anniversary of the foundation of the Bulgarian Academy of Science.

Horsemanship
A454

16s, 44s, 2 l, vert.

1954, Dec. 21

869 A454 16s Gymnastics .52 .16
870 A454 44s Wrestling .60 .20
871 A454 80s shown 1.25 .55
872 A454 2 l Skiing 3.00 1.65
Nos. 869-872 (4) 5.37 2.56

Welcoming Liberators — A455

Soldier's Return — A456

Designs: 28s, Refinery. 44s, Dimitrov and Workers. 80s, Girl and boy. 1 l, George Dimitrov.

1954, Oct. 4

Cream Paper

873 A455 12s brown car .15 .15
874 A456 16s dp carmine .15 .15
875 A455 28s indigo .15 .15
876 A455 44s redsh brn .15 .15
877 A456 80s deep blue .55 .25
878 A456 1 l dark green .55 .25
Set value 1.40 .70

10th anniversary of Bulgaria's liberation.

Recreation at Workers' Rest Home — A457

Metal Worker and Furnace — A458

Portraits: 80s, Dimitrov, Blagoev, and Kirkov.

Unwmk.

1954, Dec. 28 Photo. *Perf. 13*

Cream Paper

879 A457 16s dark green .16 .15
880 A458 44s brown orange .16 .15
881 A457 80s dp violet blue .42 .20
Nos. 879-881 (3) .74
Set value .30

50th anniversary of Bulgaria's trade union movement.

Geese — A459

Designs: 4s, Chickens. 12s, Hogs. 16s, Sheep. 28s, Telephone building. 44s, Communist party headquarters. 80s, Apartment buildings. 1 l, St. Kiradgieff Mills.

1955-56

882 A459 2s dk blue grn .16 .15
883 A459 4s olive green .28 .15
884 A459 12s dk red brn .42 .15
885 A459 16s brown orange .65 .15
886 A459 28s violet blue .32 .15
887 A459 44s lil red, *cream* .60 .15
a. 44s brown red 4.50 .15
888 A459 80s dk red brown .75 .15
889 A459 1 l dk blue green 1.50 .16
Nos. 882-889 (8) 4.68
Set value .56

Issued: #887, 4/20/56; others, 2/19/55.

Textile Worker — A460

Mother and Child — A461

Design: 16s, Woman feeding calf.

1955, Mar. 5

890 A460 12s dark brown .15 .15
891 A460 16s dark green .15 .15
892 A461 44s dk car rose .50 .15
893 A461 44s blue .50 .15
Nos. 890-893 (4) 1.30
Set value .26

Women's Day, Mar. 8, 1955.

No. 744 Surcharged in Blue

1955, Mar. 8 *Perf. 13*

894 A410 16s on 4 l red brown .45 .15

May Day Demonstration of Workers
A462

Sts. Cyril and Methodius
A463

Design: 44s, Three workers and globe.

1955, Apr. 23 Photo.

895 A462 16s car rose .15 .15
896 A462 44s blue .30 .15
Set value .15

Labor Day, May 1, 1955.

1955, May 21

Designs: 8s, Paisii Hilendarski. 16s, Nicolas Karastoyanov's printing press. 28s, Christo Botev. 44s, Ivan Vazov. 80s, Demeter Blagoev and socialist papers. 2 l, Blagoev printing plant, Sofia.

Cream Paper

897 A463 4s deep blue .15 .15
898 A463 8s olive .15 .15
899 A463 16s black .15 .15
900 A463 28s henna brn .16 .15
901 A463 44s brown .32 .15
902 A463 80s rose red .50 .16
903 A463 2 l black 1.50 .42
Nos. 897-903 (7) 2.93
Set value .80

Creation of the Cyrillic alphabet, 1100th anniv. Latin lettering at bottom on #901-903.

Sergei Rumyantzev
A464

Mother and Children
A465

Portraits: 16s, Christo Jassenov. 44s, Geo Milev.

1955, June 30 Unwmk. *Perf. 13*

Cream Paper

904 A464 12s orange brn .16 .15
905 A464 16s lt brown .16 .15
906 A464 44s grnsh blk .42 .15
Nos. 904-906 (3) .74
Set value .24

30th anniv. of the deaths of Sergei Rumyanchev, Christo Jassenov and Geo Milev. Latin lettering at bottom of No. 906.

1955, July 30

907 A465 44s brn car, *cream* .30 .15

World Congress of Mothers in Lausanne, 1955.

Young People of Three Races — A466

Friedrich Engels and Book — A467

1955, July 30

908 A466 44s blue, *cream* .30 .15

5th World Festival of Youth in Warsaw, July 31-Aug. 14.

1955, July 30

909 A467 44s brown .30 .15

60th anniv. of the death of Friedrich Engels.

Entrance to Fair, 1892 — A468

Statuary Group at Fair, 1955 — A469

Designs: 44s, "Fruit of our Land." 80s, Woman holding Fair emblem.

1955, Aug. 31

Cream Paper

910 A468	4s deep brown	.15	.15
911 A469	16s dk car rose	.15	.15
912 A468	44s olive blk	.20	.15
913 A469	80s deep blue	.45	.15
	Set value	.80	.32

16th International Plovdiv Fair. Latin lettering on Nos. 912-913.

Friedrich von Schiller — A470

Portraits: 44s, Adam Mickiewicz. 60s, Hans Christian Andersen. 80s, Baron de Montesquieu. 1 l, Miguel de Cervantes. 2 l, Walt Whitman.

1955, Oct. 31

Cream Paper

914 A470	16s brown	.15	.15
915 A470	44s brown red	.38	.15
916 A470	60s Prus blue	.60	.15
917 A470	80s black	.60	.15
918 A470	1 l rose violet	1.40	.32
919 A470	2 l olive green	1.90	.50
	Nos. 914-919 (6)	5.03	
	Set value		1.05

Various anniversaries of famous writers. Nos. 918 and 919 are issued in sheets alternating with labels without franking value. The labels show title pages for Leaves of Grass and Don Quixote in English and Spanish, respectively. Latin lettering on #915-919.

Karl Marx Industrial Plant — A471

Friendship Monument — A472

I. V. Michurin — A473

Designs: 4s, Alekandr Stamboliski Dam. 16s, Bridge over Danube. 1 l, Vladimir V. Mayakovsky.

1955, Dec. 1 **Unwmk.**

920 A471	2s slate blk	.15	.15
921 A471	4s deep blue	.15	.15
922 A471	16s dk blue grn	.15	.15
923 A472	44s red brown	.15	.15
924 A473	80s dark green	.25	.15
925 A473	1 l gray blk	.38	.15
	Set value	.90	.45

Russian-Bulgarian friendship.

Library Seal — A474

Krusto Pishurka — A475

Portrait: 44s, Bacho Kiro.

1956, Feb. 10 ***Perf. 11x10½***

926 A474	12s car lake, *cream*	.15	.15
927 A475	16s dp brn, *cream*	.15	.15
928 A475	44s slate blk, *cream*	.22	.15
	Set value	.33	.17

100th anniversary of the National Library. Latin lettering at bottom of No. 928.

Canceled to Order

Beginning about 1956, some issues were sold in sheets canceled to order. Values in second column when much less than unused are for "CTO" copies. Postally used stamps are valued at slightly less than, or the same as, unused.

Quinces — A476

Cherrywood Cannon — A477

Designs: 8s, Pears. 16s, Apples. 44s, Grapes.

1956 **Photo.** ***Perf. 13***

929 A476	4s carmine	.75	.15
930 A476	8s blue green	.32	.15
931 A476	16s lilac rose	.80	.15
932 A476	44s deep violet	.80	.16
	Nos. 929-932 (4)	2.67	
	Set value		.32

Latin lettering on #932. See #964-967. For surcharge see #1364.

1956, Apr. 28 ***Perf. 11x10½***

933 A477	16s shown	.15	.15
934 A477	44s Cavalry attack	.22	.15
	Set value		.15

April Uprising against Turkish rule, 80th anniv.

Demeter Blagoev (1856-1924), Writer, Birthplace A478

Cherries A479

1956, May 30 ***Perf. 11***

935 A478	44s Prus blue	.25	.15

1956 **Unwmk.** ***Perf. 13***

936 A479	2s shown	.15	.15
937 A479	12s Plums	.15	.15
938 A479	28s Peaches	.18	.15
939 A479	80s Strawberries	.55	.20
	Nos. 936-939 (4)	1.03	
	Set value		.35

Latin lettering on No. 939.

Gymnastics A480

Pole Vaulting A481

Designs: 12s, Discus throw. 44s, Soccer, 80s, Basketball. 1 l, Boxing.

Perf. 11x10½, 10½x11

1956, Aug. 29

940 A480	4s brt ultra	.15	.15
941 A480	12s brick red	.15	.15
942 A481	16s yellow brn	.32	.16
943 A481	44s dark green	.48	.25
944 A480	80s dark red brn	1.00	.50
945 A481	1 l deep magenta	1.65	.65
	Nos. 940-945 (6)	3.75	1.86

Latin lettering on Nos. 943-945.

16th Olympic Games at Melbourne, Nov. 22-Dec. 8, 1956.

Tobacco, Rose and Distillery A482

People's Theater A483

1956, Sept. 1 ***Perf. 13***

946 A482	44s deep carmine	.38	.16
947 A482	44s olive green	.38	.16

17th International Plovdiv Fair.

1956, Nov. 16 **Unwmk.**

Design: 44s, Dobri Woinikoff and Sawa Dobroplodni, dramatists.

948 A483	16s dull red brown	.15	.15
949 A483	44s dark blue green	.22	.15
	Set value		.15

Bulgarian Theater centenary.

Benjamin Franklin A484

Cyclists, Palms and Pyramids A485

Portraits: 20s, Rembrandt. 40s, Mozart. 44s, Heinrich Heine. 60s, Shaw. 80s, Dostoevski. 1 l, Ibsen. 2 l, Pierre Curie.

1956, Dec. 29

950 A484	16s dark olive grn	.15	.15
951 A484	20s brown	.18	.15
952 A484	40s dark car rose	.18	.15
953 A484	44s dark violet brn	.22	.15
954 A484	60s dark slate	.32	.15
955 A484	80s dark brown	.45	.15
956 A484	1 l bluish grn	.80	.30
957 A484	2 l Prus green	1.75	.52
	Nos. 950-957 (8)	4.05	
	Set value		1.20

Great personalities of the world.

1957, Mar. 6 **Photo.** ***Perf. 10½***

958 A485	80s henna brown	.50	.25
959 A485	80s Prus green	.50	.25

Fourth Egyptian bicycle race.

Woman Technician — A486

"New Times" Review — A487

Designs: 16s, Woman and children. 44s, Woman feeding chickens.

1957, Mar. 8

960 A486	12s deep blue	.15	.15
961 A486	16s henna brown	.15	.15
962 A486	44s slate green	.30	.15
	Set value	.40	.17

Women's Day. Latin lettering on 44s.

1957, Mar. 8 **Unwmk.**

963 A487	16s deep carmine	.20	.15

60th anniversary of the founding of the "New Times" review.

Fruit Type of 1956.

Designs: 4s, Quinces. 8s, Pears. 16s, Apples. 44s, Grapes.

1957 **Photo.** ***Perf. 13***

964 A476	4s yellow green	.15	.15
965 A476	8s brown orange	.15	.15
966 A476	16s rose red	.15	.15
967 A476	44s orange yellow	.40	.15
	Set value	.62	.35

Latin lettering on #967. For surcharge see #1364.

Sts. Cyril and Methodius A488

Basketball A489

1957, May 22 ***Perf. 11***

968 A488	44s olive grn & buff	.50	.15

Centenary of the first public veneration of Sts. Cyril and Methodius, inventors of the Cyrillic alphabet.

1957, June 20 **Photo.** ***Perf. 10½x11***

969 A489	44s dark green	.95	.30

10th European Basketball Championship at Sofia.

Dancer and Spasski Tower, Moscow — A490

1957, July 18 ***Perf. 13***

970 A490	44s blue	.30	.15

Sixth World Youth Festival in Moscow.

George Dimitrov (1882-1949) — A491

1957, July 18

971 A491	44s deep carmine	.50	.15

Vassil Levski — A492

1957, July 18 ***Perf. 11***

972 A492	44s grnsh black	.30	.15

120th anniversary of the birth of Vassil Levski, patriot and national hero.

No. 742 Surcharged in Carmine

1957 **Unwmk.** ***Perf. 13***

973 A408	16s on 1 l purple	.15	.15

Trnovo and Lazarus L. Zamenhof A493

1957, July 27

974 A493	44s slate green	.50	.15

50th anniv. of the Bulgarian Esperanto Society and the 70th anniv. of Esperanto.

For surcharge see No. 1235.

Bulgarian Veteran of 1877 War and Russian Soldier — A494

Design: 44s, Battle of Shipka Pass.

1957, Aug. 13

975 A494 16s dk blue grn .15 .15
976 A494 44s brown .32 .15
Set value .15

80th anniversary of Bulgaria's liberation from the Turks. Latin lettering on No. 976.

Woman Planting Tree — A495

Red Deer in Forest — A496

Designs: 16s, Dam, lake and forest. 44s, Plane over forest. 80s, Fields on edge of forest.

1957, Sept. 16 Photo. *Perf. 13*

977 A495 2s deep green .15 .15
978 A496 12s dark brown .15 .15
979 A496 16s Prus blue .15 .15
980 A496 44s Prus green .22 .15
981 A496 80s yellow green .42 .15
Set value .90 .45

Latin lettering on Nos. 980 and 981.

Lenin — A497

Designs: 16s, Cruiser "Aurora." 44s, Dove over map of communist area. 60s, Revolutionaries and banners. 80s, Oil refinery.

1957, Oct. 29 *Perf. 11*

982 A497 12s chocolate .16 .15
983 A497 16s Prus green .32 .15
984 A497 44s deep blue .65 .15
985 A497 60s dk car rose .75 .15
986 A497 80s dark green 1.25 .22
Nos. 982-986 (5) 3.13
Set value .54

40th anniv. of the Communist Revolution. Latin lettering on Nos. 984-985.

Globes A498

1957, Oct. 4 *Perf. 13*

987 A498 44s Prus blue .30 .15

4th Intl. Trade Union Cong., Leipzig, Oct. 4-15.

Vassil Kolarov Hotel A499

Bulgarian Health Resorts: 4s, Skis and Pirin Mountains. 8s, Old house at Koprivspitsa. 12s, Rest home at Velingrad. 44s, Momin-Prochod Hotel. 60s, Nesebr Hotel, shoreline and peninsula. 80s, Varna beach scene. 1 l, Hotel at Varna.

1958 Photo. *Perf. 13*

988 A499 4s blue .15 .15
989 A499 8s orange brn .15 .15
990 A499 12s dk green .15 .15
991 A499 16s green .15 .15
992 A499 44s dk blue grn .15 .15
993 A499 60s deep blue .18 .15
994 A499 80s fawn .28 .15
995 A499 1 l dk red brn .35 .18
Set value 1.14 .62

Latin lettering on 44s, 60s, 80s, and 1 l.
Issue dates: #991-994, Jan. 20. Others, July 5.
For surcharge see No. 1436.

Mikhail I. Glinka — A500

Portraits: 16s, Jan A. Komensky (Comenius). 40s, Carl von Linné. 44s, William Blake. 60s, Carlo Goldoni. 80s, Auguste Comte.

1957, Dec. 30

996 A500 12s dark brown .20 .15
997 A500 16s dark green .20 .15
998 A500 40s Prus blue .20 .15
999 A500 44s maroon .20 .15
1000 A500 60s orange brown .75 .15
1001 A500 80s deep plum 2.50 .90
Nos. 996-1001 (6) 4.05
Set value 1.25

Famous men of other countries. Latin lettering on Nos. 999-1001.

Young Couple, Flag, Dimitrov A501

People's Front Salute A502

1957, Dec. 28 *Perf. 11*

1002 A501 16s carmine rose .15 .15

10th anniversary of Dimitrov's Union of the People's Youth.

1957, Dec. 28

1003 A502 16s dk violet brn .15 .15

15th anniversary of the People's Front.

Hare — A503

Animals: 12s, Red deer (doe), vert. 16s, Red deer (stag). 44s, Chamois. 80s, Brown bear. 1 l, Wild boar.

Perf. 10½

1958, Apr. 5 Unwmk. Photo.

1004 A503 2s lt & dk ol grn .15 .15
1005 A503 12s sl grn & red brn .18 .15
1006 A503 16s bluish grn & dk red brn .20 .15
1007 A503 44s blue & brown .24 .15
1008 A503 80s bis & dk brn .75 .25
1009 A503 1 l stl bl & dk brn 1.00 .22
Nos. 1004-1009 (6) 2.52
Set value .55

Value, imperf. set $4.

Marx and Lenin A504

Designs: 16s, Marchers and flags. 44s, Lenin blast furnaces.

1958, July 2 *Perf. 11*

1010 A504 12s dark brown .16 .15
1011 A504 16s dark carmine .20 .15
1012 A504 44s dark blue .85 .15
Nos. 1010-1012 (3) 1.21
Set value .20

Bulgarian Communist Party, 7th Congress.

Wrestlers — A505

1958, June 20 *Perf. 10½*

1013 A505 60s dk carmine rose .65 .35
1014 A505 80s deep brown 1.10 .55

World Wrestling Championship, Sofia.

Chessmen and Globe A506

Perf. 10½

1958, July 18 Unwmk. Photo.

1015 A506 80s grn & yel grn 2.50 .80

5th World Students' Chess Games, Varna.

Conference Emblem A507

1958, Sept. 24

1016 A507 44s blue .40 .15

World Trade Union Conference of Working Youth, Prague, July 14-20.

Swimmer A508

1958 Students' Games: 28s, Dancer, vert. 44s, Volleyball, vert.

1958, Sept. 19 *Perf. 11x10½*

1017 A508 16s brt blue .15 .15
1018 A508 28s brown orange .22 .15
1019 A508 44s brt green .30 .15
Nos. 1017-1019 (3) .67
Set value .35

Onions — A509

Vegetables: 12s, Garlic. 16s, Peppers. 44s, Tomatoes. 80s, Cucumbers. 1 l, Eggplant.

1958, Sept. 20 *Perf. 13*

1020 A509 2s orange brown .15 .15
1021 A509 12s Prus blue .15 .15
1022 A509 16s dark green .15 .15
1023 A509 44s deep carmine .16 .15
1024 A509 80s deep green .40 .15
1025 A509 1 l brt purple .60 .15
Nos. 1020-1025 (6) 1.61
Set value .38

See No. 1072. Value, imperf. set $4.

Plovdiv Fair Building A510

1958, Sept. 14 Unwmk. *Perf. 11*

1026 A510 44s deep carmine .40 .15

18th International Plovdiv Fair.

Attack — A511

Design: 44s, Fighter dragging wounded man.

1958, Sept. 23 Photo. *Perf. 11*

1027 A511 16s orange ver .15 .15
1028 A511 44s lake .35 .15
Set value .15

35th anniv. of the September Revolution.

Emblem, Brussels Fair — A512

1958, Oct. 13 *Perf. 11*

1029 A512 1 l blk & brt blue 5.00 1.25

Brussels World's Fair, Apr. 17-Oct. 19.
Exists imperf.

Runner at Finish Line — A513

Woman Throwing Javelin A514

Sports: 60s, High jumper. 80s, Hurdler. 4 l, Shot putter.

1958, Nov. 30

1030 A513 16s red brn, *pnksh* .40 .15
1031 A514 44s olive, *yelsh* .40 .15
1032 A514 60s dk bl, *bluish* .75 .20
1033 A514 80s dp grn, *grnsh* 1.00 .20
1034 A513 4 l dp rose cl, *pnksh* 6.25 1.40
Nos. 1030-1034 (5) 7.70 2.10

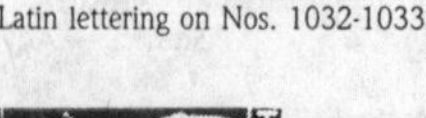

1958 Balkan Games.
Latin lettering on Nos. 1032-1033.

Christo Smirnenski — A515

1958, Dec. 22

1035 A515 16s dark carmine .15 .15

Christo Smirnenski (1898-1923), poet.

Girls Harvesting — A516

Girl Tending Calves A517

Designs: 16s, Boy and girl laborers. 40s, Boy pushing wheelbarrow. 44s, Headquarters building.

1959, Nov. 29 **Photo.**

1036 A516 8s dk olive green .15 .15
1037 A517 12s redsh brown .15 .15
1038 A516 16s violet brown .15 .15
1039 A517 40s Prus blue .15 .15
1040 A516 44s deep carmine .60 .15
Set value .95 .34

4th Congress of Dimitrov's Union of People's Youth.

UNESCO Building, Paris A518

1959, Mar. 28 **Unwmk.** ***Perf. 11***

1041 A518 2 l dp red lilac, *cream* 1.25 1.00

Opening of UNESCO Headquarters, Paris, Nov. 3, 1958. Value imperf. $2.50

Skier — A519

Soccer Players — A520

1959, Mar. 28 ***Perf. 11***

1042 A519 1 l blue, *cream* .90 .50

Forty years of skiing in Bulgaria.

1959, Mar. 25

1043 A520 2 l chestnut, *cream* 1.25 .65

1959 European Youth Soccer Championship.

Russian Soldiers Installing Telegraph Wires — A521

First Bulgarian Postal Coach A522

Designs: 60s, Stamp of 1879. 80s, First Bulgarian automobile. 1 l, Television tower. 2 l, Strike of railroad and postal workers, 1919.

1959, May 4

1044 A521 12s dk grn & cit .15 .15
1045 A522 16s deep plum .15 .15
1046 A521 60s dk brn & yel .32 .15
1047 A522 80s hn brn & sal .45 .15
1048 A521 1 l blue .60 .16
1049 A522 2 l dk red brown 1.65 .80
Nos. 1044-1049 (6) 3.32
Set value 1.25

80th anniv. of the Bulgarian post. Latin lettering on Nos. 1046-1049.

Two imperf. souvenir sheets exist with olive borders and inscriptions. One contains one copy of No. 1046 in black & ocher, and measures 92x121mm. The other sheet contains one copy each of Nos. 1044-1045 and 1047-1048 in changed colors: 12s, olive green & ocher; 16s, deep claret & ocher; 80s, dark red & ocher; 1 l, olive & ocher. Each sheet sold for 5 leva. Value, each $22.50.

Great Tits A523

Birds: 8s, Hoopoe. 16s, Great spotted woodpecker, vert. 45s, Gray partridge, vert. 60s, Rock partridge. 80s, European cuckoo.

1959, June 30 **Photo.**

1050 A523 2s olive & sl grn .15 .15
1051 A523 8s dp orange & blk .15 .15
1052 A523 16s chestnut & dk brn .22 .15
1053 A523 45s brown & blk .28 .15
1054 A523 60s dp blue & gray .65 .15
1055 A523 80s dp bl grn & gray 1.10 .18
Nos. 1050-1055 (6) 2.55
Set value .55

Bagpiper — A524

Designs: 12s, Acrobats. 16s, Girls exercising with hoops. 20s, Male dancers. 80s, Ballet dancers. 1 l, Ceramic pitcher. 16s, 20s, 80s are horizontal.

1959, Aug. 29 **Unwmk.** ***Perf. 11***
Surface-colored Paper

1056 A524 4s dk olive .15 .15
1057 A524 12s scarlet .15 .15
1058 A524 16s maroon .15 .15
1059 A524 20s dk blue .25 .15
1060 A524 80s brt green .52 .26
1061 A524 1 l brown org .95 .42
Nos. 1056-1061 (6) 2.17
Set value 1.00

7th International Youth Festival, Vienna. Latin inscriptions on Nos. 1060-1061.

Partisans in Truck A525

Designs: 16s, Partisans and soldiers shaking hands. 45s, Refinery. 60s, Tanks. 80s, Harvester. 1.25 l, Children with flag, vert.

1959, Sept. 8

1062 A525 12s red & Prus grn .15 .15
1063 A525 16s red & dk pur .15 .15
1064 A525 45s red & int bl .15 .15
1065 A525 60s red & ol grn .15 .15
1066 A525 80s red & brn .26 .15
1067 A525 1.25 l red & dp brn .65 .38
Set value 1.20 .75

15th anniversary of Bulgarian liberation.

Soccer A526

1959, Oct. 10 **Unwmk.** ***Perf. 11***

1068 A526 1.25 l dp green, *yel* 3.50 2.00

50 years of Bulgarian soccer.

Set exists imperf. in changed colors. Value $7.50 unused, $4 canceled.

Batak Defenders A527

1959, Aug. 8

1069 A527 16s deep claret .20 .15

300th anniv. of the settlement of Batak.

Post Horn and Letter — A528

Bird-shaped Lyre — A529

Design: 1.25 l, Dove and letter.

1959, Nov. 23

1070 A528 45s emerald & blk .30 .15
1071 A528 1.25 l lt blue, red & blk .50 .20
Set value .27

Intl. Letter Writing Week Oct. 5-11.

Type of 1958 Surcharged "45 CT." in Dark Blue

Design: Tomatoes.

1959 **Photo.** ***Perf. 13***

1072 A509 45s on 44s scarlet .55 .15

1960, Feb. 23 **Unwmk.** ***Perf. 10½***

1073 A529 80s shown .40 .15
1074 A529 1.25 l Lyre .70 .18
Set value .27

50th anniv. of Bulgaria's State Opera.

N. I. Vapzarov — A530

Parachute and Radio Tower — A531

1959, Dec. 14 ***Perf. 11***

1075 A530 80s yel grn & red brn .35 .15

Vapzarov, poet and patriot, 50th birth anniv.

1959, Dec. 3 **Photo.**

1076 A531 1.25 l dp grnsh bl & yel 1.25 .45

3rd Cong. of Voluntary Participants in Defense.

Cotton Picker — A532

Harvester Combine — A533

Designs: 2s, Kindergarten. 4s, Woman doctor and child. 10s, Woman milking cow. 12s, Woman holding tobacco leaves. 15s, Woman working loom. 16s, Stalin textile mill, Dimitrovgrad. 25s, Rural electrification. 28s, Woman picking sunflowers. 40s, "Cold-well" hydroelectric dam. 45s, Miner. 60s, Foundry worker. 80s. Woman harvesting grapes. 1 l, Worker and peasant with cogwheel. 1.25 l, Industrial worker. 2 l, Party leader.

1959-61 **Photo.** ***Perf. 13***

1077 A533 2s brown org ('60) .15 .15
1077A A532 4s gldn brn ('61) .15 .15
1078 A532 5s dk green .15 .15
1079 A533 10s red brn ('61) .15 .15
1080 A532 12s red brown .15 .15
1081 A532 15s red lil ('60) .15 .15
1082 A533 16s dp vio ('60) .15 .15
1083 A533 20s orange .15 .15
1084 A532 25s brt blue ('60) .15 .15
1085 A532 28s brt green .18 .15
1086 A533 40s brt grnsh bl .30 .15
1087 A532 45s choc ('60) .22 .15
1088 A533 60s scarlet .42 .15
1089 A532 80s ol ('60) .50 .15
1090 A532 1 l maroon .50 .15
1090A A533 1.25 l dull bl ('61) 1.75 .30
1091 A532 2 l dp car ('60) 1.10 .22
Nos. 1077-1091 (17) 6.32
Set value 1.25

Early completion of the 5-year plan (in 1959).

L. L. Zamenhof — A534

Path of Lunik 3 — A535

1959, Dec. 5 **Unwmk.** ***Perf. 11***

1092 A534 1.25 l dk grn & yel grn .75 .38

Lazarus Ludwig Zamenhof (1859-1917), inventor of Esperanto.

1960, Mar. 28 ***Perf. 11***

1093 A535 1.25 l Prus bl & brt yel 3.50 1.90

Flight of Lunik 3 around moon. Value, imperf. $5

Skier A536

1960, Apr. 15 **Litho.**

1094 A536 2 l ultra, blk & brn .95 .35

8th Winter Olympics, Squaw Valley, CA, Feb. 18-29. Value, imperf. $2 unused, $1 canceled.

Vela Blagoeva — A537

Portraits: 28s, Anna Maimunkova. 45s, Vela Piskova. 60s, Rosa Luxemburg. 80s, Klara Zetkin. 1.25 l, N. K. Krupskaya.

1960, Apr. 27 **Photo.** ***Perf. 11***

1095 A537 16s rose & red brn .15 .15
1096 A537 28s citron & olive .15 .15
1097 A537 45s ol grn & sl grn .20 .15
1098 A537 60s lt bl & Prus bl .20 .15
1099 A537 80s red org & dp brn .35 .15
1100 A537 1.25 l dull yel & olive .60 .18
Nos. 1095-1100 (6) 1.65
Set value .50

International Women's Day, Mar. 8, 1960.

Lenin — A538

1960, May 12

1101 A538 16s shown .50 .15
1102 A538 45s Lenin sitting 1.10 .16

90th anniversary of the birth of Lenin.

A539

A541

1960, June 3 — *Perf. 11*

1103 A539 1.25 l yel & slate grn .85 .35

Seventh European Women's Basketball championships.

1960, June 29 — **Litho.**

1105 A541 16s Parachutist .55 .30
1106 A541 1.25 l Parachutes 1.50 .45

5th International Parachute Championships.

Yellow Gentian — A542

Flowers: 5s, Tulips. 25s, Turk's-cap lily. 45s, Rhododendron. 60s, Lady's-slipper. 80s, Violets.

1960, July 27 — **Photo.** — *Perf. 11*

1107 A542 2s beige, grn & yel .15 .15
1108 A542 5s yel grn, grn & car rose .15 .15
1109 A542 25s pink, grn & org .20 .15
1110 A542 45s pale lil, grn & rose lil .35 .15
1111 A542 60s yel, grn & org .75 .15
1112 A542 80s gray, grn & vio bl .90 .22
Nos. 1107-1112 (6) 2.50
Set value .55

Soccer A543

Sports: 12s, Wrestling. 16s, Weight lifting. 45s, Woman gymnast. 80s, Canoeing. 2 l, Runner.

1960, Aug. 29 — **Unwmk.** — *Perf. 11*

Athletes' Figures in Pink

1113 A543 8s brown .15 .15
1114 A543 12s violet .15 .15
1115 A543 16s Prus blue .15 .15
1116 A543 45s deep plum .18 .15
1117 A543 80s blue .30 .15
1118 A543 2 l deep green 1.25 .35
Set value 2.00 .75

17th Olympic Games, Rome, Aug. 25-Sept. 11.
Value, set imperf. in changed colors, $3.50.

Globes A544

Unwmk.

1960, Oct. 12 — **Photo.** — *Perf. 11*

1125 A544 1.25 l blue & ultra .50 .20

15th anniversary of the World Federation of Trade Unions.

Alexander Popov — A545

1960, Oct. 12

1126 A545 90s blue & blk .75 .15

Centenary of the birth of Alexander Popov, radio pioneer.

Bicyclists A546

1960, Sept. 22

1127 A546 1 l yel, red org & blk .90 .45

The 10th Tour of Bulgaria Bicycle Race.

Jaroslav Vésin — A547

1960, Nov. 22 — **Unwmk.** — *Perf. 11*

1128 A547 1 l brt cit & ol grn 2.75 .65

Birth centenary of Jaroslav Vesin, painter.

UN Headquarters A548

Costume of Kyustendil A549

1961, Jan. 14 — **Photo.** — *Perf. 11*

1129 A548 1 l brown & yel 1.00 .45
a. Souvenir sheet 4.00 2.75

15th anniv. of the UN. #1129 sold for 2 l.
Value, imperf. $3.50.
No. 1129a sold for 2.50 l and contains one copy of No. 1129, imperf, in dark olive and pink.

1961, Jan. 28

Designs (Regional Costumes): 16s, Pleven. 28s, Sliven. 45s, Sofia. 60s, Rhodope. 80s, Karnobat.

1130 A549 12s sal, sl grn & yel .15 .15
1131 A549 16s pale lil, brn vio & buff .15 .15
1132 A549 28s pale grn, sl grn & rose .15 .15
1133 A549 45s blue & red .30 .15
1134 A549 60s grnsh bl, Prus bl & yel .48 .15
1135 A549 80s yel, sl grn & pink .60 .26
Nos. 1130-1135 (6) 1.83
Set value .60

Theodor Tiro (Fresco) A550

Designs: 60s, Boyana Church. 1.25 l, Duchess of Dessislava (fresco).

1961, Jan. 28 — **Photo.**

1136 A550 60s yel grn, blk & grn .50 .15
1137 A550 80s yel, sl grn & org .50 .15
1138 A550 1.25 l yel grn, hn brn & buff 1.00 .22
Nos. 1136-1138 (3) 2.00
Set value .40

700th anniv. of murals in Boyana Church.

Clock Tower, Vratsa — A551

Wooden Jug — A552

Designs: 12s, Clock tower, Bansko. 20s, Anguchev House, Mogilitsa. 28s, Oslekov House, Koprivspitsa, horiz. 40s, Pasha's house. Melnik, horiz. 45s, Lion sculpture. 60s, Man on horseback, Madara. 80s, Fresco, Bratchkovo monastery. 1 l, Tsar Assen coin.

1961, Feb. 25 — **Unwmk.** — *Perf. 11*

Denomination and Stars in Vermilion

1139 A551 8s olive grn .15 .15
1140 A551 12s lt violet .15 .15
1141 A552 16s dk red brn .15 .15
1142 A551 20s brt blue .15 .15
1143 A551 28s grnsh blue .15 .15
1144 A551 40s red brown .15 .15
1145 A552 45s olive gray .16 .15
1146 A552 60s slate .32 .15
1147 A552 80s dk olive gray .55 .15
1148 A552 1 l green .70 .16
Set value 2.25 .65

Capercaillie — A553

Birds: 4s, Dalmatian pelican. 16s, Ringnecked pheasant. 80s, Great bustard. 1 l, Lammergeier. 2 l, Hazel hen.

1961, Mar. 31

1149 A553 2s blk, sal & Prus grn .15 .15
1150 A553 4s blk, yel grn & org .15 .15
1151 A553 16s brn, lt grn & org .15 .15
1152 A553 80s brn, bluish grn & yel .35 .15
1153 A553 1 l blk, lt bl & yel .65 .15
1154 A553 2 l brn, bl & yel 1.65 .55
Nos. 1149-1153 (5) 1.45
Set value 1.00

Radio Tower and Winged Anchor — A554

1961, Apr. 1 — **Unwmk.** — *Perf. 11*

1155 A554 80s brt green & blk .45 .20

50th anniv. of the Transport Workers' Union.

T. G. Shevchenko — A555

Water Polo — A556

1961, Apr. 27

1156 A555 1 l olive & blk 2.50 .65

Centenary of the death of Taras G. Shevchenko, Ukrainian poet.

1961, May 15

Designs: 5s, Tennis. 16s, Fencing. 45s, Throwing the discus. 1.25 l, Sports Palace. 2 l, Basketball. 5 l, Sports Palace, different view. 5s, 16s, 45s and 1.25 l, are horizontal.

Black Inscriptions

1157 A556 4s lt ultra .15 .15
1158 A556 5s orange ver .15 .15
1159 A556 16s olive grn .15 .15
1160 A556 45s dull blue .15 .15
1161 A556 1.25 l yellow brn .60 .18
1162 A556 2 l lilac .85 .40
Nos. 1157-1162 (6) 2.05
Set value .75

Souvenir Sheet

Imperf

1163 A556 5 l yel grn, dl bl & yel 7.50 6.50

1961 World University Games, Sofia, Aug. 26-Sept. 3.
Value, Nos. 1157-1162 in changed colors, imperf. $4.50.

Monk Seal A557

Black Sea Fauna: 12s, Jellyfish. 16s, Dolphin. 45s, Black Sea sea horse, vert. 1 l, Starred sturgeon. 1.25 l, Thornback ray.

1961, June 19 — *Perf. 11*

1164 A557 2s green & blk .15 .15
1165 A557 12s Prus grn & pink .15 .15
1166 A557 16s ultra & vio bl .15 .15
1167 A557 45s lt blue & brn .28 .15
1168 A557 1 l yel grn & Prus grn .65 .20
1169 A557 1.25 l lt vio bl & red brn 1.10 .35
Nos. 1164-1169 (6) 2.48
Set value .90

Hikers — A558

Designs: 4s, "Sredetz" hostel, horiz. 16s, Tents. 1.25 l, Mountain climber.

1961, Aug. 25 — **Litho.** — *Perf. 11*

1170 A558 4s yel grn, yel & blk .15 .15
1171 A558 12s lt bl, cr & blk .15 .15
1172 A558 16s green, cr & blk .15 .15
1173 A558 1.25 l bister, cr & blk .45 .15
Set value .65 .30

"Know Your Country" campaign.

Demeter Blagoev Addressing 1891 Congress at Busludja — A559

1961, Aug. 5 — **Photo.**

1174 A559 45s dk red & buff .20 .15
1175 A559 80s blue & pink .30 .15
1176 A559 2 l dk brn & pale citron .75 .25
Nos. 1174-1176 (3) 1.25 .55

70th anniversary of the first Congress of the Bulgarian Social-Democratic Party.

The Golden Girl — A560

Fairy Tales: 8s, The Living Water. 12s, The Golden Apple. 16s, Krali-Marko, hero. 45s, Samovila-Vila, Witch. 80s, Tom Thumb.

1961, Oct. 10 — **Unwmk.** — *Perf. 11*

1177 A560 2s blue, blk & org .18 .15
1178 A560 8s rose lil, blk & gray .24 .15
1179 A560 12s bl grn, blk & pink .24 .15
1180 A560 16s red, blk, bl & gray .38 .15
1181 A560 45s ol grn, blk & pink .75 .22
1182 A560 80s ocher, blk & dk car 1.10 .28
Nos. 1177-1182 (6) 2.89
Set value .80

Caesar's Mushroom A561 — Miladinov Brothers and Title Page A562

Designs: Various mushrooms.

1961, Dec. 20 — Photo. — *Perf. 11*

Denominations in Black

1183 A561 2s lemon & red .15 .15
1184 A561 4s ol grn & red brn .15 .15
1185 A561 12s bister & red brn .15 .15
1186 A561 16s lilac & red brn .15 .15
1187 A561 45s car rose & yel .15 .15
1188 A561 80s brn org & sep .18 .15
1189 A561 1.25 l vio & dk brn .40 .18
1190 A561 2 l org brn & brn .70 .40
Set value 1.55 1.00

Value, denomination in dark grn, imperf. set $5 unused, $1.75 canceled.

1961, Dec. 21 — Unwmk. — *Perf. 10½*

1191 A562 1.25 l olive & blk .60 .20

Centenary of the publication of "Collected Folk-songs" by the Brothers Miladinov, Dimitri and Konstantin.

Nos. 1079-1085, 1087, 992, 1023, 1090-1091 and 806 Surcharged with New Value in Black, Red or Violet

1962, Jan. 1

1192 A533 1s on 10s red brown .15 .15
1193 A532 1s on 12s red brown .15 .15
1194 A532 2s on 15s red lilac .15 .15
1195 A533 2s on 16s dp vio (R) .15 .15
1196 A533 2s on 20s orange .15 .15
a. "2 CT." on 2 lines .15 .15
1197 A532 3s on 25s brt bl (R) .15 .15
a. Black surcharge 7.00 4.00
1198 A532 3s on 28s brt grn (R) .15 .15
1199 A532 5s on 45s chocolate .15 .15
1200 A499 5s on 44s dk bl grn (R) .15 .15
1201 A509 5s on 44s dp car (V) .15 .15
1202 A532 10s on 1 l maroon .25 .15
1203 A532 20s on 2 l dp car .70 .22
1204 A430 40s on 4 l rose lake (V) 1.50 .48
Nos. 1192-1204 (13) 3.95
Set value 1.30

Freighter "Varna" A563

Designs: 5s, Tanker "Komsomoletz." 20s, Liner "G. Dimitrov."

1962, Mar. 1 — Photo. — *Perf. 10½*

1205 A563 1s lt grn & brt bl .15 .15
1206 A563 5s lt blue & grn .18 .15
1207 A563 20s gray bl & grnsh bl .70 .16
Nos. 1205-1207 (3) 1.03
Set value .26

Dimitrov Working as Printer — A564 — Roses — A565

Design: 13s, Griffin, emblem of state printing works.

1962, Mar. 19 — Unwmk.

1208 A564 2s ver, blk & yel .15 .15
1209 A564 13s red org, blk & yel .42 .15
Set value .50 .15

80th anniversary (in 1961) of the George Dimitrov state printing works.

1962, Mar. 28

Various Roses in Natural Colors

1210 A565 1s deep violet .15 .15
1211 A565 2s salmon & dk car .15 .15
1212 A565 3s gray & car .15 .15
1213 A565 4s dark green .16 .15
1214 A565 5s ultra .22 .15
1215 A565 6s bluish grn & dk car .48 .15
1216 A565 8s citron & car 1.10 .18
1217 A565 13s blue 2.25 .60
Nos. 1210-1217 (8) 4.66
Set value 1.15

For overprint and surcharges see Nos. 1281-1283.

Malaria Eradication Emblem and Mosquito A566

Design: 20s, Malaria eradication emblem.

1962, Apr. 19

1218 A566 5s org brn, yel & blk .40 .15
1219 A566 20s emerald, yel & blk .85 .35

WHO drive to eradicate malaria.
Value, imperf. $2.50 unused, $1.50 canceled.

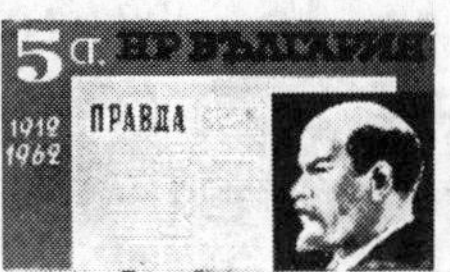

Lenin and First Issue of Pravda A567

1962, May 4 — Unwmk. — *Perf. 10*

1220 A567 5s deep rose & slate .50 .15

50th anniversary of Pravda, Russian newspaper founded by Lenin.

Blackboard and Book — A568

1962, May 21 — Photo.

1221 A568 5s Prus bl, blk & yel .25 .15

The 1962 Teachers' Congress.

Soccer Player and Globe — A569

1962, May 26 — *Perf. 10½*

1222 A569 13s brt grn, blk & lt brn .65 .25

World Soccer Championship, Chile, May 30-June 17. Value, imperf. in changed colors, $2.50 unused, $1.65 canceled.

George Dimitrov A570

1962, June 18 — Photo.

1223 A570 2s dark green .20 .15
1224 A570 5s turq blue .40 .15
Set value .15

80th anniv. of the birth of George Dimitrov (1882-1949), communist leader and premier of the Bulgarian Peoples' Republic.

Bishop — A571

1962, July 7 — Unwmk. — *Perf. 10½*

1225 A571 1s shown .15 .15
1226 A571 2s Rook .15 .15
1227 A571 3s Queen .15 .15
1228 A571 13s Knight .65 .22
1229 A571 20s Pawn 1.10 .42
Nos. 1225-1229 (5) 2.20
Set value .95

15th Chess Olympics, Varna. Nos. 1225-1229 were also issued imperf. in changed colors.

An imperf. souvenir sheet contains one 20s horizontal stamp showing five chessmen. Size: 75x66mm.

Rila Mountain A572

Designs: 2s, Pirin mountain. 6s, Nesebr, Black Sea. 8s, Danube. 13s, Vidin Castle. 1 l, Rhodope mountain.

1962-63 — *Perf. 13*

1230 A572 1s dk blue grn .15 .15
1231 A572 2s blue .15 .15
1232 A572 6s grnsh blue .15 .15
1233 A572 8c lilac .16 .15
1234 A572 13s yellow grn .38 .15
1234A A572 1 l dp green ('63) 3.25 .30
Nos. 1230-1234A (6) 4.24
Set value .58

No. 974 Surcharged in Red

XXXV КОНГРЕС
1962

13 =

1962, July 14 — *Perf. 13*

1235 A493 13s on 44s slate grn 2.25 .80

25th Bulgarian Esperanto Congress, Burgas, July 14-16.

Girl and Festival Emblem A573

Design: 5s, Festival emblem.

1962, Aug. 18 — Photo. — *Perf. 10½*

1236 A573 5s green, lt bl & pink .20 .15
1237 A573 13s lilac, lt bl & gray .35 .15
Set value .15

8th Youth Festival for Peace and Friendship, Helsinki, July 28-Aug. 6, 1962.

Parnassius Apollo A574

1962, Sept. 13

Various Butterflies in Natural Colors

1238 A574 1s pale cit & dk grn .15 .15
1239 A574 2s rose & brown .15 .15
1240 A574 3s buff & red brn .15 .15
1241 A574 4s gray & brown .15 .15
1242 A574 5s lt gray & brn .16 .15
1243 A574 6s gray & black .18 .15
1244 A574 10s pale grn & blk 1.25 .25
1245 A574 13s buff & red brn 1.90 .40
Nos. 1238-1245 (8) 4.09
Set value 1.00

Planting Machine A575

Designs: 2s, Electric locomotive. 3s, Blast furnace. 13s, Blagoev and Dimitrov and Communist flag.

1962, Nov. 1 — *Perf. 11½*

1246 A575 1s bl grn & dk ol grn .15 .15
1247 A575 2s bl & Prus bl .15 .15
1248 A575 3s carmine & brn .18 .15
1249 A575 13s plum, red & blk .55 .20
Nos. 1246-1249 (4) 1.03
Set value .45

Bulgarian Communist Party, 8th Congress.

Title Page of "Slav-Bulgarian History" — A576

Paisii Hilendarski Writing History — A577

1962, Dec. 8 — Unwmk. — *Perf. 10½*

1250 A576 2s olive grn & blk .15 .15
1251 A577 5s brown org & blk .15 .15
Set value .25 .20

200th anniv. of "Slav-Bulgarian History."

Aleco Konstantinov (1863-1897), Writer — A578

1963, Mar. 5 — Photo. — *Perf. 11½*

1252 A578 5s red, grn & blk .25 .15

Printed with alternating red brown and black label showing Bai Ganu, hero from Konstantinov's books.

A579 — Sofia University — A580

Designs: No. 1255, Levski Stadium, Sofia. No. 1256, Arch, Nissaria. No. 1257, Parachutist.

1963, Feb. 20 — Unwmk. — *Perf. 10*

1253 A579 1s brown red .15 .15
1254 A580 1s red brown .15 .15
1255 A580 1s blue green .15 .15
1256 A580 1s dark green .15 .15
1257 A580 1s brt blue .15 .15
Set value .25 .25

Vassil Levski — A581

Boy, Girl and Dimitrov — A582

1963, Apr. 11 Photo.

1258 A581 13s grnsh blue & buff .75 .25

90th anniversary of the death of Vassil Levski, revolutionary leader in the fight for liberation from the Turks.

1963, Apr. 25 Unwmk. *Perf. 11½*

Design: 13s, Girl with book and boy with hammer.

1259 A582 2s org, ver, red brn & blk .15 .15
1260 A582 13s bluish grn, brn & blk .42 .15
Set value .20

10th Congress of Dimitrov's Union of the People's Youth.

Red Squirrel — A583

Sun Coast Promenade — A584

Animals: 2s, Hedgehog. 3s, European polecat. 5s, Pine marten. 13s, Badger. 20s, Otter. 2s, 3s, 13s, horiz.

1963, Apr. 30

Red Numerals

1261 A583 1s grn & brn, *grnsh* .15 .15
1262 A583 2s grn & blk, *yel* .15 .15
1263 A583 3s grn & brn, *bis* .15 .15
1264 A583 5s vio & red brn, *lil* .20 .15
1265 A583 13s red brn & blk, *pink* .80 .16
1266 A583 20s blk & brn, *blue* 1.25 .20
Nos. 1261-1266 (6) 2.70
Set value .60

1963, Mar. 12 Unwmk. *Perf. 13*

Black Sea Resorts: 2s, 3s, 13s, Views of Gold Sand. 5s, 20s, Sun Coast.

1267 A584 1s blue .15 .15
1268 A584 2s vermilion .26 .15
1269 A584 2s car rose .38 .15
1270 A584 3s ocher .18 .15
1271 A584 5s lilac .18 .15
1272 A584 13s blue green .52 .15
1273 A584 20s green .95 .20
Nos. 1267-1273 (7) 2.62
Set value .53

Freestyle Wrestling — A585

Design: 20s, Freestyle wrestling, horiz.

1963, May 31 *Perf. 11½*

1274 A585 5s yel bister & blk .16 .15
1275 A585 20s org brn & blk .80 .18
Set value .24

15th International Freestyle Wrestling Competitions, Sofia.

"Women for Peace" A586

1963, June 24 Unwmk. *Perf. 11½*

1276 A586 20s blue & blk .60 .15

World Congress of Women, Moscow, June 24-29.

Esperanto Emblem and Arms of Sofia — A587

Moon, Earth and Lunik 4 — A588

1963, June 29 Photo.

1277 A587 13s multicolored .60 .15

48th World Esperanto Congress, Sofia, Aug. 3-10.

1963, July 22

Designs: 2s, Radar equipment. 3s, Satellites and moon.

1278 A588 1s ultra .15 .15
1279 A588 2s red lilac .15 .15
1280 A588 3s greenish blue .15 .15
Set value .25 .15

Russia's rocket to the moon, Apr. 2, 1963.

MOSTRA EUROPEISTICA·1963
13
RICCIONE

Nos. 1211-1212 and 1215 Overprinted or Surcharged in Green, Ultramarine or Black

1963, Aug. 31 *Perf. 10½*

1281 A565 2s (G) .25 .15
1282 A565 5s on 3s (U) .38 .15
1283 A565 13s on 6s .70 .22
Nos. 1281-1283 (3) 1.33
Set value .40

Intl. Stamp Fair, Riccione, Aug. 31.

Women's Relay Race A589

Designs: 2s, Hammer thrower. 3s, Women's long jump. 5s, Men's high jump. 13s, Discus thrower.

Perf. 11½

1963, Sept. 13 Photo. Unwmk.

Flags in National Colors

1284 A589 1s slate green .15 .15
1285 A589 2s purple .15 .15
1286 A589 3s Prus blue .16 .15
1287 A589 5s maroon .45 .30
1288 A589 13s chestnut brn 1.65 1.25
Nos. 1284-1288 (5) 2.56 2.00

Balkan Games. A multicolored, 50s, imperf. souvenir sheet shows design of women's relay race. Size: 74x70mm.

"Slav-Bulgarian History" — A590

1963, Sept. 19 *Perf. 10½*

1289 A590 5s sal pink, slate & yel .20 .15

5th International Slavic Congress.

Revolutionists A591

Christo Smirnenski A592

1963, Sept. 22 *Perf. 11½*

1290 A591 2s brt red & blk .15 .15

40th anniversary of the September Revolution.

1963, Oct. 28 *Perf. 10½*

1291 A592 13s pale lilac & indigo .45 .15

Christo Smirnenski, poet, 65th birth anniv.

Columbine A593

Horses A594

1963, Oct. 9 Photo. *Perf. 11½*

1292 A593 1s shown .15 .15
1293 A593 2s Edelweiss .15 .15
1294 A593 3s Primrose .15 .15
1295 A593 5s Water lily .15 .15
1296 A593 6s Tulips .16 .15
1297 A593 8s Larkspur .30 .15
1298 A593 10s Alpine clematis .70 .16
1299 A593 13s Anemone 1.25 .25
Nos. 1292-1299 (8) 3.01
Set value .90

1963, Dec. 28 Unwmk. *Perf. 10½*

Designs: 2s, Charioteer and chariot. 3s, Trumpeters. 5s, Woman carrying tray with food. 13s, Man holding bowl. 20s, Woman in armchair. Designs are from a Thracian tomb at Kazanlik.

1300 A594 1s gray, org & dk red .15 .15
1301 A594 2s gray, ocher & pur .15 .15
1302 A594 3s gray, dl yel & sl grn .15 .15
1303 A594 5s pale grn, ocher & brn .15 .15
1304 A594 13s pale grn, bis & blk .42 .15
1305 A594 20s pale grn, org & dk car .75 .30
Set value 1.50 .75

World Map and Emblem A595

Designs: 2s, Blood transfusion. 3s, Nurse bandaging injured wrist. 5s, Red Cross nurse. 13s, Henri Dunant.

1964, Jan. 27 *Perf. 10½*

1306 A595 1s lem, blk & red .15 .15
1307 A595 2s ultra, blk & red .15 .15
1308 A595 3s gray, sl, blk & red .15 .15
1309 A595 5s brt bl, blk & red .15 .15
1310 A595 13s org yel, blk & red .42 .15
Set value .80 .32

Centenary of International Red Cross.

Speed Skating A596

Sports: 2s, 50s, Women's figure skating. 3s, Cross-country skiing. 5s, Ski jump. 10s, Ice hockey goalkeeper. 13s, Ice hockey players.

1964, Feb. 21 Unwmk. *Perf. 10½*

1311 A596 1s grnsh bl, ind & ocher .15 .15
1312 A596 2s brt pink, ol grn & dk sl grn .15 .15
1313 A596 3s dl grn, dk grn & brn .15 .15
1314 A596 5s bl, blk & yel brn .18 .15
1315 A596 10s gray, org & blk .40 .18
1316 A596 13s lil, blk & lil rose .70 .28
Nos. 1311-1316 (6) 1.73
Set value .60

Miniature Sheet

Imperf

1317 A596 50s gray, Prus grn & pink 3.75 3.00

9th Winter Olympic Games, Innsbruck, Jan. 29-Feb. 9, 1964.

Mask of Nobleman, 2nd Century — A597

Designs: 2s, Thracian horseman. 3s, Ceramic jug. 5s, Clasp and belt. 6s, Copper kettle. 8s, Angel. 10s, Lioness. 13s, Scrub woman, contemporary sculpture.

1964, Mar. 14 Photo. *Perf. 10½*

Gray Frame

1318 A597 1s dp green & red .15 .15
1319 A597 2s ol gray & red .15 .15
1320 A597 3s bister & red .15 .15
1321 A597 5s indigo & red .16 .15
1322 A597 6s org brn & red .22 .15
1323 A597 8s brn red & red .38 .15
1324 A597 10s olive & red .42 .15
1325 A597 13s gray ol & red .65 .22
Nos. 1318-1325 (8) 2.28
Set value .75

2,500 years of Bulgarian art.

"The Unborn Maid" A598

Fairy Tales: 2s, Grandfather's Glove. 3s, The Big Turnip. 5s, The Wolf and the Seven Kids. 8s, Cunning Peter. 13s, The Wheat Cake.

1964, Apr. 17 Unwmk. *Perf. 10½*

1326 A598 1s bl grn, red & org brn .15 .15
1327 A598 2s ultra, ocher & blk .15 .15
1328 A598 3s cit, red & blk .15 .15
1329 A598 5s dp rose, brn & blk .15 .15
1330 A598 8s yel grn, red & blk .20 .15
1331 A598 13s lt vio bl, grn & blk .70 .18
Set value 1.25 .46

Ascalaphus Otomanus A599

Insects: 2s, Nemoptera coa., vert. 3s, Saga natalia (grasshopper). 5s, Rosalia alpina, vert. 13s, Anisoplia austriaca, vert. 20s, Scolia flavitrons.

1964, May 16 Photo. *Perf. 11½*

1332 A599 1s brn org, yel & blk .15 .15
1333 A599 2s dl bl grn, bis & blk .15 .15
1334 A599 3s gray, grn & blk .15 .15
1335 A599 5s lt ol grn, blk & vio .15 .15
1336 A599 13s vio, bis & blk .55 .16
1337 A599 20s gray bl, yel & blk .85 .28
Nos. 1332-1337 (6) 2.00
Set value .75

Soccer — A600

Designs: 13s, Women's volleyball. 60s, Map of Europe and European Women's Volleyball Championship Cup (rectangular, size: 60x69mm).

1964, June 8 Unwmk. *Perf. 11½*

1338 A600 2s bl, dk bl, ocher & red .15 .15
1339 A600 13s bl, dk bl, ocher & red .52 .22
Set value .30

Miniature Sheet

Imperf

1340 A600 60s ultra, ocher, red & gray 3.00 2.25

Levski Physical Culture Assoc., 50th anniv.

Peter Beron and Title Page of Primer A601

1964, June 22 *Perf. 11½*

1341 A601 20s red brn & dk brn, *grysh* 1.00 .60

140th anniversary of the publication of the first Bulgarian primer.

Robert Stephenson's "Rocket" Locomotive, 1825 — A602

Designs: 2s, Modern steam locomotive. 3s, Diesel locomotive. 5s, Electric locomotive. 8s, Freight train on bridge. 13s, Diesel locomotive and tunnel.

1964, July 1 Photo. *Perf. 11½*

1342 A602 2s multicolored .15 .15
1343 A602 2s multicolored .15 .15
1344 A602 3s multicolored .15 .15
1345 A602 5s multicolored .15 .15
1346 A602 8s multicolored .32 .15
1347 A602 13s multicolored .80 .20
Nos. 1342-1347 (6) 1.72
Set value .50

German Shepherd A603

1964, Aug. 22 Photo.

1348 A603 1s shown .15 .15
1349 A603 2s Setter .15 .15
1350 A603 3s Poodle .15 .15
1351 A603 4s Pomeranian .16 .15
1352 A603 5s St. Bernard .20 .15
1353 A603 6s Terrier .26 .15
1354 A603 10s Pointer 1.40 .22
1355 A603 13s Dachshund 2.75 .42
Nos. 1348-1355 (8) 5.22
Set value .90

Partisans — A604

Designs: 2s, People welcoming Soviet army. 3s, Russian aid to Bulgaria. 4s, Blast furnace, Kremikovski. 5s, Combine. 6s, Peace demonstration. 8s, Sentry. 13s, Demeter Blagoev and George Dimitrov.

1964, Sept. 9 Unwmk. *Perf. 11½*

Flag in Red

1356 A604 1s lt & dp ultra .15 .15
1357 A604 2s ol bis & dp ol .15 .15
1358 A604 3s rose lil & mar .15 .15
1359 A604 4s lt vio & vio .15 .15
1360 A604 5s org & red brn .15 .15
1361 A604 6s bl & dp bl .15 .15
1362 A604 8s lt grn & grn .20 .15
1363 A604 13s fawn & red brn .42 .15
Set value 1.00 .50

20th anniv. of People's Government of Bulgaria.

ММ панаир
ПЛОВДИВ - 1964
ST 20

No. 967 Surcharged

1964, Sept. 13 *Perf. 13*

1364 A476 20s on 44s org yel 1.00 .35

International Plovdiv Fair.

Gymnast on Parallel Bars A606

Vratcata Mountain Road A607

Sports: 2s, Long jump. 3s, Woman diver. 5s, Soccer. 13s, Women's volleyball. 20s, Wrestling.

1964, Oct. 10 *Perf. 11½*

1366 A606 1s pale grn, grn & red .15 .15
1367 A606 2s pale vio, vio bl & red .15 .15
1368 A606 3s bl grn, brn & red .15 .15
1369 A606 5s pink, pur & red .16 .15
1370 A606 13s bl, Prus grn & red .52 .15
1371 A606 20s yel, grn & red .90 .22
Set value 1.75 .60

18th Olympic Games, Tokyo, Oct. 10-25. See No. B27.

1964, Oct. 26 Photo. *Perf. 12½x13*

Bulgarian Views: 2s, Ritlite mountain road. 3s, Pines, Malovica peak. 4s, Pobitite rocks. 5s, Erkupria. 6s, Rhodope mountain road.

1372 A607 1s dk slate grn .15 .15
1373 A607 2s brown .15 .15
1374 A607 3s grnsh blue .15 .15
1375 A607 4s dk red brn .15 .15
1376 A607 5s deep green .20 .15
1377 A607 6s blue violet .30 .15
Set value .80 .35

Mail Coach, Plane and Rocket A608

1964, Oct. 3 Unwmk. *Perf. 11½*

1378 A608 20s greenish blue 1.25 .48

First national stamp exhibition, Sofia, Oct. 3-18. Issued in sheets of 12 stamps and 12 labels (woman's head and inscription, 5x5) arranged around one central label showing stylized bird design.

Students Holding Book — A609

1964, Dec. 30 Photo.

1379 A609 13s lt blue & blk .45 .15

8th Intl. Students' Congress, Sofia.

500-Year-Old Walnut Tree at Golemo Drenovo A610

Designs: Various old trees.

1964, Dec. 28

1380 A610 1s blk, buff & cl brn .15 .15
1381 A610 2s blk, pink & dp cl .15 .15
1382 A610 3s blk, yel & dk brn .15 .15
1383 A610 4s blk, lt bl & Prus bl .15 .15
1384 A610 10s blk, pale grn & grn .22 .15
1385 A610 13s blk, pale bis & dk ol grn .42 .15
Set value .84 .42

Soldiers' Monument — A611

1965, Jan. 1 Unwmk.

1386 A611 2s red & black .20 .15

Bulgarian-Soviet friendship.

Olympic Medal Inscribed "Olympic Glory" — A612

1965, Jan. 27 Photo. *Perf. 11½*

1387 A612 20s org brn, gold & blk .60 .16

Bulgarian victories in the 1964 Olympic Games.

"Victory Over Fascism" A613

Design: 13s, "Fight for Peace" (dove and globe).

1965, Apr. 16 *Perf. 11½*

1388 A613 5s gray, blk & ol bis .15 .15
1389 A613 13s gray, blk & blue .26 .16
Set value .21

20th anniv. of victory over Fascism, May 9, 1945.

Vladimir M. Komarov and Section of Globe — A614

Designs: 2s, Konstantin Feoktistov. 5s, Boris B. Yegorov. 13s, Komarov, Feoktistov and Yegorov. 20s, Spaceship Voskhod.

1965, Feb. 15 Photo.

1390 A614 1s pale lil & dk bl .15 .15
1391 A614 2s lt bl, ind & dl vio .15 .15
1392 A614 5s pale grn, grn & ol grn .15 .15
1393 A614 13s pale pink, dp rose & mar .42 .15
1394 A614 20s lt bl, vio bl, grnsh bl & yel .75 .16
Nos. 1390-1394 (5) 1.62
Set value .42

Russian 3-man space flight, Oct. 12-13, 1964.

Imperfs. in changed colors. Four low values se-tenant. Value, set $2 unused, $1 canceled.

Bullfinch — A615

Birds: 2s, European golden oriole. 3s, Common rock thrush. 5s, Barn swallow. 8s, European roller. 10s, European goldfinch. 13s, Rosy pastor starling. 20s, Nightingale.

1965, Apr. 20 Unwmk. *Perf. 11½*

Birds in Natural Colors

1395 A615 1s blue green .15 .15
1396 A615 2s rose lilac .15 .15
1397 A615 3s rose .15 .15
1398 A615 5s brt blue .15 .15
1399 A615 8s citron .32 .15
1400 A615 10s gray 1.10 .15
1401 A615 13s lt vio blue 1.10 .18
1402 A615 20s emerald 2.25 .35
Nos. 1395-1402 (8) 5.37
Set value .88

Black Sea Fish — A616

1965, June 10 Photo. *Perf. 11½*

Gray Frames

1403 A616 1s Sting ray .15 .15
1404 A616 2s Belted bonito .15 .15
1405 A616 3s Hogfish .15 .15
1406 A616 5s Gurnard .18 .15
1407 A616 10s Scad .75 .16
1408 A616 13s Turbot 1.10 .26
Nos. 1403-1408 (6) 2.48
Set value .64

Plane, Bus, Train, Ship and Whale — A617

1965, Apr. 30

1409 A617 13s multicolored .45 .15

4th Intl. Conf. of Transport, Dock and Fishery Workers, Sofia, May 10-14.

ITU Emblem and Communications Symbols — A618

1965, May 17

1410 A618 20s multicolored .65 .30

Centenary of the ITU.

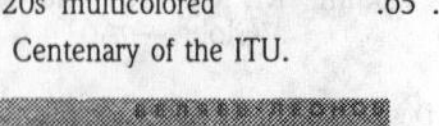

Col. Pavel Belyayev and Lt. Col. Alexei Leonov A619

Design: 20s, Leonov floating in space.

1965, May 20 **Unwmk.**

1411 A619 2s gray, dull bl & dk brn .15 .20
1412 A619 20s multicolored 1.00 .45

Space flight of Voskhod 2 and the first man floating in space, Lt. Col. Alexei Leonov.

ICY Emblem — A620

1965, May 15 **Photo.**

1413 A620 20s orange, olive & blk .65 .15

International Cooperation Year, 1965.

Corn A621

Marx and Lenin A622

1965, Apr. 1 ***Perf. 12½x13***

1414 A621 1s shown .15 .15
1415 A621 2s Wheat .15 .15
1416 A621 3s Sunflowers .15 .15
1417 A621 4s Sugar beet .15 .15
1418 A621 5s Clover .15 .15
1419 A621 10s Cotton .42 .15
1420 A621 13s Tobacco .60 .15
Set value 1.40 .42

1965, June ***Perf. 10½***

1421 A622 13s red & dk brn .65 .15

6th Conference of Postal Ministers of Communist Countries, Peking, June 21-July 15.

Film and UNESCO Emblem A623

1965, June 30

1422 A623 13s dp bl, blk & lt gray .50 .15

Balkan Film Festival, Varna.

Ballerina — A624

1965, July 10 **Photo.**

1423 A624 5s dp lil rose & blk .60 .25

2nd Intl. Ballet Competition, Varna.

Map of Balkan Peninsula and Dove with Letter — A625

Col. Pavel Belyayev and Lt. Col. Alexei Leonov — A626

Designs: 2s, Sailboat and modern buildings. 3s, Fish and plants. 13s, Symbolic sun and rocket. 40s, Map of Balkan Peninsula and dove with letter (like 1s).

1965, July 23-Aug. 7 ***Perf. 10½***

1424 A625 1s sil, dp ultra & yel .15 .15
1425 A625 2s sil, pur & yel .15 .15
1426 A625 3s gold, grn & yel .15 .15
1427 A625 13s gold, hn brn & yel .55 .50
1428 A626 20s sil, bl & brn .70 .55
Nos. 1424-1428 (5) 1.70
Set value 1.25

Miniature Sheet

Imperf

1429 A625 40s gold & brt bl 1.75 1.00

Balkanphila 1965 Philatelic Exhibition, Varna, Aug. 7-15, and visit of Russian astronauts Belyayev and Leonov. The 20s and 40s were issued Aug. 7.

Value, No. 1428 imperf. in changed colors, 90 cents.

Woman Gymnast — A627

Designs: 2s, Woman gymnast on parallel bars. 3s, Weight lifter. 5s, Automobile and chart. 10s, Women basketball players. 13s, Automobile and map of rally.

1965, Aug. 14 ***Perf. 10½***

1430 A627 1s crim, brn & blk .15 .15
1431 A627 2s rose vio, dp cl & blk .15 .15
1432 A627 3s dp car, brn & blk .15 .15
1433 A627 5s fawn, red brn & blk .15 .15
1434 A627 10s dp lil rose, dp cl & blk .52 .15
1435 A627 13s lilac, claret & blk .65 .16
Set value 1.45 .48

Sports events in Bulgaria during May-June, 1965.

No. 989 Surcharged

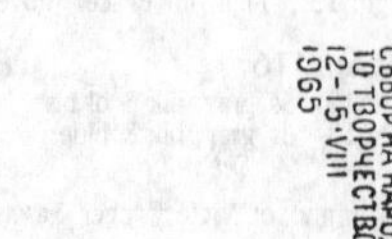

1965, Aug. 12 ***Perf. 13***

1436 A499 2s on 8s orange brn .75 .26

1st Natl. Folklore Competition, Aug. 12-15.

Escaping Prisoners A628

Fruit A629

1965, July 23 ***Perf. 10½***

1437 A628 2s slate .20 .15

40th anniversary of the escape of political prisoners from Bolshevik Island.

1965, July 1 ***Perf. 13***

1438 A629 1s Apples .15 .15
1439 A629 2s Grapes .15 .15
1440 A629 3s Pears .15 .15
1441 A629 4s Peaches .15 .15
1442 A629 5s Strawberries .20 .15
1443 A629 6s Walnuts .32 .15
Set value .75 .34

Horsemanship — A630

1965, Sept. 30 **Unwmk.** ***Perf. 10½***

1444 A630 1s Dressage .15 .15
1445 A630 2s Three-day test .15 .15
1446 A630 3s Jumping .15 .15
1447 A630 5s Race .15 .15
1448 A630 10s Steeplechase .75 .20
1449 A630 13s Hurdle race 1.40 .28
Nos. 1444-1449 (6) 2.75
Set value .75

See No. B28.

Smiling Children — A631

Designs: 2s, Two girl Pioneers. 3s, Bugler. 5s, Pioneer with model plane. 8s, Two singing girls in national costume. 13s, Running boy.

1965, Oct. 24 **Photo.**

1450 A631 1s dk bl grn & yel grn .15 .15
1451 A631 2s vio & deep rose .15 .15
1452 A631 3s olive & lemon .15 .15
1453 A631 5s dp blue & bister .15 .15
1454 A631 8s olive bister & org .28 .15
1455 A631 13s rose car & vio .65 .24
Set value 1.25 .60

Dimitrov Pioneer Organization.

U-52 Plane over Trnovo A632

Designs: 2c, 1L-14 over Plovdiv. 3s, Mi-4 Helicopter over Dimitrovgrad. 5s, Tu-104 over Ruse. 13s, IL-18 over Varna. 20s, Tu-114 over Sofia.

1965, Nov. 25 ***Perf. 10½***

1456 A632 1s gray, blue & red .15 .15
1457 A632 2s gray, lilac & red .15 .15
1458 A632 3s gray, grnsh bl & red .15 .15
1459 A632 5s gray, orange & red .15 .15
1460 A632 13s gray, bister & red .70 .15
1461 A632 20s gray, lt grn & red 1.00 .28
Set value 2.00 .60

Development of Bulgarian Civil Air Transport.

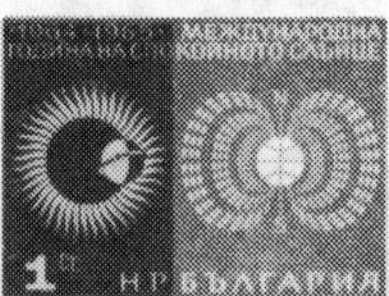

IQSY Emblem, and Earth Radiation Zones A633

Designs (IQSY Emblem and): 2s, Sun with corona. 13s, Solar eclipse.

1965, Dec. 15 **Photo.** ***Perf. 10½***

1462 A633 1s grn, yel & ultra .15 .15
1463 A633 2s yel, red lil & red .15 .15
1464 A633 13s bl, yel & blk .32 .15
Set value .42 .24

International Quiet Sun Year, 1964-65.

"North and South Bulgaria" A634

"Martenitsa" Emblem A635

1965, Dec. 6

1465 A634 13s brt yel grn & blk .50 .25

Union of North and South Bulgaria, cent.

1966, Jan. 10 **Photo.** ***Perf. 10½***

"Spring" in Folklore: 2s, Drummer. 3s, Bird ornaments. 5s, Dancer "Lazarka." 8s, Vase with flowers. 13s, Bagpiper.

1466 A635 1s rose lil, vio bl & gray .15 .15
1467 A635 2s gray, blk & crim .15 .15
1468 A635 3s red, vio & gray .15 .15
1469 A635 5s lil, blk & crim .15 .15
1470 A635 8s rose lil, brn & pur .22 .15
1471 A635 13s bl, blk & rose lil .50 .20
Set value 1.00 .50

Church of St. John the Baptist, Nessebr A636

Designs: 1s, Christ, fresco from Bojana Church. 2s, Ikon "Destruction of Idols," horiz. 3s, Bratchkovo Monastery. 4s, Zemen Monastery, horiz. 13s, Nativity, ikon from Arbanassi. 20s, Ikon "Virgin and Child," 1342.

1966, Feb. 25 **Litho.** ***Perf. 11½***

1472 A636 1s gray & multi *3.50 1.25*
1473 A636 2s gray & multi .25 .15
1474 A636 3s multicolored .25 .15
1475 A636 4s multicolored .25 .15
1476 A636 5s multicolored .25 .15
1477 A636 13s gray & multi .50 .15
1478 A636 20s multicolored .95 .35
Nos. 1472-1478 (7) *5.95 2.35*

2,500 years of art in Bulgaria.

Georgi Benkovski and T. Kableshkov A637

Designs: 1s, Proclamation of April Uprising, Koprivstitsa. 3s, Dedication of flag, Panaguriste. 5s, V. Petleshkov and Z. Dyustabanov. 10s, Botev landing at Kozlodui. 13s, P. Volov and Ilarion Dragostinov.

1966, Mar. 3 **Photo.** ***Perf. 10½***

Center in Black

1479 A637 1s red brn & gold .15 .15
1480 A637 2s brt red & gold .15 .15
1481 A637 3s ol grn & gold .15 .15

1482 A637 5s steel bl & gold .15 .15
1483 A637 10s brt rose lil & gold .20 .15
1484 A637 13s lt vio & gold .48 .15
Set value .95 .34

April Uprising against the Turks, 90th anniv.

Sofia Zoo Animals A638

1966, May 23 **Litho.**

1485 A638 1s Elephant .15 .15
1486 A638 2s Tiger .15 .15
1487 A638 3s Chimpanzee .15 .15
1488 A638 4s Siberian ibex .18 .15
1489 A638 5s Polar bear .25 .15
1490 A638 8s Lion .25 .15
1491 A638 13s Bison .80 .20
1492 A638 20s Kangaroo 1.50 .30
Nos. 1485-1492 (8) 3.43
Set value .85

WHO Headquarters, Geneva — A639

1966, May 3 **Photo.**

1493 A639 13s dp blue & silver .60 .25

Inauguration of the WHO Headquarters, Geneva.

Worker A640

1966, May 9 **Photo.** ***Perf. 10½***

1494 A640 20s gray & rose .65 .15

Sixth Trade Union Congress.

Yantra River Bridge, Biela — A641

Designs: No. 1496, Maritsa River Bridge, Svilengrad. No. 1497, Fountain, Samokov. No. 1498, Ruins of Fort, Kaskovo. 8s, Old Fort, Ruse. 13s, House, Gabrovo.

1966, Feb. 10 **Photo.** ***Perf. 13***

1495 A641 1s Prus blue .15 .15
1496 A641 1s brt green .15 .15
1497 A641 2s olive green .15 .15
1498 A641 2s dk red brown .15 .15
1499 A641 8s red brown .25 .15
1500 A641 13s dark blue .42 .15
Set value .95 .36

Souvenir Sheet

Moon Allegory — A642

1966, Apr. 29 ***Imperf.***

1501 A642 60s blk, plum & sil 2.50 1.25

1st Russian soft landing on the moon by Luna 9, Feb. 3, 1966.

Steamer Radetzky and Bugler A643

1966, May 28 ***Perf. 10½***

1502 A643 2s multicolored .15 .15

90th anniv. of the participation of the Danube steamer Radetzky in the uprising against the Turks.

Standard Bearer Nicola Simov-Kuruto A644

1966, May 30

1503 A644 5s bis, grn & ol .25 .15

Hero of the Turkish War.

UNESCO Emblem — A645

1966, June 8

1504 A645 20s gold, blk & ver .60 .16

20th anniv. of UNESCO.

Youth Federation Badge — A646

1966, June 6 **Photo.** ***Perf. 10½***

1505 A646 13s silver, bl & blk .40 .15

7th Assembly of the Intl. Youth Federation.

Soccer — A647

Designs: Various soccer scenes. 50s, Jules Rimet Cup.

1966, June 27

1506 A647 1s gray, yel brn & blk .15 .15
1507 A647 2s gray, crim & blk .15 .15
1508 A647 5s gray, ol bis & blk .15 .15
1509 A647 13s gray, ultra & blk .35 .15
1510 A647 20s gray, Prus bl & blk .60 .20
Nos. 1506-1510 (5) 1.40
Set value .45

Miniature Sheet

Imperf

1511 A647 50s gray, dp lil rose & gold 2.25 1.50

World Soccer Cup Championship, Wembley, England, July 11-30. Size of No. 1511: 60x64mm.

Woman Javelin Thrower — A648

Designs: No. 1513, Runner. No. 1514, Young man and woman carrying banners, vert.

1966 **Photo.** ***Perf. 10½***

1512 A648 2s grn, yel & ver .15 .15
1513 A648 13s dp grn, yel & sal pink .40 .15
1514 A648 13s bl, lt bl & salmon .40 .15
Nos. 1512-1514 (3) .95
Set value .26

Nos. 1512-1513: 3rd Spartacist Games; issued Aug. 10. No. 1514: 3rd congress of the Bulgarian Youth Federation; issued May 25.

Wrestlers Nicolas Petrov and Dan Kolov — A649

1966, July 29

1515 A649 13s bis brn, dk brn & lt ol grn .40 .20

3rd International Wrestling Championships.

Map of Balkan Countries, Globe and UNESCO Emblem — A650

1966, Aug. 26 ***Perf. 10½x11½***

1516 A650 13s ultra, lt grn & pink .40 .15

First Congress of Balkanologists.

Children with Building Blocks — A651

Designs: 2s, Bunny and teddy bear with book. 3s, Children as astronauts. 13s, Children with pails and shovel.

1966, Sept. 1 ***Perf. 10½***

1517 A651 1s dk car, org & blk .15 .15
1518 A651 2s emerald, blk & red brn .15 .15
1519 A651 3s ultra, org & blk .15 .15
1520 A651 13s blue, rose & blk .60 .15
Set value .80 .29

Children's Day.

Yuri A. Gagarin and Vostok 1 — A652

Designs: 2s, Gherman S. Titov, Vostok 2. 3s, Andrian G. Nikolayev, Pavel R. Popovich, Vostoks 3 & 4. 5s, Valentina Tereshkova, Valeri Bykovski, Vostoks 5 & 6. 8s, Vladimir M. Komarov, Boris B. Yegorov, Konstantin Feoktistov, Voskhod 1. 13s, Pavel Belyayev, Alexei Leonov, Voskhod 2.

1966, Sept. 29 **Photo.** ***Perf. 11½x11***

1521 A652 1s slate & gray .15 .15
1522 A652 2s plum & gray .15 .15
1523 A652 3s yel brn & gray .15 .15
1524 A652 5s brn red & gray .15 .15
1525 A652 8s ultra & gray .15 .15
1526 A652 13s Prus bl & gray .48 .15
Set value, #1521-1526, B29 1.90 .72

Russian space explorations.

St. Clement, 14th Century Wood Sculpture — A653

1966, Oct. 27 **Photo.** ***Perf. 11½x11***

1527 A653 5s red, buff & brn .20 .15

1050th anniversary of the birth of St. Clement of Ochrida.

Metodi Shatorov A654

Portraits: 3s, Vladimir Trichkov. 5s, Valcho Ivanov. 10s, Raiko Daskalov. 13s, General Vladimir Zaimov.

1966, Nov. 8 ***Perf. 11x11½***

Gold Frame, Black Denomination

1528 A654 2s crimson & bl vio .15 .15
1529 A654 3s magenta & blk .15 .15
1530 A654 5s car rose & dk bl .15 .15
1531 A654 10s orange & olive .28 .15
1532 A654 13s red & brown .40 .15
Set value .90 .32

Fighters against fascism.

George Dimitrov — A655

Steel Worker — A656

1966, Nov. 14 **Photo.** ***Perf. 11½x11***

1533 A655 2s magenta & blk .15 .15
1534 A656 20s fawn, gray & blk .70 .15
Set value .17

Bulgarian Communist Party, 9th Congress.

Deer's Head Drinking Cup A667

Gold Treasure: 2s, 6s, 10s, Various Amazon's head jugs. 3s, Ram's head cup. 5s, Circular plate. 8s, Deer's head cup. 13s, Amphora. 20s, Ram drinking horn.

1966, Nov. 28 ***Perf. 12x11½***

Vessels in Gold and Brown; Black Inscriptions

1535 A667 1s gray & violet .15 .15
1536 A667 2s gray & green .15 .15
1537 A667 3s gray & dk bl .15 .15
1538 A667 5s gray & red brn .15 .15
1539 A667 6s gray & Prus bl .15 .15
1540 A667 8s gray & brn ol .85 .15
1541 A667 10s gray & sepia .85 .18
1542 A667 13s gray & dk vio bl .85 .28
1543 A667 20s gray & vio brn .95 .32
Nos. 1535-1543 (9) 4.25
Set value 1.25

The gold treasure from the 4th century B.C. was found near Panagyurishte in 1949.

Tourist House, Bansko — A668

Tourist Houses: No. 1545, Belogradchik. No. 1546, Triavna. 20s, Rila.

1966, Nov. 29 Photo. *Perf. 11x11½*

1544 A668 1s dark blue .15 .15
1545 A668 2s dark green .15 .15
1546 A668 2s brown red .15 .15
1547 A668 20s lilac .42 .15
Set value .65 .25

Decorated Tree — A669

Design: 13s, Jug with bird design.

1966, Dec. 12 *Perf. 11*

1548 A669 2s grn, pink & gold .18 .15
1549 A669 13s brn lake, rose, emer & gold .38 .15
Set value .15

New Year, 1967.

Pencho Slavikov, Author — A670

Dahlia — A671

Portraits: 2s, Dimcho Debeljanov, author. 3s, P. H. Todorov, author. 5s, Dimitri Dobrovich, painter. 8s, Ivan Markvichka, painter. 13s, Ilya Bezhkov, painter.

1966, Dec. 15 *Perf. 10½x11*

1550 A670 1s blue, olive & org .15 .15
1551 A670 2s orange, brn & gray .15 .15
1552 A670 3s olive, bl & org .15 .15
1553 A670 5s gray, red brn & org .15 .15
1554 A670 8s lilac, dk gray & bl .30 .15
1555 A670 13s blue, vio & lil .38 .15
Set value .95 .34

1966, Dec. 29

Flowers: No. 1557, Clematis. No. 1558, Foxglove. No. 1559, Narcissus. 3s, Snowdrop. 5s, Petunia. 13s, Tiger lily. 20s, Bellflower.

Flowers in Natural Colors

1556 A671 1s gray & lt brn .15 .15
1557 A671 1s gray & dull bl .15 .15
1558 A671 2s gray & dull lil .15 .15
1559 A671 2s gray & brown .15 .15
1560 A671 3s gray & dk grn .16 .15
1561 A671 5s gray & dp ultra .22 .15
1562 A671 13s gray & brown .60 .15
1563 A671 20s gray & ultra .95 .15
Nos. 1556-1563 (8) 2.53
Set value .55

Ringnecked Pheasant A672

Game: 2s, Rock partridge. 3s, Gray partridge. 5s, Hare. 8s, Roe deer. 13s, Red deer.

1967, Jan. 28 *Perf. 11x10½*

1564 A672 1s lt ultra, dk brn & ocher .15 .15
1565 A672 2s pale yel grn & dk grn .15 .15
1566 A672 3s lt bl, blk & cr .16 .15
1567 A672 5s lt grn & blk .16 .15
1568 A672 8s pale bl, dk brn & ocher .70 .15
1569 A672 13s bl & dk brn 1.25 .25
Nos. 1564-1569 (6) 2.57
Set value .60

Bulgaria No. 1, 1879 — A673

Thracian Coin, 6th Century, B.C. — A674

1967, Feb. 4 Photo. *Perf. 10½*

1570 A673 10s emerald, blk & yel .75 .22

Bulgarian Philatelic Union, 10th Congress.

1967, Mar. 30 *Perf. 11½x11*

Coins: 2s, Macedonian tetradrachma, 2nd cent. B.C. 3s, Tetradrachma of Odessus, 2nd cent. B.C. 5s, Philip II of Macedonia, 4th cent., B.C. 13s, Thracian King Seuthus VII, 4th cent., B.C., obverse and reverse. 20s, Apollonian coin, 5th cent., B.C., obverse and reverse.

Size: 25x25mm

1571 A674 1s brn, blk & sil .15 .15
1572 A674 2s red lil, blk & sil .15 .15
1573 A674 3s grn, blk & sil .15 .15
1574 A674 5s brn org, blk & sil .16 .15

Size: 37½x25mm

1575 A674 13s brt bl, blk & brnz .70 .24
1576 A674 20s vio, blk & sil 1.25 .45
Nos. 1571-1576 (6) 2.56
Set value .88

Partisans Listening to Radio — A675

Design: 20s, George Dimitrov addressing crowd and Bulgarian flag.

1967, Apr. 20 *Perf. 11x11½*

1577 A675 1s red, gold, buff & sl grn .15 .15
1578 A675 20s red, gold, dl red, grn & blk .55 .15
Set value .17

25th anniversary of the Union of Patriotic Front Organizations.

Nikolas Kofardjiev A676

Portraits: 2s, Petko Napetov. 5s, Petko D. Petkov. 10s, Emil Markov. 13s, Traitcho Kostov.

1967, Apr. 24 *Perf. 11½x11*

1579 A676 1s brn red, gray & blk .15 .15
1580 A676 2s ol grn, gray & blk .15 .15
1581 A676 5s brn, gray & blk .15 .15
1582 A676 10s dp bl, gray & blk .20 .15
1583 A676 13s mag, gray & blk .42 .15
Set value .85 .30

Fighters against fascism.

Symbolic Flower and Flame — A677

1967, May 18 Photo. *Perf. 11x11½*

1584 A677 13s gold, yel & lt grn .45 .15

First Cultural Congress, May 18-19.

Gold Sand Beach and ITY Emblem A678

Designs: 20s, Hotel, Pamporovo. 40s, Nessebr Church.

1967, June 12 Photo. *Perf. 11x11½*

1585 A678 13s ultra, yel & blk .28 .15
1586 A678 20s Prus bl, blk & buff .42 .15
1587 A678 40s brt grn, blk & ocher 1.00 .28
Nos. 1585-1587 (3) 1.70 .58

International Tourist Year, 1967.

Angora Cat — A679

Cats: 2s, Siamese, horiz. 3s, Abyssinian. 5s, Black European. 13s, Persian, horiz. 20s, Striped domestic.

Perf. 11½x11, 11x11½

1967, June 19

1588 A679 1s dl vio, dk brn & buff .15 .15
1589 A679 2s ol, sl & brt bl .15 .15
1590 A679 3s dull blue & brn .15 .15
1591 A679 5s grn, blk & yel .20 .15
1592 A679 13s dl red brn, sl & org .90 .15
1593 A679 20s gray grn, brn & buff 1.65 .25
Nos. 1588-1593 (6) 3.20
Set value .56

Scene from Opera "The Master of Boyana" by K. Iliev — A680

Songbird on Keyboard — A681

1967, June 19

1594 A680 5s gray, vio bl & dp car .38 .15
1595 A681 13s gray, dp car & dk bl 1.10 .15
Set value .15

3rd Intl. Competition for Young Opera Singers.

George Kirkov (1867-1919), Revolutionist A682

1967, June 24 *Perf. 11x11½*

1596 A682 2s rose red & dk brn .15 .15

Symbolic Tree and Stars — A683

1967, July 28 Photo. *Perf. 11½x11*

1597 A683 13s dp bl, car & blk .30 .15

11th Congress of Dimitrov's Union of the People's Youth.

Roses and Distillery A684

Designs: No. 1599, Chick and incubator. No. 1600, Cucumbers and hothouse. No. 1601, Lamb and sheep farm. 3s, Sunflower and oil mill. 4s, Pigs and pig farm. 5s, Hops and hop farm. 6s, Corn and irrigation system. 8s, Grapes and Bolgar tractor. 10s, Apples and cultivated tree. 13s, Bees and honey. 20s, Bee, blossoms and beehives.

1967 *Perf. 11x11½*

1598 A684 1s multicolored .15 .15
1599 A684 1s dk car, yel & blk .15 .15
1600 A684 2s vio, lt grn & blk .15 .15
1601 A684 2s brt grn, gray & blk .15 .15
1602 A684 3s yel grn, yel & blk .15 .15
1603 A684 4s brt pur, yel & blk .15 .15
1604 A684 5s ol bis, yel grn & blk .15 .15
1605 A684 6s ol, brt grn & blk .15 .15
1606 A684 8s grn, bis & blk .15 .15
1607 A684 10s multicolored .25 .15
1608 A684 13s grn, bis brn & blk .42 .15
1609 A684 20s grnsh bl, brt pink & blk .55 .15
Set value 2.00 .80

Issue dates: Nos. 1598-1601, 1607, 1609, July 15; Nos. 1602-1606, 1608, July 24.

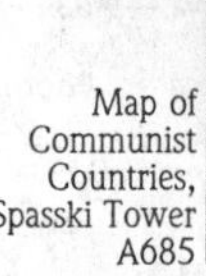

Map of Communist Countries, Spasski Tower A685

Designs: 2s, Lenin speaking to soldiers. 3s, Fighting at Wlodaja, 1918. 5s, Marx, Engels and Lenin. 13s, Oil refinery. 20s, Molniya communication satellite.

1967, Aug. 25 *Perf. 11*

1610 A685 1s multicolored .15 .15
1611 A685 2s magenta & olive .15 .15
1612 A685 3s magenta & dull vio .15 .15
1613 A685 5s magenta & red .15 .15
1614 A685 13s magenta & ultra .25 .15
1615 A685 20s magenta & blue .45 .15
Set value 1.10 .50

50th anniv. of the Russian October Revolution.

Rod, "Fish" and Varna — A686

1967, Aug. 29 Photo. *Perf. 11*

1616 A686 10s multicolored .35 .15

7th World Angling Championships, Varna.

Skiers and Winter Olympics' Emblem — A687

Sports and Emblem: 2s, Ski jump. 3s, Biathlon. 5s, Ice hockey. 13s, Figure skating couple.

1967, Sept. 20 Photo. *Perf. 11*

1617 A687 1s dk bl grn, red & blk .15 .15
1618 A687 2s ultra, blk & ol .15 .15
1619 A687 3s vio brn, bl & blk .15 .15
1620 A687 5s green, yel & blk .15 .15
1621 A687 13s vio bl, blk & buff .35 .15
Nos. 1617-1621,B31 (6) 2.05
Set value .50

10th Winter Olympic Games, Grenoble, France, Feb. 6-18, 1968.

Mountain Peaks — A688

1967, Sept. 25 Engr. *Perf. 11½*

1622 A688 1s Bogdan .15 .15
1623 A688 2s Czerny .15 .15
1624 A688 3s Ruen, vert. .15 .15
1625 A688 5s Persenk .15 .15
1626 A688 10s Botev .15 .15
1627 A688 13s Rila, vert. .25 .15
1628 A688 20s Vihren .55 .15
Set value 1.25 .50

George Rakovski A689

1967, Oct. 20 Photo. *Perf. 11*

1629 A689 13s yellow grn & blk .40 .15

Centenary of the death of George Rakovski, revolutionary against Turkish rule.

Yuri A. Gagarin, Valentina Tereshkova and Alexei Leonov — A690

Designs: 2s, Lt. Col. John H. Glenn, Jr., and Maj. Edward H. White. 5s, Earth and Molniya 1. 10s, Gemini 6 and 7. 13s, Luna 13 moon probe. 20s, Gemini 10 and Agena rocket.

1967, Nov. 25

1630 A690 1s Prus bl, blk & yel .15 .15
1631 A690 2s dl bl, blk & dl yel .15 .15
1632 A690 5s vio bl, grnsh bl & blk .15 .15
1633 A690 10s dk bl, blk & red .35 .15
1634 A690 13s grnsh bl, brt yel & blk .55 .15
1635 A690 20s dl bl, blk & red .75 .20
Nos. 1630-1635 (6) 2.10
Set value .50

Achievements in space exploration.

View of Trnovo — A691

Various Views of Trnovo.

1967, Dec. 5 Photo. *Perf. 11*

1636 A691 1s multicolored .15 .15
1637 A691 2s multicolored .15 .15
1638 A691 3s multicolored .15 .15
1639 A691 5s multicolored .16 .15
1640 A691 13s multicolored .32 .15
1641 A691 20s multicolored .50 .15
Nos. 1636-1641 (6) 1.43
Set value .46

Restoration of the ancient capital Veliko Trnovo.

Ratchenitza Folk Dance, by Ivan Markvichka — A692

1967, Dec. 9

1642 A692 20s gold & gray green 1.00 .80

Belgo-Bulgarian Philatelic Exposition, Brussels, Dec. 9-10. Printed in sheets of 8 stamps and 8 labels.

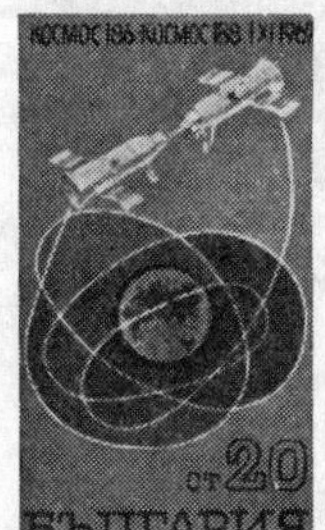

Cosmos 186 and 188 Docking — A693

Design: 40s, Venus 4 and orbits around Venus, horiz.

1968, Jan.

1643 A693 20s vio, gray & pink .55 .15
1644 A693 40s multicolored 1.00 .24

Docking maneuvers of the Russian spaceships Cosmos 186 and Cosmos 188, Nov. 1, 1967, and the flight to Venus of Venus 4, June 12-Nov. 18, 1967.

Crossing the Danube, by Orenburgski A694

Paintings: 2s, Flag of Samara, by J. Veschin, vert. 3s, Battle of Pleven by Orenburgski. 13s, Battle of Orlovo Gnezdo, by N. Popov, vert. 20s, Welcome for Russian Soldiers, by D. Gudienov.

1968, Jan. 25 Photo. *Perf. 11*

1645 A694 1s gold & dk green .15 .15
1646 A694 2s gold & dk blue .15 .15
1647 A694 3s gold & chocolate .15 .15
1648 A694 13s gold & dk vio .32 .15
1649 A694 20s gold & Prus grn .48 .18
Set value .95 .45

90th anniv. of the liberation from Turkey.

Shepherds, by Zlatyn Boyadjiev — A695

Paintings: 2s, Wedding dance, by V. Dimitrov, vert. 3s, Partisans' Song, by Ilya Petrov. 5s, Portrait of Anna Penchovich, by Nikolai Pavlovich, vert. 13s, Self-portrait, by Zachary Zograf, vert. 20s, View of Old Plovdiv, by T. Lavrenov. 60s, St. Clement of Ochrida, by A. Mitov.

1967, Dec. Litho. *Perf. 11½*

Size: 45x38mm, 38x45mm

1650 A695 1s gray & multi .15 .15
1651 A695 2s gray & multi .15 .15

Size: 55x35mm

1652 A695 3s gray & multi .22 .15

Size: 38x45mm, 45x38mm

1653 A695 5s gray & multi .40 .15
1654 A695 13s gray & multi .90 .22
1655 A695 20s gray & multi 1.25 .40
Nos. 1650-1655 (6) 3.07
Set value .88

Miniature Sheet

Size: 65x84mm

Imperf

1656 A695 60s multicolored 3.25 1.90

Marx Statue, Sofia — A696

Maxim Gorky — A697

1968, Feb. 20 Photo. *Perf. 11*

1657 A696 13s black & red .35 .15

150th anniversary of birth of Karl Marx.

1968, Feb. 20

1658 A697 13s ver & grnsh blk .40 .15

Maxim Gorky (1868-1936), Russian writer.

Folk Dancers — A698

Designs: 5s, Runners. 13s, Doves. 20s, Festival poster, (head, flowers and birds). 40s, Globe and Bulgaria No. 1 under magnifying glass.

1968, Mar. 20

1659 A698 2s multicolored .15 .15
1660 A698 5s multicolored .15 .15
1661 A698 13s multicolored .22 .15
1662 A698 20s multicolored .48 .20
1663 A698 40s multicolored 1.10 .40
Nos. 1659-1663 (5) 2.10
Set value .80

9th Youth Festival for Peace and Friendship, Sofia, July 28-Aug. 6.

Bellflower — A699

1968, Apr. 25 *Perf. 11*

1664 A699 1s shown .15 .15
1665 A699 2s Gentian .15 .15
1666 A699 3s Crocus .15 .15
1667 A699 5s Iris .16 .15
1668 A699 10s Dog-tooth violet .20 .15
1669 A699 13s Sempervivum .70 .15
1670 A699 20s Dictamnus .95 .22
Nos. 1664-1670 (7) 2.46
Set value .60

"The Unknown Hero," Tale by Ran Bosilek A700

Design: 20s, The Witch and the Young Man (Hans Christian Andersen fairy tale.)

1968, Apr. 25 Photo. *Perf. 10½*

1671 A700 13s black & multi .35 .15
1672 A700 20s black & multi .52 .20

Bulgarian-Danish Philatelic Exhibition.

Memorial Church, Shipka — A701

Steeplechase — A702

1968, May 3

1673 A701 13s multicolored .60 .20

Bulgarian Stamp Exhibition in Berlin.

1968, June 24 Photo. *Perf. 10½*

Designs (Olympic Rings and): 1s, Gymnast on bar. 3s, Fencer. 10s, Boxer. 13s, Woman discus thrower.

1674 A702 1s red & black .15 .15
1675 A702 2s gray, blk & rose brn .15 .15
1676 A702 3s magenta, gray & blk .15 .15
1677 A702 10s grnsh bl, blk & lem .15 .15
1678 A702 13s vio bl, gray & pink .55 .18
Nos. 1674-1678,B33 (6) 2.15
Set value .75

19th Olympic Games, Mexico City, Oct. 12-27.

Battle of Buzluja A703

Design: 13s, Haji Dimitr and Stefan Karaja.

1968, July 1

1679 A703 2s silver & red brn .15 .15
1680 A703 13s gold & sl grn .32 .15
Set value .40 .17

Centenary of the death of the patriots Haji Dimitr and Stefan Karaja.

Lakes of Smolian — A704

Sofia Zoo, Cent. — A705

Bulgarian Scenes: 2s, Ropotamo Lake. 3s, Erma-Idreloto mountain pass. 8s, Isker River dam. 10s, Slanchev Breg (sailing ship). 13s, Cape Caliacra. 40s, Old houses, Sozopol. 2 l, Chudnite Skali ("Strange Mountains").

1968 Photo. *Perf. 13*

1681 A704 1s Prus green .15 .15
1682 A704 2s dark green .15 .15
1683 A704 3s dark brown .15 .15
1684 A704 8s olive green .15 .15
1685 A704 10s redsh brown .15 .15
1686 A704 13s dk olive grn .22 .15
1687 A704 40s Prus blue .60 .24
1688 A704 2 l sepia 3.75 .85
Nos. 1681-1688 (8) 5.32
Set value 1.40

1968, July 29 *Perf. 10½*

1689 A705 1s Cinereous vulture .15 .15
1690 A705 2s Crowned crane .15 .15
1691 A705 3s Zebra .22 .15
1692 A705 5s Cheetah .38 .15
1693 A705 13s Indian python .70 .15
1694 A705 20s African crocodile 1.25 .30
Nos. 1689-1694 (6) 2.85
Set value .75

Human Rights Flame — A706

1968, July 8
1695 A706 20s dp blue & gold .60 .15

International Human Rights Year, 1968.

Congress Hall, Varna, and Emblem A707

1968, Sept. 17 Photo. *Perf. 10½*
1696 A707 20s bister, grn & red .50 .15

56th International Dental Congress, Varna.

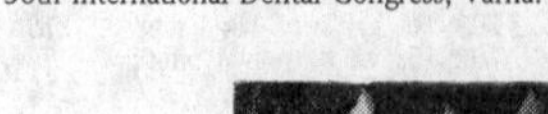

Flying Swans — A708

Rose A709

Stag Beetle A710

Designs: 2s, Jug. 20s, Five Viking ships.

1968 Photo. *Perf. 10½*
1697 A709 2s green & ocher .75 .50
1698 A708 5s dp blue & gray .75 .50
1699 A709 13s dp plum & lil rose .75 .50
1700 A708 20s dp vio & gray .75 .50
Nos. 1697-1700 (4) 3.00 2.00

Cooperation with the Scandinavian countries. Nos. 1697 and 1700 are printed with connecting label showing bridge made of flags of Scandinavian countries.

Issue dates: 5s, 13s, Sept. 12. Others, Nov. 22.

Perf. 12½x13, 13x12½
1968, Aug. 26

Insects: No. 1702, Ground beetle (Procerus scabrosus). No. 1703, Ground beetle (Calosoma sycophania). No. 1704, Scarab beetle, horiz. No. 1705, Saturnid moth, horiz.

1701 A710 1s brown olive .15 .15
1702 A710 1s dark blue .15 .15
1703 A710 1s dark green .15 .15
1704 A710 1s orange brown .15 .15
1705 A710 1s magenta .15 .15
Set value .30 .25

Turks Fighting Insurgents, 1688 A711

1968, Aug. 22 *Perf. 10½*
1706 A711 13s multicolored .45 .15

280th anniversary of the Tchiprovtzi insurrection.

Christo Smirnenski (1898-1923), Poet — A712

1968, Sept. 28 Litho. *Perf. 10½*
1707 A712 13s gold, red org & blk .40 .15

Dalmatian Pelican A713

Birds: 2s, Little egret. 3s, Crested grebe. 5s, Common tern. 13s, European spoonbill. 20s, Glossy ibis.

1968, Oct. 28 Photo.
1708 A713 1s silver & multi .15 .15
1709 A713 2s silver & multi .15 .15
1710 A713 3s silver & multi .15 .15
1711 A713 5s silver & multi .15 .15
1712 A713 13s silver & multi .52 .15
1713 A713 20s silver & multi 1.10 .32
Nos. 1708-1713 (6) 2.22
Set value .65

Srebirna wild life reservation.

Carrier Pigeon A714

1968, Oct. 19
1714 A714 20s emerald .70 .25
a. Sheet of 4 + labels 5.00 1.65

2nd Natl. Stamp Exhib. in Sofia, Oct. 25-Nov. 15. No. 1714a contains 4 No. 1714 and 5 labels.

Man and Woman from Lovetch — A715

Regional Costumes: 1s, Silistra. 3s, Jambol. 13s, Chirpan. 20s, Razgrad. 40s, Ihtiman.

1968, Nov. 20 Litho. *Perf. 13½*
1715 A715 1s dp org & multi .15 .15
1716 A715 2s Prus bl & multi .15 .15
1717 A715 3s multicolored .16 .15
1718 A715 13s multicolored .28 .15
1719 A715 20s multicolored .55 .25
1720 A715 40s green & multi 1.40 .45
Nos. 1715-1720 (6) 2.69
Set value 1.00

St. Arsenius A716

Designs (10th century Murals and Icons): 2s, Procession with relics of St. Ivan Rilsky, horiz. 3s, St. Michael Torturing the Soul of the Rich Man. 13s, St. Ivan Rilski. 20s, St. John. 40s, St. George. 1 l, Procession meeting relics of St. Ivan Rilsky, horiz.

Perf. 11½x12½, 12½x11½
1968, Nov. 25 Photo.
1721 A716 1s gold & multi .15 .15
1722 A716 2s gold & multi .15 .15
1723 A716 3s gold & multi .15 .15
1724 A716 13s gold & multi .42 .16
1725 A716 20s gold & multi .95 .28
1726 A716 40s gold & multi 1.40 .60
Nos. 1721-1726 (6) 3.22
Set value 1.25

Souvenir Sheet
Imperf

1727 A716 1 l gold & multi 3.75 2.75

Millenium of Rila Monastery. No. 1727 also: Sofia 1969 Intl. Phil. Exhib., May 31-June 8, 1969. No. 1727 contains one stamp, size: 57x51mm.

Medlar A717

Herbs: No. 1729, Camomile. 2s, Lily-of-the-valley. 3s, Belladonna. 5s, Mallow. 10s, Buttercup. 13s, Poppies. 20s, Thyme.

1969, Jan. 2 Litho. *Perf. 10½*
1728 A717 1s black, grn & org red .15 .15
1729 A717 1s black, grn & yel .15 .15
1730 A717 2s black, emer & grn .15 .15
1731 A717 3s black & multi .15 .15
1732 A717 5s black & multi .15 .15
1733 A717 10s black, grn & yel .16 .15
1734 A717 13s black & multi .30 .15
1735 A717 20s black, lil & grn .65 .15
Set value 1.50 .60

Silkworms and Spindles A718

Designs: 2s, Silkworm, cocoons and pattern. 3s, Cocoons and spinning wheel. 5s, Cocoons, woof-and-warp diagram. 13s, Silk moth, Cocoon and spinning frame. 20s, Silk moth, eggs and shuttle.

1969, Jan. 30 Photo. *Perf. 10½*
1736 A718 1s bl, grn, sl & blk .15 .15
1737 A718 2s dp car, sil & blk .15 .15
1738 A718 3s Prus bl, sil & blk .15 .15
1739 A718 5s pur, ver, sil & blk .15 .15
1740 A718 13s red lil, ocher, sil & blk .25 .15
1741 A718 20s grn, org, sil & blk .45 .15
Set value .95 .45

Bulgarian silk industry.

Attack and Capture of Emperor Nicephorus — A719

Sts. Cyril and Methodius, Mural, Troian Monastery — A720

Designs (Manasses Chronicle): No. 1742, Death of Ivan Asen. 3s, Khan Kroum feasting after victory. No. 1748, Invasion of Bulgaria by Prince Sviatoslav of Kiev. No. 1750, Russian invasion and campaigns of Emperor John I Zimisces, c. 972 A.D. 40s, Tsar Ivan Alexander, Jesus and Constantine Manasses.

Horizontal designs: No. 1743, Kings Nebuchadnezzar, Balthazar, Darius and Cyrus. No. 1745, Kings Cambyses, Gyges and Darius. 5s, King David and Tsar Ivan Alexander. No. 1749, Persecution of Byzantine army after battle of July 26, 811. No. 1751, Christening of Bulgarian Tsar Boris, 865. 60s, Arrival of Tsar Simeon in Constantinople and his succeeding surprise attack on that city.

1969 Photo. *Perf. 14x13½, 13½x14*
1742 A719 1s multicolored .15 .15
1743 A719 1s multicolored .15 .15
1744 A719 2s multicolored .15 .15
1745 A719 2s multicolored .15 .15
1746 A719 3s multicolored .15 .15
1747 A719 5s multicolored .15 .15
1748 A719 13s multicolored .38 .15
1749 A719 13s multicolored .38 .15
1750 A719 20s multicolored .80 .15
1751 A719 20s multicolored .80 .15
1752 A719 40s multicolored 1.25 .38
1753 A719 60s multicolored 2.25 .42
Nos. 1742-1753 (12) 6.76
Set value 1.50

1969, Mar. 23
1754 A720 28s gold & multi .75 .45

Post Horn — A721

Designs: 13s, Bulgaria Nos. 1 and 534. 20s, Street fighting at Stackata, 1919.

1969, Apr. 15 Photo. *Perf. 10½*
1755 A721 2s green & yel .15 .15
1756 A721 13s multicolored .40 .15
1757 A721 20s dk bl & lt bl .48 .18
Nos. 1755-1757 (3) 1.03
Set value .35

90th anniversary of the Bulgarian postal administration.

The Fox and the Rabbit A722

Children's Drawings: 2s, Boy reading to wolf and fox. 13s, Two birds and cat singing together.

1969, Apr. 21
1758 A722 1s emer, org & blk .15 .15
1759 A722 2s org, lt bl & blk .15 .15
1760 A722 13s lt bl, ol & blk .38 .15
Set value .50 .25

Issued for Children's Week.

ILO Emblem — A723

1969, Apr. 28
1761 A723 13s dull grn & blk .30 .15

50th anniv. of the ILO.

St. George and SOFIA 69 Emblem — A724

Designs: 2s, Virgin Mary and St. John Bogoslov. 3s, Archangel Michael. 5s, Three Saints. 8s, Jesus Christ. 13s, Sts. George and Dimitrie. 20s, Christ, the Almighty. 40s, St. Dimitrie. 60s, The 40 Martyrs. 80s, The Transfiguration.

1969, Apr. 30 *Perf. 11x12*
1762 A724 1s gold & multi .15 .15
1763 A724 2s gold & multi .15 .15
1764 A724 3s gold & multi .15 .15
1765 A724 5s gold & multi .15 .15
1766 A724 8s gold & multi .16 .15
1767 A724 13s gold & multi .32 .15
1768 A724 20s gold & multi .65 .22

1769 A724 40s gold & multi		1.40	.42
a. Sheet of 4		5.75	5.00
1770 A724 60s gold & multi		1.75	.85
1771 A724 80s gold & multi		2.75	1.00
Nos. 1762-1771 (10)		7.63	
Set value			3.00

Old Bulgarian art from the National Art Gallery. No. 1769a contains 4 of No. 1769 with center gutter showing Alexander Nevski Shrine. See note on SOFIA 69 after Nos. C112-C120.

St. Cyril Preaching — A725

Design: 28s, St. Cyril and followers.

1969, June 20 Litho. *Perf. 10½*

1772 A725 2s sil, grn & red	.16	.15
1773 A725 28s sil, dk bl & red	.75	.22
Set value		.27

St. Cyril (827-869), apostle to the Slavs, inventor of Cyrillic alphabet. Issued in sheets of 25 with se-tenant labels; Cyrillic inscription on label of 2s, Glagolitic inscription on label of 28s.

St. Sophia Church — A726

Sofia Through the Ages: 1s, Roman coin with inscription "Ulpia Serdica." 2s, Roman coin with Aesculapius Temple. 4s, Bojana Church. 5s, Sobranic Parliament. 13s, Vasov National Theater. 20s, Alexander Nevski Shrine. 40s, Clement Ochrida University. 1 l, Coat of arms.

1969, May 25 *Perf. 13x12½*

1774 A726 1s gold & blue	.15	.15
1775 A726 2s gold & ol grn	.15	.15
1776 A726 3s gold & red brn	.15	.15
1777 A726 4s gold & purple	.15	.15
1778 A726 5s gold & plum	.15	.15
1779 A726 13s gold & brt grn	.28	.15
1780 A726 20s gold & vio bl	.45	.15
1781 A726 40s gold & dp car	1.10	.25
Nos. 1774-1781 (8)	2.58	
Set value		.75

Souvenir Sheet

Imperf

1782 A726 1 l grn, gold & red	2.25	2.00

Historic Sofia in connection with the International Philatelic Exhibition, Sofia, May 31-June 8.

#1782 contains one 43½x43½mm stamp. Emblems of 8 preceding philatelic exhibitions in metallic ink in margin; gold inscription.

No. 1782 was overprinted in green "IBRA 73" and various symbols, and released May 4, 1973, for the Munich Philatelic Exhibition. The overprint also exists in gray.

St. George — A727

1969, June 9 Litho. *Perf. 11½*

1783 A727 40s sil, blk & pale rose	1.25	.50

38th FIP Congress, June 9-11.

Hand Planting Sapling A728

1969, Apr. 28 Photo. *Perf. 11*

1784 A728 2s ol grn, blk & lilac	.15	.15

25 years of the reforestation campaign.

Partisans A729

Designs: 2s, Combine harvester. 3s, Dam. 5s, Flutist and singers. 13s, Factory. 20s, Lenin, Dimitrov, Russian and Bulgarian flags.

1969, Sept. 9

1785 A729 1s blk, pur & org	.15	.15
1786 A729 2s blk, ol bis & org	.15	.15
1787 A729 3s blk, bl grn & org	.15	.15
1788 A729 5s blk, brn red & org	.15	.15
1789 A729 13s blk, bl & org	.30	.15
1790 A729 20s blk, brn & org	.50	.15
Set value	1.10	.45

25th anniversary of People's Republic.

Women Gymnasts A730

1969, Sept. Photo. *Perf. 11*

1791 A730 2s shown	.15	.15
1792 A730 20s Wrestlers	.42	.22
Set value		.30

Third National Spartakiad.

Tchanko Bakalov Tcherkovski, Poet. Birth Cent. — A731

1969, Sept.

1793 A731 13s multicolored	.35	.15

Woman Gymnast A732

Designs: 2s, Two women with hoops. 3s, Woman with hoop. 5s, Two women with spheres.

1969, Oct.

Gymnasts in Light Gray

1794 A732 1s green & dk blue	.15	.15
1795 A732 2s blue & dk blue	.15	.15
1796 A732 3s emer & sl grn	.15	.15
1797 A732 5s orange & pur	.15	.15
Set value, #1794-1797, B35-B36	1.45	.70

World Championships for Artistic Gymnastics, Varna.

The Priest Rilski, by Zachary Zograf — A733

Paintings from the National Art Gallery. 2s, Woman at Window, by Vasil Stoilov. 3s, Workers at Rest, by Nenko Balkanski, horiz. 4s, Woman Dressing (Nude), by Ivan Nenov. 5s, Portrait of a Woman, by N. Pavlovich. 13s, Falstaff, by Duzunov Kr. Sarafov. No. 1804, Portrait of a Woman, by N. Mihajlov, horiz. No. 1805, Workers at Mealtime, by Stojan Sotirov, horiz. 40s, Self-portrait, by Tcheno Togorov.

Perf. 11½x12, 12x11½

1969, Nov. 10

1798 A733 1s gold & multi	.15	.15
1799 A733 2s gold & multi	.15	.15
1800 A733 3s gold & multi	.15	.15
1801 A733 4s gold & multi	.15	.15
1802 A733 5s gold & multi	.15	.15
1803 A733 13s gold & multi	.32	.15
1804 A733 20s gold & multi	.70	.22
1805 A733 20s gold & multi	.70	.22
1806 A733 40s gold & multi	1.40	.60
Nos. 1798-1806 (9)	3.87	
Set value		1.50

Roman Bronze Wolf A734

Design: 2s, Roman statue of woman, found at Silistra, vert.

1969, Oct. Photo. *Perf. 11*

1807 A734 2s sil, ultra & gray	.15	.15
1808 A734 13s sil, dk grn & gray	.42	.15
Set value		.17

City of Silistra's 1,800th anniversary.

Worker and Factory — A735

1969 *Perf. 13*

1809 A735 6s ultra & blk	.15	.15

25th anniversary of the factory militia.

European Hake — A736

Designs: No. 1811, Deep-sea fishing trawler. Fish: 2s, Atlantic horse mackerel. 3s, Pilchard. 5s, Dentex macrophthalmus. 10s, Chub mackerel. 13s, Otolithes macrognathus. 20s, Lichia vadigo.

1969 *Perf. 11*

1810 A736 1s ol grn & blk	.15	.15
1811 A736 1s ultra, ind & gray	.15	.15
1812 A736 2s lilac & blk	.15	.15
1813 A736 3s vio bl & blk	.15	.15
1814 A736 5s rose cl, pink & blk	.24	.15
1815 A736 10s gray & blk	.48	.15
1816 A736 13s ver, sal & blk	.70	.15
1817 A736 20s ocher & black	1.25	.18
Nos. 1810-1817 (8)	3.27	
Set value		.58

Marin Drinov A737

1969, Nov. 10 Litho. *Perf. 11*

1818 A737 20s black & red org	.35	.15

Centenary of the Bulgarian Academy of Science, founded by Marin Drinov.

Trapeze Artists A738

Pavel Bania Sanatorium A739

Circus Performers: 2s, Jugglers. 3s, Jugglers with loops. 5s, Juggler and bear on bicycle. 13s, Woman and performing horse. 20s, Musical clowns.

1969 Photo. *Perf. 11*

1819 A738 1s dk blue & multi	.15	.15
1820 A738 2s dk green & multi	.15	.15
1821 A738 3s dk violet & multi	.15	.15
1822 A738 5s multicolored	.15	.15
1823 A738 13s multicolored	.30	.15
1824 A738 20s multicolored	.55	.20
Set value	1.10	.50

1969, Dec. Photo. *Perf. 10½-14*

Health Resorts: 5s, Chisar Sanatorium. 6s, Kotel Children's Sanatorium. 20s, Narechen Polyclinic.

1825 A739 2s blue	.15	.15
1826 A739 5s ultra	.15	.15
1827 A739 6s green	.15	.15
1828 A739 20s emerald	.32	.15
Set value	.65	.22

G. S. Shonin, V. N. Kubasov and Spacecraft — A740

Designs: 2s, A. V. Filipchenko, V. N. Volkov, V. V. Gorbatko and spacecraft. 3s, Vladimir A. Shatalov, Alexei S. Yeliseyev and spacecraft. 28s, Three spacecraft in orbit.

1970, Jan. Photo. *Perf. 11*

1829 A740 1s rose car, ol grn & blk	.15	.15
1830 A740 2s bl, dl cl & blk	.15	.15
1831 A740 3s grnsh bl, vio & blk	.15	.15
1832 A740 28s vio bl, lil rose & lt bl	.70	.16
Set value	.90	.31

Russian space flights of Soyuz 6, 7 and 8, Oct. 11-13, 1969.

Khan Krum and Defeat of Emperor Nicephorus, 811 — A741

Bulgarian History: 1s, Khan Asparuch and Bulgars crossing the Danube (679). 3s, Conversion of Prince Boris to Christianity, 865. 5s, Tsar Simeon and battle of Akhelo, 917. 8s, Tsar Samuel defeating the Byzantines, 976. 10s, Tsar Kaloyan defeating Emperor Baldwin, 1205. 13s, Tsar Ivan Assen II defeating Greek King Theodore Komnine, 1230. 20s, Coronation of Tsar Ivailo, 1277.

1970, Feb. Perf. 10½

1833 A741 1s gold & multi .15 .15
1834 A741 2s gold & multi .15 .15
1835 A741 3s gold & multi .15 .15
1836 A741 5s gold & multi .15 .15
1837 A741 8s gold & multi .18 .15
1838 A741 10s gold & multi .30 .15
1839 A741 13s gold & multi .40 .15
1840 A741 20s gold & multi .70 .15
Nos. 1833-1840 (8) 2.18
Set value .56

See Nos. 2126-2133.

Bulgarian Pavilion, EXPO '70 — A742

1970 Perf. 12½

1841 A742 20s brown, sil & org .75 .50

EXPO '70 International Exposition, Osaka, Japan, Mar. 15-Sept. 13, 1970.

Soccer A743

Designs: Various views of soccer game.

1970, Mar. 4 Photo. Perf. 12½

1842 A743 1s blue & multi .15 .15
1843 A743 2s rose car & multi .15 .15
1844 A743 3s ultra & multi .15 .15
1845 A743 5s green & multi .15 .15
1846 A743 20s emerald & multi .55 .15
1847 A743 40s red & multi 1.25 .28
Nos. 1842-1847 (6) 2.40
Set value .65

9th World Soccer Championships for the Jules Rimet Cup, Mexico City, May 30-June 21, 1970. See No. B37.

Lenin (1870-1924) A744

1970, Apr. 22

1848 A744 2s shown .15 .15
1849 A744 13s Portrait .32 .15
1850 A744 20s Writing .70 .15
Nos. 1848-1850 (3) 1.17
Set value .26

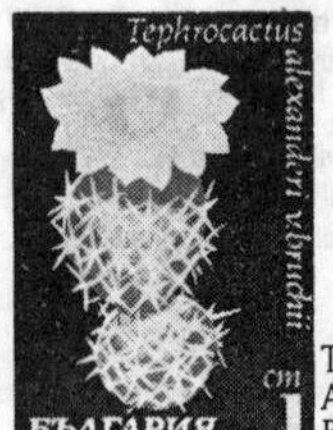

Tephrocactus Alexanderi V. Bruchii — A745

Cacti: 2s, Opuntia drummondii. 3s, Hatiora cilindrica. 5s, Gymnocalycium vatteri. 8s, Heliantho cereus grandiflorus. 10s, Neochilenia andreaeana. 13s, Peireskia vargasii v. longispina. 20s, Neobesseya rosiflora.

1970 Photo. Perf. 12½

1851 A745 1s multicolored .15 .15
1852 A745 2s dk green & multi .15 .15
1853 A745 3s multicolored .15 .15
1854 A745 5s blue & multi .15 .15
1855 A745 8s brown & multi .28 .15
1856 A745 10s vio bl & multi 1.00 .16
1857 A745 13s brn red & multi 1.00 .16
1858 A745 20s purple & multi 1.40 .32
Nos. 1851-1858 (8) 4.28
Set value 1.00

Rose — A746

Designs: Various Roses.

1970, June 8 Litho. Perf. 13½

1859 A746 1s gray & multi .15 .15
1860 A746 2s gray & multi .15 .15
1861 A746 3s gray & multi .15 .15
1862 A746 4s gray & multi .15 .15
1863 A746 5s gray & multi .15 .15
1864 A746 13s gray & multi .16 .15
1865 A746 20s gray & multi 1.10 .25
1866 A746 28s gray & multi 1.90 .42
Nos. 1859-1866 (8) 3.91
Set value 1.10

Gold Bowl — A747

Designs: Various bowls and art objects from Gold Treasure of Thrace.

1970, June 15 Photo. Perf. 12½

1867 A747 1s blk, bl & gold .15 .15
1868 A747 2s blk, lt vio & gold .15 .15
1869 A747 3s blk, ver & gold .15 .15
1870 A747 5s blk, yel grn & gold .15 .15
1871 A747 13s blk, org & gold .70 .15
1872 A747 20s blk, lil & gold .85 .18
Nos. 1867-1872 (6) 2.15
Set value .50

EXPO Emblem, Rose and Bulgarian Woman — A748

Designs (EXPO Emblem and): 2s, Three women. 3s, Woman and fruit. 28s, Dancers. 40s, Mt. Fuji and pavilions.

1970, June 20

1873 A748 1s gold & multi .15 .15
1874 A748 2s gold & multi .15 .15
1875 A748 3s gold & multi .15 .15
1876 A748 28s gold & multi .70 .22
Nos. 1873-1876 (4) 1.15
Set value .45

Miniature Sheet

Imperf

1877 A748 40s gold & multi 1.00 .60

EXPO '70 International Exposition, Osaka, Japan, Mar. 15-Sept. 13. No. 1877 contains one stamp with simulated perforations.

Ivan Vasov — A749

1970, Aug. 1 Photo. Perf. 12½

1878 A749 13s violet blue .40 .15

120th anniv. of the birth of Ivan Vasov, author.

UN Emblem — A750

1970, Aug. 1

1879 A750 20s Prus bl & gold .50 .20

25th anniversary of the United Nations.

George Dimitrov A751

Retriever A752

1970, Aug.

1880 A751 20s blk, gold & org .60 .15

BZNC (Bulgarian Communist Party), 70th anniv.

1970 Photo. Perf. 12½

Dogs: 1s, Golden retriever, horiz. 3s, Great Dane. 4s, Boxer. 5s, Cocker spaniel. 13s, Doberman pinscher. 20s, Scottish terrier. 28s, Russian greyhound, horiz.

1881 A752 1s multicolored .15 .15
1882 A752 2s multicolored .15 .15
1883 A752 3s multicolored .15 .15
1884 A752 4s multicolored .15 .15
1885 A752 5s multicolored .15 .15
1886 A752 13s multicolored .52 .15
1887 A752 20s multicolored 1.10 .26
1888 A752 28s multicolored 1.65 .32
Nos. 1881-1888 (8) 4.02
Set value .94

Volleyball — A753

Designs: No. 1890, Two women players. No. 1891, Woman player. No. 1892, Man player.

1970, Sept. Photo. Perf. 12½

1889 A753 2s dk red brn, bl & blk .15 .15
1890 A753 2s ultra, org & blk .15 .15
1891 A753 20s Prus bl, yel & blk .48 .15
1892 A753 20s grn, yel & blk .48 .15
Nos. 1889-1892 (4) 1.26
Set value .34

World Volleyball Championships.

Enrico Caruso and "I Pagliacci" by Ruggiero Leoncavallo — A754

Opera Singers and Operas: 2s, Christina Morfova and "The Bartered Bride" by Bedrich Smetana. 3s, Peter Reitchev and "Tosca" by Giacomo Puccini. 10s, Svetana Tabakova and "The Flying Dutchman" by Richard Wagner. 13s, Katia Popova and "The Masters" by Paroshkev Hadjev. 20s, Feodor Chaliapin and "Boris Godunov" by Modest Musorgski.

1970, Oct. 15 Photo. Perf. 14

1893 A754 1s black & multi .15 .15
1894 A754 2s black & multi .15 .15
1895 A754 3s black & multi .15 .15
1896 A754 10s black & multi .20 .15
1897 A754 13s black & multi .28 .16
1898 A754 20s black & multi 1.00 .25
Nos. 1893-1898 (6) 1.93
Set value .80

Honoring opera singers in their best roles.

Ivan Assen II Coin — A755

Coins from 14th Century with Ruler's Portrait: 2s, Theodor Svetoslav. 3s, Mikhail Chichman. 13s, Ivan Alexander and Mikhail Assen. 20s, Ivan Stratsimir. 28s, Ivan Chichman (initials).

1970, Nov. Perf. 12½

1899 A755 1s buff & multi .15 .15
1900 A755 2s gray & multi .15 .15
1901 A755 3s multicolored .15 .15
1902 A755 13s multicolored .22 .15
1903 A755 20s lt blue & multi .60 .15
1904 A755 28s multicolored .85 .22
Nos. 1899-1904 (6) 2.12
Set value .65

Fire Protection A756

1970 Litho. Perf. 12½

1905 A756 1s Fireman .15 .15
1906 A756 3s Fire engine .15 .15
Set value .20 .15

Bicyclists — A757

Congress Emblem — A758

1970 Photo.

1907 A757 20s grn, yel & pink .50 .20

20th Bulgarian bicycle race.

1970

1908 A758 13s gold & multi .35 .15

7th World Congress of Sociology, Varna, Sept. 14-19.

Ludwig van Beethoven — A759

Friedrich Engels — A760

1970

1909 A759 28s lil rose & dk bl .90 .40

Beethoven (1770-1827), composer.

1970 Photo. Perf. 12½

1910 A760 13s ver, tan & brn .30 .15

Friedrich Engels (1820-1895), German socialist, collaborator of Karl Marx.

Miniature Sheets

Luna 16
A761

Russian moon mission: 80s, Lunokhod 1, unmanned vehicle on moon, horiz.

1970 Photo. *Imperf.*

No.	Type	Value	Description	Unused	Used
1911	A761	80s	plum, sil, blk & bl	2.00	2.00
1912	A761	1 l	vio bl, sil & red	4.00	2.75

No. 1911 , Lunokhod 1, Nov. 10-17. No. 1912, Luna 16 mission, Sept. 12-24.
Issue dates: 80s, Dec. 18; 1 l, Nov. 10.

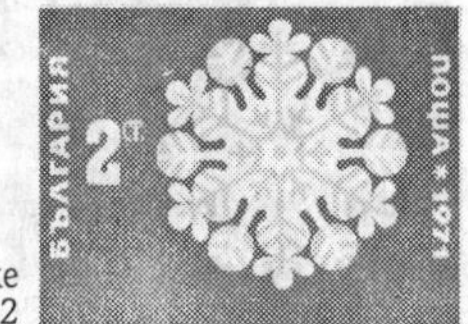

Snowflake
A762

1970, Dec. 15 Photo. *Perf. 12½x13*

No.	Type	Value	Description	Unused	Used
1913	A762	2s	ultra & multi	.15	.15

New Year 1971.

Birds and Flowers
A763

Folk Art: 2s, Bird and flowers. 3s, Flying birds. 5s, Birds and flowers. 13s, Sun. 20s, Tulips and pansies.

1971, Jan. 25 *Perf. 12½x13½*

No.	Type	Value	Description	Unused	Used
1914	A763	1s	multicolored	.15	.15
1915	A763	2s	multicolored	.15	.15
1916	A763	3s	multicolored	.15	.15
1917	A763	5s	multicolored	.15	.15
1918	A763	13s	multicolored	.16	.15
1919	A763	20s	multicolored	.55	.15
			Set value	.95	.40

Spring 1971.

Girl, by Zeko Spiridonov
A764

Modern Bulgarian Sculpture: 2s, Third Class (people looking through train window), by Ivan Funev. 3s, Bust of Elin Pelin, by Marko Markov. 13s, Bust of Nina, by Andrej Nikolov. 20s, Monument to P. K. Yavorov (kneeling woman), by Ivan Lazarov. 28s, Engineer, by Ivan Funev. 1 l, Refugees, by Sekul Krimov, horiz.

1971, Feb. *Perf. 12½*

No.	Type	Value	Description	Unused	Used
1920	A764	1s	gold & vio	.15	.15
1921	A764	2s	gold & dk ol grn	.15	.15
1922	A764	3s	gold & rose brn	.15	.15
1923	A764	13s	gold & dk grn	.30	.15
1924	A764	20s	gold & red brn	.52	.15
1925	A764	28s	gold & dk brn	.80	.20
			Nos. 1920-1925 (6)	2.07	
			Set value		.65

Souvenir Sheet

Imperf

No.	Type	Value	Description	Unused	Used
1926	A764	1 l	gold, dk brn & buff	2.00	1.75

Runner
A765

Design: 20s, Woman putting the shot.

1971, Mar. 13 Photo. *Perf. 12½x13*

No.	Type	Value	Description	Unused	Used
1927	A765	2s	brown & multi	.15	.15
1928	A765	20s	dp grn, org & blk	.90	.22
			Set value		.30

2nd European Indoor Track and Field Championships.

Bulgarian Secondary School, Bolgrad — A766

Educators: 20s, Dimiter Mitev, Prince Bogoridi and Sava Radoulov.

1971, Mar. 16 *Perf. 12½*

No.	Type	Value	Description	Unused	Used
1929	A766	2s	silver, brn & grn	.15	.15
1930	A766	20s	silver, brn & vio	.52	.15
			Set value		.20

First Bulgarian secondary school, 1858, in Bolgrad, USSR.

Communards — A767

1971, Mar. 18 Photo. *Perf. 12½x13*

No.	Type	Value	Description	Unused	Used
1931	A767	20s	rose mag & blk	.50	.20

Centenary of the Paris Commune.

Dimitrov Facing Goering, Quotation, FIR Emblem
A768

1971, Apr. 11 *Perf. 12½*

No.	Type	Value	Description	Unused	Used
1932	A768	2s	grn, gold, blk & red	.15	.15
1933	A768	13s	plum, gold, blk & red	.70	.15
			Set value		.15

Intl. Fed. of Resistance Fighters (FIR), 20th anniv.

George S. Rakovski (1821-1867), Revolutionary Against Turkish Rule — A769

1971, Apr. 14

No.	Type	Value	Description	Unused	Used
1934	A769	13s	olive & blk brn	.30	.15

Edelweiss Hotel, Borovets — A770

Designs: 2s, Panorama Hotel, Pamporovo. 4s, Boats at Albena, Black Sea. 8s, Boats at Rousalka. 10s, Shtastlivetsa Hotel, Mt. Vitosha.

1971 *Perf. 13*

No.	Type	Value	Description	Unused	Used
1935	A770	1s	brt green	.15	.15
1936	A770	2s	olive gray	.15	.15
1937	A770	4s	brt blue	.15	.15
1938	A770	8s	blue	.15	.15
1939	A770	10s	bluish green	.25	.15
			Set value	.65	.30

Technological Progress — A771

Designs: 1s, Mason with banner, vert. 13s, Two men and doves, vert.

1971, Apr. 20 Photo. *Perf. 12½*

No.	Type	Value	Description	Unused	Used
1940	A771	1s	gold & multi	.15	.15
1941	A771	2s	gray blue & multi	.15	.15
1942	A771	13s	lt green & multi	.52	.16
			Set value	.70	.30

10th Cong. of Bulgarian Communist Party.

Panayot Pipkov and Anthem
A772

1971, May 20

No.	Type	Value	Description	Unused	Used
1943	A772	13s	sil, blk & brt grn	.45	.15

Panayot Pipkov, composer, birth cent.

Mammoth
A773

Prehistoric Animals: 2s, Bear, vert. 3s, Hipparion (horse). 13s, Platybelodon. 20s, Dinotherium, vert. 28s, Saber-tooth tiger.

1971, May 29 *Perf. 12½*

No.	Type	Value	Description	Unused	Used
1944	A773	1s	dull bl & multi	.15	.15
1945	A773	2s	lilac & multi	.15	.15
1946	A773	3s	multicolored	.15	.15
1947	A773	13s	multicolored	.48	.15
1948	A773	20s	dp grn & multi	.80	.18
1949	A773	28s	multicolored	1.40	.28
			Nos. 1944-1949 (6)	3.13	
			Set value		.75

Khan Asparuch Crossing Danube, 679 A.D., by Boris Angelushev — A774

Historical Paintings: 3s, Reception at Trnovo, by Ilya Petrov. 5s, Chevartov's Troops at Benkovsky, by P. Morozov. 8s, Russian Gen. Gurko and People in Sofia, 1878, by D. Gudjenko. 28s, People Greeting Red Army, by S. Venov.

1971, Mar. 6 *Perf. 13½x14*

No.	Type	Value	Description	Unused	Used
1950	A774	2s	gold & multi	.15	.15
1951	A774	3s	gold & multi	.15	.15
1952	A774	5s	gold & multi	.16	.15
1953	A774	8s	gold & multi	.32	.15
a.			Souv. sheet of 4, #1950-1953	1.00	.50
1954	A774	28s	gold & multi	2.75	.85
			Nos. 1950-1954 (5)	3.53	
			Set value		1.20

In 1973, No. 1953a was surcharged 1 lev and overprinted "Visitez la Bulgarie," airline initials and emblems, and, on the 5s stamp, "Par Avion."

Freed Black, White and Yellow Men — A775

1971, May 20 Photo. *Perf. 12½*

No.	Type	Value	Description	Unused	Used
1955	A775	13s	blue, blk & yel	.35	.15

Intl. Year against Racial Discrimination.

Map of Europe, Championship Emblem — A776

"XXX" Supporting Barbell — A777

1971, June 19

No.	Type	Value	Description	Unused	Used
1956	A776	2s	lt blue & multi	.15	.15
1957	A777	13s	yellow & multi	.60	.18
			Set value	.65	.25

30th European Weight Lifting Championships, Sofia, June 19-27.

Facade, Old House, Koprivnica
A778

Designs: Decorated facades of various old houses in Koprivnica.

1971, July 10 Photo. *Perf. 12½*

No.	Type	Value	Description	Unused	Used
1958	A778	1s	green & multi	.15	.15
1959	A778	2s	brown & multi	.15	.15
1960	A778	6s	violet & multi	.15	.15
1961	A778	13s	dk red & multi	.42	.15
			Set value	.65	.30

Frontier Guard and German Shepherd
A779

1971, July 31 *Perf. 13*

No.	Type	Value	Description	Unused	Used
1962	A779	2s	green & ol grn	.15	.15

25th anniversary of the Frontier Guards.

Congress of Busludja, Bas-relief — A780

1971, July 31 *Perf. 12½*

No.	Type	Value	Description	Unused	Used
1963	A780	2s	dk red & ol grn	.15	.15

80th anniversary of the first Congress of the Bulgarian Social Democratic party.

Young Woman, by Ivan Nenov — A781

Paintings: 2s, Lazarova in Evening Gown, by Stefan Ivanov. 3s, Performer in Dress Suit, by Kyril Zonev. 13s, Portrait of a Woman, by Detchko Uzunov. 20s, Woman from Kalotina, by Vladimir Dimitrov. 40s, Gorjanin (Mountain Man), by Stoyan Venev.

1971, Aug. 2 *Perf. 14x13½*

1964	A781	1s green & multi	.15	.15
1965	A781	2s green & multi	.15	.15
1966	A781	3s green & multi	.15	.15
1967	A781	13s green & multi	.38	.15
1968	A781	20s green & multi	.75	.30
1969	A781	40s green & multi	1.65	.45
		Nos. 1964-1969 (6)	3.23	
		Set value		1.00

National Art Gallery.

Wrestlers A782

Designs: 13s, Wrestlers.

1971, Aug. 27 *Perf. 12½*

1970	A782	2s green, blk & bl	.15	.15
1971	A782	13s red org, blk & bl	.48	.15
		Set value		.20

European Wrestling Championships.

Young Workers A783

Post Horn Emblem A784

1971 **Photo.** *Perf. 13*

1972	A783	2s dark blue	.15	.15

25th anniv. of the Young People's Brigade.

1971, Sept. 15 *Perf. 12½*

1973	A784	20s dp green & gold	.45	.20

8th meeting of postal administrations of socialist countries, Varna.

FEBS Waves Emblem — A785

1971, Sept. 20

1974	A785	13s black, red & mar	.50	.20

7th Congress of European Biochemical Association (FEBS), Varna.

Statue of Republic — A786

Design: 13s, Bulgarian flag.

1971, Sept. 20 *Perf. 13x12½*

1975	A786	2s gold, yel & dk red	.15	.15
1976	A786	13s gold, grn & red	.38	.20
		Set value	.45	.25

Bulgarian People's Republic, 25th anniv.

Cross Country Skiing and Winter Olympics Emblem A787

Sport and Winter Olympics Emblem: 2s, Downhill skiing. 3s, Ski jump and skiing. 4s, Women's figure skating. 13s, Ice hockey. 28s, Slalom skiing. 1 l, Torch and stadium.

1971, Sept. 25 *Perf. 12½*

1977	A787	1s dk green & multi	.15	.15
1978	A787	2s vio blue & multi	.15	.15
1979	A787	3s ultra & multi	.15	.15
1980	A787	4s dp plum & multi	.15	.15
1981	A787	13s dk blue & multi	.40	.15
1982	A787	28s multicolored	.90	.35
		Set value	1.50	.75

Miniature Sheet

Imperf

1983	A787	1 l multicolored	3.50	1.65

11th Winter Olympic Games, Sapporo, Japan, Feb. 3-13, 1972.

Factory, Botevgrad A788

Industrial Buildings: 2s, Petro-chemical works, Pleven, vert. 10s, Chemical works, Vratsa. 13s, Maritsa-Istok Power Station, Dimitrovgrad. 40s, Electronics works, Sofia.

1971 **Photo.** *Perf. 13*

1984	A788	1s violet	.15	.15
1985	A788	2s orange	.15	.15
1986	A788	10s deep purple	.18	.15
1987	A788	13s lilac rose	.22	.15
1988	A788	40s deep brown	.70	.15
		Nos. 1984-1988 (5)	1.40	
		Set value		.32

UNESCO Emblem A789

1971, Nov. 4 *Perf. 12½*

1989	A789	20s lt bl, blk, gold & red	.45	.15

25th anniv. of UNESCO.

Soccer Player, by Kyril Zonev (1896-1971) A790

Paintings by Kyril Zonev: 2s, Landscape, horiz. 3s, Self-portrait. 13s, Lilies. 20s, Landscape, horiz. 40s, Portrait of a Young Woman.

1971, Nov. 10 *Perf. 11x12*

1990	A790	1s gold & multi	.15	.15
1991	A790	2s gold & multi	.15	.15
1992	A790	3s gold & multi	.15	.15
1993	A790	13s gold & multi	.22	.15
1994	A790	20s gold & multi	.85	.24
1995	A790	40s gold & multi	1.25	.35
		Nos. 1990-1995 (6)	2.77	
		Set value		.85

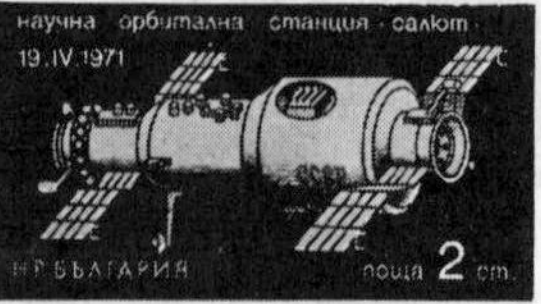
Salyut Space Station — A791

Astronauts Dobrovolsky, Volkov and Patsayev — A792

Designs: 13s, Soyuz 11 space transport. 40s, Salyut and Soyuz 11 joined.

1971, Dec. 20 *Perf. 12½*

1996	A791	2s dk grn, yel & red	.15	.15
1997	A791	13s multicolored	.22	.16
1998	A791	40s dk blue & multi	1.25	.40
		Nos. 1996-1998 (3)	1.62	.71

Souvenir Sheet

Imperf

1999	A792	80s multicolored	2.00	1.50

Salyut-Soyuz 11 space mission, and in memory of the Russian astronauts Lt. Col. Georgi T. Dobrovolsky, Vladislav N. Volkov and Victor I. Patsayev, who died during the Soyuz 11 space mission, June 6-30, 1971.

Oil Tanker Vihren A793

1972, Jan. 8 **Photo.** *Perf. 12½*

2000	A793	18s lil rose, vio & blk	.75	.25

Bulgarian shipbuilding industry.

Goce Delchev A794

Portraits: 5s, Jan Sandanski. 13s, Damjan Gruev.

1972, Jan. 21 **Photo.** *Perf. 12½*

2001	A794	2s brick red & blk	.15	.15
2002	A794	5s green & blk	.15	.15
2003	A794	13s lemon & blk	.35	.15
		Set value	.50	.22

Centenary of the births of Bulgarian patriots Delchev (1872-1903) and Sandanski, and of Macedonian Gruev (1871-1906).

Gymnast with Ball, Medals — A795

Designs: 18s, Gymnast with hoop, and medals. 70s, Gymnasts with hoops, and medals.

1972, Feb. 10

2004	A795	13s multicolored	.42	.15
2005	A795	18s multicolored	.55	.16
		Set value		.25

Miniature Sheet

Imperf

2006	A795	70s multicolored	2.25	2.00

5th World Women's Gymnastic Championships, Havana, Cuba.

View of Melnik, by Petar Mladenov — A796

Paintings from National Art Gallery: 2s, Plower, by Pencho Georgiev. 3s, Funeral, by Alexander Djendov. 13s, Husband and Wife, by Vladimir Dimitrov. 20s, Nursing Mother, by Nenko Balkanski. 40s, Paisii Hilendarski Writing History, by Koio Denchev.

1972, Feb. 20 *Perf. 13½x14*

2007	A796	1s green & multi	.15	.15
2008	A796	2s green & multi	.15	.15
2009	A796	3s green & multi	.15	.15
2010	A796	13s green & multi	.42	.15
2011	A796	20s green & multi	.75	.20
2012	A796	40s green & multi	1.25	.35
		Nos. 2007-2012 (6)	2.87	
		Set value		.90

Paintings from National Art Gallery.

Worker — A797

1972, Mar. 7 *Perf. 12½*

2013	A797	13s silver & multi	.20	.15

7th Bulgarian Trade Union Congress.

Singing Harvesters A798

Designs: Paintings by Vladimir Dimitrov.

Perf. 11½x12, 12x11½

1972, Mar. 31

2014	A798	1s shown	.15	.15
2015	A798	2s Harvester	.15	.15
2016	A798	3s Women Diggers	.15	.15
2017	A798	13s Fabric Dyers	.35	.15
2018	A798	20s "My Mother"	.70	.15
2019	A798	40s Self-portrait	1.40	.32
		Nos. 2014-2019 (6)	2.90	
		Set value		.80

Vladimir Dimitrov, painter, 90th birth anniv.

"Your Heart is your Health" — A799

St. Mark's Basilica and Wave — A800

1972, Apr. 30 ***Perf. 12½***

2020 A799 13s red, blk & grn .70 .30

World Health Day.

1972, May 6 ***Perf. 13x12½***

Design: 13s, Ca' D'Oro and wave.

2021 A800 2s ol grn, bl grn & lt bl .15 .15
2022 A800 13s red brn, vio & lt grn .52 .18
Set value .60 .25

UNESCO campaign to save Venice.

Dimitrov in Print Shop, 1901 — A801

Designs: Life of George Dimitrov.

1972, May 8 **Photo.** ***Perf. 12½***

2023 A801 1s shown .15 .15
2024 A801 2s Dimitrov as leader of 1923 uprising .15 .15
2025 A801 3s Leipzig trial, 1933 .15 .15
2026 A801 5s As Communist functionary, 1935 .15 .15
2027 A801 13s As leader and teacher, 1948 .15 .15
2028 A801 18s Addressing youth rally, 1948 .42 .15
2029 A801 28s With Pioneers, 1948 .65 .16
2030 A801 40s Mausoleum 1.00 .32
2031 A801 80s Portrait 2.75 .45
a. Souvenir sheet 4.25 2.50
Nos. 2023-2031 (9) 5.57 1.83

90th anniversary of the birth of George Dimitrov (1882-1949), communist leader.

No. 2031a contains one imperf. stamp similar to No. 2031, but in different colors.

Value, No. 2031 imperf. in slightly changed colors, $5.

Paisii Hilendarski — A802

Design: 2s, Flame and quotation.

1972, May 12

2032 A802 2s gold, grn & brn .15 .15
2033 A802 13s gold, grn & brn .50 .15
Set value .15

Paisii Hilendarski (1722-1798), monk, writer of Bulgarian-Slavic history.

Canoeing, Motion and Olympic Emblems — A803

Designs (Motion and Olympic emblems and): 2s, Gymnastics. 3s, Swimming, women's. 13s, Volleyball. 18s, Jumping. 40s, Wrestling. 80s, Stadium and sports.

1972, June 25

Figures of Athletes in Silver & Black

2034 A803 1s lt blue & multi .15 .15
2035 A803 2s orange & multi .15 .15
2036 A803 3s multicolored .15 .15
2037 A803 13s yellow & multi .15 .15
2038 A803 18s multicolored .42 .18
2039 A803 40s pink & multi 1.25 .30
Nos. 2034-2039 (6) 2.27
Set value .75

Miniature Sheet

Imperf

Size: 62x60mm

2040 A803 80s gold, ver & yel 1.75 1.00

20th Olympic Games, Munich, Aug. 26-Sept. 11.

Angel Kunchev A804

1972, June 30 **Photo.** ***Perf. 12½***

2041 A804 2s mag, dk pur & gold .15 .15

Centenary of the death of Angel Kunchev, patriot and revolutionist.

Zlatni Pyassatsi — A805

1972, Sept. 16

2042 A805 1s shown .15 .15
2043 A805 2s Drouzhba .15 .15
2044 A805 3s Slunchev Bryag .15 .15
2045 A805 13s Primorsko .15 .15
2046 A805 28s Roussalka .60 .24
2047 A805 40s Albena .85 .30
Nos. 2042-2047 (6) 2.05
Set value .80

Bulgarian Black Sea resorts.

Bronze Medal, Olympic Emblems, Canoeing A806

Designs (Olympic Emblems and): 2s, Silver medal, broad jump. 3s, Gold medal, boxing. 18s, Gold medal, wrestling. 40s, Gold medal, weight lifting.

1972, Sept. 29

2048 A806 1s Prus bl & multi .15 .15
2049 A806 2s dk green & multi .15 .15
2050 A806 3s orange brn & multi .15 .15
2051 A806 18s olive & multi .50 .16
2052 A806 40s multicolored 1.00 .30
Nos. 2048-2052 (5) 1.95
Set value .65

Bulgarian victories in 20th Olympic Games. For overprint see No. 2066.

Stoj Dimitrov — A807

Resistance Fighters: 2s, Cvetko Radoinov. 3s, Bogdan Stivrodski. 5s, Mirko Laiev. 13s, Nedelyo Nikolov.

1972, Oct. 30 **Photo.** ***Perf. 12½x13***

2053 A807 1s olive & multi .15 .15
2054 A807 2s multicolored .15 .15
2055 A807 3s multicolored .15 .15
2056 A807 5s multicolored .15 .15
2057 A807 13s multicolored .28 .15
Set value .60 .30

"50 Years USSR" A808

1972, Nov. 3 **Photo.** ***Perf. 12½x13***

2058 A808 13s gold, red & yel .35 .15

50th anniversary of Soviet Union.

Turk's-cap Lily — A809

Protected Plants: 2s, Gentian. 3s, Sea daffodil. 4s, Globe flower. 18s, Primrose. 23s, Pulsatilla vernalis. 40s, Snake's-head.

1972, Nov. 25 ***Perf. 12½***

Flowers in Natural Colors

2059 A809 1s olive bister .15 .15
2060 A809 2s olive bister .15 .15
2061 A809 3s olive bister .15 .15
2062 A809 4s olive bister .15 .15
2063 A809 18s olive bister .28 .15
2064 A809 23s olive bister .75 .20
2065 A809 40s olive bister 1.40 .35
Nos. 2059-2065 (7) 3.03
Set value .90

No. 2052 Overprinted in Red СВЕТОВЕН ПЪРВЕНЕЦ

1972, Nov. 27

2066 A806 40s multicolored .95 .24

Bulgarian weight lifting Olympic gold medalists.

Dobri Chintulov — A810

1972, Nov. 28 **Photo.** ***Perf. 12½***

2067 A810 2s gray, dk & lt grn .20 .15

Dobri Chintulov, writer, 150th birth anniversary.

Forehead Band — A811

Designs (14th-19th Century Jewelry): 2s, Belt buckles. 3s, Amulet. 8s, Pendant. 23s, Earrings. 40s, Necklace.

1972, Dec. 27 **Engr.** ***Perf. 14x13½***

2068 A811 1s red brn & blk .15 .15
2069 A811 2s emerald & blk .15 .15
2070 A811 3s Prus bl & blk .15 .15
2071 A811 8s dk red & blk .15 .15
2072 A811 23s red org & multi .50 .20
2073 A811 40s violet & blk 1.10 .42
Set value 1.90 .90

Skin Divers A812

Designs: 2s, Shelf-1 underwater house and divers. 18s, Diving bell and diver, vert. 40s, Elevation balloon and divers, vert.

1973, Jan. 24 **Photo.** ***Perf. 12½***

2074 A812 1s lt bl, blk & yel .15 .15
2075 A812 2s blk, bl & org yel .15 .15
2076 A812 18s blk, Prus bl & dl org .42 .15
2077 A812 40s blk, ultra & bister .95 .30
Nos. 2074-2077 (4) 1.67
Set value .54

Bulgarian deep-sea research in the Black Sea.

A souvenir sheet of four contains imperf. 20s stamps in designs of Nos. 2074-2077 with colors changed. Sold for 1 l. Value $3.50 unused, $3 canceled.

Execution of Levski, by Boris Angelushev — A813

Design: 20s, Vassil Levski, by Georgi Danchev.

1973, Feb. 19 ***Perf. 13x12½***

2078 A813 2s dull rose & Prus grn .15 .15
2079 A813 20s dull grn & brn .90 .18
Set value .23

Centenary of the death of Vassil Levski (1837-1873), patriot, executed by the Turks.

Kukersky Mask, Elhovo Region A814

Nicolaus Copernicus A815

Kukersky Masks at pre-Spring Festival: 2s, Breznik. 3s, Hissar. 13s, Radomir. 20s, Karnobat. 40s, Pernik.

1973, Feb. 26 ***Perf. 12½***

2080 A814 1s dp rose & multi .15 .15
2081 A814 2s emerald & multi .15 .15
2082 A814 3s violet & multi .15 .15
2083 A814 13s multicolored .35 .15
2084 A814 20s multicolored .38 .15
2085 A814 40s multicolored 2.25 1.10
Nos. 2080-2085 (6) 3.43
Set value 1.45

1973, Mar. 21 **Photo.** ***Perf. 12½***

2086 A815 28s ocher, blk & cl 1.25 .60

500th anniversary of the birth of Nicolaus Copernicus (1473-1543), Polish astronomer.

Vietnamese Worker and Rainbow — A816

1973, Apr. 16

2087 A816 18s lt blue & multi .35 .15

Peace in Viet Nam.

A817

A818

Wild flowers.

1973, May **Photo.** ***Perf. 13***

2088	A817	1s	Poppy	.15	.15
2089	A817	2s	Daisy	.15	.15
2090	A817	3s	Peony	.15	.15
2091	A817	13s	Centaury	.25	.15
2092	A817	18s	Corn cockle	2.75	1.10
2093	A817	28s	Ranunculus	.60	.22
			Nos. 2088-2093 (6)	4.05	
			Set value		1.50

1973, June 2

2094	A818	2s	pale grn, buff & brn	.15	.15
2095	A818	18s	pale brn, gray & grn	.65	.42

Christo Botev (1848-1876), poet.

"Suffering Worker" — A819

Design: 1s, Asen Halachev and revolutionists.

1973, June 6 **Photo.** ***Perf. 13***

2096	A819	1s	gold, red & blk	.15	.15
2097	A819	2s	gold, org & dk brn	.15	.15
			Set value	.15	.15

50th anniversary of Pleven uprising.

Muskrat A820

Perf. 12½x13, 13x12½

1973, June 29 **Litho.**

2098	A820	1s	shown	.15	.15
2099	A820	2s	Racoon	.15	.15
2100	A820	3s	Mouflon, vert.	.15	.15
2101	A820	12s	Fallow deer, vert.	.22	.15
2102	A820	18s	European bison	.50	.15
2103	A820	40s	Elk	2.50	1.00
			Nos. 2098-2103 (6)	3.67	
			Set value		1.35

Aleksandr Stamboliski A821

1973, June 14 **Photo.** ***Perf. 12½***

2104	A821	18s	dp brown & org	.35	.18
a.			18s orange	2.50	.75

Aleksandr Stamboliski (1879-1923), leader of Peasants' Party and premier.

Trade Union Emblem — A822

Stylized Sun, Olympic Rings — A823

1973, Aug. 27 **Photo.** ***Perf. 12½***

2105	A822	2s	yellow & multi	.15	.15

8th Congress of World Federation of Trade Unions, Varna, Oct. 15-22.

1973, Aug. 29 ***Perf. 13***

Designs: 28s, Emblem of Bulgarian Olympic Committee and Olympic rings. 80s, Soccer, emblems of Innsbruck and Montreal 1976 Games, horiz.

2106	A823	13s	multicolored	.70	.32
2107	A823	28s	multicolored	1.25	.40

Souvenir Sheet

2108	A823	80s	multicolored	3.25	1.75

Olympic Congress, Varna. No. 2108 contains one stamp. It also exists imperf.; also with violet margin, imperf.

Revolutionists with Communist Flag — A824

Designs: 5s, Revolutionists on flatcar blocking train. 13s, Raising Communist flag, vert. 18s, George Dimitrov and Vassil Kolarov.

1973, Sept. 22 **Photo.** ***Perf. 12½***

2109	A824	2s	magenta & multi	.15	.15
2110	A824	5s	magenta & multi	.15	.15
2111	A824	13s	magenta & multi	.30	.15
2112	A824	18s	magenta & multi	.85	.32
			Nos. 2109-2112 (4)	1.45	
			Set value		.50

50th anniv. of the September Revolution.

Warrior Saint — A825

Murals from Boyana Church: 1s, Tsar Kaloyan and 2s, his wife Dessislava. 5s, "St. Wystratti." 10s, Tsar Constantine Assen. 13s, Deacon Laurentius. 18s, Virgin Mary. 20s, St. Ephraim. 28s, Jesus. 80s, Jesus in the Temple, horiz.

1973, Sept. 24

2113	A825	1s	gold & multi	.15	.15
2114	A825	2s	gold & multi	.15	.15
2115	A825	3s	gold & multi	.15	.15
2116	A825	5s	gold & multi	.15	.15
2117	A825	10s	gold & multi	.35	.15
2118	A825	13s	gold & multi	.45	.15
2119	A825	18s	gold & multi	.70	.15
2120	A825	20s	gold & multi	.95	.18
2121	A825	28s	gold & multi	3.50	.35
			Nos. 2113-2121 (9)	6.55	
			Set value		1.00

Miniature Sheet

Imperf

2122	A825	80s	gold & multi	3.75	2.25

No. 2122 contains one stamp with simulated perforations.

Christo Smirnenski — A826

1973, Sept. 29 **Photo.** ***Perf. 12½***

2123	A826	1s	multicolored	.15	.15
2124	A826	2s	vio blue & multi	.18	.15
			Set value	.25	.15

75th anniversary of the birth of Christo Smirnenski (1898-1923), poet.

Human Rights Flame — A827

1973, Oct. 10

2125	A827	13s	dk blue, red & gold	.30	.16

25th anniversary of the Universal Declaration of Human Rights.

Type of 1970

History of Bulgaria: 1s, Tsar Theodor Svetoslav receiving Byzantine envoys. 2s, Tsar Mihail Shishman's army in battle with Byzantines. 3s, Tsar Ivan Alexander's victory at Russocastro. 4s, Patriarch Euthimius at the defense of Turnovo. 5s, Tsar Ivan Shishman leading horsemen against the Turks. 13s, Momchil attacking Turks at Umour. 18s, Tsar Ivan Stratsimir meeting King Sigismund's crusaders. 28s, The Boyars Balik, Theodor and Dobrotitsa, meeting ship bringing envoys from Anne of Savoy.

1973, Oct. 23 ***Perf. 13***

Silver and Black Vignettes

2126	A741	1s	olive bister	.15	.15
2127	A741	2s	Prus blue	.15	.15
2128	A741	3s	lilac	.15	.15
2129	A741	4s	green	.15	.15
2130	A741	5s	violet	.15	.15
2131	A741	13s	orange & brn	.22	.15
2132	A741	18s	olive green	.40	.18
2133	A741	28s	yel brn & brn	1.10	.48
			Nos. 2126-2133 (8)	2.47	
			Set value		1.25

Finn Class — A828

Sailboats: 2s, Flying Dutchman. 3s, Soling class. 13s, Tempest class. 20s, Class 470. 40s, Tornado class.

1973, Oct. 29 **Litho.** ***Perf. 13***

2134	A828	1s	ultra & multi	.15	.15
2135	A828	2s	green & multi	.15	.15
2136	A828	3s	dk blue & multi	.15	.15
2137	A828	13s	dull vio & multi	.28	.15
2138	A828	20s	gray bl & multi	.60	.32
2139	A828	40s	dk blue & multi	2.50	2.00
			Nos. 2134-2139 (6)	3.83	2.92

Value, set imperf. in changed colors, $10.

Village, by Bencho Obreshkov — A829

Paintings: 2s, Mother and Child, by Stoyan Venev. 3s, Rest (woman), by Tsenko Boyadjiev. 13s, Flowers in Vase, by Sirak Skitnik. 18s, Meri Kuneva (portrait), by Ilya Petrov. 40s, Winter in Plovdiv, by Zlatyu Boyadjiev. 13s, 18s, 40s, vert.

Perf. 12½x12, 12x12½

1973, Nov. 10

2140	A829	1s	gold & multi	.15	.15
2141	A829	2s	gold & multi	.15	.15
2142	A829	3s	gold & multi	.15	.15
2143	A829	13s	gold & multi	.22	.15
2144	A829	18s	gold & multi	.42	.20
2145	A829	40s	gold & multi	2.25	.75
			Nos. 2140-2145 (6)	3.34	
			Set value		1.20

Souvenir Sheet

Paintings by Stanislav Dospevski: a, Domnica Lambreva. b, Self-portrait. Both vert.

2146		Sheet of 2	2.75	1.75
a.	A829	50s gold & multi	.70	.52
b.	A829	50s gold & multi	.70	.52

Bulgarian paintings. No. 2146 commemorates the 150th birth anniv. of Stanislav Dospevski.

Souvenir Sheet

Soccer A830

1973, Dec. 10 **Photo.** ***Perf. 13***

2147	A830	28s	multicolored	4.00	3.50

No. 2147 sold for 1 l. Exists overprinted for Argentina 78.

Angel and Ornaments — A831

Designs: 1s, Attendant facing right. 2s, Passover table and lamb. 3s, Attendant facing left. 8s, Abraham and ornaments. 13s, Adam and Eve. 28s, Expulsion from Garden of Eden.

1974, Jan. 21 **Photo.** ***Perf. 13***

2148	A831	1s	fawn, yel & brn	.15	.15
2149	A831	2s	fawn, yel & brn	.15	.15
2150	A831	3s	fawn, yel & brn	.15	.15
a.			Strip of 3, #2148-2150	.25	.20
2151	A831	5s	slate grn & yel	.15	.15
2152	A831	8s	slate grn & yel	.20	.15
a.			Pair, #2151-2152	.30	.25
2153	A831	13s	lt brown, yel & ol	.28	.24
2154	A831	28s	lt brown, yel & ol	.52	.32
a.			Pair, #2153-2154	.80	.35
			Set value	1.28	1.00

Woodcarvings from Rozhen Monastery, 19th century.

Lenin, by N. Mirtchev — A832

Design: 18s, Lenin visiting Workers, by W. A. Serov.

1974, Jan. 28 Litho. *Perf. 12½x12*

2155 A832 2s ocher & multi .15 .15
2156 A832 18s ocher & multi .48 .22
Set value .30

50th anniversary of the death of Lenin.

1974, Jan. 28

Design: Demeter Blagoev at Rally, by G. Kowachev.

2157 A832 2s multicolored .15 .15

50th anniversary of the death of Demeter Blagoev, founder of Bulgarian Communist Party.

Domestic Animals A833

1974, Feb. 1 Photo. *Perf. 13*

2158 A833 1s Sheep .15 .15
2159 A833 2s Goat .15 .15
2160 A833 3s Pig .15 .15
2161 A833 5s Cow .16 .15
2162 A833 13s Buffalo cow .30 .15
2163 A833 20s Horse .80 .28
Nos. 2158-2163 (6) 1.71
Set value .75

Comecon Emblem A834

1974, Feb. 11 Photo. *Perf. 13*

2164 A834 13s silver & multi .40 .15

25th anniversary of the Council of Mutual Economic Assistance.

Soccer — A835

Designs: Various soccer action scenes.

1974, Mar. Photo. *Perf. 13*

2165 A835 1s dull green & multi .15 .15
2166 A835 2s brt green & multi .15 .15
2167 A835 3s slate grn & multi .15 .15
2168 A835 13s olive & multi .15 .20
2169 A835 28s blue grn & multi .65 .42
2170 A835 40s emerald & multi 1.50 .70
Nos. 2165-2170 (6) 2.75 1.77

Souvenir Sheet

2171 A835 1 l green & multi 3.00 1.65

World Soccer Championship, Munich, June 13-July 7. No. 2171 exists imperf.

Salt Production A836

Children's Paintings: 1s, Cosmic Research for Peaceful Purposes. 3s, Fire Dancers. 28s, Russian-Bulgarian Friendship (train and children). 60s, Spring (birds).

1974, Apr. 15 Photo. *Perf. 13*

2172 A836 1s lilac & multi .15 .15
2173 A836 2s lt green & multi .15 .15
2174 A836 3s blue & multi .15 .15
2175 A836 28s slate & multi 1.75 .95
Nos. 2172-2175 (4) 2.20 1.40

Souvenir Sheet

Imperf

2176 A836 60s blue & multi 2.25 1.75

Third World Youth Philatelic Exhibition, Sofia, May 23-30. No. 2176 contains one stamp with simulated perforations.

Folk Singers — A837

Designs: 2s, Folk dancers (men). 3s, Bagpiper and drummer. 5s, Wrestlers. 13s, Runners (women). 18s, Gymnast.

1974, Apr. 25 *Perf. 13*

2178 A837 1s vermilion & multi .15 .15
2179 A837 2s orange brn & multi .15 .15
2180 A837 3s brn red & multi .15 .15
2181 A837 5s blue & multi .15 .15
2182 A837 13s ultra & multi .75 .24
2183 A837 18s violet bl & multi .42 .15
Set value 1.45 .58

4th Amateur Arts and Sports Festival

Flowers A838

1974, May Photo. *Perf. 13*

2184 A838 1s Aster .15 .15
2185 A838 2s Petunia .15 .15
2186 A838 3s Fuchsia .15 .15
2187 A838 18s Tulip .28 .15
2188 A838 20s Carnation .60 .22
2189 A838 28s Pansy 1.65 .55
Nos. 2184-2189 (6) 2.98
Set value 1.10

Souvenir Sheet

2190 A838 80s Sunflower 1.75 .85

Automobiles and Emblems A839

1974, May 15 Photo. *Perf. 13*

2191 A839 13s multicolored .30 .15

International Automobile Federation (FIA) Spring Congress, Sofia, May 20-24.

Old and New Buildings, UNESCO Emblem A840

1974, June 15

2192 A840 18s multicolored .30 .15

UNESCO Executive Council, 94th Session, Varna.

Postrider A841

Designs: 18s, First Bulgarian mail coach. 28s, UPU Monument, Bern.

1974, Aug. 5

2193 A841 2s ocher, blk & vio .15 .15
2194 A841 18s ocher, blk & grn .38 .15
Set value .45 .19

Souvenir Sheet

2195 A841 28s ocher, blk & bl 2.00 1.50

UPU cent. No. 2195 exists imperf.

Pioneer and Komsomol Girl — A842

Designs: 2s, Pioneer and birds. 60s, Emblem with portrait of George Dimitrov.

1974, Aug. 12

2196 A842 1s green & multi .15 .15
2197 A842 2s blue & multi .15 .15
Set value .15 .15

Souvenir Sheet

2198 A842 60s red & multi 1.65 1.10

30th anniversary of Dimitrov Pioneer Organization, Septemvrilche.

"Bulgarian Communist Party" — A843

Symbolic Designs: 2s, Russian liberators. 5s, Industrialization. 13s, Advanced agriculture and husbandry. 18s, Scientific and technical progress.

1974, Aug. 20

2199 A843 1s blue gray & multi .15 .15
2200 A843 2s blue gray & multi .15 .15
2201 A843 5s gray & multi .15 .15
2202 A843 13s gray & multi .26 .15
2203 A843 18s gray & multi .35 .15
Set value .85 .30

30th anniversary of the People's Republic.

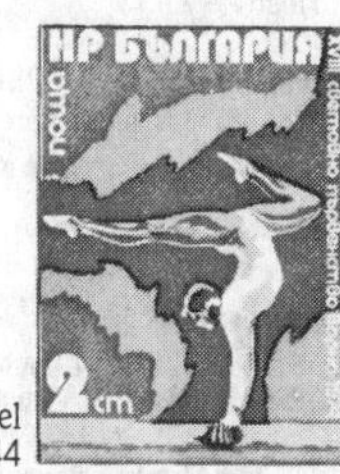

Gymnast on Parallel Bars — A844

Design: 13s, Gymnast on vaulting horse.

1974, Oct. 18 Photo. *Perf. 13*

2204 A844 2s multicolored .15 .15
2205 A844 13s multicolored .28 .20
Set value .35 .25

18th Gymnastic Championships, Varna.

Souvenir Sheet

Symbols of Peace — A845

1974, Oct. 29 Photo. *Perf. 13*

2206 A845 Sheet of 4 2.50 1.10
a. 13s Doves .18 .15
b. 13s Map of Europe .18 .15
c. 13s Olive Branch .18 .15
d. 13s Inscription .18 .15

1974 European Peace Conference. "Peace" in various languages written on Nos. 2206a-2206c. Sold for 60s. Exists imperf.

Nib and Envelope — A846

1974, Nov. 20

2207 A846 2s yellow, blk & grn .15 .15

Introduction of postal zone numbers.

Flowers A847

1974, Dec. 5

2208 A847 2s emerald & multi .15 .15

St. Todor, Ceramic Icon — A848

Fruit Tree Blossoms — A849

Designs: 2s, Medallion, Veliko Turnovo. 3s, Carved capital. 5s, Silver bowl. 8s, Goblet. 13s, Lion's head finial. 18s, Gold plate with Cross. 28s, Breastplate with eagle.

1974, Dec. 18 Photo. *Perf. 13*

2209 A848 1s orange & multi .15 .15
2210 A848 2s pink & multi .15 .15
2211 A848 3s blue & multi .15 .15
2212 A848 5s lt vio & multi .15 .15
2213 A848 8s brown & multi .15 .15
2214 A848 13s multicolored .22 .15
2215 A848 18s red & multi .32 .16
2216 A848 28s ultra & multi 1.00 .60
Set value 1.90 1.25

Art works from 9th-12th centuries.

1975, Jan. Photo. *Perf. 13*

2217 A849 1s Apricot .15 .15
2218 A849 2s Apple .15 .15
2219 A849 3s Cherry .15 .15
2220 A849 19s Pear .28 .15
2221 A849 28s Peach .70 .25
Set value 1.10 .50

Tree and Book A850

1975, Mar. 25 Photo. *Perf. 13*

2222 A850 2s gold & multi	.15	.15

Forestry High School, 50th anniversary.

Souvenir Sheet

Farmers' Activities (Woodcuts) — A851

1975, Mar. 25

2223 A851 Sheet of 4	.80	.48
a. 2s Farmer with ax and flag		
b. 5s Farmers on guard		
c. 13s Dancing couple		
d. 18s Woman picking fruit		

Bulgarian Agrarian Peoples Union, 75th anniv.

Michelangelo, Self-portrait A852

Designs: 13s, Night, horiz. 18s, Day, horiz. Both designs after sculptures from Medici Tomb, Florence.

1975

2224 A852 2s plum & dk blue	.15	.15
2225 A852 13s vio bl & plum	.24	.15
2226 A852 18s brown & green	.52	.15
Nos. 2224-2226 (3)	.91	
Set value		.30

Souvenir Sheet

2227 A852 2s olive & red	1.25	1.25

Michelangelo Buonarotti (1475-1564), Italian sculptor, painter and architect. No. 2227 issued to publicize ARPHILA 75 Intl. Phil. Exhib., Paris, June 6-16. Sheet sold for 60s.

Issued: #2224-2226, 3/28; #2227, 3/31.

Souvenir Sheet

Spain No. 1 and España 75 Emblem A853

1975, Apr. 4

2228 A853 40s multicolored	3.75	3.00

Espana 75 International Philatelic Exhibition, Madrid, Apr. 4-13.

Gabrov Costume — A854

Regional Costumes: 3s, Trnsk. 5s, Vidin. 13s, Gocedelchev. 18s, Risen.

1975, Apr. Photo. *Perf. 13*

2229 A854 2s blue & multi	.15	.15
2230 A854 3s emerald & multi	.15	.15
2231 A854 5s orange & multi	.15	.15
2232 A854 13s olive & multi	.35	.15
2233 A854 18s multicolored	.80	.24
Nos. 2229-2233 (5)	1.60	
Set value		.50

Red Star and Arrow — A855

Standard Kilogram and Meter — A856

Design: 13s, Dove and broken sword.

1975, May 9

2234 A855 2s red, blk & gold	.15	.15
2235 A855 13s blue, blk & gold	.32	.15
Set value	.37	.19

Victory over Fascism, 30th anniversary.

1975, May 9 *Perf. 13x13½*

2236 A856 13s silver, lil & blk	.35	.15

Cent. of Intl. Meter Convention, Paris, 1875.

IWY Emblem, Woman's Head — A857

Ivan Vasov — A858

1975, May 20 Photo. *Perf. 13*

2237 A857 13s multicolored	.35	.15

International Women's Year 1975.

1975, May

Design: 13s, Ivan Vasov, seated.

2238 A858 2s buff & multi	.15	.15
2239 A858 13s gray & multi	.32	.15
Set value	.40	.15

125th birth anniversary of Ivan Vasov.

Nikolov and Sava Kokarechkov — A859

Designs: 2s, Mitko Palaouzov and Ivan Vassilev. 5s, Nicolas Nakev and Stevtcho Kraychev. 13s, Ivanka Pachkoulova and Detelina Mintcheva.

1975, May 30

2240 A859 1s multicolored	.15	.15
2241 A859 2s multicolored	.15	.15
2242 A859 5s multicolored	.15	.15
2243 A859 13s multicolored	.28	.15
Set value	.50	.35

Teen-age resistance fighters, killed during World War II.

Mother Feeding Child, by John E. Millais — A861

Etchings: 2s, The Dead Daughter, by Goya. 3s, Reunion, by Beshkov. 13s, Seated Nude, by Renoir. 20s, Man in a Fur Hat, by Rembrandt. 40s, The Dream, by Daumier, horiz. 1 l, Temptation, by Dürer.

Photogravure and Engraved

1975, Aug. *Perf. 12x11½, 11½x12*

2248 A861 1s yel grn & multi	.15	.15
2249 A861 2s orange & multi	.15	.15
2250 A861 3s lilac & multi	.15	.15
2251 A861 13s lt blue & multi	.26	.15
2252 A861 20s ocher & multi	.40	.18
2253 A861 40s rose & multi	1.10	.28
Set value	1.95	.70

Souvenir Sheet

2254 A861 1 l emerald & multi	2.00	1.25

World Graphics Exhibition.

Letter "Z" from 12th Century Manuscript A862

Initials from Illuminated Manuscripts: 2s, "B" from 17th cent. prayerbook. 3s, "V" from 16th cent. Bouhovo Gospel. 8s, "B" from 14th cent. Turnovo collection. 13s, "V" from Dobreisho's Gospel, 13th cent. 18s, "E" from 11th cent. Enina book of the Apostles.

1975, Aug. Litho. *Perf. 11½*

2255 A862 1s multicolored	.15	.15
2256 A862 2s multicolored	.15	.15
2257 A862 3s multicolored	.15	.15
2258 A862 8s multicolored	.15	.15
2259 A862 13s multicolored	.25	.15
2260 A862 18s multicolored	.65	.16
Set value	1.25	.50

Bulgarian art.

Whimsical Globe — A863

1975, Aug. Photo. *Perf. 13*

2261 A863 2s multicolored	.15	.15

Festival of Humor and Satire.

Lifeboat Dju IV and Gibraltar-Cuba Route — A864

1975, Aug. 5 Photo. *Perf. 13*

2262 A864 13s multicolored	.25	.15

Oceanexpo 75, 1st Intl. Ocean Exhib., Okinawa, July 20, 1975-Jan. 18, 1976.

Sts. Cyril and Methodius A865

Sts. Constantine and Helena A866

St. Sophia Church, Sofia, Woodcut by V. Zahriev — A867

1975, Aug. 21

2263 A865 2s ver, yel & brn	.15	.15
2264 A866 13s green, yel & brn	.25	.15
Set value	.30	.20

Souvenir Sheet

2265 A867 50s orange & multi	1.25	.80

Balkanphila V, philatelic exhibition, Sofia, Sept. 27-Oct. 5.

Peace Dove and Map of Europe — A868

1975, Nov. Photo. *Perf. 13*

2266 A868 18s ultra, rose & yel	.45	.22

European Security and Cooperation Conference, Helsinki, Finland, July 30-Aug. 1. No. 2266 printed in sheets of 5 stamps and 4 labels, arranged checkerwise.

Acherontia Atropos A869

Designs: Moths.

1975 Photo. *Perf. 13*

2267 A869 1s *shown*	.15	.15
2268 A869 2s *Daphnis nerii*	.15	.15
2269 A869 3s *Smerinthus ocellata*	.15	.15
2270 A869 10s *Deilephila nicea*	.20	.15

2271	A869	13s	*Choerocampa elpenor*	.24	.15
2272	A869	18s	*Macroglossum fuciformis*	.90	.24
			Set value	1.50	.53

Soccer Player — A870

1975, Sept. 21

2273	A870	2s	multicolored	.15	.15

8th Inter-Toto (soccer pool) Soccer Championships, Varna.

Constantine's Rebellion Against the Turks, 1403 — A871

Designs (Woodcuts): 2s, Campaign of Vladislav III, 1443-1444. 3s, Battles of Turnovo, 1598 and 1686. 10s, Battle of Liprovsko, 1688. 13s, Guerrillas, 17th century. 18s, Return of exiled peasants.

1975, Nov. 27 **Photo.** ***Perf. 13***

2274	A871	1s	bister, grn & blk	.15	.15
2275	A871	2s	blue, car & blk	.15	.15
2276	A871	3s	yellow, lil & blk	.15	.15
2277	A871	10s	orange, grn & blk	.16	.15
2278	A871	13s	green, lil & blk	.22	.15
2279	A871	18s	pink, grn & blk	.45	.18
			Set value	1.00	.45

Bulgarian history.

Red Cross and First Aid — A872

Design: 13s, Red Cross and dove.

1975, Dec. 1

2280	A872	2s	red brn, red & blk	.15	.15
2281	A872	13s	bl grn, red & blk	.22	.15
			Set value	.30	.15

90th anniversary of Bulgarian Red Cross.

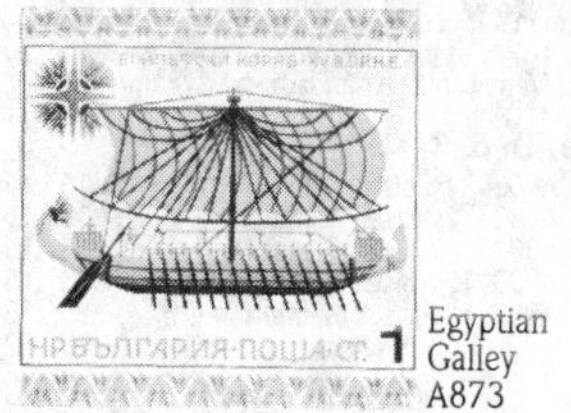

Egyptian Galley A873

Historic Ships: 2s, Phoenician galley. 3s, Greek trireme. 5s, Roman galley. 13s, Viking longship. 18s, Venetian galley.

1975, Dec. 15 **Photo.** ***Perf. 13***

2282	A873	1s	multicolored	.15	.15
2283	A873	2s	multicolored	.15	.15
2284	A873	3s	multicolored	.15	.15
2285	A873	5s	multicolored	.15	.15
2286	A873	13s	multicolored	.32	.15
2287	A873	18s	multicolored	.60	.16
			Set value	1.25	.46

See Nos. 2431-2436, 2700-2705.

Souvenir Sheet

Ethnographical Museum, Plovdiv — A874

1975, Dec. 17

2288		Sheet of 3	4.50	2.50
a.	A874	80s green, yellow & dark brown	1.25	.65

European Architectural Heritage Year. No. 2288 contains 3 stamps and 3 labels showing stylized bird.

Dobri Hristov — A875

1975, Dec. ***Perf. 13***

2289	A875	5s	brt green, yel & brn	.15	.15

Dobri Hristov, musician, birth centenary.

United Nations Emblem — A876

1975, Dec.

2290	A876	13s	gold, blk & mag	.20	.15

United Nations, 30th anniversary.

Glass Ornaments A877

Design: 13s, Peace dove, decorated ornament.

1975, Dec. 22 **Photo.** ***Perf. 13***

2291	A877	2s	brt violet & multi	.15	.15
2292	A877	13s	gray & multi	.20	.15
			Set value	.25	.15

New Year 1976.

Downhill Skiing — A878

Designs (Winter Olympic Games Emblem and): 2s, Cross country skier, vert. 3s, Ski jump. 13s, Biathlon, vert. 18s, Ice hockey, vert. 23s, Speed skating, vert. 80s, Figure skating, pair, vert.

1976, Jan. 30 ***Perf. 13½***

2293	A878	1s	silver & multi	.15	.15
2294	A878	2s	silver & multi	.15	.15
2295	A878	3s	silver & multi	.15	.15
2296	A878	13s	silver & multi	.22	.15
2297	A878	18s	silver & multi	.32	.15
2298	A878	23s	silver & multi	.80	.30
			Set value	1.50	.68

Souvenir Sheet

2299	A878	80s	silver & multi	1.65	1.10

12th Winter Olympic Games, Innsbruck, Austria, Feb. 4-15.

Electric Streetcar, Sofia, 1976 — A879

Design: 13s, Streetcar and trailer, 1901.

1976, Jan. 12 **Photo.** ***Perf. 13½x13***

2300	A879	2s	gray & multi	.15	.15
2301	A879	13s	gray & multi	.38	.15
			Set value		.15

75th anniversary of Sofia streetcars.

Stylized Bird — A880

Designs: 5s, Dates "1976" and "1956" and star. 13s, Hammer and sickle. 50s, George Dimitrov.

1976, Mar. 1 ***Perf. 13***

2302	A880	2s	gold & multi	.15	.15
2303	A880	5s	gold & multi	.15	.15
2304	A880	13s	gold & multi	.25	.15
			Set value	.45	.18

Souvenir Sheet

2305	A880	50s	gold & multi	1.00	.45

11th Bulgarian Communist Party Congress.

A. G. Bell and Telephone, 1876 A881

1976, Mar. 10

2306	A881	18s	dk brn, yel & ocher	.25	.15

Centenary of first telephone call by Alexander Graham Bell, Mar. 10, 1876.

Mute Swan — A882

Waterfowl: 2s, Ruddy shelduck. 3s, Common shelduck. 5s, Garganey teal. 13s, Mallard. 18s, Red-crested pochard.

1976, Mar. 27 **Litho.** ***Perf. 11½***

2307	A882	1s	vio bl & multi	.15	.15
2308	A882	2s	yel grn & multi	.15	.15
2309	A882	3s	blue & multi	.15	.15
2310	A882	5s	multicolored	.22	.15
2311	A882	13s	purple & multi	.65	.15
2312	A882	18s	green & multi	.90	.15
			Nos. 2307-2312 (6)	2.22	
			Set value		.40

Guerrillas — A883

Designs (Woodcuts by Stoev): 2s, Peasants with rifle and proclamation. 5s, Raina Knaginia with horse and guerrilla. 13s, Insurgents with cherrywood cannon.

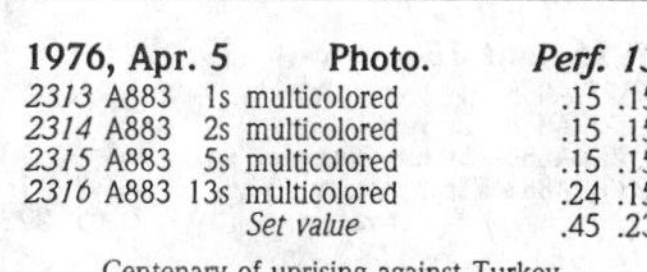

1976, Apr. 5 **Photo.** ***Perf. 13***

2313	A883	1s	multicolored	.15	.15
2314	A883	2s	multicolored	.15	.15
2315	A883	5s	multicolored	.15	.15
2316	A883	13s	multicolored	.24	.15
			Set value	.45	.23

Centenary of uprising against Turkey.

Guard and Dog A884

Design: 13s, Men on horseback, observation tower.

1976, May 15

2317	A884	2s	multicolored	.15	.15
2318	A884	13s	multicolored	.20	.15
			Set value	.25	.15

30th anniversary of Border Guards.

Construction Worker — A885

1976, May 20

2319	A885	2s	multicolored	.15	.15

Young Workers Brigade, 30th anniversary.

Busludja, Bas-relief — A886

AES Complex — A887

Design: 5s, Memorial building.

1976, May 28 **Photo.** ***Perf. 13***

2320	A886	2s	green & multi	.15	.15
2321	A886	5s	violet bl & multi	.15	.15
			Set value	.20	.15

First Congress of Bulgarian Social Democratic Party, 85th anniversary.

1976, Apr. 7

Designs: 8s, Factory. 10s, Apartment houses. 13s, Refinery. 20s, Hydroelectric station.

2322	A887	5s	green	.15	.15
2323	A887	8s	maroon	.16	.15
2324	A887	10s	green	.20	.15
2325	A887	13s	violet	.32	.15
2326	A887	20s	brt green	.42	.15
			Nos. 2322-2326 (5)	1.25	
			Set value		.32

Five-year plan accomplishments.

Children Playing Around Table — A888

Designs (Kindergarten Children): 2s, with doll carriage and hobby horse. 5s, playing ball. 23s, in costume.

1976, June 15

2327 A888 1s green & multi .15 .15
2328 A888 2s yellow & multi .15 .15
2329 A888 5s lilac & multi .15 .15
2330 A888 23s rose & multi .42 .15
Set value .65 .29

Demeter Blagoev — A889

Christo Botev — A890

1976, May 28

2331 A889 13s bluish blk, red & gold .25 .15

Demeter Blagoev (1856-1924), writer, political leader, 120th birth anniversary.

1976, May 25

2332 A890 13s ocher & slate grn .25 .15

Christo Botev (1848-1876), poet, death centenary. Printed se-tenant with yellow green and ocher label, inscribed with poem.

Boxing, Montreal Olympic Emblem — A891

Belt Buckle — A892

Designs (Montreal Olympic Emblem): 1s, Wrestling, horiz. 3s, 1 l, Weight lifting. 13s, One-man kayak. 18s, Woman gymnast. 28s, Woman diver. 40s, Woman runner.

1976, June 25

2333 A891 1s orange & multi .15 .15
2334 A891 2s multicolored .15 .15
2335 A891 3s lilac & multi .15 .15
2336 A891 13s multicolored .18 .15
2337 A891 18s multicolored .28 .15
2338 A891 28s blue & multi .38 .16
2339 A891 40s lemon & multi .75 .30
Set value 1.75 .75

Souvenir Sheet

2340 A891 1 l orange & multi 1.65 1.10

21st Olympic Games, Montreal, Canada, July 17-Aug. 1.

1976, July 30 Photo. *Perf. 13*

Thracian Art (8th-4th Centuries): 2s, Brooch. 3s, Mirror handle. 5s, Helmet cheek cover. 13s, Gold ornament. 18s, Lion's head (harness decoration). 20s, Knee guard. 28s, Jeweled pendant.

2341 A892 1s brown & multi .15 .15
2342 A892 2s blue & multi .15 .15
2343 A892 3s multicolored .15 .15
2344 A892 5s claret & multi .15 .15
2345 A892 13s purple & multi .24 .15
2346 A892 18s multicolored .32 .15
2347 A892 20s multicolored .42 .15
2348 A892 28s multicolored .60 .18
Set value 1.85 .68

Composite of Bulgarian Stamp Designs A893

1976, June 5

2349 A893 50s red & multi 1.65 .65

International Federation of Philately (F.I.P.), 50th anniversary and 12th Congress.

Partisans at Night, by Ilya Petrov — A894

Paintings: 5s, Old Town, by Tsanko Lavenov. 13s, Seated Woman, by Petrov, vert. 18s, Seated Boy, by Petrov, vert. 28s, Old Plovdiv, by Lavenov, vert. 80s, Ilya Petrov, self-portrait, vert.

1976, Aug. 11 Photo. *Perf. 14*

2350 A894 2s multicolored .15 .15
2351 A894 5s multicolored .15 .15
2352 A894 13s ultra & multi .32 .15
2353 A894 18s multicolored .45 .15
2354 A894 28s multicolored .65 .18
Nos. 2350-2354 (5) 1.72
Set value .45

Souvenir Sheet

2354A A894 80s multicolored 1.25 .95

Souvenir Sheet

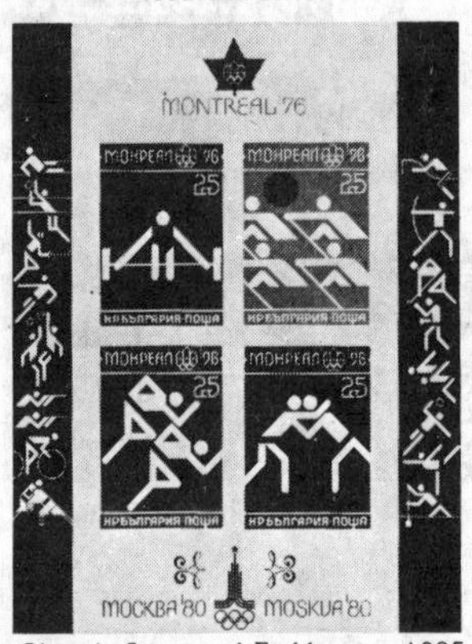

Olympic Sports and Emblems — A895

1976, Sept. 6 Photo. *Perf. 13*

2355 A895 Sheet of 4 1.65 1.00
a. 25s Weight Lifting .35 .18
b. 25s Rowing .35 .18
c. 25s Running .35 .18
d. 25s Wrestling .35 .18

Medalists, 21st Olympic Games, Montreal.

Souvenir Sheet

Fresco and UNESCO Emblem — A896

1976, Dec. 3

2356 A896 50s red & multi 1.25 .55

UNESCO, 30th anniv.

"The Pianist" by Jendov — A897

Fish and Hook — A898

Designs (Caricatures by Jendov): 5s, Imperialist "Trick or Treat." 13s, The Leader, 1931.

1976, Sept. 30 Photo. *Perf. 13*

2357 A897 2s green & multi .15 .15
2358 A897 5s purple & multi .15 .15
2359 A897 13s magenta & multi .32 .15
Set value .50 .18

Alex Jendov (1901-1953), caricaturist.

1976, Sept. 21 Photo. *Perf. 13*

2360 A898 5s multicolored .15 .15

World Sport Fishing Congress, Varna.

St. Theodore A899

Frescoes: 3s, St. Paul. 5s, St. Joachim. 13s, Melchizedek. 19s, St. Porphyrius. 28s, Queen. 1 l, The Last Supper.

1976, Oct. 4 Litho. *Perf. 12x12½*

2361 A899 2s gold & multi .15 .15
2362 A899 3s gold & multi .15 .15
2363 A899 5s gold & multi .15 .15
2364 A899 13s gold & multi .32 .15
2365 A899 19s gold & multi .35 .15
2366 A899 28s gold & multi .65 .20
Set value 1.50 .56

Miniature Sheet

Perf. 12

2367 A899 1 l gold & multi 1.50 .95

Zemen Monastery frescoes, 14th cent.

Document — A900

1976, Oct. 5

2368 A900 5s multicolored .15 .15

State Archives, 25th anniversary.

Cinquefoil — A901

1976, Oct. 14 Photo. *Perf. 13*

2369 A901 1s Chestnut .15 .15
2370 A901 2s shown .15 .15
2371 A901 5s Holly .15 .15
2372 A901 8s Yew .15 .15
2373 A901 13s Daphne .32 .15
2374 A901 23s Judas tree .60 .18
Set value 1.25 .46

Dimitri Polianov — A902

1976, Nov. 19

2375 A902 2s dk purple & ocher .15 .15

Dimitri Polianov (1876-1953), poet.

Christo Botev, by Zlatyu Boyadjiev A903

Paintings: 2s, Partisan Carrying Cherrywood Cannon, by Ilya Petrov. 3s, "Necklace of Immortality" (man's portrait), by Detchko Uzunov. 13s, "April 1876," by Georgi Popoff. 18s, Partisans, by Stoyan Venev. 60s, The Oath, by Svetlin Ruseff.

1976, Dec. 8

2376 A903 1s bister & multi .15 .15
2377 A903 2s bister & multi .15 .15
2378 A903 3s bister & multi .15 .15
2379 A903 13s bister & multi .24 .15
2380 A903 18s bister & multi .35 .15
Set value .80 .32

Souvenir Sheet

Imperf

2381 A903 60s gold & multi .95 .55

Uprising against Turkish rule, centenary.

"Pollution" and Tree A904

Design: 18s, "Pollution" obscuring sun.

1976, Nov. 10 *Perf. 13*

2382	A904	2s ultra & multi	.15	.15
2383	A904	18s blue & multi	.30	.15
		Set value	.35	.15

Protection of the environment.

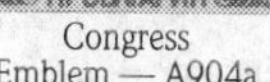
Congress Emblem — A904a

Flags — A904b

1976, Nov. 28 **Photo.** *Perf. 13*

2384	A904a	2s multicolored	.15	.15
2384A	A904b	13s multicolored	.26	.15
		Set value		.15

33rd BSIS Cong. (Bulgarian Socialist Party).

Tobacco Workers, by Stajkov A905

Paintings by Stajkov: 2s, View of Melnik. 13s, Shipbuilder.

1976, Dec. 16 **Photo.** *Perf. 13*

2385	A905	1s multicolored	.15	.15
2386	A905	2s multicolored	.15	.15
2387	A905	13s multicolored	.28	.15
		Set value	.38	.20

Veselin Stajkov (1906-1970), painter.

Snowflake A906

1976, Dec. 20

2388	A906	2s silver & multi	.15	.15

New Year 1977.

Zachary Stoyanov (1851-1889), Historian — A907

1976, Dec. 30

2389	A907	2s multicolored	.15	.15

Bronze Coin of Septimus Severus — A908

Roman Coins: 2s, 13s, 18s, Bronze coins of Caracalla, diff. 23s, Copper coin of Diocletian.

1977, Jan. 28 **Photo.** *Perf. 13½x13*

2390	A908	1s gold & multi	.15	.15
2391	A908	2s gold & multi	.15	.15
2392	A908	13s gold & multi	.20	.15
2393	A908	18s gold & multi	.26	.15
2394	A908	23s gold & multi	.45	.20
		Set value	1.00	.52

Coins struck in Serdica (modern Sofia).

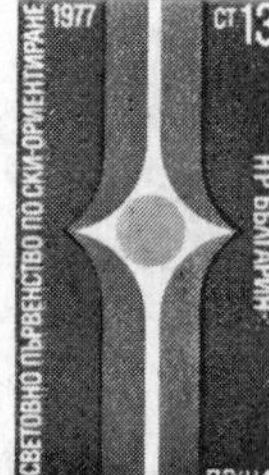
Skis and Compass — A909

Tourist Congress Emblem — A910

1977, Feb. 14 *Perf. 13*

2395	A909	13s ultra, red & lt bl	.25	.15

2nd World Ski Orienteering Championships.

1977, Feb. 24 **Photo.** *Perf. 13*

2396	A910	2s multicolored	.15	.15

5th Congress of Bulgarian Tourist Organization.

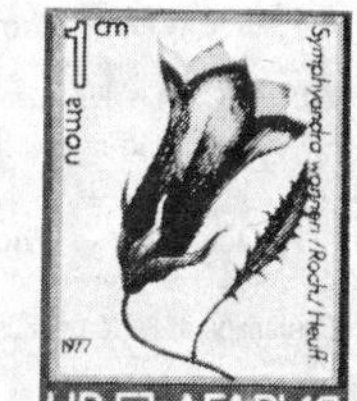

Bellflower — A911

Designs: Various bellflowers.

1977, Mar. 2

2397	A911	1s yellow & multi	.15	.15
2398	A911	2s rose & multi	.15	.15
2399	A911	3s lt blue & multi	.15	.15
2400	A911	13s multicolored	.30	.15
2401	A911	43s yellow & multi	1.10	.28
		Set value	1.50	.50

Vasil Kolarov — A912

Union Congress Emblem — A913

1977, Mar. 21 **Photo.** *Perf. 13*

2402	A912	2s blue & black	.15	.15

Vasil Kolarov (1877-1950), politician.

1977, Mar. 25

2403	A913	2s multicolored	.15	.15

8th Bulgarian Trade Union Cong., Apr. 4-7.

Wolf A914

Wild Animals: 2s, Red fox. 10s, Weasel. 13s, European wildcat. 23s, Jackal.

1977, May 16 **Litho.** *Perf. 12½x12*

2404	A914	1s multicolored	.15	.15
2405	A914	2s multicolored	.15	.15
2406	A914	10s multicolored	.18	.15
2407	A914	13s multicolored	.35	.15
2408	A914	23s multicolored	.60	.18
		Nos. 2404-2408 (5)	1.43	
		Set value		.40

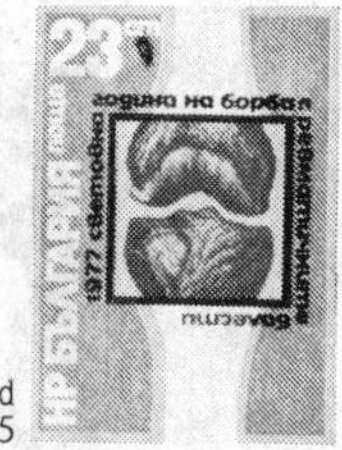
Diseased Knee — A915

1977, Mar. 31 **Photo.** *Perf. 13*

2409	A915	23s multicolored	.40	.15

World Rheumatism Year.

Writers' Congress Emblem A916

1977, June 7

2410	A916	23s lt bl & yel grn	.65	.20

International Writers Congress: "Peace, the Hope of the Planet." No. 2410 printed in sheets of 8 stamps and 4 labels with signatures of participating writers.

Old Testament Trinity, Sofia, 16th Century A917

Icons: 1s, St. Nicholas, Nessebur, 13th cent. 3s, Annunciation, Royal Gates, Veliko Turnovo, 16th cent. 5s, Christ Enthroned, Nessebur, 17th cent. 13s, St. Nicholas, Elena, 18th cent. 23s, Presentation of the Virgin, Rila Monastery, 18th cent. 35s, Virgin and Child, Tryavna, 19th cent. 40s, St. Demetrius on Horseback, Provadia, 19th cent. 1 l, The 12 Holidays, Rila Monastery, 18th cent.

1977, May 10 **Photo.** *Perf. 13*

2411	A917	1s black & multi	.15	.15
2412	A917	2s green & multi	.15	.15
2413	A917	3s brown & multi	.15	.15
2414	A917	5s blue & multi	.15	.15
2415	A917	13s olive & multi	.30	.15
2416	A917	23s maroon & multi	.50	.15
2417	A917	35s green & multi	.80	.25
2418	A917	40s dp ultra & multi	1.10	.38
		Nos. 2411-2418 (8)	3.30	
		Set value		1.00

Miniature Sheet

Imperf

2419	A917	1 l gold & multi	2.25	1.10

Bulgarian icons. See Nos. 2615-2619.

Souvenir Sheet

St. Cyril A918

1977, June 7 **Photo.** *Perf. 13*

2420	A918	1 l gold & multi	1.75	.90

1150th anniversary of the birth of St. Cyril (827-869), reputed inventor of Cyrillic alphabet.

Congress Emblem — A919

1977, May 9

2421	A919	2s red, gold & grn	.15	.15

13th Komsomol Congress.

Newspaper Masthead A920

1977, June 3 **Photo.** *Perf. 13*

2422	A920	2s multicolored	.15	.15

Cent. of Bulgarian daily press and 50th anniv. of Rabotnichesko Delo newspaper.

Patriotic Front Emblem — A921

Weight Lifting — A922

1977, May 26

2423	A921	2s gold & multi	.15	.15

8th Congress of Patriotic Front.

1977, June 15

2424	A922	13s dp brown & multi	.25	.15

European Youth Weight Lifting Championships, Sofia, June.

Women Basketball Players — A923

1977, June 15 *Perf. 13*

2425	A923	23s multicolored	.50	.18

7th European Women's Basketball Championships.

Wrestling — A924

Designs (Games Emblem and): 13s, Running. 23s, Basketball. 43s, Women's gymnastics.

1977, Apr. 15

2426 A924 2s multicolored .15 .15
2427 A924 13s multicolored .20 .15
2428 A924 23s multicolored .38 .15
2429 A924 43s multicolored .70 .26
Nos. 2426-2429 (4) 1.43
Set value .50

UNIVERSIADE '77, University Games, Sofia, Aug. 18-27.

TV Tower, Berlin — A925

1977, Aug. 12 **Litho.** ***Perf. 13***

2430 A925 25s blue & dk blue .50 .16

SOZPHILEX 77 Philatelic Exhibition, Berlin, Aug. 19-28.

Ship Type of 1975

Historic Ships: 1s, Hansa cog. 2s, Santa Maria, caravelle. 3s, Golden Hind, frigate. 12s, Santa Catherina, carrack. 13s, La Corone, galleon. 43s, Mediterranean galleass.

1977, Aug. 29 **Photo.** ***Perf. 13***

2431 A873 1s multicolored .15 .15
2432 A873 2s multicolored .15 .15
2433 A873 3s multicolored .15 .15
2434 A873 12s multicolored .25 .15
2435 A873 13s multicolored .25 .15
2436 A873 43s multicolored 1.00 .26
Set value 1.65 .52

Ivan Vasov National Theater — A926

Buildings, Sofia: 13s, Party Headquarters. 23s, House of the People's Army. 30s, Clement Ochrida University. 80s, National Gallery. 1 l, National Assembly.

1977, Aug. 30 **Photo.** ***Perf. 13***

2437 A926 12s red, *gray* .18 .15
2438 A926 13s red brn, *gray* .18 .15
2439 A926 23s blue, *gray* .30 .15
2440 A926 30s olive, *gray* .40 .15
2441 A926 80s violet, *gray* 1.10 .42
2442 A926 1 l claret, *gray* 1.40 .52
Nos. 2437-2442 (6) 3.56 1.54

Map of Europe A927

1977, June 10

2443 A927 23s brown, bl & grn .40 .18

21st Congress of the European Organization for Quality Control, Varna.

Union of Earth and Water, by Rubens A928

Rubens Paintings: 23s, Venus and Adonis. 40s, Pastoral Scene (man and woman). 1 l, Portrait of a Lady in Waiting.

1977, Sept. 23 **Litho.** ***Perf. 12***

2444 A928 13s gold & multi .45 .15
2445 A928 23s gold & multi .65 .15
2446 A928 40s gold & multi 1.10 .25
Nos. 2444-2446 (3) 2.20
Set value .44

Souvenir Sheet

2447 A928 1 l gold & multi 2.50 1.65

Peter Paul Rubens (1577-1640).

George Dimitrov A929

1977, June 17 **Photo.** ***Perf. 13***

2448 A929 13s red & deep claret .35 .15

George Dimitrov (1882-1947).

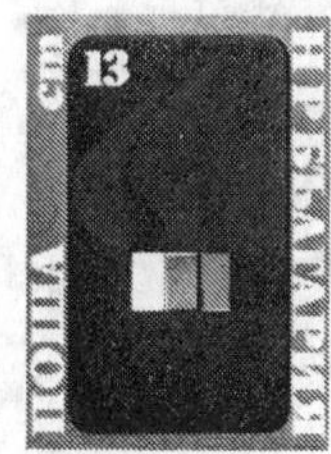

Flame with Star — A930

Smart Pete on Donkey, by Ilya Beshkov — A931

1977, May 17

2449 A930 13s gold & multi .25 .15

3rd Bulgarian Culture Congress.

1977, May 19

2450 A931 2s multicolored .15 .15

11th National Festival of Humor and Satire Gabrovo.

Elin Pelin — A932

Dr. Pirogov — A934

13th Canoe World Championships — A933

Albena, Black Sea A933a

Writers: 2s, Pelin (Dimitur Ivanov Stojanov, (1877-1949). 5s, Peju K. Jaworov (1878-1914).
Artists: 13s, Boris Angelushev (1902-1966), 23s, Ceno Todorov (Ceno Todorov Dikov, 1877-1953).
Each printed with label showing scenes from authors' works or illustrations by the artists.

1977, Aug. 26 **Photo.** ***Perf. 13***

2451 A932 2s gold & brown .15 .15
2452 A932 5s gold & gray grn .15 .15
2453 A932 13s gold & claret .22 .15
2454 A932 23s gold & blue .45 .15
Set value .80 .28

1977, Sept. 1 **Photo.** ***Perf. 13***

2455 A933 2s shown .15 .15
2456 A933 23s 2-man canoe .42 .18
Set value .25

1977, Oct. 5 **Photo.** ***Perf. 13***

2456A A933a 35s shown .65 .25
2456B A933a 43s Rila Monastery .80 .30

Sheet contains 4 each plus label.

1977, Oct. 14 **Photo.** ***Perf. 13***

2457 A934 13s olive, ocher & brown .25 .15

Centenary of visit by Russian physician N. J. Pirogov during war of liberation from Turkey.

Peace Decree, 1917 A935

Old Soldier with Grandchild A936

Designs: 13s, Lenin, 1917. 23s, "1917" as a flame.

1977, Oct. 21

2458 A935 2s black, buff & red .15 .15
2459 A935 13s multicolored .24 .15
2460 A935 23s multicolored .45 .15
Nos. 2458-2460 (3) .84
Set value .30

60th anniv. of Russian October Revolution.

1977, Sept. 30

Designs (Festival Posters): 13s, "The Bugler." 23s, Liberation Monument, Sofia (detail). 25s, Samara flag.

2461 A936 2s multicolored .15 .15
2462 A936 13s multicolored .25 .15
2463 A936 23s multicolored .42 .15
2464 A936 25s multicolored .52 .22
Nos. 2461-2464 (4) 1.34
Set value .50

Liberation from Turkish rule, centenary.

Souvenir Sheet

Games' and Sports Emblems — A937

1977, Aug. 10 **Photo.** ***Perf. 13½x13***

2465 A937 1 l multicolored 1.50 1.25

University Games '77, Sofia.

Conference Building — A938

1977, Sept. 12 ***Perf. 13½***

2466 A938 23s multicolored .40 .18

64th Interparliamentary Union Conference, Sofia.

Bulgarian Worker's Newspaper, Anniversaries A939

1977, Sept. 12 **Photo.** ***Perf. 13***

2467 A939 2s yel grn, blk & red .15 .15

Ornament A940

New Year 1978: 13s, Different ornament.

1977, Dec. 1

2468 A940 2s gold & multi .15 .15
2469 A940 13s silver & multi .26 .15
Set value .15

Railroad Bridge — A941

1977, Nov. 9

2470 A941 13s green, yel & gray .30 .15

Transport Organization, 50th anniversary.

A942 A943

1977, Nov. 15

2471 A942 8s gold & vio brn .15 .15

Petko Ratchev Slaveikov (1827-95), poet, birth sesquicentennial. No. 2471 printed in sheets of 8 stamps and 8 labels in 4 alternating vertical rows.

1978, Jan. 30 Photo. *Perf. 13*

Designs: 23s, Soccer player and Games' emblem. 50s, Soccer players.

2472 A943 13s multicolored .24 .15
2473 A943 23s multicolored .45 .15
Set value .19

Souvenir Sheet

2474 A943 50s ultra & multi 1.00 .85

11th World Cup Soccer Championship, Argentina, June 1-25.

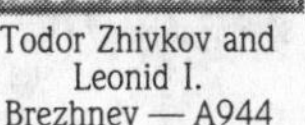

Todor Zhivkov and Leonid I. Brezhnev — A944

Ostankino Tower, Moscow, Bulgarian Post Emblem — A945

1977, Sept. 7 Photo. *Perf. 13*

2475 A944 18s gold, car & brn .30 .15

Bulgarian-Soviet Friendship. No. 2475 issued in sheets of 3 stamps and 3 labels.

1978, Mar. 1

2476 A945 13s multicolored .25 .15

20th anniversary of the Comecon Postal Organization (Council of Mutual Economic Assistance).

Leo Tolstoy — A946

Shipka Pass Monument — A947

Portraits: 5s, Fedor Dostoevski. 13s, Ivan Sergeevich Turgenev. 23s, Vasili Vasilievich Vershchagin. 25s, Giuseppe Garibaldi. 35s, Victor Hugo.

1978, Mar. 28 Photo. *Perf. 13*

2477 A946 2s yellow & dk grn .15 .15
2478 A946 5s lemon & brown .15 .15
2479 A946 13s tan & sl grn .22 .15
2480 A946 23s gray & vio brn .35 .15
2481 A946 25s yel grn & blk .40 .15
2482 A946 35s lt bl & vio bl .80 .38
Nos. 2477-2482 (6) 2.07
Set value .73

Souvenir Sheet

2483 A947 50s multicolored .80 .60

Bulgaria's liberation from Ottoman rule, cent.

Bulgarian and Russian Colors A948

1978, Mar. 18

2484 A948 2s multicolored .15 .15

30th anniv. of Russo-Bulgarian co-operation.

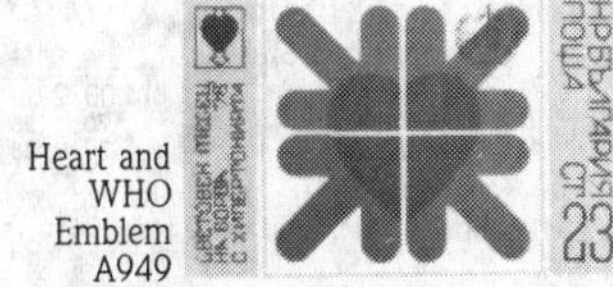

Heart and WHO Emblem A949

1978, May 12

2485 A949 23s gray, red & org .32 .15

World Health Day, fight against hypertension.

Goddess A950

Ceramics (2nd-4th Centuries) and Exhibition Emblem: 5s, Mask of bearded man. 13s, Vase. 23s, Vase. 35s, Head of Silenus. 53s, Cock.

1978, Apr. 26

2486 A950 2s green & multi .15 .15
2487 A950 5s multicolored .15 .15
2488 A950 13s multicolored .26 .15
2489 A950 23s multicolored .48 .16
2490 A950 35s multicolored .75 .24
2491 A950 53s carmine & multi 1.25 .32
Nos. 2486-2491 (6) 3.04
Set value .90

Philaserdica Philatelic Exhibition.

Nikolai Roerich, by Svyatoslav Roerich — A951

"Mind and Matter," by Andrei Nikolov — A952

1978, Apr. 5

2492 A951 8s multicolored .16 .15
2493 A952 13s multicolored .28 .15
Set value .15

Nikolai K. Roerich (1874-1947) and Andrei Nikolov (1878-1959), artists.

Bulgarian Flag and Red Star — A953

1978, Apr. 18

2494 A953 2s vio blue & multi .15 .15

Bulgarian Communist Party Congress.

Young Man, by Albrecht Dürer A954

Paintings: 23s, Bathsheba at Fountain, by Rubens. 25s, Portrait of a Man, by Hans Holbein the Younger. 35s, Rembrandt and Saskia, by Rembrandt. 43s, Lady in Mourning, by Tintoretto. 60s, Old Man with Beard, by Rembrandt. 80s, Knight in Armor, by Van Dyck.

1978, June 19 Photo. *Perf. 13*

2495 A954 13s multicolored .16 .15
2496 A954 23s multicolored .30 .15
2497 A954 25s multicolored .32 .15
2498 A954 35s multicolored .45 .15
2499 A954 43s multicolored .55 .20
2500 A954 60s multicolored .85 .26
2501 A954 80s multicolored 1.10 .38
Nos. 2495-2501 (7) 3.73
Set value 1.18

Dresden Art Gallery paintings.

Doves and Festival Emblem — A955

1978, May 31

2502 A955 13s multicolored .25 .15

11th World Youth Festival, Havana, July 28-Aug. 5.

Fritillaria Stribrnyi — A956

Rare Flowers: 2s, Fritillaria drenovskyi. 3s, Lilium rhodopaeum. 13s, Tulipa urumoffii. 23s, Lilium jankae. 43s, Tulipa rhodopaea.

1978, June 27

2503 A956 1s multicolored .15 .15
2504 A956 2s multicolored .15 .15
2505 A956 3s multicolored .15 .15
2506 A956 13s multicolored .26 .15
2507 A956 23s multicolored .45 .15
2508 A956 43s multicolored .90 .30
Nos. 2503-2508 (6) 2.06
Set value .67

Yacht Cor Caroli and Map of Voyage A957

1978, May 19 Photo. *Perf. 13*

2509 A957 23s multicolored .50 .18

First Bulgarian around-the-world voyage, Capt. Georgi Georgiev, Dec. 20, 1976-Dec. 20, 1977.

Market, by Naiden Petkov — A958

Views of Sofia: 5s, Street, by Emil Stoichev. 13s, Street, by Boris Ivanov. 23s, Tolbukhin Boulevard, by Nikola Tanev. 35s, National Theater, by Nikola Petrov. 53s, Market, by Anton Mitov.

1978, Aug. 28 Litho. *Perf. 12½x12*

2510 A958 2s multicolored .15 .15
2511 A958 5s multicolored .15 .15
2512 A958 13s multicolored .18 .15
2513 A958 23s multicolored .30 .15
2514 A958 35s multicolored .52 .18
2515 A958 53s multicolored .85 .28
Nos. 2510-2515 (6) 2.15
Set value .72

Miniature Sheet

Sleeping Venus, by Giorgione — A959

1978, Aug. 7 Photo. *Imperf.*

2516 A959 1 l multicolored 2.00 .85

View of Varna — A960

1978, July 13 Photo. *Perf. 13*

2517 A960 13s multicolored .25 .15

63rd Esperanto Cong., Varna, July 29-Aug. 5.

Black Woodpecker — A961

Woodpeckers: 2s, Syrian. 3s, Three-toed. 13s, Middle spotted. 23s, Lesser spotted. 43s, Green.

1978, Sept. 1

2518 A961 1s multicolored .15 .15
2519 A961 2s multicolored .15 .15
2520 A961 3s multicolored .15 .15
2521 A961 13s multicolored .26 .15
2522 A961 23s multicolored .42 .15
2523 A961 43s multicolored 1.10 .24
Set value 1.95 .58

"September 1923" A962

1978, Sept. 5
2524 A962 2s red & brn .25 .15

55th anniversary of September uprising.

Souvenir Sheet

National Theater, Sofia A963

Photogravure and Engraved

1978, Sept. 1 *Perf. 12x11½*
2525 Sheet of 4 2.50 1.00
a. A963 40s shown .60 .16
b. A963 40s Festival Hall, Sofia .60 .16
c. A963 40s Charles Bridge, Prague .60 .16
d. A963 40s Belvedere Palace, Prague .60 .16

PRAGA '78 and PHILASERDICA '79 Philatelic Exhibitions.

Black and White Hands, Human Rights Emblem — A964

1978, Oct. 3 Photo. *Perf. 13x13½*
2526 A964 13s multicolored .25 .15

Anti-Apartheid Year.

Gotse Deltchev — A965

Bulgarian Calculator — A966

1978, Aug. 1 Photo. *Perf. 13*
2527 A965 13s multicolored .25 .15

Gotse Deltchev (1872-1903), patriot.

1978, Sept. 3
2528 A966 2s multicolored .15 .15

International Sample Fair, Plovdiv.

Guerrillas — A967

1978, Aug. 1
2529 A967 5s blk & rose red .15 .15

75th anniversary of the Ilinden and Preobrazhene revolts.

"Pipe Line" and Flags A968

1978, Oct. 3
2530 A968 13s multicolored .25 .15

Construction of gas pipe line from Orenburg to Russian border.

A969 A970

1978, Oct. 4 *Perf. 13x13½*
2531 A969 13s Three acrobats .25 .15

3rd World Acrobatic Championships, Sofia, Oct. 6-8.

1978, Sept. 18 Photo. *Perf. 13*
2532 A970 2s dp claret & ocher .15 .15

Christo G. Danov (1828-1911), 1st Bulgarian publisher. No. 2532 printed with se-tenant label showing early printing press.

Insurgents, by Todor Panajotov A971

1978, Sept. 20
2533 A971 2s multicolored .15 .15

Vladaja mutiny, 60th anniversary.

A972 A973

1978, Oct. 11 Photo. *Perf. 13*
2534 A972 13s dk brn & org red .25 .15

Salvador Allende (1908-1973), president of Chile.

1978, Oct. 18
2535 A973 23s Human Rights flame .50 .20

Universal Declaration of Human Rights, 30th anniversary.

A974 A975

Burgarian Paintings: 1s, Levski and Matei Mitkaloto, by Kalina Tasseva. 2s, "Strength for my Arm" by Zlatyu Boyadjiev. 3s, Rumena, woman military leader, by Nikola Mirchev, horiz. 13s, Kolju Ficeto, by Elza Goeva. 23s, Family, National Revival Period, by Naiden Petkov.

Perf. 12x12½, 12½x12

1978, Oct. 25 Litho.
2536 A974 1s multicolored .15 .15
2537 A974 2s multicolored .15 .15
2538 A974 3s multicolored .15 .15
2539 A974 13s multicolored .24 .15
2540 A974 23s multicolored .42 .15
Set value .85 .30

1300th anniversary of Bulgaria (in 1981).

Designs: a, Tourism building, Plovdiv. b, Chrelo Tower, Rila Cloister.

1978, Nov. 1 Photo. *Perf. 13*

Souvenir Sheet

2541 Sheet of 5 + label 4.00 2.00
a. A975 43s multicolored .70 .28
b. A975 43s multicolored .70 .28

Conservation of European architectural heritage. No. 2541 contains 3 No. 2541a & 2 No. 2541b.

Ferry, Map of Black Sea with Route A976

1978, Nov. 1 Photo. *Perf. 13*
2542 A976 13s multicolored .25 .15

Opening of Ilychovsk-Varna Ferry.

Bird, from Marble Floor, St. Sofia Church — A977

1978, Nov. 20
2543 A977 5s multicolored .15 .15

3rd Bulgaria '78, National Philatelic Exhibition, Sofia. Printed se-tenant with label showing emblems of Bulgaria '78 and Philaserdica '79.

Initial, 13th Century Gospel — A978

Designs: 13s, St. Cyril, miniature, 1567. 23s, Book cover, 16th century. 80s, St. Methodius, miniature, 13th century.

1978, Dec. 15 Photo. *Perf. 13*
2544 A978 2s multicolored .15 .15
2545 A978 13s multicolored .20 .15
2546 A978 23s multicolored .35 .15
Nos. 2544-2546 (3) .70
Set value .24

Souvenir Sheet

2547 A978 80s multicolored 1.25 1.00

Cent. of the Cyril and Methodius Natl. Library.

Bulgaria No. 53 A979

Bulgarian Stamps: 13s, No. 534. 23s, No. 968. 35s, No. 1176, vert. 53s, No. 1223, vert. 1 l, No. 1.

1978, Dec. 30
2548 A979 2s ol grn & red .15 .15
2549 A979 13s ultra & rose car .18 .15
2550 A979 23s rose lil & ol grn .32 .15
2551 A979 35s brt bl & blk .48 .20
2552 A979 53s ver & sl grn .90 .32
Nos. 2548-2552 (5) 2.03
Set value .74

Souvenir Sheet

2553 A979 1 l multicolored 1.50 1.25

Philaserdica '79, International Philatelic Exhibition, Sofia, May 18-27, 1979, and centenary of Bulgarian stamps. No. 2553 exists imperf. See Nos. 2560-2564.

St. Clement of Ochrida — A980

1978, Dec. 8
2554 A980 2s multicolored .15 .15

Clement of Ochrida University, 90th anniv.

Ballet Dancers A981

1978, Dec. 22
2555 A981 13s multicolored .30 .15

Bulgarian ballet, 50th anniversary.

Nikola Karastojanov A982

1978, Dec. 12
2556 A982 2s multicolored .15 .15

Nikola Karastojanov (1778-1874), printer. No. 2556 printed se-tenant with label showing printing press.

Christmas Tree Made of Birds A983

1978, Dec. 22
2557 A983 2s shown .15 .15
2558 A983 13s Post horn .20 .15
Set value .25 .15

New Year 1979.

COMECON Building, Moscow, Members' Flags — A984

1979, Jan. 25 **Photo.** ***Perf. 13***
2559 A984 13s multicolored .25 .15

Council for Mutual Economic Aid (COMECON), 30th anniversary.

Philaserdica Type of 1978
Designs as Before

1979, Jan. 30
2560 A979 2s brt bl & red .15 .15
2561 A979 13s grn & dk car .18 .15
2562 A979 23s org brn & multi .32 .15
2563 A979 35s dl red & blk .50 .22
2564 A979 53s vio & dk ol .90 .35
Nos. 2560-2564 (5) 2.05
Set value .78

Philaserdica '79.

Bank Building, Commemorative Coin — A985

1979, Feb. 13
2565 A985 2s yel, gray & sil .15 .15

Centenary of Bulgarian People's Bank.

Aleksandr Stamboliski A986

1979, Feb. 28
2566 A986 2s orange & dk brn .15 .15

Aleksandr Stamboliski (1879-1923), leader of peasant's party and premier.

Flower with Child's Face, IYC Emblem — A987

1979, Mar. 8
2568 A987 23s multicolored .40 .15

International Year of the Child.

Stylized Heads, World Association Emblem — A988

1979, Mar. 20
2569 A988 13s multicolored .25 .15

8th World Cong. for the Deaf, Varna, June 20-27.

"75" and Trade Union Emblem — A989

1979, Mar. 20
2570 A989 2s slate grn & org .15 .15

75th anniversary of Bulgarian Trade Unions.

Souvenir Sheet

Sculptures in Sofia — A990

Designs: 2s, Soviet Army Monument (detail). 5s, Mother and Child, Central Railroad Station. 13s, 23s, 25s, Bas-relief from Monument of the Liberators.

1979, Apr. 2 **Photo.** ***Perf. 13***
2571 A990 Sheet of 5 + label 1.25 .60
a. 2s multicolored .15
b. 5s multicolored .15
c. 13s multicolored .22
d. 23s multicolored .38
e. 25s multicolored .48

Centenary of Sofia as capital.

Rocket Launch, Space Flight Emblems — A991

Designs (Intercosmos and Bulgarian-USSR Flight Emblems and): 25s, Link-up, horiz. 35s, Parachute descent. 1 l, Globe, emblems and orbit, horiz.

1979, Apr. 11
2572 A991 12s multicolored .20 .15
2573 A991 25s multicolored .45 .15
2574 A991 35s multicolored .60 .22
Nos. 2572-2574 (3) 1.25 .52

Souvenir Sheet

2575 A991 1 l multicolored 1.50 .75

1st Bulgarian cosmonaut on Russian space flight.
A slightly larger imperf. sheet similar to No. 2575 with control numbers at bottom and rockets at sides exists.

Nicolai Rukavishnikov — A992

Design: 13s, Rukavishnikov and Soviet cosmonaut Georgi Ivanov.

1979, May 14 **Photo.** ***Perf. 13***
2576 A992 2s multicolored .15 .15
2577 A992 13s multicolored .32 .15
Set value .40 .15

Col. Rukavishnikov, 1st Bulgarian astronaut.

Souvenir Sheet

Thracian Gold-leaf Collar — A993

1979, May 16
2578 A993 1 l multicolored 2.00 1.50

48th International Philatelic Federation Congress, Sofia, May 16-17.

Post Horn, Carrier Pigeon, Jet, Globes and UPU Emblem — A994

Designs (Post Horn, Globes and ITU Emblem): 5s, 1st Bulgarian and modern telephones. 13s, Morse key and teleprinter. 23s, Old radio transmitter and radio towers. 35s, Bulgarian TV tower and satellite. 50s, Ground receiving station

1979, May 8 ***Perf. 13½x13***
2579 A994 2s multicolored .15 .15
2580 A994 5s multicolored .15 .15
2581 A994 13s multicolored .20 .15
2582 A994 23s multicolored .38 .15
2583 A994 35s multicolored .60 .22
Nos. 2579-2583 (5) 1.48
Set value .48

Souvenir Sheet
Perf. 13

2584 A994 50s vio, blk & gray 1.00 .65

Intl. Telecommunications Day and cent. of Bulgarian Postal & Telegraph Services. Size of stamp in #2584: 39x28mm. #2584 exists imperf.

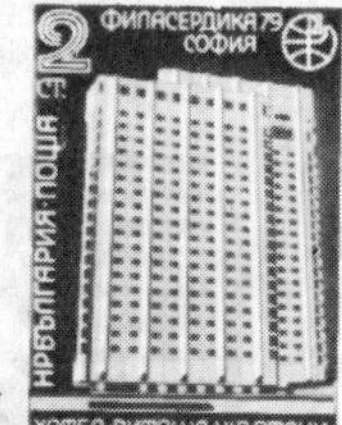

Hotel Vitosha-New Otani — A996

1979, May 20
2586 A996 2s ultra & pink .15 .15

Philaserdica '79 Day.

Horseman Receiving Gifts, by Karellia and Boris Kuklievi A997

1979, May 23
2587 A997 2s multicolored .15 .15

Bulgarian-Russian Friendship Day.

A998 A999

Design: Man on Donkey, by Boris Angeloushev.

1979, May 23 **Photo.** ***Perf. 13½***
2588 A998 2s multicolored .15 .15

12th National Festival of Humor and Satire, Gabrovo.

Lithographed and Engraved
1979, May 31 ***Perf. 14x13½***

Durer Engravings: 13s, Four Women. 23s, Three Peasants. 25s, The Cook and his Wife. 35s, Portrait of Helius Eobanus Hessus. 80s, Rhinoceros, horiz.

2589 A999 13s multicolored .24 .15
2590 A999 23s multicolored .40 .15
2591 A999 25s multicolored .45 .15
2592 A999 35s multicolored .65 .18
Nos. 2589-2592 (4) 1.74
Set value .49

Souvenir Sheet
Imperf

2593 A999 80s multicolored 1.50 1.25

Albrecht Durer (1471-1528), German engraver and painter.

R. Todorov (1879-1916) A1000

Bulgarian Writers: No. 2595, Dimitri Dymov (1909-1966). No. 2596, S. A. Kostov (1879-1939).

1979, June 26 **Photo.** ***Perf. 13***
2594 A1000 2s multicolored .15 .15
2595 A1000 2s slate grn & yel grn .15 .15
2596 A1000 2s dp claret & yel .15 .15
Set value .25 .15

Nos. 2594-2596 each printed se-tenant with label showing title page or character from writer's work.

Moscow '80 Emblem, Runners — A1001

Moscow '80 Emblem and: 13s, Pole vault, horiz. 25s, Discus. 35s, Hurdles, horiz. 43s, High jump, horiz. 1 l, Long jump.

1979, May 15 *Perf. 13*

2597 A1001 2s multicolored .15 .15
2598 A1001 13s multicolored .20 .15
2599 A1001 25s multicolored .40 .15
2600 A1001 35s multicolored .80 .24
2601 A1001 43s multicolored 1.00 .30
2602 A1001 1 l multicolored 2.25 .65
Nos. 2597-2602 (6) 4.80 1.64

Souvenir Sheet

2602A A1001 2 l multicolored 6.00 3.25

22nd Summer Olympic Games, Moscow, July 19-Aug. 3, 1980.

Rocket — A1002

Designs: 5s, Flags of USSR and Bulgaria. 13s, "35."

1979, Sept. 4 **Photo.**

2603 A1002 2s multicolored .15 .15
2604 A1002 5s multicolored .15 .15
2605 A1002 13s multicolored .18 .15
Set value .30 .18

35th anniversary of liberation.

Moscow '80 Emblem, Gymnast A1003

Designs: Moscow '80 Emblem and gymnasts. 13s horiz.

1979, July 31 **Photo.** *Perf. 13*

2606 A1003 2s multicolored .15 .15
2607 A1003 13s multicolored .20 .15
2608 A1003 25s multicolored .48 .15
2609 A1003 35s multicolored .75 .22
2610 A1003 43s multicolored 1.00 .25
2611 A1003 1 l multicolored 2.25 .80
Nos. 2606-2611 (6) 4.83 1.72

Souvenir Sheet

2612 A1003 2 l multicolored 6.00 3.25

22nd Summer Olympic Games, Moscow, July 19-Aug. 3, 1980.

A1004

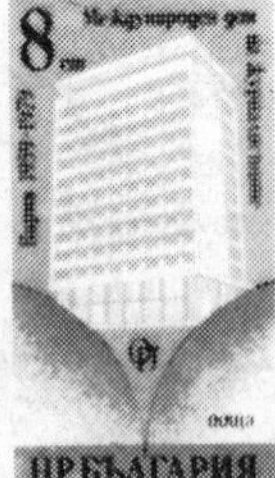

A1005

1979, July 8 **Photo.** *Perf. 13*

2613 A1004 13s ultra & blk .18 .15

Theater Institute, 18th Congress.

1979, July 17

2614 A1005 8s multicolored .15 .15

Journalists' Vacation House, Varna, 20th Anniv.

Icon Type of 1977

Virgin and Child by: 13s, 23s, Nesebar, 16th cent., diff. 35s, 43s, Sozopol, 16th cent., diff. 53s, Samokov, 19th cent. Inscribed 1979.

1979, Aug. 7 **Litho.** *Perf. 12½*

2615 A917 13s multicolored .20 .15
2616 A917 23s multicolored .35 .15
2617 A917 35s multicolored .50 .15
2618 A917 43s multicolored .60 .16
2619 A917 53s multicolored .85 .24
Nos. 2615-2619 (5) 2.50
Set value .69

A1006

A1007

1979, Aug. 9 **Photo.** *Perf. 13x13½*

2620 A1006 2s Anton Besenschek .15 .15

Bulgarian stenography centenary.

1979, Aug. 28 *Perf. 13*

2621 A1007 2s multicolored .15 .15

Bulgarian Alpine Club, 50th anniv.

Public Health Ordinance A1008

1979, Aug. 31 *Perf. 13½*

2622 A1008 2s multicolored .15 .15

Public Health Service centenary. No. 2622 printed with label showing Dimitar Mollov, founder.

Isotope Measuring Device — A1009

1979, Sept. 8 *Perf. 13½x13*

2623 A1009 2s multicolored .15 .15

International Sample Fair, Plovdiv.

Games' Emblem — A1010

1979, Sept. 20 *Perf. 13*

2624 A1010 5s multicolored .15 .15

Universiada '79, World University Games, Mexico City, Sept.

Sofia Locomotive Sports Club, 50th Anniversary — A1011

1979, Oct. 2

2625 A1011 2s blue & org red .15 .15

Ljuben Karavelov (1837-1879), Poet and Freedom Fighter — A1012

1979, Oct. 4 **Photo.** *Perf. 13*

2626 A1012 2s blue & slate grn .15 .15

A1013

A1014

1979, Oct. 20

2627 A1013 2s Biathlon .15 .15
2628 A1013 13s Speed skating .22 .15
2629 A1013 23s Downhill skiing .38 .15
2630 A1013 43s Luge .75 .22
Nos. 2627-2630 (4) 1.50
Set value .44

Souvenir Sheet

Imperf

2631 A1013 1 l Slalom 1.75 1.10

13th Winter Olympic Games, Lake Placid, NY, Feb. 12-24.

1979, Oct. 31 *Perf. 14*

Decko Uzunov, 80th Birthday: 12s, Apparition in Red. 13s, Woman from Thrace. 23s, Composition.

2632 A1014 12s multicolored .24 .15
2633 A1014 13s multicolored .24 .15
2634 A1014 23s multicolored .38 .15
Nos. 2632-2634 (3) .86
Set value .22

Swimming, Moscow '80 Emblem A1016

1979, Nov. 30 **Photo.** *Perf. 13*

2636 A1016 2s Two-man kayak, vert. .15 .15
2637 A1016 13s Swimming, vert. .18 .15
2638 A1016 25s shown .40 .15
2639 A1016 35s One-man kayak .80 .20
2640 A1016 43s Diving, vert 1.00 .40
2641 A1016 1 l Diving, vert. (diff.) 2.25 .70
Nos. 2636-2641 (6) 4.78 1.75

Souvenir Sheet

2642 A1016 2 l Water polo, vert. 6.00 3.25

22nd Summer Olympic Games, Moscow, July 19-Aug. 3, 1980.

Nikola Vapzarov A1017

1979, Dec. 7 **Photo.** *Perf. 13*

2643 A1017 2s claret & rose .15 .15

Vapzarov (1909-1942), poet and freedom fighter. No. 2643 printed with label showing smokestacks.

The First Socialists, by Bojan Petrov — A1018

Paintings: 13s, Demeter Blagoev Reading Newspaper, by Demeter Gjudshenov, 1892. 25s, Workers' Party March, by Sotir Sotirov, 1917. 35s, Dawn in Plovdiv, by Johann Leviev, vert.

Perf. 12½x12, 12x12½

1979, Dec. 10 **Litho.**

2644 A1018 2s multicolored .15 .15
2645 A1018 13s multicolored .22 .15
2646 A1018 25s multicolored .38 .15
2647 A1018 35s multicolored .55 .15
Nos. 2644-2647 (4) 1.30
Set value .36

Sharpshooting, Moscow '80 Emblem — A1019

1979, Dec. 22 **Photo.** *Perf. 13*

2648 A1019 2s shown .15 .15
2649 A1019 13s Judo, horiz. .20 .15
2650 A1019 25s Wrestling, horiz. .40 .16
2651 A1019 35s Archery .80 .25
2652 A1019 43s Fencing, horiz. 1.00 .50
2653 A1019 1 l Fencing 2.25 .90
Nos. 2648-2653 (6) 4.80 2.11

Souvenir Sheet

2654 A1019 2 l Boxing 6.00 4.00

Procession with Relics, 11th Century Fresco A1020

Frescoes of Sts. Cyril and Methodius, St. Clement's Basilica, Rome: 13s, Reception by Pope Hadrian II. 23s, Burial of Cyril the Philosopher, 18th century. 25s, St. Cyril. 35s, St. Methodius.

1979, Dec. 25

2655 A1020 2s multicolored .15 .15
2656 A1020 13s multicolored .24 .15
2657 A1020 23s multicolored .42 .15
2658 A1020 25s multicolored .45 .15
2659 A1020 35s multicolored .65 .18
Nos. 2655-2659 (5) 1.91
Set value .48

Bulgarian Television Emblem A1021

1979, Dec. 29 *Perf. 13½*

2660 A1021 5s violet bl & lt bl .15 .15

Bulgarian television, 25th anniversary. No. 2660 printed with label showing Sofia television tower.

Doves in Girl's Hair A1022

Design: 2s, Children's heads, mosaic, vert.

1979 *Perf. 13*

2661 A1022 2s multicolored .15 .15
2662 A1022 13s multicolored .16 .15
Set value .25 .15

International Year of the Child. Issue dates: 2s, July 17; 13s, Dec. 14.

Puppet on Horseback, IYC Emblem — A1023

Thracian Rider, Votive Tablet, 3rd Century — A1024

1980, Jan. 22 Photo. *Perf. 13*

2663 A1023 2s multicolored .15 .15

UNIMA, Intl. Puppet Theater Organization, 50th anniv. (1979); Intl. Year of the Child (1979).

1980, Jan. 29 Photo. *Perf. 13x13½*

National Archaeological Museum Centenary; 13s, Deines stele, 5th century B.C.

2664 A1024 2s brown & gold .15 .15
2665 A1024 13s multicolored .20 .15
Set value .25 .15

Dimitrov Meeting Lenin in Moscow, by Alexander Poplilov A1026

1980, Mar. 28 *Perf. 12x12½*

2667 A1026 13s multicolored .20 .15

Lenin, 110th birth anniversary.

A1027

A1027a

Circulatory system, lungs enveloped in smoke.

1980, Apr. 7 *Perf. 13*

2668 A1027 5s multicolored .15 .15

World Health Day fight against cigarette smoking.

1980, Apr. 10 Photo. *Perf. 13*

2669 A1027a 2s Basketball .15 .15
2670 A1027a 13s Soccer .18 .15
2671 A1027a 25s Hockey .40 .15
2672 A1027a 35s Cycling .80 .20
2673 A1027a 43s Handball 1.00 .40
2674 A1027a 1 l Volleyball 2.25 .70
Nos. 2669-2674 (6) 4.78 1.75

Souvenir Sheet

2675 A1027a 2 l Weightlifting 6.50 4.25

Souvenir Sheet

Intercosmos Emblem, Cosmonauts — A1028

1980, Apr. 22 *Perf. 12*

2676 A1028 50s multicolored 1.00 .45

Intercosmos cooperative space program.

Penio Penev (1930-1959), Poet — A1029

1980, Apr. 22 Photo. *Perf. 13*

2677 A1029 5s multicolored .15 .15

Se-tenant with label showing quote from author's work.

Penny Black — A1030

1980, Apr. 24 *Perf. 13*

2678 A1030 25s dark red & sepia .60 .45

London 1980 International Stamp Exhibition, May 6-14; printed se-tenant with label showing Rowland Hill between every two stamps.

Demeter H. Tchorbadjiiski, Self-portrait — A1031

1980, Apr. 29

2679 A1031 5s shown .15 .15
2680 A1031 13s "Our People" .18 .15
Set value .25 .15

Nikolai Giaurov — A1032

Raising Red Flag Reichstag Building, Berlin — A1033

1980, Apr. 30

2681 A1032 5s multicolored .15 .15

Nikolai Giaurov (b. 1930), opera singer; printed se-tenant with label showing Boris Godunov.

1980, May 6 *Perf. 13x13½*

Armistice, 35th Anniversary: 13s, Soviet Army memorial, Berlin-Treptow.

2682 A1033 5s multicolored .15 .15
2683 A1033 13s multicolored .18 .15
Set value .25 .15

Numeral — A1034

1979 *Perf. 14*

2684 A1034 2s ultra .15 .15
2685 A1034 5s rose car .15 .15
Set value .20 .15

A1034a

A1035

1980, May 12 Photo. *Perf. 13*

2685A A1034a 5s multicolored .15 .15

75th Anniv. of Teachers' Union.

1980, May 14 Photo. *Perf. 13*

2686 A1035 13s multicolored .20 .15

Warsaw Pact, 25th anniv.

A1036

A1037

Statues.

1980, June 10

2687 A1036 2s multicolored .15 .15
2688 A1036 13s multicolored .18 .15
2689 A1036 25s multicolored .40 .15
2690 A1036 35s multicolored .80 .30
2691 A1036 43s multicolored 1.00 .60
2692 A1036 1 l multicolored 2.25 1.10
Nos. 2687-2692 (6) 4.78 2.45

Souvenir Sheet

2693 A1036 2 l multicolored 6.00 3.25

22nd Summer Olympic Games, Moscow, July 19-Aug. 3.

1980, Sept. Photo. *Perf. 13*

2694 A1037 13s multicolored .25 .15

10th Intl. Ballet Competition, Varna.

Hotel Europa, Sofia A1038

Hotels: No. 2696, Bulgaria, Burgas, vert. No. 2697, Plovdiv, Plovdiv. No. 2698, Riga, Russe, vert. No. 2699, Varna, Djuba.

1980, July 11

2695 A1038 23s lt ultra & multi .30 .15
2696 A1038 23s orange & multi .30 .15
2697 A1038 23s gray & multi .30 .15
2698 A1038 23s blue & multi .30 .15
2699 A1038 23s yellow & multi .30 .15
Nos. 2695-2699 (5) 1.50
Set value .60

See No. 2766.

Ship Type of 1975

Ships of 16th, 17th Centuries: 5s, Christ of Lubeck, galleon. 8s, Roman galley. 13s, Eagle, Russian galleon. 23s, Mayflower. 35s, Maltese galley. 53s, Royal Louis, galleon.

1980, July 14

2700 A873 5s multicolored .15 .15
2701 A873 8s multicolored .15 .15
2702 A873 13s multicolored .25 .15
2703 A873 23s multicolored .45 .18
2704 A873 35s multicolored .70 .20
2705 A873 53s multicolored 1.10 .35
Nos. 2700-2705 (6) 2.80
Set value .92

Int'l Year of the Child, 1979 — A1040

Designs: Children's drawings and IYC emblem. 43s, Tower. 5s, 25s, 43s, vert.

1980 Litho. *Perf. 12½x12, 12x12½*

2708 A1040 3s multicolored .15 .15
2709 A1040 5s multicolored .15 .15
2710 A1040 8s multicolored .15 .15
2711 A1040 13s multicolored .20 .15
2712 A1040 25s multicolored .38 .15
2713 A1040 35s multicolored .52 .15
2714 A1040 43s multicolored .65 .18
Nos. 2708-2714 (7) 2.20
Set value .64

Helicopter, Missile Transport, Tank — A1041

1980, Sept. 23 Photo. *Perf. 13*

2715 A1041 3s shown .15 .15
2716 A1041 5s Jet, radar, rocket .15 .15
2717 A1041 8s Helicopter, ships .16 .15
Set value .35 .15

Bulgarian People's Army, 35th anniversary.

St. Anne, by Leonardo da Vinci A1042

Da Vinci Paintings: 8s, 13s, Annunciation (diff.). 25s, Adoration of the Kings. 35s, Lady with the Ermine. 50s, Mona Lisa.

1980, Nov.

2718 A1042 5s multicolored .15 .15
2719 A1042 8s multicolored .15 .15
2720 A1042 13s multicolored .20 .15
2721 A1042 25s multicolored .38 .15
2722 A1042 35s multicolored .55 .18
Nos. 2718-2722 (5) 1.43
Set value .45

Souvenir Sheet

Imperf

2723 A1042 50s multicolored 1.00 .35

International Peace Conference, Sofia — A1043

1980, Sept. 4 Photo. *Perf. 13*
2724 A1043 25s multicolored .35 .15

Jordan Jowkov (1880-1937), Writer — A1044

1980, Sept. 19
2725 A1044 5s multicolored .15 .15

Se-tenant with label showing scene from Jowkov's work.

International Samples Fair, Plovdiv — A1045

1980, Sept. 24 *Perf. 13½x13*
2726 A1045 5s multicolored .15 .15

Blooming Cacti — A1045a

1980, Nov. 4 Photo. *Perf. 13*
2726A A1045a 5s multicolored .15 .15
2726B A1045a 13s multicolored .20 .15
2726C A1045a 25s multicolored .42 .16
2726D A1045a 35s multicolored .60 .25
2726E A1045a 53s multicolored 1.00 .32
Nos. 2726A-2726E (5) 2.37 1.03

Souvenir Sheet

25th Anniv. of Bulgarian UN Membership — A1045b

1980, Nov. 25
2726F A1045b 60s multicolored 2.25 2.00

World Ski Racing Championship, Velingrad — A1046

1981, Jan. 17 Photo. *Perf. 13*
2727 A1046 43s multicolored .60 .22

Hawthorn — A1047 Slalom — A1048

Designs: Medicinal herbs.

1981, Jan.
2728 A1047 3s shown .15 .15
2729 A1047 5s St. John's wort .15 .15
2730 A1047 13s Common elder .20 .15
2731 A1047 25s Blackberries .38 .15
2732 A1047 35s Lime .55 .20
2733 A1047 43s Wild briar .65 .24
Nos. 2728-2733 (6) 2.08
Set value .75

1981, Feb. 27 Photo. *Perf. 13*
2734 A1048 43s multicolored .60 .25

Evian Alpine World Ski Cup Championship, Borovets.

Nuclear Traces, Research Institute — A1049

1981, Mar. 10 *Perf. 13½x13*
2735 A1049 13s gray & blk .20 .15

Nuclear Research Institute, Dubna, USSR, 25th anniversary.

Congress Emblem A1050

1981, Mar. 12 *Perf. 13½*
2736 A1050 5s shown .15 .15
2737 A1050 13s Stars .20 .15
2738 A1050 23s Teletape .35 .15
Nos. 2736-2738 (3) .70
Set value .24

Souvenir Sheet
2739 A1050 50s Demeter Blagoev, George Dimitrov .80 .48

12th Bulgarian Communist Party Congress. Nos. 2736-2738 each printed se-tenant with label.

Paintings by Zachary Zograf — A1050a

1981, Mar. 23 Photo. *Perf. 12x12½*
2739A A1050a 5s multicolored .15 .15
2739B A1050a 13s multicolored .22 .15
2739C A1050a 23s multicolored .42 .15
2739D A1050a 25s multicolored .48 .15
2739E A1050a 35s multicolored .70 .18
Nos. 2739A-2739E (5) 1.97
Set value .55

Nos. 2739A-2739C are vert.

EXPO '81, Plovdiv A1050b

1981, Apr. 7
2739F A1050b 5s multicolored .15 .15
2739G A1050b 8s multicolored .15 .15
2739H A1050b 13s multicolored .25 .15
2739J A1050b 25s multicolored .45 .15
2739K A1050b 53s multicolored 1.00 .24
Nos. 2739F-2739K (5) 2.00
Set value .55

Centenary of Bulgarian Shipbuilding — A1050c

1981, Apr. 15 Photo. *Perf. 13*
2739L A1050c 35s Georgi Dimitrov, liner .55 .20
2739M A1050c 43s 5th from RMS, freighter .65 .25
2739N A1050c 53s Khan Asparuch, tanker .80 .28
Nos. 2739L-2739N (3) 2.00 .73

Arabian Horse A1051

1980, Nov. 27 Litho. *Perf. 12½x12*
2740 A1051 3s multicolored .15 .15
2741 A1051 5s multicolored .15 .15
2742 A1051 13s multicolored .30 .15
2743 A1051 23s multicolored .45 .15
2744 A1051 35s multicolored .75 .20
Nos. 2740-2744 (5) 1.80
Set value .48

Vassil Stoin, Ethnologist, Birth Centenary — A1052

1980, Dec. 5 Photo. *Perf. 13½x13*
2745 A1052 5s multicolored .15 .15

12th Bulgarian Communist Party Congress — A1052a

1980, Dec. 26 Photo. *Perf. 13x13½*
2745A A1052a 5s Party symbols .15 .15

New Year A1053

1980, Dec. 8 *Perf. 13*
2746 A1053 5s shown .15 .15
2747 A1053 13s Cup, date .18 .15
Set value .25 .15

Culture Palace, Sofia A1053a

1981, Mar. 13 Photo. *Perf. 13*
2747A A1053a 5s multicolored .15 .15

Vienna Hofburg Palace A1054

1981, May 15 Photo. *Perf. 13*
2748 A1054 35s multicolored .45 .18

WIPA 1981 Intl. Philatelic Exhibition, Vienna, May 22-31.

34th Farmers' Union Congress A1055

1981, May 18 *Perf. 13½*
2749 A1055 5s shown .15 .15
2750 A1055 8s Flags .15 .15
2751 A1055 13s Flags, diff. .20 .15
Set value .40 .18

Wild Cat A1056

1981, May 27
2752 A1056 5s shown .15 .15
2753 A1056 13s Boar .22 .15
2754 A1056 23s Mouflon .40 .15
2755 A1056 25s Mountain goat .45 .15
2756 A1056 35s Stag .60 .18
2757 A1056 53s Roe deer 1.00 .26
Nos. 2752-2757 (6) 2.82
Set value .82

Souvenir Sheet
Perf. 13½x13
2758 A1056 1 l Stag, diff. 1.65 .85

EXPO '81 Intl. Hunting Exhibition, Plovdiv. Nos. 2752-2757 each se-tenant with labels showing various hunting rifles. No. 2758 contains one stamp, size: 48½x39mm.

25th Anniv. of UNESCO Membership A1057

1981, June 11 *Perf. 13*
2759 A1057 13s multicolored .20 .15

Hotel Type of 1980

1981, July 13 Photo. *Perf. 13*
2766 A1038 23s Veliko Tirnovo Hotel .35 .15

Flying Figure, Sculpture by Velichko Minekov — A1059

Bulgarian Social Democratic Party Buzludja Congress, 90th Anniv. (Minkov Sculpture): 13s, Advancing Female Figure.

1981, July 16 *Perf. 13½*
2767 A1059 5s multicolored .15 .15
2768 A1059 13s multicolored .18 .15
Set value .25 .15

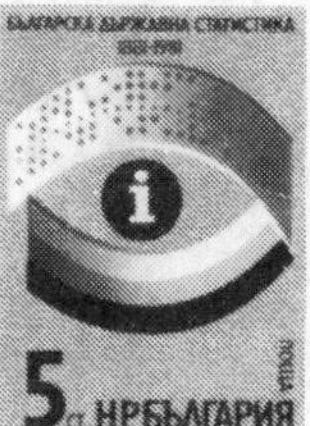

Kukeri, by Georg Tschapkanov A1060

Statistics Office Centenary A1061

1981, May 28 Photo. *Perf. 13*
2769 A1060 5s multicolored .15 .15

13th Natl. Festival of Humor and Satire.

1981, June 9
2770 A1061 5s multicolored .15 .15

Gold Dish A1063

Designs: Goldsmiths' works, 7th-9th cent.

1981, July 21
2772 A1063 5s multicolored .15 .15
2773 A1063 13s multicolored .20 .15
2774 A1063 23s multicolored .35 .22
2775 A1063 25s multicolored .40 .25
2776 A1063 35s multicolored .55 .35
2777 A1063 53s multicolored .90 .38
Nos. 2772-2777 (6) 2.55 1.50

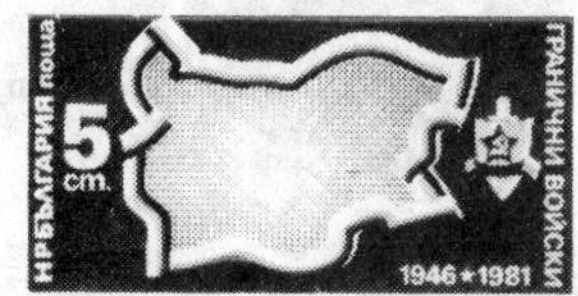

35th Anniv. of Frontier Force — A1064

1981, July 28 *Perf. 13½x13*
2778 A1064 5s multicolored .15 .15

1300th Anniv. of First Bulgarian State — A1065

Designs: No. 2779, Sts. Cyril and Methodius. No. 2780, 9th cent. bas-relief. 8s, Floor plan, Round Church, Preslav, 10th cent. 12s, Four Evangelists of King Ivan Alexander, miniature, 1356. No. 2783, King Ivan Asen II memorial column. No. 2784, Warriors on horseback. 16s, April uprising, 1876. 23s, Russian liberators, Tirnovo. 25s, Social Democratic Party founding, 1891. 35s, September uprising, 1923. 41s, Fatherland Front. 43s, Prime Minister George Dimitrov, 5th Communist Party Congress, 1948. 50s, Lion, 10th cent. bas-relief. 53s, 10th Communist Party Congress. 55s, Kremikovski Metalurgical Plant. 1 l, Brezhnev, Gen. Todor Zhivkov.

1981, Aug. 10
2779 A1065 5s multicolored .15 .15
2780 A1065 5s multicolored .15 .15
2781 A1065 8s multicolored .15 .15
2782 A1065 12s multicolored .18 .15
2783 A1065 13s multicolored .18 .15
2784 A1065 13s multicolored .18 .15
2785 A1065 16s multicolored .22 .15
2786 A1065 23s multicolored .30 .15
2787 A1065 25s multicolored .35 .15
2788 A1065 35s multicolored .48 .20
2789 A1065 41s multicolored .55 .22
2790 A1065 43s multicolored .60 .24
2791 A1065 53s multicolored .75 .30
2792 A1065 55s multicolored .75 .30
Nos. 2779-2792 (14) 4.99
Set value 2.00

Souvenir Sheets

2793 A1065 50s multicolored .90 .55
2794 A1065 1 l multicolored 1.90 1.10

European Volleyball Championship A1066

1981, Sept. 16 *Perf. 13*
2795 A1066 13s multicolored .20 .15

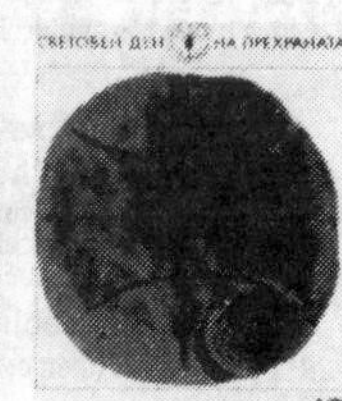

Pegasus, Bronze Sculpture (Word Day) — A1067

World Food Day — A1068

1981, Oct. 2
2796 A1067 5s olive & cream .15 .15

1981, Oct. 16
2797 A1068 13s multicolored .16 .15

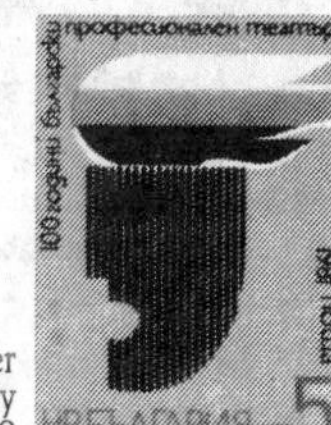

Professional Theater Centenary A1069

1981, Oct. 30
2798 A1069 5s multicolored .15 .15

Anti-Apartheid Year — A1070

1981, Dec. 2
2799 A1070 5s multicolored .15 .15

Espana '82 World Cup Soccer — A1071

Designs: Various soccer players.

1981, Dec.
2800 A1071 5s multicolored .15 .15
2801 A1071 13s multicolored .24 .18
2802 A1071 43s multicolored .70 .24
2803 A1071 53s multicolored .95 .35
Nos. 2800-2803 (4) 2.04 .92

Heritage Day A1072

1981, Nov. 21 Photo. *Perf. 13*
2804 A1072 13s multicolored .20 .15

Souvenir Sheet

2804A A1072 60s multicolored 4.25 1.10

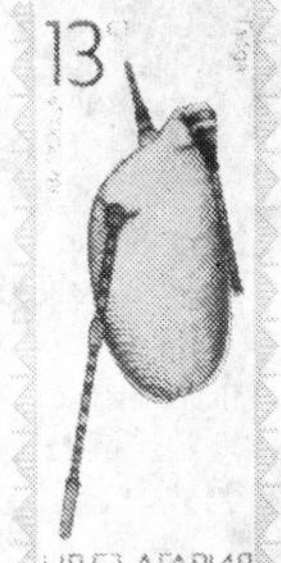

Bagpipe — A1073

Public Libraries and Reading Rooms, 125th Anniv — A1074

1982, Jan. 14
2805 A1073 13s shown .20 .15
2806 A1073 25s Flutes .40 .18
2807 A1073 30s Rebec .50 .20
2808 A1073 35s Flute, recorder .55 .24
2809 A1073 44s Mandolin .75 .30
Nos. 2805-2809 (5) 2.40 1.07

1982, Jan. 20
2810 A1074 5s dk grn .15 .15

Souvenir Sheet

Intl. Decade for Women (1975-1985) — A1075

1982, Mar. 8
2811 A1075 1 l multicolored 1.65 1.00

New Year 1982 A1076

1981, Dec. 22 Photo. *Perf. 13*
2812 A1076 5s Ornament .15 .15
2813 A1076 13s Ornament, diff. .18 .15
Set value .25 .15

The Sofia Plains, by Nicolas Petrov (1881-1916) — A1077

1982, Feb. 10 *Perf. 12½*
2814 A1077 5s shown .15 .15
2815 A1077 13s Girl Embroidering .20 .15
2816 A1077 30s Fields of Peshtera .48 .20
Nos. 2814-2816 (3) .83
Set value .33

25th Anniv. of UNICEF (1981) — A1078

Mother and Child Paintings.

1982, Feb. 25 *Perf. 14*
2817 A1078 53s Vladimir Dimitrov .80 .32
2818 A1078 53s Basil Stoilov .80 .32
2819 A1078 53s Ivan Milev .80 .32
2820 A1078 53s Liliana Russeva .80 .32
Nos. 2817-2820 (4) 3.20 1.28

Figures, by Vladamir Dimitrov (1882-1961) — A1079

1982, Mar. 8 **Litho.**

2821 A1079 5s shown .15 .15
2822 A1079 8s Landscape .15 .15
2823 A1079 13s View of Istanbul .22 .15
2824 A1079 25s Harvesters, vert. .42 .16
2825 A1079 30s Woman in a Landscape, vert. .50 .20
2826 A1079 35s Peasant Woman, vert. .60 .25
Nos. 2821-2826 (6) 2.04
Set value .78

Souvenir Sheet

2827 A1079 50s Self-portrait .80 .65

No. 2827 contains one stamp, size: 54x32mm.

Trade Union Congress A1080

1982, Apr. 8 **Photo.** ***Perf. 13½***

2828 A1080 5s Dimitrov reading union paper .15 .15
2829 A1080 5s Culture Palace .15 .15
Set value .25 .15

#2828-2829 se-tenant with label showing text.

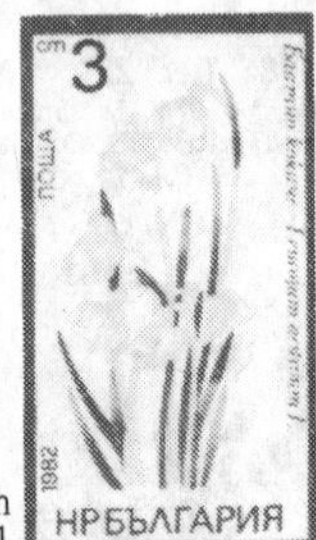

Marsh Snowdrop — A1081

Designs: Medicinal plants.

1982, Apr. 10 **Photo.** ***Perf. 13***

2830 A1081 3s shown .15 .15
2831 A1081 5s Chicory .15 .15
2832 A1081 8s Chamaenerium angustifolium .15 .15
2833 A1081 13s Solomon's seal .25 .15
2834 A1081 25s Violets .50 .20
2835 A1081 35s Centaury .70 .26
Nos. 2830-2835 (6) 1.90
Set value .70

Cosmonauts' Day — A1082

1982, Apr. 12 ***Perf. 13½***

2836 A1082 13s Salyut-Soyuz link-up .20 .15

Se-tenant with label showing K.E. Tsiolkovsky (space pioneer).

> *Foreign postal stationery (stamped envelopes, postal cards and air letter sheets) is beyond the scope of this catalogue.*

Souvenir Sheet

SOZFILEX Stamp Exhibition — A1083

1982, May 7 ***Perf. 13***

2837 A1083 50s Dimitrov, emblems .80 .45

14th Komsomol Congress (Youth Communists) — A1084

1982, May 25

2838 A1084 5s multicolored .15 .15

PHILEXFRANCE '82 Intl. Stamp Exhibition, Paris, June 11-21 — A1085

1982, May 28

2839 A1085 42s France #1, Bulgaria #1 .65 .25

19th Cent. Fresco A1086

Designs: Various floral pattern frescoes.

1982, June 8 ***Perf. 11½***

2840 A1086 5s red & multi .15 .15
2841 A1086 13s green & multi .30 .15
2842 A1086 25s violet & multi .50 .16
2843 A1086 30s ol grn & multi .60 .22
2844 A1086 42s blue & multi .90 .26
2845 A1086 60s brown & multi 1.25 .42
Nos. 2840-2845 (6) 3.70 1.36

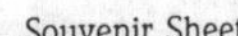

Souvenir Sheet

George Dimitrov (1882-1949), First Prime Minister — A1087

1982, June 15 ***Perf. 13***

2846 A1087 50s multicolored 1.00 .45

9th Congress of the National Front — A1088

1982, June 21 **Photo.** ***Perf. 13***

2847 A1088 5s Dimitrov .15 .15

35th Anniv. of Balkan Bulgarian Airline A1089

1982, June 28 ***Perf. 13½x13***

2848 A1089 42s multicolored .65 .26

A1090

A1091

1982, July 15 ***Perf. 13***

2849 A1090 13s multicolored .25 .15

Nuclear disarmament.

1982, July **Photo.** ***Perf. 13***

2850 A1091 5s multicolored .15 .15
2851 A1091 13s multicolored .18 .15
Set value .25 .15

Souvenir Sheet

2852 A1091 1 l multicolored 1.50 .75

Ludmila Zhivkova (b. 1942), artist.

5th Congress of Bulgarian Painters — A1092

1982, July 27 ***Perf. 13½***

2853 A1092 5s multicolored .20 .15

Se-tenant with label showing text.

Flag of Peace Youth Assembly — A1093

Various children's drawings.

1982, Aug. 10 ***Perf. 14***

2853A A1093 3s multicolored .15 .15
2853B A1093 5s multicolored .15 .15
2853C A1093 8s multicolored .15 .15
2853D A1093 13s multicolored .22 .15
Set value .46 .23

Souvenir Sheet

Perf. 14, Imperf.

2853E A1093 50s In balloon 3.00 .35

See Nos. 2864-2870, 3052-3058, 3321-3327.

10th Anniv. of UN Conference on Human Environment, Stockholm — A1093a

1982, Nov. 10 ***Perf. 13***

2854 A1093a 13s dk blue & grn .20 .15

A1094

A1095

Designs: No. 2855, Park Hotel Moskva, Sofia. No. 2856, Tchernomore, Varna.

1982, Oct. 20 **Photo.** ***Perf. 13***

2855 A1094 32s lt blue & multi .42 .18
2856 A1094 32s pink & multi .42 .18

1982, Nov. 4

2857 A1095 13s Cruiser Aurora, Sputnik II .16 .15

October Revolution, 65th anniv.

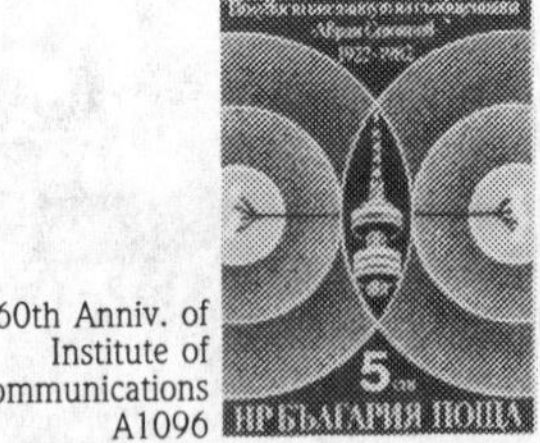

60th Anniv. of Institute of Communications A1096

1982, Dec. 9

2858 A1096 5s ultra .15 .15

60th Anniv. of USSR A1097

1982, Dec. 9

2859 A1097 13s multicolored .18 .15

The Piano, by Pablo Picasso (1881-1973) A1098

Perf. 11½x12½

1982, Dec. 24 **Litho.**

2860 A1098 13s shown .20 .15
2861 A1098 30s Portrait of Jacqueline .40 .18
2862 A1098 42s Maternity .60 .26
Nos. 2860-2862 (3) 1.20 .59

Souvenir Sheet

2863 A1098 1 l Self-portrait 2.50 .75

Children's Drawings Type of 1982

Various children's drawings. 8s, 13s, 50s vert.

1982, Dec. 28 ***Perf. 14***

2864 A1093 3s multicolored .15 .15
2865 A1093 5s multicolored .15 .15
2866 A1093 8s multicolored .15 .15
2867 A1093 13s multicolored .20 .15
2868 A1093 25s multicolored .35 .15
2869 A1093 30s multicolored .40 .18
Nos. 2864-2869 (6) 1.40
Set value .56

Souvenir Sheet

Perf. 14, Imperf.

2870 A1093 50s Shaking hands 2.50 .35

New Year A1100

1982, Dec. 28 **Photo.** ***Perf. 13***

2872 A1100 5s multicolored .15 .15
2873 A1100 13s multicolored .18 .15
Set value .25 .15

A1101 A1102

1982, Dec. 28

2874 A1101 25s Robert Koch .38 .15
2875 A1101 30s Simon Bolivar .42 .18
2876 A1101 30s Rabindranath Tagore (1861-1941) .42 .18
Nos. 2874-2876 (3) 1.22 .51

No. 2874 also for TB bacillus cent.

1983, Jan. 10 **Photo.** ***Perf. 13x13½***

2877 A1102 5s olive & brown .15 .15

Vassil Levski (1837-73), revolutionary.

Universiade Games — A1103

1983, Feb. 15 ***Perf. 13***

2878 A1103 30s Downhill skiing .35 .18

Fresh-water Fish — A1104

1983, Mar. 24 **Photo.** ***Perf. 13½x13***

2879 A1104 3s Pike .15 .15
2880 A1104 5s Sturgeon .15 .15
2881 A1104 13s Chub .20 .15
2882 A1104 25s Perch .38 .15
2883 A1104 30s Catfish .42 .18
2884 A1104 42s Trout .55 .24
Nos. 2879-2884 (6) 1.85
Set value .75

Karl Marx (1818-1883) A1105

1983, Apr. 5 ***Perf. 13x13½***

2885 A1105 13s multicolored .20 .15

Jaroslav Hasek (1883-1923) — A1106

1983, Apr. 20 **Photo.** ***Perf. 13***

2886 A1106 13s multicolored .20 .15

Martin Luther (1483-1546) A1107

1983, May 10

2887 A1107 13s multicolored .20 .15

55th Anniv. of Komsomol Youth Movement — A1108

1983, May 13

2888 A1108 5s "PMC" .15 .15

A1109 A1111

National costumes.

1983, May 17 **Litho.** ***Perf. 14***

2889 A1109 5s Khaskovo .15 .15
2890 A1109 8s Pernik .15 .15
2891 A1109 13s Burgas .20 .15
2892 A1109 25s Tolbukhin .38 .15
2893 A1109 30s Blagoevgrad .40 .15
2894 A1109 42s Topolovgrad .55 .22
Nos. 2889-2894 (6) 1.83
Set value .68

1983, May 20

6th Intl. Satire and Humor Biennial, Gabrovo: Old Man Feeding Chickens.

2900 A1111 5s multicolored .15 .15

Christo Smirnensky (1898-1983), Poet — A1112

1983, May 25

2901 A1112 5s multicolored .15 .15

17th Intl. Geodesists' Congress — A1113

1983, May 27

2902 A1113 30s Emblem .45 .20

Interarch '83 Architecture Exhibition, Sofia — A1114

1983, June 6

2903 A1114 30s multicolored .45 .20

8th European Chess Championships, Plovdiv — A1115

1983, June 20 **Photo.** ***Perf. 13***

2904 A1115 13s Chess pieces, map of Europe .20 .15

Souvenir Sheet

BRASILIANA '83 Philatelic Exhibition — A1116

1983, June 24

2905 A1116 1 l Brazilian and Bulgarian stamps 1.50 .95

Social Democratic Party Congress of Russia, 80th Anniv. A1118

Design: Lenin addressing congress.

1983, July 29 **Photo.** ***Perf. 13***

2907 A1118 5s multicolored .15 .15

Ilinden-Preobrazhensky Insurrection, 80th Anniv. — A1119

1983, July 29

2908 A1119 5s Gun, dagger, book .15 .15

Institute of Mining and Geology, Sofia, 30th Anniv. — A1120

1983, Aug. 10

2909 A1120 5s multicolored .15 .15

60th Anniv. of September 1923 Uprising — A1121

1983, Aug. 19

2910 A1121 5s multicolored .15 .15
2911 A1121 13s multicolored .18 .15
Set value .25 .15

Angora Cat A1123

1983, Sept. 26 ***Perf. 13***

2917 A1123 5s shown .15 .15
2918 A1123 13s Siamese .22 .15
2919 A1123 20s Abyssinian, vert. .38 .15
2920 A1123 25s Persian .45 .18
2921 A1123 30s European, vert. .55 .22
2922 A1123 42s Indochinese .75 .30
Nos. 2917-2922 (6) 2.50 1.15

Animated Film Festival — A1124

1983, Sept. 15 **Photo.** ***Perf. 14x13½***

2923 A1124 5s Articulation layout .15 .15

Trevethick's Engine, 1804 — A1125

Locomotives: 13s, Blenkinsop's Prince Royal, 1810. 42s, Hedley's Puffing Billy, 1812. 60s, Adler (first German locomotive), 1835.

1983, Oct. 20 *Perf. 13*

2924 A1125 5s multicolored .15 .15
2925 A1125 13s multicolored .32 .15
2926 A1125 42s multicolored .95 .30
2927 A1125 60s multicolored 1.40 .42
Nos. 2924-2927 (4) 2.82
Set value .84

See Nos. 2983-2987.

Souvenir Sheet

Liberation Monument, Plovdiv — A1126

1983, Nov. 4

2928 A1126 50s multicolored .80 .60

Philatelic Federation, 90th anniv.

Sofia Opera, 75th Anniv. — A1127

Composers' Assoc., 50th Anniv. — A1128

1983, Dec. 2 *Perf. 13x13½*

2929 A1127 5s Mask, lyre, laurel .15 .15

1983, Dec. 5

Composers: 5s, Ioan Kukuzel (14th cent.) 8s, Atanasov. 13s, Petko Stainov. 20s, Veselin Stodiov. 25s, Liubomir Pipkov. 30s, Pancho Vladigerov. Se-tenant with labels showing compositions.

2930 A1128 5s multicolored .15 .15
2931 A1128 8s multicolored .15 .15
2932 A1128 13s multicolored .18 .15
2933 A1128 20s multicolored .30 .15
2934 A1128 25s multicolored .38 .16
2935 A1128 30s multicolored .48 .20
Nos. 2930-2935 (6) 1.64
Set value .65

New Year 1984 A1129

1983, Dec. 10 *Perf. 13*

2936 A1129 5s multicolored .15 .15

Angelo Donni, by Raphael — A1130

1983, Dec. 22 *Perf. 14*

2937 A1130 5s shown .15 .15
2938 A1130 13s Cardinal .20 .15
2939 A1130 30s Baldassare Castiglioni .45 .20
2940 A1130 42s Donna Belata .68 .30
Nos. 2937-2940 (4) 1.48
Set value .62

Souvenir Sheet

2941 A1130 1 l Sistine Madonna 1.65 1.25

Bat, World Wildlife Emblem A1131

Various bats and rodents.

1983, Dec. 30 *Perf. 13*

2942 A1131 12s multicolored .16 .15
2943 A1131 13s multicolored .18 .15
2944 A1131 20s multicolored .28 .15
2945 A1131 30s multicolored .45 .22
2946 A1131 42s multicolored .65 .30
Nos. 2942-2946 (5) 1.72
Set value .79

Dmitri Mendeleev (1834-1907), Russian Chemist — A1132

1984, Mar. 14

2947 A1132 13s multicolored .22 .15

Ljuben Karavelov, Poet and Freedom Fighter, Birth Sesquicentenary A1133

1984, Jan. 31 *Perf. 13x13½*

2948 A1133 5s multicolored .15 .15

Tanker Gen. V.I. Zaimov A1137

1984, Mar. 22 *Perf. 13½*

2959 A1137 5s shown .15 .15
2960 A1137 13s Mesta .22 .15
2961 A1137 25s Veleka .42 .16
2962 A1137 32s Ferry .52 .22
2963 A1137 42s Cargo ship Rossen .70 .28
Nos. 2959-2963 (5) 2.01
Set value .78

Souvenir Sheet

World Cup Soccer Commemorative of 1982, Spain No. 2281 — A1137a

1984, Apr. 18 Photo. *Perf. 13x13½*

2963A A1137a 2 l multicolored 3.00 2.50

ESPANA '84.

Dove with Letter over Globe — A1138

Berries — A1139

1984, Apr. 24 *Perf. 13*

2964 A1138 5s multicolored .15 .15

World Youth Stamp Exhibition, Pleven, Oct. 5-11.

1984, May 5

2965 A1139 5s Cherries .15 .15
2966 A1139 8s Strawberries .15 .15
2967 A1139 13s Blackberries .20 .15
2968 A1139 20s Raspberries .35 .15
2969 A1139 42s Currants .70 .32
Nos. 2965-2969 (5) 1.55
Set value .62

A1140 A1142

1984, May 23

2970 A1140 13s Athlete, doves .20 .15

6th Republican Spartikiade games.

1984, June 12

2972 A1142 5s Folk singer, drum .15 .15

6th amateur art festival.

Bulgarian-Soviet Relations, 50th Anniv. — A1143

1984, June 27

2973 A1143 13s Initialed seal .15 .15

Doves and Pigeons — A1144

1984, July 6 Litho. *Perf. 14*

2974 A1144 5s Rock dove .15 .15
2975 A1144 13s Stock dove .20 .15
2976 A1144 20s Wood pigeon .35 .15
2977 A1144 30s Turtle dove .48 .20
2978 A1144 42s Domestic pigeon .70 .28
Nos. 2974-2978 (5) 1.88
Set value .74

1st Natl. Communist Party Congress, 60th Anniv. — A1145

1984, May 18 Photo. *Perf. 13½x13*

2979 A1145 5s multicolored .15 .15

Souvenir Sheet

Intl. Stamp Exhibition, Essen, May 26-31 — A1146

Europa Conference stamps: No. 2980a, 1980. No. 2980b, 1981.

1984, May 22 *Perf. 13x13½*

2980 A1146 Sheet of 2 12.00 10.00
a.-b. 1.50 l multi 6.00 5.00

Mount Everest — A1147

1984, May 31 *Perf. 13*

2981 A1147 5s multicolored .15 .15

1st Bulgarian Everest climbing expedition, Apr. 20-May 9.

Souvenir Sheet

UPU Congress, Hamburg — A1148

1984, June 11 *Perf. 13½x13*

2982 A1148 3 l Sailing ship 12.00 10.00

Locomotives Type of 1983

1984, July 31 *Perf. 13*

2983 A1125 13s Best Friend of Charleston, 1830, US .24 .15
2984 A1125 25s Saxonia, 1836, Dresden .42 .25
2985 A1125 30s Lafayette, 1837, US .52 .30
2986 A1125 42s Borsig, 1841, Germany .75 .42
2987 A1125 60s Philadelphia, 1843, Austria 1.10 .65
Nos. 2983-2987 (5) 3.03 1.77

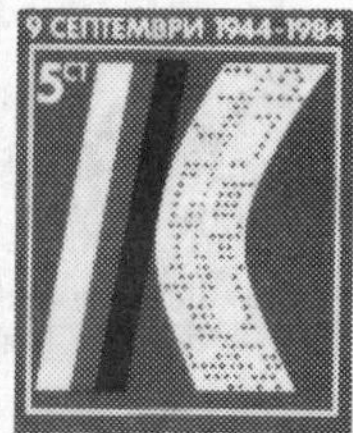

September 9 Revolution, 40th Anniv. — A1149

1984, Aug. 4

2988 A1149 5s K, production quality emblem .15 .15
2989 A1149 20s Victory Monument, Sofia .35 .20
2990 A1149 30s Star, "9" .55 .30
Nos. 2988-2990 (3) 1.05
Set value .55

Paintings by Nenko Balkanski (1907-1977) — A1150

1984, Sept. 17 *Perf. 14*

2991 A1150 5s Boy Playing Harmonica, vert. .15 .15
2992 A1150 30s A Paris Window, vert. .55 .30
2993 A1150 42s Double Portrait .80 .42
Nos. 2991-2993 (3) 1.50 .87

Souvenir Sheet

2994 A1150 1 l Self-portrait, vert. 1.75 1.25

MLADPOST '84 International Youth Stamp Exhibition, Pleven — A1151

Buildings in Pleven: 5s, Mausoleum to Russian soldiers, 1877-78 Russo-Turkish War. 13s, Panorama Building.

1984, Sept. 20 *Perf. 13*

2995 A1151 5s multicolored .15 .15
2996 A1151 13s multicolored .28 .15
Set value .19

Septembrist Young Pioneers Org., 40th Anniv. A1152

1984, Sept. 21 **Photo.** *Perf. 13*

2997 A1152 5s multicolored .15 .15

Nikola Vapzarov A1153

1984, Oct. 2

2998 A1153 5s maroon & pale yel .15 .15

Natl. Soccer, 75th Anniv. A1154

1984, Oct. 3

2999 A1154 42s multicolored .75 .42

Souvenir Sheet

MLADPOST '84 — A1155

1984, Oct. 5 **Photo.** *Perf. 13*

3000 A1155 50s multicolored 1.00 .50

Bridges and Maps — A1156

1984, Oct. 5 **Photo.** *Perf. 13½x13*

3001 A1156 5s Devil's Bridge, Arda River .15 .15
3002 A1156 13s Koljo-Fitscheto, Bjala .28 .15
3003 A1156 30s Asparuchow, Warna .65 .32
3004 A1156 42s Bebresch Highway Bridge, Botevgrad .90 .45
Nos. 3001-3004 (4) 1.98 1.07

Intl. Olympic Committee, 90th Anniv. A1158

1984, Oct. 24 **Photo.** *Perf. 13*

3007 A1158 13s multicolored .25 .15

A1159 A1160

Pelecanus crispus.

1984, Nov. 2

3008 A1159 5s Adult, young .15 .15
3009 A1159 13s Two adults .28 .15
3010 A1159 20s Adult in water .40 .20
3011 A1159 32s In flight .65 .32
Nos. 3008-3011 (4) 1.48 .82

World Wildlife Fund.

1984, Nov. 2

3012 A1160 5s multicolored .15 .15

Anton Ivanov (1884-1942), labor leader.

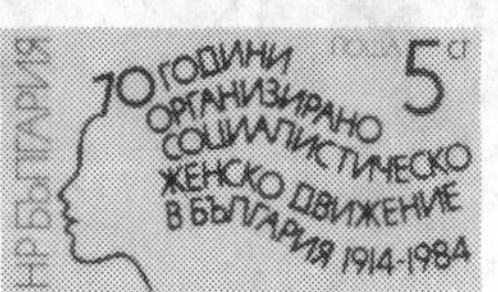

Women's Socialist Movement, 70th Anniv. — A1161

1984, Nov. 9

3013 A1161 5s multicolored .15 .15

Telecommunication Towers — A1162

1984, Nov. 23

3014 A1162 5s Snezhanka .15 .15
3015 A1162 1 l Orelek 1.90 1.00

Snowflakes, New Year 1985 — A1163

1984, Dec. 5

3016 A1163 5s Doves, posthorns .15 .15
3017 A1163 13s Doves, blossom .22 .15
Set value .30 .19

Paintings by Stoyan Venev (b. 1904) — A1164

1984, Dec. 10 **Litho.**

3018 A1164 5s September Nights .15 .15
3019 A1164 30s Man with Three Medals .48 .30
3020 A1164 42s The Best .70 .42
Nos. 3018-3020 (3) 1.33 .87

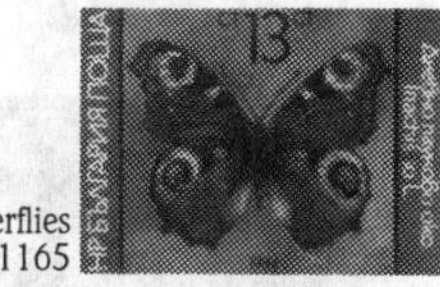

Butterflies A1165

1984, Dec. 14 *Perf. 11½*

3021 A1165 13s Inachis io .25 .15
3022 A1165 25s Papilio machaon .42 .25
3023 A1165 30s Brintesia circe .52 .30
3024 A1165 42s Anthocaris cardamines .75 .42
3025 A1165 60s Vanessa atalanta 1.00 .60
Nos. 3021-3025 (5) 2.94 1.72

Souvenir Sheet

3026 A1165 1 l Limenitis populi 2.00 1.00

A1166 A1167

1984, Dec. 18 **Photo.** *Perf. 13x13½*

3027 A1166 13s multicolored .25 .15

Cesar Augusto Sandino (1895-1934), Nicaraguan freedom fighter.

1984, Dec. 28 **Litho.** *Perf. 14*

3028 A1167 5s The Three Graces .15 .15
3029 A1167 13s Cupid and the Graces .28 .15
3030 A1167 30s Original Sin .55 .30
3031 A1167 42s La Fornarina .80 .42
Nos. 3028-3031 (4) 1.78 1.02

Souvenir Sheet

3032 A1167 1 l Galatea 2.00 1.00

Raphael, 500th birth anniv. (1983).

Cruise Ship Sofia, Maiden Voyage — A1168

1984, Dec. 29 **Photo.** *Perf. 13*

3033 A1168 13s blue, dk bl & yel .25 .15

Predators A1170

1985, Jan. 17

3035 A1170 13s Conepatus leuconotus .25 .15
3036 A1170 25s Prionodon linsang .42 .25
3037 A1170 30s Ictonix striatus .52 .30
3038 A1170 42s Hemigalus derbyanus .75 .42
3039 A1170 60s Galidictis fasciata 1.00 .60
Nos. 3035-3039 (5) 2.94 1.72

Nikolai Liliev (1885-1960), Poet, UNESCO Emblem — A1171

1985, Jan. 25

3040 A1171 30s multicolored .50 .30

Zviatko Radojnov (1895-1942), Labor Leader — A1172

1985, Jan. 29

3041 A1172 5s dk red & dk brn .15 .15

Dr. Assen Zlatarov (1885-1936), Chemist — A1173

1985, Feb. 14

3042 A1173 5s multicolored .15 .15

Souvenir Sheet

Akademik, Research Vessel — A1174

1985, Mar. 1

3043 A1174 80s multicolored 1.25 .80

UNESCO Intl. Oceanographic Commission, 25th anniv.

Souvenir Sheet

Lenin — A1175

1985, Mar. 12

3044 A1175 50s multicolored .85 .50

A1176 A1177

1985, Mar. 19

3045 A1176 13s multicolored .25 .15

Warsaw Treaty Org., 30th anniv.

1985, Mar. 25

Composers.

3046 A1177 42s Bach .75 .42
3047 A1177 42s Mozart .75 .42
3048 A1177 42s Tchaikovsky .75 .42
3049 A1177 42s Mussorgsky .75 .42
3050 A1177 42s Verdi .75 .42
3051 A1177 42s Tenev .75 .42
Nos. 3046-3051 (6) 4.50 2.52

Children's Drawings Type of 1982

Inscribed 1985. Various children's drawings.

1985, Mar. 26 Litho. *Perf. 14*

3052 A1093 5s multicolored .15 .15
3053 A1093 8s multicolored .15 .15
3054 A1093 13s multicolored .24 .15
3055 A1093 20s multicolored .35 .20
3056 A1093 25s multicolored .42 .25
3057 A1093 30s multicolored .52 .30
Nos. 3052-3057 (6) 1.83 1.20

Souvenir Sheet

3058 A1093 50s Children dancing, vert. 1.00 .50

3rd Flag of Peace Intl. Assembly, Sofia. No. 3058 exists imperf. with blue control number, same value.

St. Methodius, 1100th Death Anniv. — A1179

1985, Apr. 6 Photo. *Perf. 13*

3059 A1179 13s multicolored .25 .15

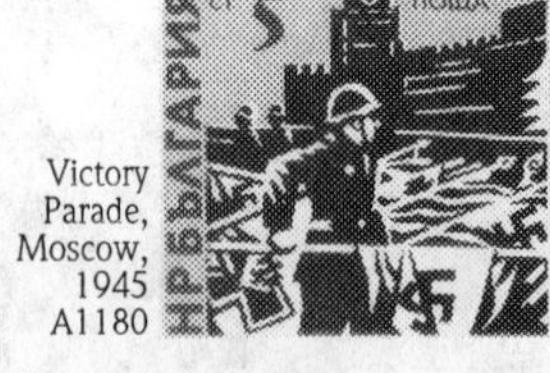

Victory Parade, Moscow, 1945 A1180

Designs: 13s, 11th Infantry on parade, Sofia. 30s, Soviet soldier, orphan. 50s, Soviet flag-raising, Berlin.

1985, Apr. 30 *Perf. 13½*

3060 A1180 5s multicolored .15 .15
3061 A1180 13s multicolored .24 .15
3062 A1180 30s multicolored .52 .30
Nos. 3060-3062 (3) .91
Set value .50

Souvenir Sheet

Perf. 13

3063 A1180 50s multicolored 1.00 .50

Defeat of Nazi Germany, end of World War II, 40th anniv. Nos. 3060-3062 printed se-tenant with labels picturing Soviet (5s, 30s) and Bulgarian medals of honor.

7th Intl. Humor and Satire Biennial A1181

1985, Apr. 30 *Perf. 13½*

3064 A1181 13s yel, sage grn & red .25 .15

No. 3064 printed se-tenant with label picturing Gabrovo Cat emblem.

Intl. Youth Year — A1182

1985, May 21 *Perf. 13*

3065 A1182 13s multicolored .25 .15

Ivan Vasov (1850-1921), Poet — A1183

1985, May 30 *Perf. 13½*

3066 A1183 5s tan & sepia .15 .15

No. 3066 printed se-tenant with label picturing Vasov's birthplace in Sopot.

Soviet War Memorial, Haskovo City Arms A1184

1985, June 1 *Perf. 13*

3067 A1184 5s multicolored .15 .15

Haskovo millennium.

12th World Youth Festival, Moscow — A1185

1985, June 25

3068 A1185 13s multicolored .25 .15

Indira Gandhi (1917-1984), Prime Minister of India — A1186

1985, June 26

3069 A1186 30s org yel, sep & ver .60 .30

Vasil Aprilov, Founder — A1187

1985, June 30

3070 A1187 5s multicolored .15 .15

1st secular school, Gabrovo, 150th anniv.

INTERSTENO '85 — A1188

1985, June 30

3071 A1188 13s multicolored .25 .15

Congress for the Intl. Union of Stenographers and Typists, Sofia.

Alexander Nevski Cathedral A1189

1985, July 9

3072 A1189 42s multicolored .80 .42

World Tourism Org., general assembly, Sofia.

UN, 40th Anniv. A1190

1985, July 16

3073 A1190 13s multicolored .25 .15

A1191

Roses — A1192

1985, July 16
3074 A1191 13s multicolored .25 .15

Admission of Bulgaria to UN, 30th anniv.

1985, July 20 **Litho.**
3075 A1192 5s Rosa damascena .15 .15
3076 A1192 13s Rosa trakijka .24 .15
3077 A1192 20s Rosa radiman .35 .20
3078 A1192 30s Rosa marista .50 .30
3079 A1192 42s Rosa valentina .75 .42
3080 A1192 60s Rosa maria 1.00 .60
a. Min. sheet of 6, #3075-3080 3.50 2.00
Nos. 3075-3080 (6) 2.99 1.82

Helsinki Conference, 10th Anniv. — A1193

1985, Aug. 1 **Photo.**
3081 A1193 13s multicolored .25 .15

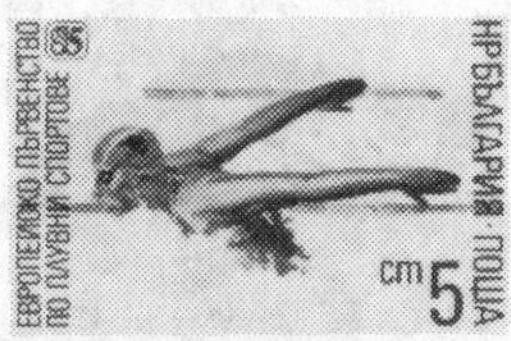

European Swimming Championships, Sofia — A1194

1985, Aug. 2 **Litho.** ***Perf. 12½***
3082 A1194 5s Butterfly stroke .15 .15
3083 A1194 13s Water polo, vert. .25 .15
3084 A1194 42s Diving, vert. .80 .42
3085 A1194 60s Synchronized swimming 1.10 .50
Nos. 3082-3085 (4) 2.30 1.22

The 60s exists with central design inverted.

Natl. Tourism Assoc., 90th Anniv. A1195

1985, Aug. 15 **Photo.** ***Perf. 13***
3086 A1195 5s multicolored .15 .15

1986 World Cup Soccer Championships, Mexico — A1196

Various soccer plays. Nos. 3087-3090 vert.

1985, Aug. 29 ***Perf. 13***
3087 A1196 5s multicolored .15 .15
3088 A1196 13s multicolored .28 .15
3089 A1196 30s multicolored .60 .30
3090 A1196 42s multicolored .85 .42
Nos. 3087-3090 (4) 1.88 1.02

Souvenir Sheet

3091 A1196 1 l multicolored 2.00 1.00

Union of Eastern Rumelia and Bulgaria, 1885 — A1197

1985, Aug. 29 ***Perf. 14x13½***
3092 A1197 5s multicolored .15 .15

Computer Design Portraits — A1198

1985, Sept. 23 ***Perf. 13***
3093 A1198 5s Boy .15 .15
3094 A1198 13s Youth .24 .15
3095 A1198 30s Cosmonaut .52 .30
Nos. 3093-3095 (3) .91
Set value .50

Intl. Exhibition of the Works of Youth Inventors, Plovdiv.

St. John the Baptist Church, Nessebar — A1199

Natl. restoration projects: 13s, Tyrant Hreljo Tower, Rila Monastery. 35s, Soldier, fresco, Ivanovo Rock Church. 42s, Archangel Gabriel, fresco, Bojana Church. 60s, Thracian Woman, fresco, Tomb of Kasanlak, 3rd century B.C. 1 l, The Horseman of Madara, bas-relief.

1985, Sept. 25 **Litho.** ***Perf. 12½***
3096 A1199 5s multicolored .15 .15
3097 A1199 13s multicolored .22 .15
3098 A1199 35s multicolored .60 .32
3099 A1199 42s multicolored .75 .40
3100 A1199 60s multicolored 1.10 .60
Nos. 3096-3100 (5) 2.82 1.62

Souvenir Sheet

Imperf

3101 A1199 1 l multicolored 1.75 1.00

UNESCO, 40th anniv.

Souvenir Sheet

Ludmila Zhishkova Cultural Palace, Sofia — A1200

1985, Oct. 8 ***Perf. 13***
3102 A1200 1 l multicolored 1.75 1.00

UNESCO 23rd General Assembly, Sofia.

Colosseum, Rome A1201

1985, Oct. 15 **Photo.** ***Perf. 13½***
3103 A1201 42s multicolored .75 .42

ITALIA '85. No. 3103 printed se-tenant with label picturing the exhibition emblem.

Souvenir Sheet

Cultural Congress, Budapest — A1202

Designs: No. 3104a, St. Cyril, patron saint of Europe. No. 3104b, Map of Europe. No. 3104c, St. Methodius, patron saint of Europe.

Perf. 13, 13 Vert. (#3104b)

1985, Oct. 22 **Photo.**
3104 A1202 Sheet of 3 2.75 1.50
a.-c. 50s, any single .90 .50

Helsinki Congress, 10th anniv.

Flowers — A1203

1985, Oct. 22 **Photo.** ***Perf. 13x13½***
3105 A1203 5s Gladiolus hybridy .15 .15
3106 A1203 5s Iris germanica .15 .15
3107 A1203 5s Convolvulus tricolor .15 .15
Set value .25 .15

See Nos. 3184-3186.

Historic Sailing Ships A1204

1985, Oct. 28 **Photo.** ***Perf. 13***
3108 A1204 5s Dutch .15 .15
3109 A1204 12s Sea Sovereign, Britain .22 .15
3110 A1204 20s Mediterranean .35 .20
3111 A1204 25s Royal Prince, Britain .45 .25
3112 A1204 42s Mediterranean .75 .42
3113 A1204 60s British battleship 1.10 .60
Nos. 3108-3113 (6) 3.02 1.77

Souvenir Sheet

PHILATELIA '85, Cologne — A1205

Designs: a, Cologne Cathedral. b, Alexander Nevski Cathedral, Sofia.

1985, Nov. 4 ***Imperf.***
3114 A1205 Sheet of 2 1.25 .65
a.-b. 30s, any single .60 .30

Conspiracy to Liberate Bulgaria from Turkish Rule, 150th Anniv. — A1206

Freedom fighters and symbols: No. 3115, Georgi Stojkov Rakowski (1820-1876). No. 3116, Batscho Kiro (1835-1876). No. 3117, Sword, Bible and hands.

1985, Nov. 6 ***Perf. 13***
3115 A1206 5s multicolored .15 .15
3116 A1206 5s multicolored .15 .15
3117 A1206 13s multicolored .22 .15
Set value .40 .22

Liberation from Byzantine Rule, 800th Anniv. A1207

Paintings: 5s, The Revolt 1185, by G. Bogdanov. 13s, The Revolt 1185, by Alexander Tersiev. 30s, Battle Near Klokotnitza, by B. Grigorov and M. Ganowski. 42s, Velika Tarnovo Town Wall, by Zanko Lawrenov. 1 l, St. Dimitriev Church, 12th cent.

1985, Nov. 15 **Litho.**
3118 A1207 5s multicolored .15 .15
3119 A1207 13s multicolored .22 .15
3120 A1207 30s multicolored .52 .30
3121 A1207 42s multicolored .75 .42
Nos. 3118-3121 (4) 1.64 1.02

Souvenir Sheet

Imperf

3122 A1207 1 l multicolored 2.00 1.00

Souvenir Sheet

BALKANPHILA '85 — A1208

1985, Nov. 29 Photo. *Perf. 13*
3123 A1208 40s Dove, posthorn .75 .40

Intl. Post and Telecommunications Development Program — A1209

1985, Dec. 2
3124 A1209 13s multicolored .25 .15

Anton Popov (1915-1942), Freedom Fighter — A1210

1985, Dec. 11 Photo. *Perf. 13*
3125 A1210 5s lake .15 .15

New Year 1986 A1211

1985, Dec. 11 Photo. *Perf. 13*
3126 A1211 5s Doves, snowflake .15 .15
3127 A1211 13s Doves .22 .15
Set value .30 .19

Hunting Dogs and Prey — A1212

Designs: 5s, Pointer and partridge. 8s, Irish setter and pochard. 13s, English setter and mallard. 20s, Cocker spaniel and woodcock. 25s, German pointer and rabbit. 30s, Balkan hound and boar. 42s, Shorthaired dachshund and fox.

1985, Dec. 27 Litho. *Perf. 13x12½*
3128 A1212 5s multicolored .15 .15
3129 A1212 8s multicolored .16 .15
3130 A1212 13s multicolored .28 .15
3131 A1212 20s multicolored .40 .20
3132 A1212 25s multicolored .50 .25
3133 A1212 30s multicolored .60 .30
3134 A1212 42s multicolored .85 .42
Nos. 3128-3134 (7) 2.94 1.62

Intl. Year of the Handicapped — A1213

1985, Dec. 30 Photo. *Perf. 13*
3135 A1213 5s multicolored .15 .15

George Dimitrov (1882-1949) — A1214

1985, Dec. 30 Photo. *Perf. 13*
3136 A1214 13s brn lake .25 .15

7th Intl. Communist Congress, Moscow.

UN Child Survival Campaign — A1215

1986, Jan. 21 Photo. *Perf. 13*
3137 A1215 13s multicolored .25 .15

UNICEF, 40th anniv.

Demeter Blagoev (1856-1924) — A1216

1986, Jan. 28 Photo. *Perf. 13*
3138 A1216 5s dk lake, car & dk red .15 .15

Intl. Peace Year — A1217

1986, Jan. 31 *Perf. 13½*
3139 A1217 5s multicolored .15 .15

Orchids — A1218

1986, Feb. 12 Litho. *Perf. 13x12½*
3140 A1218 5s Dactylorhiza romana .15 .15
3141 A1218 13s Epipactis palustris .25 .15
3142 A1218 30s Ophrys cornuta .60 .30
3143 A1218 32s Limodorum abortivum .60 .32
3144 A1218 42s Cypripedium calceolus .85 .42
3145 A1218 60s Orchis papilionacea 1.25 .60
a. Min. sheet of 6, #3140-3145 4.00 2.00
Nos. 3140-3145 (6) 3.70 1.94

Hares and Rabbits A1219

1986, Feb. 24 *Perf. 12½x12*
3146 A1219 5s multicolored .15 .15
3147 A1219 25s multicolored .45 .25
3148 A1219 30s multicolored .55 .30
3149 A1219 32s multicolored .60 .32
3150 A1219 42s multicolored .75 .42
3151 A1219 60s multicolored 1.00 .60
Nos. 3146-3151 (6) 3.50 2.04

Bulgarian Eagle, Newspaper, 140th Anniv. — A1220

Design: Front page of first issue and Ivan Bogorov, journalist.

1986, Feb. 2 Photo. *Perf. 13*
3152 A1220 5s multicolored .15 .15

Souvenir Sheet

Halley's Comet A1221

Comet's orbit in the Solar System: a, 1980. b, 1910-86. c, 1916-70. d, 1911.

1986, Mar. 7 *Perf. 13½x13*
3153 Sheet of 4 1.75 1.25
a.-d. A1221 25s, any single .42 .30

XIII КОНГРЕС НА БКП
1986
5 СТ
НРБЪЛГАРИЯ ПОЩА

A1222 A1223

1986, Mar. 12 *Perf. 13x13½*
3154 A1222 5s dp bl & bl .15 .15

Vladimir Bachev (1935-1967), poet.

1986, Mar. 17 *Perf. 13*
3155 A1223 5s Wavy lines .15 .15
3156 A1223 8s Star .15 .15
3157 A1223 13s Worker .24 .15
Set value .45 .27

Souvenir Sheet

Imperf

3158 A1223 50s Scaffold, flags .90 .50

13th Natl. Communist Party Congress.

Souvenir Sheet

1st Manned Space Flight, 25th Anniv. — A1224

Designs: a, Vostok I, 1961. b, Yuri Gagarin (1934-68), Russian cosmonaut.

1986, Mar. 28 *Perf. 13½x13*
3159 Sheet of 2 1.75 1.00
a.-b. A1224 50s, any single 1.00 .50

April Uprising against the Turks, 110th Anniv. — A1225

Monuments: 5s, 1876 Uprising monument, Panagjuriste. 13s, Christo Botev, Vraca.

1986, Mar. 30 *Perf. 13*
3160 A1225 5s multicolored .15 .15
3161 A1225 13s multicolored .26 .15
Set value .20

A1225a

Levsky-Spartak Sports Club, 75th Anniv. — A1226

1986 *Perf. 13*
3161A A1225a 5s multicolored .15 .15

Souvenir Sheet

Imperf

3162 A1226 50s Rhythmic gymnastics .80 .50

Issue dates: 5s, Dec. 50s, May 12.

A1227 A1228

1986, May 19 *Perf. 13*
3163 A1227 5s Congress emblem .15 .15
3164 A1227 8s Emblem on globe .15 .15
3165 A1227 13s Flags .24 .15
Set value .45 .27

35th Congress of Bulgarian farmers, Sofia.

1986, May 27 *Perf. 13x13½*
3166 A1228 13s multicolored .25 .15

Conference of Transport Ministers from Socialist Countries.

17th Intl. Book Fair, Sofia — A1229

1986, May 28

3167 A1229 13s blk, brt red & grysh blk .25 .15

1986 World Cup Soccer Championships, Mexico — A1230

Various soccer plays; attached labels picture Mexican landmarks.

1986, May 30 *Perf. 13½*

3168	A1230	5s multi, vert.	.15	.15
3169	A1230	13s multicolored	.25	.15
3170	A1230	20s multicolored	.35	.20
3171	A1230	30s multicolored	.55	.30
3172	A1230	42s multicolored	.75	.42
3173	A1230	60s multi, vert.	1.10	.60
		Nos. 3168-3173 (6)	3.15	1.82

Souvenir Sheet

Perf. 13

3174 A1230 1 l Azteca Stadium 1.75 1.00

Treasures of Preslav — A1231

Gold artifacts: 5s, Embossed brooch. 13s, Pendant with pearl cross, vert. 20s, Crystal and pearl pendant. 30s, Embossed shield. 42s, Pearl and enamel pendant, vert. 60s, Enamel shield.

1986, June 7 *Perf. 13½x13, 13x13½*

3175	A1231	5s multicolored	.15	.15
3176	A1231	13s multicolored	.25	.15
3177	A1231	20s multicolored	.35	.20
3178	A1231	30s multicolored	.55	.30
3179	A1231	42s multicolored	.75	.42
3180	A1231	60s multicolored	1.00	.60
		Nos. 3175-3180 (6)	3.05	1.82

World Fencing Championships, Sofia, July 25-Aug. 3 — A1232

1986, July 25 **Photo.** *Perf. 13*

3181	A1232	5s Head cut, lunge	.15	.15
3182	A1232	13s Touche	.25	.15
3183	A1232	25s Lunge, parry	.45	.25
		Nos. 3181-3183 (3)	.85	
		Set value		.44

Flower Type of 1985

1986, July 29 *Perf. 13x13½*

3184	A1203	8s Ipomoea tricolor	.15	.15
3185	A1203	8s Anemone coronaria	.15	.15
3186	A1203	32s Lilium auratum	.55	.32
		Nos. 3184-3186 (3)	.85	
		Set value		.48

A1233

A1234

1986, Aug. 25

3187 A1233 42s sep, sal brn & lake .75 .42

STOCKHOLMIA '86. No. 3187 printed in sheets of 3 + 3 labels picturing folk art.

Miniature Sheet

Environmental Conservation: a, Ciconia ciconia. b, Nuphar lutea. c, Salamandra salamandra. d, Nymphaea alba.

1986, Aug. 25 **Litho.** *Perf. 14*

3188		Sheet of 4 + label	2.00	.90
a.-d.		A1234 30s any single	.50	.22

No. 3188 contains center label picturing the oldest oak tree in Bulgaria, Granit Village.

Natl. Arms, Building of the Sobranie — A1235

1986, Sept. 13 **Photo.** *Perf. 13*

3189 A1235 5s Prus grn, yel grn & red .15 .15

People's Republic of Bulgaria, 40th anniv.

15th Postal Union Congress — A1236

1986, Sept. 24

3190 A1236 13s multicolored .25 .15

Natl. Youth Brigade Movement, 40th Anniv. A1237

Intl. Organization of Journalists, 10th Congress A1238

1986, Oct. 4

3191 A1237 5s multicolored .15 .15

1986, Oct. 13

3192 A1238 13s blue & dark blue .25 .15

Sts. Cyril and Methodius, Disciples A1239

1986, Oct. 23 *Perf. 13½*

3193 A1239 13s dark brown & buff .25 .15

Sts. Cyril and Methodius in Bulgaria, 1100th anniv. No. 3193 printed se-tenant with inscribed label.

Telephones in Bulgaria, Cent. A1240

1986, Nov. 5 *Perf. 13*

3194 A1240 5s multicolored .15 .15

World Weight Lifting Championships — A1241

1986, Nov. 6

3195 A1241 13s multicolored .25 .15

Ships A1242

1986, Nov. 20

3196	A1242	5s King of Prussia	.15	.15
3197	A1242	13s East Indiaman, 18th cent.	.25	.15
3198	A1242	25s Shebek, 18th cent.	.45	.25
3199	A1242	30s St Paul	.55	.30
3200	A1242	32s Topsail schooner, 18th cent.	.60	.32
3201	A1242	42s Victory	.80	.42
		Nos. 3196-3201 (6)	2.80	1.59

Souvenir Sheet

European Security and Cooperation Congress, Vienna — A1243

Various buildings and emblems: a, Bulgaria. b, Austria. c, Donau Park, UN.

Perf. 13, Imperf. x13 (#3202b)

1986, Nov. 27

3202	Sheet of 3	3.00	1.50
a.-c.	A1243 50s any single	1.00	.50

Exists imperf. bearing control number.

Rogozen Thracian Pitchers A1244

1986, Dec. 5 *Perf. 13*

3203	A1244	10s Facing left	.18	.15
3204	A1244	10s Facing right	.18	.15
		Set value		.20

Union of Bulgarian Philatelists, 14th Congress. Nos. 3203-3204 printed se-tenant with labels picturing carved figures on pitchers in blocks of 4.

New Year 1987 A1245

1986, Dec. 9

3205	A1245	5s shown	.15	.15
3206	A1245	13s Snow flakes	.26	.15
		Set value		.19

Home Amateur Radio Operators in Bulgaria, 60th Anniv. — A1246

1986, Dec. 10

3207 A1246 13s multicolored .25 .15

Miniature Sheet

Paintings by Bulgarian Artists — A1247

Designs: a, Red Tree, by Danail Dechev (1891-1962). b, Troopers Confront Two Men, by Ilya Beshkov (1901-58). c, View of Melnik, by Veselin Stajkov (1906-70). d, View of Houses through Trees, by Kyril Zonev (1896-1961).

1986, Dec. 10 **Litho.** *Perf. 14*

3208	Sheet of 4	2.25	1.10
a.-b.	A1247 25s any single	.50	.25
c.-d.	A1247 30s any single	.60	.30

Sofia Academy of Art, 90th anniv.

Augusto Cesar Sandino (1893-1934), Nicaraguan Revolutionary, and Flag — A1248

1986, Dec. 16 **Photo.** *Perf. 13*

3209 A1248 13s multicolored .25 .15

Sandinista movement in Nicaragua, 25th anniv.

Smoyan Mihylovsky (b. 1856), Writer — A1249

Ran Bossilek (b. 1886) — A1250

Title Page from Bulgarian Folk Songs of the Miladinov Brothers — A1251

Annivs. and events: No. 3211, Pentcho Slaveyckov (b. 1861), writer. No. 3212, Nickola Atanassov (b. 1886), musician.

1986, Dec. 17

3210	A1249	5s multicolored	.15	.15
3211	A1249	5s multicolored	.15	.15
3212	A1249	8s multicolored	.16	.15
3213	A1250	8s multicolored	.16	.15
3214	A1251	10s multicolored	.20	.15
		Nos. 3210-3214 (5)	.82	
		Set value		.36

A1252

Paintings by Titian — A1253

Various portraits.

1986, Dec. 23 Litho. *Perf. 14*

3215	A1252	5s multicolored	.15	.15
3216	A1252	13s multicolored	.28	.15
3217	A1252	20s multicolored	.40	.20
3218	A1252	30s multicolored	.60	.30
3219	A1252	32s multicolored	.65	.32
3220	A1252	42s multicolored	.85	.42
a.		Min. sheet of 6, #3215-3220	3.00	1.50
		Nos. 3215-3220 (6)	2.93	1.54

Souvenir Sheet

3221	A1253	1 l multicolored	2.25	1.00

Sports Cars — A1255

1986, Dec. 30 Litho. *Perf. 13½*

3223	A1255	5s 1905 Fiat	.15	.15
3224	A1255	10s 1928 Bugatti	.18	.15
3225	A1255	25s 1936 Mercedes	.45	.25
3226	A1255	32s 1952 Ferrari	.55	.32
3227	A1255	40s 1985 Lotus	.70	.40
3228	A1255	42s 1986 McLaren	.75	.42
		Nos. 3223-3228 (6)	2.78	1.69

Varna Railway Inauguration, 120th Anniv. — A1257

1987, Jan. 19 Photo.

3229	A1257	5s multicolored	.15	.15

Dimcho Debelianov (1887-1916), Poet — A1258

1987, Jan. 20 Photo. *Perf. 13*

3230	A1258	5s blue, dull yel & dp blue	.15	.15

L.L. Zamenhof, Creator of Esperanto A1259

1987, Feb. 12

3231	A1259	13s multicolored	.15	.15

Mushrooms A1260

10th Natl. Trade Unions Congress A1261

1987, Feb. 6 Litho. *Perf. 11½*

3232	A1260	5s Amanita rubescens	.15	.15
3233	A1260	20s Boletus regius	.50	.30
3234	A1260	30s Leccinum aurantiacum	.70	.45
3235	A1260	32s Coprinus comatus	.75	.48
3236	A1260	40s Russula vesca	1.00	.60
3237	A1260	60s Cantharellus cibarius	1.40	.90
a.		Min. sheet of 6, #3232-3237	5.25	
		Nos. 3232-3237 (6)	4.50	2.88

1987, Mar. 20 Photo. *Perf. 13*

3238	A1261	5s dark red & violet	.15	.15

Rogozen Thracian Treasure A1262

Embossed and gilded silver artifacts: 5s, Plate, Priestess Auge approaching Heracles. 8s, Pitcher, lioness attacking stag. 20s, Plate, floral pattern. 30s, Pitcher, warriors on horseback dueling. 32s, Urn, decorative pattern. 42s, Pitcher (not gilded), winged horses.

1987, Mar. 31

3239	A1262	5s multicolored	.15	.15
3240	A1262	8s multicolored	.20	.15
3241	A1262	20s multicolored	.48	.30
3242	A1262	30s multicolored	.70	.45
3243	A1262	32s multicolored	.75	.48
3244	A1262	42s multicolored	1.00	.62
		Nos. 3239-3244 (6)	3.28	2.15

Miniature Sheet

Modern Architecture — A1263

Designs: a, Ludmila Zhivkova conf. center, Varna. b, Ministry of Foreign Affairs, Sofia. c, Interpred Building, Sofia. d, Hotel, Sandanski.

1987, Apr. 7 *Perf. 13½x13*

3245		Sheet of 4	3.00	1.80
a.-d.		A1263 30s any single	.75	.45

Exists imperf. with black control number.

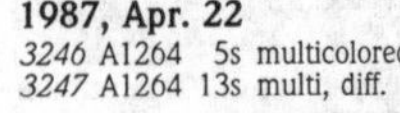

European Freestyle Wrestling Championships A1264

1987, Apr. 22 *Perf. 13*

3246	A1264	5s multicolored	.15	.15
3247	A1264	13s multi, diff.	.38	.18

CAPEX '87, Toronto A1265

1987, Apr. 24

3248	A1265	42s multicolored	1.00	.42

10th Congress of the Natl. Front — A1266

1987, May 11

3249	A1266	5s multicolored	.15	.15

15th Communist Youth Congress A1267

1987, May 13

3250	A1267	5s George Dimitrov	.15	.15

8th Intl. Humor and Satire Biennial, Gabrovo — A1268

1987, May 15 *Perf. 13x13½*

3251	A1268	13s multicolored	.35	.15

13th World Rhythmic Gymnastics Championships, Varna — A1269

Gymnasts.

1987, Aug. 5 Photo. *Perf. 13*

3252	A1269	5s Maria Gigova	.15	.15
3252A	A1269	8s Iliana Raeva	.18	.15
3252B	A1269	13s Anelia Ralenkova	.28	.16
3252C	A1269	25s Pilyana Georgieva	.55	.32
3252D	A1269	30s Lilia Ignatova	.65	.38
3252E	A1269	42s Bianca Panova	.90	.52
		Nos. 3252-3252E (6)	2.71	1.68

Souvenir Sheet

Perf. 13x13½

3252F	A1269	1 l Neshka Robeva, coach	2.25	1.50

Exists imperf. with black control number.

Vassil Kolarov — A1270

1987, June 3 *Perf. 13*

3253	A1270	5s dk red, yel & dk bl	.15	.15

Rayko Daskalov (b. 1886), Politician A1254

1986, Dec. 23 Photo. *Perf. 13*

3222	A1254	5s deep claret	.15	.15

Stela Blagoeva (b. 1887) — A1271

1987, June 4

3254 A1271	5s pink & sepia		.15	.15

Rabotnichesko Delo Newspaper, 60th Anniv. — A1272

1987, May 28

3255 A1272	5s black & lake	.15	.15

Deer A1273

1987, June 23 **Litho.**

3256 A1273	5s Capreolus capreolus, vert.	.15	.15
3257 A1273	10s Alces alces	.25	.15
3258 A1273	32s Dama dama, vert.	.75	.25
3259 A1273	40s Cervus nippon, vert.	1.10	.30
3260 A1273	42s Cervus elaphus	1.10	.32
3261 A1273	60s Rangifer tarandus, vert.	1.40	.45
a.	Min. sheet of 6, #3256-3261, imperf.	5.50	2.85
	Nos. 3256-3261 (6)	4.75	1.62

Vassil Levski (1837-73) A1274

Various portraits.

1987, June 19 **Photo.**

3262 A1274	5s red brn & dark grn	.15	.15
3263 A1274	13s dark grn & red brn	.35	.20
	Set value		.26

Namibia Day A1275

1987, July 8

3264 A1275	13s org, blk & dark red	.30	.20

Georgi Kirkov (1867-1919), Revolutionary A1276

1987, July 17 ***Perf. 13x13½***

3265 A1276	5s claret & deep claret	.15	.15

Bees and Plants — A1277

1987, July 29 **Litho.** ***Perf. 13***

3266 A1277	5s Phacelia tanacetifolia	.15	.15
3267 A1277	10s Helianthus annuus	.25	.15
3268 A1277	30s Robinia pseudoacacia	.75	.45
3269 A1277	32s Lavandula vera	.80	.48
3270 A1277	42s Tilia parvifolia	1.10	.62
3271 A1277	60s Onobrychis sativa	1.50	.90
a.	Min. sheet of 6, #3266-3271	5.00	2.75
	Nos. 3266-3271 (6)	4.55	2.75

BULGARIA '89 — A1278

1987, Sept. 3 ***Perf. 13½x13***

3272 A1278	13s No. 1	.40	.20

HAFNIA '87 — A1279

1987, Sept. 8 ***Perf. 13***

3273 A1279	42s multicolored	1.00	.62

No. 3273 issued in sheets of 3 plus 2 labels picturing emblems of the HAFNIA '87 and BULGARIA '89 exhibitions, and 1 label with background similar to Denmark Type A32 with castle instead of denomination.

Portrait of a Girl, by Stefan Ivanov — A1280

Paintings in the Sofia City Art Galler: 8s, Grape-gatherer, by Bencho Obreshkov. 20s, Portrait of a Lady with a Hat, by David Perets. 25s, Listeners of Marimba, by Kiril Tsonev. 32s, Boy with an Harmonica, by Nenko Balkanski. 60s, Rumyana, by Vasil Stoilov.

1987, Sept. 15 **Litho.** ***Perf. 14***

3274 A1280	5s shown	.15	.15
3275 A1280	8s multicolored	.22	.15
3276 A1280	20s multicolored	.52	.30
3277 A1280	25s multicolored	.65	.38
3278 A1280	32s multicolored	.85	.48
3279 A1280	60s multicolored	1.50	.90
	Nos. 3274-3279 (6)	3.89	2.36

Intl. Atomic Energy Agency, 30th Anniv. A1281

1987, Sept. 15 **Photo.** ***Perf. 13½x13***

3280 A1281	13s red, lt blue & emer	.35	.20

Songbirds A1282

1987, Oct. 12 **Litho.** ***Perf. 12½x12***

3281 A1282	5s Troglodytes troglodytes	.15	.15
3282 A1282	13s Emberiza citrinella	.35	.16
3283 A1282	20s Sitta europaea	.55	.25
3284 A1282	30s Turdus merula	.80	.35
3285 A1282	42s Coccothraustes coccothraustes	1.10	.50
3286 A1282	60s Cinclus cinclus	1.50	.75
a.	Min. sheet of 6, #3281-3286	5.00	2.25
	Nos. 3281-3286 (6)	4.45	2.16

Balkan War, 75th Anniv. A1283

1987, Sept. 15 **Photo.** ***Perf. 13½***

3287 A1283	5s buff, blk & brt org	.15	.15

Newspaper Anniversaries — A1283a

1987, Sept. 24 **Photo.** ***Perf. 13***

3287A A1283a	5s multicolored	.15	.15

Rabotnik, 95th anniv., *Rabotnicheski Vstnik*, 90th anniv. and *Rabotnichesko Delo*, 60th anniv.

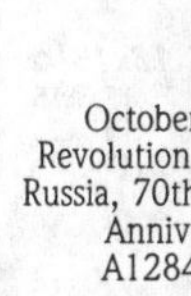

October Revolution, Russia, 70th Anniv. A1284

Lenin and: 5s, Revolutionary. 13s, Cosmonaut.

1987, Oct. 27 **Photo.** ***Perf. 13***

3288 A1284	5s rose brn & red org	.15	.15
3289 A1284	13s brt ultra & red org	.35	.20
	Set value		.26

1988 Winter Olympics, Calgary — A1285

1987, Oct. 27 **Litho.** ***Perf. 13x13½***

3290 A1285	5s Biathlon	.15	.15
3291 A1285	13s Slalom	.38	.20
3292 A1285	30s Women's figure skating	.85	.45
3293 A1285	42s 4-Man bobsled	1.10	.62
	Nos. 3290-3293 (4)	2.48	1.42

Souvenir Sheet

3294 A1285	1 l Ice hockey	2.75	1.50

No. 3294 exists imperf.

Souvenir Sheet

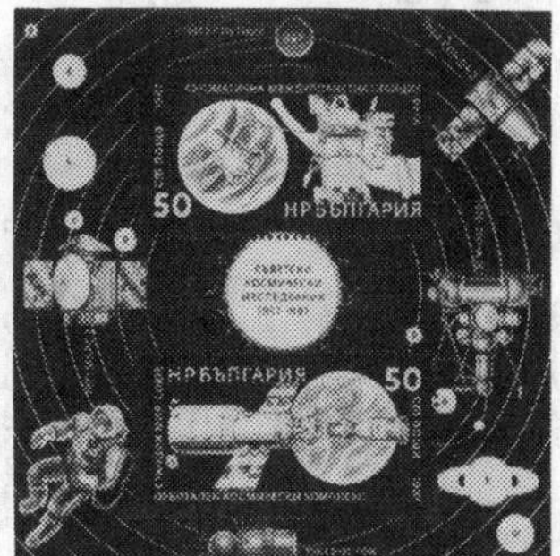
Soviet Space Achievements, 1937-87 — A1286

Designs: No. 3295a, Vega probe. No. 3295b, Mir-Soyuz Space Station.

1987, Dec. 24 **Photo.** ***Perf. 13½x13***

3295 A1286	Sheet of 2	2.75	1.50
a.-b.	50s any single	1.25	.75

Exists imperf.

New Year 1988 A1287

Sofia stamp exhibition emblem within folklore patterns.

1987, Dec. 25 ***Perf. 13***

3296 A1287	5s multicolored	.15	.15
3297 A1287	13s multi, diff.	.35	.20
	Set value		.26

Souvenir Sheet

European Security Conferences A1288

Conferences held in Helsinki, 1973, and Vienna, 1987: a, Helsinki Conf. Center. b, Map of Europe. c, Vienna Conf. Center.

Perf. 13x13½ on 2 or 4 Sides

1987, Dec. 30

3298	Sheet of 3	4.00	3.00
a.-c.	A1288 50s any single	1.50	.75

Exists imperf.

A1289 A1290

1988, Jan. 20
3299 A1289 5s multicolored .15 .15

Christo Kabaktchiev (b. 1878), party leader.

1988, Jan. 25 **Litho.** ***Perf. 12***

Marine flowers.

3300 A1290 5s Scilla bythynica .15 .15
3301 A1290 10s Geum rhodopaeum .24 .15
3302 A1290 13s Caltha polypetala .32 .20
3303 A1290 25s Nymphoides peltata .60 .38
3304 A1290 30s Cortusa matthioli .75 .45
3305 A1290 42s Stratiotes aloides 1.00 .62
a. Min. sheet of 6, #3300-3305 3.50 2.00
Nos. 3300-3305 (6) 3.06 1.95

Liberation of Bulgaria, 110th Anniv. A1291

1988, Feb. 15 **Photo.** ***Perf. 13***
3306 A1291 5s Officer, horse .15 .15
3307 A1291 13s Soldiers .35 .20
Set value .26

8th Intl. Civil Servants Congress, Sofia A1292

1988, Mar. 22 **Photo.** ***Perf. 13***
3308 A1292 13s multicolored .30 .16

State Railways, Cent. — A1293

Locomotives: 5s, Jantra, 1888. 13s, Christo Botev, 1905. 25s, 0-10-1, 1918. 32s, 4-12-1 heavy duty, 1943. 42s, Diesel, 1964. 60s, Electric, 1979.

1988, Mar. 25 **Litho.** ***Perf. 11***
3309 A1293 5s multicolored .15 .15
3310 A1293 13s multicolored .28 .16
3311 A1293 25s multicolored .52 .30
3312 A1293 32s multicolored .70 .40
3313 A1293 42s multicolored .95 .52
3314 A1293 60s multicolored 1.25 .72
a. Min. sheet of 6, #3309-3314 4.00 2.00
Nos. 3309-3314 (6) 3.85 2.25

Ivan Nedyalkov (1880-1925) A1294

Postal workers, heroes of socialism: 8s, Delcho Spasov (1918-43). 10s, Nikola Ganchev (1915-43). 13s, Ganka Stoyanova Rasheva (1921-44).

1988, Mar. 31 **Photo.** ***Perf. 13½x13***
3315 A1294 5s buff & dark rose brn .15 .15
3316 A1294 8s pale ultra & violet blue .16 .15
3317 A1294 10s pale olive grn & olive grn .22 .15
3318 A1294 13s pale pink & lake .26 .16
Nos. 3315-3318 (4) .79
Set value .44

Georgi Traikov (b. 1898), Statesman A1295

Intl. Red Cross and Red Crescent Organizations, 125th Annivs. A1296

1988, Apr. 8 **Litho.** ***Perf. 13x13½***
3319 A1295 5s orange & brn .15 .15

1988, Apr. 26 **Photo.** ***Perf. 13***
3320 A1296 13s multicolored .25 .16

Children's Drawings Type of 1982

Designs: 5s, Girl wearing a folk costume, vert. 8s, Painter at easel, vert. 13s, Children playing. 20s, Ringing bells for peace. 32s, Accordion player, vert. 42s, Cosmonaut, vert. 50s, Assembly emblem.

1988, Apr. 28 **Litho.** ***Perf. 14***
3321 A1093 5s multicolored .15 .15
3322 A1093 8s multicolored .18 .15
3323 A1093 13s multicolored .28 .16
3324 A1093 20s multicolored .42 .25
3325 A1093 32s multicolored .65 .40
3326 A1093 42s multicolored .90 .52
Nos. 3321-3326 (6) 2.58 1.63

Souvenir Sheet

3327 A1093 50s multicolored 1.00 .62

4th Intl. Children's Assembly, Sofia. No. 3327 exists imperf.

Karl Marx A1297

1988, May 5 ***Perf. 13***
3328 A1297 13s multicolored .30 .16

Birds — A1297a

1988, May 6 **Litho.** ***Perf. 13x13½***
3328A A1297a 5s *Ciconia ciconia* .15 .15
3328B A1297a 5s *Larus argentatus* .15 .15
3328C A1297a 8s *Ardea cinerea* .18 .15
3328D A1297a 8s *Corvus corone cornix* .18 .15
3328E A1297a 10s *Accipiter gentilis* .22 .15
3328F A1297a 42s *Bubo bubo* .90 .50
Nos. 3328A-3328F (6) 1.78
Set value .94

Dated 1987.

Sofia Zoo, Cent. A1298

1988, May 20
3329 A1298 5s Loxodonta africana .15 .15
3330 A1298 13s Ceratotherium simum .25 .16
3331 A1298 25s Lycaon pictus .50 .30
3332 A1298 30s Pelecanus onocrotalus .65 .36
3333 A1298 32s Bucorvus abissinicus .70 .40
3334 A1298 42s Nyctea scandiaca .90 .52
a. Min. sheet of 6, #3329-3334 3.60 1.80
Nos. 3329-3334 (6) 3.15 1.89

FINLANDIA '88 — A1299

1988, June 7
3335 A1299 30s Finland No. 1 .70 .35

No. 3335 printed in miniature sheets of 3 plus 3 labels picturing skyline, SOFIA '89 and FINLANDIA '88 exhibition emblems.

Exists imperf.

2nd Joint USSR-Bulgaria Space Flight — A1300

1988, June 7
3336 A1300 5s shown .15 .15
3337 A1300 13s Rocket, globe .30 .16
Set value .22

EXPO '91, Plovdiv — A1301

1988, June 7 ***Perf. 13½x13***
3338 A1301 13s multicolored .30 .16

1988 European Soccer Championships — A1302

1988, June 10 ***Perf. 13***
3339 A1302 5s Corner kick .15 .15
3340 A1302 13s Heading the ball .25 .16
3341 A1302 30s Referee, player .55 .36
3342 A1302 42s Player holding trophy .85 .55
Nos. 3339-3342 (4) 1.80 1.22

Souvenir Sheet

3343 A1302 1 l Stadium 2.25 1.25

Paintings by Dechko Usunov (1899-1986) A1303

Designs: 5s, *Portrait of a Young Girl.* 13s, *Portrait of Maria Wassilewa.* 30s, *Self-portrait.*

1988, June 14 ***Perf. 13x13½***
3344 A1303 5s multicolored .15 .15
3345 A1303 13s multicolored .32 .16
3346 A1303 30s multicolored .72 .36
Nos. 3344-3346 (3) 1.19 .67

Souvenir Sheet

1st Woman in Space, 25th Anniv. — A1304

1988, June 16 ***Perf. 13½x13***
3347 A1304 1 l multicolored 2.50 1.50

Valentina Tereshkova's flight, June 16-19, 1963.

Kurdzhali Region Religious Art — A1305

Designs: 5s, *St. John the Baptist,* 1592. 8s, *St. George Slaying the Dragon,* 1841.

1988, June 27 ***Perf. 13x13½***
3348 A1305 5s multicolored .15 .15
3349 A1305 8s multicolored .20 .15
Set value .16

1988 Summer Olympics, Seoul — A1306

1988, July 25 **Litho.** ***Perf. 13***
3350 A1306 5s High jump .15 .15
3351 A1306 13s Weight lifting .28 .16
3352 A1306 30s Greco-Roman wrestling .65 .38
3353 A1306 42s Rhythmic gymnastics .90 .52
Nos. 3350-3353 (4) 1.98 1.21

Souvenir Sheet

3354 A1306 1 l Volleyball 2.50 1.25

No. 3354 exists imperf.

Dimitr and Karaja A1307

1988, July 25 **Litho.** ***Perf. 13***
3355 A1307 5s blk, dark olive bister & grn .15 .15

120th anniv. of the deaths of Haji Dimitr and Stefan Karaja, patriots killed during the Balkan Wars.

Problems of Peace and Socialism, 30th Anniv. A1308

1988, July 26 **Photo.**

3356 A1308 13s multicolored .25 .16

Paintings in the Ludmila Zhivkova Art Gallery — A1309

Paintings: No. 3357, *Harbor, Algiers,* by Albermarke (1875-1947). No. 3358, *Portrait of Ermin David in the Studio,* by Jul Pasken (1885-1930). No. 3359, *Madonna with Child and Sts. Sebastian and Roko,* by Giovanni Rosso (1494-1540). No. 3360, *The Barren Tree,* by Roland Udo (1879-1982).

1988, July 27 **Litho.** ***Perf. 14***

3357 A1309 30s multicolored .65 .38
3358 A1309 30s multicolored .65 .38
3359 A1309 30s multicolored .65 .38
3360 A1309 30s multicolored .65 .38
Nos. 3357-3360 (4) 2.60 1.52

St. Clement of Ohrid University, Sofia, 100th Anniv. A1310

1988, Aug. 22 ***Perf. 13***

3361 A1310 5s blk & pale yel .15 .15

PRAGA '88 A1311

1988, Aug. 22

3362 A1311 25s Czechoslovakia #2 in vermilion .60 .30

Printed in miniature sheets of 3 plus 3 labels picturing skyline, PRAGA '88 and SOFIA '89 exhibition emblems.
Exists imperf.

OLYMPHILEX '88 — A1312

1988, Sept. 1

3363 A1312 62s Korea No. 1 1.25 .75

Printed in miniature sheets of 3 plus 3 labels picturing skyline, OLYMPHILEX '88 and SOFIA '89 exhibition emblems.
Exists imperf.

A1313 A1314

1988, Sept. 15

3364 A1313 5s deep blue, lt blue & red .15 .15

Kremikovtsi steel mill, 25th anniv.

1988, Sept. 16 ***Perf. 13½x13***

3365 A1314 13s dark red & ultra .25 .16

80th Interparliamentary Conference.

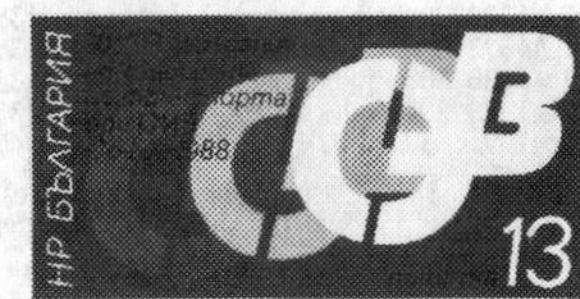

Transportation Commission 80th Congress — A1315

1988, Oct. 17

3366 A1315 13s deep lil rose & blk .25 .16

Kurdzhali Region Artifacts A1316

Designs: 5s, Earthenware bowl, 13th-14th cent. 8s, Medieval fortification, Gorna Krepost Village, vert.

1988, Sept. 20 ***Perf. 13***

3367 A1316 5s multicolored .15 .15
3368 A1316 8s multicolored .20 .15
Set value .16

Chiprovo Uprising, 300th Anniv. — A1317

1988, Sept. 23

3369 A1317 5s multicolored .15 .15

Bears A1318

1988, Sept. 26 ***Perf. 12½***

3370 A1318 5s *Ursus arctos* .15 .15
3371 A1318 8s *Thalassarctos maritimus* .18 .15
3372 A1318 13s *Melursus ursinus* .30 .16
3373 A1318 20s *Helarctos malayanus* .45 .25
3374 A1318 32s *Selenarctos thibetanus* .70 .40
3375 A1318 42s *Tremarctos ornatus* .95 .52
a. Min. sheet of 6, #3370-3375 3.00 1.50
Nos. 3370-3375 (6) 2.73 1.63

ECOFORUM for Peace — A1319

1988, Oct. 29 ***Perf. 13***

3376 A1319 20s multicolored .50 .25

PLOVDIV '88 A1320

Design: Amphitheater ruins, PRAGA '88 and PLOVDIV '88 emblems.

1988, Nov. 2

3377 A1320 5s multicolored .15 .15

Exists in imperf. sheet of six.

Radio & Television Authority, 25th Anniv. — A1321

1988, Nov. 17 **Litho.** ***Perf. 13***

3378 A1321 5s multicolored .15 .15

BULGARIA '89 A1321a

1988, Nov. 22 **Litho.** ***Perf. 13***

3379 A1321a 42s No. 1 1.10 .58

Printed in miniature sheets of 3+3 labels picturing exhib. emblem and conf. center.
Exists imperf.

Souvenir Sheet

Danube Cruise Excursion Industry, 40th Anniv. — A1321b

1988, Nov. 25 ***Perf. 13½x13***

3380 Sheet of 2 4.75 2.75
a. A1321b 1 l *Russia* 2.50 1.35
b. A1321b 1 l *Aleksandr Stamboliski* 2.50 1.35

Traffic Safety A1321c

1988, Nov. 28

3381 A1321c 5s multicolored .15 .15

New Year 1989 — A1321d

1988, Dec. 20 ***Perf. 13***

3382 A1321d 5s shown .15 .15
3383 A1321d 13s multi, diff. .35 .25

Hotels in Winter A1322

1988, Dec. 19 **Litho.** ***Perf. 13½x13***

3384 A1322 5s shown .15 .15
3385 A1322 8s multi, diff. .18 .15
3386 A1322 13s multi, diff. .28 .16
3387 A1322 30s multi, diff. .70 .38
Nos. 3384-3387 (4) 1.31
Set value .70

Souvenir Sheet

Soviet Space Shuttle *Energija-Buran* — A1322a

1988, Dec. 28 ***Perf. 13½x13***

3387A A1322a 1 l dark blue 2.75 1.50

BULGARIA '89 — A1322b

Traditional modes of postal conveyance.

1988, Dec. 29 ***Perf. 13½x13***

3387B A1322b 25s Mail coach .50 .30
3387C A1322b 25s Biplane .50 .30
3387D A1322b 25s Truck .50 .30
3387E A1322b 25s Steam packet .50 .30
Nos. 3387B-3387E (4) 2.00 1.20

Philatelic Exhibitions A1323

1989 **Litho.** ***Perf. 13***

3388 A1322 42s France No. 1 1.00 .52
3389 A1322 62s India No. 200 1.50 .78

BULGARIA '89 and PHILEXFRANCE '89 (42s) or INDIA '89 (62s).

Issue dates: 42s, Feb. 23; 62s, Jan. 14. Nos. 3388-3389 printed in miniature sheets of 3 plus 3 labels picturing skylines, BULGARIA '89 and PHILEXFRANCE or INDIA exhibition labels. Exist imperf.

Exist in sheet of four also.

Souvenir Sheet

Universiade Winter Games, Sofia — A1324

Designs: a, Downhill skiing. b, Ice hockey. c, Cross-country skiing. d, Speed skating.

1989, Jan. 30 Litho. *Imperf.*
Simulated Perforations

3390	Sheet of 4	2.25	1.25
a.-d.	A1324 25s multicolored	.55	.30

No. 3390 exists imperf. without simulated perforations and containing black control number.

Humor and Satire Festival, Gabrovo A1325

1989, Feb. 7 *Perf. 13½x13*
3391 A1325 13s Don Quixote .30 .16

Endangered Plant Species — A1326

1989, Feb. 22 *Perf. 13x13½*

3392	A1326 5s *Ramonda serbica*	.15	.15
3393	A1326 10s *Paeonia maskula*	.20	.15
3394	A1326 25s *Viola perinensis*	.50	.30
3395	A1326 30s *Dracunculus vulgaris*	.60	.35
3396	A1326 42s *Tulipa splendens*	.85	.50
3397	A1326 60s *Rindera umbellata*	1.25	.70
a.	Min. sheet of 6, #3392-3397	4.00	2.50
	Nos. 3392-3397 (6)	3.55	2.15

World Wildlife Fund A1327

Bats.

1989, Feb. 27 *Perf. 13*

3398	A1327 5s *Nyctalus noctula*	.15	.15
3399	A1327 13s *Rhinolophus ferrumequinum*	.30	.15
3400	A1327 30s *Myotis myotis*	.70	.35
3401	A1327 42s *Vespertilio murinus*	1.00	.50
a.	Min. sheet of 4, #3398-3401	2.25	1.25
	Nos. 3398-3401 (4)	2.15	1.15

Aleksandr Stamboliski (1879-1923), Premier — A1328

1989, Mar. 1 *Perf. 13½x13*
3402 A1328 5s brt org & blk .15 .15

Souvenir Sheet

Soviet-Bulgarian Joint Space Flight, 10th Anniv. — A1329

Designs: a, Liftoff. b, Crew.

1989, Apr. 10 *Perf. 13*

3403	A1329 Sheet of 2	2.25	1.25
a.-b.	50s any single	1.10	.62

Exists imperf.

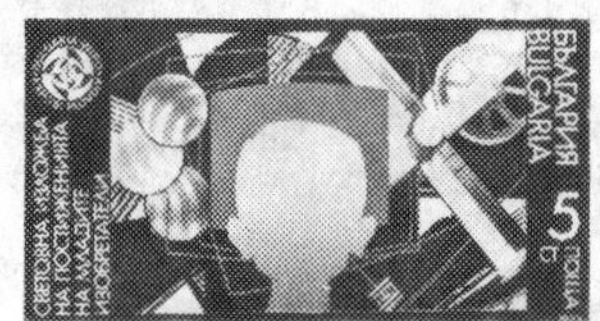

EXPO '91 Young Inventors Exhibition, Plovdiv — A1330

1989, Apr. 20 *Perf. 13½x13*
3404 A1330 5s multicolored .15 .15

Petko Enev (b. 1889) A1331

Stanke Dimitrov Marek (b. 1889) — A1332

Perf. 13½x13, 13x13½
1989, Apr. 28

3405	A1331 5s scarlet & black	.15	.15
3406	A1332 5s scarlet & black	.15	.15
	Set value		.15

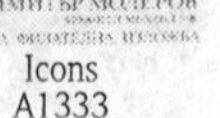

Icons A1333

Photocopier A1334

Paintings by Bulgarian artists: No. 3407, Archangel Michael, by Dimiter Molerov. No. 3408, Mother and Child, by Toma Vishanov. No. 3409, St. John, by Vishanov. No. 3410, St. Dimitri, by Ivan Terziev.

1989, Apr. 28 *Perf. 13x13½*

3407	A1333 30s multicolored	.65	.35
3408	A1333 30s multicolored	.65	.35
3409	A1333 30s multicolored	.65	.35
3410	A1333 30s multicolored	.65	.35
	Nos. 3407-3410 (4)	2.60	1.40

Nos. 3408, 3410 exist in sheets of four. Nos. 3407-3410 exist in souvenir sheets of four and together in one sheet of four, imperf.

1989, May 5

3411	A1334 5s shown	.15	.15
3412	A1334 8s Computer	.18	.15
3413	A1334 35s Telephone	.80	.45
3414	A1334 42s Dish receiver	.90	.52
	Nos. 3411-3414 (4)	2.03	1.27

Bulgarian Communications, 110th anniv. Nos. 3411-3413 exist in imperf. sheets of six.

Souvenir Sheet

58th FIP Congress — A1335

1989, May 22
3415 A1335 1 l Charioteer 2.00 1.00

Exists imperf.

1st Communist Party Congress in Bulgaria, 70th Anniv. — A1336

Famous Men — A1337

1989, June 15
3416 A1336 5s mar, blk & dk red .15 .15

1989

Portraits: No. 3417, Ilya Blaskov. No. 3418, Sofronii, Bishop of Vratza. No. 3419, Vassil Aprilov (b. 1789), educator, historian. No. 3420, Christo Jassenov (1889-1925). 10s, Stoyan Zagorchinov (1889-1969).

3417	A1337 5s black & gray olive	.15	.15
3418	A1337 5s blk, brn blk & pale green	.15	.15
3419	A1337 8s lt blue, blk & vio blk	.28	.15
3420	A1337 8s tan, blk & dark red brown	.22	.15
3421	A1337 10s blk, pale pink & gray blue	.28	.15
	Nos. 3417-3421 (5)	1.08	
	Set value		.50

Issued: #3417-3418, June 15; #3419, Aug. 1; #3420, Sept. 25; 10s, Aug. 5.

French Revolution, Bicent. — A1338

1989, June 26 *Perf. 13½x13*

3422	A1338 13s Anniv. emblem	.26	.15
3423	A1338 30s Jean-Paul Marat	.60	.35
3424	A1338 42s Robespierre	.85	.50
	Nos. 3422-3424 (3)	1.71	1.00

7th Army Games A1339

1989, June 30 *Perf. 13*

3425	A1339 5s Gymnast	.15	.15
3426	A1339 13s Equestrian	.28	.16
3427	A1339 30s Running	.65	.38
3428	A1339 42s Shooting	.95	.52
	Nos. 3425-3428 (4)	2.03	1.21

22nd World Canoe and Kayak Championships, Plovdiv — A1340

1989, Aug. 11 Litho. *Perf. 13*

3429	A1340 13s Woman paddling	.28	.15
3430	A1340 30s Man rowing	.60	.25

Photography, 150th Anniv. — A1341

1989, Aug. 29 *Perf. 13½x13*
3431 A1341 42s blk, buff & yellow .85 .45

September 9 Revolution, 45th Anniv. — A1342

1989, Aug. 30 *Perf. 13*

3432	A1342 5s Revolutionaries	.15	.15
3433	A1342 8s Couple embracing	.16	.15
3434	A1342 13s Faces in a crowd	.25	.16
	Nos. 3432-3434 (3)	.56	
	Set value		.32

Natural History Museum, Cent. A1343

1989, Aug. 31

3435 A1343 13s multicolored .30 .16

Postal Workers Killed in World War II — A1343a

Designs: 5s, L.D. Dardjikov. 8s, I.B. Dobrev. 10s, N.P. Antonov.

1989, Sept. 22 Litho. *Perf. 13*

3436 A1343a 5s multicolored .15 .15
3437 A1343a 8s multicolored .18 .15
3438 A1343a 13s multicolored .32 .18
Nos. 3436-3438 (3) .65
Set value .34

12th Shipping Unions Congress (FIATA) A1344

1989, Sept. 25 Litho. *Perf. 13½x13*

3439 A1344 42s light blue & dark blue .85 .45

Jawaharlal Nehru, 1st Prime Minister of Independent India — A1346

1989, Oct. 10

3440 A1346 13s blk, pale yel & brn .32 .16

Souvenir Sheet

European Ecology Congress — A1347

1989, Oct. 12 *Perf. 13*

3441 A1347 Sheet of 2 3.50 1.75
a. 50s multicolored 1.20 .60
b. 1 l multicolored 2.25 1.15

Snakes A1368

1989, Oct. 20 Litho. *Perf. 13*

3491 A1368 5s *Eryx jaculus turcicus* .15 .15
3492 A1368 10s *Elaphe longissima* .22 .15
3493 A1368 25s *Elaphe situla* .55 .30
3494 A1368 30s *Elaphe quatuorlineata* .65 .35
3495 A1368 42s *Telescopus fallax* .90 .50
3496 A1368 60s *Coluber rubriceps* 1.25 .70
a. Min. sheet of 6, #3491-3496 4.00 2.05
Nos. 3491-3496 (6) 3.72 2.15

Intl. Youth Science Fair, Plovdiv, 1989 — A1369

1989, Nov. 4

3497 A1369 13s multicolored .25 .15

1990 World Soccer Championships, Italy — A1370

Various athletes: No. 3502a, Athletes facing right. No. 3502b, Athletes facing left.

1989, Dec. 1

3498 A1370 5s shown .15 .15
3499 A1370 13s multi, diff. .30 .15
3500 A1370 30s multi, diff. .70 .35
3501 A1370 42s multi, diff. .98 .50
Nos. 3498-3501 (4) 2.13 1.15

Souvenir Sheet

3502 Sheet of 2 2.30 1.15
a.-b. A1370 50s any single 1.15 .57

Air Sports A1371

1989, Dec. 8

3503 A1371 5s Glider planes .15 .15
3504 A1371 13s Hang glider .30 .15
3505 A1371 30s Sky diving .70 .35
3506 A1371 42s Three sky divers .98 .50
Nos. 3503-3506 (4) 2.13 1.15

82nd General conference of the FAI, Varna.

Traffic Safety A1372

1989, Dec. 12

3507 A1372 5s multicolored .15 .15

New Year 1990 — A1373

1989, Dec. 25 Litho. *Perf. 13*

3508 A1373 5s Santa's sleigh .15 .15
3509 A1373 13s Snowman .32 .16

Cats — A1374

Designs: No. 3510, Persian. No. 3511, Tiger. 8s, Tabby. No. 3513, Himalayan. No. 3514, Persian, diff. 13s, Siamese. Nos. 3511 and 3514-3515 vert.

Perf. 13½x13, 13x13½

1989, Dec. 26 Background Color

3510 A1374 5s gray .15 .15
3511 A1374 5s yellow .15 .15
3512 A1374 8s orange .20 .15
3513 A1374 10s blue .24 .15
3514 A1374 10s brown orange .24 .15
3515 A1374 13s red .30 .15
Nos. 3510-3515 (6) 1.28
Set value .61

Explorers and Their Ships A1375

1990, Jan. 17 *Perf. 13*

3516 A1375 5s Christopher Columbus .15 .15
3517 A1375 8s Vasco da Gama .20 .15
3518 A1375 13s Fernando Magellan .30 .15
3519 A1375 32s Sir Francis Drake .78 .38
3520 A1375 42s Henry Hudson 1.00 .50
3521 A1375 60s James Cook 1.45 .72
a. Min. sheet of 6, #3516-3521 3.85 1.90
Nos. 3516-3521 (6) 3.88 2.05

Natl. Esperanto Movement, Cent. — A1376

1990, Feb. 23 Litho. *Perf. 13*

3522 A1376 10s multicolored .25 .15

Paintings by Foreign Artists in the Natl. Museum — A1377

Artists: No. 3523, Suzanna Valadon (1867-1938). No. 3524, Maurice Brianchon (1899-1978). No. 3525, Moise Kisling (1891-1953). No. 3526, Giovanni Beltraffio (1467-1516).

1990, Mar. 23 *Perf. 14*

3523 A1377 30s multicolored .65 .38
3524 A1377 30s multicolored .65 .38
3525 A1377 30s multicolored .65 .38
3526 A1377 30s multicolored .65 .38
Nos. 3523-3526 (4) 2.60 1.52

1990 World Soccer Championships, Italy — A1378

Various athletes.

1990, Mar. 26 *Perf. 13*

3527 A1378 5s multicolored .15 .15
3528 A1378 13s multi, diff. .28 .15
3529 A1378 30s multi, diff. .70 .38
3530 A1378 42s multi, diff. .95 .50
Nos. 3527-3530 (4) 2.08 1.18

Souvenir Sheet

3531 Sheet of 2 2.25 1.20
a. A1378 50s Three players 1.10 .60
b. A1378 50s Two players 1.10 .60

Bavaria No. 1 A1379

1990, Apr. 6 Litho. *Perf. 13*

3532 A1379 42s ver & blk 1.00 .50

ESSEN '90, Germany, Apr. 12-22. No. 3532 printed in sheets of 3 + 3 labels.

Souvenir Sheet

Penny Black, 150th Anniv. A1380

1990, Apr. 10

3533 Sheet of 2 2.25 1.20
a. A1380 50s Great Britain #1 1.10 .60
b. A1380 50s Sir Rowland Hill 1.10 .60

Cooperative Farming in Bulgaria, Cent. — A1381

1990, Apr. 17

3534 A1381 5s multicolored .15 .15

Dimitar Chorbadjiski-Chudomir (1890-1967) — A1382

1990, Apr. 24

3535 A1382 5s multicolored .15 .15

Labor Day, Cent. — A1383

1990, May 1 *Perf. 13x13½*

3536 A1383 10s multicolored .25 .15

ITU, 125th Anniv. — A1384

1990, May 13 Litho. *Perf. 13½x13*

3537 A1384 20s blue, red & black .45 .24

Belgium No. 1 A1385

1990, May 23 *Perf. 13*

3538 A1385 30s multicolored .75 .38

Belgica '90. No. 3538 printed in sheets of 3 + 3 labels.

Lamartine (1790-1869), French Poet — A1386

1990, June 15 *Perf. 13½x13*

3539 A1386 20s multicolored .45 .25

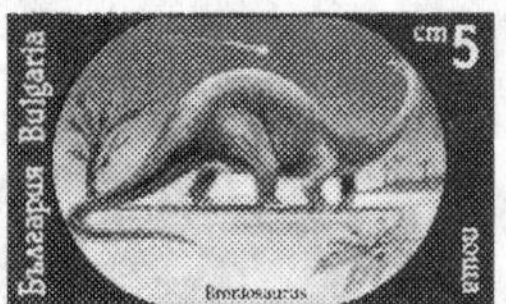

Dinosaurs — A1387

1990, June 19 *Perf. 12½*

3540 A1387 5s Brontosaurus .15 .15
3541 A1387 8s Stegosaurus .20 .15
3542 A1387 13s Edaphosaurus .32 .16
3543 A1387 25s Rhamphorhynchus .62 .30
3544 A1387 32s Protoceratops .80 .40
3545 A1387 42s Triceratops 1.05 .55
a. Min. sheet of 6, #3540-3545 3.25 1.60
Nos. 3540-3545 (6) 3.14 1.71

1992 Summer Olympic Games, Barcelona — A1388

1990, July 13 *Perf. 13½x13*

3546 A1388 5s Swimming .15 .15
3547 A1388 13s Handball .32 .16
3548 A1388 30s Hurdling .75 .38
3549 A1388 42s Cycling 1.05 .55
Nos. 3546-3549 (4) 2.27 1.24

Souvenir Sheet

3550 Sheet of 2 2.50 1.25
a. A1388 50s Tennis, forehand 1.25 .62
b. A1388 50s Tennis, backhand 1.25 .62

Butterflies A1389

1990, Aug. 8 Litho. *Perf. 13*

3551 A1389 5s Zerynthia Polyxena .15 .15
3552 A1389 10s Panaxia quadripunctaria .22 .15
3553 A1389 20s Proserpinus proserpina .45 .24
3554 A1389 30s Hyles lineata .65 .36
3555 A1389 42s Thecla betulae .95 .55
3556 A1389 60s Euphydryas cynthia 1.25 .72
a. Min. sheet of 6, #3551-3556 4.00 2.10
Nos. 3551-3556 (6) 3.67 2.17

Airplanes — A1390

1990, Aug. 30 Litho. *Perf. 13½x13*

3557 A1390 5s Airbus A-300 .15 .15
3558 A1390 10s Tu-204 .18 .15
3559 A1390 25s Concorde .42 .30
3560 A1390 30s DC-9 .52 .36
3561 A1390 42s Il-86 .75 .55
3562 A1390 60s Boeing 747 1.00 .72
a. Min. sheet of 6, #3557-3562 3.25 2.15
Nos. 3557-3562 (6) 3.02 2.23

Exarch Joseph I (1840-1915), Religious Leader — A1391

1990, Sept. 27 *Perf. 13*

3563 A1391 5s blk, pur & grn .15 .15

Intl. Traffic Safety Year A1392

1990, Oct. 9 Litho. *Perf. 13*

3564 A1392 5s multicolored .15 .15

Olymphilex '90, Varna — A1393

1990, Oct. 16 *Perf. 13x13½*

3565 A1393 5s Shot put .15 .15
3566 A1393 13s Discus .25 .15
3567 A1393 42s Hammer throw .90 .55
3568 A1393 60s Javelin 1.25 .72
a. Souv. sheet of 4, #3565-3568, imperf. 12.00 1.50
Nos. 3565-3568 (4) 2.55 1.57

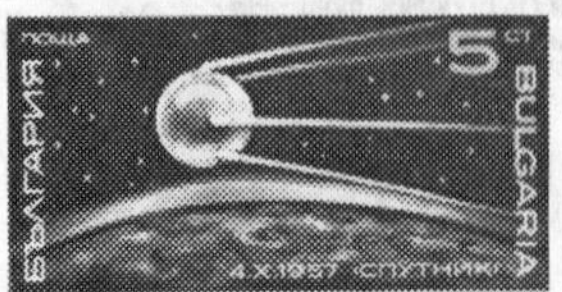

Space Exploration — A1394

Designs: 5s, Sputnik, 1957, USSR. 8s, Vostok, 1961, USSR. 10s, Voshkod 2, 1965, USSR. 20s, Apollo-Soyuz, 1975, US-USSR. 42s, Space Shuttle Columbia, 1981, US. 60s, Galileo, 1989-1996, US. 1 l, Apollo 11 Moon landing, 1969, US.

1990, Oct. 22 *Perf. 13½x13*

3569 A1394 5s multicolored .15 .15
3570 A1394 8s multicolored .16 .15
3571 A1394 10s multicolored .20 .15
3572 A1394 20s multicolored .40 .24
3573 A1394 42s multicolored .90 .55
3574 A1394 60s multicolored 1.25 .72
Nos. 3569-3574 (6) 3.06 1.96

Souvenir Sheet

3575 A1394 1 l multicolored 2.75 1.50

St. Clement of Okhrida — A1395

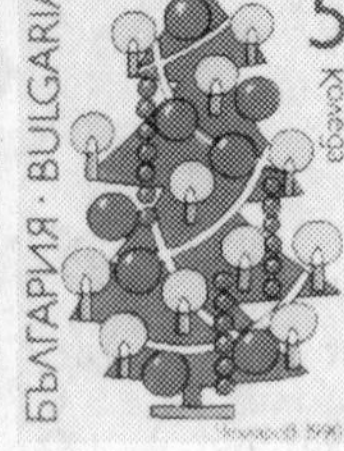

Christmas — A1396

1990, Nov. 29 Litho. *Perf. 13*

3576 A1395 5s multicolored .15 .15

1990, Dec. 25 Litho. *Perf. 13*

3577 A1396 5s Christmas tree .15 .15
3578 A1396 20s Santa Claus .40 .24
Set value .30

European Figure Skating Championships, Sofia — A1397

1991, Jan. 18 *Perf. 13½x13*

3579 A1397 15s multicolored .35 .18

Farm Animals — A1398

1991-92 *Perf. 14x13½*

3581 A1398 20s Sheep .30 .18
3582 A1398 25s Goose .35 .22
3583 A1398 30s Hen, chicks .42 .28
3584 A1398 40s Horse .55 .35
3585 A1398 62s Goat .85 .55
3586 A1398 86s Sow 1.25 .75
3587 A1398 95s Goat .70 .42
3588 A1398 1 l Donkey 1.40 .90
3589 A1398 2 l Bull 2.75 1.75
3590 A1398 5 l Turkey 7.00 4.25
3591 A1398 10 l Cow 14.00 8.50
Nos. 3581-3591 (11) 29.57 18.15

Issued: 20s, 25s, 40s, 86s, 1 l, Aug. 21; 10 l, Feb. 22; 95s, May 5, 1992; others, Feb. 11, 1991.

Mushrooms A1399

1991, Mar. 19 *Perf. 12½x13*

3597 A1399 5s Amanita phalloides .15 .15
3598 A1399 10s Amanita verna .16 .15
3599 A1399 20s Amanita pantherina .32 .18
3600 A1399 32s Amanita muscaria .55 .30
3601 A1399 42s Gyromitra esculenta .70 .38
3602 A1399 60s Boletus satanas .95 .55
a. Min. sheet of 6, #3597-3602 3.00 1.50
Nos. 3597-3602 (6) 2.83 1.71

French Impressionists A1400

Designs: 20s, Good Morning, by Gauguin. 43s, Madame Dobini, by Degas. 62s, Peasant Woman, by Pissarro. 67s, Woman with Black Hair, by Manet. 80s, Blue Vase, by Cezanne. 2 l, Jeanny Samari, by Renoir. 3 l, Self portrait, by Van Gogh.

1991, Apr. 1 *Perf. 13*

3603 A1400 20s multicolored .22 .18
3604 A1400 43s multicolored .50 .38
3605 A1400 62s multicolored .70 .55
3606 A1400 67s multicolored .80 .60
3607 A1400 80s multicolored 1.00 .75
3608 A1400 2 l multicolored 2.25 1.75
Nos. 3603-3608 (6) 5.47 4.21

Miniature Sheet

3609 A1400 3 l multicolored 4.50 2.65

Swiss Confederation, 700th Anniv. — A1401

1991, Apr. 11

3610 A1401 62s multicolored .90 .55

Philatelic Review, Cent. — A1402

1991, May 7 Litho. *Perf. 13*

3611 A1402 30s multicolored .45 .25

Europa — A1403

1991, May 10 *Perf. 13x13½*

3612 A1403 43s Meteosat .70 .38
3613 A1403 62s Ariane rocket 1.00 .55

Horses A1404

1991, May 21 *Perf. 13x12½*

3614 A1404 5s Przewalski's horse .15 .15
3615 A1404 10s Tarpan .16 .15
3616 A1404 25s Arabian .40 .22
3617 A1404 35s Arabian .55 .32
3618 A1404 42s Shetland pony .65 .38
3619 A1404 60s Draft horse .90 .55
a. Min. sheet of 6, #3614-3619 3.00 1.65
Nos. 3614-3619 (6) 2.81 1.77

EXPO 91, Plovdiv — A1405

1991, June 6 Litho. *Perf. 13½x13*
3620 A1405 30s multicolored .45 .28

Wolfgang Amadeus Mozart A1406

1991, July 2 *Perf. 13*
3621 A1406 62s multicolored .95 .55

Space Shuttle Missions, 10th Anniv. A1407

1991, July 23 Litho. *Perf. 13*
3622 A1407 12s Columbia .16 .15
3623 A1407 32s Challenger .45 .30
3624 A1407 50s Discovery .70 .45
3625 A1407 86s Atlantis, vert. 1.25 .75
3626 A1407 1.50 l Buran, vert. 2.25 1.30
3627 A1407 2 l Atlantis, diff., vert. 2.75 1.75
Nos. 3622-3627 (6) 7.56 4.70

Souvenir Sheet
3628 A1407 3 l US shuttle, earth 4.50 2.65

1992 Winter Olympics, Albertville — A1408

1991, Aug. 7 Litho. *Perf. 13x13½*
3629 A1408 30s Luge .40 .28
3630 A1408 43s Slalom skiing .52 .38
3631 A1408 67s Ski jumping .85 .60
3632 A1408 2 l Biathlon 2.50 1.75
Nos. 3629-3632 (4) 4.27 3.01

Souvenir Sheet
3633 A1408 3 l Two-man bobsled 4.50 2.65

Sheraton Sofia Hotel Balkan A1409

1991, Sept. 6 Litho. *Perf. 13*
3634 A1409 62s multicolored 1.10 .55
a. Sheet of 3 + 3 labels 3.30 1.65

Dogs — A1410

1991, Oct. 11 *Perf. 13x13½*
3635 A1410 30s Japanese .52 .26
3636 A1410 43s Chihuahua .75 .38
3637 A1410 62s Pinscher 1.10 .55
3638 A1410 80s Yorkshire terrier 1.40 .70
3639 A1410 1 l Chinese 1.75 .90
3640 A1410 3 l Pug 5.25 2.65
a. Min. sheet of 6, #3635-3640 10.80 5.45
Nos. 3635-3640 (6) 10.77 5.44

Cologne '91, Intl. Philatelic Exhibition A1411

1991, Oct. 21 *Perf. 13*
3641 A1411 86s multicolored 1.50 .75

Printed in sheets of 3 + 3 labels.

Souvenir Sheet

Brandenburg Gate, Bicent. — A1412

1991, Oct. 23
3642 A1412 4 l multicolored 7.00 3.50

Exists imperf.

Phila Nippon '91 A1413

1991, Nov. 11
3643 A1413 62s Japan #1 1.10 .55

Printed in miniature sheets of 3 + 3 labels.

Bulgarian Railroad, 125th Anniv. — A1414

1991, Nov. 30
3644 A1414 30s Locomotive .55 .28
3645 A1414 30s Passenger car .55 .28

Medicinal Plants A1415

Designs: 30s, Pulsatilla vernalis. 40s, Pulsatilla pratensis. 55s, Pulsatilla halleri. 60s, Aquilegia nigricans. 1 l, Hippophae rhamnoides. 2 l, Ribes nigrum.

1991, Nov. 20 Litho. *Perf. 13*
3646 A1415 30s +15s label .78 .38
3647 A1415 40s multicolored .70 .35
3648 A1415 55s multicolored .95 .48
3649 A1415 60s multicolored 1.05 .58
3650 A1415 1 l multicolored 1.75 .90
3651 A1415 2 l multicolored 3.50 1.75
a. Min. sheet of 6, #3646-3651 8.75 4.45
Nos. 3646-3651 (6) 8.73 4.44

No. 3646 printed se-tenant with label. No. 3651a sold for 5 l, but does not contain the 15s label printed with No. 3646.

Basketball, Cent. A1416

1991, Dec. 6 *Perf. 13½x13*
3652 A1416 43s Ball below rim .75 .38
3653 A1416 62s Ball at rim 1.10 .55
3654 A1416 90s Ball in cylinder 1.60 .80
3655 A1416 1 l Ball in basket 1.75 .90
Nos. 3652-3655 (4) 5.20 2.63

El Greco, 450th Birth Anniv. — A1417

Paintings: 43s, Christ Carrying the Cross. 50s, Holy Family with St. Anne. 60s, St. John the Evangelist and St. John the Baptist. 62s, St. Andrew and St. Francis. 1 l, Holy Family with St. Mary Magdalene. 2 l, Cardinal Nino de Guevara. 3 l, Holy Family with St. Anne (detail).

1991, Dec. 13 *Perf. 13*
3656 A1417 43s multicolored .75 .38
3657 A1417 50s multicolored .90 .45
3658 A1417 60s multicolored 1.05 .52
3659 A1417 62s multicolored 1.10 .55
3660 A1417 1 l multicolored 1.75 .90
3661 A1417 2 l multicolored 3.50 1.75
Nos. 3656-3661 (6) 9.05 4.55

Souvenir Sheet
3662 A1417 3 l multicolored 5.25 2.65

No. 3662 contains one 43x53mm stamp.

Christmas A1418

1991, Dec. 18
3663 A1418 30s Snowman, candle, bell, heart .55 .28
3664 A1418 62s Star, angel, flower, house, tree 1.10 .55

Marine Mammals — A1419

Designs: 30s, Phogophoca graenlandica. 43s, Orcinus orca. 62s, Odobenus rosmarus. 68s, Tursiops truncatus. 1 l, Monachus monachus. 2 l, Phocaena phocaena.

1991, Dec. 24
3665 A1419 30s multicolored .52 .26
3666 A1419 43s multicolored .75 .38
3667 A1419 62s multicolored 1.10 .55
3668 A1419 68s multicolored 1.20 .60
3669 A1419 1 l multicolored 1.75 .90
3670 A1419 2 l multicolored 3.50 1.75
a. Min. sheet of #3665-3670 8.85 4.45
Nos. 3665-3670 (6) 8.82 4.44

Settlement of Jews in Bulgaria, 500th Anniv. — A1420

1992, Mar. 5 Litho. *Perf. 13*
3671 A1420 1 l multicolored 1.75 .90

Gioacchino Rossini (1792-1868), Composer — A1421

1992, Mar. 11
3672 A1421 50s multicolored .88 .45

Plovdiv Fair, Cent. A1422

1992, Mar. 25
3673 A1422 1 l buff & black 1.75 .90

Fiat Croma — A1423

Automobiles.

1992, Mar. 26 *Perf. 13½x13*
3674 A1423 30s Volvo 740 .52 .26
3675 A1423 45s Ford Escort .80 .40
3676 A1423 50s shown .90 .45
3677 A1423 50s Mercedes 600 .90 .45
3678 A1423 1 l Peugeot 605 1.75 .90
3679 A1423 2 l BMW 316 3.50 1.75
Nos. 3674-3679 (6) 8.37 4.21

Francisco de Orellana — A1424

Explorers: No. 3681, Vespucci. No. 3682, Magellan. No. 3683, Gonzalo Jimenez de Quesada (1500-1579). 2 l, Drake. 3 l, Pedro de Valdivia (1500-1553). 4 l, Columbus.

1992, Apr. 22 Litho. *Perf. 13*
3680 A1424 50s multicolored .45 .22
3681 A1424 50s multicolored .45 .22
3682 A1424 1 l multicolored .90 .45
3683 A1424 1 l multicolored .90 .45
3684 A1424 2 l multicolored 1.80 .90
3685 A1424 3 l multicolored 2.70 1.35
Nos. 3680-3685 (6) 7.20 3.59

Souvenir Sheet
3686 A1424 4 l multicolored 3.50 1.75

Granada '92
A1425

1992, Apr. 23

3687	A1425	62s multicolored	.55	.28

No. 3687 printed in sheets of 3 + 3 labels.

Discovery of America, 500th Anniv.
A1426

1992, Apr. 24

3688	A1426	1 l Ships, map	.90	.45
3689	A1426	2 l Columbus, ship	1.80	.90
a.		Pair, #3688-3689	2.60	1.30

Europa.

SOS Children's Village
A1427

1992, June 15 Litho. *Perf. 13*

3690	A1427	1 l multicolored	.90	.45

1992 Summer Olympics, Barcelona
A1428

1992, July 15 *Perf. 13½x13*

3691	A1428	50s Swimming	.45	.22
3692	A1428	50s Long jump	.45	.22
3693	A1428	1 l High jump	.90	.45
3694	A1428	3 l Gymnastics	2.70	1.35
		Nos. 3691-3694 (4)	4.50	2.24

Souvenir Sheet

Perf. 13x13½

3695	A1428	4 l Torch, vert.	3.60	1.80

Motorcycles
A1429

Designs: 30s, 1902 Laurin & Klement. No. 3697, 1928 Puch 200 Luxus. No. 3698, 1931 Norton CS1. 70s, 1950 Harley Davidson. 1 l, 1986 Gilera SP 01. 2 l, 1990 BMW K1.

1992, July 30 *Perf. 13*

3696	A1429	30s multicolored	.28	.15
3697	A1429	50s multicolored	.45	.22
3698	A1429	50s multicolored	.45	.22
3699	A1429	70s multicolored	.62	.30
3700	A1429	1 l multicolored	.90	.45
3701	A1429	2 l multicolored	1.80	.90
		Nos. 3696-3701 (6)	4.50	2.24

Genoa '92 Intl. Philatelic Exhibition
A1430

1992, Sept. 18 *Perf. 13*

3702	A1430	1 l multicolored	.90	.45

Issued: This is a developing set. Numbers may change.

Insects — A1431

1992 Litho. *Perf. 14x13½*

3710	A1431	1 l Dragonfly	.15	
3711	A1431	2 l Mayfly	.22	
3712	A1431	3 l Locust	.32	
3713	A1431	4 l Stag beetle	.45	
3714	A1431	5 l Carrion beetle	.55	
3715	A1431	7 l Ant	.75	
3718	A1431	20 l Bee	2.25	
3718A	A1431	50 l Praying mantis	5.75	
		Nos. 3710-3718A (8)	10.44	

Issued: 7, 20 l, Sept. 25; 3, 50 l, Nov. 30; 1, 2, 4, 5 l, Dec. 15, 1993.

This is a developing set. Numbers may change.

Based on available currency exchange rates the face value of No. 3718A is about $2. It appears that Bulgarian stamps are appearing in the market at significantly higher prices.

A1432 A1433

1992, Sept. 30 *Perf. 13*

3719	A1432	1 l blk, pink & rose	.90	.45

Higher Institute of Architecture and Building, 50th anniv.

1992, Oct. 16 Litho. *Perf. 13*

Trees: No. 3720, Quercus mestensis. No. 3721, Aesculus hippocastanum. No. 3722, Quercus thracica. No. 3723, Pinus peuce. 2 l, Acer heldreichii. 3 l, Pyrus bulgarica.

3720	A1433	50s multicolored	.45	.22
3721	A1433	50s multicolored	.45	.22
3722	A1433	1 l multicolored	.90	.45
3723	A1433	1 l multicolored	.90	.45
3724	A1433	2 l multicolored	1.80	.90
3725	A1433	3 l multicolored	2.70	1.35
		Nos. 3720-3725 (6)	7.20	3.59

Ethnographical Museum, Cent. — A1434

1992, Oct. 23

3726	A1434	1 l multicolored	.90	.45

Tanker Bulgaria — A1435

1992, Oct. 30 Litho. *Perf. 13*

3727	A1435	30s Freighter Bulgaria	.28	.15
3728	A1435	50s Castor	.45	.22
3729	A1435	1 l Hero of Sevastopol	.90	.45
3730	A1435	2 l shown	1.80	.90
3731	A1435	2 l Aleko Constantinov	1.80	.90
3732	A1435	3 l Varna	2.70	1.35
		Nos. 3727-3732 (6)	7.93	3.97

Bulgarian Merchant Fleet, Cent.

Bulgaria, Member of the Council of Europe — A1436

1992, Nov. 6 Litho. *Perf. 13*

3733	A1436	7 l multicolored	6.30	3.15

Souvenir Sheet

4th World Congress of Popular Sports, Varna — A1437

1992, Nov. 17 Litho. *Perf. 13*

3734	A1437	4 l multicolored	4.00	

Christmas
A1438

1992, Dec. 1 *Perf. 13½x13*

3735	A1438	1 l Santa Claus	.75	
3736	A1438	7 l Madonna & Child	5.25	

Wild Cats — A1439

1992, Dec. 18 Litho. *Perf. 13*

3737	A1439	50s Panthera pardus	.38	
3738	A1439	50s Acinonyx jubatus	.38	
3739	A1439	1 l Panthera onca	.75	
3740	A1439	2 l Panthera tigris	1.50	
3741	A1439	2 l Felis concolor	1.50	
3742	A1439	3 l Panthera leo	2.25	
		Nos. 3737-3742 (6)	6.76	

Sports
A1440

1992, Dec. 18

3743	A1440	50s Baseball	.38	
3744	A1440	50s Cricket	.38	
3745	A1440	1 l Polo	.75	
3746	A1440	1 l Harness racing	.75	
3747	A1440	2 l Field hockey	1.50	
3748	A1440	3 l Football	2.25	
		Nos. 3743-3748 (6)	6.01	

Owls
A1441

1992, Dec. 23

3749	A1441	30s Aegolius funereus	.25	
3750	A1441	50s Strix aluco	.38	
3751	A1441	1 l Asio otus	.75	
3752	A1441	2 l Otus scops	1.50	
3753	A1441	2 l Asio flammeus	1.50	
3754	A1441	3 l Tyto alba	2.25	
		Nos. 3749-3754 (6)	6.63	

Nos. 3749, 3751, 3753-3754 are vert.

Paintings Depicting History of Bulgaria
A1442

Artists: 50s, Dimiter Gyudzhenov. 1 l, 3 l, Nikolai Pavlovich. 2 l, Dimiter Panchev. 4 l, Mito Ganovski.

1992, Dec. 28

3755	A1442	50s multicolored	.38	
3756	A1442	1 l multicolored	.75	
3757	A1442	2 l multicolored	1.50	
3758	A1442	3 l multicolored	2.25	
		Nos. 3755-3758 (4)	4.88	

Souvenir Sheet

3759	A1442	4 l multicolored, vert.	3.00	

Archeological Museum, Cent. — A1443

1993 World Biathlon Championships, Borovetz — A1444

1993, Jan. 1 Litho. *Perf. 13x13½*

3760	A1443	1 l multicolored	.75	

1993, Feb. 5

3761	A1444	1 l Woman aiming rifle	.75	
3762	A1444	7 l Skiing	5.25	

Neophit Rilski, Birth Bicent.
A1445

1993, Apr. 22 Litho. *Perf. 13½x13*

3763	A1445	1 l henna brn & ol bis	.75	

Contemporary Art — A1446

Europa: 3 l, Sculpture of centaur, by Georgi Chapkinov. 8 l, Painting of geometric forms, by D. Bujukliski.

1993, Apr. 29 *Perf. 13x13½*

3764 A1446 3 l multicolored 2.25
3765 A1446 8 l multicolored 6.00

Fish A1447

1993, June 29 **Litho.** *Perf. 13*

3766 A1447 1 l C.a.j. bicaudatus .75
3767 A1447 2 l Mollienesia velifera 1.50
3768 A1447 3 l Aphyosemion bivittatum 2.25
3769 A1447 3 l Pterophyllum eimekei 2.25
3770 A1447 4 l Symphysodon discus 3.00
3771 A1447 8 l Trichogaster leeri 6.00
Nos. 3766-3771 (6) 15.75

Fruit — A1448

1993, July 8 *Perf. 13x13½*

3772 A1448 1 l Malus domestica .75
3773 A1448 2 l Pyrus sativa 1.50
3774 A1448 2 l Persica vulgaris 1.50
3775 A1448 3 l Cydonia oblonga 2.25
3776 A1448 5 l Punica granatum 3.75
3777 A1448 7 l Ficus carica 5.25
Nos. 3772-3777 (6) 15.00

Claudio Monteverdi (1567-1643), Composer A1449

1993, July 20 **Litho.** *Perf. 13½x13*

3778 A1449 1 l multicolored .75

17th World Summer Games for the Deaf A1450

1993, July 20 *Perf. 13*

3779 A1450 1 l shown .75
3780 A1450 2 l Swimming 1.50
3781 A1450 3 l Cycling 2.25
3782 A1450 4 l Tennis 3.00
Nos. 3779-3782 (4) 7.50

Souvenir Sheet

3783 A1450 5 l Soccer

Miniature Sheet

A1451

Council of Preslav, Cyrillic Alphabet in Bulgaria, 1100th Anniv.: a, Baptism of Christian convert. b, Tsar Boris I (852-889). c, Tsar Simeon (893-927). d, Battle between Bulgarians and Byzantines.

1993, Sept. 16 **Litho.** *Perf. 13½x13*

3784 A1451 5 l Sheet of 4, #a.-d. 3.50

Alexander of Battenberg (1857-93), Prince of Bulgaria — A1452

1993, Sept. 23 *Perf. 13x13½*

3785 A1452 3 l multicolored .50

Peter I. Tchaikovsky (1840-93) A1453

1993, Sept. 30 *Perf. 13½x13*

3786 A1453 3 l multicolored .50

Small Arms A1454

Isaac Newton (1643-1725) A1455

1993, Oct. 22 **Litho.** *Perf. 13½x14*

3787 A1454 1 l Crossbow, 16th cent. .18
3788 A1454 2 l Pistol, 18th cent. .35
3789 A1454 3 l Luger, 1908 .50
3790 A1454 3 l Pistol, 1873 .50
3791 A1454 5 l Rifle, 1938 .85
3792 A1454 7 l Kalashnikov, 1947 1.25
Nos. 3787-3792 (6) 3.63

1993, Oct. 29 *Perf. 13½x13*

3793 A1455 1 l multicolored .18

Organized Philately in Bulgaria, Cent. A1456

1993, Nov. 16

3794 A1456 1 l multicolored .18

Ecology A1457

1993, Nov. 17

3795 A1457 1 l shown .18
3796 A1457 7 l Ecology 1.25

Game Animals A1458

1993, Nov. 25

3797 A1458 1 l Anas platrhynchos .18
3798 A1458 1 l Phasianus colchicus .18
3799 A1458 2 l Vulpes vulpes .35
3800 A1458 3 l Capreolus capreolus .50
3801 A1458 6 l Lepus europaeus 1.00
3802 A1458 8 l Sus scrofa 1.40
Nos. 3797-3802 (6) 3.61

Christmas A1459

Signs of Zodiac on sundial: No. 3803a, Taurus, Gemini, Cancer. b, Libra, Virgo, Leo.
No. 3804a, Aquarius, Pisces, Aries. b, Capricorn, Sagittarius, Scorpio.

1993, Dec. 1

3803 A1459 1 l Pair, #a.-b. .35
3804 A1459 7 l Pair, #a.-b. 2.50

When placed together, Nos. 3803-3804 form a complete sundial.

Regional Folk Costumes for Men
A1460 A1461

1993, Dec. 16 **Litho.** *Perf. 13½x14*

3805 A1460 1 l Sofia .15
3806 A1461 1 l Plovdiv .15
3807 A1460 2 l Belogradchik .22
3808 A1460 3 l Shumen .32
3809 A1461 3 l Oryakhovitsa .32
3810 A1461 8 l Kurdzhali .90
Nos. 3805-3810 (6) 2.06

1994 Winter Olympics, Lillehammer A1462

1994, Feb. 8 *Perf. 13*

3811 A1462 1 l Freestyle skiing .15
3812 A1462 2 l Speed skating .22
3813 A1462 3 l 2-Man luge .32
3814 A1462 4 l Hockey .45
Nos. 3811-3814 (4) 1.14

Souvenir Sheet

3815 A1462 5 l Downhill skiing .55

Nikolai Pavlovich (1835-94) A1463

1994, Feb. 16 *Perf. 13½x13*

3816 A1463 3 l multicolored .32

Dinosaurs A1464

1994, Apr. 27 **Litho.** *Perf. 13*

3817 A1464 2 l Plesiosaurus .15
3818 A1464 3 l Iguanodon .15
3819 A1464 3 l Archaeopteryx .15
3820 A1464 4 l Edmontonia .16
3821 A1464 5 l Styracosaurus .20
3822 A1464 7 l Tyrannosaurus Rex .28
Nos. 3817-3822 (6) 1.09

1994 World Cup Soccer Championships, US — A1465

Players in championships of : 3 l, Chile, 1962. 6 l, England, 1966. 7 l, Mexico, 1970. 9 l, West Germany, 1974. No. 3827a, Mexico, 1986, vert. b, US, 1994.

1994, Apr. 28

3823 A1465 3 l multicolored .15
3824 A1465 6 l multicolored .22
3825 A1465 7 l multicolored .28
3826 A1465 9 l multicolored .35
Nos. 3823-3826 (4) 1.00

Souvenir Sheet

3827 A1465 5 l Sheet of 2, #a.-b. .40

For No. 3827 with inscription reading up along the left margin, see No. 3851.

European Discoveries A1466

Europa: 3 l, Axis of symmetry. 15 l, Electrocardiogram.

1994, Apr. 29 **Litho.** *Perf. 13½*

3828 A1466 3 l multicolored .15
3829 A1466 15 l multicolored .60

Boris Hristov (1914-93) — A1467

1994, May 18 **Litho.** *Perf. 13*

3830 A1467 3 l brown & bister .15

Cricetus Cricetus — A1468

Designs: 3 l, In nest. 7 l, Emerging from burrow. 10 l, Standing on hind legs. 15 l, Finding berry.

1994, Sept. 23 **Litho.** *Perf. 13*

3831 A1468 3 l multicolored .15
3832 A1468 7 l multicolored .28
3833 A1468 10 l multicolored .40
3834 A1468 15 l multicolored .60
Nos. 3831-3834 (4) 1.43

World Wildlife Fund.

Space Program — A1469

Intl. Olympic Committee, Cent. — A1470

1994, Nov. 4 Litho. *Perf. 13*

3835 A1469 3 l multicolored .15

1994, Nov. 7

3836 A1470 3 l multicolored .15

Icons A1471

Christmas A1472

1994, Nov. 24 Litho. *Perf. 13x13½*

3837	A1471	2 l	Christ	.15
3838	A1471	3 l	Christ, the healer	.15
3839	A1471	5 l	Crucifixion	.16
3840	A1471	7 l	Archangel Michael	.22
3841	A1471	8 l	Sts. Cyril, Methodius	.25
3842	A1471	15 l	Madonna & Child	.45
			Nos. 3837-3842 (6)	1.38

1994, Dec. 1

3843	A1472	3 l	Ancient coin	.20
3844	A1472	15 l	Coin, diff.	1.00

Roses A1473

1994, Dec. 12 *Perf. 13*

Color of Rose

3845	A1473	2 l	yellow	.15
3846	A1473	3 l	rose red	.15
3847	A1473	5 l	white	.16
3848	A1473	7 l	salmon	.22
3849	A1473	10 l	carmine	.32
3850	A1473	15 l	orange & yellow	.45
			Nos. 3845-3850 (6)	1.45

Souvenir Sheet

No. 3827 with Additional Inscription in Left Sheet Margin

1994, Dec. 15 Litho. *Perf. 13*

3851 A1465 5 l Sheet of 2, #a.-b. .40

Trams A1474

1994, Dec. 29

3852	A1474	1 l	Model 1912	.15
3853	A1474	2 l	Model 1928	.15
3854	A1474	3 l	Model 1931	.15
3855	A1474	5 l	Model 1942	.16
3856	A1474	8 l	Model 1951	.25
3857	A1474	10 l	Model 1961	.32
			Set value	.88

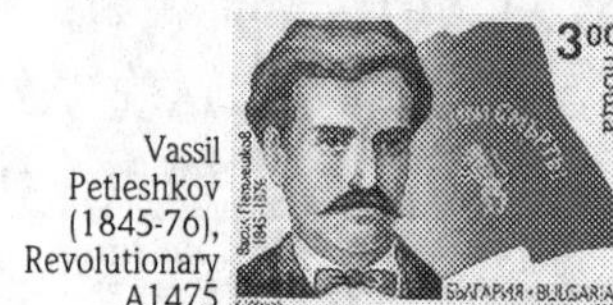
Vassil Petleshkov (1845-76), Revolutionary A1475

1995, Feb. 27 Litho. *Perf. 13½x13*

3858 A1475 3 l multicolored .15

End of World War II, 50th Anniv. — A1476

Europa: 15 l, Dove holding olive branch standing on gun barrel.

1995, May 3 Litho. *Perf. 13*

3859	A1476	3 l	multicolored	.15
3860	A1476	15 l	multicolored	.45

Souvenir Sheet

Men's World Volleyball League, Cent. A1477

Designs: a, 10 l, Player digging ball. b, 15 l, Player spiking ball, vert.

1995, May 25 Litho. *Perf. 13*

3861 A1477 Sheet of 2, #a.-b. .75

Souvenir Sheet

European Nature Conservation Year — A1478

Designs: a, 10 l, Pancratium maritimum. b, 15 l, Aquila heliaca. Illustration reduced.

1995, June 23 Litho. *Perf. 13*

3862 A1478 Sheet of 2, #a.-b. .75

Antarctic Wildlife — A1479

Designs: 1 l, Euphausia superba. 2 l, Chaenocephalus. 3 l, Physeter catodon. 5 l, Leptonychotes weddelli. 8 l, Stercorarius skua. 10 l, Aptenodytes forsteri, vert.

1995, June 29

3863	A1479	1 l	multicolored	.15
3864	A1479	2 l	multicolored	.15
3865	A1479	3 l	multicolored	.15
3866	A1479	5 l	multicolored	.15
3867	A1479	8 l	multicolored	.25
3868	A1479	10 l	multicolored	.30
			Set value	.65

Stephan Stambolov (1854-95), Revolutionary Leader, Politician — A1480

1995, July 6 Litho. *Perf. 13*

3869 A1480 3 l multicolored .15

1996 Summer Olympics, Atlanta A1481

Designs: 3 l, Pole vault. 7 l, High jump. 10 l, Women's long jump. 15 l, Track.

1995, July 17

3870	A1481	3 l	multicolored	.15
3871	A1481	7 l	multicolored	.20
3872	A1481	10 l	multicolored	.30
3873	A1481	15 l	multicolored	.45
			Nos. 3870-3873 (4)	1.10

Legumes — A1482

1995, July 31

3874	A1482	2 l	Pisum sativum	.15
3875	A1482	3 l	Glicine	.15
3876	A1482	3 l	Cicer arietinum	.15
3877	A1482	4 l	Spinacia oleracea	.15
3878	A1482	5 l	Arachis hypogaea	.15
3879	A1482	15 l	Lens esculenta	.45
			Set value	.95

Organized Tourism in Bulgaria, Cent. A1483

1995, Aug. 21 Litho. *Perf. 13*

3880 A1483 3 l multicolored .15

Vassil Zahariev (1895-1971), Graphic Artist — A1484

Designs: 2 l, Woodcut of a man. 3 l, Woodcut of building in valley. 5 l, Self-portrait. 10 l, Carving of two women.

1995, Sept. 4 Litho. *Perf. 13*

3881	A1484	2 l	multicolored	.15
3882	A1484	3 l	multicolored	.15
3883	A1484	5 l	multicolored	.15
3884	A1484	10 l	multicolored	.30
			Set value	.60

UN, 50th Anniv. A1485

1995, Sept. 12

3885 A1485 3 l multicolored .15

Airplanes — A1486

1995, Sept. 26 Litho. *Perf. 13*

3886	A1486	3 l	PO-2	.15
3887	A1486	5 l	Li-2	.15
3888	A1486	7 l	JU52-3M	.20
3889	A1486	10 l	FV-58	.30
			Nos. 3886-3889 (4)	.80
			Set value	.75

Motion Pictures, Cent. — A1487

Designs: 2 l, Charlie Chaplin, Mickey Mouse. 3 l, Marilyn Monroe, Marlene Dietrich. 5 l, Humphrey Bogart. 8 l, Sophia Loren, Liza Minnelli. 10 l, Toshiro Mifune. 15 l, Katya Paskaleva.

1995, Oct. 16

3890 A1487	2 l multicolored	.15	
3891 A1487	3 l multicolored	.15	
3892 A1487	5 l multicolored	.15	
3893 A1487	8 l multicolored	.25	
3894 A1487	10 l multicolored	.30	
3895 A1487	15 l multicolored	.45	
	Set value	1.25	

Minerals A1488

1995, Nov. 20 Litho. *Perf. 13*

3896 A1488	1 l Agate	.15	
3897 A1488	2 l Sphalerite	.15	
3898 A1488	5 l Calcite	.15	
3899 A1488	7 l Quartz	.20	
3900 A1488	8 l Pyromorphite	.25	
3901 A1488	10 l Almandine	.30	
	Nos. 3896-3901 (6)	1.20	

Christmas A1489

1995, Dec. 8 Litho. *Perf. 13*

3902 A1489	3 l shown	.15	
3903 A1489	15 l Magi	.45	

SEMI-POSTAL STAMPS

Catalogue values for unused stamps in this section are for Never Hinged items.

Regular Issues of 1911-20 Surcharged:

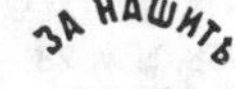
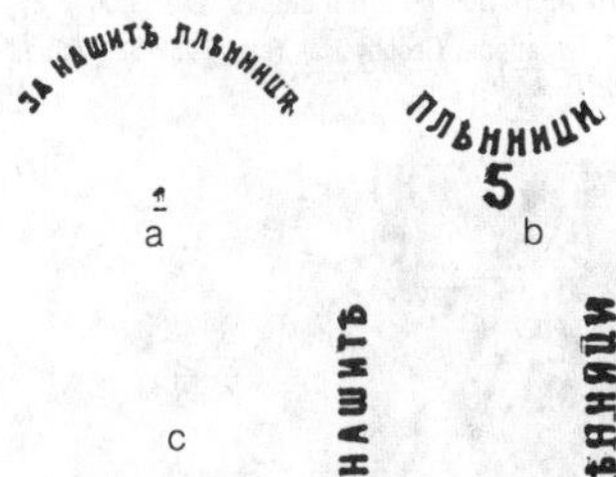

Perf. 11½x12, 12x11½

1920, June 20 Unwmk.

B1 A43 (a)	2s + 1s ol grn	.15	.15
B2 A44 (b)	5s + 2½s grn	.15	.15
B3 A44 (b)	10s + 5s rose	.15	.15
B4 A44 (b)	15s + 7½s vio	.15	.15
B5 A44 (b)	25s + 12½s dp bl	.15	.15
B6 A44 (b)	30s + 15s choc	.15	.15
B7 A44 (b)	50s + 25s yel brn	.15	.15
B8 A29 (c)	1 l + 50s dk brn	.15	.15
B9 A37a (a)	2 l + 1 l brn org	.24	.24
B10 A38 (a)	3 l + 1½ l claret	.55	.42
	Set value	1.50	1.10

Surtax aided ex-prisoners of war. Value, Nos. B1-B7 imperf., $7.75.

Tsar Boris Type of 1937
Souvenir Sheet

1937, Nov. 22 Photo. *Imperf.*

B11 A140 2 l + 18 l ultra 4.50 2.50

19th anniv. of the accession of Tsar Boris III to the throne.

Stamps of 1917-21 Surcharged in Black

Наводнението
1939
1+1
лева

1939, Oct. 22 *Perf. 12½, 12*

B12 A34	1 l + 1 l on 15s slate	.15	.15
B13 A69	2 l + 1 l on 1½ l ol grn	.15	.15
B14 A69	4 l + 2 l on 2 l dp grn	.18	.15
B15 A69	7 l + 4 l on 3 l Prus bl	.50	.28
B16 A69	14 l + 7 l on 5 l red brn	.85	.48
	Nos. B12-B16 (5)	1.83	
	Set value		1.00

Surtax aided victims of the Sevlievo flood. The surcharge on #B13-B16 omits "leva."

Map of Bulgaria — SP2

1947, June 6 Typo. *Perf. 11½*

B17 SP2 20 l + 10 l dk brn red & grn .45 .30

30th Jubilee Esperanto Cong., Sofia, 1947.

Postman — SP3

Radio Towers — SP6

Designs: 10 l+5 l, Lineman. 20 l+10 l, Telephone operators.

1947, Nov. 5

B18 SP3	4 l + 2 l ol brn	.15	.15
B19 SP3	10 l + 5 l brt red	.15	.15
B20 SP3	20 l + 10 l dp ultra	.15	.15
B21 SP6	40 l + 20 l choc	.70	.55
	Nos. B18-B21 (4)	1.15	
	Set value		.80

Christo Ganchev — SP7

Actors' Portraits: 10 l+6 l, Adriana Budevska. 15 l+7 l, Vasil Kirkov. 20 l+15 l, Sava Ognianov. 30 l+20 l, Krostyu Sarafov.

1947, Dec. 8 Litho. *Perf. 10½*

B22 SP7	9 l + 5 l Prus grn	.15	.15
B23 SP7	10 l + 6 l car lake	.20	.15
B24 SP7	15 l + 7 l rose vio	.20	.15
B25 SP7	20 l + 15 l ultra	.20	.15
B26 SP7	30 l + 20 l vio brn	.48	.30
	Nos. B22-B26 (5)	1.23	
	Set value		.73

National Theater, 50th anniversary.

Souvenir Sheet

Olympic Emblem — SP8

1964, Oct. 10 Litho. *Imperf.*

B27 SP8 40s + 20s bis, red & bl 2.75 1.40

18th Olympic Games, Tokyo, Oct. 10-25.

Horsemanship Type of 1965
Miniature Sheet

1965, Sept. 30 Photo. *Imperf.*

B28 A630 40s + 20s Hurdle race 2.00 1.00

Space Exploration Type of 1966

Designs: 20s+10s, Yuri A. Gagarin, Alexei Leonov and Valentina Tereshkova. 30s+10s, Rocket and globe.

1966, Sept. 29 Photo. *Perf. 11½x11*

B29 A652 20s + 10s pur & gray 1.00 .35

Miniature Sheet

B30 A652 30s + 10s gray, fawn & blk 2.00 .95

Winter Olympic Games Type of 1967

Sports and Emblem: 20s+10s, Slalom. 40s+10s, Figure skating couple.

1967, Sept. Photo. *Perf. 11*

B31 A687 20s + 10s multi 1.10 .28

Souvenir Sheet
Imperf

B32 A687 40s + 10s multi 2.00 .85

Type of Olympic Games Issue, 1968

Designs: 20s+10s, Rowing. 50s+10s, Stadium, Mexico City, and communications satellite.

1968, June 24 Photo. *Perf. 10½*

B33 A702 20s + 10s vio bl, gray & pink 1.00 .32

Miniature Sheet
Imperf

B34 A702 50s + 10s gray, blk & Prus bl 2.25 1.50

Sports Type of Regular Issue, 1969

Designs: 13s+5s, Woman with ball. 20s+10s, Acrobatic jump.

1969, Oct. Photo. *Perf. 11*
Gymnasts in Light Gray

B35 A732	13s + 5s brt rose & vio	.40	.15
B36 A732	20s + 10s cit & bl grn	.70	.30

Miniature Sheet

Soccer Ball — SP9

1970, Mar. 4 Photo. *Imperf.*

B37 SP9 80s + 20s multi 2.25 1.40

9th World Soccer Championships for the Jules Rimet Cup, Mexico City, May 30-June 21, 1970.

Souvenir Sheet

Yuri A. Gagarin — SP10

1971, Apr. 12 Photo. *Imperf.*

B38 SP10 40s + 20s multi 2.00 1.10

10th anniversary of the first man in space.

SP11

SP12

Bulgarian lion, magnifying glass, stamp tongs

1971, July 10 Photo. *Perf. 12½*

B39 SP11 20s + 10s brn org, blk & gold .90 .40

11th Congress of Bulgarian Philatelists, Sofia, July, 1971.

1989, Nov. 10 Litho. *Perf. 13x13½*

Toys: a, Skateboarding. b, Doll, ball. c, Rope. d, Train set.

Souvenir Sheet

B40	Sheet of 4	2.75	1.40
a.-d.	SP12 30s +15s any single	.65	.35

For the benefit of the Children's Foundation.

AIR POST STAMPS

Regular Issues of 1925-26 Overprinted in Various Colors

1927-28 Unwmk. *Perf. 11½*

C1 A76	2 l ol (R) ('28)	1.10	.70
C2 A74	4 l lake & yel (Bl)	1.10	.70
C3 A77	10 l brn blk & brn org (G) ('28)	17.00	13.00

Overprinted Vertically and Surcharged with New Value

C4 A77	1 l on 6 l dp bl & pale lem (C)	1.10	.70
a.	Inverted surcharge	*325.00*	*275.00*
b.	Pair, one without surcharge	*425.00*	
	Nos. C1-C4 (4)	20.30	15.10

Nos. C2-C4 overprinted in changed colors were not issued, value set $10.50.

Dove Delivering Message — AP1

Junkers Plane, Rila Monastery — AP2

1931, Oct. 28 **Typo.**

C5 AP1 1 l dk green .18 .15
C6 AP1 2 l maroon .18 .15
C7 AP1 6 l dp blue .28 .20
C8 AP1 12 l carmine .28 .30
C9 AP1 20 l dk violet .70 .55
C10 AP1 30 l dp orange 1.10 1.25
C11 AP1 50 l orange brn 2.25 1.40
Nos. C5-C11 (7) 4.97 4.00

Counterfeits exist. See Nos. C15-C18.

1932, May 9

C12 AP2 18 l blue grn 14.00 11.00
C13 AP2 24 l dp red 14.00 11.00
C14 AP2 28 l ultra 14.00 11.00
Nos. C12-C14 (3) 42.00 33.00

Catalogue values for unused stamps in this section, from this point to the end of the section, are for Never Hinged items.

1938, Dec. 27

C15 AP1 1 l violet brown .24 .15
C16 AP1 2 l green .18 .15
C17 AP1 6 l deep rose .70 .28
C18 AP1 12 l peacock blue .85 .32
Nos. C15-C18 (4) 1.97 .90

Counterfeits exist.

Mail Plane — AP3

Plane over Tsar Assen's Tower — AP4

Designs: 4 l, Plane over Bachkovski Monastery. 6 l, Bojurishte Airport, Sofia. 10 l, Plane, train and motorcycle. 12 l, Planes over Sofia Palace. 16 l, Plane over Pirin Valley. 19 l, Plane over Rila Monastery. 30 l, Plane and Swallow. 45 l, Plane over Sofia Cathedral. 70 l, Plane over Shipka Monument. 100 l, Plane and Royal Cipher.

1940, Jan. 15 **Photo.** ***Perf. 13***

C19 AP3 1 l dk green .15 .15
C20 AP4 2 l crimson 1.10 .15
C21 AP4 4 l red orange .15 .15
C22 AP3 6 l dp blue .20 .15
C23 AP4 10 l dk brown .30 .15
C24 AP3 12 l dull brown .52 .18
C25 AP3 16 l brt bl vio .55 .24
C26 AP3 19 l sapphire .75 .32
C27 AP4 30 l rose lake 1.10 .48
C28 AP4 45 l gray violet 2.75 .95
C29 AP4 70 l rose pink 2.75 1.25
C30 AP4 100 l dp slate bl 9.00 3.75
Nos. C19-C30 (12) 19.32 7.92

Nos. 368 and 370 Overprinted in Black

1945, Jan. 26

C31 A181 1 l bright green .15 .15
C32 A181 4 l red orange .15 .15
Set value .18 .15

A similar overprint on Nos. O4, O5, O7 and O8 was privately applied.

Type of Parcel Post Stamps of 1944 Surcharged or Overprinted in Various Colors

Imperf

C37 PP5 10 l on 100 l dl yel (Bl) .18 .15
C38 PP5 45 l on 100 l dl yel (C) .28 .15
C39 PP5 75 l on 100 l dl yel (G) .38 .25
C40 PP5 100 l dl yel (V) .70 .35
Nos. C37-C40 (4) 1.54 .90

Plane and Sun — AP16

Pigeon with Letter — AP17

Plane, Letter — AP18

Wings, Posthorn — AP19

Winged Letter — AP20

Plane, Sun — AP21

Pigeon, Posthorn — AP22

Mail Plane — AP23

Conventionalized Figure Holding Pigeon — AP24

1946, July 15 **Litho.** ***Perf. 13***

C41 AP16 1 l dull lilac .15 .15
C42 AP16 2 l slate gray .15 .15
C43 AP17 4 l violet blk .15 .15
C44 AP18 6 l blue .15 .15
C45 AP19 10 l turq green .15 .15
C46 AP19 12 l yellow brn .15 .15
C47 AP20 16 l rose violet .15 .15
C48 AP19 19 l carmine .15 .15
C49 AP21 30 l orange .15 .15
C50 AP22 45 l lt ol grn .18 .15
C51 AP22 75 l red brown .24 .15
C52 AP23 100 l slate blk .65 .24
C53 AP24 100 l red .65 .24
Set value 2.50 1.25

No. C47 exists imperf. Value $90.

People's Republic

Plane over Plovdiv AP25

1947, Aug. 31 **Photo.** ***Imperf.***

C54 AP25 40 l dull olive grn .60 .50

Plovdiv International Fair, 1947.

Baldwin's Tower — AP26

1948, May 23 **Litho.** ***Perf. 11½***

C55 AP26 50 l ol brn, *cr* .75 .60

Stamp Day and the 10th Congress of Bulgarian Philatelic Societies, June 1948.

Romanian and Bulgarian Parliament Buildings AP27

Romanian and Bulgarian Flags, Bridge over Danube AP28

1948, Nov. 3 **Photo.**

C56 AP27 40 l ol gray, *cr* .22 .15
C57 AP28 100 l red vio, *cr* .52 .32

Romanian-Bulgarian friendship.

Mausoleum of Pleven — AP29

1949, June 26

C58 AP29 50 l brown 2.00 1.25

7th Congress of Bulgarian Philatelic Associations, June 26-27, 1949.

Symbols of the UPU — AP30

Frontier Guard and Dog — AP31

1949, Oct. 10 ***Perf. 11½***

C59 AP30 50 l violet blue 1.50 .75

75th anniv. of the UPU.

1949, Oct. 31

C60 AP31 60 l olive black 1.25 .90

Dimitrov Mausoleum AP32

1950, July 3 ***Perf. 10½***

C61 AP32 40 l olive brown 3.00 1.10

1st anniv. of the death of George Dimitrov.

Belogradchic Rocks — AP33

Air View of Plovdiv Fair — AP34

Designs: 16s, Beach, Varna. 20s, Harvesting grain. 28s, Rila monastery. 44s, Studena dam. 60s, View of Dimitrovgrad. 80s, View of Trnovo. 1 l, University building, Sofia. 4 l, Partisans' Monument.

1954, Apr. 1 **Unwmk.** ***Perf. 13***

C62 AP33 8s olive black .15 .15
C63 AP34 12s rose brown .15 .15
C64 AP33 16s brown .15 .15
C65 AP33 20s brn red, *cream* .15 .15
C66 AP33 28s dp bl, *cream* .18 .15
C67 AP33 44s vio brn, *cream* .18 .15
C68 AP33 60s red brn, *cream* .26 .15
C69 AP34 80s dk grn, *cream* .26 .18
C70 AP33 1 l dk bl grn, *cream* 1.25 .35
C71 AP34 4 l deep blue 3.00 .80
Nos. C62-C71 (10) 5.73 2.38

Glider on Mountainside AP35

Designs: 60s, Glider over airport. 80s, Three gliders.

1956, Oct. 15 **Photo.**

C72 AP35 44s brt blue .16 .15
C73 AP35 60s purple .30 .15
C74 AP35 80s dk blue grn .48 .15
Nos. C72-C74 (3) .94
Set value .31

30th anniv. of glider flights in Bulgaria.

Passenger Plane AP36

1957, May 21 **Unwmk.** ***Perf. 13***

C75 AP36 80s deep blue .60 .32

10th anniv. of civil aviation in Bulgaria.

Sputnik 3 over Earth — AP37

1958, Nov. 28 ***Perf. 11***

C76 AP37 80s brt grnsh blue 3.00 2.25

International Geophysical Year, 1957-58. Value, imperf. $7.50.

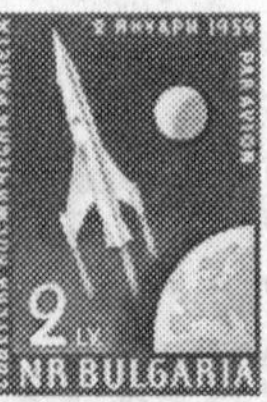

Lunik 1 Leaving Earth for Moon — AP38

1959, Feb. 28 ***Perf. 10½***

C77 AP38 2 l brt blue & ocher 3.00 2.75

Launching of 1st man-made satellite to orbit moon. Value, imperf. in slightly different colors, $7.50 unused, $5.25 canceled.

Statue of Liberty and Tu-110 Airliner AP39

Perf. 10½

1959, Nov. 11 Photo. Unwmk.
C78 AP39 1 l violet bl & pink 1.75 1.50

Visit of Khrushchev to US. Value, imperf. $5.

Lunik 2 and Moon — AP40

1960, June 23 Litho. *Perf. 11*
C79 AP40 1.25 l blue, blk & yel 3.50 1.65

Russian rocket to the Moon, Sept. 12, 1959.

Sputnik 5 and Dogs Belka and Strelka AP41

1961, Jan. 14 Photo. *Perf. 11*
C80 AP41 1.25 l brt grnsh bl & org 4.00 2.50

Russian rocket flight of Aug. 19, 1970.

Maj. Yuri A. Gagarin and Vostok 1 AP42

1961, Apr. 26 Unwmk.
C81 AP42 4 l grnsh bl, blk & red 2.50 1.50

First manned space flight, Apr. 12, 1961.

Soviet Space Dogs — AP43

1961, June 28 *Perf. 11*
C82 AP43 2 l slate & dk car 2.00 1.00

Venus-bound Rocket — AP44

1961, June 28
C83 AP44 2 l brt bl, yel & org 4.00 2.50

Issued to commemorate the Soviet launching of the Venus space probe, Feb. 12, 1961.

Maj. Gherman Titov — AP45

Design: 1.25 l, Spaceship Vostok 2.

1961, Nov. 20 Photo. *Perf. 11x10½*
C84 AP45 75s dk ol grn & gray grn 1.75 1.25
C85 AP45 1.25 l vio bl, lt bl & pink 2.25 1.75

1st manned space flight around the world, Maj. Gherman Titov of Russia, Aug. 6-7, 1961.

Iskar River Narrows — AP46

Designs: 2s, Varna and sailboat. 3s, Melnik. 10s, Trnovo. 40s, Pirin mountains.

1962, Feb. 3 Unwmk. *Perf. 13*
C86 AP46 1s bl grn & gray bl .15 .15
C87 AP46 2s blue & pink .15 .15
C88 AP46 3s brown & ocher .22 .15
C89 AP46 10s black & lemon .45 .15
C90 AP46 40s dk green & green 1.10 .28
Nos. C86-C90 (5) 2.07
Set value .48

Ilyushin Turboprop Airliner AP47

1962, Aug. 18 *Perf. 11*
C91 AP47 13s blue & black .60 .25

15th anniversary of TABSO airline.

Konstantin E. Tsiolkovsky and Rocket Launching AP48

Design: 13s, Earth, moon and rocket on future flight to the moon.

1962, Sept. 24 *Perf. 11*
C92 AP48 5s dp green & gray 1.90 .85
C93 AP48 13s ultra & yellow 1.10 .35

13th meeting of the International Astronautical Federation.

Maj. Andrian G. Nikolayev — AP49

Designs: 2s, Lt. Col. Pavel R. Popovich. 40s, Vostoks 3 and 4 in orbit.

1962, Dec. 9 Photo. Unwmk.
C94 AP49 1s bl, sl grn & blk .15 .15
C95 AP49 2s bl grn, grn & blk .24 .15
C96 AP49 40s dk bl grn, pink & blk 1.65 .85
Nos. C94-C96 (3) 2.04 1.15

First Russian group space flight of Vostoks 3 and 4, Aug. 12-15, 1962.

Spacecraft "Mars 1" Approaching Mars — AP50

Design: 13s, Rocket launching spacecraft, Earth, Moon and Mars.

1963, Feb. 25 Unwmk. *Perf. 11*
C97 AP50 5s multicolored .50 .28
C98 AP50 13s multicolored 1.00 .45

Launching of the Russian spacecraft "Mars 1," Nov. 1, 1962.

Lt. Col. Valeri F. Bykovski AP51

Designs: 2s, Lt. Valentina Tereshkova. 5s, Globe and trajectories.

1963, Aug. 26 Unwmk. *Perf. 11½*
C99 AP51 1s pale vio & Prus bl .15 .15
C100 AP51 2s citron & red brn .15 .15
C101 AP51 5s rose & dk red .15 .15
Set value .24 .15

The space flights of Valeri Bykovski, June 14-19, and Valentina Tereshkova, first woman cosmonaut, June 16-19, 1963. An imperf. souvenir sheet contains one 50s stamp showing Spasski tower and globe in lilac and red brown. Light blue border with red brown inscription. Size: 77x67mm. Value $2.50. See No. CB3.

Nos. C99-C100 Surcharged in Magenta or Green

МЕЖДУНАРОДНА КОСМИЧЕСКА ИЗЛОЖБА РИЧИОНЕ 1964 ST 10

1964, Aug. 22
C102 AP51 10s on 1s (M) .32 .18
C103 AP51 20s on 2s .65 .22

International Space Exhibition in Riccione, Italy. Overprint in Italian on No. C103.

St. John's Monastery, Rila — AP52

Design: 13s, Notre Dame, Paris; French inscription.

1964, Dec. 22 Photo. *Perf. 11½*
C104 AP52 5s pale brn & blk .18 .15
C105 AP52 13s lt ultra & sl bl .65 .20
Set value .27

The philatelic exhibition at St. Ouen (Seine) organized by the Franco-Russian Philatelic Circle and philatelic organizations in various People's Democracies.

Paper Mill, Bukijovtz AP53

Designs: 10s, Metal works, Plovdiv. 13s, Metal works, Kremikovtsi. 20s, Oil refinery, Stara-Zagora. 40s, Fertilizer plant, Stara-Zagora. 1 l, Rest home, Meded.

1964-68 Unwmk. *Perf. 13*
C106 AP53 8s grnsh blue .15 .15
C107 AP53 10s red lilac .15 .15
C108 AP53 13s brt violet .22 .15
C109 AP53 20s slate blue .70 .15
C110 AP53 40s dk olive grn 1.10 .18
C111 AP53 1 l red ('68) 1.90 .32
Nos. C106-C111 (6) 4.22
Set value .75

Issue dates: 1 l, May 6. Others, Dec. 7.

Three-master — AP54 Veliko Turnovo — AP55

Means of Communication: 2s, Postal coach. 3s, Old steam locomotive. 5s, Early cars. 10s, Montgolfier balloon. 13s, Early plane. 20s, Jet planes. 40s, Rocket and satellites. 1 l, Postrider.

1969, Mar. 31 Photo. *Perf. 13x12½*
C112 AP54 1s gray & multi .15 .15
C113 AP54 2s gray & multi .15 .15
C114 AP54 3s gray & multi .15 .15
C115 AP54 5s gray & multi .15 .15
C116 AP54 10s gray & multi .15 .15
C117 AP54 13s gray & multi .25 .15
C118 AP54 20s gray & multi .50 .22
C119 AP54 40s gray & multi .90 .38
Set value 2.00 1.00

Miniature Sheet

Imperf

C120 AP54 1 l gold & org 2.25 1.50

SOFIA 1969 Philatelic Exhibition, Sofia, May 31-June 8.

1973, July 30 Photo. *Perf. 13*

Designs: Historic buildings in various cities.

C121 AP55 2s shown .15 .15
C122 AP55 13s Roussalka .25 .15
C123 AP55 20s Plovdiv 1.50 .80
C124 AP55 28s Sofia .65 .18
Nos. C121-C124 (4) 2.55 1.28

Aleksei A. Leonov and Soyuz AP56

Designs: 18s, Thomas P. Stafford and Apollo. 28s, Apollo and Soyuz over earth. 1 l, Apollo Soyuz link-up.

1975, July 15
C125 AP56 13s blue & multi .30 .15
C126 AP56 18s purple & multi .40 .15
C127 AP56 28s multicolored 1.00 .28
Nos. C125-C127 (3) 1.70
Set value .38

Souvenir Sheet

C128 AP56 1 l violet & multi 2.00 1.25

Apollo Soyuz space test project (Russo-American cooperation), launching July 15; link-up July 17.

Balloon Over Plovdiv — AP57

1977, Sept. 3
C129 AP57 25s yellow, brn & red .50 .20

Alexei Leonov Floating in Space — AP58

Designs: 25s, Mariner 6, US spacecraft. 35s, Venera 4, USSR Venus probe.

1977, Oct. 14 Photo. *Perf. 13½*
C130 AP58 12s multicolored .20 .15
C131 AP58 25s multicolored .42 .15
C132 AP58 35s multicolored .60 .22
Nos. C130-C132 (3) 1.22 .52

Space era, 20 years.

TU-154, Balkanair Emblem — AP59

1977 *Perf. 13*
C133 AP59 35s ultra & multi .75 .35

30th anniv. of Bulgarian airline, Balkanair. Issued in sheets of 6 stamps + 3 labels (in lilac) with inscription and Balkanair emblem.

Baba Vida Fortress AP60

Design: 35s, Peace Bridge, connecting Rousse, Bulgaria, with Giurgiu, Romania.

1978 Photo. *Perf. 13*
C134 AP60 25s multicolored .40 .40
C135 AP60 35s multicolored .55 .55

The Danube, European Intercontinental Waterway. Issued in sheets containing 5 each of Nos. C134-C135 and 2 labels, one showing course of Danube, the other hydrofoil and fish.

Red Cross AP61

1978, Mar. Photo. *Perf. 13*
C136 AP61 25s multicolored .50 .16

Centenary of Bulgarian Red Cross.

AP62 AP63

Clock towers.

1979, June 5 Litho. *Perf. 12x12½*
C137 AP62 13s Byalla Cherkva .16 .15
C138 AP62 23s Botevgrad .30 .15
C139 AP62 25s Pazardgick .32 .15
C140 AP62 35s Grabovo .42 .18
C141 AP62 53s Tryavna .75 .30
Nos. C137-C141 (5) 1.95 .93

1980, Oct. 22 Photo. *Perf. 12x12½*
C142 AP62 13s Bjala .20 .15
C143 AP62 23s Rasgrad .35 .22
C144 AP62 25s Karnabat .40 .18
C145 AP62 35s Serlievo .52 .25
C146 AP62 53s Berkovitza .80 .35
Nos. C142-C146 (5) 2.27 1.15

1980
C147 AP63 13s shown .20 .15
C148 AP63 25s Parachutist .40 .15
Set value .21

15th World Parachute Championships, Kazanluk.

DWVY-1 Aircraft — AP64

1981, June 27 Litho. *Perf. 12½*
C149 AP64 5s shown .15 .15
C150 AP64 12s LAS-7 .20 .15
C151 AP64 25s LAS-8 .40 .15
C152 AP64 35s DAR-1 .52 .20
C153 AP64 45s DAR-3 .70 .26
C154 AP64 55s DAR-9 .88 .32
Nos. C149-C154 (6) 2.85 1.23

AP65 AP66

1983, June 28
C155 Sheet of 2 1.50 1.00
a. AP65 50s Valentina Tereshkova .75 .50
b. AP65 50s Svetlana Savitskaya .75 .50

Women in space, 20th anniv.

1983, July 20 Photo. *Perf. 13*
C156 AP66 5s TV tower, Tolbukhin .15 .15
C157 AP66 13s Postwoman .25 .15
C158 AP66 30s TV tower, Mt. Botev .60 .30
a. Strip of 3, #C156-C158 .95 .50
Nos. C156-C158 (3) 1.00
Set value .47

World Communications Year. Emblems of World Communications Year, Bulgarian Post, UPU and ITU on attached margins.

Souvenir Sheet

Geophysical Map of the Moon, Russia's Luna I, II and III Satellites — AP67

1984, Oct. 24 Photo. *Perf. 13*
C159 AP67 1 l multicolored 2.00 1.00

Conquest of Space.

Intl. Civil Aviation Org., 40th Anniv. — AP68

1984, Dec. 21 Photo. *Perf. 13*
C160 AP68 42s Balkan Airlines jet .85 .42

Balkan Airlines — AP69

Design: Helicopter MU-8, passenger jet TU-154 and AN-21 transport plane.

1987, Aug. 25 Photo.
C161 AP69 25s multicolored .75 .35

2nd Joint Soviet-Bulgarian Space Flight — AP70

Cosmonauts: A. Aleksandrov, A. Solovov and V. Savinich.

1989, June 7 Litho. *Perf. 13½x13*
C162 AP70 13s multicolored .35 .18

AIR POST SEMI-POSTAL STAMPS

Catalogue values for unused stamps in this section are for Never Hinged items.

Statue of Liberty, Plane and Bridge — SPAP1

Perf. 11½.
1947, May 24 Unwmk. Litho.
CB1 SPAP1 70 l + 30 l red brn .95 .95

5th Philatelic Congress, Trnovo, and CIPEX, NYC, May, 1947.

Bulgarian Worker SPAP2

1948, Feb. 28 Photo. *Perf. 12x11½.*
CB2 SPAP2 60 l hn brn, *cr* .45 .35

2nd Bulgarian Workers' Congress, and sold by subscription only, at a premium of 16 l over face value.

Type of Air Post Stamps, 1963

Design: Valeri Bykovski and Valentina Tereshkova.

1963, Aug. 26 Unwmk. *Perf. 11½*
CB3 AP51 20s + 10s pale bluish grn & dk grn 1.25 .45

See note after No. C101.

SPECIAL DELIVERY STAMPS

Catalogue values for unused stamps in this section are for Never Hinged items.

Postman on Bicycle — SD1

Mail Car — SD2

Postman on Motorcycle — SD3

1939 Unwmk. Photo. *Perf. 13*
E1 SD1 5 l deep blue .60 .15
E2 SD2 6 l copper brn .24 .15
E3 SD3 7 l golden brn .35 .15
E4 SD2 8 l red orange .60 .15
E5 SD1 20 l bright rose 1.25 .38
Nos. E1-E5 (5) 3.04 .98

POSTAGE DUE STAMPS

D1

D2

Large Lozenge Perf. 5½ to 6½
1884 Typo. Unwmk.
J1 D1 5s orange 150.00 15.00
J2 D1 25s lake 75.00 10.00
J3 D1 50s blue 12.00 5.00
Nos. J1-J3 (3) 237.00 30.00

1886 *Imperf.*
J4 D1 5s orange 75.00 2.50
J5 D1 25s lake 120.00 2.50
J6 D1 50s blue 5.00 2.75
Nos. J4-J6 (3) 200.00 7.75

1887 *Perf. 11½*
J7 D1 5s orange 9.50 1.00
J8 D1 25s lake 9.50 1.00
J9 D1 50s blue 3.50 1.00
Nos. J7-J9 (3) 22.50 3.00

Same, Redrawn
24 horizontal lines of shading in upper part instead of 30 lines

1892 *Perf. 10½, 11½*
J10 D1 5s orange 7.50 1.25
J11 D1 25s lake 7.50 1.25

1893

Pelure Paper
J12 D2 5s orange 10.00 3.50

D3

D4

1895 *Imperf.*
J13 D3 30s on 50s blue 7.00 2.00

Perf. 10½, 11½
J14 D3 30s on 50s blue 7.00 2.00

Wmk. Coat of Arms in the Sheet
1896 *Perf. 13*
J15 D4 5s orange 3.00 .75
J16 D4 10s purple 2.00 .75
J17 D4 30s green 1.40 .45
Nos. J15-J17 (3) 6.40 1.95

Nos. J15-J17 are also known on unwatermarked paper from the edges of sheets.

In 1901 a cancellation, "T" in circle, was applied to Nos. 60-65 and used provisionally as postage dues.

D5

D6

1901-04 Unwmk. *Perf. 11½*

J19	D5	5s dl rose	.20	.15
J20	D5	10s yel grn	.42	.15
J21	D5	20s dl bl ('04)	3.25	.16
J22	D5	30s vio brn	.35	.16
J23	D5	50s org ('02)	5.50	4.00
		Nos. J19-J23 (5)	9.72	4.62

Nos. J19-J23 exist imperf. and in pairs imperf. between. Value, imperf., $250.

1915 Unwmk. *Perf. 11½*

Thin Semi-Transparent Paper

J24	D6	5s green	.15	.15
J25	D6	10s purple	.20	.15
J26	D6	20s dl rose	.20	.15
J27	D6	30s dp org	1.10	.20
J28	D6	50s dp bl	.35	.17
		Nos. J24-J28 (5)	2.00	
		Set value		.52

1919-21 *Perf. 11½, 12x11½*

J29	D6	5s emerald	.15	.15
a.		5s gray green ('21)	.30	.15
J30	D6	10s violet	.15	.15
J31	D6	20s salmon	.15	.15
a.		20s yellow	.15	.15
J32	D6	30s orange	.15	.15
a.		30s red orange ('21)	.65	.65
J33	D6	50s blue	.15	.15
J34	D6	1 l emerald ('21)	.18	.15
J35	D6	2 l rose ('21)	.18	.15
J36	D6	3 l brown org ('21)	.30	.15
		Set value	1.16	.42

Stotinki values of the above series surcharged 10s or 20s were used as ordinary postage stamps. See Nos. 182-185.

The 1919 printings are on thicker white paper with clean-cut perforations, the 1921 printings on thicker grayish paper with rough perforations.

Most of this series exist imperforate and in pairs imperforate between.

Heraldic Lion — D7

Lion of Trnovo — D8

National Arms
D9 D10

1932, Aug. 15

Thin Paper

J37	D7	1 l olive bister	.24	.20
J38	D7	2 l rose brown	.24	.20
J39	D7	6 l brown violet	.75	.35
		Nos. J37-J39 (3)	1.23	.75

1933, Apr. 10

J40	D8	20s dk brn	.15	.15
J41	D8	40s dp bl	.15	.15
J42	D8	80s car rose	.15	.15
J43	D9	1 l org brn	.24	.18
J44	D9	2 l olive	.30	.25
J45	D9	6 l dl vio	.15	.15
J46	D9	14 l ultra	.24	.15
		Set value	1.00	.78

Catalogue values for unused stamps in this section, from this point to the end of the section, are for Never Hinged items.

1947, June Typo. *Perf. 10½*

J47	D10	1 l chocolate	.15	.15
J48	D10	2 l deep claret	.15	.15
J49	D10	8 l deep orange	.15	.15
J50	D10	20 l blue	.22	.15
		Set value	.42	.25

Arms of the People's Republic — D11

1951 *Perf. 11½x10½*

J51	D11	1 l chocolate	.15	.15
J52	D11	2 l claret	.15	.15
J53	D11	8 l red orange	.22	.15
J54	D11	20 l deep blue	.60	.32
		Set value	.92	.52

OFFICIAL STAMPS

Catalogue values for unused stamps in this section are for Never Hinged items.

Bulgarian Coat of Arms
O1 O2

1942 Unwmk. Typo. *Perf. 13*

O1	O1	10s yel grn	.15	.15
O2	O1	30s red	.15	.15
O3	O1	50s bister	.15	.15
O4	O2	1 l vio bl	.15	.15
O5	O2	2 l dk grn	.15	.15
O6	O2	3 l lilac	.15	.15
O7	O2	4 l rose	.15	.15
O8	O2	5 l carmine	.16	.15
		Set value	.65	.40

1944 *Perf. 10½x11½*

O9	O2	1 l blue	.20	.15
O10	O2	2 l brt red	.20	.15

Lion Rampant
O3 O4

O5

1945 *Imperf.*

O11	O5	1 l pink	.15	.15

Perf. 10½x11½, Imperf.

O12	O3	2 l blue green	.15	.15
O13	O4	3 l bister brown	.15	.15
O14	O4	4 l light ultra	.15	.15
O15	O5	5 l brown lake	.15	.15
		Set value	.25	.25

In 1950, four stamps prepared for official use were issued as regular postage stamps. See Nos. 724-727.

PARCEL POST STAMPS

Catalogue values for unused stamps in this section are for Never Hinged items.

Weighing Packages — PP1

Parcel Post — PP2

Designs: 3 l, 8 l, 20 l, Parcel post truck. 4 l, 6 l, 10 l, Motorcycle.

Perf. 12½x13½, 13½x12½

1941-42 Photo. Unwmk.

Q1	PP1	1 l slate grn	.15	.15
Q2	PP2	2 l crimson	.15	.15
Q3	PP2	3 l dull brn	.15	.15
Q4	PP2	4 l red org	.15	.15
Q5	PP1	5 l deep blue	.15	.15
Q6	PP1	5 l slate grn ('42)	.15	.15
Q7	PP2	6 l red vio	.15	.15
Q8	PP2	6 l henna brn ('42)	.15	.15
Q9	PP1	7 l dark blue	.15	.15
Q10	PP1	7 l dk brn ('42)	.15	.15
Q11	PP2	8 l brt bl grn	.15	.15
Q12	PP2	8 l green ('42)	.15	.15
Q13	PP2	9 l olive gray	.15	.15
Q14	PP2	9 l dp olive ('42)	.15	.15
Q15	PP2	10 l orange	.15	.15
Q16	PP2	20 l gray vio	.42	.15
Q17	PP2	30 l dull blk	.55	.15
Q18	PP2	30 l sepia ('42)	.50	.15
		Set value	2.50	1.00

Arms of Bulgaria — PP5

1944 Litho. *Imperf.*

Q21	PP5	1 l dk carmine	.15	.15
Q22	PP5	3 l blue grn	.15	.15
Q23	PP5	5 l dull bl grn	.15	.15
Q24	PP5	7 l rose lilac	.15	.15
Q25	PP5	10 l deep blue	.15	.15
Q26	PP5	20 l orange brn	.15	.15
Q27	PP5	30 l dk brn car	.15	.15
Q28	PP5	50 l red orange	.30	.15
Q29	PP5	100 l blue	.52	.22
		Set value	1.30	.75

For overprints and surcharges see Nos. 448-454, C37-C40.

POSTAL TAX STAMPS

The use of stamps Nos. RA1 to RA18 was compulsory on letters, etc., to be delivered on Sundays and holidays. The money received from their sale was used toward maintaining a sanatorium for employees of the post, telegraph and telephone services.

View of Sanatorium PT1

Sanatorium, Peshtera PT2

1925-29 Unwmk. Typo. *Perf. 11½*

RA1	PT1	1 l blk, *grnsh bl*	2.75	.15
RA2	PT1	1 l chocolate ('26)	2.75	.15
RA3	PT1	1 l orange ('27)	3.00	.15
RA4	PT1	1 l pink ('28)	4.50	.15
RA5	PT1	1 l vio, *pnksh* ('29)	4.25	.15
RA6	PT2	2 l blue green	.35	.15
RA7	PT2	2 l violet ('27)	.35	.16
RA8	PT2	5 l deep blue	3.00	.80
RA9	PT2	5 l rose ('27)	3.75	.40
		Nos. RA1-RA9 (9)	24.70	2.26

St. Constantine Sanatorium PT3

1930-33

RA10	PT3	1 l red brn & ol grn	4.00	.16
RA11	PT3	1 l ol grn & yel ('31)	.50	.16
RA12	PT3	1 l red vio & ol brn ('33)	.50	.16
		Nos. RA10-RA12 (3)	5.00	.48

Trojan Rest Home — PT4

Sanatorium PT5

1935 Wmk. 145 *Perf. 11, 11½*

RA13	PT4	1 l choc & red org	.32	.15
RA14	PT4	1 l emer & indigo	.32	.15
RA15	PT5	5 l red brn & indigo	1.40	.35
		Nos. RA13-RA15 (3)	2.04	
		Set value		.51

St. Constantine Sanatorium PT6

Designs: 2 l, Children at seashore. 5 l, Rest home.

1941 Unwmk. Photo. *Perf. 13*

RA16	PT6	1 l dark olive green	.15	.15
RA17	PT6	2 l red orange	.15	.15
RA18	PT6	5 l deep blue	.30	.15
		Set value	.50	.22

See Nos. 702-705 for same designs in smaller size issued as regular postage.

BURKINA FASO

bůr-'kē-nə-'fä-sō

Upper Volta

LOCATION — Northwestern Africa, north of Ghana
GOVT. — Republic
AREA — 105,869 sq. mi.
POP. — 6,695,500 (est. 1984)
CAPITAL — Ouagadougou

In 1919 the French territory of Upper Volta was detached from the southern section of Upper Senegal and Niger and made a separate colony. In 1933 the colony was divided among its neighbors: French Sudan, Ivory Coast, and Niger Territory. The Republic of Upper Volta was proclaimed December 11, 1958; the name was changed to Burkina Faso on August 4, 1984.

100 Centimes = 1 Franc

Catalogue values for unused stamps in this country are for Never Hinged items, beginning with Scott 70 in the regular postage section, Scott B1 in the semi-postal section, Scott C1 in the airpost section, Scott J21 in the postage due section, and Scott O1 in the official section.

Stamps and Types of Upper Senegal and Niger, 1914-17, Overprinted in Black or Red **HAUTE-VOLTA**

1920-28 Unwmk. *Perf. 13½x14*

1 A4 1c brn vio & vio .15 .15
2 A4 2c gray & brn vio (R) .15 .15
3 A4 4c blk & bl .15 .15
4 A4 5c yel grn & bl grn .25 .15
5 A4 5c ol brn & dk brn ('22) .15 .15
6 A4 10c red org & rose .40 .35
7 A4 10c yel grn & bl grn ('22) .15 .15
8 A4 10c claret & bl ('25) .25 .25
a. Overprint omitted 80.00
9 A4 15c choc & org .40 .30
10 A4 20c brn vio & blk (R) .65 .55
11 A4 25c ultra & bl .65 .30
12 A4 25c blk & bl grn ('22) .45 .40
a. Overprint omitted 65.00
13 A4 30c ol brn & brn (R) 1.10 .65
14 A4 30c red org & rose ('22) .40 .35
15 A4 30c vio & brn red ('25) .40 .35
16 A4 30c dl grn & bl grn ('27) .70 .45
17 A4 35c car rose & vio .45 .30
18 A4 40c gray & car rose .45 .35
19 A4 45c bl & brn (R) .35 .20
20 A4 50c blk & grn 1.50 1.10
21 A4 50c ultra & bl ('22) .15 .15
22 A4 50c red org & bl ('25) .40 .35
23 A4 60c org red ('26) .15 .15
24 A4 65c bis & pale bl ('28) .70 .45
25 A4 75c org & brn .30 .30
26 A4 1fr brn & brn vio .65 .40
27 A4 2fr grn & bl 1.00 .65
28 A4 5fr vio & blk (R) 2.50 1.75
Nos. 1-28 (28) 15.00 11.00

No. 9 Surcharged in Various Colors **0,01 ═ 0,01**

1922

29 A4 0,01c on 15c (Bk) .40 .40
a. Double surcharge 50.00 50.00
30 A4 0,02c on 15c (Bl) .40 .40
31 A4 0,05c on 15c (R) .40 .40
Nos. 29-31 (3) 1.20 1.20

Type of 1920 Surcharged **60 ═ 60**

1922

32 A4 60c on 75c vio, *pnksh* .35 .35

Stamps and Types of 1920 Surcharged with New Value and Bars

1924-27

33 A4 25c on 2fr grn & bl .45 .45
34 A4 25c on 5fr vio & blk .45 .45
35 A4 65c on 45c bl & brn ('25) .50 .50
36 A4 85c on 75c org & brn ('25) .70 .70
37 A4 90c on 75c brn red & sal pink ('27) .70 .70
38 A4 1.25fr on 1fr dp bl & lt bl (R) ('26) .45 .45
39 A4 1.50fr on 1fr dp bl & ultra ('27) 1.25 1.25
40 A4 3fr on 5fr dl red & brn org ('27) 1.65 1.65
41 A4 10fr on 5fr ol grn & lil rose ('27) 7.25 7.25
42 A4 20fr on 5fr org brn & vio ('27) 10.00 10.00
Nos. 33-42 (10) 23.40 23.40

Hausa Chief — A5

Hausa Woman — A6

Hausa Warrior A7

1928 Typo. *Perf. 13½x14*

43 A5 1c indigo & grn .15 .15
44 A5 2c brn & lil .15 .15
45 A5 4c blk & yel .15 .15
46 A5 5c indigo & gray bl .20 .20
47 A5 10c indigo & pink .50 .50
48 A5 15c brn & bl .90 .90
49 A5 20c brn & grn .90 .90
50 A6 25c brn & yel 1.10 1.10
51 A6 30c dp grn & grn 1.10 1.10
52 A6 40c blk & pink 1.10 1.10
53 A6 45c brn & blue 1.10 1.10
54 A6 50c blk & grn 1.10 1.10
55 A6 65c indigo & bl 1.65 1.65
56 A6 75c blk & lil 1.10 1.10
57 A6 90c brn red & lil 1.10 1.10

Perf. 14x13½

58 A7 1fr brn & grn 1.10 1.10
59 A7 1.10fr indigo & lil 1.10 1.10
60 A7 1.50fr ultra & grysh 1.75 1.75
61 A7 2fr blk & bl 2.25 2.25
62 A7 3fr brn & yel 2.25 2.25
63 A7 5fr brn & lil 2.25 2.25
64 A7 10fr blk & grn 9.00 9.00
65 A7 20fr blk & pink 13.00 13.00
Nos. 43-65 (23) 45.00 45.00

Colonial Exposition Issue

Common Design Types

1931 Engr. *Perf. 12½*

Country Name Typo. in Black

66 CD70 40c dp grn 1.50 1.50
67 CD71 50c violet 1.50 1.50
68 CD72 90c red org 1.50 1.50
69 CD73 1.50fr dull blue 2.00 2.00
Nos. 66-69 (4) 6.50 6.50

Common Design Types pictured in section at front of book.

Catalogue values for unused stamps in this section, from this point to the end of the section, are for Never Hinged items.

Republic

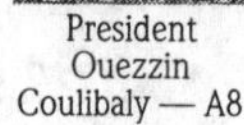

President Ouezzin Coulibaly — A8

Deer Mask and Deer — A9

1959 Unwmk. Engr. *Perf. 13*

70 A8 25fr black & mag .25 .15

1st anniv. of the proclamation of the Republic; Ouezzin Coulibaly, Council President, who died in December, 1958.

Imperforates

Most Upper Volta stamps from 1959 onward exist imperforate in issued and trial colors, and also in small presentation sheets in issued colors.

1960

Animal Masks: 1fr, 2fr, 4fr, Wart hog. 5fr, 6fr, 8fr, Monkey. 10fr, 15fr, 20fr, Buffalo. 25fr, Coba (antelope). 30fr, 40fr, 50fr, Elephant. 60fr, 85fr, Secretary bird.

71 A9 30c rose & vio .15 .15
72 A9 40c buff & dp claret .15 .15
73 A9 50c bl grn & gray ol .15 .15
74 A9 1fr red, blk & red brn .15 .15
75 A9 2fr emer, yel grn & dk grn .15 .15
76 A9 4fr bl, vio & ind .15 .15
77 A9 5fr ol bis, red & brn .15 .15
78 A9 6fr grnsh bl & vio brn .15 .15
79 A9 8fr org & red brn .15 .15
80 A9 10fr lt yel grn & plum .15 .15
81 A9 15fr org, ultra & brn .15 .15
82 A9 20fr green & ultra .22 .15
83 A9 25fr bl, emer & dp claret .25 .15
84 A9 30fr dk bl grn, blk & brn .30 .15
85 A9 40fr ultra, ind & dk car .38 .15
86 A9 50fr brt pink, brn & grn .42 .18
87 A9 60fr org brn & bl .55 .25
88 A9 85fr gray ol & dk bl .80 .32
Set value 3.60 1.80

C.C.T.A. Issue

Common Design Type

1960 Engr. *Perf. 13*

89 CD106 25fr vio bl & slate .35 .35

Emblem of the Entente — A9a

Pres. Maurice Yameogo — A10

1960 Photo. *Perf. 13x13½*

90 A9a 25fr multicolored .40 .35

Council of the Entente.

1960, May 1 Engr. *Perf. 13*

91 A10 25fr dk vio brn & slate .25 .16

Flag, Village and Couple — A11

1960, Aug. 5 Unwmk. *Perf. 13*

92 A11 25fr red brn, blk & red .35 .25

Proclamation of independence, Aug. 5, 1960.

World Meteorological Organization Emblem — A12

1961, May 4

93 A12 25fr blk, bl & red .30 .25

First World Meteorological Day.

Arms of Republic — A13

1961, Dec. 8 Photo. *Perf. 12x12½*

94 A13 25fr multicolored .25 .25

The 1961 independence celebrations.

WMO Emblem, Weather Station and Sorghum Grain — A14

1962, Mar. 23 Unwmk. *Perf. 13*

95 A14 25fr dk bl, emer & brn .30 .25

UN 2nd World Meteorological Day, Mar. 23.

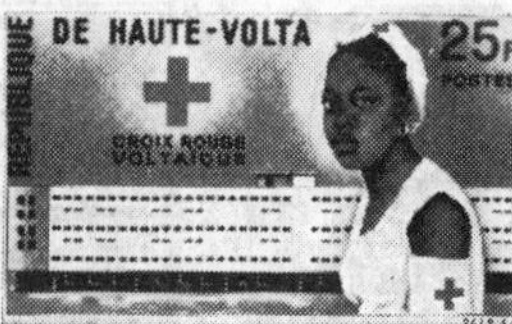

Hospital and Nurse — A15

1962, June 23 *Perf. 13x12*

96 A15 25fr multicolored .35 .35

Founding of Upper Volta Red Cross.

Buffalos at Water Hole — A16

Designs: 10fr, Lions, horiz. 15fr, Defassa waterbuck. 25fr, Arly reservation, horiz. 50fr, Diapaga reservation, horiz. 85fr, Buffon's kob.

Perf. 12½x12, 12x12½

1962, June 30 Engr.

97 A16 5fr sepia, bl & grn .15 .15
98 A16 10fr red brn, grn & yel .16 .15
99 A16 15fr sepia, grn & yel .25 .16
100 A16 25fr vio brn, bl & grn .45 .20
101 A16 50fr vio brn, bl & grn .80 .55
102 A16 85fr red brn, bl & grn 1.20 .80
Nos. 97-102 (6) 3.01 2.01

Abidjan Games Issue

Common Design Type

Designs: 20fr, Soccer. 25fr, Bicycling. 85fr, Boxing. All horiz.

1962, July 21 Photo. *Perf. 12½x12*

103 CD109 20fr multicolored .25 .18
104 CD109 25fr multicolored .30 .25
105 CD109 85fr multicolored .60 .40
Nos. 103-105 (3) 1.15 .83

African-Malgache Union Issue

Common Design Type

1962, Sept. 8 Unwmk.

106 CD110 30fr red, bluish grn & gold .70 .65

Weather Map and UN Emblem A17

1963, Mar. 23 *Perf. 12x12½*

107 A17 70fr multicolored .60 .45

3rd World Meteorological Day, Mar. 23.

Friendship Games, Dakar, Apr. 11-21 — A18

1963, Apr. 11 Engr. *Perf. 13*

108 A18 20fr Basketball .22 .15
109 A18 25fr Discus .25 .15
110 A18 50fr Judo .55 .25
Nos. 108-110 (3) 1.02 .55

Amaryllis A19

Flowers: 50c, Hibiscus. 1fr, Oldenlandia grandiflora. 1.50fr, Rose moss (portulaca). 2fr,

Tobacco. 4fr, Morning glory. 5fr, Striga senegalensis. 6fr, Cowpea. 8fr, Lepidagathis heudelotiana. 10fr, Spurge. 25fr, Argyreia nervosa. 30fr, Rangoon creeper. 40fr, Water lily. 50fr, White plumeria. 60fr, Crotalaria retusa. 85fr, Hibiscus. Nos. 111-119 are vert.

1963 **Photo.**

111 A19	50c	multicolored	.15	.15
112 A19	1fr	multicolored	.15	.15
113 A19	1.50fr	multicolored	.15	.15
114 A19	2fr	multicolored	.15	.15
115 A19	4fr	multicolored	.15	.15
116 A19	5fr	multicolored	.15	.15
117 A19	6fr	multicolored	.15	.15
118 A19	8fr	multicolored	.15	.15
119 A19	10fr	multicolored	.16	.15
120 A19	15fr	multicolored	.20	.15
121 A19	25fr	multicolored	.30	.16
122 A19	30fr	multicolored	.35	.20
123 A19	40fr	multicolored	.40	.30
124 A19	50fr	multicolored	.55	.38
125 A19	60fr	multicolored	.65	.42
126 A19	85fr	multicolored	.90	.55
		Set value	4.00	2.75

Centenary Emblem and Globe — A20

Scroll — A21

1963, Oct. 21 **Unwmk.** ***Perf. 12***
127 A20 25fr multicolored .50 .40

Centenary of International Red Cross.

1963, Dec. 10 **Photo.** ***Perf. 13x12½***
128 A21 25fr dp claret, gold & bl .30 .20

15th anniv. of the Universal Declaration of Human Rights.

Sound Wave Patterns A22

1964, Jan. 16 ***Perf. 12½x13***
129 A22 25fr multicolored .25 .20

Upper Volta's admission to the ITU.

Barograph and WMO Emblem A23

1964, Mar. 23 **Engr.** ***Perf. 13***
130 A23 50fr dk car rose, grn & bl .55 .40

4th World Meteorological Day, Mar. 23.

World Connected by Letters and Carrier Pigeon — A24

Design: 60fr, World connected by letters and jet plane.

1964, Mar. 29 **Photo.** ***Perf. 13x12***
131 A24 25fr gray brn & ultra .25 .20
132 A24 60fr gray brn & org .60 .42

Upper Volta's admission to the UPU.

IQSY Emblem and Seasonal Allegories — A25

1964, Aug. 17 **Engr.** ***Perf. 13***
133 A25 30fr grn, ocher & car .35 .25

International Quiet Sun Year.

Cooperation Issue
Common Design Type

1964, Nov. 7 **Unwmk.** ***Perf. 13***
134 CD119 70fr dl bl grn, dk brn & car .65 .42

Hotel Independance, Ouagadougou A26

1964, Dec. 11 **Litho.** ***Perf. 12½x13***
135 A26 25fr multicolored 1.00 .35

Pigmy Long-tailed Sunbird — A27

Comoe Waterfall — A28

1965, Mar. 1 **Photo.** ***Perf. 13x12½***
Size: 22x36mm
136 A27 10fr shown .20 .16
137 A27 15fr Olive-bellied Sunbird .25 .20
138 A27 20fr Splendid Sunbird .40 .25
Nos. 136-138,C20 (4) 6.35 3.11

1965 **Engr.** ***Perf. 13***

Design: 25fr, Great Waterfall of Banfora, horiz.

139 A28 5fr yel grn, bl & red brn .15 .15
140 A28 25fr dk red, brt bl & grn .25 .16
Set value .23

Soccer — A29

Abraham Lincoln — A30

Designs: 25fr, Boxing gloves and ring. 70fr, Tennis rackets, ball and net.

1965, July 15 **Unwmk.** ***Perf. 13***
141 A29 15fr brn, red & dk grn .16 .15
142 A29 25fr pale org, bl & brn .28 .18
143 A29 70fr dk car & brt grn .60 .32
Nos. 141-143 (3) 1.04 .65

1st African Games, Brazzaville, July 18-25.

1965, Nov. 3 **Photo.** ***Perf. 13x12½***
144 A30 50fr green & multi .50 .38

Centenary of death of Abraham Lincoln.

Pres. Maurice Yameogo — A31

1965, Dec. 11 **Photo.** ***Perf. 13x12½***
145 A31 25fr multicolored .25 .16

Mantis A32

Wart Hog A33

Headdress A34

1966 ***Perf. 13x12½, 12½x13***

146 A33	1fr	Nemopistha imperatrix	.15	.15
147 A33	2fr	Ball python	.15	.15
148 A32	3fr	shown	.15	.15
149 A32	4fr	Grasshopper	.15	.15
150 A33	5fr	shown	.15	.15
151 A32	6fr	Scorpion	.15	.15
152 A33	8fr	Green monkey	.15	.15
153 A32	10fr	Dromedary	.15	.15
154 A33	15fr	Leopard	.20	.15
155 A32	20fr	Cape buffalo	.22	.16
156 A33	25fr	Hippopotamus	.30	.16
157 A32	30fr	Agama lizard	.38	.20
158 A33	45fr	Common puff adder	.55	.22
159 A33	50fr	Chameleon	.60	.35
160 A33	60fr	Ugada limbata	.70	.42
161 A33	85fr	Elephant	.90	.50
		Nos. 146-161 (16)	5.05	
		Set value		2.65

1966, Apr. 9 **Photo.** ***Perf. 13x12½***

Designs: 25fr, Plumed headdress. 60fr, Male dancer.

162 A34 20fr yel grn, choc & red .20 .15
163 A34 25fr multicolored .25 .16
164 A34 60fr org, dk brn & red .60 .35
Nos. 162-164 (3) 1.05 .66

Intl. Negro Arts Festival, Dakar, Senegal, 4/1-24.

Pô Church A35

Design: No. 166, Bobo-Dioulasso Mosque.

1966, Apr. 15 ***Perf. 12½x13***
165 A35 25fr multicolored .22 .16
166 A35 25fr bl, cream & red brn .22 .16

The Red Cross Helping the World — A36

1966, June **Photo.** ***Perf. 13x12½***
167 A36 25fr lemon, blk & car .22 .15

Issued to honor the Red Cross.

Boy Scouts in Camp — A37

Design: 15fr, Two Scouts on a cliff exploring the country.

1966, June 15 ***Perf. 12½x13***
168 A37 10fr multicolored .15 .15
169 A37 15fr blk, bis brn, & dl yel .16 .15
Set value .17

Issued to honor the Boy Scouts.

Cow Receiving Injection A38

1966, Aug. 16 **Photo.** ***Perf. 12½x13***
170 A38 25fr yel, blk & blue .25 .20

Campaign against cattle plague.

Plowing with Donkey A39

Design: 30fr, Crop rotation, Kamboince Experimental Station.

1966, Sept. 15 **Photo.** ***Perf. 12½x13***
171 A39 25fr multicolored .22 .15
172 A39 30fr multicolored .25 .16

Natl. and rural education; 3rd anniv. of the Kamboince Experimental Station (No. 172).

UNESCO Emblem and Map of Africa — A40

UNICEF Emblem and Children A41

1966, Dec. 10 **Engr.** ***Perf. 13***
173 A40 50fr brt bl, blk & red .50 .25
174 A41 50fr dk vio, dp lil & dk red .50 .25

20th anniv. of UNESCO and of UNICEF.

Arms of Upper Volta — A42

Symbols of Agriculture, Industry, Men and Women — A43

1967, Jan. 2 **Photo.** ***Perf. 12½x13***
175 A42 30fr multicolored .22 .15

Europafrica Issue

1967, Feb. 4 **Photo.** ***Perf. 12½***
176 A43 60fr multicolored .50 .30

Scout Handclasp and Jamboree Emblem A44

Design: 5fr, Jamboree emblem and Scout holding hat.

1967, June 8 Photo. *Perf. 12½x13*
177 A44 5fr multicolored .20 .15
178 A44 20fr multicolored .55 .40

12th Boy Scout World Jamboree, Farragut State Park, Idaho, Aug. 1-9. See No. C41.

Bank Book and Hands with Coins — A45

1967, Aug. 22 Engr. *Perf. 13*
179 A45 30fr slate grn, ocher & olive .25 .15

National Savings Bank.

Mailman on Bicycle — A46

1967, Oct. 15 Engr. *Perf. 13*
180 A46 30fr dk bl, emer & brn .30 .16

Stamp Day.

Monetary Union Issue
Common Design Type

1967, Nov. 4 Engr. *Perf. 13*
181 CD125 30fr dk vio & dl bl .25 .15

View of Nizier — A47

Designs (Olympic Emblem and): 50fr, Les Deux-Alps, vert. 100fr, Ski lift and view of Villard-de-Lans.

1967, Nov. 28
182 A47 15fr brt bl, grn & brn .16 .15
183 A47 50fr brt bl & slate grn .45 .20
184 A47 100fr brt bl, grn & red .90 .45
Nos. 182-184 (3) 1.51 .80

10th Winter Olympic Games, Grenoble, France, Feb. 6-18, 1968.

White and Black Men Holding Human Rights Emblem A48

1968, Jan. 2 Photo. *Perf. 12½x13*
185 A48 20fr brt bl, gold & dp car .20 .15
186 A48 30fr grn, gold & dp car .30 .16

International Human Rights Year.

Administration School and Student — A49

1968, Feb. 2 Engr. *Perf. 13*
187 A49 30fr ol bis, Prus bl & brt grn .25 .15

National School of Administration.

WHO Emblem and Sick People — A50

1968, Apr. 7 Engr. *Perf. 13*
188 A50 30fr ind, brt bl & car rose .30 .16
189 A50 50fr brt bl, sl grn & lt brn .45 .22

WHO, 20th anniversary.

Telephone Office, Bobo-Dioulasso — A51

1968, Sept. 30 Photo. *Perf. 12½x12*
190 A51 30fr multicolored .28 .15

Opening of the automatic telephone office in Bobo-Dioulasso.

Weaver A52

1968, Oct. 30 Engr. *Perf. 13*
Size: 36x22mm
191 A52 30fr mag, brn & ocher .30 .16

See No. C58.

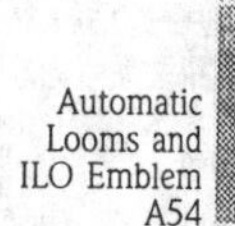

Grain Pouring over World, Plower and FAO Emblem — A53

1969, Jan. 7 Engr. *Perf. 13*
192 A53 30fr slate, vio bl & maroon .25 .15

UNFAO world food program.

Automatic Looms and ILO Emblem A54

1969, Mar. 15 Engr. *Perf. 13*
193 A54 30fr brt grn, mar & ind .25 .15

ILO, 50th anniversary.

Smith — A55

1969, Apr. 3 Engr. *Perf. 13*
Size: 36x22mm
194 A55 5fr magenta & blk .15 .15

See No. C64.

Blood Donor — A56

1969, May 15 Engr. *Perf. 13*
195 A56 30fr blk, bl & car .25 .16

League of Red Cross Societies, 50th anniv.

Nile Pike — A57

Fish: 20fr, Nannocharax gobioides. 25fr, Hemigrammocharax polli. 55fr, Alestes luteus. 85fr, Micralestes voltae.

1969 Engr. *Perf. 13*
Size: 36x22mm
196 A57 20fr brt bl, brn & yel .32 .20
197 A57 25fr slate, brn & dk brn .32 .20
198 A57 30fr dk olive & blk .45 .25
199 A57 55fr dk grn, yel & ol .60 .42
200 A57 85fr slate brn & pink 1.25 .90
Nos. 196-200,C66-C67 (7) 5.24 3.01

Development Bank Issue
Common Design Type

1969, Sept. 10 Engr. *Perf. 13*
201 CD130 30fr sl grn, grn & ocher .22 .15

Millet — A58

Design: 30fr, Cotton.

1969, Oct. 30 Photo. *Perf. 12½x13*
202 A58 15fr dk brn, grn & yel .16 .15
203 A58 30fr dp claret & brt bl .30 .16

See Nos. C73-C74.

ASECNA Issue
Common Design Type

1969, Dec. 12 Engr. *Perf. 13*
204 CD132 100fr brown .80 .50

Niadale Mask — A59

Carvings from National Museum: 30fr, Niaga. 45fr, Man and woman, Iliu Bara. 80fr, Karan Weeba figurine.

1970, Mar. 5 Engr. *Perf. 13*
207 A59 10fr dk car rose, org & dk brn .15 .15
209 A59 30fr dk brn, brt vio & grnsh bl .22 .15
211 A59 45fr yel grn, brn & bl .32 .15
212 A59 80fr pur, rose lil & brn .60 .25
Nos. 207-212 (4) 1.29
Set value .55

African Huts and European City — A60

1970, Apr. 25 Engr. *Perf. 13*
213 A60 30fr dk brn, red & bl .25 .15

Issued for Linked Cities' Day.

Mask for Nebwa Gnomo Dance — A61

Designs: 8fr, Cauris dancers, vert. 20fr, Gourmantchés dancers, vert. 30fr, Larlé dancers.

1970, May 7 Photo. *Perf. 13*
214 A61 5fr lt brn, vio bl & blk .15 .15
215 A61 8fr org brn, car & blk .15 .15
216 A61 20fr dk brn, sl grn & ocher .16 .15
217 A61 30fr dp car, dk gray & brn .25 .15
Set value .58 .36

Education Year Emblem, Open Book and Pupils — A62

Design: 90fr, Education Year emblem, telecommunication and education symbols.

1970, May 14 *Perf. 12½x12*
218 A62 40fr black & multi .35 .20
219 A62 90fr olive & multi .65 .35

International Education Year.

UPU Headquarters Issue

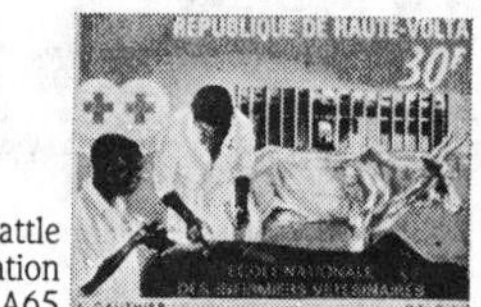

Abraham Lincoln, UPU Headquarters and Emblem — A63

1970, May 20 Engr. *Perf. 13*
220 A63 30fr dk car rose, ind & red brn .30 .16
221 A63 60fr dk bl grn, vio & red brn .50 .25

See note after CD133, Common Design section.

Ship-building Industry A64

Designs: 45fr, Chemical industry. 80fr, Electrical industry.

1970, June 15
222 A64 15fr brt pink, red brn & blk .15 .15
223 A64 45fr emerald, dp bl & blk .35 .20
224 A64 80fr red brn, claret & blk .65 .35
Nos. 222-224 (3) 1.15 .70

Hanover Fair.

Cattle Vaccination A65

1970, June 30 Photo. *Perf. 13*
225 A65 30fr Prus bl, yel & sep .30 .15

National Veterinary College.

Vaccination and Red Cross — A66

1970, Aug. 28 Engr. *Perf. 12½x13*
226 A66 30fr choc & car .25 .16

Issued for the Upper Volta Red Cross. For surcharge see No. 252.

Europafrica Issue

Nurse with Child, by Frans Hals — A67

Paintings: 30fr, Courtyard of a House in Delft, by Pieter de Hooch. 150fr, Christina of Denmark, by Hans Holbein. 250fr, Courtyard of the Royal Palace at Innsbruck, Austria, by Albrecht Dürer.

1970, Sept. 25 Litho. *Perf. 13x14*

227 A67	25fr multicolored	.22	.15
228 A67	30fr multicolored	.30	.16
229 A67	150fr multicolored	1.40	.65
230 A67	250fr multicolored	2.00	1.00
	Nos. 227-230 (4)	3.92	1.96

Citroen — A68

Design: 40fr, Old and new Citroen cars.

1970, Oct. 16 Engr. *Perf. 13*

231 A68	25fr ol brn, mar & sl grn	.22	.15
232 A68	40fr brt grn, plum & sl	.40	.20

57th Paris Automobile Salon.

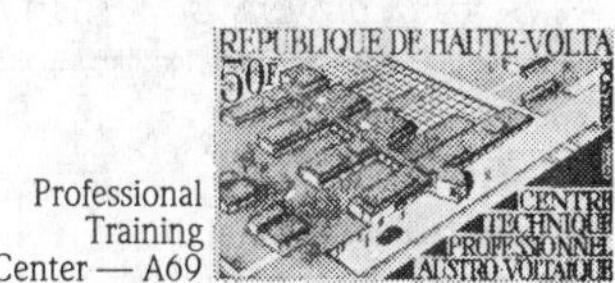

Professional Training Center — A69

1970, Dec. 10 Engr. *Perf. 13*

233 A69	50fr grn, bis & brn	.38	.16

Opening of Professional Training Center under joint sponsorship of Austria and Upper Volta.

Upper Volta Arms and Soaring Bird — A70

1970, Dec. 10 Photo.

234 A70	30fr lt blue & multi	.22	.15

Tenth anniversary of independence, Dec. 11.

Political Maps of Africa — A71

1970, Dec. 14 Litho. *Perf. 13½*

235 A71	50fr multicolored	.40	.20

10th anniv. of the declaration granting independence to colonial territories and countries.

Beingolo Hunting Horn — A72

Musical Instruments: 15fr, Mossi guitar, vert. 20fr, Gourounsi flutes, vert. 25fr, Lunga drums.

1971, Mar. 1 Engr. *Perf. 13*

236 A72	5fr blue, brn & car	.15	.15
237 A72	15fr green, crim rose & brn	.15	.15
238 A72	20fr car rose, bl & gray	.16	.15
239 A72	25fr brt grn, red brn & ol gray	.20	.15
	Nos. 236-239 (4)	.66	
	Set value		.37

Voltaphilex I, National Phil. Exhibition.

Four Races — A73

1971, Mar. 21 Engr. *Perf. 13*

240 A73	50fr rose cl, lt grn & dk brn	.40	.22

Intl. year against racial discrimination.

Telephone and Globes — A74

1971, May 17 Engr. *Perf. 13*

241 A74	50fr brn, gray & dk pur	.40	.20

3rd World Telecommunications Day.

Cane Field Worker, Banfora Sugar Mill — A75

Cotton and Voltex Mill Emblem — A76

1971, June 24 Photo. *Perf. 13*

242 A75	10fr multicolored	.15	.15
243 A76	35fr multicolored	.25	.15
	Set value		.19

Industrial development.

Gonimbrasia Hecate A77

Butterflies and Moths: 2fr, Hamanumida daedalus. 3fr, Ophideres materna. 5fr, Danaus chrysippus. 40fr, Hypolimnas misippus. 45fr, Danaus petiverana.

1971, June 30

244 A77	1fr blue & multi	.15	.15
245 A77	2fr lt lilac & multi	.15	.15
246 A77	3fr multicolored	.15	.15
247 A77	5fr gray & multi	.15	.15
248 A77	40fr ocher & multi	.60	.35
249 A77	45fr multicolored	.80	.50
	Set value	1.65	1.10

Kabuki Actor — A78

Design: 40fr, African mask and Kabuki actor.

1971, Aug. 12 Photo. *Perf. 13*

250 A78	25fr multicolored	.20	.15
251 A78	40fr multicolored	.30	.15
	Set value		.24

Philatokyo 71, Philatelic Exposition, Tokyo, Apr. 19-29.

100F

No. 226 Surcharged

1971 Engr. *Perf. 12½x13*

252 A66	100fr on 30fr choc & car	.65	.40

10th anniversary of Upper Volta Red Cross.

Seed Preparation A79

Designs: 75fr, Old farmer with seed packet, vert. 100fr, Farmer in rice field.

1971, Sept. 30 Photo. *Perf. 13*

253 A79	35fr ocher & multi	.22	.15
254 A79	75fr lt blue & multi	.50	.20
255 A79	100fr brown & multi	.65	.35
	Nos. 253-255 (3)	1.37	.70

National campaign for seed protection.

Outdoor Classroom A80

Design: 50fr, Mother learning to read.

1971, Oct. 14

256 A80	35fr multicolored	.22	.15
257 A80	50fr multicolored	.38	.16

Women's education.

Joseph Dakiri, Soldiers Driving Tractors — A81

Children and UNICEF Emblem — A84

Spraying Lake, Fly, Man Leading Blind Women A82

Design: 40fr, Dakiri and soldiers gathering harvest.

1971, Oct. 13 *Perf. 12x12½*

258 A81	15fr blk, yel & red brn	.15	.15
259 A81	40fr blue & multi	.25	.16

Joseph Dakiri (1938-1971), inaugurator of the Army-Aid-to-Agriculture Program.

1971, Nov. 26 Photo. *Perf. 13*

260 A82	40fr dk brn, yel & bl	.25	.16

Drive against onchocerciasis, roundworm infestation.

For surcharge see No. 295.

1971, Dec. 11 *Perf. 13*

262 A84	45fr red, bis & blk	.35	.16

UNICEF, 25th anniv.

Peulh House — A85

Upper Volta Houses: 20fr, Gourounsi house. 35fr, Mossi houses. 45fr, Bobo house, vert. 50fr, Dagari house, vert. 90fr, Bango house, interior.

Perf. 13x13½, 13½x13

1971-72 Photo.

263 A85	10fr ver & multi	.15	.15
264 A85	20fr multicolored	.16	.15
265 A85	35fr brt grn & multi	.22	.15
266 A85	45fr multi ('72)	.35	.16
267 A85	50fr multi ('72)	.40	.20
268 A85	90fr multi ('72)	.60	.35
	Nos. 263-268 (6)	1.88	1.16

Town Halls of Bobo-Dioulasso and Chalons-sur-Marne — A86

1971, Dec. 23 *Perf. 13x12½*

269 A86	40fr yellow & multi	.25	.15

Kinship between the cities of Bobo-Dioulasso, Upper Volta, and Chalons-sur-Marne, France.

Louis Armstrong — A87

1972, May 17 *Perf. 14x13*

270 A87	45fr multicolored	.45	.25

Black musician. See No. C104.

Red Crescent, Cross and Lion Emblems A88

1972, June 23 *Perf. 13x14*

271 A88	40fr yellow & multi	.35	.16

World Red Cross Day. See No. C105.

Coiffure of Peulh Woman — A89

Designs: Various hair styles.

1972, July 23 Litho. *Perf. 13*

272 A89	25fr blue & multi	.20	.15
273 A89	35fr emerald & multi	.22	.15
274 A89	75fr yellow & multi	.45	.18
	Nos. 272-274 (3)	.87	
	Set value		.38

Classroom A90

Designs: 15fr, Clinic. 20fr, Factory. 35fr, Cattle. 40fr, Plowers. 85fr, Road building machinery.

1972, Oct. 30 Engr. *Perf. 13*

275 A90	10fr sl grn, lt grn & choc	.15	.15
276 A90	15fr brt grn, brn org & brn	.15	.15
277 A90	20fr bl, lt brn & grn	.15	.15

278 A90 35fr grn, brn & brt bl .18 .15
279 A90 40fr choc, pink & sl grn .22 .16
Nos. 275-279,C106 (6) 1.30
Set value .75

2nd Five-Year Plan.

West African Monetary Union Issue
Common Design Type

1972, Nov. 2
280 CD136 40fr brn, bl & gray .25 .15

Lottery Office and Emblem — A91

1972, Nov. 6 **Litho.**
281 A91 35fr multicolored .22 .15

5th anniversary of National Lottery.

Domestic Animals — A92

1972, Dec. 4 Litho. ***Perf. 13½x12½***
282 A92 5fr Donkeys .15 .15
283 A92 10fr Geese .15 .15
284 A92 30fr Goats .20 .15
285 A92 50fr Cow .35 .15
286 A92 65fr Dromedaries .42 .20
Nos. 282-286 (5) 1.27
Set value .52

Mossi Woman's Hair Style, and Village — A93

1973, Jan. 24 **Engr.** ***Perf. 13***
287 A93 5fr slate grn, org & choc .15 .15
288 A93 40fr bl, org & chocolate .22 .15
Set value .27 .19

Eugene A. Cernan and Lunar Module A94

Designs: 65fr, Ronald E. Evans and splashdown. 100fr, Capsule, in orbit and interior, horiz. 150fr, Harrison H. Schmitt and lift-off. 200fr, Conference and moon-buggy. 500fr, Moon-buggy and capsule, horiz.

Perf. 12½x13½, 13½x12½

1973, Mar. 29 **Litho.**
289 A94 50fr multi .32 .16
290 A94 65fr multi .38 .18
291 A94 100fr multi .60 .30
292 A94 150fr multi .90 .45
293 A94 200fr multi 1.25 .60
Nos. 289-293 (5) 3.45 1.69

Souvenir Sheet

294 A94 500fr multi 3.50 1.60

Apollo 17 moon mission.

No. 260 Surcharged in Red

O. M. S.
25e Anniversaire
45F

1973, Apr. 7 **Photo.** ***Perf. 13***
295 A82 45fr on 40fr multi .25 .16

WHO, 25th anniversary.

Scout Bugler — A95

1973, July 18 **Litho.** ***Perf. 12½x13***
296 A95 20fr multicolored .15 .15
Nos. 296,C160-C163 (5) 3.30 1.70

African Postal Union Issue
Common Design Type

1973, Sept. 12 **Engr.** ***Perf. 13***
297 CD137 100fr brt red, mag & dl yel .65 .25

Pres. Kennedy, Saturn 5 on Assembly Trailer — A96

Pres. John F. Kennedy (1917-1963) and: 10fr, Atlas rocket carrying John H. Glenn. 30fr, Titan 2 rocket and Gemini 3 capsule.

1973, Sept. 12 **Litho.** ***Perf. 12½x13***
298 A96 5fr multicolored .15 .15
299 A96 10fr multicolored .15 .15
300 A96 30fr multicolored .20 .15
Nos. 298-300,C167-C168 (5) 3.90 2.10

Cross-examination — A97

Designs: 65fr, "Diamond Ede." 70fr, Forensic Institute. 150fr, Robbery scene.

1973, Sept. 15 ***Perf. 13x12½***
301 A97 50fr multicolored .32 .16
302 A97 65fr multicolored .38 .18
303 A97 70fr multicolored .40 .20
304 A97 150fr multicolored .90 .45
Nos. 301-304 (4) 2.00 .99

Interpol, 50th anniversary. See No. C170.

Market Place, Ouagadougou — A98

Design: 40fr, Swimming pool, Hotel Independence.

1973, Sept. 30
305 A98 35fr multicolored .22 .15
306 A98 40fr multicolored .25 .15

Tourism. See Nos. C171-C172.

Protestant Church — A99

Design: 40fr, Ouahigouya Mosque.

1973, Sept. 28 ***Perf. 13x12½***
307 A99 35fr multicolored .22 .15
308 A99 40fr multicolored .25 .15

Houses of worship. See No. C173.

Kiembara Dancers A100

Design: 40fr, Dancers.

1973, Nov. 30 **Litho.** ***Perf. 12½x13***
309 A100 35fr multicolored .22 .15
310 A100 40fr multicolored .25 .15

Folklore. See Nos. C174-C175.

Yuri Gagarin and Aries — A101

Famous Men and their Zodiac Signs: 10fr, Lenin and Taurus. 20fr, John F. Kennedy, rocket and Gemini. 25fr, John H. Glenn, orbiting capsule and Cancer. 30fr, Napoleon and Leo. 50fr, Goethe and Virgo. 60fr, Pelé and Libra. 75fr, Charles de Gaulle and Scorpio. 100fr, Beethoven and Sagittarius. 175fr, Conrad Adenauer and Capricorn. 200fr, Edwin E. Aldrin, Jr. (Apollo XI) and Aquarius. 250fr, Lord Baden-Powell and Pisces.

1973, Dec. 15 **Litho.** ***Perf. 13x14***
311 A101 5fr multicolored .15 .15
312 A101 10fr multicolored .15 .15
313 A101 20fr multicolored .15 .15
314 A101 25fr multicolored .15 .15
315 A101 30fr multicolored .16 .15
316 A101 50fr multicolored .30 .15
317 A101 60fr multicolored .38 .18
318 A101 75fr multicolored .42 .20
319 A101 100fr multicolored .60 .30
320 A101 175fr multicolored 1.10 .55
321 A101 200fr multicolored 1.20 .55
322 A101 250fr multicolored 1.50 .70
Nos. 311-322 (12) 6.26 3.38

See Nos. C176-C178.

Rivera with Italian Flag and Championship '74 Emblem — A102

Design: 40fr, World Cup, soccer ball, World Championship '74 emblem and Pelé with Brazilian flag.

1974, Jan. 15 ***Perf. 13x12½***
323 A102 5fr multicolored .15 .15
324 A102 40fr multicolored .25 .15
Nos. 323-324,C179-C181 (5) 3.15 1.70

10th World Cup Soccer Championship, Munich, June 13-July 7.

Charles de Gaulle A103

Designs: 40fr, De Gaulle memorial. 60fr, Pres. Charles de Gaulle.

1974, Feb. 4 **Litho.** ***Perf. 12½x13***
325 A103 35fr multicolored .20 .15
326 A103 40fr multicolored .20 .15
327 A103 60fr multicolored .35 .16
Nos. 325-327,C183 (4) 2.75 1.46

Gen. Charles de Gaulle (1890-1970), president of France. #325-327 printed se-tenant. See #C184.

N'Dongo and Cameroun Flag — A104

World Cup, Emblems and: 20fr, Kolev and Bulgarian flag. 50fr, Keita and Mali flag.

1974, Mar. 19
328 A104 10fr multicolored .15 .15
329 A104 20fr multicolored .15 .15
330 A104 50fr multicolored .35 .16
Nos. 328-330,C185-C186 (5) 2.90 1.59

10th World Cup Soccer Championship, Munich, June 13-July 7.

Map and Flags of Members A105

1974, May 29 **Photo.** ***Perf. 13x12½***
331 A105 40fr blue & multi .22 .15

15th anniversary of the Council of Accord.

UPU Emblem and Mail Coach — A106

UPU emblem and: 40fr, Steamship. 85fr, Mailman.

1974, July 23 Litho. *Perf. 13½*

332 A106 35fr multicolored .22 .15
333 A106 40fr multicolored .25 .15
334 A106 85fr multicolored .55 .28
Nos. 332-334,C189-C191 (6) 4.02 2.08

Universal Postal Union centenary.
For overprints see #339-341, C197-C200.

Soccer Game, Winner Italy, in France, 1938 — A107

World Cup, Game and Flags: 25fr, Uruguay, in Brazil, 1950. 50fr, East Germany, in Switzerland, 1954.

1974, Sept. 2 Litho. *Perf. 13½*

335 A107 10fr multicolored .15 .15
336 A107 25fr multicolored .16 .15
337 A107 50fr multicolored .35 .16
Nos. 335-337,C193-C195 (6) 4.66 2.41

World Cup Soccer winners.

Map and Farm Woman — A108

1974, Oct. 2 Litho. *Perf. 13x12½*

338 A108 35fr yellow & multi .20 .15

Kou Valley Development.

Nos. 332-334 Overprinted in Red "100e ANNIVERSAIRE DE L'UNION POSTALE UNIVERSELLE / 9 OCTOBRE 1974"

1974, Oct. 9

339 A106 35fr multicolored .22 .15
340 A106 40fr multicolored .25 .15
341 A106 85fr multicolored .55 .28
Nos. 339-341,C197-C199 (6) 5.07 2.58

Universal Postal Union centenary.

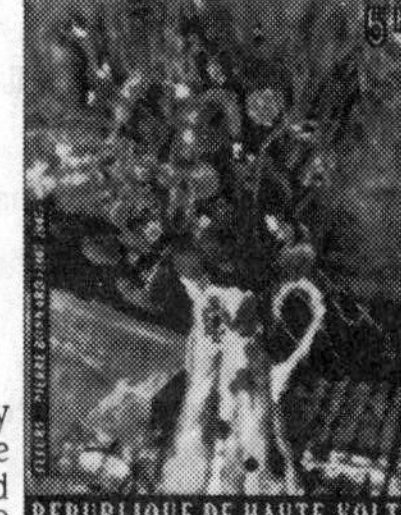

Flowers, by Pierre Bonnard A109

Flower Paintings by: 10fr, Jan Brueghel. 30fr, Jean van Os. 50fr, Van Brussel.

1974, Oct. 31 Litho. *Perf. 12½x13*

342 A109 5fr multicolored .15 .15
343 A109 10fr multicolored .15 .15
344 A109 30fr multicolored .16 .15
345 A109 50fr multicolored .25 .15
Nos. 342-345,C201 (5) 2.71
Set value 1.30

Churchill as Officer of India Hussars — A110

Churchill: 75fr, As Secretary of State for Interior. 100fr, As pilot. 125fr, meeting with Roosevelt, 1941. 300fr, As painter. 450fr, and "HMS Resolution."

1975, Jan. 11 *Perf. 13½*

346 A110 50fr multicolored .30 .15
347 A110 75fr multicolored .42 .20
348 A110 100fr multicolored .55 .28
349 A110 125fr multicolored .70 .38
350 A110 300fr multicolored 1.60 .80
Nos. 346-350 (5) 3.57 1.81

Souvenir Sheet

351 A110 450fr multicolored 2.50 1.25

Sir Winston Churchill, birth centenary.

US No. 619 and Minutemen — A111

US Stamps: 40fr, #118 and Proclamation of Independence. 75fr, #798 and Signing the Constitution. 100fr, #703 and Surrender at Yorktown. 200fr, #1003 and George Washington. 300fr, #644 and Surrender of Burgoyne at Saratoga. 500fr, #63, 68, 73, 157, 179, 228 and 1483a.

1975, Feb. 17 Litho. *Perf. 11*

352 A111 35fr multicolored .20 .15
353 A111 40fr multicolored .22 .15
354 A111 75fr multicolored .42 .20
355 A111 100fr multicolored .55 .28
356 A111 200fr multicolored 1.20 .55
357 A111 300fr multicolored 1.60 .80
Nos. 352-357 (6) 4.19 2.13

Souvenir Sheet

Imperf

358 A111 500fr multicolored 3.00 1.50

American Bicentennial.

"Atlantic" No. 2670, 1904-12 — A112

Locomotives from Mulhouse, France, Railroad Museum: 25fr, No. 2029, 1882. 50fr, No. 2129, 1882.

1975, Feb. 28 Litho. *Perf. 13x12½*

359 A112 15fr multicolored .15 .15
360 A112 25fr multicolored .16 .15
361 A112 50fr multicolored .35 .16
Nos. 359-361,C203-C204 (5) 2.71 1.46

French Flag and Renault Petit Duc, 1910 — A113

Flags and Old Cars: 30fr, US and Ford Model T, 1909. 35fr, Italy and Alfa Romeo "Le Mans," 1931.

1975, Apr. 6 *Perf. 14x13½*

362 A113 10fr multicolored .15 .15
363 A113 30fr multicolored .20 .15
364 A113 35fr multicolored .22 .15
Nos. 362-364,C206-C207 (5) 2.97 1.60

Washington and Lafayette — A114

American Bicentennial: 40fr, Washington reviewing troops at Valley Forge. 50fr, Washington taking oath of office.

1975, May 6 Litho. *Perf. 14*

365 A114 30fr multicolored .20 .15
366 A114 40fr multicolored .25 .15
367 A114 50fr multicolored .35 .16
Nos. 365-367,C209-C210 (5) 4.20 2.11

Souvenir Sheet

367A A114 500fr multicolored 3.50 1.60

Schweitzer and Pelicans — A115

Design: 15fr, Albert Schweitzer and bateleur eagle.

1975, May 25 Litho. *Perf. 13½*

368 A115 5fr multicolored .15 .15
369 A115 15fr multicolored .15 .15
Nos. 368-369,C212-C214 (5) 3.90 2.00

Albert Schweitzer, birth centenary.

Apollo and Soyuz Orbiting Earth — A116

Design: 50fr, Apollo and Soyuz near link-up.

1975, July 18

370 A116 40fr multicolored .25 .15
371 A116 50fr multicolored .35 .16
Nos. 370-371,C216-C218 (5) 4.65 2.31

Apollo-Soyuz space test project, Russo-American cooperation, launched July 15, link-up July 17.

Maria Picasso Lopez, Artist's Mother A117

Paintings by Pablo Picasso (1881-1973): 60fr, Self-portrait. 90fr, First Communion.

1975, Aug. 7

372 A117 50fr multicolored .35 .16
373 A117 60fr multicolored .40 .20
374 A117 90fr multicolored .60 .30
Nos. 372-374,C220-C221 (5) 4.60 2.36

Expo '75 Emblem and Tanker, Idemitsu Maru — A118

Oceanographic Exposition, Okinawa: 25fr, Training ship, Kaio Maru. 45fr, Firefighting ship, Hiryu. 50fr, Battleship, Yamato. 60fr, Container ship, Kamakura Maru.

1975, Sept. 26 Litho. *Perf. 11*

375 A118 15fr multicolored .15 .15
376 A118 25fr multicolored .16 .15
377 A118 45fr multicolored .30 .15
377A A118 50fr multicolored .35 .16
378 A118 60fr multicolored .40 .20
Nos. 375-378,C223 (6) 2.11 1.19

Woman, Globe and IWY Emblem — A119

1975, Nov. 20 Photo. *Perf. 13*

379 A119 65fr multicolored .38 .22

International Women's Year.

Msgr. Joanny Thevenoud and Cathedral — A120

Design: 65fr, Father Guillaume Templier and Cathedral.

1975, Nov. 20 Engr. *Perf. 13x12½*

380 A120 55fr grn, blk & dl red .20 .15
381 A120 65fr blk, org & dl red .26 .16

75th anniv. of the Evangelization of Upper Volta.

Farmer's Hat, Hoe and Emblem A121

1975, Dec. 10 Photo. ***Perf. 13x13½***

382 A121 15fr buff & multi .15 .15
383 A121 50fr lt green & multi .18 .15
Set value .24 .16

Development of the Volta valleys.

Sledding and Olympic Emblem — A122

Innsbruck Background, Olympic Emblem and: 45fr, Figure skating. 85fr, Skiing.

1975, Dec. 16 Litho. ***Perf. 13½***

384 A122 35fr multicolored .18 .15
385 A122 45fr multicolored .22 .15
386 A122 85fr multicolored .45 .22
Nos. 384-386,C225-C226 (5) 2.90 1.52

12th Winter Olympic Games, Innsbruck, Austria, Feb. 4-15, 1976.

Gymnast and Olympic Emblem — A123

Olympic Emblem and: 50fr, Sailing. 100fr, Soccer.

1976, Mar. 17

387 A123 40fr multicolored .20 .15
388 A123 50fr multicolored .25 .15
389 A123 100fr multicolored .55 .28
Nos. 387-389,C228-C229 (5) 2.40 1.26

21st Olympic Games, Montreal, Canada, July 17-Aug. 1.

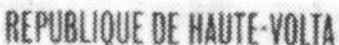

Olympic Emblem and Sprinters A124

Olympic Emblem and: 55fr, Equestrian. 75fr, Hurdles.

1976, Mar. 25 Litho. ***Perf. 11***

390 A124 30fr multicolored .16 .15
391 A124 55fr multicolored .30 .15
392 A124 75fr multicolored .42 .20
Nos. 390-392,C231-C232 (5) 2.63 1.38

21st Olympic Games, Montreal.
For overprints see #420-422, C245-C247.

Blind Woman and Man — A125

1976, Apr. 7 Engr. ***Perf. 13***

393 A125 75fr dk brn, grn & org .40 .25
394 A125 250fr dk brn, ocher & org 1.40 .80

Drive against onchocerciasis, roundworm infestation.

"Deutschland" over Friedrichshafen — A126

Airships: 40fr, "Victoria Louise" over sailing ships. 50fr, "Sachsen" over German countryside.

1976, May 11 Litho. ***Perf. 11***

395 A126 10fr multicolored .70 .15
396 A126 40fr multicolored .25 .15
397 A126 50fr multicolored .35 .16
Nos. 395-397,C234-C236 (6) 5.35 2.46

75th anniversary of the Zeppelin.

Viking Lander and Probe on Mars — A127

Viking Mars project: 55fr, Viking orbiter in flight. 75fr, Titan rocket start for Mars, vert.

1976, June 24 ***Perf. 13½***

398 A127 30fr multicolored .15 .15
399 A127 55fr multicolored .22 .15
400 A127 75fr multicolored .32 .16
Nos. 398-400,C238-C239 (5) 3.19 1.71

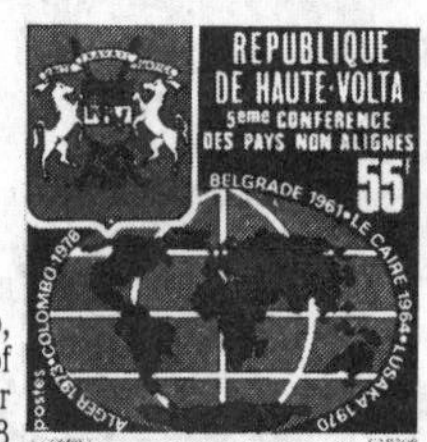

World Map, Arms of Upper Volta — A128

Design: 100fr, World map, arms and dove.

1976, Aug. 19 Litho. ***Perf. 12½***

401 A128 55fr brown & multi .22 .16
402 A128 100fr blue & multi .42 .30

5th Summit Conference of Non-aligned Countries, Colombo, Sri Lanka, Aug. 9-19.

Bicentennial, Interphil 76 Emblems and Washington at Battle of Trenton — A129

Design: 90fr, Bicentennial, Interphil 76 emblems and Seat of Government, Pennsylvania.

1976, Sept. 30 ***Perf. 13½***

403 A129 60fr multicolored .40 .16
404 A129 90fr multicolored .55 .22
Nos. 403-404,C241-C243 (5) 5.00 2.38

American Bicentennial, Interphil 76, Philadelphia, Pa., May 29-June 6.

UPU and UN Emblems — A130

1976, Dec. 8 Engr. ***Perf. 13***

405 A130 200fr red, ol & bl 1.00 .60

UN Postal Administration, 25th anniv.

Arms of Tenkodogo A131

Bronze Statuette A132

Coats of Arms: 20fr, 100fr, Ouagadougou.

1977, May 2 Litho. ***Perf. 13***

406 A131 10fr multicolored .15 .15
407 A131 20fr multicolored .15 .15
408 A131 65fr multicolored .35 .25
409 A131 100fr multicolored .55 .40
Nos. 406-409 (4) 1.20
Set value .78

1977, June 13 Photo. ***Perf. 13***

Design: 65fr, Woman with bowl, bronze.

410 A132 55fr multicolored .30 .20
411 A132 65fr multicolored .35 .20

#410-411 issued in sheets and coils with black control number on every 5th stamp.

Granaries — A133

Handbags — A134

1977, June 20 Photo. ***Perf. 13½x13***

412 A133 5fr Samo .15 .15
413 A133 35fr Boromo .20 .15
414 A133 45fr Banfora .22 .15
415 A133 55fr Mossi .30 .20
Nos. 412-415 (4) .87
Set value .50

1977, June 20

416 A134 30fr Gouin .16 .15
417 A134 40fr Bissa .20 .15
418 A134 60fr Lobi .35 .20
419 A134 70fr Mossi .38 .22
Nos. 416-419 (4) 1.09 .72

Nos. 390-392 Overprinted in Gold:
a. VAINQUEUR 1976 / LASSE VIREN / FINLANDE
b. VAINQUEUR 1976 / ALWIN SCHOCKEMOHLE / R.F.A.
c. VAINQUEUR 1976 / JOHANNA SCHALLER / R.D.A.

1977, July 4 Litho. ***Perf. 11***

420 A124 (a) 30fr multicolored .16 .15
421 A124 (b) 55fr multicolored .30 .15
422 A124 (c) 75fr multicolored .40 .20
Nos. 420-422,C245-C246 (5) 3.26 1.65

Winners, 21st Olympic Games.

Crinum Ornatum — A135

Haemanthus Multiflorus — A136

Hannoa Undulata — A137

Designs: Flowers, flowering branches and wild fruits. 175fr, 300fr, horiz.

1977 Litho. ***Perf. 12½***

423 A137 2fr Cordia myxa .15 .15
424 A137 3fr Opilia celtidifolia .15 .15
425 A135 15fr shown .15 .15
426 A136 25fr shown .15 .15
427 A137 50fr shown .25 .20
428 A135 90fr Cochlospermum planchonii .45 .35
429 A135 125fr Clitoria ternatea .65 .50
430 A136 150fr Cassia alata .80 .60
431 A136 175fr Nauclea latifolia .90 .65
432 A136 300fr Bombax costatum 1.60 1.20
433 A135 400fr Eulophia cucullata 2.00 1.60
Nos. 423-433 (11) 7.25 5.70

Issued: 25fr, 150fr, 175fr, 300fr, Aug. 1; 2fr, 3fr, 50fr, Aug. 8; 15fr, 90fr, 125fr, 400fr, Aug. 23.

De Gaulle and Cross of Lorraine A138

Designs: 200fr, King Baudouin of Belgium.

1977, Aug. 16 ***Perf. 13½x14***

434 A138 100fr multicolored .55 .22
435 A138 200fr multicolored 1.10 .42

Elizabeth II A139

Designs: 300fr, Elizabeth II taking salute. 500fr, Elizabeth II after Coronation.

1977, Aug. 16

436 A139 200fr multicolored .80 .32
437 A139 300fr multicolored 1.20 .50

Souvenir Sheet

438 A139 500fr multicolored 2.00 .90

25th anniv. of reign of Queen Elizabeth II.
For overprints see Nos. 478-480.

Lottery Tickets, Cars and Map of Upper Volta in Flag Colors — A140

1977, Sept. 16 Photo. *Perf. 13*

439 A140 55fr multicolored .30 .22

10th anniversary of National Lottery.

Selma Lagerlof, Literature — A141

Nobel Prize Winners: 65fr, Guglielmo Marconi, physics. 125fr, Bertrand Russell, literature. 200fr, Linus C. Pauling, chemistry. 300fr, Robert Koch, medicine. 500fr, Albert Schweitzer, peace.

1977, Sept. 22 Litho. *Perf. 13½*

440 A141 55fr multicolored .30 .15
441 A141 65fr multicolored .38 .16
442 A141 125fr multicolored .65 .25
443 A141 200fr multicolored 1.10 .42
444 A141 300fr multicolored 1.60 .65
Nos. 440-444 (5) 4.03 1.63

Souvenir Sheet

445 A141 500fr multicolored 2.50 1.20

The Three Graces, by Rubens A142

Paintings by Peter Paul Rubens (1577-1640): 55fr, Heads of Black Men, horiz. 85fr, Bathsheba at the Fountain. 150fr, The Drunken Silenus. 200fr, 300fr, Life of Maria de Medicis, diff.

1977, Oct. 19 Litho. *Perf. 14*

446 A142 55fr multicolored .30 .15
447 A142 65fr multicolored .38 .16
448 A142 85fr multicolored .45 .22
449 A142 150fr multicolored .80 .40
450 A142 200fr multicolored 1.10 .45
451 A142 300fr multicolored 1.60 .60
Nos. 446-451 (6) 4.63 1.98

Lenin in His Office A143

Designs: 85fr, Lenin Monument, Kremlin. 200fr, Lenin with youth. 500fr, Lenin and Leonid Brezhnev.

1977, Oct. 28 Litho. *Perf. 12*

452 A143 10fr multicolored .15 .15
453 A143 85fr multicolored .45 .25
454 A143 200fr multicolored 1.10 .65
455 A143 500fr multicolored 2.50 1.60
Nos. 452-455 (4) 4.20 2.65

Russian October Revolution, 60th anniv.

Stadium and Brazil No. C79 — A144

Stadium and: 65fr, Brazil #1144. 125fr, Gt. Britain #458. 200fr, Chile #340. 300fr, Switzerland #350. 500fr, Germany #1147.

1977, Dec. 30 Litho. *Perf. 13½*

456 A144 55fr multicolored .30 .15
457 A144 65fr multicolored .38 .16
458 A144 125fr multicolored .65 .25
459 A144 200fr multicolored 1.10 .42
460 A144 300fr multicolored 1.60 .65
Nos. 456-460 (5) 4.03 1.63

Souvenir Sheet

461 A144 500fr multicolored 2.50 1.20

11th World Cup Soccer Championship, Argentina. For overprints see Nos. 486-491.

Jean Mermoz and Seaplane — A145

History of Aviation: 75fr, Anthony H. G. Fokker. 85fr, Wiley Post. 90fr, Otto Lilienthal, vert. 100fr, Concorde. 500fr, Charles Lindbergh and "Spirit of St. Louis."

1978, Jan. 2 Litho. *Perf. 13½*

462 A145 65fr multicolored .38 .16
463 A145 75fr multicolored .40 .20
464 A145 85fr multicolored .45 .20
465 A145 90fr multicolored .50 .20
466 A145 100fr multicolored .55 .22
Nos. 462-466 (5) 2.28 .98

Souvenir Sheet

467 A145 500fr multicolored 2.50 1.25

Crataeva Religiosa — A146

1978, Feb. 28 Litho. *Perf. 12½*

468 A146 55fr shown .30 .22
469 A146 75fr Fig tree .40 .30

Souvenir Sheet

Virgin and Child, by Rubens A147

1978, May 24 Litho. *Perf. 13½x14*

470 A147 500fr multicolored 2.50 1.20

Peter Paul Rubens (1577-1640).

Antenna and ITU Emblem A148

1978, May 30 *Perf. 13*

471 A148 65fr silver & multi .38 .16

10th World Telecommunications Day.

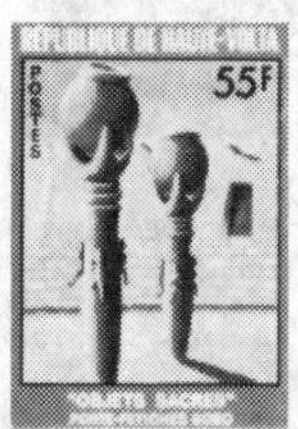

Fetish Gate of Bobo — A149

1978, July 10 Litho. *Perf. 13½*

472 A149 55fr shown .30 .15
473 A149 65fr Mossi fetish .38 .16

Capt. Cook and "Endeavour" — A150

Capt. James Cook (1728-1779) and: 85fr, Death on Hawaiian beach. 250fr, Navigational instruments. 350fr, "Resolution."

1978, Sept. 1 Litho. *Perf. 14½*

474 A150 65fr multicolored .38 .16
475 A150 85fr multicolored .45 .20
476 A150 250fr multicolored 1.40 .65
477 A150 350fr multicolored 1.90 .80
Nos. 474-477 (4) 4.13 1.81

Nos. 436-438 Overprinted Vertically in Silver: "ANNIVERSAIRE DU COURONNEMENT 1953-1978"

1978, Oct. 24 Litho. *Perf. 13½x14*

478 A139 200fr multicolored 1.10 .42
479 A139 300fr multicolored 1.60 .65

Souvenir Sheet

480 A139 500fr multicolored 2.50 1.20

25th anniversary of Coronation of Queen Elizabeth II. Overprint in 3 lines on 200fr, in 2 lines on 300fr and 500fr.

#478-480 exist with overprint in metallic red.

Trent Castle, by Dürer A151

Paintings by Albrecht Durer (1471-1528): 150fr, Virgin and Child with St. Anne, vert. 250fr, Sts. George and Eustachius, vert. 350fr, Hans Holzschuher, vert.

Perf. 14x13½, 13½x14

1978, Nov. 20 Litho.

481 A151 65fr multicolored .38 .16
482 A151 150fr multicolored .80 .38
483 A151 250fr multicolored 1.40 .65
484 A151 350fr multicolored 1.90 .65
Nos. 481-484 (4) 4.48 1.84

Human Rights Emblem A152

1978, Dec. 10 Litho. *Perf. 12½*

485 A152 55fr multicolored .30 .15

Universal Declaration of Human Rights, 30th anniv.

Nos. 456-461 Overprinted in Silver

a, VAINQUEURS 1950 URUGUAY / 1978 / ARGENTINE
b, VAINQUEURS 1970 BRESIL / 1978 ARGENTINE
c, VAINQUEURS 1966 GRANDE BRETAGNE / 1978 ARGENTINE
d, VAINQUEURS / 1962 BRESIL / 1978 ARGENTINE
e, VAINQUEURS 1954 ALLEMAGNE (RFA) / 1978 ARGENTINE
f, VAINQUEURS 1974 ALLEMAGNE (RFA) / 1978 ARGENTINE

1979, Jan. 4 Litho. *Perf. 13½*

486 A144(a) 55fr multicolored .30 .15
487 A144(b) 65fr multicolored .38 .16
488 A144(c) 125fr multicolored .65 .25
489 A144(d) 200fr multicolored 1.10 .40
490 A144(e) 300fr multicolored 1.60 .65
Nos. 486-490 (5) 4.03 1.61

Souvenir Sheet

491 A144(f) 500fr multicolored 2.50 1.20

Winners, World Soccer Cup Championships 1950-1978.

Radio Station A153

Design: 65fr, Mail plane at airport.

1979, Mar. 30 Litho. *Perf. 12½*

492 A153 55fr multicolored .30 .15
493 A153 65fr multicolored .38 .16

Post and Telecommunications Org., 10th anniv.

Teacher and Pupils, IYC Emblem — A154

1979, Apr. 9 *Perf. 13½*

494 A154 75fr multicolored .40 .20

International Year of the Child.

Telecommunications A155

1979, May 17 Litho. *Perf. 13*

495 A155 70fr multicolored .45 .20

11th Telecommunications Day.

Basketmaker and Upper Volta No. 111 — A156

Design: No. 497, May of Upper Volta, Concorde, truck and UPU emblem.

1979, June 8 Photo.

496 A156 100fr multicolored .65 .35
497 A156 100fr multicolored .65 .35

Philexafrique II, Libreville, Gabon, June 8-17. Nos. 496, 497 each printed in sheets of 10 and 5 labels showing exhibition emblem.

Synodontis Voltae A157

Fresh-water Fish: 50fr, Micralestes comoensis. 85fr, Silurus.

1979, June 10 Litho. *Perf. 12½*

498 A157 20fr multicolored .15 .15
499 A157 50fr multicolored .35 .16
500 A157 85fr multicolored .55 .30
Nos. 498-500 (3) 1.05 .61

Rowland Hill, Train and Upper Volta No. 60 — A158

Sir Rowland Hill (1795-1879), originator of penny postage, Trains and Upper Volta Stamps: 165fr, #59. 200fr, #57. 300fr, #56. 500fr, #55.

1979, June Litho. *Perf. 13½*

501 A158 65fr multicolored .42 .20
502 A158 165fr multicolored 1.10 .55
503 A158 200fr multicolored 1.40 .65
504 A158 300fr multicolored 2.00 1.00
Nos. 501-504 (4) 4.92 2.40

Souvenir Sheet

505 A158 500fr multicolored 3.50 1.60

Wildlife Fund Emblem and Protected Animals — A159

1979, Aug. 30 Litho. *Perf. 14½*

506 A159 30fr Waterbuck .20 .15
507 A159 40fr Roan antelope .25 .15
508 A159 60fr Caracal .40 .20
509 A159 100fr African bush elephant .65 .35
510 A159 175fr Hartebeest 1.20 .55
511 A159 250fr Leopard 1.60 .80
Nos. 506-511 (6) 4.30 2.20

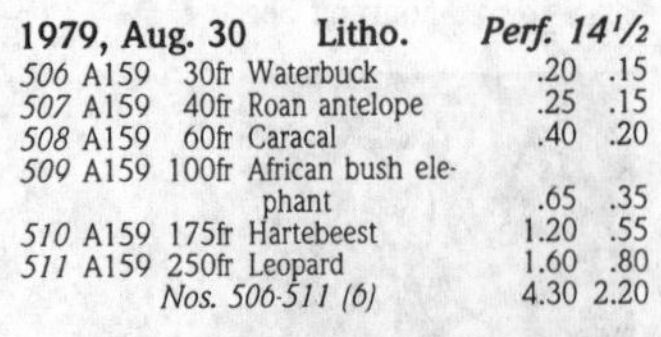
Adult Students and Teacher — A160

Design: 55fr, Man reading book, vert.

Perf. 12½x13, 13x12½

1979, Sept. 8

512 A160 55fr multicolored .38 .18
513 A160 250fr multicolored 1.60 .85

World Literacy Day.

Map of Upper Volta, Telephone Receiver and Lines, Telecom Emblem — A161

1979, Sept. 20 *Perf. 13x12½*

514 A161 200fr multicolored 1.40 .65

3rd World Telecommunications Exhibition, Geneva, Sept. 20-26.

King Vulture — A162

1979, Oct. 26 Litho. *Perf. 13*

515 A162 5fr shown .15 .15
516 A162 10fr Hoopoe .15 .15
517 A162 15fr Bald vulture .15 .15
518 A162 25fr Herons .16 .15
519 A162 35fr Ostrich .22 .15
520 A162 45fr Crowned crane .30 .15
521 A162 125fr Eagle .80 .40
Nos. 515-521 (7) 1.93
Set value .90

Control Tower, Emblem, Jet — A163

1979, Dec. 12 Photo. *Perf. 13x12½*

522 A163 65fr multicolored .42 .20

ASECNA (Air Safety Board), 20th anniv.

Central Bank of West African States — A164

1979, Dec. 28 Litho. *Perf. 12½*

523 A164 55fr multicolored .38 .18

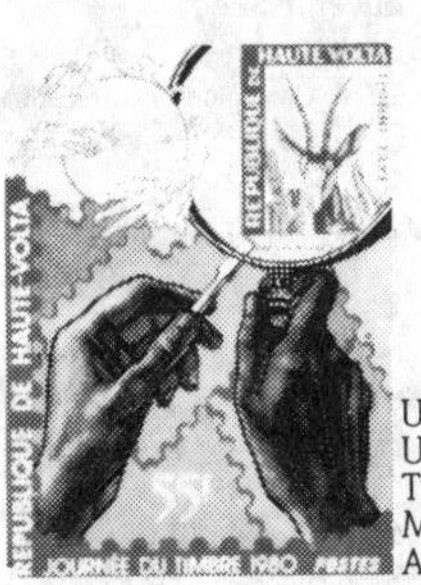
Eugene Jamot, Map of Upper Volta, Tsetse Fly — A165

1979, Dec. 28 *Perf. 13x13½*

524 A165 55fr multicolored .38 .18

Eugene Jamot (1879-1937), discoverer of sleeping sickness cure.

UPU Emblem, Upper Volta Type D4 under Magnifier A166

1980, Feb. 26 Litho. *Perf. 12½x13*

525 A166 55fr multicolored .38 .18

Stamp Day.

World Locomotive Speed Record, 25th Anniversary A167

1980, Mar. 30 Litho. *Perf. 12½*

526 A167 75fr multicolored .50 .25
527 A167 100fr multicolored .65 .35

Pres. Sangoule Lamizana, Pope John Paul II, Cardinal Pau Zoungrana, Map of Upper Volta — A168

1980, May 10 Litho. *Perf. 12½*

528 A168 65fr shown .42 .20

Size: 21x36mm

529 A168 100fr Pope John Paul II .65 .35

Visit of Pope John Paul II to Upper Volta.

A169 A170

1980, May 17 *Perf. 13x12½*

530 A169 50fr multicolored .35 .16

12th World Telecommunications Day.

1980, June 12 Litho. *Perf. 13*

531 A170 65fr Sun and earth .42 .20
532 A170 100fr Solar energy .65 .35

Downhill Skiing, Lake Placid '80 Emblem A171

1980, June 26 *Perf. 14½*

533 A171 65fr shown .35 .16
534 A171 100fr Women's downhill .55 .30
535 A171 200fr Figure skating 1.25 .55
536 A171 350fr Slalom, vert. 1.90 1.00
Nos. 533-536 (4) 4.05 2.01

Souvenir Sheet

537 A171 500fr Speed skating 3.50 1.60

12th Winter Olympic Game Winners, Lake Placid, NY, Feb. 12-24.

Map of Europe and Africa, Jet — A172
Hand Holding Back Sand Dune — A173

Europafrica Issue

1980, July 14 Litho. *Perf. 13*

538 A172 100fr multicolored .65 .35

1980, July 18

Operation Green Sahel: 55fr, Hands holding seedlings.

539 A173 50fr multicolored .35 .16
540 A173 55fr multicolored .38 .20

Gourmantche Chief Initiation — A174

1980, Sept. 12 Litho. *Perf. 14*

541 A174 30fr shown .20 .15
542 A174 55fr Moro Naba, Mossi Emperor .38 .18
543 A174 65fr Princess Guimbe Quattara, vert. .42 .20
Nos. 541-543 (3) 1.00 .53

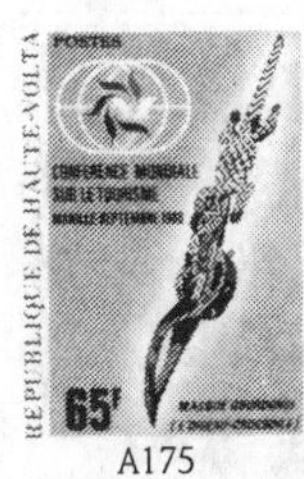

A175 A176

Gourounsi mask, conference emblem.

1980, Oct. 6 *Perf. 13½x13*
544 A175 65fr multicolored .42 .20

World Tourism Conf., Manila, Sept. 27.

1980, Nov. 5 Litho. *Perf. 12½*
545 A176 55fr Agriculture .38 .18
546 A176 65fr Transportation .42 .20
547 A176 75fr Dam, highway .50 .25
548 A176 100fr Industry .65 .35
Nos. 545-548 (4) 1.95 .98

West African Economic Council, 5th anniv.

20th Anniv. of Independence — A177

1980, Dec. 11 *Perf. 13*
549 A177 500fr multicolored 3.50 1.60

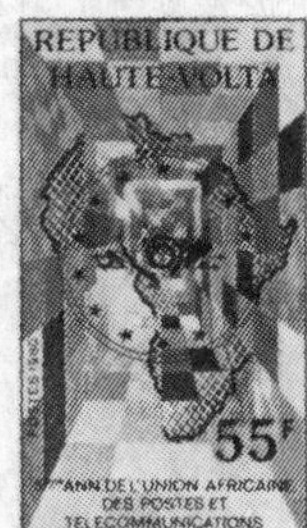

Madonna and Child, by Raphael — A178

West African Postal Union, 5th Anniv. — A179

Christmas: Paintings of Madonna and Child, by Raphael.

1980, Dec. 22 *Perf. 12½*
550 A178 60fr multicolored .40 .20
551 A178 150fr multicolored 1.00 .50
552 A178 250fr multicolored 1.60 .80
Nos. 550-552 (3) 3.00 1.50

1980, Dec. 24 Photo. *Perf. 13½*
553 A179 55fr multicolored .38 .20

Dung Beetle — A180

Perf. 13x13½, 13½x13

1981, Mar. 10 Litho.
554 A180 5fr shown .15 .15
555 A180 10fr Crickets .15 .15
556 A180 15fr Termites .15 .15
557 A180 20fr Praying mantis, vert. .15 .15
558 A180 55fr Emperor moth .38 .25
559 A180 65fr Locust, vert. .42 .20
Set value 1.15 .65

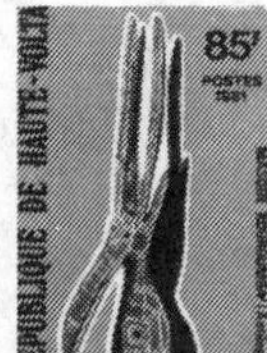

Antelope Mask, Kouroumba — A181

Designs: Various ceremonial masks.

1981, Mar. 20 Litho. *Perf. 13*
560 A181 45fr multicolored .26 .15
561 A181 55fr multicolored .32 .16
562 A181 85fr multicolored .48 .25
563 A181 105fr multicolored .60 .30
Nos. 560-563 (4) 1.66 .86

Notre Dame of Kologh' Naba College, 25th Anniv. A182

1981, Mar. 30
564 A182 55fr multicolored .32 .18

Heinrich von Stephan, UPU Founder, Birth Sesquicentennial — A183

1981, May 4 Litho. *Perf. 13*
565 A183 65fr multicolored .35 .18

13th World Telecommunications Day — A184

1981, May 17 *Perf. 13½x13*
566 A184 90fr multicolored .52 .25

Diesel Train, Abidjan-Niger Railroad A185

Designs: Trains.

1981, July 6 Litho. *Perf. 13*
567 A185 25fr shown .16 .15
568 A185 30fr Gazelle .20 .15
569 A185 40fr Belier .25 .15
Nos. 567-569 (3) .61
Set value .32

Tree Planting Month — A186

1981, July 15
570 A186 70fr multicolored .45 .22

Natl. Red Cross, 20th Anniv. A187

1981, July 31 *Perf. 12½x13*
571 A187 70fr multicolored .45 .22

Intl. Year of the Disabled — A188

1981, Aug. 20 Litho. *Perf. 13x12½*
572 A188 70fr multicolored .45 .22

View of Koudougou A189

1981, Sept. 3 Litho. *Perf. 12½*
573 A189 35fr shown .22 .15
574 A189 45fr Toma .30 .15
575 A189 85fr Volta Noire .55 .28
Nos. 573-575 (3) 1.07 .58

World Food Day A190

1981, Oct. 16 *Perf. 13*
576 A190 90fr multicolored .60 .30

Elephant A191

Designs: Various protected species.

1981, Oct. 21 Photo. *Perf. 14*
577 A191 5fr multicolored .15 .15
578 A191 15fr multicolored .15 .15
579 A191 40fr multicolored .25 .15
580 A191 60fr multicolored .40 .20
581 A191 70fr multicolored .45 .22
Nos. 577-581 (5) 1.40
Set value .65

Fight Against Apartheid — A192

Mangoes — A193

1981, Dec. 9 Litho. *Perf. 12½*
582 A192 90fr red orange .60 .30

Perf. 13x13½, 13½x13

1981, Dec. 15
583 A193 20fr Papayas, horiz. .15 .15
584 A193 35fr Fruits, vegetables, horiz. .22 .15
585 A193 75fr shown .50 .25
586 A193 90fr Melons, horiz. .60 .30
Nos. 583-586 (4) 1.47 .85

Guinea Hen — A194

West African Rice Development Assoc., 10th Anniv. — A195

Designs: Breeding animals. 10fr, 25fr, 70fr, 250fr, 300fr horiz.

1981, Dec. 22 *Perf. 13*
587 A194 10fr Donkey .15 .15
588 A194 25fr Pig .16 .15
589 A194 70fr Cow .45 .22
590 A194 90fr shown .60 .30
591 A194 250fr Rabbit 1.60 .80
Nos. 587-591 (5) 2.96 1.62

Souvenir Sheet

592 A194 300fr Sheep 2.00 1.00

1981, Dec. 29
593 A195 90fr multicolored .60 .30

20th Anniv. of World Food Program — A196

1982, Jan. 18
594 A196 50fr multicolored .35 .16

Traditional Houses — A197

1982, Apr. 23 Litho. *Perf. 12½*
595 A197 30fr Morhonaba Palace, vert. .20 .15
596 A197 70fr Bobo .45 .22
597 A197 100fr Gourounsi .65 .35
598 A197 200fr Peulh 1.40 .65
599 A197 250fr Dagari 1.60 .80
Nos. 595-599 (5) 4.30 2.17

14th World Telecommunications Day — A198

1982, May 17
600 A198 125fr multicolored .85 .40

Water Lily — A199

25th Anniv. of Cultural Aid Fund — A201

African Postal Union A200

1982, Sept. 22 *Perf. 13x12½*
601 A199 25fr shown .15 .15
602 A199 40fr Kapoks .20 .15
603 A199 70fr Frangipani .35 .18
604 A199 90fr Cochlospermum planchonii .60 .22
605 A199 100fr Cotton .50 .25
Nos. 601-605 (5) 1.80 .95

1982, Oct. 7
606 A200 70fr multicolored .45 .22
607 A200 90fr multicolored .60 .30

1982, Nov. 10 *Perf. 12½x13*
608 A201 70fr multicolored .45 .22

Map, Hand Holding Grain, Steer Head — A202

1982 *Perf. 12½*
609 A202 90fr multicolored .60 .30

Traditional Hairstyle A203

1983, Jan. Litho. *Perf. 12½*
610 A203 90fr lt green & multi .52 .25
611 A203 120fr lt blue & multi .70 .35
612 A203 170fr pink & multi .95 .48
Nos. 610-612 (3) 2.17 1.08

For overprints see Nos. 884-886.

8th Film Festival, Ouagadougou — A204

1983, Feb. 10 Litho. *Perf. 13x12½*
613 A204 90fr Scene .60 .30
614 A204 500fr Filmmaker Dumarou Ganda 3.50 1.60

UN Intl. Drinking Water and Sanitation Decade, 1981-90 — A205

1983, Apr. 21 Litho. *Perf. 13½x13*
615 A205 60fr Water drops .40 .20
616 A205 70fr Carrying water .45 .22

Manned Flight Bicentenary A206

Portraits and Balloons: 15fr, J.M. Montgolfier, 1783. 25fr, Etienne Montgolfier's balloon, 1783, Pilatre de Rozier. 70fr, Charles & Roberts flight, 1783, Jacques Charles. 90fr, Flight over English Channel, John Jeffries. 100fr, Testu-Brissy's horse-back flight, Wilhemine Reichardt. 250fr, Andree's Spitzbergen flight, 1897, S.A. Andree. 300fr, Piccard's stratosphere flight, 1931, August Piccard.

1983, Apr. 15 Litho. *Perf. 13½*
617 A206 15fr multicolored .15 .15
618 A206 25fr multicolored .16 .15
619 A206 70fr multicolored .45 .22
620 A206 90fr multicolored .60 .30
621 A206 100fr multicolored .65 .35
622 A206 250fr multicolored 1.60 .80
Nos. 617-622 (6) 3.61 1.97

Souvenir Sheet

623 A206 300fr multicolored 2.00 1.00

No. 623 contains one stamp 38x47mm. Nos. 621-623 airmail.

World Communications Year — A207

1983, May 26 Litho. *Perf. 12½*
624 A207 30fr Man reading letter .16 .15
625 A207 35fr Like No. 624 .18 .15
626 A207 45fr Aircraft over stream .25 .15
627 A207 90fr Girl on telephone .50 .25
Nos. 624-627 (4) 1.09
Set value .55

Fishing Resources A208

1983, July 28 Litho. *Perf. 13*
628 A208 20fr Synadontis gambiensis .15 .15
629 A208 30fr Palmotochromis .15 .15
630 A208 40fr Boy fishing, vert. .15 .15
631 A208 50fr Fishing with net .16 .15
632 A208 75fr Fishing with basket .25 .15
Set value .72 .37

Anti-deforestation — A209

1983, Sept. 13 Litho. *Perf. 13*
633 A209 10fr Planting saplings .15 .15
634 A209 50fr Tree nursery .16 .15
635 A209 100fr Prevent forest fires .35 .16
636 A209 150fr Woman cooking .50 .25
637 A209 200fr Prevent felling, vert. .65 .35
Nos. 633-637 (5) 1.81
Set value .88

Fresco Detail, by Raphael — A210

Paintings: 120fr, Self-portrait, by Pablo Picasso, 1901, vert. 185fr, Self-portrait at the palette, by Manet, 1878, vert. 350fr, Fresco Detail, diff., by Raphael. 500fr, Goethe, by George Oswald May, 1779, vert.

1983, Nov. Litho. *Perf. 13*
638 A210 120fr multicolored .40 .20
639 A210 185fr multicolored .62 .32
640 A210 300fr multicolored 1.00 .50
641 A210 350fr multicolored 1.20 .60
642 A210 500fr multicolored 1.60 .80
Nos. 638-642 (5) 4.82 2.42

25th Anniv. of the Republic A211

1983, Dec. 9 Litho. *Perf. 14*
643 A211 90fr Arms .30 .15
644 A211 500fr Family, flag 1.60 .80

A212

Scouting — A213

1984, May 29 Litho. *Perf. 12½*
645 A212 90fr multicolored .30 .15
646 A212 100fr multicolored .35 .16

Council of Unity, 25th anniv.

1984, June 15 Litho. *Perf. 13½*
647 A213 25fr Polystictus leoninus .15 .15
648 A213 185fr Pterocarpus Lucens .90 .45
649 A213 200fr Phlebopus colossus sudanicus 1.10 .50
650 A213 250fr Cosmos sulphureus 1.25 .62
651 A213 300fr Trametes versicolor 1.50 .80
652 A213 400fr Ganoderma lucidum 2.00 1.10
Nos. 647-652 (6) 6.90 3.62

Souvenir Sheet

653 A213 600fr Leucocoprinus cepaestipes 3.25 1.60

Nos. 651-653 are airmail. For overprints see Nos. 669-674.

Wildlife A214

Wildlife — A215

1984, July 19
654 A214 15fr Cheetah, four cubs .15 .15
655 A214 35fr Two adults .15 .15
656 A214 90fr One adult .35 .16
657 A214 120fr Cheetah, two cubs .45 .22
658 A214 300fr Baboons 1.20 .55
659 A214 400fr Vultures 1.50 .80
Nos. 654-659 (6) 3.80 2.03

Souvenir Sheet

660 A215 1000fr Antelopes 4.00 1.90

World Wildlife Fund (Nos. 654-567); Rotary Intl. (Nos. 658, 660); Natl. Boy Scouts (No. 659). Nos. 658-660 are airmail.

Sailing Ships and Locomotives — A216

1984, Aug. 14 *Perf. 12½*
661 A216 20fr Maiden Queen .15 .15
662 A216 40fr CC 2400 ch .16 .15
663 A216 60fr Scawfell .22 .15
664 A216 100fr PO 1806 .38 .18
665 A216 120fr Harbinger .45 .22
666 A216 145fr Livingstone .55 .28
667 A216 400fr True Briton 1.50 .80
668 A216 450fr Pacific C51 1.60 .85
Nos. 661-668 (8) 5.01 2.78

Natl. Defense — A216a

Design: 120fr, Capt. Sankara, crowd, horiz.

1984, Nov. 21 Litho. *Perf. 13½*
668A A216a 90fr multicolored
668B A216a 120fr multicolored

Burkina Faso

Nos. 647-652 Ovptd. with Two Bars and "BURKINA FASO"

1985, Mar. 5 Litho. *Perf. 13½*
669 A213 25fr multicolored .15 .15
670 A213 185fr multicolored .55 .25
671 A213 200fr multicolored .60 .30
672 A213 250fr multicolored .75 .38
673 A213 300fr multicolored .90 .45
674 A213 400fr multicolored 1.20 .60
Nos. 669-674 (6) 4.15 2.13

A217

Designs: 5fr, 120fr, Flag. 15fr, 150fr, Natl. Arms, vert. 90fr, 185fr, Map.

1985, Mar. 8 Litho. *Perf. 12½*
675 A217 5fr multicolored
676 A217 15fr multicolored
677 A217 90fr multicolored

678	A217	120fr	multicolored		
679	A217	150fr	multicolored		
680	A217	185fr	multicolored		

Nos. 678-680 are airmail.

1986 World Cup Soccer Championships, Mexico — A218

A219

Various soccer plays and Aztec artifacts.

1985, Apr. 20 Litho. *Perf. 13*

681	A218	25fr	multicolored	.15	.15
682	A218	45fr	multicolored	.16	.15
683	A218	90fr	multicolored	.35	.16
684	A218	100fr	multicolored	.38	.18
685	A218	150fr	multicolored	.55	.25
686	A218	200fr	multicolored	.70	.38
687	A218	250fr	multicolored	.90	.45
			Nos. 681-687 (7)	3.19	1.72

Souvenir Sheet

688	A219	500fr	multicolored	1.90	1.20

Nos. 681-685 vert. No. 684-688 are airmail.

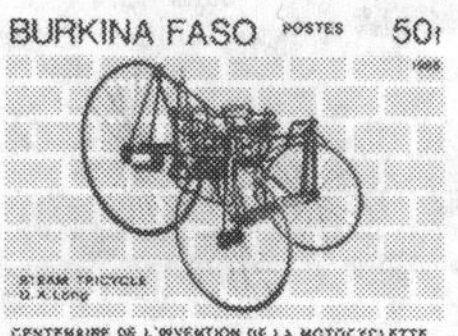

Motorcycle, Cent. — A220

1985, May 26

689	A220	50fr	Steam tricycle, G.A. Long	.18	.15
690	A220	75fr	Pope	.28	.15
691	A220	80fr	Manet-90	.30	.15
692	A220	100fr	Ducati	.38	.18
693	A220	150fr	Jawa	.55	.28
694	A220	200fr	Honda	.70	.38
695	A220	250fr	B.M.W.	.90	.45
			Nos. 689-695 (7)	3.29	1.74

Nos. 692-695 are airmail.

Reptiles A221

1985, June 20

696	A221	5fr	Chamaeleon dilepis	.15	.15
697	A221	15fr	Agama stellio	.15	.15
698	A221	35fr	Lacerta Lepida	.15	.15
699	A221	85fr	Hiperolius marmoratus	.32	.16
700	A221	100fr	Echis leucogaster	.38	.18
701	A221	150fr	Kinixys erosa	.55	.28
702	A221	250fr	Python regius	.90	.45
			Nos. 696-702 (7)	2.60	
			Set value		1.24

#696-697 vert. #700-702 are airmail.

British Queen Mother, 85th Birthday A222

1985, June 21 *Perf. 13½*

703	A222	75fr	On pony bobs	.22	.15
704	A222	85fr	Wedding, 1923	.25	.15
705	A222	500fr	Holding infant Elizabeth, 1926	1.60	.80
706	A222	600fr	Coronation of King George VI, 1937	1.90	.90
			Nos. 703-706 (4)	3.97	2.00

Souvenir Sheet

707	A222	1000fr	Christening of Prince William, 1982	3.25	1.60

Nos. 705-707 are airmail.

Vintage Autos and Aircraft — A223

1985, June 21

708	A223	5fr	Benz Victoria, 1893	.15	.15
709	A223	25fr	Peugeot 174, 1927	.15	.15
710	A223	45fr	Louis Bleriot	.16	.15
711	A223	50fr	Breguet 14	.20	.15
712	A223	500fr	Bugatti Coupe Napoleon T41 Royale	1.90	.90
713	A223	500fr	Airbus A300-P4	1.90	.90
714	A223	600fr	Mercedes-Benz 540K, 1938	2.25	1.20
715	A223	600fr	Airbus A300B	2.25	1.20
			Nos. 708-715 (8)	8.96	4.80

Souvenir Sheet

716	A223	1000fr	Louis Bleriot, Karl Benz	4.00	1.90

Automobile, cent. Nos. 712-716 are airmail.

Audubon Birth Bicent. A224

Illustrations of No. American bird species by Audubon and scouting trefoil.

1985, June 21

717	A224	60fr	Aix sponsa	.22	.15
718	A224	100fr	Mimus polyglotos	.38	.18
719	A224	300fr	Icterus galbula	1.20	.60
720	A224	400fr	Sitta carolinensis	1.50	.80
721	A224	500fr	Asyndesmus lewis	1.50	.90
722	A224	600fr	Buteo cagopus	2.25	1.10
			Nos. 717-722 (6)	7.05	3.73

Souvenir Sheet

723	A224	1000fr	Columba leucocephala	4.00	1.90

Nos. 721-723 are airmail.

ARGENTINA '85, Buenos Aires — A225

Various equestrians.

1985, July 5 *Perf. 13*

724	A225	25fr	Gaucho, piebald	.15	.15
725	A225	45fr	Horse and rider, Andes Mountains	.16	.15
726	A225	90fr	Rodeo	.32	.16
727	A225	100fr	Hunting gazelle	.38	.18
728	A225	150fr	Gauchos, 3 horses	.55	.25
729	A225	200fr	Rider beside mount	.70	.35
730	A225	250fr	Contest	.90	.42
			Nos. 724-730 (7)	3.16	1.66

Souvenir Sheet

731	A225	500fr	Foal	1.90	.70

Nos. 727-731 are airmail.

Locomotives — A226

1985, July 23

732	A226	50fr	105-30 electric, tank wagon	.18	.15
733	A226	75fr	Diesel shunting locomotive	.25	.15
734	A226	80fr	Diesel locomotive	.28	.15
735	A226	100fr	Diesel railcar	.38	.18
736	A226	150fr	No. 6093	.55	.25
737	A226	200fr	No. 105 diesel railcar	.70	.35
738	A226	250fr	Diesel, passenger car	.90	.42
			Nos. 732-738 (7)	3.24	1.65

Nos. 735-738 are airmail.

Artifacts — A227

Fungi — A228

1985, July 27 *Perf. 13x12½*

739	A227	10fr	4-legged jar, Tikare	.15	.15
740	A227	40fr	Lidded pot with bird handles, P. Bazega	.15	.15
741	A227	90fr	Mother and child, bronze statue, Ouagadougou	.35	.16
742	A227	120fr	Drummer, bronze statue, Ouagadougou	.42	.20
			Nos. 739-742 (4)	1.07	
			Set value		.48

No. 742 is airmail.

1985, Aug. 8 *Perf. 13*

743	A228	15fr	Philiota mutabilis	.15	.15
744	A228	20fr	Hypholoma (nematoloma) fasciculare	.15	.15
745	A228	30fr	Ixocomus granulatus	.15	.15
746	A228	60fr	Agaricus campestris	.22	.15
747	A228	80fr	Trachypus scaber	.30	.15
748	A228	150fr	Armillaria mellea	.55	.25
749	A228	250fr	Marasmius scorodonius	.90	.42
			Nos. 743-749 (7)	2.42	
			Set value		1.05

Nos. 748 is airmail.

ITALIA '85 — A228a

Paintings by Botticelli: 25fr, Virgin and Child. 45fr, Portrait of a Man. 90fr, Mars and Venus. 100fr, Birth of Venus. 150fr, Allegory of the Calumny. 200fr, Pallas and the Centaur. 250fr, Allegory of Spring. 500fr, The Virgin of Melagrana.

1985, Oct. 25 Litho. *Perf. 12½x13*

749A	A228a	25fr	multicolored	.15	.15
749B	A228a	45fr	multicolored	.22	.15
749C	A228a	90fr	multicolored	.45	.22
749D	A228a	100fr	multicolored	.50	.25
749E	A228a	150fr	multicolored	.70	.38
749F	A228a	200fr	multicolored	1.00	.50
749G	A228a	250fr	multicolored	1.25	.60
			Nos. 749A-749G (7)	4.27	2.25

Souvenir Sheet

749H	A228a	500fr	multicolored	2.50	1.25

No. 749D-749H are airmail.

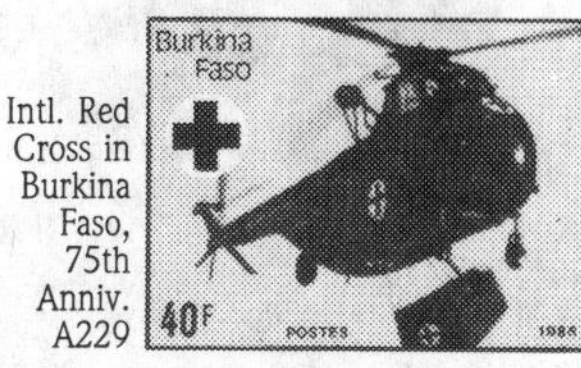

Intl. Red Cross in Burkina Faso, 75th Anniv. A229

1985, Nov. 10

750	A229	40f	Helicopter	.15	.15
751	A229	85fr	Ambulance	.30	.15
752	A229	150fr	Henri Dunant	.55	.25
753	A229	250fr	Physician, patient	.90	.42
			Nos. 750-753 (4)	1.90	.97

Nos. 752-753 are vert. and airmail.

Child Survival — A230

1986, Jan. 6

754	A230	90fr	Breast-feeding	.48	.25

Dated 1985.

Dodo Carnival A231

1986, Jan. 6 *Perf. 12½*

755	A231	20fr	Three children, drummer	.15	.15
756	A231	25fr	Lion, 4 dancers	.15	.15
757	A231	40fr	Two dancers, two drummers	.22	.15
758	A231	45fr	Three dancers	.25	.15
759	A231	90fr	Zebra, ostrich, dancers	.48	.25
760	A231	90fr	Elephant, dancer	.48	.25
			Nos. 755-760 (6)	1.73	
			Set value		.86

Dated 1985.

Christopher Columbus (1451-1506) — A232

Columbus: 250fr, At Court of King of Portugal, the Nina. 300fr, Using astrolable, the Santa Maria. 400fr, Imprisonment at Hispanola, 1500, the Santa Maria. 450fr, At San Salvador, 1492, the Pinta. 1000fr, Fleet departing Palos harbor, 1492.

1986, Feb. 10 *Perf. 13½*

761 A232 250fr multicolored 1.35 .68
762 A232 300fr multicolored 1.65 .82
763 A232 400fr multicolored 2.25 1.15
764 A232 450fr multicolored 2.50 1.25
Nos. 761-764 (4) 7.75 3.90

Souvenir Sheet

765 A232 1000fr multicolored 5.50 2.75

Nos. 764-765 are airmail. Dated 1985.

Railroad Construction — A233

1986, Feb. 10

766 A233 90fr Man, woman carrying rail .50 .25
767 A233 120fr Laying rails .65 .32
768 A233 185fr Diesel train on new tracks 1.00 .50
769 A233 500fr Adler locomotive, 1835 2.75 1.40
Nos. 766-769 (4) 4.90 2.47

Souvenir Sheet

770 A233 1000fr Electric train, Series 290 diesel 5.00 2.75

German Railways, sesquicentennial. Nos. 769-770 are airmail. Dated 1985.

Intl. Peace Year — A234

World Health by the Year 2000 — A235

1986, Oct. 10 Photo. *Perf. 12½x13*

771 A234 90fr blue 1.10 .55

1986, Aug. 8 Litho. *Perf. 13*

Designs: 100fr, Primary care medicine. 150fr, Mass inoculations.

772 A235 90fr multicolored .65 .32

Size: 26x30mm

Perf. 12½x13

773 A235 100fr multicolored .72 .35
774 A235 120fr multicolored .85 .42
Nos. 772-774 (3) 2.22 1.09

Insects — A236

World Post Day — A237

1986, Sept. 10 Litho. *Perf. 12½x13*

775 A236 15fr Phryneta aurocinta .15 .15
776 A236 20fr Sternocera interrupta .18 .15
777 A236 40fr Prosoprocera lactator .36 .18
778 A236 45fr Gonimbrasia hecate .42 .20
778A A236 85fr Charaxes epijasius .78 .36
Nos. 775-778A (5) 1.89 1.04

1986, Oct. 9 *Perf. 13*

779 A237 120fr multicolored .68 .35

UN Child Survival Campaign — A238

Designs: 30fr, Mother feeding child. 90fr, Nurse vaccinating child.

1986, Oct. 8 Litho. *Perf. 11½x12*

780 A238 30fr multicolored
782 A238 90fr multicolored

Numbers have been reserved for 60fr and 120fr stamps in this set.

Mammals A239

Designs: 50fr, Warthog. 65fr, Hyena. 90fr, Antelope. 100fr, Gazelle. 120fr, Bushbuck. 145fr, Kudu. 500fr, Gazelle, diff.

1986, Nov. 3 Litho. *Perf. 13x12½*

784 A239 50fr multicolored
784A A239 65fr multicolored
784B A239 90fr multicolored
784C A239 100fr multicolored
784D A239 120fr multicolored
784E A239 145fr multicolored
784F A239 500fr multicolored

Traditional Dances — A240

Designs: 10fr, Namende. 25fr, Mouhoun. 90fr, Houet. 105fr, Seno. 120fr, Ganzourgou.

1986, Nov. 3 Litho. *Perf. 12½x13*

785 A240 10fr multicolored
785A A240 25fr multicolored
785B A240 90fr multicolored
785C A240 105fr multicolored
785D A240 120fr multicolored

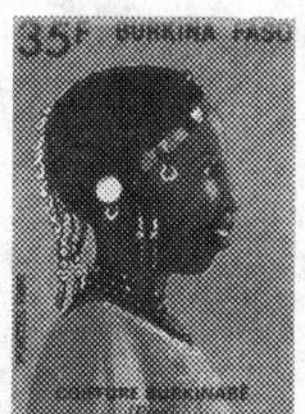

Hairstyles — A241

1986, Nov. 4 Litho. *Perf. 12½x13*

788 A241 35fr Peul .28 .15
789 A241 75fr Dafing .60 .30
790 A241 90fr Peul, diff. .70 .35
791 A241 120fr Mossi .95 .48
792 A241 185fr Peul, diff. 1.50 .75
Nos. 788-792 (5) 4.03 2.03

10th African Film Festival — A242

Intl Women's Day — A243

1987, Feb. 21 Litho. *Perf. 12x12½*

793 A242 90fr Maps, cameras
794 A242 120fr Jolson, cameramen
795 A242 185fr Charlie Chaplin

60th Anniv. of the film *The Jazz Singer* (120fr); 10th anniv. of the death of Charlie Chaplin (185fr).

1987, Mar. 8 *Perf. 13½*

796 A243 90fr multicolored

Flora — A244

Fight Against Leprosy — A245

1987, June 6 Litho. *Perf. 12½x13*

797 A244 70fr Calotropis procera .48 .24
798 A244 75fr Acacia seyal .52 .25
799 A244 85fr Parkia biglobosa .60 .30
800 A244 90fr Sterospernum kunthianum .62 .30
801 A244 100fr Dichrostachys cinerea .70 .35
802 A244 300fr Combretum paniculatum 2.10 1.05
Nos. 797-802 (6) 5.02 2.49

1987, Aug. 6 *Perf. 13*

Raoul Follereau (1903-1977) and: 90fr, Doctors examining African youth. 100fr, Laboratory research. 120fr, Gerhard Hansen (1841-1912), microscope, bacillus under magnification. 300fr, Follereau embracing cured leper.

803 A245 90fr multicolored .62 .30
804 A245 100fr multicolored .70 .35
805 A245 120fr multicolored .85 .42
806 A245 300fr multicolored 2.10 1.05
Nos. 803-806 (4) 4.27 2.12

World Environment Day — A246

1987, Aug. 18 Litho. *Perf. 13x12½*

807 A246 90fr shown .68 .35
808 A246 145fr Emblem, huts 1.10 .55

Pre-Olympic Year — A247

1987, Aug. 31 *Perf. 12½*

809 A247 75fr High jump .55 .28
810 A247 85fr Tennis, vert. .62 .30
811 A247 90fr Ski jumping .68 .35
812 A247 100fr Soccer .75 .38
813 A247 145fr Running 1.10 .55
814 A247 350fr Pierre de Coubertin, tennis, vert. 2.60 1.30
Nos. 809-814 (6) 6.30 3.16

Pierre de Coubertin (1863-1937).

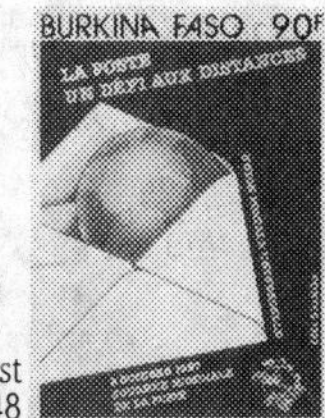

World Post Day — A248

1987, Oct. 5 Litho. *Perf. 12½x13*

815 A248 90fr multicolored

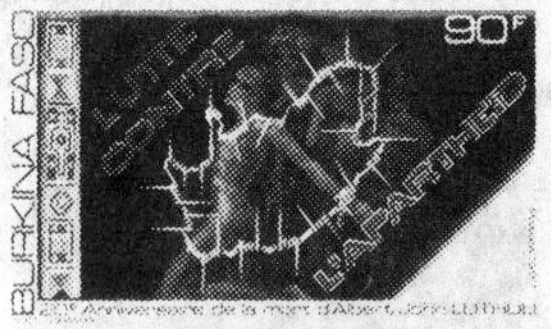

Fight Against Apartheid — A249

1987, Nov. 11 Litho. *Perf. 13*

816 A249 90fr shown 1.00 .50
817 A249 100fr Luthuli, book, 1962 1.10 .55

Albert John Luthuli (1898-1967), South African reformer, author and 1960 Nobel Peace Prize winner. No. 817 incorrectly inscribed "1899-1967."

Traditional Costumes — A250

1987, Dec. 4 Litho. *Perf. 11½x12*

820 A250 90fr Mossi
821 A250 200fr Senoufo

Numbers have been reserved for 10fr, 30fr and 500fr stamps in this set.

Traditional Musical Instruments A251

Perf. 12x11½, 11½x12

1987, Dec. 4 Litho.

823 A251 20fr Xylophone .18 .15
824 A251 25fr 3-Stringed lute, vert. .22 .15
825 A251 35fr Zither .30 .15
826 A251 90fr Conical drum .78 .40
827 A251 1000fr Calabash drum, vert. 8.50 4.25
Nos. 823-827 (5) 9.98 5.10

Intl. Year of Shelter for the Homeless — A252

1987, Dec. 4 Litho. *Perf. 13*

828 A252 90fr multicolored .65 .32

Five-year Natl. Development Plan — A253

1987, Dec. 15 *Perf. 13½*

829 A253 40fr Small businesses .30 .15
830 A253 55fr Agriculture .40 .20
831 A253 60fr Constructing schools .45 .22
832 A253 90fr Transportation and communications .65 .32

833 A253 100fr Literacy .72 .35
834 A253 120fr Animal husbandry .88 .45
Nos. 829-834 (6) 3.40 1.69

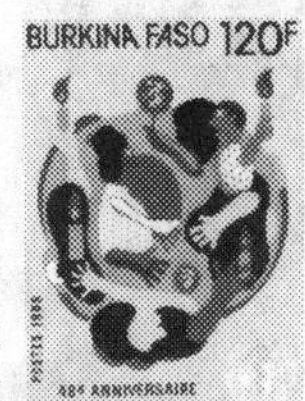

World Health Organization, 40th Anniv. — A254

1988, Mar. 31 Litho. *Perf. 12½x13*
835 A254 120fr multicolored .78 .40

1988 Summer Olympics, Seoul — A255

1988, May 5 *Perf. 13x12½*
836 A255 30fr shown .20 .15
837 A255 160fr Torch, vert. 1.05 .52
838 A255 175fr Soccer 1.15 .58
839 A255 235fr Volleyball, vert. 1.50 .75
840 A255 450fr Basketball, vert. 2.90 1.45
Nos. 836-840 (5) 6.80 3.45

Souvenir Sheet
Perf. 12½x13
841 A255 500fr Runners 3.25 1.65

No. 841 contains one stamp, size: 40x52mm plus two labels.

Ritual Masks A256

1988, May 30 Litho. *Perf. 13*
842 A256 10fr Epervier, Houet .15 .15
843 A256 20fr Jeunes Filles, Oullo .15 .15
844 A256 30fr Bubale, Houet .20 .15
845 A256 40fr Forgeron, Mouhoun .28 .15
846 A256 120fr Nounouma, Ouri .80 .40
847 A256 175fr Chauve-souris, Ouri 1.20 .60
Nos. 842-847 (6) 2.78
Set value 1.35

Nos. 842-846 vert.

Handicrafts A257

1988, Aug. 22 Litho. *Perf. 13½*
848 A257 5fr Kieriebe ceramic pitcher, vert. .15 .15
849 A257 15fr Mossi basket .15 .15
850 A257 25fr Gurunsi chair .18 .15
851 A257 30fr Bissa basket .20 .15
852 A257 45fr Ougadougou leather box .35 .18
853 A257 85fr Ougadougou bronze statue, vert. .68 .35
854 A257 120fr Ougadougou leather valise .80 .40
Nos. 848-854 (7) 2.51
Set value 1.20

World Post Day — A258

1988, Oct. 9 Litho. *Perf. 13*
855 A258 120fr multicolored .80 .40

Aquatic Fauna — A259

1988, Oct. 31 *Perf. 12*
856 A259 70fr Angler martin .48 .25
857 A259 100fr Mormyrus rume .68 .35
858 A259 120fr Frog .80 .40
859 A259 160fr Duck 1.10 .55
Nos. 856-859 (4) 3.06 1.55

Civil Rights and Political Activists A260

Designs: 80fr, Mohammed Ali Jinnah (1876-1948), 1st Governor General of Pakistan. 120fr, Mahatma Gandhi (1869-1948), India. 160fr, John F. Kennedy. 235fr, Martin Luther King, Jr.

1988, Nov. 22 Litho. *Perf. 14*
860 A260 80fr multicolored .52 .25
861 A260 120fr multicolored .78 .40
862 A260 160fr multicolored 1.00 .50
863 A260 235fr multicolored 1.50 .75
Nos. 860-863 (4) 3.80 1.90

A261

A262

Christmas: Stained-glass windows.

1988, Dec. 2 *Perf. 12*
864 A261 120fr Adoration of the shepherds .78 .40
865 A261 160fr Adoration of the Magi 1.00 .50
866 A261 450fr Madonna and child 2.90 1.45
867 A261 1000fr Flight into Egypt 6.35 3.15
Nos. 864-867 (4) 11.03 5.50

1989, Feb. 25 Litho. *Perf. 14*
868 A262 75fr shown .24 .15
869 A262 500fr Ababacar Makharam 1.60 .80
870 A262 500fr Jean Tchissoukou 1.60 .80
871 A262 500fr Paulin Vieyra 1.60 .80
Nos. 868-871 (4) 5.04 2.55

Souvenir Sheet
872 Sheet of 3 9.00 4.50
a.-c. A262 500fr like #869-871, inscribed in gold 3.00 1.50

Panafrican Film Festival (FESPACO), 20th anniv. Nos. 869-872 are airmail.

World Fight Against AIDS A263

1989, Apr. 7 Litho. *Perf. 13*
873 A263 120fr multicolored .78 .40

Council for Rural Development, 30th Anniv. A264

1989, May 3 Litho. *Perf. 15x14*
874 A264 75fr multicolored .48 .25

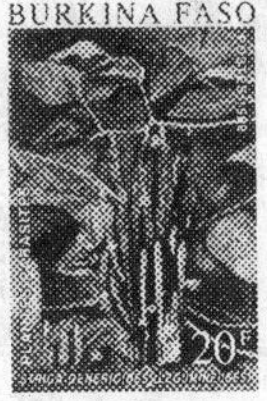

Parasitic Plants — A265

Legumes and cereals.

1989, Oct. 9 Litho. *Perf. 11½*
Granite Paper
875 A265 20fr *Striga generiodes* .15 .15
876 A265 50fr *Striga hermonthica* .32 .16
877 A265 235fr *Striga aspera* 1.50 .78
878 A265 450fr *Alectra vogelii* 3.00 1.50
Nos. 875-878 (4) 4.97 2.59

Dogs A266

1989, Oct. 9 *Perf. 15x14½*
879 A266 35fr Sahel .24 .15
880 A266 50fr Puppy .35 .18
881 A266 60fr Hunting dog .40 .20
882 A266 350fr Guard dog 2.30 1.15
Nos. 879-882 (4) 3.29 1.68

Solidarity with the Palestinian People — A267

1989, Nov. 15 *Perf. 13*
883 A267 120fr Monument, Place de la Palestine .80 .40

Nos. 610-612 Overprinted

1988, Dec. 21 Litho. *Perf. 12½*
884 A203 90fr multicolored .62 .30
885 A203 120fr multicolored .85 .42
886 A203 170fr multicolored 1.20 .60
Nos. 884-886 (3) 2.67 1.32

Visit of Pope John Paul II — A268

1990, Jan. 1 Litho. *Perf. 15x14*
887 A268 120fr Our Lady of Yagma .85 .42
888 A269 160fr Pope, crowd 1.20 .60

150th Anniv. of the Postage Stamp A269

1990, Mar. 20 Litho. *Perf. 15x14*
889 A269 120fr multicolored 1.00 .50

Souvenir Sheet
Perf. 14x15
890 A269 500fr Penny Black, ship 4.00 2.00

Stamp World London '90.

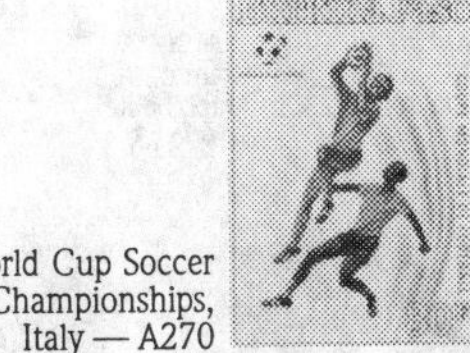

World Cup Soccer Championships, Italy — A270

1990, Apr. 26 Litho. *Perf. 11½*
891 A270 30fr multicolored .22 .15
892 A270 150fr multi, diff. 1.10 .55

Souvenir Sheet
893 A270 1000fr multi, horiz. 7.25 3.65

Intl. Literacy Year — A271

1990, July 10 Litho. *Perf. 13*
894 A271 40fr multicolored .28 .15
895 A271 130fr multicolored .90 .45

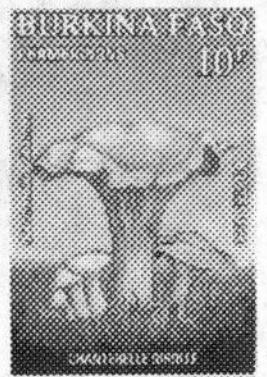

Mushrooms — A272

1990, May 17 Litho. *Perf. 11½*
896 A272 10fr Cantharellus cibarius .15 .15
897 A272 15fr Psalliota bispora .15 .15
898 A272 60fr Amanita caesarea .48 .24
899 A272 190fr Boletus badius 1.50 .75
a. Souv. sheet of 4, #896-899 2.25 1.10
Nos. 896-899 (4) 2.28
Set value 1.10

Intl. Exposition of Handicrafts — A273

1990, Sept. 25 Litho. *Perf. 13*

900 A273 35fr Masks, fans, vert. .30 .15
901 A273 45fr shown .40 .20
902 A273 270fr Rattan chair, vert. 2.35 1.20
Nos. 900-902 (3) 3.05 1.55

Gen. Charles de Gaulle (1890-1970) A274

1990, Nov. 22 Litho. *Perf. 13*

903 A274 200fr multicolored 1.75 .90

Minerals A275

1991, Feb. 4 Litho. *Perf. 15x14*

904 A275 20fr Quartz .15 .15
905 A275 50fr Granite .40 .20
906 A275 280fr Amphibolite 2.25 1.12
Nos. 904-906 (3) 2.80 1.47

African Film Festival — A276

Fight Against Drugs — A277

1991, Feb. 20 *Perf. 11½*

907 A276 150fr multicolored 1.20 .60

Souvenir Sheet

908 A276 1000fr Award 8.00 4.00

1991, Feb. 20

909 A277 130fr multicolored 1.05 .55

Samuel F.B. Morse (1791-1872), Inventor — A278

1991, May 17 Litho. *Perf. 13*

910 A278 200fr multicolored 1.60 .80

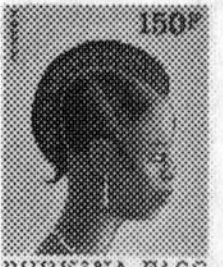

Native Girl — A279

Flowers — A280

1991-93 Litho. *Perf. 14½x15*

911 A279 5fr gray & multi .15 .15
912 A279 10fr yellow & multi .15 .15
913 A279 25fr lilac rose & multi .15 .15
914 A279 50fr red lilac & multi .28 .15
915 A279 130fr blue & multi 1.10 .55
916 A279 150fr multicolored 1.20 .60
920 A279 200fr multicolored 1.60 .80
922 A279 330fr orange & multi 2.75 1.40
Nos. 911-922 (8) 7.38 3.95

Issued: 150fr, 200fr, 6/20/91; 130fr, 330fr, 1/15/93; 5-50fr, 1994.
This is an expanding set. Numbers may change.

1991, July 31 Litho. *Perf. 11½*

926 A280 5fr Grewia tenax .15 .15
927 A280 15fr Hymenocardia acide .15 .15
928 A280 60fr Cassia sieberiana, vert. .48 .24
929 A280 100fr Adenium obesum .78 .40
930 A280 300fr Mitragyna inermis 2.40 1.20
Nos. 926-930 (5) 3.96 2.14

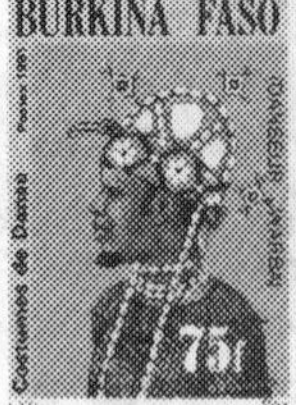

Traditional Dance Costumes — A281

World Post Day — A282

1991, Aug. 20 *Perf. 12½*

931 A281 75fr Warba .60 .30
932 A281 130fr Wiskamba 1.05 .52
933 A281 280fr Pa-zenin 2.20 1.10
Nos. 931-933 (3) 3.85 1.92

1991, Oct. 9 *Perf. 13½*

934 A282 130fr multicolored 1.05 .52

Cooking Utensils A283

1992, Jan. 8 Litho. *Perf. 11½*

935 A283 45fr Pancake fryer .35 .18
936 A283 130fr Cooking pot, vert. 1.00 .50
937 A283 310fr Mortar & pestle, vert. 2.40 1.20
938 A283 500fr Ladle, calabash 4.00 2.00
Nos. 935-938 (4) 7.75 3.88

1992 African Soccer Championships, Senegal — A284

1992, Jan. 17 *Perf. 13½*

939 A284 50fr Yousouf Fofana .40 .20
940 A284 100fr Francois-Jules Bocande .78 .40

Souvenir Sheet

Perf. 13x12½

941 A284 500fr Trophy 4.00 2.00

UN Decade For the Handicapped A285

1992, Mar. 31 Litho. *Perf. 12½*

942 A285 100fr multicolored .85 .42

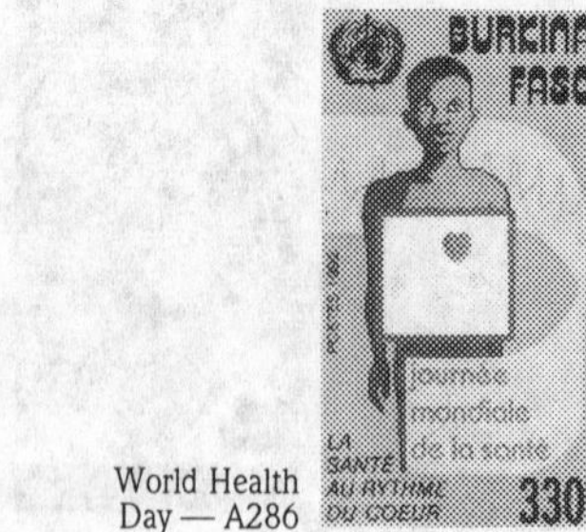

World Health Day — A286

1992, Apr. 7 *Perf. 13*

943 A286 330fr multicolored 2.70 1.35

Discovery of America, 500th Anniv. A287

1992, Aug. 12 Litho. *Perf. 12½*

944 A287 50fr Columbus, Santa Maria .42 .22
945 A287 150fr Ships, natives 1.25 .65

Souvenir Sheet

946 A287 350fr Map 3.00 1.50

Genoa '92. No. 946 contains one 52x31mm stamp.

A288

A289

Insects.

1992, Aug. 17 *Perf. 15x14*

947 A288 20fr Dysdercus voelkeri .18 .15
948 A288 40fr Rhizopertha dominica .35 .18
949 A288 85fr Orthetrum microstigma .75 .35
950 A288 500fr Apis mellifera 4.25 2.25
Nos. 947-950 (4) 5.53 2.93

1992, Dec. 21 Litho. *Perf. 11½*

Christmas: 10fr, Boy, creche. 130fr, Children decorating creche. 1000fr, Boy holding painting of Madonna and Child.

951 A289 10fr multicolored .15 .15
952 A289 130fr multicolored 1.00 .50
953 A289 1000fr multicolored 8.00 4.00
Nos. 951-953 (3) 9.15 4.65

Invention of the Diesel Engine, Cent. A290

1993, Jan. 25 Litho. *Perf. 11½*

954 A290 1000fr multicolored 8.00 4.00

The date of issue is in question.

Paris '94, Philatelic Exhibition A291

1993, July 15

955 A291 400fr multicolored 3.50 1.75
956 A291 650fr multi, diff. 5.50 2.75

African Film Festival — A292

Birds — A293

Designs: 250fr, Monument to the cinema. 750fr, M. Douta (1919-1991), comedian, horiz.

Perf. 11½x12, 12x11½

1993, Feb. 16 Litho.

957 A292 250fr multicolored 2.00 1.00
958 A292 750fr multicolored 6.00 3.00

1993, Mar. 31 *Perf. 11½x12*

Designs: 100fr, Mycteria ibis. 200fr, Leptoptilos crumeniferus. 500fr, Ephippiorhynchus senegalensis.

959 A293 100fr multicolored .80 .40
960 A293 200fr multicolored 1.60 .80
961 A293 500fr multicolored 4.00 2.00
a. Souvenir sheet of 3, #959-961 9.60 4.80
Nos. 959-961 (3) 6.40 3.20

No. 961a sold for 1200fr.

1994 World Cup Soccer Championships, US — A294

1993, Apr. 8 *Perf. 15*

962 A294 500fr shown 4.00 2.00
963 A294 1000fr Players, US flag 8.00 4.00

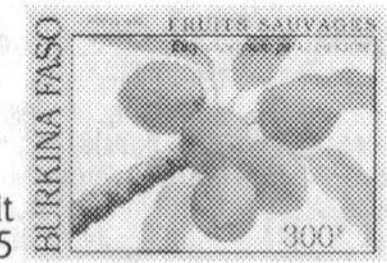

Fruit Trees — A295

Designs: 150fr, Saba senegalensis, vert. 300fr, Butyrospermum parkii. 600fr, Adansonia digitata, vert.

1993, June 2 Litho. *Perf. 11½*

964 A295 150fr multicolored 1.25 .65
965 A295 300fr multicolored 2.50 1.25
966 A295 600fr multicolored 5.00 2.50
Nos. 964-966 (3) 8.75 4.40

Traditional Jewelry — A296

1993, Sept. 25 Litho. *Perf. 11½*

967 A296 200fr Ring for hair 1.65 .85
968 A296 250fr Agate necklace, vert. 2.00 1.00
969 A296 500fr Bracelet 4.00 2.00
Nos. 967-969 (3) 7.65 3.85

Gazella Rufifrons A297

1993, Dec. 10 Litho. *Perf. 14½*

970 A297 30fr shown .25 .15
971 A297 40fr Two facing left .32 .16
972 A297 60fr Two standing .50 .25
973 A297 100fr Young gazelle .80 .40
a. Souvenir sheet, #970-973 3.25 1.65
Nos. 970-973 (4) 1.87 .96

World Wildlife Fund (#970-973). No. 973a sold for 400fr.

Kingfishers — A298

1994, Mar. 8 Litho. *Perf. 11½*

974 A298	600fr	Halcyon senegalensis	2.00	1.00
975 A298	1200fr	Halcyon chelicuti	4.25	2.25

Souvenir Sheet

976 A298	2000fr	Ceyx picta	7.00	3.50

1994 World Cup Soccer Championships, US — A299

1994, Mar. 28

977 A299	1000fr	Players, US map	3.50	1.75
978 A299	1800fr	Soccer ball, players	6.50	3.25
a.		Souvenir sheet of 1	7.00	3.50

No. 978a sold for 2000fr.

First Manned Moon Landing, 25th Anniv. — A300

1994 Litho. *Perf. 11½*

979 A300	750fr	Astronaut, flag	3.75	1.90
980 A300	750fr	Lunar module, earth	3.75	1.90
a.		Pair, #979-980	7.50	3.75

No. 980a is a continuous design.

First Stamp Exhibition, Paris, 1994 A301

1994

981 A301	1500fr	Dogs	7.75	3.75
a.		Souvenir sheet of 1	7.75	3.75

Legumes — A302

Designs: 40fr, Hibiscus sabdariffa. 45fr, Solanum aethiopicum. 75fr, Solanum melongena. 100fr, Hibiscus esculentus.

1994 Litho. *Perf. 11½*

982 A302	40fr	multicolored	.20	.15
983 A302	45fr	multicolored	.22	.15
984 A302	75fr	multicolored	.38	.20
985 A302	100fr	multicolored	.50	.25
		Nos. 982-985 (4)	1.30	.75

Intl. Olympic Committee, Cent. — A303

Domestic Animals — A304

1994 *Perf. 15*

986 A303	320fr	multicolored	1.65	.80

1994 *Perf. 11½*

987 A304	150fr	Pig, horiz.	.75	.35
988 A304	1000fr	Capra hircus	4.75	2.50
989 A304	1500fr	Ovis aries, horiz.	7.25	3.75
		Nos. 987-989 (3)	12.75	6.60

Elvis Presley (1935-77) A305

Portraits in feature films: 300fr, Loving You. 500fr, Jailhouse Rock. 1000fr, Blue Hawaii. 1500fr, Marilyn Monroe, Presley.

1995 Litho. *Perf. 13½*

990-992 A305	Set of 3	7.50	3.75

Souvenir Sheet

993 A305	1500fr	multicolored	6.00	3.00

Nos. 990-992 exist in souvenir sheets of one. No. 993 contains one 51x42mm stamp with continuous design.

See Nos. 1012-1015.

Crocodile — A306

1995 Litho. *Perf. 15x14½*

994 A306	10fr	brown & multi	.15	.15
995 A306	20fr	lilac & multi	.15	.15
996 A306	25fr	olive brn & multi	.15	.15
997 A306	30fr	green & multi	.15	.15
998 A306	40fr	red brown & multi	.20	.15
999 A306	50fr	gray & multi	.25	.15
1000 A306	75fr	gray violet & multi	.38	.18
1001 A306	100fr	gray brown & multi	.50	.25
1002 A306	150fr	olive & multi	.75	.38
1003 A306	175fr	gray blue & multi	.90	.45
1004 A306	250fr	brown lake & multi	1.25	.65
1005 A306	400fr	blue green & multi	2.00	1.00
		Nos. 994-1005 (12)	6.83	3.81

World Tourism Organization, 20th Anniv. — A307

Designs: 150fr, Man riding donkey, vert. 350fr, Bobo-Dioulasso railroad station. 450fr, Grand Mosque, Bani. 650fr, Gazelle, map.

1995 Litho. *Perf. 11½*

1006 A307	150fr	multicolored	.75	.38
1007 A307	350fr	multicolored	1.75	.90
1008 A307	450fr	multicolored	2.25	1.10
1009 A307	650fr	multicolored	3.25	1.65
		Nos. 1006-1009 (4)	8.00	4.03

FESPACO '95 — A308

Motion pictures: 150fr, "Rabi," Gaston Kabore. 250fr, "Tilai," Idrissa Ouedraogo.

1995 *Perf. 13½*

1010 A308	150fr	multicolored	.80	.40
1011 A308	250fr	multicolored	1.40	.70

Nos. 1010-1011 exist in souvenir sheets of one. Motion pictures, cent.

Stars of Motion Pictures Type of 1995

Marilyn Monroe in feature films: 400fr, The Joyful Parade. 650fr, The Village Tramp. 750fr, Niagara.

1500fr, The Seven Year Itch.

1995 Litho. *Perf. 13½*

1012-1014 A305	Set of 3	7.50	3.75

Souvenir Sheet

1015 A305	1500fr	multicolored	6.00	3.00

Nos. 1012-1014 exist in souvenir sheets of 1. No. 1015 contains one 42x51mm stamp with continuous design.

Birds — A309

Designs: 450fr, Laniarius barbarus. 600fr, Estrilda bengala. 750fr, Euplectes afer.

1995 Litho. *Perf. 11½*

1016 A309	450fr	multicolored	2.00	1.00
1017 A309	600fr	multicolored	2.75	1.40
1018 A309	750fr	multicolored	3.50	1.75
a.		Souvenir sheet of 3, #1016-1018	9.00	4.50
		Nos. 1016-1018 (3)	8.25	4.15

No. 1018a sold for 2000fr.

Reptiles A310

Designs: 450fr, Psammophis sibilans. 500fr, Eryx muelleri. 1500fr, Turtle.

1995

1019 A310	450fr	multicolored	2.00	1.00
1020 A310	500fr	multicolored	2.25	1.10
1021 A310	1500fr	multicolored	6.75	3.50
		Nos. 1019-1021 (3)	11.00	5.60

1996 Summer Olympics, Atlanta — A311

1995 Litho. *Perf. 13½*

1022 A311	150fr	Basketball	.70	.35
1023 A311	250fr	Baseball	1.25	.60
1024 A311	650fr	Tennis	3.00	1.50
1025 A311	750fr	Table tennis	3.50	1.75
		Nos. 1022-1025 (4)	8.45	4.20

Souvenir Sheet

1026 A311	1500fr	Equestrian event	7.00	7.00

Sports Figures — A312

Designs: 300fr, Juan Manuel Fangio, race car driver, 1955 Mercedes W 196. 400fr, Andre Agassi, US tennis player. 500fr, Ayrton Senna (1960-94), race car driver, McLaren MP 4/6 Honda. 1000fr, Michael Schumacher, race car driver, 1995 Benetton B 195.

1500fr, Enzo Ferrari, 412 TR, F40.

1995

1027 A312	300fr	multicolored	2.25	1.10
1028 A312	400fr	multicolored	3.25	1.65
1029 A312	500fr	multicolored	4.00	2.00
1030 A312	1000fr	multicolored	8.00	4.00
		Nos. 1027-1030 (4)	17.50	8.75

Souvenir Sheet

1031 A312	1500fr	multicolored	*7.00*	*3.50*

Nos. 1027-1030 exist in souvenir sheets of 1. No. 1031 contains one 55x48mm stamp.

See French West Africa Nos. 67, 84 for additional stamps inscribed "Haute Volta" and "Afrique Occidentale Francaise."

SEMI-POSTAL STAMPS

Catalogue values for unused stamps in this section are for Never Hinged items.

Anti-Malaria Issue

Common Design Type

Perf. 12½x12

1962, Apr. 7 Engr. Unwmk.

B1	CD108	25fr + 5fr red org	.50	.50

Freedom from Hunger Issue

Common Design Type

1963, Mar. 21 *Perf. 13*

B2	CD112	25fr + 5fr dk grn, bl & brn	.50	.50

AIR POST STAMPS

Catalogue values for unused stamps in this section are for Never Hinged items.

Plane over Map Showing Air Routes — AP1

Designs: 200fr, Plane at airport, Ouagadougou. 500fr, Champs Elysees, Ouagadougou.

Unwmk.

1961, Mar. 4 Engr. *Perf. 13*

C1	AP1	100fr multicolored	.85	.28
C2	AP1	200fr multicolored	1.65	.55
C3	AP1	500fr multicolored	4.00	1.50
		Nos. C1-C3 (3)	6.50	2.33

Air Afrique Issue

Common Design Type

1962, Feb. 17

C4	CD107	25fr brt pink, dk pur & lt grn	.30	.18

UN Emblem and Upper Volta Flag — AP2

Perf. 13½x12½

1962, Sept. 22 **Photo.**

C5 AP2 50fr multicolored .42 .22
C6 AP2 100fr multicolored .85 .48

Admission to UN, second anniversary.

Post Office, Ouagadougou — AP3

1962, Dec. 11 ***Perf. 13x12***

C7 AP3 100fr multicolored .75 .42

Jet Over Map AP4

1963, June 24

C8 AP4 200fr multicolored 1.65 .65

First jet flight, Ouagadougou to Paris.
For surcharge see No. C10.

African Postal Union Issue
Common Design Type

1963, Sept. 8 **Unwmk.** ***Perf. 12½***

C9 CD114 85fr dp vio, ocher & red .70 .48

No. C8 Surcharged in Red

AIR AFRIQUE
19-11-63
50F

1963, Nov. 19 ***Perf. 13x12***

C10 AP4 50fr on 200fr multi .52 .42

See note after Mauritania No. C26.

Europafrica Issue
Common Design Type

Design: 50fr, Sunburst and Europe linked with Africa.

1964, Jan. 6 ***Perf. 12x13***

C11 CD116 50fr multicolored .75 .52

Ramses II, Abu Simbel — AP5

Greek Sculptures — AP6

1964, Mar. 8 **Engr.** ***Perf. 13***

C12 AP5 25fr dp green & choc .35 .30
C13 AP5 100fr brt bl & brn 1.40 1.20

UNESCO world campaign to save historic monuments of Nubia.

1964, July 1 **Unwmk.** ***Perf. 13***

C14 AP6 15fr Greek Portrait Head .20 .15
C15 AP6 25fr Seated boxer .25 .20
C16 AP6 85fr Victorious athlete .80 .60
C17 AP6 100fr Venus of Milo 1.10 .70
a. Min. sheet of 4, #C14-C17 3.50 3.50
Nos. C14-C17 (4) 2.35 1.65

18th Olympic Games, Tokyo, Oct. 10-25.

West African Gray Woodpecker AP7

President John F. Kennedy (1917-1963) AP8

1964, Oct. 1 **Engr.** ***Perf. 13***

C18 AP7 250fr multicolored 2.75 1.90

1964, Nov. 25 **Photo.** ***Perf. 12½***

C19 AP8 100fr orange, brn & lil .70 .70
a. Souvenir sheet of 4 4.50 4.50

Bird Type of Regular Issue, 1965

1965, Mar. 1 **Photo.** ***Perf. 13***
Size: 27x48mm

C20 A27 500fr Abyssinian roller 5.50 2.50

Earth and Sun AP9

1965, Mar. 23 **Engr.**

C21 AP9 50fr multicolored .45 .16

5th World Meteorological Day.

Hughes Telegraph, ITU Emblem and Dial Telephone — AP10

1965, May 17 **Unwmk.** ***Perf. 13***

C22 AP10 100fr red, sl grn & bl grn .80 .40

ITU, centenary.

Intl. Cooperation Year — AP10a

1965, June 21 **Photo.** ***Perf. 13***

C23 AP10a 25fr multicolored .20 .15
C24 AP10a 100fr multicolored .55 .26
a. Min. sheet, 2 each #C23-C24 1.90 1.90

Sacred Sabou Crocodile — AP11

1965, Aug. 9 **Engr.** ***Perf. 13***

C25 AP11 60fr shown .60 .30
C26 AP11 85fr Lion, vert. .80 .42

Early Bird Satellite over Globe — AP12

Tiros Satellite and Weather Map — AP13

1965, Sept. 15 **Unwmk.** ***Perf. 13***

C27 AP12 30fr brt bl, brn & brn red .28 .16

Space communications.

1966, Mar. 23 **Engr.** ***Perf. 13***

C28 AP13 50fr dk car, brt bl & blk .40 .28

6th World Meteorological Day.

FR-1 Satellite over Ouagadougou Space Tracking Station AP14

1966, Apr. 28 ***Perf. 13***

C29 AP14 250fr mag, ind & org brn 2.00 .90

Inauguration of WHO Headquarters, Geneva — AP15

1966, May 3 **Photo.**

C30 AP15 100fr yel, blk & bl .80 .45

Air Afrique Issue
Common Design Type

1966, Aug. 31 **Photo.** ***Perf. 13***

C31 CD123 25fr tan, blk & yel grn .30 .15

Sir Winston Churchill, British Lion and "V" Sign — AP16

1966, Nov. 5 **Engr.** ***Perf. 13***

C32 AP16 100fr sl grn & car rose 1.00 .55

Sir Winston Spencer Churchill (1874-1965), statesman and WWII leader.

Pope Paul VI, Peace Dove, UN General Assembly and Emblem — AP17

1966, Nov. 5

C33 AP17 100fr dk blue & pur 1.00 .55

Pope Paul's appeal for peace before the UN General Assembly, Oct. 4, 1965.

Blind Man and Lions Emblem — AP18

1967, Feb. 28 **Engr.** ***Perf. 13***

C34 AP18 100fr dk vio bl, brt bl & dk brn 1.40 .55

50th anniversary of Lions Intl.

UN Emblem and Rain over Landscape — AP19

Diamant Rocket — AP20

1967, Mar. 23 **Engr.** ***Perf. 13***

C35 AP19 50fr ultra, dk grn & bl grn .50 .22

7th World Meteorological Day.

1967, Apr. 18 **Engr.** ***Perf. 13***

French Spacecraft: 20fr, FR-1 satellite, horiz. 30fr, D1-C satellite. 100fr, D1-D satellite, horiz.

C36 AP20 5fr brt bl, sl grn & org .15 .15
C37 AP20 20fr lilac & slate blue .20 .15
C38 AP20 30fr red brn, brt bl & emer .32 .16
C39 AP20 100fr emer & dp claret .90 .45
Nos. C36-C39 (4) 1.57 .91

For overprint see No. C69.

Albert Schweitzer (1875-1965), Medical Missionary and Organ Pipes — AP21

1967, May 12 **Engr.** ***Perf. 13***

C40 AP21 250fr claret & blk 1.75 .95

World Map and 1967 Jamboree Emblem — AP22

1967, June 8 **Photo.**
C41 AP22 100fr multicolored 1.00 .55

12th Boy Scout World Jamboree, Farragut State Park, Idaho, Aug. 1-9.

Madonna and Child, 15th Century AP23

Paintings: 20fr, Still life by Paul Gauguin. 50fr, Pietà, by Dick Bouts. 60fr, Anne of Cleves, by Hans Holbein the Younger. 90fr, The Money Lender and his Wife, by Quentin Massys (38x40mm). 100fr, Blessing of the Risen Christ, by Giovanni Bellini. 200fr, The Handcart, by Louis Le Nain, horiz. 250fr, The Four Evangelists, by Jacob Jordaens.

Perf. 12½x12, 12x12½, 13½ (90fr)
1967-68 **Photo.**
C42 AP23 20fr multi ('68) .25 .15
C43 AP23 30fr multicolored .30 .15
C44 AP23 50fr multicolored .50 .25
C45 AP23 60fr multi ('68) .60 .25
C46 AP23 90fr multi ('68) .85 .42
C47 AP23 100fr multicolored 1.00 .38
C48 AP23 200fr multi ('68) 2.00 .70
C49 AP23 250fr multicolored 2.75 1.00
Nos. C42-C49 (8) 8.25 3.30

See Nos. C70-C72.

African Postal Union Issue, 1967
Common Design Type

1967, Sept. 9 **Engr.** ***Perf. 13***
C50 CD124 100fr brn red, dp bl & bl grn .80 .35

Caravelle "Ouagadougou" — AP24

1968, Feb. 29 **Engr.** ***Perf. 13***
C51 AP24 500fr bl, dp cl & blk 3.75 1.40

WMO Emblem, Sun, Rain, Wheat — AP25

1968, Mar. 23 **Engr.** ***Perf. 13***
C52 AP25 50fr dk red, ultra & gray grn .45 .22

8th World Meteorological Day.

Europafrica Issue

Clove Hitch — AP25a

1968, July 20 **Photo.** ***Perf. 13***
C53 AP25a 50fr yel bis, blk & dk red .40 .20

See note after Niger No. C89.

Vessel in Form of Acrobat with Bells, Colima Culture — AP26

Mexican Sculptures: 30fr, Ballplayer, Veracruz, vert. 60fr, Javelin thrower, Colima, vert. 100fr, Seated athlete with cape, Jalisco.

1968, Oct. 14 **Engr.** ***Perf. 13***
C54 AP26 10fr dk red, ocher & choc .15 .15
C55 AP26 30fr bl grn, brt grn & dk brn .22 .15
C56 AP26 60fr ultra, ol & mar .45 .22
C57 AP26 100fr brt grn, bl & mar .65 .35
Nos. C54-C57 (4) 1.47 .87

19th Olympic Games, Mexico City, Oct. 12-27.

Artisan Type of Regular Issue

1968, Oct. 30 **Engr.** ***Perf. 13***
Size: 48x27mm
C58 A52 100fr Potter .70 .32

PHILEXAFRIQUE Issue

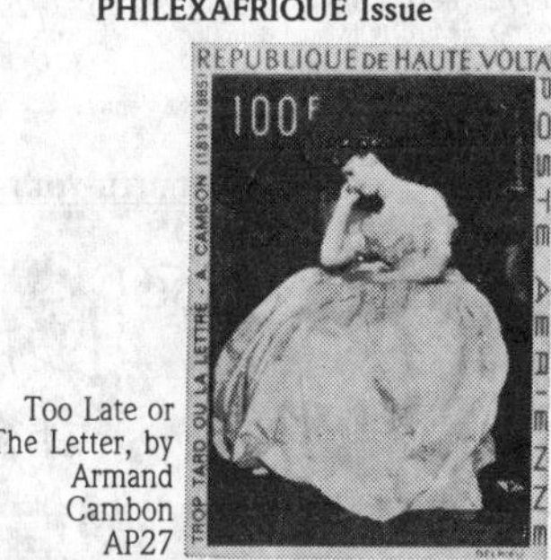

Too Late or The Letter, by Armand Cambon AP27

1968, Nov. 22 **Photo.** ***Perf. 12½***
C59 AP27 100fr multicolored 1.00 .75

PHILEXAFRIQUE, Phil. Exhib., Abidjan, Feb. 14-23, 1969. Printed with alternating rose claret label.

Albert John Luthuli — AP28

Design: No. C61, Mahatma Gandhi.

1968, Dec. 16 **Photo.** ***Perf. 12½***
C60 AP28 100fr dk grn, yel grn & blk .75 .40
C61 AP28 100fr dk grn, yel & blk .75 .40
a. Min. sheet, 2 each #C60-C61 3.00 3.00

Exponents of non-violence.

2nd PHILEXAFRIQUE Issue
Common Design Type

Design: 50fr, Upper Volta No. 59, dancers and musicians.

1969, Feb. 14 **Engr.** ***Perf. 13***
C62 CD128 50fr pur, bl car & brn .55 .55

Weather Sonde, WMO Emblem, Mule and Cattle in Irrigated Field — AP29

1969, Mar. 24 **Engr.** ***Perf. 13***
C63 AP29 100fr dk brn, brt bl & grn .90 .50

9th World Meteorological Day.

Artisan Type of Regular Issue

Design: 150fr, Basket weaver.

1969, Apr. 3 **Engr.** ***Perf. 13***
Size: 48x27mm
C64 A55 150fr brn, bl & blk 1.20 .60

Lions Emblem, Eye and Blind Man — AP30

1969, Apr. 30 **Photo.**
C65 AP30 250fr red & multi 2.50 1.00

12th Congress of District 403 of Lions Intl., Ouagadougou, May 2-3.

Fish Type of Regular Issue

Designs: 100fr, Phenacogrammus pabrensis. 150fr, Upside-down catfish.

1969 **Engr.** ***Perf. 13***
Size: 48x27mm
C66 A57 100fr slate, pur & yel .90 .42
C67 A57 150fr org brn, gray & slate 1.40 .62

Earth and Astronaut — AP31

Embossed on Gold Foil
1969 ***Die-cut Perf. 10½x10***
C68 AP31 1000fr gold 8.25 8.25

Apollo 8 mission, which put the first man into orbit around the moon, Dec. 21-27, 1968.

No. C39 Overprinted in red with Lunar Landing Module and: "L'HOMME SUR LA LUNE / JUILLET 1969 / APOLLO 11"

1969, July 25 **Engr.** ***Perf. 13***
C69 AP20 100fr emer & dp claret 2.25 1.90

See note after Mali No. C80.

Painting Type of 1967-68

Paintings: 50fr, Napoleon Crossing Great St. Bernard Pass, by Jacques Louis David. 150fr, Napoleon Awarding the First Cross of the Legion of Honor, by Jean-Baptiste Debret. 250fr, Napoleon Before Madrid, by Carle Vernet.

1969, Aug. 18 **Photo.** ***Perf. 12½x12***
C70 AP23 50fr carmine & multi .45 .35
C71 AP23 150fr violet & multi 1.10 .80
C72 AP23 250fr green & multi 2.25 1.40
Nos. C70-C72 (3) 3.80 2.55

Napoleon Bonaparte (1769-1821).

Agriculture Type of Regular Issue

1969, Oct. 30 **Photo.** ***Perf. 12½x13***
Size: 47½x27mm
C73 A58 100fr Peanuts .75 .28
C74 A58 200fr Rice 1.65 .55

AP32 AP33

Tree of Life, symbols of science, agriculture and industry.

1969, Nov. 21 **Photo.** ***Perf. 12x13***
C75 AP32 100fr multicolored .65 .35

See note after Mauritania No. C28.

1970, Apr. 22 **Photo.** ***Perf. 12½***

Designs: 20fr, Lenin. 100fr, Lenin Addressing Revolutionaries in Petrograd, by V. A. Serov, horiz.

C76 AP33 20fr ocher & brn .15 .15
C77 AP33 100fr blk, lt grn & red .65 .38

Lenin (1870-1924), Russian communist leader.

Pres. Roosevelt with Stamp Collection — AP34

Design: 10fr, Franklin Delano Roosevelt, vert.

1970, June 4 **Photo.** ***Perf. 12½***
C78 AP34 10fr dk brn, emer & red brn .15 .15
C79 AP34 200fr vio bl, gray & dk car 1.40 .45
Set value .50

Soccer Game and Jules Rimet Cup — AP35

Design: 100fr, Goalkeeper catching ball and globe.

1970, June 4 **Engr.** ***Perf. 13***
C80 AP35 40fr olive, brt grn & brn .40 .20
C81 AP35 100fr blk, lil, brn & grn .90 .40

9th World Soccer Championships for the Jules Rimet Cup, Mexico City, May 30-June 21, 1970.

EXPO Emblem, Monorail and "Cranes at the Seashore" — AP36

UN Emblem, Dove and Star — AP37

Design: 150fr, EXPO emblem, rocket, satellites and "Geisha."

1970, Aug. 7 Photo. *Perf. 12½*

C82 AP36 50fr multicolored .35 .16
C83 AP36 150fr green & multi 1.00 .60

Issued to publicize EXPO '70 International Exhibition, Osaka, Japan, Mar. 15-Sept. 13.

1970, Oct. 2 Engr. *Perf. 13*

Design: 250fr, UN emblem and doves, horiz.

C84 AP37 60fr dk bl, bl & grn .40 .20
C85 AP37 250fr dk red brn, vio bl & ol 1.60 .65

25th anniversary of the United Nations.

Holy Family AP38

Silver Embossed

1970, Nov. 27 *Die-Cut Perf. 10*

C86 AP38 300fr silver 2.50 2.50

Gold Embossed

C87 AP38 1000fr gold 9.00 9.00

Christmas.

Family and Upper Volta Flag — AP39

Gamal Abdel Nasser — AP41

UN "Key to a Free World" — AP40

Litho.; Gold Embossed

1970, Dec. 10 *Perf. 12½*

C88 AP39 500fr gold, blk & red 2.50 1.50

10th anniversary of independence, Dec. 11.

1970, Dec. 14 Engr. *Perf. 13*

C89 AP40 40fr red, bister & blue .35 .16

UN Declaration of Independence for Colonial Peoples, 10th anniv.

1971, Jan. 30 Photo. *Perf. 12½*

C90 AP41 100fr green & multi .65 .30

Nasser (1918-1970), president of Egypt.

Herons, Egyptian Art, 1354 — AP42

Design: 250fr, Page from Koran, Egypt, 1368-1388, vert.

1971, May 13 Photo. *Perf. 13*

C91 AP42 100fr multicolored .55 .25
C92 AP42 250fr multicolored 1.40 .70

Olympic Rings and Various Sports — AP43

1971, June 10 Engr. *Perf. 13*

C93 AP43 150fr vio bl & red 1.00 .60

Pre-Olympic Year.

Boy Scout and Buildings — AP44

1971, Aug. 12 Photo. *Perf. 12½*

C94 AP44 45fr multicolored .35 .16

13th Boy Scout World Jamboree, Asagiri Plain, Japan, Aug. 2-10.

De Gaulle, Map of Upper Volta, Cross of Lorraine — AP45

Charles de Gaulle — AP46

1971, Nov. 9 Photo. *Perf. 13x12*

C95 AP45 40fr lt brn, grn & blk .40 .35

Lithographed; Gold Embossed

Perf. 12½

C96 AP46 500fr gold & grn 4.00 3.75

Gen. Charles de Gaulle (1890-1970), president of France.

African Postal Union Issue, 1971
Common Design Type

Design: 100fr, Mossi dancer and UAMPT building, Brazzaville, Congo.

1971, Nov. 13 Photo. *Perf. 13x13½*

C97 CD135 100fr bl & multi .65 .35

Gen. Sangoule Lamizana — AP47

Kabuki Actor and Ice Hockey — AP48

1971, Dec. 11 *Perf. 12½*

C98 AP47 35fr sep, blk, gold & ultra .22 .15

Inauguration of 2nd Republic of Upper Volta.

1972, Feb. 15 Engr. *Perf. 13*

C99 AP48 150fr red, bl & pur 1.00 .60

11th Winter Olympic Games, Sapporo, Japan, Feb. 3-13.

Music, by Pietro Longhi AP49

Design: 150fr, Gondolas and general view, by Ippolito Caffi, horiz.

1972, Feb. 28 Photo. *Perf. 13*

C100 AP49 100fr gold & multi .65 .35
C101 AP49 150fr gold & multi 1.10 .40

UNESCO campaign to save Venice.

Running and Olympic Rings — AP50

Design: 200fr, Discus and Olympic rings.

1972, May 5 Engr. *Perf. 13*

C102 AP50 65fr dp bl, brn & grn .35 .15
C103 AP50 200fr dp bl & brn 1.10 .35
a. Min. sheet of 2, #C102-C103 1.65 1.65

20th Olympic Games, Munich, Aug. 26-Sept. 10.

Musician Type of Regular Issue

Design: 500fr, Jimmy Smith and keyboard.

1972, May 17 Photo. *Perf. 14x13*

C104 A87 500fr green & multi 4.00 1.90

Red Crescent Type of Regular Issue

1972, June 23 *Perf. 13x14*

C105 A88 100fr yellow & multi .65 .25

2nd Plan Type of Regular Issue

Design: 85fr, Road building machinery.

1972, Oct. 30 Engr. *Perf. 13*

C106 A90 85fr brick red, bl & blk .45 .22

Presidents Pompidou and Lamizana — AP51

Design: 250fr, Presidents Pompidou and Lamizana, different design.

1972, Nov. 20 Photo. *Perf. 13*

Size: 48x37mm

C107 AP51 40fr gold & multi .45 .35

Photogravure; Gold Embossed

Size: 56x36mm

C108 AP51 250fr yel grn, dk grn & gold 2.50 2.50

Visit of Pres. Georges Pompidou of France, Nov. 1972.

Skeet-shooting, Scalzone, Italy — AP52

Gold-medal Winners: 40fr, Pentathlon, Peters, Great Britain. 45fr, Dressage, Meade, Great Britain. 50fr, Weight lifting, Talts, USSR. 60fr, Boxing, lightweight, Seales, US 65fr, Fencing, Ragno-Lonzi, Italy. 75fr, Gymnastics, rings, Nakayama, Japan. 85fr, Gymnastics, Touritcheva, USSR. 90fr, 110m high hurdles, Milburn, US 150fr, Judo, Kawaguchi, Japan. 200fr, Sailing, Finn class, Maury, France. 250fr, Swimming, Spitz, US (7 gold). 300fr, Women's high jump, Meyfarth, West Germany. 350fr, Field Hockey, West Germany. 400fr, Javelin, Wolfermann, West Germany. No. C124, Women's diving, King, US No. C125, Cycling, Morelon, France. No. C126, Individual dressage, Linsenhoff, West Germany.

1972-73 Litho. *Perf. 12½*

C109 AP52 35fr multi ('73) .18 .15
C110 AP52 40fr multicolored .20 .15
C111 AP52 45fr multi ('73) .22 .15
C112 AP52 50fr multi ('73) .25 .15
C113 AP52 60fr multi ('73) .30 .15
C114 AP52 65fr multicolored .35 .16
C115 AP52 75fr multi ('73) .40 .20
C116 AP52 85fr multicolored .42 .20
C117 AP52 90fr multi ('73) .45 .22
C118 AP52 150fr multi ('73) .80 .40
C119 AP52 200fr multicolored 1.10 .50
C120 AP52 250fr multi ('73) 1.40 .65
C121 AP52 300fr multicolored 1.60 .80
C122 AP52 350fr multi ('73) 1.90 .90
C123 AP52 400fr multi ('73) 2.00 1.10
Nos. C109-C123 (15) 11.57 5.88

Souvenir Sheets

C124 AP52 500fr multicolored 2.25 1.60
C125 AP52 500fr multi ('73) 2.25 1.60
C126 AP52 500fr multi ('73) 2.25 1.60

20th Olympic Games, Munich.

Nativity, by Della Notte — AP53

Christmas: 200fr, Adoration of the Kings, by Albrecht Dürer.

1972, Dec. 23 Photo. *Perf. 13*

C127 AP53 100fr gold & multi .50 .22
C128 AP53 200fr gold & multi 1.10 .65

Madonna and Child, by Albrecht Dürer — AP54

Christmas: 75fr, Virgin Mary, Child and St. John, by Joseph von Führich. 100fr, The Virgin of Grand Duc, by Raphael. 125fr, Holy Family, by David. 150fr, Madonna and Child, artist unknown. 400fr, Flight into Egypt, by Gentile da Fabriano, horiz.

1973, Mar. 22 Litho. *Perf. 12½x13*

C129 AP54 50fr multi .35 .16
C130 AP54 75fr multi .50 .25
C131 AP54 100fr multi .65 .35
C132 AP54 125fr multi .80 .40
C133 AP54 150fr multi 1.00 .50
Nos. C129-C133 (5) 3.30 1.66

Souvenir Sheet

C134 AP54 400fr multi 2.50 1.40

Manned Lunar Buggy on Moon — AP55

Moon Exploration: 65fr, Lunakhod, Russian unmanned vehicle on moon. 100fr, Lunar module returning to orbiting Apollo capsule. 150fr, Apollo capsule in moon orbit. 200fr, Space walk. 250fr, Walk in Sea of Tranquillity.

1973, Apr. 30 Litho. *Perf. 13x12½*

C135 AP55 50fr multi .35 .16
C136 AP55 65fr multi .42 .20
C137 AP55 100fr multi .65 .35
C138 AP55 150fr multi 1.00 .50
C139 AP55 200fr multi 1.40 .65
Nos. C135-C139 (5) 3.82 1.86

Souvenir Sheet

C140 AP55 250fr multi 1.60 .80

Giraffes AP56

African Wild Animals: 150fr, Elephants. 200fr, Leopard, horiz. 250fr, Lion, horiz. 300fr, Rhinoceros, horiz. 500fr, Crocodile, horiz.

Perf. 12½x13, 13x12½

1973, May 3 Litho.

C141 AP56 100fr multi .65 .35
C142 AP56 150fr multi 1.00 .50
C143 AP56 200fr multi 1.40 .65
C144 AP56 250fr multi 1.60 .80
C145 AP56 500fr multi 3.50 1.60
Nos. C141-C145 (5) 8.15 3.90

Souvenir Sheet

C146 AP56 300fr multi 2.00 1.00

Europafrica Issue

Girl Reading Letter, by Jan Vermeer AP57

Paintings: 65fr, Portrait of a Lady, by Roger van der Weyden. 100fr, Young Lady at her Toilette, by Titian. 150fr, Jane Seymour, by Hans Holbein. 200fr, Mrs. Williams, by John Hoppner. 250fr, Milkmaid, by Jean-Baptiste Greuze.

1973, June 7 Litho. *Perf. 12½x13*

C147 AP57 50fr multi .35 .16
C148 AP57 65fr multi .42 .20
C149 AP57 100fr multi .65 .35
C150 AP57 150fr multi 1.00 .50
C151 AP57 200fr multi 1.40 .65
Nos. C147-C151 (5) 3.82 1.86

Souvenir Sheet

C152 AP57 250fr multi 1.60 .80

For overprint see No. C165-C166.

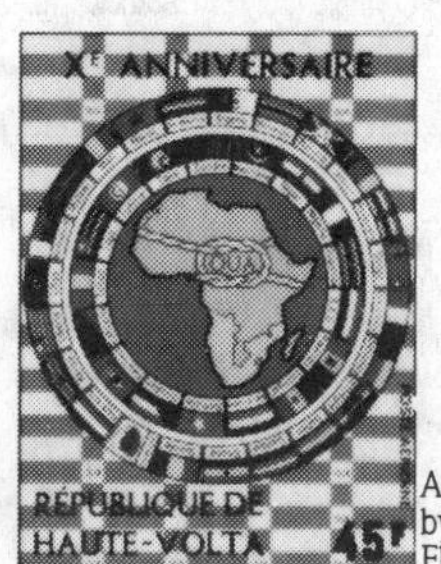

Africa Encircled by OAU Flags — AP58

1973, June 7

C153 AP58 45fr multi .30 .15

10th anniv. of Org. for African Unity.

Locomotive "Pacific" 4546, 1908 — AP59

Locomotives from Railroad Museum, Mulhouse, France: 40fr, No. 242, 1927. 50fr, No. 2029, 1882. 150fr, No. 701, 1885-92. 250fr, "Coupe-Vent" No. C145, 1900. 350fr, Buddicomb No. 33, Paris to Rouen, 1884.

1973, June 30 *Perf. 13x12½*

C154 AP59 10fr multi .15 .15
C155 AP59 40fr multi .25 .15
C156 AP59 50fr multi .35 .16
C157 AP59 150fr multi 1.00 .50
C158 AP59 250fr multi 1.60 .80
Nos. C154-C158 (5) 3.35 1.76

Souvenir Sheet

C159 AP59 350fr multi 2.25 1.20

Boy Scout Type of 1973

Boy Scouts: 40fr, Flag signaling. 75fr, Skiing. 150fr, Cooking. 200fr, Hiking. 250fr, Studying stars.

1973, July 18 Litho. *Perf. 12½x13*

C160 A95 40fr multi .25 .15
C161 A95 75fr multi .50 .25
C162 A95 150fr multi 1.00 .50
C163 A95 200fr multi 1.40 .65
Nos. C160-C163 (4) 3.15 1.55

Souvenir Sheet

C164 A95 250fr multi 1.60 .80

Nos. C148 and C150 Surcharged in Silver New Value and "SECHERESSE / SOLIDARITE AFRICAINE / ET INTERNATIONALE"

1973, Aug. 16

C165 AP57 100fr on 65fr multi .65 .35
C166 AP57 200fr on 150fr multi 1.40 .65

Drought relief.

Kennedy Type, 1973

John F. Kennedy and: 200fr, Firing Saturn 1 rocket, Apollo program. 300fr, First NASA manned space capsule. 400fr, Saturn 5 countdown.

1973, Sept. 12 Litho. *Perf. 12½x13*

C167 A96 200fr multi 1.40 .65
C168 A96 300fr multi 2.00 1.00

Souvenir Sheet

C169 A96 400fr multi 2.50 1.40

10th death anniv. of Pres John F. Kennedy.

Interpol Type of 1973
Souvenir Sheet

Design: Victim in city street.

1973, Sept. 15 *Perf. 13x12½*

C170 A97 300fr multi 2.00 1.00

Tourism Type of 1973

1973, Sept. 30

C171 A98 100fr Waterfalls .65 .35

Souvenir Sheet

C172 A98 275fr Elephant 1.90 .90

House of Worship Type of 1973

Design: Cathedral of the Immaculate Conception.

1973, Sept. 28

C173 A99 200fr multi 1.40 .65

Folklore Type of 1973

Designs: 100fr, 225fr, Bobo masked dancers, diff.

1973, Nov. 30 Litho. *Perf. 12½x13*

C174 A100 100fr multi .65 .35
C175 A100 225fr multi 1.50 .70

Zodiac Type of 1973
Souvenir Sheets

Zodiacal Light and: #C176, 1st 4 signs of Zodiac. #C177, 2nd 4 signs. #C178, Last 4 signs.

1973, Dec. 15 *Perf. 13x14*

C176 A101 250fr multi 1.60 .80
C177 A101 250fr multi 1.60 .80
C178 A101 250fr multi 1.60 .80

Nos. C176-C178 have multicolored margin showing night sky and portraits: No. C176, Louis Armstrong; No. C177, Mahatma Gandhi; No. C178, Martin Luther King.

Soccer Championship Type, 1974

Championship '74 emblem and: 75fr, Gento, Spanish flag. 100fr, Bereta, French flag. 250fr, Best, British flag. 400fr, Beckenbauer, West German flag.

1974, Jan. 15 Litho. *Perf. 13x12½*

C179 A102 75fr multi .50 .25
C180 A102 100fr multi .65 .35
C181 A102 250fr multi 1.60 .80
Nos. C179-C181 (3) 2.75 1.40

Souvenir Sheet

C182 A102 400fr multi 2.50 1.40

De Gaulle Type, 1974

Designs: 300fr, De Gaulle and Concorde, horiz. 400fr, De Gaulle and French space shot.

Perf. 13x12½, 12½x13

1974, Feb. 4 Litho.

C183 A103 300fr multi 2.00 1.00

Souvenir Sheet

C184 A103 400fr multi 2.50 1.40

Soccer Cup Championship Type, 1974

World Cup, Emblems and: 150fr, Brindisis, Argentinian flag. No. C186, Kenko, Zaire flag. No. C187, Streich, East German flag. 400fr, Cruyff, Netherlands flag.

1974, Mar. 19 *Perf. 12½x13*

C185 A104 150fr multi .75 .38
C186 A104 300fr multi 1.50 .75

Souvenir Sheets

C187 A104 300fr multi 1.50 .75
C188 A104 400fr multi 2.00 1.00

UPU Type, 1974

UPU Emblem and: 100fr, Dove carrying mail. 200fr, Air Afrique 707. 300fr, Dish antenna. 500fr, Telstar satellite.

1974, July 23 *Perf. 13½*

C189 A106 100fr multi .50 .25
C190 A106 200fr multi 1.00 .50
C191 A106 300fr multi 1.50 .75
Nos. C189-C191 (3) 3.00 1.50

Souvenir Sheet

C192 A106 500fr multi 2.50 1.25

For overprint see No. C197-C200.

Soccer Cup Winners Type, 1974

World Cup, Game and Flags: 150fr, Brazil, in Sweden, 1958. 200fr, Brazil, in Chile, 1962. 250fr, Brazil, in Mexico, 1970. 450fr, England, in England, 1966.

1974, Sept. 2

C193 A107 150fr multi 1.00 .50
C194 A107 200fr multi 1.40 .65
C195 A107 250fr multi 1.60 .80
Nos. C193-C195 (3) 4.00 1.95

Souvenir Sheet

C196 A107 450fr multi 3.00 1.50

Nos. C189-C192 Overprinted in Red "100e ANNIVERSAIRE DE L'UNION POSTALE UNIVERSELLE / 9 OCTOBRE 1974"

1974, Oct. 9

C197 A106 100fr multi .65 .35
C198 A106 200fr multi 1.40 .65
C199 A106 300fr multi 2.00 1.00
Nos. C197-C199 (3) 4.05 2.00

Souvenir Sheet

C200 A106 500fr multi 3.00 1.40

Universal Postal Union, centenary.

Flower Type of 1974

Flower Paintings by: 300fr, Auguste Renoir. 400fr, Carl Brendt.

1974, Oct. 31 Litho. *Perf. 12½x13*

C201 A109 300fr multi 2.00 1.00

Souvenir Sheet

C202 A109 400fr multi 2.50 1.40

Locomotive Type of 1975

Locomotives from Railroad Museum. Mulhouse, France: 100fr, Crampton No. 80, 1852. 200fr, No. 701, 1885-92. 300fr, "Forquenot," 1882.

1975, Feb. 28 Litho. *Perf. 13x12½*

C203 A112 100fr multi .65 .35
C204 A112 200fr multi 1.40 .65

Souvenir Sheet

C205 A112 300fr multi 2.00 1.00

Old Cars Type, 1975

Flags and Old Cars: 150fr, Germany and Mercedes-Benz, 1929. 200fr, Germany and Maybach, 1936. 400fr, Great Britain and Rolls Royce Silver Ghost, 1910.

1975, Apr. 6 *Perf. 14x13½*

C206 A113 150fr multi 1.00 .50
C207 A113 200fr multi 1.40 .65

Souvenir Sheet

C208 A113 400fr multi 2.50 1.40

American Bicentennial Type of 1975

American Bicentennial: 200fr, Washington crossing Delaware. 300fr, Hessians Captured at Trenton.

1975, May 6 Litho. *Perf. 14*

C209 A114 200fr multi 1.40 .65
C210 A114 300fr multi 2.00 1.00

Schweitzer Type of 1975

Albert Schweitzer and: 150fr, Toucan. 175fr, Vulturine guinea fowl. 200fr, King vulture. 450fr, Crested corythornis.

1975, May 25 Litho. *Perf. 13½*

C212 A115 150fr multi 1.00 .50
C213 A115 175fr multi 1.20 .55
C214 A115 200fr multi 1.40 .65
Nos. C212-C214 (3) 3.60 1.70

Souvenir Sheet

C215 A115 450fr multi 3.00 1.50

Apollo Soyuz Type of 1975

Designs: 100fr, Apollo and Soyuz near link-up. 200fr, Cosmonauts Alexei Leonov and Valeri Kubasov. 300fr, Astronauts Donald K. Slayton, Vance Brand and Thomas P. Stafford. 500fr, Apollo Soyuz emblem, US and USSR flags.

1975, July 18 Litho. *Perf. 13½*
C216 A116 100fr multi .65 .35
C217 A116 200fr multi 1.40 .65
C218 A116 300fr multi 2.00 1.00
Nos. C216-C218 (3) 4.05 2.00

Souvenir Sheet

C219 A116 500fr multi 3.50 1.60

Picasso Type of 1975

Picasso Paintings: 150fr, El Prado, horiz. 350fr, Couple in Patio. 400fr, Science and Charity.

1975, Aug. 7
C220 A117 150fr multi 1.00 .50
C221 A117 350fr multi 2.25 1.20

Souvenir Sheet

C222 A117 400fr multi 2.50 1.40

EXPO '75 Type of 1975

Expo '75 emblem and: 150fr, Passenger liner Asama Maru. 300fr, Future floating city Aquapolis.

1975, Sept. 26 Litho. *Perf. 11*
C223 A118 150fr multi .75 .38

Souvenir Sheet

Perf. 13½

C224 A118 300fr multi 1.50 .75

Winter Olympic Games Type of 1975

Innsbruck Background, Olympic Emblem and: 100fr, Ice hockey. 200fr, Ski jump. 300fr, Speed skating.

1975, Dec. 15 *Perf. 13½*
C225 A122 100fr multi .65 .35
C226 A122 200fr multi 1.40 .65

Souvenir Sheet

C227 A122 300fr multi 2.00 1.00

Olympic Games Type of 1976

Olympic Emblem and: 125fr, Heavyweight judo. 150fr, Weight lifting. 500fr, Sprint.

1976, Mar. 17 Litho. *Perf. 13½*
C228 A123 125fr multi .65 .30
C229 A123 150fr multi .75 .38

Souvenir Sheet

C230 A123 500fr multi 2.50 1.25

Summer Olympic Games Type of 1976

Olympic emblem and: 150fr, Pole vault. 200fr, Gymnast on balance beam. 500fr, Two-man sculls.

1976, Mar. 25 *Perf. 11*
C231 A124 150fr multi .75 .38
C232 A124 200fr multi 1.00 .50

Souvenir Sheet

C233 A124 500fr multi 2.50 1.25

For overprint see No. C245-C247.

Zeppelin Type of 1976

Airships: 100fr, Graf Zeppelin over Swiss Alps. 200fr, LZ-129 over city. 300fr, Graf Zeppelin. 500fr, Zeppelin over Bodensee.

1976, May 11
C234 A126 100fr multi .65 .35
C235 A126 200fr multi 1.40 .65
C236 A126 300fr multi 2.00 1.00
Nos. C234-C236 (3) 4.05 2.00

Souvenir Sheet

C237 A126 500fr multi 3.50 1.60

Viking Mars Type of 1976

Designs: 200fr, Viking lander assembly. 300fr, Viking orbiter in descent on Mars. 450fr, Viking in Mars orbit.

1976, June 24 Litho. *Perf. 13½*
C238 A127 200fr multi 1.00 .50
C239 A127 300fr multi 1.50 .75

Souvenir Sheet

C240 A127 450fr multi 2.25 1.10

American Bicentennial Type of 1976

Bicentennial and Interphil '76 Emblems and: 100fr, Siege of Yorktown. 200fr, Battle of Cape St. Vincent. 300fr, Peter Francisco's bravery. 500fr, Surrender of the Hessians.

1976, Sept. 30 Litho. *Perf. 13½*
C241 A129 100fr multi .65 .35
C242 A129 200fr multi 1.40 .65
C243 A129 300fr multi 2.00 1.00
Nos. C241-C243 (3) 4.05 2.00

Souvenir Sheet

C244 A129 500fr multi 3.50 1.60

Nos. C231-C233 Overprinted in Gold:
a. VAINQUEUR 1976 / TADEUSZ SLUSARSKI / POLOGNE
b. VAINQUEUR 1976 / NADIA COMANECI / ROUMANIE
c. VAINQUEUR 1976 / FRANK ET ALF HANSEN / NORVEGE

1976, July 4 Litho. *Perf. 11*
C245 A124(a) 150fr multi 1.00 .50
C246 A124(b) 200fr multi 1.40 .65

Souvenir Sheet

C247 A124(c) 500fr multi 3.50 1.60

Winners, 21st Olympic Games.

UPU Emblem over Globe — AP60

1978, Aug. 8 Litho. *Perf. 13*
C248 AP60 350fr multi 2.25 1.50

Congress of Paris, establishing UPU, cent.

Jules Verne, Apollo 11 Emblem, Footprint on Moon, Neil Armstrong — AP61

Space Conquest: 50fr, Yuri Gagarin and moon landing. 100fr, Montgolfier hot air balloon and memorial medal, 1783; Bleriot's monoplane, 1909.

1978, Sept. 27 Litho. *Perf. 13x12½*
C249 AP61 50fr multi .35 .16
C250 AP61 60fr multi .40 .20
C251 AP61 100fr multi .65 .35
Nos. C249-C251 (3) 1.40 .71

Anti-Apartheid Year — AP62

1978, Oct. 12 Litho. *Perf. 13*
C252 AP62 100fr blue & multi .65 .35

Philexafrique II-Essen Issue

Common Design Types

Designs: #C253, Hippopotamus and Upper Volta #C18. #C254, Hummingbird and Hanover #1.

1978, Nov. 1 Litho. *Perf. 12½*
C253 CD138 100fr multi .65 .35
C254 CD139 100fr multi .65 .35

Nos. C253-C254 printed se-tenant.

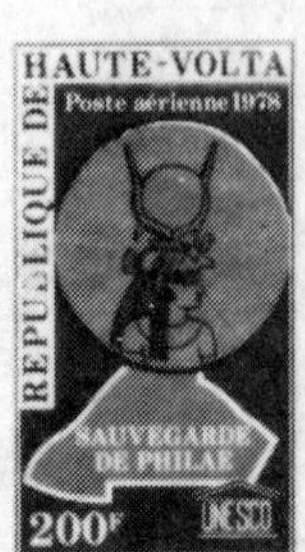

Sun God Horus with Sun — AP63

Jules Verne and Balloon — AP64

Design: 300fr, Falcon with cartouches and UNESCO emblem.

1978, Dec. 4
C255 AP63 200fr multi 1.40 .65
C256 AP63 300fr multi 2.00 1.00

UNESCO Campaign to safeguard monuments at Philae.

1978, Dec. 10 Engr. *Perf. 13*
C257 AP64 200fr multi 1.40 .65

Verne (1828-1905), science fiction writer.

Bicycling, Olympic Rings AP65

Designs: Bicycling scenes.

1980 *Perf. 14½*
C258 AP65 65fr multi .65 .32
C259 AP65 150fr multi, vert. 1.00 .50
C260 AP65 250fr multi 1.60 .80
C261 AP65 350fr multi 2.25 1.20
Nos. C258-C261 (4) 5.50 2.82

Souvenir Sheet

C262 AP65 500fr multi 3.50 1.60

22nd Summer Olympic Games, Moscow, July 19-Aug. 3.

Nos. C258-C262 Overprinted with Name of Winner and Country

1980, Nov. 22 Litho. *Perf. 14½*
C263 AP65 65fr multi .42 .20
C264 AP65 150fr multi 1.00 .50
C265 AP65 250fr multi 1.60 .80
C266 AP65 350fr multi 2.25 1.20
Nos. C263-C266 (4) 5.27 2.70

Souvenir Sheet

C267 AP65 500fr multi 3.50 1.60

1982 World Cup — AP66

Designs: Various soccer players.

1982, June 22 Litho. *Perf. 13½*
C268 AP66 70fr multi .45 .22
C269 AP66 90fr multi .60 .30
C270 AP66 150fr multi 1.00 .50
C271 AP66 300fr multi 2.00 1.00
Nos. C268-C271 (4) 4.05 2.02

Souvenir Sheet

C272 AP66 500fr multi 3.50 1.60

Anniversaries and Events — AP67

1983, June Litho. *Perf. 13½*
C273 AP67 90fr Space Shuttle .30 .15
C274 AP67 120fr World Soccer Cup .40 .20
C275 AP67 300fr Cup, diff. 1.00 .50
C276 AP67 450fr Royal Wedding 1.50 .70
Nos. C273-C276 (4) 3.20 1.55

Souvenir Sheet

C277 AP67 500fr Prince Charles, Lady Diana 1.60 1.60

Pre-Olympics, 1984 Los Angeles AP68

1983, Aug. 1 Litho. *Perf. 13*
C278 AP68 90fr Sailing .30 .15
C279 AP68 120fr Type 470 .40 .20
C280 AP68 300fr Wind surfing 1.00 .50
C281 AP68 400fr Wind surfing, diff. 1.40 .65
Nos. C278-C281 (4) 3.10 1.50

Souvenir Sheet

C282 AP68 520fr Soling Class, Wind surfing 1.60 1.60

Christmas AP69

Rubens Paintings.

1983 Litho. *Perf. 13*
C283 AP69 120fr Adoration of the Shepherds .40 .20
C284 AP69 350fr Virgin of the Garland 1.20 .60
C285 AP69 500fr Adoration of the Kings 1.60 .80
Nos. C283-C285 (3) 3.20 1.60

1984 Summer Olympics — AP70

1984, Mar. 26 Litho. *Perf. 12½*
C286 AP70 90fr Handball, vert. .30 .15
C287 AP70 120fr Volleyball, vert. .40 .20
C288 AP70 150fr Handball, diff. .50 .25
C289 AP70 250fr Basketball .80 .42
C290 AP70 300fr Soccer 1.00 .50
Nos. C286-C290 (5) 3.00 1.52

Souvenir Sheet

C291 AP70 500fr Volleyball, diff. 1.60 .80

Local Birds AP71

1984, May 14 Litho. *Perf. 12½*
C292 AP71 90fr Phoenicopterus roseus .30 .15
C293 AP71 185fr Choriotis kori, vert. .62 .32
C294 AP71 200fr Buphagus erythrorhynchus, vert. .65 .35
C295 AP71 300fr Bucorvus leadbeateri 1.00 .50
Nos. C292-C295 (4) 2.57 1.32

AP72

Famous Men — AP73

Designs: 5fr, Houari Boumediene (1927-1978), president of Algeria 1965-78. 125fr, Gottlieb Daimler (1834-1900), German automotive pioneer, and 1886 Daimler. 250fr, Louis Bleriot (1872-1936), French aviator, first to fly the English Channel in a heavier-than-air craft. 300fr, Abraham Lincoln. 400fr, Henri Dunant (1828-1910), founder of the Red Cross. 450fr, Auguste Piccard (1884-1962), Swiss physicist, inventor of the bathyscaphe Trieste, 1948. 500fr, Robert Baden-Powell (1856-1941), founder of Boy Scouts. 600fr, Anatoli Karpov, Russian chess champion. 1000fr, Paul Harris (1868-1947), founder of Rotary Intl.

1984, May 21 Litho. *Perf. 13½*

C296 AP72 5fr multi .15 .15
C297 AP72 125fr multi .50 .25
C298 AP72 250fr multi 1.00 .50
C299 AP72 300fr multi 1.20 .60
C300 AP72 400fr multi 1.60 .80
C301 AP72 450fr multi 1.90 .90
C302 AP72 500fr multi 2.00 1.00
C303 AP72 600fr multi 2.25 1.20
Nos. C296-C303 (8) 10.60 5.40

Souvenir Sheet

C304 AP73 1000fr multi 4.00 2.00

No. C304 contains one 51x30mm stamp.

Burkina Faso

Butterflies — AP73a

1984, May 23 *Perf. 13½*

C305 AP73a 10fr Graphium pylades .15 .15
C306 AP73a 120fr Hypolimnas misippus .50 .22
C307 AP73a 400fr Danaus chrysippus 1.60 .80
C308 AP73a 450fr Papilio demodocus 1.90 .90
Nos. C305-C308 (4) 4.15 2.07

Philexafrica '85, Lome — AP74

1985, May 20 Litho. *Perf. 13*

C309 AP74 200fr Solar & wind energy .55 .25
C310 AP74 200fr Children .55 .25

Nos. C309-C310 se-tenant with center label picturing a map of Africa or the exhibition emblem.

PHILEXAFRICA '85, Lome — AP75

National development: No. C311, Youth. No. C312, Communications and transportation.

1985, Nov. 16 Litho. *Perf. 13*

C311 AP75 250fr multi .90 .45
C312 AP75 250fr multi .90 .45

Intl. Youth Year (No. C311). Nos. C311-C312 printed se-tenant with center label picturing PHILEXAFRICA '85 emblem or outline map of Africa.

French Revolution, Bicent. — AP76

Illustration reduced.

Designs: 150fr, *Oath of the Tennis Court,* by David. 200fr, *Storming of the Bastille,* by Thevenin. 600fr, *Rouget de Lisle Singing La Marseillaise,* by Pils.

1989, May 3 Litho. *Perf. 13*

C313 AP76 150fr multi .90 .45
C314 AP76 200fr multi 1.20 .60
C315 AP76 600fr multi 3.60 1.80
Nos. C313-C315 (3) 5.70 2.85

PHILEXFRANCE '89. Printed se-tenant with label containing the exhibition emblem.

POSTAGE DUE STAMPS

Postage Due Stamps of Upper Senegal and Niger, 1914, Overprinted in Black or Red **HAUTE-VOLTA**

1920 Unwmk. *Perf. 14x13½*

J1 D2 5c green .30 .30
J2 D2 10c rose .30 .30
J3 D2 15c gray .30 .30
J4 D2 20c brown (R) .40 .40
J5 D2 30c blue .45 .45
J6 D2 50c black (R) .65 .65
J7 D2 60c orange .65 .65
J8 D2 1fr violet .90 .90
Nos. J1-J8 (8) 3.95 3.95

Type of 1914 Issue Surcharged

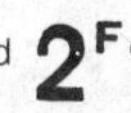

1927

J9 D2 2fr on 1fr lilac rose 2.25 2.25
J10 D2 3fr on 1fr orange brn 2.50 2.50

D3

Red-fronted Gazelle — D4

1928 Typo.

J11 D3 5c green .30 .30
J12 D3 10c rose .30 .30
J13 D3 15c dark gray .40 .40
J14 D3 20c dark brown .40 .40
J15 D3 30c dark blue .50 .50
J16 D3 50c black 1.60 1.60
J17 D3 60c orange 2.00 2.00
J18 D3 1fr dull violet 3.25 3.25
J19 D3 2fr lilac rose 6.00 6.00
J20 D3 3fr orange brn 6.25 6.25
Nos. J11-J20 (10) 21.00 21.00

Catalogue values for unused stamps in this section, from this point to the end of the section, are for Never Hinged items.

Republic

1962, Jan. 31 *Perf. 14x13½*

Denomination in Black

J21 D4 1fr bright blue .15 .15
J22 D4 2fr orange .15 .15
J23 D4 5fr brt vio blue .15 .15
J24 D4 10fr red lilac .20 .20
J25 D4 20fr emerald .45 .45
J26 D4 50fr rose red 1.10 1.10
Nos. J21-J26 (6) 2.20 2.20

OFFICIAL STAMPS

Catalogue values for unused stamps in this section are for Never Hinged items.

Elephant O1

Perf. 12½

1963, Feb. 1 Unwmk. Photo.

Center in Sepia

O1 O1 1fr red brown .15 .15
O2 O1 5fr yel green .15 .15
O3 O1 10fr deep vio .20 .20
O4 O1 15fr red org .25 .25
O5 O1 25fr brt rose lilac .35 .35
O6 O1 50fr brt green .55 .55
O7 O1 60fr brt red .70 .70
O8 O1 85fr dk slate grn 1.10 1.10
O9 O1 100fr brt blue 1.75 1.75
O10 O1 200fr bright rose 3.00 3.00
Nos. O1-O10 (10) 8.20 8.20

BURUNDI

bú-'rün-dē

LOCATION — Central Africa, adjoining the ex-Belgian Congo Republic, Rwanda and Tanzania
GOVT. — Republic
AREA — 10,759 sq. mi.
POP. — 4,920,000 (est. 1983)
CAPITAL — Bujumbura

Burundi was established as an independent country on July 1, 1962. With Rwanda, it had been a UN trusteeship territory (Ruanda-Urundi) administered by Belgium. A military coup overthrew the monarchy November 28, 1966.

100 Centimes = 1 Franc

Catalogue values for all unused stamps in this country are for Never Hinged items.

Flower Issue of Ruanda-Urundi, 1953 Overprinted:

Royaume
du

Burundi

Perf. 11½

1962, July 1 Unwmk. Photo.

Flowers in Natural Colors

1 A27 25c dk grn & dull org .15 .15
2 A27 40c green & salmon .15 .15
3 A27 60c blue grn & pink .20 .15
4 A27 1.25fr dk green & blue 7.00 6.50
5 A27 1.50fr vio & apple grn .30 .25
6 A27 5fr dp plum & lt bl grn .42 .30
7 A27 7fr dk green & fawn .85 .55
8 A27 10fr dp plum & pale ol 1.20 .85
Nos. 1-8 (8) 10.27 8.90

Animal Issue of Ruanda-Urundi, 1959-61 with Similar Overprint or Surcharge in Black or Violet Blue

Size: 23x33mm, 33x23mm

9 A29 10c brn, crim & blk brn .15 .15
10 A30 20c gray, ap grn & blk .15 .15
11 A29 40c mag, blk & gray grn .15 .15
12 A30 50c grn, org yel & brn .15 .15
a. Larger overprint and bar .15 .15
13 A29 1fr brn, ultra & blk .15 .15
14 A30 1.50fr blk, gray & org (VB) .15 .15
15 A29 2fr grnsh bl, ind & brn .15 .15
16 A30 3fr brn, dp car & blk .15 .15
17 A30 3.50fr on 3fr brn, dp car & blk .15 .15
18 A30 4fr on 10fr multi ("XX" 6mm wide) .15 .15
a. "XX" 4mm wide .45 .45
19 A30 5fr multicolored .15 .15
20 A30 6.50fr red, org yel & brn .25 .18
21 A30 8fr bl, mag & blk .30 .22
a. Violet blue overprint .65 .65
22 A30 10fr multicolored .30 .30

Size: 45x26½mm

23 A30 20fr multicolored .65 .65
24 A30 50fr multi (ovpt. bars 2mm wide) 1.25 1.10
a. Overprint bars 4mm wide 1.90 1.10
Set value 3.65 3.35

On #12a, "Burundi" is 13mm long; bar is continuous line across sheet. On #12, "Burundi" is 10mm; bar is 29mm. #12a was issued in 1963.

Two types of overprint exist on 10c, 40c, 1fr and 2fr: I, "du" is below "me"; bar 22½mm. II, "du" below "oy"; bar 20mm.

The 50c and 3fr exist in two types, besides the larger 50c overprint listed as No. 12: I, "du" is closer to "Royaume" than to "Burundi"; bar is less than 29mm; wording is centered above bar. II, "du" is closer to "Burundi"; bar is more than 30mm; wording is off-center leftward.

King Mwami Mwambutsa IV and Royal Drummers — A1

Flag and Arms of Burundi — A2

Design: 2fr, 8fr, 50fr, Map of Burundi and King.

Unwmk.

1962, Sept. 27 Photo. *Perf. 14*

25 A1 50c dull rose car & dk brn .15 .15
26 A2 1fr dk green, red & emer .15 .15
27 A1 2fr brown ol & dk brn .15 .15
28 A1 3fr vermilion & dk brn .22 .15
29 A2 4fr Prus blue, red & emer .18 .15
30 A1 8fr violet & dk brn .32 .15
31 A1 10fr brt green & dk brn .50 .15
32 A2 20fr brown, red & emer 1.25 .20
33 A1 50fr brt pink & dk brn 2.25 .40
Nos. 25-33 (9) 5.17
Set value 1.00

Burundi's independence, July 1, 1962.
See #47-50. For overprints see #45-46, 51-52.

Ruanda-Urundi Nos. 151-152 Surcharged:

HOMMAGE A
DAG HAMMARSKJÖLD
3.50F
ROYAUME DU BURUNDI

Photogravure, Surcharge Engraved

1962, Oct. 31 *Perf. 11½*

Inscription in French

34 A31 3.50fr on 3fr ultra & red .15 .15
35 A31 6.50fr on 3fr ultra & red .20 .15
36 A31 10fr on 3fr ultra & red .30 .25

Inscription in Flemish

37 A31 3.50fr on 3fr ultra & red .15 .15
38 A31 6.50fr on 3fr ultra & red .20 .15
39 A31 10fr on 3fr ultra & red .30 .25
Nos. 34-39 (6) 1.30 1.10

Dag Hammarskjold, Secretary General of the United Nations, 1953-61.

King Mwami Mwambutsa IV, Map of Burundi and Emblem — A3

1962, Dec. 10 Photo. *Perf. 14*

40	A3	8fr yel, bl grn & blk brn	.65	.15
41	A3	50fr gray grn, bl grn & blk brn	1.75	.35

WHO drive to eradicate malaria.

Stamps of type A3 without anti-malaria emblem are listed as Nos. 27, 30 and 33.

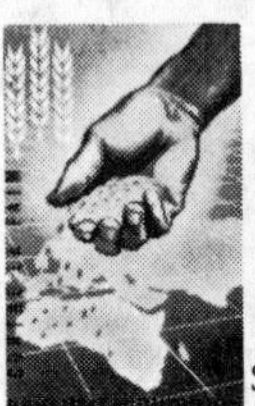

Sowing Seed over Africa — A4

1963, Mar. 21 *Perf. 14x13*

42	A4	4fr olive & dull pur	.15	.15
43	A4	8fr dp org & dull pur	.15	.15
44	A4	15fr emerald & dull pur	.20	.15
		Set value	.41	.30

FAO "Freedom from Hunger" campaign.

Nos. 27 and 33 Overprinted in Dark Green

1963, June 19 Unwmk. *Perf. 14*

45	A1	2fr brn olive & dk brn	1.65	1.25
46	A1	50fr brt pink & dk brn	1.90	1.25

Conquest and peaceful use of outer space.

Types of 1962 Inscribed: "Premier Anniversaire" in Red or Magenta

1963, July 1 Photo.

47	A2	4fr olive, red & emer (R)	.15	.15
48	A1	8fr orange & dk brn (M)	.15	.15
49	A1	10fr lilac & dk brn (M)	.20	.15
50	A2	20fr gray, red & emer (R)	.40	.25
		Nos. 47-50 (4)	.90	
		Set value		.50

First anniversary of independence.

Nos. 26 and 32 Surcharged in Brown

1963, Sept. 24 Unwmk. *Perf. 14*

51	A2	6.50fr on 1fr multi	.38	.15
52	A2	15fr on 20fr multi	.75	.25

Red Cross Flag over Globe with Map of Africa — A5

1963, Sept. 26 *Perf. 14x13*

53	A5	4fr emer, car & gray	.15	.15
54	A5	8fr brn ol, car & gray	.25	.15
55	A5	10fr blue, car & gray	.38	.18
56	A5	20fr lilac, car & gray	.75	.30
		Nos. 53-56 (4)	1.53	.78

Centenary of International Red Cross. See No. B7.

"1962", Arms of Burundi, UN and UNESCO Emblems A6

UN Agency Emblems: 8fr, ITU. 10fr, World Meteorological Organization. 20fr, UPU. 50fr, FAO.

1963, Nov. 4 Unwmk. *Perf. 14*

57	A6	4fr yel, ol grn & blk	.15	.15
58	A6	8fr pale lil, Prus bl & blk	.15	.15
59	A6	10fr blue, lil & blk	.20	.15
60	A6	20fr yel grn, grn & blk	.35	.15
61	A6	50fr yel, red brn & blk	.90	.30
a.		Souvenir sheet of 2	3.00	3.00
		Nos. 57-61 (5)	1.75	
		Set value		.65

1st anniv. of Burundi's admission to the UN. No. 61a contains two imperf. stamps with simulated perforations similar to Nos. 60-61. The 20fr stamp shows the FAO and the 50fr the WMO emblems.

UNESCO Emblem, Scales and Map — A7

Designs: 3.50fr, 6.50fr, Scroll, scales and "UNESCO." 10fr, 20fr, Abraham Lincoln, broken chain and scales.

1963, Dec. 10 Litho. *Perf. 14x13½*

62	A7	50c pink, lt bl & blk	.15	.15
63	A7	1.50fr org, lt bl & blk	.15	.15
64	A7	3.50fr fawn, lt grn & blk	.15	.15
65	A7	6.50fr lt vio, lt grn & blk	.18	.15
66	A7	10fr blue, bis & blk	.30	.15
67	A7	20fr pale brn, ocher, bl & blk	.60	.18
		Set value	1.25	.55

15th anniv. of the Universal Declaration of Human Rights and the cent. of the American Emancipation Proclamation (Nos. 66-67).

Ice Hockey — A8

Impala — A9

Designs: 3.50fr, Women's figure skating. 6.50fr, Torch. 10fr, Men's speed skating. 20fr, Slalom.

Unwmk.

1964, Jan. 25 Photo. *Perf. 14*

68	A8	50c olive, blk & gold	.15	.15
69	A8	3.50fr lt brown, blk & gold	.15	.15
70	A8	6.50fr pale gray, blk & gold	.38	.15
71	A8	10fr gray, blk & gold	.50	.15
72	A8	20fr tan, blk & gold	1.00	.32
		Nos. 68-72 (5)	2.18	
		Set value		.65

Issued to publicize the 9th Winter Olympic Games, Innsbruck, Jan. 29-Feb. 9, 1964.

A souvenir sheet contains two stamps (10fr+5fr and 20fr+5fr) in tan, black and gold.

Canceled to Order

Starting about 1964, values in the used column are for "canceled to order" stamps. Postally used copies sell for much more.

1964 Litho. *Perf. 14x13, 13x14*

Animals: 1fr, 5fr, Hippopotamus, horiz. 1.50fr, 10fr, Giraffe. 2fr, 8fr, Cape buffalo, horiz. 3fr, 6.50fr, Zebra, horiz. 3.50fr, 15fr, Defassa waterbuck. 20fr, Cheetah. 50fr, Elephant. 100fr, Lion.

Size: 21½x35mm, 35x21½mm

73	A9	50c multi	.15	.15
74	A9	1fr multi	.15	.15
75	A9	1.50fr multi	.15	.15
76	A9	2fr multi	.15	.15
77	A9	3fr multi	.18	.15
78	A9	3.50fr multi	.20	.15

Size: 26x42mm, 42x26mm

79	A9	4fr multi	.22	.15
80	A9	5fr multi	.28	.15
81	A9	6.50fr multi	.32	.15
82	A9	8fr multi	.40	.15
83	A9	10fr multi	.50	.15
84	A9	15fr multi	.65	.18

Perf. 14

Size: 53x33mm

85	A9	20fr multi	.85	.20
86	A9	50fr multi	2.25	.32
87	A9	100fr multi	4.00	.65
		Nos. 73-87,C1-C7 (22)	13.12	
		Set value		2.80

Burundi Dancer — A10

Designs: Various Dancers and Drummers.

Unwmk.

1964, Aug. 21 Litho. *Perf. 14*

Dancers Multicolored

88	A10	50c gold & emerald	.15	.15
89	A10	1fr gold & vio blue	.15	.15
90	A10	4fr gold & brt blue	.15	.15
91	A10	6.50fr gold & red	.20	.15
92	A10	10fr gold & brt blue	.30	.15
93	A10	15fr gold & emerald	.45	.15
94	A10	20fr gold & red	.65	.22
a.		Souvenir sheet of 3, #92-94	1.50	1.50
		Nos. 88-94 (7)	2.05	
		Set value		.73

1965, Sept. 10

Dancers Multicolored

88a	A10	50c silver & emerald	.15	.15
89a	A10	1fr silver & violet blue	.15	.15
90a	A10	4fr silver & bright blue	.15	.15
91a	A10	6.50fr silver & red	.15	.15
92a	A10	10fr silver & bright blue	.18	.15
93a	A10	15fr silver & emerald	.20	.18
94b	A10	20fr silver & red	.30	.30
c.		Souvenir sheet of 3, #92a-94b	1.50	1.50
		Set value	.95	.80

New York World's Fair, 1964-65.

Pope Paul VI and King Mwami Mwambutsa IV — A11

22 Sainted Martyrs — A12

Designs: 4fr, 14fr, Pope John XXIII and King Mwami.

1964, Nov. 12 Photo. *Perf. 12*

95	A11	50c brt bl, gold & red brn	.15	.15
96	A12	1fr mag, gold & slate	.15	.15
97	A11	4fr pale rose lil, gold & brn	.18	.15
98	A12	8fr red, gold & brn	.18	.15
99	A11	14fr lt grn, gold & brn	.42	.15
100	A11	20fr red brn, gold & grn	.65	.30
		Nos. 95-100 (6)	1.73	
		Set value		.68

Canonization of 22 African martyrs, 10/18/64.

Shot Put — A13

African Purple Gallinule — A14

Sports: 1fr, Discus. 3fr, Swimming, horiz. 4fr, Running. 6.50fr, Javelin, woman. 8fr, Hurdling, horiz. 10fr, Broad jump, horiz. 14fr, Diving, woman. 18fr, High jump, horiz. 20fr, Vaulting, horiz.

1964, Nov. 18 Litho. *Perf. 14*

101	A13	50c olive & multi	.15	.15
102	A13	1fr brt pink & multi	.15	.15
103	A13	3fr multi	.15	.15
104	A13	4fr multi	.15	.15
105	A13	6.50fr multi	.15	.15
106	A13	8fr lt bl & multi	.16	.15
107	A13	10fr multi	.20	.15
108	A13	14fr multi	.26	.15
109	A13	18fr bister & multi	.32	.18
110	A13	20fr gray & multi	.35	.22
		Set value	1.60	.95

18th Olympic Games, Tokyo, Oct. 10-25, 1964. See No. B8.

1965 Unwmk. *Perf. 14*

Birds: 1fr, 5fr, Little bee eater. 1.50fr, 6.50fr, Secretary bird. 2fr, 8fr, Yellow-billed stork. 3fr, 10fr, Congo peacock. 3.50fr, 15fr, African anhinga. 20fr, Saddle-billed stork. 50fr, Abyssinian ground hornbill. 100fr, Crowned crane.

Birds in Natural Colors

Size: 21x35mm

111	A14	50c tan, grn & blk	.15	.15
112	A14	1fr pink, mag & blk	.15	.15
113	A14	1.50fr blue & blk	.15	.15
114	A14	2fr yel grn, dk grn & blk	.15	.15
115	A14	3fr yellow, brn & blk	.15	.15
116	A14	3.50fr yel grn, dk grn & blk	.15	.15

Size: 26x43mm

117	A14	4fr tan, grn & blk	.15	.15
118	A14	5fr pink, mag & blk	.15	.15
119	A14	6.50fr blue & blk	.15	.15
120	A14	8fr yel grn, dk grn & blk	.15	.15
121	A14	10fr yel, brn & blk	.20	.15
122	A14	15fr yel grn, dk grn & blk	.38	.15

Size: 33x53mm

123	A14	20fr rose lilac & blk	.50	.30
124	A14	50fr yellow, brn & blk	1.25	.20
125	A14	100fr green, yel & blk	2.75	.40
		Nos. 111-125 (15)	6.58	
		Set value		1.50

Issue dates: Nos. 111-116, Mar. 31. Nos. 117-122, Apr. 16. Nos. 123-125, Apr. 30.

For overprints see #174-184, C35A-C35I.

Relay Satellite and Morse Key — A15

Designs: 3fr, Telstar and old telephone handpiece. 4fr, Relay satellite and old wall telephone. 6.50fr, Orbiting Geophysical Observatory and radar screen. 8fr, Telstar II and headphones. 10fr, Sputnik II and radar aerial. 14fr, Syncom and transmission aerial. 20fr, Interplanetary Explorer and tracking aerial.

1965, July 3 Litho. *Perf. 13*

126 A15	1fr	multi	.15	.15
127 A15	3fr	multi	.15	.15
128 A15	4fr	multi	.15	.15
129 A15	6.50fr	multi	.15	.15
130 A15	8fr	multi	.15	.15
131 A15	10fr	multi	.18	.15
132 A15	14fr	multi	.25	.15
133 A15	20fr	multi	.30	.18
		Set value	1.10	.74

Cent. of the ITU. Perf. and imperf. souv. sheets of 2 contain Nos. 131, 133. Size: 120x86mm. Value, both sheets, $7.50.

Globe and ICY Emblem — A16

Designs: 4fr, Map of Africa and UN development emblem. 8fr, Map of Asia and Colombo Plan emblem. 10fr, Globe and UN emblem. 18fr, Map of the Americas and Alliance for Progress emblem. 25fr, Map of Europe and EUROPA emblems. 40fr, Map of Outer Space and satellite with UN wreath.

1965, Oct. 1 Litho. *Perf. 13*

134 A16	1fr	ol green & multi	.15	.15
135 A16	4fr	dull blue & multi	.15	.15
136 A16	8fr	pale yellow & multi	.15	.15
137 A16	10fr	lilac & multi	.16	.15
138 A16	18fr	salmon & multi	.25	.15
139 A16	25fr	gray & multi	.50	.15
140 A16	40fr	blue & multi	.75	.16
a.		Souvenir sheet of 3, #138-140	1.65	1.65
		Nos. 134-140 (7)	2.11	
		Set value		.70

International Cooperation Year.

Protea A17

Flowers: 1fr, 5fr, Crossandra. 1.50fr, 6.50fr, Ansellia. 2fr, 8fr, Thunbergia. 3fr, 10fr, Schizoglossum. 3.50fr, 15fr, Dissotis. 4fr, 20fr, Protea. 50fr, Gazania. 100fr, Hibiscus. 150fr, Markhamia.

1966 Unwmk. *Perf. 13½*

Size: 26x26mm

141 A17	50c	multi	.15	.15
142 A17	1fr	multi	.15	.15
143 A17	1.50fr	multi	.15	.15
144 A17	2fr	multi	.15	.15
145 A17	3fr	multi	.15	.15
146 A17	3.50fr	multi	.15	.15

Size: 31x31mm

147 A17	4fr	multi	.15	.15
148 A17	5fr	multi	.15	.15
149 A17	6.50fr	multi	.15	.15
150 A17	8fr	multi	.15	.15
151 A17	10fr	multi	.15	.15
152 A17	15fr	multi	.30	.15

Size: 39x39mm

153 A17	20fr	multi	.38	.15
154 A17	50fr	multi	1.00	.25
155 A17	100fr	multi	1.90	.38
156 A17	150fr	multi	2.75	.55
		Nos. 141-156,C17-C25 (25)	12.02	
		Set value		3.00

Issue dates: Nos. 141-147, Feb. 28; Nos. 148-153, May 18; Nos. 154-156, June 15.

For overprints see Nos. 159-173, C27-C35.

Souvenir Sheets

Allegory of Prosperity and Equality Tapestry by Peter Colfs — A18

1966, Nov. 4 Litho. *Perf. 13½*

157 A18	Sheet of 7 (1.50fr)		.65	.25
158 A18	Sheet of 7 (4fr)		1.65	.65

20th anniv. of UNESCO. Each sheet contains 6 stamps showing a reproduction of the Colfs tapestry from the lobby of the General Assembly Building, NYC, and one stamp with the UNESCO emblem plus a label. The labels on Nos. 157-158 and C26 are inscribed in French or English. The 3 sheets with French inscription have light blue marginal border. The 3 sheets with English inscription have pink border. See No. C26.

Republic

Nos. 141-152, 154-156 Overprinted

REPUBLIQUE
DU
BURUNDI

1967 Litho. *Perf. 13½*

Size: 26x26mm

159 A17	50c	multi	.15	.15
160 A17	1fr	multi	.15	.15
161 A17	1.50fr	multi	.15	.15
162 A17	2fr	multi	.15	.15
163 A17	3fr	multi	.15	.15
164 A17	3.50fr	multi	.15	.15

Size: 31x31mm

165 A17	4fr	multi	.80	.30
166 A17	5fr	multi	.16	.15
167 A17	6.50fr	multi	.20	.15
168 A17	8fr	multi	.25	.15
169 A17	10fr	multi	.32	.15
170 A17	15fr	multi	.38	.15

Size: 39x39mm

171 A17	50fr	multi	3.75	1.25
172 A17	100fr	multi	6.25	2.50
173 A17	150fr	multi	5.00	2.25
		Nos. 159-173,C27-C35 (24)	29.24	
		Set value		9.59

Nos. 111, 113, 116, 118-125 Overprinted "REPUBLIQUE DU BURUNDI" and Horizontal Bar

1967 Litho. *Perf. 14*

Birds in Natural Colors

Size: 21x35mm

174 A14	50c	multi	1.25	.65
175 A14	1.50fr	blue & black	.15	.15
176 A14	3.50fr	multi	.15	.15

Size: 26x43mm

177 A14	5fr	multi	.15	.15
178 A14	6.50fr	blue & black	.15	.15
179 A14	8fr	multi	.18	.15
180 A14	10fr	yel, brn & blk	.32	.15
181 A14	15fr	multi	.65	.15

Size: 33x53mm

182 A14	20fr	multi	2.00	.38
183 A14	50fr	multi	4.00	1.40
184 A14	100fr	multi	6.00	2.75
		Nos. 174-184 (11)	15.00	6.23

Haplochromis Multicolor — A19

Various Tropical Fish.

1967 Photo. *Perf. 13½*

Size: 42x19mm

186 A19	50c	multi	.15	.15
187 A19	1fr	multi	.15	.15
188 A19	1.50fr	multi	.15	.15
189 A19	2fr	multi	.15	.15
190 A19	3fr	multi	.15	.15
191 A19	3.50fr	multi	.15	.15

Size: 50x25mm

192 A19	4fr	multi	.16	.15
193 A19	5fr	multi	.20	.15
194 A19	6.50fr	multi	.25	.15
195 A19	8fr	multi	.28	.15
196 A19	10fr	multi	.32	.15
197 A19	15fr	multi	.50	.15

Size: 59x30mm

198 A19	20fr	multi	.65	.15
199 A19	50fr	multi	1.40	.18
200 A19	100fr	multi	3.00	.30
201 A19	150fr	multi	4.25	.45
		Nos. 186-201,C46-C54 (25)	17.27	
		Set value		2.50

Issue Dates: Nos. 186-191, Apr. 4; Nos. 192-197, Apr. 28; Nos. 198-201, May 18.

Ancestor Figures, Ivory Coast — A20

African Art: 1fr, Seat of Honor, Southeast Congo. 1.50fr, Antelope head, Aribinda Region. 2fr, Buffalo mask, Upper Volta. 4fr, Funeral figures, Southwest Ethiopia.

1967, June 5 Photo. *Perf. 13½*

202 A20	50c	silver & multi	.15	.15
203 A20	1fr	silver & multi	.15	.15
204 A20	1.50fr	silver & multi	.15	.15
205 A20	2fr	silver & multi	.15	.15
206 A20	4fr	silver & multi	.15	.15
		Set value, #202-206, C36-C40	1.30	.80

Scouts on Hiking Trip — A21

Designs: 1fr, Cooking at campfire. 1.50fr, Lord Baden-Powell. 2fr, Boy Scout and Cub Scout giving Scout sign. 4fr, First aid.

1967, Aug. 9 Photo. *Perf. 13½*

207 A21	50c	silver & multi	.15	.15
208 A21	1fr	silver & multi	.15	.15
209 A21	1.50fr	silver & multi	.15	.15
210 A21	2fr	silver & multi	.15	.15
211 A21	4fr	silver & multi	.15	.15
		Set value, #207-211, C41-C45	2.00	.90

60th anniv. of the Boy Scouts and the 12th Boy Scout World Jamboree, Farragut State Park, Idaho, Aug. 1-9.

The Gleaners, by Francois Millet A22

Paintings Exhibited at EXPO '67: 8fr, The Water Carrier of Seville, by Velazquez. 14fr, The Triumph of Neptune and Amphitrite, by Nicolas Poussin. 18fr, Acrobat Standing on a Ball, by Picasso. 25fr, Marguerite van Eyck, by Jan van Eyck. 40fr, St. Peter Denying Christ, by Rembrandt.

1967, Oct. 12 Photo. *Perf. 13½*

212 A22	4fr	multi	.15	.15
213 A22	8fr	multi	.18	.15
214 A22	14fr	multi	.25	.15
215 A22	18fr	multi	.32	.15
216 A22	25fr	multi	.50	.18
217 A22	40fr	multi	.75	.25
a.		Souvenir sheet of 2, #216-217	1.25	1.00
		Nos. 212-217 (6)	2.15	
		Set value		.69

EXPO '67 International Exhibition, Montreal, Apr. 28-Oct. 27. Printed in sheets of 10 stamps and 2 labels inscribed in French or English. No. 217a exists imperf.

Place de la Revolution and Pres. Michel Micombero — A23

Designs: 5fr, President Michel Micombero and flag. 14fr, Formal garden and coat of arms. 20fr, Modern building and coat of arms.

1967, Nov. 23 *Perf. 13½*

218 A23	5fr	multi	.15	.15
219 A23	14fr	multi	.20	.15
220 A23	20fr	multi	.30	.15
221 A23	30fr	multi	.45	.22
		Nos. 218-221 (4)	1.10	
		Set value		.47

First anniversary of the Republic.

Madonna by Carlo Crivelli — A24

Designs: 1fr, Adoration of the Shepherds by Juan Bautista Mayno. 4fr, Holy Family by Anthony Van Dyck. 14fr, Nativity by Maitre de Moulins.

1967, Dec. 7 Photo. *Perf. 13½*

222 A24	1fr	multi	.15	.15
223 A24	4fr	multi	.15	.15
224 A24	14fr	multi	.25	.15
225 A24	26fr	multi	.60	.25
		Nos. 222-225 (4)	1.15	
		Set value		.50

Christmas 1967.

Printed in sheets of 25 and one corner label inscribed "Noel 1967" and giving name of painting and painter.

Slalom — A25

Designs: 10fr, Ice hockey. 14fr, Women's skating. 17fr, Bobsled. 26fr, Ski jump. 40fr, Speed skating. 60fr, Hand holding torch, and Winter Olympics emblem.

1968, Feb. 16 Photo. *Perf. 13½*

226	A25	5fr silver & multi	.15	.15
227	A25	10fr silver & multi	.20	.15
228	A25	14fr silver & multi	.25	.15
229	A25	17fr silver & multi	.30	.15
230	A25	26fr silver & multi	.50	.15
231	A25	40fr silver & multi	.75	.15
232	A25	60fr silver & multi	1.25	.20
		Nos. 226-232 (7)	3.40	
		Set value		.60

Issued to publicize the 10th Winter Olympic Games, Grenoble, France, Feb. 6-18. Issued in sheets of 10 stamps and label.

The Lacemaker, by Vermeer A26

Paintings: 1.50fr, Portrait of a Young Man, by Botticelli. 2fr, Maja Vestida, by Goya, horiz.

1968, Mar. 29 Photo. *Perf. 13½*

233	A26	1.50fr gold & multi	.15	.15
234	A26	2fr gold & multi	.15	.15
235	A26	4fr gold & multi	.15	.15
		Nos. 233-235,C59-C61 (6)	1.80	
		Set value		.69

Issued in sheets of 6.

Moon Probe — A27

Designs: 6fr, Russian astronaut walking in space. 8fr, Weather satellite. 10fr, American astronaut walking in space.

1968, May 15 Photo. *Perf. 13½*

Size: 35x35mm

236	A27	4fr silver & multi	.15	.15
237	A27	6fr silver & multi	.15	.15
238	A27	8fr silver & multi	.20	.15
239	A27	10fr silver & multi	.22	.15
		Nos. 236-239,C62-C65 (8)	2.42	
		Set value		.65

Issued to publicize peaceful space explorations.

A souvenir sheet contains one 25fr stamp in Moon Probe design and one 40fr in Weather Satellite design. Stamp size: 41x41mm. Value $2. Sheet exists imperf. Price $3.

Salamis Aethiops — A28

Butterflies: 1fr, 5fr, Graphium ridleyanus. 1.50fr, 6.50fr, Cymothoe. 2fr, 8fr, Charaxes eupale. 3fr, 10fr, Papilio bromius. 3.50fr, 15fr, Teracolus annae. 20fr, Salamis aethiops. 50fr, Papilio zonobia. 100fr, Danais chrysippus. 150fr, Salamis temora.

1968

Size: 30x33½mm

240	A28	50c gold & multi	.15	.15
241	A28	1fr gold & multi	.15	.15
242	A28	1.50fr gold & multi	.15	.15
243	A28	2fr gold & multi	.15	.15
244	A28	3fr gold & multi	.15	.15
245	A28	3.50fr gold & multi	.15	.15

Size: 33½x37½mm

246	A28	4fr gold & multi	.15	.15
247	A28	5fr gold & multi	.15	.15
248	A28	6.50fr gold & multi	.28	.15
249	A28	8fr gold & multi	.32	.15
250	A28	10fr gold & multi	.38	.15
251	A28	15fr gold & multi	.45	.15

Size: 41x46mm

252	A28	20fr gold & multi	.75	.15
253	A28	50fr gold & multi	1.50	.15
254	A28	100fr gold & multi	2.50	.28
255	A28	150fr gold & multi	3.75	.40
		Nos. 240-255,C66-C74 (25)	16.26	
		Set value		2.25

Issue dates: Nos. 240-245, June 7; Nos. 246-251, June 28. Nos. 252-255, July 19.

Women, Along the Manzanares, by Goya — A29

Paintings: 7fr, The Letter, by Pieter de Hooch. 11fr, Woman Reading a Letter, by Gerard Terborch. 14fr, Man Writing a Letter, by Gabriel Metsu.

1968, Sept. 30 Photo. *Perf. 13½*

256	A29	4fr multi	.15	.15
257	A29	7fr multi	.15	.15
258	A29	11fr multi	.20	.15
259	A29	14fr multi	.30	.15
		Nos. 256-259,C84-C87 (8)	2.74	
		Set value		.80

International Letter Writing Week.

Soccer — A30

Designs: 7fr, Basketball. 13fr, High jump. 24fr, Relay race. 40fr, Javelin.

1968, Oct. 24

260	A30	4fr gold & multi	.15	.15
261	A30	7fr gold & multi	.15	.15
262	A30	13fr gold & multi	.18	.15
263	A30	24fr gold & multi	.35	.15
264	A30	40fr gold & multi	.60	.30
		Nos. 260-264,C88-C92 (10)	3.98	
		Set value		1.25

19th Olympic Games, Mexico City, Oct. 12-27. Printed in sheets of 8.

Virgin and Child, by Fra Filippo Lippi — A31

Paintings: 5fr, The Magnificat, by Sandro Botticelli. 6fr, Virgin and Child, by Albrecht Durer. 11fr, Madonna del Gran Duca, by Raphael.

1968, Nov. 26 Photo. *Perf. 13½*

265	A31	3fr multi	.15	.15
266	A31	5fr multi	.15	.15
267	A31	6fr multi	.15	.15
268	A31	11fr multi	.22	.15
a.		Souvenir sheet of 4, #265-268	1.00	1.00
		Nos. 265-268,C93-C96 (8)	1.72	
		Set value		.75

Christmas 1968. For overprints see Nos. 272-275, C100-C103.

WHO Emblem and Map of Africa — A32

1969, Jan. 22

269	A32	5fr gold, dk grn & yel	.15	.15
270	A32	6fr gold, vio & ver	.15	.15
271	A32	11fr gold, pur & red lil	.22	.15
		Nos. 269-271 (3)	.52	
		Set value		.21

20th anniv. of WHO in Africa.

Nos. 265-268 Overprinted in Silver

1969, Feb. 17 Photo. *Perf. 13½*

272	A31	3fr multi	.15	.15
273	A31	5fr multi	.15	.15
274	A31	6fr multi	.15	.15
275	A31	11fr multi	.22	.15
		Nos. 272-275,C100-C103 (8)	2.00	
		Set value		.85

Man's 1st flight around the moon by the US spacecraft Apollo 8, Dec. 21-27, 1968.

Map of Africa, and CEPT Emblem — A33

Designs: 14fr, Plowing with tractor. 17fr, Teacher and pupil. 26fr, Maps of Europe and Africa and CEPT (Conference of European Postal and Telecommunications Administrations) emblem, horiz.

1969, Mar. 12 Photo. *Perf. 13*

276	A33	5fr multi	.15	.15
277	A33	14fr multi	.20	.15
278	A33	17fr multi	.25	.15
279	A33	26fr multi	.32	.15
		Nos. 276-279 (4)	.92	
		Set value		.35

5th anniv. of the Yaounde (Cameroun) Agreement, creating the European and African-Malgache Economic Community.

Resurrection, by Gaspard Isenmann A34

Paintings: 14fr, Resurrection by Antoine Caron. 17fr, Noli me Tangere, by Martin Schongauer. 26fr, Resurrection, by El Greco.

1969, Mar. 24

280	A34	11fr gold & multi	.15	.15
281	A34	14fr gold & multi	.20	.15
282	A34	17fr gold & multi	.25	.15
283	A34	26fr gold & multi	.38	.15
a.		Souvenir sheet of 4, #280-283	1.50	1.50
		Nos. 280-283 (4)	.98	
		Set value		.34

Easter 1969.

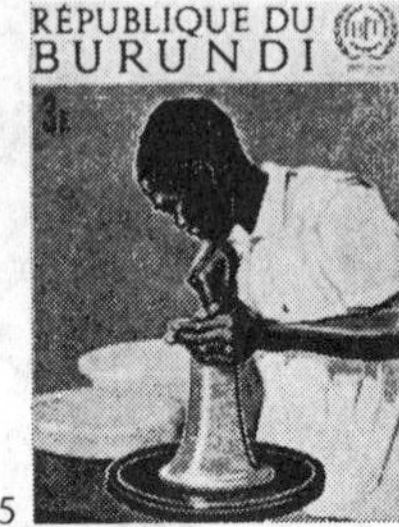

Potter — A35

Designs (ITU Emblem and): 5fr, Farm workers. 7fr, Foundry worker. 10fr, Woman testing corn crop.

1969, May 17 Photo. *Perf. 13½*

284	A35	3fr multicolored	.15	.15
285	A35	5fr multicolored	.15	.15
286	A35	7fr multicolored	.15	.15
287	A35	10fr multicolored	.20	.15
		Set value	.51	.25

50th anniv. of the ILO.

Industry and Bank's Emblem A36

Designs (African Development Bank Emblem and): 17fr, Communications. 30fr, Education. 50fr, Agriculture.

1969, July 29 Photo. *Perf. 13½*

288	A36	10fr gold & multi	.18	.15
289	A36	17fr gold & multi	.30	.15
290	A36	30fr gold & multi	.50	.15
291	A36	50fr gold & multi	.80	.25
a.		Souvenir sheet of 4, #288-291	1.90	1.90
		Nos. 288-291 (4)	1.78	
		Set value		.55

5th anniversary of the African Development Bank.

Girl Reading Letter, by Vermeer A37

Paintings: 7fr, Graziella (young woman), by Auguste Renoir. 14fr, Woman writing a letter, by Gerard Terborch. 26fr, Galileo Galilei, painter unknown. 40fr, Ludwig van Beethoven, painter unknown.

1969, Oct. 24 Photo. *Perf. 13½*

292 A37 4fr multicolored .15 .15
293 A37 7fr multicolored .15 .15
294 A37 14fr multicolored .32 .15
295 A37 26fr multicolored .55 .15
296 A37 40fr multicolored .75 .20
a. Souvenir sheet of 2, #295-296 1.75 1.75
Nos. 292-296 (5) 1.92
Set value .52

Intl. Letter Writing Week, Oct. 7-13.

Rocket Launching A38

Moon Landing: 6.50fr, Rocket in space. 7fr, Separation of landing module from capsule. 14fr, 26fr, Landing module landing on moon. 17fr, Capsule in space. 40fr, Neil A. Armstrong leaving landing module. 50fr, Astronaut on moon.

1969, Nov. 6 Photo. *Perf. 13½*

297 A38 4fr blue & multi .15 .15
298 A38 6.50fr vio blue & multi .22 .15
299 A38 7fr vio blue & multi .22 .15
300 A38 14fr black & multi .35 .20
301 A38 17fr vio blue & multi .55 .25
Nos. 297-301,C104-C106 (8) 3.64 1.95

Souvenir Sheet

302 Sheet of 3 3.00 3.00
a. A38 26fr multicolored .50 .50
b. A38 40fr multicolored .75 .75
c. A38 50fr multicolored 1.00 1.00

See note after Algeria No. 427.

Madonna and Child, by Rubens — A39

Paintings: 6fr, Madonna and Child with St. John, by Giulio Romano. 10fr, Magnificat Madonna, by Botticelli.

1969, Dec. 2 Photo.

303 A39 5fr gold & multi .15 .15
304 A39 6fr gold & multi .15 .15
305 A39 10fr gold & multi .25 .15
a. Souvenir sheet of 3, #303-305 .75 .75
Nos. 303-305,C107-C109 (6) 2.33
Set value .65

Christmas 1969.

Sternotomis Bohemani A40

Designs: Various Beetles and Weevils.

1970 *Perf. 13½*

Size: 39x28mm

306 A40 50c multicolored .15 .15
307 A40 1fr multicolored .15 .15
308 A40 1.50fr multicolored .15 .15
309 A40 2fr multicolored .15 .15
310 A40 3fr multicolored .15 .15
311 A40 3.50fr multicolored .15 .15

Size: 46x32mm

312 A40 4fr multicolored .15 .15
313 A40 5fr multicolored .15 .15
314 A40 6.50fr multicolored .15 .15
315 A40 8fr multicolored .20 .15
316 A40 10fr multicolored .25 .15
317 A40 15fr multicolored .38 .15

Size: 52x36mm

318 A40 20fr multicolored .50 .15
319 A40 50fr multicolored 1.00 .18
320 A40 100fr multicolored 1.90 .35
321 A40 150fr multicolored 2.75 .50
Nos. 306-321,C110-C118 (25) 19.11
Set value 2.85

Issue dates: Nos. 306-313, Jan. 20; Nos. 314-318, Feb. 17; Nos. 319-321, Apr. 3.

Jesus Condemned to Death — A41

Stations of the Cross, by Juan de Aranoa y Carredano: 1.50fr, Jesus carries His Cross. 2fr, Jesus falls the first time. 3fr, Jesus meets His mother. 3.50fr, Simon of Cyrene helps carry the cross. 4fr, Veronica wipes the face of Jesus. 5fr, Jesus falls the second time.

1970, Mar. 16 Photo. *Perf. 13½*

322 A41 1fr gold & multi .15 .15
323 A41 1.50fr gold & multi .15 .15
324 A41 2fr gold & multi .15 .15
325 A41 3fr gold & multi .15 .15
326 A41 3.50fr gold & multi .15 .15
327 A41 4fr gold & multi .15 .15
328 A41 5fr gold & multi .15 .15
a. Souv. sheet of 7, #322-328 + label .60 .60
Set value, #322-328, C119-C125 2.60 1.15

Easter 1970.

Parade and EXPO '70 Emblem — A42

Designs (EXPO '70 Emblem and): 6.50fr, Aerial view. 7fr, African pavilions. 14fr, Pagoda, vert. 26fr, Recording pavilion and pool. 40fr, Tower of the Sun, vert. 50fr, Flags of participating nations.

1970, May 5 Photo. *Perf. 13½*

329 A42 4fr gold & multi .15 .15
330 A42 6.50fr gold & multi .15 .15
331 A42 7fr gold & multi .15 .15
332 A42 14fr gold & multi .22 .15
333 A42 26fr gold & multi .38 .15
334 A42 40fr gold & multi .55 .15
335 A42 50fr gold & multi .80 .20
Nos. 329-335 (7) 2.40
Set value .65

EXPO '70 Intl. Exhibition, Osaka, Japan, Mar. 15-Sept. 13, 1970. See No. C126.

White Rhinoceros — A43

Designs, FAUNA: Camel, dromedary, okapi, addax, Burundi cow (2 stamps of each animal in 2 different poses). MAP OF THE NILE: Delta and pyramids, dhow, cataract, Blue Nile and crowned crane, Victoria Nile and secretary bird, Lake Victoria and source of Nile on Mt. Gikizi.

1970, July 8 Photo. *Perf. 13½*

336 Sheet of 18 7.00 1.50
a. A43 7fr any single .38 .15

Issued in sheets of 18 (3x6) stamps of different designs, to publicize the southernmost source of the Nile on Mt. Gikizi in Burundi. See No. C127.

Winter Wren, Firecrest, Skylark and Crested Lark — A44

Birds: 2fr, 3.50fr and 5fr, vertical; others horizontal.

1970, Sept. 30 Photo. *Perf. 13½*

Stamp Size: 44x33mm

337 A44 Block of 4 .38 .15
a. 2fr Northern shrike .15
b. 2fr European starling .15
c. 2fr Yellow wagtail .15
d. 2fr Bank swallow .15
338 A44 Block of 4 .55 .15
a. 3fr Winter wren .15
b. 3fr Firecrest .15
c. 3fr Skylark .15
d. 3fr Crested lark .15
339 A44 Block of 4 .75 .15
a. 3.50fr Woodchat shrike .18
b. 3.50fr Common rock thrush .18
c. 3.50fr Black redstart .18
d. 3.50fr Ring ouzel .18
340 A44 Block of 4 .80 .15
a. 4fr European Redstart .20
b. 4fr Hedge sparrow .20
c. 4fr Gray wagtail .20
d. 4fr Meadow pipit .20
341 A44 Block of 4 1.00 .15
a. 5fr Eurasian hoopoe .25
b. 5fr Pied flycatcher .25
c. 5fr Great reed warbler .25
d. 5fr Eurasian kingfisher .25
342 A44 Block of 4 1.25 .15
a. 6.50fr House martin .30
b. 6.50fr Sedge warbler .30
c. 6.50fr Fieldfare .30
d. 6.50fr European Golden oriole .30
Nos. 337-342,C132-C137 (12) 23.63 3.25

Nos. 337-342 are printed in sheets of16.

Library, UN Emblem — A45

Designs: 5fr, Students taking test, and emblem of University of Bujumbura. 7fr, Students in laboratory and emblem of Ecole Normale Superieure of Burundi. 10fr, Students with electron-microscope and Education Year emblem.

1970, Oct. 23

343 A45 3fr gold & multi .15 .15
344 A45 5fr gold & multi .15 .15
345 A45 7fr gold & multi .15 .15
346 A45 10fr gold & multi .15 .15
Set value .41 .20

Issued for International Education Year.

Pres. and Mrs. Michel Micombero — A46

Designs: 7fr, Pres. Michel Micombero and Burundi flag. 11fr, Pres. Micombero and Revolution Memorial.

1970, Nov. 28 Photo. *Perf. 13½*

347 A46 4fr gold & multi .15 .15
348 A46 7fr gold & multi .15 .15
349 A46 11fr gold & multi .20 .15
a. Souvenir sheet of 3 .50 .50
Set value .40 .20

4th anniv. of independence. No. 349a contains 3 stamps similar to Nos. 347-349, but inscribed "Poste Aerienne." Exists imperf.

See Nos. C140-C142.

Lenin with Delegates A47

Designs (Lenin, Paintings): 5fr, addressing crowd. 6.50fr, with soldier and sailor. 15fr, speaking from balcony. 50fr, Portrait.

1970, Dec. 31 Photo. *Perf. 13½*

Gold Frame

350 A47 3.50fr dk red brown .15 .15
351 A47 5fr dk red brown .15 .15
352 A47 6.50fr dk red brown .15 .15
353 A47 15fr dk red brown .32 .15
354 A47 50fr dk red brown 1.10 .18
Nos. 350-354 (5) 1.87
Set value .46

Lenin's birth centenary (1870-1924).

Lion — A48

1971, Mar. 19 Photo. *Perf. 13½*

Size: 38x38mm

355 Strip of 4 .20 .15
a. A48 1fr Lion .15
b. A48 1fr Cape buffalo .15
c. A48 1fr Hippopotamus .15
d. A48 1fr Giraffe .15
356 Strip of 4 .24 .15
a. A48 2fr Hartebeest .15
b. A48 2fr Black rhinoceros .15
c. A48 2fr Zebra .15
d. A48 2fr Leopard .15
357 Strip of 4 .32 .15
a. A48 3fr Grant's gazelles .15
b. A48 3fr Cheetah .15
c. A48 3fr African white-backed vultures .15
d. A48 3fr Johnston's okapi .15
358 Strip of 4 .50 .20
a. A48 5fr Chimpanzee .15
b. A48 5fr Elephant .15
c. A48 5fr Spotted hyenas .15
d. A48 5fr Beisa .15
359 Strip of 4 .65 .42
a. A48 6fr Gorilla .15
b. A48 6fr Gnu .15
c. A48 6fr Wart hog .15
d. A48 6fr Cape hunting dog .15
360 Strip of 4 1.40 .45
a. A48 11fr Sable antelope .32
b. A48 11fr Caracal lynx .32
c. A48 11fr Ostriches .32
d. A48 11fr Bongo .32
Nos. 355-360,C146-C151 (12) 15.31 3.31

For overprints and surcharges see Nos. C152, CB15-CB18.

The Resurrection, by Il Sodoma — A49

Paintings: 6fr, Resurrection, by Andrea del Castagno. 11fr, Noli me Tangere, by Correggio.

1971, Apr. 2

361 A49 3fr gold & multi .15 .15
362 A49 6fr gold & multi .15 .15
363 A49 11fr gold & multi .28 .15
a. Souvenir sheet of 3, #361-363 .60 .60
Nos. 361-363,C143-C145 (6) 1.30
Set value .46

Easter 1971. No. 363a exists imperf.

Young Venetian Woman, by Dürer — A50

Dürer Paintings: 11fr, Hieronymus Holzschuher. 14fr, Emperor Maximilian I. 17fr, Holy Family, from Paumgartner Altar. 26fr, Haller Madonna. 31fr, Self-portrait, 1498.

1971, Sept. 20

364 A50 6fr multicolored .15 .15
365 A50 11fr multicolored .22 .15
366 A50 14fr multicolored .38 .15
367 A50 17fr multicolored .45 .22
368 A50 26fr multicolored .65 .35
369 A50 31fr multicolored .80 .40
a. Souvenir sheet of 2, #368-369 1.60 1.60
Nos. 364-369 (6) 2.65 1.42

International Letter Writing Week. Albrecht Dürer (1471-1528), German painter and engraver. No. 369a exists imperf.

Nos. 364-369, 369a Overprinted in Black and Gold: "VIème CONGRES / DE L'INSTITUT INTERNATIONAL / DE DROIT D'EXPRESSION FRANCAISE"

1971, Oct. 8

370 A50 6fr multicolored .15 .15
371 A50 11fr multicolored .22 .15
372 A50 14fr multicolored .28 .15
373 A50 17fr multicolored .35 .15
374 A50 26fr multicolored .50 .15
375 A50 31fr multicolored .65 .18
a. Souvenir sheet of 2 1.25 1.25
Nos. 370-375 (6) 2.15
Set value .62

6th Congress of the Intl. Legal Institute of the French-speaking Area, Bujumbura, Aug. 10-19.

Madonna and Child, by Il Perugino — A51

Paintings of the Madonna and Child by: 5fr, Andrea del Sarto. 6fr, Luis de Morales.

1971, Nov. 2 Photo. *Perf. 13½*

376 A51 3fr dk green & multi .15 .15
377 A51 5fr dk green & multi .15 .15
378 A51 6fr dk green & multi .15 .15
a. Souvenir sheet of 3, #376-378 .38 .38
Nos. 376-378,C153-C155 (6) 1.55
Set value .62

Christmas 1971. No. 378a exists imperf.
For surcharges see #B49-B51, CB19-CB21.

Lunar Orbiter — A52

Designs: 11fr, Vostok. 14fr, Luna 1. 17fr, Apollo 11 astronaut on moon. 26fr, Soyuz 11. 40fr, Lunar Rover (Apollo 15).

1972, Jan. 15

379 A52 6fr gold & multi .18 .15
380 A52 11fr gold & multi .22 .15
381 A52 14fr gold & multi .28 .15
382 A52 17fr gold & multi .40 .20
383 A52 26fr gold & multi .40 .32
384 A52 40fr gold & multi .62 .32
a. Souvenir sheet of 6 2.25 2.25
Nos. 379-384 (6) 2.10 1.29

Conquest of space. See No. C156.
No. 384a contains one each of Nos. 379-384 inscribed "APOLLO 16."

Slalom and Sapporo '72 Emblem — A53

Designs (Sapporo '72 Emblem and): 6fr, Figure skating, pairs. 11fr, Figure skating, women's. 14fr, Ski jump. 17fr, Ice hockey. 24fr, Speed skating, men's. 26fr, Snow scooter. 31fr, Downhill skiing. 50fr, Bobsledding.

1972, Feb. 3

385 A53 5fr silver & multi .15 .15
386 A53 6fr silver & multi .15 .15
387 A53 11fr silver & multi .18 .15
388 A53 14fr silver & multi .22 .15
389 A53 17fr silver & multi .28 .15
390 A53 24fr silver & multi .38 .15
391 A53 26fr silver & multi .40 .15
392 A53 31fr silver & multi .50 .15
393 A53 50fr silver & multi .80 .20
Nos. 385-393 (9) 3.06
Set value .82

11th Winter Olympic Games, Sapporo, Japan, Feb. 3-13. Printed in sheets of 12. See No. C157. Issued: #385-390, Feb. 1; #391-393, Feb. 21.

Ecce Homo, by Quentin Massys — A54

Paintings: 6.50fr, Crucifixion, by Rubens. 10fr, Descent from the Cross, by Jacopo da Pontormo. 18fr, Pieta, by Ferdinand Gallegos. 27fr, Trinity, by El Greco.

1972, Mar. 20 Photo. *Perf. 13½*

394 A54 3.50fr gold & multi .15 .15
395 A54 6.50fr gold & multi .15 .15
396 A54 10fr gold & multi .15 .15
397 A54 18fr gold & multi .25 .15
398 A54 27fr gold & multi .65 .15
a. Souv. sheet of 5, #394-398 + label 1.50 1.25
Nos. 394-398 (5) 1.35
Set value .42

Easter 1972. Printed in sheets of 8 with label. No. 398a exists imperf.

Gymnastics, Olympic Rings and "Motion" A55

1972, May 19

399 A55 5fr shown .15 .15
400 A55 6fr Javelin .15 .15
401 A55 11fr Fencing .22 .15
402 A55 14fr Bicycling .25 .15
403 A55 17fr Pole vault .32 .15
Nos. 399-403,C158-C161 (9) 2.94
Set value .95

Souvenir Sheet

404 Sheet of 2 1.75 1.25
a. A55 31fr Discus .45 .45
b. A55 40fr Soccer .60 .60

20th Olympic Games, Munich, Aug. 26-Sept. 11.

Prince Rwagasore, Pres. Micombero, Burundi Flag, Drummers A56

Designs: 7fr, Rwagasore, Micombero, flag, map of Africa, globe. 13fr, Micombero, flag, globe.

1972, Aug. 24 Photo. *Perf. 13½*

405 A56 5fr silver & multi .15 .15
406 A56 7fr silver & multi .15 .15
407 A56 13fr silver & multi .22 .15
a. Souvenir sheet of 3, #405-407 .50
Nos. 405-407,C162-C164 (6) 1.52
Set value .52

10th anniversary of independence.

Madonna and Child, by Andrea Solario — A57

Paintings of the Madonna and Child by: 10fr, Raphael. 15fr, Botticelli.

1972, Nov. 2

408 A57 5fr lt blue & multi .15 .15
409 A57 10fr lt blue & multi .15 .15
410 A57 15fr lt blue & multi .22 .15
a. Souvenir sheet of 3, #408-410 .50
Nos. 408-410,C165-C167 (6) 1.80
Set value .56

Christmas 1972. Sheets of 20 stamps + label.
For surcharges see #B56-B58, CB26-CB28.

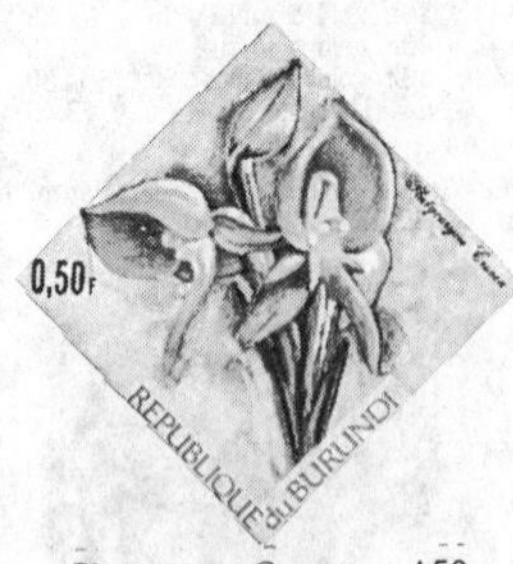

Platycoryne Crocea — A58

1972

Size: 33x33mm

411 A58 50c *shown* .15 .15
412 A58 1fr *Cattleya trianaei* .15 .15
413 A58 2fr *Eulophia cucullata* .15 .15
414 A58 3fr *Cymbidium hamsey* .15 .15
415 A58 4fr *Thelymitra pauciflora* .15 .15
416 A58 5fr *Miltassia* .15 .15
417 A58 6fr *Miltonia* .15 .15

Size: 38x38mm

418 A58 7fr Like 50c .15 .15
419 A58 8fr Like 1fr .15 .15
420 A58 9fr Like 2fr .15 .15
421 A58 10fr Like 3fr .18 .15
Set value, #411-421, C168-C174 3.25 1.20

Orchids. Issue dates: Nos. 411-417, Nov. 6; Nos. 418-421, Nov. 29.

Henry Morton Stanley — A59

Designs: 7fr, Porters, Stanley's expedition. 13fr, Stanley entering Ujiji.

1973, Mar. 19 Photo. *Perf. 13½*

422 A59 5fr gold & multi .15 .15
423 A59 7fr gold & multi .15 .15
424 A59 13fr gold & multi .20 .15
Nos. 422-424,C175-C177 (6) 1.40
Set value .48

Exploration of Africa by David Livingstone (1813-1873) and Henry Morton Stanley (John Rowlands; 1841-1904).

Crucifixion, by Roger van der Weyden — A60

Easter (Paintings): 5fr, Flagellation of Christ, by Caravaggio. 13fr, The Burial of Christ, by Raphael.

1973, Apr. 10

425 A60 5fr gold & multi .15 .15
426 A60 7fr gold & multi .15 .15
427 A60 13fr gold & multi .20 .15
a. Souvenir sheet of 3, #425-427 .60 .60
Nos. 425-427,C178-C180 (6) 1.63
Set value .46

INTERPOL Emblem, Flag — A61

Design: 10fr, INTERPOL flag and emblem. 18fr, INTERPOL Headquarters and emblem.

1973, May 19 Photo. *Perf. 13½*

428 A61 5fr silver & multi .15 .15
429 A61 10fr silver & multi .15 .15
430 A61 18fr silver & multi .28 .15
Nos. 428-430,C181-C182 (5) 1.46
Set value .59

50th anniversary of International Criminal Police Organization (INTERPOL).

Signs of the Zodiac, Babylon — A62

Designs: 5fr, Greek and Roman gods representing planets. 7fr, Ptolemy (No. 433a) and Ptolemaic solar system. 13fr, Copernicus (No. 434a) and heliocentric system.
a, UL. b, UR. c, LL. d, LR.

1973, July 27 Photo. *Perf. 13½*

431 A62 3fr Block of 4, #a.-d. .20 .15
432 A62 5fr Block of 4, #a.-d. .25 .15
433 A62 7fr Block of 4, #a.-d. .32 .15
434 A62 13fr Block of 4, #a.-d. .75 .20
e. Souvenir sheet of 4, #431-434 2.75 1.40
Nos. 431-434,C183-C186 (8) 9.32 2.50

500th anniversary of the birth of Nicolaus Copernicus (1473-1543), Polish astronomer.

Flowers and Butterflies — A63

Designs: Each block of 4 contains 2 flower and 2 butterfly designs. The 1fr, 2fr, 5fr and 11fr have flower designs listed as "a" and "d" numbers, butterflies as "b" and "c" numbers; the arrangement is reversed for the 3fr and 6fr.

1973, Sept. 3 Photo. *Perf. 13*
Stamp Size: 34x41½mm

435 A63 Block of 4 .20 .15
a. 1fr *Protea cynaroides* .15 .15
b. 1fr *Precis octavia* .15 .15
c. 1fr *Epiphora bauhiniae* .15 .15
d. 1fr *Gazania longiscapa* .15 .15
436 A63 Block of 4 .20 .15
a. 2fr *Kniphofia* .15 .15
b. 2fr *Cymothoe coccinata* .15 .15
c. 2fr *Nudaurelia zambesina* .15 .15
d. 2fr *Freesia refracta* .15 .15
437 A63 Block of 4 .24 .15
a. 3fr *Calotis eupompe* .15 .15
b. 3fr *Narcissus* .15 .15
c. 3fr *Cineraria hybrida* .15 .15
d. 3fr *Cyrestis camillus* .15 .15
438 A63 Block of 4 .40 .15
a. 5fr *Iris tingitana* .15 .15
b. 5fr *Pappilio demodocus* .15 .15
c. 5fr *Catopsilia avelaneda* .15 .15
d. 5fr *Nerine sarniensis* .15 .15
439 A63 Block of 4 .50 .20
a. 6fr *Hypolimnas dexithea* .15 .15
b. 6fr *Zantedeschia tropicalis* .15 .15
c. 6fr *Sandersonia aurantiaca* .15 .15
d. 6fr *Drurya antimachus* .15 .15
440 A63 Block of 4 1.00 .22
a. 11fr *Nymphaea capensis* .25 .15
b. 11fr *Pandoriana pandora* .25 .15
c. 11fr *Precis orythia* .25 .15
d. 11fr *Pelargonium domestica* .25 .15
Nos. 435-440,C187-C192 (12) 22.04 3.52

Virgin and Child, by Giovanni Bellini — A64

Virgin and Child by: 10fr, Jan van Eyck. 15fr, Giovanni Boltraffio.

1973, Nov. 13 Photo. *Perf. 13*

441 A64 5fr gold & multi .15 .15
442 A64 10fr gold & multi .15 .15
443 A64 15fr gold & multi .22 .15
a. Souvenir sheet of 3, #441-443 .50 .50
Nos. 441-443,C193-C195 (6) 1.80
Set value .52

Christmas 1973.
For surcharges see #B59-B61, CB29-CB31.

Pietá, by Paolo Veronese — A65

Paintings: 10fr, Virgin and St. John, by van der Weyden. 18fr, Crucifixion, by van der Weyden. 27fr, Burial of Christ, by Titian. 40fr, Pietá, by El Greco.

1974, Apr. 19 Photo. *Perf. 14x13½*

444 A65 5fr gold & multi .15 .15
445 A65 10fr gold & multi .15 .15
446 A65 18fr gold & multi .28 .15
447 A65 27fr gold & multi .42 .15
448 A65 40fr gold & multi .65 .15
a. Souvenir sheet of 5, #444-448 1.65 1.65
Nos. 444-448 (5) 1.65
Set value .46

Easter 1974.

Fish — A66

1974, May 30 Photo. *Perf. 13*
Stamp Size: 35x35mm

449 A66 Block of 4 .20 .20
a. 1fr *Haplochromis multicolor* .15 .15
b. 1fr *Pantodon buchholzi* .15 .15
c. 1fr *Tropheus duboisi* .15 .15
d. 1fr *Distichodus sexfasciatus* .15 .15
450 A66 Block of 4 .20 .15
a. 2fr *Pelmatochromis kribensis* .15 .15
b. 2fr *Nannaethiops tritaeniatus* .15 .15
c. 2fr *Polycentropsis abbreviata* .15 .15
d. 2fr *Hemichromis bimaculatus* .15 .15
451 A66 Block of 4 .20 .20
a. 3fr *Ctenopoma acutirostre* .15 .15
b. 3fr *Synodontis angelicus* .15 .15
c. 3fr *Tilapia melanopleura* .15 .15
d. 3fr *Aphyosemion bivittatum* .15 .15
452 A66 Block of 4 .32 .15
a. 5fr *Monodactylus argenteus* .15 .15
b. 5fr *Zanclus canescens* .15 .15
c. 5fr *Pygoplites diacanthus* .15 .15
d. 5fr *Cephalopholis argus* .15 .15
453 A66 Block of 4 .38 .15
a. 6fr *Priacanthus arenatus* .15 .15
b. 6fr *Pomacanthus arcuatus* .15 .15
c. 6fr *Scarus guacamaia* .15 .15
d. 6fr *Zeus faber* .15 .15
454 A66 Block of 4 .65 .20
a. 11fr *Lactophrys quadricornis* .16 .15
b. 11fr *Balistes vetula* .16 .15
c. 11fr *Acanthurus bahianus* .16 .15
d. 11fr *Holocanthus ciliaris* .16 .15
Nos. 449-454,C207-C212 (12) 12.25 2.65

Soccer and Cup — A67

Designs: Various soccer scenes and cup.

1974, July 4 Photo. *Perf. 13*

455 A67 5fr gold & multi .15
456 A67 6fr gold & multi .15
457 A67 11fr gold & multi .16
458 A67 14fr gold & multi .22
459 A67 17fr gold & multi .25
a. Souvenir sheet of 3 1.40
Nos. 455-459,C196-C198 (8) 2.23

World Soccer Championship, Munich, June 13-July 7. No. 459a contains 3 stamps similar to Nos. C196-C198 without "Poste Aerienne."
Nos. 455-459 and 459a exist imperf.

Flags over UPU Headquarters, Bern — A68

Designs: No. 461, G.P.O., Bujumbura. No. 462, Mailmen ("11F" in UR). No. 463, Mailmen ("11F" in UL). No. 464, UPU emblem. No. 465, Means of transportation. No. 466, Pigeon over globe showing Burundi. No. 467, Swiss flag, pigeon over map showing Bern.

1974, July 23

460 A68 6fr gold & multi .18
461 A68 6fr gold & multi .18
462 A68 11fr gold & multi .30
463 A68 11fr gold & multi .30
464 A68 14fr gold & multi .38
465 A68 14fr gold & multi .38
466 A68 17fr gold & multi .45
467 A68 17fr gold & multi .50
a. Souvenir sheet of 8, #460-467 2.75
Nos. 460-467,C199-C206 (16) 9.97
Set, used 1.00

Cent. of UPU. Stamps of same denomination printed se-tenant (continuous design).

St. Ildefonso Writing Letter, by El Greco — A69

Paintings: 11fr, Lady Sealing Letter, by Chardin. 14fr, Titus at Desk, by Rembrandt. 17fr, The Love Letter, by Vermeer. 26fr, The Merchant G. Gisze, by Holbein. 31fr, Portrait of Alexandre Lenoir, by David.

1974, Oct. 1 Photo. *Perf. 13*

468 A69 6fr gold & multi .15
469 A69 11fr gold & multi .16
470 A69 14fr gold & multi .22
471 A69 17fr gold & multi .25
472 A69 26fr gold & multi .40
473 A69 31fr gold & multi .45
a. Souvenir sheet of 2, #472-473 1.10
Nos. 468-473 (6) 1.63

International Letter Writing Week, Oct. 6-12. No. 473a exists imperf.

Virgin and Child, by Bernaert van Orley — A70

Paintings of the Virgin and Child: 10fr, by Hans Memling. 15fr, by Botticelli.

1974, Nov. 7 Photo. *Perf. 13*

474 A70 5fr gold & multi .15
475 A70 10fr gold & multi .15
476 A70 15fr gold & multi .22
a. Souvenir sheet of 3, #474-476 .50
Nos. 474-476,C213-C215 (6) 1.80

Christmas 1974. Sheets of 20 stamps and one label. No. 476a exists imperf.

Apollo-Soyuz Space Mission and Emblem — A71

1975, July 10 Photo. *Perf. 13*

477 A71 Block of 4 .80
a. 26fr A.A. Leonov, V.N. Kubasov, Soviet flag .20
b. 26fr Soyuz and Soviet flag .20
c. 26fr Apollo and American flag .20
d. 26fr D.K. Slayton, V.D. Brand, T.P. Stafford, American flag .20
478 A71 Block of 4 1.25
a. 31fr Apollo-Soyuz link-up .28
b. 31fr Apollo, blast-off .28
c. 31fr Soyuz, blast-off .28
d. 31fr Kubasov, Leonov, Slayton, Brand, Stafford .28
Nos. 477-478,C216-C217 (4) 4.35

Apollo Soyuz space test project (Russo-American cooperation), launching July 15; link-up, July 17.

Addax — A72

1975, July 31 Photo. *Perf. 13½*

479 Strip of 4 .20
a. A72 1fr shown .15
b. A72 1fr Roan antelope .15
c. A72 1fr Nyala .15
d. A72 1fr White rhinoceros .15
480 Strip of 4 .20
a. A72 2fr Mandrill .15
b. A72 2fr Eland .15
c. A72 2fr Salt's dik-dik .15
d. A72 2fr Thomson's gazelles .15
481 Strip of 4 .20
a. A72 3fr African small-clawed otter .15
b. A72 3fr Reed buck .15
c. A72 3fr Indian civet .15
d. A72 3fr Cape buffalo .15
482 Strip of 4 .35
a. A72 5fr White-tailed gnu .15
b. A72 5fr African wild asses .15
c. A72 5fr Black-and-white colobus monkey .15
d. A72 5fr Gerenuk .15
483 Strip of 4 .36
a. A72 6fr Dama gazelle .15
b. A72 6fr Black-backed jackal .15
c. A72 6fr Sitatungas .15
d. A72 6fr Zebra antelope .15
484 Strip of 4 .65
a. A72 11fr Fennec .16
b. A72 11fr Lesser kudus .15
c. A72 11fr Blesbok .16
d. A72 11fr Serval .16
Nos. 479-484,C218-C223 (12) 12.61

For overprints see Nos. C224-C227.

Jonah, by Michelangelo — A73

Designs: Paintings from Sistine Chapel.

1975, Dec. 3 Photo. *Perf. 13*

485 A73 5fr shown .15
486 A73 5fr Libyan Sybil .15
487 A73 13fr Prophet Isaiah .20
488 A73 13fr Delphic Sybil .20
489 A73 27fr Daniel .40
490 A73 27fr Cumaean Sybil .40
a. Souvenir sheet of 6, #485-490 2.00
Nos. 485-490,C228-C233 (12) 5.10

Michelangelo Buonarotti (1475-1564), Italian sculptor, painter and architect. Stamps of same denominations printed se-tenant in sheets of 18 stamps and 2 labels.
For surcharges see Nos. B65-B70, CB35-CB40.

Speed Skating — A74

Basketball — A75

Designs (Innsbruck Games Emblem and): 24fr, Figure skating, women's. 26fr, Two-man bobsled. 31fr, Cross-country skiing.

1976, Jan. 23 Photo. *Perf. 14x13½*

491 A74 17fr dp bl & multi .30
492 A74 24fr multi .45
493 A74 26fr multi .48
494 A74 31fr plum & multi .55
a. Souvenir sheet of 3 2.25
Nos. 491-494,C234-C236 (7) 3.70

12th Winter Olympic Games, Innsbruck, Austria, Feb. 4-15.

No. 494a contains 3 stamps similar to Nos. C234-C236, perf. 13½, without "POSTE AERIENNE."

1976, May 3 Litho. *Perf. 13½*

Designs (Montreal Games Emblem and): Nos. 496, 499, 503b, Pole vault. Nos. 497, 500, 503d, Running. Nos. 498, 501, 503a, Soccer. No. 502, 503c, Basketball.

495 A75 14fr blue & multi .25
496 A75 14fr olive & multi .25
497 A75 17fr magenta & multi .30
498 A75 17fr vermilion & multi .30
499 A75 28fr olive & multi .48
500 A75 28fr magenta & multi .48
501 A75 40fr vermilion & multi .70
502 A75 40fr blue & multi .70
Nos. 495-502,C237-C242 (14) 7.20

Souvenir Sheet

503 Sheet of 4 1.65
a. A75 14fr red & multi .22
b. A75 17fr olive & multi .25
c. A75 28fr blue & multi .40
d. A75 40fr magenta & multi .60

21st Olympic Games, Montreal, Canada, July 17-Aug. 1. Stamps of same denomination printed se-tenant in sheets of 20.

Virgin and Child, by Dirk Bouts — A76

Virgin and Child by: 13fr, Giovanni Bellini. 27fr, Carlo Crivelli.

1976, Oct. 18 Photo. *Perf. 13½*

504 A76 5fr gold & multi .15
505 A76 13fr gold & multi .20
506 A76 27fr gold & multi .40
a. Souvenir sheet of 3, #504-506 .75
Nos. 504-506,C250-C252 (6) 2.05

Christmas 1976. Sheets of 20 stamps and descriptive label.

For surcharges see #B71-B73, CB41-CB43.

St. Veronica, by Rubens A77

Paintings by Rubens: 21fr, Christ on the Cross. 27fr, Descent from the Cross. 35fr, The Deposition.

1977, Apr. 5 Photo. *Perf. 13*

507 A77 10fr gold & multi .15
508 A77 21fr gold & multi .32
509 A77 27fr gold & multi .40
510 A77 35fr gold & multi .55
a. Souvenir sheet of 4 1.50
Nos. 507-510 (4) 1.42

Easter 1977. Sheets of 30 stamps and descriptive label. No. 510a contains 4 stamps similar to Nos. 507-510 inscribed "POSTE AERIENNE."

Alexander Graham Bell — A78

Intelsat Satellite, Modern and Old Telephones — A79

Designs: No. 513, Switchboard operator, c. 1910, and wall telephone. No. 514, Intelsat and radar. No. 515, A.G. Bell and first telephone. No. 516, Satellites around globe and videophone.

1977, May 17 Photo. *Perf. 13*

511 A78 10fr multi .15
512 A79 10fr multi .15
513 A78 17fr multi .15
514 A79 17fr multi .15
515 A78 26fr multi .22
516 A79 26fr multi .22
Nos. 511-516,C253-C256 (10) 1.84

Centenary of first telephone call by Alexander Graham Bell, Mar. 10, 1876. Stamps of same denomination printed se-tenant in sheets of 32.

Buffon's Kob — A80

1977, Aug. 22 Photo. *Perf. 14x14½*

517 Strip of 4 .20
a. A80 2fr shown .15
b. A80 2fr Marabous .15
c. A80 2fr Brindled gnu .15
d. A80 2fr River hog .15
518 Strip of 4 .35
a. A80 5fr Zebras .15
b. A80 5fr Shoebill .15
c. A80 5fr Striped hyenas .15
d. A80 5fr Chimpanzee .15
519 Strip of 4 .48
a. A80 8fr Flamingos .15
b. A80 8fr Nile crocodiles .15
c. A80 8fr Green mamba .15
d. A80 8fr Greater kudus .15
520 Strip of 4 .70
a. A80 11fr Hyrax .16
b. A80 11fr Cobra .16
c. A80 11fr Jackals .16
d. A80 11fr Verreaux's eagles .16
521 Strip of 4 1.40
a. A80 21fr Honey badger .32
b. A80 21fr Harnessed antelopes .32
c. A80 21fr Secretary bird .32
d. A80 21fr Klipspringer .32
522 Strip of 4 1.40
a. A80 27fr African big-eared fox .35
b. A80 27fr Elephants .35
c. A80 27fr Vulturine guineafowl .35
d. A80 27fr Impalas .35
Nos. 517-522,C258-C263 (12) 20.68

The Goose Girl, by Grimm — A81

Fairy Tales: 5fr, by Grimm Brothers. 11fr, by Aesop. 14fr, by Hans Christian Andersen. 17fr, by Jean de La Fontaine. 26fr, English fairy tales.

1977, Sept. 14 *Perf. 14*

523 Block of 4 .38
a. A81 5fr shown .15
b. A81 5fr The Two Wanderers .15
c. A81 5fr The Man of Iron .15
d. A81 5fr Snow White and Rose Red .15
524 Block of 4 .85
a. A81 11fr The Quarreling Cats .20
b. A81 11fr The Blind and the Lame .20
c. A81 11fr The Hermit and the Bear .20
d. A81 11fr The Fox and the Stork .20
525 Block of 4 1.00
a. A81 14fr The Princess and the Pea .25
b. A81 14fr The Old Tree Mother .25
c. A81 14fr The Ice Maiden .25
d. A81 14fr The Old House .25
526 Block of 4 1.25
a. A81 17fr The Oyster and the Suitors .30
b. A81 17fr The Wolf and the Lamb .30
c. A81 17fr Hen with the Golden Egg .30
d. A81 17fr The Wolf as Shepherd .30
527 Block of 4 2.00
a. A81 26fr Three Heads in the Well .50
b. A81 26fr Mother Goose .50
c. A81 26fr Jack and the Beanstalk .50
d. A81 26fr Alice in Wonderland .50
Nos. 523-527 (5) 5.48

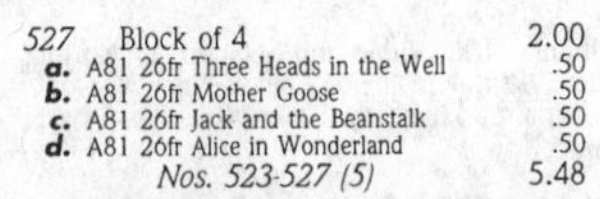

Security Council Chamber, UN Nos. 28, 46, 37, C7 — A82

Designs (UN Stamps and): 8fr, UN General Assembly, interior. 21fr, UN Meeting Hall.

1977, Oct. 10 Photo. *Perf. 13½*

528 A82 Block of 4 .65
a. 8fr No. 25 .15
b. 8fr No. C5 .15
c. 8fr No. 23 .15
d. 8fr No. 2 .15
529 A82 Block of 4 .75
a. 10fr No. 28 .18
b. 10fr No. 46 .18
c. 10fr No. 37 .18
d. 10fr No. C7 .18
530 A82 Block of 4 1.50
a. 21fr No. 45 .35
b. 21fr No. 42 .35
c. 21fr No. 17 .35
d. 21fr No. 13 .35
e. Souvenir sheet of 3 .65
Nos. 528-530,C264-C266 (6) 10.05

25th anniv. (in 1976) of the UN Postal Administration. No. 530e contains 8fr in design of No. 529d, 10fr in design of No. 530b, 21fr in design of No. 528c.

Virgin and Child — A83

Designs: Paintings of the Virgin and Child.

1977, Oct. 31 Photo. *Perf. 14x13*

531 A83 5fr By Meliore Toscano .15
532 A83 13fr By J. Lombardos .20
533 A83 27fr By Emmanuel Tzanes, 1610-1680 .40
a. Souvenir sheet of 3, #531-533 .75
Nos. 531-533,C267-C269 (6) 2.11

Christmas 1977. Sheets of 24 stamps with descriptive label.

For surcharges see #B74-B76, CB44-CB46.

Cruiser Aurora, Russia Nos. 211, 303, 1252, 187 — A84

Designs (Russian Stamps and): 8fr, Kremlin, Moscow. 11fr, Pokrovski Cathedral, Moscow. 13fr, Labor Day parade, 1977 and 1980 Olympic Games emblem.

1977, Nov. 14 Photo. *Perf. 13*

534 A84 Block of 4 .38
a. 5fr No. 211 .15
b. 5fr No. 303 .15
c. 5fr No. 1252 .15
d. 5fr No. 187 .15
535 A84 Block of 4 .65
a. 8fr No. 856 .15
b. 8fr No. 1986 .15
c. 8fr No. 908 .15
d. 8fr No. 2551 .15
536 A84 Block of 4 .85
a. 11fr No. 3844b .20
b. 11fr No. 3452 .20
c. 11fr No. 3382 .20
d. 11fr No. 3837 .20
537 A84 Block of 4 1.00
a. 13fr No. 4446 .25
b. 13fr No. 3497 .25
c. 13fr No. 2926 .25
d. 13fr No. 2365 .25
Nos. 534-537 (4) 2.88

60th anniv. of Russian October Revolution.

Ship at Dock, Arms and Flag — A85

Burundi Arms and Flag and: 5fr, Men at lathes. 11fr, Male leopard dance. 14fr, Coffee harvest. 17fr, Government Palace.

1977, Nov. 25 Photo. *Perf. 13½*

538 A85 1fr sil & multi .15
539 A85 5fr sil & multi .15
540 A85 11fr sil & multi .16
541 A85 14fr sil & multi .20
542 A85 17fr sil & multi .25
Set value .74

15th anniversary of independence.

A86

A87

Paintings of the Virgin and Child by: 13fr, Rubens. 17fr, Solario. 27fr, Tiepolo. 31fr, Gerard David. 40fr, Bellini.

1979, Feb. Photo. *Perf. 14x13*

543 A86 13fr multi .20
544 A86 17fr multi .25
545 A86 27fr multi .40
546 A86 31fr multi .48
547 A86 40fr multi .60
Nos. 543-547 (5) 1.93

Christmas 1978. See No. C270.

1979 Photo. *Perf. 13½x13*

548 A87 1fr *Abyssinian hornbill* .15
549 A87 2fr *Snakebird* .15
550 A87 3fr *Melittophagus pusillus* .15
551 A87 5fr *Flamingo* .15
552 A87 8fr *Afropavo congenis* .15
553 A87 10fr *Gallinule* .18
554 A87 20fr *Martial eagle* .32
555 A87 27fr *Ibis* .42
556 A87 50fr *Saddle-billed stork* .85
Nos. 548-556,C273-C281 (18) 6.96

Mother and Infant, IYC Emblem A88

IYC Emblem and: 20fr, Infant. 27fr, Girl with doll. 50fr, Children in Children's Village.

1979, July 19 Photo. *Perf. 14*

557 A88 10fr multi .15
558 A88 20fr multi .25
559 A88 27fr multi .32
560 A88 50fr multi .55
Nos. 557-560 (4) 1.27

Intl. Year of the Child. See No. B82.

A89

A90

Virgin and Child by: 20fr, del Garbo. 27fr, Giovanni Penni. 31fr, G. Romano. 50fr, Jacopo Bassano.

1979, Oct. 12

561 A89 20fr multi .30
562 A89 27fr multi .40
563 A89 31fr multi .48
564 A89 50fr multi .75
Nos. 561-564,B83-B86 (8) 3.95

Christmas 1979. See Nos. C271, CB48.

1979, Nov. 6

Designs: 20fr, Rowland Hill, Penny Black.

Stamps of Burundi: 27fr, German East Africa Nos. 17, N17. 31fr, Nos. 4, 24. 40fr, Nos. 29, 294. 60fr, Heinrich von Stephan, Nos. 464-465.

565 A90 20fr multi .30
566 A90 27fr multi .40
567 A90 31fr multi .48
568 A90 40fr multi .60
569 A90 60fr multi .90
Nos. 565-569 (5) 2.68

Sir Rowland Hill (1795-1879), originator of penny postage. See No. C272.

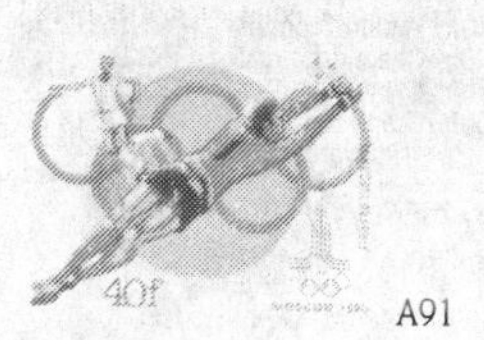

A91

1980, Oct. 24 Photo. *Perf. 13x13½*

570 A91 20fr 110-meter hurdles .38
571 A91 20fr Hurdles, Thomas Munkelt .38
572 A91 20fr Hurdles, R.D.A. .38
573 A91 30fr Discus .55
574 A91 30fr Discus, V. Rassh-chupkin .55
575 A91 30fr Discus, U.R.S.S. .55
576 A91 40fr Soccer, Tchecoslovaquie .75
577 A91 40fr "Football" .75
578 A91 40fr shown .75
Nos. 570-578 (9) 5.04

22nd Summer Olympic Games, Moscow, July 19-Aug. 3. Stamps of same denomination se-tenant.

See No. C282.

Virgin and Child, by Mainardi — A92

Christmas 1980 (Paintings): 30fr, Holy Family, by Michelangelo. 40fr, Virgin and Child, by di Cosimo. 45fr, Holy Family, by Fra Bartolomeo.

1980, Dec. 12 Photo. *Perf. 13½x13*

579 A92 10fr multi .15
580 A92 30fr multi .30
581 A92 40fr multi .42
582 A92 45fr multi .45
Nos. 579-582,B87-B90 (8) 2.71

UPRONA Party National Congress, 1979 — A93

1980, Dec. 29 *Perf. 14x13½*

583 A93 10fr multi .15
584 A93 40fr multi .60
585 A93 45fr multi .65
Nos. 583-585 (3) 1.40

Johannes Kepler, Dish Antenna A94

1981, Feb. 12 *Perf. 14*

586 A94 10fr shown .15
587 A94 40fr Satellite .60
588 A94 45fr Satellite, diff. .65
a. Souvenir sheet of 3, #586-588 1.50
Nos. 586-588 (3) 1.40

350th death anniv. of Johannes Kepler and 1st earth satellite station in Burundi.

Lion A95

1983, Apr. 22 Photo. *Perf. 13*

589 A95 2fr shown .15
590 A95 3fr Giraffes .15
591 A95 5fr Rhinoceros .15
592 A95 10fr Water buffalo .15
593 A95 20fr Elephant .30
594 A95 25fr Hippopotamus .38
595 A95 30fr Zebra .45
596 A95 50fr Warthog .75
597 A95 60fr Oryx .90
598 A95 65fr Wild dog 1.00
599 A95 70fr Leopard 1.10
600 A95 75fr Wildebeest 1.25
601 A95 85fr Hyena 1.75
Nos. 589-601 (13) 8.48

Nos. 589-601 Overprinted in Silver with World Wildlife Fund Emblem

1983 Photo. *Perf. 13*

589a A95 2fr multi .15
590a A95 3fr multi .15
591a A95 5fr multi .15
592a A95 10fr multi .15
593a A95 20fr multi .30
594a A95 25fr multi .38
595a A95 30fr multi .45
596a A95 50fr multi .75
597a A95 60fr multi .90
598a A95 65fr multi 1.00
599a A95 70fr multi 1.10
600a A95 75fr multi 1.15
601a A95 85fr multi 1.25
Nos. 589a-601a (13) 7.88

20th Anniv. of Independence, July 1, 1982 — A96

Flags, various arms, map or portrait.

1983 *Perf. 14*

602 A96 10fr multi .15
603 A96 25fr multi .38
604 A96 30fr multi .45
605 A96 50fr multi .75
606 A96 65fr multi 1.00
Nos. 602-606 (5) 2.73

Christmas 1983 — A97

Virgin and Child paintings: 10fr, by Luca Signorelli (1450-1523). 25fr, by Esteban Murillo (1617-1682). 30fr, by Carlo Crivelli (1430-1495). 50fr, by Nicolas Poussin (1594-1665).

1983, Oct. 3 Litho. *Perf. 14½x13½*

607 A97 10fr multi .15
608 A97 25fr multi .38
609 A97 30fr multi .45
610 A97 50fr multi .75
Nos. 607-610,B91-B94 (8) 3.52

See Nos. C285, CB50.

Butterflies A98

1984, June 29 Photo. *Perf. 13*

611 A98 5fr Cymothoe coccinata .15
612 A98 5fr Papilio zalmoxis .15
613 A98 10fr Asterope pechueli .25
614 A98 10fr Papilio antimachus .25
615 A98 30fr Papilio hesperus .70
616 A98 30fr Bebearia mardania .70
617 A98 35fr Euphaedra neophron .85
618 A98 35fr Euphaedra perseis .85
619 A98 65fr Euphaedra imperialis 1.50
620 A98 65fr Pseudocraea striata 1.50
Nos. 611-620 (10) 6.90

Stamps of the same denomination printed horizontally se-tenant.

For surcharges see Nos. 654D-654E.

19th UPU Congress, Hamburg A99

UPU emblem and: 10fr, German East Africa, Nos. 17, N17. 30fr, Nos. 4, 24. 35fr, Nos. 294, 595. 65fr, Dr. Heinrich von Stephan, Nos. 464-465.

1984, July 14 Litho. *Perf. 13x13½*

621 A99 10fr multi .15
622 A99 30fr multi .45
623 A99 35fr multi .50
624 A99 65fr multi 1.00
Nos. 621-624 (4) 2.10

See No. C286.

1984 Summer Olympics A100

Gold medalists: 10fr, Jesse Owens, US, track and field, Berlin, 1936. 30fr, Rafer Johnson, US, decathlon, 1960. 35fr, Bob Beamon, US, long jump, 1968. 65fr, Kipchoge Keino, Kenya, 3000-meter steeplechase, 1972.

1984, Aug. 6 *Perf. 13½x13*

625 A100 10fr multi .25
626 A100 30fr multi .70
627 A100 35fr multi .85
628 A100 65fr multi 1.50
Nos. 625-628 (4) 3.30

See No. C287.

Christmas 1984 — A101

Paintings: 10fr, Rest During the Flight into Egypt, by Murillo (1617-1682). 25fr, Virgin and Child, by R. del Garbo. 30fr, Virgin and Child, by Botticelli (1445-1510). 50fr, The Adoration of the Shepherds, by Giacomo da Bassano (1517-1592).

1984, Dec. 15 *Perf. 13½*

629 A101 10fr multi .15
630 A101 25fr multi .38
631 A101 30fr multi .45
632 A101 50fr multi .75
Nos. 629-632,B95-B98 (8) 3.52

See Nos. C288, CB51.

Flowers — A102

1986, July 31 Photo. *Perf. 13x13½*

633 A102 2fr Thunbergia .15
634 A102 3fr Saintpaulia .15
635 A102 5fr Clivia .15
636 A102 10fr Cassia .15
637 A102 20fr Strelitzia .16
638 A102 35fr Gloriosa .28
Nos. 633-638,C289-C294 (12) 5.54

Intl. Peace Year — A103

1986, May 1 Litho. *Perf. 14*

639 A103 10fr Rockets as housing .15
640 A103 20fr Atom as flower .18
641 A103 30fr Handshake .28
642 A103 40fr Globe, chicks .35
a. Souvenir sheet of 4, #639-642 .90
Nos. 639-642 (4) .96

No. 642a exists imperf.

Great Lake Nations Economic Community (CEPGI), 10th Anniv. — A104

Outline maps of Lake Tanganyika, CEPGI emblem and: 5fr, Aviation. 10fr, Agriculture. 15fr, Industry. 25fr, Electrification. 35fr, Flags of Burundi, Rwanda and Zaire.

1986, May 1 Photo. *Perf. 13½x14½*

643 A104 5fr multi .15
644 A104 10fr multi .15
645 A104 15fr multi .20
646 A104 25fr multi .32
647 A104 35fr multi .45
a. Souv. sheet of 5, #643-647 + label 1.25
Nos. 643-647 (5) 1.27

Intl. Year of Shelter for the Homeless A105

1987, June **Litho.** *Perf. 14*

648 A105 10fr Hovel .28
649 A105 20fr Drain pipe shelter .55
650 A105 80fr Shoveling sand 2.15
651 A105 150fr Children, house model 4.00
a. Souvenir sheet of 4, #648-651 7.00
Nos. 648-651 (4) 6.98

A106 A107

1987(?) **Litho.** *Perf. 14*

652 A106 5fr shown .15
653 A106 20fr Skull, lungs .30
654 A106 80fr Cigarette, face 1.25
Nos. 652-654 (3) 1.70

WHO Anti-smoking campaign.

Nos. 615-616 Surcharged **80f**

1989 **Photo.** *Perf. 13*

654D A98 80fr on 30fr #615
654E A98 80fr on 30fr #616

Numbers have been reserved for additional values in this set.

1990 **Litho.** *Perf. 14*

655 A107 5fr red lil & multi .15
656 A107 10fr blue & multi .24
657 A107 20fr gray & multi .48
658 A107 30fr ol grn & multi .72
659 A107 50fr brt blue & multi 1.20
660 A107 80fr grn bl & multi 1.95
a. Souv. sheet of 6, #655-660, perf. 13½ 4.75
Nos. 655-660 (6) 4.74

Visit of Pope John Paul II.

Animals A108

1991, Oct. 4 **Litho.** *Perf. 14*

661 A108 5fr Hippopotamus .15
662 A108 10fr Chickens .15
663 A108 20fr Lion .32
664 A108 30fr Elephant .48
665 A108 50fr Guinea fowl .80
666 A108 80fr Crocodile 1.25
a. Souv. sheet of 6, #661-666, perf. 13½ 3.15
Nos. 661-666,C298-C301 (10) 12.95

No. 666a exists imperf.

Flowers — A108a

1992, June 2 **Litho.** *Perf. 14*

666B A108a 15fr Impatiens petersiana .40
666C A108a 20fr Lachenalia aloides .50
666D A108a 30fr Nymphaea lotus .80
666E A108a 50fr Clivia miniata 1.30
f. Souvenir sheet of 4, #666B-666E, perf. 13½ 3.00
Nos. 666B-666E (4) 3.00

A109

Native Music and Dancing A110

Designs: 15fr, Native drummer. 30fr, Two dancers. 115fr, Drummers. 200fr, Five dancers.

1992, Apr. 2 **Litho.** *Perf. 14*

667 A109 15fr multicolored .25
668 A109 30fr multicolored .48
669 A110 115fr multicolored 1.80
670 A110 200fr multicolored 3.10
a. Souvenir sheet 5.65
Nos. 667-670 (4) 5.63

No. 670a contains one each of Nos. 667-668, perf. 13x13½, and Nos. 669-670, perf. 13½x13.

Independence, 30th Anniv. — A111

Designs: 30fr, 140fr, People with flag. 85fr, 115fr, Natl. flag. 110fr, 200fr, Monument, vert. 120fr, 250fr, Map, vert.

1992, June 30 **Litho.** *Perf. 15*

671 A111 30fr multicolored .35
672 A111 85fr multicolored 1.00
673 A111 110fr multicolored 1.25
674 A111 115fr multicolored 1.35
675 A111 120fr multicolored 1.40
676 A111 140fr multicolored 1.65
677 A111 200fr multicolored 2.35
678 A111 250fr multicolored 3.00
Nos. 671-678 (8) 12.35

Discovery of America, 500th Anniv. A112

Columbus' fleet, globe and: 200fr, Pre-Columbian artifacts. 400fr, Fruits and vegetables.

1992, Oct. 12 **Litho.** *Perf. 15*

679 A112 200fr multicolored 3.00
680 A112 400fr multicolored 6.25

Felis Serval A113

1992, Oct. 16

681 A113 30fr shown .48
682 A113 130fr Two seated 2.00
683 A113 200fr One standing, one lying 3.10
684 A113 220fr Two faces 3.40
Nos. 681-684 (4) 8.98

World Wildlife Fund.

Mushrooms A114 1992 Summer Olympics, Barcelona A115

Designs: 10fr, Russula ingens. 15fr, Russula brunneorigida. 20fr, Amanita zambiana. 30fr, Russula subfistulosa. 75fr, 85fr, Russula meleagris. 100fr, Russula immaculata. 110fr, like #685. 115fr, like #686. 120fr, 130fr, Russula sejuncta. 250fr, Afroboletus luteolus.

1992-93 *Perf. 11½x12*

Granite Paper

685 A114 10fr multicolored .15
686 A114 15fr multicolored .24
687 A114 20fr multicolored .32
688 A114 30fr multicolored .48
689 A114 75fr multicolored 1.15
690 A114 85fr multicolored 1.35
691 A114 100fr multicolored 1.55
691A A114 110fr multicolored 1.65
691B A114 115fr multicolored 1.75
692 A114 120fr multicolored 1.90
693 A114 130fr multicolored 2.00
694 A114 250fr multicolored 3.75
Nos. 685-694 (12) 16.29

Issued: 110fr, 115fr, 1993; others, 9/30/92.

1992, Nov. 6 *Perf. 15*

695 A115 130fr Runners 2.00
696 A115 500fr Hurdler 7.75

A116 A116a

Christmas (Details of Adoration of the Kings, by Gentile da Fabriano): a, 100fr, Crowd, horses. b, 130fr, Kings. c, 250fr, Nativity scene.

1992, Dec. 7 **Litho.** *Perf. 11½*

697 A116 Strip of 3, #a.-c. 5.25
d. Souvenir sheet of 3, #697a-697c 6.50

Nos. 697a-697c have white border. No. 697d has continuous design and sold for 580fr.

1992, Dec. 5 **Litho.** *Perf. 15*

Designs: 200fr, Emblems. 220fr, Profile of person made from fruits and vegetables.

697E A116a 200fr multicolored 5.25
697F A116a 220fr multicolored 5.75

Intl. Conference on Nutrition, Rome.

European Common Market A117

Designs: 130fr, Flags, stars. 500fr, Europe, Africa, clasped hands, stars.

1993, Mar. 29 **Litho.** *Perf. 15*

698 A117 130fr multicolored 1.50
699 A117 500fr multicolored 5.75

1994 World Cup Soccer Championships, US — A118

Players, stadium, US flag and: 130fr, Statue of Liberty. 200fr, Golden Gate Bridge.

1993, July 5 **Litho.** *Perf. 15*

700 A118 130fr multicolored 1.50
701 A118 200fr multicolored 2.30

Traditional Musical Instruments A119

1993, Apr. 30 **Litho.** *Perf. 15*

702 A119 200fr Indonongo 2.30
703 A119 220fr Ingoma 2.50
704 A119 250fr Ikembe 2.75
705 A119 300fr Umuduri 3.50
Nos. 702-705 (4) 11.05

A120 A121

1993, June 4 **Litho.** *Perf. 11½*

706 A120 130fr Papilio bromius 1.50
707 A120 200fr Charaxes eupale 2.25
708 A120 250fr Cymothoe caenis 2.75
709 A120 300fr Graphium ridleyanus 3.50
a. Souvenir sheet of 4, #706-709 11.50
Nos. 706-709 (4) 10.00

No. 709a sold for 980fr.

1993, Dec. 9 *Perf. 14*

710 A121 100fr Cattle 1.10
711 A121 120fr Sheep 1.40
712 A121 130fr Pigs 1.50
713 A121 250fr Goats 2.75
Nos. 710-713 (4) 6.75

Christmas — A122 Rock Stars — A123

Natives adoring Christ Child: a, 100fr, Woman carrying baby, two people kneeling. b, 130fr, With Christ Child. 250fr, c, Woman carrying baby, three other people.

1993, Dec. 10 *Perf. 11½*

714 A122 Strip of 3, #a.-c. 5.00
d. Souvenir sheet of 3, #714a-714c 6.00

Nos. 714a-714c have white border. No. 714d has continuous design and sold for 580fr.

1994 **Litho.** *Perf. 15*

715 A123 60fr Elvis Presley .65
716 A123 115fr Mick Jagger 1.25
717 A123 120fr John Lennon 1.25
718 A123 200fr Michael Jackson 2.25
a. Souvenir sheet, #715-718 6.50
Nos. 715-718 (4) 5.40

No. 718a sold for 600fr.

A124

A125

1994, Oct. 10 Litho. *Perf. 15*
719 A124 150fr multicolored 1.10

Intl. Olympic Committee, cent.

1994, Dec. 14 Photo. *Perf. 15*

Christmas (Madonna and Child): a, 115fr, Chinese. b, 120fr, Japanese. c, 250fr, Polish.

720 A125 Strip of 3, #a.-c. 5.00
d. Souvenir sheet of 1, #720c 2.75

A126

A127

Designs: 115fr, FAO, 50th anniv. 120fr, UN, 50th anniv.

1995, Feb. 21 Litho. *Perf. 11½*
721 A126 115fr multicolored 1.25
722 A126 120fr multicolored 1.25

1995 Litho. *Perf. 11½*

Flowers: 15fr, Cassia didymobotrya. 20fr, Mitragyna rubrostipulosa. 30fr, Phytolacca dodecandra. 85fr, Acanthus pubescens. 100fr, Bulbophyllum comatum. 110fr, Angraecum evradianum. 115fr, Eulophia burundiensis. 120fr, Habenaria adolphii.

Granite Paper

723 A127 15fr multicolored .15
724 A127 20fr multicolored .20
725 A127 30fr multicolored .30
726 A127 85fr multicolored .80
727 A127 100fr multicolored .90
728 A127 110fr multicolored 1.00
729 A127 115fr multicolored 1.00
730 A127 120fr multicolored 1.10
Nos. 723-730 (8) 5.45

SEMI-POSTAL STAMPS

Prince Louis Rwagasore — SP1

Prince and Stadium SP2

Design: 1.50fr+75c, 6.50fr+3fr, Prince and memorial monument.

Perf. 14x13, 13x14
1963, Feb. 15 Photo. Unwmk.
B1 SP1 50c + 25c brt vio .15 .15
B2 SP2 1fr + 50c red org & dk bl .15 .15
B3 SP2 1.50fr + 75c lem & dk vio .15 .15
B4 SP1 3.50fr + 1.50fr lil rose .15 .15
B5 SP2 5fr + 2fr rose pink & dk bl .15 .15
B6 SP2 6.50fr + 3fr gray ol & dk vio .15 .15
Set value .50 .39

Issued in memory of Prince Louis Rwagasore (1932-61), son of King Mwami Mwambutsa IV and Prime Minister. The surtax was for the stadium and monument in his honor.

Red Cross Type of Regular Issue
Souvenir Sheet

1963, Sept. 26 Litho. *Imperf.*
B7 Sheet of 4 2.00 2.00
a. A5 4fr + 2fr fawn, red & black .32 .32
b. A5 8fr + 2fr green, red & black .38 .38
c. A5 10fr + 2fr gray, red & black .42 .42
d. A5 20fr + 2fr ultra, red & black .65 .65

Surtax for Red Cross work in Burundi.

Olympic Type of Regular Issue
Souvenir Sheet

Designs: 18fr+2fr, Hurdling, horiz. 20fr+5fr, Vaulting, horiz.

1964, Nov. 18 *Perf. 13½*
B8 Sheet of 2 3.00 2.75
a. A13 18fr + 2fr yel grn & multi 1.25 1.00
b. A13 20fr + 5fr brt pink & multi 1.25 1.00

Scientist with Microscope and Map of Burundi — SP3

Lithographed and Photogravure
1965, Jan. 28 Unwmk. *Perf. 14½*
B9 SP3 2fr + 50c multi .15 .15
B10 SP3 4fr + 1.50fr multi .15 .15
B11 SP3 5fr + 2.50fr multi .20 .15
B12 SP3 8fr + 3fr multi .25 .15
B13 SP3 10fr + 5fr multi .38 .16
Nos. B9-B13 (5) 1.13
Set value .47

Souvenir Sheet
Perf. 13x13½
B14 SP3 10fr + 10fr multi .85 .85

Issued for the fight against tuberculosis.

Coat of Arms, 10fr Coin, Reverse SP4

Designs (Coins of Various Denominations): 4fr+50c, 8fr+50c, 15fr+50c, 40fr+50c, King Mwambutsa IV, obverse.

Lithographed; Embossed on Gilt Foil
1965, Aug. 9 *Imperf.*

Diameter: 39mm
B15 SP4 2fr + 50c crim & org .15 .15
B16 SP4 4fr + 50c ultra & ver .15 .15

Diameter: 45mm
B17 SP4 6fr + 50c org & gray .15 .15
B18 SP4 8fr + 50c bl & mag .15 .15

Diameter: 56mm
B19 SP4 12fr + 50c lt grn & red lil .25 .25
B20 SP4 15fr + 50c yel grn & lt lil .30 .30

Diameter: 67mm
B21 SP4 25fr + 50c vio bl & buff .50 .50
B22 SP4 40fr + 50c brt pink & red brn .75 .75
Nos. B15-B22 (8) 2.40 2.40

Stamps are backed with patterned paper in blue, orange and pink engine-turned design.

Prince Louis Rwagasore and Pres. John F. Kennedy SP5

Designs: 4fr+1fr, 20fr+5fr, Prince Louis and memorial. 20fr+2fr, 40fr+5fr, Pres. John F. Kennedy and library shelves. 40fr+2fr, King Mwambutsa IV at Kennedy grave, Arlington, vert.

1966, Jan. 21 Photo. *Perf. 13½*
B23 SP5 4fr + 1fr gray bl & dk brn .15 .15
B24 SP5 10fr + 1fr pale grn, ind & brn .18 .15
B25 SP5 20fr + 2fr lil & dp grn .38 .15
B26 SP5 40fr + 2fr gray grn & dk brn .65 .15
Nos. B23-B26 (4) 1.36
Set value .28

Souvenir Sheet
B27 Sheet of 2 1.50 1.00
a. SP5 20fr + 5fr gray blue & dk brn .50 .45
b. SP5 40fr + 5fr lilac & deep green .75 .50

Issued in memory of Prince Louis Rwagasore and President John F. Kennedy.

Republic

Winston Churchill and St. Paul's, London SP6

Designs: 15fr+2fr, Tower of London and Churchill. 20fr+3fr, Big Ben and Churchill.

1967, Mar. 23 Photo. *Perf. 13½*
B28 SP6 4fr + 1fr multi .15 .15
B29 SP6 15fr + 2fr multi .35 .15
B30 SP6 20fr + 3fr multi .45 .18
Nos. B28-B30 (3) .95
Set value .33

Issued in memory of Sir Winston Churchill (1874-1965), statesman and World War II leader.

A souvenir sheet contains one airmail stamp, 50fr+5fr, with Churchill portrait centered. Size: 80x80mm. Exists perf. and imperf. Value, each sheet, $3.50.

Nos. B28-B30 Overprinted

1967, July 14 Photo. *Perf. 13½*
B31 SP6 4fr + 1fr multi .15 .15
B32 SP6 15fr + 2fr multi .42 .20
B33 SP6 20fr + 3fr multi .65 .30
Nos. B31-B33 (3) 1.22 .65

50th anniversary of Lions International.
Exist with dates transposed.
The souvenir sheets described below No. B30 also received this Lions overprint. Value, each $3.50.

Blood Transfusion and Red Cross — SP7

Designs: 7fr+1fr, Stretcher bearers and wounded man. 11fr+1fr, Surgical team. 17fr+1fr, Nurses tending blood bank.

1969, June 26 Photo. *Perf. 13½*
B34 SP7 4fr + 1fr multi .15 .15
B35 SP7 7fr + 1fr multi .15 .15
B36 SP7 11fr + 1fr multi .30 .15
B37 SP7 17fr + 1fr multi .32 .15
Nos. B34-B37,CB9-CB11 (7) 2.50
Set value .68

League of Red Cross Societies, 50th anniv.

Pope Paul VI and Map of Africa — SP8

Designs: 3fr+2fr, 17fr+2fr, Pope Paul VI, vert. 10fr+2fr, Flag made of flags of African Nations. 14fr+2fr, View of St. Peter's, Rome. 40fr+2fr, 40fr+5fr, Martyrs of Uganda. 50fr+2fr, 50fr+5fr, Pope on Throne. All designs include portrait of Pope Paul VI.

1969, Sept. 12 Photo. *Perf. 13½*
B38 SP8 3fr + 2fr multi .15 .15
B39 SP8 5fr + 2fr multi .15 .15
B40 SP8 10fr + 2fr multi .30 .15
B41 SP8 14fr + 2fr multi .42 .15
B42 SP8 17fr + 2fr multi .50 .15
B43 SP8 40fr + 2fr multi 1.00 .18
B44 SP8 50fr + 2fr multi 1.10 .20
Nos. B38-B44 (7) 3.62
Set value .66

Souvenir Sheet
B45 Sheet of 2 2.00 1.75
a. SP8 40fr + 5fr multi .90 .75
b. SP8 50fr + 5fr multi 1.00 .90

Visit of Pope Paul VI to Uganda, July 31-Aug. 2.

Virgin and Child, by Albrecht Dürer — SP9

Christmas (Paintings): 11fr+1fr, Madonna of the Eucharist, by Sandro Botticelli. 20fr+1fr, Holy Family, by El Greco.

1970, Dec. 14 Photo. *Perf. 13½*
Gold Frame
B46 SP9 6.50fr + 1fr multi .15 .15
B47 SP9 11fr + 1fr multi .22 .15
B48 SP9 20fr + 1fr multi .42 .15
a. Souvenir sheet of 3B46-B48 .90 .90
Nos. B46-B48,CB12-CB14 (6) 2.14
Set value .70

Nos. 376-378 Surcharged in Gold and Black

1971, Nov. 27
B49 A51 3fr + 1fr multi .15 .15
B50 A51 5fr + 1fr multi .15 .15
B51 A51 6fr + 1fr multi .18 .15
a. Souvenir sheet of 3 .55 .55
Nos. B49-B51,CB19-CB21 (6) 1.78
Set value .56

UNICE, 25th anniv. #B51a contains 3 stamps similar to #B49-B51 with 2fr surtax each.

"La Polenta," by Pietro Longhi SP10

Designs: 3fr+1fr, Archangel Michael, Byzantine icon from St. Mark's 6fr+1fr, "Gossip," by Pietro Longhi. 11fr+1fr, "Diana's Bath," by Giovanni Batista Pittoni. All stamps inscribed UNESCO.

1971, Dec. 27
B52 SP10 3fr + 1fr gold & multi .15 .15
B53 SP10 5fr + 1fr gold & multi .15 .15
B54 SP10 6fr + 1fr gold & multi .18 .15
B55 SP10 11fr + 1fr gold & multi .30 .15
a. Souvenir sheet of 4 .75 .50
Nos. B52-B55,CB22-CB25 (8) 2.26
Set value .75

The surtax was for the UNESCO campaign to save the treasures of Venice. No. B55a contains 4 stamps similar to Nos. B52-B55, but with 2fr surtax. Sheet exists imperf.

Nos. 408-410 Surcharged "+1F" in Silver

1972, Dec. 12 Photo. *Perf. 13½*

B56 A57 5fr + 1fr multi .15 .15
B57 A57 10fr + 1fr multi .22 .15
B58 A57 15fr + 1fr multi .32 .15
a. Souvenir sheet of 3 .75 .70
Nos. B56-B58,CB26-CB28 (6) 2.02
Set value .60

Christmas 1972. No. B58a contains 3 stamps similar to Nos. B56-B58, but with 2fr surtax.

Nos. 441-443 Surcharged "+1F" in Silver

1973, Dec. 14 Photo. *Perf. 13*

B59 A64 5fr + 1fr multi .15 .15
B60 A64 10fr + 1fr multi .20 .15
B61 A64 15fr + 1fr multi .30 .15
a. Souvenir sheet of 3 .65 .65
Nos. B59-B61,CB29-CB31 (6) 1.93
Set value .60

Christmas 1973. No. B61a contains 3 stamps similar to Nos. B59-B61 with 2fr surtax each.

Christmas Type of 1974

1974, Dec. 2 Photo. *Perf. 13*

B62 A70 5fr + 1fr multi .15 .15
B63 A70 10fr + 1fr multi .20 .15
B64 A70 15fr + 1fr multi .30 .18
a. Souvenir sheet of 3 .75 .75
Nos. B62-B64,CB32-CB34 (6) 2.17 1.40

No. B64a contains 3 stamps similar to Nos. B62-B64 with 2fr surtax each.

Nos. 485-490 Surcharged "+ 1F" in Silver and Black

1975, Dec. 22 Photo. *Perf. 13*

B65 A73 5fr + 1fr #485 .15
B66 A73 5fr + 1fr #486 .15
B67 A73 13fr + 1fr #487 .28
B68 A73 13fr + 1fr #488 .28
B69 A73 27fr + 1fr #489 .50
B70 A73 27fr + 1fr #490 .50
a. Souvenir sheet of 6 2.50
Nos. B65-B70,CB35-CB40 (12) 5.16

Michelangelo Buonarroti (1475-1564), 500th birth anniversary. No. B70a contains 6 stamps similar to Nos. B65-B70 with 2fr surcharge each.

Nos. 504-506 Surcharged "+1f" in Silver and Black

1976, Nov. 25 Photo. *Perf. 13½*

B71 A76 5fr + 1fr multi .15
B72 A76 13fr + 1fr multi .22
B73 A76 27fr + 1fr multi .42
a. Souvenir sheet of 3 .85
Nos. B71-B73,CB41-CB43 (6) 2.19

Christmas 1976. No. B73a contains 3 stamps similar to Nos. B71-B73 with 2fr surtax each.

Nos. 531-533 Surcharged "+1fr" in Silver and Black

1977 Photo. *Perf. 14x13*

B74 A83 5fr + 1fr multi .15
B75 A83 13fr + 1fr multi .22
B76 A83 27fr + 1fr multi .42
a. Souvenir sheet of 3 .85
Nos. B74-B76,CB44-CB46 (6) 2.17

Christmas 1977. No. B76a contains 3 stamps similar to Nos. B74-B76 with 2fr surtax each.

Christmas Type of 1979

1979, Feb. Photo. *Perf. 14x13*

B77 A86 13fr + 1fr multi .22
B78 A86 17fr + 1fr multi .28
B79 A86 27fr + 1fr multi .42
B80 A86 31fr + 1fr multi .50
B81 A86 40fr + 1fr multi .60
Nos. B77-B81 (5) 2.02

IYC Type of 1979

1979, July 19 Photo. *Perf. 14*

B82 Sheet of 4 1.25 1.00
a. A88 10fr + 2fr like #557 .15 .15
b. A88 20fr + 2fr like #558 .24 .15
c. A88 27fr + 2fr like #559 .28 .20
d. A88 50fr + 2fr like #560 .55 .32

Christmas Type of 1979

1979, Dec. 10 Photo. *Perf. 13½*

B83 A89 20fr + 1fr like #561 .32
B84 A89 27fr + 1fr like #562 .42
B85 A89 31fr + 1fr like #563 .48
B86 A89 50fr + 1fr like #564 .80
Nos. B83-B86 (4) 2.02

Christmas Type of 1980

1981, Jan. 16 Photo. *Perf. 13½x13*

B87 A92 10fr + 1fr like #579 .15
B88 A92 30fr + 1fr like #580 .32
B89 A92 40fr + 1fr like #581 .42
B90 A92 50fr + 1fr like #582 .50
Nos. B87-B90 (4) 1.39

Christmas Type of 1983

1983, Nov. 2 Litho. *Perf. 14½x13½*

B91 A97 10fr + 1fr like #607 .16
B92 A97 25fr + 1fr like #608 .40
B93 A97 30fr + 1fr like #609 .48
B94 A97 50fr + 1fr like #610 .75
Nos. B91-B94 (4) 1.79

Christmas Type of 1984

1984, Dec. 15 *Perf. 13½*

B95 A101 10fr + 1fr like #629 .16
B96 A101 25fr + 1fr like #630 .40
B97 A101 30fr + 1fr like #631 .48
B98 A101 50fr + 1fr like #632 .75
Nos. B95-B98 (4) 1.79

Multi-party Elections, 1st Anniv.
SP11 SP12

Designs: 30fr+10fr, Pres. Buyoya handing Baton of Power to Pres. Ndadaye. 110fr+10fr, Pres. Ndadaye giving inauguration speech. 115fr+10fr, Arms, map of Burundi. 120fr+10fr, Warrior, flag of Burundi, trees, map of Burundi.

1994, Oct. 20 Litho. *Perf. 15*

B99 SP11 30fr +10fr multi .30
B100 SP11 110fr +10fr multi .90
B101 SP12 115fr +10fr multi .95
B102 SP12 120fr +10fr multi 1.00
Nos. B99-B102 (4) 3.15

AIR POST STAMPS

Animal Type of Regular Issue

Animals: 6fr, Zebra. 8fr, Cape buffalo (bubalis). 10fr, Impala, vert. 14fr, Hippopotamus. 15fr, Defassa waterbuck, vert. 20fr, Cheetah. 50fr, Elephant.

Unwmk.

1964, July 2 Litho. *Perf. 14*

Size: 42x21mm, 21x42mm

C1 A9 6fr multi .15 .15
C2 A9 8fr multi .16 .15
C3 A9 10fr multi .22 .15
C4 A9 14fr multi .30 .15
C5 A9 15fr multi .32 .15

Size: 53x32½mm

C6 A9 20fr multi .42 .15
C7 A9 50fr multi 1.10 .38
Nos. C1-C7 (7) 2.67
Set value .85

Bird Type of Regular Issue

Birds: 6fr, Secretary bird. 8fr, African anhinga. 10fr, African peacock. 14fr, Bee eater. 15fr, Yellow-billed stork. 20fr, Saddle-billed stork. 50fr, Abyssinian ground hornbill. 75fr, Martial eagle. 130fr, Lesser flamingo.

1965, June 10 Litho. *Perf. 14*

Size: 26x43mm

C8 A14 6fr multi .15 .15
C9 A14 8fr multi .15 .15
C10 A14 10fr multi .20 .15
C11 A14 14fr multi .25 .15
C12 A14 15fr multi .30 .15

Size: 33x53mm

C13 A14 20fr multi .35 .15
C14 A14 50fr multi .90 .20
C15 A14 75fr multi 1.25 .25
C16 A14 130fr multi 2.25 .38
Nos. C8-C16 (9) 5.80
Set value 1.15

For overprints see Nos. C35A-C35I.

Flower Type of Regular Issue

Flowers: 6fr, Dissotis. 8fr, Crossandra. 10fr, Ansellia. 14fr, Thunbergia. 15fr, Schizoglossum. 20fr, Gazania. 50fr, Protea. 75fr, Hibiscus. 130fr, Markhamia.

1966, Oct. 10 Unwmk. *Perf. 13½*

Size: 31x31mm

C17 A17 6fr multi .15 .15
C18 A17 8fr multi .15 .15
C19 A17 10fr multi .18 .15
C20 A17 14fr multi .22 .15
C21 A17 15fr multi .22 .15

Size: 39x39mm

C22 A17 20fr multi .22 .15
C23 A17 50fr multi .60 .18
C24 A17 75fr multi .80 .22
C25 A17 130fr multi 1.50 .32
Nos. C17-C25 (9) 4.04
Set value 1.10

For overprints see Nos. C27-C35.

Tapestry Type of Regular Issue
Souvenir Sheet

1966, Nov. 4 Unwmk. *Perf. 13½*

C26 A18 Sheet of 7 (14fr) 1.25 .65

See note after No. 158.

Republic
Nos. C17-C25 Overprinted

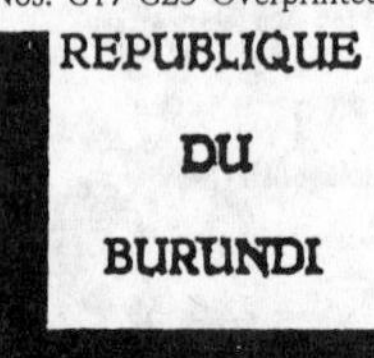

1967 Litho. *Perf. 13½*

Size: 31x31mm

C27 A17 6fr multi .20 .15
C28 A17 8fr multi .22 .15
C29 A17 10fr multi .25 .15
C30 A17 14fr multi .48 .15
C31 A17 15fr multi .48 .15

Size: 39x39mm

C32 A17 20fr multi .70 .18
C33 A17 50fr multi 1.90 .50
C34 A17 75fr multi 3.00 .50
C35 A17 130fr multi 4.00 1.10
Nos. C27-C35 (9) 11.23 3.03

Nos. C8-C16 Overprinted "REPUBLIQUE / DU / BURUNDI" and Horizontal Bar

1967 Litho. *Perf. 14*

Size: 26x43mm

C35A A14 6fr multi *.15*
C35B A14 8fr multi *.18*
C35C A14 10fr multi *.20*
C35D A14 14fr multi *.30*
C35E A14 15fr multi *.48*

Size: 33x53mm

C35F A14 20fr multi *.75*
C35G A14 50fr multi *1.90*
C35H A14 75fr multi *3.00*
C35I A14 130fr multi *3.50*
Nos. C35A-C35I (9) *10.46*

African Art Type of Regular Issue

African Art: 10fr, Spirit of Bakutu figurine, Equatorial Africa. 14fr, Pearl throne of Sultan of the Bamum, Cameroun. 17fr, Bronze head of Mother Queen of Benin, Nigeria. 24fr, Statue of 109th Bakouba king, Kata-Mbula, Central Congo. 26fr, Baskets and lances, Burundi.

1967, June 5 Photo. *Perf. 13½*

C36 A20 10fr gold & multi .15 .15
C37 A20 14fr gold & multi .15 .15
C38 A20 17fr gold & multi .15 .15
C39 A20 24fr gold & multi .22 .15
C40 A20 26fr gold & multi .42 .25
Nos. C36-C40 (5) 1.09
Set value .55

Boy Scout Type of Regular Issue

Designs: 10fr, Scouts on hiking trip. 14fr, Cooking at campfire. 17fr, Lord Baden-Powell. 24fr, Boy Scout and Cub Scout giving Scout sign. 26fr, First aid.

1967, Aug. 9 *Perf. 13½*

C41 A21 10fr gold & multi .15 .15
C42 A21 14fr gold & multi .22 .15
C43 A21 17fr gold & multi .28 .15
C44 A21 24fr gold & multi .42 .18
C45 A21 26fr gold & multi .70 .18
Nos. C41-C45 (5) 1.77
Set value .66

A souvenir sheet of 2 contains one each of Nos. C44-C45 and 2 labels in the designs of Nos. 208-209 with commemorative inscriptions was issued Jan. 8, 1968. Size: 100x100mm

Fish Type of Regular Issue

Designs: Various Tropical Fish

1967, Sept. 8 Photo. *Perf. 13½*

Size: 50x23mm

C46 A19 6fr multi .15 .15
C47 A19 8fr multi .16 .15
C48 A19 10fr multi .18 .15
C49 A19 14fr multi .25 .15
C50 A19 15fr multi .25 .15

Size: 58x27mm

C51 A19 20fr multi .32 .15
C52 A19 50fr multi .80 .15
C53 A19 75fr multi 1.25 .16
C54 A19 130fr multi 2.00 .26
Nos. C46-C54 (9) 5.36
Set value .80

Boeing 707 of Air Congo and ITY Emblem — AP1

Designs: 14fr, Boeing 727 of Sabena over lake. 17fr, Vickers VC10 of East African Airways over lake. 26fr, Boeing 727 of Sabena over airport.

1967, Nov. 3 Photo. *Perf. 13*

C55 AP1 10fr blk, yel brn & sil .15 .15
C56 AP1 14fr blk, org & sil .20 .15
C57 AP1 17fr blk, brt bl & sil .25 .15
C58 AP1 26fr blk, brt rose lil & sil .42 .15
Nos. C55-C58 (4) 1.02
Set value .38

Opening of the jet airport at Bujumbura and for International Tourist Year, 1967.

Paintings Type of Regular Issue

Paintings: 17fr, Woman with Cat, by Renoir. 24fr, The Jewish Bride, by Rembrandt, horiz. 26fr, Pope Innocent X, by Velazquez.

1968, Mar. 29 Photo. *Perf. 13½*

C59 A26 17fr multi .35 .15
C60 A26 24fr multi .45 .18
C61 A26 26fr multi .55 .20
Nos. C59-C61 (3) 1.35 .53

Issued in sheets of 6.

Space Type of Regular Issue

Designs: 14fr, Moon Probe. 18fr, Russian astronaut walking in space. 25fr, Weather satellite. 40fr, American astronaut walking in space.

1968, May 15 Photo. *Perf. 13½*

Size: 41x41mm

C62 A27 14fr sil & multi .25 .15
C63 A27 18fr sil & multi .30 .15
C64 A27 25fr sil & multi .45 .15
C65 A27 40fr sil & multi .70 .18
Nos. C62-C65 (4) 1.70
Set value .42

Butterfly Type of Regular Issue

Butterflies: 6fr, Teracolus annae. 8fr, Graphium ridleyanus. 10fr, Cymothoe. 14fr, Charaxes eupale. 15fr, Papilio bromius. 20fr, Papilio zenobia. 50fr, Salamis aethiops. 75fr, Danais chrysippus. 130fr, Salamis temora.

1968, Sept. 9 Photo. *Perf. 13½*

Size: 38x42mm

C66 A28 6fr gold & multi .15 .15
C67 A28 8fr gold & multi .15 .15
C68 A28 10fr gold & multi .18 .15
C69 A28 14fr gold & multi .20 .15
C70 A28 15fr gold & multi .20 .15

Size: 44x49mm

C71 A28 20fr gold & multi .30 .15
C72 A28 50fr gold & multi .70 .15
C73 A28 75fr gold & multi 1.25 .15
C74 A28 130fr gold & multi 2.00 .20
Nos. C66-C74 (9) 5.13
Set value .72

Painting Type of Regular Issue

Paintings: 17fr, The Letter, by Jean H. Fragonard. 26fr, Young Woman Reading Letter, by Jan Vermeer. 40fr, Lady Folding Letter, by Elisabeth Vigée-Lebrun. 50fr, Mademoiselle Lavergne, by Jean Etienne Liotard.

1968, Sept. 30 Photo. Perf. 13½
C84 A29 17fr multi .22 .15
C85 A29 26fr multi .42 .15
C86 A29 40fr multi .60 .15
C87 A29 50fr multi .70 .18
Nos. C84-C87 (4) 1.94
Set value .48

Olympic Games Type of 1968

Designs: 10fr, Shot put. 17fr, Running. 26fr, Hammer throw. 50fr, Hurdling. 75fr, Broad jump.

1968, Oct. 24
C88 A30 10fr gold & multi .15 .15
C89 A30 17fr gold & multi .22 .15
C90 A30 26fr gold & multi .38 .15
C91 A30 50fr gold & multi .70 .20
C92 A30 75fr gold & multi 1.10 .30
Nos. C88-C92 (5) 2.55
Set value .70

Christmas Type of 1968

Paintings: 10fr, Virgin and Child, by Correggio. 14fr, Nativity, by Federigo Baroccio. 17fr, Holy Family, by El Greco. 26fr, Adoration of the Magi, by Maino.

1968, Nov. 26 Photo. Perf. 13½
C93 A31 10fr multi .15 .15
C94 A31 14fr multi .22 .15
C95 A31 17fr multi .28 .15
C96 A31 26fr multi .40 .15
a. Souv. sheet of 4, #C93-C96 1.10
Nos. C93-C96 (4) 1.05
Set value .45

For overprints see Nos. C100-C103.

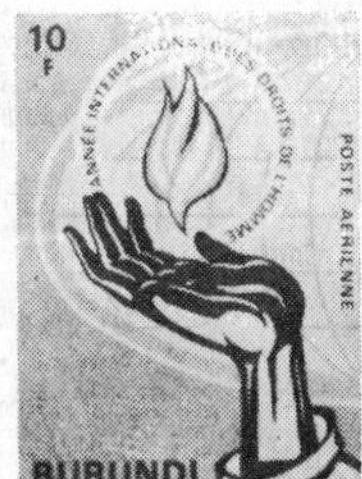

Human Rights Flame, Hand and Globe — AP2

1969, Jan. 22
C97 AP2 10fr multi .15 .15
C98 AP2 14fr multi .22 .15
C99 AP2 26fr lil & multi .40 .15
Nos. C97-C99 (3) .77
Set value .22

International Human Rights Year, 1968.

Nos. C93-C96 Overprinted in Silver

1969, Feb. 17 Photo. Perf. 13½
C100 A31 10fr multi .20 .15
C101 A31 14fr multi .28 .15
C102 A31 17fr multi .35 .15
C103 A31 26fr multi .50 .22
Nos. C100-C103 (4) 1.33 .67

Man's 1st flight around the moon by the US spacecraft Apollo 8, Dec. 21-27, 1968.

Moon Landing Type of 1969

Designs: 26fr, Neil A. Armstrong leaving landing module. 40fr, Astronaut on moon. 50fr, Splashdown in the Pacific.

1969, Nov. 6 Photo. Perf. 13½
C104 A38 26fr gold & multi .50 .25
C105 A38 40fr gold & multi .75 .38
C106 A38 50fr gold & multi .90 .42
Nos. C104-C106 (3) 2.15 1.05

Christmas Type of 1969

Paintings: 17fr, Madonna and Child, by Benvenuto da Garofalo. 26fr, Madonna and Child, by Jacopo Negretti. 50fr, Madonna and Child, by Il Giorgione. All horizontal.

1969, Dec. 2 Photo.
C107 A39 17fr gold & multi .38 .15
C108 A39 26fr gold & multi .50 .15
C109 A39 50fr gold & multi .90 .28
a. Souv. sheet of 3, #C107-C109 1.90 1.50
Nos. C107-C109 (3) 1.78
Set value .48

Insect Type of Regular Issue

Designs: Various Beetles and Weevils.

1970 Perf. 13½

Size: 46x32mm
C110 A40 6fr gold & multi .15 .15
C111 A40 8fr gold & multi .15 .15
C112 A40 10fr gold & multi .18 .15
C113 A40 14fr gold & multi .25 .15
C114 A40 15fr gold & multi .30 .15

Size: 52x36mm
C115 A40 20fr gold & multi 1.00 .15
C116 A40 50fr gold & multi 2.00 .25
C117 A40 75fr gold & multi 3.00 .25
C118 A40 130fr gold & multi 3.75 .40
Nos. C110-C118 (9) 10.78
Set value 1.20

Issue dates: Nos. C110-C115, Jan. 20. Nos. C116-C118, Feb. 27.

Easter Type of 1970

Stations of the Cross, by Juan de Aranoa y Carredano: 8fr, Jesus meets the women of Jerusalem. 10fr, Jesus falls a third time. 14fr, Jesus stripped. 15fr, Jesus nailed to the cross. 18fr, Jesus dies on the cross. 20fr, Descent from the cross. 50fr, Jesus laid in the tomb.

1970, Mar. 16 Photo. Perf. 13½
C119 A41 8fr gold & multi .15 .15
C120 A41 10fr gold & multi .15 .15
C121 A41 14fr gold & multi .22 .15
C122 A41 15fr gold & multi .25 .15
C123 A41 18fr gold & multi .28 .15
C124 A41 20fr gold & multi .30 .15
C125 A41 50fr gold & multi .70 .30
a. Souv. sheet of 7, #C119-C125 + label 2.25 1.75
Nos. C119-C125 (7) 2.05
Set value .84

EXPO '70 Type of Regular Issue
Souvenir Sheet

Designs: 40fr, Tower of the Sun, vert. 50fr, Flags of participating nations, vert.

1970, May 5 Photo. Perf. 13½
C126 Sheet of 2 1.40 1.40
a. A42 40fr multi .50 .50
b. A42 50fr multi .60 .60

Rhinoceros Type of Regular Issue

Designs, FAUNA: Camel, dromedary, okapi, rhinoceros, addax, Burundi cow (2 stamps of each animal in 2 different poses). MAP OF THE NILE: Delta and pyramids, dhow, cataract, Blue Nile and crowned crane, Victoria Nile and secretary bird, Lake Victoria and source of Nile on Mt. Gikizi.

1970, July 8 Photo. Perf. 13½
C127 Sheet of 18 5.25
a. A43 14fr any single .28 .15

Issued in sheets of 18 (3x6) stamps of different designs, to publicize the southernmost source of the Nile on Mt. Gikizi in Burundi.

UN Emblem and Headquarters, NYC — AP3

25th Anniv. of the UN (UN Emblem and): 11fr, Security Council and mural by Per Krohg. 26fr, Pope Paul VI and U Thant. 40fr, Flags in front of UN Headquarters, NYC.

1970, Oct. 23 Photo. Perf. 13½
C128 AP3 7fr gold & multi .15 .15
C129 AP3 11fr gold & multi .18 .15
C130 AP3 26fr gold & multi .40 .15
C131 AP3 40fr gold & multi .60 .15
a. Souvenir sheet of 2 1.10 .90
Nos. C128-C131 (4) 1.33
Set value .30

No. C131a contains 2 stamps similar to Nos. C130-C131 but without "Poste Aerienne". Exists imperf.

Bird Type of Regular Issue

Birds: 8fr, 14fr, 30fr, vertical; 10fr, 20fr, 50fr, horizontal.

1970 Photo. Perf. 13½

Stamp size: 52x44mm
C132 A44 Block of 4 1.25 .15
a. 8fr Northern shrike .30 .15
b. 8fr European starling .30 .15
c. 8fr Yellow wagtail .30 .15
d. 8fr Bank swallow .30 .15
C133 A44 Block of 4 1.50 .18
a. 10fr Winter wren .35 .15
b. 10fr Firecrest .35 .15
c. 10fr Skylark .35 .15
d. 10fr Crested lark .35 .15
C134 A44 Block of 4 1.90 .25
a. 14fr Woodchat shrike .45 .15
b. 14fr Common rock thrush .45 .15
c. 14fr Black redstart .45 .15
d. 14fr Ring ouzel .45 .15
C135 A44 Block of 4 3.00 .32
a. 20fr European redstart .70 .15
b. 20fr Hedge sparrow .70 .15
c. 20fr Gray wagtail .70 .15
d. 20fr Meadow pipit .70 .15
C136 A44 Block of 4 4.25 .55
a. 30fr Eurasian hoopoe 1.00 .15
b. 30fr Pied flycatcher 1.00 .15
c. 30fr Great reed warbler 1.00 .15
d. 30fr Eurasian kingfisher 1.00 .15
C137 A44 Block of 4 7.00 .90
a. 50fr House martin 1.75 .20
b. 50fr Sedge warbler 1.75 .20
c. 50fr Fieldfare 1.75 .20
d. 50fr European Golden oriole 1.75 .20
Nos. C132-C137 (6) 18.90 2.35

Queen Fabiola and King Baudouin of Belgium AP4

Designs: 20fr, Pres. Michel Micombero and King Baudouin. 40fr, Pres. Micombero and coats of arms of Burundi and Belgium.

1970, Nov. 28 Photo. Perf. 13½
C140 AP4 6fr multicolored .15 .15
C141 AP4 20fr multicolored .45 .15
C142 AP4 40fr multicolored .90 .30
a. Souvenir sheet of 3 1.50 1.50
Nos. C140-C142 (3) 1.50
Set value .50

Visit of the King and Queen of Belgium. No. C142a contains 3 stamps similar to Nos. C140-C142, but without "Poste Aerienne." No. C142a exists imperf.

Easter Type of Regular Issue

Paintings of the Resurrection: 14fr, by Louis Borrassá. 17fr, Piero della Francesca. 26fr, Michel Wohlgemuth.

1971, Apr. 2 Photo. Perf. 13½
C143 A49 14fr gold & multi .20 .15
C144 A49 17fr gold & multi .22 .15
C145 A49 26fr gold & multi .30 .15
a. Souv. sheet of 3, #C143-C145 1.00 .75
Nos. C143-C145 (3) .72
Set value .29

Easter 1971. No. C145a sheet exists imperf.

Animal Type of Regular Issue

1971 Photo. Perf. 13½

Size: 44x44mm
C146 Strip of 4 1.00 .15
a. A48 10fr Lion .22 .15
b. A48 10fr Cape buffalo .22 .15
c. A48 10fr Hippopotamus .22 .15
d. A48 10fr Giraffe .22 .15
C147 Strip of 4 1.50 .22
a. A48 14fr Hartebeest .35 .15
b. A48 14fr Black rhinoceros .35 .15
c. A48 14fr Zebra .35 .15
d. A48 14fr Leopard .35 .15
C148 Strip of 4 1.75 .25
a. A48 17fr Grant's gazelles .40 .15
b. A48 17fr Cheetah .40 .15
c. A48 17fr African white-backed vultures .40 .15
d. A48 17fr Johnston's okapi .40 .15
C149 Strip of 4 2.25 .32
a. A48 24fr Chimpanzee .50 .15
b. A48 24fr Elephant .50 .15
c. A48 24fr Spotted Hyenas .50 .15
d. A48 24fr Beisa .50 .15
C150 Strip of 4 2.50 .40
a. A48 26fr Gorilla .55 .15
b. A48 26fr Gnu .55 .15
c. A48 26fr Warthog .50 .15
d. A48 26fr Cape hunting dog .55 .15
C151 Strip of 4 3.00 .45
a. A48 31fr Sable antelope .70 .15
b. A48 31fr Caracal lynx .70 .15
c. A48 31fr Ostriches .70 .15
d. A48 31fr Bongo .70 .15
Nos. C146-C151 (6) 12.00 1.79

For overprint and surcharges see Nos. C152, CB15-C18.

No. C146 Overprinted in Gold and Black

LUTTE CONTRE LE RACISME ET
LA DISCRIMINATION RACIALE

1971, July 20 Photo. Perf. 13½
C152 Strip of 4 .60 .15
a. A48 10fr Lion .15 .15
b. A48 10fr Cape buffalo .15 .15
c. A48 10fr Hippopotamus .15 .15
d. A48 10fr Giraffe .15 .15

Intl. Year Against Racial Discrimination.

Christmas Type of Regular Issue

Paintings of the Madonna and Child by: 14fr, Cima de Conegliano. 17fr, Fra Filippo Lippi. 31fr, Leonardo da Vinci.

1971, Nov. 2 Photo. Perf. 13½
C153 A51 14fr red & multi .28 .15
C154 A51 17fr red & multi .32 .15
C155 A51 31fr red & multi .50 .20
a. Souv. sheet of 3, #C153-C155 1.10 1.10
Nos. C153-C155 (3) 1.10 .50

Christmas 1971. No. C155a exists imperf.
For surcharges see Nos. CB19-CB21.

Spacecraft Type of Regular Issue
Souvenir Sheet

1972, Jan. 15 Photo. Perf. 13½
C156 Sheet of 6 1.50 1.00
a. A52 6fr Lunar Orbiter .15 .15
b. A52 11fr Vostok .15 .15
c. A52 14fr Luna I .18 .15
d. A52 17fr Apollo 11 astronaut on moon .22 .15
e. A52 26fr Soyuz 11 .35 .18
f. A52 40fr Lunar rover (Apollo 15) .50 .25

Sapporo '72 Type of Regular Issue
Souvenir Sheet

Designs (Sapporo '72 Emblem and): 26fr, Snow scooter. 31fr, Downhill skiing. 50fr, Bobsledding.

1972, Feb. 3
C157 Sheet of 3 1.50 1.25
a. A53 26fr silver & multi .35 .25
b. A53 31fr silver & multi .40 .30
c. A53 50fr silver & multi .65 .40

No. C157 contains 3 stamps, arranged vertically.

Olympic Games Type of 1972

1972, July 24 Photo. Perf. 13½
C158 A55 24fr Weight lifting .35 .15
C159 A55 26fr Hurdles .40 .15
C160 A55 31fr Discus .50 .15
C161 A55 40fr Soccer .60 .20
Nos. C158-C161 (4) 1.85 .65

Independence Type of 1972

Designs: 15fr, Prince Rwagasore, Pres. Micombero, Burundi flag, drummers. 18fr, Rwagasore, Micombero, flag, map of Africa, globe. 27fr, Micombero, flag, globe.

1972, Aug. 24 Photo. Perf. 13½
C162 A56 15fr gold & multi .25 .15
C163 A56 18fr gold & multi .30 .15
C164 A56 27fr gold & multi .45 .15
a. Souv. sheet of 3, #C162-C164 1.10 1.10
Nos. C162-C164 (3) 1.00
Set value .34

Christmas Type of 1972

Paintings of the Madonna and Child by: 18fr, Sebastiano Mainardi. 27fr, Hans Memling. 40fr, Lorenzo Lotto.

1972, Nov. 2 Photo. Perf. 13½
C165 A57 18fr dk car & multi .28 .15
C166 A57 27fr dk car & multi .40 .15
C167 A57 40fr dk car & multi .60 .18
a. Souv. sheet of 3, #C165-C167 1.40 1.40
Nos. C165-C167 (3) 1.28
Set value .39

For surcharges see Nos. CB26-CB28.

Orchid Type of Regular Issue

1973, Jan. 18 Photo. Perf. 13½

Size: 38x38mm
C168 A58 13fr *Thelymitra pauciflora* .22 .15
C169 A58 14fr *Miltassia* .22 .15
C170 A58 15fr *Miltonia* .25 .15
C171 A58 18fr *Platycoryne crocea* .28 .15
C172 A58 20fr *Cattleya trinaei* .30 .15
C173 A58 27fr *Eulophia cucullata* .42 .15
C174 A58 36fr *Cymbidium hamsey* .55 .15
Nos. C168-C174 (7) 2.24
Set value .59

African Exploration Type of 1973

Designs: 15fr, Livingstone writing his diary. 18fr, "Dr. Livingstone, I presume." 27fr, Livingstone and Stanley discussing expedition.

1973, Mar. 19 Photo. *Perf.* $13^1/_2$

C175 A59 15fr gold & multi .22 .15
C176 A59 18fr gold & multi .28 .15
C177 A59 27fr gold & multi .40 .15
a. Souv. sheet of 3 1.10 1.10
Nos. C175-C177 (3) .90
Set value .31

#C177a contains 3 stamps similar to #C175-C177, but without "Poste Aerienne."

Easter Type of 1973

Paintings: 15fr, Christ at the Pillar, by Guido Reni. 18fr, Crucifixion, by Mathias Grunewald. 27fr, Descent from the Cross, by Caravaggio.

1973, Apr. 10

C178 A60 15fr gold & multi .28 .15
C179 A60 18fr gold & multi .35 .15
C180 A60 27fr gold & multi .50 .15
a. Souv. sheet of 3, #C178-C180 1.25 1.25
Nos. C178-C180 (3) 1.13
Set value .30

INTERPOL Type of Regular Issue

Designs: 27fr, INTERPOL emblem and flag. 40fr, INTERPOL flag and emblem.

1973, May 19 Photo. *Perf.* $13^1/_2$

C181 A61 27fr gold & multi .40 .16
C182 A61 40fr gold & multi .48 .20

Copernicus Type of Regular Issue

Designs: 15fr, Copernicus (C183a), Earth, Pluto, and Jupiter. 18fr, Copernicus (No. C184a), Venus, Saturn, Mars. 27fr, Copernicus (No. C185a), Uranus, Neptune, Mercury. 36fr, Earth and various spacecrafts.

a, UL. b, UR. c, LL. d, LR.

1973, July 27 Photo. *Perf.* $13^1/_2$

C183 A62 15fr Block of 4, #a.-d. 1.40 .30
C184 A62 18fr Block of 4, #a.-d. 1.65 .35
C185 A62 27fr Block of 4, #a.-d. 2.00 .50
C186 A62 36fr Block of 4, #a.-d. 2.75 .70
e. Souv. sheet of 4, #C183-C186 7.00 7.00
Nos. C183-C186 (4) 7.80 1.85

Flower-Butterfly Type of 1973

Designs: Each block of 4 contains 2 flower and 2 butterfly designs. The 10fr, 14fr, 24fr and 31fr have flower designs listed as "a" and "d" numbers, butterflies as "b" and "c" numbers; the arrangement is reversed for the 17fr and 26fr.

1973, Sept. 28 Photo. *Perf.* 13
Stamp Size: 35x45mm

C187 A63 Block of 4 2.00 .20
a. 10fr *Protea cynaroides* .45 .15
b. 10fr *Precis octavia* .45 .15
c. 10fr *Epiphora bauhiniae* .45 .15
d. 10fr *Gazania longiscapa* .45 .15
C188 A63 Block of 4 2.50 .28
a. 14fr *Kniphofia* .60 .15
b. 14fr *Cymothoe coccinata* .60 .15
c. 14fr *Nudaurelia zambesina* .60 .15
d. 14fr *Freesia refracta* .60 .15
C189 A63 Block of 4 3.00 .32
a. 17fr *Calotis eupompe* .70 .15
b. 17fr *Narcissus* .70 .15
c. 17fr *Cineraria hybrida* .70 .15
d. 17fr *Cyrestis camillus* .70 .15
C190 A63 Block of 4 3.50 .50
a. 24fr *Iris tingitana* .85 .15
b. 24fr *Papilio demodocus* .85 .15
c. 24fr *Catopsilia avelaneda* .85 .15
d. 24fr *Nerine sarniensis* .85 .15
C191 A63 Block of 4 4.00 .55
a. 26fr *Hypolimnas dexithea* 1.00 .15
b. 26fr *Zantedeschia tropicalis* 1.00 .15
c. 26fr *Sandersonia aurantiaca* 1.00 .15
d. 26fr *Drurya antimachus* 1.00 .15
C192 A63 Block of 4 4.50 .65
a. 31fr *Nymphaea capensis* 1.10 .15
b. 31fr *Pandoriana pandora* 1.10 .15
c. 31fr *Precis orythia* 1.10 .15
d. 31fr *Pelargonium domestica* 1.10 .15
Nos. C187-C192 (6) 19.50 2.50

Christmas Type of 1973

Virgin and Child by: 18fr, Raphael. 27fr, Pietro Perugino. 40fr, Titian.

1973, Nov. 19

C193 A64 18fr gold & multi .28 .15
C194 A64 27fr gold & multi .40 .15
C195 A64 40fr gold & multi .60 .16
a. Souv. sheet of 3, #C193-C195 1.40 1.40
Nos. C193-C195 (3) 1.28
Set value .36

For surcharges see Nos. CB239-CB31.

Soccer Type of Regular Issue

Designs: Various soccer scenes and cup.

1974, July 4 Photo. *Perf.* 13

C196 A67 20fr gold & multi .30
C197 A67 26fr gold & multi .40
C198 A67 40fr gold & multi .60
Nos. C196-C198 (3) 1.30

For souvenir sheet see No. 459a.

UPU Type of 1974

Designs: No. C199, Flags over UPU Headquarters, Bern. No. C200, G.P.O., Usumbura. No. C201, Mailmen ("26F" in UR). No. C202, Mailmen ("26F" in UL). No. C203, UPU emblem. No. C204, Means of transportation. No. C205, Pigeon over globe showing Burundi. No. C206, Swiss flag, pigeon over map showing Bern.

1974, July 23

C199 A68 24fr gold & multi .65
C200 A68 24fr gold & multi .65
C201 A68 26fr gold & multi .75
C202 A68 26fr gold & multi .75
C203 A68 31fr gold & multi 1.00
C204 A68 31fr gold & multi 1.00
C205 A68 40fr gold & multi 1.25
C206 A68 40fr gold & multi 1.25
a. Souv. sheet of 8, #C199-C206 7.50
Nos. C199-C206 (8) 7.30

Stamps of same denomination printed setenant (continuous design) in sheets of 40.

Fish Type of 1974

1974, Sept. 9 Photo. *Perf.* 13
Size: 35x35mm

C207 A66 Block of 4 1.00 .15
a. 10fr *Haplochromis multicolor* .25 .15
b. 10fr *Pantodon buchholzi* .25 .15
c. 10fr *Tropheus duboisi* .25 .15
d. 10fr *Distichodus sexfasciatus* .25 .15
C208 A66 Block of 4 1.25 .20
a. 14fr *Pelmatochromis kribensis* .30 .15
b. 14fr *Nannaethiops tritaeniatus* .30 .15
c. 14fr *Polycentropsis abbreviata* .30 .15
d. 14fr *Hemichromis bimaculatus* .30 .15
C209 A66 Block of 4 1.65 .20
a. 17fr *Ctenopoma acutirostre* .38 .15
b. 17fr *Synodontis angelicus* .38 .15
c. 17fr *Tilapia melanopleura* .38 .15
d. 17fr *Aphyosemion bivittatum* .38 .15
C210 A66 Block of 4 1.90 .30
a. 24fr *Monodactylus argenteus* .45 .15
b. 24fr *Zanclus canescens* .45 .15
c. 24fr *Pygoplites diacanthus* .45 .15
d. 24fr *Cephalopholis argus* .45 .15
C211 A66 Block of 4 2.00 .35
a. 26fr *Priacanthus arenatus* .50 .15
b. 26fr *Pomacanthus arcutus* .50 .15
c. 26fr *Scarus guacamaia* .50 .15
d. 26fr *Zeus faber* .50 .15
C212 A66 Block of 4 2.50 .40
a. 31fr *Lactophrys quadricornis* .60 .15
b. 31fr *Balistes vetula* .60 .15
c. 31fr *Acanthurus bahianus* .60 .15
d. 31fr *Holocanthus ciliaris* .60 .15
Nos. C207-C212 (6) 10.30 1.60

Christmas Type of 1974

Paintings of the Virgin and Child: 18fr, by Hans Memling. 27fr, by Filippino Lippi. 40fr, by Lorenzo di Gredi.

1974, Nov. 7 Photo. *Perf.* 13

C213 A70 18fr gold & multi .28 .22
C214 A70 27fr gold & multi .40 .32
C215 A70 40fr gold & multi .60 .48
a. Souv. sheet of 3, #C213-C215 1.50 1.50
Nos. C213-C215 (3) 1.28 1.02

Christmas 1974. Sheets of 20 stamps and one label. No. C215a exists imperf.

Apollo-Soyuz Type of 1975

1975, July 10 Photo. *Perf.* 13

C216 A71 Block of 4 .90
a. 27fr A.A. Leonov, V.N. Kubasov, Soviet flag .22
b. 27fr Soyuz and Soviet flag .22
c. 27fr Apollo and American flag .22
d. 27fr Slayton, Brand, Stafford, American flag .22
C217 A71 Block of 4 1.40
a. 40fr Apollo-Soyuz link-up .32
b. 40fr Apollo, blast-off .32
c. 40fr Soyuz, blast-off .32
d. 40fr Kubasov, Leonov, Slayton, Brand, Stafford .32

Nos. C216-C217 are printed in sheets of 32 containing 8 blocks of 4.

Animal Type of 1975

1975, Sept. 17 Photo. *Perf.* $13^1/_2$

C218 Strip of 4 .90
a. A72 10fr Addax .22
b. A72 10fr Roan antelope .22
c. A72 10fr Nyala .22
d. A72 10fr White rhinoceros .22
C219 Strip of 4 1.25
a. A72 14fr Mandrill .30
b. A72 14fr Eland .30
c. A72 14fr Salt's dik-dik .30
d. A72 14fr Thomson's gazelles .30
C220 Strip of 4 1.50
a. A72 17fr African small-clawed otter .35
b. A72 17fr Reed buck .35
c. A72 17fr Indian civet .35
d. A72 17fr Cape buffalo .35
C221 Strip of 4 2.00
a. A72 24fr White-tailed gnu .50
b. A72 24fr African wild asses .50
c. A72 24fr Black-and-white colobus monkey .50
d. A72 24fr Gerenuk .50
C222 Strip of 4 2.25
a. A72 26fr Dama gazelle .55
b. A72 26fr Black-backed jackal .55
c. A72 26fr Sitatungas .55
d. A72 26fr Zebra antelope .55
C223 Strip of 4 2.75
a. A72 31fr Fennec .65
b. A72 31fr Lesser kudus .65
c. A72 31fr Blesbok .65
d. A72 31fr Serval .65
Nos. C218-C223 (6) 10.65

Nos. C218-C219 Overprinted in Black and Silver with IWY Emblem and: "ANNEE INTERNATIONALE / DE LA FEMME"

1975, Nov. 19 Photo. *Perf.* $13^1/_2$

C224 Strip of 4 .60 .15
a. A72 10fr Addax .15 .15
b. A72 10fr Roan antelope .15 .15
c. A72 10fr Nyala .15 .15
d. A72 10fr White rhinoceros .15 .15
C225 Strip of 4 .80 .20
a. A72 14fr Mandrill .20 .15
b. A72 14fr Oryx .20 .15
c. A72 14fr Dik-dik .20 .15
d. A72 14fr Thomson's gazelles .20 .15

International Women's Year 1975.

Nos. C222-C223 Overprinted in Black and Silver with UN Emblem and:"30ème ANNIVERSAIRE DES/ NATIONS UNIES"

1975, Nov. 19

C226 Strip of 4 1.65 .30
a. A72 26fr Dama gazelle .38 .15
b. A72 26fr Wild dog .38 .15
c. A72 26fr Sitatungas .38 .15
d. A72 26fr Striped duiker .38 .15
C227 Strip of 4 1.90 .32
a. A72 31fr Fennec .45 .15
b. A72 31fr Lesser kudus .45 .15
c. A72 31fr Blesbok .45 .15
d. A72 31fr Serval .45 .15

United Nations, 30th anniversary.

Michelangelo Type of 1975

Designs: Paintings from Sistine Chapel.

1975, Dec. 3 Photo. *Perf.* 13

C228 A73 18fr Zachariah .35
C229 A73 18fr Joel .35
C230 A73 31fr Erythrean Sybil .65
C231 A73 31fr Prophet Ezekiel .65
C232 A73 40fr Persian Sybil .80
C233 A73 40fr Prophet Jeremiah .80
a. Souv. sheet of 6, #C228-C233 3.75
Nos. C228-C233 (6) 3.60

Stamps of same denominations printed se-tenant in sheets of 18 stamps and 2 labels.

For surcharges see Nos. CB35-CB40.

Olympic Games Type, 1976

Designs (Olympic Games Emblem and): 18fr, Ski jump. 36fr, Slalom. 50fr, Ice hockey.

1976, Jan. 23 Photo. *Perf.* $14x13^1/_2$

C234 A74 18fr ol brn & multi .32
C235 A74 36fr grn & multi .70
C236 A74 50fr pur & multi .90
a. Souvenir sheet of 4 2.00
Nos. C234-C236 (3) 1.92

No. C236a contains 4 stamps similar to Nos. 491-494, perf. $13^1/_2$, inscribed "POSTE AERIENNE."

Hurdles — AP5

Designs (Montreal Games Emblem and): Nos. C238, C241, C243b, High jump. Nos. C239, C242, C243a, Athlete on rings. No. C240, C243c, Hurdles.

1976, May 3 Litho. *Perf.* $13^1/_2$

C237 AP5 27fr grn & multi .42
C238 AP5 27fr dk bl & multi .42
C239 AP5 31fr ocher & multi .55
C240 AP5 31fr grn & multi .55
C241 AP5 50fr dk bl & multi .90
C242 AP5 50fr ocher & multi .90
Nos. C237-C242 (6) 3.74

Souvenir Sheet

C243 Sheet of 3 1.75
a. AP5 27fr ocher & multi .38
b. AP5 31fr dark blue & multi .45
c. AP5 50fr green & multi .75

21st Olympic Games, Montreal, Canada, July 17-Aug. 1. Stamps of same denomination printed se-tenant in sheets of 20.

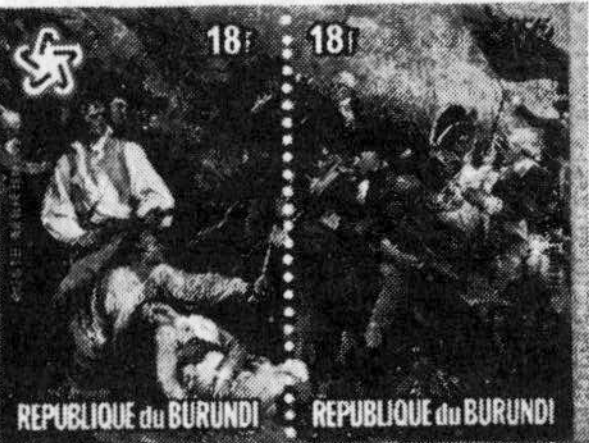

Battle of Bunker Hill, by John Trumbull
AP6 AP7

Paintings: 26fr, Franklin, Jefferson and John Adams. 36fr, Declaration of Independence, by John Trumbull.

1976, July 16 Photo. *Perf.* 13

C244 AP6 18fr gold & multi .35
C245 AP7 18fr gold & multi .35
C246 AP6 26fr gold & multi .45
C247 AP7 26fr gold & multi .45
C248 AP6 36fr gold & multi .75
C249 AP7 36fr gold & multi .75
a. Souv. sheet of 6, #C244-C249 3.25
Nos. C244-C249 (6) 3.10

American Bicentennial. Stamps of same denomination printed se-tenant in sheets of 50.

Christmas Type of 1976

Paintings: 18fr, Virgin and Child with St. Anne, by Leonardo da Vinci. 31fr, Holy Family with Lamb, by Raphael. 40fr, Madonna of the Basket, by Correggio.

1976, Oct. 18 Photo. *Perf.* $13^1/_2$

C250 A76 18fr gold & multi .25
C251 A76 31fr gold & multi .45
C252 A76 40fr gold & multi .60
a. Souv. sheet of 3, #C250-C252 1.40
Nos. C250-C252 (3) 1.30

Christmas 1976. Sheets of 20 stamps and descriptive label.

For surcharges see Nos. CB41-CB43.

A.G. Bell Type of 1977

Designs: 10fr, A.G. Bell and first telephone. Nos. C253, 17fr, A.G. Bell speaking into microphone. Nos. C254, C257e, Satellites around globe and videophone. No. C255, Switchboard operator, c.1910, and wall telephone. Nos. C256, 26fr, Intelsat satellite, modern and old telephones. No. C257c, Intelsat and radar.

1977, May 17 Photo. *Perf.* 13

C253 A78 18fr multi .15
C254 A79 18fr multi .15
C255 A78 36fr multi .25
C256 A79 36fr multi .25
C257 Sheet of 5 1.75 1.00
a. A78 10fr multi .15 .15
b. A78 17fr multi .25 .15
c. A79 18fr multi .25 .15
d. A79 26fr multi .40 .22
e. A79 36fr multi .52 .25

No. C257 contains 3 postage (10fr, 17fr, 26fr) and 2 air post stamps (18fr, 36fr).

Animal Type of 1977

1977, Aug. 22 Photo. *Perf.* $14x14^1/_2$

C258 Strip of 4 .80
a. A80 9fr Buffon's kob .20
b. A80 9fr Marabous .20
c. A80 9fr Brindled gnu .20
d. A80 9fr River hog .20
C259 Strip of 4 1.10
a. A80 13fr Zebras .25
b. A80 13fr Shoebill .25
c. A80 13fr Striped hyenas .25
d. A80 13fr Chimpanzee .25
C260 Strip of 4 2.25
a. A80 30fr Flamingos .55
b. A80 30fr Nile Crocodiles .55
c. A80 30fr Green mamba .55
d. A80 30fr Greater kudus .55
C261 Strip of 4 2.75
a. A80 35fr Hyrax .65
b. A80 35fr Cobra .65
c. A80 35fr Jackals .65
d. A80 35fr Verreaux's eagles .65
C262 Strip of 4 4.25
a. A80 54fr Honey badger 1.00
b. A80 54fr Harnessed antelopes 1.00
c. A80 54fr Secretary bird 1.00
d. A80 54fr Klipspringer 1.00
C263 Strip of 4 5.00
a. A80 70fr African big-eared fox 1.25
b. A80 70fr Elephants 1.25
c. A80 70fr Vulturine guineafowl 1.25
d. A80 70fr Impalas 1.25
Nos. C258-C263 (6) 16.15

UN Type of 1977

Designs (UN Stamps and): 24fr, UN buildings by night. 27fr, UN buildings and view of Manhattan. 35fr, UN buildings by day.

1977, Oct. 10 Photo. *Perf.* $13^1/_2$

C264 A82 Block of 4 1.90
a. 24fr No. 77 .45
b. 24fr No. 78 .45
c. 24fr No. 40 .45
d. 24fr No. 32 .45

C265 A82 Block of 4 2.00
a. 27fr No. 50 .50
b. 27fr No. 21 .50
c. 27fr No. 30 .50
d. 27fr No. 44 .50
C266 A82 Block of 4 3.25
a. 35fr No. C6 .75
b. 35fr No. 105 .75
c. 35fr No. 4 .75
d. 35fr No. 1 .75
e. Souvenir sheet of 3 1.40
Nos. C264-C266 (3) 7.15

No. C266e contains 24fr in design of No. C265b, 27fr in design of No. C266a, 35fr in design of No. C264c.

Christmas Type of 1977

Designs: Paintings of the Virgin and Child.

1977, Oct. 31 Photo. *Perf. 14x13*

C267 A83 18fr Master of Moulins .28
C268 A83 31fr Workshop of Lorenzo de Credi .48
C269 A83 40fr Palma Vecchio .60
a. Souv. sheet of 3, #C267-C269 1.50
Nos. C267-C269 (3) 1.36

Sheets of 24 stamps and descriptive label.
For surcharges see Nos. CB44-CB46.

Christmas 1978 Type of 1979
Souvenir Sheet

1979, Feb. Photo. *Perf. 14x13½*

C270 Sheet of 5 2.00
a. A86 13fr like #543 .20
b. A86 17fr like #544 .25
c. A86 27fr like #545 .40
d. A86 31fr like #546 .48
e. A86 40fr like #547 .60

Christmas Type of 1979
Souvenir Sheet

1979, Oct. 12 *Perf. 13½*

C271 Sheet of 4 2.00 1.25
a. A89 20fr like #561 .30 .16
b. A89 27fr like #562 .40 .22
c. A89 31fr like #563 .48 .28
d. A89 50fr like #564 .75 .42

Hill Type of 1979
Souvenir Sheet

1979, Nov. 6

C272 Sheet of 5 3.50 1.75
a. A90 20fr like #565 .40 .16
b. A90 27fr like #566 .55 .22
c. A90 31fr like #567 .60 .28
d. A90 40fr like #568 .80 .35
e. A90 50fr like #569 1.00 .50

Sir Rowland Hill (1795-1879), originator of penny postage.

Bird Type of 1979

1979 Photo. *Perf. 13½x3*

C273 A87 6fr like #548 .15
C274 A87 13fr like #549 .20
C275 A87 18fr like #550 .28
C276 A87 26fr like #551 .38
C277 A87 31fr like #552 .48
C278 A87 36fr like #553 .55
C279 A87 40fr like #554 .60
C280 A87 54fr like #555 .80
C281 A87 70fr like #556 1.00
Nos. C273-C281 (9) 4.44

Olympic Type of 1980
Souvenir Sheet

1980, Oct. 24 Photo. *Perf. 13½*

C282 Sheet of 9 4.25
a. A91 20fr like #570 .30
b. A91 20fr like #571 .30
c. A91 20fr like #572 .30
d. A91 30fr like #573 .45
e. A91 30fr like #574 .45
f. A91 30fr like #575 .45
g. A91 40fr like #576 .60
h. A91 40fr like #577 .60
i. A91 40fr like #578 .60

22nd Summer Olympic Games, Moscow, July 19-Aug. 3.

Christmas Type of 1980
Souvenir Sheet

1980, Dec. 12 Photo. *Perf. 13½x13*

C283 Sheet of 4 1.90 1.40
a. A92 10fr like #579 .15 .15
b. A92 30fr like #580 .45 .30
c. A92 40fr like #581 .60 .40
d. A92 45fr like #582 .65 .45

UPRONA Type of 1980
Souvenir Sheet

1980, Dec. 29 *Perf. 14½x13½*

C284 Sheet of 3 1.50
a. A93 10fr like #583 .15
b. A93 40fr like #584 .60
c. A93 45fr like #585 .65

Christmas Type of 1983
Souvenir Sheet

1983, Oct. 3 Litho. *Perf. 14½x13½*

C285 Sheet of 4 1.75
a. A97 10fr like #607 .15
b. A97 25fr like #608 .38
c. A97 30fr like #609 .45
d. A97 50fr like #610 .75

UPU Congress Type of 1984
Souvenir Sheet

1984, July 14 *Perf. 13x13½*

C286 Sheet of 4 2.25
a. A99 10fr like #621 .15
b. A99 30fr like #622 .45
c. A99 35fr like #623 .50
d. A99 65fr like #624 1.00

Summer Olympics Type of 1984
Souvenir Sheet

1984, Aug. 6 *Perf. 13½x13*

C287 Sheet of 4 2.25
a. A100 10fr like #625 .15
b. A100 30fr like #626 .45
c. A100 35fr like #627 .50
d. A100 65fr like #628 1.00

Christmas Type of 1984
Souvenir Sheet

1984, Dec. 15 *Perf. 13½*

C288 Sheet of 4 1.75
a. A101 10fr like #629 .15
b. A101 25fr like #630 .38
c. A101 30fr like #631 .45
d. A101 50fr like #632 .75

Flower Type of 1986 with Dull Lilac Border

1986, July 31 Photo. *Perf. 13x13½*

C289 A102 70fr like #633 .55
C290 A102 75fr like #634 .60
C291 A102 80fr like #635 .65
C292 A102 85fr like #636 .70
C293 A102 100fr like #637 .80
C294 A102 150fr like #638 1.20
Nos. C289-C294 (6) 4.50

Animal Type of 1991

1992, June 2 Litho. *Perf. 14*

C298 A108 100fr M. nemestrina 1.55
C299 A108 115fr Equus grevyi 1.75
C300 A108 200fr Long horn cattle 3.10
C301 A108 220fr Pelecanus onocrotalus 3.40
a. Souvenir sheet of 4, #C298-C301, perf. 13½ 10.00
Nos. C298-C301 (4) 9.80

AIR POST SEMI-POSTAL STAMPS

Coin Type of Semi-Postal Issue

Designs (Coins of Various Denominations): 3fr+1fr, 11fr+1fr, 20fr+1fr, 50fr+1fr, Coat of Arms, reverse. 5fr+1fr, 14fr+1fr, 30fr+1fr, 100fr+1fr, King Mwambutsa IV, obverse.

Lithographed; Embossed on Gilt Foil
1965, Nov. 15 *Imperf.*

Diameter: 39mm

CB1 SP4 3fr + 1fr lt & dk vio .15 .15
CB2 SP4 5fr + 1fr pale grn & red .15 .15

Diameter: 45mm

CB3 SP4 11fr + 1fr org & lilac .25 .25
CB4 SP4 14fr + 1fr red & emer .30 .30

Diameter: 56mm

CB5 SP4 20fr + 1fr ultra & blk .40 .40
CB6 SP4 30fr + 1fr dp org & mar .60 .60

Diameter: 67mm

CB7 SP4 50fr + 1fr bl & vio bl 1.00 1.00
CB8 SP4 100fr + 1fr rose & dp cl 2.25 2.25
Nos. CB1-CB8 (8) 5.10 5.10

Stamps are backed with patterned paper in blue, orange, and pink engine-turned design.

Red Cross Type of Semi-Postal Issue

Designs: 26fr+3fr, Laboratory. 40fr+3fr, Ambulance and thatched huts. 50fr+3fr, Red Cross nurse with patient.

1969, June 26 Photo. *Perf. 13½*

CB9 SP7 26fr + 3fr multi .38 .15
CB10 SP7 40fr + 3fr multi .55 .15
CB11 SP7 50fr + 3fr multi .65 .20
Nos. CB9-CB11 (3) 1.58 .50

Perf. and imperf. souvenir sheets exist containing 3 stamps similar to Nos. CB9-CB11, but without "Poste Aerienne." Size: 90½x97mm

Christmas Type of Semi-Postal Issue

Paintings: 14fr+3fr, Virgin and Child, by Velázquez. 26fr+3fr, Holy Family, by Joos van Cleve. 40fr+3fr, Virgin and Child, by Rogier van der Weyden.

1970, Dec. 14 Photo. *Perf. 13½*

CB12 SP9 14fr + 3fr multi .25 .15
CB13 SP9 26fr + 3fr multi .45 .15
CB14 SP9 40fr + 3fr multi .65 .20
a. Souv. sheet of 3, #CB12-CB14 1.50 1.50
Nos. CB12-CB14 (3) 1.35 .50

No. C147 Surcharged in Gold and Black

LUTTE CONTRE
L'ANALPHABETISME

1971, Aug. 9 Photo. *Perf. 13½*

CB15 Strip of 4 .80 .20
a. A48 14fr+2fr Hartebeest .20 .15
b. A48 14fr+2fr Black rhinoceros .20 .15
c. A48 14fr+2fr Zebra .20 .15
d. A48 14fr+2fr Leopard .20 .15

UNESCO campaign against illiteracy.

No. C148 Surcharged in Gold and Black

+1F

AIDE INTERNATIONALE
AUX REFUGIES

1971, Aug. 9

CB16 Strip of 4 1.00 .20
a. A48 17fr+1fr Grant's gazelles .22 .15
b. A48 17fr+1fr Cheetah .22 .15
c. A48 17fr+1fr African white-backed vultures .22 .15
d. A48 17fr+1fr Johnston's okapi .22 .15

International help for refugees.

Nos. C150-C151 Surcharged in Black and Gold

+1F

a 

75eme ANNIVERSAIRE DES
JEUX OLYMPIQUES MODERNES
(1896-1971)

+1F

b 

JEUX PRE-OLYMPIQUES
MUNICH 1972

1971, Aug. 16

CB17 Strip of 4 2.25 .45
a. A48(a) 26fr+1fr Gorilla .55 .15
b. A48(a) 26fr+1fr Gnu .55 .15
c. A48(a) 26fr+1fr Warthog .55 .15
d. A48(a) 26fr+1fr Cape hunting dog .55 .15
CB18 Strip of 4 3.00 .60
a. A48(b) 31fr+1fr Sable antelope .75 .15
b. A48(b) 31fr+1fr Caracal lynx .75 .15
c. A48(b) 31fr+1fr Ostriches .75 .15
d. A48(b) 31fr+1fr Bongo .75 .15

75th anniv. of modern Olympic Games (#CB17); Olympic Games, Munich, 1972 (#CB18).

Nos. C153-C155 Surcharged

1971, Nov. 27 Photo. *Perf. 13½*

CB19 A51 14fr + 1fr multi .32 .15
CB20 A51 17fr + 1fr multi .38 .15
CB21 A51 31fr + 1fr multi .60 .16
Nos. CB19-CB21 (3) 1.30
Set value .34

25th anniv. of UNICEF.

Casa D'Oro, Venice
SPAP1

Views in Venice: 17fr+1fr, Doge's Palace. 24fr+1fr, Church of Sts. John and Paul. 31fr+1fr, Doge's Palace and Piazzetta at Feast of Ascension, by Canaletto.

1971, Dec. 27

CB22 SPAP1 10fr + 1fr multi .16 .15
CB23 SPAP1 17fr + 1fr multi .32 .15
CB24 SPAP1 24fr + 1fr multi .45 .15
CB25 SPAP1 31fr + 1fr multi .55 .16
a. Souvenir sheet of 4 1.50 1.50
Nos. CB22-CB25 (4) 1.48
Set value .50

Surtax for the UNESCO campaign to save the treasures of Venice. No. CB25a contains 4 stamps similar to Nos. CB22-CB25, but with 2fr surtax.

Nos. C165-C167, C193-C195 Surcharged "+1F" in Silver

1972, Dec. 12 Photo. *Perf. 13½*

CB26 A57 18fr + 1fr multi .28 .15
CB27 A57 27fr + 1fr multi .45 .15
CB28 A57 40fr + 1fr multi .60 .18
a. Souvenir sheet of 3 1.50 1.50
Nos. CB26-CB28 (3) 1.33
Set value .38

Christmas 1972. No. CB28a contains 3 stamps similar to Nos. CB26-CB28 but with 2fr surtax.

1973, Dec. 14 Photo. *Perf. 13*

CB29 A64 18fr + 1fr multi .28 .15
CB30 A64 27fr + 1fr multi .40 .15
CB31 A64 40fr + 1fr multi .60 .20
a. Souvenir sheet of 3 1.50 1.50
Nos. CB29-CB31 (3) 1.28
Set value .40

Christmas 1973. No. CB31 contains 3 stamps similar to Nos. CB29-CB31 with 2fr surtax each.

Christmas Type of 1974

1974, Dec. 2 Photo. *Perf. 13*

CB32 A70 18fr + 1fr multi .32 .20
CB33 A70 27fr + 1fr multi .50 .30
CB34 A70 40fr + 1fr multi .70 .42
a. Souvenir sheet of 3 1.75 1.75
Nos. CB32-CB34 (3) 1.52

Christmas 1974. No. CB34a contains 3 stamps similar to Nos. CB32-CB34 with 2fr surtax.

Nos. C228-C233 Surcharged "+ 1F" in Silver and Black

1975, Dec. 22 Photo. *Perf. 13*

CB35 A73 18fr + 1fr #C228 .35
CB36 A73 18fr + 1fr #C229 .35
CB37 A73 31fr + 1fr #C230 .55
CB38 A73 31fr + 1fr #C231 .55
CB39 A73 40fr + 1fr #C232 .75
CB40 A73 40fr + 1fr #C233 .75
a. Souvenir sheet of 6 4.25
Nos. CB35-CB40 (6) 3.30

Michelangelo Buonarroti (1475-1564). No. CB40a contains 6 stamps similar to Nos. CB35-CB40 with 2fr surtax each.

Nos. C250-C252 Surcharged "+1f" in Silver and Black

1976, Nov. 25 Photo. *Perf. 13½*

CB41 A76 18fr + 1fr multi .30
CB42 A76 31fr + 1fr multi .50
CB43 A76 40fr + 1fr multi .60
a. Souvenir sheet of 3 1.50
Nos. CB41-CB43 (3) 1.40

Christmas 1976. No. CB43a contains 3 stamps similar to Nos. CB41-CB43 with 2fr surtax each.

Nos. C267-C269 Surcharged "+1fr" in Silver and Black

1977 Photo. *Perf. 14x13*

CB44 A83 18fr + 1fr multi .28
CB45 A83 31fr + 1fr multi .50
CB46 A83 40fr + 1fr multi .60
a. Souvenir sheet of 3 1.50
Nos. CB44-CB46 (3) 1.38

Christmas 1977. No. CB46a contains 3 stamps similar to Nos. CB44-CB46 with 2fr surtax each.

Christmas 1978 Type
Souvenir Sheet

1979, Feb. Photo. *Perf. 14x13*

CB47 Sheet of 5 3.00
a. A86 13fr + 2fr multi .30
b. A86 17fr + 2fr multi .36
c. A86 27fr + 2fr multi .55
d. A86 31fr + 2fr multi .70
e. A86 40fr + 2fr multi .85

Christmas Type of 1979
Souvenir Sheet

1979, Dec. 10 Photo. *Perf. 13½*

CB48 Sheet of 4 2.75
a. A89 20fr + 2fr like #561 .45
b. A89 27fr + 2fr like #562 .55
c. A89 31fr + 2fr like #563 .70
d. A89 50fr + 2fr like #564 1.00

Christmas Type of 1980
Souvenir Sheet

1981, Jan. 16 Photo. *Perf. 13½x13*

CB49 Sheet of 4 2.50
a. A92 10fr + 2fr like #579 .20
b. A92 30fr + 2fr like #580 .55
c. A92 40fr + 2fr like #581 .75
d. A92 50fr + 2fr like #582 .90

Christmas Type of 1983
Souvenir Sheet

1983, Nov. 2 Litho. *Perf. 14½x13½*

CB50 Sheet of 4 1.90
a. A97 10fr + 2fr like #607 .16
b. A97 25fr + 2fr like #608 .38
c. A97 30fr + 2fr like #609 .50
d. A97 50fr + 2fr like #610 .75

Christmas Type of 1984
Souvenir Sheet

1984, Dec. 15 *Perf. 13½*

CB51 Sheet of 4 1.90
a. A101 10fr + 2fr like #629 .16
b. A101 25fr + 2fr like #630 .38
c. A101 30fr + 2fr like #631 .50
d. A101 50fr + 2fr like #632 1.00

CAMBODIA

kam-'bō-dē-ə

(Kampuchea)

(Khmer Republic)

LOCATION — Southern Indo-China
GOVT. — Republic
AREA — 69,866 sq. mi.
POP. — 7,640,000 (est. 1974)
CAPITAL — Phnom Penh

Before 1951, Cambodia used stamps of Indo-China. In October, 1970, the Kingdom of Cambodia became the Khmer Republic.

From 1978 to 1980 money was abolished.

100 Cents = 1 Piaster
100 Cents = 1 Riel (1955)

Imperforates

Most Cambodia stamps exist imperforate in issued and trial colors, and also in small presentation sheets in issued colors.

Catalogue values for all unused stamps in this country are for Never Hinged items.

Apsaras — A1

King Norodom Sihanouk — A3

Enthronement Hall — A2

1951-52 Unwmk. Engr. *Perf. 13*

1 A1 10c dk blue green .75 .50
2 A1 20c cl & org brn .45 .20
3 A1 30c pur & indigo .45 .20
4 A1 40c ultra & brt bl grn .45 .20
5 A2 50c dk grn & dk ol grn .45 .20
6 A3 80c bl blk & dk bl grn .95 .65
7 A2 1pi indigo & purple 1.10 .65
8 A3 1.10pi dp car & brt red 1.10 .65
9 A3 1.50pi blk brn & red brn ('51) 1.40 .65
10 A1 1.50pi dp car & cerise 1.40 .65
11 A2 1.50pi indigo & dp ultra 1.40 .75
12 A3 1.90pi indigo & dp ultra 1.90 1.00
13 A2 2pi dp car & org brn 1.75 .75
14 A3 3pi dp car & org brn 2.50 1.00
15 A1 5pi indigo & purple 10.25 3.00
a. Souvenir sheet of 1 27.50
16 A2 10pi purple & indigo 20.00 6.00
a. Souvenir sheet of 1 27.50
17 A3 15pi dk purple & purple 27.50 8.00
a. Souvenir sheet of 1 32.50
Nos. 1-17 (17) 73.80 25.05

Nos. 15a, 16a, 17a sold in a booklet for 30pi.
For surcharges see Nos. B1-B4.

Phnom Daun Penh — A4

East Gate, Angkor Thom — A5

Arms of Cambodia — A6

Methods of Mail Transport — A7

1954-55 Unwmk. *Perf. 13*

18 A4 10c rose carmine .20 .15
a. Souvenir sheet of 5 ('55) 35.00
19 A4 20c dark green .20 .15
20 A4 30c indigo .20 .15
21 A4 40c dark purple .20 .15
22 A4 50c dk violet brn .20 .15
23 A5 70c chocolate .35 .25
a. Souvenir sheet of 5 ('55) 42.50
24 A5 1pi red violet .35 .25
25 A5 1.50pi red .35 .25
26 A6 2pi rose red .60 .45
a. Souvenir sheet of 5 ('55) 42.50
27 A6 2.50pi green 1.00 .75
28 A7 2.50pi blue green 1.40 .75
a. Souvenir sheet of 5 ('55) 42.50
29 A6 3pi ultra 1.50 .90
30 A7 4pi black brown 1.65 1.25
31 A6 4.50pi purple 2.00 1.25
32 A7 5pi rose red 2.00 1.25
33 A6 6pi chocolate 2.50 1.25
34 A7 10pi purple 2.50 1.90
35 A7 15pi deep blue 3.75 2.25
36 A5 20pi ultra 7.25 3.00
37 A5 30pi blue green 10.00 6.50
Nos. 18-37 (20) 38.20 23.00

The 4 souvenir sheets each contain 5 stamps: #18a (10c, 20c, 30c, 40c, 50c); #23a (70c, 1pi, 1.50pi, 20pi, 30pi); #26a (2pi, 2.50pi green, 3pi, 4.50pi, 6pi); #28a (2.50pi blue green, 4pi, 5pi, 10pi, 15pi). Size of #18a, 26a and 28a: 120x120mm. Size of #23a: 160x92mm.
For overprints see Nos. 99-100.

King Norodom Suramarit — A8

King Norodom Suramarit and Queen Kossamak Nearirat Serey Vathana — A9

Portraits: 50c (No. 39), 2.50r, 4r, 6r, 15r, Queen Kossamak Nearirat Serey Vathana.

Perf. 14x13(A8), 13(A9)

1955, Nov. 24 Engr. Unwmk.

38 A8 50c violet .20 .15
39 A8 50c indigo .20 .15
40 A8 1r car lake .20 .15
41 A9 1.50r dk brown .55 .50
42 A9 2r black & indigo .55 .40
43 A8 2r dp ultra .35 .50
44 A8 2.50r dk vio brn .55 .50
45 A9 3r brn org & car .55 .50
46 A8 4r dark green .90 .80
47 A9 5r blk & dk grn .90 .80
48 A8 6r deep plum 1.25 1.00
49 A8 7r dark brown 1.65 1.00
50 A9 10r brn car & vio 1.25 1.25
51 A8 15r purple 2.50 1.50
52 A8 20r deep green 3.00 2.50
Nos. 38-52 (15) 14.60 11.70

Coronation of King Norodom Suramarit and Queen Kossamak Nearirat Serey Vathana.
See Nos. 74-75. For surcharge see No. 122.

King Norodom Suramarit — A10

Prince Sihanouk, Globe and Flags — A11

Portrait: 3r, 5r, 50r, Queen Kossamak Nearirat Serey Vathana.

1956, Mar. 8 *Perf. 13*

53 A10 2r dark red 1.40 1.40
54 A10 3r dark blue 2.00 2.00
55 A10 5r yellow green 3.00 3.00
56 A10 10r dark green 7.75 7.75
57 A10 30r dark violet 17.00 17.00
58 A10 50r rose lilac 32.50 32.50
Nos. 53-58 (6) 63.65 63.65

Coronation of King Norodom Suramarit and Queen Kossamak Nearirat Serey Vathana.

1957, Mar. 1

59 A11 2r green, ultra & car .85 .40
60 A11 4.50r ultra .85 .40
61 A11 8.50r carmine .85 .40
Nos. 59-61 (3) 2.55 1.20

Admission to the UN, 1st anniv. (in 1956).

Type of Semi-Postal Stamps, 1957

1957, May 12 Unwmk. *Perf. 13*

62 SP1 1.50r vermilion .70 .70
63 SP1 6.50r bluish violet .90 .90
64 SP1 8r dark green .90 .90
Nos. 62-64 (3) 2.50 2.50

2500th anniv. of the birth of Buddha.

King Ang Duong — A12

1958, Mar. 4

65 A12 1.50r purple & brown .25 .25
66 A12 5r olive gray & olive .50 .50
67 A12 10r claret & dull brn .85 .85
a. Souvenir sheet of 3, #65-67 3.50 3.50
Nos. 65-67 (3) 1.60 1.60

King Ang Duong (1795-1860).
No. 67a sold for 25r.

King Norodom I — A13

1958-59 Engr. *Perf. 12½x13*

68 A13 2r ultra & olive .25 .25
69 A13 6r orange & sl grn .55 .55
70 A13 15r green & ol gray .75 .75
a. Souv. sheet of 3, #68-70 ('59) 2.75 2.75
Nos. 68-70 (3) 1.55 1.55

King Norodom I (1835-1904).
No. 70a sold for 32r.
Issued: #68-70, 11/3/58; #70a, 1/31/59.
For surcharge see No. 184.

Children of the World — A14

1959, Dec. 9 Unwmk. *Perf. 13*

71 A14 20c rose violet .25 .25
72 A14 50c blue .50 .50
73 A14 80c rose carmine .85 .85
Nos. 71-73 (3) 1.60 1.60

Issued to promote friendship among the children of the world.
For surcharges see Nos. 115, B8-B10.

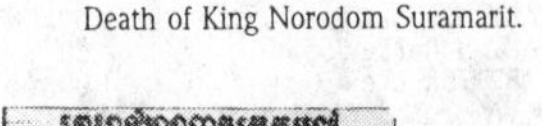

Nos. 49 and 52 with Black Border

1960 *Perf. 14x13*

74 A8 7r dk brown & blk 2.50 2.50
75 A8 20r dp green & blk 2.50 2.50

Death of King Norodom Suramarit.

Port of Sihanoukville, Prince Sihanouk and Serpent Naga — A15

20r (double size)

1960, Apr. *Perf. 13x12½*

76 A15 2r carmine & sepia .35 .35
a. Cambodian 20r 1.50 1.50
77 A15 5r ultra & dp brown .35 .35
a. Cambodian 20r 2.00 2.00
78 A15 20r lilac & dk blue 1.40 1.40
Nos. 76-78 (3) 2.10 2.10

Opening of the port of Sihanoukville. By error the denomination in Cambodian on the 2r and 5r was engraved as 20r; it was corrected later.

Ceremonial Plow — A16

1960		Perf. 12	
79 A16 1r magenta		.55	.55
80 A16 2r brown		.55	.55
81 A16 3r bluish green		.55	.55
Nos. 79-81 (3)		1.65	1.65

Feast of the Sacred Furrow.

Fight Against Illiteracy A17

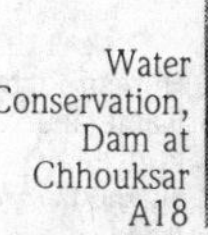

Water Conservation, Dam at Chhouksar A18

Dove, Factory and Books — A19

Buddhist Ceremony — A20

Works of Sangkum: 6r, Workman and house. 10r, Woman in rice field.

1960, Sept. 1	Engr.	Perf. 13	
82 A17 2r dk grn, brn & dk bl		.20	.20
a. Souvenir sheet of 3		3.25	3.25
83 A18 3r brown & green		.35	.25
a. Souvenir sheet of 3		3.25	3.25
84 A19 4r rose car, vio & grn		.35	.30
85 A17 6r brown, org & grn		.50	.35
86 A17 10r ultra, grn & bis		1.00	.75
87 A20 25r dk car, red & mag		2.50	1.40
Nos. 82-87 (6)		4.90	3.25

No. 82a contains one each of Nos. 82, 85 and 87, and sold for 42r. No. 83a contains one each of Nos. 83, 84 and 86, and sold for 23r. Nos. 82a-83a were issued Dec. 5, 1960.

Cambodian Flag and Dove A21

Frangipani A22

1960, Dec. 24	Engr.	Perf. 13	
Flag in Ultramarine and Red			
88 A21 1.50r brown & green		.25	.25
89 A21 5r orange red		.35	.35
90 A21 7r green & ultra		.90	.90
a. Souvenir sheet of 3, #88-90		3.50	3.50
b. Souvenir sheet of 3 (colors changed)		4.00	4.00
Nos. 88-90 (3)		1.50	1.50

Peace propaganda. No. 90a sold for 16r. No. 90b contains one of each denomination with colors changed to: 1.50r orange red, 5r green & ultramarine, 7r brown & green and sold for 20r.

1961, July 1	Unwmk.	Perf. 13	
91 A22 2r shown		.40	.40
92 A22 5r Oleander		.70	.70
93 A22 10r Amaryllis		1.40	1.40
a. Souvenir sheet of 3, #91-93		3.00	3.00
Nos. 91-93 (3)		2.50	2.50

No. 93a sold for 20r.

Krishna in Chariot, Khmer Frieze — A23

1961-63	Typo.	Perf. 14x13½	
94 A23 1r lilac		.25	.15
94A A23 2r blue ('63)		1.90	.75
95 A23 3r emerald		.35	.25
96 A23 6r orange		.70	.25
a. Souvenir sheet of 3		5.00	5.00
Nos. 94-96 (4)		3.20	1.40

Issued to honor Cambodian armed forces. No. 94A issued in coils. No. 96a contains one each of Nos. 94, 95, 96. Sold for 12r.

Independence Monument A24

1961, Nov. 9	Engr.	Perf. 13x12½	
97 A24 2r green		.65	.65
98 A24 4r gray brown		.65	.65
a. Souvenir sheet of 2, #97-98		3.00	3.00
Nos. 97-98,C15-C17 (5)		6.10	5.00

10th anniv. of Independence. For surcharge see No. 116.

Nos. 27 and 31 Overprinted in Red: "VIe CONFERENCE MONDIALE BOUDDIQUE 12-11-1961"

1961, Nov. 11		Perf. 13	
99 A6 2.50pi green		.45	.45
100 A6 4.50pi purple		.75	.75

Sixth World Conference of Buddhism.

Highway (American Aid) — A25

Foreign Aid: 2r, Power station (Czech aid). 4r, Textile factory (Chinese aid). 5r, Hospital (Russian aid). 6r, Airport (French aid).

1961, Dec.	Engr.	Perf. 13	
101 A25 2r org & rose car		.15	.15
102 A25 3r bl, grn & org brn		.25	.15
103 A25 4r dl bl, org brn & mag		.30	.15
104 A25 5r dl grn & lil rose		.35	.25
105 A25 6r dk bl & org brn		.45	.30
a. Souvenir sheet of 5, #101-105		3.00	3.00
Nos. 101-105 (5)		1.50	1.00

Malaria Eradication Emblem — A26

1962, Apr. 7	Unwmk.	Perf. 13	
106 A26 2r magenta & brown		.30	.15
107 A26 4r green & dk brown		.40	.35
108 A26 6r violet & olive bister		.55	.45
Nos. 106-108 (3)		1.25	.95

WHO drive to eradicate malaria. For surcharges see Nos. B11-B12.

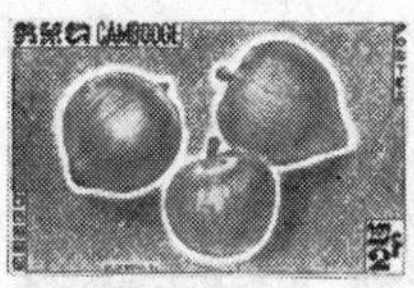

Fruits — A27

1962, June 4		Engr.	
109 A27 2r Turmeric		.45	.40
110 A27 4r Cinnamon		.45	.40
111 A27 6r Mangosteens		.75	.60
a. Souvenir sheet of 3, #109-111		2.25	2.25
Nos. 109-111 (3)		1.65	1.40

Nos. 111a sold for 15r.

Pineapples — A28

1962	Unwmk.	Perf. 13	
112 A28 2r shown		.40	.30
113 A28 5r Sugar cane		.50	.35
114 A28 9r Sugar palms		.75	.45
Nos. 112-114 (3)		1.65	1.10

No. 73 Surcharged

1962, Nov. 9		Perf. 13	
115 A14 50c on 80c rose car		.40	.40

No. 97 Surcharged with New Value in Red and Overprinted in Black with Two Bars and: "INAUGURATION / DU / MONUMENT"

1962			
116 A24 3r on 2r green		.35	.20

Dedication of Independence Monument.

Corn, Rice and FAO Emblem A29

1963, Mar. 21	Engr.	Perf. 13	
117 A29 3r multicolored		.45	.35
118 A29 6r org red, vio bl & ocher		.45	.35

FAO "Freedom from Hunger" campaign.

Preah Vihear, Ancient Temple — A30

Tonsay Lake — A31

1963, June 15		Perf. 12½x13	
119 A30 3r claret, brown & sl grn		.20	.20
120 A30 6r orange, sl grn & grnsh blk		.45	.35
121 A30 15r blue, choc & green		.80	.75
Nos. 119-121 (3)		1.45	1.30

Return by Thailand of Preah Vihear on the Mekong River. For overprint see No. 176.

No. 44 Surcharged with New Value and Bars

1963	Engr.	Perf. 14x13	
122 A8 3r on 2½r dk violet brn		.35	.35

Perf. 12x12½, 12½x12

1963, Aug. 1		Photo.	
Designs: 7r, Popokvil Falls. 20r, Beach, horiz.			
123 A31 3r multicolored		.25	.20
124 A31 7r multicolored		.55	.30
125 A31 20r multicolored		1.50	.60
Nos. 123-125 (3)		2.30	1.10

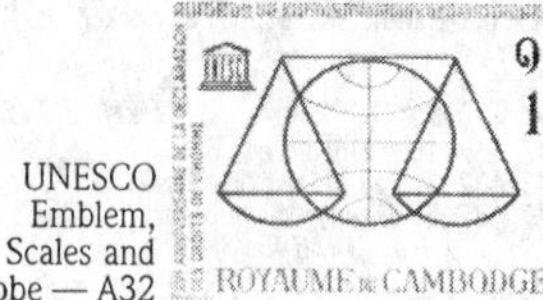

UNESCO Emblem, Scales and Globe — A32

1963, Dec. 10	Engr.	Perf. 13	
126 A32 1r vio bl, rose cl & grn		.25	.20
127 A32 3r yel grn, vio bl & rose cl		.40	.35
128 A32 12r rose cl, yel grn & vio bl		.95	.70
Nos. 126-128 (3)		1.60	1.25

15th anniversary of the Universal Declaration of Human Rights. For surcharge see No. 183.

Kouprey A33

1964, Mar. 3	Unwmk.	Perf. 13	
129 A33 50c grn, dk brn & org brn		.30	.25
130 A33 3r org, brn, dk brn & grn		.50	.45
131 A33 6r blue, dk brn & grn		.75	.55
Nos. 129-131 (3)		1.55	1.25

Black-billed Magpie — A34

1964, May 2	Engr.	Perf. 13	
132 A34 3r shown		.15	.15
133 A34 6r Kingfisher		.60	.35
134 A34 12r Gray heron		1.00	.80
Nos. 132-134 (3)		1.75	1.30

For overprint and surcharge see Nos. 303, B16.

Emblem of Royal Cambodian Airline A35

1964	Unwmk.	Perf. 13x12½	
135 A35 1.50r rose car & purple		.20	.20
136 A35 3r ver & dk blue		.25	.20
137 A35 7.50r ultra & car		.60	.45
Nos. 135-137 (3)		1.05	.85

8th anniv. of the Royal Cambodian Airline.

Prince Norodom Sihanouk — A36

1964	Engr.	Perf. 12½x13	
138 A36 2r purple		.15	.15
139 A36 3r red brown		.25	.20
140 A36 10r dark blue		.65	.50
Nos. 138-140 (3)		1.05	.85

10th anniv. of the Sangkum (political party). For overprints see Nos. 144-145.

Woman Weaver A37

Khmer Handicrafts: 3r, Metal worker. 5r, Basket maker.

1965, Feb. 1 *Perf. 13x12½*
141 A37 1r multicolored .20 .20
142 A37 3r red lil, red brn & gray ol .50 .35
143 A37 5r green, dk brn & car .65 .50
Nos. 141-143 (3) 1.35 1.05

Nos. 139-140 Overprinted in Black or Red: "CONFERENCE / DES PEUPLES / INDOCHINOIS"

1965, Mar. 1 *Perf. 12½x13*
144 A36 3r red brown .40 .35
145 A36 10r dark blue (R) .60 .45

Conference of the people of Indo-China.

ITU Emblem, Old and New Communication Equipment — A38

1965, May 17 **Engr.** *Perf. 13*
146 A38 3r green & ol bister .25 .25
147 A38 4r red & blue .35 .25
148 A38 10r violet & rose lilac .60 .45
Nos. 146-148 (3) 1.20 .95

Centenary of the ITU.

Cotton Plant — A39

Designs: 3r, Peanut plant. 7.50r, Coconut palm.

1965, Aug. 2 *Perf. 12½x13*
149 A39 1.50r orange, sl grn & pur .25 .25
150 A39 3r blue, yel, grn & brn .45 .45
151 A39 7.50r orange brn & sl grn .80 .80
Nos. 149-151 (3) 1.50 1.50

Preah Ko Temple, Rolouoh — A40

Temples at Angkor: 5r, Baksei Chamkrong, Rolouoh. 7r, Banteay Srei (Citadel of Women). 9r, Angkor Wat. 12r, Bayon, Angkor Thom.

1966, Feb. 1 **Engr.** *Perf. 13*
152 A40 3r gray ol, sal & dl grn .55 .25
153 A40 5r lil, dk grn & redsh brn .70 .40
154 A40 7r dk grn, redsh brn & bis .75 .50
155 A40 9r vio bl, pur & dk grn 1.00 .60
156 A40 12r dk grn, rose car & ver 1.25 .80
Nos. 152-156 (5) 4.25 2.55

For overprints see Nos. 172-175, 177.

WHO Headquarters, Geneva A41

1966, July 1 **Photo.** *Perf. 12½x13*
WHO Emblem in Blue and Yellow
157 A41 2r black & pale rose .30 .15
158 A41 3r black & yel grn .35 .25
159 A41 5r black & lt bl .50 .30
Nos. 157-159 (3) 1.15 .70

Inauguration of WHO Headquarters, Geneva.

Tree Planting — A42

UNESCO Emblem — A43

1966, July 22 **Engr.** *Perf. 12½x13*
160 A42 1r brn, dull brn & brt grn .15 .15
161 A42 3r org, dull brn & brt grn .30 .25
162 A42 7r gray, dull brn & brt grn .60 .35
Nos. 160-162 (3) 1.05 .75

Issued for Arbor Day.

1966 **Photo.** *Perf. 13*
163 A43 3r multicolored .25 .25
164 A43 7r multicolored .50 .25

20th anniv. of UNESCO.

Wrestlers and Games' Emblem A44

GANEFO Games (Games Emblem and): 3r, Stadium, Phnom Penh. 7r, Swordsmen. 10r, Indian club swingers. Bas-reliefs from Angkor Wat.

1966, Nov. 25 **Engr.** *Perf. 13*
165 A44 3r violet blue .25 .15
166 A44 4r green .30 .15
167 A44 7r dk car rose .40 .20
168 A44 10r dark brown .55 .30
Nos. 165-168 (4) 1.50 .80

Indian Wild Boar — A45

Perf. 13x12½, 12½x13
1967, Feb. 20 **Engr.**
169 A45 3r shown .45 .20
170 A45 5r Muntjac, vert. .60 .25
171 A45 7r Elephant .95 .40
Nos. 169-171 (3) 2.00 .85

Nos. 152-153, 155-156 and 121 Overprinted in Red: "ANNEE INTERNATIONALE DU TOURISME 1967"

1967, Apr. 27 **Engr.** *Perf. 13*
172 A40 3r multicolored .30 .25
173 A40 5r multicolored .45 .25
174 A40 9r multicolored .70 .50
175 A40 12r multicolored .85 .65
176 A30 15r multicolored .90 .70
Nos. 172-176 (5) 3.20 2.35

International Tourist Year, 1967.

No. 154 Overprinted in Red: "MILLENAIRE / DE BANTEAY SREI / 967-1967"

1967, Apr. 27
177 A40 7r multicolored .65 .40

Banteay Srei Temple at Angkor, millennium.

Royal Ballet Dancer — A46

Various Dancers

1967, June **Engr.** *Perf. 13*
178 A46 1r orange .15 .15
179 A46 3r Prus blue .25 .20
180 A46 5r ultra .35 .25
181 A46 7r carmine rose .45 .45
182 A46 10r multicolored .70 .50
Nos. 178-182 (5) 1.90 1.55

Cambodian Royal Ballet.

Nos. 128 and 70 Surcharged in Red

Journée Internationale
de l'Alphabétisation
8-9-67
6r

1967, Sept. 8 **Engr.**
183 A32 6r on 12r multi .50 .30
184 A13 7r on 15r grn & olive gray .60 .40

Intl. Literacy Day, Sept. 8. The surcharge on #184 is adapted to fit the shape of the stamp.

Symbolic Water Cycle — A47

1967, Nov. 1 **Typo.** *Perf. 13x14*
185 A47 1r black, bl & org .20 .15
186 A47 6r lilac, lt bl & org .35 .20
187 A47 10r dk blue, emer & org .60 .35
Nos. 185-187 (3) 1.15 .70

Hydrological Decade (UNESCO), 1965-74.

Royal University, Kompong Cham — A48

Designs: 6r, Engineering School, Phnom Penh. 9r, University Center, Sangkum Reastr Niyum.

1968, Mar. 1 **Engr.** *Perf. 13*
188 A48 4r violet bl & multi .25 .20
189 A48 6r slate & multi .40 .30
190 A48 9r Prus blue & multi .55 .30
Nos. 188-190 (3) 1.20 .80

Vaccination and WHO Emblem A49

WHO, 20th Anniv.: 7r, Malaria control and WHO emblem (man spraying DDT).

1968, July 8 **Engr.** *Perf. 13*
191 A49 3r ultramarine .25 .15
192 A49 7r deep blue .45 .30

Stadium, Mexico City — A50

1968, Oct. 12 **Engr.** *Perf. 13*
193 A50 1r shown .15 .15
194 A50 2r Wrestling .20 .15
195 A50 3r Bicycling .35 .20
196 A50 7.50r Boxing, vert. .45 .30
197 A50 7.50r Torch bearer, vert. .55 .35
Nos. 193-197 (5) 1.70 1.15

19th Olympic Games, Mexico City, Oct. 12-27.

Red Cross Team — A51

1968, Nov. 1 **Engr.** *Perf. 13*
198 A51 3r Prus bl, grn & red .40 .20

Issued to honor the Cambodian Red Cross.

Prince Norodom Sihanouk A52

Design: 8r, Soldiers wading through swamp.

1968, Nov. 9
199 A52 7r emer, ultra & pur .35 .20
200 A52 8r bl, grn & dp brn .40 .20

15th anniversary of independence.

Human Rights Flame and Prince Sihanouk A53

1968, Dec. 10 **Engr.** *Perf. 13*
201 A53 3r blue .30 .15
202 A53 5r bright plum .45 .20
203 A53 7r multicolored .60 .25
Nos. 201-203 (3) 1.35 .60

International Human Rights Year.

ILO Emblem A54

1969, May 1 **Engr.** *Perf. 13*
204 A54 3r ultra .20 .15
205 A54 6r dp carmine .35 .20
206 A54 9r blue green .55 .25
Nos. 204-206 (3) 1.10 .60

ILO, 50th anniversary.

Globe, Red Cross, Crescent, Lion and Sun Emblems A55

1969, May 8
207 A55 1r blue, red & yel .15 .15
208 A55 3r sl grn, red & vio brn .25 .15
209 A55 10r brt lil, red & brn .65 .25
Nos. 207-209 (3) 1.05 .55

50th anniv. of the League of Red Cross Societies.

Papilio Oeacus A56

Butterflies: 4r, Papilio agamenon. 8r, Danaus plexippus.

1969, Oct. 10 **Engr.** *Perf. 13*
210 A56 3r lilac, blk & yel .70 .25
211 A56 4r ver, blk & grn .95 .40
212 A56 8r yel grn, dk brn & org 1.40 .50
Nos. 210-212 (3) 3.05 1.15

Map of Cambodia and Diesel Engine A57

Designs: Various railroad stations and trains.

1969, Nov. 27 Engr. *Perf. 13*

213 A57 3r multicolored .50 .20
214 A57 6r slate grn & lt brn .65 .25
215 A57 8r black .90 .35
216 A57 9r dk green & blue 1.10 .35
Nos. 213-216 (4) 3.15 1.15

Issued to publicize the new rail link between Phnom Penh and Sihanoukville.

Fish — A58

1970, Jan. 29 Photo. *Perf. 13*

217 A58 3r Tripletail .30 .15
218 A58 7r Sleeper goby .50 .20
219 A58 9r Snakehead .70 .25
Nos. 217-219 (3) 1.50 .60

Wat Maniratanaram — A59

Monasteries: 2r, Wat Tepthidaram, vert. 6r, Wat Patumavati. 8r, Wat Unnalom.

1970, Apr. 29 Photo. *Perf. 13*

220 A59 2r multicolored .15 .15
221 A59 3r multicolored .25 .15
222 A59 6r multicolored .35 .20
223 A59 8r multicolored .50 .25
Nos. 220-223 (4) 1.25
Set value .65

UPU Headquarters and Monument, Bern — A60

1970, May 20

224 A60 1r green & multi .15 .15
225 A60 3r scarlet & multi .20 .15
226 A60 4r dp blue & multi .30 .20
227 A60 10r brown & multi .50 .25
Nos. 68-70 (3) 1.55
Set value .60

New UPU Headquarters in Bern.

Open Book and Satellite Earth Receiving Station — A61

1970, May 17 Photo. *Perf. 13*

228 A61 3r dk vio bl & multi .15 .15
229 A61 4r sl grn & multi .25 .15
230 A61 9r brn ol & multi .60 .15
Nos. 228-230 (3) 1.00 .45

World Telecommunications Day.

Nelumbium Speciosum A62

Flowers: 4r, Eichhornia crassipes. 13r, Nymphea lotus.

1970, Aug. 17 Photo. *Perf. 13*

231 A62 3r multicolored .25 .15
a. Cambodian and Arabic 3's transposed 3.00
232 A62 4r multicolored .40 .15
233 A62 13r multicolored .80 .20
Nos. 231-233 (3) 1.45 .50

Elephant God, Basrelief at Banteay Srei — A63

1970, Sept. 21 Engr. *Perf. 13*

234 A63 3r lil rose & dp grn .20 .15
235 A63 4r bl grn, grn & lil rose .35 .15
236 A63 7r bl grn, dk brn & grn .45 .15
Nos. 234-236 (3) 1.00 .45

Issued for World Meteorological Day.

Khmer Republic

Globe, Rocket, Dove and UN Emblem A64

1970, Nov. 9 Photo. *Perf. 12½x12*

237 A64 3r black & multi .20 .15
238 A64 5r brown red & multi .35 .20
239 A64 10r dp violet & multi .70 .40
Nos. 237-239 (3) 1.25 .75

25th anniversary of the United Nations.

Education Year Emblem A65

1970, Nov. 9 Engr. *Perf. 13x12½*

240 A65 1r blue .15 .15
241 A65 3r brt rose lilac .20 .15
242 A65 8r blue green .40 .20
Nos. 240-242 (3) .75 .50

Issued for International Education Year.

Chuon-Nath — A66

1971, Jan. 27 Photo. *Perf. 13*

243 A66 3r ol grn & multi .20 .15
244 A66 8r purple & multi .45 .15
245 A66 9r violet & multi .55 .30
Nos. 243-245 (3) 1.20 .60

In memory of Chuon-Nath (1883-1969), Cambodian language expert.

For surcharge see No. 322.

Soldiers in Battle — A67

1971, Mar. 18 Photo. *Perf. 13*

246 A67 1r gray & multi .15 .15
247 A67 3r bister & multi .20 .15
248 A67 10r blue & multi .55 .25
Nos. 246-248 (3) .90
Set value .45

National territorial defense.

For overprint see No. 321.

UN Emblem, Men of Four Races — A68

1971, Mar. 21

249 A68 3r blue & multi .15 .15
250 A68 7r green & multi .30 .15
251 A68 8r brt rose & multi .35 .20
Nos. 249-251 (3) .80
Set value .40

Intl. year against racial discrimination.

General Post Office, Phnom Penh — A69

1971, Apr. 19

252 A69 3r blue & multi .20 .15
253 A69 9r lilac rose & multi .45 .15
254 A69 10r black & multi .60 .20
Nos. 252-254 (3) 1.25
Set value .40

Symbolic Globe and Waves A70

Design: 7r, 8r, ITU emblem and waves.

1971, May 17 Photo. *Perf. 13*

255 A70 3r green, blk & bl .15 .15
256 A70 4r yellow & multi .20 .15
257 A70 7r lilac, blk & red .30 .15
258 A70 8r sal pink, blk & red .35 .15
Nos. 255-258 (4) 1.00
Set value .40

3rd World Telecommunications Day.

Erythrina Indica — A71

Wild Flowers: 3r, Bauhinia variegata. 6r, Butea frondosa. 10r, Lagerstroemia floribunda, vert.

1971, July 5 *Perf. 13x12½, 12½x13*

259 A71 2r lt ultra & multi .20 .15
260 A71 3r yel grn & multi .25 .15
261 A71 6r blue & multi .50 .20
262 A71 10r brown & multi .60 .35
Nos. 259-262 (4) 1.55 .85

Khmer Coat of Arms — A72

Flag and Square of the Republic — A73

1971, Oct. 9 Engr. *Perf. 13*

263 A72 3r brt grn & bis .20 .15
264 A73 3r purple & multi .20 .15
265 A73 4r dp claret & multi .25 .15
266 A72 8r orange & bis .30 .15
267 A72 10r lt brn & bis .60 .15
a. Souv. sheet of 3, #263, 266-267 1.40 1.40
268 A73 10r slate grn & multi .60 .15
a. Souv. sheet of 3, #264-265, 268 1.10 1.10
Nos. 263-268 (6) 2.15
Set value .70

Republic, 1st anniv. #267a sold for 25r, #268a for 20r.

For overprints and surcharges see Nos. 301-302, B13-B14.

UNICEF Emblem — A74

1971, Dec. 11

269 A74 3r black brown .15 .15
270 A74 5r ultra .20 .15
271 A74 9r dk pur & brn red .30 .20
Nos. 269-271 (3) .65
Set value .40

25th anniv. of UNICEF.

Book Year Emblem A75

1972, Feb. 7

272 A75 3r blue, grn & vio .15 .15
273 A75 8r violet, grn & bl .25 .15
274 A75 9r emerald & multi .30 .15
a. Souvenir sheet of 3, #272-274 1.10 1.10
Nos. 272-274 (3) .70 .45

Intl. Book Year. No. 274a sold for 23r.

Lion of St. Mark — A76

Designs: 5r, Waves engulfing St. Mark's Basilica. 10r, Bridge of Sighs, vert.

1972, Feb. 7 Engr. *Perf. 13*

275 A76 3r lil rose & org brn .20 .15
276 A76 5r yel grn & org brn .30 .15
277 A76 10r org brn, bl & yel grn .55 .20
a. Souvenir sheet of 3, #275-277 1.75 1.10
Nos. 275-277 (3) 1.05
Set value .40

UNESCO campaign to save Venice. No. 277a sold for 23r.

UN Emblem A77

1972, Mar. 28

278 A77 3r deep carmine .15 .15
279 A77 6r deep blue .20 .15
280 A77 9r deep orange .30 .20
a. Souvenir sheet of 3, #278-280 1.10 1.10
Nos. 278-280 (3) .65
Set value .25

25th anniv. UN Economic Commission for Asia and the Far East (ECAFE). No. 280a sold for 23r.

Dancing Apsarases A78

"UIT" A79

1972, May 5 Engr. *Perf. 13*

281 A78 1r golden brn .15 .15
282 A78 3r violet .15 .15
283 A78 7r rose claret .20 .15
284 A78 8r olive brn .25 .15
285 A78 9r blue grn .35 .15
286 A78 10r ultra .45 .15

No.	Type	Description	Unused	Used
287	A78	12r purple	.60	.20
288	A78	14r Prus blue	.65	.25
		Nos. 281-288 (8)	2.80	
		Set value		1.10

1972, May 17 **Litho.**

No.	Type	Description	Unused	Used
289	A79	3r blk, yel & grnsh bl	.15	.15
290	A79	9r blk, dp lil rose & bl grn	.25	.15
291	A79	14r blk, brn & bl grn	.45	.20
		Nos. 289-291 (3)	.85	
		Set value		.40

4th World Telecommunications Day.

"Human Environment" — A80

1972, June 5 **Engr.**

No.	Type	Description	Unused	Used
292	A80	3r org, plum & grn	.15	.15
293	A80	12r brt grn & plum	.35	.25
294	A80	15r plum & brt grn	.50	.30
a.		Souvenir sheet of 3, #292-294	1.65	1.65
		Nos. 292-294 (3)	1.00	
		Set value		.60

UN Conf. on Human Environment, Stockholm, June 5-16. No. 294a sold for 35r.

For overprints and surcharges see Nos. 304-305, B15, B17.

Javan Rhinoceros A81

1972, Aug. 1 **Engr.** ***Perf. 13***

No.	Type	Description	Unused	Used
295	A81	3r shown	.20	.15
296	A81	4r Serow	.30	.15
297	A81	6r Malayan sambar	.45	.15
298	A81	7r Banteng	.60	.15
299	A81	8r Water buffalo	.70	.15
300	A81	10r Gaur	1.00	.20
		Nos. 295-300 (6)	3.25	
		Set value		.75

Nos. 263, 267, 134, 293, 294 Overprinted in Red

XXE JEUX OLYMPIQUES MUNICH 1972

1972, Sept. 9 **Engr.** ***Perf. 13***

No.	Type	Description	Unused	Used
301	A72	3r brt grn & bis	.25	.15
302	A72	10r orange & bis	.50	.20
303	A34	12r multicolored	.75	.25
304	A80	12r brt grn & plum	.75	.25
305	A80	15r plum & brt grn	.95	.40
		Nos. 301-305 (5)	3.20	1.25

20th Olympic Games, Munich, Aug. 26-Sept. 11.

Raising Khmer Flag — A82

1972, Oct. 9 **Photo.** ***Perf. 12½x13***

No.	Type	Description	Unused	Used
306	A82	3r multicolored	.15	.15
307	A82	5r brt rose & multi	.15	.15
308	A82	9r yel grn & multi	.30	.15
		Nos. 306-308 (3)	.60	
		Set value		.35

2nd anniversary of the establishment of the Khmer Republic.

For surcharge see No. 323.

Stupa and Crest — A83

Apsaras — A84

1973, May 12 **Engr.** ***Perf. 13***

No.	Type	Description	Unused	Used
309	A83	3r ocher & multi	.15	.15
310	A83	12r yel grn & multi	.20	.15
311	A83	14r blue & multi	.30	.15
a.		Souvenir sheet of 3, #309-311	1.25	1.25
		Nos. 309-311 (3)	.65	
		Set value		.35

New Constitution. No. 311a sold for 34r.

1973, July 23 **Engr.** ***Perf. 13***

Sculptures from Angkor Wat: 8r, 10r, Devata (different).

No.	Type	Description	Unused	Used
312	A84	3r brown black	.15	.15
313	A84	8r Prus green	.20	.15
314	A84	10r olive bister	.30	.15
a.		Souvenir sheet of 3, #312-314	.90	.90
		Nos. 312-314 (3)	.65	
		Set value		.35

No. 314a sold for 25r.

INTERPOL Emblem — A85

Marshal Lon Nol — A86

1973, Oct. 2 **Engr.** ***Perf. 13***

No.	Type	Description	Unused	Used
315	A85	3r green & multi	.25	.15
316	A85	7r red brn & multi	.35	.15
317	A85	10r olive & multi	.55	.15
a.		Souvenir sheet of 3, #315-317	.75	.75
		Nos. 315-317 (3)	1.15	
		Set value		.35

50th anniv. of the Intl. Criminal Police Org. No. 317a sold for 30r.

1973, Oct. 9

No.	Type	Description	Unused	Used
318	A86	3r lt grn, blk & brn	.25	.15
319	A86	8r brown, ol & blk	.35	.15
320	A86	14r black & brn	.40	.20
a.		Souvenir sheet of 3	2.75	2.75
		Nos. 318-320 (3)	1.00	
		Set value		.35

Marshal Lon Nol, 1st pres. of the Republic. No. 320a contains stamps similar to Nos. 318-320 in changed colors. Sold for 50r.

Nos. 248, 243 and 307 Surcharged with New Value, 2 Bars and Overprinted in Red or Silver: "4th ANNIVERSAIRE/DE LA REPUBLIQUE"

1974 **Photo.** ***Perf. 13, 12½x13***

No.	Type	Description	Unused	Used
321	A67	10r multi (R)	.60	.35
322	A66	50r on 3r multi	1.25	.80
323	A82	100r on 5r multi	3.25	2.00
		Nos. 321-323 (3)	5.10	3.15

4th anniversary of independence.

Copernicus and "Nerva" — A87

Designs: Copernicus, various spacecraft and events.

1974, Sept. 10 **Litho.** ***Perf. 13***

No.	Type	Description	Unused	Used
324	A87	1r shown		
325	A87	5r Mariner II		
326	A87	10r Apollo		
327	A87	25r Telstar		
328	A87	50r Space walk		
329	A87	100r Moon landing		
330	A87	150r Separation of space-ship and module		
		Nos. 324-330, C32-C33 (9)	32.50	32.50

500th anniversary of the birth of Nicolaus Copernicus (1473-1543), Polish astronomer.

Carrier Pigeon and UPU Emblem — A88

Design: 60r, Sailing ship and UPU emblem.

1974, Nov. 2

No.	Type	Description	Unused	Used
331	A88	10r multicolored	.15	.15
332	A88	60r multicolored	.30	.20
		Nos. 331-332, C34 (3)	3.95	2.85

Cent. of UPU. A souvenir sheet containing one No. 332 exists.

1976 Summer Olympics, Montreal (ancient and modern sports), set of nine, 1, 5, 10, 25, airmail 50, 100, 150, 200, 250r, plus 9 imperf. souv. sheets and 9 souv. sheets with simulated perfs., 2 perf. souv. sheets (200r, 250r), and 2 gold foil 1200r airmail, issued Jan. 2, 1975. Nos. 7501-7531.

World Cup Soccer Championships, set of nine, 1, 5, 10, 25r, airmail 50, 100, 150, 200, 250r, plus 9 imperf. souv. sheets and 9 souv. sheets with simulated perfs., 2 perf. souv. sheets (200r, 250r), and gold foil 1200r airmail and airmail souv. sheet, issued Feb. 13, 1975. Nos. 7532-7562.

UPU Cent. (2nd issue), set of nine, 15, 20, 70, 160, 180, 235r, airmail 500, 1000, 2000r, plus 9 imperf. souv. sheets and 9 souv. sheets with simulated perfs., 2 perf. souv. sheets (1000r, 2000r), 2 gold foil embossed perf. and imperf. 1000r airmail (train and plane) and 1200r airmail souv. sheet (Chinese junks), issued Apr. 12, 1975. Nos. 7563-7594.

SEMI-POSTAL STAMPS

Nos. 8, 12, 14 and 15 Surcharged in Black

+60^{c} AIDE A L'ÉTUDIANT

1952, Oct. 20 **Unwmk.** ***Perf. 13***

No.	Type	Description	Unused	Used
B1	A3	1.10pi + 40c	3.00	2.00
B2	A3	1.90pi + 60c	3.00	2.00
B3	A3	3pi + 1pi	3.00	2.00
B4	A1	5pi + 2pi	3.00	2.00
		Nos. B1-B4 (4)	12.00	8.00

Preah Stupa — SP1

1957, Mar. 15 **Engr.** ***Perf. 13***

No.	Type	Description	Unused	Used
B5	SP1	1.50r + 50c ind, ol & red	1.00	.65
B6	SP1	6.50r + 1.50r red lil, ol & red	1.65	1.00
B7	SP1	8r + 2r bl, ol & red	2.50	1.65
		Nos. B5-B7 (3)	5.15	3.30

2500th anniv. of the birth of Buddha. See Nos. 62-64.

Type of Regular Issue, 1959, with Red Typographed Surcharge

+ 0,30

1959, Dec. 9

No.	Type	Description	Unused	Used
B8	A14	20c + 20c rose vio	.35	.35
B9	A14	50c + 30c blue	.40	.40
B10	A14	80c + 50c rose car	.90	.90
		Nos. B8-B10 (3)	1.65	1.65

The surtax was for the Red Cross.

Nos. 107-108 Surcharged and Overprinted in Red: "1863-1963 CENTENAIRE DE LA CROIX ROUGE"

1963, Oct. 1 **Unwmk.** ***Perf. 13***

No.	Type	Description	Unused	Used
B11	A26	4r + 40c grn & dk brn	.65	.65
B12	A26	6r + 60c vio & ol bis	.85	.85

Centenary of International Red Cross.

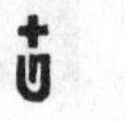

Nos. 263, 267, 293-294, 134 Surcharged in Red

SECOURS AUX VICTIMES DE GUERRE

1972, Nov. 15 **Engr.** ***Perf. 13***

No.	Type	Description	Unused	Used
B13	A72	3r + 2r multi	.25	.25
B14	A72	10r + 6r multi	.40	.35
B15	A80	12r + 7r multi	.60	.35
B16	A34	12r + 7r multi	.60	.35
B17	A80	15r + 8r multi	.90	.70
		Nos. B13-B17 (5)	2.75	2.00

Surtax was for war victims. Surcharge arranged differently on Nos. B15-B17.

AIR POST STAMPS

Kinnari — AP1

Unwmk.

1953, Apr. 16 **Engr.** ***Perf. 13***

No.	Type	Description	Unused	Used
C1	AP1	50c dp green	.55	.50
a.		Souv. sheet of 4, #C1, C3, C5, C9	40.00	40.00
C2	AP1	3pi red brown	.65	.50
a.		Souv. sheet of 3, #C2, C4, C8	40.00	40.00
C3	AP1	3.30pi rose vio	.90	.90
C4	AP1	4pi dk brn & dp bl	1.00	.90
C5	AP1	5.10pi brn, red & org	1.90	1.65
C6	AP1	6.50pi dk brn & lil rose	1.90	1.65
a.		Souv. sheet of 2, #C6-C7	40.00	40.00
C7	AP1	9pi lil rose & dp grn	2.50	2.50
C8	AP1	11.50pi multi	5.25	4.00
C9	AP1	30pi dk brn, bl grn & org	9.50	6.50
		Nos. C1-C9 (9)	24.15	19.10

#C1a sold for 50pi, #C2a for 25pi, #C6a for 20pi.

AP2

1957, Dec. 11

No.	Type	Description	Unused	Used
C10	AP2	50c maroon	.15	.15
C11	AP2	1r emerald	.20	.15
C12	AP2	4r ultra	.90	.60
C13	AP2	50r carmine rose	4.50	3.75
C14	AP2	100r grn, bl & car	7.50	5.50
a.		Souv. sheet of 5, #C10-C14	16.00	16.00
		Nos. C10-C14 (5)	13.25	10.15

No. C14a sold for 160r.

Independence Type of 1961

1961, Nov. 9 ***Perf. 13x12½***

No.	Type	Description	Unused	Used
C15	A24	7r multicolored	.65	.35
C16	A24	30r grn, car & ultra	1.40	1.10
C17	A24	50r ind, grn & ol	2.75	2.25
a.		Souv. sheet of 3, #C15-C17	6.00	6.00
		Nos. C15-C17 (3)	4.80	3.70

No. C15 Surcharged with New Value in Red and Overprinted in Black with Two Bars and: "INAUGURATION DU MONUMENT"

1962, Nov. 9

C18	A24	12r on 7r multi	1.25	1.00

Dedication of Independence Monument.

Hanuman, Monkey God — AP3

1964, Sept. 1 **Engr.** ***Perf. 13***

C19	AP3	5r multicolored	.70	.35
C20	AP3	10r ol bis, lil rose & grn	.95	.35
C21	AP3	20r vio, bl & ol bis	1.40	.75
C22	AP3	40r bl, ol bis & dk bl	3.00	1.40
C23	AP3	80r multicolored	5.00	3.50
		Nos. C19-C23 (5)	11.05	6.35

Nos. C19-C22 Surcharged in Red

12 ₹
JEUX
OLYMPIQUES
TOKYO-1964

1964, Oct.

C24	AP3	3r on 5r multi	.60	.55
C25	AP3	6r on 10r multi	.95	.85
C26	AP3	9r on 20r multi	1.25	1.10
C27	AP3	12r on 40r multi	1.90	1.65
		Nos. C24-C27 (4)	4.70	4.15

18th Olympic Games, Tokyo, Oct. 10-25.

1972 Summer Olympics, Munich, set of 4 gold foil 900r airmail, and 2 souv. sheets of 2, issued Nov. 2, 1972. Nos. 72C01-72C06.

Apollo 16, set of 2 gold foil 900r airmail, and souv. sheet of 2, perf., imperf., issued Nov. 2, 1972. Nos. 72C07-72C09.

Garuda, 12th Century, Angkor Thom — AP4

1973, Jan. 18 **Engr.** ***Perf. 13***

C28	AP4	3r carmine	.25	.15
C29	AP4	30r violet blue	1.10	.80
C30	AP4	50r dull purple	1.75	1.25
C31	AP4	100r dull green	3.75	2.25
		Nos. C28-C31 (4)	6.85	4.45

World Cup Soccer Championships, set of 4 gold foil 900r airmail, issued Nov. 19, 1973. Nos. 73C01-73C04.

John F. Kennedy and Apollo 11 Astronauts on Moon, set of 2 gold foil 110r airmail, and souv. sheet of two, issued Feb. 18, 1974. Nos. 74C01-74C03.

Copernicus Type of 1974

Designs: 200r, Copernicus and Skylab III. 250r, Copernicus, Concorde and solar eclipse.

1974, Sept. 10 **Litho.** ***Perf. 13***

C32	A87	200r multi		
C33	A87	250r multi		

A souvenir sheet containing No. C32 is perf., size 110x82mm. A souvenir sheet containing No. C33 is imperf., size 83x111mm.

Copernicus, gold foil 1200r airmail, and 1200r souv. sheet, issued Sept. 10, 1974. Nos. 74C04-74C05.

UPU Type of 1974

Design: 700r, Rocket, globe and UPU emblem.

1974, Nov. 2

C34	A88	700r gold & multi	3.50	2.50

A souvenir sheet of one exists.

UPU Cent. , set of 2 gold foil 1200r airmail, and 2 souv. sheets of 1, issued Nov. 2, 1974. Nos. 74C06-74C09.

POSTAGE DUE STAMPS

D1

Frieze, Angkor Wat — D2

1957 **Unwmk.** **Typo.** ***Perf. $13^1/_2$***

Denomination in Black

J1	D1	10c ver & pale blue	.15	.15
J2	D1	50c ver & pale blue	.15	.15
J3	D1	1r ver & pale blue	.30	.30
J4	D1	3r ver & pale blue	.45	.45
J5	D1	5r ver & pale blue	.80	.80
		Nos. J1-J5 (5)	1.85	1.85

1974, Feb. 18 **Engr.** ***Perf. $12^1/_2$x13***

J6	D2	2r ocher	.20	.15
J7	D2	6r green	.25	.20
J8	D2	8r deep carmine	.35	.30
J9	D2	10r violet blue	.45	.40
		Nos. J6-J9 (4)	1.25	1.05

CAMEROUN

ˌka–mə–ˈrün

(Kamerun)

LOCATION — On the west coast of Africa, north of the equator
GOVT. — Republic
AREA — 456,054 sq. mi.
POP. — 9,060,000 (est. 1983)
CAPITAL — Yaounde

Before World War I, Cameroun (Kamerun) was a German Protectorate. It was occupied during the war by Great Britain and France and in 1922 was mandated to these countries by the League of Nations. The French-mandated part became the independent State of Cameroun on January 1, 1960. The Southern Cameroons, a United Kingdom Trust Territory, joined this state to form the Federal Republic of Cameroun on October 1, 1961. The name was changed to United Republic of Cameroun on May 20, 1972.

Cameroun German Dominion, British and French Occupation stamps can be mounted in the Scott Germany album part 2.

Stamps of Southern Cameroons are listed under Cameroons in Volume 1.

100 Pfennig = 1 Mark
12 Pence = 1 Shilling
100 Centimes = 1 Franc

Catalogue values for unused stamps in this country are for Never Hinged items, beginning with Scott 281A in the regular postage section, Scott B13A in the semi-postal section, Scott C1 in the airpost section, Scott J24 in the postage due section, and Scott M1 in the military stamp section.

Watermark

Wmk. 125-Lozenges

Issued under German Dominion

A1

A2

Stamps of Germany, 1889-1900, Overprinted in Black

1897 **Unwmk.** ***Perf. $13^1/_2$x$14^1/_2$***

1	A1	3pf yellow brn	12.50	*17.50*
a.		3pf red brown	20.00	*65.00*
b.		3pf dark brown	16.00	*42.50*
2	A1	5pf green	5.00	*9.00*
3	A2	10pf carmine	4.00	*5.00*
4	A2	20pf ultra	4.00	*9.00*
5	A2	25pf orange	22.50	*40.00*
6	A2	50pf red brown	17.50	*32.50*
		Nos. 1-6 (6)	65.50	*113.00*

Kaiser's Yacht "Hohenzollern"
A3 A4

1900 **Unwmk.** **Typo.** ***Perf. 14***

7	A3	3pf brown	1.40	1.50
8	A3	5pf green	15.00	.90
9	A3	10pf carmine	45.00	1.25
10	A3	20pf ultra	27.50	2.40
11	A3	25pf org & blk, *yel*	1.50	*6.00*
12	A3	30pf org & blk, *sal*	1.75	*4.50*
13	A3	40pf lake & blk	1.75	*4.50*
14	A3	50pf pur & blk, *sal*	2.25	*6.50*
15	A3	80pf lake & blk, *rose*	3.00	*12.50*

Engr. ***Perf. $14^1/_2$x14***

16	A4	1m carmine	75.00	75.00
17	A4	2m blue	5.50	*70.00*
18	A4	3m black vio	6.00	*110.00*
19	A4	5m slate & car	110.00	*450.00*
		Nos. 7-19 (13)	295.65	*745.05*

1905-18 **Wmk. 125** **Typo.**

20	A3	3pf brown ('18)	.75	
21	A3	5pf green ('06)	.75	*1.75*
b.		Bklt. pane of 6, 2 #21 + 4 #22	62.50	
c.		Booklet pane of 5 + label	275.00	
22	A3	10pf carmine	.75	*1.00*
b.		Booklet pane of 5 + label	400.00	
23	A3	20pf ultra ('14)	2.50	*140.00*
24	A4	1m car ('15)	3.50	
25	A4	5m sl & car ('13)	17.50	*4,750.*
		Nos. 20-25 (6)	25.75	

The 3pf and 1m were not placed in use.

Issued under British Occupation

Stamps of German Cameroun Surcharged

C. E. F.
1/2 d.

Wmk. Lozenges (125) (#54-56, 65); Unwmk. (Other Values)

1915 ***Perf. 14, $14^1/_2$***

Blue Surcharge

53	A3	½p on 3pf brn	7.50	*12.50*
54	A3	½p on 5pf grn	3.75	*7.50*
a.		Double surcharge	400.00	*300.00*
b.		Black surcharge	12.50	*15.00*
55	A3	1p on 10pf car	3.50	*7.50*
a.		"1" with thin serifs	15.00	*17.50*
b.		Double surcharge	175.00	*175.00*
c.		Black surcharge	25.00	*37.50*
d.		As "c," "1" with thin serifs	67.50	*80.00*

Black Surcharge

56	A3	2p on 20pf ultra	5.00	*12.50*
57	A3	2½p on 25pf org & blk, *yel*	15.00	*25.00*
a.		Double surcharge	*3,500.*	
58	A3	3p on 30pf org & blk, *sal*	15.00	*25.00*
59	A3	4p on 40pf lake & blk	15.00	*25.00*
60	A3	6p on 50pf pur & blk, *sal*	15.00	*25.00*
61	A3	8p on 80pf lake & blk, *rose*	15.00	*25.00*

Surcharged

C. E. F.
1s.

62	A4	1sh on 1m car	150.00	*425.00*
a.		"S" inverted	675.00	*1,000.*
63	A4	2sh on 2m bl	150.00	*425.00*
a.		"S" inverted	675.00	*1,000.*
64	A4	3sh on 3m blk vio	160.00	*450.00*
a.		"S" inverted	700.00	*1,050.*
b.		Double surcharge	*4,000.*	
65	A4	5sh on 5m sl & car	250.00	*575.00*
a.		"S" inverted	700.00	*1,100.*
		Nos. 53-65 (13)	804.75	*2,040.*

The letters "C. E. F." are the initials of "Cameroons Expeditionary Force."

Numerous overprint varieties exist for #53-65.

Counterfeits exist of Nos. 54a, 54b.

Issued under French Occupation

Stamps of Gabon, 1910, Overprinted

Corps Expéditionnaire
Franco-Anglais
CAMEROUN

1915 **Unwmk.** ***Perf. $13^1/_2$x14***

101	A10	10c red & car	17.50	6.75
102	A13	1c choc & org	55.00	16.00
103	A13	2c blk & choc	80.00	42.50
104	A13	4c vio & dp bl	80.00	45.00
105	A13	5c ol gray & grn	17.50	7.50
105A	A13	10c red & car	*10,500.*	*11,000.*
106	A13	20c ol brn & dk vio	100.00	90.00
107	A14	25c dp bl & choc	40.00	12.50
108	A14	30c gray blk & red	95.00	85.00
109	A14	35c dk vio & grn	27.50	11.00
a.		Double overprint	900.00	900.00
110	A14	40c choc & ultra	90.00	80.00
111	A14	45c car & vio	100.00	80.00
112	A14	50c bl grn & gray	100.00	85.00
113	A14	75c org & choc	140.00	90.00
114	A15	1fr dk brn & bis	150.00	100.00
115	A15	2fr car & brn	140.00	110.00
		Nos. 101-105,106-115 (15)	1,232.	861.25

The overprint is vertical, reading up, on #101-106, 114-115, and horizontal on #107-113.

Stamps of Middle Congo, Issue of 1907, Overprinted

Occupation
Francaise
du Cameroun

1916 **Unwmk.**

116	A1	1c ol gray & brn	40.00	40.00
117	A1	2c vio & brn	55.00	50.00
118	A1	4c bl & brn	55.00	50.00
119	A1	5c dk grn & bl	14.00	12.50
120	A2	35c vio brn & bl	55.00	42.50
121	A2	45c vio & red	40.00	35.00

The overprint is vert., reading down, on #120-121.

Same Overprint On Stamps of French Congo, 1900

Wmk. Branch of Thistle (122)

122 A4 15c dl vio & ol grn 55.00 52.50
a. Inverted overprint 77.50 77.50

Wmk. Branch of Rose Tree (123)

123 A5 20c yel grn & org 100.00 60.00
124 A5 30c car rose & org 60.00 40.00
125 A5 40c org brn & brt grn 55.00 50.00
126 A5 50c gray vio & lil 60.00 40.00
127 A5 75c red vio & org 60.00 40.00

Wmk. Branch of Olive (124)

128 A6 1fr gray lil & ol 65.00 42.50
129 A6 2fr car & brn 65.00 42.50
Nos. 116-129 (14) 779.00 597.50

The overprint is horiz. on No. 122; vert., reading down or up, on Nos. 123-129.

Values are for copies centered in the grade of fine.

Counterfeits exist of Nos. 101-129.

Stamps of Middle Congo, Issue of 1907 Overprinted **CAMEROUN Occupation Française**

1916-17 Unwmk.

130 A1 1c ol gray & brn .15 .15
131 A1 2c violet & brn .15 .15
132 A1 4c blue & brn .15 .15
133 A1 5c dk grn & bl .15 .15
134 A1 10c carmine & bl .50 .30
135 A1 15c brn vio & rose ('17) .55 .25
136 A1 20c brown & bl .30 .20
137 A2 25c blue & grn .35 .25
a. Triple overprint 300.00
138 A2 30c scar & grn .20 .20
a. Double overprint 200.00
139 A2 35c vio brn & bl .35 .30
140 A2 40c dl grn & brn .75 .30
141 A2 45c violet & red .75 .35
142 A2 50c bl grn & red .75 .45
143 A2 75c brn & bl .80 .45
144 A3 1fr dp grn & vio .70 .45
145 A3 2fr vio & gray grn 4.25 2.40
146 A3 5fr blue & rose 4.75 3.25
Nos. 130-146 (17) 15.60 9.75

Nos. 130-146 exist on ordinary paper and, with the exception of No. 135, on chalk surfaced paper. Nos. 137-146 are known with inverted "S" in "Francaise."

On Nos. 137-146 there is 7mm between "Cameroun" and "Occupation."

Provisional French Mandate

Types of Middle Congo, 1907, Overprinted **CAMEROUN**

1921

147 A1 1c ol grn & org .15 .15
148 A1 2c brn & rose .15 .15
149 A1 4c gray & lt grn .15 .15
150 A1 5c dl red & org .15 .15
a. Double overprint 450.00
151 A1 10c bl grn & lt grn .20 .20
152 A1 15c bl & org .20 .20
153 A1 20c red brn & ol .25 .20
154 A2 25c sl & org .25 .20
155 A2 30c rose & ver .30 .20
156 A2 35c gray & ultra .35 .30
157 A2 40c ol grn & org .30 .25
158 A2 45c brn & rose .30 .20
159 A2 50c bl & ultra .30 .25
160 A2 75c red brn & lt grn .35 .25
161 A3 1fr sl & org .85 .65
162 A3 2fr ol grn & rose 2.75 2.00
163 A3 5fr dl red & gray 3.50 3.00
Nos. 147-163 (17) 10.50 8.50

The 2c, 4c, 15c, 25c and 50c exist with overprint omitted.

Nos. 152, 162, 163, 158, 160 Surcharged with New Value and Bars

1924-25

164 A1 25c on 15c bl & org ('25) .35 .35
165 A3 25c on 2fr ol grn & rose .35 .35
166 A3 25c on 5fr red & gray .40 .40
a. Pair, one without new value and bars
167 A2 65c on 45c brn & rose ('25) .80 .80
168 A2 85c on 75c red brn & lt grn ('25) .80 .80
Nos. 164-168 (5) 2.70 2.70

French Mandate

Herder and Cattle Crossing Sanaga River — A5

Tapping Rubber Tree — A6

Rope Suspension Bridge — A7

1925-38 Typo. *Perf. 14x13½*

170 A5 1c ol grn & brn vio, *lav* .15 .15
171 A5 2c rose & grn, *grnsh* .15 .15
172 A5 4c bl & blk .15 .15
173 A5 5c org & red vio, *lav* .15 .15
174 A5 10c red brn & org, *yel* .15 .15
175 A5 15c sl grn & grn .15 .15
176 A5 15c lil & red ('27) .45 .25

Perf. 13½x14

177 A6 20c ol brn & red brn .20 .15
178 A6 20c grn ('26) .20 .15
179 A6 20c brn red & ol brn ('27) .25 .15
180 A6 25c lt grn & blk .45 .15
181 A6 30c bluish grn & ver .20 .15
182 A6 30c dk grn & grn ('27) .25 .15
183 A6 35c brn & blk .20 .15
184 A6 35c dl grn & grn ('38) .70 .35
185 A6 40c org & vio .80 .45
186 A6 45c dp rose & cer .20 .15
187 A6 45c vio & org brn ('27) 1.25 .85
188 A6 50c lt grn & cer .20 .15
189 A6 55c ultra & car ('38) .80 .65
190 A6 60c red vio & blk .20 .15
191 A6 60c brn red ('26) .15 .15
192 A6 65c ind & brn .15 .15
193 A6 75c ind & dp bl .40 .25
194 A6 75c org brn & red vio ('27) .40 .20
195 A6 80c car & brn ('38) .75 .45
196 A6 85c dp rose & bl .45 .20
197 A6 90c brn red & cer ('27) 1.25 .65

Perf. 14x13½

198 A7 1fr indigo & brn .55 .30
199 A7 1fr dl bl ('26) .30 .25
200 A7 1fr ol brn & red vio ('27) .50 .25
201 A7 1fr grn & dk brn ('29) .80 .50
202 A7 1.10fr rose red & dk brn ('28) 2.00 1.40
203 A7 1.25fr gray & dp bl ('33) 3.25 1.75
204 A7 1.50fr dl bl ('27) .50 .25
205 A7 1.75fr brn & org ('33) .65 .40
206 A7 1.75fr dk bl & lt bl ('38) .65 .35
207 A7 2fr dl grn & brn org 1.00 .40
208 A7 3fr ol brn & red vio ('27) 3.25 .70
209 A7 5fr brn & blk, *bluish* 1.65 .70
a. Cliché of 2fr in plate of 5fr 900.00
210 A7 10fr org & vio ('27) 6.25 2.75
211 A7 20fr rose & ol grn ('27) 10.00 5.00
Nos. 170-211 (42) 42.15 22.00

Shades exist for several values.

For overprints and surcharge see Nos. 212, 264, 276, 278, 279, B7-B9, B21.

No. 199 Surcharged with New Value and Bars in Red

1926

212 A7 1.25fr on 1fr dull blue .25 .25

Common Design Types pictured in section at front of book.

Colonial Exposition Issue

Common Design Types

Name of Country in Black

1931 Engr. *Perf. 12½*

213 CD70 40c deep green 1.65 1.40
214 CD71 50c violet 2.25 2.00
215 CD72 90c red orange 2.25 2.00
216 CD73 1.50fr dull blue 2.75 2.50
Nos. 213-216 (4) 8.90 7.90

Paris International Exposition Issue

Common Design Types

1937 *Perf. 13*

217 CD74 20c dp violet .65 .65
218 CD75 30c dk green .60 .60
219 CD76 40c car rose .60 .60
220 CD77 50c dk brown .60 .60
221 CD78 90c red .65 .65
222 CD79 1.50fr ultra .65 .65
Nos. 217-222 (6) 3.75 3.75

French Colonial Art Exhibition

Common Design Type

Souvenir Sheet

1937 *Imperf.*

222A CD77 3fr org red & blk 2.25 2.25

New York World's Fair Issue

Common Design Type

1939 *Perf. 12½x12*

223 CD82 1.25fr car lake .60 .60
224 CD82 2.25fr ultra .60 .60

For overprints and surcharges see Nos. 280-281, B14-B17, B23, B25.

Mandara Woman — A19

Falls on M'bam River near Banyo — A20

Elephants A21

Man in Yaré — A22

1939-40 Engr. *Perf. 13*

225 A19 2c black brn .15 .15
226 A19 3c magenta .15 .15
227 A19 4c dp ultra .15 .15
228 A19 5c red brn .15 .15
229 A19 10c dp bl grn .15 .15
230 A19 15c rose red .15 .15
231 A19 20c plum .15 .15
232 A20 25c black brn .20 .20
233 A20 30c dk red .20 .20
234 A20 40c ultra .30 .25
235 A20 45c slate green .80 .65
236 A20 50c brown car .30 .20
237 A20 60c pck blue .35 .25
238 A20 70c plum 1.10 1.00
239 A21 80c Prus blue .80 .70
240 A21 90c Prus blue .45 .25
241 A21 1fr car rose .60 .35
242 A21 1fr choc ('40) .60 .30
243 A21 1.25fr car rose 1.60 1.10
244 A21 1.40fr org red .60 .45
245 A21 1.50fr chocolate .45 .35
246 A21 1.60fr blk brn .80 .80
247 A21 1.75fr dk blue .45 .30
248 A21 2fr dk green .50 .45
249 A21 2.25fr dk blue .45 .30
250 A21 2.50fr brt red vio .60 .45
251 A21 3fr dk violet .35 .25
252 A22 5fr black brn .45 .30
253 A22 10fr brt red vio .80 .65
254 A22 20fr dk green 1.40 1.00
Nos. 225-254 (30) 15.20 11.80

For overprints and surcharges see Nos. 255-263, 265-275, 277, 278A, 279A, B10-B13, B22, B24.

Stamps of 1925-40 Overprinted in Black or Orange "CAMEROUN FRANCAIS 27.8.40."

1940 *Perf. 14x13½, 13½x14, 13*

255 A19 2c blk brn (O) .25 .25
256 A19 3c magenta .30 .30
257 A19 4c dp ultra (O) .35 .35
258 A19 5c red brn 1.10 1.10
259 A19 10c dp bl grn (O) .30 .30
260 A19 15c rose red .45 .45
260A A19 20c plum (O) 3.25 2.50
261 A20 25c blk brn .35 .30
b. Inverted overprint 110.00 110.00
261A A20 30c dk red 3.00 2.25
262 A20 40c ultra 1.50 1.00
263 A20 45c slate green 1.10 .80
264 A6 50c lt grn & cer .60 .30
a. Inverted overprint 125.00
265 A20 60c pck bl 1.50 1.00
266 A20 70c plum .55 .55
267 A21 80c Prus bl (O) 1.50 1.25
268 A21 90c Prus bl (O) .40 .40
269 A21 1.25fr car rose .55 .35
270 A21 1.40fr org red .80 .60
271 A21 1.50fr chocolate .35 .35
272 A21 1.60fr blk brn (O) .60 .35
273 A21 1.75fr dk bl (O) .80 .85
274 A21 2.25fr dk bl (O) .45 .45
275 A21 2.50fr brt red vio .45 .45
276 A7 5fr brn & blk, *bluish* 7.50 5.50
277 A22 5fr black brn 7.50 6.50
278 A7 10fr org & vio 9.00 6.50
278A A22 10fr brt red vio 20.00 14.00
279 A7 20fr rose & ol grn 22.50 18.00
279A A22 20fr dk green 100.00 90.00

Same Overprint on Stamps of 1939

Perf. 12½x12

280 CD82 1.25fr car lake 1.50 1.50
281 CD82 2.25fr ultra 1.50 1.50
Nos. 255-281 (31) 190.00 160.00

Issued to note Cameroun's affiliation with General de Gaulle's "Free France" movement.

Numerous overprint varieties exist.

Catalogue values for unused stamps in this section, from this point to the end of the section, are for Never Hinged items.

Cattle Fording Sanaga River and Marshal Petain A22a

1941 Engr. *Perf. 12½x12*

281A A22a 1fr green .45
281B A22a 2.50fr dark blue .45

Nos. 281A-281B were issued by the Vichy government, and were not placed on sale in Cameroun.

Lorraine Cross and Joan of Arc Shield — A23

1941 Photo. *Perf. 14x14½*

282 A23 5c brown .15 .15
283 A23 10c dk blue .15 .15
284 A23 25c emerald .15 .15
285 A23 30c dp orange .15 .15
286 A23 40c dk slate green .15 .15
287 A23 80c red brown .15 .15
288 A23 1fr dp red lilac .15 .15
289 A23 1.50fr brt red .15 .15
290 A23 2fr gray black .20 .15
291 A23 2.50fr brt ultra .25 .15
292 A23 4fr dull violet .45 .35
293 A23 5fr bister .45 .45
294 A23 10fr dp brown .50 .45
295 A23 20fr dp green 1.00 .70
Set value 3.25 2.50

For surcharges see Nos. 297A-303.

Eboue Issue

Common Design Type

1945 Unwmk. Engr. *Perf. 13*

296 CD91 2fr black .20 .20
297 CD91 25fr Prus green .65 .65

Nos. 282, 284, 291 Surcharged with New Values and Bars in Red, Carmine or Black

1946 *Perf. 14x14½*

297A A23 50c on 5c (R) .20 .20
298 A23 60c on 5c (R) .25 .25
a. Inverted surcharge 60.00
299 A23 70c on 5c (R) .25 .25
300 A23 1.20fr on 5c (C) .25 .25
301 A23 2.40fr on 25c .20 .20
302 A23 3fr on 25c .45 .45
302A A23 4.50fr on 25c .70 .70
303 A23 15fr on 2.50fr (C) .70 .70
Nos. 297A-303 (8) 3.00 3.00

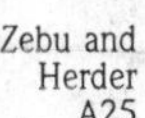

Zebu and Herder A25

Tikar Women — A26

Porters Carrying Bananas — A27

Bowman — A28

Lamido Horsemen — A29

Farmer — A30

1946 Engr. *Perf. 12½x12, 12x12½*

No.	Type	Description		
304	A25	10c blue grn	.15	.15
305	A25	30c brown org	.15	.15
306	A25	40c brt ultra	.15	.15
307	A26	50c olive brn	.15	.15
308	A26	60c dp plum	.15	.15
309	A26	80c chnt brn	.30	.15
310	A27	1fr org red	.20	.15
311	A27	1.20fr dp green	.40	.20
312	A27	1.50fr dk car	1.25	.75
313	A28	2fr black	.20	.15
314	A28	3fr dk carmine	.20	.15
314A	A28	3.60fr red brn	.65	.35
315	A28	4fr dp blue	.30	.15
316	A29	5fr brown car	.65	.15
317	A29	6fr ultra	.65	.15
318	A29	10fr slate green	.65	.15
319	A30	15fr grnsh blue	1.00	.35
320	A30	20fr dk green	1.25	.25
321	A30	25fr black	1.75	.60
		Nos. 304-321 (19)	10.20	
		Set value		3.50

Shades exist for most values.
For surcharges see Nos. 343-344, 346.

Imperforates
Most Cameroun stamps from 1952 onward exist imperforate in issued and trial colors, and also in small presentation sheets in issued colors.

Military Medal Issue
Common Design Type
Engraved and Typographed

1952 Unwmk. *Perf. 13*

No.	Type	Description		
322	CD101	15fr multicolored	3.00	2.00

Porters Carrying Bananas — A32

Picking Coffee Beans — A33

1954 Engr.

No.	Type	Description		
323	A32	8fr red vio, org brn & vio bl	.35	.20
324	A32	15fr brn red, yel & blk brn	.60	.30
325	A33	40fr blk brn, org brn & lil rose	.60	.30
		Nos. 323-325 (3)	1.55	.80

FIDES Issue
Common Design Type

Designs: 5fr, Plowmen. 15fr, Wouri bridge. 20fr, Technical instruction. 25fr, Mobile medical station.

1956 Unwmk. *Perf. 13*

No.	Type	Description		
326	CD103	5fr org brn & dk brn	.45	.30
327	CD103	15fr aqua, slate & blk	.75	.50
328	CD103	20fr grnsh bl & dp ultra	.75	.50
329	CD103	25fr dp ultra	1.00	.75
		Nos. 326-329 (4)	2.95	2.05

For surcharges see Nos. 345, 347.

Coffee Issue

Coffee — A35

1956 Engr. *Perf. 13*

No.	Type	Description		
330	A35	15fr car & brt red	.50	.25

For surcharge see No. 348.

Autonomous Government

Flag and Woman Holding Child — A36

1958

No.	Type	Description		
331	A36	20fr multicolored	.30	.15

Anniv. of the installation of the 1st autonomous government of Cameroun.

Men Looking to the Sun — A37

1958

No.	Type	Description		
332	A37	20fr sepia & brn red	.35	.25

10th anniv. of the signing of the Universal Declaration of Human Rights.

Flower Issue
Common Design Type

Design: 20fr, Randia malleifera.

1959 Photo. *Perf. 12½x12*

No.	Type	Description		
333	CD104	20fr dp grn, yel & rose	.25	.15

Loading Bananas A38

Harvesting Bananas — A39

1959 Engr. *Perf. 13*

No.	Type	Description		
334	A38	20fr dk grn & org	.20	.15
335	A39	25fr maroon & slate grn	.25	.15
		Set value		.15

For surcharge see No. 349.

Independent State

Map and Flag of Cameroun — A40

Prime Minister Ahmadou Ahidjo — A41

1960 Unwmk. Engr. *Perf. 13*

No.	Type	Description		
336	A40	20fr multicolored	.25	.15
337	A41	25fr blk, grn & pale lem	.30	.15
		Set value		.20

Declaration of independence, Jan. 1, 1960.
For surcharge see No. 350.

Uprooted Oak Emblem A42

1960

No.	Type	Description		
338	A42	30fr red brn, ultra & yel grn	.40	.38

Issued to publicize World Refugee Year, July 1, 1959-June 30, 1960.
For surcharge see No. 351.

C.C.T.A. Issue
Common Design Type

1960

No.	Type	Description		
339	CD106	50fr dull claret & slate	.65	.40

UN Headquarters, NYC, and Flag — A43

1961, May 20 *Perf. 13*
Flag in Green, Red and Yellow

No.	Type	Description		
340	A43	15fr grn, dk bl & brn	.25	.22
341	A43	25fr dk blue & grn	.30	.22
342	A43	85fr red, dk bl & vio brn	.90	.80
		Nos. 340-342 (3)	1.45	1.24

Cameroun's admission to the UN, Sept. 20, 1960.

Federal Republic

Stamps of 1946-60 Surcharged in Red or Black: **REPUBLIQUE FEDERALE 2 d**

Two types of 2sh6p:
I - Large figures. "2/6" measures 8x3¾mm.
II - Small figures. "2/6" measures 6x2½mm.

1961, Oct. 1 Engr. *Perf. 12x12½, 13*

No.	Type	Description		
343	A27	½p on 1fr (#310)	.16	.16
344	A28	1p on 2fr (#313)	.22	.16
345	CD103	1½p on 5fr (#326)	.22	.16
346	A29	2p on 10fr (#318)	.25	.20
347	CD103	3p on 15fr (#327)	.30	.22
348	A35	4p on 15fr (Bk) (#330)	.40	.30
349	A38	6p on 20fr (#334)	.50	.35
350	A41	1sh on 25fr (#337)	1.00	.80
351	A42	2sh6p on 30fr (#338) (I)	1.60	1.60
a.		Type II	4.25	4.25
		Nos. 343-351 (9)	4.65	3.95

Issued for use in the former United Kingdom Trust Territory of Southern Cameroons.
The "Republique Federale" overprint is in one line on Nos. 345, 347-349, in two vertical lines on No. 350. See Nos. C38-C40.

President Ahidjo and Prime Minister Foncha A45

1962, Jan. 1 Unwmk. Engr. *Perf. 13*

No.	Type	Description		
352	A45	20fr vio & choc	5.00	4.25
353	A45	25fr dk grn & brn	8.00	6.50
354	A45	60fr car & dl grn	22.50	20.00
		Nos. 352-354 (3)	35.50	30.75

Same Surcharged for Use in Southern Cameroons **3 d**

No.	Type	Description		
355	A45	3p on 20fr	90.00	90.00
356	A45	6p on 25fr	90.00	90.00
357	A45	2sh6p on 60fr	90.00	90.00
		Nos. 355-357 (3)	270.00	270.00

Reunification of the former French and British Sections of Cameroun. It is reported that Nos. 352-357 were withdrawn after a few days and destroyed.

Canceled to Order
Many Cameroun stamps from 1962 onward are available c-t-o. Values are for postally used copies. C-t-o copies sell for less.

Mustache Monkey A46

Designs: 1fr, 4fr, Elephant, Ntem Falls. 1.50fr, 3fr, Buffon's kob, Dschang. 2fr, 5fr, Hippopotamus. 6fr, 15fr, Mustache monkey. 8fr, 30fr, Manatee, Lake Ossa. 10fr, 25fr, Buffalo, Batouri. 20fr, 40fr, Giraffes, Waza Reservation, vert.

1962 Unwmk. Engr. *Perf. 12*

No.	Type	Description		
358	A46	50c brn, brt grn & bl	.15	.15
359	A46	1fr gray brn, bl grn & org	.15	.15
360	A46	1.50fr brn, lt grn & sl grn	.15	.15
361	A46	2fr dk gray, grnsh bl & grn	.15	.15
362	A46	3fr brn, org & lil rose	.15	.15
363	A46	4fr brn, yel grn & bl grn	.15	.15
364	A46	5fr gray brn, grn & sal	.15	.15
365	A46	6fr brn, yel & bl	.15	.15
366	A46	8fr dk bl, red & grn	.16	.15
367	A46	10fr ol blk, org & brt bl	.16	.15
368	A46	15fr brn, Prus bl & bl	.20	.15
369	A46	20fr brn & gray	.25	.15
370	A46	25fr red brn, grn & yel	.40	.20
371	A46	30fr blk, org & bl	.60	.25
372	A46	40fr dp cl, yel grn & blk	.80	.40
		Set value	3.20	1.50

See Nos. 396-397.

African and Malagasy Union Issue
Common Design Type

1962, Sept. 8 Photo. *Perf. 12½x12*

No.	Type	Description		
373	CD110	30fr multicolored	.65	.45

Village and Map of Cameroun A48

Designs: 20fr, 25fr, Sun rising over city. 50fr, Hands holding scroll.

1962, Oct. 1 Engr. *Perf. 13*

No.	Type	Description		
374	A48	9fr pur, ol & dk brn	.15	.15
375	A48	18fr grn, org brn & dk bl	.22	.16
376	A48	20fr lil rose, ol bis & ind	.22	.16
377	A48	25fr bl, red org & sep	.35	.20
378	A48	50fr dk red, sep & bl	.65	.50
		Nos. 374-378 (5)	1.59	1.17

1st anniv. of the reunification of Cameroun.

"School under the Trees" — A49

1962, Nov. 5 Photo. *Perf. 12x12½*

379 A49 20fr ver, emer & yel .25 .15

Literacy and popular education campaign.

Telstar and Globe — A50

1963, Feb. 9 Engr. *Perf. 13*

Size: 36x22mm

380 A50 1fr dk bl, olive & pur .15 .15
381 A50 2fr dk bl, claret & grn .15 .15
382 A50 3fr dk grn, ol & dp cl .15 .15
383 A50 25fr grn, dp cl & brt bl .45 .40
Set value .65 .60

1st TV connection of the US and Europe through the Telstar satellite, July 11-12, 1962. See No. C45.

High Frequency Transmission Station, Mt. Bankolo — A51

Design: 20fr, Station and wiring plan.

1963, May 18 Photo. *Perf. 12x12½*

384 A51 15fr multicolored .16 .15
385 A51 20fr multicolored .22 .16

Issued to publicize the high frequency telegraph connection Douala-Yaounde. See No. C46.

"Yaoundé-Regional Center of Textbook Production" — A52

1963, Aug. 10 Unwmk. *Perf. 12½*

386 A52 20fr emer, blk & red .22 .15
387 A52 25fr org, blk & red .30 .16
388 A52 100fr gold, blk & red 1.10 .65
Nos. 386-388 (3) 1.62 .96

UNESCO regional center for the production of school books at Yaounde.

Pres. Ahmadou Ahidjo and Flag — A53

Design: 18fr, Flag and map of Cameroun.

1963, Oct. 1 *Perf. 12x12½*

Flag in Green, Red and Yellow

389 A53 9fr grn, bl & dk brn .15 .15
390 A53 18fr grn, bl & lil .20 .16
391 A53 20fr grn, blk & yel grn .22 .20
Nos. 389-391 (3) .57 .51

Second anniversary of reunification.

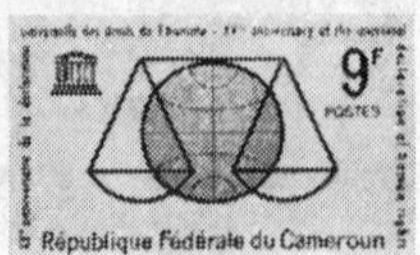

Scales, Globe, UNESCO Emblem A54

1963, Dec. 10 Photo. *Perf. 12½x12*

392 A54 9fr ultra, blk & sal .15 .15
393 A54 18fr brt yel grn, blk & rose red .20 .15
394 A54 25fr rose red, blk & brt yel grn .25 .20
395 A54 75fr yel, blk & ultra .90 .50
Nos. 392-395 (4) 1.50 1.00

Universal Declaration of Human Rights, 15th anniv.

Animal Type of 1962

Design: 10fr, 25fr, Lion, Waza National Park, North Cameroun.

1964, June 20 Engr. *Perf. 13*

396 A46 10fr red brn, bis & grn .16 .15
397 A46 25fr green & bister .35 .16
Set value .25

Soccer Game in Stadium A55

Designs: 18fr, Pile of sports equipment. 30fr, Stadium (outside), flags and map of Africa.

1964, July 11 Engr. *Perf. 13*

398 A55 10fr grn, bl & red brn .15 .15
399 A55 18fr car, grn & vio .20 .15
400 A55 30fr blk, dk bl & org brn .35 .20
Nos. 398-400 (3) .70
Set value .40

Tropics Cup Games, Yaounde, July 11-19.

Europafrica Issue, 1964

Common Design Type and

Palace of Justice, Yaounde — A56

Design: 40fr, Emblems of Science, Agriculture, Industry and Education and two sunbursts.

1964, July 20 Photo. *Perf. 12x13*

401 A56 15fr multicolored .35 .25
402 CD116 40fr multicolored .65 .60

1st anniv. of the economic agreement between the European Economic Community and the African and Malgache Union.

Hurdling and Olympic Flame — A57

Design: 10fr, Runners, vert.

1964, Oct. 10 Engr. *Perf. 13*

403 A57 9fr red, yel grn & blk .60 .40
404 A57 10fr red, vio & ol gray .60 .40

18th Olympic Games, Tokyo, Oct. 10-25. See Nos. C49, C49a.

Bamileke Dance Dress — A58

Ntem Falls, Ebolowa Region — A59

Designs: 18fr, Dance mask, Bamenda region. 25fr, Fulani horseman, North Cameroun, horiz.

1964 Unwmk. *Perf. 13*

405 A58 9fr red, yel grn & bl .15 .15
406 A58 18fr bl, red & brn .20 .15
407 A59 20fr dk car, grn & ol .22 .15
408 A58 25fr dk brn, org & car .30 .20
Nos. 405-408 (4) .87 .65

See No. C50.

Cooperation Issue

Common Design Type

1964, Nov. 7 Engr.

409 CD119 18fr dk bl, yel grn & dk brn .22 .15
410 CD119 30fr red brn, bl grn & dk brn .40 .16

Memorial Stone — A60

Diesel Train — A61

1965, Jan. 1 Engr. *Perf. 13*

411 A60 12fr bl, indigo & grn .16 .15

Typo. *Perf. 14x13*

412 A61 20fr rose car, yel & grn .25 .15
Set value .24

Laying of the 1st rail of the Mbanga-Kumba Railroad, Mar. 28, 1964.

Red Cross Station and Ambulance A62

Design: 50fr, Red Cross nurse and infant, vert.

1965, May 8 Engr. *Perf. 13*

413 A62 25fr car, slate grn & ocher .30 .16
414 A62 50fr gray, red & red brn .60 .30

Issued for the Cameroun Red Cross.

Coins Inserted in Map of Cameroun, and Bankbook — A63

Savings Bank Building — A64

Design: 20fr, Bankbook and coins inserted in cacao pod-shaped bank, horiz.

1965, June 10

Size: 22x37mm

415 A63 9fr grn, red & org .15 .15

Size: 48x27mm, 27x48mm

416 A64 15fr choc, ultra & grn .20 .16
417 A63 20fr ocher, brt grn & brn .22 .20
Nos. 415-417 (3) .57 .51

Federal Postal Savings Banks.

Soccer Players and Africa Cup — A65

Unwmk.

1965, June 26 Engr. *Perf. 13*

418 A65 9fr car, brn & yel .15 .15
419 A65 20fr car, sl bl & yel .22 .16

Cameroun Oryx Club, winner of the club champions' Africa Cup, February 1965.

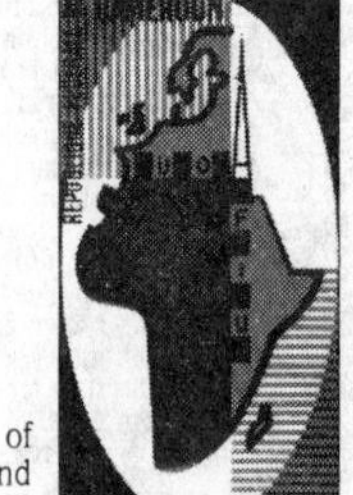

Symbolic Map of Europe and Africa — A66

Designs: 40fr, Delegates around conference table.

1965, July 20 Photo. *Perf. 12x12½*

420 A66 5fr car, blk & lil .15 .15
421 A66 40fr brn, buff, grn & ultra .45 .35

2nd, anniv. of the economic agreement between the European Economic Community and the African and Malgache Union.

UPU Monument, Bern — A67

1965, July 26 Engr. *Perf. 13*

422 A67 30fr black & red .40 .25

Cameroun's admission to the UPU, 5th anniv.

ICY Emblem — A68

1965, Sept. 11 Unwmk. *Perf. 13*

423 A68 10fr dk bl & car rose .16 .16

Issued for the International Cooperation Year, 1964-65. See No. C57.

Pres. Ahidjo and Government House — A69

Design: 9fr, 20fr, Pres. Ahidjo and Government House, vert.

Perf. 12x12½, 12½x12

1965, Oct. 1 Photo. Unwmk.

424 A69	9fr	multicolored	.15	.15
425 A69	18fr	multicolored	.20	.15
426 A69	20fr	multicolored	.22	.15
427 A69	25fr	multicolored	.30	.16
		Nos. 424-427 (4)	.87	
		Set value		.50

Reelection of Pres. Ahmadou Ahidjo.

National Tourist Office, Yaoundé A70

Designs: 9fr, Pouss Musgum houses. 18fr, Great Calao's dance (North Cameroun). 20fr, Gate of Sultan's Palace, Foumban, vert.

1965 Engr. *Perf. 13*

428 A70	9fr	brn, rose red & grn	.15	.15
429 A70	18fr	brt bl, brn & grn	.20	.16
430 A70	20fr	bl, brn & choc	.22	.15
431 A70	25fr	mar, emer & gray	.22	.15
		Nos. 428-431 (4)	.79	.61

See No. C58.

Mountain Hotel, Buea — A71

Designs: 20fr, Hotel of the Deputies, Yaoundé. 35fr, Dschang Health Center.

1966

432 A71	9fr	sl grn, rose cl & brn	.15	.15
433 A71	20fr	brt bl, sl grn & blk	.22	.15
434 A71	35fr	brn, sl grn & car	.40	.30
		Nos. 432-434,C63-C69 (10)	5.68	3.26

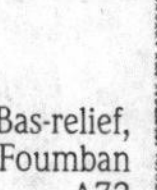

Bas-relief, Foumban A72

Designs: 18fr, Ekoi mask, vert. 20fr, Mother and child, carving, Bamiléké, vert. 25fr, Ceremonial stool, Bamoun.

1966, Apr. 15 Unwmk.

435 A72	9fr	red & blk	.16	.15
436 A72	18fr	brt grn, org brn & choc	.22	.16
437 A72	20fr	brt bl, red brn & pur	.30	.16
438 A72	25fr	pur & dk brn	.35	.20
		Nos. 435-438 (4)	1.03	.67

Intl. Negro Arts Festival, Dakar, Senegal, Apr. 1-24.

New WHO Headquarters, Geneva A73

1966, May 3 Photo. *Perf. 12½x13*

439 A73	50fr	ultra, red brn & yel	.60	.35

ITU Headquarters, Geneva A74

1966, May 3 Photo. *Perf. 12½x13*

440 A74	50fr	ultra & yellow	.60	.35

Phaeomeria Magnifica — A75

"6" and Men Dancing around UN Emblem — A76

Flowers: 18fr, Hibiscus (rose of China). 20fr, Mountain rose.

1966, May 20 *Perf. 12x12½*

Flowers in Natural Colors

Size: 22x36mm

441 A75	9fr	red brown	.15	.15
442 A75	18fr	green	.20	.15
443 A75	20fr	dark green	.22	.15
		Nos. 441-443,C70-C72 (6)	2.42	
		Set value		.75

See No. 469.

1966, Sept. 20 Engr. *Perf. 13*

Design: 50fr, UN General Assembly, horiz.

444 A76	50fr	ultra, grn & vio brn	.60	.15
445 A76	100fr	red brn, grn & ultra	1.10	.50

6th anniv. of Cameroun's admission to the UN.

Prime Minister's Residence, Buea — A77

Designs (Prime Minister's Residences): 18fr, at Yaoundé, front view. 20fr, at Yaoundé, side view. 25fr, at Buea, front view.

1966, Oct. 1 Photo.

446 A77	9fr	multicolored	.15	.15
447 A77	18fr	multicolored	.20	.15
448 A77	20fr	multicolored	.22	.15
449 A77	25fr	multicolored	.25	.16
		Nos. 446-449 (4)	.82	
		Set value		.45

5th anniversary of re-unification.

Learning to Write and UNESCO Emblem A78

Design: No. 451, Children's heads and UNICEF emblem.

1966, Nov. 24 Engr. *Perf. 13*

450 A78	50fr	red lil, bl & brn	.60	.30
451 A78	50fr	red lil, blk & brt bl	.60	.30

20th anniv. of UNESCO, 20th anniv. of UNICEF.

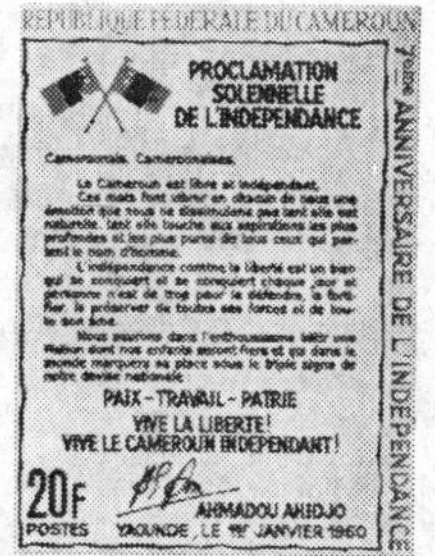

Independence Proclamation — A79

1967, Jan. 1 Engr. *Perf. 13*

452 A79	20fr	grn, red & yel	.30	.22

7th anniversary of independence.

Map of Africa and Madagascar, Railroad Tracks and Symbols — A80

Design: 25fr, Map of Africa and Madagascar and train.

1967, Feb. 21 Photo. *Perf. 13*

453 A80	20fr	multicolored	.22	.16
454 A80	25fr	multicolored	.30	.16

5th Conf. of African and Madagascan Railroad Technicians.

Lions Emblem and Forest — A81

Design: 100fr, Lions emblem and palms.

1967, Mar. 3

455 A81	50fr	multicolored	.60	.35
456 A81	100fr	multicolored	1.10	.65

Lions International, 50th anniversary.

Jet and I.C.A.O. Emblem — A82

Dove and I.A.E.A. Emblem A83

Perf. 13x12½, 12½x13

1967, Mar. 15 Photo.

457 A82	50fr	ultra, lt bl, brn & gold	.60	.35
458 A83	50fr	ultra & emer	.60	.35

UN agencies: No. 457, the ICAO; No. 458, the Intl. Atomic Energy Agency.

Rotary International Emblem A84

1967, Apr. 17 Photo. *Perf. 12½*

459 A84	25fr	crim, vio bl & gold	.30	.16

10th anniversary of the Douala, Cameroun, branch of Rotary International.

Pomelo — A85

Bird-of-Paradise Flower — A86

1967, May 10 Photo. *Perf. 12x12½*

460 A85	1fr	shown	.15	.15
461 A85	2fr	Papaya	.15	.15
462 A85	3fr	Custard apple	.15	.15
463 A85	4fr	Breadfruit	.15	.15
464 A85	5fr	Coconut	.15	.15
465 A85	6fr	Mango	.15	.15
466 A85	8fr	Avacado	.16	.15
467 A85	10fr	Pineapple	.20	.15
468 A85	30fr	Bananas	.45	.20
		Set value	1.30	.65

For surcharges see Nos. 550, 593.

1967, June 22 Photo. *Perf. 12x12½*

Size: 22x36mm

469 A86	15fr	lt blue & multi	.16	.15

Sanaga Falls and ITY Emblem — A87

1967, Aug. 14 Photo. *Perf. 13x12½*

470 A87	30fr	multicolored	.35	.20

Issued for International Tourist Year 1967.

Art of Cameroun: Coconut Harvest A88

Designs (Carved Bas-relief): 20fr, Lion hunt. 30fr, Women carrying baskets. 100fr, Carved chest.

1967, Sept. 22 *Perf. 12½x13*

471 A88	10fr	brn, bl & car	.15	.15
472 A88	20fr	brn, yel & grn	.22	.15
473 A88	30fr	emer, brn & car	.35	.15
474 A88	100fr	red org, brn & emer	1.10	.45
		Nos. 471-474 (4)	1.82	.90

Coat of Arms — A89

1968, Jan. 1 Litho. *Perf. 12½x13*
475 A89 30fr gold & multi .40 .20

Spiny Lobster A90

Designs (Fish and Crustaceans): 10fr, River crayfish. 15fr, Nile mouth-breeder. 20fr, Sole. 25fr, Common pike. 30fr, Crab. 40fr, Spadefish, vert. 50fr, Shrimp, vert. 55fr, African snakehead. 60fr, Threadfin.

1968, July 25 Engr. *Perf. 13*
476 A90 5fr brn, vio bl & dl grn .15 .15
477 A90 10fr ultra, brn ol & slate .15 .15
478 A90 15fr sal, red lil & sepia .15 .15
479 A90 20fr red brn, dp bl & sep .16 .15
480 A90 25fr lt brn, emer & slate .25 .15
481 A90 30fr mag, dk bl & dk brn .35 .15
482 A90 40fr slate bl & org .40 .15
483 A90 50fr emer, gray & rose car .50 .20
484 A90 55fr lt brn, Prus bl & dk brn .60 .25
485 A90 60fr brn, bl grn & indigo .65 .35
Nos. 476-485 (10) 3.36
Set value 1.35

Tanker, Refinery and Map of Area Served — A91

1968, July 30 Photo. *Perf. 12½*
486 A91 30fr multicolored .30 .15

Issued to commemorate the opening of the Port Gentil (Gabon) Refinery, June 12, 1968.

Human Rights Flame — A92

1968, Sept. 14 Photo. *Perf. 12½x13*
487 A92 15fr blue & salmon .16 .15

International Human Rights Year. See No. C110.

Pres. Ahmadou Ahidjo A93

1969, Apr. 10 Photo. *Perf. 12½x12*
488 A93 30fr carmine & multi .30 .15

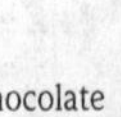
Chocolate Vat — A94

Designs: 30fr, Chocolate factory. 50fr, Candy making, vert.

1969, Apr. 24 Engr. *Perf. 13*
489 A94 15fr red brn, ind & choc .16 .15
490 A94 30fr grn, blk & red brn .30 .15
491 A94 50fr brown & multi .50 .20
Nos. 489-491 (3) .96
Set value .40

Cameroun chocolate industry.

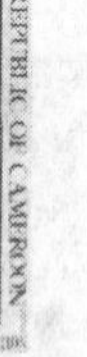

Fertility Symbol, Abbia — A95

Diesel Train on Bridge — A96

Art and Folklore from Abbia: 10fr, Two toucans, horiz. 15fr, Forest symbol. 30fr, Vulture attacking monkey, horiz. 70fr, Oliphant player.

1969, May 30 Engr. *Perf. 13*
492 A95 5fr ultra, Prus bl & brt rose lil .15 .15
493 A95 10fr bl, ol gray & org .15 .15
494 A95 15fr ultra, dk red & blk .15 .15
495 A95 30fr brt bl, lem & grn .30 .15
496 A95 70fr brt bl, dk grn & ver .70 .35
Nos. 492-496 (5) 1.45
Set value .65

Perf. 12½x13, 13x12½
1969, July 11 Photo.

Design: 30fr, Kumba Railroad station, horiz.

497 A96 30fr blue & multi .30 .15
498 A96 50fr black & multi .60 .25

Opening of Mbanga-Kumba Railroad.

Development Bank Issue
Common Design Type

1969, Sept. 10 Engr. *Perf. 13*
499 CD130 30fr vio bl, grn & ocher .35 .15

African Development Bank, 5th anniv.

ASECNA Issue
Common Design Type

1969, Dec. 12 Engr. *Perf. 13*
500 CD132 100fr slate green 1.00 .60

Red Sage — A99

Design: 30fr, Passionflower.

1970, Mar. 24 Photo. *Perf. 12x12½*
Size: 22x36½mm
501 A99 15fr yel grn & multi .16 .15
502 A99 30fr multicolored .25 .15
Set value .20

See Nos. C140-C141.

UPU Headquarters Issue
Common Design Type

1970, May 20 Engr. *Perf. 13*
503 CD133 30fr blue, pur & grn .30 .15
504 CD133 50fr gray, red & bl .50 .16

Brewery A100

Design: 30fr, Cellar with barrels.

1970, July 9 Engr. *Perf. 13*
505 A100 15fr brn, gray & dk grn .15 .15
506 A100 30fr bl grn, dk brn & brn red .25 .15
Set value .20

Cameroun brewing industry.

Ozila Dancers — A101

Cameroun Doll — A102

Design: 50fr, Ozila dancer and drummer.

1970, Oct. 19 Engr. *Perf. 13*
507 A101 30fr multicolored .25 .15
508 A101 50fr red & multi .50 .20

1970, Nov. 2

Designs: 15fr, Doll in short skirt. 30fr, Doll with basket on back.

509 A102 10fr car & multi .15 .20
510 A102 15fr dk grn & multi .18 .15
511 A102 30fr brn red & multi .35 .15
Nos. 509-511 (3) .68
Set value .35

Cogwheels and Grain A103

1970, Feb. 9 Photo. *Perf. 13*
512 A103 30fr multicolored .25 .15

Europafrica Economic Conference.

Federal University, Yaoundé A104

1971, Jan. 19 Engr.
513 A104 50fr multicolored .40 .15

Inauguration of Federal University at Yaoundé.

Presidents Ahidjo and Pompidou, Flags of Cameroun and France — A105

1971, Feb. 9 Photo. *Perf. 13*
514 A105 30fr multicolored .40 .35

Visit of Georges Pompidou, Pres. of France.

Young People, Globe, Map of Cameroun A106

1971, Feb. 11
515 A106 30fr blue & multi .22 .15

Fifth National Youth Festival, Feb. 11.

Gerbera Hybrida — A107

Men of Four Races — A108

Designs: 40fr, Opuntia polyantha (cactus). 50fr, Hemerocallis hybrida (lily).

1971, Mar. 14 Photo.
516 A107 20fr multicolored .18 .15
517 A107 40fr green & multi .30 .15
518 A107 50fr blue & multi .40 .15
Nos. 516-518 (3) .88
Set value .35

1971, Mar. 21 *Perf. 13x12½*

Design: 30fr, Hands and globe.

519 A108 20fr green & multi .18 .15
520 A108 30fr ultra & multi .25 .15
Set value .15

Intl. year against racial discrimination.

Crowned Cranes at Waza Camp A109

Designs: 20fr, Canoe on Sanaga River. 30fr, Sanaga River.

1971, Apr. 9. Engr. *Perf. 13*
521 A109 10fr red, grn & blk .15 .15
522 A109 20fr dk grn, brn & red .18 .15
523 A109 30fr red, dk grn & brt bl .22 .15
Nos. 521-523 (3) .55
Set value .20

International Court, The Hague A110

1971, June 14 Engr. *Perf. 13*
524 A110 50fr ultra, org brn & sl grn .40 .16

25th anniversary of the International Court in The Hague, Netherlands.

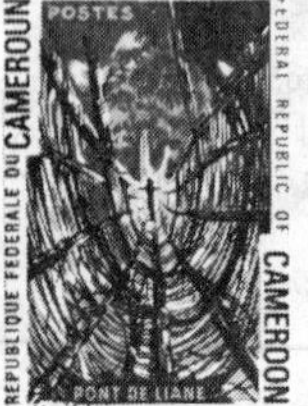

Liana Bridge — A111

Bamoun Horseman — A113

Local Market A112

1971, Aug. 16 Photo. *Perf. 13*
525 A111 40fr multicolored .35 .15
526 A112 45fr multicolored .38 .15

1971, Sept. 18

African Art: 15fr, Animal fetish statuette.

527 A113 10fr brown & yellow .15 .15
528 A113 15fr dp brn & org yel .15 .15
Set value .20 .15

Communications Satellite and Globe — A114

1971, Oct. 14 *Perf. 13x12½*
529 A114 40fr Prus bl, sl grn & org .30 .15

Pan-African telecommunications system.

UNICEF Emblem A115

Design: 50fr, UNICEF emblem and grain, vert.

1971, Dec. 11 Engr. *Perf. 13*
530 A115 40fr sl grn, bl grn & plum .40 .20
531 A115 50fr dp bl, dk red & lt grn .60 .25

25th anniv. of UNICEF.

Houses from South-Central Region A116

Design: 15fr, Adamaua round houses.

1972, Jan. 15 Photo. *Perf. 13*
532 A116 10fr dk blue & multi .15 .15
533 A116 15fr black & multi .15 .15
Set value .20 .15

Giraffe — A117

Designs: 5fr, Home industries. 10fr, Smith, horiz. 15fr, Women carrying burdens.

Perf. 13x13½, 13½x13
1972, Feb. 18 Litho.
534 A117 2fr multicolored .15 .15
535 A117 5fr black, org & red .15 .15
536 A117 10fr multicolored .15 .15
537 A117 15fr multicolored .20 .15
Set value .45 .25

Youth Day 1972.

Soccer Players and Field A118

Designs: 20fr, African Soccer Cup, vert. 45fr, Team captains shaking hands, vert.

1972, Feb. 22 *Perf. 13½*
538 A118 20fr gray & multi .15 .15
539 A118 40fr gray & multi .35 .20
540 A118 45fr yellow & multi .40 .25
Nos. 538-540 (3) .90 .60

African Soccer Cup, Yaoundé, Feb. 23-Mar. 5.

Government Building, Yaoundé, and Laurel A119

1972, Apr. 6 Photo. *Perf. 12½x12*
541 A119 40fr multicolored .22 .15

110th session of Inter-Parliamentary Council, Yaoundé, Apr. 1972.

"Fantasia," North Cameroun A120

Bororo Woman — A121

Design: 40fr, Boat on Wouri River and Mt. Cameroun.

Perf. 13x12½, 12½x13
1972, Apr. 24
542 A120 15fr dk vio & multi .16 .15
543 A121 20fr multicolored .16 .15
544 A120 40fr multicolored .25 .15
Nos. 542-544 (3) .57
Set value .30

Chemical Apparatus A122

1972, May 15 Engr. *Perf. 13*
545 A122 40fr lilac, red & grn .22 .15

President Ahmadou Ahidjo Prize.

United Republic

Solanum Macranthum A123

Design: 45fr, Wax plant.

1972, July 20 Photo. *Perf. 13*
546 A123 40fr multicolored .25 .15
547 A123 45fr yellow & multi .28 .15

Charaxes Ameliae A124

Design: 45fr, Papilio tynderaeus.

1972, Aug. 20 Photo. *Perf. 13*
548 A124 40fr bl, dk bl & gold .35 .16
549 A124 45fr lt grn, blk & gold .38 .20

No. 468 Surcharged

40 F

1972, Aug. 30 Photo. *Perf. 12x12½*
550 A85 40fr on 30fr multicolored .25 .15

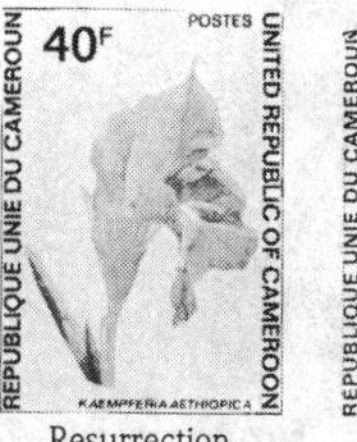
Resurrection Lily — A125

Great Blue Touraco — A126

Flowers: 45fr, Candlestick cassia. 50fr, Amaryllis.

1972, Sept. 16 *Perf. 13*
551 A125 40fr lt green & multi .25 .15
552 A125 45fr multicolored .30 .16
553 A125 50fr lt blue & multi .38 .20
Nos. 551-553 (3) .93 .51

Perf. 12½x13, 13x12½
1972, Nov. 20 Litho.

Design: 45fr, Red-faced lovebirds, horiz.

554 A126 10fr yellow & multi .15 .15
555 A126 45fr yellow & multi .30 .15
Set value .20

Cotton (North) — A127

Designs: 10fr, Cacao (south central). 15fr, Logging (southeast and southern coast). 20fr, Coffee (west). 45fr, Tea (northwest and southwest).

1973, Mar. 26 Photo. *Perf. 12½x13*
556 A127 5fr black & multi .15 .15
557 A127 10fr black & multi .15 .15
558 A127 15fr black & multi .15 .15
559 A127 20fr black & multi .15 .15
560 A127 45fr black & multi .30 .15
Set value .60 .40

Third 5-Year Plan.
For surcharge see No. 568.

Flag and Map of Cameroun, Pres. Ahidjo and No. 331 — A128

Design: 20fr, Proclamation of independence, Pres. Ahidjo and No. 336.

1973, May 20 Engr. *Perf. 13*
561 A128 10fr ultra & multi .15 .15
562 A128 20fr multicolored .15 .15
Set value .20 .15

First anniversary of the United Republic of Cameroun. See Nos. C200-C201.

Bamoun Mask — A129

Dr. Hansen — A130

Designs: Various Bamoun masks.

1973, July 10 Engr. *Perf. 13*
563 A129 5fr green, brn & blk .15 .15
564 A129 10fr lilac, brn & blk .15 .15
565 A129 45fr red, brn & blk .25 .15
566 A129 100fr ultra, brn & blk .55 .35
Set value .90 .60

1973, July 25 Engr. *Perf. 13*
567 A130 45fr multicolored .25 .15

Centenary of the discovery by Dr. Armauer G. Hansen of the Hansen bacillus, the cause of leprosy.

No. 556 Surcharged with New Value, 2 Bars, and Overprinted in Ultramarine: "SECHERESSE/SOLIDARITE AFRICAINE"

1973, Aug. 16 Photo. *Perf. 12½x13*
568 A127 100fr on 5fr multicolored .55 .40

African solidarity in drought emergency.

Dancers, South West Africa — A131

WMO Emblem — A132

Designs: Southwest African dances.

1973, Aug. 17 *Perf. 13*
569 A131 10fr multicolored .15 .15
570 A131 25fr multicolored .15 .15
571 A131 45fr multicolored .30 .15
Set value .50 .30

1973, Sept. 1 Engr. *Perf. 13*
572 A132 45fr green & ultra .25 .16

Cent. of intl. meteorological cooperation.

Garoua Party Headquarters — A133

1973, Sept. 1 Photo.
573 A133 40fr multicolored .25 .16

7th anniv. of Cameroun National Union.

African Postal Union Issue, 1973
Common Design Type

1973, Sept. 12 Engr.
574 CD137 100fr brt bl, bl & sl grn .60 .40

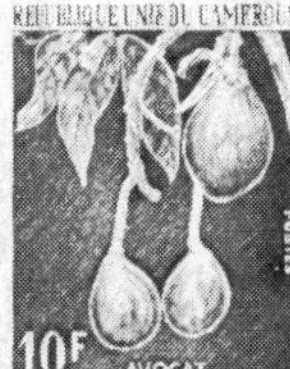
Avocados — A135

1973, Sept. 20

575 A135 10fr shown .15 .15
576 A135 20fr Mangos .20 .15
577 A135 45fr Plums .30 .15
578 A135 50fr Custard apple .45 .20
Nos. 575-578 (4) 1.10
Set value .45

Kirdi Village A136

Views: 45fr, Mabas village. 50fr, Fishing village.

1973, Oct. 25 **Engr.** ***Perf. 13***

579 A136 15fr black, bis & grn .15 .15
580 A136 45fr magenta, brn & org .30 .16
581 A136 50fr green, blk & org .35 .20
Nos. 579-581 (3) .80 .51

Handshake on Map of Africa — A137

1974, May 15 **Engr.** ***Perf. 12½x13***

582 A137 40fr carmine & multi .22 .15
583 A137 45fr indigo & multi .25 .15

Organization for African Unity, 10th anniv.

Spinning Mill — A138

1974, May 25 **Engr.** ***Perf. 13x12½***

584 A138 45fr multicolored .25 .16

CICAM Industrial Complex.

Carved Panel from Bilinga A139

Cameroun Art (Carvings): 40fr, Detail from Bubinga chair. 45fr, Detail Acajou Ngollon panel.

1974, May 30

585 A139 10fr brt grn & ocher .15 .15
586 A139 40fr red & brown .22 .15
587 A139 45fr blue & rose brn .25 .16
Nos. 585-587 (3) .62
Set value .35

Zebu — A140

1974, June 1 ***Perf. 13½***

588 A140 40fr multicolored .22 .15

North Cameroun cattle raising. See No. C210.

Laying Rail Section A141

Designs: 5fr, Map showing line Yaoundé to Ngaoundéré, vert. 40fr, Welding rail joint, vert. 100fr, Train on Djerem River Bridge.

Perf. 12½x13, 13x12½

1974, June 10 **Engr.**

589 A141 5fr multicolored .15 .15
590 A141 20fr multicolored .15 .15
591 A141 40fr multicolored .20 .15
592 A141 100fr multicolored .50 .45
Nos. 589-592 (4) 1.00
Set value .70

Opening of Yaoundé-Ngaoundéré railroad line. For surcharge see No. 596.

No. 466 Surcharged

1974, June 1 **Photo.** ***Perf. 12x12½***

593 A85 40fr on 8fr multi .25 .15

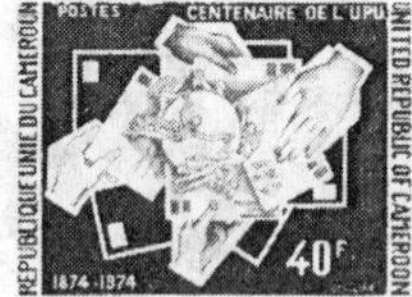

UPU Emblem, Hands Holding Letters A142

1974, Oct. 8 **Engr.** ***Perf. 13***

594 A142 40fr multicolored .20 .15

Cent. of the UPU. See Nos. C218-C219.

Presidents and Flags of Cameroun, CAR, Congo, Gabon and Meeting Center — A143

1974, Dec. 8 **Photo.** ***Perf. 13***

595 A143 40fr gold & multi .22 .15

10th anniversary of Central African Customs and Economic Union (Union Douanière et Economique de l'Afrique Centrale, UDEAC). See No. C223.

=100F

No. 589 Surcharged in Violet Blue

10 DECEMBRE
1974

1974, Dec. 10 **Engr.** ***Perf. 12½x13***

596 A141 100fr on 5fr multi .55 .45

Virgin of Autun, 15th Century Sculpture A144

Christmas: 45fr, Virgin and Child, by Luis de Morales (c. 1509-1586).

1974, Dec. 20 **Photo.** ***Perf. 13***

597 A144 40fr gold & multi .22 .16
598 A144 45fr gold & multi .25 .20

Tropical Plants — A145

1975, Mar. 10 **Photo.** ***Perf. 13***

599 A145 5fr Cockscomb .15 .15
600 A145 40fr Costus spectabilis .25 .15
601 A145 45fr Mussaenda erythrophylla .25 .16
Set value .55 .35

Fishing by Night — A146

1975, Apr. 1 **Engr.** ***Perf. 13***

602 A146 40fr shown .22 .15
603 A146 45fr Fishing by day .25 .16

Afo Akom Statue and Chief's Stool — A147

Tree Fungus — A148

1975, Apr. 1 **Photo.**

604 A147 40fr multicolored .20 .15
605 A147 45fr multicolored .22 .15
606 A147 200fr multicolored 1.10 .75
Nos. 604-606 (3) 1.52 1.05

1975, Apr. 14

607 A148 15fr shown .15 .15
608 A148 40fr Chrysalis .25 .15
Set value .20

Ministry of Posts and Telecommunications — A149

1975, July 21 **Engr.** ***Perf. 13***

609 A149 40fr brn, grn & Prus bl .22 .16
610 A149 45fr Prus bl, brn & grn .25 .20

Presbyterian Church, Elat — A150

Designs: No. 612, Foumban Mosque. 45fr, Catholic Church, Ngaoundere.

1975, Aug. 20 **Engr.** ***Perf. 13***

611 A150 40fr multicolored .20 .15
612 A150 40fr multicolored .20 .15
613 A150 45fr multicolored .25 .16
Nos. 611-613 (3) .65 .46

Plowing A151

Design: No. 615, Corn harvest, vert.

Perf. 13x12½, 12½x13

1975, Dec. 15 **Photo.**

614 A151 40fr deep green & multi .20 .15
615 A151 40fr deep green & multi .20 .15

Green revolution.

Zamengoe Satellite Monitoring Station — A152

1976, May 20 **Litho.** ***Perf. 13***

616 A152 40fr shown .20 .16
617 A152 100fr Radar, vert. .60 .40

Porcelain Rose — A153

Design: 50fr, Flower of North Cameroun.

1976, July 20 **Litho.** ***Perf. 12½***

618 A153 40fr multicolored .20 .15
619 A153 50fr multicolored .25 .16

Leopard Dance — A154

Telephone Exchange — A155

1976, Sept. 15 **Litho.** ***Perf. 12***

620 A154 40fr gray & multi .20 .16

See Nos. C233-C234.

1976, Oct. 5 ***Perf. 13***

621 A155 50fr multicolored .30 .20

Centenary of first telephone call by Alexander Graham Bell, Mar. 10, 1876.

Young Men Building House — A156

Design: 45fr, Young women working in field.

1976, Oct. 10 **Litho.** ***Perf. 12***

622 A156 40fr multicolored .20 .16
623 A156 45fr multicolored .25 .16

10th National Youth Day.

Konrad Adenauer (1876-1967), German Chancellor, Cologne Cathedral — A157

1976, Oct. 20

624 A157 100fr multicolored .60 .40

Party Headquarters, Douala — A158

Design: No. 626, Party Headquarters, Yaoundé.

1976, Dec. 28 Litho. *Perf. 12*

625 A158 50fr orange & multi .25 .20
626 A158 50fr blue & multi .25 .20

10th anniv. of the Cameroun National Union.

Bamoun Copper Pipe — A159

Ostrich — A160

1977, Feb. 4 Litho. *Perf. 12½*

627 A159 50fr multicolored .25 .20

2nd World Black and African Festival, Lagos, Nigeria, Jan. 15-Feb. 12. See No. C239.

1977, Mar. 20 Litho. *Perf. 12*

628 A160 30fr shown .16 .15
629 A160 50fr Crowned cranes .25 .16

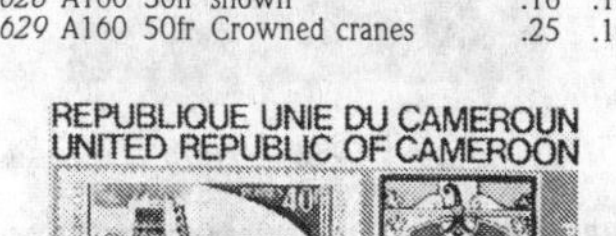

Cameroun No. 609 and Switzerland No. 3L1 — A161

1977, June 5 Litho. *Perf. 12*

630 A161 50fr multicolored .25 .20

Jufilex Philatelic Exhibition, Bern, Switzerland. See Nos. C252-C253.

Winter Olympics 1976, set of five, 40, 50fr, airmail 140, 200, 350fr, and airmail souv. sheet, 500fr, issued Aug. 10, 1977. Nos. 7701-7706.

Apollo-Soyuz, set of five, 40, 60fr, airmail 100, 250, 350fr, and airmail souv. sheet, 500fr, issued Aug. 10, 1977. Nos. 7707-7712.

No. 617 Overprinted in French and English in Red: "To the Welfare of the / families of martyrs and / freedom fighters of Palestine."

1977, Aug. 22 Litho. *Perf. 13*

635 A152 100fr multicolored .60 .40

Palestinian fighters and their families.

Chairman Mao and Great Wall — A164

1977, Sept. 9 Engr. *Perf. 13*

636 A164 100fr olive & brown .60 .40

Mao Tse-tung (1893-1976), Chinese communist leader, first death anniversary.

Nativity, by Albrecht Altdorfer A165

Design: 50fr, Madonna of the Grand Duke, by Raphael.

1977, Dec. 15 Litho. *Perf. 12½x12*

637 A165 30fr multicolored .16 .15
638 A165 50fr multicolored .25 .20

Christmas 1977. See Nos. C264-C265.

Gazelle and Rotary Emblem — A166

Pres. Ahidjo, Flag and Map of Cameroun — A167

1978, Feb. 11 Litho. *Perf. 12*

639 A166 50fr orange & multi .25 .20

Rotary Club of Yaounde, 20th anniversary.

1978, Apr. 3 Litho. *Perf. 12½*

640 A167 50fr multicolored .25 .15

New flag of Cameroun. See No. C266.

Cardioglossa Escalerae A168

Design: 60fr, Cardioglossa elegans.

1978, Apr. 5

641 A168 50fr multicolored .25 .16
642 A168 60fr multicolored .35 .22

See No. C267.

Jules Verne and "From Earth to Moon" — A169

1978, Oct. 10 Litho. *Perf. 12*

643 A169 250fr multicolored 1.60 1.40

Jules Verne (1828-1905), science fiction writer, birth sesquicentennial. See No. C276.

Hypolimnas Salmacis Drury — A170

Butterflies: 25fr, Euxanthe trajanus ward. 30fr, Euphaedra cyparissa cramer.

1978, Oct. 15

644 A170 20fr multicolored .15 .15
645 A170 25fr multicolored .16 .15
646 A170 30fr multicolored .20 .15
Nos. 644-646 (3) .51 .45

Men Planting Seedlings — A171

Carved Bamun Drum — A172

1978, Oct. 30 *Perf. 12½*

647 A171 10fr multicolored .15 .15
648 A171 15fr multicolored .15 .15
Set value .20 .15

Green barrier against the desert.

1978, Nov. 20 Litho. *Perf. 12½*

Design: 60fr, String instrument (Gueguerou) horiz.

649 A172 50fr multicolored .35 .20
650 A172 60fr multicolored .40 .25

See No. C277.

Pres. Ahidjo, Giscard D'Estaing, Flags of Cameroun and France — A173

1979, Feb. 8 Photo. *Perf. 13*

651 A173 60fr multicolored .40 .25

Visit of Pres. Valery Giscard D'Estaing of France to Cameroun.

Human Rights Emblem, Globe, Scroll and African — A174

1979, Feb. 11 Litho. *Perf. 12x12½*

652 A174 5fr multicolored .15 .15

Universal Declaration of Human Rights, 30th anniversary (in 1978). See No. C278.
See No. 803.

Boy and Girl Greeting Sun — A175

1979, Aug. 15 Litho. *Perf. 12*

653 A175 50fr multicolored .35 .20

International Year of the Child.

Protected Animals A176

Nos. 655, 658 vert.

1979, Sept. 20 *Perf. 12½*

654 A176 50fr Rhinoceros .35 .20
655 A176 60fr Giraffe .40 .25
656 A176 60fr Gorilla .40 .25
657 A176 100fr Leopard .65 .40
658 A176 100fr Elephant .65 .40
Nos. 654-658 (5) 2.45 1.50

Eugene Jamot, Map of Cameroun, Tsetse Fly — A177

1979, Nov. 5 Engr. *Perf. 13*

659 A177 50fr multicolored .35 .20

Eugene Jamot (1879-1937), discoverer of sleeping sickness cure.

Annunciation, by Fra Filippo Lippi — A178

Paintings; 50fr, Rest During the Flight to Egypt, c. 1620. No. 622, Flight into Egypt, by Jan Joest, No. 663, Nativity, by Joest. 100fr, Nativity, by Botticelli.

1979, Dec. 6 Litho. *Perf. 12½x12*

660 A178 10fr multicolored .15 .15
661 A178 50fr multicolored .38 .22
662 A178 60fr multicolored .42 .30
663 A178 60fr multicolored .42 .30
a. Pair, #662-663 .85 .65
664 A178 100fr multicolored .70 .42
Nos. 660-664 (5) 2.07 1.39

Christmas 1979.

Piper Capense A179

Medicinal Plants: 60fr, Bracken fern.

1979, Dec. 15 Litho. *Perf. 12½*

665 A179 50fr multicolored .35 .20
666 A179 60fr multicolored .40 .25

Pres. Ahidjo, Cameroun Map, Arms and No. 331 — A180

1980, Feb. 12 Litho. *Perf. 12½*

667 A180 50fr multicolored .35 .20

Independence, 20th anniversary.

Congress Building, Bafoussam A181

1980, Feb. 12

668 A181 50fr multicolored .35 .20

Cameroun National Union, 3rd Ordinary Congress, Bafoussam, Feb. 12-17.

Rotary Emblem, Map of Cameroun — A182

Rotary Intl., 75th Anniv.: #670, Anniv. emblem.

1980, Mar. 15 Litho. *Perf. 12½*

669 A182 200fr multicolored 1.40 .80
670 A182 200fr multicolored 1.40 .80
a. Souvenir sheet of 2, #669-670 2.75 1.60

Voacanga Medicinal Beans A183

1980, Dec. 3 Litho. *Perf. 12½*

671 A183 50fr shown .35 .20
672 A183 60fr Voacanga tree, vert. .40 .25
673 A183 100fr Voacanga flower, vert. .65 .40
Nos. 671-673 (3) 1.40 .85

Violet Mellowstone A184

1980, Dec. 5

674 A184 50fr shown .40 .20
675 A184 60fr Patula .45 .25
676 A184 100fr Cashmere bouquet .80 .40
Nos. 674-676 (3) 1.65 .85

Occupation of Mecca by Mohammed, 1350th Anniversary — A185

1980, Dec. 9

677 A185 50fr multicolored .50 .30

African Slender-snouted Crocodile (Endangered Species) — A186

1980, Dec. 24

678 A186 200fr shown 1.60 .80
679 A186 300fr Buffon's antelope, vert. 2.00 1.20

Bororo Girls and Roumsiki Peaks — A187

1980, Dec. 29

680 A187 50fr shown .35 .20
681 A187 60fr Dschang tourist center .40 .25

Banana Tree A188

1981, Feb. 5

682 A188 50fr shown .50 .30
683 A188 60fr Cattle, vert. .60 .40

Girl on Crutches — A189

1981, Feb. 20 Litho. *Perf. 12½*

684 A189 60fr shown .40 .25
685 A189 150fr Boy in motorized wheelchair 1.00 .65

International Year of the Disabled.

Air Terminal, Douala Airport — A190

1981, Apr. 4 Litho. *Perf. 12½*

686 A190 100fr shown .75 .55
687 A190 200fr Boeing 747 1.65 1.10
688 A190 300fr Douala Intl. Airport 2.50 1.65
Nos. 686-688 (3) 4.90 3.30

Cameroun Airlines, 10th anniv.

Pres. Ahidjo Presenting Trophy to Canon Soccer Team — A191

1981, Apr. 20

689 A191 60fr shown .60 .40
690 A191 60fr Union team captain .60 .40

1979 African Soccer Cup champions.

Scaly Anteater A192

Designs: Endangered species.

1981, July 20 Litho. *Perf. 12½*

691 A192 50fr Moutourou .35 .20
692 A192 50fr Tortoise .35 .20
693 A192 100fr shown .65 .40
Nos. 691-693 (3) 1.35 .80

Prince Charles and Lady Diana, St. Paul's Cathedral — A193

1981, July 29 Litho. *Perf. 12½*

694 A193 500fr shown 3.00 2.00
695 A193 500fr Couple, royal coach 3.00 2.00
a. Souvenir sheet of 2, #694-695 6.00 4.00

Royal wedding.

Bafoussam-Bamenda Highway — A194

1981, Sept. 10 Litho. *Perf. 12½*

696 A194 50fr multicolored .35 .20

Freighter Cam Iroko (Cameroun Shipping Line) A195

1981, Sept. 25

697 A195 60fr multicolored .60 .40

20th Anniv. of Reunification A196

1981, Oct. 10 *Perf. 12½x13*

698 A196 50fr multicolored .35 .20

Medicinal Plants — A197

1981, Dec. 31 Litho. *Perf. 12½*

699 A197 60fr Voacanga thouarsii .40 .25
700 A197 70fr Cassia alata .45 .30

Easter 1982 — A198

Paintings: 100fr, Christ in the Garden of Olives, by Delacroix. 200fr, Descent from the Cross, by Giotto. 250fr, Pieta in the Countryside, by Bellini.

1982, Apr. 10 Litho. *Perf. 13*

701 A198 100fr multicolored .55 .35
702 A198 200fr multicolored 1.00 .65
703 A198 250fr multicolored 1.40 .90
Nos. 701-703 (3) 2.95 1.90

PHILEXFRANCE '82 Stamp Exhibition, Paris, June 11-21 — A199

1982, Apr. 25 *Perf. 12*

704 A199 90fr multicolored .60 .40

Snakeskin Handbag — A200

1982, Apr. 30 *Perf. 12½*

705 A200 60fr shown .40 .25
706 A200 70fr Clay water jug .45 .35

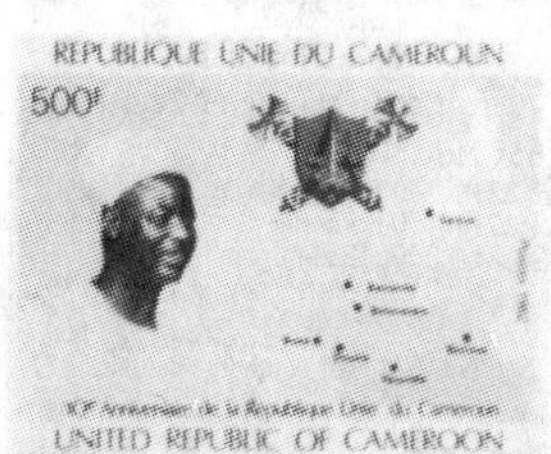

10th Anniv. of Republic — A201

1982, May 20 *Perf. 13*

707 A201 500fr multicolored 3.50 2.00

Town Hall, Douala — A202

1982, June 15 Litho. *Perf. 12½*

708 A202 40fr shown .25 .20
709 A202 60fr Yaounde .40 .25

See Nos. 730-731, 757-758, 790-791, 867.

1982 World Cup — A203

1982, July 10 *Perf. 13*

710 A203 100fr Natl. team .65 .42
711 A203 200fr Semi-finalists 1.40 .80
712 A203 300fr Players, vert. 2.00 1.25
713 A203 400fr Natl. team 2nd lineup 2.50 1.60
a. Souvenir sheet of 2, #713 6.00 3.50
Nos. 710-713 (4) 6.55 4.07

Partridge — A204

1982 *Perf. 12½x13*

714 A204 10fr shown .15 .15
715 A204 15fr Turtle dove .15 .15
716 A204 20fr Swallow .15 .15
717 A204 200fr Bongo antelope 1.40 .80
718 A204 300fr Black colobus 2.00 1.25
Nos. 714-718 (5) 3.85 2.50

Issued: 200fr, 300fr, July 20; others Aug. 10.
See No. 804.

Scouting Year — A205

1982, Sept. 30 Litho. *Perf. 13x12½*

719 A205 200fr Campfire 1.10 .80
720 A205 400fr Baden-Powell 2.25 1.60

25th Anniv. of the Presbyterian Church in Cameroun A206

Perf. 13x12½, 12½x13

1982, Oct. 30

721 A206 45fr Buea Chapel .22 .15
722 A206 60fr Nyasoso Chapel, vert. .30 .20

ITU Plenipotentiaries Conference, Nairobi, Sept. — A207

1982, Oct. 5 Litho. *Perf. 12½x13*

723 A207 70fr multicolored .35 .22

Italy's Victory in 1982 World Cup — A208

1982, Nov. *Perf. 13*

724 A208 500fr multicolored 4.00 2.00
725 A208 1000fr multicolored 7.00 4.00

30th Anniv. of Customs Cooperation Council — A209

1983, Jan. 10 *Perf. 12½x13*

726 A209 250fr Emblem 1.40 .80
727 A209 250fr Headquarters, Brussels 1.40 .80

2nd Yaoundé Medical Conference — A210

1983, Jan. 23 Litho. *Perf. 13*

728 A210 60fr grn & multi .45 .20
729 A210 70fr brn & multi .55 .22

City Hall Type of 1982

1983, Feb. 25 Litho. *Perf. 12½*

730 A202 60fr Bafoussam .40 .25
731 A202 70fr Garoua .45 .30

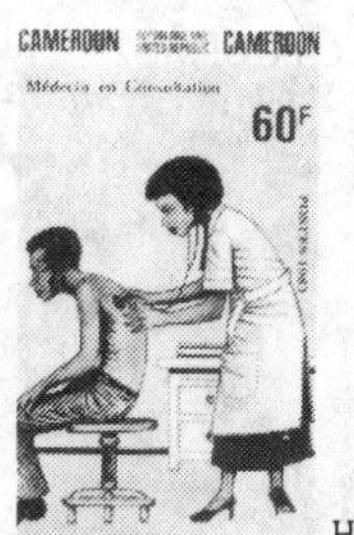

Homage to Women — A211

1983, Apr. 25 Litho. *Perf. 12½*

733 A211 60fr Nurse .40 .20
734 A211 70fr Lawyer .45 .22

11th Anniv. of Independence — A212

Flag and Pres. Paul Biya.

1983, May 18 Litho. *Perf. 13*

735 A212 60fr dk grn & multi .40 .25
736 A212 70fr dk bl & multi .45 .30

25th Anniv. of Intl. Maritime Org. — A213

1983, May 23 *Perf. 13x12½*

737 A213 500fr multicolored 2.50 1.50

Eagle — A214

1983, June 15 Litho. *Perf. 12½x13*

738 A214 25fr shown .16 .15
739 A214 30fr Sparrowhawk .20 .15
740 A214 50fr Purple heron .35 .20
Nos. 738-740 (3) .71 .50

See Nos. 798-800, 873, 882, 886.

A215

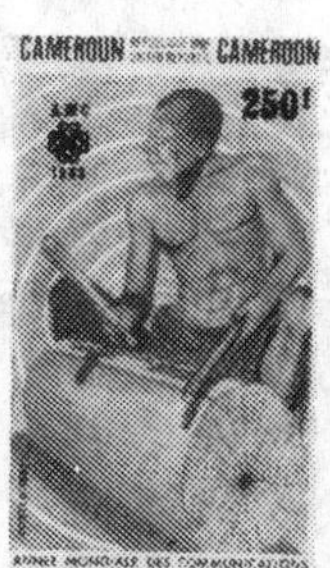

A216

1983, July 25 Litho. *Perf. 12*

741 A215 60fr Pearl mask, by Wery-Nwen-Nto, 1899 .40 .25
742 A215 70fr Basket with lid .45 .30

1983, Aug. 20 Litho. *Perf. 12*

743 A216 90fr Mobile Post Office, horiz .30 .20
744 A216 150fr Telegraph Operator .50 .35
745 A216 250fr Tom-tom .80 .55
Nos. 743-745 (3) 1.60 1.10

World Communications Year.

Endangered Species — A217

1983, Sept. 22 *Perf. 12*

746 A217 200fr Civet Cat .80 .42
747 A217 200fr Gorilla, vert .80 .42
748 A217 350fr Cobaya, vert 1.40 .80
Nos. 746-748 (3) 3.00 1.64

See No. 887.

Lake Tizon A218

1983, Nov. 25 Litho. *Perf. 13*

749 A218 60fr shown .20 .15
750 A218 70fr Mt. Cameroon .22 .16

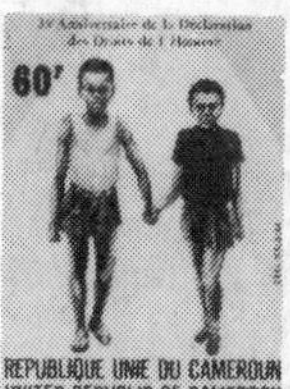

Human Rights Declaration, 35th Anniv — A219

1983, Dec. 20 Litho. *Perf. 12½x13*

751 A219 60fr multicolored .20 .15
752 A219 70fr multicolored .22 .16

Christmas 1983 — A220

Designs: 60fr, Christmas tree. 200fr, Stained glass window, Yaoundé Cathedral. No. 755, Rest during Flight into Egypt, by Philipp Otto Runge. No. 756, Angel of the Annunciation. 60fr, 200fr, No. 756 vert.

1983, Dec. 20 Litho. *Perf. 12½*

753 A220 60fr multicolored .22 .15
754 A220 200fr multicolored .80 .50
755 A220 500fr multicolored 2.00 1.20

756 A220 500fr multicolored 2.00 1.20
a. Souvenir sheet of 3, #754-756 5.00 3.25
Nos. 753-756 (4) 5.02 3.05

City Hall Type of 1982

1984, Apr. 20 Litho. *Perf. 12½*
757 A202 60fr Bamenda .30 .20
758 A202 70fr Mbalmayo .35 .22

Catholic Church, Zoetele — A221

1984, July 25 Litho. *Perf. 13*
759 A221 60fr shown .30 .22
760 A221 70fr Protestant Church, Yaounde .35 .25

Endangered Species — A222

1984, Aug. 15
761 A222 250fr Wild pig 1.00 .65
762 A222 250fr Deer 1.00 .65

1984, Oct. 10 Litho. *Perf. 13½*
763 A222 60fr Nightingale .18 .15
764 A222 60fr Vultures .18 .15

See No. 883.

Bamenda Farming Fair — A223

1984, Dec. 10 Litho. *Perf. 13*
765 A223 60fr Corn .28 .20
766 A223 70fr Cattle .32 .22
767 A223 300fr Potatoes 1.35 .90
Nos. 765-767 (3) 1.95 1.32

International Civil Aviation Organization, 40th Anniv. — A224

1984, Dec. 20 Litho. *Perf. 12½*
768 A224 200fr Icarus .90 .60
769 A224 200fr ICAO emblem, vert. .90 .60
770 A224 300fr Boeing 747 1.35 .90
771 A224 300fr Solar Princess painting 1.35 .90
Nos. 768-771 (4) 4.50 3.00

Olymphilex '85, Lausanne — A225

Wmk. CARTOR

1985, Apr. 5 Photo. *Perf. 13*
772 A225 150fr Wrestlers, exhibition emblem .42 .42

Domestic Musical Instruments — A226

1985, Apr. 23 *Perf. 13½*
773 A226 60fr Balafons (xylophone) .16 .16
774 A226 70fr Guitar .20 .20
775 A226 100fr Flute .28 .28
Nos. 773-775 (3) .64 .64

INTELSAT Org., 20th Anniv. — A227

1985, May 8 *Perf. 13*
776 A227 125fr Intelsat V .35 .35
777 A227 200fr Intelcam, Yaounde .60 .60

New York Headquarters A228

1985, May 30
778 A228 250fr multicolored 1.10 1.10
779 A228 500fr multicolored 2.25 2.25

UN, 40th anniv.

Pres. Mitterand, Biya — A229

1985, June 20
780 A229 60fr multicolored .20 .20
781 A229 70fr multicolored .22 .22

Visit of Pres. Mitterand of France.

UNICEF A230

UN Infant Survival Campaign A231

1985, July 15
782 A230 60fr multicolored .20 .20
783 A231 300fr multicolored 1.00 1.00

Visit of Pope John Paul II, Aug. 10-14 — A232

1985, Aug. 9 *Perf. 13x12½*
784 A232 60fr Pope, papal arms .20 .20
785 A232 70fr Pope, crosier .22 .22

Size: 55x38mm

786 A232 200fr Pres. Biya, John Paul II .70 .70
a. Souv. sheet of 3, #784-786 1.25 1.25
Nos. 784-786 (3) 1.12 1.12

Landscapes — A233

1985, July 25 Litho. *Perf. 12½*
787 A233 60fr Lake Barumbi, Kumba .16 .16
788 A233 70fr Bonando Pygmy Village, Doume .18 .18
789 A233 150fr Cameroun River .40 .40
Nos. 787-789 (3) .74 .74

City Hall Type of 1982

1985, July 30
790 A202 60fr Ngaoundere .16 .16
791 A202 60fr D'Ebolowa .16 .16

Wildlife — A234 Wood Sculptures — A235

1985, Aug. 20 *Perf. 13½*
792 A234 125fr Porcupine .38 .38
793 A234 200fr Squirrel .60 .60
794 A234 350fr Hedgehog 1.10 1.10
Nos. 792-794 (3) 2.08 2.08

1985, Sept. 15
795 A235 60fr Mask .20 .20
796 A235 70fr Mask, diff. .22 .22
797 A235 100fr Wood bas-relief, horiz. .30 .30
Nos. 795-797 (3) .72 .72

Bird Type of 1983
Inscribed Republic of Cameroon

1985, Nov. 10
798 A214 140fr Toucans .50 .50
799 A214 150fr Rooster .55 .55
800 A214 200fr Red-throated bee-eater .70 .70
Nos. 798-800 (3) 1.75 1.75

See No. 873. For surcharge see No. 871.

American Peace Corps in Cameroun, 25th Anniv. — A237

1986, Jan. 1 Litho. *Perf. 12½*
801 A237 70fr multicolored .38 .38
802 A237 100fr multicolored .55 .55

Stamps of 1979-1982 Redrawn

1986, Mar. *Perf. 13, 13½*
803 A174 5fr multicolored .15 .15
804 A204 10fr multicolored .15 .15
Set value .15 .15

Nos. 803-804 inscribed "Republic of Cameroon" instead of "United Republic of Cameroon."

Easter — A238 Insects — A239

Paintings: 210fr, Head of the Virgin, by Pierre-Paul Prud'Hon (1758-1823). 350fr, The Stoning of St. Steven, by Van Scorel (1495-1562).

1986, Apr. 15 *Perf. 13½*
805 A238 210fr multicolored 1.15 1.15
806 A238 350fr multicolored 1.90 1.90

1986, Apr. 20
807 A239 70fr Honeybee .38 .38
808 A239 70fr Dragonfly .38 .38
809 A239 100fr Grasshopper .55 .55
Nos. 807-809 (3) 1.31 1.31

Nos. 808-809 horiz.

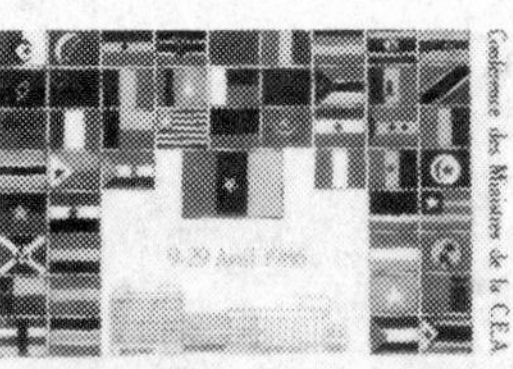

Flags, Conference Center — A240

1986, Apr. 25 Litho. *Perf. 13*
810 A240 100fr Map, vert. .55 .55
811 A240 175fr shown .95 .95

Conference of Ministers of the Economic Commission for Africa, Apr. 9-29.

Statues — A241

1986, July 5 **Litho.** *Perf. 13½*

812 A241 70fr Bronze earth mother .40 .40
813 A241 100fr Wood funerary figure .60 .60
814 A241 130fr Wood equestrian figure .80 .80
Nos. 812-814 (3) 1.80 1.80

Queen Elizabeth II, 60th Birthday — A242

1986, July 15 **Litho.** *Perf. 13*

815 A242 100fr Elizabeth .60 .60
816 A242 175fr Elizabeth, Pres. Biya 1.10 1.10
817 A242 210fr Elizabeth, diff. 1.25 1.25
Nos. 815-817 (3) 2.95 2.95

Natl. Democratic Party, 1st Anniv. — A243

1986, July 25 *Perf. 12½*

818 A243 70fr Party headquarters, Bamenda .40 .40
819 A243 70fr Pres. Biya, vert. .40 .40
820 A243 100fr Presidential address, vert. .60 .60
Nos. 818-820 (3) 1.40 1.40

Kwem Mask Dancers of the Northeast — A244

1986, Aug. 1 *Perf. 13½*

821 A244 100fr multicolored .60 .60
822 A244 130fr multicolored .80 .80

Endangered Species A245

1986, Aug. 20

823 A245 300fr Varanus niloticus 1.75 1.75
824 A245 300fr Panthera pardus 1.75 1.75

For surcharge see No. 872.

A246 A247

Intl. Peace Year: 175fr, 200fr, Desmond Tutu, South Africa, Nobel Peace Prize winner. 250fr, UN and IPY emblems.

1986, Sept. 7 **Litho.** *Perf. 13½*

825 A246 175fr multicolored 1.10 1.10
826 A246 200fr multicolored 1.25 1.25
827 A246 250fr multicolored 1.50 1.50
Nos. 825-827 (3) 3.85 3.85

1986, Oct. 30 **Litho.** *Perf. 13½*

828 A247 70fr multicolored .40 .40

Natl. Fed. of Associations for the Handicapped.

A248 A249

1986, Nov. 9

829 A248 70fr Family under umbrella .40 .40
830 A248 100fr Child immunization .55 .55

African Vaccination Year.

1986, Dec. 20 **Litho.** *Perf. 13½*

831 A249 70fr Afforestation map .40 .40
832 A249 100fr Hands, seedling .55 .55

Arbor Day.

Agricultural Development — A250

1986, Dec. 24

833 A250 70fr ONCPB seminar .40 .40
834 A250 70fr Coconut farming, Dibombari .40 .40
835 A250 200fr Pineapple farm 1.10 1.10
Nos. 833-835 (3) 1.90 1.90

Insects Destructive to Agriculture A251

1987, Sept. 25 **Litho.** *Perf. 13½*

836 A251 70fr Antestiopsis lineaticollis intricata .50 .50
837 A251 100fr Distantiella theobroma .72 .72

4th African Games, Nairobi — A252

1987, Oct. 1 *Perf. 12½*

838 A252 100fr Shot put .72 .72
839 A252 140fr Pole vault 1.00 1.00

Maroua Agricultural Show — A253

1988, Jan. 6

840 A253 70fr Millet field .50 .50
841 A253 100fr Cotton .72 .72
842 A253 150fr Cattle 1.10 1.10
Nos. 840-842 (3) 2.32 2.32

World Wildlife Fund — A254

Baboons, *Papio leucophaeus.*

1988, Apr. 25 **Litho.** *Perf. 13*

843 A254 30fr Adult .22 .22
844 A254 40fr Adult grooming young .30 .30
845 A254 70fr Baboon on branch .50 .50
846 A254 100fr Adult carrying young .72 .72
Nos. 843-846 (4) 1.74 1.74

Interparliamentary Union, Cent. — A255

1989 **Litho.** *Perf. 13½*

847 A255 50fr Natl. Assembly .32 .32

World Cup Soccer Championships, Italy — A256

1990, Oct. 27 **Litho.** *Perf. 11½*

Granite Paper

848 A256 200fr shown 1.15 1.15
849 A256 250fr Players, diff. 1.45 1.45
850 A256 250fr Goalkeeper, flags 1.45 1.45
851 A256 300fr Team 1.70 1.70
a. Souv. sheet of 4, #848-851 7.60 7.60
Nos. 848-851 (4) 5.75 5.75

Roger Milla, World Cup Soccer Player — A257

1990, July 4 **Litho.** *Perf. 11½*

Granite Paper

852 A257 500fr multicolored 4.00 4.00
a. Souv. sheet of 1 4.00 4.00

Agriculture A258

Designs: 70fr, Treating cacao plants. 100fr, Sheep.

1990, Dec. 1 **Litho.** *Perf. 13½*

853 A258 70fr multicolored .55 .55
854 A258 100fr multicolored .80 .80
a. Sheet of 2, #853-854, perf. 12½ 1.35 1.35

For surcharge see No. 894.

UN Development Program, 40th Anniv. A259

1990, Dec. 31 **Litho.** *Perf. 13½*

855 A259 50fr multicolored .40 .40

Intl. Literacy Year — A260

1990, Dec. 31

856 A260 200fr bl, blk, & lt bl 1.60 1.60

Independence, 30th Anniv. — A261

1991, Jan. 1 *Perf. 13*

857 A261 150fr shown 1.20 1.20
858 A261 1000fr Flag, Palace, #336 7.90 7.90
a. Souv. sheet. of 2, #857-858 9.10 9.10

Fight Against AIDS — A262

1991, Jan. 15

859 A262 15fr Hearts, map, vert. .15 .15
860 A262 25fr shown .20 .20

See Nos. 884-885.

Birds A263

Designs: Nos. 861, 864, Pie grieche, vert. Nos. 862, 863, Picathartes chauve.

1991, May 3 **Litho.** *Perf. 13½*

861 A263 70fr grn & multi .55 .55
862 A263 70fr bl & multi .55 .55
863 A263 300fr blk & multi 2.40 2.40
864 A263 350fr blk & multi 2.75 2.75
a. Souv. sheet of 2, #863-864 5.25 5.25
Nos. 861-864 (4) 6.25 6.25

Wild Animals A264

1991, May 8 *Perf. 13½*

865 A264 125fr Elephant 1.00 1.00
866 A264 250fr Water buffalo 2.00 2.00
a. Souvenir sheet of 2, #865-866, perf. 12½ 3.00 3.00

City Hall Type of 1982 Redrawn

1991 *Perf. 13*

867 A202 40fr multicolored .25 .20

No. 867 inscribed "Republic of Cameroon" instead of "United Republic of Cameroon."

Cameroun Catholic Church, Cent. (in 1990) A265

1991, Dec. 8 Litho. *Perf. 13½*

868 A265 125fr Mvolye church 1.00 1.00
869 A265 250fr Akono church 2.00 2.00
a. Souvenir sheet of 2, #868-869 perf. 12½x13 3.00 3.00

Intl. Savings Banks Institute, 7th Meeting of the African Group A266

1991, Dec. 9

870 A266 250fr multicolored 2.00 2.00
a. Souv. sheet of 1, perf. 12½x13 2.00 2.00

Nos. 799 & 824 Surcharged

20 F 70 F

1992 *Perf. 13½*

871 A214 20fr on 150fr #799 .16 .16
872 A245 70fr on 300fr #824 .55 .55

Bird Type of 1983

1992 Litho. *Perf. 13½*

873 A214 125fr like #800 .95 .95

Dated 1985.

Cameroun Soccer League — A267

Designs: 125fr, Mbappe Mbappe Samuel (1936-1985), soccer player, vert. 250fr, Linafoote League emblem, vert. 400fr, Linafoote emblem, diff. 500fr, Stadium.

1992, Aug. *Perf. 11½*

874 A267 125fr multicolored .95 .95
875 A267 250fr multicolored 1.90 1.90
876 A267 400fr multicolored 3.00 3.00
877 A267 500fr multicolored 3.75 3.75
Nos. 874-877 (4) 9.60 9.60

See No. 896.

Discovery of America, 500th Anniv. A268

Columbus and: 125fr, Fleet of ships. 250fr, Landing in New World. 400fr, Meeting with natives. 500fr, Map, ships.

1992, Aug.

878 A268 125fr multicolored .95 .95
879 A268 250fr multicolored 1.90 1.90
880 A268 400fr multicolored 3.00 3.00
881 A268 500fr multicolored 3.75 3.75
Nos. 878-881 (4) 9.60 9.60

Types of 1983-84 Redrawn and Inscribed "Republic of Cameroon"

1992 Litho. *Perf. 13½*

882 A214 200fr like #739 1.45 1.45
883 A222 350fr like #763 2.55 2.55

AIDS Type of 1991

1993 Litho. *Perf. 13½*

884 A262 100fr like #859 .70 .70
885 A262 175fr like #860 1.20 1.20

Types of 1983 Redrawn and Inscribed "Republic of Cameroon"

886 A214 370fr like #738 2.55 2.55

Perf. 13

887 A217 410fr like #746 2.85 2.85

1994 World Cup Soccer Championships, US — A270

Designs: 125fr, Pres. Paul Biya holding soccer ball, lion. 250fr, Logo, lion, player, map. 450fr, Players, globe, World Cup, flag. 500fr, US eagle, Cameroun lion, soccer ball.

1994 Litho. *Perf. 13*

890 A270 125fr multicolored .48 .48
891 A270 250fr multicolored .95 .95
892 A270 450fr multicolored 1.75 1.75
893 A270 500fr multicolored 1.90 1.90
a. Min. sheet of 4, #890-893 5.00 5.00
Nos. 890-893 (4) 5.08 5.08

No. 853 Surcharged in Gold and Black

125F

1993 Litho. *Perf. 13½*

894 A258 125fr on 70fr #853

A number has been reserved for an additional value in this set, which the editors would like to examine.

Cameroun Soccer League Type of 1992

1993 Litho. *Perf. 11½*

896 A267 10fr like #876

Dated 1993.

Psittacus Erithacus — A271

1995 Litho. *Perf. 11½*
Granite Paper

897 A271 125fr multicolored .50 .50

Visit of Pope John Paul II A272

1995 *Perf. 12½*

898 A272 55fr shown .20 .20
899 A272 125fr Pope, open text, cross .50 .50

UN, 50th Anniv. — A273

1995, Oct. 24 *Perf. 11½*

900 A273 200fr shown .80 .80
901 A273 250fr "50," people 1.00 1.00

SEMI-POSTAL STAMPS

Curie Issue
Common Design Type

1938 Unwmk. *Perf. 13*

B1 CD80 1.75fr + 50c brt ultra 3.00 3.00

French Revolution Issue
Common Design Type
Photogravure; Name and Value Typographed in Black

1939

B2 CD83 45c + 25c green 5.00 5.00
B3 CD83 70c + 30c brown 5.00 5.00
B4 CD83 90c + 35c red org 5.00 5.00
B5 CD83 1.25fr + 1fr rose pink 5.50 5.50
B6 CD83 2.25fr + 2fr blue 6.00 6.00
Nos. B2-B6 (5) 26.50 26.50

Stamps of 1925-33 Surcharged in Black

OEUVRES DE GUERRE
+ 2 frs.

1940 *Perf. 14x13½*

B7 A7 1.25fr + 2fr gray & dp bl 5.00 5.00
B8 A7 1.75fr + 3fr brn & org 5.00 5.00
B9 A7 2fr + 5fr dl grn & brn org 5.00 5.00
Nos. B7-B9 (3) 15.00 15.00

The surtax was used for war relief work.

Regular Stamps of 1939 Surcharged in Black

+ 5 Frs.
SPITFIRE

1940 *Perf. 13*

B10 A20 25c + 5fr blk brn 62.50 55.00
B11 A20 45c + 5fr slate grn 62.50 55.00
B12 A20 60c + 5fr pck bl 75.00 65.00
B13 A20 70c + 5fr plum 75.00 65.00
Nos. B10-B13 (4) 275.00 240.00

The surtax was used to purchase Spitfire planes for the Free French army.

Catalogue values for unused stamps in this section, from this point to the end of the section, are for Never Hinged items.

Common Design Type and

Military Doctor SP2

Cameroun Militiaman — SP4

1941 Photo. *Perf. 13½*

B13A SP2 1fr + 1fr red .50
B13B CD86 1.50fr + 3fr mar .50
B13C SP4 2.50fr + 1fr dk bl .50
Nos. B13A-B13C (3) 1.50

Nos. B13A-B13C were issued by the Vichy government, and were not placed on sale in Cameroun.

Nos. 281A-281B were surcharged "OEUVRES COLONIALES" and surtax (including change of denomination of the 2.50fr to 50c). These were issued in 1944 by the Vichy government, and not placed on sale in Cameroun.

New York World's Fair Stamps, 1939 Surcharged in Black

+
SPITFIRE 10fr.
Général de GAULLE

1941 *Perf. 12½x12*

B14 CD82 1.25fr + 10fr car lake 50.00 40.00
B15 CD82 2.25fr + 10fr ultra 50.00 40.00

New York World's Fair Stamps, 1939, Surcharged in Black or Blue

+ 10 Frs.
AMBULANCE
LAQUINTINIE

1941

B16 CD82 1.25fr + 10fr car lake (Bl) 9.00 7.25
B17 CD82 2.25fr + 10fr ultra (Bk) 9.00 7.25

The surtax was used to purchase ambulances for the Free French army.

Regular Stamps of 1933-39 Surcharged in Black

Valmy
+ 100 frs.

1943 *Perf. 14x13½, 13, 12½x12*

B21 A7 1.25fr + 100 gray & dp bl 4.50 4.50
B22 A21 1.25fr + 100fr car rose 4.50 4.50
B23 CD82 1.25fr + 100fr car lake 4.50 4.50
B24 A21 1.50fr + 100fr choc 4.50 4.50
B25 CD82 2.25fr + 100fr ultra 4.50 4.50
Nos. B21-B25 (5) 22.50 22.50

Red Cross Issue
Common Design Type

1944 Photo. *Perf. 14½x14*

B28 CD90 5fr + 20fr rose 1.25 .75

The surtax was for the French Red Cross and national relief.

Tropical Medicine Issue
Common Design Type

1950 Engr. *Perf. 13*

B29 CD100 10fr + 2fr dk bl grn & dk grn 1.60 1.60

The surtax was for charitable work.

Independent State

Map and Flag — SP7

Unwmk.

1961, Mar. 25 Engr. *Perf. 13*

B30 SP7 20fr + 5fr grn, car & yel .42 .42
B31 SP7 25fr + 10fr multi .50 .50
B32 SP7 30fr + 15fr car, yel & grn .70 .70
Nos. B30-B32 (3) 1.62 1.62

The surtax was for the Red Cross.

Federal Republic

Map of Cameroun, Lions Emblem and Physician Helping Leper — SP8

1962, Jan. 28

B33 SP8 20fr + 5fr multi .40 .40
B34 SP8 25fr + 10fr multi .45 .45
B35 SP8 50fr + 15fr multi .80 .80
Nos. B33-B35 (3) 1.65 1.65

Issued for leprosy relief work.

Anti-Malaria Issue
Common Design Type

1962, Apr. 7 *Perf. 12½x12*
B36 CD108 25fr + 5fr rose lilac .50 .45

WHO drive to eradicate malaria.

Freedom from Hunger Issue
Common Design Type

1963, Mar. 21 Engr. *Perf. 13*
B37 CD112 18fr + 5fr multi .42 .35
B38 CD112 25fr + 5fr multi .55 .40

Antelopes — SP9

Designs: 125fr+10fr, Ourebia ourebi. 250fr+20fr, Kobus defassa.

1991, Apr. 30 Litho. *Perf. 13½x13*
B39 SP9 125fr + 10fr multi 1.15 1.15
B40 SP9 250fr + 20fr multi 2.30 2.30
a. Souvenir sheet of 2, #B39-B40, perf. 12½ 3.45 3.45

AIR POST STAMPS

Catalogue values for unused stamps in this section are for Never Hinged items.

Common Design Type

1942 Unwmk. Photo. *Perf. 14½x14*

C1	CD87	1fr dk orange	.15	.15
C2	CD87	1.50fr brt red	.15	.15
C3	CD87	5fr brown red	.15	.15
C4	CD87	10fr black	.30	.30
C5	CD87	25fr ultra	.40	.40
C6	CD87	50fr dk green	.55	.55
C7	CD87	100fr plum	.75	.75
		Nos. C1-C7 (7)	2.45	2.45

Victory Issue
Common Design Type

1946, May 8 Engr. *Perf. 12½*
C8 CD92 8fr dk violet brn .40 .25

European victory of the Allied Nations in WWII.

Chad to Rhine Issue
Common Design Types

1946, June 6

C9	CD93	5fr dk blue grn	.70	.70
C10	CD94	10fr dk rose vio	.70	.70
C11	CD95	15fr red	.80	.80
C12	CD96	20fr brt blue	.80	.80
C13	CD97	25fr orange red	1.00	1.00
C14	CD98	50fr gray	1.25	1.25
		Nos. C9-C14 (6)	5.25	5.25

Plane and Map — AP9

Seaplane Alighting — AP10

Plane and Freighters AP11

1946 Photo. *Perf. 13, 13½*

C15	AP9	25c brown red	.15	.15
C16	AP9	50c green	.15	.15
C17	AP9	1fr brt violet	.15	.15
C18	AP10	2fr olive grn	.15	.15
C19	AP10	3fr chocolate	.15	.15
C20	AP10	4fr deep ultra	.15	.15
C21	AP10	6fr blue grn	.15	.15
C22	AP10	7fr brt violet	.15	.15
C23	AP10	12fr orange	2.00	2.00
C24	AP10	20fr crimson	.45	.45
C25	AP11	50fr dk ultra	.50	.50
		Nos. C15-C25 (11)	4.15	4.15

Nos. C15 to C25 were "issued" in 1941 in France by the Vichy Government, but were not sold in Cameroun until 1946.

V8

This 100fr stamp and eight denominations of types AP9, AP10 and AP11 without "RF" monogram were issued by the Vichy Government in 1943-44, but were not on sale in Cameroun.

Birds over Mountains — AP12

Cavalry and Plane — AP13

Warrior, Dance Mask and Nose of Plane — AP14

Perf. 12½

1947, Feb. 10 Unwmk. Engr.

C26	AP12	50fr dk green	1.00	.45
C27	AP13	100fr brn red	1.75	.25
C28	AP14	200fr black	3.50	.75
		Nos. C26-C28 (3)	6.25	1.45

UPU Issue
Common Design Type

1949, July *Perf. 13*
C29 CD99 25fr multicolored 2.75 2.00

Humsiki Peak — AP16

1953, Feb. 16
C30 AP16 500fr grnsh blk, dk vio & vio bl 7.50 1.75

For surcharge see No. C40.

Edéa Dam and Sacred Ibis — AP17

1953, Nov. 18
C31 AP17 15fr choc, brn lake & ultra 1.25 .60

Issued to publicize the official dedication of Edea Dam on the Sanaga River.

Liberation Issue
Common Design Type

1954, June 6
C32 CD102 15fr dk grnsh bl & bl grn 1.75 1.25

Dr. Eugene Jamot, Research Laboratory and Tsetse Flies — AP19

1954, Nov. 29
C33 AP19 15fr dk grn, ind & dk brn 1.25 1.10

75th anniv. of the birth of Dr. Eugene Jamot.

Logging — AP20

Designs: 100fr, Giraffes. 200fr, Port of Douala.

1955, Jan. 24

C34	AP20	50fr ol grn, brn & vio brn	1.25	.50
C35	AP20	100fr grnsh bl, brn & dk brn	3.75	1.25
C36	AP20	200fr dk grn, choc & dp ultra	5.00	2.25
		Nos. C34-C36 (3)	10.00	4.00

For surcharges see Nos. C38-C39.

Federal Republic
Air Afrique Issue
Common Design Type
Unwmk.

1962, Feb. 17 Engr. *Perf. 13*
C37 CD107 25fr mar, pur & lt grn .40 .38

Nos. C35-C36 and C30 Surcharged in Red with New Value, Bars and: "REPUBLIQUE FEDERALE"

Two types of 5sh:
I - "5/-" measures 6½x4mm.
II - "5/" measures 3¾x3mm, No dash after diagonal line.

Three types of 10sh:
I - "10/-" measures 9x3¾mm.
II - "10/-" measures 7x2½-3mm.
III - "1" of "10/" vertically in line with last "E" of "FEDERALE".

Two types of £1:
I - "REPUBLIQUE / FEDERALE" 17¼mm wide.
II - "REPUBLIQUE / FEDERALE" 22mm wide.

1961, Oct. 1 Engr. *Perf. 13*

C38	AP20	5sh on 100fr (I)	2.50	2.50
a.		Type II	6.50	6.50
C39	AP20	10sh on 200fr (I)	5.50	5.50
a.		Type II	22.50	22.50
b.		Type III	8.00	8.00
C40	AP16	£1 on 500fr (I)	10.00	10.00
a.		Type II	15.00	15.00
		Nos. C38-C40 (3)	18.00	18.00

Issued for use in the former United Kingdom Trust Territory of Southern Cameroons.

Kapsikis Mokolo — AP21

Designs: 50fr, Cocotieres Hotel, Douala. 100fr, Cymothoe sangaris butterflies. 200fr, Ostriches, Waza Reservation.

1962, June 15

C41	AP21	50fr sl grn, bl & dl red	.50	.30
C42	AP21	100fr multicolored	1.10	.40
C43	AP21	200fr dk grn, blk & bis	2.25	.65
C44	AP21	500fr vio brn, bl & ocher	5.00	1.60
		Nos. C41-C44 (4)	8.85	2.95

Telstar Type of Regular Issue

1963, Feb. 9

Size: 48x27mm

C45 A50 100fr dk grn & red brn 1.10 .65

See note after No. 383.

Edéa Relay Station — A22

1963, May 18 Photo. *Perf. 12x12½*
C46 AP22 100fr multicolored 1.10 .65

Issued to publicize the high frequency telegraph connection Douala-Yaoundé.

African Postal Union Issue
Common Design Type

1963, Sept. 8 Unwmk. *Perf. 12½*
C47 CD114 85fr ultra, ocher & red 1.10 1.00

Air Afrique Issue, 1963
Common Design Type

1963, Nov. 19 *Perf. 13x12*
C48 CD115 50fr pink, gray, blk & grn .60 .40

Olympic Games Type of 1964

Design: 300fr, Greco-Roman wrestlers (ancient).

1964, Oct. 10 Engr. *Perf. 13*
C49 A57 300fr red, dk brn & dl grn 3.50 2.00
a. Sheet of 3, #403-404, C49 4.25 4.25

Kribi Port — AP25

1964, Oct. 26 Unwmk. *Perf. 13*
C50 AP25 50fr red brn, ultra & grn .60 .35

Black Rhinoceros — AP26

1965, Dec. 15 Engr. *Perf. 13*
C51 AP26 250fr brn red, grn & dk brn 3.00 1.10

Pres. John F. Kennedy — AP27

1964, Dec. 8 Photo. *Perf. 12½*

C52 AP27 100fr grn, yel grn & brn 1.10 1.10
a. Souvenir sheet of 4 4.50 4.50

Pres. John F. Kennedy (1917-63).

Abraham Lincoln — AP28

1965, Apr. 20 Unwmk. *Perf. 13*

C53 AP28 100fr multicolored 1.10 .80

Abraham Lincoln, death centenary.

Syncom Satellite and ITU Emblem — AP29

1965, May 17 Engr.

C54 AP29 70fr red, dk bl, & blk .80 .60

Cent. of the ITU.

Sir Winston Spencer Churchill, Statesman and World War II Leader — AP30

Design: 18fr, Churchill, battleship and oak leaves with acorns.

Perf. 13x12½

1965, May 28 Photo. Unwmk.

C55 AP30 12fr multicolored .65 .50
C56 AP30 18fr multicolored .65 .50
a. Strip of 2, #C55-C56 + label 1.60 1.40

ICY Type of Regular Issue

1965, Sept. 11 Engr. *Perf. 13*

C57 A68 100fr dk red & dk bl 1.10 .70

Racing Boat, Sanaga River, Edéa — AP31

1965, Oct. 27 Unwmk. *Perf. 13*

C58 AP31 50fr brn, dk grn & sl .60 .35

Edward H. White Floating in Space and Gemini IV — AP32

Designs: 50fr, Vostok 6. 200fr, Gemini V and REP (rendezvous evaluation pod). 500fr, Gemini VI & VII rendezvous.

1966, Mar. 30 Engr. *Perf. 13*

C59 AP32 50fr car rose & dk sl grn .60 .35
C60 AP32 100fr red lil & vio bl 1.10 .65
C61 AP32 200fr ultra & dk pur 2.00 1.40
C62 AP32 500fr brt bl & indigo 5.50 3.00
Nos. C59-C62 (4) 9.20 5.40

Man's conquest of space.

Hotel Type of Regular Issue

Designs: 18fr, Mountain Hotel, Buea. 25fr, Hotel Akwa Palace, Douala. 50fr, Terminus Hotel, Yaoundé. 60fr, Imperial Hotel, Yaoundé. 85fr, Independence Hotel, Yaoundé. 100fr, Hunting Lodge, Mora, vert. 150fr, Boukarous (round huts), Waza Camp.

1966

C63 A71 18fr sl grn, brt bl & blk .16 .15
C64 A71 25fr car, ultra & sl .25 .16
C65 A71 50fr choc, grn & ocher .60 .35
C66 A71 60fr choc, grn & brt bl .60 .35
C67 A71 85fr dk car rose, dl bl & grn .80 .50
C68 A71 100fr brn, grn & sl 1.10 .50
C69 A71 150fr brn, dl bl & ocher 1.40 .65
Nos. C63-C69 (7) 4.91 2.66

Issued: #C63-C64, Apr. 6; #C65-C69, June 4.

Flower Type of Regular Issue

Flowers: 25fr, Hibiscus mutabilis. 50fr, Delonix regia. 100fr, Bougainvillea.

1966, May 20 Photo. *Perf. 12½*
Flowers in Natural Colors
Size: 26x45mm

C70 A75 25fr slate green .25 .15
C71 A75 50fr brt grnsh bl .50 .15
C72 A75 100fr gold 1.10 .25
Nos. C70-C72 (3) 1.85 .55

Military Police — AP33

Design: 25fr, "Army," soldier, tanks and parachutes. 60fr, "Navy," and "Vigilante." 100fr, "Air Force," plane.

1966, June 21 Engr. *Perf. 13*

C73 AP33 20fr vio bl, org brn & dl pur .20 .15
C74 AP33 25fr dk grn, dl pur & brn .25 .16
C75 AP33 60fr bl grn, bl & ind .65 .30
C76 AP33 100fr brn, Prus bl & car rose 1.10 .65
Nos. C73-C76 (4) 2.20 1.26

Issued to honor Cameroun's armed forces.

Wembley Stadium, London — AP34

1966, July 20

C77 AP34 50fr shown .55 .25
C78 AP34 200fr Soccer 2.00 1.10

8th World Cup Soccer Championship, Wembley, England, July 11-30.

Air Afrique Issue, 1966
Common Design Type

1966, Aug. 31 Photo. *Perf. 13*

C79 CD123 25fr red lil, blk & gray .25 .15

Yaoundé Cathedral — AP35

Designs: 18fr, Buea Cathedral. 30fr, Orthodox Church, Yaoundé. 60fr, Mosque, Garoua.

1966, Dec. 19 Engr. *Perf. 13*

C80 AP35 18fr choc, bl & grn .20 .16
C81 AP35 25fr brn, grn & brt vio .25 .16
C82 AP35 30fr lil, grn & dl red .30 .20
C83 AP35 60fr mar, brt grn & grn .65 .35
Nos. C80-C83 (4) 1.40 .87

Pioneer A and Moon — AP36

1967, Apr. 30 Engr. *Perf. 13*

C84 AP36 25fr shown .25 .16
C85 AP36 50fr Ranger 6 .60 .35
C86 AP36 100fr Luna 9 1.10 .65
C87 AP36 250fr Luna 10 2.50 2.00
Nos. C84-C87 (4) 4.45 3.16

"Conquest of the Moon."

Flower Type of Regular Issue

1967, June 22 Photo. *Perf. 12½*
Size: 26x46mm

C88 A86 200fr Thevetia Peruviana 2.00 .90
C89 A86 250fr Amaryllis 2.50 1.10

African Postal Union Issue, 1967
Common Design Type

1967, Sept. 9 Engr. *Perf. 13*

C90 CD124 100fr red brn, Prus bl & brt lil 1.10 .65

Skis, Ice Skates, Olympic Flame and Emblem — AP38

1967, Oct. 11 Engr. *Perf. 13*

C91 AP38 30fr ultra & sepia .40 .20

Issued to publicize the 10th Winter Olympic Games, Grenoble, Feb. 6-8, 1968.

Cameroun Exhibit, EXPO '67 — AP39

Designs: 100fr, Bangwa house poles carved with ancestor figures. 200fr, Canadian Pavilions.

1967, Oct. 18

C92 AP39 50fr mag, ol & maroon .50 .22
C93 AP39 100fr dk grn, mar & dk brn 1.10 .55
C94 AP39 200fr brn, lil rose & sl grn 2.25 1.10
Nos. C92-C94 (3) 3.85 1.87

EXPO '70, International Exhibition, Montreal, Apr. 28-Oct. 27, 1967.

See note after No. C116 regarding 1969 moon overprint.

Konrad Adenauer (1876-1967), Chancellor of West Germany (1949-63) and Cologne Cathedral — AP40

Design: 70fr, Adenauer and Chancellery, Bonn.

1967, Dec. 1 Photo. *Perf. 12½*

C95 AP40 30fr multi .35 .20
C96 AP40 70fr multi .80 .40
a. Strip of 2, #C95-C96 + label 1.20 .65

Pres. Ahidjo, King Faisal and View of Mecca — AP41

Design: 60fr, Pres. Ahidjo, Pope Paul VI and view of Rome.

1968, Feb. 18 Photo. *Perf. 12½*

C97 AP41 30fr multi .30 .16
C98 AP41 60fr multi .60 .30

Issued to commemorate President Ahidjo's Pilgrimage to Mecca and visit to Rome.

Earth on Television Transmitted by Explorer VI — AP42

Designs: 30fr, Molniya spacecraft. 40fr, Earth on television screen transmitted by Molniya.

1968, Apr. 20 Engr. *Perf. 13*

C99 AP42 20fr multi .20 .15
C100 AP42 30fr multi .30 .16
C101 AP42 40fr multi .40 .20
Nos. C99-C101 (3) .90 .51

Telecommunication by satellite.

Forge — AP43

Boxing — AP44

Designs: No. C103, Tea harvest. No. C104, Trans-Cameroun railroad (diesel train emerging from tunnel). 40fr, Rubber harvest. 60fr, Douala Harbor, horiz.

1968, June 5 Engr. *Perf. 13*

C102 AP43 20fr red brn, dk grn & ind .20 .15
C103 AP43 30fr dk brn, grn & ultra .30 .16
C104 AP43 30fr ind, sl grn & bis brn .30 .16
C105 AP43 40fr ol bis, dk grn & bl grn .35 .20
C106 AP43 60fr ultra, dk brn & sl .60 .40
Nos. C102-C106 (5) 1.75 1.07

Second Economic Development Five-Year Plan.

1968, Aug. 19 Engr. *Perf. 13*

Design: 50fr, Long jump. 60fr, Athlete on rings.

C107 AP44 30fr brt grn, dk grn & choc .30 .16
C108 AP44 50fr brt grn, brn red & choc .50 .30
C109 AP44 60fr brt grn, ultra & choc .60 .35
a. Min. sheet of 3, #C107-C109 1.50 1.50
Nos. C107-C109 (3) 1.40 .81

19th Olympic Games, Mexico City, Oct. 12-27.

Human Rights Type of Regular Issue

1968, Sept. 14 Photo. *Perf. 12½x13*

C110 A92 30fr grn & brt pink .25 .15

Martin Luther King, Jr. — AP45

Portraits: No. C112, Mahatma Gandhi and map of India. 40fr, John F. Kennedy. 60fr, Robert F. Kennedy. No. C115, Rev. Martin Luther King, Jr. No. C116, Mahatma Gandhi.

1968, Dec. 5 Photo. *Perf. 12½*

C111 AP45 30fr bl & blk .35 .20
C112 AP45 30fr multi .35 .20
C113 AP45 40fr pink & blk .40 .25
C114 AP45 60fr bluish lil & blk .60 .40
C115 AP45 70fr yel grn & blk .65 .45
a. Souvenir sheet of 4, #C112-C115 2.00 2.00
C116 AP45 70fr multi .65 .45
Nos. C111-C116 (6) 3.00 1.95

Issued to honor exponents of non-violence. The 2 King stamps (Nos. C111 and C115), the 2 Gandhi stamps (Nos. C112 and C116) and the 2 Kennedy stamps (Nos. C113-C114) are each printed as triptychs with a descriptive label between.

In 1969 Nos. C111-C116 and C94 were overprinted in carmine capitals: "Premier Homme / sur la Lune / 20 Juillet 1969" and "First Man / Landing on Moon / 20 July 1969".

PHILEXAFRIQUE Issue

The Letter, by Armand Cambon AP46

1968, Dec. 10

C117 AP46 100fr multi 1.10 .80

PHILEXAFRIQUE, Philatelic Exhibition in Abidjan, Feb. 14-23, 1969. Printed with alternating light green label.

2nd PHILEXAFRIQUE Issue

Common Design Type

Design: Cameroun #199 and Wouri Bridge.

1969, Feb. 14 Engr. *Perf. 13*

C118 CD128 50fr multi .55 .55

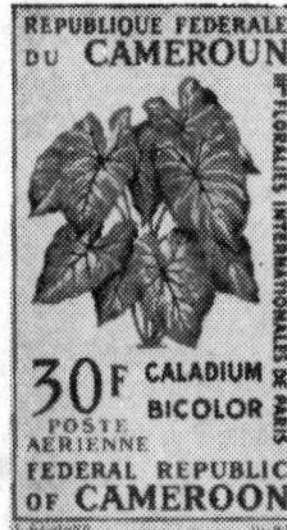

Caladium Bicolor — AP47

Flowers: 50fr, Aristolochia elegans. 100fr, Gloriosa simplex.

1969, May 14 Photo. *Perf. 12½*

C119 AP47 30fr lil & multi .30 .20
C120 AP47 50fr grn & multi .60 .35
C121 AP47 100fr brn & multi 1.00 .55
Nos. C119-C121 (3) 1.90 1.10

3rd Intl. Flower Show, Paris, Apr. 23-Oct. 5.

Douala Post Office — AP48

Designs: 50fr, Buea Post Office. 100fr, Bafoussam Post Office.

1969, June 19 Engr. *Perf. 13*

C122 AP48 30fr grn, vio bl & brn .22 .15
C123 AP48 50fr sl, emer & red brn .45 .25
C124 AP48 100fr dk brn, brt grn & brn .90 .50
Nos. C122-C124 (3) 1.57 .90

Coronation of Napoleon I, by Jacques Louis David — AP49

Napoleon Crossing Saint Bernard, after J. L. David — AP50

1969, July 4 Photo. *Perf. 12x12½*

C125 AP49 30fr vio bl & multi .50 .20

Die-cut Perf. 10

Embossed on Gold Foil

C126 AP50 1000fr gold 16.00 16.00

Bicentenary of birth of Napoleon I.

William E. B. Du Bois (1868-1963), American Writer — AP51

Portraits: 15fr, Dr. Price Mars, Haiti (1876-1969). No. C128, Aimé Cesaire, Martinique (1913-). No. C130, Langston Hughes, US (1902-1967). No. C131, Marcus Garvey, Jamaica (1887-1940). 100fr, René Maran, Martinique (1887-1960).

1969, Sept. 25 Photo. *Perf. 12½*

C127 AP51 15fr lt bl & blk .15 .15
C128 AP51 30fr lem & blk .25 .15
C129 AP51 30fr rose brn & blk .25 .15
C130 AP51 50fr gray & blk .42 .22
C131 AP51 50fr emer & blk .42 .22
C132 AP51 100fr yel & blk .90 .60
a. Min. sheet of 6, #C127-C132 2.50 2.50
Nos. C127-C132 (6) 2.39 1.49

Issued to honor Negro writers.

ILO Emblem — AP52

1969, Oct. 29 Photo. *Perf. 13*

C133 AP52 30fr blk, bl grn & gray .35 .15
C134 AP52 50fr blk, dp lil rose & gray .60 .25

50th anniv. of the ILO.

Armstrong, Collins and Aldrin Splashdown in the Pacific — AP53

Design: 500fr, Landing module and Neil A. Armstrong's first step on moon.

1969, Nov. 29 Photo. *Perf. 12½*

C135 AP53 200fr multi 2.50 1.25
C136 AP53 500fr multi 5.50 2.25

See note after Algeria No. 427.

Pres. Ahidjo, Arms and Map of Cameroun — AP54

Embossed on Gold Foil

1970, Jan. 1 *Die-cut Perf. 10*

C137 AP54 1000fr gold & multi 8.25 8.25

10th anniversary of independence.

Hotel Mont Fébé, Yaoundé — AP55

1970, Jan. 15 Engr. *Perf. 13*

C138 AP55 30fr lt brn, sl grn & gray .35 .15

Lenin — AP56

1970, Jan. 25 Photo. *Perf. 12½*

C139 AP56 50fr org & blk .45 .25

Plant Type of Regular Issue

Designs: 50fr, Cleome speciosa (caper). 100fr, Mussaenda erythrophylla (madder).

1970, Mar. 24 Photo. *Perf. 12½*

Size: 26x46mm

C140 A99 50fr blk & multi .40 .25
C141 A99 100fr multi .80 .40

Map of Africa and Lions Emblem Pinpointing Yaoundé — AP57

1970, May 2 Photo. *Perf. 12½*

C142 AP57 100fr multi 1.00 .50

13th Lions International Congress of District 13, Yaoundé, May 2, 1970.

UN Emblem and Doves — AP58

Design: 50fr, UN emblem and dove, vert.

1970, June 26 Engr. *Perf. 13*

C143 AP58 30fr brn & org .25 .16
C144 AP58 50fr Prus bl & sl bl .42 .22

25th anniversary of the United Nations.

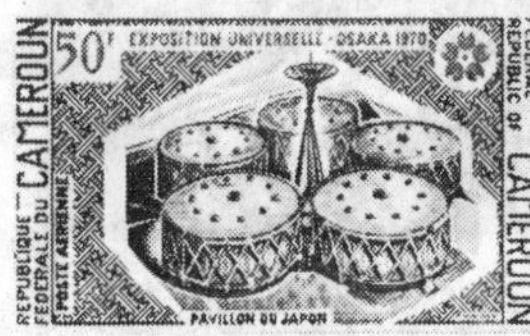

Japanese Pavilion and EXPO Emblem — AP59

Designs (EXPO Emblem and): 100fr, Map of Japan, vert. 150fr, Australian pavilion.

1970, Aug. 1 Engr. *Perf. 13*

C145 AP59 50fr ind, lt grn & ver .42 .22
C146 AP59 100fr bl, lt grn & red 1.00 .42
C147 AP59 150fr choc, bl & gray 1.40 .65
Nos. C145-C147 (3) 2.82 1.29

EXPO '70 International Exhibition, Osaka, Japan, Mar. 15-Sept. 13.

Charles de Gaulle — AP60

Pelé and Team — AP61

Design: 200fr, de Gaulle in unifrom.

1970, Aug. 27

C148 AP60 100fr grn, vio bl & ol brn 1.00 .50
C149 AP60 200fr ol brn, vio bl & grn 2.00 .90
a. Strip of 2, #C148-C149 + label 3.50 1.60

Rallying of the Free French, 30th anniv.
For overprints see Nos. C159-C160.

1970, Oct. 14 Photo. *Perf. 12½*

Designs: 50fr, Aztec Stadium, Mexico City, horiz. 100fr, Mexican soccer team, horiz.

C150 AP61 50fr multi .50 .22
C151 AP61 100fr multi 1.00 .50
C152 AP61 200fr multi 2.00 1.00
Nos. C150-C152 (3) 3.50 1.72

9th World Soccer Championships for the Jules Rimet Cup, Mexico City, May 30-June 21, and the final victory of Brazil over Italy.

Ludwig van Beethoven (1770-1827), Composer — AP62

1970, Nov. 23 Engr. *Perf. 13*

C153 AP62 250fr multi 2.00 1.00

Christ at Emmaus, by Rembrandt — AP63

Design: 150fr, The Anatomy Lesson, by Rembrandt.

1970, Dec. 5 Photo. *Perf. 12x12½*

C154 AP63 70fr grn & multi .55 .25
C155 AP63 150fr multi 1.20 .60

Charles Dickens — AP64

Designs: 50fr, Scenes from David Copperfield. 100fr, Dickens holding quill.

1970, Dec. 22 *Perf. 13*

C156 AP64 40fr blk & rose .35 .16
C157 AP64 50fr bis & multi .40 .20
C158 AP64 100fr rose & multi .80 .40
a. Strip of 3, #C156-C158 1.75 1.00

Charles Dickens (1812-1870), English novelist.

De Gaulle Type of 1970 Overprinted with Black Border and: "IN MEMORIAM / 1890-1970"

1971, Jan. 15 Engr. *Perf. 13*

C159 AP60 100fr vio bl, emer & brn red .80 .40
C160 AP60 200fr brn red, emer & vio bl 1.60 .80

In memory of Gen. Charles de Gaulle (1890-1970), President of France.

Timber Storage, Douala — AP65

Designs (Industrialization): 70fr, ALUCAM aluminum plant, Edea, vert. 100fr, Mbakaou Dam.

1971, Feb. 14 Engr. *Perf. 13*

C161 AP65 40fr dk red, bl grn & ol brn .35 .15
C162 AP65 70fr ol brn, sl grn & brt bl .55 .25
C163 AP65 100fr Prus bl, yel grn & red brn .80 .40
Nos. C161-C163 (3) 1.70 .80

Relay Race — AP66

Designs: 50fr, Torch bearer, vert. 100fr, Discus.

1971, Apr. 24 Engr. *Perf. 13*

C164 AP66 30fr dk brn, ver & ind .25 .15
C165 AP66 50fr blk, bl & choc .45 .22
C166 AP66 100fr multi .80 .35
Nos. C164-C166 (3) 1.50 .72

75th anniv. of revival of Olympic Games.

Fishing Trawler — AP67

Designs: 40fr, Local fishermen, Northern Cameroun. 70fr, Fishing harbor, Douala. 150fr, Shrimp boats, Douala.

1971, May 14 Engr. *Perf. 13*

C167 AP67 30fr lt brn, bl & grn .22 .15
C168 AP67 40fr sl grn, bl & dk brn .30 .16
C169 AP67 70fr dk brn, bl & red org .60 .25
C170 AP67 150fr multi 1.20 .60
Nos. C167-C170 (4) 2.32 1.16

Cameroun fishing industry.

Cameroun No. 123 and War Memorial, Yaoundé — AP68

Designs (Cameroun Stamps): 25fr, No. C33 and Jamot memorial. 40fr, No. 431 and government buildings, Yaoundé. 50fr, No. 19 and Imperial German postal emblem. 100fr, No. 101 and World War II memorial.

1971, Aug. 1 Engr. *Perf. 13*

C171 AP68 20fr grn, ocher & dk brn .16 .15
C172 AP68 25fr dk brn, vio bl & sl grn .20 .15
C173 AP68 40fr grn, mar & sl .30 .16
C174 AP68 50fr dk brn, blk & ver .40 .20
C175 AP68 100fr mar, sl grn & org .80 .40
Nos. C171-C175 (5) 1.86 1.06

PHILATECAM 1971 Philatelic Exhibition.

Cameroun Flag, Pres. Ahidjo and Reunification Highway — AP69

Typographed, Silk Screen, Embossed

1971, Oct. 1 *Perf. 12½*

C176 AP69 250fr gold & multi 2.50 2.00

PHILATECAM Philatelic Exhibition, Yaoundé-Douala.

African Postal Union Issue, 1971

Common Design Type

1971, Nov. 13 Photo. *Perf. 13x13½*

C177 CD135 100fr bl & multi .90 .42

Annunciation, by Fra Angelico — AP71

Christmmas (Paintings): 45fr, Virgin and Child, by Andrea del Sarto. 150fr, Christ Child with Lamb, detail from Holy Family, by Raphael, vert.

Perf. 13x13½, 13½x13

1971, Dec. 19

C178 AP71 40fr multi .25 .15
C179 AP71 45fr multi .40 .20
C180 AP71 150fr multi 1.40 .60
Nos. C178-C180 (3) 2.05 .95

Cameroun Airlines Emblem AP72

1972, Feb. 2 Photo. *Perf. 12½x12*

C181 AP72 50fr lt bl & multi .40 .20

Inauguration of Cameroun Airlines.

Doge's Palace, by Ippolito Caffi — AP73

Paintings: 100fr, 200fr, Details from "Regatta on the Grand Canal," by School of Canaletto.

1972 Photo. *Perf. 13*

C182 AP73 40fr gold & multi .35 .16
C183 AP73 100fr gold & multi .80 .40
C184 AP73 200fr gold & multi 1.60 .80
Nos. C182-C184 (3) 2.75 1.36

UNESCO campaign to save Venice.

Cosmonauts Patsayev, Dobrovolsky and Volkov — AP74

1972, May 1 Photo. *Perf. 13x13½*

C185 AP74 50fr multi .40 .16

Salute-Soyuz 11 space mission, and in memory of the Russian cosmonauts Victor I. Patsayev, Georgi T. Dobrovolsky and Vladislav N. Volkov, who died during Soyuz 11 space mission, June 6-30, 1971.

UN Headquarters, Chinese Flag and Gate of Heavenly Peace AP75

1972, May 19 *Perf. 13*

C186 AP75 50fr blk, scar & gold .35 .16

Admission of People's Republic of China to UN.

United Republic

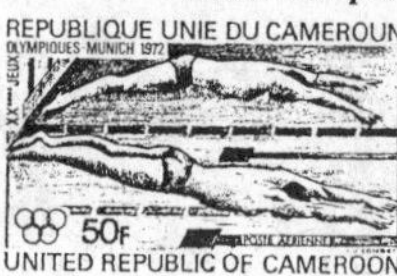

Olympic Rings, Swimming AP76

Designs (Olympic Rings and): No. C188, Boxing, vert. 200fr, Equestrian.

1972, Aug. 1 Engr. *Perf. 13*

C187 AP76 50fr lake & slate grn .40 .20
C188 AP76 50fr choc & slate .40 .20
C189 AP76 200fr cl, gray & dk brn 1.50 .70
a. Min. sheet of 3 2.25 2.25
Nos. C187-C189 (3) 2.30 1.10

20th Olympic Games, Munich, Aug. 26-Sept. 11. No. C189a contains stamps similar to Nos. C187-C189, but in changed colors. The 50fr (swimming) is Prussian blue, violet & brown; the 50c (boxing) lilac, Prussian blue & brown; the 200fr, Prussian blue & brown.

Nos. C187-C189 Overprinted in Red or Black

NATATION MARK SPITZ
MEDAILLES D'OR
a

SUPER WELTER
KOTTYSCH
MEDAILLE D'OR
b

CONCOURS COMPLET
MEADE
MEDAILLE D'OR
c

1972, Oct. 23 Engr. *Perf. 13*

C190 AP76(a) 50fr (R) .40 .20
C191 AP76(b) 50fr .40 .20
C192 AP76(c) 200fr 1.60 .80
Nos. C190-C192 (3) 2.40 1.20

Gold Medal Winners in 20th Olympic Games: Mark Spitz, US, swimming (#C190); Dieter Kottysch, West Germany, light middleweight boxing (#C191); Richard Meade, Great Britain, 3-day equestrian (#C192).

Madonna with Angels, by Cimabue AP77

Christmas: 140fr, Madonna of the Rose Arbor, by Stefan Lochner.

1972, Dec. 21 Photo. *Perf. 13*

C193 AP77 45fr gold & multi .40 .20
C194 AP77 140fr gold & multi .90 .45

St. Teresa, the Little Flower — AP78

Design: 100fr, Lisieux Cathedral and St. Teresa.

1973, Jan. 2 **Engr.**

C195	AP78	45fr vio bl, pur & mar	.35	.16
C196	AP78	100fr mag, ultra & brn	.65	.38

Centenary of the birth of St. Teresa of Lisieux (1873-1897), Carmelite nun.

African Unity Hall, Addis Ababa and Emperor Haile Selassie — AP79

1973, Mar. 14 **Photo.** ***Perf. 13***

C197	AP79	45fr yellow & multi	.25	.16

80th birthday of Emperor Haile Selassie of Ethiopia.

Corn, Grain, Healthy and Starving People — AP80

1973, Apr. 10 **Typo.** ***Perf. 13***

C198	AP80	45fr multi	.25	.15

World Food Program, 10th anniversary.

Hearts and Blood Vessels — AP81

Scout Emblem and Flags — AP82

1973, May 5 **Engr.**

C199	AP81	50fr dk car rose & dk vio bl	.25	.16

"Your Heart is Your Health" and for the 25th anniv. of the WHO.

Type of Regular Issue

Designs: 45fr, Map of Cameroun, Pres. Ahidjo and No. C176. 70fr, National colors and commemorative inscriptions.

1973, May 20 **Engr.** ***Perf. 13***

C200	A128	45fr grn & multi	.25	.16
C201	A128	70fr red & multi	.40	.25

1973, July 31 **Typo.** ***Perf. 13***

C202	AP82	40fr multi	.25	.16
C203	AP82	45fr multi	.30	.20
C204	AP82	100fr multi	.60	.42
		Nos. C202-C204 (3)	1.15	.78

Cameroun's admission to the World Scout Conference, Mar. 26, 1971.

African Weeks Issue

Head and City Hall, Brussels — AP83

1973, Sept. 17 **Engr.** ***Perf. 13***

C205	AP83	40fr dp brn & rose claret	.25	.16

African Weeks, Brussels, Sept. 15-30.

Map of Africa with Cameroun — AP84

1973, Sept. 29 **Engr.** ***Perf. 13***

C206	AP84	40fr blk, red & grn	.35	.16

Help for handicapped children.

Zamengoe Radar Station AP85

1973, Dec. 8 **Engr.** ***Perf. 13***

C207	AP85	100fr bl, lt brn & grn	.60	.40

Chancellor Rolin Madonna, by Van Eyck — AP86

Christmas: 140fr, Nativity, by Federigo Barocei.

1973, Dec. 11 **Photo.** ***Perf. 13***

C208	AP86	45fr gold & multi	.30	.20
C209	AP86	140fr gold & multi	1.00	.70

Zebu Type of 1974

1974, June 1 **Litho.** ***Perf. 13***

C210	A140	45fr Zebu herd	.25	.15

Churchill and Union Jack — AP87

1974, July 10 **Engr.** ***Perf. 13***

C211	AP87	100fr blk, bl & red	.60	.40

Winston Churchill (1874-1965).

Soccer, Arms of Frankfurt, Dortmund, Gelsenkirchen and Stuttgart — AP88

Designs: 100fr, Soccer and arms of Berlin, Hamburg, Hanover and Düsseldorf. 200fr, Soccer cup and game.

1974, Aug. 5 **Photo.** ***Perf. 13***

C212	AP88	45fr gray, sl & org	.25	.15
C213	AP88	100fr gray, sl & org	.60	.40
C214	AP88	200fr org, slate & bl	1.10	.65
a.		Strip of 3, Nos. C212-C214	2.00	1.40

World Cup Soccer Championship, Munich, June 13-July 7.

Nos. C212-C214 Overprinted in Dark Blue: "7th JULY 1974 / R.F.A. 2 HOLLANDE 1 / 7 JUILLET 1974"

1974, Sept. 16 **Photo.** ***Perf. 13***

C215	AP88	45fr multi	.25	.16
C216	AP88	100fr multi	.60	.42
C217	AP88	200fr multi	1.10	.80
a.		Strip of 3, Nos. C215-C217	2.25	1.50

World Cup Soccer Championship, 1974, victory of German Federal Republic.

UPU Type of 1974

Designs: 100fr, Cameroun No. 503. 200fr, Cameroun No. C29.

1974, Oct. 8 **Engr.** ***Perf. 13***

C218	A142	100fr blue & multi	.42	.32
C219	A142	200fr red & multi	.80	.60

Copernicus and Planets Circling Sun — AP89

1974, Oct. 15 **Engr.** ***Perf. 13***

C220	AP89	250fr multi	1.40	1.00

500th anniversary of the birth of Nicolaus Copernicus (1473-1543), Polish astronomer.

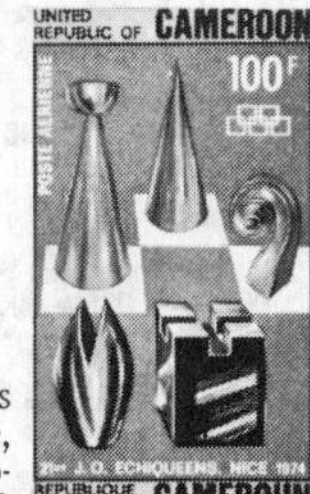

21st Chess Olympiad, Nice, France, June 6-30 — AP90

1974, Nov. 3 **Photo.** ***Perf. 13x12½***

C221	AP90	100fr Chess pieces	.50	.40

Mask and ARPHILA Emblem — AP91

1974, Nov. 30 **Engr.** ***Perf. 13***

C222	AP91	50fr choc & magenta	.25	.16

ARPHILA 75, Paris, June 6-16, 1975.

Presidents and Flags of Cameroun, CAR, Gabon and Congo — AP92

1974, Dec. 8 **Photo.**

C223	AP92	100fr gold & multi	.55	.40

See note after No. 595.

Man Landing on Moon — AP93

1974, Dec. 15 **Engr.**

C224	AP93	200fr brn, bl & car	1.10	.80

5th anniv. of man's 1st landing on the moon.

Charles de Gaulle and Félix Eboué — AP94

1975, Feb. 24 **Typo.** ***Perf. 13***

C225	AP94	45fr multi	.35	.16
C226	AP94	200fr multi	1.40	.80

Felix A. Eboué (1884-1944), Governor of Chad, first colonial governor to join Free French in WWII, 30th death anniversary.

Marquis de Lafayette — AP95

American Bicentennial: 140fr, Washington and soldiers. 500fr, Franklin and Independence Hall.

1975, Oct. 20 **Engr.** ***Perf. 13***

C227	AP95	100fr vio bl & multi	.55	.40
C228	AP95	140fr brn & multi	.70	.60
C229	AP95	500fr grn & multi	2.50	1.60
		Nos. C227-C229 (3)	3.75	2.60

The Burning Bush, by Nicolas Froment AP96

Painting: 500fr, Adoration of the Kings, by Gentile da Fabriano, horiz.

1975, Dec. 25 **Photo.** ***Perf. 13***

C230	AP96	50fr gold & multi	.35	.16
C231	AP96	500fr gold & multi	3.25	1.60

Christmas 1975.

Concorde and Route: Paris-Dakar-Rio de Janeiro — AP97

1976, July 20 Litho. *Perf. 13*

C232 AP97 500fr lt bl & multi	3.00	1.60
a. Souvenir sheet of 1	3.75	3.75

1st commercial flight of supersonic jet Concorde from Paris to Rio de Janeiro, Jan. 21. No. C232a sold for 600fr.

For overprint see No. C263.

Dance Type of 1976

Designs: 50fr, Dancers and drummer. 100fr, Woman dancer.

1976, Sept. 15 Litho. *Perf. 12*

C233 A154 50fr gray & multi	.25	.20
C234 A154 100fr gray & multi	.55	.35

Virgin and Child, by Giovanni Bellini — AP98

Paintings: 30fr, Adoration of the Shepherds, by Le Brun. 60fr, Adoration of the Kings, by Rubens. 500fr, The Newborn, by Georges de la Tour.

1976, Dec. 15 Litho. *Perf. 12½*

C235 AP98 30fr gold & multi	.16	.15
C236 AP98 60fr gold & multi	.35	.22
C237 AP98 70fr gold & multi	.38	.25
C238 AP98 500fr gold & multi	2.50	1.60
a. Souv. sheet of 4, #C235-C238	3.75	3.75
Nos. C235-C238 (4)	3.39	2.22

Christmas 1976.

Festival Type of 1977

Design: #Traditional Chief on his throne, sculpture.

1977, Feb. 4 Litho. *Perf. 12½*

C239 A159 60fr multi	.35	.22

Crucifixion, by Matthias Grunewald — AP99

Paintings: 125fr, Christ on the Cross, by Velazquez, vert. 150fr, The Deposition, by Titian.

1977, Apr. 2 Litho. *Perf. 12½*

C240 AP99 50fr gold & multi	.25	.20
C241 AP99 125fr gold & multi	.65	.40
C242 AP99 150fr gold & multi	.80	.55
a. Souv. sheet of 3, #C240-C242, perf. 12	1.75	1.75
Nos. C240-C242 (3)	1.70	1.15

Easter 1977. No. C242a sold for 350fr.

The lack of a value for a listed item does not necessarily indicate rarity.

Lions Emblem, Map of Africa — AP100

Rotary Emblem — AP101

1977, Apr. 29 Litho. *Perf. 12½*

C243 AP100 250fr multi	1.40	1.00

Lions Club of Douala, 19th Cong., Apr. 29-30.

1977, May 18

C244 AP101 60fr multi	.35	.22

Rotary Club of Douala, 20th anniversary.

Antoine de Saint-Exupéry AP102

Charles Lindbergh and Spirit of St. Louis — AP103

Designs: 50fr, Jean Mermoz and his plane. 80fr, Maryse Bastié and her plane. 100fr, Sikorsky S-43. 300fr, Concorde.

1977, May 20 Engr. *Perf. 13*

C245 AP103 50fr org & bl	.25	.20
C246 AP102 60fr mag & org	.35	.22
C247 AP103 80fr mag & bl	.40	.30
a. Souvenir sheet of 3, #C245-C247	1.10	1.10
C248 AP103 100fr grn & yel	.55	.40
C249 AP103 300fr multi	1.60	1.25
C250 AP103 500fr multi	2.50	1.75
a. Souvenir sheet of 3, #C248-C250	6.00	6.00
Nos. C245-C250 (6)	5.65	4.12

Aviation pioneers and events. No. C247a sold for 200fr. No. C250a sold for 1000fr.

For overprint see No. C262.

Sassenage Castle, Grenoble — AP104

1977, May 21 Litho. *Perf. 12½*

C251 AP104 70fr multi	.40	.25

10th anniv. of Intl. French Language Council.

Jufilex Type of 1977

Designs: 70fr, Switzerland (Zurich) No. 1L1 and Cameroun No. 16. 100fr, Switzerland (Geneva) No. 2L1 and Cameroun No. 254.

1977, June 5 Litho. *Perf. 12*

C252 A161 70fr multi	.40	.25
C253 A161 100fr multi	.55	.40

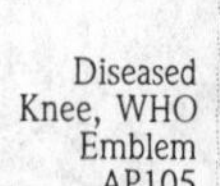

Diseased Knee, WHO Emblem AP105

1977, Oct. 15 Engr. *Perf. 13*

C260 AP105 70fr multi	.40	.25

World Rheumatism Year.

Nos. C249 and C232 Overprinted in Red: "PREMIER VOL PARIS-NEW YORK /FIRST FLIGHT PARIS-NEW YORK / 22 Nov. 1977-22nd Nov. 1977"

Engraved, Lithographed

1977, Nov. 22 *Perf. 13*

C262 AP103 300fr multi	1.60	1.20
C263 AP97 500fr multi	2.50	2.00

Concorde, 1st commercial flight Paris to NY.

Christmas Type of 1977

Paintings: 60fr, Virgin and Child with 4 Saints, by Bellini, horiz. 400fr, Adoration of the Shepherds, by George de la Tour, horiz.

1977, Dec. 15 Litho. *Perf. 12x12½*

C264 A165 60fr multi	.35	.22
C265 A165 400fr multi	2.25	1.75

Flag Type of 1978

Design: 60fr, New flag, Pres. Ahidjo and spear.

1978, Apr. 3 Litho. *Perf. 12½*

C266 A167 60fr multi	.35	.16

Frog Type of 1978

Design: 100fr, Cardioglossa trifasciata.

1978, Apr. 5

C267 A168 100fr multi	.60	.40

L'Arlesienne, by Van Gogh AP106

Painting: No. C269, Burial of Christ, by Albrecht Dürer.

1978, May 15 Litho. *Perf. 12½*

C268 AP106 200fr multi	1.40	1.10
C269 AP106 200fr multi	1.40	1.10

Leprosy Distribution on World Map, Raoul Follereau — AP107

1978, June 6 Litho. *Perf. 12*

C270 AP107 100fr multi	.65	.55

25th World Leprosy Day.

Capt. Cook and Siege of Quebec — AP108

Design: 250fr, Capt. Cook, Adventure and Resolution, map of voyages.

1978, July 26 Engr. *Perf. 13*

C271 AP108 100fr multi	.65	.55
C272 AP108 250fr multi	1.60	1.40

Capt. James Cook (1728-1779), explorer.

Argentine Soccer Team, Coat of Arms and Rimet Cup — AP109

Designs: 200fr, Two soccer players, vert. 1000fr, Soccer ball illuminating world map, vert.

1978, Sept. 1 Litho. *Perf. 13*

C273 AP109 100fr multi	.65	.55
C274 AP109 200fr multi	1.40	1.10
C275 AP109 1000fr multi	6.50	5.50
Nos. C273-C275 (3)	8.55	7.15

11th World Cup Soccer Championship, Argentina, June 1-25.

Jules Verne Type of 1978

Design: 400fr, Jules Verne and "20,000 Leagues Under the Sea," horiz.

1978, Oct. 10 Litho. *Perf. 12*

C276 A169 400fr multi	2.50	2.00

Musical Instrument Type of 1978

Design: 100fr, Man playing Mvet zither.

1978, Nov. 20 Litho. *Perf. 12½*

C277 A172 100fr multi	.65	.40

Human Rights Type of 1979

1979, Feb. 11 Litho. *Perf. 12x12½*

C278 A174 500fr multi	3.50	2.50

Lions Emblem, Map of District 403 — AP110

1979, Apr. 26 Litho. *Perf. 12½*

C279 AP110 60fr multi	.40	.25

21st Congress of Lions Club of Yaoundé.

Penny Black, Hill, Cameroun No. 9 — AP111

1979, Aug. 30 Engr. *Perf. 13*

C280 AP111 100fr multi	.65	.40

Sir Rowland Hill (1795-1879), originator of penny postage.

"TELECOM 79" — AP112

Pope Paul VI — AP113

1979, Sept. 26 Litho. *Perf. 13x12½*

C281 AP112 100fr multi .65 .40

3rd World Telecommunications Exhibition, Geneva, Sept. 20-26.

1979, Oct. 23 Engr. *Perf. 12½x13*

C282 AP113 100fr shown .65 .42
C283 AP113 100fr John Paul I .65 .42
C284 AP113 100fr John Paul II .65 .42
Nos. C282-C284 (3) 1.95 1.26

"Double Eagle" over French Coastline AP114

Design: No. C286, Balloonists and balloon.

1979, Dec. 15 Litho. *Perf. 12½*

C285 AP114 500fr multi 4.00 2.25
C286 AP114 500fr multi 4.00 2.25

First Transatlantic balloon crossing.

100-Meter Race — AP115

Designs: 150fr, Figure skating pairs. 200fr, Javelin. 300fr, Wrestling.

1980, Dec. 18 Litho. *Perf. 12½*

C287 AP115 100fr yel brn & brn .80 .48
C288 AP115 150fr bl & brn 1.25 .70
C289 AP115 200fr grn & brn 1.60 1.00
C290 AP115 300fr red & brn 2.50 1.40
Nos. C287-C290 (4) 6.15 3.58

22nd Summer Olympic Games, Moscow, July 19-Aug. 3; 13th Winter Olympic Games, Lake Placid, Feb. 12-24 (150fr).

Alan Shepard and Freedom 7 — AP116

1981, Sept. 15 Litho. *Perf. 12½*

C291 AP116 500fr shown 6.00 4.00
C292 AP116 500fr Yuri Gagarin, Vostok I 6.00 4.00

Manned space flight, 20th anniv.

4th African Scouting Conference, Abidjan, June — AP117

1981, Oct. 5

C293 AP117 100fr Emblem, salute, badge .65 .42
C294 AP117 500fr Scout saluting 3.50 2.00

Guernica (detail), by Pablo Picasso (1881-1973) — AP118

Design: No. C296, Landscape, by Paul Cezanne (1839-1906).

1981, Nov. 10 Litho. *Perf. 12½*

C295 AP118 500fr multi 3.50 2.00
C296 AP118 500fr multi 3.50 2.00

Christmas 1981 — AP119

Designs: 50fr, Virgin and Child, by Froment, vert. 60f, San Zeno Altarpiece, by Mantegna, vert. 400fr, Flight into Egypt, by Giotto.

1981, Dec. 1 Litho. *Perf. 12½*

C297 AP119 50fr multi .40 .25
C298 AP119 60fr multi .48 .32
C299 AP119 400fr multi 3.25 2.00
a. Souv. sheet of 3, #C297-C299, perf. 13x13½ 4.25 2.75
Nos. C297-C299 (3) 4.13 2.57

Still Life, by Georges Braque (1882-1963) — AP120

Paintings: No. C301, Olympia, by Edouard Manet (1832-1883).

1982, Dec. 5 Litho. *Perf. 13*

C300 AP120 500fr multi 3.00 2.00
C301 AP120 500fr multi 3.00 2.00

Pres. John F. Kennedy (1917-63) — AP121

Lions District 403 (Douala), 2nd Convention, May — AP122

1983, Mar. 15 Litho. *Perf. 13*

C302 AP121 500fr multi 3.50 2.00

1983, May 5 Litho. *Perf. 12½*

C303 AP122 70fr multi .40 .30
C304 AP122 150fr multi .90 .65

Jeanne of Aragon by Raphael AP123

Design: No. C306, Massacre of Scio by Delacroix.

1983, Oct. 15 Litho. *Perf. 13*

C305 AP123 500fr multi 2.00 1.00
C306 AP123 500fr multi 2.00 1.00

Easter 1984 — AP124

Designs: 200fr, Pieta, by G. Hernandez. 500fr, Martyrdom of St. John the Evangelist, by C. Le Brun.

1984, Mar. 30 Litho. *Perf. 13*

C307 AP124 200fr multi .75 .50
C308 AP124 500fr multi 2.00 1.40
a. Souv. sheet of 2, #C307-C308 3.00 2.00

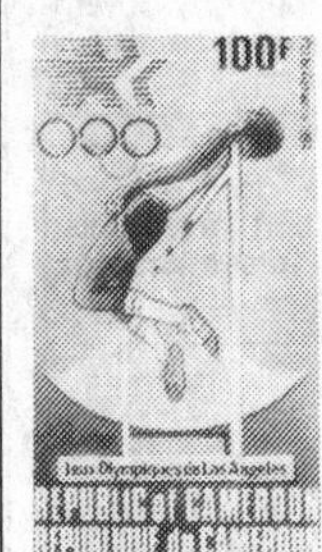

1984 Summer Olympics — AP125

European Soccer Championship, June 12-27 — AP126

1984, Apr. 30 *Perf. 12½*

C309 AP125 100fr High jump .35 .22
C310 AP125 150fr Volleyball .50 .32
C311 AP125 250fr Handball .80 .55
C312 AP125 500fr Bicycling 1.60 1.10
Nos. C309-C312 (4) 3.25 2.19

See Nos. C321-C324.

1984, June 5 Litho. *Perf. 12½*

C313 AP126 250fr Player in red shorts 1.00 .65
C314 AP126 250fr Yellow shorts 1.00 .65
C315 AP126 500fr Players 2.00 1.25
a. Souvenir sheet of 3 4.00 2.75
Nos. C313-C315 (3) 4.00 2.55

No. C315a contains Nos. C313-C315 in changed panel colors.

Presidential Oath — AP127

1984 Litho. *Perf. 13*

C316 AP127 60fr French inscription .20 .15
a. English inscription .20 .15
C317 AP127 70fr French inscription .22 .15
a. English inscription .22 .15
C318 AP127 200fr French inscription .60 .40
a. English inscription .60 .40
Nos. C316-C318 (3) 1.02 .70

Issue dates: French, Sept. 15; English, Nov.

Famous Men — AP128

Paintings: No. C316, Diana in the Bath, by Watteau (1684-1721). No. C317, Portrait of Diderot (1713-1784).

1984, Sept. 20 Litho. *Perf. 13*

C319 AP128 500fr Watteau 1.50 1.00
C320 AP128 500fr Diderot, vert. 1.50 1.00

Nos. C309-C312 in Changed Colors with Added Inscriptions

100fr: MOEGENBURG (R.F.A.) 11-08-84

150fr: U.S.A. 11-08-84

250fr: YOUGOSLAVIE 9-08-84

500fr: GORSKI (U.S.A.) 3-08-84

1984, Sept. 25 Litho. *Perf. 12½*

C321 AP125 100fr multi .30 .20
C322 AP125 150fr multi .45 .30
C323 AP125 250fr multi .70 .55
C324 AP125 500fr multi 1.50 1.00
Nos. C321-C324 (4) 2.95 2.05

Moon Landing, 15th Anniv. — AP129

1984, Nov. 15 Litho. *Perf. 12½*

C325 AP129 500fr Neil Armstrong 1.50 1.00
C326 AP129 500fr Apollo 12 launching 1.50 1.00

Louis Pasteur (1822-1895), Chemist, Microbiologist — AP130

Designs: No. 328, Mourning Woman (detail), Mausoleum of Henri Claude d'Harcourt, by sculptor Jean Baptiste Pigalle (1714-1785).

1985, Oct. 10 — Litho. — *Perf. 13*
C327 AP130 500fr multi 2.00 2.00
C328 AP130 500fr multi 2.00 2.00

Christmas AP131

Designs: 250fr, Children's gifts. 300fr, Akono Church. 400fr, Holy Family and drummer boy. 500fr, The Virgin with the Blue Diadem, by Raphael.

1985, Dec. 20 — Litho. — *Perf. 13*
C329 AP131 250fr multi .90 .90
C330 AP131 300fr multi 1.10 1.10
C331 AP131 400fr multi 1.50 1.50
C332 AP131 500fr multi 2.00 2.00
Nos. C329-C332 (4) 5.50 5.50

1986 World Cup Soccer Championships, Mexico — AP132

1986 — *Perf. 13½*
C333 AP132 250fr Argentina, winner 1.40 1.40
C334 AP132 300fr Stadium 1.65 1.65
C335 AP132 400fr Mexican team 2.25 2.25
Nos. C333-C335 (3) 5.30 5.30

Famous Men — AP133

Designs: No. C336, Pierre Curie (1859-1906), chemist, atom, and elements. No. C337, Jean Mermoz (1901-1936), aviator, and aircraft.

1986, Sept. 10 — Litho. — *Perf. 12½*
C336 AP133 500fr multi 2.75 2.75
C337 AP133 500fr multi 2.75 2.75

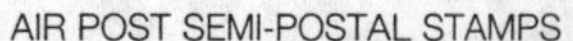

AIR POST SEMI-POSTAL STAMPS

V9-V10

Stamps of the designs shown above were issued in 1942 by the Vichy Government, but were not placed on sale in Cameroun.

POSTAGE DUE STAMPS

Man Felling Tree — D1

Perf. 14x13½
1925-27 — Unwmk. — Typo.
J1 D1 2c lt bl & blk .15 .15
J2 D1 4c ol bis & red vio .15 .15
J3 D1 5c vio & blk .25 .25
J4 D1 10c red & blk .25 .25
J5 D1 15c gray & blk .35 .35
J6 D1 20c olive grn & blk .40 .40
J7 D1 25c yel & blk .45 .45
J8 D1 30c blue & org .55 .55
J9 D1 50c brn & blk .65 .65
J10 D1 60c bl grn & rose red .80 .80
J11 D1 1fr dl red & grn, *grnsh* 1.10 1.10
J12 D1 2fr red & vio ('27) 2.00 2.00
J13 D1 3fr org brn & ultra ('27) 3.00 3.00
Nos. J1-J13 (13) 10.10 10.10

Shades occur for several values.

Carved Figures — D2

1939 — Engr. — *Perf. 14x13*
J14 D2 5c brt red vio .15 .15
J15 D2 10c Prus blue .35 .35
J16 D2 15c car rose .15 .15
J17 D2 20c blk brn .15 .15
J18 D2 30c ultra .15 .15
J19 D2 50c dk grn .15 .15
J20 D2 60c brn vio .15 .15
J21 D2 1fr dk vio .30 .30
J22 D2 2fr org red .55 .55
J23 D2 3fr dark blue .80 .80
Set value 2.50 2.50

A 10c stamp, type D2, without "RF" was issued in 1944 by the Vichy Government, but was not placed on sale in Cameroun.

Catalogue values for unused stamps in this section, from this point to the end of the section, are for Never Hinged items.

D3

1947 — Unwmk. — *Perf. 13*
J24 D3 10c dark red .15 .15
J25 D3 30c dp org .15 .15
J26 D3 50c grnsh blk .15 .15
J27 D3 1fr dark car .15 .15
J28 D3 2fr dp yel grn .20 .20
J29 D3 3fr dp red lil .22 .22
J30 D3 4fr dp ultra .22 .22
J31 D3 5fr red brn .25 .25
J32 D3 10fr peacock bl .40 .40
J33 D3 20fr sepia .65 .65
Set value 2.15 2.15

Federal Republic

Hibiscus — D4

Flowers: No. J35, Erythrine. No. J36, Plumeria lutea. No. J37, Ipomoea. No. J38, Hoodia gordonii. No. J39, Grinum. No. J40, Ochna. No. J41, Gloriosa. No. J42, Costus spectabilis. No. J43, Bougainvillea spectabilis. No. J44, Delonix regia. No. J45, Haemanthus. No. J46, Ophthalmophyllum. No. J47, Titanopsis. No. J48, Amorphophallus. No. J49, Zingiberacee.

Unwmk.
1963, Apr. 10 — Engr. — *Perf. 11*
J34 D4 50c car, bl, grn & yel .15 .15
J35 D4 50c car, bl, grn & yel .15 .15
J36 D4 1fr mag, grn & yel .15 .15
J37 D4 1fr mag, grn & yel .15 .15
J38 D4 1.50fr dk grn, lil & yel .15 .15
J39 D4 1.50fr dk grn, lil & yel .15 .15
J40 D4 2fr org ver, yel & grn .15 .15
J41 D4 2fr org ver, yel & grn .15 .15
J42 D4 5fr mag, grn & yel .15 .15
J43 D4 5fr mag, grn & yel .15 .15
J44 D4 10fr crim, grn & yel .22 .22
J45 D4 10fr crim, grn & yel .22 .22
J46 D4 20fr grn, yel & lil .45 .45
J47 D4 20fr grn, yel & lil .45 .45
J48 D4 40fr lilac & yel .80 .80
J49 D4 40fr lilac & yel .80 .80
Set value 3.50 3.50

The two types of each denomination in Nos. J34-J49 were printed tête bêche, se-tenant at the base.

MILITARY STAMP

Catalogue values for unused stamps in this section are for Never Hinged items.

M1

1963, July 1 — Unwmk. — *Perf. 13*
M1 M1 rose claret 1.50 1.50

CAPE JUBY

'kāp 'jü–bē

LOCATION — Northwest coast of Africa in Spanish Sahara
GOVT. — Spanish administration
AREA — 12,700 sq. mi.
POP. — 9,836
CAPITAL — Villa Bens (Cape Juby)

By agreement with France, Spain's Sahara possessions were extended to include Cape Juby and in 1916 Spanish troops occupied the territory. It is attached for administrative purposes to Spanish Sahara.

100 Centimos = 1 Peseta

Stamps of Rio de Oro, 1914 Surcharged in Violet, Red or Green

CABO JUBI
5
CÉNTIMOS

1916 — Unwmk. — *Perf. 13*
1 A6 5c on 4p rose (V) 70.00 12.00
2 A6 10c on 10p dl vio (R) 27.50 12.00
3 A6 15c on 50c dk brn (G) 35.00 22.50
4 A6 15c on 50c dk brn (R) 27.50 12.00
5 A6 40c on 1p red vio (G) 55.00 27.50
6 A6 40c on 1p red vio (R) 45.00 15.00
Nos. 1-6 (6) 260.00 101.00

Nos. 1-6 exist with inverted surcharge. Same values.

Stamps of Spain, 1876-1917, Overprinted in Red or Black

CABO JUBY

1919 — *Imperf.*
7 A21 ¼c bl grn (R) .15 .15

Perf. 13x12½, 14
8 A46 2c dk brn (Bk) .15 .15
a. Double overprint 15.00 6.75
b. Double overprint (Bk + R) 40.00 27.50
9 A46 5c grn (R) .40 .15
a. Double overprint 15.00 6.75
b. Inverted overprint 21.50 14.00
10 A46 10c car (Bk) .45 .15
a. Double overprint (Bk + R) 40.00 27.50
11 A46 15c ocher (Bk) 2.10 .15
b. Double overprint 15.00 6.75
c. Red control # 3.00 3.00
d. As "c," inverted overprint 11.00
12 A46 20c ol grn (R) 12.00 2.00
13 A46 25c dp bl (R) 2.00 .25
a. Double overprint 15.00 6.75
14 A46 30c bl grn (R) 2.00 .25
15 A46 40c rose (Bk) 2.00 .25
16 A46 50c sl bl (R) 2.25 .25
17 A46 1p lake (Bk) 6.50 2.00
18 A46 4p dp vio (R) 22.50 9.25
19 A46 10p org (Bk) 32.50 10.00
Nos. 7-19 (13) 85.00 25.00

Nos. 8-19 have blue control number on back. Nos. 8-13, 15, 17-19 exist imperf.

Same on Stamps of Spain, 1920-21

1922 — *Imperf.*
20 A47 1c blue green (R) 16.00 9.00

Engr. — *Perf. 13x12½*
Blue Control Number on Back
23 A46 20c violet 110.00 35.00

A 2c exists, value $150.

Same on Stamps of Spain, 1922-23

1925 — *Perf. 13½x13*
25 A49 5c red vio 4.00 1.75
26 A49 10c bl grn 12.00 1.75
28 A49 20c violet 25.00 5.75
Nos. 25-28 (3) 41.00 9.25

Exists on Spain No. 331, 2c olive green. Value $150 unused.

Seville-Barcelona Exposition Issue

Stamps of Spain, 1929, Overprinted in Red or Blue

CABO JUBY

1929 — *Perf. 11*
29 A52 5c rose lake (Bl) .15 .15
30 A53 10c green (R) .15 .15
31 A50 15c Prus bl (R) .15 .15
32 A51 20c pur (R) .15 .15
33 A50 25c brt rose (Bl) .15 .15
34 A52 30c blk brn (Bl) .20 .25
35 A53 40c dk bl (R) .20 .25
36 A51 50c dp org (Bl) .35 .50
37 A52 1p bl blk (R) 9.50 5.75
38 A53 4p dp rose (Bl) 12.00 11.50
39 A53 10p brn (Bl) 12.00 8.50
Nos. 29-39 (11) 35.00 27.50

Stamps of Spanish Morocco, 1928-33, Overprinted in Black or Red

Cabo Juby

1934 — *Perf. 14*
40 A7 1c brt rose (Bk) .25 .25
41 A2 2c dk vio (R) 2.00 .35
42 A2 5c dp bl (R) 2.00 .50
43 A2 10c dk grn (Bk) 4.50 .85
43A A10 10c dk grn (R) 1.50 1.25
44 A2 15c org brn (Bk) 9.50 3.50
45 A7 20c sl grn (R) 4.25 2.40
46 A3 25c cop red (Bk) 2.00 2.00
47 A10 30c red brn (Bk) 4.00 2.40
48 A13 40c dp bl (R) 14.00 8.50
49 A13 50c red org (Bk) 25.00 13.00
50 A4 1p yel grn (Bk) 15.00 7.50
51 A5 2.50p red vio (Bk) 35.00 16.00
52 A6 4p ultra (R) 45.00 21.00

No. 43A and 1c, 20c, 30c, 40c, 50c, with control numbers.

Same Overprint in Black on Stamp of Spanish Morocco, 1932

53 A2 1c car rose ("Ct") 1.00 .50
Nos. 40-53 (15) 165.00 80.00

Stamps of Spanish Morocco, 1933-35, Overprinted in Black, Blue or Red — CABO JUBY

1935-36
54 A8 2c grn (R) .35 .15
55 A9 5c mag (Bk) 1.40 .15
55A A10 10c dk grn (R) ('36) 7.50 1.50
56 A11 15c yel (Bl) 3.25 .95
57 A12 25c crim (Bk) 25.00 1.50
58 A8 1p sl blk (R) 4.50 2.25
59 A9 2.50p brn (Bl) 18.00 8.50
60 A11 4p yel grn (R) 25.00 11.00
61 A12 5p blk (R) 25.00 14.00
Nos. 54-61 (9) 110.00 40.00

Same Overprint in Black or Red on Stamps of Spanish Morocco, 1935

1935 *Perf. 13½*
62 A14 25c vio (R) 2.25 1.00
63 A15 30c crim (Bk) 2.25 .85
64 A14 40c org (Bk) 3.00 1.00
65 A15 50c brt bl (R) 6.00 1.00
66 A14 60c dk bl grn (R) 7.25 2.25
67 A15 2p brn lake (Bk) 40.00 14.00

Same Overprint on Stamps of Spanish Morocco, 1933

Perf. 13½, 14
68 A7 1c brt rose (Bk) .15 .15

Perf. 14
69 A7 20c slate grn (R) 3.00 1.50
Nos. 62-69 (8) 63.90 21.75

Same Overprint on Stamps of Spanish Morocco, 1937

1937 *Perf. 13½*
70 A21 1c dk bl (Bk) .20 .15
71 A21 2c org brn (Bk) .20 .15
72 A21 5c cer (Bk) .20 .15
73 A21 10c emer (Bk) .20 .15
74 A21 15c brt bl (Bk) .25 .15
75 A21 20c red brn (Bk) .25 .20
76 A21 25c mag (Bk) .25 .20
77 A21 30c red org (Bk) .25 .20
78 A21 40c org (Bk) .80 .55
79 A21 50c ultra (R) .80 .55
80 A21 60c yel grn (Bk) .80 .55
81 A21 1p bl vio (Bk) .80 .55
82 A21 2p Prus bl (Bk) 37.50 35.00
83 A21 2.50p gray blk (R) 37.50 35.00
84 A21 4p dk brn (Bk) 37.50 35.00
85 A22 10p vio blk (R) 37.50 35.00
Nos. 70-85 (16) 155.00 143.55

1st Year of the Revolution.

Same Overprint in Black on Types of Spanish Morocco, 1939

Designs: 5c, Spanish quarter. 10c, Moroccan quarter. 15c, Street scene, Larache. 20c, Tetuan.

1939 **Photo.** *Perf. 13½*
86 A25 5c vermilion .40 .30
87 A25 10c deep green .40 .30
88 A25 15c brown lake .40 .35
89 A25 20c bright blue .40 .35
Nos. 86-89 (4) 1.60 1.30

Same Overprint in Black or Red on Stamps of Spanish Morocco, 1940

1940 *Perf. 11½x11*
90 A26 1c dk brn (Bk) .15 .15
91 A27 2c ol grn (R) .15 .15
92 A28 5c dk bl (R) .15 .15
93 A29 10c dk red lil (Bk) .15 .15
94 A30 15c dk grn (R) .15 .15
95 A31 20c pur (R) .15 .15
96 A32 25c blk brn (R) .15 .15
97 A33 30c brt grn (Bk) .15 .15
98 A34 40c slate grn (R) .45 .15
99 A35 45c org ver (Bk) .45 .15
100 A36 50c brn org (Bk) .50 .15
101 A37 70c saph (R) 1.40 .55
102 A38 1p ind & brn (Bk) 3.00 .55
103 A39 2.50p choc & dk grn (Bk) 7.50 3.50
104 A40 5p dk cer & sep (Bk) 7.50 3.50
105 A41 10p dk ol grn & brn org (Bk) 18.00 13.00
Nos. 90-105 (16) 40.00 22.75

Imperfs exist.

Stamps of Spanish Morocco, 1944. Overprinted in Black or Red — CABO JUBY

1944, Oct. 2 **Unwmk.** *Perf. 12½*
106 A47 1c choc & lt bl .15 .15
107 A48 2c slate grn & lt grn .15 .15
108 A49 5c choc & grnsh blk (R) .15 .15
109 A50 10c brt ultra & red org .15 .15
110 A51 15c sl grn & lt grn .15 .15
111 A52 20c dp cl & blk (R) .15 .15
112 A53 25c lt bl & choc .15 .15
113 A47 30c yel grn & brt ultra (R) .15 .15
114 A48 40c choc & red vio .15 .15
115 A49 50c brt ultra, & red brn .15 .15
116 A50 75c yel grn & brt ultra (R) .60 .25
117 A51 1p brt ultra & choc .60 .25
118 A52 2.50p blk & brt ultra (R) 1.65 1.25
119 A53 10p sal & gray blk (R) 11.50 9.25
Nos. 106-119 (14) 15.85 12.50

Same Overprint on Stamps of Spanish Morocco, 1946

1946, Mar. *Perf. 10½x10*
120 A54 1c pur & brn .15 .15
121 A55 2c dk Prus grn & vio blk (R) .15 .15
122 A54 10c dp org vio bl .15 .15
123 A55 15c dk bl & bl grn .15 .15
124 A54 25c yel grn & ultra .15 .15
125 A56 40c dk bl & brn (R) .15 .15
126 A55 45c blk & rose .15 .15
127 A57 1p dk Prus grn & dp bl .65 .30
128 A58 2.50p dp org & grnsh gray (R) 2.00 1.50
129 A59 10p dk bl & gray (R) 6.50 4.50
Nos. 120-129 (10) 10.20 7.35

Same Overprint in Carmine, Black or Brown on Stamps of Spanish Morocco, 1948

1948, Jan. 1 *Perf. 10, 10x10½*
130 A64 2c pur & brn .15 .15
131 A65 5c dp claret & vio .15 .15
132 A66 15c brt ultra & bl grn (Bk) .15 .15
133 A67 25c blk & Prus grn .15 .15
134 A65 35c brt ultra & gray blk .15 .15
135 A68 50c red & vio (Br) .15 .15
136 A66 70c dk gray grn & ultra (Bk) .15 .15
137 A67 90c cer & dk gray grn (Bk) .15 .15
138 A68 1p brt ultra & vio (Br) .18 .18
139 A64 2.50p vio brn & sl grn .75 .45
140 A69 10p bl & dp ultra 2.50 1.90
Set value 4.05 3.15

SEMI-POSTAL STAMPS

Types of Semi-Postal Stamps of Spain, 1926, Overprinted — CABO-JUBY

1926 **Unwmk.** *Perf. 12½, 13*
B1 SP1 1c orange 6.00 3.25
B2 SP2 2c rose 6.00 3.25
B3 SP3 5c blk brn 2.00 1.50
B4 SP4 10c dk grn 1.10 1.10
B5 SP1 15c dk vio 1.10 1.10
B6 SP4 20c vio brn 1.10 1.10
B7 SP5 25c dp car 1.10 1.10
B8 SP1 30c ol grn 1.10 1.10
B9 SP3 40c ultra 1.10 1.10
B10 SP2 50c red brn 1.10 1.10
B11 SP4 1p vermilion 1.10 1.10
B12 SP3 4p bister 1.10 1.10
B13 SP5 10p lt vio 1.10 1.10
Nos. B1-B13 (13) 25.00 19.00

Nos. B12-B13 surcharged "Alfonso XIII" and new value are listed as Spain Nos. B68-B69. See Spain No. B6a.

AIR POST STAMPS

Spanish Morocco, Nos. C1 to C10 Overprinted "CABO JUBY" as on #54-61

1938, June 1 **Unwmk.** *Perf. 13½*
C1 AP1 5c brown .15 .15
C2 AP1 10c brt grn .15 .15
C3 AP1 25c crimson .15 .15
C4 AP1 40c light blue 1.50 .65
C5 AP2 50c brt mag .15 .15
C6 AP2 75c dk bl .15 .15
C7 AP1 1p sepia .15 .15
C8 AP1 1.50p dp vio 1.00 .35
C9 AP1 2p dp red brn 2.10 .85
C10 AP1 3p brn blk 5.50 2.75
Nos. C1-C10 (10) 11.00 5.50

Strait of Gibraltar — AP3

Designs: 5c, Ketama landscape. 10c, Mosque, Tangier. 15c, Velez. 90c, Sanjurjo.

1942, Apr. 1 **Photo.** *Perf. 12½*
C11 AP3 5c deep blue .15 .15
C12 AP3 10c org brn .15 .15
C13 AP3 15c grnsh blk .15 .15
C14 AP3 90c dk rose .45 .25
C15 AP3 5p black 1.60 .85
Nos. C11-C15 (5) 2.50
Set value 1.25

SPECIAL DELIVERY STAMPS

Special Delivery Stamp of Spain Ovptd. "CABO JUBY" as on #7-28

1919 **Unwmk.** *Perf. 14*
E1 SD1 20c red (Bk) 1.40 .85
b. Double overprint 21.00 12.50

Spanish Morocco No. E4 Overprinted "CABO JUBY" as on Nos. 40-52 in Red

1934
E2 SD2 20c black 4.75 4.50

Spanish Morocco No. E5 Overprinted "CABO JUBY" as on Nos. 54-61

1935
E3 SD3 20c vermilion 2.50 .75

Same Ovpt. on Spanish Morocco, No. E6

1937 *Perf. 13½*
E4 SD4 20c bright carmine .65 .40

1st Year of the Revolution.

Same Ovpt. on Spanish Morocco, No. E8

1940 *Perf. 11½x11*
E5 SD5 25c scarlet .35 .25

SEMI-POSTAL SPECIAL DELIVERY STAMP

Type of Semi-Postal Special Delivery Stamp of Spain, 1926, Overprinted "CABO-JUBY" as on Nos. B1-B13

1926 **Unwmk.** *Perf. 12½, 13*
EB1 SPSD1 20c ultra & black 1.75 1.40

CAPE VERDE

'kāp 'vərd

LOCATION — A group of 10 islands and five islets in the Atlantic Ocean, about 500 miles due west of Senegal.
GOVT. — Republic
AREA — 1,557 sq. mi.
POP. — 296,093 (1980)
CAPITAL — Praia

The Portuguese territory of Cape Verde became independent on July 5, 1975.

1000 Reis = 1 Milreis
100 Centavos = 1 Escudo (1913)

Catalogue values for unused stamps in this country are for Never Hinged items, beginning with Scott 268 in the regular postage section, Scott J31 in the postage due section, and Scott RA6 in the postal tax section.

Crown of Portugal — A1

King Luiz — A2

Perf. 12½, 13½

1877 **Unwmk.** **Typo.**
1 A1 5r black 3.00 1.00
2 A1 10r yellow 30.00 11.00
3 A1 20r bister 2.00 1.00
4 A1 25r rose 1.50 1.00
a. Perf. 13½ 7.50 4.00
5 A1 40r blue 75.00 40.00
a. Cliche of Mozambique in Cape Verde plate, in pair with #5 700.00 500.00
b. As "a," perf. 13½ 1,500. 1,500.
6 A1 50r green 75.00 40.00
7 A1 100r lilac 6.00 1.50
8 A1 200r orange 3.00 1.50
a. Perf. 13½ 8.00 4.00
9 A1 300r brown 3.00 1.50
Nos. 1-9 (9) 198.50 98.50

1881-85
10 A1 10r green 2.00 .90
11 A1 20r carmine ('85) 3.00 1.50
a. Perf. 13½ 40.00 22.50
12 A1 25r violet ('85) 3.00 1.25
13 A1 40r yellow buff 2.00 .90
a. Imperf. .75
b. Cliche of Mozambique in Cape Verde plate, in pair with #13 50.00 50.00
c. As "b," imperf. 25.00
14 A1 50r blue 5.00 2.25
Nos. 10-14 (5) 15.00 6.80

Reprints of the 1877-85 issues are on smooth white chalky paper, ungummed, and on thin white paper with shiny white gum. They are perf 13½.

1886 **Embossed** *Perf. 12½, 13½*
Chalk-Surfaced Paper
15 A2 5r black 3.00 1.50
16 A2 10r green 4.00 1.75
17 A2 20r carmine 5.00 2.50
a. Perf. 13½ 6.00 3.50
18 A2 25r violet 5.00 1.50
19 A2 40r chocolate 7.00 2.00
a. Perf. 13½ 8.00 4.00
20 A2 50r blue 6.00 1.75
21 A2 100r yel brown 6.00 2.25
22 A2 200r gray lilac 12.00 6.50
23 A2 300r orange 18.00 9.50
Nos. 15-23 (9) 66.00 29.25

The 25r, 50r and 100r have been reprinted in aniline colors with clean-cut Perf. 13½.
For surcharges see Nos. 59-67, 184-187.

King Carlos
A3 A4

Perf. 11½, 12½, 13½

1894-95 **Typo.**
24 A3 5r orange .90 .60
25 A3 10r redsh violet .90 .70
26 A3 15r chocolate 1.50 1.00
a. Perf. 12½ 100.00 67.50
27 A3 20r lavender 1.90 1.25
28 A3 25r dp green 1.90 1.40
a. Perf. 12½ 4.00 3.00
29 A3 50r lt blue 1.50 1.40
a. Perf. 13½ 8.00 3.00
30 A3 75r carmine ('95) 6.25 3.75
a. Perf. 13½ 17.50 10.50
31 A3 80r yel grn ('95) 7.75 5.00
a. Perf. 13½ 20.00 14.00
32 A3 100r brn, *buff* ('95) 5.25 1.50
a. Perf. 12½ 45.00 20.00
33 A3 150r car, *rose* ('95) 10.50 7.75
a. Perf. 12½ 125.00 100.00
b. Perf. 11½ 45.00 30.00
34 A3 200r dk blue, *lt blue* ('95) 8.75 5.50
a. Perf. 12½ 100.00 75.00
35 A3 300r dk blue, *sal* ('95) 15.00 9.50
Nos. 24-35 (12) 62.10 39.35

For surcharges see Nos. 68-78, 137, 189-193, 201-205.

1898-1903 *Perf. 11½*
Name and Value in Black except 500r
36 A4 2½r gray .20 .15
37 A4 5r orange .20 .15
38 A4 10r lt green .45 .15
39 A4 15r brown 2.50 1.00
40 A4 15r gray green ('03) .90 .70
41 A4 20r gray violet 1.00 .35
42 A4 25r sea green 2.25 .70
a. Perf. 12½ 52.50 30.00
43 A4 25r carmine ('03) .55 .20
44 A4 50r dark blue 2.25 .60
45 A4 50r brown ('03) 1.75 1.40
46 A4 65r slate blue ('03) 25.00 *40.00*
47 A4 75r rose 4.25 2.00
48 A4 75r lilac ('03) 1.50 1.25
49 A4 80r violet 3.75 2.50
50 A4 100r dk blue, *blue* 1.25 .75
51 A4 115r org brn, *pink* ('03) 12.00 *15.00*
52 A4 130r brown, *straw* ('03) 12.00 *15.00*
53 A4 150r brown, *straw* 9.00 7.50
54 A4 200r red vio, *pnksh* 1.75 1.40
55 A4 300r dk blue, *rose* 9.00 2.50
56 A4 400r dull blue, *straw* ('03) 8.00 4.25

No.	Type	Description	Unused	Used
57	A4	500r blk & red, *blue* ('01)	8.00	2.50
58	A4	700r violet, *yelsh* ('01)	14.00	8.75
		Nos. 36-58 (23)	121.55	108.80

For overprints and suecharges see Nos. 80-99, 139, 200.

Regular Issues Surcharged in Red or Black

65 RÉIS

Two spacing types of surcharge. See note above Angola No. 61.

On Issue of 1886

1902, Dec. 1 *Perf. 12½, 13½*

No.	Type	Description	Unused	Used
59	A2	65r on 5r black (R)	3.00	2.50
60	A2	65r on 200r gray lilac	3.00	2.50
61	A2	65r on 300r orange	3.00	2.50
62	A2	115r on 10r green	3.00	2.75
63	A2	115r on 20r rose	3.00	2.75
a.		Perf. 13½	27.50	18.00
64	A2	130r on 50r blue	3.00	2.50
65	A2	130r on 100r brown	3.00	2.50
66	A2	400r on 25r violet	1.50	1.25
67	A2	400r on 40r choc	2.50	2.00
a.		Perf. 13½	27.50	22.50

On Issue of 1894

Perf. 11½, 12½, 13½

No.	Type	Description	Unused	Used
68	A3	65r on 10r red violet	4.75	3.00
69	A3	65r on 20r lavender	4.50	2.50
70	A3	65r on 100r brown, *buff*	4.50	3.00
a.		Perf 12½	12.00	10.00
71	A3	115r on 5r orange	2.50	1.90
a.		Inverted surcharge	40.00	40.00
72	A3	115r on 25r blue grn	2.50	1.90
a.		Perf. 11½	14.00	6.00
73	A3	115r on 150r car, *rose*	4.50	3.75
a.		Perf. 13½	20.00	12.00
74	A3	130r on 75r car	2.50	2.00
a.		Perf. 13½	25.00	22.50
75	A3	130r on 80r yel grn	2.25	2.00
76	A3	130r on 200r dk blue, *blue*	3.00	1.90
77	A3	400r on 50r lt blue	3.00	2.50
a.		Inverted surcharge	65.00	55.00
b.		Perf. 13½	40.00	32.50
78	A3	400r on 300r dk blue, *sal*	1.50	1.10

On Newspaper Stamp of 1893

No.	Type	Description	Unused	Used
79	N1	400r on 2½r brown	1.25	1.10
a.		Inverted surcharge	25.00	
b.		Perf. 12½	30.00	20.00
		Nos. 59-79 (21)	61.75	47.90

Reprints of Nos. 59, 66, 67, and 77 have shiny white gum and clean-cut perforation 13½.

For overprint and surcharge see #137, 205-206.

Overprinted in Black On Nos. 39, 42, 44, 47

PROVISORIO

1902-03 *Perf. 11½*

No.	Type	Description	Unused	Used
80	A4	15r brown	1.50	.80
81	A4	25r sea green	1.50	.80
82	A4	50r blue ('03)	1.75	1.00
83	A4	75r rose ('03)	2.25	1.40
a.		Inverted overprint	40.00	40.00
		Nos. 80-83 (4)	7.00	4.00

For overprint see No. 139.

No. 46 Surcharged in Black

50 RÉIS

1905, July 1

No.	Type	Description	Unused	Used
84	A4	50r on 65r slate blue	1.75	1.75

Stamps of 1898-1903 Overprinted in Carmine or Green

REPUBLICA

1911, Aug. 20

No.	Type	Description	Unused	Used
85	A4	2½r gray	.20	.15
86	A4	5r orange	.20	.15
87	A4	10r lt green	.60	.50
88	A4	15r gray green	.35	.20
89	A4	20r gray violet	.65	.65
90	A4	25r carmine (G)	.65	.30
91	A4	50r brown	4.00	2.75
92	A4	75r red lilac	.85	.50
93	A4	100r dk blue, *blue*	.85	.60
94	A4	115r org brn, *pink*	.45	1.25
95	A4	130r brown, *straw*	.45	1.25
96	A4	200r red vio, *pnksh*	3.25	3.25
97	A4	400r dull bl, *straw*	1.25	1.25
98	A4	500r blk & red, *bl*	1.50	1.10
99	A4	700r violet, *straw*	1.50	1.10
		Nos. 85-99 (15)	16.75	15.00

King Manuel II — A5

Overprinted in Carmine or Green

1912 *Perf. 11½x12*

No.	Type	Description	Unused	Used
100	A5	2½r violet	.15	1.25
101	A5	5r black	.15	.15
102	A5	10r gray grn	.15	.15
103	A5	20r carmine (G)	1.25	.70
104	A5	25r vio brown	.25	.15
105	A5	50r dk blue	2.00	1.65
106	A5	75r bister brn	.45	.35
107	A5	100r brown, *lt grn*	.45	.35
108	A5	200r dk green, *sal*	.70	.60
109	A5	300r black, *azure*	.70	.60

Perf. 14½x15

No.	Type	Description	Unused	Used
110	A5	400r black & blue	2.00	1.65
111	A5	500r ol grn & vio brn	2.00	1.65
		Nos. 100-111 (12)	10.25	9.25

Vasco da Gama Issue of Various Portuguese Colonies

Common Design Types CD20-CD27 Surcharged

REPUBLICA CABO VERDE ¼ C.

On Stamps of Macao

1913, Feb. 13 *Perf. 12½ to 16*

No.	Description	Unused	Used
112	¼c on ½a blue grn	3.00	3.00
113	½c on 1a red	3.00	3.00
114	1c on 2a red violet	3.00	3.00
115	2½c on 4a yel grn	3.00	3.00
116	5c on 8a dk blue	5.00	5.00
117	7½c on 12a vio brn	4.00	4.00
118	10c on 16a bister brn	3.50	3.50
119	15c on 24a bister	4.00	4.00
	Nos. 112-119 (8)	28.50	28.50

On Stamps of Portuguese Africa

Perf. 14 to 15

No.	Description	Unused	Used
120	¼c on 2½r bl grn	.85	.85
121	½c on 5r red	.85	.85
122	1c on 10r red vio	.85	.85
123	2½c on 25r yel grn	.90	.90
124	5c on 50r dk blue	1.50	1.50
125	7½c on 75r vio brn	2.00	2.00
126	10c on 100r bis brn	1.75	1.75
127	15c on 150r bister	2.50	2.50
	Nos. 120-127 (8)	11.20	11.20

On Stamps of Timor

No.	Description	Unused	Used
128	¼c on ½a bl grn	1.10	1.10
129	½c on 1a red	1.10	1.10
130	1c on 2a red vio	1.10	1.10
131	2½c on 4a yel grn	1.10	1.10
132	5c on 8a dk blue	3.75	3.75
133	7½c On 12a vio brn	3.75	3.75
134	10c on 16a bis brn	2.25	2.25
135	15c on 24a bister	2.75	2.75
	Nos. 128-135 (8)	16.90	16.90
	Nos. 112-135 (24)	56.60	56.60

For surcharges see Nos. 197-198.

No. 75 Overprinted in Red

REPUBLICA

1913 *Perf. 11½, 12½, 13½*

No.	Type	Description	Unused	Used
137	A3	130r on 80r yel grn	2.50	2.00

Nos. 73 and 76 overprinted but not issued. Values, $10, $12.

Same Overprint on No. 83 in Green

1914 *Perf. 12*

No.	Type	Description	Unused	Used
139	A4	75r rose	2.50	2.00
a.		"PROVISORIO" double (G and R)	45.00	40.00

Ceres — A6

Perf. 11½, 12x11½, 15x14

1914-26 **Typo.**

Name and Value in Black

No.	Type	Description	Unused	Used
144	A6	¼c olive brn	.15	.15
a.		Imperf.		
145	A6	½c black	.15	.15
146	A6	1c blue grn	.85	.75
147	A6	1c yel grn ('22)	.15	.15
148	A6	1½c lilac brown	.15	.15
149	A6	2c carmine	.15	.15
150	A6	2c gray ('26)	.25	5.00
151	A6	2½c lt violet	.15	.15
152	A6	3c org ('22)	.30	.25
153	A6	4c rose ('22)	.15	1.65
154	A6	4½c gray ('22)	.15	5.00
155	A6	5c deep blue	.75	.45
156	A6	5c brt blue ('22)	.15	.15
157	A6	6c lilac ('22)	.15	2.75
158	A6	7c ultra ('22)	.15	2.75
159	A6	7½c yel brn	.15	1.00
160	A6	8c slate	.40	.30
161	A6	10c orange brn	.15	.15
162	A6	12c blue grn ('22)	.35	.25
163	A6	15c plum	6.50	6.00
164	A6	15c brn rose ('22)	.25	.15
165	A6	20c yel grn	.20	.15
166	A6	24c ultra ('26)	1.50	1.40
167	A6	25c choc ('26)	1.50	1.40
168	A6	30c brown, *grn*	3.50	3.50
169	A6	30c gray grn ('22)	.35	.25
170	A6	40c brown, *pink*	3.75	3.75
171	A6	40c turq blue ('22)	1.00	.25
172	A6	50c orange, *sal*	3.75	3.75
173	A6	50c violet ('26)	1.50	.30
174	A6	60c dk blue ('22)	1.50	.45
175	A6	60c rose ('26)	1.25	.45
176	A6	80c brt rose ('22)	2.50	1.10
177	A6	1e green, *blue*	3.75	3.75
178	A6	1e rose ('22)	5.00	2.25
179	A6	1e dp blue ('26)	7.00	1.50
180	A6	2e dk violet ('22)	10.00	4.00
181	A6	5e buff ('26)	15.00	12.00
182	A6	10e pink ('26)	30.00	25.00
183	A6	20e pale turq ('26)	60.00	40.00
		Nos. 144-183 (40)	164.65	132.75

For surcharge see No. 214.

Provisional Issue of 1902 Overprinted in Carmine

REPUBLICA

1915 *Perf. 11½, 12½, 13½*

No.	Type	Description	Unused	Used
184	A2	115r on 10r green	1.75	1.75
a.		Perf. 13½	15.00	15.00
185	A2	115r on 20r rose	1.25	1.25
a.		Perf. 13½	15.00	15.00
186	A2	130r on 50r blue	1.10	1.10
187	A2	130r on 100r brown	.70	.70
188	A3	115r on 5r orange	.50	.40
a.		Inverted overprint	30.00	
189	A3	115r on 25r blue grn	.70	.65
a.		Perf. 11½	15.00	15.00
190	A3	115r on 150r car, *rose*	.50	.35
191	A3	130r on 75r carmine	.90	.90
192	A3	130r on 80r yel grn	.70	.70
a.		Inverted overprint	30.00	
193	A3	130r on 200r bl, *bl*	.90	.90
a.		Perf. 12½	40.00	32.50
		Nos. 184-193 (10)	9.00	8.70

War Tax Stamps of Portuguese Africa Surcharged

CABO VERDE CORREIOS ½ C.

1921, Feb. 3 *Perf. 15x14, 11½*

No.	Type	Description	Unused	Used
194	WT1	¼c on 1c green	.22	.22
195	WT1	½c on 1c green	.40	.28
a.		"1/2" instead of "½" as shown	10.00	10.00
196	WT1	1c green	.40	.28

Nos. 127 and 126 Surcharged

2 C.

Perf. 14 to 15

No.	Type	Description	Unused	Used
197	CD27	2c on 15c on 150r	1.00	1.00
198	CD26	4c on 10c on 100r	1.25	1.00
a.		On No. 118 (error)	150.00	150.00

The 4c surcharge also exists on No. 134.

No. 50 Surcharged

6 c. REPUBLICA

Perf. 12

No.	Type	Description	Unused	Used
200	A4	6c on 100r dk bl, *bl*	1.25	1.25
a.		No accent on "U" of surcharge	12.50	8.00
		Nos. 194-200 (6)	4.52	4.03

No. 200 has an accent on the "U" of the surcharge.

Stamps of 1913-15 Surcharged

$04

1922, Apr. *Perf. 11½, 12½, 13½*

On No. 137

No.	Type	Description	Unused	Used
201	A3	4c on 130r on 80r	1.25	1.25

On Nos. 191-193

No.	Type	Description	Unused	Used
202	A3	4c on 130r on 75r	1.65	1.65
203	A3	4c on 130r on 80r	1.25	1.25
204	A3	4c on 130r on 200r	.85	.60
a.		Perf. 12½	15.00	15.00
		Nos. 201-204 (4)	5.00	4.75

Surcharge of Nos. 201-204 with smaller $ occurs once in sheet of 28. Value eight times normal.

Nos. 78-79 Surcharged

República 40 C.

1925 *Perf. 13½, 11½*

No.	Type	Description	Unused	Used
205	A3	40c on 400r on 300r	.60	.55
206	N1	40c on 400r on 2½r	.40	.45

No. 176 Surcharged

70 C.

1931, Nov. *Perf. 12x11½*

No.	Type	Description	Unused	Used
214	A6	70c on 80c brt rose	2.75	1.40

Ceres — A7

1934, May 1 **Wmk. 232**

No.	Type	Description	Unused	Used
215	A7	1c bister	.15	1.25
216	A7	5c olive brown	.15	.15
217	A7	10c violet	.16	.15
218	A7	15c black	.20	.15
219	A7	20c gray	.25	.15
220	A7	30c dk green	.30	.15
221	A7	40c red org	.40	.20
222	A7	45c brt blue	.75	.45
223	A7	50c brown	.70	.40
224	A7	60c olive grn	.70	.40
225	A7	70c brown org	.70	.40
226	A7	80c emerald	.70	.40
227	A7	85c deep rose	2.25	2.00
228	A7	1e maroon	1.75	.55
229	A7	1.40e dk blue	3.00	2.25
230	A7	2e dk violet	3.50	1.75
231	A7	5e apple green	12.50	4.00
232	A7	10e olive bister	21.00	9.50
233	A7	20e orange	45.00	30.00
		Nos. 215-233 (19)	94.16	54.30

For surcharge see No. 256.

Vasco da Gama Issue

Common Design Types

1938 **Unwmk.** *Perf. 13½x13*

Name and Value in Black

No.	Type	Description	Unused	Used
234	CD34	1c gray green	.15	.70
235	CD34	5c orange brn	.15	.70
236	CD34	10c dk carmine	.15	.15
237	CD34	15c dk vio brn	.55	.30
238	CD34	20c slate	.25	.15
239	CD35	30c rose vio	.35	.15
240	CD35	35c brt green	.35	.20
241	CD35	40c brown	.35	.15
242	CD35	50c brt red vio	.35	.15
243	CD36	60c gray blk	.65	.30
244	CD36	70c brown vio	.65	.20
245	CD36	80c orange	.65	.20
246	CD36	1e red	.65	.20
247	CD37	1.75e blue	1.15	.45
248	CD37	2e dk blue grn	1.75	.70
249	CD37	5e ol grn	4.50	1.40

250	CD38	10e blue vio	6.25	1.40
251	CD38	20e red brown	16.00	3.50
		Nos. 234-251 (18)	34.90	11.00

For surcharges see #255, 271-276, 288-292.

Outline Map of Africa — A8

1939, June 23 Litho. *Perf. 11½x12*

252	A8	80c vio, *pale rose*	2.00	1.40
253	A8	1.75e blue, *pale bl*	10.00	7.00
254	A8	20e brown, *buff*	35.00	25.00
		Nos. 252-254 (3)	47.00	33.40

Visit of the President of Portugal in 1939.

Nos. 239 and 221 Surcharged with New Value and Bars in Black

1948 Unwmk. *Perf. 13½x13*

255	CD35	10c on 30c rose violet	.90	1.25

Perf. 12x11½
Wmk. 232

256	A7	25c on 40c red orange	1.00	1.25

Machado Pt., Sao Vicente — A9

Brava Creek, Sao Nicoláo — A10

Designs: 10c, Ribeira Grande. 1e, Harbor, Sao Vicente. 1.75e, Mindelo, distant view. 2e, Joao de Evora Beach. 5e, Mindelo. 10e, Volcano, Fire Island. 20e, Mt. Paul.

Perf. 14½
1948, Oct. 1 Litho. Unwmk.

257	A9	5c vio brn & bis	.20	.20
258	A9	10c ol grn & pale grn	.20	.15
259	A10	50c mag & lil rose	.35	.15
260	A10	1e brn vio & rose lil	1.25	.60
261	A10	1.75e ultra & grnsh bl	1.50	1.10
262	A10	2e dk brn & buff	7.25	.90
263	A10	5e ol grn & yel	10.50	4.25
264	A10	10e red & cream	13.00	7.25
265	A10	20e dk vio & bis	32.50	12.00
		Nos. 257-265 (9)	66.75	26.60

Common Design Types pictured in section at front of book

Lady of Fatima Issue
Common Design Type

1948, Dec.

266	CD40	50c dark blue	5.00	3.00

UPU Symbols — A10a

1949, Oct. *Perf. 14*

267	A10a	1e red vio & pink	2.00	2.00

UPU, 75th anniversary.

Catalogue values for unused stamps in this section, from this point to the end of the section, are for Never Hinged items.

Holy Year Issue
Common Design Types

1950, May *Perf. 13x13½*

268	CD41	1e orange brown	.35	.30
269	CD42	2e slate	1.75	1.10

Holy Year Conclusion Issue
Common Design Type

1951, Oct. Unwmk. *Perf. 14*

270	CD43	2e purple & lilac	.75	.60

Nos. 240, 244-245, 247, 250 Surcharged with New Value and Bars

Perf. 13½x13
1951, May 21 Unwmk.

271	CD35	10c on 35c	.28	*1.00*
272	CD36	20c on 70c	.42	*1.00*
273	CD36	40c on 70c	1.00	*1.40*
274	CD36	50c on 80c	1.75	*2.00*
275	CD37	1e on 1.75e	2.00	*2.75*
276	CD38	2e on 10e	3.50	*5.25*
a.		1e on 10e	225.00	175.00
		Nos. 271-276 (6)	8.95	*13.40*

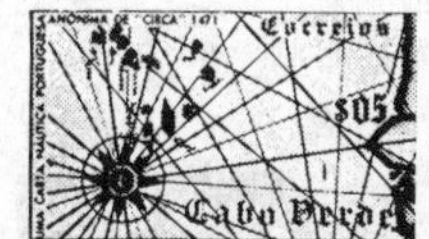

Map of Cape Verde Islands, 1502 — A11

Vicente Dias and Gonçalo de Cintra — A12

Portraits: 30c, Diogo Alfonso and Alvaro Fernandes. 50c, Lançarote and Soeiro da Costa. 1e, Diogo Gomes and Antonio da Nola. 2e, Prince Fernando and Prince Henry the Navigator. 3e, Antao Gonçalves and Dinis Dias. 5e, Alfonso Goncalves Baldaia and Joao Fernandes. 10e, Dinis Eanes da Gra and Alvaro de Freitas. 20e, Map of Cape Verde Islands, 1502.

1952, Feb. 24 *Perf. 14*

277	A11	5c multicolored	.15	.15
278	A12	10c multicolored	.15	.15
279	A12	30c multicolored	.15	.15
280	A12	50c multicolored	.15	.15
281	A12	1e multicolored	.20	.15
282	A12	2e multicolored	.60	.15
283	A12	3e multicolored	3.50	.55
284	A12	5e multicolored	1.75	.30
285	A12	10e multicolored	2.75	.65
286	A11	20e multicolored	6.00	.85
		Nos. 277-286 (10)	15.40	3.25

Medical Congress Issue
Common Design Type

Design: Hypodermic Injection.

1952, June *Perf. 13½*

287	CD44	20c ol grn & dk brn	.40	.30

No. 247 Surcharged with New Values and "X" in Black

1952, Jan. 25 *Perf. 13½x13*

288	CD37	10c on 1.75e	1.50	1.10
289	CD37	20c on 1.75e	1.50	1.10
290	CD37	50c on 1.75e	5.00	3.50
291	CD37	1e on 1.75e	.75	.45
292	CD37	1.50e on 1.75e	.75	.45
		Nos. 288-292 (5)	9.50	6.60

Facade of Jeronymos Convent — A13

Perf. 13½
1953, Jan. Unwmk. Litho.

293	A13	10c brn & pale olive	.15	.15
294	A13	50c purple & fawn	.25	.15
295	A13	1e dark green & fawn	.65	.42
		Nos. 293-295 (3)	1.05	.72

Exhibition of Sacred Missionary Art held at Lisbon in 1951.

Stamp of Portugal and Arms of Colonies — A13a

1953 Photo.

296	A13a	50c multicolored	.75	.40

Centenary of Portuguese stamps.

Sao Paulo Issue
Common Design Type

1954 Litho. *Perf. 13½*

297	CD46	1e grn, cream & gray	.35	.15

Belem Tower, Lisbon, and Colonial Arms — A14

Arms of Praia — A15

1955, May 15 Litho. *Perf. 13½*

298	A14	1e multicolored	.30	.20
299	A14	1.60e buff & multi	.50	.30

Visit of Pres. Francisco H. C. Lopes.

1958, June 14 *Perf. 12x11½*

300	A15	1e multicolored	.30	.16
301	A15	2.50e pink & multi	.60	.20

Centenary of city of Praia.

Fair Emblem, Globe and Arms — A15a

1958 *Perf. 12x11½*

302	A15a	2e multicolored	.45	.30

World's Fair, Brussels, Apr. 17-Oct. 19.

Tropical Medicine Congress Issue
Common Design Type

1958, Sept. 5 *Perf. 13½*

303	CD47	3e Aloe vera	2.00	1.25

Prince Henry — A16

Antonio da Nola — A17

1960, June 25 Litho. *Perf. 13½*

304	A16	2e multicolored	.30	.15

500th anniv. of the death of Prince Henry the Navigator.

1960, Oct. Unwmk. *Perf. 14½*

Design: 2.50e, Diogo Gomes.

305	A17	1e multicolored	.35	.24
306	A17	2.50e multicolored	.80	.50

Discovery of Cape Verde, 500th anniv.

School Children — A18

1960

307	A18	2.50e multicolored	.65	.30

10th anniv. of the Commission for Technical Cooperation in Africa South of the Sahara (C.C.T.A.).

Arms of Praia — A19

Designs: Arms of various cities and towns of Cape Verde.

1961, July Litho. *Perf. 13½*

308	A19	5c shown	.15	.15
309	A19	15c Nova Sintra	.15	.15
310	A19	20c Ribeira Brava	.15	.15
311	A19	30c Assomada	.15	.15
312	A19	1e Maio	.40	.15
313	A19	2e Mindelo	.32	.15
314	A19	2.50e Santa Maria	.60	.15
315	A19	3e Pombas	1.10	.20
316	A19	5e Sal-Rei	1.10	.20
317	A19	7.50e Tarrafal	.65	.25
318	A19	15e Maria Pia	1.10	.40
319	A19	30e San Felipe	2.25	.85
		Nos. 308-319 (12)	8.12	
		Set value		2.45

Sports Issue
Common Design Type

Sports: 50c, Javelin. 1e, Discus. 1.50e, Cricket. 2.50e, Boxing. 4.50e, Hurdling. 12.50e, Golf.

1962, Jan. 18 *Perf. 13½*

320	CD48	50c lt brown	.15	.15
321	CD48	1e lt green	.52	.18
322	CD48	1.50e lt blue grn	.30	.15
323	CD48	2.50e pale vio bl	.45	.22
324	CD48	4.50e orange	.75	.45
325	CD48	12.50e beige	1.65	1.10
		Nos. 320-325 (6)	3.82	2.25

Anti-Malaria Issue
Common Design Type

Design: Anopheles pretoriensis.

1962 Litho. *Perf. 13½*

326	CD49	2.50e multicolored	.60	.42

Airline Anniversary Issue
Common Design Type

1963, Oct. Unwmk. *Perf. 14½*

327	CD50	2.50e gray & multi	.40	.25

National Overseas Bank Issue
Common Design Type

Design: 1.50e, Jose da Silva Mendes Leal.

1964, May 16 *Perf. 13½*

328	CD51	1.50e multicolored	.40	.32

ITU Issue
Common Design Type

1965, May 17 Litho. *Perf. 14½*

329	CD52	2.50e buff & multi	1.00	.65

Militia Drummer, 1806 — A20

Designs: 1e, Soldier, Militia, 1806. 1.50e, Grenadier officer, 1833. 2.50e, Grenadier, 1833. 3e, Cavalry officer, 1834. 4e, Grenadier, 1835. 5e, Artillery officer, 1848. 10e, Drum major, infantry, 1856.

1965, Dec. 1 Litho. *Perf. 14½*

330	A20	50c multicolored	.15	.15
331	A20	1e multicolored	.20	.15
332	A20	1.50e multicolored	.30	.15
333	A20	2.50e multicolored	.65	.15

334	A20	3e multicolored	1.10	.25
335	A20	4e multicolored	.75	.25
336	A20	5e multicolored	.75	.30
337	A20	10e multicolored	1.40	1.00
		Nos. 330-337 (8)	5.30	2.40

National Revolution Issue
Common Design Type

Design: 1e, Dr. Adriano Moreira School and Health Center.

1966, May 28 Litho. ***Perf. 12***

338 CD53 1e multicolored .30 .30

Navy Club Issue
Common Design Type

Designs: 1e, Capt. Fontoura da Costa and gunboat Mandovy. 1.50e, Capt. Carvalho Araujo and minesweeper Augusto Castilho.

1967, Jan. 31 Litho. ***Perf. 13***

339	CD54	1e multicolored	.48	.24
340	CD54	1.50e multicolored	.80	.32

Virgin Mary Statue — A21

Pres. Rodrigues Thomaz — A22

1967, May 13 Litho. ***Perf. 12½x13***

341 A21 1e multicolored .20 .15

50th anniv. of the apparition of the Virgin Mary to 3 shepherd children at Fatima.

1968, Feb. 9 Litho. ***Perf. 13½***

342 A22 1e multicolored .20 .20

Issued to commemorate the 1968 visit of Pres. Americo de Deus Rodrigues Thomaz.

Cabral Issue

Pedro Alvares Cabral — A23

Design: 1e, Cantino's world map, 1502, horiz.

1968, Apr. 22 Litho. ***Perf. 14***

343	A23	1e multicolored	.70	.30
344	A23	1.50e multicolored	.80	.30

See note after Angola No. 545.
For overprint see No. 365.

Sao Vicente Harbor — A24

Physic Nut — A25

Designs: 1.50e, Peanut plant. 2.50e, Castor-oil plant. 3.50e, Yams. 4e, Date palm. 4.50e, Guavas. 5e, Tamarind. 10e, Bitter cassava. 30e, Woman carrying fruit baskets.

1968, Oct. 15 Litho. ***Perf. 14***

345	A24	50c multicolored	.15	.15
346	A25	1e multicolored	.15	.15
347	A25	1.50e multicolored	.15	.15
348	A25	2.50e multicolored	.15	.15
349	A25	3.50e multicolored	.20	.15
350	A25	4e multicolored	.20	.15
351	A25	4.50e multicolored	.25	.15
352	A25	5e multicolored	.25	.15
353	A25	10e multicolored	.52	.22
354	A25	30e multicolored	2.00	.85
		Nos. 345-354 (10)	4.02	
		Set value		1.75

For overprint see No. 372.

Admiral Coutinho Issue
Common Design Type

Design: Adm. Coutinho & map showing route of first flight from Lisbon to Rio de Janeiro, vert.

1969, Feb. 17 Litho. ***Perf. 14***

355 CD55 30c multicolored .15 .15

For surcharge see No. 388.

Vasco da Gama — A26

King Manuel I — A27

Vasco da Gama Issue

1969, Aug. 29 Litho. ***Perf. 14***

356 A26 1.50e multicolored .15 .15

Vasco da Gama (1469-1524), navigator.

Administration Reform Issue
Common Design Type

1969, Sept. 25 Litho. ***Perf. 14***

357 CD56 2e multicolored .15 .15

King Manuel I Issue

1969, Dec. 1 Litho. ***Perf. 14***

358 A27 3e multicolored .25 .15

500th anniv. of the birth of King Manuel I.

Marshal Carmona Issue
Common Design Type

Design: 2.50e, Antonio Oscar Carmona in marshal's uniform.

1970, Nov. 15 Litho. ***Perf. 14***

359 CD57 2.50e multi .25 .15

Galleons on Sanaga River — A28

1972, May 25 Litho. ***Perf. 13***

360 A28 5e lilac rose & multi .25 .15

4th centenary of the publication of The Lusiads by Luiz Camoens.

Olympic Games Issue
Common Design Type

Design: 4e, Basketball and boxing, Olympic emblem.

1972, June 20 ***Perf. 14x13½***

361 CD59 4e multicolored .25 .15

Lisbon-Rio de Janeiro Flight Issue
Common Design Type

Design: "Lusitania" landing at San Vicente.

1972, Sept. 20 Litho. ***Perf. 13½***

362 CD60 3.50e multi .32 .15

WMO Centenary Issue
Common Design Type

1973, Dec. 15 Litho. ***Perf. 13***

363 CD61 2.50e ultra & multi .32 .15

For overprint see No. 387.

Mindelo Desalination Plant — A29

1974 Litho. ***Perf. 13½***

364 A29 4e multicolored .50 .25

Opening of the Mindelo desalination plant.

Republic

No. 343 Overprinted: "INDEPENDENCIA / 5-Julho-75"

1975, Dec. 19 Litho. ***Perf. 14***

365 A23 1e multicolored .15 .15

Proclamation of Independence.

Amilcar Cabral, Flag and Crowd — A30

1976, Jan. 20

366 A30 5e multicolored .32 .15

3rd anniv. of the assassination of Amilcar Cabral (1924-73), revolutionary leader.

Rising Sun, Coat of Arms, Liberated People — A31

1976, July 5 Litho. ***Perf. 14***

367	A31	50c multicolored	.15	.15
368	A31	3e multicolored	.30	.15
369	A31	15e multicolored	.85	.40
370	A31	50e multicolored	2.75	1.25
a.		Miniature sheet of 4, #367-370	*12.00*	*12.00*
		Nos. 367-370 (4)	4.05	1.95

First anniversary of independence.

No. 351 Overprinted with Row of Stars and: "REPUBLICA / DE"

1976 Litho. ***Perf. 14***

372 A25 4.50e multi 2.00 1.50

Amilcar Cabral, Map and Flag of Cape Verde A32

1976, Sept. 19 ***Perf. 14***

373 A32 1e multicolored .15 .15

Party of Intl. Action (PAICC), 20th anniv.

Electronic Tree and ITU Emblem — A33

Ashtray — A34

1977, May 17 Litho. ***Perf. 13½x13***

374 A33 5.50e multi .25 .15

World Telecommunications Day.

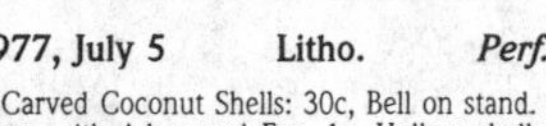

1977, July 5 Litho. ***Perf. 14***

Carved Coconut Shells: 30c, Bell on stand. 50c, Lamp with Adam and Eve. 1e, Hollow shell with Nativity. 1.50e, Desk lamp. 5e, Jar. 10e, Jar with hinged cover. 20e, Tobacco jar with palms. 30e, Stringed instrument.

375	A34	20c lilac & multi	.15	.15
376	A34	30c rose & multi	.15	.15
377	A34	50c salmon & multi	.15	.15
378	A34	1e lt green & multi	.15	.15
379	A34	1.50e orange yel & multi	.15	.15
380	A34	5e gray & multi	.25	.15
381	A34	10e lt blue & multi	.52	.15
382	A34	20e yellow & multi	1.00	.52
383	A34	30e rose lilac & multi	1.65	.85
		Nos. 375-383 (9)	4.17	
		Set value		1.95

Cape Verde No. 1 and Coat of Arms — A35

Congress Emblem — A36

1977, Sept. 12 Litho. ***Perf. 13½***

384	A35	4e blue & multi	.20	.15
385	A35	8e lilac & multi	.45	.18
		Set value		.26

Centenary of Cape Verde stamps.

1977, Nov. 15 ***Perf. 14***

386 A36 3.50e multi .20 .15

African Party of Independence of Guinea-Bissau and Cape Verde (PAIGC), 3rd congress, Nov. 15-20.

No. 363 Overprinted with Row of Stars and: "REPUBLICA / DE"

1978, May 1 ***Perf. 12***

387 CD61 2.50e ultra & multi .20 .15

No. 355 Surcharged with New Value and Bars

1978, May 1 ***Perf. 14***

388 CD55 3e on 30c multi .20 .15

Antenna and ITU Emblem — A37

1978, May 17 Litho. ***Perf. 14***

389 A37 3.50e silver & multi .20 .15

10th World Telecommunications Day.

Freighter Cabo Verde — A38

1978, June 25 Litho. ***Perf. 14***

391 A38 1e multicolored .15 .15

First ship of Cape Verde merchant marine.

Cape Verde stamps can be mounted in the Scott annual Portugal supplement.

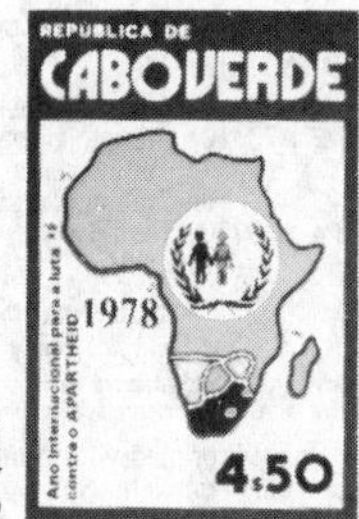

Map of Africa and Equality Emblem — A39

1978, June 21
392 A39 4.50e multi .25 .15

Anti-Apartheid Year.

Human Rights Emblem — A40

1978, Dec. 10 Litho. *Perf. 14*
393 A40 1.50e multicolored .15 .15
394 A40 2e multicolored .20 .15
Set value .15

Universal Declaration of Human Rights, 30th anniversary.

1.50

Children and Balloons, IYC Emblem — A41

IYC Emblem and Child's Drawing: 3.50e, Children and flowers.

1979, June 1 Litho. *Perf. 14*
395 A41 1.50e multi .15 .15
396 A41 3.50e multi .20 .15
Set value .15

International Year of the Child.

Pindjiguiti Massacre Monument — A42

Natl. Youth Week — A42a

1979, Aug. 3 *Perf. 13*
397 A42 4.50e multi .25 .15

Massacre of Pindjiguiti, 20th anniversary.

1979, Sept. 1 Litho. *Perf. 14*
397A A42a 3.50e Poster .45 .15

Centenary of Mindelo — A43

1980, Apr. 23 Litho. *Perf. 12½*
398 A43 4e multicolored .20 .15

Flag of Cape Verde — A44

Stylized Bird, "V" — A45

1980 Litho. *Perf. 12½*
399 A44 4e multicolored .20 .15
400 A45 4e multicolored .20 .15
401 A45 7e multicolored .40 .15
402 A45 11e multicolored .60 .20
Nos. 399-402 (4) 1.40
Set value .52

5th anniversary of independence. Issued: No. 399, June 1; others July 5.

A45a

A46

1980, May 13
402A A45a 3.50e multi .45
402B A45a 4.50e multi .60

1980 Natl. census.

1980, June 6
403 A46 1e Running .15 .15
404 A46 2.50e Boxing .15 .15
405 A46 3e Basketball .15 .15
406 A46 4e Volleyball .20 .15
407 A46 20e Swimming 1.10 .25
408 A46 50e Tennis 2.75 .65
Nos. 403-408 (6) 4.50 1.50

Souvenir Sheet

Perf. 13

409 A46 30e Soccer, horiz. *6.50*

22nd Summer Olympic Games, Moscow, July 19-Aug. 3.

Thunnus Alalunga A47

1980, Nov. 11 Litho. *Perf. 13*
410 A47 50c shown .15 .15
411 A47 4.50e Trachurus trachurus .20 .15
412 A47 8e Muraena helena .40 .15
413 A47 10e Corvina nigra .52 .15
414 A47 12e Katsuwonus pelamis .65 .20
415 A47 50e Prionace glauca 2.75 .65
Nos. 410-415 (6) 4.67 1.45

Lochnera Rosea — A48

1980, Dec. 29
416 A48 50c shown .15 .15
417 A48 4.50e Poinciana regia-bojer .20 .15
418 A48 8e Mirabilis jalapa .40 .15
419 A48 10e Nerium oleander .52 .15
420 A48 12e Bougainvillia litoralis .65 .20
421 A48 30e Hibiscus 1.65 .40
Nos. 416-421 (6) 3.57 1.20

WHO Anti-smoking Campaign — A48a

1980, Sept. 19 *Perf. 12½*
421A A48a 4e multicolored .52
421B A48a 7e multicolored .90

Arca Verde A49

1980, Nov. 30 Litho. *Perf. 12½x12*
422 A49 3e shown .15 .15
423 A49 5.50e Ilha do Maio .25 .15
424 A49 7.50e Ilha de Komo .40 .15
425 A49 9e Boa Vista .45 .15
426 A49 12e Santo Antao .65 .20
427 A49 30e Santiago 1.65 .40
Nos. 422-427 (6) 3.55 1.20

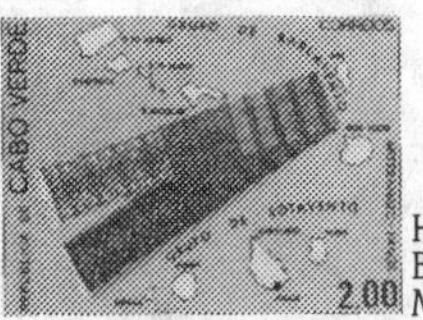

Hand-woven Bag, Map — A49a

Various hand-woven articles. 10e, vert.

1978, May 21 Litho. *Perf. 14*
427A A49a 50c multi .15
427B A49a 1.50e multi .20
427C A49a 2e multi .25
427D A49a 3e multi .40
427E A49a 10e multi 1.25
Nos. 427A-427E (5) 2.25

Desert Erosion Prevention Campaign A50

1981, Mar. 30 Litho. *Perf. 13*
428 A50 4.50e multi .25 .15
429 A50 10.50e multi .52 .20

6th Anniv. of Constitution — A51

1981, Apr. 15
430 A51 4.50e multicolored .25 .15

Souvenir Sheet

Austria No. B336 — A52

1981, May 18
431 A52 50e multicolored 2.50

WIPA '81 Philatelic Exhibition, Vienna, Austria, May 22-31.

Antenna — A53

1981, Aug. 25 Litho. *Perf. 12½*
432 A53 4.50e shown .25 .15
433 A53 8e Dish antenna .40 .15
434 A53 20e Dish antenna, diff. 1.10 .32
Nos. 432-434 (3) 1.75 .62

Intl. Year of the Disabled A54

1981, Dec. 25 Litho. *Perf. 12½*
435 A54 4.50e multicolored .20 .15

Purple Gallinule A55

1981, Dec. 30
436 A55 1e Egret, vert. .15 .15
437 A55 4.50e Barn owl, vert. .20 .15
438 A55 8e Passerine, vert. .35 .15
439 A55 10e shown .40 .15
440 A55 12e Guinea fowl .45 .15
Nos. 436-440 (5) 1.55
Set value .49

Souvenir Sheet

Perf. 13

441 A55 50e Razo Isld. lark 2.00 1.25

No. 441 contains 31x39mm one stamp.

CILSS Congress, Praia, Jan. 17 — A56

1982, Jan. 17 *Perf. 13x12½*
442 A56 11.50e multicolored .42 .20

Amilcar Cabral Soccer Championship — A57

Designs: Soccer players and flags.

1982, Feb. 10 Litho. *Perf. 12½*
443 A57 4.50e multicolored .20 .15
444 A57 7.50e multicolored .30 .15
445 A57 11.50e multicolored .50 .15
Nos. 443-445 (3) 1.00
Set value .32

1982 World Cup — A58

Designs: Soccer players and ball.

1982, Apr. 25
446 A58 1.50e multi .15 .15
447 A58 4.50e multi .20 .15
448 A58 8e multi .35 .15
449 A58 10.50e multi .40 .15
450 A58 12e multi .45 .15
451 A58 20e multi .85 .20
Nos. 446-451 (6) 2.40
Set value .71

Souvenir Sheet

452 A58 50e multi 2.00 1.25

First Anniv. of Women's Organization — A59

1982, Apr. 15 Litho. *Perf. 12½x12*
453 A59 4.50e Marching .20 .15
454 A59 8e Farming .35 .15
455 A59 12e Child care .50 .15
Nos. 453-455 (3) 1.05
Set value .32

Estaleiros Navais Port, St. Vincent — A59a

1982, July 5 Litho. *Perf. 13x12½*
455A A59a 10.50e multi .40

Natl. independence, 7th anniv.

Return of Barque Morrissey-Ernestina — A60

1982, July 5 Litho. *Perf. 13*
456 A60 12e multi .50

Butterflies A61

1982, July 27 Litho.
457 A61 2e Hypolimnas misippus .15
458 A61 4.50e Melanitis lede .15
459 A61 8e Catopsilia florella .20
460 A61 10.50e Colias electo .22
461 A61 11.50e Danaus chrysippus .30
462 A61 12e Papilio demodecus .32
Nos. 457-462 (6) 1.34

Francisco Xavier da Cruz (1905-1958), Composer — A62

Design: 14e, Eugenio Tavares (1867-1930), poet.

1983, Feb. 20 Litho. *Perf. 13*
463 A62 7e multi .18
464 A62 14e multi .35

World Communications Year — A63

1983, Oct. 10 Litho.
465 A63 13e multicolored .32

Local Seashells — A64

1983, Nov. 30 *Perf. 13½*
466 A64 50c Conus ateralbus .15
467 A64 1e Conus decoratus .15
468 A64 3e Conus salreiensis .15
469 A64 10e Conus verdensis .25
470 A64 50e Conus cuneolus 1.25
Nos. 466-470 (5) 1.95

40th Anniv. of Intl. Civil Aviation Org. A65

Airplanes: 50c, Ogma-Auster D5/160, 1966. 2e, De Havilland DH-104 Dove, 1945. 10e, Hawker Siddeley 748-200, 1972. 13e, De Havilland Dragon Rapide, 1945. 20e, De Havilland Twin Otter, 1977. 50e, Britten-Norman Islander, 1971.

1984, Feb. 15 Litho.
471 A65 50c multicolored .15
472 A65 2e multicolored .15
473 A65 10e multicolored .25
474 A65 13e multicolored .32
475 A65 20e multicolored .52
476 A65 50e multicolored 1.25
Nos. 471-476 (6) 2.64

Amilcar Cabral — A66

A67

1983, Jan. 17 Litho. *Perf. 14½*
477 A66 7e multi .15
478 A66 10.50e multi .22
a. Souvenir sheet of 2, #477-478 .75

Amilcar Cabral Symposium, Jan. 17-20. No. 478a sold for 30e.

1983, Dec. 10 Photo. *Perf. 14½*
479 A67 7e Cross overshadowing islands .30

Christianity in Cape Verde, 450th anniv.

Natl. Solidarity Campaign — A68

1984, Sept. 12 *Perf. 13½*
480 A68 6.50e multi .15
481 A68 13.50e multi .35

2nd Conference of Natl. Women's Orgs., Mar. 23-27 — A69

1985, Mar. 27 Litho. *Perf. 13½*
482 A69 8e multicolored .15

Miniature Sheet

483 A69 30e multicolored .50

Natl. Independence, 10th Anniv. — A70

1985, July 5 Litho. *Perf. 14*
484 A70 8c multicolored .18
485 A70 12e multicolored .28

Intl. Year of the Child — A71

1985, Sept. 12 Litho. *Perf. 14*
486 A71 12e multicolored .50

Vapor, by Hundertwasser A72

Photogravure and Engraved
1986, Apr. 25 *Perf. 14*
Black Surcharge

487 A72 30e on 10e multi .75

Souvenir Sheets
Background Color

488 Sheet of 4 4.50
a. A72 50e yellow & multi 1.10
489 Sheet of 4 4.50
a. A72 50e red & multi 1.10
490 Sheet of 4 4.50
a. A72 50e green & multi 1.10

No. 487 not issued without surcharge.

World Wildlife Fund — A73

Perf. 13½x14½
1986, June 15 Litho.
491 A73 8e Mabuya vaillanti .18
492 A73 10e Tarentola gigas brancoensis .22
493 A73 15e Tarentola gigas gigas .32
494 A73 30e Hemidactylus bouvieri .75
Nos. 491-494 (4) 1.47

Souvenir Sheet

495 Sheet of 2 2.25
a. A73 50e Mabuya vaillanti 1.10
b. A73 50e Hemidactylus bouvieri 1.10

No. 495 printed with center label picturing progress union emblem. Nos. 495a-495b printed without WWF emblem.

World Food Day — A74

Intl. Peace Year — A75

1986, June 20 *Perf. 14*
496 A74 8e Cauldron .18
497 A74 12e Mortar & pestle .28
498 A74 15e Quern stone .32
Nos. 496-498 (3) .78

1986, Dec. 24 Litho. *Perf. 14*
499 A75 12e multicolored .28
500 A75 30e multicolored .75

Natl. Child Survival Campaign A76

1987, Mar. 27 Litho. *Perf. 14*
501 A76 8e multicolored .18
502 A76 10e multicolored .22
503 A76 12e multicolored .28
504 A76 16e multicolored .35
505 A76 100e multicolored 2.25
Nos. 501-505 (5) 3.28

Tourism A77

1987, May 17
506 A77 1e Bay, Mindelo .15
507 A77 2.50e Hill country .15
508 A77 5e Mountain peak .15
509 A77 8e Monument .15
510 A77 10e Mountain peaks .20
511 A77 12e Beached boats .24
512 A77 100e Harbor 2.00
Nos. 506-512 (7) 3.04

Ships — A78

1987, Aug. 3 *Perf. 13½x14½*
513 A78 12e Carvalho, 1937 .24
514 A78 16e Nauta, 1943 .32
515 A78 50e Maria Sony, 1911 1.10
Nos. 513-515 (3) 1.66

Souvenir Sheet

516 Sheet of 2 2.75
a. A78 60e Madalan, 1928 1.25

Crop Protection A80

1988, May 9 Litho. *Perf. 13½*

518 A80 50c Identification of insect plague .15
519 A80 2e Use of insecticides .15
520 A80 9e Import of parasites .30
521 A80 13e Import of predators .45
522 A80 16e Locust .55
523 A80 19e Estimation of crop loss .65
Nos. 518-523 (6) 2.25

Souvenir Sheet

524 A80 50e Agricultural Research Institute 1.70

Maps — A81

1988, July 5 Litho. *Perf. 14*

525 A81 1e Dutch, 17th cent. .15
526 A81 2.50e Belgian, 18th cent. .15
527 A81 4.50e French, 18th cent. .16
528 A81 9.50e English, 18th cent. .32
529 A81 19.50e English, 19th cent. .68
530 A81 20e French, 18th cent., vert. .70
Nos. 525-530 (6) 2.16

Churches A82

Designs: 5e, St. Amaro Abade, Tarrafal, Santiago Is. 8e, Our Lady of the Light, Maio Is. 10e, Nazarene, Praia, Santiago Is. 12e, Our Lady of Rosa'rio, Sao Nicolau Is. 15e, Nazarene, Mindelo, Sao Vicente Is. 20e, Our Lady of Grace, Praia, Santiago Is.

1988, Aug. 15 *Perf. 13½x14½*

531 A82 5e multicolored .18
532 A82 8e multicolored .28
533 A82 10e multicolored .35
534 A82 12e multicolored .42
535 A82 15e multicolored .52
536 A82 20e multicolored .70
Nos. 531-536 (6) 2.45

Water Conservation A83

1988, Sept. 26 Litho. *Perf. 14*

537 A83 12e multicolored .42

Intl. Red Cross, 125th Anniv. A84

1988, Oct. 20

538 A84 7e multi .24

3rd Communist Party (PAICV) Congress — A85

Portrait of Pres. Pereira, PAICV secretary-general, and: 7e, S. Jorginho Vocational Training Center. 10.50e, UN Secretary-General Perez de Cuellar. 30e, 100e, Star and text.

Perf. 14½x13½

1988, Nov. 25 Litho.

539 A85 7e multi .22
540 A85 10.50e multi .35
541 A85 30e multi .95
Nos. 539-541 (3) 1.52

Souvenir Sheet

542 A85 100e multi 3.10

1988 Summer Olympics, Seoul — A86

1988, Dec. 26

543 A86 12e shown .38
544 A86 15e Tennis .48
545 A86 20e Soccer .62
546 A86 30e Boxing .95
Nos. 543-546 (4) 2.43

Souvenir Sheet

547 A86 50e Long jump 1.55

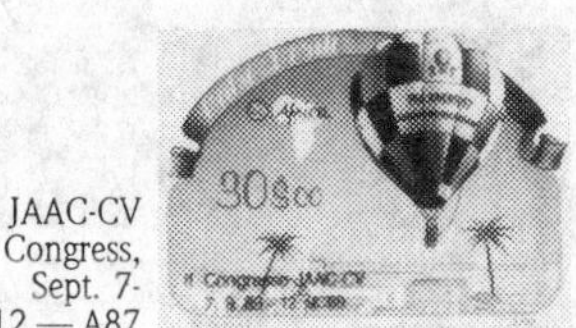

2nd JAAC-CV Congress, Sept. 7-12 — A87

1989, Apr. 7 Litho. *Perf. 14*

548 A87 30e Hot air balloon 1.00

Liberty Guiding the People — A88

Relief, Arc de Triomphe — A89

1989, July 7 Litho. *Perf. 14*

549 A88 20e multicolored .58
550 A88 24e multicolored .70
551 A88 25e multicolored .72
Nos. 549-551 (3) 2.00

Souvenir Sheet

Perf. 14½x13½

552 A89 100e multicolored 3.00

French revolution, bicent.

Interparliamentary Union, Cent. — A90

1989, Sept. 18 Litho. *Perf. 14*

553 A90 2e shown .15
554 A90 4e Dove .15
555 A90 13e Natl. Assembly Bldg. .32
Set value .46

Traditional Ceramics A91

1989, Nov. 13 Litho. *Perf. 13½*

Panel Colors

556 A91 13e lilac .32
557 A91 20e red, vert. .50
558 A91 24e brown .60
559 A91 25e orange, vert. .62
Nos. 556-559 (4) 2.04

Outdoor Toys — A92

1989, Dec. 23

560 A92 1e Yellow truck .15
561 A92 6e Car .15
562 A92 8e White truck .20
563 A92 11.50e Trucks .28
564 A92 18e Scooter .45
565 A92 100e Boat 2.50
Nos. 560-565 (6) 3.73

Visit of Pope John Paul II — A93

1990, Jan. 25

566 A93 13e blue & multi .32
567 A93 25e violet & multi .62

Souvenir Sheet

568 A93 200e multi, diff. 5.00

Turtles — A94

1990, May 17 Litho. *Perf. 13½*

569 A94 50c Chelonia mydas .15
570 A94 1e Dermochelys coriacea .15
571 A94 5e Lepidochelys olivacea .15
572 A94 10e Caretta caretta .28
573 A94 42e Eretmochelys imbricata 1.20
Nos. 569-573 (5) 1.93

Women's Congress A95

1990, Aug. 13

574 A95 9e multicolored .25

A96

A97

Various drawings of soccer players in action.

1990, Aug. 7

575 A96 4e multicolored .15
576 A96 7.50e multicolored .20
577 A96 8e multicolored .22
578 A96 100e multicolored 2.80
Nos. 575-578 (4) 3.37

Souvenir Sheet

579 A96 100e multi, diff. 2.80

World Cup Soccer Championships, Italy.

1990, Oct. 15 *Perf. 11½*

Vaccinations: 5e, Emile Roux (1853-1933), diphtheria. 13e, Robert Koch (1843-1910), tuberculosis. 20e, Gaston Ramon (1886-1963), tetanus. 24e, Jonas Salk (1914-), polio.

Granite Paper

580 A97 5e multicolored .15
581 A97 13e multicolored .38
582 A97 20e multicolored .60
583 A97 24e multicolored .70
Nos. 580-583 (4) 1.83

Intl. Literacy Year — A98

Designs: 3e, Adult literacy class. 15e, Teacher holding flash card, children. 19e, Teacher, student at blackboard.

1990, Sept. 28

Granite Paper

584 A98 2e shown .15
585 A98 3e multicolored .15
586 A98 15e multicolored .40
587 A98 19e multicolored .55
Nos. 584-587 (4) 1.25

Traditional Fairy Tales — A99

1990, Dec. 20 Litho. *Perf. 12½*

588 A99 50c shown .15
589 A99 2.50e Man catching mermaid .15
590 A99 12e Woman, snake .42
591 A99 25e Man, eggs, woman .90
Nos. 588-591 (4) 1.62

Fight Against AIDS — A100

1991, Feb. 20 Litho. *Perf. 14*

Granite Paper

592 A100 13e multicolored .50
593 A100 24e multi, diff. .90

Fishing — A101

Designs: 24e, Man removing hook from fish. 25e, Fishing boats. 50e, Two men long-line fishing.

1991, Apr. 23 Litho. *Perf. 11½*

594 A101 10e multicolored .32
595 A101 24e multicolored .78
596 A101 25e multicolored .80
597 A101 50e multicolored 1.60
Nos. 594-597 (4) 3.50

Medicinal Plants — A102

Designs: 10e, Lavandula rotundifolia. 15e, Micromeria forbesii. 21e, Sarcostemma daltonii. 24e, Periploca chevalieri. 30e, Echium hypertropicum. 35e, Erysimum caboverdeanum.

1991, July 5 Litho. *Perf. 11½*

598 A102 10e multicolored .30
599 A102 15e multicolored .45
600 A102 21e multicolored .65
601 A102 24e multicolored .70
602 A102 30e multicolored .90
603 A102 35e multicolored 1.05
Nos. 598-602 (5) 3.00

Landmarks in Old Ribeira Grande on Santiago Island A103

Designs: 12.50e, Church of Our Lady of the Rosary, 1495. 15e, Ruins of the Cathedral, 1556. 20e, Fortress of San Felipe, 1587. 30e, Ruins of the Convent of St. Francis, 1642. 100e, Pillory, 1520, vert.

1991, June 25 Litho. *Perf. 11½*

604 A103 12.50e multicolored .40
605 A103 15e multicolored .45
606 A103 20e multicolored .60
607 A103 30e multicolored .90
Nos. 604-607 (4) 2.35

Souvenir Sheet

608 A103 100e multicolored 3.00

Musical Instruments — A104

1991, Oct. 9 Litho. *Perf. 11½*

609 A104 10e 6-string guitar .30
610 A104 20e Violin .60
611 A104 29e 5-string guitar .90
612 A104 47e Cimba 1.50
Nos. 609-612 (4) 3.30

Souvenir Sheet

613 A104 60e Accordion, horiz. 1.90

Christmas A105

1991, Dec. 20 Litho. *Perf. 11½*

614 A105 31e Nativity scene 1.00
615 A105 50e Nativity scene, diff. 1.65

Discovery of America, 500th Anniv. A106

1992, Mar. 31 Litho. *Perf. 11½*

616 A106 40e shown 1.30
617 A106 40e Columbus on ship 1.30
a. Pair, #616-617 2.60

Souvenir Sheet

618 A106 Sheet of 2 5.00

Stamps in No. 618 are smaller, without white border and "Luis Duran" and "Courvoisier" inscriptions. No. 618 was printed in continuous design and sold for 150e.

Souvenir Sheet

Granada '92 — A107

1992, Apr.24 *Perf. 11½*

619 A107 50e multicolored 5.00

No. 619 sold for 150e.

Tropical Fruits A108

1992, Feb. 29 *Perf. 12x11½*

620 A108 16e Syzygium jambos .50
621 A108 25e Mangifera indica .80
622 A108 31e Anacardium occidentale 1.00
623 A108 32e Persea americana 1.05
Nos. 620-623 (4) 3.35

1992 Summer Olympics, Barcelona — A109

1992, June 30 Litho. *Perf. 13½*

624 A109 16e Women's javelin .60
625 A109 20e Weight lifting .75
626 A109 32e Women's pole vault 1.25
627 A109 40e Women's shot put 1.50
Nos. 624-627 (4) 4.10

Souvenir Sheet

628 A109 100e Women's gymnastics 3.80

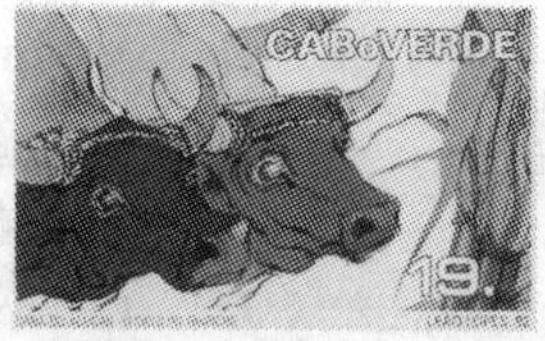

Sugar Cane Production — A110

Designs: 19e, Oxen, sugar cane. 20e, Oxen yoked to press. 37e, Man placing cane inside press. 38e, Refining process.

1992, Nov. Litho. *Perf. 11*

629 A110 19e multicolored .58
630 A110 20e multicolored .65
631 A110 37e multicolored 1.15
632 A110 38e multicolored 1.18
Nos. 629-632 (4) 3.56

Domestic Animals A111

1992, Nov. *Perf. 13½*

633 A111 16e Cat .48
634 A111 31e Chickens .95
635 A111 32e Dog, vert. 1.00
636 A111 50e Horse 1.55
Nos. 633-636 (4) 3.98

Corals A112

1993, Apr. 29 Litho. *Perf. 11½*

637 A112 5e Tubastrea aurea .15
638 A112 31e Corallium rubrum .90
639 A112 37e Porites porites 1.10
640 A112 50e Millepora alcicornis 1.50
Nos. 637-640 (4) 3.65

Treaty of Tordesillas, 500th Anniv. (in 1994) A113

Designs: No. 641, King Ferdinand, Queen Isabella of Spain, Pope Alexander VI. No. 642, Pope Julius II, King John II of Portugal. No. 643, Astrolabe, treaty signing. No. 644, Compass rose, map.

1993, Aug. 1 Litho. *Perf. 12x11½*

641 A113 37e multicolored 1.00
642 A113 37e multicolored 1.00
a. Pair, #641-642 2.00
643 A113 38e multicolored 1.05
644 A113 38e multicolored 1.05
a. Pair, #643-644 2.10
Nos. 641-644 (4) 4.10

Souvenir Sheet

Santiago Island, 1806 — A114

1993, July 30 *Perf. 13½*

645 A114 100e multicolored 2.75

Brasiliana '93.

Lobsters — A115

1993, Sept. 29 Litho. *Perf. 11½*

646 A115 2e Palinurus charlestoni .15
647 A115 10e Panulirus echinatus .15
648 A115 17e Panulirus regius .25
649 A115 38e Scyllarides latus .60
Nos. 646-649 (4) 1.15

Souvenir Sheet

650 A115 100e Panulirus regius, diff. 1.50

No. 650 contains one 51x36mm stamp.

Birds A116

1993, Oct. 29 Litho. *Perf. 12x11½*

651 A116 10e Calonectris edwardsii .28
652 A116 30e Sula leucogaster .85
653 A116 40e Fregata magnificens 1.10
a. Souvenir sheet of 1 4.25
654 A116 41e Phaeton aethereus 1.25
Nos. 651-654 (4) 3.48

Hong Kong '94 (#653a).
No. 653a sold for 150e.

Flowers A117

1993, Dec. 16 Litho. *Perf. 12x11½*

655 A117 5e Rosa alexandra .15
656 A117 30e Strelitzia reginae .90
657 A117 37e Dianthus barbatus 1.10
658 A117 50e Dahlia 1.50
Nos. 655-658 (4) 3.65

1994 World Cup Soccer Championships, US — A118

Players, US flag, and: 1e, Giant's Stadium, New Jersey. 20e, Rose Bowl Stadium, Pasadena. 37e, Foxboro Stadium, Boston. 38e, Silverdome, Pontiac. 100e, RFK Stadium, Washington DC.

1994, May 31 Litho. *Perf. 11½*

659 A118 1e multicolored .15
660 A118 20e multicolored .55
661 A118 37e multicolored 1.00
662 A118 38e multicolored 1.10
Nos. 659-662 (4) 2.80

Souvenir Sheet

663 A118 100e multicolored 2.75

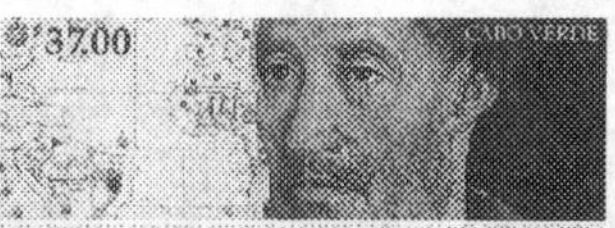

Prince Henry the Navigator (1394-1460) — A119

Illustration reduced.

1994, Mar. 4 Litho. *Perf. 12*

664 A119 37e multicolored 1.10

See Brazil #2463, Macao #719, Portugal #1987.

Sharks A120

1994, June 27 Litho. *Perf. 12x11½*

665 A120 21e Eugomphodus taurus .60
666 A120 27e Carcharhinus limbatus .80
667 A120 37e Rhiniodon typus 1.10
668 A120 38e Etmopterus spinax 1.10
Nos. 665-668 (4) 3.60

Bananas A121

1994, Aug. 16 Litho. *Perf. 11½*

669 A121 12e Prata, vert. .35
670 A121 16e Pao .48
671 A121 30e Ana roberta, vert. .90
672 A121 40e Roxa, vert. 1.25
Nos. 669-672 (4) 2.98

Souvenir Sheet

673 A121 100e Prata, diff., vert. 4.25

PHILAKOREA '94, SINGPEX '94 (#673). No. 673 sold for 150e.

Lighthouses
A122

1994, Oct. 17 *Perf. 12*
674 A122 2e Fontes Pereira de Melo .15
675 A122 37e Morro Negro 1.00
676 A122 38e Amelia, vert. 1.10
677 A122 50e Maria Pia, vert. 1.40
Nos. 674-677 (4) 3.65

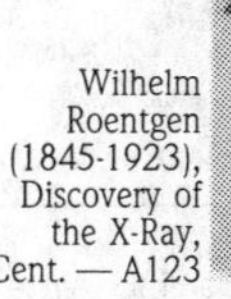
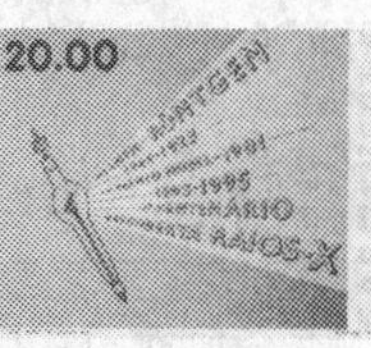
Wilhelm Roentgen (1845-1923), Discovery of the X-Ray, Cent. — A123

1995 **Litho.** *Perf. 12*
678 A123 20e yellow & multi .65
679 A123 37e blue & multi 1.25
a. Souvenir sheet of 2, #678-679 3.25

No. 679a sold for 100e.

FAO, 50th Anniv.
A124 A125

1995 **Litho.** *Perf. 12*
680 A124 37e multicolored 1.10
681 A125 38e multicolored 1.25

Dogs
A126

Dog, scene depicting story of dogs: 1e, Fox terrier, Two foxhounds and fox terrier, by John Emms. 10e, Cavalier King Charles, Shooting over Dogs, by Richard Ansdell. 40e, Rough collie, German shepherd. 50e, Braco, Hounds at Full Cry, by Thomas Blinks.

1995 **Litho.** *Perf. 12x11½*
682 A126 1e multicolored .15
683 A126 10e multicolored .30
684 A126 40e multicolored 1.25
685 A126 50e multicolored 1.50
Nos. 682-685 (4) 3.20

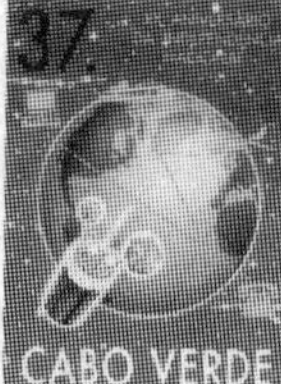
Independence, 20th Anniv. — A127

1995 **Litho.** *Perf. 12*
686 A127 37e multicolored 1.10

Traditional Festival
A128

Designs: 2e, Horse race. 10e, Horseman leading parade. 37e, People singing, playing drums. 40e, Playing game on horseback.

1995 *Perf. 12x11½*
687 A128 2e multicolored .15
688 A128 10e multicolored .30
689 A128 37e multicolored 1.10
690 A128 40e multicolored 1.25
Nos. 687-690 (4) 2.80

Souvenir Sheet

Singapore '95 — A129

Illustration reduced.

1995 *Perf. 11½*
691 A129 37e Dianthus barbatus 4.50

AIR POST STAMPS

Common Design Type
Name and Value in Black
Perf. 13½x13

1938, July 26 **Unwmk.**
C1 CD39 10c scarlet .35 .30
C2 CD39 20c purple .35 .30
C3 CD39 50c orange .35 .30
C4 CD39 1e ultra .35 .30
C5 CD39 2e lilac brown .65 .50
C6 CD39 3e dk green 1.75 1.40
C7 CD39 5e red brown 3.50 1.40
C8 CD39 9e rose carmine 5.75 3.00
C9 CD39 10e magenta 8.25 4.50
Nos. C1-C9 (9) 21.30 12.00

No. C7 exists with overprint "Exposicao Internacional de Nova York, 1939-1940" and Trylon and Perisphere.

POSTAGE DUE STAMPS

D1 D2

1904 **Unwmk.** **Typo.** *Perf. 12*
J1 D1 5r yellow grn .20 .40
J2 D1 10r slate .20 .40
J3 D1 20r yellow brn .45 .60
J4 D1 30r red orange .75 .80
J5 D1 50r gray brown .45 .80
J6 D1 60r red brown 5.00 5.00
J7 D1 100r lilac 1.10 1.50
J8 D1 130r dull blue 1.10 1.50
J9 D1 200r carmine 1.25 2.75
J10 D1 500r dull violet 3.50 5.00
Nos. J1-J10 (10) 14.00 18.75

Overprinted in Carmine or Green

REPUBLICA

1911
J11 D1 5r yellow grn .15 .15
J12 D1 10r slate .20 .15
J13 D1 20r yellow brn .20 .15
J14 D1 30r orange .20 .15
J15 D1 50r gray brown .20 .15
J16 D1 60r red brown .35 .30
J17 D1 100r lilac .45 .30
J18 D1 130r dull blue .75 .35
J19 D1 200r carmine (G) 1.25 .55
J20 D1 500r dull violet 1.50 1.25
Nos. J11-J20 (10) 5.25 3.50

1921 *Perf. 11½*
J21 D2 ½c yellow grn .15 .20
J22 D2 1c slate .15 .20
J23 D2 2c red brown .15 .20
J24 D2 3c orange .15 .20
J25 D2 5c gray brown .15 .20
J26 D2 6c lt brown .15 .15
J27 D2 10c red violet .15 .15
J28 D2 13c dull blue .30 .55
J29 D2 20c carmine .30 .55
J30 D2 50c gray .95 1.10
Nos. J21-J30 (10) 3.50
Set value 2.10

Catalogue values for unused stamps in this section, from this point to the end of the section, are for Never Hinged items.

Common Design Type
Photogravure and Typographed
1952 **Unwmk.** *Perf. 14*
Numeral in Red, Frame Multicolored
J31 CD45 10c chocolate .15 .15
J32 CD45 30c black brown .15 .15
J33 CD45 50c dark blue .15 .15
J34 CD45 1e dark blue .20 .20
J35 CD45 2e red brown .20 .20
J36 CD45 5e olive green .40 .40
Nos. J31-J36 (6) 1.25 1.25

NEWSPAPER STAMP

N1

1893 **Typo.** **Unwmk.** *Perf. 11½*
P1 N1 2½r brown .75 .50
a. Perf. 12½ 3.25 3.25
b. Perf. 13½ 5.75 3.50

For surcharges see Nos. 79, 206.

POSTAL TAX STAMPS

Pombal Issue
Common Design Types
1925 **Unwmk.** **Engr.** *Perf. 12½*
RA1 CD28 15c dull vio & blk .45 .45
RA2 CD29 15c dull vio & blk .45 .45
RA3 CD30 15c dull vio & blk .45 .45
Nos. RA1-RA3 (3) 1.35 1.35

St. Isabel — PT1

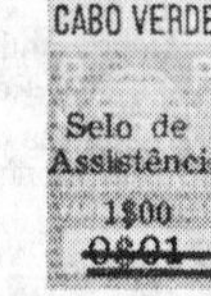
PT2

1948 **Litho.** *Perf. 11*
RA4 PT1 50c dark green 1.90 1.25
RA5 PT1 1e henna brown 3.50 2.50

Catalogue values for unused stamps in this section, from this point to the end of the section, are for Never Hinged items.

No. RA5 Surcharged with New Value and Bars

1959
RA6 PT1 50c on 1e henna brown 1.00 .50
Perf. 14
RA7 PT1 50c carmine rose 1.10 .52
RA8 PT1 1e blue 1.10 .52

St. Isabel Type Redrawn
1967-72 **Litho.** *Perf. 14*
RA9 PT1 30c (blue panel) .15 .15
RA10 PT1 50c (lilac rose panel) .50 .50
RA11 PT1 50c (red panel) ('72) *3.25 3.25*
RA12 PT1 1e (brn panel) .60 .60
RA13 PT1 1e (red lilac panel) ('72) *3.25 3.25*
Nos. RA9-RA13 (5) 7.75 7.75

Nos. RA9-RA13 are inscribed "ASSISTENCIA" in large letters in bottom panel and "PORTUGAL" and "CABO VERDE" in small letters in upper left corner.

Revenue Stamps Surcharged in Green, Blue or Black

1967-72 **Typo.** *Perf. 12*
Black "CABO VERDE" & Value
Pale Green Burelage
RA14 PT2 50c on 1c org (Bl) ('71) 1.00 .60
a. Black surcharge ('68?) *7.50 8.75*
RA15 PT2 50c on 2c org (Bk) ('69) *45.00 45.00*
c. Inverted surcharge
RA16 PT2 50c on 3c org (G) ('72) 1.50 .60
RA17 PT2 50c on 5c org (G) ('72) .70 .60
RA18 PT2 50c on 10c org (G) ('71) .85 .85
RA19 PT2 1e on 1c org (Bk) 4.50 4.00
RA20 PT2 1e on 2c org (G) ('71) 1.65 1.65
a. Blue surcharge ('71) 1.10 .60
b. Black surcharge 3.50 3.00
Nos. RA14-RA20 (7) *55.20 53.30*

POSTAL TAX DUE STAMPS

Pombal Issue
Common Design Types
1925 **Unwmk.** *Perf. 12½*
RAJ1 CD31 30c dull vio & blk .50 .50
RAJ2 CD32 30c dull vio & blk .50 .50
RAJ3 CD33 30c dull vio & blk .50 .50
Nos. RAJ1-RAJ3 (3) 1.50 1.50

CAROLINE ISLANDS

'kar–ə–,līn 'ī–lənds

LOCATION — A group of about 549 small islands in the West Pacific Ocean, north of the Equator.
GOVT. — Former German colony
AREA — 550 sq. mi.
POP. — 40,000 (approx. 1915)

100 Pfennig = 1 Mark

Watermark

Wmk. 125- Lozenges

Stamps of Germany 1889-90 Overprinted in Black

Overprinted at 56 degree Angle
1900 **Unwmk.** *Perf. 13½x14½*
1 A9 3pf dk brown 14.00 *16.00*
2 A9 5pf green 16.00 *20.00*
3 A10 10pf carmine 18.00 *22.50*
4 A10 20pf ultra 22.50 *30.00*
5 A10 25pf orange 55.00 *65.00*
6 A10 50pf red brown 55.00 *65.00*
Nos. 1-6 (6) 180.50 *218.50*

1899
Overprinted at 48 degree Angle
1a A9 3pf light brown 525.00 *750.00*
2a A9 5pf green 625.00 550.00
3a A10 10pf carmine 75.00 *150.00*
4a A10 20pf ultra 75.00 *150.00*
5a A10 25pf orange *1,500.* *3,000.*
6a A10 50pf red brown *900.00* *1,750.*

Kaiser's Yacht "Hohenzollern"
A3 A4

1901, Jan. **Typo.** *Perf. 14*
7 A3 3pf brown .90 *1.50*
8 A3 5pf green .90 *2.00*
9 A3 10pf carmine .90 *4.75*
a. Half used as 5pf on cover, backstamped in Jaluit ('05) *110.00*

10 A3 20pf ultra 1.25 *7.50*
a. Half used as 10pf on cover ('10) *9,000.*
11 A3 25pf org & blk, *yel* 1.50 *15.00*
12 A3 30pf org & blk, *sal* 1.50 *15.00*
13 A3 40pf lake & blk 1.50 *16.00*
14 A3 50pf pur & blk, *sal* 2.00 *20.00*
15 A3 80pf lake & blk, *rose* 3.00 *25.00*

***Perf.* 14½x14 Engr.**

16 A4 1m carmine 4.00 *60.00*
17 A4 2m blue 6.00 *75.00*
18 A4 3m black violet 10.00 *150.00*
19 A4 5m slate & carmine 150.00 *550.00*
Nos. 7-19 (13) 183.45

No. 9a is known as the "typhoon provisional" the stock of 5pf stamps having been destroyed during a typhoon. Covers (cards) without backstamp, value about $90.

Forged cancellations are found on #7-19.

No. 7 Handstamp Surcharged

1910, July 12

20 A3 5pf on 3pf brown *5,250.*
a. Inverted surcharge *6,000.*
b. Double surcharge *5,500.*

Values are for stamps tied to cover. Stamps on piece sell for about 40% less.

1915-19 Wmk. 125 Typo.

21 A3 3pf brown ('19) .90
22 A3 5pf green 15.00

Engr.

23 A4 5m slate & carmine 17.50
Nos. 21-23 (3) 33.40

CASTELLORIZO

ˌkäs-tə-ˈlȯr-ə-ˌzō

(Castelrosso)

LOCATION — A Mediterranean island in the Dodecanese group lying close to the coast of Asia Minor and about 60 miles east of Rhodes.
GOVT. — Former Italian Colony
AREA — 4 sq. mi.
POP. — 2,238 (1936)

Formerly a Turkish possession, Castellorizo was occupied by the French in 1915 and ceded to Italy after World War I.

25 Centimes = 1 Piaster
100 Centimes = 1 Franc

Used values in italics are for postally used copies. Stamps with CTO or fake cancels sell for about the same as hinged, unused stamps.

Issued under French Occupation

Stamps of French Offices in Turkey Overprinted

B. N. F.
CASTELLORIZO

1920 Unwmk. *Perf.* 14x13½

1 A2 1c gray 20.00 20.00
a. Inverted overprint 40.00 40.00
b. Double overprint 50.00 50.00
2 A2 2c vio brn 20.00 20.00
3 A2 3c red org 20.00 20.00
a. Inverted overprint 40.00 40.00
4 A2 5c green 20.00 20.00
a. Inverted overprint 40.00 40.00
5 A3 10c rose 22.50 22.50
6 A3 15c pale red 32.50 32.50
a. Inverted overprint 55.00 55.00
7 A3 20c brn vio 35.00 35.00
8 A5 1pi on 25c blue 35.00 35.00
9 A3 30c lilac 35.00 35.00
10 A4 40c red & pale bl 55.00 55.00
a. Inverted overprint 215.00 215.00
11 A6 2pi on 50c bis brn & lav 55.00 55.00
a. Inverted overprint 215.00 215.00
12 A6 4pi on 1fr cl & ol grn 100.00 100.00
a. Double overprint 225.00 225.00
b. Inverted overprint 225.00 225.00
13 A6 20pi on 5fr dk bl & buff 300.00 300.00
a. Double overprint 550.00 550.00
Nos. 1-13 (13) 750.00 750.00

On Nos. 10-13 the overprint is placed vertically.

No. 1-9 were overprinted in blocks of 25. Position 4 had "CASTELLORIZO" inverted and Positions 8 and 18 had "CASTELLORISO". The later variety also occurred in the setting of the form for Nos. 10-13.

"B. N. F." are the initials of "Base Navale Francaise".

Overprinted in Black or Red

O. N. F.
Castellorizo

1920
On Stamps of French Offices in Turkey

14 A2 1c gray 9.50 9.50
15 A2 2c vio brn 9.50 9.50
16 A2 3c red org 10.50 10.50
17 A2 5c green (R) 10.50 10.50
19 A3 10c rose 11.00 11.00
20 A3 15c pale red 14.00 14.00
21 A3 20c brn vio 30.00 30.00
22 A5 1pi on 25c bl (R) 27.50 27.50
23 A3 30c lilac (R) 27.50 27.50
24 A4 40c red & pale bl 27.50 27.50
25 A6 2pi on 50c bis brn & lav 27.50 27.50
26 A6 4pi on 1fr claret & ol grn 30.00 30.00
28 A6 20pi on 5fr dk bl & buff 145.00 145.00
Nos. 14-28 (13) 380.00 380.00

On Nos. 25, 26 and 28 the two lines of the overprint are set wider apart than on the lower values.

"O.N.F." are the initials of "Occupation Navale Francaise."

Overprint on 8pi on 2fr (#37), value $700.

On Stamps of France

30 A22 10c red 15.00 11.00
a. Inverted overprint 60.00
31 A22 25c blue (R) 15.00 11.00
a. Inverted overprint 60.00

This overprint exists on 8 other 1900-1907 denominations of France (5c, 15c, 20c, 30c, 40c, 50c, 1fr, 5fr). These are believed not to have been issued or postally used.

Stamps of France, 1900-1907, Handstamped in Black or Violet

1920

33 A22 5c green 65.00 65.00
34 A22 10c red 65.00 65.00
35 A22 20c vio brn 65.00 65.00
36 A22 5c blue 65.00 65.00
37 A18 50c bis brn & lav 475.00 475.00
38 A18 1fr cl & ol grn (V) 475.00 475.00
Nos. 33-38 (6) 1,210. 1,210.

Nos. 1-38 are considered speculative.

Forgeries of overprints on Nos. 1-38 exist. They abound of Nos. 33-38.

Stamps of French Offices in Turkey hand-stamped "Occupation Francaise Castellorizo" were made privately.

Issued under Italian Dominion

100 Centesimi = 1 Lira

Italian Stamps of 1906-20 Overprinted

CASTELROSSO

1922 Wmk. 140 *Perf.* 14

51 A48 5c green 1.00 *3.00*
52 A48 10c claret .40 *3.00*
53 A48 15c slate .45 *3.00*
54 A50 20c brn org .45 *3.00*
a. Double overprint 60.00
55 A49 25c blue .45 *3.00*
56 A49 40c brown 8.75 3.00
57 A49 50c violet 8.75 3.00
58 A49 60c carmine 8.75 3.00
59 A49 85c chocolate 1.00 *4.00*
Nos. 51-59 (9) 30.00 *28.00*

Map of Castellorizo; Flag of Italy — A1

1923

60 A1 5c gray green .20 *2.50*
61 A1 10c dull rose .20 *2.50*
62 A1 25c dull blue .20 *2.50*
63 A1 50c gray lilac .20 *2.50*
64 A1 1 l brown .20 *2.50*
Nos. 60-64 (5) 1.00 *12.50*

Italian Stamps of 1901-20 Overprinted

1924

65 A48 5c green .30 *10.00*
66 A48 10c claret .30 *10.00*
67 A48 15c slate .30 *10.00*
68 A50 20c brn orange .30 *10.00*
69 A49 25c blue .30 *10.00*
70 A49 40c brown .30 *10.00*
71 A49 50c violet .30 *10.00*
72 A49 60c carmine .30 *10.00*
a. Double overprint 60.00
73 A49 85c red brown .30 *10.00*
74 A46 1 l brn & green .30 *10.00*
Nos. 65-74 (10) 3.00 *100.00*

Ferrucci Issue

Types of Italian Stamps of 1930, Overprinted in Red or Blue

CASTELROSSO

1930 Wmk. Crowns (140)

75 A102 20c violet .75 *1.25*
76 A103 25c dark green .75 *1.25*
77 A103 50c black .75 *1.25*
78 A103 1.25 l deep blue .75 *1.25*
79 A104 5 l + 2 l dp car (Bl) 3.00 *6.75*
Nos. 75-79 (5) 5.80 *11.75*

Garibaldi Issue

Types of Italian Stamps of 1932, Overprinted like Nos. 75-79 in Red or Blue

1932

80 A138 10c brown 3.50 *7.25*
81 A138 20c red brn (Bl) 3.50 *7.25*
82 A138 25c dp grn 3.50 *7.25*
83 A138 30c bluish slate 3.50 *7.25*
84 A138 50c red vio (Bl) 3.50 *7.25*
85 A141 75c cop red (Bl) 3.50 *7.25*
86 A141 1.25 l dull blue 3.50 *7.25*
87 A141 1.75 l + 25c brn 3.50 *7.25*
88 A144 2.55 l + 50c org (Bl) 3.50 *7.25*
89 A145 5 l + 1 l dl vio 3.50 *7.25*
Nos. 80-89 (10) 35.00 *72.50*

CENTRAL AFRICA

ˈsen-trəl ˈa-fri-kə

LOCATION — Western Africa, north of equator
GOVT. — Republic
AREA — 241,313 sq. mi.
POP. — 2,610,000 (est. 1974)
CAPITAL — Bangui

The former French colony of Ubangi-Shari, a unit in French Equatorial Africa, proclaimed itself the Central African Republic Dec. 1, 1958. It became the Central African Empire Dec. 4, 1976. It became the Central African Republic again in 1979.

100 Centimes = 1 Franc

Catalogue values for all unused stamps in this country are for Never Hinged items.

Watermark

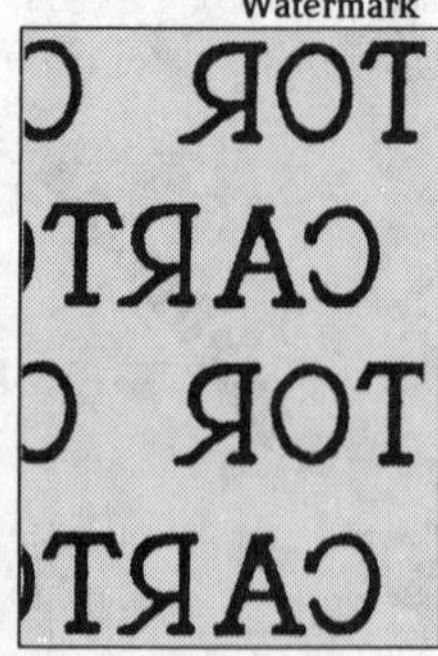

Wmk. 385

Central African Republic

Premier Barthélemy Boganda and Flag — A1

Design: 25fr, Boganda and flag, horiz.

Unwmk.

1959, Dec. 1 Engr. *Perf.* 13

1 A1 15fr multi .16 .15
2 A1 25fr multi .25 .15

1st anniv. of the Republic and honoring Premier Barthélemy Boganda (1910-59).

For overprints & surcharge see #12, 59, M1-M2.

Imperforates

Many stamps of Central African Republic exist imperforate in issued and trial colors, and also in small presentation sheets in issued colors.

C.C.T.A. Issue

Common Design Type

1960, May 21 Unwmk. *Perf.* 13

3 CD106 50fr lt grn & dk bl .80 .60

Dactyloceras Widenmanni A2

Designs: Various butterflies.

1960-61

4 A2 50c bl grn & dk red .15 .15
5 A2 1fr multi .15 .15
6 A2 2fr dk grn & brn .15 .15
7 A2 3fr yel grn & dk red .15 .15
8 A2 5fr multi .15 .15
9 A2 10fr multi .15 .15
10 A2 20fr multi .22 .15
11 A2 85fr multi .90 .55
Set value 1.50 .95

Issued: 50c-3fr, June 10, 1961; others, Sept. 3.

No. 2 Overprinted: "FETE NATIONALE 1-12-1960"

1960, Dec. 1

12 A1 25fr multi .70 .70

National Holiday, Dec. 1, 1960.

Louis Pasteur and Pasteur Institute, Bangui — A3

1961, Feb. 25 Unwmk. *Perf.* 13

13 A3 20fr multi .42 .42

Opening of Pasteur Institute at Bangui.

Common Design Types pictured in section at front of book.

Flag, Map, and UN Emblem A4

1961, Mar. 4 Engr.

14 A4 15fr multi .15 .15
15 A4 25fr multi .20 .15
16 A4 85fr multi .65 .55
Nos. 14-16 (3) 1.00 .85

Admission to the UN.

No. 15 Overprinted in Green: "FETE NATIONALE 1-12-61" and Star

1961, Dec. 1

17 A4 25fr multi .90 .90

National Holiday, Dec. 1.

No. 16 Surcharged in Red Brown: "U.A.M. CONFERENCE DE BANGUI 25-27 Mars 1962"

1962, Mar. 25

18 A4 50fr on 85fr multi .80 .80

Conf. of the African and Malgache Union at Bangui, Mar. 25-27.

Abidjan Games Issue
Common Design Type

1962, July 21 Photo. *Perf. 12½x12*

19 CD109 20fr Hurdling .20 .16
20 CD109 50fr Bicycling .55 .38
Nos. 19-20,C6 (3) 1.75 1.19

African-Malgache Union Issue
Common Design Type

1962, Sept. 8 Unwmk.

21 CD110 30fr multi .38 .30

1st anniv. of the African and Malgache Union.

Pres. David Dacko — A5

Soldiers with Flag — A6

1962 *Perf. 12*

22 A5 20fr multi .20 .15
23 A5 25fr multi .22 .15

For surcharge see No. 60.

1963, Aug. 13 Photo.

24 A6 20fr blk & multi .20 .15

National Army, third anniversary.

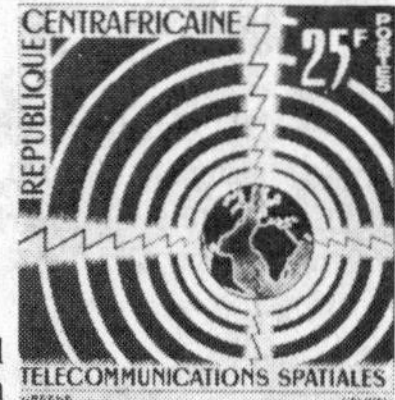

Waves Around Globe — A6a

Design: 100fr, Orbit patterns around globe.

1963, Sept. 19 Unwmk. *Perf. 12½*

25 A6a 25fr plum & grn .30 .25
26 A6a 100fr org, bl & grn 1.10 1.00

Issued to publicize space communications.

Young Pioneers A7

1963, Oct. 14 Engr. *Perf. 12½*

27 A7 50fr grnsh bl, vio bl & brn .45 .35

Issued to honor Young Pioneers.

Boali Falls — A8

1963, Oct. 28 *Perf. 13*

28 A8 30fr bl, grn & red brn .30 .20

Colotis Evippe — A9

Designs: Various butterflies.

1963, Nov. 18 Photo. *Perf. 12½x13*

29 A9 1fr multi .15 .15
30 A9 3fr multi .15 .15
31 A9 4fr multi .16 .16
32 A9 60fr multi .65 .65
Nos. 29-32 (4) 1.11 1.11

For surcharge see No. 58.

UNESCO Emblem, Scales and Tree — A9a

1963, Dec. 10 *Perf. 13*

33 A9a 25fr grn, ol & red brn .30 .22

15th anniversary of the Universal Declaration of Human Rights.

Leaves and IQSY Emblem A10

1964, Apr. 20 Engr. *Perf. 13*

34 A10 25fr org, Prus grn & bis .70 .65

International Quiet Sun Year, 1964-65.

Child — A11

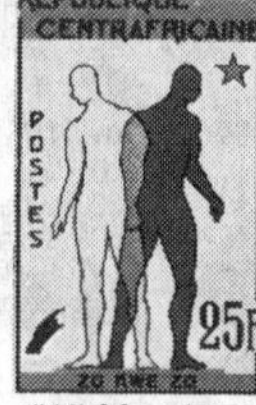

"All Men Are Men" — A12

Designs: Heads of Children.

1964, Aug. 13 Unwmk. *Perf. 13*

35 A11 20fr multi .20 .15
36 A11 25fr multi .22 .16
37 A11 40fr multi .35 .24
38 A11 50fr multi .50 .28
a. Miniature sheet of 4, #35-38 1.50 1.50
Nos. 35-38 (4) 1.27 .83

Cooperation Issue
Common Design Type

1964, Nov. 7 Engr.

39 CD119 25fr grn, mag & dk brn .30 .20

1964, Dec. 1 Litho. *Perf. 13x12½*

40 A12 25fr multi .28 .15

Issued to publicize National Unity.

Putting Yoke on Oxen — A13

Designs: 50fr, Ox pulling harrow. 85fr, Team of oxen in field. 100fr, Hay wagon.

1965, Apr. 28 Engr. *Perf. 13*

41 A13 25fr sl grn, sep & rose .25 .20
42 A13 50fr sl grn, lt bl & brn .50 .30
43 A13 85fr bl, grn & red brn .80 .50
44 A13 100fr multi 1.00 .65
Nos. 41-44 (4) 2.55 1.65

For surcharges see Nos. 63-64.

Telegraph Receiver by Pouget-Maisonneuve — A14

ITU cent.: 30fr, Chappe telegraph, vert. 50fr, Doignon regulator, vert. 85fr, Pouillet telegraph transcriber.

1965, May 17 Unwmk.

45 A14 25fr red, grn & ultra .25 .20
46 A14 30fr lake & grn .35 .22
47 A14 50fr car & vio .55 .35
48 A14 85fr red lil & slate .80 .55
Nos. 45-48 (4) 1.95 1.32

"Health" A15

Designs: 25fr, "Clothes;" shuttle, cloth and women. 60fr, "Teaching;" student and school. 85fr, "Food;" mother feeding child, tractor in wheat field.

1965, June 10 Engr. *Perf. 13*

49 A15 25fr ultra, brt grn & brn .25 .20
50 A15 50fr ultra, brn & grn .50 .35
51 A15 60fr grn, ultra & brn .60 .42
52 A15 85fr multi .90 .50
Nos. 49-52 (4) 2.25 1.47

Issued to publicize the slogans and aims of "M.E.S.A.N." (Mouvement d'Evolution Sociale de l'Afrique Noire). See No. C30.

Caterpillars and Moth on Coffee Branch — A16

Designs: 3fr, Hawk moth and caterpillar on coffee leaves, horiz. 30fr, Platyedra moth and larvae on cotton plant.

1965, Aug. 25 Engr. *Perf. 13*

53 A16 2fr dk pur, dp org & sl grn .15 .15
54 A16 3fr blk, sl grn & red .15 .15
55 A16 30fr red lil, red & sl grn .65 .25
Set value .75 .35

Issued to publicize plant protection.

Boy Scout, Tents and Animals A17

Design: 25fr, Campfire and Scout emblem.

1965, Sept. 27 Unwmk. *Perf. 13*

56 A17 25fr red org, bl & red lil .25 .15
57 A17 50fr brn & Prus bl .55 .38

Issued to honor the Boy Scouts.

Nos. 30, 1 and 22 Surcharged in Black or Brown

5 F

Engraved; Photogravure
Perf. 13, 12, 12½x13

1965, Aug. 26 Unwmk.

58 A9 2fr on 3fr multi 1.10 1.10
59 A1 5fr on 15fr multi 1.10 1.10
60 A5 10fr on 20fr multi (Br) 1.40 1.40
Nos. 58-60 (3) 3.60 3.60

The surcharges are adjusted to shape of stamps.

UN Emblem and Wheat — A18

1965, Oct. 16 Engr. *Perf. 13*

61 A18 50fr ocher, sl grn & brt bl .60 .40

FAO "Freedom from Hunger Campaign."

Diamond Cutter — A19

1966, Mar. 14 Engr. *Perf. 13*

62 A19 25fr car rose, dk pur & brn .25 .16

Nos. 43-44 Surcharged

5 F

1966, Feb.

63 A13 5fr on 85fr multi .16 .16
64 A13 10fr on 100fr multi .30 .30

Issue dates: 5fr, Feb. 17; 10fr, Feb. 15.

Statue of Mbaka Woman Porter — A20

WHO Headquarters, Geneva — A21

1966, Apr. 9 Photo. *Perf. 13x12½*

65 A20 25fr multi .25 .16

Intl. Negro Arts Festival, Dakar, Senegal, Apr. 1-24.

1966, May 3 Photo. Unwmk.

66 A21 25fr pur, bl & yel .25 .16

Inauguration of the WHO Headquarters, Geneva.

Eulophia Cucullata — A22

Orchids: 5fr, Lissochilus horsfalii. 10fr, Tridactyle bicaudata. 15fr, Polystachya. 20fr, Eulophia alta. 25fr, Microcelia macrorrhynchium.

1966, May 16 Photo. *Perf. 12x12½*
Orchids in Natural Colors

67 A22 2fr dk red .15 .15
68 A22 5fr brn org & vio .15 .15
69 A22 10fr bl grn & blk .15 .15
70 A22 15fr lt grn & dk brn .16 .15

71 A22 20fr dk grn .22 .15
72 A22 25fr lt ultra & brn .30 .15
Set value .90 .55

For surcharge see No. 78.

Congo Forest Mouse — A23

Rodents: 10fr, One-stripe mouse. 20fr, Dollman's tree mouse, vert.

1966, Sept. 15 Photo. *Perf. 12½x12*
73 A23 5fr yel & multi .15 .15
74 A23 10fr tan & multi .15 .15
75 A23 20fr lt grn & multi .22 .16
Set value .42 .30

UNESCO Emblem — A24

Pres. Jean Bedel Bokassa — A25

1966, Dec. 5 Photo. *Perf. 13*
76 A24 30fr multi .30 .16

20th anniv. of UNESCO.

1967, Jan. 1 *Perf. 12x12½*
77 A25 30fr yel grn, blk & bis brn .35 .16

No. 72 Surcharged with New Value and "XX"

1967, May 8 Photo. *Perf. 12x12½*
78 A22 10fr on 25fr multi .15 .15

See No. C43.

Central Market, Bangui — A26

1967, Aug. 8 Photo. *Perf. 12½x13*
79 A26 30fr multi .35 .20

Safari Hotel, Bangui A27

1967, Sept. 26 Photo. *Perf. 12½x13*
80 A27 30fr multi .35 .20

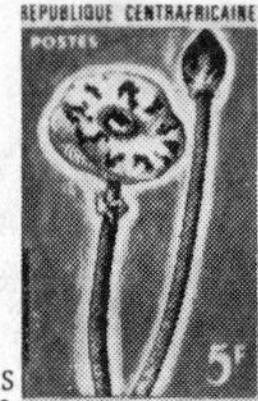

Leucocoprinus Africanus — A28

Various Mushrooms

1967, Oct. 3 Engr. *Perf. 13*
81 A28 5fr dk brn, ol & ocher .15 .15
82 A28 10fr dk brn, ultra & yel .15 .15
83 A28 15fr dk brn, sl grn & yel .16 .15
84 A28 30fr multi .40 .16
85 A28 50fr multi .60 .35
Nos. 81-85 (5) 1.46
Set value .78

Map, Radio Tower, Projector and People — A29

1967, Oct. 31
86 A29 30fr emer, ocher & indigo .35 .20

Radiovision service.

African Hair Style — A30

Various African Hair Styles.

1967, Nov. 7 Engr. *Perf. 13*
87 A30 5fr ultra, dk brn & bis brn .15 .15
88 A30 10fr car, dk brn & bis brn .15 .15
89 A30 15fr dp grn, dk brn & bis brn .16 .15
90 A30 20fr org, dk brn & bis brn .22 .15
91 A30 30fr red lil, dk brn & bis brn .35 .16
Nos. 87-91 (5) 1.03
Set value .48

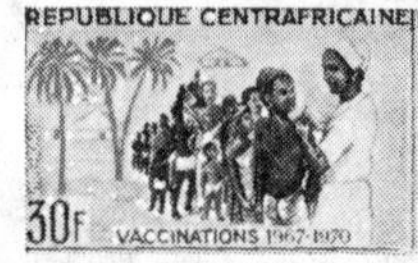

Nurse Vaccinating Children A31

1967, Nov. 14
92 A31 30fr dk red brn & brt grn .35 .16

Vaccination campaign, 1967-70.

Douglas DC-3 — A32

1967, Nov. 24
93 A32 1fr shown .15 .15
94 A32 2fr Beechcraft Baron .15 .15
95 A32 5fr Douglas DC-4 .15 .15
Nos. 93-95,C47-C49 (6) 6.20 2.95

Pierced Stone, Kwe Tribe — A33

Designs: 30fr, Primitive dwelling at Toulou, horiz. 100fr, Megaliths, Bouar. 130fr, Rock painting (people), Toulou, horiz.

1967, Dec. 26 Engr. *Perf. 13*
96 A33 30fr crim, ind & mar .35 .20
97 A33 50fr ol brn, ocher & dk grn .55 .25
98 A33 100fr dk brn, brt bl & brn 1.10 .45
99 A33 130fr dk red, brn & dk grn 1.40 .60
Nos. 96-99 (4) 3.40 1.50

6th Pan-African Prehistoric Cong., Dakar.

Tanker, Refinery and Map of Area Served — A33a

1968, July 30 Photo. *Perf. 12½*
100 A33a 30fr multi .25 .15

Issued to commemorate the opening of the Port Gentil (Gabon) Refinery, June 12, 1968.

Bulldozer Clearing Land — A34

Designs: 10fr, Baoule cattle. 20fr, 15,000-spindle spinning machine. No. 104, Automatic Diederichs looms. No. 105, Bulldozer.

1968, Oct. 1 Engr. *Perf. 13*
101 A34 5fr blk, grn & dk brn .15 .15
102 A34 10fr blk, pale grn & bis brn .15 .15
103 A34 20fr grn, red brn & yel .20 .15
104 A34 30fr brn, ol & ultra .35 .15
105 A34 30fr ind, red brn & sl grn .35 .15
Nos. 101-105 (5) 1.20
Set value .55

Issued to publicize "Operation Bokassa."

Bangui Mosque A35

1968, Oct. 14
106 A35 30fr grn, bl & ocher .30 .15

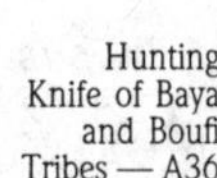

Hunting Knife of Baya and Boufi Tribes — A36

Designs: 20fr, Hunting knife of Nzakara tribe. 30fr, Crossbow of Babinga and Babenzele (pygmy) tribes.

1968, Nov. 19 Engr. *Perf. 13*
107 A36 10fr lem, Prus bl & ultra .15 .15
108 A36 20fr ultra, dk ol & sl grn .20 .15
109 A36 30fr sl grn, ultra & brn org .30 .15
Nos. 107-109 (3) .65
Set value .32

"Ville de Bangui," 1958 — A37

River Boats: 30fr, "J. B. Gouandjia," 1968. 50fr, "Lamblin," 1944.

1968, Dec. 10 Engr. *Perf. 13*
Size: 36x22mm
110 A37 10fr mag, brt grn & vio bl .15 .15
111 A37 30fr bl, grn & brn .35 .15
112 A37 50fr brn, sl & ol grn .60 .25
Nos. 110-112,C62-C63 (5) 3.50 1.65

Woman Javelin Thrower — A38

1969, Mar. 18 Photo. *Perf. 13x12½*
113 A38 5fr shown .15 .15
114 A38 10fr Women runners .15 .15
115 A38 15fr Soccer .16 .15
Nos. 113-115,C71-C72 (5) 1.96
Set value .80

BIT and ILO Emblems and Worker A39

1969, May 20 Photo. *Perf. 12½x13*
116 A39 30fr dp bl, grn & ol brn .25 .15
117 A39 50fr dp car, grn & ol brn .50 .22

50th anniv. of the ILO.

Pres. Bokassa — A40

Garayah — A41

1969, Dec. 1 Litho. *Perf. 13x13½*
118 A40 30fr vermilion & multi .25 .15

ASECNA Issue
Common Design Type

1969, Dec. 12 Engr. *Perf. 13*
119 CD132 100fr dp bl 1.00 .45

1970, Jan. 6 Engr. *Perf. 13*

Musical Instuments: 15fr, Ngombi (harp) horiz. 30fr, Xylophone, horiz. 50fr, Ndala (lute) horiz. 130fr, Gatta and babyon (drums).

120 A41 10fr yel grn, dk grn & ocher .15 .15
121 A41 15fr bl grn, ocher & dk brn .16 .15
122 A41 30fr mar, ocher & dk brn .30 .15
123 A41 50fr rose car & ind .50 .30
124 A41 130fr brt bl, brn & ol 1.40 .45
Nos. 120-124 (5) 2.51 1.20

UPU Headquarters Issue
Common Design Type

1970, May 20 Engr. *Perf. 13*
125 CD133 100fr ultra, ver & red brn .65 .35

Loading Platform and Flour Storage Bins — A42

Designs: 50fr, Flour milling machinery. 100fr, View of mill.

1970, Feb. 24 Litho. *Perf. 14*
126 A42 25fr sl & multi .22 .15
127 A42 50fr lil & multi .45 .22
128 A42 100fr red & multi .90 .50
Nos. 126-128 (3) 1.57 .87

Inauguration of SICPAD (Société Industrielle Centrafricaine des Produits Alimentaires et Dérivés), a part of Operation Bokassa, 2/22/68.

Pres. Bokassa — A43

1970, Aug. 13 Litho. *Perf. 14*

129 A43 30fr multi 2.25 1.75
130 A43 40fr multi 3.25 2.25

Cheese Factory, Sarki — A44

Silk Worm — A45

Designs: 10fr, M'Bali Ranch. 20fr, Zebu, vert.

Perf. 13x13½, 13½x13

1970, Sept. 15

131 A44 5fr red & multi .15 .15
132 A44 10fr red & multi 2.50 2.25
133 A44 20fr red & multi .42 .30
134 A45 40fr red & multi .70 .50
Nos. 131-134,C83 (5) 5.17 3.90

Issued to publicize Operation Bokassa, a national development plan.

Gnathonemus Monteiri — A46

River Fish: 20fr, Mormyrus proboscirostris. 30fr, Marcusenius wilverthi. 40fr, Gnathonemus elephas. 50fr, Gnathonemus curvirostris.

1971, Apr. 6 Photo. *Perf. 12½*

135 A46 10fr multi .15 .15
136 A46 20fr multi .20 .15
137 A46 30fr multi .35 .16
138 A46 40fr multi .42 .16
139 A46 50fr multi .55 .25
Nos. 135-139 (5) 1.67 .87

Berberati Cathedral A47

1971, July 20 Litho. *Perf. 13½*

140 A47 5fr grn & multi .15 .15

New Roman Catholic Cathedral at Berberati.

Charles de Gaulle — A48

Gray Galago — A49

1971, Aug. 20 *Perf. 13½x13*

141 A48 100fr brt bl & multi 1.00 .70

In memory of Gen. Charles de Gaulle (1890-1970), president of France.

1971, Oct. 25 Photo. *Perf. 13*

Designs: 40fr, Elegant galago. 100fr, Calabar potto, horiz. 150fr, Bosman's potto, horiz. 200fr, Oustalet's colobo, horiz.

142 A49 30fr pink & multi .35 .25
143 A49 40fr lt bl & multi .50 .35
144 A49 100fr multi .90 .65
145 A49 150fr multi 1.50 .80
146 A49 200fr multi 2.25 1.00
Nos. 142-146 (5) 5.50 3.05

Alan B. Shepard — A50

Designs: No. 148, Yuri Gagarin. No. 149, Edwin E. Aldrin, Jr. No. 150, Alexei Leonov. No. 151, Neil A. Armstrong on moon. No. 152, Lunokhod I on moon.

1971, Nov. 19 Litho. *Perf. 14*

147 A50 40fr vio & multi .35 .16
148 A50 40fr vio & multi .35 .16
149 A50 100fr multi .90 .40
150 A50 100fr multi .90 .40
151 A50 200fr red & multi 1.60 .65
152 A50 200fr red & multi 1.60 .65
Nos. 147-152 (6) 5.70 2.42

Space achievements of US and Russia.

"Operation Bokassa" and Pres. Bokassa A51

1971, Dec. 1 Photo. *Perf. 13*

153 A51 40fr red & multi .40 .15

12th anniversary of independence.

Racial Equality Emblem A52

1971, Dec. 6 Litho.

154 A52 50fr multi .40 .16

Intl. Year Against Racial Discrimination.

Bokassa School Emblem and Cadets — A53

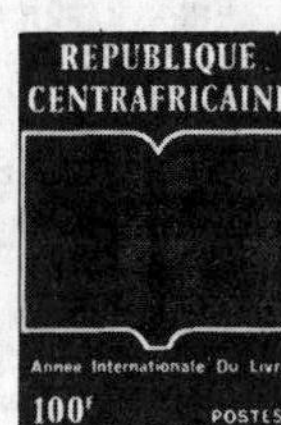

Book Year Emblem — A54

1972, Jan. 1 Photo.

155 A53 30fr gold & multi .30 .15

J. B. Bokassa Military School.

1972, Mar. 11 Photo. *Perf. 12½x13*

156 A54 100fr red brn, gold & org .70 .42

International Book Year 1972.

"Your Heart is your Health" A55

1972, Apr. 7 Photo. *Perf. 13x12½*

157 A55 100fr yel, blk & car .70 .42

World Health Day.

Red Cross Workers in Village — A56

1972, May 8 *Perf. 13*

158 A56 150fr multi 1.40 .60

25th World Red Cross Day.

Globe — A57

1972, May 17 Litho.

159 A57 50fr yel, blk & dp org .40 .20

4th World Telecommunications Day.

Pres. and Mrs. Bokassa and Family A58

1972, May 28 *Perf. 14*

160 A58 30fr yel & multi .25 .15

Mother's Day. Mothers' gold medal awarded to Catherine Bokassa.

Pres. Bokassa Planting Cotton, Map of Africa — A59

1972, June 5 Photo. *Perf. 13*

161 A59 40fr yel & multi .35 .16

Operation Bokassa, a natl. development plan.

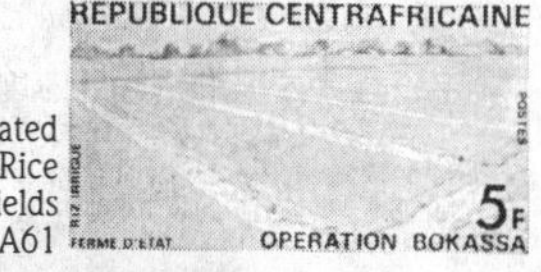

Postal Checking and Savings Center — A60

1972, June 21

162 A60 30fr yel org & multi .25 .15

Irrigated Rice Fields A61

"Le Pacifique" Apartment House — A62

Designs: 25fr, Plowing rice field. No. 166, Swimming pool, Hotel St. Sylvestre. No. 167, Entrance, Hotel St. Sylvestre. No. 168, J. B. Bokassa University.

1972 Litho. *Perf. 13x13½*

163 A61 5fr multi .15 .15
164 A61 25fr multi .22 .15

Engr. *Perf. 13*

165 A62 30fr multi .22 .15
166 A62 30fr multi .22 .15
167 A62 40fr multi .30 .16
168 A62 40fr multi .30 .15
Nos. 163-168 (6) 1.41
Set value .65

Operation Bokassa. Issued: 5fr, 25fr, Nov. 10; #165, June 27; #166-167, Dec. 9; #168, Aug. 26.

Protestant Youth Center — A64

Bull Chasing Woman on Clock Face — A63

Designs (Scenes Painted on Clock Faces): 10fr, Men and open cooking fire. 20fr, Fishermen. 30fr, Palms, monkeys and giraffe. 40fr, Warriors.

1972, July 31 Photo. *Perf. 12½*

169 A63 5fr dk red & multi .15 .15
170 A63 10fr brt bl & multi .15 .15
171 A63 20fr grn & multi .16 .15
172 A63 30fr yel & multi .30 .15
173 A63 40fr vio & multi .35 .20
Set value .92 .50

HORCEN Central African clock and watch factory.

Design: 10fr, Postal runner carrying mail in cleft stick, vert.

1972, Aug. 12 *Perf. 13*

174 A64 10fr multi .15 .15
175 A64 20fr multi .16 .15
Nos. 174-175,C95-C98 (6) 3.66 1.82

Centraphilex 1972, Central African Philatelic Exhibition, Bangui.

Mail Truck — A65

1972, Oct. 23 **Photo.** *Perf. 13*

176 A65 100fr ocher & multi .90 .35

Universal Postal Union Day.

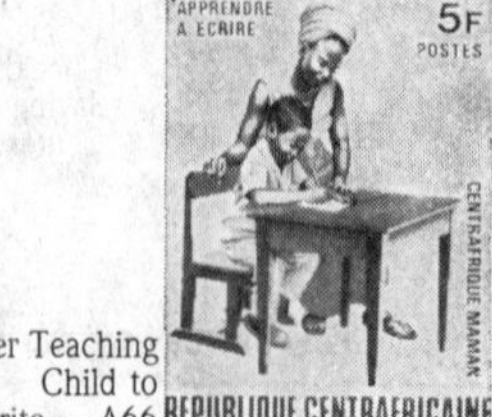

Mother Teaching Child to Write — A66

Central African Mothers: 10fr, Caring for infant. 15fr, Combing child's hair. 20fr, Teaching to read. 180fr, Nursing. 190fr, Teaching to walk.

1972, Dec. 27 *Perf. 13½x13*

177 A66 5fr multi .15 .15
178 A66 10fr lil & multi .15 .15
179 A66 15fr dl org & multi .15 .15
180 A66 20fr yel grn & multi .16 .15
181 A66 180fr multi 1.50 .50
182 A66 190fr pink & multi 1.50 .70
Nos. 177-182 (6) 3.61
Set value 1.40

Farmer Carrying Sheaf — A67

1973, May 30 **Photo.** *Perf. 13*

183 A67 50fr vio bl & multi .38 .22

10th anniv. of the World Food Program.

Garcinia Punctata A68

African Flora: 20fr, Bertiera racemosa. 30fr, Corynanthe pachyceras. 40fr, Combretodendron africanum. 50fr, Xylopia Villosa, vert.

1973, June 8

184 A68 10fr pale bl & multi .15 .15
185 A68 20fr multi .15 .15
186 A68 30fr lt gray & multi .25 .15
187 A68 40fr multi .25 .20
188 A68 50fr multi .35 .22
Nos. 184-188 (5) 1.15
Set value .64

For surcharge see No. 193.

Pygmy Chameleon A69

1973, June 26 **Photo.** *Perf. 13*

189 A69 15fr multi .15 .15

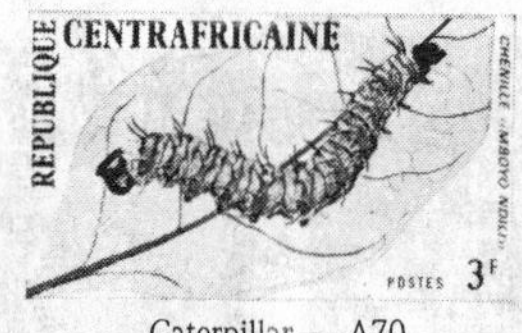

Caterpillar — A70

Designs: Various caterpillars.

1973, Aug. 6 **Photo.** *Perf. 13*

190 A70 3fr multi .15 .15
191 A70 5fr multi .15 .15
192 A70 25fr multi .20 .15
Set value .30 .20

For surcharge see No. 259.

No. 184 Surcharged with New Value, 2 Bars, and Overprinted in Red: "SECHERESSE SOLIDARITE AFRICAINE"

1973, Aug. 16

193 A68 100fr on 10fr multi .60 .50

African solidarity in drought emergency.

African Postal Union Issue
Common Design Type

1973, Sept. 12 **Engr.** *Perf. 13*

194 CD137 100fr dk brn, red org & ol .60 .42

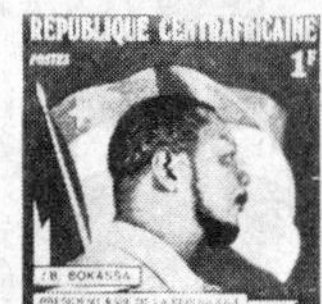

Pres. Bokassa and CAR Flag — A71

1973, Nov. 30 **Photo.** *Perf. 12½*

195 A71 1fr brn & multi .15 .15
196 A71 2fr pur & multi .15 .15
197 A71 3fr vio bl & multi .15 .15
198 A71 5fr ocher & multi .15 .15
199 A71 10fr multi .15 .15
200 A71 15fr org & multi .15 .15
201 A71 20fr multi .15 .15
202 A71 30fr dk grn & multi .20 .15
203 A71 40fr dk brn & multi .25 .20
Set value, #195-203, C117-C118 1.95 1.40

INTERPOL Emblem A72

1973, Dec. 20 *Perf. 13x12½*

204 A72 50fr yel & multi .35 .25

Intl. Criminal Police Organization, 50th anniv.

Catherine Bokassa Center — A73

Design: 40fr, Ambulance in front of Catherine Bokassa Center.

1974, Jan. 24 **Engr.** *Perf. 13*

205 A73 30fr multi .16 .15
206 A73 40fr multi .22 .16

Catherine Bokassa Center for Mothers and Children.

Cigarette-making Machine — A74

Designs: 10fr, Cigarette in ashtray, and factory. 30fr, Hand lighting cigarette, and Administration Building.

1974, Jan. 29

207 A74 5fr slate grn & multi .15 .15
208 A74 10fr slate grn & multi .15 .15
209 A74 30fr slate grn & multi .16 .15
Set value .28 .22

Publicity for Centra cigarettes.

"Communications" A75

1974, June 8 **Photo.** *Perf. 12½x13*

210 A75 100fr multi .65 .45

World Telecommunications Day.
For surcharge see No. 280.

People and WPY Emblem A76

1974, June 20 **Engr.** *Perf. 13*

211 A76 100fr red, sl grn & brn .65 .45

World Population Year.
For surcharge see No. 281.

Mother, Child, WHO Emblem — A77

1974, July 10

212 A77 100fr multi .65 .30

26th anniv. of WHO.
For surcharge see No. 282.

Hoeing A78

Veterans' activities: 10fr, Battle scene ("yesterday"). 15fr, Pastoral scene ("today"). 20fr, Rice planting. 25fr, Storehouse. 40fr, Veterans Headquarters. Borders show tanks and tractors.

1974, Nov. 15 **Litho.** *Perf. 13*

213 A78 10fr multi .15 .15
214 A78 15fr multi .15 .15
215 A78 20fr multi .15 .15
216 A78 25fr multi .15 .15
217 A78 30fr multi .16 .15
218 A78 40fr multi .22 .15
Set value .80 .46

For surcharges see Nos. 260, 265, 267.

Presidents and Flags of Cameroun, CAR, Congo, Gabon and Meeting Center — A79

1974, Dec. 8 **Photo.** *Perf. 13*

219 A79 40fr gold & multi .25 .15

See #C126 and note after Cameroun #595.
For surcharge see No. 272.

House in OCAM City — A80

Designs: Scenes in housing development, OCAM City.

1975, Feb. 1 **Photo.** *Perf. 13*

220 A80 30fr multi .20 .15
221 A80 40fr multi .25 .15
222 A80 50fr multi .30 .20
223 A80 100fr multi .60 .42
Nos. 220-223 (4) 1.35 .92

For surcharges see Nos. 269, 273.

1975, Feb. 22

Designs: Cottage scenes in J. B. Bokassa "pilot village."

224 A80 25fr multi .15 .15
225 A80 30fr multi .16 .15
226 A80 40fr multi .25 .15
Nos. 224-226 (3) .56
Set value .32

For surcharges see Nos. 268, 270, 274.

Foreign Ministry A81

Television Station — A82

1975, Feb. 28 *Perf. 13x12½*

227 A81 40fr multi .25 .15

Perf. 13

228 A82 40fr multi .25 .15

Public buildings, Bangui.
For surcharges see Nos. 275-276.

Bokassa's Saber — A83

Design: 40fr, Bokassa's baton.

1975, Feb. 22 **Photo.** *Perf. 13*

229 A83 30fr dp bl & multi .16 .15
230 A83 40fr vio bl & multi .22 .15

Jean Bedel Bokassa, President for Life and Marshal of the Republic. See Nos. C127-C128. For surcharge see No. 286.

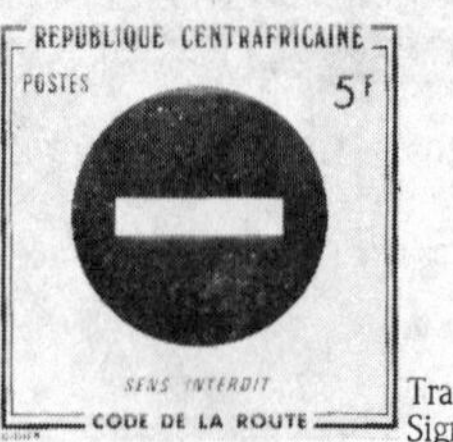

Traffic Signs — A84

1975, Mar. 20

231 A84 5fr Do Not Enter .15 .15
232 A84 10fr Stop .15 .15
233 A84 20fr No parking .15 .15
234 A84 30fr School .15 .15
235 A84 40fr Intersection .25 .15
Set value .60 .42

For surcharges see Nos. 261, 277.

Buffon's Kob — A85

1975, June 24 Photo. *Perf. 13*

No.	Type	Description	Unused	Used
236	A85	10fr shown	.15	.15
237	A85	15fr Wart hog	.15	.15
238	A85	20fr Waterbuck	.15	.15
239	A85	30fr Lion	.20	.15
		Set value	.50	.32

For surcharges see Nos. 262-263, 266, 271.

Crane Lifting Log onto Truck — A86

Designs: 10fr, Forest, vert. 15fr, Tree felling, vert. 100fr, Log pile. 150fr, Logs transported by raft. 200fr, Lumberyard.

1975, Nov. 28 Engr. *Perf. 13*

No.	Type	Description	Unused	Used
240	A86	10fr multi	.15	.15
241	A86	15fr multi	.15	.15
242	A86	50fr multi	.25	.16
243	A86	100fr multi	.50	.38
244	A86	150fr multi	.70	.60
245	A86	200fr multi	1.00	.70
		Nos. 240-245 (6)	2.75	2.14

Promotion of Central African wood.
For surcharges see Nos. 264, 279.

Women's Heads and Various Occupations — A87

1975, Dec. 10 Photo.

No.	Type	Description	Unused	Used
246	A87	40fr multi	.22	.15
247	A87	100fr multi	.50	.38

International Women's Year 1975.

Alexander Graham Bell — A88

1976, Mar. 25 Litho. *Perf. 12½x13*

No.	Type	Description	Unused	Used
248	A88	100fr yel & blk	.50	.35

Centenary of first telephone call by Alexander Graham Bell, Mar. 10, 1876.
For surcharge see No. 283.

Satellite and ITU Emblem — A89

Design: No. 250, UPU emblem, various forms of mail transport.

1976 Engr. *Perf. 13*

No.	Type	Description	Unused	Used
249	A89	100fr vio bl, cl & grn	.50	.35
250	A89	100fr car, grn & ocher	.70	.50

World Telecommunications Day (No. 249); Universal Postal Union Day (No. 250).
For surcharges see Nos. 284-285.

Soyuz on Launching Pad — A90

Design: 50fr, Apollo rocket.

1976, June 14 Litho. *Perf. 14x13½*

No.	Type	Description	Unused	Used
251	A90	40fr multi	.28	.15
252	A90	50fr multi	.38	.16
		Nos. 251-252,C135-C137 (5)	4.71	1.96

Apollo Soyuz space test project, Russo-American cooperation, launched July 15, link-up July 17, 1975.
For surcharges see Nos. 287, 290, C161, C168, C173, C177.

Drurya Antimachus — A91

Butterfly: 40fr, Argema mittrei, vert.

1976, Sept. 20 Litho. *Perf. 12½*

No.	Type	Description	Unused	Used
253	A91	30fr ocher & multi	.16	.15
254	A91	40fr ultra & multi	.22	.15
		Set value		.24

See Nos. C145-C146. For surcharge see No. 278.

Slalom, Piero Gros — A92

Design: 60fr, Karl Schnabel and Toni Innauer.

1976, Sept. 23 *Perf. 13½*

No.	Type	Description	Unused	Used
255	A92	40fr multi	.28	.15
256	A92	60fr multi	.42	.22
		Nos. 255-256,C147-C149 (5)	4.55	2.12

12th Winter Olympic Games winners, Innsbruck.
For surcharges see Nos. 288, 291, C164, C170, C174, C178.

Viking Components A93

Design: 60fr, Viking take-off.

1976, Dec.

No.	Type	Description	Unused	Used
257	A93	40fr multi	.28	.15
258	A93	60fr multi	.42	.20
		Nos. 257-258,C151-C153 (5)	4.55	1.97

Viking Mars project.
For surcharges and overprints see Nos. 289, 292, 391-392, C165, C171, C175, C179.

Empire

Stamps of 1973-76 Overprinted with Bars and "EMPIRE CENTRAFRICAIN" in Black, Green, Violet Blue, Silver, Carmine, Brown or Red

Printing and Perforations as Before

1977, Mar.

No.	Type	Description	Unused	Used
259	A70	3fr (#190; B)	.15	.15
260	A78	10fr (#213;B)	.15	.15
261	A84	10fr (#232;VB)	.15	.15
262	A85	10fr (#236;C)	.15	.15
263	A85	15fr (#237;C)	.15	.15
264	A86	15fr (#241;B)	.15	.15
265	A78	20fr (#215;B)	.15	.15
266	A85	20fr (#238;C)	.15	.15
267	A78	25fr (#216;B)	.16	.15
268	A80	25fr (#224;B)	.16	.15
269	A80	30fr (#220;VB)	.20	.16
270	A80	30fr (#225;B)	.20	.16
271	A85	30fr (#239;C)	.20	.16
272	A79	40fr (#219;B)	.22	.20
273	A80	40fr (#221;VB)	.25	.20
274	A80	40fr (#226;B)	.22	.20
275	A81	40fr (#227;B & S)	.22	.20
276	A82	40fr (#228;B)	.22	.20
277	A84	40fr (#235;VB)	.20	.16
278	A91	40fr (#254;B)	.20	.16
279	A86	50fr (#242;Br)	.30	.22
280	A75	100fr (#210;B)	.60	.45
281	A76	100fr (#211;B)	.60	.45
282	A77	100fr (#212;G)	.65	.55
283	A88	100fr (#248;R)	.65	.55
284	A89	100fr (#249;B)	.65	.55
285	A89	100fr (#250;B)	.65	.55
		Nos. 259-285 (27)	7.75	6.62

Stamps of 1975-76 Overprinted "EMPIRE CENTRAFRICAIN" in Black on Silver Panel

1977, Apr. 1

No.	Type	Description	Unused	Used
286	A83	40fr multi (#230)	.20	.16
287	A90	40fr multi (#251)	.25	.20
288	A92	40fr multi (#255)	.20	.16
289	A93	40fr multi (#257)	.20	.16
290	A90	50fr multi (#252)	.35	.22
291	A92	60fr multi (#256)	.35	.22
292	A93	60fr multi (#258)	.35	.22
		Nos. 286-292 (7)	1.90	1.34

Pierre and Marie Curie A94

Design: 60fr, Wilhelm C. Roentgen.

1977, Apr. 1 Litho. *Perf. 13½*

No.	Type	Description	Unused	Used
293	A94	40fr multi	.22	.15
294	A94	60fr multi	.40	.20
		Nos. 293-294,C180-C182 (5)	3.78	1.70

Nobel Prize winners.

Italy No. C42 and Faustine Temple, Rome — A95

Design: 60fr, Russia No. C12 and St. Basil's Cathedral, Moscow.

1977, Apr. 11 Litho. *Perf. 11*

No.	Type	Description	Unused	Used
295	A95	40fr multi	.22	.15
296	A95	60fr multi	.40	.20
		Nos. 295-296,C184-C186 (5)	4.47	1.97

75th anniversary of the Zeppelin.

Lindbergh over Paris — A96

Designs: 60fr, Santos Dumont and "14 bis." 100fr, Bleriot and monoplane. 200fr, Roald Amundsen and "N24." 300fr, Concorde. 500fr, Lindbergh and Spirit of St. Louis.

1977, Sept. 30 Litho. *Perf. 13½*

No.	Type	Description	Unused	Used
297	A96	50fr multi	.35	.16
298	A96	60fr multi	.40	.20
299	A96	100fr multi	.60	.25
300	A96	200fr multi	1.25	.50
301	A96	300fr multi	2.00	.80
		Nos. 297-301 (5)	4.60	1.91

Souvenir Sheet

No.	Type	Description	Unused	Used
302	A96	500fr multi	3.25	1.50

History of aviation, famous fliers.

Shot on Goal A97

Designs: 60fr, Heading ball in net. 100fr, Backfield defense. 200fr, Argentina '78 poster. 300fr, Mario Zagalo and stadium. 500fr, Ferenc Puskas.

1977, Nov. 18 Litho. *Perf. 13½*

No.	Type	Description	Unused	Used
303	A97	50fr multi	.35	.16
304	A97	60fr multi	.40	.20
305	A97	100fr multi	.60	.22
306	A97	200fr multi	1.25	.50
307	A97	300fr multi	2.00	.80
		Nos. 303-307 (5)	4.60	1.88

Souvenir Sheet

No.	Type	Description	Unused	Used
308	A97	500fr multi	3.25	1.50

World Soccer Championships, Argentina, June 1-25, 1978.
For overprints see Nos. 370-375.

Emperor Bokassa I, Central African Flag — A98

1977, Dec. 4 Litho. *Perf. 13½*

No.	Type	Description	Unused	Used
309	A98	40fr multi	.20	.16
310	A98	60fr multi	.35	.22
311	A98	100fr multi	.55	.40
312	A98	150fr multi	.80	.60
		Nos. 309-312,C188-C189 (6)	4.60	3.03

Coronation of Emperor Bokassa I, Dec. 4.

Lilium — A99

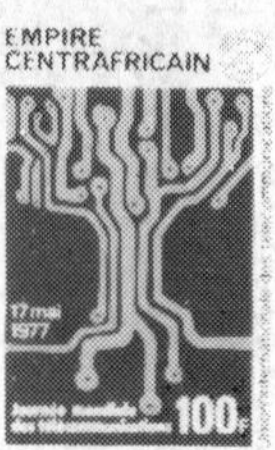

Electronic Tree, ITU Emblem — A100

1977 Litho. *Perf. 13½x14*

No.	Type	Description	Unused	Used
313	A99	5fr shown	.15	.15
314	A99	10fr Hibiscus	.15	.15
		Set value	.15	.15

For overprints see Nos. 408-409.

1977

No.	Type	Description	Unused	Used
315	A100	100fr blk, org & brn	.80	.60

World Telecommunications Day.

Bible and People A101

1977 Litho. *Perf. 14x13½*
316 A101 40fr multi .25 .15

Bible Week.

People and Rotary Emblem A102

1977
317 A102 60fr multi .40 .20

Rotary Club of Bangui, 20th anniversary.

Holy Family, by Rubens — A103

Rubens Paintings: 150fr, Marie de Medicis. 200fr, Son of artist. 300fr, Neptune. 500fr, Marie de Medicis, diff.

1978, Jan. 26
318 A103 60fr multi .40 .20
319 A103 150fr multi .90 .40
320 A103 200fr multi 1.25 .55
321 A103 300fr multi 2.00 .80
Nos. 318-321 (4) 4.55 1.95

Souvenir Sheet

322 A103 500fr gold & multi 3.25 1.50

Peter Paul Rubens (1577-1640).

Rhinoceros — A104

Endangered Animals and Wildlife Fund Emblem: 50fr, Slender-nosed crocodile. 60fr, Leopard, vert. 100fr, Giraffe, vert. 200fr, Elephant. 300fr, Gorilla, vert.

1978, Feb. 21 Litho. *Perf. 13½*
323 A104 40fr multi .22 .15
324 A104 50fr multi .35 .16
325 A104 60fr multi .40 .20
326 A104 100fr multi .60 .28
327 A104 200fr multi 1.25 .55
328 A104 300fr multi 2.00 .80
Nos. 323-328 (6) 4.82 2.14

Bokassa Sports Palace A105

Design: 60fr, Sports Palace, side view.

1978 *Perf. 14*
329 A105 40fr multi .20 .16
330 A105 60fr multi .35 .22

Automatic Telephone Exchange, Bangui A106

1978
331 A106 40fr multi .25 .15
332 A106 60fr multi .40 .20

Diligence and Satellite A107

Designs (UPU Emblem and): 50fr, Steam locomotive and communications via satellite. 60fr, Paddle-wheel steamer and ship-to-shore communication via satellite. 80fr, Old mail truck and satellite.

1978, May 17 *Perf. 13½*
333 A107 40fr multi .25 .15
334 A107 50fr multi .35 .16
335 A107 60fr multi .40 .20
336 A107 80fr multi .55 .25
Nos. 333-336,C191-C192 (6) 3.60 1.76

Posts and telecommunications, cent. pf progress.

Mask A108

Capt. Cook on "Endeavour" A109

Designs: 30fr, Mask. 60fr, Women dancers, horiz. 100fr, Men dancers, horiz.

Perf. 13½x14, 14x13½
1978, July 11 Litho.
337 A108 20fr blk & yel .15 .15
338 A108 30fr blk & brt bl .20 .15
339 A108 60fr blk & multi .40 .20
340 A108 100fr blk & multi .65 .35
Nos. 337-340 (4) 1.40
Set value .72

Black-African World Arts Festival, Lagos.
For overprints see Nos. 411-412.

1978, Aug. 30 *Perf. 14½*

Designs: 60fr, Resolution off Hawaii, horiz. 200fr, Hawaiians welcoming Capt. Cook, horiz. 350fr, Masked rowers in Hawaiian boat, horiz.

341 A109 60fr multi .40 .20
342 A109 80fr multi .55 .25
343 A109 200fr multi 1.40 .65
344 A109 350fr multi 2.25 1.10
Nos. 341-344 (4) 4.60 2.20

Capt. James Cook (1728-1779), explorer.

Dürer, Self-portrait A110

Dürer Paintings: 80fr, The Four Apostles. 200fr, Virgin and Child. 350fr, Emperor Maximilian I.

1978, Oct. 24 Litho. *Perf. 13½*
345 A110 60fr multi .40 .20
346 A110 80fr multi .55 .25
347 A110 200fr multi 1.40 .65
348 A110 350fr multi 2.25 1.10
Nos. 345-348 (4) 4.60 2.20

Albrecht Dürer (1471-1528), German painter.

Tutankhamen's Gold Mask — A111

Treasures of Tutankhamen: 60fr, King and Queen, gold back panel of throne. 80fr, Gilt folding chair. 100fr, King wearing crowns of Upper and Lower Egypt, painted wood sculpture. 120fr, Lion's head. 150fr, Tutankhamen, wood stature. 180fr, Gold throne. 250fr, Gold miniature coffin.

1978, Nov. 22
349 A111 40fr multi .25 .15
350 A111 60fr multi .40 .20
351 A111 80fr multi .55 .25
352 A111 100fr multi .65 .35
353 A111 120fr multi .80 .40
354 A111 150fr multi 1.00 .50
355 A111 180fr multi 1.20 .60
356 A111 250fr multi 1.60 .80
Nos. 349-356 (8) 6.45 3.25

Tutankhamen, c. 1358 B.C., King of Egypt.

Lenin at Smolny Institute — A112

Soviet Union, 60th anniv.: 60fr, 200fr, 300fr, Various Lenin portraits. 100fr, Ulyanov family, horiz. 150fr, Lenin, Cruiser "Aurora" and flag, horiz. 500fr, "Aurora" and star.

1978, Nov. *Perf. 14*
357 A112 40fr multi .25 .15
358 A112 60fr multi .40 .20
359 A112 100fr blk & gold .65 .35
360 A112 150fr blk, gold & red 1.00 .50
361 A112 200fr multi 1.40 .65
362 A112 300fr multi 2.00 1.00
Nos. 357-362 (6) 5.70 2.85

Souvenir Sheet

363 A112 500fr multi 3.50

Catherine Bokassa — A113

Design: 60fr, Emperor Bokassa.

1978, Dec. 4 Litho. *Perf. 13*
364 A113 40fr multi .25 .15
365 A113 60fr multi .40 .20

1st anniv. of coronation. See No. C202.

Rowland Hill, Letter Scale and G.B. No. 1 — A114

Rowland Hill and: 50fr, US #1, mailman on bicycle. 60fr, Austria #P4, 19th cent. mailman. 80fr, Switzerland #2L1, postilion and mailcoach.

1978, Dec. 9 Litho. *Perf. 13½*
366 A114 40fr multi .25 .15
367 A114 50fr multi .35 .16
368 A114 60fr multi .40 .20
369 A114 80fr multi .55 .25
Nos. 366-369,C203-C204 (6) 3.60 1.76

Sir Rowland Hill (1795-1879), originator of penny postage.

Nos. 303-307 Overprinted in Silver: "VAINQUEUR: ARGENTINE"

1978, Dec. 27
370 A97 50fr multi .35 .16
371 A97 60fr multi .40 .20
372 A97 100fr multi .65 .35
373 A97 200fr multi 1.40 .65
374 A97 300fr multi 2.00 1.00
Nos. 370-374 (5) 4.80 2.36

Souvenir Sheet

No. 308 Overprinted in Silver: "ARGENTINE-PAYS BAS 3-1 / 25 juin 1978"

375 A97 500fr multi 3.50 1.60

Argentina's victory in World Cup Soccer Championship 1978.

Children Painting and Dutch Portrait — A115

Designs (UNICEF, Eagle Emblems and): 50fr, Eskimo children skiing, and ski jump. 60fr, Children with toy racing car, and Carl Benz with early car model. 80fr, Children launching rocket, and Intelsat.

1979, Mar. 6 Litho. *Perf. 13½*
376 A115 40fr multi .25 .15
377 A115 50fr multi .35 .16
378 A115 60fr multi .40 .20
379 A115 80fr multi .55 .25
Nos. 376-379,C206-C207 (6) 3.60 1.76

International Year of the Child.

High Jump, Moscow '80 Emblem and "M" — A116

Designs (Moscow '80 Emblem, Various Sports and): 50fr, Bicycling and "O." 60fr, Weight lifting and "C." 80fr, Judo and "K."

1979, Mar. 16 Litho. *Perf. 13*
380 A116 40fr multi .22 .15
381 A116 50fr multi .25 .15
382 A116 60fr multi .32 .16
383 A116 80fr multi .40 .20
Nos. 380-383,C209-C210 (6) 3.24 1.66

22nd Olympic Games, Moscow, July 19-Aug. 3, 1980. Background letters on Nos. 380-383, C209-C210 spell "Mockba." A 1500fr gold embossed stamp showing emblems and Discobolus exists.

Memorial, Bangui, Butterfly, Hibiscus — A117

Design: 150fr, Canoe, truck and letters.

1979, June 8 Litho. *Perf. 12x12½*
384 A117 60fr multi .32 .16
385 A117 150fr multi .80 .40

Philexafrique II, Libreville, Gabon, June 8-17. Nos. 384, 385 each printed in sheets of 10 with 5 labels showing exhibition emblem.

Schoolgirl A118

1979, July 25 Litho. *Perf. 12½x12*
386 A118 70fr multi .38 .15

Intl. Bureau of Education, Geneva, 50th anniv.

Chicken A119

1979, Aug. *Perf. 13*
387 A119 10fr shown .15 .15
388 A119 20fr Bull .15 .15
389 A119 40fr Sheep .20 .15
Set value .35 .20

National Husbandry Assoc. See No. C211.

Souvenir Sheet

Virgin and Child, by Dürer A120

1979, Aug. *Perf. 13½*
390 A120 500fr lt grn & dl red 2.75 1.25

Albrecht Dürer (1471-1528), German engraver and printer.

Nos. 257-258 Overprinted "ALUNISSAGE/APOLLO XI/ juillet/1969" and Emblem

1979, Nov. 11 Litho. *Perf. 13½*
391 A93 40fr multi .22 .15
392 A93 60fr multi .32 .16
Nos. 391-392,C212-C214 (5) 3.79 1.91

Apollo 11 moon landing, 10th anniversary.

Girl and Rose A121

1979, Dec. 15
393 A121 30fr Butterfly and girl, vert. .16 .15
394 A121 40fr shown .22 .15
395 A121 60fr Hansel and Gretel, vert. .32 .16
396 A121 200fr Cinderella 1.10 .50
397 A121 250fr Mermaid, vert. 1.40 .65
Nos. 393-397 (5) 3.20 1.61

International Year of the Child.

Locomotive, US Type A27, Hill — A122

Locomotives, Hill and Stamps: 100fr, France #1. 150fr, Germany type A11. 250fr, Great Britain #32. 500fr, CAR #2.

1979, Dec. 20
398 A122 60fr multi .32 .16
399 A122 100fr multi .55 .25
400 A122 150fr multi .80 .40
401 A122 250fr multi 1.40 .65
Nos. 398-401 (4) 3.07 1.46

Souvenir Sheet

402 A122 500fr multi 3.00 1.50

Sir Rowland Hill (1795-1879), originator of penny postage.

Basketball, Moscow '80 Emblem — A123

Pre-Olympic Year: Men's or women's basketball.

1979, Dec. 28 Litho. *Perf. 14½*
403 A123 50fr multi .25 .15
404 A123 125fr multi .65 .35
405 A123 200fr multi 1.10 .55
406 A123 300fr multi 1.60 .80
407 A123 500fr multi 2.75 1.40
Nos. 403-407 (5) 6.35 3.25

For overprints see Nos. 425-429.

Nos. 313-314, 337-338 Overprinted "REPUBLIQUE CENTRAFRICAINE" in Black on Silver Panel and

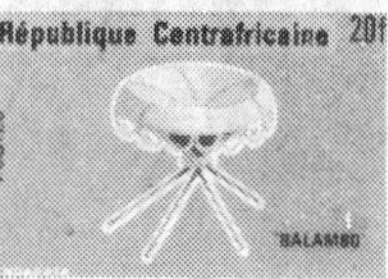

Balambo Chair — A124

Perf. 13½x14, 14x13½
1980, Mar. 20 Litho.
408 A99 5fr multi .15 .15
409 A99 10fr multi .15 .15
410 A124 20fr multi .15 .15
411 A108 20fr multi .15 .15
412 A108 30fr multi .16 .15
Set value .46 .28

Viking Satellite A125

1980, Apr. 8 *Perf. 13½*
413 A125 40fr shown .20 .15
414 A125 50fr Apollo-Soyuz .25 .15
415 A125 60fr Voyager .32 .16
416 A125 100fr European Space Agency emblem, flags .55 .25
Nos. 413-416,C221-C222 (6) 3.22 1.66

Walking, Olympic Medal, Moscow '80 Emblem — A126

1980, July 25 Litho. *Perf. 13½*
417 A126 30fr shown .16 .15
418 A126 40fr Relay race .22 .15
419 A126 70fr Running .38 .16
420 A126 80fr High jump .42 .22
Nos. 417-420,C231-C232 (6) 2.53 1.33

For overprints see Nos. 462-465, C248-C250.

Fruit A126a

1980, Aug. 1 Litho. *Perf. 13½*
420A A126a 40fr multicolored

The editors would like to see a 70fr stamp issued with No. 420A.

Agricultural Development A127

1980, Nov. 4 Litho. *Perf. 13½*
421 A127 30fr shown .16 .15
422 A127 40fr Telecommunications .22 .15
423 A127 70fr Engineering .38 .16
424 A127 100fr Civil engineering .55 .25
Nos. 421-424,C234-C235 (6) 3.21 1.66

Europe-Africa cooperation.

Nos. 403-407 Overprinted with Medal and Country

1980, Nov. 12 *Perf. 14½*
425 A123 50fr multi .25 .15
426 A123 125fr multi .65 .35
427 A123 200fr multi 1.10 .55
428 A123 300fr multi 1.60 .80
429 A123 500fr multi 2.75 1.40
Nos. 425-429 (5) 6.35 3.25

Virgin and Child, by Raphael A128

African Postal Union, 5th Anniversary A129

Christmas: Virgin & Child paintings by Raphael.

1980, Dec. 20 *Perf. 12½*
430 A128 60fr multi .35 .16
431 A128 150fr multi .80 .40
432 A128 250fr multi 1.40 .65
Nos. 430-432 (3) 2.55 1.21

1980, Dec. 24 Photo. *Perf. 13½*
433 A129 70fr multi .38 .16

Peruvian Soccer Team, Soccer Cup — A130

1981, Jan. 13 Litho. *Perf. 13½*
434 A130 10fr shown .15 .15
435 A130 15fr Scotland .15 .15
436 A130 20fr Mexico .15 .15
437 A130 25fr Sweden .15 .15
438 A130 30fr Austria .16 .15
439 A130 40fr Poland .22 .15
440 A130 50fr France .25 .15
441 A130 60fr Italy .35 .16
442 A130 70fr Germany .40 .20
443 A130 80fr Brazil .42 .22
Nos. 434-443,C237-C238 (12) 4.05
Set value 1.90

ESPANA '82 World Cup Soccer Championship.

13th World Telecommunications Day — A131

1981, May 17 Litho. *Perf. 12½*
444 A131 150fr multi .80 .40

Apollo 15 Crew on Moon A132

Space Exploration: Columbia space shuttle.

1981, June 10 Litho. *Perf. 14*
445 A132 100fr multi .55 .25
446 A132 150fr multi .80 .40
447 A132 200fr multi 1.10 .55
448 A132 300fr multi 1.60 .80
Nos. 445-448 (4) 4.05 2.00

Souvenir Sheet

449 A132 500fr multi 2.75 1.40

Family of Acrobats with Monkey, by Picasso A133

Picasso Birth Cent.: 50fr, The Balcony. 80fr, The Artist's Son as Pierrot. 100fr, The Three Dancers.

1981, June 30 *Perf. 13½*

450 A133 40fr multi .22 .15
451 A133 50fr multi .25 .15
452 A133 80fr multi .42 .22
453 A133 100fr multi .55 .25
Nos. 450-453,C245-C246 (6) 3.34 1.72

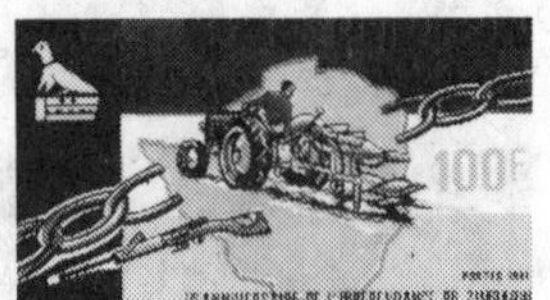

First Anniv. of Zimbabwe's Independence — A134

1981, July 9 **Litho.** *Perf. 12½*

454 A134 100fr multi .55 .25
455 A134 150fr multi .80 .40
456 A134 200fr multi 1.10 .55
Nos. 454-456 (3) 2.45 1.20

Prince Charles and Lady Diana — A135

1981, July, 24 *Perf. 14*

457 A135 75fr Charles .40 .20
458 A135 100fr Diana .55 .25
459 A135 150fr St. Paul's Cathedral .80 .40
460 A135 175fr shown .90 .45
Nos. 457-460 (4) 2.65 1.30

Souvenir Sheet

461 A135 500fr Couple 2.75 1.40

Royal Wedding.
For overprints see Nos. 529-533.

Nos. 417-420 Overprinted with Event, Winner and Country in Gold

1981 **Litho.** *Perf. 13½*

462 A126 30fr multi .16 .15
463 A126 40fr multi .22 .15
464 A126 70fr multi .38 .16
465 A126 80fr multi .42 .22
Nos. 462-465,C248-C249 (6) 2.53 1.33

Prince Charles and Lady Diana — A136

1981, Aug. 20 **Litho.** *Perf. 13½*

466 A136 40fr shown .22 .15
467 A136 50fr Crowned Prince of Wales .25 .15
468 A136 80fr Diana .42 .22
469 A136 100fr Naval training .55 .25
Nos. 466-469,C251-C252 (6) 3.34 1.72

Royal wedding.

1906 Renault — A137

1981, Sept. 22 **Litho.** *Perf. 12½*

470 A137 20fr shown .15 .15
471 A137 40fr Mercedes-Benz, 1937 .22 .15
472 A137 50fr Matra-Ford, 1969 .25 .15
473 A137 110fr Tazio Nuvolari, 1927 .60 .30
474 A137 150fr Jackie Stewart, 1965 .80 .40
Nos. 470-474 (5) 2.02 1.15

Souvenir Sheet

Perf. 10

475 A137 450fr Finish line, 1914 2.50 1.40

Grand Prix of France, 75th anniv.

World Food Day — A138

1981, Oct. 16

476 A138 90fr multi .48 .25
477 A138 110fr multi .60 .30

Navigators and their Ships — A139

1981, Sept. 4 **Litho.** *Perf. 13½*

478 A139 40fr C.V. Rietschoten .22 .15
479 A139 50fr M. Pajot .25 .15
480 A139 60fr K. Jaworski .35 .16
481 A139 80fr M. Birch .42 .22
Nos. 478-481,C254-C255 (6) 2.89 1.48

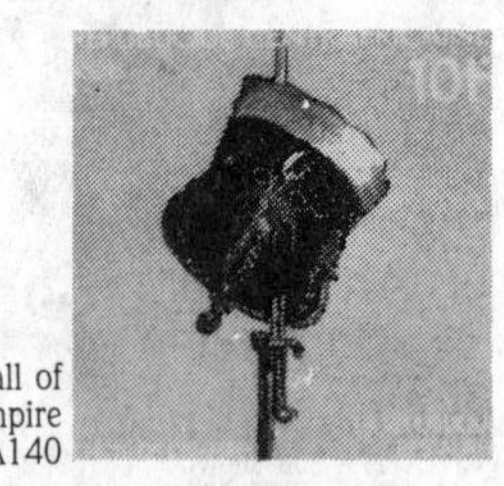

Downfall of Empire A140

1981, Oct. 6

482 A140 5fr Bayonet through crown .15 .15
483 A140 10fr like #482 .15 .15
484 A140 25fr Victory holding map .15 .15
485 A140 60fr like #484 .35 .16
486 A140 90fr Toppled Bokassa statue .48 .24
487 A140 500fr like #486 2.75 1.40
Nos. 482-487 (6) 4.03 2.25

Komba — A141

1981, Nov. 17

488 A141 50fr shown .25 .15
489 A141 90fr Dodoro, horiz. .48 .25
490 A141 140fr Kaya, horiz. .70 .40
Nos. 488-490 (3) 1.43 .80

Central African States Bank — A142

1981, Dec. 12 **Litho.** *Perf. 12½x13*

491 A142 90fr multi .48 .25
492 A142 110fr multi .60 .30

Christmas 1981 — A143

Virgin and Child Paintings.

1981, Dec. 24

493 A143 50fr Fra Angelico, 1430 .25 .15
494 A143 60fr Cosimo Tura, 1484 .35 .16
495 A143 90fr Bramantino .50 .25
496 A143 110fr Memling .45 .22
Nos. 493-496,C260-C261 (6) 3.35 1.73

Scouting Year — A144

1982, Jan. 13 *Perf. 12½*

497 A144 100fr Hiking .55 .25
498 A144 150fr Scouts, horiz. .80 .40
499 A144 200fr Hiking 1.10 .55
500 A144 300fr Salute, flag, vert. 1.60 .80
Nos. 497-500 (4) 4.05 2.00

Souvenir Sheet

Perf. 13

501 A144 500fr Scout, Baden-Powell, vert. 2.75 1.40

Elephant — A145

1982, Jan. 22 *Perf. 13½*

502 A145 60fr shown .35 .16
503 A145 90fr Giraffes .48 .25
504 A145 100fr Addaxes .55 .25
505 A145 110fr Okapi .60 .30
Nos. 502-505,C263-C264 (6) 6.33 3.16

Norman Rockwell Illustrations A146

1982, Feb. 17 *Perf. 13½x14*

506 A146 30fr Grandfather snowman .16 .15
507 A146 60fr Croquet players .35 .16
508 A146 110fr Women talking .60 .30
509 A146 150fr Searching .80 .40
Nos. 506-509 (4) 1.91 1.01

AT 16 Dirigible A147

1982, Feb. 27 **Litho.** *Perf. 13½*

510 A147 5fr shown .15 .15
511 A147 10fr Beyer-Garrat locomotive .15 .15
512 A147 20fr Bugatti 24 "Royale," 1924 .15 .15
513 A147 110fr Vickers "Valentia," 1928 .60 .30
Nos. 510-513,C266-C267 (6) 5.15 2.95

Bellvue Garden, by Edouard Manet — A148

Anniversaries: 400fr, Goethe, vert. #519-520, Princess Diana, 21st birthday, July 1, vert. 300fr, George Washington, vert.

1982, Apr. 6 **Litho.** *Perf. 13*

517 A148 200fr multi 1.10 .55
517A A148 300fr multi 1.60 .80
518 A148 400fr multi 2.00 1.10
519 A148 500fr multi 2.75 1.40
Nos. 517-519 (4) 7.45 3.85

Souvenir Sheet

520 A148 500fr multi 2.75 1.40

23rd Olympic Games, Los Angeles, 1984 — A149

1982, July 24 **Litho.** *Perf. 13½*

521 A149 5fr Soccer .15 .15
522 A149 10fr Boxing .15 .15
523 A149 20fr Running .15 .15
524 A149 110fr Long jump .60 .30
Nos. 521-524,C269-C270 (6) 5.15 2.95

21st Birthday of Princess Diana — A150

Portraits.

1982, July 20 **Litho.** *Perf. 13½*

525 A150 5fr multi .15 .15
526 A150 10fr multi .15 .15
527 A150 20fr multi .15 .15
528 A150 110fr multi .60 .30
Nos. 525-528,C272-C273 (6) 5.15 2.95

Nos. 457-461 Overprinted in Blue:
"NAISSANCE ROYALE 1982"

1982, Aug. 20 *Perf. 14*

529	A135	75fr multi	.40	.20
530	A135	110fr multi	.60	.30
531	A135	150fr multi	.80	.40
532	A135	175fr multi	.90	.45
		Nos. 529-532 (4)	2.70	1.35

Souvenir Sheet

533	A135	500fr multi	2.75	1.40

Birth of Prince William of Wales, June 21.

2nd UN Conference on Peaceful Uses of Outer Space, Vienna, Aug. 9-21 — A151

Various satellites and space scenes.

1982, Aug. 15 Litho. *Perf. 13½*

534	A151	5fr multi	.15	.15
535	A151	10fr multi	.15	.15
536	A151	20fr multi	.15	.15
537	A151	110fr multi	.60	.30
		Nos. 534-537,C277-C278 (6)	5.15	2.95

Sakpa Basket A152

Baskets and bowls.

1982, Sept. 2 *Perf. 13*

538	A152	5fr shown	.15	.15
539	A152	10fr like 5fr	.15	.15
540	A152	25fr Ngbenda gourd, vert.	.15	.15
541	A152	60fr like 25fr	.32	.16
542	A152	120fr Ta ti ngou jugs	.65	.35
543	A152	175fr Kangu bowls	1.10	.55
544	A152	300fr Kolongo bowls, vert.	1.60	.80
		Nos. 538-544 (7)	4.12	2.31

1982 World Cup Soccer Championships, Spain — A152a

Various soccer plays.

1982, Sept. Litho. *Perf. 13½x13*

Overprinted in Silver or Gold

545	A152a	60fr Italy, 1st, 2nd	.16	.15
546	A152a	150fr Poland, 3rd	.40	.20
547	A152a	300fr France, 4th	.80	.40
		Nos. 545-547 (3)	1.36	.75

Souvenir Sheet

548	A152a	500fr Italy, 1st (G)	1.40	.65

Not issued without overprint.

13th World UPU Day — A153

1982, Oct. 9

549	A153	60fr multi	.32	.16
550	A153	120fr multi	.65	.35

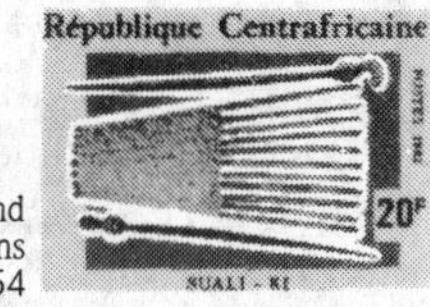

Comb and Hairpins A154

1982, Oct. 20 *Perf. 13x12½*

551	A154	20fr multi	.15	.15
552	A154	30fr multi	.16	.15
553	A154	60fr multi	.32	.16
554	A154	80fr multi	.42	.22
555	A154	120fr multi	.65	.35
		Nos. 551-555 (5)	1.70	
		Set value		.85

Artist Pierre Ndarata and No.69 A155

1982, Oct. *Perf. 13*

556	A155	40fr Jean Tubind at easel, vert.	.20	.15
557	A155	70fr shown	.38	.18
558	A155	90fr like 70fr	.48	.25
559	A155	140fr like 40fr	.90	.42
		Nos. 556-559 (4)	1.96	1.00

TB Bacillus Centenary A156

1982, Nov. 30 *Perf. 13½x13*

560	A156	100fr vio & blk	.55	.25
561	A156	120fr red org & blk	.65	.35
562	A156	175fr bl & blk	1.10	.55
		Nos. 560-562 (3)	2.30	1.15

10th Anniv. of UN Conference on Human Environment A157

1982, Dec. 8

563	A157	120fr multi	.65	.35
564	A157	150fr multi	.80	.40
565	A157	300fr multi	1.60	.80
		Nos. 563-565 (3)	3.05	1.55

Granary A158

1982, Dec. 15 *Perf. 13*

566	A158	60fr multi	.32	.16
567	A158	80fr multi	.40	.22
568	A158	120fr multi	.65	.35
569	A158	200fr multi	1.10	.55
		Nos. 566-569 (4)	2.47	1.28

A159

A160

1982, Dec.

570	A159	100fr multi	.55	.25
571	A159	120fr multi	.65	.35

ITU Plenipotentiaries Conf., Nairobi, Sept.

1983, Jan. 31 Litho. *Perf. 13½x13*

572	A160	5fr Modes of communication	.15	.15
573	A160	60fr like 5fr	.35	.16
574	A160	120fr Map, jet	.65	.35
575	A160	175fr like 120fr	1.10	.55
		Nos. 572-575 (4)	2.25	1.21

UN Decade for African Transportation and Communication, 1978-88.

Chess Champions — A161

Men and Chess Pieces: 5fr, Steinitz, first world champion, 1886. 10fr, Aaron Niemzovitch, castle. 20fr, Alexander Alekhine, knights. 110fr, Botvinnik. 300fr, Boris Spassky, glass pieces. 500fr, Bobby Fischer, king, knight. 600fr, Korchnoi, Karpov, pawn. No. 582A, Bobby Fischer. No. 582B, Reti, Larsen, Petrossian, and Mecking, horiz.

1983, Jan. 15

576	A161	5fr multi	.15	.15
577	A161	10fr multi	.15	.15
578	A161	20fr multi	.15	.15
579	A161	110fr multi	.60	.30
580	A161	300fr multi	1.60	.80
581	A161	500fr multi	2.75	1.40
		Nos. 576-581 (6)	5.40	2.95

Souvenir Sheet

582	A161	600fr multi	3.50	1.60

Litho. & Embossed

Perf. 13½

Size: 35x60mm

582A	A161	1500fr gold & multi		

Souvenir Sheet

582B	A161	1500fr gold & multi		

No. 582 contains one 56x33mm stamp, No. 582B one 35x60mm stamp. 300fr, 500fr, 600fr Nos. 581A and 582A airmail.

Marshal Tito (1892-1980) — A162

1983, Jan. 22

583	A162	20fr George Washington	.15	.15
a.		Souvenir sheet	.16	.15
584	A162	110fr shown	.60	.30
a.		Souvenir sheet	.65	.35
		Set value		.35

1982 World Cup Soccer Championships, Spain — A162a

Trophy, flags, scores, players: 5fr, Hamilton, Pezzey. 10fr, Borovski, Boniek. 20fr, Littbarski, Zamora. 110fr, Zico, Passarella. 300fr, Rossi, Smolarek. 500fr, Rummenigge, Giresse. 600fr, Rossi, Rummenigge. No. 584I, Platini. No. 584J, Rossi.

1983, Feb. 8 Litho. *Perf. 13½*

584B	A162a	5fr multicolored	.15	.15
584C	A162a	10fr multicolored	.15	.15
584D	A162a	20fr multicolored	.15	.15
584E	A162a	110fr multicolored	.60	.30
584F	A162a	300fr multicolored	1.65	.80
584G	A162a	500fr multicolored	2.75	1.40
		Nos. 584B-584G (6)	5.45	2.95

Souvenir Sheet

584H	A162a	600fr multicolored	3.25	1.65

Litho. & Embossed

584I	A162a	1500fr gold & multi		

Souvenir Sheet

584J	A162a	1500fr gold & multi		

Nos. 584F-584J are airmail.

Easter 1983 — A163

Rembrandt Paintings.

1983, Apr. 16

585	A163	100fr Entombment	.55	.25
586	A163	300fr Crucifixion	1.60	.80
587	A163	400fr Descent from the Cross	2.25	1.10
		Nos. 585-587 (3)	4.40	2.15

Vintage Cars and their Makers A164

A164a

Designs: 10fr, Emile Levassor, Rene Panhard, 1895 car. 20fr, Henry Ford, 1896 car. 30fr, Louis Renault, 1899 car. 80fr, Ettore Bugatti, type 37, 1925. 400fr, Enzo Ferrari, 815 sport, 1940. 500fr, Ferdinand Porsche, 356 coupe, 1951. 600fr, Karl Benz, velocipede, 1886. No. 594A, F.H. Royce and C.S. Rolls, 1911 Rolls-Royce Silver Ghost. No. 594B, G. Daimler, 1900 Mercedes 35CV.

1983, June 3 Litho. *Perf. 13½*

588	A164	10fr multi	.15	.15
589	A164	20fr multi	.15	.15
590	A164	30fr multi	.16	.15
591	A164	80fr multi	.42	.22
592	A164	400fr multi	2.25	1.10
593	A164	500fr multi	2.75	1.40
		Nos. 588-593 (6)	5.88	3.17

Souvenir Sheet

594	A164	600fr multi	3.50	1.60

Litho. & Embossed

594A	A164a	1500fr gold & multi		

Souvenir Sheet

594B	A164a	1500fr gold & multi		

Nos. 592-594B are airmail.

25th Anniv. of Intl. Maritime Org. — A165

1983, July 8 Litho. *Perf. 12½x13*

595 A165 40fr multi .22 .15
596 A165 100fr multi .55 .25

World Communications Year — A166

1983, July 22

597 A166 50fr multi .25 .15
598 A166 130fr multi .65 .35

Pre-Olympics, Los Angeles — A167

1984 Summer Olympics, Los Angeles A167a

1983, Aug. 3 Litho. *Perf. 13*

599 A167 5fr Gymnast .15 .15
600 A167 40fr Javelin throwing .22 .15
601 A167 60fr Pole vault .32 .16
602 A167 120fr Fencing .60 .32
603 A167 200fr Cycling 1.10 .55
604 A167 300fr Sailing 1.60 .80
Nos. 599-604 (6) 3.99 2.13

Souvenir Sheet

605 A167 600fr Handball 3.50 1.60

Litho. & Embossed

Perf. 13½

605A A167a 1500fr Shot put

Souvenir Sheet

605B A167a 1500fr Dressage, horiz.

Nos. 603-605B are airmail.

Namibia Day — A168

1983, Sept. 16 Litho. *Perf. 13*

606 A168 100fr multi .55 .25
607 A168 200fr multi 1.10 .55

Manned Flight Bicentenary — A169

A169a

Designs: 50fr, J. Montgolfier and his balloon, 1783. 100fr, J.P. Blanchard, English Channel crossing, 1785. 200fr, L.-J. Gay-Lussac, 4000-meter balloon ascent, 1804. 300fr, Giffard and his dirigible, 1852. 400fr, Santos Dumont, dirigible, Eiffel Tower. 500fr, A. Laquot, captive observation balloon, 1914. 600fr, J.A. Charles, first gas balloon; G. Tissandier, dirigible, 1883. No. 614, Marquis d'Arlandes and Jean Francois Pilatre de Rozier, Montgolfier balloon. No. 614B, Ferdinand von Zeppelin, Graf Zeppelin, horiz.

1983, Sept. 30 Litho. *Perf. 13½*

608 A169 50fr multi .16 .15
609 A169 100fr multi .35 .16
610 A169 200fr multi .65 .35
611 A169 300fr multi 1.00 .50
612 A169 400fr multi 1.40 .65
613 A169 500fr multi 1.60 .80
Nos. 608-613 (6) 5.16 2.61

Souvenir Sheet

614 A169 600fr multi 2.00 1.00

Litho. & Embossed

614A A169a 1500fr gold & multi

Souvenir Sheet

614B A169a 1500fr gold & multi

Nos. 612-614B are airmail.

Black Rhinoceros and World Wildlife Emblem A170

Various black rhinoceroses.

1983, Nov. 14

615 A170 10fr multi .15 .15
616 A170 40fr multi .15 .15
617 A170 70fr multi .22 .15
618 A170 180fr multi .60 .30
Nos. 615-618,C291A-C292 (6) 4.72 2.55

UPU Day, World Communications Year — A171

1983, Nov. 2 Litho. *Perf. 13*

619 A171 205fr multi 1.10 .55

2nd Anniv. of the Natl. Military Committee A172

Gen. Andre Kolingba, head of state.

1983, Sept. 1 *Perf. 12½*

620 A172 65fr sil & multi .22 .15
621 A172 130fr gold & multi .42 .22

Earth Satellite Receiving Station, Bangui M'Poko — A173

1983 *Perf. 13*

622 A173 130fr multi .42 .20

Natl. Day of the Handicapped and the Elderly A174

1983, Dec. 20 Engr. *Perf. 13x12½*

623 A174 65fr vio & org .22 .15
624 A174 130fr ultra & org .42 .22
625 A174 205fr dk grn & org .70 .35
Nos. 623-625 (3) 1.34 .72

Fishing Resources A175

1983, Dec. 31 Litho. *Perf. 12½*

626 A175 25fr Breeding tank .15 .15
627 A175 65fr Net fishing .22 .15
628 A175 100fr Dam fishing .35 .16
629 A175 130fr Still life with fish .42 .22
630 A175 205fr Basket trap .70 .35
Nos. 626-630 (5) 1.84 1.03

Wildlife Protection — A176

1984, Jan. 25 *Perf. 13*

631 A176 30fr Forest fire .15 .15
632 A176 130fr Hunters .42 .20
Set value .25

Packet Ship Pericles — A177

1984, June Litho. *Perf. 12½*

633 A177 65fr shown .22 .15
634 A177 110fr CC-1500 locomotive .38 .18
635 A177 120fr Three-master Pereire .40 .20
636 A177 240fr PLM series 210, 1868 .80 .40
637 A177 250fr Admella .85 .42
638 A177 350fr 231-726 locomotive, 1937 1.10 .60
639 A177 400fr Royal William 1.40 .65
640 A177 440fr Pacific S3/6, 1908 1.50 .70
641 A177 500fr Great Britain 1.60 .80
642 A177 500fr Henschel 151 series 45, 1937 1.60 .80
Nos. 633-642 (10) 9.85 4.90

For overprints see Nos. 701-704.

J. W. Goethe, Scene from Faust A178

Designs: 100fr, Henri Dunant, Red Cross Founder, Battle of Solferino, 125th anniv. 200fr, Alfred Nobel, Nobel Foundation headquarters. 300fr, Lord Baden-Powell, World Scouting Jamboree, Alberta, 1983. 400fr, John F. Kennedy, first man on the Moon, 1969. 500fr, 600fr, wedding of Prince and Princess of Wales.

1984, Feb. 25 Litho. *Perf. 13½*

643 A178 50fr multi .16 .15
644 A178 100fr multi .32 .16
645 A178 200fr multi .65 .35
646 A178 300fr multi 1.00 1.00
647 A178 400fr multi 1.25 .60
648 A178 500fr multi 1.50 .75
Nos. 643-648 (6) 4.88 3.01

Souvenir Sheet

649 A178 600fr multi 1.60 .85

Nos. 647-649 are airmail.

Old Masters A179

Paintings: 50fr, Madonna and Child, by Raphael. 100fr, Madonna with Pear, by Durer. 200fr, Aldobrandini Madonna, by Raphael. 300fr, Madonna with Carnation, by Durer. 400fr, Virgin and Child, by Correggio. 500fr, La Bohemienne, by Modigliani. 600fr, Madonna and Child on the Throne, by Raphael.

1984, Mar. 30 Litho. *Perf. 13½*

650 A179 50fr multi .16 .15
651 A179 100fr multi .32 .16
652 A179 200fr multi .60 .32
653 A179 300fr multi 1.00 .50
654 A179 400fr multi 1.40 .65
655 A179 500fr multi 1.60 .80
Nos. 650-655 (6) 5.08 2.58

Miniature Sheet

656 A179 600fr multi 2.00 1.00

No. 656 contains 1 stamp, size 30x59mm. Nos. 654-656 are airmail.

Space — A180

1984, Aug. 6 Litho. *Perf. 13½*

657 A180 20fr Galileo, Ariane rocket .15 .15
658 A180 70fr Piccard, X-15, balloon .22 .15
659 A180 150fr Oberth, satellite .50 .25
660 A180 205fr Einstein, satellites .70 .38
661 A180 300fr Curie, Viking vehicle 1.00 .50
662 A180 500fr Merbold, Spacelab 1.60 .80
Nos. 657-662 (6) 4.17 2.23

Miniature Sheet

663 A180 600fr Armstrong, Apollo 11, horiz. 2.00 1.00

No. 663 contains 1 stamp, size: 42x36mm. 300fr, 500fr and 600fr are airmail.

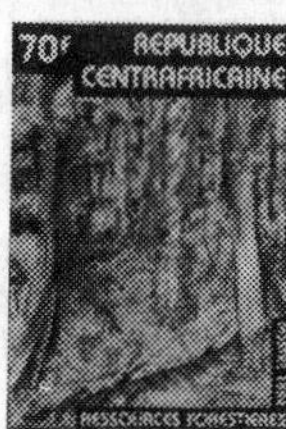

Forestry Resources — A181

UNICEF — A182

1984, Oct. 9 Litho. *Perf. 13x12½*
664 A181 70fr Forest .22 .15
665 A181 130fr Logging .42 .20

1984, Oct. 27 Litho. *Perf. 13x12½*
666 A182 10fr Weighing child .15 .15
667 A182 30fr Vaccinating child .15 .15
668 A182 65fr Giving liquids .22 .15
669 A182 100fr Balancing diet .35 .16
Set value .72 .38

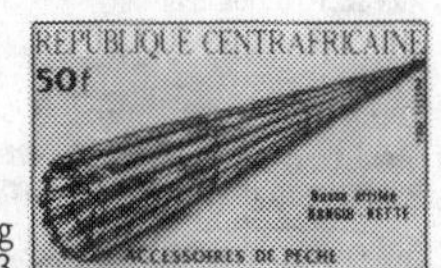

Fishing Traps — A183

1984, Nov. 6 Litho. *Perf. 13*
670 A183 50fr Bangui-Kette .16 .15
671 A183 80fr Mbres .25 .15
672 A183 150fr Bangui-Kette .50 .25
Nos. 670-672 (3) .91 .55

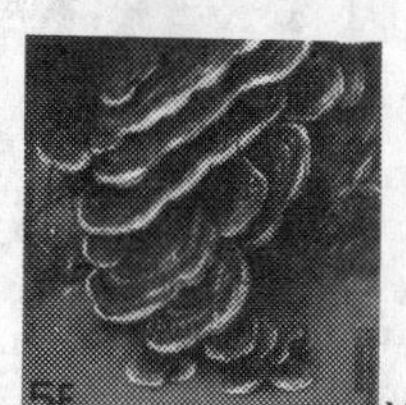

Mushrooms A184

1984, Nov. 15 Litho. *Perf. 13½*
673 A184 5fr Leptoporus lignosus .15 .15
674 A184 10fr Phlebopus sudanicus .15 .15
675 A184 40fr Termitomyces letestui .15 .15
676 A184 130fr Lepiota esculenta .35 .16
677 A184 300fr Termitomyces aurantiacus .80 .40
678 A184 500fr Termitomyces robustus 1.40 .65
Nos. 673-678 (6) 3.00
Set value 1.35

Souvenir Sheet

679 A184 600fr Tricholoma- lobayensis 1.60 .80

Nos. 677-679 are airmail.

1984 Winter Olympics, Sarajevo A184a

Gold medalists, communications satellite and events: 30fr, Gaetan Boucher, Canada, 1000 and 1500-meter speed skating. 90fr, W. Hoppe, R. Wetzig, D. Schauerhammer and A. Kirchner, German Democratic Republic, 4-man bobsled. 140fr, Paoletta Magoni, Italy, women's slalom. 200fr, Jayne Torvill and Christopher Dean, Great Britain, ice dancing. 400fr, Matti Nykaenen, Finland, 90-meter ski jumping. 500fr, USSR, ice hockey. 600fr, Bill Johnson, US, men's downhill.

1984, Nov. 30 Litho. *Perf. 13½*
679A A184a 30fr multi .15 .15
679B A184a 90fr multi .30 .15
679C A184a 140fr multi .42 .20
679D A184a 200fr multi .65 .35
679E A184a 400fr multi 1.40 .65
679F A184a 500fr multi 1.60 .80
Nos. 679A-679F (6) 4.52 2.30

Souvenir Sheet

679G A184a 600fr multi 2.00 1.00

Nos. 679E-679G are airmail.

Flowers — A185

1984, Nov. 22 Litho. *Perf. 13½*
680 A185 65fr Hibiscus .22 .15
681 A185 130fr Canna Indica .42 .22
682 A185 205fr Eichlornia Crassipes .70 .35
Nos. 680-682 (3) 1.34 .72

Economic Campaign — A186

1984, Dec. 3 Litho. *Perf. 13½*
683 A186 25fr Cotton planting .15 .15
684 A186 40fr Selling cotton crop .15 .15
685 A186 130fr Cotton market .42 .22
Nos. 683-685 (3) .72
Set value .34

World Food Day A187

1984, Dec. 10 Litho. *Perf. 13½*
686 A187 205fr Picking corn .70 .35

OLYMPHILEX '85 — A188

Publicity posters from previous Games and host city landmarks.

1985, Mar 18 Litho. *Perf. 13½*
687 A188 5fr Stockholm, 1912 .15 .15
688 A188 10fr Paris, 1924 .15 .15
689 A188 20fr London, 1948 .15 .15
690 A188 100fr Tokyo, 1964 .45 .22
691 A188 400fr Mexico 1.75 .90
692 A188 500fr Munich, 1972 2.25 1.10
Nos. 687-692 (6) 4.90 2.67

Souvenir Sheet

693 A188 600fr Athens, 1896, Baron Pierre de Coubertin 3.00 1.50

Nos. 691-693 are airmail. No. 693 contains one 60x30mm stamp.

Anniversaries and Events A189

Queen Mother, 85th Birthday A189a

Famous men: 50fr, Abraham Lincoln, American Civil War soldiers. 90fr, Auguste Piccard (1884-1962), inventor, bathyscaphe Trieste. 120fr, Gottlieb Daimler (1834-1900), 1938 Mercedes Type 540. 200fr, Louis Bleriot (1872-1936), inventor, plane. 350fr, Anatoly Karpov, world chess champion. 400fr, Jean Henri Dunant (1828-1910), Red Cross founder, worker caring for wounded soldier.

1984, Dec. 22 Litho. *Perf. 13½*
694 A189 50fr multi .15 .15
695 A189 90fr multi .25 .15
696 A189 120fr multi .35 .16
697 A189 200fr multi .55 .25
698 A189 350fr multi .90 .45
698A A189 400fr multi 1.10 .60
Nos. 694-698A (6) 3.30 1.76

Nos. 698-698A are airmail.

Souvenir Sheet

1984 Litho. *Perf. 13½*
698B A189a 600fr multi 2.75 1.40

Bangui Rotary Club and Water — A190

1984, Dec. 29
699 A190 130fr multi .35 .16
700 A190 205fr multi .60 .28

Nos. 637-640, C302A Overprinted with Exhibitions in Red

1985, Mar. 13 Litho. *Perf. 12½*
701 A177 250fr Argentina '85, Buenos Aires .65 .35
702 A177 350fr Tsukuba Expo '85 .90 .45
703 A177 400fr Italia '85, Rome 1.10 .50
704 A177 440fr Mophila '85, Hamburg 1.25 .60
Nos. 701-704 (4) 3.90 1.90

Souvenir Sheet
Perf. 13½x13

705 AP89 500fr Olymphilex '85, Lausanne 1.40 .65

500fr airmail.

Beetles — A191

1985, Mar. Litho. *Perf. 13½*
706 A191 15fr Chelorrhina polyphemus .15 .15
707 A191 20fr Fornasinius russus .15 .15
708 A191 25fr Goliathus giganteus .15 .15
709 A191 65fr Goliathus meleagris .16 .15
Set value .33 .23

Audubon Birth Bicentenary — A192

Illustrations of North American bird species by John Audubon.

1985, Mar. 25 Litho. *Perf. 13½*
710 A192 40fr Cyanocitta cristata .15 .15
711 A192 80fr Caprimulgus carolinensis .20 .15
712 A192 130fr Campephilus principales .35 .16
713 A192 250fr Calocitta formosa .65 .35
714 A192 300fr Coccizus minor, horiz. .80 .40
715 A192 500fr Hirundo rustica, horiz. 1.40 .65
Nos. 710-715 (6) 3.55 1.86

Souvenir Sheet

716 A192 600fr Dryocopus pileatus, horiz. 1.60 .80

Nos. 714-716 are airmail.

Intl. Youth Year — A193

Famous children's book authors and scenes from their best-known novels: 100fr, The Jungle Book, 1894, by Kipling, vert. 200fr, Les Cavaliers, 1967, by Joseph Kessel (1898-1979). 300fr, Twenty-Thousand Leagues Under the Sea, 1873, by Verne. 400fr, The Adventures of Tom Sawyer, 1876, by Twain.

1985, Apr. Litho. *Perf. 13*
718 A193 100fr multi .25 .15
719 A193 200fr multi .55 .25
720 A193 300fr multi .80 .40
721 A193 400fr multi 1.10 .55
Nos. 718-721 (4) 2.70 1.35

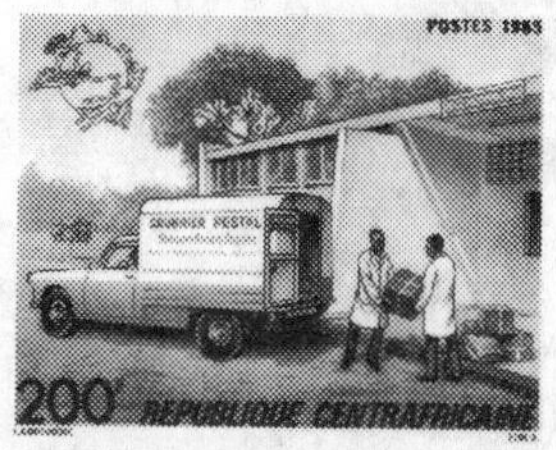

Philexafrica '85, Lome — A194

Designs: No. 722, UPU emblem, Postmen unloading parcel post van. No. 723, Exhibition emblem, scout troop.

1985, May 15 *Perf. 13x12½*
722 A194 200fr multi .55 .25
723 A194 200fr multi .55 .25

Nos. 722-723 se-tenant with center label picturing a map of Africa or the UAPT emblem.

Rabies Vaccine Cent., Louis Pasteur (1822-95), Chemist, Microbiologist — A195

Anniversaries and events: 200fr, Battle of Solferino, Founding of the Red Cross, 125th Anniv., Founder Jean-Henri Dunant (1828-1910), horiz. 300fr, Girl Guides, 75th anniv. 450fr, Elizabeth, the Queen Mother, 85th birthday. 500fr, Statue of Liberty, cent.

1985, June *Perf. 13*
724 A195 150fr multi .40 .20
725 A195 200fr multi .55 .25
726 A195 300fr multi .80 .40
727 A195 450fr multi 1.20 .60
728 A195 500fr multi 1.40 .65
Nos. 724-728 (5) 4.35 2.10

1986 World Cup Soccer Championships, Mexico — A196

Famous soccer players and match scenes.

1985, July 24 Litho. *Perf. 13½*

730 A196 5fr Pele .15 .15
731 A196 10fr Tony Schumacher .15 .15
732 A196 20fr Paolo Rossi .15 .15
733 A196 350fr Kevin Keegan 1.10 .60
734 A196 400fr Michel Platini 1.25 .65
735 A196 500fr Karl Heinz Rummenigge 1.50 .75
Nos. 730-735 (6) 4.30 2.45

Souvenir Sheet

736 A196 600fr Diego Armando Maradona 1.75 .90

Nos. 734-736 are airmail.

Kotto Waterfalls A197

1985, July 27 Litho. *Perf. 13½*

737 A197 65fr multi .20 .15
738 A197 90fr multi .25 .15
739 A197 130fr multi .40 .20
Nos. 737-739 (3) .85 .50

State Visit of Pope John Paul II — A198

Portraits.

1985, Aug. 14

740 A198 65fr multi .20 .15
741 A198 130fr multi .40 .20

Natl. Economic Development Campaign — A199

Designs: 5fr, Troops plowing. 60fr, Soldier preparing field for planting, vert. 130fr, Planting cotton seeds, vert.

1985, Sept. 1 *Perf. 13*

742 A199 5fr multi .15 .15
743 A199 60fr multi .18 .15
744 A199 130fr multi .40 .20
Nos. 742-744 (3) .73
Set value .35

Queen Mother, 85th Birthday — A200

1985, Sept. 16 Litho. *Perf. 13½*

745 A200 100fr Age 4, with brother .28 .15
746 A200 200fr Duchess of York, 1923 .52 .25
747 A200 300fr Reviewing Irish Guards, 1928 .80 .42
748 A200 350fr Family portrait, 1936 .90 .45
749 A200 400fr George VI coronation, 1937 1.10 .60
750 A200 500fr Wedding anniv., 1948 1.40 .65
Nos. 745-750 (6) 5.00 2.52

Souvenir Sheet

751 A200 600fr Christening Prince Charles, 1948 1.60 .80

Nos. 749-751 are airmail.

Dr. Rene Labusquiere (1919-1977), Promoter of Preventive Medicine A201

1985, Sept. 22 Litho. *Perf. 13½*

752 A201 10fr multi .15 .15
753 A201 45fr multi .15 .15
754 A201 110fr multi .30 .15
Set value .47 .27

Natl. Postal Service — A202

1985, Oct. 9 *Perf. 12½*

755 A202 15fr Loading mail van .15 .15
756 A202 60fr Bangui P.O., van .20 .15
757 A202 150fr Hdqtrs, Bangui, and vans .50 .25
Nos. 755-757 (3) .85
Set value .40

Space Research A203

Designs: 40fr, Yuri Gagarin and Sergei Korolev, Soviet cosmonauts. 110fr, Nicolaus Copernicus, Cassini probe. 240fr, Galileo, Viking orbiter. 300fr, Theodor von Karman (1881-1963), American aeronautical engineer, and space shuttle recovering Palapa B satellite. 450fr, Percival Lowell (1855-1916), American astronomer, and Viking probe. 500fr, Dr. U. Merbold and orbiting space station project Colombo. 600fr, Apollo 11 Project, first step on Moon by Neil Armstrong.

1985, Oct. 31 Litho. *Perf. 13½*

758 A203 40fr multi .15 .15
759 A203 110fr multi .40 .22
760 A203 240fr multi .80 .42
761 A203 300fr multi 1.10 .60
762 A203 450fr multi 1.60 .80
763 A203 500fr multi 1.75 .90
Nos. 758-763 (6) 5.80 3.09

Souvenir Sheet
Imperf

764 A203 600fr multi 2.00 1.10

Nos. 762-764 are airmail.

Solar Energy Apparatus, Damara A204

1985, Nov. 4 Litho. *Perf. 13½*

765 A204 65fr multi .22 .15
766 A204 130fr multi .45 .22

Girl Guides Nature Study — A205

1985, Nov. 16 *Perf. 13*

767 A205 250fr shown .90 .45
768 A205 250fr Quaka Sugar Refinery .90 .45

PHILEXAFRICA '85, Lome, Togo, Nov. 16-24. Nos. 767-768 se-tenant with center labels picturing map of Africa or UAPT emblem.

State Visit of Pres. Mitterand of France, Dec. 12-13 — A206

1985-86 Litho. *Perf. 13x12½*

769 A206 65fr multi .22 .15
770 A206 130fr multi .45 .22
770A A206 160fr multi ('86) .60 .28
Nos. 769-770A (3) 1.27 .65

Nos. 769-770 issued Dec. 12.

UN 40th Anniv., Central Africa Admission, 25th Anniv. — A207

1985, Dec. 18 *Perf. 13½*

771 A207 140fr multi .50 .25

Intl. Youth Year A208

Designs: 40fr, Madonna with the Carnation, 1470, by Leonardo da Vinci. 80fr, Johann Sebastian Bach. 100fr, St. John at Patmos, 1619, by Velazquez. 250fr, The Erl King score, by Franz Schubert. 400fr, Portrait of Vicente Osorio de Moscoso, by Goya. 500fr, The Young Mozart Playing in Paris, 1764. 600fr, Woman in a Plumed Hat, 1901, by Picasso.

1985, Dec. 28

772 A208 40fr multi .15 .15
773 A208 80fr multi .25 .15
774 A208 100fr multi .35 .18
775 A208 250fr multi .90 .45
776 A208 400fr multi 1.40 .65
777 A208 500fr multi 1.75 .90
Nos. 772-777 (6) 4.80 2.48

Souvenir Sheet

778 A208 600fr multi 2.25 1.10

Nos. 776-778 are airmail.

Halley's Comet A209

Designs: 100fr, Edmond Halley, British astronomer. 200fr, Sir Isaac Newton's telescope and comet sighting. 300fr, Halley and Newton observing comet. 350fr, US probe. 400fr, Soviet probe plotting comet's perihelion. 500fr, Isodensity photograph of comet. 600fr, Comet, Earth, Sun and probe.

1985, Dec. 31

779 A209 100fr multi .35 .18
780 A209 200fr multi .70 .38
781 A209 300fr multi 1.10 .60
782 A209 350fr multi 1.25 .65
783 A209 400fr multi 1.40 .65
784 A209 500fr multi 1.75 .90
Nos. 779-784 (6) 6.55 3.36

Souvenir Sheet

785 A209 600fr multi 2.25 1.10

Nos. 783-785 are airmail.

Christopher Columbus A210

Various events leading to the discovery of America and beyond.

1986

786 A210 90fr Plotting course .32 .16
787 A210 110fr Receiving blessing .40 .20
788 A210 240fr Fleet in port .80 .42
789 A210 300fr Trade with natives 1.10 .60
790 A210 400fr Storm at sea 1.40 .65
791 A210 500fr Fleet at sea 1.75 .90
Nos. 779-784 (6) 6.55 3.36

Souvenir Sheet

792 A210 600fr Portrait 2.25 1.10

Nos. 790-792 are airmail.

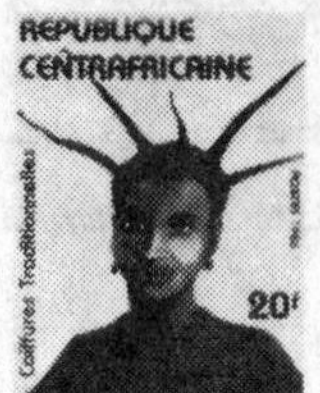

Hairstyles — A211

France- Central Africa Week — A212

1986, May 21 Litho. *Perf. 12½*

793 A211 20fr multi .15 .15
794 A211 30fr multi .15 .15
795 A211 65fr multi .16 .15
796 A211 160fr multi .60 .30
Nos. 793-796 (4) 1.06
Set value .48

1986, May 26

797 A212 40fr Communications, horiz. .15 .15
798 A212 60fr Youth, horiz. .22 .15
799 A212 100fr Basket maker .38 .18
800 A212 130fr Bicycling .45 .22
Nos. 797-800 (4) 1.20 .70

Centrapalm Palm Oil — A213

Designs: 25fr, 65fr, Refinery, Bossongo, and palm tree. 120fr, 160fr, Refinery and palm tree, vert.

1986, Aug. 12 Litho. *Perf. 13½*

801 A213 25fr multi .15 .15
802 A213 65fr multi .22 .15
803 A213 120fr multi .50 .25
804 A213 160fr multi .65 .35
Nos. 801-804 (4) 1.52
Set value .77

Dogs and Cats A214

1986, Sept. 9

805 A214 10fr Pointer .15 .15
806 A214 20fr Egyptian mau .15 .15
807 A214 200fr Newfoundland .80 .42
808 A214 300fr Borzoi 1.10 .60
809 A214 400fr Persian red 1.60 .80
Nos. 805-809 (5) 3.80 2.12

Souvenir Sheet

810 A214 500fr Spaniel, Burmese-Malayan 2.00 1.00

Nos. 808-810 are airmail.

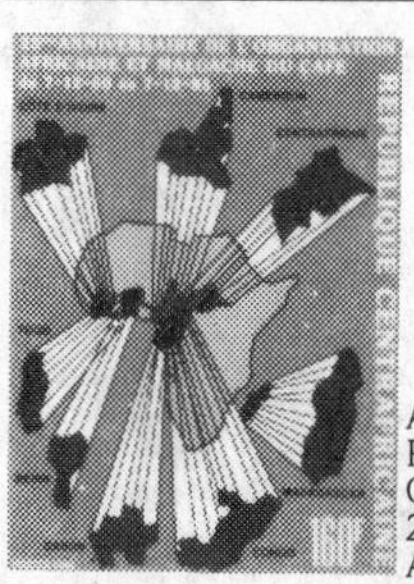
African Coffee Producers Organization, 25th Anniv. A215

1986, Sept. 25 Litho. *Perf. 13*

811 A215 160fr multi .60 .30

1986 World Cup Soccer Championships, Mexico — A216

Satellites, final scores, World Cup and athletes: 30fr, Muller, Socrates. 110fr, Scifo, Ceulemans. 160fr, Stopyra, Platini. 350fr, Brehme, Schumacher. 450fr, Maradona. 500fr, Schumacher, Burruchaga.

1986, Nov. 12 *Perf. 13½*

812 A216 30fr multi .15 .15
813 A216 110fr multi .40 .20
814 A216 160fr multi .60 .30
815 A216 350fr multi 1.40 .65
816 A216 450fr multi 1.60 .80
Nos. 812-816 (5) 4.15 2.10

Souvenir Sheet

817 A216 500fr multi 1.75 .90

Nos. 816-817 are airmail.

US Anniversaries and Events — A217

Designs: 15fr, Judith Resnik. 25fr, Frederic Auguste Bartholdi. 70fr, Elvis Presley. 300fr, Ronald McNair. 450fr, Christa McAuliffe. 500fr, Challenger Astronauts: McAuliffe, Scobee, Smith, Resnik, Onizuka, McNair, Jarvis.

1986, Nov. 19

818 A217 15fr multi .15 .15
819 A217 25fr multi .15 .15
820 A217 70fr multi .25 .15
821 A217 300fr multi 1.10 .55
822 A217 450fr multi 1.60 .80
Nos. 818-822 (5) 3.25 1.80

Souvenir Sheet

823 A217 500fr multi 1.75 1.00

US space shuttle Challenger explosion; Statue of Liberty, cent. Nos. 822-823 are airmail.
For surcharges and overprint see Nos. 850-852.

Flora and Fauna A218

1986, May 30 Litho. *Perf. 13½*

824 A218 25fr Allamanda neriifolia .15 .15
825 A218 65fr Taurotragus eurycerus .25 .15
826 A218 160fr Plumieria acuminata .60 .30
827 A218 300fr Acinonyx jubatus 1.10 .40
828 A218 400fr Eulophia erthoplata 1.50 .70
829 A218 500fr Leopard 1.75 .90
Nos. 824-829 (6) 5.35 2.60

Souvenir Sheet

830 A218 600fr Derby's eland, eulophia cucullata 2.25 1.10

Nos. 824, 826, 828 vert. Nos. 828-830 are airmail. No. 830 contains one 51x30mm stamp.

Intl. Peace Year — A219

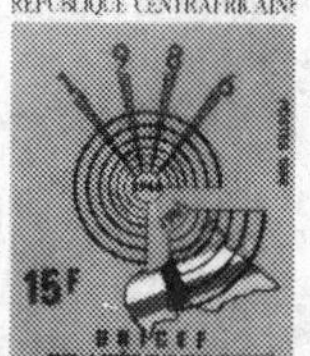
Air Africa, 25th Anniv. — A220

1986, Nov. 29

831 A219 160fr multi .60 .30

1986, Dec. 15

832 A220 200fr multi .70 .40

UNICEF, 40th Anniv. — A221

1986, Dec. 24

833 A221 15fr shown .15 .15
834 A221 130fr Child immunization .45 .22
835 A221 160fr Youth, food, map .60 .30
Nos. 833-835 (3) 1.20 .67

German Railways Sesquicentenary — A222

Inventors and locomotives: 40fr, Alfred de Glehn, Prussian Railways DH2 Green Elephant. 70fr, Rudolf Diesel, S3/6 No. 1829 Rheingold. 160fr, Carl Golsdorf, Trans-Europe Express train Type 103. 300fr, Wilhelm Schmidt, Beyer Garratt locomotive. 400fr, Monsieur de Bousquet, Series 3500 compound locomotive. 500fr, Werner von Siemens, 1980s electric locomotive.

1986, Dec. 31

836 A222 40fr multi .15 .15
837 A222 70fr multi .25 .15
838 A222 160fr multi .60 .30
839 A222 300fr multi 1.10 .40
840 A222 400fr multi 1.50 .70
Nos. 836-840 (5) 3.60 1.70

Souvenir Sheet

841 A222 500fr multi 1.75 1.00

Nos. 840-841 are airmail. No. 841 contains one 42x36mm stamp.

Agriculture Radio Project — A223

1986, Dec. 27 Litho. *Perf. 13½*

842 A223 170fr shown .65 .35
843 A223 265fr Satellite communication 1.00 .50

Pan-African Telecommunications Union congress, Dec. 7, 1986.
No. 842 exists in souvenir sheet of one.

Space — A224

Scientists and inventions: 25fr, Sir William Herschel (1738-1822), British astronomer, and Miranda satellite. 65fr, Wernher von Braun (1912-1977), American engineer, and Mars rover. 160fr, Rudolf Hanel, Mariner Mark II and Titan. 300fr, Patrick Baudry, Hermes shuttle and Eureka platform. 400fr, U. Keller, Halley's Comet and Giotto probe. 500fr, Wubbo Ockels, Ulf Merbold and Columbus European Space Station. 600fr, Wilhelm Obers (1758-1840) and Mariner Mark II surveying asteroids. No. 850 horiz.

1987, Jan. 27

844 A224 25fr multi .15 .15
845 A224 65fr multi .38 .20
846 A224 160fr multi .95 .48
847 A224 300fr multi 1.75 .90
848 A224 400fr multi 2.50 1.25
849 A224 500fr multi 3.00 1.50
Nos. 844-849 (6) 8.73 4.48

Souvenir Sheet

850 A224 600fr multi 3.50 1.75

Nos. 848-850 are airmail.

No. 820 Surcharged

1987, Feb. 20 Litho. *Perf. 13½*

851 A217 485fr on 70fr Elvis Presley 2.75 1.40

Nos. 820 and 851 Ovptd. "Elvis PRESLEY / 1977-1987."

1987, Feb. 20 Litho. *Perf. 13½*

851A A217 70fr multi .55 .28
851B A217 485fr on 70fr multi 2.75 1.40

1992 Barcelona Olympics A225

Athletes and landmarks or sights: 30fr, Soccer player, Lady with Umbrella fountain. 150fr, Judo, Barcelona Cathedral. 265fr, Cyclist, Church of the Holy Family, by Gaudi. 350fr, Gymnast, Tomb of Columbus. 495fr, Runner, human tower. 500fr, Swimmer, Statue of Columbus.

1987, June 4

852 A225 30fr multi .18 .15
853 A225 150fr multi .82 .40
854 A225 265fr multi 1.45 .72
855 A225 350fr multi 1.90 .95
856 A225 495fr multi 2.70 1.35
Nos. 852-856 (5) 7.05 3.57

Souvenir Sheet

857 A225 500fr multi 2.75 1.40

Nos. 855-857 are airmail.

A226

1988 Winter Olympics, Calgary — A227

1987, June 26

858 A226 20fr Two-man luge .15 .15
859 A226 140fr Cross-country skiing .78 .40
860 A226 250fr Women's figure skating 1.40 .80
861 A226 300fr Hockey 1.65 .82
862 A226 400fr Men's slalom 2.20 1.10
Nos. 858-862 (5) 6.18 3.27

Souvenir Sheet

863 A227 500fr Downhill skiing 2.75 1.35

Nos. 861-863 are airmail.

Intl. Peace Year — A228

1987, July 20

864 A228 50fr dull ultra, sepia & blk .28 .15
865 A228 160fr lt olive green, sepia & blk .90 .45

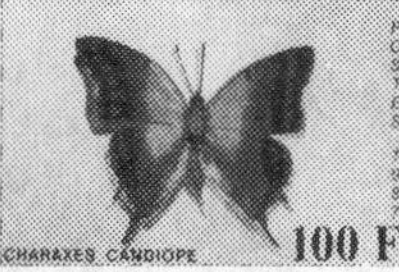
Butterflies A229

1987, Oct. 5 Litho. *Perf. 13½*

866 A229 100fr Charaxes candiope .70 .35
867 A229 120fr Graphium leonidas .85 .42
868 A229 130fr Charaxes brutus .90 .45
869 A229 160fr Salamis aetiops 1.15 .58
Nos. 866-869 (4) 3.60 1.80

Pygmy Soccer Team from Nola — A230

1987, Nov. 30 Litho. *Perf. 13*

870 A230 90fr multi .65 .32
871 A230 160fr multi 1.15 .58

Integration of the pygmy people into Central African society.

Dinosaurs — A231

Perf. 14x13½, 13½x14

1988, Mar. 19 Litho.

872 A231 50fr Brontosaurus .30 .15
873 A231 65fr Triceratops .40 .20
874 A231 100fr Ankylosaurus .60 .30
875 A231 160fr Stegosaurus .95 .48

No.	Type	Value	Description	Unused	Used
876	A231	200fr	Tyrannosaurus rex	1.20	.60
877	A231	240fr	Corythosaurus	1.45	.72
878	A231	300fr	Allosaurus	1.80	.90
879	A231	350fr	Brachiosaurus	2.10	1.05
			Nos. 872-879 (8)	8.80	4.40

Nos. 876-879 vert.

Anniversaries and Events — A232

Designs: 40fr, Pres. James Madison and "We the People..." from the US Constitution. 160fr, Elizabeth II and Duke of Edinburgh . 200fr, Steffi Graf, tennis champion. 300fr, Garri Kasparov of Russia, 1985 world chess champion. 400fr, Boris Becker, 1985-86 Wimbledon champion. 500fr, Christoph Willibald Gluck (1714-87), composer. Nos. 880-884 vert.

1988, Feb. 15 *Perf. 13½*

No.	Type	Value	Description	Unused	Used
880	A232	40fr	multi	.24	.15
881	A232	160fr	multi	.95	.48
882	A232	200fr	multi	1.20	.60
883	A232	300fr	multi	1.80	.90
884	A232	400fr	multi	2.40	1.20
			Nos. 880-884 (5)	6.59	3.33

Souvenir Sheet

No.	Type	Value	Description	Unused	Used
885	A232	500fr	multi	3.00	1.50

US Constitution bicentennial (40fr); 40th wedding anniv. of Elizabeth II and Prince Philip (160fr). Nos. 883-885 are airmail.

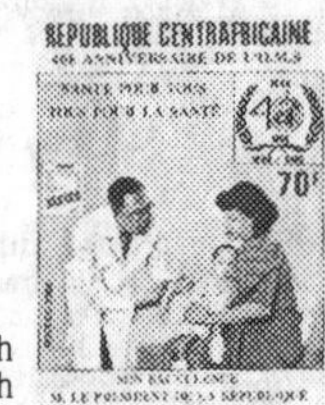

World Health Organization, 40th Anniv. — A233

1988, Apr. 7 **Litho.** *Perf. 13½*

No.	Type	Value	Description	Unused	Used
886	A233	70fr	multi	.48	.25
887	A233	120fr	multi	.80	.40

Scout Ornithological Activities A234

Scouts and: 25fr, *Merops nubicus.* 170fr, *Euplectes hordeacea.* 300fr, *Ceryle rudis.* 400fr, *Estrilda bengala.* 450fr, *Kaupifalco monogrammicus.* 500fr, *Lamprotornis splendidus.*

1988, July 1 **Litho.** *Perf. 13½*

No.	Type	Value	Description	Unused	Used
888	A234	25fr	multi	.18	.15
889	A234	170fr	multi	1.25	.62
890	A234	300fr	multi	2.25	1.15
891	A234	400fr	multi	3.00	1.50
892	A234	450fr	multi	3.40	1.70
			Nos. 888-892 (5)	10.08	5.12

Souvenir Sheet

No.	Type	Value	Description	Unused	Used
893	A234	500fr	multi	3.75	1.90

Nos. 891-893 are airmail.
For surcharges see Nos. 921-924.

1988 Summer Olympics, Seoul A235

1988, Sept. 30

No.	Type	Value	Description	Unused	Used
894	A235	150fr	Running, vert.	1.15	.58
895	A235	300fr	Judo, vert.	2.25	1.15
896	A235	400fr	Soccer, vert.	3.00	1.50
897	A235	450fr	Tennis, vert.	3.40	1.70
			Nos. 894-897 (4)	9.80	4.93

Souvenir Sheet

No.	Type	Value	Description	Unused	Used
898	A235	500fr	Boxing	3.75	1.90

Nos. 896-898 are airmail.

1988 Winter Olympics, Calgary — A236

1988, Sept. 30 **Litho.** *Perf. 13½*

No.	Type	Value	Description	Unused	Used
899	A236	170fr	Cross-country skiing	1.25	.62
900	A236	350fr	Ice hockey	2.65	1.30
901	A236	400fr	Downhill skiing	3.00	1.50
902	A236	450fr	Freestyle	3.40	1.70
			Nos. 899-902 (4)	10.30	5.12

Souvenir Sheet

No.	Type	Value	Description	Unused	Used
903	A236	500fr	shown	3.75	1.90

Nos. 899-902 vert. Nos. 901-903 are airmail.

Natl. Arbor Day — A237

1988, July 16 **Litho.** *Perf. 13½*

No.	Type	Value	Description	Unused	Used
904	A237	50fr	Students planting trees	.32	.16
905	A237	100fr	like 50fr	.65	.32
906	A237	130fr	Forest (before and after)	.85	.42
			Nos. 904-906 (3)	1.82	.90

L'Amitie Hospital, 1st Anniv. — A238

1988, Nov. 30

No.	Type	Value	Description	Unused	Used
907	A238	5fr	shown	.15	.15
908	A238	60fr	Aerial view	.40	.20
909	A238	160fr	Front gate	1.05	.52
			Nos. 907-909 (3)	1.60	.87

A239 A240

Olympic Medalists, Seoul, 1988: 150fr, Kristine Otto, DDR, swimming. 240fr, Matt Biondi, US, swimming. 300fr, Florence Griffith-Joyner, US, running. 450fr, Pierre Durand, France, equestrian. 600fr, Carl Lewis, US, running.

1989, Apr. 1

No.	Type	Value	Description	Unused	Used
910	A239	150fr	multi	.98	.50
911	A239	240fr	multi	1.55	.78
912	A239	300fr	multi	1.95	.98
913	A239	450fr	multi	2.95	1.45
a.			Souv. sheet of 4, #910-913		
			Nos. 910-913 (4)	7.43	3.71

Souvenir Sheet

No.	Type	Value	Description	Unused	Used
914	A239	600fr	multi	3.90	1.95

Nos. 913-914 airmail. No. 914 contains one 37x43mm stamp.

1989, Apr. 10 **Litho.** *Perf. 13½*

Transportation Innovations, Inventors: 20fr, Hebmuller and 1953 Volkswagen Beetle. 205fr, Werner von Siemens (1816-1892) and 1879 Locomotive B. 300fr, Dennis Conner, skipper of *Stars and Stripes,* winner of the 1988 America's Cup. 400fr, Andre Citroen (1878-1935) and 1955 Citroen-15 SIX. 450fr, Marc Seguin (1786-1875) and 1895 Decauville-Mallet 020-020. 750fr, Frederick S. Duesenberg (1876-1932), brother August, US flag and 1929 J Phaeton.

No.	Type	Value	Description	Unused	Used
915	A240	20fr	multi	.15	.15
916	A240	205fr	multi	1.35	.68
917	A240	300fr	multi	1.95	.98
918	A240	400fr	multi	2.60	1.30
919	A240	450fr	multi	2.90	1.45
			Nos. 915-919 (5)	8.95	4.56

Souvenir Sheet

No.	Type	Value	Description	Unused	Used
920	A240	750fr	multi	4.75	2.40

Nos. 919-920 airmail. No. 920 contains one 43x37mm stamp.

Nos. 889-892 Surcharged in Black or Silver

1988, Oct. 7 **Litho.** *Perf. 13½*

No.	Type	Value	Description	Unused	Used
921	A234	30fr	on 170fr No. 889 (B)	.22	.15
922	A234	70fr	on 300fr No. 890	.50	.25
923	A234	160fr	on 400fr No. 891	1.15	.58
924	A234	200fr	on 450fr No. 892	1.40	1.40
			Nos. 921-924 (4)	3.27	2.38

Nos. 923-924 are airmail.

PHILEXFRANCE '89, French Revolution Bicent. — A241

Designs: 200fr, Allegory in Honor of Liberty. 300fr, Declaration of Human Rights and Citizenship. 500fr, The Bastille, horiz.

1989, July 7 **Litho.** *Perf. 13*

No.	Type	Value	Description	Unused	Used
925	A241	200fr	multi	1.20	.60
926	A241	300fr	multi	1.75	.88

Souvenir Sheet

No.	Type	Value	Description	Unused	Used
927	A241	500fr	multi	3.00	1.50

Nos. 925-926 printed se-tenant with center label picturing the exhibition emblem.

Souvenir Sheet

Statue of Liberty — A242

Designs: a, Crown and torch observatories lit at night. b, Working on statue's coiffure. c, Face and scaffolding. d, Workman sanding copper sheeting around the crown observatory. e, Re-opening ceremony, 1986. f, Crown observatory at night.

1989, July **Litho.** **Wmk. 385** *Perf. 13*

No.	Type	Value	Description	Unused	Used
928			Sheet of 6	6.60	3.30
a.-c.	A242	150fr	any single	.95	.48
d.-f.	A242	200fr	any single	1.25	.62

Statue of Liberty cent. (in 1986). Photograph of the statue is reversed.

M. Champagnat (1789-1840), Founder of the Marist Order — A243

1989 **Litho.** *Perf. 13½*

No.	Type	Value	Description	Unused	Used
929	A243	15fr	Madonna and child, map	.15	.15
930	A243	50fr	Cross, Earth	.32	.16
931	A243	160fr	shown	1.05	.52
			Nos. 929-931 (3)	1.52	.83

Nos. 929-930 vert.

Harvest Feast, Bambari A244

1989, Oct. 15

No.	Type	Value	Description	Unused	Used
932	A244	100fr	Produce	.65	.32
933	A244	160fr	Ox plow	1.05	.52

World Food Day — A245

1989, Oct. 16

No.	Type	Value	Description	Unused	Used
934	A245	60fr	Domestic animals	.40	.20
935	A245	240fr	Arresting ivory poachers	1.50	.75

French Revolution, Bicent. — A246

Battle scenes and leaders: 160fr, Brig.-Gen. Francois-Christophe Kellermann (1735-1820), Battle of Valmy, Sept. 22, 1792. 200fr, Minister of War Charles-Francois du Perier Dumouriez (1739-1823), Battle of Jemappes, Nov. 7, 1792. 500fr, Gen. Jean-Charles Pichegru (1761-1804), capture of the Dutch fleet, Jan. 22, 1795. 600fr, Gen. Louis-Lazare Hoche (1768-97), Battle of Quiberon Bay, July 21, 1795. 1000fr, Napoleon at the Battle of Rivoli Veronese, Jan. 15, 1797.

1989, Dec. 5 **Litho.** *Perf. 13½*

No.	Type	Value	Description	Unused	Used
936	A246	160fr	multicolored	1.05	.50
937	A246	200fr	multicolored	1.30	.65
938	A246	500fr	multicolored	1.65	.85
939	A246	600fr	multicolored	2.00	1.00
a.			Souvenir sheet of 4, #936-939	6.00	6.00
			Nos. 936-939 (4)	6.00	3.00

Souvenir Sheet

No.	Type	Value	Description	Unused	Used
940	A246	1000fr	multicolored	6.50	3.25

PHILEXFRANCE '89. Nos. 938-940 are airmail.

No. 936 is incorrectly inscribed "Francois-Etienne." Jemappes is incorrectly spelled on No. 937. No. 940 is incorrectly inscribed "January 14."

1990 World Cup Soccer Championships, Italy — A247

Various athletes and Italian landmarks: 20fr, Bell tower, Palermo Cathedral. 120fr, Trinity of the Mount, Rome. 160fr, St. Francis Church apse, Bologna. 200fr, Palace, Florence. 1000fr, Milan Cathedral.

1989, Dec. 23

941 A247 20fr multicolored .15 .15
942 A247 120fr multicolored .78 .40
943 A247 160fr multicolored 1.05 .52
944 A247 200fr multicolored 1.30 .65
Nos. 941-944 (4) 3.28 1.72

Souvenir Sheet

945 A247 1000fr multicolored 6.50 3.25

Nos. 942 and 945 are airmail.

Save the Forests A247a

1989 Litho. *Perf. 13½*

945A A247a 160fr multicolored 1.15 .58

Town of Bangui, Cent. — A247b

Designs: 100fr, Governor's Palace, 1906. 160fr, Outpost. 200fr, A. Dolisie, founder of Bangui, vert. 1000fr, Signing of peace treaty between Michel Dolisie and Chief Gbembo, 1889, vert.

1989 Litho. *Perf. 13½*

945B A247b 100fr multicolored .75 .38
945C A247b 160fr multicolored 1.20 .60
945D A247b 200fr multicolored 1.50 .75
945E A247b 1000fr multicolored 7.50 3.75
Nos. 945B-945E (4) 10.95 5.48

Championship Team from Central Africa, 1987 — A248

1990, Feb. 23 Litho. *Perf. 13½*

946 A248 160fr Flag, players, trophy 1.15 .58
947 A248 240fr shown 1.70 .85
948 A248 500fr like 160fr 3.50 1.75
Nos. 946-948 (3) 6.35 3.18

African Basketball Championships. Dated 1988. Nos. 946 and 948 vert.

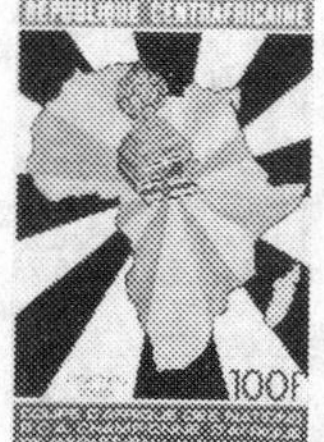

A249

A250

1990, Feb. 23 Litho. *Perf. 13½*

949 A249 100fr multicolored .72 .35
950 A249 130fr multicolored .92 .45

Central Africa, winner of the 1987 African Basketball Cup Championships, Tunis. Dated 1989.

1990, Mar. 12 Litho. *Perf. 13½*

1992 Winter Olympics, Albertville: No. 955A, Slalom skier. No. 955B, Pairs figure skating.

951 A250 10fr Speed skating .15 .15
952 A250 60fr Cross-country skiing .42 .20
953 A250 500fr Slalom 3.50 1.75
954 A250 750fr Figure skating 5.25 2.60
Nos. 951-954 (4) 9.32 4.70

Souvenir Sheet

955 A250 1000fr Downhill skiing 7.00 3.50

Litho. & Embossed

955A A250 1500fr gold & multi

Souvenir Sheet

955B A250 1500fr gold & multi

Nos. 953-955B are airmail. No. 955 contains one 36x42mm stamp. Nos. 951-954 exist in souvenir sheets of one.

Scout, *Euphaera eusemoides* A251

Boy scouts and butterflies: 65fr, *Cymothoe beckeri.* 160fr, *Pseudacraea clarki.* 250fr, *Charaxes castor.* 300fr, *Euphaedra gausape.* 500fr, *Graphium ridleyanus.* 1000fr, *Euphaedra edwardsi.* No. 962A, Antanartia delius. No. 962B, Spotted flycatcher. No. 962C, Cymothoe sangaris.

1990, Mar. 26

956 A251 25fr multicolored .18 .15
957 A251 65fr multicolored .45 .22
958 A251 160fr multicolored 1.15 .58
959 A251 250fr multicolored 1.75 .88
960 A251 300fr multicolored 2.10 1.05
961 A251 500fr multicolored 3.50 1.75
Nos. 956-961 (6) 9.13 4.63

Souvenir Sheet

962 A251 1000fr multicolored 7.00 3.50

Litho. & Embossed

Perf. 12½

962A A251 1500fr gold & multi

Perf. 13½

962B A251 1500fr gold & multi

Souvenir Sheet

962C A251 1500fr gold & multi

Nos. 962A-962C are airmail. No. 962A exists in a souvenir sheet of 1.

1992 Summer Olympics, Barcelona A252

1990, Apr. 1 Litho. *Perf. 13½*

963 A252 10fr Javelin .15 .15
964 A252 40fr Runner .28 .15
965 A252 130fr Tennis .92 .45
966 A252 240fr Hurdles 1.70 .85
967 A252 400fr Yachting 2.85 1.45
968 A252 500fr Soccer 3.50 1.75
Nos. 963-968 (6) 9.40 4.80

Souvenir Sheet

969 A252 1000fr Boxing 7.00 3.50

Nos. 963-965 vert. Nos. 967-969 are airmail.

Pres. Gorbachev, Pres. Bush — A253

Pres. Gorbachev, Pope John Paul II — A254

1990, July 27 Litho. *Perf. 13½*

970 A253 120fr multicolored .85 .42
971 A254 200fr multicolored 1.45 .72

Pope John Paul II-Gorbachev meeting Dec. 2, 1989. Bush-Gorbachev Summit Meeting Dec. 3, 1989. Nos. 970-971 exist in souvenir sheets of 1.

Great Britain No. 1, Sir Rowland Hill (1795-1879) — A255

1990, July 27

972 A255 130fr multicolored .90 .45

No. 972 exists in a souvenir sheet of 1.

Events and Anniversaries — A256

Designs: 160fr, Galileo Probe to Jupiter. 240fr, Neil Armstrong, 1st man on moon. 250fr, Concorde, rapid-transit train, Rotary Intl. emblem.

1990, July 27 Litho. *Perf. 13½*

973 A256 160fr multicolored 1.15 .58
974 A256 240fr multicolored 1.75 .88
975 A256 250fr multicolored 1.80 .90
Nos. 973-975 (3) 4.70 2.36

Wildlife Protection A258

Design: 100fr, Declining elephant population, vert.

1991, Jan. 25 Litho. *Perf. 13½*

976 A258 15fr gold & multi .15 .15
977 A258 60fr multicolored .45 .22
978 A258 100fr multicolored .75 .38
Nos. 976-978 (3) 1.35 .75

Eutropius A259

Design: 240fr, Distichodus.

1991, Jan. 26

979 A259 50fr multicolored .38 .20
980 A259 160fr gold & multi 1.20 .60
981 A259 240fr multicolored 1.80 .90
Nos. 979-981 (3) 3.38 1.70

Fight Against AIDS A260

Design: 120fr, Class speaker, vert.

1991, Jan. 24

982 A260 5fr gold & multi .15 .15
983 A260 70fr multicolored .52 .25
984 A260 120fr multicolored .90 .45
Nos. 982-984 (3) 1.57 .85

Assumption of Power by Pres. Andre Kolingba, 10th Anniv. (in 1991) — A261

1992, Sept. 1 Litho. *Perf. 13x13½*

985 A261 160fr multicolored 1.35 .65

Anniversaries and Events — A262

Designs: 80fr, Maybach Zeppelin, zeppelin airship, Count Ferdinand Zeppelin. 140fr, Child being comforted, Jean-Henri Dunant. 160fr, Benetton-Ford B 192, Michael Schumacher. 350fr, Konrad Adenauer signing Constitution of German Republic. 500fr, Pope John Paul II, mother and child, map. 600fr, Wolfgang Amadeus Mozart. 1000fr, Columbus at La Rabida, sailing ship, and building in Seville, Spain.

1992, Sept. 22 Litho. *Perf. 13½*

986 A262 80fr multicolored .58 .28
987 A262 140fr multicolored 1.00 .50
988 A262 160fr multicolored 1.15 .58
989 A262 350fr multicolored 2.55 1.25
990 A262 500fr multicolored 3.65 1.80
991 A262 600fr multicolored 4.35 2.20
Nos. 986-991 (6) 13.28 6.61

Souvenir Sheet

992 A262 1000fr multicolored 7.25 3.65

Count Zeppelin, 75th anniv. of death (#986). Jean-Henri Dunant, first recipient of Nobel Peace Prize, 90th anniv. (in 1991) (#987). Grand Prix of Monaco (#988). Brandenburg Gate, bicent (#989). Visit of Pope John Paul II to Africa (#990). Wolfgang Amadeus Mozart, bicent. of death (in 1991) (#991). Discovery of America, 500th anniv. and Expo '92, Seville (#992).

Nos. 990-992 are airmail. Nos. 986-991 exist in souvenir sheets of 1.

For overprint see No. 1073.

A264

Elvis Presley (1935-1977) A264a

Portrait of Presley, song or movie: 200fr, Heartbreak Hotel, 1956. 300fr, Love Me Tender, 1957. 400fr, Jailhouse Rock, 1957. 600fr, Harem Scarum, 1965.

1000fr, With guitar, at microphone.

No. 1001A, Holding microphone. No. 1001B, Playing guitar.

1993, July 12 Litho. *Perf. 13½*

997	A264	200fr multicolored	1.50	.75
998	A264	300fr multicolored	2.25	1.15
999	A264	400fr multicolored	3.00	1.60
1000	A264	600fr multicolored	4.50	2.25
		Nos. 997-1000 (4)	11.25	5.75

Souvenir Sheet

1001	A264	1000fr multicolored	7.50	3.75

Litho. & Embossed

1001A A264a 1500fr gold & multi

Souvenir Sheet

1001B A264a 1500fr gold & multi

Nos. 1000-1001B are airmail. Nos. 997-1000 exist imperf. and in souvenir sheets of one. No. 1001 exists imperf.

Wedding of Japan's Crown Prince Naruhito and Masako Owada — A265

A265a

Designs: 50fr, Princess Masako, parents. 65fr, Crown Prince Naruhito, parents. 160fr, Princess Masako, Harvard University 450fr, Crown Prince Naruhito, Oxford University. 750fr, Crown Prince, Princess.

1993, July 12 Litho. *Perf. 13½*

1002	A265	50fr multicolored	.38	.18
1003	A265	65fr multicolored	.48	.24
1004	A265	160fr multicolored	1.20	.60
1005	A265	450fr multicolored	3.40	1.70
		Nos. 1002-1005 (4)	5.46	2.72

Souvenir Sheet

1006	A265	750fr multicolored	5.75	2.80

Litho. & Embossed

1006A A265a 1500fr gold & multi

Nos. 1005-1006A are airmail. Nos. 1002-1005, 1006A exist imperf. and in souvenir sheets of one. No. 1006 exists imperf.

A266

1994 World Cup Soccer Championships, US — A266a

Designs show winning team, scenes from: 40fr, Amsterdam, 1928; Montevideo, 1930. 50fr, Rome, 1934; Paris, 1938. 60fr, Rio, 1950; Berne, 1954. 80fr, Stockholm, 1958; Santiago, 1962. 160fr, London, 1966; Mexico City, 1970. 200fr, Munich, 1974; Buenos Aires, 1978. 400fr, Madrid, 1982; Mexico City, 1986. 500fr, Rome, 1990; emblem for US competition, 1994.

1000fr, 1990 German team; 1994 US team.

No. 1015A, Pele, Brazil. No. 1015B, Gerd Muller, Germany.

1993, Oct. 9 Litho. *Perf. 13½*

1007	A266	40fr multicolored	.30	.15
1008	A266	50fr multicolored	.38	.18
1009	A266	60fr multicolored	.45	.22
1010	A266	80fr multicolored	.60	.30
1011	A266	160fr multicolored	1.20	.60
1012	A266	200fr multicolored	1.50	.75
1013	A266	400fr multicolored	3.00	1.50
1014	A266	500fr multicolored	3.75	1.90
		Nos. 1007-1014 (8)	11.18	5.60

Souvenir Sheet

1015	A266	1000fr multicolored	7.50	3.75

Litho. & Embossed

1015A A266a 1500fr gold & multi

Souvenir Sheet

1015B A266a 1500fr gol & multi

No. 1015 contains one 60x30mm stamp. Nos. 1007-1014 exist in souvenir sheets of one.

Nos. 1015A-1015B are airmail.

Miniature Sheets

Modern Olympic Games, Cent. (in 1996) — A267

Designs: No. 1016a, Ancient olympian. b, Baron de Coubertin, 1896. c, Charles Bennett, 1900. d, Etienne Desmarteau, 1904. e, Harry Porter, 1908. f, Patrick MacDonald, 1912. g, No games, 1916. h, Frank Loomis, 1920. i, Albert White, 1924.

No. 1017a, El Ouafi, 1928. b, Eddie Tolan, 1932. c, Jesse Owens, 1936. d, No games, 1940. e, No games, 1944. f, Tapio Rautavaara, 1948. g, Jean Boiteux, 1952. h, Petrus Kasterman, 1956. i, Sante Gaiardoni, 1960.

No. 1018a, Anton Geesink, 1964. b, Bob Beamon, 1968. c, Mark Spitz, 1972. d, Nadia Comaneci, 1976. e, Aleksandre Dityatin, 1980. f, J.F. Lamour, 1984. g, Pierre Durand, 1988. h, Michael Jordan, 1992. i, Soccer player, 1996.

1993 Litho. *Perf. 13½*

1016	A267	90fr Sheet of 9, #a.-i.	6.50	3.25
1017	A267	100fr Sheet of 9, #a.-i.	7.25	3.75
1018	A267	160fr Sheet of 9, #a.-i.	11.50	5.75

Miniature Sheet

Dinosaurs A268

Designs: No. 1019a, 25fr, Saltoposuchus. b, 25fr, Rhamphorhynchus. c, 25fr, Dimorphodon. d, 25fr, Archaeopteryx. e, 30fr, Compsognathus longipes. f, 30fr, Cryptocleidus oxoniensis. g, 30fr, Stegosaurus. h, 30fr, Cetiosaurus. i, 50fr, Brontosaurus. j, 50fr, Corythosaurus casuarius. k, 50fr, Styracosaurus. l, 50fr, Gorgosaurus. m, 500fr, Scolosaurus. n, 500fr, Trachodon. o, 500fr, Struthiomimus. p, 500fr, Tarbosaurus.

No. 1020, Tylosaur.

1993

1019	A268	Sheet of 16, #a.-p.	19.00	9.50

Souvenir Sheet

1020	A268	1000fr multicolored	7.75	3.75

No. 1020 is airmail and contains one 51x60mm stamp.

Biodiversity A269

Various fauna surrounding: 100fr, Man planting tree. 130fr, Man with local fauna, vert.

1993 Litho. *Perf. 13½*

1021	A269	100fr multicolored	.38	.18
1022	A269	130fr multicolored	.50	.25

M'Bali Dam — A270

1993, Jan. 14 Litho. *Perf. 13*

1023	A270	160fr shown	.60	.30
1024	A270	200fr Women, men with fish	.75	.38

Cooperation Council, 40th Anniv. A271

1993, Jan. 26

1025	A271	240fr multicolored	.95	.48

Intl. Conference on Nutrition, Rome — A272

1993, Apr. 1

1026	A272	90fr shown	.35	.16
1027	A272	140fr Fresh foods	.55	.28

University of Bangui A273

1993, Apr. 8

1028	A273	100fr multicolored	.38	.18

Dated 1992.

Environmental Development — A274

Designs: 160fr, Woman with vegetables, fruit. 240fr, Woman cooking food.

1993 Litho. *Perf. 13½*

1029	A274	160fr multicolored	.60	.30
1030	A274	240fr multicolored	.90	.45

Miniature Sheets

1994 Winter Olympics, Lillehammer A275

Past Winter Olympic champions: 1031a, Th. Haug, Nordic combined skiing, Chamonix, 1924. b, J. Heaton, 1-man sled, St. Moritz, 1928. c, B. Ruud, ski jumping, Lake Placid, 1932. d, I. Ballangrud, speed skating, Garmisch-Partenkirchen, 1936. e, G. Fraser, women's slalom skiing, St. Moritz, 1948. f, German 4-man bobsled, Oslo, 1952. g, USSR hockey team, Cortina D'Ampezzo, 1956. h, J. Vuarnet, downhill skiing, Squaw Valley, 1960.

No. 1032a, M. Goitschel, giant slalom, Innsbruck, 1964. b, Jean-Claude Killy, slalom skiing, Grenoble, 1968. c, U. Wehling, Nordic combined, Sapporo, 1972. d, Rodnina & Zaitsev, pairs figure skating, Innsbruck, 1976. e, E. Heiden, speed skating, Lake Placid, 1980. f, K. Witt, figure skating, Sarajevo, 1984. g, J. Mueller, luge, Calgary, 1988. h, E. Grospiron, freestyle skiing, Albertville, 1992. i, Speed skiing, Lillehammer, 1994.

1994 Litho. *Perf. 13½*

1031	A275	100fr Sheet of 8 + label	6.00	3.00
1032	A275	200fr Sheet of 9, #a.-i.	14.00	7.00

1994 Winter Olympics, Lillehammer — A276

Design: 1500fr, Women figure skaters.

1994 Litho. & Embossed ***Perf. 13½***

1033 A276 1500fr gold & multi

#1033 is airmail & exists in a souvenir sheet of 1.

Flowers, Vegetables, Fruit, & Mushrooms A277

Flowers: No. 1034a, 25fr, Ansellia africana. b, 60fr, Polystachia bella. c, 90fr, Aerangis rhodosticta. d, 500fr, Angraecum eburneum.
Vegetables: No. 1035a, 30r, Yams. b, 65fr, Manioc. c, 100fr, Corn. d, 400fr, Sweet potato.
Fruits: No. 1036a, 40fr, Orange. b, 70fr, Banana. c, 160fr, Mango. d, 300fr, Coffee.
Mushrooms: No. 1037a, 50fr, Termitomyces schimperi. b, 80fr, Sympodia arborescens. c, 200fr, Phlebopus sudanicus. d, 600fr, Leucocoprinus africanus.

1994 Litho. ***Perf. 13½***

1034 A277 Strip of 4, #a.-d. 5.00 2.50
1035 A277 Strip of 4, #a.-d. 4.50 2.25
1036 A277 Strip of 4, #a.-d. 4.25 2.00
1037 A277 Strip of 4, #a.-d. 7.00 3.50
e. Sheet of 16, #1034-1037 21.00 10.50

Catholic Church in Africa, Cent. — A278

Designs: 130fr, Monsignor Augouard, founder of mission, St. Paul of the Rapids. 160fr, Monsignor Grandin, Abbe Boganda, first sacred ordainment, 1938. 240fr, Father Louis Godart, House of Charity, Bangui.

1994 Litho. ***Perf. 13½***

1038 A278 130fr multicolored .52 .25
1039 A278 160fr multicolored .65 .32
1040 A278 240fr multicolored .95 .48
Nos. 1038-1040 (3) 2.12 1.05

Relics from Early Civilizations, Landmarks — A279

Designs: 10fr, Cabin-shaped cinerary urn, Rome. 25fr, Face of the secret denunciation, Venice, vert. 30fr, Statue of the Tetrarchs, Venice, vert. 50fr, Little cube-shaped building, Palermo, vert. 65fr, Frieze, The Alhambra, Granada, vert. 90fr, Grand Chateau, Bellinzona. 100fr, Museum D'Orsay, Paris, vert. 130fr, Granary, Galicia. 140fr, Mural, by Diego Rivera, Mexico, vert. 160fr, Guacamaya mask, Mexico, vert. 200fr, Ivory mask, Western Africa, vert. 240fr, La Sagrada Familia, Barcelona, vert. 260fr, Casbah of Amerhidil. 300fr, Gold aureus of Sulla, Rome, 82 BC. 400fr, Chimborazo volcano.

1994 ***Perf. 13***

1041-1055 A279 Set of 15 8.75 4.50

D-Day, 50th Anniv. — A280

Pegasus Bridge, June 6: No. 1056a, British troops crossing bridge, piper. b, Glider, British and German soldiers. c, German soldiers.
Operation COBRA, July 24: a, Tank, monument, soldiers. b, Bombers, soldiers, gun barrel. c, Tank, soldiers up close.

1994 Litho. ***Perf. 13½***

1056 A280 600fr Strip of 3, #a.-c. 7.50 3.75
1057 A280 600fr Strip of 3, #a.-c. 7.50 3.75

Nos. 1056b, 1057b are 30x46mm. Nos. 1056-1057 are continuous designs. See No. C359.

Anniversaries & Events — A281

Characters from "Star Wars:" a, Han Solo, Chewbaca. b, Darth Vader, Princess Leia, Luke Skywalker, R2D2, C3PO. c, Obi Wan Kenobi.
First manned moon landing, 25th anniv.: No. 1059a, 400fr, Buzz Aldrin. b, 500fr, Neil Armstrong, Apollo 11 liftoff. c, 600fr, Michael Collins.
No. 1060a, 400fr, Theodor von Karman. b, 500fr, Apollo 11 command module, Werner von Braun. c, 600fr, Hermes Rocket, Hermann Oberth.

1994 Litho. ***Perf. 13½***

1058 A281 600fr Strip of 3, #a.-c. 7.25 3.50
1059 A281 Strip of 3, #a.-c. 6.00 3.00
1060 A281 Strip of 3, #a.-c. 6.00 3.00

Motion Pictures, cent. (#1058).
Nos. 1058b, 1059b, 1060b are 60x51mm. Nos. 1058-1060 are continuous design and exist in a souvenir sheet of 1.

Natl. Assembly A282

1994

1061 A282 65fr blue & multi .28 .15
1062 A282 430fr yellow brn & multi 1.75 .90

Antoine de Saint-Exupery (1900-44), Aviator, Author — A283

1994

1063 A283 80fr Airplane .32 .16
1064 A283 235fr Portrait, vert. .95 .48

Inauguration of Pres. Ange-Felix Patasse, 1st Anniv. — A284

1994

1065 A284 65fr blue & multi .25 .15
1066 A284 300fr yellow & multi 1.25 .60
1067 A284 385fr green & multi 1.50 .75
Nos. 1065-1067 (3) 3.00 1.50

A285

Intl. Olympic Committee, Cent. — A286

1994

1068 A285 60fr blue green & multi .22 .15
1069 A285 405fr yellow grn & multi 1.65 .80

Souvenir Sheet

1070 A286 675fr Pierre de Coubertin 2.75 1.40

No. 1070 is airmail.

Nos. 1031-1032 Ovptd. with Medalist & Country Name in Gold

Overprints on No. 1031: No. 1071a, "F.B. LUNDBERG / NORVEGE." b, "G. HACKL / ALLEMAGNE." c, "B. DAEHLIE / NORVEGE." d, "J.O. KOSS / NORVEGE." e, "V. SCHNEIDER / SUISSE." f, "MEDAILLE D'OR / ALLEMAGNE." g, "MEDAILLE D'OR / SUEDE." h, "T. MOE / U.S.A."
Overprints on No. 1032: No. 1072a, "M. WASMEIER / ALLEMAGNE." b, "T. STANGASSINGER / AUTRICHE." c, "MEDAILLE D'OR / PAR EQUIPES / JAPON." d, "Y. GORDEYEVA / S. GRINKOV / RUSSIE." e, "D. JANSEN / U.S.A." f, "O. BAYUL / UKRAINE." g, "G. HACKL / ALLEMAGNE." h, "J.-L. BRASSARO / CANADA." i, "K. SEIZINGER / ALLEMAGNE."

1994

1071 A275 100fr Sheet of 8, #a.-h. + label 6.00 3.00
1072 A275 200fr Sheet of 9, #a.-i. 14.00 7.00

No. 988 Overprinted in Silver

MICHAEL SCHUMACHER
CHAMPION DU MONDE
FORMULE I 1994

1994 Litho. ***Perf. 13½***

1073 A262 160fr multicolored 9.00 4.50

No. 1073 also exists in souvenir sheet of 1.

1995 Boy Scout Jamboree, Holland — A287

Scout with mushrooms or butterflies: 300fr, Armillariela mellea. 385fr, Charaxes pleione. 405fr, Charaxes candiope. 430fr, Charaxes pollux. 500fr, Volvaria esculenta. 1000fr, Cortinarius.
2000fr, Euphaedra medon.

1995

1074-1079 A287 Set of 6 14.00 7.00

Souvenir Sheet

1080 A287 2000fr multicolored 8.75 4.25

Nos. 1074-1079 exist in souvenir sheets of 1. No. 1080 is airmail and contains one 39x57mm stamp.

1994 World Cup Soccer Championships, US — A288

Stadium: 300fr, Citrus Bowl, Orlando. 385fr, RFK Stadium, Washington, DC. 405fr, Soldier Field, Chicago. 430fr, Cotton Bowl, Dallas. 500fr, Giants Stadium, East Rutherford, NJ. 1000fr, Foxboro Stadium, Foxboro, MA.
2000fr, Rose Bowl, vert.

1995 Litho. ***Perf. 13½***

1081-1086 A288 Set of 6 13.00 6.50

Souvenir Sheet

1087 A288 2000fr multicolored 11.50 5.75

No. 1087 is airmail.

African Development Bank, 30th Anniv. — A289

1995

1088 A289 70fr multicolored .30 .15
1089 A289 200fr multicolored .90 .45

Nos. 1088-1089 also exist in souvenir sheet of 1.

Fish — A290

Designs, 25fr, 300fr, Auchenoglanis. 30fr, 50fr, Chrisicntys.

1995

1090-1093 A290 Set of 4 1.75 .90

Entertainers
A291

Designs: 300fr, Freddie Mercury (Queen). 385fr, Jimi Hendrix. 430fr, Marilyn Monroe. 500fr, Michael Jackson. 600fr, Jerry Garcia (Grateful Dead). 800fr, Elvis Presley.
2000fr, Marilyn Monroe, diff.

1995, July 21
1094-1099 A291 Set of 6 13.00 6.50

Souvenir Sheet
1100 A291 2000fr multicolored 8.75 4.25

Nos. 1094-1099 exist in souvenir sheets of 1. No. 1100 is airmail.

SEMI-POSTAL STAMPS

Central African Republic Anti-Malaria Issue
Common Design Type
Perf. 12½x12

1962, Apr. 7 Engr. Unwmk.
B1 CD108 25fr + 5fr slate .45 .45

WHO drive to eradicate malaria.

Freedom from Hunger Issue
Common Design Type

1963, Mar. 21 *Perf. 13*
B2 CD112 25fr + 5fr multi .42 .42

Guinea Fowl and Partridge
SP1

Designs: 10fr+5fr, Yellow-backed duiker and snail. 20fr+5fr, Elephant, tortoise and hippopotamus playing tug-of-war. 30fr+10fr, Cuckoo and tortoise. 50fr+20fr, Patas monkey and leopard.

1971, Feb. 9 Photo. *Perf. 12½x12*
B3 SP1 5fr + 5fr multi .80 .40
B4 SP1 10fr + 5fr multi 1.25 .80
B5 SP1 20fr + 5fr multi 1.60 1.10
B6 SP1 30fr + 10fr multi 2.25 1.60
B7 SP1 50fr + 20fr multi 4.50 3.50
Nos. B3-B7 (5) 10.40 7.40

Lengué
Dancer — SP2

Dancers: 40fr+10fr, Le Lengué. 100fr+40fr, Teke. 140fr+40fr, Englabolo.

1971 Litho. *Perf. 13*
B8 SP2 20fr + 5fr multi .22 .15
B9 SP2 40fr + 10fr multi .42 .25
B10 SP2 100fr + 40fr multi 1.10 .60
B11 SP2 140fr + 40fr multi 1.50 .80
Nos. B8-B11 (4) 3.24 1.80

AIR POST STAMPS

Central African Republic

Abyssinian Roller — AP1

Birds: 200fr, Gold Coast touraco. 500fr, African fish eagle.

Unwmk.

1960, Sept. 3 Engr. *Perf. 13*
C1 AP1 100fr vio bl, org brn & emer 1.00 .42
C2 AP1 200fr multi 2.00 .80
C3 AP1 500fr Prus bl, emer & red brn 5.00 2.00
Nos. C1-C3 (3) 8.00 3.22

French Equatorial Africa No. C37 Surcharged in Red

XVII°
OLYMPIADE
1960

REPUBLIQUE
CENTRAFRICAINE

250f

1960, Dec. 15 *Perf. 13*
C4 AP8 250fr on 500fr grnsh blk, blk & sl 4.25 4.25

17th Olympic Games, Rome, Aug. 25-Sept. 11.

Air Afrique Issue
Common Design Type

1962, Feb. 17 Unwmk. *Perf. 13*
C5 CD107 50fr vio, lt grn & red brn .50 .45

Founding of Air Afrique airline.

Pole Vault — AP1a

1962, July 21 Photo. *Perf. 12x12½*
C6 AP1a 100fr grn, yel, brn & blk 1.00 .65

Abidjan games.

Red-faced Lovebirds — AP2

1962-63 Engr. *Perf. 13*
C7 AP2 50fr Great blue touraco .50 .22
C8 AP2 250fr shown ('63) 2.50 1.40

Issued: 50fr, Nov. 15; 250fr, Mar. 11, 1963.

Runner with Torch and Palm Branch — AP3

1962, Dec. 24
C9 AP3 100fr gray grn, brn & car 1.00 .65

Tropics Cup Games, Bangui, Dec. 24-31.

African Postal Union Issue
Common Design Type

1963, Sept. 8 Photo. *Perf. 12½*
C10 CD114 85fr emer, ocher & red .80 .60

Sun Shining on Africa — AP4

1963, Nov. 9 *Perf. 13x12*
C11 AP4 25fr bl, yel & vio bl .25 .20

Issued for African unity.

Europafrica Issue
Common Design Type

1963, Nov. 30 *Perf. 12x13*
C12 CD116 50fr ultra, yel & dk brn .90 .70

Diesel Engine — AP5

Various Locomotives; 25fr, 50fr, vertical.

1963, Dec. 1 Engr. *Perf. 13*
C13 AP5 20fr brn, cl & dk grn .20 .20
C14 AP5 25fr brn, bl & choc .25 .20
C15 AP5 50r brn, red lil & vio .55 .40
C16 AP5 100fr brn, grn & dl red brn 1.10 .80
a. Min. sheet of 4, #C13-C16 2.25 2.25
Nos. C13-C16 (4) 2.10 1.60

Bangui-Douala railroad project.

Bangui Cathedral — AP6

1964, Jan. 21 Unwmk. *Perf. 13*
C17 AP6 100fr yel grn, org brn & bl 1.00 .60

Radar Tracking Station and WMO Emblem — AP7

1964, Mar. 23 Engr. *Perf. 13*
C18 AP7 50fr org brn, bl & pur .50 .42

World Meteorological Day.

Map and Presidents of Chad, Congo, Gabon and Central African Republic — AP8

1964, June 23 Photo. *Perf. 12½*
C19 AP8 100fr multi 1.00 .65

5th anniversary of the Conference of Chiefs of State of Equatorial Africa.

Javelin Throwers — AP9

Designs: 50fr, Basketball game. 100fr, Four runners. 250fr, Swimmers, one in water.

1964, June 23 Engr. *Perf. 13*
C20 AP9 25fr grn, dk brn & lt vio bl .25 .15
C21 AP9 50fr blk, car & grn .50 .25
C22 AP9 100fr grn, vio bl & dk brn 1.00 .55
C23 AP9 250fr grn, blk & car 2.50 1.50
a. Min. sheet of 4, #C20-C23 4.25 4.25
Nos. C20-C23 (4) 4.25 2.45

18th Olympic Games, Tokyo, Oct. 10-25, 1964.

John F. Kennedy — AP10

1964, July 4 Photo. *Perf. 12½*
C24 AP10 100fr lil, brn & blk 1.10 .90
a. Min. sheet of 4 5.00 5.00

Industrial Symbols, Maps of Africa and Europe — AP11

1964, Dec. 19 Unwmk. *Perf. 13x12*
C25 AP11 50fr yel, org & grn .50 .45

See note after Cameroun No. 402.

International Cooperation Year Emblem — AP12

1965, Jan. 2 *Perf. 13*
C26 AP12 100fr red brn, yel & bl 1.00 .60

International Cooperation Year.

Nimbus Weather Satellite — AP13

1965, Mar. 23 Engr. *Perf. 13*

C27 AP13 100fr org brn, ultra & blk 1.10 .65

Fifth World Meteorological Day.

Lincoln and Statue of Liberty — AP14

1965, Apr. 15 Photo. *Perf. 13*

C28 AP14 100fr bluish grn, ind & bis 1.10 .60

Centenary of death of Abraham Lincoln.

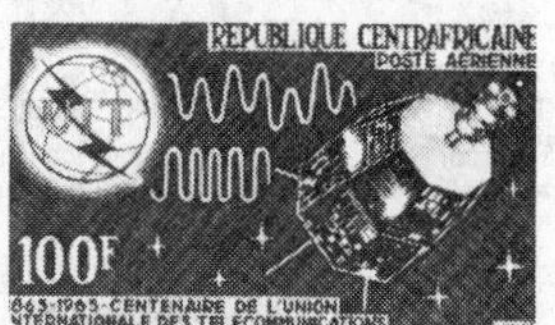

ITU Emblem and Relay Satellite — AP15

1965, May 17 Engr. *Perf. 13*

C29 AP15 100fr dk grn vio bl & brn 1.10 .60

Centenary of the ITU.

"Housing," New Home in Village — AP16

1965, June 10 Unwmk.

C30 AP16 100fr ultra, brn & sl grn 1.00 .60

See note after No. 52.

Europafrica Issue

Tractor, Cotton Picker, Cotton, Sun and Emblem — AP17

1965, Nov. 7 Photo. *Perf. 12x13*

C31 AP17 50fr multi .45 .35

See note after Chad No. C11.

Mercury by Antoine Coysevox — AP18

Father Holding Sick Child — AP19

1965, Dec. 5 Engr. *Perf. 13*

C32 AP18 100fr red brn, bl & blk 1.10 .65

5th anniv. of Central African Republic's admission to the UPU.

1965, Dec. 12

Design: 100fr, Mother and child.

C33 AP19 50fr dk bl, car & blk .50 .35

C34 AP19 100fr red brn, red & brt grn 1.00 .65

Issued to honor the Red Cross.

Air Afrique Issue
Common Design Type

1966, Aug. 31 Photo. *Perf. 13*

C35 CD123 25fr bl, blk & lem .25 .15

For surcharge see No. C43.

Surveyor Spacecraft on Moon — AP20

Designs: No. C37, Luna 9 on Moon and Earth. 200fr, Rocket take-off, Jules Verne's "From the Earth to the Moon."

1966, Oct. 24 Photo. *Perf. 12x12½*

C36 AP20 130fr multi 1.40 .80

C37 AP20 130fr multi 1.40 .80

C38 AP20 200fr multi 2.00 1.20

a. Souv. sheet of 3, #C36-C38 5.50 5.50

Nos. C36-C38 (3) 4.80 2.80

Conquest of the Moon.

For surcharges see Nos. C58, C61.

Eugene A. Cernan, Gemini 9 and Agena Rocket — AP21

Design: No. C40, Pavel R. Popovich and rocket.

1966, Nov. 14 Photo. *Perf. 13*

C39 AP21 50fr multi .50 .22

C40 AP21 50fr multi .50 .22

American and Russian astronauts.

Diamant Rocket, D-1 Satellite and Globe with Map of Africa — AP22

1966, Nov. 14 Engr.

C41 AP22 100fr brt rose lil & brn 1.10 .50

Issued to commemorate the launching of France's first satellite, Nov. 26, 1965, and the launching of the D-1 satellite, Feb. 17, 1966.

Exchange of Agricultural and Industrial Products between Africa and Europe — AP23

1966, Dec. 5 Photo. *Perf. 12x13*

C42 AP23 50fr multi .50 .30

See note after Gabon No. C46.

No. C35 Surcharged **XIX**

1967, May 8 *Perf. 13*

C43 CD123 5fr on 25fr multi .15 .15

The surcharge obliterates the "2" of the original 25fr denomination.

DC-8F Over M'Poko Airport, Bangui — AP24

1967, July 3 Engr. *Perf. 13*

C44 AP24 100fr sl, dk grn & brn 1.10 .50

View of EXPO '67, Montreal — AP25

1967, July 17

C45 AP25 100fr vio bl, dk red brn & dk grn 1.00 .45

International Exposition. EXPO '67, Montreal, Apr. 28-Oct. 27.

African Postal Union Issue, 1967
Common Design Type

1967, Sept. 9 Engr. *Perf. 13*

C46 CD124 100fr brt grn, dk car rose & plum 1.00 .45

Potez 25 TOE AP26

1967, Nov. 24 Engr. *Perf. 13*

C47 AP26 100fr shown .75 .30

C48 AP26 200fr Junkers 52 1.25 .55

C49 AP26 500fr Caravelle 11R 3.75 1.65

Nos. C47-C49 (3) 5.75 2.50

For surcharges see Nos. C59-C60.

Presidents Boganda and Bokassa — AP27

1967, Dec. 1 Photo. *Perf. 12½*

C50 AP27 130fr org, red, lt bl & blk 1.40 .90

9th anniversary of the republic.

Pres. Jean Bedel Bokassa AP28

1968, Jan. 1 *Perf. 12½x12*

C51 AP28 30fr multi .35 .20

Human Rights Flame, Men and Globe — AP29

1968, Mar. 26 Photo. *Perf. 13*

C52 AP29 200fr brt grn, vio & ver 2.00 1.00

International Human Rights Year.

Man, WHO Emblem and Tsetse Fly — AP30

1968, Apr. 8 Engr.

C53 AP30 200fr multi 2.00 1.00

20th anniv. of WHO.

Javelin Thrower — AP31

Space Probe Landing on Venus — AP32

1968, Apr. 16 **Engr.** ***Perf. 13***

C54 AP31 200fr shown 2.00 1.10
C55 AP31 200fr Downhill skier 2.00 1.10

The 1968 Olympic Games.

1968, Apr. 23

C56 AP32 100fr ultra, dk & brt grn 1.00 .45

Venus exploration by Venus IV, Oct. 18, 1967.

Marie Curie and "Cancer Destroyed" — AP33

1968, Apr. 30

C57 AP33 100fr vio, brt bl & brn 1.00 .45

Marie Curie (1867-1934), scientist.

Nos. C36-C37 and C47-C48 Surcharged with New Value

Photogravure; Engraved

1968, Sept. 16 ***Perf. 12x12½, 13***

C58 AP20 5fr on 130fr multi .15 .15
C59 AP26 10fr on 100fr multi .15 .15
C60 AP26 20fr on 200fr multi .20 .15
C61 AP20 50fr on 130fr multi .55 .38
Nos. C58-C61 (4) 1.05
Set value .58

On No. C58 the old denomination has been obliterated with "XIX," on No. C61 the obliteration is a rectangular bar. On Nos. C59-C60 the last zero of the old denomination has been obliterated with a black square.

River Boat Type of Regular Issue

Craft: 100fr, "Pie X," Bangui, 1894. 130fr, "Ballay," Bangui, 1891.

1968, Dec. 10 **Engr.** ***Perf. 13***

Size: 48x27mm

C62 A37 100fr bl, dk brn & ol 1.00 .45
C63 A37 130fr brt pink, sl grn & slate 1.40 .65

PHILEXAFRIQUE Issue

Mme. de Sévigné, French School, 17th Century AP34

1968, Dec. 17 **Photo.** ***Perf. 12½***

C64 AP34 100fr brn & multi 1.10 .90

Issued to publicize PHILEXAFRIQUE, Philatelic Exhibition in Abidjan, Feb. 14-23. Printed with alternating brown label.

2nd PHILEXAFRIQUE Issue

Common Design Type

Design: 50fr, Ubangi-Shari No. J16, cotton field and Pres. Bokassa.

1969, Feb. 14 **Engr.** ***Perf. 13***

C65 CD128 50fr bis brn, blk & dk grn .60 .60

Holocerina Angulata Aur. — AP35

Butterflies and Moths: 20fr, Nudaurelia dione fabr. 30fr, Eustera troglophylla hamp., vert. 50fr, Aurivillius aratus west. 100fr, Epiphora albida druce.

1969, Feb. 25 **Photo.**

C66 AP35 10fr yel & multi .15 .15
C67 AP35 20fr vio & multi .20 .15
C68 AP35 30fr multi .30 .15
C69 AP35 50fr multi .60 .25
C70 AP35 100fr multi 1.10 .55
Nos. C66-C70 (5) 2.35 1.25

Boxing — AP36

1969, Mar. 18 **Photo.** ***Perf. 13***

C71 AP36 50fr shown .50 .22
C72 AP36 100fr Basketball 1.00 .40

Apollo 8 over Moonscape — AP37

1969, May 27 **Photo.** ***Perf. 13***

C73 AP37 200fr dp bl, gray & yel 2.00 .90

US Apollo 8 mission, the 1st men in orbit around the moon, Dec. 21-27, 1968.
For overprint see No. C81.

Market Cross, Nuremberg, and Toys — AP38

1969, June 3

C74 AP38 100fr blk, brt rose lil & emer 1.00 .65

Intl. Toy Fair in Nuremberg, Germany.

Napoleon as First Consul, by Anne-Louis Girodet-Trioson — AP39

Designs: 130fr, Napoleon meeting Emperor Francis II, by Antoine Jean Gros, horiz. 200fr, The Wedding of Napoleon and Marie-Louise, by Georges Rouget, horiz.

1969, Nov. 4 **Photo.** ***Perf. 12½***

C75 AP39 100fr multi 1.10 .80
C76 AP39 130fr brn & multi 1.60 1.00
C77 AP39 200fr multi 2.75 2.00
Nos. C75-C77 (3) 5.45 3.80

Napoleon Bonaparte (1769-1821).

Pres. Bokassa, Map of Africa and Flag — AP40

Franklin Delano Roosevelt — AP41

1970, Jan. 1 ***Die-cut; Perf. 10½***

Embossed on Gold Foil

C78 AP40 2000fr gold 16.00 16.00

1970 **Litho.** ***Perf. 13½x14***

C79 AP41 100fr shown .90 .55
C80 AP41 100fr Lenin .80 .45

Roosevelt, 25th death anniv., Lenin, birth cent.
Issue dates: #C79, Apr. 29; #C80. Apr. 22.

No. C73 Overprinted in Red:

ATTERRISSAGE
d'APOLLO 12
19 novembre 1969

1970, June 1 **Photo.** ***Perf. 13***

C81 AP37 200fr multi 5.50 4.25

Issued to commemorate the moon landing mission of Apollo 12, Nov. 14-24, 1969.

AP42

1970, Sept. 15 **Litho.** ***Perf. 10***

C82 AP42 Pair + label 1.60 .80
a. 100fr Dancer .80 .35
b. 100fr Still life .80 .35

Knokphila 70, 6th Intl. Phil. Exhib. at Knokke, Belgium, July 4-10. Imperf. between stamps and label.

Sericulture Type of Regular Issue

1970, Sept. 15 ***Perf. 10***

C83 A45 140fr multi 1.40 .70

C.A.R. Flag, EXPO Emblem and Pavilion — AP43

1970, Dec. 18 **Litho.** ***Perf. 13½x13***

C84 AP43 200fr red & multi 1.75 .90

Intl. Exposition EXPO '70, Osaka, Japan.

Soccer AP44

1970, Dec. 8 ***Perf. 13x13½***

C85 AP44 200fr multi 1.75 .90

World Soccer Championships, Mexico, May 30-June 21, 1970.

Dove AP45

1970, Dec. 31

C86 AP45 200fr bl, yel & blk 1.75 .90

25th anniversary of the United Nations.

Presidents Mobutu, Bokassa, and Tombalbaye — AP46

1971, Jan. 10

C87 AP46 140fr multi 1.40 .60

Return of Central African Republic to the United States of Central Africa which also includes Congo Democratic Republic and Chad.

Satellite over Globe — AP47

1971, May 17 **Photo.** ***Perf. 12½***

C88 AP47 100fr multi .90 .42

3rd World Telecommunications Day.

African Postal Union Issue, 1971

Common Design Type

Design: 100fr, Carved head and UAMPT building, Brazzaville, Congo.

1971, Nov. 13 **Photo.** ***Perf. 13x13½***

C89 CD135 100fr bl & multi .90 .42

Child and Education Year Emblem — AP48

1971, Nov. 11 **Litho.** ***Perf. 13x13½***

C90 AP48 140fr multi 1.10 .50

25th anniv. of UNESCO.

Fight Against Cancer — AP49

Gamal Abdel Nasser — AP50

1971, Nov. 20 Photo. *Perf. 12½*

C91 AP49 100fr grn & multi .90 .40

1972, Jan. 15

C92 AP50 100fr dk red, blk & bister .80 .40

In memory of Gamal Abdel Nasser (1918-1970), president of Egypt.

Olympic Rings and Boxing — AP51

Design: No. C94, Track and Olympic rings, vert.

1972, May 26 Engr. *Perf. 13*

C93 AP51 100fr brn org & sepia 1.00 .40
C94 AP51 100fr green & violet 1.00 .40
a. Miniature sheet of 2 2.00 2.00

20th Olympic Games, Munich, Aug. 26-Sept. 10. No. C94a contains 2 stamps similar to Nos. C93-C94, but in changed colors. The boxing stamp is red lilac and green, the track stamp ocher and red lilac.

For overprints see Nos. C100-C101.

Tiling's Mail Rocket, 1931, and Mailman — AP52

Designs: 50fr, DC-3 and mailman riding camel, vert. 150fr, Sirio satellite and rocket, vert. 200fr, Intelsat 4 and rocket.

1972, Aug. 12

C95 AP52 40fr bl, org & indigo .35 .16
C96 AP52 50fr bl, brn & org .40 .16
C97 AP52 150fr brn, org & gray 1.10 .55
C98 AP52 200fr brn, bl & org 1.50 .65
a. Souv. sheet of 4, #C95-C98 3.50 3.50
Nos. C95-C98 (4) 3.35 1.52

Centraphilex 1972, Central African Philatelic Exhibition, Bangui.

Europafrica Issue

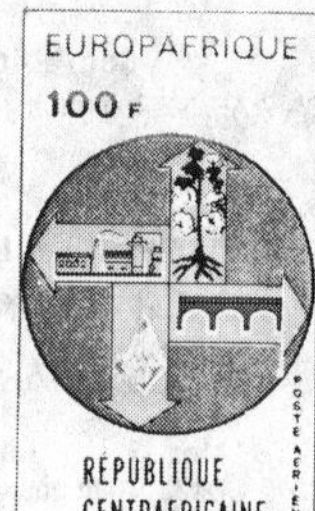

Arrows with Symbols of Agriculture and Industry — AP53

1972, Nov. 17 Litho. *Perf. 13*

C99 AP53 100fr multi .65 .40

Nos. C93-C94, C94a Overprinted
a. POIDS-MOYEN / LEMECHEV MEDAILLE D'OR
b. LONGUER / WILLIAMS MEDAILLE D'OR

1972, Nov. 24 Engr.

C100 AP51 (a) 100fr .90 .40
C101 AP51 (b) 100fr .90 .40
a. Miniature sheet of 2 2.00 2.00

Gold Medal Winners in 20th Olympic Games: Viatscheslav Lemechev, USSR, middleweight boxing; Randy Williams, US, broad jump.

Lunar Rover and Module — AP54

1972, Dec. 18 Engr. *Perf. 13*

C102 AP54 100fr slate grn, bl & gray .80 .42

Apollo 16 US moon mission, Apr. 15-27, 1972.

Virgin and Child, by Francesco Pesellino AP55

Christmas: 150fr, Adoration of the Child with St. John the Baptist and St. Romuald, by Fra Filippo Lippi.

1972, Dec. 25 Photo.

C103 AP55 100fr gold & multi .80 .42
C104 AP55 150fr gold & multi 1.25 .65

Parthenon, Athens, Spyridon Louis, Marathon, 1896 — AP56

Designs (Olympic Rings and): 40fr, Arc de Triomphe, Paris, H. Barrelet, single scull, 1900. 50fr, Old Courthouse and Western Arch, St. Louis, Myer Prinstein, triple jump, 1904. 100fr, Tower, London, Henry Taylor, swimming, 1908. 150fr, City Hall, Stockholm, Greco-Roman wrestling, 1912.

1972, Dec. 28 Engr.

C105 AP56 30fr brt grn, mag & brn .25 .15
C106 AP56 40fr vio bl, emer & brn .35 .15
C107 AP56 50fr car rose, vio bl & Prus bl .40 .16
C108 AP56 100fr sl, red lil & brn .80 .38
C109 AP56 150fr red lil, blk & Prus bl 1.25 .60
Nos. C105-C109 (5) 3.05 1.44

Olympic Games 1896-1912.

WHO Emblem, Surgeon and Nurse — AP57

1973, Apr. 7 Photo. *Perf. 13*

C110 AP57 100fr multi .80 .45

WHO, 25th anniv.

AP58

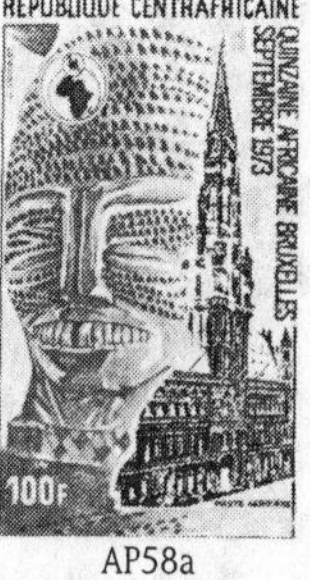

AP58a

1973, May 17 Litho. *Perf. 12½*

C111 AP58 200fr World map, arrows, waves 1.40 .80

5th International Telecommunications Day.

1973, Sept. 17 Engr. *Perf. 13*

Head and City Hall, Brussels.

C112 AP58a 100fr pur, ocher & brn .80 .45

African Weeks, Brussels, Sept. 15-30, 1973.

Europafrica Issue

Map of Central African Republic with Industry and Agriculture, Young Man — AP59

1973, Sept. 28 Engr. *Perf. 13*

C113 AP59 100fr sepia, grn & org .70 .45

Carrier Pigeon with Letter and UPU Emblem — AP60

1973, Oct. 9 Photo.

C114 AP60 200fr multi 1.50 .90

Universal Postal Union Day.

WMO Emblem, Weather Map — AP61

1973, Oct. 20 Engr. *Perf. 13*

C115 AP61 150fr brt ultra & sl grn 1.00 .50

Cent. of intl. meteorological cooperation.

Copernicus, Heliocentric System — AP62

1973, Nov. 2 Photo.

C116 AP62 100fr gold & multi .75 .45

Copernicus (1473-1543), Polish astronomer.

Pres. Bokassa AP63

Pres. Bokassa — AP64

Rocket Launch and Apollo 17 Badge — AP65

1973, Nov. 30 Photo. *Perf. 12½*

C117 AP63 50fr multi .35 .22
C118 AP64 100fr multi .65 .45

1973, Dec. 15 Engr. *Perf. 13*

Designs: 65fr, Capsule over moonscape, horiz. 100fr, Moon landing, horiz. 150fr, Astronauts on moon. 200fr, Splashdown with parachutes and badge.

C119 AP65 50fr ver, gray grn & brn .35 .25
C120 AP65 65fr dk brn, brn red & sl grn .40 .35
C121 AP65 100fr ver, slate & choc .65 .45
C122 AP65 150fr brn, ol & sl grn .90 .65
C123 AP65 200fr red, bl & sl grn 1.40 .90
Nos. C119-C123 (5) 3.70 2.60

Apollo 17 US moon mission, Dec. 7-19, 1972.

St. Teresa — AP66

UPU Emblem, Letter — AP67

1973, Dec. 25

C124 AP66 500fr vio bl & grnsh bl 3.50 2.00

St. Teresa of the Infant Jesus, the Little Flower (1873-1897), Carmelite nun.

1974, Oct. 9 Engr. *Perf. 13*

C125 AP67 500fr multi 3.50 2.25

Centenary of Universal Postal Union.

For surcharge see No. C159.

Presidents and Flags of Cameroun, CAR, Gabon and Congo — AP68

1974, Dec. 8 Photo. *Perf. 13*

C126 AP68 100fr gold & multi .60 .42

See note after Cameroun No. 595.
For surcharge see No. C155.

Marshal Bokassa AP69

Design: 100fr, Bokassa in Marshal's uniform with cape.

1975, Feb. 22 Photo. *Perf. 13*

C127 AP69 50fr tan & multi .25 .20
C128 AP69 100fr tan & multi .55 .40

Jean Bedel Bokassa, President for Life and Marshal of the Republic.

Mask, Map of Africa, Arphila Emblem — AP70

Albert Schweitzer and Dugout, Lambarene — AP71

1975, Aug. 25 Engr. *Perf. 13*

C129 AP70 100fr brt bl, red brn & red .65 .35

ARPHILA 75 International Philatelic Exhibition, Paris, June 6-16.
For surcharge see No. C156.

1975, Sept. 30 Engr. *Perf. 13*

C130 AP71 200fr blk, ultra & ol 1.40 .65

Dr. Albert Schweitzer (1875-1965), medical missionary and musician.
For surcharge see No. C158.

Pres. Bokassa's Houseboat, Bow — AP72

Design: 40fr, Pres. Bokassa's houseboat, stern.

1976, Feb. 22 Litho. *Perf. 13*

C131 AP72 30fr multi .16 .15
C132 AP72 40fr multi .22 .15

Monument to Franco-CAR Cooperation AP73

Presidents and Flags of France and CAR — AP74

1976, Mar. 5

C133 AP73 100fr multi .55 .35
C134 AP74 200fr multi 1.10 .65

Official visit of Pres. Valery Giscard d'Estaing to Central African Republic, Mar. 5-8.
For surcharge see No. C157.

Apollo Soyuz Type, 1976

Designs: 100fr, Soyuz space ship. 200fr, Apollo space ship. 300fr, Astronauts and cosmonauts in cabin. 500fr, Apollo and Soyuz after link-up.

1976, June 14 Litho. *Perf. 14x13½*

C135 A90 100fr multi .65 .25
C136 A90 200fr multi 1.40 .60
C137 A90 300fr multi 2.00 .80
Nos. C135-C137 (3) 4.05 1.65

Souvenir Sheet

C138 A90 500fr multi 3.25 1.50

For surcharges see #C161, C168, C173, C177.

French Hussar — AP75

Uniforms: 125fr, Scottish "Black Watch." 150fr, German dragoon. 200fr, British grenadier. 250fr, American ranger. 450fr, American dragoon.

1976, July 4 *Perf. 13½*

C139 AP75 100fr multi .60 .20
C140 AP75 125fr multi .80 .35
C141 AP75 150fr multi 1.00 .40
C142 AP75 200fr multi 1.25 .45
C143 AP75 250fr multi 1.50 .60
Nos. C139-C143 (5) 5.15 2.00

Souvenir Sheet

C144 AP75 450fr multi 3.00 1.25

American Bicentennial.
For surcharges see Nos. C162, C166-C167, C169, C172, C176.

Acherontia Atropos — AP76

Design: 100fr, Papilio nireus & niocha marnois.

1976, Sept. 20 Litho. *Perf. 12½*

C145 AP76 50fr multi .25 .16
C146 AP76 100fr multi .55 .35

For surcharges see Nos. C160, C163.

Olympic Winners Type, 1976

Designs: 100fr, Women's figure skating, Dorothy Hamill, vert. 200fr, Ice skating, Alexander Gorshkov and Ludmilla Pakhomova. 300fr, Men's figure skating, John Curry, vert. 500fr, Downhill skiing, Rosi Mittermaier, vert.

1976, Sept. 23 Litho. *Perf. 13½*

C147 A92 100fr multi .60 .25
C148 A92 200fr multi 1.25 .60
C149 A92 300fr multi 2.00 .90
Nos. C147-C149 (3) 3.85 1.75

Souvenir Sheet

C150 A92 500fr multi 3.25 1.50

For surcharges see #C164, C170, C174, C178.

Viking Mars Type, 1976

Designs: 100fr, Phases of Mars landing. 200fr, Viking descending on Mars, horiz. 300fr, Viking probe. 500fr, Viking flight to Mars, horiz.

1976, Dec.

C151 A93 100fr multi .60 .22
C152 A93 200fr multi 1.25 .60
C153 A93 300fr multi 2.00 .80
Nos. C151-C153 (3) 3.85 1.62

Souvenir Sheet

C154 A93 500fr multi 3.25 1.50

For surcharges and overprints see Nos. C165, C171, C175, C179, C212-C215.

Empire

Stamps of 1973-76 Overprinted with Bars and "EMPIRE CENTRAFRICAIN" in Black, Violet Blue or Gold

Printing and Perforations as Before

1977, Mar.

C155 AP68 100fr (#C126;B) .60 .45
C156 AP70 100fr (#C129;VB) .60 .45
C157 AP73 100fr (#C133;G) .60 .45
C158 AP71 200fr (#C130;B) 1.40 1.00
C159 AP67 500fr (#C125;B) 3.75 2.75
Nos. C155-C159 (5) 6.95 5.10

No bar on No. C159.

Stamps of 1976 Overprinted "EMPIRE CENTRAFRICAIN" in Black on Silver Panel

1977, Apr. 1

C160 AP76 50fr (#C145) .35 .20
C161 A90 100fr (#C135) .60 .45
C162 AP75 100fr (#C139) .55 .40
C163 AP76 100fr (#C146) .55 .40
C164 A92 100fr (#C147) .55 .40
C165 A93 100fr (#C151) .55 .50
C166 AP75 125fr (#C140) .65 .55
C167 AP75 150fr (#C141) .80 .60
C168 A90 200fr (#C136) 1.40 1.00
C169 AP75 200fr (#C142) 1.10 .80
C170 A92 200fr (#C148) 1.10 .80
C171 A93 200fr (#C152) 1.10 .80
C172 AP75 250fr (#C143) 1.40 1.00
C173 A90 300fr (#C137) 2.00 1.50
C174 A92 300fr (#C149) 1.60 1.25
C175 A93 300fr (#C153) 1.60 1.25
Nos. C160-C175 (16) 15.90 11.90

Souvenir Sheets

C176 AP75 450fr (#C144) 2.50 2.50
C177 A90 500fr (#C138) 2.75 2.75
C178 A92 500fr (#C150) 2.75 2.75
C179 A93 500fr (#C154) 2.75 2.75

Overprint on type AP75 is in upper and lower case letters.

Nobel Prize Type, 1977

Designs: 100fr, Rudyard Kipling. 200fr, Ernest Hemingway. 300fr, Luigi Pirandello. 500fr, Rabindranath Tagore.

1977, Apr. 1 Litho. *Perf. 13½*

C180 A94 100fr multi .65 .22
C181 A94 200fr multi 1.25 .60
C182 A94 300fr multi 2.00 .80
Nos. C180-C182 (3) 3.90 1.62

Souvenir Sheet

C183 A94 500fr multi 3.25 1.50

Zeppelin Type of 1977

Designs: 100fr, Germany #C42 and North Pole. 200fr, Germany #C44 and Science and Industry Building, Chicago. 300fr, Germany #C35 and Brandenburg Gate, Berlin. 500fr, US #C14 and US Capitol.

1977, Apr. 11 Litho. *Perf. 11*

C184 A95 100fr multi .60 .22
C185 A95 200fr multi 1.25 .60
C186 A95 300fr multi 2.00 .80
Nos. C184-C186 (3) 3.85 1.62

Souvenir Sheet

C187 A95 500fr multi 3.25 1.50

75th anniversary of Zeppelin.

Bokassa Type of 1977

1977, Dec. 4 Litho. *Perf. 13½*

C188 A98 200fr multi 1.10 .65
C189 A98 300fr multi 1.60 1.00
a. Souvenir sheet, 500fr 2.50 2.00

Coronation of Emperor Bokassa I, Dec. 4. No. C189a contains a horizontal stamp in similar design. A 2500fr gold embossed horizontal stamp in similar design exists.

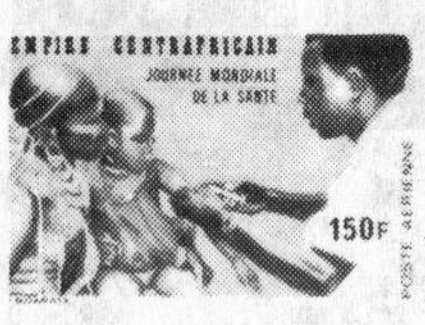

Vaccination AP77

1977 Litho. *Perf. 14x13½*

C190 AP77 150fr multi 1.00 .50

World Health Day.

Communications Type of 1978

Designs: 100fr, Balloon and spaceships docking in space. 200fr, Hydrofoil and Concorde. 500fr, Tom-tom and Zeppelin. No. C193A, Early postman and rider, UPU emblem, Concorde. No. C193B, Mail coach, dove, satellites.

1978, May 17 Litho. *Perf. 13½*

C191 A107 100fr multi .65 .35
C192 A107 200fr multi 1.40 .65

Souvenir Sheet

C193 A107 500fr multi 3.75 2.25

Cent. of progress of posts and telecommunications. No. C193 contains one 53x35mm stamp.

1978, Mar. 21 Litho. & Embossed

Size: 57x39mm

C193A A107 1500fr gold & multi

Souvenir Sheet

C193B A107 1500fr gold & multi

Nos. C193A-C193B exist imperf. No. C193A exists in a souvenir sheet of one. No. C193B contains one 57x39mm stamp.

Clement Ader and his Plane — AP78

Designs: 50fr, Wilbur and Orville Wright and plane. 60fr, John W. Alcock, Arthur W. Brown and plane. 100fr, Alan Cobham and plane 150fr, Claude Dornier and hydroplane. 500fr, Wilbur and Orville Wright and plane.

1978, Sept. 19 *Perf. 14*

C194 AP78 40fr multi .30 .15
C195 AP78 50fr multi .38 .16
C196 AP78 60fr multi .42 .20
C197 AP78 100fr multi .70 .35
C198 AP78 150fr multi 1.10 .50
Nos. C194-C198 (5) 2.90 1.36

Souvenir Sheet

C199 AP78 500fr multi 3.75 1.75

History of aviation.

Philexafrique II-Essen Issue

Common Design Types

Designs: No. C200, Crocodile and CAR #C3. No. C201, Birds and Mecklenburg-Schwerin #1.

1978, Nov. 1 Litho. *Perf. 12½*

C200 CD138 100fr multi .65 .35
C201 CD139 100fr multi .65 .35

Nos. C200-C201 printed se-tenant.

Bokassa Type of 1978

Design: 150fr, Catherine and Jean Bedel Bokassa, horiz.

1978, Dec. 4 Litho. *Perf. 13*

C202 A113 150fr multi 1.00 .50

First anniv. of coronation. A 1000fr gold embossed souvenir sheet showing Emperor Bokassa exists.

Rowland Hill Type of 1978

Designs (Rowland Hill and): 100fr, Mailman and Tuscany No. 23. 200fr, Balloon and France No. 1. 500fr, Central Africa Nos. 1-2.

1978, Dec. 27

C203 A114 100fr multi .65 .35
C204 A114 200fr multi 1.40 .65

Souvenir Sheet

C205 A114 500fr multi 3.50 1.60

Sir Rowland Hill (1795-1879), originator of penny postage. No. C205 contains one 37½x39mm stamp. 1500fr gold embossed stamp and souvenir sheet exist.

IYC Type of 1979

Designs (UNICEF, Eagle Emblems and): 100fr, Chinese girl flying kites and German Do-X flying boat, 1929. 200fr, Boys playing leapfrog, hurdler and Olympic emblem. 500fr, Child with abacus and Albert Einstein with his equation.

1979, Mar. 6 ***Perf. 13½***

C206 A115 100fr multi .65 .35
C207 A115 200fr multi 1.40 .65

Souvenir Sheet

C208 A115 500fr multi 3.50 1.60

International Year of the Child. No. C208 contains one 56x33mm stamp. 1500fr gold embossed stamp and souvenir sheet exist.

Olympic Type of 1979

Designs (Moscow '80 Emblem, various Sports and): 100fr, Hurdles and "B." 200fr, Broad jump and "A."

1979, Mar. 16 Litho. ***Perf. 13***

C209 A116 100fr multi .65 .35
C210 A116 200fr multi 1.40 .65

22nd Olympic Games, Moscow, July 19-Aug. 3, 1980. A 1500fr gold embossed souvenir sheet exists showing diver, runner and javelin.

National Husbandry Association Type

1979, Aug. Litho. ***Perf. 13***

C211 A119 60fr Horse .32 .16

Nos. C151-C154 Overprinted "ALUNISSAGE/APOLLO XI/ JUILLET 1969" and Emblem in Black or Silver

1979, Oct. Litho. ***Perf. 14x13½***

C212 A93 100fr multi .55 .25
C213 A93 200fr multi 1.10 .55
C214 A93 300fr multi 1.60 .80
Nos. C212-C214 (3) 3.25 1.60

Souvenir Sheet

C215 A93 500fr multi (S) 3.00 1.50

Apollo 11 moon landing, 10th anniversary.

Ski Jump, Lake Placid '80 Emblem — AP79

Lake Placid Emblem and: 100fr, Downhill skiing. 200fr, Hockey. 300fr, Slalom. 500fr, Bobsledding.

1979, Nov. 11 Litho. ***Perf. 13½***

C216 AP79 60fr multi .32 .16
C217 AP79 100fr multi .55 .25
C218 AP79 200fr multi 1.10 .55
C219 AP79 300fr multi 1.60 .80
Nos. C216-C219 (4) 3.57 1.76

Souvenir Sheet

C220 AP79 500fr multi 3.00 1.50

13th Winter Olympics Games, Lake Placid, NY, Feb. 12-24, 1980.

For overprints see Nos. C224-C228.

Space Type of 1980

1980, Apr. 8 Litho. ***Perf. 13½***

C221 A125 150fr Early satellites .80 .40
C222 A125 200fr Space shuttle 1.10 .55

Souvenir Sheet

C223 A125 500fr Apollo 11, Armstrong 2.75 1.40

Litho. & Embossed

1980, Apr. 8 Litho ***Perf. 13½***

Size: 51x57mm

C223A A125 1500fr Armstrong, Apollo 11

Souvenir Sheet

C223B A125 1500fr Space shuttle, horiz.

C223A-C223B exist imperf. No. C223A exists in a souvenir sheet of one. No. C223B contains one 57x51mm stamp.

Nos. C216-C220 Overprinted:

a. VAINQUEUR / INNAVER / AUTRICHE
b. VAINQUEUR / MOSER-PROELL / AUTRICHE
c. VAINQUEUR / ETATS-UNIS
d. VAINQUEUR / STENMARK / SUEDE
e. VAINQUEURS / SCHAERER-BENZ / SUISSE

1980, May 12 Litho. ***Perf. 13½***

C224 AP79 (a) 60fr multi .32 .16
C225 AP79 (b) 100fr multi .55 .25
C226 AP79 (c) 200fr multi 1.10 .55
C227 AP79 (d) 300fr multi 1.60 .80
Nos. C224-C227 (4) 3.57 1.76

Souvenir Sheet

C228 AP79 (e) 500fr multi 2.75 1.40

World Telecommunications Day — AP80

1980, June 26 Litho. ***Perf. 12½***

C229 AP80 100fr multi .55 .25
C230 AP80 150fr multi, vert. .80 .40

Olympic Type of 1980

1980, July 25 Litho. ***Perf. 13½***

C231 A126 100fr Boxing .55 .25
C232 A126 150fr Hurdles .80 .40

Souvenir Sheet

C233 A126 250fr Long jump 1.40 .65

Litho. & Embossed

C233A A126 1500fr Relay race, diff.

Souvenir Sheet

C233B A126 1500fr Basketball, vert.

22nd Summer Olympic Games, Moscow, July 19-Aug. 3. #C233 contains one 39x36mm stamp.

For overprints see Nos. C248-C250B.

Europe-Africa Type of 1980

1980, Nov. 4 Litho. ***Perf. 13½***

C234 A127 150fr Meteorology .80 .40
C235 A127 200fr Aviation 1.10 .55

Souvenir Sheet

C236 A127 500fr Concorde jet 2.75 1.40

No. C236 contains one 41½x29mm stamp.

Litho. & Embossed

Size: 42x39mm

C236A A127 1500fr Boy Scouts

Souvenir Sheet

C236B A127 1500fr Concorde

Nos. C236A-C236B exist imperf. No. C236A exists in a souvenir sheet of one. No. C236B contains one 42x39mm stamp.

Soccer Type of 1981

1981, Jan. 13 Litho. ***Perf. 13½***

C237 A130 100fr Netherlands .55 .25
C238 A130 200fr Spain 1.10 .55

Souvenir Sheet

C239 A130 500fr Argentina 2.75 1.40

Litho. & Embossed

Size: 57x39mm

C239A A130 1500fr Players, trophy

Souvenir Sheet

C239B A130 1500fr Players, trophy, diff.

Nos. C239A-C239B exist imperf. No. C239A exists in a souvenir sheet of one. No. C239B contains one 36x60mm stamp.

Jacob Wrestling with the Angel, by Rembrandt AP81

Rembrandt Paintings: 90fr, Christ during the Storm. 150fr, Jeremiah Mourning the Destruction of Jerusalem. 250fr, Tobit Accusing Anne of Theft of a Goat. 500fr, Belshazzar's Feast, horiz.

1981, Feb. 20 ***Perf. 12½***

C240 AP81 60fr multi .35 .16
C241 AP81 90fr multi .45 .22
C242 AP81 150fr multi .80 .40
C243 AP81 250fr multi 1.40 .65
Nos. C240-C243 (4) 3.00 1.43

Souvenir Sheet

C244 AP81 500fr multi 2.50 1.40

Picasso Type of 1981

Paintings: 150fr, Woman in Mirror with Self-portrait. 200fr, Woman Sleeping, The Dream. 500fr, Portrait of Maia (the Artist's Daughter). No. C247A, Two Women and Glasses, Picasso. No. C247B, Woman with Handbag, statue of standing woman, vert.

1981, June 30 Litho. ***Perf. 13½***

C245 A133 150fr multi .80 .40
C246 A133 200fr multi 1.10 .55

Souvenir Sheet

C247 A133 500fr multi 2.75 1.40

No. C247 contains one 42x46mm stamp.

Litho. & Embossed

Size: 57x39mm

C247A A133 1500fr gold & multi

Souvenir Sheet

C247B A133 1500fr gold & multi

Nos. C247A-C247B exist imperf. No. C247A exists in a souvenir sheet of one. No. C247B contains one 39x58mm stamp.

Nos. C231-C233B Overprinted with Event, Winner and Country in Gold

1981 Litho. ***Perf. 13½***

C248 A126 100fr multi .55 .25
C249 A126 150fr multi .80 .40

Souvenir Sheet

C250 A126 250fr multi 1.40 .65

Litho. & Embossed

C250A A126 1500fr on #C233A

Souvenir Sheet

C250B A126 1500fr on #C233B

Royal Wedding Type of 1981

1981, Aug. 20 Litho. ***Perf. 13½***

C251 A136 150fr Prince of Wales arms .80 .40
C252 A136 200fr Palace 1.10 .55

Souvenir Sheet

C253 A136 500fr St. Paul's Cathedral 2.75 1.40

No. C253 contains one 60x32mm stamp.

Litho. & Embossed

Size: 51x42mm

C253A A136 1500fr Diana, Charles

Souvenir Sheet

C253B A136 1500fr Charles, Diana, ship

Nos. C253A-C253B exist imperf. No. C253A exists in a souvenir sheet of one. No. C253B contains one 51x42mm stamp.

Navigator Type of 1981

1981, Sept. 4 Litho. ***Perf. 13½***

C254 A139 100fr O. Kersauson .55 .25
C255 A139 200fr Chichester 1.10 .55

Souvenir Sheet

C256 A139 500fr A. Colas 2.75 1.40

Litho. & Embossed

Size: 51x42mm

C256A A139 1500fr Riguidel

Souvenir Sheet

C256B A139 1500fr Tabarly

Nos. C256A-C256B exist imperf. No. C256A exists in a souvenir sheet of one. No. C256B contains one 51x42mm stamp.

Lizard — AP82

1981, Oct. 30 ***Perf. 12½x13***

C257 AP82 30fr shown .16 .15
C258 AP82 60fr Snake .35 .16
C259 AP82 110fr Crocodile .60 .30
Nos. C257-C259 (3) 1.11 .61

Christmas Type of 1981

1981, Dec. 24 ***Perf. 13½***

C260 A143 140fr Correggio .70 .40
C261 A143 200fr Gentileschi, 1610 1.10 .55

Souvenir Sheet

C262 A143 500fr Holy Family, by Cranach 2.75 1.40

No. C262 contains one 41x50mm stamp.

Litho. & Embossed

Size: 30x60mm

C262A A143 1500fr Hans Memling, c. 1470

Souvenir Sheet

C262B A143 1500fr Fra Angelico, 1438

Nos. C262A-C262B exist imperf. No. C262A exists in a souvenir sheet of one. No. C262B contains one 30x60mm stamp.

Animal Type of 1982

1982, Jan. 22 Litho. ***Perf. 13½***

C263 A145 300fr Mandrill 1.60 .80
C264 A145 500fr Lion 2.75 1.40

Souvenir Sheet

C265 A145 600fr Nile crocodiles 3.50 1.60

No. C265 contains one 47x38mm stamp.

Litho. & Embossed

Size: 51x57mm

C265A A145 1500fr Leopard, Rotary emblem

Souvenir Sheet

C265B A145 1500fr Emblem, eagle, horiz.

Nos. C265A-C265B exist imperf. No. C265A exists in a souvenir sheet of one. No. C265B contains one 57x51mm stamp.

Transportation Type of 1982 and

AP82a

Designs: No. C267A, Space shuttle launch, horiz. No. C268A, Shuttle, space telescope.

1982, Feb. 27 Litho. ***Perf. 13½***

C266 A147 300fr Savannah cargo ship 1.60 .80
C267 A147 500fr Columbia space shuttle 2.50 1.40

Souvenir Sheet

C268 A147 600fr Spirit of Locomotion emblem 3.50 1.60

Litho. & Embossed

C268A AP82a 1500fr gold & multi

Souvenir Sheet

C268B AP82a 1500fr gold & multi

No. C268 contains one 39x43mm stamp. No. C268B contains one 51x42mm stamp.

Olympic Type of 1982

1982, July 24	**Litho.**	***Perf. 13½***		
C269 A149	300fr Diving		1.60	.80
C270 A149	500fr Equestrian		2.50	1.40

Souvenir Sheet

C271 A149 600fr Basketball 3.50 1.60

No. C271 contains one 38x56mm stamp.

Diana Type of 1982

1982, July 20	**Litho.**	***Perf. 13½***		
C272 A150	300fr multi		1.60	.80
C273 A150	500fr multi		2.50	1.40

Souvenir Sheet

C274 A150 600fr multi 3.50 1.60

No. C274 contains one 56x32mm stamp.

Christmas 1982 — AP83

Raphael Paintings.

1982, Dec.	***Perf. 13***		
C275 AP83	150fr Beautiful Gardener	.80	.40
C276 AP83	500fr Holy Family	2.50	1.40

Space Type of 1982

Designs: Various satellites and space scenes. No. C279A, European communications satellite, controller. No. C279B, Viking on Mars, vert.

1982, Aug. 15	**Litho.**	***Perf. 13½***		
C277 A151	300fr multi		1.60	.80
C278 A151	500fr multi		2.50	1.40

Souvenir Sheet

C279 A151 600fr multi 3.50 1.60

Litho. & Embossed

Size: 60x36mm

C279A A151 1500fr gold & multi

Souvenir Sheet

C279B A151 1500fr gold & multi

Nos. C279A-C279B exist imperf. No. C279A exists in a souvenir sheet of one. No. C279B contains one 36x60mm stamp.

Birth of Prince William of Wales, June 21, 1982 — AP84

Designs: No. C281, Diana, William, Charles. No. 281B, Diana, William, vert.

1983, Jan. 22

C280 AP84 500fr Diana, William 2.50 1.40

Souvenir Sheet

C281 AP84 600fr Family 3.50 1.60

Litho. & Embossed

C281A AP84 1500fr gold & multi

Souvenir Sheet

C281B AP84 1500fr gold & multi

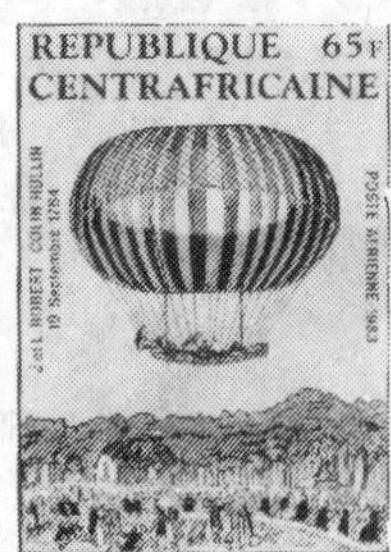

Manned Flight Bicentenary AP85

1983, Apr.

C282 AP85	65fr Robert's & Hullin's balloon	.35	.16
C283 AP85	130fr John Wise's, 1859	.70	.35
C284 AP85	350fr Mail balloon, 1870	1.75	.90
C285 AP85	400fr Dirigible Underberg	2.25	1.10
	Nos. C282-C285 (4)	5.05	2.51

Souvenir Sheet

C286 AP85 500fr Montgolfiere, 1783 2.50 1.40

Pre-Olympics — AP86

Various equestrian events.

1983, July	**Litho.**	***Perf. 13***	
C287 AP86	100fr multi	.50	.20
C288 AP86	200fr multi	1.00	.45
C289 AP86	300fr multi	1.40	.55
C290 AP86	400fr multi	1.75	.90
	Nos. C287-C290 (4)	4.65	2.10

Souvenir Sheet

C291 AP86 500fr multi 2.25 1.10

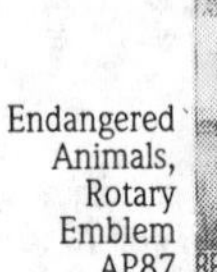

Endangered Animals, Rotary Emblem AP87

1983, Nov. 14	**Litho.**	***Perf. 13½***	
C291A AP87	400fr Black rhinoceros, parrot, zebra, scouts	2.00	1.00
C292 AP87	500fr shown	1.60	.80

Souvenir Sheet

C293 AP87 600fr Leopard 2.00 1.00

15th World Scout Jamboree, Alberta (400fr). No. C293 contains one 47x32mm stamp.

Christmas 1983 — AP88

Paintings: 130fr, Annunciation, by da Vinci. 205fr, Virgin of the Rocks, by da Vinci. 350fr, Adoration of the Shepherds, by Rubens. 500fr, Virgin and Child with Donor, by Rubens.

1984, Jan. 3	**Litho.**	***Perf. 13***	
C294 AP88	130fr multi	.45	.22
C295 AP88	205fr multi	.70	.35
C296 AP88	350fr multi	1.10	.55
C297 AP88	500fr multi	1.60	.80
	Nos. C294-C297 (4)	3.85	1.92

1984 Summer Olympics — AP89

Various gymnastic and rhythmic gymnastic events. 65fr, 100fr, 205fr, 350fr vert.

1984, Mar. 13	**Litho.**	***Perf. 13***	
C298 AP89	65fr multi	.22	.15
C299 AP89	100fr multi	.35	.16
C300 AP89	130fr multi	.42	.22
C301 AP89	205fr multi	.70	.35
C302 AP89	350fr multi	1.10	.60
	Nos. C298-C302 (5)	2.79	1.48

Souvenir Sheet

Perf. 13½x13

C302A AP89 500fr Rhythmic formation 1.60 .80

For overprint see No. 705.

Summer Olympics Winners AP90

1985, Jan. 7	**Litho.**	***Perf. 14***	
C303 AP90	60fr 400 meter relay	.16	.15
C304 AP90	140fr 400 meter hurdles	.40	.20
C305 AP90	300fr 5000 meter race	.90	.45
C306 AP90	440fr Decathlon	1.20	.60
	Nos. C303-C306 (4)	2.66	1.40

Souvenir Sheet

C307 AP90 500fr 800 meter race, horiz. 1.40 .65

Christmas 1984 — AP91

Paintings by Titian: 130fr, Virgin and Infant Jesus. 350fr, Virgin with Rabbit. 400fr, Virgin and Child.

1985, Jan. 17	**Litho.**	***Perf. 13***	
C308 AP91	130fr multi	.38	.20
C309 AP91	350fr multi	.90	.50
C310 AP91	400fr multi	1.10	.60
	Nos. C308-C310 (3)	2.38	1.30

Audubon Bicentenary — AP92

1985, Jan. 25	**Litho.**	***Perf. 13***	
C311 AP92	60fr Otus asio	.16	.15
C312 AP92	110fr Coccizus minor, vert.	.32	.16
C313 AP92	200fr Zenaidura macroura, vert.	.60	.28
C314 AP92	500fr Aix sponsa	1.40	.70
	Nos. C311-C314 (4)	2.48	1.29

Christmas 1985 — AP93

Religious paintings: 100fr, Virgin with Angels, by the Master of Burgo de Osma. 200fr, Nativity, by Louis Le Nain (1593-1648). 400fr, Virgin and Child with Dove, by Piero de Cosimo (1462-1521).

1985, Dec. 24	**Litho.**	***Perf. 13***	
C315 AP93	100fr multi	.35	.20
C316 AP93	200fr multi	.70	.38
C317 AP93	400fr multi	1.50	.70
	Nos. C315-C317 (3)	2.55	1.28

Halley's Comet — AP94

1986, Mar. 8			
C318 AP94	110fr Edmond Halley	.40	.20
C319 AP94	130fr Giotto probe	.45	.22
C320 AP94	200fr Comet, planet	.70	.38
C321 AP94	300fr Vega probe	1.10	.55
C322 AP94	400fr Space shuttle	1.50	.70
	Nos. C318-C322 (5)	4.15	2.05

Christmas AP95

Painting details: 250fr, Nativity, by Giotto. 440fr, Adoration of the Magi, by Botticelli, vert. 500fr, Nativity, by Giotto, diff.

1986, Dec. 24	**Litho.**	***Perf. 13½***	
C323 AP95	250fr multi	.90	.45
C324 AP95	440fr multi	1.60	.80
C325 AP95	500fr multi	1.75	.90
	Nos. C323-C325 (3)	4.25	2.15

Tennis at the 1988 Olympics — AP96

Various plays.

1986, Dec. 31	***Perf. 12½***		
C326 AP96	150fr multi	.55	.25
C327 AP96	250fr multi, vert.	.90	.45
C328 AP96	440fr multi, vert.	1.60	.80
C329 AP96	600fr multi	2.25	1.10
	Nos. C326-C329 (4)	5.30	2.60

1988 Summer Olympics, Seoul — AP97

1987, June 15 Litho. *Perf. 13*

C330 AP97 100fr Triple jump, vert. .55 .28
C331 AP97 200fr High jump 1.10 .55
C332 AP97 300fr Long jump 1.65 .82
C333 AP97 400fr Pole vault, vert. 2.25 1.10
Nos. C330-C333 (4) 5.55 2.75

Souvenir Sheet

C334 AP97 500fr High jump, diff. 2.75 1.40

1988 Summer Olympics, Seoul — AP98

Stamps on stamps and gymnasts: 90fr, No. C94, balance beam, vert. 200fr, No. C21, balance beam, diff. 300fr, No. C22, pommel horse. 400fr, No. C23, parallel bars. 500fr, No. C93, rings.

1988, July 26 Litho. *Perf. 13*

C335 AP98 90fr multi .58 .30
C336 AP98 200fr multi 1.30 .65
C337 AP98 300fr multi 1.90 .95
C338 AP98 400fr multi 2.60 1.30
Nos. C335-C338 (4) 6.38 3.20

Souvenir Sheet

C339 AP98 500fr multi 3.25 1.60

1st Moon Landing, 20th Anniv. AP99

1989, Aug. 4 Litho. *Perf. 13*

C340 AP99 40fr Apollo 11 .25 .15
C341 AP99 80fr Apollo 15 .52 .25
C342 AP99 130fr Apollo 16 .85 .42
C343 AP99 1000fr Apollo 17 6.40 3.20
Nos. C340-C343 (4) 8.02 4.02

World Cup Soccer Championships, Italy — AP100

1990, July 7 Litho. *Perf. 13*

C344 AP100 5fr multicolored .15 .15
C345 AP100 30fr multi, diff. .22 .15
C346 AP100 500fr multi, diff. 3.75 1.90
C347 AP100 1000fr multi, diff. 7.50 3.75
Nos. C344-C347 (4) 11.62 5.95

Charles de Gaulle (1890-1979) — AP101

1990, July 27 *Perf. 13½*

C348 AP101 500fr multicolored 3.50 1.75

No. C348 exists in a souvenir sheet of 1.

Don Mattingly, Baseball Player — AP102

Saturn V Rocket, Apollo 11 Astronauts AP103

Charles de Gaulle, Birth Cent. AP104

Design: No. C352, De Gaulle and Cross of Lorraine.

1990, July 27 Litho. *Perf. 13½*

C349 AP102 300fr multicolored 2.10 1.05

Souvenir Sheet

C350 AP103 1000fr multicolored 7.00 3.50

Litho. & Embossed

C351 AP104 1500fr gold & multi

Souvenir Sheet

C352 AP104 1500fr gold & multi

No. C351 exists in souvenir sheet of 1. For overprints see Nos. C355-C356.

Visit of Pope John Paul II to Africa AP105

Pope John Paul II and: No. C353, Mother Theresa, portrait. No. C354, Papal arms, globe.

1993 Litho. & Embossed *Perf. 13½*

C353 AP105 1500fr gold & multi

Souvenir Sheet

C354 AP105 1500fr gold & multi

No. C351 Ovptd. "6 JUIN / 1944"
No. C352 Ovptd. in Silver in Sheet Margin

1994 Litho. & Embossed *Perf. 13½*

C355 AP104 1500fr gold & multi

Souvenir Sheet

C356 AP104 1500fr gold & multi

Overprint on No. C356 contains map, soldiers and "50 eme ANNIVERSAIRE DU /DEBARQUEMENT." No. C355 exists in souvenir sheet of 1.

Souvenir Sheets

Japanese Exploration of Antarctica — AP106

1994

C357 AP106 1200fr Nobu Shirase 4.75 2.25
C358 AP106 1200fr Schooner Kainman Maru, horiz. 4.75 2.25

D-Day, 50th Anniv. (in 1994) — AP107

Designs: a, Gliders over Pegasus Bridge, Sword beach. b, Fighter planes over Juno, Gold and Omaha beaches. c, Planes over Utah beach, St. Mere Eglise.

1995 Litho. & Embossed *Perf. 13½*

C359 AP107 1000fr Strip of 3, #a.-c. 11.00 11.00

No. C359b is 60x45mm.

AIR POST SEMI-POSTAL STAMPS

Central African Republic

Isis of Kalabsha — SPAP1

Unwmk.

1964, Mar. 7 Engr. *Perf. 13*

CB1 SPAP1 25fr + 10fr multi .65 .65
CB2 SPAP1 50fr + 10fr multi 1.00 1.00
CB3 SPAP1 100fr + 10fr multi 1.60 1.60
Nos. CB1-CB3 (3) 3.25 3.25

UNESCO world campaign to save historic monuments in Nubia.

African Infants and Globe — SPAP2

1971, Dec. 11 Litho. *Perf. 13x13½*

CB4 SPAP2 140fr + 50fr multi 1.60 1.00

25th anniv. of UNICEF, and Children's Day.

POSTAGE DUE STAMPS

Central African Republic

Sternotomis Virescens — D1

Beetles: No. J2, Sternotomis gama. No. J3, Augosoma centaurus. No. J4, Phosphorus virescens and ceroplesis carabarica. No. J5, Cetoine scaraboidae. No. J6, Ceroplesis S.P. No. J7, Macrorhina S.P. No. J8, Cetoine scaraboidae. No. J9, Phryneta leprosa. No. J10, Taurina longiceps. No. J11, Monohamus griseoplagiatus. No. J12, Jambonus trifasciatus.

Unwmk.

1962, Oct. 15 Engr. *Perf. 11*

J1 D1 50c grn & dp org .15 .15
J2 D1 50c grn & dp org .15 .15
J3 D1 1fr blk, brn & lt grn .15 .15
J4 D1 1fr blk, brn & lt grn .15 .15
J5 D1 2fr blk, org & yel grn .15 .15
J6 D1 2fr blk & red org .15 .15
J7 D1 5fr brn, org & grn .15 .15
J8 D1 5fr brn, org, grn & red .15 .15
J9 D1 10fr blk, grn & brn .30 .30
J10 D1 10fr blk, brn & grn .30 .30
J11 D1 25fr blk, bl grn & brn .45 .45
J12 D1 25fr blk, brn & bl grn .45 .45
Set value 2.10 2.10

Each two stamps of the same denomination are printed together in the sheet, se-tenant at the base.

Giant Anteater — D2

1985, Jan. 25 Litho. *Perf. 12½*

J13 D2 5fr multi .15 .15
J14 D2 20fr multi .15 .15
J15 D2 30fr multi .15 .15
Set value .22 .15

MILITARY STAMPS

Central African Republic

No. 1 Overprinted **FM**

1962, Jan. 1 Unwmk. Engr. *Perf. 13*

M1 A1 bl, car, grn & yel 8.25 8.25

=

No. 1 Overprinted **FM**

1963

M2 A1 bl, car, grn & yel 9.00 9.00

OFFICIAL STAMPS

Central African Republic

Coat of Arms — O1

Imprint: "d'après G. RICHER SO.GE.IM."

Perf. 13x12½

1965-69 Litho. Unwmk.

Arms in Original Colors

No.	Type	Description	Unused	Used
O1	O1	1fr blk & brn org	.15	.15
O2	O1	2fr blk & violet	.15	.15
O3	O1	5fr blk & gray	.15	.15
O4	O1	10fr blk & green	.18	.15
O5	O1	20fr blk & red brn	.30	.22
O6	O1	30fr blk & emer ('69)	.55	.40
O7	O1	50fr blk & dk bl	.65	.55
O8	O1	100fr blk & bister	1.40	.80
O9	O1	130fr blk & ver ('69)	2.00	1.60
O10	O1	200fr blk & claret	3.00	2.00
		Nos. O1-O10 (10)	8.53	6.17

Redrawn

Imprint: "d'après G. RICHER DELRIEU"

1971 Photo. *Perf. 12x12½*

Arms in Original Colors

No.	Type	Description	Unused	Used
O11	O1	5fr blk & gray	.15	.15
O12	O1	30fr blk & emer	.30	.18
O13	O1	40fr blk & dp claret	.40	.22
O14	O1	100fr blk & bister	.90	.45
O15	O1	140fr blk & lt bl	1.60	.65
O16	O1	200fr blk & claret	2.25	1.10
		Nos. O11-O16 (6)	5.60	2.75

Empire

Nos. O11, O13-O16 Overprinted with Bar and "EMPIRE CENTRAFRICAIN"

1977 Litho. *Perf. 12x12½*

No.	Type	Description	Unused	Used
O17	O1	5fr multi	.15	.15
O18	O1	40fr multi	.22	.18
O19	O1	100fr multi	.55	.38
O20	O1	140fr multi	.80	.60
O21	O1	200fr multi	1.25	.90
		Nos. O17-O21 (5)	2.97	2.21

Type of 1965 Inscribed: "EMPIRE CENTRAFRICAIN"

1978, July Litho. *Perf. 12½*

No.	Type	Description	Unused	Used
O22	O1	1fr multi	.15	.15
O23	O1	2fr multi	.15	.15
O24	O1	5fr multi	.15	.15
O25	O1	10fr multi	.15	.15
O26	O1	15fr multi	.15	.15
O27	O1	20fr multi	.15	.15
O28	O1	30fr multi	.20	.20
O29	O1	40fr multi	.25	.25
O30	O1	50fr multi	.35	.35
O31	O1	60fr multi	.40	.40
O32	O1	100fr multi	.65	.65
O33	O1	130fr multi	.90	.90
O34	O1	140fr multi	.90	.90
O35	O1	200fr multi	1.40	1.40
		Nos. O22-O35 (14)	5.95	5.95

CENTRAL LITHUANIA

'sen–trəl ˌli–thə–'wā–nē–ə

LOCATION — North of Poland and east of Lithuania

CAPITAL — Vilnius

At one time Central Lithuania was a grand duchy of Lithuania but at the end of the 18th Century it fell under Russian rule. After World War I, Lithuania regained her sovereignty but certain areas were occupied by Poland. During the Russo-Polish war this territory was seized by Lithuania whose claim was promptly recognized by the Soviet Government. Under the leadership of the Polish General Zeligowski the territory was recaptured and it was during this occupation the stamps of Central Lithuania came into being. Subsequently the territory became a part of Poland.

100 Fennigi = 1 Markka

Coat of Arms — A1

Perf. 11½, Imperf.

1920-21 Typo. Unwmk.

No.	Type	Description	Unused	Used
1	A1	25f red	.20	.50
2	A1	25f dark grn ('21)	.20	.50
3	A1	1m blue	.20	.50
4	A1	1m dark brn ('21)	.20	.50
5	A1	2m violet	.25	.50
6	A1	2m orange ('21)	.25	.50
		Nos. 1-6 (6)	1.30	3.00

For surcharges see Nos. B1-B5.

Lithuanian Stamps of 1919 Surcharged in Blue or Black

Perf. 11½x12, 12½x11½, 14

1920, Nov. 23 Wmk. 145

No.	Type	Description	Unused	Used
13	A5	2m on 15sk lil	5.50	5.50
a.		Inverted surcharge	125.00	
14	A5	4m on 10sk red	5.50	5.50
a.		Inverted surcharge	125.00	
15	A5	4m on 20sk dl bl (Bk)	5.50	5.50
a.		Inverted surcharge	125.00	
16	A5	4m on 30sk buff	5.50	5.50
a.		Inverted surcharge	125.00	
17	A6	6m on 50sk lt grn	5.50	5.50
a.		4m on 50sk (error)	125.00	
b.		10m on 50sk (error)	125.00	
18	A6	6m on 60sk vio & red	5.50	5.50
a.		4m on 60sk (error)	125.00	
b.		10m on 60sk (error)	125.00	
19	A6	6m on 75sk bis & red	5.50	5.50
a.		4m on 75sk (error)	125.00	
b.		10m on 75sk (error)	125.00	
20	A8	10m on 1auk gray & red	8.25	8.25
a.		Inverted surcharge	190.00	
21	A8	10m on 3auk lt brn & red	275.00	300.00
22	A8	10m on 5auk bl grn & red	275.00	300.00
		Nos. 13-22 (10)	596.75	646.75

Reprints of Nos. 17a, 17b, 18a, 18b, 19a, 19b. Value, each $37.50.

Counterfeits of Nos. 21-22 exist.

Lithuanian Girl — A2

Warrior — A3

Holy Gate of Vilnius — A4

Tower and Cathedral, Vilnius — A5

Rector's Insignia — A6

Gen. Lucien Zeligowski — A7

Perf. 11½, Imperf.

1920 Litho. Unwmk.

No.	Type	Description	Unused	Used
23	A2	25f gray	.15	.30
24	A3	1m orange	.15	.30
25	A4	2m claret	.30	.70
26	A5	4m gray grn & buff	.40	.70
27	A6	6m rose & gray	.80	.85
28	A7	10m brown & yellow	1.40	2.00
		Nos. 23-28 (6)	3.20	4.85

For surcharges see Nos. B13-B14, B17-B19.

St. Anne's Church, Vilnius — A8

St. Stanislas Cathedral, Vilnius — A9

White Eagle, White Knight Vytis — A10

Queen Hedwig and King Ladislas II Jagello — A11

Coat of Arms of Vilnius A12

Poczobut Astronomical Observatory A13

Union of Lithuania and Poland — A14

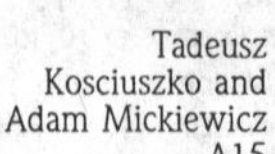

Tadeusz Kosciuszko and Adam Mickiewicz A15

1921 *Perf. 13½, 14, Imperf.*

No.	Type	Description	Unused	Used
35	A8	1m dk gray & yel	.30	.45
36	A9	2m rose & green	.30	.45
37	A10	3m dark green	.30	.45
38	A11	4m brown & buff	.30	.45
39	A12	5m red brown	.30	.45
40	A13	6m slate & buff	.30	.60
41	A14	10m red vio & buff	.75	1.00
42	A15	20m blk brn & buff	.90	1.00
		Nos. 35-42 (8)	3.45	4.85

Peasant Girl Sowing — A16

White Eagle and Vytis — A17

Great Theater at Vilnius A18

Allegory: Peace and Industry A19

Gen. Zeligowski Entering Vilnius A20

Gen. Zeligowski A21

1921-22 *Perf. 11½, Imperf.*

No.	Type	Description	Unused	Used
53	A16	10m brown ('22)	2.50	2.75
54	A17	25m red & yel ('22)	2.50	2.75
55	A18	50m dk blue ('22)	2.75	2.75
56	A19	75m violet ('22)	4.00	4.00
57	A20	100m bl & bister	2.75	3.75
58	A21	150m ol grn & brn	3.00	4.00
		Nos. 53-58 (6)	17.50	20.00

Opening of the Natl. Parliament, Nos. 53-56; anniv. of the entry of General Zeligowski into Vilnius, Nos. 57-58.

SEMI-POSTAL STAMPS

Nos. 1-6 Surcharged in Black or Red

NA
ŚLĄSK
2 M.

1921 Unwmk. *Perf. 11½, Imperf.*

No.	Type	Description	Unused	Used
B1	A1	25f + 2m red (Bk)	.70	1.10
B2	A1	25f + 2m dk green	.70	1.10
B3	A1	1m + 2m blue	.90	1.10
B4	A1	1m + 2m dk brown	.90	1.10
B5	A1	2m + 2m violet	.90	1.10
B6	A1	2m + 2m orange	.90	1.10
		Nos. B1-B6 (6)	5.00	6.60

The surcharge means "For Silesia 2 marks." The stamps were intended to provide a fund to assist the plebiscite in Upper Silesia.

Nos. 25, 26 Surcharged:

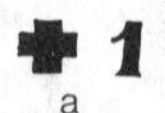

a

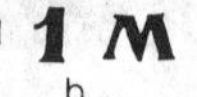

b

Perf. 11½, Imperf.

No.	Type	Description	Unused	Used
B13	A4 (a)	2m + 1(m) claret	1.65	1.90
B14	A5 (b)	4m + 1m gray green & buff	1.65	1.90

Nos. 25-26, 28 with inset

Perf. 11½, Imperf.

No.	Type	Description	Unused	Used
B17	A4	2m + 1m claret	.90	.90
B18	A5	4m + 1m gray green & buff	.90	.90
B19	A7	10m + 2m brn & yel	.90	.90
		Nos. B13-B19 (5)	6.00	6.50

POSTAGE DUE STAMPS

University, Vilnius — D1

Castle Hill, Vilnius — D2

Castle Ruins, Troki — D3

Holy Gate, Vilnius — D4

St. Stanislas Cathedral — D5

St. Anne's Church, Vilnius — D6

1920-21 Unwmk. *Perf. 11½, Imperf.*

J1 D1 50f red violet .25 *.50*
J2 D2 1m green .25 *.50*
J3 D3 2m red violet .25 *.50*
J4 D4 3m red violet .50 *.75*
J5 D5 5m red violet .75 *1.00*
J6 D6 20m scarlet 2.00 *2.25*
Nos. J1-J6 (6) 4.00 *5.50*

CHAD

'chad

(Tchad)

LOCATION — Central Africa, south of Libya
GOVT. — Republic
AREA — 495,572 sq. mi.
POP. — 5,122,000 (est. 1984)
CAPITAL — N'djamena

A former dependency of Ubangi-Shari, Chad became a separate French colony in 1920. In 1934, the colonies of Chad, Gabon, Middle Congo and Ubangi-Shari were grouped in a single administrative unit known as French Equatorial Africa, with the capital at Brazzaville. The Republic of Chad was proclaimed November 28, 1958.

100 Centimes = 1 Franc

Catalogue values for unused stamps in this country are for Never Hinged items, beginning with Scott 64 in the regular postage section, Scott B1 in the semi-postal section, Scott C1 in the air post section, Scott CB1 in the air post semi-postal section, Scott J23 in the postage due section, Scott M1 in the military stamp section, and Scott O1 in the officials section.

See French Equatorial Africa No. 190 for stamp inscribed "Tchad."

Types of Middle Congo, 1907-17, Overprinted **TCHAD**

Perf. 14x13½, 13½x14

1922 Unwmk.

1 A1 1c red & violet .15 .15
a. Overprint omitted 75.00
2 A1 2c ol brn & salmon .25 .25
a. Overprint omitted 125.00
3 A1 4c ind & vio .30 .30
4 A1 5c choc & grn .40 .40
5 A1 10c dp grn & gray grn .65 .65
6 A1 15c vio & red .90 .90
7 A1 20c grn & vio 2.25 2.25
8 A2 25c ol brn & brn 4.00 4.00
9 A2 30c rose & pale rose .50 .50
10 A2 35c dl bl & dl rose 1.00 1.00
11 A2 40c choc & grn 1.00 1.00
12 A2 45c vio & grn 1.00 1.00
13 A2 50c dk bl & pale bl 1.10 1.10
14 A2 60c on 75c vio, *pnksh* 1.75 1.75
a. "TCHAD" omitted 125.00
b. "60" omitted 125.00
15 A1 75c red & violet 1.00 1.00
16 A3 1fr indigo & salmon 4.50 4.50
17 A3 2fr indigo & violet 7.25 7.25
18 A3 5fr ind & olive brn 6.00 6.00
Nos. 1-18 (18) 34.00 34.00

Stamps of 1922 Overprinted in Various Colors:

AFRIQUE EQUATORIALE FRANÇAISE — Nos. 19-28

AFRIQUE EQUATORIALE FRANÇAISE — Nos. 29-50

1924-33

19 A1 1c red & vio .15 .15
a. "TCHAD" omitted 75.00
b. Double overprint 65.00
20 A1 2c ol brn & sal .15 .15
a. "TCHAD" omitted 75.00
b. Double overprint 80.00
21 A1 4c ind & vio .15 .15
a. "TCHAD" omitted 400.00
22 A1 5c choc & grn (Bl) .45 .45
a. "TCHAD" omitted 75.00
23 A1 5c choc & grn .25 .25
a. "TCHAD" omitted 90.00
24 A1 10c dp grn & gray grn (Bl) .25 .25
25 A1 10c dp grn & gray grn .25 .25
26 A1 10c red org & blk ('25) .20 .20
27 A1 15c vio & red .25 .25
28 A1 20c grn & vio .25 .25
29 A2 25c ol brn & brn .25 .25
30 A2 30c rose & pale rose .15 .15
31 A2 30c gray & bl (R) ('25) .15 .15
32 A2 30c dk grn & grn ('27) .45 .45
a. "Afrique Equatoriale Francaise" omitted 110.00
33 A2 35c ind & dl rose .15 .15
34 A2 40c choc & grn .45 .45
a. Dbl. overprint (R + Bk) 110.00
35 A2 45c vio & grn .35 .35
a. Dbl. overprint (R + Bk) 110.00
36 A2 50c dk bl & pale bl .35 .35
a. Inverted overprint 60.00
37 A2 50c grn & vio ('25) .45 .45
38 A2 65c org brn & bl ('28) 1.00 1.00
39 A2 75c red & vio .30 .30
40 A2 75c dp bl & lt bl (R) ('25) .20 .20
a. "TCHAD" omitted 75.00
41 A2 75c rose & dk brn ('28) 1.00 1.00
42 A2 90c brn red & pink ('30) 3.00 3.00
43 A3 1fr ind & salmon .65 .65
44 A3 1.10fr dl grn & bl ('28) 1.00 1.00
45 A3 1.25fr org brn & lt bl ('33) 3.00 3.00
46 A3 1.50fr ultra & bl ('30) 3.00 3.00
47 A3 1.75fr ol brn & vio ('33) 22.50 22.50
48 A3 2fr ind & vio 1.10 1.10
49 A3 3fr red vio ('30) 4.25 4.25
50 A3 5fr ind & ol brn .90 .90
Nos. 19-50 (32) 47.00 47.00

Types of 1922 Overprinted like Nos. 29-50 and Surcharged with New Values

1924-27

51 A2 60c on 75c dk vio, *pnksh* .25 .25
a. "60" omitted 57.50
52 A3 65c on 1fr brn & ol grn ('25) .70 .70
53 A3 85c on 1fr brn & ol grn ('25) .70 .70
54 A2 90c on 75c brn red & rose red ('27) .70 .70
55 A3 1.25fr on 1fr dk bl & ultra (R) ('26) .20 .20
a. "Afrique Equatoriale Francaise" omitted 75.00
56 A3 1.50fr on 1fr ultra & bl ('27) .70 .70
57 A3 3fr on 5fr org brn & dl red ('27) 1.75 1.75
58 A3 10fr on 5fr ol grn & cer ('27) 4.50 4.50
59 A3 20fr on 5fr vio & ver ('27) 7.00 7.00
Nos. 51-59 (9) 16.50 16.50

Colonial Exposition Issue

Common Design Types

1931 Engr. *Perf. 12½*

Name of Country in Black

60 CD70 40c deep green 1.75 1.75
61 CD71 50c violet 1.75 1.75
62 CD72 90c red orange 1.75 1.75
63 CD73 1.50fr dull blue 1.75 1.75
Nos. 60-63 (4) 7.00 7.00

Catalogue values for unused stamps in this section, from this point to the end of the section, are for Never Hinged items.

Republic

"Birth of the Republic" A1

"Solidarity of the Community" A2

1959 Unwmk. Engr. *Perf. 13*

64 A1 15fr ultra, grn & maroon .15 .15
65 A2 25fr dk grn & dp claret .25 .15
Set value .15

1st anniv. of the proclamation of the Republic.

Common Design Types pictured in section at front of book.

Imperforates

Most Chad stamps from 1959 onward exist imperforate in issued and trial colors, and also in small presentation sheets in issued colors.

C.C.T.A. Issue

Common Design Type

1960

66 CD106 50fr rose lil & dk pur .55 .50

Flag and Map of Chad and UN Emblem — A3

Unwmk.

1961, Jan. 11 Engr. *Perf. 13*

Flag in blue, yellow and carmine

67 A3 15fr brn & dk bl .20 .15
68 A3 25fr org brn & dk bl .25 .15
69 A3 85fr slate grn & dk bl .80 .45
Nos. 67-69 (3) 1.25 .75

Admission of Chad to United Nations.

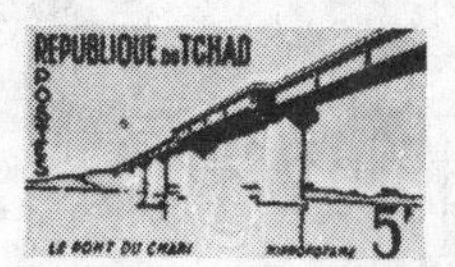

Chari Bridge and Hippopotamus — A4

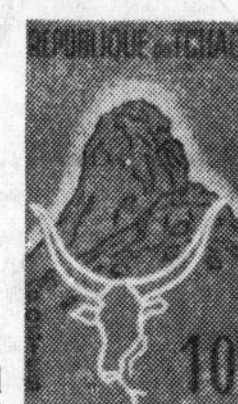

Abtouyoua Mountain and Ox — A5

Designs: 50c, Biltine and dorcas gazelle. 1fr, Logone and elephant. 2fr, Batha and lion. 3fr, Salamat and buffalo. 4fr, Ouaddai and Kudu. 15fr, Bessada and giant eland. 20fr, Tibesti mountains and mouflon. 25fr, Rocherg and antelope. 30fr, Kanem and cheetah. 60fr, Borkou and oryx. 85fr, Gorge of Archet and addax.

Perf. 13½x14, 14x13½

1961-62 Typo.

70 A5 50c yel grn & dk grn ('62) .15 .15
71 A5 1fr bl grn & dk bl grn ('62) .15 .15
72 A5 2fr dk red brn & blk ('62) .15 .15
73 A5 3fr ocher & dl grn ('62) .15 .15
74 A5 4fr dk crim & blk ('62) .15 .15
75 A4 5fr yellow & blk .15 .15
76 A5 10fr pink & blk .15 .15
77 A5 15fr lilac & blk ('62) .16 .15
78 A5 20fr red & blk .20 .15
79 A5 25fr blue & blk ('62) .25 .15
80 A5 30fr ultra & blk ('62) .35 .15
81 A5 60fr yel & ol grn ('62) .60 .20
82 A5 85fr org & blk .80 .35
Set value 2.75 1.30

First anniversary of Independence.
For overprint see No. M1.

Abidjan Games Issue

Common Design Type

1962, July 21 Photo. *Perf. 12½x12*

83 CD109 20fr Relay race .20 .15
84 CD109 50fr High jump .40 .30

See No. C8.

African-Malgache Union Issue

Common Design Type

1962, Sept. 8 Unwmk.

85 CD110 30fr dk bl, bluish grn, red & gold .35 .30

Pres. Ngarta Tombalbaye — A7

1963, Apr. 22 *Perf. 12x12½*

86 A7 20fr multi .20 .15
87 A7 85fr multi .80 .30

Space Communciations Issue

Waves Around Globe — A8

Design: 100fr, Orbit patterns around globe.

Perf. 12½

1963, Sept. 19 Unwmk. Photo.

88 A8 25fr grn & pur .25 .22
89 A8 100fr pink & ultra 1.00 .70

Ancestral Mask — A9

Excavated Sao Art: 5fr, Clay weight. 25fr, Ancestral clay statuette. 60fr, Gazelle, bronze. 80fr, Bronze pectoral.

1963, Dec. 2 Engr. *Perf. 13*

90 A9 5fr brt grn & red brn .15 .15
91 A9 15fr gray, dl cl & red .16 .15
92 A9 25fr dk bl & org brn .25 .16
93 A9 60fr org brn & slate grn .60 .25
94 A9 80fr org red & olive .80 .25
Nos. 90-94 (5) 1.96
Set value .80

UNESCO Emblem, Scales and Tree — A10

1963, Dec. 10

95 A10 25fr green & maroon .25 .20

15th anniv. of the Universal Declaration of Human Rights.

Potter — A11

Perf. 12½

1964, Feb. 5 Unwmk. Engr.

96 A11 10fr shown .15 .15
97 A11 30fr Boatmaker .30 .15
98 A11 50fr Weaver .50 .20
99 A11 85fr Smiths .55 .35
Nos. 96-99 (4) 1.50 .85

Barograph and WMO Emblem A12

1964, Mar. 23 *Perf. 13*

100	A12	50fr red lil, pur & ultra	.55	.30

Fourth World Meteorological Day.

Cotton — A13

Design: 25fr, Royal poinciana.

1964, Apr. 6 Photo. *Perf. 12½x13*

101	A13	20fr multi	.25	.15
102	A13	25fr multi	.25	.15

Co-operation Issue

Common Design Type

1964, Nov. 7 Engr. *Perf. 13*

103	CD119	25fr ver, dk bl & dk brn	.25	.20

National Guard and Map of Chad — A14

Design: 25fr, Infantry, flag and map, vert.

Perf. 12½x13, 13x12½

1964, Dec. 11 Photo.

104	A14	20fr multi	.22	.15
105	A14	25fr lt bl & multi	.25	.15

Issued to honor the army of Chad.

Aoudad or Barbary Sheep — A15

Animals: 10fr, Addax. 20fr, Oryx. 25fr, Derby's eland, vert. 30fr, Giraffe, buffalo and lion, Zakouma Park, vert. 85fr, Great kudu at water hole., vert.

Perf. 12½x12, 12x12½

1965, Jan. 11 Unwmk.

106	A15	5fr dk brn, ultra & yel	.15	.15
107	A15	10fr ultra, org & blk	.15	.15
108	A15	20fr multi	.20	.15
109	A15	25fr multi	.25	.15
110	A15	30fr multi	.30	.16
111	A15	85fr multi	.80	.42
		Nos. 106-111 (6)	1.85	
		Set value		.95

Olsen Perforator A16

Designs: 60fr, Mildé telephone, vert. 100fr, Distributor of Baudot telegraph.

1965, May 17 Engr. *Perf. 13*

112	A16	30fr multi	.30	.20
113	A16	60fr multi	.60	.40
114	A16	100fr multi	.90	.65
		Nos. 112-114 (3)	1.80	1.25

Cent. of the ITU.

Motorized Police — A17

Perf. 12½x12

1965, June 22 Photo. Unwmk.

115	A17	25fr ol, dk grn, gold & brn	.25	.16

Issued to honor the national police.

Guitar — A18

Musical Instruments from National Museum: 1fr, Drum and stool, vert. 3fr, Shoulder drums, vert. 15fr, Viol. 60fr, Harp, vert.

1965, Oct. 26 Engr. *Perf. 13*

Size: 22x36mm, 36x22mm

116	A18	1fr car, emer & brn	.15	.15
117	A18	2fr red, brt lil & brn	.15	.15
118	A18	3fr red & sepia	.15	.15
119	A18	15fr red, ocher & sl grn	.16	.15
120	A18	60fr maroon & slate grn	.60	.25
		Nos. 116-120,C23 (6)	2.11	
		Set value		.80

Head and Bowl — A19

WHO Headquarters, Geneva — A20

Sao Art: 20fr, Head. 60fr, Head with crown. 80fr, Circlet with human head. From excavations at Bouta Kebira and Gawi.

1966, Apr. 1 Engr. *Perf. 13*

121	A19	15fr ol, choc & ultra	.15	.15
122	A19	20fr dk red, brn & bl grn	.20	.15
123	A19	60fr brt bl, choc & ver	.60	.35
124	A19	80fr brn org, grn & pur	.80	.40
		Nos. 121-124 (4)	1.75	1.05

Issued to publicize the International Negro Arts Festival, Dakar, Senegal, Apr. 1-24.

No. 86 Surcharged with New Value and Two Bars in Orange

1966, Apr. 15 Photo. *Perf. 12x12½*

125	A7	25fr on 20fr multi	.25	.15

1966, May 3

126	A20	25fr car, lt ultra & yel	.25	.20
127	A20	32fr emer, ultra & yel	.30	.22

New WHO Headquarters, Geneva.

Staff of Mercury and Map of Africa — A21

1966, May 24 *Perf. 12½x12*

128	A21	30fr multi	.30	.15

Central African Customs and Economic Union (Union Douaniere et Economique de l'Afrique Centrale, UDEAC).

Soccer Player — A22

Design: 60fr, Soccer player facing left.

1966, July 12 Engr. *Perf. 13*

129	A22	30fr grn, bl grn & mar	.30	.16
130	A22	60fr dk bl, gray & car	.60	.35

8th World Cup Soccer Championship, Wembley, England, July 11-30.

Young Men, Flag and Emblem A23

1966, Aug. 11 Photo. *Perf. 12½x13*

131	A23	25fr dk bl & multi	.25	.16

Chad Youth Movement.

Greek Columns and UNESCO Emblem — A24

1966, Aug. 23 Engr. *Perf. 13*

132	A24	32fr sl bl, vio & car rose	.35	.20

20th anniv. of UNESCO.

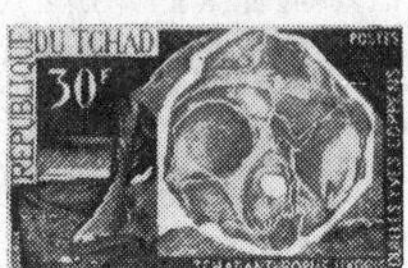

Reconstructed Skull of Chadanthropus — A25

1966, Sept. 20 Engr. *Perf. 13*

133	A25	30fr gray, red & ocher	.30	.15

Yves Coppens' discovery of Lake Chad man.

Stone Axe — A26

Prehistoric Tools: 30fr, Flint arrow head. 85fr, Bone harpoon. 100fr, Sandstone millstone with grinder.

1966, Dec. 11 Engr. *Perf. 13*

134	A26	25fr dp bl, red & dk brn	.22	.15
135	A26	30fr brn, dp bl & blk	.30	.15
136	A26	85fr dk red, brt bl & brn	.80	.38
137	A26	100fr Prus grn, dk brn & bis brn	.90	.45
a.		Miniature sheet of 4, #134-137	2.50	2.60
		Nos. 134-137 (4)	2.22	1.13

Map of Chad and Various Sports — A27

1967, Apr. 10 Photo. *Perf. 12x12½*

138	A27	25fr multi	.25	.16

Issued for Sports Day, Apr. 10, 1967.

Colotis Protomedia A28

Various Butterflies.

1967, May 23 Photo. *Perf. 12½x12*

139	A28	5fr blue & multi	.15	.15
140	A28	10fr emerald & multi	.15	.15
141	A28	20fr orange & multi	.20	.15
142	A28	130fr red & multi	1.10	.60
		Nos. 139-142 (4)	1.60	
		Set value		.87

WHO Headquarters, Brazzaville A29

1967, Sept. 23 Photo. *Perf. 12½x13*

143	A29	30fr vio bl & multi	.30	.16

Opening of the Regional Office of the WHO, Brazzaville.

Jamboree Emblem and Boy Scouts — A30

Design: 32fr, Jamboree emblem and Boy Scout.

1967, Oct. 17 Photo. *Perf. 12½x13*

144	A30	25fr multi	.22	.15
145	A30	32fr multi	.35	.16

12th Boy Scout World Jamboree, Farragut State Park, Idaho, Aug. 1-9.

Great Mills of Chad — A31

30fr, Lake reclamation project, grain fields.

1967, Nov. 14 Engr. *Perf. 13*

146	A31	25fr brt bl, ind & sep	.22	.15
147	A31	30fr ultra, emer & ol brn	.25	.16

Economic development of Chad.

Woman and Harp Player — A32

Rock Paintings: 30fr, Giraffes. 50fr, Camel rider hunting ostrich.

1967, Dec. 19 Engr. *Perf. 13*

Size: 36x22mm

148	A32	15fr bl, sal & mar	.15	.15
149	A32	30fr grnsh bl, sal & mar	.30	.16
150	A32	50fr emer, sal & mar	.50	.20
		Nos. 148-150,C38-C39 (5)	3.20	1.53

Balloud expedition in the Ennedi Mountains. See Nos. 163-166.

Rotary Emblem — A33

Map of Chad, WHO Emblem, Well, Physicians, Mother and Child — A34

1968, Jan. 9 Photo. *Perf. 13x12½*

151	A33	50fr multi	.50	.22

Rotary Club of Chad, 10th anniversary.

1968, Apr. 6 *Perf. 13x12½*

152	A34	25fr multi	.22	.15
153	A34	32fr multi	.35	.20

20th anniv. of WHO.

"Water" Aiding Agriculture and Industry A35

1968, Apr. 23 Engr. *Perf. 13*

154 A35 50fr grnsh bl, brn & brt grn .45 .20

Hydrological Decade (UNESCO), 1965-74.

National Administration School — A36

1968, Aug. 20 Engr. *Perf. 13*

155 A36 25fr sl, brn red & rose vio .22 .15

Boy Learning to Write — A37

1968, Sept. 10

156 A37 60fr dk bl, dk brn & blk .50 .22

Issued for National Literacy Day.

Cotton Harvest A38

Loom, Fort Archambault Factory — A39

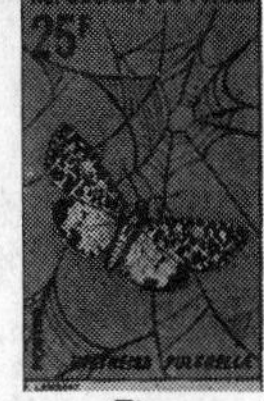
Tiger Moth — A40

1968, Sept. 24 Engr. *Perf. 13*

157	A38	25fr Prus bl, choc & dk grn	.22	.15
158	A39	30fr brt grn, ol & ultra	.30	.15
		Set value		.24

Issued to publicize the cotton industry.

1968, Oct. 1 **Photo.**

Moths: 30fr, Owlet. 50fr, Saturnid (Gynanisa maja). 100fr, Saturnid (Epiphora bauhiniae).

159	A40	25fr multi	.20	.15
160	A40	30fr multi	.25	.15
161	A40	50fr multi	.45	.22
162	A40	100fr multi	.80	.35
		Nos. 159-162 (4)	1.70	.87

Rock Paintings Type of 1967

Rock Paintings: 2fr, Archers. 10fr, Costumes (4 women, 1 man). 20fr, Funeral vigil. 25fr, Dispute.

1968, Nov. 19 Engr. *Perf. 13*

Size: 36x22mm

163	A32	2fr scar, salmon & brn	.15	.15
164	A32	10fr pur, salmon & dk red	.15	.15
165	A32	20fr grn, salmon & maroon	.20	.15
166	A32	25fr bl, salmon & maroon	.25	.15
		Set value	.60	.34

Man and Human Rights Flame — A41

St. Paul — A42

1968, Dec. 10 Engr. *Perf. 13*

167 A41 32fr grn, brt bl & red .35 .20

International Human Rights Year.

1969, May 6 Litho. *Perf. 12½x13*

Apostles: 1fr, St. Peter. 2fr, St. Thomas. 5fr, St. John the Evangelist. 10fr, St. Bartholomew. 20fr, St. Matthew. 25fr, St. James the Less. 30fr, St. Andrew. 40fr, St. Jude. 50fr, St. James the Greater. 85fr, St. Philip. 100fr, St. Simon.

168	A42	50c multi	.15	.15
169	A42	1fr multi	.15	.15
170	A42	2fr multi	.15	.15
171	A42	5fr multi	.15	.15
172	A42	10fr multi	.15	.15
173	A42	20fr multi	.18	.15
174	A42	25fr multi	.22	.15
175	A42	30fr multi	.28	.15
176	A42	40fr multi	.40	.16
177	A42	50fr multi	.42	.20
178	A42	85fr multi	.65	.40
179	A42	100fr multi	.80	.40
		Set value	3.25	1.75

Jubilee Year of the Catholic Church in Chad. #168-179 printed se-tenant in sheets of 12 (4x3).

Tractors and Trucks — A43

1969, June 19 Engr. *Perf. 13*

180 A43 32fr grn, red brn & ind .25 .16

50th anniv. of the ILO.

Deborah Meyer, US, 200 Meter Freestyle — A44

Woman with Flowers, by Veneto — A45

Winners of 1968 Olympic Games: #182, Roland Matthes, East Germany, 100m backstroke. #183, Klaus DiBiasi, Italy, springboard diving. #184, Bruno Cipolla, Primo Baran and Renzo Sambo, Italy, pair with coxswain. #185, Annemarie Zimmermann and Rosewitha Esser, West Germany, women's kayak tandem. #186, Sailing, G.B. #187, Pierre Trentin, France, 1000 meter bicycling. #188, Pier Franco Vianelli, Italy, 196k bicycle road race. #189, Daniel Morelon and Pierre Trentin, France, tandem. #190, Daniel R. Rebillard, France, 4000m pursuit (bicycle). #191, Ingrid Becker, West Germany, pentathlon. #192, Jean J. Guyon, France, equestrian. #193, Olympic dressage team, West Germany. #194, Bernd Klinger, West Germany, small bore rifle. #195, Manfred Wolke, East Germany, welterweight. #196, Randy Matson, US, shot put. #197, Colette Besson, France, 400m run. #198, Mohammed Gammoudi, Tunisia, 5,000m run. #199, Tommie Smith, US, 200m run. #200, David Hemery, G.B., 200m hurdles. #201, Willie Davenport, US, 110m hurdles. #202, Bob Beamon, US, long jump. #203, Sawao Kato, Japan, all around gymnastics. #204, Dick Fosbury, US, high jump.

Paintings: #206, Holy Family, by Murillo, horiz. #207, Adoration of the Magi, by Rubens. #208, Portrait of an African Woman, by Bezombes. #209, Three Black Men, by Rubens. #210, Mother and Child, by Gauguin.

1969, June 30 Litho. *Perf. 12½x13*

181-204 A44 1fr set of 24 5.00 5.00

Perf. 12½x13, 13x12½

205-210 A45 1fr set of 6 1.25 1.25

Issued to stress the brotherhood of mankind. For overprints see Nos. 244A-244F, 245A-245X.

Cochlospermum Tinctorium — A46

Flowers: 4fr, Parkia biglobosa. 10fr, Pancratium trianthum. 15fr, Morning glory.

1969, July 8 Photo. *Perf. 12½x13*

211	A46	1fr pink, yel & blk	.15	.15
212	A46	4fr dk grn, yel & red	.15	.15
213	A46	10fr dk grn, yel & gray	.15	.15
214	A46	15fr vio bl & multi	.15	.15
		Set value	.34	.22

Meat Freezer, Farcha — A47

Design: 30fr, Cattle at Farcha slaughterhouse.

1969, Aug. 19 Engr. *Perf. 13*

215	A47	25fr sl grn, ocher & red brn	.22	.15
216	A47	30fr red brn, sl grn & gray	.25	.16

Economic development in Chad.

Development Bank Issue

Common Design Type

1969, Sept. 10

217 CD130 30fr dl red, grn & ocher .25 .15

Tilapia Nilotica A48

Fish: 3fr, Citharinus latus. 5fr, Tetraodon fahaka strigosus. 20fr, Hydrocyon forskali.

1969, Nov. 25 Engr. *Perf. 13*

218	A48	2fr choc, grn & gray	.15	.15
219	A48	3fr gray, red & bl	.15	.15
220	A48	5fr ocher, blk & yel	.15	.15
221	A48	20fr blk, red & grn	.22	.15
		Set value	.39	.27

ASECNA Issue

Common Design Type

1969, Dec. 12 Engr. *Perf. 13*

222 CD132 30fr orange .20 .15

Pres. François Tombalbaye — A49

Lenin — A50

1970, Jan. 11 Litho. *Perf. 14*

223 A49 25fr multi .25 .15

1970, Apr. 22 Photo. *Perf. 11½*

224 A50 150fr gold, blk & buff 1.10 .65

Lenin (1870-1924), Russian communist leader.

UPU Headquarters Issue

Common Design Type

1970, May 20 Engr. *Perf. 13*

225 CD133 30fr dk red, pur & brn .25 .15

During the 1970-73 period three different agents had entered into contracts to produce stamps with various officials of the Chad government, apparently including Pres. Tombalbaye. In June 1973, Tombalbaye declared that some of the stamps produced by these agents were not recognized by the Chad government but might be put on sale at a later date, and that other stamps produced and shipped to Chad were refused by the government. In July 1973, the Chad government announced that the stamps that were not recognized would be put on sale by the end of the year. We have no evidence that this actually happened.

Apollo Program A50a

Designs: 15fr, Apollo 11 in Lunar orbit. 25fr, Apollo 12 astronaut deploying lunar research equipment. 40fr, Astronaut, lunar module on moon. 50fr, Astronauts Conrad and Bean in life raft after splashdown, horiz.

1970, June 12 Litho. *Perf. 12x12½*

225A A50a Strip of 3

Souvenir Sheet

Perf. 13½x13

225C A50a 50fr multicolored

No. 225C contains one 66x44mm stamp. No. 225C, 15fr, 25fr are airmail.

Expo '70, Japan — A50b

Japanese prints of women: 50c, by Kiyonaga. 1fr, by Utamaro. 2fr, from Heian period.

1970, June 12 Litho. *Perf. 12x12½*

225E A50b Strip of 3

For overprint see No. 239C.

Adult Education Class and UN Emblem A52

1970, June 16 Litho. *Perf. 14*
226 A52 100fr blue & multi .80 .20

International Education Year.

Bull's Head, Symbols of Weather and Agriculture — A53

1970, July 22 Engr. *Perf. 13*
227 A53 50fr org, gray & grn .38 .15

Issued for World Meteorological Day.

1970 World Cup Soccer Championships, Mexico City — A53a

Designs: 1fr, Three players, Italian flag. 4fr, Franz Beckenbauer, German flag. Nos. 227C, 227E, English players receiving World Cup trophy, 1966. No. 227D, Three players, Brazilian flag. No. 227F, Four players, "1970."

1970-71 Litho. *Perf. 12*
227A A53a 1fr multicolored
227B A53a 4fr multicolored
227C A53a 5fr multicolored
227D A53a 5fr multicolored

Embossed
Die Cut Perf 13
227E A53a 5fr gold

Souvenir Sheet
Litho.
Perf. 13½x13
227F A53a 15fr multicolored

No. 227F contains one 66x44mm stamp. Nos. 227D, 227F are airmail.
Issue dates: Nos. 227A-227D, 227F, July 2, 1970. No. 227E, Nov. 1, 1971.
For overprints see Nos. 267A-267E.

Christmas A53b

Virgin and Child by: 3fr, Solario. 25fr, Durer. 32fr, Fouquet.

1970, Aug. 19 Litho. *Perf. 12x12½*
227G A53b 3fr multicolored
227H A53b 25fr multicolored
227I A53b 32fr multicolored

No. 227I is airmail.

Ahmed Mangue, Minister of Education — A54

1970, Sept. 15 Litho. & Engr.
228 A54 100fr gold, car & blk .65 .16

1972 Summer Olympics, Munich — A54a

Designs: No. 228A, 3fr, Horses pulling chariot. 8fr, Men running. 19fr, No. 228C, Woman hurdling. No. 228B, 20fr, Equestrian. 35fr, Woman diving. No. 228D, Woman diver in tuck position.

1970 Litho. *Perf. 12½x12*
228A A54a Strip of 3
Perf. 12x12½
228B A54a Pair + label

Embossed
Die Cut Perf 13
228C A54a 10fr gold

Souvenir Sheet
Litho.
Perf. 13½x13
228D A54a 40fr multicolored

19fr, 35fr, Nos. 228C-228D are airmail. No. 228D contains one 66x43mm stamp. Issue dates: Nos. 228A-228B, 228D, Sept. No. 228C, Oct. 14.
For overprints see Nos. 239D-239F.

Tanner — A55

Designs: 2fr, Cloth dyer, vert. 3fr, Camel turning oil press. 4fr, Water carrier. 5fr, Copper worker.

1970, Oct. 10 Engr. *Perf. 13*

229	A55	1fr ol brn, bl & brn	.15	.15
229A	A55	2fr dk brn, ol & ind	.15	.15
229B	A55	3fr pur, ol brn & rose car	.15	.15
229C	A55	4fr choc, lem & bl grn	.15	.15
229D	A55	5fr red, choc & sl grn	.15	.15
		Set value	.25	.25

UN Emblem, Grain and Dove — A56

1970, Oct. 24 Photo. *Perf. 12x12½*
230 A56 32fr dk bl & multi .25 .16

25th anniversary of United Nations.

OCAM Headquarters, Map of Africa, Stars — A57

1971, Jan. 23 Photo. *Perf. 12½x12*
231 A57 30fr dk grn & multi .25 .16

OCAM (Organisation Commune Africaine, Malgache et Mauricienne) Summit Conference, N'djamena, Jan. 22-30.

Space Exploration — A57a

Illustration reduced.

1971, Feb. 16 Litho. *Perf. 13x13½*
231A A57a 8fr shown
231B A57a 10fr Apollo 11
231C A57a 35fr Soviet space station

Embossed
Die Cut Perf 13
231D A57a 8fr gold, like #231A
f. Sheet of 1, Imperf.

Souvenir Sheet
Perf. 13½x13
231E A57a 40fr John F. Kennedy, Apollo spacecraft, vert.

Nos. 231C, 231E are airmail. No. 231f contains one 73x45mm stamp with same size design as No. 231D. No. 231E contains one 33x50mm stamp.
Nos. 231D, 231f probably were not available in Chad.

1972 Winter Olympics, Sapporo A57b

Paintings by Kiyonaga: 50c, Cherry Trees in Bloom, Tokyo. 1fr, Snowy Morning. 2fr, Sake Party.

1971 Litho. *Perf. 12x12½*
231G A57b 50c multicolored
231H A57b 1fr multicolored
231I A57b 2fr multicolored

Embossed
Die Cut Perf 13
231J A57b 2fr gold, like #231I
k. Sheet of 1, Imperf.

Issue dates: Nos. 231G-231I, Feb. 16. Nos. 231J-231k, Nov. 1, 1971. No. 231k contains one 43x54mm stamp with same size design as No. 231I.
For overprints see Nos. 246A-246C.
Nos. 231J-231k probably were not available in Chad.

Portraits of French Royalty A57c

Designs: No. 232A, 25fr, The Dauphin (Louis XVII), by J.M. Vien the Younger. 32fr, Marie Antoinette, by E. Vigee-Lebrun. 60fr, Louis XVI, by J.S. Duplessis.
No. 232B, 25fr, Comtesse du Barry, by E. Vigee-Lebrun. 40fr, Louis XV, by M.Q. Delatour.
No. 232C, 40fr, Marie Antoinette, by Charpentier. 50fr, Louis XVI (Dauphin), by Michel Van Loo.
No. 232D, 35fr, Madame de Pompadour (detail), by Delatour. 70fr, Louis XV by Delatour.
No. 232E, 30fr, Madame de Pompadour (entire), by Delatour. 60fr, Marie Leszczynska, by Jean Marc Nattier. 80fr, Louis XV, by Van Loo.
No. 232F, 40fr, Duc D'Orleans as Regent, by 19th cent. French school. 200fr, Louis XIV, by H. Rigaud.
No. 232G, 100fr, Madame de Montespan, by Henry Gascard. 100fr, Madame de Maintenon, by Pierre Mignard.
No. 232H, 50fr, Colbert, by Claude Lefebvre. 200fr, Louis XIV, by J. Garnier.
No. 232J, 50fr, Marie Therese, by Mignard. 200fr, Louis XIV, by Marot.
No. 232K, 50fr, Marie de la Valliere, by English school. 200fr, Louis XIV, by French school.
No. 232L, 100fr, Giulio Cardinal Mazarin, by Mignard. 100fr, Anne of Austria, by Rubens.
No. 232M, 50fr, Vicomte de Turenne, by Champaigne. 200fr, Louis XIV as a Boy, by Mignard.
No. 232N, 100fr, Marquis de Cinq-Mars, by M. le Nain. 150fr, Cardinal Richelieu, by Champaigne.
No. 232P, 150fr, Anne of Austria, by Rubens, diff. 250fr, Louis XIII (detail), by Simon Vouet.
No. 232Q, 150fr, Marriage of Marie de Medicis (looking right), by Rubens. 150fr, Mirror image.
No. 232R, Duke of Sully, by Quesnel. Mirror image.
No. 232S, 150fr, Henry IV, by Rubens. 150fr, Marie de Medicis, by Rubens.
No. 232T, 200fr, Gabrielle d'Estrees, by unknown artist. 250fr, Henry IV, by French school, c. 1595.
No. 232U, 150fr, Jeanne d'Albret, by Francois Clouet. Marie de Medicis as a Girl, by Angelo Bronzino.
No. 232V, 200fr, Henry III, by Clouet. 250fr, Ambroise Pare, by 16th century French school.
No. 232W, 150fr, Catherine de Medicis, by Clouet. 250fr, Henry II, by Clouet.
No. 233A, 200fr, Elizabeth of Austria, by Clouet. Charles IX, by Clouet.
No. 233B, 200fr, Mary Stuart, by 16th cent. Scottish school. 300fr, Diane of Poitiers, by Fontainbleu school.
No. 233C, 200fr, Elizabeth of Valois, by Alonso S. Coello. 250fr, Francis, Duke of Alencon, by Clouet.
No. 233D, 150fr, Marguerite d'Angouleme, by Clouet. 300fr, Francis I, by Clouet.
No. 233E, 200fr, Francis I, by Titian. 300fr, Francis I as Dauphin, by Corneille of Lyon.
No. 233F, 100fr, Anne of Austria, by Coello. 250fr, Louis XIII, by Champaigne.
No. 233G, 200fr, Marie de Medicis, by Rubens, diff. 200fr, Marie de Medicis, Louis XIII, by Rubens.
No. 233H, 150fr, The Exchange of Princess Elizabeth of France and Princess Anne of Austria on the Andaye River, by Rubens. 250fr, Louis XIII of France and Navarre, by Vouet.
No. 233J, 250fr, Marie de Medicis, by Rubens, diff. 250fr, Henry IV, by Rubens.
No. 233K, Louis XV and the Dauphin at Battle of Fontenoy. No. 233L, The Grand Dauphin and his Family, by Mignard. No. 233M, Madame de Montespan, horiz. No. 233N, Madame de la Valliere and her Children. No. 233P, The Birth of Louis XIII at Fontainebleau, by Rubens. No. 233Q, Reconciliation of the Queen and Louis XIII, by Rubens. No. 233R, Henry IV Entrusting Regency to Marie de Medici, by Rubens. No. 233S, The Majority of Louis XIII, by Rubens. No. 233T, The Apotheosis of Henry IV and the Proclamation of Regency, by Rubens. No. 233U, Felicity of the Regency, by Rubens.

1971-73 Litho. *Perf. 12½x13*
232A A57c Strip of 3
232B A57c Pair
232C A57c Pair
232D A57c Pair
232E A57c Strip of 3
232F A57c Pair
232G A57c Pair
232H A57c Pair
232J A57c Pair
232K A57c Pair
232L A57c Pair

232M A57c Pair
232N A57c Pair
232P A57c Pair
232Q A57c Pair
232R A57c Pair
232S A57c Pair
232T A57c Pair
232U A57c Pair
232V A57c Pair
232W A57c Pair
233A A57c Pair
233B A57c Pair
233C A57c Pair
233D A57c Pair
233E A57c Pair
233F A57c Pair
233G A57c Pair
233H A57c Pair
233J A57c Pair

Souvenir Sheets

Perf. 13x13½, 13½x13, 13½

233K A57c 75fr multi
233L A57c 100fr multi
233M A57c 200fr multi
233N A57c 300fr multi
233P A57c 350fr multi
233Q A57c 400fr multi
233R A57c 400fr multi
233S A57c 400fr multi
233T A57c 400fr multi
233U A57c 500fr multi

Nos. 232A 60fr, 232B 40fr, 232C 50fr, 232D 70fr, 232E 80fr, 232F 200fr, 232G, 232H 200fr, 232J 200fr, 232K, 232L, 232M 200fr, 232N-233U are airmail.

Issue dates: 1971 - #232A, Feb. 24. #232B, Mar. 30. #232C, Mar. 4. #232D, 233K, Mar. 15. #232E, Apr. 12. #232F, 233L, Apr. 26. #232G, Aug. 10. #232H, Sept. 6. #232J, Sept. 23. #232K, Oct. 6. #232L, Oct. 26. #232M, Nov. 16. #232N, Nov. 20.

1972 - #232P, 233P, Jan. #232Q, 233M-233N, Feb. #233Q-233R, May. #232R, 233S, June 15. #232S, 233T, June 26. #232T, Aug. 8. #232U, Aug. 17. #232V, Aug. 30. #232W, 233U, Dec. 11. #233A, Dec. 18. #233B, Dec. 28.

1973 - #233C-233J.

Nos. 233K-233L, 233T-233U each contain one 37x62mm stamp. Nos. 233N, 233P each contain one 32x50mm stamp. No. 233M contains one 45x65mm stamp. Nos. 233Q-233R, 233U each contain one 65x45mm stamp.

Nos. 232Q-232V, 233G, 233J, 233R-233U and possibly 232P, 232W-233F, 233H probably were not available in Chad.

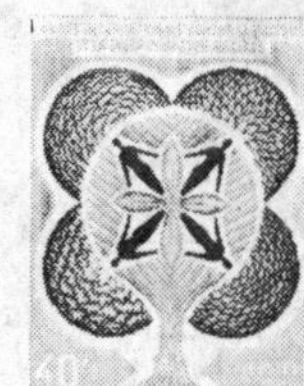

Symbolic Tree — A58

1971, Mar. 21 Engr. *Perf. 13*

236 A58 40fr bl grn, dk red & grn .35 .16

Intl. year against racial discrimination.

Paintings of Flowers A58a

Designs: 1fr, The Three Graces (detail), by Rubens. 4fr, Imperial Bouquet, by Van Os. 5fr, Bouquet, by Jan Brueghel.

1971, Apr. 28 Litho. *Perf. 12x12½*

236A A58a Strip of 3

For overprint see No. 278A.

Summer Olympic Games — A58b

Designs: 15fr, Swimming, vert. 20fr, Women's relay races, vert. 25fr, Swimming, medals. 50fr, Running.

Perf. 12x12½, 12½x12

1971, Apr. 28 Litho.

236B A58b 15fr multicolored
236C A58b 20fr multicolored
236D A58b 25fr multicolored

Embossed

Perf. 13

236E A58b 25fr gold, like No. 236D

Souvenir Sheet

Litho.

Die Cut Perf 13

236F A58b 50fr multicolored

Nos. 236D-236F are airmail. No. 236F contains one 62x36mm stamp.

Issued: #236B-236D, 236F, Apr. 28; #236E, Nov. 1.

For overprints see Nos. 251A-251D.

No. 236E probably was not available in Chad.

Map of Africa, Radar Antenna A59

Designs (Map of Africa and): 40fr, Communications tower. 50fr, Communications satellite.

1971, May 17 Engr. *Perf. 13*

237 A59 5fr ultra, org & dk red	.15	.15
238 A59 40fr pur, emer & brn	.25	.15
239 A59 50fr dk red, blk & brn	.40	.20
Nos. 237-239 (3)	.80	
Set value		.39

3rd World Telecommunications Day.

Apollo 11 — A59a

1971, July 5 Embossed *Perf. 13*

239A A59a 10fr gold
b. Sheet of 1, Imperf.

No. 239b contains one 73x45mm stamp with same size design as No. 239A.

Nos. 239A-239b probably were not available in Chad.

No. 225E Ovptd. in Gold

1971, July 17 Litho. *Perf. 12x12½*

239C A50b Strip of 3

1972 Winter Olympics, Sapporo.

Nos. 228A-228B, 228D Ovptd. with "MUNICH 72" and Olympic Rings in Gold

Perf. 12½x12, 12x12½

1971, Nov. 1 Litho.

239D A54a Strip of 3
239E A54a Pair + label

Souvenir Sheet

Perf. 13½x13

239F A54a 40fr on #228D

UNICEF Emblem and Children — A60

1971, Dec. 11 Engr. *Perf. 13*

240 A60 50fr Prus bl, emer & brt pink .40 .20

25th anniv. of UNICEF.

Gorane Nangara Dancers A61

Dancers: 15fr, Girls' initiation dance, Yondo. 30fr, Women of M'Boum, vert. 40fr, Men of Sara Kaba, vert.

1971, Dec. 18 Litho. *Perf. 13*

241 A61 10fr blk & multi	.15	.15
242 A61 15fr brn org & multi	.16	.15
243 A61 30fr bl & multi	.35	.15
244 A61 40fr yel grn & multi	.42	.15
Nos. 241-244 (4)	1.08	
Set value		.32

Nos. 205-210 Ovptd. in Gold

noël 1971

1971 Litho. *Perf. 12½x13, 13x12½*

244A-244F A45 1fr on #205-210

Nos. 244A-244F probably were not available in Chad.

Presidents Pompidou and Tombalbaye, Map with Paris and Fort Lamy — A62

1972, Jan. 25 Photo. *Perf. 13*

245 A62 40fr blue & multi .35 .20

Visit of Pres. Georges Pompidou of France, Jan. 1972.

Nos. 181-204 Ovptd. with "MUNICH 72" and Olympic Rings in Gold

1972, Feb. 7 Litho. *Perf. 12½x13*

245A-245X A44 1fr on #181-204

Nos. 245A-245X probably were not available in Chad.

Nos. 231G-231I Ovptd. in Gold

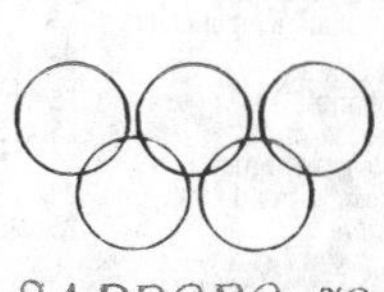

1972, Feb. Litho. *Perf. 12x12½*

246A A57b 50c Pair, #a.-b.
246B A57b 1fr Pair, #a.-b.
246C A57b 2fr Pair, #a.-b.

Nos. 246A-246C probably were not available in Chad.

President Tombalbaye A63

1972, Apr. 13 Litho. *Perf. 13*

247 A63 30fr multi	.20	.15
247A A63 40fr multi	.25	.15
Set value		.24

See Nos. C112-C113.

Downhill Skiing — A64

Designs: 75fr, Women's figure skating. 150fr, Luge.

1972, Apr. 13 *Perf. 13½*

248 A64 25fr multi	.16	.15
249 A64 75fr multi	.50	.25
250 A64 150fr multi	1.00	.50
Nos. 248-250,C114-C115 (5)	3.91	1.95

11th Winter Olympic Games, Sapporo, Japan.

Heart — A65

Gorrizia Dubiosa — A66

1972, Apr. 25 Engr. *Perf. 13*

251 A65 100fr purple, bl & car .80 .16

"Your heart is your health," World Health Month.

Nos. 236B-236D, 236F Ovptd. with "MUNICH 72" and Olympic Rings in Gold

1972 Litho. *Perf. 12x12½, 12½x12*

251A A58b 15fr multicolored
251B A58b 20fr multicolored
251C A58b 25fr multicolored

Souvenir Sheet

Die Cut Perf 13

251D A58b 50fr multicolored

Nos. 251C-251D are airmail.

1972, May 6 **Photo.**

Insects: 2fr, Spider (argiope sector). 3fr, Silk spider (nephila senegalense). 4fr, Beetle (oryctes boas). 5fr, Dragonfly (hemistigma albipunctata).

252 A66 1fr green & multi .15 .15
253 A66 2fr blue & multi .15 .15
254 A66 3fr car rose & multi .15 .15
255 A66 4fr yellow grn & multi .15 .15
256 A66 5fr dp green & multi .15 .15
Set value .25 .25

Trains A66a

1972 **Litho.** ***Perf. 12***

256A A66a 10fr Orient Express
256B A66a 40fr Osaka Express
256C A66a 50fr St. Germain
256D A66a 150fr Blue train
256E A66a 200fr Trans-Europe Express

Souvenir Sheet

256F A66a 300fr Rogers "Madison," 1855

No. 256F contains one 60x40mm stamp.
See note before No. 225A.

Scout Greeting — A67

70fr, Mountain climbing. 80fr, Canoeing.

1972, May 15 **Photo.**

257 A67 30fr multi .20 .15
258 A67 70fr multi .45 .22
259 A67 80fr multi .55 .25
Nos. 257-259,C118-C119 (5) 2.55 1.50

Scout Jamboree.

Hurdles, Motion and Olympic Emblems A68

Motion and Olympic Emblems and: 130fr, Gymnast on rings. 150fr, Swimming. 300fr, Bicycling.

1972, June 9 **Litho.** ***Perf. 13½***

260 A68 50fr blk & multi .40 .15
261 A68 130fr blk & multi .90 .25
262 A68 150fr blk & multi 1.20 .30
Nos. 260-262 (3) 2.50 .70

Souvenir Sheet

263 A68 300fr blk & multi 2.25 2.00

20th Olympic Games, Munich, Aug. 26-Sept. 10.

Ski Jump, Kasaya, Japan — A69

Designs: 75fr, Cross-country skiing, P. Tyldum, Sweden. 100fr, Figure-skating, pairs, L. Rodnina and A. Ulanov, USSR. 130fr, Men's speed skating, A. Schenk, Netherlands.

1972, June 15 ***Perf. 14½***

264 A69 25fr gold & multi .16 .15
265 A69 75fr gold & multi .50 .25
266 A69 100fr gold & multi .65 .35
267 A69 130fr gold & multi .90 .42
Nos. 264-267,C130-C131 (6) 4.41 2.25

11th Winter Olympic Games, gold-medal winners. Nos. 264-267 exist se-tenant with label showing earth satellite.

Nos. 227A-227D, 227F Overprinted With Soccer Ball, "MUNICH 72" and Olympic Rings in Gold

1972 **Litho.** ***Perf. 12***

267A A53a 1fr multicolored
267B A53a 4fr multicolored
267C A53a 5fr multicolored
267D A53a 5fr multicolored

Souvenir Sheet

Perf. 13½x13

267E A53a 15fr multicolored

Nos. 267D-267E are airmail.
Nos. 267A-267E probably were not available in Chad.

TV Tower and Weight-lifting — A70

Designs (TV Tower, Munich and): 40fr, Woman sprinter. 60fr, Soccer goalkeeper.

1972, Aug. 15 **Litho.** ***Perf. 14½***

268 A70 20fr gold & multi .15 .15
269 A70 40fr gold & multi .25 .15
270 A70 60fr gold & multi .40 .20
Nos. 268-270,C135-C137 (6) 3.10 1.70

20th Summer Olympic Games, Munich. Nos. 268-270 exist se-tenant with label showing arms of Munich.

Domestic Animals A71

1972, Aug. 29 **Engr.** ***Perf. 13***

271 A71 25fr Dromedary .22 .15
272 A71 30fr Horse .25 .15
273 A71 40fr Dog .35 .15
274 A71 45fr Goat .38 .15
Nos. 271-274 (4) 1.20
Set value .42

For surcharge see No. 293.

Tobacco Cultivation A72

1972, Oct. 24 **Engr.** ***Perf. 13***

275 A72 40fr shown .25 .15
276 A72 50fr Plowing .35 .16

Massa Warrior — A73

Design: 20fr, Moundang warrior.

1972, Nov. 15 **Photo.** ***Perf. 14x13***

277 A73 15fr orange & multi .16 .16
278 A73 20fr yellow & multi .20 .16

No. 236A Overprinted "Noel 1972" in gold

1972 **Litho.** ***Perf. 12x12½***

278A A58a Strip of 3

No. 228A probably was not available in Chad.

King Faisal and Pres. Tombalbaye — A74

1972, Nov. 17 **Litho.** ***Perf. 13***

279 A74 100fr gold & multi .65 .40

Visit of King Faisal of Saudi Arabia. See No. C143.

Gen. Gowon and Pres. Tombalbaye — A75

1972, Dec. 7

280 A75 70fr multi .50 .25

Visit of Gen. Yakubu Gowon of Nigeria.

Olympic Emblem and 100-meter Sprint, Valeri Borzov, USSR — A76

Designs (Olympic Emblem and): 20fr, Shotput, Komar, Poland. 40fr, Hammer throw, Bondartchuk, USSR. 60fr, Discus, Danek, Czechoslovakia.

1972, Dec. 22 ***Perf. 11***

281 A76 10fr multi .15 .15
282 A76 20fr multi .15 .15
283 A76 40fr multi .25 .15
284 A76 60fr multi .40 .20
Nos. 281-284,C148-C149 (6) 3.40 1.95

20th Summer Olympic Games, winners.

Olympic Emblem and Fencing, Woyda, Poland — A77

Designs (Olympic Emblem and): 30fr, 3-day equestrian event, Richard Meade, Gt. Britain. 50fr, Two-man sculls, Brietzke-Mager, East Germany.

1972, Dec. 22

285 A77 20fr gold & multi .15 .15
286 A77 30fr gold & multi .20 .15
287 A77 50fr gold & multi .35 .16
Nos. 285-287,C151-C152 (5) 3.15 1.74

20th Summer Olympic Games, winners.

1972 Summer Olympics Gold Medalists — A77a

Designs: 20fr, Teofilo Stevenson, boxing, Cuba. 25fr, Yugoslavia, team handball. 30fr, M. Peters, pentathlon, Great Britain. 40fr, basketball, USSR. No. 287E, W. Ruska, judo, Netherlands. No. 287F, Women's gynmastics, Ludmila Tourischeva, USSR. 75fr, Men's volleyball, Japan. No. 287H, A. Scalzone, shooting, Italy. No. 287I, Soccer, Poland. 130fr, J. Williams, archery, US. No. 287K, A. Nakayama, men's rings, Japan. No. 287L, Field hockey, West Germany. 200fr, Vassily Alexeiev, weight lifting, USSR. 250fr, D. Morelon, cycling, France.

1972, Dec. 22 **Litho.** ***Perf. 11½***

287A A77a 20fr multicolored
287B A77a 25fr multicolored
287C A77a 30fr multicolored
287D A77a 40fr multicolored
287E A77a 50fr multicolored
287F A77a 50fr multicolored
287G A77a 75fr multicolored
287H A77a 100fr multicolored
287I A77a 100fr multicolored
287J A77a 130fr multicolored
287K A77a 150fr multicolored
287L A77a 150fr multicolored

Souvenir Sheets

Perf. 15

287M A77a 200fr multicolored
287N A77a 250fr multicolored

Nos. 287G-287N are airmail.

Soviet Flag and Shield — A78

1972, Dec. 30 **Litho.** ***Perf. 12***

288 A78 150fr red & multi 1.00 .42

50th anniversary of the Soviet Union.

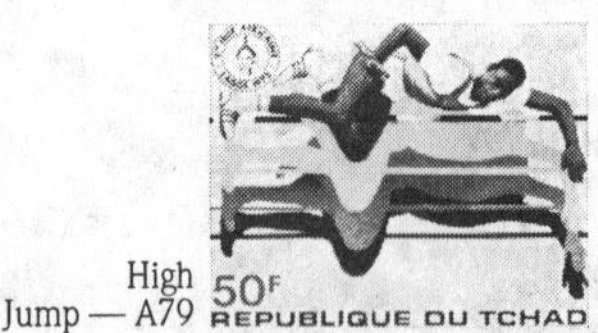

High Jump — A79

Designs (Games Emblem and): 125fr, Running. 200fr, Shot put. 250fr, Discus.

1973, Jan. 17 **Litho.** ***Perf. 13½x13***

289 A79 50fr vio bl & multi .35 .15
290 A79 125fr olive & multi .80 .40
291 A79 200fr lilac & multi 1.40 .65
Nos. 289-291 (3) 2.55 1.20

Souvenir Sheet

292 A79 250fr brn & multi 2.00 2.00

2nd African Games, Lagos, Nigeria, Jan. 7-18.

Paintings with Musical Instruments — A79a

Details from Paintings: 30fr, Madeleine Playing her Lute, by unknown artist. 70fr, A Concert, by Lorenzo Costa. 100fr, Bass and Sheet Music, by Jean-Baptiste Oudry, horiz. 125fr, St. Cecilia and Angel, by Carlo Saraceni. 150fr, Woman Listening to Violinist, by Gabriel Metsu. 300fr, Still Life with Musical Instruments, by Pieter Claesz, horiz.

1973, Apr. Litho. *Perf. 11½*

292A A79a 30fr multicolored
292B A79a 70fr multicolored
292C A79a 100fr multicolored
292D A79a 125fr multicolored
292E A79a 150fr multicolored

Souvenir Sheet

Perf. 15

292F A79a 300fr multicolored

Nos. 292D-292F are airmail.

No. 271 Surcharged with New Value, 2 Bars, and Overprinted in Red: "SECHERESSE SOLIDARITE AFRICAINE"

1973, Aug. 16 Engr. *Perf. 13*

293 A71 100fr on 25fr multi .65 .42

African solidarity in drought emergency.

African Postal Union Issue

Common Design Type

1973, Sept. 17 Engr. *Perf. 13*

294 CD137 100fr cl, sl grn & brn ol .65 .40

Easter A79b

Details from paintings: 40fr, Christ on the Cross, by Lucas Cranach. 60fr, Supper in Emmaus, by Titian, horiz. 120fr, The Crucifixion, by Durer. 150fr, The Tribute, by Titian. 250fr, The Pieta, by Botticelli. 400fr, Entombment of Christ, by Gaspard Isenmann, horiz.

1973 Litho. *Perf. 11½*

294A A79b 40fr multicolored
294B A79b 60fr multicolored
294C A79b 120fr multicolored
294D A79b 150fr multicolored
294E A79b 250fr multicolored

Souvenir Sheet

Perf. 15

294F A79b 400fr multicolored

Nos. 294A, 294D-294F are airmail.

Animals A79c

1973 Litho. *Perf. 13½*

294G A79c 20fr Sheep
294H A79c 30fr Camels
294J A79c 100fr Cats
294K A79c 130fr Dogs
294L A79c 150fr Horses

Nos. 294J-294L are airmail.
See note before No. 225A.

Christmas — A79d

Designs: 30fr, The Virgin and Infant Surrounded by Saints, by Lorenzo Lotto. 40fr, The Holy Family, by Tintoretto, vert. 55fr, Nativity Scene, by Martin Schongauer, vert. 60fr, Nativity Scene, by Federico Barocci, vert. 250fr, Adoration of the Magi, by Stephan Lochner, vert. 400fr, Epiphany, by Hans Memling.

1973 Litho. *Perf. 11½*

294M A79d 30fr multicolored
294N A79d 40fr multicolored
294P A79d 55fr multicolored
294Q A79d 60fr multicolored
294R A79d 250fr multicolored

Souvenir Sheet

Perf. 15

294S A79d 400fr multicolored

Nos. 294Q-294S are airmail.
See note before No. 225A.

Dinothrombium Tinctorium A80

Rotary Emblem A81

1974, Sept. 3 Photo. *Perf. 13*

295 A80 25fr *shown* .15 .15
296 A80 30fr *Bupreste sternocera* .16 .15
297 A80 40fr *Diptere hyperechia* .22 .15
298 A80 50fr *Chrysis* .30 .18
299 A80 100fr *Longicorn beetle* .60 .25
300 A80 130fr *Spider* .75 .35
Nos. 295-300 (6) 2.18 1.23

1975, Apr. 11 Typo. *Perf. 13*

301 A81 50fr multi .30 .16

Rotary International, 70th anniversary.

Craterostigma Plantagineum A82

Flowers: 10fr, Tapinanthus globiferus. 15fr, Commelina forskalaei, vert. 20fr, Adenium obesum. 25fr, Yellow hibiscus. 30fr, Red hibiscus. 40fr, Kigelia africana.

1975, Sept. 25 Photo. *Perf. 13*

302 A82 5fr org & multi .15 .15
303 A82 10fr gray bl & multi .15 .15
304 A82 15fr yel grn & multi .15 .15
305 A82 20fr lt brn & multi .15 .15
306 A82 25fr lil & multi .15 .15
307 A82 30fr bis & multi .15 .15
308 A82 40fr ultra & multi .18 .15
Set value .73 .42

A. G. Bell, Satellite and Waves — A83

1976, June 10 Litho. *Perf. 12½*

309 A83 100fr bl, brn & ocher .48 .30
310 A83 125fr lt grn, brn & ocher .60 .38

Centenary of first telephone call by Alexander Graham Bell, Mar. 10, 1876.

Ice Hockey, USSR — A84

Design: 90fr, Ski jump, Karl Schnabl, Austria.

1976, June 21 *Perf. 14*

311 A84 60fr multi .35 .18
312 A84 90fr multi .48 .20

12th Winter Olympic Games, winners. See Nos. C178-C180.

High Hurdles A85

1976, July 12 Litho. *Perf. 13½*

313 A85 45fr multi .28 .15

21st Summer Olympic Games, Montreal, Canada. See Nos. C187-C190.

Mars Landing and Viking Rocket — A86

Design (Mars Landing and): 90fr, Viking trajectory, Earth to Mars.

1976, July 23 *Perf. 14*

314 A86 45fr multi .25 .15
315 A86 90fr multi .55 .28
Nos. 314-315,C191-C193 (5) 4.30 1.90

Viking Mars project.

For overprints see Nos. 379-380.

Robert Koch, Medicine — A87

Design: 90fr, Anatole France, literature.

1976, Dec. 15

316 A87 45fr multi .30 .15
317 A87 90fr multi .52 .25
Nos. 316-317,C196-C198 (5) 4.57 1.97

Nobel Prize winners.

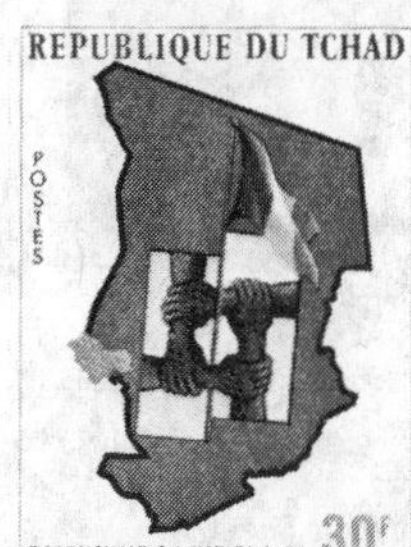

Map and Flag of Chad, Clasped Hands A88

Designs: 120fr, Map of Chad, people and various occupations.

1976, Sept. 15 Litho. *Perf. 12½x13*

318 A88 30fr multi .15 .15
319 A88 60fr orange & multi .30 .18
320 A88 120fr brown & multi .60 .42
Nos. 318-320 (3) 1.05 .75

National reconciliation.

Freed Political Prisoners — A89

Designs: 60fr, Parade of cadets.

1976, Sept. 25 Litho. *Perf. 12½*

321 A89 30fr bl & multi .15 .15
322 A89 60fr blk & multi .30 .18
323 A89 120fr red & multi .60 .40
Nos. 321-323 (3) 1.05 .73

Revolution of Apr. 13, 1975, 1st anniv.

Decorated Calabashes — A90

Designs: Various pyrographed calabashes.

1976, Nov. Litho. *Perf. 12½x13*

324 A90 30fr multi .15 .15
325 A90 60fr multi .30 .18
326 A90 120fr multi .60 .40
Nos. 324-326 (3) 1.05 .73

Germany No. C57 and Friedrichshafen, Germany — A91

1977, Mar. 30 *Perf. 14*

327 A91 100fr multi	.60	.25
Nos. 327,C206-C209 (5)	4.85	1.89

75th anniversary of the Zeppelin.

Elizabeth II in Coronation Regalia and Clergy — A92

Design: 450fr, Elizabeth II and Prince Philip.

1977, June 15 Litho. *Perf. 14x13½*

328 A92 250fr multi	1.75	.45

Souvenir Sheet

329 A92 450fr multi	3.00	1.40

25th anniv. of the reign of Elizabeth II.
For overprints see Nos. 347-348.

Simon Bolivar — A93

Famous Personalities: 175fr, Joseph J. Roberts. No. 332, Queen Wihelmina of Netherlands. No. 333, Charles de Gaulle. 325fr, King Baudouin and Queen Fabiola of Belgium.

1977, June 15 *Perf. 13½x14*

330 A93 150fr multi	.70	.25
331 A93 175fr multi	.80	.30
332 A93 200fr multi	.90	.38
333 A93 200fr multi	.90	.38
334 A93 325fr multi	1.75	.50
Nos. 330-334 (5)	5.05	1.81

Post and Telecommunications Emblem — A94

Map of Chad and Waves — A95

Society Emblem — A96

1977, Aug. 15 Litho. *Perf. 13*

335 A94 30fr yel & blk	.15	.15

Perf. 12½

336 A95 60fr multi	.30	.18

Perf. 13½x13

337 A96 120fr multi	.60	.40
Nos. 335-337 (3)	1.05	.73

Telecommunications (30fr); Natl. Telecommunications School, 10th anniv. (60fr); Intl. Telecommunication Soc. of Chad (120fr).

WHO Emblem and Man (Back Pain) — A97

World Rheumatism Year (WHO Emblem and): 60fr, Woman's head (neck pain), horiz. 120fr, Leg (knee pain).

Perf. 12½x13, 13x12½

1977, Nov. 10 Engr.

338 A97 30fr multi	.15	.15
339 A97 60fr multi	.30	.18
340 A97 120fr multi	.60	.40
Nos. 338-340 (3)	1.05	.73

World Cup Emblems and Saving a Goal — A98

Designs (Argentina '78, World Cup Emblems and): 60fr, Heading the ball. 100fr, Referee whistling a goal. 200fr, World Cup poster. 300fr, Pelé. 500fr, Helmut Schoen and Munich stadium.

1977, Nov. 25 Litho. *Perf. 13½*

341 A98 40fr multi	.22	.15
342 A98 60fr multi	.38	.18
343 A98 100fr multi	.55	.25
344 A98 200fr multi	1.25	.50
345 A98 300fr multi	1.90	.75
Nos. 341-345 (5)	4.30	1.83

Souvenir Sheet

346 A98 500fr multi	3.00	1.10

World Cup Soccer Championship, Argentina '78.
For overprints see Nos. 359-364.

Nos. 328-329 Overprinted in Silver: "ANNIVERSAIRE DU COURONNEMENT 1953-1978"

1978, Sept. 13 *Perf. 14x13½*

347 A92 250fr multi	1.25	.60

Souvenir Sheet

348 A92 450fr multi	2.50	1.25

25th anniv. of coronation of Elizabeth II.

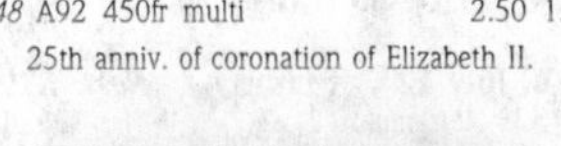

Abraham and Melchisedek, by Rubens — A99

Rubens Paintings: 120fr, Helene Fourment, vert. 200fr, David and the Elders of Israel. 300fr, Anne of Austria, vert. 500fr, Marie de Medicis, vert.

1978, Nov. 23 Litho. *Perf. 13½*

349 A99 60fr multi	.38	.18
350 A99 120fr multi	.75	.38
351 A99 200fr multi	1.25	.60
352 A99 300fr multi	1.90	.95
Nos. 349-352 (4)	4.28	2.11

Souvenir Sheet

353 A99 500fr multi	3.50	1.75

Peter Paul Rubens (1577-1640).

Dürer Portrait A100

Dürer Paintings: 150fr, Jacob Muffel. 250fr, Young Woman. 350fr, Oswolt Krel.

1978, Nov. 23

354 A100 60fr multi	.38	.18
355 A100 150fr multi	.90	.50
356 A100 250fr multi	1.50	.80
357 A100 350fr multi	2.25	1.10
Nos. 354-357 (4)	5.03	2.58

Head, Village and Fly — A101

1978, Nov. 28 *Perf. 13*

358 A101 60f multi	.38	.18

National Health Day.

Nos. 341-346 Overprinted in Silver:
a. 1962 BRESIL-TCHECOSLOVAQUIE / 3-1
b. 1966 / GRANDE BRETAGNE / - ALLEMAGNE (RFA) / 4-2
c. 1970 BRESIL-ITALIE 4-1
d. 1974 ALLEMAGNE (RFA)- / PAYS BAS 2-1
e. 1978 / ARGENTINE -/ PAYS BAS / 3-1
f. ARGENTINE -PAYS BAS / 3-1

1978, Dec. 30 Litho. *Perf. 13½*

359 A98(a) 40fr multi	.22	.15
360 A98(b) 60fr multi	.38	.18
361 A98(c) 100fr multi	.55	.32
362 A98(d) 200fr multi	1.25	.60
363 A98(e) 300fr multi	1.90	.95
Nos. 359-363 (5)	4.30	2.20

Souvenir Sheet

364 A98(f) 500fr multi	3.00	1.50

World Soccer Championship winners.

UPU Emblems, Camel Caravan, Satellites — A102

Design: 150fr, Obus woman and houses, Massa Territory, hibiscus.

1979, June 8 Litho. *Perf. 12x12½*

365 A102 60fr multi	.38	.18
366 A102 150fr multi	.90	.50

Philexafrique II, Libreville, Gabon, June 8-17. Nos. 365, 366 each printed in sheets of 10 with 5 labels showing exhibition emblem.

Wildlife Fund Emblem and Gazelle A103

Protected Animals: 50fr, Addax. 60fr, Oryx antelope. 100fr, Cheetah. 150fr, Zebra. 300fr, Rhinoceros.

1979, Sept. 15 Litho. *Perf. 14½*

367 A103 40fr multi	.25	.15
368 A103 50fr multi	.32	.15
369 A103 60fr multi	.38	.18
370 A103 100fr multi	.60	.32
371 A103 150fr multi	.95	.50
372 A103 300fr multi	1.90	.95
Nos. 367-372 (6)	4.40	2.25

Souvenir Sheet

Holy Family, by Dürer A104

1979, Sept. 1 *Perf. 13½*

373 A104 500fr brown & dull red	3.50	1.75

Boy and Handpainted Doors — A105

IYC Emblem and: 75fr, Oriental girl. 100fr, Caucasian girl, doves. 150fr, African boys. 250fr, Pencil and outlines of child's hands.

1979, Sept. 19 Litho. *Perf. 13½*

374 A105 65fr multi	.40	.20
375 A105 75fr multi	.48	.25
376 A105 100fr multi	.60	.32
377 A105 150fr multi	.95	.48
Nos. 374-377 (4)	2.43	1.25

Souvenir Sheet

378 A105 20fr multi	1.90	.95

Nos. 314-315 Overprinted "ALUNISSAGE/APOLLO XI/JUILLET 1969" and Emblem

1979, Nov. 26 Litho. *Perf. 13½x14*

379 A86 45fr multi	.28	.15
380 A86 90fr multi	.55	.32
Nos. 379-380,C240-C242 (5)	4.18	2.19

Apollo 11 moon landing, 10th anniversary.

Ski Jump, Lake Placid '80 Emblem A106

Lake Placid '80 Emblem and: 20fr, Slalom, vert. 40fr, Biathlon, vert. 150fr, Women's slalom, vert. 350fr, Cross-country skiing. 500fr, Downhill skiing.

1979, Dec. 18 *Perf. 14½*

381 A106 20fr multi	.16	.15
382 A106 40fr multi	.30	.15
383 A106 60fr multi	.45	.20
384 A106 150fr multi	1.10	.55
385 A106 350fr multi	2.50	1.25
386 A106 500fr multi	3.75	1.75
Nos. 381-386 (6)	8.26	4.05

13th Winter Olympic Games, Lake Placid, NY, Feb. 12-24, 1980.

Jet over Map of Africa A107

1980, Feb. 20 Litho. *Perf. 12½*

387	A107	15fr yellow & multi	.15	.15
388	A107	30fr blue & multi	.20	.15
389	A107	60fr red & multi	.42	.20
		Nos. 387-389 (3)	.77	
		Set value		.35

ASECNA (Air Safety Board), 20th anniv.

1982 World Cup Soccer Championships, Spain — A108

1982 Litho. *Perf. 13½*

390	A108	30fr Hungary	.15	.15
391	A108	40fr Italy	.15	.15
392	A108	50fr Algeria	.15	.15
393	A108	60fr Argentina	.15	.15
		Nos. 390-393,C258-C259 (6)	1.60	
		Set value		.75

21st Birthday of Princess Diana A109

1982, July 2 Litho. *Perf. 13½*

395	A109	30fr 1961	.18	.15
396	A109	40fr 1965	.25	.15
397	A109	50fr 1967	.32	.15
398	A109	60fr 1975	.38	.18
		Nos. 395-398,C260-C261 (6)	3.53	1.83

For overprints see Nos. 413-419B.

A110

1984 Summer Olympics, Los Angeles — A110a

Designs: No. 405A, Runner. No. 405B, Long jumper, vert.

1982, Aug. 2 Litho. *Perf. 13½*

399	A110	30fr Gymnast	.18	.15
400	A110	40fr Equestrian	.25	.15
401	A110	50fr Judo	.32	.15
402	A110	60fr High jump	.38	.18
403	A110	80fr Hurdles	.50	.25
404	A110	300fr Woman gymnast	1.90	.95
		Nos. 399-404 (6)	3.53	1.83

Souvenir Sheet

405	A110	500fr Relay race	3.25	1.50

For surcharge see No. C302.

1982, July 31 Litho. & Embossed

405A A110a 1500fr gold & multi

Souvenir Sheet

405B A110a 1500fr gold & multi

No. 405 contains one 56x39mm stamp. Nos. 403-405B airmail.

Scouting Year — A111

Boy Scouts, 75th Anniv. A111a

Scouts from various countries. No. 412A, Lord Robert Baden-Powell. No. 412B, Scouts at campsite, Baden-Powell, horiz.

1982, July 15

406	A111	30fr West Germany	.18	.15
407	A111	40fr Upper Volta	.25	.15
408	A111	50fr Mali	.32	.15
409	A111	60fr Scotland	.38	.18
410	A111	80fr Kuwait	.50	.25
411	A111	300fr Chad	1.90	.95
		Nos. 401-411 (11)	9.88	4.86

Souvenir Sheet

412	A111	500fr Chad, diff.	3.25	1.50

Litho. & Embossed

412A A111a 1500fr gold & multi

Souvenir Sheet

412B A111a 1500fr gold & multi

No. 412 contains one 53x35mm stamp. Nos. 410-412B airmail.
For overprints see Nos. 466-472B.

Nos. 395-398, C260-C262B Overprinted: "21 JUIN 1982 / WILLIAM ARTHUR PHILIP LOUIS/ PRINCE DE GALLES"

1982, Oct. 4 Litho. *Perf. 13½*

413	A109	30fr multi	.18	.15
414	A109	40fr multi	.25	.15
415	A109	50fr multi	.32	.15
416	A109	60fr multi	.38	.18
417	A109	80fr multi	.50	.25
418	A109	300fr multi	1.90	.95
		Nos. 413-418 (6)	3.53	1.83

Souvenir Sheet

419	A109	500fr multi	3.25	1.50

Litho. & Embossed

419A AP71b 1500fr on #C262A

Souvenir Sheet

419B AP71b 1500fr on #C262B

Birth of Prince William of Wales, June 21. Nos. 417-419B airmail.

A112

1982 World Cup Soccer Championships, Spain — A112a

Various players and flags. No. 426A, Dino Zoff, Italy, holding World Cup trophy. No. 426B, Paolo Rossi, Italy, two players, trophy, horiz.

1982, Nov. 30

420	A112	30fr multi	.18	.15
421	A112	40fr multi	.25	.15
422	A112	50fr multi	.32	.15
423	A112	60fr multi	.38	.18
424	A112	80fr multi	.50	.25
425	A112	300fr multi	1.90	.95
		Nos. 420-425 (6)	3.53	1.83

Souvenir Sheet

426	A112	500fr multi	3.25	1.50

Litho. & Embossed

426A A112a 1500fr gold & multi

Souvenir Sheet

426B A112a 1500fr gold & multi

No. 426 contains one 56x32mm stamp. Nos. 424-426B airmail. For surcharge see No. C306.

A113

Chess Champions — A113a

Designs: No. 433A, Bobby Fischer. No. 433B, William Steinitz.

1982, Dec. 24

427	A113	30fr Philidor	.18	.15
428	A113	40fr Paul Morphy	.25	.15
429	A113	50fr Howard Staunton	.32	.15
430	A113	60fr Capablanca	.38	.18
431	A113	80fr Boris Spassky	.50	.25
432	A113	300fr Anatoly Karpov	1.90	.95
		Nos. 427-432 (6)	3.53	1.83

Souvenir Sheet

433	A113	500fr Victor Korchnoi	3.25	1.50

Litho. & Embossed

433A A113a 1500fr gold & multi

Souvenir Sheet

433B A113a 1500fr gold & multi

No. 433 contains one 53x35mm stamp. Nos. 431-433B airmail.
For overprints see Nos. 459-465.

2nd UN Conference on Peaceful Uses of Outer Space, Vienna, Aug. 9-21 — A114

A114a

Inventors and Satellites: 30fr, K.E. Tsiolkovsky, Soyuz. 40fr, R.H. Goddard, space telescope design. 50fr, Korolev, ultraviolet telescope. 60fr, von Braun, Columbia space shuttle. 80fr, Esnault Pelterie, Ariana rocket. 300fr, H. Oberth, orbital space station. 500fr, Pres. Kennedy, Apollo 11 badge, lunar rover. No. 440A, Sir Bernard Lovell, Viking I & II. No. 440B, Sir Isaac Newton, satellite TDF 1.

1983, Jan. 31 Litho. *Perf. 13½*

434	A114	30fr multi	.18	.15
435	A114	40fr multi	.25	.15
436	A114	50fr multi	.32	.15
437	A114	60fr multi	.38	.18
438	A114	80fr multi	.50	.25
439	A114	300fr multi	1.90	.95
		Nos. 434-439 (6)	3.53	1.83

Souvenir Sheet

440	A114	500fr multi	3.25	1.50

Litho. & Embossed

440A A114a 1500fr gold & multi

Souvenir Sheet

440B A114a 1500fr gold & multi

No. 440 contains one 42x50mm stamp. Nos. 438-440B airmail.

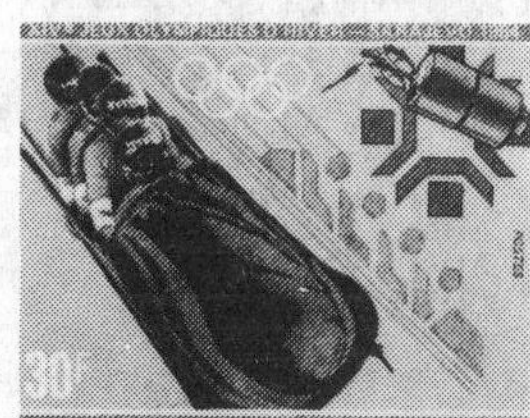

Bobsledding — A115

Woman Figure Skater A115a

Design: No. 447B, Slalom skier, horiz.

1983, Apr. 25 Litho. *Perf. 13½*

441	A115	30fr shown	.15	.15
442	A115	40fr Speed skating	.18	.15
443	A115	50fr Cross-country skiing	.25	.15
444	A115	60fr Hockey	.32	.18
445	A115	80fr Ski jumping	.40	.25
446	A115	300fr Downhill skiing	1.50	.95
		Nos. 441-446 (6)	2.80	1.83

Souvenir Sheet

447	A115	500fr Figure skating	2.50	1.50

Litho. & Embossed

447A A115a 1500fr gold & multi

Souvenir Sheet

447B A115a 1500fr gold & multi

14th Winter Olympic Games, Sarajevo, Yugoslavia, Feb. 8-19, 1984. Nos. 445-447B airmail. For surcharge see No. C298.

First Manned Balloon Flight, 200th Anniv. A116

Designs: 25fr, Hot air balloon, Montgolfier Brothers. 45fr, Captive balloon, Pilatre De Rozier. 50fr, First parachute descent, Jacques Garnerin. 60fr, Chelsea balloon, J.P. Blanchard.

1983, May 30 Litho. *Perf. 13½*

448	A116	25fr multi	.15	.15
449	A116	45fr multi	.28	.15
450	A116	50fr multi	.32	.15
451	A116	60fr multi	.38	.18
		Nos. 448-451,C268-C269 (6)	2.43	1.26

Automobiles — A116a

Automobiles and their builders: 25fr, 1927 Mercedes Type S, Gottlieb Daimler and Karl Benz. 45fr, 1913 Torpedo Martini Type GC 32-2, 6L, Friedrich Martini. 50fr, 1926 Chrysler "70," Walter P. Chrysler. 60fr, 1929 Alfa Romeo 6C 1750 Grand Sport, Nicola Romeo. 80fr, 1934 Phantom II Continental, Stewart Rolls and Henry Royce. 250fr, 1948 Talbot Lago, Lord Shrewsbury and Talbot.

1983, July 15 Litho. *Perf. 13½*

451A	A116a	25fr multicolored
451B	A116a	45fr multicolored
451C	A116a	50fr multicolored
451D	A116a	60fr multicolored
451E	A116a	80fr multicolored
451F	A116a	250fr multicolored

Nos. 451E-451F are airmail.

1984 Summer Olympics, Los Angeles — A117

A117a

1983, Nov. 15 Litho. *Perf. 13½*

452	A117	25fr Kayak	.15	.15
453	A117	45fr Long jump	.15	.15
454	A117	50fr Boxing	.15	.15
455	A117	60fr Discus	.18	.15
456	A117	80fr Running	.25	.15
457	A117	350fr Equestrian	1.10	.55
		Nos. 452-457 (6)	1.98	
		Set value		.94

Souvenir Sheet

458	A117	500fr Gymnastics	1.50	.80

Litho. & Embossed

458A A117a 1500fr Hurdles

Souvenir Sheet

458B A117a 1500fr Equestrian, vert.

Nos. 456-458B are airmail.

Nos. 427-433 Overprinted: "60e ANNIVERSAIRE FEDERATION / MONDIALE D'ECHECS 1924-1984"

1983, Dec. 27 Litho. *Perf. 13½*

459	A113	30fr multi	.15	.15
460	A113	40fr multi	.15	.15
461	A113	50fr multi	.15	.15
462	A113	60fr multi	.18	.15
463	A113	80fr multi	.25	.15
464	A113	300fr multi	.95	.50
		Nos. 459-464 (6)	1.83	
		Set value		.88

Souvenir Sheet

465	A113	500fr multi	1.50	.80

World Chess Fedn., 60th anniv.

Nos. 406-412B Ovptd. with Emblem for the 15th World Scout Jamboree, Alberta, Canada, 1983

1983, Dec. 27 Litho. *Perf. 13½*

466	A111	30fr multi	.15	.15
467	A111	40fr multi	.15	.15
468	A111	50fr multi	.15	.15
469	A111	60fr multi	.18	.15
470	A111	80fr multi	.25	.15
471	A111	300fr multi	.95	.50
		Nos. 466-471 (6)	1.83	
		Set value		.88

Souvenir Sheet

472	A111	500fr multi	1.50	.80

Litho. & Embossed

472A A111a 1500fr on #412A

Souvenir Sheet

472B A111a 1500fr on #412B

Locomotive "Lady," 1879 A118

1984, Mar. 15

473	A118	50fr shown	.15	.15
474	A118	200fr Sailboat, Lake Chad	.60	.32
475	A118	300fr Graf Zeppelin	.90	.45
476	A118	350fr Renault desert transport, 1930	1.10	.55
477	A118	400fr Bloch 120 monoplane	1.25	.60
478	A118	500fr Air Africa DC-8	1.40	.70
		Nos. 473-478 (6)	5.40	2.77

Souvenir Sheet

479	A118	600fr Intelsat V satellite	1.75	.85

Nos. 477-479 airmail. For surcharge see No. 579.

Liberation, 2nd Anniv. — A119

Pres. Hissein Habre — A120

1984, June 6 *Perf. 12½*

480	A119	50fr multi	.15	.15

1984, June 18 *Perf. 12½x13*

481	A120	125fr multi	.38	.18

Anniversaries and Events — A121

Designs: 50fr, Pres. Habre, civil war martyrs. 200fr, Paul Harris, Rotary Intl. headquarters, Illinois. 300fr, Alfred Nobel, will establishing fund for Prizes. 350fr, Raphael, detail from Virgin with Child and St. John the Baptist. 400fr, Rembrandt, detail from The Holy Family. 500fr, J.W. Goethe, scene from Faust. 600fr, Rubens, detail from Helene Forement and Her Two Children.

1984, Jan. 16 Litho. *Perf. 13½*

482	A121	50fr multi	.15	.15
483	A121	200fr multi	.55	.32
484	A121	300fr multi	.85	.45
485	A121	350fr multi	1.10	.55
486	A121	400fr multi	1.25	.60
487	A121	500fr multi	1.40	.70
		Nos. 482-487 (6)	5.30	2.77

Souvenir Sheet

488	A121	600fr multi	1.75	.85

Nos. 486-488 are airmail.

Homage to Our Martyred Dead — A122

1984, Feb. 22 Litho. *Perf. 13½*

500	A122	50fr multi	.15	.15
501	A122	80fr multi	.24	.15
502	A122	120fr multi	.35	.18
503	A122	200fr multi	.65	.28
504	A122	250fr multi	.80	.40
		Nos. 500-504 (5)	2.19	1.16

#503-504 airmail. For surcharge see #C303.

World Communications Year — A123

1984, Feb. 29 Litho. *Perf. 13½*

505	A123	50fr sil & multi	.15	.15
506	A123	60fr sil & multi	.18	.15
507	A123	70fr sil & multi	.20	.15
508	A123	125fr sil & multi	.38	.18
509	A123	250fr sil & multi	.80	.40
		Nos. 505-509 (5)	1.71	
		Set value		.83

#508-509 airmail. For surcharge see #C304.

Anniversaries and Events — A123a

Designs: 50fr, Durer, detail from Madonna of the Rosary. 200fr, Henri Dunant, Red Cross founder, Battle of Solferino. 300fr, Early telephone, Goonhilly Downs Satellite Station, Britain. 350fr, J.F. Kennedy, Neil Armstrong's first step on Moon, 1969. 400fr, Europe-Africa Satellite infrared photograph. 500fr, Prince Charles and Lady Diana. 600fr, Wedding photograph of Prince Charles and Lady Diana.

1984

510	A123a	50fr multi	.15	.15
511	A123a	200fr multi	.55	.28
512	A123a	300fr multi	.85	.45
513	A123a	350fr multi	1.10	.52
514	A123a	400fr multi	1.25	.55
515	A123a	500fr multi	1.50	.80
a.		Souvenir sheet of one	2.25	1.10
		Nos. 510-515 (6)	5.40	2.75

Souvenir Sheet

516 A121 600fr multicolored

Nos. 514-516 are airmail. For surcharge see No. 578.

Development of Communications — A123b

Ships and locomotives.

1984, Aug. 1 Litho. *Perf. 12½*

517	A123b	90fr Indiaman, East India Co.	.25	.15
518	A123b	100fr Nord 701, 1885	.28	.15
519	A123b	125fr Vera Cruz	.38	.18
520	A123b	150fr Columbia, 1888	.42	.20
521	A123b	200fr Carlisle Castle	.55	.28
522	A123b	250fr Rete Mediterranea, 1900	.80	.40
523	A123b	300fr Britannia	.85	.45
524	A123b	350fr Mav 114	1.10	.52
		Nos. 517-524 (8)	4.63	2.33

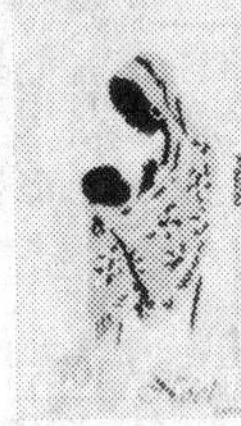
Christmas — A124

1984, Dec. 28 Litho. *Perf. 13*

525	A124	50fr lt bl & org brn	.15	.15
526	A124	60fr ver & org brn	.15	.15
527	A124	80fr emer & org brn	.20	.15
528	A124	85fr rose lil & org brn	.22	.15
529	A124	100fr org yel & org brn	.25	.15
530	A124	135fr dp bl vio & org brn	.38	.18
		Nos. 525-530 (6)	1.35	
		Set value		.73

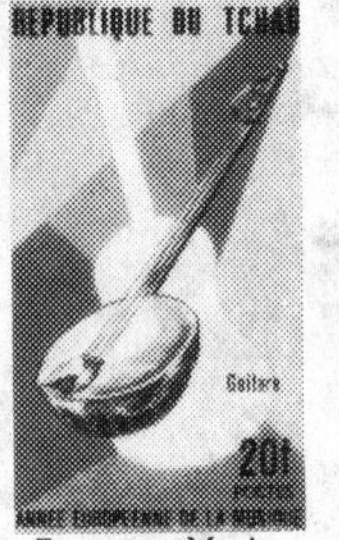

European Music Year A125

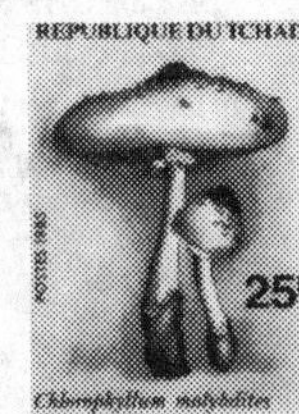

Mushrooms A126

Instruments.

1985, Apr. 30 Litho. *Perf. 12x12½*

531	A125	20fr Guitar	.15	.15
532	A125	25fr Harp	.15	.15
533	A125	30fr Xylophone	.15	.15
534	A125	50fr Shoulder drum	.15	.15
535	A125	70fr like #534	.18	.15
536	A125	80fr like #532	.20	.15
537	A125	100fr like #531	.25	.15
538	A125	250fr like #533	.60	.32
		Set value	1.50	.84

1985, May 15 Litho. *Perf. 12½*

539	A126	25fr Chlorophyllum molybdites	.15	.15
540	A126	30fr Tulostoma volvulatum	.15	.15
541	A126	50fr Lentinus tuber-regium	.15	.15
542	A126	70fr like #541	.18	.15
543	A126	80fr Podaxis pistillaris	.20	.15
544	A126	100fr like #539	.25	.32
		Set value	.88	.66

Anniversaries and Events — A127

Designs: 25fr, Abraham Lincoln. 45fr, Henri Dunant, Geneva birthplace and red cross. 50fr, Gottlieb Daimler, 1887 Motor Carriage. 60fr, Louis Bleriot, Bleriot XI monoplane, 1909. 80fr, Paul Harris, Chicago site of Rotary Intl. founding. 350fr, Auguste Piccard, bathyscaphe Trieste, 1953. 600fr, Anatoly Karpov, 1981 world chess champion. 1500fr, Paul Harris.

1985, May 25 Litho. *Perf. 13½*

545 A127 25fr multi .15 .15
546 A127 45fr multi .15 .15
547 A127 50fr multi .15 .15
548 A127 60fr multi .15 .15
549 A127 80fr multi .22 .15
550 A127 350fr multi .85 .45
Nos. 545-550 (6) 1.67
Set value .80

Souvenir Sheets

551 A127 600fr multi 1.75 .85

Litho. & Embossed

551A A127 150fr multi

No. 551A contains one 130x90mm stamp. Nos. 548-551A are airmail.

Souvenir sheets of one exist for Nos. 545-551.

Intl. Youth Year — A128

1985, May 30 Litho. *Perf. 13*

552 A128 70fr Development levels, vert. .18 .15
553 A128 200fr Globe .50 .25

A129

3rd Anniv. of the Republic A130

Perf. 13, 12½x13

1985, June 7 Litho.

554 A129 70fr Hand, claw .18 .15
555 A129 70fr Hands, map .18 .15
556 A130 70fr Pres. Hissein Habre .18 .15
557 A129 110fr like #554 .28 .15
558 A129 110fr like #555 .28 .15
559 A130 110fr like #556 .28 .15
Nos. 554-559 (6) 1.38
Set value .63

Audubon Birth Bicent. — A131

Mammals — A132

1985, July 20 Engr. *Perf. 13*

560 A131 70fr Stork .18 .15
561 A131 110fr Ostrich .32 .15
562 A131 150fr Marabou .45 .22
563 A131 200fr Snake eagle .55 .28
Nos. 560-563 (4) 1.50 .80

Souvenir Sheet

564 A131 500fr like 200fr 1.40 .70

1985, Oct. 1

565 A132 50fr Waterbuck .15 .15
566 A132 70fr Kudus, horiz. .38 .18
567 A132 250fr Shaggy mouflon .80 .40
Nos. 565-567 (3) 1.33 .73

Souvenir Sheet

568 A132 500fr White rhinoceros 1.75 .85

UN, 40th Anniv. — A133

1985, Oct. 24

569 A133 200fr brt bl, red & brn .55 .28

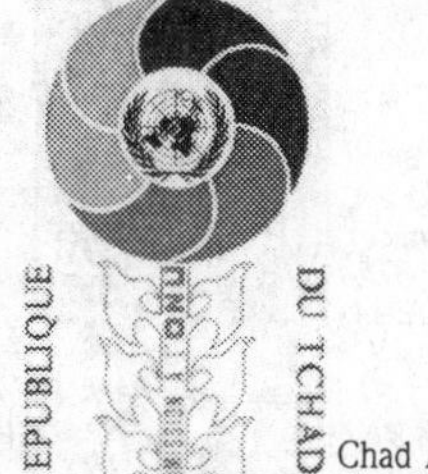

Chad Admission to UN, 25th Anniv. — A134

1985, Oct. 24

570 A134 300fr red, brt bl & yel 1.00 .50

President's Visit to the Nation's Interior A135

1986, June 7 Litho. *Perf. 12½x13*

571 A135 100fr multi .45 .22
572 A135 170fr multi .75 .38
573 A135 200fr multi .90 .45
Nos. 571-573 (3) 2.10 1.05

World Wildlife Fund — A136

Various mouflons, *Ammotragus lervia.*

1988, Nov. 10 Litho. *Perf. 13*

574 A136 25fr shown .18 .15
575 A136 45fr Adult, young .30 .15
576 A136 70fr Two adults, diff. .48 .25
577 A136 100fr Adults, young .68 .35
Nos. 574-577 (4) 1.64 .90

Nos. 512 and 475 Surcharged

1989 Litho. *Perf. 13½*

578 A123a 170fr on 300fr #512
579 A118 240fr on 300fr #475

Liberation — A137

1989 *Perf. 11½x12*

580 A137 20fr multi .15 .15
581 A137 25fr multi .15 .15
582 A137 40fr multi .24 .15
583 A137 100fr multi .60 .30
584 A137 170fr multi 1.05 .52
Nos. 580-584 (5) 2.19 1.27

Visit of Pope John Paul II — A138

Cathedral in Chad and: 20fr, 100fr, Pope holding crosier. 80fr, 170fr, Pope, diff.

1990, Jan. 30 Litho. *Perf. 13*

585 A138 20fr multicolored .15 .15
586 A138 80fr multicolored .58 .30
587 A138 100fr multicolored .70 .35
588 A138 170fr multicolored 1.20 .60
Nos. 585-588 (4) 2.63 1.40

Vaccinations A140

1991 Photo. *Perf. 11½*

Granite Paper

593 A140 30fr brown & multi .26 .15
594 A140 100fr green & multi .90 .45
595 A140 170fr vio & multi 1.50 .75
596 A140 180fr blue & multi 1.60 .80
597 A140 200fr red & multi 1.75 .90
Nos. 593-597 (5) 6.01 3.05

A141

A142

1991 Litho.

598 A141 10fr green & multi .15 .15
599 A141 20fr lilac & multi .18 .15
600 A141 40fr yellow & multi .35 .18
601 A141 70fr blue & multi .60 .30
602 A141 130fr tan & multi 1.15 .58
603 A141 200fr pink & multi 1.75 .90
Nos. 598-603 (6) 4.18 2.26

Liberty and Democracy Day, Dec. 1, 1990.

1992, Nov. 15 Litho. *Perf. 11½*

604 A142 20fr bright yel & multi .15 .15
605 A142 45fr golden yel & multi .35 .18
606 A142 85fr pink & multi .68 .35
607 A142 170fr blue & multi 1.35 .68
608 A142 300fr gray & multi 2.35 1.20
Nos. 604-608 (5) 4.88 2.56

Doctors Without Borders, 20th anniv.

Campaign Against Illiteracy A143

1992, Nov. 30

609 A143 25fr yellow green & multi .20 .15
610 A143 40fr golden yel & multi .32 .15
611 A143 70fr pink & multi .55 .28
612 A143 100fr lilac & multi .78 .40
613 A143 180fr blue & multi 1.40 .70
614 A143 200fr gray & multi 1.60 .80
Nos. 609-614 (6) 4.85 2.48

Intl. Conference on Nutrition, Rome — A144

1992, Dec. 15

615 A144 10fr yellow & multi .15 .15
616 A144 60fr pink & multi .48 .24
617 A144 120fr yellow green & multi .95 .48
618 A144 500fr blue & multi 4.00 2.00
Nos. 615-618 (4) 5.58 2.87

SEMI-POSTAL STAMPS

Catalogue values for unused stamps in this section are for Never Hinged items.

Anti-Malaria Issue

Common Design Type

Perf. 12½x12

1962, Apr. 7 Engr. Unwmk.

B1 CD108 25fr + 5fr orange .42 .42

Freedom from Hunger Issue

Common Design Type

1963, Mar. 21 *Perf. 13*

B2 CD112 25fr + 5fr dk grn, dk bl & brn .42 .42

Red Cross, Mother and Children — SP1

1974, Oct. 2 Photo. *Perf. 12½x13*

B3 SP1 30fr + 10fr multi .22 .20

Red Cross of Chad, first anniversary.

AIR POST STAMPS

> Catalogue values for unused stamps in this section are for Never Hinged items.

Olympic Games Issue

French Equatorial Africa No. C37 Surcharged in Red

Unwmk.

1960, Dec. 15 Engr. *Perf. 13*
C1 AP8 250fr on 500fr grnsh blk, blk & slate 6.00 6.00

17th Olympic Games, Rome, Aug. 25-Sept. 11. Surcharge 46mm wide; illustration reduced.

Red Bishops — AP1

Discus Thrower — AP2

Designs (birds in pairs): 100fr, Scarlet-chested sunbird. 200fr, African paradise flycatcher. 250fr, Malachite kingfisher. 500fr, Nubian carmine bee-eater.

1961-63 Unwmk. Engr. *Perf. 13*
C2 AP1 50fr dk grn, mag & blk .40 .16
C3 AP1 100fr multi 1.00 .45
C4 AP1 200fr multi 2.00 .80
C5 AP1 250fr dk bl, grn & dp org ('63) 2.75 1.40
C6 AP1 500fr multi 6.00 2.50
Nos. C2-C6 (5) 12.15 5.31

Air Afrique Issue

Common Design Type

1962, Feb. 17 Unwmk. *Perf. 13*
C7 CD107 25fr lt bl, org brn & blk .25 .15

Abidjan Games Issue

1962, July 21 Photo. *Perf. 12x12½*
C8 AP2 100fr brn, lt grn & blk 1.00 .60

African Postal Union Issue

Common Design Type

1963, Sept. 8 Unwmk. *Perf. 12½*
C9 CD114 85fr dk bl, ocher & red .65 .30

Air Afrique Issue, 1963

Common Design Type

1963, Nov. 19 *Perf. 13x12*
C10 CD115 50fr multi .60 .40

Europafrica Issue

Common Design Type

1963, Nov. 30 Photo. *Perf. 12x13*
C11 CD116 50fr dp grn, yel & dk brn .50 .38

Mail Truck and Broussard Plane — AP4

Unwmk.

1963, Dec. 16 Engr. *Perf. 13*
C12 AP4 100fr sl grn, ultra & red brn 1.00 .35

Chiefs of State Issue

Map and Presidents of Chad, Congo, Gabon and Central African Republic AP4a

1964, June 23 Photo. *Perf. 12½*
C13 AP4a 100fr multi .90 .42

See note after Central African Republic No. C19.

Europafrica Issue, 1964

Globe and Emblems of Industry and Agriculture — AP5

1964, July 20 *Perf. 13x12*
C14 AP5 50fr brn, pur & dp org .42 .30

See note after Cameroun No. 402.

Soccer — AP6

Designs: 50fr, Javelin throw, vert. 100fr, High jump, vert. 200fr, Runners.

1964, Aug. 12 Engr. *Perf. 13*
C15 AP6 25fr yel grn, sl grn & org brn .25 .16
C16 AP6 50fr org brn, ind & brt bl .45 .32
C17 AP6 100fr blk, red & brt grn 1.00 .65
C18 AP6 200fr bis, blk & car 2.00 1.25
a. Min. sheet of 4, #C15-C18 3.75 3.75
Nos. C15-C18 (4) 3.70 2.38

18th Olympic Games, Tokyo, Oct. 10-25, 1964.

Communications Symbols — AP7

1964, Nov. 2 Litho. *Perf. 12½x13*
C19 AP7 25fr lil, dk brn & lt red brn .25 .15

Pan-African and Malagasy Posts and Telecommunications Cong., Cairo, Oct. 24-Nov. 6.

President John F. Kennedy (1917-63) — AP8

1964, Nov. 3 Photo. *Perf. 12½*
C20 AP8 100fr multi 1.10 .80
a. Souvenir sheet of 4 3.50 3.50

ICY Emblem — AP9

1965, July 5 Photo. *Perf. 13*
C21 AP9 100fr multi 1.00 .60

International Cooperation Year, 1965.

Abraham Lincoln — AP10

1965, Sept. 7 Unwmk. *Perf. 13*
C22 AP10 100fr multi 1.00 .60

Centenary of death of Abraham Lincoln.

Musical Instrument Type of Regular Issue

Design: 100fr, Xylophone (marimba).

1965, Oct. 26 Engr. *Perf. 13*
Size: 48x27mm
C23 A18 100fr ocher, brt bl & vio bl .90 .30

Sir Winston Spencer Churchill (1874-1965) — AP11

1965, Nov. 23 Engr. *Perf. 13*
C24 AP11 50fr dk grn & blk .50 .22

Dr. Albert Schweitzer and Outstretched Hands — AP12

1966, Feb. 15 Photo. *Perf. 12½*
C25 AP12 100fr multi 1.00 .50

Dr. Albert Schweitzer (1875-1965), medical missionary, theologian and musician.

Air Afrique Issue, 1966

Common Design Type

1966, Aug. 31 Photo. *Perf. 13*
C26 CD123 30fr yel grn, blk & gray .30 .16

White-throated Bee-eater — AP13

Birds: 50fr, Blue-eared glossy starling. 200fr, African pygmy kingfisher. 250fr, Red-throated bee-eater. 500fr, Little green bee-eater.

1966-67 Photo. *Perf. 13x12½*
C27 AP13 50fr gold & multi .35 .16
C28 AP13 100fr bluish gray & multi .65 .30
C29 AP13 200fr grnsh gray & multi 1.40 .65
C30 AP13 250fr pale bl & multi 1.60 .80
C31 AP13 500fr pale sal & multi 3.00 1.60
Nos. C27-C31 (5) 7.00 3.51

Issue dates: 100fr, 200fr, 500fr, Oct. 18, 1966. Others, Mar. 21, 1967.

For surcharges see Nos. C67-C69.

Congress Hall — AP14

1967, Jan. 5 Photo. *Perf. 12½*
C32 AP14 25fr multi .25 .15

Opening of the new Congress Hall.

Breguet 19 Biplane — AP15

Planes: 30fr, Latécoère 631 hydroplane. 50fr, Douglas DC-3. 100fr, Piper Cherokee 6.

1967, Aug. 1 Engr. *Perf. 13*
C33 AP15 25fr sky bl, sl grn & lt brn .25 .15
C34 AP15 30fr sky bl, indigo & grn .30 .16
C35 AP15 50fr sky bl, ol bis & sl grn .50 .25
C36 AP15 100fr dk bl, sl grn & dk red 1.00 .50
Nos. C33-C36 (4) 2.05 1.06

First anniversary of Air Chad.

African Postal Union Issue, 1967

Common Design Type

1967, Sept. 9 Engr. *Perf. 13*
C37 CD124 100fr ol, brt pink & red brn .90 .45

Rock Painting Type of Regular Issue

1967, Dec. 19 Engr. *Perf. 13*
Size: 48x27mm
C38 A32 100fr Masked dancers 1.00 .42
C39 A32 125fr Rabbit hunt 1.25 .60

Downhill Skiing — AP16

1968, Feb. 5 Engr. *Perf. 13*
C40 AP16 30fr shown .30 .16
C41 AP16 100fr Ski jump, vert. 1.00 .60

10th Winter Olympic Games, Grenoble, France, Feb. 6-18.

Konrad Adenauer (1876-1967), Chancellor of West Germany (1949-63) — AP17

1968, Mar. 19 Photo. *Perf. 12½*
C42 AP17 52fr grn, dk brn & lt lil .55 .30
a. Souvenir sheet of 4 2.25 2.25

The Snake Charmer, by Henri Rousseau AP18

Design: 130fr, "War" by Henri Rousseau.

1968, May 14 Photo. *Perf. 13½*
Size: 41x41mm

C43 AP18 100fr ultra & multi 1.00 .40

Size: 48x35mm
Perf. 12½

C44 AP18 130fr brn & multi 1.10 .55

Hurdlers — AP19

1968, Oct. 16 Engr. *Perf. 13*

C45 AP19 32fr shown .35 .15
C46 AP19 80fr Relay race .65 .20

19th Olympic Games, Mexico City, Oct. 12-27.

PHILEXAFRIQUE Issue

The Actor Wolf (Bernard), by Jacques L. David AP20

1969, Jan. 15 Photo. *Perf. 12½*

C47 AP20 100fr multi .95 .55

PHILEXAFRIQUE, Philatelic Exhib. in Abidjan, Feb. 14-23. Printed with alternating label.

2nd PHILEXAFRIQUE Issue

Common Design Type

50fr, Chad #J12 and Moundang Dancers.

1969, Feb. 14 Engr. *Perf. 13*

C48 CD128 50fr red, brt bl, brn & grn .48 .32

Gustav Nachtigal and Tibesti Gorge, 1869 — AP21

Design: No. C50, Heinrich Barth and Lake Chad, 1851.

1969, Feb. 17

C49 AP21 100fr vio bl, dk brn & brn .80 .25
C50 AP21 100fr grn, pur & bl .80 .25

German explorers Gustav Nachtigal (1834-85) and Heinrich Barth (1821-65), and state visit of the Pres. of West Germany Heinrich Lubke.

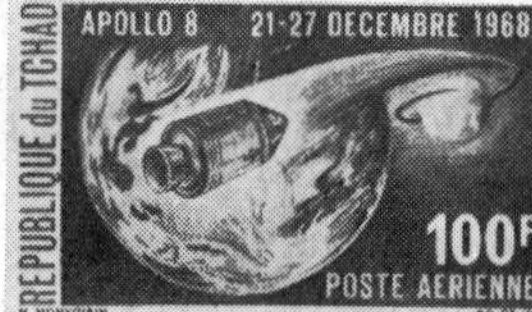
Apollo 8, Earth and Moon — AP22

1969, Apr. 10 Photo. *Perf. 13*

C51 AP22 100fr multi .80 .45

US Apollo 8 mission, the 1st men in orbit around the moon, Dec. 21-27, 1968.

Mahatma Gandhi — AP23

Portraits: No. C53, John F. Kennedy. No. C54, Dr. Martin Luther King, Jr. No. C55, Robert F. Kennedy.

1969, May 20 Photo. *Perf. 12½*

C52 AP23 50fr blk & lt grn .42 .25
C53 AP23 50fr blk & tan .42 .25
C54 AP23 50fr blk & pink .42 .25
C55 AP23 50fr blk & lt vio bl .42 .25
a. Souvenir sheet of 4, #C52-C55 2.50 2.50
Nos. C52-C55 (4) 1.68 1.00

Issued to honor exponents of non-violence.

Presidents Tombalbaye and Mobutu, Map and Flags of Chad and Congo — AP24

Embossed on Gold Foil

1969 *Die-cut; Perf. 13½*

C56 AP24 1000fr gold, dk bl & red 10.00 10.00

1st anniv. of the establishment of the Union of Central African States, comprising Chad, Congo Democratic Republic and Central African Republic.

Napoleon Visiting Hospital, by Alexandre Veron-Bellecourt — AP25

Paintings: 85fr, Battle of Wagram, by Horace Vernet. 130fr, Battle of Austerlitz, by Francois Pascal Gerard.

1969, July 23 Photo. *Perf. 12x12½*

C57 AP25 30fr multi .38 .28
C58 AP25 85fr multi 1.10 .70
C59 AP25 130fr multi 1.90 1.10
Nos. C57-C59 (3) 3.38 2.08

Bicentenary of birth of Napoleon I.

Apollo 11 Issue

Astronaut on Moon — AP26

Embossed on Gold Foil

1969, Oct. 17 *Die-cut; Perf. 13½*

C60 AP26 1000fr gold 10.00 10.00

See note after Algeria No. 427.

Village Life, by Goto Narcisse — AP27

Designs: No. C62, Women at the Market, by Iba N'Diaye. No. C63, Woman with Flowers, by Iba N'Diaye, vert.

1970 Photo. *Perf. 12x12½, 12½x12*

C61 AP27 100fr multi .55 .15
C62 AP27 250fr grn & multi 2.00 .35
C63 AP27 250fr brn & multi 2.00 .35
Nos. C61-C63 (3) 4.55 .85

Issue dates: Mar. 17, 100fr; Aug. 28, #C62-C63.

Napoleon — AP27a

Designs: Nos. C63A, C63E, Napoleon II, Duke of Reichstadt, vert.

No. C63B, 10fr, Crossing the Grand St. Bernard, by David. 25fr, Emperor Napoleon, by Gerard. 32fr, Marriage of Napoleon and Marie Louise, by Rouget. 40fr, Napoleon after return from Elba, vert.

Perf. 12x12½, 12½x12

1970-71 Litho.

C63A AP27a 10fr multicolored
C63B AP27a Strip of 3

Embossed
Perf. 13

C63C AP27a 10fr gold
f. Sheet of 1, Imperf.

Souvenir Sheets
Litho.
Perf. 13x13½

C63D AP27a 40fr multicolored

Embossed
Imperf

C63E AP27a 10fr gold, like #C63A

#C63A is printed se-tenant with label. #C63D contains one 43x67mm stamp. #C63f contains one 53x42mm stamp with same size design as #C63B, 10fr. #C63E contains one 43x104mm stamp with same size design as #C63A.

No. C63E probably was not available in Chad.

Issue dates: No. C63B, June 12. Nos. C63A, C63D-C63E, Apr. 1971. No. C63C, Nov. 1, 1971.

EXPO Emblem and Osaka Print — AP28

Designs (EXPO Emblem and): 100fr, Tower of the Sun. 125fr, Osaka print (diff. design).

1970, June 30 Engr. *Perf. 13*

C64 AP28 50fr bl, red brn & sl grn .42 .15
C65 AP28 100fr red, yel grn & Prus bl .80 .18
C66 AP28 125fr blk, dk red & bis 1.00 .25
Nos. C64-C66 (3) 2.22 .58

Issued to publicize EXPO '70 International Exhibition, Osaka, Japan, Mar. 15-Sept. 13.

1968 Summer Olympics, 1970 World Cup Soccer Championships, Mexico — AP28a

1970, July 1 Litho. *Perf. 12½x12*

C66A AP28a 5fr Flags, soccer players

Souvenir Sheet
Perf. 13½x13

C66C AP28a 15fr Olympic torch, soccer player

No. C66A printed in sheets of 2 + 2 labels. No. C66C contains one 66x43mm stamp.

For overprints see Nos. C88A-C88B.

Nos. C28-C30 Surcharged in Carmine with New Value and Bars and Overprinted:

a. "APOLLO XI / 1er débarquement sur la lune/20 juillet 1969"
b. "APOLLO XII / Exploration de la lune / 19 Novembre 1969"
c. "APOLLO XIII / Exploit spatial / 11-17 avril 1970"

1970, July 9 Photo. *Perf. 13x12½*

C67 AP13 (a) 50fr on 100fr multi .40 .25
C68 AP13 (b) 100fr on 200fr multi .80 .38
C69 AP13 (c) 125fr on 250fr multi 1.00 .50
Nos. C67-C69 (3) 2.20 1.13

Space missions of Apollo 11, 12 and 13.

DC-8 "Fort Lamy" over Airport AP29

1970, Aug. 5 *Perf. 12½*

C70 AP29 30fr dk sl grn & multi .25 .15

Souvenir Sheet

Apollo 12
AP29a

1970, Sept. Embossed ***Imperf.***

C70A AP29a 25fr gold

No. C70A probably was not available in Chad.

The Visitation, Venetian School, 15th Century
AP30

Paintings, Venetian School: 25fr, Nativity, 15th century. 30fr, Virgin and Child, c. 1350.

1970, Dec. 15 Photo. ***Perf. 12½x12***

C71 AP30 20fr gold & multi .18 .15
C72 AP30 25fr gold & multi .20 .15
C73 AP30 30fr gold & multi .25 .15
Nos. C71-C73 (3) .63 .45

Christmas 1970. See Nos. C105-C108.

Post Office Mauritius and Emblem
AP31

1971, Jan. 23 Engr. ***Perf. 13***

C74 AP31 10fr shown .15 .15
C75 AP31 20fr Tuscany #23 .15 .15
C76 AP31 30fr France #8 .25 .15
C77 AP31 60fr US #2 .42 .15
C78 AP31 80fr Japan #8 .55 .25
C79 AP31 100fr Saxony #1 .80 .28
a. Souvenir sheet of 6, #C74-C79 3.25 3.25
Nos. C74-C79 (6) 2.32
Set value .85

Publicity for PHILEXOCAM, philatelic exhibition, Fort Lamy, Jan. 23-30.

Gamal Abdel Nasser — AP32

1971, Feb. 16 Photo. ***Perf. 12½***

C80 AP32 75fr multi .48 .15

In memory of Gamal Abdel Nasser (1918-1970), President of Egypt.

Presidents Mobutu, Bokassa and Tombalbaye — AP33

1971, Apr. 28 Photo. ***Perf. 13***

C81 AP33 100fr multi .65 .32

Return of Central African Republic to the United States of Central Africa which also includes Congo Democratic Republic and Chad.

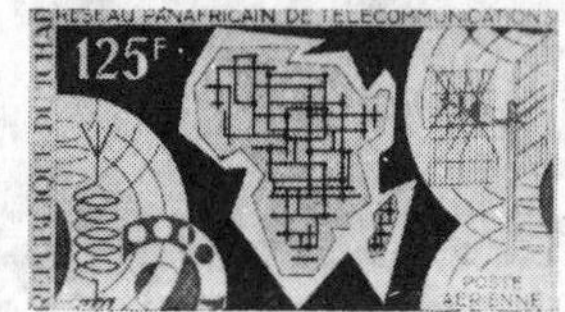

Map of Africa, Communications Network and Symbols — AP34

1971, May 17 Engr. ***Perf. 13***

C82 AP34 125fr ultra, sl grn & brn red .85 .18

Pan-African telecommunications system.

Boys Around Campfire, Torii — AP35

1971, Aug. 24 Photo. ***Perf. 12½***

C83 AP35 250fr multi 1.75 .55

13th Boy Scout World Jamboree, Asagiri Plain, Japan, Aug. 2-10.

White Egret
AP36

1971, Sept. 28 Photo. ***Perf. 13x12½***

C84 AP36 1000fr blk, dk bl & ocher 6.25 4.50

Greek Marathon Runners — AP37

Designs: 45fr, Ancient Olympic Stadium. 75fr, Greek wrestlers. 130fr, Olympic Stadium, Athens, 1896.

1971, Oct. 5 ***Perf. 12½***

C85 AP37 40fr multi .32 .15
C86 AP37 45fr multi .35 .22
C87 AP37 75fr multi .52 .25
C88 AP37 130fr multi .85 .42
Nos. C85-C88 (4) 2.04 1.04

75th anniv. of modern Olympic Games.

Nos. C66A, C66C Ovptd. in Gold

1971 Litho. ***Perf. 12½x12***

C88A AP28a 5fr on #C66A

Souvenir Sheet

Perf. 13½x13

C88B AP28a 15fr on #C66C

Overprint on No. C88B is 36mm long.

Duke Ellington — AP38

Charles de Gaulle — AP39

Portraits: 50fr, Sidney Bechet. 100fr, Louis Armstrong.

1971, Oct. 20 Litho. ***Perf. 13***

C89 AP38 50fr multi .40 .15
C90 AP38 75fr lt bl & multi .55 .28
C91 AP38 100fr multi .80 .40
Nos. C89-C91 (3) 1.75 .83

Famous American jazz musicians.

Lithographed and Embossed

1971, Nov. 9 ***Perf. 12½***

Design: No. C93, Félix Eboué.

C92 AP39 200fr grn, yel grn & gold 2.50 2.50
C93 AP39 200fr bl, lt bl & gold 2.50 2.50
a. Souv. sheet of 2, #C92-C93 + label 5.00 5.00

Charles de Gaulle (1890-1970), pres. of France.

African Postal Union Issue, 1971

Common Design Type

Design: 100fr, Sao antelope head and UAMPT building, Brazzaville, Congo.

1971, Nov. 13 Photo. ***Perf. 13x13½***

C94 CD135 100fr bl & multi .70 .22

Apollo 15 Rocket
AP40

Designs: 80fr, Apollo 15 capsule, horiz. 150fr, Lunar module on Moon, horiz. 250fr, Astronaut making tests. 300fr, Moon-buggy. No. C100, Successful splashdown, horiz. No. C101, Apollo 15 insignia.

1972, Jan. 5 Litho. ***Perf. 13½***

C95 AP40 40fr multi .20 .15
C96 AP40 80fr multi .40 .18
C97 AP40 150fr multi .75 .38
C98 AP40 250fr multi 1.25 .60
C99 AP40 300fr multi 1.50 .75
C100 AP40 500fr multi 2.50 1.25
Nos. C95-C100 (6) 6.60 3.31

Souvenir Sheet

C101 AP40 500fr multi 2.50 1.10

Apollo 15 moon landing.

Soyuz 2 Link-up — AP41

Designs: 30fr, Soyuz 2 on launching pad, vert. 50fr, No. C108, Cosmonauts in uniform. 200fr, V. I. Patsayev. No. C106, V. N. Volkov. 400fr, G. L. Dobrovolsky. No. C109, Three cosmonauts.

1972, Jan. 5 ***Perf. 13½x13***

C102 AP41 30fr multi .15 .15
C103 AP41 50fr multi .25 .15
C104 AP41 100fr multi .50 .25
C105 AP41 200fr multi 1.00 .50
C106 AP41 300fr multi 1.50 .75
C107 AP41 400fr multi 2.25 1.00
Nos. C102-C107 (6) 5.65 2.80

Souvenir Sheets

C108 AP41 300fr multi 1.90 .95
C109 AP41 400fr multi 2.50 1.25

Soyuz 2 link-up project.

Bobsledding — AP42

Design: 100fr, Slalom.

1972, Feb. 24 Engr. ***Perf. 13***

C110 AP42 50fr Prus bl & rose red .38 .15
C111 AP42 100fr red lil & slate grn .75 .22

11th Winter Olympic Games, Sapporo, Japan, Feb. 3-13.

Pres. Tombalbaye Type, 1972

1972, Apr. 13 Litho. ***Perf. 13***

C112 A63 70fr multi .42 .22
C113 A63 80fr multi .50 .25

11th Winter Olympic Type, 1972

Designs: 130fr, Speed skating. No. C115, Ice hockey. No. C116, Ski jumping. 250fr, 4-man bobsled.

1972, Apr. 13 ***Perf. 13½***

C114 A64 130fr multi .75 .45
C115 A64 200fr multi 1.50 .60

Souvenir Sheets

C116 A64 200fr multi 1.50 .60
C117 A64 250fr multi 1.75 .95

Scout Jamboree Type, 1972

Designs: 100fr, Cooking preparation. 120fr, Lord Baden Powell. 250fr, Hiking.

1972, May 15

C118 A67 100fr multi .60 .38
C119 A67 120fr multi .75 .50

Souvenir Sheet

C120 A67 250fr multi 1.50 .95

Zebras — AP43

African wild animals: 30fr, Mandrills. 100fr, African elephants. 130fr, Gazelles. 150fr, Hippopotamuses. 200fr, Lion cub.

1972, May 15 Litho. ***Perf. 13***

C121 AP43 20fr multi .15 .15
C122 AP43 30fr multi .18 .15
C123 AP43 100fr multi .60 .32
C124 AP43 130fr multi .80 .40
C125 AP43 150fr multi .95 .50
Nos. C121-C125 (5) 2.68 1.52

Souvenir Sheet

C126 AP43 200fr multi 1.25 .60

View of Venice, by Caffi — AP44

Paintings by Ippolito Caffi: 40fr, Sailing ship and Doge's Palace, vert. 140fr, Grand Canal, vert.

1972, May 23 **Photo.**

C127 AP44 40fr gold & multi .32 .15
C128 AP44 45fr gold & multi .38 .15
C129 AP44 140fr gold & multi .95 .60
Nos. C127-C129 (3) 1.65 .90

UNESCO campaign to save Venice.

11th Winter Olympic Winners Type, 1972

Designs: 150fr, Slalom, B. Cochran, US. 200fr, Women's figure skating, B. Schuba, Austria. 250fr, Ice hockey, USSR. 300fr, 2-man bobsled. W. Zimmerer and P. Utzschneider, West Germany.

1972, June 15 ***Perf. 14½***

C130 A69 150fr gold & multi .95 .48
C131 A69 200fr gold & multi 1.25 .60

Souvenir Sheets

C132 A69 250fr gold & multi 1.25 .80
C133 A69 300fr gold & multi 1.90 1.10

Nos. C130-C131 exist se-tenant with label showing earth satellite.

Daudet, "Tartarin de Tarascon," Book Year Emblem — AP45

1972, July 22 **Engr.** ***Perf. 13***

C134 AP45 100fr dk red, lil & dk brn .75 .18

Intl. Book Year, 1972, and to honor Alphonse Daudet (1840-1897), French writer.

20th Summer Olympics Type, 1972

Designs (TV Tower, Munich and): 100fr, Gymnast. 120fr, Pole vault. 150fr, Fencing. 250fr, Hammer throw. 300fr, Boxing.

1972, Aug. 15

C135 A70 100fr gold & multi .60 .32
C136 A70 120fr gold & multi .75 .38
C137 A70 150fr gold & multi .95 .50
Nos. C135-C137 (3) 2.30 1.20

Souvenir Sheets

C138 A70 250fr gold & multi 1.75 .90
C139 A70 300fr gold & multi 2.00 1.00

Nos. C135-C137 exist se-tenant with label showing arms of Munich.

Lunokhod on Moon — AP46

Russian moon missions: 100fr, Luna 16 on moon and rocket in flight, vert.

1972, Sept. 19

C140 AP46 100fr dk bl, pur & bis .75 .32
C141 AP46 150fr slate, brn & lil 1.10 .50

Farcha Laboratory, Cattle, Scientist — AP47

1972, Nov. 11 **Photo.** ***Perf. 13***

C142 AP47 75fr yellow & multi .42 .22

20th anniversary of the Farcha Laboratory for veterinary research.

King Faisal and Holy Kaaba, Mecca — AP48

1972, Nov. 17

C143 AP48 75fr multi .48 .25

Visit of King Faisal of Saudi Arabia.

Christmas Type of 1970

Christmas: 40fr, Virgin and Child, by Giovanni Bellini. 75fr, Virgin and Child, by Dall'Occhio. 80fr, Nativity, by Fra Angelico, horiz. 95fr, Adoration of the Kings, by Il Perugino.

1972, Dec. 15 **Photo.** ***Perf. 13***

C144 AP30 40fr gold & multi .32 .15
C145 AP30 75fr gold & multi .55 .15
C146 AP30 80fr gold & multi .60 .18
C147 AP30 95fr gold & multi .65 .25
Nos. C144-C147 (4) 2.12 .73

Summer Olympic Winners Type, 1972

Designs (Olympic Emblems and): 150fr, Pole vault, Nordwig, East Germany. 250fr, Hurdles, Milburn, US 300fr, Javelin, Wolfermann, West Germany.

1972, Dec. 22

C148 A76 150fr multi .95 .50
C149 A76 250fr multi 1.50 .80

Souvenir Sheet

C150 A76 300fr multi 2.00 .95

Summer Olympic Winners Type, 1972

Designs (Olympic Emblem and): 150fr, Dressage, Mancinelli, Italy. No. C152; Finn class sailing, Serge Maury, France. No. C153, Swimming, Mark Spitz.

1972, Dec. 22 **Litho.** ***Perf. 11***

C151 A77 150fr gold & multi .95 .48
C152 A77 250fr gold & multi 1.50 .80

Souvenir Sheet

C153 A77 250fr multi 1.50 .80

Copernicus and Solar System — AP49

1973, Mar. 31 **Engr.** ***Perf. 13***

C154 AP49 250fr gray, mag & brn 1.75 .95

500th anniversary of the birth of Nicolaus Copernicus (1473-1543), Polish astronomer.

Horses — AP49a

Details from paintings: 20fr, A Horse Frightened by Lightning, by Theordore Gericault. 60fr, The White Horse, by Paul Potter. 100fr, Mares and Foals, by George Stubbs. 150fr, Horse Head, by Theordore Gericault, vert. 500fr, The Carriage, by Vernet.

1973 **Litho.** ***Perf. 11½***

C154A AP49a 20fr multicolored
C154B AP49a 60fr multicolored
C154C AP49a 100fr multicolored
C154D AP49a 150fr multicolored

Souvenir Sheet

Perf. 15

C154E AP49a 500fr multicolored

See note before No. 225A.

Airplanes — AP49b

1973 **Litho.** ***Perf. 12***

C154F AP49b 5fr Fokker F VII/3M
C154G AP49b 25fr DH 89A Rapide
C154H AP49b 70fr Viscount
C154J AP49b 150fr Boeing 747
C154K AP49b 200fr Concorde

Souvenir Sheet

Perf. 12

C154L AP49b 350fr Concorde, diff.

Nos. C154L contains one 60x40mm stamp. See note before No. 225A.

Skylab over Africa — AP50

1974, Aug. 6 **Engr.** ***Perf. 13***

C155 AP50 100fr shown .60 .35
C156 AP50 150fr Skylab .85 .48

Exploits of Skylab, US manned space station.

Soccer — AP51

Designs: 125fr, 150fr, Soccer players; 125fr, vert.

1974, Oct. 22 **Engr.** ***Perf. 13***

C157 AP51 50fr dl red & choc .28 .15
C158 AP51 125fr red & dp grn .65 .40
C159 AP51 150fr grn & rose red .80 .48
Nos. C157-C159 (3) 1.73 1.03

World Cup Soccer Championship, Munich, June 13-July 7.

Family and WPY Emblem — AP52

1974, Nov. 11

C160 AP52 250fr multi 1.50 .95

World Population Year.

Mail Delivery by Canoe — AP53

UPU Cent.: 40fr, Diesel train. 100fr, Jet. 150fr, Spacecraft.

1974, Dec. 20 **Engr.** ***Perf. 13***

C161 AP53 30fr car & multi .18 .15
C162 AP53 40fr ultra & blk .22 .15
C163 AP53 100fr brn, ultra & blk .55 .35
C164 AP53 150fr grn, lil & ol .85 .52
Nos. C161-C164 (4) 1.80 1.17

Women of Different Races, IWY Emblem — AP54

1975, June 25 **Photo.** ***Perf. 13***

C165 AP54 250fr bl & multi 1.40 .80

International Women's Year 1975.

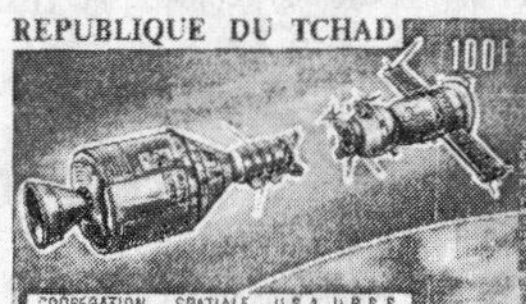

Apollo and Soyuz Before Link-up — AP55

Design: 130fr, Apollo and Soyuz after link-up.

1975, July 15 **Engr.** ***Perf. 13***

C166 AP55 100fr ultra, choc & grn .60 .32
C167 AP55 130fr vio bl, brn & grn .75 .48

Apollo Soyuz space test project (Russo-American space cooperation), launching July 15; link-up July 17.

For overprints see Nos. C171-C172.

Soccer Player, View of Montreal — AP56

Designs (Olympic Rings, Montreal Skyline): 100fr, Discus thrower. 125fr, Runner.

1975, Oct. 14 Engr. *Perf. 13*

C168 AP56	75fr car & sl grn	.42	.25
C169 AP56	100fr car, choc & bl grn	.60	.32
C170 AP56	125fr brn, bl & car	.80	.50
	Nos. C168-C170 (3)	1.82	1.07

Pre-Olympic Year 1975.

Nos. C166-C167 Overprinted: "JONCTION / 17 JUILLET 1975"

1975, Nov. 4 Engr. *Perf. 13*

C171 AP55	100fr multi	.60	.32
C172 AP55	130fr multi	.75	.42

Apollo-Soyuz link-up in space, July 17.

Stylized British and American Flags, "200" — AP57

1975, Dec. 5 Engr. *Perf. 13*

C173 AP57	150fr vio bl, car & ol bis	.80	.50

American Bicentennial.

Adoration of the Shepherds, by Murillo — AP58

Christmas (Paintings): 75fr, Adoration of the Shepherds, by Georges de La Tour. 80fr, Virgin and Child with Bible, by Rogier van der Weyden, vert. 100fr, Holy Family, by Raphael, vert.

1975, Dec. 15 Litho. *Perf. 13x12½*

C174 AP58	40fr yel & multi	.25	.15
C175 AP58	75fr yel & multi	.42	.25
C176 AP58	80fr yel & multi	.50	.25
C177 AP58	100fr yel & multi	.60	.28
	Nos. C174-C177 (4)	1.77	.93

12th Winter Olympic Winners Type, 1976

Designs: 250fr, 4-man bobsled, West Germany. 300fr, Speed skating, J. E. Storholt, Norway. 500fr, Downhill skiing, F. Klammer, Austria.

1976, June 21 *Perf. 14*

C178 A84	250fr multi	1.40	.70
C179 A84	300fr multi	1.75	.95

Souvenir Sheet

C180 A84	500fr multi	3.25	1.25

Paul Revere's Ride and Portrait by Copley — AP59

American Bicentennial: 125fr, Washington crossing Delaware. 150fr, Lafayette offering his services to America. 200fr, Rochambeau at Yorktown with Washington. 250fr, Franklin presenting Declaration of Independence. 400fr, Count de Grasse's victory at Cape Charles.

1976, July 4 Litho. *Perf. 14*

C181 AP59	100fr multi	.60	.32
C182 AP59	125fr multi	.75	.38
C183 AP59	150fr multi	.85	.42
C184 AP59	200fr multi	1.25	.55
C185 AP59	250fr multi	1.90	.60
	Nos. C181-C185 (5)	5.35	2.27

Souvenir Sheet

C186 AP59	400fr multi	2.75	1.25

Summer Olympics Type, 1976

Designs: 100fr, Boxing. 200fr, Pole vault. 300fr, Shot put. 500fr, Sprint.

1976, July 12

C187 A85	100fr multi	.50	.32
C188 A85	200fr multi	1.25	.55
C189 A85	300fr multi	1.90	.70
	Nos. C187-C189 (3)	3.65	1.57

Souvenir Sheet

C190 A85	500fr multi	2.50	1.25

Viking Mars Project Type, 1976

Designs (Mars Lander and): 100fr, Viking landing on Mars. 200fr, Capsule over Mars. 250fr, Lander over Mars. 450fr, Lander and probe.

1976, July 23 Litho. *Perf. 14*

C191 A86	100fr multi	.60	.32
C192 A86	200fr multi	1.40	.55
C193 A86	250fr multi	1.50	.60
	Nos. C191-C193 (3)	3.50	1.47

Souvenir Sheet

C194 A86	450fr multi	2.75	1.25

For overprints see Nos. C240-C243.

Concorde — AP60

1976, Oct. 15 Litho. *Perf. 12½*

C195 AP60	250fr bl, blk & ver	1.25	.38

First commercial flight of supersonic jet Concorde, Jan. 21.

Nobel Prize Type, 1976

Designs: 100fr, Albert Einstein, physics. 200fr, Dag Hammarskjold, peace. 300fr, Shinichiro Tomanaga, physics. 500fr, Alexander Fleming, medicine.

1976, Dec. 15

C196 A87	100fr multi	.60	.32
C197 A87	200fr multi	1.25	.55
C198 A87	300fr multi	1.90	.70
	Nos. C196-C198 (3)	3.75	1.57

Souvenir Sheet

C199 A87	500fr multi	3.00	1.25

Adoration of the Shepherds, by Gerard van Honthorst — AP61

Christmas (Paintings): 30fr, Nativity, by Albrecht Altdorfer, vert. 60fr, Nativity, by Hans Holbein, vert. 150fr, Adoration of the Kings, by Gerard David.

1976, Dec. 22 Litho. *Perf. 12½*

C200 AP61	30fr gold & multi	.15	.15
C201 AP61	60fr gold & multi	.32	.18
C202 AP61	120fr gold & blk	.60	.38
C203 AP61	150fr gold & blk	.75	.42
	Nos. C200-C203 (4)	1.82	1.13

Lesdiguières Bridge, by Jongkind — AP62

Design: 120fr, Sailing Ship and Boats, by Johan Barthold Jongkind (1819-1891).

1976, Dec. 27 Photo. *Perf. 13*

C204 AP62	100fr multi	.50	.28
C205 AP62	120fr multi	.60	.38

Centenary of impressionism.

Zeppelin Type of 1977

Designs: 125fr, Germany #C40, North Pole. 150fr, Germany #C45, Chicago department store. 175fr, Germany #C38 and scenes of NYC and London. 200fr, 500fr, US #C15, NYC.

1977, Mar. 30 *Perf. 11*

C206 A91	125fr multi	.75	.32
C207 A91	150fr multi	.90	.38
C208 A91	175fr multi	1.10	.42
C209 A91	200fr multi	1.50	.52
	Nos. C206-C209 (4)	4.25	1.64

Souvenir Sheet

C210 A91	500fr multi	3.00	1.25

Sassenage Castle, Grenoble — AP63

1977, May 21 Litho. *Perf. 12½*

C211 AP63	100fr multi	.50	.28

Intl. French Language Council, 10th Anniv.

Lafayette and Ships — AP64

American Bicentennial: 120fr, Abraham Lincoln, eagle and flags, vert. 150fr, James Madison and family.

1977, July 30 Engr. *Perf. 13*

C212 AP64	100fr multi	.50	.38
C213 AP64	120fr multi	.60	.42
C214 AP64	150fr multi	.75	.55
	Nos. C212-C214 (3)	1.85	1.35

Lindbergh and Spirit of St. Louis — AP65

Designs: 100fr, Concorde. 150fr, 200fr, 300fr, Various Lindbergh portraits and Spirit of St. Louis.

1977, Sept. 27

C215 AP65	100fr multi	.50	.38
C216 AP65	120fr multi	.60	.42
C217 AP65	150fr multi	.75	.55
C218 AP65	200fr multi	1.00	.70
C219 AP65	300fr multi	1.50	1.00
	Nos. C215-C219 (5)	4.35	3.05

Charles A. Lindbergh's solo transatlantic flight from NY to Paris, 50th anniv., and 1st supersonic transatlantic flight of Concorde.

For overprint see No. C227.

Mariner 10 — AP66

Spacecraft: 200fr, Lunokhod on moon, Luna 21. 300fr, Viking on Mars.

1977, Oct. 10 Engr. *Perf. 13*

C220 AP66	100fr multi	.50	.38
C221 AP66	200fr multi	1.00	.75
C222 AP66	300fr multi	1.50	1.00
	Nos. C220-C222 (3)	3.00	2.13

Running — AP67

1977, Oct. 24 Engr. *Perf. 13*

C223 AP67	30fr shown	.15	.15
C224 AP67	60fr Volleyball	.32	.22
C225 AP67	120fr Soccer	.60	.42
C226 AP67	125fr Basketball	.60	.48
	Nos. C223-C226 (4)	1.67	1.27

No. C215 Overprinted: "PARIS NEW-YORK / 22.11.77"

1977, Nov. 22

C227 AP65	100fr multi	.50	.38

Concorde, 1st commercial flight Paris to New York.

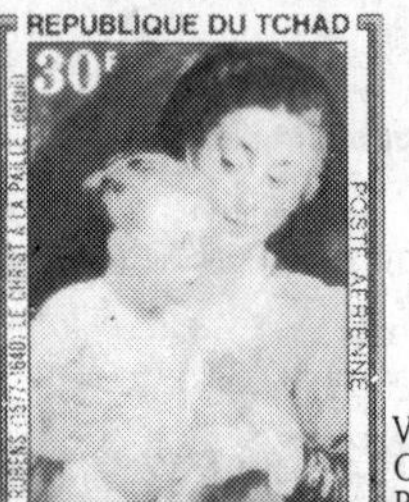

Virgin and Child, by Rubens AP68

Rubens Paintings: 60fr, Virgin and Child and Two Donors. 100fr, Adoration of the Shepherds. 125fr, Adoration of the Kings.

1977, Dec. 20 Litho. *Perf. 12½x12*

C228 AP68	30fr multi	.15	.15
C229 AP68	60fr multi	.32	.22
C230 AP68	100fr multi	.50	.38
C231 AP68	125fr multi	.60	.48
	Nos. C228-C231 (4)	1.57	1.23

Christmas 1977.

Antoine de Saint-Exupéry — AP69

Designs: 50fr, Wilbur and Orville Wright and Flyer. 80fr, Hugo Junkers and his plane. 100fr, Gen. Italo Balbo and his plane. 120fr, Concorde. 500fr, Wilbur and Orville Wright and Flyer.

1978, Oct. 25 Litho. *Perf. 13½*

C232 AP69	40fr multi	.25	.15
C233 AP69	50fr multi	.32	.15
C234 AP69	80fr multi	.50	.25
C235 AP69	100fr multi	.60	.32
C236 AP69	120fr multi	.75	.38
	Nos. C232-C236 (5)	2.42	1.25

Souvenir Sheet

C237 AP69	500fr multi	3.50	1.75

History of aviation and 75th anniversary of 1st powered flight.

Philexafrique II-Essen Issue

Common Design Types

Designs: No. C238, Rhinoceros and Chad No. C6. No. C239, Kingfisher and Mecklenburg-Strelitz No. 1.

1978, Nov. 1 *Perf. 12½*

C238 CD138	100fr multi	.60	.32
C239 CD139	100fr multi	.60	.32

Nos. C238-C239 printed se-tenant.

Nos. C191-C194 Overprinted "ALUNISSAGE/APOLLO XI/ JUILLET 1969"

1979, Nov. 26 Litho. *Perf. 13½x14*

C240 A86 100fr multi .60 .32
C241 A86 200fr multi 1.25 .60
C242 A86 250fr multi 1.50 .80
Nos. C240-C242 (3) 3.35 1.72

Souvenir Sheet

C243 A86 450fr multi 3.00 1.50

Apollo 11 moon landing, 10th anniversary.

Hurdles, Moscow '80 Emblem — AP70

Moscow '80 Emblem and: 30fr, Field hockey. 250fr, Swimming. 350fr, Running. 500fr, Yachting.

1979, Nov. 30 *Perf. 13½*

C244 AP70 15fr multi .15 .15
C245 AP70 30fr multi .25 .15
C246 AP70 250fr multi 1.90 .80
C247 AP70 350fr multi 2.50 1.25
Nos. C244-C247 (4) 4.80 2.35

Souvenir Sheet

C248 AP70 500fr multi 3.75 1.90

Pre-Olympic Year.
For overprints see Nos. C254-C255.

Austria Jubilee Issue of 1910, Canoe, Hill AP71

Hill, Stamps and Vessels: 100fr, US type A97, dhow. 200fr, France No. 21, Sidewheeler. 300fr, Holstein No. 16, ocean liner. 500fr, Chad No. J13, ocean liner.

1979, Dec. 3 *Perf. 14x13½*

C249 AP71 65fr multi .50 .25
C250 AP71 100fr multi .65 .32
C251 AP71 200fr multi 1.50 .60
C252 AP71 300fr multi 2.25 .95
Nos. C249-C252 (4) 4.90 2.12

Souvenir Sheet

C253 AP71 500fr multi 3.75 1.90

Sir Rowland Hill (1795-1879), originator of penny postage.
For overprints see Nos. C256-C257.

Nos. C244-C245, C249-C250 Overprinted: "POSTES 1981" in Red or Overprinted and Surcharged Silver on Red

Perf. 13½, 14x13½

1981, Nov. 15 Litho.

C254 AP70 30fr on 15fr multi .18 .15
C255 AP70 30fr multi .18 .15
C256 AP71 60fr on 65fr multi .38 .18
C257 AP71 60fr on 100fr multi .38 .18
Nos. C254-C257 (4) 1.12 .66

Soccer Type of 1982 and

1982 World Cup Soccer Championships, Spain — AP71a

Design: No. C259C, Soccer players, ball, and trophy, vert.

1982 Litho. *Perf. 13½*

C258 A108 80fr Brazil .20 .15
C259 A108 300fr W. Germany .80 .42

Souvenir Sheet

C259A A108 500fr like 300fr 1.40 .70

Litho. & Embossed

C259B AP71a 1500fr gold & multi

Souvenir Sheet

C259C AP71a 1500fr gold & multi

No. C259A contains one 42x51mm stamp.
For surcharge see No. C305.

Diana Type of 1982 and

Princess Diana, 21st Birthday AP71b

Design: No. C262A, Portrait, horiz.

1982, July 2 Litho. *Perf. 13½*

C260 A109 80fr 1977 .50 .25
C261 A109 300fr 1980 1.90 .95

Souvenir Sheet

C262 A109 500fr 1981 3.00 1.50

Litho. & Embossed

C262A AP71b 1500fr gold & multi

Souvenir Sheet

C262B AP71b 1500fr gold & multi

For overprints see Nos. 419A-419B.

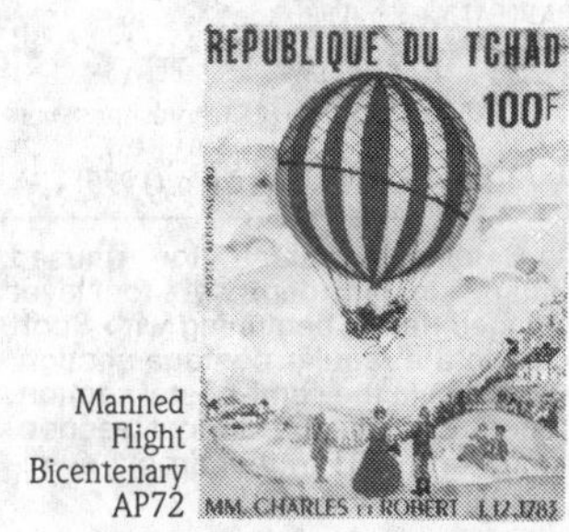

Manned Flight Bicentenary AP72

Balloons: 100fr, Charles' and Roberts', 1783, vert. 200fr, J.P. Blanchard, Berlin, 1788, vert. 300fr, Charles Green, London, 1837. 400fr, Modern blimp. 500fr, Montgolfiere, 1783, vert.

1983, Apr. Litho. *Perf. 13*

C263 AP72 100fr multi .48 .25
C264 AP72 200fr multi .95 .48
C265 AP72 300fr multi 1.40 .70
C266 AP72 400fr multi 1.90 .95
Nos. C263-C266 (4) 4.73 2.38

Souvenir Sheet

C267 AP72 500fr multi 3.00 1.50

Balloon Type and

First Balloon Ascension, Bicent. — AP72a

Designs: 80fr, Steam Powered Airship, H. Giffard. 250fr, Graf Zeppelin; Airship L-1, 1st flight. 300fr, 1st Balloon Flight, Montgolfier and Rozier. No. C270A, Airship Hindenburg, Count Ferdinand von Zeppelin. No. C270B, Jean-Francois Pilatre de Rozier and Marquis d'Arlandes, first balloon ascension.

1983, May 30 Litho. *Perf. 13*

C268 A116 80fr multi .50 .25
C269 A116 250fr multi .80 .38

Souvenir Sheet

C270 A116 300fr multi 1.90 .95

Litho. & Embossed

Perf. 13½

C270A AP72a 1500fr gold & multi

Souvenir Sheet

C270B AP72a 1500fr gold & multi

For surcharge see No. C299.

1984 Summer Olympics — AP73

Various kayak scenes.

1984, Mar. 1 Litho. *Perf. 13*

C271 AP73 100fr multi .28 .15
C272 AP73 200fr multi .55 .28
C273 AP73 300fr multi .85 .42
C274 AP73 400fr multi 1.10 .55
Nos. C271-C274 (4) 2.78 1.40

Souvenir Sheet

C275 AP73 500fr multi 1.40 .70

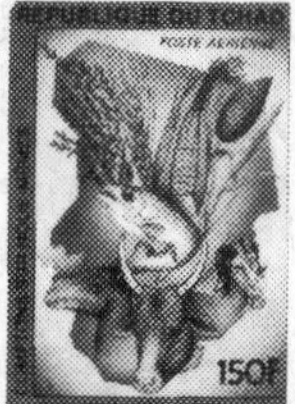

Natl. Goals — AP73a

Designs: Nos. C276, C278, Peace and reconciliation. Nos. C277, C279, Self-sufficiency in food production.

1983, Dec. 26 Litho. *Perf. 13½*

C276 AP73a 150fr multi .85 .42
C277 AP73a 150fr multi .85 .42
C278 AP73a 200fr multi 1.10 .55
C279 AP73a 200fr multi 1.10 .55
Nos. C276-C279 (4) 3.90 1.94

For surcharges see Nos. C300-C301.

Paul P. Harris (1868-1947), Founder of Rotary Intl. — AP73b

Litho. & Embossed

1984, Jan. 16 *Perf. 13½*

C279B AP73b 1500fr gold & multi

IYY, PHILEXAFRICA '85 — AP74

1985, May 2 Litho. *Perf. 13*

C280 AP74 200fr Boy scout, tree .50 .25
C281 AP74 200fr Air Chad Fokker 27 .50 .25

Printed se-tenant with center label.

IYY, PHILEXAFRICA Type of 1985

1985, Nov. 1 Litho. *Perf. 13x12½*

C283 AP74 250fr Girl, Scout ceremony .85 .42
C284 AP74 250fr Communications and transportation .85 .42

Nos. C283-C284 printed se-tenant with center labels picturing map of Africa or UAPT emblem.

ASCENA Airlines, 25th Anniv. — AP75

1985, Aug. 15 *Perf. 12½*

C285 AP75 70fr bl & multi .18 .15
C286 AP75 110fr org & multi .28 .15
C287 AP75 250fr yel & multi .70 .35
Nos. C285-C287 (3) 1.16 .65

Victor Hugo (1802-1885), French Novelist — AP76

Scene from Les Miserables.

1985, Nov. 24 Engr. *Perf. 13*

C288 AP76 70fr org brn, chlky bl & dp brn .18 .15
C289 AP76 110fr lake, dk brn & dk grn .38 .18
C290 AP76 250fr brt org, blk & dk red .90 .42
C291 AP76 300fr dk red, cl & sl bl 1.00 .52
Nos. C288-C291 (4) 2.46 1.27

Christmas 1985 — AP77

1985, Dec. 22 Litho. *Perf. 13½*

C292 250fr Adoration of the Magi .85 .42

1988 Summer Olympics, Seoul — AP78

1988, June 1 Litho. *Perf. 13*

C293 AP78 100fr 400-Meter hurdles, vert. .65 .32
C294 AP78 170fr 5000-Meter race 1.10 .55
C295 AP78 200fr Long jump 1.30 .65
C296 AP78 600fr Triple jump, vert. 3.85 1.95
Nos. C293-C296 (4) 6.90 3.47

Souvenir Sheet

C297 AP78 750fr 10,000-Meter race, vert. 5.00 2.50

Stamps of 1982-84 Surcharged

1989 *Perfs. as Before*

C298 A115 100 on 300fr #446
C299 A116 100 on 250fr #C269
C300 AP73a 100 on 200fr #C278
C301 AP73a 100 on 200fr #C279
C302 A110 170 on 300fr #404
C303 A122 170 on 200fr #503
C304 A123 170 on 250fr #509
C305 A108 170 on 300fr #C259
C306 A112 240 on 300fr #425

AIR POST SEMI-POSTAL STAMPS

Catalogue values for unused stamps in this section are for Never Hinged items.

Ramses II Battling the Hittites (from Abu Simbel) — SPAP1

Unwmk.

1964, Mar. 9 Engr. *Perf. 13*

CB1	SPAP1	10fr + 5fr multi	.22	.20
CB2	SPAP1	25fr + 5fr multi	.35	.25
CB3	SPAP1	50fr + 5fr multi	.65	.60
		Nos. CB1-CB3 (3)	1.22	1.05

UNESCO world campaign to save historic monuments in Nubia.

Lions Emblem — SPAP2

1967, July 5 Photo. *Perf. 13*

CB4	SPAP2	50fr + 10fr multi	.60	.22

50th anniv. of Lions Intl. and to publicize the Lions work for the blind.

POSTAGE DUE STAMPS

TCHAD

Postage Due Stamps of France Overprinted

A. E. F.

1928 Unwmk. *Perf. 14x13½*

J1	D2	5c light blue	.15	.15
J2	D2	10c gray brown	.15	.15
J3	D2	20c olive green	.20	.20
J4	D2	25c bright rose	.35	.35
J5	D2	30c light red	.40	.40
J6	D2	45c blue green	.55	.55
J7	D2	50c brown violet	.65	.65
J8	D2	60c yellow brown	.75	.75
J9	D2	1fr red brown	.75	.75
J10	D2	2fr orange red	2.50	2.50
J11	D2	3fr bright violet	1.25	1.25
		Nos. J1-J11 (11)	7.70	7.70

Huts — D3

Canoe — D4

1930 Typo. *Perf. 14x13½, 13½x14*

J12	D3	5c dp bl & olive	.20	.20
J13	D3	10c dk red & brn	.30	.30
J14	D3	20c grn & brn	.50	.50
J15	D3	25c lt bl & brn	.60	.60
J16	D3	30c bis brn & Prus bl	.60	.60
J17	D3	45c Prus bl & olive	.85	.85
J18	D3	50c red vio & brn	1.10	1.10
J19	D3	60c gray lil & bl blk	1.25	1.25
J20	D4	1fr bis brn & bl blk	1.25	1.25
J21	D4	2fr vio & brn	2.50	2.50
J22	D4	3fr dp red & brn	20.00	20.00
		Nos. J12-J22 (11)	29.15	29.15

In 1934 stamps of Chad were superseded by those of French Equatorial Africa.

Catalogue values for unused stamps in this section, from this point to the end of the section, are for Never Hinged items.

Republic

Rhinoceros — D5

Tibesti Pictographs: No. J24, Kudu. No. J25, Two antelopes. No. J26, Three antelopes. No. J27, Ostrich. No. J28, Horned bull. No. J29, Bull. No. J30, Wild swine. No. J31, Elephant. No. J32, Rhinoceros. No. J33, Warrior with spear and shield. No. J34, Masked archer.

Unwmk.

1962, Apr. 20 Engr. *Perf. 13*

J23	D5	50c olive bister	.15	.15
J24	D5	50c brown red	.15	.15
J25	D5	1fr blue	.15	.15
J26	D5	1fr green	.15	.15
J27	D5	2fr vermilion	.15	.15
J28	D5	2fr maroon	.15	.15
J29	D5	5fr slate green	.15	.15
J30	D5	5fr violet blue	.15	.15
J31	D5	10fr brown	.35	.35
J32	D5	10fr orange brown	.35	.35
J33	D5	25fr carmine rose	.80	.80
J34	D5	25fr violet	.80	.80
		Set value	3.00	3.00

The two designs of the same denomination are printed se-tenant.

Dolls — D6

1969, Sept. 19 Engr. *Perf. 14x13*

J35	D6	1fr Kanem	.15	.15
J36	D6	2fr Kotoko	.15	.15
J37	D6	5fr Leather	.15	.15
J38	D6	10fr Kotoko	.15	.15
J39	D6	25fr Guera	.30	.16
		Set value	.65	.45

MILITARY STAMPS

Catalogue values for unused stamps in this section are for Never Hinged items.

No. 78 Overprinted "F.M."

1965 Typo. *Perf. 14x13½*

M1	A5	20fr red & black	100.00	100.00

Flag Bearer and Map of Chad — M1

1st Regiment Emblem — M2

1968 Unwmk. Litho. *Perf. 13x12½*

M2	M1	tan & multi	1.00	.60

1972, Jan. 21 Photo. *Perf. 13*

M3	M2	blue & multi	.45	.25

OFFICIAL STAMPS

Catalogue values for unused stamps in this section are for Never Hinged items.

Flag and Map of Chad — O1

Perf. 13½x14

1966-71 Typo. Unwmk.

Flag in blue, yellow and carmine

O1	O1	1fr light blue	.15	.15
O2	O1	2fr gray	.15	.15
O3	O1	5fr black	.15	.15
O4	O1	10fr violet blue	.15	.15
O5	O1	25fr orange	.20	.15
O6	O1	30fr bright green	.25	.15
O7	O1	40fr carmine ('71)	.30	.15
O8	O1	50fr red lilac	.40	.20
O9	O1	85fr green	.65	.30
O10	O1	100fr brown	1.00	.35
O11	O1	200fr red	1.60	.60
		Nos. O1-O11 (11)	5.00	
		Set value		2.00

CHILE

'chi-lē

LOCATION — Southwest corner of South America
GOVT. — Republic
AREA — 292,135 sq. mi.
POP. — 11,682,260 (est. 1982)
CAPITAL — Santiago

100 Centavos = 1 Peso
1000 Milésimos = 100 Centésimos = 1 Escudo (1960)
100 Centavos = 1 Peso (1975)

Catalogue values for unused stamps in this country are for Never Hinged items, beginning with Scott 257 in the regular postage section, Scott B3 in the semi-postal section, Scott C125 in the airpost section, and Scott CB1 in the airpost semi-postal section.

Pen cancellations are common on the 1862-67 issues. Such stamps sell for much less than the quoted values which are for those with hand-stamped postal cancellations.

Watermarks

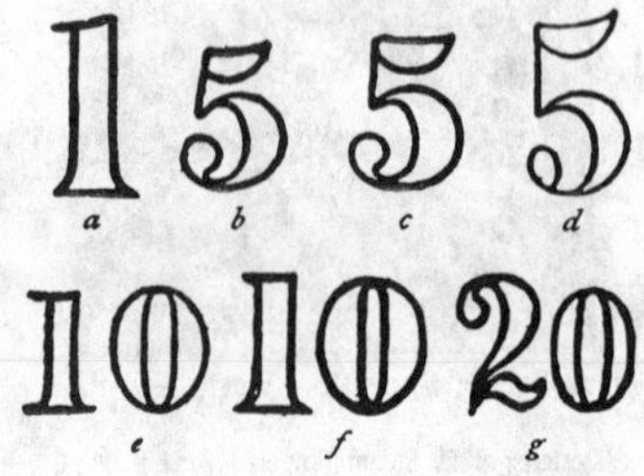

Wmk. 215- Small Star in Shield, Multiple

Christopher Columbus — A1

London Prints

1853 Wmk. b Engr. *Imperf.*

Blued Paper

1	A1	5c brown red	*375.00*	45.00
a.		White paper		72.50

Wmk. e

White Paper

2	A1	10c dp brt bl	*600.00*	90.00
a.		Blued paper		*475.00*
b.		Diag. half used as 5c on cover		*350.00*

Santiago Prints

Impressions Fine and Clear

1854 Wmk. b and e

White Paper

3	A1	5c pale red brn	325.00	32.50
a.		5c deep red brown	*350.00*	35.00
b.		5c chestnut	*575.00*	110.00
4	A1	5c burnt sienna	*1,050.*	165.00
a.		5c dull chocolate	*2,000.*	850.00
5	A1	10c deep blue	*875.00*	87.50
a.		10c slate blue		87.50
b.		10c greenish blue		850.00
c.		Half used as 5c on cover		400.00
6	A1	10c lt dl bl	*875.00*	87.50
a.		10c pale blue		87.50
b.		Diag. half used as 5c on cover		275.00

Litho.

7	A1	5c pale brown	*1,100.*	165.00
a.		5c red brown	*1,600.*	210.00

London Print

1855 Blued Paper Wmk. c Engr.

8	A1	5c brown red	125.00	8.75

Santiago Prints

Impressions Worn and Blurred

1856-62 Wmk. b and e

White Paper

9	A1	5c rose red ('58)	27.50	4.25
a.		5c carmine red ('62)	70.00	14.00
b.		5c orange red ('61)	175.00	105.00
c.		5c dull redsh brn ('57)	175.00	17.50
d.		Printed on both sides		*450.00*
e.		Double impression		
10	A1	10c deep blue	140.00	17.50
a.		10c sky blue ('57)	140.00	17.50
b.		10c light blue	140.00	17.50
c.		10c indigo blue	175.00	52.50
d.		Half used as 5c on cover		*125.00*

London Prints

1862 Wmk. a, f and g

11	A1	1c lemon yellow	22.50	27.50
a.		Double impression		*675.00*
12	A1	10c bright blue	35.00	6.00
a.		10c deep blue	35.00	6.00
b.		Blued paper	87.50	17.50
c.		Wmkd. "20" (error)	*5,000.*	*4,000.*
d.		Half used as 5c on cover		105.00
13	A1	20c green	52.50	32.50
a.		20c emerald		
		Nos. 11-13 (3)	110.00	66.00

Santiago Print

1865 Wmk. d

14	A1	5c rose red	21.00	8.75
a.		5c carmine red	25.00	8.75
b.		Printed on both sides	300.00	*210.00*
c.		Laid paper		*165.00*
d.		Double impression		*165.00*

The 5c rose red (shades) on unwatermaked paper, either wove or ribbed, and on paper watermarked Chilean arms in the sheet are reprints made about 1870.

No. 13 has been reprinted in the color of issue and in fancy colors, both from the original engraved plate and from lithographic transfers. The reprints are on paper without watermark or with watermark CHILE and Star.

A2

A3

1867 Unwmk. *Perf. 12*

15 A2 1c orange 12.50 1.75
Pen cancellation .25
16 A2 2c black 16.00 2.75
Pen cancellation .40
17 A2 5c red 12.50 .90
Pen cancellation .15
18 A2 10c blue 12.50 1.75
Pen cancellation .25
19 A2 20c green 17.50 2.75
Pen cancellation .35
Nos. 15-19 (5) 71.00 9.90

Unused values for Nos. 15-19 are for stamps with original gum.

1877 *Rouletted*

20 A3 1c gray 2.00 1.00
21 A3 2c orange 11.00 2.75
22 A3 5c dull lake 12.50 .75
23 A3 10c blue 11.00 1.75
a. Diagonal half used as 5c on cover
24 A3 20c green 11.50 2.75
Nos. 20-24 (5) 48.00 9.00

The panel inscribed "CENTAVO" is straight on No. 22.

A4

A5

Columbus — A6

1878-99 *Rouletted*

25 A4 1c green ('81) .75 .15
26 A4 2c rose ('81) 1.00 .15
27 A5 5c dull lake ('78) 3.75 .35
28 A5 5c ultra ('83) 1.00 .15
29 A5 10c orange ('85) 1.50 .30
a. 10c yellow 5.50 .75
30 A5 15c dk grn ('92) 1.25 .35
31 A5 20c gray ('86) 1.00 .35
32 A5 25c org brn ('92) 1.50 .40
33 A5 30c rose car ('99) 3.50 1.50
34 A5 50c lilac ('78) 35.00 7.00
35 A5 50c violet ('85) 1.75 .75
36 A6 1p dk brn & blk ('92) 18.00 1.50
a. Imperf. horiz. or vert., pair 90.00
Nos. 25-36 (12) 70.00 12.95

For surcharge and overprint see Nos. 50, O16.

Columbus
A7 A8

1894 Re-engraved

37 A7 1c blue green .70 .15
38 A7 2c carmine lake .70 .15

In type A4 there is a small colorless ornament at each side of the base of the numeral, above the "E" and "V" of "CENTAVO." In type A7 these ornaments are missing, the figure "1" is broader than in type A4 and the head of the figure "2" is formed by a curved line instead of a ball.

1900-01

Type I- There is a heavy shading of short horizontal lines below "Chile" and the adjacent ornaments.

Type II- There is practically no shading below "Chile" and the ornaments.

Type I

39 A8 1c yel grn .75 .15
40 A8 2c brn rose 1.50 .15
41 A8 5c dp bl 9.00 .15
42 A8 10c violet 5.50 .30
a. Horizontal pair, imperf. between
43 A8 20c gray 3.50 .75
44 A8 30c dp org ('01) 4.25 .75
45 A8 50c red brn 5.50 1.25
a. Horiz. pair, imperf. btwn. 52.50
Nos. 39-45 (7) 30.00 3.50

Type II

46 A8 1c yel grn ('01) .75 .15
47 A8 2c rose ('01) .75 .15
48 A8 5c dull blue ('01) 3.50 .15
a. Printed on both sides
49 A8 10c vio ('01) 4.50 .35
Nos. 46-49 (4) 9.50 .80

For surcharge see No. 57.

Columbus
A9 A10

1900

Black Surcharge

50 A9 5c on 30c rose car .70 .15
a. Inverted surcharge 27.50 14.00
b. Double surcharge 90.00 57.50
c. Double surcharge, both invtd. 90.00 57.50
d. Double surcharge, one invtd. 90.00 57.50
e. Surcharged on front and back 90.00 57.50

1901-02 *Perf. 12*

51 A10 1c green .25 .15
52 A10 2c carmine .35 .15
53 A10 5c ultra .70 .15
54 A10 10c red & blk 1.50 .35
55 A10 30c vio & blk 5.25 .35
56 A10 50c red org & blk 6.25 2.10
Nos. 51-56 (6) 14.30 3.25

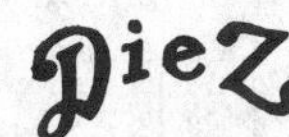

No. 44 Surcharged in Dark Blue

1903 *Rouletted*

57 A8 10c on 30c orange 1.75 .35
a. Inverted surcharge 17.50 10.50
b. Double surcharge 21.00 10.50
c. Double surch., one inverted 21.00 10.50
d. Double surch., both invtd. 21.00 10.50
e. Stamp design printed on both sides

Pedro de Valdivia
A11

Coat of Arms
A12

A13

Telegraph Stamps Surcharged or Overprinted in Black

Type I - Animal at left has neither mane nor tail.
Type II - Animal at left has mane and tail.

1904 *Perf. 12*

58 A11 1c on 20c ultra .25 .15
a. Imperf. horiz., pair 35.00 35.00
b. Inverted surcharge 42.50 42.50
59 A13 2c yel brn, I .25 .15
a. Inverted overprint 17.50 17.50
b. Pair, one without overprint 42.50 42.50
60 A13 5c red, I .45 .15
a. Inverted overprint 17.50 17.50
c. Pair, one without overprint 42.50 42.50
61 A13 10c ol grn, I 1.40 .45
a. Inverted overprint 42.50 42.50
Nos. 58-61 (4) 2.35 .90

Perf. 12½ to 16

62 A13 2c yel, brn, II 4.25 4.25
63 A11 3c on 5c brn red 42.50 37.50
a. Inverted surcharge
64 A12 3c on 1p brn, II .45 .35
a. Double surcharge 42.50 42.50
65 A13 5c red, II 7.25 7.25
a. Inverted overprint
66 A13 10c ol grn, II 17.00 10.00
67 A11 12c on 5c brn red .90 .45
a. No star at left of "Centavos" 1.90 1.25
b. Inverted surcharge 35.00 35.00
c. Double surcharge 42.50 42.50
Nos. 62-67 (6) 72.35 59.80

Counterfeits exist of the overprint and surcharge varieties of Nos. 57-67.

For overprint see No. O12.

A14

A15

Columbus — A16

1905-09 *Perf. 12*

68 A14 1c green .25 .15
69 A14 2c carmine .30 .15
70 A14 3c yel brn .55 .25
71 A14 5c ultra .55 .15
72 A15 10c gray & blk 1.05 .15
73 A15 12c lake & blk 5.00 1.75
74 A15 15c vio & blk 1.05 .15
75 A15 20c org brn & blk 2.50 .15
76 A15 30c bl grn & blk 3.25 .25
77 A15 50c ultra & blk 3.50 .25
78 A16 1p gold, grn & gray 10.50 9.00
Nos. 68-78 (11) 28.50 12.40

A 20c dull red and black, type A15, was prepared but not issued. Value $125. "Specimen" copies of Nos. 74, 76-78 exist, punched to prevent postal use.

For surcharges and overprints see Nos. 79-82, O9, O11-O15.

Nos. 73, 78 Surcharged in Blue or Red

ISLAS DE
JUAN FERNANDEZ
5
a

ISLAS DE
JUAN FERNANDEZ
10 Cts.
b

1910

79 A15 (a) 5c on 12c (Bl) .45 .15
80 A16 (b) 10c on 1p (R) 1.05 .25
81 A16 (b) 20c on 1p (R) 1.50 .55
82 A16 (b) 1p (R) 2.75 1.05
Nos. 79-82 (4) 5.75 2.00

The 1p is overprinted "ISLAS DE JUAN FERNANDEZ" only. The use of these stamps throughout Chile was authorized.

Independence Centenary Issue

Oath of Independence
A17

Monument to O'Higgins
A26

Gen. Manuel Blanco Encalada — A29

Designs: 2c, Battle of Chacabuco. 3c, Battle of Roble. 5c, Battle of Maipu. 10c, Naval Engagement of "Lautaro" and "Esmeralda." 12c, Capturing the "Maria Isabel." 15c, First Sortie of Liberating Forces. 20c, Abdication of O'Higgins. 25c, Chile's First Congress. 50c, Monument to José M. Carrera. 1p, Monument to San Martin. 5p, Gen. José Ignacio Zenteno. 10p, Adm. Lord Thomas Cochrane.

1910

Center in Black

83 A17 1c dk green .25 .15
a. Center inverted 7,000.
84 A17 2c lake .25 .15
85 A17 3c red brown .95 .45
86 A17 5c dp blue .55 .15
87 A17 10c gray brn .95 .30
88 A17 12c vermilion 2.25 1.00
89 A17 15c slate 2.25 .45
90 A17 20c red orange 3.00 .80
91 A17 25c ultra 3.75 1.50
92 A26 30c violet 3.00 .80
93 A26 50c olive grn 6.50 2.25
94 A26 1p yel org 15.00 5.25
95 A29 2p red 15.00 5.25
96 A29 5p yel grn 37.50 17.50
97 A29 10p dk violet 35.00 16.00
Nos. 83-97 (15) 126.20 52.00

Columbus
A32

De Valdivia
A33

Mateo de Toro Zambrano
A34

Bernardo O'Higgins
A35

Ramón Freire — A36

F. A. Pinto — A37

Joaquín Prieto — A38

Manuel Bulnes — A39

Manuel Montt — A40

José Joaquín Pérez — A41

Federico Errázuriz Zanartu — A42

Aníbal Pinto — A43

Designs: 2p, Domingo Santa María. 5p, José de Balmaceda. 10p, Federico Errázuriz Echaurren.

Outer backgrounds consist of horizontal and diagonal lines

1911 Engr. *Perf. 12*

98 A32 1c dp green .25 .15
99 A33 2c scarlet .25 .15
100 A34 3c sepia .75 .25
101 A35 5c dk blue .25 .15
102 A36 10c gray & blk .70 .15
a. Center inverted 1,000. 700.00
103 A37 12c carmine & blk 1.05 .15
104 A38 15c violet & blk .90 .15
a. Center inverted 1,000.
105 A39 20c org red & blk 1.75 .15
a. Center inverted 60.00 60.00
106 A40 25c lt blue & blk 2.10 .55
107 A41 30c bis brn & blk 3.25 .25
108 A42 50c myr grn & blk 3.75 .25
109 A43 1p green & blk 7.00 .30

110 A43 2p ver & blk 12.50 1.05
111 A43 5p ol grn & blk 45.00 7.00
112 A43 10p org yel & blk 37.50 5.50
Nos. 98-112 (15) 117.00 16.20

See Nos. 117, 121, 123, 127-128, 133-141, 143, 155A, 157-161, 165-169,171-172 and designs A47-A55, A57. For overprints see Nos. C6, C6B-C6D, C7-C8, C10-C11, C13-C21, O19-O22, O24-O27, O30-O34, O40.

Columbus
A47

Toro
Zambrano
A48

Freire
A49

O'Higgins
A50

1912-13 Engr. *Perf. 12*

113 A47 2c scarlet .20 .15
114 A48 4c black brn .30 .15
115 A49 8c gray 1.00 .15
116 A50 10c blue & blk 1.00 .15
 a. Center inverted 600.00 500.00
 b. Imperf. horiz. or vert., pair 50.00
117 A37 14c car & blk 1.00 .15
121 A38 40c violet & blk 4.50 .50
123 A40 60c lt blue & blk 10.00 1.25
Nos. 113-123 (7) 18.00 2.50

See Nos. 125-126, 131, 164, 170, 173. For overprints see Nos. C6E, O18, O23, O28, O29.

Cochrane
A52

Columbus
A53

1915 Engr. *Perf. 13¹/₂x14*

124 A52 5c slate blue .55 .15
 a. Imperf., pair 11.50

See Nos. 155, 162-163. For overprints see Nos. O17, O37.

1918

125 A49 8c slate 13.00 .50

No. 125 is from a plate made in Chile to resemble No. 115. The top of the head is further from the oval, the spots of color enclosed in the figures "8" are oval instead of round, and there are many small differences in the design.

1921

Worn Plate

126 A49 8c gray 25.00 6.25

No. 126 differs from No. 125 in not having diagonal lines in the frame and only a few diagonal lines above the shoulders (due to wear), while No. 125 has diagonal lines in the oval up to the level of the forehead.

1915-25 Typo. *Perf. 13¹/₂ to 14¹/₂*

127 A32 1c gray green .25 .15
128 A33 2c red .25 .15
129 A53 4c brown ('18) .35 .15

Frame Litho.; Head Engr.

131 A50 10c bl & blk 1.40 .15
 a. 10c dark blue & black 1.25 .15
 b. Imperf., pair 110.00
 c. Center inverted 325.00
133 A38 15c vio & blk 1.00 .15
134 A39 20c org red & blk 1.75 .15
 a. 20c brown orange & blk 1.75 .15
135 A40 25c dl bl & blk .65 .15
136 A41 30c bis brn & blk 2.25 .15
137 A42 50c dp grn & blk 2.50 .15

Perf. 14

138 A43 1p grn & blk 10.00 .20
139 A43 2p red & blk 12.00 .15
 a. 2p vermilion & black 32.50 .60
140 A43 5p ol grn & blk ('20) 27.50 .60
141 A43 10p org & blk ('25) 30.00 1.75
Nos. 127-141 (13) 89.90
Set value 3.50

The frames have crosshatching on the 15c, 20c, 30c, 2p, 5p and 10p. They have no crosshatching on the 10c, 25c, 50c and 1p.

Nos. 131a and 134a are printed from new head plates which give blacker and heavier impressions. No. 131a exists with; (a) frame litho., head engr.; (b) frame typo., head engr.; (c) frame typo., head litho. No. 134a is with frame typo., head engr.

A 4c stamp with portrait of Balmaceda and a 14c with portrait of Manuel de Salas were prepared but not placed in use. Both stamps were sent to the paper mill at Puente Alto for destruction. They were not all destroyed as some were privately preserved and sold.

Columbus
A54

Manuel
Rengifo
A55

Types of 1915-20 Redrawn

1918-20 *Perf. 13¹/₂x14¹/₂*

143 A32 1c gray grn ('20) .40 .15
144 A54 4c brown .50 .15

No. 143 has all the lines much finer and clearer than No. 127. The white shirt front is also much less shaded.

1921

145 A55 40c dk vio & blk 2.00 .15

For overprints see Nos. C6A, C9.

Pan-American
Congress
Building — A56

Adm. Juan José
Latorre — A57

1923, Apr. 25 Typo. *Perf. 14¹/₂x14*

146 A56 2c red .20 .15
147 A56 4c brown .20 .15

Typo.; Center Engr.

148 A56 10c blue & blk .20 .15
149 A56 20c orange & blk .50 .15
150 A56 40c dl vio & blk .75 .20
151 A56 1p green & blk .90 .30
152 A56 2p red & blk 3.25 .40
153 A56 5p dk grn & blk 11.50 3.00
Nos. 146-153 (8) 17.50 4.50

Fifth Pan-American Congress.

Typographed; Head Engraved

1927 *Perf. 13¹/₂x14¹/₂*

154 A57 80c dk brn & blk 2.00 .60

Types of 1915-25 Issues
Inscribed: "Chile Correos"

Perf. 13¹/₂x14¹/₂

1928-31 Engr. Wmk. 215

155 A52 5c slate blue 1.10 .20

Frame Typo.; Center Engr.

155A A38 15c violet & blk 350.00
156 A55 40c dk vio & blk .55 .15
157 A42 50c dp grn & blk 2.00 .15

Perf. 14

158 A43 1p green & blk .90 .15
159 A43 2p red & blk 3.25 .15
160 A43 5p ol grn & blk 7.25 .25
161 A43 10p orange & blk 7.25 1.10
Nos. 155,156-161 (7) 22.30 2.15

Paper of #155-161 varies from thin to thick.

Types of 1915-25 Issues
Inscribed: "Correos de Chile"

1928 Engr. *Perf. 13¹/₂x14¹/₂*

162 A52 5c deep blue .40 .15

1929 Litho.

163 A52 5c light green .40 .15

Frame Litho.; Center Engr.

164 A50 10c blue & blk 1.75 .15
165 A38 15c violet & blk 1.90 .15
166 A39 20c org red & blk 4.50 .15
167 A40 25c blue & blk .85 .15
168 A41 30c brown & blk .60 .20
169 A42 50c dp grn & blk .50 .15
Nos. 163-169 (7) 10.50
Set value .65

Redrawn

1929 Frame Typo.; Center Litho.

170 A50 10c blue & blk 2.00 .15
171 A38 15c violet & blk 1.75 .15
172 A39 20c org red & blk 2.75 .15
Nos. 170-172 (3) 6.50
Set value .35

1931 Unwmk.

173 A50 10c blue & blk .70 .20

In the redrawn stamps the lines behind the portraits are heavier and completely fill the ovals. There are strong diagonal lines above the shoulders. On #170 the head is larger than on #164, 173.

A58

Prosperity of Saltpeter Trade
A59 A60

Perf. 13¹/₂x14

1930, July 21 Litho. Wmk. 215

Size: 20x25mm

175 A58 5c yellow grn .35 .15
176 A58 10c red brown .35 .15
177 A58 15c violet .35 .15
178 A59 25c deep gray 1.40 .40
179 A60 70c dark blue 3.50 1.00

Perf. 14

Size: 24¹/₂x30mm

180 A60 1p dk gray grn 2.50 .50
Nos. 175-180 (6) 8.45 2.35

Cent. of the 1st shipment of saltpeter from Chile, July 21, 1830.

Manuel Bulnes
A61

Bernardo
O'Higgins
A62

1931 *Perf. 13¹/₂, 14*

181 A61 20c dark brown .90 .15

For overprints see Nos. O35, O39.

1932

182 A62 10c deep blue 1.00 .15

For overprints see Nos. O36, O38.

Mariano
Egana — A63

Joaquin
Tocornal — A64

1934 *Perf. 13¹/₂x14*

183 A63 30c magenta .50 .15

Perf. 14

184 A64 1.20p bright blue .90 .20

Centenary of the constitution.

José Joaquín Pérez — A65

1934 *Perf. 13¹/₂x14*

185 A65 30c bright pink 1.40 .15

Atacama
Desert — A66

Designs: 10c, Fishing boats. 20c, Coquito palms. 25c, Sheep. 30c, Mining. 40c, Lonquimay forest. 50c, Colliery at Port Lota. 1p, Shipping at Valparaiso. 1.20p, Puntiagudo volcano. 2p, Diego de Almagro. 5p, Cattle. 10p, Mining saltpeter.

Wmk. 215

1936, Mar. 1 Litho. *Perf. 14*

186 A66 5c vermilion .25 .15
187 A66 10c violet .15 .15
188 A66 20c magenta .15 .15
189 A66 25c grnsh blue 1.50 .50
190 A66 30c lt green .15 .15
191 A66 40c blk, *cream* 1.50 .65
192 A66 50c bl, *bluish* .75 .20

Engr.

193 A66 1p dk green .75 .30
194 A66 1.20p dp blue .90 .45
195 A66 2p dk brown .90 .55
196 A66 5p copper red 2.50 1.50
197 A66 10p dk violet 6.00 5.25
Nos. 186-197 (12) 15.50 10.00

400th anniv. of the discovery of Chile by Diego de Almagro.

Laja
Waterfall — A78

Fishing in
Chiloé — A84

Designs: 10c, Agriculture. 15c, Boldo tree. 20c, Nitrate Industry. 30c, Mineral spas. 40c, Copper mine. 50c, Mining. 1.80p, Osorno Volcano. 2p, Mercantile marine. 5p, Lake Villarrica. 10p, State railways.

Perf. 13¹/₂x14

1938-40 Litho. Wmk. 215

198 A78 5c brn car ('39) .20 .15
199 A78 10c sal pink ('39) .20 .15
200 A78 15c brn org ('40) .20 .15
201 A78 20c light blue .20 .15
202 A78 30c brt pink .20 .15
203 A78 40c lt grn ('39) .20 .15
204 A78 50c violet .20 .15

Engr. *Perf. 14*

205 A84 1p orange brn .20 .15
206 A84 1.80p deep blue .45 .25
207 A84 2p car lake .20 .15
208 A84 5p dk slate grn .35 .15
209 A84 10p rose vio ('40) .90 .15
Nos. 198-209 (12) 3.50
Set value 1.00

See Nos. 217-227. For surcharge and overprints see Nos. 253, O41-O66, O70-O71.

Map of the
Americas — A89

Unwmk.

1940, Sept. 11 Litho. *Perf. 14*

210 A89 40c dl grn & yel grn .15 .15

Pan American Union, 50th anniversary.

Camilo Henríquez — A90

Founding of Santiago A93

Designs: 40c, Pedro de Valdivia. 1.10p, Benjamin Vicuna Mackenna. 3.60p, Diego Barros Arana.

Perf. 14½x14, 14½

1941, Jan. 23 Engr. Wmk. 215

211	A90	10c	car lake	.20	.15
212	A90	40c	green	.25	.15
213	A90	1.10p	red	.90	.50
214	A93	1.80p	blue	.90	.50
215	A90	3.60p	indigo	2.75	2.00
			Nos. 211-215 (5)	5.00	3.30

400th anniversary of Santiago.

Types of 1938

Perf. 13½x14

1942-46 Unwmk. Litho.

217	A78	10c	sal pink ('43)	.20	.15
218	A78	15c	brn org ('43)	.20	.15
219	A78	20c	lt bl ('43)	.20	.15
220	A78	30c	brt pink ('43)	.20	.15
221	A78	40c	yel grn	.70	.15
222	A78	50c	vio ('43)	.20	.15

Engr. *Perf. 14*

223	A84	1p	brn org	1.40	.15
225	A84	2p	car lake ('43)	.20	.15
226	A84	5p	dk sl grn ('43)	.45	.15
227	A84	10p	rose vio ('46)	.75	.15
			Nos. 217-227 (10)	4.50	
			Set value		.70

Valentin Letelier A95

University of Chile A98

Designs: 40c, Andrés Bello. 90c, Manuel Bulnes. 1.80p, Manuel Montt.

1942, Nov. 1 *Perf. 14x14½, 14 (1p)*

228	A95	30c	rose red	.20	.15
229	A95	40c	dp grn	.20	.15
230	A95	90c	rose vio	1.00	.90
231	A98	1p	dp brn	.70	.50
232	A95	1.80p	dk bl	2.00	1.75
			Nos. 228-232 (5)	4.10	3.45

University of Chile cent. See No. C89.

Manuel Bulnes — A100

Map Showing Strait of Magellan — A104

Designs: 30c, Juan Williams Wilson. 40c, Diego Duble Almeida. 1p, José Mardones.

1944, Mar. 2 Litho. *Perf. 14*

233	A100	15c	black	.20	.15
234	A100	30c	dp rose	.20	.15
235	A100	40c	yel grn	.20	.15
236	A100	1p	brn car	.85	.15
237	A104	1.80p	ultra	1.25	.70
			Nos. 233-237 (5)	2.70	1.30

100th anniversary of the occupation of the Strait of Magellan.

Red Cross and Lamp of Life — A105

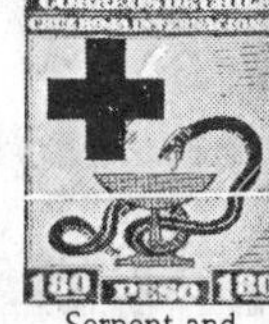
Serpent and Cup — A106

1944, Oct. 18 Unwmk.

238	A105	40c	grn, red & blk	.25	.15
239	A106	1.80p	ultra & red	.60	.35

80th anniv. of the Intl. Red Cross Soc.

Bernardo O'Higgins — A107

"Embrace of Maipú" (O'Higgins Joining San Martin) A108

Designs: 40c, Abdication of O'Higgins. 1.80p, Battle of Rancagua.

1945 Engr. *Perf. 14 (15c), 14½*
Center in Black

240	A107	15c	carmine	.25	.15
241	A108	30c	brown	.25	.15
242	A108	40c	dp grn	.25	.15
243	A108	1.80p	dk bl	1.25	.80
			Nos. 240-243 (4)	2.00	1.25

Death of Bernardo O'Higgins in 1842, cent.

A111

A112

Proposed Columbus lighthouse.

Wmk. 215

1945, Sept. 10 Litho. *Perf. 14*

244	A111	40c	light green	.20	.15

Issued in honor of the discovery of America by Columbus and the Memorial Lighthouse to be erected in his memory.

1946 Engr.

245	A112	40c	dk grn	.15	.15
246	A112	1.80p	dk bl	.15	.15
			Set value		.20

80th anniv. of the death of Andrés Bello, poet and educator.

Map Showing Chile's Claims of Antarctic Territory — A113

1947, May 12 Litho. *Perf. 14½*

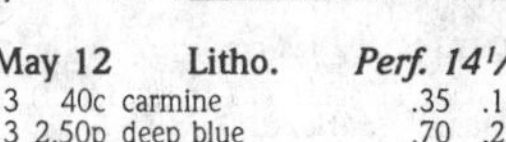

247	A113	40c	carmine	.35	.15
248	A113	2.50p	deep blue	.70	.25

Eusebio Lillo and Ramon Carnicer A114

1947, Sept. 18 Engr.

249	A114	40c	dark green	.15	.15

Centenary of national anthem.

Miguel de Cervantes Saavedra — A115

1947, Oct. 11 Wmk. 215

250	A115	40c	dk carmine	.20	.15

400th anniv. of the birth of Cervantes, novelist, playwright and poet.

Arturo Prat Chacón and Iquique Naval Battle A116

1948, Dec. 24 *Perf. 14½*

251	A116	40c	deep blue	.20	.15

Centenary of the birth of Arturo Prat Chacon, Chilean naval hero.

Bernardo O'Higgins — A117

Perf. 13½x14

1948 Wmk. 215 Litho.

252	A117	60c	black	.15	.15

See No. 262. For surcharges see Nos. 266-267.

No. 203 Surcharged in Black

VEINTE
CTS.

1948

253	A78	20c on 40c	lt grn	.15	.15

Chilean Pigeons — A118

FAUNA: a, Chilean Otter. c, Chilean pigeons. d, American skunk. f, Southern sea lions. g, Sugar-cane borer moth. h, Emperor penguins. i, Bat. j, Chinchilla. k, Grant's stag beetle. l, Trevally (fish). m, Chilean slender lizard. o, Crested caracara. q, Red-gartered coot. r, Chilean guemal (deer). s, Spiny rock lobster. u, Tilefish. v, Praying mantis. x, Torrent duck. y, Red conger.

FLORA: b, Araucarian pine (monkey puzzle tree). e, Evening primrose. n, Chilean red bell flower. p, Loxodon (flower). t, Boldo tree. w, Coquito palm trees.

Wmk. 215

1948, Dec. 6 Litho. *Perf. 14*

254	A118	60c	Block of 25	7.50	
a.-y.			any single	.25	.15
255	A118	2.60p	Block of 25	10.00	
a.-y.			any single	.35	.25

Issued in panes of 100.

Cent. (in 1944) of the publication of the 1st volume of Claudio Gay's Natural History of Chile. See No. C124.

Catalogue values for unused stamps in this section, from this point to the end of the section, are for Never Hinged items.

Benjamin Vicuna Mackenna — A121

1949, Mar. 22 Engr. *Perf. 13½x14*

257	A121	60c	deep blue	.15	.15

See No. C126.

Symbols of Arts and Crafts Education — A122

Heinrich von Stephan — A123

Design: 2.60p, Badge and book.

Unwmk.

1949, Nov. 11 Litho. *Perf. 14*

258	A122	60c	lilac rose	.20	.15
259	A122	2.60p	vio bl	.40	.35
			Nos. 258-259,C127-C128 (4)	2.20	1.50

Cent. of the foundation of Chile's School of Arts and Crafts.

1950, Jan. 6 Engr.

260	A123	60c	dp car	.20	.15
261	A123	2.50p	dp bl	.40	.30
			Nos. 260-261,C129-C130 (4)	1.45	1.05

UPU, 75th anniv.

O'Higgins Type of 1948

1950 Litho. *Perf. 13x14*

262	A117	60c	black	.15	.15

For surcharge see No. 266.

San Martín — A124

Isabella I — A125

Wmk. 215

1951, Mar. 16 Engr. *Perf. 14*

263	A124	60c	deep blue	.15	.15

Cent. of the death of Gen. José de San Martin. See No. C165.

1952, Mar. 20

264	A125	60c	brt bl	.15	.15

500th anniv. of the birth of Queen Isabella I of Spain. See No. C166.

Bernardo O'Higgins A126

Mateo de Toro Zambrano A127

1952 Unwmk. Litho. *Perf. 13½x14*
265 A126 1p dk bl grn .15 .15

See No. 275. For overprints see Nos. O67-O69.

#262, 252 Surcharged "40 Ctvs." in Red

1952, Sept.
266 A117 40c on 60c black .15 .15

Wmk. 215
267 A117 40c on 60c black .15 .15
Set value .20 .15

1953, Mar. 13 Wmk. 215
268 A127 80c green .15 .15

See No. 285.

Valdivia Arms — A128

Old Fort — A129

Designs: 3p, Modern Valdivia. 5p, Street in ancient Valdivia.

1953, May *Perf. 14*
269 A128 1p brt ultra .35 .15
270 A129 2p dl rose vio .35 .15
271 A129 3p bl grn .45 .20
272 A129 5p dp brn .45 .20
Nos. 269-272,C167 (5) 2.60 .95

4th centenary of the founding of Valdivia, capital of Valdivia province.

José Toribio Medina (1852-1930), Historian and Bibliographer A130

1953, June Engr. *Perf. 14½*
273 A130 1p brown .15 .15
274 A130 2.50p dp bl .30 .20

O'Higgins Type of 1952

Perf. 13½x14

1953, Oct. Wmk. 215 Litho.
275 A126 1p dk bl grn .15 .15

For overprint see No. O69.

A131

A132

1953, Oct. 15 Engr. *Perf. 14½*
276 A131 1p Stamp of 1853 .20 .15

Centenary of Chile's first postage stamps.

Souvenir sheet including No. 276 is noted below No. C168.

1953, Nov. 5 Litho. *Perf. 13½x14*

Census chart and map.

277 A132 1p bl grn .15 .15
278 A132 2.50p vio bl .20 .15
279 A132 3p chocolate .30 .20
280 A132 4p carmine .40 .20
Nos. 277-280 (4) 1.05 .70

12th general census of population and housing.

Arms of Angol — A133

Ignacio Domeyko — A134

1954, May 28 Unwmk. *Perf. 14*
281 A133 2p dp car .15 .15

400th anniversary of the founding of Angol, capital of Malleco province.

1954, Aug. 16 Engr. *Perf. 13½x14*
282 A134 1p greenish blue .15 .15

150th anniversary of the birth of Ignacio Domeyko (1802-89), mineralogist and educator. See No. C171.

Early Steam Locomotive A135

1954, Sept. 10 Wmk. 215 *Perf. 14½*
283 A135 1p red .15 .15

Centenary (in 1951) of the first South American railroad. See No. C172.

Adm. Arturo Prat Chacón — A136

Arms of Viña del Mar — A137

1954 Unwmk. Litho. *Perf. 14*
284 A136 2p dk vio bl .15 .15

75th anniv. of the naval Battle of Iquique.

Toro Zambrano Type of 1953

1954, Nov. 6 *Perf. 13½x14*
285 A127 80c green .15 .15

1955, Mar. 5 Wmk. 215 *Perf. 14*

Design: 2p, Arms of Valparaiso.

286 A137 1p vio bl .15 .15
287 A137 2p carmine .15 .15
Set value .20 .16

1st Intl. Phil. Exhib., Valparaiso, Mar. 1955.

Dr. Alejandro del Rio — A138

1955, May 24 *Perf. 13½x14*
288 A138 2p vio bl .15 .15

14th Pan-American Sanitary Conference.

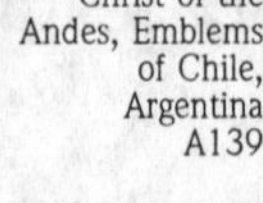

Christ of the Andes, Emblems of Chile, Argentina A139

1955, Aug. 31 Unwmk. *Perf. 14½*
289 A139 1p vio bl .15 .15

Reciprocal visits of Presidents Juan D. Peron and Carlos Ibanez del Campo. See No. C173.

Manuel Rengifo — A140

Portraits: 5p, Mariano Egana. 50p, Diego Portales.

1955-56 Unwmk. *Perf. 14x14½*
290 A140 3p vio bl .15 .15
291 A140 5p dk car rose .15 .15
292 A140 50p rose lil ('56) 1.50 .40
Nos. 290-292 (3) 1.80
Set value .56

Joaquin Prieto (1786-1854), soldier and political leader; president, 1831-41. See No. QRA1.

Jose M. Carrera — A141

Ramón Freire — A142

Portraits: 5p, Manuel Bulnes. 10p, Pres. Francisco A. Pinto. 50p, Manuel Montt.

Perf. 14x14½

1956-58 Unwmk. Litho.
293 A141 2p purple .15 .15
293A A142 3p lt vio bl .15 .15
294 A141 5p redsh brn (19½x23mm) .15 .15
a. Size 19x22mm .15 .15
295 A142 10p vio (19x22¼mm) .15 .15
a. Perf. 13½x14 (19¼x22½mm) ('58) .50 .15
296 A141 50p rose red .35 .15
Set value .80 .30

#294 has yellow gum; #294a, white gum.
For overprints see Nos. O72-O76.

Wmk. 215
297 A141 2p dl pur .15 .15
298 A142 3p vio bl .15 .15
Set value .20 .16

Federico Santa Maria — A143

Gabriela Mistral — A144

Unwmk.

1957, Jan. 31 Engr. *Perf. 14*
299 A143 5p dk red brn .15 .15

25th anniv. of the Federico Santa Maria Technical University. See Nos. C190-C191.

Souvenir sheet including No. 299 is noted below No. C191.

1958, Jan. 10
300 A144 10p red brn .15 .15

Issued in honor of Gabriela Mistral, poet and educator. See No. C192.

Arms of Osorno — A145

Arms of Santiago — A146

Design: 50p, Garcia Hdo. de Mendoza.

1958, Mar. 23 Litho. *Perf. 14*
301 A145 10p carmine .15 .15

Engr.
302 A145 50p green .30 .15

400th anniversary of the founding of the city of Osorno, capital of Osorno province.

Souvenir sheet including No. 302 in red brown is noted below No. C193.

1958, Oct. 18 Unwmk. *Perf. 14*
303 A146 10p dk vio .15 .15

Natl. Philatelic Exposition, Santiago, Oct. 18-26.

Souvenir sheet including No. 303 in deep red is noted below No. C194.

Symbolical Savings Bank — A147

Modern Map of Antarctica — A148

1958, Dec. 18
304 A147 10p dk bl .15 .15

Savings Bank for Public Employees, cent.

Souvenir sheet including No. 304 in violet is noted below No. C195.

1958, Aug. 28 Unwmk. *Perf. 14*
305 A148 40p rose car .15 .15

IGY, 1957-1958. See No. C214.

Antarctic Map and "La Araucana" A149

Map of Strait of Magellan, 1588 A150

1958 Litho. *Perf. 14*
310 A149 10p violet blue .15 .15

Engr.
311 A150 200p dull purple 2.00 1.10
Nos. 310-311,C199-C200 (4) 5.10 2.65

For overprint see No. O77.

Valdivia River Bridge — A153

1959, Feb. 9 Engr. *Perf. 14*
319 A153 40p green .20 .15

Cent. of the German School in Valdivia and to publicize the Valdivia Phil. Exhib., Feb. 9-18.

Souvenir sheet including No. 319 is noted below No. C213.

Strait of Magellan, Map by Pedro Sarmiento de Gamboa, c. 1582 — A154

1959, Aug. 27 **Litho.**
320 A154 10p dull purple .15 .15

Juan Ladrillero expedition to explore the Strait of Magellan, 1557-58, 400th anniv. See #C215.

Diego Barros Arana — A155

Henri Dunant — A156

1959, Aug. 27
321 A155 40p ultra .15 .15

50th anniv. of the death of Diego Barros Arana (1830-1907), historian. See No. C216.

1959, Oct. 6 **Unwmk.** ***Perf. 14***
322 A156 20p red & red brn .15 .15

Centenary of the Red Cross idea. See No. C217.

Manuel Bulnes — A157

Francisco A. Pinto — A158

Choshuenco Volcano — A159

Designs: No. 326, Choshuenco volcano, redrawn. 5c, Manuel Montt. 10c, Maule River Valley. 20c, 1e, Inca Lake.

1960-67 **Litho.** ***Perf. 13x14***
323 A157 5m bluish grn .15 .15
324 A158 1c carmine .15 .15

Perf. 14
Size: 29x25mm
325 A159 2c ultra ('61) .15 .15

Perf. 14x13
Size: 23½x18mm
326 A159 2c ultra ('62) .15 .15

Perf. 13x14
327 A157 5c blue .15 .15

Perf. 14
Size: 29x25mm
328 A159 10c grn ('62) .20 .15
329 A159 20c Prus bl ('62) .32 .15
329A A159 1e bluish grn ('67) .40 .20
Set value 1.20 .65

On No. 325 "Volcan Choshuenco" is at upper left, below "Correos." On No. 326, it is at bottom, above "Centesimos."
For overprint and surcharge see #O79, RA1.

Refugee Family — A160

1960, Apr. 7 ***Perf. 14½***
330 A160 1c green .15 .15

WRY, July 1, 1959-June 30, 1960. A souvenir sheet is noted below No. C218.

Type of Air Post Issue, 1962, and

Arms of Chile A161

José M. Carrera — A162

Designs: No. 332, Palace of Justice. 5c, National Memorial. 10c, Manuel de Toro y Zambrano and Martinez de Rozas. 20c, Manuel de Salas and Juan Egana. 50c, Manuel Rodriguez and Juan Mackenna.

Wmk. 215 (#331, 1e); Unwmk.
1960-65 **Engr.** ***Perf. 14½***
331 A161 1c maroon & sepia .16 .15
332 A161 1c brn & claret ('62) .15 .15
333 A162 5c grn & Prus grn ('61) .15 .15
334 AP54 10c brn & vio brn ('64) .16 .15
334A AP54 20c ind & bl grn ('65) .16 .15
335 AP54 50c red brn & mar ('65) .28 .15
336 A162 1e gray ol & brn 1.00 .40
Nos. 331-336,C218A-C220D (14) 4.56
Set value 1.90

150th anniv. of the formation of the 1st Natl. Government. A souvenir sheet is noted below No. C220B. See No. C285.

Family — A163

Design: 10c, Various buildings.

Unwmk.
1960, Jan. 18 **Litho.** ***Perf. 14***
337 A163 5c green .15 .15
338 A163 10c brt vio .15 .15
Set value .30 .16

13th population census (No. 337) and 2nd housing census (No. 338).

Chamber of Deputies A164

1961, Aug. 14 **Unwmk.** ***Perf. 14½***
339 A164 2c red brown .48 .15

150th anniv. of the 1st National Congress. See No. C245.

Soccer Players and Globe A165

Design: 5c, Goalkeeper and stadium (vert.).

1962, May 30 **Engr.** ***Perf. 14½***
340 A165 2c blue .16 .15
341 A165 5c green .24 .15
Set value .20

World Soccer Championship, Chile, May 30-June 17. Note on souvenir sheet follows No. C247.

Mother and Child — A166

Centenary Emblem — A167

1963, Mar. 21 **Litho.** ***Perf. 14***
342 A166 3c maroon .15 .15

FAO "Freedom from Hunger" campaign. See No. C248.

1963, Aug. 23 **Unwmk.** ***Perf. 14***
343 A167 3c red & gray .15 .15

Centenary of the Intl. Red Cross. See No.C249.

Fireman Carrying Woman — A168

Enrique Molina — A169

1963, Dec. 20 **Unwmk.** ***Perf. 14***
344 A168 3c violet .15 .15

Issued to commemorate the centenary of the Santiago Fire Brigade. See No. C250.

1964, Nov. 14 **Litho.** ***Perf. 14***

Design: No. 346, Magr. Carlos Casanueva.

345 A169 4c bister brown .15 .15
346 A169 4c rose claret .15 .15
Set value, #345-346, C257-C258 .42 .25

Enrique Molina, founder of the University of Concepcion, and Msgr. Carlos Casanueva, rector of the Catholic University, 1920-53.

Easter Island Statue A170

Copihue, National Flower A171

Design: 30c, Robinson Crusoe.

1965-69 **Litho.** ***Perf. 14x14½***
347 A170 6c rose lilac .15 .15
347A A170 10c rose pink ('68) .15 .15

Perf. 14
348 A171 15c yel grn & rose red .15 .15
348A A171 20c yel grn & rose red ('69) .15 .15

Perf. 14x14½
349 A170 30c rose claret .20 .15
Set value .65 .41

For surcharge see No. RA2.

Skier — A172

Lorenzo Sazie — A173

1965, Aug. 30 ***Perf. 14***
350 A172 4c bl grn .15 .15

World Skiing Championships, Chile, 1966.

1966, Feb. 9 **Litho.** ***Perf. 14x14½***
351 A173 1e green .50 .15

Cent. of the death of Dr. Lorenzo Sazie, dean of the Faculty of Medicine, University of Santiago.

German Riesco, President in 1901-1906 — A174

Portrait: 30c, Jorge Montt (1847-1922), president in 1891-1896.

1966 **Unwmk.** ***Perf. 13x14***
354 A174 30c violet .15 .15
355 A174 50c dl brn .15 .15
Set value .20 .15

William Wheelwright and S.S. Chile — A175

1966, Aug. 2 ***Perf. 14½***
358 A175 10c ultra & lt bl .15 .15

125th anniv. (in 1965) of the arrival of the paddle steamers "Chile" and "Peru." See No. C268.

Learning to Read — A176

1966, Aug. 13 **Litho.** ***Perf. 14***
359 A176 10c red brn .15 .15

Literacy campaign.

UN and ICY Emblems A177

1966, Oct. 28 **Unwmk.** ***Perf. 14½***
360 A177 1e grn & brn .80 .20

Intl. Cooperation Year, 1965. See No. C269.

Capt. Luis Pardo and Ship in Antarctica A178

1967, Jan. **Litho.** ***Perf. 14½***
361 A178 20c turq bl .15 .15

Rescue of the Shackleton South Pole expedition by Capt. Luis Pardo of Chile, 50th anniv. See #C271.

The Scott editorial staff regrettably cannot accept requests to identify, authenticate, or appraise stamps and postal markings.

Family — A179

Trees and Mountains — A180

1967, Apr. 13 Unwmk. *Perf. 14*

362 A179 10c magenta & blk .15 .15

8th Intl. Conf. for Family Planning, Santiago, Apr. 1967. See No. C272.

1967, June 9 Litho. *Perf. 14½*

363 A180 10c bl grn & lt bl .15 .15

Reforestation Campaign. See No. C274.

Lions Emblem — A181

1967, July 12 Litho. *Perf. 14*

364 A181 20c Prus bl & yel .15 .15

Nos. 269-272,C167 (5) 2.60

Set value .25

50th anniv. of Lions Intl.

Chilean Flag A182

1967, Oct. 20 Unwmk. *Perf. 14½*

365 A182 80c crim & ultra .15 .15

Natl, flag, 150th anniv. See No. C277.

José Maria Cardinal Caro — A183

1967, Dec. 4 Engr. *Perf. 14½*

366 A183 20c dp car .50 .30

Centenary of the birth of José Maria Cardinal Caro, the first Chilean cardinal. See No. C279.

San Martin and O'Higgins A184

1968, Apr. 23 Litho. Unwmk.

367 A184 3e blue .15 .15

Sesquicentennial of the Battles of Chacabuco and Maipu. See No. C280.

Farm Couple — A185

1968, June 18 *Perf. 14½*

368 A185 20c blk, org & grn .16 .15

Agrarian reforms. See No. C281.

Juan I. Molina A186

1968, Aug. 27 Litho. *Perf. 14½*

369 A186 2e red lilac .15 .15

Issued to honor Juan I. Molina, educator and scientist. See No. C282.

Hand Holding Cogwheel — A187

1968, Sept. *Perf. 14x14½*

370 A187 30c deep carmine .15 .15

Fourth census of manufacturers.

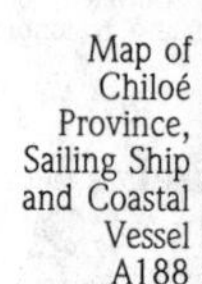

Map of Chiloé Province, Sailing Ship and Coastal Vessel A188

1968, Oct. 7 *Perf. 14½*

371 A188 30c ultra .15 .15

Anniversaries of the founding of five towns in Chiloé Province. See No. C283.

Automobile Club Emblem — A189

1968, Nov. 10 Engr. *Perf. 14½x14*

372 A189 1e car rose .15 .15

40th anniversary of the Automobile Club of Chile. See No. C284.

Francisco Garcia Huidobro A190

Design: 5e, King Philip V of Spain.

1968, Dec. 31 Litho. *Perf. 14½*

373 A190 2e pale rose & ultra .15 .15

374 A190 5e brn & yel grn .15 .15

Set value, #373-374, C288-C289 .35 .30

225th anniv. of the founding of the State Mint (Casa de Moneda de Chile).

Satellite and Radar Station A191

1969, May 20 Litho. *Perf. 14½*

375 A191 30c blue .15 .15

Inauguration of ENTEL-Chile, the 1st commercial satellite communications ground station, Longovilo.

See No. C290. For surcharge see No. 397.

Red Cross, Crescent and Lion and Sun Emblems A192

1969, Sept. Litho. *Perf. 14½*

376 A192 2e vio bl & red .15 .15

Issued to commemorate the 50th anniversary of the League of Red Cross Societies. See No. C291.

Rapel Hydroelectric Plant A193

1969, Nov. 18 Litho. *Perf. 14½*

377 A193 40c green .15 .15

See No. C292.

Col. Rodriguez Monument A194

1969, Nov. 24

378 A194 2e rose claret .15 .15

150th anniversary of the death of Col. Manuel Rodriguez. See No. C293.

EXPO '70 Emblem — A195

1969, Dec. 2 Litho. *Perf. 14*

379 A195 3e blue .15 .15

Issued to publicize EXPO '70 International Exhibition, Osaka, Japan, March 15-Sept. 13, 1970. See No. C294.

Open Book A196

1969, Dec. 3 *Perf. 14½*

380 A196 40c red brn .15 .15

400th anniv. of the translation of the Bible into Spanish by Casiodoro de Reina. See No. C295.

Globes and ILO Emblem A197

1969, Dec. 17 *Perf. 14½*

381 A197 1e grn & blk .15 .15

ILO, 50th anniv. See No. C296.

Human Rights Flame A198

1969, Dec. 18

382 A198 4e blue & red .15 .15

Human Rights Year, 1968. See No. C297.

Policarpo Toro and Easter Island A199

1970, Jan. 26 *Perf. 14½*

383 A199 5e lilac .15 .15

80th anniversary of the acquisition of Easter Island. See No. C298.

Sailing Ship and Arms of Valdivia A200

1970, Feb. 4 Litho. *Perf. 14½*

384 A200 40c dk car .15 .15

150th anniv. of the capture of Valdivia during Chile's war of independence by Thomas Cochrane (1775-1860), naval commander. See No. C299.

Paul Harris and Rotary Emblem — A201

1970, Mar. 18 Litho. *Perf. 14*

385 A201 10e vio bl .15 .15

Cent. of the birth of Paul Harris (1868-1947), founder of Rotary Intl. See No. C300.

Mahatma Gandhi — A202

Santo Domingo Church, Santiago, Chile — A203

1970, Apr. 1 Litho. *Perf. 14½*

386 A202 40c bl grn .15 .15

Issued to commemorate the centenary of the birth of Mohandas K. Gandhi (1869-1948), leader in India's fight for independence. See No. C301.

1970, Apr. 30 **Engr.**

Designs: 2e, Casa de Moneda de Chile, horiz. 3e, Pedro de Valdivia. 5e, Bridge, horiz. 10e, Ambrosio O'Higgins.

387 A203	2e vio brn		.15	.15
388 A203	3e dk red		.15	.15
389 A203	4e dk bl		.15	.15
390 A203	5e brown		.15	.15
391 A203	10e green		.15	.15
		Set value	.46	.28

Exploration and development of Chile by Spanish explorers.

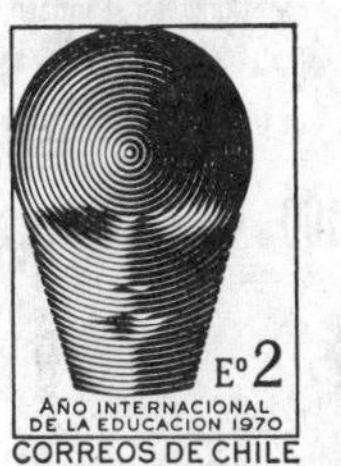

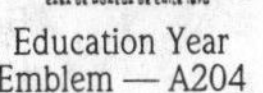

Education Year Emblem — A204

Virgin and Child — A205

1970, July 17 **Litho.** ***Perf. 14½***
392 A204 2e claret .15 .15

Issued for International Education Year. See No. C302.

1970, July 28
393 A205 40c green .15 .15

O'Higgins National Shrine at Maipu. See No. C303. For surcharge see No. 454.

Torch and Snake — A206

Copper Symbol, Chile Arms — A207

1970, Aug. 11
394 A206 40c claret & light blue .15 .15

International Cancer Congress, Houston, Texas, May 22-29. See No. C304.

1970, Oct. 21 **Litho.** ***Perf. 14½***
395 A207 40c car & lt red brn .15 .15

Nationalization of the copper industry. See No. C305. For surcharge see No. 459.

Dove and World Map A208

1970, Oct. 22
396 A208 3e rose magenta & pur .15 .15

25th anniv. of the UN. See No. C306.

No. 375 Surcharged in Red

1970, Dec. 24 **Litho.** ***Perf. 14½***
397 A191 52c on 30c blue .15 .15

Freighter and Ship's Wheel — A209

1971, Jan. 18 **Litho.** ***Perf. 14***
398 A209 52c dp car .15 .15

National Maritime Commission. See No. C307.

Bernardo O'Higgins and Ship A210

1971, Feb. 3 ***Perf. 14½***
399 A210 5e grnsh bl & grn .15 .15

150th anniv. of the expedition to liberate Peru from Spanish rule. See No. C309.

Youth, Girl and UN Emblem A211

1971, Feb. 11 **Litho.** ***Perf. 14½***
400 A211 52c dk bl & brn .15 .15

1st meeting in Latin America of the Executive Council of UNICEF, Santiago, May 20-31, 1969. See No. C310.

Chilean Boy Scout Emblem — A212

1971, Feb. 10 ***Perf. 14***
401 A212 1e grn & brn .15 .15

Founding of Chilean Boy Scouts, 60th anniversary. See No. C311.

Satellite and Radar Station A213

1971, May 25 **Litho.** ***Perf. 14½***
402 A213 40c dl grn .15 .15

First commercial Chilean satellite communications ground station, Longovilo. See No. C312.

Diver with Harpoon Gun A214

1971, Sept. 1

403 A214	1.15e lt & dk grn		.15	.15
404 A214	2.35e vio bl & dp vio bl		.15	.15
		Set value		.15

10th World Championship of Underwater Fishing.

Ferdinand Magellan and Sailing Ship — A215

1971, Nov. 3
405 A215 35c lt vio & brn vio .15 .15

450th anniv. of 1st trip through and discovery of the Strait of Magellan, Oct. 21-Nov. 28, 1520.

Dagoberto Godoy and Plane over Andes A216

1971, Nov. 4
406 A216 1.15e bl & grn .15 .15

First trans-Andean flight, Dec. 12, 1918.

Virgin of San Cristobal — A217

Chilean Flag and Congress Emblem A218

Designs (Congress Emblem and): 4.35e, Church of San Francisco. 9.35e, Central post office, horiz. 18.35e, La Posada (Inn) del Corregidor, horiz.

1971

407 A217	1.15e dk bl		.15	.15
408 A218	2.35e ultra & car		.15	.15
409 A217	4.35e brn red		.15	.15
410 A217	9.35e violet		.15	.15
411 A217	18.35e lil rose		.15	.15
		Set value	.60	.32

10th Cong. of the Postal Union of the Americas and Spain, Santiago. Issued: 2.35e, 4.35e, Nov. 5; 1.15e, Nov. 11; 9.35e, Nov. 18; 18.35e, Nov. 19.

Observation Dome, Cerro el Tololo Observatory A219

1971, Dec. 18
412 A219 1.95e lt & dk bl .15 .15

Boeing 707 over Easter Island A220

1971, Dec. 18
413 A220 2.35e dk brn & yel .15 .15

Inauguration of regular flights: Santiago, Easter Island, Tahiti.

Alonso de Ercilla y Zuniga — A221

1972, Mar. 20 **Engr.** ***Perf. 14***
414 A221 1e dk red .15 .15

4th centenary (in 1969) of "La Araucana," by Alonso de Ercilla y Zuniga (1533-1596), Spanish author. See No. C313.

Map of Antarctica and Dog Sled A222

1972, Mar. 20 **Litho.** ***Perf. 14½x15***

415 A222	1.15e vio bl & blk		.15	.15
416 A222	3.50e bl grn & grn		.15	.15
		Set value	.22	.16

10th anniversary (in 1971) of the Antarctic Treaty pledging peaceful uses of and scientific cooperation in Antarctica.

For surcharge see No. 630.

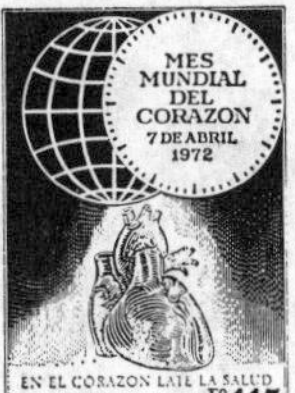

"Your Heart is your Health" — A223

1972, Apr. 2 **Litho.** ***Perf. 14½***
417 A223 1.15e blk & car .15 .15

World Health Day.

For surcharge see No. 631.

People and Statement by Pres. Allende A224

Conference Hall and UN Emblem A225

1972, Apr. 13 **Litho.** ***Perf. 14½***

418 A224	35c dl grn & buff		.15	.15
419 A225	1.15e ultra & pur		.15	.15
420 A224	4e dk pur & pale rose		.15	.15
421 A225	6e org & vio bl		.15	.15
		Nos. 418-421 (4)		.60
		Set value		.34

3rd UN Conf. on Trade and Development (UNCTAD III), Santiago, Apr.-May 1972. Design A224 is perf. horiz. in the middle.

Soldier, 1822, Andes, Military College Emblem A226

1972, June 9
422 A226 1.15e bl & yel .15 .15

Sesquicentennial of Bernardo O'Higgins Military College.

Miner Holding Copper Ingot, Chilean Flag — A227

Sailing Ship — A228

1972, July 11 Litho. *Perf. 15x14½*

423 A227	1.15e	bl & rose red	.15	.15
424 A227	5e	bl, blk & rose red	.15	.15
		Set value	.18	.15

Nationalization of copper industry.

1972, Aug. 4

425 A228	1.15e	violet brown	.15	.15

Arturo Pratt Naval Training School, sesqui.

Mt. Calan Observatory A229

1972, Aug. 31 Litho. *Perf. 14½*

426 A229	50c	ultra	.15	.15

University of Chile Mt. Calan Observatory.

Carrier Pigeon — A230

1972, Oct. 9 Litho. *Perf. 14½*

427 A230	1.15e	red lilac & vio	.15	.15

Intl. Letter Writing Week, Oct. 9-15.

René Schneider and Army Flag — A231

1972, Oct. 25 *Perf. 14*

428 A231	2.30e	multi	.15	.15

2nd anniv. of the death of Gen. René Schneider. No. 428 is perforated vertically in the middle.

Book and Young People A232

1972, Oct. 31 *Perf. 14½*

429 A232	50c	blk & dp org	.15	.15

International Book Year 1972.

Guitar and Earthen Jar — A233

Designs: 2.65e, Fish and produce. 3.50e, Stove, pots and rug, vert.

1972, Nov. 20 Litho. *Perf. 14½*

430 A233	1.15e	red & blk	.15	.15
431 A233	2.65e	ultra & rose lake	.15	.15
432 A233	3.50e	red & red brn	.15	.15
		Set value	.24	.15

Tourism Year of the Americas.

José M. Carrera Before Execution — A234

Map of Antarctica, Flag at Base — A235

1973, Feb. 1 Litho. *Perf. 14½*

433 A234	2.30e	lt ultra	.15	.15

Sesquicentennial of the death of José Miguel Carrera (1785-1821), Chilean revolutionist and dictator.

1973, Feb. 8

434 A235	10e	ultra & red	.15	.15

Bernardo O'Higgins Antarctic Base, 25th anniv.

Naval Air Service Emblem, Destroyer A236

La Silla Observatory A237

1973, Mar. 16 Litho. *Perf. 14½*

435 A236	20e	brt bl & ocher	.15	.15

Chilean Naval Aviation, 50th anniversary.

1973, Apr. 25 Litho. *Perf. 14½*

436 A237	2.30e	ultra & blk	.15	.15

INTERPOL Emblem — A238

Designs: 50e, Fingerprint over globe.

1973, Sept. 23 Litho. *Perf. 14½*

437 A238	30e	bis & ultra	.15	.15
438 A238	50e	blk & red	.25	.15
		Set value		.16

50th anniversary of International Criminal Police Organization.

Grapes — A239

Chilean wine export: 100e, Globe inscribed "Chile Exporta Vino."

1973, Dec. 10 Litho. *Perf. 14½*

439 A239	20e	buff & lilac	.15	.15
440 A239	100e	blue & claret	.15	.15
		Set value	.20	.16

UPU Headquarters, Bern — A240

1974, Apr. 4

441 A240	500e	on 45c green	.15	.15

UPU cent. No. 441 was not issued without dark green surcharge and overprint.

Bernardo O'Higgins, Armed Forces Emblems A241

1974, Apr. 11 Litho. *Perf. 14½*

442 A241	30e	shown	.15	.15
443 A241	30e	Soldiers with mortar	.15	.15
444 A241	30e	Navy anti-aircraft gunners	.15	.15
445 A241	30e	Pilot in cockpit	.15	.15
446 A241	30e	Mounted policeman	.15	.15
		Set value	.40	.25

Honoring the Armed Forces.

Soccer Ball and Globe — A242

Traffic Police — A243

Design: 1000e, Soccer ball and stadium, horiz.

1974 Litho. *Perf. 14*

447 A242	500e	dk red & org	.15	.15
448 A242	1000e	bl & indigo	.20	.15
		Set value		.15

World Cup Soccer Championship, Munich, June 13-July 7.

A souvenir sheet contains 2 imperf. stamps similar to Nos. 447-448, with blue marginal inscription. Printed on thin card. Size: 90x119mm.

Nos. 386, 355 Surcharged

1974, June Litho. *Perf. 14½*

449 A202	100e	on 40c bl grn	.15	.15

Perf. 13x14

450 A174	300e	on 50c dl brn	.15	.15
		Set value	.20	.15

1974, June 20 *Perf. 14½*

451 A243	30e	red brn & grn	.15	.15

Traffic safety.

Santiago-Australia Air Service — A244

1974, Sept. 5 Litho. *Perf. 14½x14*

452 A244		Block of 4	1.00	.50
a.	200e	Easter Island turtle	.20	.15
b.	200e	Polynesian dancer	.20	.15
c.	200e	Map of Fiji Islands	.20	.15
d.	200e	Kangaroo	.20	.15

Inauguration of air service by LAN (Chile's national airline) from Santiago to Easter Island, Tahiti, Fiji, Australia.

Globe Cut to Show Mantle and Core — A245

1974, Sept. 9 *Perf. 14x14½*

453 A245	500e	red brn & org	.15	.15

International Volcanology Congress, Santiago, Sept. 9-14.

E°100

INAUGURACION TEMPLO VOTIVO

24 OCTUBRE 1974

No. 393 Surcharged in Brown

1974, Oct. 24 Litho. *Perf. 14½*

454 A205	100e	on 40c green	.15	.15

Inauguration of the O'Higgins National Shrine at Maipu, Oct. 24, 1974.

Juan Fernandez Archipelago — A246

1974, Nov. 22 Litho. *Perf. 14½x14*

455 A246		Block of 4	.75	.50
a.	200e	Robinson Crusoe Island	.15	.15
b.	200e	Chonta palms	.15	.15
c.	200e	Mountain goat	.15	.15
d.	200e	Crayfish	.15	.15

400th anniversary of discovery of Juan Fernandez Archipelago.

O'Higgins and Bolivar A247

1974, Dec. 9 *Perf. 14½*

456 A247	100e	red brn & buff	.15	.15

Sesquicentennial of the Battles of Junin and Ayacucho.

F. Vidal Gormaz and Institute Seal A248

Albert Schweitzer A249

1975, Jan. 22 Litho. *Perf. 14½*

457 A248	100e	rose cl & bl	.15	.15

Centenary of the Naval Hydrographic Institute; F. Vidal Gormaz was first commandant.

1975, Apr. 7 Litho. *Perf. 14x14½*

458 A249	500e	yel & red brn	.15	.15

Dr. Albert Schweitzer (1875-1965), medical missionary, birth centenary.

E° 70.-

No. 395 Surcharged in Red

Revalorizada
1975

1975, Apr. 7 *Perf. 14½*
459 A207 70e on 40c car & lt red brn .15 .15

Volunteer Lifeboat Service — A250

1975, Apr. 15 **Litho.** *Perf. 14½x14*

460 A250	Block of 4	.75	.50
a.	150e Lighthouse	.15	.15
b.	150e Shipwreck	.15	.15
c.	150e Lifeboat	.15	.15
d.	150e Sailor reaching for life preserver	.15	.15

Valparaiso Volunteer Lifeboat service, 50th anniversary.

Frigate Lautaro A251

1975, May 21 **Photo. & Engr.**

461	A251	500e shown	.25	.15
462	A251	500e Corvette Baquedano	.25	.15
463	A251	500e Cruiser Chacabuco	.25	.15
464	A251	500e Brigantine Goleta Esmeralda	.25	.15
a.		Block of 4, #461-464	1.00	.75
465	A251	800e like #461	.30	.18
466	A251	800e like #462	.30	.18
467	A251	800e like #463	.30	.18
468	A251	800e like #464	.30	.18
a.		Block of 4, #465-468	1.25	1.00
469	A251	1000e like #461	.40	.20
470	A251	1000e like #462	.40	.20
471	A251	1000e like #463	.40	.20
472	A251	1000e like #464	.40	.20
a.		Block of 4, #469-472	1.75	1.25
		Nos. 461-472 (12)	3.80	2.12

Shipwreck of training frigate Lautaro, 30th anniversary. Se-tenant in sheets of 25 (5x5) with 7 Lautaro stamps and 6 each of the others.

A souvenir card contains impressions of Nos. 469-472. Size: 118x150mm.

Happy Mother, by Alfredo Valenzuela P. — A252

Diego Portales, Finance Minister — A253

Paintings: No. 474, Young Girl, by Francisco Javier Mandiola. No. 475, Lucia Guzman, by Pedro Lira Rencoret. No. 476, Woman, by Magdalena Mira Mena.

1975, Oct. 13 **Litho.** *Perf. 14½*

473 A252	50c multi	.15	.15
474 A252	50c multi	.15	.15
475 A252	50c multi	.15	.15
476 A252	50c multi	.15	.15
	Nos. 473-476 (4)	.60	.60

International Women's Year 1975. Gray inscription on back, printed beneath gum, gives details about painting shown.

A souvenir card contains impressions of Nos. 473-476.

Inscribed D. Portales

1975-78 **Litho.** *Perf. 13x14*

477	A253	10c gray grn	.15	.15
478	A253	20c vio ('76)	.15	.15
479	A253	30c org ('76)	.15	.15
480	A253	50c lt brn	.15	.15
481	A253	1p blue	.15	.15
482	A253	1.50p ocher ('76)	.15	.15
483	A253	2p gray ('77)	.15	.15
483A	A253	2.50p citron ('78)	.15	.15
483B	A253	3.50p pnksh rose ('78)	.20	.15
484	A253	5p rose claret	.20	.15
		Set value	1.20	.65

See #635-639. For surcharge see #533.

Cochrane and Liberating Squadron, 1820 A254

Designs: No. 486, Capture of Valdivia, 1820. No. 487, Capture of Three-master Esmeralda, 1820. No. 488, Cruiser Cochrane, 1874. No. 489, Destroyer Cochrane, 1962.

1976, Jan. 6 *Perf. 14½*

485 A254	1p multi	.15	.15
486 A254	1p multi	.15	.15
487 A254	1p multi	.15	.15
488 A254	1p multi	.15	.15
489 A254	1p multi	.15	.15
a.	Strip of 5, #485-489	.75	.75
	Nos. 485-489 (5)	.75	.75

Lord Thomas Cochrane, first commander of Chilean Navy, birth bicentenary.

Flags of Chile and Bolivia A255

1976, May 25 **Litho.** *Perf. 14½*
490 A255 1.50p multi .20 .15

Sesquicentennial of Bolivia's independence.

Lake of the Inca, OAS Emblem A256

1976, June 11
491 A256 1.50p multi .20 .15

6th General Assembly of the Organization of American States.

George Washington — A257

1976, July
492 A257 5p multi .38 .15

American Bicentennial.

Minerva and Academy Emblem A258

1976, July
493 A258 2.50p multi .15 .15

Polytechnic Military Academy, 50th anniv.

Araucan Indian — A259

Designs: 2p, Condor with broken chain. 3p, Winged woman, symbolizing rebirth.

1976, Sept. 20 **Litho.** *Perf. 14½*

494 A259	1p bl & multi	.15	.15
495 A259	2p bl & multi	.15	.15
496 A259	3p yel & multi	.25	.20
a.	Strip of 3, #494-496	.50	.45

3rd anniversary of the Military Junta.

View, Antarctica A260

1977, Feb. 10 **Litho.** *Perf. 14½*
497 A260 2p multi .15 .15

Visit of President Augusto Pinochet to Antarctica.

School Emblem, Planted Field — A261

Justice — A262

1977, Mar. 10 *Perf. 14½*
498 A261 2p multi .18 .15

Cent. of advanced agricultural education.

1977, Mar. 30 **Litho.** *Perf. 14½*
499 A262 2p brn & slate .18 .15

Supreme Court of Justice, sesquicentennial.

Eye with Globe, Caduceus A263

1977, Mar. 30 **Litho.** *Perf. 14½*
500 A263 2p multi .20 .15

11th Pan-American Ophthalmological Cong.

Mounted Policeman — A264

Designs: No. 502, Policewoman with children. No. 503, Paine Peaks and Osorno Volcano, crossed rifle emblem. No. 504, Crossed rifle emblem, mounted and motorcycle policemen, helicopter and automobile, horiz.

1977, Apr. 27

501 A264	2p multi	.15	.15
502 A264	2p multi	.15	.15
503 A264	2p multi	.15	.15
504 A264	2p multi	.15	.15
	Nos. 501-504 (4)	.60	.60

Chilean police organization, 50th anniv.

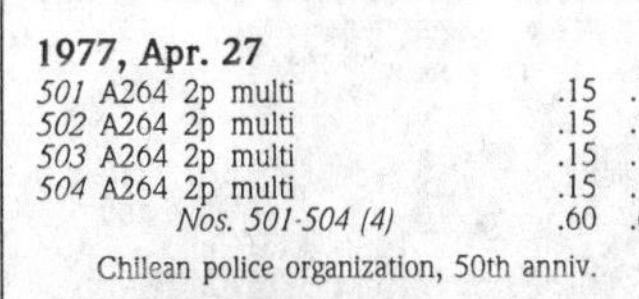

Intelsat Satellite over Globe — A265

1977, May 17 **Litho.** *Perf. 14½*
505 A265 2p multi .18 .18

World Telecommunications Day.

El Mercurio's First Front Page, Press and Ship A266

1977, July 5 **Litho.** *Perf. 14½*
506 A266 2p multi .18 .18

El Mercurio de Valparaiso, first Chilean newspaper, 150th anniversary.

St. Francis, Birds and Cross A267

Science and Technology A268

1977, July 26 **Litho.** *Perf. 14½*
507 A267 5p multi .30 .15

St. Francis of Assisi, 750th death anniv.

1977, Aug. 26 **Litho.** *Perf. 14½*
508 A268 4p multi .25 .15

Young Mother Weaving — A269

Diego de Almagro — A270

Designs: No. 510, Handicapped boy in wheelchair and nurse. No. 511, Children dancing in circle, horiz. No. 512, Old man and home, horiz.

1977, Sept. 13 **Litho.** *Perf. 14½*

509 A269	5p multi	.25	.15
510 A269	5p multi	.25	.15
511 A269	10p multi	.50	.20
512 A269	10p multi	.50	.20
	Nos. 509-512 (4)	1.50	.70

4th anniversary of Government Junta and social services of armed forces.

1977, Oct. 31 **Engr.** *Perf. 14½*
513 A270 5p rose & car .25 .15

Diego de Almagro (1475-1538), leader of Spanish expedition to Chile.

Bell, Letters, Dove and Child A271

1977, Dec. 12 **Litho.** ***Perf. 14½***
514 A271 2.50p multi .15 .15

Christmas 1977.

Loading Timber A272

1978 **Litho.** ***Perf. 15***
515 A272 10p multi .50 .20
516 A272 20p multi 1.00 .20

No. 516 inscribed "CORREOS," ship is flying Chilean flag.

Papal Arms and Globe A273

University A274

1978 **Litho.** ***Perf. 14½***
521 A273 10p multi .50 .20
522 A274 25p multi 1.25 .30

World Peace Day (10p); Catholic University of Valparaiso, 50th anniversary (25p). Issue dates: 10p, July 28; 25p, July 31.

O'Higgins, by Gil de Castro — A275

1978, Aug. 20 **Litho.** ***Perf. 15***
523 A275 10p multi .50 .20

Bernardo O'Higgins (1778-1842), soldier and statesman.

Chacabuco Victory Monument A276

1978, Sept. 11
524 A276 10p multi .50 .20

160th anniversary of O'Higgins victory at Chacabuco, and 5th anniversary of military government.

Teacher Writing on Blackboard A277

1978, Sept. 21
525 A277 15p multi .75 .20

10th anniversary and 9th Reunion of Interamerican Council for Education, Science and Culture (C.I.E.C.C.), Sept. 21-29.

First National Fleet, by Thomas Somerscales — A278

Design: 30p, Last Moments of Rancagua Battle, by Pedro Subercaseaux.

1978 **Litho.** ***Perf. 15***
526 A278 20p multi 1.00 .20
527 A278 30p multi 1.50 .35

Bernardo O'Higgins (1778-1842), soldier and statesman.
Issue dates: 20p, Oct. 9; 30p, Oct. 2.

San Martin-O'Higgins Medal, by Rene Thenot, 1942 — A279

1978, Oct. 20
528 A279 7p multi .35 .15

José de San Martin and Bernardo O'Higgins, 200th birth anniversaries.

Council Emblem — A280

1978, Nov. 27 **Litho.** ***Perf. 14½***
529 A280 50p multi 3.00 .65

Intl. Council of Military Sports, 30th anniv.

Three Kings — A281

Virgin and Child — A282

1978, Dec. 14 **Litho.** ***Perf. 14½***
530 A281 3p multi .15 .15
531 A282 11p multi .60 .28

Christmas 1978.

Philippi Brothers A283

1978, Dec. 29 **Litho.** ***Perf. 14½x15***
532 A283 3.50p multi .20 .15

Bernardo E. Philippi (1811-1852) and Rodulfo A. Philippi (1808-1904), scientists and travelers.

No. 477 Surcharged in Bright Green

1979 **Litho.** ***Perf. 13x14***
533 A253 3.50p on 10c gray grn .25 .25

Flags of Chile and Salvation Army — A284

1979, Mar. 17 **Litho.** ***Perf. 14½***
534 A284 10p multi .75 .50

Salvation Army in Chile, 70th anniversary.

Pope Paul VI (1897-1978) A285

1979, Mar. 30
535 A285 11p multi .80 .50

Battle of Maipu Monument A286

1979, Apr. 17 **Litho.** ***Perf. 14½***
536 A286 8.50p multi .65 .40

Bernardo O'Higgins (1778-1842), Liberator of Chile.

Naval Battles A287

1979, May 21 **Litho.** ***Perf. 14½***
537 A287 3.50p Angamos .35 .20
538 A287 3.50p Iquique .35 .20
539 A287 3.50p Punta Gruesa .35 .20
Nos. 537-539 (3) 1.05 .60

Centenary of victorious naval battles against Peru.

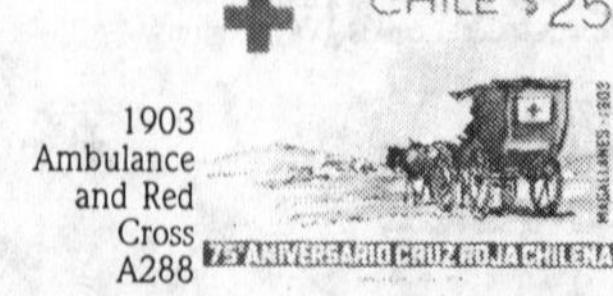

1903 Ambulance and Red Cross A288

1979, June 29 **Litho.** ***Perf. 14½***
540 A288 25p multi 1.50 .90

75th anniversary of Chilean Red Cross.

Diego Portales — A289

1979-86 **Litho.** ***Perf. 13½***
542 A289 1.50p ocher .15 .15
543 A289 2p gray ('81) .15 .15
544 A289 3.50p red .20 .15
545 A289 4.50p bl grn ('81) .25 .15
546 A289 5p rose claret .30 .15
547 A289 6p emerald .35 .20
548 A289 7p yellow ('82) .30 .20
549 A289 10p blue ('82) .45 .20
550 A289 12p orange ('86) .15 .15
Nos. 542-550 (9) 2.30
Set value 1.22

1.50p, 3.50p, 5p and 6p inscribed "D. Portales."

People and Flag — A290

1979, Aug. 28 **Litho.** ***Perf. 14½***
551 A290 10p multi .60 .35

Yugoslavian immigration, centenary.

Coat of Arms and Mt. Castillo A290a

1979, Oct. 12 **Litho.** ***Perf. 14½***
552 A290a 20p multi 1.20 .75

Coyhaique 50th anniv.

IYC Emblem, Playground A291

IYC Emblem, Children's Drawings: 11p, Girl and shadow, vert. 12p, Dancing.

1979, Oct. 9 ***Perf. 14½***
553 A291 9.50p multi .60 .35
554 A291 11p multi .65 .40
555 A291 12p multi .70 .40
Nos. 553-555 (3) 1.95 1.15

International Year of the Child.

Telecom 79 — A292

1979, Oct. 26 **Litho.** ***Perf. 14½***
556 A292 15p multi .90 .50

3rd World Telecommunications Exhibition, Geneva, Sept. 20-26.

Puerto Williams, 25th Anniversary A293

1979, Nov. 21
557 A293 3.50p multi .20 .15

Adoration of the Kings
A294

1979, Dec. 4 Litho. *Perf. 15*
558 A294 3.50p multi .20 .15

Christmas 1979.

Rafael Sotomayor, Minister of War — A295

Military Heroes: No. 560, Erasmo Escala. No. 561, Emilio Sotomayor. No. 562, Eleuterio Ramirez

1979, Dec. 29 *Perf. 13½*
559 A295 3.50p ocher & brn .20 .15
560 A295 3.50p ocher & brn .20 .15
561 A295 3.50p ocher & brn .20 .15
562 A295 3.50p ocher & brn .20 .15
a. Block of 4, #559-562 .85 .45

Bell UH-1 Rescue Helicopter at Tinguiririca Volcano, by S.O. Mococain — A296

Air Force, 50th Anniversary: No. 564, Flying boat Catalina Skua over Antarctic, by E.F. Alvarez. No. 565, F5-E Tiger II over Andes, by M.M. Barria.

1980, Mar. 21 Litho. *Perf. 13½*
563 A296 3.50p shown .25 .15
564 A296 3.50p Jet .25 .15
565 A296 3.50p Sea plane .25 .15
Nos. 563-565 (3) .75
Set value .36

The Death of Bueras, by Pedro Leon Carmona — A297

1980, Apr. 14 Litho. *Perf. 13½*
566 A297 12p multi .70 .40

Charge of Bueras, Battle of Maipo, 1818.

Rotary International, 75th Anniversary — A298

1980, Apr. 15
567 A298 10p multi .60 .30

Gen. Manuel Baquedano, by Pedro Subercaseaux
A299

Gen. Pedro Lagos, Battle Scene, by Subercaseaux — A300

Battle of Morro de Arica Centenary (Subercaseaux Paintings): No. 570, Commander Juan J. San Martin, battle scene.

1980, June 7 Litho. *Perf. 13½*
568 A299 3.50p multi .20 .15
569 A300 3.50p multi .20 .15
570 A300 3.50p multi .20 .15
Nos. 568-570 (3) .60
Set value .30

Score and Perez's Silhouette — A301

1980, June 27 Litho. *Perf. 13½*
571 A301 6p multi .35 .20

Osman Perez Freire (1880-1930), composer, and fragment from his song "Ay, Ay, Ay."

Mt. Gasherbrum II, Chilean Flag, Ice Pick — A302

1980, July 9
572 A302 15p multi .90 .50

Chilean Himalayan expedition, June 1979.

"Charity," Stained-glass Window
A303

1980, July 18
573 A303 10p multi .60 .30

Daughters of Charity, 125th anniv. in Chile.

Condor, Colors of Chile
A304

1980, Sept. 11 Litho. *Perf. 13½*
574 A304 3.50p multi .20 .15

17th anniversary of constitution.

Inca Child Mummy
A305

Pablo Burchard, by Pedro Lira
A306

1980, Sept. 14
575 A305 5p shown .30 .15
576 A305 5p Claudio Gay .30 .15
a. Pair, #575-576 + label .60 .40

Natl. Museum of Natural History (founded by Claudio Gay, 1800-73) sesqui.

1980, Sept. 27 Litho. *Perf. 13½*
577 A306 3.50p multi .20 .15

Museum of Fine Art centenary (directed by Burchard, 1932).

Santiago International Fair — A307

1980, Oct. 30
578 A307 3.50p multi .20 .15

Nativity — A308

Christmas 1980: 3.50p, Family, vert.

1980, Nov. 25 Litho. *Perf. 13½*
579 A308 3.50p multi .20 .15
580 A308 10.50p multi .65 .35

Infantryman 1879 — A309

Congress Emblem — A310

Designs: Pacific War period uniforms, 1879.

1980, Nov. 27
581 A309 3.50p shown .20 .15
582 A309 3.50p Cavalry officer .20 .15
583 A309 3.50p Artillery officer .20 .15
584 A309 3.50p Engineer colonel .20 .15
a. Block of 4, #581-584 .85 .45

See Nos. 606-609.

1980, Dec. 1
585 A310 11.50p multi .70 .40

23rd Intl. Cong. of Military Medicine & Pharmacy.

Eradication of Hoof and Mouth Disease — A311

1981, Jan. 16 Litho. *Perf. 13½*
586 A311 9.50p multi .45 .15

Moai Statues, Easter Island
A312

1981, Jan. 28 Litho. *Perf. 13½*
587 A312 3.50p shown .20 .15
588 A312 3.50p Robinson Crusoe Island .20 .15
589 A312 10.50p Penguins, Antarctic Territory .70 .50
Nos. 587-589 (3) 1.10 .80

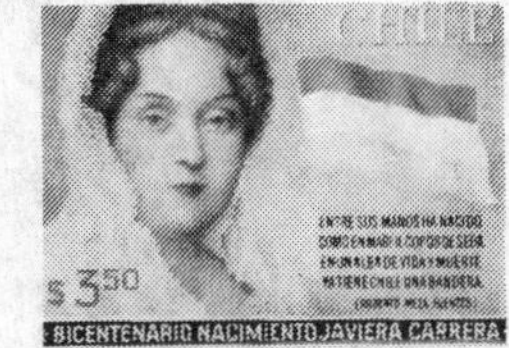

National Heroine Javiera Carrera, by O.M. Pizarro, Birth Bicentenary — A313

1981, Mar. 20
590 A313 3.50p multi .16 .15

UPU Membership Centenary
A314

1981, Apr. 1
591 A314 3.50p multi .16 .15

C130 Hercules Air Force Transport Plane Unloading Cargo — A315

1981, Apr. 21
592 A315 3.50p multi .16 .15

Lieutenant Marsh Air Force Base, 1st anniv.

13th World Telecommunications Day — A316

1981, May 17 Litho. *Perf. 13½*
593 A316 3.50p multi .16 .15

Arturo Prat Naval Base A317

1981, June 23 Litho. *Perf. 13½*
594 A317 3.50p multi .16 .15

Capt. Jose Luis Araneda — A318

1981, June 26
595 A318 3.50p multi .16 .15

Battle of Sangrar centenary.

Philatelic Society of Chile, 90th Anniv. — A319

1981, July 29 Litho. *Perf. 13½*
596 A319 4.50p multi .20 .15

Minister Recabarren and Chief Conuepan Giving Speeches, by Hector Robles Acuna — A320

1981, Aug. 7
597 A320 4.50p multi .20 .15

Temuco city centenary.

Exports — A321

1981, Aug. 31 Litho. *Perf. 13½*
598 A321 14p multi .65 .35

Presidential Palace — A322

1981, Sept. 11
599 A322 4.50p multi .20 .15

Natl. liberation, 8th anniv.

St. Vincent de Paul, 400th Birth Anniv. — A323

1981, Sept. 27 Litho. *Perf. 13½*
600 A323 4.50p multi .25 .15

Andres Bello, Statesman, Birth Bicentenary A324

1981, Sept. 29
601 A324 4.50p Coin .25 .15
602 A324 9.50p Bust, books .50 .20
603 A324 11.50p Statue, arms .60 .28
Nos. 601-603 (3) 1.35 .63

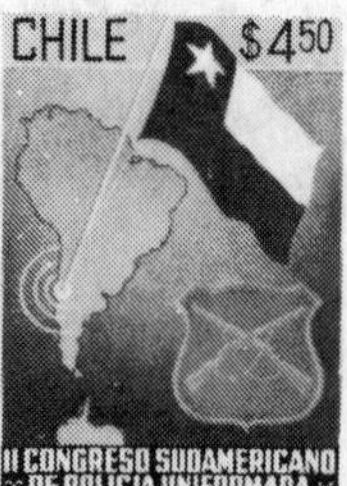
2nd Congress of South American Uniformed Police — A325

1981, Oct. 15
604 A325 4.50p multi .25 .15

World Food Day A326

1981, Oct. 16
605 A326 5.50p multi .30 .15

Uniform Type of 1980

1879 Parade Uniforms.

1981, Nov. 6 *Perf. 13½*
606 A309 5.50p Infantry private .30 .15
607 A309 5.50p Cadet .30 .15
608 A309 5.50p Cavalryman .30 .15
609 A309 5.50p Artilleryman .30 .15
a. Block of 4, #606-609 1.25 .60
Set value .48

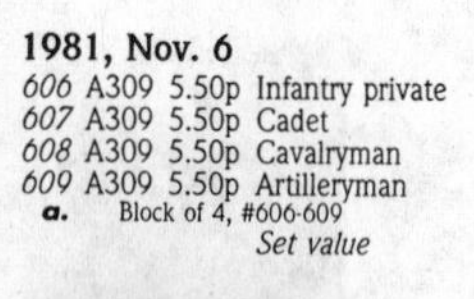

Intl. Year of the Disabled — A327

1981, Nov. 11
610 A327 5.50p multi .30 .15

Christmas 1981 — A328

1981, Nov. 25
611 A328 5.50p Nativity .30 .15
612 A328 11.50p Three Kings .60 .28

50th Anniv. of Federico Santa Maria Technical University — A329

1981, Dec 1 Litho. *Perf. 13½*
613 A329 5.50p multi .30 .15

Dario Salas (1881-1941), Educator — A330

1981, Dec. 4
614 A330 5.50p multi .30 .15

FIDA '82, 2nd Natl. Air Force Fair — A331

1982, Mar. 6 Litho. *Perf. 13½*
615 A331 4.50p multi .25 .15

1982 Constitution — A332

1982, Mar. 11
616 A332 4.50p Cardinal Caro, family .25 .15
617 A332 11p Diego Portales .65 .25
618 A332 30p Bernardo O'Higgins 1.80 .60
Nos. 616-618 (3) 2.70 1.00

Panamerican Institute of Geography and History, 12th General Assembly A333

1982, Mar. 22 Litho. *Perf. 13½*
619 A333 4.50p multi .25 .15

American Air Forces Cooperation System — A334

1982, Apr. 12
620 A334 4.50p multi .25 .15

Pedro Montt A335

Fish Exports A336

1982, Mar. 27
621 A335 4.50p light vio .25 .15

1982, May 3 Litho. *Perf. 13½*
622 A336 20p multi 1.20 .50

Scouting Year — A337

1982, May 21 Litho. *Perf. 13*
623 A337 Pair .50 .20
a.-b. 4.50p, either single .25 .15

Battle of Concepcion Centenary — A338

Chacabuco Regiment officers killed in battle.

1982, June 18 Litho. *Perf. 13½*

624	Block of 4	1.00	.60
a.	A338 4.50p I. Carrera Pinto	.25	.15
b.	A338 4.50p A. Perez Canto	.25	.15
c.	A338 4.50p J. Montt Salamanca	.25	.15
d.	A338 4.50p L. Cruz Martinez	.25	.15

UN World Assembly on Aging, July 26-Aug. 6 — A339

1982, Aug. 5

625 A339 4.50p multi .25 .15

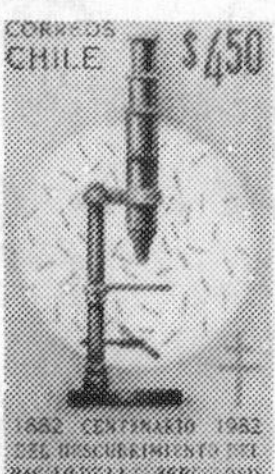

TB Bacillus Centenary — A340

1982, Aug. 31

626 A340 4.50p multi .20 .15

9th Anniv. of National Liberation — A341

1982, Sept. 11 Litho. *Perf. 13½*

627 A341 4.50p multi .20 .18

Christmas 1982 — A342

Children's drawings.

1982, Nov. 2

628 A342 10p multi		.45	.18
629 A342 25p multi, vert.		1.00	.40

Nos. 416-417 Surcharged in Green or Black

1982, Nov. *Perf. 14½x15, 14½*

630 A222 1p on 3.50p bl grn & grn (G)		.15	.15
631 A223 2p on 1.15p blk & car		.15	.15
Set value		.15	.15

Marist Alumni, 9th World Congress — A342a

Design: 7p, Virgin Mary and Marcellus Champagnat (founder of Marist Brotherhood), stained glass window, Church of the Sacred Heart of Jesus, Barcelona.

1982, Nov. 11 Litho. *Perf. 13½*

631A A342a 7p multi .30 .15

El Sur Newspaper Centenary A342b

1982, Nov. 15

631B A342b 7p Wooden handpress, masthead .30 .15

110th Anniv. of South American Steamship Co. — A342c

1982, Dec. 20

631C A342c 7p Steamer Copiapo .30 .15

60th Anniv. of Radio Club of Chile — A342d

1982, Dec. 29

631D A342d 7p multi .30 .15

First Anniv. of Postal Agreement with Order of Malta — A343

1983, Mar. 30 Litho. *Perf. 13½*

632	25p Arms of Order of Malta	1.00	.25
633	50p Chile	2.00	.50
a.	Pair, #632-633	3.00	.75

D. Portales Type of 1975 Inscribed Diego Portales and:

Ramon Barros Luco A344

Juan Luis Sanfuentes A344a

1983-88 Litho. *Perf. 13½*

634	A344	1p	grnsh bl	.15	.15
635	A253	1p	chalky bl	.15	.15
636	A253	1.50p	ocher	.15	.15
637	A344	2p	dl vio ('84)	.15	.15
638	A253	2p	ol gray	.15	.15
639	A253	2.50p	lemon	.15	.15
640	A253	5p	red lilac		
641	A344	5p	crim rose	.15	.15
642	A344a	5p	red ('84)	.15	.15
643	A344	7p	ultra	.28	.15
644	A344a	9p	brn ('84)	.22	.15
645	A344a	9p	grn ('84)	.22	.15
646	A344	10p	black	.25	.15
646A	A344a	10p	gray ('84)	.25	.15
647	A344a	15p	ultra ('87)	.15	.15
648	A344a	20p	yel ('88)	.20	.15
b.			Booklet pane of 10	2.00	

Nos. 644, 647, 648 inscribed "D.S. No. 20."
Issued: No. 640, 8/85.
For surcharge see No. 779.

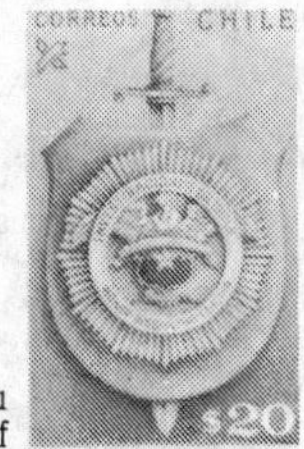

50th Anniv. of Bureau of Investigation — A345

1983, June 19 Litho. *Perf. 13½*

649 A345 20p multi .80 .35

Antonio Cardinal Samore (1905-1983) — A346

1983, June 26

650 A346 30p multi 1.20 .50

Centenary of Cliff Elevators in Valparaiso A347

1983, Aug. 19 Litho. *Perf. 13½*

651 A347 40p multi 1.00 .40

Pucara de Quitor Settlement Ruins, San Pedro de Atacama — A348

Designs: No. 653, Llamas, rock painting, Rio Ibanez, Aisen. No. 654, Duck-shaped jug with human head, Diaguita cultures. No. 655, Puoko Tangata carved stone head, Easter Isld., vert.

1983, Aug. 26

652 A348 7p multi		.20	.20
653 A348 7p multi		.20	.20
654 A348 7p multi		.20	.20
655 A348 7p multi		.20	.20
Nos. 652-655 (4)		.80	.80

10th Anniv. of National Liberation — A349

1983, Sept. 11 Litho. *Perf. 13½*

656 A349	7p Angel with broken chains	.18	.15
657 A349	7p Couple, flag	.18	.15
658 A349	10p Family, torch	.25	.15
659 A349	40p Coat of arms, "10"	1.00	.40
a.	Strip of 4, #656-659	1.75	.75
	Set value		.64

For surcharges see Nos. 669-670.

Famous Hondurans — A350

Designs: No. 660, Francisco Morazan (1792-1842), Advocate of United Central America. No. 661, Jose Cecilio Del Valle (1777-1834), Scholar and Leader of Pan Americanism.

1983, Oct. 3 Litho. *Perf. 13½*

660 A350 7p multi		.18	.15
661 A350 7p multi		.18	.15
Set value			.16

World Communications Year A351 A352

1983, Oct. 13 Litho. *Perf. 13½*

662 A351	7p Central P.O.	.18	.15
663 A352	7p Challenger spaceship	.18	.15
a.	Pair, #662-663	.40	.20

Christmas 1983 — A353

Childrens' Drawings: 10p Chilean Peasant, Hanny Chacon. 30p, Holy Family. Lucrecia Cardenas, vert.

1983, Nov. 14 Litho. *Perf. 13*

664 A353 10p multi		.25	.15
665 A353 30p multi		.75	.38

Design descriptions printed on back on top of gum.

State Railways Centenary — A354

Train Cars: a, Presidential coach, 1911. b, Service coach, 1910; tender, 1929. c, Locomotive Type 80, 1929.

1984, Jan. 4 Litho. *Perf. 13½*
666 Strip of 3 .70 .30
a.-c. A354 9p, any single .22 .15

3rd Intl. Air Fair, Santiago, Mar. 3-11 — A355

1984, Jan. 31 Litho. *Perf. 13½*
667 A355 9p Flags, plane .22 .15

20th Anniv. of Nuclear Energy Commission — A356

1984, Apr. 16 Litho. *Perf. 13*
668 A356 9p multi .22 .15

Nos. 656-657 Surcharged in Purple

1984, June 11 Litho. *Perf. 13½*
669 A349 9p on 7p #656 .18 .15
670 A349 9p on 7p #657 .18 .15
a. Pair, #669-670 .40 .20

Antarctic Colonization — A357

1984, June 18
671 A357 15p Women's expedition .30 .15
672 A357 15p Villa las Estrellas Station .30 .15
673 A357 15p Scouts, flag, Air Force base .30 .15
a. Strip of 3, #671-673 .90 .50

10th Anniv. of Regionalization — A358

Designs: a, Parinacota Church, Tarapaca. b, El Tatio geyser, Antofagasta. c, Copper mining, Atacama. d, Tololo Observatory, Coquimbo. e, Valparaiso Harbor, Valparaiso. f, Ahu Akivi head sculptures, Easter Isld. g, St. Francis Church, Santiago. h, El Hunique House, O'Higgins. i, Colburn Machicura Dam and Hydroelectric Power Station, Maule. j, Sta. Juana de Guadalcazar Fort, Bio-Bio. k, Indian woman, Araucania. l, Guar Isld. Church, Los Lagos. m, Main road, Gen. del Campo. n, Shepherds' Monument, Magellanes and Antarctic. o, Family, Villa las Estrellas Station, Antarctic.

1984, July 11
674 Sheet of 15 3.25 3.25
a.-o. A358 9p multi, any single .25 .18

Capt. Pedro Sarmiento de Gamboa, Map, 1584 — A359

1984, July 31 Litho. *Perf. 13*
675 A359 100p multi 2.00 1.00

400th anniv. of Spanish presence in Straits of Magellan.

State Bank of Chile Centenary — A360

1984, Sept. 6 Litho. *Perf. 13½*
676 A360 35p Founder Antonio Varas de la Barra, coin .70 .30

11th Anniv. of Liberation — A361

1984, Sept. 11
677 A361 20p Monument to O'Higgins .40 .20

Circus Centenary — A362

1984, Sept. 28 Litho. *Perf. 13½*
678 A362 45p Clown .90 .45

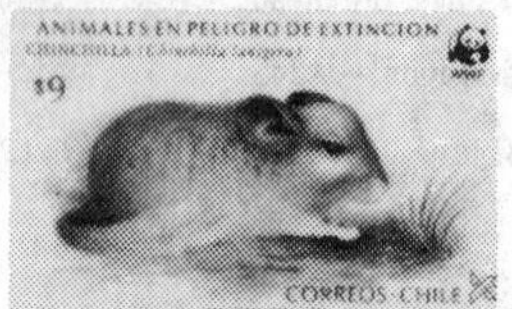

Endangered Species, World Wildlife Emblem — A363

1985, July Litho. *Perf. 13½*
679 A363 9p Chinchilla .18 .15
680 A363 9p Blue whale .18 .15
681 A363 9p Sea lions .18 .15
682 A363 9p Chilean huemuls .18 .15
a. Block of 4, #679-682 .75 .40

Christmas 1984 — A364

Children's drawings.

1984, Nov. 20 Litho. *Perf. 13½*
683 A364 9p Shepherds .18 .15
684 A364 40p Bethlehem .80 .40

Santiago University Planetarium Opening — A365

1984, Dec. 29
685 A365 10p multi .20 .15

Flora and Fauna — A366

Wildlife: a, Conepatus chinga. b, Leucocoryne purpurea. c, Himantopus himantopus. d, Lutra felina. e, Balbisia peduncularis. f, Psittacus cyanalysias. g, Pudu pudu. h, Fuschia magellanica. i, Diuca diuca. j, Dusicyon griseus. k, Alstroemeria sierrae. l, Glaucidium nanum.

1985, Feb.
686 Block of 12 2.40 2.40
a.-l. A366 10p, Any single .20 .15

American Airforces Cooperation System, 25th Anniv. — A367

1985, Mar. 26
687 A367 45p Emblem, flags .90 .45

Chile-Argentina Peace Treaty — A368

1985, May 2 Litho. *Perf. 13½*
688 A368 20p Papal arms, flags .25 .15

Fr. Joseph Kentenich (1885-1968), Founder, Intl. Schonstatt Movement of Catholic Laymen — A369

1985, May 19 Litho. *Perf. 13½*
689 A369 40p Portrait, La Florida Sanctuary, Santiago .48 .24

Antarctic Treaty, 25th Anniv. A370

Resources, research: 15p, Krill, pack ice, map. 20p, Seismological Station, O'Higgins' Base. 35p, Georeception Station, dish receiver.

1985, June 21
690 A370 15p multi .18 .15
691 A370 20p multi .24 .15
692 A370 35p multi .42 .20
Nos. 690-692 (3) .84
Set value .41

Canis Fulvipes — A371

Endangered wildlife: b, Phoenicoparrus jamesi. c, Fulica gigantea. d, Lutra provocax.

1985, Aug. 9 Litho. *Perf. 13½*
693 Block of 4 1.00 .70
a.-d. A371 20p, any single .25 .15

Intl. Youth Year A372

UN, 40th Anniv. A373

1985, Aug. 31
694 A372 15p multi .18 .15
695 A373 15p multi .18 .15
a. Pair, #694-695 .40 .25

Gen. Jose Miguel Carrera Verdugo (1785-1821) — A374

1985, Oct. 8 Litho. *Perf. 13½*
696 A374 40p multi .45 .20

Farmer and Ox-drawn Hay Cart — A375

Folklore: b, Street photographer, wet plate camera. c, One-man band. d, Basket maker.

1985, Oct.
697 Block of 4 .40 .20
a.-d. A375 10p, any single .15 .15

For surcharges see Nos. 770-771.

Christmas 1985 — A376

Holy Family — A376a

Winning children's drawings, 7th natl. design contest.

1985, Nov. 4
698 A376 15p Nativity .16 .15
699 A376 100p Father Christmas, vert. 1.10 .55

Nos. 698-699 inscribed in black on gummed side with child's name, age, school and region.

1985 Litho. *Perf. 13½*
699A A376a 10p buff & brn .15 .15

For surcharge see No. 768.

16th Armed Forces Conference — A377

Designs: 20p, Cavalryman, Directorial Escort, 1818. 35p, Officer, Grand Guard, 1813.

1985, Nov. 15 **Litho.** *Perf. 13½*
700 A377 20p multi .22 .15
701 A377 35p multi .38 .20

Halley's Comet — A378

1985, Nov. 29 **Litho.** *Perf. 13½*
702 A378 45p multi .48 .25
a. Souvenir sheet *4.00*

No. 702a exists imperf.

Natl. Solidarity Campaign — A379

1985
703 A379 5p red & blue .15 .15

Campaign for Prevention of Forest Fires — A380

1985, Dec. 27
704 A380 40p Forest .45 .25
705 A380 40p Fire destruction .45 .25
a. Pair, #704-705 .90 .50

No. 705a has continuous design.

Dungeness Point Lighthouse, Straits of Magellan — A381

1986, Jan. 26
706 A381 45p shown .50 .25
707 A381 45p Evangelistas Lighthouse .50 .25
a. Pair, #706-707 1.00 .50

No. 707a continuous design.

View of Santiago, Mackenna — A382

1986, Jan. 28
708 A382 30p multi .35 .18

Benjamin Vicuna Mackenna (d. 1886), municipal superintendent of Santiago, 1872-1875.

Diego Portales, Natl. Crest, Text A382a

1986, Feb. **Litho.** *Perf. 13½*
708A A382a 12p on 3.50p multi .15 .15

No. 708A not issued without surcharge.

1986 World Cup Soccer Championships, Mexico — A383

Host stadiums: 15p, Natl. Stadium, Chile, 1962. 20p, Aztec Stadium, Mexico, 1970. 35p, Maracana Stadium, Brazil, 1950. 50p, Wembley Stadium, Great Britain, 1966.

1986, Feb. 18
709 A383 15p multi .18 .15
710 A383 20p multi .22 .15
711 A383 35p multi .40 .20
712 A383 50p multi .55 .30
Nos. 709-712 (4) 1.35 .80

Environmental Conservation — A384

1986, Feb. 28
713 A384 20p Water .24 .15
714 A384 20p Air .24 .15
715 A384 20p Soil .24 .15
Nos. 713-715 (3) .72
Set value .36

Sailing Ship Santiaguillo, Flags — A385

1986, Mar. 20
716 A385 40p multi .48 .25

Discovery of Valparaiso Bay, 450th anniv.

A386

A387

1986, Apr. 9
717 A386 45p multi .55 .25

Interamerican Development Bank, 25th anniv.

1986, Apr. 30 **Litho.** *Perf. 13½*
718 A387 15p multi .18 .15

St. Rosa de Lima (1586-1617), sanctuary at Pelequen.

Moai Statues, Easter Is. — A388

1986, May 15
719 A388 60p Raraku Volcano .65 .40
a. Souvenir sheet *1.15* *1.15*
720 A388 100p Tongariki Ruins 1.10 .75
a. Souvenir sheet *1.90* *1.90*

AMERIPEX '86 — A389

1986, May 23
721 A389 100p multi 1.10 .55

Historic Naval Ships A390

1986, May 30
722 A390 35p Schooner Ancud, 1843 .38 .20
723 A390 35p Armed merchantman Aguilar, 1830 .38 .20
724 A390 35p Corvette Esmeralda, 1856 .38 .20
725 A390 35p Frigate O'Higgins, 1834 .38 .20
a. Block of 4, #722-725 1.75 .90

See Nos. 752-753.

Paintings by Juan Francisco Gonzalez (1853-1933) A391

1986, June 24
726 A391 30p Rush and Chrysanthemums .32 .15
727 A391 30p Gate of La Serena .32 .15

Exports — A392

Designs: a, Saltpeter. b, Iron. c, Copper. d, Molybdenum.

1986 **Litho.** *Perf. 13½*
728 A392 Block of 4 .56 .40
a.-d. 12p, any single .15 .15

Antarctic Fauna — A393

Designs: a, Sterna vittata. b, Phalacrocorax atriceps. c, Aptenodytes forsteri. d, Catharacta lonnberg.

1986, July 16 **Litho.** *Perf. 13½*
729 Block of 4 1.80 1.25
a.-d. A393 40p, any single .45 .25

Writers A394

Designs: No. 730, Pedro de Ona (1570-1643). No. 731, Vicente Huidobro (1893-1948).

1986, Aug. 19
730 A394 20p multi .22 .15
731 A394 20p multi .22 .15
a. Pair, #730-731 .45 .25

Has continuous design.

Military Academy, Cent. — A395

1986, Sept. 8 **Litho.** *Perf. 13½*
732 A395 45p Major-General, 1878 .48 .25
733 A395 45p Major, 1950 .48 .25
a. Pair, #732-733 1.00 .50

Art A396

1986, Oct. 17 *Perf. 13½*
734 A396 30p Diaguita urn, duck jug .30 .15
735 A396 30p Mapuche silver ornament, embroidery .30 .15
a. Pair, #734-735 .65 .30

Christmas — A397

8th Natl. design contest-winning children's drawings.

1986, Nov. 19 **Litho.** *Perf. 13½*
736 A397 15p multi .16 .15
737 A397 105p multi 1.10 .55

Nos. 736-737 inscribed in black on gummed side with child's name, age, school and region.

Christmas A397a

Design: Shepherds see star, Bethlehem.

1986, Nov. Litho. *Perf. 13½*
737A A397a 12p multi .15 .15

Intl. Peace Year — A398

1986, Nov. 26
738 A398 85p multi .88 .45

Natl. Women Volunteers — A399

1986, Dec. 15 Litho. *Perf. 13½*
739 A399 15p multi .16 .15

Crowning of Our Lady of Mt. Carmel, Patron of Chile, by Pius XI, 60th Anniv. — A400

1986, Dec. 19
740 A400 25p multi .28 .15

Andean Railways Kitson-Meyer No. 59, 1907, Designed by Robert Sterling — A401

1987, Jan. 27 Litho. *Perf. 13½*
741 A401 95p multi 1.05 .75

Arturo Prat Naval Base, Greenwich Island, the Antarctic, 40th Anniv. — A402

1987, Feb. 6
742 A402 100p Storage and power supplies 1.15 .60
743 A402 100p Working and living quarters 1.15 .60
a. Pair, #742-743 2.50 1.50

No. 743a has continuous design.

State Visit of Pope John Paul II, Apr. 1-6, 1987 A403

Pope John Paul II and: 20p, Christ the Redeemer statue. 25p, Votive Church, Maipu. 90p, Cross of the Seas, Straits of Magellan. 115p, Virgin of the Hill.

1987 Litho. *Perf. 13½*
744 A403 20p multi .20 .15
745 A403 25p multi .25 .15
746 A403 90p multi .90 .45
747 A403 115p multi 1.25 .65
a. Souv. sheet of one 2.50 2.50
747B A403 115p multi 1.25 .65
Nos. 744-747B (5) 3.85 2.05

No. 747a sold for 250p.

No. 747B differs from No. 747 in that the Statue of the Virgin has a halo and Pope John Paul II is smiling.

Issue date: Nos. 744-747a, Apr. 6.

Los Carabineros (Natl. Guard), 60th Anniv. A404

World Youth Soccer Championships A405

1987, Apr. 21
748 A404 50p Cavalry showmanship .50 .25
749 A404 50p Air-sea rescue .50 .25
a. Pair, #748-749 1.00 .50

1987, May 28

Designs: No. 750b, Concepcion Stadium, kick play. No. 750c, Antofagasta Stadium, dribbling the ball. No. 750d, Valparaiso Stadium, heading the ball.

750 Block of 4 1.80 1.25
a.-d. A405 45p any single .45 .25

Souvenir Sheet

751 A405 45p Four players 1.50 1.50

No. 751 sold for 150p.

Naval Ships Type of 1986

1987, May 29
752 A390 60p Battleship Almirante Latorre, 1913 .60 .30
753 A390 60p Cruiser O'Higgins, 1936 .60 .30

Diego Portales (1793-1837), Finance Minister — A406

1987, June 16
754 A406 30p multi .30 .15

Public Works Ministry, Cent. — A407

1987, June 26
755 A407 25p multi .25 .15

Infantry School, Cent. A408

1987, July 9
756 A408 50p Entrance .50 .25
757 A408 100p Soldiers, natl. flag 1.00 .50

Miniature Sheet

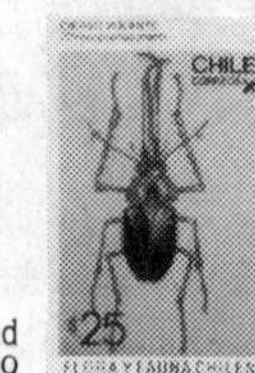

Flora and Fauna — A409

Designs: a, Chiasognathus granti. b, Calidris alba. c, Hippocamelus antisensis. d, Jubaea chilensis. e, Colias vauthieri. f, Pandion haliaetus. g, Cephalorhynchus commersonii. h, Austrocedrus chilensis. i, Jasus frontalis. j, Stephanoides fernandensis. k, Vicugna vicugna. l, Thyrsopteris elegans. m, Lithodes antarctica. n, Pterocnemia pennata. o, Lagidium viscacia. p, Cereus atacamensis.

1987, July 30
758 Sheet of 16 5.00 3.00
a.-p. A409 25p any single .30 .15

Intl. Year of Shelter for the Homeless A410

The Guitarist of Quinchamali A411

1987, Aug. 6
759 A410 40p multi .40 .20

1987, July Litho. *Perf. 13½*

Legends and folk tales: b, El Caleuche. c, El Pihuychen. d, La Lola.

760 Block of 4 .60 .40
a.-d. A411 15p any single .15 .15

Nos. 760a-760d exist ovptd. "D.S. No 20." in golden brown on back.

For surcharges see Nos. 812, 1104.

FISA '87, Santiago — A412

1987, Oct. 16 Litho. *Perf. 13½*
761 A412 20p multi .20 .15

25th Intl. agriculture and exports exhibition.

Rear Admiral Carlos Condell de la Haza (1843-1887), Naval Hero at the Battle of the Pacific — A413

1987, Nov. 7
762 A413 50p multi .45 .20

Christmas 1987 — A414

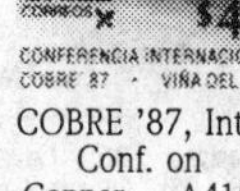

COBRE '87, Intl. Conf. on Copper — A415

Children's drawings: 30p, Holy Family. 100p, Star Over Bethlehem, horiz.

1987, Nov. 13
763 A414 30p multi .35 .15
764 A414 100p multi 1.40 .45

1987, Nov. 23
765 A415 40p Foundry .35 .15
a. Souv. sheet of one 1.35 1.35

No. 765 sold for 150p.

Natl. Antarctic Exploration Commission, 25th Anniv. — A415a

1987, Dec. 11 Litho. *Perf. 13½*
765B A415a 45p multi .40 .20

Ramon Freire Serrano (1787-1851), Chief of State A416

To Smoke Is To Contaminate A417

1987, Dec. 29 *Perf. 13x13½*
766 A416 20p pale lil & rose claret .20 .15

1987, Dec. Litho. *Perf. 13½*
767 A417 15p blue & ver .15 .15

Natl. Commission for the Control of Smoking.

$12

D.S.N°20

No. 699A Surcharged in Green

1987 Litho. *Perf. 13½*
768 A376a 12p on 10p buff & brn .15 .15

Christmas 1987 — A418

1987, Dec.
769 A418 15p ultra, org yel & blk .15 .15
a. Bklt. pane of 10 4.00

No. 769a exists ovptd. "D.S. No 20." on back.

No. 697 Surcharged with New Value and 6 Bars in Rose Red and Black

1987, Dec.

770	Block of 4	.50	.30
a.-d.	A375 12p on 10p, #697a-697d	.15	.15
771	Block of 4	.60	.40
a.-d.	A375 15p on 10p, #697a-697d	.15	.15

St. John Bosco (1815-1888), Educator Canonized in 1934 — A419

1988, Jan. 29

772 A419 40p multi .40 .20

20th Music Week, Frutillar A420

1988, Jan. 27

773 A420 30p multi .30 .15

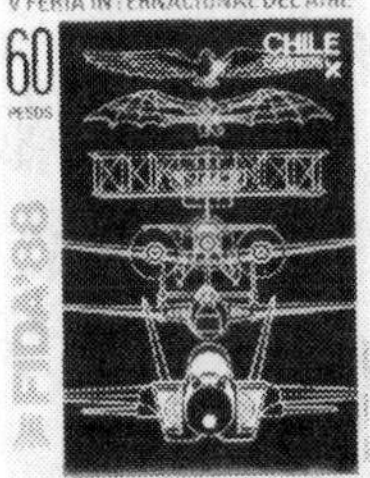

FIDA '88, 5th Intl. Aviation Fair — A421

1988, Mar. 4 **Litho.** ***Perf. 13½***

774 A421 60p dark blue & blue .50 .25

1988 Summer Olympics, Seoul — A422

Flags of Chile and Korea, events: 50p, Shot put, pole vault, javelin. 100p, Swimming, cycling, running.

1988, Mar. 18 ***Perf. 13½***

775	A422 50p multi	.40	.20
776	A422 100p multi	.80	.40
a.	Souv. sheet of 2, #775-776	2.00	2.00

No. 776a sold for 250p.

Natl. Agricultural Soc., 150th Anniv. — A423

1988, Apr. 8

777 A423 45p multi .35 .20

Intl. Red Cross and Red Crescent Organizations, 125th Annivs. — A424

1988, May 10

778 A424 150p multi 1.25 .60

$20

No. 645 Surcharged

DS Nº20

1988 **Litho.** ***Perf. 13½***

779 A344a 20p on 9p green .15 .15

Easter Island Folk Art — A425

Designs: Nos. 780, 782, Carved wooden head from Kava Kava. Nos. 781, 783, Bird man stone carving from Tangata Manu.

1988, Apr. 1 **Litho.** ***Perf. 13½***

780	A425 20p brick red & blk	.15	.15
781	A425 20p brick red & blk	.15	.15
a.	Bklt. pane, 6 #780, 4 #781	1.80	
b.	Pair, #780-781	.40	.40
782	A425 20p yel & blk	.15	.15
783	A425 20p yel & blk	.15	.15
a.	Bklt. pane, 6 #782, 4 #783	1.80	
b.	Pair, #782-783	.40	.40
	Nos. 780-783 (4)	.60	.60

Nos. 782-783 inscribed "D.S. No 20."
For surcharges see Nos. 813-816, 955-956.

Merino, Biplane, Jet Passenger Plane and Supersonic Fighter Plane — A426

1988, May 17 **Litho.** ***Perf. 13½***

784 A426 35p multi .50 .15

Commodore Arturo Merino Benitez (b. 1888), aviation pioneer.

Naval Tradition
A427 A428

Designs: No. 785, Training ship *Esmeralda*. No. 786, Capt. Arturo Pratt, a stained-glass window in the Naval Museum, Valparaiso.

1988, May 23

785	A427 50p multi	.45	.20
786	A428 50p multi	.45	.20
a.	Pair, #785-786	.90	.45

Pontifical Catholic University of Chile, Santiago, Cent. — A429

1988, June 21

787 A429 40p Papal and university arms .35 .20

Locomotives — A430

1988, July 22 **Litho.** ***Perf. 13½***

788	A430 60p Esslingen No. 3331	.45	.20
789	A430 60p North British No. 45	.45	.20
a.	Souv. sheet of 2, #788-789, imperf.	1.35	1.35
b.	Pair, #788-789	.90	.45

Arica-La Paz Railway, 75th anniv. (#788); Antofagasta Bolivia Railway, cent. (#789).

Jose Miguel Carrera Natl. Institute, 175th Anniv. — A431

1988, Aug. 10 **Litho.** ***Perf. 13½***

790 A431 45p multi .40 .20

Annexation of Easter Is., Cent. — A432

1988, Sept. 9

791	A432 50p Ship, officer	.45	.25
792	A432 50p Map, globe	.45	.25
a.	Pair, #791-792	.90	.50
793	A432 100p Easter Is. folk dancers	.90	.50
794	A432 100p Stone ruins	.90	.50
a.	Souv. sheet of 4, #791-794, imperf.	4.00	4.00
b.	Pair, #793-794	2.00	1.25
	Nos. 791-794 (4)	2.70	1.50

Miniature Sheet

Flowers — A433

Designs: a, *Chloraea chrysantha*. b, *Lapageria rosea*. c, *Nolana paradoxa*. d, *Rhodophiala advena*. e, *Schizanthus hookeri*. f, *Acacia caven*. g, *Cordia decandra*. h, *Leontochir ovallei*. i, *Alstroemeria pelegrina*. j, *Copiapoa cinerea*. k, *Salpiglossis sinuata*. l, *Leucocoryne coquimbensis*. m, *Eucryphia glutinosa*. n, *Calandrinia longiscapa*. o, *Desfontainia spinosa*. p, *Sophora macrocarpa*.

1988, Aug. 23 **Litho.** ***Perf. 13½***

795	Sheet of 16	4.50	3.00
a.-p.	A433 30p any single	.28	.15

First Domestic Airmail Route, 1919 — A434

1988, Oct. 11

796 A434 150p Clodomiro Figueroa Ponce's aircraft 1.35 .65

Christmas 1988
A435 A436

Children's drawings: 35p, Nativity, by Paulette Thiers, age 8. 100p, Going to church, by Jose M. Lamas, age 9, horiz.

1988, Nov. 17

797	A435 20p rose lake & org yel	.15	.15
a.	Bklt. pane of 10	1.80	
798	A435 20p rose lake & org yel	.30	.15
a.	Bklt. pane of 10	3.00	
	Set value		.20
799	A436 35p multi	.30	.15
800	A436 100p multi	.88	.45
	Nos. 797-800 (5)	1.63	1.10

No. 798 inscribed "D.S. No 20."

Artisans — A437

1988, Oct. 25 **Litho.** ***Perf. 13½***

801	A437 25p Potter	.22	.15
802	A437 25p Weaver	.22	.15
a.	Pair, #801-802	.45	.25

No. 802a has continuous design.

Natl. Philatelic Soc., Cent. — A438

1988, Nov. 24

803 A438 40p No. 38, cancellation .35 .15

School Crossing Guards — A439

1988, Oct. 26

804 A439 45p multi .40 .20

Commander and Battle Scene — A440

Battle Scene and Serviceman — A441

1989, Jan. 12 Litho. *Perf. 13½*

805 A440 50p Manuel Bulnes (1799-1866) .38 .18
806 A441 50p Cavalryman .38 .18
a. Pair, #805-806 .80 .40
807 A440 100p Roberto Simpson .75 .42
808 A441 100p Seaman .75 .42
a. Pair, #807-808 1.50 .90
Nos. 805-808 (4) 2.26 1.20

Battles of 1839: Yungay (50p) and Casma (100p). Nos. 806a, 808a have continuous designs.

Municipal Annivs. — A442

Municipal coats of arms and: 30p, San Ambrosio Church. 35p, Craftsman sculpting marble. 45p, Laja Spring and falls.

1989, Jan. 20

809 A442 30p multi .28 .15
810 A442 35p multi .32 .16
811 A442 45p multi .42 .20
Nos. 809-811 (3) 1.02 .51

Founding of Vallenar, 200th anniv. (30p); founding of Combarbala, 200th anniv. (35p); founding of Los Angeles, 250th anniv. (45p).

Nos. 760a-760d and 780-783 Surcharged

=

$25
a

b

1989, Mar. 20 Litho. *Perf. 13½*

812 Block of 4 .88 .60
a.-d. A411(a) 25p on 15p #760a-760d, any single .22 .15
813 A425(b) 25p on 20p #780 .22 .15
814 A425(b) 25p on 20p #781 .22 .15
815 A425(b) 25p on 20p #782 .20 .15
816 A425(b) 25p on 20p #783 .20 .15
Nos. 812-816 (5) 1.72
Set value 1.00

Surcharge differs on Nos. 814, 816.
Issued: #812-814, Mar. 20. #815-816, Nov. 30.

Women Beatified — A443

A444

1989, Mar. 21 Litho. *Perf. 13½*

818 A443 40p Sr. Teresa de Los Andes .40 .20
819 A443 40p Laura Vicuna .40 .20
a. Pair, #818-819 .80 .45

No. 819a has continuous design.

1989, Mar. 31

820 A444 100p Christopher Columbus 1.05 .52
821 A444 100p Galleons 1.05 .52
a. Pair, #820-821 2.25 1.50
b. Souvenir sheet of 2, #820-821 3.15 2.00
c. Souvenir sheet of 2, #820-821 3.15 2.00

EXFINA '89, Santiago. No. 821a has continuous design. No. 821b margin pictures Columbus's coat of arms and the Order of the Great Admiralty, No. 821c margin Nos. 55, 69, 18, 76, 37, 1, 20 and 98.

CORFO Development Corp., 50th Anniv. — A445

1989, Apr. 4

822 A445 60p Shipping .52 .26
823 A445 60p Lumber .52 .26
824 A445 60p Communication .52 .26
825 A445 60p Coal .52 .26
a. Block of 4, #822-825 2.25 1.25

Gabriela Mistral (1889-1957), Poet — A446

1989, Apr. 7 Litho. *Perf. 13½*

826 A446 30p Poet, steeple .25 .15
827 A446 30p Poet, children .25 .15
828 A446 30p Poet working .25 .15
829 A446 30p Receiving Nobel Prize, 1945 .25 .15
a. Block of 4, #826-829 1.10 .55

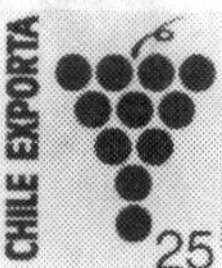

Exports — A447

Designs: Nos. 830, 832, Grapes. Nos. 831, 833, Apple.

1989, Apr. 19

830 A447 25p indigo & brt yel grn .22 .15
831 A447 25p ver & brt yel grn .22 .15
a. Bklt. pane, 5 each #830-831 2.20
b. Pair, #830-831 .45 .25
832 A447 25p indigo & pale yel org .22 .15
833 A447 25p ver & pale yel org .22 .15
a. Bklt. pane, 5 each #832-833 2.20
b. Pair, #832-833 .45 .25
Nos. 830-833 (4) .88
Set value .40

Nos. 832-833 inscribed "D.S. No 20."
See Nos. 861-864, 943-946. For surcharges see Nos. 956B-956C, 1085-1088.

Military Justice Department, 150th Anniv. — A448

1989, Apr. 24 Litho. *Perf. 13½*

834 A448 50p multicolored .45 .22

Monument to the Martyrs of Carabineros de Chile — A449

1989, Apr. 26

835 A449 35p multicolored .30 .15

Surveyor and Penguins — A450

1989, May 29

836 A450 150p multi 1.65 1.25

Antarctic Research Institute expeditions, 25th anniv.

Naval Engineers, Cent. — A451

Designs: No. 837, Naval school. No. 838, Seamen in boiler room. No. 839, Ship, helicopter, submarine. No. 840, *Aquiles* launch, Asmar-Talcahuano.

1989, May 31

837 A451 45p multicolored .38 .18
838 A451 45p multicolored .38 .18
839 A451 45p multicolored .38 .18
840 A451 45p multicolored .38 .18
a. Block of 4, #837-840 1.60 .75

Horse-drawn Carriage (Victoria), Vina del Mar — A452

Early transportation: 35p, Launch off Chiloe Is., vert. 40p, Cart, Cautin. 45p, Ferry, Rio Palena. 50p, Car transport, Lake Gral, Carretta. 60p, Incline railroad, Valparaiso. 100p, Cable car (funicular), Santiago.

1989-92 Litho. *Perf. 13½*

841 A452 30p black & orange .24 .15
842 A452 60p black & lemon .48 .24
842A A452 60p like No. 842 .38 .18
843 A452 100p black & brt yel grn .80 .40

1989-91

844 A452 35p black & brt blue .25 .15
845 A452 40p black & olive .30 .15
846 A452 45p blk & pale blue grn .32 .16
846A A452 45p black & lt ol grn .32 .16
847 A452 50p black & scarlet .35 .18
Nos. 841-847 (9) 3.44 1.77

Nos. 842A, 846A inscribed DS No. 20.
Issued: #841-842, 843, May 22, 1989; #846A, Feb. 1, 1991; #842A, 1992; others, Aug. 1989.
For surcharge see No. 1002.
This is an expanding set. Numbers will change if necessary.

Export Type of 1989

Designs: #861, 863, Grapes. #862, 864, Apple.

1989, May 22

861 A447 5p dark blue & gray .15 .15
862 A447 5p brt red, dark blue & gray .15 .15
a. Pair, #861-862 .15 .15
863 A447 10p dark blue & gray .15 .15
864 A447 10p brt red, dark blue & gray .15 .15
a. Pair, #863-864 .18 .15
Set value .26 .20

A453

A454

1989, Aug. 25 Litho. *Perf. 13½*

865 A453 250p multicolored 1.80 .90
a. Souvenir sheet of 1 2.45 1.65

World Stamp Expo '89.

1989, Oct. 12

UPAE emblem and pre-Columbian peoples: 30p, Atacamena potter. 150p, Selk'nam-onas bow hunter.

866 A454 30p multicolored .22 .15
867 A454 150p multicolored 1.05 .52

Drawing by Christina Lopez — A455

1989, Nov. 20 Litho. *Perf. 13½*

868 A455 100p multicolored .68 .32

Christmas.

Christmas Ornaments — A456

Designs: Nos. 869, 871, Balls. Nos. 870, 872, Bells.

1989

869 A456 25p dull green & org .20 .15
870 A456 25p dull green & org .20 .15
a. Bklt. pane, 5 each Nos. 869-870 2.00
b. Pair, #869-870 .40 .30
871 A456 25p dull green & ver .20 .15
872 A456 25p dull green & ver .20 .15
a. Bklt. pane, 5 each Nos. 871-872 2.00
b. Pair, #871-872 .40 .30
Nos. 869-872 (4) .80 .60

Nos. 871-872 inscribed "D.S. No 20."

Miniature Sheet

Wildlife, Natl. Parks — A457

Designs: a, Vicuna, Lauca Park. b, Chilean flamingos, Salar de Surire. c, Cactus, La Chimba Reserve. d, Guanaco, Pan de Azucar Park. e, Song bird, Father Jorge Park. f, Terns, Rapa Nui Park. g, Ferret, La Campana Park. h, Duck, Rio Clarillo Park. i, Cypress tree, Rio de Los Cipreses Reserve. j, Black-headed swan, Laguna de Torca Reserve. k, Puma, Laguna del Laja Park. l, Araucaria tree, Villarrica Park. m, Flower, Vicente Perez Rosales Park. n, Lenga tree, Dos Lagunas. o, Sea lion, Laguna San Rafael Park. p, Rhea, Torres del Paine Park.

1990, Jan. 25

873 Sheet of 16 4.50 2.50
a.-p. A457 35p any single .24 .15

1990 World Cup Soccer Championships, Italy — A458

1990, Feb. 23

874 A458 50p Cleated shoe .35 .18
875 A458 50p Hand .35 .18
876 A458 50p Soccer ball .35 .18
877 A458 50p Athlete .35 .18
a. Block of 4, #874-877 1.50 .75

Natl. Air Force
A459

Various aircraft: No. 878, Vickers Wibault. No. 879, Curtiss O1E Falcon. No. 880, Pitts S2A. No. 881, Extra 300.

1990, Mar. 16 Litho. *Perf. 13½*

878 A459 40p multicolored .28 .15
879 A459 40p multicolored .28 .15
880 A459 40p multicolored .28 .15
881 A459 40p multicolored .28 .15
a. Souvenir sheet of 4, #878-881 1.15 .56
Nos. 878-881 (4) 1.12 .60

FIDAE '90.

Discovery of America 500th Anniv. (in 1992)
A460 A461

Maps and 16th cent. men: No. 882, Incan. No. 883, Spanish infantryman.

1990, Apr. 20 Litho. *Perf. 13½*

882 A460 60p multicolored .42 .20
883 A461 60p multicolored .42 .20
a. Pair, #882-883 .85 .45

Port Cities
A462

1990, Apr. 27

884 A462 40p Valparaiso .28 .15
885 A462 40p San Vicente .28 .15
a. Pair, #884-885 .60 .30

Democracy — A463

1990, June 8 Litho. *Perf. 13½*

886 A463 20p Sunrise .15 .15
887 A463 30p Peace dove .22 .15
888 A463 60p Pleasure .45 .24
889 A463 100p Star .78 .40
a. Souvenir sheet of 4, #886-889 2.40 1.20
Nos. 886-889 (4) 1.60 .94

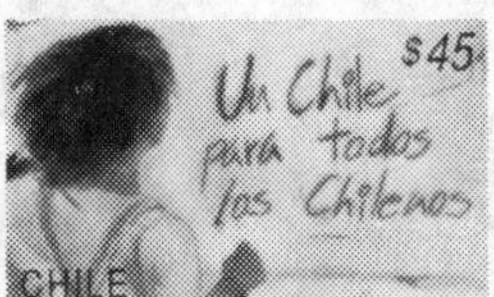

Equality — A464

1990, June 8

890 A464 45p multicolored .35 .18
a. Souvenir sheet .60 .30

No. 890a margin continues the design.

Naval Tradition — A465

Designs: No. 891, Transport ship Piloto Pardo. No. 892, Oceanographic research ship Yelcho.

1990, May 30 Litho. *Perf. 13½*

891 A465 50p multicolored .36 .18
892 A465 50p multicolored .36 .18
a. Pair, #891-892 .72 .36

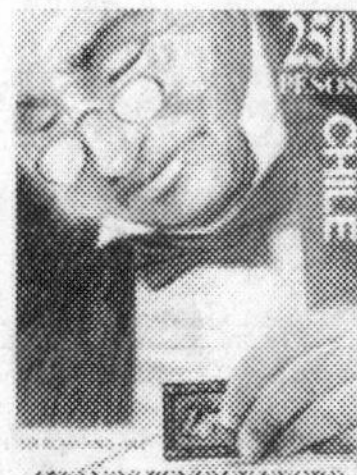

Penny Black, 150th Anniv. — A466

1990, June 12

893 A466 250p Sir Rowland Hill 2.75 1.40
a. Souvenir sheet of 1 4.10 2.00

No. 893a margin continues the design.

Organization of American States, Cent. — A467

1990, June 21

894 A467 150p multicolored 1.00 .50

Marine Resources — A468

Designs: a, Scallop. b, Clam. c, Swordfish. d, Crab. e, Fish. f, Baiting, processing.

1990, July 27 Litho. *Perf. 13½*

895 Block of 6 1.80 .90
a.-f. A468 40p any single .30 .15

Curimon Convent — A469

1990, Aug. 1

896 A469 50p multicolored .36 .18

250th anniversary of San Felipe.

Environmental Protection — A470

1990, Sept. 1 Litho. *Perf. 13½*

897 A470 35p Aerosol propellants .24 .15
898 A470 35p Deforestation .24 .15
899 A470 35p Smokestacks .24 .15
900 A470 35p Oil slick, shore .24 .15
901 A470 35p Forest fire .24 .15
a. Strip of 5, #897-901 1.20 .60
b. Bklt. pane, 2 each #897-901 2.40
Nos. 897-901 (5) 1.20
Set value .60

Inscribed "D.S. No 20"

902 A470 35p Aerosol propellants .24 .15
903 A470 35p Deforestation .24 .15
904 A470 35p Smokestacks .24 .15
905 A470 35p Oil slick, shore .24 .15
906 A470 35p Forest fire .24 .15
a. Strip of 5, #902-906 1.20 .60
b. Bklt. pane, 2 each #902-906 2.40
Nos. 902-906 (5) 1.20
Set value .60

See Nos. 988-997.

Presidents of Chile — A471

1990, Sept. 4

912 A471 35p Salvador Allende .24 .15
913 A471 35p Eduardo Frei .24 .15
914 A471 40p Jorge Alessandri .30 .15
915 A471 45p Gabriel Gonzalez V .35 .18
916 A471 50p Juan Antonio Rios .38 .20
917 A471 60p Pedro Aguirre Cerda .45 .24
918 A471 70p Juan E. Montero .52 .25
919 A471 80p Carlos Ibanez .60 .30
920 A471 90p Emiliano Figueroa .70 .35
921 A471 100p Arturo Alessandri .75 .38
Nos. 912-921 (10) 4.53 2.35

Rodeos — A472

Designs: a, Rodeo ring. b, Men on horses. c, Man stopping horse. d, Men, horses, bull.

1990, Sept. 24

926 Block of 4 1.40 .70
a.-d. A472 45p any single .35 .18

Discovery of America, 500th Anniv. (in 1992) — A473

1990, Oct. 12 Litho. *Perf. 13½*

927 A473 30p Phoenicopterus chilensis .22 .15
928 A473 150p Arctocephalus australis 1.10 .55

King and Queen of Spain's Visit — A474

Design: No. 930, Arms of King Juan Carlos I, Chilean Arms.

1990, Oct. 18

929 A474 100p shown .75 .38
930 A474 100p Denomination at LR .75 .38
a. Pair, #929-930 1.50 .76

Malleco Bridge, Cent. — A475

Design: #932, Boy waving at train on bridge.

1990, Oct. 26 Litho.

931 A475 60p multicolored
932 A475 60p multicolored
a. Pair, #931-932

Chilean Antarctic Territorial Claims, Anniv. — A476

Design: #934, Penguins, helicopter, camp.

1990, Nov. 6 *Perf. 13*

933 A476 250p multicolored 1.80
934 A476 250p multicolored 1.80
a. Souvenir sheet of 2, #933-934 5.25

A477

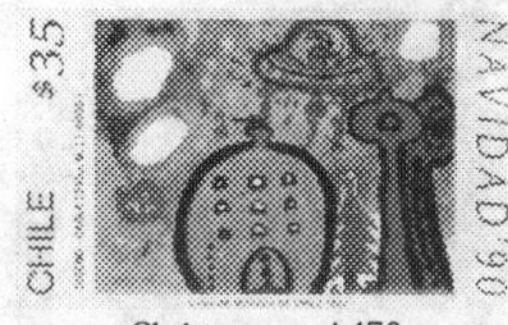

Christmas — A478

1990, Nov. 20 Litho. *Perf. 13½*

935 A477 35p lt green & bl grn .25 .15
a. Booklet pane of 10 2.50
936 A477 35p dull org & bl grn .25 .15
a. Booklet pane of 10 2.50
937 A478 35p shown .25 .15
938 A478 150p Underwater dwelling 1.10 .55
Nos. 935-938 (4) 1.85 1.00

No. 936 inscribed "D.S. No.20."

National Congress — A479

1990, Dec. 21 Litho. *Perf. 13½*

939 A479 100p Congress chamber .75 .38
940 A479 100p Early congressional session .75 .38
a. Pair, #939-940 1.50 .75

City of Santiago, 450th Anniv. — A480

1991, Feb. 7

941 A480 100p Colorado House .75 .38
942 A480 100p Skyline .75 .38
a. Pair, #941-942 1.50 .75
b. Souvenir sheet of 2, #941-942 2.00 1.00

Exports Type of 1989

Designs: Nos. 943, 945, Grapes. Nos. 944, 946, Apple.

1991, Feb. 8 *Perf. 13½ on 3 Sides*

943 A447 45p indigo & brt pink .32 .16
944 A447 45p vermilion & brt pink .32 .16
a. Bklt. pane, 5 each #943-944 3.25
945 A447 45p indigo & yel .32 .16
946 A447 45p ver & yel .32 .16
a. Bklt. pane, 5 each #945-946 3.25
Nos. 943-946 (4) 1.28 .64

Nos. 945-946 inscribed "D.S. No.20."
For surcharges see Nos. 1085-1088.

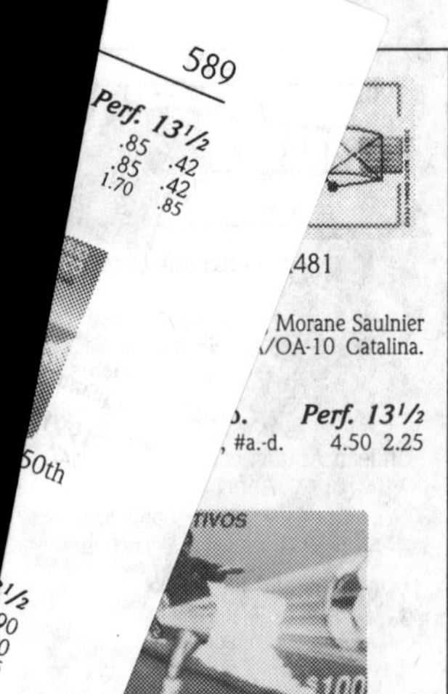

589

Perf. 13½
.85 .42
.85 .42
1.70 .85

A481

, Morane Saulnier
/OA-10 Catalina.

. *Perf. 13½*
, #a.-d. 4.50 2.25

50th

Soccer Cup, Chile — A482

12 Litho. *Perf. 13½*
100p shown .65 .32
100p Ball, goalie .65 .32
, #948-949 1.30 .65

Coal Mining A483

Design: #951, Miners dumping cart of coal.

1991, Apr. 18

950 A483 200p shown 1.30 .65
951 A483 200p multicolored 1.30 .65
a. Pair, #950-951 2.60 1.30

Cultural Art — A484

Design: #953, Small sculptures, spurs, dish.

1991, Apr. 29

952 A484 90p shown .60 .30
953 A484 90p multicolored .60 .30
a. Pair, #952-953 1.20 .60

Chilean Scientific Society, Cent. — A485

1991, Apr. 29

954 A485 45p blue grn & blk .30 .15

Nos. 782-783 Surcharged

$45 a

$45 b

1991, Apr. 30

955 A425(a) 45p on 20p, #782 .30 .15
956 A425(b) 45p on 20p, #783 .30 .15
a. Pair, #955-956 .60 .30

Nos. 832-833 Surcharged $45

1991, May 6 Litho. *Perf. 13½*

956B A447 45p on 25p, #832 .25 .15
956C A447 45p on 25p, #833 .25 .15
d. Pair, #956B-956C .50 .30

Santiago Cathedral A486

1991, May 9 Litho & Engr.

957 A486 300p red brn, sal & blk 2.00 1.00

World Telecommunications Day — A487

1991, May 17 Litho.

958 A487 90p multicolored .60 .30

A488

A489

1991, May 23

959 A488 100p Pope Leo XIII .65 .32

Rerum Novarum Encyclical, cent.

1991, May 28 Litho. *Perf. 13½*

Rescue of Shackleton Expedition, 75th anniv.: a, Lt. Luis Pardo, Sir Ernest Shackleton. b, Rescue ship, Yelcho. c, Sailor pointing to survivors. d, Shackleton's ship, Endurance.

960 A489 50p Block of 4, #a.-d. 1.30 .65
e. Miniature sheet, #960 1.30

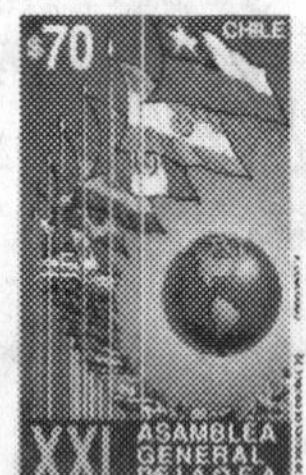

21st General Assembly of Organization of American States, Santiago — A490

1991, June 5

961 A490 70p multicolored .45 .24

New Carabinero School — A491

1991, June 12

962 A491 50p multicolored .32 .16

Natl. Merchant Marine Day — A492

1991, June 26

963 A492 45p black & red .30 .15

11th Pan American Games, Havana — A493

1991, July 23

964 A493 100p Runners, torch, flags .65 .32
965 A493 100p Cycling, running, basketball .65 .32
a. Pair, #964-965 1.30 .65

Founding of the City of Los Andes, Bicent. — A494

1991, July 29

966 A494 100p multicolored .65 .32

Miniature Sheet

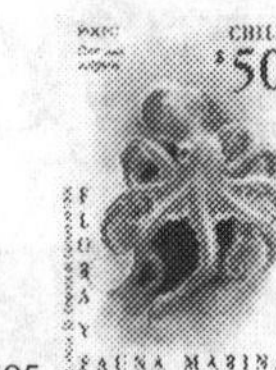

Marine Life — A495

Designs: No. 967a, Octopus vulgaris. b, Durvillaea antarctica. c, Paralichthys adspersus. d, Austromegabalanus psittacus. e, Concholepas concholepas. f, Cancer setosus. g, Lessonia nigrescens. h, Loxechinus albus. i, Homalaspis plana. j, Porphyra columbina. k, Oplegnathus insignis. l, Chorus giganteus. m, Rhynchocinetes typus. n, Engraulis ringens. o, Gracilaria spp. p, Pyura chilensis.

1991, Aug. 20 Litho. *Perf. 13½*

967 Sheet of 16 5.25 2.60
a.-p. A495 50p any single .32 .16

1891 Revolution, Cent. — A496

Jose M. Balmaceda (1840-1891) and: No. 968, Machinery. No. 969, Teacher, students at Valentin Letelier School of Medicine.

1991, Aug. 29

968 A496 100p multicolored .65 .32
969 A496 100p multicolored .65 .32
a. Pair, #968-969 1.30 .65

Chilean Art — A497

Paintings: 50p, Woman in Red, by Pedro Reszka. 70p, The Traveler, by Camilo Mori. 200p, Head of Child, by Benito Rebolledo. 300p, Boy Wearing a Fez, by A. Valenzuela Puelma.

1991, Sept. 26

970 A497 50p multicolored .32 .16
971 A497 70p multicolored .45 .24
972 A497 200p multicolored 1.30 .65
973 A497 300p multicolored 1.95 .95
Nos. 970-973 (4) 4.02 2.00

Antarctic Treaty, 30th Anniv. — A498

1991, Oct. 7 Litho. *Perf. 13½*

974 A498 80p shown .50 .25
975 A498 80p Birds, sea life .50 .25
a. Pair, #974-975 1.00 .50

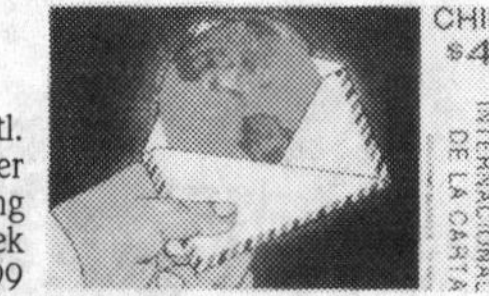

Intl. Letter Writing Week A499

1991, Oct. 9

976 A499 45p shown .30 .15
977 A499 70p Envelope filled with people .45 .22

America Issue A500

UPAEP emblem, sailing ships and: 150p, Navigator.

1991, Oct. 14

978 A500 50p multicolored .32 .16
979 A500 150p multicolored .95 .48

A501

Christmas — A502

1991, Oct. 21

980 A501 45p blue hat .30 .15
981 A501 45p red hat .30 .15
a. Pair, #980-981 .60 .30
b. Souvenir sheet of 2, #980-981 1.25 1.25

Pablo Neruda, (1904-1973), Nobel Prize winner for literature, 1971. Nos. 981a has a continuous design.

1991, Nov. 4

982 A502 45p Boy with stars .30 .15
983 A502 100p Girl with stars .65 .32

Christmas
A503 A504

1991, Nov. 18 Litho. *Perf. 13½*

984 A503 45p violet & brt pink .28 .15
985 A504 45p violet & brt pink .28 .15
a. Pair, #984-985 .56 .15
b. Bklt. pane of 5 #985a 2.80
986 A503 45p violet & brt pink .28 .15
987 A504 45p violet & brt pink .28 .15
a. Pair, #986-987 .56 .15
b. Bklt. pane of 5 #987a 2.80
Nos. 984-987 (4) 1.12 .60

Nos. 986-987 inscribed "D.S. No. 20."
For surcharges see Nos. 1016-1019.

Environmental Protection Type of 1990

1992, Jan. 28 Litho. *Perf. 13½*

988 A470 60p like #897, lem & blk .35 .18
989 A470 60p like #898, lem & blk .35 .18
990 A470 60p like #899, lem & blk .35 .18
991 A470 60p like #900, lem & blk .35 .18
992 A470 60p like #901, blk & lem .35 .18
a. Strip of 5, #988-992 1.75 .90
b. Bklt. pane, 2 each #988-992 3.50

Inscribed "D.S. No. 20"

993 A470 60p like #902, org & dk grn .35 .18
994 A470 60p like #903, org & dk grn .35 .18
995 A470 60p like #904, org & dk grn .35 .18
996 A470 60p like #905, org & dk grn .35 .18
997 A470 60p like #906, dk grn & org .35 .18
a. Strip of 5, #993-997 1.75 .90
b. Bklt. pane, 2 each #993-997 3.50
Nos. 988-997 (10) 3.50 1.80

Wolfgang Amadeus Mozart, Death Bicent. (in 1991) — A505

1992, Jan. 31

998 A505 60p shown .35 .18
999 A505 200p Hands at piano 1.15 .62
a. Sheet of 2, #998-999 2.30 1.50

FIDAE '92, Intl. Air and Space Fair — A506

1992, Mar. 5 Litho. *Perf. 13½*

1000 A506 60p multicolored .35 .18

16th Population and Housing Census — A507

1992, Mar.

1001 A507 60p multicolored .35 .18

No. 846 Surcharged in Red Brown **$60**

1992, Mar.

1002 A452 60p on 45p .35 .18

Chilean Cities — A508

Cities' coat of arms and: 80p, Church of San Jose de Maipo. 90p, People making pottery. 100p, Lircunlauta House. 150p, Wine and lumber industries. 250p, Huilquilemu cultural center. (Illustration reduced).

1992, Apr. 10 Litho. *Perf. 13½*

1003 A508 80p multicolored .45 .22
1004 A508 90p multicolored .52 .26
1005 A508 100p multicolored .58 .28
1006 A508 150p multicolored .88 .45
1007 A508 250p multicolored 1.45 .72
Nos. 1003-1007 (5) 3.88 1.93

80p, San Jose de Maipo, 200th anniv. 90p, Melipilla, 250th anniv. 100p, San Fernando, 250th anniv. 150p, Cauquenes, 250th anniv. 250p, Talca, 250th anniv.

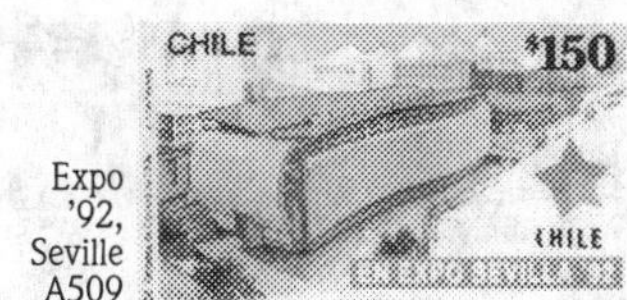

Expo '92, Seville A509

1992, Apr. 23

1008 A509 150p Pavilion .88 .45
1009 A509 200p Iceberg 1.15 .58
a. Sheet of 2, #1008-1009 *2.75 1.40*

A510

Easter Island A511

Marine life: No. 1010a, Morula praecipua, Strombus maculatus, Cypraea caputdraconis. b, Codium pocockiae. c, Myripristis tiki. d, Sargassum skottsbergii. e, Pseudolabrus fuentesi. f, Pocillopora danae. g, Panulirus pascuensis. h, Tripneustes gratilla.

No. 1011b, Natives, airplane, petroglyph.

1992, June 9 Litho. *Perf. 13½*

1010 A510 60p Sheet of 8, #a.-h. 3.30 2.20
1011 A511 200p Pair, #a.-b. 2.75 1.40

Natl. Council of the Disabled — A512

Military Chiefs of Staff, 50th Anniv. — A513

1992, June 23

1012 A512 60p multicolored .42 .20

1992, July 3

1013 A513 60p multicolored .42 .20

Submarine Forces, 75th Anniv. — A514

Coat of arms and: 250p, Officer using periscope, control room.

1992, July 4

1014 A514 150p multicolored .95 .48
1015 A514 250p multicolored 1.60 .80

Nos. 984-987 Surcharged

1992, Aug. 11 Litho. *Perf. 13½*

1016 A503 60p on 45p No. 984 .35 .18
1017 A504 60p on 45p No. 985 .35 .18
a. Pair, #1016-1017 .70 .35
1018 A503 60p on 45p No. 986 .35 .18
1019 A504 60p on 45p No. 987 .35 .18
a. Pair, #1018-1019 .70 .35
Nos. 1016-1019 (4) 1.40 .72

Nos. 1018-1019 inscribed "D.S. No. 20."

Emperor Penguins — A515

1992, Sept. 28 Litho. *Perf. 13½*

1020 A515 200p shown 1.15 .55
1021 A515 250p Adults with young 1.40 .70
a. Souvenir sheet of 2, #1020-1021 3.75 1.90

Central Post Office, Santiago, 1772 — A516

1992, Oct. 9

1022 A516 200p multicolored 1.15 .58

Discovery of America, 500th Anniv. — A517

UPAEP emblem and: 200p, Calendar stone, astrolabe, Columbus. 250p, Church, map of Central and South America, sailing ship.

1992, Oct. 20

1023 A517 200p multicolored 1.15 .58
1024 A517 250p multicolored 1.40 .70

Radio Chile, 75th Anniv. A518

Bernardo O'Higgins (1778-1842) A519

1992, Oct. 22

1025 A518 250p multicolored 1.40 .70

1992, Oct. 23

1026 A519 60p multicolored .35 .18

Claudio Arrau, Pianist A520

1992, Nov. 12 Litho. *Perf. 13½*

1027 A520 150p As child .90 .45
1028 A520 200p As adult 1.20 .60
a. Souvenir sheet of 2, #1027-1028 2.40 1.20

Natl. Human Rights Day A521

1992, Dec. 10

1029 A521 100p multicolored .58 .30
a. Souvenir sheet of 1 1.05 .52

Christmas — A522

Designs: Nos. 1030, 1032, Denomination at LR. Nos. 1031, 1033, Denomination at LL.

1992, Dec. 12 Litho. *Perf. 13½*

1030 A522 60p buff & brown .32 .16
1031 A522 60p buff & brown .32 .16
a. Pair, #1030-1031 .64 .32
b. Booklet pane of 5 #1031a 3.25
1032 A522 60p buff & red .32 .16
1033 A522 60p buff & red .32 .16
a. Pair, #1032-1033 .64 .32
b. Booklet pane of 5 #1033a 3.25
Nos. 1030-1033 (4) 1.28 .64

Nos. 1032-1033 inscribed "DS/20."

A523

A524

University of Chile, 150th Anniv.: a, Statue. b, Coat of arms, facade of building.

1992, Nov. 19 Litho. *Perf. 13½*

1034 A523 200p Pair, #a.-b. 2.30 1.15
c. Souvenir sheet of 1, #1034 2.30 1.15

Nos. 1034a-1034b have a continuous design.

1992, Dec. 12

1035 A524 70p black & yellow .42 .22

23rd meeting of Latin American Energy Ministers.

Churches of Chile — A525

Designs: Nos. 1036, 1038, Achao. Nos. 1037, 1039, Castro.

1993, Mar. 1 Litho. *Perf. 13½*

1036 A525 70p black & pink .42 .22
1037 A525 70p black & pink .42 .22
a. Pair #1036-1037 .84 .44
b. Booklet pane of 5 #1037a 4.20

Inscribed "DS/20"

1038 A525 70p black & yellow .42 .22
1039 A525 70p black & yellow .42 .22
a. Pair, #1038-1039 .84 .44
b. Booklet pane of 5 #1039a 4.20
Nos. 1036-1039 (4) 1.68 .88

See Nos. 1053-1060.
For surcharges see No. 1129-1130.

Arrival of the Jesuits, 400th Anniv. — A526

Canonization of St. Teresa of the Andes, 1993 — A527

1993 Litho. *Perf. 13½*

1040 A526 200p St. Ignatius of Loyola 1.15 .58
a. Souvenir sheet of 1 1.45 .72
1041 A527 300p St. Teresa of the Andes 1.75 .90

Issue dates: 200p, Mar. 15. 300p, Mar. 31. No. 1040a sold for 250p.

World Festival of Theatre of the Nations — A528

Clotario Blest (1899-1990), Syndicalist — A530

Second Space Conference of the Americas — A529

1993, Apr. 22

1042 A528 250p multicolored 1.45 .75

1993, Apr. 26

1043 A529 150p multicolored .90 .45
a. Souvenir sheet of 1 2.10 1.05

No. 1043a sold for 350p.

1993, Apr. 30

1044 A530 70p multicolored .40 .20

Intl. Labor Day.

Vicente Huidobro, Poet (1893-1948) — A531

1993, May 19 Litho. *Perf. 13½*

1045 A531 100p shown .58 .30
1046 A531 100p Portrait, seated .58 .30
a. Pair, #1045-1046 1.15 .60

Antique Fire Engines A532

Designs: No. 1047, 1902 Watterous Engineering Co. Ltd., Canada. No. 1048, 1872 Merryweather, England.

1993, June 30 Litho. *Perf. 13½*

1047 A532 100p multicolored .55 .28
1048 A532 100p multicolored .55 .28
a. Souvenir sheet of 2, #1047-1048 2.25 1.10

No. 1048a sold for 400p.

Aircraft A533

Designs: No. 1049, Douglas B-26 Invader. No. 1050, Mirage M50 Panther. No. 1051, Sanchez Besa. No. 1052, Bell 47D1 helicopter.

1993, July 13

1049 A533 100p multicolored .55 .28
1050 A533 100p multicolored .55 .28
1051 A533 100p multicolored .55 .28
1052 A533 100p multicolored .55 .28
a. Block of 4, #1049-1052 2.10 1.15

Church Type of 1993

Designs: 10p, Chonchi. 20p, Vilupulli. 30p, Llau-llao. 40p, Dalcahue. 50p, Tenaun. 80p, Quinchao. 90p, Quehui. 100p, Nercon.

1993, July Litho. *Perf. 13½*

1053 A525 10p green & black .15 .15
1054 A525 20p black & brown .15 .15
1055 A525 30p black & vermilion .16 .16
1056 A525 40p black & blue .22 .22
1057 A525 50p black & green blue .28 .28
1058 A525 80p black & buff .45 .45
a. Booklet pane of 10 4.25
1059 A525 90p olive & black .50 .50
a. Booklet pane of 10 5.00
Complete booklet, #1059a 5.00
1060 A525 100p gray violet & black .55 .55
Nos. 1053-1060 (8) 2.46 2.46

Issued: No. 1058a, 1/1/94; No. 1059a, 1995.
See No. 1093 for 80p black & violet.

Natl. Dance, "La Cueca" — A534

Paintings — A535

1993, Sept. 15 Litho. *Perf. 13½*

1061 A534 70p Cueca chilota .38 .16
1062 A534 70p Cueca central .38 .16
1063 A534 70p Cueca nortina .38 .16
Nos. 1061-1063 (3) 1.14 .48

1993, Sept. 28

Designs: 80p, Tarde Amanecer, by Mario Carreno, horiz. 90p, Summer, by Gracia Barrios, horiz. 150p, Figura Protegida, by Roser Bru. 200p, Tangueria-Valparaiso, by Nemesio Antunez, horiz.

1064 A535 80p multicolored .45 .22
1065 A535 90p multicolored .50 .25
1066 A535 150p multicolored .80 .40
1067 A535 200p multicolored 1.10 .55
Nos. 1064-1067 (4) 2.85 1.42

Chilean Mint, 250th Anniv. — A536

1993, Oct. 7 Litho. & Engr.

1068 A536 250p multicolored 1.40 .70
a. Souvenir sheet of 1 1.75 .90

Urban Transportation System, 25th Anniv. — A537

1993, Oct. 19 Litho.

1069 A537 80p multicolored .45 .22

America Issue — A538

1993, Oct. 12 Litho. *Perf. 13½*

1070 A538 150p Cyanoliseus patagonus .80 .40
1071 A538 200p Hippocamelus bisculcus 1.10 .55

Chilean Possession of Straits of Magellan, 150th Anniv. — A539

1993, Oct. 21

1072 A539 100p multicolored .55 .28

Naval Anniversaries — A540

1993, Oct. 27

1073 A540 80p Sailing ships .45 .22
1074 A540 80p Schooner .45 .22
1075 A540 80p Assault ship .45 .22
1076 A540 80p Patrol boat .45 .22
Nos. 1073-1076 (4) 1.80 .88

Sailing of first naval squadron (#1073), Arturo Prat Naval Academy (#1074), Marine Corps (#1075), 175th anniversaries. Alejandro Navarette School for Cadets (#1076), 125th anniv.

Intl. Year of Indigenous Peoples — A541

1993, Nov. 24

1077 A541 100p multicolored .55 .28

Christmas A542

Pygoscelis Adelie A543

1993, Dec. 1 Litho. *Perf. 13½*

1078 A542 70p tan & violet .35 .18
a. Booklet pane of 10 3.50
1079 A542 70p green & blue .35 .18
a. Booklet pane of 10 3.50

No. 1079 inscribed "DS/20."
For surcharge see No. 1131.

1993, Dec. 3

1080 A543 200p Nesting 1.00 .50
1081 A543 250p Adult, chicks 1.25 .65
a. Souv. sheet of 2, #1080-1081, imperf. 2.25 1.25

Chilean Antarctica.
No. 1081a has simulated perfs.

Chilean Cities A544

1993, Dec. 15

1082 A544 80p Rancagua .38 .20
1083 A544 80p Curico .38 .20
1084 A544 80p Ancud .38 .20
Nos. 1082-1084 (3) 1.14 .60

Rancagua and Curico, 250th anniv. Ancud, 225th anniv.

Nos. 943-946 Surcharged

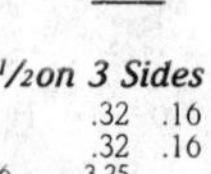

1993 Litho. *Perf. 13½ on 3 Sides*

1085 A447 60p on 45p, #943 .32 .16
1086 A447 60p on 45p, #944 .32 .16
a. Bklt. pane, 5 each #1085-1086 3.25
1087 A447 60p on 45p, #945 .32 .16
1088 A447 60p on 45p, #946 .32 .16
a. Bklt. pane, 5 each #1087-1088 3.25
Nos. 1085-1088 (4) 1.28 .64

Nos. 1087-1088 inscribed "D.S. No. 20."

Intl. Year of the Family — A545

1994, Jan. 17 Litho. *Perf. 13½*

1089 A545 100p multicolored .48 .25

Musical Instruments — A546

Designs: a, Violin. b, Cello.

1994, Jan. 27 Litho. *Perf. 13½*
1091 A546 150p Pair, #a.-b. 1.40 .70

Nos. 1091a-1091b have a continuous design.

Church Type of 1993

Design: 80p, Quinchao. 90p, Quehui.

1994-95 Litho. *Perf. 13½*
1093 A525 80p black & violet .42 .22
1095 A525 90p red & black .45 .25
a. Booklet pane of 10 4.75
Complete booklet, #1095a 4.75

Issued: 80p, 1/1/94; 90p, 1995.
Nos. 1093, 1095 inscribed "DS/20."
This is an expanding set. Numbers may change.

Souvenir Sheet

Natl. Aviation Museum, 50th Anniv. — A547

Aircraft: a, Sukhoi SU-30 Flanker. b, Vought-Sikorsky OS-2U3 Kingfisher. c, Lockheed F-117A Nighthawk. d, Northrop F-5E Tiger III.

1994, Mar. 17 Litho. *Perf. 13*
1102 A547 300p Sheet of 4, #a.-d. + 2 labels 6.00 3.00

Intl. Air and Space Fair, FIDAE '94.

College of Agronomy, 50th Anniv. — A548

1994, Apr. 28 Litho. *Perf. 13*
1103 A548 220p multicolored 1.10 .55

No. 760 Surcharged

$80

1994, May 1 Litho. *Perf. 13½*
1104 Block of 4 1.50 .75
a.-d. A411 80p on 15p any single .35 .18

Concepcion University, 75th Anniv. — A549

Sections of mural, by Jorge Gonzalez Camarena: No. 1105, Cactus plant, skeletons. No. 1106, Flags, pillars, nude woman, faces. No. 1107, Flags, bodies, woman, soldier in armor. No. 1108, Women's faces, pipelines.

1994, May 14 Litho. *Perf. 13*
1105 A549 250p multicolored 1.25 .60
1106 A549 250p multicolored 1.25 .60
1107 A549 250p multicolored 1.25 .60
1108 A549 250p multicolored 1.25 .60
a. Strip of 4, #1105-1108 + label 5.00 2.50

No. 1108a is a continuous design.

Chilean Antarctic Institute, 30th Anniv. — A550

Designs: No. 1109, Penguins, buildings. No. 1110, Buildings, coastal waters.

1994, May 31 *Perf. 13*
1109 A550 300p multicolored 1.50 .75
1110 A550 300p multicolored 1.50 .75
a. Pair, #1109-1110 3.00 1.50

No. 1110a is a continuous design.

Antique Fire Engines A551

Designs: No. 1111, Merryweather steam pumper, England, 1869. No. 1112, Western lever pumper, US, 1863. No. 1113, Mieusset steam pumper, France, 1905. No. 1114, Merryweather pumper, England, 1903.

1994, July 19 Litho. *Perf. 13*
1111 A551 150p multicolored .70 .35
1112 A551 150p multicolored .70 .35
1113 A551 150p multicolored .70 .35
1114 A551 150p multicolored .70 .35
a. Block of 4, #1111-1114 2.80 1.40

Javiera Carrera Girls' School, Cent. A552

1994, Aug. 10
1115 A552 200p multicolored .95 .48

Arms, Sights from Chilean Cities A553

Designs: 90p, Porvenir, cent. 100p, Villa Alemana, cent. 150p, Constitucion, bicent. 200p, Linares, bicent. 250p, Copiapo, 250th anniv. 300p, La Serena, 450th anniv.

1994, Aug. 26
1116 A553 90p multicolored .42 .20
1117 A553 100p multicolored .48 .24
1118 A553 150p multicolored .70 .35
1119 A553 200p multicolored .95 .48
1120 A553 250p multicolored 1.20 .60
1121 A553 300p multicolored 1.50 .75
Nos. 1116-1121 (6) 5.25 2.62

Miniature Sheet of 8

Butterflies — A554

Designs: a, Vanessa terpsichore. b, Hypsochila wagenknechti. c, Battus polydamas. d, Polythysana apollina. e, Satyridae. f, Tetraphloebia stellygera. g, Eroessa chilensis. h, Phoebis sennae.

1994, June 24 Litho. *Perf. 13*
1122 A554 100p #a.-h. 4.25 4.25

20th Intl. Conference on Data Bases — A555

1994, Sept. 21 Litho. *Perf. 13½*
1123 A555 100p multicolored .55 .28

America Issue A556

Early postal transport vehicles: 80p, Van. 220p, DH-60-G, Gypsy Moth.

1994, Oct. 12
1124 A556 80p multicolored .45 .22
1125 A556 220p multicolored 1.25 .65

Beatification of Father Alberto Hurtado — A557

1994, Oct. 31 Litho. & Engr.
1126 A557 300p multicolored 1.65 .80

Christmas — A558

1994 Litho. *Perf. 13½*
1127 A558 80p multicolored .45 .22
a. Booklet pane of 10 4.50
Complete booklet, #1127a 4.50

Inscribed "DS/20"

1128 A558 80p multicolored .45 .22
a. Booklet pane of 10 4.50
Complete booklet, #1128a 4.50

Nos. 1036-1037, 1079 Surcharged

$80

1994 Litho. *Perf. 13½ on 3 Sides*
1129 A525 80p on 70p #1036 .45 .22
1130 A525 80p on 70p #1037 .45 .22
a. Pair, #1129-1130 .90 .45
b. Booklet pane, 5 #1130a 4.75
Complete booklet, #1130b 4.75
1131 A542 80p on 70p #1079 .45 .22
a. Booklet pane, 10 #1131 4.75
Complete booklet, #1131a 4.75

Size and location of surcharge varies.

Miniature Sheet

Intl. Women's Day — A559

Designs: a, Star, "Women enriching the future." b, Moon, sun, "Women bringing harmony." c, Bird, "Women bringing peace." d, Earth, "Women changing the world."

1995, Mar. 8 Litho. *Perf. 13½*
1132 A559 90p Sheet of 4, #a.-d. 1.90 .95

Ancud Seminary of Conciliation, 150th Anniv. — A560

1995, Apr. 27
1133 A560 200p multicolored 1.10 .55

Destroyer Admiral Williams A561

1995, Apr. 21
1134 A561 100p multicolored .55 .28

World Conference on Social Development — A562

1995, Apr. 25
1135 A562 150p multicolored .80 .40

Order of St. Augustine in Chile, 400th Anniv. — A563

Design: Stained glass, Cathedral of Santiago.

1995, Apr. 28
1136 A563 250p multicolored 1.40 .70

Petroglyphs — A564

Designs: a, Ceremonial mask, Buitre, Limari Province. b, Lamas, Taira Sector, El Loa Province. c, Harpooned whale, El Medano, Taltal Province. d, Two masks, Encanto, Ovalle.

1995, June 16 Litho. ***Perf. 13½***
1137 A564 150p Block of 4, #a.-d. 3.75 1.75

Miniature Sheet

Motion Pictures, Cent. — A565

Posters: a, Director's chair, camera. b, Charlie Chaplin in "The Kid." c, Lumiere brothers' 1895 Cinematographe. d, "Valparaiso, My Love", with Aldo Francia.

1995, June 21
1138 A565 100p Sheet of 4, #a.-d. 2.50 1.25

City of Parral, Bicent. A566

1995, June 30 Litho. ***Perf. 13½***
1139 A566 200p multicolored 1.25 .60

Miniature Sheet

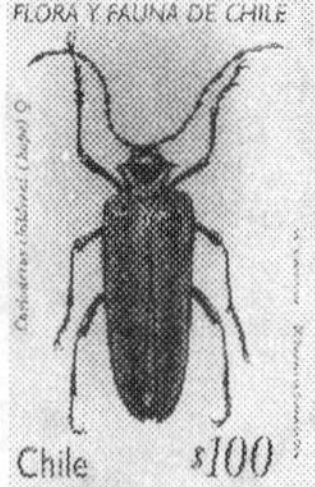

Insects and Cacti — A567

Designs: a, Cheloderus childreni. b, Eulychnia acida. c, Chiasognathus grantii. d, Browningia candelaris. e, Copiapoa dealbata. f, Acanthinodera cummingi. g, Neoporteria subgibbosa. h, Semiotus luteipennis.

1995, Aug. 10 Litho. ***Perf. 13½***
1140 A567 100p Sheet of 8, #a.-h. 4.50 2.25

2nd World Congress of Police, Santiago — A568

1995, Oct. 2
1141 A568 200p multicolored 1.25 .55

Ministry of Housing and Urban Development, 30th Anniv. — A569

Design: Tower of Babel V, by Mario Toral.

1995, Oct. 5 Litho. ***Perf. 13½***
1142 A569 200p multicolored 1.25 .60

Andres Bello (1781-1865), Scholar, Author — A570

1995, Oct. 9 Litho. & Engr.
1143 A570 250p dark brown & black 1.40 .70

Andres Bello Convenant, 25th anniv.

America Issue A572

Children's drawings of environmental protection: 100p, Family in garden, trees, vert. 250p, Three people working with trees.

1995 Litho. ***Perf. 13½***
1145 A572 100p multicolored .60 .30
1146 A572 250p multicolored 1.50 .75

51st World Congress of Cape Horn Captains — A574

1995 Litho. ***Perf. 13½***
1148 A574 250p multicolored 1.50 .75

SEMI-POSTAL STAMPS

S. S. Abtao and Captain Policarpo Toro — SP1

S. S. Abtao and Brother Eugenio Eyraud SP2

Perf. 14½x15
1940, Mar. 1 Engr. Unwmk.
B1 SP1 80c + 2.20p dk grn & lake 1.40 1.25
B2 SP2 3.60p + 6.40p lake & dk grn 1.40 1.25
a. Pair, #B1-B2 3.50 3.50

50th anniv. of Chilean ownership of Easter Is. Surtax used for charitable institutions.

Sheets containing 15 of each value, with 9 se-tenant pairs.

Catalogue values for unused stamps in this section, from this point to the end of the section, are for Never Hinged items.

Pedro de Valdivia — SP3

Portraits: 10c+10c, Jose Toribio Medina.

1961, Apr. 29 Photo. ***Perf. 13x12½***
B3 SP3 5c + 5c pale brn & sl grn .80 .18
B4 SP3 10c + 10c buff & vio blk .60 .18

Printed without charge by the Spanish Mint as a gift to Chile. The surtax was to aid the 1960 earthquake victims and to increase teachers' salaries. See Nos. CB1-CB2.

No. 402 Surcharged in Dark Green

E° 27 + 3

"Centenario de la Organización Meteorológica Mundial IMO-W-MO 1973"

1974, Mar. 25 Litho. ***Perf. 14½***
B5 A213 27e + 3e on 40c dl grn .15 .15

Cent. of intl. meteorological cooperation.

The 3e surtax of Nos. B5-B10 was for modernization of the postal system.

No. 412 Surcharged in Dark Blue

E° 27 + 3

"V Centenario del Nacimiento de Copérnico 1473 - 1973"

1974, Apr. 25 Litho. ***Perf. 14½***
B6 A219 27e + 3e on 1.95e .15 .15

500th anniversary of the birth of Nicolaus Copernicus (1473-1534), Polish astronomer.

No. 329A Surcharged

E° 27 + 3

" Centenario de la ciudad de Viña del Mar 1874 - 1974 "

1974, May 2 Litho. ***Perf. 14***
B7 A159 27e + 3e on 1e bluish grn .15 .15

Centenary of the city of Vina del Mar.

No. 377 Surcharged

1974, June 7 Litho. ***Perf. 14½***
B8 A193 47e + 3e on 40c grn .15 .15

Nos. 395 and 380 Surcharged in Red

1974
B9 A207 67e + 3e on 40c multi .15 .15
B10 A196 97e + 3e on 40c red brn .15 .15
Set value .16 .15

Issue dates: #B9, July 9; #B10, June 20.

AIR POST STAMPS

Correo Aéreo

2 pesos

Black Surcharge

Lithographed; Center Engraved
1927 Unwmk. ***Perf. 13½x14***
Black Brown & Blue
C1 40c on 10c 225.00 25.00
C2 80c on 10c 225.00 40.00
C3 1.20p on 10c 225.00 40.00
C4 1.60p on 10c 225.00 40.00
C5 2p on 10c 225.00 40.00
Nos. C1-C5 (5) 1,125. 185.00

Issued for air post service between Santiago and Valparaiso. The stamps picture Bernardo O'Higgins and are not known without surcharge.

Regular Issues of 1915-28 Overprinted or Surcharged in Black, Red or Blue

CORREO AEREO

Inscribed: "Chile Correos"

1928-29 ***Perf. 13½x14, 14***
C6 A39 20c brn org & blk (Bk) .35 .25
C6A A55 40c dk vio & blk (R) .40 .15
C6B A43 1p grn & blk (Bl) 1.00 .60
C6C A43 2p red & blk (Bl) 2.00 .30
f. 2p ver & blk (Bl) 75.00 18.00
C6D A43 5p ol grn & blk (Bl) 2.75 .80
C6E A50 6p on 10c dp bl & blk (R) 42.50 22.50
C7 A43 10p org & blk (Bk) ('29) 11.00 3.00
C8 A43 10p org & blk (Bl) 40.00 22.50
Nos. C6-C8 (8) 100.00 50.10

On Nos. C6B to C6D, C7 and C8 the overprint is larger than on the other stamps of the issue.

Same Overprint or Surcharge on Nos. 155, 156, 158-161

Inscribed: "Chile Correos"

1928-32 Wmk. 215
C9 A55 40c vio & blk (R) .50 .30
C10 A43 1p grn & blk (Bl) 1.25 .45
C11 A43 2p red & blk (Bl) 7.50 1.50
C12 A52 3p on 5c sl bl (R) 27.50 20.00
C13 A43 5p ol grn & blk (Bl) 5.75 1.50
C14 A43 10p org & blk (Bk) 27.50 7.25
Nos. C9-C14 (6) 70.00 31.00

Same Overprint on Nos. 166-169, 172 and 158 in Black or Red

Inscribed: "Correos de Chile"

1928-30
C15 A39 20c (#166) ('29) .90 .50
C16 A39 20c (#172) ('30) .30 .15
C17 A40 25c bl & blk (R) .45 .15
C18 A41 30c brn & blk .25 .15
a. Double ovpt., one inverted *250.00 250.00*
C19 A42 50c dp grn & blk (R) .35 .15
Nos. C15-C19 (5) 2.25 1.10

Inscribed: "Chile Correos"

1932 ***Perf. 13½x14, 14***
C21 A43 1p yel grn & blk (Bk) 2.75 1.50

Condor on Andes — AP1a

Airplane Crossing Andes — AP3

Los Cerrillos Airport — AP2

1931 Litho. ***Perf. 13½x14, 14½x14***
C22 AP1a 5c yellow grn .25 .15
C23 AP1a 10c yellow brn .25 .15
C24 AP1a 20c rose .25 .15
C25 AP2 50c dark blue 1.05 .40
C26 AP3 50c black brn .60 .20
C27 AP3 1p purple .45 .20
C28 AP3 2p blue blk .90 .25
a. 2p bluish slate .90 .25
C29 AP2 5p lt red 2.25 .25
Nos. C22-C29 (8) 6.00 1.75

For surcharges see Nos. C51-C53.

Airplane over City — AP4

Two Airplanes over Globe — AP9

Designs: 30c, 40c, 50c, Wings over Chile. 60c, Condor. 70c, Airplane and Star of Chile. 80c, Condor and Statue of Canpolican. 3p, 4p, 5p, Seaplane. 6p, 8p, 10p, Airplane. 20p, 30p, Airplane and Southern Cross. 40p, 50p, Airplane and symbols of space.

Perf. 13½x14

1934-39 Engr. Wmk. 215

C30 AP4 10c yel grn ('35) .25 .15
C31 AP4 15c dk grn ('35) .35 .20
C32 AP4 20c dp bl ('36) .20 .15
C33 AP4 30c blk brn ('35) .20 .15
C34 AP4 40c indigo ('38) .20 .15
C35 AP4 50c dk brn ('36) .20 .15
C36 AP4 60c vio blk ('35) .20 .15
C37 AP4 70c blue ('35) .35 .20
C38 AP4 80c ol blk ('35) .20 .15

Perf. 14

C39 AP9 1p slate blk .20 .15
C40 AP9 2p grnsh bl .20 .15
C41 AP9 3p org brn ('35) .25 .15
C42 AP9 4p brn ('35) .25 .15
C43 AP9 5p org red .25 .15
C44 AP9 6p yel brn ('35) .35 .20
a. 6p brown ('39) 3.75 2.00
C45 AP9 8p grn ('35) .30 .15
C46 AP9 10p brn lake .35 .20
C47 AP9 20p olive .35 .20
C48 AP9 30p gray blk .40 .20
C49 AP9 40p gray vio 1.00 .60
C50 AP9 50p brn vio 1.25 .60
Nos. C30-C50 (21) 7.30 4.35

Nos. C30-C50 have been re-issued in slightly different colors, with white gum. The first printings are considerably scarcer.

See Nos. C90-C107B, C148-C154.

Types of 1931 Surcharged in Black or Red

Perf. 13½x14, 14½x14

1940 Wmk. 215

C51 AP1a 80c on 20c lt rose .35 .15
C52 AP2 1.60p on 5p lt red 2.25 .70
C53 AP3 5.10p on 2p sl bl (R) 1.65 1.00
Nos. C51-C53 (3) 4.25 1.85

The surcharge on #C52 measures 21½mm.

Plane and Weather Vane — AP14

Plane and Caravel — AP23

Designs (Plane and): 20c, Globe. 30c, Chilean flag. 40c, Star of Chile and Southern Cross. 50c, Mountains. 60c, Tree. 70c, Lakes. 80c, Shore. 90c, Sunrise. 2p, Compass. 3p, Telegraph lines. 4p, Rainbow. 5p, Factory. 10p, Snow-capped mountain.

1941-42 Wmk. 215 Litho. Perf. 14

C54 AP14 10c ol gray .15 .15
C55 AP14 20c dp rose .15 .15
C56 AP14 30c blue vio .15 .15
C57 AP14 40c dl red brn .15 .15
C58 AP14 50c red org ('42) .35 .15
C59 AP14 60c dp green .15 .15
C60 AP14 70c rose .30 .25
C61 AP14 80c ultra ('42) 1.75 .45
C62 AP14 90c dk brown .45 .25
C63 AP23 1p brt blue .30 .20
C64 AP23 2p rose lake .45 .30
C65 AP23 3p dk bl grn & yel grn .65 .50
C66 AP23 4p bl vio & buff 1.00 .65
C67 AP23 5p dk org red ('42) 9.00 4.50
C68 AP23 10p gray grn & bl grn 5.00 3.50
Nos. C54-C68 (15) 20.00 11.50

The 1p, dated "1541-1941", commemorates the 400th anniversary of Santiago.

1942-46 Unwmk.

C69 AP14 10c ultra ('43) .20 .15
C70 AP14 10c rose lil ('45) .20 .15
C71 AP14 20c dull grn ('43) .20 .15
C72 AP14 20c cop brn ('45) .20 .15
C73 AP14 30c dull vio ('44) .20 .15
C74 AP14 30c ol blk ('45) .20 .15
C75 AP14 40c red brn ('44) .40 .15
C76 AP14 40c ultra ('45) .20 .15
C77 AP14 50c rose ('43) .20 .15
C78 AP14 50c org red ('45) .20 .15
C79 AP14 60c orange .20 .15
C79B AP14 60c dp grn ('46) .20 .15
C80 AP14 70c rose ('45) .50 .35
C81 AP14 80c slate grn .20 .15
C82 AP14 90c brown ('45) .55 .35
C83 AP23 1p gray grn & lt bl ('43) .25 .15
C84 AP23 2p org red ('43) .55 .15
C85 AP23 3p dk pur & pale org ('43) .55 .15
C86 AP23 4p bl grn & yel grn .55 .30
C87 AP23 5p dk rose car ('43) .45 .20
a. 5p dk car rose ('44) .20 .15
C88 AP23 10p sapphire ('43) .55 .30
Nos. C69-C88 (21) 6.75
Set value 3.30

No. C83 is without dates "1541-1941."

See Nos. C109-C123, C145-C147. For surcharges see Nos. C145-C147

Coat of Arms and Plane AP29

1942, Nov. 5 Engr. Perf. 14½

C89 AP29 100p car lake 25.00 20.00

University of Chile centenary.

Types of 1934-39

Perf. 13½x14

1944-55 Unwmk. Engr.

C90 AP4 10c yel grn ('55) .25 .20
C91 AP4 20c deep blue .15 .15
C93 AP4 30c black brn .15 .15
C94 AP4 40c indigo .15 .15
C95 AP4 50c dk brn ('47) .15 .15
C96 AP4 60c slate vio .15 .15
C97 AP4 70c blue ('48) .15 .15
C98 AP4 80c olive blk .15 .15

Perf. 14

C99 AP9 1p slate blk .15 .15
C100 AP9 2p grnsh bl .25 .15
C101 AP9 3p org brn ('45) .15 .15
C102 AP9 4p brown .15 .20
C103 AP9 5p org red .35 .15
C104 AP9 6p yel brn ('46) .40 .20
C105 AP9 8p green .40 .15
C106 AP9 10p brn lake 1.10 .15
C107 AP9 20p ol gray ('45) .75 .15
a. Imperf., pair 70.00
C107B AP9 50p rose vio ('50) 17.50 3.50
Nos. C90-C107B (18) 22.50
Set value 5.50

Plane and Radio Tower — AP30

1945 Unwmk. Litho. Perf. 14

C108 AP30 1.60p brt violet .55 .25

Types of 1941-42

1946-48 Wmk. 215

C109 AP14 10c rose lil ('47) .15 .15
C110 AP14 20c dk red brn ('48) .15 .15
C111 AP14 20c dull grn ('48) 1.50 .30
C112 AP14 30c black ('48) .15 .15
C113 AP14 40c ultra ('48) .15 .15
C114 AP14 60c ol grn ('48) .15 .15
C115 AP14 80c ol blk ('48) .15 .15
C116 AP14 90c choc ('48) .20 .15
C117 AP23 1p gray grn & lt bl ('48) .20 .15
C118 AP30 1.60p brt violet .20 .15
C119 AP30 1.80p brt vio ('48) .20 .15
C119A AP23 2p org red .40 .15
C120 AP23 3p dk pur & pale org ('47) 1.50 .30
C121 AP23 4p bl grn & yel grn ('48) 1.10 .45
C122 AP23 5p rose car ('47) .80 .20
C123 AP23 10p sapphire ('47) 1.00 .20
Nos. C109-C123 (16) 8.00
Set value 2.50

No. C117 is without dates "1541-1941."

For surcharges see Nos. C145, C147.

Flora anf Fauna Type of 1948

1948

C124 A118 3p Block of 25 25.00
a.-y. any single .60 .60

Catalogue values for unused stamps in this section, from this point to the end of the section, are for Never Hinged items.

Air Line Emblem and Planes — AP32

1949 Wmk. 215 Litho. Perf. 14

C125 AP32 2p ultra .40 .25

20th anniversary of the establishment of Chile's National Air Line.

Benjamin Vicuna Mackenna AP33

Factory, Badge and Book AP34

1949, Mar. 22 Engr. Perf. 13½x14

C126 AP33 3p dk car rose .25 .15

Unwmk.

1949, Nov. 11 Litho. Perf. 14

Design: 10p, Column and cogwheel.

C127 AP34 5p green .60 .40
C128 AP34 10p red brown 1.00 .60

Centenary of the founding of Chile's School of Arts and Crafts.

Plane and Globe — AP35

1950, Jan. Engr.

C129 AP35 5p green .25 .20
C130 AP35 10p red brown .60 .40

75th anniv. of the UPU.

Plane over Snow-capped Mountain — AP36

Araucarian Pine and Plane — AP38

Plane and: 40c, Coast and Sunrise. 60c, Over fishing boat. 2p, Chilean flag. 3p, Dock crane. 4p, Above river. 5p, Blast furnace. 10p, Mountain lake. 20p, Cable cars.

Imprint: "Especies Valoradas-Chile"

1950-54 Wmk. 215 Litho. Perf. 14

C135 AP36 20c yel brn ('54) .20 .15
C136 AP36 40c purple ('52) .20 .15
C137 AP36 60c lt bl ('53) 1.50 .75
C138 AP38 1p dull green .20 .15
C139 AP38 2p brown red .20 .15
C140 AP38 3p violet bl .20 .15
C141 AP38 4p red org ('54) .20 .15
C142 AP38 5p violet .20 .15
C143 AP38 10p yel grn ('53) .25 .15
C144 AP38 20p red brn ('54) .40 .15
Nos. C135-C144 (10) 3.55
Set value 1.65

See Nos. C155-C164, C207-C212.

Nos. C115, C81 and C116 Surcharged with New Value in Carmine or Black

1951-52 Wmk. 215

C145 AP14 40c on 80c ol blk (C) ('52) .20 .15

Unwmk.

C146 AP14 40c on 80c sl grn (C) ('52) 5.00 3.50

Wmk. 215

C147 AP14 1p on 90c choc .20 .15
Nos. C145-C147 (3) 5.40 3.80

Types of 1934-39

1951-53 Unwmk. Engr. Perf. 14

C148 AP9 1p deep blue .16 .15
C149 AP9 2p blue .28 .15
C150 AP9 6p bis brn ('52) .45 .16
C151 AP9 30p dk gray ('53) 4.00 .60
C152 AP9 40p dk pur brn 12.00 1.65
C153 AP9 50p dark purple 20.00 6.50
Nos. C148-C153 (6) 36.89 9.21

Wmk. 215

C154 AP13 50p dk pur ('52) .80 .40

Types of 1950-54

Designs as Before

Imprint: "Especies Valoradas-Chile"

1951-55 Unwmk. Litho. Perf. 14

C155 AP36 20c yel brn ('54) .16 .15
C156 AP36 40c purple .16 .15
C157 AP36 60c lt blue ('53) .25 .15
C158 AP38 1p dk bl grn ('55) .16 .15
C159 AP38 2p brown red .16 .15
C160 AP38 3p violet bl .16 .15
C161 AP38 4p red org ('52) .28 .16
C162 AP38 5p violet .28 .16
C163 AP38 10p emerald .28 .15
C164 AP38 20p brown .40 .15
Nos. C155-C164 (10) 2.29
Set value 1.05

San Martin Crossing Andes AP40

Perf. 14½

1951, Mar. 16 Wmk. 215 Engr.

C165 AP40 5p red violet .40 .25

Gen. José de San Martín, death cent.

Isabella Type of Regular Issue, 1952.

1952, Mar. 21 Perf. 14

C166 A125 10p carmine .50 .30

A souvenir card without franking value was issued for the Hispano-Chilean Philatelic Exhibition at Santiago, Oct. 12, 1969. It contains 2 imperf. stamps similar to Nos. 264 and C166-60c green and 10p rose red. Size: 115x137½mm.

Ancient Fortress — AP42

1953, Apr. 28

C167 AP42 10p brown car 1.00 .25

4th centenary of the founding of Valdivia.

Stamp Centenary Type of 1953

1953, Oct. 15 Engr. Perf. 14½

C168 A131 100p dp grnsh bl 1.25 .75

An imperf. souvenir sheet contains one each of Nos. 276 and C168, with inscriptions in black at top and bottom center. Sheet measures 178x229mm. It is stated that this sheet was not valid for postage.

Early Plane and Stylized Modern Version — AP44

Unwmk.

1954, May 26 Engr. *Perf. 14*
C170 AP44 3p deep blue .15 .15

25th anniversary of the founding of Chile's National Air Line.

Domeyko Type of Regular Issue, 1954.

1954, Aug. 16 *Perf. 13½x14*
C171 A134 5p orange brown .20 .15

Railroad Type of Regular Issue, 1954

1954, Sept. 10 Wmk. 215 *Perf. 14½*
C172 A135 10p dk purple .40 .20

An imperforate souvenir sheet contains one each of Nos. 283 and C172. Size: 174x232mm. Value, $200.

Presidential Visits Type of 1955

1955, May 24
C173 A139 100p red 1.50 1.25

Jet Plane in Clouds — AP48

Comet Air Liner — AP49

Designs: 2p, Helicopter over bridge. 10p, Oil derricks and plane. 50p, Control tower and plane. 200p, Beechcraft monoplane. 500p, Douglas DC-6.

Perf. 14½x14, 14x13½ (AP49)

1955-56 Engr. Wmk. 215

C174	AP48	1p dp red lil ('56)	.20	.15
C175	AP48	2p pale brn ('56)	.15	.15
C176	AP48	10p bluish grn ('56)	.15	.15
C177	AP48	50p rose ('56)	.60	.25
C178	AP49	100p green	.75	.15
C179	AP49	200p dp ultra	5.00	.70
C180	AP49	500p dk carmine	6.00	.70
		Nos. C174-C180 (7)	12.85	2.25

Stamps similar to type AP49, but inscribed in escudo currency, are listed as type AP58.

1956-58 Unwmk.

Designs: 5p, Train and plane. 20p, Jet plane and Easter Island statue.

C183	AP48	5p violet	.15	.15
C184	AP48	10p grn ('57)	.15	.15
C185	AP48	20p ultra	.15	.15
C186	AP48	50p rose ('57)	.15	.15
C187	AP49	100p bl grn ('57)	.40	.15
a.		Lithographed ('60)	.40	.20
C188	AP49	200p dp ultra ('57)	.50	.15
C189	AP49	500p car ('58)	.65	.20
		Nos. C183-C189 (7)	2.15	
		Set value		.70

Symbols of University Departments — AP50

Design: 100p, View of the University.

1956, Dec. 15 Unwmk. *Perf. 14½*
C190 AP50 20p green .25 .15
C191 AP50 100p dk vio bl 1.00 .60

25th anniversary of the Federico Santa Maria Technical University, Valparaiso.

A souvenir sheet contains one each of Nos. 299, C190-C191, imperf. It was not issued for postal use, though some served postally. Size: 127x160mm. Value, $25.

Mistral Type of Regular Issue, 1958

1958, Jan. 10 Engr. *Perf. 14*
C192 A144 100p green .20 .15

Ambrosio O'Higgins — AP51

1958, Mar. 23
C193 AP51 100p lt blue .25 .15

Founding of the city of Osorno, 500th anniv.

A souvenir sheet contains one each of Nos. 302 and C193, imperf. and printed in red brown. It was not issued for postal use, though some served postally. Size: 155x138mm. Value, $15.

Exhibition Type of Regular Issue

1958, Oct. 18 Unwmk.
C194 A146 50p dull green .15 .15

A souvenir sheet contains one each of Nos. 303 and C194, imperf. and printed in deep red. It was not issued for postal use, though some served postally. Size: 188x220mm. Value, $15.

Bank Type of Regular Issue, 1958.

1958, Dec. 18 Engr. *Perf. 14*
C195 A147 50p redsh brown .15 .15

A souvenir sheet contains one each of Nos. 304 and C195, printed in dull violet, imperf. It was not issued for postal use, though some served postally. Value, $150.

Antarctic Types of Regular Issue

1958 Litho. *Perf. 14*
C199 A149 20p violet .20 .15

Engr.
C200 A150 500p dark blue 2.75 1.25

Symbols of Various Religions — AP52

Perf. 14½

1959, Jan. 23 Unwmk. Engr.
C206 AP52 50p dk car rose .15 .15

10th anniversary of the Universal Declaration of Human Rights.

Types of 1950-54.

Imprint: "Casa de Moneda de Chile."

Designs: 50p, Plane silhouette over shore. 100p, Plane over map of Antarctica. 200p, Plane over natural arch rock.

1959 Litho. *Perf. 14*

C207	AP38	1p dk blue grn	.60	.35
a.		Wmk. 215	30.00	
C208	AP38	10p emerald	.40	.15
C209	AP38	20p red brown	.25	.15
C210	AP38	50p yellow grn	.25	.15
C211	AP38	100p car rose	.25	.15
C212	AP38	200p brt blue	.40	.15
		Nos. C207-C212 (6)	2.15	1.10

Carlos Anwandter — AP53

1959, June 18 Engr. *Perf. 14*
C213 AP53 20p rose carmine .20 .15

Centenary of the German School in Valdivia, founded by Carlos Anwandter.

A souvenir sheet contains one each of Nos. 319 and C213, imperf. It was not issued for postal use, though some served postally. Value, $20.

IGY Type of Regular Issue, 1958.

1959, Aug. 28 Unwmk. *Perf. 14*
C214 A148 50p green .20 .15

Ladrillero Type of Regular Issue

1959, Aug. 28 Litho.
C215 A154 50p green .20 .15

Barros Arana Type of Regular Issue

1959, Aug. 28
C216 A155 100p purple .40 .20

Red Cross Type of Regular Issue

1959, Oct. 6
C217 A156 50p red & blk .25 .15

WRY Type of Regular Issue, 1960.

1960, Apr. 7 Unwmk. *Perf. 14½*
C218 A160 10c violet .25 .15

A souvenir sheet contains two stamps similar to Nos. 330 and C218, the 1c printed in blue, the 10c airmail in maroon. The sheet is imperf., printed on thin cardboard. Size: 160x204mm. Value, $90.

Type of Regular Issue, 1960-62, and

José Agustin Eyzaguirre and José Miguel Infante — AP54

Designs: 2c, Palace of Justice. 5c, National memorial. No. C220, Arms of Chile. No. C220A, José Gaspar Marin and J. Gregorio Argomedo. 50c, Archbishop J. I. Cienfuegos and Brother Camilo Henriquez. 1e, Bernardo O'Higgins.

1960-65 Unwmk. Engr. *Perf. 14½*

C218A	AP54	2c mar & gray vio ('62)	.15	.15
C219	A162	5c vio bl & dl pur ('61)	.20	.15
		Wmk. 215		
C220	A161	10c dk brn & red brn	.20	.15
		Unwmk.		
C220A	AP54	10c vio brn & brn ('64)	.20	.15
C220B	AP54	20c dk bl & dl pur ('64)	.25	.15
C220C	AP54	50c bl grn & ind ('65)	.50	.20
C220D	A162	1e dk red & red brn ('63)	1.00	.40
		Nos. C218A-C220D (7)	2.50	
		Set value		1.10

150th anniv. of the formation of the 1st Natl. Government.

A souvenir sheet contains two airmail stamps: a 5c brown similar to No. C219 (National Memorial) and a 10c green, type A161. The sheet is imperf., printed on heavy paper with papermaker's watermark. Size: 120x168mm. Value, $30.

Map and Rotary Emblem — AP55

Unwmk.

1960, Dec. 1 Litho. *Perf. 14*
C221 AP55 10c blue .30 .15

South American Rotary Regional Conference, Santiago, 1960.

A souvenir sheet contains one 10c maroon, type AP55, with brown marginal inscription. Size: 118x158mm. Value, $14.

The souvenir sheet was overprinted in green "El Mundo Unida Contra la Malaria" and the outline of a mosquito, and released in October, 1962. Value, $27.50.

Plane over Mountain Lake — AP56

Designs: 1m, Araucarian pine and plane. 2m, Chilean flag and plane. 3m, Plane and dock crane. 4m, Plane above river (vignette like AP39). 5m, Blast furnace. 2c, Plane over cable cars. 5c, Plane silhouette over shore. 10c, Plane over map of Antarctica. 20c, Plane over natural arch rock.

Imprint: "Casa de Moneda de Chile."

1960-62 Litho. *Perf. 14*

C222	AP56	1m orange	.15	.15
C223	AP56	2m yellow grn	.15	.15
C224	AP56	3m violet	.15	.15
C225	AP56	4m gray olive	.15	.15
C226	AP56	5m brt bl grn	.15	.15
C227	AP56	1c ultra	.15	.15
C228	AP56	2c red brn ('61)	.22	.15
C229	AP56	5c yel grn ('61)	1.25	.15
C230	AP56	10c car rose ('62)	.30	.15
C231	AP56	20c brt bl ('62)	.35	.15
		Nos. C222-C231 (10)	3.02	
		Set value		.70

Oil Derricks and Douglas DC-6 — AP57

Beechcraft Monoplane — AP58

Designs: 5m, Train and plane. 2c, Jet plane and Easter Island statue. 5c, Control tower and plane. 10c, Comet airliner. 50c, Douglas DC-6.

Perf. 14x13½

1960-67 Unwmk. Litho.

C234	AP57	5m red brown	.15	.15
C235	AP57	1c dull blue	.15	.15
C236	AP57	2c ultra ('62)	.15	.15
C237	AP57	5c rose red ('64)	.15	.15
C238	AP58	10c ultra ('67)	.15	.15
C239	AP58	20c car ('62)	.15	.15
C240	AP58	50c green ('63)	.15	.15
		Set value	.44	.36

Stamps similar to type AP58, but inscribed in peso ($) currency, are listed as type AP49.

Congress Type of Regular Issue.

1961, Oct. 5 *Perf. 14½*
C245 A164 10c gray green .75 .25

Soccer Type of Regular Issue, 1962.

Designs: 5c, Goalkeeper and stadium, vert. 10c, Soccer players and globe.

1962, May 30 Unwmk. Engr.
C246 A165 5c rose lilac .15 .15
C247 A165 10c dk carmine .25 .15

A souvenir sheet of four contains one each of Nos. 340-341, C246-C247, imperf., with light brown marginal inscriptions. Size: 123x194mm. Sold for 7.50 escudos (face value, 22 centavos). Value, $5.

Hunger Type of Regular Issue.

Design: 20c, Mother with empty bowl, horiz.

1963, Mar. 21 Litho. *Perf. 14*
C248 A166 20c green .15 .15

Red Cross Type of Regular Issue.

Design: 20c, Centenary emblem and plane silhouette, horiz.

1963, Sept. 6 Unwmk. *Perf. 14*
C249 A167 20c gray & red .15 .15

Fire Engine of 1860's — AP59

1963, Dec. 20 Litho. *Perf. 14½*
C250 AP59 30c red .15 .15

Centenary of the Santiago Fire Brigade.

Western Hemisphere AP60

1964, Apr. 9 Unwmk. *Perf. 14½*

C254 AP60 4c ultra .15 .15

Issued in memory of President John F. Kennedy and to honor the Alliance for Progress.

Battle of Rancagua AP61

1965, May 7 Engr. *Perf. 14½*

C255 AP61 5c dull grn & sepia .15 .15

Battle of Rancagua, Oct. 7, 1814, 150th anniv.

ITU Emblem, Old and New Communication Equipment AP62

1965, May 7 Litho. *Perf. 14½x14*

C256 AP62 40c red & maroon .15 .15

ITU centenary.

Portrait Type of 1964

Portraits: No. C257, Enrique Molina. No. C258, Msgr. Carlos Casanueva.

1965, June Litho. *Perf. 14*

C257 A169 60c brt violet .15 .15
C258 A169 60c green .15 .15
Set value .20 .15

See note after No. 346.

Skier Type of Regular Issue 1965

Design: 20c, Skier, horiz.

1965, Aug. 30 Unwmk. *Perf. 14*

C259 A172 20c ultra .15 .15

Fishing Boats, Angelmo Harbor AP63

Aviators' Monument AP64

1965

C260 AP63 40c brown .15 .15

Perf. 14x14½

C262 AP64 1e car rose .15 .15
Set value .15

Andrés Bello (1780?-1865), Venezuela-born Writer and Educator — AP65

1965, Nov. 29 Engr. Unwmk.

C263 AP65 10c dk car rose .15 .15

Skiers — AP66

Basketball — AP67

1966, Apr. 6 Litho. *Perf. 14*

C264 AP66 4e dk bl & red brn .60 .15

World Skiing Championships, Partillo, Aug. 1966.

1966, Apr. 28

C265 AP67 13c rose carmine .15 .15

International Basketball Championships.

Slalom AP68

Perf. 14½x15

1966, July 20 Litho. Unwmk.

C266 AP68 75c rose car & lil .15 .15
C267 AP68 3e ultra & lt bl .20 .15
Set value .15

International Skiing Championships, Partillo, August 1966. A souvenir sheet of 2 contains imperf. stamps similar to Nos. C266-C267. No gum. Size: 109x140mm. Value $2.50.

Ship Type of Regular Issue

1966 Litho. *Perf. 14½*

C268 A175 70c Prus grn & yel grn .15 .15

See note below No. 358.

ICY Type of Regular Issue

1966, Oct. 28 Unwmk. *Perf. 14½*

C269 A177 3e blue & carmine .40 .20

A souvenir sheet of 2 contains imperf. stamps similar to Nos. 360 and C269. No gum. Size: 111x140mm. Value $2.25.

Chilean Flag and Ships — AP69

1966, Nov. 21 Litho. *Perf. 14*

C270 AP69 13c dull red brn .15 .15

Centenary of the city of Antofagasta.

Pardo Type of Regular Issue

Design: 40c, Pardo and map of Chile's claim to Antarctica.

1967, Jan. 6 Unwmk. *Perf. 14½*

C271 A178 40c ultra .15 .15

See note below No. 361.

Family Type of Regular Issue

1967, Apr. 13 Litho. *Perf. 14*

C272 A179 80c brt bl & blk .15 .15

Ruben Dario and Title Page of "Azul" AP70

1967, May 15 Engr. *Perf. 14½*

C273 AP70 10c dark blue .15 .15

Ruben Dario (pen name of Felix Ruben Garcia Sarmiento, 1867-1916), Nicaraguan poet, newspaper correspondent and diplomat.

Tree Type of Regular Issue

1967, June 9 Litho.

C274 A180 75c grn & pale rose .15 .15

Lions Type of Regular Issue

1967 Litho. *Perf. 14*

C275 A181 1e purple & yel .15 .15
C276 A181 5e blue & yel .80 .15
Set value .20

A souvenir sheet without franking value contains 3 imperf. stamps, 20c, 1e and 5e, in violet blue and yellow. Size: 110x140mm. Value, $7.50.

Issue dates: 1e, July 12; 5e, Aug. 11.

Flag Type of Regular Issue

1967, Oct. 20 Unwmk. *Perf. 14½*

C277 A182 50c ultra & crimson .15 .15

ITY Emblem AP71

1967, Nov. 22 Litho. *Perf. 14½*

C278 AP71 30c lt vio bl & blk .15 .15

Issued for International Tourist Year, 1967.

Caro Type of Regular Issue, 1967.

1967, Dec. 4 Engr. *Perf. 14½*

C279 A183 40c violet .50 .20

Type of Regular Issue, 1968

1968, Apr. 23 Litho. *Perf. 14½*

C280 A184 2e brt violet .15 .15

Sesquicentennial of the Battles of Chacabuco and Maipu. A souvenir sheet of 2 contains imperf. stamps similar to Nos. 367 and C280. Value, $4. A second sheet exists with the 2e in green and the 3e in brown. Size: 139½x100mm. Value, $4.

Farm Type of Regular Issue

1968, June 18 Unwmk.

C281 A185 50c blk, org & grn .15 .15

Juan I. Molina, Educator and Scientist AP72

1968, Aug. 27 Litho. *Perf. 14½*

C282 AP72 1e bright green .15 .15

Map of Chiloé Province — AP73

British Crown and Map of Chile — AP74

Perf. 14½

1968, Oct. 7 Unwmk. Litho.

C283 AP73 1e rose claret .15 .15

Anniversaries of the founding of five towns in Chiloé Province.

Auto Club Type of Regular Issue

1968, Nov. 10 Engr. *Perf. 14½x14*

C284 A189 5e ultra .20 .15

1968, Nov. 12 Litho. *Perf. 14½*

Designs: 50c, Chilean coat of arms (horiz.; similar to type A161). 3e, British coat of arms, horiz.

C285 AP74 50c green & brn .20 .15
C286 AP74 3e bl & org brn .15 .15

Engr.

C287 AP74 5e purple & mag .20 .15
Nos. C285-C287 (3) .55
Set value .28

Visit of Queen Elizabeth II of Great Britain, Nov. 11-18. A souvenir sheet of 3 contains imperf., lithographed stamps similar to Nos. C285-C287. Size: 124½x190mm. The souvenir sheet also publicizes the British-Chilean Philatelic Exhibition. Value, $8.

First Coin Minted in Chile and Coin Press AP75

Design: 1e, Chile No. 128.

1968, Dec. 31 Litho. *Perf. 14½*

C288 AP75 50c ocher & vio brn .15 .15
C289 AP75 1e lt bl & dp org .15 .15
Set value .20 .15

225th anniversary of the founding of the State Mint (Casa de Moneda de Chile).

A souvenir sheet of 4 contains imperf. stamps similar to Nos. 373-374, C288-C289. Size: 150x119mm. Value, $2.

Satellite Type of Regular Issue

1969, May 20 Litho. *Perf. 14½*

C290 A191 2e rose lilac .15 .15

Red Cross Type of Regular Issue

1969, Sept. Litho. *Perf. 14½*

C291 A192 5e black & red .15 .15

A souvenir card contains 2 imperf. stamps similar to Nos. 376 and C291, with red marginal inscription. Size: 109x140mm. Value $3.

Dam Type of Regular Issue

1969, Nov. 18 Litho. *Perf. 14½*

C292 A193 3e blue .15 .15

Rodriguez Type of Regular Issue

1969, Nov. 24

C293 A194 30c brown .15 .15

EXPO '70 Type of Regular Issue

1969, Dec. 1 Litho. *Perf. 14*

C294 A195 5e red .15 .15

Bible Type of 1969

1969, Dec. 2 *Perf. 14½*

C295 A196 1e green .15 .15

ILO Type of Regular Issue

1969, Dec. 17 *Perf. 14½*

C296 A197 2e rose lil & blk .15 .15

Human Rights Year Type of 1969

1969, Dec. 18

C297 A198 4e brown & red .15 .15

A souvenir sheet of 2 contains imperf. stamps similar to Nos. 382 and C297. Size: 110x140mm. Value, $3.50.

Easter Island Type of 1970

1970, Jan. 26

C298 A199 50c dull grnsh bl .15 .15

Ship Type of Regular Issue

1970, Feb. 4 Litho. *Perf. 14½*

C299 A200 2e deep ultra .20 .15

Rotary Type of Regular Issue

1970, Mar. 18 Litho. *Perf. 14*

C300 A201 1e rose claret .15 .15

Gandhi Type of Regular Issue

1970, Apr. 1 Litho. *Perf. 14½*

C301 A202 1e red brown .15 .15

Education Year Type of 1970

1970, July 17 Litho. *Perf. 14½*

C302 A204 4e red brown .15 .15

National Shrine Type of 1970

1970, July 28 Litho. *Perf. 14½*

C303 A205 1e ultra .15 .15

Cancer Type of Regular Issue

1970, Aug. 11

C304 A206 2e brn & lt olive .15 .15

A few copies are known inscribed "Correos de Chile" instead of "Correos Aereo Chile."

Copper Type of Regular Issue

1970, Oct. 21 Litho. *Perf. 14½*

C305 A207 3e grn & lt red brn .15 .15

United Nations Type of 1970

1970, Oct. 22

C306 A208 5e dk car & grn .32 .15

Freighter Type of Regular Issue

1971, Jan. 18 Litho. *Perf. 14*

C307 A209 5e lt red brown .15 .15

No. C290 Surcharged in Red

1971, Jan. 21 Litho. *Perf. 14½*

C308 A191 52c on 2e rose lil .20 .15

Liberation Type of Regular Issue

1971, Feb. 3 *Perf. 14½*

C309 A210 1e gray bl & brn .15 .15

UNICEF Type of Regular Issue

1971, Feb. 11 Litho. *Perf. 14½*

C310 A211 2e blue & grn .15 .15

Boy Scout Type of Regular Issue

1971, Feb. 10 *Perf. 14*

C311 A212 5c dk car & ol .15 .15

Satellite Type of Regular Issue

1971, May 25 Litho. *Perf. 14½*

C312 A213 2e brown .15 .15

De Ercilla Type of Regular Issue

1972, Mar. 20 Engr. *Perf. 14*

C313 A221 2e Prussian blue .15 .15

A souvenir card contains impressions of Nos. 414 and C313 with black marginal inscription commemorating España 75 Philatelic Exhibition. Size: 165x220mm.

AIR POST SEMI-POSTAL STAMPS

Catalogue values for unused stamps in this section are for Never Hinged items.

Type of Semi-Postal Stamps, 1961

Portraits: 10c+10c, Alonso de Ercilla. 20c+20c, Gabriela Mistral.

Perf. 13x12½

1961, Apr. 29 Photo. Unwmk.

CB1 SP3 10c + 10c sal & choc .65 .20
CB2 SP3 20c + 20c gray & dp cl .65 .20

Printed without charge by the Spanish Mint as a gift to Chile. The surtax was to aid the 1960 earthquake victims and to increase teachers' salaries.

ACKNOWLEDGMENT OF RECEIPT STAMPS

AR1

1894 Unwmk. *Perf. 11½*

H1 AR1 5c brown .75 .50
a. Imperf., pair 3.00

The black stamp of design similar to AR1 inscribed "Avis de Paiement" was prepared for use on notices of payment of funds but was not regularly issued.

POSTAGE DUE STAMPS

D1

D2

Handstamped

1894 Unwmk. *Perf. 13*

J1 D1 2c black, *straw* 11.00 5.00
J2 D1 4c black, *straw* 11.00 5.00
J3 D1 6c black, *straw* 11.00 5.00
J4 D1 8c black, *straw* 11.00 5.00
J5 D2 10c black, *straw* 11.00 5.00
J6 D1 16c black, *straw* 11.00 5.00
J7 D1 20c black, *straw* 11.00 5.00
J8 D1 30c black, *straw* 11.00 5.00
J9 D1 40c black, *straw* 11.00 5.00
Nos. J1-J9 (9) 99.00 45.00

J1a D1 2c black, *yellow* 45.00 42.50
J2a D1 4c black, *yellow* 37.50 30.00
J3a D1 6c black, *yellow* 27.50 25.00
J4a D1 8c black, *yellow* 11.00 9.00
J5a D2 10c black, *yellow* 11.00 9.00
J6a D1 16c black, *yellow* 11.00 9.00
J7a D1 20c black, *yellow* 11.00 9.00
J8a D1 30c black, *yellow* 11.00 9.00
J9a D1 40c black, *yellow* 11.00 9.00
Nos. J1a-J9a (9) 176.00 151.50

Counterfeits exist.

D3

1895 Litho. *Perf. 11*

J19 D3 1c red, *yellow* 5.00 2.00
J20 D3 2c red, *yellow* 5.00 2.00
J21 D3 4c red, *yellow* 4.25 2.00
J22 D3 6c red, *yellow* 5.00 2.00
J23 D3 8c red, *yellow* 3.25 2.00
J24 D3 10c red, *yellow* 3.25 3.00
J25 D3 20c red, *yellow* 3.25 1.50
J26 D3 40c red, *yellow* 3.25 2.00
J27 D3 50c red, *yellow* 3.25 2.00
J28 D3 60c red, *yellow* 6.50 3.00
J29 D3 80c red, *yellow* 6.50 4.25
J30 D3 1p red, *yellow* 6.50 4.25
Nos. J19-J30 (12) 55.00 30.00

Nos. J19-J30 were printed in sheets of 100 (10x10) containing all 12 denominations.
Counterfeits of Nos. J19-J42 exist.

1896 *Perf. 13½*

J31 D3 1c red, *straw* .75 .35
J32 D3 2c red, *straw* .75 .35
J33 D3 4c red, *straw* 1.00 .35
J34 D3 6c red, *straw* 2.00 .75
J35 D3 8c red, *straw* 1.00 .40
J36 D3 10c red, *straw* .75 .40
J37 D3 20c red, *straw* .75 .40
J38 D3 40c red, *straw* 12.00 10.00
J39 D3 50c red, *straw* 12.00 10.00
J40 D3 60c red, *straw* 12.00 10.00
J41 D3 80c red, *straw* 12.00 10.00
J42 D3 100c red, *straw* 25.00 21.00
Nos. J31-J42 (12) 80.00 64.00

D4

D5

1898 *Perf. 13*

J43 D4 1c scarlet .35 .30
J44 D4 2c scarlet .90 .60
J45 D4 4c scarlet .35 .30
J46 D4 10c scarlet .35 .30
J47 D4 20c scarlet .35 .30
Nos. J43-J47 (5) 2.30 1.80

1924 *Perf. 11½, 12½*

J48 D5 2c blue & red .75 .60
J49 D5 4c blue & red .75 .60
J50 D5 8c blue & red .75 .60
J51 D5 10c blue & red .75 .60
J52 D5 20c blue & red .75 .35
J53 D5 40c blue & red .75 .60
J54 D5 60c blue & red .75 .60
J55 D5 80c blue & red .75 .60
J56 D5 1p blue & red 1.00 .75
J57 D5 2p blue & red 1.75 1.25
J58 D5 5p blue & red 1.75 1.25
Nos. J48-J58 (11) 10.50 7.80

Nos. J48-J58 were printed in sheets of 150 containing all 11 denominations, and in sheets of 50 containing the five lower denominations, providing various se-tenants.

All values of this issue exist imperforate, also with center inverted, but are not believed to have been regularly issued. Those with inverted centers sell for about 10 times normal stamps.

OFFICIAL STAMPS

For Domestic Postage

O1

Single-lined frame
Control number in violet

1907 Unwmk. *Imperf.*

O1 O1 dl bl, "CARTA" org 22.50 17.50
O2 O1 red, "OFICIO" bl 22.50 17.50
O3 O1 vio, "PAQUETE" red 22.50 17.50
O4 O1 org, *bl,* "EP" vio 22.50 17.50
Nos. O1-O4 (4) 90.00 70.00

The diagonal inscription in differing color indicates type of usage: CARTA for letters of ordinary weight; OFICIO, heavy letters to 100 grams; PAQUETE, parcels to 100 grams; E P (Encomienda Postal), heavier parcels; C (Certificado), as on No. O8, registration including postage.

Varieties include CARTA, PAQUETE and E P inverted, OFICIO omitted, etc.

Double-lined frame
Large control number in black

Perf. 11

O5 O1 bl, "CARTA" yel 8.00 7.00
O6 O1 red, "OFICIO" bl 8.00 5.25
O7 O1 brn, "PAQUETE" grn 8.00 5.25
O8 O1 grn, "C" red 115.00 82.50
Nos. O5-O8 (4) 139.00 100.00

Nos. O5-O8 exist in tête bêche pairs; with CARTA, OFICIO or PAQUETE double or inverted, and other varieties.

Counterfeits of Nos. O1-O8 exist.

For Foreign Postage

Regular Issues of 1892-1909 Overprinted in Red — a

On Stamps of 1904-09

1907 *Perf. 12*

O9 A14 1c green 7.50 7.50
a. Inverted overprint 17.50
O10 A12 3c on 1p brn 14.00 14.00
a. Inverted overprint 52.50
O11 A14 5c ultra 10.50 10.50
a. Inverted overprint 35.00
O12 A15 10c gray & blk 10.50 10.50
O13 A15 15c vio & blk 14.00 14.00
O14 A15 20c org brn & blk 14.00 14.00
O15 A15 50c ultra & blk 45.00 45.00

On Stamp of 1892

Rouletted

O16 A6 1p dk brn & blk 110.00 87.50
Nos. O9-O16 (8) 225.50 203.00

Counterfeits of Nos. O9-O16 exist.

Regular Issues of 1915-25 Overprinted in Red or Blue — b

OFICIAL

1926 *Perf. 13½x14, 14*

O17 A52 5c slate bl (R) 2.50 .50
O18 A50 10c bl & blk (R) 4.00 .75
O19 A39 20c org red & blk (Bl) 2.00 .40
O20 A42 50c dp grn & blk (Bl) 2.00 .40
O21 A43 1p grn & blk (R) 2.75 .70
O22 A43 2p ver & blk (Bl) 4.00 1.00
Nos. O17-O22 (6) 17.25 3.75

Nos. O21 and O22 are overprinted vertically at each side.

Nos. O17 to O22 were for the use of the Biblioteca Nacional.

Servicio del

Regular Issue of 1915-25 Overprinted in Red — c

ESTADO

1928 *Perf. 13½x14, 14*

O23 A50 10c bl & blk 6.50 2.00
O24 A39 20c brn org & blk 3.00 1.00
O25 A40 25c dl bl & blk 7.50 1.00
O26 A42 50c dp grn & blk 4.00 1.00
O27 A43 1p grn & blk 5.00 1.50
Nos. O23-O27 (5) 26.00 6.50

The overprint on Nos. O23 to O26 is 16½mm high; on No. O27 it is 20mm.

Servicio del

Regular Issues of 1928-30 Overprinted in Red — d

ESTADO

On Stamp Inscribed: "Correos de Chile"

1930-31

O28 A50 10c bl & blk 3.00 1.50

Wmk. 215

On Stamps Inscribed: "Correos de Chile"

O29 A50 10c bl & blk 6.00 3.00
O30 A39 20c org red & blk .75 .50
O31 A40 25c bl & blk .75 .50
O32 A42 50c dp grn & blk 1.50 .75

On Stamps Inscribed: "Chile Correos"

O33 A42 50c dp grn & blk 1.50 .75
O34 A43 1p grn & blk 1.50 .75
Nos. O28-O34 (7) 15.00 7.75

Same Overprint on No. 181

1933 *Perf. 13½x14*

O35 A61 20c dk brn .75 .25

Same Overprint in Red on No. 182

1935 Wmk. 215

O36 A62 10c deep blue .75 .50

No. 163 Ovptd. Type "b" in Red
Inscribed: "Correos de Chile"

1934

O37 A52 5c lt grn .60 .50

Overprint "b" on No. 182

1935

O38 A62 10c dp bl .50 .50

Same Overprint in Black on No. 181

1936 Wmk. 215 *Perf. 13½x14*

O39 A61 20c dk brn 10.00 .50

Overprint "b" in Red on No. 158

1938 *Perf. 14*

O40 A43 1p grn & blk 2.50 1.00

Nos. 204 and 205 Overprinted Type "d" in Black

1939 *Perf. 13½x14, 14*

O41 A78 50c violet 4.00 2.50
O42 A84 1p org brn 5.00 4.00

Stamps of 1938-40 Overprinted Type "b" in Black, Red or Blue

1940-46 *Perf. 13½x14, 14*

O43 A78 10c sal pink ('45) 2.00 1.75
O44 A78 15c brn org 1.00 .40
O45 A78 20c lt bl (R) ('42) 1.50 .60
O46 A78 30c brn pink (Bl) .75 .40
O47 A78 40c lt grn .75 .40
O48 A78 50c vio ('45) 4.00 .75
O49 A84 1p org brn ('42) 2.50 .75
O50 A84 1.80p dp bl (R) ('45) 10.00 6.00
O51 A84 2p car lake ('42) 2.00 1.25
Nos. O43-O51 (9) 24.50 12.30

Overprint "b" in Black on Nos. 223, 225

Unwmk.

O58 A84 1p brn org 2.50 1.50
O59 A84 2p car lake ('46) 5.00 2.00

Regular Issues of 1938-43 Overprinted Diagonally in Carmine, Black or Blue — e

Wmk. 215, Unwmkd.

1948-54 *Perf. 13½x14, 14*

O60 A78 20c lt bl, #219 (C) .75 .35
O61 A78 30c brt pink, #202 (Bl) ('54) 1.50 .50
O62 A78 40c brt grn, #203 ('54) 2.50 1.25
O63 A78 50c vio #222 ('49) .75 .40
O64 A84 1p org brn, #205 2.50 1.00
O65 A84 2p car lake, #207 ('54) 1.00 .50
O66 A84 5p dk sl grn, #208 (C) ('51) 1.75 1.00
Nos. O60-O66 (7) 10.75 5.00

Overprint "e" Diagonally on Nos. 265 and 275 in Red or Black

Perf. 13½x14, 13x14

1953-55 Wmk. 215, Unwmkd.

O67 A126 1p dk bl grn, #265 (R) 1.00 .50
O68 A126 1p dk bl grn, #265 (Bk) ('55) .75 .50

O69 A126 1p dk bl grn, #275 (R) ('55) .75 .50
Nos. O67-O69 (3) 2.50 1.50

Overprint "e" Horizontally on Nos. 207, 209 in Black or Blue

1955-56 Wmk. 215 *Perf. 14*

O70 A84 2p car lake ('56) 1.75 .75
O71 A84 10p rose vio (Bl) 2.75 1.75

Overprint "e" Horizontally on Nos. 293-295 and Types of 1956 Regular Issue in Black or Red

1956 Unwmk. *Perf. 14x14½*

O72 A141 2p purple 1.00 .60
O73 A142 3p lt vio bl (R) 3.00 2.00
O74 A141 5p redsh brn .75 .35
O75 A142 10p vio (19x22¼mm) (R) 3.00 1.75
a. Perf. 13½x14 (19½x22½mm) ('58) .50 .40
O76 A141 50p rose red 2.50 1.00

No. 310 Overprinted in Red Vertically, Reading Down, Similar to Type "e"
Size of Overprint: 21x2½mm

1958 Litho. *Perf. 14*

O77 A149 10p vio blue 200.00 30.00

Overprint "e" Horizontally on No. 327 in Red

1960 Unwmk. *Perf. 13x14*

O79 A157 5c blue 1.75 .70

POSTAL TAX STAMPS

Talca Issue.
A 10c blue postal tax stamp, inscribed "Bicentenario de Talca" and picturing a coat of arms, was issued in 1942. It was sold only in Talca and was required for a time on all domestic letters sent from that city. The tax helped pay for Talca's bicentenary celebration. Value 15 cents.

Nos. 326 and 347 Surcharged

Eº 0,10
Art. 77
LEY
17272

1970 Unwmk. Litho. *Perf. 14x13*

RA1 A159 10c on 2c ultra .20 .15

Perf. 14x14½

RA2 A170 10c on 6c rose lil .20 .15
Set value .16

Chilean Arms — PT1

Perf. 14½x14

1970, Apr. 23 Litho. Unwmk.

RA3 PT1 10c blue .15 .15

See No. RA6.

No. RA3 Surcharged in Red

Eº0,15 (a) Eº0,15 (b)

1971-72

RA4 PT1 (a) 15c on 10c bl .15 .15
RA5 PT1 (b) 15c on 10c bl ('72) .15 .15
Set value .16

Type of 1970

1972, July Litho. *Perf. 14½x14*

RA6 PT1 15c rose red .20 .15

No. RA6 Surcharged in Ultramarine

1972-73

RA7 PT1 20c on 15c rose red .15 .15
RA8 PT1 50c on 15c rose red ('73) .15 .15
Set value .16

No. RA8 has 9 bars instead of 8.
The surtax on Nos. RA1-RA8 was for modernization of postal system. Compulsory on all inland mail.

PARCEL POST POSTAL TAX STAMP

Pres. J. J. Prieto V. — PPT1

Unwmk.

1957, Apr. 8 Litho. *Perf. 14*

QRA1 PPT1 15p green .25 .25

The surtax aided the Prieto Foundation. No. QRA1 was required on parcel post entering or leaving Chile.

CHINA

'chī–nə

LOCATION — Eastern Asia
GOVT. — Republic
AREA — 2,903,475 sq. mi.
POP. — 462,798,093 (1948)

10 Candareen = 1 Mace
10 Mace = 1 Tael
100 Cents = 1 Dollar (Yuan) (1897)

Watermarks

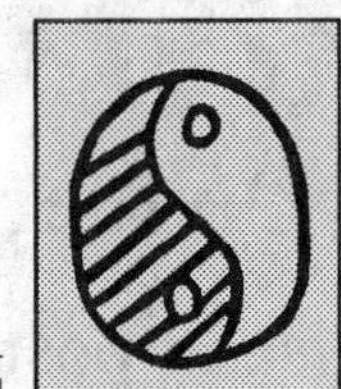

Wmk. 103- Yin-Yang Symbol

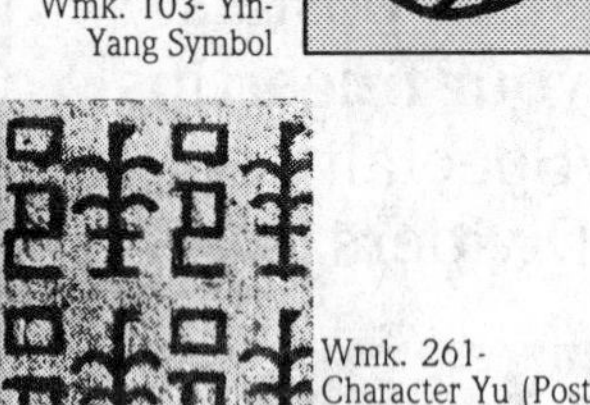

Wmk. 261- Character Yu (Post) Multiple

Issues of the Imperial Maritime Customs Post

Imperial Dragon — A1

1878 Unwmk. Typo. *Perf. 12½*
Thin Paper
Stamps printed 2½-3¼mm apart

1	A1	1c green	175.00	85.00
a.		1c dark green	325.00	150.00
2	A1	3c brown red	275.00	67.50
a.		3c vermilion	400.00	110.00
3	A1	5c orange	450.00	67.50
a.		5c bister orange	900.00	275.00

Imperforate essays of Nos. 1-3 have an extra circle near the dragon's lower left foot. Copies with the circle completely or mostly removed are proofs or unfinished stamps.

1882
Thin or Pelure Paper
Stamps printed 4½mm apart

4	A1	1c green	260.00	130.00
a.		1c dark green	275.00	140.00
5	A1	3c brown red	475.00	80.00
6	A1	5c orange yellow	10,000.	575.00

Value for No. 6 is for faulty copies.

1883 *Rough to smooth Perf. 12½*
Medium to Thick Opaque Paper
Stamps printed 2½ to 3¼mm apart

7	A1	1c green	200.00	110.00
a.		1c dark green	350.00	175.00
b.		1c light green	350.00	225.00
c.		Vert. pair, imperf. between	*15,000.*	
8	A1	3c brown red	350.00	55.00
a.		3c vermilion	700.00	60.00
b.		Vert. pair, imperf. between		*15,000.*
9	A1	5c yellow	675.00	65.00
a.		5c chrome yellow	900.00	90.00
b.		Horiz. pair, imperf. between		*15,000.*

Nos. 1-9 were printed from plates of 25, 20 or 15 individual copper dies, but only No. 5 exists in the 15-die setting. Many different printings and plate settings exist. All values occur in a wide variety of shades and papers. The effect of climate on certain papers has produced the varieties on so-called toned papers in Nos. 1-15.

Value for No. 8b is for a damaged copy.

Counterfeits, frequently with forged cancellations, occur in all early Chinese issues.

Imperial Dragon — A2

1885 Wmk. 103 *Perf. 12½*

10	A2	1c green	40.00	12.50
a.		Vert. pair, imperf. btwn.	*7,000.*	*7,000.*
b.		Horiz. pair, imperf. btwn.		
11	A2	3c lilac	80.00	12.50
a.		Horiz. pair, imperf. btwn.	*9,000.*	*9,000.*
b.		Vert. pair, imperf. btwn.		*10,000.*
12	A2	5c grnsh yellow	90.00	17.50
a.		5c bister brown	100.00	22.50
b.		Vert. pair, imperf. btwn.	*10,000.*	*10,000.*
c.		Horiz. pair, imperf. btwn.		*10,000.*
		Nos. 10-12 (3)	210.00	42.50

1888 *Perf. 11½-12*

13	A2	1c green	15.00	10.00
14	A2	3c lilac	55.00	6.00
b.		Double impression		*500.00*
15	A2	5c grnsh yellow	80.00	22.50
b.		Horiz. pair, imperf. vert.		—
c.		Double impression	450.00	450.00
		Nos. 13-15 (3)	150.00	38.50

Nos. 10-15 were printed from plates made of 40 individual copper dies, arranged in two panes of 20 each. Several different settings exist of all values.

Imperforates of Nos. 13-15 are considered proofs by most authorities.

Stamps overprinted "Formosa" in English or Chinese are proofs.

For surcharges see Nos. 25-27, 75-77.

"Shou" and "Wu Fu" — A3

Dragon and Hydrangea Leaves — A4

"Pa Kua" Signs in Corners — A5

Dragon and Peony — A6

Carp, the Messenger Fish — A7

Dragon, "Pa Kua" and Immortelle — A8

Dragons and "Shou" — A9

Dragons and Giant Peony — A10

Junk on the Yangtse — A11

1894 Lithographed in Shanghai

16	A3	1c orange red	6.50	*10.00*
a.		Vert. pair, imperf. btwn.	*1,800.*	*1,800.*
b.		Horiz. pair, imperf. btwn.	*2,500.*	*1,800.*
c.		Vert. pair, imperf. horiz.	*1,500.*	*1,500.*
17	A4	2c green	12.50	6.00
a.		Horiz. pair, imperf. btwn.	*1,500.*	*1,500.*
18	A5	3c orange	7.00	3.75
a.		Vert. pair, imperf. btwn.	*1,500.*	*1,500.*
b.		Horiz. pair, imperf. btwn.	*1,800.*	*1,500.*
19	A6	4c rose pink	45.00	40.00
a.		Horiz. pair, imperf. btwn.	*1,800.*	
20	A7	5c dull orange	80.00	75.00
a.		Horiz. pair, imperf. btwn.	*2,000.*	*2,000.*
21	A8	6c dark brown	17.50	7.50
a.		Vert. pair, imperf. btwn.	*4,500.*	
b.		Horiz. pair, imperf. btwn.	*4,500.*	
22	A9	9c dark green	55.00	12.50
a.		Imperf., pair	*750.00*	
b.		Imperf. vert., pair	*2,000.*	*2,000.*
c.		Imperf. horiz., pair	*2,000.*	
d.		Vert. pair, imperf. btwn.	*2,500.*	*2,500.*
e.		Tete beche pair, vert.	*650.00*	*700.00*
f.		Tete beche pair, imperf. horiz.	*3,000.*	
g.		Tete beche pair, imperf. vert.	*3,000.*	*3,000.*
h.		Vert. strip of 3, imperf. btwn.	*3,000.*	
i.		Tete beche pair, horiz	*750.00*	*800.00*
23	A10	12c orange	125.00	50.00
24	A11	24c carmine	190.00	40.00
a.		Vert. pair, imperf. btwn.	*5,000.*	

60th birthday of Tsz'e Hsi, the Empress Dowager. All values exist in several distinct shades.

On Mar. 20, 1896, the Customs Post was changed, by Imperial Edict, effective Jan. 1, 1897, to a National Post and the dollar was adopted as the unit of currency.

Time was required to work out details of the Imperial Post and design new stamps. As a provisional measure, stocks of Nos. 16-24 were ordered surcharged with new values in dollars and cents. It is believed that only the Shanghai office stock of Nos. 16-24 (plus any reserve stock at the printers) was surcharged with small figures of value. Other post offices throughout China were instructed to return all unoverprinted stocks on receipt of the new surcharges.

Early in the year it was apparent that all stamps would be exhausted before the new issues were ready (Nos. 86-97), and since the stones from which Nos. 16-24 had been printed no longer existed, new stones were made from the original transfers. A printing from the new stones was made early in 1897 and surcharged with large figures of value spaced 2½mm below the Chinese characters. During the surcharging, sheets from the 1894 (original) printing were received from outlying post offices and surcharged as they arrived. A small quantity of the 1897 printing reached the public without surcharge (Nos. 16n-24n).

Additional stamps were still required and another printing was made from the new stones and surcharged with large figures, but in a new setting with 1½mm between the Chinese characters and the value. Additional sheets of the 1894 printing were received from the most distant post offices and were also surcharged with the 1½mm setting. Thus there are four different sets of the large-figure surcharges. All these stamps were regularly issued but no attempt was made by the post office to separate printings. Some values are difficult to distinguish as to printing, particularly in used condition.

See No. 73. For surcharges see Nos. 28-72, 74.

1897 Lithographed in Shanghai

16n	A3	1c pink	*350.*
17n	A4	2c olive green	*500.*
18n	A5	3c chrome yellow	*375.*
p.		3c yellow buff	*750.*
19n	A6	4c pale rose	*400.*
20n	A7	5c yellow	*375.*
21n	A8	6c red brown	*550.*
22n	A9	9c yellowish green	*1,250.*
p.		9c emerald green	
23n	A10	12c yellowish orange	*1,250.*
24n	A11	24c purplish red	*1,000.*

The colors of the 1897 printings are pale or dull; the gum is thin and white. The 1894 printing has a thicker, yellowish gum.

The set of 9 values on thick unwatermarked paper is a special printing of 5,000 sets ordered by P. G. von Mollendorf, a Customs official, for presentation purposes. Value, set $1,000.

For surcharges see Nos. 47-55, 65-72.

Issues of the Chinese Government Post

Preceding Issues Surcharged in Black

暫作洋銀貳分
2
cents.

Small Numerals 2½mm Below Chinese Characters Surcharged on Nos. 13-15

1897, Jan. 2 *Perf. 11½-12*

25	A2	1c on 1c	16.00	22.50
26	A2	2c on 3c	100.00	40.00
27	A2	5c on 5c	45.00	15.00

Surcharged on Nos. 16-24

28	A5	½c on 3c	8.00	6.50
a.		"1" instead of "½"	190.00	190.00
b.		Horiz. pair, imperf. btwn.	*1,600.*	
c.		Vert. pair, imperf. horiz.	*1,600.*	*1,500.*

No.	Type	Description	Unused	Used
d.		Double surcharge	*8,500.*	*8,500.*
e.		Vert. pair, imperf. between	*1,600.*	
29	A3	1c on 1c	7.50	7.50
a.		Inverted surcharge	*1,800.*	*1,800.*
30	A4	2c on 2c	7.50	4.50
a.		Horiz. pair, imperf. vert.	*1,300.*	
b.		Vert. pair, imperf. btwn.	*1,500.*	
c.		Double surcharge	*5,000.*	
d.		Inverted surcharge	—	*10,000.*
e.		Horiz. pair, imperf. btwn.	*1,400.*	
31	A6	4c on 4c	5.00	4.50
a.		Double surcharge	*8,000.*	*8,000.*
b.		Vert. pair, imperf. btwn.	*1,500.*	*1,500.*
c.		Horiz. pair, imperf. btwn.	*1,500.*	*1,500.*
32	A7	5c on 5c	7.50	4.50
a.		Vert. pair, imperf. btwn.	*1,600.*	*1,500.*
33	A8	8c on 6c	10.00	6.00
a.		Vert. pair, imperf. btwn.	*1,000.*	*1,000.*
b.		Vert. strip of 3, imperf. btwn.	*1,100.*	*1,100.*
c.		Horiz. pair, imperf. btwn.	*1,200.*	*1,200.*
34	A8	10c on 6c	30.00	40.00
b.		Vert. pair, imperf. btwn.	*1,000.*	*1,000.*
c.		Horiz. pair, imperf. vert.	*1,200.*	*1,200.*
35	A9	10c on 9c	175.00	65.00
a.		Double surcharge	*6,000.*	*6,000.*
b.		Inverted surcharge	*10,000.*	*10,000.*
36	A10	10c on 12c	140.00	90.00
a.		Vert. pair, imperf. horiz.	*850.00*	
b.		Vert. pair, imperf. between	*1,000.*	*1,500.*
37	A11	30c on 24c	200.00	110.00
a.		Vert. pair, imperf. between	*4,000.*	

Small Numerals 4mm Below Chinese Characters

No.	Type	Description	Unused	Used
25a	A2	1c on 1c green	45.00	50.00
28f	A4	½c on 3c orange	27.50	22.50
29b	A3	1c on 1c vermilion	55.00	45.00
30f	A4	2c on 2c dark green	27.50	27.50
31d	A6	4c on 4c dark pink	27.50	27.50
32b	A7	5c on 5c dull orange	27.50	27.50
33d	A8	8c on 8c brown	17.50	17.50
35c	A9	10c on 9c dark green	225.00	225.00
37b	A11	30c on 24c dark red	300.00	160.00

貳洋暫
分銀作
2
cents.

Preceding Issues Surcharged in Black

Large Numerals

Numerals 2½mm below Chinese characters

1897, Mar.

Surcharged on Nos. 16-24

No.	Type	Description	Unused	Used
38	A5	½c on 3c	1,400.	400.
b.		Inverted surcharge		*2,750.*
39	A3	1c on 1c	90.	90.
40	A4	2c on 2c	250.	140.
41	A6	4c on 4c	250.	165.
b.		Horiz. pair, imperf. btwn.	*7,500.*	
42	A7	5c on 5c	90.	90.
43	A8	8c on 6c	1,000.	1,000.
44	A9	10c on 9c	350.	225.
45	A10	10c on 12c	4,500.	675.
46	A11	30c on 24c	675.	625.
b.		2mm spacing between "30" and "cents."	*12,000.*	

Same Surcharge on Nos. 16n-24n

No.	Type	Description	Unused	Used
47	A5	½c on 3c	6.50	11.00
a.		"cen" for "cent"	525.00	500.00
b.		Vert. pair, imperf. btwn.	*950.00*	*950.00*
c.		Vert. pair, imperf. horiz.	375.00	450.00
d.		As "a" and "c"	*6,000.*	*6,000.*
e.		As "a" and "b"	*4,000.*	*4,000.*
f.		Horiz. pair, imperf. btwn.	*800.00*	*800.00*
48	A3	1c on 1c	6.25	6.00
a.		Horiz. pair, imperf. btwn.		*1,000.*
49	A4	2c on 2c	6.25	3.75
50	A6	4c on 4c	7.50	6.25
a.		Horiz. pair, imperf. btwn.	*1,500.*	*1,500.*
b.		Vert. pair, imperf. btwn.		*1,800.*
51	A7	5c on 5c	12.50	6.25
52	A8	8c on 6c	190.00	110.00
53	A9	10c on 9c	60.00	35.00
a.		10c on 9c emerald	70.00	40.00
b.		Pair, one without surcharge	550.00	
54	A10	10c on 12c	100.00	25.00
55	A11	30c on 24c	175.00	65.00
a.		2mm spacing btwn "30" and "cents"	*1,000.*	400.00
b.		Vert. pair, imperf. btwn.	*3,750.*	

Numerals 1½mm below Chinese characters

1897, May

Surcharged on Nos. 16-24

No.	Type	Description	Unused	Used
56	A5	½c on 3c org yel	*1,500.*	*165.*
57	A3	1c on 1c	140.	95.
58	A4	2c on 2c	—	375.
59	A6	4c on 4c	125.	125.
60	A7	5c on 5c	75.	75.
61	A8	8c on 6c	700.	600.
62	A9	10c on 9c	140.	95.
63	A10	10c on 12c	675.	550.
64	A11	30c on 24c	*7,500.*	*7,500.*

Same Surcharge on Nos. 16n-24n

No.	Type	Description	Unused	Used
65	A5	½c on 3c	5.00	3.50
a.		Inverted surcharge	*1,100.*	500.00
b.		½mm spacing	*1,500.*	*1,200.*
66	A3	1c on 1c	7.00	4.50
67	A4	2c on 2c	8.00	5.50
a.		Inverted surcharge	*3,000.*	*3,000.*
b.		Vert. pair, imperf. btwn.		*5,500.*
68	A6	4c on 4c	110.00	80.00
a.		Inverted surcharge	450.00	450.00
69	A7	5c on 5c	110.00	85.00
70	A9	10c on 9c	65.00	25.00
a.		Inverted surcharge	400.00	400.00
71	A10	10c on 12c	140.00	40.00
72	A11	30c on 24c	10,000.	1,500.

Same Surcharge (1½mm Spacing) on Type A12, and

A12

A12a

Redrawn Designs

Printed from New Stones

1897

No.	Type	Description	Unused	Used
73	A12	½c on 3c yel	125.00	90.00
a.		½mm spacing	*750.00*	*750.00*
74	A12a	2c on 2c yel grn	30.00	12.00
a.		Horiz. pair, imperf. btwn.	*6,000.*	

Nos. 73 and 74 were surcharged on stamps printed from new stones, which differ slightly from the originals. On No. 73 the numeral "3" and symbols in the four corner panels have been enlarged and strengthened. On No. 74, the numeral "2" has a thick, flat base.

Surcharged on Nos. 13-15

No.	Type	Description	Unused	Used
75	A2	1c on 1c green	250.00	*375.00*
76	A2	2c on 3c lilac	625.00	*675.00*
77	A2	5c on 5c grnsh yel	125.00	*250.00*

Type A13 Surcharged in Black:

A13

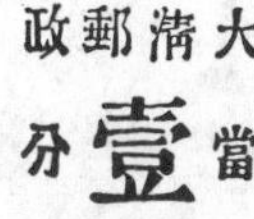

a

政郵清大
貳洋暫
分銀作
2 cents
b

政郵清大
貳洋暫
分銀作
2
cents
c

政郵清大
肆洋暫
分銀作
4
cents.
d

政郵清大
肆洋暫
分銀作
4
cents.
e

政郵清大
當壹圓
1 dollar.
f

政郵清大
當壹圓
1 dollar
g

1897 **Unwmk.** ***Perf. 12 to 15***

No.	Type	Description	Unused	Used
78	A13 (a)	1c on 3c red	80.00	60.00
a.		No period after "cent"	125.00	100.00
b.		Central character with large "box"	110.00	90.00
79	A13 (b)	2c on 3c red	175.00	85.00
a.		Inverted surcharge	*4,250.*	*2,000.*
b.		Inverted "S" in "CENTS"	200.00	150.00
c.		No period after "CENTS"	200.00	140.00
d.		Comma after "CENTS"	200.00	140.00
e.		Double surcharge	*10,000.*	*10,000.*
f.		Dbl. surch., both inverted		—
g.		Double surch. (blk & grn)	*10,000.*	
80	A13 (c)	2c on 3c red	125.00	57.50
81	A13 (d)	4c on 3c red	*7,000.*	*3,500.*
a.		Double surcharge (blk & vio)	*12,000.*	*6,500.*
82	A13 (e)	4c on 3c red	190.00	75.00
83	A13 (f)	$1 on 3c red	*225,000.*	
a.		No period after "r"		—
84	A13 (g)	$1 on 3c red	1,100.	525.00
85	A13 (g)	$5 on 3c red	7,500.	7,000.
a.		Inverted surcharge	*15,000.*	*10,000.*

A few copies of the 3c red exist without surcharge; one canceled. No. 79 with green surcharge is a trial printing.

Dragon
A14

Carp
A15

Wild Goose — A16

A17

A18

A19

"Imperial Chinese Post" Lithographed in Japan
Perf. 11, 11½, 12

1897, Aug. 16 **Wmk. 103**

No.	Type	Description	Unused	Used
86	A14	½c purple brn	2.00	1.75
a.		Horiz. pair, imperf. btwn.	325.00	
87	A14	1c yellow	2.50	1.75
88	A14	2c orange	2.00	1.10
a.		Vert. pair, imperf. horiz.	300.00	
89	A14	4c brown	3.75	1.50
a.		Horiz. pair, imperf. btwn.	500.00	
90	A14	5c rose red	4.75	1.50
91	A14	10c dk green	12.00	1.40
92	A15	20c maroon	30.00	7.50
93	A15	30c red	55.00	15.00
94	A15	50c yellow grn	37.50	22.50
a.		50c black green	325.00	
b.		50c blue green	675.00	
95	A16	$1 car & rose	125.00	95.00
a.		Horiz. pair, imperf. vert.	1,700.	
96	A16	$2 orange & yel	725.00	750.00
a.		Horiz. pair, imperf. vert.	—	
97	A16	$5 yel grn & pink	450.00	550.00

The inner circular frames and outer frames of Nos. 86-91 differ for each denomination.

No. 97 imperforate was not regularly issued. **Copies have been privately perforated and offered as No. 97.** Shades occur in most values of this issue.

"Chinese Imperial Post" Engraved in London

1898 **Wmk. 103** *Perf. 12 to 16*

No.	Type	Description	Unused	Used
98	A17	½c chocolate	1.25	.60
a.		Vert. pair, imperf. btwn.	400.00	250.00
b.		Vert. pair, imperf. horiz.	400.00	250.00
99	A17	1c ocher	1.50	.60
a.		Vert. pair, imperf. btwn.	110.00	110.00
b.		Horiz. pair, imperf. btwn.	190.00	190.00
100	A17	2c scarlet	2.50	.40
a.		Vert. pair, imperf. btwn.	90.00	90.00
b.		Horiz. pair, imperf. vert.	90.00	90.00
101	A17	4c orange brn	2.00	.55
a.		Vert. pair, imperf. btwn.	190.00	
b.		Horiz. pair, imperf. vert.	125.00	125.00
c.		Horiz. pair, imperf. btwn.	300.00	300.00
d.		Horiz. strip of 3, imperf. btwn.	425.00	425.00
102	A17	5c salmon	3.75	1.00
a.		Vert. pair, imperf. btwn.	150.00	150.00
b.		Horiz. pair, imperf. btwn.	165.00	165.00
c.		Vert. pair, imperf. horiz.	175.00	175.00
d.		5c pale reddish orange	800.00	2.00
e.		As "d," vert pair, imperf. btwn.	200.00	200.00
103	A17	10c dk blue grn	4.75	.40
a.		Vert. or horiz. pair, imperf. btwn	—	—
104	A18	20c claret	30.00	3.50
a.		Horiz. pair, imperf. btwn.	375.00	375.00
b.		Vert. pair, imperf. horiz.	375.00	375.00
c.		Vert. pair, imperf. btwn.	400.00	400.00
105	A18	30c dull rose	18.00	6.00
a.		Horiz. pair, imperf. btwn.	400.00	
b.		Vert. pair, imperf. horiz.	400.00	
c.		Vert. pair, imperf. btwn.	400.00	
106	A18	50c lt green	30.00	5.50
a.		Vert. pair, imperf. btwn.	375.00	
107	A19	$1 red & pale rose	125.00	15.00
108	A19	$2 brn, red & yel	250.00	40.00
109	A19	$5 dp green & sal	400.00	125.00
a.		Horiz. pair, imperf. btwn.	*5,000.*	
b.		Vert. pair, imperf. btwn.	*5,250.*	
		Nos. 98-109 (12)	868.75	198.55

No. 98 surcharged "B. R. A.-5-Five Cents" in three lines in black or green, was surcharged by British military authorities shortly after the Boxer riots for use from military posts in an occupied area along the Peking-Mukden railway. Usually canceled in violet.

See note following No. 122.

1900(?)-06 **Unwmk.** *Perf. 12 to 16*

No.	Type	Description	Unused	Used
110	A17	½c brown	.70	.35
a.		Horiz. pair, imperf. btwn.	175.00	175.00
b.		Vert. pair, imperf. btwn.	175.00	175.00
111	A17	1c ocher	.70	.30
a.		Horiz. pair, imperf. btwn.	125.00	125.00
b.		Vert. pair, imperf. btwn.	110.00	110.00
c.		Vert. pair, imperf. horiz.	110.00	110.00
112	A17	2c scarlet	1.25	.30
a.		Horiz. pair, imperf. btwn.	100.00	100.00
b.		Vert. pair, imperf. btwn.	100.00	100.00
c.		Vert. pair, imperf. horiz.	100.00	100.00
d.		Horiz. pair, imperf. vert.	100.00	100.00
e.		Vert. strip of 3, imperf. btwn.	100.00	100.00
113	A17	4c orange brn	1.75	.35
a.		Horiz. pair, imperf. btwn.	175.00	175.00
b.		Vert. pair, imperf. btwn.	175.00	175.00
114	A17	5c rose red	12.00	1.50
a.		Vert. pair, imperf. btwn.	160.00	160.00
b.		Vert. pair, imperf. horiz.	135.00	135.00
115	A17	5c orange	12.00	2.00
a.		5c yellow	135.00	18.00
b.		Vert. pair, imperf. btwn.	190.00	190.00
c.		Horiz. pair, imperf. btwn.	190.00	190.00
116	A17	10c green	9.00	.30
a.		Vert. pair, imperf. btwn.	140.00	
b.		Horiz. pair, imperf. btwn.	140.00	
c.		Vert. pair, imperf. horiz.	140.00	
d.		Vert. strip of 3, imperf. btwn.	250.00	
117	A18	20c red brown	12.50	1.00
a.		Horiz. pair, imperf. btwn.	225.00	
b.		Vert. pair, imperf. btwn.	200.00	
c.		Vert. pair, imperf. horiz.	200.00	
118	A18	30c dull red	11.00	.65
a.		Vert. pair, imperf. btwn.	400.00	
119	A18	50c yellow grn	20.00	1.50
a.		Horiz. pair, imperf. btwn.	575.00	
120	A19	$1 red & pale rose ('06)	70.00	9.00
121	A19	$2 brn red & yel ('06)	190.00	16.00
122	A19	$5 dp green & sal	275.00	90.00
		Nos. 110-122 (13)	615.90	123.25

See #124-130. For surcharges and overprints see #123, 134-177, J1-J6, Offices in Tibet 1-11.

Diagonal Half of No. 112 Surcharged on Stamp and Envelope

Postage
1 Cent
Paid

1903

No.	Type	Description	Unused	Used
123	A17	1c on half of 2c scarlet, on cover		*900.00*

Used Oct. 22 to Oct. 24. Value is for cover mailed to post office other than sending office (Foochow) and bearing backstamp showing arrival date. Locally addressed or unaddressed covers without backstamps properly used are worth approximately $275. Others are worth less.

Forgeries are plentiful, particularly on pieces of cover.

1905-10

No.	Type	Description	Unused	Used
124	A17	2c green ('08)	.80	.35
a.		Horiz. pair, imperf. btwn.	190.00	190.00
b.		Vert. pair, imperf. btwn.	190.00	190.00
c.		Horiz. pair, imperf. vert.	190.00	190.00
d.		Horiz. strip of 4, imperf. btwn.	400.00	400.00
125	A17	3c slate grn ('10)	1.90	.35
a.		Horiz. pair, imperf. btwn.	135.00	
b.		Vert. pair, imperf. btwn.	135.00	
126	A17	4c ver ('09)	1.90	.35
127	A17	5c violet	3.00	.60
a.		5c lilac	4.50	.40
b.		Horiz. pair, imperf. btwn.	200.00	
c.		Vert. pair, imperf. btwn.	200.00	
d.		Vert. pair, imperf. horiz.	175.00	
128	A17	7c maroon ('10)	7.50	4.00
129	A17	10c ultra ('08)	8.00	.30
a.		Horiz. pair, imperf. btwn.	225.00	
b.		Vert. pair, imperf. btwn.	225.00	
c.		Vert. pair, imperf. horiz.	190.00	190.00
130	A18	16c olive grn ('07)	25.00	7.50
		Nos. 124-130 (7)	48.10	13.45

Temple of Heaven, Peking — A20

1909 *Perf. 14*

No.	Type	Description	Unused	Used
131	A20	2c orange & green	3.00	*4.00*
132	A20	3c orange & blue	6.00	*10.00*
133	A20	7c orange & brn vio	4.00	*5.00*
		Nos. 131-133 (3)	13.00	*19.00*

1st year of the reign of Hsuan T'ung, who later became Henry Pu-yi and then Emperor Kang Teh of Manchukuo.

Stamps of 1902-10 Overprinted with Chinese Characters

Foochow Issue

Overprinted in Red or Black 立中時臨

1912 *Perf. 12 to 16*

No.	Type	Description	Unused	Used
134	A17	3c slate grn (R)	150.	70.
135	A19	$1 red & pale rose	1,400.	1,200.
136	A19	$2 brn red & yel	1,900.	1,250.
137	A19	$5 dp grn & sal	3,000.	1,800.

The overprint "Ling Shih Chung Li" or "Provisional Neutrality," signified that the P.O. was conducted neutrally by agreement between the Manchu and opposing forces.

Nanking Issue

Overprinted in Red or Black 中華 立中時臨 民國

No.	Type	Description	Unused	Used
138	A17	1c ocher (R)	90.	60.
139	A17	3c slate grn (R)	85.	55.
140	A17	7c maroon	225.	175.
141	A18	16c olive grn (R)	1,400.	1,400.
142	A18	50c yellow grn (R)	1,500.	1,100.
143	A19	$1 red & pale rose	1,400.	1,000.
144	A19	$2 brown red & yel	2,750.	2,750.
145	A19	$5 dp green & sal	4,750.	4,750.

Vertical overprint reads: "Chung Hwa Min Kuo" (Republic of China).

Stamps of this issue were also used in Shanghai and Hankow.

Additional values were overprinted but not issued. Excellent forgeries of the overprints of Nos. 134-145 exist.

Issues of the Republic

Overprinted in Black or Red 中華民國

Overprinted by the Maritime Customs Statistical Department, Shanghai

No.	Type	Description	Unused	Used
146	A17	½c brown	.65	.25
a.		Inverted overprint	25.00	25.00
b.		Double overprint	60.00	
147	A17	1c ocher (R)	.95	.25
a.		Vert. pair, imperf. horiz.	110.00	110.00
b.		Inverted overprint	95.00	60.00
c.		Double overprint	110.00	90.00
d.		Horiz. pair, imperf. btwn.	175.00	150.00
e.		Horiz. pair, imperf. vert.	85.00	
f.		Pair, one without overprint	85.00	
148	A17	2c green (R)	.95	.25
a.		Vert. pair, imperf. btwn.	110.00	110.00
149	A17	3c slate grn (R)	1.25	.25
a.		Inverted overprint	65.00	35.00
b.		Horiz. or vert. pair, imperf. btwn	175.00	175.00
d.		Horiz. pair, imperf. vert.	70.00	
150	A17	4c vermilion	2.25	.30
a.		Vert. pair, imperf. btwn.	475.00	
151	A17	5c violet (R)	2.75	.25
a.		Horiz. pair, imperf. btwn.		
152	A17	7c maroon	4.00	.90
153	A17	10c ultra (R)	4.25	.50
a.		Double overprint	110.00	
b.		Pair, one without overprint	425.00	
c.		Brownish red overprint	11.00	6.00
d.		Inverted overprint	150.00	150.00
154	A18	16c olive grn (R)	7.50	3.50
155	A18	20c red brown	7.50	2.00
156	A18	30c rose red	9.50	2.00
157	A18	50c yel grn (R)	17.50	2.00
158	A19	$1 red & pale rose	125.00	11.00
a.		Inverted overprint		*5,500.*
159	A19	$2 brn red & yel	95.00	24.00
a.		Inverted overprint	175.00	175.00
160	A19	$5 dp grn & sal	300.00	200.00
		Nos. 146-160 (15)	579.05	247.45

Stamps with blue overprint similar to the preceding were not an official issue but were privately made by a printer in Tientsin.

Overprinted in Red 中華民國

Overprinted by the Commercial Press, Shanghai

This type differs in that the top character is shifted slightly to right and the bottom character is larger and has small "legs".

No.	Type	Description	Unused	Used
161	A17	1c ocher	3.00	.40
a.		Inverted overprint	90.00	90.00
b.		Vert. pair, imperf. btwn.	150.00	
c.		Double overprint	95.00	
162	A17	2c green	19.00	1.25
a.		Inverted overprint	725.00	600.00
b.		Vert. pair, imperf. btwn.	175.00	
c.		Horiz. pair, imperf. btwn.	200.00	
d.		Horiz. strip of 3, imperf. btwn.	325.00	

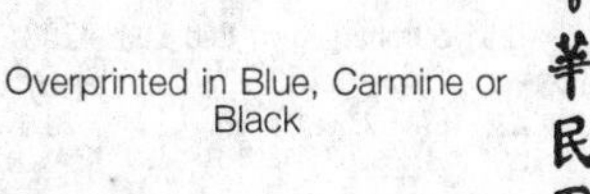

Overprinted in Blue, Carmine or Black

Overprinted by Waterlow & Sons, London

No.	Type	Description	Unused	Used
163	A17	½c brown (Bl)	.70	.40
a.		Vert. pair, imperf. btwn.	700.00	700.00
164	A17	1c ocher (C)	.70	.40
a.		Horiz. pair, imperf. btwn.	125.00	
165	A17	2c green (C)	1.25	.50
166	A17	3c slate grn (C)	1.50	.60
a.		Inverted overprint		1,100.
167	A17	4c vermilion (Bk)	2.00	.80
168	A17	5c violet (C)	3.00	.70
169	A17	7c maroon (Bk)	17.50	11.00
170	A17	10c ultra (C)	6.00	1.25
a.		Vert. pair, imperf. btwn.	350.00	350.00
171	A18	16c olive grn (R)	21.00	6.00
172	A18	20c red brn (Bk)	11.00	2.00
173	A18	30c dull red (Bk)	42.50	3.00
174	A18	50c yellow grn (R)	60.00	4.75
175	A19	$1 red & pale rose (Bk)	85.00	6.00
176	A19	$2 brn red & yel (Bk)	200.00	100.00
177	A19	$5 dp grn & sal (C)	275.00	225.00
		Nos. 163-177 (15)	727.15	362.40

Due to instructions issued to postmasters throughout China at the time of the Revolution, a number of them prepared unauthorized overprints using the same characters as the overprints prepared by the government. While many were made in good faith, some, like the blue overprints from Tientsin, were bogus, and the status of certain others is extremely dubious.

Dr. Sun Yat-sen — A21

1912, Dec. 14 — ***Perf. 14½***

No.	Type	Description	Unused	Used
178	A21	1c orange	2.50	2.75
179	A21	2c yellow grn	2.50	2.75
180	A21	3c slate grn	2.50	2.75
181	A21	5c rose lilac	3.75	1.75
182	A21	8c dp brown	3.75	2.75
183	A21	10c dull blue	3.75	2.75
184	A21	16c olive grn	9.00	7.00
185	A21	20c maroon	17.50	7.00
186	A21	50c dk green	30.00	22.50
187	A21	$1 brown red	150.00	37.50
188	A21	$2 yellow brn	275.00	225.00
189	A21	$5 gray	110.00	110.00
		Nos. 178-189 (12)	610.25	424.50

Honoring the leader of the Revolution.

President Yuan Shih-kai — A22

1912, Dec. 14

No.	Type	Description	Unused	Used
190	A22	1c orange	1.25	1.10
191	A22	2c yellow green	1.25	1.10
192	A22	3c slate green	1.25	1.10
193	A22	5c rose lilac	1.25	1.10
194	A22	8c deep brown	3.75	1.50
195	A22	10c dull blue	1.50	1.25
196	A22	16c olive green	4.50	7.00
197	A22	20c maroon	3.50	4.50
198	A22	50c dark green	18.00	17.00
199	A22	$1 brown red	60.00	35.00
200	A22	$2 yellow brown	80.00	25.00
201	A22	$5 gray	225.00	225.00
		Nos. 190-201 (12)	401.25	320.65

Honoring the 1st pres. of the Republic.

Junk — A24

Reaping Rice — A25

Gateway, Hall of Classics, Peking — A26

DESIGN A24

London Printing: Vertical shading lines under top panel fine, junk with clear diagonal shading lines on sails, right pennant of junk usually long, lines in water weak except directly under junk.

Peking Printing: Vertical shading lines under top panel and inner vertical frame line much heavier, water and sails of junk more evenly and strongly colored, white wave over "H" of "CHINA" pointed upward, touching the junk.

DESIGN A25

London: Front hat brim thick and nearly straight, left foot touches shadow.

Peking: Front hat brim thin and strongly upturned, left foot and sickle clearly outlined in white, shadow of middle tree lighter than those of the right and left trees.

DESIGN A26

London: Light colored walk clearly defined almost to the doorway, figure in right doorway "T" shaped with strong horizontal cross-bar, white panel in base of central tower rectangular, vertical stroke in top left character uniformly thick at its base, tree to right of doorway ends in minute dots.

Peking: Walk more heavily shaded near doorway, especially at right; figure in right doorway more like a "Y", white panel at base of central tower is a long oval, right vertical stroke in top left character incurved near its base, tree at right has five prominent dots at top.

London Printing: By Waterlow & Sons, London, perf. 14 to 15.

Peking Printing: By the Chinese Bureau of Engraving and Printing, Peking, perf. 14.

London Printing

1913, May 5 — ***Perf. 14-15***

No.	Type	Description	Unused	Used
202	A24	½c black brn	.45	.15
a.		Horiz. or vert. pair, imperf. btwn.	110.00	
203	A24	1c orange	.45	.15
a.		Horiz. pair, imperf. btwn.	165.00	
b.		Vert. pair, imperf. btwn.	90.00	
c.		Horiz. strip of 5, imperf. btwn	475.00	
204	A24	2c yellow grn	1.40	.15
a.		Horiz. pair, imperf. btwn.	275.00	
205	A24	3c blue grn	2.25	.15
a.		Horiz. pair, imperf. btwn.	110.00	
b.		Vert. pair, imperf. btwn.		275.00
206	A24	4c scarlet	5.00	.40
207	A24	5c rose lilac	14.00	.40
208	A24	6c gray	2.25	.55
209	A24	7c violet	10.50	4.00
210	A24	8c brown org	20.00	1.40
211	A24	10c dk blue	17.50	.60
a.		Horiz. pair, imperf. btwn.	225.00	225.00
b.		Vert. pair, imperf. btwn.	250.00	175.00
212	A25	15c brown	15.00	3.50
213	A25	16c olive grn	8.00	1.10
214	A25	20c brown red	14.00	.90
215	A25	30c brown vio	14.00	1.10
a.		Horiz. pair, imperf. btwn.	250.00	200.00
216	A25	50c green	27.50	1.65
217	A26	$1 ocher & blk	70.00	2.00
218	A26	$2 blue & blk	110.00	9.00
219	A26	$5 scarlet & blk	200.00	70.00
220	A26	$10 yel grn & blk	675.00	575.00
		Nos. 202-220 (19)	1,207.	672.20

First Peking Printing

1915 — ***Perf. 14***

No.	Type	Description	Unused	Used
221	A24	½c black brn	.45	.15
222	A24	1c orange	.45	.15
223	A24	2c yellow grn	.85	.15
224	A24	3c blue grn	.85	.15
225	A24	4c scarlet	8.50	.15
226	A24	5c rose lilac	2.75	.15
a.		Booklet pane of 4	110.00	
227	A24	6c gray	8.50	.25
228	A24	7c violet	8.50	3.00
229	A24	8c brown org	5.75	.25
230	A24	10c dk blue	5.75	.45
a.		Booklet pane of 4	110.00	
231	A25	15c brown	18.00	2.75
232	A25	16c olive grn	7.00	.45
233	A25	20c brown red	5.75	.45
234	A25	30c brown vio	7.00	.45
235	A25	50c green	17.00	.45
236	A26	$1 ocher & blk	57.50	.55
237	A26	$2 blue & blk	110.00	2.00
a.		Center inverted	*20,000.*	
238	A26	$5 scarlet & blk	275.00	18.00
239	A26	$10 yel grn & blk	400.00	140.00
		Nos. 221-239 (19)	939.60	169.95

1919

No.	Type	Description	Unused	Used
240	A24	1½c violet	1.65	.40
241	A25	13c brown	4.00	.45
242	A26	$20 yellow & blk	1,600.	1,800.

Nos. 226 and 230 overprinted in red with five characters in vertical column were for postal savings use.

The higher values of the 1913-19 issues are often overprinted with Chinese characters, which are the names of various postal districts. Stamps were frequently stolen while in transit to post offices. The overprints served to protect them, since the stamps could only be used in the districts for which they were overprinted.

For surcharges and overprints see Nos. 247, 288, B1-B3, Sinkiang 1-38.

Yeh Kung-cho, Hsu Shi-chang and Chin Yun-peng — A27

1921, Oct. 10

No.	Type	Description	Unused	Used
243	A27	1c orange	4.25	1.10
244	A27	3c blue green	4.25	1.10
245	A27	6c gray	4.25	1.10
246	A27	10c blue	4.25	1.10
		Nos. 243-246 (4)	17.00	4.40

National Post Office, 25th anniversary.

For overprints see Sinkiang Nos. 39-42.

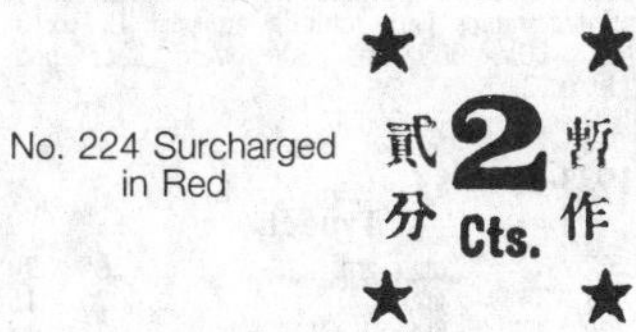

No. 224 Surcharged in Red

1922

No.	Type	Description	Unused	Used
247	A24	2c on 3c blue green	1.10	.40
a.		Inverted surcharge	*19,000.*	

Second Peking Printing

A29

A30

A31

Types of 1913-19 Issues Re-engraved

Type A29: Most of the whitecaps in front of the junk have been removed and the water made darker. The shading lines have been removed from the arabesques and pearls above the top inscription. The inner shadings at the top and sides of the picture have been cut away.

Type A30: The heads of rice in the side panels have a background of crossed lines instead of horizontal lines. The Temple of Heaven is strongly shaded and has a door. There are rows of pearls below the Chinese characters in the upper corners. The arabesques above the top inscription have been altered and are without shading lines.

Type A31: The curved line under the inscription at top is single instead of double. There are four vertical lines, instead of eight, at each side of the picture. The trees at the sides of the temple had foliage in the 1913-19 issues, but now the branches are bare. There are numerous other alterations in the design.

1923 — ***Perf. 14***

No.	Type	Description	Unused	Used
248	A29	½c black brown	.70	.15
a.		Horiz. pair, imperf. btwn.	165.00	165.00
b.		Horiz. pair, imperf. vert.	140.00	140.00
249	A29	1c orange	.45	.15
a.		Imperf., pair	85.00	
b.		Horiz. pair, imperf. vert.	85.00	
c.		Booklet pane of 6	90.00	
d.		Booklet pane of 4	45.00	
250	A29	1½c violet	.90	.70
251	A29	2c yellow grn	.75	.15
252	A29	3c blue green	1.65	.15
a.		Booklet pane of 6	75.00	

No.	Type	Description	Unused	Used
253	A29	4c gray	9.00	.60
254	A29	5c claret	1.10	.35
a.		Booklet pane of 4	90.00	
255	A29	6c scarlet	3.00	.35
256	A29	7c violet	3.00	.35
257	A29	8c orange	5.75	.35
258	A29	10c blue	4.50	.25
a.		Booklet pane of 6	110.00	
b.		Booklet pane of 2	140.00	
259	A30	13c brown	10.50	.45
260	A30	15c dp blue	3.50	.45
261	A30	16c olive grn	4.50	.45
262	A30	20c brown red	3.50	.30
263	A30	30c purple	11.00	.30
264	A30	50c dp green	20.00	.45
265	A31	$1 org brn & sep	21.00	.45
266	A31	$2 blue & red brn	30.00	.60
267	A31	$5 red & slate	45.00	1.75
268	A31	$10 green & claret	225.00	27.50
269	A31	$20 plum & blue	450.00	70.00
		Nos. 248-269 (22)	854.80	106.25

Nos. 249 and 275 exist with webbing watermark from experimental printing.

To prevent speculation and theft, the dollar denominations were overprinted with single characters in red for use in Kwangsi ($1-$20) and Kweichow ($1-$5).

See Nos. 275, 324. For surcharges and overprints see Nos. 274, 289, 311, 325, 330, 339-340, Szechwan 1-3, Yunnan 1-20, Manchuria 1-20, Sinkiang 47-69, 114, C1-C4.

Temple of Heaven, Peking — A32

1923, Oct. 17 *Perf. 14*

No.	Type	Description	Unused	Used
270	A32	1c orange	3.50	.90
271	A32	3c blue green	3.50	1.90
272	A32	4c red	7.50	1.90
273	A32	10c blue	11.00	1.90
		Nos. 270-273 (4)	25.50	6.60

Adoption of Constitution, October, 1923.

For overprints see Sinkiang Nos. 43-46.

No. 253 Surcharged in Red

叁 3 暫
分 Cts. 作

1925

No.	Type	Description	Unused	Used
274	A29	3c on 4c gray	1.75	.15
a.		Inverted surcharge	*22,500.*	*10,000.*
b.		Vert. pair, imperf. btwn.		

Junk Type of 1923

1926

No.	Type	Description	Unused	Used
275	A29	4c olive green	1.10	.15
a.		Horiz. pair, imperf. vert.	175.00	
b.		Horiz. pair, imperf. btwn.	175.00	
c.		Horiz. strip of 3, imperf. btwn.	225.00	

Marshal Chang Tso-lin — A34

President Chiang Kai-shek — A35

1928, Mar. 1 *Perf. 14*

No.	Type	Description	Unused	Used
276	A34	1c brown orange	1.10	1.10
277	A34	4c olive green	3.00	3.50
278	A34	10c dull blue	7.00	4.50
279	A34	$1 red	40.00	57.50
		Nos. 276-279 (4)	51.10	66.60

Assumption of office by Marshal Chang Tso-lin. The stamps of this issue were only available for postage in the Provinces of Chihli and Shantung and at the Offices in Manchuria and Sinkiang.

For overprints see Manchuria Nos. 21-24, Sinkiang 70-73.

1929, May

No.	Type	Description	Unused	Used
280	A35	1c brown orange	1.10	.45
281	A35	4c olive green	1.90	.90
282	A35	10c dark blue	9.00	1.90
283	A35	$1 dark red	80.00	70.00
		Nos. 280-283 (4)	92.00	73.25

Unification of China.

For overprints see Yunnan Nos. 21-24, Manchuria 25-28, Sinkiang 74-77.

Sun Yat-sen Mausoleum, Nanking — A36

1929, May 30 *Perf. 14*

No.	Type	Description	Unused	Used
284	A36	1c brown orange	1.10	.80
285	A36	4c olive green	1.00	1.75
286	A36	10c dark blue	6.50	2.25
287	A36	$1 dark red	62.50	27.50
		Nos. 284-287 (4)	71.10	32.30

The transfer of Dr. Sun Yat-sen's remains from Peiping to the mausoleum at Nanking.

For overprints see Yunnan Nos. 25-28, Manchuria 29-32, Sinkiang 78-81.

Nos. 224 and 252 Surcharged in Red

壹 1 暫
分 Ct. 作

1930

No.	Type	Description	Unused	Used
288	A24	1c on 3c blue green	1.10	1.90
289	A29	1c on 3c blue green	.85	.35
a.		No period after "Ct"	17.50	17.50

See Nos. 311, 325, 330.

Dr. Sun Yat-sen — A37

Type I - Double-lined circle in the sun.
Type II - Heavy, single-lined circle in the sun.

Printed by De la Rue & Co., Ltd., London

Perf. 11½x12½, 12½x13, 12½, 13½

1931 **Engr.**

Type I

No.	Type	Description	Unused	Used
290	A37	1c orange	.45	.15
291	A37	2c olive green	.55	.30
292	A37	4c green	.90	.15
293	A37	20c ultra	1.00	.15
294	A37	$1 org brn & dk brn	7.50	.35
295	A37	$2 blue & org brn	18.00	1.75
296	A37	$5 dull red & blk	27.50	3.50
		Nos. 290-296 (7)	55.90	6.35

Stamps issued prior to 1933 were printed by a wet-paper process, and owing to shrinkage such stamps are 1-1½mm narrower than the later dry-printed stamps. Early printings are perf. 12½x13. Nos. 304, 305 and 306 were later perf. 11½x12½.

1931-37

Type II

No.	Type	Description	Unused	Used
297	A37	2c olive grn	.35	.20
298	A37	4c green	.35	.15
299	A37	5c green ('33)	.35	.15
300	A37	15c dk green	3.75	.85
301	A37	15c scarlet ('34)	.40	.15
302	A37	20c ultra ('37)	.40	.15
303	A37	25c ultra	.40	.60
304	A37	$1 org brn & dk brn	7.50	.35
305	A37	$2 blue & org brn	14.00	.75
306	A37	$5 dull red & blk	30.00	3.50
		Nos. 297-306 (10)	57.50	6.85

See #631-635. For surcharges and overprints see #341, 343, 678, 682, 684-685, 689-691, 768, 843, 1N1, 2N1-2N5, 2N57-2N59, 2N83-2N84, 2N101-2N106, 2N116, 2N124-2N126, 3N1-3N5, 4N1-4N5, 5N1-5N4, 6N1-6N5, 7N1-7N4, 7N54, 8N2-8N3, 8N43-8N44, 8N54, 8N57, 8N69-8N71, 8N85, 9N1-9N5, Taiwan 19, 21-22, Northeastern Provinces 44, Szechwan 4-11, Yunnan 29-44, Sinkiang 82-97.

"Nomads in the Desert" — A38

1932 **Unwmk.** *Perf. 14*

No.	Type	Description	Unused	Used
307	A38	1c deep orange	25.00	19.00
308	A38	4c olive green	25.00	19.00
309	A38	5c claret	25.00	19.00
310	A38	10c deep blue	25.00	19.00
		Nos. 307-310 (4)	100.00	76.00

Northwest Scientific Expedition of Sven Hedin. A small quantity of this issue was sold at face at Peking and several other cities. The bulk of the issue was furnished to Hedin and sold at $5 (Chinese) a set for funds to finance the expedition.

#252 Surcharged in Black Like #288

1932

No.	Type	Description	Unused	Used
311	A29	1c on 3c blue green	1.75	1.10

Martyrs Issue

Teng Keng — A39

Ch'en Ying-shih — A40

Chu Chih-hsin — A45

Sung Chiao-jen — A46

Huang Hsing — A47

Liao Chung-kai — A48

1932-34 *Perf. 14*

No.	Type	Description	Unused	Used
312	A39	½c black brown	.15	.15
313	A40	1c orange ('34)	.15	.15
314	A39	2½c rose lilac ('33)	.15	.15
315	A48	3c dp brown ('33)	.15	.15
316	A45	8c brown orange	.35	.15
317	A46	10c dull violet	.30	.15
318	A45	13c blue green	.40	.15
319	A46	17c brown olive	.35	.15
320	A47	20c brown red	.70	.15
321	A48	30c brown violet	1.10	.15
322	A47	40c orange	.95	.25
323	A40	50c green ('34)	3.50	.25
		Nos. 312-323 (12)	8.25	
		Set value		.75

Perfs. 12 to 13 and compound and with secret marks are listed as Nos. 402-439. No. 316 re-drawn is No. 485.

For overprints and surcharge see Nos. 342, 472, 474, 478-479, 486-487, 490, 531-536, 539-541, 544-549, 616, 619, 622-624, 647-659, 662-663, 665, 669, 672, 698, 704, 711, 713-715, 720-721, 831, 846-847, 867, 870, 872, 881-882, J120-J121, 1N14-1N15, 1N59, 2N6-2N9, 2N32-2N56, 2N60, 2N76-2N82, 2N85, 2N87-2N90, 2N107-2N115, 2N118, 2N121-2N123, 3N6-3N10, 3N34-3N55, 3N59, 4N6-4N9, 4N39-4N64, 4N69, 5N5-5N8, 5N34-5N60, 5N65, 6N6-6N8, 6N35-6N61, 6N66, 7N5-7N7, 7N30-7N53, 7N55, 7N59, 8N1, 8N4, 8N28-8N42, 8N45, 8N47-8N50, 8N60-8N61, 8N68, 8N73, 8N76-8N79, 8N89, 8N97, 8N99-8N100, 8N103-8N104, 9N72-9N77, Taiwan 14-17, 20, 28A, 74, Northeastern Provinces 6-8, 11, Szechwan 12-23, Yunnan 49-60, Sinkiang 102-113, 140-161, 197.

Junk Type of 1923 Issue

1933 *Perf. 14*

No.	Type	Description	Unused	Used
324	A29	6c brown	18.00	1.10

#275 Surcharged in Red Like #288

1933

No.	Type	Description	Unused	Used
325	A29	1c on 4c olive green	1.40	.30
a.		No period after "Ct"	17.50	17.50

Tan Yuan-chang — A49

1933, Jan. 9

No.	Type	Description	Unused	Used
326	A49	2c olive green	2.25	.35
327	A49	5c green	2.25	.35
328	A49	25c ultra	7.00	1.10
329	A49	$1 red	55.00	14.00
		Nos. 326-329 (4)	66.50	15.80

Tan Yuan-chang, more commonly known as Tan Yen-kai, a prominent statesman in China since the revolution of 1912 and Pres. of the Executive Dept. of the Natl. Government. Placed on sale Jan. 9, 1933, the date of the ceremony in celebration of the completion of the Tan Yuan-chang Memorial Hall and Tomb at Mukden.

For overprints see Yunnan Nos. 45-48, Sinkiang 98-101.

#251 Surcharged in Red Like #288

1935 *Perf. 14*

No.	Type	Description	Unused	Used
330	A29	1c on 2c yellow grn	2.25	.15

Emblem of New Life Movement A50

Four Virtues of New Life A51

Lighthouse — A52

1936, Jan. 1

No.	Type	Description	Unused	Used
331	A50	2c olive green	.65	.15
332	A50	5c green	1.00	.15
333	A51	20c dark blue	5.00	.70
334	A52	$1 rose red	22.50	3.00
		Nos. 331-334 (4)	29.15	4.00

"New Life" movement.

Methods of Mail Transportation A53

Maritime Scene — A54

Shanghai General Post Office — A55

Ministry of Communications, Nanking — A56

1936, Oct. 10

No.	Type	Description	Unused	Used
335	A53	2c orange	.40	.15
336	A54	5c green	.50	.15
337	A55	25c blue	3.50	.40
338	A56	$1 dk carmine	22.50	3.00
		Nos. 335-338 (4)	26.90	3.70

Founding of the Chinese PO, 40th anniv.

Nos. 260 and 261 Surcharged in Red

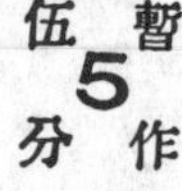

1936, Oct. 11

No.	Type	Description	Unused	Used
339	A30	5c on 15c dp blue	.90	.35
340	A30	5c on 16c olive grn	1.90	.85

No. 298 Surcharged in Red

壹 暫
分 1 作

1937

341 A37 1c on 4c green, type II .60 .25
a. Upper left character missing

Nos. 322 and 303 Surcharged in Black or Red

捌 暫
分 8 作

1938 *Perf. 12½, 14*

342 A47 8c on 40c orange (Bk) 1.00 .50
343 A37 10c on 25c ultra (R) .60 .20

Dr. Sun Yat-sen — A57

Type I - Coat button half circle. Six lines of shading above head. Top frame partially shaded with vertical lines.

Type II - Coat button complete circle. Nine lines of shading above head. Top frame partially shaded with vertical lines.

Type III - Coat button complete circle. Nine lines of shading above head. Top frame line fully shaded with vertical lines.

Printed by the Chung Hwa Book Co.

1938 Unwmk. Engr. *Perf. 12½*

Type I

344 A57 $1 henna & dk brn 65.00 9.00
345 A57 $2 dp blue & org brn 13.00 3.25
346 A57 $5 red & grnsh blk 100.00 10.00
Nos. 344-346 (3) 178.00 22.25

1939

Type II

347 A57 $1 henna & dk brn 13.00 .65
348 A57 $2 dp blue & org brn 16.00 3.00

1939-43

Type III

349 A57 2c olive green .15 .15
350 A57 3c dull claret .15 .15
351 A57 5c green .15 .15
352 A57 5c olive green .15 .15
353 A57 8c olive green .15 .15
354 A57 10c green .15 .15
355 A57 15c scarlet 1.10 1.10
356 A57 15c dk vio brn ('43) 14.00 *27.50*
357 A57 16c olive gray 1.50 .40
358 A57 25c dk blue .35 .60
359 A57 $1 henna & dk brn 1.75 .60
360 A57 $2 dp blue & org brn 3.25 .50
a. Imperf., pair 275.00
361 A57 $5 red & grnsh blk 2.25 .50
362 A57 $10 dk green & dull pur 13.00 1.75
363 A57 $20 rose lake & dk blue 45.00 32.50
Nos. 349-363 (15) 83.10 *66.35*

Several values exist imperforate, but these were not regularly issued. No. 361 imperforate is printer's waste.

See Nos. 368-401, 506-524. For surcharges and overprints see Nos. 440-448, 473, 475-477, 480-481, 482-484, 489, 537-538, 615, 618, 620, 660-661, 664, 666-668, 673-676, 680-681, 686, 688, 699-703, 707-709, 717, 719, 830, J67-J68, M2, M11-M12, 1N2-1N13, 1N23-1N42, 1N57-1N58, 2N10-2N31, 2N61-2N75, 2N86, 2N91-2N93, 2N117, 2N119-2N120, 3N11-3N33, 3N56-3N58, 3N60-3N61, 4N10-4N38, 4N65-4N68, 4N70-4N71, 5N9-5N33, 5N61-5N64, 5N66-5N68, 6N9-6N34, 6N62-6N65, 6N67-6N69, 7N8-7N29, 7N56-7N58, 7N60-7N61, 8N5-8N27, 8N46, 8N51-8N53, 8N55-8N56, 8N58-8N59, 8N62-8N67, 8N72, 8N74-8N75, 8N80-8N84, 8N86-8N88, 8N90, 8N95-8N96, 8N98, 8N101-8N102, 8N105-8N106, 9N6-9N71, 9N97, 9N99, Taiwan 78, 84, Northeastern Provinces 9-10, Sinkiang 115-139, 174-188, 196, 198.

Chinese and American Flags and Map of China — A58

Printed by American Bank Note Co.

Frame Engr., Center Litho.

1939, July 4 Unwmk. *Perf. 12*

Flag in Deep Rose and Ultramarine

364 A58 5c dark green 1.50 .50
365 A58 25c deep blue 1.50 .75
366 A58 50c brown 3.50 1.00
367 A58 $1 rose carmine 5.50 2.00
Nos. 364-367 (4) 12.00 4.25

150th anniv. of the US Constitution.

Type of 1939-41 Issue
Re-engraved

2c, 1939-41

Re-engraved

8c, 1939-41

Re-engraved

1940 *Perf. 12½*

368 A57 2c olive green .15 .15
369 A57 8c olive green .15 .15
Set value .20 .20

Type of 1938-41 Issue

1940 Unwmk. *Perf. 14*

Type III

370 A57 2c olive green 2.25 .85
371 A57 5c green 4.50 2.25
372 A57 $1 henna & dk brn 75.00 16.00
373 A57 $2 dp blue & org brn 16.00 4.50
374 A57 $5 red & grnsh blk 22.50 11.00
375 A57 $10 dk grn & dull pur 65.00 7.75
Nos. 370-375 (6) 185.25 42.35

See surcharge note following No. 363.

Type of 1939-41

1940 Wmk. 261 *Perf. 12½*

Type III

376 A57 $1 henna & dk brn 3.00 *7.50*
377 A57 $2 dp blue & org brn 3.00 *7.50*
378 A57 $5 red & grnsh blk 8.00 *15.00*
379 A57 $10 dk green & dull pur 12.00 *25.00*
380 A57 $20 rose lake & dp blue 16.00 *25.00*
Nos. 376-380 (5) 42.00 *80.00*

See surcharge note following No. 363.

Printed by the Dah Tung Book Co.

Type III with Secret Marks

Five Cent

Type III- Characters joined

Secret Mark- Characters not joined

Eight Cent

Type III- Characters not joined

Secret Mark- Characters joined

Ten Cent

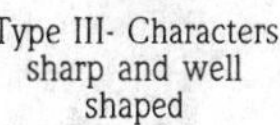

Type III- Characters sharp and well shaped

Secret Mark- Characters coarse and varying in thickness

Dollar Values

Type III

Secret Mark

1940 Unwmk. *Perf. 14*

381 A57 5c green .15 .15
382 A57 5c olive green .15 .15
383 A57 8c olive green .35 .15
a. Without "star" in uniform button 1.50 1.50
384 A57 10c green .15 .15
385 A57 30c scarlet .35 .15
386 A57 50c dk blue .45 .15
387 A57 $1 org brn & sepia 2.25 .15
388 A57 $2 dp blue & yel brn .90 .35
389 A57 $5 red & slate grn .90 .45
390 A57 $10 dk grn & dull pur 3.75 1.10
391 A57 $20 rose lake & dk blue 11.00 2.75
Nos. 381-391 (11) 20.40 5.70

Type III with Secret Marks

1940 Wmk. 261 *Perf. 14*

392 A57 5c green .15 .15
393 A57 5c olive green .15 .15
394 A57 10c green .35 .15
395 A57 30c scarlet .15 .15
396 A57 50c dk blue .55 .15
397 A57 $1 org brn & sepia 4.50 2.25
398 A57 $2 dp blue & yel brn 11.00 11.00
399 A57 $5 red & slate grn 4.50 *6.50*
400 A57 $10 dk grn & dull pur 13.00 14.00
401 A57 $20 rose lake & dk blue 21.00 15.00
Nos. 392-401 (10) 55.35 49.50

Nos. 383, 384, 385, 397, 400 and 401 exist perf. 12½, but were not issued with this perforation.

See surcharge note following No. 363.

Types of 1932-34 Martyrs Issue with Secret

1932-34 Issue. In the left Chinese character in bottom row, the two parts are not joined.

Secret Mark, 1940-41 Issue. The two parts are joined.

Perf. 12½, 13 and Compound

1940-41 Wmk. 261

402 A39 ½c olive blk .25 .15
403 A40 1c orange .25 .15
404 A46 2c dp blue ('41) .25 .15
405 A39 2½c rose lilac .25 .15
406 A48 3c dp yellow brn .25 .15
407 A39 4c pale vio ('41) .25 .15
408 A48 5c dull red org ('41) .25 .15
409 A45 8c dp orange .25 .15
410 A46 10c dull violet .25 .15
411 A45 13c dp yellow grn .25 .15
412 A48 15c brown car .25 .15
413 A46 17c brown olive .25 .15
414 A47 20c lt blue .25 .15
415 A45 21c olive brn ('41) .25 .15
416 A40 25c red vio ('41) .25 .15
417 A46 28c olive ('41) .25 .15
418 A48 30c brown car .25 .15
a. Vert. pair, imperf. btwn. 125.00
419 A47 40c orange .25 .15
420 A40 50c green .25 .15

Unwmk.

421 A39 ½c olive black .15 .15
422 A40 1c orange .15 .15
a. Without secret mark 2.25 2.25
b. Horiz. pair, imperf. vert. 110.00
423 A46 2c dp blue .15 .15
a. Vert. pair, imperf. horiz. 50.00
b. Horiz. pair, imperf. between 165.00
424 A39 2½c rose lilac .15 .15
425 A48 3c dp yellow brn .15 .15
426 A39 4c pale violet .15 .15
427 A48 5c dull red org .15 .15
428 A45 8c dp orange .15 .15
429 A46 10c dull violet 2.75 .35
430 A45 13c dp yel grn .15 .15
431 A48 15c brown car .15 .15
432 A46 17c brn olive .15 .15
433 A47 20c lt blue .15 .15
a. Vert. pair, imperf. horiz. 125.00
b. Horiz. pair, imperf. vert. 125.00
434 A45 21c olive brn .15 .15
435 A40 25c rose vio .15 .15
436 A46 28c olive .15 .15
437 A48 30c brown car 2.25 2.25
438 A47 40c orange .15 .15
439 A40 50c green .15 .15
Nos. 402-439 (38) 12.30

Several values exist imperforate, but they were not regularly issued.

Used values are for favor cancels. Postally used copies sell for more.

See surcharge note following No. 323.

Regional Surcharges.

The regional surcharges, Nos. 440-448, 482-484, 486-491, 525-549, have been listed according to the basic stamps, with black or red surcharges. The surcharges of the individual provinces, plus Hong Kong and Shanghai, are noted in small type. The numeral following each letter is the surcharge denomination. These surcharges are identified by the following letters:

a- Hong Kong
b- Shanghai
bx- Anhwei
c- Hunan
d- Kansu
e- Kiangsi
f- Eastern Szechwan
g- Chekiang
h- Fukien
i- Kwangsi
j- Kwangtung
k- Western Szechwan
l- Yunnan
m- Honan
n- Shensi
o- Kweichow
p- Hupeh

Regional Surcharges on Stamps of 1939-40:

肆 暫
分 4 作
Hong Kong a4

叁 暫
分 3 作
Shanghai b3

叁 暫
分 3 作
Hunan — c3

叁 暫
分 3 作
Kansu — d3

叁 暫
分 3 作
Kiangsi — e3

叁 暫
分 3 作
Eastern Szechwan — f3

叁 暫
分 3 作
Chekiang — g3

1940-41 Unwmk. *Perf. 12½, 14*

Carmine Surcharge

440 A57 4c on 5c ol grn (#382) .55 .55
r. Lower right character duplicated at left 22.50 32.50

Black Surcharge

441 A57 3c on 5c grn (#351) (b3) 1.10 1.25
442 A57 3c on 5c ol grn (#352) (c3, d3) .60 1.65
443 A57 3c on 5c grn (#381) (b3) .55 1.10
444 A57 3c on 5c ol grn (#382) (e3) .65 .85
r. Lower left character duplicated at right (Kiangsi) 40.00 40.00
(b3) Shanghai .65 1.40
(f3) Eastern Szechwan .65 1.65

The Kansu surcharges of #442 are of 6 types. Differences include formation of top part of fen character (at left of "3"), fen with low right hook, height of "3" (5-4mm), space between upper and lower characters (6-9mm), etc.

1940-41 Wmk. 261 *Perf. 14*

445 A57 3c on 5c grn (#392) (e3) .55 1.25
r. Lower left character duplicated at right (Kiangsi) 32.50 32.50
(b3, c3) Shanghai, Hunan .55 1.40
446 A57 3c on 5c ol grn (#393) (f3) .65 1.65
(b3) Shanghai .85 1.65

r.	Lower left character duplicated at right (f3)	60.00	65.00

Red Surcharge

No.	Description	Unused	Used
447	A57 3c on 5c grn (#392) (g3)	1.10	1.10
448	A57 3c on 5c ol grn (#393) (g3)	2.75	3.00

Dr. Sun Yat-sen — A59

Printed by American Bank Note Co.

1941 Unwmk. Engr. *Perf. 12*

No.	Type	Description	Unused	Used
449	A59	½c sepia	.15	.30
450	A59	1c orange	.15	.15
451	A59	2c brt ultra	.15	.15
452	A59	5c green	.15	.20
453	A59	8c red orange	.15	.25
454	A59	8c turq green	.15	.15
455	A59	10c brt green	.15	.20
456	A59	17c olive	3.00	9.00
457	A59	25c rose violet	.15	.35
458	A59	30c scarlet	.20	.25
459	A59	50c dk blue	.20	.20
460	A59	$1 brown & blk	.30	.20
461	A59	$2 blue & blk	.30	.20
a.		Center inverted	*12,500.*	
462	A59	$5 scarlet & blk	.50	.20
463	A59	$10 green & blk	3.50	1.00
464	A59	$20 rose vio & blk	2.00	3.00
		Set value		7.00

For surcharges see Nos. 488, 491, 542-543, 617, 621, 670, 677, 687, 705-706, 712, 716, 718, M1, M3-M4, 1N16-1N22, 1N43-1N56, 9N78-9N96, 9N98, 9N100.

Industry and Agriculture — A60

1941, June 21 *Perf. 12½*

No.	Type	Description	Unused	Used
465	A60	8c green	.15	.20
466	A60	21c red brown	.15	.20
467	A60	28c dk olive grn	.20	.20
468	A60	33c vermilion	.85	1.50
469	A60	50c dp ultra	1.10	.85
470	A60	$1 dk violet	1.40	.85
		Nos. 465-470 (6)	3.85	3.80

Souvenir Sheet

Imperf

Typo.

No.	Description	Unused	Used
471	Sheet of 6	35.00	35.00
a.	A60 8c dull green	2.00	2.00
b.	A60 21c dark orange brown	2.00	2.00
c.	A60 28c dull yellow green	2.00	2.00
d.	A60 33c red	2.00	2.00
e.	A60 50c dull blue	2.00	2.00
f.	A60 $1 dark violet	2.00	2.00

The Thrift Movement and its aim to "Save for Reconstruction."

Issued in sheets measuring 155x171mm, without gum.

This sheet exists with additional blue marginal overprints in Russia, French and Chinese reading "Souvenir of the Exhibition of the Russian Philatelic Society in China, Shanghai, China, Feb. 28, 1943."

The overprinting was applied by the society, and when so overprinted this sheet had no franking power.

Stamps of 1939-41 Overprinted in Carmine or Blue

中華民國創立
三十週年紀念
三十年十月十日

1941, Oct. 10 *Perf. 12½, 14, 13*

No.	Type	Description	Unused	Used
472	A40	1c dull orange	.20	*.60*
473	A57	2c olive grn (C)	.20	*.60*
474	A39	4c pale violet (C)	.20	*.60*
475	A57	8c ol grn (#369) (C)	.20	*.60*
476	A57	10c green (#354) (C)	.20	*.60*
477	A57	16c ol gray (#357) (C)	.20	*.60*
478	A45	21c olive brn (C)	.20	*.60*
479	A46	28c olive (C)	.35	*1.65*
480	A57	30c scarlet	.65	*3.50*
481	A57	$1 hn & dk brn (#359)	3.50	3.50
		Nos. 472-481 (10)	5.90	*12.85*

Chinese Republic, 30th anniversary.

Kiangsi e7

Eastern Szechwan f7

Chekiang — g7

Fukien — h7

1941 Unwmk. *Perf. 12½, 14*

No.	Description	Unused	Used
482	A57 7c on 8c (#353) (g7, h7)	.55	1.10
483	A57 7c on 8c (#369) (f7)	.45	.55
484	A57 7c on 8c (#383) (h7)	.55	.90
	(e7) Kiangsi	.65	.90
	(g7) Chekiang	.65	1.10
r.	Without "star" in uniform button	65.00	

Type of 1932-34 Re-engraved

1941 Unwmk. *Perf. 14*

No.	Description	Unused	Used
485	A45 8c deep orange	11.00	55.00

The original stamps are 19½mm wide, the re-engraved 21mm.

Eleven other values of the Martyrs Issue and types A37 and A57 exist re-engraved, but were not issued.

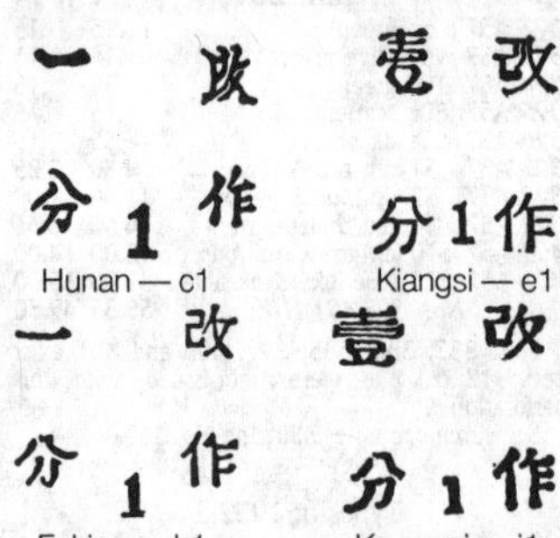

Hunan — c1

Kiangsi — e1

Fukien — h1

Kwangsi — i1

Kwangtung — j1

1942

Red Surcharge

No.	Description	Unused	Used
486	A39 1c on ½c blk brn (#312) (i1)	.85	.55
	(c1) Hunan	1.65	*2.75*
487	A39 1c on ½c ol blk (#421) (e1)	.45	1.65
	(c1) Hunan	.55	*2.00*
	(i1) Kwangsi	1.65	*2.50*
	(h1) Fukien	5.00	*8.00*
488	A59 1c on ½c sepia (#449) (j1)	.85	*1.65*
	(c1) Hunan	1.10	*2.50*

Hunan c40

Eastern Szechwan f40

Western Szechwan k40

Yunnan l40

Red Surcharge

No.	Description	Unused	Used
489	A57 40c on 50c dk bl (#386) (f40)	.65	1.10
	(k40) Western Szechwan	3.75	*5.00*
	(l40) Yunnan	3.25	*3.25*
r.	Inverted surcharge (Yunnan)	90.00	

Wmk. 261

No.	Description	Unused	Used
490	A40 40c on 50c grn (#420) (c40)	1.65	*5.50*

Unwmk.

No.	Description	Unused	Used
491	A59 40c on 50c dk bl (#459) (c40)	2.75	*6.50*

Dr. Sun Yat-sen — A62

Central Trust Printing

Perf. 10½-11, 11½-12½, 13 and Compounds

1942-43 Typo.

Without Gum

No.	Type	Description	Unused	Used
492	A62	10c dp green ('43)	.15	.35
493	A62	16c dull ol brn	10.00	*30.00*
a.		Perf 10½	200.00	175.00
494	A62	20c dk ol grn ('43)	.15	.15
a.		Perf. 11	6.00	6.00
495	A62	25c brown vio	.15	.15
496	A62	30c dull ver	.15	.15
a.		Perf. 11	2.75	2.75
497	A62	40c dk red brn ('43)	.20	.25
a.		Perf. 11x13	85.00	
b.		Perf. 11	12.00	12.00
498	A62	50c sage green	.15	.15
a.		Perf. 11	6.00	*12.00*
499	A62	$1 rose lake	.30	.15
a.		Perf. 11	35.00	35.00
500	A62	$1 dull grn ('43)	.30	.30
501	A62	$1.50 dp blue ('43)	.30	.30
a.		Perf. 11	250.00	250.00
502	A62	$2 dk blue grn	.30	.30
503	A62	$3 dk yellow ('43)	.30	.30
504	A62	$4 red brown	.30	.30
505	A62	$5 cerise ('43)	.30	.30
		Nos. 492-505 (14)	13.05	33.15

Many shades and part-perforate varieties exist.

See Nos. 550 to 563 for other stamps of type A62 with secret mark and new values and colors. For surcharges and overprints see Nos. 525-530, 671, 683, 692-694, 696, 771, 773, 807-809, 811-820, 824-827, 832, 834-834A, 836, 848-850, 852-854, 857, 860-863, 876, 879, M5-M10, Taiwan 55, 86, 99, Kwangsi 6-7, Sinkiang 162-173, 194-195.

Type of 1938

Thin Paper Without Gum

1942-44 Unwmk. Engr. *Imperf.*

No.	Type	Description	Unused	Used
506	A57	$10 red brown	.35	.15
507	A57	$20 blue grn	.35	.30
508	A57	$20 rose red ('44)	4.75	1.50
509	A57	$30 dull vio ('43)	.35	.35
510	A57	$40 rose red ('43)	.45	.35
511	A57	$50 blue	.90	.50
512	A57	$100 org brn ('43)	1.75	1.75

Rouletted

No.	Type	Description	Unused	Used
513	A57	$5 lilac gray ('44)	4.75	6.00
a.		Rouletted x perf. 12½	25.00	30.00
514	A57	$10 red brown	3.00	2.50
515	A57	$50 blue	3.00	2.50
a.		Rouletted x imperf.		
		Nos. 506-515 (10)	19.65	15.90

1942-45 *Perf. 12½ to 15*

No.	Type	Description	Unused	Used
516	A57	$4 dp blue ('43)	.20	.20
517	A57	$5 lilac gray ('43)	.35	.30
518	A57	$10 red brown	.35	.30
519	A57	$20 blue grn ('43)	.30	.30
520	A57	$20 rose red ('45)	55.00	65.00
521	A57	$30 dull vio ('43)	.50	.35
522	A57	$40 rose ('43)	.50	.40
523	A57	$50 blue	.50	.40
524	A57	$100 org brn ('45)	65.00	70.00
		Nos. 516-524 (9)	122.70	137.25

See surcharge note following No. 363.

No. 493 Overprinted in Black or Red

國內平信
附加已付

1942

No.	Description	Unused	Used
525	A62 (i) 16c (Bk)	40.00	85.00
	(c) Hunan	325.00	
	(k) Western Szechwan	75.00	90.00
	(m) Honan	600.00	650.00
r.	Perf. 10½ (Kwangsi)	400.00	
	(n) Shensi	125.00	150.00
s.	Inverted ovpt. (Shensi)	175.00	
526	A62 (d) 16c (R)	10.00	17.50
	(bx) Anhwei	425.00	425.00
	(e) Kiangsi	21.00	40.00
	(f) Eastern Szechwan	40.00	50.00
r.	Perf. 10½ (E. Szechwan)	475.00	
	(h) Fukien	165.00	175.00
	(j) Kwangtung	425.00	425.00
	(l) Yunnan	21.00	35.00
s.	Horiz. pair, imperf. btwn (Yunnan)	250.00	
	(o) Kweichow	125.00	125.00
	(p) Hupeh, perf. 10½	725.00	600.00
t.	Perf. 13 (Hupeh)	1,400.	1,100.

This overprint means "Domestic Ordinary Letter Surcharge Paid." It was applied in various sizes and types by 14 districts, 9 using red ink, 5 using black. (The Anhwei overprint comes in two types.) These overprinted stamps were briefly sold for $1.16 before the government ordered their sale suspended. The vertical bars and 50c surcharge of Nos. 527-528 were then applied.

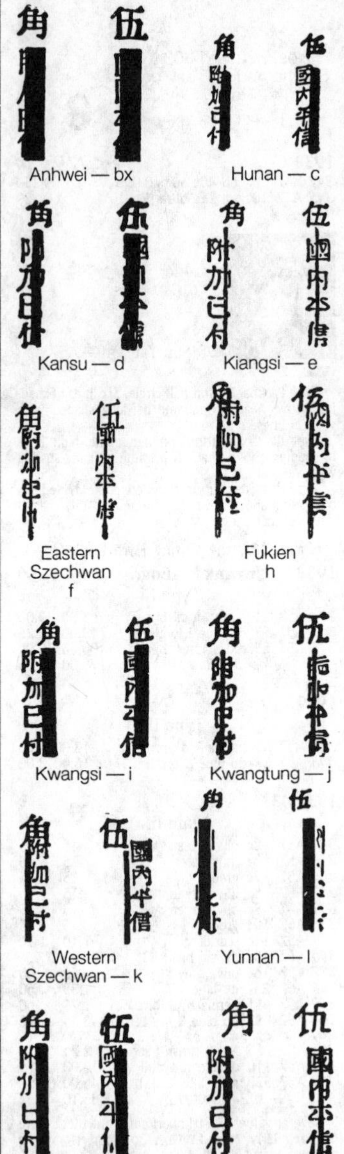

Anhwei — bx

Hunan — c

Kansu — d

Kiangsi — e

Eastern Szechwan f

Fukien h

Kwangsi — i

Kwangtung — j

Western Szechwan — k

Yunnan — l

Honan — m

Shensi — n

Kweichow — o

Hupeh — p

Nos. 525-526 Surcharged "50 cents" and 2 Vertical Bars in Black or Red

1942 Unwmk.

No.	Description	Unused	Used
527	A62 50c on 16c (Bk) (c,f)	2.00	2.50
	(i) Kwangsi	3.75	4.75
	(k) Western Szechwan	6.00	6.00
r.	Inverted surch. (W. Szech.)	110.00	
s.	"k" surcharge on #493	110.00	
	(m) Honan	5.50	6.50
	(n) Shensi	3.00	3.50
528	A62 50c on 16c (R) (d)	3.00	4.75
	(bx) Anhwei	35.00	55.00
	(e) Kiangsi	4.75	9.00
	(h) Fukien	5.50	6.00
	(j) Kwangtung	5.50	5.00
	(l) Yunnan	5.50	7.00
	(o) Kweichow	3.00	6.00

r. Inverted surch. (Kweichow) 90.00
(p) Hupeh 3.00 4.25
s. "p" surch. on #526(f) 110.00 110.00

Many varieties of Nos. 527-528 exist, including narrow or wide spacing between the two top characters, or between the vertical bars, or both.

Surcharges on stamps perf. 10½ (basic No. 493a) usually sell at much higher prices.

伍 改
角50作
General Issue

伍 改
角50作
Hunan — c50

伍 改
角50作
Eastern Szechwan — f50

伍 改
角50作
Chekiang — g50

伍 改
角50作
Kwangsi — i50

伍 改
角50作
Kwangtung — j50

伍 改
角 50 作
Western Szechwan — k50

伍 改
角 50 作
Honan — m50

伍 改
角 50 作
Shensi — n50

伍 改
角50作
Kweichow — o50

No. 493 Surcharged in Black, Red or Carmine

1943 **Unwmk.**

529 A62 50c on 16c (Bk) (m50) 3.75 4.50
(n50) Shensi 6.50 6.00
r. Perf. 11x13 (Shensi) 80.00
530 A62 50c on 16c (C) .85 1.50
(c50) Hunan 2.50 5.00
r. Inverted surch. (Hunan) 40.00
(f50) Eastern Szechwan 3.00 2.50
(g50) Chekiang 30.00 35.00
(i50) Kwangsi 5.50 6.50
(j50) Kwangtung 4.00 6.50
(k50) Western Szechwan 4.00 5.50
(m50) Honan 7.00 8.00
(o50) Kweichow 9.00 11.00
s. "05" instead of "50" (Kweichow) 300.00

Many varieties of Nos. 529-530 exist, such as narrow or wide spacing horizontally or vertically between the overprinted Chinese characters.

Surcharges on No. 493a (perf. 10½) usually sell at much higher pricess.

The General Issue type, No. 530, was distributed to all head offices, which in turn supplied the post offices under their direction. It is surcharged in carmine; the other stamps listed under No. 530 are surcharged in red or carmine.

貳 改
角20作
Hunan — c20

貳 改
角 (20) 作
Kansu — d20

貳 改
角20作
Kiangsi e20

貳 改
角20作
Eastern Szechwan f20

貳 改
角20作
Fukien h20

貳 改
角20作
Kwangsi i20

貳 改
角 20 作
Kwangtung j20

貳 改
角 20 作
Western Szechwan k20

貳 改
角 20 作
Yunnan — l20

貳 改
角 20 作
Honan — m20

貳 改
角 20 作
Shensi n20

貳 改
角20作
Kweichow o20

貳 改
角20作
Hupeh — p20

1943 **Wmk. 261, Unwmkd.**

On No. 318

531 A45 20c on 13c (k20) .70 *1.40*
(d20) Kansu 1.10 *3.00*
(n20) Shensi .90 *2.25*
532 A45 20c on 13c (i20;R) .65 1.65
(c20) Hunan 550.00
(e20) Kiangsi 140.00
(j20) Kwangtung 40.00 55.00
(p20) Hupeh 1.10 *2.25*

On No. 411

533 A45 20c on 13c (n20) 1.00 *2.50*
(d20) Kansu 1.10 *4.50*
(k20) Western Szechwan 1.00 *4.50*
(l20) Yunnan 11.00 8.00
(m20) Honan 225.00
534 A45 20c on 13c (p20;R) .75 *3.25*
(c20) Hunan 1.50 1.10
(e20) Kiangsi 1.10 1.25
(f20) Eastern Szechwan 1.10 *1.65*
(h20) Fukien 5.00 *5.50*
(i20) Kwangsi .85 *1.40*
(j20) Kwangtung 9.00 10.00
(o20) Kweichow 1.65 *2.00*

On No. 430

535 A45 20c on 13c (l20) .75 *2.75*
(d20) Kansu 1.10 *1.65*
(k20) Western Szechwan 22.50 *25.00*
(m20) Honan 2.25 *5.50*
(n20) Shensi 1.10 *3.25*
536 A45 20c on 13c (f20;i20;R) .70 *2.00*
(c20) Hunan 5.50 *5.75*
(e20) Kiangsi 2.25 *2.25*
(j20) Kwangtung 1.10 *1.65*
(o20) Kweichow 1.10 *6.00*
(p20) Hupeh 1.10 *2.25*

On No. 357

537 A57 20c on 16c (k20) .90 *1.25*
(c20) Hunan 1.40 *8.00*
(d20) Kansu 1.10 *8.00*
(m20) Honan 3.25 *11.00*
(n20) Shensi .90 *8.00*
538 A57 20c on 16c (e20;R) 1.10 *8.00*
(c20) Hunan 7.00 *11.00*
(i20) Kwangsi 2.25 *8.00*
(j20) Kwangtung 22.50 *32.50*
(o20) Kweichow 1.65 *8.00*

On No. 413

539 A46 20c on 17c (c20;R) .90 *2.50*
(i20) Kwangsi 1.10 *1.65*
(j20) Kwangtung 22.50 27.50

On No. 432

540 A46 20c on 17c (k20) 2.25 3.25
(d20) Kansu 2.25 3.75
(m20) Honan 22.50 27.50
541 A46 20c on 17c (e20;R) 1.10 *3.25*
(j20) Kwangtung 2.25 *7.50*
(o20) Kweichow 1.40 *4.00*

On No. 456

542 A59 20c on 17c (m20) 140.00 150.00
543 A59 20c on 17c (c20;R) 13.00 15.00

On No. 415

544 A45 20c on 21c (e20;R) 6.50 7.50

On No. 434

545 A45 20c on 21c (c20, k20) 1.00 *2.25*
(d20) Kansu 1.40 *4.00*
(l20) Yunnan 1.10 *2.25*
(m20) Honan 2.25 *5.50*
546 A45 20c on 21c (f20;R) .55 *2.50*
(e20) Kiangsi .90 *3.25*
(h20) Fukien 1.10 *2.75*
(i20) Kwangsi 1.40 *2.25*
(j20) Kwangtung 1.40 *2.75*
(o20) Kweichow 1.40 *1.65*
(p20) Hupeh .90 *3.25*

On No. 417

547 A46 20c on 28c (e20;R) 325.00 375.00

On No. 436

548 A46 20c on 28c (l20) 1.10 *3.75*
(d20) Kansu 11.00 14.00
(k20) Western Szechwan 22.50 32.50
(m20) Honan 17.00 27.50
549 A46 20c on 28c (e20;R) .80 *2.00*
(c20) Hunan 1.10 *2.75*
(h20) Fukien 1.10 *2.75*
(i20) Kwangsi .80 *2.75*
(j20) Kwangtung 1.00 *3.75*
(o20) Kweichow 2.50 *2.75*

Many varieties of Nos. 531-549 exist, such as narrow or wide spacing between the overprinted Chinese characters, and "20" higher or lower than illustrated.

Type of 1942-43
Pacheng Printing

1944-46 **Unwmk.** ***Perf. 12***

Without Gum

550 A62 30c chocolate .35 *10.00*
551 A62 $1 green 3.00 3.00
552 A62 $2 dk vio brn .15 .15
a. Imperf., pair 12.00 12.00
553 A62 $2 dk bl grn .15 .15
a. Perf. 10½ 35.00 26.00
554 A62 $2 deep blue 1.25 1.25
555 A62 $3 lt yellow 1.00 .60
556 A62 $4 violet brn .15 .15
a. Imperf., pair 60.00
557 A62 $5 car ('46) .15 .15
a. Perf. 10½ 45.00 4.00
558 A62 $6 gray vio ('45) .15 .15
559 A62 $10 red brn ('45) .15 .15
a. Imperf., pair 60.00
560 A62 $20 dp ultra ('46) .15 .15
561 A62 $50 dk green ('46) 1.25 .20
562 A62 $70 lilac ('46) .50 .20
563 A62 $100 lt brown ('46) .15 .15
Set value 5.00 *10.80*

In the Pacheng printing of the Central Trust type stamps, the secret mark "C" has been added below the lower left foliate ornament beneath the sun emblem. On the $3, it is below the right ornament. New values also include a "P" at right of sun emblem on the $6 and $10, and at right of necktie on the $20. Some values of Pacheng printing exist on paper with elephant watermark in sheet.

See surcharge note following No. 505.

Dr. Sun Yat-sen
A63

Allegory of Savings
A64

1944-46 **Unwmk.** **Typo.** ***Perf. 12½***

Without Gum

565 A63 40c brown red .25 .25
566 A63 $2 gray brown .25 .25
567 A63 $3 red .25 .25
a. $3 orange red 2.50 3.00
568 A63 $3 lt red brown ('45) .60 .35
569 A63 $6 pale lilac gray ('45) .25 .25
570 A63 $10 dull lake ('45) .25 .25
571 A63 $20 rose ('45) .25 .25
a. Perf. 15½ 150.00 150.00
572 A63 $50 lt brown ('46) .40 .40
573 A63 $70 rose violet ('46) .40 .40
Nos. 565-573 (9) 2.90 2.65

For surcharges see Nos. 772, 774, 828, 833, 835, 836A, 839, 842, 851, 864, 868, 873-875, 877, 880. Taiwan 81, 98, Sinkiang 200-201.

1944-45 **Engr.** ***Perf. 13***

Without Gum

574 A64 $40 indigo ('45) .20 .20
575 A64 $50 yellow grn ('45) .20 .20
576 A64 $100 yellow brn .20 .20
577 A64 $200 dk green ('45) .20 .20
Nos. 574-577 (4) .80 .80

All four values were printed on thick paper; the first three were also printed on thin paper.

For surcharges see Szechwan Nos. F1, F3.

Dr. Sun Yat-sen
A65 A66

1944, Dec. 25 **Litho.**

Without Gum

578 A65 $2 deep green .30 .30
579 A65 $5 fawn .30 .60
580 A65 $6 dull rose vio .90 1.25
581 A65 $10 violet blue 1.75 2.00
582 A65 $20 carmine 3.00 3.25
Nos. 578-582 (5) 6.25 7.40

50th anniversary of the Kuomintang.

1945, Mar. 12

Without Gum

583 A66 $2 gray green .30 .60
584 A66 $5 red brown .40 .60
585 A66 $6 dk vio blue .45 .90
586 A66 $10 lt blue .70 .90
587 A66 $20 rose .95 1.10
588 A66 $30 buff 1.50 1.75
Nos. 583-588 (6) 4.30 5.85

Death of Dr. Sun Yat-sen, 20th anniv.

Dr. Sun Yat-sen — A67

1945-46 **Without Gum** ***Perf. 12½***

589 A67 $2 green .25 .35
590 A67 $5 dull green .25 .35
591 A67 $10 dk blue .25 .35
a. Imperf., pair 70.00
592 A67 $20 carmine ('46) .25 .35
a. Imperf., pair 70.00
Nos. 589-592 (4) 1.00 1.40

For surcharges see Nos. 695, 697, 837, 855, Taiwan 58, 82, 87-88.

Statue of Liberty, Map of China, Flags of Great Britain, China and United States, and Chiang Kai-shek
A68

1945, July 7 **Unwmk.** **Engr.** ***Perf. 12***

Flags in Dark Blue and Red

593 A68 $1 dp blue .15 .15
594 A68 $2 dull green .30 .35
595 A68 $5 olive gray .30 .35
596 A68 $6 brown .65 .80
597 A68 $10 rose lilac 2.75 *4.50*
598 A68 $20 car rose 2.00 *5.50*
Nos. 593-598 (6) 6.15 *11.65*

Signing of a Treaty in 1943 between Great Britain, the US and China.

Pres. Lin Sen (1864-1943)
A69

Pres. Chiang Kai-shek
A70

1945, Aug. **Unwmk.** ***Perf. 12***

599 A69 $1 dp ultra & blk .15 .15
600 A69 $2 myrtle grn & blk .15 .15
601 A69 $5 red & blk .15 .15
602 A69 $6 purple & blk 1.00 .75
603 A69 $10 choc & blk 1.50 *2.00*
604 A69 $20 olive grn & blk 2.00 *2.50*
Nos. 599-604 (6) 4.95 *5.70*

1945, Oct. 10

Flag in Rose Red and Violet Blue

605 A70 $2 green .50 .90
606 A70 $4 dk blue .50 .90
607 A70 $5 olive gray .50 .90
608 A70 $6 bister brown 1.25 2.00
609 A70 $10 gray 1.75 2.25
610 A70 $20 red violet 3.00 4.25
Nos. 605-610 (6) 7.50 11.20

Inauguration of Chiang Kai-shek as president, Oct. 10, 1943.

President Chiang Kai-shek — A71

1945, Oct. 10 Typo. *Perf. 13*

Without Gum

Flag in Carmine and Blue

611 A71 $20 green & blue .25 .20
612 A71 $50 bister brn & bl .50 .35
613 A71 $100 blue .45 .35
614 A71 $300 rose red & blue .45 .35
Nos. 611-614 (4) 1.65 1.25

Victory of the Allied Nations over Japan.

C. N. C. Surcharges

The green surcharges on Nos. 615 to 621, and the surcharges on Nos. 647 to 721, and 768 to 774 represent Chinese National Currency and were applied at Shanghai.

Stamps of 1938-41 Surcharged in Black with Chinese Characters and New Value in Checkered Rectangle at Bottom, Resurcharged in Green

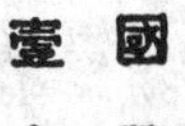

1945 *Perf. 12, 12½*

615 A57 10c on $20 on 3c (#350) .15 .20
616 A46 15c on $30 on 2c (#423) .15 .35
a. Horiz. pair, imperf. between 90.00
b. Vert. pair, imperf. between 85.00
617 A59 25c on $50 on 1c (#450) .15 .20
618 A57 50c on $100 on 3c (#350) .15 .20
619 A40 $1 on $200 on 1c (#422) .15 .20
a. Horiz. pair, imperf. between 90.00
620 A57 $2 on $400 on 3c (#350) .15 .20
621 A59 $5 on $1000 on 1c (#450) .15 .20
Set value .30
Nos. 615-621 (7) 1.55

The black (first) surcharges on Nos. 615 to 621 represent Nanking puppet government currency.

In the green surcharge, the characters at the left express the new value and are either two or four in number.

Types of 1932-34, Re-engraved, and Surcharged in Green with Horizontal Bar and Four or Five Chinese Characters and Overprinted in Black:

Perf. 14

622 A47 $10 on 20c brown red 4.00 5.50
623 A47 $20 on 40c orange 21.00 24.00
a. Green surcharge inverted 60.00
624 A48 $50 on 30c violet brn 14.00 18.00
Nos. 622-624 (3) 39.00 47.50

These provisional surcharges were applied in Honan in National currency to stamps of the Hwa Pei (North China) government. The black overprint reads: "Hwa Pei."

The two-character "Hwa Pei" overprint was applied to various stamps in 1941-43 by the North China puppet government. See Nos. 8N1-8N53, 8N60-8N84.

Dr. Sun Yat-sen
A72 A73

1945, Dec. Typo. *Perf. 12*

Without Gum

625 A72 $20 dp carmine .25 .25
626 A72 $30 dp blue .25 .25
627 A72 $40 orange .25 .25
628 A72 $50 green .25 .25
629 A72 $100 dk brown .25 .25
630 A72 $200 brown violet .25 .25
Nos. 625-630 (6) 1.50 1.50

For surcharges see Nos. 810, 829, 838, 865, J110-J119, Taiwan 75, Kwangsi F2, Szechwan F2, F4, Yunnan 66-67, 71.

Type of 1931-37

Perf. 12½, 13x12½, 13½

1946 Unwmk.

631 A37 $1 dk violet .30 .20
632 A37 $2 olive green .30 .15
633 A37 $20 brt yellow grn .30 .25
634 A37 $30 chocolate .30 .25
635 A37 $50 red orange .30 .15
Nos. 631-635 (5) 1.50 1.00

For surcharges see Nos. 678, 684, 689-690, 768, 843.

1946-47 Engr. *Perf. 14*

Without Gum

636 A73 $20 carmine .70 .15
637 A73 $30 dk blue ('47) .15 .15
638 A73 $50 purple .15 .15
639 A73 $70 red org ('47) 16.00 1.40
640 A73 $100 dk carmine .15 .15
641 A73 $200 olive grn ('47) .15 .15
642 A73 $500 brt bl grn ('47) .15 .15
643 A73 $700 red brown ('47) .15 .15
644 A73 $1000 rose lake .35 .35
645 A73 $3000 blue 1.00 .35
646 A73 $5000 dp green & ver .95 .35
Nos. 636-646 (11) 19.90
Set value 2.00

For surcharges see Nos. 679, 769, 775, 823, 837A, 844-845, 856, 866, 875A, 878, Taiwan 18, 23-28, 54, 76-77, 100, Northeastern Provinces 41-43, Fukien 5-6, Hunan 1, E1, F1, Kwangsi 11, F2, Szechwan F5-F8, Sinkiang 202-204, People's Republic of China 3L53, 3L67-3L68, 6L28.

Stamps of 1932-41 Surcharged in Black

Perf. 12½, 13, 13x12, 14

Wmk. 261

647 A45 $20 on 8c (#409) .15 .65
648 A39 $30 on ½c (#402) 1,000.
649 A45 $50 on 21c (#415) .15 .15
650 A45 $70 on 13c (#411) .15 .20
651 A46 $100 on 28c (#417) .15 .65

Unwmk.

652 A39 $3 on 2½c (#424) 5.50 5.50
653 A48 $10 on 15c (#431) .20 .20
654 A45 $20 on 8c (#428) .20 .20
655 A47 $20 on 20c (#433) .35 .35
656 A39 $30 on ½c (#421) .20 .20
657 A45 $50 on 21c (#434) .35 .45
657A A45 $70 on 13c (#318) 95.00 80.00
658 A45 $70 on 13c (#430) .35 .45
659 A46 $100 on 28c (#436) .35 .35

國幣 伍拾圓 50.00

Stamps and Types of 1931-1946 Surcharged in Black or Carmine

Perf. 12½, 13, 14

1946-47 Wmk. 261

660 A57 $50 on 5c green (#392) .35 .85
661 A57 $50 on 5c ol grn (#393) 21.00 17.50
662 A48 $50 on 5c dl red org (#408) .15 1.10
663 A40 $100 on 1c org (#403) .15 1.10

Perf. 12, 12½, 12½x13, 13, 14

1946-47 Unwmk.

664 A57 $20 on 3c (#350) .15 .35
665 A45 $20 on 8c (#428) .15 .20
666 A57 $50 on 3c (#350) .15 .15
667 A57 $50 on 5c (#352) .15 .20
668 A57 $50 on 5c (#382) .85 1.65
669 A48 $50 on 5c (#427) .15 .15
670 A59 $50 on 5c (#452) .20 .20
671 A62 $50 on $1 (#500) .15 .15
672 A40 $100 on 1c (#422) .15 .15
a. Without secret mark (#422a) 65.00 65.00
673 A57 $100 on 3c (#350) .15 .15
674 A57 $100 on 8c (#353) 11.00 11.00
675 A57 $100 on 8c (#369) .55 .35
676 A57 $100 on 8c (#383) .35 .35
a. Without "star" in uniform button (No. 383a) 25.00 16.00
677 A59 $100 on 8c (#454) .15 .15
678 A37 $100 on $1 (#631) .20 .20
679 A73 $100 on $20 (#636) .35 .35
680 A57 $200 on 10c (#354) .25 .25
681 A57 $200 on 10c (#384) .25 1.10
682 A37 $200 on $4 dl bl .15 .15
a. Double surcharge 16.00
683 A62 $250 on $1.50 (#501) .20 .20
a. Perf. 11 375.00 375.00
684 A37 $250 on $2 (#632) .20 .20
685 A37 $250 on $5 car .15 .15
686 A57 $300 on 10c (#354) .15 .15
687 A59 $300 on 10c (#455) .15 .15
688 A57 $500 on 3c (#350) .15 .15
689 A37 $500 on $20 (#633) .15 .15
690 A37 $800 on $30 (#634) .15 .15
691 A37 $1000 on 2c (#297) .55 .35
692 A62 $1000 on $2 (#552) .15 .15
a. Imperf., pair 16.00 16.00
693 A62 $1000 on $2 (#553) .15 .25
694 A62 $1000 on $2 (#554) .25 .55
695 A67 $1000 on $2 (#589) .15 .15
696 A62 $2000 on $5 (#557) .15 .15
697 A67 $2000 on $5 dl grn (C) (#590) .15 .15
Nos. 664-697 (34) 18.35 20.30

Nos. 682 and 685 were not issued without surcharge. No. 682 is perf. 13x13½; No. 685, perf. 12x12½.

The characters at the left express the new value and vary in number.

Stamps of 1938-41 Surcharged in Black

國幣 伍拾圓 50.00

Perf. 12, 12½, 13, 14

1946 Wmk. 261

698 A45 $20 on 8c (#409) 100.00 100.00
699 A57 $50 on 5c (#392) .15 .55
700 A57 $50 on 5c (#393) .15 1.10

1946-48 Unwmk.

700A A57 $20 on 5c (#381) 600.00
701 A57 $20 on 8c (#353) .15 .35
702 A57 $20 on 8c (#369) .35 .35
703 A57 $20 on 8c (#383) .15 .15
a. Without "star" in uniform button (No. 383a) 4.50 4.50
b. Inverted surcharge 20.00
c. Dbl. surch., one on back 32.50 32.50
d. Double surcharge 32.50
704 A45 $20 on 8c (#428) .15 .15
a. Double surcharge 22.50
705 A59 $20 on 8c (#453) .15 .15
706 A59 $20 on 8c (#454) .15 .15
a. Inverted surcharge 13.00
b. Double surcharge 13.00
707 A57 $50 on 5c (#351) 6.50 6.00
708 A57 $50 on 5c (#352) .15 .15
a. Inverted surcharge 27.50
709 A57 $50 on 5c (#381) .70 .70
710 A57 $50 on 5c (#382) .15 .35
711 A48 $50 on 5c (#427) .15 .15
a. Inverted surcharge 27.50
712 A59 $50 on 5c (#452) .15 .15
a. Double surcharge 16.00

國幣 拾圓

Stamps of 1939-41 Surcharged in Blue or Red

1946 Wmk. 261 *Perf. 12½*

713 A40 $10 on 1c org (#403) .15 .15
a. Inverted surcharge 40.00
714 A48 $20 on 3c dp yel brn (#406) 450.00 450.00

1946 Unwmk. *Perf. 12, 12½, 13*

715 A40 $10 on 1c org (#422) .15 .15
a. Without secret mark (#422a) 10.00 12.00
b. Inverted surcharge 8.00 10.00
716 A59 $10 on 1c org (#450) .15 .15
a. Double surcharge 27.50
717 A57 $20 on 2c ol grn (R) (#368) .15 .15
718 A59 $20 on 2c brt ultra (R) (#451) .15 .15
a. Inverted surcharge 20.00
b. Double surcharge 16.00
719 A57 $20 on 3c dl cl (#350) .15 .15
a. Double surcharge 22.50
720 A48 $20 on 3c dp yel brn (#425) .15 .35
721 A39 $30 on 4c pale vio (R) (#426) .15 .25
a. Inverted surcharge 9.00
Set value .56 1.10

President Chiang Kai-shek — A74

Perf. 10½-11½

1946, Oct. 31 Engr. Unwmk.

722 A74 $20 carmine .35 .40
723 A74 $30 green .35 .40
724 A74 $50 vermilion .35 .40
725 A74 $100 yellow grn .35 .40
726 A74 $200 yellow org .35 .40
727 A74 $300 magenta .35 .40
Nos. 722-727 (6) 2.10 2.40

60th birthday of Chiang Kai-shek.

Printed by Dah Yeh Printing Co.; the earlier ones are gumless, the later ones gummed.

See Taiwan Nos. 29-34, Northeastern Provinces 30-35.

Printed by Dah Tung Book Co.

Without Gum

Perf. 14

722a A74 $20 carmine 1.00 1.40
723a A74 $30 green 1.00 1.40
724a A74 $50 vermilion 1.00 1.40
725a A74 $100 yellow green 1.00 1.40
726a A74 $200 yellow orange 1.00 1.40
727a A74 $300 magenta 1.00 1.40
Nos. 722a-727a (6) 6.00 8.40

Assembly House, Nanking — A75

1946, Nov. 15 Litho. *Perf. 14*

Without Gum

728 A75 $20 green .60 .25
729 A75 $30 blue .60 .25
730 A75 $50 dk brown .60 .25
a. Horiz. pair, imperf. between 50.00 60.00
731 A75 $100 carmine .60 .25
Nos. 728-731 (4) 2.40 1.00

Convening of National Assembly.

For surcharges see Taiwan Nos. 10-13, Northeastern Provinces 26-29.

Entrance to Dr. Sun Yat-sen Mausoleum — A76

Dr. Sun Yat-sen — A77

1947, May 5 Engr.

732 A76 $100 dp green .35 .20
733 A76 $200 deep blue .35 .20
734 A76 $250 carmine .35 .20
735 A76 $350 lt brown .35 .20
736 A76 $400 dp claret .35 .20
Nos. 732-736 (5) 1.75 1.00

First anniversary of return of Chinese National Government to Nanking.

See Taiwan Nos. 35-39, Northeastern Provinces 36-40.

1947 *Perf. 12½, 11½x12½*

737 A77 $500 olive green .15 .15
738 A77 $1000 green & car .15 .15
739 A77 $2000 dp blue & red brn .15 .15
740 A77 $5000 org red & blk .15 .15
Nos. 737-740 (4) .60 .60

For surcharge see Szechwan No. 50.

Confucius
A78

Confucius' Lecturing School
A79

Tomb of Confucius — A80

Temple of Confucius — A81

1947, Aug. 27 **Litho.** ***Perf. 14***

Without Gum

741 A78 $500 carmine rose .40 *.25*

Engr.

742 A79 $800 yellow brown .40 *.25*
743 A80 $1250 blue green .40 *.25*
744 A81 $1800 blue .40 *.25*
Nos. 741-744 (4) 1.60 1.00

Sun Yat-sen and Plum Blossoms A82

Chinese Flag and Map of Taiwan A83

1947-48 **Engr.** ***Perf. 14***

Without Gum

745 A82 $150 dk blue .15 *.25*
746 A82 $250 dp lilac .25 .20
747 A82 $500 blue grn .15 .15
748 A82 $1000 red .15 .15
749 A82 $2000 vermilion .20 .20
750 A82 $3000 blue .15 .15
751 A82 $4000 gray ('48) .20 .20
752 A82 $5000 dk brown .15 .15
753 A82 $6000 rose lilac ('48) .20 .20
754 A82 $7000 lt red brn ('48) .20 .20
755 A82 $10,000 dp blue & car .85 .20
756 A82 $20,000 car & yel grn .25 .20
757 A82 $50,000 grn & dk bl .85 .20
758 A82 $100,000 dl yel & ol grn ('48) 1.40 .20
759 A82 $200,000 vio brn & dp bl ('48) 1.65 .45
760 A82 $300,000 sep & org brn ('48) 1.65 .45
761 A82 $500,000 dk Prus grn & sep ('48) 2.25 .45
Nos. 745-761 (17) 10.70 4.00

See Nos. 788-799. For similar type see Formosa A1. For surcharges see Nos. 770, 804-806, 821-822, 840-841, 858-859, 869, 871, 880A-880B, 885A-885E, 1025-1036, Taiwan 56-57, 59, 89, Fukien 1-4, 7-12, 19-23, Hunan 2-5, C1, Kiangsi 1-3, C1, E1, F1-F2, Kwangsi 8-10, 12-17, Shensi 1-2, C1, E1, Szechwan 24-49, Yunnan 61-62, 69, 205-207, People's Republic of China 3L69-3L70, 3L76, 4L63-4L64, 6L22, 6L27, 6L29, 6L32.

1947, Oct. 25

With Gum

762 A83 $500 carmine .25 .25
763 A83 $1250 deep green .25 .25

Restoration of Taiwan to China, 2nd anniv.

Mobile Post Office — A84

Street-Corner Branch Post Office — A85

1947, Nov. 5

764 A84 $500 carmine .25 .15
765 A85 $1000 lilac .25 .15
766 A85 $1250 green .25 .15
767 A84 $1800 deep blue .25 .15
Nos. 764-767 (4) 1.00
Set value .50

Stamps and Type of 1943-47 Surcharged in Black or Green

1947-48 **Unwmk.** ***Perf. 12½, 13, 14***

768 A37 $500 on $20 brt yel grn (#633) .15 .15
769 A73 $1250 on $70 red org (#639) .15 .15
770 A82 $1800 on $350 yel org .15 .15
771 A62 $2000 on $3 dk yel ('48) (#503) .15 .15
772 A63 $2000 on $3 red (#567) .15 .15
a. On #567a 3.25 2.25
773 A62 $3000 on $3 lt yel ('48) (#555) .15 .15
774 A63 $3000 on $3 lt red brn (G) ('48) (#568) .15 .15
Set value .35 .60

The characters at the left express the new value and vary in number.

No. 640 Surcharged

1948, Aug. ***Perf. 14***

775 A73 $5000 on $100 dk car 4.50 *35.00*

No. 775 received its surcharge in Kwangsi for use in that province.

Map of China and Mail-carrying Vehicles — A86

Rural Mail Delivery — A87

Early and Modern Mail Transportation A88

1947, Dec. 16 **Engr.** ***Perf. 12***

776 A86 $100 violet .25 .15
777 A87 $200 brt green .25 .15
778 A87 $300 red brown .25 .15
779 A88 $400 scarlet .25 .15
780 A88 $500 brt vio blue .25 .15
Nos. 776-780 (5) 1.25
Set value .65

Chinese Postal Administration, 50th anniv.

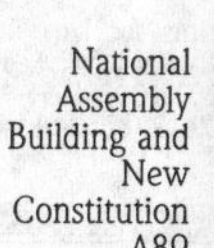

National Assembly Building and New Constitution A89

1947, Dec. 25 ***Perf. 14***

Without Gum

781 A89 $2000 brt red .25 .20
782 A89 $3000 blue .25 .20
783 A89 $5000 deep green .25 .20
Nos. 781-783 (3) .75 .60

1st anniv. of the adoption of China's new constitution, Dec. 25, 1946.

Chinese Stamps of 1947 and 1912 — A90

Perf. 14, Imperf.

1948, Mar. 20 **Litho.**

Without Gum

784 A90 $5000 dk car rose .50 1.00
a. Vert. pair, imperf. btwn 30.00
785 A90 $5000 dk green .50 1.00
a. Vert. pair, imperf. btwn 20.00

Stamp exhibitions at Nanking, Mar. 20 (No. 784), and at Shanghai, May 19 (No. 785).

Sun Yat-sen Memorial Hall, Taipei — A91

1948, Apr. 28 **Engr.** ***Perf. 14***

786 A91 $5000 violet .15 .15
787 A91 $10000 red .15 .15
Set value .20

Restoration of Formosa to China, 3rd anniv.

Sun Yat-sen Type of 1947-48

1948

Without Gum

788 A82 $20000 rose pink .35 .15
789 A82 $30000 chocolate .20 .15
790 A82 $40000 green .20 .15
791 A82 $50000 dp blue .20 .15
792 A82 $100000 dull grn .20 .15
793 A82 $200000 brn vio .55 .15
794 A82 $300000 yel grn .85 .15
795 A82 $500000 lil rose .85 .15
796 A82 $1000000 claret .55 .15
797 A82 $2000000 vermilion 1.10 .15
798 A82 $3000000 ol bis 2.25 .25
799 A82 $5000000 ultra 4.00 .55
Nos. 788-799 (12) 11.30
Set value 1.40

Zeros for "cents" omitted.
For surcharges see Nos. 841, 871, 880A-880B, 885A-885E, 1025-1028, 1031-1036.

Early Ship and Modern Hai Tien — A92

Passenger Ship Kiang Ya — A93

1948, Aug. 16

Without Gum

800 A92 $20000 blue .15 .15
801 A92 $30000 rose lilac .15 .15
802 A93 $40000 yel brown .15 .15
803 A93 $60000 vermilion .15 .15
Set value .20

75th anniversary of the China Merchants' Steam Navigation Company.

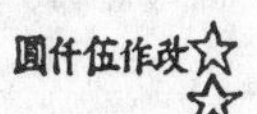

Type of 1947-48 Surcharged in Black

1948 **Unwmk.** ***Perf. 14***

804 A82 $4000 on $100 car .15 .65
805 A82 $5000 on $100 car .15 .15
806 A82 $8000 on $700 red brn .15 .15
Nos. 804-806 (3) .95
Set value .20

Stamps of 1942-46 Surcharged in Black or Red

1948 ***Perf. 12½, 13***

807 A62 $5000 on $1 (#500) .20 .20
808 A62 $5000 on $1 (#551) 13.00 13.00
809 A62 $5000 on $2 (#502) .20 .20
810 A72 $10000 on $20 (#625) .20 .20
811 A62 $20000 on 10c (#492) .20 .20
812 A62 $20000 on 50c (#498;R) .20 .20
813 A62 $30000 on 30c (#496) .20 .20
a. Perf. 10½ 16.00 16.00
Nos. 807-813 (7) 14.20 14.20

Nos. 492, 556 and 558 Surcharged in Black or Carmine

1948

814 A62 $15,000 on 10c dp grn .15 .15
815 A62 $15,000 on $4 vio brn .15 .15
816 A62 $15,000 on $6 gray vio (C) .15 .15
Set value .25 .35

No. 498, 494 and 504 Surcharged in Black

1948 **Unwmk.** ***Perf. 11½, 13***

817 A62 $15,000 on 50c, perf. 13 .20 .15
a. Perf. 11½ 7.75
818 A62 $40,000 on 20c dk ol grn .20 .15
a. Perf. 11 7.00 5.50
819 A62 $60,000 on $4 red brn .20 .15
Nos. 817-819 (3) .60
Set value .35

Gold Yuan Surcharges

(Nos. 820-885E)

Stamps of 1942-47 Surcharged in Black, Carmine or Red

1948 ***Perf. 14, 13, 11***

820 A62 ½c on 30c (#496) .15 .15
821 A82 ½c on $500 (Bk) (#747) .15 .15
822 A82 ½c on $500 (C) (#747) .15 .15
823 A73 1c on $20 (#636) .15 .15
824 A62 2c on $1.50 (R) (#501) .15 .15
825 A62 3c on $5 (#505) .15 .15
826 A62 4c on $1 (#499) .15 .15
827 A62 5c on 50c (#498) .15 .15
a. Perf. 11 4.50 4.50
Set value 1.00 1.00

On No. 820-827, the position of the surcharged denomination and "Gold Yuan" characters varies, the aim being to obliterate the original denomination.

Stamps of 1940-48 Surcharged in Black, Violet, Carmine, Blue or Green

Perf. 12, 12½, 13, 14, 12½x13

1948-49

828 A63 5c on $20 (#571) .15 .15
829 A72 5c on $30 (C) (#626) .15 .15
a. Double surcharge 16.00
830 A57 10c on 2c (#368) .15 .15
831 A39 10c on 2½c (#424) .15 .15
832 A62 10c on 25c (V) (#495) .15 .15
833 A63 10c on 40c (#565) .15 .15
834 A62 10c on $1 (#500) .15 .15
834A A62 10c on $1 (#551) 150.00 150.00
835 A63 10c on $2 (#566) .15 .15
836 A62 10c on $20 (C) (#560) .15 .15
836A A63 10c on $20 (#571) 90.00 95.00
837 A67 10c on $20 (#592) .15 .15
837A A73 10c on $20 (#636) .65 *2.00*
838 A72 10c on $30 (C) (#626) .15 *.30*
839 A63 10c on $70 (#573) .15 .15
a. Double surcharge 13.00
840 A82 10c on $7000 (#754) .15 .15
841 A82 10c on $20,000 (#788) .15 .15
842 A63 20c on $6 (#569) .15 .15
843 A37 20c on $30 (#634) .35 *1.10*
844 A73 20c on $30 (C) (#637) .15 .15
845 A73 20c on $100 (#640) .15 .15
a. Inverted surcharge 19.00
b. Double surcharge 14.00
846 A39 50c on ½c (#312) 35.00 35.00
847 A39 50c on ½c (#421) .15 .15
a. Inverted surcharge 27.50
848 A62 50c on 20c (#494) .15 .15
849 A62 50c on 30c (Bl) (#496) .15 .15

850 A62 50c on 40c (V) (#497) .15 .15
a. Perf. 11 6.50 7.25
851 A63 50c on 40c (V) (#565) .15 .15
852 A62 50c on $4 (#556) .15 .15
853 A62 50c on $4 (Bl) (#556) .15 .15
854 A62 50c on $20 (C) (#560) .15 .15
855 A67 50c on $20 (V) (#592) .15 .20
856 A73 50c on $20 (#636) .15 .15
857 A62 50c on $70 (C) (#562) .15 .15
858 A82 50c on $6000 (#753) .15 .15
859 A82 50c on $6000 (Bl) (#753) .15 .15
860 A62 $1 on 30c (#550) .15 .15
a. Perf. 11 16.00 16.00
861 A62 $1 on 40c (#497) .15 .15
a. Perf. 11 2.75 2.75
862 A62 $1 on $1 (#499) .15 .15
863 A62 $1 on $5 (#557) .15 .15
864 A63 $2 on $2 (R) (#566) .15 .15
865 A72 $2 on $20 (#625) .15 .15
866 A73 $2 on $100 (#640) .15 .15
867 A46 $5 on 17c (#432) .15 .15
868 A63 $5 on $2 (#566) .15 .15
869 A82 $5 on $3000 (C) (#750) .15 .15
870 A47 $8 on 20c (#433) .15 .15
871 A82 $8 on $30,000 (C) (#789) .15 .15
872 A47 $10 on 40c (#438) .15 .15
873 A63 $10 on $2 (G) (#566) .15 .15
874 A63 $10 on $2 (C) (#566) .15 .15
875 A63 $20 on $2 (C) (#566) .15 .15
875A A73 $20 on $20 (#636) 1.40 1.65
876 A62 $50 on 30c (#496) .15 .15
877 A63 $50 on $2 (Bl) (#566) .15 .15
878 A73 $80 on $20 (#636) .15 .15
879 A62 $100 on $1 (#551) .15 .85
a. Perf. 11 40.00 40.00
880 A63 $100 on $2 (C) (#566) .15 .15

880A A82 $50,000 on $20,000 (#788) .85 .35
880B A82 $100,000 on $30,000 (V) (#789) 2.00 .65

Wmk. 261

881 A39 10c on 2½c (#405) .40 4.00
882 A39 50c on ½c (#402) .15 .85
Nos. 828-882 (61) 288.45 298.45

Characters at left express the new value. Style of characters and numerals varies.

Nos. Q7 to Q9 Surcharged in Black or Carmine

改作郵票 金圓伍佰圓 500.00

1948 Unwmk. Perf. 12½

883 PP2 $200 on $3000 red org .15 .15
884 PP2 $500 on $5000 dk bl (C) .15 .15
885 PP2 $1000 on $10,000 vio .15 .15
Set value .40 .40

Nos. 788-791 Surcharged in Gold Yuan in Red (Nos. 885A, 885D-885E) or Black (Nos. 885B-885C) at Foochow

金圓 念萬圓 200000

1949, Apr. 30 Unwmk. Perf. 14

885A $20,000 on $40,000 11.00 13.00
885B $50,000 on $30,000 11.00 13.00
885C $100,000 on $20,000 11.00 13.00
885D $200,000 on $40,000 11.00 13.00
885E $200,000 on $50,000 11.00 13.00
Nos. 885A-885E (5) 55.00 65.00

Issued in Fukien Postal District.

Dr. Sun Yat-sen — A94

1949 Unwmk. Engr. Perf. 14
Without Gum

886 A94 $1 orange .35 .35
887 A94 $10 green .35 .35
888 A94 $20 vio brown .35 .35
889 A94 $50 dk Prus grn .35 .35
890 A94 $100 org brn .35 .35
891 A94 $200 red org .35 .35
892 A94 $500 rose lilac .35 .35
893 A94 $800 car rose .35 .45
894 A94 $1000 blue .35 .35

Redrawn
Engr.
Perf. 12½

895 A94 $10 green .35 2.25
a. Perf. 14 2.50 3.50
896 A94 $20 violet brn .35 .35
a. Perf. 14 .65 1.65
Nos. 886-896 (11) 3.85 .75

Small "T" at left of necktie on #895-896a.

Redrawn

1949 Litho. Perf. 12½
Without Gum

897 A94 $50 grnsh gray .15 1.40
898 A94 $100 dk org brn .15 .20
899 A94 $200 orange red .15 1.40
900 A94 $500 rose lilac .15 .15
901 A94 $1000 deep blue .15 .25
902 A94 $2000 violet .15 .15
903 A94 $5000 light blue .15 .15
904 A94 $10,000 sepia .15 .15
905 A94 $20,000 apple grn .15 .25
906 A94 $50,000 rose pink .15 .20
907 A94 $80,000 brn red .45 .65
908 A94 $100,000 bl grn .20 .20
Set value 1.40
Nos. 897-908 (12) 5.15

Diagonal lines have been added to the background of the redrawn design.
Zeros for "cents" omitted on No. 908.
See Nos. 973-981. For surcharges see Nos. 991-1006, 1057-1060, Fukien 13-17, Szechwan 51, Tsingtau 1-4, Yunnan 63-65, 68, 70, People's Republic of China 4L34-4L44, 4L48-4L60, 5L43-5L50, 5L54-5L59, 5L91-5L95, 6L1-6L16, 6L23-6L26, 6L30-6L31, 7L6-7L8, 7L13-7L16, 8L12-8L13, 8L48-8L51.

50

Plane, Train and Ship — A95

Two types, 50c on $20:
I - Thick numerals in "20." Vertical stroke in lower right corner of vignette. (Dah Tung Book Co.)
II - Thin "20." No vertical stroke in corner. (Central Trust.)

Two types, $2 on $50, $10 on $30, $100 on $50 and $300 on $50:
III - "Y" in lower right corner of vignette. (Dah Yeh Printing Co.)
IV - No "Y" in corner. (Dah Tung, Central Trust or Chung Ming.)

Two types, $50 on $300 and $1000 on $100:
V - Projection on left frame column below foliate ornament. (Dah Yeh Printing Co.)
VI - No projection. (Dah Tung Book Co.)

Gold Yuan Surcharge in Black or Other Colors on Revenue Stamps Type A95

Litho.; Nos. 923, 933, 935-936 Engr.
1949 Perf. 12½, 13, 14
Without Gum

913 50c on $20 red brn, I .15 .15
a. 50c on $20 brown, II .15 .15
914 $1 on $15 red org .15 .15
915 $2 on $50 dk bl, IV (C) .15 .15
a. Type III .25 .25
916 $3 on $50 dk bl (Bl) .15 .15
917 $3 on $50 dk bl .15 .15
918 $5 on $500 brn .15 .15
919 $10 on $30 dk vio, III (Bl) .15 .15
a. Type IV .45 .45
b. Double surcharge, IV
920 $15 on $20 org brn (Bl) .15 .15
921 $25 on $20 org brn (G) .15 .15
922 $50 on $50 dk bl (R O) .15 .15
923 $50 on $300 grn, VI (C) .15 .15
a. $50 on $300 yel grn, V (C) .15 .15
924 $80 on $50 dk bl (Dk Br) .15 .15
925 $100 on $50 dk bl, IV .15 .15
a. Type III 2.25 7.50
926 $200 on $50 dk bl .15 .15
927 $200 on $500 brn (Bl) .15 .15
928 $300 on $50 dk bl, III (C) .15 .15
a. Type IV .65 1.10
929 $300 on $50 dk bl (Br) .60 .60
930 $500 on $15 red org (Bl) .25 .25
931 $500 on $30 dk vio .25 .25
932 $1000 on $50 dk bl (C) .30 .30
933 $1000 on $100 ol grn, V .30 .30
a. Type VI 2.75 5.00
934 $1500 on $50 dk bl (Bl) 1.50 1.50
935 $2000 on $300 grn (Bl) .30 .30
a. Horiz. pair, imperf. between
936 $5000 on $100 ol grn (C) 250.00
Set value, #913-935 5.00 5.10

No. 936 was officially authorized, but never issued.

Key pattern of overprinted border inverted and in 2 or 3 detached sections at top and bottom in Blue, Black or Green

1949 Hankow Prints Litho.
Without Gum
Type A95

937 $50 on $10 (Bk) 6.50 6.50
938 $100 on $10 7.75 7.75
939 $500 on $10 (Bk) 5.50 4.50
940 $1000 on $10 4.50 4.50
941 $5000 on $20 11.00 11.00
942 $10,000 on $20 (Bk) 11.00 6.50
943 $50,000 on $20 12.00 11.00
944 $100,000 on $20 (Bk) 16.00 11.00
945 $500,000 on $20 225.00 110.00
946 $2,000,000 on $20 (G) 550.00 165.00
947 $5,000,000 on $20 1,000. 325.00
Nos. 937-944 (8) 74.25 62.75

The $10 stamp is slate green, the $20 red brown.
The basic revenue stamps of Nos. 915-947 were the work of several printers. There are three main types, differing in the bottom label. Nos. 922 and 925 are in a second type: Nos. 923 and 930 in a third. Varieties of paper, color and overprint exist.
Counterfeits exist of Nos. 945-947.
For surcharges and overprints see Nos. 960-970, C63, E13, F3, J122-J126, Hopeh 1-2, People's Republic of China 5L51-5L53, 6L17-6L21.

Redrawn Coarse Impression

1949 Litho.
Without Gum
Size: 18¼x20¾mm

951 A94 $50 green .35 21.00
952 A94 $1000 dp blue .40 .25
953 A94 $5000 carmine .40 .25
954 A94 $10,000 brown 1.10 3.50
955 A94 $20,000 orange .85 .55
956 A94 $50,000 blue 1.10 1.10
957 A94 $200,000 violet 2.25 1.40
958 A94 $500,000 vio brn 3.50 .65
Nos. 951-958 (8) 9.95 28.70

Zeros for "cents" omitted on Nos. 957-958.
See surcharge note following No. 900.

Locomotive and Ship — A96

1949, May 1 Litho. Perf. 12½
Without Gum

959 A96 orange 1.65 1.10
a. Rouletted 8.75 4.00

Nos. 959, C62, E12 and F2 were printed without denomination and sold at the daily rate of the yuan. This was necessitated by the gold yuan inflation.
For surcharges and overprints see Nos. 1130, 1213, Taiwan 97, Fukien 18, Kansu 1, People's Republic of China 24-29, 101-104, 4L31-4L33, 4L45-4L47, 4L61-4L62, 7L9-7L12, 8L52-8L54.

Revenue Stamps Overprinted in Black

1949, May Perf. 12½, 13, 14
Without Gum

960 A95 $30 dark violet 70.00 50.00

Engr.

961 A95 $200 violet brown 9.00 5.50
962 A95 $500 dark green 12.00 9.00
Nos. 960-962 (3) 91.00 64.50

A similar overprint appears on #C63, E13, F3, differing in 2nd and 3rd characters of bottom row.

Silver Yuan Surcharge in Black or Other Colors

10

1949 Litho.

963 A95 1c on $5000 brn (G) 5.00 2.25
964 A95 4c on $100 ol grn (Bl) 2.25 .90
965 A95 4c on $3000 org) 2.25 .55
966 A95 10c on $50 dk bl (RV) 3.50 .65
967 A95 10c on $1000 car 4.50 .90
a. Inverted surcharge 60.00
968 A95 20c on $1000 red (V) 4.50 1.65
b. Inverted surcharge 27.50
968A A95 50c on $30 dk vio (C) 27.50 2.25
969 A95 50c on $50 dk bl (C) 5.50 1.10
970 A95 $1 on $50 dk bl 10.00 10.00
Nos. 963-970 (9) 65.00 20.25

Nos. 963-965 and 967 are engraved.

Sun Type of 1949 Redrawn
Coarse Impression

1949 Perf. 12½, 13 or Compound

973 A94 1c apple green 16.00 1.75
974 A94 2c orange 3.50 2.00
975 A94 4c blue green .15 .15
976 A94 10c deep lilac .15 .20
977 A94 16c orange red .45 2.25
978 A94 20c blue .25 .25
979 A94 50c dk brown 1.40 5.00
980 A94 100c deep blue 225.00 200.00
981 A94 500c scarlet 250.00 225.00
Nos. 973-981 (9) 496.90 436.60

For surcharges see Nos. 1057-1060.

Flying Geese Over Globe — A97

Pigeons, Globe and Wreath — A98

1949, May Litho. Perf. 12½
Without Gum

984 A97 $1 brown org 4.50 6.00
985 A97 $2 blue 35.00 9.00
986 A97 $5 car rose 35.00 11.00
987 A97 $10 blue grn 35.00 25.00
Nos. 984-987 (4) 109.50 51.00

Five other denominations - 10c, 16c, 50c, $20 and $50 - were also printed at Shanghai, but were not issued.
For surcharges see Nos. 1007-1011, 1042-1045, 1061-1063, People's Republic of China 49-56, 5LQ17-5LQ26, 7L17-7L18, 8L14-8L16.

Engraved and Typographed
1949, Aug. 1 Without Gum Imperf.

988 A98 $1 org red & blk 5.50 7.00

75th anniv. of the UPU.
Exists with black denomination omitted.

Summer Palace, Peiping — A99

Bronze Bull and Kunming Lake — A100

Engraved and Typographed
1949, Aug. Rouletted
Without Gum

989 A99 15c org brn & grn 2.50 4.00
990 A100 40c dl grn & car 2.75 4.00
a. 2nd and 3rd characters at top transposed 65.00 80.00

Silver Yuan Surcharge in Black on 1949 Sun Yat-sen Issues

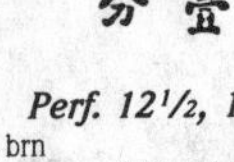

1949 Perf. 12½, 14

991 A94 1c on $100 org brn (890) 8.50 4.00
992 A94 1c on $100 dk org brn (898) 8.50 4.00
993 A94 2½c on $500 rose lil (892) 11.00 4.50
a. Inverted surcharge 35.00
994 A94 2½c on $500 rose lil (900) 11.00 5.00
995 A94 15c on $10 grn (887) 17.50 17.50
a. Inverted surcharge 40.00

996 A94 15c on $20 vio brn (896) 25.00 27.50
Nos. 991-996 (6) 81.50 62.50

5 伍分

Silver Yuan Surcharge in Black or Carmine

997 A94 2½c on $50 grn (951) 1.65 1.65
998 A94 2½c on $50,000 bl (956) 4.50 1.65
999 A94 5c on $1000 dp bl (952) (C) 3.50 1.65
1000 A94 5c on $20,000 org (955) 2.25 1.40
1001 A94 5c on $200,000 vio (957) (C) 3.50 1.40
1002 A94 5c on $500,000 vio brn (958) 2.25 1.40
1003 A94 10c on $5000 car (953) 6.50 3.50
1004 A94 10c on $10,000 brn (954) 6.50 3.50
1005 A94 15c on $200 red org (891) 8.00 5.50
1006 A94 25c on $100 dk org brn (896) 16.00 13.00
Nos. 997-1006 (10) 54.65 34.65

REPUBLIC OF CHINA

ri-'pə-blik of 'chī-nə

(Taiwan)

LOCATION — Taiwan (Formosa) (since 1949)
GOVT. — Republic
AREA — 13,892 sq. mi.
POP. — 16,700,000 (est. 1978)
CAPITAL — Taipei

Stamps issued and used in Taiwan after Communist forces occupied the Chinese mainland include Taiwan Nos. 91-96, 101-103, J10-J17.

Catalogue values for unused stamps in this country are for Never Hinged items, beginning with Scott 1124 in the regular postage section, Scott C69 in the airpost section, and Scott J142 in the postage due section.

Watermarks

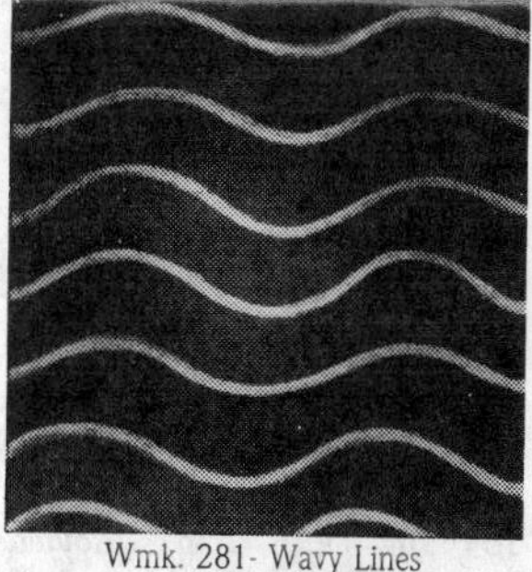

Wmk. 281- Wavy Lines

Wmk. 323- Seal Character (found with "Yu" in various arrangements)

Wmk. 368- JEZ Multiple

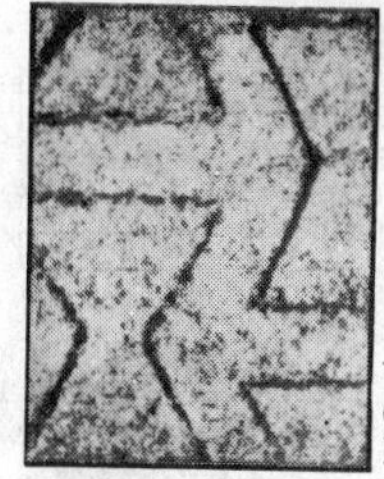

Wmk. 370- Geometrical Design

壹 臺
圓 幣
1.00

Type of 1949 with Value Omitted Surcharged in Various Colors

1950, Jan. 1 Unwmk. *Perf. 12½*

1007 A97 $1 green (Bk) 150.00 5.00
1008 A97 $2 green (C) 150.00 12.50
1009 A97 $5 green (V) 1,500. 42.50
1010 A97 $10 green (Br) 1,400. 65.00
1011 A97 $20 green (Dk Bl) 3,000. 475.00
Nos. 1007-1011 (5) 6,200. 600.00

Two printings of the $1 and $2 show minor differences.

Cheng Ch'eng-kung (Koxinga) — A101

1950, June 26 Typo. *Rouletted*
Without Gum

1012 A101 3c dk gray grn .90 1.25
1013 A101 10c orange brn .90 .15
1014 A101 15c orange yel 15.00 3.00
1015 A101 20c emerald 2.50 .15
1016 A101 30c claret 32.50 15.00
1017 A101 40c red orange 3.75 .15
1018 A101 50c chocolate 7.75 .80
1019 A101 80c carmine 7.75 3.00
1020 A101 $1 ultra 8.25 1.25
1021 A101 $1.50 green 24.00 2.75
1022 A101 $1.60 blue 32.50 2.75
1023 A101 $2 red violet 40.00 3.75
1024 A101 $5 aqua 125.00 11.00
Nos. 1012-1024 (13) 300.80 45.00

Part perf pairs exist of the 10c, 20c, 80c.
For surcharges see Nos. 1070-1072, 1105-1108, 1118-1119.

Nos. 751, 753, 788-791, 793, 795-799 Surcharged in Carmine or Black

1950, Mar. 25 Engr. *Perf. 14*

1025 A82 3c on $30,000 4.75 2.25
1026 A82 3c on $40,000 (C) 4.75 2.25
1027 A82 3c on $50,000 (C) 6.00 3.00
1028 A82 5c on $200,000 6.00 2.25
1029 A82 10c on $4000 12.00 4.50
1030 A82 10c on $6000 19.00 4.50
1031 A82 10c on $20,000 19.00 4.50
1032 A82 10c on $2,000,000 19.00 4.50
1033 A82 20c on $500,000 45.00 4.50
1034 A82 20c on $1,000,000 57.50 8.00
1035 A82 30c on $3,000,000 65.00 10.00
1036 A82 50c on $5,000,000 (C) 125.00 10.00
Nos. 1025-1036 (12) 383.00 60.25

Inverted Surcharge

1029a A82 10c on $4000 140.00
1030a A82 10c on $6000 325.00
1032a A82 10c on $2,000,000 190.00
1033a A82 20c on $500,000 250.00
1034a A82 20c on $1,000,000 250.00

No. 1031 exists with inverted surcharge.

Allegory of Election — A102

Perf. 12x12½, Imperf.
1951, Mar. 20 Engr. Unwmk.
Without Gum

1037 A102 40c carmine 12.50 .75
a. Horiz. pair, imperf. btwn. 90.00
1038 A102 $1 dp blue 22.50 1.75
1039 A102 $1.60 purple 32.50 3.25
1040 A102 $2 brown 52.50 5.25
Nos. 1037-1040 (4) 120.00 11.00

Souvenir Sheet
Imperf

1041 A102 $2 dp blue grn *400.00 400.00*

Adoption of local self-government in Taiwan.

Type A97 Surcharged A103

Farmer and Scroll Announcing Tax Reduction A104

Surcharge in Various Colors

1951, July 19 *Perf. 12½*
Without Gum

1042 A103 $5 green (R Br) 32.50 10.00
1043 A103 $10 green (Bk) 87.50 10.00
1044 A103 $20 green (R) 400.00 22.50
1045 A103 $50 green (P) 725.00 80.00
Nos. 1042-1045 (4) 1,245. 122.50

1952, Jan. 1 *Perf. 14*
Without Gum

1046 A104 20c red orange 6.75 2.25
1047 A104 40c dk green 14.00 3.25
1048 A104 $1 brown 17.50 7.75
1049 A104 $1.40 dp blue 27.50 6.50
1050 A104 $2 dk gray 52.50 22.50
1051 A104 $5 brown car 67.50 12.50
Nos. 1046-1051 (6) 185.75 54.75

Land tax reduction of 37.5% in Taiwan.
Value, imperf. set, $500.

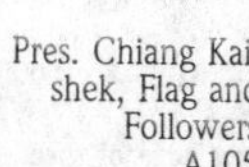

Pres. Chiang Kai-shek, Flag and Followers A105

1952, Mar. 1 Unwmk. *Perf. 14*
Without Gum
Flag in Violet Blue and Carmine

1052 A105 40c rose car 8.50 1.50
a. Vert. pair, imperf. btwn. 85.00
1053 A105 $1 dp green 15.00 3.75
1054 A105 $1.60 brown org 32.50 3.00
a. Horiz. pair, imperf. btwn. 175.00
1055 A105 $2 brt blue 52.50 13.00
1056 A105 $5 violet brn 60.00 6.25
Nos. 1052-1056 (5) 168.50 27.50

2nd anniv. of Chiang Kai-shek's return to the presidency.
Value, imperf. set, $325.
See Nos. 1064-1069.

叁 臺
分 幣

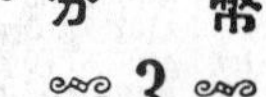

Nos. 975-976, 978-979 Surcharged in Black

1952 *Perf. 12½*

1057 A94 3c on 4c bl grn 4.00 4.00
1058 A94 3c on 10c dp lil 4.00 4.00
a. Inverted surcharge
1059 A94 3c on 20c blue 4.00 4.00
1060 A94 3c on 50c dk brn 4.00 4.00
Nos. 1057-1060 (4) 16.00 16.00

圓拾壹幣

Geese Type of 1949 with Value Omitted Surcharged

1952, Dec. 8

1061 A97 $10 green (P) 60.00 10.00
1062 A97 $20 green (R) 225.00 24.00
1063 A97 $50 green (Bk) 1,300. 675.00

Chiang Type of 1952
Redrawn
Perf. 12½
1953, Mar. 1 Engr. Unwmk.
Without Gum
Flag in Dark Blue & Carmine

1064 A105 10c red orange 17.50 1.75
1065 A105 20c green 17.50 1.75
1066 A105 40c rose pink 32.50 2.50
1067 A105 $1.40 blue 57.50 3.75
1068 A105 $2 brown 80.00 6.75
1069 A105 $5 rose violet 150.00 10.50
Nos. 1064-1069 (6) 355.00 27.00

Chiang Kai-shek's return to presidency, 3rd anniv.
Many differences in redrawn design. Value, imperf. set, $475.

3 cts. 叁分

Nos. 1020, 1014, 1016 and 1022 Surcharged in Various Colors

1953-54 *Rouletted*

1070 A101 3c on $1 ultra (C) 1.10 .80
1070A A101 10c on 15c org yel (G) ('54) 10.00 1.40
1071 A101 10c on 30c cl (Bl) 1.10 .70
1072 A101 20c on $1.60 bl (Bk) 1.10 .70
Nos. 1070-1072 (4) 13.30 3.60

Chinese characters and ornamental device at bottom differ on each value.

Nurse and Patients — A106

1953, July 1 Litho. *Perf. 12½*
Without Gum
Cross in Red, Burelage Color in Italics

1073 A106 40c brown, *buff* 17.50 1.65
1074 A106 $1.60 blue, *bl* 25.00 1.40
1075 A106 $2 green, *yel* 62.50 2.25
1076 A106 $5 red org, *org* 80.00 7.75
Nos. 1073-1076 (4) 185.00 13.05

Chinese Anti-Tuberculosis Association.

Pres. Chiang Kai-shek — A107

1953, Oct. 31 Engr.
Without Gum

1077 A107 10c dk brown 1.50 .15
1078 A107 20c lilac 4.50 .15
1079 A107 40c dp green 4.50 .15

1080 A107 50c dp pink 4.50 .30
1081 A107 80c brown bis 24.00 3.25
1082 A107 $1 dp olive grn 11.00 .20
1083 A107 $1.40 dp blue 20.00 .45
1084 A107 $1.60 dp carmine 24.00 .35
1085 A107 $1.70 apple grn 15.00 3.00
1086 A107 $2 brown 16.00 .20
1087 A107 $3 dark blue 87.50 7.50
1088 A107 $4 aqua 35.00 .75
1089 A107 $5 red orange 17.50 1.00
1090 A107 $10 dk green 32.50 1.50
1091 A107 $20 dk brn lake 87.50 3.25
a. Souvenir folder 400.00
Nos. 1077-1091 (15) 385.00 22.20

67th birthday of Pres. Chiang Kai-shek.
No. 1091a contains Nos. 1077-1091 imperf., arranged in 3 sheets of 5 stamps each.

Silo Highway Bridge A108

Forest of Evergreens A109

Design: $1.60 and $5, Silo bridge, side view.

1954, Jan. 28 Unwmk. *Perf. 12½*
Without Gum
Various Frames

1092 A108 40c vermilion 7.75 1.10
1093 A108 $1.60 blue vio 110.00 2.25
1094 A108 $3.60 sepia 37.50 4.75
1095 A108 $5 magenta 125.00 6.75
a. Souvenir folder *1,000.*
Nos. 1092-1095 (4) 280.25 14.85

Opening of Silo bridge, 1st anniversary.
No. 1095a contains one sheet of 4 containing Nos. 1092-1095 imperforate.

1954, Mar. 12 *Perf. 12x12½*
Without Gum

1096 A109 40c shown 32.50 .85
1097 A109 $10 Nursery 95.00 5.50

Issued to publicize forest conservation.

Runner — A110

Globe, Bridge and Ship — A111

1954, Mar. 29
Without Gum

1098 A110 40c dp ultra 24.00 2.00
1099 A110 $5 carmine 62.50 8.00

11th Youth Day, Mar. 29, 1954.

1954, Oct. 21 *Perf. 12*
Without Gum

1100 A111 40c red orange 15.00 .60
1101 A111 $5 deep blue 12.00 3.00

2nd Overseas Chinese Day, Oct. 21, 1954.

Ex-Prisoner with Broken Chains — A112

Designs: $1, Ex-prisoner with torch and flag, UN emblem. $1.60, Torch and date.

1955, Jan. 23

1102 A112 40c blue green 1.90 .80
a. Vert. pair, imperf. btwn. 150.00
1103 A112 $1 sepia 13.00 5.00
1104 A112 $1.60 lake 17.00 4.25
Nos. 1102-1104 (3) 31.90 10.05

Honoring Chinese who fought on the side of the North Korean army, who, when released January 23, 1955, chose to return to the Republic of China.

Nos. 1019-1021, 1017 Surcharged in Brown, Blue or Green:

a b

c

1955 *Rouletted*

1105 A101(a) 3c on $1 (Br) 3.00 .75
1106 A101(b) 10c on 80c (Bl) 3.00 .75
1107 A101(b) 10c on $1.50 (Bl) 3.00 .75
1108 A101(c) 20c on 40c (G) 3.00 .75
Nos. 1105-1108 (4) 12.00 3.00

Hand Planting Evergreen Tree — A113

Chiang Kai-shek, Flags, Building — A114

Design: $50, Seedling and map of Taiwan.

1955, Apr. 1 *Perf. 12*
Without Gum

1109 A113 $20 dp carmine 26.00 1.75
1110 A113 $50 blue 62.50 4.25

Issued to publicize forest conservation.

1955, May 20 Engr. *Perf. 12*
Without Gum

1111 A114 20c olive 3.50 .15
1112 A114 40c blue green 3.25 .15
1113 A114 $2 carmine rose 8.25 .85
1114 A114 $7 dp ultra 12.50 2.00
a. Souv. sheet of 4, #1111-1114, imperf. *165.00 165.00*
Nos. 1111-1114 (4) 27.50 3.15

First anniversary of Pres. Chiang Kai-shek's re-election.
No. 1114a is perf. 12 at right edge of sheet. Value is for sheet with right selvage.

Armed Forces Emblem — A115

1955, Sept. 3
Without Gum

1115 A115 40c dk blue 1.25 .30
1116 A115 $2 orange ver 15.00 .70
1117 A115 $7 blue green 15.00 3.00
a. Sheet of 3, #1115-1117, imperf. *425.00 425.00*
Nos. 1115-1117 (3) 31.25 4.00

Armed Forces Day, Sept. 3.
No. 1117a is perf. 12 at right edge of sheet. Value is for sheet with right selvage.

Nos. 1017, 1018 and C64 Surcharged in Magenta

1955 Typo. *Rouletted*

1118 A101 20c on 40c red orange 4.50 .45
1119 A101 20c on 50c chocolate 4.50 .45
1120 AP6 20c on 60c dp blue 4.50 .45
Nos. 1118-1120 (3) 13.50 1.35

Flags of UN and China A116

1955, Oct. 24 Engr. *Perf. 11½*
Without Gum

1121 A116 40c dk blue 2.50 .15
1122 A116 $2 dk car rose 7.00 1.00
1123 A116 $7 slate green 8.75 2.25
Nos. 1121-1123 (3) 18.25 3.40

10th anniv. of the UN, Oct. 24, 1955.

Catalogue values for unused stamps in this section, from this point to the end of the section, are for Never Hinged items.

Pres. Chiang Kai-shek A117

Birthplace of Sun Yat-sen A118

1955, Oct. 31 Photo. *Perf. 13½*

1124 A117 40c dk bl, red & brn 3.75 .15
1125 A117 $2 grn, red & dk bl 11.00 1.10
1126 A117 $7 brn, red & grn 15.00 2.25
a. Souv. sheet of 3, #1124-1126, imperf. *150.00 150.00*
Nos. 1124-1126 (3) 29.75 3.50

69th birthday of Pres. Chiang Kai-shek.
No. 1126a is perf. 12 at right edge of sheet. Value is for sheet with right selvage.

1955, Nov. 12 Engr. *Perf. 12*
Without Gum

1127 A118 40c blue 2.50 .45
1128 A118 $2 red brown 5.75 1.40
1129 A118 $7 rose lake 10.00 2.50
Nos. 1127-1129 (3) 18.25 4.35

90th anniversary, birth of Sun Yat-sen.

No. 959a Surcharged in Bright Green

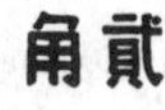

1956 Litho. *Rouletted*

1130 A96 20c on orange .30 .15

See No. 1213.

China Map and Transportation Methods — A119

Wmk. 281
1956, Mar. 20 Engr. *Perf. 12*
Without Gum

1131 A119 40c dk carmine 1.25 .15
1132 A119 $1 intense blk 2.50 .75
1133 A119 $1.60 chocolate 4.75 .30
1134 A119 $2 dk green 6.50 .75
Nos. 1131-1134 (4) 15.00 1.95

60th anniv. of the founding of the modern Chinese postal system.

Souvenir Sheets
Imperf

1135 A119 $2 magenta *45.00 20.00*
1136 A119 $2 red *45.00 20.00*

Exhib. for the 60th anniv. of the modern Chinese postal system, Mar. 20, 1956.

Children at Play A120

Early and Modern Locomotives A121

1956, Apr. 4 Unwmk. *Perf. 12*
Without Gum

1137 A120 40c emerald 1.10 .15
1138 A120 $1.60 dk blue 3.25 .20
1139 A120 $2 dk carmine 3.75 1.10
Nos. 1137-1139 (3) 8.10 1.45

Children's Day, Apr. 4, 1956.

1956, June 9 Wmk. 281 Vert.
Without Gum

1140 A121 40c rose car 2.50 .20
1141 A121 $2 blue 3.25 .35
1142 A121 $8 green 9.25 1.75
Nos. 1140-1142 (3) 15.00 2.30

75th anniversary of Chinese Railroads.

Pres. Chiang Kai-shek
A122 A123

A124

Various Portraits of Chiang
Perf. 14½x13½, 14½ (A123), 13½x14½

1956, Oct. 31 Photo. Unwmk.

1143 A122 20c red orange 2.75 .15
1144 A122 40c carmine rose 4.75 .15
1145 A123 $1 brt ultra 5.75 .20
1146 A123 $1.60 red lilac 7.00 .20
1147 A124 $2 red brown 14.00 .20
1148 A124 $8 brt grnsh blue 35.00 1.10
Nos. 1143-1148 (6) 69.25 2.00

70th birthday of Pres. Chiang Kai-shek.

Types of Special Delivery, Air Post and Registration Stamps of 1949 Surcharged in Black or Maroon

a b c

1956 Unwmk. Litho. *Rouletted*
Without Gum

1150 SD2(a) 3c red violet 1.00 .25
a. Perf. 12½ 3.00 .40
1151 AP5(b) 3c blue green (M) 1.00 .25
1152 R2(c) 10c brt red 1.00 .25
Nos. 1150-1152 (3) 3.00 .75

Telecommunications Emblem and Radio Tower — A125

Wmk. 281
1956, Dec. 28 Engr. *Perf. 12*
Without Gum
1153 A125 40c deep ultra .40 .15
1154 A125 $1.40 carmine .80 .15
1155 A125 $1.60 dark green 1.00 .15
1156 A125 $2 chocolate 5.75 .50
Nos. 1153-1156 (4) 7.95 .95

Chinese telegraph service, 75th anniv.

Map of China — A126

Mother Instructing Mencius — A127

Pin Perf., Perf. 12x12½
1957 Litho. Wmk. 281
Without Gum
1157 A126 3c brt blue 1.10 .15
1158 A126 10c violet 1.10 .15
1159 A126 20c red orange 1.10 .15
1160 A126 40c rose red 1.10 .15
Unwmk.
1161 A126 $1 orange brown 1.90 .15
1162 A126 $1.60 green 2.50 .15
Nos. 1157-1162 (6) 8.80
Set value .65

Map inscription reads: "Recovery of Mainland." See Nos. 1177-1182.

Unwmk.
1957, May 12 Engr. *Perf. 12*

Design: $3, Mother tattooing Yueh Fei.

Without Gum
1163 A127 40c green .85 .25
1164 A127 $3 redsh brown 2.25 .50

Issued to honor Mother's Day, 1957.

Badge of Chinese Boy Scouts A128

1957, Aug. 11
Without Gum
1165 A128 40c lilac .70 .20
1166 A128 $1 green 1.10 .30
1167 A128 $1.60 dk blue 1.65 .40
Nos. 1165-1167 (3) 3.45 .90

Cent. of the birth of Lord Baden-Powell and to publicize the World Scout Jubilee Jamboree, England, Aug. 1-12.

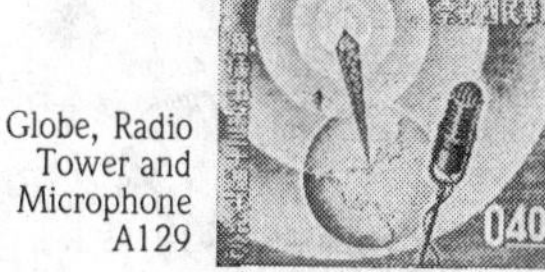
Globe, Radio Tower and Microphone A129

1957, Sept. 16
Without Gum
1168 A129 40c vermilion .35 .20
1169 A129 50c brt rose lilac .75 .35
1170 A129 $3.50 dark blue 1.90 .60
Nos. 1168-1170 (3) 3.00 1.15

30th anniv. of Chinese broadcasting.

Map of Taiwan — A130

1957, Oct. 26
Without Gum
1171 A130 40c blue green 2.00 .25
1172 A130 $1.40 lt ultra 5.25 1.10
1173 A130 $2 gray 6.75 1.65
Nos. 1171-1173 (3) 14.00 3.00

Start of construction on the Cross Island Highway, Taiwan.

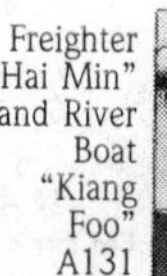

Freighter "Hai Min" and River Boat "Kiang Foo" A131

1957, Dec. 16 Engr. *Perf. 12*
Without Gum
1174 A131 40c deep ultra .40 .15
1175 A131 80c rose lake 1.00 .30
1176 A131 $2.80 vermilion 2.50 .90
Nos. 1174-1176 (3) 3.90 1.35

85th anniv. of the establishment of the China Merchants Steam Navigation Co.

Type of 1957
Pin Perf., Perf. 12x12½
1957, Dec. 25 Typo. Unwmk.
Without Gum
Dark Blue Frames
1177 A126 3c brt blue .85 .15
1178 A126 10c violet .85 .15
1179 A126 20c brick red .85 .15
1180 A126 40c rose red 2.00 .15
1181 A126 $1 dp org brn 2.00 .15
1182 A126 $1.60 dp green 3.00 .15
Nos. 1177-1182 (6) 9.55
Set value .70

Butterfly A132

Mme. Chiang Kai-shek Orchid A133

Perf. 13½
1958, Mar. 20 Unwmk. Photo.
Various Insects in Natural Colors
1183 A132 10c pale grn, grn & blk 1.90 .20
1184 A132 40c lem, pink, grn & blk 1.90 .40
1185 A132 $1 yel grn & mar 2.25 .40
1186 A132 $1.40 yel, org & blk 3.00 .50
1187 A132 $1.60 pale brn & dk pur 3.50 .50
1188 A132 $2 brt yel, org & blk 4.50 .75
Nos. 1183-1188 (6) 17.05 2.75

1958, Mar. 20

Orchids: 20c, Formosan Wilson, horiz. $1.40, Klotzsch. $3, Fitzgerald, horiz.

Orchids in Natural Colors
1189 A133 20c chocolate 1.75 .20
1190 A133 40c purple 1.75 .20
1191 A133 $1.40 dk vio brn 3.50 .35
1192 A133 $3 dark blue 5.25 .75
Nos. 1189-1192 (4) 12.25 1.50

World Health Organization Emblem A134

1958, May 28 Engr. *Perf. 12*
Without Gum
1193 A134 40c dark blue .50 .15
1194 A134 $1.60 brick red .50 .15
1195 A134 $2 deep red lilac .70 .50
Nos. 1193-1195 (3) 1.70 .80

10th anniv. of the WHO.

President's Mansion, Taipei — A135

Wmk. 323
1958, Sept. 20 Engr. *Perf. 12*
Without Gum
1196 A135 $10 blue green 11.00 .15
a. Granite paper ('63) 7.50 .15
1197 A135 $20 car rose 17.00 .35
a. Granite paper ('63) 12.00 .15
1198 A135 $50 red brown 55.00 2.00
1199 A135 $100 dk blue 95.00 3.50
Nos. 1196-1199 (4) 178.00 6.00

See #1349-1351. For surcharge see #J131.

Taiwan Farm Scene A136

1958, Oct. 1 Unwmk.
Without Gum
1200 A136 20c emerald .45 .25
1201 A136 40c black .45 .25
1202 A136 $1.40 brt magenta 1.75 .25
1203 A136 $3 ultra 4.75 .50
Nos. 1200-1203 (4) 7.40 1.25

10th anniversary of the Joint Commission on Rural Reconstruction.

Pres. Chiang Kai-shek — A137

1958, Oct. 31 Photo. *Perf. 13½*
1204 A137 40c multicolored .90 .35

Pres. Chiang Kai-shek on his 72nd birthday.

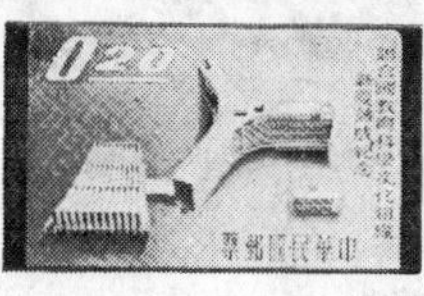
UNESCO Building, Paris A138

1958, Nov. 3 Engr. *Perf. 12*
Without Gum
1205 A138 20c dark blue .15 .15
1206 A138 40c green .25 .15
1207 A138 $1.40 orange ver .90 .45
1208 A138 $3 red lilac 1.40 .65
Nos. 1205-1208 (4) 2.70 1.40

UNESCO Headquarters in Paris opening, Nov. 3.

Flame from Liberty Torch Encircling Globe — A139

1958, Dec. 10 Unwmk.
Without Gum
1209 A139 40c green .15 .15
1210 A139 60c gray brown .20 .15
1211 A139 $1 carmine .52 .15
1212 A139 $3 ultra 1.00 .40
Nos. 1209-1212 (4) 1.87 .85

10th anniversary of the signing of the Universal Declaration of Human Rights.

0.20
No. 959a Surcharged in Bright Green
貳角

Rouletted
1958, Dec. 11 Litho. Unwmk.
Without Gum
1213 A96 20c on orange .30 .15

Ballot Box, Scales and Constitution A140

1958, Dec. 25 Engr. *Perf. 12*
Without Gum
1214 A140 40c green .50 .25
1215 A140 50c dull pur .70 .25
1216 A140 $1.40 car rose 2.25 .30
1217 A140 $3.50 dk blue 4.00 .90
Nos. 1214-1217 (4) 7.45 1.70

Adoption of the constitution, 10th anniv.

Chu Kwang Tower, Quemoy — A141

1959-60 Wmk. 323 Litho. *Perf. 12*
Without Gum
1218 A141 3c orange .20 .15
1218A A141 5c lt yel grn ('60) .20 .15
1219 A141 10c lilac .20 .15
1220 A141 20c ultra .20 .15
1221 A141 40c brown .40 .15
1222 A141 50c bluish grn .75 .15
1223 A141 $1 rose red 1.40 .15
1224 A141 $1.40 yel grn 1.65 .15
1225 A141 $2 gray grn 1.65 .15
1226 A141 $2.80 rose pink 3.50 .15
1227 A141 $3 slate blue 3.75 .15
Nos. 1218-1227 (11) 13.90 1.65

See Nos. 1270-1283.

ILO Emblem and Headquarters, Geneva A142

1959, June 15 Engr. *Perf. 12*
Without Gum
1228 A142 40c blue .15 .15
1229 A142 $1.60 dk brown .25 .15
1230 A142 $3 brt blue grn .50 .25
1231 A142 $5 orange ver 1.50 .60
Nos. 1228-1231 (4) 2.40 1.15

40th anniversary of the ILO.

Bugler and Tents A143

1959, July 8 **Unwmk.**

Without Gum

1232 A143 40c carmine .40 .25
1233 A143 50c dark blue 1.10 .25
1234 A143 $5 green 3.25 .95
Nos. 1232-1234 (3) 4.75 1.45

10th World Boy Scout Jamboree, Makiling National Park, Philippines, July 17-26.

Inscribed Stone, Mt. Tai-wu, Quemoy — A144

Map of Taiwan Straits A145

1959, Sept. 3 **Engr.** ***Perf. 12***

Without Gum

1235 A144 40c brown .45 .15
1236 A145 $1.40 ultra 1.10 .15
1237 A145 $2 green 2.50 .15
1238 A144 $3 dk blue 3.00 .35
Nos. 1235-1238 (4) 7.05
Set value .70

Defense of Quemoy and Matsu islands.
For overprints see Nos. 1258-1259.

Pigeons Circling Globe A146

1959, Oct. 4

Without Gum

1239 A146 40c blue .20 .15
1240 A146 $1 rose carmine .45 .25
1241 A146 $2 gray brown .70 .15
1242 A146 $3.50 red orange 1.65 .60
Nos. 1239-1242 (4) 3.00 1.15

Intl. Letter Writing Week, Oct. 4-10.

National Taiwan Science Hall, Taipei — A147

1959, Nov. 12 **Photo.** ***Perf. 13x13½***

1243 A147 40c shown 1.00 .25
1244 A147 $3 Front view 2.00 .75

Emblem A148

1959, Dec. 7 **Engr.** ***Perf. 12***

Without Gum

1245 A148 40c blue green .25 .20
1246 A148 $1.60 red lilac .70 .30
1247 A148 $3 orange 1.10 .60
Nos. 1245-1247 (3) 2.05 1.10

Intl. Confederation of Free Trade Unions, 10th anniv.

Sun Yat-sen, Lincoln and Flags A149

Perf. 13½, 12

1959, Dec. 25 **Photo.** **Unwmk.**

1248 A149 40c multicolored .60 .35
1249 A149 $3 multicolored .90 .65

Issued to honor Sun Yat-sen and Abraham Lincoln as "Leaders of Democracy."

Mailman on Motorcycle Delivering Night Mail — A150

Postal Launch A151

1960, Mar. 20 **Engr.** ***Perf. 11½***

Without Gum

1250 A150 $1.40 dk violet brn .75 .20
1251 A151 $1.60 ultra 1.10 .50

Issued to publicize the Prompt Delivery Service.

WRY Uprooted Oak Emblem — A152

1960, Apr. 7 **Photo.** ***Perf. 13***

1252 A152 40c blk, red brn & emer .45 .15
1253 A152 $3 blk, red org & grn .95 .40

Issued to publicize World Refugee Year, July 1, 1959-June 30, 1960.

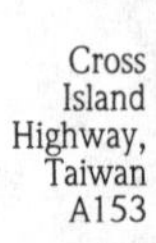

Cross Island Highway, Taiwan A153

Design: $1, $2, Road through tunnel, vert.

Perf. 11½

1960, May 9 **Engr.** **Unwmk.**

Without Gum

1254 A153 40c green .60 .15
1255 A153 $1 dk blue 2.25 .35
1256 A153 $2 brown vio .80 .20
1257 A153 $3 brown 3.00 .25
a. Souv. sheet of 2, #1255, 1257, wmk. 323 *190.00* *75.00*
Nos. 1254-1257 (4) 6.65 .95

Opening of the Cross Island Highway, Taiwan.

Red Overprint on Nos. 1237-1238 Chinese and English: "Welcome U.S. President Dwight D. Eisenhower 1960"

1960, June 18 **Unwmk.** ***Perf. 12***

1258 A145 $2 green 1.25 .30
a. Inverted overprint 200.00 200.00
1259 A144 $3 dk blue 2.50 .50

Eisenhower's visit to China, June 18, 1960.

Phonopost — A154

1960, June 27

Without Gum

1260 A154 $2 red orange 1.10 .35

Phonopost Service of the Chinese armed forces.

Two Horses and Groom, by Han Kan — A155

Paintings from Palace Museum, Taichung: $1, Two Riders, by Wei Yen. $1.60, Flowers and Birds by Hsiao Yung, vert. $2, Pair of Mandarin Ducks by Monk Hui Ch'ung.

1960, Aug. 4 **Photo.** ***Perf. 13***

1261 A155 $1 ol gray, blk & brn 5.00 1.50
1262 A155 $1.40 bis brn, blk & fawn 6.50 1.50
1263 A155 $1.60 multicolored 7.75 1.50
1264 A155 $2 beige, blk & gray grn 14.00 1.90
Nos. 1261-1264 (4) 33.25 6.40

Chinese paintings, 7th-11th centuries.

For other painting types with large straight numerals in the upper corners and large Chinese characters on the side see A186, A241 and A285.

Youth Corps Flag and Summer Activities A156

Reforestation A157

Design: $3, similar to 50c, horiz.

1960, Aug. 20 **Engr.** ***Perf. 12***

Without Gum

1265 A156 50c slate green .30 .15
1266 A156 $3 copper brown 1.10 .55

Summer activities of China Youth Corps.

1960, Aug. 29 **Photo.** ***Perf. 13½x13***

Designs: $2, Protection of forest. $3, Timber industry.

1267 A157 $1 multicolored 1.50 .15
1268 A157 $2 multicolored 3.75 .65
1269 A157 $3 multicolored 3.75 .65
a. Souvenir sheet of 3 24.00 16.00
Nos. 1267-1269 (3) 9.00 1.45

Fifth World Forestry Congress, Seattle, Washington, Aug. 29-Sept. 10.

No. 1269a contains Nos. 1267-1269 assembled as a triptych, 65½x40mm and imperf., but with simulated black perforations.

Chu Kwang Tower, Quemoy — A158

Sports — A159

1960-61 **Wmk. 323** **Litho.** ***Perf. 12***

Without Gum

1270 A158 3c lt red brown .15 .15
1271 A158 40c pale violet .15 .15
1272 A158 50c orange ('61) .15 .15
1273 A158 60c rose lilac .15 .15
1274 A158 80c pale green .25 .15
1275 A158 $1 gray green ('61) 2.00 .15
1276 A158 $1.20 gray olive .95 .15
1277 A158 $1.50 ultra .95 .15
1278 A158 $2 car rose ('61) 2.25 .15
1279 A158 $2.50 pale blue 2.25 .15
1280 A158 $3 bluish green 2.00 .15
1281 A158 $3.20 lt red brown 3.50 .15
1282 A158 $3.60 vio blue ('61) 3.00 .35
1283 A158 $4.50 vermilion 5.75 .50
Nos. 1270-1283 (14) 23.50
Set value 2.00

1962-64

Granite Paper

Without Gum

1270a A158 3c light red brown 1.25 .15
1270B A158 10c emerald ('63) 3.00 .15
1271a A158 40c pale violet 1.25 .15
1274a A158 80c pale green 2.25 .15
1275a A158 $1 gray green ('63) 8.50 .15
1278a A158 $2 carmine rose 9.25 .15
1281a A158 $3.20 red brown ('64) 9.25 .15
1282A A158 $4 brt blue grn 20.00 .25
1283a A158 $4.50 vermilion 9.25 .40
Nos. 1270a-1283a (9) 64.00
Set value 1.25

Two types of No. 1271a: I. Seven lines in "0" of "40." II. Eight lines in "0."

Perf. 12½

1960, Oct. 25 **Photo.** **Unwmk.**

1284 A159 50c Diving .95 .15
1285 A159 80c Discus thrower .95 .20
1286 A159 $2 Basketball 1.50 .30
1287 A159 $2.50 Soccer 2.50 .35
1288 A159 $3 Hurdling 2.75 .55
1289 A159 $3.20 Runner 4.75 .70
Nos. 1284-1289 (6) 13.40 2.25

Bronze Wine Container, 1751-1111 B.C. — A160

Flat Bowl, 1111-771 B.C. — A161

Ancient Chinese Art Treasures: $1, Cauldron, 1111-771 B.C. $1.20, Porcelain vase, 960-1126 A.D. $1.50, Perforated tube, 1111-771 B.C. $2, Jug in shape of monk's cap, 1368-1661 A.D. $2.50, Jade flower vase, 1368-1661, A.D.

1961 **Photo.** ***Perf. 13***

1290 A160 80c lt ol, blk & dk vio 3.00 .30
1291 A160 $1 sal, bl & blk 3.00 .35
1292 A160 $1.20 yel, brn & ultra 4.00 .75
1293 A160 $1.50 lil, bl & sep 4.00 1.00
1294 A160 $2 pale grn, dk grn & red brn 5.25 .75
1295 A160 $2.50 grnsh bl & dk vio 6.00 .85
Nos. 1290-1295 (6) 25.25 4.00

Issue dates: Nos. 1290, 1292, 1295, Feb. 1. Nos. 1291, 1293-1294, May 1.

1961

Designs: 80c, Palace perfumer, 1662-1911. $1, Corn vase, 770-221 B.C. $2, Jade tankard, 960-1126 A.D. $4, Glazed washer, 1127-1279 A.D. $4.50, Jade chimera, 8 B.C.-206 A.D.

1296 A160 80c pink, brn, bl & yel 1.75 .30
1297 A160 $1 cit, blk & brn 5.25 .30
1298 A161 $1.50 sal & ind 5.25 1.50
1299 A160 $2 bl, blk & rose 5.25 1.10
1300 A161 $4 red, blk & bluish gray 17.50 1.10
1301 A161 $4.50 grnsh bl, blk & brn 15.00 3.00
Nos. 1296-1301 (6) 50.00 7.30

Issue dates: Nos. 1296-1298, Aug. 15. Nos. 1299-1301, Sept. 15.

1962

Designs: 80c, Topaz twin wine vessels, 1662-1911 A.D. $1, Squat pouring vase, 1751-1111 B.C. $2.40, Vase, 1368-1661 A.D. $3, Wine vase, 1751-1111 B.C. $3.20, Covered porcelain jar, 1662-1911 A.D. $3.60, Perforated disc, 206 B.C.-8 A.D.

1302 A160	80c	crim, blk & ocher	2.00	.15
1303 A160	$1	blue & vio blk	3.25	.15
1304 A160	$2.40	hn brn, blk & bl	7.75	.50
1305 A160	$3	blue, blk & pink	19.00	1.50
1306 A160	$3.20	ultra, lt grn & red	22.50	.15
1307 A160	$3.60	yel, blk & brn	19.00	1.00
		Nos. 1302-1307 (6)	73.50	3.45

Issue dates: Nos. 1303-1304, 1307, Jan. 15. Nos. 1302, 1305-1306, Feb. 15.

Farmer with Mechanized Plow — A162

Madame Chiang Kai-shek and League Emblem — A163

1961, Feb. 4 Engr. *Perf. 12*
Without Gum

1308 A162	80c	rose violet	1.10	.15
1309 A162	$2	green	3.50	.60
1310 A162	$3.20	vermilion	3.50	.25
		Nos. 1308-1310 (3)	8.10	1.00

1961 agricultural census.

Unwmk.
1961, Mar. 8 Photo. *Perf. 13*
Portrait in Black

1311 A163	80c	lt grn & car rose	1.10	.30
1312 A163	$1	yel grn & car rose	2.50	.60
1313 A163	$2	org brn & car rose	2.50	.60
1314 A163	$3.20	lil & car rose	6.00	1.25
		Nos. 1311-1314 (4)	12.10	2.75

10th anniversary of the Chinese Women's Anti-Aggression League.

Spiny Lobster and Mail Order Service Emblem — A164

Jeme Tien-yow and Pataling Tunnel — A165

1961, Mar. 20 Engr. *Perf. 11½*
Without Gum

1315 A164	$3	slate green	2.50	.35

Issued to publicize the mail order service for consumer goods.

1961, Apr. 26 *Perf. 11½*
Without Gum

Design: $2, Jeme Tien-yow and 1909 locomotive, horiz.

1316 A165	80c	lilac	.65	.15
1317 A165	$2	black	2.75	.60

Centenary of the birth of Jeme Tien-yow, builder of the Peking-Kalgan railroad.

Map of China inscribed: "Recovery of the Mainland" — A166

Pres. Chiang Kai-shek — A167

1961, May 20 Photo. *Perf. 13½*

1318 A166	80c	multicolored	1.40	.25
1319 A167	$2	multicolored	4.75	1.25
a.		Souvenir sheet of 2	14.00	*30.00*

1st anniversary of Pres. Chiang Kai-shek's 3rd term inauguration.

No. 1319a contains one each of Nos. 1318-1319, imperf. with simulated perforations. Without gum.

Convair 880-M, Biplane of 1921 and Flag — A168

1961, July 1 *Perf. 13x12½*

1320 A168	$10	multicolored	3.75	1.50

40th anniversary of civil air service.

Sun Yat-sen and Chiang Kai-shek — A169

Flag and Map of China — A170

Perf. 13½
1961, Oct. 10 Unwmk. Photo.

1321 A169	80c	gray, lt brn & sl	1.10	.15
1322 A170	$5	gray, ultra, red & beige	4.50	1.75
a.		Souvenir sheet of 2	10.00	10.00

50th anniv. of the Republic of China. No. 1322a contains one each of Nos. 1321-1322, imperf. with simulated perforations. No gum.

Green Lake — A171

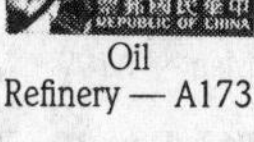

Oil Refinery — A173

Lotus Pond A172

Taiwan Scenery: $2, Sun-Moon Lake. $3.20, Wulai waterfalls.

Perf. 13½x14, 14x13½
1961, Oct. 31 Unwmk.

1323 A171	80c	multicolored	3.00	.20
1324 A172	$1	multicolored	8.75	.75
1325 A172	$2	multicolored	8.75	.75
1326 A171	$3.20	multicolored	20.00	1.10
		Nos. 1323-1326 (4)	40.50	2.80

1961, Nov. 14 *Perf. 11½*

Designs: $1.50, Steel works. $2.50, Aluminum plant. $3.20, Fertilizer plant, horiz.

1327 A173	80c	multicolored	1.10	.15
1328 A173	$1.50	multicolored	3.50	.75
1329 A173	$2.50	multicolored	3.50	.75
1330 A173	$3.20	multicolored	6.75	.65
		Nos. 1327-1330 (4)	14.85	2.30

Chinese industrial development and the Golden Jubilee Convention of the Chinese Institute of Engineers, Nov. 13-16.

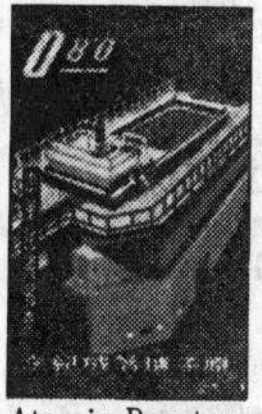

Atomic Reactor, Tsing-Hwa University A174

Atomic Reactor in Operation A175

Design: $3.20, Atomic symbol and laboratory, Tsing-Hwa, horiz.

1961-62 Photo. *Perf. 12½*

1331 A174	80c	multicolored	1.50	.15
1332 A175	$2	multi ('62)	3.25	1.65
1333 A175	$3.20	multi ('62)	5.25	1.10
		Nos. 1331-1333 (3)	10.00	2.90

Inauguration on Apr. 13, 1961, of the 1st Chinese atomic reactor at the National Tsing-Hwa University Institute of Nuclear Science.

Microwave Reflector and Telegraph Wires — A176

Design: $3.20, Microwave parabolic antenna and mountains, horiz.

1961, Dec. 28 *Perf. 12½*

1334 A176	80c	multicolored	.45	.15
1335 A176	$3.20	multicolored	2.50	1.00

80th anniv. of Chinese telecommunications.

Mechanical Postal Equipment and Twine Tying Machine A176a

Perf. 11½
1962, Mar. 20 Engr. Wmk. 323
Without Gum

1336 A176a	80c	chocolate	1.00	.35

Yu Shan Observatory A177

Observation Balloon, Earth and Cumulus Clouds A178

Design: $1, Map showing route of typhoon Pamela, Sept. 1961, horiz.

1962
Without Gum

1337 A177	80c	brown	.40	.15
1338 A178	$1	bluish black	2.75	.45
1339 A178	$2	green	1.65	.90
		Nos. 1337-1339 (3)	4.80	1.50

Issue dates: 80c, $2, Mar. 23; $1, May 7.

World Meteorological Day, Mar. 23.

Child Receiving Milk, UN Emblem A179

1962, Apr. 4
Without Gum

1340 A179	80c	rose red	.30	.15
1341 A179	$3.20	green	2.00	.55
a.		Souvenir sheet of 2	12.00	4.00

15th anniv. of UNICEF. No. 1341a contains one each of Nos. 1340-1341 imperf. with simulated perforations.

Malaria Eradication Emblem — A180

Perf. 12½
1962, Apr. 7 Unwmk. Photo.

1342 A180	80c	dk bl, red & lt grn	.65	.20
1343 A180	$3.60	brn, pink & grn	1.40	1.10

WHO drive to eradicate malaria.

Yu Yu-jen — A181

Cheng Ch'eng-kung (Koxinga) — A182

1962, Apr. 24 *Perf. 13*

1344 A181	80c	gray, blk & pink	1.65	.25

Issued to honor Yu Yu-jen, newspaper reporter, revolutionary leader and co-worker of Sun Yat-sen, on his 84th birthday.

1962, Apr. 29

1345 A182	80c	deep claret	1.10	.30
1346 A182	$2	dark green	3.00	.75

300th anniversary (in 1961) of the recovery of Taiwan from the Dutch by Koxinga.

Emblem of Intl. Cooperative Alliance — A183

Clasped Hands Across Globe — A184

Wmk. 323
1962, July 7 Engr. *Perf. 12*
Without Gum

1347 A183	80c	brown	.55	.15
1348 A184	$2	violet	1.50	.50

Intl. Cooperative Movement and 40th Intl. Cooperative Day, July 7, 1962.

Mansion Type of 1958

1962, July 20
Without Gum

1349 A135	$5	gray green	2.25	.15
1350 A135	$5.60	violet	2.50	.15
1351 A135	$6	orange	2.75	.15
		Nos. 1349-1351 (3)	7.50	.45

1963

Granite Paper

1349a A135 $5 gray green 3.00 .15
1350a A135 $5.60 violet 4.75 .15
1351a A135 $6 orange 5.25 .15
Nos. 1349a-1351a (3) 13.00 .45

"Art and Science" — A185

Designs: $2, "Education," book and UNESCO emblem, horiz. $3.20, "Communications," globes, horiz.

1962, Aug. 28 Wmk. 323 *Perf. 12*

Without Gum

1352 A185 80c lilac rose .30 .15
1353 A185 $2 rose claret 1.65 .50
1354 A185 $3.20 yellow green 1.50 .35
Nos. 1352-1354 (3) 3.45 1.00

UNESCO activities in China.

Emperor T'ai Tsung, T'ang Dynasty, 627-649 A186

Emperors: $2, T'ai Tsu, Sung dynasty, 960-975. $3.20, T'ai Tsu, Yuan dynasty (Genghis Khan), 1206-27. $4, T'ai Tsu, Ming dynasty, 1368-98.

1962, Sept. 20 Photo. Unwmk.

1355 A186 80c multicolored *8.25* *1.50*
1356 A186 $2 multicolored *42.50* *9.25*
1357 A186 $3.20 multicolored *47.50* *10.00*
1358 A186 $4 multicolored *42.50* *9.25*
Nos. 1355-1358 (4) *140.75* *30.00*

Lions International Emblem — A187

1962, Oct. 8 *Perf. 13*

1359 A187 80c multicolored .65 .20
1360 A187 $3.60 multicolored 3.00 1.00
a. Souvenir sheet of 2 15.00 8.00

45th anniv. of Lions Intl. No. 1360a contains one each of Nos. 1359-1360, imperf. with simulated perforations.

Pole Vaulting — A188

Shooting A189

1962, Oct. 25 Unwmk. *Perf. 13*

1361 A188 80c multicolored 1.10 .20
1362 A189 $3.20 multicolored 2.25 .45

Sports meet.

Young Farmers and 4-H Emblem A190

Flag, Liner of China Merchants' Steam Navigation Co. A191

Design: $3.20, 4-H emblem and rice.

Wmk. 323

1962, Dec. 7 Engr. *Perf. 12*

Without Gum

1363 A190 80c carmine .50 .20
1364 A190 $3.20 green 1.50 .55
a. Souvenir sheet of 2 15.00 10.00

10th anniv. of the 4-H Club in China. No. 1364a contains one each of Nos. 1363-1364, imperf. with simulated perforations.

Perf. 13½

1962, Dec. 16 Unwmk. Photo.

Design: $3.60, Company's Pacific navigation chart and freighter, horiz.

1365 A191 80c multicolored 1.25 .20
1366 A191 $3.60 multicolored 3.75 1.00

90th anniversary of the China Merchants' Steam Navigation Co., Ltd.

Farm Woman, Tractor and Plane Dropping Food over Mainland — A192

Perf. 12½

1963, Mar. 21 Unwmk. Photo.

1367 A192 $10 multicolored 4.50 .90

FAO "Freedom from Hunger" campaign.

Torch, Young Couple and Martyrs' Monument, Canton A193

Perf. 11½

1963, Mar. 29 Wmk. 323 Engr.

Without Gum

1368 A193 80c purple .35 .15
1369 A193 $3.20 green 1.65 .45

Issued for the 20th Youth Day.

Swallows, Pagoda and AOPU Emblem — A194

Designs: $2, Northern gannet, horiz. $6, Japanese crane and pine.

Unwmk.

1963, Apr. 1 Photo. *Perf. 13*

1370 A194 80c multicolored 3.50 .20
1371 A194 $2 multicolored 3.50 .20
1372 A194 $6 multicolored 12.00 3.25
Nos. 1370-1372 (3) 19.00 3.65

1st anniversary of the formation of the Asian-Oceanic Postal Union, AOPU.

Refugee Girl (Li Ying) and Map of China — A195

Refugees Fleeing Mainland A196

Perf. 11½

1963, June 27 Wmk. 323 Engr.

Without Gum

1373 A195 80c bluish black .90 .25
1374 A196 $3.20 dp claret 2.00 .35

1st anniv. of the evacuation of Chinese mainland refugees from Hong Kong to Taiwan. Designs from photographs of refugees.

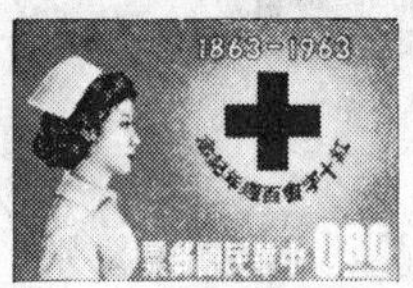

Nurse and Red Cross — A197

Design: $10, Globe and Red Cross.

Perf. 12½

1963, Sept. 1 Unwmk. Photo.

1375 A197 80c black & carmine 3.00 .25
1376 A197 $10 slate, gray & car 8.50 2.50

Centenary of International Red Cross.

Basketball Player, Stadium and Asian Cup — A198

Design: $2, Hands reaching for ball and Asian cup.

Wmk. 323

1963, Nov. 20 Engr. *Perf. 12*

Without Gum

1377 A198 80c lilac rose .40 .15
1378 A198 $2 violet 2.25 .75

The 2nd Asian Basketball Championship, Taipei, Nov. 20.

UN Emblem, Torch and Men — A199

Scales and Men of Various Races — A200

1963, Dec. 10 Wmk. 323 *Perf. 11½*

Without Gum

1379 A199 80c brt green .55 .25
1380 A200 $3.20 maroon 1.40 .40

Universal Declaration of Human Rights, 15th anniversary.

Village and Orchids A201

"Kindle the Fire of Conscience" A202

Perf. 13½x13

1963, Dec. 17 Photo. Unwmk.

1381 A201 40c multicolored 1.75 .45
1382 A202 $4.50 multicolored 6.50 2.00

Contribution of the Good-People-Good-Deeds campaign to improve ethical standards.

Sun Yat-sen and Book, "Three Principles of the People" A203

1963, Dec. 25 *Perf. 13*

1383 A203 $5 blue & multi 10.00 1.25

"Land-to-the-Tillers" program, 10th anniv. An 80c was prepared but not issued.

Torch A204

Hands Unchained A205

Perf. 11½

1964, Jan. 23 Wmk. 323 Engr.

Without Gum

1384 A204 80c red orange .35 .20
1385 A205 $3.20 indigo 2.25 .40

Liberty Day, 10th anniversary.

Broadleaf Cactus A206

Wu Chih-hwei A207

Designs: $1, Crab cactus. $3.20, Nopalxochia. $5, Grizzly bear cactus.

Perf. 12½

1964, Feb. 27 Unwmk. Photo.

Plants in Original Colors

1386 A206 80c dp plum & fawn 1.75 .20
1387 A206 $1 dk blue & car 5.00 1.00
1388 A206 $3.20 green 7.50 .20
1389 A206 $5 lilac & yellow 10.50 1.00
Nos. 1386-1389 (4) 24.75 2.40

Perf. 11½

1964, Mar. 25 Engr. Wmk. 323

Without Gum

1390 A207 80c black brown 1.50 .15

Centenary of the birth of Wu Chih-hwei (1865-1953), politician and leader of the Kuomintang.

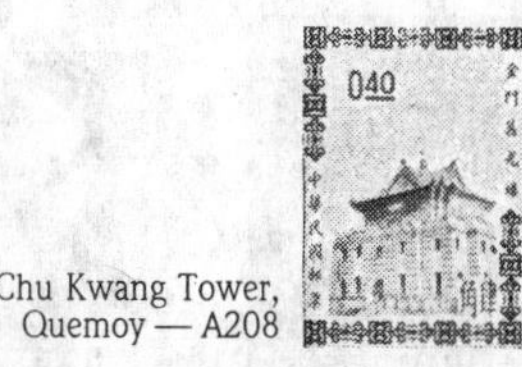

Chu Kwang Tower, Quemoy — A208

Perf. 13x12½

1964-66 Wmk. 323 Litho.

Granite Paper; Without Gum

1391	A208	3c	sepia	.35	.15
1392	A208	5c	brt yel grn ('65)	.35	.15
1393	A208	10c	yellow grn	.35	.15
1394	A208	20c	slate grn ('65)	.35	.15
1395	A208	40c	rose red	.35	.15
1396	A208	50c	brown	.35	.15
1397	A208	80c	orange ('65)	.80	.15
1398	A208	$1	violet ('65)	1.10	.15
1399	A208	$1.50	brt lilac ('66)	1.50	.25
1400	A208	$2	lilac rose	1.50	.15
1401	A208	$2.50	ultra ('65)	1.50	.15
1402	A208	$3	slate	2.75	.15
1403	A208	$3.20	brt blue	3.50	.15
1404	A208	$4	brt green	4.25	.15
		Nos. 1391-1404 (14)		19.00	
		Set value			1.50

Nurses Holding Candles — A209

Florence Nightingale and Student Nurse — A210

1964, May 12 Engr. *Perf. 11½*

Without Gum

1406	A209	80c	violet blue	.95	.30
1407	A210	$4	red	3.00	.55

Issued for Nurses Day.

Shihmen Reservoir A211

Designs: $1, Irrigation system. $3.20, Main dam and power plant. $5, Spillway.

Perf. 12½

1964, June 14 Unwmk. Photo.

1408	A211	80c	multicolored	2.25	.20
1409	A211	$1	multicolored	2.25	.25
1410	A211	$3.20	multicolored	4.00	.55
1411	A211	$5	multicolored	11.00	2.00
		Nos. 1408-1411 (4)		19.50	3.00

Completion of Shihmen Reservoir.

15th Century Ship, Modern Liner — A212

Perf. 11½

1964, July 11 Engr. Wmk. 323

Without Gum

1412	A212	$2	orange	.60	.30
1413	A212	$3.60	brt green	1.25	.50

China's 10th Navigation Day.

Bananas A213

Unwmk.

1964, July 25 Photo. *Perf. 14*

1414	A213	80c	shown	*9.50*	.45
1415	A213	$1	Oranges	*16.00*	1.40
1416	A213	$3.20	Pineapple	*21.00*	.90
1417	A213	$4	Watermelon	*35.00*	2.25
		Nos. 1414-1417 (4)		*81.50*	5.00

Artillery, Warships, Jet Fighters — A214

Perf. 11½

1964, Sept. 3 Wmk. 323 Engr.

Without Gum

1418	A214	80c	dk blue	.60	.15
1419	A214	$6	violet brown	3.25	.60

Issued for the 10th Armed Forces Day.

Unisphere, Flags of China and US — A215

Chinese Pavilion, NY World's Fair — A216

1964, Sept. 10 Photo. Unwmk.

1420	A215	80c	violet & multi	.45	.25
1421	A216	$5	blue & multi	3.50	1.00

NY World's Fair, 1964-65. See #1450-1451.

Cowboy Carrying Calf, and Ranch A217

Bicycling A218

Perf. 11½

1964, Sept. 24 Wmk. 323 Engr.

Without Gum

1422	A217	$2	brown lake	1.25	.20
1423	A217	$4	dark violet blue	3.25	.75

Animal Protection Week, Sept. 24-30.

1964, Oct. 10 Without Gum

Sports: $1, Runner. $3.20, Gymnast on rings. $10, High jump.

1424	A218	80c	violet blue	.55	.15
1425	A218	$1	rose red	.90	.20
1426	A218	$3.20	dull blue grn	2.00	.20
1427	A218	$10	lilac	5.50	1.90
		Nos. 1424-1427 (4)		8.95	2.45

18th Olympic Games, Tokyo, Oct. 10-25.

Hsü Kuang-chi A219

Pharmaceutical Industry A220

Textile Industry — A221

1964, Nov. 8 Engr. *Perf. 11½*

Without Gum

1428	A219	80c	indigo	2.00	.15

Issued to honor Hsü Kuang-chi (1562-1633), scholar and statesman.

1964, Nov. 11 Photo. Unwmk.

Designs: $2, Chemical industry. $3.60, Cement industry.

1429	A220	40c	multi	1.40	.40
1430	A221	$1.50	multi	3.75	1.25
1431	A220	$2	multi	4.25	.50
1432	A221	$3.60	multi	8.50	1.00
		Nos. 1429-1432 (4)		17.90	3.15

Dr. Sun Yat-sen — A222

Eleanor Roosevelt and Scales of Justice — A223

1964, Nov. 24 Engr. Wmk. 323

Without Gum

1433	A222	80c	green	2.25	.30
1434	A222	$3.60	purple	3.50	.50

Founding of the Kuomintang by Sun Yat-sen, 70th anniversary.

Unwmk.

1964, Dec. 10 Photo. *Perf. 13*

1435	A223	$10	violet & brown	1.50	.50

Issued to honor Eleanor Roosevelt (1884-1962) on the 16th anniversary of the Universal Declaration of Human Rights.

Scales, Code Book and Plum Blossom A224

Rotary Emblem and Mainspring A225

Perf. 11½

1965, Jan. 11 Wmk. 323 Engr.

Without Gum

1436	A224	80c	carmine rose	.65	.30
1437	A224	$3.20	dull slate grn	.65	.40

The 20th Judicial Day.

1965, Feb. 23 Wmk. 323 *Perf. 11½*

Without Gum

1438	A225	$1.50	vermilion	.25	.15
1439	A225	$2	emerald	.75	.25
1440	A225	$2.50	blue	1.00	.35
		Nos. 1438-1440 (3)		2.00	.75

Rotary International, 60th anniversary.

Double Carp Design — A226

Madame Chiang Kai-shek — A227

Perf. 11½

1965, Mar. 29 Wmk. 323 Engr.

Granite Paper; Without Gum

1441	A226	$5	purple	14.00	.30
1442	A226	$5.60	dp blue	8.00	4.00
1443	A226	$6	brown	7.00	1.00
1444	A226	$10	lilac rose	16.00	.25
1445	A226	$20	rose car	18.00	.75
1446	A226	$50	green	35.00	2.75
1447	A226	$100	crimson rose	80.00	4.75
		Nos. 1441-1447 (7)		178.00	13.80

1965, Apr. 17 Photo. Unwmk.

1448	A227	$2	multicolored	11.00	.30
1449	A227	$6	salmon & multi	27.50	3.50

Chinese Women's Anti-Aggression League, 15th anniversary.

Unisphere and Chinese Pavilion — A228

"100 Birds Paying Homage to Queen Phoenix" and Unisphere — A229

1965, May 8

1450	A228	$2	blue & multi	9.50	.35
1451	A229	$10	red, ocher & bis	35.00	2.00

New York World's Fair, 1964-65.

ITU Emblem, Old and New Communication Equipment A230

Design: $5, similar to 80c, vert.

Perf. 13½x13, 13x13½

1965, May 17 Photo. Unwmk.

1452	A230	80c	multicolored	.50	.15
1453	A230	$5	multicolored	2.50	.65

Centenary of the ITU.

Red Sea Bream A231

Fish: 80c, White pomfret. $2, Skipjack, vert. $4, Moonfish.

1965, July 1 *Perf. 13*

1454	A231	40c	multicolored	2.00	.60
1455	A231	80c	multicolored	4.25	.60
1456	A231	$2	multicolored	5.50	.75
1457	A231	$4	multicolored	13.00	1.65
		Nos. 1454-1457 (4)		24.75	3.60

Issued for Fishermen's Day.

Confucius A232

ICY Emblem A233

Portraits: $2.50, Yueh Fei. $3.50, Wen Tien-hsiang. $3.60, Mencius.

Perf. 11½

1965-66 Wmk. 323 Engr.

Without Gum

1458	A232	$1	deep carmine	2.25	.35
1459	A232	$2.50	black brown	2.25	.45
1460	A232	$3.50	dark red	4.50	.55
1461	A232	$3.60	dark blue	6.00	.65
		Nos. 1458-1461 (4)		15.00	2.00

Issue dates: Nos. 1458, 1461, Sept. 28, 1965. Nos. 1459-1460, Sept. 3, 1966.

The $2.50 and $3.50 have colored background. See Nos. 1507-1508.

Unwmk.

1965, Oct. 24 Photo. *Perf. 13*

Design: $6, ICY emblem, horiz.

1462 A233 $2 brn, blk & gold	.95	.15
1463 A233 $6 brt grn, red & gold	4.75	1.10

International Cooperation Year, 1965.

Street Crossing, Traffic Light A234

Sun Yat-sen A235

Perf. 11½

1965, Nov. 1 Wmk. 323 Engr.

Without Gum

1464 A234 $1 brown violet	1.50	.45
1465 A234 $4 crimson rose	2.75	1.10

Issued to publicize traffic safety.

Perf. 13½

1965, Nov. 12 Unwmk. Photo.

Designs: $4, Dr. Sun Yat-sen, portrait at right. $5, Sun Yat-sen and flags, horiz.

1466 A235 $1 multicolored	1.90	.15
1467 A235 $4 multicolored	5.75	.40
1468 A235 $5 multicolored	10.50	1.90
Nos. 1466-1468 (3)	18.15	2.45

Children with New Year's Firecrackers A236

Dragon Dance, "Dragon Playing Ball" A237

1965, Dec. 1 Photo. *Perf. 13*

1469 A236 $1 multi	5.25	.35
1470 A237 $4.50 multi	6.25	1.25

Lien Po from "Marshal and Prime Minister Reconciled" — A238

Facial Paintings for Chinese Operas: $3, Kuan Yü from "Reunion at Ku City." $4, Gen. Chang Fei from "The Battle of Chang Pan Hill." $6, Buddha from "The Flower-Scattering Angel."

1966, Feb. 15 Unwmk. *Perf. 11½*

1471 A238 $1 olive & multi	21.00	.45
1472 A238 $3 multicolored	20.00	.35
1473 A238 $4 multicolored	21.00	.45
1474 A238 $6 ver & multi	35.00	2.75
Nos. 1471-1474 (4)	97.00	4.00

Postal Service Emblem Held by Carrier Pigeon — A239

Stone, Mt. Tai-wu, Quemoy, and Mailman A240

Designs (postal service emblem and): $3, Postal Museum. $4, Mailman climbing symbolic slope.

1966, Mar. 20 Photo. *Perf. 12½*

1475 A239 $1 green & multi	2.25	.25
1476 A240 $2 multicolored	2.25	.25
1477 A240 $3 multicolored	3.50	.30
1478 A239 $4 multicolored	6.50	.95
Nos. 1475-1478 (4)	14.50	1.75

China postal service, 70th anniversary.

Fishing on a Snowy Day, "Five Dynasties" (907-960) A241

Paintings from Palace Museum: $3.50, Calves on the Plain, Sung artist (960-1126). $4.50, Winter landscape, Sung artist (960-1126). $5, Magpies, by Lin Ch'un, Southern Sung dynasty (1127-1279).

1966, May 20 Photo. *Perf. 13*

1479 A241 $2.50 blk, brn & red	8.25	.40
1480 A241 $3.50 bis brn, blk & gray	6.75	.55
1481 A241 $4.50 blk, buff & sl	6.75	1.25
1482 A241 $5 multicolored	18.00	1.65
Nos. 1479-1482 (4)	39.75	3.85

Inauguration of Pres. Chiang Kai-shek for a 4th term.

Dragon Boat Race — A242

Lion Dance — A243

Design: $4, Lady Chang O flying to the Moon.

1966 Unwmk.

1483 A242 $2.50 multi	5.75	.40
1484 A242 $4 multi	3.25	.40
1485 A243 $6 multi	3.00	.75
Nos. 1483-1485 (3)	12.00	1.55

Issued for the Dragon Boat, Mid-Autumn and Lunar New Year Festivals. Issue dates: $2.50, June 23; $4, Sept. 29; $6, Nov. 26.

Flags of China and Argentina A244

1966, July 9 Photo. *Perf. 13*

1486 A244 $10 multicolored	3.00	.60

150th anniversary of Argentina's Independence.

Lin Sen — A245

Flying Geese — A246

Perf. 11½

1966, Aug. 1 Wmk. 323 Engr.

Without Gum

1487 A245 $1 dk brown	1.50	.15

Centenary of the birth of Lin Sen (1867-1943), Chairman of the Nationalist Government of China (1931-43).

1966-67 *Perf. 11½ Rough*

Granite Paper; Without Gum

1496 A246 $3.50 brown	.55	.15
1497 A246 $4 vermilion	.70	.15
1498 A246 $4.50 brt green	.95	.25
1499 A246 $5 rose lilac	.95	.15
1500 A246 $5.50 yel grn ('67)	.95	.25
1501 A246 $6 brt blue	2.75	.65
1502 A246 $6.50 violet	1.75	.40
1503 A246 $7 black	1.50	.15
1504 A246 $8 car rose ('67)	1.75	.25
Nos. 1496-1504 (9)	11.85	2.40

The $4.50, $5, $6, $7 and $8 were reissued with gum in 1970-71.

Pres. Chiang Kai-shek in Chung San Robe — A247

Design: $5, Chiang Kai-shek in marshal's uniform.

Unwmk.

1966, Oct. 31 Photo. *Perf. 13*

1505 A247 $1 multicolored	1.00	.25
1506 A247 $5 multicolored	5.00	1.40

Chiang Kai-shek's inauguration for a fourth term as president, May 20, 1966.

Famous Men Type of 1965-66 with Frame Line

Portraits: No. 1507, Tsai Yuan-pei (1868-1940), educator. No. 1508, Chiu Ching (1875-1907), woman educator and revolutionist.

1967 Wmk. 323 Engr. *Perf. 11½*

Without Gum

1507 A232 $1 violet blue	1.50	.25
1508 A232 $1 black	1.50	.25

Issue dates: #1507, Jan. 11. #1508, July 15. No. 1507 is on granite paper.

Motorized Mailman and Microwave Station — A248

"Transportation" and Radar Weather Station — A249

Unwmk.

1967, Mar. 15 Photo. *Perf. 13*

1511 A248 $1 multicolored	1.10	.25
1512 A249 $5 multicolored	1.90	.75

Issued to publicize the progress in communication and transportation services.

Pres. Chiang Kai-shek and Chinese Flag — A250

Chu Yuan, 332-295 B.C. — A251

Design: $4, Different frame.

1967, May 20 Litho. *Perf. 13*

1513 A250 $1 multicolored	1.25	.50
1514 A250 $4 multicolored	2.75	.60

First anniversary of President Chiang Kai-shek's 4th-term inauguration.

Perf. 11½

1967, June 12 Wmk. 323 Engr.

Portraits: $2, Li Po (705-760). $2.50, Tu Fu (712-770). $3, Po Chu-i (772-846).

Granite Paper; Without Gum

1515 A251 $1 black	1.90	.15
1516 A251 $2 brown	3.25	.25
1517 A251 $2.50 brown blk	3.75	.40
1518 A251 $3 grnsh black	3.75	.30
Nos. 1515-1518 (4)	12.65	1.10

Issued for Poets' Day.

Hotei, Wood Carving — A252

World Map — A253

Handicrafts: $2.50, Vase and plate. $3, Dolls. $5, Palace lanterns.

Perf. 11½

1967, Aug. 12 Unwmk. Photo.

1519 A252 $1 gray & multi	1.40	.55
1520 A252 $2.50 multi	2.75	.55
1521 A252 $3 multi	3.75	.65
1522 A252 $5 multi	5.50	2.50
Nos. 1519-1522 (4)	13.40	4.25

Taiwan handicraft industry.

Perf. 11½

1967, Sept. 25 Wmk. 323 Engr.

Granite Paper; Without Gum

1523 A253 $1 vermilion	.20	.15
1524 A253 $5 blue	1.00	.45

1st Conference of the World Anti-Communist League, WACL, Taipei, Sept. 25-29.

Players on Stilts: "The Fisherman and the Woodcutter" A254

Unwmk.

1967, Oct. 10 Photo. *Perf. 13*

1525 A254 $4.50 multi	1.50	.30

Issued for the 56th National Day.

Maroon Oriole A255

Formosan Birds: $1, Formosan barbet, vert. $2.50, Formosan green pigeon. $3, Formosan blue magpie. $5, Crested serpent eagle, vert. $8, Mikado pheasants.

1967, Nov. 25 Photo. *Perf. 11*
Granite Paper

1526 A255 $1 multi 1.50 .20
1527 A255 $2 multi 3.25 .20
1528 A255 $2.50 multi 3.25 .30
1529 A255 $3 multi 3.50 .30
1530 A255 $5 multi 9.25 .40
1531 A255 $8 multi 13.00 1.00
Nos. 1526-1531 (6) 33.75 2.40

Chung Hsing Pagoda — A256

Buddha, Changhua A257

Designs: $2.50, Seashore, Yeh Liu Park. $5, National Palace Museum, Taipei.

Unwmk.
1967, Dec. 10 Photo. *Perf. 13*

1532 A256 $1 multi .90 .15
1533 A257 $2.50 multi 2.75 .50
1534 A257 $4 multi 3.75 .30
1535 A257 $5 multi 5.75 .85
Nos. 1532-1535 (4) 13.15 1.80

Issued for International Tourist Year 1967.

China Park, Manila, and Flags — A258

1967, Dec. 30 *Perf. 13½*

1536 A258 $1 multicolored .50 .20
1537 A258 $5 multicolored 1.50 .45

Sino-Philippine Friendship Year 1966-67.

Sun Yat-sen Building, Yangmingshan
A259 A259a

Perf. 13x12½
1968-75 Litho. Wmk. 323
Granite Paper

1538 A259 5c lt brown .20 .15
1539 A259 10c grnsh black .20 .15
1540 A259 50c brt rose lilac .20 .15
1541 A259 $1 vermilion .50 .15
1542 A259 $1.50 emerald 1.00 .20
1543 A259 $2 plum 1.00 .15
1544 A259 $2.50 blue 1.00 .15
1545 A259 $3 grnsh blue 2.00 .20
Nos. 1538-1545 (8) 6.10
Set value 1.00

For overprints see Nos. 1723-1725.

Coil Stamps
Perf. 13 Horiz.
Photo. Unwmk.

1546 A259a $1 carmine rose .25 .25
1547 A259a $1 vermilion .25 .25

Issued dates: 50c, $1, $2.50, Jan. 23, 1968; No. 1546, Mar. 20, 1970; No. 1547, Jan. 28, 1975; others July 11, 1968.

Inscription on No. 1546 is in color with white background. On No. 1547 it is white with colored background.

Harvesting Sugar Cane A260

Jade Cabbage, 1662-1911 A261

Unwmk.
1968, Mar. 1 Photo. *Perf. 13*

1548 A260 $1 olive & multi 1.25 .15
1549 A260 $4 multicolored 1.75 .45

1968, Mar. 29 Unwmk. *Perf. 13*

Ancient Art Treasures: $1.50, Jade battle axe. $2, Porcelain flower bowl, 960-1126 A.D., horiz. $2.50, Cloisonné enamel vase, 1723-1736 A.D. $4, Agate flower holder in shape of finger citrus, 1662-1911 A.D., horiz. $5, Sacrificial kettle, 1111-771 B.C.

1550 A261 $1 rose & multi 1.25 .25
1551 A261 $1.50 blue & multi 2.50 .45
1552 A261 $2 blue & multi 3.50 .15
1553 A261 $2.50 dull rose & multi 3.50 .45
1554 A261 $4 pink & multi 3.75 .50
1555 A261 $5 blue & multi 5.25 .70
Nos. 1550-1555 (6) 19.75 2.50

For similar artifact designs inscribed "Republic of China," with single-color denominations in slanted numerals and the cents underlined, see types A276, A291, A323, A336, A372, A384, A395, A411.

Artifact designs with denominations in outlined numerals begin with type A439.

View of City in Cathay (1) — A262

Views: No. 1557, City and wall of Forbidden City (2). No. 1558, Wall at right, bridge at left (3). No. 1559, Queen's ship landing at left (4). No. 1560, Palace (5). $5, City wall and gate. $8, Suburb around Great Bridge. Design from scroll "A City in Cathay," painted 1736.

1968, June 18 Photo. *Perf. 13½*
Size: 50x29mm

1556 A262 $1 multicolored 1.25 .20
1557 A262 $1 multicolored 1.25 .20
1558 A262 $1 multicolored 1.25 .20
1559 A262 $1 multicolored 1.25 .20
1560 A262 $1 multicolored 1.25 .20
a. Strip of 5, #1556-1560 6.75 6.75

Size: 60x31mm
Perf. 13x13½

1561 A262 $5 multicolored 9.25 1.75
1562 A262 $8 multicolored 14.00 2.00
Nos. 1556-1562 (7) 29.50

Nos. 1556-1560 printed se-tenant in sheet of 50 with horizontal strips of five containing one of each.

See Nos. 1610-1614. For similar designs see types A281, A299, A326, A343.

Entrance Gate, Taroko Gorge — A263

Design: $8, Sun Yat-sen Building, Yangmingshan.

1968, Feb. 12 Photo. *Perf. 13*

1563 A263 $5 multicolored 2.50 .25
1564 A263 $8 multicolored 2.50 .30

The 17th Annual Conference of the Pacific Area Travel Association.

Vice President Chen Cheng — A264

Flying Geese — A265

1968, Mar. 5

1565 A264 $1 brown & multi 1.00 .20

Vice President Chen Cheng (1898-1965).

Wmk. 323
1968, Mar. 20 Litho. *Perf. 12*
Granite Paper

1566 A265 $1 vermilion 1.00 .20

Souvenir Sheet
Imperf

1567 A265 $3 green 9.50 1.50

90th anniv. of Chinese postage stamps. No. 1567 contains one stamp with simulated perforations.

WHO Emblem and "20" — A266

Symbolic Water Cycle — A267

1968, Apr. 7 Engr. *Perf. 12*
Granite Paper

1568 A266 $1 green .30 .15
1569 A266 $5 scarlet .70 .40

20th anniv. of WHO.

Perf. 11½
1968, June 6 Wmk. 323 Litho.
Granite Paper

1570 A267 $1 green & org .35 .20
1571 A267 $4 brt blue & org .85 .20

Hydrological Decade (UNESCO) 1965-74.

Broadcasting to Mainland China A268

Dual Carriers for FM Broadcasting A269

Wmk. 323
1968, Aug. 1 Litho. *Perf. 12*
Granite Paper

1572 A268 $1 bl, vio bl & gray .35 .20
1573 A269 $4 lt ultra & ver .85 .20

40th anniv. of the Broadcasting Corp. of China, and the inauguration of frequency modulation broadcasting.

Human Rights Flame — A270

Crop Improvement and Extension Work — A271

1968, Sept. 3
Granite Paper

1574 A270 $1 multicolored .40 .20
1575 A270 $5 multicolored 1.10 .20

International Human Rights Year 1968.

Wmk. 323
1968, Sept. 30 Litho. *Perf. 12*
Granite Paper

1576 A271 $1 yel, bister & dk brn .35 .15
1577 A271 $5 yel, emer & dk grn .85 .40

Joint Commission on Rural Reconstruction, 20th anniversary.

Javelin — A272

Designs: $2.50, Weight lifting. $5, Pole vault, horiz. $8, Woman hurdling, horiz.

Unwmk.
1968, Oct. 12 Photo. *Perf. 13*

1578 A272 $1 multi .35 .15
1579 A272 $2.50 multi .55 .20
1580 A272 $5 multi .85 .15
1581 A272 $8 pink & multi 1.25 .50
Nos. 1578-1581 (4) 3.00 1.00

19th Olympic Games, Mexico City, Oct. 12-27.

Pres. Chiang Kai-shek and Whampoa Military Academy A273

Designs: $2, Pres. Chiang Kai-shek reviewing forces of the Northern Expedition. $2.50, Suppression of bandits, reconstruction work and New Life Movement emblem. $3.50, Marco Polo Bridge near Peking and victory parade, Nanking. $4, Original copy of Constitution of Republic of China. $5, Nationalist Chinese flag flying over mainland China.

1968, Oct. 31 *Perf. 11½x12*

1582 A273 $1 multi .70 .25
1583 A273 $2 multi 1.10 .30
1584 A273 $2.50 multi 1.10 .30
1585 A273 $3.50 multi 1.40 .30
1586 A273 $4 multi 1.75 .65
1587 A273 $5 multi 2.00 .65
Nos. 1582-1587 (6) 8.05 2.45

Chiang Kai-shek's achievements for China.

Cock — A274

Flag — A275

1968, Nov. 12 Litho. *Perf. 12*
Granite Paper

1588 A274 $1 pink & multi 27.50 .30
1589 A274 $4.50 lilac & multi 27.50 5.25

Issued for use on New Year's greetings.

1968, Dec. 25 Wmk. 323 *Perf. 12½*
Granite Paper

1590 A275 $1 multicolored .40 .20
1591 A275 $5 lt blue & multi .90 .40

Constitution of the Republic of China, 20th anniversary.

Jade Belt Buckle, 1662-1911 A276

Ancient Art Treasures: $1.50, Yellow jade vase, 960-1126 A.D., vert. $2, Cloisonne enamel square teapot, 1662-1911 A.D. $2.50, Kuei, sacrificial bronze vessel, 722-481 B.C. $4, Heavenly ball vase, 1368-1661 A.D., vert. $5, Gourd-shaped vase, 1662-1911 A.D., vert.

Unwmk.

1969, Jan. 15 Photo. *Perf. 13*

1592 A276 $1 dl rose & multi .90 .15
1593 A276 $1.50 rose & multi 1.10 .25
1594 A276 $2 brt rose & multi 1.10 .20
1595 A276 $2.50 lt blue & multi 2.00 .35
1596 A276 $4 tan & multi 2.50 .35
1597 A276 $5 pale blue & multi 3.25 .70
Nos. 1592-1597 (6) 10.85 2.00

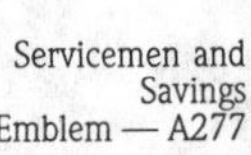

Servicemen and Savings Emblem — A277

Wmk. 323

1969, Feb. 1 Engr. *Perf. 12*

Granite Paper

1598 A277 $1 dull red brown .25 .20
1599 A277 $4 deep blue .75 .30

Military Savings Program, 10th anniv.

Ti (Flute) A278

Musical Instruments: $2.50, Sheng (13 bamboo pipes connected at the base). $4, P'i p'a (lute). $5, Cheng (zither).

Unwmk.

1969, Mar. 16 Photo. *Perf. 13*

1600 A278 $1 buff & multi .40 .15
1601 A278 $2.50 lt ap grn & multi .85 .15
1602 A278 $4 pink & multi 1.75 .50
1603 A278 $5 lt grnsh bl & multi 1.75 .25
Nos. 1600-1603 (4) 4.75 1.05

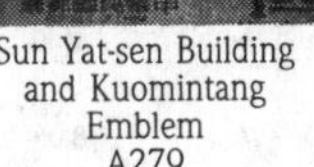

Sun Yat-sen Building and Kuomintang Emblem A279

Double Carp Design A280

1969, Mar. 29 Litho. *Perf. 13½*

1604 A279 $1 multicolored .50 .20

10th Natl. Cong. of the Chinese Nationalist Party (Kuomintang), Mar. 29. A $2.50 stamp portraying Sun Yat-sen and Chiang Kai-shek was prepared but not issued.

Perf. 13½x12½

1974 Engr. Wmk. 323

Granite Paper

1606 A280 $10 dark blue 1.40 .15
1607 A280 $20 dark brown 2.75 .15
1608 A280 $50 green 6.75 .35
1609 A280 $100 bright red 11.00 1.00
Nos. 1606-1609 (4) 21.90 1.65

1969

Perf. 11½

1606a A280 $10 2.00 .15
1607a A280 $20 2.75 .15
1608a A280 $50 7.50 .25
1609a A280 $100 11.50 .65
Nos. 1606a-1609a (4) 23.75 1.20

The 1969 issue is 27mm high; 1974, 28mm. See No. 1980.

Bridal Procession — A281

Designs: No. 1610, Musicians and standard bearer from bridal procession. $2.50, Emigrant farm family in oxcart. $5, Art gallery. $8, Roadside food stands. Designs from scroll "A City in Cathay," painted in 1736.

Perf. 13½

1969, May 20 Unwmk. Photo.

1610 A281 $1 multi 1.00 .15
1611 A281 $1 multi 1.00 .15
a. Pair, #1610-1611 2.25 .25
1612 A281 $2.50 multi 3.00 .45
1613 A281 $5 multi 3.25 .55
1614 A281 $8 multi 5.50 .90
Nos. 1610-1614 (5) 13.75 2.20

ILO Emblem — A282

Perf. 11½

1969, June 15 Engr. Wmk. 323

Granite Paper

1615 A282 $1 dark blue .35 .15
1616 A282 $8 dark carmine 1.10 .40

ILO, 50th anniversary.

Family at Dinner Table and Dressing — A283

Pupils in Laboratory and Playing — A284

Designs: $2.50, Housecleaning and obeying traffic rules. $4, Recreation (music, fishing, basketball) and education.

Perf. 11½

1969, July 15 Engr. Wmk. 323

1617 A283 $1 brick red .15 .15
1618 A283 $2.50 blue .50 .30
1619 A283 $4 green .50 .20
Nos. 1617-1619 (3) 1.15 .65

Model Citizen's Life Movement.

1969, Sept. 1 Wmk. 323 *Perf. 11½*

Design: $1, $5, Pupils with book and various school activities, horiz.

Granite Paper

1620 A284 $1 brt red .35 .15
1621 A284 $2.50 brt green .50 .20
1622 A284 $4 dk blue .65 .25
1623 A284 $5 brown .90 .30
Nos. 1620-1623 (4) 2.40 .90

Free 9-year education system, 1st anniv.

Wild Flowers and Pheasants, by Lu Chih (Ming) — A285

Paintings: $2.50, Bamboo and birds, Sung dynasty. $5, Flowers and Birds, Sung dynasty. $8, Cranes and Flowers, by G. Castiglione, S.J. (1688-1766).

1969, Oct. 9 Photo. *Perf. 13½*

1624 A285 $1 multi 1.25 .20
1625 A285 $2.50 multi 2.50 .35
1626 A285 $5 multi 5.00 .55
1627 A285 $8 multi 9.25 .90
Nos. 1624-1627 (4) 18.00 2.00

Golden Scepter Rose — A286

Rocket and Radar Station — A287

Roses: $1, "Charles Mollerin," called black rose. $5, Peace. $8, Josephine Bruce.

1969, Oct. 31 Litho. *Perf. 14*

1628 A286 $1 lt vio & multi .75 .15
1629 A286 $2.50 lt bl & multi 1.75 .15
1630 A286 $5 dl org & multi 3.25 .45
1631 A286 $8 ap grn & multi 3.75 .35
Nos. 1628-1631 (4) 9.50 1.10

Perf. 11½

1969, Nov. 21 Wmk. 323 Engr.

1632 A287 $1 rose claret .80 .15

The 30th Air Defense Day.

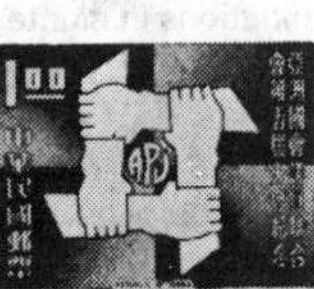

Symbol of International Cooperation A288

Pekingese A289

1969, Nov. 25

1633 A288 $1 rose claret .25 .15
1634 A288 $5 green .75 .25

5th General Assembly of the Asian Parliamentary Union, Taipei, Nov. 24-28.

1969, Dec. 1 Litho. *Perf. 12*

Granite Paper

1635 A289 50c red & multi 1.00 .30
1636 A289 $4.50 green & multi 7.00 1.65

Issued for use on New Year's greetings.

Satellite, Earth Station and Map of Taiwan A290

Unwmk.

1969, Dec. 28 Photo. *Perf. 13*

1637 A290 $1 brown & multi .50 .15
1638 A290 $5 vio blue & multi 1.50 .30
1639 A290 $8 purple & multi 1.65 .55
Nos. 1637-1639 (3) 3.65 1.00

Inauguration of the Communication Satellite Earth Station at Chin-Shan-Li, Dec. 28.

Agate Grinding Stone, 1662-1911 A291

Ancient Art Treasures: $1, Carved lacquer ware vase, 1662-1911, vert. $2, White jade Chin-li-chih melons, 1662-1911. $2.50, Black jade shepherd and ram, 206 B.C.-220 A.D. $4, Chien-lung twin porcelain vase, 1736-1796, vert. $5, Ju porcelain vase with 3 bulls, 960-1126, vert.

1970, Jan. 23

1640 A291 $1 lt grnsh bl & multi .50 .20
1641 A291 $1.50 pale bl & multi .90 .30
1642 A291 $2 green & multi .90 .30
1643 A291 $2.50 pink & multi 1.65 .30
1644 A291 $4 ol bis & multi 2.50 .30
1645 A291 $5 ultra & multi 3.25 .60
Nos. 1640-1645 (6) 9.70 2.00

Hsuan Chuang A292

Chu Hsi A293

Design: $2.50, Hua To.

Perf. 11½

1970, Feb. 20 Wmk. 323 Engr.

Granite Paper

1646 A292 $1 car rose .80 .20
1647 A293 $2.50 blue grn 1.25 .25
1648 A293 $4 blue 1.75 .30
Nos. 1646-1648 (3) 3.80 .75

Issued in memory of Hsuan Chuang (602-664), who propagated Buddhism in China; Chu Hsi (1130-1200), who developed Neo-Confucianism, and Hua To (3rd century A.D.) physician and surgeon.

EXPO '70 Pavilion, Emblem and Flags of Participants A294

Design: $5, Chinese pavilion, EXPO '70 emblem, exhibition and Chinese flags.

Unwmk.

1970, Mar. 13 Photo. *Perf. 13*

1649 A294 $5 org red & multi .65 .30
1650 A294 $8 lt blue & multi 1.10 .45

EXPO '70 International Exhibition, Osaka, Japan, Mar. 15-Sept. 13.

Nimbus III and WMO Emblem — A295

Design: $1, Agricultural meteorological station and tropical landscape, vert.

Perf. 14x13½, 13½x14

1970, Mar. 23 Litho. Wmk. 323

Granite Paper

1651 A295 $1 green & multi .30 .15
1652 A295 $8 blue & multi .95 .45

10th Annual World Meteorological Day.

Martyrs' Shrine, Taipei — A296

Shrine's Gate — A297

Unwmk.

1970, Mar. 29 Photo. *Perf. 13*

1653 A296 $1 multicolored .55 .15
1654 A297 $8 multicolored 1.75 .45

Completion of the Martyrs' Shrine in Northern Taipei, dedicated to the memory of 72 young revolutionaries who died Mar. 29, 1911.

Yueh Fei Fighting for Lost Territories A298

Characters from Chinese Operas: $2.50, Emperor Shun and stepmother. $5, The Lady Warrior Chin Liang-yu. $8, Kuan Yu and groom.

1970, May 4 Unwmk. *Perf. 13½*

1655 A298 $1 multi 1.00 .20
1656 A298 $2.50 multi 1.75 .40
1657 A298 $5 multi 2.50 .55
1658 A298 $8 multi 5.50 .85
Nos. 1655-1658 (4) 10.75 2.00

"One Hundred Horses" (Detail) by Lang Shih-ning — A299

Three Horses Playing — A300

Designs (Horses): No. 1660, Trees in left background. No. 1661, Tree trunk in lower left corner. No. 1662, Group of trees at right. No. 1663, Barren tree at right. $8, Groom roping horses. Designs from scroll "One Hundred Horses" by Lang Shih-ning (Giuseppe Castiglione, 1688-1766).

Perf. 13½

1970, June 18 Unwmk. Photo.

1659 A299 $1 multi .95 .20
1660 A299 $1 multi .95 .20
1661 A299 $1 multi .95 .20
1662 A299 $1 multi .95 .20
1663 A299 $1 multi .95 .20
a. Strip of 5, #1659-1663 4.75
1664 A300 $5 bister & multi 4.50 .90
1665 A300 $8 dl yel & multi 6.00 1.10
Nos. 1659-1665 (7) 15.25 3.00

Lai-tsu Amusing his Old Parents — A301

Chinese Fairy Tales: No. 1667, Man disguised as deer, and hunters. No. 1668, Boy cooling his father's bed. No. 1669, Boy fishing through ice. No. 1670, Son reunited with old mother. No. 1671, Emperor tasting mother's medicine. No. 1672, Boy saving oranges for mother. No. 1673, Boy saving father from tiger.

Perf. 13½

1970, July 10 Wmk. 323 Litho.

Granite Paper

1666 A301 10c red & multi .15 .15
1667 A301 10c car rose & multi .15 .15
1668 A301 10c lt vio & multi .15 .15
1669 A301 10c gray & multi .15 .15
1670 A301 10c emerald & multi .15 .15
1671 A301 50c bister & multi .20 .15
1672 A301 $1 sky blue & multi .50 .20
1673 A301 $1 dp blue & multi .50 .20
Nos. 1666-1673 (8) 1.95
Set value .70

See Nos. 1726-1733.

Man's First Step onto Moon — A302

Designs: $1, Pres. Chiang Kai-shek's message brought to the moon. $5, Neil A. Armstrong, Michael Collins, Edwin E. Aldrin, Jr., and moon, horiz.

Perf. 13½x13, 13x13½

1970, July 21 Photo. Unwmk.

1674 A302 $1 yellow & multi .55 .15
1675 A302 $5 lt yel grn & multi .95 .30
1676 A302 $8 blue & multi 1.50 .65
Nos. 1674-1676 (3) 3.00 1.10

1st anniv. of man's 1st landing on the moon.

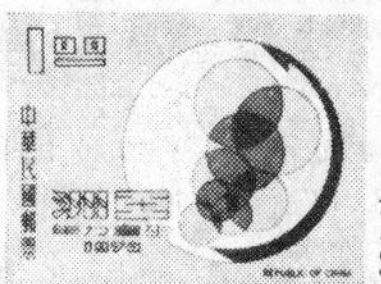

Asian Productivity Year Symbol — A303

Perf. 13½

1970, Aug. 18 Wmk. 323 Litho.

Granite Paper

1677 A303 $1 emerald & multi .40 .15
1678 A303 $5 blue & multi .90 .40

Issued to publicize Asian Productivity Year.

Flags of China and UN — A304

1970, Sept. 19 Wmk. 323 *Perf. 12*

Granite Paper

1679 A304 $5 blue, car & blk 1.40 .50

25th anniversary of the United Nations.

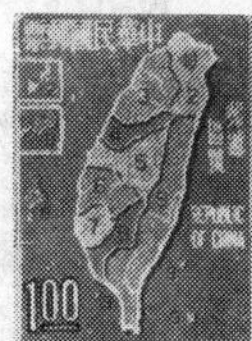

Postal Zone Map — A305

Postal Code Emblem — A306

1970, Oct. 8 Litho.

1680 A305 $1 lt blue & multi .45 .20
1681 A306 $2.50 green & multi 1.00 .35

Issued to publicize the postal code system.

Eleventh Month Scroll — A307

Designs: A scroll series, "Activities of the 12 Months," painted on silk by a group of painters of the Ch'ien Lung court (1736-1796). Chinese number in parenthesis at right of denomination tells month.

Jan., Feb., Mar.

(一) (二) (三)

Perf. 13½x13

1970-71 Photo. Unwmk.

1682 A307 $1 multi .95 .50
1683 A307 $2.50 multi 2.25 .70
1684 A307 $5 multi 3.75 1.10

Apr., May, June

(四) (五) (六)

1685 A307 $1 multi .95 .40
1686 A307 $2.50 multi 2.25 .80
1687 A307 $5 multi 3.75 .80

July, Aug., Sept.

(七) (八) (九)

1688 A307 $1 multi .95 .30
1689 A307 $2.50 multi 2.25 .40
1690 A307 $5 multi 3.75 .70

Oct., Nov., Dec.

(十) (一十) (二十)

1691 A307 $1 multi 5.75 .30
1692 A307 $2.50 multi 7.50 .40
1693 A307 $5 multi 13.00 .70
Nos. 1682-1693 (12) 47.10 7.10

Issue dates: Nos. 1691-1693, Oct. 21, 1970. Nos. 1682-1684, Jan. 14, 1971. Nos. 1685-1687, Apr. 26, 1971. Nos. 1688-1690, Aug. 27, 1971.

Family at Home — A308

Piggy Bank — A309

Design: $4, Family of 5 going on an excursion, vert.

Perf. 13½x14, 14x13½

1970, Nov. 11 Litho. Wmk. 323

Granite Paper

1694 A308 $1 multicolored .50 .20
1695 A308 $4 yel grn & multi 1.50 .30

Issued to publicize family planning.

1970, Dec. 1 *Perf. 12½x12*

Granite Paper

1696 A309 50c multi .95 .35
1697 A309 $4.50 blue & multi 4.50 .65

Issued for use on New Year's greetings.

Tibia Fusus Shells — A310

Rare Taiwan Shells: $2.50, Harpeola kurodai. $5, Conus stupa kuroda. $8, Entemnotrochus rumphii.

1971, Feb. 25 *Perf. 13x13½*

1698 A310 $1 vio & multi .45 .15
1699 A310 $2.50 multi .65 .30
1700 A310 $5 org & multi 1.65 .50
1701 A310 $8 grn & multi 2.75 .30
Nos. 1698-1701 (4) 5.50 1.25

Sun Yat-sen Building, Yangmingshan A311

Passbook and Postal Savings Certificate A312

Perf. 13½x12½

1971 Litho. Wmk. 323

Granite Paper

1702 A311 5c brown .15 .15
1703 A311 10c dk gray .15 .15
1704 A311 50c brt rose lilac .15 .15
1705 A311 $1 vermilion .15 .15
1706 A311 $1.50 ultra .85 .15
1707 A311 $2 plum .85 .15
1708 A311 $2.50 emerald 1.65 .15
1709 A311 $3 aqua 1.65 .15
Nos. 1702-1709 (8) 5.60
Set value .75

Perf. 13½x14

1971, Mar. 20 Litho. Wmk. 323

Design: $4, People and hand dropping coin into bank.

1712 A312 $1 yel grn & multi .15 .15
1713 A312 $4 ver & multi 1.10 .30

Publicizing Chinese Postal Savings Service.

Cooperation Emblem, Farmers A313

Rock Monkey A314

Design: $8, Chinese teaching rice farming to Africans, horiz.

Unwmk.

1971, May 20 Photo. *Perf. 13*

1714 A313 $1 multicolored .25 .15
1715 A313 $8 multicolored 1.10 .40

Sino-African Technical Cooperation Committee, 10th anniversary.

1971, June 25 *Perf. 11½*

Taiwan Animals: $2, White-face flying squirrel. $3, Chinese pangolin. $5, Formosan sika deer. $2, $3, $5 are horiz.

1716 A314 $1 gold & multi .65 .20
1717 A314 $2 gold & multi .65 .20
1718 A314 $3 gold & multi 1.75 .55
1719 A314 $5 gold & multi 1.75 .55
Nos. 1716-1719 (4) 4.80 1.50

Pitcher — A315

Designs: $2.50, Players at base, horiz. $4, Batter and catcher.

1971, July 29 Photo. *Perf. 13*

1720 A315 $1 multi .25 .15
1721 A315 $2.50 multi .35 .20
1722 A315 $4 multi .65 .25
Nos. 1720-1722 (3) 1.25 .60

Pacific Regional competition for the 1971 Little League World Series.

Nos. 1541, 1544-1545 Overprinted in Magenta or Red

Perf. 13x12½

1971, Sept. 9 Litho. Wmk. 323

Granite Paper

1723 A259	$1	ver (M)	.20	.15
1724 A259	$2.50	blue (R)	.55	.20
1725 A259	$3	grnsh blue (R)	.40	.30
	Nos. 1723-1725 (3)		1.15	.65

Chinese victory in 1971 Little League World Series, Williamsport, Pa., Aug. 24.

Fairy Tale Type of 1970

Chinese Fairy Tales (Filial Piety): No. 1726, Birds and elephant helping in rice field. No. 1727, Son gathering mulberries for mother. No. 1728, Son gathering firewood. No. 1729, Son, mother and bandits. No. 1730, Son carrying heavy burden. 50c, Son digging for bamboo shoots in winter. No. 1732, Man and wife working as slaves. No. 1733, Father, son and carriage.

1971, Sept. 22 *Perf. 13½*

Granite Paper

1726 A301	10c	dp org & multi	.15	.15
1727 A301	10c	lilac & multi	.15	.15
1728 A301	10c	ocher & multi	.15	.15
1729 A301	10c	dp car & multi	.15	.15
1730 A301	10c	lt ultra & multi	.15	.15
1731 A301	50c	multicolored	.15	.15
1732 A301	$1	emerald & multi	.40	.15
1733 A301	$1	lt red brn & multi	.40	.15
	Nos. 1726-1733 (8)		1.70	
	Set value			.75

Flag of China, "Double Ten" and Anniversary Emblems A316

Designs (Flag of China and): $2.50, National anthem. $5, Gen. Chiang Kai-shek. $8, Sun Yat-sen.

1971, Oct. 10 Photo. *Perf. 13*

1734 A316	$1	orange & multi	.25	.15
1735 A316	$2.50	multi	.40	.15
1736 A316	$5	green & multi	.80	.35
1737 A316	$8	olive & multi	1.10	.35
	Nos. 1734-1737 (4)		2.55	1.00

60th National Day.

Bird in Flight (AOPU Emblem) A317

Perf. 13½x14

1971, Nov. 8 Litho. Wmk. 323

1738 A317	$2.50	yellow & multi	.50	.20
1739 A317	$5	orange & multi	.50	.20

Asian-Oceanic Postal Union Executive Committee Session, Taipei, Nov. 8-15.

"White Frost Hawk," by Lang Shih-ning A318

Dog Series I

Designs: $2, "Star-Glancing Wolf." $2.50, "Golden-Winged Face." $5, "Young Black Dragon." $8, "Young Gray Dragon."

Designs from painting series "Ten Prized Dogs," by Lang Shih-ning (Giuseppe Castiglione, 1688-1766).

Perf. 13½x13

1971, Nov. 16 Litho. Unwmk.

1740 A318	$1	Facing left	.95	.20
1741 A318	$2	Lying down	1.40	.30
1742 A318	$2.50	Scratching	1.50	.50
1743 A318	$5	Facing right	2.75	.80
1744 A318	$8	Looking back	5.50	1.65
	Nos. 1740-1744 (5)		12.10	3.45

Dog Series II

Designs: $1, "Black with Snow-white Paws." $2, "Yellow Leopard." $2.50, "Flying Magpie." $5, "Heavenly Lion." $8, "Mottled Tiger."

1972, Jan. 12

1745 A318	$1	Facing right	3.25	.20
1746 A318	$2	Walking	3.75	.25
1747 A318	$2.50	Sleeping	4.75	.45
1748 A318	$5	Facing left	8.50	1.00
1749 A318	$8	Sitting	20.00	1.65
	Nos. 1745-1749 (5)		40.25	3.55

Squirrels A319

Perf. 13½x12½

1971, Dec. 1 Wmk. 323

1750 A319	Block of 4	3.75	.20
a.	50c in UL corner	.65	.15
b.	50c in UR corner	.65	.15
c.	50c in LL corner	.65	.15
d.	50c in LR corner	.65	.15
1751 A319	Block of 4	16.00	2.50
a.	$4.50 in UL corner	3.75	.60
b.	$4.50 in UR corner	3.75	.60
c.	$4.50 in LL corner	3.75	.60
d.	$4.50 in LR corner	3.75	.60

New Year 1972.

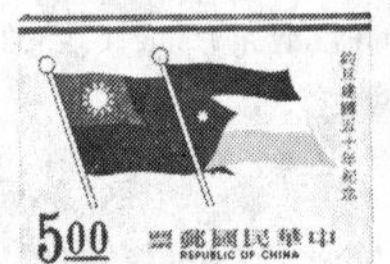

Flags of China and Jordan — A320

1971, Dec. 16 *Perf. 13½*

Granite Paper

1752 A320	$5 multicolored	1.00	.25

50th anniversary of the founding of the Hashemite Kingdom of Jordan.

Cargo Ship "Hai King" — A321

Design: $7, Ocean liner and map of Pacific Ocean, vert.

1971, Dec. 16 *Perf. 12½*

1753 A321	$4 grn, dk bl & red	.45	.45
1754 A321	$7 ocher & multi	.75	.50

Cent. of China Merchants Steam Navigation Co.

Downhill Skiing, Olympic Rings — A322

Designs: $5, Cross-country skiing. $8, Giant slalom.

1972, Feb. 3 *Perf. 13½*

1755 A322	$1 org, blk & bl	.15	.15
1756 A322	$5 yel grn, dp org & blk	.45	.20
1757 A322	$8 red, gray & blk	.60	.20
	Nos. 1755-1757 (3)	1.20	.55

11th Winter Olympic Games, Sapporo, Japan, Feb. 3-13.

Vase, 18th Century — A323

Porcelain Series I

Porcelain Masterworks of Ching Dynasty: $2, Covered jar. $2.50, Pitcher. $5, Vase with 5 openings and dragon design. $8, Covered jar with children design.

Perf. 11½

1972, Mar. 20 Photo. Unwmk.

1758 A323	$1	violet & multi	.90	.15
1759 A323	$2	plum & blue	.90	.20
1760 A323	$2.50	org ver & bl	.90	.25
1761 A323	$5	bis brn & bl	2.00	.35
1762 A323	$8	sl grn & multi	2.50	.55
	Nos. 1758-1762 (5)		7.20	1.50

See Nos. 1812-1821, 1864-1868.

Nine Flying Doves — A324

Perf. 13½x14

1972, Apr. 1 Litho. Wmk. 323

1763 A324	$1 lt blue & blk	.30	.20
1764 A324	$5 lt violet & blk	.90	.35

Asian-Oceanic Postal Union, 10th anniv.

"Dignity with Self-reliance" — A325

Perf. 13½x12½

1972-75 Litho. Wmk. 323

1765 A325	5c	brown & yel	.15	.15
1766 A325	10c	blue & org	.15	.15
1767 A325	20c	cl & yel grn ('75)	.15	.15
1768 A325	50c	lil & lil rose	.15	.15
1769 A325	$1	red & brt bl	.15	.15
1770 A325	$1.50	yel & dk bl	.35	.15
1771 A325	$2	maroon & org	.35	.15
1772 A325	$2.50	emer & ver	.35	.15
1773 A325	$3	red & lt grn	.50	.15
	Set value		2.00	.75

Souvenir Sheet

Imperf

1775 A325	Sheet of 2	5.00	2.00

No. 1775 commemorates ROCPEX '72 Philatelic Exhibition, Taipei, Oct. 24-Nov. 2. It contains 2 stamps similar to Nos. 1771 and 1773 with simulated perforations.

Issued: $1, $1.50, $2, $3, May 20, 1972; 5c, 10c, 50c, $2.50, No. 1775, Oct. 24, 1972; 20c, 1975.

For overprints see Nos. 1787-1790.

Emperor Shih-tsung's Procession — A326

Messengers on Horseback — A327

Designs from scrolls depicting Emperor Shih-tsung's (reigned 1522-1566) journey to and from tombs at Cheng-tien. No. 1776 shows land journey departure and is designed from right to left. No. 1779 shows return trip by boat and is designed from left to right. The 5 stamps of Nos. 1776 and 1780 are numbered 1 to 5 in Chinese (see illustrations with Nos. 1682-1686 for numerals).

1972 Photo. Unwmk. *Perf. 13½*

1776		Strip of 5	3.00	.60
a.	A326 $1	shown (1)	.60	.15
b.	A326 $1	Seven carriages (2)	.60	.15
c.	A326 $1	Carriage drawn by 23 horses (3)	.60	.15
d.	A326 $1	Procession (4)	.60	.15
e.	A326 $1	Emperor under 2 canopies (5)	.60	.15
1777 A327	$2.50	shown	1.65	.15
1778 A327	$5	Guards with flags, fans & spears	2.50	.20
1779 A327	$8	Sedan chair carried by 28 men	4.25	.45
1780		Strip of 5	3.00	.60
a.	A326 $1	Three barges (1)	.60	.15
b.	A326 $1	Procession, sedan chairs (2)	.60	.15
c.	A326 $1	Two barges with trunks (3)	.60	.15
d.	A326 $1	Procession on land (4)	.60	.15
e.	A326 $1	Procession, 2 sedan chairs (5)	.60	.15
1781 A327	$2.50	Courtiers at city welcoming Emperor	1.65	.15
1782 A327	$5	Orchestra on horseback	2.50	.20
1783 A327	$8	Barges	2.50	.45
	Nos. 1776-1783 (8)		21.05	2.80

Issue dates: No. 1776-1779, June 14; Nos. 1780-1783, July 12.

First Day Covers A328

Magnifying Glass, Tongs, Gauge A329

Design: $2.50, Sun Yat-sen stamp of 1971 (type A311) under magnifying glass.

Wmk. 323

1972, Aug. 9 Engr. *Perf. 12*

1784 A328	$1	dk vio blue	.15	.15
1785 A328	$2.50	brt green	.20	.15
1786 A329	$8	scarlet	.65	.25
	Nos. 1784-1786 (3)		1.00	.55

Promotion of philately. Printed in sheets of 40. Each sheet contains 4 blocks of 10 stamps surrounded by margins with inscriptions.

Nos. 1768-1770, 1772 Overprinted in Dark Blue or Red

Perf. 13½x12½

1972, Sept. 9 Litho. Wmk. 323

1787 A325	$1	red & brt bl (DB)	.15	.15
1788 A325	$1.50	yel & dk bl (R)	.25	.30
1789 A325	$2	maroon & org (R)	.30	.15
1790 A325	$3	red & lt grn (DB)	.30	.20
	Nos. 1787-1790 (4)		1.00	.80

China's championship victories in the Little League World Series, Gary, Ind., and in the Senior League World Series, Williamsport, Pa., Aug. 1972.

Emperor Yao (2357-2258 B.C.) — A330

Mountain Climbing — A331

Rulers: $4, Emperor Shun (ruled 2255-2208 B.C.). $4.50, Yu, the Great (ruled 2205-2198 B.C.). $5, King T'ang (ruled 1783-1754 B.C.). $5.50, King Wen (ruled 1171-1122 B.C.). $6, King Wu (ruled 1121-1114 B.C.). $7, Chou Kung (died 1105 B.C.). $8, Confucius (551-479 B.C.).

1972-73 Engr. *Perf. 12*
Granite Paper

1791 A330 $3.50 dk blue .60 .25
1792 A330 $4 rose red .60 .25
1793 A330 $4.50 bluish lil .70 .25
1794 A330 $5 brt green .85 .25
1795 A330 $5.50 dp org ('73) 1.25 .25
1796 A330 $6 dp claret ('73) 1.25 .30
a. Perf. 13½x12½ ('76) 1.25 .30
1797 A330 $7 sepia ('73) 1.25 .30
a. Perf. 13½x12½ ('76) 1.25 .30
1798 A330 $8 indigo ('73) 1.25 .35
a. gray, perf. 13½x12½ ('76) 1.75 .35
Nos. 1791-1798 (8) 7.75 2.20

In the first printing, Nos. 1791-1794, 1796-1798 measure 32mm high. In a 1974 reissue they are 33mm.

Unwmk.
1972, Oct. 31 Photo. *Perf. 12*

Designs (China Youth Corps emblem and): $2.50, Skiing (skiers forming circle). $4, Diving. $8, Parachute jumping.

1800 A331 $1 green & multi .15 .15
1801 A331 $2.50 blue & multi .35 .15
1802 A331 $4 orange & multi .50 .15
1803 A331 $8 multicolored 1.10 .30
Nos. 1800-1803 (4) 2.10 .75

China Youth Corps, 20th anniversary.

JCI Emblem — A332

1972, Nov. 12 Litho. Wmk. 323

1804 A332 $1 multicolored .15 .15
1805 A332 $5 orange & multi .30 .20
1806 A332 $8 multicolored .55 .50
Nos. 1804-1806 (3) 1.00 .85

27th Junior Chamber International (JCI) World Congress, Taipei, Nov. 12-19.

Electronic Mail Sorter A333

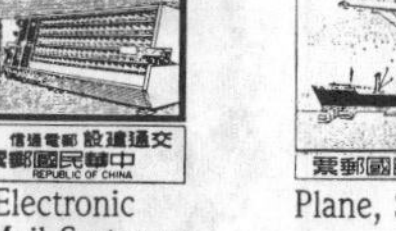
Plane, Ship and Pier A334

Progress of Communications System on Taiwan: $5, Highway overpass over railroad.

Perf. 11½
1972, Nov. 12 Wmk. 323 Engr.

1807 A333 $1 red .15 .15
1808 A334 $2.50 blue .25 .25
1809 A334 $5 dk violet brn .60 .45
Nos. 1807-1809 (3) 1.00 .85

Cow and Calf (Parental Love) — A335

1972, Dec. 1 Litho. *Perf. 12*

1810 A335 50c red & blk 1.50 .40
1811 A335 $4.50 yel, red & brn 4.00 1.10

New Year 1973. Printed in sheets of 80, divided into 4 panes of 20, separated by vertical and horizontal gutters 2 rows wide. 20 red chops meaning "Happy New Year" are printed in the gutters.

Porcelain Type of 1972 and

Stem Bowl with Dragons A336

Porcelain Series II

Porcelain Masterworks of Ming Dynasty: $1, Covered vase with fruits and flowers. $2, Vase with ornamental and floral design. $2.50, Vase imitating ancient bronze. $5, Flask with flowers of 4 seasons. $8, Garlic head vase.

1973 Photo. *Perf. 11½*

1812 A323 $1 gray & multi .35 .15
1813 A323 $2 lt brn & multi .50 .25
1814 A323 $2.50 brt grn & multi 1.25 .30
1815 A323 $5 ultra & multi 2.50 .50
1816 A323 $8 olive & multi 3.50 .85
Nos. 1812-1816 (5) 8.10 2.05

Porcelain Series III

Ming Porcelain: $2, Refuse container with dragons. $2.50, Covered jar with lotus. $5, Covered jar with horses. $8, Bowl with figures of immortals.

1817 A336 $1 gray & multi .20 .20
1818 A336 $2 lt vio & multi .30 .30
1819 A336 $2.50 dk red & multi .85 .30
1820 A336 $5 blue & multi .85 .50
1821 A336 $8 dp org & multi 1.90 .80
Nos. 1817-1821 (5) 4.10 2.10

Issue dates: Nos. 1812-1816, Jan. 10; Nos. 1817-1821, Mar. 24.
See Nos. 1865-1868.

Oyster Fairy and Fisherman's Dance — A337

1973, Feb. 7 Photo. *Perf. 11½*
Granite Paper

1822 A337 $1 Kicking shuttlecock, vert. .45 .15
1823 A337 $4 Shown .80 .20
1824 A337 $5 Rowing boat over land .80 .25
1825 A337 $8 Old man carrying young lady, vert. 1.10 .40
Nos. 1822-1825 (4) 3.15 1.00

Chinese folklore popular entertainment.

Bamboo Boat — A338

Taiwanese Handicrafts: $2.50, Painted marble vase, vert. $5, Painted glass plate. $8, Doll, bridegroom carrying bride on back, vert.

Perf. 13½x14½, 14½x13½
1973, Mar. 9 Photo.

1826 A338 $1 multi .25 .15
1827 A338 $2.50 multi .50 .25
1828 A338 $5 multi .80 .30
1829 A338 $8 multi .85 .45
Nos. 1826-1829 (4) 2.40 1.15

Federation Emblem, Cargo Hook, Crane — A339

Emblem, Tractor, New Buildings — A340

Perf. 12½
1973, Apr. 2 Litho. Wmk. 323

1830 A339 $1 salmon & multi .15 .15
1831 A340 $5 blue & blk .65 .35

12th convention of International Federation of Asian and Western Pacific Contractors Association, Taipei, Apr. 2-10.

Pres. Chiang Kai-shek, Flag of China — A341

Lin Tse-hsü — A342

Design: $4, like $1 with different border.

Unwmk.
1973, May 20 Photo. *Perf. 12*

1832 A341 $1 yellow & multi .35 .25
1833 A341 $4 dk grn & multi .90 .60

First anniversary of Pres. Chiang Kai-shek's inauguration for a fifth term.

Wmk. 323
1973, June 3 Engr. *Perf. 12*

1834 A342 $1 sepia .40 .25

Lin Tse-hsü (1785-1850), Governor of Hunan and Kwantung, who destroyed large quantity of opium at Humen, Kwantung, June 3, 1839.

Willows and Palace Gate in the Morning — A343

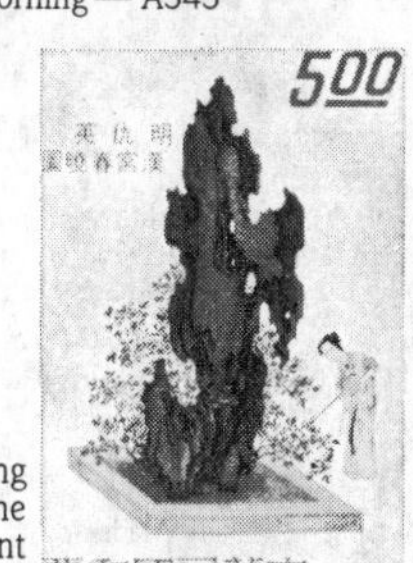
Lady Watering Peonies, Stone Ornament A344

Design from scroll "Spring Morning in the Han Palace," by Chiu Ying. The five stamps of No. 1835 are numbered 1 to 5 and the five stamps of No. 1838 are numbered 6-10 in Chinese (see illustrations with Nos. 1682-1691 for numerals). The stamps are numbered and listed from right to left.

1973 Photo. Unwmk. *Perf. 11½*
Granite Paper

1835 Strip of 5 3.00 1.25
a. A343 $1 shown (1) .20 .15
b. A343 $1 Ladies feeding peacocks (2) .20 .15
c. A343 $1 Lady watering peonies (3) .20 .15
d. A343 $1 Pear tree in bloom (4) .20 .15
e. A343 $1 Lady musicians (5) .20 .15
1836 A344 $5 shown 2.75 .60
1837 A344 $8 Lady musicians 3.25 1.00
1838 Strip of 5 3.00 1.25
a. A343 $1 Ladies playing go (6) .20 .15
b. A343 $1 Various games (7) .20 .15
c. A343 $1 Talking and playing music (8) .20 .15
d. A343 $1 Artist painting portrait (9) .20 .15
e. A343 $1 Sentries guarding wall (10) .20 .15
1839 A344 $5 Ladies playing go 2.75 .60
1840 A344 $8 Girl chasing butterfly 3.25 1.00
Nos. 1835-1840 (6) 18.00 5.70

Issued: #1835-1837, 6/20; #1838-1840, 7/18.

Fan, Bamboo Design, by Hsiang Te-hsin — A345

Designs: Painted fans, Ming dynasty.

Perf. 12½x13
1973, Aug. 15 Photo. Wmk. 368

1841 A345 $1 bister & multi .20 .15
1842 A345 $2.50 bister & multi .45 .25
1843 A345 $5 bister & multi .75 .35
1844 A345 $8 bister & multi 1.10 .60
Nos. 1841-1844 (4) 2.50 1.35

See Nos. 1934-1937.

Little League Emblem A346

INTERPOL Emblem A347

Perf. 13½
1973, Sept. 9 Litho. Wmk. 370

1845 A346 $1 yel, car & dk bl .35 .20
1846 A346 $4 yel, grn & dk bl 1.50 .40

Chinese victory in Little League Twin Championships, Gary, Ind., and Williamsport, Pa.

Wmk. 370
1973, Sept. 11 Litho. *Perf. 12*

1847 A347 $1 blue & org .15 .15
1848 A347 $5 green & org .40 .30
1849 A347 $8 magenta & org .60 .50
Nos. 1847-1849 (3) 1.15 .95

Intl. Criminal Police Organization, 50th anniv.

Ch'iu Feng-chia — A348

Perf. 11½
1973, Oct. 5 Wmk. 323 Engr.

1850 A348 $1 violet black .50 .30

2nd meeting of overseas Hakkas, Taipei, Oct. 5-7, and to honor Ch'iu Feng-chia (1864-1912), Hakka scholar, poet and revolutionist.

Tsengwen Reservoir A349

Tsengwen Dam — A350

Perf. 13½

1973, Oct. 31 Photo. Unwmk.

1851 Strip of 3 .60 .50
a. A349 $1 Upper shore .20 .15
b. A349 $1 shown .20 .15
c. A349 $1 Lower shore .20 .15

Perf. 12x11½

1852 A350 $5 shown .70 .40
1853 A350 $8 Spillway 1.10 .70
Nos. 1851-1853 (3) 2.40 1.60

Inauguration of Tsengwen Reservoir. No. 1851 printed se-tenant in sheets of 15.

Tiger — A351

Perf. 12½

1973, Dec. 1 Litho. Wmk. 370

1854 A351 50c multi .50 .30
1855 A351 $4.50 multi 1.65 .60

New Year 1974.

"Snow-dotted Eagle," by Lang Shih-ning — A352

Designs: No. 1857, "Comfortable Ride." No. 1858, "Red Flower Eagle." No. 1859, "Cloud-running Steed." No. 1860, "Sky-running steed." $2.50, "Red Jade Seat." $5, "Thunderclap Steed." $8, "Arabian Champion." Designs from painting series "Ten Prized Horses," by Lang Shih-ning (Giuseppe Castiglione, 1688-1766).

1973 Litho. Unwmk. Perf. 13

Without Gum

1856 A352 50c shown .20 .20
1857 A352 $1 Pinto, blk tail .75 .20
1858 A352 $1 Facing left .75 .20
1859 A352 $1 Facing right .75 .20
1860 A352 $1 Pinto, white tail .75 .20
a. Block of 4, #1857-1860 3.25 3.00
1861 A352 $2.50 Palomino 1.75 .40
1862 A352 $5 Grazing 2.50 .60
a. Souvenir sheet of 4 20.00 7.50
1863 A352 $8 Brown stallion 4.25 .75
Nos. 1856-1863 (8) 11.70 2.75

No. 1862a contains 4 stamps with simulated perforations similar to Nos. 1856-1857, 1861-1862.
Issued: 50c, $2.50, $5, Nov. 21; others Dec. 21.

Porcelain Types of 1972-73
Porcelain Series IV

Porcelain Masterworks of Sung Dynasty: $1, Vase. $2, Three-tiered vase. $2.50, Lotus-shaped bowl. $5, Incense burner. $8, Incense burner on stand.

1974, Jan. 16 Photo. Perf. 11½

1864 A323 $1 ultra & multi .20 .15
1865 A336 $2 multicolored .45 .20
1866 A336 $2.50 red & multi .60 .25
1867 A336 $5 lilac & multi 1.00 .35
1868 A336 $8 green & multi 1.40 .55
Nos. 1864-1868 (5) 3.65 1.50

Juggler — A353

Taroko Gorge, Hualien — A354

Design: $8, Magician producing dishes from his robe, horiz.

1974, Feb. 6 Photo. Perf. 11½

1869 A353 $1 yellow & multi .20 .15
1870 A353 $8 yellow & multi 1.25 .15
Set value .15

1974, Mar. 22 Photo. Perf. 12

Designs: $2.50, Luce Chapel, Tunghai University. $5, Tzu En Pagoda, Sun Moon Lake. $8, Goddess of Mercy, Keelung.

1871 A354 $1 multi .30 .15
1872 A354 $2.50 multi .75 .15
1873 A354 $5 multi 1.10 .20
1874 A354 $8 multi 1.75 .25
Nos. 1871-1874 (4) 3.90 .75

Taiwan landmarks.

Fighting Cocks (Brass) A355

Designs: $2.50, Grapes and bowl with fruit (imitation jade). $5, Fisherman (wood carving), vert. $8, Basket with plastic roses, vert.

Perf. 13½x14½, 14½x13½

1974, Apr. 10

1875 A355 $1 blue grn & multi .15 .15
1876 A355 $2.50 brown & multi .50 .25
1877 A355 $5 crimson & multi .80 .30
1878 A355 $8 multicolored 1.25 .50
Nos. 1875-1878 (4) 2.70 1.20

Taiwanese handicraft products.

Sun Yat-sen Memorial Hall — A356

Taiwan landmarks: $2.50, Reaching-moon Tower, Cheng Ching Lake. $5, Orchid Island (boats). $8, Penghu Interisland Bridge.

1974, May 15 Photo. Perf. 11½

Granite Paper

1879 A356 $1 blue & multi .15 .15
1880 A356 $2.50 blue & multi .45 .15
1881 A356 $5 blue & multi .70 .15
1882 A356 $8 blue & multi 1.25 .20
Nos. 1879-1882 (4) 2.55
Set value .55

Pres. Chiang and Gate of Whampoa Military Academy — A357

Marching Cadets and Entrance Gate — A358

Perf. 11½

1974, June 16 Engr. Wmk. 323

1883 A357 $1 carmine rose .15 .15
1884 A358 $14 violet blue .65 .50

50th anniversary of the founding of the Whampoa Military Academy.

Long-distance Runner and Olympic Rings — A359

The Boy Wang Ch'i Fighting Invaders — A360

Design: $8, Women's relay race and Olympic rings.

1974, June 23 Litho. Perf. 12½

1885 A359 $1 blue, blk & red .15 .15
1886 A359 $8 pink, blk & red .80 .45

80th anniv. of Intl. Olympic Committee.

1974, July 15 Wmk. 370 Perf. 13½

Folk Tales: No. 1888, T'i Ying pleading for her father before the Emperor. No. 1889, Wen Yen-po flushing out ball caught in tree. No. 1890, Boy Wang Hua returning gold piece he found. No. 1891, Pu Shih, a rich sheep raiser and benefactor. No. 1892, K'ung Yung as a child choosing smallest pear. No. 1893, Tung Yu studying. No. 1894, Szu Ma-kuang saving playmate from drowning in water jar.

1887 A360 50c olive & multi .15 .15
1888 A360 50c ultra & multi .15 .15
1889 A360 50c ocher & multi .15 .15
1890 A360 50c red brn & multi .15 .15
a. Block of 4, #1887-1890 .60 .60
1891 A360 $1 green & multi .35 .35
1892 A360 $1 lilac & multi .35 .35
1893 A360 $1 blue & multi .35 .35
1894 A360 $1 car & multi .35 .35
a. Block of 4, #1891-1894 1.50 1.50
Nos. 1887-1894 (8) 2.00 2.00

For similar designs see types A380, A427, A456, A495.

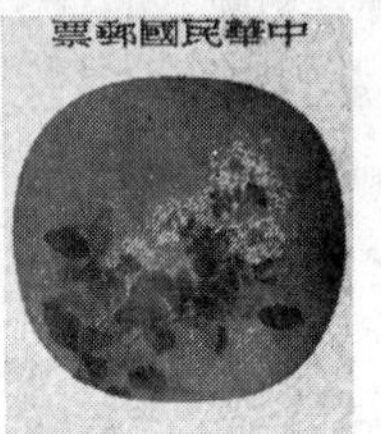

Myrtle, by Wei Sheng — A361

Silk Fan Paintings, Sung Dynasty (960-1279 A.D.): $2.50, Cabbage and Insects, by Hsu Ti. $5, Hibiscus, Cat and Dog, by Li Ti. $8, Pomegranate and Birds, by Wu Ping. Fans from National Palace Museum.

Perf. 13x12½

1974, Aug. 14 Photo. Wmk. 368

1895 A361 $1 multi .20 .15
1896 A361 $2.50 multi .50 .25
1897 A361 $5 multi 1.00 .30
1898 A361 $8 multi 1.25 .50
Nos. 1895-1898 (4) 2.95 1.20

See Nos. 1950-1953.

Battle at Marco Polo Bridge, July 7, 1937 A362

Perf. 13½

1974, Sept. 3 Litho. Wmk. 370

1899 A362 $1 multicolored .15 .15

Souvenir Sheet

Wmk. 323

Without Gum; Granite Paper

1900 Sheet of 8 7.25 7.25
a. A362 $1, single stamp .60 .60

20th Armed Forces Day. No. 1900 commemorates Armed Forces Stamp Exhibition, Sun Yat-sen Memorial Hall, Sept. 3-9.

Chrysanthemum A363

Designs: Various chrysanthemums.

Unwmk.

1974, Sept. 30 Photo. Perf. 12

Granite Paper

1901 A363 $1 lilac & multi .15 .15
1902 A363 $2.50 multi .55 .20
1903 A363 $5 orange & multi .80 .30
1904 A363 $8 multi 1.25 .45
Nos. 1901-1904 (4) 2.75 1.10

Rep. of China Pavilion, EXPO Emblem A364

Map of Fair Grounds, Chinese Flag A364a

Wmk. 370

1974, Oct. 10 Litho. Perf. 13

1905 A364 $1 multi .15 .15
1906 A364a $8 multi .50 .50

EXPO '74, Spokane, Wash., May 4-Nov. 4. Theme, "Preserve the Environment."

Steel Mill, Kaohsiung A365

Taichung Harbor A366

Designs: $1, Taiwan North Link Railroad and map. $2, Oil refinery. $2.50, Electric train. $3.50, Taoyuan International Airport. $4, Taiwan North-South Highway and map. $4.50, Kaohsiung shipyard. $5, Su-ao Port.

Perf. 13x12½, 12½x13

1974, Oct. 31 Wmk. 323

1907 A365 50c lilac, yel & brn .15 .15
1908 A365 $1 green & org .15 .15
1909 A365 $2 blue & yel .15 .15
1910 A365 $2.50 emer & org .15 .15
1911 A366 $3 ocher & ultra .15 .15
1912 A366 $3.50 sl grn & yel .15 .15
1913 A366 $4 brown & yel .20 .15
1914 A366 $4.50 ver & bl .20 .15
1915 A366 $5 sepia & dk bl .25 .15
Set value 1.10 .75

Major construction projects.
See Nos. 2009-2017, 2068-2076. For overprints see Nos. 2064-2065, 2112-2113.

Agaricus Bisporus — A367

Edible Mushrooms: $2.50, Pleurotus ostreatus. $5, Dictyophora indusiata. $8, Flammulina velutipes.

Perf. 11½

1974, Nov. 15 Unwmk. Photo.

1916 A367 $1 multi .15 .15
1917 A367 $2.50 multi .45 .20
1918 A367 $5 multi .80 .25
1919 A367 $8 multi .95 .40
Nos. 1916-1919 (4) 2.35 1.00

9th Intl. Scientific Congress on the Cultivation of Edible Fungi, Taipei, Nov. 1974.

Batters and World Map — A368

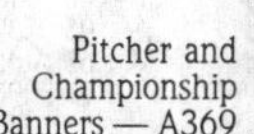

Pitcher and Championship Banners — A369

Perf. 13½

1974, Nov. 24 Wmk. 323 Litho.

1920 A368 $1 multicolored .15 .15
1921 A369 $8 multicolored .50 .40

China's victory in 1974 Little League Baseball World Series Triple Championships.

Rabbit — A370 Acrobat with Iron Rod — A371

Perf. 12½

1974, Dec. 10 Photo. Wmk. 323

1922 A370 50c orange & multi .25 .20
1923 A370 $4.50 brown & multi 1.10 .35

New Year 1975.

1975, Jan. 15 Unwmk. *Perf. 11½*

Design: $5, Two acrobats spinning tops, horiz.

Granite Paper

1924 A371 $4 yellow & multi .50 .50
1925 A371 $5 yellow & multi .90 .55

Children Watching Puppet Show — A372

Ceremonial New Year Greetings — A373

Designs from scroll "Festivals for the New Year," by Ting Kuan-p'eng. Nos. 1926a-1926e are numbered 1-5 in Chinese.

1975, Feb. 25 Photo. *Perf. 11½*

Granite Paper

1926 Strip of 5 2.00 .55
a. A372 $1 Ceremonial New Year Greetings (1) .30 .15
b. A372 $1 Man with trained monkey (2) .30 .15
c. A372 $1 Crowd and musicians (3) .30 .15
d. A372 $1 Picnic under a tree (4) .30 .15
e. A372 $1 shown (5) .30 .15
1927 A373 $2.50 shown 1.25 .30
1928 A373 $5 Children buying firecrackers 2.00 .60
1929 A373 $8 Children and man with trained monkey 4.75 .95
Nos. 1926-1929 (4) 10.00 2.40

Sun Yat-sen Memorial Hall, Taipei A374

Sun Yat-sen's Handwriting A375

Sun Yat-sen, Bronze Statue in Memorial Hall — A376

Sun Yat-sen Memorial Hall, St. John's University, NY — A377

Perf. 13½x14, 14x13½

1975, Mar. 12 Litho.

1930 A374 $1 green & multi .15 .15
1931 A375 $4 yel grn & multi .40 .20
1932 A376 $5 yellow & multi .50 .25
1933 A377 $8 gray & multi .85 .40
Nos. 1930-1933 (4) 1.90 1.00

Dr. Sun Yat-sen (1866-1925), statesman and revolutionary leader.

Fan Type of 1973 Inscribed "Landscape" (1st Character, 2nd Row)

山水

Designs: Painted fans, Ming Dynasty. Second row of inscription gives design description.

Perf. 12½x13

1975, Apr. 16 Photo. Wmk. 368

1934 A345 $1 bister & multi .20 .15
1935 A345 $2.50 bister & multi .70 .20
1936 A345 $5 bister & multi 1.00 .40
1937 A345 $8 bister & multi 1.10 .65
Nos. 1934-1937 (4) 3.00 1.40

Yuan-chin coin, 1122-221 B.C. — A378

Ancient Chinese Coins: $4, Pan-liang, 221-207 B.C. $5, Five chu, 206 B.C.-220 A.D. $8, Five chu, 502-557 A.D.

Wmk. 323

1975, May 20 Litho. *Perf. 13*

1938 A378 $1 salmon & multi .20 .15
1939 A378 $4 yellow & multi .70 .20
1940 A378 $5 dl yel & multi .90 .20
1941 A378 $8 lt vio & multi 1.75 .35
Nos. 1938-1941 (4) 3.55 .90

The Cloth-bag Monk, by Chang Hung (1577-1668) A379

Chinese Paintings: $4, Lao-tzu Riding Buffalo, by Chao Pu-chih (1053-1110). $5, Portrait of Shih-te, by Wang Wen (1497-1576). $8, Splashed-ink Immortal, by Liang K'ai (early 13th century).

Perf. 11½

1975, June 18 Photo. Unwmk.

Granite Paper

1942 A379 $2 blk, buff & ver .60 .15
1943 A379 $4 blk, gray & red 1.40 .30
1944 A379 $5 blk, yel & ver 1.75 .40
1945 A379 $8 tan, red & blk 3.25 .60
Nos. 1942-1945 (4) 7.00 1.45

Chu Yin Reading by the Light of Fireflies — A380

Folk Tales: No. 1947, Hua Mu-lan going to war for her father. No. 1948, King Kou Chien tasting gall. $5, Chou Ch'u killing tiger.

Perf. 14x13½

1975, July 16 Litho. Wmk. 368

1946 A380 $1 olive & multi .15 .15
1947 A380 $2 bis brn & multi .25 .25
1948 A380 $2 lt grn & multi .25 .25
1949 A380 $5 blue & multi .75 .35
Nos. 1946-1949 (4) 1.40 1.00

See Nos. 2108-2111.

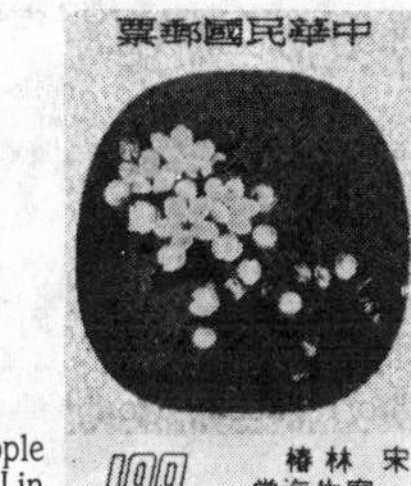

Cherry-Apple Blossoms, by Lin Ch'un — A381

Silk Fan Paintings, Sung Dynasty: $2, Spring Blossoms and Butterfly, by Ma K'uei. $5, Monkeys and Deer, by I Yüan-chih. $8, Tame Sparrow among Bamboo.

Perf. 13x12½

1975, Aug. 15 Litho. Wmk. 323

1950 A381 $1 multicolored .20 .15
1951 A381 $2 multicolored .55 .20
1952 A381 $5 multicolored 1.10 .25
1953 A381 $8 multicolored 1.40 .60
Nos. 1950-1953 (4) 3.25 1.20

See Nos. 2001-2004.

Gen. Chang Tzu-chung (1891-1940) — A382

Portraits: No. 1955, Maj. Gen. Kao Chih-hong (1908-37). No. 1956, Capt. Sha Shih-chiun (1896-1938). No. 1957, Maj. Gen. Hsieh Chin-yuan (1905-41). No. 1958, Lt. Yen Hai-wen (1916-37). No. 1959, Lt. Gen. Tai An-lan (1905-42).

Wmk. 323

1975, Sept. 3 Engr. *Perf. 12*

1954 A382 $2 carmine .15 .15
1955 A382 $2 sepia .15 .15
1956 A382 $2 dull green .15 .15
1957 A382 $5 violet black .25 .25
1958 A382 $5 violet blue .25 .25
1959 A382 $5 dark blue .25 .25
Nos. 1954-1959 (6) 1.20 1.20

Martyrs of the resistance fight against Japan.

Lotus Pond with Willows, by Madame Chiang — A383

Paintings by Madame Chiang Kai-shek: $5, Sun Breaks through Mountain Clouds. $8, A Pair of Pine Trees. $10, Fishing and Farming.

Perf. 13½

1975, Oct. 31 Litho. Unwmk.

1960 A383 $2 multicolored .80 .20
1961 A383 $5 multicolored 2.00 .35
1962 A383 $8 multicolored 2.75 .60
1963 A383 $10 multicolored 3.50 .85
Nos. 1960-1963 (4) 9.05 2.00

For similar design see type A404.

Cauldron with Phoenix Handles, 481-221 B.C. — A384

Ancient Bronzes: $2, Rectangular cauldron, 1122-722 B.C., vert. $8, Flat jar, 481-221 B.C. $10, 3-legged wine vessel, 1766-1122 B.C., vert.

1975, Nov. 12 Photo. *Perf. 12*

1964 A384 $2 pink & multi .15 .15
1965 A384 $5 lt blue & multi .55 .20
1966 A384 $8 yellow & multi .80 .30
1967 A384 $10 lilac & multi 1.10 .35
Nos. 1964-1967 (4) 2.60 1.00

For similar design see type A395. No. 1964 has 7 Chinese characters at left, No. 2005 has 4. No. 1967 has 4 characters at left, No. 2008 has 5.

Dragon, Nine-Dragon Wall, Peihai — A385 Techi Dam — A386

Perf. 12½

1975, Dec. 1 Litho. Wmk. 323

1968 A385 $1 orange & multi .20 .20
1969 A385 $5 green & multi 1.00 .75

New Year 1976.

1975, Dec. 17 Unwmk. *Perf. 13½*

Design: $10, Panoramic view of Techi Dam.

1970 A386 $2 green & multi .15 .15
1971 A386 $10 blue & multi .55 .55

Completion of Techi Dam, Tachia River.

Biathlon and Olympic Rings — A387

Designs (Olympic Rings and): $5, Luge. $8, Skiing.

1976, Jan. 15 Litho. *Perf. 13½*

1972 A387 $2 blue & multi .20 .15
1973 A387 $5 blue & multi .40 .20
1974 A387 $8 blue & multi .60 .35
Nos. 1972-1974 (3) 1.20 .70

12th Winter Olympic Games, Innsbruck, Austria, Feb. 4-15.

Chin, Oldest Chinese Instrument A388

Musical Instruments: $5, Se, c. 2900 B.C. $8, Standing kong-ho (harp). $10, Sleeping kong-ho.

1976, Feb. 11 Unwmk. *Perf. 14*

1975 A388	$2 yellow & multi		.25	.15
1976 A388	$5 org & multi		.45	.20
1977 A388	$8 grnsh bl & multi		.65	.25
1978 A388	$10 multicolored		.90	.40
	Nos. 1975-1978 (4)		2.25	1.00

For similar design see Type A407.

Double Carp Type of 1969

Perf. 13½x12½

1976, Dec. 15 Engr. Unwmk.

1980 A280	$14 car rose	.80	.50

Mail Collecting A389

Mail Sorting — A390

Postal Service, 80th Anniv.: $8, Mail transport. $10, Mail delivery.

Perf. 13½

1976, Mar. 20 Litho. Wmk. 323

1984 A389	$2 yellow & multi	.15	.15
1985 A390	$5 green & multi	.30	.15
1986 A390	$8 blue & multi	.50	.20
1987 A389	$10 orange & multi	.60	.30
a.	Souv. sheet of 4, #1984-1987	8.00	7.00
	Nos. 1984-1987 (4)	1.55	.80

Pres. Chiang Kai-shek A391

People Paying Homage — A392

Designs: No. 1990, Pres. Chiang lying in state. No. 1991, Hearse leaving funeral chapel. $5, People along funeral route. $8, Spirit tablet in Tzuhu Guest House. $10, Tzuhu Guest House, Pres. Chiang's burial place.

1976, Apr. 4

1988 A391	$2 gray & multi	.15	.15
1989 A392	$2 gray & multi	.15	.15
1990 A392	$2 gray & multi	.15	.15
1991 A392	$2 gray & multi	.15	.15
1992 A392	$5 gray & multi	.35	.20
1993 A392	$8 gray & multi	.55	.30
1994 A392	$10 gray & multi	.65	.40
	Nos. 1988-1994 (7)	2.15	1.50

Pres. Chiang Kai-shek (1887-1975), first death anniversary.

Flags of China and US — A393

Perf. 13½

1976, May 29 Litho. Wmk. 323

1995 A393	$2 multicolored	.15	.15
1996 A393	$10 yellow & multi	.55	.40

American Bicentennial.

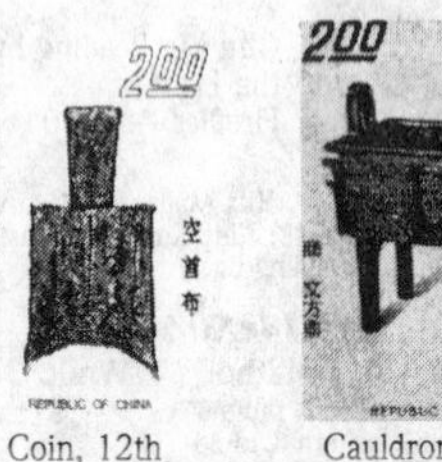

Coin, 12th Century B.C. — A394

Cauldron, Shang Dynasty — A395

Bronze Shovel Coins (pu): $5, Pointed-feet coin, 481-221 B.C. $8, Round-feet coin, 722-481 B.C. $10, Square-feet coin, 3rd-2nd centuries B.C.

1976, June 16

1997 A394	$2 salmon & multi	.15	.15
1998 A394	$5 lt blue & multi	.40	.15
1999 A394	$8 gray & multi	.60	.25
2000 A394	$10 multicolored	.85	.35
	Nos. 1997-2000 (4)	2.00	.90

Fan Painting Type of 1975

Silk Fan Paintings, Sung Dynasty: $2, Hibiscus, by Li Tung. $5, Lilies, by Lin Ch'un. $8, Deer and Pine, by Mou Chung-fu. $10, Quail and Wild Flowers, by Li An-chung.

Perf. 13x12½

1976, July 14 Litho. Wmk. 323

2001 A381	$2 multicolored	.30	.20
2002 A381	$5 multicolored	.90	.25
2003 A381	$8 multicolored	1.25	.35
2004 A381	$10 multicolored	1.50	.40
	Nos. 2001-2004 (4)	3.95	1.20

1976, Aug. 25 Photo. *Perf. 11½*

Granite Paper

Ancient Bronzes: $5, 3-legged cauldron, Chou Dynasty (1122-722 B.C.). $8, Wine container, Chou Dynasty. $10, Wine vessel with spout, Shang Dynasty (1766-1122 B.C.).

2005 A395	$2 rose & multi	.20	.15
2006 A395	$5 lt blue & multi	.60	.20
2007 A395	$8 yellow & multi	.80	.25
2008 A395	$10 lilac & multi	1.10	.40
	Nos. 2005-2008 (4)	2.70	1.00

Construction Types of 1974

Designs: $1, Taiwan North Link railroad and map. $2, Railroad electrification. $3, Taichung Harbor. $4, Taiwan North-South Highway and map. $5, Steel Mill, Kaohsiung. $6, Taoyuan International Airport. $7, Kao-hsiung shipyard. $8, Oil refinery. $9, Su-ao Port.

Perf. 13½x12½, 12½x13½

1976 Litho. Wmk. 323

2009 A365	$1 carmine & grn	.15	.15
2010 A365	$2 orange & multi	.15	.15
2011 A366	$3 violet & multi	.20	.15
2012 A366	$4 carmine & multi	.25	.15
2013 A365	$5 green & brn	.30	.15
2014 A366	$6 brown & multi	.35	.15
2015 A366	$7 brown & multi	.40	.15
2016 A365	$8 carmine & grn	.50	.20
2017 A366	$9 olive & blue	.50	.20
	Nos. 2009-2017 (9)	2.80	
	Set value		.90

Chiang Kai-shek and Mother — A396

Sun Yat-sen and Chiang Kai-shek at Canton Station — A397

Design: $5, Chiang Kai-shek, portrait.

1976, Oct. 31 Litho. *Perf. 13½*

2023 A396	$2 multicolored	.20	.15
2024 A396	$5 multicolored	.40	.20
2025 A397	$10 multicolored	.75	.50
	Nos. 2023-2025 (3)	1.35	.85

Pres. Chiang Kai-shek, 90th anniv. of birth.

Flags of Kuomintang and China — A398

Sun Yat-sen and Chiang Kai-shek A399

1976, Nov. 12 *Perf. 13½x14*

2026 A398	$2 multicolored	.15	.15
2027 A399	$10 multicolored	.55	.35
a.	Souv. sheet of 2, #2026-2027	4.00	4.00

11th National Kuomintang Cong., Taipei.

Brazen Serpent — A400

1976, Dec. 15 Wmk. 323 *Perf. 12½*

2028 A400	$1 red, lilac & gold	.25	.15
2029 A400	$5 plum, yel & gold	1.25	.30

New Year 1977.

Bird and Plum Blossoms, by Ch'en Hung-shou A401

Chinese Paintings: $8, "Wintry Days" (pine), by Yang Wei-chen. $10, Rock and Bamboo, by Hsia Ch'ang.

Perf. 11½

1977, Jan. 12 Photo. Unwmk.

Granite Paper

2030 A401	$2 multicolored	.60	.15
2031 A401	$8 multicolored	1.75	.40
2032 A401	$10 multicolored	2.50	.45
	Nos. 2030-2032 (3)	4.85	1.00

Black-naped Orioles — A402

Birds of Taiwan: $8, Common Kingfisher. $10, Chinese pheasant-tailed jacana.

1977, Feb. 16 Litho.

2033 A402	$2 multicolored	.40	.15
2034 A402	$8 multicolored	.95	.30
2035 A402	$10 multicolored	1.65	.45
	Nos. 2033-2035 (3)	3.00	.90

See Nos. 2163-2165.

Census Emblem, Industry and Commerce A403

Perf. 13½

1977, Mar. 16 Litho. Unwmk.

2036 A403	$2 red & multi	.15	.15
2037 A403	$10 purple & multi	.50	.50

Industry and Commerce Census.

Green Mountains Rising into Clouds, by Madame Chiang — A404

Landscapes, by Madame Chiang Kai-shek: $5, Boat in the Beauty of Spring. $8, Scholar beside Waterfall. $10, Water Rises to Meet the Bridge.

Perf. 11½

1977, Mar. 31 Unwmk. Photo.

Granite Paper

2038 A404	$2 multi	.60	.15
2039 A404	$5 multi	1.25	.35
2040 A404	$8 multi	1.90	.55
2041 A404	$10 multi	2.25	.70
	Nos. 2038-2041 (4)	6.00	1.75

League Emblem A405

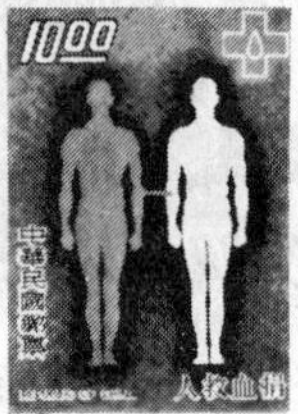

Blood Donation A406

1977, Apr. 18 Litho. *Perf. 12½*

2042 A405	$2 carmine & multi	.15	.15
2043 A405	$10 green & multi	.45	.45

10th World Anti-Communist League Conference.

1977, May 5 Wmk. 323 *Perf. 13½*

Design: $2, Donating blood, horiz.

2044 A406	$2 red & black	.15	.15
2045 A406	$10 red & black	.45	.45

Blood donation movement.

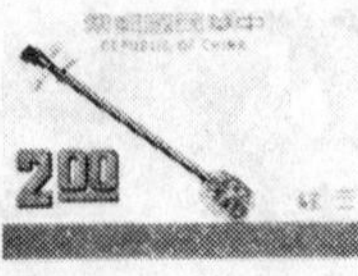

San-hsien A407

Musical Instruments: $5, Tung-hsiao (bamboo flute). $8, Yang-chin (butterfly harpsichord). $10, Pai-hsiao (pipes). Background shows musician playing instrument.

Unwmk.

1977, June 21 Photo. *Perf. 14*

2046 A407	$2 multicolored	.15	.15
2047 A407	$5 multicolored	.35	.20
2048 A407	$8 multicolored	.45	.30
2049 A407	$10 multicolored	.55	.35
	Nos. 2046-2049 (4)	1.50	1.00

Idea Leuconoe — A408

Protected Butterflies: $4, Hebomoia glaucippe formosana. $6, Stichophthalma howqua formosana. $10, Atrophaneura horishana.

1977, July 20 Litho. *Perf. 13½*
2050 A408 $2 ver & multi .35 .20
2051 A408 $4 lt grn & multi .75 .25
2052 A408 $6 lt bl & multi 1.10 .35
2053 A408 $10 yellow & multi 1.40 .50
Nos. 2050-2053 (4) 3.60 1.30

National Palace Museum A409

Temple — A410

Children's Drawings: $2, Sea Goddess Festival. $4, Boats on Shore of Lan-yu.

Perf. 13½
1977, Aug. 27 Litho. Wmk. 323
2054 A409 $1 multicolored .15 .15
2055 A409 $2 multicolored .20 .15
2056 A409 $4 multicolored .35 .25
2057 A410 $5 multicolored .40 .25
Nos. 2054-2057 (4) 1.10
Set value .60

8th Exhib. of World School Children's Art.

Carved Lacquer Plate, Wan-li Ware — A411

Ancient Carved Lacquer Ware: $5, Bowl, Ching dynasty. $8, Round box, Ming dynasty. $10, Four-tiered box, Ching dynasty.

Perf. 13x14
1977, Sept. 28 Photo. Wmk. 368
2058 A411 $2 multicolored .30 .15
2059 A411 $5 multicolored .60 .20
2060 A411 $8 multicolored .95 .30
2061 A411 $10 multicolored 1.25 .35
Nos. 2058-2061 (4) 3.10 1.00

Lions International, Emblem and Activities — A412

Unwmk.
1977, Oct. 8 Litho. *Perf. 13*
2062 A412 $2 multicolored .15 .15
2063 A412 $10 multicolored .50 .45

Intl. Association of Lions Clubs, 60th anniv.

Nos. 2069 and 2075 Overprinted in Claret

1977
中華民國青年、青少年及少年棒球隊再獲世界三冠軍紀念

Perf. 13½x12½
1977, Sept. 9 Litho. Unwmk.
2064 A365 $2 orange & multi .15 .15
2065 A365 $8 carmine & grn .45 .35

Little League baseball championship.

Chinese Quality Mark — A413

Perf. 13x12½
1977, Oct. 14 Litho. Unwmk.
2066 A413 $2 red & multi .45 .15
2067 A413 $10 blue & multi 1.75 .35

International Standardization Day.

Construction Types of 1974
Redrawn: Numerals Outlined

Designs as 1976 Issue.

Perf. 13½x12½, 12½x13½
1977 Litho. Unwmk.
Granite Paper
2068 A365 $1 car & dp grn .15 .15
2069 A365 $2 ver & multi .15 .15
2070 A366 $3 violet & multi .20 .15
2071 A366 $4 carmine & multi .20 .15
2072 A365 $5 green & multi .30 .15
2073 A366 $6 sepia & multi .30 .15
2074 A366 $7 sepia & multi .35 .20
2075 A365 $8 red lil & multi .40 .20
2076 A366 $9 olive & multi .40 .20
Nos. 2068-2076 (9) 2.45
Set value 1.35

Numerals are in solid color on #1907-1915, 2009-2017; in outline on #2068-2076.
For overprints see #2064-2065, 2112-2113.

Man and Heart — A414

White Stallion — A415

Perf. 13½x12½
1977, Nov. 12 Litho. Wmk. 323
2077 A414 $2 multicolored .15 .15
2078 A414 $10 multicolored .50 .50

Physical health, cardiac care.

Perf. 12½
1977, Dec. 1 Unwmk. Litho.

New Year 1978: $5, Two horses, horiz. Designs from painting "100 Horses," by Lang Shih-ning.

2079 A415 $1 red & multi .25 .15
2080 A415 $5 emerald & multi 1.25 .35

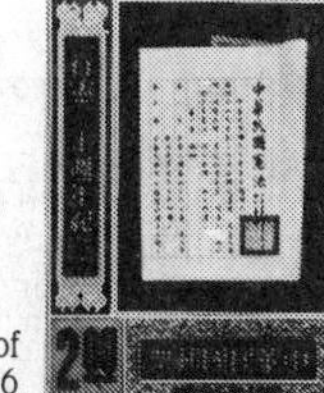
First Page of Constitution — A416

Pres. Chiang Accepting Constitution, 1946 — A417

1977, Dec. 25 Litho. *Perf. 13½*
2081 A416 $2 multicolored .15 .15
2082 A417 $10 multicolored .65 .40

30th anniversary of the Constitution.

Knife Coin with 3 Characters, 403-221 B.C. — A418

Designs: Ancient knife coins.

1978, Jan. 18 Wmk. 323 *Perf. 13½*
2083 A418 $2 salmon & multi .25 .15
2084 A418 $5 lt blue & blk .55 .15
2085 A418 $8 lt gray & multi .80 .25
2086 A418 $10 tan & multi 1.10 .30
Nos. 2083-2086 (4) 2.70 .85

China No. 1 and Flag of China — A419

Designs: $5, No. 464 (Sun Yat-sen). $10, No. 1204 (Chiang Kai-shek).

1978, Feb. 21 Litho. *Perf. 13½*
2087 A419 $2 brown & multi .15 .15
2088 A419 $5 blue & multi .35 .25
2089 A419 $10 orange & multi .60 .50
a. Souv. sheet of 3, #2087-2089 8.00 4.00
Nos. 2087-2089 (3) 1.10 .90

Centenary of Chinese postage stamps.

Sun Yat-Sen Memorial Hall — A420

China Nos. 2079 and 2 — A421

Perf. 14x12½, 12½x14
1978, Mar. 20 Wmk. 323
2090 A420 $2 multicolored .15 .15
2091 A421 $10 multicolored .50 .40

ROCPEX '78 Phil. Exhib., Taipei, Mar. 20-29.

Chiang Kai-shek with Revolutionary Army — A422

Pres. Chiang Kai-shek (1887-1975); $2, as young man, 1912, vert. $8, Making speech at Mt. Lu, July 17, 1937. $10, Reviewing Armed Forces on National Day, 1956, and Chinese flags, vert.

1978, Apr. 5 Wmk. 323 *Perf. 13½*
2092 A422 $2 violet & multi .15 .15
2093 A422 $5 green & multi .45 .25
2094 A422 $8 blue & multi .60 .50
2095 A422 $10 vio blue & multi .75 .55
Nos. 2092-2095 (4) 1.95 1.45

Nuclear Reactor and Plant — A423

Poem by Wen Cheng-ming (1470-1559) — A424

Perf. 13½x12½
1978, Apr. 28 Unwmk.
2096 A423 $10 multicolored .65 .25

First nuclear power plant on Taiwan.

Perf. 13½
1978, May 20 Wmk. 323 Litho.

Chinese Calligraphy: $2, Letter by Wang Hsi-chih (307-365). $4, Eulogy by Chu Sui-liang (596-658). $8, From Autobiography of Huai-su, Tang Dynasty. $10, Poem by Ch'ang Piao, Sung Dynasty.

2097 A424 $2 multicolored *.65* .15
2098 A424 $4 multicolored *1.10* .30
2099 A424 $6 multicolored *1.65* .40
2100 A424 $8 multicolored *2.25* .55
2101 A424 $10 multicolored *3.25* .70
Nos. 2097-2101 (5) *8.90* 2.10

Head and Dao Cancer Fund Emblem — A425

Carved Lacquer Vase, Ming Dynasty — A426

1978, June 15 Litho. *Perf. 13½*
2102 A425 $2 red, org & ol .15 .15
2103 A425 $10 dk & lt bl & grn .55 .40

Cancer prevention.

1978, July 12

Ancient Carved Lacquer Ware: $2, Box with dragon and cloud design, Ch'ing dynasty, horiz. $5, Double box on legs, Ch'ing dynasty, horiz. $8, Round box with peonies, Ming dynasty, horiz.

2104 A426 $2 gray olive & multi .25 .15
2105 A426 $5 gray olive & multi .35 .20
2106 A426 $8 gray olive & multi .60 .25
2107 A426 $10 gray olive & multi .80 .30
Nos. 2104-2107 (4) 2.00 .90

Tsu Ti Practicing with his Sword — A427

Folk Tales: No. 2109, Pan Ch'ao, diplomat and governor. No. 2110, Tien Tan's "Fire Bull Battle." $5, Liang Hung-yu, a general's wife, who served as drummer in battle.

Perf. 13½
1978, Aug. 16 Litho. Wmk. 323
2108 A427 $1 multicolored .20 .15
2109 A427 $2 bis & multi .45 .20
2110 A427 $2 gray & multi .45 .20
2111 A427 $5 multicolored .80 .35
Nos. 2108-2111 (4) 1.90 .90

For similar designs see types A456, A495.

Nos. 2071 and 2073 Overprinted in Red

1978
中華民國青年青少年及少年棒球隊三榮世界三冠軍紀念

1978, Sept. 9 *Perf. 12½x13*

2112 A366 $4 multicolored .20 .20
2113 A366 $6 multicolored .35 .35

Triple championships won by Chinese teams in Little League World Series. "1978" overprint on $4 at left, on $6 at right.

Ixias Pyrene — A428

Protected Butterflies: $4, Euploea sylvestor swinhoei. $6, Cyrestis thyodamas formosana. $10, Byasa polyeuctes termessus.

1978, Sept. 20

2114 A428 $2 multicolored .45 .20
2115 A428 $4 multicolored .70 .25
2116 A428 $6 multicolored .95 .40
2117 A428 $10 multicolored 1.75 .60
Nos. 2114-2117 (4) 3.85 1.45

Scout Symbols — A429

Tropical Tomatoes — A430

1978, Oct. 5 **Litho.** *Perf. 13½*

2118 A429 $2 multicolored .20 .20
2119 A429 $10 multicolored .35 .35

5th Chinese Boy Scout Jamboree, Cheng Ching Lake, Oct. 5-12.

1978, Oct. 23 **Wmk. 323**

Design: $10, Tropical tomatoes, horiz.

2120 A430 $2 multicolored .25 .15
2121 A430 $10 multicolored 1.25 .45

International Symposium on Tropical Tomatoes, Taiwan, Oct. 23-28.

Sino-Saudi Bridge A431

Design: $6, Buttresses of bridge, flags of Taiwan and Saudi Arabia, horiz.

1978, Oct. 31

2122 A431 $2 multicolored .35 .20
2123 A431 $6 multicolored 1.10 .40

Completion of Sino-Saudi Bridge over Cho-Shui River.

National Flag — A432

1978-80 *Perf. 13½*

2124 A432 $1 red & dk bl, I .15 .15
a. Bklt. pane of 16 ($5, $6, $8, $10, 3 $1, 9 $2) 10.00
b. Type II .15 .15
2125 A432 $2 red & dk bl, I .15 .15
a. Bklt. pane of 15 + label 14.00
b. Type II .15 .15
2126 A432 $3 yel grn & multi ('80) .45 .15
2127 A432 $4 bis & multi ('80) .50 .15
2128 A432 $5 dk grn & multi, I .40 .15
a. Type II .40 .15
2129 A432 $6 brn org & multi .45 .15
2130 A432 $7 dk brn & multi ('80) .50 .15
2131 A432 $8 dk grn & multi, I .65 .20
a. Type II .65 .20
2132 A432 $10 brt bl & multi ('79) .90 .20
2133 A432 $12 brt rose lil & multi ('80) .90 .25
Nos. 2124-2133 (10) 5.05
Set value 1.50

Two types exist: I. Second line (red) below flag is same width as blue line. II. Second line is a hairline, notably thinner. The $3, $4, $7 and $12 were issued only in type II; $6, $10, Nos. 2134, 2124a, only in type I.

Nos. 2129-2133 have colorless inscriptions and denomination in a panel of solid color.

Nos. 2124a, 2125a have selvage inscribed in blue. 1980 printings are in green or red.

Coil Stamp

1980, Jan. 15 *Perf. 12 Horiz.*

2134 A432 $2 multicolored .25 .15

See Nos. 2288-2300. For overprints see Nos. 2540-2541.

Three Rams, by Emperor Hsuan-tsung A433

Taoyuan International Airport A434

Perf. 12½

1978, Dec. 1 **Litho.** **Wmk. 323**

2135 A433 $1 multicolored .20 .15
2136 A433 $5 multicolored 1.00 .45

New Year 1979.

1978, Dec. 31 *Perf. 13½*

Design: $10, Passenger terminal and control tower, horiz.

2137 A434 $2 multicolored .15 .15
2138 A434 $10 multicolored .65 .45

Completion of Taoyuan Intl. Airport.

Oracle Bones and Inscription, 1766-1123 B.C. — A435

Antiquities and Inscriptions: $5, Lehchi cauldron, 722-481 B.C. $8, Small seal (turtle), 206 B.C.-8 A.D. $10, Inscribed stone tablet, 175-183 A.D.

1979, Jan. 17

2139 A435 $2 multicolored .30 .15
2140 A435 $5 multicolored .80 .35
2141 A435 $8 multicolored 1.65 .55
2142 A435 $10 multicolored 2.00 .75
Nos. 2139-2142 (4) 4.75 1.80

Origin and development of Chinese characters.

Chihkan Tower, 1653 — A436

Taiwan Scenery: $5, Shrine of Confucius, 1665. $8, Shrine of Koxinga, 1661. $10, Eternal Castle and moat.

1979, Feb. 11 **Litho.** *Perf. 13½*

2143 A436 $2 multicolored .20 .15
2144 A436 $5 multicolored .40 .20
2145 A436 $8 multicolored .75 .30
2146 A436 $10 multicolored 1.00 .35
Nos. 2143-2146 (4) 2.35 1.00

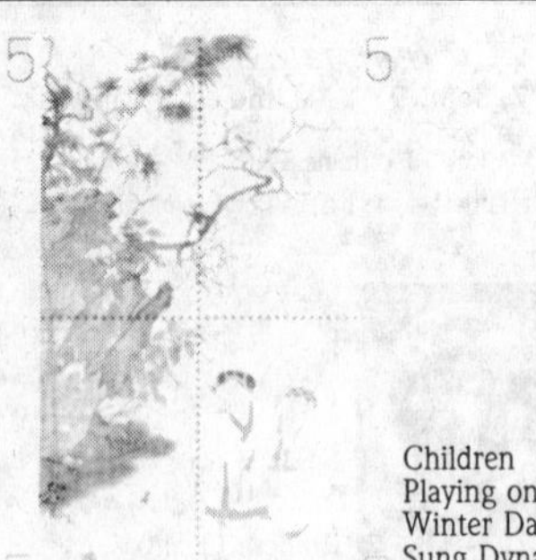

Children Playing on Winter Day, Sung Dynasty A437

1979, Mar. 8

2147 A437 Block of 4 8.00 2.00
a. $5 in UL corner 2.00 .45
b. $5 in UR corner 2.00 .45
c. $5 in LL corner 2.00 .45
d. $5 in LR corner 2.00 .45
e. Souvenir sheet of 4, #2147 16.00 5.00

Lu Hao-tung — A438

Yellow Jade Brush Holder — A439

Perf. 13x12½

1979, Mar. 29 **Engr.** **Wmk. 323**

2148 A438 $2 blue .35 .20

Lu Hao-tung (1868-1895), revolutionist.

Unwmk.

1979, Apr. 12 **Photo.** *Perf. 12*

Ancient Brush Washers: $5, White jade, Ming Dynasty. $8, Dark green jade, Ch'ing Dynasty. $10, Bluish jade, Ch'ing Dynasty. All horiz.

Granite Paper

2149 A439 $2 multicolored .15 .15
2150 A439 $5 multicolored .60 .35
2151 A439 $8 multicolored 1.00 .60
2152 A439 $10 multicolored 1.25 .75
Nos. 2149-2152 (4) 3.00 1.85

For similar artifacts designs with single-color background and denominations in outlined numerals with the cents, see types A453, A469, A489, A523, A547, A582.

Plum Blossoms, Natl. Flower A440 A440a

Perf. 13½x12½

1979-92 **Engr.** **Wmk. 323**

Granite Paper

2153 A440 $10 dk blue .40 .15
a. Plain paper ('88) .80 .30
2154 A440 $20 brown .65 .15
b. Plain paper ('87) 1.60 .60
2154A A440 $40 brt car, plain paper ('85) 1.25 .15
2155 A440 $50 dull green 1.65 .15
a. Plain paper ('87) 1.90 .65
2156 A440 $100 vermilion 4.00 1.25
e. Plain paper ('92) 4.00 4.75

Perf. 14x13½

2156A A440a $300 pur & red org ('83) 21.00 4.25
c. Plain paper ('91) 25.00 4.25
2156B A440a $500 ver & brn ('82) 35.00 7.50
d. Plain paper ('91) 40.00 7.50
Nos. 2153-2156B (7) 63.95 13.60

Issued: #2156c-2156d, May 1. #2156e, Jan. 7

City Houses and Garden — A441

Design: $10, Rural landscape, horiz.

Perf. 13x12½, 12½x13

1979, June 5 **Litho.**

2157 A441 $2 multicolored .15 .15
2158 A441 $10 multicolored .85 .40

Protection of the Environment.

Bankbook and Computer Department A442

Designs: $2, Children at counter, vert. $5, People standing in line, vert. $10, Hand putting coin in savings bank, symbolic tree.

1979, July 1 **Wmk. 323** *Perf. 13½*

2159 A442 $2 multicolored .15 .15
2160 A442 $5 multicolored .30 .15
2161 A442 $8 multicolored .50 .20
2162 A442 $10 multicolored .55 .30
Nos. 2159-2162 (4) 1.50 .80

Postal savings, 60th anniversary.

Bird Type of 1977

Birds of Taiwan: $2, Swinoe's pheasant. $8, Steere's babbler. $10, Formosan yuhina.

1979, Aug. 8 *Perf. 11½*

2163 A402 $2 multicolored .25 .15
2164 A402 $8 multicolored .95 .30
2165 A402 $10 multicolored 1.10 .35
Nos. 2163-2165 (3) 2.30 .80

Rowland Hill, Penny Black A443

Perf. 13½x13

1979, Aug. 27 **Litho.** **Wmk. 323**

2166 A443 $10 multicolored .80 .30

Sir Rowland Hill (1795-1879), originator of penny postage.

Jar with Rope Design, Shang Dynasty — A444

Ancient Chinese Pottery: $5, Two-handled jar, Shang dynasty. $8, Red jar with "ears," Han dynasty. $10, Green glazed jar, Han dynasty.

1979, Sept. 12 *Perf. 13½*

2167 A444 $2 multicolored .30 .15
2168 A444 $5 multicolored .85 .15
2169 A444 $8 multicolored 1.40 .30
2170 A444 $10 multicolored 1.65 .35
Nos. 2167-2170 (4) 4.20 .95

Children and IYC Emblem — A445

1979, Sept. 28 Litho. *Perf. 13½*
2171 A445 $2 multicolored .15 .15
2172 A445 $10 multicolored .50 .40

International Year of the Child.

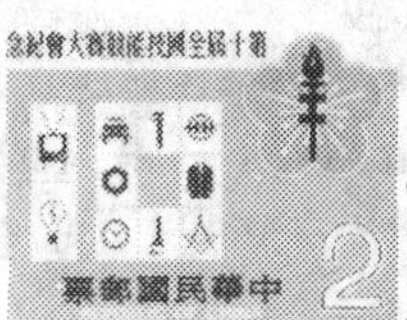

Trade Symbols, Competition Emblem A446

1979, Nov. 11 Litho. *Perf. 13½*
2173 A446 $2 blue & multi .15 .15
2174 A446 $10 green & multi .50 .40

10th National Vocational Training Competition, Taichung, Nov. 11.

Trees on a Winter Plain, by Li Ch'eng — A447

Paintings: $5, Bamboo, Wen T'ung. $8, Old tree, bamboo and rock, by Chao Meng-fu. $10, Twin Pines, by Li K'an.

1979, Nov. 21
2175 A447 $2 multicolored .35 .20
2176 A447 $5 multicolored 1.25 .30
2177 A447 $8 multicolored 2.25 .45
2178 A447 $10 multicolored 2.75 .55
Nos. 2175-2178 (4) 6.60 1.50

Monkey — A448

1979, Dec. 1 *Perf. 12½*
2179 A448 $1 yellow & multi .45 .15
2180 A448 $6 tan & multi 2.50 .60

New Year 1980.

Rotary Emblem and "75" — A449

Rotary Intl., 75th Anniv.: $12, Anniv. emblem.

1980, Feb. 23 Litho. *Perf. 13½*
2181 A449 $2 multicolored .15 .15
2182 A449 $12 multi, vert. .85 .45

Mt. Hohuan A450

Taiwan Landscapes (East-West Cross-Island Highway): $2, Tunnel of Nine Turns, vert. $12, Bridge, Tien Hsiang, vert.

1980, Mar. 1 Wmk. 323
2183 A450 $2 multicolored .15 .15
2184 A450 $8 multicolored .75 .20
2185 A450 $12 multicolored 1.10 .45
Nos. 2183-2185 (3) 2.00 .80

A451

A452

Perf. 13½x12½
1980, Mar. 29 Engr.
Granite Paper
2186 A451 $2 red brown .20 .15

Shih Chien-Ju (1879-1900), revolutionist.

1980, Apr. 4 Litho. *Perf. 13½*
2187 A452 $2 Chung-cheng Memorial Hall .15 .15
2188 A452 $8 Quotation .40 .30
2189 A452 $12 Bronze statue .55 .55
Nos. 2187-2189 (3) 1.10 1.00

Chiang Kai-shek (1887-1975), 5th anniv. of death.

Melon-shaped Jade Brush Washer, Ming Dynasty A453

Jade Pottery: $2, Jar with dragons, Sung dynasty, vert. $8, Monk's alms bowl, Ch'ing dynasty. $10, Yellow jade brush washer, Ch'ing dynasty.

1980, May 20 Photo. *Perf. 12*
Granite Paper
2190 A453 $2 multicolored .15 .15
2191 A453 $5 multicolored .50 .20
2192 A453 $8 multicolored .80 .30
2193 A453 $10 multicolored 1.10 .35
Nos. 2190-2193 (4) 2.55 1.00

Energy Conservation — A454

1980, July 15 Litho. *Perf. 13½*
2194 A454 $2 multicolored .15 .15
2195 A454 $12 multicolored .60 .45

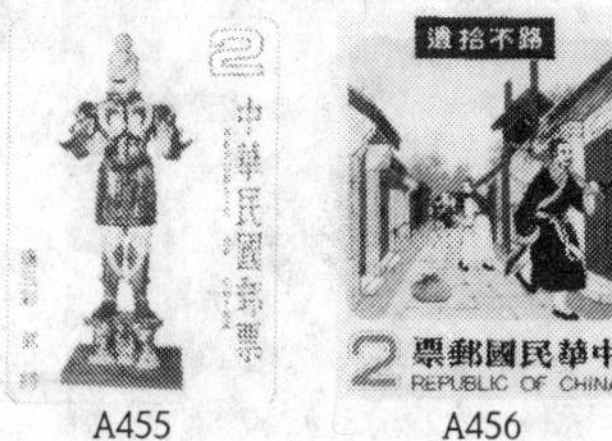

A455 A456

T'ang Dynasty pottery.

1980, Aug. 18 Litho. *Perf. 13½*
2196 A455 $2 Soldier .20 .15
2197 A455 $5 Roosters .65 .20
2198 A455 $8 Horse 1.25 .30
2199 A455 $10 Camel 1.50 .35
Nos. 2196-2199 (4) 3.60 1.00

Perf. 14x13½
1980, Sept. 23 Litho. Wmk. 323

Folk Tales: $1, Grinding mortar into a needle. No. 2201, Confucius Returning Lost Article (shown). No. 2202, Wen Tien-hsiang in jail. $5, Sending coal in snow.

2200 A456 $1 multicolored .15 .15
2201 A456 $2 multicolored .25 .15
2202 A456 $2 multicolored .25 .20
2203 A456 $5 multicolored .85 .35
Nos. 2200-2203 (4) 1.50 .85

Railroad Electrification A457

1980, Oct. 10 *Perf. 13½x14*
2204 A457 $2 shown .35 .20
2205 A457 $2 Taichung Harbor .35 .20
2206 A457 $2 Chiang Kai-shek Airport .35 .20
2207 A457 $2 Steel Mill .35 .20
2208 A457 $2 Sun Yat-sen Freeway .35 .20
2209 A457 $2 Nuclear power plant .35 .20
2210 A457 $2 Petrochemical plants .35 .20
2211 A457 $2 Su-ao Harbor .35 .20
2212 A457 $2 Kaohsiung shipyard .35 .20
2213 A457 $2 North link railroad .35 .20
a. Souv. sheet of 10, #2204-2213 9.00 9.00
b. Block of 10, #2204-2213 3.50 3.50
Nos. 2204-2213 (10) 3.50 2.00

Completion of major construction projects.

10th National Savings Day — A458

Perf. 13½
1980, Oct. 25 Litho. Wmk. 323
2214 A458 $2 Ancient coin and coin banks .15 .15
2215 A458 $12 shown .85 .45

Landscape, by Ch'iu Ying, Ming Dynasty A459

1980, Nov. 12 Litho. *Perf. 13½*
2216 A459 Block of 4 7.50 2.25
a. $5 in UL corner 1.75 .50
b. $5 in UR corner 1.75 .50
c. $5 in LL corner 1.75 .50
d. $5 in LR corner 1.75 .50
e. Souvenir sheet 16.00 16.00

Cock — A460

Faces, Flag, Census Form — A461

1980, Dec. 1 *Perf. 12½*
2217 A460 $1 multicolored .30 .15
2218 A460 $6 multicolored 2.00 .45
a. Souv. sheet, 2 each #2217-2218 8.00 8.00

New Year 1981.

1980, Dec. 13 *Perf. 13½*
2219 A461 $2 shown .15 .15
2220 A461 $12 Buildings, horiz. .70 .45

1980 population and housing census.

TIROS-N Satellite — A462

Design: $10, Central weather bureau, horiz.

1981, Jan. 28 Litho. *Perf. 13½*
2221 A462 $2 multicolored .15 .15
2222 A462 $10 multicolored .65 .45

Completion of meteorological satellite ground station, Taipei.

"Happiness" A463

New Year 1981 (Calligraphy): No. 2224, Wealth. No. 2225, Longevity. No. 2226, Joy.

1981, Feb. 3 *Perf. 13½x12½*
2223 A463 $5 multi, 5 at B .90 .15
2224 A463 $5 multi, 5 at R .90 .15
2225 A463 $5 multi, 5 at L .90 .15
2226 A463 $5 multi, 5 at T .90 .15
a. Block of 4, #2223-2226 4.00 2.00

International Year of the Disabled A464

1981, Feb. 19 Litho. *Perf. 13½*
2227 A464 $2 multicolored .15 .15
2228 A464 $12 multicolored .50 .25
Set value .30

Mt. Ali A465

1981, Mar. 1
2229 A465 $2 shown .15 .15
2230 A465 $7 Oluanpi Beach .75 .30
2231 A465 $12 Sun Moon Lake 1.40 .35
Nos. 2229-2231 (3) 2.30 .80

A $2 multicolored stamp for the 12th National Kuomintang Congress at Taipei was prepared for release Mar. 29, 1981, but not issued. It showed Sun Yat-sen, Chiang Kai-shek, flags of China and the Kuomintang and a map of China.

Children in Forest A467

Children's Day: Drawings.

1981, Apr. 4
2233 A467 $1 multicolored .15 .15
2234 A467 $2 multicolored .15 .15
2235 A467 $5 multicolored .15 .15
2236 A467 $7 multicolored .25 .25
Set value .50 .50

Chiang Kai-shek Memorial Hall — A468

1981, Apr. 5 *Perf. 12½x13½*

2237 A468 20c bluish lilac .15 .15
a. Photo. ('87) .15 .15
2238 A468 40c crim rose .15 .15
a. Photo. ('87) .15 .15
2239 A468 50c dull red brn .15 .15
a. Photo. ('88) .15 .15
Set value .35 .25

Chiang Kai-shek (1887-1975).
See Nos. 2601-2603.

Cloisonne Enamel Brush Washer, 15th Cent. — A469

Cloisonne Enamel: $5, Ritual vessel, 15th cent., vert. $8, Plate, 17th cent. $10, Vase, Ming Dynasty, vert.

1981, May 20 Photo. *Perf. 12*
Granite Paper

2240 A469 $2 multicolored .20 .15
2241 A469 $5 multicolored .50 .20
2242 A469 $8 multicolored .75 .30
2243 A469 $10 multicolored 1.00 .35
Nos. 2240-2243 (4) 2.45 1.00

For similar enamelware stamps see Nos. 2318-2321, 2348-2351, 2410-2413.

Early & Modern Locomotives — A470
Linnaeus Crab — A471

Perf. 12½
1981, June 9 Litho. Wmk. 323

2244 A470 $2 shown .15 .15
2245 A470 $14 Trains, horiz. .90 .50

Railroad service centenary.

1981, June 14 *Perf. 13½*

2246 A471 $2 De Haan crab, horiz. .15 .15
2247 A471 $5 shown .40 .20
2248 A471 $8 Miers crab, horiz. .70 .30
2249 A471 $14 Rathbun crab 1.10 .45
Nos. 2246-2249 (4) 2.35 1.10

Central Weather Bureau, 40th Anniv. — A472

1981, July 1 Litho. *Perf. 13½*

2250 A472 $2 multicolored .15 .15
2251 A472 $14 multicolored .90 .50

Scene from The Cowherd and the Weaving Maid — A473

Designs: Scenes from the Cowherd and the Weaving Maid.

1981, Aug. 6 Litho. *Perf. 13½x14*

2252 A473 $2 multicolored .20 .15
2253 A473 $4 multicolored .45 .20
2254 A473 $8 multicolored 1.10 .35
2255 A473 $14 multicolored 2.25 .65
Nos. 2252-2255 (4) 4.00 1.35

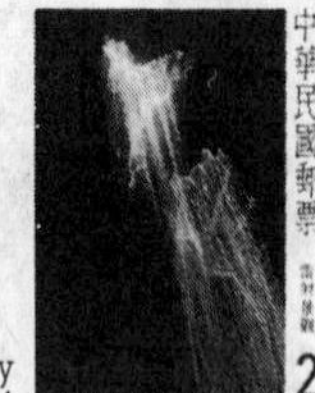

First Lasography Exhibition — A474

Lasography Designs.

1981, Aug. 15 *Perf. 13½*

2256 A474 $2 multicolored .15 .15
2257 A474 $5 multicolored .30 .30
2258 A474 $8 multicolored .55 .45
2259 A474 $14 multicolored 1.00 .75
Nos. 2256-2259 (4) 2.00 1.65

Soccer Players
A475 A476

1981, Sept. 9 Litho. *Perf. 13½*

2260 A475 $5 multicolored .50 .15
2261 A476 $5 multicolored .50 .15
a. Pair, #2260-2261 1.00 .60
Set value .20

Sports Day.

A477

70th Anniv. of Republic: No. 2263, Eastward Expedition (soldiers on Hill). No. 2264, Northward Expedition (Chiang on horse). No. 2265, Resistance War with Japan (Chiang, fist raised). No. 2266, Suppression of Communist Rebels (Battle scene). No. 2267, Counter-offensive and unification. $8, Chiang Kai-shek. $14, Sun Yat-sen.

1981, Oct. 10 *Perf. 13½*

2262 A477 $2 multicolored .15 .15
2263 A477 $2 multicolored .15 .15
2264 A477 $2 multicolored .15 .15
2265 A477 $2 multicolored .15 .15
2266 A477 $3 multicolored .20 .20
2267 A477 $3 multicolored .20 .20
2268 A477 $8 multicolored .50 .30
2269 A477 $14 multicolored 1.00 .45
a. Souv. sheet of 8, #2262-2269 7.00 3.00
Nos. 2262-2269 (8) 2.50
Set value 1.35

No. 2269a issued Oct. 25.

ROCPEX TAIPEI '81 Intl. Philatelic Exhibition, Taipei, Oct. 25-Nov. 2 — A478

1981, Oct. 25

2270 A478 $2 multicolored .15 .15
2271 A478 $14 multicolored .55 .40

Boys Playing Games (#2272a) A479

Designs: a.-j. "One Hundred Boys," Sung Dynasty scroll (each stamp is numbered from 1 to 10 in Chinese. See illustrations with Nos. 1682-1691 for numerals.) Two strips of 5 each in continuous design.

1981, Nov. 12

2272 Block of 10 15.00 3.50
a.-e. A479 $2 single (top row) 1.40 .25
f.-j. A479 $2 single (bottom row) 1.40 .25

New Year 1982 (Year of the Dog) — A480
Information Week, Dec. 6-12 — A481

Perf. 12½
1981, Dec. 1 Litho. Wmk. 323

2273 A480 $1 multicolored .25 .15
2274 A480 $10 multicolored 2.25 .50
a. Souv. sheet, 2 each #2273-2274 10.00 1.25

1981, Dec. 7 *Perf. 14x13½*

2275 A481 $2 multicolored .25 .15

Telecommunications Centenary — A482

Perf. 14x13½, 13½x14
1981, Dec. 28

2276 A482 $2 Telephone, vert. .15 .15
2277 A482 $3 Old, new phones .15 .15
2278 A482 $8 Submarine cable .40 .20
2279 A482 $18 Computers, vert. .95 .50
Nos. 2276-2279 (4) 1.65 1.00

Floral Arrangement — A483

Designs: Various floral arrangements in Ming vases.

Perf. 13½
1982, Jan. 23 Litho. Wmk. 323

2280 A483 $2 multicolored .15 .15
2281 A483 $3 multicolored .15 .15
2282 A483 $8 multicolored .50 .25
2283 A483 $18 multicolored 1.25 .55
Nos. 2280-2283 (4) 2.05 1.10

Compare with designs A559, A584.

The Ku Cheng Reunion — A484

Designs: Opera scenes.

Perf. 13½
1982, Feb. 15 Litho. Wmk. 323

2284 A484 $2 multicolored .35 .15
2285 A484 $3 multicolored .45 .20
2286 A484 $4 multicolored 1.10 .25
2287 A484 $18 multicolored 4.00 .85
Nos. 2284-2287 (4) 5.90 1.45

Flag Type of 1978
Value Colorless in Colored Panel

1981 Litho. *Perf. 13½*
Panel Color

2288 A432 $1 dk blue .15 .15
2289 A432 $1.50 lt olive .15 .15
2290 A432 $2 dk olive bis .15 .15
2291 A432 $3 red .15 .15
2292 A432 $4 blue .30 .15
2293 A432 $5 sepia .40 .15
2294 A432 $6 orange .45 .20
2295 A432 $7 green .50 .20
2296 A432 $8 magenta .60 .20
2297 A432 $9 olive grn .65 .20
2298 A432 $10 dk purple .70 .25
2299 A432 $12 lilac .90 .30
2300 A432 $14 dk green 1.00 .35
Nos. 2288-2300 (13) 6.10
Set value 2.10

Second line (red) below flag is a hairline, notably thinner.
For overprints see Nos. 2540-2541.

Tubercle Bacillus Centenary A485
Cheng Shih-liang, Revolutionary A486

Perf. 13½
1982, Mar. 24 Litho. Wmk. 323

2309 A485 $2 multicolored .15 .15

Perf. 13½x12½
1982, Mar. 29 Engr.
Granite Paper

2310 A486 $2 carmine rose .15 .15

Children's Day — A487

Designs: Various children's drawings.

1982, Apr. 4 Litho.

2311 A487 $2 multi, vert. .15 .15
2312 A487 $3 multicolored .25 .15
2313 A487 $5 multicolored .60 .15
2314 A487 $8 multicolored 1.00 .20
Nos. 2311-2314 (4) 2.00 .65

Dentists' Day — A488

1982, May 4 Litho. *Perf. 13½*

2315 A488 $2 Tooth, boy .25 .15
2316 A488 $3 Flossing, brushing .30 .15
2317 A488 $10 Examination 1.40 .40
Nos. 2315-2317 (3) 1.95
Set value .60

Champleve Enamel Cup and Saucer, 18th Cent. A489

Painted Enamelware: $5, Cloisonne gold-plated duck Ch'ien-lung period (1736-1795), vert. $8, Incense burner, K'ang-hsi period (1662-1722). $12, Cloisonne pitcher, Ch'ien-lung period, vert.

1982, May 20 Photo. *Perf. 12*
Granite Paper

2318 A489 $2 multicolored .35 .15
2319 A489 $5 multicolored .80 .15
2320 A489 $8 multicolored 1.40 .15
2321 A489 $12 multicolored 2.25 .25
Nos. 2318-2321 (4) 4.80
Set value .56

See Nos. 2348-2351.

Poets' Day — A490

Tang Dynasty Poetry Illustrations (618-906): $2, Spring Dawn, by Meng Hao-Jan. $3, On Looking for a Hermit and Not Finding Him, by Chia Tao. $5, Summer Dying, by Liu Yu-Hsi. $18, Looking at the Snow Drifts on South Mountain, by Tsu Yung. Chinese characters are to the left of the denominations on Nos. 2322-2325, Nos. 2396-2399 have no characters to the left of the denominations.

Perf. 13½

1982, June 25 Litho. Wmk. 323

2322 A490 $2 multicolored *1.00* .20
2323 A490 $3 multicolored *1.65* .25
2324 A490 $5 multicolored *4.00* .45
2325 A490 $18 multicolored *13.00* 1.25
Nos. 2322-2325 (4) *19.65* 2.15

See Nos. 2352-2355.

5th World Women's Softball Championship, Taipei, July 1-12 — A491

1982, July 2

2326 A491 $2 lt grn & multi .15 .15
2327 A491 $18 tan & multi 1.10 .50

Scouting Year A492

1982, July 18

2328 A492 $2 Crossing bridge, Baden-Powell .15 .15
2329 A492 $18 Emblem, camp .90 .55

Stamp in Tongs — A493

1982, Aug. 9

2330 A493 $2 shown .15 .15
2331 A493 $18 Album stamps magnified .90 .55

Carved Lion, Tsu Shih Temple — A494

Hsun Kuan Saving Hsiang-cheng City — A495

Tsu Shih Temple of Sanhsia Architecture: $3, Lion brackets, horiz. $5, Sub-lintels. $18, Tiled roof, horiz.

1982, Sept. 1 Litho. *Perf. 13½*

2332 A494 $2 multicolored .15 .15
2333 A494 $3 multicolored .30 .15
2334 A494 $5 multicolored .50 .15
2335 A494 $18 multicolored 1.65 .55
Nos. 2332-2335 (4) 2.60 1.00

1982, Oct. 15 *Perf. 14x13½*

Designs: Scenes from The Thirty-Six Examples of Filial Piety, Folk Tale collection by Wu Yen-huan.

2336 A495 $1 multicolored .15 .15
2337 A495 $2 multicolored .30 .15
2338 A495 $3 multicolored .45 .20
2339 A495 $5 multicolored 1.25 .25
Nos. 2336-2339 (4) 2.15
Set value .60

30th Anniv. of China Youth Corps A496

1982, Oct. 31

2340 A496 $2 Riding .15 .15
2341 A496 $3 Raising flag, vert. .15 .15
2342 A496 $18 Mountain climbing .85 .60
Nos. 2340-2342 (3) 1.15
Set value .75

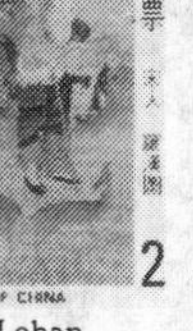

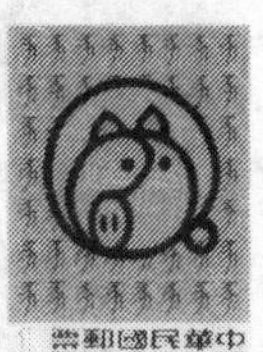

Seated Lohan (Buddhist Saint) — A497

New Year 1983 (Year of the Boar) — A498

Paintings of Lohan, Hanging Scrolls by Liu Sung-nien, 13th cent.

Perf. 13x12½

1982, Nov. 12 Litho. Wmk. 323

2343 A497 $2 multicolored .55 .15
2344 A497 $3 multicolored .75 .20
2345 A497 $18 multicolored 6.75 1.10
a. Souv. sheet of 3, #2343-2345 *17.00* 10.00
Nos. 2343-2345 (3) 8.05 1.45

No. 2345a comes overprinted in red in the sheet margins.

1982, Dec. 1 *Perf. 12½*

2346 A498 $1 multicolored .35 .15
2347 A498 $10 multicolored 3.75 .60
a. Souv. sheet, 2 each #2346-2347 *12.00* 2.50
Set value .65

Enamelware Type of 1982

Designs: $2, Square basin, Ch'ing Dynasty (1644-1911). $3, Vase, Ch'ien-lung period (1736-1795), vert. $4, Tea pot, Ch'ien-lung period. $18, Elephant vase, Ch'ing Dynasty, vert.

1983, Jan. 5 Photo. *Perf. 12*
Granite Paper

2348 A489 $2 multicolored .15 .15
2349 A489 $3 multicolored .20 .15
2350 A489 $4 multicolored .40 .20
2351 A489 $18 multicolored 2.00 .60
Nos. 2348-2351 (4) 2.75
Set value .90

Poetry Illustration Type of 1982

Sung Dynasty Poetry: $2, Seeing the Flowers Fade Away. $3, River. $5, Freckled with Clouds is the Azure Sky. $11, Yielding Fine Fragrance in the Snow. Nos. 2352-2355 vert.

Perf. 13½

1983, Feb. 10 Litho. Wmk. 323

2352 A490 $2 multicolored *1.65* .30
2353 A490 $3 multicolored *1.90* .40
2354 A490 $5 multicolored *5.00* .55
2355 A490 $11 multicolored *10.50* 1.00
Nos. 2352-2355 (4) *19.05* 2.25

Mt. Jade, Taiwan — A499

1983, Mar. 1

2356 A499 $2 Wawa Valley, vert. .20 .15
2357 A499 $3 University Pond, vert. .25 .15
2358 A499 $18 shown 2.00 .75
Nos. 2356-2358 (3) 2.45 1.05

400th Anniv. of Arrival of Matteo Ricci (1552-1610), Italian Missionary — A500

Perf. 14x13½

1983, Apr. 3 Litho. Wmk. 323

2359 A500 $2 Globe .20 .15
2360 A500 $18 Great Wall 1.50 .50

Mandarin Phonetic Symbols, 70th Anniv. — A501

Scenes from Lady White Snake Fairytale — A502

Perf. 13½

1983, May 22 Litho. Wmk. 323

2361 A501 $2 Wu Ching-heng, inventor .15 .15
2362 A501 $18 Children writing 1.10 .50

1983, June 15 *Perf. 14x13½*

2363 A502 $2 multicolored .20 .15
2364 A502 $3 lt blue & multi .25 .15
2365 A502 $3 orange & multi .25 .15
2366 A502 $18 multicolored 2.50 .70
Nos. 2363-2366 (4) 3.20 1.15

A503 A504

Various bamboo carved objects. Nos. 2367-2369 Ch'ing dynasty.

Perf. 13½

1983, July 14 Litho. Wmk. 323

2367 A503 $2 Bamboo jug .25 .15
2368 A503 $3 Tao-t'ieh motif vase .40 .15
2369 A503 $4 Landscape sculpture .55 .20
2370 A503 $18 Brush holder, Ming dynasty 3.75 .55
Nos. 2367-2370 (4) 4.95 1.05

Perf. 13½

1983, Aug. 5 Litho. Wmk. 323

2371 A504 $2 Globe .15 .15
2372 A504 $18 Emblem .90 .50

World Communications Year.

Fishing Industry (Local Fish) A505

1983, Aug. 20

2373 A505 $2 Epinephelus tauvina .15 .15
2374 A505 $18 Saurida undosquamis 1.00 .50

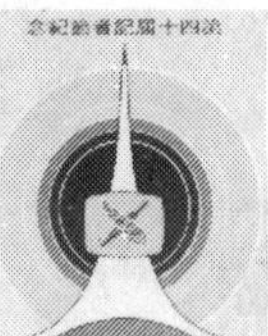

40th Journalists' Day — A506

1983, Sept. 1

2375 A506 $2 multicolored .20 .15

Views of Mongolia and Tibet — A507

1983, Sept. 15

2376 A507 $2 Village .20 .15
2377 A507 $3 Potala Palace .25 .15
2378 A507 $5 Sheep grazing .60 .25
2379 A507 $11 Camel caravan 1.40 .50
Nos. 2376-2379 (4) 2.45 1.05

2nd East Asian Bird Protection Conference, Oct. — A508

1983, Oct. 8 Litho. *Perf. 13½*

2380 A508 $2 Lanius cristatus, vert. .15 .15
2381 A508 $18 Butastur indicus 1.90 .50

A509

A510

Plum Blossoms, Photography by Hu Ch'ung-hsien.

1983, Oct. 31 Litho. *Perf. 14x13½*

2382 A509 $2 multicolored .15 .15
2383 A509 $3 multi, diff. .25 .15
2384 A509 $5 multi, diff. .50 .20
2385 A509 $11 multi, diff. 1.10 .40
Nos. 2382-2385 (4) 2.00 .90

1983, Nov. 6 *Perf. 13x13½, 13½x13*

2386 A510 $2 JCI and Congress emblems .15 .15
2387 A510 $18 Globe and emblems, horiz .90 .50

Jaycees Intl., 38th World Congress, Taipei.

8th Asian-Pacific Cardiology Congress — A511

1983, Nov. 27 Litho. *Perf. 13½*

2388 A511 $2 shown .15 .15
2389 A511 $18 Electrocardiogram 1.10 .50

New Year 1984 (Year of the Rat) — A512

1983, Dec. 1 Litho. *Perf. 12½*

2390 A512 $1 multicolored .45 .15
2391 A512 $10 multicolored 5.50 .65
a. Souv. sheet, 2 each #2390-2391 *24.00* 7.50

Literacy Week A513

1983, Dec. 17 Litho. *Perf. 13½*

2392 A513 $2 shown .15 .15
2393 A513 $18 Modern family, vert. .90 .50

World Freedom Day — A514

1984, Jan. 23 Litho. *Perf. 13½*

2394 A514 $2 Korean War Patriots .15 .15
2395 A514 $18 Intl. support 1.10 .50

Drama Day — A515

Yuan Dynasty Poetry Illustrations by Tien-shih Lin (Poems by): $2, Kuan Yun-shih. $3, Po Pu. $5, Chang Ko-chiu. $18, Shang Cheng-shu. (See note with Nos. 2322-2325.)

1984, Feb. 15 Litho. *Perf. 13½*

2396 A515 $2 multicolored *.85* .20
2397 A515 $3 multicolored *1.40* .25
2398 A515 $5 multicolored *3.00* .30
2399 A515 $18 multicolored *12.00* 1.25
Nos. 2396-2399 (4) *17.25* 2.00

A516

A517

A518

Arbor Day — A519

1984, Mar. 12 Litho. *Perf. 13½x14*

2400 A516 $2 multicolored 1.00 .15
2401 A517 $2 multicolored 1.00 .15
2402 A518 $2 multicolored 1.00 .15
2403 A519 $2 multicolored 1.00 .15
a. Block of 4, #2400-2403 4.00 1.00
Set value .25

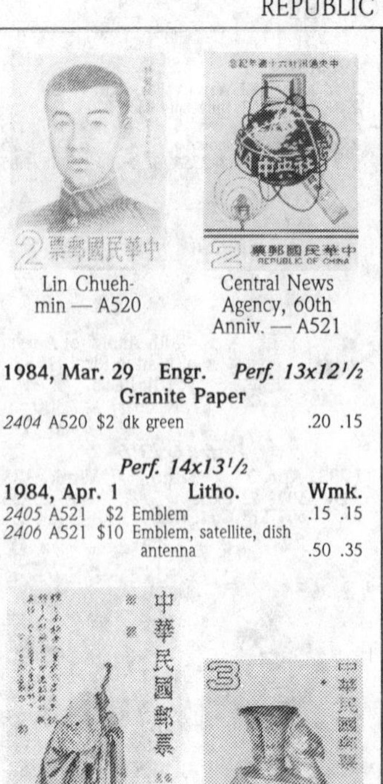

Lin Chueh-min — A520

Central News Agency, 60th Anniv. — A521

1984, Mar. 29 Engr. *Perf. 13x12½*

Granite Paper

2404 A520 $2 dk green .20 .15

Perf. 14x13½

1984, Apr. 1 Litho. Wmk.

2405 A521 $2 Emblem .15 .15
2406 A521 $10 Emblem, satellite, dish antenna .50 .35

God of Longevity A522

Ch'ing Dynasty Enamelware A523

Paintings by Chang Ta-chien (1899-1983): $2, Five Auspicious Tokens. $18, Lotus Blossoms in Ink Splash.

Perf. 11½

1984, Apr. 20 Litho. Wmk. 323

2407 A522 $2 multicolored .55 .15
2408 A522 $5 multicolored 1.65 .15
2409 A522 $18 multicolored 5.75 .60
Nos. 2407-2409 (3) 7.95 .90

1984, May 20 Photo. *Perf. 12*

Granite Paper

2410 A523 $2 Cup, pot, plate, horiz. .15 .15
2411 A523 $3 Wine jug .20 .15
2412 A523 $4 Teapot .35 .15
2413 A523 $18 Candle holder 1.65 .55
Nos. 2410-2413 (4) 2.35 1.00

China Airlines World-wide Service Inauguration A524

1984, May 31 Litho. *Perf. 13½x14*

2414 A524 $2 Jet circling globe .15 .15
2415 A524 $7 Globe, jet .35 .20
2416 A524 $11 New York City .55 .40
2417 A524 $18 Amsterdam .85 .50
Nos. 2414-2417 (4) 1.90 1.25

30th Navigation Day — A525

Perf. 13½x13

1984, July 11 Litho. Wmk. 323

2418 A525 $2 Container ship .20 .15
2419 A525 $18 Oil tanker 2.50 .50

1984 Summer Olympics — A526

Alpine Plants — A527

Perf. 13½x14, 14x13½

1984, July 28

2420 A526 $2 Judo, horiz. .15 .15
2421 A526 $5 Archery .25 .15
2422 A526 $18 Swimming, horiz. 1.10 .65
Nos. 2420-2422 (3) 1.50 .95

1984, Aug. 8 *Perf. 13*

2423 A527 $2 Gentiana arisanensis .25 .15
2424 A527 $3 Epilobium nankotaizanense .35 .15
2425 A527 $5 Adenophora uehatae .65 .15
2426 A527 $18 Aconitum fukutomei 2.75 .85
Nos. 2423-2426 (4) 4.00
Set value 1.00

The Eighteen Scholars, Sung Dynasty Hanging Scroll — A528

Details.

Wmk. 323

1984, Aug. 20 Litho. *Perf. 13*

2427 A528 $2 Playing instruments *1.10* .15
2428 A528 $3 Playing chess *1.65* .15
2429 A528 $5 Practicing calligraphy *3.50* .25
2430 A528 $18 Painting *15.00* .95
Nos. 2427-2430 (4) *21.25* 1.50

Athletics Day
A529 A530

1984, Sept. 9

2431 A529 $5 Two players .50 .15
2432 A530 $5 One player .50 .15
a. Pair, #2431-2432 1.00 .60
Set value .20

A531 A532

1984, Sept. 9

2433 A531 $10 "20," map of Asia .50 .25

Asian-Pacific Parliamentarians' Union, 20th anniv.

1984, Oct. 10 Litho. *Perf. 12½*

2434 A532 $2 No. 1458 .15 .15
2435 A532 $5 No. 296 .25 .15
2436 A532 $18 Museum 1.00 .70
a. Souv. sheet of 3, #2434-2436 8.00 2.00
Nos. 2434-2436 (3) 1.40 1.00

Postal Museum opening.

Flag, Alliance Emblem — A533

Veteran's Assistance — A534

1984, Oct. 16 *Perf. 13½*

2437 A533 $2 multicolored .25 .15

Grand Alliance for China's Reunification Under the Three Principles of the People Convention, Taipei, Oct. 16-17.

1984, Nov. 1 Litho. *Perf. 13½*

2438 A534 $2 Vignettes .25 .15

Pine Tree A535

Bamboo A535a

Plum Tree — A535b

1984-88

2439 A535 $2 multicolored .15 .15
2440 A535a $8 multicolored .45 .15
2441 A535b $10 grayish tan background .50 .15
a. Pale yellow bister background .35 .15
Nos. 2439-2441 (3) 1.10
Set value .30

Issue dates: Nos. 2439-2441, Nov. 12. No. 2441a, Jan. 12, 1988. See Nos. 2495-2503.

A536

A537

1984, Dec. 1 *Perf. 12x12½*

2442 A536 $1 multicolored .30 .15
2443 A536 $10 multicolored 3.00 .40
a. Min. sheet, 2 each #2442-2443 *6.50* 2.50
Set value .45

New Year 1985 (Year of the Ox).

1985, Jan. 11 Litho. *Perf. 13½*

2444 A537 $5 Scales, legal codes .30 .15

Judicial Day 1985.

Quemoy and Matsu Scenes — A538

1985, Jan. 23 Litho. *Perf. 13½x14*

2445 A538 $2 Ku-kang Lake, Quemoy .15 .15
2446 A538 $5 Kuang-hai Stone, Quemoy .50 .20
2447 A538 $8 Sheng-li Reservoir, Matsu .80 .25
2448 A538 $10 Tung-chu Lighthouse, Matsu .90 .30
Nos. 2445-2448 (4) 2.35 .90

Sir Robert Hart (1835-1911) — A539

1985, Feb. 15 Litho. *Perf. 14x13½*

2449 A539 $2 No. 1 .30 .15

Inspector General of Chinese Customs, 1863-1908, and founder of the Chinese Postal Service.

Lo Fu-hsing (1886-1914) A540

Tsou Jung (1882-1905) A541

1985, Feb. 24 *Perf. 13x13½*

2450 A540 $2 multicolored .30 .15

Perf. 13½x12½

1985, Mar. 29 Engr.

Granite Paper

2451 A541 $3 green .30 .15

Chung-cheng Memorial Hall Main Gate — A542

1985, Apr. 5 Litho. *Perf. 13*

2452 A542 $2 shown .15 .15
2453 A542 $8 Tzuhu Memorial .70 .25
2454 A542 $10 Chiang Kai-shek, vert. .95 .30
Nos. 2452-2454 (3) 1.80 .70

Tenth death anniv. of Chiang Kai-shek.

A543

A544

1985, May 8 Litho. *Perf. 13½*

2455 A543 $2 Carnation .70 .15
2456 A543 $2 Day lily .70 .15
a. Pair, #2455-2456 1.50 .15

Mother's Day.

1985, May 18

2457 A544 $5 Tunnel to Chi-chin Island .35 .25

Kaohsiung Cross-Harbor Tunnel, 1st anniv.

Girl Scouts, 75th Anniv. — A545

Perf. 13½

1985, June 1 Litho. Wmk. 323

2458 A545 $2 multicolored .15 .15
2459 A545 $18 multicolored 1.10 .50

The Book of Odes, Confucius A545a

1985, June 22 Litho. Wmk. 323

2460 A545a $2 Spring *.80* .15
2461 A545a $5 Summer *2.50* .30
2462 A545a $8 Fall *4.00* .45
2463 A545a $10 Winter *4.50* .60
Nos. 2460-2463 (4) *11.80* 1.50

Fruit — A546

Perf. 13½x14

1985, July 5 Litho. Wmk. 323

2464 A546 $2 Wax Jambo .30 .15
2465 A546 $3 Guava .40 .15
2466 A546 $5 Carambola .90 .20
2467 A546 $8 Litchi nut 1.75 .25
Nos. 2464-2467 (4) 3.35 .75

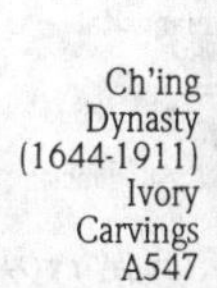

Ch'ing Dynasty (1644-1911) Ivory Carvings A547

1985, July 18 Wmk. 323 *Perf. 13½*

2468 A547 $2 Dragon Boat .15 .15
2469 A547 $3 Landscape .20 .15
2470 A547 $5 Melon, water container .50 .15
2471 A547 $18 Brush holder, vert. 2.00 .55
Nos. 2468-2471 (4) 2.85 1.00

T'ang Dynasty (618-907) Aristocrat — A548

Designs: $5, Sung Dynasty (960-1280) palace woman. $8, Yuan Dynasty (1280-1368) aristocrat. $11, Ming Dynasty (1368-1644) aristocrat.

1985, Aug. 1 Wmk. 323 *Perf. 13½*

2472 A548 $2 multicolored .35 .15
2473 A548 $5 multicolored 1.25 .15
2474 A548 $8 multicolored 2.25 .25
2475 A548 $11 multicolored 2.50 .35
Nos. 2472-2475 (4) 6.35 .90

4th Asian Conf. on Costume, Aug. 3.

See #2549-2552, 2605-2608, 2660-2663. In the 2 rows of Chinese characters above the denomination, the right row has 3 characters and a dot on #2472-2475, 4 characters and a dot on #2549-2552. #2605-2608, 2660-2663 have solid black numerals.

Social Welfare Program A549

Perf. 13½x14

1985, Aug. 1 Wmk. 323

2476 A549 $2 Heart, bird feeding young .25 .15

Historic Sites A550

Perf. 13½

1985, Sept. 3 Litho. Wmk. 323

2477 A550 $2 Taipei North Gate .20 .15
2478 A550 $5 San Domingo Fort, Tamsui .50 .15
2479 A550 $8 Lung Shun Temple, Lukang .85 .20
2480 A550 $10 Confucius Temple, Changhua 1.10 .30
Nos. 2477-2480 (4) 2.65 .80

Bonsai — A551

Trade Shows — A552

Perf. 13½x14

1985, Sept. 22 Wmk. 323

2481 A551 $2 Oak .15 .15
2482 A551 $5 Five-leaf pine .30 .15
2483 A551 $8 Lohan pine .55 .25
2484 A551 $18 Banyan 1.25 .60
Nos. 2481-2484 (4) 2.25 1.15

1985, Oct. 5 *Perf. 13½*

Taipei World Trade Center and show emblems: a, Sporting goods. b, Toys and gifts. c, Electronics. d, Machinery. Se-tenant in continuous design.

2485 Strip of 4 2.75 .45
a.-d. A552 $2 any single .65 .15

Scenes of Modern Taiwan, Map, Flag — A553

1985, Oct. 25

2486 A553 $2 shown .20 .15
2487 A553 $18 Chiang Kai-shek, Triumphal Arch 1.75 .50

Defeat of Japanese army, end of World War II, and return of Taiwan to control of the Republic, 40th anniv.

7th Asian Conference on Mental Retardation A554

Sun Yat-sen and Birthplace A555

1985, Nov. 8 *Perf. 14x13½*

2488 A554 $2 multicolored .15 .15
2489 A554 $11 multicolored .90 .35
Set value .40

1985, Nov. 12 *Perf. 13½*

2490 A555 $2 multicolored .15 .15
2491 A555 $18 multicolored 1.40 .50

Postal Life Insurance, 50th Anniv. — A556

New Year 1986 (Year of the Tiger) — A557

1985, Dec. 1

2492 A556 $2 multicolored .30 .15

1985, Dec. 1 *Perf. 12½*

2493 A557 $1 multicolored .20 .15
2494 A557 $10 multicolored 1.75 .40
a. Min. sheet, 2 each #2493-2494 *9.50* 3.50
Set value .45

Flora Types of 1984

1986, Jan. 10 Litho. *Perf. 13½*

2495 A535 $1 multicolored .15 .15
2496 A535a $11 multicolored .50 .15
2497 A535b $18 multicolored .75 .15

1988, Feb. 12

2498 A535 $1.50 multicolored .15 .15
2499 A535a $7.50 multicolored .45 .15
2500 A535b $16 multicolored 1.10 .35

#2500 has value expressed in dollars and cents.

1989, Feb. 24

2501 A535 $3 multicolored .20 .15
2502 A535a $16.50 multicolored 1.10 .35
2503 A535b $21 multicolored 1.25 .40
Nos. 2495-2503 (9) 5.65 2.00

Cultural Renaissance Movement — A558

Painting: Hermit Anglers on a Mountain Stream, Ming Dynasty, 1386-1644. Se-tenant in a continuous design. (Each stamp is numbered from 1 to 5 in Chinese. See illustrations with Nos. 1682-1691 for numerals.)

1986, Jan. 28 Litho. *Perf. 13½*

2507 Strip of 5 *9.50* .30
a.-e. A558 $2 any single *1.90* .15

See No. 2604.

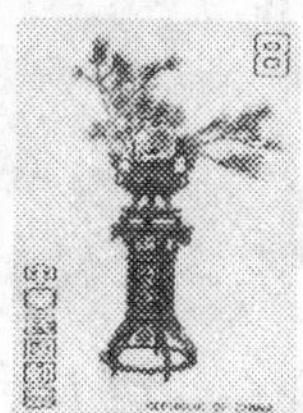

Floral Arrangements A559

Perf. 13½

1986, Feb. 20 Litho. Wmk. 323

2517 A559 $2 denom. UL .15 .15
2518 A559 $5 denom. UR .40 .15
2519 A559 $8 shown .65 .25
2520 A559 $10 denom. UL .80 .30
Nos. 2517-2520 (4) 2.00 .85

Compare with designs A483, A584.

Natl. Postal Service, 90th Anniv. A560

Designs: $2, Unloading express mail at airport. $5, Motorcycle delivery, vert. $8, Technological innovations, vert. $10, Electronic sorting machine.

1986, Mar. 20

2521 A560 $2 multicolored .15 .15
2522 A560 $5 multicolored .30 .15
2523 A560 $8 multicolored .45 .25
2524 A560 $10 multicolored .60 .30
a. Souv. sheet of 4, #2521-2524 4.75 2.00
Nos. 2521-2524 (4) 1.50 .85

Chen Tien-hua (1875-1905), Revolutionary — A561

Perf. 13½x12½

1986, Mar. 29 **Engr.**

Granite Paper

2525 A561 $2 violet .15 .15

Yushan Natl. Park — A562

1986, Apr. 10 **Litho.** ***Perf. 13½***

2526 A562 $2 multicolored .30 .15
2527 A562 $5 multi, diff. .95 .15
2528 A562 $8 multi, diff. 1.65 .30
2529 A562 $10 multi, diff. 1.90 .40
Nos. 2526-2529 (4) 4.80 1.00

Power Plants — A563

1986, Apr. 29

2530 A563 $2 Hydro-electric .15 .15
2531 A563 $8 Thermo-electric .50 .20
2532 A563 $10 Nuclear .60 .30
Nos. 2530-2532 (3) 1.25 .65

Economic prosperity through energy development.

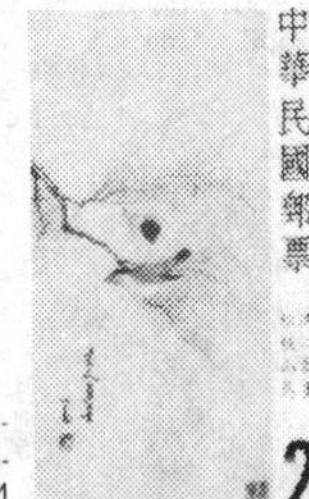

Paintings by P'u Hsin-yu (1896-1963) — A564

1986, May 22 ***Perf. 11½***

2533 A564 $2 Bird .70 .15
2534 A564 $8 Landscape 3.25 .35
2535 A564 $10 Woman in forest 4.50 .40
Nos. 2533-2535 (3) 8.45 .90

Asian Productivity Org., 25th Anniv. A565

1986, June 3 ***Perf. 13x13½***

2536 A565 $2 multicolored .15 .15
2537 A565 $11 multicolored .80 .35
Set value .40

Natl. Productivity Center, 30th anniv.

Coral-reef Fish — A566

Designs: a, Chrysiptera starcki. b, Chelmon rostratus. c, Chaetodon xanthurus. d, Chaetodon quadrimaculatus. e, Chaetodon meyeri. f, Genicanthus semifasciatus. g, Genicanthus semifasciatus. h, Pomacanthus annularis. i, Lienardella fasciata. j, Balistapus undulatus.

1986, June 3 ***Perf. 13½***

2538 Block of 10 4.00 1.25
a.-j. A566 $2 any single .40 .15

Protection of Intellectual Property Rights — A567

1986, June 12

2539 A567 $2 Macaw .50 .15

Nos. 2294, 2297 Surcharged

1986, July 9 **Litho.** ***Perf. 13½***

2540 A432 $2 on $6 multi .15 .15
2541 A432 $8 on $9 multi .50 .30

60th Anniv. of northward expedition by the national revolutionary army.

Bridges A568

1986, July 30

2542 A568 $2 Tzu Mu, 1965 .30 .15
2543 A568 $5 Chang Hung, 1968 .70 .15
2544 A568 $8 Kuan Fu, 1977 1.25 .25
2545 A568 $10 Kuan Tu, 1983 1.75 .30
Nos. 2542-2545 (4) 4.00 .85

Love between Liang Shanpo and Chu Yingtai, Folk Tale — A569

Cartoons by Huang Mu-ts'un: a, Yingtai disguised to go to school. b, Yingtai and Shanpo meet in class. c, The friends at pond. d, Yingtai summoned home for arranged marriage. e, Yingtai and Shanpo ascend to heaven as butterflies (each stamp is numbered from 1 to 5 in Chinese. See illustrations with Nos. 1682-1691 for numerals.)

1986, Aug. 12 ***Perf. 12½***

2546 Strip of 5 4.00 .75
a.-e. A569 $5 any single .75 .15

Social Awareness Campaign A570

1986, Sept. 12 **Litho.** ***Perf. 13½***

2547 A570 $2 Rainbow, children .15 .15
2548 A570 $8 Children, adults .60 .30

Folk Costumes — A571

Designs: $2, Shang Dynasty (1766-1122 B.C.) aristocrat. $5, Warring States (403-221 B.C.) aristocrat. $8, Later Han Dynasty (A.D. 25-221) empress. $10, Flying ribbons gown, Wei and Tsin Dynasties (A.D. 221-420) aristocrat.

1986, Sept. 23 **Litho.** ***Perf. 13½***

2549 A571 $2 multicolored .50 .15
2550 A571 $5 multicolored 1.10 .20
2551 A571 $8 multicolored 1.75 .30
2552 A571 $10 multicolored 2.50 .35
Nos. 2549-2552 (4) 5.85 1.00

Ch'ing Dynasty Ju-i Scepters A572

1986, Oct. 10 **Photo.** ***Perf. 14½x15***

2553 A572 $2 White jade .20 .15
2554 A572 $3 Red coral .25 .15
2555 A572 $4 Redwood and gems .35 .15
2556 A572 $18 Gilded wood 1.65 .55
Nos. 2553-2556 (4) 2.45 1.00

See Nos. 2582-2585.

Chiang Kai-shek A573

Portrait and: $5, Map and flag. $8, Emblem. $10, Flags on globe.

1986, Oct. 31 **Litho.** ***Perf. 13½***

2557 A573 $2 multicolored .25 .15
2558 A573 $5 multicolored .55 .15
2559 A573 $8 multicolored .95 .25
2560 A573 $10 multicolored 1.10 .30
a. Souv. sheet of 4, #2557-2560 7.25 3.00
Nos. 2557-2560 (4) 2.85 .85

Cultural Heritage A574

Architecture: $2, Chin-Kuang Fu land development and defense fund building, 1826. $5, Erh-shawan Gun Emplacement, Keelung, 1841, restored 1979. $8, Fort Hsi T'ai, 1886. $10, Matsu Temple, Peng-hu, renovated 1563-1624.

1986, Nov. 14 **Litho.** ***Perf. 13½***

2561 A574 $2 multicolored .20 .15
2562 A574 $5 multicolored .40 .20
2563 A574 $8 multicolored .70 .30
2564 A574 $10 multicolored .90 .35
Nos. 2561-2564 (4) 2.20 1.00

New Year 1987 (Year of the Hare) — A575

1986, Dec. 1 ***Perf. 12½***

2565 A575 $1 dl pink & multi .20 .15
2566 A575 $10 pale grn & multi 1.75 .40
a. Souv. sheet, 2 each #2565-2566 *13.00* 2.50

Kenting, 1st Natl. Park — A576

1987, Jan. 8 **Litho.** ***Perf. 13½***

2567 A576 $2 Garden .35 .15
2568 A576 $5 Shore rocks .65 .20
2569 A576 $8 Shore and hill 1.10 .30
2570 A576 $10 Shore and rocks, diff. 1.40 .40
Nos. 2567-2570 (4) 3.50 1.05

Folk Art — A577

Puppets: $2, Hand puppet. $5, Marionette. $18, Shadow puppet.

1987, Feb. 12 **Litho.** ***Perf. 14x13½***

2571 A577 $2 multicolored .30 .15
2572 A577 $5 multicolored .50 .15
2573 A577 $18 multicolored 2.25 .60
Nos. 2571-2573 (3) 3.05
Set value .75

Speedpost A578

Wu Yueh (1878-1905), Revolutionary A579

1987, Mar. 20 **Litho.** ***Perf. 14x13½***

2574 A578 $2 multicolored .15 .15
2575 A578 $18 multicolored .90 .55
Set value .60

Stamp Day.

Perf. 13½x12½

1987, Mar. 29 **Engr.**

2576 A579 $2 orange .70 .15

Landscapes Painted by Madame Chiang Kai-shek — A580

Designs: $2, Singing Creek with Bamboo Orchestra. $5, Mountains Draped in Clouds. $8, Vista of Tranquility. $10, Mountains after a Snowfall.

1987, Apr. 10 **Litho.** ***Perf. 13½***

2577 A580 $2 blk, buff & ver .55 .15
2578 A580 $5 blk, buff & ver 1.50 .25
2579 A580 $8 blk, buff & ver 2.25 .40
2580 A580 $10 blk, buff & ver 2.75 .50
Nos. 2577-2580 (4) 7.05 1.30

Stone Sculptures — A581

Designs: a, Head of a Bodhisattva, sandstone, Norther Wei Dynasty (386-534). b, Standing Buddha, limestone, Northern Ch'i Dynasty (550-577). c, Head of a Bodhisattva, sandstone, T'ang Dynasty (618-907). d, Seated Buddha, alabaster, T'ang Dynasty.

1987, Apr. 23
2581 Strip of 4 3.00 1.40
a.-d. A581 $5 any single .65 .35

No. 2581a shows seven Chinese characters at left; No. 2581c shows five.

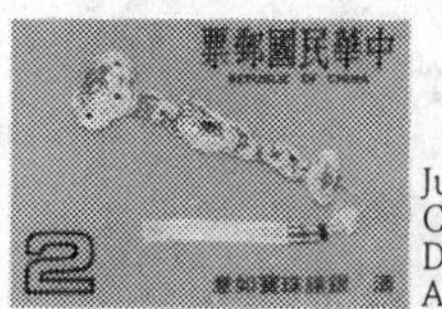

Ju-i Scepters, Ch'ing Dynasty A582

1987, May 7 Photo. *Perf. 14½x15*
2582 A582 $2 Silver and gems .45 .15
2583 A582 $3 Gold and gems .70 .15
2584 A582 $4 Gilded, jade and inlaid gems .95 .15
2585 A582 $18 Gilded, inlaid malachite 4.00 .65
Nos. 2582-2585 (4) 6.10
Set value .90

Feitsui Reservoir Inauguration A583

1987, June 6 Litho. *Perf. 13½x14*
2586 A583 $2 Reservoir .15 .15
2587 A583 $18 Hsintien Stream, reservoir 1.65 .65

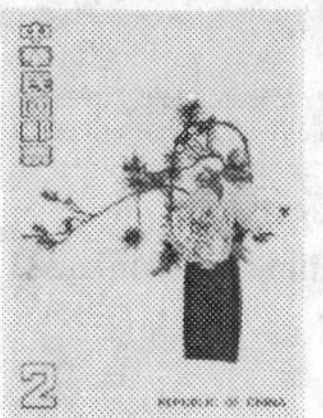

Flower Arrangements by Huang Yung-ch'uan A584

Lions Club Intl. 70th Annual Convention, Taipei A585

1987, June 19 *Perf. 13½*
2588 A584 $2 denom. LL .20 .15
2589 A584 $5 denom. LL .50 .20
2590 A584 $8 Flowers in brown vase .75 .30
2591 A584 $10 denom. UR .95 .35
Nos. 2588-2591 (4) 2.40 1.00

Compare with designs A483, A559.

1987, July 1
2592 A585 $2 multicolored .15 .15
2593 A585 $18 multicolored 1.10 .65

Sino-Japanese War, 50th Anniv. A586

Wang Yun-wu (1888-1979), Lexicographer A587

1987, July 7 *Perf. 14x13½*
2594 A586 $1 Battle front .15 .15
2595 A586 $2 Chiang Kai-shek giving speech .15 .15
2596 A586 $5 Public donating funds .30 .15
2597 A586 $6 Troops marching .40 .20
2598 A586 $8 Signing of peace treaty .50 .25
2599 A586 $18 Parade 1.10 .50
Nos. 2594-2599 (6) 2.60 1.40

1987, Aug. 14 *Perf. 13½*
2600 A587 $2 gray black .20 .15

Memorial Hall Type of 1981

Perf. 12½x13½

1987, Sept. 24 Photo.
2601 A468 10c lake .15 .15
2602 A468 30c brt green .15 .15
2603 A468 60c brt blue .30 .15
Set value .50 .25

A588

Cultural Renaissance Movement — A589

Scroll, 1543, by Weng Chen-ming (1470-1559), a copy of Chao Po-su's *Red Cliff.* Nos. 2604a-2604e and 2604f-2604j are printed in continuous designs. (Each stamp is numbered from 1 to 10 in Chinese. See illustrations with Nos. 1682-1691 for numerals.)

1987, Sept. 22 Engr. *Perf. 13½*
2604 Block of 10 10.00 3.50
a.-e. A588 $3 any single .75 .30
f.-j. A589 $3 any single .75 .30

Folk Costumes — A590

Designs: $1.50, Han woman, early Ch'ing Dynasty (1644-1911). $3, Wife of a Ch'ing Dynasty Manchu Bannerman. $7.50, Urban woman wearing Manchu ch'i-p'ao dress, c. 1912. $18, Short jacket over long skirt, c. 1920.

1987, Oct. 2 Litho.
2605 A590 $1.50 multicolored *.30* .15
2606 A590 $3 multicolored *.60* .15
2607 A590 $7.50 multicolored *1.40* .25
2608 A590 $18 multicolored *3.50* .65
Nos. 2605-2608 (4) *5.80* 1.20

Nos. 2605-2608 have 3 groups of 2 smaller Chinese characters above denomination. Nos. 2660-2663 have 2 groups of 2 and 4 characters.

A591

A592

1987, Nov. 12 *Perf. 13½x14*
2609 A591 $3 Ta Chen Tian temple, Taichung .25 .15
2610 A591 $18 Confucius 1.40 .65

Intl. Symposium on Confucianism, Taipei, Nov. 12-17.

1987, Dec. 1 *Perf. 12½*
2611 A592 $1.50 multicolored .30 .15
2612 A592 $12 multicolored 2.00 .40
a. Souv. sheet, 2 each #2611-2612 11.00 3.00
Set value .45

New Year 1988 (Year of the Dragon).

Constitution, 40th Anniv. A593

1987, Dec. 25 Litho. *Perf. 13½*
2613 A593 $3 multicolored .15 .15
2614 A593 $16 multi, diff. .85 .65

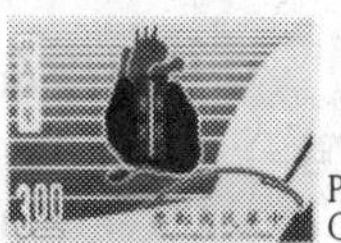

Prevent Hypertension Campaign — A594

1988, Jan. 8 *Perf. 12½x13½*
2615 A594 $3 multicolored .25 .15

Fruit Tree Blossoms — A595

Perf. 13½

1988, Feb. 4 Litho. Wmk. 323
2616 A595 $3 Prunus mume .70 .15
2617 A595 $7.50 Prunus armeniaca 1.65 .45
2618 A595 $12 Prunus persica 2.50 .70
a. Min. sheet of 3, #2616-2618 *24.00 24.00*

Perf. 13½

1988, May 5 Litho. Wmk. 323
2619 A595 $3 Paeonia suffruticosa .70 .15
2620 A595 $7.50 Punica granatum 1.65 .45
2621 A595 $12 Nelumbo nucifera 2.50 .70
a. Min. sheet of 3, #2619-2621 *15.00 15.00*

Perf. 13½

1988, Aug. 9 Litho. Wmk. 323
2622 A595 $3 Impatiens balsamina .70 .15
2623 A595 $7.50 Osmanthus fragrans 1.65 .45
2624 A595 $12 Chrysanthemum morifolium 2.50 .70
a. Min. sheet of 3, #2622-2624 *11.00 11.00*

Perf. 13½

1988, Nov. 7 Litho. Wmk. 323
2625 A595 $3 Hibiscus mutabilis .50 .15
2626 A595 $7.50 Camellia japonica 1.10 .45
2627 A595 $12 Narcissus tazetta 1.65 .70
a. Min. sheet of 3, #2625-2627 *12.50 12.50*
Nos. 2616-2627 (12) 17.80 5.20

Tourism Day — A596

Folk art: $3, Modeled dough figurines. $7.50, Blown sweet-malt sugar candy. $16, Sugar paintings.

Perf. 13½x14

1988, Mar. 2 Litho. Wmk. 323
2628 A596 $3 multicolored .45 .15
2629 A596 $7.50 multicolored .90 .45
2630 A596 $16 multicolored 2.25 .90
Nos. 2628-2630 (3) 3.60 1.50

A597

A598

Perf. 13½x12½

1988, Mar. 29 Engr. Wmk. 323
2631 A597 $3 brown .30 .20

Hsu Hsi-lin (1873-1907), hero of the revolution.

1988 Litho. *Perf. 13½*
2632 A598 $1.50 Biotechnology .15 .15
2633 A598 $3 Energy resources .20 .15
2634 A598 $7 Immunization .40 .35
2635 A598 $7.50 Automation .45 .40
2636 A598 $10 Telecommunications .60 .50
2637 A598 $12 Laser technology .70 .60
2638 A598 $16 Micro-optics .95 .80
2639 A598 $16.50 Agricultural research .95 .85
Nos. 2632-2639 (8) 4.40 3.80

Industrialization by technological development. Issued: $3, $7.50, $10, $16, Apr. 22; other, May 9.

Police Day — A599

Perf. 13½

1988, June 15 Litho. Wmk. 323
2640 A599 $3 Traffic control .20 .20
2641 A599 $12 Rescue operations .80 .70

Amphibians A600

1988, July 8 *Perf. 13½x14*
2642 A600 $1.50 Microhyla butleri *.45* .15
2643 A600 $3 Rana taipehensis *.85* .20
2644 A600 $7.50 Microhyla inornata *2.25* .45
2645 A600 $16 Rhacophorus smaragdinus *4.50* 1.00
Nos. 2642-2645 (4) *8.05* 1.80

China Broadcasting Corp. (BBC), 60th Anniv. A601

Perf. 13½

1988, Aug. 1 Litho. Wmk. 323
2646 A601 $3 multicolored .25 .20

Victory at the Battle of Kinmen, 30th Anniv. A602

Designs: $1.50, Chiang Kai-shek and artillery commander. $3, With troops. $7.50, Cannon. $12, Tanks.

1988, Aug. 23
2647 A602 $1.50 multicolored .15 .15
2648 A602 $3 multicolored .20 .20
2649 A602 $7.50 multicolored .45 .45
2650 A602 $12 multicolored .75 .60
Nos. 2647-2650 (4) 1.55 1.40

Sports Promotion — A603

Designs: Nos. 2651-2652, Basketball. Nos. 2653-2654, Baseball.

1988, Sept. 9

2651 A603 $5 Players .85 .30
2652 A603 $5 Players .85 .30
a. Pair, #2651-2652 1.75 1.25
2653 A603 $5 Batter .85 .30
2654 A603 $5 Catcher .85 .30
a. Pair, #2653-2654 1.75 1.25
Nos. 2651-2654 (4) 3.40 1.20

#2652a, 2654a have continuous designs.

Yangmingshan Natl. Park — A604

1988, Sept. 16

2655 A604 $1.50 Volcanic crater *.15* .15
2656 A604 $3 Lake *.25* .15
2657 A604 $7.50 Tatun Volcanic Range *.70* .30
2658 A604 $16 Dormant volcano *1.40* .65
Nos. 2655-2658 (4) *2.50* 1.25

Lofty Mount Lu, a Hanging Scroll, 1467, By Shen Chou (1427-1509) — A605

Painting details: a, UL. b, UR. c, LL. d, LR.

Perf. 11½

1988, Oct. 9 Litho. Wmk. 323

2659 A605 Block of 4 *6.00* 1.25
a.-d. $5 any single *1.50* .30

Folk Costumes — A606

Designs: $2, Shang Dynasty (1766-1122 B.C.) nobleman. $3, Warring States (403-221) B.C.) ruler. $7.50, Wei-Chin Period (221-420) official. $12, Northern Dynasties (502-581) official.

Perf. 13½x14

1988, Mar. 2 Litho. Wmk. 323

2660 A606 $2 multicolored *.40* .15
2661 A606 $3 multicolored *.60* .20
2662 A606 $7.50 multicolored *1.50* .45
2663 A606 $12 multicolored *2.50* .70
Nos. 2660-2663 (4) *5.00* 1.50

Nos. 2721-2724 have groups of 2 and 6 Chinese characters above denomination; Nos. 2660-2663 groups of 2 and 4; #2794-2797 groups of 1 and 5.

A607

A608

1988, Dec. 1 *Perf. 12½*

2664 A607 $2 multicolored *.70* .15
2665 A607 $13 multicolored *4.50* .80
a. Souv. sheet, 2 each #2664-2665 *15.00* 15.00

New Year 1989 (Year of the Snake).

Perf. 13½

1989, Jan. 4 Litho. Wmk. 323

2666 A608 $3 black .45 .20

Tai Ch'uan-hsien (1890-1949), party leader.

Pres. Chiang Ching-kuo (1910-88) A609

1989, Jan. 13

2667 A609 $3 shown .15 .15
2668 A609 $6 Suffrage .35 .25
2669 A609 $7.50 Industry .40 .35
2670 A609 $16 Children .90 .75
Nos. 2667-2670 (4) 1.80 1.50

Ni Ying-tien (1884-1910), Revolution Leader — A610

Perf. 13½x12½

1989, Mar. 28 Engr. Wmk. 323

2671 A610 $3 black .25 .20

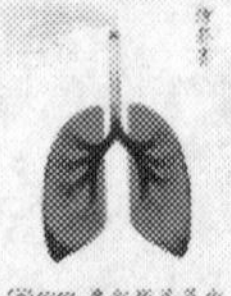

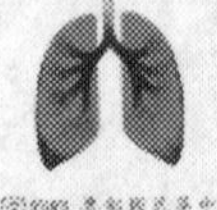

Stop Smoking — A611

Lighthouses — A612

Perf. 13½x12½

1989, Apr. 7 Litho. Wmk. 323

2672 A611 $3 multicolored .25 .20

1989-91 *Perf. 13½*

2673 A612 75c Mu Tou Yu .15 .15
2674 A612 $2 Lu Tao .20 .15
2675 A612 $2.25 Pen Chia Yu .25 .15
2676 A612 $3 Pitou Chiao .30 .15
2677 A612 $4.50 Tungyin Tao .35 .15
2678 A612 $6 Chilai Pi .55 .30
2679 A612 $7 Fukwei Chiao .65 .40
2680 A612 $7.50 Hua Yu .70 .40
2681 A612 $9 Oluan Pi .80 .30
2682 A612 $10 Kaohsiung .90 .50
2683 A612 $10.50 Yuweng Tao .95 .40
2683A A612 $12 Tungchu Tao 1.10 .60
2683B A612 $13 Yeh Liu 1.25 .50
2683C A612 $15 Tungchi Yu 1.40 .90
2684 A612 $16.50 Chimei Yu 1.50 .85
Nos. 2673-2684 (15) 11.05 5.90

Issue dates: $7, $15, May 19, 1990. $6, $12, Jan. 9, 1991. $2, $3, $7.50, $10, $16.50, May 20, 1991. Others, 1989.

See Nos. 2811-2823.

1st Natl. Wealth Survey A613

1989, May 18 Litho. *Perf. 13½*

2685 A613 $3 multicolored .45 .20

Ch'u Ts'u Collection of Poems, 722-481 B.C. — A614

Excerpts: $3, "I once tended nine fields of orchids; Also I had planted a hundred rods of melilotus" (Li Sao). $7.50, "No grief is greater than parting of the living; No joy is more than making new friends" (Chiu Ko, shao ssu ming). $12, "Since my heart is straight and good, Why should I be chagrined at living remote and neglected?" (Chiu Chang, she chiang). $16, "The steed will not gallop itself into servitude; The phoenix has no appetite for slave food." (Chiu Pien).

Perf. 11½x12

1989, June 7 Photo. Granite Paper

2686 A614 $3 Man overlooking fields .35 .20
2687 A614 $7.50 Map, woman on path .90 .50
2688 A614 $12 Man holding staff 1.50 .80
2689 A614 $16 Man, stallion, stone gate 2.00 1.10
Nos. 2686-2689 (4) 4.75 2.60

Compare with types A629, A663. Nos. 2686-2689 have two Chinese characters near denomination. Nos. 2725-2728 have groups of 3 and 4 characters.

Taipei Subway Inauguration A615

1989, June 27 Litho. *Perf. 13½*

2690 A615 $3 Subway tunnel .25 .20
2691 A615 $16 Entering underground 1.25 1.10

Butterflies A616

Designs: $2, *Graphium sarpedon connectens.* $3, *Papilio memnon heronus.* $7.50, *Princeps demoleus libanius.* $9, *Pachliopa aristolochiae interpositas.*

Perf. 13½

1989, July 14 Litho. Wmk. 323

2692 A616 $2 multicolored .45 .15
2693 A616 $3 multicolored .70 .15
2694 A616 $7.50 multicolored 1.75 .40
2695 A616 $9 multicolored 2.25 .50
Nos. 2692-2695 (4) 5.15 1.20

Compare with design A627.

Ch'ing Dynasty Teapots from I-Hsing of Kiangsu, 1644-1911 A617

1989, July 28 *Perf. 13½x14*

2696 A617 $2 multicolored .25 .15
2697 A617 $3 multi, diff. .50 .15
2698 A617 $12 multi, diff. 1.75 .65
2699 A617 $16 multi, diff. 2.50 .90
Nos. 2696-2699 (4) 5.00 1.85

For stamps with teapot designs and solid black denominations see Nos. 2760-2764.

Intl. Seminar on Fan Chung-yen (989-1052), Military Leader and Civil Service Reformer — A618

Perf. 14x13½

1989, Sept. 1 Litho. Wmk. 323

2700 A618 $12 multicolored .90 .65

Autumn Colors on the Ch'iao and Hua Mountains, 14th Cent., by Ch'iao Meng-fu A619

Designs: a, Right side of mountain, trees. b, Trees, left side of mountain. c, House, trees. d, shown.

Perf. 13½

1989, Oct. 5 Litho. Wmk. 323

2701 Strip of 4 9.50 3.00
a.-d. A619 $7.50 any single 2.25 .75

Social Welfare A619a

1989, Nov. 3 Litho. *Perf. 13½*

2701E A619a $3 multicolored .25 .15

Taroko Natl. Park — A620

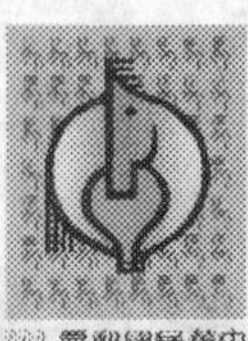

New Year 1990 (Year of the Horse) — A621

Designs: $2, Marble gorge, Liwu River. $3, Hohuan Mountain. $12, Waterfall, Cirque of Nanhu. $16, Chingshui Cliff.

Perf. 13½

1989, Nov. 28 Litho. Wmk. 323

2702 A620 $2 multicolored .15 .15
2703 A620 $3 multicolored .15 .15
2704 A620 $12 multicolored .65 .65
2705 A620 $16 multicolored .90 .90
Nos. 2702-2705 (4) 1.85 1.85

1989, Dec. 1 *Perf. 12½*

2706 A621 $2 multicolored .20 .15
2707 A621 $13 multicolored 1.65 .75
a. Souv. sheet, 2 each #2706-2707 9.00 3.00

Yu Lu — A622

Men Shen, "guardian spirits" (likenesses of legendary beings placed on residence doors at the new year): No. 2708, Yu Lu. No. 2709, Shen Shu. No. 2710, Wei-ch'ih Ching-te. No. 2711, Ch'in Shu-pao.

Perf. 13½

1990, Jan. 19 Litho. Wmk. 323

2708 A622 $3 shown 1.50 .20
2709 A622 $3 "$3" at LR 1.50 .20
a. Pair, #2708-2709 3.00 3.50
2710 A622 $7.50 "$7.50" at LL 3.25 .55
2711 A622 $7.50 "$7.50" at LR 3.25 .55
a. Pair, #2710-2711 6.50 7.50
Nos. 2708-2711 (4) 9.50 1.50

Nos. 2709a, 2711a have continuous designs.

A623

Scenery — A624

Designs: $2, Lishan House, Pear Mountain. $18, Tayu Pass, Tayuling, vert.

Perf. 13½

1990, Feb. 10 Litho. Wmk. 323

2712 A623 $2 multicolored .20 .15
2713 A624 $18 multicolored 1.75 1.10

Labor Insurance System, 40th Anniv. — A625

1990, Mar. 1

2714 A625 $3 multicolored .50 .20

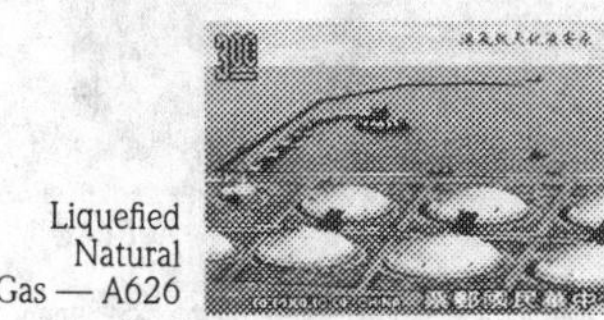

Liquefied Natural Gas — A626

Designs: $3, Terminal, Yung-an Hsiang of Kaohsiung. $16, Container ship, map, refinery, vert.

1990, Mar. 31 Litho. *Perf. 13½*

2715 A626 $3 multicolored .25 .20
2716 A626 $16 multicolored 1.25 .90

Butterflies A627

1990, Apr. 20

2717 A627 $2 *Salatura genutia* .15 .15
2718 A627 $3 *Hypolimnas misippus* .30 .20
2719 A627 $7.50 *Pieris canidia* .75 .40
2720 A627 $9 *Precis almana* .80 .50
Nos. 2717-2720 (4) 2.00 1.25

Compare with design A616.

Folk Costumes — A628

Designs: $2, Official, Sui and T'ang Dynasties (589-907). $3, Official, T'ang and Sung Dynasties (618-1280). $7.50, Royal guardsman, Chin and Yuan Dynasties (1115-1368). $12, Highest ranking civil official, Ming Dynasty (1368-1644).

1990, May 10 Litho. *Perf. 13½*

2721 A628 $2 multicolored .25 .15
2722 A628 $3 multicolored .45 .20
2723 A628 $7.50 multicolored 1.00 .40
2724 A628 $12 multicolored 1.90 .70
Nos. 2721-2724 (4) 3.60 1.45

See note after No. 2663.

Yueh Fu Classical Poetry — A629

Lyrics from Tzu-yeh folk songs, Six Dynasties (222-589): $3, Spring Song at Midnight. $7.50, Summer Song at Midnight. $12, Autumn Song at Midnight. $16, Winter Song at Midnight.

Perf. 11½

1990, June 27 Litho. Wmk. 323

Granite Paper

2725 A629 $3 shown .55 .20
2726 A629 $7.50 Couple, river 1.40 .50
2727 A629 $12 Washing clothes, river 2.25 .80
2728 A629 $16 River in winter 3.25 1.10
Nos. 2725-2728 (4) 7.45 2.60

Bonsai A630

Designs: $3, *Pinus thunbergii parl.* $6.50, *Ehretia microphylla lamk.* $12, *Buxus harlandii hance.* $16, *Celtis sinensis pers.*

1990, July 20 Litho. *Perf. 13½*

2729 A630 $3 multicolored .20 .20
2730 A630 $6.50 multicolored .50 .40
2731 A630 $12 multicolored .85 .80
2732 A630 $16 multicolored 1.10 1.00
Nos. 2729-2732 (4) 2.65 2.40

Snuff Bottles — A631

1990, Aug. 9

2733 A631 $3 Bamboo stem shaped .20 .20
2734 A631 $6 Peony motif .40 .40
2735 A631 $9 Amber .60 .55
2736 A631 $16 White jade 1.10 1.00
Nos. 2733-2736 (4) 2.30 2.15

Formosan Firecrest A632

1990, Aug. 20 Litho. *Perf. 13½*

2737 A632 $2 shown .15 .15
2738 A632 $3 Laughing thrush .20 .15
2739 A632 $7.50 White-eared sibia .50 .35
2740 A632 $16 Yellow tit 1.10 .80
Nos. 2737-2740 (4) 1.95 1.45

Sports — A633

1990, Sept. 8 Litho. *Perf. 13½*

2741 A633 $2 Sprint .15 .15
2742 A633 $3 Long jump .20 .15
2743 A633 $7 Pole vault .50 .40
2744 A633 $16 High hurdle 1.10 .80
Nos. 2741-2744 (4) 1.95 1.50

Flying Tigers, 50th Anniv. A634

1990, Sept. 26 Litho. *Perf. 13½*

2745 A634 $3 multicolored .45 .15

Children's Drawings A635

1990, Oct. 9

2746 A635 $2 Cat .15 .15
2747 A635 $3 Peacocks .25 .15
2748 A635 $7.50 Chickens .60 .40
2749 A635 $12 Cattle 1.00 .65
Nos. 2746-2749 (4) 2.00 1.35

National Theater A636

Photo. & Engr.

1990, Oct. 30 *Perf. 13½*

2750 A636 $3 shown .30 .15
2751 A636 $12 Natl. concert hall 1.10 .65

A637

A638

Ancient money.

1990, Nov. 5 Litho. *Perf. 13x13½*

2752 A637 $2 Shell .15 .15
2753 A637 $3 Oyster .15 .15
2754 A637 $6.50 Bone .35 .35
2755 A637 $7.50 Jade .40 .40
2756 A637 $9 Bronze .50 .50
Nos. 2752-2756 (5) 1.55 1.55

1990, Dec. 1 *Perf. 12½*

2757 A638 $2 multicolored .50 .15
2758 A638 $13 multicolored 1.75 .65
a. Souv. sheet, 2 each #2757-2758 *8.50* 2.50

New Year 1991 (Year of the Sheep).

Hu Shih (1891-1962), Educator — A639

Perf. 13½

1990, Dec. 17 Engr. Wmk. 323

2759 A639 $3 purple .20 .15

Teapots, Natl. Palace Museum A640

Teapots: $2, Blue phoenix, Ming Dynasty. $3, Dragon handle and spout, Ming Dynasty. $9, Blue landscape, flowered top, Ch'ing Dynasty. $12, Rectangular, passion flower motif, Ch'ing Dynasty. $16, Rectangular, flower motif, Ch'ing Dynasty.

1991, Jan. 18 Photo. *Perf. 12*

Granite Paper

2760 A640 $2 yel, blk & blue .15 .15
2761 A640 $3 brt yel grn & blk .20 .15
2762 A640 $9 pink & multi .60 .45
2763 A640 $12 vio & multi .80 .60
2764 A640 $16 lt bl & multi 1.10 .95
Nos. 2760-2764 (5) 2.85 2.30

God of Happiness — A641

God of Joy — A642

1991, Feb. 7 Litho. *Perf. 13½*

2765 A641 $3 shown .45 .15
2766 A641 $3 God of Wealth .45 .15
2767 A642 $7.50 shown 1.10 .40
2768 A642 $7.50 God of Longevity 1.10 .40
Nos. 2765-2768 (4) 3.10 1.10

1991 *Perf. 13½ Vert.*

2765a A641 $3 *.80* .15
2766a A641 $3 *.80* .15
2767a A642 $7.50 *.80* .15
2768a A642 $7.50 *.80* .15
b. Bklt. pane of 8, 2 each #2765a-2768a + label *9.50*

Native Plants A643

Designs: $2, Petasites formosanus. $3, Heloniopsis acutifolia. $7.50, Disporum shimadai. $9, Viola nagasawai.

1991, Mar. 12 Litho. *Perf. 13½*

2769 A643 $2 multicolored .15 .15
2770 A643 $3 multicolored .25 .15
2771 A643 $7.50 multicolored .65 .40
2772 A643 $9 multicolored .80 .45

1991, June 12

Designs: $2, Gaultheria itoana. $3, Lysionotus montanus. $7.50, Leontopodium microphyllum. $9, Gentiana flavo-maculata.

2773 A643 $2 multicolored .15 .15
2774 A643 $3 multicolored .30 .15
2775 A643 $7.50 multicolored .80 .40
2776 A643 $9 multicolored 1.00 .45

1991, Sept. 12

Designs: $3.50, Rosa transmorrisonensis. $5, Impatiens devolii. $9, Impatiens uniflora. $12, Impatiens tayemonii.

2777 A643 $3.50 multicolored .30 .20
2778 A643 $5 multicolored .50 .25
2779 A643 $9 multicolored .85 .45
2780 A643 $12 multicolored 1.10 .60

1991, Dec. 12

Designs: $3.50, Kalanchoe garambiensis. $5, Pieris taiwanensis. $9, Pleione formosana. $12, Elaeagnus oldhamii.

2781 A643 $3.50 multicolored .30 .15
2782 A643 $5 multicolored .40 .25
2783 A643 $9 multicolored .80 .50
2784 A643 $12 multicolored 1.00 .60
Nos. 2769-2784 (16) 9.35 5.30

Hsiung Cheng-Chi (1887-1910), Revolutionary — A644

Perf. 13½x12½

1991, Mar. 28 Engr.

2785 A644 $3 blue .20 .15

Republic of China, 80th Anniv. A645

1991, Mar. 28 Litho. *Perf. 13½*

2786 A645 $3 Agriculture .20 .15
2787 A645 $7.50 Science & technology .55 .40
2788 A645 $12 Cultural activities .85 .60
2789 A645 $16 Transportation 1.25 .80
Nos. 2786-2789 (4) 2.85 1.95

Children's Toys — A646

Folk Costumes — A647

1991, Apr. 20 Litho. *Perf. 13½*

2790 A646 $3 Bamboo pony .25 .15
2791 A646 $3 Woven-grass grasshopper .25 .15
2792 A646 $3 Top .25 .15
2793 A646 $3 Pinwheels .25 .15
a. Souv. sheet of 4, #2790-2793 5.75 2.00
Nos. 2790-2793 (4) 1.00 .60

See Nos. 2840-2843. Compare with designs A676, A696.

1991 *Perf. 13½ Vert.*

2790a A646 $3 .90 .15
2791a A646 $3 .90 .15
2792a A646 $3 .90 .15
2793b A646 $3 .90 .15
c. Bklt. pane, 2 each #2790a-2793b + label 8.00
Nos. 2790a-2793b (4) 3.60 .60

1991, June 29 Litho. *Perf. 13½*

Ch'ing Dynasty (1644-1911): $2, Winter court hat, Mang robe. $3, Summer court hat, surcoat. $7.50, Winter overcoat. $12, Common hat, traveling robe.

2794 A647 $2 multicolored .35 .15
2795 A647 $3 multicolored .50 .15
2796 A647 $7.50 multicolored 1.25 .40
2797 A647 $12 multicolored 1.90 .60
Nos. 2794-2797 (4) 4.00 1.30

See note after No. 2724.

Nos. 2794-2797 have groups of one and five Chinese characters.

Traffic Safety Year — A648

1991, July 17 Litho. *Perf. 13½*

2798 A648 $3 shown .35 .15
2799 A648 $7.50 Don't drink & drive .85 .40

Cloisonne Enamel Lions, Ch'ing Dynasty (1644-1911)
A649 A649a

1991, July 20 Litho. *Perf. 12½*

2800 A649 yel grn & multi
2801 A649a violet & multi
Set value 2.00

#2800 paid basic domestic rate, #2801 paid basic express mail rate on date of issue.

Fruits — A650 Birds — A651

1991, Aug. 10 Litho. *Perf. 14x13½*

2802 A650 $3 Strawberry .20 .15
2803 A650 $7.50 Grapes .50 .40
2804 A650 $9 Mango .60 .50
2805 A650 $16 Sugar apple 1.10 .85
Nos. 2802-2805 (4) 2.40 1.90

1991, Aug. 24 *Perf. 13½*

Designs: a, Myiophoneus insularis. b, Cinclus pallasii. c, Aix galericulata. d, Nycticorax nycticorax. e, Egretta garzetta. f, Rhyacornis fuliginosus. g, Enicurus scouleri. h, Motacilla cinerea. i, Alcedo atthis. j, Motacilla alba.

2806 Block of 10 4.50 2.75
a.-j. A651 $5 any single .45 .25

Outdoor Activities A652

Perf. 13½

1991, Sept. 27 Litho. Wmk. 323

2807 A652 $2 Rock climbing .15 .15
2808 A652 $3 Fishing .25 .15
2809 A652 $7.50 Bird watching .55 .40
2810 A652 $10 Playing in water .75 .60
Nos. 2807-2810 (4) 1.70 1.30

Intl. Federation of Camping and Caravaning, 1991 Rally.

Lighthouse Type of 1989
Inscription Panel in Blue

1991-92 *Perf. 13½*

2811 A612 50c like #2683C .15 .15
2811A A612 $1 like #2683 .15 .15
2812 A612 $3.50 like #2678 .25 .20
2813 A612 $5 like #2679 .40 .25
a. Booklet pane of 10 4.00
2814 A612 $12 like #2683A .90 .60
a. $12 Booklet pane of 5 + label 4.75
2816 A612 $19 like #2684A 1.40 1.00
2817 A612 $20 like #2678 1.50 1.00
2818 A612 $26 like #2683 2.00 1.40
2819 A612 $28 like #2684 2.00 1.40

1992

2820 A612 $7 like #2676 .50 .35
2821 A612 $9 like #2681 .70 .45
2822 A612 $10 like #2682 .75 .50
2823 A612 $13 like #2675 .95 .65
Nos. 2811-2823 (13) 11.65 8.10

Issue dates: 50c, $3.50, $5, $12, Oct. 2; No. 2814a, Sept. 26, 1992; $1, $19, $20, Mar. 2, 1992; $26, $28, May 20, 1992; $7, $9, $10, $13, Aug. 21, 1992.

This is an expanding set. Numbers will change.

Peacocks by Lan Shih-ning (Giuseppe Castiglione, 1688-1768) A653

Design: $20, Peacock spreading tail feathers.

Perf. 12x11½

1991, Oct. 30 Photo. Unwmk.
Granite Paper

2826 A653 $5 multicolored .45 .25
2827 A653 $20 multicolored 1.75 1.20
a. Souvenir sheet of 1 4.00 2.00

New Year 1992 (Year of the Monkey) — A654

Perf. 12½

1991, Nov. 30 Litho. Wmk. 323

2828 A654 $3.50 org & multi .25 .20
2829 A654 $13 tan & multi 1.00 .70
a. Souv. sheet, 2 each #2828-2829 4.75 2.00

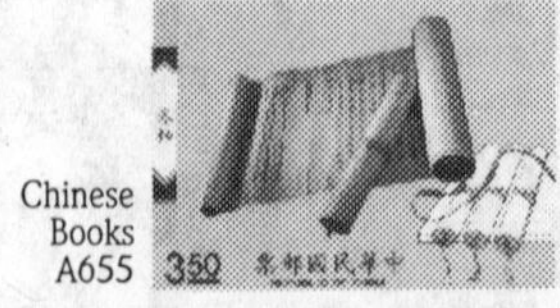

Chinese Books A655

Perf. 13½

1992, Jan. 17 Litho. Wmk. 323

2830 A655 $3.50 Scroll .25 .20
2831 A655 $5 Fold bindings .40 .25
2832 A655 $9 Butterfly bindings .70 .45
2833 A655 $15 String bindings 1.10 .85
Nos. 2830-2833 (4) 2.45 1.75

Good Fortune and Satisfaction A656

Five Blessings Upon the House A657

Nienhwa paintings: No. 2835, Peace in the Wake of Firecrackers. No. 2837, An Abundance for Every Year.

1992, Jan. 27 Litho. *Perf. 13½*

2834 A656 $5 multicolored .35 .25
2835 A656 $5 multicolored .35 .25
2836 A657 $12 multicolored .90 .60
2837 A657 $12 multicolored .90 .60
a. Bklt. pane, 2 each #2834-2837 + label 8.00
Nos. 2834-2837 (4) 2.50 1.70

Lunar New Year.

A658 A659

Lunar New Year: a, like #2664. b, like #2611. c, like #2565. d, like #2493. e, like #2442. f, like #2390. g, like #2346. h, like #2273. i, like #2217. j, like #2828. k, like #2757. l, like #2706.

Perf. 12½

1992, Feb. 18 Litho. Wmk. 323

2838 A658 $5 Block of 12, #a.-l., ver & multi 4.50 3.00
m. Sheet of 12, #2838a-2838l 4.50 3.00

1992, Mar. 12 *Perf. 13½*

Trees: a, Chamaecyparis formosensis. b, Chamaecyparis taiwanensis. c, Calocedrus formosana. d, Cunninghamia konishii. e. Taiwania cryptomerioides.

2839 A659 $5 Strip of 5, #a.-e. 2.00 .65

Children's Toys Type of 1991

1992, Apr. 29 Litho. *Perf. 13½*

2840 A646 $5 Walking on iron pots .40 .25
2841 A646 $5 Chopstick gun .40 .25
2842 A646 $5 Hoop rolling .40 .25
2843 A646 $5 Grass fighting .40 .25
a. Sheet of 4, #2840-2843 4.75 4.75
b. As "a," imperf. (simulated perfs), red inscription in sheet margin 14.00 14.00
c. Bklt. pane, 2 each #2840-2843 + label 3.25
Nos. 2840-2843 (4) 1.60 1.00

Issue date: No. 2843b, May 15.

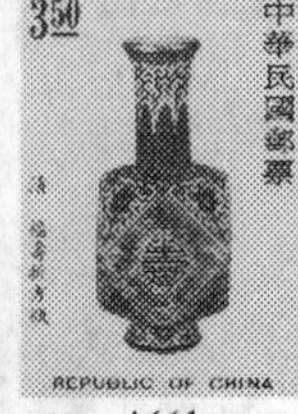

A660 A661

Mother and son in: $3.50, Spring. $5, Summer. $9, Autumn. $10, Winter.

Perf. 13½

1992, May 9 Litho. Wmk. 323

2844 A660 $3.50 multicolored .25 .20
2845 A660 $5 multicolored .40 .25
2846 A660 $9 multicolored .75 .45
2847 A660 $10 multicolored .80 .50
Nos. 2844-2847 (4) 2.20 1.40

Parent-child relationships.

Perf. 13½

1992, June 25 Litho. Wmk. 323

Glassware Decorated with Enamel - Vases: $3.50, Faceted, decorated with bats and longevity characters. $5, Double-lobed, with children at play. $7, Flowered. $17, Tutoring scene.

Background colors

2848 A661 $3.50 pink .25 .20
2849 A661 $5 green .40 .25
2850 A661 $7 bister .55 .40
2851 A661 $17 blue 1.40 1.00
Nos. 2848-2851 (4) 2.60 1.85

Stone Lion of Lugouqiao A662

Various stone lions.

Perf. 13½

1992, July 7 Engr. Wmk. 323

2852 A662 $5 olive green & purple .40 .25
2853 A662 $5 blue & brown .40 .25
2854 A662 $12 orange & olive green .95 .60
2855 A662 $12 purple & black .95 .60
Nos. 2852-2855 (4) 2.70 1.70

Ku Shih Classical Poetry — A663

Excerpts: $3.50, "Flesh and body are as closely linked as leaves to a tree." $5, "Once a man and woman get married, conjugal love will last forever without doubt." $9, "Man takes pains to uphold virtue." $15, "Tartar horses lean toward the northern wind."

1992, Aug. 8 Litho.

2856 A663 $3.50 Children playing near tree .30 .20
2857 A663 $5 Man & woman .50 .25
2858 A663 $9 Couple near stream .85 .45
2859 A663 $15 Horse, tree 1.40 .70
Nos. 2856-2859 (4) 3.05 1.60

Life in the Countryside A664

Scenes of temple fair: a, Two women, man beating drum, crowd. b, Vendor with basket. c, People playing musical instruments. d, Man with food cart. e, Women with umbrella, basket.

Perf. 11½

1992, Sept. 22 Litho. Wmk. 323

2860 A664 $5 Strip of 5, #a.-e. 2.50 .60

Silk Tapestries A665

Ming Dynasty Silk Tapestry Drawing on Life: $5, Two Birds Perched on a Red Camellia Branch. $12, Two Birds Playing on a Peach Branch.

1992, Oct. 9 Litho. *Perf. 11½*

Granite Paper

2861 A665 $5 multicolored .40 .25
2862 A665 $12 multicolored 1.10 .60
a. Sheet of 2, #2861-2862 1.50 .85

Chinese Opera — A666

Actors, props: $3.50, Nin Hsiang-ju's carting to a party from "The General and Premier." $5, Hsao En rowing a boat from "The Lucky Pearl." $9, Wang Chao-chun making peace with the frontier from "Chao-chun Serves as an Envoy." $12, Scene with red sedan chair from "Escort to the Wedding."

Perf. 13½

1992, Oct. 21 Litho. Wmk. 323

2863 A666 $3.50 multicolored .25 .20
2864 A666 $5 multicolored .40 .25
2865 A666 $9 multicolored .65 .45
2866 A666 $12 multicolored .90 .60
Nos. 2863-2866 (4) 2.20 1.50

Alishan Forest Railway — A667

1992, Nov. 5 *Perf. 11½*

2867 A667 $5 Steam engine .40 .25
2868 A667 $15 Diesel engine 1.25 .75

Endangered Mammals of Taiwan A668

Designs: a, Lutra lutra chinensis. b, Pteropus dasymallus formosus. c, Neofelis nebulosa brachyurus. d, Selenarctos thibetanus formosanus.

Perf. 11½x12

1992, Nov. 25 Photo. Unwmk.

Granite Paper

2869 A668 $5 Block of 4, #a.-d. 1.65 1.00

New Year 1993 (Year of the Rooster) — A669

Design: $13, Rooster facing left.

Perf. 12½

1992, Dec. 1 Litho. Wmk. 323

2870 A669 $3.50 red & multi .25 .20
a. Perf. 13½ vert. .30 .20
2871 A669 $13 pur & multi .95 .60
a. Souv. sheet, 2 each #2870-2871 2.50 2.50
b. As "a" with added inscription in border 2.50 2.50
c. Bklt. pane, 5 ea #2870-2871 6.25
d. Perf. 13½ vert. 1.00 .70
e. Booklet pane, 6 each #2870a, 2871d + label 8.00

Inscription on No. 2871b reads "Philippine Stamp Exhibition 1992-Taipei" in English and Chinese.

Johann Adam Schall von Bell (1592-1666), Astronomer and Missionary A670

1992 Dec. 10 *Perf. 11½*

2872 A670 $5 multicolored .35 .25

Traditional Nienhwas of Window Frames — A671

Perf. 11½

1993, Jan. 7 Litho. Wmk. 323

Background Color

2873 A671 $5 brt green .35 .25
2874 A671 $5 red lilac .35 .25
2875 A671 $12 yellow .90 .60
2876 A671 $12 red .90 .60
Nos. 2873-2876 (4) 2.50 1.70

Lunar New Year.

Perf. 13½ Vert.

2873a A671 $5 *1.25* .25
2874a A671 $5 *1.25* .25
2875a A671 $12 *1.25* .60
2876a A671 $12 *1.25* .60
b. Booklet pane, 2 each #2873a-2876a + label *11.00*

Nos. 2873a-2876a are 29x43mm.

Traditional Crafts A672

1993, Jan. 16

2877 A672 $3.50 Clip & paste moldings .25 .20
2878 A672 $5 Lanterns .35 .25
2879 A672 $9 Pottery jars .60 .45
2880 A672 $15 Oil paper umbrella 1.00 .75
Nos. 2877-2880 (4) 2.20 1.65

Chinese Creation Story — A673

Designs: $3.50, Pan Gu's creation of the universe, vert. $5, Pan Gu transmitted himself into all creatures. $9, Nu Wa created human beings with pestled earth. $19, Nu Wa mended sky with smelted stone, vert.

1993, Feb. 6 *Perf. 12x11½, 11½x12*

2881 A673 $3.50 multicolored .25 .20
2882 A673 $5 multicolored .35 .25
2883 A673 $9 multicolored .60 .45
2884 A673 $19 multicolored 1.25 1.00
Nos. 2881-2884 (4) 2.45 1.90

Lucky Animals — A674 Water Plants — A675

Perf. 13½

1993, Mar. 2 Litho. Wmk. 323

2885 A674 $3.50 Mandarin duck .25 .20
2886 A674 $5 Chinese unicorn .40 .25
2887 A674 $10 Deer .80 .50
2888 A674 $15 Crane 1.25 .80
Nos. 2885-2888 (4) 2.70 1.75

See Nos. 2920-2923.

1993, Mar. 12 *Perf. 11½*

2889 A675 $5 Nymphaea x hybrida .40 .25
2890 A675 $9 Nuphar shimadai .70 .45
2891 A675 $12 Eichhornia crassipes .95 .60
Nos. 2889-2891 (3) 2.05 1.30

A676

1993 Litho. Wmk. 323 *Perf. 11½*

2892 A676 $5 Sandbag tossing .40 .25
2893 A676 $5 Bamboo dragonfly twisting .40 .25
2894 A676 $5 Rubber band skipping .40 .25
2895 A676 $5 Waist-strength dueling .40 .25
a. Souvenir sheet of 4, #2892-2895 2.50 2.50
b. As "a," with green & black inscriptions in border 2.50 2.50
c. As "a," with red inscription in border 2.50 2.50
Nos. 2892-2895 (4) 1.60 1.00

Inscriptions on No. 2895b read "AUSTRALIAN STAMP EXHIBITION 1993-TAIPEI" in Chinese and English.

Inscription on No. 2895c reads "Chinese Stamp Exhibition-Thailand" in Chinese.

Nos. 2895b-2895c each have perforations extending into the margin at top (#2895c) or bottom (#2895b).

Issue dates: Nos. 2892-2895, 2895a, Apr. 20; No. 2895b, Apr. 23; No. 2895c, Apr. 30.

Perf. 13½ Vert.

2892a A676 $5 *.80* .25
2893a A676 $5 *.80* .25
2894a A676 $5 *.80* .25
2895d A676 $5 *.80* .25
e. Bklt. pane, 2 each #2892a-2894a, 2895d + label *6.50*

A677

Yangtze River A678

Designs: No. 2896, Source on Ching-Kang-Chang Plateau. No. 2897, Abrupt bend, Chinsha River. No. 2898, Narrow waterway, Roaring Tiger Gorge, Chinsha River. No. 2899, Sheer cliffs, Chuntang Gorge. $9, Three Small Gorges (Dragon Gate, Pawu, and Titsui).

Perf. 13x13½

1993, May 15 Litho. Wmk. 323

2896 A677 $3.50 shown .25 .15
2897 A677 $3.50 multicolored .25 .15
2898 A678 $5 shown .40 .25
2899 A677 $5 multicolored .40 .25
2900 A677 $9 multicolored .70 .45
Nos. 2896-2900 (5) 2.00 1.25

Environmental Protection
A679 A680

Children's paintings: $5, No More Noise Pollution, by Yen Chao-min. $17, Clothing My Hometown with Green, by Hu Hui-chun.

Perf. 12½x13½, 13½x12½

1993, June 5

2901 A679	$5	multicolored	.35	.25
2902 A680	$17	multicolored	1.25	1.00

Ch'eng-hua Porcelain, Natl. Palace Museum
A681

Cups decorated in tou-ts'ai: $3.50, Human figures. $5, Chickens. $7, Flowers and fruits. $9, Dragon.

1993, June 30 *Perf. 12*

2903 A681	$3.50	multicolored	.25	.20
2904 A681	$5	multicolored	.40	.25
2905 A681	$7	multicolored	.55	.40
2906 A681	$9	multicolored	.70	.50
		Nos. 2903-2906 (4)	1.90	1.35

Vocational Training
A682

Perf. 12½

1993, July 24 Litho. Wmk. 323

2907 A682	$3.50	Graphic artist	.25	.20
2908 A682	$5	Computer operator	.35	.25
2909 A682	$9	Carpenter	.65	.50
2910 A682	$12	Welder	.85	.70
		Nos. 2907-2910 (4)	2.10	1.65

Parent-Child Relationship
A683

Silhouettes: $3.50, Adult carrying child on shoulders. $5, Father playing flute for daughter. $9, Father teaching daughter. $10, Father, adult son enjoying wildlife.

Perf. 11½

1993, Aug. 4 Litho. Wmk. 323

Background Color

2911 A683	$3.50	tan	.25	.20
2912 A683	$5	green	.35	.25
2913 A683	$9	lilac	.65	.50
2914 A683	$10	red brown	.75	.60
		Nos. 2911-2914 (4)	2.00	1.55

Souvenir Sheet

Taipei '93, Asian Intl. Philatelic Exhibition — A684

Enjoying Antiques, by Tu Chin, 15th cent: a, Man carrying stick. b, Man selecting antiques from table. c, Man seated in chair. d, Two people at table.

Perf. 12x11½

1993, Aug. 14 Photo. Unwmk.

Granite Paper

2915 A684	$5 Sheet of 4, #a.-d.	2.50	1.15

Persimmon A685 — Loquat A686

1993, Sept. 10 Litho. *Perf. 12½*

2916 A685	$5	shown	.35	.25
2917 A685	$5	Peach	.35	.25
2918 A686	$12	shown	.90	.70
2919 A686	$12	Papaya	.90	.70
		Nos. 2916-2919 (4)	2.50	1.90

Lucky Animals Type of 1993

Perf. 13½

1993, Sept. 29 Litho. Wmk. 323

2920 A674	$1	Blue dragon	.15	.15
2921 A674	$2.50	White tiger	.20	.15
2922 A674	$9	Linnet	.65	.40
2923 A674	$19	Black tortoise	1.40	.90
		Nos. 2920-2923 (4)	2.40	1.60

Taiwan Area Games, Taoyuan A687 — Stone Lions A688

Designs: a, Taekwondo. b, Pommel horse.

Perf. 12½

1993, Oct. 20 Litho. Wmk. 323

2924 A687	$5 Pair, #a.-b.	.75	.75

1993, Oct. 30

Stone lions from: $3.50, Taipei New Park. $5, Hsinchu City Council. $9, Hsinchu City God Temple. $12, Fort Providentia, Tainan.

2925 A688	$3.50	multicolored	.25	.15
2926 A688	$5	multicolored	.40	.25
2927 A688	$9	multicolored	.65	.45
2928 A688	$12	multicolored	.90	.60
		Nos. 2925-2928 (4)	2.20	1.45

Syrmaticus Mikado
A689

Designs: a, Hatchling. b, Mother with chicks. c, Immature female, male. d, Adult female, male (profile, showing plumage).

Perf. 11½

1993, Nov. 17 Photo. Unwmk.

Granite Paper

2929 A689	$5 Strip of 4, #a.-d.	1.50	1.50

New Year 1994 (Year of the Dog) — A690

Design: $13, Dog facing left.

Perf. 12½

1993, Dec. 1 Litho. Wmk. 323

2930 A690	$3.50	red & multi	.25	.15
a.		Perf. 13½ vert.	.25	.15
b.		As "a," bklt. pane of 12 + label	3.00	
2931 A690	$13	green & multi	1.00	.65
a.		Souvenir sheet, 2 each #2930-2931	1.25	.85
b.		As "a," overprinted in red	1.25	.85

No. 2931b is inscribed in Chinese for Kaohsiung Kuo-kuang Stamp Exhibition-1993, and has additional perforations extending into top and bottom margins.

Asian Vegetable Research and Development Center, 20th Anniv. — A691

1993, Dec. 7

2932 A691	$5	shown	.35	.25
2933 A691	$13	Researchers in field	1.00	.65

Formation of Constitutional Court — A692

Perf. 12½

1994, Jan. 11 Litho. Wmk. 323

2934 A692	$5	multicolored	.35	.25

Paper Making — A693 — Flowers — A694

Designs: No. 2935, Cutting bamboo. No. 2936, Cooking bamboo. No. 2937, Pouring syrup into wooden panel. No. 2938, Stacking panel. No. 2939, Drying paper.

1994, Jan. 24 *Perf. 12x12½*

2935 A693	$3.50	multicolored	.25	.20
2936 A693	$3.50	multicolored	.25	.20
2937 A693	$5	multicolored	.40	.25
2938 A693	$5	multicolored	.40	.25
2939 A693	$12	multicolored	.90	.60
		Nos. 2935-2939 (5)	2.20	1.50

See Nos. 2993-2997.

1994, Feb. 17 *Perf. 12½*

2940 A694	$5	Clivia miniata	.35	.25
2941 A694	$12	Cymbidium sinense	.90	.60
2942 A694	$19	Primula malacoides	1.40	.95
		Nos. 2940-2942 (3)	2.65	1.80

Kinmen Wind Lion Lords — A695

Various Wind Lion Lords.

1994, Mar. 18 Litho. *Perf. 12½*

2943 A695	$5	green & multi	.40	.25
2944 A695	$9	yellow & multi	.70	.45
2945 A695	$12	orange yellow & multi	.90	.60
2946 A695	$17	blue & multi	1.25	.80
		Nos. 2943-2946 (4)	3.25	2.10

Children at Play — A696

Designs: No. 2947, Playing with paper boat. No. 2948, Fighting with water gun. No. 2949, Throwing paper airplane. No. 2950, Playing "train" with rope.

Perf. 12½

1994, Apr. 2 Litho. Wmk. 323

2947 A696	$5	multicolored	.35	.25
2948 A696	$5	multicolored	.35	.25
2949 A696	$5	multicolored	.35	.25
2950 A696	$5	multicolored	.35	.25
a.		Souvenir sheet of 4, #2947-2950	1.50	1.00
		Nos. 2947-2950 (4)	1.40	1.00

Perf. 13½ Vert.

2947a	A696	$5	.35	.25
2948a	A696	$5	.35	.25
2949a	A696	$5	.35	.25
2950b	A696	$5	.35	.25
c.		Booklet pane, 2 each #2947a-2949a, 2950b + label	3.25	

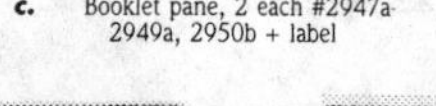

A697 — A698

Life in the countryside: $5, Playing chess. $10, Playing musical instruments. $12, Telling stories. $19, Drinking tea.

Perf. 12½

1994, Apr. 25 Litho. Wmk. 323

2951 A697	$5	multicolored	.35	.25
2952 A697	$10	multicolored	.75	.45
2953 A697	$12	multicolored	.90	.60
2954 A697	$19	multicolored	1.40	.95
		Nos. 2951-2954 (4)	3.40	2.25

1994, May 7

Mother, baby birds: $5, Malay bittern. $7, Little tern, horiz. $10, Common noddy, horiz. $12, Muller's barbet.

2955 A698	$5	multicolored	.35	.25
2956 A698	$7	multicolored	.50	.35
2957 A698	$10	multicolored	.75	.50
2958 A698	$12	multicolored	.90	.55
		Nos. 2955-2958 (4)	2.50	1.65

A699 — A700

Protection of Intellectual Property Rights: $5, Palm-shaped book. $15, Human head, computer disk.

Perf. 12½

1994, May 28 Litho. Wmk. 323

2959 A699	$5	multicolored	.40	.25
2960 A699	$15	multicolored	1.10	.70

1994, June 11

Designs: $5, Care for Lost Children. $17, Care for the aged.

2961 A700	$5	multicolored	.35	.25
2962 A700	$17	multicolored	1.25	.85

Intl. Olympic Committee, Cent. — A701

1994, June 23

2963 A701	$5	shown	.40	.25
2964 A701	$15	Sporting events	1.10	.70

A702 — A703

Shei-pa Natl. Park: $5, Tapachienshan. $7, Shei-san Landslide Scar. $10, Holy Ridge. $17, Shiah-tsuei Lake.

Perf. 12½

1994, July 1 Litho. Wmk. 323

2965 A702 $5 multicolored .40 .25
2966 A702 $7 multicolored .50 .35
2967 A702 $10 multicolored .75 .45
2968 A702 $17 multicolored 1.25 .85
Nos. 2965-2968 (4) 2.90 1.90

1994, July 30 ***Perf. 11½x12***

Design: $5, Portrait of Chien Mu (b. 1895), educator.

2969 A703 $5 multicolored .40 .25

Intl. Year of the Family A704

Designs: $5, Rainbow, window. $15, Globe, house.

1994, Aug. 25 ***Perf. 11½***

2970 A704 $5 multicolored .40 .25
2971 A704 $15 yel & multi 1.10 .70

Invention Myths — A705

Designs: $5, Sueirenjy digging wood to obtain fire. $10, Fushijy drawing Pa-Kua. $12, Shennungjy making agricultural tools. $15, Tsang-jier creating written characters.

1994, Sept. 17 Photo. ***Perf. 11½***
Granite Paper

2972 A705 $5 multicolored .35 .25
2973 A705 $10 multicolored .75 .45
2974 A705 $12 multicolored .90 .60
2975 A705 $15 multicolored 1.10 .70
Nos. 2972-2975 (4) 3.10 2.00

A706

A707

Design: $5, Dr. Lin Yutang, linguist, writer, 100th birthday.

Perf. 12½

1994, Oct. 8 Litho. Wmk. 323

2976 A706 $5 multicolored .40 .25

1994, Oct. 17

Designs: $5, Cheng Ho's ship. $17, Chart, ship, Cheng Ho.

2977 A707 $5 multicolored .40 .25
2978 A707 $17 multicolored 1.25 .85

World Trade Week.

Sun Yat-sen, Founding of Kuomintang, Cent. — A708

Design: $19, Democratic elections, factories, economic development.

Perf. 12½

1994, Nov. 24 Litho. Wmk. 323

2979 A708 $5 multicolored .40 .25
2980 A708 $19 multicolored 1.40 .95

A709

A710

1994, Nov. 29

2981 A709 $3.50 Facing right .30 .20
a. Perf. 13½ vert. .30 .20
b. As "a," booklet pane of 6 1.75
Complete booklet, 2 #2981b + label 3.50
2982 A709 $13 Facing left 1.00 .65
a. Souvenir sheet, 2 each #2981-2982 2.50 1.65

New Year 1995 (Year of the Boar).

1994, Dec. 24 Litho. ***Perf. 12½***

2983 A710 $5 Portrait .40 .25
2984 A710 $15 Greeting farm family 1.10 .70

Pres. Yen Chia-kan, 1st death anniv.

Traditional Architecture A711

Roof lines: No. 2985, Horse's back (illustrated). No. 2986, Swallow's tail. $12, Talisman (stove and bowl). $19, Cylinder-shaped brick.

Perf. 12½x12

1995, Jan. 10 Litho. Wmk. 323

2985 A711 $5 multicolored .35 .25
2986 A711 $5 multicolored .35 .25
2987 A711 $12 multicolored .90 .60
2988 A711 $19 multicolored 1.40 .95
Nos. 2985-2988 (4) 3.00 2.05

Ancient Chinese Engravings — A712

Various floral designs.

1995, Jan. 24 ***Perf. 13½***

2989 A712 $3.50 multicolored .25 .20
2990 A712 $5 multicolored .35 .25
2991 A712 $19 multicolored 1.40 .95
2992 A712 $26 multicolored 2.00 1.40
Nos. 2989-2992 (4) 4.00 2.80

See Nos. 3018-3021, 3044-3047.

Ancient Skills Type of 1994

Methods of irrigation: No. 2993, Water wheel. No. 2994, Gear-driven bucket lift. $5, Pedal-powered hoist. $12, Hand-cranked hoist. $13, Using pole with counter-weight to raise bucket.

Perf. 12x11½

1994, Feb. 14 Litho. Wmk. 323

2993 A693 $3.50 multicolored .28 .18
2994 A693 $3.50 multicolored .28 .18
2995 A693 $5 multicolored .38 .25
2996 A693 $12 multicolored .90 .60
2997 A693 $13 multicolored 1.00 .65
Nos. 2993-2997 (5) 2.84 1.86

Beauties on an Outing, by Lee Gong-lin — A713

Designs: a, Two riders. b, Rider on black horse, woman with child on horse. c, Three riders. d, One rider.

Unwmk.

1995, Mar. 3 Photo. ***Perf. 12***
Granite Paper

2998 A713 $9 Strip of 4, #a.-d. 2.75 1.90
e. Souvenir sheet of 2, #2998b-2998c 1.40 .90

No. 2998 is a continuous design.

Natl. Health Insurance Plan — A714

Flowers — A715

Perf. 11½x12½

1995, Mar. 11 Litho. Wmk. 323

2999 A714 $12 multicolored .90 .60

1995, Mar. 20 Litho. ***Perf. 12½***

3000 A715 $5 Lilium speciosum .38 .25
3001 A715 $12 Haemanthus multiflorus .90 .60
3002 A715 $19 Hyacinthus orientalis 1.40 .95
Nos. 3000-3002 (3) 2.68 1.80

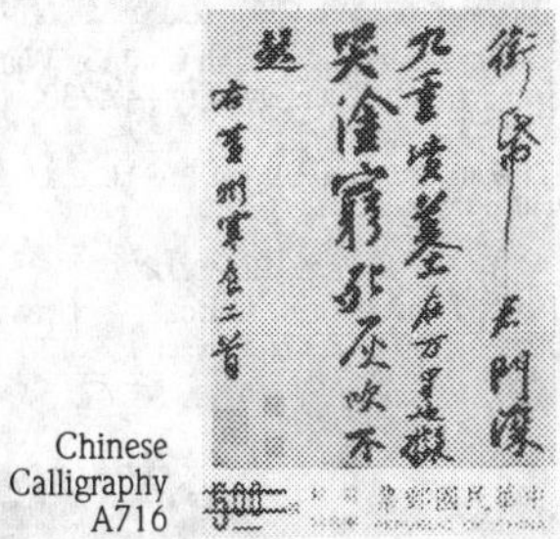

Chinese Calligraphy A716

Cold Food Observance, poem by Su Shih, red inscriptions at: a, Lower left. b, Middle. c, Upper right. d, Right half of design.

1995, Apr. 6 ***Perf. 13½***

3003 Strip of 4 1.50 1.00
a.-d. A716 $5 any single .38 .25

Paintings by Tsou I Kuei's — A717

1995, May 5 Photo. ***Die Cut***
Self-Adhesive

3004 A717 $5 Red peony .38 .25
3005 A717 $5 Pink peony .38 .25
a. Booklet pane, 9 each #3004-3005 7.00

By its nature, No. 3005a is a complete booklet. The peelable backing serves as a booklet cover.

Campaign Against Illegal Drugs — A718

Perf. 12½

1995, June 1 Litho. Wmk. 323

3006 A718 $5 shown .38 .25
3007 A718 $15 Arm, hypodermic needle 1.10 .70

Natl. Taiwan University Hospital, Cent. — A719

Designs: $5, Medical treatment, old hospital. $19, Medical research, new hospital.

1995, June 20

3008 A719 $5 multicolored .38 .25
3009 A719 $19 multicolored 1.40 .95

East Coast Scenes — A720

Designs: No. 3010, Green hills above Chichi Bay. No. 3011, Rocky promontory, Shihyuesan. $12, Hsiaoyehlieu. $15, Changhong Bridge.

Perf. 12½

1995, July 1 Litho. Wmk. 323

3010 A720 $5 multicolored .38 .25
3011 A720 $5 multicolored .38 .25
3012 A720 $12 multicolored 1.00 .60
3013 A720 $15 multicolored 1.25 .75
Nos. 3010-3013 (4) 3.01 1.85

Oncorhynchus Masou Formosanus A721

Designs: $5, Mating. $7, Female digging a spot to lay eggs. $10, Hatching of fry. $17, Fry swimming in river.

Perf. 14x14½

1995, July 27 Litho. Unwmk.

3014 A721 $5 multicolored .38 .25
3015 A721 $7 multicolored .55 .35
3016 A721 $10 multicolored .75 .50
3017 A721 $17 multicolored 1.40 .85
Nos. 3014-3017 (4) 3.08 1.95

Ancient Chinese Engraving Type of 1995

Various pictures of birds on tree branches.

Perf. 13½

1995, Aug. 18 Litho. Wmk. 323

3018 A712 $2.50 multicolored .20 .15
3019 A712 $7 multicolored .55 .30
3020 A712 $13 multicolored 1.00 .60
3021 A712 $28 multicolored 2.25 1.25
Nos. 3018-3021 (4) 4.00 2.30

Marine Life A722

Louis Pasteur (1822-95) A723

Designs: No. 3022, Tubastraea aurea. No. 3023, Chromodoris elizabethina. $5, Spirobranchus gigateus. $17, Himerometra magnipinna.

Perf. 12½

1995, Sept. 7 Litho. Wmk. 323

3022 A722 $3.50 multicolored .25 .15
3023 A722 $3.50 multicolored .25 .15
3024 A722 $5 multicolored .40 .22
3025 A722 $17 multicolored 1.25 .75
Nos. 3022-3025 (4) 2.15 1.27

1995, Sept. 20

3026 A723 $17 multicolored 1.25 .75

Natl. Palace Museum, 70th Anniv. — A724

Designs: No. 3027, Painting, "Strange Peaks and Myriad Trees." No. 3028, Greenish blue porcelain vase, vert. $5, Bronze X Fu-K'uei Ting vessel, vert. $26, Calligraphy of quatrain in seven-character verse, "The Fragrance of Flowers."

Perf. 12x11½, 11½x12

1995, Oct. 9 Photo. Unwmk.

3027 A724 $3.50 multicolored .25 .15
3028 A724 $3.50 multicolored .25 .15
3029 A724 $5 multicolored .40 .20
3030 A724 $26 multicolored 2.00 1.10
Nos. 3027-3030 (4) 2.90 1.60

End of World War II, 50th Anniv. — A725

Designs: $5, Chinese soldiers in battle. $19, Flag, outline map of Taiwan, presidential mansion.

Perf. 11½x12

1995, Oct. 24 Litho. Wmk. 323

3031 A725 $5 multicolored .40 .20
3032 A725 $19 multicolored 1.50 .75
a. Souvenir sheet, #3031-3032 2.00 1.00

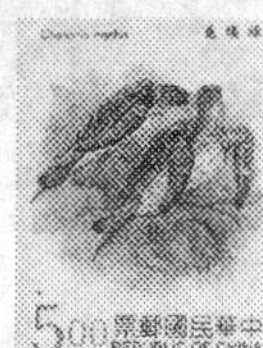

Sea Turtles — A726

Designs: No. 3033, Chelonia mydas. No. 3034, Caretta caretta. No. 3035, Lepidochelys olivacea. No. 3036, Eretmochelys imbricata.

Perf. 12½

1995, Nov. 10 Litho. Wmk. 323

3033 A726 $5 multicolored .40 .20
3034 A726 $5 multicolored .40 .20
3035 A726 $5 multicolored .40 .20
3036 A726 $5 multicolored .40 .20
Nos. 3033-3036 (4) 1.60 .80

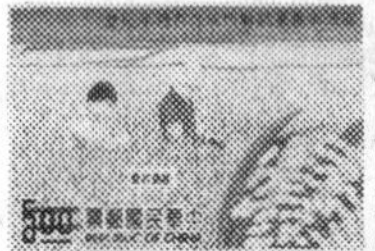

Taiwan Agricultural Research Institute, Cent. — A727

Perf. 12x11½

1995, Nov. 22 Litho. Wmk. 323

3037 A727 $5 In rice field .40 .20
3038 A727 $28 In anthurium field 2.00 1.00

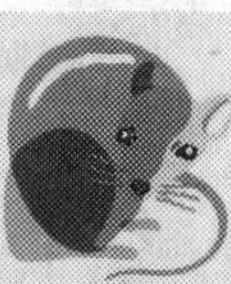

New Year 1996 (Year of the Rat) — A728

Designs: $3.50, $13, Different stylized rats.

Perf. 12½

1995, Dec. 1 Litho. Wmk. 323

3039 A728 $3.50 pink & multi .25 .15
a. Perf. 13½vert. .25 .15
b. As "a," booklet pane of 6 1.50
Complete booklet, 2 #3039b + gutter 3.00
3040 A728 $13 olive & multi 1.00 .50
a. Souvenir sheet, 2 each #3039-3040 2.50 1.25

Traditional Wedding Ceremony A729

Designs: $5, Escorting bride. $12, Kowtowing Heaven, Earth, and ancestors. $19, Seated in bridal chamber.

1996, Jan. 10

3041 A729 $5 multicolored .40 .20
3042 A729 $12 multicolored 1.00 .50
3043 A729 $19 multicolored 1.50 .75
Nos. 3041-3043 (3) 2.90 1.45

Ancient Chinese Engraving Type of 1995

Various pictures of fruit.

Perf. 13½

1996, Jan. 25 Litho. Wmk. 323

3044 A712 $9 multicolored .65 .30
3045 A712 $12 multicolored .90 .45
3046 A712 $15 multicolored 1.10 .55
3047 A712 $17 multicolored 1.25 .60
Nos. 3044-3047 (4) 3.90 1.90

Scenic Dwelling at Chü-Ch'ü, by Wang Meng, Yüan Dynasty — A730

Denominations: a, UL. b, UR. c, LL. d, LR. Illustration reduced.

Perf. 12½x12

1996, Feb. 15 Litho. Unwmk.

3048 A730 Block of 4, #a.-d. 1.65 .85
a.-d. $5 any single .40 .20

Flowers — A731

Designs: $5, Bougainvillea spectabilis. $12, Wisteria sinensis. $19, Merremia tuberosa.

1996, Mar. 8 Unwmk. *Perf. 12½*

3049 A731 $5 multicolored .40 .20
3050 A731 $12 multicolored .90 .45

Wmk. 323

3051 A731 $19 multicolored 1.50 .75
Nos. 3049-3051 (3) 2.80 1.40

SEMI-POSTAL STAMPS

SP1

Red or Blue Surcharge

1920, Dec. 1 Unwmk. *Perf. 14, 15*

B1 SP1 1c on 2c green 4.00 1.25
B2 SP1 3c on 4c scar (B) 5.50 2.25
B3 SP1 5c on 6c gray 8.00 2.75
Nos. B1-B3 (3) 17.50 6.25

The surcharge represents the actual franking value. The extra cent helped victims of the 1919 Yellow River flood.

War Refugees SP2

Black Surcharge

1944, Oct. 10 Engr. *Perf. 12*

B4 SP2 $2 +$2 on 50c + 50c .20 .25
B5 SP2 $4 +$4 on 8c + 8c .20 .25
B6 SP2 $5 +$5 on 21c + 21c .55 .75
B7 SP2 $6 +$6 on 28c + 28c .85 1.00
B8 SP2 $10 +$10 on 33c + 33c 1.40 1.75
B9 SP2 $20 +$20 on $1 + $1 2.75 3.50
a. Sheet of 6, #B4-B9 32.50 20.00
Nos. B4-B9 (6) 5.95 7.50

The borders of each stamp differ slightly in design. The surtax was for war refugees.

Nos. B4-B8 exist without surcharge, but were not regularly issued.

Great Wall of China — SP4

Chinese Refugee Family — SP5

1948, July 5 Litho. *Perf. 14, Imperf.*

Without Gum

Cross in Carmine

B11 SP4 $5000 + $2000 vio .15 .15
B12 SP4 $10,000 + $2000 brn .15 .15
B13 SP4 $15,000 + $2000 gray .15 .15
a. Cross omitted
Set value .35 .35

The surtax was for anti-tuberculosis work.

Republic of China (Taiwan)

1954, Oct. 1 Engr. *Perf. 12*

Without Gum

B14 SP5 40c + 10c dp bl 20.00 2.00
B15 SP5 $1.60 + 40c lil rose 50.00 20.00
B16 SP5 $5 + $1 red 110.00 110.00
Nos. B14-B16 (3) 180.00 132.00

The surtax was used to aid in the evacuation of Chinese from North Viet Nam.

AIR POST STAMPS

Curtiss "Jenny" over Great Wall (Bars of Republic flag on tail) — AP1

1921, July 1 Unwmk. Engr. *Perf. 14*

C1 AP1 15c bl grn & blk 24.00 24.00
C2 AP1 30c scar & blk 24.00 24.00
C3 AP1 45c dull vio & blk 24.00 24.00
C4 AP1 60c dk blue & blk 30.00 30.00
C5 AP1 90c ol grn & blk 42.50 42.50
Nos. C1-C5 (5) 144.50 144.50

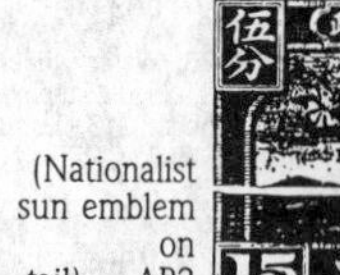

(Nationalist sun emblem on tail) — AP2

1929, July 5

C6 AP2 15c blue grn & blk 3.00 .60
C7 AP2 30c dk red & blk 4.75 2.00
C8 AP2 45c dk vio & blk 11.00 6.50
C9 AP2 60c dk blue & blk 11.00 8.00
C10 AP2 90c ol grn & blk 12.00 14.00
Nos. C6-C10 (5) 41.75 31.10

Junkers F-13 over Great Wall — AP3

1932-37

C11 AP3 15c gray grn .40 .40
C12 AP3 25c orange ('33) .40 .40
C13 AP3 30c red 1.75 .40
C14 AP3 45c brown vio .40 .40
C15 AP3 50c dk brown ('33) .40 .40
C16 AP3 60c dk blue .40 .40
C17 AP3 90c olive grn .40 .40
C18 AP3 $1 yellow grn ('33) .40 .40
C19 AP3 $2 brown ('37) 1.00 .40
C20 AP3 $5 brown car ('37) 2.50 3.25
Nos. C11-C20 (10) 8.05 6.85

See #C21-C40. For surcharges and overprints see #C41-C52, C54-C60, 9N111-9N114, 9NC1-9NC7, Szechwan C1, C3-C6, Sinkiang C5-C19.

Type of 1932-37, with secret mark

1932-37 Issue. Lower part of left character joined

Secret Mark, 1940-41 Issue. Separated.

Perf. 12, 12½, 12½x13, 13

1940-41 Wmk. 261

C21 AP3 15c gray green .45 .45
C22 AP3 25c yellow org .45 .45
C23 AP3 30c red .45 .45
a. Vert. pair, imperf. between 200.00
C24 AP3 45c dull rose vio ('41) .45 .45
C25 AP3 50c brown .45 .45
C26 AP3 60c dp blue ('41) .45 .45
C27 AP3 90c olive ('41) .45 .45
C28 AP3 $1 apple grn ('41) .45 .45
C29 AP3 $2 lt brown ('41) .45 .45
C30 AP3 $5 lake 1.10 1.10
Nos. C21-C30 (10) 5.15 5.15

Unwmk.

Perf. 12½, 13, 13½

C31 AP3 15c gray green ('41) .30 .30
C32 AP3 25c lt orange ('41) .30 .30
C33 AP3 30c lt red ('41) .30 .30
C34 AP3 45c dl rose vio ('41) .30 .30
C35 AP3 50c brown .30 .30
C36 AP3 60c blue ('41) .30 .30
C37 AP3 90c lt olive ('41) .30 .30
C38 AP3 $1 apple grn ('41) .55 .55
C39 AP3 $2 lt brown ('41) 1.40 1.40
C40 AP3 $5 lake ('41) 1.10 1.10
Nos. C31-C40 (10) 5.15 5.15

For surcharges see note following No. C20.

Nos. C11 and C12 Surcharged

圓叁拾伍幣國

5300

1946, May 2 Unwmk. *Perf. 14*

C41 AP3 $53 on 15c .40 *.90*
C42 AP3 $73 on 25c 700.00 750.00

Forgeries of No. C42 exist.

On Nos. C23, C21, C22, C29 and C30

Perf. 13, 13x12, 12½

Wmk. 261

C43 AP3 $23 on 30c red .15 *.35*
C44 AP3 $53 on 15c gray grn 14.00 *17.50*
C45 AP3 $73 on 25c yel org .15 *.35*
C46 AP3 $100 on $2 lt brown .15 *.15*
C47 AP3 $200 on $5 lake .25 *.15*
Nos. C43-C47 (5) 14.70 18.50

On Nos. C33, C31, C32, C39 and C40

Perf. 13, 13x12, 13x12½, 12½

Unwmk.

C48 AP3 $23 on 30c lt red .15 .25
a. Inverted surcharge 100.00
b. "2300" omitted 50.00
c. Last character (kuo) of surch. omitted 65.00
C49 AP3 $53 on 15c gray grn .15 .25
a. Horiz. pair, imperf. brwn. 675.00
C50 AP3 $73 on 25c lt orange .15 .25
a. Inverted surcharge 525.00
C51 AP3 $100 on $2 lt brown .15 .15
C52 AP3 $200 on $5 lake .15 .15
a. Inverted surcharge 80.00
Set value, #C48-C52 .30

The surcharges on #C41-C52 represent Chinese natl. currency and were applied at Shanghai.

Douglas DC-4 over Sun Yat-sen Mausoleum, Nanking AP4

1946, Sept. 10 Litho. *Perf. 14*
Without Gum

C53 AP4 $27 blue .15 .35

For surcharges see Nos. C61, Szechwan C2.

No. C23 Surcharged in Black

圓萬壹作改
10000.00

1948, May 18 Wmk. 261 *Perf. 13x12*

C54 AP3 $10,000 on 30c red .15 *.35*

Same, in Black or Carmine, on Nos. C33, C32, C37, C36, C18 and C38

Perf. 12½, 13x12½, 14
Unwmk.

C55 AP3 $10,000 on 30c lt red .15 *.15*
C56 AP3 $20,000 on 25c lt org .20 *.20*
C57 AP3 $30,000 on 90c lt ol (C) .15 *.15*
C58 AP3 $50,000 on 60c blue (C) .15 *.20*
C59 AP3 $50,000 on $1 yel grn (C) 75.00 70.00
C60 AP3 $50,000 on $1 ap grn (C) .15 *.20*

No. C53 Surcharged in Black

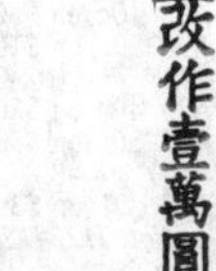

Perf. 14

C61 AP4 $10,000 on $27 bl .15 .55
Nos. C54-C61 (8) 76.10 71.80

Douglas DC-4 and Arrow — AP5

Perf. 12½
1949, May 2 Unwmk. Litho.
Without Gum

C62 AP5 blue green 3.50 4.00
a. Rouletted 4.50 5.75

See note after No. 959.
For overprints see Taiwan #C1, Fukien #C1, Kansu #C1, PRC #102.

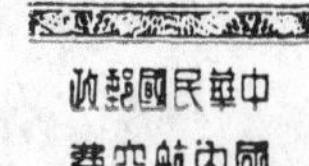

Revenue Stamp Overprinted in Blue

1949, May Engr. *Perf. 14*

C63 A95 $100 olive green 30.00 30.00

See note after No. 962.

Republic of China (Taiwan)

Cheng Ch'eng-kung (Koxinga) — AP6

Rouletted
1950, Sept. 26 Unwmk. Typo.
Without Gum

C64 AP6 60c deep blue 11.00 5.00

For surcharge see No. 1120.

Plane over City Gate, Taipei — AP7

Jet Planes above Chung Shan Bridge — AP8

Two Doves Near Koxinga Shrine — AP9

1954 Engr. *Perf. 11½*
Without Gum

C65 AP7 $1 dk brown 19.00 .75
a. Vert. pair, imperf. btwn. 225.00
C66 AP8 $1.60 olive blk 14.00 .65
a. Vert. pair, imperf. btwn. 150.00
b. Horiz. pair, imperf. btwn. 110.00 130.00
C67 AP9 $5 grnsh blue 17.00 .75
Nos. C65-C67 (3) 50.00 2.15

No. C67 Surcharged in Red

1958, Dec. 11
Without Gum

C68 AP9 $3.50 on $5 grnsh bl 4.00 1.50

Catalogue values for unused stamps in this section, from this point to the end of the section, are for Never Hinged items.

Sea Gull — AP10

Sabre Jets in Bomb Burst Formation — AP11

1959, Mar. 20 Photo. *Perf. 13*

C69 AP10 $8 bl, gray & blk 4.00 .40

1960, Feb. 29 Unwmk. *Perf. 13*

Plane Formations: $2, Loop, horiz. $5, Diamond formation passing over grounded plane, horiz.

C70 AP11 $1 multicolored 4.00 .45
C71 AP11 $2 multicolored 4.00 .30
C72 AP11 $5 multicolored 8.00 .55
Nos. C70-C72 (3) 16.00 1.30

Issued to honor the Chinese Air Force and the "Thunder Tiger" aerobatic team.

Jet Airliner over Pitan Bridge — AP12

Designs: $6, Jet over Tropic of Cancer monument, Kiai, vert. $10, Jet over Lion Head mountain, Sinchu, vert.

1963, Aug. 14 Photo. *Perf. 13*

C73 AP12 $2.50 multi 4.75 .15
C74 AP12 $6 multi 8.75 .15
C75 AP12 $10 multi 16.00 .85
Nos. C73-C75 (3) 29.50 1.15

Boeing 727 over Chilin Pavilion, Grand Hotel — AP13

Wild Geese Flying over Mountains — AP14

Design: $8, Boeing 727 over National Palace Museum, Taipei.

1967, Apr. 1 Unwmk. *Perf. 13*

C76 AP13 $5 multicolored 2.75 .15
C77 AP13 $8 multicolored 3.75 .55

1969, Aug. 14 Photo. *Perf. 13*

Wild Geese flying over: $5, The sea. $8, The land, horiz.

C78 AP14 $2.50 multicolored 2.25 .15
C79 AP14 $5 multicolored 3.75 .35
C80 AP14 $8 multicolored 5.00 .50
Nos. C78-C80 (3) 11.00 1.00

Presidental Palace and Tzu-Ch'iang Squadron AP15

1980, June 18 Litho. *Perf. 13½*

C81 AP15 $5 shown .25 .20
C82 AP15 $7 China Airlines jet .45 .30
C83 AP15 $12 China flag, jet .75 .50
Nos. C81-C83 (3) 1.45 1.00

Civil Aeronautics Administration, 37th Anniv. — AP16

Jet Airliners over: $7, Chiang Kai-shek Intl. Airport, vert. $11, Chung Cheng Memorial Hall. $18, Sun Yat-sen Memorial Hall.

Perf. 14x13½, 13½x14
1984, Jan. 20 Litho.

C84 AP16 $7 multicolored .40 .15
C85 AP16 $11 multicolored .65 .20
C86 AP16 $18 multicolored 1.10 .40
Nos. C84-C86 (3) 2.15 .75

Airplane AP17

1987, Aug. 4 Litho. *Perf. 13½*

C87 AP17 $9 multicolored .55 .30
C88 AP17 $14 multicolored .85 .55
C89 AP17 $18 multicolored 1.10 .65
Nos. C87-C89 (3) 2.50 1.50

SPECIAL DELIVERY STAMPS

Design: Dragon in irregular oval.

Stamp 8x2½ inches, divided into four parts by perforation or serrate rouletting.

Values of Nos. E1-E8 are for used mailer's receipts. Complete unused strips of four are exceptionally scarce because the first section (#1) was to remain in the P.O. booklet.

The mailer received the righthand section (#4), usually canceled, as a receipt. The middle two sections were canceled and attached to the letter. Upon arrival at the destination P.O. they were canceled again, usually on the back, with the righthand copy (#3) retained by that P.O. The lefthand copy (#2) was signed by the recipient and returned to the original P.O. as evidence of delivery. Sections 2 and 3 usually are thin or badly damaged.

Unused strips of three (#2-4) can be found of Nos. E3-E8.

"Chinese Imperial Post Office" in lines, repeated to form the background which is usually lighter in color than the rest of the design.

Dragon's head facing downward
Background with period after "POSTOFFICE."
No Date

1905 Unwmk. *Perf. 11*

E1 10c grass green 425.00

Serrate Roulette in Black

E2 10c deep green 300.00

1907-10

Dragon's head facing forward
Background with no period after "POSTOFFICE"
No Date

E3 10c light bluish green 175.00

1909-11

Background with date at bottom

E4 10c green (Feby 1909) 125.00
E5 10c bl grn (Jan. 1911) 125.00

1912

"Imperial Post Office" in serifed letters repeated to form the background.
No Date, No Border
Background of 30 or 28 lines

E6 10c green (30 lines) 65.00
a. 28 lines 65.00

Background of 35 lines of sans-serif letters
Colored Border

E8 10c green 125.00

On No. E8 the medallion in the third section has Chinese characters in the background instead of the usual English inscriptions. E6 and E8 occur with many types of four-character overprints reading "Republic of China," applied locally but unofficially at various post offices.

1913

Design: Wild Goose. Stamp 7½x2¾ inches, divided into five parts.
"Chinese Post Office" in sans-serif letters, repeated to form the background of 28 lines. With border.
Serrate Roulette in Black

E9 10c green 350.00 24.00

Unused values for Nos. E9-E10 are for complete strips of five parts. Used values are for single parts.

1914

"Chinese Post Office" in antique letters, forming a background of 29 or 30 lines. No border.
Serrate Roulette in Green

E10 10c green 90.00 3.00

On No. E9 the background is in sans-serif capitals, the Chinese and English inscriptions are on white tablets and the serial numbers are in black.

On No. E10 the background is in antique capitals and extends under the inscriptions. The serial numbers are in green.

NOTE:

In February, 1916, the Special Delivery Stamps were demonetized and became merely receipts without franking value. To mark this, four of the five sections of the stamp had the letters A, B, C, D either handstamped or printed on them.

SD1

1941 Unwmk. Typo. *Rouletted*
Without Gum

E11 SD1 ($2) car & yel 22.50 22.50

Motorcycle Messenger — SD2

1949, July Litho. *Perf. 12½*
Without Gum

E12 SD2 red violet 5.00 *11.00*
a. Rouletted 6.00 *11.00*

See note after No. 959.
For surcharge and overprints see Nos. 1150, Taiwan E1, Fukien E1.

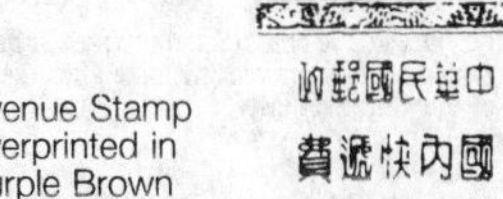

Revenue Stamp Overprinted in Purple Brown

1949

Without Gum

E13 A95 $10 grnsh gray 16.00 16.00

See note after No. 962.

REGISTRATION STAMPS

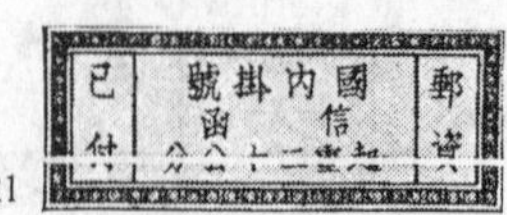

R1

1941 Unwmk. Typo. *Rouletted*

Without Gum

F1 R1 ($1.50) green & buff 18.00 12.00

Mountain Scene — R2

1949, July Litho. *Perf. 12½*

Without Gum

F2 R2 carmine 5.50 *8.00*
a. Rouletted 6.50 *11.00*

See note after No. 959.

For surcharge and overprints see Nos. 1152, Taiwan F1, Fukien F1, PRC 103.

Revenue Stamp Overprinted in Carmine

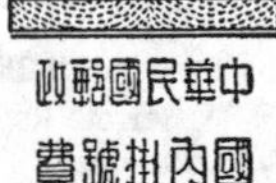

1949

F3 A95 $50 dark blue 13.00 13.00

See note after No. 962.

POSTAGE DUE STAMPS

Regular Issue of 1902-03 Overprinted in Black

POSTAGE DUE
資 欠

1904 Unwmk. *Perf. 14 to 15*

J1 A17 ½c chocolate 5.75 1.90
J2 A17 1c ocher 6.50 2.50
J3 A17 2c scarlet 7.25 3.00
J4 A17 4c red brn 7.75 4.00
J5 A17 5c salmon 15.00 7.25
J6 A17 10c dk blue grn 25.00 11.00
a. Vert. pair, imperf. btwn. 475.00
Nos. J1-J6 (6) 67.25 29.65

D1

1904 Engr.

J7 D1 ½c blue 2.25 .50
a. Horiz. pair, imperf. btwn. 300.00 275.00
J8 D1 1c blue 4.25 .50
J9 D1 2c blue 3.00 .50
a. Horiz. pair, imperf. btwn. 350.00 300.00
J10 D1 4c blue 5.50 .60
J11 D1 5c blue 7.25 .60
J12 D1 10c blue 7.25 1.50
J13 D1 20c blue 20.00 3.00
J14 D1 30c blue 25.00 20.00
Nos. J7-J14 (8) 74.50 27.20

Arabic numeral of value at left on #J12-J14.

1911

J15 D1 1c brown 6.00 1.50
J16 D1 2c brown 12.50 12.50

The ½c, 4c, 5c and 20c in brown exist but were not issued as they arrived in China after the downfall of the Ching dynasty.

Issue of 1904 Overprinted in Red 立中時臨

1912

J19 D1 ½c blue 425. 325.
J20 D1 4c blue 475. 400.
J21 D1 5c blue 550. 575.
J22 D1 10c blue 850. 650.
J23 D1 20c blue 1,800. 1,500.
J24 D1 30c blue 1,800. 1,500.

Nos. J15-J16 exist with this overprint, but were not regularly issued.

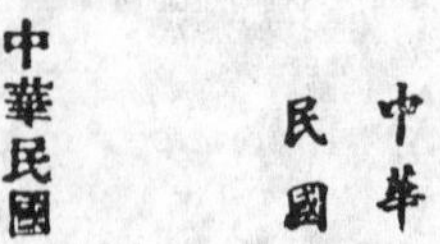

Nos. J25-J33 Nos. J34-J42

1912

Overprinted in Red

J25 D1 ½c blue .15 .15
J26 D1 1c brown .30 .30
a. Horiz. pair, imperf. btwn. 450.00
b. Inverted overprint 175.00
J27 D1 2c brown .35 .30
J28 D1 4c blue 2.50 3.00
J29 D1 5c blue 85.00 85.00
J30 D1 5c brown 1.25 .80
a. Inverted overprint 150.00 125.00
J31 D1 10c blue 4.75 1.10
J32 D1 20c blue 7.75 5.25
J33 D1 30c blue 11.00 10.00
Nos. J25-J33 (9) 113.05 105.90

1912

Overprinted in Black

J34 D1 ½c blue 6.00 1.50
J35 D1 ½c brown .70 .30
J36 D1 1c brown .65 .55
a. Inverted overprint 175.00 150.00
J37 D1 2c brown 2.50 4.25
J38 D1 4c blue 4.75 5.50
J39 D1 5c brown 9.00 6.00
a. Horiz. pair, imperf. btwn. 600.00
J40 D1 10c blue 11.00 16.00
J41 D1 20c brown 26.00 30.00
J42 D1 30c blue 55.00 35.00
Nos. J34-J42 (9) 115.60 99.10

D4 D5 D6

Printed by Waterlow & Sons

1913, May *Perf. 14, 15*

J43 D4 ½c blue .60 .20
a. Horiz. pair, imperf. btwn. 200.00
J44 D4 1c blue 1.10 .20
J45 D4 2c blue 2.50 1.75
J46 D4 4c blue 1.75 .20
J47 D4 5c blue 3.00 .15
J48 D4 10c blue 6.00 4.25
J49 D4 20c blue 14.00 7.75
J50 D4 30c blue 18.00 3.50
Nos. J43-J50 (8) 46.95 17.95

Printed by the Chinese Bureau of Engraving & Printing

1915 Re-engraved *Perf. 14*

J51 D4 ½c blue .50 .55
J52 D4 1c blue 1.25 .15
J53 D4 2c blue 1.25 .15
J54 D4 4c blue 1.25 .15
J55 D4 5c blue 2.50 .50
J56 D4 10c blue 3.00 .70
J57 D4 20c blue 8.00 1.25
J58 D4 30c blue 30.00 3.00
Nos. J51-J58 (8) 47.75 6.45

In the upper part of the stamps of type D4 there is an ornament of five marks like the letter "V". Below this is a curved label with an inscription in Chinese characters. On the 1913 stamps there are two complete background lines between the ornament and the label. The 1915 stamps show only one unbroken line at this place. There are other minute differences in the engraving of the stamps of the two issues.

1932 *Perf. 14*

J59 D5 ½c orange .15 .15
J60 D5 1c orange .15 .15
J61 D5 2c orange .15 .15
J62 D5 4c orange .40 .20
J63 D5 5c orange .40 .20
J64 D5 10c orange .85 .45
J65 D5 20c orange 1.10 .55
J66 D5 30c orange 1.75 .55
Nos. J59-J66 (8) 4.95 2.40

See Nos. J69-J79. For surcharges see Nos. 1NJ1, 9NJ1-9NJ4.

Regular Stamps of 1939 Overprinted in Black or Red

欠 暫

1940

J67 A57 $1 henna & dk brn (Bk) 1.65 *4.50*
J68 A57 $2 dl bl & org brn (R) 1.65 *5.50*

Type of 1932

Printed by The Commercial Press, Ltd.

Perf. 12½, 12½x13, 13

1940-41 Engr.

J69 D5 ½c yellow orange .20 .30
J70 D5 1c yellow orange .20 .30
J71 D5 2c yellow orange ('41) .20 .30
J72 D5 4c yellow orange .20 .30
J73 D5 5c yellow orange ('41) .55 .30
J74 D5 10c yellow orange ('41) .20 .30
J75 D5 20c yellow orange ('41) .20 .30
J76 D5 30c yellow orange .20 .30
J77 D5 50c yellow orange .35 .35
J78 D5 $1 yellow orange .35 .60
J79 D5 $2 yellow orange .60 .60
Nos. J69-J79 (11) 3.25 3.95

For surcharge see No. 1NJ1.

Thin Paper Without Gum

1944 Typo. *Perf. 13*

J80 D6 10c bluish green .15 *.45*
J81 D6 20c light chalky blue .15 *.45*
J82 D6 40c dull rose .15 *.45*
J83 D6 50c bluish green .15 *.40*
J84 D6 60c dull blue .15 *.70*
J85 D6 $1 dull rose .15 *.35*
J86 D6 $2 lilac brown .15 *.35*
Set value .85 .84

D7 D8

1945 Without Gum Unwmk.

J87 D7 $2 rose carmine .15 *.85*
J88 D7 $6 rose carmine .15 *.85*
J89 D7 $8 rose carmine .15 *.85*
J90 D7 $10 rose carmine .15 *1.10*
J91 D7 $20 rose carmine .15 *1.10*
J92 D7 $30 rose carmine .40 *1.10*
Set value .70
Nos. J87-J92 (6) *5.85*

For surcharges see Nos. J102-J109.

Thin Paper Without Gum

1947 Litho. *Perf. 14*

J93 D8 $50 plum .15 *.35*
J94 D8 $80 plum .15 *.35*
J95 D8 $100 plum .15 *.35*
J96 D8 $160 plum .15 *.35*
J97 D8 $200 plum .15 *.35*
J98 D8 $400 violet brown .15 *.35*
J99 D8 $500 violet brown .15 *.35*
a. Vert. pair, imperf. between 20.00
J100 D8 $800 violet brown .15 *.35*
J101 D8 $2000 violet brown .15 *.35*
Set value .75
Nos. J93-J101 (9) *3.15*

Type of 1945, Redrawn

Surcharged with New Value in Black

1948 Engr. *Perf. 13½x14*

Without Gum

J102 D7 $1000 on $20 dp claret .15 *.50*
J103 D7 $2000 on $30 dp claret .15 *.50*
J104 D7 $3000 on $50 dp claret .15 *.50*
J105 D7 $4000 on $100 dp claret .15 *.50*
J106 D7 $5000 on $200 dp claret .15 *.50*
J107 D7 $10,000 on $300 dp claret .15 *.55*
J108 D7 $20,000 on $500 dp claret .15 *.55*
J109 D7 $30,000 on $1000 deep cl .15 *.70*
Set value .90
Nos. J102-J109 (8) *4.30*

There are many differences in the redrawn design.

No. 627 Surcharged in Black

資欠作改
壹 金
分 圓
1

1949 *Perf. 12*

J110 A72 1 (c) on $40 orange .15 *.45*
J111 A72 2 (c) on $40 orange .15 *.45*
J112 A72 5 (c) on $40 orange .15 *.45*
J113 A72 10 (c) on $40 orange .15 *.45*
J114 A72 20 (c) on $40 orange .15 *.45*
J115 A72 50 (c) on $40 orange .15 *.50*
J116 A72 $1 on $40 orange .15 *.50*
J117 A72 $2 on $40 orange .15 *.50*
J118 A72 $5 on $40 orange .15 *.70*
J119 A72 $10 on $40 orange .20 *.50*
Set value 1.25
Nos. J110-J119 (10) *4.95*

Republic of China (Taiwan)

No. 438 Surcharged in Green or Black

肆 臺
角 幣

1951 Unwmk. *Perf. 12½*

J120 A47 40c on 40c org (G) 15.00 20.00
J121 A47 80c on 40c org (Bk) 15.00 20.00

Revenue Stamps Surcharged in Various Colors

政郵國民華中
角壹幣台資欠
10

1953 Unwmk. *Perf. 12½, 14*

Without Gum

J122 A95 10c on $50 dk bl (O) 18.00 3.75
J123 A95 20c on $100 ol grn (Dk Br) 18.00 3.75
J124 A95 40c on $20 org brn 18.00 1.10
J125 A95 80c on $500 sl grn (Dk Bl) 26.00 2.25
J126 A95 $1 on $30 dk vio (G) 26.00 7.50
Nos. J122-J126 (5) 106.00 18.35

D9 D10 D11

1956 Unwmk. Litho. *Perf. 12½*

Without Gum

J127 D9 20c rose car, & lt bl .90 .20
J128 D9 40c green & buff 1.75 .20
J129 D9 80c brown & gray 3.75 .20
J130 D9 $1 ultra & pink 3.75 .20
Nos. J127-J130 (4) 10.15 .80

No. 1197 Surcharged in Dark Violet

500
資 欠
伍

Wmk. 323

1961, Dec. 28 Engr. *Perf. 12*

Without Gum

J131 A135 $5 on $20 car rose 2.00 .65

Nos. 1274, 1282-1283 Surcharged in Black, Carmine Rose or Blue

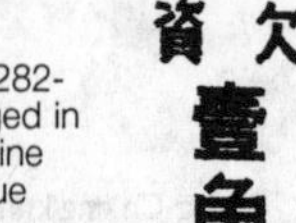

1964-65 Litho.

J132 A158 10c on 80c pale grn .15 .15
J133 A158 20c on $3.60 vio bl (CR) ('65) .30 .15
J134 A158 40c on $4.50 ver (B) ('65) .55 .15
Nos. J132-J134 (3) 1.00
Set value .30

1966-76 Wmk. 323 *Perf. 12½*
Granite Paper; Without Gum

J135 D10 10c dk brn & lil .25 .15
J136 D10 20c blue & yel .40 .15
J137 D10 50c vio bl & lt bl ('70) .65 .15
J138 D10 $1 purple & sal .50 .15
J139 D10 $2 grn & lt bl .65 .15
J140 D10 $5 red & sal 1.25 .30
a. $5 org red & pale yel 1.25 .30
J141 D10 $10 lil rose & pink ('76) *20.00* .60
Nos. J135-J141 (7) *23.70*
Set value 1.30

The 50c, $10 and No. J140a are gummed. The $1 and $2 were reissued with gum in 1968 and 1973 respectively. No. J140a and the $10 are on ordinary paper.

Catalogue values for unused stamps in this section, from this point to the end of the section, are for Never Hinged items.

1984-88 Litho. *Perf. 12½*

J142 D11 $1 rose & violet .15 .15
J143 D11 $2 yellow & blue .15 .15
J143A D11 $3 pale grn & brt rose lil .25 .20
J144 D11 $5 blue & yellow .25 .15
J144B D11 $5.50 rose lil & brt blue .45 .35
J144C D11 $7.50 bister yel & dp violet .60 .45
J145 D11 $10 yel & lil rose .50 .30
J155 D11 $20 sky blue & citron 1.65 1.25
Nos. J142-J155 (8) 4.00 3.00

Issued: $3, $5.50, $7.50, $20, Apr. 1, 1988; others, Mar. 15, 1984.

PARCEL POST STAMPS

PP1

PP2

PP3

1945-48 Unwmk. Engr. *Perf. 13*
Without Gum

Q1 PP1 $500 green 2.00 .15
Q2 PP1 $1000 blue 2.00 .15
Q3 PP1 $3000 rose red 6.50 .15
Q4 PP1 $5000 brown 100.00 3.50
Q5 PP1 $10,000 lil gray 165.00 4.25
Q6 PP1 $20,000 red org *1,600.*
Nos. Q1-Q5 (5) 275.50 8.20

No. Q6 was prepared but not issued.
For surcharges see People's Republic of China Nos. 5LQ1-5LQ2, 5LQ27-5LQ28.

Perf. 12½

Q7 PP2 $3000 red org 17.50 .55
Q8 PP2 $5000 dk blue 27.50 .55
Q9 PP2 $10,000 violet 27.50 .55
Q10 PP2 $20,000 dk red 27.50 .55

Perf. 13½

Q11 PP3 $1000 org yel 5.00 .85
Q12 PP3 $3000 bl grn 5.50 .85
Q13 PP3 $5000 org red 5.50 .85
Q14 PP3 $7000 dl blue 5.50 .85
Q15 PP3 $10,000 car rose 6.25 .85
Q16 PP3 $30,000 olive 6.25 .85
Q17 PP3 $50,000 indigo 6.25 .85
Q18 PP3 $70,000 org brn 9.00 .85
Q19 PP3 $100,000 dp plum 9.00 .85

Denomination Tablet Without Inner Frame

Q20 PP3 $200,000 dk grn 12.00 1.65
Q21 PP3 $300,000 pink 12.00 1.65
Q22 PP3 $500,000 vio brn 12.00 1.90
Q23 PP3 $3,000,000 sl blue 13.00 2.75
Q24 PP3 $5,000,000 lilac 13.00 2.75
Q25 PP3 $6,000,000 ol gray 14.00 3.50
Q26 PP3 $8,000,000 scarlet 14.00 3.75
Q27 PP3 $10,000,000 sage grn 17.50 4.50
Nos. Q11-Q27 (17) 165.75 30.10

Zeros for "cents" omitted on Nos. Q23-Q27.
See Taiwan Nos. Q1-Q5. For surcharges see Nos. 883-885, Northeastern Provinces Q1, Szechwan Q1, People's Republic of China 3LQ1-3LQ9, 5LQ3-5LQ16, 5LQ29-5LQ30.

Nos. Q11-Q15, Q23-Q24 Surcharged in Black or Carmine

圓拾圓金
10
圓拾圓金

1949 Unwmk. *Perf. 13½*

Q32 PP3 $10 on $3000 4.50 .15
Q33 PP3 $20 on $5000 4.50 .15
Q34 PP3 $50 on $10,000 4.50 .15
Q35 PP3 $100 on $3,000,000 (C) 5.50 .15
Q36 PP3 $200 on $5,000,000 10.00 .15
Q37 PP3 $500 on $1000 20.00 .15
Q38 PP3 $1000 on $7000 20.00 .25
Nos. Q32-Q38 (7) 69.00
Set value .85

5 characters in each line on Nos. Q33-Q38.

MILITARY STAMPS

No. 454 Overprinted in Dull Red 郵 軍

1943-44 Unwmk. *Perf. 12*

M1 A59 8c turquoise green 2.25 4.00

Nos. 383, 453-454 Overprinted in Red or Black 郵 軍

6mm between characters
Perf. 14, 12½

M2 A57 8c olive green 2.75 4.50
a. 8mm between characters 2.75 4.25
M3 A59 8c red orange (B) 275.00
M4 A59 8c turquoise green 5.50 5.00

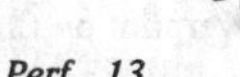
No. 493 Overprinted in Red 郵 軍

Perf. 13

M5 A62 16c dull olive brn 3.25 3.25
a. Perf. 10½-11 110.00

No. M5 overprinted in black is a proof.

Stamps of 1942-44 Overprinted in Carmine or Black 郵 軍

M6 A62 50c sage green (C) 2.00 3.50
M7 A62 $1 rose lake 3.00 4.25
M8 A62 $1 dull green 3.00 4.25
M9 A62 $2 dk blue grn (C) 4.75 7.00
M10 A62 $2 dk vio brn ('44) 75.00 75.00
Nos. M6-M10 (5) 87.75 94.00

Nos. 383 and 357 Overprinted in Red 郵 軍

1944 *Perf. 12, 14*

M11 A57 8c olive green 2.75 4.00
a. Right character inverted 165.00
M12 A57 16c olive gray 40.00 40.00

Anti-Aircraft Guns — M1

1945, Jan. 1 Typo. *Perf. 12½*
Thin Paper Without Gum

M13 M1 rose .60 *4.00*

For overprints see Northeastern Provinces Nos. M2-M3.

TAIWAN

(Formosa)
100 Sen = 1 Yen
100 Cents = 1 Dollar

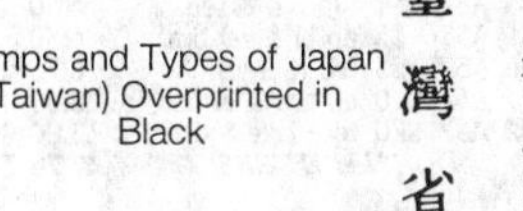
Stamps and Types of Japan (Taiwan) Overprinted in Black

Values in Sen and Yen
Black Overprint

1945 Unwmk. Litho. *Imperf.*
Stamps Divided by Lines of Colored Dashes

1 A1 3s carmine .60 .85
2 A1 5s blue grn .70 .65
3 A1 10s pale blue 1.00 .65
a. Inverted overprint 85.00
b. Double overprint 95.00
4 A1 30s dk blue 3.25 3.50
5 A1 40s violet 2.75 3.50
6 A1 50s gray brn 3.25 3.25
7 A1 1y olive grn 4.50 4.50

Same Overprint on Types of Japan

8 A99 5y gray grn 16.00 16.00
9 A100 10y brown vio 22.50 22.50
a. Inverted overprint 150.00
Nos. 1-9 (9) 54.55 55.40

The basic stamps of this issue were prepared by Japanese authorities for Taiwan use before the end of World War II when the island reverted to Chinese control. They are printed on crude buff or white wove paper. The overprint translates: "For Use in Taiwan, Chinese Republic."
A second overprinting of Nos. 2-3 was made with a different font.

China, Nos. 728-731, Surcharged in Black

70 限臺灣省貼用 錢拾柒

1946 *Perf. 14*
Without Gum

10 A75 70s on $20 green 1.65 *3.50*
a. Inverted surcharge 150.00
11 A75 1y on $30 blue 2.25 *4.00*
12 A75 2y on $50 dk brn 2.00 *4.00*
13 A75 3y on $100 car 2.25 *4.00*
Nos. 10-13 (4) 8.15 *15.50*

Convening of the Chinese Natl. Assembly.

China Issues and Types of 1940-1946 Surcharged in Black

用貼灣臺限

a

Perf. 12½, 12½x13, 13, 13x12½, 14
1946-47

14 A46 2s on 2c dp bl .15 .40
15 A48 5s on 5c dl red org .15 .25
16 A39 10s on 4c pale vio .15 .30
17 A48 30s on 15c brn car .15 .25
18 A73 50s on $20 car .25 .20
19 A37 65s on $20 brt yel grn .30 *1.65*
20 A47 1y on 20c lt bl .15 *1.10*
a. Inverted surcharge 70.00
21 A37 1y on $30 choc .20 *1.10*
22 A37 2y on $50 red org .35 .40
23 A73 3y on $100 dk car .15 .20
24 A73 5y on $200 ol grn .15 .20
25 A73 10y on $500 brt bl grn .20 .30
26 A73 20y on $700 red brn .65 .55
27 A73 50y on $1000 rose lake 1.10 .80
28 A73 100y on $3000 blue 2.75 .80
Nos. 14-28 (15) 6.85 *8.50*

The bottom line of the surcharge expresses the new value and consists of 2, 3 or 4 characters.
Nos. 14, 18-19, 21-28 issued in 1947.

Same Surcharge on China No. 412

1947 Wmk. 261 *Perf. 13*

28A A48 30s on 15c brn car 50.00 85.00

Type of China, 1946, Inscribed:

1947 Unwmk. Engr. *Perf. 11, 11½*

29 A74 70c carmine 1.50 *2.25*
30 A74 $1 green 1.50 *2.25*
31 A74 $2 vermilion 1.50 *2.25*
32 A74 $3 yel grn 1.50 *2.25*
33 A74 $7 yel org 1.50 *2.25*
34 A74 $10 magenta 1.50 *2.25*
Nos. 29-34 (6) 9.00 *13.50*

60th birthday of Chiang Kai-shek.

Type of China, 1947, Inscribed:

用貼灣臺

1947 *Perf. 14*

35 A76 50c deep green 1.50 2.50
36 A76 $3 deep blue 1.50 2.50
37 A76 $7.50 carmine 1.50 2.50
38 A76 $10 light brown 1.50 2.50
39 A76 $20 deep claret 1.50 2.50
Nos. 35-39 (5) 7.50 12.50

First anniversary of return of Chinese National Government to Nanking.

Dr. Sun Yat-sen — A1

1947, July 10
Without Gum

40 A1 $1 dk brown 2.25 .25
41 A1 $2 org brn .55 .25
42 A1 $3 blue grn .55 .25
43 A1 $5 vermilion .55 .25
44 A1 $9 deep blue .55 .25
45 A1 $10 brt rose car .55 .25
46 A1 $20 deep green .55 .30
47 A1 $50 rose lilac .55 .25
48 A1 $100 blue .55 .50
49 A1 $200 dark red .55 .50
Nos. 40-49 (10) 7.20 3.05

The 30c gray and $7.50 orange were not regularly issued without surcharge.
See #63-68. For overprint and surcharges see #51-53, 69-73, 101-103, J10-J17.

Type of 1947 Surcharged in Black

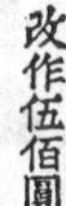
500⁰⁰
b

1948 Unwmk. *Perf. 14*

51 A1 $25 on $100 blue 1.10 1.10
52 A1 $500 on $7.50 org 1.10 .55
53 A1 $1000 on 30c gray 4.50 3.50
Nos. 51-53 (3) 6.70 5.15

Stamps of China, 1943-48, Surcharged Type "a" in Black or Carmine

1948-49 *Perf. 12½, 14*

54 A73 $5 on $70 red org .50 *2.25*
55 A62 $10 on $3 dk yel 1.65 2.25
56 A82 $10 on $150 dk bl (C) .45 .55
57 A82 $20 on $250 dp lil (C) .85 .55
58 A67 $100 on $20 car 575.00 575.00
59 A82 $1000 on $20,000 rose pink ('49) 2.25 1.65
Nos. 54-59 (6) 580.70 582.25

The bottom line of the surcharge expresses the new value and consists of 2 or 3 characters.

Type of 1947

1949 Engr. *Perf. 14*

63 A1 $25 olive grn .55 .25
64 A1 $5000 ocher 5.50 .45
65 A1 $10,000 apple grn 6.00 3.25
66 A1 $20,000 ol bister 6.00 3.25
67 A1 $30,000 indigo 6.00 .65
68 A1 $40,000 violet brn 5.00 .55
Nos. 63-68 (6) 29.05 8.40

For overprint and surcharges see #101, 103, J12.

No. 42 and Type of 1947 Surcharged Type "b" in Black, Carmine Violet or Red Violet

1949

69 A1 $300 on $3 bl grn .65 .20
70 A1 $1000 on $3 bl grn (C) 1.65 .55
71 A1 $2000 on $3 bl grn (V) 1.65 .55
72 A1 $3000 on $3 bl grn (RV) 3.50 1.10
73 A1 $3000 on $7.50 org 50.00 1.65
Nos. 69-73 (5) 57.45 4.05

For overprints see Nos. J10-J11.

Stamps of China, 1940-47, Surcharged Type "a" in Black or Carmine
Perf. 12½, 13x13½, 14

74 A39 $2 on 2½c rose lil (#424) .55 *1.65*
75 A72 $5 on $40 org (#627) .65 *1.10*
76 A73 $5 on $50 pur (C) (#638) .65 .25
77 A73 $5 on $100 dk car (#640) .65 .45
78 A57 $20 on 2c ol grn (#368) .65 .55
81 A63 $100 on $20 rose (#571) 1.10 .45

82 A67 $200 on $10 dk bl (C) (#591) 1.65 1.00
84 A57 $500 on $30 dl vio (#521) 5.50 2.00
86 A62 $800 on $4 red brn (#504) 4.50 3.25
87 A67 $5000 on $10 dk bl (#591) 5.50 2.75
88 A67 $10,000 on $20 car (#592) 9.00 3.00
89 A82 $200,000 on $3000 bl (C) (#750) 325.00 22.50
Nos. 74-89 (12) 355.40 38.95

臺幣 貳分

Northeastern Provinces No. 47, Surcharged in Green, Red Violet, Black or Blue

2 ★★★ 2

1949-50

91 A2 2c on $44 (G) 27.50 3.25
92 A2 5c on $44 (RV) ('50) 27.50 6.50
a. Violet surcharge 40.00 6.50
93 A2 10c on $44 (RV) ('50) 40.00 6.50
94 A2 20c on $44 (Bk) ('50) 50.00 6.50
a. Double surcharge 65.00
95 A2 30c on $44 (Bl) ('50) 55.00 11.00
96 A2 50c on $44 (Bl) ('50) 70.00 15.00
Nos. 91-96 (6) 270.00 48.75

China 959a, Overprinted in Black 限臺灣貼用

Overprint 15mm Wide

1949 Unwmk. Rouletted 9½

97 A96 orange 1.10 .20

China Nos. 567, 498 and 640 Surcharged Type "a" in Black

1948-49 Unwmk. Perf. 12½, 13, 14

98 A63 $20 on $3 red 2.25 1.40
99 A62 $50 on 50c sage grn 2.25 1.10
a. Perf. 11 14.00 13.00
100 A73 $600 on $100 dk car 8.50 2.75
Nos. 98-100 (3) 13.00 5.25

Botton line of surcharge consists of 3 characters.
No. 99 has two settings of surcharge: I. Spacing 10mm between rows of characters. II. Spacing 12mm.

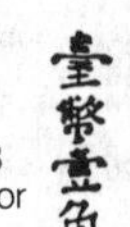

Nos. 67, 47 and 68 Surcharged in Violet or Black

10

1949 Perf. 14

101 A1 2c on $30,000 ind (V) 32.50 11.00
102 A1 10c on $50 rose lil 22.50 4.50
103 A1 10c on $40,000 vio brn 60.00 13.00
Nos. 101-103 (3) 115.00 28.50

Numerals slightly larger on Nos. 101-103.
For similar surcharges on China type A82 see China Nos. 1025-1036.

AIR POST STAMP

China No. C62a, Overprinted in Black 限臺灣貼用

Overprint 15mm Wide

1949 Unwmk. Rouletted 9½

C1 AP5 blue green 4.00 1.10

SPECIAL DELIVERY STAMP

China No. E12a, Overprinted in Black 限臺灣貼用

Overprint 12½mm Wide

1950 Unwmk. Rouletted 9½

E1 SD2 red violet 2.75 2.75

REGISTRATION STAMP

China No. F2a Overprinted in Black 限臺灣貼用

Overprint 12mm Wide

1950 Unwmk. Rouletted 9½

F1 R2 carmine 1.65 1.10

TAIWAN POSTAGE DUE STAMPS

D1

Unwmk.

1948, Feb. 10 Litho. Perf. 14

Without Gum

J1 D1 $1 blue 1.10 2.75
J2 D1 $3 blue 1.10 3.75
J3 D1 $5 blue 1.10 3.75
J4 D1 $10 blue 1.10 4.50
J5 D1 $20 blue 1.10 2.75
Nos. J1-J5 (5) 5.50 17.50

Nos. J1-J4 Surcharged in Carmine 改作伍拾圓 50.00

1948, Dec. 4

J6 D1 $50 on $1 blue 7.75 7.75
J7 D1 $100 on $3 blue 7.75 7.75
J8 D1 $300 on $5 blue 7.75 7.75
J9 D1 $500 on $10 blue 7.75 7.75
Nos. J6-J9 (4) 31.00 31.00

Nos. 70, 72 and 64 Handstamped in Violet 欠資

1949, Aug. 5

J10 A1 $1000 on $3 bl grn 13.00 13.00
J11 A1 $3000 on $3 bl grn 16.00 16.00
J12 A1 $5000 ocher 27.50 27.50
Nos. J10-J12 (3) 56.50 56.50

欠資 臺幣肆分

No. 48 Surcharged in Various Colors

4

1950

J13 A1 4c on $100 bl (Br) 16.00 9.00
J14 A1 10c on $100 bl (RV) 27.50 25.00
J15 A1 20c on $100 bl (Bk) 11.00 20.00
J16 A1 40c on $100 bl (C) 55.00 80.00
J17 A1 $1 on $100 bl (Bl) 40.00 45.00
Nos. J13-J17 (5) 149.50 179.00

TAIWAN PARCEL POST STAMPS

Type of China, Parcel Post Stamps of 1945-48 With Added Inscription:

1949 Unwmk. Engr. Perf. 14

Q1 PP3 $100 bluish grn 140.00 .15
Q2 PP3 $300 rose car 140.00 .15
Q3 PP3 $500 olive green 140.00 .15
Q4 PP3 $1000 slate 140.00 .15
Q5 PP3 $3000 deep plum 140.00 .15
Nos. Q1-Q5 (5) 700.00
Set value .50

Chinese characters in lower corners have colorless background; denomination tablet in color.

OCCUPATION STAMPS

Issued Under Japanese Occupation

Canceled Stamps
Postally used stamps of the Japanese occupation generally have heavy, smudgy cancels.

Kwangtung

China No. 297 Overprinted in Black

1942 Unwmk. Perf. 12½

1N1 A37 2c olive green 3.75 3.75
a. Inverted overprint 65.00

Same Overprint in Red or Black on Stamps of China, 1939-41

Perf. 12½, 14

1N2 A57 3c dl cl (#350) 2.25 2.25
1N3 A57 8c ol grn (#383) 2.25 2.25
1N4 A57 10c grn (#354) (R) 2.25 2.25
1N5 A57 10c grn (#384) (R) 2.75 2.75
1N6 A57 16c ol gray (#357) 3.50 5.50
1N7 A57 30c scar (#385) 2.75 2.75
1N8 A57 50c dk bl (#386) (R) 2.75 2.75
1N9 A57 $1 org brn & sep (#387) 5.50 6.50
1N10 A57 $2 dp bl & yel brn (#388) 7.00 9.00
1N11 A57 $5 red & sl grn (#389) 6.50 7.50
1N12 A57 $10 dk grn & dl pur (#390) 12.00 13.00
1N13 A57 $20 rose lake & dk bl (#391) 6.50 8.75

Same Overprint on China Nos. 422 and 433

Perf. 12½

1N14 A40 1c orange 1.65 2.25
a. Inverted overprint 65.00 65.00
1N15 A47 20c lt blue 2.75 3.50

Same Overprint on Stamps of China, 1941

Perf. 12

1N16 A59 1c orange 2.25 3.25
1N17 A59 5c green 2.25 3.25
1N18 A59 8c turq grn 2.25 3.25
1N19 A59 10c brt green 2.75 3.25
1N20 A59 17c olive 2.75 3.25
1N21 A59 30c scarlet 2.75 3.25
1N22 A59 50c dk blue 2.75 3.25
Nos. 1N1-1N22 (22) 81.90 97.50

粵省 貼用

Stamps of China, 1939-41 Overprinted in Black

1942 Perf. 12½, 14

1N23 A57 2c olive grn (#368) .55 .80
1N24 A57 3c dl claret (#350) .55 .80
1N25 A57 5c olive grn (#352) .55 1.10
1N26 A57 8c olive grn (#353) 200.00
1N27 A57 8c olive grn (#369) .65 .80
1N28 A57 10c green (#354) 1.00 1.10
1N29 A57 16c ol gray (#357) 1.00 1.10
1N30 A57 25c dk bl (#358) 1.00 2.25
1N31 A57 30c scarlet (#385) .65 1.40
1N32 A57 50c dk blue (#386) 2.25 1.65
1N33 A57 $1 org brn & sep (#387) 5.50 6.50
1N34 A57 $2 dp bl & yel brn (#388) 7.00 8.75
1N35 A57 $5 red & sl grn (#389) 9.00 11.00
1N36 A57 $10 dk grn & dl pur (#390) 14.00 16.00
1N37 A57 $20 rose lake & dk bl (#391) 13.00 16.00
Nos. 1N23-1N25,1N27-1N37 (14) 56.70 69.25

No. 1N26 is valued in fine condition.

Same Overprint on China Nos. 397-401

1942 Wmk. 261 Perf. 14

1N38 A57 $1 org brn & sep 6.50 7.50
1N39 A57 $2 dp bl & yel brn 6.50 8.00
1N40 A57 $5 red & sl grn 8.75 13.00
1N41 A57 $10 dk grn & dl pur 13.00 16.00
1N42 A57 $20 rose lake & dk bl 13.00 15.00
Nos. 1N38-1N42 (5) 47.75 59.50

Same Overprint on Stamps of China, 1941

1942 Unwmk. Perf. 12

1N43 A59 2c brt ultra .25 .40
1N44 A59 5c green .25 .40
1N45 A59 8c red org .30 .40
1N46 A59 8c turq grn .30 .75
1N47 A59 10c brt green .50 .55
1N48 A59 17c olive .55 .85
1N49 A59 25c rose vio .55 .85
1N50 A59 30c scarlet .55 .90
1N51 A59 50c dk blue .55 .90
1N52 A59 $1 brn & blk 4.00 6.50
1N53 A59 $2 bl & blk 5.00 7.50
1N54 A59 $5 scar & blk 4.00 4.00
1N55 A59 $10 grn & blk 7.00 11.00
1N56 A59 $20 rose vio & blk 8.50 16.00
Nos. 1N43-1N56 (14) 32.30 51.00

粵省 貼用 暫售價佰圓

China Nos. 354 and 369 Surcharged in Black

1945 Unwmk. Perf. 12½

1N57 A57 $200 on 10c grn 90.00 55.00
1N58 A57 $400 on 8c ol grn 100.00 60.00

China No. 422 Surcharged in Black

1945

1N59 A40 $400 on 1c org 500.00 500.00

OCCUPATION POSTAGE DUE STAMPS

China, No. J79 Surcharged Diagonally with New Value Between Parallel Lines in Black

1945 Unwmk. Perf. 12½

1NJ1 D5 $100 on $2 yel org 550.00 600.00
a. Inverted surcharge 800.00

MENG CHIANG (Inner Mongolia)

Nos. 297-298, 301-303 Overprinted

Characters 4mm High — I

Characters 5mm High — II

1941 Engr. Unwmk.

2N1 A37 2c #297, I 1.10 1.40
a. Type II 1.40 1.65
2N2 A37 4c #298, II 40.00 40.00
a. Type I 40.00 40.00
2N3 A37 15c #301, I 3.25 4.50
a. Type II 3.75 4.50
2N4 A37 20c #302, I 8.75 11.00
a. Type II 6.50 6.50
2N5 A37 25c #303, II 4.50 5.50
a. Type I 40.00 40.00

For surcharge see No. 2N116.

On Nos. 312, 314, 318, 321

1941 Perf. 14

2N6 A39 ½c #312, I 11.00 13.00
a. Type II 16.00 16.00
2N7 A39 2½c #314, II 3.25 2.25
a. Type I 5.50 5.50
2N8 A45 13c #318, II 1.10 1.10
a. Type I 90.00 95.00
2N9 A48 30c #321, II 65.00 65.00

On Stamps of 1939-41

1941 Perf. 12½

2N10 A57 2c #368, II 1.65 1.65
2N11 A57 3c #350, I 1.10 1.10
a. Type II .85 .85
2N12 A57 5c #352, I 2.25 2.25
a. Type II 1.65 2.25
2N13 A57 8c #353, I .85 .85
a. Type II 1.65 1.65
2N14 A57 8c #369, II 4.50 4.00
2N15 A57 10c #354, II 1.90 1.65
2N16 A57 16c #357, II 2.75 2.75
2N17 A57 $1 #359, II 8.00 8.00
a. Type I 275.00 275.00
b. #347, I 65.00 65.00
2N18 A57 $5 #361, II 55.00 55.00

For surcharges see Nos. 2N117, 2N119.

On Stamps of 1940 with Secret Marks

1941 Unwmk. Perf. 14

2N19 A57 5c #382, II 1.10 1.10
2N20 A57 8c #383, I 2.75 2.25
a. Type II 40.00 40.00
2N21 A57 10c #384, I 2.75 2.75
a. Type II 2.25 1.65
2N22 A57 30c #385, I 4.00 3.25
a. Type II 2.25 2.25
2N23 A57 50c #386, I 5.50 5.50
a. Type II 5.50 5.50
2N24 A57 $1 #387, I 8.75 9.00
a. Type II 16.00 14.00

2N25 A57 $2 #388, I 11.00 13.00
a. Type II 27.50 32.50
2N26 A57 $5 #389, I 45.00 45.00
a. Type II 55.00 55.00
2N27 A57 $10 #390, II 50.00 50.00
a. Type I 55.00 55.00
2N28 A57 $20 #391, II 70.00 70.00
a. Type I 75.00 75.00

For surcharge see No. 2N120.

On Stamps of 1940 with Secret Marks

1941 Wmk. 261 *Perf. 14*

2N29 A57 10c #394, II 4.00 4.00
2N30 A57 30c #395, II 4.00 4.50
a. Type I 55.00 55.00
2N31 A57 50c #396, II 3.50 3.50
Nos. 2N29-2N31 (3) 11.50 12.00

On Stamps of 1940-41 (Martyrs) with Secret Marks

Perf. 12½, 13 & Compound

1941 Wmk. 261

2N32 A39 ½c #402, II 10.00 11.00
2N33 A40 1c #403, I 2.75 1.65
a. Type II .85 .85
2N34 A39 2½c #405, II 65.00 65.00
a. Type I 50.00 50.00
2N35 A48 3c #406, II 2.25 2.75
2N36 A46 10c #410, I 11.00 11.00
a. Type II 11.00 11.00
2N37 A46 17c #413, II 40.00 40.00
a. Type I 65.00 65.00
2N38 A40 25c #416, II 2.75 2.75
2N39 A48 30c #418, II 50.00 55.00
a. Type I 60.00 60.00
2N40 A47 40c #419, II 4.00 4.00
a. Type I 6.50 6.50
2N41 A40 50c #420, I 8.50 8.50
a. Type II 40.00 40.00

Unwmk.

2N42 A39 ½c #421, I 2.25 2.50
a. Type II 1.10 .85
2N43 A40 1c #422, I 1.40 1.10
a. Type II 2.75 2.75
2N44 A46 2c #423, I 3.25 2.75
2N45 A48 3c #425, I 3.00 3.00
a. Type II 2.00 2.00
2N46 A39 4c #426, II 1.65 1.40
2N47 A45 8c #428, II 16.00 16.00
a. Type I 65.00 65.00
2N48 A46 10c #429, I 15.00 15.00
a. Type II 50.00 50.00
2N49 A45 13c #430, I 5.50 5.50
a. Type II 16.00 16.00
2N50 A48 15c #431, II 3.25 3.25
2N51 A46 17c #432, I 3.25 3.75
a. Type II 3.25 3.25
2N52 A47 20c #433, II 2.00 2.50
a. Type I 3.25 3.25
2N53 A45 21c #434, II 3.25 3.25
2N54 A40 25c #435, I 3.75 3.25
2N55 A46 28c #436, II 3.25 3.25
2N56 A40 50c #439, II 5.50 5.50
a. Type I 11.00 11.00

For surcharges see Nos. 2N114-2N115, 2N118, 2N121-2N122.

China Nos. 297-298, 302 Surcharged in Black

疆 蒙
分 壹

1942 Unwmk. *Perf. 12½, 13*

2N57 A37 1c on 2c ol grn 6.50 6.50
2N58 A37 2c on 4c grn 5.00 3.75
2N59 A37 10c on 20c ultra 20.00 20.00
Nos. 2N57-2N59 (3) 31.50 30.25

Same, on China No. 313

Perf. 14

2N60 A40 ½c on 1c org 14.00 14.00

Same, on Stamps of China, 1938-41

Perf. 12½

2N61 A57 1c on 2c (#368) 1.40 1.10
2N62 A57 4c on 8c (#353) 4.75 3.75
a. Inverted surcharge 55.00 55.00
2N63 A57 4c on 8c (#369) 1.10 1.10
2N64 A57 5c on 10c (#354) .85 .55
2N65 A57 8c on 16c (#357) 3.25 2.25
2N66 A57 50c on $1 (#359) 7.75 7.75
a. On No. 347 45.00 45.00
b. On No. 344 325.00 325.00
2N67 A57 $1 on $2 (#360) 45.00 45.00
Nos. 2N61-2N67 (7) 64.10 61.50

No. 2N66b was issued without gum.

Same, on Stamps of China, 1940

Perf. 14

2N68 A57 4c on 8c (#383) .35 .35
2N69 A57 15c on 30c (#385) 4.50 3.25
a. Inverted surcharge 55.00 55.00
2N70 A57 25c on 50c (#386) 5.50 5.50
2N71 A57 50c on $1 (#387) 3.75 3.25
2N72 A57 $1 on $2 (#388) 11.00 11.00
2N73 A57 $5 on $10 (#390) 40.00 40.00
2N74 A57 $10 on $20 (#391) 65.00 65.00
Nos. 2N68-2N74 (7) 130.10 128.35

Same, on China No. 395

1942 Wmk. 261 *Perf. 14*

2N75 A57 15c on 30c scar 65.00 65.00

Same, on China Nos. 418 and 419

Perf. 12½, 13

2N76 A48 15c on 30c brn car 32.50 32.50
2N77 A47 20c on 40c org 6.50 7.75

Same, on Stamps of China, 1940-41

1942 Unwmk.

2N78 A40 ½c on 1c org .20 .30
2N79 A39 2c on 4c pale vio 3.75 3.75
2N80 A47 10c on 20c lt bl 5.00 5.00
2N81 A47 20c on 40c org 11.00 11.00
2N82 A40 25c on 50c grn 16.00 16.00
Nos. 2N78-2N82 (5) 35.95 36.05

Same Surcharge on "New Peking" Prints

Perf. 14

2N83 A37 1c on 2c ol grn 4.00 4.00
2N84 A37 2c on 4c dl grn .55 .55
2N85 A46 5c on 10c dl vio 3.50 4.50
2N86 A57 8c on 16c ol gray 1.25 .75
2N87 A47 10c on 20c red brn 4.00 3.50
2N88 A48 15c on 30c brn car 1.50 2.50
2N89 A47 20c on 40c org 5.50 6.00
2N90 A40 25c on 50c grn 1.75 3.00
2N91 A57 50c on $1 org brn & sep 7.00 7.00
2N92 A57 $1 on $2 dp bl & org brn 20.00 19.00
2N93 A57 $5 on $10 dk grn & dl pur 45.00 45.00
Nos. 2N83-2N93 (11) 94.05 95.80

The "New Peking" printings were made by the Chinese Bureau of Engraving and Printing for use in Japanese controlled areas of North China. They are on thin, poor quality paper, with dull gum or without gum and there are slight alterations in the designs.

Dragon-Carved Pillar and Doves — A1

Mining Coal — A2

Wmk. Characters in Circle in Sheet

1943 Engr. *Perf. 12xPin-perf. 12*

2N94 A1 4f deep orange .20 .65
2N95 A1 8f dark blue .25 .85

5th anniv. of the Inner Mongolia post and telegraph service.

The watermark, which is 40mm in diameter and covers four stamps, occurs three times in the sheet.

1943 Unwmk. Photo. *Perf. 12*

2N96 A2 8f Prus green .20 .85
2N97 A2 4f brown red .25 1.00

2nd anniv. of the "Greater East Asia War."

Flying Horse — A3

Yun Wang — A4

1944 *Perf. 12½x12, 12x12½*

2N98 A3 4f rose .15 .85
2N99 A4 8f dull blue .25 .85

5th anniv. of the founding of the Federal Autonomous Government of Mongolia, Sept. 1, 1939.

Industrial Plant — A5

1944, Dec. 8 Photo. *Perf. 12x12½*

2N100 A5 8f red brown .25 1.50

3rd anniv. of the "Greater East Asia War" and to encourage production increase.

New Peking Printings of 1942 Overprinted in Black

1945 Unwmk. Engr. *Perf. 14*

Without Gum

2N101 A37 2c olive grn 9.50 9.50
2N102 A37 4c dull grn 14.00 14.00
2N103 A37 5c green 9.50 9.50
2N104 A57 $1 org brn & sep 2.50 2.50
2N105 A57 $2 dp bl & org brn 9.50 9.50
2N106 A57 $5 red & grnsh blk 25.00 25.00

Same Overprint on New Peking Printings of Martyrs Issue

2N107 A40 1c orange .70 .70
2N108 A45 8c dp orange .35 .35
2N109 A46 10c dl violet .20 .20
2N110 A47 20c red brown 1.50 1.50
2N111 A48 30c brown car .35 .35
2N112 A47 40c orange .35 .35
2N113 A40 50c green 6.00 6.00
Nos. 2N101-2N113 (13) 79.45 79.45

For surcharges see Nos. 2N123-2N127.

Stamps of Meng Chiang, 1941, Surcharged in Red or Black

角伍
50c

角壹 圓壹
10c $1

1945

2N114 A39 10c on ½c ol blk (#2N42a) (R) 1.10 1.50
a. 10c on ½c ol blk (#2N42) 4.50 3.75
2N115 A40 10c on 1c org (#2N43a) (R) .85 1.10
a. Without secret mark (China #313) 32.50 32.50
b. On #2N43 2.25 2.75
2N116 A37 50c on 2c ol grn (#2N1a) (Bk) 15.00 15.00
b. On #2N1 20.00 20.00
2N117 A57 50c on 2c ol grn (#2N10) (Bk) .65 .85
2N118 A39 50c on 4c pale vio (#2N46) (R) .65 .85
2N119 A57 50c on 5c ol grn (#2N12a) (R) .45 1.10
a. On #2N12 8.50 8.50
2N120 A57 50c on 5c ol grn (#2N19) (R) .85 1.10
Nos. 2N114-2N120 (7) 19.55 21.50

Same Surcharge on #2N32, 2N33a

1945 Wmk. 261

2N121 A39 10c on ½c ol blk (R) 14.00 16.00
2N122 A40 10c on 1c orange (R) .85 1.10
a. On #2N33 16.00 22.50

Same Surcharge on Nos. 2N107, 2N101-2N103 and 2N108

1945 Unwmk.

2N123 A40 10c on 1c org (R) .20 .20
2N124 A37 50c on 2c ol grn (Bk) 2.50 2.50
2N125 A37 50c on 4c dl grn (R) 3.50 3.50
2N126 A37 50c on 5c green .40 .40
2N127 A45 $1 on 8c dp org (R) .60 .60
Nos. 2N123-2N127 (5) 7.20 7.20

NORTH CHINA

Honan

Nos. 297-298, 301-303 Overprinted

南河 南河
I II

1941 Engr. Unwmk.

3N1 A37 2c #297, II 4.50 3.25
a. Type I 5.50 5.50
3N2 A37 4c #298, I 5.50 5.00
a. Type II 20.00 20.00
3N3 A37 15c #301, II 2.25 1.65
a. Type I 1.40 1.65
3N4 A37 20c #302, I 5.50 5.50
3N5 A37 25c #303, II 15.00 15.00

1941 *Perf. 14*

3N6 A39 ½c #312, I 1.65 2.25
a. Type II 19.00 19.00
3N7 A39 2½c #314, II 1.50 1.50
a. Type I 1.10 1.10
3N8 A45 13c #318, II 1.10 1.10
a. Type I 70.00 70.00
3N9 A48 30c #321, II 11.00 11.00
3N10 A47 40c #322, II 75.00 75.00

On Stamps of 1939-41

1941 *Perf. 12½*

3N11 A57 2c #368, II 1.10 1.10
3N12 A57 3c #350, II .85 .85
a. Type I .50 .50
3N13 A57 5c #352, II 1.10 .55
a. Type I 1.65 1.65
3N14 A57 8c #353, II 1.10 1.10
a. Type I 1.10 1.10
3N15 A57 10c #354, II 1.10 1.10
3N16 A57 16c #357, II 1.00 1.00
3N17 A57 $1 #359, II 10.00 10.00
a. Type I 225.00 225.00
b. On #347, I 45.00 45.00
3N18 A57 $5 #361, II 55.00 55.00

For overprints see Nos. 3N56, 3N58, 3N61.

On Stamps of 1940 with Secret Marks

1941 Unwmk. *Perf. 14*

3N20 A57 5c #382, II 1.40 .55
3N21 A57 8c #383, II .40 .40
3N22 A57 10c #384, II 1.10 .65
3N23 A57 30c #385, I 5.50 5.50
a. Type II 7.75 7.75
3N24 A57 50c #386, I 2.25 2.25
a. Type II 9.00 9.00
3N25 A57 $1 #387, I 5.50 2.75
a. Type II 45.00 45.00
3N26 A57 $2 #388, I 11.00 13.00
a. Type II 16.00 16.00
3N27 A57 $5 #389, I 22.50 22.50
a. Type II 55.00 55.00
3N28 A57 $10 #390, II 40.00 40.00
a. Type I 95.00 95.00
3N29 A57 $20 #391, II 75.00 75.00
a. Type I 85.00 85.00

On Stamps of 1940 with Secret Marks

1941 Wmk. 261 *Perf. 14*

3N30 A57 5c #392, II 16.00 5.50
3N31 A57 5c #393, II 9.00 4.50
3N32 A57 30c #395, I 15.00 15.00
a. Type II 27.50 27.50
3N33 A57 50c #396, II 14.00 14.00

On Stamps of 1940-41 (Martyrs) with Secret Marks

Perf. 12½, 13 & Compound

1941 Wmk. 261

3N34 A39 ½c #402, II 1.75 2.25
3N35 A40 1c #403, II .65 .65
a. Type I 1.10 1.10
3N36 A39 2½c #405, II 9.00 9.00
3N37 A46 10c #410, I 22.50 11.00
a. Type II 9.00 9.00
3N38 A45 13c #411, II 3.00 3.00
3N39 A46 17c #413, II 2.75 2.75
a. Type I 7.00 7.00
3N40 A40 25c #416, II 2.25 2.25
3N41 A47 40c #419, II 3.50 3.50
a. Type I 11.00 11.00

Unwmk.

3N42 A39 ½c #421, II .85 .85
a. Type I 2.25 2.25
3N43 A40 1c #422, I 1.40 1.40
a. Type II 2.75 2.75
3N44 A46 2c #423, I 6.50 6.50
3N45 A48 3c #425, I 1.10 1.65
3N46 A39 4c #426, II .55 .55
3N47 A46 10c #429, I 25.00 25.00
3N48 A45 13c #430, I 2.25 2.25
a. Type I 11.00 11.00
3N49 A48 15c #431, II 1.65 1.65
3N50 A46 17c #432, II 2.75 2.75
a. Type I 11.00 11.00
3N51 A47 20c #433, II 1.40 1.40
a. Type I 32.50 32.50
3N52 A45 21c #434, II 2.25 2.25
3N53 A40 25c #435, I 3.25 3.25
3N54 A46 28c #436, II 2.25 2.25

For overprints see Nos. 3N55, 3N59.

Overprinted in Red

坡嘉新
念紀落陷

1942

3N55 A39 4c #3N46 2.25 3.25
3N56 A57 8c #3N14 17.50 22.50
3N57 A57 8c #369, II 3.75 9.00
Nos. 3N55-3N57 (3) 23.50 34.75

The fall of Singapore.

Overprinted in Red

國建國洲滿
念紀年週十

1942

3N58 A57 2c #3N11 6.50 9.00
3N59 A39 4c #3N46 11.00 16.00
3N60 A57 8c #369, II 27.50 32.50
3N61 A57 8c #3N14 22.50 27.50
Nos. 3N58-3N61 (4) 67.50 85.00

Formation of Manchukuo, 10th anniv.

Hopei

Nos. 297-298, 301-303 Overprinted

北河 北河
I II

1941 Engr. Unwmk.

4N1 A37 2c #297, II .90 .90
a. Type I 2.25 2.25

4N2 A37 4c #298, I 2.25 2.25
a. Type II 55.00 55.00
4N3 A37 15c #301, II 2.25 2.25
a. Type I 3.50 2.75
4N4 A37 20c #302, II 1.10 1.10
4N5 A37 25c #303, II 5.00 5.75
a. Type I 75.00 65.00

On Nos. 312, 314, 318, 321

1941 ***Perf. 14***
4N6 A39 ½c #312, II .35 .55
a. Type I .80 .80
4N7 A39 2½c #314, II .45 .45
a. Type I .45 .55
4N8 A45 13c #318, II 1.10 1.10
a. Type I 1.90 1.90
4N9 A48 30c #321, II 3.00 3.00

On Stamps of 1939-41

1941 ***Perf. 12½***
4N10 A57 2c #368, II .55 .55
4N11 A57 2c #349, II .55 .50
4N12 A57 3c #350, II .30 .30
a. Type I 1.40 1.40
4N13 A57 5c #352, II .55 .40
a. Type I 1.40 1.25
4N14 A57 8c #353, II .30 .30
a. Type I 1.25 1.25
4N15 A57 8c #369, II 2.75 2.75
4N16 A57 10c #354, II .55 .55
4N17 A57 16c #357, II 1.65 .65
4N18 A57 $1 #359, II 6.00 6.00
a. On #347, I 190.00 190.00
4N19 A57 $2 #360, II 9.00 9.00
a. Type I 32.50 27.50
4N20 A57 $5 #361, II 27.50 27.50
a. Type I 32.50 32.50
4N21 A57 $10 #362, II 140.00 140.00
4N22 A57 $20 #363, II 275.00 275.00

For overprints see Nos. 4N66-4N68, 4N70.

On Stamps of 1940 with Secret Marks

1941 Unwmk. ***Perf. 14***

Type II
4N24 A57 5c #382 .40 .40
4N25 A57 8c #383 1.10 1.10
4N26 A57 10c #384 .55 .35
4N27 A57 30c #385 .85 .85
4N28 A57 50c #386 1.65 1.65
4N29 A57 $1 #387 3.25 3.00
4N30 A57 $2 #388 8.75 8.75
4N31 A57 $5 #389 32.50 32.50
4N32 A57 $10 #390 32.50 32.50
4N33 A57 $20 #391 45.00 45.00
Nos. 4N24-4N33 (10) 126.55 126.10

For overprints see Nos. 4N65, 4N71.

Type I
4N24a A57 5c 1.10 1.10
4N25a A57 8c 45.00 45.00
4N26a A57 10c 1.10 1.10
4N28a A57 50c 1.40 1.40
4N29a A57 $1 5.00 3.25
4N30a A57 $2 22.50 22.50
4N31a A57 $5 45.00 37.50
4N32a A57 $10 50.00 35.00
4N33a A57 $20 70.00 65.00
Nos. 4N24a-4N33a (9) 241.10 211.85

On Stamps of 1940 with Secret Marks

1941 Wmk. 261 ***Perf. 14***
4N34 A57 5c #392, II .35 .35
4N35 A57 5c #393, II 1.10 1.10
4N36 A57 10c #394, II .85 .55
4N37 A57 30c #395, II 2.50 2.50
a. Type I 3.25 3.25
4N38 A57 50c #396, II 4.50 3.75
Nos. 4N34-4N38 (5) 9.30 8.25

On Stamps of 1940-41 (Martyrs) with Secret Marks

Perf. 12½, 13 & Compound

1941 Wmk. 261

Type II
4N39 A39 ½c #402 .85 .85
4N40 A40 1c #403 1.10 1.00
4N41 A46 2c #404 .65 .65
4N42 A39 2½c #405 .85 .85
4N43 A48 3c #406 1.50 1.75
4N44 A46 10c #410 1.65 1.65
4N45 A45 13c #411 1.65 1.65
4N46 A46 17c #413 2.25 2.25
4N47 A40 25c #416 2.25 2.25
4N48 A48 30c #418 8.75 8.75
4N49 A47 40c #419 2.25 2.25
Nos. 4N39-4N49 (11) 23.75 23.90

Type I
4N40a A40 1c .65 2.25
4N44a A46 10c 1.10 1.10
4N46a A46 17c 2.75 2.75
4N48a A48 30c 22.50 22.50
4N49a A47 40c 3.75 3.75
Nos. 4N40a-4N49a (5) 30.75 32.35

Unwmk.

Type II
4N50 A39 ½c #421 .85 .85
4N51 A40 1c #422 1.65 1.10
4N53 A48 3c #425 1.65 2.25
4N54 A39 4c #426 .85 .85
4N55 A45 8c #428 1.10 1.10
4N56 A46 10c #429 2.25 2.25
4N57 A45 13c #430 3.25 3.25
4N58 A48 15c #431 2.75 2.75
4N59 A46 17c #432 2.25 2.25
4N60 A47 20c #433 2.25 2.25
4N61 A45 21c #434 3.25 3.25
4N62 A40 25c #435 2.25 2.25
4N63 A46 28c #436 2.25 2.50
Nos. 4N50-4N63 (13) 26.60 26.90

Type I
4N50a A39 ½c 1.10 1.10
4N51a A40 1c 1.65 1.10
4N52 A46 2c #423 .35 .35
4N53a A48 3c .85 .85
4N55a A45 8c 2.50 2.50
4N57a A45 13c 2.25 2.25
4N59a A46 17c 3.75 3.75
4N60a A47 20c 2.75 2.75
4N62a A40 25c 3.25 3.25
Nos. 4N50a-4N62a (9) 18.45 17.90

For overprints see Nos. 4N64, 4N69.

Honan Singapore Overprint in Red

1942
4N64 A39 4c #4N54 .85 2.25
4N65 A57 8c #4N25 2.75 3.00
4N66 A57 8c #4N14 2.00 2.25
4N67 A57 8c #4N15 6.50 8.75
Nos. 4N64-4N67 (4) 12.10 16.25

Honan Anniv. of Manchukuo Overprint in Red

1942
4N68 A57 2c #4N10 4.75 5.50
4N69 A39 4c #4N54 4.50 5.50
4N70 A57 8c #4N14 50.00 55.00
4N71 A57 8c #4N25 6.50 7.00
Nos. 4N68-4N71 (4) 65.75 73.00

Shansi

Nos. 297-298, 301, 303 Overprinted

西 山 I 西 山 II

1941 Engr. Unwmk.
5N1 A37 2c #297, II 2.75 2.75
a. Type I 3.75 2.75
5N2 A37 4c #298, I 45.00 45.00
a. Type II 90.00 90.00
5N3 A37 15c #301, I 5.50 5.50
a. Type II 3.50 3.50
5N4 A37 25c #303, II 5.50 5.50
a. Type I 40.00 40.00

On Nos. 312, 314, 318, 321

1941 ***Perf. 14***
5N5 A39 ½c #312, II .85 1.10
a. Type I 1.40 2.00
5N6 A39 2½c #314, II 1.10 1.10
a. Type I 1.75 1.75
5N7 A45 13c #318, II 1.40 1.40
a. Type I 110.00 110.00
5N8 A48 30c #321, II 7.00 7.00
Nos. 5N5-5N8 (4) 10.35 10.60

On Stamps of 1939-41

1941 ***Perf. 12½***
5N9 A57 2c #368, II .55 .55
5N10 A57 3c #350, II .85 .85
a. Type I 10.00 10.00
5N11 A57 5c #352, II 2.25 2.25
a. Type I 3.25 3.25
5N12 A57 8c #353, II 1.10 1.10
a. Type I 2.75 2.75
5N13 A57 8c #369, II 27.50 16.00
5N14 A57 10c #354, II 1.40 1.40
5N15 A57 16c #357, II 3.25 3.25
5N16 A57 $1 #359, II 8.25 8.25
5N17 A57 $2 #360, II 32.50 32.50
5N18 A57 $5 #361, II 40.00 40.00
Nos. 5N9-5N18 (10) 117.65 106.15

For overprints see Nos. 5N62-5N64, 5N66-5N67.

On Stamps of 1940 with Secret Marks

1941 Unwmk. ***Perf. 14***
5N19 A57 5c #382, II .55 .50
5N20 A57 8c #383, II 1.10 1.10
5N21 A57 10c #384, I .85 1.10
a. Type II 2.75 2.75
5N22 A57 30c #385, I 1.90 1.90
a. Type II 1.65 1.65
5N23 A57 50c #386, I 2.50 2.50
a. Type II 3.75 3.75
5N24 A57 $1 #387, I 7.75 7.75
a. Type II 22.00 16.00
5N25 A57 $2 #388, I 16.00 16.00
a. Type II 13.00 16.00
5N26 A57 $5 #389, II 32.50 27.50
a. Type I 65.00 65.00
5N27 A57 $10 #390, II 50.00 50.00
a. Type I 50.00 50.00
5N28 A57 $20 #391, II 60.00 60.00
a. Type I 65.00 65.00

For overprints see Nos. 5N61, 5N68.

On Stamps of 1940 with Secret Marks

1941 Wmk. 261 ***Perf. 14***
5N29 A57 5c #392, II 1.00 1.00
5N30 A57 5c #393, II .85 .85
5N31 A57 10c #394, II 2.25 2.25
5N32 A57 30c #395, I 55.00 50.00
5N33 A57 50c #396, I 5.00 5.00
Nos. 5N29-5N33 (5) 64.10 59.10

On Stamps of 1940-41 (Martyrs) with Secret Marks

Perf. 12½, 13 & Compound

1941 Wmk. 261
5N34 A39 ½c #402, II .85 .85
5N35 A40 1c #403, II .70 .70
a. Type I .85 .85
5N36 A46 2c #404, II 1.65 1.65
5N37 A39 2½c #405, I 6.00 6.00
5N38 A46 10c #410, I 5.00 5.00
5N39 A45 13c #411, II 2.75 2.75
5N40 A46 17c #413, I 22.50 22.50
5N41 A40 25c #416, II 2.25 2.25
5N42 A48 30c #418, II 75.00 75.00
a. Type I 90.00 90.00
5N43 A47 40c #419, II 3.75 3.75
a. Type I 22.50 22.50
5N44 A40 50c #420, II 4.50 4.50
a. Type I 22.50 22.50

Unwmk.
5N45 A39 ½c #421, II 2.00 2.00
a. Type I 2.75 2.75
5N46 A40 1c #422, II .85 .85
a. Type I 1.75 1.75
5N47 A46 2c #423, II .50 .50
5N48 A48 3c #425, I 5.50 5.50
5N49 A39 4c #426, II .85 .85
5N50 A45 8c #428, I 10.00 10.00
a. Type II 11.00 11.00
5N51 A46 10c #429, I 27.50 27.50
a. Type II 32.50 32.50
5N52 A45 13c #430, I 13.00 13.00
a. Type II 13.00 13.00
5N53 A48 15c #431, II 2.75 2.75
5N54 A46 17c #432, II 2.75 2.75
a. Type I 3.75 3.75
5N55 A47 20c #433, II 2.25 2.25
a. Type I 2.25 2.25
5N56 A45 21c #434, II 2.75 2.75
5N57 A40 25c #435, I 2.25 2.50
5N58 A46 28c #436, II 2.75 2.75
5N59 A40 50c #439, II 7.75 7.75

For overprints see Nos. 5N60, 5N65.

Honan Singapore Overprint in Red

1942
5N60 A39 4c #5N49 2.00 2.50
5N61 A57 8c #5N20 3.25 3.25
5N62 A57 8c #5N12 4.75 6.50
5N63 A57 8c #5N13 6.50 9.00
Nos. 5N60-5N63 (4) 16.50 21.25

Honan Anniv. of Manchukuo Overprint in Red

1942
5N64 A57 2c #5N9 5.50 6.50
5N65 A39 4c #5N49 8.25 11.00
5N66 A57 8c #5N12 27.50 32.50
5N67 A57 8c #5N13 50.00 55.00
5N68 A57 8c #5N20 27.50 27.50
Nos. 5N64-5N68 (5) 118.75 132.50

Shantung

Nos. 297-298, 301-303 Overprinted

東 山 I 東 山 II

1941 Engr. Unwmk.
6N1 A37 2c #297, II 1.10 1.10
a. Type I 2.75 2.75
6N2 A37 4c #298, II 3.25 3.25
a. Type I 5.50 4.50
6N3 A37 15c #301, II 1.65 1.65
a. Type I 2.25 2.25
6N4 A37 20c #302, II 2.25 2.00
6N5 A37 25c #303, II 3.50 3.00
a. Type I 150.00 150.00

On Nos. 312, 314, 318

1941 ***Perf. 14***
6N6 A39 ½c #312, II .85 .85
a. Type I 1.65 1.10
6N7 A39 2½c #314, II 1.10 1.10
a. Type I .85 .85
6N8 A45 13c #318, II 1.10 1.10
a. Type I 16.00 16.00
Nos. 6N6-6N8 (3) 3.05 3.05

On Stamps of 1939-41

1941 ***Perf. 12½***
6N9 A57 2c #349, II .55 .55
6N10 A57 2c #368, II .85 .85
6N11 A57 3c #350, II .55 .55
a. Type I 1.10 1.10
6N12 A57 5c #352, II .85 .85
a. Type I .85 .85
6N13 A57 8c #353, II .55 .35
a. Type I .55 .55
6N14 A57 8c #369, II .55 .55
6N15 A57 10c #354, II .55 .55
6N16 A57 16c #357, II 3.50 3.50
6N17 A57 $1 #359, II 8.25 8.25
a. Type I 190.00 190.00
b. On No. 347, I 45.00 45.00
6N18 A57 $5 #361, II 32.50 32.50
Nos. 6N9-6N18 (10) 48.70 48.50

For overprints see Nos. 6N62, 6N64-6N65, 6N67-6N68.

On Stamps of 1940 with Secret Marks

1941 Unwmk. ***Perf. 14***
6N20 A57 5c #382, II 1.10 .85
6N21 A57 8c #383, I 1.10 .85
a. Type II .25 .25
6N22 A57 10c #384, II .85 .55
6N23 A57 30c #385, II 1.40 1.10
a. Type I 4.50 4.50
6N24 A57 50c #386, II 5.50 4.75
a. Type I 5.00 3.75
6N25 A57 $1 #387, II 4.50 3.25
a. Type I .1100 11.00
6N26 A57 $2 #388, II 11.00 11.00
a. Type I 16.00 16.00
6N27 A57 $5 #389, II 22.50 22.50
a. Type I 32.50 27.50
6N28 A57 $10 #390, II 45.00 32.50
a. Type I 55.00 55.00
6N29 A57 $20 #391, II 65.00 60.00
a. Type I 65.00 60.00

For overprints see Nos. 6N63, 6N69.

On Stamps of 1940 with Secret Marks

1941 Wmk. 261 ***Perf. 14***
6N30 A57 5c #392, II .85 .85
6N31 A57 5c #393, II .85 .85
6N32 A57 10c #394, II 5.50 5.50
6N33 A57 30c #395, II 3.25 2.75
a. Type I 16.00 14.00
6N34 A57 50c #396, II 2.75 2.75
a. Type I 6.50 6.50
Nos. 6N30-6N34 (5) 13.20 12.70

On Stamps of 1940-41 (Martyrs) with Secret Marks

Perf. 12½, 13 & Compound

1941 Wmk. 261
6N35 A39 ½c #402, II 1.65 1.65
6N36 A40 1c #403, II 1.65 1.65
a. Type I 1.65 1.65
6N37 A39 2½c #405, II 5.50 5.50
6N38 A46 10c #410, I 2.25 2.25
6N39 A45 13c #411, II 2.75 2.75
6N40 A46 17c #413, II 3.00 3.00
a. Type I 6.50 6.50
6N41 A40 25c #416, II 2.75 2.75
6N42 A48 30c #418, II 20.00 22.50
6N43 A47 40c #419, II 2.75 2.75
a. Type I 20.00 20.00
6N44 A40 50c #420, II 5.50 5.50
Nos. 6N35-6N44 (10) 47.80 50.30

Unwmk.
6N45 A39 ½c #421, II 1.10 1.10
a. Type I 2.25 2.25
6N46 A40 1c #422, II 1.10 1.10
a. Type I 2.25 2.25
b. On No. 422a, II 55.00 55.00
6N48 A46 2c #423, II 1.10 1.10
6N49 A48 3c #425, I 2.75 3.00
a. Type II 3.25 3.75
6N50 A39 4c #426, II .85 .85
6N51 A45 8c #428, II 2.25 2.25
a. Type I 20.00 20.00
6N52 A46 10c #429, I 6.50 6.50
6N53 A45 13c #430, I 2.75 2.75
a. Type II 3.25 3.25
6N54 A48 15c #431, II 1.75 1.75
6N55 A46 17c #432, II 2.25 2.25
a. Type I 3.25 3.25
6N56 A47 20c #433, II 3.25 3.25
a. Type I 4.50 4.50
6N57 A45 21c #434, II 3.25 2.75
6N58 A40 25c #435, I 3.75 2.75
6N59 A46 28c #436, II 3.25 2.75
6N60 A40 50c #439, II 8.00 8.00

For overprints see Nos. 6N61, 6N66.

Honan Singapore Overprint in Red

1942
6N61 A39 4c #6N50 1.65 2.25
6N62 A57 8c #6N13 13.00 16.00
6N63 A57 8c #6N21a 16.00 16.00
6N64 A57 8c #6N14 3.25 3.75
Nos. 6N61-6N64 (4) 33.90 38.00

Honan Anniv. of Manchukuo Overprint in Red

1942
6N65 A57 2c #6N10 2.75 3.25
6N66 A39 4c #6N50 3.25 3.00
6N67 A57 8c #6N13 13.00 16.00
6N68 A57 8c #6N14 32.50 40.00
6N69 A57 8c #6N21a 2.75 3.25
Nos. 6N65-6N69 (5) 54.25 65.50

Supeh

Nos. 297-298, 301-302 Overprinted

北 蘇 北 蘇

I II

1941 Engr. Unwmk.

7N1 A37 2c #297, I 5.50 4.75
a. Type II 11.00 11.00
7N2 A37 4c #298, I 27.50 27.50
a. Type II 60.00
7N3 A37 15c #301, I 2.75 2.75
a. Type II 2.25 2.25
7N4 A37 20c #302, II 2.75 2.75

On Nos. 312, 314, 318

1941 ***Perf. 14***

7N5 A39 ½c #312, I 2.75 2.75
7N6 A39 2½c #314, II 1.10 1.10
a. Type I 1.10 1.10
7N7 A45 13c #318, II 1.10 1.10
a. Type I 75.00 75.00

On Stamps of 1939-41

1941 ***Perf. 12½***

7N8 A57 2c #368, II 1.10 1.10
7N9 A57 3c #350, II 1.10 1.10
a. Type I 16.00 14.00
7N10 A57 5c #352, II 1.10 1.50
a. Type I 2.75 2.25
7N11 A57 8c #353, I 1.75 1.75
a. Type II 2.75 2.75
7N12 A57 8c #369, II 27.50 22.50
7N13 A57 10c #354, II 1.65 1.40
7N14 A57 16c #357, II 1.10 1.65
7N15 A57 $1 #359, II 11.00 11.00
a. On No. 347, I 140.00 140.00
Nos. 7N8-7N15 (8) 46.30 42.00

For overprints see Nos. 7N56-7N58, 7N60-7N61.

On Stamps of 1940 with Secret Marks

1941 Unwmk. ***Perf. 14***

7N17 A57 5c #382, II 1.10 1.00
7N18 A57 8c #383, II .85 .85
7N19 A57 10c #384, I 2.75 2.75
a. Type II 2.75 2.25
7N20 A57 30c #385, II 5.50 5.50
a. Type I 2.25 2.25
7N21 A57 50c #386, II 3.25 3.25
a. Type I 3.25 3.25
7N22 A57 $1 #387, I 16.00 16.00
a. Type II 27.50 22.50
7N23 A57 $2 #388, II 16.00 16.00
a. Type I 27.50 32.50
7N24 A57 $5 #389, I 27.50 27.50
a. Type II 60.00 60.00
7N25 A57 $10 #390, II 55.00 55.00
a. Type I 30.00 40.00
7N26 A57 $20 #391, II 65.00 65.00
a. Type I 70.00 60.00

On Stamps of 1940 with Secret Marks

1941 Wmk. 261 ***Perf. 14***

7N27 A57 10c #394, II 3.25 3.25
7N28 A57 30c #395, I 11.00 11.00
7N29 A57 50c #396, I 11.00 11.00
Nos. 7N27-7N29 (3) 25.25 25.25

On Stamps of 1940-41 (Martyrs) with Secret Marks

Perf. 12½, 13 & Compound

1941 Wmk. 261

7N30 A39 ½c #402, II 2.25 2.25
7N31 A40 1c #403, I 1.10 1.10
a. Type II 2.25 2.25
7N32 A46 2c #404, II 1.10 1.10
7N33 A39 2½c #405, I 22.50 22.50
7N34 A46 10c #410, I 13.00 13.00
7N35 A45 13c #411, II 4.50 3.50
7N36 A46 17c #413, II 4.00 3.75
a. Type I 65.00 65.00
7N37 A40 25c #416, II 2.75 2.75
7N38 A48 30c #418, I 8.00 8.00
7N39 A47 40c #419, II 3.75 3.75
a. Type I 5.50 5.50
7N40 A40 50c #420, I 65.00 65.00
Nos. 7N30-7N40 (11) 127.95 126.70

Unwmk.

7N41 A39 ½c #421, II 2.75 2.75
a. Type I 2.75 2.75
7N42 A40 1c #422, II 1.10 1.10
7N43 A46 2c #423, I 8.00 8.00
7N44 A46 3c #425, I 3.25 3.25
7N45 A39 4c #426, II .85 .85
7N46 A46 10c #429, I 27.50 27.50
7N47 A45 13c #430, I 4.50 4.50
7N48 A48 15c #431, II 3.25 3.25
7N49 A46 17c #432, II 3.25 3.25
a. Type I 4.25 4.25
7N50 A47 20c #433, II 3.25 3.25
a. Type I 4.50 4.50
7N51 A45 21c #434, II 3.25 3.25
7N52 A40 25c #435, I 4.00 3.25
a. Type II 11.00 11.00
7N53 A46 28c #436, II 3.50 3.50
Nos. 7N41-7N53 (13) 68.45 67.70

For overprints see Nos. 7N55, 7N59.

Honan Singapore Overprint in Red

1942

7N54 A37 4c #298, II 35.00 35.00
7N55 A39 4c #7N45 4.00 4.50
7N56 A57 8c #7N11a 11.00 13.00
7N57 A57 8c #7N12 10.00 11.00
Nos. 7N54-7N57 (4) 60.00 63.50

Honan Anniv. of Manchukuo Overprint in Red

1942

7N58 A57 2c #7N8 10.00 11.00
7N59 A39 4c #7N45 9.50 11.00
7N60 A57 8c #7N11a 50.00 55.00
7N61 A57 8c #7N12 55.00 60.00
Nos. 7N58-7N61 (4) 124.50 137.00

North China

For use in Honan, Hopei, Shansi, Shantung and Supeh (Northern Kiangsu)

Stamps of China, 1931-37 Surcharged North China (Hwa Pei) and Half of Original Value

北 華
分 壹

1942 Unwmk. ***Perf. 14, 12½***

8N1 A40 ½c on 1c (#313) .50 .70
8N2 A37 1c on 2c (#297) .55 .35
8N3 A37 2c on 4c (#298) 1.10 .85
8N4 A45 4c on 8c (#316) 125.00

Same Surcharge on Stamps of 1938-41

Perf. 12½

8N5 A57 1c on 2c (#349) 2.75 2.75
8N6 A57 1c on 2c (#368) .35 .35
8N7 A57 4c on 8c (#353) 1.40 .85
8N8 A57 4c on 8c (#369) .40 .40
8N9 A57 5c on 10c grn .50 .50
8N10 A57 8c on 16c ol gray 1.40 .55
8N11 A57 50c on $1 (#359) 5.50 5.50
8N12 A57 50c on $1 (#344) 475.00 475.00
8N13 A57 50c on $1 (#347) 80.00 80.00
8N14 A57 $1 on $2 (#360) 8.00 8.00
8N15 A57 $1 on $2 (#345) 27.50 27.50
8N16 A57 $1 on $2 (#348) 100.00 100.00

No. 8N12 was issued without gum.
For overprint see No. 8N58.

Same Surcharge on China Nos. 383-388, 390-391

Perf. 14

8N17 A57 4c on 8c ol grn .55 .55
8N18 A57 5c on 10c grn .65 1.00
8N19 A57 15c on 30c scar 1.10 .85
a. Inverted surcharge 65.00 65.00
8N20 A57 25c on 50c dk bl 1.10 1.10
8N21 A57 50c on $1 org brn & sep 2.50 2.50
8N22 A57 $1 on $2 dp bl & yel brn 4.50 4.50
8N23 A57 $5 on $10 dk grn & dl pur 32.50 32.50
8N24 A57 $10 on $20 rose lake & dk bl 32.50 32.50
Nos. 8N17-8N24 (8) 75.40 75.50

For overprint see No. 8N55.

Same Surcharge on China Nos. 394-396

Wmk. 261

8N25 A57 5c on 10c grn .50 .75
8N26 A57 15c on 30c scarlet 2.25 2.75
8N27 A57 25c on 50c dk bl 1.00 1.10
Nos. 8N25-8N27 (3) 3.75 4.60

Same Surcharge on Stamps of 1940-41

1942 Wmk. 261 ***Perf. 12½, 13***

8N28 A40 ½c on 1c org .30 .30
8N29 A46 1c on 2c dp bl 1.65 1.65
8N30 A45 4c on 8c dp org 13.00 14.00
8N31 A46 5c on 10c dl vio 1.65 2.25
8N32 A48 15c on 30c brn car 6.50 6.50
8N33 A47 20c on 40c org 3.75 3.25
8N34 A40 25c on 50c grn 3.25 3.25
Nos. 8N28-8N34 (7) 30.10 31.20

Unwmk.

8N35 A40 ½c on 1c org (#422) .20 .15
a. ½c on 1c org (#422a) 10.00 10.00
8N36 A46 1c on 2c dp bl .85 .85
8N37 A39 2c on 4c pale vio .65 .55
8N38 A45 4c on 8c dp org .85 .85
8N39 A46 5c on 10c dl vio 1.65 1.65
8N40 A47 10c on 20c lt bl 1.10 .55
8N41 A47 20c on 40c org 2.75 .85
8N42 A40 25c on 50c grn 2.25 2.25
Nos. 8N35-8N42 (8) 10.30 7.70

Same Surcharge on "New Peking" Prints

Perf. 14

8N43 A37 1c on 2c ol grn .30 .15
8N44 A37 2c on 4c dl grn .55 .15
a. Inverted surcharge 35.00
8N45 A45 4c on 8c dp org .30 .15
8N46 A57 8c on 16c ol gray .30 .15
8N47 A47 10c on 20c red brn 1.50 1.25
8N48 A48 15c on 30c brn car .60 .60
8N49 A47 20c on 40c org 1.25 .20
a. Inverted surcharge 45.00
8N50 A40 25c on 50c grn 1.25 1.00
8N51 A57 50c on $1 org brn & sep 2.50 2.50
8N52 A57 $1 on $2 dp bl & org brn 3.50 2.50
8N53 A57 $5 on $10 dk grn & dl pur 14.00 14.00
Nos. 8N43-8N53 (11) 26.05 22.65

See note after No. 2N93.
For overprints see #8N54, 8N56-8N57, 8N59.

Nos. 8N44, 8N17 and 8N46 with Additional Overprint in Red

邦友
界租 還交
念紀

1943 Unwmk. ***Perf. 14***

8N54 A37 2c on 4c dl grn .20 .60
8N55 A57 4c on 8c ol grn 1.00 1.25
8N56 A57 8c on 16c ol gray 1.00 1.25
Nos. 8N54-8N56 (3) 2.20 3.10

Return of the Foreign Concessions to China.

Nos. 8N44, 8N8 and 8N46 with Additional Overprint in Red

局總 政郵
立成
念紀年週五

1943, Aug. 15 ***Perf. 14, 12½***

8N57 A37 2c on 4c dl grn .30 .45
8N58 A57 4c on 8c ol grn .30 .45
8N59 A57 8c on 16c ol gray .40 .60
Nos. 8N57-8N59 (3) 1.00 1.50

North China Postal Service, 5th anniv.

Stamps of China, 1934-41, Overprinted in Black

北 華

1943, Nov. 1

8N60 A40 1c org (#313) .60 .60
8N61 A40 1c org (#422) .70 .60
8N62 A57 10c grn (#354) .40 .40
8N63 A57 $2 dp bl & yel brn (#388) 25.00 25.00
8N64 A57 $5 red & grnsh blk (#361) 13.00 13.00
8N65 A57 $5 red & sl grn (#389) 8.00 8.00
8N66 A57 $10 dk grn & dl pur (#390) 12.50 8.00
8N67 A57 $20 rose lake & dk bl (#391) 65.00 65.00
Nos. 8N60-8N67 (8) 125.20 120.60

Same Overprint on "New Peking" Prints

8N68 A40 1c orange .25 .15
8N69 A37 2c olive grn .25 .40
8N70 A37 4c dull green .25 .40
8N71 A37 5c green .25 .30
8N72 A57 9c olive grn .25 .40
8N73 A46 10c dl violet .25 .15
8N74 A57 16c olive gray .25 .40
8N75 A57 18c olive gray .25 .40
8N76 A47 20c henna .35 .40
8N77 A48 30c brown car .25 .15
8N78 A47 40c brt orange .25 .20
a. Inverted overprint 35.00 35.00
8N79 A40 50c green 1.75 1.75
8N80 A57 $1 org brn & sep 3.00 .75
8N81 A57 $2 bl & org brn 1.75 1.50
8N82 A57 $5 red & sl grn 3.50 4.75
8N83 A57 $10 dk grn & dl pur 6.00 5.00
8N84 A57 $20 rose lake & dk bl 7.00 7.00
Nos. 8N68-8N84 (17) 25.85 24.10

See note after No. 2N93.
For overprints see Nos. 8N85-8N90, 8N95-8N106.

Nos. 8N70 and 8N62 with Additional Overprint in Red

戰 參
念紀年週一

1944, Jan. 9

8N85 A37 4c dull green .25 .25
8N86 A57 10c green .25 .30

1st anniv. of the declaration of war against the Allies by North China.

Nos. 8N72, 8N75, 8N79 and 8N80 with Additional Overprint in Red

會員委務政
念紀年週四

1944, Mar. 30

8N87 A57 9c olive green .40 .60
8N88 A57 18c olive gray .40 .60
8N89 A40 50c green 3.50 4.00
8N90 A57 $1 org brn & sepia 2.00 2.50
a. Red overprint inverted 30.00 30.00
Nos. 8N87-8N90 (4) 6.30 7.70

4th anniv. of the North China Political Council.

Shanghai-Nanking Nos. 9N101-9N104 Surcharged North China (Hwa Pei) and New Value in Red or Black

a: 華北玖分
b: 華北壹角捌分
c: 華北叁角陸分
d: 華北玖角

1944 ***Perf. 12½x12, 12x12½***

8N91 OS1 (a) 9c on 50c org .90 1.25
8N92 OS1 (b) 18c on $1 grn (R) 1.10 1.50
a. Double surcharge 30.00 30.00
8N93 OS2 (c) 36c on $2 dp bl (R) 1.25 1.50
8N94 OS2 (d) 90c on $5 car rose 1.50 1.75
Nos. 8N91-8N94 (4) 4.75 6.00

Nos. 8N72, 8N75, 8N79 and 8N80 Overprinted in Red or Blue

立成局總政郵
念紀年週六

1944, Aug. 15

8N95 A57 9c olive grn .60 1.00
8N96 A57 18c olive gray .60 1.00
8N97 A40 50c green 1.25 1.50
8N98 A57 $1 org brn & sep (Bl) 2.50 2.75
Nos. 8N95-8N98 (4) 4.95 6.25

6th anniv. of the General P.O. Dept. of North China.

North China Nos. 8N76, 8N79-8N81 Overprinted in Blue or Black

席 主 汪
念 紀 典 葬

1944, Dec. 5

8N99 A47 20c henna (Bl) 2.00 2.25
8N100 A40 50c green (Bl) 2.00 2.25
8N101 A57 $1 org brn & sep (Bl) 4.00 4.50
8N102 A57 $2 bl & org brn 1.25 1.20
Nos. 8N99-8N102 (4) 9.25 10.20

Death of Wang Ching-wei, puppet ruler of China.

North China Nos. 8N76, 8N79-8N81 Overprinted in Red or Black

年週二戰參
念 紀

1945

8N103 A47 20c henna 1.50 1.75
8N104 A40 50c green (R) 3.00 3.00
8N105 A57 $1 org brn & sep 2.00 2.25
8N106 A57 $2 bl & org brn 1.50 1.75
Nos. 8N103-8N106 (4) 8.00 8.75

2nd anniv. of the declaration of war.

Shanghai-Nanking Nos. 9N105-9N106 Surcharged in Red

華北伍角

1945 ***Perf. 12x12½***

8N107 OS3 50c on $3 lt org .45 .60
8N108 OS3 $1 on $6 blue .45 .60

Return of the foreign concessions in Shanghai.

Dragon Pillar — OS1

Dr. Sun Yat-sen — OS2

Designs: $2, Long Bridge and White Pagoda. $5, Tower in Imperial City. $10, Marble Boat, Summer Palace.

1945 Unwmk. Litho. *Perf. 14*
Various Papers

8N109	OS1 $1 dull yellow	1.25	1.25
8N110	OS1 $2 deep blue	.25	.40
8N111	OS1 $5 carmine	.75	.50
8N112	OS1 $10 dull green	.35	.60
	Nos. 8N109-8N112 (4)	2.60	2.75

North China Political Council, 5th anniv.

1945
Without Gum; Various Papers

8N113	OS2 $1 bister	.25	.25
8N114	OS2 $2 dark blue	.90	.90
8N115	OS2 $5 fawn	1.75	1.75
8N116	OS2 $10 sage green	1.75	1.50
8N117	OS2 $20 dull violet	1.50	1.25
8N118	OS2 $50 brown	35.00	35.00
	Nos. 8N113-8N118 (6)	41.15	40.65

Nos. 8N113-8N118 without "Hwa Pei" overprint are proofs.

Wutai Mountain, Shansi — OS3

Designs: $10, Kaifeng Iron Pagoda. $20, International Bridge, Tientsin. $30, Taishan Mountain, Shantung. $50, General Post Office, Peking.

1945, Aug. 15
Without Gum; Various Papers

8N119	OS3 $5 gray green	.25	.60
8N120	OS3 $10 dull brown	.60	.60
8N121	OS3 $20 dull purple	.45	.60
8N122	OS3 $30 slate blue	.90	1.25
8N123	OS3 $50 carmine	1.75	1.75
	Nos. 8N119-8N123 (5)	3.95	4.80

North China Postal Directorate, 7th anniv.

Shanghai and Nanking

China Nos. 299-303 Surcharged

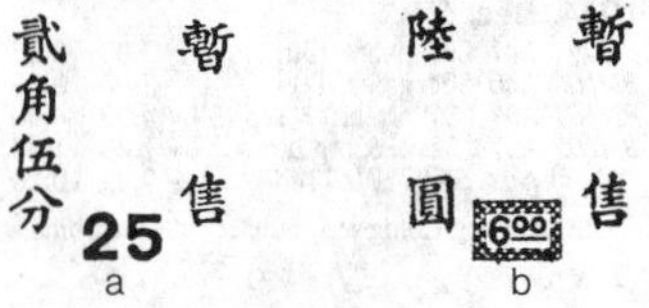

Overprinted Type "b"

1942-45 Unwmk. *Perf. 12½, 13½*

9N1	A37 $6 on 5c green	1.65	1.65
9N2	A37 $20 on 15c scar	.30	.85
9N3	A37 $500 on 15c dk grn	1.10	1.75
9N4	A37 $1000 on 20c ultra	1.65	1.10
9N5	A37 $1000 on 25c ultra	1.65	2.25
	Nos. 9N1-9N5 (5)	6.35	7.60

A $1000 on 20c ultramarine, No. 293, exists.

Surcharged Type "a" (Nos. 9N6-9N10) or Type "b" (Nos. 9N11-9N40) on Type A57 Stamps of 1939-41
Perf. 12½

9N6	25c on 5c (#352)	.20	.25
9N7	30c on 2c (#368)	.20	.25
9N8	50c on 3c (#350)	.20	.25
9N9	50c on 5c (#352)	.20	.20
9N10	50c on 8c (#353)	.20	.20
9N11	$1 on 8c (#353)	.20	.15
9N12	$1 on 8c (#369)	11.00	13.00
9N13	$1 on 15c (#356)	.20	.15
9N14	$1.30 on 16c (#357)	.20	.35
9N15	$1.50 on 3c (#350)	.20	.35
9N16	$2 on 5c (#352)	.90	.90
9N17	$2 on 10c (#354)	.20	.30
9N18	$3 on 15c (#356)	.20	.30
9N19	$4 on 16c (#357)	.35	.20
9N20	$5 on 15c (#356)	.20	.20
9N21	$6 on 5c (#351)	.55	1.10
a.	Perf. 14 (#371)	35.00	35.00
9N22	$6 on 5c (#352)	.20	.30
9N23	$6 on 8c (#353)	.35	.35
9N24	$6 on 8c (#369)	550.00	550.00
9N25	$6 on 10c (#354)	.20	.20
9N26	$10 on 10c (#354)	.20	.20
9N27	$10 on 16c (#357)	.40	.20
9N28	$20 on 3c (#350)	.20	.35
9N29	$20 on 15c (#355)	.90	1.10
9N30	$20 on 15c (#356)	.35	.35
9N31	$20 on $2 (#360)	1.25	2.25
9N32	$100 on 3c (#350)	.40	.35
9N33	$500 on 8c (#353)	1.10	1.40
9N34	$500 on 8c (#369)	20.00	22.50
9N35	$500 on 10c (#354)	.85	.85
9N36	$500 on 15c (#355)	1.10	1.40
9N37	$500 on 15c (#356)	.85	.85
9N38	$500 on 16c (#357)	1.10	1.10
9N39	$1000 on 25c (#358)	.85	1.75
9N40	$2000 on $5 (#361)	1.10	1.75
	Nos. 9N1-9N23,9N25-9N40 (39)	52.95	63.00

Nos. 381-391 (Type A57) Surcharged with Type "b"
Perf. 14

9N41	$1 on 8c ol grn	.20	.25
9N42	$1.70 on 30c scar	.25	.40
a.	Perf. 12½	2.75	2.75
9N43	$2 on 5c ol grn	.35	.45
9N44	$2 on 1c org brn & sep	.85	1.40
9N45	$3 on 8c ol grn	.50	.45
a.	$3 on 8c olive green (#383a)	27.50	27.50
b.	"3" with flat top	.35	.35
9N46	$6 on 5c grn	.35	.45
9N47	$6 on 5c ol grn	.35	.65
9N48	$6 on 8c ol grn	.35	.65
9N49	$10 on 10c grn	.35	1.10
a.	Perf. 12½	1.65	2.75
9N50	$20 on $2 dp bl & yel brn	1.10	1.10
9N51	$50 on 30c scar	.50	.55
9N52	$50 on 50c dk bl	.55	.55
9N53	$50 on $5 red & sl grn	.80	.80
9N54	$50 on $20 rose lake & dk bl	2.00	2.25
9N55	$100 on $10 dk grn & dl pur	1.00	1.00
9N56	$200 on $20 rose lake & dk bl	.55	.55
9N57	$500 on 8c ol grn	9.00	11.00
a.	$500 on 8c ol grn (#383a)	18.00	20.00
9N58	$500 on 10c grn	1.65	2.00
9N59	$1000 on 30c scar	1.75	2.25
9N60	$1000 on 50c dk bl	.85	1.10
9N61	$1000 on $2 dp bl & yel brn	2.25	2.25
9N62	$2000 on $5 red & sl grn	1.10	1.40

China Nos. 392-395 and 399-401 (Type A57) Surcharged with Type "b"

1942-45 Wmk. 261 *Perf. 14*

9N63	$2 on $1 org brn & sep, perf. 12½	.70	.90
9N64	$6 on 5c grn	.35	.35
9N65	$6 on 5c ol grn	.85	.85
9N66	$50 on $5 red & sl grn	.55	.85
a.	Numeral tablet violet	.65	.85
9N67	$100 on $10 dk grn & dl pur	.40	.45
9N68	$200 on $20 rose lake & dk bl	.45	.45
9N69	$500 on 10c grn	1.10	1.10
9N70	$1000 on 30c scar	2.25	2.75
9N71	$5000 on $10 dk grn & dl pur, perf. 12½	6.00	6.00
a.	Perf. 14	55.00	45.00
	Nos. 9N41-9N71 (31)	39.30	46.30

Nos. 9N63 and 9N71 were not issued without surcharge. A $50 on 30c scarlet exists.

Same Surch. on Stamps of 1940-41
Perf. 12½, 13
Wmk. 261

9N72	A46 $30 on 2c dp bl	65.00	65.00

A $7.50 on ½c and a $15 on 1c are known.

Unwmk.

9N73	A39 $7.50 on ½c ol blk	.55	1.50
9N74	A40 $15 on 1c org	.30	.45
a.	Without secret mark	32.50	32.50
9N75	A46 $30 on 2c dp bl	.85	1.10
9N76	A40 $200 on 1c org	.35	.45
9N77	A45 $200 on 8c dp org	.45	.55
	Nos. 9N73-9N77 (5)	2.50	4.05

Surcharged Type "a" (Nos. 9N78-9N81) or Type "b" (Nos. 9N82-9N96) on Type A59 Stamps of 1941
Perf. 12

9N78	5c on ½c sepia	.20	.20
9N79	10c on 1c orange	.20	.20
9N80	20c on 1c orange	.20	.20
9N81	40c on 5c green	.20	.20
9N82	$5 on 5c green	.20	.20
9N83	$10 on 10c brt grn	.20	.20
9N84	$50 on ½c sepia	.20	.20
9N85	$50 on 1c orange	.30	.35
9N86	$50 on 17c olive	.30	.45
9N87	$200 on 5c green	.30	.35
9N88	$200 on 8c turq grn	.20	.20
9N89	$200 on 8c red org	.30	.50
9N90	$500 on $5 scar & blk	.30	.35
9N91	$1000 on 1c orange	.30	.45
9N92	$1000 on 25c rose vio	.35	.45
9N93	$1000 on 30c scarlet	.85	.45
9N94	$1000 on $2 bl & blk	.75	.80
9N95	$1000 on $10 grn & blk	.35	.45
9N96	$2000 on $5 scar & blk	.85	.85
	Nos. 9N78-9N96 (19)	6.55	7.05

Stamps of China 1939-41 Surcharged in Red or Blue

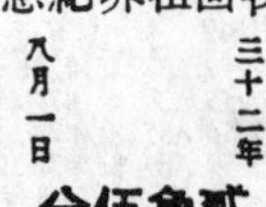

1943 Unwmk. *Perf. 12, 12½*

9N97	A57 25c on 5c grn	.15	*1.10*
9N98	A59 50c on 8c red org (Bl)	.15	*.40*
9N99	A57 $1 on 16c ol gray	.15	*.40*
9N100	A59 $2 on 50c dk bl	.15	*.40*
	Set value		.30

Return of the foreign concessions in Shanghai.

Wheat and Cotton — OS1

Purple Mountain, Nanking OS2

Perf. 12½x12, 12x12½
1944 Engr. Unwmk.

9N101	OS1 50c orange	.15	*.30*
9N102	OS1 $1 green	.15	*.30*
9N103	OS2 $2 dp bl	.15	*.35*
9N104	OS2 $5 car rose	.15	*.35*
	Set value	.25	

4th anniv. of the puppet government at Nanking.
For surcharges see Nos. 8N91-8N94, 9N107-9N110.

Map of Foreign Concessions in Shanghai — OS3

1944 *Perf. 12x12½*

9N105	OS3 $3 lt org	.15	*.30*
9N106	OS3 $6 blue	.15	*.30*
	Set value	.15	

1st anniversary of the return of the foreign concessions in Shanghai.
For surcharges see Nos. 8N107-8N108.

Nos. 9N101-9N104 Surcharged in Black with Type "b"

1945, Mar. 30

9N107	OS1 $15 on 50c org	.15	*.30*
9N108	OS1 $30 on $1 grn	.15	*.30*
9N109	OS2 $60 on $2 dp bl	.15	*.35*
9N110	OS2 $200 on $5 car rose	.15	*.35*
	Set value	.25	

China Nos. C31, C32, C36 and C38 Surcharged in Red, Green, Orange or Carmine

1945 *Perf. 12½, 13*

9N111	AP3 $150 on 15c (R)	.15	*.15*
9N112	AP3 $250 on 25c (G)	.15	*.30*
9N113	AP3 $600 on 60c (O)	.15	*.30*
9N114	AP3 $1,000 on $1 (C)	.15	*.30*
	Set value	.35	

Issue as air raid precaution propaganda.

SHANGHAI AND NANKING AIR POST STAMPS

China Nos. C35 and C38 Surcharged in Black

10

付已費空航之片明內國

The surcharges on Nos. 9NC1-9NC7 were in Japanese currency because all air mail then was carried by Japanese planes.

The surcharges translate: (10c) "Airmail fee for postcard within the nation has been paid." (20c) "Airmail fee for letter within the nation has been paid."

1941 Unwmk. *Perf. 12½*

9NC1	AP3 10(s) on 50c brown	.35	*.35*
9NC2	AP3 20(s) on $1 apple grn	.15	*.30*

Two types of surcharge exist on No. 9NC1.

Similar Surcharge on No. C28

1941 Wmk. 261 *Perf. 13*

9NC3	AP3 20(s) on $1 ap grn	13.00	15.00

Nos. C37 and C39 Surcharged

35

付已費空航函信本日寄

The surcharges translate: (18c and 25c) "Airmail fee for postcard to Japan has been paid." (35c) "Airmail fee for letter to Japan has been paid."

1941 Unwmk. *Perf. 12½, 13*

9NC4	AP3 18(s) on 90c lt olive	.15	*.45*
9NC5	AP3 25(s) on 90c lt olive	.15	*.35*
9NC6	AP3 35(s) on $2 lt brn	.15	*.35*
	Nos. 9NC4-9NC6 (3)	.45	*1.15*

No. 9NC6 with Additional Surcharge in Red
Perf. 12½

9NC7	AP3 60(s) on 35(s) on $2	.15	*.30*

SHANGHAI AND NANKING POSTAGE DUE STAMPS

Postage Due Stamps of China 1932 Surcharged in Black

壹 改
圓 作
1.00

1945 Unwmk. *Perf. 14*

9NJ1	D5 $1 on 2c org	.15	*.35*
9NJ2	D5 $2 on 5c org	.15	*.35*
9NJ3	D5 $5 on 10c org	.15	*.35*
9NJ4	D5 $10 on 20c org	.15	*.35*
	Nos. 9NJ1-9NJ4 (4)	.60	*1.40*

Northeastern Provinces

民 中

國 華

With the end of World War II and the collapse of Manchukuo, the Northeastern Provinces reverted to China. In many Manchurian towns and cities, the Manchukuo stamps were locally handstamped in ideograms: "Republic of China," "China Postal Service" or "Temporary Use for China." A typical example is shown above.

Dr. Sun Yat-sen
A1 A2

Black Surcharge

1946, Feb. Unwmk. Typo. *Perf. 14*

1 A1 50c on $5 red .15 .85
2 A1 50c on $10 grn .50 1.25
3 A1 $1 on $10 grn .15 .90
4 A1 $2 on $20 brn vio .15 .85
5 A1 $4 on $50 brn .15 .55
Set value .85

The two characters at left express the new value.

Stamps of China, 1938-41 Overprinted 限東北貼用

1946, Apr. *Perf. 12½, 13, 13½, 14*

6 A40 1c org (#422) .20 .85
7 A48 3c dp yel brn (#425) .20 .85
8 A48 5c dl red org (#427) .20 .55
9 A57 10c grn (#354) .20 .55
10 A57 10c grn (#384) .20 .85
11 A47 20c lt bl (#433) .20 1.65
a. Horiz. pair, imperf. btwn 50.00
Nos. 6-11 (6) 1.20 5.30

1946, July Engr. *Perf. 14*
Without Gum

12 A2 5c lake .15 .90
13 A2 10c orange .15 .90
14 A2 20c yel grn .15 2.50
15 A2 25c blk brn .15 1.25
16 A2 50c red org .15 .60
17 A2 $1 blue .15 .60
18 A2 $2 dk vio .15 .60
19 A2 $2.50 indigo .15 .90
20 A2 $3 brown .15 .60
21 A2 $4 org brn .15 .90
22 A2 $5 dk grn .15 .60
23 A2 $10 crimson .15 .60
24 A2 $20 olive .15 .60
25 A2 $50 blue vio .15 .60
Nos. 12-25 (14) 2.10 12.15

Two types of $4, $10, $20 and $50: I- Character *kuo* directly left of sun emblem is open at upper and lower left corners of "box." Diagonal stroke from top center to lower right has no hook at bottom. II- Character is closed at left corners. Diagonal stroke has hook at bottom.

See Nos. 47-52, 61-63. For surcharges see Nos. M1, Taiwan 91-96, People's Republic of China 35-48, 3L37-3L52, 3L55-3L66, 3L71-3L75.

China Nos. 728-731 Surcharged in Black

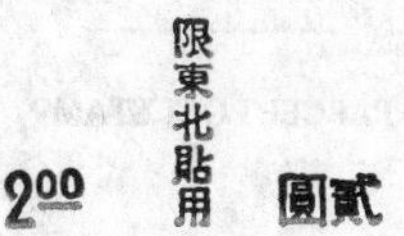

1946

26 A75 $2 on $20 green .15 .80
27 A75 $3 on $30 blue .15 1.25
28 A75 $5 on $50 dark brown .15 .50
29 A75 $10 on $100 carmine .15 .80
Nos. 26-29 (4) .60

Convening of Chinese National Assembly.

Type of China, 1946, Inscribed: 東北貼用

1947 Engr. *Perf. 11, 11½*

30 A74 $2 carmine .30 1.00
31 A74 $3 green .40 1.00
32 A74 $5 vermilion .40 1.00
33 A74 $10 yel grn .75 1.00
34 A74 $20 yel org .60 1.00
35 A74 $30 magenta .60 1.00
Nos. 30-35 (6) 3.05 6.00

60th birthday of Chiang Kai-shek.

Type of China, 1947, Inscribed: 用貼北東

1947 Unwmk. Engr. *Perf. 14*

36 A76 $2 deep green .20 .50
37 A76 $4 deep blue .20 .50
38 A76 $6 carmine .20 .50
39 A76 $10 lt brown .20 .50
40 A76 $20 deep claret .20 .50
Nos. 36-40 (5) 1.00 2.50

First anniversary of return of Chinese National Government to Nanking.

China Nos. 644 to 646 and 634 Surcharged in Black 用貼北東限 叁佰圓 改作 300.00

1947 *Perf. 12½, 14*

41 A73 $100 on $1000 rose lake .35 1.10
42 A73 $300 on $3000 bl .35 1.10
43 A73 $500 on $5000 dp grn & ver .35 1.10
44 A37 $500 on $30 choc 1.10 1.65
Nos. 41-44 (4) 2.15

Type of 1946

1947 Engr. *Perf. 14*
Without Gum

47 A2 $44 dk car rose 20.00 30.00
48 A2 $100 dp grn .15 .35
49 A2 $200 rose brn .15 .55
50 A2 $300 bluish grn .20 1.10
51 A2 $500 rose car .20 .35
52 A2 $1000 dp orange .25 .35
Nos. 47-52 (6) 20.95 32.70

For surcharges see note following No. 25.

Stamps and Types of 1946-47 Surcharged in Black or Red 壹仟伍佰圓 1500 改作

1948 Unwmk. *Perf. 14*

53 A2 $1500 on 20c yel grn .50 2.25
54 A2 $3000 on $1 blue .20 .55
55 A2 $4000 on 25c blk brn (R) .20 .55
56 A2 $8000 on 50c red org .20 .55
57 A2 $10,000 on 10c org .25 .55
58 A2 $50,000 on $109 dk grn (R) .85 2.00
59 A2 $100,000 on $65 dl grn .50 2.00
60 A2 $500,000 on $22 gray (R) 1.10 1.65
Nos. 53-60 (8) 3.80 10.10

Type of 1946

1947, Nov. 5
Without Gum

61 A2 $22 gray 40.00
62 A2 $65 dull green 45.00
63 A2 $109 dark green 55.00
Nos. 61-63 (3) 140.00

For surcharges see note following No. 25.

POSTAGE DUE STAMPS

D1

1947 Unwmk. Engr. *Perf. 14*
Without Gum

J1 D1 10c dark blue .15 4.00
J2 D1 20c dark blue .15 4.00
J3 D1 50c dark blue .15 3.00
J4 D1 $1 dark blue .15 2.00
J5 D1 $2 dark blue .20 3.00
J6 D1 $5 dark blue .20 2.00
Set value .75

Nos. J1 to J3 Surcharged in Red 拾圓 改作

1948

J7 D1 $10 on 10c dark blue .15 3.50
J8 D1 $20 on 20c dark blue .15 3.50
J9 D1 $50 on 50c dark blue .15 3.50
Set value .35

The surcharge reads "Changed to . . . dollars." Characters at the left express the new value and vary on each denomination.

MILITARY STAMPS

No. 16 Surcharged in Black 軍郵 暫作 肆拾肆圓

1947 Unwmk. *Perf. 14*

M1 A2 $44 on 50c red org 3.50 6.75

The surcharge reads: "Army Post. Temporarily for 44 dollars."

China No. M13 Overprinted in Black 限東北貼用

Thin Paper Without Gum
Perf. 12½

M2 M1 rose .85 3.50

China No. M13 Overprinted in Black 限東北貼用

M3 M1 rose 27.50 22.50

PARCEL POST STAMP

China No. Q25 Surcharged in Black 限東北貼用 伍拾萬圓 改作

1948 Unwmk. Engr. *Perf. 13½*
Without Gum

Q1 PP3 $500,000 on $5,000,000 lilac 110.00

The use of this handstamp from Anhwei has not been verified.

Fukien Province

Stamps of China, 1945-49, Surcharged

1949 Engr. *Perf. 14*
Without Gum

1 A82 1c on $500 bl grn 6.00 6.50
2 A82 1c on $7000 lt red brn 14.00 18.00
3 A82 2c on $2,000,000 ver 3.50 4.00
4 A82 2½c on $50,000 dp bl 18.00 18.00
5 A73 4c on $100 dk car 3.00 3.00
6 A73 10c on $200 ol grn 4.00 4.50
7 A82 10c on $3000 bl 2.50 3.00
8 A82 10c on $4000 gray 3.50 4.00
9 A82 10c on $6000 rose lil 3.50 4.00
10 A82 10c on $100,000 dl grn 3.50 4.00
11 A82 10c on $1,000,000 cl 3.50 4.00
12 A82 40c on $200,000 brn vio 5.50 7.00
Nos. 1-12 (12) 70.50 80.00

The surcharge on No. 2 is handstamped and in slightly larger characters.

Issue dates: No. 2, May 10; others, June.

China Nos. 973, 975-978 Overprinted 福州

1949, June Litho. *Perf. 12½, 13*

13 A94 1c apple grn 12.00 6.00
14 A94 4c blue green 6.00 1.25
15 A94 10c deep lilac 35.00 18.00
16 A94 16c orange red 7.00 18.00
17 A94 20c blue 35.00 14.00
Nos. 13-17 (5) 95.00 57.25

Same Overprint on China No. 959

1949, July Litho. *Perf. 12½*

18 A96 orange 45.00 40.00

Same Overprint on Fukien Nos. 1, 3-4, 8, 11 in Black or Red

1949, June Engr. *Perf. 14*

19 A82 1c on $500 bl grn 90.00 90.00
20 A82 2c on $2,000,000 ver 30.00 30.00
21 A82 2½c on $50,000 dp bl 50.00 50.00
22 A82 10c on $4000 gray 25.00 25.00
23 A82 10c on $1,000,000 claret 80.00 75.00
Nos. 19-23 (5) 275.00 270.00

AIR POST STAMP

China No. C62 Overprinted as Nos. 13-17

1949, July Litho. *Perf. 12½*

C1 AP5 blue green 45.00 25.00

SPECIAL DELIVERY STAMP

China No. E12 Overprinted as Nos. 13-17

1949, July Litho. *Perf. 12½*

E1 SD2 red violet 30.00 18.00

REGISTRATION STAMP

China No. F2 Overprinted as Nos. 13-17

1949, July Litho. *Perf. 12½*

F1 R2 carmine 30.00 18.00

Hunan Province

China No. 640 Surcharged 國內平信 湘 郵資已付

1949, May Engr. *Perf. 14*

1 A73 on $100 dk car 9.00 5.50

The first printing of surcharge on No. 1 is in smaller characters.

China Nos. 797, 788, 750, 747 Surcharged 伍分 湘

1949, May Engr. *Perf. 14*

2 A82 1c on $2,000,000 ver 18.00 18.00
3 A82 2c on $20,000 rose pink 18.00 18.00
4 A82 5c on $3000 blue 24.00 24.00
5 A82 10c on $500 blue grn 18.00 18.00
Nos. 2-5 (4) 78.00 78.00

AIR POST STAMP

China No. 790 Surcharged 國內航空 湘 郵資已付

1949, May Engr. *Perf. 14*

C1 A82 On $40,000 green 14.00 15.00

SPECIAL DELIVERY STAMP

China No. 637 Surcharged as No. F1 in Red

1949, May Engr. *Perf. 14*

E1 A73 On $30 dark blue 18.00 18.00

REGISTRATION STAMP

China No. 754 Surcharged 國內挂號 湘 郵資已付

1949, May Engr. *Perf. 14*

F1 A73 On $7000 lt red brn 18.00 18.00

Hupeh Province

China Type A95 Surcharged

1949, May **Litho.**

1 A95 1c on $20 red brn 40.00 35.00
2 A95 10c on $20 red brn 40.00 35.00

Kansu Province

China No. 959 Handstamped in Purple

1949, Aug. **Litho.** ***Perf. 12½***

1 A96 orange 550.00

AIR POST STAMP

Same Handstamp Overprinted on China No. C62 in Red

1949, Aug. **Litho.** ***Perf. 12½***

C1 AP5 blue green 550.00

Counterfeits exist.

Kiangsi Province

China Nos. 789-791 Surcharged

1949 **Engr.** ***Perf. 14***

1 A82 On $30,000 choc 35.00 30.00
2 A82 On $40,000 green 35.00 30.00
3 A82 On $50,000 dp bl 35.00 30.00
Nos. 1-3 (3) 105.00 90.00

AIR POST STAMP

Similar Surcharge on China No. 754

1949 **Engr.** ***Perf. 14***

C1 A82 On $7000 lt red brn 40.00 40.00

Third and fourth characters in right column of surcharge read "Air Mail" in Chinese on No. C1, "Registered" on Nos. F1-F2.

SPECIAL DELIVERY STAMP

Similar Surcharge on China No. 750

1949 **Engr.** ***Perf. 14***

E1 A82 On $3000 blue 45.00 30.00

See note below No. C1.

REGISTRATION STAMPS

Similar Surcharge on China Nos. 747 and 754

1949 **Engr.** ***Perf. 14***

F1 A82 On $500 bl grn 45.00 30.00
F2 A82 On $7000 lt red brn 45.00 30.00

Kwangsi Province

China Nos. 811 and 818 Also Surcharged in Red

1949, May 21 **Typo.**

6 A62 5c on $20,000 on 10c dp grn 18.00 18.00
7 A62 5c on $40,000 on 20c dk ol grn 45.00 45.00

China Stamps of 1946-48 Surcharged in Black or Red

a b

1949 **Engr.** ***Perf. 14***

Type "a" Surcharge

8 A82 ½c on $500,000 lil rose 25.00 14.00
9 A82 1c on $200,000 brn vio 12.00 4.75
10 A82 2c on $300,000 yel grn 50.00 25.00
11 A73 5c on $3000 blue 12.00 6.00
12 A82 5c on $3000 blue 9.50 5.50
13 A82 5c on $40,000 grn 9.50 6.00

Type "b" Surcharge

14 A82 13c on $50,000 dp bl (R) 12.00 7.00
15 A82 13c on $50,000 dp bl 30.00 14.00
16 A82 17c on $7000 lt red brn 14.00 9.00
17 A82 21c on $100,000 dl grn 17.00 10.00
Nos. 8-17 (10) 191.00 101.25

Shensi Province

China Nos. 747, 750 Surcharged

1949, May **Engr.** ***Perf. 14***

1 A82 On $500 bl grn 30.00 30.00
2 A82 On $3000 blue 30.00 30.00

AIR POST STAMP

Similar Surcharge on China No. 754

1949, May **Engr.** ***Perf. 14***

C1 A82 On $7000 lt red brn 35.00 35.00

SPECIAL DELIVERY STAMP

Similar Surcharge on China No. 746 in Red

1949, May **Engr.** ***Perf. 14***

E1 A82 On $250 dp lil 40.00 40.00

REGISTRATION STAMPS

Similar Surcharge on China Nos. 626, 637 in Red

1949, May **Typo.** ***Perf. 12***

F1 A72 on $30 dp bl 40.00 40.00
F2 A73 on $30 dk bl 35.00 35.00

Szechwan Province

Re-engraved Issue of China, 1923, Overprinted

1933 **Unwmk.** ***Perf. 14***

1 A29 1c orange 5.75 .60
2 A29 5c claret 5.75 .75
3 A30 50c deep green 17.50 3.50
Nos. 1-3 (3) 29.00 4.85

The overprint reads "For use in Szechwan Province exclusively"

Same on Sun Yat-sen Issue of 1931-37 Type II

1933-34 ***Perf. 12½***

4 A37 2c olive grn .60 .60
5 A37 5c green 12.50 1.40
6 A37 15c dk green 2.25 1.75
7 A37 15c scar ('34) 3.50 7.00
8 A37 25c ultra 3.00 1.10
9 A37 $1 org brn & dk brn 11.00 2.25
10 A37 $2 bl & org brn 25.00 3.50
11 A37 $5 dl red & blk 70.00 17.50
Nos. 4-11 (8) 127.85 35.10

Same on Martyrs Issue of 1932-34

1933 ***Perf. 14***

12 A39 ½c black brn .35 .30
13 A40 1c orange .30 .30
14 A39 2½c rose lilac 1.75 1.75
15 A48 3c deep brown 1.40 1.40
16 A45 8c brown org 1.10 .90
17 A46 10c dull violet 2.50 .30
18 A45 13c blue green 2.50 .60
19 A46 17c brown olive 2.75 .85
20 A47 20c brown red 3.00 .60
21 A48 30c brown violet 2.75 .60
22 A47 40c orange 7.00 .60
23 A40 50c green 17.50 .85
Nos. 12-23 (12) 42.90 9.05

Stamps of China, 1947-48, Surcharged

1949 **Engr.** ***Perf. 14***

24 A82 on $150 dk bl 40.00 30.00
25 A82 on $250 dp lil 40.00 30.00
26 A82 on $500 bl grn 12.00 7.00
27 A82 on $1000 red 30.00 25.00
28 A82 on $2000 ver 12.00 9.00
29 A82 on $3000 blue 12.00 9.00
30 A82 on $4000 gray 12.00 9.00
31 A82 on $5000 dk brn 30.00 35.00
32 A82 on $6000 rose lil 12.00 12.00
33 A82 on $7000 lt red brn 30.00 25.00
34 A82 on $10,000 dk bl & car 12.00 9.00
35 A82 on $20,000 rose pink 12.00 9.00
36 A82 on $30,000 choc 18.00 12.00
37 A82 on $50,000 grn & dk bl 18.00 15.00
38 A82 on $50,000 dp bl 18.00 12.00
39 A82 on $100,000 dl yel & ol 18.00 12.00
40 A82 on $100,000 dl grn 18.00 15.00
41 A82 on $200,000 vio brn & dp bl 18.00 12.00
42 A82 on $200,000 brn vio 18.00 12.00
43 A82 on $300,000 sep & org brn 25.00 18.00
44 A82 on $300,000 yel grn 25.00 18.00
45 A82 on $500,000 dk Prus grn & sep 18.00 12.00
46 A82 on $1,000,000 claret 30.00 18.00
47 A82 on $2,000,000 ver 18.00 15.00
48 A82 on $3,000,000 ol bis 18.00 15.00
49 A82 on $5,000,000 ultra 60.00 40.00
Nos. 24-49 (26) 574.00 435.00

Several of Nos. 24-49 exist with inverted surcharge and a few with bottom character of left row repeated in right row, same position.

Counterfeits exist.

China No. 737 Surcharged in Purple

1949 ***Perf. 12½***

50 A77 2c on $500 ol grn 25.00 30.00

China No. 975 Handstamp Surcharged in Purple

1949 **Litho.**

51 A94 2½c on 4c bl grn 20.00 25.00

SZECHWAN AIR POST STAMPS

China Nos. C55-C58, C60-C61 Surcharged

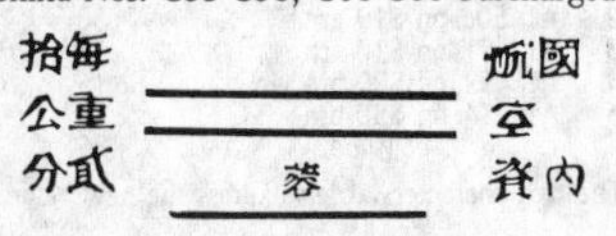

Perf. 12½, 13x12½, 14

1949, July **Unwmk.**

C1 AP3 On $10,000 on 30c 4.00 4.00
  a. On #C54 500.00
C2 AP4 On $10,000 on $27 7.00 10.00
  a. Second surch. invtd. 225.00
  b. On #C53 125.00
C3 AP3 On $20,000 on 25c 6.00 7.00
C4 AP3 On $30,000 on 90c 8.00 9.00
C5 AP3 On $50,000 on 60c 60.00 70.00
C6 AP3 On $50,000 on $1 11.00 15.00
Nos. C1-C6 (6) 96.00 115.00

On No. C2 characters of overprint are arranged in two horizontal rows, and two of four lines are vertical.

SZECHWAN REGISTRATION STAMPS

Stamps of China, 1944-47, Surcharged

Engraved; Typographed (A72)

1949 ***Perf. 12, 13, 14***

F1 A64 On $100 yel brn 55.00
F2 A72 On $100 dk brn 60.00
F3 A64 On $200 dk grn 40.00
F4 A72 On $200 brn vio 60.00
F5 A73 On $200 ol grn 100.00
F6 A73 On $500 brt bl grn 100.00
F7 A73 On $700 red brn 175.00
F8 A73 On $5000 dp grn & ver 75.00
Nos. F1-F8 (8) 665.00

PARCEL POST STAMP

China No. Q10 Surcharged

1949 **Engr.** ***Perf. 12½***

Q1 PP2 1c on $20,000 dk red 250.00

No. Q1 is also found with surcharged value repeated in 5 characters at top of stamp.

Tsingtau

China Nos. 890, 903, 945, 894 Handstamp Surcharged in Purple Blue or Red

Engraved; Lithographed

1949, May ***Perf. 14, 12½***

1 A94 1c on $100 org brn (P) 60.00 22.50
2 A94 4c on $5000 lt bl (P) 60.00 35.00
3 A94 6c on $500 rose lil (B) 60.00 40.00
4 A94 10c on $1000 bl (R) 60.00 35.00
Nos. 1-4 (4) 240.00 132.50

Yunnan Province

Stamps of China, 1923-26, Overprinted

The overprint reads "For exclusive use in the Province of Yunnan". It was applied to prevent stamps being purchased in the depreciated currency of Yunnan and used elsewhere.

1926 **Unwmk.** ***Perf. 14***

1 A29 ½c blk brn 1.10 .20
2 A29 1c orange 1.10 .15
3 A29 1½c violet 2.25 2.25
4 A29 2c yellow grn 1.75 .30
5 A29 3c blue green 1.75 .20
6 A29 4c olive grn 1.75 .30

No.	Type	Description	Unused	Used
7	A29	5c claret	1.75	.30
8	A29	6c red	3.00	.70
9	A29	7c violet	3.00	1.10
10	A29	8c brown org	2.25	.75
11	A29	10c dark blue	1.75	.15
12	A30	13c brown	1.10	1.10
13	A30	15c dark blue	1.10	1.00
14	A30	16c olive grn	1.75	1.10
15	A30	20c brown red	4.00	1.75
16	A30	30c brown vio	3.00	3.00
17	A30	50c deep green	3.00	3.00
18	A31	$1 org brn & sep	11.00	7.50
19	A31	$2 blue & red brn	20.00	7.50
20	A31	$5 red & slate	125.00	125.00
		Nos. 1-20 (20)	191.40	157.35

Unification Issue of China, 1929, Overprinted in Red 貼 滇 用 省

1929 *Perf. 14*

No.	Type	Description	Unused	Used
21	A35	1c brown org	1.10	1.10
22	A35	4c olive grn	2.25	3.50
23	A35	10c dark blue	4.00	4.50
24	A35	$1 dark red	70.00	60.00
		Nos. 21-24 (4)	77.35	69.10

Similar Overprint in Black on Sun Yat-sen Mausoleum Issue

Characters 15½-16mm apart

No.	Type	Description	Unused	Used
25	A36	1c brown orange	.85	.85
26	A36	4c olive green	1.10	*2.25*
27	A36	10c dark blue	3.00	4.00
28	A36	$1 dark red	45.00	45.00
		Nos. 25-28 (4)	49.95	52.10

London Print Issue of China, 1931-37, Overprinted 用貼省滇限

1932-34 **Unwmk.** *Perf. 12½*

Type I (double circle)

No.	Type	Description	Unused	Used
29	A37	1c orange	1.75	1.75
30	A37	2c olive grn	2.00	3.00
31	A37	4c green	2.00	3.00
32	A37	20c ultra	1.75	1.75
33	A37	$1 org brn & dk brn	26.00	26.00
34	A37	$2 bl & org brn	50.00	50.00
35	A37	$5 dl red & blk	150.00	150.00
		Nos. 29-35 (7)	233.50	235.50

Type II (single circle)

No.	Type	Description	Unused	Used
36	A37	2c olive grn	4.00	4.00
37	A37	4c green	2.25	1.75
38	A37	5c green	7.00	5.75
39	A37	15c dk green	4.00	4.00
40	A37	15c scar ('34)	4.00	5.00
41	A37	25c ultra	4.00	4.50
42	A37	$1 org brn & dk brn	35.00	35.00
43	A37	$2 bl & org brn	70.00	57.50
44	A37	$5 dl red & blk	150.00	150.00
		Nos. 36-44 (9)	280.25	267.50

Nos. 36-39, 41-44 were overprinted in London as well as in Peking. The overprints differ in minor details. Value of London overprints (8), $350.

Tan Yuan-chang Issue of China, 1933, Overprinted 貼 滇 用 省

1933 *Perf. 14*

No.	Type	Description	Unused	Used
45	A49	2c olive green	1.10	1.10
46	A49	5c green	1.50	1.50
47	A49	25c ultra	3.25	3.25
48	A49	$1 red	45.00	45.00
		Nos. 45-48 (4)	50.85	50.85

Martyrs Issue of China, 1932-34, Overprinted 用貼省滇限

1933

No.	Type	Description	Unused	Used
49	A39	½c blk brown	.60	.45
50	A40	1c orange	.85	.70
51	A39	2½c rose lilac	1.75	2.00
52	A48	3c deep brown	3.50	1.25
53	A45	8c brown org	1.10	1.10
54	A46	10c dull vio	1.75	2.00
55	A45	13c blue grn	1.10	.60
56	A46	17c brn olive	3.50	2.25
57	A47	20c brown red	1.50	1.50
58	A48	30c brown vio	4.50	4.00
59	A47	40c orange	19.00	19.00
60	A40	50c green	20.00	19.00
		Nos. 49-60 (12)	59.15	53.85

China No. 324 was overprinted with characters arranged vertically, like Sinkiang No. 114, but was not issued.

China Stamps of 1945-49 Surcharged in Black or Blue 壹 滇省貼用 角10

Engraved; Lithographed; Typographed

1949 *Perf. 12, 12½, 14*

No.	Type	Description	Unused	Used
61	A82	1c on $200,000 brn vio	12.00	12.00
62	A82	1.2c on $40,000 grn	12.00	12.00
63	A94	6c on $200 red org	12.00	12.00
64	A94	10c on $20,000 org	12.00	12.00
65	A94	12c on $50 dk Prus grn (Bl)	12.00	12.00
66	A72	12c on $50 grnsh gray (Bl)	12.00	12.00
67	A72	12c on $200 brn vio (Bl)	12.00	12.00
68	A94	30c on $20 vio brn	12.00	12.00
69	A82	$1.20 on $100,000 dl grn	18.00	18.00
		Nos. 61-69 (9)	114.00	114.00

China No. 888 and 630 Surcharged 4 肆分 郵資 滇

1949 **Engr.** *Perf. 14*

No.	Type	Description	Unused	Used
70	A94	4c on $20 vio brn	200.00	

Typo. *Perf. 12*

No.	Type	Description	Unused	Used
71	A72	12c on $200 brn vio	200.00	

Manchuria

Kirin and Heilungkiang Issue

Stamps of China, 1923-26, Overprinted

用貼黑吉限

The overprint reads: "For use in Ki-Hei District" the two names being abbreviated.

The intention of the overprint was to prevent the purchase of stamps in Manchuria, where the currency was depreciated, and their resale elsewhere.

1927 **Unwmk.** *Perf. 14*

No.	Type	Description	Unused	Used
1	A29	½c black brn	1.10	.20
2	A29	1c orange	1.10	.15
3	A29	1½c violet	1.50	1.10
4	A29	2c yellow grn	1.50	.20
5	A29	3c blue grn	.85	.45
6	A29	4c olive grn	.30	.15
7	A29	5c claret	.85	.20
8	A29	6c red	1.50	1.10
9	A29	7c violet	3.00	1.10
10	A29	8c brown org	1.75	1.10
11	A29	10c dk blue	1.10	.30
12	A30	13c brown	2.25	1.75
13	A30	15c dk blue	2.25	1.75
14	A30	16c olive grn	2.25	1.50
15	A30	20c brown red	3.50	1.75
16	A30	30c brown vio	4.50	2.00
17	A30	50c dp green	7.00	2.25
18	A31	$1 org brn & sep	14.00	4.50
19	A31	$2 bl & red brn	37.50	11.00
20	A31	$5 red & slate	175.00	150.00
		Nos. 1-20 (20)	262.80	182.55

Several values of this issue exist with inverted overprint, double overprint and in pairs with one overprint omitted. These "errors" were not regularly issued. Forgeries also exist.

Chang Tso-lin Stamps of 1928 Overprinted in Red or Blue 貼 吉 用 黑

1928 *Perf. 14*

No.	Type	Description	Unused	Used
21	A34	1c brown org (R)	1.75	1.10
22	A34	4c olive grn (R)	1.10	1.10
23	A34	10c dull blue (R)	3.00	2.25
24	A34	$1 red (Bl)	30.00	27.50
		Nos. 21-24 (4)	35.85	31.95

Unification Issue of China, 1929, Overprinted in Red as in 1928

1929

No.	Type	Description	Unused	Used
25	A35	1c brown orange	.80	.80
26	A35	14c olive green	2.25	1.75
27	A35	10c dark blue	8.00	7.50
28	A35	$1 dark red	55.00	65.00
		Nos. 25-28 (4)	66.05	75.05

Similar Overprint in Black on Sun Yat-sen Mausoleum Issue of China

Characters 15-16mm apart

1929 *Perf. 14*

No.	Type	Description	Unused	Used
29	A36	1c brown orange	1.50	1.75
30	A36	4c olive green	2.00	2.00
31	A36	10c dark blue	5.50	3.50
32	A36	$1 dark red	55.00	52.50
		Nos. 29-32 (4)	64.00	59.75

Sinkiang

Stamps of China, 1913-19, Overprinted in Black or Red 限新省貼用

The first character of overprint is ½mm out of alignment, to the left, and the overprint measures 16mm.

1915 **Unwmk.** *Perf. 14, 15*

No.	Type	Description	Unused	Used
1	A24	½c black brn	1.10	.60
2	A24	1c orange	1.10	.45
3	A24	2c yellow grn	1.50	.80
4	A24	3c slate grn	1.50	.40
5	A24	4c scarlet	3.00	.70
6	A24	5c rose lilac	2.25	.60
7	A24	6c gray	4.00	1.75
8	A24	7c violet	4.00	4.00
9	A24	8c brown orange	3.50	1.75
10	A24	10c dark blue	3.50	1.75
11	A25	15c brown	4.00	2.25
12	A25	16c olive grn	8.00	4.50
13	A25	20c brown red	8.00	4.50
14	A25	30c brown violet	9.00	6.00
15	A25	50c deep green	25.00	10.00
16	A26	$1 ocher & blk (R)	85.00	40.00
a.		Second & third characters of overprint transposed	*7,500.*	
		Nos. 1-16 (16)	164.45	80.05

Stamps of China, 1913-19, Overprinted in Black or Red 限新省貼用

The five characters of overprint are correctly aligned and measure 15½mm.

1916-19

No.	Type	Description	Unused	Used
17	A24	½c black brn	1.10	1.50
18	A24	1c orange	1.75	1.10
19	A24	1½c violet	2.25	2.25
20	A24	2c yellow grn	1.75	1.10
21	A24	3c slate grn	3.00	.45
22	A24	4c scarlet	3.00	.70
23	A24	5c rose lilac	3.00	.50
24	A24	6c gray	4.50	.70
25	A24	7c violet	4.00	4.50
26	A24	8c brown org	4.50	5.00
27	A24	10c dark blue	4.50	.70
28	A25	13c brown	3.00	4.50
29	A25	15c brown	3.50	4.50
30	A25	16c olive grn	3.00	2.75
31	A25	20c brown red	2.50	1.75
32	A25	30c brown vio	4.00	3.50
33	A25	50c deep green	5.00	3.25
34	A26	$1 ocher & blk (R)	16.00	6.50
35	A26	$2 dk bl & blk (R)	17.50	7.00
36	A26	$5 scar & blk (R)	60.00	22.50
37	A26	$10 yel grn & blk (R)	150.00	100.00
38	A26	$20 yel & blk (R)	400.00	300.00
		Nos. 17-38 (22)	697.85	474.75

For overprint see No. C4.

China Nos. 243-246 Overprinted 用貼省新限

1921 *Perf. 14*

No.	Type	Description	Unused	Used
39	A27	1c orange	1.10	1.10
40	A27	3c blue green	2.25	2.25
41	A27	6c gray	8.50	6.00
42	A27	10c blue	45.00	45.00
		Nos. 39-42 (4)	56.85	54.35

Constitution Issue of China, 1923, Overprinted 貼 新疆 用 省

1923

No.	Type	Description	Unused	Used
43	A32	1c orange	3.50	3.50
44	A32	3c blue green	4.25	4.25
45	A32	4c red	6.00	6.00
46	A32	10c blue	17.50	17.50
		Nos. 43-46 (4)	31.25	31.25

Stamps of China, 1923-26, Overprinted as in 1916-19, in Black or Red

1924

Re-engraved

No.	Type	Description	Unused	Used
47	A29	½c black brn	.70	1.10
48	A29	1c orange	.70	.70
49	A29	1½c violet	1.50	2.25
50	A29	2c yellow grn	1.75	.70
51	A29	3c blue grn	1.75	.70
52	A29	4c gray	2.25	3.00
53	A29	5c claret	.85	.60
54	A29	6c red	3.50	1.50
55	A29	7c violet	4.00	3.50
56	A29	8c org brn	*8.00*	*3.50*
57	A29	10c dark blue	3.00	1.10
58	A30	13c red brown	2.75	4.00
59	A30	15c deep blue	5.00	4.00
60	A30	16c olive grn	5.00	4.50
61	A30	20c brown red	4.50	3.25
62	A30	30c brown vio	5.00	2.75
63	A30	50c deep green	5.00	2.75
64	A31	$1 org brn & sep (R)	10.00	3.00
65	A31	$2 bl & red brn (R)	20.00	6.00
66	A31	$5 red & sl (R)	50.00	17.50
67	A31	$10 grn & cl (R)	150.00	75.00
68	A31	$20 plum & bl (R)	225.00	150.00
		Nos. 47-68 (22)	510.25	291.40

See #69, 114. For overprints see #C1-C3.

Same Overprint on China No. 275

1926

No.	Type	Description	Unused	Used
69	A29	4c olive green	2.25	2.25

Chang Tso-lin Stamps of China, 1928, Overprinted in Red or Blue 貼 新 用 疆

1928 *Perf. 14*

No.	Type	Description	Unused	Used
70	A34	1c brn org (R)	1.10	1.10
71	A34	4c ol grn (R)	1.75	1.75
72	A34	10c dull bl (R)	4.00	4.00
73	A34	$1 red (Bl)	35.00	35.00
		Nos. 70-73 (4)	41.85	41.85

Unification Issue of China, 1929, Overprinted in Red as in 1928

1929

No.	Type	Description	Unused	Used
74	A35	1c brown org	1.75	1.75
75	A35	4c olive grn	3.00	3.00
76	A35	10c dk blue	7.00	7.00
77	A35	$1 dk red	55.00	55.00
		Nos. 74-77 (4)	66.75	66.75

Similar Overprint in Black on Sun Yat-sen Mausoleum Issue of China

Characters 15mm apart

1929 *Perf. 14*

No.	Type	Description	Unused	Used
78	A36	1c brown org	1.10	1.10
79	A36	4c olive grn	1.75	1.75
80	A36	10c dark blue	4.00	4.00
81	A36	$1 dark red	50.00	50.00
		Nos. 78-81 (4)	56.85	56.85

Stamps of Sun Yat-sen Issue of 1931-37 Overprinted 用貼省新限

1932 **Type I** *Perf. 12½*

No.	Type	Description	Unused	Used
82	A37	1c orange	.90	1.10
83	A37	2c olive grn	1.75	2.25
84	A37	4c green	1.50	2.75
85	A37	20c ultra	2.25	3.00
86	A37	$1 org brn & dk brn	6.00	7.00
87	A37	$2 bl & org brn	14.00	17.50
88	A37	$5 dl red & blk	22.50	30.00
		Nos. 82-88 (7)	48.90	63.60

No. 83 was overprinted in Shanghai in 1938. The overprint differs in minor details.

1932-38

Type II

No.	Type	Description	Unused	Used
89	A37	2c olive grn	.25	.60
90	A37	4c green	.70	.90
91	A37	5c green	.45	.70
92	A37	15c dk green	.60	1.75
93	A37	15c scar ('34)	.60	1.75
93A	A37	20c ultra ('38)	.45	1.00
94	A37	25c ultra	.70	.70
95	A37	$1 org brn & dk brn	5.00	5.00
96	A37	$2 bl & org brn	11.00	11.00
97	A37	$5 dl red & blk	22.50	30.00
		Nos. 89-97 (10)	42.25	53.40

Nos. 89, 90 and 94 were overprinted in London, Peking and Shanghai. Nos. 92, 95-97 exist with London and Peking overprints. Nos. 91 and 93 exist with Peking and Shanghai overprints. No. 93A is a Shanghai overprint. The overprints differ in minor details.

Tan Yuan-chang Issue of China, 1933, Overprinted as in 1928

1933 *Perf. 14*

No.	Type	Description	Unused	Used
98	A49	2c olive grn	2.25	2.25
99	A49	5c green	3.00	3.00
100	A49	25c ultra	8.50	8.50
101	A49	$1 red	45.00	45.00
		Nos. 98-101 (4)	58.75	58.75

Stamps of China Martyrs Issue of 1932-34 Overprinted 用貼省新限

1933-34

No.	Type	Description	Unused	Used
102	A39	½c black brown	.15	.45
103	A40	1c orange	1.10	1.50
104	A39	2½c rose lilac	.25	.45
105	A48	3c deep brown	.25	.45
106	A45	8c brown orange	.70	1.10
107	A46	10c dull violet	.20	.45

108 A45 13c blue green .25 .70
109 A46 17c brown olive .25 .45
110 A47 20c brown red 1.10 1.50
111 A48 30c brown violet .40 .60
112 A47 40c orange .60 .70
113 A40 50c green .70 .70
Nos. 102-113 (12) 5.95 9.05

Nos. 102-113 were originally overprinted in Peking. In 1938, Nos. 103-105, 108-112 were overprinted in Shanghai. The two overprints differ in minor details. No. 105, Shanghai overprint, is scarce. Value $35.

China No. 324 Overprinted as in 1916-19

1936 *Perf. 14*
114 A29 6c brown 11.00 11.00

Stamps of China, 1939-40 Overprinted in Black

1940-45 Unwmk. *Perf. 12½*
Type III

115 A57 2c olive green .85 1.00
116 A57 3c dull claret ('41) .15 *1.40*
117 A57 5c green .15 .30
118 A57 5c olive green .15 .40
119 A57 8c olive green ('41) .20 .40
120 A57 10c green ('41) .15 .40
121 A57 15c scarlet .55 *2.25*
122 A57 16c olive gray ('41) .35 *1.00*
123 A57 25c dark blue .50 *2.25*
124 A57 $1 hn & dk brn (type II) 5.50 *11.00*
125 A57 $2 dp bl & org brn (type I) 4.50 *11.00*
126 A57 $5 red & grnsh blk 22.50 *27.50*
Nos. 115-126 (12) 35.55 *58.90*

Perf. 14
With Secret Marks

127 A57 8c ol grn (#383a) 1.10 *1.65*
a. On #383 16.00 *22.50*
128 A57 10c green ('41) 7.00 8.25
129 A57 30c scarlet ('45) .30 *.75*
130 A57 50c dk blue ('45) .55 *.75*
131 A57 $1 org brn & sep .55 *.95*
132 A57 $2 dp bl & org brn .55 *1.65*
133 A57 $5 red & sl grn .65 *3.25*
134 A57 $10 dk grn & dl pur 1.65 *2.75*
135 A57 $20 rose lake & dk bl 3.00 *4.75*
Nos. 127-135 (9) 15.35 24.75

Wmk. Character Yu (Post) (261)
Perf. 14

136 A57 5c olive green .20 .45
137 A57 10c green .30 .65
138 A57 30c scarlet .30 .85
139 A57 50c dark blue .35 .65
Nos. 136-139 (4) 1.15 2.60

Martyrs Issue, 1940-41, Overprinted in Black 用貼省新限

Perf. 12, 12½, 13, 13x12, 13½x13

1941-45 Wmk. 261

140 A40 1c orange .20 *.45*
141 A39 2½c rose lilac .20 *1.10*
142 A45 8c dp org ('45) 2.75 *2.25*
143 A46 10c dull vio .25 *.85*
144 A45 13c dp yel grn .55 *2.00*
145 A46 17c brown olive .55 *1.65*
146 A40 25c red vio ('45) 1.10 *2.00*
147 A47 40c orange ('45) 1.65 *2.25*
Nos. 140-147 (8) 7.25 *12.55*

Unwmk.

148 A39 ½c olive blk .20 *.55*
149 A40 1c orange ('45) .20 *.45*
150 A46 2c dp blue ('45) .30 *.65*
151 A48 3c dp yel brn .15 *1.00*
152 A39 4c pale vio ('45) .15 *.90*
153 A45 8c dp orange .20 *1.10*
154 A45 13c dp yel grn ('45) .35 *.80*
155 A48 15c brn car ('45) .15 *.80*
156 A46 17c brn ol ('45) .55 *.90*
157 A47 20c lt blue ('45) .20 *.55*
158 A45 21c ol brn ('45) .35 *.90*
159 A46 28c olive ('45) .40 *1.10*
160 A47 40c orange ('45) 1.65 *3.25*
161 A40 50c green ('45) .55 *1.40*
Nos. 148-161 (14) 5.40 *14.35*

Stamps of China, 1942-43 Overprinted in Carmine, Black or Red 用貼省新限

1944 *Perf. 12½, 13*
Without Gum

162 A62 10c dp grn (C) .90 *2.75*
163 A62 20c dk ol grn (C) 1.25 *2.75*
164 A62 25c violet brn .15 *3.00*
165 A62 30c dk orange .60 *3.25*
166 A62 40c red brown .15 *3.00*
167 A62 50c sage green .15 *1.75*
a. Perf. 11 7.00 8.50
168 A62 $1 rose lake 1.75 *1.75*
169 A62 $1 dull green .15 *3.00*
170 A62 $1.50 dp bl (C) .15 *3.25*
171 A62 $2 dk bl grn (R) 1.25 *2.50*
172 A62 $3 yellow .15 *4.25*
173 A62 $5 cerise 1.25 *4.00*
Nos. 162-173 (12) 7.90 *35.25*

For surcharges see Nos. 194-195.

Same Overprint on Stamps of China, 1942-43, in Black

1944-46 *Imperf.*

174 A57 $10 red brown 40.00 40.00
175 A57 $20 rose red 1.75 *6.00*
176 A57 $30 dull vio 1.25 *5.50*
177 A57 $40 rose red 1.75 *5.75*
178 A57 $50 blue ('46) 550.00 600.00
179 A57 $100 orange brn 2.50 *6.25*

Perf. 13½

180 A57 $4 dp blue .15 *3.50*
181 A57 $5 lilac gray .30 *3.00*
182 A57 $10 red brn .30 *3.00*
183 A57 $20 blue grn .90 *3.25*
184 A57 $20 rose red 55.00 55.00
185 A57 $30 dull vio 1.25 *4.25*
186 A57 $40 rose 1.25 *4.25*
187 A57 $50 blue 1.50 *3.50*
188 A57 $100 orange brn 45.00 45.00
Nos. 174-177,179-188 (14) 152.90 *188.25*

Nos. 162 and 164 Surcharged in Black

1944, Aug. 1

194 A62 12c on 10c dp grn 1.25 *2.50*
195 A62 24c on 25c brn vio 1.50 *2.75*

Stamps of China, 1940-41, Overprinted in Black at Chengtu, Szechwan 用貼省新限

1943

196 A57 10c green (#354) 5.50 8.25
197 A47 20c lt blue (#433) 4.50 7.00

Wmk. 261 *Perf. 14*

198 A57 50c dk blue (#396) 5.50 8.25

China Nos. 565 and 567 Overprinted in Black 用貼省新限

1945 Unwmk. *Perf. 12½*

200 A63 40c brown red .30 .90
201 A63 $3 red .30 .90

China Nos. 640-642, 788, 751, 753 Surcharged in Black or Red 伍分 改作 用貼省新限

1949 Engr. *Perf. 14*

202 A73 1c on $100 dk car 15.00 18.00
203 A73 3c on $200 ol grn (R) 15.00 18.00
204 A73 5c on $500 brt bl grn (R) 15.00 18.00
205 A82 10c on $20,000 rose pink 15.00 18.00
206 A82 50c on $4000 gray (R) 55.00 *55.00*
207 A82 $1 on $6000 rose lil 65.00 *65.00*
Nos. 202-207 (6) 180.00 192.00

AIR POST STAMPS

Sinkiang Nos. 53, 57, 59, 32 Overprinted in Red 空航

1932-33 Unwmk. *Perf. 14*

C1 A29 5c claret ('33) 125. 75.
C2 A29 10c dk blue ('33) 125. 60.
C3 A30 15c deep blue 1,000. 250.
C4 A25 30c brown vio 375. 275.

Counterfeits exist of Nos. C1-C19.

Air Post Stamps of China, 1932-37 Handstamped in Dull Red

用貼省新限

1942

C5 AP3 15c gray green 3.50 3.50
C6 AP3 25c orange 225.00 200.00
C7 AP3 30c red 8.00 14.00
C8 AP3 45c brown vio 5.50 8.50
C9 AP3 50c dk brown 22.50 25.00
C10 AP3 60c dk blue 5.00 9.50
C11 AP3 90c olive grn 27.50 35.00
C12 AP3 $1 yellow grn 6.25 10.00
Nos. C5-C12 (8) 303.25 305.50

Same Handstamped Overprint on Air Post Stamps of China, 1940-41 in Dull Red

Perf. 12½, 13, 13½

1942 Wmk. 261

C13 AP3 15c gray green 2.75 3.25
C14 AP3 25c yellow org 2.75 3.25

1942 Unwmk.

C15 AP3 25c lt orange 2.25 2.25
C16 AP3 30c lt red 3.50 3.50
C17 AP3 50c brown 4.50 4.50
C18 AP3 $2 lt brown 22.50 22.50
C19 AP3 $5 lake 22.50 22.50
Nos. C15-C19 (5) 55.25 55.25

Twelve values exist with this overprint in black. Their status has not been determined. Inverted overprints exist in both red and black.

Official Perforated Characters

For use on official mail, various Sinkiang stamps were perforated with an arrangement of four Chinese characters ("For Official Business Only"). These include Nos. 1-38, 47-69, 114.

OFFICES IN TIBET

12 Pies = 1 Anna
16 Annas = 1 Rupee

Stamps of China, Issues of 1902-10, Surcharged

分半
Three Pies

1911 Unwmk. *Perf. 12 to 16*

1 A17 3p on 1c ocher 9.00 15.00
a. Inverted surcharge 775.00
2 A17 ½a on 2c grn 9.00 15.00
3 A17 1a on 4c ver 9.00 15.00
4 A17 2a on 7c mar 9.00 9.00
5 A17 2½a on 10c ultra 12.00 14.00
6 A18 3a on 16c ol grn 24.00 24.00
a. Large "S" in "Annas" 600.00
7 A18 4a on 20c red brn 24.00 24.00
8 A18 6a on 30c rose red 35.00 35.00
9 A18 12a on 50c yel grn 110.00 140.00
10 A19 1r on $1 red & pale rose 300.00 350.00
11 A19 2r on $2 red & yel 600.00 725.00
Nos. 1-11 (11) 1,141. 1,366.

CHINA, PEOPLE'S REPUBLIC OF

'pē-pəls ri-'pə-blik of 'chī-nə

LOCATION — Eastern Asia
GOVT. — Communist Republic
POP. — 1,015,400,000 (est. 1983)
CAPITAL — Beijing (Peking)

The communists completed their conquest of all mainland China in 1949. They established the Central Government and General Postal Administration in Peking. They ordered all but two regions to stop selling regional issues by June 30, 1950, extending validity one year from that date. The Northeast and Port Arthur-Dairen regions were exempted because their currency had a different value. These two regions stopped using separate issues at the end of 1950. Thereafter unified issues were used throughout mainland China.

After currency revaluation Mar. 1, 1955, reprints were prepared and put on sale by the Philatelic Agency in order to supply stocks of exhausted issues for collectors. Minor differences in design or paper distinguish the reprints. They are of commemorative and special issues up to the gymnastics set of 1952. Reprints are less expensive. Values are for original issues. Reprint distinctions are footnoted.

Most used stamps before 1970 exist primarily canceled to order. Postally used copies generally sell for ½ the unused value.

Commemorative issues, beginning in 1949, and special issues, beginning in 1951, bear 4 numbers in lower margin: 1. Issue number. 2. Total of stamps in set. 3. Position of stamp in set. 4. Cumulative number of stamp (usually in parenthesis). A fifth number, the year of issue, was added in 1952.

The numbering system varies at times, with all numbers omitted on Scott 938-1046.

In certain sets listings include parenthetically the position-in-set number. During some periods these parentheses in listings hold the stamp's cumulative number. Issue numbers are noted when one or more designs are not illustrated.

All stamps to the beginning of 1960 were issued without gum, except as noted. After that date, most stamps have gum, which is translucent and almost invisible. All issues are unwatermarked, unless otherwise noted.

100 fen = 1 yuan ($)

Catalogue values for unused stamps in this country are for Never Hinged items, beginning with Scott 487 in the regular postage section, Scott B1 in the semi-postal section.

Lantern and Gate of Heavenly Peace — A1

Globe and Hand Holding Hammer — A2

1949, Oct. 8 Litho. *Perf. 12½*

1 A1 $30 blue 1.40 1.75
2 A1 $50 rose red 1.40 1.75
3 A1 $100 green 1.40 1.75
4 A1 $200 maroon 1.40 1.75
Nos. 1-4 (4) 5.60 7.00

1st session of Chinese People's Consultative Political Conference. See #1L121-1L124.

Original — Reprint

Reprints have altered ornament on lantern base. On originals, it is a full oval; in reprints, only a partial circle. Value, set, $1.75.

1949, Nov. 16

5 A2 $100 carmine 5.25 4.50
6 A2 $300 slate green 5.25 4.50
7 A2 $500 dark blue 5.25 4.50
Nos. 5-7 (3) 15.75 13.50

Asiatic and Australasian Congress of the World Federation of Trade Unions, Peking.

The $100, imperf., is of dubious status.

See Nos. 1L133-1L135.

Original

Reprint

Reprints show heavier shading on index finger and thumb. Value, set $4.25.

Conference Hall, Peking — A3

Mao Tse-tung on Rostrum — A4

1950, Feb. 1 Engr. *Perf. 14*

8	A3	$50 red	3.00	3.00
9	A3	$100 blue	3.00	3.00
10	A4	$300 red brown	3.00	2.75
11	A4	$500 green	3.00	2.75
		Nos. 8-11 (4)	12.00	11.50

Chinese People's Consultative Political Conference. See Nos. 1L136-1L139.

Original

Reprint

Nos. 8-9: First character in top inscription shows a square, reprints an oblong.

Nos. 10-11: Originals have heavy crosshatching and lines which touch back of head and top of rostrum. Reprints have lighter lines which do not touch head or top of rostrum. Reprints, value set $4.50.

Gate of Heavenly Peace (same size) — A5

First Issue: Top line of shading broken at right.

1950, Feb. 10 Litho. *Perf. 12½*

12	A5	$200 green	6.00	1.25
13	A5	$300 brn red	.20	.25
14	A5	$500 red	.20	.15
15	A5	$800 orange	57.50	.20
16	A5	$1000 dull violet	1.50	.15
17	A5	$2000 olive	9.00	.50
18	A5	$5000 brt pink	.20	.75
19	A5	$8000 blue	.20	2.50
20	A5	$10,000 brown	.75	1.25
		Nos. 12-20 (9)	75.55	7.00

1950, June 9 Typo.

Second Issue: Top line of shading extends to frame line at right.

21	A5	$1000 dull violet	1.40	.15
22	A5	$3000 red brown	1.40	.15
23	A5	$10,000 brown	1.40	.15
		Nos. 21-23 (3)	4.20	.45

Other Gate of Heavenly Peace issues are illustrated where they are listed. See A10, A13, A14 and A42 for similar designs.

For similar types with Chinese characters in upper right corner see Northeast China A28, A29, Port Arthur & Darien A11, North China A8.

中國人民郵政 貳佰圓

China Nos. 959, C62, E12, F2 Surcharged in Blue, Black, Green or Red

Rouletted, Perf. 12½ (#27, 29)

1950, Mar. Litho.

24	SD2	$100 on red vio (Bl)	.25	.75
a.		Perf. 12½	7.50	3.00
25	R2	$200 on red (Bk)	2.50	.60
a.		Perf. 12½	30.00	3.00
26	AP5	$300 on bl grn (Bk)	.25	.75
a.		Perf. 12½	.25	1.00
27	A96	$500 on orange (Bk)	.15	.30
a.		Perf. 14	95.00	55.00
28	A96	$800 on orange (R)	2.50	.20
a.		Perf. 12½	14.00	1.00
b.		Perf. 14	140.00	55.00
29	A96	$1000 on orange (Bk)	.15	.20
a.		Perf. 14	.15	.20
		Nos. 24-29 (6)	5.80	2.80

No. 27 exists with green surcharge.

Harvesters with Ox — A6

1950, May

30	A6	$20,000 on $10,000 red	400.00	25.00

No. 30 is surcharged on an unissued stamp of East China.

Flag, Mao Tse-tung, Gate of Heavenly Peace — A7

1950, July 1 *Perf. 14*

Yellow Stars

31	A7	$800 green & red	8.75	2.50
32	A7	$1000 brown & red	13.00	5.00
33	A7	$2000 dk brown & red	17.00	6.00
34	A7	$3000 dk blue & red	17.00	7.00
		Nos. 31-34 (4)	55.75	20.50

Inauguration of the People's Republic, Oct. 1, 1949. See Nos. 1L150-1L153.

Original

Reprint

Originals have a single curved line in jacket button, reprints have an extra dot in button. Value, set $6.

中國人民郵政 伍拾圓 ☆

Sun Yat-sen Stamps of Northeastern Provinces Surcharged in Red, Black or Blue

1950, July 1 Engr.

35	A2	$50 on 20c yel grn	2.50	6.00
36	A2	$50 on 25c blk brn	4.50	2.00
37	A2	$50 on 50c red org (Bk)	.35	.60
38	A2	$100 on $2.50 ind	1.25	.60
39	A2	$100 on $3 brn (Bk)	15.00	.60
40	A2	$100 on $4 org brn, Type II (Bl)	11.00	3.50
a.		Type I	400.00	125.00
41	A2	$100 on $5 dk grn (Bk)	15.00	.60
42	A2	$100 on $10 crim, Type II (Bl)	18.00	5.00
a.		Type I	800.00	
43	A2	$400 on $20 ol, Type II (Bl)	18.00	5.00
a.		Type I	300.00	100.00
44	A2	$400 on $44 dk car rose (Bl)	.75	3.00
45	A2	$400 on $65 dl grn	72.50	10.00
46	A2	$400 on $100 dp grn	16.00	3.00
47	A2	$400 on $200 rose brn (Bk)	82.50	4.00
48	A2	$400 on $300 bluish grn	82.50	4.00
		Nos. 35-48 (14)	339.85	47.90

中國人民郵政 貳佰圓 ★★ 200

Flying Geese Type of China Surcharged in Red, Blue, Green, Brown or Black

1950, Aug. 1 *Perf. 12½, Imperf.*

49	A97	$50 on 10c dk bl (R)	.15	.35
50	A97	$100 on 16c ol, imperf. (Bl)	.15	.35
51	A97	$100 on 50c dl grn, imperf. (Bl)	.15	.15
52	A97	$200 on $1 org (G)	.15	.15
53	A97	$200 on $2 bl (Br)	6.00	.75
54	A97	$400 on $5 car rose (Bk)	.15	.35
55	A97	$400 on $10 bl grn (Bk)	.15	1.00
56	A97	$400 on $20 pur (Bk)	.20	2.50
		Nos. 49-56 (8)	7.10	5.60

Dove of Peace, by Picasso — A8

Chinese Flag and "1" — A9

1950, Aug. 1 Engr. *Perf. 14*

57	A8	$400 brown	4.00	1.00
58	A8	$800 green	4.00	1.00
59	A8	$2000 blue	4.00	1.00
		Nos. 57-59 (3)	12.00	3.00

World Peace Campaign. See Nos. 1L154-1L156.

Paper of originals appears bright under ultraviolet lamp. That of reprints looks dull. Value, set $4.

1950 Engr. & Litho.

Flag in Red & Yellow

60	A9	$100 purple	12.00	3.25
61	A9	$400 red brown	12.00	5.50
62	A9	$800 green	12.00	3.25
63	A9	$1000 lt olive	12.00	3.50
64	A9	$2000 blue	12.00	5.50
		Nos. 60-64 (5)	60.00	21.00

First anniversary of the Chinese People's Republic. Size of $800: 38x46mm; others 26x32mm.

Issue dates: No. 62, Oct. 1; others Oct. 31. See Nos. 1L157-1L161.

$800

Original

Reprint

Reprints are a brighter red, leaves beside "1" are gray brown instead of reddish brown. On the $800 the arrangement of dots in background differs in relationship to large star. Value, set $5.

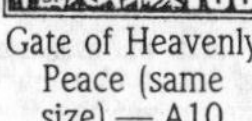
Gate of Heavenly Peace (same size) — A10

"Communication" and Map of China — A11

Third Issue: Cloud almost touches character at upper left. Cloud breaks inner frame line at top.

1950 Litho.

65	A10	$100 lt grnsh bl	37.50	*7.00*
66	A10	$200 green	300.00	*8.75*
67	A10	$300 dk car	2.75	*3.00*
68	A10	$400 grnsh gray	1.10	*3.00*
69	A10	$500 carmine	.75	*3.25*
70	A10	$800 orange	5.75	.25
71	A10	$2000 gray olive	1.50	.40
		Nos. 65-71 (7)	349.35	*25.65*

Issue dates: $800, Oct. 8; $500, $2000, Dec. 1; others, Oct. 6.

1950, Nov. 1 Litho.

72	A11	$400 grn & brn	5.00	3.50
73	A11	$800 car & grn	5.00	3.50

First All-China Postal Conference, Peking. See Nos. 1L162-1L163.

Original

Reprint

Originals have 3 lines below horizontal bar below the 2nd character; reprints have four. Value, set $1.50.

Stalin and Mao Tse-tung — A12

1950, Dec. 1 Engr. *Perf. 14*

74	A12	$400 red	9.50	4.00
75	A12	$800 dp green	9.50	3.00
76	A12	$2000 dk blue	9.50	4.00
		Nos. 74-76 (3)	28.50	11.00

Signing of Sino-Soviet Treaty of Friendship, Alliance and Mutual Assistance. See Nos. 1L176-1L178.

Paper of originals appears bright under ultraviolet lamp. That of reprints looks dull. Value, set $3.50.

East China Issue of 1949 Surcharged in Red, Black, Brown or Blue

Train and Postal Runner — A12a

1950, Dec. Litho. *Perf. 12½*

77	A12a	$50 on $10 dp ultra (R)	.15	.15
78	A12a	$100 on $15 org ver (Bk)	.15	.15
a.		$100 on $15 red (Bk), perf. 14	.15	.15
79	A12a	$300 on $50 car (Bk)	.15	.15
80	A12a	$400 on $1600 vio bl (Br)	.95	.15
81	A12a	$400 on $2000 brn vio (Bl)	.45	.15
		Nos. 77-81 (5)	1.85	
		Set value		.50

East China Issue of 1949 Surcharged in Red or Black

Chairman Mao — A12b

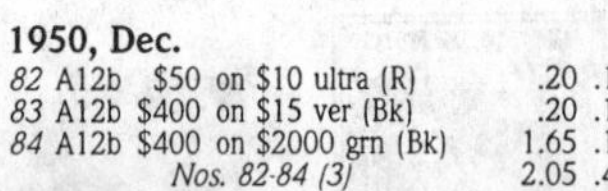

1950, Dec.

82	A12b	$50 on $10 ultra (R)	.20	.15
83	A12b	$400 on $15 ver (Bk)	.20	.15
84	A12b	$400 on $2000 grn (Bk)	1.65	.15
		Nos. 82-84 (3)	2.05	.45

(same size) — A13

(same size) — A14

Fourth Issue: Similar to 3rd issue, but large cloud does not break inner frame line at top.

1950-51 **Litho.**

85	A13	$100 lt blue	2.50	.75
86	A13	$200 dull green	2.75	.75
87	A13	$300 dull lilac	.55	*5.25*
88	A13	$400 gray grn	.55	1.00
89	A13	$500 carmine	.15	*1.10*
90	A13	$800 orange	92.50	1.50
a.		Imperf., pair	*4,000.*	
91	A13	$1000 violet	.70	.75
92	A13	$2000 olive	325.00	3.00
93	A13	$3000 brown	.15	*6.00*
94	A13	$5000 pink	.15	*6.00*
		Nos. 85-94 (10)	425.00	*26.10*

Issue dates: $200, $300, $500, $800, $2000, $5000, Dec. 22, 1950; others June 8, 1951.

1951, Jan. 18 **Engr.** ***Perf. 14***

Fifth Issue: Colored network on surface in salmon.

95	A14	$10,000 brown	1.50	*11.00*
96	A14	$20,000 olive	1.50	*9.25*
97	A14	$30,000 green	22.50	*37.50*
98	A14	$50,000 violet	67.50	19.00
99	A14	$100,000 scarlet	2,000.	190.00
100	A14	$200,000 blue	2,000.	190.00
		Nos. 95-100 (6)	4,093.	456.75

Unit Issue of China Surcharged

中國人民郵政
伍
圓

1951, May 2 **Litho.** ***Perf. 12½***

101	SD2	$5 on rose lilac	3.00	.50
102	AP5	$10 on brt grn	.20	.25
103	R2	$15 on red	.15	.25
104	A96	$25 on orange	.65	.25
		Nos. 101-104 (4)	4.00	1.25

Issued for use in Northeast China, but available for use throughout China. Nos. 101-104 rouletted were sold for philatelic purposes only. Value, set $1.50.

Chairman Mao Tse-tung — A15

1951, July 1 **Engr.** ***Perf. 14***

105	A15	$400 chestnut	4.00	1.25
106	A15	$500 deep green	4.00	1.25
107	A15	$800 crimson	4.00	1.25
		Nos. 105-107 (3)	12.00	3.75

Chinese Communist Party, 30th anniv.

Reprints are on whiter, thinner and harder paper. Value, set $2.50.

Picasso Dove — A16

1951, Aug. 15 ***Perf. 12½***

108	A16	$400 orange brn	8.25	5.00
109	A16	$800 blue grn	8.25	3.00
110	A16	$1000 dull vio	8.25	4.00
		Nos. 108-110 (3)	24.75	12.00

Reprints are perf 14. Value, set $7.

Remittance Stamp of China Surcharged in Carmine or Black

(same size) — A17

Engraved, Commercial Press

1951, Sept. ***Perf. 12½***

111	A17	$50 on $2 bl grn (C)	.30	*1.00*

Typo., Kang Hwa Printing Co.
Rouletted 9½

112	A17	$50 on $2 gray bl (C)	.65	1.00
113	A17	$50 on $5 red org (Bk)	.15	*1.00*
114	A17	$50 on $50 gray (C)	6.25	1.00

Lithographed, Central Trust Co.
Perf. 13

115	A17	$50 on $50 gray blk (C)	.15	*1.00*

Lithographed, Chung Hwa Book Co.
Perf. 11½x10

116	A17	$50 on $50 gray (C)	1.00	1.00
a.		Perf. 11½	2.25	.75
		Nos. 111-116 (6)	8.50	6.00

National Emblem — A18

Engraved; Background Network Lithographed in Yellow

1951, Oct. 1 ***Perf. 14***

117	A18	$100 Prus blue	5.00	2.25
118	A18	$200 brown	5.00	2.25
119	A18	$400 orange	5.00	2.50
120	A18	$500 green	5.00	1.50
121	A18	$800 carmine	5.00	1.50
		Nos. 117-121 (5)	25.00	10.00

Reprints exist but difficult to distinguish; paper whiter, and colors slightly brighter. Value, set $2.50.

Rough Perfs

Rough perforations are normal on many early issues. These include Nos. 122-123, 136-140, 155-176, 239-240, 299-300, 453-456, 467-482, 629-634, 684-707, 737-745 and probably others.

Lu Hsun and Quotation A19

1951, Oct. 19 **Litho.** ***Perf. 12½***

122	A19	$400 lilac	3.50	2.25
123	A19	$800 green	3.50	2.25

15th anniversary of the death of Lu Hsun (1881-1936), writer.

Original

Reprint

Reprints have dot in triangle at lower right; no dot in original. Value, set, 75 cents.

Peasant Uprising, Chintien — A20

Design: Nos. 126-127, Coin of Taiping Regime and decrees of peasant government.

1951, Dec. 15 **Engr.** ***Perf. 14***

124	A20	$400 green	7.00	2.00
125	A20	$800 scarlet	7.00	2.00
126	A20	$800 orange	7.00	2.00
127	A20	$1000 dp blue	7.00	3.00
		Nos. 124-127 (4)	28.00	9.00

Centenary of Taiping Peasant Rebellion.

Original

Reprint

Reprints of Nos. 124-125 have additional short stroke at upper left.

Original

Reprint

Reprints of Nos. 126-127 have two short strokes on scale near tail of right dragon on coin. Value, Nos. 124-127, $1.50.

Old and New Methods of Agriculture A21

1952, Jan. 1

128	A21	$100 scarlet	3.50	2.50
129	A21	$200 bright blue	3.50	2.50
130	A21	$400 deep brown	3.50	1.65
131	A21	$800 green	3.50	1.65
		Nos. 128-131 (4)	14.00	8.30

Agrarian reform.

Original

Reprint

One short horizontal line between legs of plower; 2 lines in reprints. Value, set $1.25.

Potala Monastery, Lhasa — A22

Designs: Nos. 134-135, Farmer plowing with yaks.

1952, Mar. 15 ***Perf. 12½***

132	A22	$400 vermilion	4.25	2.50
133	A22	$800 claret	4.25	2.50
134	A22	$800 bl grn	4.25	1.65
135	A22	$1000 dl vio	4.25	1.65
		Nos. 132-135 (4)	17.00	8.30

Liberation of Tibet.

Reprints, perf 14, have a small Chinese character at lower left of the vignette which is missing in the original. Value, set $1.50.

Children of Four Races — A23

Hammer and Sickle on Numeral 1 — A24

1952, Apr. 12 **Litho.**

136 A23 $400 dull grn .50 .30
137 A23 $800 vio blue .50 .30

Intl. Child Protection Conf., Vienna.

1952, May 1

Labor Day: No. 139, Dove rising from worker's hand. No. 140, Dove, hammer, wheat and chimneys.

138 A24 $800 scarlet .20 .20
139 A24 $800 blue grn .20 .20
140 A24 $800 orange brn .55 .20
Nos. 138-140 (3) .95 .60

Physical Exercises — A25

Stamps printed in blocks of four for each color, each block representing a specific setting-up exercise; exercises coincided with a national radio program. Where exercise positions are identical within the block, the serial number (in parenthesis) is the only means of differentiation.

1952, June 20

141 A25 Block of 4 22.50 22.50
a. $400 vermilion (1) 3.00 1.00
b. $400 vermilion (2) 3.00 1.00
c. $400 vermilion (3) 3.00 1.00
d. $400 vermilion (4) 3.00 1.00
142 A25 Block of 4 22.50 22.50
a. $400 blue (5) 3.00 1.00
b. $400 blue (6) 3.00 1.00
c. $400 blue (7) 3.00 1.00
d. $400 blue (8) 3.00 1.00
143 A25 Block of 4 22.50 22.50
a. $400 brown red (9) 3.00 1.00
b. $400 brown red (10) 3.00 1.00
c. $400 brown red (11) 3.00 1.00
d. $400 brown red (12) 3.00 1.00
144 A25 Block of 4 22.50 22.50
a. $400 yellow green (13) 3.00 1.00
b. $400 yellow green (14) 3.00 1.00
c. $400 yellow green (15) 3.00 1.00
d. $400 yellow green (16) 3.00 1.00
145 A25 Block of 4 22.50 22.50
a. $400 red orange (17) 3.00 1.00
b. $400 red orange (18) 3.00 1.00
c. $400 red orange (19) 3.00 1.00
d. $400 red orange (20) 3.00 1.00
146 A25 Block of 4 22.50 22.50
a. $400 dull blue (21) 3.00 1.00
b. $400 dull blue (22) 3.00 1.00
c. $400 dull blue (23) 3.00 1.00
d. $400 dull blue (24) 3.00 1.00
147 A25 Block of 4 22.50 22.50
a. $400 orange (25) 3.00 1.00
b. $400 orange (26) 3.00 1.00
c. $400 orange (27) 3.00 1.00
d. $400 orange (28) 3.00 1.00
148 A25 Block of 4 22.50 22.50
a. $400 dull purple (29) 3.00 1.00
b. $400 dull purple (30) 3.00 1.00
c. $400 dull purple (31) 3.00 1.00
d. $400 dull purple (32) 3.00 1.00
149 A25 Block of 4 22.50 22.50
a. $400 yellow bister (33) 3.00 1.00
b. $400 yellow bister (34) 3.00 1.00
c. $400 yellow bister (35) 3.00 1.00
d. $400 yellow bister (36) 3.00 1.00
150 A25 Block of 4 22.50 22.50
a. $400 sky blue (37) 3.00 1.00
b. $400 sky blue (38) 3.00 1.00
c. $400 sky blue (39) 3.00 1.00
d. $400 sky blue (40) 3.00 1.00
Nos. 141-150 (10) 225.00 225.00

Originals are on thin gray paper, colors darker. Reprints on thicker white paper, colors brighter. Value, set $13.

Hunting, Wei Dynasty, A.D. 386-580 A26

Designs from Murals in Cave Temples at Tunhuang, Kansu Province: No. 152, Lady attendants, Sui Dynasty, 581-617 A.D. No. 153, Gandharvas (mythology), Tang Dynasty, 618-906. No. 154, Dragon, Tang Dynasty.

1952, July 1 **Engr.**

151 A26 $800 slate green (1) .50 .25
152 A26 $800 chocolate (2) .50 .25
153 A26 $800 indigo (3) .50 .25
154 A26 $800 dk vio (4) .50 .25
Nos. 151-154 (4) 2.00 1.00

"Glorious Mother Country," 1st series.

Marco Polo Bridge, near Peking A27

Designs: No. 156, Cavalry passing through Great Wall. No. 157, Departure of New Fourth Army. No. 158, Mao Tse-tung and Gen. Chu Teh planning counter-attack.

1952, July 7 **Litho.** ***Perf. 14***

155 A27 $800 brt blue .30 .30
156 A27 $800 blue grn .65 .65
157 A27 $800 plum .30 .30
158 A27 $800 scarlet .15 .15
Nos. 155-158 (4) 1.40 1.40

15th anniversary of war against Japan.

Soldier and Tanks — A28

Designs: No. 159, Soldier, sailor and airman, vert. No. 161, Sailor and warships. No. 162, Airman and planes.

1952, Aug. 1 **Engr.** ***Perf. 12½***

159 A28 $800 carmine .30 .20
160 A28 $800 deep green .50 .30
161 A28 $800 purple .30 .20
162 A28 $800 orange brown .30 .20
Nos. 159-162 (4) 1.40 .90

25th anniv. of People's Liberation Army.

Huai River Sluice Dam A29

Designs: No. 164, Train on the Chengtu-Chungking Railway. No. 165, Oil refinery and derricks in the Northwest. No. 166, Mechanized state farm.

1952, Oct. 1 ***Perf. 14***

163 A29 $800 dk violet .30 .15
164 A29 $800 red .30 .15
165 A29 $800 dk vio brn .30 .15
166 A29 $800 dp green .30 .15
Nos. 163-166 (4) 1.20 .60

"Glorious Mother Country," 2nd series.

Doves and Globe A30

Designs: Nos. 167-168, Picasso dove over Pacific, vert. $2500, as No. 169.

1952, Oct. 2 ***Perf. 14***

167 A30 $400 maroon .30 .30
168 A30 $800 red .30 .30
169 A30 $800 brown orange .30 .30
170 A30 $2500 deep green .60 .60
Nos. 167-170 (4) 1.50 1.50

Peace Conf. of the Asian and Pacific Regions.

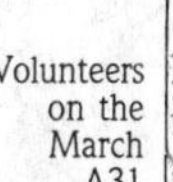

Volunteers on the March A31

Designs: No. 172, Chinese peasants loading supplies. No. 173, Volunteers attacking across river. No. 174, Meeting of Chinese and Korean troops.

1952, Oct. 25

171 A31 $800 blue green (1) .20 .15
172 A31 $800 vermilion (2) .20 .15
173 A31 $800 violet (3) .30 .20
174 A31 $800 lake brown (4) .40 .25
Nos. 171-174 (4) 1.10 .75

2nd anniv. of Chinese Volunteers in Korea.

Woman Textile Worker A32

Design: No. 176, Farm woman with sickle.

1953, Mar. 10

175 A32 $800 carmine .35 .20
176 A32 $800 emerald .40 .20

International Women's Day.

Textile Worker — A33

Karl Marx — A34

Designs: $200, Shepherdess. $250, Stone lion. $800, Lathe operator. $1600, Coal miners. $2000, Corner tower of Forbidden City, Peking.

1953 **Litho.** ***Perf. 14, 12½ ($250)***

177 A33 $50 magenta .65 .15
178 A33 $200 emerald .35 .20
179 A33 $250 ultra 4.75 1.25
180 A33 $800 blue grn .20 .15
181 A33 $1600 gray .65 .20
182 A33 $2000 red org .20 .15
Nos. 177-182 (6) 6.80 2.10

Issued: #177-181, Mar. 25; #182, May 23.

1953, May 20 **Engr.** ***Perf. 14***

183 A34 $400 dk brown .35 .15
184 A34 $800 slate grn .65 .25

135th anniv. of the birth of Karl Marx.

Workers and Banners — A35

1953, June 25

185 A35 $400 Prus blue .35 .15
186 A35 $800 carmine .25 .15

7th All-China Trade Union Congress.

Picasso Dove — A36

1953, July 25

187 A36 $250 blue grn .65 .15
188 A36 $400 org brn .35 .15
189 A36 $800 purple .50 .20
Nos. 187-189 (3) 1.50 .50

World Peace.

Groom, Wei Dynasty, 386-580 A37

Scenes from Tunhuang Murals: No. 191, Court Players, Wei Dynasty. No. 192, Battle Scene, Sui Dynasty, 581-617. No. 193, Ox-drawn palanquin, Tang Dynasty, 618-906.

1953, Sept. 1

190 A37 $800 dp green (1) 1.00 .15
191 A37 $800 red org (2) .20 .15
192 A37 $800 Prus blue (3) .50 .15
193 A37 $800 carmine (4) .20 .15
Nos. 190-193 (4) 1.90 .60

"Glorious Mother Country," 3rd series.

Stalin and Mao on Kremlin Terrace A38

Statue of Stalin at Volga-Don Canal — A39

Designs: No. 195, Lenin proclaiming Soviet power. No. 197, Stalin as orator.

1953, Oct. 5

194 A38 $800 green (1) 1.10 .40
195 A38 $800 carmine (2) .50 .15
196 A39 $800 brt blue (3) .45 .15
197 A39 $800 org brn (4) .35 .15
Nos. 194-197 (4) 2.40 .85

Russian October Revolution, 35th anniv.

Stamps in same designs with two additional characters meaning "Soviet" in the single-line Chinese inscription, and in different colors, were unofficially released at several small post offices in Hunan, Fukien and Canton areas in February, 1953, but were withdrawn after only a small number had been sold. Value, set $3,500 unused, $2,000 canceled.

Compass, 3rd Century B.C. — A40

Designs: No. 199, Seismoscope, later Han Dynasty. No. 200, Drum cart to measure distance, Chin Dynasty. No. 201, Armillary sphere, Ming Dynasty.

1953, Dec. 1

198 A40 $800 indigo (1) .75 .15
199 A40 $800 dk green (2) .15 .15
200 A40 $800 dk blue (3) .40 .15
201 A40 $800 choc (4) .40 .15
Nos. 198-201 (4) 1.70 .60

Major inventions by ancient and medieval Chinese scientists.
"Glorious Mother Country," 4th series.

Francois Rabelais — A41

(same size) Gate of Heavenly Peace — A42

Designs: $400, Jose Marti, Cuban revolutionary. $800, Chu Yuan (350-275 B.C.), philosopher. $2200, Nicolaus Copernicus, astronomer.

1953, Dec. 30

202 A41 $250 slate grn (3) .40 .25
203 A41 $400 brown blk (4) .40 .25
204 A41 $800 indigo (1) .40 .25
205 A41 $2200 choc (2) .40 .25
Nos. 202-205 (4) 1.60 1.00

1954, Apr. 16 **Litho.**

Sixth Issue: Inscription at upper right.

206 A42 $50 carmine .15 .15
207 A42 $100 lt blue .15 .15
208 A42 $200 green .15 .15
209 A42 $250 ultra 3.00 .20
210 A42 $400 gray grn .15 .20
211 A42 $800 orange .15 .15
212 A42 $1600 gray .15 *.75*
213 A42 $2000 olive .15 *.35*
Nos. 206-213 (8) 4.05 2.10

Textile Plant, Harbin — A43

Lenin — A44

Designs: $200, Tangku Harbor. $250, Tienshui-Lanchow railroad bridge, Kansu Province. $400, Heavy machine-building plant, Taiyuan, Shansi. No. 218, Automatic blast, furnace, Anshan, Manchuria. No. 219, Fushun open-cut coal mine. $2000, Automatic power plant, Northeast. $3200, Prospecting in Tayeh district, Hupeh.

1954, May 1 **Engr.**

214 A43 $100 brown olive .25 .15
215 A43 $200 blue green .25 .15
216 A43 $250 violet .15 .15
217 A43 $400 black .25 .15
218 A43 $800 claret .15 .15
219 A43 $800 indigo .15 .15
220 A43 $2000 red .15 .15
221 A43 $3200 dark brown .40 .40
Nos. 214-221 (8) 1.75
Set value 1.30

Economic progress.

1954, June 30 **Engr.**

Designs: $400, Lenin and Stalin Monument, Gorki, horiz. $2000, Lenin proclaiming Soviet power.

222 A44 $400 deep green .45 .20
223 A44 $800 dark brown .20 .15
224 A44 $2000 deep carmine 1.75 .30
Nos. 222-224 (3) 2.40 .65

30th anniversary of the death of Lenin.

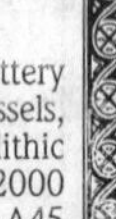

Pottery Vessels, Neolithic Period, 2000 B. C. — A45

Archeological Treasures: No. 226, Stone clime, Shang Dynasty, c. 1200 B.C. No. 227, Kuo Chi Tsu-pai bronze basin, Middle Chou Dynasty, 816 B.C. No. 228, Lacquered box and wine cup, Warring States Period, 403-221 B.C.

1954, Aug. 25

225 A45 $800 brown .50 .15
226 A45 $800 indigo .50 .15
227 A45 $800 Prus bl .50 .15
228 A45 $800 dk car .50 .15
Nos. 225-228 (4) 2.00 .60

"Glorious Mother Country," 5th series.

Pipe Production, Anshan Steel Mill — A46

Stalin Statue, by Tomsky — A47

Design: $800, Rolling mill, Anshan.

1954, Oct. 1

229 A46 $400 Prus green .55 .30
230 A46 $800 vio brown .55 .30

1954, Oct. 15

Designs: $800, Stalin portrait. $2000, Stalin viewing hydroelectric plant.

Size: 21x45mm

231 A47 $400 black 1.65 .30

Size: 26x37mm

232 A47 $800 black brn .35 .15

Size: 42x26mm

233 A47 $2000 dp red .35 .15
Nos. 231-233 (3) 2.35 .60

First anniversary of the death of Stalin.

Exhibition Building, Peking — A48

1954, Nov. 7

234 A48 $800 brown, *cream* 7.00 3.00
a. Size: 53½x24mm 10.00 3.00

Russian Economic and Cultural Exhibition, Peking. No. 234 measures 52½x24½mm.

Apprentices and Lathe — A49

Progress in Technology: $800, Heavy machinery and workers.

1954, Dec. 15

235 A49 $400 dk olive grn .25 .15
236 A49 $800 brt red .15 .15

Woman Worker Voting — A50

People Celebrating Opening of Congress — A51

1954, Dec. 30

237 A50 $400 deep claret .15 .15
238 A51 $800 bright red .65 .20
Set value .25

First National Congress.

Flags, Worker and Woman Holding Constitution — A52

1954, Dec. 30

239 A52 $400 brown, *buff* .30 .15
240 A52 $800 brt red, *yel* .30 .15

Adoption of Constitution.

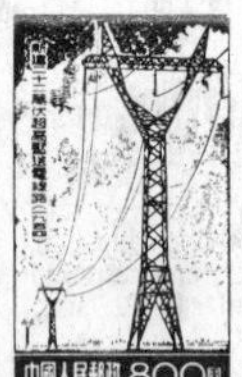
High-tension Pylon — A53

1955, Feb. 25

241 A53 $800 dk Prus bl .80 .20

Development of electric power.

Factory Health Workers and Red Cross — A54

1955, June 25 **Engr.; Cross Typo.**

242 A54 8f dp grn & red 7.00 1.00

50th anniversary of Chinese Red Cross.

Stalin and Mao in Kremlin A55

Soviet Specialist and Chinese Worker — A56

1955, July 25 **Engr.**

243 A55 8f brown red 6.00 .50
244 A56 20f olive blk 6.00 1.50

5th anniv. of Sino-Soviet Friendship Treaty.

Chang Heng (78-139), Astronomer — A57

Portraits of Scientists: No. 246, Tsu Chung-chih (429-500), mathematician. No. 247, Chang Sui (683-727), astronomer. No. 248, Li Shih-chen (1518-1593), physician and pharmacologist.

1955, Aug. 25 ***Perf. 14***

245 A57 8f sepia, *buff* 1.10 .30
a. Min. sheet, sepia, *white* 12.50 5.00
246 A57 8f dp grn, *buff* 1.10 .30
a. Min. sheet, deep green, *white* 12.50 5.00
247 A57 8f black, *buff* 1.10 .30
a. Min. sheet, blk, *white* 12.50 5.00
248 A57 8f claret, *buff* 1.10 .30
a. Min. sheet, claret, *white* 12.50 5.00
Nos. 245-248 (4) 4.40 1.20

Miniature sheets contain one imperf. stamp.

Steel Pouring Ladle A58

1955-56 **Litho.**

Position-in-set number in ( )

249 A58 8f shown (1) .50 .15
250 A58 8f High tension line (2) .50 .15
251 A58 8f Mechanized coal mining (3) .50 .15
252 A58 8f Tank cars and derricks (4) .50 .15
253 A58 8f Heavy machine shop (5) .50 .15
254 A58 8f Soldier on guard (6) .50 .15
255 A58 8f Spinning machine (7) .50 .15
256 A58 8f Workers discussing 5-year plan (8) .50 .15
257 A58 8f Combine harvester (9) .50 .15
258 A58 8f Milk production (10) .50 .15
259 A58 8f Dam (11) .50 .15
260 A58 8f Pottery industry (12) ('56) .50 .15
261 A58 8f Truck (13) .50 .15
262 A58 8f Ship at dock (14) .50 .15
263 A58 8f Geological survey (15) .50 .15
264 A58 8f Higher education (16) .50 .15
265 A58 8f Family (17) .50 .15
266 A58 8f Workers' rest home (18) ('56) .50 .15
Nos. 249-266 (18) 9.00
Set value 2.25

1st 5 Year Plan. Issued: #249-257, Oct. 1; #258-259, 261-265, Dec. 15; #260, 266, Feb. 24, 1956.

Lenin — A59

Engels — A60

1955, Dec. 15 **Engr.** ***Perf. 14***
267 A59 8f dk blue grn 6.00 .25
268 A59 20f dk rose car 6.00 2.25

85th anniversary of the birth of Lenin.

1955, Dec. 15
269 A60 8f deep orange 5.50 .25
270 A60 20f brown 5.50 2.25

135th anniversary of the birth of Friedrich Engels (1820-1895), German socialist.

Storming Lu Ting Bridge A61

Crossing Great Snow Mountains — A62

1955, Dec. 30
271 A61 8f dark red 4.75 .45
272 A62 8f dark blue 4.75 2.00

Long March of Chinese Communist army, 20th anniversary.

Miner A63

Gate of Heavenly Peace A64

Designs: 1f, Machinist. 2f, Airman. 2½f, Nurse. 4f, Soldier. 8f, Steel worker. 10f, Scientist. 20f, Farm woman. 50f, Sailor.

1955-56 **Litho.** ***Perf. 14***
273 A63 ½f orange brn 2.50 .25
274 A63 1f purple 2.50 .25
275 A63 2f green 2.50 .15
276 A63 2½f blue ('56) 2.50 .15
277 A63 4f gray olive 2.50 .25
278 A63 8f red org (Peking printing) 2.50 .95
a. Perf. 12½ (Shanghai printing) 140.00 8.00
279 A63 10f claret ('56) 21.00 .15
280 A63 20f dp blue 4.00 .15
281 A63 50f gray 4.00 .15
Nos. 273-281 (9) 44.00 2.45

Engr.
282 A64 $1 claret ('56) .95 .25
283 A64 $2 sepia ('55) 1.65 .25
284 A64 $5 indigo ('56) 2.75 .40
285 A64 $10 dp org ('56) 8.25 4.25
286 A64 $20 gray vio ('56) 14.00 17.00
Nos. 282-286 (5) 27.60 22.15

Nos. 282-286 are the 7th Gate Issue.

Trucks, Mountains, Highway Map — A65

Suspension Bridge over Tatu River — A66

Design: No. 289, First truck arriving in Lhasa, and the Potala.

1956, Mar. 10 **Engr.**
287 A65 4f dp blue .50 .15
288 A66 8f dk brown .50 .15
289 A65 8f carmine .50 .15
Nos. 287-289 (3) 1.50 .45

Completion of Sikang-Tibet and Chinghai-Tibet Highways.

Summer Palace and Marble Boat — A67

Famous Views of Imperial Peking: No. 291, Peihai Park with Jade Belt Marble Bridge. No. 292, Gate of Heavenly Peace. No. 293, Temple of Heaven. No. 294, Great Throne Hall, Forbidden City.

1956-57
290 A67 4f car rose (1) 1.50 .25
291 A67 4f bl grn (2) 1.50 .25
292 A67 8f red org (3) ('57) 1.50 .25
293 A67 8f Prus bl (4) 1.50 .25
294 A67 8f yel brn (5) 1.50 .25
Nos. 290-294 (5) 7.50 1.25

Issued: #292, Feb. 20, 1957; others, June 15, 1956.
No. 292 exists with sun rays in background.

Salt Making A68

Designs: No. 296, Dwelling of the Eastern Han period. No. 297, Duck hunting and harvesting. No. 298, Carriage crossing bridge.

1956, Oct. 1
295 A68 4f gray olive .25 .15
296 A68 4f slate blue .25 .15
297 A68 8f gray brown .25 .15
298 A68 8f sepia .25 .15
Nos. 295-298 (4) 1.00
Set value .50

Murals, Tung Han Dynasty, 250 B.C.-220 A.D., found near Chengtu.

Ancient Coins and "Save" — A69

1956, Oct. 1
299 A69 4f yellow brown 6.00 .70
300 A69 8f rose red 6.00 .70

Promotion of saving.

Gate of Heavenly Peace — A70

Sun Yat-sen — A71

1956, Nov. 10
301 A70 4f dk green 5.00 .50
302 A70 8f brt red 5.00 .50
303 A70 16f dk carmine 5.00 1.00
Nos. 301-303 (3) 15.00 2.00

8th National Congress of the Communist Party of China.

1956, Nov. 12
304 A71 4f brown, *cream* 6.00 .15
305 A71 8f dp blue, *cream* 6.00 1.40

90th anniversary of birth of Sun Yat-sen.

Weight Lifting — A72

1957, Mar. 20 **Litho.** ***Perf. 12½***
Hibiscus red and green; inscription brown
306 A72 4f Shot put (2) 1.00 .20
307 A72 4f shown (5) 1.00 .20
308 A72 8f Track (1) 1.00 .20
309 A72 8f Soccer (3) 1.00 .20
310 A72 8f Bicycling (4) 1.00 .20
Nos. 306-310 (5) 5.00 1.00

First National Workers' Sports Meeting.

Truck Factory No. 1, Changchun — A73

China's truck industry: 8f, Trucks rolling off assembly line.

1957, May 1 **Engr.** ***Perf. 14***
311 A73 4f light brown .35 .20
312 A73 8f slate green .35 .20

Nanchang Uprising — A74

Designs: No. 314, Mao and Chu Teh at Chingkanshan. No. 315, Crossing Yellow River. No. 316, Liberation of Nanking, Apr. 23, 1949.

1957
313 A74 4f blk vio (1) 4.00 .90
314 A74 4f slate grn (2) 4.00 1.50
315 A74 8f red brn (3) 4.00 .60
316 A74 8f dp blue (4) 4.00 .60
Nos. 313-316 (4) 16.00 3.60

30th anniversary of People's Liberation Army. Issue dates: Nos. 313, 315, Aug. 10; No. 314, Aug. 30; No. 316, Dec. 30.

Congress Emblem — A75

1957, Sept. 30
317 A75 8f chocolate 3.50 .45
318 A75 22f indigo 3.50 .75

4th Intl. Trade Union Cong., Leipzig, Oct. 4-15.

Yangtze River Bridge A76

Design: 20f, Road leading to and over bridge.

1957, Oct. 1
319 A76 8f scarlet .50 .25
320 A76 20f slate blue .50 .15

Completion of Yangtze River Bridge at Wuhan.

Fireworks over Kremlin — A77

Designs: 8f, Hammer and sickle over globe and broken chain. 20f, Stylized dove and olive branch. 22f, Hands of three races holding book with Marx and Lenin. 32f, Star and pylon.

1957, Nov. 7
321 A77 4f brt red 4.00 .40
322 A77 8f chocolate 4.00 .40
323 A77 20f dp green 4.00 .40
324 A77 22f red brown 4.00 .40
325 A77 32f dp blue 4.00 2.50
Nos. 321-325 (5) 20.00 4.10

40th anniv. of Russian October Revolution.

Map of Yellow River Basin A78

Designs: No. 327, Sanmen Gorge dam and powerhouse. No. 328, Ocean liner on Yellow River. No. 329, Dam, irrigation canals and tree-bordered fields.

1957, Dec. 30
326 A78 4f deep orange (1) 3.75 1.50
327 A78 4f deep blue (2) 3.75 1.90
328 A78 8f deep lake (3) 3.75 .75
329 A78 8f blue green (4) 3.75 .75
Nos. 326-329 (4) 15.00 4.90

Yellow River control plan.

Old Man and Young Drummer A79

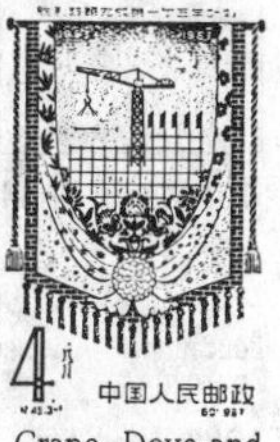

Crane, Dove and Flowers A80

1957, Dec. 30 **Litho.**
330 A79 8f shown (1) .60 .20
331 A79 8f Plowman (2) .60 .15
332 A79 8f Woman planting tree (3) .60 .15
333 A79 8f Harvest (4) .60 .15
Nos. 330-333 (4) 2.40
Set value .50

Agricultural cooperation.

1958, Jan. 30 **Engr.**

Designs (Congratulatory Banner and): 8f, Crane with hot ingots, cotton bolls and wheat. 16f, Train on bridge, ship and plane.

334 A80 4f emer, *cream* .30 .15
335 A80 8f red, *cream* .30 .25
336 A80 16f ultra, *cream* .30 .15
Nos. 334-336 (3) .90
Set value .45

Fulfillment of First Five-Year Plan.

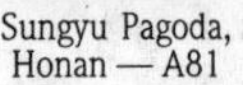

Sungyu Pagoda, Honan — A81

Trilobite, Kaoli — A82

Ancient Pagodas: No. 338, Chienhsun Pagoda, Yunnan. No. 339, Sakyamuni Pagoda, Shansi. No. 340, Flying Rainbow Pagoda, Shansi.

1958, Mar. 15 **Engr.**

337 A81 8f sepia (1) .90 .15
338 A81 8f Prus blue (2) .90 .15
339 A81 8f maroon (3) .90 .15
340 A81 8f dp green (4) .90 .25
Nos. 337-340 (4) 3.60 .70

1958, Apr. 15

Designs: 8f, Lufeng dinosaur. 16f, Choukoutien sino-megaceros.

341 A82 4f black .35 .15
342 A82 8f sepia .35 .25
343 A82 16f slate green .35 .15
Nos. 341-343 (3) 1.05 .55

Prehistoric animals of China.

Heroes Monument A83

1958, May 1

344 A83 8f scarlet 9.00 1.40
a. Souvenir sheet, imperf. 60.00 30.00

Unveiling of People's Heroes Monument, Peking. No. 344a issued May 30.

Karl Marx — A84

Cogwheels and Factories — A85

Design: 22f, Marx Speaking to German Workers' Educational Association, London, painting by Zhukow.

1958, May 5

345 A84 8f chocolate 6.00 1.00
346 A84 22f dk green 6.00 2.00

Karl Marx (1818-83), 140th birth anniv.

1958, May 25

347 A85 4f brt grnsh bl 5.00 *3.25*
348 A85 8f red lilac 5.00 .75

8th All-China Trade Union Cong., Peking.

Dove over Globe — A86

Mother and Child — A87

1958, June 1

349 A86 8f vio blue 5.00 .25
350 A86 20f blue grn 5.00 3.25

4th Congress of the Intl. Democratic Women's Federation, Vienna, June 1958.

1958, June 1 **Litho.**

Children's Day: No. 352, Watering sunflowers. No. 353, Playing hide-and-seek. No. 354, Sailing toy boat.

351 A87 8f green & multi (1) 5.00 1.00
352 A87 8f green & multi (2) 5.00 1.00
353 A87 8f green & multi (3) 5.00 1.00
354 A87 8f green & multi (4) 5.00 1.00
Nos. 351-354 (4) 20.00 4.00

Kuan Han-ching — A88

Designs (Operas): 4f, "Dream of Butterflies." 20f, "The Riverside Pavilion."

1958, June 20 **Engr.**

355 A88 4f indigo, *cr* 9.25 *2.25*
356 A88 8f brown, *cr* 9.25 .40
357 A88 20f black, *cr* 9.25 .60
a. Souvenir sheet of 3, *ivory* 140.00 70.00
Nos. 355-357 (3) 27.75 *3.25*

700th anniversary of publication of works of Kuan Han-ching (1210-1280), dramatist. No. 357a contains 3 imperf. stamps similar to Nos. 355-357. Size: 130x100mm. Issued June 28.

Planetarium A89

Design: 20f, Telescope and stars over Peking.

1958, June 25

358 A89 8f dk green 5.00 1.00
359 A89 20fr indigo 5.00 2.00

First Chinese planetarium, Peking.

Marx and Engels — A90

Wild Goose and Broadcasting Tower — A91

Design: 8f, Cover of first edition of the Communist Manifesto.

1958, July 1

360 A90 4f dk red vio 6.50 2.25
361 A90 8f Prus blue 6.50 .25

110th anniversary of publication of the Communist Manifesto.

1958, July 10

362 A91 4f ultra 5.00 .35
363 A91 8f dp green 5.00 1.10

1st Conference of the Ministers of Posts and Telecommunications of Socialist Countries, Moscow, Dec. 3-17, 1957.

Peony and Doves — A92

Bronze Weather Vane — A93

Designs: 8f, Olive branch with ribbon and clouds. 22f, Atomic energy symbol over factories.

1958, July 20

364 A92 4f red 7.50 1.00
365 A92 8f green 7.50 7.00
366 A92 22f red brown 7.50 3.00
Nos. 364-366 (3) 22.50 11.00

Congress for Disarmament and International Cooperation, Stockholm, July 17-22.

1958, Aug. 25

Designs: No. 368, Weather balloon. No. 369, Typhoon tower and weather map of Asia.

367 A93 8f yel bis & blk (1) .40 .15
368 A93 8f blue & blk (2) .40 .15
369 A93 8f brt grn & blk (3) .40 .15
Nos. 367-369 (3) 1.20 .45

Meteorological services in ancient and modern China.

"5" Encircling IUS Emblem — A94

1958, Sept. 4

370 A94 8f rose lilac 5.50 .40
371 A94 22f dp blue grn 5.50 1.10

5th Congress of the International Union of Students, Peking, Sept. 4-13.

Telegraph Building, Peking — A95

1958, Sept. 29

372 A95 4f greenish black 1.25 .20
373 A95 8f rose red 1.25 .20

Opening of Telegraph Building, Peking.

Exhibition Emblem and Exhortation — A96

Designs: No. 375, Dragon over clouds signifying "aiming high." No. 376, Flying horses, signifying "great leap forward" in production.

1958, Oct. 1

374 A96 8f slate grn (1) 4.50 .25
375 A96 8f rose car (2) 4.50 .25
376 A96 8f red brown (3) 4.50 1.00
Nos. 374-376 (3) 13.50 1.50

National Exhibition of Industry and Communications, Peking.

Worker and Excavator A97

Design: 8f, Completed dam and pylon.

1958, Oct. 25

377 A97 4f dk brown .55 .15
378 A97 8f dp Prus blue .65 .15

13 Ming Tombs Reservoir completion.

Sputnik over Armillary Sphere — A98

Designs: 8f, Sputnik 3 in orbit. 10f, Trajectories of 3 Sputniks over earth.

1958, Oct. 30

379 A98 4f scarlet 2.75 .35
380 A98 8f dp vio bl 2.75 .35
381 A98 10f dp grn 2.75 2.00
Nos. 379-381 (3) 8.25 2.70

Anniversary of first earth satellite launched by the USSR.

Chinese and North Korean Soldiers A99

Designs: No. 383, Chinese soldier embracing Korean woman. No. 384, Chinese girl presenting flowers to returning soldier.

1958, Nov. 20

382 A99 8f brt purple (1) .65 .25
383 A99 8f chestnut (2) .65 .15
384 A99 8f rose car (3) .65 .15
Nos. 382-384 (3) 1.95
Set value .50

Return of the Chinese Volunteers from Korea.

Forest and Mountains A100

Peony A101

Afforestation: No. 386, Mounted forest patrol. No. 387, Mechanized lumbering, horiz. No. 388, Tree-planting: "Turning the Country Green," horiz.

1958, Dec. 15

385 A100 8f dp blue grn (1) 2.00 .55
386 A100 8f slate grn (2) 2.00 .20
387 A100 8f dk purple (3) 2.00 .20
388 A100 8f indigo (4) 2.00 .35
Nos. 385-388 (4) 8.00 1.30

1958, Sept. 25 **Litho.**

Designs: 3f, Lotus. 5f, Chrysanthemums.

389 A101 1½f lilac rose 4.00 .30
390 A101 3f blue grn 4.00 .90
391 A101 5f dp orange 4.00 .15
Nos. 389-391 (3) 12.00 1.35

Atomic Reactor A102

1958, Dec. 30 **Engr.**

392 A102 8f shown 4.75 *3.00*
393 A102 20f Cyclotron 4.75 .50

Inauguration of China's first atomic reactor and cyclotron, Peking.

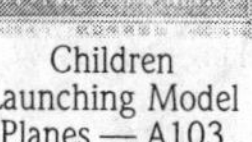

Children Launching Model Planes — A103

Camel Carrying Load — A104

Designs: 8f, Gliders over trees. 10f, Parachutists descending. 20f, Small monoplanes in mid-air.

1958, Dec. 30

394 A103 4f carmine .60 .20
395 A103 8f dp slate grn .60 .15
396 A103 10f dk brown .60 .15
397 A103 20f Prus blue .60 .15
Nos. 394-397 (4) 2.40
Set value .55

Sports-aviation publicity.

1959, Jan. 1

Designs: No. 399, Pomegranates. No. 400, Rooster. No. 401, Theatrical figure.

398 A104 8f vio & blk (1) 4.75 .15
399 A104 8f dp lil grn & blk (2) 4.75 .60
400 A104 8f red & blk (3) 4.75 .60
401 A104 8f dp bl & blk (4) 4.75 1.65
Nos. 398-401 (4) 19.00 3.00

Paper cut-outs (folk art).

Red Flag, Mao and Workers — A105

Women Workers and Atomic Model — A106

Designs: 8f, Traditional and modern blast furnaces. 10f, Steel works and workers.

1959

402 A105 4f brt red 5.00 .45
403 A105 8f lake 5.00 .45
404 A105 10f deep red 5.00 .45
Nos. 402-404 (3) 15.00 1.35

"Great Leap Forward" in steel production. Issue dates: 4f, 8f, Feb. 19; 10f, May 25.

1959, Mar. 8

Design: 22f, Chinese and Soviet women holding banners dated "3.8".

405 A106 8f emerald, *cr* .45 .30
406 A106 22f magenta, *cr* .45 .15

International Women's Day.

Natural History Museum — A107

1959, Apr. 1

407 A107 4f greenish blue .50 .15
408 A107 8f olive brown .50 .15
Set value .25

Opening of Museum of Natural History, Peking.

Wheat — A108

Designs on Chinese Flag: No. 410, Rice. No. 411, Cotton bolls. No. 412, Soybeans, rapeseed and peanuts.

1959, Apr. 25

409 A108 8f red (1) 1.65 .25
410 A108 8f red (2) 1.65 .25
411 A108 8f red (3) 1.65 .25
412 A108 8f red (4) 1.65 .25
a. Block of 4, #409-412 9.00 2.00

Successful harvest, 1958.

A109 A110

Designs: 4f, Marx, Lenin and workers. 8f, Black, yellow and white fists holding banner. 22f, Steel workers parading with banners dated "5.1."

1959, May 1

413 A109 4f ultra 6.00 .50
414 A109 8f red 6.00 .50
415 A109 22f emerald 6.00 .50
Nos. 413-415 (3) 18.00 1.50

International Labor Day.

1959, June 20

Design: 8f, Peking airport. 10f, Plane loading on runway.

416 A110 8f lilac & blk 7.25 .90
417 A110 10f ol gray & blk 7.25 .90

Opening of new Peking Airport.

Students with Marx-Lenin Banners A111

Design: 8f, Workers with banners of Mao.

1959, July 1 **Photo.** ***Perf. 11x11½***

418 A111 4f gray, red & dk brn 10.50 3.00
419 A111 8f bis, red & dk brn 10.50 3.00

40th anniv. of the May 4th students' uprising.

Frederick Joliot-Curie — A112

Design: 22f, Three races, dove and olive branch.

1959, July 25 **Engr.** ***Perf. 11½***

420 A112 8f violet brn 6.00 *3.50*
421 A112 22f dk violet 6.00 .15

10th anniv. of the World Peace Movement.

Stamp Printing Plant, Peking A113

1959, Aug. 15 ***Perf. 11x11½***

422 A113 8f dp blue grn 7.75 2.50

Sino-Czechoslovak cooperation in stamp production.

Table Tennis — A114

1959, Aug. 30 **Litho.** ***Perf. 14***

423 A114 4f black & blue 2.50 .45
424 A114 8f black & red 2.50 .30

25th World Table Tennis Championships, Dortmund, German Democratic Republic.

Soviet Space Rocket A115

Backyard Steel Production A116

1959, Sept. 10 **Photo.** ***Perf. 11½***

425 A115 8f Prus bl, red & blk 10.00 3.00

Launching of first Russian space rocket, Jan. 2, 1959.

1959, Sept. 25 **Engr.**

Designs: #426, Sun rising over "industry and agriculture." #428, Farming. #429, Trade. #430, Education. #431, Militia. #432, Communal dining. #433, Nursery. #434, Care for the aged. #435, Health services. #436, Flutist; culture and sports. #437, Flower symbolizing unity of industry, agriculture, trade, education and armed forces.
Position-in-set number in ( ).

426 A116 8f rose (1) .45 .15
427 A116 8f violet brn (2) .45 .15
428 A116 8f dp orange (3) .45 .15
429 A116 8f slate grn (4) .45 .15
430 A116 8f dp blue (5) .45 .15
431 A116 8f olive (6) .45 .15
432 A116 8f indigo (7) .45 .15
433 A116 8f lilac rose (8) .45 .15
434 A116 8f gray blk (9) .45 .15
435 A116 8f emerald (10) .45 .15
436 A116 8f dk violet (11) .45 .15
437 A116 8f red (12) .45 .15
Nos. 426-437 (12) 5.40 1.80

First anniversary of Peoples' Communes.

Mao and Gate of Heavenly Peace — A117

National Emblem — A118

Blast Furnaces — A119

Celebration at Gate of Heavenly Peace — A120

Mao Proclaiming Republic — A121

Designs: #439, Marx, Lenin and Kremlin. 22f, Dove over globe.

1959, Sept. 28 **Photo.** ***Perf. 11½x11***

With Gum

438 A117 8f lt brown & red 10.00 5.50
439 A117 8f dull blue & red 10.00 1.75
440 A117 22f blue grn & red 10.00 1.00
Nos. 438-440 (3) 30.00 8.25

1959, Oct. 1 **Litho.** ***Perf. 14***

441 A118 4f pale grn, red & gold 4.75 4.25
442 A118 8f gray, red & gold 4.75 .40
443 A118 10f lt blue, red & gold 4.75 .40
444 A118 20f pale brn, red & gold 4.75 2.50
Nos. 441-444 (4) 19.00 7.55

Engraved and Photogravure

1959, Oct. 1 ***Perf. 11½x11***

Designs: No. 446, Large coal mine. No. 447, Planer, Wuhan heavy machinery plant. No. 448, Wuhan Yangtze River Bridge. No. 449, Combine harvester. No. 450, Hsinankiang hydroelectric station. No. 451, Spinning machine. No. 452, Kirin chemical fertilizer plant.

With Gum

445 A119 8f brown & rose red (1) .90 .25
446 A119 8f brown & gray (2) .90 .25
447 A119 8f brown & yel brn (3) .90 .25
448 A119 8f brown & stl bl (4) .90 .25
449 A119 8f brown & org (5) .90 .25
450 A119 8f brown & ol (6) .90 .25
451 A119 8f brown & bl grn (7) .90 .25
452 A119 8f brown & vio (8) .90 .25
Nos. 445-452 (8) 7.20 2.00

1959, Oct. 1 **Litho.** ***Perf. 14***

Designs: 10f, Workers and factory, vert. 20f, People rejoicing, vert.

453 A120 8f cream & multi 3.00 .75
454 A120 10f cream & multi 3.00 .75
455 A120 20f cream & multi 3.00 .75
Nos. 453-455 (3) 9.00 2.25

1959, Oct. 1 **Engr.**

456 A121 20f deep carmine 18.00 9.00

Nos. 438-456 commemorate 10th anniversary of the Proclamation of the People's Republic of China.

A122

A123

Designs: No. 457, Pioneers' emblem. No. 458, Pioneer Bugler. No. 459, Schoolgirl. No. 460, Girl using rain gauge. No. 461, Boy planting tree. No. 462, Girl figure skater.

1959, Nov. 10 **Photo.** ***Perf. 11½***

457 A122 4f red yel & blk (1) 2.50 .30
458 A122 4f Prus bl & red (2) 2.50 .30
459 A122 8f brn & red (3) 2.50 .30
460 A122 8f dk bl & red (4) 2.50 .30
461 A122 8f red & grn (5) 2.50 .30
462 A122 8f mag & red (6) 2.50 .30
Nos. 457-462 (6) 15.00 1.80

10th anniversary of the Young Pioneers. Black inscription on No. 457 engraved.

1959, Dec. 1 **Engr.**

Designs: 4f, Exhibition emblem, communications symbols. 8f, Exhibition emblem and chimneys.

463 A123 4f dark blue .50 .15
464 A123 8f red .50 .15
Set value .25

Exhibition of Industry and Communications, Peking.

Palace of Nationalities A124

Engraved, Frame Lithographed

1959, Dec. 10 *Perf. 14*

465 A124 4f red & blk 2.75 .65
466 A124 8f brt grn & blk 2.75 .95

Inauguration of the Cultural Palace of Nationalities, Peking.

Athletes' Monument and Track — A125

Designs: No. 468, Parachuting. No. 469, Marksmanship. No. 470, Diving. No. 471, Table tennis. No. 472, Weight lifting. No. 473, High jump. No. 474, Rowing. No. 475, Track. No. 476, Basketball. No. 477, Traditional Chinese fencing. No. 478, Motorcycling. No. 479, Gymnastics. No. 480, Bicycling. No. 481, Horsemanship. No. 482, Soccer.

1959, Dec. 28 **Litho.**

467 A125 8f bis, blk & gray (1) 1.25 .20
468 A125 8f dl bl, blk & gray (2) 1.25 .30
469 A125 8f red brn & blk (3) 1.25 .20
470 A125 8f grn, blk & brn (4) 1.25 .20
471 A125 8f brt grn, blk, brn & gray (5) 1.25 .20
472 A125 8f gray, blk & brn (6) 1.25 .20
473 A125 8f dl bl, blk & brn (7) 1.25 .20
474 A125 8f Prus grn, blk & brn (8) 1.25 .20
475 A125 8f org, blk & brn (9) 1.25 .20
476 A125 8f dl vio, blk & brn (10) 1.25 .20
477 A125 8f lt ol, blk & brn (11) 1.25 .20
478 A125 8f bl, blk & gray (12) 1.25 .20
479 A125 8f gray bl, blk, grn, & bl (13) 1.25 .20
480 A125 8f gray, blk, brn, & vio (14) 1.25 .20
481 A125 8f red org, blk, brn, & gray (15) 1.25 .20
482 A125 8f lt gray, blk, brn, & red (16) 1.25 .20
Nos. 467-482 (16) 20.00 3.30

First National Sports Meeting, Peking.

Wheat and Main Pavilion A126

Designs (Pavilion and): 8f, Meteorological symbols. 10f, Domestic animals. 20f, Fish.

1960, Jan. 20 **Engr. & Litho.**

Cream Background

483 A126 4f black & org .60 .15
484 A126 8f black & dull bl .60 .15
485 A126 10f black & org brn .60 .15
486 A126 20f black & grnsh bl .60 .30
Nos. 483-486 (4) 2.40 .75

Opening of the National Agricultural Exhibition Halls, Peking.

With Gum

From No. 487 onward all stamps were issued with gum except as noted.

Catalogue values for unused stamps in this section, from this point to the end of the section, are for Never Hinged items.

Conference Hall, Tsunyi A127

Designs: 8f, Mao addressing conference. 10f, Crossing Chinsha River.

Engraved (4f, 10f); Photogravure (8f)

1960, Jan. 25 *Perf. 11x11½*

487 A127 4f violet & blue 8.75 .70
488 A127 8f red & multi 8.75 *4.00*
489 A127 10f slate green 8.75 1.40
Nos. 487-489 (3) 26.25 *6.10*

25th anniversary of the Communist Party Conference at Tsunyi.

Clara Zetkin (1857-1933) A128

Chinese and Russian Workers A129

Designs: 8f, Mother, child and dove. 10f, Woman tractor driver. 22f, Women of three races.

1960, Mar. 8 **Photo.** *Perf. 11½x11*

490 A128 4f black & multi 1.25 .55
491 A128 8f black & multi 1.25 .55
492 A128 10f black & multi 1.25 .55
493 A128 22f black & multi 1.25 .55
Nos. 490-493 (4) 5.00 2.20

50th anniv. of International Women's Day.

1960, Mar. 10

Designs: 8f, Chinese and Russian flags. 10f, Chinese and Russian soldiers.

494 A129 4f dk brown 8.75 1.50
495 A129 8f red, yel & blk 8.75 1.50
496 A129 10f dp blue 8.75 6.00
Nos. 494-496 (3) 26.25 9.00

10th anniv. of Sino-Soviet Treaty of Friendship. Black inscription engraved on No. 495.

Flags of Hungary and China A130

Design: 8f, Parliament Building, Budapest.

1960, Apr. 4 *Perf. 11x11½*

497 A130 8f yel, blk, red & grn 7.25 1.50
498 A130 8f blue, red & blk 7.25 5.50

15th anniv. of the liberation of Hungary.

Lenin Speaking — A131

Lunik 2, Earth and Russian Arms — A132

Designs: 8f, Portrait of Lenin. 20f, Lenin talking with Smolny Palace guard.

Engraved (4f, 20f); Engraved and Photogravure (8f)

1960, Apr. 22 *Perf. 11½x11*

499 A131 4f violet brn 9.00 1.40
500 A131 8f org red & blk 9.00 5.25
501 A131 20f dk brown 9.00 1.40
Nos. 499-501 (3) 27.00 8.05

90th anniversary of the birth of Lenin.

1960, Apr. 30 **Engr.** *Perf. 11½*

Design: 10f, Lunik 3 over earth.

502 A132 8f red 4.00 1.25
503 A132 10f green 4.00 1.25

Russian space flights.

Pioneers and Flags of Czechoslovakia and China — A133

View of Prague with Charles Bridge A134

Perf. 11½x11; 11x11½

1960, May 9 **Photo.**

504 A133 8f yellow & multi 6.50 3.00
505 A134 8f dp green 6.50 3.00

Liberation of Czechoslovakia, 15th anniv.

Nostril Bouquet A135

Designs: Various goldfish.

1960, June 1 *Perf. 11x11½*

506 A135 4f shown (1) 15.00 .85
507 A135 4f Black-back dragon eye (2) 15.00 .85
508 A135 4f Bubble eye (3) 15.00 .85
509 A135 4f Red tiger head (4) 15.00 .85
510 A135 8f Pearl scale (5) 15.00 .85
511 A135 8f Blue dragon eye (6) 15.00 .85
512 A135 8f Skyward eye (7) 15.00 .85
513 A135 8f Red cap (8) 15.00 .85
514 A135 8f Purple cap (9) 15.00 6.00
515 A135 8f Red head (10) 15.00 6.00
516 A135 8f Red and white dragon eye (11) 15.00 6.00
517 A135 8f Red dragon eye (12) 15.00 6.00
Nos. 506-517 (12) 180.00 30.80

Sow with Litter A136

Designs: No. 519, Pig being inoculated. No. 520, Pigs. No. 521, Pig and mechanized feeding. No. 522, Pig and bales.

1960, June 15

518 A136 8f red & blk (1) 9.00 1.00
519 A136 8f dp grn & blk (2) 9.00 1.00
520 A136 8f lil rose & blk (3) 9.00 1.00
521 A136 8f lt yel grn & blk (4) 9.00 1.00
522 A136 8f org & blk (5) 9.00 6.00
Nos. 518-522 (5) 45.00 10.00

Flag Inscribed "Serving the Workers" — A137

Flowers, Flags of North Korea and China — A138

Design: 8f, Inscribed stone seal.

1960, July 30 **Photo.** *Perf. 11½x11*

523 A137 4f lt grn, red, pink & brn 7.00 2.00

Photogravure & Engraved

524 A137 8f pale bl, red & bis 7.00 2.00

3rd Natl. Cong. for Literature and Arts, Peking.

1960, Aug. 15 **Photo.**

Design: 8f, Flying horse of Korea.

525 A138 8f red & multi 10.00 3.00
526 A138 8f ultra, red & ind 10.00 3.00

15th anniversary of the liberation of Korea.

Railroad Station, Peking — A139

Design: 10f, Train arriving at station.

1960, Aug. 30 *Perf. 11½*

527 A139 8f blue, cr & brn 10.00 3.25
528 A139 10f bluish grn, cr & ind 10.00 3.25

Opening of new Peking Railroad Station.

Girls and Flags of North Viet Nam and China A140

Lake of the Returning Sword, Hanoi A141

Worker and Fresh-air Installation A142

Perf. 11x11½, 11½x11

1960, Sept. 2

529 A140 8f red & multi 4.25 2.25
530 A141 8f red, gray grn & gray 4.25 1.40

15th anniversary of the Democratic Republic of North Viet Nam.

1960, Sept. 10 *Perf. 11½*

Designs: No. 532, Exterminator. No. 533, Window cleaning. No. 534, Medical examination of child. No. 535, Physical exercise.

531 A142 8f black & org (1) 1.25 .15
532 A142 8f indigo & sl (2) 1.25 .25
533 A142 8f brown & bl (3) 1.25 .30
534 A142 8f maroon & ocher (4) 1.25 .45
535 A142 8f indigo & brt grn (5) 1.25 .35
Nos. 531-535 (5) 6.25 1.50

National health campaign.

Great Hall of the People — A143

Design: 10f, Inside view.

1960, Oct. 1

536 A143 8f yellow & multi 10.00 3.75
537 A143 10f brown & multi 10.00 3.75

Completion of the Great Hall of the People, Peking.

Dr. Norman Bethune — A144

Engels Addressing Congress at The Hague — A145

Design: No. 539, Dr. Bethune operating on a soldier.

Photo. (No. 538); Engr. (No. 539)

1960, Nov. 20 *Perf. 11½x11*

538 A144 8f red & multi 3.00 .65
539 A144 8f sepia 3.00 .65

Dr. Norman Bethune (1890-1939), Canadian surgeon with 8th Army.

Engr. (8f); Photo. (10f)

1960, Nov. 28

Designs: 10f, Portrait of Engels.

540 A145 8f brown 8.00 3.00
541 A145 10f blue & multi 8.00 3.00

140th anniversary of the birth of Friedrich Engels (1820-1895), German Socialist.

"Hwang Shi Ba" A146

Freighter A147

1960-61 **Photo.**

Various Chrysanthemums in Natural Colors

542 A146 4f bl gray (1) 10.00 3.00
543 A146 4f pink (2) 10.00 3.00
544 A146 8f dk gray (3) 10.00 3.00
545 A146 8f dp blue (4) 10.00 3.00
546 A146 8f green (5) 10.00 3.00
547 A146 8f magenta (6) 10.00 3.00
548 A146 8f olive (7) 10.00 3.00
549 A146 8f grnsh bl (8) 10.00 3.00
550 A146 10f gray (9) 10.00 3.00
551 A146 10f choc (10) 10.00 3.00
552 A146 20f dp blue (11) 10.00 3.00
553 A146 20f brt red (12) 10.00 3.00
554 A146 22f olive bis (13) 10.00 3.00
555 A146 22f carmine (14) 10.00 3.00
556 A146 30f grnsh gray (15) 10.00 3.00
557 A146 30f brt pink (16) 10.00 3.00
558 A146 35f dp green (17) 10.00 3.00
559 A146 52f brt lilac rose (18) 10.00 3.00
Nos. 542-559 (18) 180.00 54.00

Issue dates: Nos. 548-550, 557-559, Dec. 10, 1960; Nos. 545-547, 554-556, Jan. 18, 1961; Nos. 542-544, Feb. 24, 1961.

1960, Dec. 15 *Perf. 11½*

Without Gum

560 A147 8f deep blue 4.25 2.00

1st 10,000-ton Chinese-built freighter, launching.

Pantheon, Paris — A148

Design: 8f, Proclamation of the Commune.

Engraved and Photogravure

1961, Mar. 18 *Perf. 11½x11*

561 A148 8f gray blk & red 6.25 1.25
562 A148 8f brown & red 6.25 1.25

90th anniversary of the Paris Commune.

Championship Symbol and Jasmine — A149

Designs: 10f, Table tennis racket and ball; Temple of Heaven. 20f, Table tennis match. 22f, Peking workers' gymnasium.

1961, Apr. 5 **Photo.** *Perf. 11*

563 A149 8f multicolored 1.25 .30
564 A149 10f multicolored 1.25 .20
565 A149 20f multicolored 1.25 .20
566 A149 22f multicolored 1.25 .50
a. Souvenir sheet of 4, #563-566 *500.00 250.00*
Nos. 563-566 (4) 5.00 1.20

26th World Table Tennis Championships, Peking.

Jeme Tien-yow — A150

Design: 10f, Train and tunnel, Peking-Changchow Railroad.

1961, June 20 *Perf. 11½x11*

567 A150 8f ol grn & blk 2.75 .75
568 A150 10f org brn & brn 2.75 .75

Centenary of the birth of Jeme Tien-yow, railroad construction engineer.

Congress Building, Shanghai — A151

Designs: 8f, August 1st Building, Nanchang. 10f, Provisional Central Government Office, Juikin. 20f, Pagoda Hill, Yenan. 30f, Gate of Heavenly Peace, Peking.

1961, July 1 *Perf. 11½*

569 A151 4f gold, red & cl 11.00 1.00
570 A151 8f gold, red & bl grn 11.00 1.00
571 A151 10f gold, red & yel brn 11.00 2.25
572 A151 20f gold, red & ultra 11.00 1.00
573 A151 30f gold, red & org red 11.00 1.25
Nos. 569-573 (5) 55.00 6.50

40th anniv. of the Chinese Communist Party.

August 1 Building, Nanchang — A152

Designs: 3f, 4f, 5f, Trees and Sha Cho Pa Building, Juikin. 8f, 10f, 20f, Pagoda Hill, Yenan. 22f, 30f, 50f, Gate of Heavenly Peace, Peking.

1961-62 **Engr.** *Perf. 11*

Without Gum

Size: 24x16mm

574 A152 1f vio blue 5.25 1.25
575 A152 1½f maroon 5.25 .25
576 A152 2f indigo 5.25 1.25
577 A152 3f dull vio 5.25 .25
578 A152 4f green 5.25 .25
579 A152 5f gray 5.25 1.25
580 A152 8f sepia 5.25 .25
581 A152 10f brt lil rose 5.25 .25
582 A152 20f grnsh bl 5.25 .25
583 A152 22f brown 5.25 .25
584 A152 30f blue 5.25 .25
585 A152 50f vermilion 5.25 .25
Nos. 574-585 (12) 63.00 6.00

Issue dates: 1f, 1½f, 5f, July 20, 1962; others July 20, 1961.

See Nos. 647-654, 1059-1064.

Flowers, Flags of Mongolia and China A153

Design: 10f, Parliament, Ulan Bator, and statue of Sukhe Bator.

1961, July 11 **Photo.** *Perf. 11x11½*

586 A153 8f crimson, ultra & yel 11.00 .90
587 A153 10f orange, blk & yel 11.00 4.75

40th anniv. of the Mongolian People's Republic.

Military Museum — A154

Photo. & Engr.

1961, Aug. 1 *Perf. 11½*

588 A154 8f gray bl, brn & grn 12.00 2.75
589 A154 10f gray, blk & grn 12.00 .30

Opening of the People's Revolutionary Military Museum.

Uprising at Wuchang A155

Sun Yat-sen — A156

Perf. 11x11½, 11½x11

1961, Oct. 10 **Photo.**

590 A155 8f gray & blk 10.00 *3.25*
591 A156 10f tan & black 10.00 .35

50th anniversary of the 1911 Revolution.

Donkey — A157

Rejoicing Tibetans — A158

Designs: 8f, 10f, 20f, 22f, Horses; 30f, 50f, Camels. Ceramic statuettes from Tang Dynasty (618-906) graves.

1961, Nov. 10 *Perf. 11½x11*

Statuettes in Original Colors

592 A157 4f dull blue 7.00 1.75
593 A157 8f gray green 7.00 1.75
594 A157 8f dp purple 7.00 1.75
595 A157 10f dp blue 7.00 1.65
596 A157 20f olive 7.00 1.75
597 A157 22f blue grn 7.00 .75
598 A157 30f red brown 7.00 1.75
599 A157 50f slate 7.00 1.75
Nos. 592-599 (8) 56.00 12.90

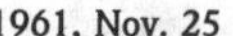

1961, Nov. 25

Designs: 8f, Woman sower. 10f, Celebration of bumper crop. 20f, People's representatives. 30f, Tibetan children.

600 A158 4f brn & ocher 13.00 .15
601 A158 8f brn & lt bl grn 13.00 .50
602 A158 10f brn & yel 13.00 .15
603 A158 20f brn & rose 13.00 5.00
604 A158 30f brn & bluish gray 13.00 5.00
Nos. 600-604 (5) 65.00 10.80

Rebirth of the Tibetan people.

Lu Hsun — A159

1962, Feb. 26

605 A159 8f red brown & blk 1.00 .25

80th anniv. of the birth of Lu Hsun, writer.

An Chi Bridge, Chao Hsien — A160

Bridges of Ancient China: 8f, Pao Tai, Soochow. 10f, Chu Pu, Kwan Hsien. 20f, Chen Yang, San Kiang.

1962, May 15 *Perf. 11*

606 A160 4f dk gray blue 1.40 .25
607 A160 8f dp green 1.40 .25
608 A160 10f brown 1.40 .15
609 A160 20f grnsh blue 1.40 1.40
Nos. 606-609 (4) 5.60 2.05

Tu Fu — A161

Cranes and Bamboo — A162

Design: 4f, Tu Fu memorial pavilion, Chengtu.

1962, May 25 *Perf. 11½x11*

610 A161 4f ol bis & blk 10.50 .75
611 A161 8f grnsh bl & blk 10.50 1.50

Poet Tu Fu, 1,250th anniversary of birth.

1962, June 10

Designs: 10f, Two cranes in flight. 20f, Crane on rock.

612 A162 8f tan & multi 13.00 3.50
613 A162 10f blue & multi 13.00 2.25
614 A162 20f bister & multi 13.00 2.25
Nos. 612-614 (3) 39.00 10.00

"The Sacred Crane," from paintings by Chen Chi-fo.

Cuban Soldier and Flag — A163

Designs: 10f, Sugar cane worker. 22f, Militiaman and woman.

1962, July 10 *Perf. 11x11½*

615 A163 8f car, rose & blk 25.00 2.00
616 A163 10f green & blk 25.00 .70
617 A163 22f ultra & blk 25.00 12.50
Nos. 615-617 (3) 75.00 15.20

Support of Cuba.

Torch and Map of Algeria — A164

Mei Lan-fang — A165

Design: 22f, Algerian soldiers and flag.

1962, July 10 *Perf. 11½x11*

618 A164 8f dp brown & red org 1.00 .70
619 A164 22f ocher & dp brn 1.00 1.10

Support of Algeria.

1962 *Perf. 11½x11, 11x11½*

Designs (Mei Lan-fang in Women's Roles): No. 621, Beating drum. No. 622, With fan. 10f, Lady Yu with swords. 20f, With bag. 22f, Heavenly Maiden, horiz. 30f, With spinning wheel, horiz. 50f, Kneeling, horiz. $3, Scene from opera "Drunken Beauty."

620 A165 4f tan & multi 32.50 4.00
621 A165 8f tan & multi 32.50 4.00
622 A165 8f gray & multi 32.50 .40
623 A165 10f gray & multi 32.50 4.00
624 A165 20f lt green & multi 32.50 2.00
625 A165 22f cream & multi 32.50 15.00
626 A165 30f lt blue & multi 32.50 19.00
627 A165 50f buff & multi 32.50 22.50
Nos. 620-627 (8) 260.00 70.90

Souvenir Sheet

Perf. 11

628 A165 $3 brown & multi *1,600. 600.00*

Stage art of Mei Lan-fang, actor.
Issue dates: 4f, 8f, 10f, Aug. 8; $3, Sept. 15; others Sept. 1.
Nos. 620-627 exist imperf. Value, set $1,400.
No. 628 contains one 48x58mm stamp and almost always has some faults.

Flower Drum Dance, Han — A166

Folk Dances: 8f, Ordos, Mongolia. 10f, Catching shrimp, Chuang. 20f, Friend, Yi. 30f, Fiddle dance, Tibet. 50f, Tambourine dance, Uighur.
Cumulative numbers 246-251 at lower right.

1962, Oct. 15 **Litho.** *Perf. 12½*

Without Gum

629 A166 4f cream & multi 1.00 .15
630 A166 8f cream & multi 1.00 .15
631 A166 10f cream & multi 1.00 .20
632 A166 20f cream & multi 1.00 .50
633 A166 30f cream & multi 1.00 .45
634 A166 50f cream & multi 1.00 .55
Nos. 629-634 (6) 6.00 2.00

See Nos. 696-707.

Soldiers Storming Winter Palace — A167

Design: 8f, Lenin leading soldiers, vert.

1962, Nov. 7 **Photo.** *Perf. 11½*

635 A167 8f black & red 12.50 .80
636 A167 20f slate grn & red 12.50 2.75

45th anniversary of the Russian Revolution.

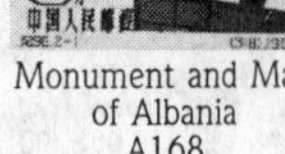
Monument and Map of Albania A168

Tsai Lun, Inventor of Papermaking A169

Design: 10f, Albanian flag and Girl Pioneer.

1962, Nov. 28 *Perf. 11½x11*

637 A168 8f Prus blue & sepia 1.25 .30
638 A168 10f red, yel, & blk 1.25 .30

50th anniversary of Albanian independence.

1962, Dec. 1 *Perf. 11½x11*

Designs: No. 640, Paper making. No. 641, Sun Szu-miao, physician. No. 642, Writing medical treatise. No. 643, Shen Ko, geologist. No. 644, Making field notes. No. 645, Kuo Shou-chin, astronomer. No. 646, Astronomical instrument.
Cumulative numbers 297-304 at lower right.

639 A169 4f multicolored 3.50 .50
640 A169 4f multicolored 3.50 .25
641 A169 8f multicolored 3.50 .25
642 A169 8f multicolored 3.50 .50
643 A169 10f multicolored 3.50 .25
644 A169 10f multicolored 3.50 .55
645 A169 20f multicolored 3.50 .55
646 A169 20f multicolored 3.50 .55
Nos. 639-646 (8) 28.00 3.40

Scientists of ancient China.

Building Type of 1961

Designs: 1f, 2f, Building, Nanchang. 3f, 4f, Trees and Sha Cho Pa Building. 8f, 10f, 20f, Pagoda Hill, Yenan. 30f, Gate of Heavenly Peace, Peking.

1962, Jan. **Litho.** ***Rough Perf. 12½***

Size: 21x16mm

Without Gum

647 A152 1f ultra .95 .20
648 A152 2f greenish gray .95 .20
649 A152 3f violet gray .95 .20
650 A152 4f green .95 .20
651 A152 8f dk olive, perf. 14 .95 .20
b. Perf. 11x11½ 5.00
652 A152 10f brt rose lilac .95 .20
653 A152 20f slate blue .95 .20
654 A152 30f dull blue .95 .20
Nos. 647-654 (8) 7.60 1.60

Tank Monument, Havana A170

Crowd in Havana — A171

Designs: No. 656, Cuban revolutionaries. No. 658, Crowd in Peking. No. 659, Cuban soldier. No. 660, Castro and Cuban flag.

Perf. 11½, 11x11½

1963, Jan. 1 **Photo.**

655 A170 4f red & blk brn 20.00 .15
656 A170 4f green & blk 20.00 .15
657 A171 8f dull red & brn 20.00 1.10
658 A171 8f dull red & brn 20.00 .20
659 A170 10f ocher & blk 20.00 4.50
660 A170 10f red, blue & blk 20.00 *15.00*
Nos. 655-660 (6) 120.00 *21.10*

4th anniversary of the Cuban revolution.

Green Dragontail A172

Karl Marx A173

1963 **Without Gum** *Perf. 11*

661 A172 4f Tibetan clouded yellow (1) 7.00 .80
662 A172 4f Tritailed glory (2) 7.00 .80
663 A172 4f Neumogeni jungle queen (3) 7.00 .80
664 A172 4f Washan swordtail (4) 7.00 1.75
665 A172 4f Striped ringlet (5) 7.00 .80
666 A172 8f shown (6) 7.00 .45
667 A172 8f Dilunulated peacock (7) 7.00 .80
668 A172 8f Yamfly (8) 7.00 .35
669 A172 8f Golden kaiser-i-hind (9) 7.00 .35
670 A172 8f Mushaell hairstreak (10) 7.00 .35
671 A172 10f Yellow orange-tip (11) 7.00 .35
672 A172 10f Great jay (12) 7.00 .45
673 A172 10f Striped punch (13) 7.00 .35
674 A172 10f Hainan violet-beak (14) 7.00 .35
675 A172 10f Omeiskipper (15) 7.00 .35
676 A172 20f Philippines birdwing (16) 7.00 .80
677 A172 20f Richtofenis red apollo (17) 7.00 .80
678 A172 22f Blue-banded king crow (18) 7.00 1.00
679 A172 30f Solskyi copper (19) 7.00 2.50
680 A172 50f Yunnan clipper (20) 7.00 6.00
Nos. 661-680 (20) 140.00 20.20

Issue dates: Nos. 666-675, July 15; others Apr. 5.

1963, May 5 *Perf. 11½*

Designs: No. 682, "Workers of the World, Unite" on cover of first edition of Communist Manifesto. No. 683, Marx and Engels.

Without Gum

681 A173 8f black, gold & sal (1) 7.50 2.25
682 A173 8f gold & red (2) 7.50 2.25
683 A173 8f gold & choc (3) 7.50 2.25
Nos. 681-683 (3) 22.50 6.75

145th anniversary of birth of Karl Marx (1818-1883), German political philosopher.

Child with Top — A174

Designs (Child): No. 685, eating berries. No. 686, as traffic policeman. No. 687, with windmill. No. 688, listening to caged cricket. No. 689, with sword. No. 690, embroidering. No. 691, with umbrella. No. 692, playing with sand. No. 693, playing table tennis. No. 694, learning to add. No. 695, with kite.

1963, June 1 **Litho.** *Perf. 12½*

Without Gum

Multicolored Designs

684 A174 4f grnsh gray (1) 1.00 .15
685 A174 4f tan (2) 1.00 .15
686 A174 8f gray (3) 1.00 .15
687 A174 8f blue (4) 1.00 .15
688 A174 8f tan (5) 1.00 .15
689 A174 8f dp gray (6) 1.00 .15
690 A174 8f citron (7) 1.00 .15
691 A174 8f gray (8) 1.00 .15
692 A174 10f green (9) 1.00 .25
693 A174 10f violet (10) 1.00 .25
694 A174 20f bister (11) 1.00 .80
695 A174 20f green (12) 1.00 .80
Nos. 684-695 (12) 12.00
Set value 3.00

Children's Day. Value, imperf set $100.

Dance Type of 1962

Folk Dances: 4f, Weavers' dance, Puyi. 8f, Kazakh. 10f, Olunchun. 20f, Labor dance, Kaochan. 30f, Reed pipe dance, Miao. 50f, Fan dance, Korea.
Cumulative numbers 261-266 at lower right.

1963, June 15 *Perf. 12½*

Without Gum

696 A166 4f cream & multi .90 .15
697 A166 8f cream & multi .90 .15
698 A166 10f cream & multi .90 .25
699 A166 20f cream & multi .90 .55
700 A166 30f cream & multi .90 .60
701 A166 50f cream & multi .90 .90
Nos. 696-701 (6) 5.40 2.60

1963, June 30 **Without Gum**

Folk Dances: 4f, "Wedding Ceremony," Yu. 8f, "Encircling Mountain Forest," Pai. 10f, Long drum dance, Yao. 20f, Third day of the third month dance, Li. 30f, Knife dance, Kawa. 50f, Peacock dance, Thai.
Cumulative numbers 279-284 at lower right.

702 A166 4f cream & multi 1.10 .15
703 A166 8f cream & multi 1.10 .15
704 A166 10f cream & multi 1.10 .20
705 A166 20f cream & multi 1.10 .65
706 A166 30f cream & multi 1.10 .65
707 A166 50f cream & multi 1.10 .90
Nos. 702-707 (6) 6.60 2.70

Giant Panda Eating Apples — A175

Table Tennis Player — A176

Designs: No. 709, Giant panda eating bamboo shoots. 10f, Two pandas, horiz.

1963, Aug. 5 **Photo.** *Perf. 11½x11*

Size: 28x38mm

708 A175 8f pale blue & blk 22.50 .70
709 A175 8f pale blue & blk 22.50 6.00

Size: 50x29mm

Perf. 11½

710 A175 10f olive & blk 22.50 .70
Nos. 708-710 (3) 67.50 7.40

Value, imperf set $125.

1963, Sept. 10 **Engr.** *Perf. 11½*

Design: No. 712, Trophies won by Chinese team.

711 A176 8f dk olive grn 10.50 3.25
712 A176 8f brown 10.50 .25

27th World Table Tennis Championships.

Snub-nosed Langur — A177

Jade-green Screen Mountain — A178

Designs: 10f, Two monkeys playing. 22f, Two monkeys grooming.

1963, Sept. 23 Photo. *Perf. 11½x11*

713 A177 8f gray & multi 10.00 .40
714 A177 10f gray & multi 10.00 .40
715 A177 22f gray & multi 10.00 6.75
Nos. 713-715 (3) 30.00 7.55

Value, imperf set $80.

Engraved and Photogravure

1963, Oct. 15 *Perf. 11½*

Hwang Shan Landscapes (Yellow Mountains), Anhwei Province. #724-731 horiz.

716 A178 4f shown (1) 16.00 3.00
717 A178 4f "Guests Welcoming Pines" (2) 16.00 3.00
718 A178 4f Pines and Rock Behind the Sea (3) 16.00 3.00
719 A178 4f Terrace of Keeping Cool (4) 16.00 3.00
720 A178 8f Mount of Heavenly Capital (5) 16.00 3.00
721 A178 8f Mount of Scissors (6) 16.00 3.00
722 A178 8f Forest of Ten Thousand Pines (7) 16.00 3.00
723 A178 8f "Brush Blooming in Dream" (8) 16.00 3.00
724 A178 10f Mount of Lotus Flower (9) 16.00 3.00
725 A178 10f Cumulus Cloud over West Sea (10) 16.00 3.00
726 A178 10f Old Pines of Hwang Shan (11) 16.00 3.00
727 A178 10f "Watching the Clouds over West Sea" (12) 16.00 3.00
728 A178 20f Mount of Stalagmites (13) 16.00 3.00
729 A178 22f "Stone Monkey Watching the Sea" (14) 16.00 3.00
730 A178 30f Forest of Lions (15) 16.00 *15.00*
731 A178 50f Three Fairy Tales of Pen Lai (16) 16.00 3.00
Nos. 716-731 (16) 256.00 *60.00*

Soccer Player — A179

Athletes and Banners — A180

Designs: No. 733, Discus, women's. No. 734, Diving, men's. No. 735, Gymnastics, women's.

Engraved and Photogravure

1963, Nov. 17 *Perf. 11*

732 A179 8f gray, red & blk (1) 9.00 1.00
733 A179 8f gray, ultra & blk (2) 9.00 1.00
734 A179 8f lt grn, brn & blk (3) 9.00 1.00
735 A179 8f gray, lil rose & blk (4) 9.00 1.00

Photo. *Perf. 11½*

736 A180 10f red & multi (5) 9.00 2.25
Nos. 732-736 (5) 45.00 6.25

Games of the Newly Emerging Forces, Djakarta.

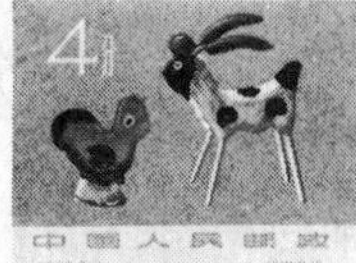
Clay Rooster and Goat — A181

Chinese Folk Toys: No. 738, Cloth camel. No. 739, Cloth tigers. No. 740, Clay ox and rider. No. 741, Cloth rabbit, wooden doll, clay roosters. No. 742, Straw rooster. No. 743, Cloth donkey and bird. No. 744, Clay lion. No. 745, Cloth tiger and tumbler doll.

1963, Dec. 10 Litho. *Perf. 11½*

Toys Multicolored; Without Gum

737 A181 4f bister (1) .55 .15
738 A181 4f gray (4) .55 .15
739 A181 4f lt blue (7) .55 .15
740 A181 8f bister (2) .55 .15
741 A181 8f gray (5) .55 .15
742 A181 8f lt blue (8) .55 .15
743 A181 10f bister (3) .55 .15
744 A181 10f gray (6) .55 .15
745 A181 10f lt blue (9) .55 .15
Nos. 737-745 (9) 4.95 1.35

Armed Vietnamese Family — A182

Flags of Cuba and China — A183

Liberation of South Viet Nam: No. 747, Militia with Vietnamese flag.

1963, Dec. 20 Photo. *Perf. 11½x11*

746 A182 8f tan, blk & red 2.50 1.50
747 A182 8f red & multi 2.50 2.00

1964, Jan. 1

Design: No. 749, Boy waving Cuban flag.

748 A183 8f red, yel, bl & ind 11.00 .65
749 A183 8f multicolored 11.00 3.25

5th anniversary of the liberation of Cuba.

Woman Driving Tractor — A184

Woman of the People's Commune: No. 751, harvesting. No. 752, picking cotton. No. 753, picking fruit. No. 754, reading book. No. 755, on guard duty.

1964, Mar. 8

750 A184 8f ol, pink & brn (1) .75 .25
751 A184 8f brn yel & org (2) .75 .25
752 A184 8f gray & multi (3) .75 .25
753 A184 8f black, org & bl (4) .75 .25
754 A184 8f green & multi (5) .75 .25
755 A184 8f lilac & multi (6) .75 .25
Nos. 750-755 (6) 4.50 1.50

Chinese and African Men — A185

Design: No. 757, African drummer.

1964, Apr. 12 Photo. *Perf. 11*

756 A185 8f red & multi .85 .25
757 A185 8f black & dk brn .85 .25

African Freedom Day.

Marx, Engels, Lenin and Stalin — A186

Design: No. 759, Banners and workers.

1964, May 1 *Perf. 11½*

758 A186 8f gold, red & blk 11.00 *4.50*
759 A186 8f gold, red & blk 11.00 *4.50*

Labor Day.

Orchard, Yenan — A187

Yenan, Shrine of the Chinese Revolution: No. 761, Central Auditorium, Yang Chia Ling. No. 762, Mao's office and residence. No. 763, Auditorium, Wang Chia Ping. No. 764, Border Region Assembly Hall. No. 765, Pagoda Hill and Bridge.

1964, July 1 Photo. *Perf. 11x11½*

760 A187 8f multicolored (1) 5.75 .70
761 A187 8f multicolored (2) 5.75 .70
762 A187 8f multicolored (3) 5.75 .70
763 A187 8f multicolored (4) 5.75 .70
764 A187 8f multicolored (5) 5.75 .70
765 A187 52f multicolored (6) 5.75 3.00
Nos. 760-765 (6) 34.50 6.50

Map and Flag of Viet Nam — A188

Alchemist's Glowing Crucible — A189

1964, July 20 *Perf. 11½*

766 A188 8f multicolored 15.00 3.00

Victory in South Viet Nam.

1964, Aug. 5 *Perf. 11½x11*

767 A189 4f shown (1) 9.00 .50
768 A189 4f Night-shining jade (2) 9.00 .50
769 A189 8f Purple Kuo's cap (3) 9.00 .25
770 A189 8f Chao pink (4) 9.00 .25
771 A189 8f Yao yellow (5) 9.00 .50
772 A189 8f Twin beauty (6) 9.00 .25
773 A189 8f Ice-veiled ruby (7) 9.00 .25
774 A189 10f Gold-sprinkled Chinese ink (8) 9.00 .35
775 A189 10f Cinnabar jar (9) 9.00 .35
776 A189 10f Lan Tien jade (10) 9.00 .25
777 A189 10f Imperial robe yellow (11) 9.00 .35
778 A189 10f Hu red (12) 9.00 .35
779 A189 20f Pea green (13) 9.00 9.00
780 A189 43f Wei purple (14) 9.00 9.00
781 A189 52f Intoxicated celestial peach (15) 9.00 9.00
Nos. 767-781 (15) 135.00 31.15

Souvenir Sheet

Perf. 11½

Without Gum

782 A189 $2 Glorious crimson & great gold pink *700.00 300.00*

No. 782 contains one 48x59mm stamp.

Wine Cup — A190

Grain Harvest — A191

Designs: Sacrificial bronze vessels of Yin dynasty, prior to 1050 B.C.

Engraved and Photogravure

1964, Aug. 25 *Perf. 11½x11*

783 A190 4f shown (1) 5.00 1.75
784 A190 4f Ku beaker (2) 5.00 1.75
785 A190 8f Kuang wine urn (3) 5.00 .25
786 A190 8f Chia wine cup (4) 5.00 .25
787 A190 10f Tsun wine vessel (5) 5.00 .30
788 A190 10f Yu wine urn (6) 5.00 .30
789 A190 20f Tsun wine vessel (7) 5.00 .55
790 A190 20f Ceremonial cauldron (8) 5.00 .55
Nos. 783-790 (8) 40.00 5.70

1964, Sept. 26 Photo.

Designs: #792, Students planting trees. #793, Study period. #794, Scientific experimentation.

791 A191 8f multicolored (1) 1.00 .25
792 A191 8f multicolored (2) 1.00 .25
793 A191 8f multicolored (3) 1.00 .25
794 A191 8f multicolored (4) 1.00 .25
Nos. 791-794 (4) 4.00 1.00

Youth helping in agriculture.

Marx, Engels, Trafalgar Square, London — A192

People with Banners — A193

1964, Sept. 28 *Perf. 11½*

795 A192 8f red, gold & red brn 25.00 18.00

Centenary of the First International.

1964, Oct. 1

Designs: No. 797, Gate of Heavenly Peace and Chinese flag. No. 798, People with banners, facing left.

796 A193 8f cream & multi (1) 16.00 1.75
797 A193 8f cream & multi (2) 16.00 1.75
798 A193 8f cream & multi (3) 16.00 1.75
a. Souvenir sheet of 3 *1,400. 475.00*
b. Strip of 3, #796-798 72.50 9.00
Nos. 796-798 (3) 48.00 5.25

15th anniv. of the People's Republic.

No. 798a contains No. 798b in continuous design without separating perfs. No. 798a almost always has some faults.

Oil Derricks — A194

Oil industry: 4f, Geological surveyors and truck, horiz. 8f, "Christmas tree" and extraction accessories. 10f, Oil refinery. 20f, Tank cars, horiz.

1964, Oct. 1

799 A194 4f lt blue & multi 24.00 .15
800 A194 8f lt blue & multi 24.00 .15
801 A194 8f lilac & multi 24.00 .20
802 A194 10f slate & multi 24.00 .15
803 A194 20f brown & multi 24.00 *14.00*
Nos. 799-803 (5) 120.00 *14.65*

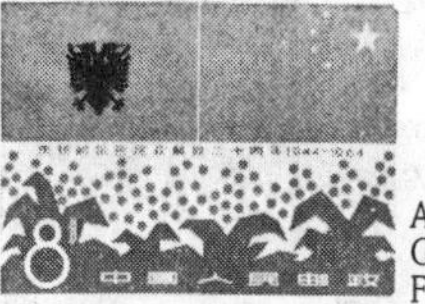
Albanian and Chinese Flags — A195

Design: 10f, Enver Hoxha and Albanian coat of arms.

1964, Nov. 29 *Perf. 11x11½*

804	A195	8f red & multi	12.50	*1.00*
805	A195	10f red, yel & blk	12.50	10.00

20th anniv. of the liberation of Albania.

Power Dam Construction A196

Designs: No. 807, Installation of turbogenerator rotor. No. 808, Main dam. 20f, Pylon.

1964, Dec. 15 *Perf. 11½*

806	A196	4f multicolored	25.00	.20
807	A196	8f multicolored	25.00	.20
808	A196	8f multicolored	25.00	.15
809	A196	20f multicolored	25.00	12.50
		Nos. 806-809 (4)	100.00	13.05

Hsin An Kiang Dam and hydroelectric power station.

Fertilizer Industry — A197

Designs (Chemical Industry): No. 811, Plastics. No. 812, Medicines. No. 813, Rubber. No. 814, Insecticides. No. 815, Industrial acids. No. 816, Industrial alkalies. No. 817, Synthetic fibers.

1964, Dec. 30 **Photo. & Engr.**

810	A197	8f red & blk (1)	1.25	.30
811	A197	8f yel grn & blk (2)	1.25	.20
812	A197	8f brown & blk (3)	1.25	.20
813	A197	8f lilac rose & blk (4)	1.25	.20
814	A197	8f blue & blk (5)	1.25	.20
815	A197	8f orange & blk (6)	1.25	.40
816	A197	8f violet & blk (7)	1.25	.40
817	A197	8f brt green & blk (8)	1.25	.40
		Nos. 810-817 (8)	10.00	2.30

Mao Studying Map — A198

Mao Tse-tung — A199

Design: No. 819, Victory at Lushan Pass.

1965, Jan. 31 **Photo.** *Perf. 11*

818	A198	8f red & multi	24.00	5.00
819	A198	8f red & multi	24.00	5.00

Perf. 11½x11

820	A199	8f gold & multi	24.00	5.00
		Nos. 818-820 (3)	72.00	15.00

Tsunyi Conference, 30th anniversary.

Conference Hall, Bandung — A200

Lenin — A201

Design: No. 822, Asians and Africans applauding.

1965, Apr. 18 *Perf. 11½x11*

821	A200	8f cream & multi	1.00	.20
822	A200	8f cream & multi	1.00	.20

10th anniversary of the Bandung, Indonesia, Conference, Apr. 1955.

1965, Apr. 25 *Perf. 11½*

823	A201	8f red, choc & sal	14.00	7.25

95th anniversary of the birth of Lenin.

Chinese Player — A202

1965, Apr. 25 *Perf. 11½*

824	A202	8f shown (1)	.60	.15
825	A202	8f European woman (2)	.60	.15
826	A202	8f Chinese woman (3)	.60	.15
827	A202	8f European man (4)	.60	.15
a.		Block of 4, #824-827	2.50	.60
		Set value		.40

28th World Table Tennis Championships, Ljubljana, Yugoslavia, Apr. 15-25.

Climbers on Mt. Minya Konka — A203

Marx and Lenin — A204

Mountain Climbers: No. 829, on Muztagh Ata. No. 830, on Mt. Jolmo Lungma (Mt. Everest). No. 831, Women camping on Kongur Tiubie Tagh. No. 832, on Shisha Pangma.

1965, May 25 **Photo. & Engr.**

828	A203	8f blue, blk & ol (1)	3.25	1.00
829	A203	8f blue, blk & ol (2)	3.25	1.00
830	A203	8f ultra, blk & gray (3)	3.25	1.00
831	A203	8f lt bl, blk & yel gray (4)	3.25	1.00
832	A203	8f ultra, blk & gray (5)	3.25	1.00
		Nos. 828-832 (5)	16.25	5.00

Chinese mountaineering achievements, 1957-64.

1965, June 21 **Photo.** *Perf. 11½x11*

833	A204	8f red, yel & blk	13.00	7.25

Postal Ministers' Congress, Peking.

Tseping Valley A205

Chingkang Mountains, Cradle of the Chinese Revolution.

1965, July 1 *Perf. 11x11½*

834	A205	4f shown (1)	10.00	.15
835	A205	8f San Wan Tsun (2)	10.00	.15
836	A205	8f Octagon Bldg., Mao Ping (3)	10.00	.20
837	A205	8f River and Bridge at Lung Shih (4)	10.00	1.10
838	A205	8f Ta Ching Tsun (5)	10.00	.15
839	A205	10f Bridge across the Lung Yuan (6)	10.00	.15
840	A205	10f Hwang Yang Mountain (7)	10.00	2.50
841	A205	52f Chingkang peaks (8)	10.00	2.50
		Nos. 834-841 (8)	80.00	6.90

Soldiers with Books — A206

1965, Aug. 1 *Perf. 11½*

Without Gum

842	A206	8f shown (1)	10.00	2.75
843	A206	8f Soldiers reading Little Red Books (2)	10.00	2.75
844	A206	8f With shell and artillery (3)	10.00	.35
845	A206	8f Rifle instruction (4)	10.00	.35
846	A206	8f Sewing jacket (5)	10.00	.35
847	A206	8f Bayonet charge (6)	10.00	4.00
848	A206	8f With Banner (7)	10.00	4.00
849	A206	8f Military band (8)	10.00	4.00
		Nos. 842-849 (8)	80.00	18.55

People's Liberation Army. Nos. 846-849 vertical.

"Welcome to Peking" — A207

Designs: No. 851, Chinese and Japanese young men. No. 852, Chinese and Japanese girls. No. 853, Musical entertainment. No. 854, Emblem of meeting.

1965, Aug. 25 *Perf. 11½x11*

850	A207	4f yellow & multi	1.25	.20
851	A207	8f pink & multi	1.25	.25
852	A207	8f multicolored	1.25	.25
853	A207	10f multicolored	1.25	.25
854	A207	22f lt blue & multi	1.25	.50
		Nos. 850-854 (5)	6.25	1.45

Chinese-Japanese Youth Meeting, Peking.

North Vietnamese Soldier — A208

Peoples of the World — A209

Designs: No. 856, Soldier with guns. No. 857, Soldier giving victory salute.

1965, Sept. 2 *Perf. 11½x11*

855	A208	8f red & red brn (1)	1.10	.20
856	A208	8f red & blk (2)	1.10	.20
857	A208	8f red & vio brn (3)	1.10	.20

Perf. 11½

858	A209	8f black & red (4)	1.10	.20
		Nos. 855-858 (4)	4.40	.80

Struggle of the people of Viet Nam.

Mao Tse-tung at His Desk — A210

Crossing Yellow River — A211

Victory Monument — A212

Design: No. 862, Recruits in cart.

1965, Sept. 3 *Perf. 11*

859	A210	8f red & multi (1)	7.50	2.25

Perf. 11x11½, 11½x11

860	A211	8f red & dk grn (2)	7.50	6.75
861	A212	8f red & dk brn (3)	7.50	.55
862	A211	8f red & dk grn (4)	7.50	.55
		Nos. 859-862 (4)	30.00	10.10

20th anniversary of victory over Japan.

2nd National Games — A213

National Games Opening Ceremonies — A214

Perf. 11½x11, 11 (A214)

1965, Sept. 28

863	A213	4f Soccer (1)	12.00	.70
864	A213	4f Archery (2)	12.00	.70
865	A213	8f Javelin (3)	12.00	.70
866	A213	8f Gymnastics (4)	12.00	.70
867	A213	8f Volleyball (5)	12.00	.70
868	A214	10f shown (6)	12.00	.70
869	A213	10f Bicyling (7)	12.00	.70
870	A213	20f Diving (8)	12.00	1.65
871	A213	22f Hurdles (9)	12.00	2.25
872	A213	30f Weight lifting (10)	12.00	3.75
873	A213	43f Basketball (11)	12.00	7.50
		Nos. 863-873 (11)	132.00	20.05

Government Building A215

Textile Workers A216

Designs: 1 1/2f, 5f, 22f, Gate of Heavenly Peace. 2f, 8f, 30f, People's Hall. 3f, 10f, 50f, Military Museum.

1965-66 *Perf. 11 1/2x11*

Without Gum

874 A215 1f brown .15 .15
875 A215 1 1/2f red lil .15 *.50*
876 A215 2f green .15 .15
877 A215 3f bl grn .15 .15
878 A215 4f brt bl .15 .15
879 A215 5f vio brn ('66) .25 .15
880 A215 8f rose red .25 .15
881 A215 10f gray ol .25 .15
882 A215 20f violet .25 .15
883 A215 22f orange 1.10 .15
884 A215 30f yel grn 1.10 .15
885 A215 50f dp bl ('66) 1.10 *1.50*
Nos. 874-885 (12) 5.05 *3.50*

1965, Nov. 30

886 A216 8f shown (1) 9.50 .15
887 A216 8f Machine shop (2) 9.50 .15
888 A216 8f Welder (3) 9.50 .15
889 A216 8f Students (4) 9.50 2.75
890 A216 8f Militia (5) 9.50 2.75
Nos. 886-890 (5) 47.50 5.95

Women workers.

Soccer — A217

Children's Sports: No. 892, Racing. No. 893, Tobogganing and skating. No. 894, Gymnastics. No. 895, Swimming. No. 896, Rifle practice. No. 897, Jumping rope. No. 898, Table tennis.

1966, Feb. 25 *Perf. 11*

891 A217 4f emerald & multi (1) .15 .15
892 A217 4f yel brown & multi (2) .15 .15
893 A217 8f blue & multi (3) .25 .25
894 A217 8f yellow & multi (4) .25 .25
895 A217 8f grnsh bl & multi (5) .25 .25
896 A217 8f green & multi (6) .25 .25
897 A217 10f orange & multi (7) .35 .30
898 A217 52f grnsh gray & multi (8) 2.00 1.40
Nos. 891-898 (8) 3.65 3.00

Mobile Transformer A218

New Industrial Machinery: No. 900, Electron microscope, vert. No. 901, Lathe. No. 902, Vertical boring and turning machine, vert. No. 903, Gear-grinding machine. No. 904, Hydraulic press. No. 905, Milling machine. No. 906, Electron accelerator, vert.

Perf. 11x11 1/2, 11 1/2x11

1966, Mar. 30 **Photo. & Engr.**

899 A218 4f yellow & blk (1) 10.00 .40
900 A218 8f blk & lt ultra (2) 10.00 .40
901 A218 8f sal pink & blk (3) 10.00 .40
902 A218 8f olive & blk (4) 10.00 .40
903 A218 8f rose lil & blk (5) 10.00 .40
904 A218 10f gray & blk (6) 10.00 2.75
905 A218 10f bl grn & blk (7) 10.00 2.75
906 A218 22f lilac & blk (8) 10.00 2.75
Nos. 899-906 (8) 80.00 10.25

Military and Civilian Workers A219

Women in Various Occupations: No. 908, Train conductor. No. 909, Red Cross worker. No. 910, Kindergarten teacher. No. 911, Road sweeper. No. 912, Hairdresser. No. 913, Bus conductor. No. 914, Traveling saleswoman. No. 915, Canteen worker. No. 916, Rural mail carrier.

1966, May 10 *Perf. 11x11 1/2*

907 A219 8f red & multi (1) .40 .20
908 A219 8f pale grn & multi (2) .40 .20
909 A219 8f yellow & multi (3) .40 .20
910 A219 8f green & multi (4) .40 .20
911 A219 8f salmon & multi (5) .40 .20
912 A219 8f pale bl & bl (6) .40 .20
913 A219 8f yellow & multi (7) .40 .20
914 A219 8f tan & multi (8) .40 .20
915 A219 8f yel grn & multi (9) .40 .20
916 A219 8f green & multi (10) .40 .20
Nos. 907-916 (10) 4.00 2.00

Statue "Thunderstorm" — A220

Design: 22f, Open book and association emblem.

1966, June 27 *Perf. 11*

917 A220 8f red & black 2.00 .50
918 A220 22f red, gold & yel 3.25 .75

Afro-Asian Writers' Assoc. Conf., Peking.

Sun Yat-sen — A221

1966, Nov. 12 *Perf. 11 1/2x11*

919 A221 8f sepia & lt buff 18.00 6.00

Birth centenary of Sun Yat-sen.

Athletes Holding Portrait of Mao — A222

Two Women Athletes with Little Red Book — A223

Designs: No. 921, Athletes holding Little Red Books. No. 923, Athletes reading Mao texts.

1966, Dec. 31 *Perf. 11*

920 A222 8f red & multi (1) 12.50 3.50
921 A222 8f red & multi (2) 12.50 3.50

Perf. 11x11 1/2

922 A223 8f blue & multi (3) 12.50 3.50
923 A223 8f blue & multi (4) 12.50 3.50
Nos. 920-923 (4) 50.00 14.00

1st Athletic Games of the New Emerging Nations.

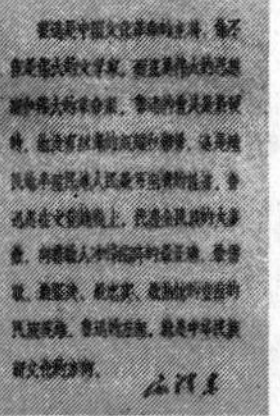
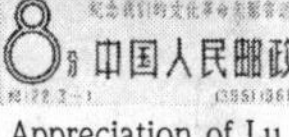

Appreciation of Lu Hsun by Mao — A224

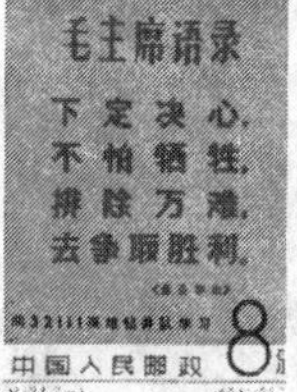

"Be Resolute ...," by Mao Tse-tung — A225

Designs: No. 925, Portrait of Lu Hsun. No. 926, Lu Hsun's handwriting (3 vert. rows).

Engr. & Photo.; Photo. (#925)

1966, Dec. 31 *Perf. 11 1/2*

924 A224 8f red & black (1) 21.00 5.25
925 A224 8f red & multi (2) 21.00 5.25
926 A224 8f red & black (3) 21.00 5.25
Nos. 924-926 (3) 63.00 15.75

Lu Hsun, Revolutionary writer (1881-1936).

Perf. 11 1/2x11, 11 1/2 (No. 928)

1967, Mar. 10 **Photo.**

Designs: No. 928, Drilling crew fighting natural gas fire, horiz. No. 929, Attempt to close fire-engulfed valve.

Sizes: Nos. 927, 929, 26x38mm; No. 928, 49x29mm

927 A225 8f red, gold & blk 16.00 3.00
928 A225 8f brick red & blk 16.00 3.00
929 A225 8f brick red & blk 16.00 3.00
Nos. 927-929 (3) 48.00 9.00

Heroic oil well firefighters.

Liu Ying-chun — A226

1967, Mar. 25 *Perf. 11 1/2x11*

930 A226 8f shown (1) 10.50 2.75
931 A226 8f With book by Mao (2) 10.50 2.75
932 A226 8f Holding bridle of horse (3) 10.50 2.75
933 A226 8f With film slide (4) 10.50 2.75
934 A226 8f Lecturing (5) 10.50 2.75
935 A226 8f Fatal attempt to stop runaway horse (6) 10.50 2.75
Nos. 930-935 (6) 63.00 16.50

In memory of soldier Liu Ying-chun, hero.

Industrial Growth — A227

Design: No. 937, Banners and people facing left: agricultural growth.

1967, Apr. 15 *Perf. 11*

936 A227 8f red & multi 16.00 3.50
937 A227 8f red & multi 16.00 3.50

Third Five-Year Plan.

Mao Tse-tung — A228

Thoughts of Mao — A229

1967, Apr. 20 *Perf. 11 1/2*

938 A228 8f red & multi 35.00 14.00

Red & Gold

939 A229 8f 39 characters 35.00 14.00
940 A229 8f 50 characters 35.00 14.00
941 A229 8f 39 characters in 6 lines 35.00 14.00
942 A229 8f 53 characters 35.00 14.00
943 A229 8f 46 characters 35.00 14.00
a. Strip of 5, #939-943 225.00 125.00

Gold & Red

944 A229 8f 41 characters 35.00 14.00
945 A229 8f 49 characters 35.00 14.00
946 A229 8f 35 characters 35.00 14.00
947 A229 8f 22 characters 35.00 14.00
948 A229 8f 29 characters 35.00 14.00
a. Strip of 5, #944-948 225.00 125.00
Nos. 938-948 (11) 385.00 154.00

Thoughts of Mao Tse-tung.

No numbers appear below design on Nos. 938-1046.

Gate of Heavenly Peace and Text from C. C. P. Communique Praising Mao — A230

Mao and Lin Piao — A231

Designs: No. 950, Mao and poem. No. 951, Mao among people of various races. No. 952, Mao facing left and Red Guards with books. No. 953, Mao with upraised right hand. No. 954, Mao leaning on rail, horiz. 10f, Mao and Lin Piao in discussion, horiz.

Engraved and Photogravure

1967 *Perf. 11x11 1/2*

Size: 36x56mm

949 A230 4f yel, red & mar 22.50 3.75

Photo.

950 A230 8f yel, brn, & red 22.50 3.75
951 A230 8f yel, red & multi 22.50 3.75
952 A230 8f yel, red & multi 22.50 3.75

Size: 36x50mm, 50x36mm

Perf. 11

953 A231 8f black & multi 22.50 3.75
954 A231 8f black & multi 110.00 32.50
955 A231 8f lt blue & multi 42.50 32.50
956 A231 10f black & multi 90.00 32.50
Nos. 949-956 (8) 355.00 116.25

"Mao Tse-tung Our Great Teacher."

Issued: #949-953, May 1; #954-956, Sept. 20.

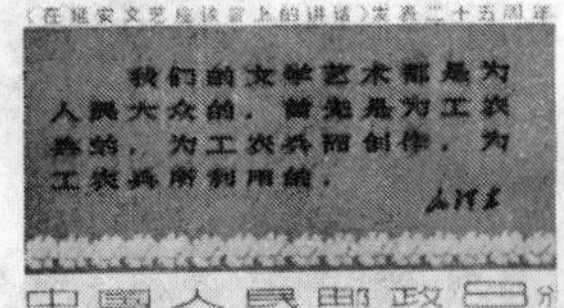

Mao Text (4 lines) — A232

Parade of Supporters — A233

Design: No. 958, Mao text (5 lines).

Engraved and Photogravure

1967, May 23 *Perf. 11½*

957 A232 8f black, red & yel 75.00 25.00
958 A232 8f black, red & yel 75.00 25.00

Photo. *Perf. 11*

959 A233 8f multicolored 75.00 25.00
Nos. 957-959 (3) 225.00 75.00

25th anniversary of Mao Tse-tung's "Talks on Literature and Art" in Yenan.

Mao Tse-tung — A234

1967 **Engr.** *Perf. 11*

960 A234 4f brown 30.00 12.00
961 A234 8f carmine 30.00 12.00
962 A234 35f dk brown 30.00 12.00
963 A234 43f vermilion 30.00 12.00
964 A234 52f carmine 30.00 12.00
Nos. 960-964 (5) 150.00 60.00

46th anniv. of Chinese Communist Party. Issue dates: 8f, July 1, others Sept.

Mao, "Sun of the Revolution" — A235

Design: No. 966, Mao and people of various races.

1967, Oct. 1 *Perf. 11½x11*

965 A235 8f multicolored 20.00 20.00
966 A235 8f multicolored 20.00 20.00

People's Republic of China, 18th anniv.

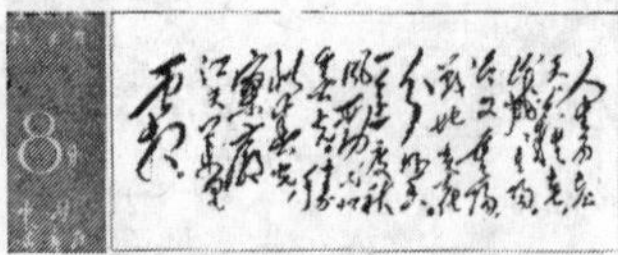
"September 9" — A236

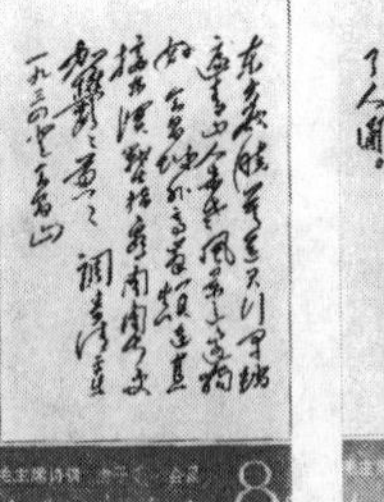
"Huichang" A237

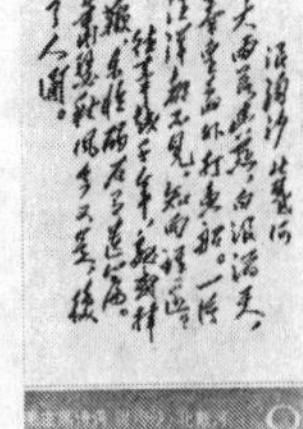
"Peitaiho" A238

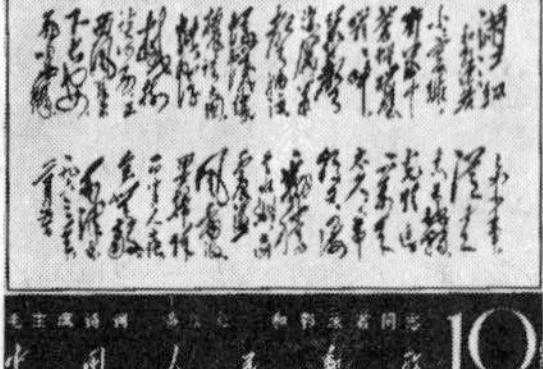
Reply to Comrade Kuo Mo-jo — A239

Mao Tse-tung Writing Poems — A240

Designs (Poems by Mao): No. 967, "The Long March." No. 968, "Liupanshan." No. 969, shown. No. 970, "The Cave of the Fairies." No. 971, "Snow." No. 972, "Lushan Pass." No. 975, "Conquest of Nanking." No. 976, "The Yellow Crane Pavilion." No. 977, "Swimming." No. 979, "Changsha."

1967-68 **Photo.** *Perf. 11*

Size: 79x18½mm

967 A236 4f 9 characters, UL panel ('68) 47.50 7.00
968 A236 4f 11 characters, UL panel ('68) 47.50 7.00

Size: 60x24mm

Perf. 11½

969 A236 8f shown, 10 characters in UL panel 30.00 2.75
970 A236 8f 21 characters in UL panel 30.00 2.75
971 A236 8f 11 characters in UL panel 47.50 7.00
972 A236 8f 9 characters in UL panel 47.50 7.00

Size: 29x50mm

973 A237 8f shown 30.00 2.75
974 A238 8f shown 47.50 7.00
975 A238 8f 3 rows in bottom panel 30.00 2.75
976 A238 8f 2 rows in bottom panel 47.50 7.00

Size: 52x38mm

Perf. 11

977 A239 8f 3 short vert. rows, at left of poem 47.50 7.00
978 A239 10f shown 47.50 7.00
979 A239 10f undivided text 30.00 2.75
980 A240 10f red, yel & multi 37.50 7.00
Nos. 967-980 (14) 567.50 76.75

Poems by Mao Tse-tung. Issue dates: Nos. 969-970, 980, Oct. 1, 1967; Nos. 973-974, 977, May 20, 1968; others July 20, 1968.

Lin Piao's Epigram on Mao Tse-tung A241

1967, Dec. 26 **Photo.** *Perf. 11x11½*

981 A241 8f red & gold 24.00 5.00

Mao and Parade of Artists — A242

"Raid on White Tiger Regiment" — A243

"Red Detachment of Women" — A244

1968 *Perf. 11½x11; 11 (983, 990)*

982 A242 8f shown (56x36mm) 11.00 2.00
983 A242 8f "The Red Lantern," vert. 11.00 2.00
984 A243 8f shown 11.00 2.00
985 A243 8f "Shachiapang" (women & soldier) 11.00 2.00
986 A243 8f "On the Dock" 11.00 2.00
987 A243 8f "Taking Bandits' Fort" 11.00 2.00
988 A244 8f shown 22.50 6.00
989 A244 8f "The White-haired Girl" 22.50 6.00
990 A242 8f Mao with Orchestra & Chorus (50x36mm) 16.00 6.00
Nos. 982-990 (9) 127.00 30.00

Mao's direction for revolutionary literature and art. Issued: #982-987, Jan. 30; #988-990, May 1.

"Unite still more closely . . ." — A245

1968, May 31 **Photo.** *Perf. 11*

991 A245 8f red, gold & red brn 35.00 7.25

Mao Tse-tung's statement of support of Afro-Americans.

Statement about Cultural Revolution — A246

Directives of Chairman Mao: No. 993, Experiences of Revolutionary Committee. No. 994, Leadership role of Revolutionary Committee. No. 995, Basic principle of reform. No. 996, Purpose of Cultural Revolution.

1968, July 20 **Photo.** *Perf. 11½*

No. of Lines Over Signature

992 A246 8f shown 40.00 18.00
993 A246 8f 5 40.00 18.00
994 A246 8f 4½ 40.00 18.00
995 A246 8f 4 40.00 18.00
996 A246 8f 8 40.00 18.00
a. Strip of 5, #992-996 *750.00* 225.00
Nos. 992-996 (5) 200.00 90.00

Lin Piao's Statement, July 26, 1965 — A247

1968, Aug. 1 **Engr. & Photo.**

997 A247 8f red, gold & blk 8.50 6.00

Chinese People's Liberation Army, 41st anniv.

Mao Tse-tung Going to An Yuan, 1921 — A248

1968, Aug. 1 *Perf. 11x11½*

998 A248 8f multicolored 21.00 3.50

Shade varieties include varying amount of red in clouds.

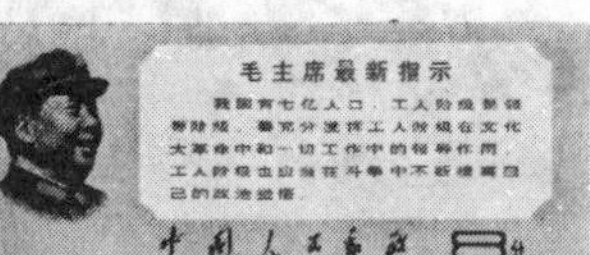
Directive of Chairman Mao — A249

1968, Nov. 30 *Perf. 11½*

999 A249 8f red & blk brn 25.00 8.75

China Map, Worker, Farmer and Soldier — A249a

1968, Nov. **Photo.** *Perf. 11½x11*

999A A249a 8f red, bl & bis *5,750.* *3,000.*

Map inscribed: "The entire nation is red." Issued in Canton and quickly withdrawn because Taiwan appears white instead of red.

Woman, Miner and Soldier Holding Little Red Book — A250

1968, Dec. 26 *Perf. 11x11½*

1000 A250 8f multicolored 11.00 3.50

Canceled-to-order
From about this point on stamps are valued postally used.

Yangtze Bridge, Nanking A251

Road across Bridge — A252

Designs: No. 1003, Side view. 10f, Aerial view.

Lithographed, *Perf.* 11½x11 (A251); Photogravure, *Perf.* 11½ (A252)

1969

Without Gum

1001	A251	4f multicolored	5.00	2.50
1002	A252	8f multicolored	5.00	4.75
1003	A252	8f multicolored	5.00	2.50
1004	A251	10f multicolored	5.00	2.50
		Nos. 1001-1004 (4)	20.00	12.25

Inauguration of Yangtze Bridge at Nanking on Dec. 29, 1968.

Singer and Pianist A253

Designs (Piano Music from the Opera, "The Red Lantern"): No. 1006, Woman singer and pianist.

1969, Aug. Photo. *Perf.* 11x11½

Without Gum

1005	A253	8f multicolored	20.00	2.50
1006	A253	8f multicolored	20.00	2.50

Harvest A254

1969, Oct.

1007	A254	4f shown	8.75	2.00
a.		Brown omitted	50.00	40.00
1008	A254	8f Two harvesters	8.75	2.00
1009	A254	8f Harvesters with Little Red Books	17.50	8.00
1010	A254	10f Red Cross worker examining baby	8.75	1.00
		Nos. 1007-1010 (4)	43.75	13.00

Agriculture students.

Armed Forces and Slogan — A255

Guarding the Coast — A256

Designs: No. 1013, 43f, Snow patrol, vert.

1969, Oct. *Perf.* 11½

1011	A255	8f red & multi	4.50	*4.00*
a.		Bayonets omitted	80.00	40.00
1012	A256	8f blue & multi	4.50	*4.00*
1013	A256	8f blue & multi	4.50	*4.00*
1014	A256	35f black & multi	4.50	*5.00*
1015	A256	43f black & multi	4.50	*5.00*
		Nos. 1011-1015 (5)	22.50	*22.00*

Defense of Chen Pao-tao (Damansky Islands) in Ussuri River.

Farm Woman — A257

Designs: 8f, Foundry worker. 10f, Soldier.

1969, Dec. *Perf.* 10; 11½ (#1017)

Without Gum

1016	A257	4f ver & dk pur	.55	1.25
1017	A257	8f ver & dk brn	.55	1.25
1018	A257	10f ver & blk	.55	1.25
		Nos. 1016-1018 (3)	1.65	3.75

Perforation

Nos. 1016-1018 and some succeeding issues bear two kinds of perforation: clean (Peking) and rough (Shanghai).

Building — A258

Communist Party Building, Shanghai — A259

Agriculture Building, Canton — A260

Foundry Worker — A261

Two types of 8f Gate of Heavenly Peace:
I- Strong, definite halo around sun.
II- Halo missing, white shades gradually into red.

1969-72 Photo. *Perf.* 10, 11½

Without Gum

1019	A258	1f shown	.15	*.20*
1020	A259	1½f shown	.95	.70
a.		Perf. 11½	5.50	5.00
1021	A260	2f shown	.15	*.15*
1022	A260	3f 1929 Party Day House, Pu Tien	.15	.15
1023	A260	4f Mao's Home and Office, Yunnan	.15	*.15*
1024	A261	5f Woman Tractor Driver	1.25	.75
1025	A260	8f Gate of Heavenly Peace, type II	1.25	.35
a.		Type I	2.00	.60
1026	A259	8f Heroes Monument	1.25	.70
a.		Perf. 11½	4.00	4.00
1027	A260	8f Pagoda Hill, Yenan	1.25	*3.50*
1028	A260	8f Gate of Heavenly Peace (no sun)	.15	.15
1029	A260	10f Monument, Tsu Ping	.20	.20
1030	A259	20f Conference Hall, Tsunyi	1.25	1.40
a.		Perf. 11½	5.50	4.00
1031	A260	20f Highway ('72)	.25	.20
1032	A260	22f Shao Shan Village, Birthplace of Mao	.30	.35
1033	A260	35f Conference Hall	.40	.35
1034	A260	43f Chingkang Peaks	.50	.35
1035	A259	50f as 4f, different view	2.75	1.40
1036	A260	52f People's Hall, Peking	.65	.35
1037	A261	$1 shown ('70)	2.75	2.75
		Nos. 1019-1037 (19)	15.75	14.15

Kin Hsün-hua — A262

Mounted Patrol — A263

1970, Jan. Without Gum *Perf.* 11½

1045	A262	8f red & black	11.00	*10.50*
a.		8f red & gray brown	12.50	7.50

Death of Kin Hsün-hua in Kirin border flood.

1970, Aug. 1

Without Gum

1046	A263	8f yel grn & multi	4.50	4.50

People's Liberation Army, 43rd anniv.

Beginning with No. 1047 commemorative stamps carry a cumulative number in parenthesis at lower left and the year at lower right. Where such numbers help to identify, they are quoted in parenthesis.

Cpl. Yang Tse-jung — A264

Ensemble — A265

1970, Aug. 1 *Perf.* 11½x11, 11x11½

1047	A264	8f shown (1)	6.00	3.50
1048	A264	8f Armed guards (2)	6.00	3.50
1049	A264	8f Yang leaping through forest (3)	6.00	3.50
1050	A265	8f shown (4)	6.00	3.50
1051	A265	8f Yang in folk costume (5)	6.00	3.50
1052	A265	8f Four actors (6)	6.00	3.50
		Nos. 1047-1052 (6)	36.00	21.00

Scenes from opera "Taking Tiger Mountain by Strategy." Nos. 1048, 1052, horizontal.

Frontier Guard A266

1971, Jan. Litho. *Perf.* 10

Without Gum

1053	A266	4f multicolored	1.00	1.00
a.		Perf. 11½	2.00	.75
b.		Perf. 11½x10	4.00	
c.		Perf. 10x11½	5.00	

Banner of the Commune — A267

Street Battle, Paris, 1871 — A268

Designs: 10f, Proclamation of the Commune. 22f, Rally.

***Perf.* 11½x11, 11x11½**

1971, Mar. 18 Litho. & Engr.

1054	A267	4f salmon & multi	14.00	3.00
1055	A268	8f ver, pink & brn	14.00	6.00
1056	A267	10f ver, pink & dk brn	14.00	2.00
1057	A268	22f ver, pink & dk brn	14.00	2.00
		Nos. 1054-1057 (4)	56.00	13.00

Centenary of the Paris Commune.

Redrawn Building Type of 1961

Designs: 2f, 3f, August 1 building, Nanchang. 4f, 52f, Gate of Heavenly Peace, Peking. 10f, 20f, Pagoda Hill, Yenan.

1971 Litho. *Perf.* 11x11½

Size: 21x16mm

Without Gum

1059	A152	2f slate green	2.00	.50
1060	A152	3f sepia	2.00	.50
1061	A152	4f brt pink	2.00	1.00
1062	A152	10f brt rose lil	2.00	1.00
1063	A152	20f dk blue grn	2.00	1.00
1064	A152	52f orange	2.00	2.00
		Nos. 1059-1064 (6)	12.00	6.00

Paper of Nos. 1059-1064 is white. That of Nos. 647-654 is toned.

Communist Party Building, Shanghai — A269

People and Factories — A270

Designs: No. 1068, Peasant Movement Training Institute. No. 1069, Ching Kang Peaks. No. 1070, Conference Building, Tsunyi. No. 1071, Pagoda Hill, Yenan. No. 1073, People and People's Hall, Peking. No. 1074, People and Pagoda Hill, Yenan. 22f, Gate of Heavenly Peace, Peking.

1971, July 1 Photo. *Perf.* 11½

Red and Gold Frame

1067	A269	4f vermilion (12)	3.00	.60
1068	A269	4f brt grn (13)	3.00	.60
1069	A269	8f grnsh bl & red (14)	3.00	.60
1070	A269	8f ol blk (15)	3.00	.60
1071	A269	8f bis, grn & red (16)	3.00	.60
1072	A270	8f yel, red & multi (18)	3.00	.60
1073	A270	8f yel, red & multi (19)	3.00	.60
1074	A270	8f yel, red & multi (20)	3.00	.60
a.		Strip of 3, #1072-1074	10.00	10.00
1075	A269	22f red, gold & brn (17)	3.00	1.25
		Nos. 1067-1075 (9)	27.00	6.05

50th anniv. of the Chinese Communist Party. No. 1074a has a continuous design.

Chinese Welcome — A271 Enver Hoxha — A272

Designs: No. 1077, Chinese and African players. No. 1078, Chinese and African girl players. 43f, Games' emblem.

1971, Nov. 3 Litho. *Perf. 11½*

1076 A271 8f lilac rose & multi 1.25 .65
1077 A271 8f lt yellow & multi 1.25 .65
1078 A271 8f dk green & multi 1.25 .65
1079 A271 43f grn, gold & org 7.00 1.65
Nos. 1076-1079 (4) 10.75 3.60

Afro-Asian Table Tennis Games, Peking.

1971, Nov. 3 Photo. *Perf. 11*

Designs: No. 1081, Party's birthplace. No. 1082, Albanian flag. 52f, Albanian partisans, horiz.

1080 A272 8f Prus blue & multi 3.25 3.00
1081 A272 8f buff & multi 3.25 1.00
1082 A272 8f red, yel & multi 3.25 1.00
1083 A272 52f lt blue & multi 3.25 3.00
Nos. 1080-1083 (4) 13.00 8.00

30th anniversary of the founding of Albanian Communist Party.

Yenan Pagoda and 1942 Meeting House A273

1972, May 23 Photo. *Perf. 11*

1084 A273 8f shown (33) 3.50 1.00
1085 A273 8f Uniformed choir (34) 3.50 1.00
1086 A273 8f "Brother & Sister" (35) 3.50 1.00
1087 A273 8f Outdoor performance (36) 3.50 1.00
1088 A273 8f "The Red Signal Lantern" (37) 3.50 1.00
1089 A273 8f Dancer from "The Red Company of Women" (38) 3.50 1.00
Nos. 1084-1089 (6) 21.00 6.00

30th anniversary of the publication of the Discussions on Literature and Art at the Yenan Forum.

Various Ball Games — A274

Workers' Gymnastics — A275

1972, June 10

1090 A274 8f shown (39) 1.65 .50
1091 A275 8f shown (40) 1.65 .50
1092 A275 8f Tug of war (41) 1.65 .50
1093 A275 8f Mountain climbers and tents (42) 1.65 .50
1094 A275 8f Children diving & swimming (43) 1.65 .50
Nos. 1090-1094 (5) 8.25 2.50

10th anniversary of Mao Tse-tung's edict on physical culture.

Ocean Freighter Fenglei — A276

1972, July 10 Photo. *Perf. 11½*

1095 A276 8f shown (29) 2.75 .80
1096 A276 8f Tanker Taching No. 30 (30) 2.75 .80
1097 A276 8f Cargo-passenger ship Changzeng (31) 2.75 .80
1098 A276 8f Dredger Xienfeng (32) 2.75 .80
Nos. 1095-1098 (4) 11.00 3.20

Table Tennis Players' Welcome A277

Perf. 11½x11, 11x11½

1972, Sept. 2

1099 A277 8f Championship emblem, vert (45) .80 .60
1100 A277 8f shown (46) .80 .60
1101 A277 8f Table tennis (47) .80 .60
1102 A277 22f Women from different countries, vert. (48) 3.50 1.40
Nos. 1099-1102 (4) 5.90 3.20

First Asian table tennis championships.

Wang Chin-hsi — A278 Workers on Cliffs along Canal — A279

Engraved and Photogravure

1972, Dec. 25 *Perf. 11½x11*

1103 A278 8f multicolored (44) 2.50 1.00

Wang Chin-hsi, the Iron Man, fighter for the working class.

1972, Dec. 30

Designs: No. 1105, Canal flowing through tunnel. No. 1106, Bridge. No. 1107, Canal along cliffs.

1104 A279 8f multicolored (49) 1.00 .60
1105 A279 8f multicolored (50) 1.00 .60
1106 A279 8f multicolored (51) 1.00 .60
1107 A279 8f multicolored (52) 1.00 .60
Nos. 1104-1107 (4) 4.00 2.40

Construction of Red Flag Canal, Linhsien county, Honan.

Giant Panda — A280 Woman Coal Miner — A281

Designs: Pandas in various positions. The 8f stamps are horizontal.

Perf. 11½x11, 11x11½

1973, Jan. 15 Photo.

Designs in Black and Red

1108 A280 4f lt yel grn (61) 10.50 3.00
1109 A280 8f buff (59) 10.50 3.00
1110 A280 8f lt tan (60) 10.50 3.00
1111 A280 10f pale green (58) 10.50 3.00
1112 A280 20f pale bl gray (57) 10.50 3.00
1113 A280 43f pale lilac (62) 10.50 3.00
Nos. 1108-1113 (6) 63.00 18.00

1973, Mar. 8 Photo. *Perf. 11½x11*

1114 A281 8f shown (63) 1.25 .90
1115 A281 8f Committee member (64) 1.25 .90
1116 A281 8f Telephone line worker (65) 1.25 .90
Nos. 1114-1116 (3) 3.75 2.70

Intl. Working Women's Day. Designs are after paintings from an exhib. for 30th anniv. of the Yenan Forum on Literature and Art.

Dancing Girl — A282 Tournament Emblem — A283

1973, June 1 Photo. *Perf. 11*

1117 A282 8f shown (86) .70 .55
1118 A282 8f Musician, boy (87) .70 .55
1119 A282 8f Girl with scarf (88) .70 .55
1120 A282 8f Boy with tambourine (89) .70 .55
1121 A282 8f Girl with drum (90) .70 .55
a. Strip of 5, #1117-1121 4.00 3.00
Nos. 1117-1121 (5) 3.50 2.75

1973, Aug. 25 Photo. *Perf. 11½*

Designs: No. 1123, Visitors from Asia, Africa and Latin America arriving by plane. No. 1124, Woman player. 22f, African, Asian and Latin American women.

1122 A283 8f multicolored (91) 1.25 .40
1123 A283 8f multicolored (92) 1.25 .40
1124 A283 8f multicolored (93) 1.25 .40
1125 A283 22f multicolored (94) 1.25 1.00
Nos. 1122-1125 (4) 5.00 2.20

Asian, African and Latin American Table Tennis Friendship Invitational Tournament.

The White-haired Girl — A284

Designs: Scenes from the ballet "The White-haired Girl." Nos. 1126, 1129 vert.

1973, Sept. 25 Photo. *Perf. 11½*

1126 A284 8f multicolored (53) 2.25 .80
1127 A284 8f multicolored (54) 2.25 .80
1128 A284 8f multicolored (55) 2.25 .80
1129 A284 8f multicolored (56) 2.25 .80
Nos. 1126-1129 (4) 9.00 3.20

Fair Building, Canton — A285

1973, Oct. 15 Photo. *Perf. 11*

1130 A285 8f multicolored (95) 2.50 1.75

Export Commodities Fall Fair, Canton.

Teapot with Blue Phoenix Design — A286

Excavated Works of Art: No. 1132, Silver pot with horse design. No. 1133, Black pottery horse. No. 1134, Woman, clay figurine. No. 1135, Carved stone pillar base. No. 1136, Galloping bronze horse. No. 1137, Bronze inkwell (toad). No. 1138, Bronze lamp, Chang Hsin Palace. No. 1139, Bronze tripod. No. 1140, Square bronze pot. 20f, Bronze wine vessel. 52f, Painted red clay tripod.

1973, Nov. 20 *Perf. 11½*

1131 A286 4f ol bis & multi (66) .40 .40
1132 A286 4f ver & multi (67) .40 .40
1133 A286 8f yel grn & multi (68) .40 .40
1134 A286 8f brt rose & multi (69) .40 .40
1135 A286 8f lt vio & multi (70) .40 .40
1136 A286 8f yel bis & multi (71) .40 .40
1137 A286 8f lt bl & multi (72) .40 .40
1138 A286 8f gray & multi (73) .40 .40
1139 A286 10f yel bis & multi (74) .40 .40
1140 A286 10f dp org & multi (75) .40 .40
1141 A286 20f lil & multi (76) 1.00 1.00
1142 A286 52f grn & multi (77) 2.75 2.75
Nos. 1131-1142 (12) 7.75 7.75

Marginal Markings

Marginal inscriptions on stamps of 1974-91 start at lower left with "J" for commemoratives and "T" for "special issues," followed by three numbers indicating (a) set sequence for the year, (b) total of stamps in set, and (c) number of stamp within set. At right appears the year date. Listings include the "c" number parenthetically. The "a" number is included only when it will help identify stamps not illustrated.

Example: T26 (6-3), the 3rd stamp of 6 from the 26th special set. Set numbers and or positions will be shown only when they help identify a stamp. An illustrated single stamp set will not have these numbers in the listings.

Woman Gymnast — A287

Designs: No. 1144, Gymnast on rings. No. 1145, Aerial split over balance beam, woman. No. 1146, Gymnast on parallel bars. No. 1147, Uneven bars, woman. No. 1148, Gymnast on horse. T.1.

1974, Jan. 1 Photo. *Perf. 11½x11*

1143 A287 8f lt grn & multi (1) 5.00 2.50
1144 A287 8f lt vio & multi (2) 5.00 2.50
1145 A287 8f lt blue & multi (3) 5.00 2.50
1146 A287 8f sal & multi (4) 5.00 2.50
1147 A287 8f yel & multi (5) 5.00 2.50
1148 A287 8f lil rose & multi (6) 5.00 2.50
Nos. 1143-1148 (6) 30.00 15.00

Girls Twirling Bamboo Diabolos — A288

Designs: No. 1149, Lion Dance, vert. No. 1150, Handstand on chairs, vert. No. 1152, Men balancing jar. No. 1153, Plate spinning, vert. No. 1154, Twirling umbrella, vert. T.2.

1974, Jan. 21 *Perf. 11*

1149 A288 8f brown & multi (1) 4.50 2.00
1150 A288 8f Prus bl & multi (2) 4.50 2.00
1151 A288 8f lilac & multi (3) 4.50 2.00
1152 A288 8f dull bl & multi (4) 4.50 2.00
1153 A288 8f ol grn & multi (5) 4.50 2.00
1154 A288 8f gray & multi (6) 4.50 2.00
Nos. 1149-1154 (6) 27.00 12.00

Traditional acrobatics.

Shao Shan — A289

Transportation by Railroad A290

Designs: 1½f, Site of 1st National Communist Party Congress. 2f, Peasant Movement Institute, Kwangchow. 3f, Headquarters of Nanchang Uprising. 4f, Great Hall of the People, Peking. 5f, View of Wen Chia Shih. 8f, Tien An Men. 10f, Tzeping in Chingkang Mountains. 20f, Site of Kutien Meeting. 22f, Tsunyi Conference site. 35f, Yenan (bridge). 43f, Hsi Pai Ho, Communist Party meeting site. 50f, Fairy Cave, Lushan. 52f, Monument to People's Heroes. $2, Trucks on mountain road.

1974 Litho. *Perf. 11*
Without Gum

1163	A289	1f sl grn & pale grn	.15	.15
1164	A289	1½f car & buff	.15	.45
1165	A289	2f dk blue & pale grn	.15	.15
1166	A289	3f dk ol & yel	.15	.15
1167	A289	4f red & yel	.15	.15
1168	A289	5f brn & lt yel	.15	.15
1169	A289	8f dull mag & buff	.15	.15
a.		Perf. 11½x12	4.00	
1170	A289	10f blue & pink	.15	.15
1171	A289	20f dk red & buff	.20	.15
1172	A289	22f vio & lt yel	.40	.15
1173	A289	35f mar & lt yel	.60	.60
1174	A289	43f red brn & buff	1.00	*1.00*
1175	A289	50f dk blue & pink	*1.50*	*1.50*
1176	A289	52f sepia & buff	2.00	2.00

Photogravure & Engraved

1177	A290	$1 multicolored	.70	.15
1178	A290	$2 multicolored	1.50	.35
		Nos. 1163-1178 (16)	9.10	7.40

Capital Stadium — A290a

Design: 8f, Hotel Peking.

1974, Dec. 1 Photo. *Perf. 11*
Without Gum

1179	A290a	4f black & yel grn	.20	.15
1180	A290a	8f black & ultra	.30	.15
		Set value		.20

"Veteran Secretary" — A291

Well Diggers — A292

Designs: Nos. 1183-1186 horizontal. T.3.

1974, Apr. 20 Photo. *Perf. 11*

1181	A291	8f shown (1)	1.65	1.00
1182	A292	8f shown (2)	1.65	1.00
1183	A291	8f Spring hoeing (3)	1.65	1.00
1184	A291	8f Farmers (4)	1.65	1.00
1185	A292	8f Farm (5)	1.65	1.00
1186	A291	8f Bumper crops (6)	1.65	1.00
		Nos. 1181-1186 (6)	9.90	6.00

Paintings by farmers of Huhsien County, shown at exhibition in Peking.

Mailman on Motorcycle — A293

1974, May 15 Photo. *Perf. 11*

1187	A293	8f shown (1)	5.00	3.00
1188	A293	8f People of the world (2)	5.00	3.00
1189	A293	8f Great Wall (3)	5.00	3.00
		Nos. 1187-1189 (3)	15.00	9.00

Centenary of the UPU. J.1.

Barefoot Doctor Inoculating Children A294

Designs (Barefoot Doctors): No. 1191, Crossing stream at night to reach patient, vert. No. 1192, Gathering herbs, vert. No. 1193, Acupuncture treatment for farmer in the field.

Perf. 11x11½, 11½x11
1974, June 26 Photo.

1190	A294	8f multicolored (82)	1.00	.75
1191	A294	8f multicolored (83)	1.00	.75
1192	A294	8f multicolored (84)	1.00	.75
1193	A294	8f multicolored (85)	1.00	.75
		Nos. 1190-1193 (4)	4.00	3.00

Steel Worker Wang Chin-hsi — A295

Designs: No. 1195, Workers studying Mao's writings around campfire. No. 1196, Drilling for oil in winter. No. 1197, Scientific industrial management. No. 1198, Oil derricks and farms. T.4.

1974, Sept. 30 Photo. *Perf. 11*

1194	A295	8f multicolored (5-1)	1.25	1.00
1195	A295	8f multicolored (5-2)	1.25	1.00
1196	A295	8f multicolored (5-3)	1.25	1.00
1197	A295	8f multicolored (5-4)	1.25	1.00
1198	A295	8f multicolored (5-5)	1.25	1.00
		Nos. 1194-1198 (5)	6.25	5.00

The workers of Taching as examples of achievement.

Members of Tachai Commune — A296

Designs: No. 1200, Farmers leveling mountains and fields in winter. No. 1201, Scientific farming. No. 1202, Trucks carrying surplus harvest. No. 1203, Young workers with banner. T.5.

1974, Sept. 30

1199	A296	8f multi (5-1)	1.25	.90
1200	A296	8f multi (5-2)	1.25	.90
1201	A296	8f multi (5-3)	1.25	.90
1202	A296	8f multi (5-4)	1.25	.90
1203	A296	8f multi (5-5)	1.25	.90
		Nos. 1199-1203 (5)	6.25	4.50

The farmers of Tachai as examples of achievement.

Arms of Republic and Members of Ethnic Groups — A297

1974, Oct. 1

1204	A297	8f multi (1-1)	4.75	3.00

Taching Steel Worker — A298

Designs: No. 1206, Tachai farm woman. No. 1207, Soldier, planes and ships. J.3.

1974, Oct. 1

1205	A298	8f multi (3-1)	1.40	1.25
1206	A298	8f multi (3-2)	1.40	1.25
1207	A298	8f multi (3-3)	1.40	1.25
a.		Strip of 3, #1205-1207	4.50	4.00

People's Republic of China, 25th anniv.

Export Commodities Fair Building, Canton — A299

1974, Oct. 15

1208	A299	8f multicolored	3.50	1.50

Chinese Export Commodities Fair, Canton.

Guerrillas' Monument, Permet, Albania — A300

Albanian Patriots and Coat of Arms — A301

1974, Nov. 29 Photo. *Perf. 11½x11*

1209	A300	8f multicolored	3.00	1.25
1210	A301	8f multicolored	3.00	1.25

Albania's liberation, 30th anniversary.

Water-cooled Generator — A302

Industrial Products: No. 1212, Motorized rice sprouts transplanter. No. 1213, Universal cylindrical grinding machine. No. 1214, Open-air rock drill, vert. All dated 1973.

Photogravure and Engraved
1974, Dec. 23 *Perf. 11*

1211	A302	8f violet & multi (78)	3.50	1.25
1212	A302	8f yel grn & multi (79)	3.50	1.25
1213	A302	8f ver & multi (80)	3.50	1.25
1214	A302	8f blue & multi (81)	3.50	1.25
		Nos. 1211-1214 (4)	14.00	5.00

Congress Delegates — A303

Designs: No. 1216, Red flags, constitution and flowers. No. 1217, Worker, farmer and soldier, agriculture and industry. J.5.

1975, Jan. 25 Photo. *Perf. 11½*

1215	A303	8f gold & multi (3-1)	4.00	1.50
1216	A303	8f gold & multi (3-2)	4.00	1.50
1217	A303	8f gold & multi (3-3)	4.00	1.50
		Nos. 1215-1217 (3)	12.00	4.50

Fourth National People's Congress, Peking.

Teacher Studying Revolutionary Works A304

Designs: No. 1219, Teacher, children and horse. No. 1220, Outdoors class. No. 1221, Class held in boat. T.9.

1975, Mar. 8 Photo. *Perf. 11*

1218	A304	8f multi (4-1)	4.50	1.50
1219	A304	8f multi (4-2)	4.50	1.50
1220	A304	8f multi (4-3)	4.50	1.50
1221	A304	8f multi (4-4)	4.50	1.50
		Nos. 1218-1221 (4)	18.00	6.00

Rural women teachers and for International Working Women's Day.

"Broadsword," Encounter Position — A305

Designs: No. 1223, Exercise with 2 swords (woman). No. 1224, Graceful boxing (woman). No. 1225, Man leaping with spear. No. 1226, Woman holding cudgel. 43f, Two women with spears against man with cudgel.

1975, June 10 Photo. *Perf. 11x11½*
Size: 39x29mm

1222	A305	8f (6-1)	1.65	1.10
1223	A305	8f (6-2)	1.65	1.10
1224	A305	8f (6-3)	1.65	1.10
1225	A305	8f (6-4)	1.65	1.10
1226	A305	8f (6-5)	1.65	1.10

Size: 59x29mm

1227	A305	43f red & multi (6-6)	11.00	11.00
		Nos. 1222-1227 (6)	19.25	16.50

Wushu ("Kung Fu"), self-defense exercises. Tête bêche in sheets of 50 (5x10).

Mass Judgment and Criticisms — A306

Designs: No. 1229, Brigade leader writing wall newspaper. No. 1230, Study and criticism on battlefield, horiz. No. 1231, Former "slave" led into battle by criticism of Lin Piao and Confucius, horiz. T.8.

Perf. 11½x11, 11x11½
1975, Aug. 20 Photo.

1228	A306	8f red & multi (4-1)	3.75	1.50
1229	A306	8f red & multi (4-2)	3.75	1.50
1230	A306	8f red & multi (4-3)	3.75	1.50
1231	A306	8f red & multi (4-4)	3.75	1.50
		Nos. 1228-1231 (4)	15.00	6.00

Campaign to encourage criticism of Lin Piao and Confucius.

Athletes Studying Theory of Dictatorship of Proletariat — A307

3rd National Sports Meet: No. 1232, Women athletes leading parade, vert. No. 1234, Women volleyball players. No. 1235, Runner, soldier, farmer and worker, vert. No. 1236, Young athlete and various sports. No. 1237, Athletes of various races and horse race. 35f, Children and diving tower, vert. J.6.

1975, Sept. 12 Photo. *Perf. 11½*

1232	A307	8f multi (7-1)	.80	.60
1233	A307	8f multi (7-2)	.80	.60
1234	A307	8f multi (7-3)	.80	.60
1235	A307	8f multi (7-4)	.80	.60
1236	A307	8f multi (7-5)	.80	.60
1237	A307	8f multi (7-6)	.80	.60
1238	A307	35f multi (7-7)	3.50	2.50
		Nos. 1232-1238 (7)	8.30	6.10

Mountaineers A308

Mt. Everest A309

Design: No. 1240, Mountaineers raising Chinese flag on summit, horiz. T.15.

1975 Photo. *Perf. 11½x11, 11x11½*

1239 A308	8f multi (3-2)		.45	.35
1240 A308	8f multi (3-3)		.45	.35
1241 A309	43f multi (3-1)		1.65	1.00
	Nos. 1239-1241 (3)		2.55	1.70

Chinese Mt. Everest expedition.

Agricultural Workers with Book — A310

Designs: No. 1243, Workers carrying load. No. 1244, Woman driving harvester combine. J.7.

1975, Oct. 1 *Perf. 11½*

1242 A310	8f multi (3-1)	3.00	1.00
1243 A310	8f multi (3-2)	3.00	1.00
1244 A310	8f multi (3-3)	3.00	1.00
	Nos. 1242-1244 (3)	9.00	3.00

National Conference to promote learning from Tachai's achievements in agriculture.

Girl Giving Boy Red Scarf — A311

Designs (Children): No. 1246, Putting up wall posters criticizing Lin Piao and Confucius. No. 1247, Studying. No. 1248, Harvesting. 52f, Physical training. T.14.

1975, Dec. 1 Photo. *Perf. 11½*

1245 A311	8f multi (5-1)	.70	.70
1246 A311	8f multi (5-2)	.70	.70
1247 A311	8f multi (5-3)	.70	.70
1248 A311	8f multi (5-4)	.70	.70
1249 A311	52f multi (5-5)	5.25	3.00
	Nos. 1245-1249 (5)	8.05	5.80

Moral, intellectual and physical progress of Chinese children.

Woman Plowing Rice Field — A312

Designs: No. 1251, Mechanized rice planting. No. 1252, Drainage and irrigation. No. 1253, Woman spraying insecticide over cotton field. No. 1254, Combine. T.13.

1975, Dec. 15 *Perf. 11*

1250 A312	8f multi (5-1)	1.65	1.00
1251 A312	8f multi (5-2)	1.65	1.00
1252 A312	8f multi (5-3)	1.65	1.00
1253 A312	8f multi (5-4)	1.65	1.00
1254 A312	8f multi (5-5)	1.65	1.00
	Nos. 1250-1254 (5)	8.25	5.00

Priority program of farm mechanization.

Farmland and Irrigation Canal — A313

Designs of Nos. 1255-1270 numbered J.8.

1976, Feb. 20 Photo. *Perf. 11½*

1255 A313	8f shown (16-1)	2.50	1.25
1256 A313	8f Irrigation canal (16-2)	2.50	1.25
1257 A313	8f Fertilizer plant (16-3)	2.50	1.25
1258 A313	8f Textile plant (16-4)	2.50	1.25
1259 A313	8f Anshan Iron and Steel Co. (16-5)	2.50	1.25

Nos. 1255-1270 commemorate fulfillment of 4th Five-year Plan.

1976, Apr. 9

1260 A313	8f Coal freight trains (16-6)	2.50	1.25
1261 A313	8f Hydroelectric station (16-7)	2.50	1.25
1262 A313	8f Ship building (16-8)	2.50	1.25
1263 A313	8f Oil industry (16-9)	2.50	1.25
1264 A313	8f Pipe line and port (16-10)	2.50	1.25

1976, June 12

1265 A313	8f Train on viaduct (16-11)	2.50	1.25
1266 A313	8f Scientific research (16-12)	2.50	1.25
1267 A313	8f Classroom (16-13)	2.50	1.25
1268 A313	8f Health Center (16-14)	2.50	1.25
1269 A313	8f Apartment houses (16-15)	2.50	1.25
1270 A313	8f Department store (16-16)	2.50	1.25
	Nos. 1255-1270 (16)	40.00	20.00

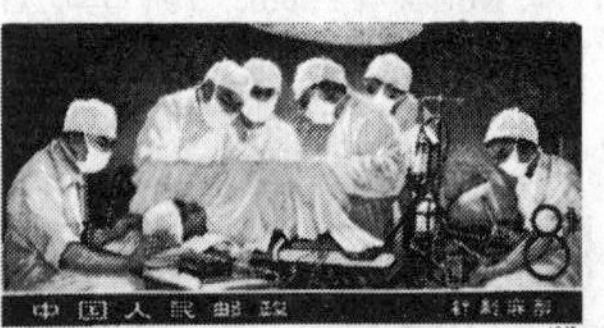

Heart Surgery with Acupuncture Anesthesia — A314

Designs (Operating Room and): No. 1272, Man driving tractor with severed arm restored. No. 1273, Man exercising broken arm in cast. No. 1274, Patient threading needle after cataract operation. T.12.

1976, Apr. 9 Photo. *Perf. 11½*

1271 A314	8f brn & multi (4-1)	2.50	1.00
1272 A314	8f yel grn & multi (4-2)	2.50	1.00
1273 A314	8f bl grn & multi (4-3)	2.50	1.00
1274 A314	8f vio bl & multi (4-4)	2.50	1.00
	Nos. 1271-1274 (4)	10.00	4.00

Achievements in medical and health services.

Students in May 7 School — A315

Designs: No. 1276, Students as farm workers. No. 1277, Production brigade. J.9.

1976, May 7 Photo. *Perf. 11½*

1275 A315	8f multi (3-1)	1.50	1.25
1276 A315	8f multi (3-2)	1.50	1.25
1277 A315	8f multi (3-3)	1.50	1.25
	Nos. 1275-1277 (3)	4.50	3.75

Chairman Mao's May 7 Directive, 10th anniv.

Mass Training in Swimming — A316

Designs: No. 1279, Swimmers crossing Yangtze River. No. 1280, Swimmers walking into the surf. J.10.

1976, July 16 Photo. *Perf. 11½*

Size: 47x27mm

1278 A316	8f multi (3-1)	1.50	1.00

Size: 35x27mm

1279 A316	8f multi (3-2)	1.50	1.00
1280 A316	8f multi (3-3)	1.50	1.00
	Nos. 1278-1280 (3)	4.50	3.00

Chairman Mao's swim in Yangtze River, 10th anniversary.

Workers, Peasants and Soldiers Going to College — A317

Designs: No. 1282, Classroom. No. 1283, Instruction on construction site. No. 1284, Computer room. No. 1285, Graduates returning home. T.18.

1976, Sept. 6 Photo. *Perf. 11½*

1281 A317	8f multi (5-1)	1.75	1.00
1282 A317	8f multi (5-2)	1.75	1.00
1283 A317	8f multi (5-3)	1.75	1.00
1284 A317	8f multi (5-4)	1.75	1.00
1285 A317	8f multi (5-5)	1.75	1.00
	Nos. 1281-1285 (5)	8.75	5.00

Success of proletarian education system.

Power Line Repair by Woman — A318

Designs: No. 1287, Insulator repair. No. 1288, Cherry picker. No. 1289, Transformer repair. T.16.

1976, Sept. 15

1286 A318	8f multi (4-1)	1.50	1.00
1287 A318	8f multi (4-2)	1.50	1.00
1288 A318	8f multi (4-3)	1.50	1.00
1289 A318	8f multi (4-4)	1.50	1.00
	Nos. 1286-1289 (4)	6.00	4.00

Maintenance of high power lines.

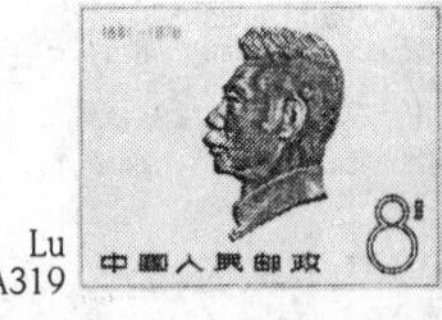

Lu Hsun — A319

Designs: No. 1291, Lu Hsun sick, writing in bed. No. 1292, Lu Hsun with worker, soldier and peasant. J.11.

Photo. & Engr.

1976, Oct. 19 *Perf. 11x11½*

1290 A319	8f multi (3-1)	4.00	1.75

Photo.

1291 A319	8f multi (3-2)	4.00	1.75
1292 A319	8f multi (3-3)	4.00	1.75
	Nos. 1290-1292 (3)	12.00	5.25

Lu Hsun (1881-1936), writer and revolutionary leader.

Old Farmer Tying Towel on Student's Head — A320

Designs: No. 1294, Student teaching farm woman, horiz. No. 1295, Students climbing mountain for new water resources. No. 1296, Student testing wheat, horiz. 10f, Student feeding lamb. 20f, Frontier guards, horiz. T.17.

1976, Dec. 22 Photo. *Perf. 11½*

1293 A320	4f multi (6-1)	.90	.50
1294 A320	8f multi (6-2)	.90	.50
1295 A320	8f multi (6-3)	.90	.50
1296 A320	8f multi (6-4)	.90	.50
1297 A320	10f multi (6-5)	.90	.50
1298 A320	20f multi (6-6)	4.00	1.65
	Nos. 1293-1298 (6)	8.50	4.15

Students' efforts to help poor country people.

Mao's Home, Shaoshan — A321

Shaoshan, Mao's birthplace: No. 1300, School building. No. 1301, Farmers' Association building. 10f, Railroad station. T.11.

1976, Dec. 26 *Perf. 11*

1299 A321	4f multi (4-1)	1.40	1.00
1300 A321	8f multi (4-2)	1.40	1.00
1301 A321	8f multi (4-3)	1.40	1.00
1302 A321	10f multi (4-4)	1.40	1.00
	Nos. 1299-1302 (4)	5.60	4.00

Chou En-lai — A322

Designs: No. 1304, Chou giving report at 10th Party Congress. No. 1305, Chou with Wang Chinhsi, famous oil worker, horiz. No. 1306, Chou with people of Tachai, 1973, horiz. J.13.

1977, Jan. 8 Photo. *Perf. 11½*

1303 A322	8f multi (4-1)	1.00	.60
1304 A322	8f multi (4-2)	1.00	.60
1305 A322	8f multi (4-3)	1.00	.60
1306 A322	8f multi (4-4)	1.00	.60
	Nos. 1303-1306 (4)	4.00	2.40

Premier Chou En-lai (1898-1976), a founder of Chinese Communist Party, 1st death anniversary.

Liu Hu-lan, an Inspiration — A323

Liu Hu-lan, Chinese heroine: No. 1307, Liu Hu-lan monument. No. 1308, Mao Tse-tung quotation: "A great life-a glorious death." J.12.

1977, Jan. 31

1307 A323	8f multi (3-1)	3.00	2.00
1308 A323	8f multi (3-2)	3.00	2.00
1309 A323	8f multi (3-3)	3.00	2.00
	Nos. 1307-1309 (3)	9.00	6.00

Uprising in Taiwan A324

Design: 10f, Gate of Heavenly Peace, Peking; Sun Moon Lake, Taiwan, Taiwanese people holding PRC flag. J.14.

1977, Feb. 28 Photo. *Perf. 11*

1310	A324	8f multi (2-1)	1.65	1.00
1311	A324	10f multi (2-2)	1.65	1.50

Uprising of the people of Taiwan, Feb. 28, 1947.

Sharpshooters — A325

Militia Women: No. 1313, Women horseback riders. No. 1314, Underground defense tunnel. T.10.

1977, Mar. 8 *Perf. 11½*

1312	A325	8f multi (3-1)	3.00	2.00
1313	A325	8f multi (3-2)	3.00	2.00
1314	A325	8f multi (3-3)	3.00	2.00
		Nos. 1312-1314 (3)	9.00	6.00

Forestry — A326

Designs: 1f, Coal mining. 1½f, Sheepherding. 2f, Export (loading railroad car onto ship). 4f, Hydroelectric station. 5f, Fishery. 8f, Combine in field. 10f, Radio tower and mail truck. 20f, Steel production. 30f, Trucks on mountain road. 40f, Textiles. 50f, Tractor assembly line. 60f, Offshore oil rigs and birds, setting sun. 70f, Railroad bridge, Yangtze Gorge. No numbers.

1977 Photo. *Perf. 11½*

1315	A326	1f yel grn, red & blk	.15	.15
1316	A326	1½f bl grn, yel grn & brn	.15	*.50*
1317	A326	2f org, bl & blk	.15	.15
1318	A326	3f ol & dk grn	.15	.15
1319	A326	4f lil, org & blk	.15	.15
1320	A326	5f lt ol & ultra	.15	.15
1321	A326	8f red & yel	.15	.15
1322	A326	10f lt grn, org & bl	.15	.15
1323	A326	20f org, yel & brn	.25	.15
1324	A326	30f bl, lt grn & blk	.30	.15
1325	A326	40f multicolored	.35	.35
1326	A326	50f cit, red & blk	.40	.20
1327	A326	60f pur, yel & org	.55	.30
1328	A326	70f blue & multi	.65	.45
		Nos. 1315-1328 (14)	3.70	
		Set value		2.50

Address by Party Committee A327

Designs: No. 1330, Planting new rice fields. No. 1331, Farmers reading wall newspaper. No. 1332, Land reclamation. T.22.

1977, Apr. 9 *Perf. 11x11½*

1329	A327	8f multi (4-1)	.75	.60
1330	A327	8f multi (4-2)	.75	.60
1331	A327	8f multi (4-3)	.75	.60
1332	A327	8f multi (4-4)	.75	.60
		Nos. 1329-1332 (4)	3.00	2.40

Building Tachai-type communities throughout China.

Worker at Microphone — A328

Designs: No. 1334, Drilling for oil during snowstorm. No. 1335, Crowd advancing under Red banner. No. 1336, Workers, industrial complex, rocket blast-off. J.15.

1977, Apr. 25 *Perf. 11*

1333	A328	8f multi (4-1)	.95	.70
1334	A328	8f multi (4-2)	.95	.70
1335	A328	8f multi (4-3)	.95	.70
1336	A328	8f multi (4-4)	.95	.70
		Nos. 1333-1336 (4)	3.80	2.80

Conference on learning from Taching workers in industry.

Mongolians Hailing Anniversary A329

Designs: 10f, Iron and steel complex, iron ore train. 20f, Cattle grazing in improved pasture. J.16.

1977, May 1 *Perf. 11x11½*

1337	A329	8f multi (3-1)	.65	.30
1338	A329	10f multi (3-2)	.65	.40
1339	A329	20f multi (3-3)	1.25	.80
		Nos. 1337-1339 (3)	2.55	1.50

30th anniversary of Inner Mongolian Autonomous Region.

1877 Flag of Romania and Oak Leaves — A330

Mihai Viteazu Memorial (16th Century Hero) — A331

Design: 10f, Battle of Smirdan, by N. Grigorescu. J.17.

1977, May 9 Photo. *Perf. 11*

1340	A330	8f multi (3-1)	.95	.60
1341	A331	10f multi (3-2)	.95	.95
1342	A331	20f multi (3-3)	2.00	1.65
		Nos. 1340-1342 (3)	3.90	3.20

Centenary of Romanian independence.

Yenan "Let 100 Flowers Bloom" A332

Design: No. 1344, Hammer, sickle, gun and flowers; "Proletarian revolutionary literature will prosper." J.18.

1977, May, 23

1343	A332	8f grn, red & gold	.75	.50
1344	A332	8f lt brn, red & gold	.75	.50

Yenan Forum on Literature and Art, 35th anniversary.

Chu Teh — A333

Designs: No. 1346, Chu Teh, last address to Congress. No. 1347, Chu Teh at his desk, horiz. No. 1348, Chu Teh on horseback as commander of Red Army. J.19.

1977, July 6 Photo. *Perf. 11½*

1345	A333	8f multi (4-1)	.35	.35
1346	A333	8f multi (4-2)	.35	.35
1347	A333	8f multi (4-3)	.35	.35
1348	A333	8f multi (4-4)	.35	.35
		Nos. 1345-1348 (4)	1.40	1.40

Chu Teh (1886-1976), Commander of Red Army, Chairman of National People's Congress.

Military under Mao's Banner — A334

Designs: No. 1350, Red Flag, Soldiers, Chingkang Mountains. No. 1351, Guerrilla fighters returning to base. No. 1352, Guerrillas crossing Yangtze. No. 1353, National defense. J.20.

1977, Aug. 1

1349	A334	8f multi (5-1)	1.00	.80
1350	A334	8f multi (5-2)	1.00	.80
1351	A334	8f multi (5-3)	1.00	.80
1352	A334	8f multi (5-4)	1.00	.80
1353	A334	8f multi (5-5)	1.00	.80
		Nos. 1349-1353 (5)	5.00	4.00

Liberation Army Day, 50th anniversary of People's Army.

Gate of Heavenly Peace, People and Red Flags — A335

Designs: No. 1355, People marching under Red Flag with Mao's portrait. No. 1356, People marching under Red Flag with hammer and sickle. J.23.

1977, Aug. 22 Photo. *Perf. 11½x11*

1354	A335	8f multi (3-1)	1.65	1.65
1355	A335	8f multi (3-2)	1.65	1.65
1356	A335	8f multi (3-3)	1.65	1.65
		Nos. 1354-1356 (3)	4.95	4.95

11th National Congress of the Communist Party of China.

Chairman Mao — A336

Designs (Mao Portraits): No. 1358, as young man in Shansi. No. 1359, addressing Communist Party in Plenary Session. No. 1360, Proclaiming People's Republic at Gate of Heavenly Peace. No. 1361, at airport with Chou En-lai and Chu Teh, horiz. No. 1362, Reviewing Army as old man. J.21.

1977, Sept. 9 Photo. *Perf. 11½*

1357	A336	8f multi (6-1)	.45	.35
1358	A336	8f multi (6-2)	.45	.35
1359	A336	8f multi (6-3)	.45	.35
1360	A336	8f multi (6-4)	.45	.35
1361	A336	8f multi (6-5)	.45	.35
1362	A336	8f multi (6-6)	.45	.35
		Nos. 1357-1362 (6)	2.70	2.10

Mao-Tse-tung (1893-1976), first death anniversary.

Mao Memorial Hall — A337

Completion of Mao Memorial Hall: No. 1364, Chairman Hua's inscription. J.22.

1977, Sept. 9

1363	A337	8f lt ultra & multi	2.00	1.40
1364	A337	8f lt grn, tan & gold	2.00	1.40

Tractors Moving Drilling Tower — A338

Designs: No. 1366, Shui Pow Tsi oil well and women workers. No. 1367, Construction of oil pipe line, Taching, and silos. No. 1368, Tung Fang Hung oil refinery, Peking. No. 1369, Taching oil loaded into tanker in harbor. 20f, Off-shore drilling platform "Pohai No. 1." T.19.

1978, Jan. 31 Photo. *Perf. 11*

1365	A338	8f multi (6-1)	.55	.55
1366	A338	8f multi (6-2)	.55	.55
1367	A338	8f multi (6-3)	.55	.55
1368	A338	8f multi (6-4)	.55	.55
1369	A338	8f multi (6-5)	.55	.55
1370	A338	20f multi (6-6)	1.00	.80
		Nos. 1365-1370 (6)	3.75	3.55

Development of Chinese oil industry.

"Army Teaching Militia" — A339

Design: No. 1372, "Army helping with rice planting." T.23.

1978, Feb. 5 Photo. *Perf. 11*

1371	A339	8f multi (2-1)	1.00	1.00
1372	A339	8f multi (2-2)	1.00	1.00

Army and people working as a family.

Red Flags, Mao Tse-tung — A340

Constitution and Red Flags — A341

Design: No. 1375, Atom symbol over symbols of agriculture and industry. All designs include Great Hall of the People, Peking, and flowers. J.24.

1978, Feb. 26

1373	A340	8f multi (3-1)	.60	.50
1374	A341	8f multi (3-2)	.60	.50
1375	A340	8f multi (3-3)	.60	.50
		Nos. 1373-1375 (3)	1.80	1.50

5th National People's Congress.

Mao's Eulogy for Lei Feng — A342

Lei Feng, Studying Mao's Works — A343

Design: No. 1377, Chairman Hua's thoughts (5 lines). J.26.

1978, Mar. 5

1376 A342 8f gold & red (3-1) .65 .65
1377 A342 8f gold & red (3-2) .65 .65
1378 A343 8f multicolored (3-3) .65 .65
Nos. 1376-1378 (3) 1.95 1.95

Lei Feng (1940-1962), communist fighter; 15th anniversary of Chairman Mao's eulogy "Learn from Comrade Lei Feng."

Hsiang Ching-yu — A344

Yang Kai-hui — A345

1978, Mar. 8

1379 A344 8f multi (2-1) .50 .50
1380 A345 8f multi (2-2) .50 .50

Hsiang Ching-yu, pioneer of Women's Movement, executed 1928; Yang Kai-hui, communist fighter, executed 1930. J.27.

Conference Emblem — A346

Designs: No. 1382, Banners symbolizing industry, agriculture, defense and science. No. 1383, Red flag, atom symbol and globe. J.25.

1978, Mar. 18 Litho. *Perf. 11½x11*

1381 A346 8f gold & red (3-1) .40 .40
1382 A346 8f multi (3-2) .40 .40
1383 A346 8f multi (3-3) .40 .40
a. Souvenir sheet of 3 *125.00*
Nos. 1381-1383 (3) 1.20 1.20

Natl. Science Conf. No. 1383a contains Nos. 1381-1383 with simulated perforations. Sold for 50 fen.

Release of Weather Balloon A347

Weather Observations: No. 1385, Radar station, typhoon watch. No. 1386, Computer, weather maps. No. 1387, Local weather observers. No. 1388, Rockets intercepting hail clouds. T.24.

1978, Apr. 25 Photo. *Perf. 11x11½*

1384 A347 8f multi (5-1) .30 .30
1385 A347 8f multi (5-2) .30 .30
1386 A347 8f multi (5-3) .30 .30
1387 A347 8f multi (5-4) .25 .25
1388 A347 8f multi (5-5) .25 .25
Nos. 1384-1388 (5) 1.40 1.40

Galloping Horse — A348

Children Playing Soccer — A349

Designs: Galloping Horses, by Hsu Peihung (1895-1953). 40f, 50f, 60f, 70f, $5, horiz. T.28.

1978, May 5 *Perf. 11½x11, 11x11½*

1389 A348 4f multi (10-1) .30 .30
1390 A348 8f multi (10-2) .30 .30
1391 A348 8f multi (10-3) .30 .30
1392 A348 10f multi (10-4) .30 .30
1393 A348 20f multi (10-5) .90 .75
1394 A348 30f multi (10-6) 1.10 .95
1395 A348 40f multi (10-7) 1.65 1.40
1396 A348 50f multi (10-8) 1.75 1.50
1397 A348 60f multi (10-9) 2.50 2.00
1398 A348 70f multi (10-10) 2.75 2.25
Nos. 1389-1398 (10) 11.85 10.05

Souvenir Sheet

1399 A348 $5 multicolored *100.00*

No. 1399 contains one stamp showing 4 horses, size: 89x39mm.

1978, June 1 *Perf. 11½*

Designs: No. 1401, Children on the beach. No. 1402, Little girls dancing. No. 1403, Children taking long walks. 20f, Children exercising for good health. T.21.

Size: 22x27mm

1400 A349 8f multi (5-2) .25 .25
1401 A349 8f multi (5-3) .25 .25
1402 A349 8f multi (5-4) .25 .25
1403 A349 8f multi (5-5) .25 .25

Size: 48x28mm

1404 A349 20f multi (5-1) .50 .40
Nos. 1400-1404 (5) 1.50 1.40

Build up your health while young.

Synthetic Fiber Feeder A350

Designs: No. 1406, Drawing out threads. No. 1407, Weaving. No. 1408, Dyeing and printing. No. 1409, Finished products. T.25.

1978, June 15 Photo. *Perf. 11½*

1405 A350 8f multi (5-1) .40 .40
1406 A350 8f multi (5-2) .40 .40
1407 A350 8f multi (5-3) .40 .40
1408 A350 8f multi (5-4) .40 .40
1409 A350 8f multi (5-5) .40 .40
a. Strip of 5, #1405-1409 2.00 2.00
Nos. 1405-1409 (5) 2.00 2.00

Chemical fiber industry. No. 1409a has continuous design.

Conference Emblem A351

"Develop Economy and Ensure Supplies" A352

1978, June 20 *Perf. 13*

1410 A351 8f multi (2-1) .45 .45
1411 A352 8f multi (2-2) .45 .45

Natl. Conf. on Learning from Taching and Tachai in Finance and Trade. J.28.

New Pastures, Mongolia — A353

Designs: No. 1413, Kazakh shepherds selecting sheep for breeding. No. 1414, Mechanized shearing of sheep, Tibet, T.27.

1978, June 30 Photo. *Perf. 11½*

1412 A353 8f multi (3-1) .65 .40
1413 A353 8f multi (3-2) .65 .40
1414 A353 8f multi (3-3) .65 .40
Nos. 1412-1414 (3) 1.95 1.20

Learning from Tachai in developing animal husbandry and new pastoral areas.

Coke Oven — A354

Iron and Steel Industry: No. 1416, Iron furnace. No. 1417, Pouring steel. No. 1418, Steel rolling. No. 1419, Finished iron and steel products. T.26.

1978, July 22

1415 A354 8f multi (5-1) .50 .35
1416 A354 8f multi (5-2) .50 .35
1417 A354 8f multi (5-3) .50 .35
1418 A354 8f multi (5-4) .50 .35
1419 A354 8f multi (5-5) .50 .35
Nos. 1415-1419 (5) 2.50 1.75

Iron Fist to Prevent Revisionism A355

Jug in Shape of Sheep A356

Designs: No. 1421, "Carrying forward revolutionary tradition." No. 1422, "Strenuous training in military skills to wipe out enemy." T.32.

1978, Aug. 1 Photo. *Perf. 11½*

1420 A355 8f multi (3-1) .70 .40
1421 A355 8f multi (3-2) .70 .40
1422 A355 8f multi (3-3) .70 .40
Nos. 1420-1422 (3) 2.10 1.20

"Learn from Hard-boned 6th Company." (A military unit since 1939).

Souvenir Sheets
Booklet Panes
Heavy speculation in stamps in China is centered around the souvenir sheets and booklet panes. These generally are trading by the 100 in China and being held off the normal philatelic market.

1978, Aug. 26

Arts and Crafts: 4f, Giant lion (toy; horiz.). No. 1425, Rhinoceros (lacquer ware; horiz). 10f, Cat (embroidery). 20f, Bag (weaving; horiz.). 30f, Teapot in shape of peacock (cloisonné). 40f, Plate with lotus, and swan-shaped box (lacquer ware; horiz.). 50f, Dragon flying in sky (ivory). 60f, Sun rising (jade; horiz.). 70f, Flight to human world (ivory). $3, Flying fairies (arts and crafts; horiz.). T.29.

1423 A356 4f multi (10-1) .15 .15
1424 A356 8f multi (10-2) .15 .15
1425 A356 8f multi (10-3) .15 .15
1426 A356 10f multi (10-4) .15 .15
1427 A356 20f multi (10-5) .40 .40
1428 A356 30f multi (10-6) .50 .50
1429 A356 40f multi (10-7) .65 .65
1430 A356 50f multi (10-8) .85 .85
1431 A356 60f multi (10-9) 1.10 1.10
1432 A356 70f multi (10-10) 1.40 1.40
Nos. 1423-1432 (10) 5.50 5.50

Souvenir Sheet

1433 A356 $3 multi *150.00*

No. 1433 contains one 85x36mm stamp.

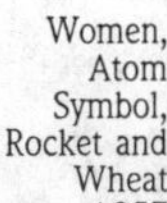

Women, Atom Symbol, Rocket and Wheat A357

1978, Sept. 8 Photo. *Perf. 11*

1434 A357 8f multicolored 1.00 .70

4th National Women's Congress.

Ginseng — A358

Flag, Wheat, Cogwheel, Plane, Atom Symbols — A359

Medicinal Plants: No. 1436, Horn of plenty. No. 1437, Blackberry lily. No. 1438, Balloonflower. 55f, Rhododendron dauricum. T.30.

1978, Sept. 15

1435 A358 8f multi (5-1) .25 .25
1436 A358 8f multi (5-2) .25 .25
1437 A358 8f multi (5-3) .25 .25
1438 A358 8f multi (5-4) .25 .25
1439 A358 55f multi (5-5) 2.00 .70
Nos. 1435-1439 (5) 3.00 1.70

1978, Oct. 11 Photo. *Perf. 11*

1440 A359 8f multicolored 1.00 .80

9th National Trade Union Congress.

Youth League Emblem A360

1978, Oct. 16

1441 A360 8f multicolored 1.25 .80

10th Natl. Communist Youth League Cong.

Chinese and Japanese Girls Exchanging Gifts — A361

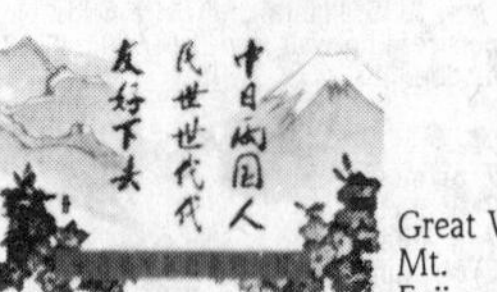

Great Wall and Mt. Fuji — A362

1978, Oct. 22

1442 A361 8f multicolored .25 .25
1443 A362 55f multicolored 1.50 1.50

Signing of Sino-Japanese Peace and Friendship Treaty.

Moslem, Chinese and Mongolian People — A363

Chinsha River Bridge, West Szechuan — A364

Designs: No. 1445, Loading coal at Holan Mountain. 10f, Irrigated rice fields and boxthorn. J.29.

1978, Oct. 25

1444	A363	8f multi (3-1)	.50	.50
1445	A363	8f multi (3-2)	.50	.50
1446	A363	10f multi (3-3)	.50	.50
		Nos. 1444-1446 (3)	1.50	1.50

20th anniversary of founding of Ningsia Moslem Autonomous Region.

1978, Nov. 1 Photo. *Perf. 11½x11*

Highway Bridges: No. 1448, Hsinhong bridge, Wuhsi. No. 1449, Chiuhsikou bridge, Fengdu. No. 1450, Chinsha River bridge, West Szechuan. 60f, Shangyeh bridge, Sanmen. $2, Hsiang-kiang River bridge. T.31.

1447	A364	8f multi (5-1)	.25	.25
1448	A364	8f multi (5-2)	.25	.25
1449	A364	8f multi (5-3)	.25	.25
1450	A364	8f multi (5-4)	.25	.25
1451	A364	60f multi (5-5)	2.50	1.00
		Nos. 1447-1451 (5)	3.50	2.00

Souvenir Sheet

1452 A364 $2 multi *125.00*

No. 1452 contains one 86x37mm stamp.

Mechanical Transplanting of Rice Seedlings — A365

Paintings: No. 1454, Spraying fields. No. 1455, Seed selection. No. 1456, Trade. No. 1457, Delivery of public grain in city. T.34.

1978, Nov. 30 *Perf. 11½*

1453	A365	8f multi (5-1)	2.75	1.50
1454	A365	8f multi (5-2)	2.75	1.50
1455	A365	8f multi (5-3)	2.75	1.50
1456	A365	8f multi (5-4)	2.75	1.50
1457	A365	8f multi (5-5)	2.75	1.50
a.		Strip of 5, #1453-1457	14.00	8.00

Agricultural progress. No. 1457a has a continuous design.

Dancers and Fireworks — A366

Designs: No. 1459, Industry, vert. 10f, Agriculture, vert. J.33.

1978, Dec. 11 Photo. *Perf. 11*

1458	A366	8f multi (3-1)	1.00	.50
1459	A366	8f multi (3-2)	1.00	.50
1460	A366	10f multi (3-3)	1.00	.50
		Nos. 1458-1460 (3)	3.00	1.50

20th anniversary of Kwangsi Chuang Autonomous Region.

Miners with Pneumatic Drill — A367

Mine Development: 4f, Old Tibetan peasant reporting to surveyor. 10f, Open-cut mining with power shovel. 20f, Loaded electric train in pit. T.20.

1978, Dec. 29 Photo. & Engr.

1461	A367	4f multi (4-1)	.20	.20
1462	A367	8f multi (4-2)	.40	.30
1463	A367	10f multi (4-3)	.55	.40
1464	A367	20f multi (4-4)	.85	.65
		Nos. 1461-1464 (4)	2.00	1.55

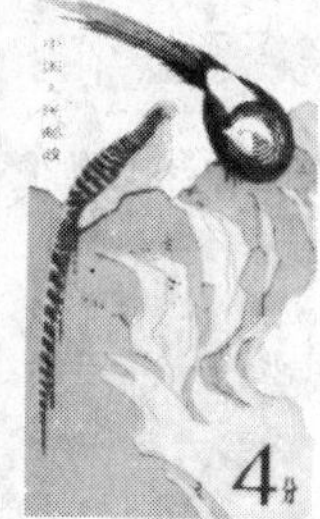
A368

A369

Golden Pheasants: 4f, Roosting on rock. 8f, In flight. 45f, Seeking food. T.35.

1979, Jan. 25 Photo. *Perf. 11½*

1465	A368	4f multi (3-1)	.75	.30
1466	A368	8f multi (3-2)	.75	.30
1467	A368	45f multi (3-3)	3.00	3.00
		Nos. 1465-1467 (3)	4.50	3.60

1979, Mar. 14 Photo. *Perf. 11½x11*

1468 A369 8f Albert Einstein, equation 1.00 .75

Phoenix Battling Monster, Praying Woman A370

Design: 60f, Man riding dragon to heaven. Designs from silk paintings found in Changsha tomb, Warring States Period (475-221 B.C.). T.33.

1979, Mar. 29 *Perf. 11*

1469	A370	8f multi (2-1)	.55	.40
1470	A370	60f multi (2-2)	2.75	2.00

Summer Palace — A371

Photo., Photo. & Engr. ($5)

1979-80 *Perf. 13*

1471	A371	$1 Pagoda ('80)	.65	.25
1472	A371	$2 Shown	1.25	.55
1473	A371	$5 Temple, Beihai Park ('80)	4.50	1.25
		Nos. 1471-1473 (3)	6.40	2.05

Hammer and Sickle "51" and Bars from "International" — A372

1979, May 1 Photo. *Perf. 11*

1474 A372 8f multicolored .60 .60

International Labor Day, 90th anniv.

"Tradition of May 4th Movement" A373

Young Woman, Rocket, Antenna, Nuclear Reactor A374

1979, May 4

1475	A373	8f multicolored	.50	.40
1476	A374	8f multicolored	.50	.40

60th anniversary of May 4th Movement.

IYC Emblem, Children Holding Balloons — A375

Children of Three Races, IYC Emblem — A376

1979, May 25 *Perf. 11½*

1477	A375	8f multicolored	.65	.45
1478	A376	60f multicolored	4.50	3.25

International Year of the Child.

Great Wall in Spring A377

Designs (The Great Wall): No. 1480, in summer. No. 1481, in autumn. 60f, in winter. $2, Guard tower. T.38.

1979, June 25 Photo. *Perf. 11*

1479	A377	8f multi (4-1)	.80	.75
1480	A377	8f multi (4-2)	.80	.75
1481	A377	8f multi (4-3)	.80	.75
1482	A377	60f multi (4-4)	4.50	4.00
		Nos. 1479-1482 (4)	6.90	6.25

Souvenir Sheet

1483 A377 $2 multi *65.00*

For overprint see No. 1492.

Roaring Tiger — A379

Manchurian Tiger: 8f, Two young tigers. 60f, Tiger at rest. T.40.

1979, July 20 *Perf. 11½x11*

1484	A379	4f multi (3-1)	.35	.30
1485	A379	8f multi (3-2)	.35	.30
1486	A379	60f multi (3-3)	2.25	1.25
		Nos. 1484-1486 (3)	2.95	1.85

Mechanical Harvesting — A380

Work of the Communes: No. 1488, Forestry. No. 1489, Raising ducks. No. 1490, Women weaving baskets. 10f, Fishing. T.39.

1979, Aug. 10 *Perf. 11½*

1487	A380	4f multi (5-1)	.65	.65
1488	A380	8f multi (5-2)	.65	.65
1489	A380	8f multi (5-3)	.65	.65
1490	A380	8f multi (5-4)	.65	.65
1491	A380	10f multi (5-5)	.65	.65
		Nos. 1487-1491 (5)	3.25	3.25

No. 1483 Overprinted with Gold Inscription and "1979" Souvenir Sheet

1979, Aug. 25 Photo. *Perf. 11*

1492 A377 $2 multicolored *225.00*

31st International Stamp Exhibition, Riccione, Italy. J41 (1-1).

Forged overprints exist.

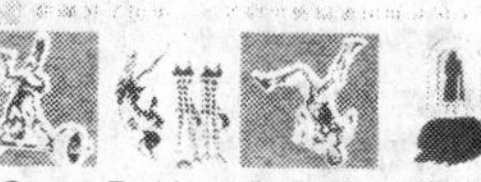
Games Emblem, Sports — A381

Emblem and: No. 1494, Soccer, badminton, high jump, speed skating. No. 1495, Fencing, skiing, gymnastics, diving. No. 1496, Motorcycling, table tennis, basketball, archery. No. 1497, Emblem only, vert. J.43.

1979, Sept. 15 *Perf. 11½x11*

1493	A381	8f multi (4-1)	.35	.35
1494	A381	8f multi (4-2)	.35	.35
1495	A381	8f multi (4-3)	.35	.35
1496	A381	8f multi (4-4)	.35	.35
a.		Block of 4, #1493-1496	1.50	1.50

Souvenir Sheet

Perf. 11½

1497 A381 $2 multi

4th National Games. Size of stamp in No. 1497: 22x26mm.

Flag and Rainbow — A382

Design: No. 1499, Flag and mountains.

1979, Oct. 1 Photo. *Perf. 11½*

1498	A382	8f multicolored	1.00	.80
1499	A382	8f multicolored	1.00	.80

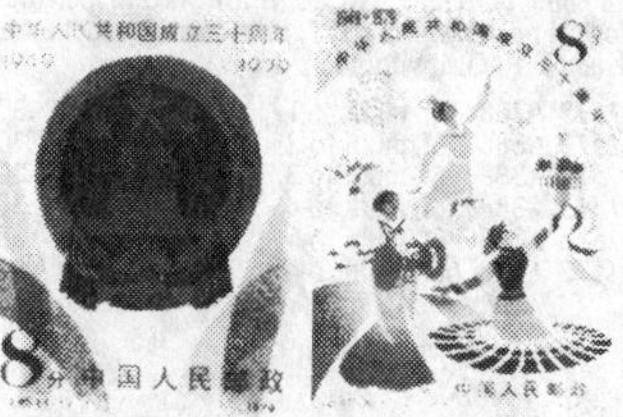
National Emblem — A383

Dancers — A384

1979, Oct. 1 Photo. *Perf. 11½*

1500 A383 8f multicolored 1.25 .60

Souvenir Sheet

1501 A383 $1 multicolored *30.00*

1979, Oct. 1 Photo. *Perf. 11½*

Designs: #1503-1505, various dances. J.47.

1502	A384	8f multi (4-1)	.35	.15
1503	A384	8f multi (4-2)	.35	.15
1504	A384	8f multi (4-3)	.35	.15
1505	A384	8f multi (4-4)	.35	.15
a.		Block of 4, #1502-1505	1.50	1.25

Tractor, Aerial Crop Spraying, Irrigation — A385

Designs: No. 1507, Gear, computers. No. 1508, Rocket, submarine, jets. No. 1509, Atom symbol. J.48.

1979, Oct. 1 Photo. *Perf. 11½*

1506 A385 8f multi (4-1) .40 .40
1507 A385 8f multi (4-2) .40 .40
1508 A385 8f multi (4-3) .40 .40
1509 A385 8f multi (4-4) .40 .40
Nos. 1506-1509 (4) 1.60 1.60

National Anthem A386

1979, Oct. 1 Engr. *Perf. 11*

1510 A386 8f multicolored 1.00 1.00

Exhibition Emblem — A387

Children Flying Model Planes — A388

1979, Oct. 3

1511 A387 8f multicolored .75 .50

Junior National Scientific and Technological Exhibition.

1979, Oct. 3

Designs: No. 1513, Girls and microscope. No. 1514, Children and telescope. No. 1515, Boy catching butterflies. No. 1516, Girl taking meteorological readings. No. 1517, Boys sailing model boat. No. 1518, Girl with book. T.41.

1512 A388 8f multi (6-1) .30 .30
1513 A388 8f multi (6-2) .30 .30
1514 A388 8f multi (6-3) .30 .30
1515 A388 8f multi (6-4) .30 .30
1516 A388 8f multi (6-5) .30 .30
1517 A388 60f multi (6-6) 1.10 .80
Nos. 1512-1517 (6) 2.60 2.30

Souvenir Sheet

Perf. 11

1518 A388 $2 multi

Study Science from Childhood. No. 1518 contains one stamp, size: 90x40mm.

Yu Shan Mountain A389

Taiwan Landscapes: No. 1520, Sun and Moon Lake. No. 1521, Chihkan Tower. No. 1522, Suao-Hualien Highway. 55f, Tian Xiang Falls. 60f, Banping Mountain. T.42.

1979, Oct. 20 Photo. *Perf. 11x11½*

1519 A389 8f multi (6-1) .50 .50
1520 A389 8f multi (6-2) .50 .50
1521 A389 8f multi (6-3) .50 .50
1522 A389 8f multi (6-4) .50 .50
1523 A389 55f multi (6-5) 2.50 1.00
1524 A389 60f multi (6-6) 2.50 2.00
Nos. 1519-1524 (6) 7.00 5.00

Arts Symbols A390

Design: 8f, Seals and modernization symbols. J.39.

1979, Oct. 30

1525 A390 4f multicolored .40 .30
1526 A390 8f multicolored .70 .45

4th Natl. Cong. of Literary and Art Workers.

Train in Tunnel A391

Railroads: No. 1528, Mountain bridge. No. 1529, Freight train. T.36.

1979, Oct. 30 Photo. & Engr.

1527 A391 8f multi (3-1) .50 .50
1528 A391 8f multi (3-2) .50 .50
1529 A391 8f multi (3-3) .50 .50
Nos. 1527-1529 (3) 1.50 1.50

Chrysanthemum Petal — A392

Camellias: No. 1531, Lion head. No. 1532, Camellia chryantha. 10f, Small osmanthus leaf. 20f, Baby face. 30f, Cornelian. 40f, Peony camellia. 50f, Purple gown. 60f, Dwarf rose. 70f, Willow leaf spinel pink. $2, Red jewelry. T.37.

1979, Nov. 10 Photo. *Perf. 11x11½*

1530 A392 4f multi (10-1) .45 .20
1531 A392 8f multi (10-2) .45 .20
1532 A392 8f multi (10-3) .45 .20
1533 A392 10f multi (10-4) .45 .20
1534 A392 20f multi (10-5) .75 .30
1535 A392 30f multi (10-6) .95 .60
1536 A392 40f multi (10-7) 1.65 .80
1537 A392 50f multi (10-8) 1.65 1.00
1538 A392 60f multi (10-9) 1.90 1.20
1539 A392 70f multi (10-10) 2.25 1.40
Nos. 1530-1539 (10) 10.95 6.10

Souvenir Sheet

Perf. 11½x11

1540 A392 $2 multi *75.00*

No. 1540 contains one 86x36mm stamp.

No. 1540 Overprinted and Numbered in Gold in Margin
Souvenir Sheet

1979, Nov. 10

1541 A392 $2 multicolored *200.00*

People's Republic of China Phil. Exhib., Hong Kong, 1979. J.42 (1-1).
Forged overprints exist.

Norman Bethune Treating Soldier — A393

Design: 70f, Bethune statue.

1979, Nov. 12

1542 A393 8f multi (2-2) .30 .30
1543 A393 70f multi (2-1) 2.75 2.75

Dr. Norman Bethune, 40th death anniv. J.50.

Central Archives Hall — A394

Intl. Archives Weeks: No. 1545, Gold archive cabinet, vert. 60f, Pavilion. J.51.

Perf. 11x11½, 11½x11

1979, Nov. 26 Photo.

1544 A394 8f multi (3-1) .60 .25
1545 A394 8f multi (3-2) .60 .25
1546 A394 60f multi (3-3) 2.50 1.25
Nos. 1544-1546 (3) 3.70 1.75

Monkey King in Waterfall Cave — A395

Monkey King, Scenes from Pilgrimage to the West (Novel): No. 1548, Fighting Necha, son of Prince Li. No. 1549, In Mother Queen's peach orchard. No. 1550, In the alchemy furnace. 10f, Subduing the white bone demon. 20f, With palm leaf fan. 60f, In cobweb cave. 70f, Walking on scripture-seeking route. T.43.

1979, Dec. 1 *Perf. 11½x11*

1547 A395 8f multi (8-1) .80 .75
1548 A395 8f multi (8-2) .80 .75
1549 A395 8f multi (8-3) .80 .75
1550 A395 8f multi (8-4) .80 .75
1551 A395 10f multi (8-5) .80 .75
1552 A395 20f multi (8-6) 1.40 1.25
1553 A395 60f multi (8-7) 4.50 4.25
1554 A395 70f multi (8-8) 5.00 4.75
Nos. 1547-1554 (8) 14.90 14.00

Stalin Delivering Speech A396

Joseph Stalin (1879-1953): No. 1555, Portrait of Stalin, vert. J.49.

Perf. 11x11½, 11½x11

1979, Dec. 21 Engr.

1555 A396 8f brown (2-1) .55 .55
1556 A396 8f black (2-2) .55 .55

A397 A398

1980 Photo. *Perf. 11½*

1557 A397 4f Peony (16-1) .35 .30
1558 A397 4f Squirrels and grapes (16-2) .35 .30
1559 A397 8f Crabs candle and wine (16-3) .35 .30
1560 A397 8f Tadpoles in mountain spring (16-4) .35 .30
1561 A397 8f Chicks (16-5) .35 .30
1562 A397 8f Lotus (16-6) .35 .30
1563 A397 8f Red plum (16-7) .35 .30
1564 A397 8f Kingfisher (16-8) .35 .30
1565 A397 10f Bottle gourd (16-9) .35 .30
1566 A397 20f Voice of autumn (16-10) .35 .25
1567 A397 30f Wisteria (16-11) .75 .50
1568 A397 40f Chrysanthemums (16-12) 1.10 .80
1569 A397 50f Shrimp (16-13) 1.65 1.00
1570 A397 55f Litchi (16-14) 2.25 1.50
1571 A397 60f Cabbages, mushrooms (16-15) 2.75 2.00
1572 A397 70f Peaches (16-16) 3.25 2.50
Nos. 1557-1572 (16) 15.25 11.25

Souvenir Sheet

1573 A397 $2 Evergreen *47.50*

Qi Baishi paintings. Issue dates: Nos. 1557-1560, 1569-1572, Jan. 15; others, May 20. No. 1573 contains one 37½x61mm stamp. T. 44.

1980, Jan. 25 *Perf. 11½x11*

Opera Masks: No. 1574, Meng Liang Mask from Hongyang Cave Opera. No. 1575, Li Kui, from Black Whirlwind. No. 1576, Huang Gai, from Meeting of Heroes. No. 1577, 10f, Lu Zhishen, from Wild Boar Forest. 20f, Lian Po, from Reconciliation between the General and Minister. 60f, Zhang Fei, from Reed Marsh. 70f, Dou Erdun, from Stealing the Emperor's Horse, T. 45.

1574 A398 4f multi (8-1) .75 .35
1575 A398 4f multi (8-2) .75 .35
1576 A398 8f multi (8-3) .75 .35
1577 A398 8f multi (8-4) .75 .35
1578 A398 10f multi (8-5) .75 .35
1579 A398 20f multi (8-6) 1.50 1.50
1580 A398 60f multi (8-7) 5.50 2.50
1581 A398 70f multi (8-8) 5.50 3.00
Nos. 1574-1581 (8) 16.25 8.75

Speed Skating, Olympic Rings — A399

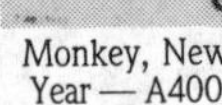
Monkey, New Year — A400

Olympic Rings and: No. 1582, Chinese flag. No. 1584, Figure skating. 60f, Downhill skiing. J.54.

1980, Feb. 13

1582 A399 8f multi (4-1) .50 .25
1583 A399 8f multi (4-2) .50 .25
1584 A399 8f multi (4-3) .50 .25
1585 A399 60f multi (4-4) 2.50 1.00
Nos. 1582-1585 (4) 4.00 1.75

13th Winter Olympic Games, Lake Placid, NY, Feb. 12-24.

Engraved and Photogravure

1980, Feb. 15 *Perf. 11½*

1586 A400 8f multicolored *65.00 25.00*

Clara Zetkin — A401

Photogravure & Engraved

1980, Mar. 8 *Perf. 11½x11*

1587 A401 8f black & yel 1.00 .80

International Working Women's Day, 70th anniv., founded by Clara Zetkin (1857-1933).

Orchard A402

Afforestation: 8f, Trees lining highway. 10f, Aerial seeding. 20f, Trees surrounding factory. T.48.

1980, Mar. 12 *Perf. 11x11½*

1588 A402 4f multi (4-1) .35 .25
1589 A402 8f multi (4-2) .50 .25
1590 A402 10f multi (4-3) .70 .25
1591 A402 20f multi (4-4) 1.50 1.00
Nos. 1588-1591 (4) 3.05 1.75

Apsaras, Symbols of Modernization — A403

1980, Mar. 15 **Photo.** *Perf. 11½*

1592 A403 8f multicolored 1.00 .80

2nd National Conference of the Scientific and Technical Association of China.

Mail Transport (T.49) — A404

1980, Mar. 20 *Perf. 11x11½*

1593 A404 2f Ship (4-1) 1.10 1.00
1594 A404 4f Bus (4-2) 1.10 1.00
1595 A404 8f Train (4-3) 1.50 1.00
1596 A404 10f Jet (4-4) 2.00 1.50
Nos. 1593-1596 (4) 5.70 4.50

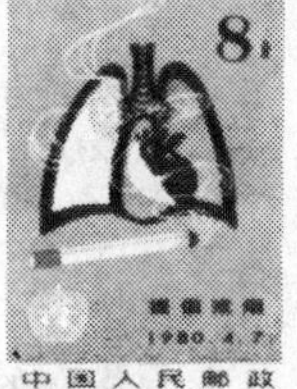

Lungs, Heart, Cigarette, WHO Emblem — A405

Statue of Chien Chen (688-763) — A406

1980, Apr. 7 *Perf. 11½x11*

1597 A405 8f shown (2-1) .50 .35
1598 A405 60f Faces (2-2) 3.50 2.50

Fight against cigarette smoking. J.56.

Perf. 11x11½, 11½x11

1980, Apr. 13

Loan to China by Japan of statue of Chien Chen (Jian Zhen), Buddhist missionary to Japan (754-763): No. 1600, Chien Chen Memorial Hall, Yangchou, horiz. 60f, Chien Chen's ship, horiz. His name in Japan is Ganjin. J.55.

1599 A406 8f multi (3-1) 1.50 .40
1600 A406 8f multi (3-2) 1.50 .40
1601 A406 60f multi (3-3) 10.00 5.00
Nos. 1599-1601 (3) 13.00 5.80

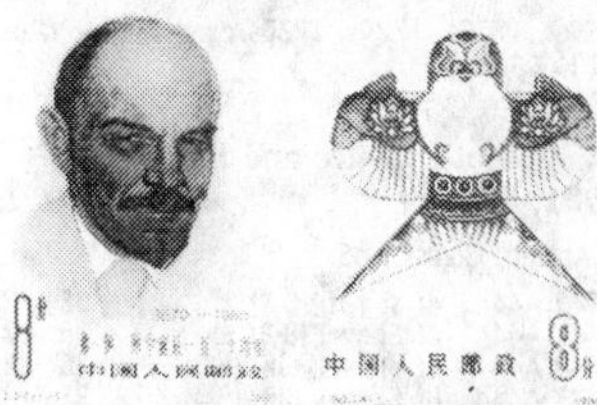

Lenin's 110th Birthday — A407

Swallow Chick Kite — A408

Photogravure and Engraved

1980, Apr. 22 *Perf. 11½x11*

1602 A407 8f multicolored 1.10 .80

1980, May 10 **Photo.** *Perf. 11½*

Designs: Kites. T.50.

1603 A408 8f shown (4-1) 1.10 .45
1604 A408 8f Slender-swallow (4-2) 1.10 .45
1605 A408 8f Semi-slender swallow (4-3) 1.10 .45
1606 A408 70f Dual swallows (4-4) 7.00 4.50
Nos. 1603-1606 (4) 10.30 5.85

Hare Running from Fallen Papaya — A409

1980, June 1 **Photo.** *Perf. 11x11½*

1607 Strip of 4 + label 5.50 5.50
a. A409 8f shown (4-1) 1.25 1.25
b. A409 8f Hare fox, monkey running away (4-2) 1.25 1.25
c. A409 8f Lion instructing animals (4-3) 1.25 1.25
d. A409 8f Discovery of fallen papaya (4-4) 1.25 1.25

Gu Dong fairy tale. T.51.

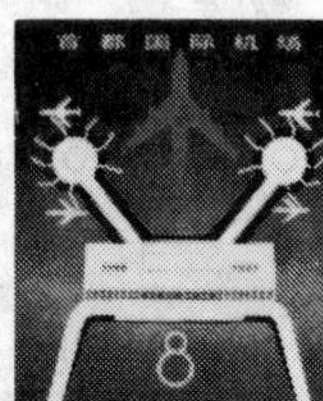

Terminal Building, Jets — A410

1980, June 20 *Perf. 11½*

1608 A410 8f Shown (2-1) .90 .40
1609 A410 10f Runways, jets (2-2) 1.10 1.10

Peking Intl. Airport opening. T.47.

Sika Stag — A411

White Lotus — A412

1980, July 18 **Photo.** *Perf. 11½*

1610 A411 4f Shown (3-1) .60 .60
1611 A411 8f Doe and fawn (3-2) .60 .50
1612 A411 60f Herd (3-3) 3.25 2.50
Nos. 1610-1612 (3) 4.45 3.60

T.52.

1980, Aug. 4

1613 A412 8f Shown (4-1) 1.10 .90
1614 A412 8f Rose-tipped snow (4-2) 1.10 .90
1615 A412 8f Buddha's seat (4-3) 1.10 .90
1616 A412 70f Variable charming face (4-4) 10.50 8.00
Nos. 1613-1616 (4) 13.80 10.70

Souvenir Sheet

1617 A412 $1 Fresh lotus on rippling water *65.00*

#1617 contains one 48x88mm stamp. T.54.

Pearl Cave, Sword-cut Stone Sculptures — A413

Guilin Landscapes: No. 1619, Three mountains, distant views. No. 1620, Nine-horse fresco hill. No. 1621, Egrets around aged banyan. No. 1622, Western hills at sunset, vert. No. 1623, Moonlight on Lijiang River, vert. 60f, Springhead, ancient ferry, vert. 70f, Scenic path, Yangshue, vert. T.53.

1980, Aug. 30 **Photo.** *Perf. 11½*

1618 A413 8f multi (8-1) .85 .65
1619 A413 8f multi (8-2) .85 .65
1620 A413 8f multi (8-3) .85 .65
1621 A413 8f multi (8-4) .85 .65
1622 A413 8f multi (8-5) .85 .65
1623 A413 8f multi (8-6) .85 .65
1624 A413 60f multi (8-7) 5.50 2.00
1625 A413 70f multi (8-8) 6.25 2.00
Nos. 1618-1625 (8) 16.85 7.90

Entrance Gate and Good Fairies A414

Great Wall, Symbols of Chicago, San Francisco and New York — A415

1980, Sept. 13 **Photo.** *Perf. 11x11½*

1626 A414 8f multicolored .35 .35
1627 A415 70f multicolored 3.25 1.65

Exhibitions of the People's Republic of China in San Francisco, Chicago and New York, Sept.-Dec. Sheets of 12 were sold only at US exhibitions at varying prices.

Romanian Flag, Warrior and Scroll — A416

1980, Sept. 20 **Photo.** *Perf. 11½x11*

1628 A416 8f multicolored .90 .70

2050th anniversary of Dacia, first independent Romanian state.

UNESCO Exhibition of Drawings and Paintings (J.60) — A417

1980, Oct. 8 *Perf. 11½*

1629 A417 8f Sea of Clouds, by Liu Haisu (3-1) .85 .40
1630 A417 8f Oriole and Magnolia, by Yu Feian, vert., (3-2) .85 .40
1631 A417 8f Camels, by Wu Zuoren (3-3) .85 .40
Nos. 1629-1631 (3) 2.55 1.20

Scenes from Tarrying Garden (T.56) — A418

1980, Oct. 25 **Photo.** *Perf. 11½*

1632 A418 8f Quxi Tower (4-1) 2.75 2.00
1633 A418 8f Yuancui Pavilion (4-2) 2.75 2.00
1634 A418 10f Hanbi Shanfang (4-3) 3.50 2.00
1635 A418 60f Guanyun Peak (4-4) 20.00 7.00
Nos. 1632-1635 (4) 29.00 13.00

Xu Guangpi (1562-1633), Agronomist A419

Shooting, Olympic Rings A420

Scientists of Ancient China: No. 1637, Li Bing, hydraulic engineer, 3rd century B.C. No. 1638, Jia Sixie, agronomist, 5th century. 60f, Huang Daopo, textile expert, 13th century. J.58.

Photogravure and Engraved

1980, Nov. 20 *Perf. 11½x11*

1636 A419 8f multi (4-1) 1.00 .65
1637 A419 8f multi (4-2) 1.00 .65
1638 A419 8f multi (4-3) 1.00 .65
1639 A419 60f multi (4-4) 7.00 3.00
Nos. 1636-1639 (4) 10.00 4.95

1980, Nov. 26 **Photo.**

1640 A420 4f shown (5-1) .15 .15
1641 A420 8f Gymnastics (5-2) .30 .20
1642 A420 8f Diving (5-3) .30 .20
1643 A420 10f Volleyball (5-4) .45 .30
1644 A420 60f Archery (5-5) 2.75 1.00
Nos. 1640-1644 (5) 3.95 1.85

Return to International Olympic Committee, 1st anniversary. J.62.

Chinese River Dolphin A421

Photogravure & Engraved

1980, Dec. 25 *Perf. 11x11½*

1645 A421 8f shown (2-1) .35 .25
a. Booklet pane of 6 3.75
1646 A421 60f Dolphins (2-2) 2.25 1.50
a. Booklet pane of 1 3.75

Cock — A422

Photogravure & Engraved

1981, Jan. 5 *Perf. 11½*

1647 A422 8f multicolored *3.00* *1.50*
a. Booklet pane of 12 17.00

New Year 1981.

Early Morning in Xishuang Bana (T.55) — A423

Perf. 11x11½, 11½x11

1981, Jan. 20 **Photo.**

1648 A423 4f shown (6-1) .35 .25
1649 A423 4f Dai mountain village (6-2) .35 .25
1650 A423 8f Rainbow over Lanchang River (6-3) .75 .50
1651 A423 8f Ancient temple vert. (6-4) .75 .50
1652 A423 8f Moonlit night, vert. (6-5) .75 .50
1653 A423 60f Phoenix tree, vert. (6-6) 6.50 3.50
Nos. 1648-1653 (6) 9.45 5.50

Flower Basket Palace Lantern — A424

Designs: Palace lanterns. T.60.

1981, Feb. 19 **Photo.** *Perf. 11½*

1654 A424 4f multi (6-1) .35 .25
1655 A424 8f multi (6-2) .75 .55
1656 A424 8f multi (6-3) .75 .55
1657 A424 8f multi (6-4) .75 .55

1658	A424	20f multi (6-5)	1.50	1.10
1659	A424	60f multi (6-6)	5.50	4.00
		Nos. 1654-1659 (6)	9.60	7.00

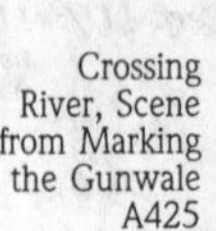

Crossing River, Scene from Marking the Gunwale — A425

Designs: Scenes from Marking the Gunwale fable. T.59.

1981, Mar. 10 Photo. *Perf. 11x11½*

1660	A425	8f Text (5-1)	.60	.35
1661	A425	8f shown (5-2)	.60	.35
1662	A425	8f Dropping sword in water (5-3)	.60	.35
1663	A425	8f Marking gunwale (5-4)	.60	.35
1664	A425	8f Searching for sword (5-5)	.60	.35
a.		Bklt. pane, 2 each #1660-1664	6.00	
b.		Strip of 5, #1660-1664	3.00	2.50

Chinese Juniper — A426

Designs: Miniature landscapes. T.61.

1981, Mar. 31 *Perf. 11½*

1665	A426	4f Chinese elm, vert. (6-1)	.25	.25
1666	A426	8f Juniper, vert. (6-2)	.45	.45
1667	A426	8f Maidenhair tree, vert. (6-3)	.45	.45
1668	A426	10f shown (6-4)	.55	.55
1669	A426	20f Persimmon (6-5)	1.25	1.25
1670	A426	60f Juniper (6-6)	3.50	3.50
		Nos. 1665-1670 (6)	6.45	6.45

Vase with Tiger-shaped Handles — A427

Cizhou Kiln Ceramic Pottery: 4f, Vase with two tigers, Song Dynasty, vert. No. 1672, Black glazed jar, Jin Dynasty. No. 1673, Amphora, vert. No. 1674, Jar with two phoenixes (Yuan Dynasty). 10f, Flat flask, Yuan Dynasty. T.62.

1981, Apr. 15 Photo. *Perf. 11½x11*

1671	A427	4f multi (6-1)	.20	.20
1672	A427	8f multi (6-2)	.40	.40
1673	A427	8f multi (6-3)	.40	.40
1674	A427	8f multi (6-4)	.40	.40
1675	A427	10f multi (6-5)	.45	.45
1676	A427	60f multi (6-6)	2.75	2.75
		Nos. 1671-1676 (6)	4.60	4.60

Panda and Colored Stamps — A428

1981, Apr. 29 Photo. *Perf. 11½x11*

1677	A428	8f shown (2-1)	.20	.15
1678	A428	60f Boat, bird (2-2)	1.25	.85
a.		Booklet pane (8 #1677, souv. sheet with 1677-1678)	3.50	

Qinchuan Steer — A429

Cattle Breeds: No. 1680, Binhu buffalo. No. 1681, Yak. No. 1682, Black and white dairy cows. 10f, Pasture red cow. 55f, Simmental cross-breed. T.63.

1981, May 5 *Perf. 11x11½*

1679	A429	4f multi (6-1)	.20	.15
1680	A429	8f multi (6-2)	.35	.30
1681	A429	8f multi (6-3)	.35	.30
1682	A429	8f multi (6-4)	.35	.30
1683	A429	10f multi (6-5)	.45	.35
1684	A429	55f multi (6-6)	2.25	1.50
		Nos. 1679-1684 (6)	3.95	2.90

Mail Delivery Slogan — A430

13th World Telecommunications Day — A431

1981, May 9 *Perf. 11*

1685	A430	8f multicolored	.80	.20

1981, May 17 *Perf. 11½x11*

1686	A431	8f multicolored	.80	.20

Construction Worker — A432

Telephone Building, Peking — A433

1981, May 20 *Perf. 11½*

1687	A432	8f shown (4-1)	.25	.20
1688	A432	8f Miner (4-2)	.25	.20
1689	A432	8f Children crossing street (4-3)	.25	.20
1690	A432	8f Farm worker (4-4)	.25	.20
		Nos. 1687-1690 (4)	1.00	.80

National Safety Month. J.65.

1981, June 5 Engr. *Perf. 11½x11*

1691	A433	8f violet brown	.25	.25

Swaythling Cup, Men's Team Table Tennis — A434

36th World Table Tennis Championships Victory: No. 1692a, St. Bride Vase, men's singles (7-3). No. 1692b, Iran Cup, men's doubles (7-4). No. 1692c, G. Geist Prize, women's singles (7-5). No. 1692d, W.J. Pope Trophy, women's doubles (7-6). No. 1692e, Heydusek Prize, mixed doubles (7-7). No. 1694, Marcel Corbillon Cup, women's team. Nos. 1693-1694 printed in sheets of 16 (8 each) with 2 labels. J.71.

1981, June 30 Photo. *Perf. 11½x11*

1692		Strip of 5	.75	.75
a.-e.		A434 8f multi	.15	.15
1693	A434	20f multi (7-1)	.35	.35
1694	A434	20f multi (7-2)	.35	.35

Chinese Communist Party, 60th Anniv. A435

1981, July 1 Photo. *Perf. 11x11½*

1695	A435	8f multi	.60	.30

Hanpo Pass, Lushan Mountains (T.67) A436

Photogravure & Engraved

1981, July 20 *Perf. 12½x12*

1696	A436	8f Five-veteran Peak, vert. (7-1)	.40	.40
1697	A436	8f shown (7-2)	.40	.40
1698	A436	8f Yellow Dragon Pool, vert. (7-3)	.40	.40
1699	A436	8f Sunlit Peak (7-4)	.40	.40
1700	A436	8f Three-layer Spring, vert. (7-5)	.40	.40
1701	A436	8f Stone and pines (7-6)	.40	.40
1702	A436	60f Dragon-head Cliff, vert. (7-7)	5.50	2.50
		Nos. 1696-1702 (7)	7.90	4.90

Tremella Fuciformis — A437

Designs: Edible mushrooms. T.66.

1981, Aug. 6 Photo. *Perf. 11½*

1703	A437	4f shown (6-1)	.20	.20
1704	A437	8f Dictyophora indusiata (6-2)	.40	.30
1705	A437	8f Hericium erinaceus (6-3)	.40	.30
1706	A437	8f Russula rubra (6-4)	.40	.30
1707	A437	10f Lentinus edodes (6-5)	.45	.35
1708	A437	70f Agaricus bisporus (6-6)	3.25	2.00
		Nos. 1703-1708 (6)	5.10	3.45

Quality Month (J.66) — A438

Lunan Stone Forest, Yunn — A439

1981, Sept. 1 Photo. *Perf. 11½x11*

1709	A438	8f Silver medal (2-1)	.25	.25
1710	A438	8f Gold medal (2-2)	.25	.25

1981, Sept. 18 *Perf. 11½*

Designs: Views of limestone formations, Lunan Stone Forest. #1711-1713 horiz. T.64.

1711	A439	8f multi (5-1)	.30	.30
1712	A439	8f multi (5-2)	.30	.30
1713	A439	8f multi (5-3)	.30	.30
1714	A439	10f multi (5-4)	.35	.35
1715	A439	70f multi (5-5)	3.25	3.25
		Nos. 1711-1715 (5)	4.50	4.50

Lu Xun, Writer, Birth Centenary (J.67) — A440

1981, Sept. 25

1716	A440	8f shown (2-1)	.20	.15
1717	A440	20f Portrait (diff.) (2-2)	.45	.35

Sun Yat-sen and Text — A441

70th Anniv. of 1911 Revolution: No. 1719, 72 Martyrs Grave, Huang Hua Gang. No. 1720, Hubei Provincial Government Headquarters, 1911. J.68.

1981, Oct. 10 Photo. *Perf. 11x11½*

1718	A441	8f multi (3-1)	.40	.25
1719	A441	8f multi (3-2)	.40	.25
1720	A441	8f multi (3-3)	.40	.25
		Nos. 1718-1720 (3)	1.20	.75

Asian Conference of Parliamentarians on Population and Development, Peking, Oct. 27 (J.73) — A442

Perf. 11½x11, 11x11½

1981, Oct. 27

1721	A442	8f Tree, vert. (2-1)	.15	.15
1722	A442	70f shown (2-2)	.90	.90

Huang Guo Shu Falls — A443

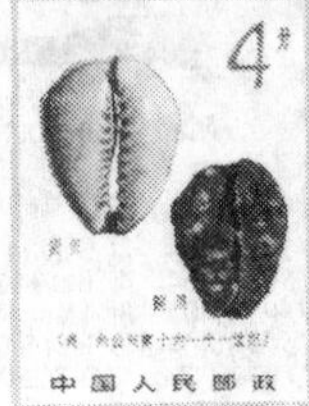

Cowrie Shell and Shell-shaped Coin — A444

1981-83 Engr. *Perf. 13x13½*

1723	A443	1f Xishuang Banna	.15	.15
1724	A443	1½f Mt. Hua	.15	.15
1725	A443	2f Mt. Tai	.15	.15
1726	A443	3f shown	.15	.15
1727	A443	4f Hainan Isld.	.15	.15
1728	A443	5f Tiger Hill, Suzhou	.15	.15
1729	A443	8f Great Wall	.15	.15
1730	A443	10f Immense Forest	.15	.15
1731	A443	20f Mt. Tian	.15	.15
1732	A443	30f Grassland, Inner Mongolia	.20	.20
1733	A443	40f Stone Forest	.30	.25
1734	A443	50f Banping Mountain	.35	.30
1735	A443	70f Mt. Qomolangma	.50	.45
1736	A443	80f Seven-Star Crag	.60	.55
1737	A443	$1 Three Gorges, Changjiang River	.70	.60
1738	A443	$2 Guilin landscape	1.40	1.25
1739	A443	$5 Mt. Huangshan	3.50	3.00
		Nos. 1723-1739 (17)	8.90	7.95

Issue dates: Nos. 1737-1739, Oct. 9, 1982; Nos. 1732, 1734-1736 Apr. 1, 1983.

Photo. *Perf. 11½*

1726a	A443	3f	.15	.15
1727a	A443	4f	.15	.15
1729a	A443	8f	.20	.20
1730a	A443	10f	.25	.25
1731a	A443	20f	.50	.50
		Nos. 1726a-1731a (5)	1.25	1.25

Nos. 1727a, 1729a, 1730a exist tagged. Values 10-15% higher.

Photogravure and Engraved

1981, Oct. 29 *Perf. 11½x11*

Ancient Coins. T.65.

1740	A444	4f shown (8-1)	.35	.25
1741	A444	4f Shovel (8-2)	.35	.25
1742	A444	8f Shovel, diff. (8-3)	.35	.25
1743	A444	8f Shovel, diff. (8-4)	.35	.25
1744	A444	8f Knife (8-5)	.35	.25
1745	A444	8f Knife (8-6)	.35	.25
1746	A444	60f Knife, diff. (8-7)	2.00	1.00
1747	A444	70f Gong (8-8)	2.75	1.50
		Nos. 1740-1747 (8)	6.85	4.00

See Nos. 1765-1772.

A445 A446

1981, Nov. 10 Photo. ***Perf. 11½x11***

1748 A445 8f multicolored .35 .20

Intl. Year of the Disabled.

1981-82 Photo. ***Perf. 11***

Twelve Beauties, from The Dream of Red Mansions, by Cao Xueqin.

1749	A446	4f Daiyu (12-1)	.25	.20
1750	A446	4f Baochai (12-2)	.25	.20
1751	A446	8f Yuanchun (12-3)	.45	.40
1752	A446	8f Yingchun (12-4)	.45	.40
1753	A446	8f Tanchun (12-5)	.45	.40
1754	A446	8f Xichun (12-6)	.45	.40
1755	A446	8f Xiangyuh (12-7)	.45	.40
1756	A446	10f Liwan (12-8)	.65	.40
1757	A446	20f Xifeng (12-9)	1.25	.60
1758	A446	30f Sister Qiao (12-10)	1.90	1.00
1759	A446	40f Keqing (12-11)	2.25	1.50
1760	A446	80f Miaoyu (12-12)	5.00	2.00
		Nos. 1749-1760 (12)	13.80	7.90

Souvenir Sheet

1761 A446 $2 Baoyu, Daiyu *35.00*

No. 1761 contains one 59x39mm stamp. Issue dates: Nos. 1749, 1751, 1753, 1755, 1757, 1759, 1761, Nov. 20, 1981; others, Apr. 24, 1982. T.69.

A447 A448

1981, Dec. 21 **Photo.**

1762 A447 8f Girl playing (2-1) .35 .25

1763 A447 20f Girl holding trophy (2-2) .65 .55

Women's team victory in 3rd World Cup Volleyball Championship (J.76).

Photogravure & Engraved

1982, Jan. 5 ***Perf. 11½***

1764 A448 8f multicolored 1.00 .60

a. Booklet pane of 10 + label *7.00*

New Year 1982 (Year of the Dog).

Coin Type of 1981

1982, Feb. 12

1765	A444	4f Guilian mask (8-1)	.15	.15
1766	A444	4f Shu shovel (8-2)	.15	.15
1767	A444	8f Xia zhuan shovel (8-3)	.15	.15
1768	A444	8f Han Dan shovel (8-4)	.15	.15
1769	A444	8f Knife (8-5)	.15	.15
1770	A444	8f Ming knife (8-6)	.15	.15
1771	A444	70f Jin hua knife (8-7)	1.65	1.25
1772	A444	80f Yi Liu Hua coin (8-8)	1.90	1.40
		Nos. 1765-1772 (8)	4.45	3.55

T.71.

Nie Er (1912-1935), Natl. Anthem Composer A449

1982, Feb. 15 ***Perf. 11x11½***

1773 A449 8f multicolored .30 .25

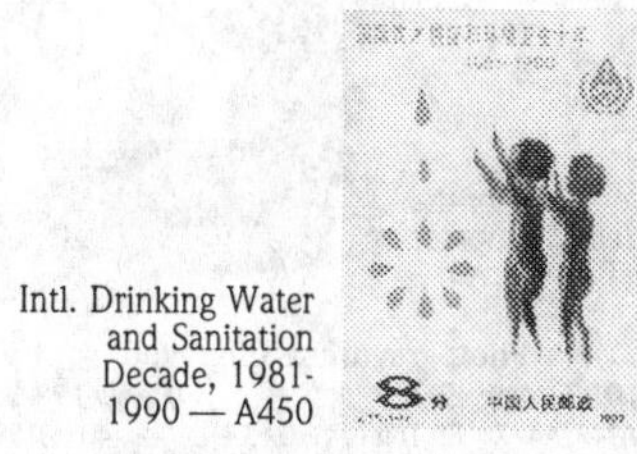

Intl. Drinking Water and Sanitation Decade, 1981-1990 — A450

1982, Mar. 1 ***Perf. 11½x11***

1774 A450 8f multicolored .30 .20

TB Bacillus Centenary A451

1982, Mar. 24 ***Perf. 11x11½***

1775 A451 8f multicolored .30 .20

Fire Control (T.76) — A452

1982, May 8 Photo. ***Perf. 11½x11***

1776 A452 8f Water hoses (2-1) .50 .25

1777 A452 8f Chemical extinguisher (2-2) .50 .25

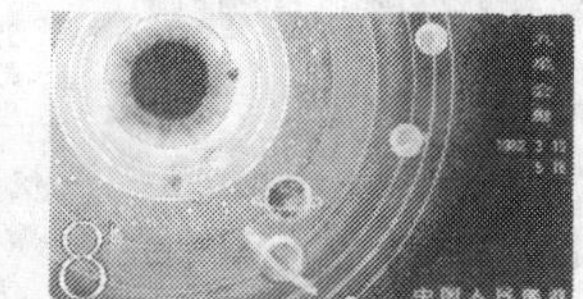

Syzygy of the Nine Planets, Mar. 10 and May 16 — A453

1982, May 16 ***Perf. 11½***

1778 A453 8f multicolored .75 .30

Medicinal Herbs — A454

Soong Ching Ling (1893-1981), Sun Yat-sen's Widow — A455

1982, May 20 ***Perf. 11½x11***

1779	A454	4f Hemerocallis flava (6-1)	.15	.15
1780	A454	8f Fritillaria unibracteata (6-2)	.15	.15
1781	A454	8f Aconitum carmichaeli (6-3)	.15	.15
1782	A454	10f Lilium brownii (6-4)	.25	.20
1783	A454	20f Arisaema (6-5)	.40	.30
1784	A454	70f Paeonia lactiflora (6-6)	1.75	1.40
		Nos. 1779-1784 (6)	2.85	2.35

Souvenir Sheet

1785 A454 $2 Iris tectorum maxim *8.00*

No. 1785 contains one 89x39mm stamp. Nos. 1779-1784 numbered T.72.

1982, May 29 ***Perf. 11½***

1786 A455 8f Addressing Consultative Conf. (2-1) .20 .20

1787 A455 20f Portrait (2-2) .60 .60

J.82.

Sable (T.68) A456

1982, June 20 Photo. ***Perf. 11½***

1788 A456 8f shown (2-1) .35 .20

1789 A456 80f Sable, diff. (2-2) 1.65 1.25

a. Bklt. pane of 8, 6 8f plus sheetlet of 2 (8f, 80f) 4.25

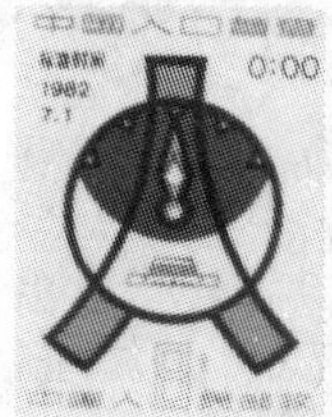

A457 A458

1982, June 30 ***Perf. 11½x11***

1790 A457 8f multicolored .20 .15

Natl. census, July 1.

1982, July 25 Photo. ***Perf. 11½x11***

1791 A458 8f multicolored .20 .15

2nd UN Conference on Peaceful Uses of Outer Space, Vienna, Aug. 9-21.

Strolling in Autumn Woods, by Shen Zhou, Ming Dynasty — A459

Fan Paintings (Ming or Qing Dynasty): No. 1793, Jackdaw on Withered Tree, by Tang Yin. No. 1794 Bamboo and Sparrows, by Zhou Zhimian. 10f, Writing Poem under Pine, by Chen Hongshou and Bai Han. 20f, Chrysanthemums, by Yun Shouping, Qing. 70f, Birds, Crape Myrtle and Chinese Parasol, by Wang Wu, Qing. T.77.

1982, July 31 ***Perf. 11½***

1792	A459	4f multi (6-1)	.25	.20
1793	A459	8f multi (6-2)	.25	.20
1794	A459	8f multi (6-3)	.25	.20
1795	A459	10f multi (6-4)	.35	.25
1796	A459	20f multi (6-5)	.80	.60
1797	A459	70f multi (6-6)	2.50	2.00
		Nos. 1792-1797 (6)	4.40	3.45

A460 A461

1982, Aug. 25 ***Perf. 11½x11***

1798 A460 8f multicolored .20 .15

60th anniv. of Chinese Geological Society.

1982, Aug. 25 Photo. ***Perf. 11½x11***

1799	A461	4f Orpiment (4-1)	.15	.15
1800	A461	8f Stibnite (4-2)	.15	.15
1801	A461	10f Cinnabar (4-3)	.25	.20
1802	A461	20f Wolframite (4-4)	.55	.40
		Nos. 1799-1802 (4)	1.10	.90

T.73.

Souvenir Sheet

Messenger, Tomb Mural, Jiayu Pass, Wei-Jin Period — A462

1982, Aug. 25

1803 A462 $1 multicolored *6.00*

All-China Philatelic Federation, 1st Cong.

12th Natl. Communist Party Congress — A463

Hoopoe — A464

1982, Sept. 1 ***Perf. 11½***

1804 A463 8f multicolored .20 .20

1982, Sept. 10 ***Perf. 11½x11***

1805	A464	8f shown (5-1)	.20	.20
1806	A464	8f Swallows (5-2)	.20	.20
1807	A464	8f Oriole (5-3)	.20	.20
1808	A464	20f Swifts (5-4)	.60	.50
1809	A464	70f Woodpecker (5-5)	2.75	2.25
		Nos. 1805-1809 (5)	3.95	3.35

Souvenir Sheet

1810 A464 $2 Cuckoos *10.00*

#1810 contains one 56x36mm stamp. T.79.

Japan-China Relations Normalization, 10th Anniv. — A465

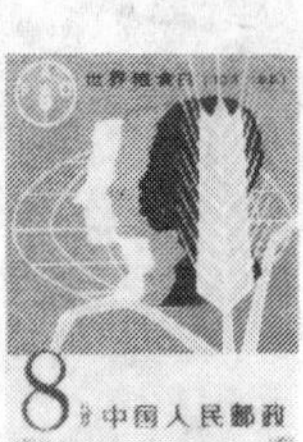

World Food Day — A466

Flower Paintings: 8f, Plum blossoms, by Guan Shanyue. 70f, Hibiscus, by Xiao Shufang. J.84.

1982, Sept. 29 ***Perf. 11***

1811 A465 8f multi (2-1) .15 .15

1812 A465 70f multi (2-2) 1.10 1.10

1982, Oct. 16 ***Perf. 11½***

1813 A466 8f multicolored .25 .25

Guo Morou (1892-1978), Acad. of Sciences Pres. — A467

Bodhisattva, 11th Cent. Sculpture — A468

Designs: Portraits. J.87.

1982, Nov. 16 Photo. *Perf. 11½x11*

1814 A467 8f multi (2-1) .15 .15
1815 A467 20f multi (2-2) .25 .25

1982, Nov. 19 *Perf. 11*

Liao Dynasty Buddha Sculptures, Lower Huayan Monastery. T.74.

1816 A468 8f multi (4-1) .25 .25
1817 A468 8f multi (4-2) .25 .25
1818 A468 8f multi (4-3) .25 .25
1819 A468 70f multi (4-4) 2.25 1.50
Nos. 1816-1819 (4) 3.00 2.25

Souvenir Sheet

Perf. 11x11½

1820 A468 $2 multicolored *12.00*

No. 1820 contains one 36x55mm stamp.

Dr. D.S. Kotnis, Indian Physician in 8th Army (J.83) A469

Perf. 11½x11, 11x11½

1982, Dec. 9 Photo.

1821 A469 8f Portrait, vert. (2-1) .15 .15
1822 A469 70f Riding horse (2-2) .85 .50

11th Communist Youth League Natl. Congress A470

1982, Dec. 20 *Perf. 11x11½*

1823 A470 8f multicolored .20 .20

Bronze Wine Container — A471

Western Zhou Dynasty Bronze (1200-771 B.C.): No. 1825, Three-legged cooking pot. No. 1826, Food bowl. No. 1827, Three-legged cooking pot (diff.). No. 1828, Animal-shaped wine container. 10f, Wine container with lid. 20f, Round food bowl. 70f, Square wine container. T.75.

Photogravure & Engraved

1982, Dec. 25 *Perf. 11*

1824 A471 4f multi (8-1) .20 .15
1825 A471 4f multi (8-2) .20 .15
1826 A471 8f multi (8-3) .40 .30
1827 A471 8f multi (8-4) .40 .30
1828 A471 8f multi (8-5) .40 .30
1829 A471 10f multi (8-6) .60 .40
1830 A471 20f multi (8-7) 1.00 .70
1831 A471 70f multi (8-8) 4.25 3.00
Nos. 1824-1831 (8) 7.45 5.30

New Year 1983 (Year of the Pig) — A472

1983, Jan. 5 *Perf. 11½*

1832 A472 8f multicolored *1.25 1.10*
a. Booklet pane of 12 *15.00*

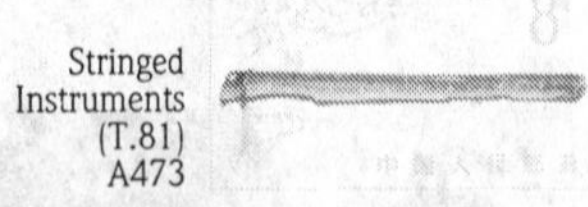
Stringed Instruments (T.81) A473

Perf. 11½x11, 11x11½

1983, Jan. 20

1833 A473 4f Konghou (5-1) *.40* .20
1834 A473 8f Ruan (5-2) *.95* .45
1835 A473 8f Qin, horiz. (5-3) *.95* .45
1836 A473 10f Piba (5-4) *1.25* .60
1837 A473 70f Sanxian (5-5) *8.50* 2.50
Nos. 1833-1837 (5) *12.05* 4.20

60th Anniv. of Peking-Hankow Railroad Workers' Strike (J.89) — A474

1983, Feb. 7 Photo. *Perf. 11½x11*

1838 A474 8f Memorial Tower, Zhengzhou (2-1) .25 .20
1839 A474 8f Monument, Jiangan (2-2) .25 .20

The Western Chamber, Traditional Opera, by Wang Shifu (1271-1368) A475

Scenes from the opera.

1983, Feb. 21 Photo. *Perf. 11x11½*

1840 A475 8f multi (4-1) .65 .50
1841 A475 8f multi (4-2) .65 .50
1842 A475 10f multi (4-3) .85 .70
1843 A475 80f multi (4-4) 8.25 4.00
Nos. 1840-1843 (4) 10.40 5.70

Souvenir Sheet

Photogravure and Engraved

Perf. 12

1844 A475 $2 multicolored *32.50*

#1844 contains one 27x48mm stamp. T.82.

Karl Marx (1818-1883) (J.90) — A476

Photogravure & Engraved

1983, Mar. 14 *Perf. 11½x11*

1845 A476 8f Portrait (2-1) .20 .15
1846 A476 20f Making speech (2-2) .40 .20

Tomb of the Yellow Emperor (T.84) — A477

Photogravure & Engraved

1983, Apr. 5 *Perf. 11½*

1847 A477 8f Tomb, vert. (3-1) .40 .15
1848 A477 10f Hall of Founder of Chinese Culture (3-2) .50 .20
1849 A477 20f Cypress tree, vert. (3-3) 1.10 .30
Nos. 1847-1849 (3) 2.00 .65

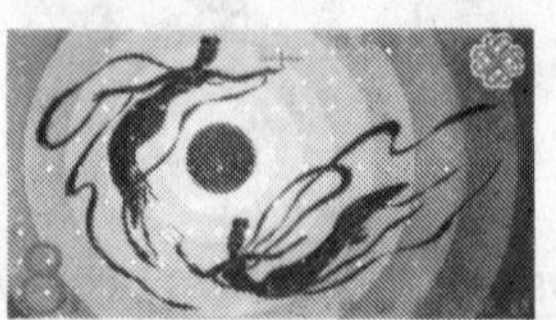
World Communications Year — A478

1983, Apr. 28 Photo. *Perf. 11½*

1850 A478 8f multicolored .50 .20

Male Chinese Alligator (T.85) — A479

Photogravure & Engraved

1983, May 24 *Perf. 11*

1851 A479 8f shown (2-1) .45 .25
1852 A479 20f Female, hatching eggs (2-2) 1.00 .55

Kitten, by Tan Arxi — A480

Various children's drawings. T.86.

1983, June 1 *Perf. 11½x11*

1853 A480 8f multi (4-1) .25 .20
1854 A480 8f multi (4-2) .25 .20
1855 A480 8f multi (4-3) .25 .20
1856 A480 8f multi (4-4) .25 .20
Nos. 1853-1856 (4) 1.00 .80

6th Natl. People's Congress (J.94) A481

1983, June 6 *Perf. 11x11½*

1857 A481 8f Hall (2-1) .15 .15
1858 A481 20f Natl. anthem score (2-2) .35 .35

Terra Cotta Figures, Qin Dynasty (221-207 BC) — A482

1983, June 30

1859 A482 8f Soldiers (4-1) .35 .25
1860 A482 8f Heads (4-2) .35 .25
1861 A482 10f Soldiers, horses (4-3) .55 .35
1862 A482 70f Excavation site (4-4) 3.75 2.50
a. Bklt. pane of 8 (#1859, 3 #1860, 3 #1861, #1862)
Nos. 1859-1862 (4) 5.00 3.35

Souvenir Sheet

1863 A482 $2 Soldier leading horse *18.00*
a. Booklet pane

#1863 contains one 59x39mm stamp. T.88.

A483 A484

Female roles in Peking opera (T.87).

1983, July 20 Photo. *Perf. 11*

1864 A483 4f Sun Yujiao (8-1) .25 .15
1865 A483 8f Chen Miaochang (8-2) .45 .30
1866 A483 8f Bai Suzhen (8-3) .45 .30
1867 A483 8f Sister Thirteen (8-4) .45 .30
1868 A483 10f Qin Xianglian (8-5) .50 .35
1869 A483 20f Yang Yuhuan (8-6) 1.10 .75
1870 A483 50f Cui Yingying (8-7) 2.50 1.75
1871 A483 80f Mu Guiying (8-8) 4.25 3.00
Nos. 1864-1871 (8) 9.95 6.90

1983, Aug. 10 Photo. *Perf. 11½*

Paintings by Liu Lingcang.

1872 A484 8f Li Bai (4-1) .30 .20
1873 A484 8f Du Fu (4-2) .30 .20
1874 A484 8f Han Yu (4-3) .30 .20
1875 A484 70f Liu Zongyuan (4-4) 3.50 2.00
Nos. 1872-1875 (4) 4.40 2.60

Poets and philosophers of ancient China (J.92).

5th Natl. Women's Congress — A485

1983, Sept. 1 Photo. *Perf. 11½*

1876 A485 8f multicolored .20 .15

5th National Games (J.93) — A486

1983, Sept. 16 Photo. *Perf. 11½*

1877 A486 4f Emblem (6-1) .15 .15
1878 A486 8f Gymnast (6-2) .15 .15
1879 A486 8f Badminton (6-3) .15 .15
1880 A486 8f Diving (6-4) .15 .15
1881 A486 20f High jump (6-5) .40 .40
1882 A486 70f Wind surfing (6-6) 1.75 1.65
Nos. 1877-1882 (6) 2.75 2.65

Family Planning (T.91) A487

1983, Sept. 19 *Perf. 11x11½*

1883 A487 8f One child (2-1) .20 .20
1884 A487 8f Cultivated land (2-2) .20 .20

10th Intl. Trade Union Congress — A488

1983, Oct. 18 Litho. *Perf. 11½*

1885 A488 8f multicolored .20 .15

Swans (T.83) — A489

Perf. 11x11½ on 3 sides

1983, Nov. 18 Photo.

1886 A489 8f (4-1) .20 .20
1887 A489 8f (4-2) .20 .20
1888 A489 10f (4-3) .20 .20
1889 A489 80f (4-4) 1.65 1.65
a. Booklet pane, 7 #1886, 1 each #1887-1889 *4.00*
Nos. 1886-1889 (4) 2.25 2.25

A490 A491

Various photos. J.96.

1983, Nov. 24 Photo. *Perf. 11½*

1890 A490 8f multi (4-1) .15 .15
1891 A490 8f multi (4-2) .15 .15
1892 A490 8f multi (4-3) .15 .15
1893 A490 8f multi (4-4) .15 .15
Nos. 1890-1893 (4) .60 .60

85th birth anniv. of Liu Shaoqi, political leader.

1983, Nov. 29 Photo. *Perf. 11½*

1894 A491 8f No. 117 (2-1) .20 .15
1895 A491 20f No. 4L1 (2-2) .50 .25

CHINAPEX '83 Natl. Philatelic Exhibition (J.99).

A492 A493

Various portraits. J.97.

1983, Dec. 26 Photo. *Perf. 11½*

1896 A492 8f 1925 (4-1) .15 .15
1897 A492 8f 1945 (4-2) .15 .15
1898 A492 10f 1952 (4-3) .15 .15
1899 A492 20f 1961 (4-4) .40 .40
Nos. 1896-1899 (4) .85 .85

90th birth anniv. of Mao Tse-tung.

Photogravure and Engraved

1984, Jan. 5 *Perf. 11½*

1900 A493 8f multicolored 1.25 .60
a. Booklet pane of 12 7.00

New Year 1984 (Year of the Rat).

Souvenir Sheets Booklet Panes

Heavy speculation in stamps in China is centered around the souvenir sheets and booklet panes. These generally are trading by the 100 in China and being held off the normal philatelic market.

Beauties Wearing Flowers — A494

Portions of painting by Zhou Fang (Tang Dynasty). T.89.

1984, Mar. 24 Photo. *Perf. 11*

1901 A494 8f multi (3-1) .30 .25
1902 A494 10f multi (3-2) .45 .35
1903 A494 70f multi (3-3) 3.75 2.00
Nos. 1901-1903 (3) 4.50 2.60

Souvenir Sheet

1904 A494 $2 Entire painting *45.00*

No. 1904 contains one 162x40mm stamp.

Chinese Roses (T.93) — A495 Ren Bishi (1904-50), Statesman — A496

1984, Apr. 20 Photo. *Perf. 11½*

1905 A495 4f Spring of Shanghai (6-1) .15 .15
1906 A495 8f Rosy Dawn of Pujiang River (6-2) .15 .15
1907 A495 8f Pearl (6-3) .15 .15
1908 A495 10f Black whirlwind (6-4) .20 .20
1909 A495 20f Yellow flower in battlefield (6-5) .40 .25
1910 A495 70f Blue Phoenix (6-6) 1.50 .80
Nos. 1905-1910 (6) 2.55 1.70

1984, Apr. 30 *Perf. 11½x11*

1911 A496 8f multicolored .15 .15

Crested Ibis (T.94) A497

1984, May 15 Photo. *Perf. 11x11½*

1912 A497 8f Flying (3-1) .20 .15
1913 A497 8f Wading (3-2) .20 .15
1914 A497 80f Perching (3-3) 1.10 .80
Nos. 1912-1914 (3) 1.50 1.10

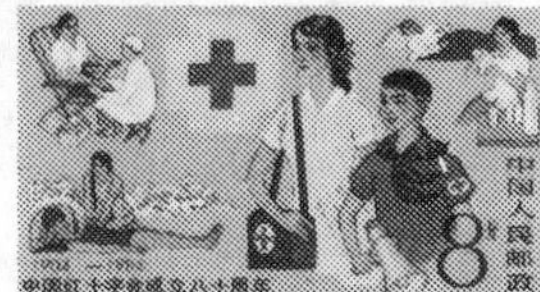

Chinese Red Cross Society, 80th Anniv. — A498

1984, May 29 *Perf. 11½*

1915 A498 8f multicolored .15 .15

Gezhou Dam, Yangtze River (T.95) — A499

1984, June 15 Photo.

1916 A499 8f Dam (3-1) .15 .15
1917 A499 10f Bridge, vert. (3-2) .20 .20
1918 A499 20f Lock Gate #2 (3-3) .45 .45
Nos. 1916-1918 (3) .80 .80

Zhuo Zheng Garden, Suzhou (T.96) — A500

Photogravure & Engraved

1984, June 30 *Perf. 11½x11*

1919 A500 8f Inverted Image Tower (4-1) .15 .15
1920 A500 8f Loquat Garden (4-2) .15 .15
1921 A500 10f Water Court, Xiao Cang Lang (4-3) .15 .15
1922 A500 70f Yuanxiang Hall, Yiyu Study (4-4) 1.25 .60
Nos. 1919-1922 (4) 1.70
Set value .90

1984 Summer Olympics A501

1984, July 28 Photo. *Perf. 11½*

1923 A501 4f Shooting (6-1) .15 .15
1924 A501 8f High jump (6-2) .15 .15
1925 A501 8f Weight lifting (6-3) .15 .15
1926 A501 10f Gymnastics (6-4) .15 .15
1927 A501 20f Volleyball (6-5) .20 .20
1928 A501 80f Diving (6-6) .95 .40
Nos. 1923-1928 (6) 1.75 1.20

Souvenir Sheet

1929 A501 $2 Athletes, rings *3.00*

#1929 contains one 61x38mm stamp. J.103.

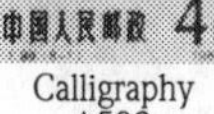

Calligraphy A502 Luanhe River Water Diversion Project (T.97) A503

Artworks by Wu Changshuo. T.98.

1984, Aug. 27 Photo. *Perf. 11½*

1930 A502 4f shown (8-1) .15 .15
1931 A502 4f A Pair of Peaches (8-2) .15 .15
1932 A502 8f Lotus (8-3) .15 .15
1933 A502 8f Wistaria (8-4) .15 .15
1934 A502 8f Peony (8-5) .15 .15
1935 A502 10f Chrysanthemum (8-6) .20 .20
1936 A502 20f Plum Blossom (8-7) .40 .35
1937 A502 70f Seal Cutting (8-8) 1.50 1.25
Nos. 1930-1937 (8) 2.85 2.55

Perf. 11½x11, 11 (#1939)

1984, Sept. 11 Photo.

1938 A503 8f multi (3-1) .15 .15
1939 A503 10f multi, horiz. (3-2) .15 .15
1940 A503 20f multi (3-3) .30 .30
Set value .50 .50

Chinese-Japanese Youth (J.104) — A504

1984, Sept. 24 Photo. *Perf. 11½*

1941 A504 8f Neighbors (3-1) .15 .15
1942 A504 20f Planting tree (3-2) .20 .20
1943 A504 80f Dancing (3-3) .90 .85
Nos. 1941-1943 (3) 1.25 1.20

People's Republic, 35th Anniv. (J.105) — A505

1984, Oct. 1 Photo. *Perf. 11½x11*

Size: 26x35mm

1944 A505 8f Engineer (5-1) .15 .15
1945 A505 8f Farm woman (5-2) .15 .15
1946 A505 8f Scientist (5-4) .15 .15
1947 A505 8f Soldier (5-5) .15 .15

Size: 36x48mm

Perf. 11

1948 A505 20f Birds (5-3) .20 .20
Set value .55 .55

110th Birth Anniv. of Chen Jiageng (J.106) A506

1984, Oct. 21 Photo. *Perf. 12½x12*

1949 A506 8f Chen Jiageng (2-1) .15 .15
1950 A506 80f Jimei School (2-2) .75 .50

The Maiden's Study — A507

Scenes from The Peony Pavilion, by Tang Xianzu. T.99.

Photogravure & Engraved

1984, Oct. 30 *Perf. 11*

1951 A507 8f shown (4-1) .15 .15
1952 A507 8f In the dreamland (4-2) .15 .15
1953 A507 20f Du Liniang drawing self-portrait (4-3) .30 .30
1954 A507 70f Married to Liu Mengmai (4-4) 1.40 1.40
Nos. 1951-1954 (4) 2.00 2.00

Souvenir Sheet

Perf. 11½

1955 A507 $2 Playing in the garden *7.00*

No. 1955 contains one 90x60mm stamp.

Emei Shan Mountain Scenery (T.100) — A508

1984, Nov. 16 *Perf. 11*

1956 A508 4f Baoguo Temple (6-1) .15 .15
1957 A508 8f Leiyin Temple (6-2) .15 .15
1958 A508 8f Hongchun Lawn (6-3) .15 .15
1959 A508 10f Elephant bath (6-4) .15 .15
1960 A508 20f Woyun Temple (6-5) .35 .35
1961 A508 80f Shining Cloud Sea at Jinding (6-6) 1.65 1.25
Nos. 1956-1961 (6) 2.60 2.20

A509

A510

Portraits.

1984, Dec. 15 Photo. *Perf. 11½x11*

1962 A509 8f During the Long March (3-1) .15 .15
1963 A509 10f At 7th Natl. Party Congress (3-2) .15 .15
1964 A509 20f In motorcade (3-3) .30 .20
Set value .50 .40

Former party secretary Ren Bishi (1904-50).

1984, Dec. 25 *Perf. 11*

1965 A510 8f Flower arrangement .20 .20

Chinese insurance industry.

New Year 1985 (Year of the Ox) — A511

Photogravure & Engraved

1985, Jan. 5 *Perf. 11½*

1966 A511 8f T.102 .25 .20
a. Bklt. pane of 4 + 8 plus label 5.00

Zunyi Meeting, 50th Anniv. — A512

Paintings: 8f, The Zunyi Meeting, by Liu Xiangping. 20f, The Red Army Successfully Arrived in Northern Shaanxi, by Zhao Yu. J.107.

1985, Jan. 15 Photo. *Perf. 11x11½*

1967 A512 8f multi (2-1) .15 .15
1968 A512 20f multi (2-2) .25 .25
Set value .30 .30

15-Cent Minimum Value
The minimum value for a single stamp is 15 cents. This value reflects the costs of handling inexpensive stamps.

A513 A514

Lantern Folk Festival: No. 1969, Lotus of Good Luck. No. 1970, Auspicious dragon and phoenix. No. 1971, A hundred flowers blossoming. 70f, Prosperity and affluence. T.104.

1985, Feb. 28 *Perf. 11½*

1969 A513 8f multi (4-1) .20 .15
1970 A513 8f multi (4-2) .20 .15
1971 A513 8f multi (4-3) .20 .15
1972 A513 70f multi (4-4) 1.25 .60
Nos. 1969-1972 (4) 1.85 1.05

1985, Mar. 8

1973 A514 20f multicolored .20 .15

UN Decade for Women (1976-85).

Mei (Prunus mume) (T.103) — A515

1985, Apr. 5 *Perf. 11*

1974 A515 8f Green calyx (6-1) .15 .15
1975 A515 8f Pendant mei (6-2) .15 .15
1976 A515 8f Contorted dragon (6-3) .15 .15
1977 A515 10f Cinnabar (6-4) .15 .15
1978 A515 20f Versicolor mei (6-5) .25 .15
1979 A515 80f Apricot mei (6-6) 1.10 .55
Nos. 1974-1979 (6) 1.95
Set value .90

Souvenir Sheet

Perf. 11½

1980 A515 $2 Duplicate and condensed fragrance mei 7.00

No. 1980 contains one 93x52mm stamp.

A516 A518

A517

1985, May 1 Photo. *Perf. 11*

1981 A516 8f Huizo Guild Hall, Guangzhou .15 .15

All-China Fed. of Trade Unions.

1985, May 4 **Photo.**

1982 A517 20f multicolored .20 .15

Intl. Youth Year.

1985, May 24 *Perf. 11½*

Paintings of giant pandas: 8f, 20f, 50f, 80f, by Han Meilin; $3, by Wu Zuoren. T.106.

1983 A518 8f multi (4-1), vert. .15 .15
1984 A518 20f multi (4-2) .15 .15
1985 A518 50f multi (4-3), vert. .30 .30
1986 A518 80f multi (4-4) .45 .40
Nos. 1983-1986 (4) 1.05 1.00

Souvenir Sheet

Perf. 11x11½

1987 A518 $3 multi, vert. 2.00

No. 1987 contains one 39x59mm stamp.

Xian Xinghai (1905-1945), Composer — A519

Agnes Smedley, 1892-1950 (3-1) — A520

Design: Bust, by Cao Chongen and music from The Yellow River Cantata.

1985, June 13 Photo. *Perf. 11½x11*

1988 A519 8f multicolored .15 .15

1985, June 25

American journalists: 20f, Anna Louise Strong, 1885-1970 (3-2). 80f, Edgar Snow, 1905-1972 (3-3). J.112.

1989 A520 8f multicolored .15 .15
1990 A520 20f multicolored .20 .20
1991 A520 80f multicolored .80 .75
Nos. 1989-1991 (3) 1.15 1.10

Zheng He's West Seas Expedition, 580th Anniv. — A521

Designs: No. 1992, Portrait of the navigator (4-1). No. 1993, Peace envoy (4-2). 20f, Trade, cultural exchange (4-3). 80f, Honored for navigational feats (4-4). J.113.

1985, July 11 *Perf. 11½*

1992 A521 8f multicolored .15 .15
1993 A521 8f multicolored .15 .15
1994 A521 20f multicolored .20 .20
1995 A521 80f multicolored .80 .40
Nos. 1992-1995 (4) 1.30 .90

Xu Beihong, 1895-1953, Painter (J.114) A522

Perf. 11½x11, 11x11½

1985, July 19

1996 A522 8f Self-portrait (2-1), vert. .25 .15
1997 A522 20f shown (2-2) .75 .20

A523 A524

Designs: 8f, Lin Zexu, 1785-1850, statesman, patriot. 80f, Burning opium at Humen, bas-relief.

1985, Aug. 30 *Perf. 11*

1998 A523 8f multi (2-1) .15 .15

Size: 51x22mm

1999 A523 80f multi (2-2) .45 .45

Lin Zexu's ban of the opium trade catalyzed the Anglo-Chinese Opium Wars. J.115.

1985, Sept. 1 *Perf. 11½x11*

2000 A524 8f Prosperity (3-1) .15 .15
2001 A524 10f Celebration (3-2) .20 .20
2002 A524 20f Abundant Harvest (3-3) .50 .50
Nos. 2000-2002 (3) .85 .85

Tibet Autonomous Region, 20th anniv. (J.116).

End of World War II, 40th Anniv. A525

Woodcuts by Wu Biduan: 8f, The Chinese Army Rose Against the Japanese Agressors at Logouqiao (2-1). 80f, The Eighth Route Army and Militia Fought Around the Great Wall (2-2). J.117.

1985, Sept. 3 *Perf. 11*

2003 A525 8f multi .15 .15
2004 A525 80f multi .45 .40
Set value .50 .45

2nd Natl. Worker's Games, Sept. 8-15, Beijing A526

Competitors from various events and: 8f, Men's bicycling (2-1). 20f, Women hurdlers (2-2). J.118.

1985, Sept. 8 *Perf. 11x11½*

2005 A526 8f multi .15 .15
2006 A526 20f multi .25 .25
Set value .30 .30

Xinjiang Uygur Autonomous Region, 30th Anniv. (J.119) — A527

1985, Oct. 1 Photo. *Perf. 11½*

2007 A527 8f Oasis in the Gobi, woman (3-1) .15 .15
2008 A527 10f Oil field, Lake Tianchi (3-2) .15 .15
2009 A527 20f Tianshan pasture, woman (3-3) .20 .20
Set value .40 .40

Size of No. 2008, 60x30mm.

1st Natl. Youth Games, Oct. 6-15, Zhengzhou (J.121) — A528

1985, Oct. 6 *Perf. 11½x11*

2010 A528 8f Girls' track & field (2-1) .15 .15
2011 A528 20f Boys' basketball (2-2) .35 .35

Forbidden City Main Buildings — A529

1985, Oct. 10 *Perf. 11½*

2012 A529 8f multi (4-1) .15 .15
2013 A529 8f multi (4-2) .15 .15
2014 A529 20f multi (4-3) .15 .15
2015 A529 80f multi (4-4) .60 .60
a. Vert. strip of 4, #2012-2057 1.10 1.10

Palace Museum, 60th anniv. J.120.

Zou Taofen (1895-1935), Journalist (J.122) — A530

1985, Nov. 5 *Perf. 11½x11*

2016	A530	8f Portrait (2-1)	.15	.15
2017	A530	20f Epitaph by Zhou Enlai (2-2)	.20	.20
a.		Pair, #2016-2017	.30	.30

December 9th Revolution, 50th Anniv. — A531

1985, Dec. 9 *Perf. 11½*

2018	A531	8f Memorial Pavilion	.15	.15

New Year 1986 — A532

Natl. Space Industry — A533

Photogravure & Engraved

1986, Jan. 5 *Perf. 11½*

2019	A532	8f multicolored	.25	.25
a.		Bklt. pane of 4 + 8 with label btwn	3.00	

1986, Feb. 1 **Photo.**

Designs: 4f, 1st experimental satellite. No. 2021, Recoverable satellite. No. 2022, Underwater rocket launch. 10f, Rocket launch. 20f, Earth satellite receiver. 70f, Satellite trajectory diagram. T.108.

2020	A533	4f multi (6-1)	.15	.15
2021	A533	8f multi (6-2)	.15	.15
2022	A533	8f multi (6-3)	.15	.15
2023	A533	10f multi (6-4)	.15	.15
2024	A533	20f multi (6-5)	.15	.15
2025	A533	70f multi (6-6)	.55	.45
		Nos. 2021-2025 (5)	1.15	
		Set value	.90	.65

Dong Biwu (1886-1975), Party Founder (J.123) — A534

Lin Boqu (1886-1960), Party Leader (J.124) — A535

Photogravure and Engraved

1986, Mar. 5 *Perf. 11½x11*

2026	A534	8f 1975 (2-1)	.15	.15
2027	A534	20f 1945 (2-2)	.25	.25
		Set value	.35	.35

1986, Mar. 20

2028	A535	8f shown (2-1)	.15	.15
2029	A535	20f Boqu standing (2-2)	.25	.25
		Set value	.35	.35

Marshal He Long (1896-1969), Revolution Leader (J.126) A536

1986, Mar. 22 *Perf. 11x11½*

2030	A536	8f shown (2-1)	.15	.15
2031	A536	20f Long on horseback (2-2)	.25	.25
		Set value	.35	.35

Halley's Comet — A537

1986, Apr. 11 **Photo.** *Perf. 11½*

2032	A537	20f dk bl & gray	.30	.25

White Crane (T.110) A538

Perf. 11x11½, 11½x11

1986, May 22

2033	A538	8f Two cranes (3-1)	.15	.15
2034	A538	10f One flying (3-2), vert.	.15	.15
2035	A538	70f Four cranes (3-3), vert.	.90	.45
		Nos. 2033-2035 (3)	1.20	
		Set value		.55

Souvenir Sheet

2036	A538	$2 Flock	2.50	

No. 2036 contains one 116x25mm stamp.

Li Weihan (1896-1984), Party Leader (J.127) A539

1986, June 2 *Perf. 11x11½*

2037	A539	8f Portrait (2-1)	.15	.15
2038	A539	20f Writing (2-2)	.25	.25
		Set value	.35	.35

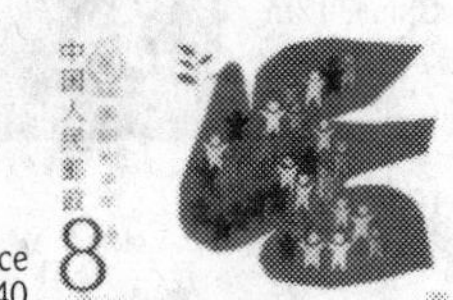

Intl. Peace Year — A540

1986, June 16 *Perf. 11*

2039	A540	8f multi	.15	.15

Mao Dun (1896-1981), Writer (J.129) A541

1986, July 4 *Perf. 11x11½*

2040	A541	8f Portrait (2-1)	.15	.15
2041	A541	20f Portrait, diff. (2-2)	.25	.25
		Set value	.35	.35

Wang Jiaxiang (1906-1974), Party Leader (J.130) A542

1986, Aug. 15

2042	A542	8f Portrait (2-1)	.15	.15
2043	A542	20f Portrait, diff. (2-2)	.25	.25
		Set value	.35	.35

Teacher's Day — A543

1986, Sept. 10 *Perf. 11*

2044	A543	8f multi	.15	.15

Magnolia Liliflora (T.111) A544

1986, Sept. 23 *Perf. 11x11½*

2045	A544	8f Blossom (3-1)	.15	.15
2046	A544	8f Two blossoms (3-2)	.15	.15
2047	A544	70f Blossom, diff. (3-3)	.80	.80
		Nos. 2045-2047 (3)	1.10	1.10

Souvenir Sheet

2048	A544	$2 Three blossoms	4.00	

No. 2048 contains one 132x70mm stamp.

Folk Houses — A545

Perf. 13x13½, 11x11½, (1½f, 3f, #2057-2062)

1986, Apr. 1 **Photo.**

2049	A545	1f Inner Mongolia	.15	.15
2050	A545	1½f Tibet	.15	.15
2051	A545	2f Northeastern China	.15	.15
2052	A545	3f Hunan	.15	.15
2053	A545	4f So. Yangtze River	.15	.15
2054	A545	8f Beijing	.15	.15
2055	A545	10f Yunnan	.15	.15
2056	A545	20f Shanghai	.15	.15
2057	A545	30f Anhui	.25	.25
2058	A545	40f No. Shaanxi	.30	.30
2059	A545	50f Sichuan	.40	.40
2060	A545	90f Taiwan	.75	.75
2061	A545	$1 Fujian	.85	.85
2062	A545	$1.10 Zhejiang	.95	.95
		Set value	4.00	4.00

Issue dates: 3f, Dec. 25. 4f, $1, Oct. 15. 20f, 50f, Sept. 10. 40f, Nov. 15. Others, Apr. 1.

Postal forgeries of No. 2056 exist.

See Nos. 2198-2207.

1989-90 **Photo.**

2055a	Perf. 11x11½ ('89)	.15	.15
2056a	Perf. 11x11½ ('89)	.25	.15
2057a	Perf. 13x13½ ('90)	.45	.25
2058a	Perf. 13x13½	.60	.30
2059a	Perf. 13x13½ ('89)	.75	.40
2061a	Perf. 13x13½ ('90)	1.50	.80

Souvenir Sheet

All-China Philatelic Federation, 2nd Congress — A546

1986, Oct. 17 **Litho.** *Perf. 11½*

2063	A546	$2 Jade lion	4.00	

Leaders of the 1911 Revolution (J.132) A547

1986, Oct. 10 **Photo.** *Perf. 11x11½*

2064	A547	8f Sun Yat-sen (3-1)	.15	.15
2065	A547	10f Huang Xing (3-2)	.15	.15
2066	A547	40f Zhang Taiyan (3-3)	.80	.80
		Set value	.90	.90

Souvenir Sheet

Sun Yat-sen (1866-1925) — A548

1986, Nov. 12 *Perf. 11½*

2067	A548	$2 multicolored	3.50	

Marshal Zhu De (1886-1976) (J.134) — A549

Designs: 20f, Orating.

1986, Dec. 1 **Engr.** *Perf. 11½x11*

2068	A549	8f sepia (2-1)	.15	.15
2069	A549	20f myrtle grn (2-2)	.30	.20
		Set value	.40	.25

Sports of Ancient China — A550

Stone carvings. T.113.

Perf. 11½x11, 11x11½

1986, Dec. 20 **Photo.**

2070	A550	8f Archery (4-1), vert.	.15	.15
2071	A550	8f Weiqi (4-2)	.15	.15
2072	A550	10f Golf (4-3)	.15	.15
2073	A550	50f Soccer (4-4), vert.	1.40	.70
		Nos. 2070-2073 (4)	1.85	1.15

A551 A552

Photogravure & Engraved

1987, Jan. 5 *Perf. 11½*

2074	A551	8f blk, dk pink & yel grn	.25
a.		Bklt. pane of 4 + 8 + label	3.50

New Year 1987 (Year of the Hare).

1987, Feb. 20 **Photo.** *Perf. 11½*

2075	A552	8f Traveling (3-1)	.15
2076	A552	20f Cave writing (3-2)	.50
2077	A552	40f Mountain climbing (3-3)	1.00
		Nos. 2075-2077 (3)	1.65

Xu Xiake (1587-1621), Ming Dynasty geographer (J.136).

Birds of Prey (T.114) — A553

1987, Mar. 20

2078	A553	8f Kite (4-1)	.15	.15
2079	A553	8f Sea eagle (4-2), vert.	.15	.15
2080	A553	10f Vulture (4-3), vert.	.20	.15
2081	A553	90f Buzzard (4-4)	2.25	.90
		Nos. 2078-2081 (4)	2.75	1.35

Liao Zhongkai (1877-1925), National Party Leader (J.137) — A554

1987, Apr. 23 *Perf. 11½x11*

2082	A554	8f shown (2-1)	.15	
2083	A554	20f Liao, He Xiangning (2-2)	.30	
		Set value	.35	

Kites (T.115) — A555

A556

1987, Apr. 1

2084	A555	8f Hawk (4-1)	.20	
2085	A555	8f Dragon (4-2)	.20	
a.		Pair, #2084-2085	.40	
2086	A555	30f Symbolic octagon (4-3)	1.00	
2087	A555	30f Phoenix (4-4)	1.00	
a.		Pair, #2086-2087	2.00	
		Nos. 2084-2087 (4)	2.40	

Nos. 2085a, 2087a have continuous designs.

1987, Apr. 28

Portraits of Ye Jianying (1897-1986), central committee vice chairman (J.138).

2088	A556	8f multi (3-3)	.15	.15
2089	A556	10f multi (3-2)	.15	.15
2090	A556	30f multi (3-1)	.55	.55
		Nos. 2088-2090 (3)	.85	.85

Caves of the Thousand Buddhas, Dunhuang, Gansu Province — A557

Petroglyphs: 8f, Worshipping Bodhisattvas, Northern Liang Dynasty. 10f, Deer King Jatka, Northern Wei Dynasty. 20f, Heavenly Musicians, Northern Wei Dynasty. 40f, Flying Devata, Northern Wei Dynasty. $2, Mahasattva Jataka. T.116.

1987, May 20 *Perf. 11½*

2091	A557	8f multi (4-1)	.20	.15
2092	A557	10f multi (4-2)	.20	.20
2093	A557	20f multi (4-3)	.50	.40
2094	A557	40f multi (4-4)	1.10	.85
		Nos. 2091-2094 (4)	2.00	1.60

Souvenir Sheet

2095	A557	$2 multi	*6.00*

No. 2095 contains one 92x73mm stamp.
See Nos. 2149-2152, 2283-2286, 2407-2411, 2505-2508.

Children's Day Festival A558

Children's drawings: No. 2096, Happy Holiday, by Yan Qinghui, age 7. No. 2097, Peace and Happiness, by Liu Yuan, age 7. T.117.

1987, June 1 *Perf. 12½x12*

2096	A558	8f shown (2-1)	.15	.15
2097	A558	8f multi, vert. (2-2)	.15	.15
		Set value	.20	.20

Rural Development A559

Postal Savings Bank Inauguration A560

1987, June 25 *Perf. 11½*

2098	A559	8f Village, southeast China (4-1)	.15	.15
2099	A559	8f Market (4-2)	.15	.15
2100	A559	10f Dairy industry (4-3)	.15	.15
2101	A559	20f Theater (4-4)	.30	.30
		Nos. 2098-2101 (4)	.75	.75

Nos. 2099-2100 horiz. T.118.

1987, July 1

2102	A560	8f multicolored	.15	.15

Esperanto Language Movement, Cent. — A561

1987, July 26

2103	A561	8f lt olive grn, blk & brt blue	.15

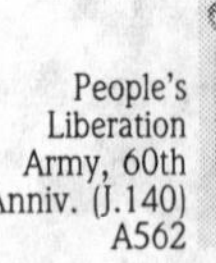

People's Liberation Army, 60th Anniv. (J.140) A562

1987, Aug. 1 *Perf. 11*

2104	A562	8f Flag, Great Wall (4-1)	.15
2105	A562	8f Rocket launch, soldier, village (4-2)	.15
2106	A562	10f Submarine, sailor (4-3)	.15
2107	A562	30f Aircraft, pilot (4-4)	.35
		Nos. 2104-2107 (4)	.80

Intl. Year of Shelter for the Homeless A563

1987, Aug. 20 *Perf. 11*

2108	A563	8f gray, dk car rose & blk	.15

Chinese Art Festival, Sept. 5-25, Beijing — A564

Fairy Tales — A565

1987, Sept. 5 *Perf. 11*

2109	A564	8f brt red, gold & blk	.15

1987, Sept. 25 *Perf. 11½*

Designs: 4f, Pan Gu inventing the universe. No. 2111, Nu Wa creating man. No. 2112, Yi shooting nine suns. 10f, Chang'e flying to the moon. 20f, Kua Fu pursuing the sun. 90f, Jing Wei filling the sea. T.120.

2110	A565	4f multi (6-1)	.15	.15
2111	A565	8f multi (6-2)	.15	.15
2112	A565	8f multi (6-3)	.15	.15
2113	A565	10f multi (6-4)	.15	.15
2114	A565	20f multi (6-5)	.20	.20
2115	A565	90f multi (6-6)	.95	.75
		Set value	1.50	1.20

Communist Party of China, 13th Natl. Congress A566

1987, Oct. 25 *Perf. 11*

2116	A566	8f multicolored	.15

Yellow Crane Tower (T.121) A567

1987, Oct. 30

2117	A567	8f shown (4-1)	.15
2118	A567	8f Yue Yang Tower (4-2)	.15
2119	A567	10f Teng Wang Pavilion (4-3)	.20
2120	A567	90f Peng Lai Pavilion (4-4)	1.50
a.		Min. sheet of 4, #2117-2120	*4.75*
		Nos. 2117-2120 (4)	2.00

No. 2120a sold for $1.50.

6th Natl. Games (J.144) — A568

1987, Nov. 20 *Perf. 11½x11*

2121	A568	8f Pole vault (4-1)	.15
2122	A568	8f Softball (4-2)	.15
2123	A568	30f Weight lifting (4-3)	.20
2124	A568	50f Diving (4-4)	.30
		Set value	.65

Souvenir Sheet

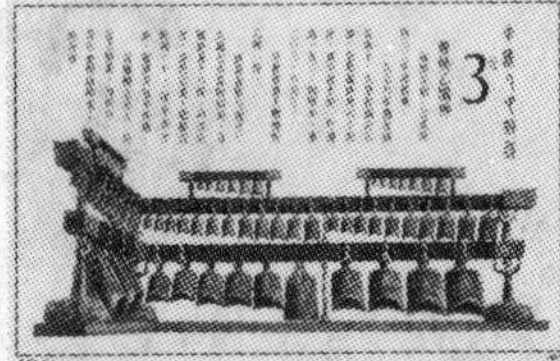
Bronze Bells from the Tomb of Marquis Yi of the Zeng State (c. 433 B.C.), Hubei Province — A569

1987, Dec. 10 **Litho.** *Imperf.*

2125	A569	$3 multicolored	*3.50*

Classic Literature — A570

Outlaws of the Marsh: 8f, Shi Jin practicing martial arts. 10f, Sagacious Lu, the "Tattooed Monk," uprooting a willow tree. 30f, Lin Chong seeking shelter from snow storm at the Mountain Spirit Temple. 50f, Song Jiang helps Ward Chief Chao Gai flee. $2, Outlaws of the Marsh capture treasures. T.123.

1987, Dec. 20 **Photo.** *Perf. 11*

2126	A570	8f multi (4-1)	.15
2127	A570	10f multi (4-2)	.20
2128	A570	30f multi (4-3)	.65
2129	A570	50f multi (4-4)	1.00
		Nos. 2126-2129 (4)	2.00

Souvenir Sheet

Perf. 11½x11

2130	A570	$2 multi	*5.75*

No. 2130 contains one 90x60mm stamp.
See Nos. 2216-2219, 2373-2377, 2449-2452.

New Year 1988 (Year of the Dragon) — A571

Cai Yuanpei (1868-1940), Education Reformer ((J.145) — A572

Photo. & Engr.

1988, Jan. 5 *Perf. 11½*

2131	A571	8f multicolored	*.25*
a.		Bklt. pane of 4 + 8 with label between	2.25

1988, Jan. 11 **Photo.** *Perf. 11½x11*

2132	A572	8f shown (2-1)	.15
2133	A572	20f Seated (2-2)	.15
		Set value	.20

Tao Zhu (1908-1969), Party Leader (J.146) A573

1988, Jan. 16 *Perf. 11x11½*

2134	A573	8f shown (2-1)	.15
2135	A573	20f Zhu, diff. (2-2)	.15
		Set value	.20

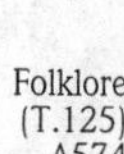

Folklore (T.125) A574

1988, Feb. 10

2136 A574 8f shown (4-1) .15
2137 A574 10f multi, diff. (4-2) .15
2138 A574 20f multi, diff. (4-3) .15
2139 A574 30f multi, diff. (4-4) .35
Nos. 2136-2139 (4) .80

A575 A576

1988, Mar. 25 Photo. *Perf. 11½*

2140 A575 8f multicolored .15

7th Natl. People's Congress.

1988, Apr. 20 Photo. *Perf. 11½*

2141 A576 8f Wuzhi Mountain (4-1) .15
2142 A576 10f Wanquan River (4-2) .15
2143 A576 30f "End of the Earth" (4-3) .15
2144 A576 $1.10 "Deer Turning Its Head" (4-4) .70
Nos. 2141-2144 (4) 1.15

Establishment of Hainan Province (J.148).

Modern Scientists A577

Designs: 8f, Li Siguang, geologist. 10f, Zhu Kezhen, meteorologist and geographer. 20f, Wu Youxun, physicist. 30f, Hua Luogeng, mathematician. J.149.

1988, Apr. 28 *Perf. 11x11½*

2145 A577 8f multi (4-1) .15
2146 A577 10f multi (4-2) .15
2147 A577 20f multi (4-3) .15
2148 A577 30f multi (4-4) .25
Set value .55

Dunhuang Petroglyphs Type of 1987

Petroglyphs from the Caves of the Thousand Buddhas, Dunhuang, Gansu Province: No. 2149, Hunting, Western Wei Dynasty. No. 2150, Fishing, Western Wei Dynasty. 10f, Farming, Northern Zhou Dynasty. 90f, Building a Pagoda, Northern Zhou Dynasty. T.126.

1988, May 25 *Perf. 11½x11*

2149 A557 8f multi (4-1) *.15*
2150 A557 8f multi (4-2) *.15*
2151 A557 10f multi (4-3) *.15*
2152 A557 90f multi (4-4) *1.10*
Nos. 2149-2152 (4) *1.55*

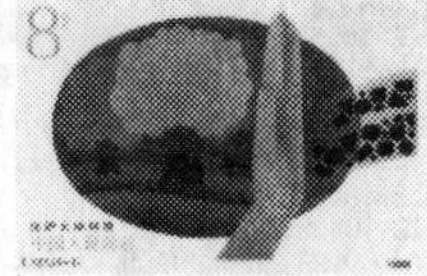

Environmental Protection — A578

1988, June 5 Photo. *Perf. 11*

2153 A578 8f Soil (4-1) .15
2154 A578 8f Air (4-2) .15
2155 A578 8f Water (4-3) .15
2156 A578 8f Prevent noise pollution (4-4) .15
a. Block of 4, #2153-2156 .40

Souvenir Sheet

China Nos. 1-3 — A579

1988, July 2 Photo. & Engr. *Perf. 13*

2157 A579 $3 multicolored *2.50*

Postage stamps of China, 110th anniv.

11th Asian Games (in 1990), Beijing (J.151) A580

1988, July 20 Photo. *Perf. 11x11½*

2158 A580 8f Emblem (2-1) .15
2159 A580 30f Character trademark (2-2) .30
Set value .35

See No. 2300a.

Signing of the Sino-Japanese Peace Treaty, 10th Anniv. (J.152) — A581

1988, Aug. 12 Photo. *Perf. 11*

2160 A581 8f Peony (2-1) .15
2161 A581 $1.60 Sakura (2-2) .75
a. Pair, #2160-2161 .80

Achievements in Construction A582

Designs: 8f, Coal-loading wharf, Ch'in-huang-tao Port. 10f, Ethylene refinery, Qilu. 20f, Pao-shan steel plant, Shanghai. 30f, Central Television Broadcasting Station. T.128.

1988, Sept. 2 Photo. *Perf. 11*

2162 A582 8f multi (4-1) .15
2163 A582 10f multi (4-2) .15
2164 A582 20f multi (4-3) .15
2165 A582 30f multi (4-4) .15
Set value .40

See Nos. 2221-2224, 2279-2282, 2354-2357.

Mt. T'ai Shan, Shantung Province (T.130) — A583

1988, Sept. 14 Photo. & Engr.

2166 A583 8f T'ai Shan Temple (4-1) .15
2167 A583 10f Ladder to Heaven (4-2) .20
2168 A583 20f Daguang peak (4-3) .45
2169 A583 90f Sun-watching peak (4-4) 1.90
Nos. 2166-2169 (4) 2.70

Liao Chengzhi (1908-1983), Party Leader (J.153) — A584

1988, Sept. 25 Photo. *Perf. 11½x11*

2170 A584 8f shown (2-1) .15
2171 A584 20f Writing (2-2) .15
Set value .20

Marshal Peng Dehuai (1898-1974), Party Leader (J.155) A585

1988, Oct. 24 Photo. *Perf. 11x11½*

2172 A585 8f shown (2-1) .15
2173 A585 20f Peng in uniform (2-2) .15
Set value .20

1st Natl. Farmers' Games (J.154) A586

1988, Oct. 9 Photo. *Perf. 11½*

2174 A586 8f Cycling (2-1) .15
2175 A586 20f Javelin (2-2) .15
Set value .25

Literary Masterpieces — A587

The Romance of the Three Kingdoms, by Luo Guanzhong, 14th cent.: No. 2176, Three heroes' sworn brotherhood (4-1). No. 2177, Battle between Lu Bu and the heroes, vert. (4-2). No. 2178, Struggle between man and woman at Fengyi Pavilion (4-3). No. 2179, Two noblemen, vert. (4-4). No. 2180, Guan Yu's battle through five passes. T.131.

Perf. 11½x11, 11x11½

1988, Nov. 25 Photo.

2176 A587 8f multicolored .20
2177 A587 8f multicolored .20
2178 A587 30f multicolored .60
2179 A587 50f multicolored 1.00
Nos. 2176-2179 (4) 2.00

Souvenir Sheet

Perf. 11

2180 A587 $3 multicolored *8.00*

See Nos. 2310-2313, 2403-2406, 2539-2543.

A588 A589

1988, Dec. 5 Photo. *Perf. 11*

2181 A588 20f multi .15

Intl Volunteers' Day.

1988, Dec. 20 Photo. *Perf. 11½x11*

Milu, *Elaphurus davidianus* (T.132).

2182 A589 8f Buck (2-1) .15
2183 A589 40f Herd (2-2) .65

Exist imperf. Value, each $2.

Orchids (T.129) — A590

1988, Dec. 25 *Perf. 12*

2184 A590 8f Da yi pin (4-1) .15
2185 A590 10f Dragon (4-2) .20
2186 A590 20f Large phoenix tail (4-3) .35
2187 A590 50f Silver-edged black (4-4) .90
a. Strip of 4, #2184-2187 1.75
Nos. 2184-2187 (4) 1.60

Souvenir Sheet

Perf. 11½x11

2188 A590 $2 Red lotus petal *4.00*

No. 2188 contains one 55x37mm stamp.

A591 A592

Grotto Statuary: $2, Buddha. $5, Warrior, Longmen Grotto, Henan. $10, Goddess. $20, Woman and birds.

Perf. 11½x11

1988-89 Photo & Engr.

2189 A591 $2 buff & reddish blk .40 .25
2190 A591 $5 buff & grnh blk 1.10 .60
2191 A591 $10 buff & brn blk 2.50 1.40
a. Souv. sheet of 1, buff & sepia *9.00*
2192 A591 $20 buff & indigo 5.00 2.75
Nos. 2189-2192 (4) 9.00 5.00

Issue dates: $2, Nov. 30; $5, Aug. 10; $10, Oct. 15; $20, Oct. 20.

No. 2191a released on Oct. 12, 1989, for the China Natl. Philatelic Exhibition and the 40th anniv. of the People's Republic.

Nos. 2189-2192, 2191a are almost always found with small ink spots on the stamps. Values are for stamps in this condition.

Photo. & Engr.

1989, Jan. 5 *Perf. 11½*

2193 A592 8f multicolored .20
a. Bklt. pane of 4+8 with label between 2.00

New Year 1989 (Year of the Snake).

Qu Qiubai (1899-1935), Party Leader (J.157) A593

1989, Jan. 29 Photo. *Perf. 11x11½*

2194 A593	8f multi (2-1)	.15	
2195 A593	20f multi, diff. (2-2)	.15	
	Set value	.20	

Brown-eared Pheasant, *Crossoptilon mantchuricum* (T.134) — A594

1989, Feb. 21 *Perf. 11½*

2196 A594	8f multi (2-1)	.15	
2197 A594	50f multi, diff. (2-2)	.40	

Folk Houses Type of 1986

1989-91 Photo. *Perf. 13x13½*

2198 A545	5f Shandong	.15	.15
2199 A545	15f Guangxi	.15	.15
2200 A545	25f Ningxia	.15	.15
2201 A545	80f Shanxi	.40	.20
2204 A545	$1.30 Qinghai	.50	.35
2206 A545	$1.60 Guizhou	.65	.45
2207 A545	$2 Jiangxi	.55	.55
	Nos. 2198-2207 (7)	2.55	2.00

Issue dates: 5f, June 10, 1991; 15f, Nov. 25, 1990; 25f, Nov. 10, 1990; 80f, Sept. 20, 1990; $1.30, $1.60, Mar. 10, 1989; $2, Apr. 25, 1991.

This is an expanding set. Numbers will change again if necessary.

Silk Painting Excavated from Han Tomb No. 1 at Mawangdui, Changsha (T.135) — A595

1989, Mar. 25 Photo. *Perf. 11½*

2208 A595	8f In the Heavens (3-1)	.15	
2209 A595	20f On the Earth, vert. (3-2)	.15	
2210 A595	30f In the Netherworld, vert. (3-3)	.20	
	Set value	.35	

Textured Paper, Without Gum

Size: 90x165mm

Imperf

2211 A595	$5 Entire painting	*2.50*	

Prevention and Resistance of Cancer (T.136) — A596

1989, Apr. 7 Litho. *Perf. 12*

2212 A596	8f shown (2-1)	.15	
2213 A596	20f Woman's thermogram (2-2)	.15	
	Set value	.20	

May Fourth Movement, 70th Anniv. (J.158) A597

1989, May 4 Photo. *Perf. 11*

2214 A597	8f Bas-relief	.15	

Interparliamentary Union, Cent. — A598

1989, June 29 Photo. *Perf. 11x11½*

2215 A598	20f multi	.15	

Literature Type of 1987

Outlaws of the Marsh: 8f, Wu Song slaying a tiger on Jingyang Ridge. 10f, Qin Ming dodging arrows. 20f, Hua Rong shooting a wild goose on Mt. Liangshan. $1.30, Li Kui fighting Zhang Shun from a junk. T.138.

1989, July 25 Photo. *Perf. 11*

2216 A570	8f multi (4-1)	.15	
2217 A570	10f multi (4-2)	.15	
2218 A570	20f multi (4-3)	.25	
2219 A570	$1.30 multi (4-4)	1.65	
	Nos. 2216-2219 (4)	2.20	

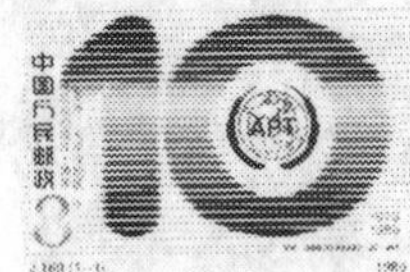

Asia-Pacific Telecommunity, 10th Anniv. — A599

1989, Aug. 4 Litho. *Perf. 12*

2220 A599	8f multi	.15	

Type of 1988

Achievements in Engineering and Construction: 8f, Beijing Intl. Telecommunications Building, vert. 10f, Xi Qu Coal Mine, Gu Jiao, Shanxi Province. 20f, Long Yang Gorge Hydroelectric Power Station, Qinghai Province. 30f, Da Yao Shan Tunnel of the Guangzhou-Heng Yang Railway. T.139.

1989, Aug. 10 Photo. *Perf. 11*

2221 A582	8f multi (4-1)	.15	
2222 A582	10f multi (4-2)	.15	
2223 A582	20f multi (4-3)	.15	
2224 A582	30f multi (4-4)	.15	
	Set value	.35	

Mt. Huashan — A601

Designs: 8f, Five prominent peaks. 10f, View from atop Huashan. 20f, 1000-foot precipice. 90f, Blue Dragon Ridge. T.140.

1989, Aug. 25 Photo. & Engr.

2225 A601	8f multi (4-1)	.15	
2226 A601	10f multi (4-2)	.15	
2227 A601	20f multi (4-3)	.20	
2228 A601	90f multi (4-4)	.85	
	Nos. 2225-2228 (4)	1.35	

Modern Art — A602

Paintings: 8f, *The Fable of the White Snake*, by Ye Qianyu. 20f, *Lijiang River in Fine Rain*, by Li Keran. 50f, *Marching Together*, by Wu Zuoren. T.141

1989, Sept. 1 Photo.

2229 A602	8f multi (3-1)	.15	
2230 A602	20f multi (3-2)	.20	
2231 A602	50f multi (3-3)	.50	
	Nos. 2229-2231 (3)	.85	

People's Political Conference — A603

1989, Sept. 21 *Perf. 12*

2232 A603	8f No. 2	.15	

A604

Confucius (551-479 B.C.) — A605

Designs: 8f, The lecture in the Apricot Temple, Qufu. $1.60, Confucius riding in an ox cart. J.162.

1989, Sept. 28 Photo. *Perf. 11*

2233 A604	8f shown (2-1)	.15	
2234 A604	$1.60 multi (2-2)	.90	

Souvenir Sheet

Litho. *Imperf.*

Without Gum

2235 A605	$3 multi	*2.50*	

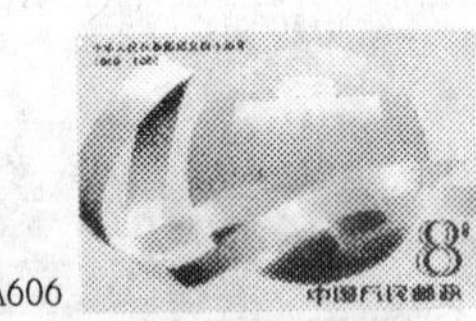

A606

Gate of Heavenly Peace — A607

1989, Oct. 1 Photo. *Perf. 11x11½*

2236 A606	8f shown (4-1)	.15	
2237 A606	10f Flowers (4-2)	.15	
2238 A606	20f Five stars (4-3)	.15	
2239 A606	40f Construction (4-4)	.25	
	Set value	.50	

Souvenir Sheet

Litho. *Imperf.*

Without Gum

2240 A607	$3 shown	*2.50*	

PRC, 40th anniv. J.163.

Photography, Sesquicentennial — A608

1989, Oct. 15 Photo. *Perf. 11*

2241 A608	8f multicolored	.15	

Li Dazhao (1889-1927), Party Leader (J.164) — A609

1989, Oct. 29 Photo. *Perf. 11½*

2242 A609	8f Dazhao, soldiers (2-1)	.15	
2243 A609	20f Dazhao, text (2-2)	.15	
	Set value	.15	

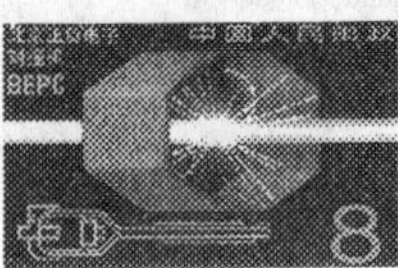

Positron Collider Produced in Beijing A610

1989, Nov. 1 *Perf. 11*

2244 A610	8f multicolored	.15	

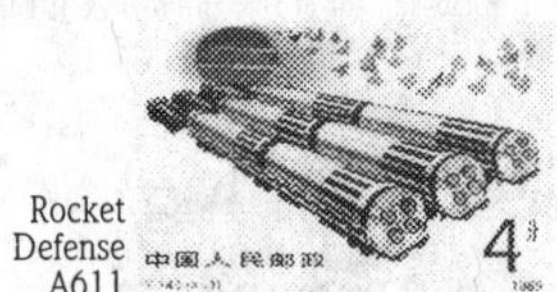

Rocket Defense A611

Designs: 4f, Transporting 3 rockets. 8f, Disassembled rocket on transport. 10f, Launch, vert. 20f, Stage separation in space. T.143.

1989, Nov. 15 Litho. *Perf. 12*

2245 A611	4f multicolored (4-1)	.15	
2246 A611	8f multicolored (4-2)	.15	
2247 A611	10f multicolored (4-3)	.15	
2248 A611	20f multicolored (4-4)	.15	
	Set value	.30	

A612

Views of West Lake (T.144) — A613

1989, Nov. 25 Photo. *Perf. 11x11½*

2249 A612	8f multi (4-1)	.15	
2250 A612	10f multi, diff. (4-2)	.15	
2251 A612	30f multi, diff. (4-3)	.30	
2252 A612	40f multi, diff. (4-4)	.35	
	Set value	.80	

Souvenir Sheet

Perf. 11½x11

2253 A613	$5 multicolored	*3.00*	

11th Asian Games A614

Various stadiums. J.165.

1989, Dec. 15 ***Perf. 11x11½***
2254 A614 8f multi (4-1) .15
2255 A614 10f multi (4-2) .15
2256 A614 30f multi (4-3) .15
2257 A614 $1.60 multi (4-4) .70
Set value .90

See Nos. 2295-2300.

A615

Narcissus (T.147) — A616

Photo & Engr.

1990, Jan. 5 ***Perf. 11½***
2258 A615 8f multicolored .40 .20
a. Bklt. pane of 12 + 4 labels 2.00

New Year 1990 (Year of the Horse).

1990, Feb. 10 Photo. ***Perf. 11x11½***
2259 A616 8f multi (4-1) .15
2260 A616 20f multi, diff. (4-2) .15
2261 A616 30f multi, diff. (4-3) .15
2262 A616 $1.60 multi, diff. (4-4) .75
Set value 1.00

Norman Bethune (1890-1939), Surgeon (J.166) A617

Perf. 11x11½

1990, Mar. 3 **Litho. & Engr.**
2263 A617 8f In Canada (2-2) .15
2264 A617 $1.60 In China (2-1) .65
a. Pair, #2263-2264 .70

See Canada #1264-1265.

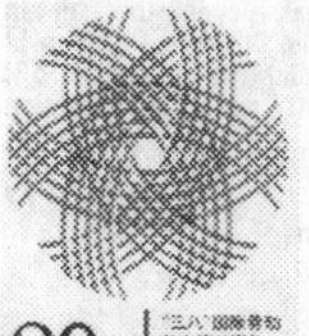

Intl. Women's Day — A618

1990, Mar. 8 Photo. ***Perf. 11½x11***
2265 A618 20f multicolored .15

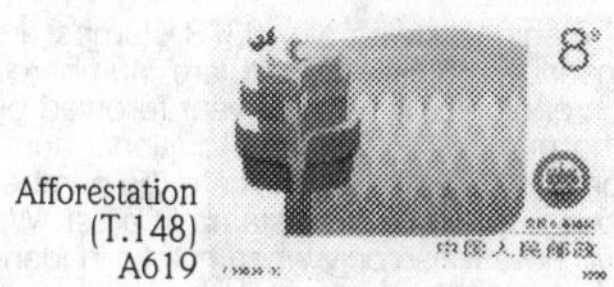

Afforestation (T.148) A619

1990, Mar. 12 ***Perf. 11***
2266 A619 8f Bird, flora (4-1) .15
2267 A619 10f Buildings (4-2) .15
2268 A619 20f Great Wall, forest, (4-3) .15
2269 A619 30f Bushes, evergreens (4-4) .15
Set value .35

Pottery (T.149) — A620

1990, Apr. 10 Litho. ***Perf. 12***
2270 A620 8f multi (4-1) .15
2271 A620 20f multi (4-2) .15
2272 A620 30f multi (4-3) .15
2273 A620 50f multi (4-4) .20
Set value .50

Li Fuchun (1900-1975), Party Leader (J.168) A621

1990, May 22 Photo. ***Perf. 11x11½***
2274 A621 8f shown .15
2275 A621 20f In uniform (2-2) .15
Set value .20

Bronze Head — A622

Bronze treasures from Emperor Qin Shi Huang Mausoleum: 50f, Horse head. $5, Chariots. T.151.

1990, June 20 Photo. ***Perf. 11½x11***
2276 A622 8f shown (2-1) .15
2277 A622 50f multicolored (2-2) .25
Set value .30

Miniature Sheet

Size: 141x79mm

2278 A622 $5 multicolored *2.50*

Achievements Type of 1988

Designs: 8f, 2nd automobile factory. 10f, Yizheng Joint Corporation of Chemical Fiber Industry. 20f, Shengli Oil Field. 30f, Qinshan Nuclear Power Station. T.152.

1990, June 30 Litho. ***Perf. 12***
2279 A582 8f shown (4-1) .15
2280 A582 10f multicolored (4-2) .15
2281 A582 20f multicolored (4-3) .15
2282 A582 30f multicolored (4-4) .20
Set value .45

Type of Dunhuang Petroglyphs of 1987

Murals: 8f, Flying Devatas. 10f, Worshipping Bodhisatva. 30f, Savior Avolokitesvara. 50f, Indra. T.150.

1990, July 10 ***Perf. 11½x11***
2283 A557 8f multi (4-1) .15
2284 A557 10f multi, vert. (4-2) .15
2285 A557 30f multi, vert. (4-3) .45
2286 A557 50f multi (4-4) .75
Nos. 2283-2286 (4) 1.50

Snow Leopard (Uncia Uncia) (T.153) A624

1990, July 20 Photo. ***Perf. 11½***
2287 A624 8f multicolored (2-1) .15
2288 A624 50f multicolored (2-2) .25
Set value .30

Chinese Soviet Post Stamp of 1931 A625

Design: 20f, Chinese Red Post issue of West Fukien, 1929. J.169.

1990, Aug. 1 Litho. ***Perf. 12***
2289 A625 8f multi (2-1) .15
2290 A625 20f multi, diff. (2-2) .15
Set value .20

Zhang Wentian (1900-1990) (J.170) A626

1990, Aug. 30 ***Perf. 11x11½***
2291 A626 8f shown (2-1) .15
2292 A626 20f multi, diff. (2-2) .15
Set value .20

Intl. Literacy Year — A627

Chinese Films — A628

1990, Sept. 8 ***Perf. 11½x11***
2293 A627 20f multicolored .15

1990, Sept. 21 Litho. ***Perf. 11***
2294 A628 20f multicolored .15

11th Asian Games, Beijing (J.172) — A629

1990, Sept. 22 ***Perf. 11x11½***
2295 A629 4f Running (6-1) .15
2296 A629 8f Gymnastics (6-2) .15
2297 A629 10f Karate (6-3) .15
2298 A629 20f Volleyball (6-4) .15
2299 A629 30f Swimming (6-5) .20
2300 A629 $1.60 Shooting (6-6) .95
a. Souv. sheet of 12, #2158-2159, 2254-2257, 2295-2300 *5.00*
Set value 1.40

Souvenir Sheet

Sportphilex '90, Beijing — A629a

1990, Sept. 21 Litho. ***Perf. 11½***
2300B A629a $10 multicolored *16.00*

Modern Scientists A630

Designs: 8f, Lin Qiaozhi, obstetrician. 10f, Zhang Yuzhe, astronomer. 20f, Hou Debang, chemist. 30f, Ding Ying, agronomist. J.173.

1990, Oct. 10 Litho. ***Perf. 12***
2301 A630 8f multicolored (4-1) .15
2302 A630 10f multicolored (4-2) .15
2303 A630 20f multicolored (4-3) .20
2304 A630 30f multicolored (4-4) .25
Set value .60

Mt. Hengshan — A631

Designs: 8f, Towering Temple. 10f, South Sacred Mountain. 20f, Forested mountainside. 50f, Imposing Zhurong Peak. T.155.

1990, Nov. 5 Photo. & Engr. ***Perf. 11***
2305 A631 8f multicolored (4-1) .15
2306 A631 10f multicolored (4-2) .15
2307 A631 20f multicolored (4-3) .20
2308 A631 50f multicolored (4-4) .55
Nos. 2305-2308 (4) 1.05

See Nos. 2342-2345. 2628-2631.

Souvenir Sheet

China Philatelic Federation, 3rd Congress — A632

1990, Nov. 28 ***Perf. 11½x11***
2309 A632 $2 multicolored *3.00*

Two types of No. 2309 exist. Either two or three of the horizontal bars in seventh character from top right are connected at left side.

Literature Type of 1988

Romance of the Three Kingdoms by Luo Guanzhong: No. 2310, Night Attack on Wuchao. No. 2311, Making Three Calls at the Thatched Cottage. 30f, Rescuing the Master Single-handedly. 50f, Turning the Changban Bridge Upside Down. T.157.

1990, Dec. 10 Photo. ***Perf. 11½x11***
2310 A587 20f multicolored (4-1) .15
2311 A587 20f multi, vert. (4-2) .15
2312 A587 30f multicolored (4-3) .25
2313 A587 50f multi, vert. (4-4) .45
Nos. 2310-2313 (4) 1.00

Han Xizai's Night Revels by Gu Hongzhong — A633

Designs: a, Guests enjoying food, music (5-1). b, Music and dance (5-2). c, Hand washing (5-3). d, Musicians (5-4). e, Guests departing (5-5). T.158. (Illustration reduced).

1990, Dec. 20 Litho. ***Perf. 12***
2314 Strip of 5 2.50
a.-e. A633 50f any single .50

New Year 1991 (Year of the Sheep) — A634

Photo. & Engr.

1991, Jan. 5 ***Perf. 11½***

2315 A634 20f multicolored .40
 a. Bklt. pane of 12 + label 2.00

Dujiangyan Irrigation Project — A635

Designs: 20f, Yuzui, flood control. 50f, Feishayan, drainage. 80f, Baopingkou, water volume control. T.156.

1991, Feb. 20 Photo. ***Perf. 11½x11***

2316 A635 20f multicolored .15
2317 A635 50f multicolored .30
2318 A635 80f multicolored .55
 Nos. 2316-2318 (3) 1.00

A636 A637

1991, Mar. 18

2319 A636 20f multicolored .15

Paris Commune, 120th anniv.

1991, Apr. 20 Photo. ***Perf. 10***

2320 A637 20f multi (2-1) .15
 a. Perf. 11½x11 .40

Perf. 11½x11

2321 A637 50f Child & adult hands (2-2) .20

Family planning (T.160).

Horned Animals (T.161) A638

1991, May 10 ***Perf. 11x11½***

2322 A638 20f Saiga tatarica (4-1) .15
2323 A638 20f Budorcas taxicolor (4-2) .15
2324 A638 50f Ovis ammon (4-3) .15
2325 A638 $2 Capra ibex (4-4) .75
 Nos. 2322-2325 (4) 1.20

A639 A640

1991, May 23 Photo. ***Perf. 11***

2326 A639 25f Song and dance (2-1) .15
2327 A639 50f Golden bridge (2-2) .25

Souvenir Sheet

2328 A639 $2 No. 132, cranes 3.00

Occupation of Tibet, 40th anniv. (J.176).

1991, June 22 ***Perf. 11½x11***

2329 A640 20f multicolored .15

Antarctic Treaty, 30th anniv.

Rhododendrons — A641

Varieties of rhododendrons. T.162.

1991, June 25 Litho. ***Perf. 12***

2330 A641 10f Delavayi (8-1) .15
2331 A641 15f Molle (8-2) .15
2332 A641 20f Simsii (8-3) .15
2333 A641 20f Fictolacteum (8-4) .15
2334 A641 50f Agglutinatum, vert. (8-5) .20
2335 A641 80f Fortunei, vert. (8-6) .35
2336 A641 90f Giganteum, vert. (8-7) .40
2337 A641 $1.60 Rex, vert. (8-8) .70
 Nos. 2330-2337 (8) 2.25

Souvenir Sheet

Perf. 11½

2338 A641 $5 Wardii 4.00

No. 2338 contains one 80x40mm stamp.

Chinese Communist Party, 70th Anniv. (J.178) A642

1991, July 1 Photo. ***Perf. 11x11½***

2339 A642 20f shown (2-1) .15
2340 A642 50f Hammer and sickle (2-2) .25

Peasant Uprising, 209B.C. A643

1991, July 7

2341 A643 20f brown .15

Mt. Hengshan Type of 1990

Designs: No. 2342, Monastery on mountainside. No. 2343, Snow-covered mountain top. 55f, Inscription carved into mountainside. 80f, Hidden monastery. T.163.

1991, July 20 Photo. & Engr. ***Perf. 11***

2342 A631 20f multi (4-1) .20
2343 A631 20f multi (4-2) .20
2344 A631 55f multi (4-3) .45
2345 A631 80f multi (4-4) .65
 Nos. 2342-2345 (4) 1.50

Intl. Union for Quaternary Research, 13th Conf. — A644

1991, Aug. 2 Photo. ***Perf. 11x11½***

2346 A644 20f multicolored .15

Chengde Mountain Resort — A645

Ch'ing Dynasty Royal Gardens: 15f, Pine valleys. 20f, Mid-lake pavilion. 90f, Islet, maple trees. $2, Chengde Royal Summer Resort. T.164.

1991 ***Perf. 11½x11***

2347 A645 15f multi (3-1) .15
2348 A645 20f multi (3-2) .15
2349 A645 90f multi (3-3) .70
 Nos. 2347-2349 (3) 1.00

Souvenir Sheet

2350 A645 $2 multicolored *2.50*

No. 2350 contains one 90x40mm stamp. Issue dates: $2, Aug. 19. Others, Aug. 10.

A646 A647

Chen Yi, (b. 1901), party leader (J.181).

1991, Aug. 26 Photo. ***Perf. 11½x11***

2351 A646 20f shown (2-1) .15
2352 A646 50f Verse (2-2) .25

1991, Sept. 14

2353 A647 80f Disaster relief .30

Achievements Type of 1988

Designs: 20f, Luoyang glassworks. 25f, Urumchi chemical fertilizer project. 55f, Dalian expressway, Shenyang. 80f, Xichang satellite launching center. T.165.

1991, Sept. 20 Litho. ***Perf. 12***

2354 A582 20f multi (4-1) .15
2355 A582 25f multi (4-2) .15
2356 A582 55f multi (4-3) .20
2357 A582 80f multi (4-4) .30
 Nos. 2354-2357 (4) .80

Revolutionary Heroes A648

Designs: No. 2358, Xu Xilin (1873-1907). No. 2359, Qiu Jin (1879-1907). No. 2360, Song Jiaoren (1882-1913). J.182.

1991, Oct. 10 Photo. ***Perf. 11x11½***

2358 A648 20f multi (3-1) .15
 a. Perf. 10 .50

Perf. 10

2359 A648 20f multi (3-2) .15
2360 A648 20f multi (3-3) .15

Jingdezhen Chinaware A649

Designs: 15f, Glazed wine pot and warming bowl, Song Dynasty, vert. No. 2362, Porcelain vase, Yuan Dynasty, vert. No. 2363, Jar, Ming Dynasty. 25f, Porcelain vase, Ch'ing Dynasty, vert. 50f, Modern underglazed plate, vert. $2, Modern octagonal eggshell bowl, T.166.

Perf. 11½, 11½x11 (#2362), 11x11½ (#2363)

1991, Oct. 11 **Photo.**

2361 A649 15f multi (6-1) .15
2362 A649 20f multi (6-2) .15
2363 A649 20f multi (6-3) .15
2364 A649 25f multi (6-4) .15
2365 A649 50f multi (6-5) .20
2366 A649 $2 multi (6-6) .75
 Set value 1.20

1991

2361a Perf. 11½x11 .15
2362a Perf. 11x11½ .15
2363a Perf. 11½ .15
2364a Perf. 11½x11 .20
2365a Perf. 11½x11 .35
2366a Perf. 11x11½ 1.40

Tao Xingzhi, Educator, Birth Cent. (J.183) — A650

1991, Oct. 18 Litho. ***Perf. 12***

2367 A650 20f shown (2-1) .15
2368 A650 50f Wearing robe (2-2) .20
 Set value .30

Xu Xiangqian, Revolutionary Leader, 90th Birth Anniv. (J.184) A651

1991, Nov. 8 ***Perf. 11x11½***

2369 A651 20f shown (2-1) .15
2370 A651 50f In uniform (2-2) .20
 Set value .30

1st Women's Soccer World Championships, Guangdong Province (J.185) — A652

Designs: 50f, Woman kicking soccer ball.

1991, Nov. 16 ***Perf. 11½x11***

2371 A652 20f red & multi (2-1) .15
2372 A652 50f grn & multi (2-2) .20
 Set value .30

Literature Type of 1987

Outlaws of the Marsh: 20f, Dai Zong sends a false letter from Liangshan Marsh. No. 2374, Ten feet of steel alone captures Stumpy Tiger Wang. No. 2375, Mistress Gu breaks open the jail in Dengzhou to rescue the Xie Brothers. 90f, Sun Li offers a plan to attack Zhu Family manor. $3, Mount Liangshan gallants raid the execution grounds. T.167.

1991, Nov. 19 ***Perf. 11***

2373 A570 20f multi (4-1) .15
2374 A570 25f multi (4-2) .15
2375 A570 25f multi (4-3) .15
2376 A570 90f multi (4-4) .45
 Nos. 2373-2376 (4) .90

Souvenir Sheet

Perf. 11x11½

2377 A570 $3 multicolored *3.00*

No. 2377 contains one 60x90mm stamp.

Beginning with No. 2378 stamps are inscribed "CHINA" and are numbered chronologically with the year followed by the number of the set. Additional numbers in parentheses indicate the number and position of each stamp in a set. We will note these only when helpful in identifying stamps.

New Year 1992, Year of the Monkey

A653 A654

Photo. & Engr.

1992, Jan. 25 ***Perf. 11½***

2378 A653 20f Monkey, peach .15
2379 A654 50f Magpies, plum branches .20

Storks — A655 Conifers — A656

1992, Feb. 20 Photo. *Perf. 11x11½*
2380 A655 20f Ciconia nigra .15
2381 A655 $1.60 Ciconia ciconia .75

1992, Mar. 10 Litho. *Perf. 12½*

Designs: 20f, Metasequoia glyptostroboides. 30f, Cathaya argyrophylla. 50f, Taiwania flousiana. 80f, Abies beshanzuensis.

2382 A656 20f multicolored .15
2383 A656 30f multicolored .15
2384 A656 50f multicolored .20
2385 A656 80f multicolored .40
Nos. 2382-2385 (4) .90

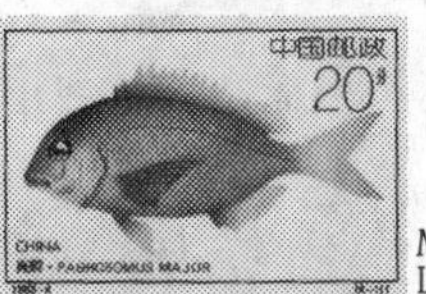

Marine Life — A660

1992, Apr. 15 Photo. *Perf. 11*
2386 A660 20f Pagrosomus major .15
2387 A660 25f Penaeus chinesis .15
2388 A660 50f Chlamys farreri .20
2389 A660 80f Laminaria japonica .25
Set value .60

Publication of "Discussions on Literature and Art at the Yenan Forum," 50th Anniv. — A661

1992, May 23 Photo. *Perf. 11½x11*
2390 A661 20f orange, black & red .15

A662 A663

1992, June 5 Litho. *Perf. 12*
2392 A662 20f multicolored .15

UN Conf. on Human Development, 20th anniv.

1992, June 28

Insects: 20f, Coccinella septempunctata. 30f, Sympetrum croceolum. 50f, Chrysopa septempunctata. $2, Tenodera aridifolia sinensis.

2393 A663 20f multicolored .15
2394 A663 30f multicolored .15
2395 A663 50f multicolored .25
2396 A663 $2 multicolored .90
Nos. 2303-2396 (4) 1.45

1992 Summer Olympics, Barcelona A664

1992, July 25 Photo. *Perf. 11*
2397 A664 20f Basketball, vert. .15
2398 A664 25f Women's gymnastics .15
2399 A664 50f Women's diving .20
2400 A664 80f Weight lifting, vert. .25
Nos. 2397-2400 (4) .75

Souvenir Sheet

2401 A664 $5 Runners *2.00*

No. 2401 contains one 54x40mm stamp.

Intl. Space Year — A665

1992, Aug. 18 Litho. *Perf. 12*
2402 A665 20f multicolored .15

Literature Type of 1988

Romance of the Three Kingdoms by Luo Guanzhong: 20f, Verbal battle with scholars. 50f, Goading Sun Quan with sarcasm, vert. 30f, Jiang Gan stealing the letter. $1.60, Gathering arrows with straw-covered boats, vert.

Perf. 11½x11, 11x11½

1992, Aug. 25 Photo.
2403 A587 20f multi (4-1) .15
2404 A587 30f multi (4-2) .15
2405 A587 50f multi (4-3) .15
2406 A587 $1.60 multi (4-4) .60
Nos. 2403-2406 (4) 1.05

Dunhuang Petroglyphs Type of 1987

Murals: 20f, Bodhisattva, vert. 25f, Musical performance, vert. 55f, Flight of a dragon. 80f, Envoy to the western regions. $5, Avalokitesvara-Bodhisattva, vert.

1992, Sept. 15 *Perf. 11*
2407 A557 20f multi (4-1) .15
2408 A557 25f multi (4-2) .15
2409 A557 55f multi (4-3) .30
2410 A557 80f multi (4-4) .45
Nos. 2407-2410 (4) 1.05

Souvenir Sheet

Perf. 11½

2411 A557 $5 multicolored *2.00*

No. 2411 contains one 52x70mm stamp.

Normalization of Diplomatic Relations Between China and Japan, 20th Anniv. A666

Designs: 20f, Cranes, Great Wall of China, Mt. Fuji. $2, Japanese, Chinese children, dove.

1992, Sept. 29 Photo. *Perf. 11x11½*
2412 A666 20f multi (2-1) .15
2413 A666 $2 multi (2-2) .75

A667 A667a

Statue of Mazu, Chinese Goddess of the Sea.

1992, Oct. 4 Litho. *Perf. 12*
2414 A667 20f multicolored .15

1992, Oct. 12 Photo. *Perf. 11½x11*
2414A A667a 20f multicolored .15

14th Chinese Communist Party Congress.

Jiao Yulu (1922-1964), Communist Party Leader — A668

1992, Oct. 28 Litho. *Perf. 12*
2415 A668 20f multicolored .15

Famous Men — A669

Designs: 20f, Xiong Qinglai, mathematician. 30f, Tang Feifan, microbiologist. 50f, Zhang Xiaoqian, physician. $1, Liang Sicheng, architect.

1992, Nov. 20
2416 A669 20f multi (4-1) .15
2417 A669 30f multi (4-2) .15
2418 A669 50f multi (4-3) .20
2419 A669 $1 multi (4-4) .35
Set value .75

Luo Ronghuan, Leader of People's Army, 90th Anniv. of Birth — A670

1992, Nov. 26 Photo. *Perf. 11x11½*
2420 A670 20f In dress uniform (2-1) .15
2421 A670 50f In field uniform (2-2) .20
Set value .30

Constitution of the People's Republic of China, 10th Anniv. — A671

1992, Dec. 4 *Perf. 11½x11*
2422 A671 20f multicolored .15

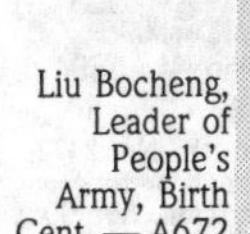

Liu Bocheng, Leader of People's Army, Birth Cent. — A672

Designs: 20f, In dress uniform. 50f, During period of Long March, vert.

1992, Dec. 4 *Perf. 11x11½, 11½x11*
2423 A672 20f multi (2-1) .15
2424 A672 50f multi (2-2) .20
Set value .30

Quingtian Stone Carvings — A673

1992, Dec. 15 Litho. *Perf. 12*
2425 A673 10f Spring (4-1) .15
2426 A673 20f Chinese sorghum (4-2) .15
2427 A673 40f Harvest (4-3) .15
2428 A673 $2 Blooming flowers, full moon (4-4) .75
Set value 1.00

New Year 1993 (Year of the Rooster)
A674 A675

Photo. & Engr.

1993, Jan. 5 *Perf. 11½*
2429 A674 20f red & black (2-1) .15
2430 A675 50f red, white & blk (2-2) .20
Set value .30

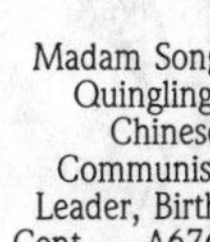

Madam Song Quingling, Chinese Communist Leader, Birth Cent. — A676

1993, Jan. 20 Photo. *Perf. 11x11½*
2431 A676 20f Portrait (2-1) .15
2432 A676 $1 With children (2-2) .40
Set value .50

Camelus Bactrianus Ferus A677

1993, Feb. 20 Litho. *Perf. 12*
2433 A677 20f shown (2-1) .15
2434 A677 $1.60 Adult, young (2-2) .65
Set value .62

8th Natl. People's Congress A678

1993, Mar. 15 Litho. *Perf. 12*
2435 A678 20f multicolored .15

A679 A680

Game of Weiqi (Go): 20f, Painting of players of ancient times. $1.60, Game board showing Chinese-style position.

1993, Apr. 30 Litho. *Perf. 12*
2436 A679 20f multi (2-1) .15
2437 A679 $1.60 multi (2-2) .55

1993, May 15 Litho. *Perf. 12*

20th Cent. Revolutionaries: 20f, Li Jishen (1885-1959), horiz. 30f, Zhang Lan (1872-1955). 50f, Shen Junru (1875-1963). $1, Huang Yanpei (1878-1965), horiz.

2438 A680 20f multi (4-1) .15
2439 A680 30f multi (4-2) .15
2440 A680 50f multi (4-3) .20
2441 A680 $1 multi (4-4) .40
Nos. 2438-2441 (4) .90

See Nos. 2483-2486.

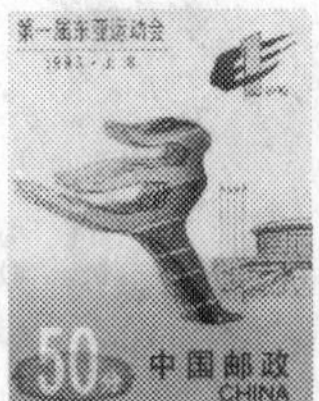

First East Asian Games — A681

1993, May 9 Photo. *Perf. 12*

2442 A681 50f Runner (2-1) .20
2443 A681 50f Mascot (2-2) .20
a. Pair, #2442-2443 .40

No. 2443a printed in continuous design.

Bamboo — A682

Designs: 20f, Phyllostachys nigra. 30f, Phyllostachys aureosulcata spectabilis. 40f, Bambusa ventricosa. $1, Pseudosasa amabilis. $5, Phyllostachys heterocycla pubescens, horiz.

1993, June 15 Litho. *Perf. 12½*

2444 A682 20f multi (4-1) .15
2445 A682 30f multi (4-2) .15
2446 A682 40f multi (4-3) .15
2447 A682 $1 multi (4-4) .40
Nos. 2444-2447 (4) .85

Souvenir Sheet

Photo.

Perf. 11

2448 A682 $5 multicolored 2.25

No. 2448 contains one 54x40mm stamp.

Literature Type of 1987

Outlaws of the Marsh: 20f, Chai Jin is trapped in Gaotang. 30f, Shi Qian steals armor. 50f, Xu Ning teaches how to use barbed lance. $2, Shi Xiu leaps from building to rescue condemned man from execution.

1993, Aug. 20 Photo. *Perf. 11*

2449 A570 20f multi (4-1) .15
2450 A570 30f multi (4-2) .15
2451 A570 50f multi (4-3) .15
2452 A570 $2 multi (4-4) .65
Set value .90

Changbai Mountains — A683

1993, Sept. 3 *Perf. 11½x11*

2453 A683 20f Tianchi (4-1) .15
2454 A683 30f Alpine tundra (4-2) .15
2455 A683 50f Waterfall (4-3) .15
2456 A683 $1 Mixed forest (4-4) .30
Set value .60

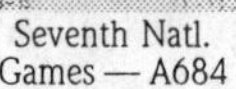

Seventh Natl. Games — A684 Longmen Grottoes — A685

1993, Sept. 4

2457 A684 20f multicolored .15

1993, Sept. 5 Litho. *Perf. 12*

Designs: 20f, Rocana, Ancestor Worshipping Temple. 30f, Sakyamuni, Middle Binyang Cave, Northern Wei. 50f, Maharaja, devas treading on Yaksha. $1, Bodhisattva at the left side of Rocana, Guyang Cave, Northern Wei. $5, Ancestor Worshipping Temple.

2458 A685 20f multi (4-1) .15
2459 A685 30f multi (4-2) .15
2460 A685 50f multi (4-3) .15
2461 A685 $1 multi (4-4) .30
Set value .60

Souvenir Sheets

2462 A685 $5 multicolored *2.00*
a. Ovptd. in gold 5.00

No. 2462 contains one 120x40mm stamp.
Overprint in margin of No. 2462a includes Chinese characters and "PJZ-1." Bangkok '95 (#2462a). No. 2462a sold for $6.
Issued: No. 2462a, 8/95.

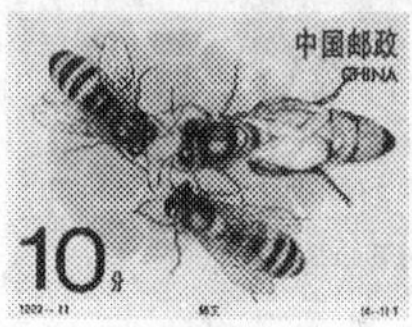

Honey Bees — A686

1993, Sept. 21 Photo. *Perf. 11½*

2463 A686 10f Queen and two bees (4-1) .15
2464 A686 15f Extracting nectar (4-2) .15
2465 A686 20f Two Zhonghua bees (4-3) .15
2466 A686 $2 Two bees in flight (4-4) .65
Set value 1.00

Lacquerware — A687

1993, Oct. 20 Photo. *Perf. 12*

2467 A687 20f Bowl (4-1) .15
2468 A687 30f Duck (4-2) .15
2469 A687 50f Round tray (4-3) .15
2470 A687 $1 Lidded box (4-4) .30
Set value .60

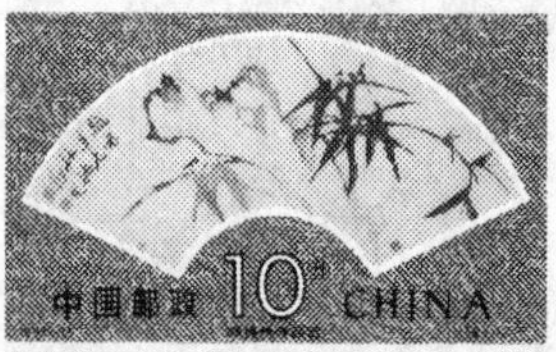

Paintings, by Zheng Banqiao — A688

Designs: 10f, Bamboo, rock on fan. No. 2472, Orchard. No. 2473, Orchard, bamboo, rock on scroll, vert. 30f, Bamboo, rock on scroll, vert. 50f, Vase and chrysanthemums. $1.60, Chinese calligraphy on fan.

1993, Nov. 22 Litho. *Perf. 12½*

2471 A688 10f multi (6-1) .15
2472 A688 20f multi (6-2) .15
2473 A688 20f multi (6-3) .15
2474 A688 30f multi (6-4) .15
2475 A688 50f multi (6-5) .15
2476 A688 $1.60 multi (6-6) .50
Set value .90

A689 A690

1993, Nov. 26 *Perf. 12*

2477 A689 20f multicolored .15

Yang Hucheng, birth cent.

1993 Photo. *Perf. 11½*

Mao Tse-tung (1893-1976).

2478 A690 20f shown (2-1) .15
2479 A690 $1 Portrait, seated (2-2) .30
Set value .35

Souvenir Sheet

2480 A690 $5 Standing by Great Wall *1.90*

Issue dates: $5, Nov. 16. 20f, $1, Dec. 26. No. 2480 contains one 48x58mm stamp.

New Year 1994 (Year of the Dog)
A691 A692

1994, Jan. 5 Photo. *Perf. 11½*

2481 A691 20f multi (2-1) .15
2482 A692 50f yel, red & blk (2-2) .30
Set value .40

20th Cent. Revolutionaries Type

Designs: No. 2483, Chen Qiyou, horiz. No. 2484, Chen Shutong. No. 2485, Ma Xulun. No. 2486, Xu Deheng, horiz.

1994, Feb. 25 Litho. *Perf. 12*

2483 A680 20f blk & brn (4-1) .15
2484 A680 20f blk & brn (4-2) .15
2485 A680 50f blk & brn (4-3) .20
2486 A680 50f blk & brn (4-4) .20
Set value .50

Sturgeon — A693

Designs: 20f, Huso dauricus. 40f, Acipenser sinensis. 50f, Psephurus gladius. $1, Acipenser dabryanus.

1994, Mar. 18 Litho. *Perf. 12½*

2487 A693 20f multi (4-1) .15
2488 A693 40f multi (4-2) .15
2489 A693 50f multi (4-3) .15
2490 A693 $1 multi (4-3) .35
Nos. 2487-2490 (4) .80

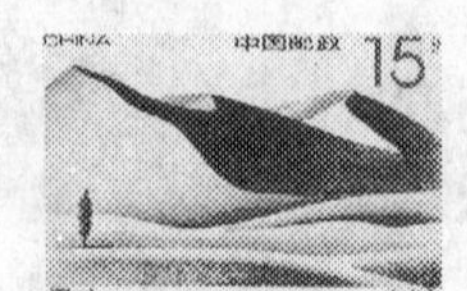

Afforestation Campaign — A694

Designs: 15f, Sand dunes. 20f, Flowers on sand dune. 40f, Forest of poplars. 50f, Oasis.

1994, Apr. 21 Litho. *Perf. 12*

2491 A694 15f multi (4-1) .15
2492 A694 20f multi (4-2) .15
2493 A694 40f multi (4-3) .15
2494 A694 50f multi (4-4) .15
Set value .50

Teapots — A695

Style of teapot: 20f, Round, three-legged. 30f, Square, four-legged. 50f, Eight diagrams. $1, Round-eared.

1994, May 5 Litho. *Perf. 12*

2495 A695 20f multi (4-1) .15
2496 A695 30f multi (4-2) .15
2497 A695 50f multi (4-3) .15
2498 A695 $1 multi (4-4) .30
Set value .55

Huangpu Military School, 70th Anniv. A696

1994, June 16 Litho. *Perf. 12*

2499 A696 20f multicolored .15

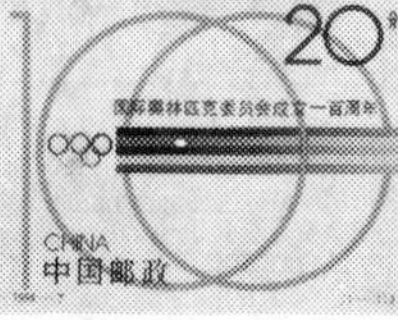

Intl. Olympic Committee, Cent. — A697

1994, June 23

2500 A697 20f multicolored .15

Ancient Chinese Writers — A698

Designs: 20f, Tao Yuanming holding basket of flowers. 30f, Cao Zhi holding sword at side. 50f, Si Maqian writing on scroll. $1, Qu Yuan walking away with sword under arm.

1994, June 25

2501 A698 20f multi (4-1) .15
2502 A698 30f multi (4-2) .15
2503 A698 50f multi (4-3) .15
2504 A698 $1 multi (4-4) .25
Set value .50

Dunhuang Petroglyphs Type of 1987

Frescos: 10f, Flying Devata. 20f, Vimalakirti. 50f, Z. Yichao on the march. $1.60, Sorceresses.

1994, July 16 Photo. *Perf. 11*

2505 A557 10f multi (4-1) .15
2506 A557 20f multi (4-2) .15
2507 A557 50f multi (4-3) .15
2508 A557 $1.60 multi (4-4) .40
Set value .65

Zhaojun's Marriage to Xiongnu — A699

1994, Aug. 25 Photo. *Perf. 11½x11*

2509 A699 20f Zhaojun (2-1) .15 .15
2510 A699 50f Leaving home (2-2) .15 .15

Souvenir Sheet

Perf. 11½

2511 A699 $3 Wedding .75 .75

No. 2511 contains one 85x46mm stamp.

Sixth Far East and South Pacific Games for the Disabled, Beijing — A700

1994, Sept. 4 Litho. *Perf. 12*
2512 A700 20f multicolored .15 .15

Wulingyuan State Forest Park — A701

Designs: 20f, South Gate to Heaven, vert. 30f, Shentangwan, vert. 50f, No. One Bridge. $1, Writing-brush Peak. $3, Picturesque corridor.

1994, Sept. 25 Litho. *Perf. 12*
2513 A701 20f multi (4-1) .15
2514 A701 30f multi (4-2) .15
2515 A701 50f multi (4-3) .15
2516 A701 $1 multi (4-4) .25
Set value .50

Souvenir Sheet
Perf. 11½x12
2517 A701 $3 multicolored .75

No. 2517 contains one 50x36mm stamp.

Wuyi Mountains — A702

Designs: a, Jade-girl Peak (4-1). b, Nine-bend Brook (4-2). c, Guadun Village (4-3). d, Alpine Grassland (4-4).

1994, Sept. 30 *Perf. 12*
2518 Strip of 4 .60
a.-d. A702 50f any single .15

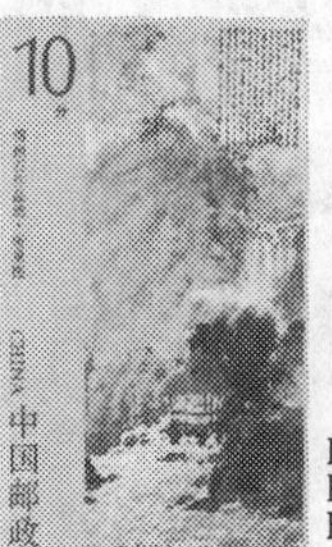

Listening to the Rapids, by Fu Baoshi (1904-65) A703

Paintings: No. 2520, Appreciating a Painting. No. 2521, Dadi's Thatched Hut. 40f, Playing the Ruan. 50f, At Hupao. $1, The Road to Shanyin.

1994, Oct. 5
2519 A703 10f multi (6-1) .15
2520 A703 20f multi (6-2) .15
2521 A703 20f multi (6-3) .15
2522 A703 40f multi (6-4) .15
2523 A703 50f multi (6-5) .15
2524 A703 $1 multi (6-6) .30
Set value .65

Nos. 2525-2527 are not assigned.

Cranes — A704

Photo. & Engr.
1994, Oct. 9 *Perf. 11x11½*
2528 A704 20f Whooping crane (2-1) .15 .15
2529 A704 $2 Black-necked crane (2-2) .50 .50

See US Nos. 2867-2868.

Souvenir Sheet

UPU, 120th Anniv. — A705

Illustration reduced.

1994, Oct. 9 Litho. *Perf. 12*
2530 A705 $3 multicolored .75

Gorges of Yangtze River — A706

Designs: 10f, Baidicheng. No. 2532, Qutang Gorge. No. 2533, Wuxia Gorge. 30f, Goddess Peak. 50f, Xiling Gorge. $1, Qu Yuan Memorial Temple. $5, The Three Gorges.

1994, Nov. 4 Photo. *Perf. 12*
2531 A706 10f multi (6-1) .15
2532 A706 20f multi (6-2) .15
2533 A706 20f multi (6-3) .15
2534 A706 30f multi (6-4) .15
2535 A706 50f multi (6-5) .15
2536 A706 $1 multi (6-6) .25
Set value .60

Souvenir Sheet
Perf. 11½x11
2537 A706 $5 multicolored 1.25

No. 2537 contains one 116x35mm stamp.

Souvenir Sheet

All-China Philatelic Federation, 4th Congress — A707

Illustration reduced.

1994, Nov. 17 Litho. *Perf. 11*
2538 A707 $3 multicolored .75

Literature Type of 1988

Romance of the Three Kingdoms by Luo Guanzhong: 20f, Composing a poem with a lance in hands. 30f, Liu Bei's marriage, vert. 50f, Overwhelming Xiaoyaojin with prowess. $1, Campsites burned, vert.
$5, Fierce battle at Chibi.

Perf. 11½x11, 11x11½
1994, Nov. 24 Photo.
2539 A587 20f multi (4-1) .15
2540 A587 30f multi (4-2) .15
2541 A587 50f multi (4-3) .15
2542 A587 $1 multi (4-4) .25
Set value .50

Souvenir Sheet
Perf. 11
2543 A587 $5 multicolored 1.25

No. 2543 contains one 158x36mm stamp.

Special Economic Zones A708

Designs: a, Shenzhen (5-1). b, Zhuhai (5-2). c, Shantou (5-3). d, Xiamen (5-4). e, Hainan (5-4).

1994, Dec. 10 Litho. *Perf. 12*
2544 A708 50f Strip of 5, #a.-e. .60

Pagodas of Ancient China — A709

Designs: No. 2545, Dayan Pagoda, Cien Temple. No. 2546, Zhenguo Pagoda, Kaiyuan Temple. 50f, Liuhe Pagoda, Kaihua Temple. $2, Youguo Temple.

Photo. & Engr.
1994, Dec. 15 *Perf. 11½x11*
2545 A709 20f tan, brn & blk (4-1) .15
2546 A709 20f tan, brn & blk (4-2) .15
2547 A709 50f tan, brn & blk (4-3) .15
2548 A709 $2 tan, brn & blk (4-4) .50
a. Souvenir sheet of 4, #2545-2548 1.10
Set value .70

No. 2548a sold for $5.

New Year 1995 (Year of the Boar)
A711 A712

Photo. & Engr.
1995, Jan. 5 *Perf. 11½*
2550 A711 20f multi (2-1) .15
2551 A712 50f multi (2-2) .15
Set value .15

Winter Scenes A713

Designs: 20f, Snow willows, Cold River. 50f, Ice & snow on jade trees, vert.

1995, Jan. 12 Litho. *Perf. 12*
2552 A713 20f multicolored .15
2553 A713 50f multicolored .15
Set value .15

Mt. Dinghushan — A714

Designs: 15f, Topographical map. No. 2555, Stream flowing down from mountain. No. 2556, Buildings on mountain side. $2.30, Peacocks.

1995, Feb. 15 Litho. *Perf. 12½*
2554 A714 15f multi (4-1) .15
2555 A714 20f multi (4-2) .15
2556 A714 20f multi (4-3) .15
2557 A714 $2.30 multi (4-4) .55
Set value .65

World Summit for Social Development, Copenhagen A715

1995, Mar. 6 Photo. *Perf. 11x11½*
2558 A715 20f multicolored .15

Owls — A716

1995, Mar. 22 Photo. *Perf. 11½*
2559 A716 10f Eagle owl (4-1) .15
2560 A716 20f Long-eared owl (4-2) .15
2561 A716 50f Snowy owl (4-3) .15
2562 A716 $1 Grass owl (4-4) .25
Set value .45

Sweet Osmanthus A717

1995, Apr. 14 Litho. *Perf. 12*
2563 A717 20f Thunbergii (4-1) .15
2564 A717 20f Latifolius (4-2) .15
2565 A717 50f Aurantiacus (4-3) .15
2566 A717 $1 Semperflorens (4-4) .25
Set value .45

43rd World Table Tennis Championships, Tianjin — A718

1995, May 1 Litho. *Perf. 12*
2567 A718 20f Athlete (2-1) .15
2568 A718 50f Arena (2-2) .15
a. Souv. sheet of 2, #2567-2568
Set value .15

No. 2568a was issued 8/14/95 and sold for $7.

Spring Outing — A719

Designs: No. 2569, Group riding horses. No. 2570, Three riding horses.

1995, May 23 Litho. *Perf. 12*

2569 A719 50f multi (2-1) .15
2570 A719 50f multi (2-2) .15
a. Pair, #2569-2570 .25

No. 2570a is a continuous design.

Shadow Play — A720

Various costumed characters.

1995, June 8 Photo. *Perf. 12x12½*

2571 A720 20f multi (4-1) .15
2572 A720 40f multi (4-2) .15
2573 A720 50f multi (4-3) .15
2574 A720 50f multi (4-4) .15
Set value .40

Highway Interchanges, Beijing — A721

1995, June 20 Photo. *Perf. 11½x11*

2575 A721 20f Siyuan (4-1) .15
2576 A721 30f Tianningsi (4-2) .15
2577 A721 50f Yuting (4-3) .15
2578 A721 $1 Anhui (4-4) .25
Set value .50

Diplomatic Relations Between China & Thailand, 20th Anniv. — A722

Designs: No. 2579, Elephants walking right into water. No. 2580, Elephants walking left into water.

1995, July 1

2579 A722 $1 multi (2-1) .25
2580 A722 $1 multi (2-2) .25
a. Pair, #2579-2580 .50

No. 2580a is a continuous design.

Taihu Lake A723

Lake scenes: No. 2581, Yellow trees. No. 2582, Structures on bank, boats, hills. No. 2583, Structures across inlet. No. 2584, Red trees, home. $2.30, Winter scene. $5, Houses on cliff, lighthouse.

1995, July 20 Photo. *Perf. 11½*

2581 A723 20f multi (5-1) .15
2582 A723 20f multi (5-2) .15
2583 A723 50f multi (5-3) .15
2584 A723 50f multi (5-4) .15
2585 A723 $2.30 multi (5-5) .55
Set value .90

Souvenir Sheet

Perf. 11

2586 A723 $5 multicolored 1.25

No. 2586 contains one 90x60mm stamp with continuing design.

Posts of Ancient China A724

1995, Aug. 17 Photo. *Perf. 12*

2587 A724 20f Yucheng (2-1) .15
2588 A724 50f Jimingshan (2-2) .15
Set value .20

Shaolin Temple, 1500th Anniv. A725

1995, Aug. 30

2589 A725 20f Entrance (4-1) .15
2590 A725 20f Pagoda Forest (4-2) .15
2591 A725 50f Martial arts (4-3) .15
2592 A725 $1 Historical rescue (4-4) .25
Set value .45

Cultural Relics of Tibet — A726

1995, Sept. 1

2593 A726 20f Jar (4-1) .15
2594 A726 30f Casque (4-2) .15
2595 A726 50f Celestial motion chart (4-3) .15
2596 A726 $1 Pearl mandala (4-4) .25
Set value .45

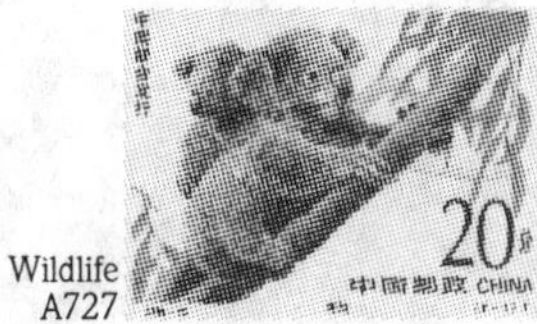

Wildlife A727

1995, Sept. 1 *Perf. 11x11½*

2597 A727 20f Koalas .15
2598 A727 $2.90 Pandas .70

See Australia No. 1459.

End of World War II, 50th Anniv. A728

Designs: 10f, July 7th event. No. 2600, Victory at Taier village. No. 2601, Soldier, hundred-regiment battle. No. 2602, Guerrilla war. No. 2603, Troops on parade, joining forces at Mangyo. 60f, Aircraft donated by Chinese living abroad. No. 2605, Taiwan recovered. No. 2606, Japanese surrender aboard USS Missouri.

1995, Sept. 3

2599 A728 10f multi (8-1) .15
2600 A728 20f multi (8-2) .15
2601 A728 20f multi (8-3) .15
2602 A728 50f multi (8-4) .15
2603 A728 50f multi (8-5) .15
2604 A728 60f multi (8-6) .15
2605 A728 $1 multi (8-7) .25
2606 A728 $1 multi (8-8) .25
Set value 1.00

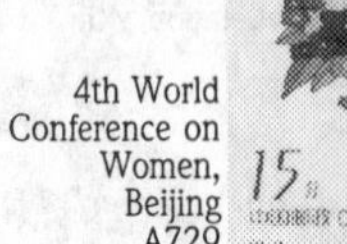

4th World Conference on Women, Beijing A729

Symbols of: 15f, Equality. 20f, Development. 50f, Peace. 60f, Friendship.

1995, Sept. 4 *Perf. 12*

2607 A729 15f multi (4-1) .15
2608 A729 20f multi (4-2) .15
2609 A729 50f multi (4-3) .15
2610 A729 60f multi (4-4) .15
Set value .35

The Great Wall — A730

Jiuhua Mountains — A731

1995, Oct. 5 Photo. *Perf. 12½*

2611 A730 60f shown .15
2612 A730 $2.30 Shanhaiguan Pass .55
2613 A730 $2.90 Jinshanling .70
Nos. 2611-2613 (3) 1.40

1995, Oct. 9 *Perf. 12*

Designs: 10f, Sunrise at Peak Terrace, horiz. No. 2615, Hall of Meditation. No. 2616, Temple of Bodhisattva, horiz. No. 2617, Sunset at Zhiyuan, horiz. No. 2618, Great Roc. No. 2619, Phoenix Pine, horiz.

2614 A731 10f multi (6-1) .15
2615 A731 20f multi (6-2) .15
2616 A731 20f multi (6-3) .15
2617 A731 50f multi (6-4) .15
2618 A731 50f multi (6-5) .15
2619 A731 $2.90 multi (6-6) .70
Set value 1.10

Motion Pictures, Cent. — A732

Projector and: 20f, Black and white film. 50f, Color film.

1995, Oct. 13

2620 A732 20f blue & black (2-1) .15
2621 A732 50f multicolored (2-2) .15
Set value .20

UN, 50th Anniv. A733

Designs: 20f, UN flag, Headquarters. 50f, Stylized flags, UN emblem, "50."

1995, Oct. 24 Litho.

2622 A733 20f multi (2-1) .15
2623 A733 50f multi (2-2) .15
Set value .20

Sanqing Mountains — A734

Designs: No. 2624, Good Fortune Land. No. 2625, Sichun Goddess. 50f, Bodhisattva Enjoys Music. $1, Huge Boa out of Mountain.

1995, Nov. 1 Photo. *Perf. 12*

2624 A734 20f multi (4-1) .15
2625 A734 20f multi (4-2) .15
2626 A734 50f multi, vert. (4-3) .15
2627 A734 $1 multi, vert. (4-4) .25
Set value .45

Mt. Hengshan Type of 1990

Songshan Mountains: 20f, Ancient Temple of Mount Song. 50f, Moon waiting at Songmen Gate. 60f, Shaolin Temple. $1, Panorama view of Mt. Song.

Photo. & Engr.

1995, Nov. 10 *Perf. 11*

2628 A631 20f multi (4-1) .15
2629 A631 50f multi (4-2) .15
2630 A631 60f multi (4-3) .15
2631 A631 $1 multi (4-4) .25
Set value .55

Scenic Views of Hong Kong A735

Designs: 20f, Victoria Harbor. 50f, Central Plaza at night. 60f, Hong Kong Cultural Center. $2.90, Repulse Bay.

1995, Nov. 28 **Photo.** *Perf. 12*

2632 A735 20f multi (4-1) .15
2633 A735 50f multi (4-2) .15
2634 A735 60f multi (4-3) .15
2635 A735 $2.90 multi (4-4) .70
Set value 1.00

Sun Zi's Art of War — A736

Drawings depicting: No. 2637, Discussing strategy. 30f, Capturing Ying. 50f, Battle at Ailing. $1, Meeting of sovereigns, Huangchi.

1995, Dec. 4 *Perf. 11x11½*

2636 A736 20f multi (5-1) .15
2637 A736 20f multi (5-2) .15
2638 A736 30f multi (5-3) .15
2639 A736 50f multi (5-4) .15
2640 A736 $1 multi (5-5) .25
Set value .55

New Year 1996 (Year of the Rat)
A737 A738

Photo. & Engr.

1996, Jan. 5 *Perf. 11½*

2641 A737 20f multi (2-1) .15
2642 A738 50f multi (2-2) .15
Set value .15

3rd Asian Winter Games A739

Designs: No. 2643, Speed skating. No. 2644, Ice hockey. No. 2645, Figure skating. No. 2646, Skiing.

1996, Feb. 4 **Litho.** *Perf. 12*

2643 A739 50f multi (4-1) .15
2644 A739 50f multi (4-2) .15
2645 A739 50f multi (4-3) .15
2646 A739 50f multi (4-4) .15
a. Block of 4, #2643-2646 .50
Set value .50

SEMI-POSTAL STAMPS

Catalogue values for unused stamps in this section are for Never Hinged items.

Girl Holding Ball — SP1

Hands Reading Braille — SP2

1984, Feb. 16 **Photo.** *Perf. 11½*

B1 SP1 8f + 2f shown (2-1) .15 .20
B2 SP1 8f + 2f Boy, panda (2-2) .15 .20

Surtax for China Children's Fund. T.92.

1985, Mar. 15 **Photo.** *Perf. 11½*

B3 SP2 8f + 2f shown (4-1) .15 .15
B4 SP2 8f + 2f Sign language, lip reading (4-2) .15 .15
B5 SP2 8f + 2f Artificial limb (4-3) .15 .15
B6 SP2 8f + 2f Handicapped person in wheelchair (4-4) .15 .15
Nos. B3-B6 (4) .60 .60

Surtax for China Welfare Fund. T.105.

Children (T.137) SP3

1989, June 1 **Litho.** *Perf. 12*

B7 SP3 8f +4f Friends (4-1) .15 .15
B8 SP3 8f +4f Penguins (4-2) .15 .15
B9 SP3 8f +4f Bird, Moon, Sun (4-3) .15 .15
B10 SP3 8f +4f Girl, boy playing ball (4-4) .15 .15
a. Strip of 4, #B7-B10 .35 .50
Set value .35 .35

Intl Children's Day, 40th anniv., and 10th Intl. Year of the Child. Surtax for China Children's Fund.

AIR POST STAMPS

Mail Plane and Temple of Heaven — AP1

1951, May 1 **Engr.** *Perf. 12½*

Without Gum

C1 AP1 $1000 carmine .15 .15
C2 AP1 $3000 green .15 .15
C3 AP1 $5000 orange .15 .15
C4 AP1 $10,000 vio brn & grn .15 .25
C5 AP1 $30,000 dk bl & brn 4.50 .75
Nos. C1-C5 (5) 5.10 1.45

Planes at Airport — AP2

Designs: 28f, Plane over winding mountain highway. 35f, Plane over railroad yard. 52f, Plane over ship.

1957-58 *Perf. 14*

Without Gum

C6 AP2 16f indigo 7.50 .15
C7 AP2 28f olive black 7.50 .15
C8 AP2 35f slate 7.50 4.00
C9 AP2 52f Prus blue ('58) 7.50 .50
Nos. C6-C9 (4) 30.00 4.80

POSTAGE DUE STAMPS

Grain and Cogwheel — D1

D2

1950, Sept. 1 **Typo.** *Perf. 12½*

Without Gum

J1 D1 $100 steel blue .15 .15
J2 D1 $200 steel blue .15 .15
J3 D1 $500 steel blue .15 .15
J4 D1 $800 steel blue 18.00 .15
J5 D1 $1000 steel blue .30 .40
J6 D1 $2000 steel blue .30 .40
J7 D1 $5000 steel blue .20 .60
J8 D1 $8000 steel blue .20 1.00
J9 D1 $10,000 steel blue .40 2.00
Nos. J1-J9 (9) 19.85 5.00

1954, Aug. 18 **Litho.** *Perf. 14*

Without Gum

J10 D2 $100 red 1.65 .15
J11 D2 $200 red .50 .15
J12 D2 $500 red 1.65 .15
J13 D2 $800 red .15 .15
J14 D2 $1600 red .15 .15
Nos. J10-J14 (5) 4.10
Set value .47

MILITARY STAMP

Red Star, 8-1 in Center — M1

1953, Aug. 1 **Litho.** *Perf. 14*

Without Gum

M1 M1 $800 yel, orange & red (Army) 20.00 27.50

This stamp was printed in deep purple, orange & red for the Air Force, and blue, orange & red for the Navy. These were not issued.

NORTHEAST CHINA

The first post war issues were local overprints on stamps of Manchukuo. In early 1946, a Ministry of Posts and Telegraphs served the areas already liberated, and in August, 1946, a Communications Committee of the Political Council was established. In June, 1947, these postal services were subordinated to the Harbin General Post Office, and this was extended to Changchun on Oct. 22, 1948, and to Mukden on Nov. 4, 1948. It was rapidly extended to cover all Manchuria.

Rough Perfs

Rough perforations are normal on most regional issues.

All Stamps Issued without Gum

Mao Tse-tung
A1 A2

1946, Feb. **Unwmk.** **Litho.** *Perf. 11*

1L1 A1 $1 violet 12.00 9.00
1L2 A2 $2 vermilion .75 1.00
1L3 A2 $5 orange .75 1.00
a. Booklet pane of 6 150.00
1L4 A2 $10 blue .75 1.00
a. Booklet pane of 6 150.00
Nos. 1L1-1L4 (4) 14.25 12.00

Value, imperf set $90.

For surcharges see Nos. 1L20-1L23, 1L49-1L50, 1L89, 1L91, 1L93.

Map of China, Lion, Hyena and Chiang Kai-shek — A3

1946, Dec. 12 *Perf. 10½*

1L5 A3 $1 violet 1.50 1.50
1L6 A3 $2 orange 1.50 1.50
1L7 A3 $5 org brn 7.00 7.00
1L8 A3 $10 lt grn 10.00 10.00
a. Imperf., pair 47.50
Nos. 1L5-1L8 (4) 20.00 20.00

10th anniversary of the capture of Chiang Kai-shek at Sian.

Railroad Workers, Chengchow — A4

1947, Feb. 7 *Perf. 10½*

1L9 A4 $1 pink .35 *1.00*
1L10 A4 $2 dull grn .70 *1.00*
1L11 A4 $5 pink 1.40 1.40
1L12 A4 $10 dull grn 3.50 3.50
Nos. 1L9-1L12 (4) 5.95 6.90

24th anniversary of the Chengchow railroad workers' strike and massacre.

Women (Worker, Soldier and Farmer) — A5

Wmk. Chinese Characters in Sheet

1947, Mar. 8 *Perf. 10½x11*

1L13 A5 $5 brick red .85 .85
1L14 A5 $10 brown .85 .85

International Women's Day, March 8.
Exists imperf.

郵 東

Same Overprinted in Green ("Northeast Postal Service")

政 北

1947, Mar. 18

1L15 A5 $5 brick red 2.75 3.25
1L16 A5 $10 brown 2.75 3.25

Exists imperf.

Children Carrying Banner — A6

1947, Apr. 4 *Perf. 11x10½*

Granite Paper

1L17 A6 $5 rose red 3.00 2.25
1L18 A6 $10 lt green 3.00 3.00
1L19 A6 $30 orange 3.00 4.00
Nos. 1L17-1L19 (3) 9.00 9.25

Children's Day.

伍 拾 圓

Nos. 1L1-1L2 Surcharged in Red, Brown, Black, Blue or Green

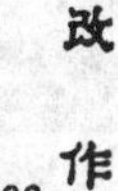

1947, Apr. **Unwmk.** *Perf. 11*

1L20 A1 $50 on $1 vio (R) 19.00 19.00
a. Brown surcharge 19.00 19.00
1L21 A2 $50 on $2 ver 19.00 19.00
a. Brown surcharge 19.00 19.00

1L22 A1 $100 on $1 vio 19.00 19.00
a. Green surcharge 19.00 19.00
1L23 A2 $100 on $2 ver (Bl) 19.00 19.00
a. Green surcharge 19.00 19.00
Nos. 1L20-1L23 (4) 76.00 76.00

Farmer and Worker — A7

Ax Severing Chain — A8

Wmk. Chinese Characters in Sheet
1947, May 1 ***Perf. 10½x11***
Granite Paper

1L24 A7 $10 orange red 1.25 1.25
1L25 A7 $30 ultra 1.75 1.75
1L26 A7 $50 gray green 3.00 3.00
Nos. 1L24-1L26 (3) 6.00 6.00

Labor Day. Value, imperf. pairs, set $300.

1947, May 4 ***Perf. 11***
1L27 A8 $10 brt green 2.50 2.50
1L28 A8 $30 brown 2.50 2.50
1L29 A8 $50 violet 3.00 3.00
Nos. 1L27-1L29 (3) 8.00 8.00

28th anniversary of the students' revolt at Peking University against the 1918 peace treaty. Value, imperf. pairs, set $350.

Workers with Banner: "Oppose Imperialist Aggression" A9

1947, May 30 ***Perf. 10½x11***
Banner in Red
1L30 A9 $2 brt lilac 2.75 2.75
1L31 A9 $5 brt green 2.75 2.75
1L32 A9 $10 yellow 2.75 2.75
1L33 A9 $20 violet 2.75 2.75
1L34 A9 $30 red brn 2.75 2.75
1L35 A9 $50 dk blue 2.75 2.75
1L36 A9 $100 brown 2.75 2.75
a. Souvenir sheet of 7 65.00
Nos. 1L30-1L36 (7) 19.25 19.25

22nd anniversary of the Shanghai-Nanking Road incident. No. 1L36a is on granite paper and contains 7 imperf. stamps similar to Nos. 1L30-1L36. Size: 215x158mm. Value, imperf. pairs, ordinary paper, set $900.

Mao and Communist Flag — A10

1947, July 1 ***Perf. 10½x11***
1L37 A10 $10 red 5.00 5.00
1L38 A10 $30 brt lilac 5.00 5.00
1L39 A10 $50 rose brn 12.00 12.00
1L40 A10 $100 vermilion 14.00 14.00
Nos. 1L37-1L40 (4) 36.00 36.00

26th anniversary of the founding of the Chinese Communist Party.

Hand Holding Rifle — A11

1947, July 7 ***Perf. 10½***
1L41 A11 $10 orange 4.50 4.50
1L42 A11 $30 green 4.50 4.50
1L43 A11 $50 dull blue 4.50 4.50
1L44 A11 $100 brown 4.50 4.50
a. Souvenir sheet of 4 80.00 50.00
Nos. 1L41-1L44 (4) 18.00 18.00

10th anniversary of the start of Sino-Japanese War. No. 1L44a contains 4 imperf. stamps similar to Nos. 1L41-1L44. Size: 149x107mm.
Exist imperf. Value, set of pairs $800.

White Mountain and Black Water, Northeast China — A12

Wmk. Zigzag Lines (141)
1947, Aug. 15 ***Perf. 10½***
1L45 A12 $10 brown org 12.00 10.00
1L46 A12 $30 lt ol grn 1.50 10.00
1L47 A12 $50 blue grn 1.50 10.00
1L48 A12 $100 sepia 12.00 10.00
Nos. 1L45-1L48 (4) 27.00 40.00

2nd anniversary of the reoccupation of Northeast China and the surrender of Japan.
Exist imperf. Value, set of pairs $425.

Nos. 1L1-1L2 Surcharged in Black, Red, Green or Blue

拾 改
圓 作
1000

1947, Aug. 29 **Unwmk.** ***Perf. 11***
1L49 A1 $5 on $1 vio 22.50 22.50
a. Red surcharge 22.50 22.50
b. Green surcharge 22.50 22.50
1L50 A2 $10 on $2 ver 22.50 22.50
a. Blue surcharge 22.50 22.50
b. Green surcharge 22.50 22.50

Map of Manchuria — A13

1947, Sept. 18 **Unwmk.**
White Paper
1L51 A13 $10 gray grn 8.50 8.50
1L52 A13 $20 rose lil 8.50 8.50
1L53 A13 $30 blk brn 8.50 8.50
1L54 A13 $50 carmine 8.50 8.50
Nos. 1L51-1L54 (4) 34.00 34.00

16th anniversary of Japanese attack on Mukden, Sept. 18, 1931.

Northeast Political Council Offices — A14

Mao Tse-tung (Value figures repeated) — A15

1947, Oct. 10 ***Perf. 10½***
1L55 A14 $10 yel org 21.00 21.00
1L56 A14 $20 rose red 21.00 21.00
1L57 A14 $100 brown 60.00 60.00
Nos. 1L55-1L57 (3) 102.00 102.00

35th anniversary of the founding of the Chinese Republic.

1947, Oct. 10 **White Paper** ***Perf. 11***
1L58 A15 $1 brown .20 1.50
1L59 A15 $5 gray grn 4.00 1.50
1L60 A15 $10 brt grn 12.00 8.00
1L61 A15 $15 bluish lil 12.00 8.00
1L62 A15 $20 brt rose .15 1.50
1L63 A15 $30 green .15 2.00
1L64 A15 $50 blk brn 15.00 12.00
1L65 A15 $90 blue 4.00 4.00
Nos. 1L58-1L65 (8) 47.50 38.50

Newsprint
1L66 A15 $100 red .40
a. White paper 3.00 4.00
1L67 A15 $500 red org 16.00 16.00
a. White paper 25.00 25.00

Type A22 resembles A15, but has "YUAN" at upper right.
The $1, $90 were also printed on newsprint.
See footnote following No. 1L72.
See Nos. 1L68-1L72. For surcharges see Nos. 1L84-1L88, 1L90, 1L92, 1L94.

1947, Nov. **Redrawn**
White Paper
1L68 A15 $50 lt grn .75 1.50
1L69 A15 $150 red org, wmkd. Chinese characters 2.00 1.50
a. Unwatermarked 2.50
1L70 A15 $250 bluish lil .25 1.50
a. Wmkd. Chinese characters .90 1.50

Nos. 1L69 and 1L69a exist in same sheet.

1947, Dec. **Unwmk.**
Newsprint
1L71 A15 $300 green 40.00 25.00
1L72 A15 $1000 yellow 1.00 1.00
a. White paper 1.00 1.00
Nos. 1L68-1L72 (5) 44.00 30.50

Panel below portrait 8½x3mm on Nos. 1L68-1L70; 7x3mm on No. 1L58-1L67. Nos. 1L68-1L70 have different ornamental border. Nos. 1L71-1L72 without zeros for cents.
For surcharges see Nos. 1L90, 1L92, 1L94.

Hand Holding Torch — A16

1947, Dec. 12 **Unwmk.** ***Perf. 11***
White Paper
1L73 A16 $30 rose red 7.00 7.00
1L74 A16 $90 dk bl 7.00 7.00
1L75 A16 $150 green 7.00 7.00
Nos. 1L73-1L75 (3) 21.00 21.00

11th anniversary of the capture of Chiang Kai-shek at Sian.

Tomb of Gen. Li Chao-lin — A17

Globe and Banner — A18

1948, Mar. 9 **Unwmk.** ***Perf. 10½x11***
1L76 A17 $30 green 10.00 10.00
a. Granite paper, wmkd. 9.00 9.00
1L77 A17 $150 vio gray 10.00 10.00
a. Granite paper, wmkd. 9.00 9.00

2nd anniversary of the assassination of Gen. Li Chao-lin, Commander of 3rd Army.

Wmk. Chinese Characters in Sheet
1948, May 1 ***Perf. 11x10½***
1L78 A18 $50 red 6.00 10.00
1L79 A18 $150 green .75 15.00
1L80 A18 $250 lilac .75 30.00
Nos. 1L78-1L80 (3) 7.50 55.00

Labor Day.

Student, Torch and Banner — A19

1948, May 4 **Unwmk.** ***Perf. 10½x11***
Granite paper
1L81 A19 $50 green 10.00 5.00
1L82 A19 $150 brown 10.00 8.00
1L83 A19 $250 red 10.00 12.00
Nos. 1L81-1L83 (3) 30.00 25.00

Youth Day, May 4.

Nos. 1L58, 1L61, 1L59, 1L63, 1L65, 1L2-1L4, 1L68-1L69, 1L71 Surcharged in Black, Blue, Red or Green

壹 改
佰
圓 作
10000

1948-49 ***Perf. 11***
1L84 A15 $100 on $1 60.00 45.00
a. Blue surcharge 50.00 50.00
1L85 A15 $100 on $15 17.50 17.50
a. Blue surcharge 50.00 50.00
1L86 A15 $300 on $5 (R) 55.00 25.00
1L87 A15 $300 on $30 (R) 8.50 10.00
1L88 A15 $300 on $90 (R) 8.50 10.00
1L89 A2 $500 on $2 5.00 5.00
1L90 A15 $500 on $50 (R, '49) 27.50 20.00
1L91 A2 $1500 on $5 (Bl) 5.00 5.00
1L92 A15 $1500 on $150 (G; '49) 6.00 6.00
1L93 A2 $2500 on $10 (R) 5.00 5.00
1L94 A15 $2500 on $300 ('49) 5.00 5.00
Nos. 1L84-1L94 (11) 203.00 153.50

Crane Operator — A20

Wmk. Chinese Characters in Sheet
1948, May ***Perf. 11***
1L95 A20 $100 red & pink .45 .45
1L96 A20 $300 vio brn & yel 1.50 1.50
1L97 A20 $500 bl & grn 1.50 1.50
Nos. 1L95-1L97 (3) 3.45 3.45

6th All-China Labor Conference, Harbin.

Farmer, Worker and Soldier Saluting — A21

Mao Tse-tung ("YUAN" at upper right) — A22

1948, Dec. 3 **Unwmk.** ***Perf. 11x10½***
White paper
1L98 A21 $500 vermilion 4.00 4.00
1L99 A21 $1500 brt grn 7.50 7.50
1L100 A21 $2500 brown 12.50 12.50
Nos. 1L98-1L100 (3) 24.00 24.00

Liberation of Northeast China.

1949, Feb. ***Perf. 11***
1L101 A22 $300 olive .35 .40
1L102 A22 $500 orange .90 .40
1L103 A22 $1500 bl grn .35 .60
1L104 A22 $4500 brown .35 .60
1L105 A22 $6500 dk bl .35 .80
Nos. 1L101-1L105 (5) 2.30 2.80

See type A15. For surcharges see Nos. 1L126-1L129, 1L131-1L132.

Workers, Globe and Flag — A23

Fields and Factories — A24

1949, May 1 ***Perf. 11½***
1L106 A23 $1000 red & dl bl .15 .25
1L107 A23 $1500 red & pale bl .15 .25
1L108 A23 $4500 rose & ol brn .15 .35
1L109 A23 $6500 dl org & grn .50 .40
1L110 A23 $10,000 mar & ultra .50 .50
Nos. 1L106-1L110 (5) 1.45 1.75

Labor Day.

1949 ***Perf. 10, 11***
1L111 A24 $5000 Prus bl 4.25 2.00
1L112 A24 $10,000 org brn .50 1.00
1L113 A24 $50,000 green .15 *1.50*
1L114 A24 $100,000 violet .15 *8.00*
Nos. 1L111-1L114 (4) 5.05 *12.50*

Production in agriculture and industry.

Workers with Flags — A25

Heroes' Monument, Harbin — A26

1949, July 1 *Perf. 11*

1L115 A25 $1500 vio, lt bl & red .15 .40
1L116 A25 $4500 dk brn, lt bl & ver 1.75 .40
1L117 A25 $6500 gray, lt bl & rose red .20 .80
Nos. 1L115-1L117 (3) 2.10 1.60

28th anniversary of the founding of the Chinese Communist Party.

1949, Aug. 15 *Perf. 11½x11*

1L118 A26 $1500 brick red .20 .80
1L119 A26 $4500 yel grn .40 .80
1L120 A26 $6500 lt blue 1.90 .80
Nos. 1L118-1L120 (3) 2.50 2.40

4th anniversary of the Reoccupation, and the surrender of Japan.

(Enlarged)

"Northeast Postal Service"

The following commemorative issues are similar to those of the People's Republic of China, with the 4 characters shown added in different sizes and various arrangements. Reprints were also issued similar to those of the PRC.

Chinese Lantern Type of PRC, 1949

1949, Sept. 12 Litho. *Perf. 12½*

1L121 A1 $1000 dp blue 3.75 4.00
1L122 A1 $1500 scarlet 3.75 4.00
1L123 A1 $3000 green 3.75 5.00
1L124 A1 $4500 maroon 3.75 6.00
Nos. 1L121-1L124 (4) 15.00 19.00

Reprints exist. Value, set $2.

Factory — A27

1949, Oct. *Perf. 11x10½*

1L125 A27 $1500 orange .25 *.80*

For surcharge see No. 1L130.

Nos. 1L101, 1L103-1L105, 1L125 Surcharged in Black or Green

1949, Nov. 20

1L126 A22 $2000 on $300 32.50 2.50
1L127 A22 $2000 on $4500 (G) 18.00 20.00
1L128 A22 $2500 on $1500 .50 3.00
1L129 A22 $2500 on $6500 18.00 20.00
1L130 A27 $5000 on $1500 .40 1.00
1L131 A22 $20,000 on $4500 .25 3.00
1L132 A22 $35,000 on $300 .35 4.00
Nos. 1L126-1L132 (7) 70.00 53.50

Globe and Hammer Type of PRC

1949, Nov. 15 *Perf. 12½*

1L133 A2 $5000 crimson 67.50 60.00
1L134 A2 $20,000 dp green 67.50 60.00
1L135 A2 $35,000 vio blue 67.50 60.00
Nos. 1L133-1L135 (3) 202.50 180.00

Reprints, Value, set $55.

Mao and Conference Hall Types of PRC

1950, Feb. 1 *Perf. 14*

1L136 A3 $1000 vermilion 8.75 7.00
1L137 A3 $1500 dp blue 8.75 7.00
1L138 A4 $5000 dk vio brn 8.75 8.00
1L139 A4 $20,000 green 8.75 11.00
Nos. 1L136-1L139 (4) 35.00 33.00

Reprints exist. Value, set $4.50.

Gate of Heavenly Peace (same size) — A28

1950 *Perf. 10½*

Narrow horizontal shading

1L140 A28 $500 olive .85 .50
1L141 A28 $1000 orange .85 .50
1L142 A28 $1000 lil rose 3.25 .50
1L143 A28 $2000 gray grn .40 .15
1L144 A28 $2500 yellow 1.65 .15
1L145 A28 $5000 dp org 35.00 .20
1L146 A28 $10,000 brn org 1.65 .50
1L147 A28 $20,000 vio brn .40 .20
1L148 A28 $35,000 dp blue .40 .35
1L149 A28 $50,000 brt grn .85 .70
Nos. 1L140-1L149 (10) 45.30 3.75

See A29.

Flag and Mao Type of PRC

1950, July 1 *Perf. 14*

Yellow Stars

1L150 A7 $5000 grn & red 15.00 11.00
1L151 A7 $10,000 brn & red 15.00 11.00
1L152 A7 $20,000 dk brn & red 15.00 11.00
1L153 A7 $30,000 dk vio bl & red 16.00 12.00
Nos. 1L150-1L153 (4) 61.00 45.00

Reprints exist. Value, set $6.

Picasso Dove Type of PRC

1950, Aug. 1 Engr. *Perf. 14*

1L154 A8 $2500 brown 8.25 8.00
1L155 A8 $5000 green 8.25 8.00
1L156 A8 $20,000 blue 8.25 8.00
Nos. 1L154-1L156 (3) 24.75 24.00

Reprints exist. Value, set $6.

Flag Type of PRC

1950, Oct. 1 Engr. & Litho.

Flag in Red & Yellow

1L157 A9 $1000 purple 20.00 11.00
1L158 A9 $2500 org brn 20.00 11.00
1L159 A9 $5000 dp grn 20.00 11.00
1L160 A9 $10,000 olive 20.00 11.00
1L161 A9 $20,000 blue 20.00 11.00
Nos. 1L157-1L161 (5) 100.00 55.00

Size of #1L159: 38x47mm, others 26x33mm.
Reprints exist. Value, set $6.

Postal Conference Type of PRC

1950, Nov. 1 Litho.

1L162 A11 $2500 grn & dp org 7.50 4.75
1L163 A11 $5000 car & grn 7.50 4.75

Reprints exist. Value, set, $4.

Gate of Heavenly Peace (same size) — A29

1950-51 *Perf. 10½*

Wide horizontal shading

1L164 A29 $5000 orange 5.00 1.25
1L165 A29 $30,000 scarlet .90 *3.00*
1L166 A29 $100,000 violet 10.50 3.25

Wmk. Zigzag Lines (141)

1L167 A29 $250 brown .75 .30
1L168 A29 $500 olive .75 .30
1L169 A29 $1000 lil rose .90 .50
1L170 A29 $2000 dl grn ('51) .35 .50
1L171 A29 $2500 yellow .40 .50
1L172 A29 $5000 orange .75 .50
1L173 A29 $10,000 brn org ('51) 1.10 .50
1L174 A29 $12,500 maroon .35 .50
1L175 A29 $20,000 dp brn ('51) 1.10 1.00
Nos. 1L164-1L175 (12) 22.85 12.10

A $50,000 green was prepared, but not issued. Value $10.

Stalin and Mao Tse-tung Type of PRC

Unwmk.

1950, Dec. 1 Engr. *Perf. 14*

1L176 A12 $2500 red 14.00 6.75
1L177 A12 $5000 dp green 14.00 6.75
1L178 A12 $20,000 dk blue 14.00 6.75
Nos. 1L176-1L178 (3) 42.00 20.25

Reprints exist. Value, set $6.

NORTHEAST CHINA PARCEL POST STAMPS

Locomotive — PP1

1951 Litho. *Perf. 10½*

1LQ1 $100,000 purple 40.00

Imperf

1LQ2 $300,000 brown 165.00
1LQ3 $500,000 grnsh bl 250.00
1LQ4 $1,000,000 ver 400.00

Value, Nos. 1LQ2-1LQ4 perf. 10½, $1,000.
For similar type see North China PP1.

PORT ARTHUR AND DAIREN

The Liaoning Postal Administration was established on April 1, 1946, in accordance with the Sino-Soviet Treaty, but was renamed one week later the Port Arthur and Dairen Postal Administration. On Apr. 3, 1947, it was combined with telecommunications and renamed the Kwantung Post and Telegraph General Administration. On May 1, 1949, the name was again changed to Port Arthur and Dairen Post and Telegraph Administration. Postal tariffs were based on local currency and both Manchukuo and Japanese stamps were overprinted for use.

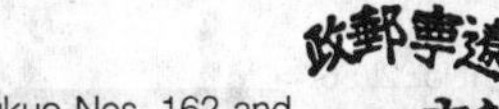

Manchukuo Nos. 162 and 94 Handstamp Surcharged in Violet ("Liaoning Post")

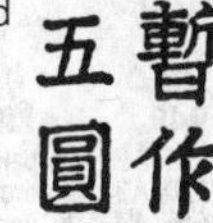

1946, Mar. 15

With Gum

2L1 A19 20f on 30f buff 60.00 60.00
2L2 A18 1y on 12f org 35.00 35.00

Same Surcharge on Japan Nos. 260, 337, 195, 244, 263, 342 in Violet, Red or Black

1946, Apr. 1

2L3 A85 20f on 3s grn (V) 12.50 12.50
2L4 A151 1y on 17s gray vio (R) 10.50 10.50
2L5 A57 5y on 6s car 27.50 27.50
2L6 A57 5y on 6s crim 27.50 27.50
2L7 A88 5y on 6s org 20.00 20.00
2L8 A154 15y on 40s dk vio 77.50 77.50
Nos. 2L1-2L8 (8) 270.50 270.50

Surcharge sideways on Nos. 2L5-2L6.

Japan Nos. 260 and 263 Surcharged

1946, Apr.

2L9 A85 1y on 3s grn *350.00*
2L10 A88 5y on 6s org *230.00*

Sha Ho Kow (suburb of Dairen) issue.
The status of this issue is in question.

Manchukuo Nos. 84, 88 and 98 Handstamp Surcharged in Green, Red or Black

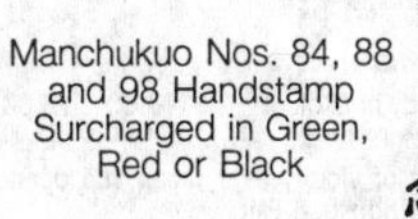

1946, May 1

2L11 A16 1y on 1f red brn (G) 17.00 17.00
2L12 A18 5y on 4f lt ol grn (R) 22.50 22.50
2L13 A19 15y on 30f chnt brn 45.00 45.00
Nos. 2L11-2L13 (3) 84.50 84.50

Transfer of postal administration and Labor Day.

Manchukuo Nos. 159, 86 and 94 Surcharged in Green, Red or Black

1946, July 7

2L14 A17 1y on 6f crim rose (G) 15.00 15.00
2L15 A17 5y on 2f lt grn (R) 65.00 65.00
2L16 A18 15y on 12f dp org 90.00 90.00
Nos. 2L14-2L16 (3) 170.00 170.00

Outbreak of war with Japan, 9th anniv.

Manchukuo Nos. 94, 84 and 158 Surcharged in Black, Green or Red

1946, Aug. 15

2L17 A18 1y on 12f dp org 27.50 27.50
2L18 A16 5y on 1f red brn (G) 50.00 50.00
2L19 A10 15y on 5f gray blk (R) 100.00 100.00
Nos. 2L17-2L19 (3) 177.50 177.50

Surrender of Japan, first anniversary.

Manchukuo Nos. 159, 94 and 86 Surcharged in Green, Black or Red

1946, Oct. 10

2L20 A17 1y on 6f crim rose (G) 27.50 27.50
2L21 A18 5y on 12f dp org 50.00 50.00
2L22 A17 15y on 2f lt grn (R) 100.00 100.00
Nos. 2L20-2L22 (3) 177.50 177.50

35th anniversary of Chinese revolution.

Manchukuo Nos. 84, 159 and 94 Surcharged in Black, Green or Blue

1946, Oct. 19

2L23 A16 1y on 1f red brn 45.00 45.00
2L24 A17 5y on 6f crim rose (G) 70.00 70.00
2L25 A18 15y on 12f dp org (Bl) 110.00 110.00
Nos. 2L23-2L25 (3) 225.00 225.00

10th anniversary of the death of Lu Hsun (1881-1936), writer.

Manchukuo Nos. 86, 159 and 95 Surcharged in Red, Green or Black

1947, Feb. 20

2L26 A17 1y on 2f lt grn (R) 45.00 45.00
2L27 A17 5y on 6f crim rose (G) 85.00 85.00
2L28 A18 15y on 13f dk red brn 190.00 190.00
Nos. 2L26-2L28 (3) 320.00 320.00

29th anniversary of the Red (USSR) Army.

Manchukuo Nos. 86, 159 and 162 Surcharged in Red, Green or Black

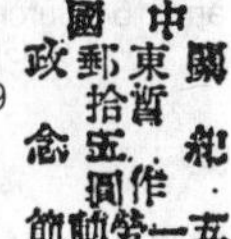

1947, May 1

2L29 A17 1y on 2f lt grn (R) 22.50 22.50
2L30 A17 5y on 6f crim rose (G) 65.00 65.00
2L31 A19 15y on 30f buff 100.00 100.00
Nos. 2L29-2L31 (3) 187.50 187.50

Labor Day.

Manchukuo Nos. 86, 88, 98 and 162 Surcharged ("Kwantung Postal Service, China")

1947, Sept. 15

2L32	A17	5y on 2f lt grn	30.00	30.00
2L33	A18	15y on 4f lt ol grn	50.00	50.00
2L34	A19	20y on 30f red brn	75.00	75.00
2L35	A19	20y on 30f buff	80.00	80.00
		Nos. 2L32-2L35 (4)	235.00	235.00

Manchukuo Nos. 86 and 159 Surcharged in Red and Green

Sacred Golden Kite (same size) — A1

1948, Feb. 20

2L36	A17	10y on 2f lt grn (R)	100.00	100.00
2L37	A17	20y on 6f crim rose (G)	120.00	120.00
2L38	A1	100y on bl & red brn	500.00	500.00

30th anniversary of the Red (USSR) Army. No. 2L38 is on an ungummed label for the 2600th anniv. of the Japanese Empire.

Japan No. 260 and Manchukuo Nos. 84, 86 and 88 Surcharged in Red, Blue or Black

1948, July

2L39	A85	5y on 3s grn (R)	80.00	80.00
2L40	A16	10y on 1f red brn (Bl)	145.00	145.00
2L41	A17	50y on 2f lt grn	325.00	325.00
2L42	A18	100y on 4f lt ol grn (R)	600.00	600.00

Smaller Characters on Bottom Line

2L43	A17	10y on 2f lt grn (R)	200.00	145.00
2L44	A16	50y on 1f red brn	250.00	200.00

Stamps of Manchukuo Nos. 84, 86 and 88 Surcharged in Blue, Red or Black

1948, Nov. 1

2L45	A16	10y on 1f red brn (Bl)	500.00	500.00
2L46	A17	50y on 2f lt grn (R)	500.00	500.00
2L47	A18	100y on 4f lt ol grn	525.00	525.00

31st anniversary of the Russian Revolution.

Manchukuo Nos. 86 and 161 Surcharged in Red or Green

1948, Nov. 15

2L48	A17	10y on 2f lt grn	700.00	400.00
2L49	A17	50y on 20f brn (G)	800.00	800.00

Kwantung Agricultural and Industrial Exhibition.

Manchukuo Nos. 86, 88 and 161 Surcharged in Red, Black or Green

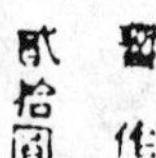

1949, Jan.

2L50	A17	20y on 2f lt grn (R)	500.00	
2L51	A18	50y on 4f lt ol grn	700.00	
2L52	A17	100y on 20f brn (G)	700.00	

Without Gum

From No. 2L56 onward all stamps were issued without gum except as noted.

Farmer and Worker — A2

Train and Ship — A3

Ship at Dock (No. 2L55) — A4

(No. 2L56)

1949 Litho. *Perf. 11, 11½*

2L53	A2	5y pale grn	1.50	2.50
2L54	A3	10y orange	10.00	7.00
2L55	A4	50y vermilion	15.00	10.00
2L56	A4	50y red (redrawn)	20.00	15.00
		Nos. 2L53-2L56 (4)	46.50	34.50

Issue dates: #2L56, July 7; others Apr. 1.

For surcharges see Nos. 2L62-2L66.

Worker, Flag and Means of Transport — A5

1949, May 1 *Perf. 11*

2L57	A5	10y rose pink	10.50	10.00
a.		10y vermilion	75.00	75.00

Labor Day. #2L57a is from a worn plate.

Mao Tse-tung and Red Flag — A6

Heroes Monument, Dairen — A7

1949, July 1

2L59	A6	50y red	20.00	20.00

28th anniversary of the founding of the Chinese Communist Party.

1949, Sept.

2L60	A7	10y red, bl & ol	13.00	13.00
a.		10y red, bl & pale bl	100.00	85.00

4th anniversary of victory over Japan and opening of the Dairen Industrial Fair.

Nos. 2L53-2L54 Surcharged in Red or Black

a b

c

1949, Sept. With Gum

2L62	A2(a)	7y on 5y (R)	30.00	25.00
2L63	A2(a)	7y on 5y	30.00	25.00
2L64	A2(b)	50y on 5y (R)	85.00	70.00
2L65	A3(b)	100y on 10y	450.00	350.00
2L66	A3(c)	500y on 10y (R)	600.00	400.00
		Nos. 2L62-2L66 (5)	1,195.	870.00

Size of surcharge on No. 2L63: 16x19mm.

A 500y on 5y, red surcharge "c," and a 500y on 10y orange, surcharge "b" were prepared but not issued.

Stalin and Lenin — A8

1949, Nov. 7 *Perf. 11x11½*

2L68	A8	10y dl bl grn (shades)	10.00	10.00

32nd anniversary of the Russian Revolution.

Workers Saluting Mao, Star and Flag — A9

1949, Nov. 16 *Perf. 11*

2L69	A9	35y dk bl, red, & yel	12.50	12.00

Founding of the People's Republic of China.

Stalin — A10

(same size) Gate of Heavenly Peace — A11

1949, Dec. 20 *Perf. 11½*

2L70	A10	20y dl mag	25.00	27.50
2L71	A10	35y rose red	25.00	27.50

70th birthday of Stalin.

1950, Mar. 10 Typo. *Perf. 10½*

2L72	A11	10y Prus blue	7.00	*4.00*
2L73	A11	20y dull grn	30.00	25.00
2L74	A11	35y red	1.25	*3.00*
2L75	A11	50y deep pur	3.00	*5.00*
2L76	A11	100y lilac rose	1.00	*8.00*
		Nos. 2L72-2L76 (5)	42.25	*45.00*

NORTH CHINA

The North China Liberation Area included the provinces of Hopeh, Chahar, Shansi and Suiyuan. The original postal service, begun in the Shansi-Hopeh-Chahar Border Area in December, 1937, became the North China Postal and Telegraph Administration in May, 1949.

All Stamps Issued without Gum

Large Victory Issue

Cavalry Man Holding Nationalist Flag — A1

Wmk. Wavy Lines

1946, Mar. *Perf. 10½*

Granite Paper

Size: 34½x42mm

3L1	A1	$1 red brown	1.00	1.40
a.		Newsprint	11.00	11.00
3L2	A1	$2 gray grn	1.00	1.25
3L3	A1	$4 vermilion	1.10	1.25
3L4	A1	$5 vio brn	1.10	1.25
3L5	A1	$8 vio bl	1.10	1.25
3L6	A1	$10 dp car	1.10	1.25
3L7	A1	$12 yellow	3.75	4.50
3L8	A1	$20 lt green	6.75	8.00
		Nos. 3L1-3L8 (8)	16.90	20.15

Defeat of Japan.

Small Victory Issue

Perf. 10½x10, 9½ rough

1946, May Unwmk.

Granite paper

Size: 20x21mm

3L9	A1	$1 red org	1.00	1.00
3L10	A1	$2 green	1.50	1.00
3L11	A1	$3 lt lilac	3.00	*4.00*
3L12	A1	$5 dull pur	4.00	.15
3L13	A1	$8 dk blue	6.00	*8.00*
3L14	A1	$10 rose red	1.50	*2.00*
3L15	A1	$15 purple	*30.00*	*20.00*
3L16	A1	$20 green	3.00	3.00
3L17	A1	$30 brt grnsh bl	2.50	*3.50*
3L18	A1	$40 brt rose lilac	3.00	*3.00*
3L19	A1	$50 brown	*20.00*	.25
3L20	A1	$60 myrtle green	*30.00*	.75

Wmk. Wavy Lines

3L21	A1	$100 orange	1.00	*2.00*
3L22	A1	$200 dull blue	1.00	*2.00*
3L23	A1	$500 rose	*10.00*	*25.00*
		Nos. 3L9-3L23 (15)	117.50	*75.65*

North China Postal and Telegraph Administration

Charging Infantrymen A2

Agriculture and Industry A3

1949, Jan. Unwmk. *Imperf.*

White Paper

3L24	A2	50c brown lake	.90	.40
3L25	A2	$1 Prussian blue	.90	1.50

Newsprint

3L26	A2	$2 apple green	.90	.40
3L27	A2	$3 dull violet	.90	.40
3L28	A2	$5 brown	.90	.40
3L29	A3	$6 deep rose	.90	.60
a.		White paper	.90	.80
3L30	A2	$10 blue grn	.15	*.30*
3L31	A2	$12 dp car	.90	.80
		Nos. 3L24-3L31 (8)	6.45	4.80

No. 3L29 issued in Peking, others in Tientsin.

Remittance Stamps of China Surcharged

A4

壹 $1

叁 $3

1949, Jan. Engr. *Perf. 13*

Small Central Characters

3L32	A4	50c on $50 brn blk	3.25	2.00
3L33	A4	$1 on $50 gray blk	2.50	1.00
3L34	A4	$3 on $50 gray	2.50	3.00

Large Central Characters

3L35	A4	50c on $50 blk	1.50	1.50
3L36	A4	$6 on $20 dk vio brn	1.50	2.00
		Nos. 3L32-3L36 (5)	11.25	9.50

Issued in Tientsin.

For surcharges see Nos. 3LQ10-3LQ21.

Sun Yat-sen Type A2 of Northeastern Provinces and China No. 640 Surcharged in Black, Red, Green or Blue

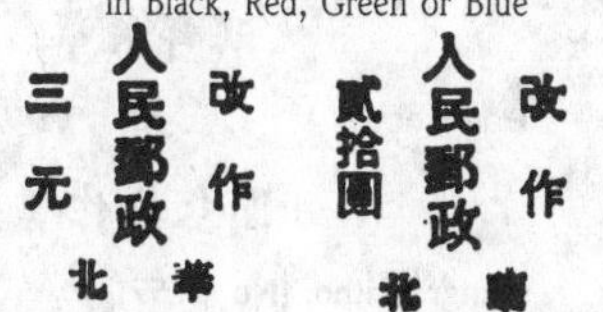

#3L37-3L45, 3L47-3L50, 3L52 — #3L46, 3L51, 3L53

c

Type "b," bottom character of left vertical row (yuan) differs. Type "c," top character of right vertical row differs.

1949, Mar. 7 *Perf. 14*

3L37 A2 50c on 5c lake .20 1.25
3L38 A2 $1 on 10c org .20 1.00
3L39 A2 $2 on 20c yel grn 37.50 12.00
3L40 A2 $3 on 50c red org .20 .75
3L41 A2 $4 on $5 dk grn 3.75 1.00
3L42 A2 $6 on $10 crim .90 1.00
3L43 A2 $10 on $300 bluish grn 1.10 *2.00*
3L44 A2 $12 on $1 bl 1.10 *1.50*
3L45 A2 $18 on $3 brn 1.10 .75
3L46 A2 $20 on 50c red org (Bl) 1.10 .50
3L47 A2 $20 on $20 ol, II 1.10 2.00
a. Type I 9.00 9.00
3L48 A2 $30 on $2.50 ind (R) 1.10 *2.00*
3L49 A2 $40 on 25c blk brn (R) 3.75 3.00
3L50 A2 $50 on $109 dk grn (R) 8.00 4.00
3L51 A2 $80 on $1 bl (R) 13.00 1.50
3L52 A2 $100 on $65 dl grn (R) 16.00 4.00
3L53 A73 $100 on $100 dk car, surch. 16mm wide (Bl) 22.50 1.50
a. Surcharge 14mm wide 24.00 10.00

1949, Apr.

3L55 A2 (c) $2 on 20c yel grn 1.10 1.50
3L56 A2 (c) $3 on 50c red org .18 *1.00*
3L57 A2 (c) $4 on $5 dk grn 8.00 *2.00*
3L58 A2 (c) $6 on $10 crim, II 3.75 2.00
a. Type I 8.00 10.00
3L59 A2 (c) $12 on $1 blue .65 .65

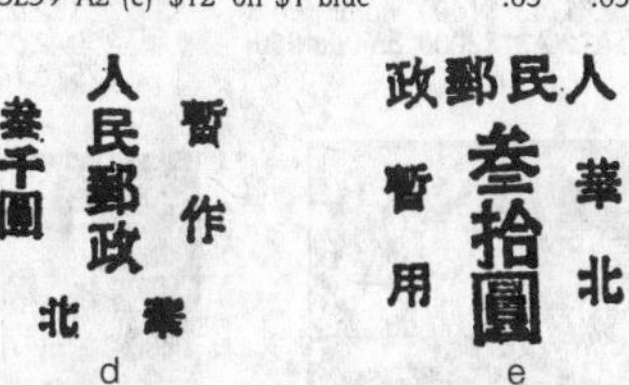

d e

1949, Apr.

Type "d"

3L60 A2 $1 on 25c blk grn (G) .15 *.60*
3L61 A2 $10 on $300 bluish grn (R) 8.00 2.75
3L62 A2 $20 on 50c red org (G) 11.00 12.00
3L63 A2 $20 on $20 ol (R) 5.50 2.00
3L64 A2 $40 on 25c blk brn (R) 5.50 2.25
3L65 A2 $50 on $109 dk grn, surch. 15mm wide (R) 8.00 6.00
a. Surcharge 13mm wide 27.50 8.00
3L66 A2 $80 on $1 bl (R) 5.50 3.00

Type "d" On Stamps on China

3L67 A73 $100 on $100 dk car (G) 45.00 15.00
3L68 A73 $300 on $700 red brn (Bl) 9.00 6.00
3L69 A82 $500 on $500 bl grn (R) 6.75 2.00
3L70 A82 $3000 on $3000 bl (R) 9.00 2.00

Type "e" On Stamps of Northeastern Provinces

1949, Aug.

3L71 A2 $10 on $10 crim, II (Bl) 5.50 1.50
a. Type I 11.00 11.00
3L72 A2 $30 on 20c yel grn (R) 5.50 1.00
3L73 A2 $50 on $44 dk car rose (Bl) 5.50 .55
3L74 A2 $100 on $3 brn (Bl) 9.00 3.00
3L75 A2 $200 on $4 org brn, II (Bl) 16.00 10.00
a. Type I 300.00 150.00

On China No. 754 in Blue

3L76 A82 $10 on $7000 lt red brn 9.00 4.00
Nos. 3L37-3L76 (39) 290.18 120.55

Overprints on Nos. 3L71 and 3L76 have 2 characters in center row.

Farmer and Worker on Globe — A5

1949, May 1 **Engr.** *Perf. 14*

3L77 A5 $20 crimson 1.65 .65
3L78 A5 $40 dark blue 1.65 .80
3L79 A5 $60 brown org 1.65 .65
3L80 A5 $80 dk green 1.65 1.00
3L81 A5 $100 purple 1.65 1.00
Nos. 3L77-3L81 (5) 8.25 4.10

Labor day. Exists imperf. Value, set $10. Also issued in blocks of 4, imperf between.

Mao Tse-tung (Chinese Numeral) — A6

Mao Tse-tung (Arabic Numeral) — A7

1949, July 1 *Perf. 14*

3L82 A6 $10 red .65 *.60*
3L83 A7 $20 dk blue .65 *.60*
3L84 A6 $50 orange 3.75 .60
3L85 A7 $80 dk green .80 *1.00*
3L86 A6 $100 purple 3.75 1.00
3L87 A7 $120 olive .55 *1.00*
3L88 A6 $140 vio brn 3.75 1.00
Nos. 3L82-3L88 (7) 13.90 5.80

28th anniv. of the founding of the Chinese Communist Party. Value, imperf, set $35.

(same size) Gate of Heavenly Peace — A8

Farmers and Factory — A9

1949, Nov. 26 **Litho.** *Perf. 12½*

3L89 A8 $50 orange .20 *2.75*
3L90 A8 $100 crimson .15 .80
3L91 A8 $200 green .50 .80
3L92 A8 $300 rose brn 8.00 1.65
3L93 A8 $400 blue 8.00 1.65
3L94 A8 $500 brown 8.00 1.00
3L95 A8 $700 violet 2.75 2.75
Nos. 3L89-3L95 (7) 27.60 11.40

1949, Dec. **Engr.** *Perf. 14*

3L96 A9 $1000 orange 2.00 .50
3L97 A9 $3000 dark blue .15 .40
3L98 A9 $5000 crimson .15 .75
3L99 A9 $10,000 red brown .15 1.50
Nos. 3L96-3L99 (4) 2.45 3.15

NORTH CHINA PARCEL POST STAMPS

Parcel Post Stamps of China Nos. Q23-Q27 (Type PP3) Surcharged in Red, Black or Blue

a b

1949, June

Surcharged Type "a"

3LQ1 $300 on $6,000,000 (R) 30.00
3LQ2 $400 on $8,000,000 (Bl) 30.00
3LQ3 $500 on $10,000,000 (R) 30.00
3LQ4 $800 on $5,000,000 (R) 30.00
3LQ5 $1000 on $3,000,000 (R) 40.00

Surcharged Type "b"

3LQ6 $500 on $3,000,000 40.00
3LQ7 $1000 on $5,000,000 50.00
3LQ8 $3000 on $8,000,000 125.00
3LQ9 $5000 on $10,000,000 165.00
Nos. 3LQ1-3LQ9 (9) 540.00

Nos. 3LQ8-3LQ9 have large numerals unboxed.

Remittance Stamps of China (like North China Type A4) Surcharged in Black or Red

a b

Peking Surcharge "a"

1949, June **Litho.** *Perf. 13*

3LQ10 $6 on $5 ver 3.25
3LQ11 $20 on $50 gray 3.25
3LQ12 $50 on $20 dk vio brn 3.25
3LQ13 $100 on $10 ol grn 6.50

Tientsin Surcharge "b"

Engr. *Perf. 14*

3LQ14 $20 on $1 brn org 12.00 5.25
a. Perf. 12½ 20.00 7.00
3LQ15 $30 on $2 dk grn 12.00 3.75
a. Red surcharge 20.00 7.00
3LQ16 $30 on $10 ol grn *90.00 40.00*
3LQ17 $100 on $10 gray grn (R) 12.00 5.25

Litho.

Perf. 13

3LQ18 $50 on $5 red 12.00 5.25

Engr.

Perf. 14

3LQ19 $20 on $1 org brn 35.00 16.00

Perf. 12½

3LQ20 $100 on $10 yel grn (R) 60.00 30.00

Typo.

Roulette 9½

3LQ21 $30 on $2 bl grn (R) 45.00 20.00

The surcharge on No. 3LQ19 is without first and last lines.

Locomotive — PP1

1949, Nov. **Engr.** *Perf. 14*

3LQ22 PP1 $500 crimson 5.00 5.00
3LQ23 PP1 $1000 deep blue 8.50
3LQ24 PP1 $2000 green 12.50
3LQ25 PP1 $5000 dp olive 27.50
3LQ26 PP1 $10,000 orange 50.00
3LQ27 PP1 $20,000 red brn 130.00
3LQ28 PP1 $50,000 brn pur 250.00
Nos. 3LQ22-3LQ28 (7) 483.50

NORTHWEST CHINA

The Northwest China Liberation Area consisted of the provinces of Sinkiang, Tsinghai, Ningsia and the western part of Shensi. The area was first established as the Shensi-Kansu-Ningsia Border Area in October, 1936, after the Long March to Yenan. Remote Sinkiang was not included until late 1949.

All Stamps Issued without Gum

Pagoda on Yenan Hill — A1

1945, Mar. **Litho.** *Imperf.*

4L1 A1 $1 green 15.00
4L2 A1 $5 dk blue 100.00
4L3 A1 $10 rose red 14.00
4L4 A1 $50 dull pur 11.00
4L5 A1 $100 yel org 14.00
Nos. 4L1-4L5 (5) 154.00

Rouletted 9

4L1a A1 $1 80.00
4L2a A1 $5 115.00
4L3a A1 $10 80.00

First issue; denomination in Chinese and Arabic. Heavy shading at top of vignette. Columns at sides.

See types A2, A3 and A4. For surcharges see Nos. 4L6-4L10, 4L23.

Nos. 4L1-4L2 Surcharged in Red:

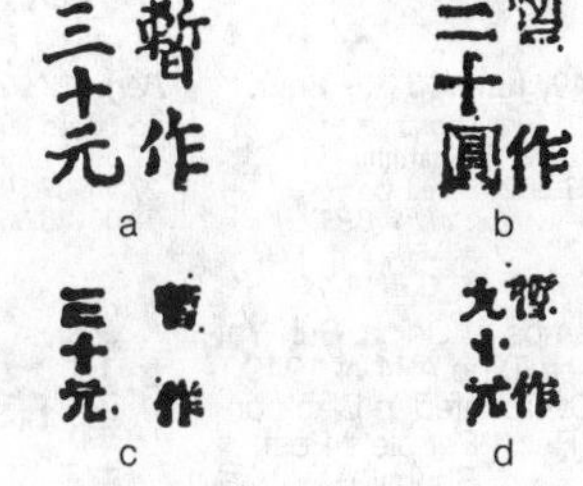

a b c d

1946, Nov.

4L6 A1 (a) $30 on $1 grn 20.00
4L7 A1 (b) $30 on $1 grn *100.00*
a. Rectangular lower left character 675.00
4L8 A1 (c) $30 on $1 grn 15.00
4L9 A1 (b) $60 on $1 grn
4L10 A1 (d) $90 on $5 dk bl 20.00

Surcharges on Nos. 4L7a and 4L9 are type "b" as illustrated. Surcharge on No. 4L7 differs from "b," having lower left character as in type "a."

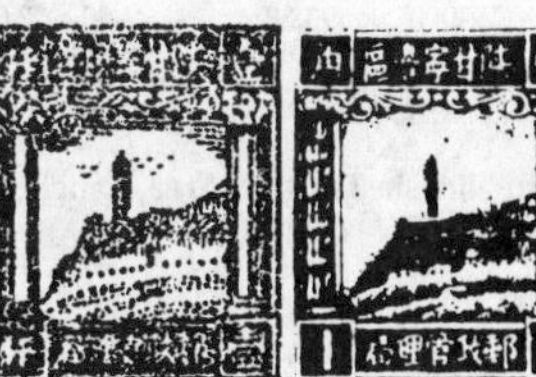

Pagoda on Yenan Hill (same size)
A2 A3

1948, June

4L11 A2 $100 buff 140.00
4L12 A2 $300 rose pink 1.00
4L13 A2 $500 red 3.50
4L14 A2 $1000 blue 3.50
4L15 A2 $2000 yel grn 24.00
4L16 A2 $5000 dull pur 10.00
Nos. 4L11-4L16 (6) 182.00

Second issue; denominations in Chinese only. Many shades and proofs exist.

For surcharge see No. 4L24.

1948, Dec.

4L17 A3 10c yel org 1.50
4L18 A3 20c lemon 1.50
4L19 A3 $1 dk blue 1.50
4L20 A3 $2 vermilion 1.50
4L21 A3 $5 pale bl grn 9.00
4L22 A3 $10 violet 13.50
Nos. 4L17-4L22 (6) 28.50

Third issue; ornamental border at sides. Many shades exist.

Nos. 4L2 and 4L13 Surcharged in Red or Black

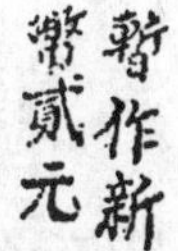

1949, Jan.
4L23 A1 $1 on $5 dk bl 45.00
4L24 A2 $2 on $500 red 20.00

Pagoda on Yenan Hill — A4

1949, May 1
4L25 A4 50c yel to olive .15 .20
4L26 A4 $1 dl bl to indigo .15 .20
4L27 A4 $3 ol yel to org yel .15 .20
4L28 A4 $5 blue green .80 .20
4L29 A4 $10 vio to dp vio 3.00 3.50
4L30 A4 $20 pink to rose red 4.00 8.00
Nos. 4L25-4L30 (6) 8.25 12.30

Fourth issue; light shading at top of vignette, columns without ornaments at sides. Many shades exist.

China Nos. 959, F2 and E12 Overprinted ("People's Post, Shensi")

1949, June 13 Engr. *Perf. 12½*
4L31 A96 orange 15.00 15.00
4L32 R2 carmine 27.50 27.50
4L33 SD2 red vio 27.50 27.50
Nos. 4L31-4L33 (3) 70.00 70.00

Stamps of China, Sun Yat-sen Type A94 of 1949, Overprinted in Black or Red ("People's Post, Shensi")

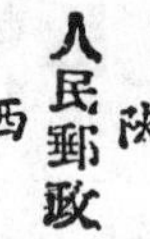

Lithographed; Engraved
1949, July 1 *Perf. 14, 12½*
4L34 $10 green (887) 1.10 1.00
4L35 $20 vio brn (888) 2.25 2.00
4L36 $20 vio brn (896) 1.10 1.00
4L37 $50 dk Prus grn (889; R) 5.75 5.00
4L38 $50 grn (951) 5.75 5.00
4L39 $100 org brn (890) 14.00 6.00
4L40 $500 ros lil (892) 20.00 6.00
4L41 $1000 dp bl (952; R) 27.50 10.00
4L42 $2000 vio (902;R) 27.50 12.00
4L43 $5000 car (953) 40.00 25.00
4L44 $10,000 brn (954) 75.00 50.00
Nos. 4L34-4L44 (11) 219.95 123.00

Kansu-Ningsia-Tsinghai Area, Lanchow Overprints

China Nos. 959a, F2 and E12 Overprinted ("People's Post, Kansu")

1949, Oct. Engr. *Rouletted*
4L45 A96 orange 18.00 18.00

Perf. 12½
4L46 R2 carmine 25.00 25.00
4L47 SD2 red vio 25.00 25.00
Nos. 4L45-4L47 (3) 68.00 68.00

Stamps of China, Sun Yat-sen Type A94 of 1949, Overprinted ("People's Post, Kansu")

郵政 人民 (甘)

Engraved; Lithographed
1949, Oct. *Perf. 14, 12½*
4L48 $10 grn (887) 3.25 1.50
4L49 $20 vio brn (888) 3.25 3.00
4L50 $50 dk Prus grn (889) 9.00 8.00
4L51 $100 org brn (890) 3.25 3.00
4L52 $100 dk org brn (898) 5.00 4.00
4L53 $200 red org (891) 6.50 5.00
4L54 $500 rose lil (892) 6.50 5.00
4L55 $1000 blue (894) 3.25 3.00
4L56 $1000 dp bl (901) 6.50 5.00
4L57 $2000 vio (902) 11.00 9.00
4L58 $5000 lt bl (903) 22.00 18.00
4L59 $10,000 sepia (904) 30.00 25.00
4L60 $20,000 ap grn (905) 60.00 50.00
Nos. 4L48-4L60 (13) 169.50 139.50

No. 4L54-4L60 exist with wider spaced overprints.

China Nos. 959, F2 and 791-792 Surcharged in Black or Red ("People's Post, Sinkiang")

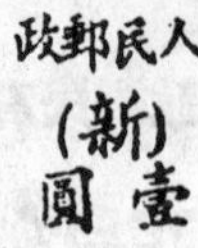

1949, Oct.
4L61 A96 $1 on org 27.50 25.00
4L62 R2 $3 on car 27.50 25.00
4L63 A82 10c on $50,000 dp bl (R) 27.50 25.00
4L64 A82 $1.50 on $100,000 dl grn (R) 27.50 30.00
Nos. 4L61-4L64 (4) 110.00 105.00

Northwest People's Post

Mao Tse-tung — A5

Great Wall — A6

1949, Oct. 15 Litho. *Imperf.*
4L65 A5 $50 rose 2.00 1.50
 a. $200 cliche in $50 plate 120.00
4L66 A6 $100 dark blue .15 .60
4L67 A5 $200 orange .15 2.50
4L68 A6 $400 sepia 2.00 2.50
Nos. 4L65-4L68 (4) 4.30 7.10

EAST CHINA

The East China Liberation Area included the provinces of Shantung, Kiangsu, Chekiang, Anhwei and Fukien. The original postal service established in Shantung in 1941, became the East China Posts and Telegraph General Office in July, 1948.

All Stamps Issued without Gum

Mao Tse-tung — A1

Transportation and Tower — A2

1948, Mar. Litho. *Perf. 10½*
5L1 A1 $50 yel org 1.40 1.00
5L2 A1 $100 dp rose 4.50 3.50
5L3 A1 $200 dk vio bl 4.50 3.50
5L4 A1 $300 brt grn 4.50 3.50
5L5 A1 $500 dp blue 1.75 1.50
5L6 A1 $800 vermilion 4.50 4.00
5L7 A1 $1000 dk blue 9.00 8.00
5L8 A1 $5000 rose 18.00 15.00
5L9 A1 $10,000 dp car 32.50 30.00
Nos. 5L1-5L9 (9) 80.65 70.00

Many varieties, including unissued imperforates exist.

Perf. 9 to 11 and compound
1949, Apr. Litho.
5L10 A2 $1 yel grn .15 .15
5L11 A2 $2 blue grn .15 .15
5L12 A2 $3 dull red .15 .15
5L13 A2 $5 pale brn (ovpt. 4x4mm) .15 .15
 a. Without overprint 60.00 60.00
 b. Overprint 3x3mm 1.00 1.00
5L14 A2 $10 ultra .15 .15
5L15 A2 $13 brt vio .15 .15
5L16 A2 $18 brt blue .15 .15
5L17 A2 $21 vermilion .20 .20
5L18 A2 $30 gray .20 .20
5L19 A2 $50 crimson .25 *.35*
5L20 A2 $100 olive 10.50 9.00
Nos. 5L10-5L20 (11) 12.20 10.80

Seventh anniv. of Shantung Communist Postal Administration. The overprint on the $5, character "yu" meaning "Posts," obliterates Japanese flag on tower, erroneously included in design. Value, imperfs. of Nos. 5L10-5L12, 5L13a, 5L14-5L20 on different paper, set $75.

Train and Postal Runner (1949.2.7) A3

Mao, Soldiers, Map A4

1949, Apr. Litho. *Perf. 8 to 11*
5L21 A3 $1 brt emer .15 .15
5L22 A3 $2 blue grn .15 .15
5L23 A3 $3 dk red .15 .15
5L24 A3 $5 brown .15 .15
5L25 A3 $10 ultra .30 .15
5L26 A3 $13 brt vio .15 .15
5L27 A3 $18 brt blue .15 .15
5L28 A3 $21 vermilion .15 .15
5L29 A3 $30 slate .15 .20
5L30 A3 $50 crimson .20 .20
5L31 A3 $100 olive .40 .40
Set value 1.45 1.55

7th anniv. of Shantung P. O., Feb. 7. Imperf. sets were sold by the Philatelic Dept., Tientsin P.O. Value $25. See Nos. 5L69-5L76. For surcharges see People's Republic of China Nos. 77-81.

1949, Apr. *Perf. 9½ to 11 and comp.*
5L32 A4 $1 brt emer .15 .15
5L33 A4 $2 blue grn .15 .15
5L34 A4 $3 dull red .15 .15
5L35 A4 $5 brown .15 .15
5L36 A4 $10 ultra .15 .15
5L37 A4 $13 brt vio .15 .15
5L38 A4 $18 brt blue .15 .15
5L39 A4 $21 vermilion .15 .15
5L40 A4 $30 gray .15 .15
5L41 A4 $50 crimson .15 .15
5L42 A4 $100 olive 1.40 1.40
Set value 2.10 2.10

Victory of Hwai-Hai (Hwaiying and Haichow). Imperf. sets were sold by the Philatelic Dept., Tientsin P.O. Value, set $60.

Stamps of China, Sun Yat-sen Type of 1949, Surcharged in Red or Black

政郵東華 京 圓壹作暫
(Nanking)
a

人民券 伍拾圓 東華
(Wuhu)
b

1949, May 4 Engr. *Perf. 12½*
5L43 A94 (a) $1 on $10 grn (895, R) .50 .50
 a. Perf. 13 3.00 3.00
5L44 A94 (a) $3 on $20 vio brn (896) .50 .50
 a. Perf. 13 .75 2.00
 b. Perf. 14 5.50 5.50
 c. Surcharge inverted 200.00

Sun Yat-sen Type A94 Surcharged Type "b"

Lithographed, Engraved
1949, May *Perf. 12½, 14*
5L45 $30 on $1000 dp bl (901 7.50 5.00
5L46 $30 on $1000 bl (894) 7.50 5.00
5L47 $50 on $200 org red (899) 7.50 5.00
5L48 $100 on $5000 lt bl (903, R) 16.00 13.00
5L49 $300 on $10,000 sep (904, R) 50.00 40.00
5L50 $500 on $200 org red (899) 75.00 60.00
Nos. 5L45-5L50 (6) 163.50 128.00

Many varieties exist.

China Nos. 913a and 913 Surcharged in Blue, Green, Black or Red

(East China)

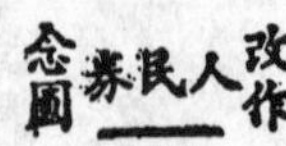

1949, May Litho. *Perf. 12½*
5L51 A95 $5 on 50c on $20 brn, II (B) 14.00 10.00
 a. Green surcharge 100.00 *50.00*
5L52 A95 $10 on 50c on $20 brn, II 14.00 10.00
5L53 A95 $20 on 50c on $20 red brn, II (R) 14.00 10.00
 a. Type I (R) 20.00 20.00
Nos. 5L51-5L53 (3) 42.00 30.00

Stamps of China, Sun Yat-sen Type of 1949, Surcharged in Black or Red

(Hangchow)

政郵東華 杭 圓叁拾作暫

Engr., Litho. (No. 5L57)
1949, June 25 *Perf. 14, 12½*
5L54 A94 $1 on $1 org (886) 1.40 1.25
5L55 A94 $3 on $20 vio brn (896, R) .75 .70
5L56 A94 $5 on $100 org brn (890) 3.75 1.65
5L57 A94 $5 on $100 dk org brn (898) 1.75 .50
5L58 A94 $10 on $50 dk Prus grn (889, R) 13.00 10.50
5L59 A94 $13 on $10 grn (895) .30 *.60*
Nos. 5L54-5L59 (6) 20.95 15.20

East China Liberation Area

Maps of Shanghai and Nanking — A5

1949, May 30 Litho. *Perf. 8½ to 11*
5L60 A5 $1 org ver .15 *.20*
5L61 A5 $2 blue grn .15 *.20*
5L62 A5 $3 brt vio .15 *.15*
5L63 A5 $5 vio brn .15 *.15*
5L64 A5 $10 ultra .15 .15
5L65 A5 $30 slate .15 *.20*
5L66 A5 $50 carmine .15 *.40*
5L67 A5 $100 olive .15 *.30*
5L68 A5 $500 orange 1.25 1.50
Set value 2.00

Liberation of Shanghai and Nanking. Many shades, paper and perforation varieties and imperfs. exist.

Train and Postal Runner Type Dated "1949"

1949, July-1950, Feb. *Perf. 12½, 14*
5L69 A3 $10 dp ultra .15 *.15*
5L70 A3 $15 org ver .15 *.40*
 a. $15 red, perf. 14 .25 .15
5L71 A3 $30 slate grn .15 .15
 a. Perf. 12½ .15 .15
5L72 A3 $50 carmine .15 *.40*
5L73 A3 $60 bl grn, perf. 14 .15 *.60*
5L74 A3 $100 ol, perf. 14 2.25 .40
5L75 A3 $1600 vio bl ('50) .55 *2.00*
5L76 A3 $2000 brn vio ('50) .70 *2.00*
Nos. 5L69-5L76 (8) 4.25 *6.10*

Chu Teh, Mao, Troops with Flags A7

Mao Tse-tung A8

1949, Aug. 17 *Perf. 12½*
5L77 A7 $70 orange .15 *.15*
5L78 A7 $270 crimson .15 *.15*
5L79 A7 $370 emerald .30 .30
5L80 A7 $470 vio brn .50 .40
5L81 A7 $570 blue .15 *.30*
Nos. 5L77-5L81 (5) 1.25 1.30

22nd anniv. of the People's Liberation Army. For similar type see Southwest China A1.

1949, Oct.
5L82 A8 $10 dk blue 1.50 *2.00*
5L83 A8 $15 vermilion 1.90 *2.50*
5L84 A8 $70 brown .15 .15
5L85 A8 $100 vio brn .15 .15
5L86 A8 $150 orange .15 .15
5L87 A8 $200 grnsh gray .15 .15
5L88 A8 $500 gray bl .15 .15
5L89 A8 $1000 rose .15 .15
5L90 A8 $2000 emerald .15 .15
Nos. 5L82-5L90 (9) 4.45 *5.55*

For surcharges see People's Republic of China Nos. 82-84.

Stamps of China, Sun Yat-sen Type of 1949 Surcharged in Black or Red

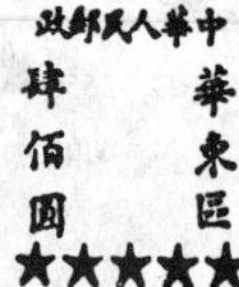

1949, Nov. **Litho.** *Perf. 12½*

5L91	A94	$400 on $200 org red (899)	24.00	1.00
5L92	A94	$1000 on $50 grnsh gray (897, R)	2.00	.65
5L93	A94	$1200 on $100 dk org brn (898)	.15	*1.00*
5L94	A94	$1600 on $20,000 ap grn (905)	.15	*2.00*
5L95	A94	$2000 on $1000 dp bl (952,R)	.15	*.65*
a.		Perf. 14	90.00	25.00
		Nos. 5L91-5L95 (5)	26.45	*5.30*

EAST CHINA PARCEL POST STAMPS

Parcel Post Stamps of China 1945-48 Surcharged

200.00

(Shantung)

1949, Aug. 1 **Engr.** *Perf. 13*

5LQ1	PP1	$200 on $500 grn	8.00	8.00
5LQ2	PP1	$500 on $1000 bl	8.00	8.00

Type PP3 *Perf. 13½*

5LQ3	$200 on $200,000 dk grn	40.00	30.00
5LQ4	$200 on $10,000,000 sage grn	8.00	8.00
5LQ5	$500 on $7000 dl bl	90.00	60.00
5LQ6	$500 on $50,000 indigo	8.00	8.00
5LQ7	$1000 on $10,000 car rose	8.00	8.00
5LQ8	$1000 on $100,000 dk rose brn	8.00	8.00
5LQ9	$1000 on $300,000 pink	6.00	6.00
5LQ10	$1000 on $500,000 vio brn	50.00	45.00
5LQ11	$1000 on $8,000,000 org ver	8.00	8.00
5LQ12	$2000 on $5,000,000 dl vio	12.00	12.00
5LQ13	$2000 on $6,000,000 brn blk	12.00	12.00
5LQ14	$3000 on $30,000 ol	20.00	17.50
5LQ15	$3000 on $70,000 org brn	20.00	17.50
5LQ16	$5000 on $3,000,000 dl bl	25.00	22.50
	Nos. 5LQ1-5LQ16 (16)	331.00	278.50

China Type A97, No. 987 Surcharged

$200 $500

$1000 $2000

$5000 $10,000

1949, Sept. 7 **Litho.** *Perf. 12½*

5LQ17	$200 on $10	32.50	15.00
5LQ18	$500 on $10	32.50	15.00
5LQ19	$1000 on $10	32.50	15.00
5LQ20	$2000 on $10	32.50	15.00
5LQ21	$5000 on $10	32.50	15.00
5LQ22	$10,000 on $10	32.50	15.00
	Nos. 5LQ17-5LQ22 (6)	195.00	90.00

Flying Geese Type of China, 1949, and China Nos. 984-986 Surcharged in Red or Black

1950, Jan. 28

5LQ23	A97	$5000 on 10c bl vio (R)	97.50	50.00
5LQ24	A97	$10,000 on $1 brn org	97.50	50.00
5LQ25	A97	$20,000 on $2 bl	97.50	50.00
5LQ26	A97	$50,000 on $5 car rose	97.50	50.00
		Nos. 5L23-5L26 (4)	390.00	200.00

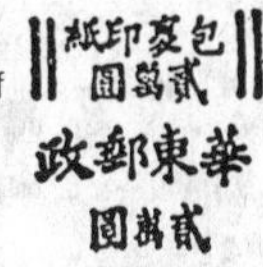

Parcel Post Stamps of China Type PP3, Nos. Q1-Q2, Q12-Q13 Surcharged in Red or Black

1950, Jan. 28 **Engr.** *Perf. 13, 13½*

5LQ27	$5000 on $500 grn (R)	.20	*50.00*
5LQ28	$10,000 on $1000 bl (R)	120.00	50.00
5LQ29	$20,000 on $3000 bl grn	120.00	80.00
5LQ30	$50,000 on $5000 org red	12.00	50.00
	Nos. 5L27-5L30 (4)	252.20	230.00

CENTRAL CHINA

The Central Chinese Liberation Area included the provinces of Honan, Hupeh, Hunan and Kiangsi. The area was established between August and September, 1949, following the liberation of Hankow.

All Stamps Issued without Gum

Hupeh Postal and Telegraph Administration

Stamps of China, Sun Yat-sen Type A94 of 1949, Surcharged ("Chinese P.O., Temporary Use")

100

Engraved; Lithographed

1949, June 4 *Perf. 14, 12½*

Thin parallel lines

6L1	$1 on $200 red org (891)	.75	.75
6L2	$6 on $10,000 sep (904)	.75	.75
6L3	$15 on $1 org (886)	.75	.75
6L4	$30 on $100 org brn (890)	3.50	1.50
6L5	$30 on $100 dk org brn (898)	.75	.75
6L6	$50 on $20 vio brn (896)	12.00	7.00
6L7	$80 on $1000 dp bl (901)	2.25	1.00

Thick parallel lines

6L8	$1 on $200 red org (891)	3.50	3.50
6L9	$3 on $5000 lt bl (903)	.50	.50
6L10	$10 on $500 rose lil (892)	.50	.50
6L11	$10 on $500 rose lil (900)	3.50	3.50
6L12	$50 on $20 vio brn (888)	3.50	3.50
6L13	$50 on $20 vio brn (896)	1.00	1.00
6L14	$80 on $1000 bl (894)	3.50	3.50
6L15	$80 on $1000 dp bl (901)	12.00	8.00
6L16	$100 on $50 dk Prus grn (903)	1.50	2.50
	Nos. 6L1-6L16 (16)	50.25	39.00

Kiangsi Postal and Telegraph Administration.

Central Trust Revenue Stamps of China Surcharged ("People's Post, Kiangsi")

(same size) — A1

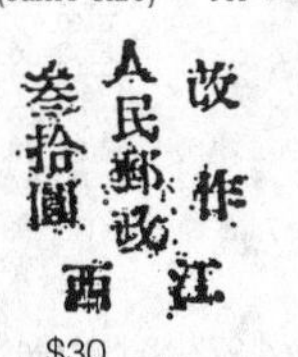

$30 $60

1949, June 20 **Engr.** *Perf. 12½*

6L17	A1	$3 on $30 pur	1.00	1.00
6L18	A1	$15 on $15 red org	1.00	1.00
6L19	A1	$30 on $50 dk bl	1.00	1.00
6L20	A1	$60 on $50 dk bl	1.00	1.00
6L21	A1	$130 on $15 red org	1.00	1.00

The $15 surcharge has 3 characters in left vertical row, the $130 surcharge has 5.

Same Surcharge on Sun Yat-sen Issues of China, 1945-49

Engraved, Lithographed

Perf. 14, 12½

6L22	A82	$1 on $250 dp lil (746)	3.00	3.00
6L23	A94	$5 on $1000 dp bl (901)	3.00	3.00
6L24	A94	$5 on $2000 vio (902)	3.00	3.00
6L25	A94	$5 on $5000 lt bl (903)	1.00	1.00
6L26	A94	$10 on $1000 bl (894)	3.00	3.00
6L27	A82	$20 on $4000 gray	3.00	1.00
6L28	A73	$30 on $100 dk car	3.00	3.00
6L29	A82	$30 on $20,000 rose pink	1.00	1.00
6L30	A94	$30 on $500 rose lil (900)	1.00	1.00
6L31	A94	$100 on $1000 dp bl (901)	1.00	1.00
6L32	A82	$200 on $250 dp lil	2.00	2.00
		Nos. 6L17-6L32 (16)	27.00	27.00

Central China Posts and Telegraph Administration

Farmer, Soldier and Worker
A2 A3

I- Top white line of square character (yuan) at upper left does not touch left vertical stroke. No gap in shading between soldier's feet.

II- Top line connects with left vertical stroke. Gap in shading between feet.

Perf. 10 to 11½ & Comp.

1949 **Litho.**

6L33	A2	$1 orange	7.25	1.50
6L34	A2	$3 brn org	2.50	1.50
6L35	A2	$6 emerald	2.50	1.50
6L36	A3	$7 yel brn	.40	1.50
6L37	A2	$10 bl grn	.15	.30
6L38	A3	$14 org brn	14.00	9.00
6L39	A2	$15 ultra	.30	.40
6L40	A2	$30 grn, type I	.15	.30
a.		Type II	.15	.20
6L41	A3	$35 gray bl	9.50	10.00
6L42	A2	$50 rose vio	8.00	4.75
6L43	A3	$70 dp grn	.15	.15
6L44	A2	$80 pink	.40	.80
6L45	A3	$100 bl grn	.25	.30
6L46	A3	$220 rose red	3.25	.60
		Nos. 6L33-6L46 (14)	48.80	32.60

For surcharges & overprints see #6L63-6L65, 6L66-6L73, 6L75, 6L90-6L98, 6L100-6L108.

Star Enclosing Map of Hankow Area — A4

Two types of $500:
I- Thick numerals of "500." No period after "500."
II- Thin numerals and period.

Two types of $1000:
I- No period after "1000."
II- Period after "1000."

1949, July

6L48	A4	$110 org brn	.25	.80
6L49	A4	$130 violet	3.75	1.25
6L50	A4	$200 dp org	.15	.25
6L51	A4	$290 brown	1.50	.20
6L52	A4	$370 dk bl	1.50	.80
6L53	A4	$500 lt bl, I	3.75	.50
a.		$500 blue, II	18.00	4.00
6L54	A4	$1000 dk red, I	25.00	5.00
a.		$1000 dull red, II	18.00	1.00
6L55	A4	$5000 brown	.75	2.00
6L56	A4	$10,000 brt pink	1.50	4.00
		Nos. 6L48-6L56 (9)	38.15	14.80

For surcharges and overprints see Nos. 6L74, 6L76-6L81, 6L99, 6L109.

Hankow River Customs Building A5

River Wall, Wuchang — A6

Design: $290, $370, River scene, Hanyang.

1949, Aug. 16 *Perf. 11, Imperf.*

6L57	A5	$70 green	1.10	.70
6L58	A5	$220 crimson	1.10	1.00
6L59	A5	$290 brown	1.10	1.00
6L60	A5	$370 brt blue	1.10	1.00
6L61	A6	$500 purple	1.10	*1.25*
6L62	A6	$1000 vermilion	1.00	*1.25*
		Nos. 6L57-6L62 (6)	6.50	*6.20*

Liberation of Hankow, Wuchang and Hanyang.
For overprints see Nos. 6L82-6L87.

Nos. 6L35, 6L39 and 6L40 Surcharged in Red ("Honan Renminbi Currency")

1949, July

6L63	A2	$7 on $6 emer	6.50	6.50
6L64	A2	$14 on $15 ultra	7.50	7.50
6L65	A2	$70 on $30 grn	11.00	11.00
		Nos. 6L63-6L65 (3)	25.00	25.00

Surcharge shown is for $70. The $7 has 5 characters in left column and no bottom line.

Issues of 1949 Overprinted ("Honan Renminbi Currency")

1949, Aug.

6L66	A2	$3 brn org	.85	.85
6L67	A3	$7 yel brn	.85	.85
6L68	A2	$10 bl grn	1.75	1.75
6L69	A3	$14 org brn	1.75	1.75
6L70	A2	$30 yel grn (6L40a)	1.75	1.75
6L71	A3	$35 gray bl	.85	.85
6L72	A2	$50 rose vio	6.25	6.25
6L73	A3	$70 dp grn	1.75	1.75
6L74	A4	$110 org brn	12.00	12.00
6L75	A3	$220 rose red	3.50	3.50
6L76	A4	$290 brown	12.00	12.00
6L77	A4	$370 blue	14.00	14.00
6L78	A4	$500 bl, II	20.00	20.00
6L79	A4	$1000 dk red, I	30.00	30.00
6L80	A4	$5000 brown	77.50	77.50
6L81	A4	$10,000 brt pink	165.00	165.00
		Nos. 6L66-6L81 (16)	349.80	349.80

Width of the overprint varies slightly.

Nos. 6L57-6L62 Overprinted ("Honan Renminbi Currency")

1949, Aug. *Perf. 11, Imperf.*

6L82	A5	$70 green	4.50	1.25
6L83	A5	$220 crimson	4.50	2.50
6L84	A5	$290 brown	4.50	2.50
6L85	A5	$370 brt bl	4.50	3.50
6L86	A6	$500 purple	4.50	3.50
6L87	A6	$1000 vermilion	4.50	5.00
		Nos. 6L82-6L87 (6)	27.00	18.25

Width of overprint on Nos. 6L82-6L85, 7mm; on Nos. 6L86-6L87, 12mm.

Changchow Issue Surcharged in Red ("Honan Renminbi Currency")

(same size) Mao Tsetung — A7

1949, Sept. *Perf. 10*

6L88	A7	$290 on $30 yel grn	45.00	30.00
6L89	A7	$370 on $30 yel grn	60.00	40.00

Issues of 1949 Surcharged

200.00

1950, Jan.

6L90	A2	$200 on $1	.45	1.00
6L91	A2	$200 on $3	2.75	1.00
6L92	A2	$200 on $6	.45	1.00
6L93	A3	$200 on $7	2.75	1.00
6L94	A3	$200 on $14	2.75	1.00
6L95	A3	$200 on $35	2.75	1.50
6L96	A3	$200 on $70	2.75	1.00
6L97	A2	$200 on $80	2.75	1.00

6L98 A3 $200 on $220 2.75 1.00
6L99 A4 $200 on $370 .45 1.00
6L100 A3 $300 on $70 .45 1.50
6L101 A2 $300 on $80 .45 1.00
6L102 A3 $300 on $220 .15 1.00
6L103 A2 $1200 on $3 27.50 15.00
6L104 A3 $1200 on $7 5.50 3.00
6L105 A3 $1500 on $14 8.00 4.00
6L106 A2 $2100 on $1 37.50 15.00
6L107 A2 $2100 on $6 37.50 15.00
6L108 A3 $2100 on $35 11.50 6.00
6L109 A4 $5000 on $370 4.50 3.00
Nos. 6L90-6L109 (20) 153.65 75.00

Two types of surcharge exist, differing in spacing of characters in top row.

CENTRAL CHINA PARCEL POST STAMPS

Star and Map of Hankow — PP1

1949, Nov. Litho. *Perf. 11, 11½*
6LQ1 PP1 $5000 brown .85 2.00
6LQ2 PP1 $10,000 scarlet 6.00 5.00
6LQ3 PP1 $20,000 dk sl grn 2.25 7.00
6LQ4 PP1 $50,000 vermilion .85 20.00
Nos. 6LQ1-6LQ4 (4) 9.95 34.00

SOUTH CHINA

The South China Liberation Area included the provinces of Kwangtung and Kwangsi and Hainan Island. The South China Postal and Telegraph Administration was organized on or about Nov. 4, 1949.

All Stamps Issued without Gum

Pearl River Bridge, Canton — A1

1949, Nov. 4 Litho. *Imperf.*
7L1 A1 $10 green .15 .15
7L2 A1 $20 sepia .15 .15
7L3 A1 $30 violet .15 .15
7L4 A1 $50 carmine .15 .15
7L5 A1 $100 ultramarine .20 .15
Set value .45 .35

For surcharges see Nos. 7L19-7L23.

China Nos. 993-995 With Additional Overprint in Red ("Liberation of Swatow") 暫用 解放

1949, Nov. 9
7L6 A94 2½c on $500 rose lil (993) 12.50 12.50
a. Handstamped 30.00 30.00
7L7 A94 2½c on $500 rose lil (994) 20.00 20.00
a. Handstamped 30.00 30.00
7L8 A94 15c on $10 grn (995) 15.00 15.00
a. Handstamped 40.00 40.00

On Unit Issues of China, 1949

7L9 A96 org (959) 15.00 12.00
7L10 AP5 bl grn (C62) 15.00 18.00
7L11 SD2 red vio (E12) 15.00 18.00
7L12 R2 car (F2) 15.00 18.00

On Sun Yat-sen and Flying Geese Issues of China

7L13 A94 2c org (974) 100.00 125.00
7L14 A94 4c bl grn (975) 350.00 250.00
7L15 A94 10c dp lil (976) 18.00 14.00
7L16 A94 20c bl (978) 18.00 14.00
7L17 A97 $1 brn org (984) 30.00 15.00
7L18 A97 $10 bl grn (987) 300.00 250.00
Nos. 7L6-7L18 (13) 923.50 781.50

300

Nos. 7L1-7L3 Surcharged in Red or Green

1950, Jan.
7L19 A1 $300 on $30 vio (R) 3.50 1.00
7L20 A1 $500 on $20 brn (R) 3.50 1.00
7L21 A1 $800 on $30 vio (G) 3.50 1.25
7L22 A1 $1000 on $10 gray grn (R) 3.50 1.00
7L23 A1 $1000 on $20 brn (R) 3.50 1.00
Nos. 7L19-7L23 (5) 17.50 5.25

SOUTHWEST CHINA

The Southwest China Liberation Area included the provinces of Kweichow, Szechwan, Yunnan, Sikang and Tibet. The Southwest Postal and Telegraph Administration was organized on or about Nov. 15, 1949 after the liberation of Kweiyang, capital of Kweichow Province.

All Stamps Issued without Gum

Chu Teh, Mao and Troops — A1

1949, Dec. Litho. *Perf. 12½*
8L1 A1 $10 deep blue 1.50 2.50
8L2 A1 $20 rose claret .15 .80
8L3 A1 $30 dp org .15 .80
8L4 A1 $50 gray grn .35 .80
8L5 A1 $100 carmine .15 .50
8L6 A1 $200 blue .50 .60
8L7 A1 $300 bl vio .75 .90
8L8 A1 $500 dk gray 1.90 1.25
8L9 A1 $1000 pale pur 3.75 4.00
8L10 A1 $2000 green 11.00 13.00
8L11 A1 $5000 orange 30.00 40.00
Nos. 8L1-8L11 (11) 50.20 65.15

For surcharges and overprints see Nos. 8L21-8L29, 8L40-8L47, 8L55.

China Nos. 974-975, 984, 986-987 Surcharged ("Kweichow People's Post")

1949, Dec. 1 *Perf. 12½*
8L12 A94 $20 on 2c org 4.50 4.50
8L13 A94 $50 on 4c bl grn 4.50 4.50
8L14 A97 $100 on $1 brn org 7.25 7.25
8L15 A97 $400 on $5 car rose 22.50 22.50
8L16 A97 $2000 on $10 bl grn 55.00 55.00
Nos. 8L12-8L16 (5) 93.75 93.75

Map of China, Flag Planted in Southwest — A2

1950, Jan. Litho. *Perf. 9 to 11½*
8L17 A2 $20 dark blue .15 .40
8L18 A2 $30 green .50 .40
8L19 A2 $50 red .20 .60
8L20 A2 $100 brown .20 .60
Nos. 8L17-8L20 (4) 1.05 2.00

Liberation of the Southwest.
For surcharges see #8L30-8L39, 8L56-8L59.

Nos. 8L5-8L6 Surcharged 圓仟貳作改

Perf. 12½
8L21 A1 $300 on $100 car 10.50 2.50
8L22 A1 $500 on $100 car .15 2.50
8L23 A1 $1200 on $100 car .70 5.00
8L24 A1 $1500 on $200 bl .70 5.00
8L25 A1 $2000 on $200 bl 17.50 7.00
Nos. 8L21-8L25 (5) 29.55 22.00

Nos. 8L5-8L6 Overprinted ("East Szechwan") （川東）

1950, Jan.
8L26 A1 $100 carmine 4.00 5.00
8L27 A1 $200 blue 4.00 5.00

Nos. 8L5-8L6 Handstamp Surcharged

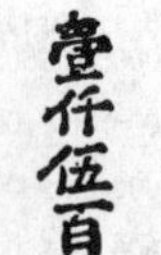

1950, Jan.
8L28 A1 $1200 on $100 car 15.00 18.00
8L29 A1 $1500 on $200 bl 60.00 18.00

Many varieties, including wide and narrow settings, exist.

Nos. 8L17-8L20 Surcharged in Black or Red

叁仟圓 改作 伍仟圓
$3000 $5000
壹萬圓 貳萬圓 伍萬圓
$10,000 $20,000 $50,000
陸拾圓 叁佰圓
$60 $300

1950 *Perf. 9 to 11½*
8L30 A2 $60 on $30 20.00 6.00
8L31 A2 $150 on $30 20.00 6.00
8L32 A2 $300 on $20 (R) 2.00 3.00
8L33 A2 $300 on $100 20.00 6.00
8L34 A2 $1500 on $100 24.00 15.00
8L35 A2 $3000 on $50 6.00 15.00
8L36 A2 $5000 on $50 5.00 15.00
8L37 A2 $10,000 on $50 50.00 30.00
8L38 A2 $20,000 on $50 3.00 30.00
8L39 A2 $50,000 on $50 5.00 40.00
Nos. 8L30-8L39 (10) 155.00 166.00

Nos. 8L5-8L7 Overprinted ("West Szechwan") 川 西

1950, Jan. *Perf. 12½*
8L40 A1 $100 carmine 20.00 7.00
8L41 A1 $200 pale blue 20.00 12.00
8L42 A1 $300 blue violet 20.00 18.00
Nos. 8L40-8L42 (3) 60.00 37.00

Nos. 8L4-8L7 Surcharged

蓉
圓百伍作改
蓉
圓仟貳作改
$2000

1950, Jan.
8L43 A1 $500 on $100 8.00 6.00
a. Narrow spacing 70.00 60.00
8L44 A1 $800 on $100 8.00 6.00
8L45 A1 $1000 on $50 10.00 7.00
8L46 A1 $2000 on $200 17.50 18.00
8L47 A1 $3000 on $300 32.50 30.00
Nos. 8L43-8L47 (5) 76.00 67.00

Two lines of surcharge 7mm apart on No. 8L43, 4mm on No. 8L43a.

China Nos. 975 and 977 Surcharged

政郵民人 政郵民人
蓉 蓉
圓百貳 圓仟壹
$200 $1000

Perf. 12½, 13 or Compound
1950, Jan.
8L48 A94 $100 on 4c 8.00 8.00
8L49 A94 $200 on 4c 15.00 15.00
8L50 A94 $800 on 16c 47.50 47.50
8L51 A94 $1000 on 16c 200.00 250.00
Nos. 8L48-8L51 (4) 270.50 320.50

Unit Issue of China Overprinted ("Southwest People's Post")

1950, Jan. Engr. *Perf. 12½*
8L52 A96 orange 150.00 175.00
a. Rouletted 150.00 175.00
8L53 SD2 red violet 150.00 175.00
8L54 R2 carmine 150.00 175.00
Nos. 8L52-8L54 (3) 450.00 525.00

On No. 8L54, space between overprint columns is 3mm and right column is raised to height of left.

Nos. 8L3, 8L17-8L20 Surcharged in Black or Red

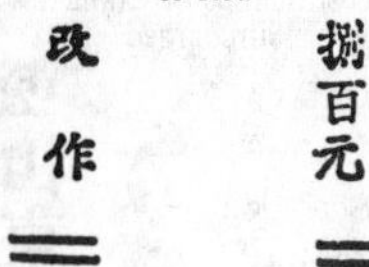

1950, Mar. *Perf. 12½, 9 to 11½*
8L55 A1 $800 on $30 42.00 35.00
8L56 A2 $1000 on $50 9.00 8.00
8L57 A2 $2000 on $100 12.00 12.00
8L58 A2 $4000 on $20 (R) 35.00 25.00
8L59 A2 $5000 on $30 55.00 37.50
Nos. 8L55-8L59 (5) 153.00 117.50

CILICIA

sə-'li-sh(ē-)ə

LOCATION — A territory of Turkey, in Southeastern Asia Minor
GOVT. — Former French occupation
AREA — 6,238 sq. mi.
POP. — 383,645
CAPITAL — Adana

British and French forces occupied Cilicia in 1918 and in 1919 its control was transferred to the French. Eventually part of Cilicia was assigned to the French Mandated Territory of Syria but by the Lausanne Treaty of 1923 which fixed the boundary between Syria and Turkey, Cilicia reverted to Turkey.

40 Paras = 1 Piaster

Issued under French Occupation

The overprint on Nos. 2-93 is often found inverted, double, etc.
Numbers in parentheses are those of basic Turkish stamps.

Turkish Stamps of 1913-19 Handstamped CILICIE

Perf. 11½, 12, 12½, 13½
1919 Unwmk.

On Pictorial Issue of 1913

2 A24 2pa red lil (254) .45 .45
3 A25 4pa dk brn (255) .45 .45
4 A27 6pa dk bl (257) 3.50 2.25
5 A32 1¾pi sl & red brn (262) .75 .50

On Issue of 1915

6 A17 1pi bl (300) .40 .40
7 A21 20pa car rose (318) .45 .45
9 A22 20pa car rose (330) .55 .55

On Commemorative Issue of 1916

10 A41 20pa ultra (347) .40 .40
11 A41 1pi vio & blk (348) .65 .65
12 A41 5pi yel brn & blk (349) .40 .40

On Issue of 1916-18

13 A44 10pa grn (424) .40 .40
14 A47 50pa ultra (428) 6.00 2.00
15 A51 25pi car, *straw* (434) .60 .60
16 A52 50pi car (437) .75 .75
17 A52 50pi ind (438) 8.00 8.00

On Issue of 1917

18 A53 5pi on 2pa Prus bl (547) 2.00 1.65

On Issue of 1919

19 A47 50pa ultra (555) 5.00 1.50
20 A48 2pi org brn & ind (556) 5.00 1.50
21 A49 5pi pale bl & blk (557) 3.75 .90

On Newspaper Stamp of 1916

22 N3 5pa on 10pa gray grn (P137) .45 .45

On Semi-Postal Stamps of 1916

23 A17 1pi bl (B19) .40 .40
24 A21 20pa car rose (B28) .30 .30
25 A21 1pi ultra (B29) .75 .75
Nos. 2-25 (23) 41.40 25.70

Turkish Stamps of 1913-18 Handstamped CILICIE

1919

On Pictorial Issue of 1913

31 A24 2pa red lil (254) .40 .40
32 A25 4pa dk brn (255) .40 .40

On Issue of 1915

33 A17 1pi bl (300) .50 .50
34 A22 20pa car rose (330) .40 .40

On Commemorative Issue of 1916

35 A41 20pa ultra (347) 1.00 1.00
36 A41 1pi vio & blk (348) .25 .25

On Issue of 1917

40 A53 5pi on 2pa Prus bl (547) 1.25 1.25

On Newspaper Stamp of 1916

41 N3 5pa on 10pa gray grn (P137) 1.00 1.00

On Semi-Postal Stamps of 1916

42 A17 1pi blue (B19) .50 .50
43 A21 20pa car rose (B28) .40 .40
Nos. 31-43 (10) 6.10 6.10

Turkish Stamps of 1913-19 Handstamped *Cilicie*

1919

On Pictorial Issue of 1913

51 A24 2pa red lil (254) .40 .40
52 A25 4pa dk brn (255) .40 .40

On Issue of 1915

53 A17 1pi blue (300) .25 .25
55 A22 5pa ocher (328) 2.50 1.40
56 A22 20pa car rose (330) .25 .25

On Commemorative Issue of 1916

57 A41 20pa ultra (347) .40 .40
58 A41 1pi vio & blk (348) .40 .40
59 A41 5pi yel brn & blk (349) .50 .50

On Issue of 1916

59A A17 1pi blue (372) 27.50 27.50

On Issue of 1916-18

60 A43 5pa org (421) 3.50 3.50
61 A46 1pi dl vio (426) 2.00 1.40
63 A52 50pi grn, *straw* (439) 15.00 5.00

On Issue of 1917

64 A53 5pi on 2pa Prus bl (547) 5.50 2.50

On Newspaper Stamp of 1916

65 N3 5pa on 10pa gray grn (P137) .40 .40

On Semi-Postal Stamps of 1916

66 A17 1pi blue (B19) 2.50 1.00
67 A19 20pa car (B26) 7.50 3.00
68 A21 20pa car rose (B28) 57.50 22.50
69 A21 20pa car rose (B31) 1.50 1.50
Nos. 51-69 (18) 128.00 72.30

Turkey No. 424 Handstamped *T.E.O. Cilicie*

1919

71 A44 10pa green .40 .40

"T.E.O." stands for "Territoires Ennemis Occupés."

Turkish Stamps of 1913-19 Overprinted in Black, Red or Blue T. E. O. Cilicie

In this setting there are various broken and wrong font letters and the letter "i" is sometimes replaced by a "t."

1919 **On Pictorial Issue of 1913**

75 A30 1pi blue (R) (260) .20 .15

On Issue of 1915

76 A21 20pa car rose (318) 2.00 2.00

On Commemorative Issue of 1916

77 A41 20pa ultra (347) .20 .20
78 A41 1pi vio & blk (348) .40 .25

On Issue of 1916-18

79 A43 5pa org (Bl) (421) .15 .15
80 A44 10pa grn (424) .20 .20
81 A45 20pa dp rose (Bk) (425) 5.00 5.00
82 A45 20pa dp rose (Bl) (425) .15 .15
83 A48 2pi org brn & ind (429) .25 .25
83C A49 5pi pale bl & blk (R) (430) .30 .25
84 A51 25pi car, *straw* (434) 5.00 3.50
85 A52 50pi grn, *straw* (439) 32.50 25.00

On Issue of 1917

85A A53 5pi on 2pa Prus bl (547)
86 A53 5pi on 2pa Prus bl (548) 1.75 1.75

On Newspaper Stamps of 1916-19

87 N3 5pa on 10p gray grn (P137) 1.00 1.00
88 N4 5pa on 2pa ol grn (F173) .15 .15

On Semi-Postal Stamps of 1915-17

90 A21 20pa car rose (B28) 1.10 1.10
91 A41 10pa car (B42) .15 .15
92 A11 10pa on 20pa vio brn (B38) .15 .15
93 SP1 10pa red vio (B46) .25 .25

It is understood that the newspaper and semi-postal stamps overprinted "Cilicie" were used as ordinary postage stamps.

A1

1920 **Blue Surcharge** *Perf. 11½*

98 A1 70pa on 5pa red .50 .50
99 A1 3½pi on 5pa red 1.10 1.10

Nos. 98-99 exist with surcharge double, inverted, double with one inverted, "OCCUPT-TION," etc. Value, $1 to $2 each.

French Offices in Turkey No. 26 Surcharged T. E. O 20 PARAS

1920 *Perf. 14x13½*

100 A3 20pa on 10c rose red .30 .30
a. "PARAS" omitted 9.00 9.00
b. Surcharged on back 1.65 1.65

Three types of "20" exist on No. 100.

Stamps of France, 1900-17, Surcharged O. M. F. Cilicie 5 PARAS

1920

101 A16 5pa on 2c vio brn .25 .25
102 A22 10pa on 5c grn .30 .30
103 A22 20pa on 10c red .40 .40
104 A22 1pi on 25c bl .50 .50
105 A20 2pi on 15c gray grn 4.00 4.00
106 A18 5pi on 40c red & gray bl 6.00 6.00
107 A18 10pi on 50c bis brn & lav 5.50 5.50
108 A18 50pi on 1fr cl & ol grn 37.50 37.50
109 A18 100pi on 5fr dk bl & buff 425.00 425.00
Nos. 101-109 (9) 479.45 479.45

Nos. 106 to 109 surcharged in four lines.

"O.M.F." stands for "Occupation Militaire Francaise."

Stamps of France, 1917, Surcharged O. M. F. Cilicie SAND. EST 20 PARAS

1920

110 A16 5pa on 2c vio brn 2.50
111 A22 10pa on 5c grn 2.50
112 A22 20pa on 10c red 1.25
113 A22 1pi on 25c blue 1.25
114 A20 2pi on 15c gray grn 6.00
115 A18 5pi on 40c red & gray bl 37.50
116 A18 20pi on 1fr cl & ol grn 52.50
Nos. 110-116 (7) 103.50

On Nos. 115 and 116 "SAND. EST" is placed vertically. "Sand. Est" is an abbreviation of Sandjak de l'Est (Eastern County).

Nos. 110-116 were prepared for use, but never issued.

Stamps of France, 1900-17, Surcharged O. M. F. Cilicie 10 PARAS

1920

117 A16 5pa on 2c vio brn .15 .15
a. Inverted surcharge 5.00 4.75
b. Double surcharge 6.00
c. "Cillie" 4.75 4.75
d. Surcharge 5pi (error) 10.00 10.00
119 A22 10pa on 5c grn .15 .15
a. Inverted surcharge 5.00 4.50
b. Surch. 5pa (error), invtd. 10.00 10.00
121 A22 20pa on 10c red .15 .15
a. Inverted surcharge 5.00 4.50
b. Surch. 10pa (error), invtd. 11.00 11.00
122 A22 1pi on 25c bl .15 .15
a. Double surcharge 8.00
b. Inverted surcharge 5.00 4.50
123 A20 2pi on 15c gray grn .25 .25
a. Double surcharge 8.00
b. Inverted surcharge 5.00 4.50
124 A18 5pi on 40c red & gray bl .55 .55
a. Double surcharge 12.00
b. Inverted surcharge 7.00 6.50
c. "PIASRTES" 10.00 10.00
125 A18 10pi on 50c bis brn & lavender 1.00 1.00
a. "PIASRTES" 10.00 10.00
126 A18 50pi on 1fr claret & ol grn 3.00 3.00
a. "PIASRTES" 12.50 12.50
b. Inverted surcharge 14.00 12.00
127 A18 100pi on 5fr dk bl & buff 7.50 7.50
a. "PIASRTES" 25.00 25.00
Nos. 117-127 (9) 12.90 12.90

This surcharge has "O.M.F." in thicker letters than the preceding issues.

There were two printings of this surcharge which may be distinguished by the space of 1 or 2mm between "Cilicie" and the numeral.

For overprints see Nos. C1-C2.

AIR POST STAMPS

Nos. 123 and 124 Handstamped POSTE PAR AVION

Perf. 14x13½

1920, July 15 **Unwmk.**

C1 A20 2pi on 15c gray grn
C2 A18 5pi on 40c red & gray bl
a. "PIASRTES"

A very limited number of Nos. C1 and C2 were used on two air mail flights between Adana and Aleppo. At a later date impressions from a new handstamp were struck "to oblige" on stamps of the regular issue of 1920 (Nos. 123, 124, 125 and 126) that were in stock at the Adana Post Office.

Counterfeits exist.

POSTAGE DUE STAMPS

Turkish Postage Due Stamps of 1914 Handstamped

Handstamped CILICIE

1919 **Unwmk.** *Perf. 12*

J1 D1 5pa claret 1.75 1.75
J2 D2 20pa red 1.75 1.75
J3 D3 1pi dark blue 3.25 3.25
J4 D4 2pi slate 3.25 3.25
Nos. J1-J4 (4) 10.00 10.00

Handstamped CILICIE

J5 D1 5pa claret 1.50 1.50
J6 D2 20pa red 1.50 1.50
J7 D3 1pi dark blue 4.00 4.00
J8 D4 2pi slate 3.25 3.25
Nos. J5-J8 (4) 10.25 10.25

Handstamped *Cilicie*

J9 D1 5pa claret 1.65 1.65
J10 D2 20pa red 1.65 1.65
J11 D3 1pi dark blue 3.25 3.25
J12 D4 2pi slate 4.00 4.00
Nos. J9-J12 (4) 10.55 10.55

Postage Due Stamps of France Surcharged O. M. F. Cilicie 2 PIASTRES

1921

J13 D2 1pi on 10c choc 3.25 3.25
J14 D2 2pi on 20c olive grn 3.50 3.50
J15 D2 3pi on 30c red 4.00 4.00
J16 D2 4pi on 50c vio brn 3.25 3.25
Nos. J13-J16 (4) 14.00 14.00

COCHIN CHINA

'kō–chən 'chī–nə

LOCATION — The southernmost state of French Indo-China in the Cambodian Peninsula.
GOVT. — French Colony
AREA — 26,476 sq. mi.
POP. — 4,615,968
CAPITAL — Saigon

100 Centimes = 1 Franc

Values for unused stamps are for examples without gum, as most stamps were issued in that condition.

Surcharged in Black on Stamps of French Colonies:

5 (a) 5 C. CH. (b) 5 (c)

1886-87 **Unwmk.** *Perf. 14x13½*

1 A9(a) 5c on 25c yel, *straw* 125.00 90.00
2 A9(b) 5c on 2c brn, *buff* 9.00 9.00
3 A9(b) 5c on 25c yel, *straw* 10.00 10.00
4 A9(c) 5c on 25c blk, *rose* ('87) 30.00 25.00
a. Double surch., one of type b 2,750. 1,250.
b. Triple surch., two of type b
c. Inverted surcharge
Nos. 1-4 (4) 174.00 134.00

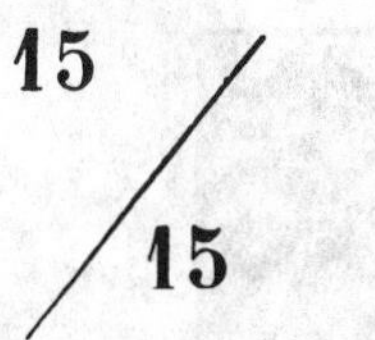

1888

5 A9 15c on half of 30c brn, *bis* 32.50

No. 5 was prepared but not issued.

The so-called Postage Due stamps were never issued.

Stamps of Cochin China were superseded by those of Indo-China in 1892.

Cilicia stamps can be mounted n the Scott annual Turkey supplement.

COLOMBIA

kə-'ləm-bē-ə

LOCATION — On the northwest coast of South America, bordering on the Caribbean Sea and the Pacific Ocean
GOVT. — Republic
AREA — 456,535 sq. mi.
POP. — 28,240,000 (est. 1984)
CAPITAL — Bogota

In 1810 the Spanish Viceroyalty of New Granada gained its independence and with Venezuela and Ecuador formed the State of Greater Colombia. In 1832 this state split into three independent units as Venezuela, Ecuador and the Republic of New Granada. The name of the country has been, successively, Granadine Confederation (1858-61), United States of New Granada (1861), United States of Colombia (1861-65), and the Republic of Colombia (1885 to date).

100 Centavos = 1 Peso

Catalogue values for unused stamps in this country are for Never Hinged items, beginning with Scott 594 in the regular postage section, Scott B1 in the semi-postal section, Scott C200 in the airpost section, Scott CE1 in the airpost special delivery section, Scott E2 in the special delivery section, and Scott RA33 in the postal tax section.

In the earlier days many towns did not have handstamps for canceling and stamps were canceled with pen and ink. Pen cancellations, therefore, do not indicate fiscal use. (Postage stamps were not used for revenue purposes.) Used values for Nos. 1-128 are for stamps with illegible manuscript cancels or handstamp cancels of Bogota or Medellin. Stamps with legible manuscript or other handstamped town-name cancels sell for more.

Fractions of many Colombian stamps of both early and late issues are found canceled, their use to pay postage having been tolerated even though forbidden by the postal laws and regulations. Many are known to have been made for philatelic purposes.

Watermarks

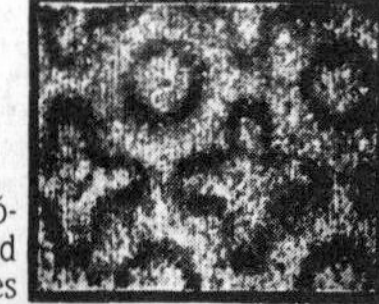
Wmk. 116- Crosses and Circles

Wmk. 127- Quatrefoils

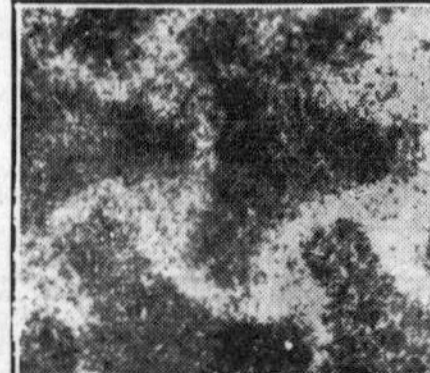
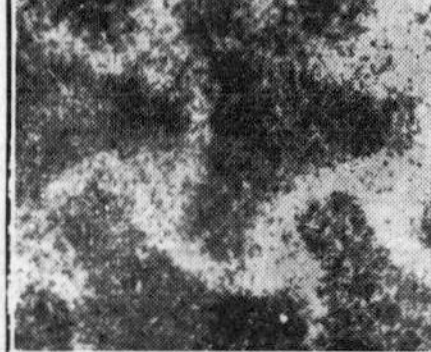
Wmk. 194- Multiple Curvilinear Triangles

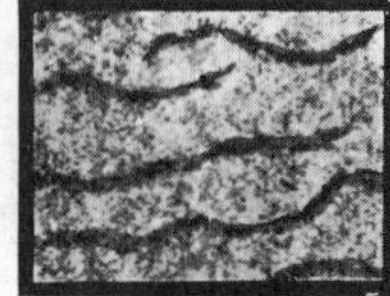
Wmk. 229- Wavy Lines

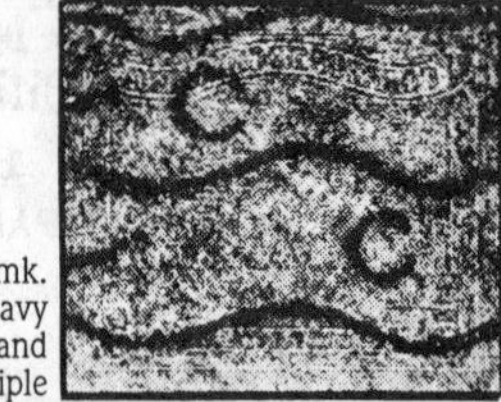
Wmk. 255- Wavy Lines and C Multiple

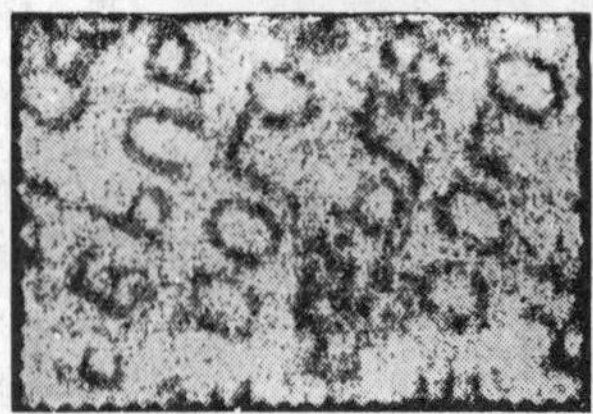
Wmk. 331- REPUBLICA DE COLOMBIA

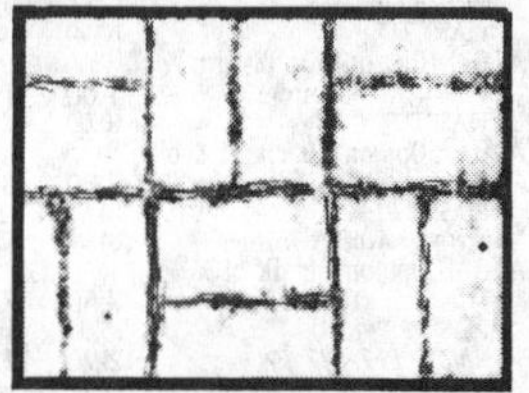
Wmk. 334- Rectangles

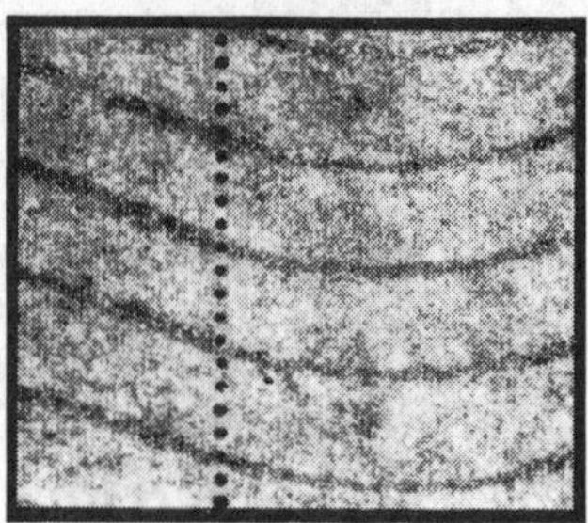
Wmk. 346- Parallel Curved Lines

Stamps inscribed "Colombia" that show the Panama Canal area were used in Panama and can be found in Vol. 4.

Granadine Confederation

Coat of Arms
A1 A2

Type A1 - Asterisks in frame. Wavy lines in background.

Type A2 - Diamond-shaped ornaments in frame. Straight lines in background. Numerals larger.

1859 Unwmk. Litho. *Imperf.*

Wove Paper

1	A1	2½c green	87.50	87.50
a.		2½c yellow green	87.50	87.50
2	A1	5c blue	110.00	70.00
a.		Tête bêche pair	*3,500.*	*5,750.*
3	A1	5c violet	225.00	90.00
b.		"50" instead of "5"		—
4	A1	10c red brown	100.00	62.50
a.		10c buff	100.00	62.50
6	A1	20c blue	90.00	55.00
a.		20c gray blue	90.00	55.00
b.		Se-tenant with 5c		
c.		Tête bêche pair	*25,000.*	*25,000.*
7	A1	1p carmine	55.00	95.00
a.		1p rose	55.00	95.00
8	A1	1p rose, *bluish*	325.00	

The 10c green is an essay.

Reprints of No. 7 are in brown rose or brown red. Wavy lines of background are much broken; no dividing lines between stamps.

1860

Laid Paper

9	A2	5c lilac	250.00	175.00

Wove Paper

10	A2	5c gray lilac	62.50	50.00
a.		5c lilac	62.50	50.00
11	A2	10c yellow buff	62.50	45.00
a.		Tête bêche pair	*7,000.*	
12	A2	20c blue	165.00	110.00

United States of New Granada

Arms of New Granada — A3

1861

13	A3	2½c black	1,100.	275.00
14	A3	5c yellow	325.00	140.00
a.		5c buff	325.00	140.00
16	A3	10c blue	950.00	140.00
17	A3	20c red	400.00	190.00
18	A3	1p pink	950.00	300.00

There are 54 varieties of the 5c, 20c, and 1 peso.

Forgeries exist of Nos. 13-18.

United States of Colombia

Coat of Arms
A4 A5 A6

1862

19	A4	10c blue	190.	95.
20	A4	20c red	*3,500.*	550.
21	A4	50c green	190.	125.
22	A4	1p red lilac	450.	125.
23	A4	1p red lil, *bluish*	*4,000.*	*1,450.*

No. 23 is on a thinner, coarser wove paper than Nos. 19-22.

1863

24	A5	5c orange	75.00	50.00
a.		Star after "Cent"	87.50	57.50
25	A5	10c blue	165.00	19.00
a.		Period after "10"	175.00	22.50
26	A5	20c red	175.00	60.00
a.		Star after "Cent"	190.00	67.50
b.		Transfer of 50c in stone of 20c	*14,000.*	*4,500.*

Bluish Paper

28	A5	10c blue	125.00	27.50
a.		Period after "10"	140.00	29.00
29	A5	50c green	165.00	60.00
a.		Star after "Cent"	165.00	67.50

Ten varieties of each.

1864

Wove Paper

30	A6	5c orange	57.50	30.00
a.		Tête bêche pair	350.00	325.00
31	A6	10c blue	42.50	12.00
a.		Period after 10	42.50	12.00
32	A6	20c scarlet	75.00	45.00
33	A6	50c green	62.50	45.00
34	A6	1p red violet	275.00	140.00

Two varieties of each.

Arms of Colombia
A7 A9

A8

1865

35	A7	1c rose	8.00	8.00
a.		bluish pelure paper	22.50	17.50
36	A8	2½c black, *lilac*	15.00	10.00
37	A9	5c yellow	35.00	16.00
a.		5c orange	35.00	16.00
38	A9	10c violet	50.00	3.50
39	A9	20c blue	50.00	16.00
40	A9	50c green	87.50	42.50
41	A9	50c grn (small figures)	87.50	42.50
42	A9	1p vermilion	95.00	14.00
a.		1p rose red	95.00	14.00
b.		Period after "PESO"	110.00	16.00

Ten varieties of each of the 5c, 10c, 20c, and 50c, and six varieties of the 1 peso. No. 36 was used as a carrier stamp.

A10 A11 A12

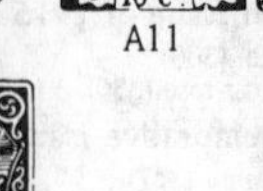

A13 A14

A15 A16

1866

White Wove Paper

45	A10	5c orange	55.00	22.50
46	A11	10c lilac	12.50	4.00
a.		Pelure paper	17.50	10.00
47	A12	20c light blue	32.50	17.50
a.		Pelure paper	50.00	42.50
48	A13	50c green	13.00	10.00
49	A14	1p rose red, *bluish*	72.50	25.00
a.		1p vermilion	72.50	25.00
51	A15	5p blk, *green*	375.00	175.00
52	A16	10p blk, *vermilion*	275.00	160.00

There are several varieties of the 1 peso having the letters "U," "N," "S" and "O" smaller.

A17 A18

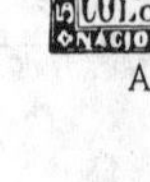
A19 A20

A21

TEN CENTAVOS:

Type I - "B" of "COLOMBIA" over "V" of "CENTAVOS".

Type II - "B" of "COLOMBIA" over "VO" of "CENTAVOS."

ONE PESO:

Type I - Long thin spear heads. Diagonal lines in lower part of shield.

Type II - Short thick spear heads. Horizontal and a few diagonal lines in lower part of shield.

Type III - Short thick spear heads. Crossed lines in lower part of shield. Ornaments at each side of circle are broken. (See No. 97.)

1868

53	A17	5c orange	55.00	42.50
54	A18	10c lilac (I)	3.25	.90
a.		10c red violet (I)	3.25	.90
b.		10c lilac (II)	3.25	.90
c.		10c red violet (II)	3.25	.90
d.		Printed on both sides	6.25	2.00
55	A19	20c blue	2.25	1.00
56	A20	50c yellow green	2.50	1.60

57 A21 1p ver (II)	3.25	1.75
a. Tête bêche pair	100.00	85.00
b. 1p rose red (I)	45.00	22.50
c. 1p rose red (II)	3.00	1.75
Nos. 53-57 (5)	66.25	47.75

See Nos. 83-84, 96-97.

Counterfeits or reprints.

10c - There is a large white dot at the upper left between the circle enclosing the "X" and the ornament below.

50c - There is a shading of dots instead of dashes below the ribbon with motto. There are crossed lines in the lowest section of the shield instead of diagonal or horizontal ones.

1p - The ornaments in the lettered circle are broken. There are crossed lines in the lowest section of the shield. These counterfeits, or reprints, are on white paper, wove and laid, on colored wove paper and in fancy colors.

A22

Two varieties

1869-70

Wove Paper

59 A22 2½c black, *violet*	3.50	2.00
a. Laid paper ('70)	250.00	210.00
b. Laid batonné paper ('70)	22.50	19.00

Nos. 59, 59a and 59b were used as carrier stamps.

Counterfeits, or reprints, are on magenta paper wove or ribbed.

A23

A24

1870

Wove Paper

62 A23 5c orange	1.65	1.10
a. 5c yellow	1.65	1.10
63 A24 25c black, *blue*	12.50	11.00

See No. 89.

In the counterfeits, or reprints, of No. 63, the top of the "2" of "25" does not touch the down stroke. The counterfeits are on paper of various colors.

A25

A26

5 pesos - The ornament at the left of the "C" of "Cinco" cuts into the "C," and the shading of the flag is formed of diagonal lines.

10 pesos - The stars have extra rays between the points, and the central part of the shield has some horizontal lines of shading at each end.

1870

Surface Colored, Chalky Paper

64 A25 5p blk, *green*	75.00	52.50
65 A26 10p blk, *vermilion*	87.50	52.50

See Nos. 77-79, 125-126.

A27

A28

A29

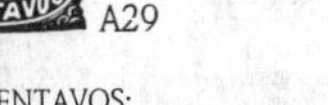

TEN CENTAVOS:

Type I - "S" of "CORREOS" 2½mm high. First "N" of "NACIONALES" small.

Type II - "S" of "CORREOS" 2mm high. First "N" of "NACIONALES" wide.

1871-74

Thin Porous Paper

66 A27 1c green ('72)	2.75	2.75
67 A27 1c rose ('73)	2.75	2.75
a. 1c carmine ('73)	2.75	2.75
68 A28 2c brown	1.25	1.25
a. 2c red brown	1.25	1.25
69 A29 10c vio (I) ('74)	1.90	1.65
a. 10c lilac (I) ('74)	1.90	1.65
b. 10c violet (II) ('74)	1.90	1.65
c. 10c lilac (II) ('74)	1.90	1.65
d. Laid paper, as #69 ('72)	110.00	110.00
e. Laid paper, as "b" ('72)	110.00	110.00
Nos. 66-69 (4)	8.65	8.40

Counterfeits or reprints.

1c - The outer frame of the shield is broken near the upper left corner and the "A" of "Colombia" has no cross-bar.

2c - There are scratches across "DOS" and many white marks around the letters on the large "2." The counterfeits, or reprints, are on white wove and bluish white laid paper.

Condor — A30

Liberty Head

A31 A32

5 pesos, redrawn - The ornament at the left of the "C" only touches the "C," and the shading of the flag is formed of vertical and diagonal lines.

10 pesos, redrawn - The stars are distinctly five pointed, and there is no shading in the central part of the shield.

1877

Wove Paper

73 A30 5c purple	5.25	1.75
a. 5c lilac	5.25	1.75
74 A31 10c bister brown	2.50	.70
a. 10c red brown	2.50	.70
b. 10c violet brown	2.50	.70
75 A32 20c blue	3.25	1.10
a. 20c violet blue	6.50	2.75
77 A26 10p blk, *rose*	87.50	55.00
78 A25 5p blk, *lt grn*, redrawn	32.50	27.50
79 A26 10p blk, *rose*, redrawn	12.50	2.25
a. 10p blk, *dark rose*, redrawn	12.50	2.25
Nos. 73-79 (6)	143.50	88.30

Stamps of the issues of 1871-77 are known with private perforations of various gauges, also with sewing machine perforation.

In the counterfeits, or reprints, of the 5 pesos the ornament at the left of the "C" of "Cinco" is separated from the "C" by a black line.

In the counterfeits, or reprints, of the 10 pesos the outer line of the double circle containing "10" is broken at the top, below "OS" of "Unidos," and the vertical lines of shading contained in the double circle are very indistinct. There is a colorless dash below the loop of the "P" of "Pesos."

1876-79

Laid Paper

80 A30 5c lilac	62.50	50.00
81 A31 10c brown	35.00	2.25
82 A32 20c blue	75.00	55.00
83 A20 50c green ('79)	77.50	52.50
84 A21 1p pale red (II) ('79)	50.00	12.50
Nos. 80-84 (5)	300.00	172.25

1879

Wove Paper

89 A24 25c green	25.00	25.00

1881

Blue Wove Paper

93 A30 5c violet	15.00	10.00
a. 5c lilac	15.00	10.00
94 A31 10c brown	8.75	2.00
95 A32 20c blue	8.75	3.00
96 A20 50c yellow green	9.50	6.00
97 A21 1p ver (III)	13.00	6.00
Nos. 93-97 (5)	55.00	27.00

For types of 1p, see note over No. 53.

Reprints of the 10c and 20c are much worn. On the 10c the letters "TAVOS" of "CENTAVOS" often touch. On the 20c the letters "NT" of "VEINTE" touch and the left arm of the "T" is too long. Reprints of the 25c, 50c and 1p have the characteristics previously described. The reprints are on white wove or laid paper, on colored papers, and in fancy colors. Stamps on green paper exist only as reprints.

A34

A35

A36

1 centavo - The period before "UNION" is round and there are rays between the stars and the condors.

2 centavos - The "2's" and "C's" in the corners are placed upright.

5 centavos - The last star at the right almost touches the frame.

10 centavos - The letters of the inscription are thin; there are rays between the stars and the condor.

1881 ***Imperf.***

White Wove Paper

103 A34 1c green	3.75	3.25
104 A35 2c vermilion	1.65	1.25
a. 2c rose	1.90	1.25
106 A34 5c blue	4.50	1.40
a. Printed on both sides		
107 A36 10c violet	3.25	1.00
108 A34 20c black	3.50	1.60
Nos. 103-108 (5)	16.65	8.50

The stamps of this issue are found with perforations of various gauges, also sewing machine perforation, all of which are unofficial.

See Nos. 112, 114-115.

Liberty Head — A37

A37a

1881 ***Imperf.***

109 A37 1c blk, *green*	2.50	3.75
110 A37 2c blk, *lilac rose*	2.50	3.75
111 A37 5c blk, *lilac*	6.25	1.40
Nos. 109-111 (3)	11.25	8.90

Nos. 109 to 111 are found with regular or sewing machine perforation, unofficial.

Reprints:

1c - The top line of the stamp and the top frame extend to the left. 2c - There is a curved line over the scroll below the "AV" of "CENTAVOS."

5c - There are scratches across the "5" in the upper left corner. All three values were reprinted on the three colors of paper of the originals.

Redrawn

1 centavo - The period before "UNION" is square and the rays between the stars and the condor have been wholly or partly erased.

2 centavos - The "2's" and "C's" in the corners are placed diagonally.

5 centavos - The last star at the right touches the wing of the condor.

10 centavos - The letters of the inscription are thick; there are no rays under the stars; the last star at the right touches the wing of the condor and this wing touches the frame.

1883 ***Imperf.***

112 A34 1c green	4.75	4.25
113 A37a 2c rose	1.65	1.40
114 A34 5c blue	3.75	1.00
a. 5c ultramarine	3.75	1.00
b. Printed on both sides, reverse ultra	25.00	20.00
115 A36 10c violet	5.00	1.40
Nos. 112-115 (4)	15.15	8.05

The stamps of this issue are found with regular or sewing machine perforation, privately applied.

A38

A39

1883 ***Perf. 10½, 12, 13½***

116 A38 1c gray grn, *grn*	.75	.75
a. Imperf., pair	3.75	3.75
117 A39 2c red, *rose*	.75	1.00
a. 2c org red, *rose*	.75	1.00
b. 2c red, *buff*	5.50	5.50
c. Imperf., pair (#117 or 117a)	3.75	3.75
d. "DE LOS" in very small caps	11.00	11.00
118 A38 5c blue, *bluish*	1.90	1.25
a. 5c dk bl, *bluish*	1.90	.90
b. 5c blue	2.75	1.90
c. Imperf., pair (#118 or 118a)	6.50	6.50
d. As "b," imperf., pair	9.50	9.50
119 A39 10c org, *yel*	.95	1.10
a. "DE LOS" in large caps	45.00	20.00
b. Imperf., pair	5.75	5.75
120 A39 20c vio, *lilac*	1.10	1.10
a. Imperf., pair	3.75	3.75
122 A38 50c brn, *buff*	2.25	2.50
a. Perf. 12	2.25	2.50
123 A38 1p claret, *bluish*	4.00	1.50
a. Imperf., pair	12.50	12.50
Nos. 116-123 (7)	11.70	9.20

Redrawn Types of 1877

1883 (?) ***Perf. 10½, 12***

125 A25 5p orange brown	8.00	4.50
126 A26 10p black, *gray*	8.00	4.50

1886 ***Perf. 10½, 11½, 12***

127 A38 5p brown, *straw*	5.75	5.75
a. Imperf., pair	25.00	25.00
128 A38 10p black, *rose*	7.00	7.00
a. Imperf., pair	25.00	25.00

Republic of Colombia

A40

Simón Bolívar — A41

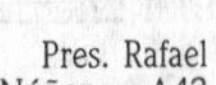

Pres. Rafael Núñez — A42

1886 *Perf. 10½ and 13½*

No.	Description		
129 A40	1c grn, *grn*	1.25	.60
a.	Imperf., pair	5.00	5.00
130 A41	5c blue, *bl*	1.25	.35
a.	5c ultra, *blue*	1.25	.35
b.	Imperf., pair (#130)	5.00	5.00
131 A42	10c orange	2.75	.60
a.	Imperf., pair	7.00	7.00
b.	Pelure paper	3.50	.85
	Nos. 129-131 (3)	5.25	1.55

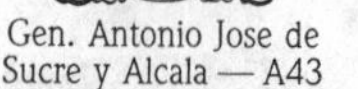
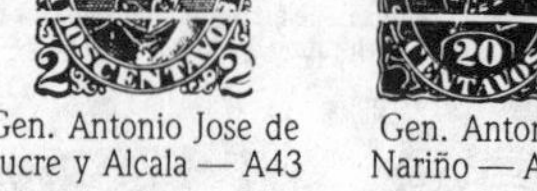

Gen. Antonio Jose de Sucre y Alcala — A43

Gen. Antonio Nariño — A44

1887

No.	Description		
133 A43	2c org red, *rose*	1.75	.85
a.	2c orange red, *yellowish*	4.50	4.50
b.	2c orange red	5.25	5.25
c.	Imperf., pair (#133)	7.75	7.75
134 A44	20c pur, *grysh*	2.25	.85
a.	Imperf., pair	6.25	6.25
b.	Pelure paper	2.75	1.75

Impressions of No. 134 on white, blue or greenish blue paper were not regularly issued.

Arms — A45

Nariño — A46

1888

No.	Description		
135 A45	50c brn, *buff*	1.25	1.40
a.	Imperf., pair	4.50	4.50
136 A45	1p claret, *bluish*	6.00	1.75
137 A45	1p claret	2.50	1.25
138 A45	5p org brn	6.25	4.25
139 A45	5p black	11.00	7.00
140 A45	10p black, *rose*	13.00	5.25
	Nos. 135-140 (6)	40.00	20.90

See Nos. 154, 156-157.

1889

No.	Description		
141 A46	20c pur, *grayish*	1.40	1.00
a.	Imperf., pair	6.75	6.75

Impressions on white, blue or greenish blue paper were not regularly issued.

A47

A48

A49

A50

A51

1890-91 *Perf. 10½, 13½, 11*

No.	Description		
142 A47	1c grn, *grn*	1.40	1.25
143 A48	2c org red, *rose*	.60	.70
144 A49	5c bl, *grnsh bl*	1.00	.35
a.	5c deep blue, *blue*	1.00	.35
b.	Imperf., pair	4.00	4.00
146 A50	10c brn, *yel*	.60	.35
a.	10c brown, *buff*	.60	.35
147 A51	20c vio, pelure paper	2.75	3.50
	Nos. 142-147 (5)	6.35	6.15

A52

A52a

A53

A53a

A54

Perf. 10½, 12, 13½, 14 to 15½

1892-99

Ordinary Paper

No.	Description		
148 A47	1c red, *yel*	.65	.35
149 A52	2c red, *rose*	32.50	32.50
150 A52	2c green	.40	.25
a.	2c yellow green	.40	.25
151 A49	5c blk, *buff*	5.50	.30
152 A52a	5c org brn, *pale buff*	.85	.25
a.	5c red brown, *salmon* ('97)	.85	.25
153 A50	10c bis brn, *rose*	.60	.35
a.	10c brown, *brownish*	.60	.35
154 A53	20c brn, *bl*	.60	.35
a.	20c red brown, *blue*	.60	.35
b.	20c yel brn, *grnsh bl* ('97)	4.00	10.00
c.	20c brown, *buff* ('97)	14.00	10.00
155 A45	50c vio, *vio*	.95	.60
156 A53a	50c red vio, *vio* ('99)	1.25	
157 A54	1p bl, *grnsh*	1.60	.70
a.	1p blue, *buff*	1.60	.70
158 A45	5p red, *pale rose*	6.25	2.50
159 A45	10p blue	12.00	2.75
a.	Thin, pale rose paper	22.50	6.00
	Nos. 148-159 (12)	63.15	40.90

Type A53a is a redrawing of type A45. The letters of the inscriptions are slightly larger and the numerals "50" slightly smaller than in type A45.

The 20c brown on white paper is believed to be a chemical changeling.

Nos. 148, 150-152a, 153-155, 157, 159 exist imperf. Value per pair, $5-$7.50.

A56

1899

No.	Description		
162 A56	1c red, *yellow*	.50	.30
163 A56	5c red brn, *sal*	.50	.30
164 A56	10c brn, *lil rose*	1.50	.75
165 A56	50c blue, *lilac*	1.00	.95
	Nos. 162-165 (4)	3.50	2.30

Cartagena Issues

A57

1899 **Blue Overprint** *Imperf.*

No.	Description		
167 A57	5c red, *buff*	24.00	24.00
a.	Sewing machine perf.	24.00	24.00
168 A57	10c ultra, *buff*	24.00	24.00
a.	Sewing machine perf.	24.00	24.00

Nos. 168 and 168a differ slightly from the illustration.

Bolivar No. 55 Overprinted with 7 Parallel Wavy Lines and:

A58

A59

A60

A61

Perf. 14 (#169), Sewing Machine Perf.

1899 **Purple Overprint**

No.	Description		
169 A18	1c black	50.00	50.00
170 A58	1c brn, *buff*	17.00	17.00
a.	Altered from 10c	25.00	25.00
171 A59	2c blk, *buff*	17.00	17.00
a.	Altered from 10c	25.00	25.00
172 A60	5c mar, *grnsh bl*	14.00	14.00
a.	Perf. 12	14.00	14.00
b.	Without overprint	8.75	8.75
173 A61	10c red, *sal*	14.00	14.00
a.	Perf. 12	14.00	14.00
	Nos. 169-173 (5)	112.00	112.00

Types A58 and A59 illustrate Nos. 170a and 171a, which were made from altered plates of the 10c (No. 168). Nos. 170 and 171 were made from altered plate of the 5c denomination (No. 167), show part of the top flag of the "5" and differ slightly from the illustrations.

Nos. 170-173 exist imperf. Values about same as perf.

A62

1900 *Imperf.*

Purple Overprint

No.	Description		
174 A62	5c red	20.00	20.00
a.	Perf. 12	27.50	27.00

A63

A64

"Gobierno Provisorio" at Top

1900 **Litho.** *Perf. 12 Vertically*

No.	Description		
175 A63	1c (ctvo) blk, *bl grn*	35.00	6.00
a.	"cvo."	90.00	12.00
b.	"cvos."	35.00	6.00
c.	"centavo"	42.50	6.00
176 A63	2c black	25.00	3.50
177 A63	5c blk, *pink*	25.00	3.50
a.	Name at side (V)	50.00	6.50
178 A63	10c blk, *pink*	25.00	4.00
a.	Name at side (V)	50.00	7.50
179 A63	20c blk, *yellow*	35.00	6.00
a.	Name at side (G)	70.00	10.00
	Nos. 175-179 (5)	145.00	23.00

"Gobierno Provisional" at Top

Name at Side in Black or Green

No.	Description		
180 A64	1c (ctvo.) blk, *bl grn*	35.00	5.00
a.	"centavo"	100.00	15.00
181 A64	2c blk, *bl grn*	20.00	4.00
182 A64	5c blk (G)	20.00	4.00
a.	"ctvos." smaller	40.00	6.00
183 A64	10c blk, *pink*	20.00	4.00
184 A64	20c blk, *yel* (G)	35.00	6.00
	Nos. 180-184 (5)	130.00	23.00

Issues of the rebel provisional government in Cucuta.

A65

A66

1901 *Sewing Machine Perf.*

Purple Overprint

No.	Description		
185 A65	1c black	.85	.85
a.	Without overprint	1.90	1.90
b.	Double overprint	2.00	2.00
c.	Imperf., pair	2.00	2.00
d.	Inverted overprint	1.00	1.00
186 A66	2c blk, *rose*	.85	.85
a.	Imperf., pair	2.00	2.00
b.	Without overprint	1.90	1.90
c.	Double overprint	2.00	2.00

A67

A68

1901

Rose Overprint

No.	Description		
187 A67	1c blue	.85	.85
a.	Imperf., pair	3.00	3.00
188 A68	2c brown	.85	.85
a.	Imperf., pair	3.00	3.00
b.	Without overprint	.85	.85

A69

A70

Sewing Machine or Regular Perf. 12, 12½

1902

Magenta Overprint

No.	Description		
189 A69	5c violet	1.75	1.75
a.	Without overprint	1.75	1.75
b.	Double overprint	1.75	1.75
c.	Imperf., pair	3.75	3.75
190 A70	10c yel brn	1.75	1.75
a.	Double overprint	1.75	1.75
b.	Imperf., pair	3.75	3.75
c.	Without overprint	1.75	1.75
d.	Printed on both sides	2.50	2.50

A71

A72

1902

Magenta Overprint

No.	Description		
191 A71	5c yel brn	1.75	1.75
a.	Without overprint	1.65	1.65
b.	Imperf., pair	5.00	5.00
192 A71	10c black	1.25	1.25
a.	Without overprint	1.00	1.00
b.	Imperf., pair	7.50	7.50
193 A72	20c maroon	4.00	2.50
b.	Imperf., pair	12.50	12.50
	Nos. 191-193 (3)	7.00	5.50

Nos. 191-193 exist tête bêche. Value of 10c and 20c, each $12.50.

Washed copies of Nos. 167-174, 185-193 are offered as "without overprint."

Barranquilla Issues

Magdalena River — A75

Iron Quay at Sabanilla — A76

La Popa Hill — A77

1902-03 *Imperf.*

No.	Description		
194 A75	2c green	1.25	1.25
195 A75	2c dk bl	1.25	1.25
196 A75	2c rose	17.50	17.50
197 A76	10c scarlet	.85	.70
198 A76	10c orange	10.00	10.00
199 A76	10c rose	.85	.70
200 A76	10c maroon	1.40	1.40
201 A76	10c claret	1.40	1.40
202 A77	20c violet	2.75	2.75
a.	Laid paper		
203 A77	20c dl bl	7.50	7.50
204 A77	20c dl bl, *pink*	*110.00*	*110.00*
205 A77	20c car rose	16.00	16.00
	Nos. 194-205 (12)	*170.75*	*170.45*

Sewing Machine Perf. and Perf. 12

No.	Description		
194a A75	2c green	7.50	7.50
195a A75	2c dark blue	7.50	7.50
196a A75	2c carmine	*35.00*	*35.00*
197a A76	10c scarlet	3.50	3.50
198a A76	10c orange	*27.50*	*27.50*
199a A76	10c rose	5.50	5.50
200a A76	10c maroon	5.50	5.50
201a A76	10c claret	5.50	5.50

202b	A77	20c	purple	.55	.55
c.		20c	lilac	.55	.55
203a	A77	20c	dull blue	7.50	7.50
204a	A77	20c	dull blue, *rose*	*140.00*	*140.00*
205b	A77	20c	carmine rose	*55.00*	*55.00*
	Nos. 194a-205b (12)			*300.55*	*300.55*

See Nos. 240-245.

Cruiser "Cartagena" — A78

Bolívar — A79

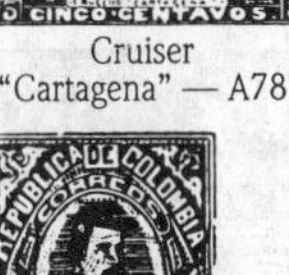

General Próspero Pinzón — A80

A81

A82

1903-04 *Imperf.*

209	A78	5c	blue	2.00	2.00
210	A78	5c	bister	2.75	2.75
211	A79	50c	yellow	3.00	3.00
212	A79	50c	green	3.50	3.50
213	A79	50c	scarlet	3.50	3.50
214	A79	50c	carmine	3.50	3.50
a.		50c	rose	3.50	3.50
215	A79	50c	pale brown	3.50	3.50
216	A80	1p	yellow brn	1.40	1.40
217	A80	1p	rose	2.00	2.00
218	A80	1p	blue	2.00	2.00
219	A80	1p	violet	20.00	20.00
220	A81	5p	claret	4.25	4.25
221	A81	5p	pale brown	6.50	6.50
222	A81	5p	blue green	6.00	6.00
223	A82	10p	pale green	6.25	6.25
224	A82	10p	claret	20.00	20.00
	Nos. 209-224 (16)			90.15	90.15

Nos. 216 and 217 measure 20½x26½mm and No. 218, 18x24mm. Stamps of this issue exist with forged perforations.

Perf. 12

209a	A78	5c	blue	7.00	7.00
210a	A78	5c	bister	7.50	7.50
211a	A79	50c	yellow	12.50	12.50
b.		50c	orange	12.50	12.50
212a	A79	50c	green	20.00	20.00
213a	A79	50c	scarlet	9.00	9.00
214b	A79	50c	rose	9.00	9.00
215a	A79	50c	pale brown	9.00	9.00
216a	A80	1p	yellow brown	4.00	4.00
217a	A80	1p	rose	6.00	6.00
218a	A80	1p	blue	6.00	6.00
219a	A80	1p	violet	50.00	50.00
220a	A81	5p	claret	16.00	16.00
221a	A81	5p	pale brown	18.00	18.00
222a	A81	5p	blue green	15.00	15.00
223a	A82	10p	pale green	25.00	25.00
224a	A82	10p	claret	60.00	60.00
	Nos. 209a-224a (16)			274.00	274.00

Laid Paper *Imperf.*

240	A76	10c	dk bl, *lil*	5.00	5.00
241	A76	10c	dk bl, *bluish*	3.00	3.00
242	A76	10c	dk bl, *brn*	3.00	3.00
243	A76	10c	dk bl, *sal*	7.00	7.00
244	A76	10c	dk bl, *grnsh bl*	4.00	4.00
245	A76	10c	dk bl, *dp rose*	3.00	3.00
	Nos. 240-245 (6)			25.00	25.00

Perf. 12

240a	A76	10c	dk bl, *lilac*	10.50	10.50
241a	A76	10c	dk bl, *bluish*	7.50	7.50
242a	A76	10c	dk bl, *brn*	7.50	7.50
243a	A76	10c	dk bl, *salmon*	55.00	55.00
244a	A76	10c	dk bl, *grnsh bl*	16.00	16.00
245a	A76	10c	dk bl, *deep rose*	7.50	7.50
	Nos. 240a-245a (6)			104.00	104.00

A82a

Imperf., Sewing Machine Perf.

1902 **Typeset**

255	A82a	10c	black, *rose*	3.50	3.50
256	A82a	20c	blk, *orange*	2.50	2.50

This issue was printed in either Cali or Popayan.

Medellin Issue

A83

1902

257	A83	1c	grn, *straw*	.22	.42
258	A83	2c	salmon, *rose*	.22	.42
259	A83	5c	dp bl, *grnsh*	.22	.42
260	A83	10c	pale brn, *straw*	.22	.42
261	A83	20c	pur, *rose*	.35	.42
262	A83	50c	dl rose, *grnsh*	1.75	2.50
263	A83	1p	blk, *yellow*	3.50	5.25
264	A83	5p	slate, *blue*	27.50	27.50
265	A83	10p	dk brn, *rose*	17.50	17.50
	Nos. 257-265 (9)			51.48	54.85

For overprint see No. L8.

Imperf., Pairs

257a	A83	1c	8.50	8.50
258a	A83	2c	8.50	8.50
259a	A83	5c	8.50	8.50
260a	A83	10c	8.50	8.50
261a	A83	20c	8.50	8.50
262a	A83	50c	8.50	8.50
263a	A83	1p	22.50	22.50
264a	A83	5p	62.50	62.50
265a	A83	10p	50.00	50.00

Regular Issue

A84

A85

A86

A87

A88

A89

A90

A91

A92

1902 *Imperf.*

266	A84	2c	blk, *rose*	.20	.20
267	A85	4c	red, *grn*	.20	.20
268	A86	5c	grn, *bl*	.20	.20
269	A87	10c	blk, *pink*	.20	.20
c.		10c	blk, *rose*	.75	.50
270	A88	20c	brn, *buff*	.20	.20
271	A89	50c	dk grn, *rose*	1.10	1.10
272	A90	1p	pur, *buff*	.45	.45
273	A91	5p	grn, *bl*	3.25	3.25
274	A92	10p	grn, *pale grn*	10.00	5.00
	Nos. 266-274 (9)			15.80	10.80

For overprint see No. H13.

Sewing Machine Perf.

266a	A84	2c	blk, *rose*	1.50	1.50
267a	A85	4c	red, *grn*	1.25	1.25
268a	A86	5c	grn, *blue*	1.50	1.50
269a	A87	10c	blk, *pink*	1.50	1.50
270a	A88	20c	brn, *buff*	2.50	2.00
271a	A89	50c	dk grn, *rose*	5.00	4.00
272a	A90	1p	pur, *buff*	6.00	5.00
273a	A91	5p	grn, *blue*	27.50	27.50
274a	A92	10p	grn, *pale grn*	50.00	50.00
	Nos. 266a-274a (9)			96.75	94.25

1903 *Perf. 12*

266b	A84	2c	blk, *rose*	1.10	1.10
269b	A87	10c	blk, *pink*	1.25	1.25
270b	A88	20c	brn, *buff*	1.25	1.25
272b	A90	1p	pur, *buff*	2.50	2.50
273b	A91	5p	grn, *blue*	22.50	22.50
274b	A92	10p	grn, *pale grn*	40.00	35.00
	Nos. 266b-274b (6)			68.60	63.60

1903 *Imperf.*

284	A85	4c	blue, *grn*	.22	.22
285	A86	5c	blue, *blue*	.22	.22
286	A88	20c	blue, *buff*	.22	.22
288	A89	50c	blue, *rose*	1.40	1.40
	Nos. 284-288 (4)			2.06	2.06

Sewing Machine Perf.

284a	A85	4c	blue, *grn*	1.75	1.40
285a	A86	5c	blue, *blue*	1.75	1.40
286a	A88	20c	blue, *buff*	2.50	2.00
288a	A89	50c	blue, *rose*	5.00	4.50
	Nos. 284a-288a (4)			11.00	9.30

Perf. 12

284b	A85	4c	blue, *grn*	2.00	2.00
285b	A86	5c	blue, *blue*	2.00	2.00
286b	A88	20c	blue, *buff*	2.75	2.75
288b	A89	50c	blue, *rose*	7.50	7.50
	Nos. 284b-288b (4)			14.25	14.25

A93

1904 **Pelure Paper** *Imperf.*

303	A93	½c	yellow brn	1.00	1.00
304	A90	1c	blue green	1.00	1.00
a.		1c	yellow green	1.00	1.00
306	A84	2c	blue	.90	.60
307	A86	5c	carmine	1.00	1.00
308	A87	10c	violet	1.00	.90
	Nos. 303-308 (5)			4.90	4.50

For overprint see No. H13.

1904 *Perf. 13*

303a	A93	½c	yellow brown	3.00	3.00
304b	A90	1c	blue green	4.00	3.50
c.		1c	yellow green	5.00	4.50
306a	A84	2c	blue	2.50	2.50

Perf. 12

307a	A86	5c	carmine	2.25	2.25
308a	A87	10c	violet	2.25	2.25
	Nos. 303a-308a (5)			14.00	13.50

A94

A95

Pres. José Manuel Marroquín — A96

Imprint: "Lit. J.L.Arango Medellin. Col."

1904 **Wove Paper** *Perf. 12*

314	A94	½c	yellow	.65	.15
315	A94	1c	green	.65	.15
316	A94	2c	rose	.65	.15
317	A94	5c	blue	1.00	.15
318	A94	10c	violet	1.40	.15
319	A94	20c	black	1.40	.22
320	A95	1p	brown	15.00	2.50
321	A96	5p	red & blk, *yel*	45.00	45.00
322	A96	10p	bl & blk, *grnsh*	45.00	45.00
	Nos. 314-322 (9)			110.75	93.47

Redrawn

314a	A94	½c	.65	.15
315a	A94	1c	.65	.15
316a	A94	2c	.65	.15
317a	A94	5c	1.00	.15
319a	A94	20c	1.40	.22
	Nos. 314a-319a (5)		4.35	.82

Imperf., Pairs

314b	A94	½c	2.50	2.50
315b	A94	1c	2.00	2.00
316b	A94	2c	2.50	2.50
317b	A94	5c	2.50	2.50
318a	A94	10c	3.25	3.25
319b	A94	20c	6.00	6.00
320a	A95	1p	50.00	50.00

On the redrawn types, the imprint is close to the base of the design instead of being spaced from it. On the redrawn 2c and 5c, the lower end of the vertical white line below "OR" of "CORREOS" forms a hook which turns to the right instead of to the left as in the originals.

See Nos. 325-330. For surcharges see Nos. 351-354, L1-L7, L9-L13, L15-L25.

A97

100p has different frame.

1903 *Imperf.*

323	A97	50p	org yel, *pale pink*	70.00	70.00
324	A97	100p	dk bl, *dk rose*	60.00	60.00

Imprint: "Lit. Nacional"

Perf. 10, 13, 13½ and Compound

1908

325	A94	½c	orange	.60	.15
a.		½c	yellow	.60	.15
b.			Imperf., pair	2.00	1.50
c.			Without imprint	4.00	4.00
326	A94	1c	yel grn	.60	.15
a.			Without imprint	.60	.15
d.			Imperf., pair	3.00	2.50
327	A94	2c	red	.60	.15
a.		2c	carmine	.60	.15
b.			Imperf., pair	3.00	2.50
328	A94	5c	blue	.52	.15
a.			Imperf., pair	5.00	4.00
329	A94	10c	violet	*40.00*	.70
330	A94	20c	gray blk	*40.00*	.50
	Nos. 325-330 (6)			*82.32*	
	Set value				1.45

The above stamps may be easily distinguished from those of 1904 by the perforation, by the height of the design, 24mm instead of 23mm, and by the "Lit. Nacional" imprint.

Camilo Torres A99

Policarpa Salavarrieta A100

Bolívar Demanding Liberation of Slaves — A105

Designs: 2c, Nariño. 5c, Bolívar. 10c, Francisco José de Caldas. 20c, Francisco de Paula Santander. 10p, Bolívar Resigning.

1910, Aug. **Engr.** *Perf. 12*

331	A99	½c	violet & blk	.48	.38
a.			Center inverted	425.00	425.00
332	A100	1c	deep green	.38	.38
333	A100	2c	scarlet	.32	.25
334	A100	5c	deep blue	1.25	.45
335	A100	10c	plum	10.00	5.00
336	A100	20c	black brn	15.00	5.50
337	A105	1p	dk violet	50.00	18.00
338	A105	10p	claret	200.00	140.00
	Nos. 331-338 (8)			277.43	169.96

Colombian independence centenary.

Caldas A107

Monument to Battle of Boyacá A113

View of Cartagena — A114

Coat of Arms — A118

Designs: 1c, Torres. 2c, Narino. 4c, Santander. 5c, Bolivar. 10c, Jose Maria Cordoba. 1p, Sucre. 2p, Rufino Cuervo. 5p, Antonio Ricaurte y Lozano.

1917 **Engr.** ***Perf. 14***

339 A107 ½c bister .35 .15
340 A107 1c green .30 .15
341 A107 2c car rose .30 .15
342 A107 4c violet .90 .30
343 A107 5c dull blue 1.40 .16
344 A107 10c gray 1.25 .16
345 A113 20c red 3.00 .18
346 A114 50c carmine 1.50 .18
347 A107 1p brt blue 11.00 .40
348 A107 2p orange 10.00 .45
349 A107 5p gray 17.50 6.00
350 A118 10p dk brown 32.50 12.00
Nos. 339-350 (12) 80.00 20.28

The 1c, 5c, 10c, 50c, 2p, 5p and 10p also exist perf. 11½ and 11½ compounded with 14.

Litho. varieties of Nos. 343, 345 and 346 are counterfeits made to defraud the government.

Imperforate copies of Nos. 339-350 are not known to have been regularly issued.

See Nos. 373-374, 400-405. For overprints and surcharges see Nos. 369-370, 377, 409-410, 440, C1, O3, O5-O9.

Nos. 318-319, 329-330 Surcharged in Red

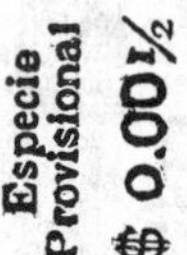

1918

On Issue of 1904

351 A94 ½c on 20c black 1.00 .25
352 A94 3c on 10c violet 2.50 .70

On Issue of 1908

353 A94 ½c on 20c gray blk 8.00 5.00
354 A94 3c on 10c violet 12.00 4.25
Nos. 351-354 (4) 23.50 10.20

Nos. 351-354 inclusive exist with surcharge reading up or down. On one stamp in each sheet the letter "S" in "Especie" is omitted. All denominations exist with a small zero before the decimal in the surcharge.

A119

A120

1918 **Litho.** ***Perf. 13½***

358 A119 3c red .50 .15
a. Imperf., pair 4.00 4.00

1920 **Engr.** ***Perf. 14***

359 A120 3c red, *org* .30 .15
a. Imperf., pair 3.00 3.00

See Nos. 371-372. For surcharge see No. 453.

A121

A122

A123

Perf. 10, 13½ and Compound

1920-21 **Litho.**

360 A121 ½c yellow .52 .22
361 A121 1c green .85 .15
362 A121 2c red .65 .15
363 A122 3c green .65 .15
a. 3c yellow green .65 .15
364 A121 5c blue .95 .22
365 A121 10c violet 3.00 1.50
366 A121 20c deep green 8.00 3.50
367 A123 50c dark red 8.00 3.50
Nos. 360-367 (8) 22.62 9.39

The tablet with "PROVISIONAL" was added separately to each design on the various lithographic stones and its position varies slightly on different stamps in the sheet. For some values there were two or more stones, on which the tablet was placed at various angles.

Nos. 360-366 exist imperf.

See No. 375.

No. 342 Surcharged in Red

PROVISIONAL $003 — a

PROVISIONAL $0.03 (15mm wide) — b

1921

369 A107 (a) 3c on 4c violet .80 .25
a. Double surcharge 13.00
370 A107 (b) 3c on 4c violet 3.50 2.00

See No. 377.

Types of 1917-21

1923-24 **Engr.** ***Perf. 13½***

371 A120 1½c chocolate 1.00 .50
372 A120 3c blue .50 .15
373 A107 5c claret ('24) 2.00 .18
374 A107 10c blue 7.50 .40

Litho.

375 A121 10c dark blue 10.00 6.00
Nos. 371-375 (5) 21.00 7.23

No. 342 Surcharged in Red

(18mm wide) PROVISIONAL $003

1924

377 A107 3c on 4c vio 3.00 1.25
a. Double surcharge 12.00
b. Double surch., one invtd. 12.00
c. With added surch. "3cs." in red

A124

1924-25 **Litho.** ***Perf. 10, 10x13½***

379 A124 1c red .70 .18
380 A124 3c dp blue ('25) .70 .18

Exist imperf. Value, each pair $5.

A125

A126

Black, Red or Green Surch. & Ovpt.

Imprint of Waterlow & Sons

1925 ***Perf. 14, 14½***

382 A125 1c on 3c bis brn .30 .15
383 A126 4c violet (R) .38 .20
a. Inverted surcharge 7.00 7.00

Imprint of American Bank Note Co.

Perf. 12

384 A125 1c on 3c bis brn 6.00 5.00
a. Inverted surcharge 15.00 15.00
385 A126 4c violet (G) .40 .30
a. Inverted overprint 7.50 7.50
Nos. 382-385 (4) 7.08 5.65

Correos

Provisional

Revenue stamps of basic types A125 and A126 were handstamped as above in violet or blue by the Cali post office in 1925, but were not authorized by the government. Denominations so overprinted are 1c, 2c, 3c, 4c and 5c.

A127

A128

Perf. 10, 13½x10

1926 **Litho.** **Wmk. 194**

395 A127 1c gray green .35 .15
396 A128 4c deep blue .35 .15

Exist imperf. Value, each pair $4.

Types of 1917 and

Sabana Station — A129

1926-29 **Unwmk.** **Engr.** ***Perf. 14***

400 A107 4c deep blue .40 .15
401 A118 8c dark blue .50 .15
402 A107 30c olive bister 4.75 .60
403 A129 40c brn & yel brn 7.50 1.00
404 A107 5p violet 7.50 .70
a. Perf. 11 ('29) 12.00 1.00
405 A118 10p green 12.00 2.00
a. Perf. 11 ('29) 25.00 4.00
Nos. 400-405 (6) 32.65 4.60

For surcharges and overprint see #09-410, O4.

Death of Bolívar A130

1930, Dec. 17 ***Perf. 12½***

408 A130 4c dk blue & blk .28 .24

Cent. of the death of Simón Bolívar. See Nos. C80-C82.

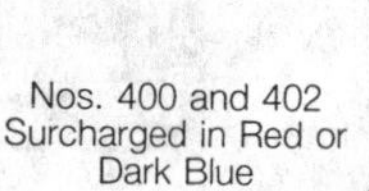
Nos. 400 and 402 Surcharged in Red or Dark Blue

1 CENTAVO

1932, Jan. 20 ***Perf. 14***

409 A107 1c on 4c dp bl (R) .30 .15
a. Inverted surcharge 5.25 5.25
410 A107 20c on 30c ol bis 8.00 .70
a. Inverted surcharge 17.50
b. Double surcharge 17.50

Emerald Mine — A131

Oil Wells — A132

Coffee Cultivation — A133

Platinum Mine — A134

Gold Mining A135

Christopher Columbus A136

Imprint: "Waterlow & Sons Ltd. Londres"

1932 **Wmk. 229** ***Perf. 12½***

411 A131 1c green .50 .15
412 A132 2c red .50 .15
413 A133 5c brown .55 .15
414 A134 8c blue blk 3.50 .48
415 A135 10c yellow 2.75 .15
416 A136 20c dk blue 8.00 .35
Nos. 411-416 (6) 15.80
Set value 1.05

See #441-442, 464-466a, 517. For surcharges see #455, 527, O1, O10-O11, O13, RA30.

Pedro de Heredia — A137

Coffee Picking — A138

Perf. 11½

1934, Jan. 10 **Unwmk.** **Litho.**

417 A137 1c dark green 2.25 .65
418 A137 5c chocolate 3.00 .55
419 A137 8c dark blue 2.25 .65
Nos. 417-419 (3) 7.50 1.85

400th anniv. of Cartagena. See Nos. C111-C114.

1934, Dec. **Engr.** ***Perf. 12***

420 A138 5c brown 2.25 .15

Discus Thrower — A139

Post and Telegraph Building — A145

Allegory of Olympic Games at Barranquilla A140

Foot Race — A141

Tennis A142

Pier at Puerto Colombia A143

View of the Bay — A144

Designs: 2c, Soccer. 10c, Hurdling. 15c, Athlete in stadium. 18c, Baseball. 24c, Swimming. 50c, View of Barranquilla. 2p, Monument to Flag. 5p, Coat of Arms. 10p, Condor.

1935, Jan. 26 **Litho.** ***Perf. 11½***

421 A139 2c bluish grn & buff 1.25 .40
422 A139 4c deep green 1.25 .40
423 A140 5c dk brn & yel 1.25 .40
a. Horiz. pair, imperf. btwn. 200.00
424 A141 7c dk carmine 2.50 1.50
425 A142 8c blk & pink 2.00 1.90
426 A141 10c brown & bl 2.75 1.50
427 A143 12c indigo 3.25 2.50

428 A141 15c bl & red brn 5.50 4.25
429 A141 18c dk vio & buff 7.50 6.50
430 A144 20c purple & grn 6.50 5.50
431 A144 24c bluish grn & ultra 6.50 5.25
432 A144 50c ultra & buff 10.00 8.50
433 A145 1p drab & blue 90.00 50.00
434 A145 2p dull grn & gray 110.00 90.00
435 A145 5p pur blk & bl 350.00 275.00
436 A145 10p black & gray 425.00 400.00
Nos. 421-436 (16) 1,025. 853.60

3rd Natl. Olympic Games, Barranquilla. Counterfeits of 10p exist.

Oil Wells — A155

Gold Mining — A157

Imprint: "American Bank Note Co."

1935, Mar. Unwmk. Engr. *Perf. 12*

437 A155 2c carmine rose .35 .15
439 A157 10c deep orange 19.00 .15
Set value .15

See Nos. 468, 470, 498, 516. For surcharge and overprints see Nos. 496, 596, O2.

No. 347 Surcharged in Black — 12 CENTAVOS

1935, Aug. *Perf. 14*

440 A107 12c on 1p brt bl 3.00 1.40

Types of 1932
Imprint: "Lit. Nacional Bogotá"

1935-36 Litho. *Perf. 11, 11½, 12½*

441 A131 1c lt green .15 .15
a. Imperf., pair 3.50
442 A133 5c brown ('36) .55 .15
a. Imperf., pair 4.00 4.00
Set value .15

For surcharge see No. 527.

Bolívar A159

Tequendama Falls A160

Wmk. Wavy Lines. (229)

1937 Engr. *Perf. 12½*

443 A159 1c deep green .20 .15
a. Perf. 14
444 A160 12c deep blue 2.50 .95

See No. 570. For surcharges and overprints see Nos. 454, 456, C231, C326, O12.

Soccer Player — A161

Runner — A163

Discus Thrower — A162

1937, Jan. 4 Photo. Unwmk.

445 A161 3c lt green 1.40 .85
446 A162 10c carmine rose 2.75 1.75
447 A163 1p black 27.50 24.00
Nos. 445-447 (3) 31.65 26.60

National Olympic Games, Manizales.
For surcharge see No. 452.

Exposition Palace A164

Stadium at Barranquilla A165

Monument to the Colors — A166

1937, Jan. 4

448 A164 5c violet brown .45 .30
449 A165 15c blue 3.50 3.50
450 A166 50c orange brn 9.25 7.50
Nos. 448-450 (3) 13.20 11.30

Barranquilla National Exposition.

Stamps of 1926-37 Surcharged in Black — 1 CENTAVO

1937-38 Unwmk. *Perf. 12½*

452 A161 1c on 3c lt grn .75 .75
a. Inverted surcharge 1.75 1.75
453 A118 5c on 8c dk bl .40 .35
a. Inverted surcharge 1.75 1.75

Wmk. 229

454 A160 2c on 12c dp bl .40 .35
455 A134 5c on 8c bl blk .45 .55
a. Invtd. surcharge 1.50 1.50
456 A160 10c on 12c dp bl ('38) 4.25 .85
a. Dbl. surcharge 8.50 8.50
Nos. 452-456 (5) 6.25 2.85

Calle del Arco — A168

Entrance to Church of the Rosary — A169

Arms of Bogotá — A170

Gonzálo Jiménez de Quesada — A171

Bochica A172

Santo Domingo Convent A173

Mass of the Conquistadors — A174

1938, July 27 Unwmk. *Perf. 12½*

457 A168 1c yellow green .15 .15
458 A169 2c scarlet .15 .15
459 A170 5c brown blk .25 .15
460 A171 10c brown .60 .30
461 A172 15c brt blue 2.50 1.25
462 A173 20c brt red vio 2.50 1.25
463 A174 1p red brown 37.50 22.50
Nos. 457-463 (7) 43.65 25.75

Bogotá, 400th anniversary.

Types of 1932
Imprint: "Litografia Nacional Bogotá"

1938, Dec. 5 Litho. *Perf. 10½, 11*

464 A132 2c rose .80 .30
465 A135 10c yellow 2.00 .30
466 A136 20c dull blue 7.50 1.00
a. 20c dk bl, perf. 12½ ('44) 50.00 5.00
Nos. 464-466 (3) 10.30 1.60

Types of 1935 and

Bolívar A175

Coffee Picking A176

Arms of Colombia A177

Christopher Columbus A178

Caldas A179

Sabana Station A180

Imprint: "American Bank Note Co."

Wmk. 255

1939, Mar. 3 Engr. *Perf. 12*

467 A175 1c green .15 .15
468 A155 2c car rose .20 .15
469 A176 5c dull brown .20 .15
470 A157 10c deep orange .85 .15
471 A177 15c dull blue 2.50 .15
472 A178 20c violet blk 6.00 .20
473 A179 30c olive bister 3.50 .30
474 A180 40c bister brn 10.00 2.75
Nos. 467-474 (8) 23.40 4.00

See Nos. 497-499, 515, 518, 574. For surcharges and overprints see Nos. 506-507, 520-522, 596, RA26, RA47.

Gen. Santander A181

Allegory A182

Gen. Santander A183

Statue at Cúcuta A184

Birthplace of Santander A185

Church at Rosario A186

Paya — A187

Bridge at Boyacá — A188

Death of General Santander — A189

Invasion of the Liberators — A190

Perf. 13x13½, 13½x13

1940, May 6 Engr. Wmk. 229

475 A181 1c olive green .20 .20
476 A182 2c dk carmine .40 .30
477 A183 5c sepia .20 .15
478 A184 8c carmine 1.50 1.50
479 A185 10c orange yel .65 .50
480 A186 15c dark blue 1.75 1.10
481 A187 20c green 2.25 1.75
482 A188 50c violet 5.25 5.00
483 A189 1p deep rose 17.00 17.00
484 A190 2p orange 52.50 52.50
Nos. 475-484 (10) 81.70 80.00

Centenary of the death of General Francisco Santander.

Tobacco Plant — A194

Gen. Santander — A195

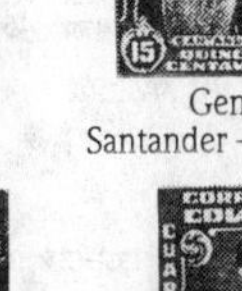
Garcia Rovira A196

R. Galan A197

Antonio Sucre — A198

Arms of Palmira — A199

1940-43 Engr. Wmk. 255 *Perf. 12*

488 A194 8c rose car & grn 1.00 .55
489 A195 15c dp blue ('43) 1.10 .25
490 A196 20c gray blk ('41) 2.75 .35
491 A197 40c brown bis ('41) 1.90 .35
492 A198 1p black 6.75 .50
Nos. 488-492 (5) 13.50 2.00

See #500, 554. For overprint see #RA28.

Unwmk.

1942, July 4 Litho. *Perf. 11*

493 A199 30c claret 1.70 .60

8th Natl. Agricultural Exposition, held at Palmira.

Paradise of Isaacs, Palmira — A200

Signing Treaty of the Wisconsin — A201

1942, July 4

494 A200 50c lt blue grn 2.25 .85

Issued in honor of the writer, Jorge Isaacs.

1942, Nov. 21 *Perf. 10½*

495 A201 10c dull orange 1.10 .50
a. "2. XI.1902" instead of "21. XI. 1902" 14.00 15.00
b. Perf. 12 3.00 3.00

40th anniv. of the signing of the Treaty of the Wisconsin, Nov. 21, 1902.

No. 470 Surcharged in Black

5
Centavos

1944 Wmk. 255 *Perf. 12*
496 A157 5c on 10c dp org .15 .15

Counterfeits exist of No. 496 with inverted or double surcharge.

Types of 1935-41 and

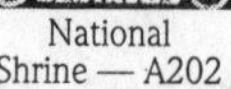
National Shrine — A202

San Pedro Alejandrino — A203

Imprint: "Columbian Bank Note Co."

1944-45 Unwmk. Engr. *Perf. 11*
497 A175 1c green .15 .15
498 A155 2c rose .15 .15
499 A176 5c dull brown .15 .15
500 A196 20c gray black 2.50 .75
501 A202 30c dl ol grn ('45) 1.40 .95
502 A203 50c rose 1.75 .95
Nos. 497-502 (6) 6.10 3.10

No. 499 Surcharged in Black

1
CENTAVO

1944, Oct.
506 A176 1c on 5c dull brn .15 .15
507 A176 2c on 5c dull brn .15 .15
Set value .20 .20

Nos. 506 and 507 exist with inverted or double surcharge, created by favor.

Flag — A204

Arms — A205

Murillo Toro — A206

Hospital of St. John of God — A207

Virrey Solis — A208

1944, Oct. 10 Litho.
508 A204 2c ultra & bis .20 .20
 a. Sheet of 18 10.00
 b. Imperf., pair 10.00
509 A205 5c ultra & bis .20 .20
 a. Sheet of 22 12.00
 b. Imperf., pair 10.00
510 A206 20c blk & bluish grn .80 .80
 a. Sheet of 8 10.00
 b. Imperf., pair 15.00
511 A207 40c blk & red 3.75 3.75
 a. Sheet of 4 13.00
512 A208 1p blk & red 8.00 8.00
 a. Sheet of 2 17.00
Nos. 508-512 (5) 12.95 12.95

Souvenir Sheet

Perf. 11x11½ All Around, Stamps Imperf.
513 Sheet of 5, #508-512 12.00 12.00

75th anniv. of Gen. Benevolent Assoc. of Cundinamarca.

Nos. 508-513 were printed in composite sheets containing one each of Nos. 508a, 509a, 510a, 511a and 512a, and two of 513. Fifty of these were presented to government officials.

Murillo Toro A210

San Pedro Alejandrino A211

1944, Nov. 10 *Perf. 11*
514 A210 5c lt brown .30 .15

Types of 1932-39 and A211
Imprint: "Litografia Nacional Bogota"

1944 Litho. *Perf. 12½*
515 A175 1c dp green .35 .15
 a. 1c olive green .35 .15
 b. Imperf., pair 1.75 1.75
516 A155 2c dk carmine .40 .15
 a. Imperf., pair 1.75 1.75
517 A135 10c yellow org 2.75 .45
518 A179 30c gray olive 7.50 3.50
 a. Imperf., pair 27.50
519 A211 50c rose 8.00 3.75
Nos. 515-519 (5) 19.00 8.00

No. 469 Overprinted in Green, Blue or Red

Wmk. 255

1945, July 19 Engr. *Perf. 12*
520 A176 5c dull brn (G) .20 .15
521 A176 5c dull brn (R) .20 .15
522 A176 5c dull brn (Bl) .20 .15
Nos. 520-522 (3) .60
Set value .25

Portraits are Joseph Stalin, Franklin D. Roosevelt and Winston Churchill.

Clock Tower, Cartagena — A212

1945, Nov. 15
523 A212 50c olive black 3.75 1.25

For overprints see Nos. 543-544.

Sierra Nevada of Santa Marta — A213

Designs: 30c, Seaplane Tolima. 50c, San Sebastian Fort, Cartagena.

Unwmk.

1945, Dec. 14 Litho. *Perf. 11*
524 A213 20c light green 1.50 1.00
525 A213 30c pale blue 1.50 1.00
526 A213 50c salmon pink 1.50 1.00
Nos. 524-526 (3) 4.50 3.00

25th anniv. of the 1st airmail service in America, according to the inscription, but earlier services are known to have existed.

No. 442 Surcharged in Black

1
UN CENTAVO

1946, Mar. 8 *Perf. 11x11½, 12½*
527 A133 1c on 5c brown .15 .15
 a. Inverted surcharge .90

Gen. Antonio Jose de Sucre — A216

Wmk. 255

1946, Apr. 16 Engr. *Perf. 12*
Size: 19x26½mm
528 A216 1c brn & turq grn .15 .15
529 A216 2c vio & rose car .15 .15

Size: 23x31mm
530 A216 5c sepia & blue .15 .15
531 A216 9c dk grn & red .55 .55
532 A216 10c ultra & org .40 .35
533 A216 20c blk & dp org .40 .25
534 A216 30c brn red & grn .65 .25
535 A216 40c ol blk & red vio .65 .30
536 A216 50c dp brn & vio .65 .30
Nos. 528-536 (9) 3.75 2.45

Map of South America A217

National Observatory A218

Unwmk.

1946, June 7 Litho. *Perf. 11*
537 A217 15c ultra .50 .30
 a. Imperf., pair 4.00

1946, Aug.
538 A218 5c fawn .32 .15
 a. Imperf., pair 4.00

See No. 565.

Andrés Bello — A219

Joaquín de Cayzedo y Cuero — A220

Wmk. 255

1946, Sept. 3 Engr. *Perf. 12*
539 A219 3c sepia .15 .15
540 A219 10c orange .55 .30
541 A219 15c slate black .60 .35
Nos. 539-541 (3) 1.30 .80

80th anniv. of the death of Andrés Bello (1781-1865), poet and educator. See No. C145.

1946, Sept. 20 Wmk. 229 *Perf. 12½*
542 A220 2p bluish green 4.50 1.25

See No. 568. For surcharge see No. 613.

Type of 1945, Overprinted in Black or Green

V JUEGOS C.
A. Y DEL C.
1946

1946, Dec. 6 Wmk. 255 *Perf. 12*
543 A212 50c red (Bk) 4.00 2.25
 a. Double overprint 25.00
544 A212 50c red (G) 4.00 2.25
 a. Double overprint 25.00

5th Central American and Caribbean Championship Games.

Coffee — A221

Engraved and Lithographed

1947, Jan. 10 Wmk. 229 *Perf. 12½*
545 A221 5c multicolored .40 .15

Colombian Orchid: Masdevallia Nycterina — A222

Designs (Orchids): 2c, Miltonia vexillaria. No. 548, Cattleya chocoensis. No. 549, Odontoglossum crispum. No. 550, Cattleya dowiana aurea. 10c, Cattleya labiata trianae.

1947, Feb. 7 Wmk. 255 *Perf. 12*
546 A222 1c multicolored .32 .15
547 A222 2c multicolored .32 .15
548 A222 5c multicolored .75 .15
549 A222 5c multicolored .75 .15
550 A222 5c multicolored .75 .15
551 A222 10c multicolored 1.25 .32
Nos. 546-551 (6) 4.14 1.07

Antonio Nariño — A228

Alberto Urdaneta y Urdaneta — A229

Perf. 12½

1947, May 9 Litho. Unwmk.
552 A228 5c blue, *grnsh* .26 .15
553 A229 10c red brn, *grnsh* .32 .15
Nos. 552-553,C146-C147 (4) 1.43 .95

4th Pan-American Press Congress, 1946.

Sucre Type of 1940

1947 Wmk. 255 Engr. *Perf. 12*
554 A198 1p violet 2.50 1.00

José Celestino Mutis and José Jerónimo Triana — A230

Miguel A. Caro and Rufino J. Cuervo — A231

1947 Wmk. 229 *Perf. 12½*
555 A230 25c olive green .65 .24
556 A231 3p dark purple 4.00 3.25

See Nos. 567, 569. For surcharge see No. 610.

Metropolitan Cathedral, Plaza Bolívar, Bogotá A232

National Capitol A233

Ministry of Foreign Affairs A234

A235

1948, Apr. 2

557 A232	5c black brown	.15	.15
558 A233	10c orange	.55	.55
559 A234	15c dark blue	.55	.55
	Nos. 557-559,C148-C149 (5)	2.30	2.30

Miniature Sheet

Imperf

560 A235	50c slate	1.50	1.50

9th Pan-American Conf., Bogotá.

No. RA5A Overprinted in Black

1948 Unwmk. *Perf. 12½*

Without Gum

561 PT3	1c yellow orange	.15	.15

The letter "C" is the initial of "CORREOS."

Nos. RA33, RA24 and RA25 Overprinted in Black CORREOS

1948 Wmk. 255 *Perf. 12.*

562 PT6	1c olive	.15	.15
563 PT6	2c green	.15	.15
564 PT6	20c brown	.16	.15
	Set value	.26	.15

Nos. 561-564 exist with inverted and double overprints.

Observatory Type of 1946

Unwmk.

1948, June 30 Litho. *Perf. 11*

565 A218	5c blue	.20	.15

Simón Bolívar — A236

Carlos Martinez Silva — A237

Wmk. 255

1948, May 29 Engr. *Perf. 12*

566 A236	15c green	.40	.18

Types of 1946-47

1948 Unwmk. *Perf. 12½*

567 A230	25c green	.30	.15
568 A220	2p dp green	.55	.15
569 A231	3p dp red violet	.70	.15
	Nos. 567-569 (3)	1.55	
	Set value		.35

Falls Type of 1937

1948 Wmk. 229

570 A160	10c red	.15	.15

For overprints see Nos. C231, C326.

Perf. 13½

1948, Dec. 21 Unwmk. Litho.

571 A237	40c carmine	.40	.25

Juan de Dios Carrasquilla A238

1949, May 20 Wmk. 229 *Perf. 12½*

572 A238	5c bister	.15	.15

75th anniv. of the foundation of the Colombian Soc. of Agriculture.

Julio Garavito Armero A239

Arms of Colombia A240

Wmk. 229

1949, Apr. 24 Engr. *Perf. 12*

573 A239	4c green	.32	.15

Issued to honor Julio Garavito Armero (1865-1920), mathematician.

Coffee Type of 1939.

Imprint: "American Bank Note Co."

1949, Aug. 4 Wmk. 255

574 A176	5c blue	.15	.15

1949, Oct. 7 Unwmk. *Perf. 13*

575 A240	15c blue	.18	.15

Issued to honor the new Constitution. See Nos. C164-C165.

Shield and Tree A241

Francisco Javier Cisneros A242

1949, Oct. 13 Wmk. 229 *Perf. 12½*

576 A241	5c olive	.15	.15

4th anniv. of Colombia's 1st Forestry Cong. and propaganda for the government's reforestation program.

1949, Dec. 15 Photo. Unwmk.

577 A242	50c red vio & yel	1.00	.60
578 A242	50c green & vio	1.00	.60
579 A242	50c brown & lt bl	1.00	.60
	Nos. 577-579 (3)	3.00	1.80

50th anniv. (in 1948) of the death of Francisco Javier Cisneros.

Masdevallia Chimaera — A243

Odontoglossum Crispum — A244

Eastern Hemisphere — A245

Designs: 3c, Cattleya labiata trianae. 4c, Masdevallia nycterina. 5c, Cattleya dowiana aurea. 11c, Miltonia vexillaria. 18c, Santo Domingo post office.

1950, Aug. 22 Photo. *Perf. 13*

580 A243	1c brown	.15	.15
581 A244	2c violet	.15	.15
582 A243	3c rose lilac	.16	.15
583 A243	4c emerald	.24	.15
584 A243	5c red orange	.65	.15
585 A244	11c red	1.50	1.50
586 A244	18c ultra	1.25	.55
	Nos. 580-586 (7)	4.10	2.80

Miniature Sheet

Imperf

587 A245	50c orange yel	1.25	1.25

75th anniv. (in 1949) of the UPU. See No. C199. For surcharge see No. C232.

Antonio Baraya — A246

Perf. 12½

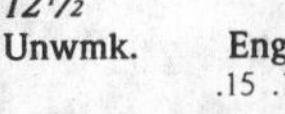

1950, Nov. 27 Unwmk. Engr.

588 A246	2c red	.15	.15

Colombian Farm A247

1950, Dec. 28 Photo. *Perf. 11½*

589 A247	5c dp car & buff	.20	.15
590 A247	5c bl grn & gray	.20	.15
591 A247	5c vio bl & gray	.20	.15
	Nos. 589-591 (3)	.60	
	Set value		.21

Issued to publicize rural life.

Arms of Bogotá A248

Arms of Colombia A249

Perf. 12x12½

1950, Dec. 28 Engr. Wmk. 255

592 A248	5p deep green	2.50	.38
593 A249	10p red orange	7.50	.65

Catalogue values for unused stamps in this section, from this point to the end of the section, are for Never Hinged items.

Map and Badge A250

Guillermo Valencia A251

Perf. 12½x13

1951, Jan. 30 Photo. Unwmk.

594 A250	20c red, yel & bl	.40	.15

60th anniversary (in 1947) of the formation of the Colombian Society of Engineers.

1951, Oct. 20 Engr. *Perf. 13x13½*

595 A251	25c black	.90	.20

Issued to honor Guillermo Valencia (1873-1943), newspaper founder, governor of Cauca, presidential candidate, author.

No. 468 Overprinted in Black

REVERSION
CONCESION MARES
25 Agosto 1951

1951, Dec. 11 Wmk. 255 *Perf. 12*

596 A155	2c carmine rose	.15	.15

Issued to publicize the reversion of the Mares oil concession to Colombia.

Nicolas Osorio — A252

Portraits: No. 598, Pompilio Martinez. No. 599, Ezequiel Uriocoechea. No. 600, Jose M. Lombana.

Perf. 11½

1952, Aug. 6 Unwmk. Engr.

Various Frames

597 A252	1c deep blue	.15	.15
598 A252	1c deep blue	.15	.15
599 A252	1c deep blue	.15	.15
600 A252	1c deep blue	.15	.15
	Set value	.28	.20

Nos. 597-600 were printed in a single sheet containing four panes of twenty-five each, separated by double rows of ornamental tabs. Although inscribed "sobretasa," the stamps were for ordinary postage.

Types of Postal Tax Stamps of 1945-50 and

Communications Building A253 A253a

1952 *Perf. 12*

601 A253	5c ultra	.25	.15

Wmk. 255

602 PT10	20c brown	7.50	.16
603 PT6	25c dk gray	7.50	3.50
604 PT10	25c blue green	.75	.15
605 A253a	50c orange yel	20.00	10.00
606 A253a	1p rose carmine	2.00	.32
607 A253a	2p lilac rose	20.00	8.00
608 A253a	2p violet	2.25	.50
	Nos. 601-608 (8)	60.25	22.78

Although inscribed "sobretasa," Nos. 601-608 were issued for ordinary postage.

For surcharges see Nos. 612, RA48.

Cathedral of Manizales — A254

Perf. 11½

1952, Oct. 10 Photo. Unwmk.

609 A254 23c blue & gray blk .35 .20

Centenary of city of Manizales.
For surcharge see No. 619.

No. 555 Surcharged in Blue

1ª CONFERENCIA 19 52 SIDERURGICA
LATINO-AMERICANA.
15

1952, Oct. 30 Wmk. 229 *Perf. 12½*

610 A230 15c on 25c olive green .40 .20

Latin American Siderurgical Conf., 1952. See No. C226.

Queen Isabella I and Monument — A255

Perf. 12½

1953, Mar. 10 Unwmk. Engr.

611 A255 23c blue & black .60 .50

5th centenary of the birth of Queen Isabella I of Spain.
For surcharge see No. 693.

Nos. 606 and 568 Surcharged with New Values in Dark Blue

1953, Oct. 19 Wmk. 255

612 A253a 40c on 1p rose car 1.25 .15
613 A220 50c on 2p dp green 1.25 .15

Manuel Ancizar — A256

Portraits: 23c, José Jeronimo Triana. 30c, Manuel Ponce de Leon. 1p, Agustin Codazzi.

Perf. 12½x13

1953, Nov. Engr. Unwmk.

Frames in Black

614 A256 14c rose red .50 .50
615 A256 23c ultra .40 .20
616 A256 30c chocolate .35 .15
617 A256 1p emerald .35 .15
Nos. 614-617 (4) 1.60 1.00

Cent. (in 1950) of the establishment of the Chorographic Commission. See Nos. 687, 690, 692. For surcharges and overprint see Nos. 620, 687, 690, 692, C284.

Murillo Toro and Map — A257

Engraved and Lithographed

1953, Dec. 12 Wmk. 255 *Perf. 12*

Black Surcharge

618 A257 5c on 5p multi .25 .15

2nd Natl. Phil. Exhib., Bogotá, Dec. 1953. See No. C237.

Nos. 609 and 614 Surcharged with New Value or New Value and Ornaments

1953 Unwmk. *Perf. 11½, 12½x13*

619 A254 5c on 23c (C) .35 .20
620 A256 5c on 14c (Bk) .35 .25

No. 614 surcharged "CINCO" in blue is listed as No. 687.

Symbolical of St. Francis Receiving Christ's Wounds — A258

1954, Apr. 23 Photo. *Perf. 11½*

621 A258 5c sepia & green .25 .15

400th anniversary of the establishment of Colombia's first Franciscan community.

Soldier, Map and Arms A259

1954, June 13 Engr. *Perf. 13*

622 A259 5c dull blue .18 .15

1st anniv. of the assumption of the presidency by Gen. Gustavo Rojas Pinilla. See Nos. C255, 637a.

Sports Emblem — A260

Design: 10c, Stadium and athlete holding arms of Colombia.

1954, July 18 Unwmk.

623 A260 5c deep blue .40 .15
624 A260 10c red .60 .15
Nos. 623-624,C256-C257 (4) 2.55 .80

7th Natl. Athletic Games, Cali, July 1954.

History Academy Seal — A261

1954, July 24

625 A261 5c ultra & green .20 .15

50th anniversary (in 1952) of the Colombian Academy of History.

Convent and Cell of St. Peter Claver — A262

1954, Sept. 9

627 A262 5c dark green .15 .15
a. Souvenir sheet 2.25 2.25

300th anniversary of the death of St. Peter Claver.

No. 627a contains one stamp similar to No. 627, but printed in greenish black. Sheet size: 121x129½mm. See Nos. C258-C258a.

Mercury — A263

1954, Oct. 29

628 A263 5c orange .28 .15
Nos. 557-559,C148-C149 (5) 2.30
Set value .25

1st Intl. Fair and Exhibition, Bogota, 1954.

Tapestry Madonna A264

College Cloister A265

Designs: 10c, Brother Cristobal de Torres. 20c, College chapel and arms.

Perf. 12½x11½, 11½x12½

1954, Dec. 6

629 A264 5c orange & blk .24 .15
630 A264 10c blue .24 .15
631 A265 15c violet brn .28 .15
632 A265 20c black & brn .55 .35
a. Souvenir sheet 3.75 3.75
Nos. 629-632,C263-C266 (8) 3.48
Set value 1.55

300th anniv. (in 1953) of the founding of the Senior College of Our Lady of the Rosary, Bogota.

No. 632a contains four stamps similar to Nos. 629-632, but printed in different colors: 5c yellow and black, 10c green, 15c dull violet, 20c black and light-blue.

Steel Mill — A266

José Marti — A267

1954, Dec. 12 *Perf. 12½x13*

633 A266 5c ultra & blk .20 .15

Issued to mark the opening of the Paz del Rio steel mill, October 1954. See No. C267.

1955, Jan. 28 *Perf. 13½x13*

634 A267 5c deep carmine .15 .15

Centenary of the birth of José Marti (1853-1895), Cuban patriot. See No. C268.

Arms, Flags and Soldiers Building Bridge A268

1955, Mar. 23 *Perf. 12½*

635 A268 10c claret .20 .15

Issued to honor Colombian soldiers who served in Korea, 1951-53. See Nos. 637a, C269.

Fleet Emblem — A269

M. S. City of Manizales and New York Skyline A270

1955, Apr. 12 Unwmk.

636 A269 15c deep green .20 .15
637 A270 20c violet .20 .15
a. Souvenir sheet 4.00 4.25
Nos. 636-637,C270-C271 (4) 1.23
Set value .20

Grand-Colombian Merchant Fleet.

No. 637a contains four stamps similar to Nos. 622, 635-637, but printed in different colors: 5c blue, 10c dark carmine, 15c green, 20c purple.

Hotel Tequendama and Church of San Diego — A271

1955, May 16 Photo. *Perf. 11½x12*

638 A271 5c blue .15 .15

See No. C273.

Bolivar's Country Estate, Bogotá A272

1955, Sept. 28 Engr. *Perf. 12½*

639 A272 5c deep ultra .15 .15

50th anniv. of Rotrary Intl. See No. C274.

Belalcazar, Jiménez de Quesada and Balboa A273

Caravels and Columbus A274

Design: 5c, San Martin, Bolivar and Washington.

Engraved and Photogravure

1955, Oct. 29 *Perf. 13x12½*

640 A273 2c yel grn & brn .15 .15
641 A273 5c brt bl & brn .15 .15
642 A274 23c lt ultra & blk .25 .15
a. Souvenir sheet 8.00 5.00
Nos. 640-642,C275-C280 (9) 11.10 10.05

7th Cong. of the Postal Union of the Americas and Spain, Bogota, Oct. 12-Nov. 9, 1955.

No. 642a contains one each of Nos. 640-642, printed in slightly different shades.

José Eusebio Caro — A275

1955, Nov. 29 Engr. *Perf. 13½x13*

643 A275 5c brown .15 .15

José Eusebio Caro (1817-53), poet. See #C281.

Departmental Issue

Map — A276

View of San Andres Harbor — A277

Cattle at Waterhole A278

Designs: 2c, Docks, Atlantico. 3c, "Industry," Antioquia. 4c, Cartagena Harbor, Bolivar. No. 647, Steel Mill, Boyaca. No. 648, Cattle, Cordoba. No. 649, Map. No. 650, San Andres Harbor. No. 651, Cacao picker, Cauca. 10c, Coffee picker, Caldas. 15c, Salt Mine Chapel, Zipaquira, Cundinamarca. 20c, Tropical plants and map, Choco. 23c, Harvester, Huila. 25c, Banana Plantation, Magdalena. 30c, Gold mining, Nariño. 40c, Tobacco plantation, Santander. 50c, Oil wells, North Santander. 60c, Cotton plantation, Tolima. 1p, Sugar industry, Cauca. 3p, Amazon river at Leticia, Amazonas. 5p, Windmills and panoramic view, La Guajira. 10p, Rubber plantation, Vaupes.

Perf. 13½x13, 13x13½, 13

Engr.; Engr. & Litho.

1956 Unwmk.

Various Frames

644 A277 2c car & grn .15 .15
645 A276 3c brn vio & blk .15 .15
646 A277 4c grn & blk .15 .15
647 A276 5c dk brn & bl .15 .15
648 A277 5c ol & dk vio brn .25 .15
649 A276 5c bl & blk .22 .15
650 A277 5c car & grnsh bl .18 .15
651 A277 5c ol grn & red brn .18 .15
652 A276 10c org & blk .18 .15
653 A276 15c ultra & blk .22 .15
654 A276 20c dk brn & bl .18 .15
655 A277 23c ultra & ver .30 .18
656 A277 25c ol grn & blk .30 .18
657 A277 30c ultra & brn .18 .15
658 A277 40c dl pur & red brn .18 .15
659 A277 50c dk grn & blk .18 .15
660 A277 60c pale brn & grn .18 .15
661 A278 1p mag & grnsh bl 1.40 .18
662 A278 2p grn & red brn 1.75 .22
663 A278 3p car & blk 2.25 .50
664 A278 5p brn & lt ultra 4.00 1.25
665 A276 10p red brn & grn 10.00 6.50
Nos. 644-665 (22) 22.73
Set value 9.75

Nos. 645, 647, 649, 652-654 measure 27x32mm. No. 665 27x37mm. See Nos. 681-684, 685, 688-689. For surcharges and overprints see Nos. 685, 688-689, C289, C312.

Columbus and Proposed Lighthouse A279

1956, Oct. 12 Photo. *Perf. 12*

666 A279 3c gray black .15 .15

Issued in honor of Christopher Columbus. See Nos. C285, C306.

Altar of St. Elizabeth and Tomb of Jimenez de Quesada — A280

1956, Nov. 19 Unwmk.

667 A280 5c red lilac .15 .15

7th cent. of St. Elizabeth of Hungary, patron saint of Sante Fé de Bogotá. See No. C286.

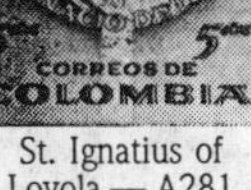

St. Ignatius of Loyola — A281

Javier Pereira — A282

1956, Nov. 26 Engr. *Perf. 12½x13*

668 A281 5c blue .18 .15

400th anniv. of the death of St. Ignatius of Loyola. See No. C287. For overprint see No. C324.

1956, Dec. 28 Unwmk. *Perf. 12*

669 A282 5c blue .15 .15

Issued to honor 167-year-old Javier Pereira. See No. C288.

Emblem and Dairy Farm — A283

Designs: 2c, Emblem and tractor. 5c, Emblem, coffee and corn.

1957, Mar. 5 Photo. *Perf. 14x13½*

670 A283 1c lt ol grn .15 .15
671 A283 2c lt brn .15 .15
672 A283 5c lt bl .15 .15
Set value, #670-672, C292-C296 1.30 .85

Agrarian Savings Bank of Colombia, 25th anniv. For overprint see No. C322.

Arms of Military Academy and Gen. Rafael Reyes A284

Design: 10c, Arms and Academy.

1957, July 20 Engr. *Perf. 12½*

673 A284 5c blue .15 .15
674 A284 10c orange .15 .15
a. Souv. sheet of 2 10.50 10.50
Set value, #673-674, C299-C300 .55 .25

50th anniv. of the Colombian Military Academy.

No. 674a contains one each of Nos. 673-674 in slightly different shades.

For overprints see Nos. C328, C312.

Statue of José Matias Delgado — A285

1957, Sept. 16 Photo. *Perf. 12*

675 A285 2c rose brn .15 .15

Issued in honor of Jose Matias Delgado, liberator of El Salvador. See No. C301.

Santo Michelena, Marcos V. Crespo, P. Alcantara Herran and UPU Monument A286

1957, Oct. 10 Unwmk.

676 A286 5c green .15 .15
677 A286 10c gray .15 .15
Set value, #676-677, C302-C303 .48 .30

Intl. Letter Writing Week and 14th UPU Cong.

St. Vincent de Paul and Children — A287

1957, Oct. 18

678 A287 1c dark olive green .15 .15

Colombian Society of St. Vincent de Paul, cent. See No. C304. For overprint see No. C323.

Fencer A288

1957, Nov. 22 Photo. *Perf. 12*

679 A288 4c lilac .15 .15

3rd South American Fencing Championship. See No. C305. For overprint see No. C332.

Francisco José de Caldas and Hypsometer A289

1958, May 12 Unwmk. *Perf. 12*

680 A289 10c black .25 .15
Nos. 680,C309-C310 (3) 1.05
Set value .30

International Geophysical Year, 1957-58.

Departmental Issue

Type of 1956

Designs as before.

1958 Engr. *Perf. 13*

681 A276 3c ultra & brn .15 .15
682 A276 3c ol grn & pur .15 .15
683 A276 10c grn & brn .15 .15
684 A276 10c dk bl & brn .15 .15
Set value .36 .20

Nos. 646, C291, 614, 653, 655, 616, C308, 615 and 611 Surcharged with New Value, and Old Value Obliterated, or Overprinted in Dark Blue or Green

Perf. 12½, 12½x13, 13

1958-59 Unwmk.

685 A277 2c on 4c grn & blk .15 .15
686 AP48 5c dp plum & multi ('59) .15 .15
687 A256 5c on 14c blk & rose red ("CINCO") ('59) .30 .30
688 A276 5c on 15c ultra & blk .15 .15
689 A277 5c on 23c ultra & ver (G) .24 .16
690 A256 5c on 30c blk & choc .15 .15
691 AP40 10c on 25c rose vio .15 .15
692 A256 20c on 23c blk & ultra (G) ('59) .24 .18
693 A255 20c on 23c bl & blk ('59) .24 .18
Set value 1.50 1.10

On No. 686 the words "Correo Extra Rapido" are obliterated in dark blue.

Father Rafael Almanza and Church of San Diego, Bogota — A290

1958, Oct. 23 Photo. *Perf. 14x13*

695 A290 10c purple .15 .15
Nos. 695,C313-C314 (3) .55
Set value .20

For overprint see #C336.

Msgr. R. M. Carrasquilla and Church — A291

1959, Jan. 22 *Perf. 14x13*

696 A291 10c dk red brn .15 .15
Nos. 696,C315-C316 (3) .95
Set value .26

Cent. of the birth of Msgr. R. M. Carrasquilla (1857-1930), rector of Our Lady of the Rosary Seminary, Bogotá. For overprints see #C335, C341.

Miss Universe 1959 — A292

Jorge Eliecer Gaitan — A293

1959, June 26 Photo. *Perf. 11½*

697 A292 10c multi .15 .15
Nos. 697,C317-C318 (3) 34.05 33.75

Luz Marina Zuluaga, Miss Universe, 1959. For overprint see No. C342.

1959, July 28 Engr. *Perf. 12x13½*

698 A293 10c on 3c gray bl (Bl) .15 .15
699 A293 30c rose vio .40 .20
Nos. 698-699,C319-C320 (4) 3.35 2.85

Issued in honor of Jorge Eliecer Gaitan (1898-1948), lawyer and politician.

No. 698 exists without blue surcharge.

Gen. Francisco de Paula Santander — A294

Designs: Nos. 701, 703, Simon Bolivar.

1959 Litho. Wmk. 331 *Perf. 12½*

700 A294 5c brown & yel .15 .15
701 A294 5c ultra & bl .15 .15
702 A294 10c gray & grn .15 .15
703 A294 10c gray & red .15 .15
Nos. 700-703,C389 (5) 3.60
Set value .80

Capitol, Bogota A295

1959

704 A295 2c dk bl & red brn .15 .15
705 A295 3c blk brn & lil .15 .15
Set value .20 .18

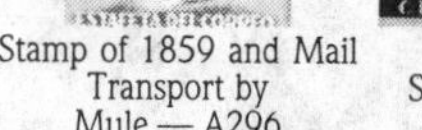

Stamp of 1859 and Mail Transport by Mule — A296

Two-Toed Sloth — A297

Designs (various stamps of 1859 and): 10c, Mail boat on the Magdalena river. 25c, Train.

Unwmk.

1959, Dec. 1 Photo. *Perf. 12*

709 A296 5c org & grn .15 .15
710 A296 10c rose cl & bl .15 .15
711 A296 15c car rose & grn .32 .32
712 A296 25c bl & red brn .42 .32
Nos. 709-712,C351-C354 (8) 4.69 2.93

Centenary of Colombian postage stamps.

1960, Feb. 12 *Perf. 12*

Designs: 10c, Alexander von Humboldt. 20c, Spider monkey.

713 A297 5c grnsh bl & brn .25 .15
714 A297 10c blk & dp car .25 .15
715 A297 20c cit & gray brn .25 .15
Nos. 713-715,C357-C359 (6) 4.75 3.25

Cent. of the death of Alexander von Humboldt (1769-1859), German naturalist and geographer.
For overprint and surcharge see #C411, C413.

Anthurium Andreanum A298

Lincoln Statue, Washington A299

Flower: 20c, Espeletia grandiflora.

1960, May 10

716 A298 5c multi .15 .15
717 A298 20c brn, yel & gray ol .15 .15
Nos. 716-717,C360-C370 (13) 12.90 14.80

See #C420-C425. For overprint see #C412.

Perf. 10½

1960, June 10 Litho. Wmk. 331

718 A299 20c rose lil & blk .18 .20
Nos. 718,C375-C376 (3) 1.28 .95

Floredo House, Cradle of the Republic A300

Arms of Santa Cruz de Mompox — A301

Design: 5c, First coins of Republic.

Unwmk.

1960, July 19 Photo. *Perf. 12*

719 A301 5c grn & ocher .15 .15
720 A300 20c ol bis & mar .15 .15
721 A301 20c multi .15 .18
Nos. 719-721,C377-C385 (12) 5.80 4.58

Colombia's independence, 150th anniv.

St. Isidore and Farm Animals — A302

Design: 20c, Nativity by Gregorio de Arce Vasquez y Ceballos.

1960, Sept. 26 *Perf. 12*

722 A302 10c multi .15 .15
723 A302 20c multi .15 .15
Nos. 722-723,C387 (3) .46
Set value .35

St. Isidore the Farmer, patron saint of the rural people.
See Nos. 747, C388, C439-C440.

UN Headquarters and Emblem — A303

Wmk. 331

1960, Oct. 24 Litho. *Perf. 11*

724 A303 20c blk & pink .15 .15

Souvenir Sheet

Imperf

725 A303 50c dk brn, brt grn & blk 2.50 2.50

15th anniversary of the United Nations.

Pan-American Highway through Colombia — A304

Alfonso Lopez — A305

1961, Mar. 7 Unwmk. *Perf. 10½x11*

726 A304 20c brn & grnsh bl .60 .60
Nos. 726,C390-C393 (5) 2.60 3.20

8th Pan-American Highway Congress, Bogota, May 20-29, 1960.

1961, Mar. 22 Photo. *Perf. 12½*

727 A305 10c brt rose & brn .16 .15
728 A305 20c vio & brn .16 .15
Nos. 727-728,C394-C395 (4) 1.00
Set value .38

Alfonso Lopez (1886-1959), President of Colombia. See No. C396.

Cauca River Bridge, Cali A306

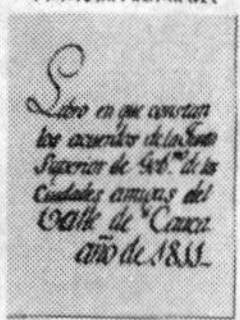

Page from Resolutions of Confederated Cities — A307

1961-62 *Perf. 12½x13, 13½x13*

729 A306 10c red brn, bl, grn & red ('62) .15 .15
730 A307 20c pale brn & blk .15 .15
Nos. 729-730,C397-C401 (7) 2.75
Set value 1.30

50th anniversary (in 1960) of the Department of Valle del Cauca.

View of Cucuta and Arms A308

Design: No. 732, Arms of Ocana and Pamplona.

1961, Aug. 29 *Perf. 13x13½*

731 A308 20c bl, blk, yel & red .15 .15
732 A308 20c ocher, ultra & red .15 .15
Nos. 731-732,C402-C403 (4) 1.05
Set value .25

50th anniv. (in 1960) of the Department of North Santander.

Arms of Popayan A309

Basketball A310

Designs: No. 734, Arms of Barranquilla. No. 735, Arms of Bucaramanga.

Perf. 12½x13

1961, Oct. 10 Unwmk.

Arms in Multicolor

733 A309 10c blue & silver .15 .15
734 A309 20c blue & yellow .15 .15
735 A309 20c blue & gold .15 .15
Nos. 733-735,C404-C408 (8) 2.40
Set value .60

Issued to honor Atlantico Department.

1961, Dec. 16 Litho. *Perf. 13½x14*

736 A310 20c shown .15 .15
737 A310 20c Runners .15 .15
738 A310 20c Boxers .24 .15
739 A310 25c Soccer .15 .15
Nos. 736-739,C414-C418 (9) 3.04
Set value 1.00

4th Bolivarian Games, Barranquilla, 1961.

Colombian Anti-Malaria Emblem — A311

Engineers Society Emblem — A312

Design: 50c, Malaria eradication emblem and mosquito in swamp.

1962, Apr. 12 Unwmk. *Perf. 12*

740 A311 20c lt bis & red .15 .15
741 A311 50c bis & ultra .16 .15
Nos. 740-741,C426-C428 (5) 4.45 4.37

1962, June 12 Photo. *Perf. 11½x12*

742 A312 10c multi .25 .22
Nos. 742,C429-C432 (5) 2.30 2.18

Colombian Society of Engineers, 75th anniv.

Flags of American Nations — A313

Woman Casting Ballot and Statue of Policarpa Salavarrieta — A314

1962, June 28 *Perf. 13*

Flags in National Colors

743 A313 25c blk & org ver .15 .15

Souvenir Sheet

744 A313 2.50p blk & yel 3.00 3.00

70th anniv. of the founding of the Organization of American States.
See No. C433.

Perf. 12x12½

1962, July 20 Litho. Wmk. 229

745 A314 10c lt bl, gray & blk .15 .15

Issued to publicize women's political rights. See Nos. 752, C434, C448-C450.

Scouts at Campfire and Tents A315

Railroad Map of Colombia A316

Perf. 11½x12

1962, July 28 Photo. Unwmk.

746 A315 10c brt grnsh bl & brn .32 .32
Nos. 746,C435-C438 (5) 5.41 4.74

Colombian Boy Scouts, 30th anniv.

St. Isidore Type of 1960 Redrawn

1962, Aug. 28 *Perf. 12*

747 A302 10c pink & multi .15 .15
Nos. 747,C439-C440 (3) 3.80 3.80

The frame on No. 747 is solid color with white inscription similar to type AP82.

1962, Sept. 28 *Perf. 12½*

748 A316 10c blk, gray, grn & red .15 .15
Nos. 748,C441-C444 (5) 5.60 4.35

Progress of Colombian railroads and the completion of the Atlantic Line from Santa Marta to Bogota.

Post Horn — A317

Perf. 13½x14

1962, Oct. 18 Litho. Wmk. 346

749 A317 20c gold, dl gray vio & blk .15 .15
Nos. 749,C445-C446 (3) .65
Set value .20

50th anniv. of the founding of the Postal Union of the Americas and Spain, UPAE.

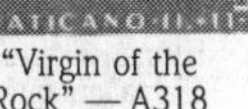
"Virgin of the Rock" — A318

Red Cross Centenary Emblem — A319

1963, Mar. 11 **Wmk. 346**
750 A318 60c multi .15 .15

Vatican II, the 21st Ecumenical Council of the Roman Catholic Church. See No. C447.

1963, May 1 ***Perf. 12x12½***
751 A319 5c olive bister & red .15 .15

Centenary of International Red Cross.

Women's Rights Type of 1962

1963, July 11 **Wmk. 346**
752 A314 5c org, gray & blk .15 .15
Nos. 752,C448-C450 (4) .94
Set value .20

Manuel Mejia J. and Flag of National Coffee Growers Assn. A320

Perf. 12½x13

1965, Feb. 10 **Engr.** **Unwmk.**
753 A320 25c rose & blk .15 .15
Nos. 753,C464-C466 (4) 4.30 .85

Manuel Mejia J. (1887-1958), banker and manager of the National Coffee Growers Association.

Julio Arboleda (1817-62), Writer, Soldier and Statesman A321

1966, Mar. 9 **Litho.** ***Perf. 14x13½***
754 A321 5c lt brn, lt yel grn & blk .15 .15

Spanish Galleon, 16th Century A322

History of Maritime Mail: 15c, Rio Hacha brigantine, 1850. 20c, Uraba canoe. 40c, Magdalena River steamship and barge, 1900. 50c, Modern motor ship and sea gull.

1966, June 16 **Photo.** **Unwmk.**
755 A322 5c org & multi .15 .15
756 A322 15c car rose, blk & brn .15 .15
757 A322 20c brt grn, org & blk .15 .15
758 A322 40c dp bl & multi .20 .15
759 A322 50c pale bl & multi .50 .22
Nos. 755-759 (5) 1.15
Set value .44

Plumed Hogfish A323

Design: 10p, Bat ray and brittle starfish.

1966, Aug. 25 **Photo.** ***Perf. 12½x13***
760 A323 80c multi .16 .15
761 A323 10p multi 5.00 6.00
Nos. 760-761,C481-C483 (5) 15.26 16.05

Arms of Venezuela, Colombia and Chile — A324

1966, Oct. 11 **Litho.** ***Perf. 14x13½***
762 A324 40c yel & multi .15 .15
Nos. 762,C484-C485 (3) .59
Set value .20

Visits of Eduardo Frei and Raul Leoni, presidents of Chile and Venezuela.

Camilo Torres, 1766-1816, Lawyer — A325

Portraits: 60c, Jorge Tadeo Lozano (1771-1816), naturalist. 1p, Francisco Antonio Zea (1776-1822), naturalist and politician.

Perf. 13½x14

1967, Jan. 18 **Litho.** **Unwmk.**
763 A325 25c vio & bis .15 .15
764 A325 60c dk red brn & bis .15 .15
765 A325 1p grn & bis .30 .15
Set value, #763-765, C486-C487 .75 .42

Issued to honor famous men of Colombia.

Map of South America and Arms — A326

1967, Feb. 2 **Litho.** ***Perf. 14x13½***
766 A326 40c multi .15 .15
767 A326 60c multi .15 .15
Nos. 766-767,C488 (3) .65
Set value .30

Declaration of Bogota for cooperation and world peace, signed by Colombia, Chile, Ecuador, Peru and Venezuela.

Monochaetum Orchid and Bee — A327

Orchid: 2p, Passiflora vitifolia and butterfly.

1967, May 23 **Litho.** ***Perf. 14***
768 A327 25c multi .15 .15
769 A327 2p multi 1.00 1.00
Nos. 768-769,C489-C491 (5) 2.94 1.75

1st Natl. Orchid Exhib. and the Topical Phil. Flora and Fauna Exhib., Medellin, Apr. 1967.

Lions Emblem — A328

SENA Emblem — A329

1967, July 12 **Litho.** ***Perf. 13½x14***
770 A328 10p multi 3.00 2.00

50th anniv. of Lions Intl. See No. C492.

Lithographed and Embossed

1967, Sept. 20 **Unwmk.**
771 A329 5p gold, brt grn & blk 1.10 .25

10th anniv. of Natl. Apprenticeship Service, SENA. See No. C494.

Gold Diadem in Calima Style — A330

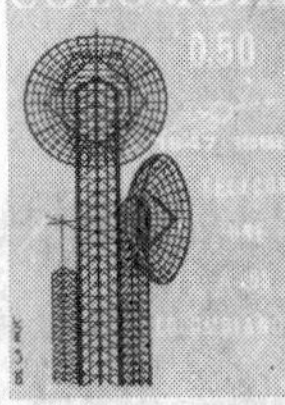
Radar Installation — A331

Pre-Columbian Art: 3p, Gold statuette, ornamental globe and bird, horiz.

Perf. 13½x14, 14x13½

1967, Oct. 13 **Photo.**
772 A330 1.60p brt rose lil, gold & brn .50 .15
773 A330 3p dk bl, gold & brn .70 .28
Nos. 772-773,C495-C497 (5) 11.25 9.15

Meeting of the UPU Committee of Postal Studies, Bogota, Oct., 1967.

1968, May 14 **Litho.** ***Perf. 13½x14***

Design: 1p, Map of communications network.

774 A331 50c brt yel grn, blk & org brn .15 .15
775 A331 1p multi .20 .15
Nos. 774-775,C498-C499 (4) .66
Set value .25

20th anniv. of the National Telecommunications Service (TELECOM).

The Eucharist — A332

St. Augustin, by Gregorio Vasquez — A333

1968, June 6 **Litho.** ***Perf. 13½x14***
776 A332 60c multi .15 .15
Nos. 776,C500-C501 (3) .60
Set value .20

39th Eucharistic Congress, Bogotá, Aug. 18-25.

1968, Aug. 13 **Photo.** ***Perf. 13***

Designs: 60c, The Gathering of Manna, by Gregorio Vasquez. 1p, The Marriage of the Virgin, by Baltazar de Figueroa. 5p, Jeweled monstrance, c. 1700. 10p, Pope Paul VI, painting by Roman Franciscan nuns.

777 A333 25c multicolored .15 .15
778 A333 60c multicolored .15 .15
779 A333 1p multicolored .15 .15
780 A333 5p multicolored .52 .15
781 A333 10p multicolored 1.10 .45
a. Souvenir sheet of 2 1.90 .95
Nos. 777-781,C502-C506 (10) 7.50
Set value 2.90

39th Eucharistic Congress. Bogotá, Aug. 18-25. No. 781a contains two imperf. stamps similar to Nos. 780-781.

Pope Paul VI — A334

Arms of National University — A335

1968, Aug. 22 **Litho.** ***Perf. 13½x14***
782 A334 25c multi .15 .15
Nos. 782,C507-C509 (4) .80
Set value .30

Visit of Pope Paul VI to Colombia, Aug. 22-24.

1968, Oct. 29 **Litho.** ***Perf. 13½x14***
783 A335 80c multi .15 .15

Centenary of the founding of the National University. See No. C510.

Stamp of Antioquia, 1868 — A336

Institute Emblem — A337

1968, Nov. 20 **Litho.** ***Perf. 12x12½***
784 A336 30c emer & bl .15 .15

Souvenir Sheet

785 A336 5p lt olive & blue 2.50 2.50

Cent. of the 1st postage stamps of Antioquia and the 7th Natl. Phil. Exhib., Medellin, Nov. 20-29.

1969, Mar. 5 **Litho.** ***Perf. 13½x14***
786 A337 20c multi .15 .15

25th anniv. (in 1967) of the Inter-American Agricultural Sciences Institute. See No. C511.

Battle of Boyaca (Detail), by José Maria Espinosa — A338

Design: 30c, Army of liberation crossing Pisba Pass, by Francisco Antonio Caro.

1969, July 24 **Litho.** ***Perf. 13½x14***
787 A338 20c gold & multi .15 .15
788 A338 30c gold & multi .15 .15
Nos. 787-788,C517 (3) .78
Set value .30

Sesquicentennial of the fight for independence.

"Poverty" A339

1970, Mar. 1 **Litho.** ***Perf. 14***
789 A339 30c bl & multi .15 .15

Colombian Institute for Family Welfare and 10th anniv. of the Children's Rights Law.

The index in each volume of the Scott Catalogue contains many listings that help identify stamps.

Greek Mask and Pre-Columbian Symbol of Literary Contest — A340

1970, Sept. 12 Litho. *Perf. 14x13½*

790 A340 30c dk brn, red org & ocher .15 .15

3rd Latin American Theatrical Festival of the Universities, Manizales, Sept. 12-20.

Colombian Stamps, Envelope and Emblem A341

1970, Sept. 24 Litho. *Perf. 14x13½*

791 A341 2p brt bl & multi .30 .15

Issued to publicize Philatelic Week.

Arms of Ibague and Discobolus A342

1970, Oct. 13

792 A342 80c buff, emer & sepia .20 .15

9th National Games in Ibague.

St. Theresa, by Baltazar de Figueroa — A343

1970, Oct. 28 Litho. *Perf. 13½x14*

793 A343 2p multi .40 .15

Elevation of St. Theresa (1515-1582), to Doctor of the Church. See No. C568. For overprint see No. C568.

Casa Cural A344

1971, May 20 Litho. *Perf. 14x13½*

794 A344 1.10p multi .26 .15

Fourth centenary (in 1970) of the founding of Guacari, Valle. See No. 809.

Dancers and Music, Currulao — A345

Design: 1p, Chicha Maya dancers and music.

1971 Litho. *Perf. 13½x14*

795 A345	1p pink & multi	.30	.15
796 A345	1.10p lt bl & multi	.30	.15
	Set value		.16

Souvenir Sheets

Imperf

797	Sheet of 3	3.25	3.00
a.	A345 2.50p Napanga	.35	.35
b.	A345 2.50p Joropo	.35	.35
c.	A345 5p Guabina	.70	.70
798	Sheet of 3	3.25	3.00
a.	A345 4p Bambuco	.55	.55
b.	A345 4p Cumbia	.55	.55
c.	A345 4p Currulao	.55	.55

Issue dates: No. 795, Dec. 20; No. 796, Aug. 5; Nos. 797-798, Aug. 10.

Constitutional Assembly, by Delgado — A346

1971, Oct. 2 *Perf. 14*

801 A346 80c multi .20 .15

Sequicentennial of Gran Colombian Constitutional Assembly in Rosario del Cucuta. See No. C589. For overprint see No. C589.

Arrows Emblem — A347

1972, Feb. 24 *Perf. 13½x14*

802 A347 60c blk & gray .28 .15

Inter-Governmental Committee on European Migration, 20th anniversary.

Student and World Map — A348

1972, Mar. 15 *Perf. 14x13½*

803 A348 1.10p lt grn & brn .20 .15

20th anniv. of ICETEX, an organization which furnishes financial help for educational purposes and for technical studies abroad.

UN Emblem, Soldier and Frigate A349

1972, Apr. 7

804 A349 1.20p lt bl & multi .20 .15

20th anniv. of the Colombian Battalion in Korea.

Mother Francisca Josefa del Castillo — A350

Handicraft — A351

1972, Apr. 6 *Perf. 13½x14*

805 A350 1.20p brn & multi .20 .15

Tercentenary (in 1971) of the birth of Mother Francisca Josefa del Castillo, Poor Clare abbess and writer.

1972, Apr. 11

806 A351 1.10p multi .35 .15

Nos. 806,C569-C571 (4) 1.55 .70

Colombian artisans.

Maxillaria Triloris — A352

Emeralds — A353

1972, Apr. 20

807 A352 20p green & multi 3.75 1.25

10th Natl. Phil. Exhib., Medellin.

1972, June 16 Litho. *Perf. 13½x14*

808 A353 1.10p multi .50 .15

Type of 1971

Design: Antonio Nariño House.

1972, June 17 *Perf. 14x13½*

809 A344 1.10p multi .50 .15

4th centenary, town of Leyva.

San Andres and Providencia Islands — A354

1972, June 24 *Perf. 13½x14*

810 A354 60c bl & multi .20 .15

Sesquicentennial of annexation by Colombia of San Andres and Providencia Islands.

Postal Service Emblem — A355

1972, Nov. 15 Litho. *Perf. 12½x12*

811 A355 1.10p emerald .15 .15

Family — A356

1972, Nov. 23

812 A356 60c orange .15 .15

Social progress.

Radio League Emblem A357

Human Figure, Tamalameque A358

1973, Apr. 6 Litho. *Perf. 12x12½*

813 A357 60c lt bl, ultra & red .20 .15

40th anniversary of the Colombian Radio Amateurs' League.

1973, June 15 Litho. *Perf. 13½x14*

Excavated Ceramic Artifacts: 1p, Winged urn, Tairona. 1.10p, Jug, Muisca.

814 A358	60c lt bl & multi	.24	.15
815 A358	1p org & multi	.45	.15
816 A358	1.10p vio bl & multi	.30	.15
	Nos. 814-816,C583-C586 (7)	4.14	
	Set value		1.75

Antonio Nariño, by José M. Espinosa — A359

Child — A360

1973, Dec. 13 Litho. *Perf. 13½x14*

817 A359 60c multi .15 .15

Sesquicentennial of the death of General Antonio Nariño (1765-1823).

1973, Dec. 17

818 A360 1.10p multi .20 .15

National Campaign for Children's Welfare.

Symbols of Financial Controls A361

1973, Dec. 20 Litho. *Perf. 14x13½*

819 A361 80c ultra, ocher & blk .15 .15

50th anniv. of Comptroller-general's Office.

Mother Laura Montoya — A362

1974, June 18 Litho. *Perf. 13½x14*

820 A362 1p multi .20 .15

Mother Laura Montoya (1874-1949), founder and Mother Superior of the Missionaries of Mary Immaculata and St. Catherine of Siena.

Runner and Games' Emblem A363

1974, July 18 Litho. *Perf. 14x13½*
821 A363 2p ver, yel & brn .25 .15

10th National Games, Pereira.

José Rivera A364

1974, Aug. 3 Litho. *Perf. 14x13½*
822 A364 10p grn & multi 1.10 .15

50th anniv. of the publication of "La Voragine" (The Whirlpool) by José Eustasio Rivera.

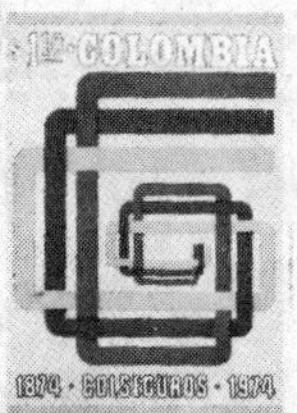

Abstract Pattern — A365

Train Emerging from Tunnel — A366

1974, Oct. 24 Litho. *Perf. 13½x14*
823 A365 1.10p multi .25 .15

Cent. of Natl. Insurance Co. See No. C610.

1974, Nov. 27 Litho. *Perf. 13½x14*
824 A366 1.10p multi .20 .15

Centenary of the Antioquia railroad.

Boy, Puppy and Soccer Ball — A367

Christmas: 1p, Girl with racket and kitten.

1974, Dec. 9
825 A367 80c multi .20 .15
826 A367 1p multi .20 .15
Set value .15

A368

1975, Apr. 11 Litho. *Perf. 14x13½*
827 A368 80c Gold Animal .40 .15
828 A368 1.10p Gold necklace .40 .15
Nos. 827-828,C621-C622 (4) 6.20
Set value .85

Pre-Columbian Sinu culture artifacts. For surcharge see No. 840.

Guglielmo Marconi — A369

Santa Marta Cathedral — A370

1975, June 2 Litho. *Perf. 13½x14*
829 A369 3p multi .16 .15

Birth centenary of Guglielmo Marconi (1874-1937), Italian electrical engineer and inventor.

1975, July 26
830 A370 80c multi .15 .15

400th anniv. of Santa Marta City. See #C623.

Rafael Nuñez — A371

Arms of Medellin — A372

1975, Sept. 28 Litho. *Perf. 13½x14*
831 A371 1.10p multi .15 .15

Rafael Nunez (1825-1894), philosopher, poet, political leader, birth sesquicentenary.
For surcharge see No. 848.

1975-79 *Perf. 13½x14, 12 (1.20p)*

832	A372	1p	shown	.30	.15
833	A372	1.20p	Ibagué	.15	.15
834	A372	1.20p	Tunja	.15	.15
835	A372	1.50p	Cucuta	.30	.15
836	A372	1.50p	Cartagena	.15	.15
836A	A372	4p	Sogamoso	.50	.15
837	A372	5p	Popayan	.30	.15
838	A372	5p	Barranquilla	.28	.15
839	A372	10p	San Gil	.50	.15
839A	A372	10p	Socorro	.50	.15
			Nos. 832-839A (10)	3.13	
			Set value		.75

1p for the tercentenary of Medellin; No. 835, the cent. of Cucuta's reconstruction.
Issued: 1975- 1p, Nov. 4; No. 835, Nov. 29; 1976- No. 836, Feb. 10; No. 833, July 30; No. 834, Dec. 20; 1977- No. 837, Aug. 30; No. 838, Sept. 20; 1979- 10p, Aug. 9; 4p, Sept. 14.
See #905-913, C818. For surcharge see #849.

No. 827 Surcharged **$ 1.20**

1975 *Perf. 14x13½*
840 A368 1.20p on 80c multi .15 .15

Purace Indians, Cauca — A373

1976, Nov. 10 Litho. *Perf. 13½x14*
841 A373 1.50p multi .15 .15

Callicore A374

Designs: 5p, Morpho (butterfly). 20p, Anthurium.

1976, Nov. 17 *Perf. 12*
842 A374 3p multicolored .85 .15
843 A374 5p multicolored 1.25 .20
844 A374 20p multicolored 3.75 .75
Nos. 842-844 (3) 5.85 1.10

Rotary Emblem — A375

1976, Dec. 3 Litho. *Perf. 12*
845 A375 1p multicolored .15 .15

Rotary Club of Colombia, 50th anniversary.

Declaration of Independence, by John Trumbull — A376

1976, Dec. 21 Litho. *Perf. 12*
846 A376 Strip of 3 9.00 10.50
a.-c. 30p any single 2.75 2.00

American Bicentennial. No. 846 printed in sheets of 4 triptychs.

Policeman with Dog — A377

1976, Dec. 29 *Perf. 13½x14*
847 A377 1.50p multicolored .20 .15

Honoring the National Police.
For surcharge see No. 850.

Nos. 831, 834, 847 Surcharged in Light Brown

1977, June Litho. *Perf. 13½x14, 12*
848 A371 2p on 1.10p multi .20 .15
849 A372 2p on 1.20p multi .15 .15
850 A377 2p on 1.50p multi .25 .15
Nos. 848-850 (3) .60
Set value .25

Souvenir Sheet

Postal Museum, Bogota — A378

1977, July 27 Litho. *Perf. 14*
855 A378 25p multi 2.50 2.50

Postal Museum, Bogota.

Mother and Child — A379

1977-78 Litho. *Perf. 12*
856 A379 2p multi .15 .15
857 A379 2.50p multi ('78) .90 .15
Set value .15

National good nutrition plan. Issue dates: 2p, Aug. 30. 2.50p, Jan. 26.

Jacana and Eichhornia A380

Fidel Cano, by Francisco Cano A381

Design: 20p, Mayan cotinga and pyrostegia venusta.

1977, Sept. 6 Litho. *Perf. 14*
858 A380 10p multicolored 2.00 .25
859 A380 20p multicolored 3.00 .40
Nos. 858-859,C644-C647 (6) 8.20 1.25

1977, Sept. 16 *Perf. 14*
860 A381 4p multicolored .20 .15

90th anniversary of El Espectador, newspaper founded by Fidel Cano.

Abacus and Alphabet A382

Cattleya Triannae A383

1977, Sept. 16 *Perf. 13½x14*
861 A382 3p multicolored .15 .15

Popular education.

1978-79 Litho. *Perf. 12*
862 A383 2.50p multi .15 .15
863 A383 3p multi ('79) .16 .15
Set value .15

Issue dates: 2.50p, Apr. 18. 3p, May 10.

Sprinting and Games Emblem A384

Sports: a, sprinting. b, basketball. c, baseball. d, boxing. e. bicycling. f, fencing. g, soccer. h, gymnastics. i, judo. j, weight lifting. k, wrestling. l, swimming. m, tennis. n, target shooting. o, volleyball. p, water polo.

1978, June 27 Litho. *Perf. 14*
868 Sheet of 16 22.50 3.50
a.-p. A384 10p, any single .90 .20

13th Central American and Caribbean Games, Medellin.

"Sigma 2" by Alvaro Herrán A385

1978, June 30
869 A385 8p multicolored .40 .16

Chamber of Commerce, Bogota, centenary.

Gen. Tomás Cipriano de Mosquera (1778-1878), Statesman A386

1978, Oct. 6 Litho. *Perf. 12*
870 A386 6p multicolored .42 .15

Anthurium Narinenses — A387

1979, July 23 *Perf. 12*
871 A387 3p red & multi .16 .15
872 A387 3p purple & multi .16 .15
873 A387 3p rose & purple .16 .15
874 A387 3p white & multi .16 .15
a. Block of 4, #871-874 .65 .25

Gen. Rafael Uribe, by Acevedo Bernal — A388

1979, Oct. 31 Litho. *Perf. 12*
875 A388 8p multicolored .40 .15

Gen. Rafael Uribe, statesman, 60th death anniversary.

Village, by Leonor Alarcon — A389

1979, Nov. 22 *Perf. 14*
876 A389 15p multicolored 1.00 .35

Community Work Boards, 20th anniversary.

Introduction of Color Television A390

1980, Mar. 4 Litho. *Perf. 14*
877 A390 5p multicolored .35 .15

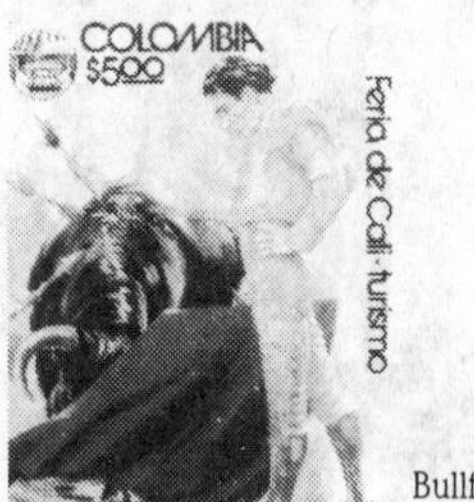

Bullfight, Arms of Cali — A391

1980, Mar. 25
878 A391 5p multicolored .50 .15

Cali Tourist Festival, Dec. 25, 1979-Jan. 2, 1980.

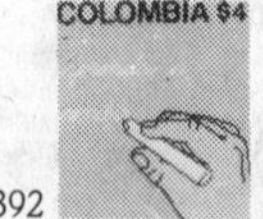

"Learn to Write" — A392

1980, Apr. 25 Litho. *Perf. 12½*
879 Block of 30 10.00 10.00
a. A392 4p, any single .20 .15

Each stamp shows letter of alphabet and corresponding animal or subject. Issued in sheets of 90 (30x3).

Villavicencio Festival — A393

Design: 9p, Vallenato festival.

1980 Litho. *Perf. 14*
880 A393 5p multicolored .30 .15
881 A393 9p multicolored .30 .15

Issue dates: 5p, July 15; 9p, June 17.

Gustavo Uribe Ramirez and Tree A394

1980, Aug. 5 Litho. *Perf. 12*
882 A394 10p multicolored .30 .15

Gustavo Uribe Ramirez (1893-1968), ecologist.

Narino Palace (Former Presidential Residence) — A395

1980, Sept. 19 Litho. *Perf. 14*
883 A395 5p multicolored .45 .15

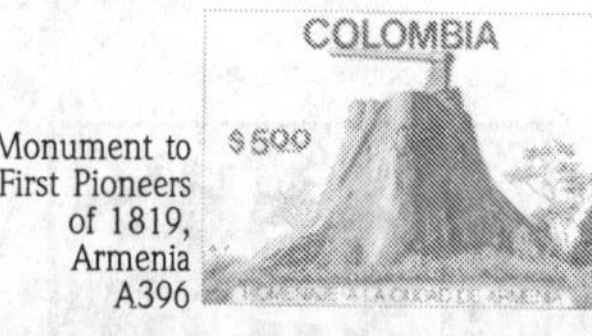

Monument to First Pioneers of 1819, Armenia A396

1980, Oct. 14
884 A396 5p multicolored .40 .15

11th National Games, Neiva — A397

Fight against Cancer — A398

1980, Nov. 28 *Perf. 13½x14*
885 A397 5p multicolored .45 .15

1980, Dec. 9
886 A398 10p multicolored .30 .15

Xavier University Law Faculty, 50th Anniversary A399

1980, Dec. 16 Litho. *Perf. 14½*
887 A399 20p multicolored .55 .15

Death of Bolivar — A400

1980, Dec. 17 *Perf. 12*
888 A400 25p multicolored 1.00 .60

Simon Bolivar, death sesquicentennial. See No. C696.

José Maria Obando, President of Colombia A401

115th Anniv. of Constitution (Former Presidents): b, Jose Hilario Lopez. c, Manuel Murillo Toro. d, Santiago Perez. e, Rafael Reyes. f, Carlos E. Restrepo. g, Jose Vicente Concha. h, Miguel Abadia Mendez. i, Eduardo Santos. j, Mariano Ospina Perez.

1981, June 9 Litho. *Perf. 12*
889 Strip of 10 1.50
a.-j. A401 5p multicolored .15 .15

1981, Sept. 23 Litho. *Perf. 12*

Designs: a, Rafael Nunez (1825-94). b, Marco Fidel Suarez (1855-1927). c, Pedro Nel Ospina (1858-1927). d, Enrique Olaya Herrera (1880-1937). e, Alfonso Lopez Pumarejo (1886-1959). f, Aquileo Parra (1825-1900). g, Santos Gutierrez (1820-72). h, Tomas Cipriano de Mosquera (1789-1878). i, Mariano Ospina Rodriguez. j, Pedro Alcantara Herran (1800-72).

890 Strip of 10 25.00
a.-j. A401 7p multicolored 2.50 .35

1981, Aug. 11 Litho. *Perf. 12*

Designs like No. 889.

891 Strip of 10 40.00
a.-j. A401 7p multicolored 4.00 .75

1981, Nov. 11 Litho. *Perf. 12*

Designs: a, Manuel Maria Mallarino. b, Santos Acosta. c, Eustorgio Salgar. d, Julian Trujillo. e, Francisco Javier Zaldua. f, Guillermo Leon Valencia. g, Laureano Gomez. h, Manuel A. Sanclemente. i, Miguel Antonio Caro. j, Jose Eusebio Otalora.

892 Strip of 10 18.00
a.-j. A401 7p multicolored 1.75 .25

1981, Dec. 15 Litho. *Perf. 12*

Designs: a, Ruben Piedrahita Arango. b, Jorge Holguin. c, Ramon Gonzalez Valencia. d, Jose Manuel Marroquin. e, Carlos Holguin. f, Bartolome Calvo. g, Sergio Camargo. h, Jose Maria Rojas Garrido. i, J.M. Campo Serrano. j, Eliseo Payan.

893 Strip of 10 14.00
a.-j. A401 7p multicolored 1.40 .20

1982, May 3 *Perf. 12*

Designs: a, Simon Bolivar. b, Francisco de Paula Santander. c, Joaquin Mosquera. d, Domingo Caicedo. e, Jose Ignacio de Marquez. f, Roberto Urdaneta Arbelaez. g, Carlos Lozano y Lozano. h, Guillermo Quintero Calderon. i, Jose de Obaldia. j, Juan de Dios Aranzazu.

894 Strip of 10 12.00
a.-j. A401 7p multicolored 1.25 .20

See No. 1110.

Jose Maria Villa and West Bridge over Cauca River — A404

1981, Nov. 25 Litho. *Perf. 14x13½*
895 A404 60p multicolored 1.00 .25

Agrarian, Mineral and Industrial Credit Bank, 50th Anniv. — A405

Los Nevados Park — A406

1981, Dec. 9 Litho. *Perf. 14*
896 A405 15p multicolored .35 .15

1981, Dec. 10 Litho. *Perf. 13½x14*
897 A406 20p multicolored .60 .15

Girl Sitting on Fence — A407

1982, Feb. 22 Litho. *Perf. 12½x12*
898 Strip of 3 2.00 1.10
a. A407 30p shown .60 .25
b. A407 30p Girl, basket .60 .25
c. A407 30p Boy, wheelbarrow .60 .25

Floral Bouquet — A408

Hipotecario Bank, 50th Anniv. — A409

Designs: Various floral arrangements.

1982, July 28
900 Strip of 10 3.50 3.50
a. A408 7p, any single .30 .15

1982, July 29 *Perf. 14*
901 A409 9p black & green .20 .15

St. Thomas Aquinas (1225-1274) — A410

Paintings by Zurbaran.

1982 Litho. *Perf. 12*
902 A410 5p multicolored .15 .15
903 A410 5p St. Teresa of Avila .15 .15
904 A410 5p St. Francis of Assisi .15 .15
Nos. 902-904 (3) .45
Set value .15

Issued: #902, Aug. 6; #903, Sept. 28; #904, Oct. 4.

Arms Type of 1975

1982-90 Litho. *Perf. 14, 12 (50p)*

905	A372	10p shown	.24	.15
905A	A372	10p San Juan de Pasto	.24	.15
906	A372	16p Rionegro	.45	.20
907	A372	20p Santa Fe de Bogota	.42	.20
907A	A372	20p Santiago de Cali	.24	.15
908	A372	23p Honda	.55	.25
911	A372	50p Cartago	.30	.15
913	A372	55p Antioquia ('86)	.60	.25
		Nos. 905-913 (8)	3.04	1.50

Issue dates: 16p, 23p, No. 905, Dec. 7; No. 907, Mar. 1, 1983; No. 905A, Apr. 12, 1983; No. 907A, July 25, 1986; 55p, Aug. 5, 1986; 50p, May 30, 1990.

See No. C818.

This is an expanding set. Numbers will change if necessary.

Gabriel Marquez, 1982 Nobel Prize, Literature — A412

1982, Dec. 10 *Perf. 13½x14*

917 A412 7p gray & grn .20 .15

See No. C731-C732.

Public Education Bicentenary (Society of Mary for Education) A413

1983, May 6

918 A413 9p gold & blk .35 .20

José Maria Espinosa Prieto, Painter — A414

250th Anniv. of City of Cucuta — A415

1983, June 3 *Perf. 12*

919 A414 9p Self-portrait, 1860 .16 .15

1983, June 23 Litho. *Perf. 12*

920 A415 9p multicolored .16 .15

Porfirio Barba-Jacob (1883-1942), Poet — A416

1983, July 29 Litho. *Perf. 13½x14*

921 A416 9p Portrait .16 .15

Simon Bolivar, 200th Birth Anniv. A417

1983, July 24 *Perf. 12*

922 A417 9p multicolored .20 .15

See Nos. C736-C737.

Royal Spanish Botanical Exhibition, 200th Anniv. — A418

1983, Aug. 18 *Perf. 14*

923	A418	9p Cinchona lancefolia	.20	.15
924	A418	9p Passiflora laurifolia	.20	.15
925	A418	60p Cinchona cordiflora	1.10	.50
		Nos. 923-925,C738-C740 (6)	3.45	
		Set value		1.08

Dawn in the Andes, by Alejandro Obregon A420

1983, Oct. 5 Litho. *Perf. 12*

928 A420 20p multicolored .40 .15

See No. C741.

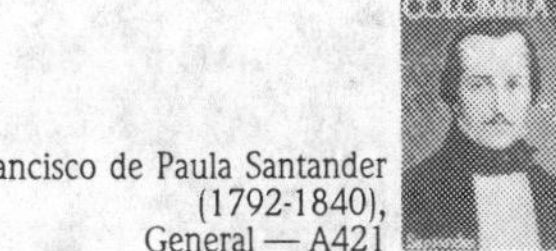

Francisco de Paula Santander (1792-1840), General — A421

1984, Mar. 6 Litho. *Perf. 14½x14*

929	A421	12p light olive green	.20	.15
930	A421	12p pale carmine	.20	.15
931	A421	12p light ultra	.20	.15
		Nos. 929-931 (3)	.60	
		Set value		.21

Admiral Jose Prudencio Padilla (1784-1831) A423

1984, May 17 Litho. *Perf. 12*

933 A423 10p multicolored .16 .15

Luis Antonio Calvo (1882-1945) Composer A424

1984, July 26

934 A424 18p multicolored .30 .15

Diego Fallon (1834-1905), Educator, Musician, Poet — A425

1984, Aug. 31 *Perf. 12*

935 A425 20p multicolored .30 .15

Candelario Obeso (1849-1884), Writer A426

1984, Sept. 4 *Perf. 14x13½*

936 A426 20p multicolored .30 .15

Site of Marandua, Future City — A427

1984, Sept. 28 *Perf. 12*

937 A427 15p multicolored .22 .15

See No. C744.

Christmas 1984 — A428

Nativity and Children Playing, by Jose Uriel Sierra, Age 7.

1984, Dec. 14

938 A428 12p multicolored .20 .15

See No. C746.

Dr. Luis Eduardo Lopez, Education Minister A429

1984, Dec. 21

939 A429 22p multicolored .35 .15

Maria Concepcion Loperena de Fernandez de Castro, Independence War Heroine — A430

1985, Jan. 6

940 A430 12p multicolored .22 .15

Gonzalo Mejia (1885-1956) A431

1985, Feb. 25

941 A431 12p Portrait, biplane, camera .20 .15

Aviation, motion picture and meat exporting industrialist.

Self-portrait with Wife — A432

1985, Feb. 25

942 A432 37p multicolored .62 .30

Pedro Nel Gomez (1899-1984), painter. See No. C748.

Fauna — A433

1985 *Perf. 14*

943 A433 12p Hydrochaeris hydrochaeris .16 .15

Perf. 13

944	A433	15p Felis pardalis	.20	.15
945	A433	15p Tremarctos ornatus, vert.	.20	.15
946	A433	20p Tapirus pinchaque	.28	.15
		Nos. 943-946,C758 (5)	1.49	
		Set value		.57

Carlos Gardel (1890-1935), Entertainer A434

Camina Literacy Program A435

1985, June 23 *Perf. 14*

947 A434 15p Portrait, Fokker F-31 Tri-motor .20 .15

1985, Nov. 25 *Perf. 13½x14*

948 A435 15p Tree, alphabet .20 .15

Christmas 1985 — A436

1985, Dec. 4 Litho. *Perf. 13*

949 A436 15p multicolored .20 .15

Rafael Pombo Children's Foundation. See No. C755.

Eduardo Carranza (b. 1913), Poet — A437

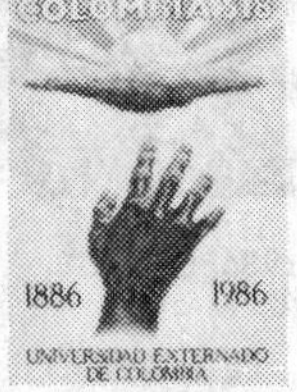

Colombian Free University, Cent. — A438

1986, Feb. 13

950 A437 18p multicolored .24 .15

1986, Feb. 14

951 A438 18p multicolored .24 .15

Gen. Antonio Ricaurte (b. 1786), Liberator
A439

1986, May 7 Litho. *Perf. 13*
952 A439 18p Leiva birthplace .24 .15

Jose Asuncion Silva (1865-1896), Poet, and Scene from Nocturno
A440

1986, May 30 Litho. *Perf. 12*
953 A440 18p multicolored .22 .15

Fernando Gomez Martinez (1897-1985), Journalist — A441

1986, June 19
954 A441 24p multicolored .30 .15

Santiago de Cali, 450th Anniv.
A442

1986, July 25 Litho. *Perf. 13*
955 A442 25p La Merced .30 .15

A443

A444

Monsignor Jose Vicente Castro Silva (1885-1968), rector of the Mayor del Rosario School: portrait by Ricardo Gomez.

1986, Aug. 4 Litho. *Perf. 12*
956 A443 20p multicolored .22 .15

1986, Oct. 14 Litho. *Perf. 12*
957 A444 40p Natl. University .45 .15

Faculties: Fine Arts, cent., and Architecture, 50th anniv.

Rafael Maya (1897-1980), Poet, and Salamanca University Entrance
A445

1986, Oct. 15
958 A445 25p multicolored .28 .15

See No. C772.

Condor in Flight — A446

Deroptius Accipritrinus — A446a

Designs: No. 962, Inia goefrenis. No. 963, Procyon cancrivorus. No. 964, Monachus tropicalis. No. 965, Pteronura brasiliensis. No. 966, Trichechus manatus. No. 967, Odocoileus virginianus. No. 968, Trogon personatos personatos. Nos. 962-968 horiz.

1986-89 Litho. *Perf. 12*
959 A446 20p ultra .22 .15
960 A446 25p ultra ('87) .30 .15

Perf. 14½x14, 14x14½
961 A446a 30p grn ('87) .35 .15
962 A446a 30p dull vio ('87) .35 .15

Engr.
Wmk. 334
963 A446a 35p chest brn ('88) .35 .15
964 A446a 35p dark grn ('88) .35 .15
965 A446a 40p deep org ('88) .40 .15
966 A446a 40p gray ('88) .28 .15
967 A446a 40p tan ('89) .28 .15
968 A446a 45p dark vio ('88) .32 .15
Nos. 959-968 (10) 3.20
Set value 1.08

Issue dates: 20p, Nov. 6. 25p, May 25. No. 961, June 8. No. 962, Dec. 24. No. 963, Aug. 6. No. 964, Sept. 20. No. 965, Sept. 20. No. 966, Nov. 29. No. 967, Apr. 29. No. 968, Dec. 16.
See Nos. 996, 1000, C778-C781.

A447

A448

1987, Jan. 29 Unwmk. *Perf. 12*
969 A447 25p multicolored .45 .15

Pedro Uribe Mejia (1886-1972), pioneer of Colombian coffee industry.

1987, May 3 *Perf. 13½x13*
970 A448 500p Santa Barbara Church 4.75 1.60

Mompox, 450th anniv.

Writers
A449

Portraits and scenes from works: 70p, Jorge Isaacs (1837-1895), novelist, and scene from *Maria.* 90p, Aurelio Martinez Mutis (1884-1954), poet, and scene from *La Epopeya del Condor.*

1987 *Perf. 12*
971 A449 70p multicolored .75 .25
972 A449 90p multicolored 1.00 .32

Issue dates: 70p, July 28. 90p, Sept. 2.

A450

A451

1987 Litho. *Perf. 13½x13*
Social Security & Communications.
973 A450 35p multicolored .38 .15

1988, May 25 Litho. *Perf. 12*
Natl. Anthem, Cent.: Score, lyricist Rafael Nunez and composer Oreste Sindici. Dated 1987.
974 A451 70p multicolored .65 .22

Human Rights — A452

Perf. 14½x14, 14x14½
1988-89 Engr.
975 A452 30p Life .28 .15
976 A452 35p Suffrage .32 .15
977 A452 40p Association, horiz. .38 .15
978 A452 45p Culture, horiz. .30 .15
Nos. 975-978 (4) 1.28
Set value .42

Issue dates: 30p, 35p, May 12. 40p, July 1. 45p, Oct. 27, 1989.
See Nos. C797, C807.

Pasto, 450th Anniv.
A453

1988, May 20 Litho. *Perf. 12*
979 A453 60p Cathedral, Pasto .60 .20

Dated 1987.

Bogota Aqueduct and Sewage System, Cent. — A454

1988, May 20
980 A454 100p Waterfall .95 .32

Maria Currea de Aya (1888-1985), Women's Rights Activist
A455

1988, May 27
981 A455 80p multicolored .75 .25

A456

A457

Sailfish, *Istiaophorus Americanus.*

Perf. 14x13½
1988, July 19 Engr. Wmk. 334
982 A456 (A) dark blue 3.75 2.00
983 A456 (B) Prus blue .95 .32

At the time of issue, No. 982 was sold for 400p and No. 983 for 100p. See type A486.

Unwmk.
1988, Aug. 10 Litho. *Perf. 12*
984 A457 120p multicolored 1.05 .35

San Bartolome College, founded in 1604.

Jorge Alvarez Lleras (1885-1952), Engineer and Director of the Natl. Astronomical Observatory
A458

1988, Aug. 17
985 A458 90p multicolored .80 .20

Pres. Eduardo Santos (1888-1974) — A459

1988, Aug. 30
986 A459 80p multicolored .70 .18

Andres Bello Seminary
A460

Unwmk.
1988, Dec. 27 Litho. *Perf. 12*
987 A460 115p multicolored .82 .28

Adpostal, 25th Anniv.
A461

1989, May 3
988 A461 45p multicolored .32 .15

Military Leaders — A462

Bolivar and Santander at the Los Llanos Campaign — A463

1989 Litho. *Perf. 12*
989 A462 40p Santander .28 .15
990 A462 40p Bolivar .28 .15
991 A463 45p multicolored .38 .15
Nos. 989-991 (3) .94
Set value .30

Liberation campaign, 170th anniv.
Issued: #989, Aug. 25; #990, July 25; 45p, Aug. 7.

From Boyaca to Santa Fe
A464 A465

1989, Aug. 7 Litho. *Perf. 12*

992 A464 45p multicolored	.38	.15
993 A465 45p multicolored	.38	.15
a. Pair, #992-993	.80	.30

Liberation campaign, 170th anniv.

Liberation Campaign Triptych — A466

Designs: a, Gen. Santander, liberation force. b, Simon Bolivar riding mount. c, Insurgent cavalry.

Unwmk.

1989, Aug. 7 Litho. *Perf. 13*

994 A466 Strip of 3	.90	.30
a.-c. 45p any single	.30	.15

Liberation Campaign, 170th anniv.

Tunja, 450th Anniv. A467

1989, Aug. 8 *Perf. 12*

995 A467 45p multicolored	.30	.15

Fauna Type of 1988

Designs: No. 996, Harpia harpyja, horiz. No. 997, Urocyon cinereoargenteus. No. 998, Dendrobates histrionicus. No. 1000, Phenacosaurus indenenae. No. 1001, Cebuella pygmaea. No. 1002, Eurypyga helias, horiz.

Perf. 14½x14, 14x14½

1989-90 Engr. Wmk. 334

996 A446a 45p black	.30	.15
997 A446a 50p blue gray	.30	.15
998 A446a 50p deep claret	.30	.15
1000 A446a 55p red brown	.38	.15
1001 A446a 60p brown	.35	.15
1002 A446a 60p org brown	.35	.15
Nos. 996-1002 (6)	1.98	
Set value		.66

Issue dates: 45p, Sept. 7; Nos. 997, 1001, Mar. 1, 1990; No. 998, Apr. 25; 55p, Aug. 18; No. 1002, Aug. 6.

This is an expanding set. Numbers will change if necessary.

A468 A469

1989, Aug. 30 Unwmk. *Perf. 12*

1011 A468 135p multicolored	.90	.30

City of Armenia, cent.

1990, Mar. 28 Litho. *Perf. 12*

1012 A469 60p Espeletia hartwegiana	.35	.15

Gen. Francisco De Paula Santander (1792-1840) A470

1990, May 6 *Perf. 14x13½*

1013 A470 50p multicolored	.30	.15
Nos. 1013,C823-C827 (6)	3.40	
Set value		.45

See Nos. 1046-1047.

General Santander Police Academy, 50th Anniv. — A471

1990, May 16 *Perf. 12*

1014 A471 60p multicolored	.35	.15

Department of La Guajira A473

1990, July 1 *Perf. 12*

1016 A473 60p multicolored	.35	.15

Ceiba Pentandra A474

1990, July 15 Litho. *Perf. 12*

1017 A474 60p multicolored	.35	.15

A475 A476

1990, Aug. 8 Litho. *Perf. 12*

1018 A475 70p Tibouchina lepidota	.65	.23

Unwmk.

1990, Aug. 28 Litho. *Perf. 14*

1019 A476 70p Ceroxylon quindiuense	.38	.15

A477 A478

1990, Sept. 28 *Perf. 12*

1020 A477 60p St. John Bosco	.35	.15

Salesian Order in Colombia, cent.

1991, Mar. 28 Litho. *Perf. 12*

1021 A478 70p multicolored	.38	.15

Miraculous Christ, Pilgrimage Church of Buga.

Moths and Butterflies A479

1991, Apr. 18 Litho. *Perf. 14*

1022 A479 70p Callithea philotima	.50	.15
1023 A479 70p Anaea syene, vert.	.50	.15
1024 A479 80p Thecla coronata, vert.	.65	.15
1025 A479 80p Agrias amydon	.65	.15
1026 A479 170p Morpho rhetenor	1.25	.28
1027 A479 190p Heliconius longarenus	1.50	.30
Nos. 1022-1027 (6)	5.05	1.18

Nos. 1025-1027 are airmail.

New Constitution A480

1991, July 4 Litho. *Perf. 14*

1028 A480 70p multicolored	.35	.15

A481 A482

1991, July 19 *Perf. 12*

1029 A481 80p multicolored	.38	.15

Pres. Dario Echandia Olaya (1897-1989). See No. 1042.

1991, Aug. 7

1030 A482 70p multicolored	.35	.15

Col. Antanasio Girardot (1791-1813).

A483 A484

1991, Aug. 15 Litho. *Perf. 14*

1031 A483 80p multicolored	.40	.15

Luis Carlos Galan Sarmiento (1943-1989), political reformer.

1991, Aug. 24 *Perf. 12*

Pre-Columbian Artifacts: 80p, Statue of cat god. No. 1033, Pitcher from tomb of high official. No. 1034, Statue with two heads. 210p, Flying fish, horiz.

1032 A484 80p multicolored	.40	.15
1033 A484 90p multicolored	.50	.15
1034 A484 90p multicolored	.50	.15
1035 A484 210p multicolored	1.10	.30
Nos. 1032-1035 (4)	2.50	.75

Nos. 1034-1035 are airmail.

Colonial Architecture A485

Designs: 80p, Cloister of St. Augustine, Tunja. No. 1037, Community Bridge, Chia. No. 1038, Roadside Chapel, Pamplona, vert. 190p, Church of Immaculate Conception, Bogota, vert.

1991 Litho. *Perf. 12*

1036 A485 80p multicolored	.40	.15
1037 A485 90p multicolored	.50	.15
1038 A485 90p multicolored	.45	.15
1039 A485 190p multicolored	.95	.25
Nos. 1036-1039 (4)	2.30	
Set value		.60

Issue dates: No. 1037, Sept. 9. Others, Sept. 27. Nos. 1038-1039 are airmail.

Istiaphorus Americanus A486

1991, Sept. 3 *Perf. 14*

1040 A486 830p multicolored	5.50	1.40

Colombian Police Force, Cent. — A487

1991, Oct. 12 *Perf. 12*

1041 A487 80p multicolored	.42	.15

President Type of 1991

Pres. Alberto Lleras Camargo (1906-1990)

1991, Nov. 5

1042 A481 80p multicolored	.42	.15

A489 A490

1991, Dec. 17 Litho. *Perf. 12*

1043 A489 80p Sogamoso City Hall	.42	.15

1992 Litho. *Perf. 14*

Designs: No. 1044, Diana Turbay Quintero (1950-91), journalist. No. 1045, Indalecio Lievano Aguirre (1917-82), diplomat.

1044 A490 80p multicolored	.42	.15
1045 A490 80p multicolored	.38	.15

Issued: #1044, Jan. 24; #1045, Apr. 21.

Santander Type of 1990 and

Battle of Boyaca — A491a

1992, Apr. 2 *Perf. 14*

Size: 26x37mm

1046 A470 80p Monument .38 .15
1047 A470 190p Portrait .85 .25

Souvenir Sheet

Perf. 13½x14

1047A A491a 950p multicolored 5.00 5.00

Nos. 1047-1047A are airmail. Gen. Francisco de Paula Santander, bicent. of birth.

A492

A493

Ministers of Justice: 100p, Enrique Low Murtra (1939-1991). 110p, Rodrigo Lara Bonilla (1946-1984).

1992, Apr. 30 **Litho.** *Perf. 12*

1048 A492 100p multicolored .42 .15
1049 A492 110p multicolored .48 .15
Set value .15

1992, May 18 *Perf. 14*

1050 A493 110p multicolored .48 .32

15th natl. games, Barranquilla.

Wildlife — A494

1992, Apr. 14 **Litho.** *Perf. 12*

1051 A494 (B) Oroaetus icidori 1.00 .48
1052 A494 (A) Tremarctos ornatus 5.00 2.25

Nos. 1051-1052 had face values of 200p and 950p respectively on date of issue.

Endangered Species A495

1992, Aug. 4

1053 A495 100p Crocodylus acatus .45 .30
1054 A495 100p Vultur gryphus, vert. .45 .30

A496

A497

1992, Aug. 24 **Litho.** *Perf. 14*

1055 A496 100p multicolored .40 .28
1056 A496 110p multicolored .45 .30

Maria Lopez de Escobar, founder of the House of the Mother and Child. No. 1056 is airmail.

1992, Sept. 23 **Litho.** *Perf. 12*

1057 A497 100p multicolored .42 .30

Conference of First Ladies of the Americas and Caribbean, Cartagena.

Recycling — A498

1992, Oct. 9 **Litho.** *Perf. 12*

1058 A498 100p multicolored .42 .30

Discovery of America, 500th Anniv. — A499

Paintings: 100p, Zenaida, by Ana Mercedes Hoyos. No. 1060, Estudio Para 1/500, by Beatriz Gonzalez. No. 1061, Blue Eagle, by Alejandro Obregon. 230p, Cantileo, by Luis Luna. 260p, Corn, by Antonio Caro. 400p, Grand Curtain, by Luis Caballero. 440p, Homage to Guatavita, by Alejandro Obregon.

1992, Oct. 5 **Litho.** *Perf. 13½x14*

1059 A499 100p multicolored .42 .30
1060 A499 110p multicolored .45 .32
1061 A499 110p multicolored .45 .32
1062 A499 230p multicolored .95 .68
1063 A499 260p multicolored 1.10 .78
Nos. 1059-1063 (5) 3.37 2.40

Souvenir Sheets

Perf. 12

1064 A499 400p multicolored 1.65 1.65
1065 A499 440p multicolored 1.80 1.80

Nos. 1061-1063 are airmail.

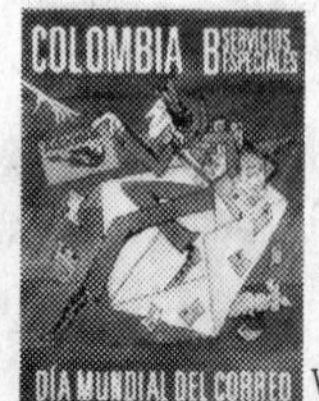

World Post Day — A500

1992, Oct. 19 **Litho.** *Perf. 12*

1066 A500 (B) multicolored .95 .65

No. 1066 had face value of 200p on day of issue.

Christmas — A501

Children's paintings of: 100p, Nativity scene. 110p, Adoration of the Magi.

1992, Nov. 20 **Litho.** *Perf. 12*

1067 A501 100p multicolored .40 .28
1068 A501 110p multicolored .45 .32

No. 1068 is airmail.

Three Musicians, by Fernando Botero A502

1993, Feb. 5 **Litho.** *Perf. 12*

1069 A502 (B) multicolored .95 .65

No. 1069 had a face value of 250p on day of issue.

Lions Intl. Campaign Against Amblyopia A503

1993, Mar. 26 *Perf. 14*

1070 A503 100p multicolored .38 .28

Holy Week in Popayan A504

1993, Apr. 5 *Perf. 14x13½*

1071 A504 (B) multicolored .95 .65

No. 1071 had a face value of 250p on day of issue.

A505 A506

1993, Apr. 7 *Perf. 12*

1072 A505 (B) multicolored .95 .65

Pan American Health Organization, 90th anniv.

No. 1072 had a face value of 250p on day of issue.

1993, Apr. 14

1073 A506 (B) multicolored .95 .65

Franciscans of Mary Immaculate, cent. No. 1073 had a face value of 250p on day of issue.

A507

A508

1993, Apr. 22 **Litho.** *Perf. 14*

1074 A507 (B) multicolored .90 .60

EXFILBO '93, 18th Natl. Philatelic Exhibition. No. 1074 had a face value of 250p on day issue.

1993, July 2 **Litho.** *Perf. 12*

1075 A508 250p Guillermo Cano, writer .95 .65

Human Rights A509

Designs: a, 150p, Rights of prisoners. b, 150p, Rights of the elderly. c, 200p, Rights of the infirm. d, 200p, Children's rights. e, 220p, Women's rights. f, 220p, Rights of the poor. g, 460p, Right to clean environment. h, 520p, Rights of indigenous people.

Painting: 800p, Peace, Rights, and Freedom, by Alfredo Vivero, vert.

1993, June 10 *Perf. 14*

1076 A509 Block of 8, #a.-h. 8.00 5.60

Souvenir Sheet

1077 A509 800p multicolored 3.00 2.00

Nos. 1076e-1076h are airmail.

Amazon Region of Colombia — A510

Designs: No. 1078a, Parrot. No. 1078b, Anaconda. No. 1079a, Victoria regia. No. 1079b, Flor ipecacuana. 880p, Map, native, horiz.

1993 **Litho.** *Perf. 12*

1078 A510 150p Pair, #a.-b. 1.10 .75
1079 A510 220p Pair, #a.-b. 1.65 1.00

Souvenir Sheet

1080 A510 880p multicolored 3.00 2.00

Nos. 1079-1080 are airmail.

Famous People — A511

Designs: a, 150p, Alberto Pumarejo (1893-1970). b, 150p, Lorencita Villegas de Santos (1892-

1960). c, 200p, Meliton Rodriguez (1875-1942). d, 200p, Tomas Carrasquilla (1858-1940).

1993 Litho. *Perf. 14x13½*
1081 A511 Block of 4, #a.-d. 2.50 1.65

Christmas — A512

1993, Nov. 30 *Perf. 12*
1082 A512 200p Holy Family .70 .48
1083 A512 220p Shepherd 1.50 1.00

No. 1083 is airmail.

Tourism A513

Designs: No. 1084a, San Andres Providence. b, Cocuy Natl. Park. c, Lake Cocha. d, Waterfalls, Serrania de la Macarena. 250p, Lake Otun. No. 1086a, Chicamocha River. b, Sierra Nevada de Santa Marta mountains. 520p, Penol Reservoir.

1993, Dec. 1 Litho. *Perf. 12*
1084 A513 220p Block of 4, #a.-d. 3.00 2.00
1085 A513 250p multicolored .85 .55
1086 A513 460p Pair, #a.-b. 3.00 2.00
1087 A513 520p multicolored 1.75 1.10
Nos. 1084-1087 (4) 8.60 5.65

Nos. 1084, 1086-87 are airmail.

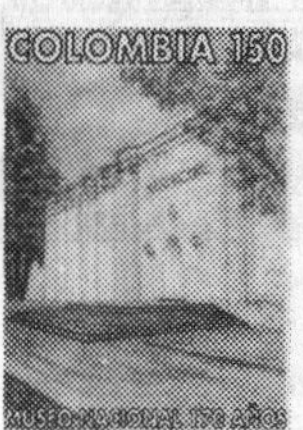

A514 A515

1993, Dec. 21 Litho. *Perf. 14*
1088 A514 150p multicolored .52 .35

Natl. Museum, 170th anniv.

1994, Jan. 25 Litho. *Perf. 14*
1089 A515 300p Marie Poussepin 1.10 .70

A516 A517

Birds: 180p, Ognorhynchus icterotis. 240p, Rallus semiplumbeus. 270p, Semnornis ramphastinus, horiz. 560p, Anas cyanoptera, horiz.

1994, Mar. 4
1090 A516 180p multicolored .65 .42
1091 A516 240p multicolored .85 .55
1092 A516 270p multicolored 1.00 .65
1093 A516 560p multicolored 2.00 1.25
Nos. 1090-1093 (4) 4.50 2.87

Nos. 1092-1093 are airmail.

1994, Apr. 11 Litho. *Perf. 14*
1094 A517 300p multicolored .95 .60

Air Force, 75th anniv.

Latin American Presidential Summit, Cartagena — A518

1994, June 14 Litho. *Perf. 14*
1095 A518 300p shown .95 .60
1096 A518 630p Flags 2.00 1.40

No. 1096 is airmail.

1994 World Cup Soccer Championships, US — A519

World Cup Trophy and: 180p, Soccer player, Colombian flag. 270p, Two players with ball. 560p, Soccer ball, Colombian flag, vert.
1110p, Soccer player offering hand to another.

1994, May 26 *Perf. 12*
1097 A519 180p multicolored .60 .38
1098 A519 270p multicolored .90 .55
1099 A519 560p multicolored 1.90 1.25
Nos. 1097-1099 (3) 3.40 2.18

Souvenir Sheet

1100 A519 1110p multicolored 3.75 2.50

Nos. 1098-1099 are airmail.

Ricardo Rendon (1894-1931), Artist — A520

1993 Census — A521

1994, June 30 Litho. *Perf. 12*
1101 A520 240p black .70 .45

1994, Aug. 12 *Perf. 14*
1102 A521 240p multicolored .70 .45

Ministry of Communications Inravision, 30th Anniv. — A522

1994, Aug. 3
1103 A522 180p multicolored .52 .32

Intl. Year of the Family A523

1994, Sept. 1 Litho. *Perf. 14*
1104 A523 300p multicolored 1.00 .65

America Issue — A524

Methods of mail delivery: 270p, Horse, bicycle. 300p, Men holding stamps showing truck, ship, plane.

1994, Oct. 18 Litho. *Perf. 13*
1105 A524 270p multicolored .90 .60
1106 A524 300p multicolored 1.00 .65

No. 1105 is airmail.

Colombian Society of Engineers, Cent. A525

1994, Oct. 20 Litho. *Perf. 12*
1107 A525 180p multicolored .60 .40

Christmas — A526

1994, Nov. 22 Litho. *Perf. 13½x13*
1108 A526 270p Magi .90 .60
1109 A526 300p Holy family 1.00 .65

No. 1108 is airmail.

Former President Type of 1981
Miniature Sheet of 20

Designs: a, Jose Miguel Pey. b, Jorge Tadeo Lozano. c, Antonio Narino. d, Camilo Torres. e, Jose Fernandez Madrid. f, Jose Maria del Castillo y Rada. g, Custodio Garcia Rovira. h, Antonio Villavicencio. i, Liborio Mejia. j, Rafael Urdaneta. k, Juan Garcia del Rio. l, Jose Maria Melo. m, Tomas Herrera. n, Froilan Largacha. o, Salvador Camacho Roldan. p, Ezequiel Hurtado. q, Dario Echandia Olaya. r, Alberto Lleras Camargo. s, Gustavo Rojas Pinilla. t, Carlos Lleras Restrepo.

1995, Apr. 4 Litho. *Perf. 12*
1110 A401 270p #a.-t. 18.00 12.00

World Offroad Bicycle Championships, Melgar — A527

1995, Mar. 30 *Perf. 14*
1111 A527 400p multicolored 1.40 .90

A528 A529

1995, Oct. 12 Litho. *Perf. 12*
1112 A528 220p multicolored .45 .30

Gen. Jose Maria Obando (1795-1861), President.

1995 *Perf. 14*
1113 A529 400p Clean air .80 .55
1114 A529 400p Clean water .80 .55

Preserve the environment. America issue.

Christmas A530

Stained glass windows: 220p, Flight into Egypt. 330p, Nativity.

1995 *Perf. 12*
1115 A530 220p multicolored .45 .30
1116 A530 330p multicolored .65 .45

No. 1116 is airmail.

SEMI-POSTAL STAMP

Catalogue values for unused stamps in this section are for Never Hinged items.

Girl Giving First Aid — SP1

Perf. 13½x14

1966, Apr. 26 Litho. Unwmk.
B1 SP1 5c + 5c multicolored .15 .15

Issued for the Red Cross.

AIR POST STAMPS

No. 341 Overprinted

1er.
Servicio
Postal
Aereo
6.-18-19

1919 Unwmk. *Perf. 14*
C1 A107 2c car rose 2,750. 1,200.
a. Numerals "1" with serifs *5,500. 3,250.*

Used for the first experimental flight from Barranquilla to Puerto Colombia, June 18, 1919.
Values are for faulty copies.

Issued by Compania Colombiana de Navegacion Aerea

From 1920 to 1932 the internal airmail service of Colombia was handled by the Compania Colombiana de Navegacion

Aerea (1920) and the Sociedad Colombo-Alemana de Transportes Aéreos, known familiarly as "SCADTA" (1920-1932). These organizations under government contracts operated and maintained their own post offices, and issued stamps which were the only legal franking for airmail service during this period, both in the internal and international mails. All letters had to bear government stamps as well.

Woman and Boy Watching Plane — AP1

Designs: No. C3, Clouds and small biplane at top. No. C4, Tilted plane viewed close-up from above. No. C5, Flier in plane watching biplane. No. C6, Lighthouse. No. C7, Fuselage and tail of biplane. No. C8, Condor on cliff. No. C9, Plane at rest; pilot foreground. No. C10, Ocean liner.

1920, Feb. Unwmk. Litho. *Imperf.*
Without Gum

C2 AP1	10c multicolored	2,000.	1,500.
C3 AP1	10c multicolored	2,400.	1,500.
C4 AP1	10c multicolored	3,000.	1,500.
C5 AP1	10c multicolored	2,750.	1,500.
C6 AP1	10c multicolored	2,400.	1,500.
C7 AP1	10c multicolored	6,750.	3,000.
C8 AP1	10c multicolored	3,000.	2,400.
a.	Without overprint		
C9 AP1	10c multicolored	2,250.	1,500.
C10 AP1	10c multicolored	3,000.	2,100.

Flier in Plane Watching Biplane — AP2

1920, Mar.

C11 AP2	10c green	47.50	*75.00*

Four other 10c stamps, similar to No. C11, have two designs showing plane, mountains and water. They are printed in deep green or light brown red. Some authorities state that these four were not used regularly.

Issued by Sociedad Colombo-Alemana de Transportes Aereos (SCADTA)

Seaplane over Magdalena River — AP3

1920-21 Litho. *Perf. 12*

C12 AP3	10c yellow ('21)	35.00	27.50
C13 AP3	15c blue ('21)	35.00	30.00
C14 AP3	30c blk, *rose*	15.00	11.00
C15 AP3	30c rose ('21)	35.00	27.50
C16 AP3	50c pale green	35.00	30.00
	Nos. C12-C16 (5)	155.00	126.00

For surcharges see Nos. C17-C24, C36-C37.

No. C16 Handstamp Surcharged in Violet or Black:

(Illustrations of types "a" to "e" are reduced in size.)

VALOR 10 CENTAVOS
a

VALOR 10 CENTAVOS
b

Valor 10 Céntavos
c

VALOR 30 Ctvos
S.C.A.T.A
d

30¢ 30¢
e

$030
f

$030¢
g

1921

C17 AP3 (a)	10c on 50c	450.	450.
C18 AP3 (b)	10c on 50c	450.	450.
C19 AP3 (c)	10c on 50c	*875.*	*700.*
C20 AP3 (b)	30c on 50c	450.	450.
C21 AP3 (d)	30c on 50c	550.	550.
C22 AP3 (e)	30c on 50c	1,000.	1,000.
C23 AP3 (f)	30c on 50c	775.	750.
C24 AP3 (g)	30c on 50c	775.	750.

Plane over Magdalena River — AP4

Plane over Bogota Cathedral — AP5

1921 *Perf. 11½*

C25 AP4	5c orange yellow	3.50	3.50
C26 AP4	10c slate green	1.25	.80
C27 AP4	15c orange brown	1.25	.90
C28 AP4	20c red brown	2.00	1.25
a.	Horiz. pair, imperf. vert.	*140.00*	
C29 AP4	30c green	1.50	.40
C30 AP4	50c blue	2.00	.65
C31 AP4	60c vermilion	10.00	7.00
C32 AP5	1p gray black	12.50	7.00
C33 AP5	2p rose	21.00	14.00
C34 AP5	3p violet	45.00	45.00
C35 AP5	5p olive green	300.00	300.00
	Nos. C25-C35 (11)	400.00	380.50

Exist imperf.
For surcharge see No. C52.

Nos. C16 and C12 Handstamp Surcharged

(Illustration of type "h" is reduced in size.)

VALOR 20 Ctvs.
h

30 cent.
i

1921-22 *Perf. 12*

C36 AP3 (h)	20c on 50c	1,200.	850.
C37 AP3 (i)	30c on 10c	500.	325.

Seaplane over Magdalena River — AP6

Plane over Bogota Cathedral — AP7

1923-28 Wmk. 116 *Perf. 14x14½*

C38 AP6	5c orange yellow	1.00	.20
C39 AP6	10c green	1.00	.20
C40 AP6	15c carmine	1.00	.15
C41 AP6	20c gray	1.00	.15
C42 AP6	30c blue	1.00	.15
C43 AP6	40c purple ('28)	7.25	5.25
C44 AP6	50c green	1.25	.20
C45 AP6	60c brown	2.00	.20
C46 AP6	80c olive grn ('28)	20.00	19.00
C47 AP7	1p black	9.00	2.00
C48 AP7	2p red orange	13.00	4.00
C49 AP7	3p violet	27.50	17.50
C50 AP7	5p olive green	45.00	24.00
	Nos. C38-C50 (13)	130.00	73.00

For surcharges and overprints see Nos. C51, C53-C54, CF1.

Nos. C41 and C31 Surcharged in Carmine and Dark Blue:

30 30 No. C51 | 30 30 No. C52

1923

C51 AP6	30c on 20c gray (C)	60.00	35.00
C52 AP4	30c on 60c ver	50.00	27.50

Nos. C41-C42 Overprinted in Black

1928 Wmk. 116 *Perf. 14x14½*

C53 AP6	20c gray	50.00	50.00
C54 AP6	30c blue	50.00	50.00

Goodwill flight of Lt. Benjamin Mendez from New York to Bogota.

Magdalena River and Tolima Volcano AP8

Columbus' Ship and Plane AP9

1929, June 1 Wmk. 127 *Perf. 14*

C55 AP8	5c yellow org	.75	.35
C56 AP8	10c red brown	.75	.25
C57 AP8	15c deep green	.75	.35
C58 AP8	20c carmine	.75	.15
C59 AP8	30c gray blue	.75	.30
C60 AP8	40c dull violet	.90	.30
C61 AP8	50c dk olive grn	1.75	.40
C62 AP8	60c orange brown	1.75	.40
C63 AP8	80c green	6.00	4.00
C64 AP9	1p blue	7.00	2.50
C65 AP9	2p brown orange	11.00	4.00
C66 AP9	3p pale rose vio	22.50	20.00
C67 AP9	5p olive green	52.50	40.00
	Nos. C55-C67 (13)	107.15	73.00

For surcharges and overprints see Nos. C80-C95, CF2, CF4.

For International Airmail

AP10

AP11

1929, June 1 Wmk. 127 *Perf. 14*

C68 AP10	5c yellow org	4.00	5.00
C69 AP10	10c red brown	.75	2.00
C70 AP10	15c deep green	.75	2.00
C71 AP10	20c carmine	.75	2.50
C72 AP10	25c violet blue	.75	.45
C73 AP10	30c gray blue	.75	.65
C74 AP10	50c dk olive grn	.75	1.25
C75 AP10	60c brown	1.75	2.00
C76 AP11	1p blue	3.50	5.00
C77 AP11	2p red orange	5.00	7.00
C78 AP11	3p violet	65.00	62.50
C79 AP11	5p olive green	80.00	90.00
	Nos. C68-C79 (12)	163.75	180.35

This issue was sold abroad for use on correspondence to be flown from coastal to interior points of Colombia. Cancellations are those of the country of origin rather than Colombia.
For overprint see No. CF3.

Nos. C63, C66 and C64 Surcharged in Black:

m

1830 1930
SIMON BOLIVAR
30 cts. 30 cts.
n

1930, Dec. 15

C80 AP8(m)	10c on 80c	4.25	4.50
C81 AP9(n)	20c on 3p	8.25	9.00
C82 AP9(n)	30c on 1p	9.00	9.00
	Nos. C80-C82 (3)	21.50	22.50

Simon Bolivar (1783-1830).

Colombian Government Issues
Nos. C55-C67 Overprinted in Black:

CORREO AEREO
o

CORREO AEREO
p

Wmk. 127
1932, Jan. 1 Typo. *Perf. 14*

C83 AP8(o)	5c yellow org	8.00	8.00
C84 AP8(o)	10c red brown	1.75	.50
C85 AP8(o)	15c deep green	3.00	3.00
C86 AP8(o)	20c carmine	1.50	.30
C87 AP8(o)	30c gray blue	1.50	.50
C88 AP8(o)	40c dull violet	2.00	1.00
C89 AP8(o)	50c dk ol grn	4.00	3.00
C90 AP8(o)	60c orange brn	3.25	3.00
C91 AP8(o)	80c green	14.00	14.00
C92 AP9(p)	1p blue	11.00	9.00
C93 AP9(p)	2p brown org	30.00	27.50
C94 AP9(p)	3p pale rose vio	60.00	52.50
C95 AP9(p)	5p olive green	100.00	110.00
	Nos. C83-C95 (13)	240.00	232.30

Coffee AP12

Gold AP16

Designs: 10c, 50c, Cattle. 15c, 60c, Petroleum. 20c, 40c, Bananas. 3p, 5p, Emerald.

1932-39 Wmk. 127 Photo. *Perf. 14*

C96 AP12	5c org & blk brn	.90	.26
C97 AP12	10c lake & blk	1.00	.22
C98 AP12	15c bl grn & vio blk	.45	.16
C99 AP12	15c ver & vio blk ('39)	2.50	.15
C100 AP12	20c car & ol blk	.70	.15
C101 AP12	20c turq grn & ol blk ('39)	3.50	.32
C102 AP12	30c dk bl & blk brn	1.65	.16
C103 AP12	40c dk vio & ol bis	.85	.15
C104 AP12	50c dk grn & brnsh blk	3.50	1.25
C105 AP12	60c dk brn & blk vio	1.10	.26
C106 AP12	80c grn & blk brn	5.50	2.00
C107 AP16	1p dk bl & ol bis	9.00	1.25
C108 AP16	2p org brn & ol bis	10.00	2.25
C109 AP16	3p dk vio & emer	17.00	6.25
C110 AP16	5p gray blk & emer	47.50	20.00
	Nos. C96-C110 (15)	105.15	34.83

For overprint see No. CF5.

Nos. C104, C106-C108 Surcharged:

a

1533 1933

CARTAGENA

20 centavos 20

b

1934, Jan. 5

C111	AP12(a)	10c on 50c	3.50	3.50
C112	AP12(a)	15c on 80c	4.75	4.75
C113	AP16(b)	20c on 1p	5.25	5.25
C114	AP16(b)	30c on 2p	5.75	5.75
		Nos. C111-C114 (4)	19.25	19.25

400th anniversary of Cartagena.

Nos. C100 and C103 Surcharged in Black or Carmine:

5 cts **15**

1939, Jan. 15

C115	AP12	5c on 20c (Bk)	.35	.35
C116	AP12	5c on 40c (C)	.35	.25
C117	AP12	15c on 20c (Bk)	1.50	.50
a.		Double surcharge	12.00	
b.		Pair, one with dbl. surch.	14.00	
c.		Inverted surcharge	12.00	12.00

No. CF5 Surcharged in Black

C118	AP12	5c on 20c	.70	.70
		Nos. C115-C118 (4)	2.90	1.80

Nos. C102-C103 Surcharged in Black or Red

15 cts

1940, Oct. 20

C119	AP12	15c on 30c	1.25	.50
a.		Inverted surcharge	12.00	
C120	AP12	15c on 40c (R)	2.50	.85
a.		Double surcharge	12.00	

Pre-Columbian Monument — AP18

Proclamation of Independence AP22

Designs: 10c, 40c, Symbol of Legend of El Dorado. 15c, 50c, Spanish Fortifications, Cartagena. 20c, 60c, Colonial Bogotá. 2p, 5p, National Library, Bogota.

Unwmk.

1941, Jan. 28 **Engr.** ***Perf. 12***

C121	AP18	5c gray black	.15	.15
C122	AP18	10c yellow org	.15	.15
C123	AP18	15c carmine rose	.16	.15
C124	AP18	20c yellow grn	.35	.15
a.		Horiz. pair, imperf. vert.	87.50	
C125	AP18	30c deep blue	.35	.15
C126	AP18	40c rose lake	.70	.15
C127	AP18	50c turq green	.70	.15
C128	AP18	60c sepia	.70	.15
C129	AP18	80c olive blk	1.90	.50
C130	AP22	1p blue & blk	3.25	.50
C131	AP22	2p red org & blk	5.25	2.00
C132	AP22	3p violet & blk	14.00	5.00
C133	AP22	5p lt green & blk	27.50	17.50
		Nos. C121-C133 (13)	55.16	26.70

See #C151-C163, C217-C225. For overprints see #C175-C198, C200-C216, C226, C290.

Bay of Santa Maria — AP24

National Capitol, Bogotá — AP27

Designs: 5c, 20c, 50c, San Sebastian Fort, Cartagena. 10c, 30c, 60c, Tequendama Waterfall.

Unwmk.

1945, Nov. 3 **Litho.** ***Perf. 11***

C134	AP24	5c blue gray	.15	.15
C135	AP24	10c yellow org	.15	.15
C136	AP24	15c rose	.15	.15
C137	AP24	20c lt yel grn	.30	.15
C138	AP24	30c ultra	.30	.15
C139	AP24	40c claret	.52	.15
C140	AP24	50c bluish grn	.55	.15
C141	AP24	60c lt vio brn	2.25	.80
C142	AP24	80c dk slate grn	3.50	.80
C143	AP27	1p dk blue	5.00	.75
C144	AP27	2p red orange	7.00	2.50
		Nos. C134-C144 (11)	19.87	5.90

Part-perforate varieties exist for all denominations except 80c.

Imperf., Pairs

C134a	AP24	5c	8.50
C135a	AP24	10c	8.50
C136a	AP24	15c	8.50
C137a	AP24	20c	8.50
C138a	AP24	30c	8.50
C139a	AP24	40c	8.50
C140a	AP24	50c	8.50
C141a	AP24	60c	8.50
C142a	AP24	80c	10.50
C143a	AP27	1p	17.50
C144a	AP27	2p	60.00

Bello Type of Regular Issue, 1946

Wmk. 255

1946, Sept. 3 **Engr.** ***Perf. 12***

C145	A219	5c deep blue	.16	.15

Francisco José de Caldas — AP29

Manuel del Socorro Rodriguez — AP30

Perf. 12½

1947, May 9 **Litho.** **Unwmk.**

C146	AP29	5c dp bl, *grnsh*	.35	.20
C147	AP30	10c red org, *grnsh*	.50	.45

4th Pan-American Press Congress (1946).

Chancellery Patio AP31

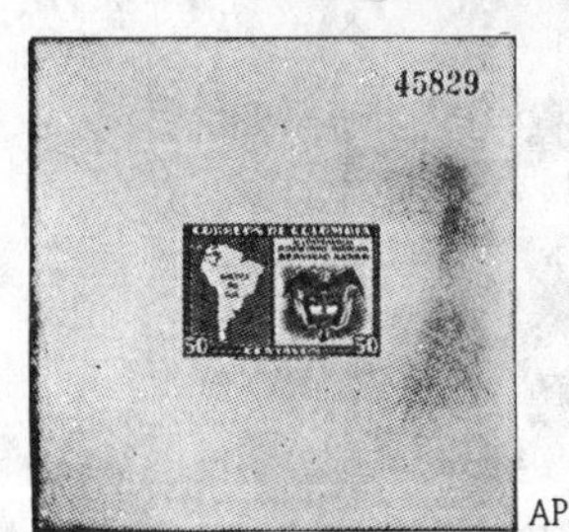

Capitol, Patio Rafael Nunez AP32

45829

AP33

1948, Apr. 2 **Engr.** **Wmk. 229**

C148	AP31	5c dark brown	.15	.15
C149	AP32	15c deep blue	.90	.90

Miniature Sheet

Imperf

C150	AP33	50c brown	1.40	1.40

9th Pan-American Conference, Bogotá.

Types of 1941

1948, July 21 **Unwmk.** ***Perf. 12***

C151	AP18	5c orange yel	.15	.15
C152	AP18	10c scarlet	.15	.15
C153	AP18	15c deep blue	.15	.15
C154	AP18	20c violet	.15	.15
C155	AP18	30c yellow grn	.35	.15
C156	AP18	40c gray	.40	.15
C157	AP18	50c rose lake	.42	.15
C158	AP18	60c olive gray	.70	.15
C159	AP18	80c red brn	.85	.16
C160	AP22	1p ol grn & vio brn	1.40	.32
C161	AP22	2p dp grn & brt bl	2.50	.65
C162	AP22	3p rose car & blk	5.50	3.75
C163	AP22	5p lt brn & turq grn	14.00	7.00
		Nos. C151-C163 (13)	26.72	13.08

"Air Week" 5c Blue

The War and Air Department issued a 5c blue stamp in May, 1949, to publicize Air Week (Semana de Aviacion). The design shows a coat-of-arms, inscribed "FAC," superimposed upon an outline map of Colombia. This stamp had no franking value and its use was optional during May 16-23.

Justice and Liberty AP34

Wing AP35

Design: 10c, Liberty holding tablet of laws.

1949, Oct. 7 **Unwmk.** ***Perf. 13***

C164	AP34	5c blue green	.15	.15
C165	AP34	10c orange	.15	.15
		Set value	.20	.15

Issued to honor the new Constitution.

For Domestic Postage

1950, June 22 **Litho.** ***Perf. 12***

C166	AP35	5c orange yellow	.25	.25
C167	AP35	10c brown red	.35	.35
C168	AP35	15c lt blue	.40	.30
C169	AP35	20c lt green	.60	.75
C170	AP35	30c lilac gray	1.50	2.00
C171	AP35	60c chocolate	1.90	2.50

With Network as in Parenthesis

C172	AP35	1p gray (buff)	14.00	16.00
C173	AP35	2p bl (pale grn)	14.00	16.00
C174	AP35	5p red brn (red brn)	40.00	45.00
		Nos. C166-C174 (9)	73.00	83.15

No. C172 was issued both with and without network.

Nos. C151-C157 and C160-C163 Overprinted in Black

L

1950, July 18

C175	AP18	5c orange yel	.15	.15
C176	AP18	10c scarlet	.15	.15
C177	AP18	15c deep blue	.15	.15
C178	AP18	20c violet	.20	.15
C179	AP18	30c yellow green	.32	.20
C180	AP18	40c gray	.80	.32
C181	AP18	50c rose lake	.42	.26
C182	AP22	1p ol grn & vio brn	2.50	2.25
C183	AP22	2p dp grn & brt bl	3.75	3.25
C184	AP22	3p rose car & blk	11.00	11.00
C185	AP22	5p lt brn & turq grn	24.00	24.00
		Nos. C175-C185 (11)	43.44	41.88

Nos. C151-C163 Overprinted in Black

1950, July 12

C186	AP18	5c orange yel	.15	.15
C187	AP18	10c scarlet	.15	.15
C188	AP18	15c deep blue	.15	.15
C189	AP18	20c violet	.18	.15
C190	AP18	30c yellow green	.18	.15
C191	AP18	40c gray	.42	.15
C192	AP18	50c rose lake	.42	.15
C193	AP18	60c olive gray	.70	.16
C194	AP18	80c red brown	1.00	.40
C195	AP22	1p ol grn & vio brn	1.10	.50
C196	AP22	2p dp grn & brt bl	3.00	1.40
C197	AP22	3p rose car & blk	7.25	6.50
C198	AP22	5p lt brn & turq grn	16.00	14.00
		Nos. C186-C198 (13)	30.70	24.01

On Nos. C175-C198, "L" stands for LANSA, "A" for AVIANCA.

UPU Type

Miniature Sheet

Unwmk.

1950, Aug. 22 **Photo.** ***Imperf.***

C199	A245	50c gray	1.00	1.00

75th anniv. (in 1949) of the UPU.

Catalogue values for unused stamps in this section, from this point to the end of the section, are for Never Hinged items.

Types of 1941 Overprinted at Lower Right in Black

Unwmk.

1951, Sept. 15 **Engr.** ***Perf. 12***

C200	AP18	40c orange yel	1.50	1.25
C201	AP18	50c ultra	1.50	1.25
C202	AP18	60c gray	1.50	1.25
C203	AP18	80c carmine rose	1.10	.95
C204	AP22	1p red org & red brn	3.75	3.00
C205	AP22	2p rose car & bl	4.00	3.00
C206	AP22	3p choc & emer	10.00	8.00
C207	AP22	5p org & gray	30.00	30.00
		Nos. C200-C207 (8)	53.35	48.70

Types of 1941 Overprinted at Lower Right in Black

1951-54

C208	AP18	40c orange yellow	3.25	.55
C209	AP18	50c ultra	4.00	.60
C210	AP18	60c gray	3.00	.45
a.		Overprint centered	1.65	.52
C211	AP18	80c car rose	.85	.30
C212	AP22	1p red org & red brn	3.25	.50
C213	AP22	1p ol grn & vio brn ('54)	4.00	.75
C214	AP22	2p rose car & bl	3.25	.52
C215	AP22	3p choc & emer	5.00	1.40
C216	AP22	5p org & gray	10.00	1.90
		Nos. C208-C216 (9)	36.60	6.97

All values except the 2p and 3p exist without overprint.

Types of 1941

1952, May 10 **Engr.**

C217	AP18	5c ultra	.30	.15
C218	AP18	10c ultra	.30	.16
C219	AP18	15c ultra	.30	.16
C220	AP18	20c ultra	.70	.25
C221	AP18	30c ultra	1.75	.55

Color Change

C222	AP18	5c car rose	.30	.15
C223	AP18	10c car rose	.30	.16
C224	AP18	20c car rose	.70	.18
C225	AP18	30c car rose	1.40	.28
		Nos. C217-C225 (9)	6.05	2.04

Type of 1941 Surcharged in Blue

1a CONFERENCIA 1952 SIDERURGICA LATINO AMERICANA 70 Ctvos.

1952, Oct. 30

C226	AP18	70c on 80c car rose	1.50	.70

Latin American Siderurgical Conf., 1952.

Type of Postal Tax Stamps, 1948-50, Nos. 602 and 604 Surcharged or Overprinted in Black

CORREO 5 AEREO

1953 **Wmk. 255** ***Perf. 12***

C227	PT10	5c on 8c blue	.15	.15
C228	PT10	15c on 20c brown	.24	.15
C229	PT10	15c on 25c bl grn	1.00	.15
C230	PT10	25c blue green	.35	.15
		Nos. C227-C230 (4)	1.74	
		Set value		.24

Many varieties of overprint or surcharge exist on Nos. C227-C231.

No. 570 Overprinted "AEREO" in Blue

1953, Aug. Wmk. 229 ***Perf. 12½***
C231 A160 10c red .15 .15

"Extra Rapido"

Stamps inscribed "Extra Rapido" are for use on domestic airmail carried by airlines other than AVIANCA.

No. 585 Surcharged and Overprinted "Extra Rapido" in Dark Blue

CORREO 5 EXTRA RAPIDO 5

1953 Unwmk. ***Perf. 13***
C232 A244 5c on 11c red .35 .35

Capitol and Arms — AP37

Revenue Stamps Overprinted "Correo Extra-Rapido"
Gray Security Paper

1953 Wmk. 255 Engr. ***Perf. 12***
C233 AP37 1c on 2c green .15 .15
C234 AP37 50c red orange .16 .15
Set value .15

AP38

Real Estate Tax Stamps Ovptd. "Correo Extra-Rapido" in Black or Carmine

1953
C235 AP38 5c red orange .20 .15
C236 AP38 20c brown (C) .25 .15
Set value .15

On 20c, overprint is at bottom of stamp and two lines of ornaments cover real estate tax inscription at top.

Castillo y Rada and Map — AP39

Real Estate Tax Stamp Surcharged "Correo Aereo, II Exposicion Filatelica Nacional, Bogota Dicbre 1953, 15 Centavos"

1953, Dec. 12 Engr. & Litho.
C237 AP39 15c on 10p multi .35 .16

2nd Natl. Philatelic Exhib., Bogota, Dec. 1953.

No. RA45 Overprinted in Black

CORREO
EXTRA-RAPIDO

1953
C238 PT10 10c purple .15 .15

Galeras Volcano — AP40

Retreat of San Diego — AP41

Designs: No. C241, Las Lajas Shrine, Narino. No. C242, 50c, Bolivar monument. 20c, 80c, Ruiz mountain, Manizales. 40c, George Isaacs monument, Cali. 60c, Monkey Fountain, Tunja. 1p, Stadium, Medellin. 2p, Pastelillo Fort, Cartagena. 3p, Santo Domingo University gate. 5p, Las Lajas Shrine. 10p, Map of Colombia.

Perf. 13½x13, 13

1954, Jan. 15 Engr. Unwmk.
C239 AP40 5c dp red vio .15 .15
C240 AP41 10c black .15 .15
C241 AP40 15c red orange .18 .15
C242 AP40 15c car rose .18 .15
C243 AP40 20c brown .18 .15
C244 AP40 30c brown org .18 .15
C245 AP40 40c blue .18 .15
C246 AP40 50c dk violet brn .22 .15
C247 AP40 60c dk brown .30 .15
C248 AP40 80c red brown .65 .15

Size: 37x27mm

Center in Black

C249 AP41 1p deep blue 2.25 .32
C250 AP41 2p dark green 3.50 .30
C251 AP41 3p carmine rose 8.00 1.00

Size: 38x32mm, 32x38mm

C252 AP41 5p dk grn & red brn 8.75 2.50
C253 AP40 10p gray grn & red org 11.00 6.00
Nos. C239-C253 (15) 35.87 11.62

See Nos. C307-C308. For surcharges and overprints see Nos. 691, C321, C325, C330, C333-C334, C343-C346.

Condor Carrying Shield — AP42

Inscribed: "Correo Extra-Rapido"

1954, Apr. 23 Litho. ***Perf. 12½***
C254 AP42 5c lilac rose .60 .28

For overprint see No. RA53.

Soldier-Map-Arms Type of Regular Issue, 1954

1954, June 13 Engr. ***Perf. 13***
C255 A259 15c carmine .28 .15

See No. C271a.

Games Type of Regular Issue, 1954

Design: 20c, Stadium and Athlete holding arms of Colombia.

1954, July 18
C256 A260 15c chocolate .55 .15
C257 A260 20c deep blue green 1.00 .35

Church of St. Peter Claver, Cartagena — AP45

1954, Sept. 9
C258 AP45 15c brown .24 .15
a. Souvenir sheet 2.25 2.25

St. Peter Claver, 300th death anniv.

No. C258a contains one stamp similar to No. C258, but printed in red brown.

Mercury Type of Regular Issue, 1954.

1954, Oct. 29
C259 A263 15c deep blue .30 .15

Inscribed "Extra Rapido"

C260 A263 50c scarlet .28 .15
Set value .15

Archbishop Manuel José Mosquera, Death Cent. — AP47

Inscribed: "Correo Extra Rapido"

1954, Nov. 17
C261 AP47 2c yellow green .15 .15

Virgin of Chiquinquira AP48

Inscribed: "Correo Extra Rapido"

1954, Dec. 4 Engr. & Litho.
C262 AP48 5c org brn & multi .15 .15

See No. C291. For overprint see No. 686.

College Types of Regular Issue, 1954.

Designs: 20c, Brother Cristobal de Torres. 50c, College chapel and arms.

Perf. 12½x11½, 11½x12½

1954, Dec. 6 Engr. Unwmk.
C263 A264 15c orange & blk .24 .15
C264 A264 20c ultra .35 .15
C265 A265 25c dark brown .48 .15
C266 A265 50c black & car 1.10 .60
a. Souvenir sheet 4.00 4.00
Nos. C263-C266 (4) 2.17 1.05

No. C266a contains four stamps similar to Nos. C263-C266, but printed in different colors: 15c red and black, 20c pale purple, 25c brown, 50c black and olive green.

Steel Mill Type of Regular Issue

1954, Dec. 12 ***Perf. 12½x13***
C267 A266 20c green & blk 1.00 .60

Marti Type of Regular Issue, 1955

1955, Jan. 28 ***Perf. 13½x13***
C268 A267 15c deep green .28 .15

Korean Veterans Type of Regular Issue, 1955

1955, Mar. 23 ***Perf. 12½***
C269 A268 20c dark green .50 .16

Merchant Fleet Types of Regular Issue, 1955

1955, Apr. 12 ***Perf. 12½***
C270 A269 25c black .28 .15
C271 A270 50c dark green .55 .32
a. Souvenir sheet 4.00 4.00

No. C271a contains four stamps similar to Nos. C255, C269-C271, but printed in different colors; 15c lilac red, 20c olive, 25c bluish black, 50c bluish green.

Marco Fidel Suarez (1855-1927), Pres. 1918-21 — AP56

Inscribed: "Correo Extra Rapido"

1955, April 23 ***Perf. 13***
C272 AP56 10c deep blue .15 .15

Hotel-Church Type of Regular Issue, 1955

1955, May 16 Photo. ***Perf. 11½x12***
C273 A271 15c rose brown .25 .15

Rotary Type of Regular Issue, 1955

Unwmk.

1955, Oct. 17 Engr. ***Perf. 13***
C274 A272 15c dk carmine rose .25 .15

O'Higgins, Santander and Sucre AP59

Ferdinand the Catholic and Queen Isabella I AP60

Designs: 2c, Atahualpa, Tisquesuza and Montezuma. 20c, Marti, Hidalgo and Petion. 1p, Artigas, Solano Lopez and Murillo. 2p, Abdon Calderon, Baron de Rio Branco and José de La Mar.

1955, Oct. 12 Engr. & Photo.

Inscribed: "Extra Rapido"

C275 AP59 2c dull brn & blk .15 .15
C276 AP60 5c dk brn & yel .15 .15

Regular Air Post

C277 AP59 15c rose car & blk .20 .15
C278 AP59 20c pale brn & blk .30 .15
a. Souvenir sheet of 2 10.00 6.50

Inscribed: "Extra Rapido"

C279 AP60 1p ol gray & brn 5.75 5.00
C280 AP60 2p violet & blk 4.00 4.00
Nos. C275-C280 (6) 10.55 9.60

7th Cong. of the Postal Union of the Americas and Spain, Bogota, Oct. 12-Nov. 9, 1955.

No. C278a contains one each of Nos. C277-C278 printed in different shades.

Caro Type of Regular Issue, 1955

1955, Nov. 29 Engr. ***Perf. 13½x13***
C281 A275 15c gray green .24 .15

University of Salamanca AP62

Inscribed: "Extra Rapido"

1955, Nov. 29 Unwmk. ***Perf. 13***
C282 AP62 20c dark brown .15 .15

University of Salamanca, 7th centenary.

Type of Postal Tax Stamp of 1948-50 Surcharged

CORREO
2
EXTRA-RAPIDO

1956 Wmk. 255 Engr. ***Perf. 12***
C283 PT10 2c on 8c blue .15 .15

No. 617 Overprinted in Black

EXTRA-RAPIDO

1956 Unwmk. ***Perf. 12½x13***
C284 A256 1p black & emerald .25 .15

Columbus Type of Regular Issue

1956, Oct. 11 Photo. ***Perf. 12***
C285 A279 15c intense blue .50 .15

See No. C306.

St. Elizabeth Type of Regular Issue

1956, Nov. 19
C286 A280 15c red brown .28 .18

St. Ignatius Type of Regular Issue

1956, Nov. 26 Engr. ***Perf. 12½x13***
C287 A281 5c brown .18 .15

Javier Pereira — AP63

1956, Dec. 28 Unwmk. *Perf. 12*

C288 AP63 20c rose carmine .15 .15

Issued to honor 167-year-old Javier Pereira.

No. 649 and Type of 1941 Overprinted in Red "EXTRA RAPIDO"

1957 *Perf. 13½x13*

C289 A276 5c blue & black 6.50 2.50

Perf. 12

C290 AP22 5p orange & gray 5.75 5.75

The overprint measures 14mm.

Virgin Type of 1954

Engraved and Lithographed

1957, May 23 Unwmk. *Perf. 13*

C291 AP48 5c dp plum & multi .15 .15

Bank Type of Regular Issue, 1957.

Designs: C292, 20c, Emblem and dairy farm. 10c, Emblem and tractor. 15c, Emblem, coffee and corn. C293, Emblem, cow, horse and herd.

1957 Photo. *Perf. 14x13½*

C292 A283 5c chocolate .15 .15
C293 A283 5c orange .15 .15
C294 A283 10c green .48 .38
C295 A283 15c black .26 .15
C296 A283 20c dull red .16 .18
Nos. C292-C296 (5) 1.20
Set value .72

No. C292 is inscribed "Extra Rapido."
No. C292 issued Mar. 5, others May 23.

Cyclist AP64

1957, July 6 Unwmk. *Perf. 12*

C297 AP64 2c brown .15 .15
C298 AP64 5c ultra .16 .16
Set value .28 .28

Seventh Bicycle Tour of Colombia.

Academy Type of Regular Issue

Designs: 15c, Coat of arms and Gen. Rafael Reyes. 20c, Coat of arms and Academy.

1957, July 20 Engr. *Perf. 12½*

C299 A284 15c rose carmine .15 .15
C300 A284 20c brown .26 .15
Set value .15

Delgado Type of Regular Issue, 1957

1957, Sept. 15 Photo. *Perf. 12*

C301 A285 10c slate blue .16 .15

UPU Type of Regular Issue, 1957

1957, Oct. 10

C302 A286 15c dark red brown .16 .15
C303 A286 25c dark blue .16 .15
Set value .16

St. Vincent de Paul Type of Regular Issue, 1957

1957, Oct. 18

C304 A287 5c rose brown .16 .15

Fencing Type of Regular Issue, 1957

1957, Nov. 23 *Perf. 12*

C305 A288 20c dark red brown .24 .16

Columbus Type of Regular Issue, 1956, Inscribed "Extra Rapido"

1958, Jan. 8 Unwmk. *Perf. 12*

C306 A279 3c dark green .15 .15

Scenic Type of 1954

Design: 25c, Las Lajas Shrine.

1958, June 20 Engr. *Perf. 13*

C307 AP40 25c dark blue .28 .15
C308 AP40 25c rose violet .28 .15
Set value .15

IGY Type of Regular Issue, 1958

1958, May 12 Photo. *Perf. 12*

C309 A289 25c green .48 .15

Inscribed "Extra Rapido"

C310 A289 1p purple .32 .15
Set value .20

No. 659 Overprinted "AEREO" in Carmine

1958, Oct. 16 Engr. *Perf. 13*

C312 A277 50c dk green & blk .40 .15

Almanza Type of Regular Issue, 1958

1958, Oct. 23 Photo. *Perf. 14x13*

C313 A290 25c dark gray .25 .15

Inscribed "Extra Rapido"

C314 A290 10c olive green .15 .15
Set value .15

Carrasquilla Type of Regular Issue

1959, Jan. 22 Photo. *Perf. 14x13*

C315 A291 25c carmine rose .20 .15
C316 A291 1p dark blue .60 .16
Set value .21

Miss Universe Type of Regular Issue

1959, June 26 Unwmk. *Perf. 11½*

C317 A292 1.20p multicolored 1.40 1.10
C318 A292 5p multicolored 32.50 32.50

Gaitan Type of Regular Issue, 1959, Inscribed "Extra Rapido" and Surcharged in Black or Blue

1959, July 28 Engr. *Perf. 12x13½*

C319 A293 2p on 1p black 1.40 1.25
C320 A293 2p on 1p black (Bl) 1.40 1.25

The 1p black, type A293, exists without surcharge.

No. C247 Surcharged with New Value in Dark Blue; Old Value Obliterated

1959, Aug. 24 Unwmk. *Perf. 13*

C321 AP40 50c on 60c dk brown 1.25 .40

Regular and Air Post Issues of 1948-59 Overprinted in Black or Red

1959-60

C322 A283 5c orange .25 .25
C323 A287 5c rose brn ('60) .40 .50
C324 A281 5c brown (R) .30 .30
C325 AP41 10c black .15 .15
a. Double overprint 2.50 2.50
C326 A160 10c red, #C231 .28 .15
a. Double overprint 1.40 1.40
C328 A284 15c rose carmine .20 .15
a. Inverted overprint 3.00 3.00
C330 AP40 20c brown .15 .15
a. Double overprint 1.40 1.40
C331 A284 20c brown .16 .16
C332 A288 20c dk red brn ('60) .15 .20
C333 AP40 25c rose vio ('60) .15 .15
C334 AP40 25c dark blue .15 .15
C335 A291 25c carmine rose .16 .15
C336 A290 25c dark gray .15 .15
C338 AP40 30c brown orange .15 .15
C340 AP40 50c on 60c dk brn .28 .15
C341 A291 1p dark blue .65 .15
a. Double overprint 2.50 2.50
C342 A292 1.20p brn, ultra, car & ol 1.00 .80
C343 AP41 2p dk grn & blk 1.40 .20
C344 AP41 3p car rose & blk 3.75 .48
a. Double overprint 8.50 8.50
C345 AP41 5p dk grn & red brn 5.25 1.10
a. Double overprint 8.50 8.50
b. Inverted overprint 8.50 8.50
C346 AP40 10p gray grn & red org 6.50 2.25
Nos. C322-C346 (21) 21.63
Set value 6.95

Issued following agreement between the Colombian government and AVIANCA to unify the air postage used on all mail carried by AVIANCA.
Vertical overprint on Nos. C342 and C346.

Airmail Stamp of 1919 and Planes AP66

Designs: 60c, No. C349a, C350a, Planes of 1919 and 1959. C349b, C350b, Stamp of 1919 and Planes.

Unwmk.

1959, Dec. 5 Photo. *Perf. 12*

C347 AP66 35c lt bl, blk & red .60 .15
C348 AP66 60c yel grn & gray .40 .15
Set value .15

Souvenir Sheets

C349 Sheet of 2 4.50 4.50
a. AP66 1p orange & gray .65 .65
b. AP66 1p lilac, gray & red .65 .65

Inscribed "Extra Rapido"

1960, May 17

C350 Sheet of 2 4.50 4.50
a. AP66 1.50p red orange & gray .85 .85
b. AP66 1.50p olive, gray & rose .85 .85

Nos. C347-C350 for the 40th anniv. of air post service and of the AVIANCA company.

Type of Regular Issue, 1959 and

1859 Stamp and Seaplane AP67

Tête Bêche 5c Stamps of 1859 — AP68

Designs (various stamps of 1859 and): 10c, Map of Colombia. 25c, Pres. Mariano Ospina. 1.20p, Plane over mountains.

1959, Dec. 1 Photo. *Perf. 12*

C351 A296 25c choc & red .50 .24
C352 AP67 50c ver & ultra 1.00 .50
C353 AP67 1.20p yel grn & car 2.00 1.10

Inscribed "Extra Rapido"

C354 A296 10c lemon & vio .15 .15
Nos. C351-C354 (4) 3.65 1.99

Souvenir Sheet

Wmk. 331

1959, Dec. 23 Litho. *Imperf.*

C355 AP68 5p blue, *pink* 11.00 11.00

Cent. of Colombian postage stamps.
No. C355 exists with inscription "VALOR $5.10" instead of "VALOR $5."

Eldorado Airport, Bogota — AP69

1960, Jan. 5 Wmk. 331 *Perf. 12½*

C356 AP69 35c black & ocher .50 .25
C356A AP69 60c ver & gray .65 .42

Inscribed "Extra Rapido"

C356B AP69 1p Prus bl & gray .85 .60
Nos. C356-C356B (3) 2.00 1.27

Ant Bear — AP70

Designs: 1.30p, Armadillo. 1.45p, Parrot fish.

Unwmk.

1960, Feb. 12 Photo. *Perf. 12*

C357 AP70 35c sepia .85 .15
C358 AP70 1.30p rose car & dk brn 1.75 1.40
C359 AP70 1.45p lt bl, bl & yel 1.40 1.25
Nos. C357-C359 (3) 4.00 2.80

Alexander von Humboldt, German naturalist and geographer (1769-1859).

Flower Type of Regular Issue, 1960

Flowers: Nos. C360, C362, C366, Passiflora mollissima. Nos. C361, C364, C367, Odontoglossum luteo purpureum. Nos. C363, C369, Anthurium andreanum. Nos. C365, C370, Stanhopea tigrina. No. C368, Espeletia grandiflora.

1960, May 10 Photo. *Perf. 12*

Flowers in Natural Colors

C360 A298 5c dark blue .15 .15
C361 A298 35c maroon .40 .15
C362 A298 60c dark blue .75 .55
C363 A298 1.45p dark brown 1.00 .85

Inscribed "Extra Rapido"

C364 A298 5c maroon .15 .15
C365 A298 10c brown .15 .15
C366 A298 1p dark blue 2.00 2.50
C367 A298 1p maroon 2.00 2.50
C368 A298 1p brown 2.00 2.50
C369 A298 1p brown 2.00 2.50
C370 A298 1p brown 2.00 2.50
Nos. C360-C370 (11) 12.60 14.50

See Nos. C420-C425.

Fleeing Family and Uprooted Oak Emblem — AP71

Perf. 10, 11

1960, May 24 Litho. Wmk. 331

C371 AP71 60c bl grn & gray .30 .20

World Refugee Year, July 1, 1959-June 30, 1960.

Souvenir Sheet

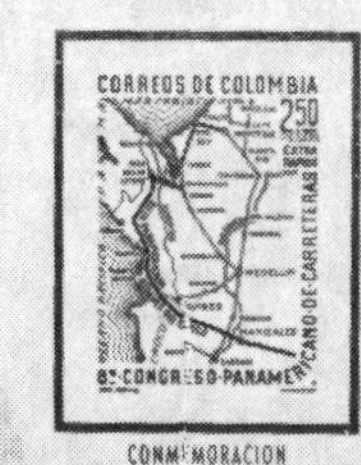

Pan-American Highway Through Colombia — AP72

1960, May 28 Litho. *Imperf.*

C372 AP72 2.50p brown & aqua 5.00 5.00

8th Pan-American Highway Congress, Bogota, May 20-29.

Lincoln Type of Regular Issue

1960, June 6 *Perf. 10½*

C375 A299 40c dl red brn & blk .85 .60
C376 A299 60c rose red & blk .25 .15

Type of Regular Issue and

Joaquin Camacho, Jorge Tadeo Lozano and Jose Miguel Pey — AP73

> ***15-Cent Minimum Value***
> *The minimum catalogue value is 15 cents. Separating se-tenant pieces into individual stamps does not increase the value of the stamps since demand for the separated stamps may be small.*

Flag, Coins and Arms of Mompox and Cartagena — AP74

Designs: No. C378, Arms of Cartagena. 35c, 1.45p, Colombian flag. 60c, Andres Rosillo, Antonio Villavicencio and Joaquin Caicedo. 1p, Manuel de Bernardo Alvarez and Joaquin Gutierrez. 1.20p, Jose Antonio Galan statue. 1.30p, Front page of newspaper La Bagatela, 1811. 1.65p, Antonia Santos, Jose Acevedo y Gomez and Liborio Mejia.

Unwmk.

1960, July 20 Photo. *Perf. 12*

C377 AP73 5c lilac & brn .15 .15
C378 A301 5c dp bl grn & multi .15 .15
C379 AP73 35c multicolored .15 .15
C380 AP73 60c red brn & grn .40 .15
C381 AP73 1p ver & sl grn .85 .60
C382 A301 1.20p ultra & ind .85 .60
C383 AP73 1.30p orange & blk .85 .60
C384 AP73 1.45p multicolored 1.10 .85
C385 AP73 1.65p green & brn .85 .85
Nos. C377-C385 (9) 5.35 4.10

Souvenir Sheet

Stamps Inscribed "Extra Rapido"

C386 AP74 Sheet of 4 3.75 3.75
a. 50c deep claret & multi .60 .60
b. 50c green & multi .60 .60
c. 1p brown olive, yel, blue & car .60 .60
d. 1p lilac & gray .60 .60

150th anniv. of Colombia's independence.

St. Isidore Type of Regular Issue, 1960

Designs: 35c, No. C388a, St. Isidore and farm animals. No. C388b, Nativity.

Unwmk.

1960, Sept. 26 Photo. *Perf. 12*

C387 A302 35c multicolored .16 .15

Souvenir Sheet

Stamps Inscribed "Extra Rapido"

C388 A302 Sheet of 2 6.00 6.00
a. 1.50p multicolored 2.00 2.00
b. 1.50p multicolored 2.00 2.00

See Nos. C439-C440.

Type of Regular Issue, 1959

Perf. 12½

1960, Nov. 23 Litho. Wmk. 331

C389 A294 35c Bolivar 3.00 .40

Pan-American Highway Type of Regular Issue, 1961

1961, Mar. 7 Unwmk. *Perf. 10½x11*

C390 A304 10c rose lil & emer .50 .65
C391 A304 20c ver & lt bl .50 .65
C392 A304 30c black & emer .50 .65

Inscribed "Extra Rapido"

C393 A304 10c dk blue & emer .50 .65
Nos. C390-C393 (4) 2.00 2.60

8th Pan-American Highway Congress, Bogota, May 20-29, 1960.

Lopez Type of Regular Issue, 1961

1961, Mar. 22 Photo. *Perf. 12½*

C394 A305 35c blue & brown .52 .15

Inscribed "Extra Rapido"

C395 A305 10c emerald & brn .16 .15
Set value .17

Souvenir Sheet

C396 A305 1p lilac & brn 3.50 3.50

Brother Damian and San Francisco Church, Cali AP75

Designs: 10c, View of Cali, vert. No. 398, Emblem of University del Valle, vert. 1.30p, Fine Arts School, Cali. 1.45p, Agricultural College, Palmira.

Perf. 13x13½, 13½x13

1961, Aug. 17 Photo. Unwmk.

C397 AP75 35c vio brn & ol .30 .15
C398 AP75 35c olive & grn .30 .15
C399 AP75 1.30p sepia & pink .85 .45
C400 AP75 1.45p multicolored .85 .60

Inscribed: "Extra Rapido"

C401 AP75 10c brn & yel grn .15 .15
Nos. C397-C401 (5) 2.45
Set value 1.20

50th anniv. (in 1960) of the department of Valle del Cauca.

View of Cucuta AP76

Design: 10c, Church of the Rosary, Cucuta, vert.

1961, Aug. 29

C402 AP76 35c brn ol & grn .60 .15

Inscribed: "Extra Rapido"

C403 AP76 10c dk brn & gray grn .15 .15
Set value .15

50th anniv. (in 1960) of the department of North Santander.

Old and New Ships of Barranquilla AP77

Arms and View of San Gil — AP78

Hotel, Popayan AP79

Statue of Christ in Procession AP80

Design: 1.45p, View of Velez.

Perf. 12½x13, 13x12½

1961, Oct. 10 Photo. Unwmk.

C404 AP77 35c gold & bl .45 .15
C405 AP78 35c bl grn, yel & red .45 .15
C406 AP79 35c carmine & brn .45 .15
C407 AP78 1.45p brown & grn .45 .20

Inscribed: "Extra Rapido"

C408 AP80 10c brown & yel .15 .15
Nos. C404-C408 (5) 1.95
Set value .46

Souvenir Sheets

Types of Regular and Air Post Issues

Designs, No. C409: 35c, Barranquilla arms. 40c, Popayan arms. c, Arms and view of San Gil. d, Holy Week in Popayan.

No. C410: a, Old and new ships at Barranquilla. b, Hotel, Popayan. c, Bucaramanga arms. d, Holy Week in Popayan.

C409 Sheet of 4 5.00 5.50
a. A309 35c gold & multi .45 .45
b. A309 40c gold & multi .45 .45
c. AP78 1p blue, yellow & red .90 .90
d. AP80 1p carmine rose & yellow .90 .90

Stamps Inscribed: "Extra Rapido"

C410 Sheet of 4 5.00 5.50
a. AP77 50c gold & carmine rose .70 .70
b. AP79 50c gold & blue .70 .70
c. A309 50c pink & multi .70 .70
d. AP80 50c blue & yellow .70 .70

Nos. C404-C408 are in honor of the Atlantico Department. Nos. C409-C410 are in honor of the Departments of Atlantico, Cauca and Santander.

Nos. 713, 716 and 715 Overprinted and Surcharged

AEREO

1961, Sept. *Perf. 12*

C411 A297 5c grnsh bl & brn .15 .15
C412 A298 5c multicolored .15 .15
C413 A297 10c on 20c cit & gray brn .15 .15
Set value .30 .19

"Aereo" in script on No. C412.

See Nos. C420-C425.

Sports Type of Regular Issue, 1961

Designs: No. C414, Women divers. No. C415, Tennis, mixed doubles. 1.45p, No. C419b, Baseball. No. C417, Torch bearer. Nos. C418, C419a, Bolivar statue and flags of six participating nations. No. C419c, Soccer. No. C419d, Basketball.

1961, Dec. 16 Litho. *Perf. 13½x14*

C414 A310 35c ultra, yel & brn .60 .15
C415 A310 35c car, yel & brn .60 .15
C416 A310 1.45p Prus grn, yel & brn .85 .55

Inscribed: "Extra Rapido"

C417 A310 10c car lake, yel & brn .15 .15
C418 A310 10c ol, yel, bl & red .15 .15
Nos. C414-C418 (5) 2.35
Set value .75

Souvenir Sheet

Stamps Inscribed: "Extra Rapido"

Imperf

C419 Sheet of 4 5.00 5.00
a. A310 50c multi .42 .42
b. A310 50c multi .42 .42
c. A310 1p multi .85 .85
d. A310 1p multi .85 .85

Flower Type of 1960

Flowers: 5c, Passiflora mollissima. 10c, Espeletia grandiflora. 20c, 2p, Odontoglossum luteo purpureum. 25c, Stanhopea tigrina. 60c, Anthurium Andreanum.

Unwmk.

1962, Jan. 30 Photo. *Perf. 12*

Flowers in Natural Colors

C420 A298 5c gray .15 .15
C421 A298 10c gray blue .15 .15
C422 A298 20c rose lilac .15 .15
C423 A298 25c citron .25 .15
C424 A298 60c light brown .25 .25

Inscribed "Extra Rapido"

C425 A298 2p salmon pink 2.00 1.75
Nos. C420-C425 (6) 2.95
Set value 1.92

Anti-Malaria Type of Regular Issue.

Designs: 40c, Colombian anti-malaria emblem. 1p, 1.45p, Malaria eradication emblem and mosquito in swamp.

1962, Apr. 12 Litho. *Perf. 12*

C426 A311 40c yellow & red .16 .15
C427 A311 1.45p gray & ultra .48 .42

Inscribed "Extra Rapido"

C428 A311 1p yel grn & ultra 3.50 3.50
Nos. C426-C428 (3) 4.14 4.07

WHO drive to eradicate malaria.

Type of Regular Issue, 1962 and

Abelardo Ramos and Engineering School, Cauca — AP81

Designs: 10c, Miguel Triana, Andres A. Arroyo and Monserrate shrine with cable cars. 15c, Diodoro Sanchez and first meeting place of Engineers Society. 2p, Engineers Society emblem.

1962, June 12 Photo. *Perf. 11½x12*

C429 AP81 5c blue & dp rose .15 .15
C430 AP81 10c green & sepia .15 .15
C431 AP81 15c lilac & sepia .25 .16

Inscribed: "Extra Rapido"

C432 A312 2p blk, yel, red & bl 1.50 1.50
Nos. C429-C432 (4) 2.05 1.96

75th anniv. of the founding of the Colombian Soc. of Engineers and 6th Natl. Cong. of Engineers.

American States Type of 1962

1962, June 28 Photo. *Perf. 13*

Flags in National Colors

C433 A313 35c black & blue .35 .15

Women's Rights Type of 1962

Perf. 12x12½

1962, July 20 Litho. Wmk. 229

C434 A314 35c ocher, gray & blk .20 .15

See Nos. C448-C450.

Scout Type of 1962

Designs: 15c, No. C438, Scouts at campfire and tents. 40c and No. C437, Girl Scouts.

Perf. 11½x12

1962, July 26 Photo. Unwmk.

C435 A315 15c brown & rose .20 .15
C436 A315 40c dp claret & pink .24 .20
C437 A315 1p blue & buff .90 .32

Inscribed "Extra Rapido"

C438 A315 1p purple & yellow 3.75 3.75
Nos. C435-C438 (4) 5.09 4.42

Nos. C435 and C438 for 30th anniv. of the Colombian Boy Scouts. Nos. C436 and C437 for the 25th anniv. of the Girl Scouts.

Nativity by Gregorio Vasquez — AP82

Design: 2p, St. Isidore, similar to type A302.

Inscribed "Extra Rapido"

Unwmk.

1962, Aug. 28 Photo. *Perf. 12*

C439 AP82 10c gray & multi .15 .15
C440 AP82 2p gray & multi 3.50 3.50

See Nos. C387-C388.

Type of Regular Issue, 1962 and

Pres. Aquileo Parra and Magdalena River Bridge AP83

Design: 5c, Locomotives of 1854 and 1961. 10c, Railroad map of Colombia.

1962, Sept. 28 Photo. *Perf. 12½*

C441 AP83 5c sep & slate grn .15 .15
C442 A316 10c multicolored .15 .15

Engr.

C443 AP83 1p dull pur & brn 1.40 .15

Inscribed: "Extra Rapido."

C444 AP83 5p bl, brn & dl grn 3.75 3.75
Nos. C441-C444 (4) 5.45 4.20

Progress of Colombian railroads and completion of the Atlantic Line from Santa Maria to Bogota.

UPAE Type of Regular Issue

Designs: 50c, Map of Americas and carrier pigeon. 60c, Post horn.

Perf. 13½x14

1962, Oct. 18 Litho. Wmk. 346

C445 A317 50c slate grn & gold .28 .15
C446 A317 60c gold & plum .22 .15
Set value .15

Pope John XXIII — AP84

1963, Mar. 11

C447 AP84 60c gold, red brn, buff & red .20 .15

Vatican II, the 21st Ecumenical Council of the Roman Catholic Church.

Women's Rights Type of 1962

1963-64 ***Perf. 12x12½***
C448 A314 5c sal, gray & blk ('64) .15 .15
C449 A314 45c pale grn, gray & blk .32 .15
C450 A314 45c brt pink, gray & blk .32 .15
Nos. C448-C450 (3) .79
Set value .15

Games Emblem — AP85

1963, Aug. 12 ***Perf. 13x14***
C451 AP85 20c gray & multi .15 .15
C452 AP85 80c buff & multi .15 .15
Set value .15

South American Athletic Championships (22nd for men, 12th for women), Cali, June 30-July 7.

Bolivar Statue by Arenas-Betancourt — AP86

Perf. 14x13½

1963, Aug. 30 **Unwmk.**
C453 AP86 1.90p olive bis & blue .20 .15

Centenary of the city of Pereira.
For surcharge see No. C574.

Tennis Player — AP87

1963, Oct. 11 ***Perf. 13½x14***
C454 AP87 55c multicolored .15 .15

30th South American Tennis Championships, Medellin, Oct. 3-13.

Pres. John F. Kennedy and Alliance for Progress Emblem AP88

1963, Dec. 17 **Litho.** ***Perf. 14x13½***
C455 AP88 10c multicolored .15 .15

President John F. Kennedy (1917-1963).

Church of the True Cross, National Pantheon, Bogota — AP89

Design: 2p, Christ of the Martyrs, bell and tomb.

Perf. 13½x14

1964, Mar. 10 **Photo.** **Unwmk.**
C459 AP89 1p multicolored .25 .15
C460 AP89 2p multicolored .32 .18
Set value .25

View of Cartagena AP90

1964, Mar. 18 **Litho.** ***Perf. 14x13½***
C461 AP90 3p vio, bl, ocher & brn 1.40 .60

Cartagena's independence in 1811, Simon Bolivar's visit in 1812 and the siege of 1815.

Eleanor Roosevelt — AP91

1964, Nov. 10 **Photo.** ***Perf. 12***
C462 AP91 20c ol & dl red brn .15 .15

Eleanor Roosevelt (1884-1962).

Alberto Castilla and Score of "El Bunde" — AP92

1964, Nov. 10 **Unwmk.**
C463 AP92 30c ol bis & Prus grn .15 .15

Department of Tolima and Maestro Alberto Castilla (1878-1937) who in 1906 founded the Tolima Conservatory of Music in Ibague.

Mejia Type of Regular Issue

Designs (Mejia portrait and): 45c, Women picking coffee. 5p, Mules carrying coffee bags. 10p, Loading coffee on freighter "Manuel Mejia."

1965, Feb. 10 **Engr.** ***Perf. 12½x13***
C464 A320 45c brown & blk .15 .15
C465 A320 5p gray grn & blk 1.75 .30
C466 A320 10p ultra & blk 2.25 .25
Nos. C464-C466 (3) 4.15 .70

ITU Emblem AP93

1965, Oct. 25 **Photo.** ***Perf. 12***
C467 AP93 80c Prus bl, lt bl & red .15 .15

Cent. of the ITU.

Cattleya Truanae — AP94

Cent. of the Telegraph in Colombia — AP95

1965, Oct. 3 **Litho.** ***Perf. 13½x14***
C468 AP94 20c yellow & multi .15 .15

Fifth Philatelic Exhibition.

1965, Nov. 1 ***Perf. 13½x14, 14x13½***

Design: No. C469, Pres. Manuel Murillo Toro statue, telegraph and orbits. No. C470, Telegraph and satellites over South America, horiz.

C469 AP95 60c multicolored .15 .15
C470 AP95 60c multicolored .15 .15
Set value .15

Junkers F-13 Seaplane, 1920 AP96

History of Colombian Aviation: 10c, Dornier Wal, 1924. 20c, Dornier Mercur, 1926. 50c, Trimotor Ford, 1932. 60c, De Havilland biplane, 1930. 1p, Douglas DC-4, 1947. 1.40p, Douglas DC-3, 1944. 2.80p, Superconstellation 1049, 1951. 3p, Boeing 720B jet, 1961.

Perf. 14x13½

1965-66 **Photo.** **Unwmk.**
C471 AP96 5c multicolored .15 .15
C472 AP96 10c multicolored .15 .15
C473 AP96 20c multicolored .15 .15
C474 AP96 50c multicolored .15 .15
C475 AP96 60c multicolored .30 .15
C476 AP96 1p multicolored .60 .15
C477 AP96 1.40p multicolored .80 .15
C478 AP96 2.80p multicolored 1.50 .60
C479 AP96 3p multicolored 2.00 .85
Nos. C471-C479 (9) 5.80
Set value 1.90

Issue dates: 5c, 60c, 3p, Dec. 13, 1965; 10c, 1p, 1.40p, July 15, 1966; 20c, 50c, 2.80p, Dec. 14, 1966.

Automobile Club Emblem and Car on Road — AP97

1966, Feb. 16 **Litho.** ***Perf. 14x13½***
C480 AP97 20c multicolored .15 .15

25th anniv. (in 1965) of the Automobile Club of Colombia.

Fish Type of Regular Issue

Fish: 2p, Flying fish. 2.80p, Queen angelfish. 20p, King mackerel.

1966, Aug. 25 **Photo.** ***Perf. 12½x13***
C481 A323 2p multicolored .35 .15
C482 A323 2.80p multicolored 1.00 1.00
C483 A323 20p multicolored 8.75 8.75
Nos. C481-C483 (3) 10.10 9.90

Coat of Arms Type of Regular Issue

1966, Oct. 11 **Litho.** ***Perf. 14x13½***
C484 A324 1p ultra & multi .24 .15
C485 A324 1.40p red & multi .20 .15
Set value .15

Portrait Type of Regular Issue

Portraits: 80c, Father Felix Restrepo Mejia, S.J. (1887-1965), theologian and scholar. 1.70p, José Joaquin Casas (1866-1951), educator and diplomat.

Perf. 13½x14

1967, Jan. 18 **Litho.** **Unwmk.**
C486 A325 80c dk bl & bis .15 .15
C487 A325 1.70p blk & bis .24 .15
Set value .17

Declaration of Bogota Type

1967, Feb. 2 **Litho.** ***Perf. 14x13½***
C488 A326 3p multicolored .35 .16

See note after No. 767.

Orchid Type of Regular Issue

Orchids: 1p, Cattleya dowiana aurea, vert. 1.20p, Masdevallia coccinea, vert. 5p, Catasetum macrocarpum and bee.

1967, May 23 **Litho.** ***Perf. 14***
C489 A327 1p multicolored .32 .15
C490 A327 1.20p multicolored .22 .15
C491 A327 5p multicolored 1.25 .30
a. Souv. sheet of 3, #C489-C491 2.00 2.00
Nos. C489-C491 (3) 1.79
Set value .48

Lions Type of Regular Issue

1967, July 12 **Litho.** ***Perf. 13½x14***
C492 A328 25c multicolored .15 .15

"First Caesarean Section" by Grau — AP98

Perf. 14x13½

1967, Sept. 7 **Litho.** **Unwmk.**
C493 AP98 80c multicolored .15 .15

Issued to publicize the 6th Congress of Colombian Surgeons, Bogota, Sept. 25.

SENA Type of Regular Issue

Lithographed and Embossed

1967, Sept. 20 ***Perf. 13½x14***
C494 A329 2p gold, ver & blk .48 .15

Pre-Columbian Art Type

Designs: 30c, Bird pectoral. 5p Ornamental pectoral. 20p, Pitcher.

1967, Oct. 13 **Photo.** ***Perf. 13½x14***
C495 A330 30c ver, gold & brn .15 .15
C496 A330 5p red, gold & brn 1.65 .32
a. Souvenir sheet of 2 2.00 1.65
C497 A330 20p vio, gold & brn 8.25 8.25
Nos. C495-C497 (3) 10.05 8.72

No. C496a also commemorates the 6th Natl. Phil. Exhib. No. C496a contains 2 imperf. stamps in changed colors similar to Nos. C495-C496 (30c has green background and 5p maroon background).

Telecommunications Type

Designs: 50c, Signal lights. 1p, Early Bird satellite, Southern Cross and radar.

Perf. 13½x14

1968, May 14 **Litho.** **Unwmk.**
C498 A331 50c blk, ver & emer .15 .15
C499 A331 1p ultra, yel & gray .16 .15
Set value .15

Eucharist Type of Regular Issue

1968, June 6 **Litho.** ***Perf. 13½x14***
C500 A332 80c rose lil, red, yel & blk .15 .15
C501 A332 3p bl, red, yel & blk .30 .15
Set value .15

Eucharistic Congress Type

Designs: 80c, The Last Supper, by Gregorio Vasquez, horiz. 1p, St. Francis Xavier Preaching, by Gregorio Vasquez. 2p, The Dream of the Prophet Elias, by Gregorio Vasquez. 3p, Monstrance, c. 1700. 20p, Pope Paul VI, painting by Roman Franciscan nuns.

1968, Aug. 13 **Photo.** ***Perf. 13***
C502 A333 80c multicolored .18 .15
C503 A333 1p multicolored .25 .15
C504 A333 2p multicolored .35 .15
C505 A333 3p lil & multi .65 .15
C506 A333 20p gold & multi 4.00 2.00
Nos. C502-C506 (5) 5.43
Set value 2.20

Shrine of the Eucharist, Bogotá AP99

Designs: 1.20p, Pope Paul VI giving blessing and Papal arms, vert. 1.80p, Cathedral of Bogotá, vert.

Perf. 14x13½, 13½x14

1968, Aug. 22 **Litho.**
C507 AP99 80c multicolored .15 .15
C508 AP99 1.20p multicolored .20 .15
C509 AP99 1.80p multicolored .30 .15
Nos. C507-C509 (3) .65
Set value .26

Visit of Pope Paul VI to Colombia.

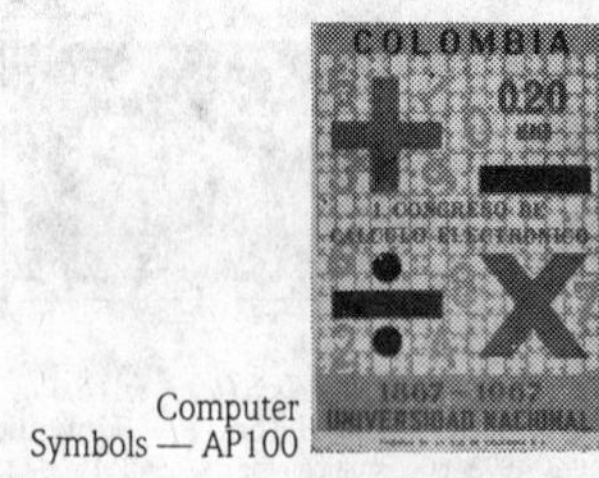

Computer Symbols — AP100

1968, Oct. 29 Litho. *Perf. 13½x14*

C510 AP100 20c buff, car & grn .15 .15

Cent. of the Natl. University and the 1st Data Processing Cong. in 1967 at the University.

Agriculture Institute Type of Regular Issue

1968, Mar. 5 Litho. *Perf. 13½x14*

C511 A337 1p gray & multi .18 .15

Microscope and Pen — AP101

1969, Mar. 24 Litho. *Perf. 14*

C512 AP101 5p blk, yel, ver & pur 1.10 .15

20th anniv. (in 1968) of the University of the Andes.

Alexander von Humboldt and Andes AP102

1969, May 3 Litho. *Perf. 14x13½*

C513 AP102 1p grn & brn .15 .15

Alexander von Humboldt (1769-1859), German naturalist and traveler.

Map of Colombia, Amphibian Plane and Letter AP103

Design: 1.50p, No. C516b, Globe, letter, and jet of Avianca airlines.

1969, June 18 Litho. *Perf. 14x13½*

C514 AP103 1p multicolored .16 .15
C515 AP103 1.50p multicolored .24 .15
Set value .15

Souvenir Sheet

Imperf

C516 Sheet of 2 3.50 3.50
a. AP103 5p green & multi .70 .70
b. AP103 5p violet & multi .70 .70

50th anniv. of the 1st air post flight in Colombia. No. C516 also for 8th Natl. Philatelic Exhibition, EXFILBA 69, Barranquilla, June 18-22. No. C516 contains 2 stamps in the designs of the 1p and 1.50p.

Independence Type of Regular Issue

Design: 2.30p, Simon Bolivar, José Antonio Anzoategui, Francisco de Paula Santander and victorious army entering Bogotá, Sept. 18, 1819; painting by Ignacio Castillo Cervantes.

1969, July 24 Litho. *Perf. 13½x14*

C517 A338 2.30p gold & multi .48 .16

Social Security Emblem — AP104

Neurosurgeons' Congress Emblem — AP105

1969, Oct. 29 Litho. *Perf. 13½x14*

C518 AP104 20c emer & blk .15 .15

20th anniv. of the Colombian Institute of Social Security.

1969, Oct. 29

C519 AP105 70c vio, red & yel .25 .15

Issued to publicize the 13th Congress of Latin-American Neurosurgeons, Bogotá.

Junkers F-13 AP106

Designs: No. C521, C522b, Globe with airlines from Bogota and Boeing jet. No. C522a, like No. C520.

1969, Nov. 28 Litho. *Perf. 14x13½*

C520 AP106 2p grn & multi .32 .15
C521 AP106 3.50p ultra & multi .48 .28

Souvenir Sheet

Imperf

C522 Sheet of 2 3.50 3.50
a. AP106 3.50p light green & multi .52 .52
b. AP106 5p ultra & multi .75 .75

50th anniv. of AVIANCA; No. C522 also publicizes the 1st Interamerican Phil. Exhib., Bogota, Nov. 28-Dec. 7.

No. C522 contains 2 imperf. stamps.

Child Mailing Letter — AP107

Christmas: 1.50p, Praying child and gifts.

1969, Dec. 16 Litho. *Perf. 13½x14*

C523 AP107 60c ocher & multi .42 .18
C524 AP107 1p multicolored .42 .15
C525 AP107 1.50p multicolored .48 .18
Nos. C523-C525 (3) 1.32 .51

Radar Station and Pre-Columbian Head — AP108

1970, Mar. 25 Litho. *Perf. 14x13½*

C526 AP108 1p dl grn, blk & brick red .28 .15

Issued to publicize the opening of the communications satellite earth station at Chocontá in Cundinamarca Province.

Emblem of Colombian Youth Sports Institute — AP109

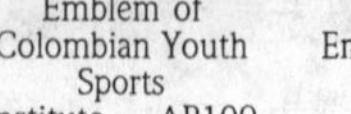

Art Exhibition Emblem — AP110

Design: 2.30p, Games' emblem (dove and 3 rings).

1970, Apr. 6 Litho. *Perf. 13½x14*

C527 AP109 1.50p dk ol grn, yel & blk .28 .16
C528 AP109 2.30p red & multi .42 .16

9th Natl. Youth Games, Ibague, July 10-20.

1970, Apr. 30 Litho. *Perf. 13½x14*

C529 AP110 30c multicolored .15 .15

2nd Biennial Art Exhib., Medellin, May 1-June 14.

Eduardo Santos, Rural and Urban Buildings AP111

1970, June 18 Litho. *Perf. 14x13½*

C530 AP111 1p grn, yel & blk .16 .15

Issued to commemorate the founding (in 1939) of the Territorial Credit Institute.

UN Emblem, Scales and Dove — AP112

EXFILCA Emblem — AP113

1970, June 26 *Perf. 13½x14*

C531 AP112 1.50p dk bl, lt bl & yel .16 .15

25th anniversary of United Nations.

1970, Nov. Litho. *Perf. 13½x14*

C532 AP113 10p bl, gold & blk 3.50 .26

EXFILCA 70, 2nd Interamerican Philatelic Exhib., Caracas, Venezuela, Nov. 27-Dec. 6.

Mother Juana Ruperta in Napanga Costume and Music by Efrain Orozco — AP114

Designs: 1p, Dancers from Eastern Plains and music by Alejandro Wills. No. C535, Guabina man, woman and folk song. No. C536, Bambuco man and woman, and music. No. C537, Man and woman dancing the Cumbia, and music.

1970-71 Litho. *Perf. 13½x14*

C533 AP114 60c dp lil rose & multi .48 .25
C534 AP114 1p ultra & multi .32 .15
C535 AP114 1.30p bl & multi .42 .15
C536 AP114 1.30p emer & multi ('71) .42 .15
C537 AP114 1.30p lil & multi ('71) .32 .15
Nos. C533-C537 (5) 1.96
Set value .52

Athlete and Games Emblem — AP115

Design: 2p, Games emblem.

1971, Mar. 11

C542 AP115 1.50p multicolored .90 .90
C543 AP115 2p blk, org & grn .80 .55

6th Pan-American Games, Cali, July 30-Aug. 13.

Gilberto Alzate Avendano AP116

1971, Apr. 29 Litho. *Perf. 14x13½*

C544 AP116 1p bl & multi .40 .26

Avendano (1910-60), journalist and popular leader.

Commemorative Medal — AP117

Lithographed and Embossed

1971, June 21 *Perf. 14x13½*

C545 AP117 1p sl grn & gold .50 .28

Centenary (in 1970) of the Bank of Bogota.

Olympic Center — AP118

Soccer — AP119

Designs (Games Emblem and): #C546-C546C, Olympic Center. #547, Soccer. #C548, Wrestling. #C549, Bicycling. #C550, Volleyball. #C551, Diving (women). #C552, Fencing. #C553, Sailing. #C554, Equestrian. #C555, Jumping. #C556, Rowing. #C557, Cali emblem. #C558, Basketball (women). #C559, Stadium. #C560, Baseball. #C561, Hockey. #C562, Weight lifting. #C563, Medals. #C564, Boxing. #C565, Gymnastics (women). #C566, Sharpshooting.

1971, July 16 Litho. *Perf. 13½x14*

Multicolored and Emblem Color:

C546 AP118 1.30p yellow 1.25 .28
C546A AP118 1.30p green 1.25 .28
C546B AP118 1.30p blue 1.25 .28
C546C AP118 1.30p carmine 1.25 .28
C547 AP119 1.30p emerald 1.25 .28
C548 AP119 1.30p lilac 1.25 .28
C549 AP119 1.30p blue 1.25 .28
C550 AP119 1.30p carmine 1.25 .28
C551 AP119 1.30p blue 1.25 .28
C552 AP119 1.30p carmine 1.25 .28
C553 AP119 1.30p blue 1.25 .28
C554 AP119 1.30p gray 1.25 .28
C555 AP119 1.30p green 1.25 .28
C556 AP119 1.30p blue 1.25 .28
C557 AP118 1.30p orange 1.25 .28
C558 AP119 1.30p carmine 1.25 .28
C559 AP118 1.30p light blue 1.25 .28
C560 AP119 1.30p plum 1.25 .28
C561 AP119 1.30p yel grn 1.25 .28
C562 AP119 1.30p pink 1.25 .28
C563 AP118 1.30p deep org 1.25 .28
C564 AP119 1.30p plum 1.25 .28
C565 AP119 1.30p lilac rose 1.25 .28
C566 AP119 1.30p green 1.25 .28
a. Sheet of 25, #C546-C566 32.50 7.00

6th Pan American Athletic Games, Cali. No. C546B appears twice in sheet.

Battle of Carabobo, by Martin Tovar y Tovar — AP120

1971, Nov. 25 Litho. *Perf. 13½x14*

C567 AP120 1.50p multicolored 1.00 .16

Sesquicentennial of the Battle of Carabobo.

St. Theresa Type of Regular Issue Overprinted "AEREO"

1972 Litho. *Perf. 13½x14*

C568 A343 2p multicolored .30 .15

See note after No. 793.

Vendor — AP121

Designs: 50c, Woman wearing shawl, and woven shawl. 3p, Fruit vendor (puppet).

1971, Apr. 11 Litho. *Perf. 13½x14*

C569	AP121	50c multicolored	.35	.16
C570	AP121	1p multicolored	.35	.15
C571	AP121	3p multicolored	.50	.24
		Nos. C569-C571 (3)	1.20	.55

Colombian artisans.

Mormodes Rolfeanum AP122

1972, Apr. 20 *Perf. 14x13½*

C572 AP122 1.30p multicolored .45 .15

7th World Orchidology Congress, Medellin.

Congo Grande Dancer — AP123

Laureano Gomez, by Ridriguez Cubillos — AP124

1972, June 21 Litho. *Perf. 13½x14*

C573 AP123 1.30p multicolored .50 .15

International Carnival of Barranquilla.

No. C453 Surcharged in Brown **$ 1.30**

1972, Oct. 5 Litho. *Perf. 14x13½*

C574 AP86 1.30p on 1.90p .55 .16

1972 *Perf. 13½x14*

Design: 1.30p, Guillermo Leòn Valencia Muñoz.

C575	AP124	1.30p multicolored	.15	.15
C576	AP124	1.30p multicolored	.18	.15
		Set value		.15

Laureano Gomez (1898-1966), Guillermo Leon Valencia Munoz (1909-71), Presidents of Colombia. Issued: No. C575, Oct. 17. No. C576, Nov. 28.

Benito Juarez — AP125

Rebecca Fountain — AP126

1972, Dec. 12 *Perf. 13½x14*

C577 AP125 1.50p multicolored .20 .15

Centenary of the death of Benito Juarez (1806-1872), revolutionary leader and president of Mexico.

1972, Dec. 19 Litho.

C578	AP126	80c multicolored	.45	.45
C579	AP126	1p multicolored	.40	.15

"Bucaramanga" — AP127

1972, Dec. 22 *Perf. 14x13½*

C580 AP127 5p multicolored .85 .15

350th anniversary of the founding of Bucaramanga.

Xavier University AP128

1973, May 8 Litho. *Perf. 14x13½*

C581	AP128	1.30p lt grn & sep	.25	.15
C582	AP128	1.50p lt bl & sep	.25	.15
		Set value		.15

350th anniversary of the founding of Xavier University in Bogotá.

Ceramic Type of Regular Issue

Excavated Ceramic Artifacts: 1p, Winged urn, Tairona. 1.30p, Woman and child, Sinu. 1.70p, Two-headed figure, Quimbaya. 3.50p, Man, Tumaco.

1973 Litho. *Perf. 13½x14*

C583	A358	1p multicolored	1.00	1.00
C584	A358	1.30p multicolored	.50	.15
C585	A358	1.70p multicolored	.55	.24
C586	A358	3.50p multicolored	1.10	.28
		Nos. C583-C586 (4)	3.15	1.67

Issue dates: 1p, Oct. 11; others, June 15.

Battle of Maracaibo, by Manuel F. Rincon AP129

1973, July 24 Litho. *Perf. 14x13½*

C587 AP129 10p bl & multi 2.00 .16

Battle of Maracaibo, sesquicentennial.

Bank Emblem AP130

1973, Oct. 1 Litho. *Perf. 14x13½*

C588 AP130 2p multicolored .20 .15

50th anniv. of the Bank of the Republic.

No. 801 Overprinted "AEREO"

1973, Oct. 11 *Perf. 14*

C589 A346 80c multicolored .28 .15

Pres. Pedro Nel Ospina, by Coroleano Leudo — AP131

Arms of Toro — AP132

1973, Nov. 9 *Perf. 13½x14*

C590 AP131 1.50p multicolored .25 .15

50th anniversary of the Ministry of Communications founded under Pres. Ospina.

1973, Dec. 1

C591 AP132 1p multicolored .15 .15

4th centenary of the founding of Toro, Valle del Cauca.

Bolivar, Battle of Bombona AP133

1973, Dec. 7 Litho. *Perf. 14x13½*

C592 AP133 1.30p multicolored .15 .15

Sesquicentennial (in 1972) of the Battle of Bombona.

Nicolaus Copernicus AP134

Andes, Map of South America AP135

1974, Feb. 19 Litho. *Perf. 13½x14*

C593 AP134 2.50p multicolored .50 .16

500th anniversary of the birth of Nicolaus Copernicus (1473-1543), Polish astronomer.

1974, May 11 Litho. *Perf. 14*

C594 AP135 2p multicolored .35 .15

Meeting of Communications Ministers of Members of the Andean Group, Cali, May 7-11, 1974.

Television Set — AP136

1974, July 16 Litho. *Perf. 14x13½*

C595 AP136 1.30p org, blk & brn .16 .15

20th anniversary of Colombian television and 10th anniversary of INRAVISION, the National Institute of Radio and Television.

Championship Emblem AP137

1974, Aug. 5 Litho. *Perf. 14x13½*

C596 AP137 4.50p multicolored .30 .15

2nd World Swimming Championships, Cali.

Condor — AP138

1974, Aug. 28 *Perf. 14*

C597 AP138 1.50p multicolored .25 .15

Bank of Colombia centenary.

UPU Envelope AP139

1974, Sept. 9 Litho. *Perf. 14*

C598 AP139 20p multicolored 2.50 .28

Centenary of Universal Postal Union.

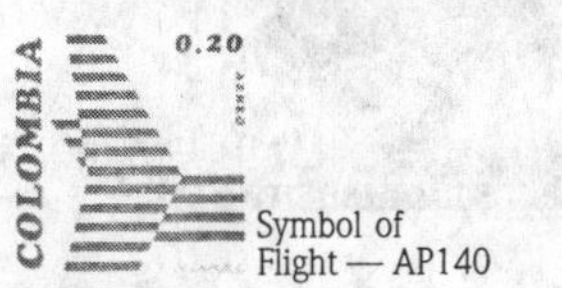

Symbol of Flight — AP140

1974, Sept. *Perf. 12x12½*

C599 AP140 20c olive .15 .15

Gen. José Maria Cordoba — AP141

White-tailed Trogon, Letter — AP142

1974, Oct. 14 Litho. *Perf. 13½x14*

C609 AP141 1.30p multicolored .20 .15

Sesquicentennial of the Battles of Junin and Ayacucho.

Insurance Type of 1974

Design: 3p, Abstract pattern.

1974, Oct. 24 Litho. *Perf. 13½x14*

C610 A365 3p multicolored .28 .15

Perf. 13½x14, 14x13½

1974, Nov. 14

Designs (UPU Letter and): 1.30p, Keelbilled Toucan, horiz. 2p, Peruvian cock-of-the-rock, horiz. 2.50p, Scarlet macaw.

C611	AP142	1p multicolored	.16	.15
C612	AP142	1.30p multicolored	.20	.15
C613	AP142	2p multicolored	.28	.15
C614	AP142	2.50p multicolored	.30	.15
		Nos. C611-C614 (4)	.94	
		Set value		.28

Centenary of Universal Postal Union. For surcharge see No. C656.

Forest No. 1, by Roman Roncancio — AP143

Boy with Thorn in Finger, by Gregorio Vazquez AP144

Paintings: 3p, Women Fruit Vendors, by Miguel Diaz Vargas (1886-1956). 5p, Annunciation, Santafereña School, 17th-18th cent.

Perf. 13½x14, 14x13½

1975, Mar. 12 **Litho.**

C615 AP143	2p multicolored	.60	.15
C616 AP144	3p multicolored	.40	.15
C617 AP144	4p multicolored	.50	.16
C618 AP144	5p multicolored	1.00	.25
	Nos. C615-C618 (4)	2.50	
	Set value		.55

Modern and Colonial Colombian paintings.

Trees and Lake AP145

Design: 6p, Victoria regia, Amazon River.

1975, Mar. 12 ***Perf. 14x13½***

C619 AP145	1p yellow & multi	.15	.15
C620 AP145	6p yellow & multi	.60	.15
	Set value		.15

Nature conservation of trees and Amazon Region.

Gold Treasure Type of 1975

Designs: 2p, Nose pendant. 10p, Alligator-shaped staff ornament.

1975, Apr. 11 **Litho.** ***Perf. 14x13½***

C621 A368	2p grn, gold & brn	.90	.15
C622 A368	10p multicolored	4.50	.60

El Rodadero, Santa Maria AP146

1975, July 26 **Litho.** ***Perf. 14x13½***

C623 AP146	2p multicolored	.15	.15

400th anniversary of Santa Maria City.

AP147

AP148

1975, Aug. 31 **Litho.** ***Perf. 13½x14***

C624 AP147	4p multicolored	.20	.15

Intl. Women's Year 1975. Maria de Jesus Paramo de Collazos founded 1st normal school for women in Bucaramanga in 1875.

1976, Mar. 12 **Litho.** ***Perf. 13½x14***

C625 AP148	5p "Sugar Cane"	.85	.30

4th Congress of Latin-American and Caribbean sugar-exporting countries, Cali, Mar. 8-12.

View of Bogota — AP149

1976, July 2 **Litho.** ***Perf. 12***

C626 AP149	10p shown	1.25	.90
C627 AP149	10p Barranquilla	1.25	.90
C628 AP149	10p Cali	1.25	.90
C629 AP149	10p Medellin	1.25	.90
a.	Block of 4, #C626-C629	5.00	4.00

Habitat, UN Conf. on Human Settlements, Vancouver, Canada, May 31-June 11.

University Emblem and "90" — AP150

1976, Aug. 6 **Litho.** ***Perf. 13½x14***

C630 AP150	5p lt blue & multi	.52	.15

University of Colombia, 90th anniversary.

Miguel Samper — AP151

Telephone, 1895 — AP152

1976, Oct. 29 **Litho.** ***Perf. 13½x14***

C631 AP151	2p multicolored	.20	.15

Samper (1825-99), economist and writer.

1976, Nov. 2

C632 AP152	3p multicolored	.16	.15

Centenary of first telephone call by Alexander Graham Bell, Mar. 10, 1876.

747 Jumbo Jet — AP153

1976, Dec. 3 **Litho.** ***Perf. 12***

C633 AP153	2p multicolored	.15	.15

Inauguration of 747 jumbo jet service by Avianca. For surcharge see No. C636.

Convent, Church and Plaza de San Francisco — AP154

1976, Dec. 29 **Litho.** ***Perf. 14***

C634 AP154	6p multicolored	.50	.15

150th anniv. of the Congress of Panama.

Souvenir Sheet

Bank of the Republic Emblem — AP155

1977, June 6 **Litho.** ***Perf. 14***

C635 AP155	25p multicolored	5.50	5.50

Opening of Philatelic Museum of Medellin under auspices of Banco de la Republica.

No. C633 Surcharged in Light Brown

1977, June **Litho.** ***Perf. 12***

C636 AP153	3p on 2p multi	.15	.15

Coffee AP156

Coffee Grower, Pack Mule AP157

1977-78 **Litho.** ***Perf. 12½***

C640 AP156	3p multicolored	.15	.15
C641 AP156	3.50p multicolored ('78)	.16	.15
	Set value		.15

Colombian coffee.

1977, Aug. 9 **Litho.** ***Perf. 13½x14***

C642 AP157	10p multicolored	.50	.15

National Federation of Coffee Growers, 50th anniversary.

Beethoven and 9th Symphony AP158

Games' Emblem AP159

1977, Aug. 17

C643 AP158	8p multicolored	.50	.15

Sesquicentennial of the death of Ludwig van Beethoven (1770-1827).

Bird Type of 1977

Tropical Birds and Plants: No. C644, Woodpecker and meriania. C645, Purple gallinule and water lilies. No. C646, Xipholaena punicea and cochlospermum orinocense. No. C647, Crowned flycatcher and jacaranda copaia.

1977, Sept. 6 **Litho.** ***Perf. 14***

C644 A380	5p multicolored	.70	.15
C645 A380	5p multicolored	.70	.15
C646 A380	10p multicolored	.90	.15
C647 A380	10p multicolored	.90	.15
	Nos. C644-C647 (4)	3.20	.60

1977, Sept. 9 ***Perf. 12x12½***

C648 AP159	6p multicolored	.24	.15

13th Central American and Caribbean Games, Medellin, 1978.

La Cayetana, by Enrique Grau AP160

Design: No. C650, Water Nymphs, by Beatriz Gonzalez.

1977, Sept. 13 ***Perf. 14x13½***

C649 AP160	8p multicolored	.45	.15
C650 AP160	8p multicolored	.45	.15

Women's suffrage, 20th anniversary.

Judge Francisco Antonio Moreno, by Joaquin Gutierrez AP161

Design: 25p, Viceroy Manuel de Guirior.

1977, Sept. 13 ***Perf. 12***

C651 AP161	20p multicolored	1.25	.75
C652 AP161	25p multicolored	1.75	1.10

Bicentenary of National Library.

Federico Lleras Acosta — AP162

Cauca University Arms — AP163

1977, Sept. 27 **Litho.** *Perf. 14*

C653 AP162 5p multicolored .26 .15

Dr. Federico Lleras Acosta, veterinarian and bacteriologist; birth centenary.

1977, Oct. 14

C654 AP163 5p multicolored .28 .15

Sesquicentennial of the University of Cauca.

CUDECOM Building, Bogota AP164

1977, Oct. 14

C655 AP164 1.50p multicolored .15 .15

Colombian Society of Engineers, 90th anniversary.

No. C612 Surcharged with New Value and Bars in Brown

1977, Dec. 3 **Litho.** *Perf. 14x13½*

C656 AP142 2p on 1.30p multi .28 .15

Lost City, Tayrona Culture AP165

Creator of Energy, by Arenas Betancourt AP166

1978, Apr. 18 **Litho.** *Perf. 12½*

C657 AP165 3.50p multicolored .20 .15

1978, Apr. 25 *Perf. 12*

C658 AP166 4p blue & multi .24 .15

Sesquicentennial of Antioquia University Law School.

Column of the Slaves — AP167

Statue of Catalina, Cartagena — AP168

1978, May 9

C659 AP167 2.50p multicolored .24 .15

Sesquicentennial of Ocana Convention (meeting of various political groups).

1978, May 30 **Litho.** *Perf. 12*

C660 AP168 4p blk & lt bl .24 .15

Sesquicentennial of University of Cartagena.

Gold Pendant, Tolima — AP169

1978, July 11 **Litho.** *Perf. 12x12½*

C661 AP169 3.50p multicolored .20 .15

Apotheosis of Spanish Language, by Luis Alberto Acuña — AP170

1978, Aug. 9 *Perf. 14*

C662 AP170 Strip of 3 4.75 4.75

a.-c. 11p, any single 1.10 1.10

Millennium of Spanish language.

Presidential Guard — AP171

Figure, Muisca Culture — AP172

1978, Aug. 16 *Perf. 13½x14*

C663 AP171 9p multicolored .45 .45

Presidential Guard Battalion, 50th anniv.

1978, Sept. 12 **Litho.** *Perf. 12½*

C664 AP172 3.50p multicolored .20 .15

Apse of Carmelite Church — AP173

1978, Oct. 12 *Perf. 13*

C665 AP173 30p multicolored 2.50 .40

Souvenir Sheet

Perf. 13½x14

C666 AP173 50p multicolored 3.25 3.25

ESPAMER '78 Philatelic Exhibition, Bogota, Oct. 12-21.

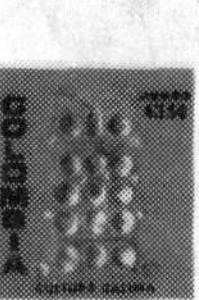

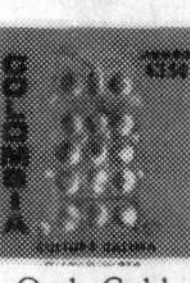

Owl, Gold Ornament, Calima AP174

Virgin and Child, by Gregorio Vasquez AP175

Designs: No. C669, Gold frog, Quimbaya culture. No. C670, Gold nose pendant, Tairona, horiz.

1978-80 **Litho.** *Perf. 12½*

C667 AP174 3.50p multicolored .20 .15

C668 AP174 4p multi ('79) .20 .15

C669 AP174 4p multi ('79) .20 .15

C670 AP174 5p multi ('80) .20 .15

Nos. C667-C670 (4) .80

Set value .21

1978, Nov. 28 *Perf. 13½x14*

C671 AP175 2.50p multicolored .15 .15

Christmas 1978.

Bull Ring, Cathedral, Manizales AP176

1979, Jan. 6 **Litho.** *Perf. 14*

C672 AP176 7p multicolored .60 .20

Manizales Fair.

Children Playing Hopscotch, and IYC Emblem — AP177

Designs: No. C674, Child at blackboard and UNESCO emblem, horiz. No. C675, The Paper Collector, by Omar Gordillo, and UN emblem.

Perf. 13½x14, 14x13½

1979, July 19

C673 AP177 8p multicolored .30 .30

C674 AP177 12p multicolored .45 .45

C675 AP177 12p multicolored .45 .45

Nos. C673-C675 (3) 1.20 1.20

International Year of the Child.

Rio Prado Hydroelectric Station — AP178

1979, Aug. 24 *Perf. 13½x14*

C676 AP178 5p multicolored .48 .15

Tomb, 6th Century — AP179

1979, Sept. 25 **Litho.** *Perf. 14*

C677 AP179 8p multicolored .55 .35

San Augustin Archaeological Park.

Gonzalo Jimenez de Quesada, by C. Leudo — AP180

1979, Oct. 11 *Perf. 12*

C678 AP180 20p multicolored 1.50 .48

Gonzalo Jimenez de Quesada (1500-1579), Spanish conquistador.

Hill, Penny Black, Colombia No. 1 — AP181

1979, Oct. 23 *Perf. 13½x14*

C679 AP181 15p multicolored .60 .20

Sir Rowland Hill (1795-1879), originator of penny postage.

Amazon Region — AP182

Tourism: 14p, San Fernando Fortress.

1979 **Litho.** *Perf. 13½x14*

C680 AP182 7p multicolored .35 .15

C681 AP182 14p multicolored .90 .60

Issue dates: 7p, Nov. 16; 14p, Nov. 9.

See Nos. C717-C719.

Nativity — AP183

Creche Sculptures: No. C682, Three Kings and soldiers. No. C684, Shepherds.

1979, Nov. 30 *Perf. 12*

C682 AP183 3p multicolored .35 .35

C683 AP183 3p multicolored .35 .35

C684 AP183 3p multicolored .35 .35

a. Strip of 3, #C682-C684 1.15 1.00

Christmas 1979.

AP184 AP185

Magdalena Bridge, Avianca emblem.

1979, Dec. 5 *Perf. 14*

C685 AP184 15p multicolored .60 .16

Barranquilla, 350th anniversary; Avianca National Airline, 60th anniversary.

1980, Feb. 15 *Perf. 13½x14*

Boy Playing Flute, by Judith Leyster.

C686 AP185 6p multicolored .45 .20

2nd International Music Competition, Ibague, Dec. 1979.

Gen. Antonio José de Sucre, 150th Death Anniversary AP186

1980, Feb. 15 Litho. *Perf. 12½x12*
C687 AP186 12p multicolored .45 .16

The Watchman, by Edgar Negret AP187

1980, Feb. 26 *Perf. 12x12½*
C688 AP187 25p multicolored 1.65 .80

Virgin Mary, by Real del Sarte, 1929 — AP188

1980, May 23 Litho. *Perf. 14x13½*
C689 AP188 12p multicolored .30 .15

Apparition of the Virgin Mary to Sister Catalina Labouri Gontard, 150th anniv.

San Gil Produce Market, by Luis Roncancio — AP189

1980, May 27 *Perf. 13½x14*
C690 AP189 12p multicolored .50 .25

Pres. Enrique Olaya Herrera, by Miguel Diaz Vargas — AP190

1980, Oct. 28 Litho. *Perf. 12*
C691 AP190 20p multicolored 1.00 .40

Enrique Olaya Herrera (1880-1936), president, 1930-1934.

The Boy Fishing in a Bucket AP191

Christmas 1980 (Christmas Stories by Rafael Pombo): No. C693, The Frog and the Mouse. No. C694, The Seven Lives of the Cat.

1980, Nov. 21 Litho. *Perf. 14½*
C692 AP191 4p multicolored .20 .16
C693 AP191 4p multicolored .20 .16
C694 AP191 4p multicolored .20 .16
Nos. C692-C694 (3) .60 .48

28th World Golf Cup, Cajica — AP192

1980, Dec. 9 Litho. *Perf. 13½x14*
C695 AP192 30p multicolored 1.40 .40

Bolivar Type of 1980

Simon Bolivar Death Sesquicentennial: 6p, Portrait, last words to Colombia, vert.

1980, Dec. 17 *Perf. 12*
C696 A400 6p multicolored .60 .45

St. Peter Claver Holding Cross — AP193

1981, Jan. 13 *Perf. 14½*
C697 AP193 15p multicolored .48 .16

St. Peter Claver (1580-1654), helped American Indians.

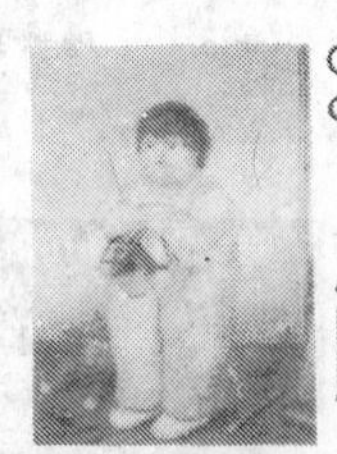
Sculptured Bird, San Augustin — AP194

Archaeological Finds: No. C699, Funeral chamber, Tierradentro. No. C700, Chamber hallway, Tierradentro. No. C701, Statue of man, San Augustin.

1981, May 12 Litho. *Perf. 14*
C698 AP194 7p multicolored .35 .15
C699 AP194 7p multicolored .35 .15
C700 AP194 7p multicolored .35 .15
C701 AP194 7p multicolored .35 .15
a. Block of 4, #C698-C701 1.40 .75

See Nos. C707-C710D.

Child with Hobby Horse, by Fernando Botero — AP195

4th Biennial Arts show, Medellin: 20p, Square Abstract, by Omar Rayo. 25p, Flowers, by Alejandro Obregon.

1981, May 15 *Perf. 12*
C702 AP195 20p multicolored .85 .16
C703 AP195 25p multicolored 1.00 .28
C704 AP195 50p multicolored 1.75 .75
Nos. C702-C704 (3) 3.60 1.19

8th South American Swimming Championships, Medellin — AP196

1981, June 5
C705 AP196 15p multicolored .50 .25

Santamaria Bull Ring, 50th Anniv. — AP197

1981, June 9 Litho. *Perf. 12*
C706 AP197 30p multicolored 2.00 1.25

AP197a AP197b

AP197c AP197d

Quimbaya Culture

1981, Sept. 23 Litho. *Perf. 14*

Yellow Background

C707 AP197a 9p Man .45 .15
C708 AP197b 9p Seated man .45 .15
C709 AP197c 9p Seal, print .45 .15
C710 AP197d 9p Jug .45 .15
e. Block of 4, #C707-C710 1.80 .75

AP197e AP197f

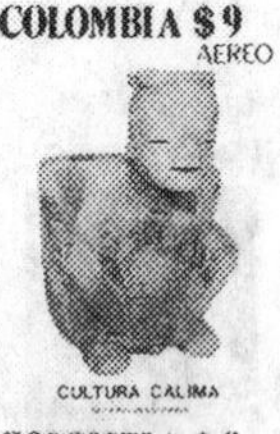

AP197g AP197h

Calima Culture

1981, Dec. 17

White Background

C710A AP197e 9p Anthropomorphic container .45 .15
C710B AP197f 9p Jar .45 .15
C710C AP197g 9p Anthropomorphic jar .45 .15
C710D AP197h 9p Urn .45 .15
f. Block of 4, #C710A-C710D 1.80 .75

Fruit AP198

1981, Nov. 3 Litho. *Perf. 14*
C711 Block of 6 8.50 6.25
a.-f. AP198 25p, any single 1.25 .55

Revolt of the Comuneros, 200th Anniv. — AP199

1981, Nov. 21 Litho. *Perf. 12*
C712 AP199 20p multicolored .55 .28

Jose Manuel Restrepo, Historian, 1775?-1860? AP200

Andres Bello, 1780?-1865 AP201

1981, Dec. 1 Litho. *Perf. 12*
C713 AP200 35p multicolored .90 .35

1981, Dec. 11 Litho. *Perf. 12*
C714 AP201 18p multicolored .48 .15

Colombia's Admission to UPU, 100th Anniv. AP202

Designs: 30p, No. 103. 50p, Hemispheres, Nos. 104-108.

1981 Litho. *Perf. 12*
C715 AP202 30p multicolored .70 .35

Size: 100x70mm

Imperf

C716 AP202 50p multicolored 1.40 1.25

Dates of issue: #C715, Dec. 18. #C716, Dec. 28.

Tourism Type of 1979

1982 Litho. *Perf. 12*
C717 AP182 20p Solano Bay .48 .20
C718 AP182 20p Tota Lake, Boyaca .48 .20
C719 AP182 20p Corrales, Boyaca .48 .20
Nos. C717-C719 (3) 1.44 .60

Issue dates: #C717, June 2; others, June 16.

1982 World Cup — AP202a

Designs: Players and team emblems.

1982, June 21 *Perf. 14*
C720 Sheet of 15 5.00 3.00
a. AP202a 9p, any single .30 .15

Bogota Gun Club Centenary AP202b

1982, July 16 *Perf. 12*
C721 AP202b 20p multicolored .50 .15

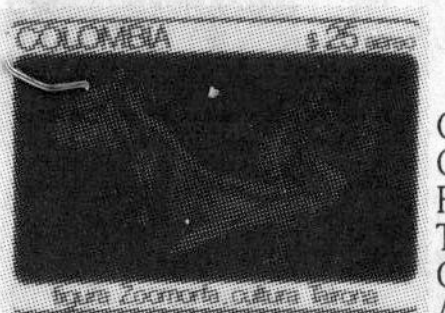
Gold Crocodile Figure, Tairona Culture AP202c

Tairona Culture Exhibit, Gold Museum: Various figures. Nos. C723-C727 vert.

1982, July 28
Gold, Black and:

C722	AP202c	25p	light brown	.70	.40
C723	AP202c	25p	bright pink	.70	.40
C724	AP202c	25p	green	.70	.40
C725	AP202c	25p	dark blue	.70	.40
C726	AP202c	25p	violet	.70	.40
C727	AP202c	25p	red	.70	.40
	Nos. C722-C727 (6)			4.20	2.40

Government Buildings, Pereira — AP203

1982, Aug. 4 **Litho.** *Perf. 12*
C728 AP203 35p multicolored .85 .40

Biplane in Flight, by Edgar Antonio Bustos AP204

1982, Aug. 5 *Perf. 14*
C729 AP204 18p multicolored .50 .20

American Air Forces Cooperation System.

Magdalena River AP205

1982, Oct. 21 **Litho.** *Perf. 12*
C730 AP205 30p multicolored .70 .35

Marquez Type of 1982

1982, Dec. 10 *Perf. 13½x14*
C731 A412 25p gray & blue .60 .16
C732 A412 30p gray & brown .85 .20

San Andres Archipelago — AP206

1983, Apr. 9 **Litho.** *Perf. 12*
C733 AP206 25p Liberty Fort .48 .15

Opening of Las Gaviotas (The Seagulls) Ecological Center, Bogota — AP207

1983, June 1 **Litho.**
C734 AP207 12p multicolored .30 .15

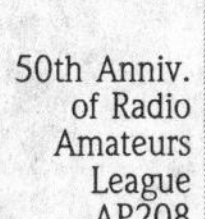

50th Anniv. of Radio Amateurs League AP208

1983, June 11 *Perf. 14x13½*
C735 AP208 12p multicolored .30 .15

Bolivar Type of 1983

1983, July 24 *Perf. 12*
C736 A417 30p multicolored .60 .20
C737 A417 100p multicolored 2.00 1.50

Botanical Exhibition Type of 1983

1983, Aug. 18 *Perf. 14*
C738 A418 12p Begonia guaduensis .35 .15
C739 A418 12p Chinchona ovaliflora .35 .15
C740 A418 40p Begonia urticae 1.25 .40
Nos. C738-C740 (3) 1.95 .70

Cartagena, 450th Anniv. — AP208a

1983, Sept. 9 **Litho.** *Perf. 12*
C740A AP208a 12p Customs Square .24 .15
C740B AP208a 35p Historic sites, Cartagena .70 .30

Painting Type of 1983

1983, Oct. 5 **Litho.** *Perf. 12*
C741 A420 30p multicolored .50 .15

Scouting Year — AP209

Coffee Beans — AP210

1983, Oct. 24
C742 AP209 12p multicolored .20 .15

1984, Mar. 28 **Litho.** *Perf. 14½x14*
C743 AP210 14p multicolored .20 .15

Marandua City Type of 1984

1984, Sept. 28 *Perf. 12*
C744 A427 30p multicolored .48 .15

AP211

AP212

1984, Nov. 2
C745 AP211 45p multicolored .70 .22

45th Congress of Americanists, Bogota, 1985.

Christmas Type of 1984

1984, Dec. 14
C746 A428 14p multicolored .22 .15

1985, Feb. 15

Design: Dove, map and flags of Colombia, Mexico, Costa Rica and Venezuela.

C747 AP212 40p multicolored .68 .32

Contadora Group of Latin American countries.

Gomez Type of 1985

1985, Feb. 25
C748 A432 40p multicolored .68 .32

Birds — AP213

AP214

1985
C749 AP213 14p Dryocopus lineatus nuperus .20 .15
C750 AP213 20p Xiphorhynchus picus .28 .15
C751 AP213 50p Eriocnemis cupreoventris .70 .22
C752 AP213 55p Momotus momota .78 .25
Nos. C749-C752 (4) 1.96 .77

Issue dates: 14p, Apr. 12. 20p, 50p, Aug. 6. 55p, Aug. 29.

1985, July 15
C753 AP214 20p multicolored .28 .15

Almirante Padilla Naval School, 50th anniv.

1985 Census AP215

1985, Oct. 15 *Perf. 12*
C754 AP215 20p multicolored .28 .15

Christmas Type of 1985

1985, Dec. 4 **Litho.** *Perf. 13*
C755 A436 20p Girl, Christmas tree .28 .15

Alfonso Lopez Pumarejo (1886-1959), President, 1934-38, 1942-45 — AP216

1986, Jan. 31
C756 AP216 24p multicolored .30 .15

Coffee Berries, Natl. Cycling Team AP217

1986, Feb. 4
C757 AP217 60p multicolored .75 .25

Natl. Coffee Producers Assoc. sponsorship of natl. cycling team, 25th anniv.

Fauna Type of 1985

1986, Feb. 18
C758 A433 50p Pudu mephistophiles .65 .22

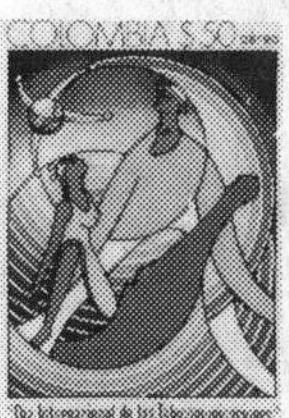

World Communications Day — AP218

Intl. Peace Year — AP219

1986, May 17 **Litho.** *Perf. 13*
C759 AP218 50p multicolored .65 .22

1986, June 13 **Litho.** *Perf. 13*
C760 AP219 55p multicolored .65 .22

AP220

AP221

1986, July 1 **Litho.** *Perf. 13*
C761 AP220 24p Portrait, papal arms .32 .15
C762 AP220 55p Portrait, Medellin cathedral, horiz. .65 .22
C763 AP220 60p Blessing crowd, horiz. .70 .24
Nos. C761-C763 (3) 1.67 .61

Souvenir Sheet

C764 AP220 200p Praying, Madonna of Bogota 1.40 1.40

Visit of Pope John Paul II.
Nos. C762-C763 each printed in sheets of 20 with se-tenant labels picturing religious symbols.

1986, July 15 *Perf. 12*
C765 AP221 25p multicolored .30 .15

Enrique Santos Montejo (1886-1971), journalist.

Bach, Handel and Schutz, Composers AP222

1986, July 17 *Perf. 13*
C766 AP222 70p Bach .82 .40
C767 AP222 100p Text, music 1.15 .55

Salesian Order Education in Colombia, Cent. AP223

1986, July 23 *Perf. 12*
C768 AP223 25p De La Salle, founder .30 .15

Completion of Coal Mining Complex, El Cerrejon AP224

1986, July 29 **Litho.** ***Perf. 12***
C769 AP224 55p multi .62 .20

AP225

Natl. Constitution, Cent. — AP226

Designs: 25p, The Five Signators, by R. Vasquez, detail, and Bogota Cathedral. 200p, Pres. Nunez and Miguel Antonio Caro, Natl. Council of Delegates chairman, and Presidential Palace, constitution.

1986, Aug. 5 **Litho.** ***Perf. 14***
C770 AP225 25p multi .28 .15

Souvenir Sheet
Perf. 12
C771 AP226 200p multi 2.25 .75

Poet Type of 1986

Design: Federico Garcia Lorca (1898-1936), poet, and birthplace, Fuentevaqueros, Granada, Spain.

1986, Sept. 26 **Litho.** ***Perf. 12***
C772 A445 60p multi .68 .24

Gratitude for Intl. Aid after the Armero Mudslide Disaster AP227

1986, Nov. 13
C773 AP227 50p multi .55 .18

Christmas — AP228

Wood sculpture: Virgin Mestiza, Nerina.

1986, Dec. 19 **Litho.** ***Perf. 12***
C774 AP228 25p multi .28 .15

The Apotheosis of Popayan, by Ephrain Martinez Zambrano (1898-1956) — AP229

1987, Jan. 13
C775 AP229 100p Popayan riding horse 1.10 .50
C776 AP229 100p Onlookers 1.10 .50
a. Pair, #C775-C776 2.25 2.25

No. C776a has a continuous design.

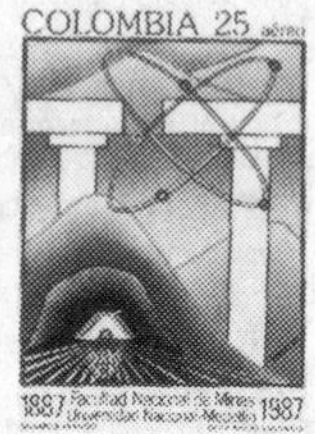
AP230 AP231

1987, Mar. 16 **Litho.** ***Perf. 12***
C777 AP230 30p multi .32 .15

The Conversion of St. Augustine of Hippo, 1600th anniv.

Type of 1987

Designs: 30p, Phoenicopterus ruber. 35p, Pseudemys scripta, horiz. No. C780, Crax alberti. No. C781, Symphysodon aequifasciatum, horiz.

Perf. 14½x14, 14x14½
1987-89 **Wmk. 334**
C778 A446a 30p lake .35 .15
C779 A446a 35p dark red brn .40 .15
C780 A446a 45p dark blue gray .32 .15
C781 A446a 45p blue .32 .15
Nos. C778-C781 (4) 1.39
Set value .49

Issue dates: 30p, June 8. 35p, Dec. 24. No. C780, Dec. 6, 1988. No. C781, June 23, 1989.
This is an expanding set. Numbers will change if necessary.

Perf. 13½x13
1987, Apr. 10 **Unwmk.**
C783 AP231 25p multi .30 .15

Natl. University School of Mining, Medellin, cent.

Purebred Horses AP232

1987, June 17 ***Perf. 12***
C784 AP232 60p White horse .70 .22
C785 AP232 70p Black horse .85 .28

El Espectador Newspaper, Cent. — AP233

Design: Frontispieces from 1887, 1915, 1948, 1974 and portraits of founder Don Fidel Cano, editors Don Luis Cano, Luis Gabriel Cano Isaza and Alfonso Cano Isaza.

1987, July 24 ***Perf. 12½x12***
C786 AP233 60p multi .70 .22

Intl. Year of Shelter for the Homeless — AP234

1987, Sept. 21 ***Perf. 14***
C787 AP234 60p multi .65 .22

Flags AP235

1987, Nov. 27 **Litho.** ***Perf. 13x13½***
C788 AP235 80p multi .82 .28

Ist Meeting of the eight Latin-American Presidents, Acapulco, Nov.

Christmas — AP236

1987, Dec. 8 **Litho.** ***Perf. 14***
C789 AP236 30p multi .30 .15

Rural Telephone System AP237

1988, Feb. 4 **Litho.** ***Perf. 14***
C790 AP237 70p multi .80 .28

Founding of Bogota, 450th Anniv. — AP238

1988, Apr. 11 **Litho.** ***Perf. 12***
C791 AP238 70p multi .65 .22

Bogota, 450th Anniv. AP238a

Unwmk.
1988, July 1 **Litho.** ***Perf. 12***
C792 AP238a 80p Modern district, vert. .75 .25
C793 AP238a 90p Colonial district .85 .28

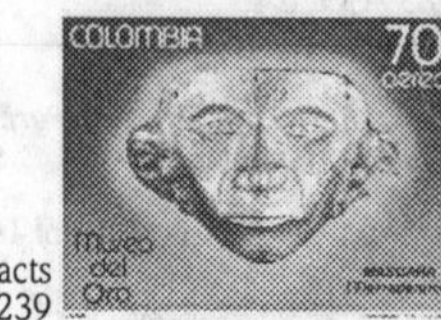
Gold Artifacts AP239

Artifacts in the Gold Museum: 70p, Mask. 80p, Two-headed human figure inside a circle, Muisca tribe. 90p, Ritual figure of the Quimbaya.

1988 ***Perf. 12***
C794 AP239 70p multi .65 .30
C795 AP239 80p multi .65 .22
C796 AP239 90p multi .72 .35
Nos. C794-C796 (3) 2.02 .87

Issue dates: 70p, May 13, 80p, 90p, Oct. 7.

Human Rights Type of 1988
Perf. 14x14½
1988, July 1 **Engr.** **Wmk. 334**
C797 A452 40p Communication, horiz. .38 .15

AP240

Christmas — AP241

1988, Sept. 28 **Litho.** ***Perf. 12***
C798 AP240 80p multi .70 .18

Zipa Tisquesusa (d. 1538), Chibcha Indian leader during revolt against Spanish Conquistadors.

1988, Nov. 23 **Litho.** ***Perf. 12***
C799 AP241 40p multi .35 .15

Agustin Nieto Caballero (1889-1975), Educator AP242

Unwmk.
1989, Mar. 18 **Litho.** ***Perf. 12***
C800 AP242 100p multi .72 .25

Pres. Laureano Gomez (1889-1965) AP243

1989, Mar. 29
C801 AP243 45p multi .32 .15

Intl. Coffee Organization AP244

1989, Apr. 3
C802 AP244 110p multi .82 .28

12th Session of the UN Commission on Human Rights — AP245

1989, Apr. 28
C803 AP245 100p multi .72 .25

French Revolution, Bicent. AP246

1989, June 29 **Litho.** *Perf. 12*
C804 AP246 100p multi .70 .24

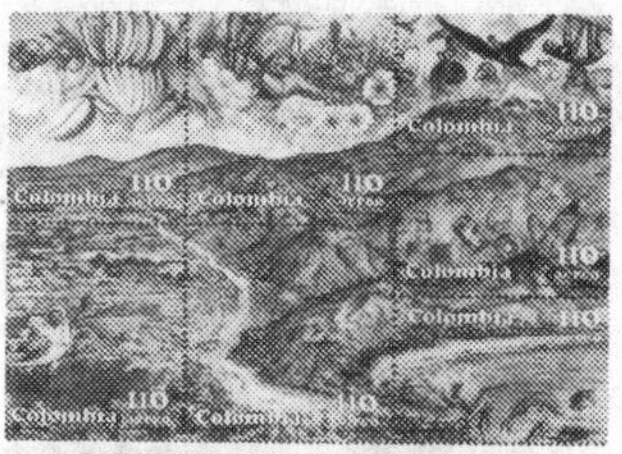
PHILEXFRANCE '89 — AP247

Designs: a, Bananas, tropical fruits. b, Fruits, flowers. c, Birds, animals. d, Precious gems, metals and mineral resources. e, View of fields, Colombian carrying produce basket. f, Waterfall. g, Fish, coast. (Illustration reduced.)

1989 **Litho.** *Perf. 14*
C805 AP247 Pane of 7 5.25 2.00
a.-g. 110p any single .75 .25

No. C805 printed in sheets containing panes of 7, rouletted between.

Souvenir Sheet

Los Lanceros, by R. Arenas Betancur — AP248

1989 **Litho.** *Perf. 12*
C806 AP248 250p multicolored 1.65 .55

Human Rights Type of 1988

Perf. 14½x14

1989, Aug. 18 **Engr.** **Wmk. 334**
C807 A452 55p Family .38 .15

Natl. Anti-Drugs Campaign — AP249

Unwmk.

1989, Aug. 23 **Litho.** *Perf. 12*
C808 AP249 115p multicolored .75 .25

America Issue AP250

UPAE emblem and artifacts or customs of pre-Columbian peoples: 115p, Quimbaya, Calima or Tolima gold smiths. 130p, Potter and Sinu ceramic figurine.

1989 *Perf. 12*
C809 AP250 115p multicolored .75 .25
C810 AP250 130p multicolored .88 .28

Issue dates: 115p, Oct. 12; 130p, Aug. 23.

Joaquin Quijano Mantilla (1878-1944), Journalist AP251

1989, Sept. 29 *Perf. 12*
C811 AP251 170p multicolored 1.15 .38

Arts and Crafts in Barro-Raquira AP252

1989 **Litho.** *Perf. 12*
C812 AP252 55p multicolored .38 .15

Christmas.

Boeing 767 AP253

1989, Dec. 5 **Litho.** *Perf. 12*
C813 AP253 130p multicolored .90 .30

Bolivar Installed at the Congress of Angostura, by Tito Salas — AP254

1989, Dec. 12
C814 AP254 130p multicolored .90 .30

Creation of the Republic, 1819.

Fathers of the Nation Leaving the Constitutional Convention AP255

1989, Dec. 12
C815 AP255 130p shown .90 .30
C816 AP255 130p Arms .90 .30
C817 AP255 130p Temple of the Rosary .90 .30
Nos. C815-C817 (3) 2.70 .90

Constitution of the Republic, 1821.

Arms Type of Regular Issue, 1982

1990, Mar. 1 **Litho.** *Perf. 12*
C818 A372 60p Velez .30 .15

Presidential Summit, Cartagena AP256

1990, Feb. 15 **Litho.** *Perf. 12*
C819 AP256 130p Plaza de la Aduana .55 .18

Colombian National Radio, 50th Anniv. — AP257

1990, Feb. 16 **Litho.** *Perf. 12*
C820 AP257 150p multicolored .65 .20

Teresa Cuervo Borda (1889-1976), Art Historian AP258

1990, Mar. 28 **Litho.** *Perf. 12*
C821 AP258 60p multicolored .35 .15

Second Latin American Theater Festival, Bogota — AP259

1990, Apr. 10
C822 AP259 150p buff, tan & gold .78 .26

Santander Type of 1990

Designs: No. C823, Santander holding the Constitution. No. C824, Central Cemetery, Bogata and National Pantheon. No. C825, Santander, as organizer of public education. No. C826, "Postman of New Granada" (Man and burro) by Joseph Brown and Jose Maria del Castillo, horiz. 500p, Santander on death bed.

1990, May 6 *Perf. 14x13½*
C823 A470 60p multicolored .25 .15
C824 A470 60p multicolored .25 .15
C825 A470 70p multicolored .30 .15
C826 A470 70p multicolored .30 .15
Nos. C823-C826 (4) 1.10
Set value .36

Souvenir Sheet

Perf. 12

C827 A470 500p multi 2.00 .66

No. C827 contains one 54x40mm stamp.

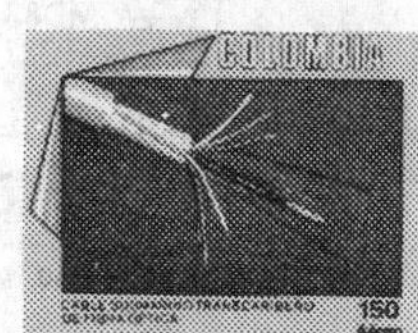
First Postage Stamp, 150th Anniv. AP260

1990, May 6 *Perf. 14*
C828 AP260 150p multicolored .65 .22

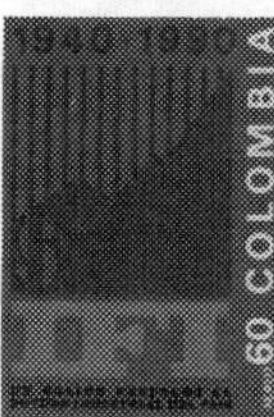
Trans-Caribbean Fiber Optic Cable — AP261

1990, May 19 *Perf. 12*
C829 AP261 150p multicolored .65 .22

Institute of Industrial Development, 25th Anniv. — AP262

1990, May 22
C830 AP262 60p multicolored .35 .15

Souvenir Sheet

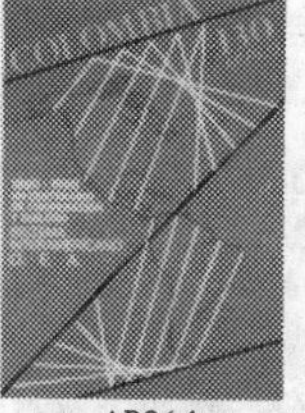
World Cup Soccer Championships, Italy — AP263

1990, June 8
C831 AP263 500p multicolored 2.00 .66

AP264

AP265

1990, June 27
C832 AP264 130p multicolored .55 .18

Organization of American States, cent.

1990, July 26
C833 AP265 170p multicolored .72 .24

Museum of Gold, 50th Anniv.

Dolphins, Marine Birds AP266

1990, Oct. 12 **Litho.** *Perf. 12*
C834 AP266 150p shown .58 .20
C835 AP266 170p Jungle fauna, vert. .65 .22

AP267 AP268

1990, Nov. 16 **Litho.** *Perf. 12*
C836 AP267 70p multicolored .38 .15

Monastery of Our Lady of Las Lajas..

1991, Feb. 8 **Litho.** *Perf. 12*
C837 AP268 170p multicolored .80 .30

Newspaper Publishing, 200th Anniv.

AP269

AP270

1990, Nov. 1 **Litho.** ***Perf. 12***
C838 AP269 70p multicolored .38 .15

Christmas.

1991, May 31 **Litho.** ***Perf. 14***

Whales and Dolphins: 80p, Megaptera novaeangliae, breaching. 170p, Megaptera novaeangliae, diving. 190p, Inia geoffrensis, Sotalia fluviatilis, horiz.

C839 AP270 80p multicolored .35 .15
C840 AP270 170p multicolored .75 .30
C841 AP270 190p multicoloed .85 .32
Nos. C839-C841 (3) 1.95 .77

America Issue AP271

1991, Oct. 11 **Litho.** ***Perf. 14***
C842 AP271 90p shown .45 .15
C843 AP271 190p Ship arriving in New World .85 .25

Adoration of the Magi — AP272

1991, Dec. 20 **Litho.** ***Perf. 14***
C844 AP272 90p multicolored .45 .15

Christmas.

AP273

AP274

1991, Dec. 2
C845 AP273 190p Country flags .85 .25

Fifth summit of Latin American presidents.

1992, Feb. 8 **Litho.** ***Perf. 12***
C846 AP274 210p multicolored .95 .28

8th UNCTAD Conference, Cartagena.

Proclamation of New Constitution, July 4, 1991 AP275

1991, Nov. 27 **Litho.** ***Perf. 14***
C847 AP275 90p multicolored .40 .15

Export Products — AP276

Copyright Protection — AP277

1992, Mar. 11 ***Perf. 12***
C848 AP276 90p Flowers .40 .15
C849 AP276 210p Fruits, vegetables, horiz. .95 .28

1992, Apr. 13 **Litho.** ***Perf. 12***
C850 AP277 190p multicolored .85 .25

1992 Summer Olympics — AP278

1992, June 4 **Litho.** ***Perf. 14***
C851 AP278 110p multicolored .48 .32

Earth Summit '92 — AP279

Designs: a, Tree, mountain landscape. b, Birds in tree.

1992, June 2 **Litho.** ***Perf. 14***
C852 A279 230p Pair, #a.-b. 2.10 1.40

America Issue — AP280

Paintings: 230p, Discovery of America by Christopher Columbus, by Salvador Dali. 260p, Magical America, Myth and Legend, by Alfredo Vivero.

1992, July 22 ***Perf. 14x13½***
C853 AP280 230p multicolored 1.00 .70
C854 AP280 260p multicolored 1.15 .75

McDonnell Douglas MD83 AP281

1992, Sept. 22 **Litho.** ***Perf. 12***
C855 AP281 110p multicolored .45 .30

Curtain of Colon Theatre AP282

1992, Oct. 12 **Litho.** ***Perf. 12***
C856 AP282 230p multicolored .95 .65

AP283

AP284

1992, Nov. 27 **Litho.** ***Perf. 12***
C857 AP283 230p Gloria Lara, 1938-82 .95 .65

1993, June 7 **Litho.** ***Perf. 12***
C858 AP284 220p multicolored .85 .60

1993 American Soccer Cup, Ecuador.

Intl. Year of Indigenous People — AP285

1993, July 1 ***Perf. 14***
C859 AP285 460p multicolored 1.75 1.25

South American Eliminations for 1994 World Cup Soccer Championships, US — AP286

1993, July 31 **Litho.** ***Perf. 12***
C860 AP286 220p multicolored .80 .52

AP287

AP288

America Issue (Endangered species): a, 220p, Saguinus oedipus. b, 220p, Porphyrula martinica. c, 460p, Rupicola peruviana. d, 520p, Trichecus manatus.

1993, Oct. 19 **Litho.** ***Perf. 12***
C861 AP287 Block of 4, #a.-d. 4.75 3.25

1994, Mar. 21 **Litho.** ***Perf. 12***
C862 AP288 630p multicolored 2.25 1.40

Intl. Decade for Natural Disaster Reduction.

Beatification of Josemaria Escriva de Balaguer — AP289

1994, May 17 **Litho.** ***Perf. 13½x14***
C863 AP289 560p multicolored 1.90 1.25

First Airmail Delivery, 75th Anniv. AP290

Design: 270p, William Knox Martin, airplane over Port Colombia, 1919.

1994, July 29 **Litho.** ***Perf. 14***
C864 AP290 270p multicolored .90 .55

Natl. Institute of Medical Law & Forensic Sciences, 80th Anniv. AP291

1994, Oct. 27 **Litho.** ***Perf. 12***
C865 AP291 560p multicolored 1.90 1.20

Sociedad Colombo-Alemana de Transportes Aereos (SCADTA), 75th Anniv. — AP292

1995, Jan. 2 **Litho.** ***Perf. 12***
C866 AP292 330p #C15 .75 .48

Flora and Fauna — AP293

Iguana iguana: No. C867a, Facing right. b, Facing left.

Rain forest: No. C868a, Nuts on branch, flowers. b, Waterfall, hanging red flower.

1995, Jan. 17
C867 AP293 650p Pair, #a.-b. 3.00 1.90
C868 AP293 750p Pair, #a.-b. 3.50 2.25

Nos. C867-C868 are continuous designs.

SCADTA, 75th Anniv. AP294

1995, Mar. 30 **Litho.** ***Perf. 14***
C869 AP294 330p No. C9 1.10 .75

FAO, 50th Anniv. AP295

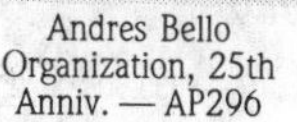

1995, Apr. 25 Litho. *Perf. 13x13½*
C870 AP295 750p multicolored 1.50 1.00

Andres Bello Organization, 25th Anniv. — AP296

Colombian Firefighters, Cent. — AP297

1995, Apr. 27 *Perf. 13½x13*
C871 AP296 650p multicolored 1.30 .85

1995, May 5 *Perf. 12*
C872 AP297 330p multicolored .70 .45

Fenalco, 50th Anniv. — AP298

UN, 50th Anniv. — AP299

1995, May 25 *Perf. 13½*
C873 AP298 330p multicolored .70 .45

1995, June 21 *Perf. 12*
C874 AP299 750p multicolored 1.50 1.00

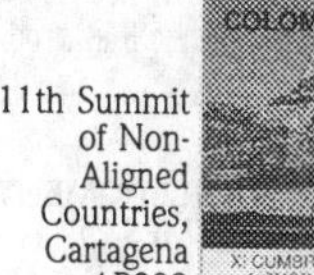

First Pacific Ocean Games — AP300

1995, June 23
C875 AP300 750p multicolored 1.50 1.00

11th Summit of Non-Aligned Countries, Cartagena AP302

1995, Oct. 13 Litho. *Perf. 12*
C877 AP302 650p multicolored 1.30 .90

Motion Pictures, Cent. AP303

Design: 330p, Charlie Chaplin and Jackie Coogan in "The Kid," Estela López Pomareda in "Maria," first Colombian feature length film.

1995, Oct. 19 *Perf. 14*
C878 AP303 330p black & sepia .65 .45

AP304

AP305

1995 *Perf. 12*
C879 AP304 650p multicolored 1.30 .90

Andes Development Corporation (CAF), 25th Anniv.

1995 *Perf. 14*

Fight against illegal drug trafficking: No. C880, Locating illegally grown plants. No. C881, Hands in handcuffs, horiz.

C880 AP305 330p multicolored .65 .45
C881 AP305 330p multicolored .65 .45

Miniature Sheet of 16

Myths and Legends — AP306

Madre-Monte: a.-d.
La Llorna: e.-h.
El Mohán: i.-l.
Hombre Caimán: m.-p.
Background color changes from top to bottom rows. Top row is blue. Row 2 is blue green. Row 3 is green. Row 4 is lilac. Each design comes in all four colors.

1995
C882 AP306 750p #a.-p. 24.00 12.00

AIR POST SPECIAL DELIVERY STAMPS

Catalogue values for unused stamps in this section are for Never Hinged items.

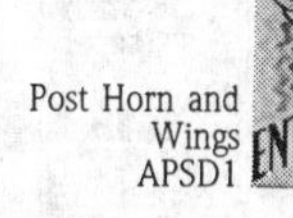

Post Horn and Wings APSD1

Unwmk.
1958, May 19 Litho. *Perf. 12*
CE1 APSD1 25c dk bl & red .35 .15

Same Overprinted Vertically in Red

1959
CE2 APSD1 25c dk bl & red .30 .15

Jet Plane and Envelope — APSD2

1963, Oct. 4 *Perf. 14*
CE3 APSD2 50c red & blk .20 .15

Aviation Type of Air Post Issue

History of Colombian Aviation: 80c, Boeing 727 jet, 1966.

Perf. 14x13½
1966, Dec. 14 Photo. Unwmk.
CE4 AP96 80c crim & multi .35 .15

AIR POST REGISTRATION STAMPS

Issued by Sociedad Colombo-Alemana de Transportes Aereos (SCADTA)

No. C41 Overprinted in Red R

1923 Wmk. 116 *Perf. 14x14½*
CF1 AP6 20c gray 2.50 1.10

No. C58 Overprinted in Black R

1929 Wmk. 127 *Perf. 14*
CF2 AP8 20c carmine 4.00 1.10

Same Overprint on No. C71
CF3 AP10 20c carmine 6.50 6.00

Colombian Government Issues
Same Overprint on No. C86

1932
CF4 AP8 20c carmine 6.50 6.00

No. C100 Overprinted R

CF5 AP12 20c car & ol blk 4.50 1.25

SPECIAL DELIVERY STAMPS

Special Delivery Messenger — SD1

1917 Unwmk. Engr. *Perf. 14*
E1 SD1 5c gray green 1.00 1.50

Catalogue values for unused stamps in this section, from this point to the end of the section, are for Never Hinged items.

SD2

1987, July 31 Litho. *Perf. 14*
E2 SD2 25p emerald & ver .30 .30
E3 SD2 30p emerald & ver .35 .35

REGISTRATION STAMPS

R1

R2

1865 Unwmk. Litho. *Imperf.*
F1 R1 5c black 80.00 40.00
F2 R2 5c black 75.00 40.00

R3

R4

1870

White Paper

Vertical Lines in Background
F3 R3 5c black 2.25 1.90
F4 R4 5c black 2.25 1.90

Horizontal Lines in Background
F5 R3 5c black 7.50 6.50
F6 R4 5c black 2.25 1.90
Nos. F3-F6 (4) 14.25 12.20

Reprints of Nos. F3 to F6 show either crossed lines or traces of lines in background.

R5

R6

1881 *Imperf.*
F7 R5 10c violet 47.50 40.00
a. Sewing machine perf. 55.00 47.50
b. Perf. 11 60.00 50.00

1883 *Perf. 12, 13½*
F8 R6 10c red, *orange* 1.50 1.90

R7

1889-95 *Perf. 12, 13½*
F9 R7 10c red, *grysh* 5.25 2.50
F10 R7 10c red, *yelsh* 5.25 2.50
F11 R7 10c dp brn, *rose buff* ('95) 1.50 1.25
F12 R7 10c yel brn, *lt buff* ('92) 1.50 1.25
Nos. F9-F12 (4) 13.50 7.50

Nos. F9-F12 exist imperf. Values same as for perf.

R9

1902 *Imperf.*
F13 R9 20c red brown, *blue* 1.40 1.40
a. Sewing machine perf. 3.75 3.75
b. Perf. 12 3.75 3.75

Medellin Issue

R10

1902 *Perf. 12*

Laid Paper
F16 R10 10c blk vio 12.50 12.50
a. Wove paper 17.50 17.50

Regular Issue

1903 *Imperf.*

F17 R9 20c blue, *blue* 1.40 1.40
a. Sewing machine perf. 4.00 4.00
b. Perf. 12 4.00 4.00

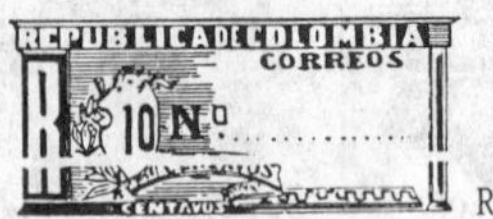
R11

1904 **Pelure Paper** *Imperf.*

F19 R11 10c purple 3.00 3.00
a. Sewing machine perf. 4.00 3.00
b. Perf. 12 5.00 4.00

R12

Imprint: "J. L. Arango"

1904 *Perf. 12*

Wove Paper

F20 R12 10c purple 2.00 .50
a. Imperf., pair 6.25 6.25

Imprint: "Lit. Nacional"

1909 *Perf. 10, 14, 10x14, 14x10*

F21 R12 10c purple 2.25 .70
a. Imperf., pair 5.00 5.00

For overprints see Nos. LF1-LF4.

Execution at Cartagena in 1816
R13

1910, July 20 **Engr.** *Perf. 12*

F22 R13 10c red & black 17.50 *75.00*

Centenary of National Independence.

Pier at Puerto Colombia
R14

Tequendama Falls — R15

Perf. 11, 11½, 14, 11½x14

1917, Aug. 25

F23 R14 4c green & ultra .50 *2.50*
a. Center inverted 575.00 575.00
F24 R15 10c deep blue 1.90 .60

R16

1925 **Litho.** *Perf. 10x13½*

F25 R16 (10c) blue 3.50 1.50
a. Imperf., pair 12.00 10.00
b. Perf. 13½x10 6.00 4.00

ACKNOWLEDGMENT OF RECEIPT STAMPS

AR1

AR2

1893 **Unwmk.** **Litho.** *Perf. 13½*

H1 AR1 5c ver, *blue* 4.25 4.25

1894 *Perf. 12*

H2 AR1 5c vermilion 3.50 4.00

1902-03 *Imperf.*

H3 AR2 10c blue, *blue* 2.75 2.75
a. 10c, blue, *greenish blue* 2.75 2.75
b. Sewing machine perf. 2.75 2.75
c. Perf. 12 2.75 2.75

The handstamp "AR" in circle is believed to be a postmark.

AR2a

Purple Handstamp

1903 *Imperf.*

H4 AR2a 10c black, *pink* 20.00 20.00

AR3

AR4

1904 **Pelure Paper** *Imperf.*

H12 AR3 5c pale blue 10.50 10.50
a. Perf. 12 10.50 10.50

No. 307 Overprinted in Black, Green or Violet **A R**

H13 A86 5c carmine 17.50 17.50

1904 *Perf. 12*

H16 AR4 5c blue 3.25 2.75
a. Imperf., pair 8.75 8.75

For overprints see Nos. LH1-LH2.

General José Acevedo y Gómez — AR5

1910, July 20 **Engr.**

H17 AR5 5c orange & green 5.75 *16.00*

Centenary of National Independence.

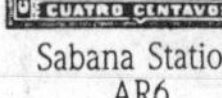
Sabana Station
AR6

Map of Colombia
AR7

1917 *Perf. 14*

H18 AR6 4c bister brown 1.75 2.00
H19 AR7 5c orange brown 1.50 1.75
a. Imperf., pair 11.00

LATE FEE STAMPS

LF1

LF2

1886 **Unwmk.** **Litho.** *Perf. 10½*

I1 LF1 2½c blk, *lilac* 3.25 2.50
a. Imperf., pair 12.00 12.00

1892 *Perf. 12, 13½*

I2 LF2 2½c dk bl, *rose* 2.75 2.00
a. Imperf., pair 12.00
I3 LF2 2½c ultra, *pink* 2.75 2.00

LF3

LF4

1902 *Imperf.*

I4 LF3 5c purple, *rose* .85 .85
a. Perf. 12 1.75 1.75

1914 *Perf. 10, 13½*

I6 LF4 2c vio brown 4.00 4.00
I7 LF4 5c blue green 4.00 3.25

Retardo

Refardo
1921

Overprints illustrated above are unauthorized and of private origin.

POSTAGE DUE STAMPS

These are not, strictly speaking, postage due stamps but were issued to cover an additional fee, "Sobreporte," charged on mail to foreign countries with which Colombia had no postal conventions.

D1

D2

D3

1866 **Unwmk.** **Litho.** *Imperf.*

J1 D1 25c black, *blue* 45.00 45.00
J2 D2 50c black, *yellow* 45.00 45.00
J3 D3 1p black, *rose* 125.00 100.00
Nos. J1-J3 (3) 215.00 190.00

DEPARTMENT STAMPS

These stamps are said to be for interior postage, to supersede the separate issues for the various departments.

Regular Issues Handstamped in Black, Violet, Blue or Green — a

Correos
Departa-
mentales

On Stamps of 1904

1909 **Unwmk.** *Perf. 12*

L1 A94 ½c yellow 2.00 2.00
a. Imperf., pair 6.00 6.00
L2 A94 1c yel grn 3.00 2.00
L3 A94 2c red 4.50 3.00
a. Imperf., pair 12.50 12.50
L4 A94 5c blue 5.00 3.25
L5 A94 10c violet 7.00 7.00
L6 A94 20c black 11.00 10.00
L7 A95 1p brown 18.00 17.00

On Stamp of 1902

L8 A83 10p dk brn, *rose* 20.00 20.00
Nos. L1-L8 (8) 70.50 64.25

On Stamps of 1908

Perf. 10, 13, 13½ and Compound

L9 A94 ½c orange 2.00 2.00
a. Imperf., pair 6.00 6.00
L10 A94 1c green 4.00 3.25
a. Without imprint 5.00 5.00
L11 A94 2c red 4.50 3.25
a. Imperf., pair
L12 A94 5c blue 4.50 3.25
a. Imperf., pair 12.50 12.50
L13 A94 10c violet 6.00 6.00

On Tolima Stamp of 1888

Perf. 10½

L14 A23 1p red brn 12.50 12.50
Nos. L9-L14 (6) 33.50 30.25

Regular Issues Handstamped — b

On Stamps of 1904

Perf. 12

L15 A94 ½c yellow 2.00 2.00
L16 A94 1c yellow grn 3.50 3.00
L17 A94 2c red 6.00 5.00
L18 A94 5c blue 6.00 5.00
L19 A94 10c violet 8.00 6.00
L20 A94 20c black 11.00 11.00
L21 A94 1p brown 20.00 20.00
Nos. L15-L21 (7) 56.50 52.00

On Stamps of 1908

Perf. 10, 13, 13½

L22 A94 ½c orange 2.25 2.25
L23 A94 1c yellow grn 6.25 6.25
L24 A94 2c red 5.00 5.00
a. Imperf., pair 12.50 12.50
L25 A94 5c light blue 6.00 5.00
Nos. L22-L25 (4) 19.50 18.50

The handstamps on Nos. L1-L25 are, as usual, found inverted and double.

DEPARTMENT REGISTRATION STAMPS

Registration Stamps Handstamped like Nos. L1-L25

On Registration Stamp of 1904

1909 **Unwmk.** *Perf. 12*

LF1 R12 (a) 10c purple 25.00 25.00
LF2 R12 (b) 10c purple 25.00 25.00

On Registration Stamp of 1909

Perf. 10, 13

LF3 R12 (a) 10c purple 25.00 25.00
LF4 R12 (b) 10c purple 25.00 25.00
Nos. LF1-LF4 (4) 100.00 100.00

Nos. LF1-LF4 exist imperf. Value per pair, $100.

DEPARTMENT ACKNOWLEDGMENT OF RECEIPT STAMPS

Acknowledgment of Receipt Stamp of 1904 Handstamped like Nos. L1-L25

1909 **Unwmk.** *Perf. 12*

LH1 AR4 (a) 5c blue 25.00 25.00
a. Imperf., pair 100.00
LH2 AR4 (b) 5c blue 25.00 25.00
a. Imperf., pair 100.00

LOCAL STAMPS FOR THE CITY OF BOGOTA

A1

Pelure Paper

1889 Unwmk. Litho. *Perf. 12*

LX1 A1 ½c black .95 .95
a. Imperf., pair 6.00 6.00

Impressions on bright blue and blue-gray paper were not regularly issued.

A2

A3

White Wove Paper

1896 *Perf. 12, 13½*

LX2 A2 ½c black .95 .95

1903 *Imperf.*

LX3 A3 10c black, *pink* 1.25 1.25
a. Perf. 12 5.00 5.00

OFFICIAL STAMPS

Stamps of 1917-1937 Overprinted in Black or Red:

OFICIAL a   OFICIAL b

1937 Unwmk. *Perf. 11, 12, 13½*

O1 A131 (a) 1c green .15 .15
O2 A157 (a) 10c dp org .15 .15
O3 A107 (b) 30c olive bis 1.75 1.00
O4 A129 (b) 40c brn & yel brn 1.50 .80
O5 A114 (b) 50c car 1.00 .50
O6 A107 (b) 1p lt bl 5.00 4.00
O7 A107 (b) 2p org 10.00 6.50
O8 A107 (b) 5p gray 37.50 27.50
O9 A118 (b) 10p dk brn 110.00 100.00

Wmk. 229

Perf. 12½

O10 A132 (a) 2c red .15 .15
O11 A133 (a) 5c brn .15 .15
O12 A160 (a) 12c dp bl (R) 1.00 .50
O13 A136 (b) 20c dk bl (R) 1.65 .60
Nos. O1-O13 (13) 170.00 142.00

Tall, wrong font "I's" in OFICIAL exist on all stamps with "a" overprint.

POSTAL TAX STAMPS

"Greatest Mother" PT1

Perf. 11½

1935, May 27 Unwmk. Litho.

RA1 PT1 5c olive blk & scar 2.00 .75

Required on all mail during Red Cross Week in 1935 (May 27-June 3) and in 1936.

Mother and Child — PT2

Perf. 10½, 10½x11

1937, May 24 Unwmk.

RA2 PT2 5c red .70 .28

Required on all mail during Red Cross Week. The tax was for the Red Cross.

Ministry of Posts and Telegraphs Building

PT3   PT4

1939-45 Litho. *Perf. 10½, 12½*

RA3 PT3 ¼c dp bl .15 .15
RA3A PT3 ¼c dk vio brn ('45) .15 .15
RA4 PT3 ½c pink .15 .15
RA5 PT3 1c violet .30 .15
RA5A PT3 1c yel org ('45) 1.50 .60
RA6 PT3 2c pck grn .40 .15
RA7 PT3 20c lt brn 3.50 1.25
Nos. RA3-RA7 (7) 6.15
Set value 1.65

Obligatory on all mail. The tax was for the construction of the new Communications Building.

The 25c of type PT3 and PT4 were not usable on postal matter.

For overprint see No. 561.

Perf. 12½x13

1940, Jan. 20 Engr. Wmk. 229

RA8 PT4 ¼c ultra .15 .15
RA9 PT4 ½c carmine .15 .15
RA10 PT4 1c violet .15 .15
RA11 PT4 2c bl grn .24 .15
RA12 PT4 20c brown 1.00 .24
Set value 1.35 .44

See note after No. RA7. See No. RA18.

"Protection" — PT5

1940, Apr. 25 Wmk. 255 *Perf. 12*

RA13 PT5 5c rose carmine .24 .15

See No. RA17.

Postal Tax Stamps of 1939 Surcharged in Black

$ 0,0½
MEDIO CENTAVO

1943 Unwmk. *Perf. 10½*

RA14 PT3 ½c on 1c violet .15 .15
a. Inverted surcharge 1.50
RA15 PT3 ½c on 2c pck grn .15 .15
RA16 PT3 ½c on 20c lt brn .15 .15
Set value .20 .20

Types of 1940

Imprint: "Litografia Colombia Bogota S.A."

1944 Litho. *Perf. 11*

RA17 PT5 5c dark rose .30 .15

Imprint: "Lito-Colombia Bogota-Colombia"

RA18 PT4 ¼c ultra .15 .15
Set value .36 .20

Ministry of Posts and Telegraphs Building — PT6

1945-48 Wmk. 255 Engr. *Perf. 12*

RA19 PT6 ¼c ultra .15 .15
RA20 PT6 ¼c sepia ('46) .15 .15
RA21 PT6 ½c car rose .15 .15
RA22 PT6 ½c dp mag ('46) .15 .15
RA23 PT6 1c vio ('46) .15 .15
RA23A PT6 1c red org ('46) .15 .15
RA24 PT6 2c grn ('46) .15 .15
RA25 PT6 20c brn ('46) .90 .22
a. 20c red brown ('48) .60 .15
Set value 1.25 .55

These stamps were obligatory on all mail. The surtax was for the construction of the new Communications Building. See Nos. 603, RA33. For overprints see Nos. 562-564.

No. 469 Overprinted in Carmine

1946, May 25

RA26 A176 5c dull brown .35 .15

The surtax was for the Red Cross.

Ministry of Posts and Telegraphs Building — PT7

1946 Unwmk. Litho. *Perf. 11*

RA27 PT7 3c blue .15 .15

No. 490 Overprinted in Carmine SOBRETASA

1947 Wmk. 255 *Perf. 12*

RA28 A196 20c gray black 3.00 1.25

Arms of Colombia and Red Cross — PT8

PT9

Perf. 12½

1947, Sept. Unwmk. Engr.

RA29 PT8 5c car lake .15 .15

The surtax of Nos. RA29 and RA40 was for the Red Cross. See No. RA40.

No. 466 Overprinted Like No. RA28 in Carmine

RA30 A136 20c dark blue 10.00 7.00

Catalogue values for unused stamps in this section, from this point to the end of the section, are for Never Hinged items.

Type of 1945

1947 Wmk. 255 Engr. *Perf. 12*

RA33 PT6 1c olive bister .15 .15

Black Surcharge

1948 Unwmk. Litho. *Perf. 11*

RA36 PT9 1c on 5c lt brn .15 .15
RA37 PT9 1c on 10c lt vio .15 .15
RA38 PT9 1c on 25c red .15 .15
RA39 PT9 1c on 50c ultra .15 .15
Set value .24 .20

Type of 1947

1948 *Perf. 10½*

RA40 PT8 5c vermilion .15 .15

Ministry of Posts and Telegraphs Building — PT10

Mother and Child — PT11

1948-50 Wmk. 255 Engr. *Perf. 12*

RA41 PT10 1c rose car ('49) .15 .15
RA42 PT10 2c green ('50) .15 .15
RA43 PT10 3c blue .15 .15
RA44 PT10 5c gray .15 .15
RA45 PT10 10c purple .22 .15
Set value .47 .25

A 25c stamp of type PT10 was for use on telegrams, later for regular postage. See Nos. 602, 604. For overprints and surcharge see Nos. C227-C230, C238, C283, RA51.

Unwmk.

1950, May 25 Litho. *Perf. 11*

Dark Blue Surcharge

RA46 PT11 5c on 2c gray, red, blk & yel .75 .30
a. "195" instead of "1950" 1.40 1.40
b. Top bar and "19" of "1950" omitted 1.40 1.40

Marginal perforations omitted, creating 26 straight-edged copies in each sheet of 44. Surtax for Red Cross.

No. 574 Overprinted in Black SOBRETASA

1950, May 26 Wmk. 255 *Perf. 12*

RA47 A176 5c blue .15 .15
a. Inverted overprint .90

Telegraph Stamp Surcharged in Black

RA48 A253a 8c on 50c org yel .15 .15
Set value .15

Fiscal stamps of type A253a were available for postal use after May 9, 1952. See Nos. 605-608.

Arms and Cross — PT12

Bartolome de Las Casas Aiding Youth — PT13

Perf. 12½

1951, May Unwmk. Engr.

RA49 PT12 5c red .22 .15
RA50 PT13 5c carmine .22 .15
Set value .15

The surtax was for the Red Cross.

No. RA43 Surcharged with New Value in Black

1951 Wmk. 255 *Perf. 12*

RA51 PT10 1c on 3c blue .15 .15

Type of 1951

Engraved; Cross Lithographed

1953 Unwmk. *Perf. 12½*

RA52 PT13 5c grn & car .22 .15

Surtax of Nos. RA52-RA60 for the Red Cross.

No. C254 Overprinted with Cross and Bar in Carmine

1954

RA53 AP42 5c lilac rose .60 .50

St. Peter Claver Offering Gifts to Slaves — PT14

Engraved; Cross Typographed

1955, May 2 Unwmk. *Perf. 13*

RA54 PT14 5c dp plum & red .22 .15

Death of St. Peter Claver, 300th anniv.

Jean Henri Dunant and Santiago Samper Brush PT15

Photo.; Red Cross & "Cruz Roja" Engr.

1956, June 1 Unwmk. *Perf. 13*

RA55 PT15 5c brown & red .22 .15

Nurses and Ambulances — PT16

1958, June 2 Photo. *Perf. 12*

RA56 PT16 5c gray & red .15 .15

St. Louisa de Marillac and Church PT17

Design: No. RA58, Henri Dunant and battle scene.

1960, Sept. 1 Litho. *Perf. 11*

RA57 PT17 5c brown & rose .22 .15
RA58 PT17 5c vio blue & rose .22 .15
Set value .16

No. RA57 for 3rd cent. of the Sisters of Charity. No. RA58 for cent. (in 1959) of the Red Cross idea.

Manuelita de la Cruz — PT18

Red Cross Worker, Patient — PT19

1961, Nov. 2 Engr. *Perf. 13*

RA59 PT18 5c dull pur & red .15 .15
RA60 PT18 5c brown & red .15 .15
Set value .15

Issued in memory of Red Cross Nurse Manuelita de la Cruz, who died in the line of duty during the floods of 1955. Obligatory on domestic mail for a month.

1965, Apr. 30 Photo. *Perf. 12*

RA61 PT19 5c blue gray & red .15 .15

Obligatory on domestic mail during May.

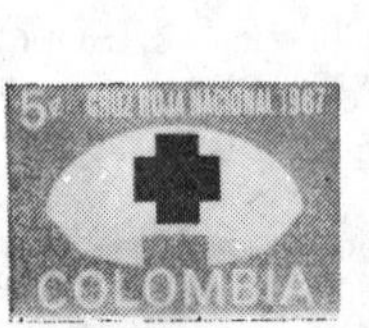

Nurse's Cap — PT20

Red Cross — PT21

1967, June 1 Litho. *Perf. 12*

RA62 PT20 5c brt bl & red .15 .15

1969, July 1 Litho. *Perf. 12x12½*

RA63 PT21 5c vio bl & red .15 .15

Child Care — PT22

1970, July 1 Litho. *Perf. 12½x12*

RA64 PT22 5c light bl & red .15 .15

ANTIOQUIA

ˌant-ē-ˈō-kē-ə

Originally a State, now a Department of the Republic of Colombia. Until the revolution of 1885, the separate states making up the United States of Colombia were sovereign governments in their own right. On August 4, 1886, the National Council of Bogotá, composed of two delegates from each state, adopted a new constitution which abolished the sovereign rights of states, which then became departments with governors appointed by the President of the Republic. The nine original states represented at the Bogotá Convention retained some of their previous rights, as management of their own finances, and all issued postage stamps until as late as 1904. For Panama's issues, see Panama Nos. 1-30.

Coat of Arms

A1 A2

A3 A4

Wove Paper

1868 Unwmk. Litho. *Imperf.*

1 A1 2½c blue 750. 450.
2 A2 5c green 575. 325.
3 A3 10c lilac 1,700. 600.
4 A4 1p red 450. 300.

Reprints of Nos. 1, 3 and 4 are on a bluish white paper and all but No. 3 have scratches across the design.

A5 A6

A7 A8

A9 A10

1869

5 A5 2½c blue 3.25 2.75
6 A6 5c green 5.00 4.50
7 A7 5c green 5.00 4.50
8 A8 10c lilac 6.25 3.25
9 A9 20c brown 6.25 3.25
10 A10 1p rose red 12.50 11.00
a. 1p vermilion 25.00 22.50
Nos. 5-10 (6) 38.25 29.25

Reprints of Nos. 7, 8 and 10 are on a bluish white paper; reprints of Nos. 5 and 10a on white paper. The 10c blue is believed to be a reprint.

A11 A12

A13 A14

A15 A16

A17 A18

1873

12 A11 1c yellow grn 4.50 3.50
a. 1c green 4.50 3.50
13 A12 5c green 7.50 5.50
14 A13 10c lilac 22.50 19.00
15 A14 20c yellow brn 7.50 6.50
a. 20c dark brown 7.50 6.50
16 A15 50c blue 1.75 1.50
17 A16 1p vermilion 3.25 2.75
18 A17 2p black, *yellow* 7.75 7.00
19 A18 5p black, *rose* 55.00 47.50

A19 A20

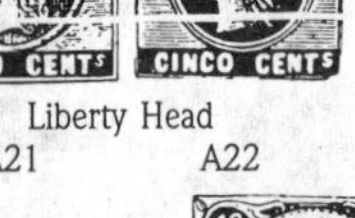

Liberty Head

A21 A22

Pedro Justo Berrio — A23

1875-85

20 A19 1c blk, *grn*, unglazed ('76) 1.65 1.40
a. Glazed paper 2.25 1.90
b. 1c blk, *lt grn*, laid paper ('85) 3.75 3.50
21 A19 1c black ('76) 1.10 1.00
a. Laid paper 140.00 100.00
22 A19 1c bl grn ('85) 2.25 1.90
23 A19 1c red lil, laid paper ('85) 2.25 1.90
24 A20 2½c blue 2.25 1.90
a. Pelure paper ('78) *1,700. 1,250.*
25 A21 5c green 15.00 12.50
a. Laid paper 140.00 80.00
26 A22 5c green 15.00 12.50
a. Laid paper 140.00 80.00
27 A23 10c lilac 22.50 19.00
a. Laid paper 140.00 110.00
28 A20 10c vio, pelure paper ('78) *900.00 675.00*

Arms — A24 Liberty — A25

A26 A27

1878-85

29 A24 2½c blue, pelure paper 2.50 2.25
30 A24 2½c green ('83) 2.25 1.90
a. Laid paper ('83) 70.00 47.50
31 A24 2½c blk, *buff* ('85) 6.25 5.50
32 A25 5c green ('83) 3.75 3.25
a. Pelure paper 30.00 25.00
b. Laid paper ('82) 37.50 11.00
33 A25 5c violet ('83) 8.75 6.50
a. 5c blue violet ('83) 8.75 6.50
34 A26 10c vio, laid paper ('82) 165.00 55.00
35 A26 10c scar ('83) 2.25 1.90
a. Tete beche pair 50.00 45.00
36 A27 20c brown ('83) 3.75 3.25
a. Laid paper ('82) 5.00 4.50

A28 A29

Liberty — A30

Coat of Arms — A31

1883-85

37 A28 5c brown 4.50 3.00
a. Laid paper 190.00 75.00
38 A28 5c green ('85) 125.00 40.00
a. Laid paper ('85) 140.00 65.00
39 A28 5c yel, laid paper ('85) 5.00 4.00
40 A29 10c bl grn, laid paper 5.00 4.50
41 A29 10c bl, *bl* ('85) 5.00 4.00
42 A29 10c lil, laid paper ('85) 9.50 6.50
a. Wove paper ('85) 100.00 40.00
43 A30 20c bl, laid paper ('85) 4.50 4.00

1886

Wove Paper

55 A31 1c grn, *pink* .55 .50
56 A31 2½c blk, *orange* .55 .50
57 A31 5c ultra, *buff* 1.75 1.60
a. 5c blue, *buff* 3.25 2.75
58 A31 10c rose, *buff* 1.65 1.40
a. Transfer of 50c in stone of 10c 75.00 65.00
59 A31 20c dk vio, *buff* 1.65 1.40
61 A31 50c yel brn, *buff* 2.75 2.50
62 A31 1p yel, *grn* 4.50 4.00
63 A31 2p green, *vio* 4.50 4.00
Nos. 55-63 (8) 17.90 15.90

1887-88

64 A31 1c red, *vio* .45 .40
65 A31 2½c lil, *pale lil* .45 .55
66 A31 5c car, *buff* .60 .55
67 A31 5c red, *grn* 3.25 1.60
68 A31 10c brn, *grn* .65 .80
Nos. 64-68 (5) 5.40 3.90

Medellin Issue

A32 A33

A34 A35

1888 Typeset

69 A32 2½c blk, *yellow* 14.00 12.50
70 A33 5c blk, *yellow* 7.50 6.75
71 A34 5c red, *yellow* 4.50 4.00
Nos. 69-71 (3) 26.00 23.25

Two varieties of No. 69, six of No. 70 and ten of No. 71.

1889

72 A35 2½c red 7.00 6.00

Ten varieties including "eentavos."

Regular Issue

Coat of Arms
A36 A37

A38 A39

A40 A41

1889 Litho. *Perf. 13½*

No.	Type	Denom.	Color	Unused	Used
73	A36	1c	blk, *rose*	.25	.25
74	A36	2½c	blk, *blue*	.25	.25
75	A36	5c	blk, *yellow*	.30	.30
76	A36	10c	blk, *green*	.30	.30
			Nos. 73-76 (4)	1.10	1.10

1890

No.	Type	Denom.	Color	Unused	Used
78	A37	20c	blue	1.25	1.25
79	A38	50c	vio brn	2.50	2.50
a.			Transfer of 20c in stone of 50c	82.50	82.50
80	A38	50c	green	2.00	2.00
81	A39	1p	red	1.75	1.75
82	A40	2p	blk, *mag*	12.50	12.50
83	A41	5p	blk, *org red*	20.00	20.00
			Nos. 78-83 (6)	40.00	40.00

Nos. 73-76, 82-83 exist imperf.

The so-called "errors" of Nos. 73 to 76, printed on paper of wrong colors, are essays or, possibly, reprints. They exist perforated and imperforate.

See No. 96.

A42 A43

A44 A45

1890 Typeset *Perf. 14*

No.	Type	Denom.	Color	Unused	Used
84	A42	2½c	blk, *buff*	2.00	2.00
85	A43	5c	blk, *orange*	2.00	2.00
86	A44	10c	blk, *buff*	6.00	6.00
87	A44	10c	blk, *rose*	7.50	7.50
88	A45	20c	blk, *orange*	7.50	7.50
			Nos. 84-88 (5)	25.00	25.00

20 varieties of the 5c, 10 each of the other values.

A46 A47

1892 Litho. *Perf. 13½*

No.	Type	Denom.	Color	Unused	Used
89	A46	1c	brn, *brnsh*	.35	.35
90	A46	2½c	pur, *lil*	.35	.35
92	A46	5c	blk, *gray*	1.00	.50
a.			Transfer of 2½c in stone of 5c	150.00	
			Nos. 89-92 (3)	1.70	1.20

1893

No.	Type	Denom.	Color	Unused	Used
93	A46	1c	blue	.25	.25
94	A46	2½c	green	.35	.35
95	A46	5c	vermilion	.25	.25
96	A36	10c	pale brown	.25	.25
			Nos. 93-96 (4)	1.10	1.10

1896 *Perf. 14*

No.	Type	Denom.	Color	Unused	Used
97	A47	2c	gray	.25	.25
98	A47	2c	lilac rose	.25	.25
99	A47	2½c	brown	.25	.25
100	A47	2½c	steel blue	.25	.25
101	A47	3c	orange	.25	.25
102	A47	3c	olive grn	.25	.25
103	A47	5c	green	.25	.25
104	A47	5c	yellow buff	.30	.30
105	A47	10c	brown vio	.55	.55
106	A47	10c	violet	.55	.55
107	A47	20c	brown org	1.25	1.25
108	A47	20c	blue	1.25	1.25
109	A47	50c	gray brn	1.25	1.25
110	A47	50c	rose	1.10	1.10
111	A47	1p	blue & blk	16.00	16.00
112	A47	1p	rose red & blk	16.00	16.00
113	A47	2p	orange & blk	47.50	47.50
114	A47	2p	dk grn & blk	47.50	47.50
115	A47	5p	red vio & blk	82.50	82.50
116	A47	5p	purple & blk	82.50	82.50
			Nos. 97-116 (20)	300.00	300.00

#115-116 with centers omitted are proofs.

General José María Córdoba — A48

1899 *Perf. 11*

No.	Type	Denom.	Color	Unused	Used
117	A48	½c	grnsh bl	.15	.15
118	A48	1c	slate blue	.15	.15
119	A48	2c	slate brown	.15	.15
120	A48	3c	red	.15	.15
121	A48	4c	bister brown	.15	.15
122	A48	5c	green	.15	.15
123	A48	10c	scarlet	.15	.15
124	A48	20c	gray violet	.15	.15
125	A48	50c	olive bister	.15	.15
126	A48	1p	greenish blk	.15	.15
127	A48	2p	olive gray	.15	.15
			Set value	.70	1.10

Numerous part-perf. and imperf. varieties of Nos. 117-127 exist.

A49

A50

A50a

1901 Typeset *Perf. 12*

No.	Type	Denom.	Color	Unused	Used
128	A49	1c	red	.20	.20
129	A50	1c	ultra	.60	.60
130	A50	1c	bister	.60	.60
130A	A50a	1c	dull red	.60	.60
130B	A50a	1c	ultra	4.00	4.00
			Nos. 128-130B (5)	6.00	6.00

Eight varieties of No. 128, four varieties of Nos. 129-130B.

A51 A52

Atanasio Girardot
A53

Dr. José Félix Restrepo
A54

1902 Litho. Wove Paper

No.	Type	Denom.	Color	Unused	Used
131	A51	1c	brt rose	.15	.15
a.			Laid paper	.60	.60
b.			Imperf., pair	2.50	
132	A51	2c	blue	.15	.15
a.			Transfer of 3c in stone of 2c	5.00	5.00
133	A51	3c	green	.15	.15
a.			Imperf., pair	4.00	
134	A51	4c	dull violet	.15	.15
135	A52	5c	rose red	.18	.18
136	A53	10c	rose lilac	.15	.15
a.			Small head	5.00	5.00
b.			10c rose	.15	.15
137	A53	20c	gray green	.18	.18
138	A53	30c	brt rose	.18	.18
139	A53	40c	blue	.18	.18
140	A53	50c	brn, *yel*	.18	.18

Laid Paper

No.	Type	Denom.	Color	Unused	Used
141	A54	1p	purple & blk	.70	.70
142	A54	2p	rose & blk	.70	.70
143	A54	5p	sl bl & blk	1.25	1.25
			Nos. 131-143 (13)	4.30	4.30

1903

Wove Paper

No.	Type	Denom.	Color	Unused	Used
143A	A51	1c	blue	.15	.15
144	A51	2c	violet	.15	.15
a.			Imperf.	2.50	

A55 A56 A57

Designs: 1p, Francisco Antonio Zea. 2p, Custodio Garcia Rovira. 3p, La Pola (Policarpa Salavarrieta). 4p, J. M. Restrepo. 5p, José Fernández Madrid. 10p, Juan del Corral.

1903-04

No.	Type	Denom.	Color	Unused	Used
145	A55	4c	yellow brn	.20	.20
146	A55	5c	blue	.20	.20
147	A56	10c	yellow	.20	.20
148	A56	20c	purple	.20	.20
149	A56	30c	brown	.60	.60
150	A56	40c	green	.60	.60
151	A56	50c	rose	.20	.20
152	A57	1p	olive gray	.60	.60
153	A57	2p	purple	.60	.60
154	A57	3p	dark blue	.60	.60
155	A57	4p	dull red	1.00	1.00
156	A57	5p	red brown	3.00	1.50
157	A57	10p	scarlet	6.50	3.50
			Nos. 145-157 (13)	14.50	10.00

Nos. 145-146, 151, 153-157 exist imperf. Value of pairs, $3 to $4.

Manizales Issue

Stamps of these designs are local private post issues.

OFFICIAL STAMPS Stamps of 1903-04 with overprint "OFICIAL" were never issued.

REGISTRATION STAMPS

R1

1896 Unwmk. Litho. *Perf. 14*

No.	Type	Denom.	Color	Unused	Used
F1	R1	2½c	rose	1.10	1.10
F2	R1	2½c	dull blue	1.10	1.10

Córdoba
R2

R3 R4

1899 *Perf. 11*

No.	Type	Denom.	Color	Unused	Used
F3	R2	2½c	dull blue	.25	.25
F4	R3	10c	red lilac	.25	.25

1902 *Perf. 12*

No.	Type	Denom.	Color	Unused	Used
F5	R4	10c	purple, *blue*	.30	.30
a.			Imperf.		

ACKNOWLEDGMENT OF RECEIPT STAMPS

AR1

1902-03 Unwmk. Litho. *Perf. 12*

No.	Type	Denom.	Color	Unused	Used
H1	AR1	5c	black, *rose*	.90	.90
H2	AR1	5c	slate ('03)	.30	.30

LATE FEE STAMPS

Córdoba — LF1

1899 Unwmk. Litho. *Perf. 11*

No.	Type	Denom.	Color	Unused	Used
I1	LF1	2½c	dark green	.25	.25
a.			Imperf., pair	2.75	

LF2

LF3

1901 Typeset *Perf. 12*

No.	Type	Denom.	Color	Unused	Used
I2	LF2	2½c	red violet	.50	.50
a.			2½c purple	.50	.50

1902 Litho.

No.	Type	Denom.	Color	Unused	Used
I3	LF3	2½c	violet	.20	.20

City of Medellin

Stamps of the designs shown were not issued by any governmental agency but by the Sociedad de Mejoras Publicas.

BOLIVAR

bə-ˈlē-ˌvär

Originally a State, now a Department of the Republic of Colombia. (See Antioquia.)

A1

1863-66 Unwmk. Litho. *Imperf.*
1 A1 10c green 1,100. 550.00
a. Five stars below shield 2,400. 2,200.
2 A1 10c red ('66) 25.00 27.50
a. Diagonal half used as 5c on cover 55.00
b. Five stars below shield 75.00 67.50
3 A1 1p red 6.25 7.25

Fourteen varieties of each. Counterfeits of Nos. 1 and 1a exist.

Coat of Arms
A2 A3

A4 A5

1873
4 A2 5c blue 7.00 7.00
5 A3 10c violet 7.00 7.00
6 A4 20c yellow green 30.00 30.00
7 A5 80c vermilion 60.00 60.00
Nos. 4-7 (4) 104.00 104.00

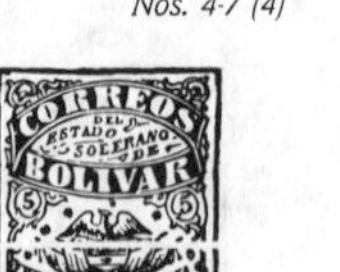

A6 A7

A8 Bolívar — A9

1874-78
8 A6 5c blue 25.00 12.50
9 A7 5c blue ('78) 7.75 7.00
10 A8 10c violet ('77) 3.75 3.50
Nos. 8-10 (3) 36.50 23.00

Dated "1879"

1879 White Wove Paper *Perf. 12½*
11 A9 5c blue .25 .25
a. Imperf., pair .80
12 A9 10c violet .20 .20
13 A9 20c red .25 .25
a. 20c green (error) 10.00 10.00

Bluish Laid Paper
15 A9 5c blue .25 .25
a. Imperf., pair 2.00
16 A9 10c violet 1.65 1.65
a. Imperf., pair 4.00
17 A9 20c red .40 .40
a. Imperf., pair 1.75
Nos. 11-17 (6) 3.00 3.00

Stamps of 80c and 1p on white wove paper and 1p on bluish laid paper were prepared but not placed in use.

Dated "1880"

1880 White Wove Paper *Perf. 12½*
19 A9 5c blue .25 .25
a. Imperf., pair 1.65
20 A9 10c violet .35 .35
a. Imperf., pair 1.65
21 A9 20c red .35 .35
a. 20c green (error) 13.00 13.00

23 A9 80c green 2.25 2.25
24 A9 1p orange 2.50 2.50
a. Imperf., pair 5.50
Nos. 19-24 (5) 5.70 5.70

Bluish Laid Paper
25 A9 5c blue .25 .25
a. Imperf., pair 1.25
26 A9 10c violet 2.25 2.25
27 A9 20c red .35 .35
a. Imperf., pair 2.75
28 A9 1p orange 400.00
a. Imperf. 450.00

A11 A12

A13 A15

A16

Dated "1882"
White Wove Paper

1882 *Perf. 12, 16x12*
29 A11 5c blue .35 .35
30 A12 10c lilac .25 .25
31 A13 20c red .35 .35
33 A15 80c green .65 .65
34 A16 1p orange .65 .65
Nos. 29-34 (5) 2.25 2.25

Nos. 29, 30 and 34 are known imperforate. They are printer's waste and were not issued through post offices.

A17 A18

1882 Engr. *Perf. 12*
35 A17 5p blue & rose red .60 .60
a. Imperf., pair 4.75
b. Perf. 16 7.50 6.25
c. Perf. 14 6.25 6.25
36 A17 10p brown & blue 1.65 1.65
a. Imperf., pair 8.00
b. Perf. 16 7.00 5.50
c. Rouletted 8.00 8.00

Dated "1883"

1883 Litho. *Perf. 12, 16x12*
37 A11 5c blue .18 .18
a. Imperf., pair .80
b. Perf. 12 3.00 1.00
38 A12 10c lilac .24 .24
39 A13 20c red .24 .24
41 A15 80c green .32 .32
42 A16 1p orange .60 .60
a. Perf. 16x12 2.00 2.00
Nos. 37-42 (5) 1.58 1.58

Dated "1884"

1884
43 A11 5c blue .32 .32
a. Perf. 12 10.00 9.25
44 A12 10c lilac .18 .18
45 A13 20c red .18 .18
a. Perf. 12 4.25 4.25
47 A15 80c green .24 .24
a. Perf. 12 2.00 2.00
48 A16 1p orange .32 .32
Nos. 43-48 (5) 1.24 1.24

Dated "1885"

1885
49 A11 5c blue .15 .15
50 A12 10c lilac .15 .15
51 A13 20c red .15 .15
53 A15 80c green .24 .24
54 A16 1p orange .32 .32
Nos. 49-54 (5) 1.01 1.01

The note after No. 34 will also apply to imperforate stamps of the 1884-85 issues.

1891 *Perf. 14*
55 A18 1c black .32 .32
56 A18 5c orange .32 .32
a. Imperf., pair .80
57 A18 10c carmine .32 .32
58 A18 20c blue .60 .60
59 A18 50c green .90 .90
60 A18 1p purple .90 .90
Nos. 55-60 (6) 3.36 3.36

For overprint see Colombia No. 169.

Bolívar A19 José Fernández Madrid A20

Manuel Rodriguez Torices A21 José María García de Toledo A22

1903 Laid Paper *Imperf.*
62 A19 50c dk bl, *pink* .60 .60
a. Bluish paper .60 .60
63 A19 50c sl grn, *pink* .60 .60
a. Rose paper 2.00 2.00
b. Greenish blue paper 3.00 3.00
c. Yellow paper 4.00 4.00
d. Brown paper 4.00 4.00
e. Salmon paper 7.50 7.50
64 A19 50c pur, *pink* 2.00 2.00
a. White paper 4.00 4.00
b. Brown paper 4.00 4.00
c. Greenish blue paper 4.00 4.00
d. Lilac paper 4.00 4.00
e. Rose paper 3.50 3.50
f. Yellow paper 4.00 4.00
g. Salmon paper 6.00 6.00
h. As "a," wove paper 9.00 9.00
65 A20 1p org, *sal* .60 .60
a. Yellow paper 4.50 4.50
b. Greenish blue paper 15.00 15.00
66 A20 1p gray grn, *lil* 1.40 1.40
a. Yellow paper 6.50 6.50
b. Salmon paper 7.50 7.50
c. Green paper 7.50 7.50
d. White wove paper 10.00
67 A21 5p car rose, *lil* .60 .60
a. Brown paper 1.10 1.10
b. Yellow paper 1.10 1.10
c. Greenish blue paper 4.50 4.50
d. Bluish paper 6.00 6.00
e. Salmon paper 7.50 7.50
f. Rose paper 9.00 9.00
68 A22 10p dk bl, *bluish* 1.25 1.25
a. Greenish blue paper 1.25 1.25
b. Rose paper 7.50 7.50
c. Salmon paper 7.50 7.50
d. Yellow paper 7.50 7.50
e. Brown paper 8.50 8.50
f. Lilac paper 10.00 10.00
g. White paper 9.00 9.00
69 A22 10p pur, *grnsh bl* 3.50 3.50
a. Bluish paper 7.50 7.50
b. Rose paper 6.75 6.75
c. Yellow paper 7.50 7.50
d. Brown paper 7.50 7.50
Nos. 62-69 (8) 10.55 10.55

Sewing Machine Perf.
Laid Paper
70 A19 50c dk bl, *pink* 1.00 1.00
a. Bluish paper 1.00 1.00
71 A19 50c sl grn, *pink* 2.00 2.00
72 A19 50c pur, *grnsh bl* 4.00 4.00
a. Bluish paper 4.00 4.00
b. White wove paper 7.50
73 A20 1p org, *sal* 2.00 2.00
74 A20 1p gray grn, *lil* 9.00 9.00
a. Yellow paper 9.00 9.00
75 A21 5p car rose, *yel* 1.65 1.65
a. Lilac paper 4.00 4.00
b. Brown paper 4.00 4.00
c. Bluish paper 5.50 5.50
d. White wove paper 9.00
76 A22 10p dk bl, *grnsh bl* 4.50 4.50
a. Bluish paper 7.00 7.00
b. Yellow paper 9.00 9.00
c. As "b," wove paper 10.00
77 A22 10p pur, *grnsh bl* 7.00 7.00
a. Bluish paper 11.00 11.00
b. Rose paper 8.00 8.00
c. Yellow paper 11.00 11.00
Nos. 70-77 (8) 31.15 31.15

José María del Castillo y Rada — A23 Manuel Anguiano — A24

Pantaleón C. Ribón — A25

1904 *Sewing Machine Perf.*
89 A23 5c black .24 .24
90 A24 10c brown .24 .24
91 A25 20c red .30 .30
92 A25 20c red brown .60 .60
Nos. 89-92 (4) 1.38 1.38

Imperf., pairs
89a A23 5c black 3.50 3.50
90a A24 10c brown 2.75 2.75
91a A25 20c red 6.50 6.50
92a A25 20c red brown 6.50 6.50

A26 A27

A28

1904 *Imperf.*
93 A26 ½c black .60 .60
a. Tête bêche pair 3.50 3.50
94 A27 1c blue 1.10 1.10
95 A28 2c purple 1.25 1.25
Nos. 93-95 (3) 2.95 2.95

REGISTRATION STAMPS

Simón Bolívar
R1 R2

White Wove Paper
Perf. 12½, 16x12

1879 Unwmk. Litho.
F1 R1 40c brown .70 .70

Bluish Laid Paper
F2 R1 40c brown .70 .70
a. Imperf., pair 3.25

Dated "1880"

1880

White Wove Paper
F3 R1 40c brown .32 .32

Bluish Laid Paper
F4 R1 40c brown .65 .65
a. Imperf., pair 3.50

Dated "1882" to "1885"
White Wove Paper

1882-85 *Perf. 16x12*

F5 R2 40c brown (1882)	.32	.32
F6 R2 40c brown (1883)	.24	.24
F7 R2 40c brown (1884)	.24	.24
F8 R2 40c brown (1885)	.32	.32
Nos. F5-F8 (4)	1.12	1.12

Perf. 12

F5a R2 40c	18.00
F6a R2 40c	9.25
F7a R2 40c	9.50
F8a R2 40c	2.50
Nos. F5a-F8a (4)	39.25

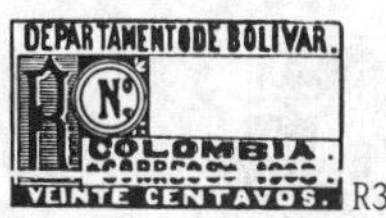
R3

Laid Paper

1903 *Imperf.*

F9 R3 20c orange, *rose*	.60	.60
a. Salmon paper	1.10	1.10
b. Greenish blue paper	6.00	6.00

Sewing Machine Perf.

F10 R3 20c orange, *rose*	2.50	2.50
a. Salmon paper	2.50	2.50
b. Greenish blue paper	6.00	6.00

R4

1904
Wove Paper

F11 R4 5c black	3.25	3.25

ACKNOWLEDGMENT OF RECEIPT STAMPS

AR1

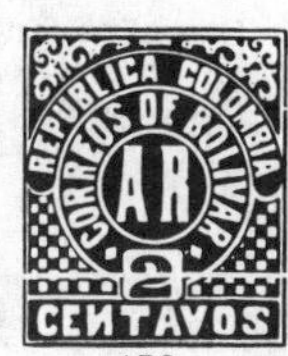
AR2

1903 Unwmk. Litho. *Imperf.*
Laid Paper

H1 AR1 20c org, *rose*	2.50	2.50
a. Yellow paper	1.25	1.25
b. Greenish blue paper	5.00	5.00
H2 AR1 20c dk bl, *yel*	2.00	2.00
a. Brown paper	3.50	3.50
b. Rose paper	2.50	2.50
c. Salmon paper	7.00	7.00
d. Greenish blue paper	7.00	7.00

Sewing Machine Perf.

H3 AR1 20c org, *grnsh bl*	6.25	6.25
a. Yellow paper	7.25	7.25
H4 AR1 20c dk bl, *yel*	7.25	7.25
a. Lilac paper	7.25	7.25
Nos. H1-H4 (4)	18.00	18.00

1904
Wove Paper

H5 AR2 2c red	1.10	1.10

LATE FEE STAMPS

LF1

1903 Unwmk. Litho. *Imperf.*
Laid Paper

I1 LF1 20c car rose, *bluish*	.60	.60
I2 LF1 20c pur, *bluish*	.55	.55
a. Rose paper	2.00	2.00
b. Brown paper	2.00	2.00
c. Lilac paper	2.00	2.00
d. Yellow paper	6.25	6.25

Sewing Machine Perf.

I3 LF1 20c car rose, *bluish*	3.50	3.50
I4 LF1 20c pur, *bluish*	3.50	3.50
a. Rose paper	6.00	6.00
b. Lilac paper	6.00	6.00
c. Yellow paper	10.00	10.00
Nos. I1-I4 (4)	8.15	8.15

BOYACA

Originally a State, now a Department of the Republic of Colombia. (See Antioquia.)

Diego Mendoza Pérez — A1

1902 Unwmk. Litho. *Perf. 13½*
Wove Paper

1 A1 5c blue green	.70	.70
a. Bluish paper	90.00	90.00
b. Imperf., pair	12.50	

Laid Paper
Perf. 12

2 A1 5c green	100.00	100.00

Coat of Arms
A2 A3

Gen. Próspero Pinzón — A4

A5

Monument of Battle of Boyacá — A6

President José Manuel Marroquin — A7

1903 Litho. *Imperf.*

4 A2 10c dark gray	.24	.24
5 A3 20c red brown	.32	.32
6 A5 1p red	3.00	3.00
a. 1p claret	3.50	3.50
8 A6 5p black, *rose*	1.10	1.10
a. 5p black, *buff*	11.00	11.00
9 A7 10p black, *buff*	1.10	1.10
a. 10p black, *rose*	11.00	11.00
b. Tête bêche pair	15.00	
Nos. 4-9 (5)	5.76	5.76

Perf. 12

10 A2 10c dark gray	.30	.30
11 A3 20c red brown	.35	.35
12 A4 50c green	.32	.32
13 A4 50c dull blue	2.00	2.00
14 A5 1p red	.32	.32
a. 1p claret	3.00	3.00
16 A6 5p black, *rose*	11.00	11.00
a. 5p black, *buff*	9.50	9.50
17 A7 10p black, *buff*	1.10	1.10
a. 10p black, *rose*	11.00	11.00
b. Tête bêche pair	12.00	12.00
Nos. 10-17 (7)	15.39	15.39

Statue of Bolívar — A8

1904

18 A8 10c orange	.24	.24
a. Imperf., pair	3.50	3.50

CAUCA

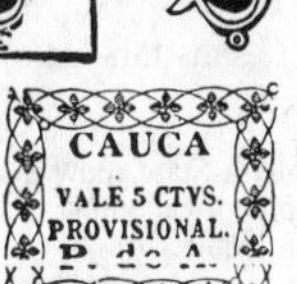

Stamps of these designs were issued by a provincial post between 1879 (?) and 1890.

Stamps of this design are believed to be of private origin and without official sanction.

Items inscribed "No hay estampillas" (No stamps available) and others inscribed "Manuel E. Jiménez" are considered by specialists to be receipt labels, not postage stamps.

CUNDINAMARCA

ˌkün–di–nə–ˈmär–kə

Originally a State, now a Department of the Republic of Colombia.
(See Antioquia.)

Coat of Arms
A1 A2

1870 Unwmk. Litho. *Imperf.*

1 A1 5c blue	4.75	4.75
2 A2 10c red	15.00	15.00

The counterfeits, or reprints, show traces of the cuts made to deface the dies.

A3

A4

A5

A6

1877-82

3 A3 10c red ('82)	3.25	3.25
a. Laid paper ('77)	4.25	4.25
4 A4 20c green ('82)	7.00	7.00
a. Laid paper ('77)	11.00	11.00
7 A5 50c purple ('82)	7.75	7.75
8 A6 1p brown ('82)	11.00	11.00
Nos. 3-8 (4)	29.00	29.00

A7

1884

10 A7 5c blue	.75	.75
11 A7 5c blue (redrawn)	.75	.75
a. Tête bêche pair	75.00	75.00

The redrawn stamp has no period after "COLOMBIA."

A8

CUNDINAMARCA.
CINCUENTA CVOS.
A9

1 CUNDINAMARCA 1
EE. UU. de Colombia
PROVISIONAL
CORREOS
1883
1 CUNDINAMARCA 1
A10

E. U. DE COLOMBIA
E.S. DE CUNDINAMARCA
SELLO PROVISORIO
CORREOS DEL ESTADO
VALE DOS REALES
A11

1883 **Typeset**

13 A8 10c blk, *yellow*	12.50	12.50
14 A9 50c blk, *rose*	12.50	12.50
15 A10 1p blk, *brown*	35.00	35.00
16 A11 2r blk, *green*	*2,000.*	

Typeset varieties exist: 4 of the 10c, 2 each of 50c and 1p.

Some experts doubt that No. 16 was issued. The variety without signature and watermarked "flowers" is believed to be a proof. Forgeries exist.

A12

1886 **Litho.**

17 A12 5c blue	.75	.75
18 A12 10c red	4.50	4.50
19 A12 10c red, *lilac*	2.50	2.50
20 A12 20c green	3.75	3.75
a. 20c yellow green	4.50	4.50
21 A12 50c purple	5.00	5.00
22 A12 1p orange brown	5.25	5.25
Nos. 17-22 (6)	21.75	21.75

Nos. 17 to 22 have been reprinted. The colors are aniline and differ from those of the original stamps. The impression is coarse and blurred.

A13

A14

A15

A16

A17

A18

A19

A20

A21

1904 *Perf. 10½, 12*

23	A13	1c orange	.25	.25
24	A14	2c gray blue	.25	.25
25	A15	3c rose	.35	.35
26	A15	5c olive grn	.35	.35
27	A16	10c pale brn	.35	.35
28	A17	15c pink	.35	.35
29	A18	20c blue, *grn*	.35	.35
30	A18	20c blue	.60	.60
31	A19	40c blue	.60	.60
32	A19	40c blue, *buff*	17.50	17.50
33	A20	50c red vio	.60	.60
34	A21	1p gray grn	.45	.45
		Nos. 23-34 (12)	22.00	22.00

Imperf

23a	A13	1c orange	.75	.75
24a	A14	2c blue	.75	.75
b.		2c slate	6.00	6.00
25a	A15	3c rose	.90	.90
26a	A15	5c olive green	1.50	1.50
27a	A16	10c pale brown	2.00	2.00
28a	A17	15c pink	.50	.50
29a	A18	20c blue, *green*	2.00	2.00
30a	A18	20c blue	2.00	2.00
31a	A19	40c blue	.70	.70
32a	A19	40c blue, *buff*	17.50	17.50
33a	A20	50c red violet	.70	.70
34a	A21	1p gray green	.70	.70
		Nos. 23a-34a (12)	30.00	30.00

REGISTRATION STAMPS

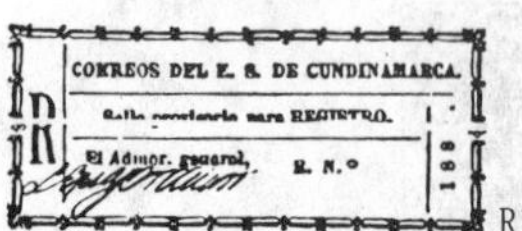

R1

1883 **Unwmk.** *Imperf.*

F1	R1	black, *orange*	15.00	16.00

R2

1904 *Perf. 12*

F2	R2	10c bister	.80	.80
a.		Imperf.	3.50	3.50

Magdalena

Items inscribed "No hay estampillas" (No stamps available) are considered by specialists to be not postage stamps but receipt labels.

Panama

Issues of Panama as a state and later Department of Colombia are listed with the Republic of Panama issues (Nos. 1-30).

SANTANDER

ˌsän-ˌtän-ˈde(ə)r

Originally a State, now a Department of the Republic of Colombia.
(See Antioquia.)

Coat of Arms
A1 A2

1884 **Unwmk.** **Litho.** *Imperf.*

1	A1	1c blue	.30	.30
a.		1c gray blue	.50	.50
2	A2	5c red	.50	.50
3	A2	10c bluish purple	1.75	1.75
a.		Tête bêche pair		
		Nos. 1-3 (3)	2.55	2.55

No. 2 exists unofficially perforated 14.

A3

A4

1886 *Imperf.*

4	A3	1c blue	.90	.90
5	A3	5c red	.30	.30
6	A3	10c red violet	.50	.50
a.		10c deep violet	.50	.50
b.		Inscribed "CINCO CENTAVOS"	25.00	25.00
		Nos. 4-6 (3)	1.70	1.70

The numerals in the upper corners are omitted on No. 5, while on No. 6 there are no numerals in the side panels. No. 6 exists unofficially perforated 12.

1887

7	A4	1c blue	.25	.25
a.		1c ultramarine	1.65	1.65
8	A4	5c red	1.65	1.65
9	A4	10c violet	5.00	5.00
		Nos. 7-9 (3)	6.90	6.90

A5

A6

A7

1889 *Perf. 11½ and 13½*

10	A5	1c blue	.30	.30
11	A6	5c red	1.25	1.25
12	A7	10c purple	.45	.45
a.		Imperf., pair	16.00	
		Nos. 10-12 (3)	2.00	2.00

A8

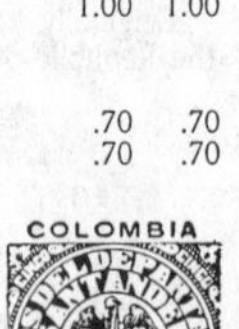
A9

1892 *Perf. 13½*

13	A8	5c red, *rose buff*	1.00	1.00

1895-96

14	A9	5c brown	.70	.70
15	A9	5c yel grn ('96)	.70	.70

A10

A11

A12

1899 *Perf. 10*

16	A10	1c black, *green*	.35	.35
17	A11	5c black, *pink*	.35	.35

Perf. 13½

18	A12	10c blue	.70	.70
a.		Perf. 12	1.00	1.00
		Nos. 16-18 (3)	1.40	1.40

A13

1903 *Imperf.*

19	A13	50c red	.55	.55
a.		50c rose	.55	.55
b.		"SANTENDER"	2.50	2.50
c.		"Corrcos"	2.50	2.50
d.		"Corceos"	2.50	2.50
e.		Tête bêche pair	4.75	4.75
f.		Pair, one without overprint	2.75	2.75

The overprint "Correos de Departmento Bucaramanga" on the 50c red revenue stamp has been proved to be a cancellation.

A14

A15

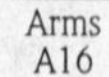
Arms
A16

Locomotive
A17

A18

A19

A20

1904 *Imperf.*

22	A14	5c dark green	.25	.25
a.		5c yellow green	.40	.40
24	A15	10c rose	.15	.15
25	A16	20c brown violet	.15	.15
26	A17	50c yellow	.15	.15
27	A18	1p black	.15	.15
28	A19	5p dark blue	.35	.35
29	A20	10p carmine	.40	.40
		Nos. 22-29 (7)	1.60	1.60

1905

30	A14	5c pale blue	.40	.40
31	A15	10c red brown	.40	.40
32	A16	20c yellow green	.40	.40
33	A17	50c red violet	.60	.60
34	A18	1p dark blue	.60	.60
35	A19	5p pink	.60	.60
36	A20	10p red	1.65	1.65
		Nos. 30-36 (7)	4.65	4.65

A21

1907 *Imperf.*

37	A21	½c on 50c rose	.55	.55

City of Cucuta

Stamps of these and similar designs on white and yellow paper, with and without surcharges of ½c, 1c or 2c, are believed to have been produced without government authorization.

TOLIMA

tə-lē-mə

Originally a State, now a Department of the Republic of Colombia.
(See Antioquia.)

A1

1870 **Unwmk.** **Typeset** *Imperf.*

White Wove Paper

1	A1	5c black	60.00	30.00
2	A1	10c black	60.00	30.00

Printed from two settings. Setting I, ten types of 5c. Setting II, six types of 5c and four types of 10c.

Blue Laid Batonné Paper

3	A1	5c black	*950.00*	

Buff Laid Batonné Paper

4	A1	5c black	140.00	80.00

Blue Wove Paper

5	A1	5c black	70.00	45.00

Blue Vertically Laid Paper

6	A1	5c black	110.00	70.00
a.		Paper with ruled blue vertical lines		

Blue Horizontally Laid Paper

7	A1	5c black	110.00	70.00

Blue Quadrille Paper

8	A1	5c black	110.00	90.00

Ten varieties each of Nos. 3-5 and 7; 20 varieties each of Nos. 6 and 8.

Official imitations were made in 1886 from new settings of the type. There are only 2 varieties of each value. They are printed on blue and white paper, wove, batonné, laid, etc.

A2

A3

A4

A5

Yellowish White Wove Paper

1871 Litho. *Imperf.*

9	A2	5c deep brown	2.25	2.25
a.		5c red brown	2.25	2.25
b.		Value reads "CINGO"	37.50	37.50
10	A3	10c blue	6.00	6.00
11	A4	50c green	7.75	7.75
12	A5	1p carmine	12.00	12.00
		Nos. 9-12 (4)	28.00	28.00

The 5p stamps, type A2, are bogus varieties made from an altered die of the 5c.

The 10c, 50c and 1 peso stamps have been reprinted on bluish white wove paper. They are from new plates and most copies show traces of fine lines with which the dies had been defaced. Reprints of the 5c have a large cross at the top. The 10c on laid batonné paper is known only as a reprint.

A6

A7

A8

A9

1879

Grayish or White Wove Paper

14	A6	5c yellow brown	.45	.45
a.		5c purple brown	.45	.45
15	A7	10c blue	.50	.50
16	A8	50c green, *bluish*	.50	.50
a.		White paper	1.65	1.65
17	A9	1p vermilion	2.25	2.25
a.		1p carmine rose	9.00	9.00
		Nos. 14-17 (4)	3.70	3.70

A10

Coat of Arms — A12

1883 *Imperf.*

18	A6	5c orange	.45	.45
19	A7	10c vermilion	.90	.90
20	A10	20c violet	1.40	1.40
		Nos. 18-20 (3)	2.75	2.75

1884 *Imperf.*

23	A12	1c gray	.15	.15
24	A12	2c rose lilac	.15	.15
a.		2c slate	.15	.15
25	A12	2½c dull orange	.15	.15
26	A12	5c brown	.15	.15
27	A12	10c blue	.35	.35
a.		10c slate	.25	.25
28	A12	20c lemon	.35	.35
a.		Laid paper	5.00	5.00
29	A12	25c black	.30	.30
30	A12	50c green	.30	.30
31	A12	1p vermilion	.40	.40
32	A12	2p violet	.60	.60
a.		Value omitted	27.50	27.50
33	A12	5p yellow	.40	.40
34	A12	10p lilac rose	1.10	1.10
a.		Laid paper	30.00	30.00
b.		10p gray	*165.00*	
		Nos. 23-34 (12)	4.40	4.40

A13

A14

Condor with Long Wings Touching Flagstaffs

A15 A16

1886 Litho. *Perf. 10½, 11*

White Paper

36	A13	5c brown	1.25	1.25
a.		5c yellow brown	1.25	1.25
b.		Imperf., pair	16.00	
37	A14	10c blue	3.50	3.50
a.		Imperf., pair	16.00	
38	A15	50c green	3.00	3.00
a.		Imperf., pair	16.00	
39	A16	1p vermilion	2.50	2.50
a.		Imperf., pair	24.00	
		Nos. 36-39 (4)	10.25	10.25

No. 38 has been reprinted in pale gray green, perforated 10½, and No. 39 in bright vermilion, perforated 11½. The impressions show many signs of wear.

Lilac Tinted Paper

36c	A13	5c orange brown	12.00	12.00
37b	A14	10c blue	12.00	12.00
38b	A15	50c green	9.00	9.00
39b	A16	1p vermilion	8.00	8.00
		Nos. 36c-39b (4)	41.00	41.00

Items similar to A15 and A16 but with condor with long wings and upper flagstaffs omitted are forgeries.

A17

A18

Condor with Short Wings

A19 A20

1886 White Paper *Perf. 12*

44	A19	1c gray	6.25	6.25
45	A17	2c rose lilac	6.50	6.50
46	A18	2½c dull org	19.00	19.00
47	A19	5c brown	8.50	8.00
48	A20	10c blue	8.00	8.00
49	A20	20c lemon	6.50	6.50
a.		Tête bêche pair	225.00	225.00
50	A20	25c black	6.25	6.25
51	A20	50c green	3.50	3.00
52	A20	1p vermilion	5.00	4.25
53	A20	2p violet	7.25	7.25
b.		Tête bêche pair	175.00	175.00
54	A20	5p orange	13.00	13.00
55	A20	10p lilac rose	7.25	7.25
		Nos. 44-55 (12)	97.00	95.25

Imperf., Pairs

44a	A19	1c	16.00
47a	A19	5c	27.50
48a	A20	10c	27.50
52a	A20	1p	20.00
53a	A20	2p	25.00
54a	A20	5p	32.50
55a	A20	10p	16.00

A23

1888 *Perf. 10½*

62	A23	5c red	.15	.15
63	A23	10c green	.30	.30
64	A23	50c blue	.80	.80
65	A23	1p red brown	1.75	1.75
		Nos. 62-65 (4)	3.00	3.00

For overprint see Colombia No. L14.

1895 *Perf. 12, 13½*

66	A23	1c blue, *rose*	.24	.24
67	A23	2c grn, *lt grn*	.24	.24
68	A23	5c red	.15	.15
69	A23	10c green	.50	.50
70	A23	20c blue, *yellow*	.30	.30
71	A23	1p brown	2.00	2.00
		Nos. 66-71 (6)	3.43	3.43

Imperf., Pairs

62a	A23	5c	2.75	
63a	A23	10c	3.25	
64a	A23	50c	4.75	4.75
65a	A23	1p	7.25	
66a	A23	1c	7.25	
67a	A23	2c	7.25	
70a	A23	20c	8.00	

"No Hay Estampillas"

Items inscribed "No hay estampillas" (No stamps available) are considered by specialists to be not postage stamps but receipt labels.

"Honda Issue"

This item seems to be of private origin.

Regular Issue

A24

A25

A26

A27

A28

A29

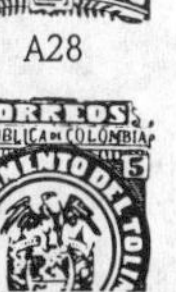

A30

A31

Sewing Machine or Regular Perf. 12

1903-04 Litho.

79	A24	4c black, *green*	.25	.25
80	A25	10c dull blue	.25	.25
81	A26	20c orange	.50	.50
82	A27	50c black, *rose*	.25	.25
a.		50c black, *buff*	.20	.18
84	A28	1p brown	.20	.18
85	A29	2p gray	.20	.18
86	A30	5p red	.20	.18
a.		Tête bêche pair	5.00	5.00
87	A31	10p black, *blue*	.25	.25
a.		10p black, *light green*	.25	.25
b.		10p black, *grn,* glazed	3.50	3.50
		Nos. 79-87 (8)	2.10	2.04

Imperf

79a	A24	4c black, *green*	.25	.25
80a	A25	10c dull blue	.20	.20
81a	A26	20c orange	1.10	1.10
82b	A27	50c black, *rose*	1.50	1.50
c.		50c black, *buff*	1.50	1.50
84a	A28	1p brown	.20	.20
85a	A29	2p gray	.25	.25
86b	A30	5p red	.25	.25
c.		Tête bêche pair	5.00	5.00
87c	A31	10p black, *blue*	2.25	2.25
d.		Tête bêche pair		
e.		10p black, *light green*	3.50	3.50
f.		10p black, *green,* glazed	18.00	18.00
		Nos. 79a-87c (8)	6.00	6.00

COMORO ISLANDS

'kä–mə–,rō 'ī–ləndz

LOCATION — In Mozambique Channel between Madagascar and Mozambique

GOVT. — Republic

AREA — 838 sq. mi.

POP. — 385,000 (est. 1983)

CAPITAL — Moroni

The Comoro Archipelago consists of the islands of Mayotte, Anjouan, Grand Comoro (Grande Comore) and Moheli, which issued their own stamps as French protectorates or colonies from 1887-1914. The archipelago was attached to Madagascar from 1914 to 1946, when it became a separate French territory. In July 1975, Anjouan, Grand Comoro and Moheli united to declare independence as the State of Comoro. Mayotte remained French.

100 Centimes = 1 Franc

Catalogue values for all unused stamps in this country are for Never Hinged items.

Anjouan Bay — A2

Comoro Woman Grinding Grain — A3

Moroni Mosque on Grand Comoro — A4

1950 Unwmk. Engr. *Perf. 13*

30	A2	10c blue	.15	.15
31	A2	50c green	.15	.15
32	A2	1fr dk ol brn	.15	.15
33	A3	2fr brt grn	.20	.20
34	A3	5fr purple	.20	.20
35	A3	6fr vio brn	.28	.28
36	A4	7fr red	.28	.28
37	A4	10fr dk grn	.35	.35
38	A4	11fr dp ultra	.42	.42
		Nos. 30-38 (9)	2.18	2.18

Imperforates

Most Comoro Islands stamps exist imperforate in issued and trial colors, and also in small presentation sheets in issued colors.

Military Medal Issue.

Common Design Type

1952 Engraved and Typographed

39	CD101	15fr multi	21.00	21.00

Mosque of Ouani, Anjouan — A5

Coelacanth A6

1952-54 **Engr.**
40 A5 15fr dark brown .45 .45
41 A5 20fr red brown .60 .60
42 A6 40fr aqua & indigo ('54) 8.00 6.25
Nos. 40-42 (3) 9.05 7.30

FIDES Issue
Common Design Type

1956 **Unwmk.** ***Perf. 13x12½***
43 CD103 9fr dp vio .50 .40

Human Rights Issue
Common Design Type

1958 **Engr.** ***Perf. 13***
44 CD105 20fr ol grn & dk bl 3.00 3.00

Flower Issue
Common Design Type

1959 **Photo.** ***Perf. 12½x12***
45 CD104 10fr Colvillea 1.50 1.00

View of Dzaoudzi and Radio Symbol — A8

Comoro radio station: 25fr, Radio tower and radio waves over Islands.

1960, Dec. 23 **Engr.** ***Perf. 13***
46 A8 20fr maroon, vio bl & grn .45 .40
47 A8 25fr ultra, brn & grn .60 .60

Harpa Conoidalis — A9

Sea Shells: 50c, Cypraecassis rufa. 2fr, Murex ramosus. 5fr, Turbo marmoratus. 20fr, Pterocera scorpio. 25fr, Charonia tritonis.

1962, Jan. 13 **Photo.**
Shells in Natural Colors
48 A9 50c lilac & brn .20 .20
49 A9 1fr yel & red .20 .20
50 A9 2fr pale grn & pink .25 .25
51 A9 5fr yel & grn .55 .55
52 A9 20fr salmon & brn 1.25 1.25
53 A9 25fr bister & pink 1.60 1.60
Nos. 48-53,C5-C6 (8) 14.05 13.55

Wheat Emblem and Globe — A10

1963, Mar. 21 **Engr.** ***Perf. 13***
54 A10 20fr choc & dk grn 1.50 1.40

FAO "Freedom from Hunger" campaign.

Red Cross Centenary Issue
Common Design Type

1963, Sept. 2 **Unwmk.** ***Perf. 13***
55 CD113 50fr emer, gray & car 2.50 2.25

Human Rights Issue
Common Design Type

1963, Dec. 10 **Engr.**
56 CD117 15fr dk red & yel grn 2.25 2.00

Tobacco Pouch — A13

Grand Comoro Canoe — A14

Designs: 4fr, Censer. 10fr, Carved lamp.

1963, Dec. 27 ***Perf. 13***
Size: 22x36mm
57 A13 3fr multi .15 .15
58 A13 4fr org, dp cl & sl grn .16 .16
59 A13 10fr org brn, dk red brn & grn .35 .35
Nos. 57-59,C8-C9 (5) 3.66 2.51

Common Design Types pictured in section at front of book.

Philatec Issue
Common Design Type

1964, Mar. 31
60 CD118 50fr dk bl, red & grn 1.10 1.10

1964, Aug. 7 **Photo.** ***Perf. 13x12½***

Design: 30fr, Boutre felucca.

Size: 22x37mm
61 A14 15fr multi .40 .40
62 A14 30fr lt grn & multi .65 .65

See Nos. C10-C11.

Spiny Lobster — A15

Designs: 12fr, Hammerhead shark, horiz. 20fr, Turtle, horiz. 25fr, Merou fish.

1965, Dec. 20 **Engr.** ***Perf. 13***
63 A15 1fr grn, lil & ocher .15 .15
64 A15 12fr org red, slate & gray .35 .25
65 A15 20fr org, red & bl grn .40 .35
66 A15 25fr bl grn, dk brn & red .45 .40
Nos. 63-66 (4) 1.35 1.15

Hotel Itsandra, Moroni — A16

Design: 15fr, Lake Salé, Grand Comoro.

1966, Dec. 19 **Photo.** ***Perf. 12½x13***
67 A16 15fr multi .25 .20
68 A16 25fr multi .35 .20

See Nos. C18-C19.

Comoro Sunbird A17

Birds: 10fr, Malachite kingfisher. 15fr, Rothschild's fody. 30fr, Cuckoo-roller.

1967, June 20 **Photo.** ***Perf. 12½x13***
Size: 36x23mm
69 A17 2fr ocher & multi .40 .40
70 A17 10fr lil & multi .55 .55
71 A17 15fr yel grn & multi .65 .65
72 A17 30fr pink & multi 1.10 1.10
Nos. 69-72,C20-C21 (6) 5.00 3.62

For surcharge see No. 133.

WHO Anniversary Issue
Common Design Type

1968, May 4 **Engr.** ***Perf. 13***
73 CD126 40fr grn, vio & dp car .55 .45

Surgeonfish A19

Design: 25fr, Imperial angelfish.

1968, Aug. 1 **Engr.** ***Perf. 13***
Size: 36x22mm
74 A19 20fr vio bl, yel & red brn .25 .25
75 A19 25fr Prus bl, dk bl & org .35 .35

See Nos. C23-C24. For surcharge and overprint see Nos. C52, C74.

Human Rights Year Issue
Common Design Type

1968, Aug. 10 **Engr.** ***Perf. 13***
76 CD127 60fr brn, grn & org .60 .60

Msoila Prayer Rug and Praying Man — A20

Designs: Each stamp shows a different prayer position.

1969, Feb. 27 **Engr.** ***Perf. 13***
77 A20 20fr bl grn, rose red & pur .20 .16
78 A20 30fr pur, rose red & bl grn .25 .22
79 A20 45fr rose red, pur & bl grn .40 .35
Nos. 77-79 (3) .85 .73

Vanilla Flower A21

Design: 15fr, Flower of ylang-ylang tree. 25fr, Poinsettia (country name in upper right corner).

1969-70 **Photo.** ***Perf. 12½x13***
Size: 36x23mm
80 A21 10fr multi .16 .15
81 A21 15fr multi .22 .18
82 A21 25fr multi ('70) .35 .22
Nos. 80-82,C26-C28 (6) 4.13 2.95

Issue dates: #80-81, Mar. 20. #82, Mar. 5.

ILO Issue
Common Design Type

1969, Nov. 24 **Engr.** ***Perf. 13***
83 CD131 5fr org, emer & gray .16 .15

UPU Headquarters Issue
Common Design Type

1970, May 20 **Engr.** ***Perf. 13***
84 CD133 65fr pur, bl grn & red brn .80 .55

Chiromani Costume, Anjouan — A22

Friday Mosque — A23

Design: 25fr, Bouiboui costume, Grand Comoro.

1970, Oct. 30 **Photo.** ***Perf. 12½x13***
85 A22 20fr grn, yel & red .25 .22
86 A22 25fr brn, yel & dk bl .35 .25

1970, Dec. 18 **Engr.** ***Perf. 13***
87 A23 5fr rose car, grn & grnsh bl .16 .15
88 A23 10fr dp lil, grn & vio .22 .16
89 A23 40fr cop red, grn & dp brn .38 .30
Nos. 87-89 (3) .76 .61

Great White Egret — A24

Pyrostegia Venusta — A25

Birds: 10fr, Comoro pigeon. 15fr, Green-backed heron. 25fr, Comoro blue pigeon. 35fr, Humbolt's flycatcher. 40fr, Allen's gallinule.

1971, Mar. 12 **Photo.** ***Perf. 12½x13***
90 A24 5fr multi .15 .15
91 A24 10fr yel & multi .18 .15
92 A24 15fr bl & multi .20 .15
93 A24 25fr org & multi .30 .22
94 A24 35fr yel grn & multi .55 .40
95 A24 40fr gray & multi .65 .55
Nos. 90-95 (6) 2.03 1.62

For overprint see No. 145.

1971, July 19 **Photo.** ***Perf. 13***

Flowers: 3fr, Dogbane, horiz. 20fr, Frangipani.

Size: 22x36mm, 36x22mm
96 A25 1fr ver & grn .15 .15
97 A25 3fr yel, grn & red .16 .15
98 A25 20fr ver & grn .45 .30
Nos. 96-98,C37-C38 (5) 2.11 1.35

For surcharges see Nos. 131-132, C75, C83.

Lithograph Cone — A26

Sea Shells: 10fr, Pacific lettered cone. 20fr, Aulicus cone. 35fr, Polita nerita. 60fr, Snake-head cowrie.

1971, Oct. 4
99 A26 5fr lt ultra & multi .15 .15
100 A26 10fr multi .16 .15
101 A26 20fr vio & multi .22 .20
102 A26 35fr lt bl & multi .40 .30
103 A26 60fr lt vio & multi .55 .55
Nos. 99-103 (5) 1.48 1.35

For surcharge see No. 150.

De Gaulle Issue
Common Design Type

Designs: 20fr, Gen. de Gaulle, 1940. 35fr, Pres. de Gaulle, 1970.

1971, Nov. 9 **Engr.** ***Perf. 13***
104 CD134 20fr dk car & blk .35 .16
105 CD134 35fr dk car & blk .45 .38

Louis Pasteur, Slides, Microscope A27

1972, Aug. 2
106 A27 65fr indigo, org, & ol brn .65 .50

Sesquicentennial of the birth of Louis Pasteur (1822-1895), chemist.

Type of Air Post Issue 1971

Designs: 10fr, View of Goulaivoini. 20fr, Bay, Mitsamiouli. 35fr, Gate and fountain, Foumbouni. 50fr, View of Moroni.

1973, June 28 Photo. *Perf. 13*

107 AP10 10fr bl & multi	.16	.15
108 AP10 20fr grn & multi	.25	.22
109 AP10 35fr bl & multi	.45	.42
110 AP10 50fr bl & multi	.55	.50
Nos. 107-110,C53 (5)	2.66	2.09

For overprint see No. 143.

Bank of Madagascar and Comoros A28

Buildings in Moroni: 15fr, Post and Telecommunications Administration. 20fr, Prefecture.

1973, July 10 Photo. *Perf. 13x12½*

111 A28 5fr multi	.15	.15
112 A28 15fr multi	.15	.15
113 A28 20fr multi	.25	.22
Nos. 111-113 (3)	.55	.52

For surcharge see No. 134.

Salimata Hamissi Mosque A29

Design: 20fr, Zaouiyat Chaduli Mosque, vert.

Perf. 12½x13, 13x12½

1973, Oct. 20 Photo.

114 A29 20fr multi	.22	.20
115 A29 35fr multi	.42	.40

For surcharges see Nos. 135, 138.

Cheikh Mausoleum A30

Design: 50fr, Mausoleum of President Said Mohamed Cheikh (different view).

1974, Mar. 16 Engr. *Perf. 13*

116 A30 35fr grn, ol brn & blk	.38	.30
117 A30 50fr grn, ol brn & blk	.50	.42

For surcharge see No. 140.

Koran Stand, Anjouan A31

Designs: 15fr, Carved combs, vert. 20fr, 3-legged table, vert. 75fr, Sugar press.

1974, May 10 Photo. *Perf. 12½x13*

118 A31 15fr emer & multi	.16	.15
119 A31 20fr grn & multi	.22	.16
120 A31 35fr multi	.35	.25
121 A31 75fr multi	.60	.55
Nos. 118-121 (4)	1.33	1.11

For overprints and surcharge see #137, 141, 149.

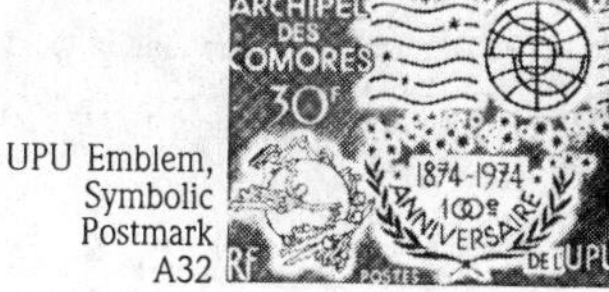

UPU Emblem, Symbolic Postmark A32

1974, Oct. 9 Engr. *Perf. 13x12½*

122 A32 30fr multi	.25	.22

Centenary of Universal Postal Union.
For surcharge see No. 155.

Bracelet A33

1975, Feb. 28 Engr. *Perf. 13*

123 A33 20fr shown	.22	.20
124 A33 35fr Diadem	.38	.35
125 A33 120fr Saber	1.10	1.00
126 A33 135fr Dagger	1.20	1.10
Nos. 123-126 (4)	2.90	2.65

For surcharges see Nos. 136, 142, 151, 154.

Mohani Village, Moheli — A34

Designs: 50fr, Djoezi Village, Moheli. 55fr, Chirazi tombs.

1975, May 26 Photo. *Perf. 13*

127 A34 30fr vio bl & multi	.20	.15
128 A34 50fr Prus bl & multi	.38	.25
129 A34 55fr grn & multi	.40	.42
Nos. 127-129 (3)	.98	.82

For overprints and surcharge see #139, 146, 148.

Skin Diver Photographing Coelacanth — A35

1975, June 27 Engr. *Perf. 13*

130 A35 50fr multi	.55	.40

1975 coelacanth expedition.
For overprint see No. 147.

STATE OF COMORO

In 1978 the islands' name became the Federal and Islamic Republic of the Comoros.

Issues of 1971-75 Surcharged and Overprinted with Bars and: "ETAT COMORIEN" in Black, Silver or Red.

Tambourine Player — A36

Design: No. 153, Women dancers and tambourine players.

Printing & Perforations as Before, Photogravure (A36)

1975 *Perf. 13 (A36)*

131 A25	5fr on 1fr	.15	.15
132 A25	5fr on 3fr	.15	.15
133 A17	10fr on 2fr	.30	.30
134 A28	15fr on 20fr (R)	.15	.15
135 A29	15fr on 20fr (S)	.15	.15
136 A33	15fr on 20fr	.15	.15
137 A31	20fr	.18	.15
138 A29	25fr on 35fr	.22	.20
139 A34	30fr	.25	.22
140 A30	30fr on 35fr	.25	.22
141 A31	30fr on 35fr	.25	.22
142 A33	30fr on 35fr	.25	.22
143 AP10	35fr	.30	.25
144 SP2	35fr on 35fr + 10fr	.30	.25
145 A24	40fr	.38	.30
146 A34	50fr	.45	.40
147 A35	50fr	.45	.40
148 A34	50fr on 55fr (S)	.45	.40
149 A31	75fr	.75	.60
150 A26	75fr on 60fr (S)	.75	.60
151 A33	100fr on 120fr	.90	.80
152 A36	100fr bl & multi	.90	.80
153 A36	100fr on 150fr (S)	.90	.80
154 A33	200fr on 135fr	1.75	1.50
155 A32	500fr on 30fr	4.50	4.00
	Nos. 131-155 (25)	15.23	13.38

Nos. 152-153 exist without overprint or surcharge. No. 155 exists with red surcharge.

Litho. & Embossed "Gold Foil" Stamps

These stamps generally are of a different design format than the rest of the issue. Since there is a commemorative inscription tying them to the issue a separate illustration is not being shown.

Apollo-Soyuz — A37

Spacecraft and astronauts: 10fr, Soyuz lift-off, Alexei A. Leonov and Valeri N. Kubasov, vert. 30fr, Apollo lift-off, Thomas P. Stafford, Vance D. Brand, Donald K. Slayton, vert. 50fr, Meeting in space, vert. 100fr, Chairman Brezhnev, President Ford talking with astronauts and cosmonauts. 200fr, Spacecraft preparing to dock. 400f, Return to Earth. 500fr, Spacecraft, mission emblems. 1500fr, Apollo-Soyuz crew. No. 164, Preparing to dock, diff.

1975, Dec. 15 Litho. *Perf. 13½*

156 A37	10fr multicolored
157 A37	30fr multicolored
158 A37	50fr multicolored
159 A37	100fr multicolored
160 A37	200fr multicolored
161 A37	400fr multicolored

Litho. & Embossed

Size: 45x45mm

162 A37 1500fr gold & multi

Souvenir Sheets

Litho.

163 A37 500fr multicolored

Litho. & Embossed

164 A37 1500fr gold & multi

Nos. 159-164 are airmail. No. 163 contains one 64x44mm stamp. No. 164 contains one 45x45mm stamp.

For overprints see Nos. 477-478.

A38

American Revolution, Bicent. — A39

Designs: 15fr, Lewis and Clark, Blackfoot Indian. 25fr, John C. Fremont, Kit Carson, Indian dancer. 35fr, Daniel Boone, Buffalo Bill Cody, wagon train. 40fr, Richard E. Egan, Johnny Frey, Pony Express. 75fr, Henry Wells, William G. Fargo, stagecoach. 400fr, Frontiersman, Indian. 500fr, Leland Stanford, Thomas C. Dunant, transcontinental railroad. 1000fr, George Washington, winter at Valley Forge. 1500fr, John Paul Jones, ship.

1976, Jan. 15 Litho.

165 A38	15fr multicolored
166 A38	25fr multicolored
167 A38	35fr multicolored
168 A38	40fr multicolored
169 A38	75fr multicolored
170 A38	500fr multicolored

Litho. & Embossed

171 A39 1000fr gold & multi

Souvenir Sheets

Litho.

172 A38 400fr multicolored

Litho. & Embossed

173 A39 1500fr gold & multi

Nos. 170-173 are airmail. See Nos. 230, 232 and note after No. 479.

1976 Winter Olympics, Innsbruck — A40

1976, Mar. 30 Litho.

174 A40	5fr Women's figure skating
175 A40	30fr Slalom skiing
176 A40	35fr Speed skating
177 A40	50fr Downhill skiing
178 A40	200fr Ski jumping
179 A40	400fr Cross country skiing

Litho. & Embossed

Size: 56x35mm

180 A40 1000fr Downhill skier, hockey

Souvenir Sheets

Litho.

181 A40 500fr Hockey

Litho. & Embossed

182 A40 1000fr Olympic Rings

Nos. 178-182 are airmail. Nos. 181-182 contain one 58x35mm stamp. For overprint see No. 471.

1976 Summer Olympics, Montreal — A41

1976, Mar. 30 Litho.

183 A41	20fr Runner, Athens, 1896
184 A41	25fr Sprints
185 A41	40fr High jump, Paris, 1900
186 A41	75fr High jump
187 A41	100fr Women stretching, St. Louis, 1904
188 A41	500fr Uneven parallel bars

Souvenir Sheet

189 A41 400fr Olympic Stadium, Montreal

Nos. 187-189 are airmail.
For overprint see No. 476.

Fairy Tales — A42

1976, June 28

190 A42	15fr Hansel & Gretel
191 A42	30fr Alice in Wonderland
192 A42	35fr Pinocchio
193 A42	40fr Good Little Henry

194 A42 50fr Peter and the Wolf
195 A42 400fr Thousand and One Nights

#195 is airmail. #190-191, 193, 195 are vert.

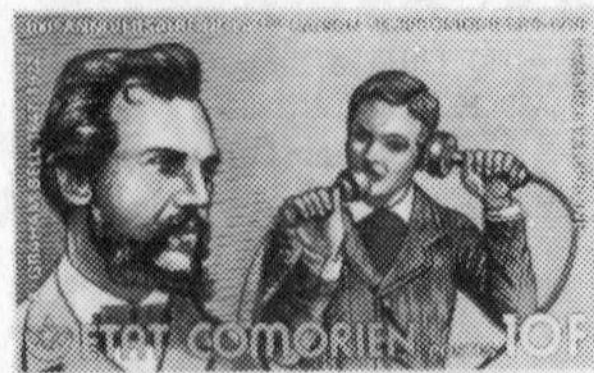
Invention of Telephone, Cent. — A43

Designs: 10fr, A. G. Bell, 1st telephone. 25fr, Charles Bourseul, Paris-London phone service, 1891. 75fr, Philipp Reis, telephone operators. 100fr, Earth to Moon to Earth communications. 200fr, Satellite. 400fr, Ship-to-Satellite communications. No. 201, Satellite in orbit, antenna. No. 203, Global communications.

1976, July 1

196 A43 10fr multicolored
197 A43 25fr multicolored
198 A43 75fr multicolored
199 A43 100fr multicolored
200 A43 200fr multicolored
201 A43 500fr multicolored

Souvenir Sheets

202 A43 400fr multicolored
203 A43 500fr multicolored

Nos. 199-203 are airmail. Nos. 202-203 contain a 73x44mm stamp. For overprint see No. 472.

Comoro Flag, Map and Government Buildings A44

1976, Nov. 18 Litho. *Perf. 13½*

204 A44 30fr multi .16 .15
205 A44 50fr multi .25 .16

1st anniversary of independence.
For overprints and surcharges see Nos. 353-356 and footnote after No. 356.

Viking Probe to Mars — A45

Designs: 5fr, Nicolaus Copernicus, rocket launch. 10fr, Albert Einstein, Carl Sagan, Thomas Young, horiz. 25fr, Viking probe orbiting Mars. 35fr, Discovery of America by Vikings, horiz. 100fr, Flag, Viking landing on Mars. 500fr, Viking emblem, surface of Mars, horiz. 400fr, Viking probe. No. 212, Wagon train, frontiersman, rocket launch. No. 214, Viking on Martian surface, robotic shovel.

1976, Nov. 23

206 A45 5fr multicolored
207 A45 10fr multicolored
208 A45 25fr multicolored
209 A45 35fr multicolored
210 A45 100fr multicolored
211 A45 500fr multicolored

Litho. & Embossed
Size: 57x39mm

212 A45 1500fr gold & multi

Souvenir Sheets
Litho.

213 A45 400fr multicolored

Litho. & Embossed

214 A45 1500fr gold & multi

American Revolution, bicentennial. Nos. 211-214 are airmail. No. 213 contains one 60x42mm stamp.

UN Postal Administration, 25th Anniv. — A46

Designs: 15fr, UN #24, irrigating field. 30fr, UN #43, doctor, nurse. 50fr, UN #162, mother holding child. 75fr, UN #42, communications satellite in orbit. 200fr, UN #32, Concorde, Zeppelin. 400fr, UN #18, cargo plane. 500fr, People passing letters around globe.

1976, Nov. 25 Litho.

215 A46 15fr multicolored
216 A46 30fr multicolored
217 A46 50fr multicolored
218 A46 75fr multicolored
219 A46 200fr multicolored
220 A46 400fr multicolored

Souvenir Sheet

221 A46 500fr multicolored

Nos. 219-221 are airmail. No. 221 contains one 57x40mm stamp. For overprints see Nos. 282-284, 473.

Comoro Flag, UN Headquarters and Emblem A47

1976, Nov. 25

222 A47 40fr multi .20 .15
223 A47 50fr multi .25 .16

1st anniv. of UN membership.

Type of 1976 and

US Bicentennial — A48

Civil War Battles: 10fr, Fort Sumter, Lincoln. 30fr, Bull Run, Gen. P.G.T. Beauregard, vert. 50fr, Antietam, Gen. Joseph E. Johnston. 100fr, Gettysburg, Gen. Meade. 200fr, Chattanooga, Gen. Sherman, vert. 400fr, Appomattox, Gen. Pickett. 500fr, Surrender at Appomattox, Generals Lee and Grant. 1000fr, Lincoln, battlefield. No. 230, Pres. Kennedy, lunar lander.

1976, Dec. 30 Litho.

224 A48 10fr multicolored
225 A48 30fr multicolored
226 A48 50fr multicolored
227 A48 100fr multicolored
228 A48 200fr multicolored
229 A48 400fr multicolored

Litho. & Embossed
Size: 61x51mm

230 A39 1500fr gold & multi

Souvenir Sheets
Litho.

231 A48 500fr multicolored

Litho. & Embossed

232 A39 1000fr gold & multi

American Revolution bicentennial. Nos. 227-232 are airmail. No. 231 contains one 60x42mm stamp.

Endangered Species — A49

1976, Dec. 30 Litho.

233 A49 15fr Andean condor, vert.
234 A49 20fr Australian tiger cat
235 A49 35fr Leopard, vert.
236 A49 40fr White rhinoceros
237 A49 75fr Nyala, vert.
238 A49 400fr Orangutan

Souvenir Sheet

239 A49 500fr Lemur, vert.

Nos. 238-239 airmail. No. 239 contains one 40x58mm stamp.
See note after No. 479.

Endangered Species A50

1977, Apr. 14

240 A50 10fr Wolf
241 A50 30fr Aye-aye
242 A50 40fr Cephalopus zebra
243 A50 50fr Giant tortoise
244 A50 200fr Ocelot
245 A50 400fr Penguin

Souvenir Sheet

246 A50 500fr Sumatran tiger

Nos. 244-246 airmail. No. 246 contains one 58x40mm stamp.

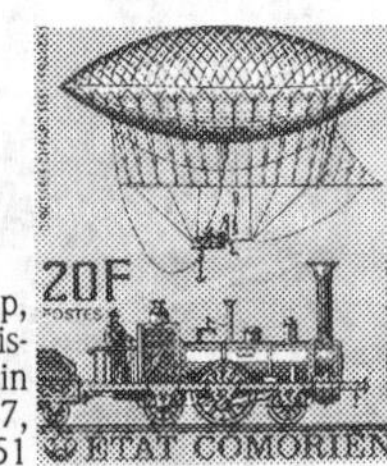
Giffard Airship, 1851 and Paris-St. Germain Train, 1837, France — A51

Airships & Locomotives: 25fr, Santos-Dumont's airship, 1906, Brazilian Tander 120FIN, Brazil. 50fr, Astra, 1914, Trans-Siberian Express, 1905, Russia. 75fr, R.34, 1919, Southern Belle, 1910, Great Britain. 200fr, Navy airship, Pacific Class locomotive, 1930, US. No. 252, Hindenburg, Rheingold Express, 1933, Germany. No. 253, Graf-Zeppelin, 1928, Nord-Express Type 231, 1925, Germany.

1977, Apr. 14

247 A51 20fr multicolored
248 A51 25fr multicolored
249 A51 50fr multicolored
250 A51 75fr multicolored
251 A51 200fr multicolored
252 A51 500fr multicolored

Souvenir Sheet

253 A51 500fr multi, horiz.

Nos. 251-253 are airmail. No. 253 contains one 58x39mm stamp.

Nobel Prize, 75th Anniv. — A52

Nobel Prize winners: 30fr, Medicine. 40fr, Physics. 50fr, Literature. 100fr, Physics. 200fr, Chemistry. 400fr, Peace.

1977, July 7

254 A52 30fr multicolored
255 A52 40fr multicolored
256 A52 50fr multicolored
257 A52 100fr multicolored
258 A52 200fr multicolored
259 A52 400fr multicolored

Souvenir Sheet

260 A52 500fr Nobel medal

Nos. 258-260 are airmail.
See note after No. 479.

Peter Paul Rubens, 400th Birth Anniv. — A53

Portraits: 20fr, Portrait of the Artist's Daughter, Clara. 25fr, Suzanne Fourment. 50fr, Toilet of Venus, (detail). 75fr, Ceres (detail). 200fr, Young Woman with Blonde Braided Hair. No. 266, Helene Fourment in her Wedding Dress. No. 267, Self-portrait.

1977, July 7

261 A53 20fr multicolored
262 A53 25fr multicolored
263 A53 50fr multicolored
264 A53 75fr multicolored
265 A53 200fr multicolored
266 A53 500fr multicolored

Souvenir Sheet

267 A53 500fr multicolored

Nos. 265-267 are airmail.
See note after No. 479.

Fish A54

1977, Nov. 21

268 A54 30fr Swordfish
269 A54 40fr Gaterin
270 A54 50fr Sea scorpion
271 A54 100fr Chaetodon lunula
272 A54 200fr Amphiprion
273 A54 400fr Tetrodon

Souvenir Sheet

274 A54 500fr Coelacanth

Nos. 272-274 airmail. No. 274 contains one 52x47mm stamp.

Space Exploration — A55

1977, Nov. 21

275 A55 30fr Jupiter lander
276 A55 50fr Voyager probe, Uranus, vert.
277 A55 75fr Pioneer probe, Venus
278 A55 100fr Space shuttle, vert.
279 A55 200fr Viking III, Mars
280 A55 400fr Apollo-Soyuz, vert.

Souvenir Sheet

281 A55 500fr Allegory of the Sun

Nos. 279-281 airmail. No. 281 contains one 52x42mm stamp.

No. 219 Overprinted in One Line in Gold, Silver or Red
"Paris-New-York - 22 nov. 1977"

1977, Nov. 22

282 A46 200fr multicolored
283 A46 200fr multicolored (S)
284 A46 200fr multicolored (R)

Birds — A56

1978, Feb. 6

285 A56 15fr Porphyrula alleni
286 A56 20fr Merops supercimosus
287 A56 35fr Alcedo vintsioides johannae
288 A56 40fr Terpsiphone
289 A56 75fr Nectarinia comorensis
290 A56 400fr Egretta alba

Souvenir Sheet

291 A56 500fr Foudia eminentissima, horiz.

Nos. 290-291 are airmail. For overprint and surcharges see Nos. 444-448.

World Cup Soccer Championships, Argentina — A57

Designs: 30fr, Greece, 5th. cent. B.C. 50fr, Brittany, 19th cent. 75fr, London, 14th cent. 100fr, Italy, 18th cent. 200fr, England, 19th cent. 400fr, English Cup match, 1891. 500fr, English Cup final, 1962. No. 298, Player, satellite. No. 300, Players.

1978, Feb. 6

292 A57 30fr multicolored
293 A57 50fr multicolored
294 A57 75fr multicolored
295 A57 100fr multicolored
296 A57 200fr multicolored
297 A57 400fr multicolored

Litho. & Embossed

Size: 60x42mm

298 A57 1000fr gold & multi

Souvenir Sheets

Litho.

299 A57 500fr multicolored

Litho. & Embossed

300 A57 1000fr gold & multi

Nos. 296-300 are airmail. No. 300 contains one 60x42mm stamp. For overprints and surcharges see Nos. 402-408, 449-453.

Composers — A58

1978, Apr. 5 **Litho.**

301 A58 30fr J.S. Bach
302 A58 40fr W.A. Mozart
303 A58 50fr Berlioz
304 A58 100fr Verdi
305 A58 200fr Tchaikovsky
306 A58 400fr George Gershwin

Souvenir Sheet

307 A58 500fr Beethoven

Nos. 305-307 are airmail. For overprints and surcharges see Nos. 454-458.

Albrecht Durer, 450th Death Anniv. A59

Portraits: 20fr, Oswolt Krel. 25fr, Elspeth Tucher. 50fr, Hieronymus Holzschuher. 75fr, Young Woman. 200fr, Emperor Maximilian I. No. 313, Young Woman, (detail). No. 314, Self-portrait.

1978, Apr. 5

308 A59 20fr multicolored
309 A59 25fr multicolored
310 A59 50fr multicolored
311 A59 75fr multicolored
312 A59 200fr multicolored
313 A59 500fr multicolored

Souvenir Sheet

314 A59 500fr multicolored

Nos. 312-314 airmail. No. 314 contains one 42x52mm stamp. See note after No. 479.

Issues Not Valid for Postage

The government changed in May, 1978. A number of sets that had not been issued seem to have been invalid for postage until they were overprinted with the new country name. These are a set of 9 for the 25th anniv. of Elizabeth's coronation, a set of 7 for butterflies, a set of 6 for the 10th Intl. Communications Year, a set of 7 for the history of aviation, a set of 9 for Rubens, and a set of 9 for Durer.

These unoverprinted sets are no scarcer than the previous listed issues. See note after No. 479.

Islamic Republic

Nos. 204-205 Surcharged and Overprinted with 3 Lines and: "République / Fédérale / et Islamique / des Comores"

1978, July 24 **Litho.** ***Perf. 13½***

353 A44 30fr multi
354 A44 40fr on 30fr multi
355 A44 50fr multi
356 A44 100fr on 50fr multi

Nos. 353 and 355 were also overprinted to commemorate Queen Elizabeth II coronation anniversary; Capt. James Cook; World Cup Soccer winner; Albrecht Dürer; First powered flight; Railroad anniversary; Voyager I and II; Intl. Year of the Child; 1980 Olympic Games; World Cup Soccer, Espana '82.

Europe-Africa A66

Various satellites or spacecraft.

1978, Dec. 16

386 A66 10fr multicolored
387 A66 25fr multicolored
388 A66 35fr multicolored
389 A66 50fr multicolored
390 A66 100fr multicolored
391 A66 500fr multicolored

Souvenir Sheet

392 A66 500fr multicolored

Nos. 390-392 airmail. No. 392 contains one 61x40mm stamp.

Sir Rowland Hill — A67

1978, Dec. 16

393 A67 20fr Saxony #1
394 A67 30fr Netherlands #1
395 A67 40fr Great Britain #2
396 A67 75fr US #2
397 A67 200fr France #33
398 A67 400fr Basel #3L1

Litho. & Embossed

Size: 39x58mm

399 A67 1500fr British Guiana #13

Souvenir Sheets

Litho.

400 A67 500fr Moheli, Mayotte, Anjouan, Grand Comoro #1

Litho. & Embossed

401 A67 1500fr Hill, Mauritius #3

Nos. 397-401 are airmail. No. 400 contains one 57x49mm stamp. No. 401 contains one 58x39mm stamp.

Nos. 292-297 Ovptd. with New Country Name in Black on Silver and

1 ARGENTINE
2 HOLLANDE
3 BRESIL

1978, Dec. 16

402 A57 30fr multicolored
403 A57 50fr multicolored
404 A57 75fr multicolored
405 A57 100fr multicolored
406 A57 200fr multicolored
407 A57 400fr multicolored

Nos. 406-407 are airmail. No. 408 is the souvenir sheet.

Exists with Country name in red on silver.

Galileo and Voyager I — A68

Exploration of Solar System: 30fr, Kepler and Voyager II. 40fr, Copernicus and Voyager I, 100fr, Huygens and Voyager II. 200fr, William Herschel and Voyager II. 400fr, Urbain Leverrier and Voyager II. 500fr, Voyagers I and II, symbolic solar system.

1979, Feb. 19 **Litho.** ***Perf. 13***

409 A68	20fr multi		.15	.15
410 A68	30fr multi		.15	.15
411 A68	40fr multi		.22	.15
412 A68	100fr multi		.45	.22
413 A68	200fr multi		.90	.40
414 A68	400fr multi		2.00	.80
	Nos. 409-414 (6)		3.87	1.87

Souvenir Sheet

415 A68 500fr multi 2.75 1.10

Nos. 413-415 airmail.

Philidor, Anderssen, Steinitz and King — A69

Design: 100fr, Chess pieces and board, Venetian chess player. 500fr, Chess Grand Masters Alekhine, Spassky, Fischer, and bishop.

1979, Feb. 19

416 A69	40fr multi	.18	.15
417 A69	100fr multi	.45	.16
418 A69	500fr multi	2.25	.90
	Nos. 416-418 (3)	2.88	1.21

Chess Grand Masters. No. 418 airmail.

Nos. 419-425 are reserved for Summer Olympics set of 6 with one souvenir sheet, released Mar. 28, 1979.

Charaxes Defulvata — A71

Birds: 50fr, Leptosomus discolor. 75fr, Bee eater.

1979, Apr. 10 **Litho.** ***Perf. 12½***

426 A71	30fr multi	.20	.15
427 A71	50fr multi	.35	.15
428 A71	75fr multi	.55	.22
	Nos. 426-428 (3)	1.10	.52

Otto Lilienthal and Glider — A72

History of Aviation: No. 430, Wright brothers and Flyer A. No. 431, Louis Bleriot and Bleriot XI. 100fr, Claude Dornier and Dornier-Wal hydrofoil. 200fr, Charles Lindbergh and Spirit of St. Louis.

1979, May 2 ***Perf. 13***

Black Overprint and Surcharge

429 A72	30fr multi	.20	.20
430 A72	50fr multi	.65	.65
431 A72	50fr on 75fr multi	.70	1.70
432 A72	100fr multi	1.40	1.40
433 A72	200fr multi	1.10	1.10
	Nos. 429-433 (5)	4.05	5.05

No. 433 airmail.

For unoverprinted stamps see note after No. 314.

Papilio Dardanus Cenea A73

Butterflies: 15fr, Papilio dardanus. 30fr, Chrysiridia croesus. 50fr, Precis octavia. 75fr, Bunaea alcinoe.

1979, May 2

Black Overprint and Surcharge

434 A73	5fr on 20fr multi	.15	.15
435 A73	15fr multi	.15	.15
436 A73	30fr multi	.25	.25
437 A73	50fr multi	.50	.50
438 A73	75fr multi	.80	.80
	Nos. 434-438 (5)	1.85	1.85

For unoverprinted stamps see note after No. 314.

Market value for a particular scarce stamp may remain relatively low if few collectors want it.

Man Reading Proclamation — A74

1979, May 2 Litho. *Perf. 13½*

Black Surcharge and Overprint

No.	Type	Description	Unused	Used
439	A74	5fr on 25fr coronation coach		
440	A74	10fr Drummer		
441	A74	50fr on 40fr with crown, orb, scepter		
442	A74	50fr on 200fr shown		
443	A74	100fr St. Edward's Crown		

No. 442 is airmail.
For unoverprinted stamps see note after No. 314.

Nos. 285-289 Overprinted or Surcharged like A72-A74

1979, May 2 Litho. *Perf. 13*

No.	Type	Description	Unused	Used
444	A56	15fr multi	.15	.15
445	A56	30fr on 35fr multi	.25	.25
446	A56	50fr on 20fr multi	.55	.55
447	A56	50fr on 40fr multi	.55	.55
448	A56	200fr on 75fr multi	1.40	1.40
		Nos. 444-448 (5)	2.90	2.90

Nos. 292-296 Overprinted or Surcharged like A72-A74

1979, May 2 Litho. *Perf. 13*

No.	Type	Description	Unused	Used
449	A57	1fr on 100fr multi	.15	.15
450	A57	2fr on 75fr multi	.15	.15
451	A57	3fr on 30fr multi	.15	.15
452	A57	50fr multi	.40	.40
453	A57	200fr multi	1.40	1.40
		Nos. 449-453 (5)	2.25	2.25

No. 453 airmail.

Nos. 301-305 Overprinted or Surcharged like A72-A74

1979, May 2 *Perf. 13½*

No.	Type	Description	Unused	Used
454	A58	5fr on 100fr multi	.15	.15
455	A58	30fr multi	.20	.20
456	A58	40fr multi	.22	.22
457	A58	50fr multi	.38	.38
458	A58	50fr on 200fr multi	.40	.40
		Nos. 454-458 (5)	1.35	1.35

No. 458 airmail.

Nos. 459-465 are reserved for Intl. Year of the Child set of 6 with one souvenir sheet, released May 30, 1979.

Litchi Nuts — A76 Basketball Players — A77

1979, June 15 Litho. *Perf. 12½*

No.	Type	Description	Unused	Used
466	A76	60fr shown	.40	.20
467	A76	70fr Papayas	.45	.22
468	A76	100fr Avocados	.65	.30
469	A76	125fr Bananas	.80	.50
		Nos. 466-469 (4)	2.30	1.22

For surcharges see Nos. 515, 533.

1979, Aug. 28 Litho. *Perf. 13*

No.	Type	Description	Unused	Used
470	A77	200fr multi	1.10	.80

Indian Ocean Olympics.

Nos. 176, 198, 218, 187, 159-160 and Type A78 Overprinted in Black

Mariner — A78

Designs: No. 475, Apollo-Soyuz. No. 479, Molniya.

Printing & Perfs. as Before, Litho. (A78)

1979, Sept. 15 *Perf. 13 (A78)*

No.	Type	Description	Unused	Used
471	A40	35fr multi	.22	
472	A43	75fr multi	.50	
473	A46	75fr multi	.50	
474	A78	75fr multi	.50	
475	A78	100fr multi	.65	
476	A41	100fr multi	.70	
477	A37	100fr multi	.65	
478	A37	200fr multi	1.40	
479	A78	200fr multi	1.40	
		Nos. 471-479 (9)	6.52	

Nos. 476-479 airmail.
For type A78 see note after No. 314.

Nos. 166-167, 169, 235-236, 257, 262, 309, 311, the unissued Rubens set (4 values) and Durer set (5 values) exist with this overprint, supposedly also issued Sept. 15.

Dugout on Beach — A80

Anjouan Puppet — A81

1980, Jan. 4 Litho. *Perf. 13*

No.	Type	Description	Unused	Used
498	A80	60fr multi	.25	.15
499	A81	100fr multi	.40	.20

For surcharge see No. 534.

Sultan Said Ali — A82

1980, Feb. 20 *Perf. 12½x13*

No.	Type	Description	Unused	Used
500	A82	40fr shown	.15	.15
501	A82	60fr Sultan Ahmed	.25	.15

Sherlock Holmes, Doyle — A83

1980, Feb. 25 *Perf. 12½*

No.	Type	Description	Unused	Used
502	A83	200fr multi	1.40	.75

Sir Arthur Conan Doyle (1859-1930), writer.
For surcharge see No. 513.

Grand Mosque, Holy Ka'aba, Mecca — A84

1980, Mar. 12 *Perf. 13x12½*

No.	Type	Description	Unused	Used
503	A84	75fr multi	.30	.20

Hegira, 1500th anniv.
For surcharge see No. 514.

Year of the Holy City of Jerusalem A85

1980, Mar. 12 *Perf. 13x13½*

No.	Type	Description	Unused	Used
504	A85	60fr multi	.25	.15

Kepler, Copernicus and Pluto — A86

1980, Apr. 30 Litho. *Perf. 12½*

No.	Type	Description	Unused	Used
505	A86	400fr multi	2.00	1.50

Discovery of Pluto, 50th anniversary.
For surcharge see No. 531.

Muscle System, Avicenna — A87

1980, Apr. 30 Engr. *Perf. 13*

No.	Type	Description	Unused	Used
506	A87	60fr multi	.25	.20

Avicenna, Arab physician, birth millennium.

Soccer Players — A88

World Cup Soccer 1982; Various soccer scenes. 60fr, 150fr, 500fr, vert.

1981, Feb. 20 Litho. *Perf. 12½*

No.	Type	Description	Unused	Used
507	A88	60fr multi	.30	.15
508	A88	75fr multi	.35	.15
509	A88	90fr multi	.42	.20
510	A88	100fr multi	.55	.25
511	A88	150fr multi	.80	.28
		Nos. 507-511 (5)	2.42	1.03

Souvenir Sheet

No.	Type	Description	Unused	Used
512	A88	500fr multi	2.50	1.00

For overprints & surcharge see #532, 555-560.

Nos. 502-503, 469 Surcharged and

Merops Superciliosus — A89

Perf. 12½, 13x12½ (No. 514)

1981, Feb. Litho.

Red, Black or Blue Surcharge

No.	Type	Description	Unused	Used
513	A83	15fr on 200fr multi	.15	.15
514	A84	20fr on 75fr multi	.15	.15
515	A76	40fr on 125fr multi (Bk)	.25	.25
516	A89	60fr on 75fr multi (Bl)	.40	.40
		Nos. 513-516 (4)	.95	.95

A90

Space Exploration: 50fr, Apollo program, vert. 75fr, 100fr, 500fr, Columbia space shuttle.

1981, July 13 Litho. *Perf. 14*

No.	Type	Description	Unused	Used
517	A90	50fr multi	.22	.15
518	A90	75fr multi	.30	.15
519	A90	100fr multi	.42	.25
520	A90	450fr multi	2.00	1.00
		Nos. 517-520 (4)	2.94	1.55

Souvenir Sheet

No.	Type	Description	Unused	Used
521	A90	500fr multi	2.50	1.00

For overprint see No. 599.

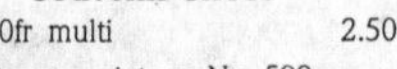

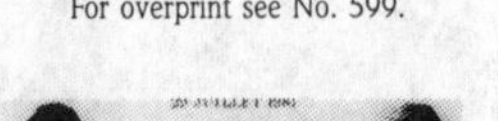

Prince Charles and Lady Diana, Buckingham Palace — A91

1981, Sept. 1 Litho. *Perf. 14½*

No.	Type	Description	Unused	Used
522	A91	125fr shown	.50	.20
523	A91	200fr Highwood House	1.00	.40
524	A91	450fr Carnarvon Castle	2.00	.90
a.		Souvenir sheet of 3	3.50	1.50
		Nos. 522-524 (3)	3.50	1.50

Royal wedding. No. 524a contains Nos. 522-524 in changed colors.
For overprints see Nos. 551-553.

Flag Type of 1979

1981, Oct. Litho. *Perf. 13*

No.	Type	Description	Unused	Used
526	O1	5fr multi	.15	.15
527	O1	15fr multi	.15	.15
528	O1	25fr multi	.15	.15

No.	Type	Description	Unused	Used
529	O1	35fr multi	.15	.15
530	O1	75fr multi	.30	.20
		Set value	.65	.43

Nos. 505, 509, 468, 499 Surcharged

1981, Nov. Litho. *Perf. 12½*

No.	Type	Description	Unused	Used
531	A86	5fr on 400fr multi	.15	.15
532	A88	20fr on 90fr multi	.15	.15
533	A76	45fr on 100fr multi	.20	.15
534	A81	45fr on 100fr multi	.20	.15
		Set value	.50	.26

75th Anniv. of Grand Prix — A92

Designs: Winners and their Cars.

1981, Dec. 28 Litho. *Perf. 12½*

No.	Type	Description	Unused	Used
535	A92	20fr Mercedes, 1914	.15	.15
536	A92	50fr Delage, 1925	.22	.15
537	A92	75fr Rudi Caracciola, 1926	.38	.15
538	A92	90fr Stirling Moss, 1955	.40	.20
539	A92	150fr Maserati, 1957	.65	.30
		Nos. 535-539 (5)	1.80	.95

Souvenir Sheet

Perf. 13

No.	Type	Description	Unused	Used
540	A92	500fr Changing wheels, vert.	2.25	1.00

For overprint see No. 600.

Scouting Year — A93

1982, Jan. 5 *Perf. 12½*

No.	Type	Description	Unused	Used
541	A93	50fr Climbing rocks	.22	.15
542	A93	75fr Boating	.35	.15
543	A93	250fr Sailing	1.10	.50
544	A93	350fr Sailing, diff.	1.60	.75
		Nos. 541-544 (4)	3.27	1.55

Souvenir Sheet

Perf. 13

No.	Type	Description	Unused	Used
545	A93	500fr Baden-Powell	2.50	1.10

For overprint see No. 601.

21st Birthday of Princess of Wales — A94

Designs: Various portraits of Princess Diana.

1982, July 1 Litho. *Perf. 14*

No.	Type	Description	Unused	Used
546	A94	200fr multi	.80	.40
547	A94	300fr multi	1.10	.60

Souvenir Sheet

No.	Type	Description	Unused	Used
548	A94	500fr multi	2.00	1.00

Johannes von Goethe (1749-1832) A95

1982, July

No.	Type	Description	Unused	Used
549	A95	75fr multi	.30	.15
550	A95	350fr multi	1.40	.65

Nos. 522-524a Overprinted in Blue: "NAISSANCE ROYALE 1982"

1982, July 31 *Perf. 14½*

No.	Type	Description	Unused	Used
551	A91	125fr multi	.50	.40
552	A91	200fr multi	.75	.60
553	A91	450fr multi	1.75	1.50
a.		Souvenir sheet of 3	2.50	3.50
		Nos. 551-553 (3)	3.00	2.50

Birth of Prince William of Wales, June 21.

Nos. 507-512 Overprinted with Finalists and Score in Red

1982, Sept. 20 Litho. *Perf. 12½*

No.	Type	Description	Unused	Used
555	A88	60fr multi	.25	.18
556	A88	75fr multi	.30	.22
557	A88	90fr multi	.35	.25
558	A88	100fr multi	.40	.30
559	A88	150fr multi	.55	.40
		Nos. 555-559 (5)	1.85	1.35

Souvenir Sheet

No.	Type	Description	Unused	Used
560	A88	500fr multi	2.00	2.00

Italy's victory in 1982 World Cup.

Paintings by Norman Rockwell A96

1982, Oct. 11 Litho. *Perf. 14*

No.	Type	Description	Unused	Used
561	A96	60fr 1931	.30	.15
562	A96	75fr 1925	.38	.15
563	A96	100fr 1922	.45	.20
564	A96	150fr 1919	.75	.30
565	A96	200fr 1924	1.00	.35
566	A96	300fr 1918	1.50	.60
		Nos. 561-566 (6)	4.38	1.75

Sultans of Anjouan — A97

1982, Dec. *Perf. 12½x13, 13x12½*

No.	Type	Description	Unused	Used
567	A97	30fr Said Mohamed Sidi, vert.	.15	.15
568	A97	60fr Ahmed Abdallah, vert.	.25	.15
569	A97	75fr Salim	.30	.20
570	A97	300fr Sidi, Abdallah	1.10	.80
		Nos. 567-570 (4)	1.80	1.30

Landscapes — A98

1983, Sept. 30 Litho. *Perf. 13*

No.	Type	Description	Unused	Used
571	A98	60fr D'Ziani Lake	.25	.15
572	A98	100fr Sunset	.40	.25
573	A98	175fr Anjouan, vert.	.75	.40
574	A98	360fr Itsandra	1.40	.80
575	A98	400fr Anjouan, diff.	1.60	1.10
		Nos. 571-575 (5)	4.40	2.70

Woman from Moheli A99

1983, Oct. 17 Litho. *Perf. 12½x13*

No.	Type	Description	Unused	Used
576	A99	30fr shown	.15	.15
577	A99	45fr Woman, diff.	.20	.15
578	A99	50fr Man from Mayotte	.22	.15
		Nos. 576-578 (3)	.57	
		Set value		.34

Horses — A100

1983, Nov. 30 Litho. *Perf. 13*

No.	Type	Description	Unused	Used
579	A100	75fr Arabian	.30	.15
580	A100	100fr Anglo-Arabian	.40	.18
581	A100	125fr Lippizaner	.50	.20
582	A100	150fr Tennessee	.60	.25
583	A100	200fr Appaloosa	.80	.35
584	A100	300fr Pure English	1.10	.55
585	A100	400fr Clydesdale	1.60	.65
586	A100	500fr Andalusian	2.00	1.00
		Nos. 579-586 (8)	7.30	3.33

Double Portrait, by Raphael A101

1983, Dec. 30 Litho. *Perf. 13*

No.	Type	Description	Unused	Used
587	A101	100fr shown	.40	.20
588	A101	200fr Girl, fresco detail	.80	.30
589	A101	300fr St. George Killing Dragon	1.10	.60
590	A101	400fr Balthazar Castiglione	1.60	.75
		Nos. 587-590 (4)	3.90	1.85

For surcharge see No. 703.

Ships and Automobiles — A102

1984, Oct. 9 Litho. *Perf. 12½*

No.	Type	Description	Unused	Used
591	A102	100fr William Fawcett	.28	
592	A102	100fr De Dion, 1885	.28	
593	A102	150fr Lightning	.40	
594	A102	150fr Benz Victoria, 1893	.40	
595	A102	200fr Rapido	.60	
596	A102	200fr Columbia Electric, 1901	.60	
597	A102	350fr Sindia	.80	
598	A102	350fr Fiat, 1902	.80	
		Nos. 591-598 (8)	4.16	

Souvenir Sheets

Nos. 521, 540, 545, C126, C131 Ovptd. with Exhibition in Black, Blue, Red or Gold

1985, Mar. 11 *Perf. 14, 13*

No.	Type	Description	Unused	Used
599	A90	500fr '85 / HAMBOURG (Bk)	1.50	
600	A92	500fr TSUKUBA EXPO '85 (Bl)	1.50	
601	A93	500fr ARGENTINA '85/BUENOS AIRES (R)	1.50	
602	AP31	500fr Rome, ITALIA '85 emblem (R)	1.50	
603	AP32	500fr OLYM - PHILEX/ '85 / LAUSANNE (G)	1.50	
		Nos. 599-603 (5)	7.50	

Nos. 602-603 airmail.

Victor Hugo (1802-1885), Author, Pantheon, Paris — A103

Anniversaries and events: 200fr, IYY, Jules Verne (1828-1905), author. 300fr, IYY, Mark Twain (1835-1910), author. 450fr, Queen Mother, 85th birthday, vert. 500fr, Statue of Liberty, cent., vert.

1985, May 27 Litho. *Perf. 13*

No.	Type	Description	Unused	Used
604	A103	100fr multi	.25	
605	A103	200fr multi	.55	
606	A103	300fr multi	.75	
607	A103	450fr multi	1.10	
608	A103	500fr multi	1.40	
		Nos. 604-608 (5)	4.05	

For surcharge see No. 704.

Sea Shells A104

1985, Oct. 23 *Perf. 14*

No.	Type	Description	Unused	Used
609	A104	75fr Lambis chiragra	.20	
610	A104	125fr Strombe lentifinosum	.35	
611	A104	200fr Tonna gala	.55	
612	A104	300fr Cymbium glans	.75	
613	A104	450fr Lambis crocata	1.10	
		Nos. 609-613 (5)	2.95	

Comoros Admission to UN, 10th Anniv. — A105

1985, Nov. 12 Litho. *Perf. 13x12½*

No.	Type	Description	Unused	Used
614	A105	5fr multi	.15	.15
615	A105	30fr multi	.15	.15
616	A105	75fr multi	.25	.15
617	A105	125fr multi	.42	.22
618	A105	400fr multi	1.40	.65
		Nos. 614-618 (5)	2.37	
		Set value		1.10

Moroni Rotary Club, 20th Anniv. — A106

Perf. 13

[...] multi .15 .15
[...] multi .25 .15
[...] multi .42 .22
[...] multi 1.75 1.00
Nos. [6]19-622 (4) 2.57 1.52

Mushrooms — A107

1985, Dec. 24 *Perf. 13½*

623 A107 75fr Boletus edulis .25 .15
624 A107 125fr Sarcoscypha coccinea .42 .22
625 A107 200fr Hypholoma fasciculare .70 .38
626 A107 350fr Astraeus hygrometricus 1.25 .60
627 A107 500fr Armillariella mellea 2.00 1.00
Nos. 623-627 (5) 4.62 2.35

Health Year — A108

1986, Oct. 2 Litho. *Perf. 15x14½*

628 A108 25fr Pediatric examination .15 .15
629 A108 100fr Weighing child .65 .32
630 A108 200fr Immunization 1.40 .70
Nos. 628-630 (3) 2.20 1.17

For surcharge see No. 705.

Musical Instruments A109

1986, Dec. 24 Litho. *Perf. 13*

631 A109 75fr Ndzoumara .40 .20
632 A109 125fr Ndzedze .70 .35
633 A109 210fr Gaboussi 1.15 .58
634 A109 500fr Ngoma 2.75 1.40
Nos. 631-634 (4) 5.00 2.53

Role of Women in National Development — A110

1987, Mar. 7 Litho. *Perf. 13*

635 A110 75fr Working fields .40 .20
636 A110 125fr Harvesting crops, vert. .68 .35
637 A110 1000fr Basketweaving 5.25 2.65
Nos. 635-637 (3) 6.33 3.20

Service Organizations A111

Emblems and activities: 75fr, Nos. 642, Kiwanis or 643c, Rotary Intl. for child survival. 125fr, Nos. 641, Kiwanis or 643b, Lions Intl. for aid to the handicapped. 210fr, No. 643a, Kiwanis helping poor and homeless children.

1988 Litho. *Perf. 13½*

638 A111 75fr dk bl, lt bl & multi .52 .25
639 A111 125fr dk brn, lt brn & multi .90 .45
640 A111 210fr org, yel & multi 1.50 .75
641 A111 425fr red, pink & multi 3.00 1.50
642 A111 500fr bl, yel & multi 3.60 1.80
643 Strip of 3 8.10 4.05
a. A111 210fr grn, lt grn & multi 1.50 .75
b. A111 425fr pur, pink & multi 3.00 1.50
c. A111 500fr red, org & multi 3.60 1.80
Nos. 638-643 (6) 17.62 8.80

For surcharges see Nos. 654-656.

A112

1988 Olympics, Calgary and Seoul — A113

1988 Litho. *Perf. 13½*

644 A112 75fr Women's figure skating .52 .25
645 A112 100fr Running .70 .35
646 A112 125fr Women's speed skating .88 .45
647 A112 150fr Equestrian 1.05 .52
648 A112 350fr Two-man luge 2.50 1.25
649 A112 400fr Biathlon 2.80 1.40
650 A112 500fr Pole vault 3.50 1.75
651 A112 600fr Soccer 4.25 2.10
Nos. 644-651 (8) 16.20 8.07

Souvenir Sheets

652 A113 750fr Women's downhill skiing, satellite 5.25 5.25
653 A113 750fr Track, satellite 5.25 5.25

Nos. 649 and 651-653 are airmail.

No. 643 and Service Organization Types Surcharged

Designs: No. 655, like #643b. No. 656, like #643c.

1988, July 18 Litho. *Perf. 13½*

654 Strip of 3 3.75 1.90
a. A111 75fr on 210fr #643a .48 .25
b. A111 200fr on 425fr #643b 1.30 .65
c. A111 300fr on 500fr #643c 1.95 1.00
655 A111 125fr on 425fr pur, lt pur & multi, blk letters .80 .40
656 A111 400fr on 500fr car, pink & multi 2.60 1.30
Nos. 654-656 (3) 7.15 3.60

Nos. 655-656 not issued without surcharge.

Discovery of America, 500th Anniv. (in 1992) — A114

Designs: 75fr, Christopher Columbus, *Santa Maria*. 125fr, Martin Alonzo Pinzon (c. 1441-1493), *Pinta*. 150fr, Vicente Yanez Pinzon (c. 1460-1523), *Nina*. 250fr, Search for Cipango, legendary rich islands off the coast of Asia. 375fr, *Santa Maria* shipwrecked. 450fr, Preparing for 4th voyage. 750fr, Samana Cay landing.

1988, Apr. 18 Litho. *Perf. 13½*

657 A114 75fr multi .50 .25
658 A114 125fr multi .82 .40
659 A114 150fr multi .98 .50
660 A114 250fr multi 1.65 .82
661 A114 375fr multi 2.45 1.20
662 A114 450fr multi 3.00 1.50
Nos. 657-662 (6) 9.40 4.67

Souvenir Sheet

663 A114 750fr multi, horiz. 5.00 5.00

Nos. 661-663 airmail. No. 663 contains one 42x30mm stamp.

For surcharge see No. 702.

1992 Summer Olympics, Barcelona A115

1988, Apr. 18

664 A115 75fr Discus, vert. .50 .25
665 A115 100fr shown .65 .32
666 A115 125fr Cycling .82 .40
667 A115 150fr Wrestling .98 .50
668 A115 375fr Basketball, vert. 2.45 1.20
669 A115 600fr Tennis, vert. 3.90 1.95
Nos. 664-669 (6) 9.30 4.62

Souvenir Sheet

670 A115 750fr Marathon, vert. 5.00 5.00

Nos. 668-670 are airmail.

Famous Men — A116

Rotary Intl. — A117

Design: 150fr, Yuri Gagarin (1934-1968), USSR, cosmonaut. 300fr, Jean-Henri Dunant, Red Cross founder. 400fr, Roger Clemens, baseball player. 500fr, Gary Kasparov, USSR, 1985 world chess champion. 600fr, Paul Harris, US, Rotary founder. 750fr, Neil Armstrong walking on the Moon, John F. Kennedy. No. 678, The Thinker by Rodin, Rotary Intl. emblem.

1988, Dec. 6 Litho. *Perf. 13½*

671 A116 150fr multi 1.05 .52
672 A116 300fr multi 2.10 1.05
673 A116 400fr multi 2.70 1.35
674 A116 500fr multi 3.50 1.75
675 A116 600fr multi 4.25 2.15
a. Souv. sheet of 5, #671-675 + label
Nos. 665-669 (5) 8.80 4.37

Litho. & Embossed

676 A117 1500fr gold & multi

Souvenir Sheets

Litho.

677 A116 750fr multi 5.25 5.25

Litho. & Embossed

678 A117 1500fr gold & multi

Intl. Red Cross, 125th anniv. (300fr), Rotary Intl. (600fr, Nos. 676, 678). Nos. 674-678 are airmail.

Inventors and Sportsmen A118

Portraits and modes of transportation: Designs: 75fr, Alain Prost, F-1 MacLaren-Honda. 125fr, George Stephenson and locomotive *Borsig of 1935*. 500fr, Ettore Bugatti (1881-1947), 1939 Bugatti Aravis Type 57. 600fr, Rudolf Diesel (1858-1913) and V200 BB diesel-electric locomotive. 750fr, Dennis Conner, captain of the *Stars and Stripes*, winner of the 1987 America's Cup. No. 684, Michael Fay, patron of the *New Zealand*, an entry in the America's Cup. No. 685, Enzo Ferrari and 1989 Ferrari Formula 1, horiz.

1988, Dec. 27 Litho. *Perf. 13½*

679 A118 75fr multi .52 .25
680 A118 125fr multi .82 .40
681 A118 500fr multi 3.50 1.75
682 A118 600fr multi 3.90 1.95
683 A118 750fr multi 4.75 2.35
684 A118 1000fr multi 6.50 3.25
Nos. 679-684 (6) 19.99 9.95

Souvenir Sheet

685 A118 1000fr multi 6.50 6.50

Nos. 683-685 are airmail.

Scouts, Butterflies and Birds — A119

Scouts involved in various activities and species: 50fr, Gathering specimens, *Papilio nireus aristophontes oberthur* female. 75fr, Studying specimen and male. 150fr, Cooking out, *Charaxes fulvescens separanus poulton*. 375fr, Picking mushrooms, *Lonchura cucullatus*. 450fr, Examining specimen, *Charaxes castor comoranus rothschild*. 500fr, Identifying specimen, *Zosterops maderaspatana*. 750fr, Studying specimens, *Foudia omissa* and *Charaxes paradoxa lathy* female. No. 692, Photographing specimen, Junonia rhadama. No. 694, Examining specimen, Agapornis cana cana.

1989 **Litho.**

686 A119 50fr multi .32 .16
687 A119 75fr multi .48 .25
688 A119 150fr multi .98 .50
689 A119 375fr multi 2.45 1.20
690 A119 450fr multi 2.90 1.45
691 A119 500fr multi 3.25 1.60
Nos. 686-691 (6) 10.38 5.16

Litho. & Embossed

692 A119 1500fr gold & multi

Souvenir Sheets

Litho.

693 A119 750fr multi 4.75 4.75

Litho. & Embossed

694 A119 1500fr gold & multi

Nos. 690-694 are airmail. Issue dates: Nos. 692, 694, May 15, others, Mar. 15.

Gold Medalists of the 1988 Summer Olympics A120

Communication satellites, various equestrians and their mounts: 75fr, Nicole Uphoff, West Germany, individual dressage, and Aussat K3. 150fr, Pierre Durand, France, individual jumping, and Brazilsat. 375fr, Janos Martinek, Hungary, individual modern pentathlon, and ECS 4. 600fr, Mark Todd, New Zealand, individual three-day event, and Olympus. 750fr, Team jumping, West Germany, and satellite. No. 699, Pierre Durand, France, individual show jumping. No. 701, Nicole Uphoff, West Germany, individual dressage.

1989, Apr. 10 Litho. *Perf. 13½*

695 A120 75fr multi .48 .25
696 A120 150fr multi .95 .48
697 A120 375fr multi 2.40 1.20
698 A120 600fr multi 3.75 1.90
Nos. 695-698 (4) 7.58 3.83

Litho. & Embossed

699 A120 1500fr gold & multi

Souvenir Sheets
Litho.

700	A120	750fr multi	4.75	4.75

Litho. & Embossed

701	A120	1500fr gold & multi		

No. 701 contains one 39x38mm stamp. Nos. 698-701 are airmail.

Nos. 660, 588, 605 and 630 Surcharged

1989 Litho. ***Perfs. as Before***

702	A114	25fr on 250fr #660	.18	.15
703	A101	150fr on 200fr #588	1.05	.52
704	A103	150fr on 200fr #605	1.05	.52
705	A108	150fr on 200fr #630	1.05	.52
		Nos. 702-705 (4)	3.33	1.71

1992 Summer Olympics, Barcelona — A121

1989, Apr. 26 Litho. ***Perf. 13½***

706	A121	75fr Running	.50	.25
707	A121	150fr Soccer	1.00	.50
708	A121	300fr Tennis	2.00	1.00
709	A121	375fr Baseball	2.50	1.25
710	A121	500fr Pommel horse	3.25	1.60
711	A121	600fr Table tennis	4.00	2.00
		Nos. 706-711 (6)	13.25	6.60

Souvenir Sheet

712	A121	750fr Equestrian	5.00	5.00

Nos. 710-712 are airmail.

Dr. Joseph-Ignace Guillotin (1738-1814) — A122

French Revolution, Bicentennial: 150fr, French artillery, Gen. Francois-Christophe Kellerman (1735-1820). 375fr, Royalist insurgents and leader, Jean Cotterau (1757-1794). 600fr, King Louis XVI (1774-1792), troops. 1000fr, Storming of the Bastille and Jacques Necker, statesman (1732-1804). No. 717, Lafayette, Mounier, Sieyes and Declaration of the Rights of Man and Citizen. No. 719, Robespierre and St. Just before the Convention on 9 Thermidor.

1989, Oct. 25 Litho. ***Perf. 13½***

713	A122	75fr multicolored	.60	.30
714	A122	150fr multicolored	1.10	.55
715	A122	375fr multicolored	2.80	1.40
716	A122	600fr multicolored	4.50	2.25
		Nos. 713-716 (4)	9.00	4.50

Litho. & Embossed

717	A122	1500fr gold & multi		

Souvenir Sheets
Litho.

718	A122	1000fr multicolored	7.50	3.75

Litho. & Embossed

719	A122	1500fr gold & multi		

Philexfrance 1989. No. 716-719 are airmail. No. 714 incorrectly inscribed "Francois-Etienne." Nos. 713-717 exist in souvenir sheets of 1.

Airport Pavilion A124

Designs: 10fr, 25fr, Airport pavilion. 50fr, 75fr, 150fr, Federal Assembly.

1990, Apr. 1 Litho. ***Perf. 13***

722	A124	5fr brn, org & brt red	.15	.15
723	A124	10fr brn, org & brt bl	.15	.15
724	A124	25fr brn, org & brt grn	.20	.15
725	A124	50fr blk & brt red	.40	.20
726	A124	75fr blk & brt bl	.60	.30
727	A124	150fr blk & grn	1.20	.60
		Nos. 722-727 (6)	2.70	
		Set value		1.30

World Cup Soccer Championships, Italy — A125

Players from: 50fr, Brazil. 75fr, England. 100fr, Federal Republic of Germany. 150fr, Belgium. 375fr, Italy. 600fr, Argentina. 750fr, Argentina and Italy.

1990 Litho. ***Perf. 13½***

728	A125	50fr multicolored	.40	.20
729	A125	75fr multicolored	.60	.30
730	A125	100fr multicolored	.75	.38
731	A125	150fr multicolored	1.10	.55
732	A125	375fr multicolored	2.80	1.40
733	A125	600fr multicolored	4.50	2.25
		Nos. 728-733 (6)	10.15	5.08

Litho. & Embossed

734	A125	1500fr gold & multi		

Souvenir Sheets
Litho.

735	A125	750fr multicolored	5.00	5.00

Litho. & Embossed

736	A125	1500fr gold & multi		

Nos. 732-736 are airmail.

Telecom '91 A125a

1990, Oct. 29 Litho. ***Perf. 13½***

736A	A125a	75fr Emblem, vert.	1.25	.60
736B	A125a	150fr shown	2.50	1.25

Nos. 736A-736B exist imperf.

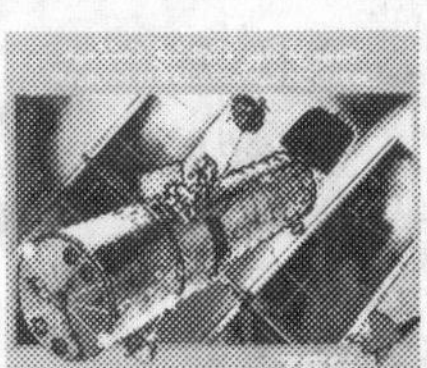

A126

Designs: 75fr, Hubble Space Telescope placed in orbit. 150fr, Pope John Paul II, Pres. Gorbachev meet Dec. 3, 1989. 200fr, Kevin Mitchell, San Francisco Giants, Natl. League Most Valuable Player, 1989. 250fr, De Gaulle, France, and Adenauer, West Germany, meet in Sept. 1962. 300fr, Cassini probe to Titan, 2002. 375fr, Bullet train and Concorde, France. 450fr, Gary Kasparov, World Chess Champion. 500fr, Paul Harris (1868-1947), founder of Rotary Intl.

1990, Nov. 26 Litho. ***Perf. 13½***

737	A126	75fr sil & multi	.70	.35
738	A126	150fr sil & multi	1.40	.70
739	A126	200fr sil & multi	1.90	.95
740	A126	250fr sil & multi	2.35	1.15
741	A126	300fr sil & multi	2.80	1.40
742	A126	375fr sil & multi	3.50	1.75
743	A126	450fr sil & multi	4.20	2.10
744	A126	500fr sil & multi	4.70	2.35
		Nos. 737-744 (8)	21.55	10.75

Nos. 743-744 are airmail.

A127 A128

Winter Olympics participants: 75fr, Edi Reinalter, Switzerland, slalom, 1948. 100fr, Canadian hockey team, 1924. 375fr, Gratia Van der Oye, women's slalom, Holland, 1936. 600fr, Heikki Hasu, Finland, combined cross country and ski jumping, 1948. 750fr, Helene Engelman & Alfred Berger, Austria, pairs figure skating, 1924. No. 751, Speed skater, horiz. No. 751A, Luge, horiz.

1990, Dec. 10

746	A127	75fr multicolored	.70	.35
747	A127	100fr multicolored	.95	.48
748	A127	375fr multicolored	3.50	1.75
749	A127	600fr multicolored	5.60	2.80
		Nos. 746-749 (4)	10.75	5.38

Souvenir Sheet

750	A127	750fr multicolored	7.00	3.50

Litho. & Embossed

751	A127	1500fr gold & multi		

Souvenir Sheet

751A	A127	1500fr gold & multi		

1992 Winter Olympics, Albertville. Nos. 748-751A are airmail. No. 750 contains one 36x41mm stamp.

1991, May 17 Litho. ***Perf. 13½***

Ground station, Moroni Volo-Volo.

752	A128	75fr multicolored	.55	.28
753	A128	150fr multicolored	1.15	.58
754	A128	225fr multicolored	1.70	.85
755	A128	300fr multicolored	2.30	1.15
756	A128	500fr multicolored	3.80	1.90
		Nos. 752-756 (5)	9.50	4.76

Indian Ocean Conference A129

1991, June 17

757	A129	75fr multicolored	.60	.30
758	A129	150fr multicolored	1.15	.60
759	A129	225fr multicolored	1.70	.85
		Nos. 757-759 (3)	3.45	1.75

World War II, 50th Anniv. A130

Actors, Films: 150fr, Errol Flynn, Objective Burma. 300fr, Henry Fonda, The Longest Day. 450fr, Humphrey Bogart, Sahara.

1991, Aug. 5

760	A130	150fr sil & multi	1.15	.58
761	A130	300fr sil & multi	2.30	1.15
762	A130	450fr sil & multi	3.45	1.75
		Nos. 760-762 (3)	6.90	3.48

No. 762 is airmail. Nos. 760-762 exist in souvenir sheets of 1.

A131

Charles de Gaulle A132

De Gaulle and: 125fr, Battle of Koufra. 375fr, Battle of Britain. 500fr, Battle of Monte Cassino. 1000fr, Airplanes. 1500fr, De Gaulle at podium.

1991, Aug. 5 Litho. ***Perf. 13½***

763	A131	125fr multi	.95	.48
764	A131	375fr multi	2.85	1.45
765	A131	500fr multi	3.80	1.90
		Nos. 763-765 (3)	7.60	3.83

Souvenir Sheet

766	A131	1000fr multi	7.60	3.80

Litho. & Embossed

767	A132	1500fr gold & multi		

Nos. 765-767 are airmail. No. 767 exists in souvenir sheet of 1.

Anniversaries and Events — A133

Designs: 100fr, Satellite Columbus in polar orbit. 150fr, Gandhi. 250fr, Jean-Henri Dunant. 300fr, Wolfgang Amadeus Mozart. 375fr, Brandenburg Gate. 400fr, Konrad Adenauer. 450fr, Elvis Presley. 500fr, Ferdinand von Zeppelin.

1991, Nov. 18 Litho. ***Perf. 13½***

768	A133	100fr multicolored	1.65	.85
769	A133	150fr multicolored	2.50	1.25
770	A133	250fr multicolored	4.25	2.00
771	A133	300fr multicolored	5.00	2.50
772	A133	375fr multicolored	6.25	3.00
773	A133	400fr multicolored	6.50	3.25
774	A133	450fr multicolored	7.50	3.75
a.		Souv. sheet, 1 each #771, #774	12.50	6.25
775	A133	500fr multicolored	8.50	4.25
a.		Souv. sheet, 1 each #772-773, 775	21.50	
		Nos. 768-775 (8)	42.15	20.85

Nobel Peace Prize, 90th anniv. (#770). Mozart, bicent. of death (#771). Brandenburg Gate, bicent. (#772). Konrad Adenauer, 25th anniv. of death (#773). Elvis Presley, 15th anniv. of death (in 1992) (#774). Count Zeppelin, 75th anniv. of death (in 1992) (#775).

Nos. 774-775 are airmail. Nos. 768-775 exist in souvenir sheets of 1.

Mushrooms A134

	Litho.	*Perf. 13½*	
	…epe comestible	.58	.30
	…eastre en etoile	1.10	.58
	…ezize ecarlate	4.75	2.50
	…6-778 (3)	6.43	3.38

No. 778 is airmail. Nos. 776-778 exist imperf. and in souvenir sheets of one.

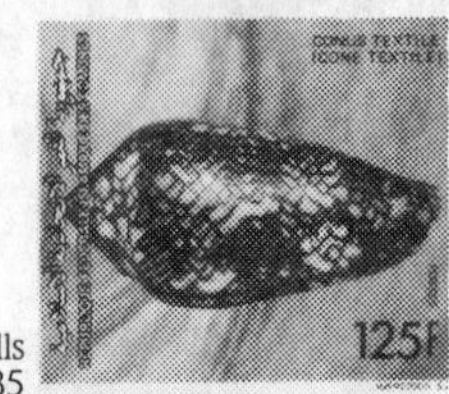

Shells A135

1992, Mar. 23

No.	Type	Description	Unused	Used
779	A135	125fr Conus textile	1.00	.50
780	A135	150fr Cypraecassis rufa	1.10	.58
781	A135	500fr Leporicypraea mappa	4.00	2.00
		Nos. 779-781 (3)	6.10	3.08

Souvenir Sheet

No.	Type	Description	Unused	Used
782	A135	750fr Nautilus pompilius	6.00	3.00

Nos. 781-782 are airmail. Nos. 779-781 exist imperf. and in souvenir sheets of one. No. 782 exists imperf.

Space Programs A136

Designs: 75fr, Mercury rocket, chimpanzee Ham, US. 125fr, Mars Observer, US. No. 785, Veronica rocket, cat Felix, France. No. 786, Mars rover, US, Mars car, USSR. 500fr, Phobos project, USSR. 600fr, Sputnik II, dog Laika, USSR. 1000fr, Viking, US, vert.

1992, Mar. 30 Litho. *Perf. 13½*

No.	Type	Description	Unused	Used
783	A136	75fr multicolored	.60	.30
784	A136	125fr multicolored	1.00	.50
785	A136	150fr multicolored	1.20	.60
786	A136	150fr multicolored	1.20	.60
787	A136	500fr multicolored	4.00	2.00
a.		Souv. sheet of 3, #784, 786-787	*11.50*	*5.75*
788	A136	600fr multicolored	4.80	2.40
a.		Souv. sheet of 3, #783, 785, 788	*11.50*	*5.75*
		Nos. 783-788 (6)	12.80	6.40

Souvenir Sheet

No.	Type	Description	Unused	Used
789	A136	1000fr multicolored	8.00	4.00

Nos. 787-789 are airmail. Nos. 783-788 exist imperf. and in souvenir sheets of one. No. 789 contains one 30x42mm stamp.

Voyages of Discovery A137

Designs: 75fr, Space shuttle Endeavour, sailing ship Endeavour, Capt. Cook. 100fr, Satellite, sailing ship Golden Hinde, Sir Francis Drake. 150fr, ISO observation satellite, sailing ship Susan Constant, John Smith. 225fr, Probe B, sailing ship Discovery, Robert F. Scott. 375fr, Magellan probe over Venus, sailing ship, Ferdinand Magellan. 500fr, Newton probe, sailing ship Sao Gabriel, Vasco da Gama.

1992, May 28 Litho. *Perf. 13½*

No.	Type	Description	Unused	Used
790	A137	75fr multicolored	.70	.35
791	A137	100fr multicolored	.95	.48
792	A137	150fr multicolored	1.50	.70
793	A137	225fr multicolored	2.25	1.10
794	A137	375fr multicolored	3.50	1.75
795	A137	500fr multicolored	4.75	2.50
		Nos. 790-795 (6)	13.65	6.88

Nos. 794-795 are airmail. Nos. 790-795 exist imperf. in souvenir sheets of one. A number has been reserved for a 1000fr souvenir sheet issued with this set.

Organization of African Unity, 30th Anniv. — A138

1993, Feb. 15 Litho. *Perf. 13½x13*

No.	Type	Description	Unused	Used
797	A138	25fr blue & multi	.20	.15
798	A138	50fr pink & multi	.40	.20

Perf. 12

No.	Type	Description	Unused	Used
799	A138	75fr green & multi	.60	.30
800	A138	150fr vermilion & multi	1.20	.60
		Nos. 797-800 (4)	2.40	1.25

1994 World Cup Soccer Championships, US — A139

Intl. Telecommunications Day — A140

1993, May 12 Litho. *Perf. 13x12½*

No.	Type	Description	Unused	Used
801	A139	25fr red & multi	.20	.15
802	A139	75fr brown & multi	.60	.30
803	A139	100fr blue & multi	.80	.40
804	A139	150fr green & multi	1.20	.60
		Nos. 801-804 (4)	2.80	1.45

1993, May 17

No.	Type	Description	Unused	Used
805	A140	50fr red & multi	.40	.20
806	A140	75fr blue & multi	.60	.30
807	A140	100fr green & multi	.80	.40
808	A140	150fr black & multi	1.20	.60
		Nos. 805-808 (4)	3.00	1.50

Miniature Sheet

Prehistoric Animals A141

Designs: a, 75fr, Edaphosaurus. b, 75fr, Moschops. c, 75fr, Sauroctonus. d, 75fr, Ornitholestes. e, 75fr, Kentrosaurus. f, 75fr, Compsognathus. g, 75fr, Styracosaurus. h, 75fr, Acanthopholis. i, 150fr, Edmontonia. j, 150fr, Struthiomimus. k, 450fr, Dromiceiomimus. l, 450fr, Iguanodon. m, 150fr, Diatryma. n, 150fr, Uintatherium. o, 525fr, Synthetoceras. p, 525fr, Euryapteryx.

1200fr, Tyrannosaurus rex.

1994, Apr. 5 Litho. *Perf. 13½*

No.	Type	Description	Unused	Used
809	A141	Sheet of 16, #a.-p.	18.00	9.00

Souvenir Sheet

No.	Type	Description	Unused	Used
810	A141	1200fr multicolored	6.75	3.50

No. 810 is airmail and contains one 42x60mm stamp.

Miniature Sheet

Flora A142

Orchids: No. 811a, 75fr, Hibiscus syriacus. 150fr, Pyrostegia venusta. 525fr, Allamanda cathartica.

Vegetables: No. 811b, 75fr, Anacardier. 150fr, Manioc. 525fr, Cacao.

Mushrooms: No. 811c, 75fr, Suillus lutens. 150fr, Lycogala epidendron. 525fr, Clathrus ruber.

Butterflies, insects: No. 812a, 75fr, Colotis zoe. b, 150fr, Acherontia atropos. c, 450fr, Danaus chrysippus. d, 75fr, Charaxes comoranus. e, 150fr, Euchloron megaera. f, 450fr, Papilio phorbanta. g, 75fr, Hypurgus ova. h, 150fr, Onthophagus catta. i, 450fr, Echinosoma bolivari.

1994 Litho. *Perf. 13½*

No.	Type	Description	Unused	Used
811	A142	Sheet of 3	12.00	6.00
a.		Strip of 3	*4.00*	*2.00*
b.		Strip of 3	*4.00*	*2.00*
c.		Strip of 3	*4.00*	*2.00*
d.		Souvenir sheet, #811a	*12.00*	*6.00*
e.		Souvenir sheet, #811b	*12.00*	*6.00*
f.		Souvenir sheet, #811c	*12.00*	*6.00*

Miniature Sheet

No.	Type	Description	Unused	Used
812	A142	Sheet of 9, #a.-i.	11.00	5.50
j.		Souvenir sheet, #812a-812c	*12.00*	*6.00*
k.		Souvenir sheet, #812d-812f	*12.00*	*6.00*
l.		Souvenir sheet, #812g-812i	*12.00*	*6.00*

SEMI-POSTAL STAMPS

Anti-Malaria Issue

Common Design Type

Perf. 12½x12

1962, Apr. 7 Engr. Unwmk.

No.	Type	Description	Unused	Used
B1	CD108	25fr + 5fr brt pink	1.10	1.10

WHO drive to eradicate malaria.

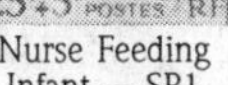

Nurse Feeding Infant — SP1

Mother and Child — SP2

1967, July 3 Engr. *Perf. 13*

No.	Type	Description	Unused	Used
B2	SP1	25fr + 5fr multi	.75	.75

For the Red Cross.

1974, Aug. 10 Engr. *Perf. 13*

No.	Type	Description	Unused	Used
B3	SP2	35fr + 10fr red & dk brn	.55	.55

For the Red Cross.

For surcharge see No. 144.

Miniature Sheet

Space Achievements — SP3

World Philatelic Programs emblems (stamp collecting or Halley's Comet) and astronomer or satellite: a, Galileo. b, Copernicus. c, Kepler. d, Halley. e, *Planet A*, Japan, and 3 stars. f, *ICE*, US. g, *Planet A*, 5 stars. h, *Vega*, USSR.

1988 Litho. *Perf. 13½*

No.	Type	Description	Unused	Used
B4		Sheet of 8	11.25	11.25
a.-h.	SP3	200fr +10fr multi	1.40	1.40

See No. C193.

AIR POST STAMPS

Comoro Village — AP1

Comoro Men and Moroni Mosque — AP2

Design: 200fr, Mosque of Ouani, Anjouan.

1950-54 Unwmk. Engr. *Perf. 13*

No.	Type	Description	Unused	Used
C1	AP1	50fr grn & red brn	1.40	.65
C2	AP2	100fr dk brn & red	2.00	.65
C3	AP1	200fr dk grn, rose brn & pur ('54)	8.00	4.00
		Nos. C1-C3 (3)	11.40	5.30

Liberation Issue

Common Design Type

1954, June 6

No.	Type	Description	Unused	Used
C4	CD102	15fr sep & red	11.00	8.00

Madrepora Fructicosa — AP3

Design: 100fr, Coral, shells and sea anemones.

1962, Jan. 13 Photo. *Perf. 12½x13*

No.	Type	Description	Unused	Used
C5	AP3	100fr multi	2.00	2.00
C6	AP3	500fr multi	8.00	7.50

Telstar Issue

Common Design Type

1962, Dec. 5 Engr. *Perf. 13*

No.	Type	Description	Unused	Used
C7	CD111	25fr dp vio, dl pur & red lil	1.50	.80

Type of Regular Issue, 1963

Unwmk.

1963, Dec. 27 Engr. *Perf. 13*

Size: 26½x48mm

No.	Type	Description	Unused	Used
C8	A13	65fr Baskets	1.00	.60
C9	A13	200fr Pendant	2.00	1.25

Boat Type of Regular Issue

1964, Aug. 7 Photo. *Perf. 13*

Size: 27x48mm

No.	Type	Description	Unused	Used
C10	A14	50fr Mayotte pirogue	.75	.30
C11	A14	85fr Schooner	1.10	.65

Olympic Torch and Boxers — AP4

Order of Star of Grand Comoro — AP5

1964, Oct. 10 Engr. *Perf. 13*

C12 AP4 100fr red brn, dk brn & gray grn 1.25 1.25

18th Olympic Games, Tokyo, Oct. 10-25.

1964, Dec. 10 Photo. *Perf. 13*

C13 AP5 500fr multi 5.50 3.25

ITU Issue
Common Design Type

1965, May 17 Engr. *Perf. 13*

C14 CD120 50fr gray, grnsh bl & ol 4.25 3.75

French Satellite A-1 Issue
Common Design Type

Designs: 25fr, Diamant rocket and launching installations. 30fr, A-1 satellite.

1966, Jan. 17 Engr. *Perf. 13*

C15 CD121 25fr dk pur & ultra .80 .80
C16 CD121 30fr dk pur & ultra 1.25 1.25
a. Strip of 2, #C15-C16 + label 2.50 2.50

French Satellite D-1 Issue
Common Design Type

1966, May 16 Engr. *Perf. 13*

C17 CD122 30fr dk grn, org & brn .90 .60

Old Gun Battery, Dzaoudzi — AP6

Design: 200fr, Ksar Castle, Mutsamudu, vert.

1966, Dec. 19 Photo. *Perf. 13*

C18 AP6 50fr multi .50 .42
C19 AP6 200fr multi 1.75 1.00

Bird Type of Regular Issue

Birds: 75fr, Madagascar paradise flycatchers. 100fr, Blue-cheeked bee eaters.

1967, June 20 Photo. *Perf. 13*
Size: 27x48mm

C20 A17 75fr yel grn & multi .90 .32
C21 A17 100fr lt bl & multi 1.40 .60

Woman Skier — AP7

1968, Apr. 29 Engr. *Perf. 13*

C22 AP7 70fr brt grn, lt bl & choc .80 .50

10th Winter Olympic Games, Grenoble, France, Feb. 6-18, 1968.

Fish Type of Regular Issue

Designs: 50fr, Moorish idol. 90fr, Diagramma lineatus.

1968, Aug. 1 Engr. *Perf. 13*
Size: 47½x27mm

C23 A19 50fr plum blk & yel .65 .60
C24 A19 90fr brt grn, yel & gray grn 1.10 .90

For surcharge and overprint see Nos. C52, C74.

Swimmer, Butterfly Stroke — AP8

1969, Jan. 27 Photo. *Perf. 12½*

C25 AP8 65fr ver, grnsh bl & blk .90 .65

Issued to commemorate the 19th Olympic Games, Mexico City, Oct. 12-27.

Flower Type of Regular Issue, 1969.

Designs: 50fr, Heliconia sp., vert. 85fr, Tuberose, vert. 200fr, Orchid (angraecum eburneum), vert.

1969, Mar. 20 Photo. *Perf. 13*
Size: 27x48mm

C26 A21 50fr gray & multi .65 .50
C27 A21 85fr multi 1.00 .65
C28 A21 200fr dk red & multi 1.75 1.25
Nos. C26-C28 (3) 3.40 2.40

Concorde Issue
Common Design Type

1969, Apr. 17 Engr.

C29 CD129 100fr pur & brn org 3.75 3.00

View of EXPO, Globe and Moon — AP9

Design: 90fr, Geisha, map of Japan and EXPO emblem.

1970, Sept. 13 Photo. *Perf. 13*

C30 AP9 60fr slate & multi .60 .40
C31 AP9 90fr multi .60 .40

EXPO '70 International Exposition, Osaka, Japan, Mar. 15-Sept. 13.

Sunset over Mutsamudu — AP10

Map of Archipelago — AP11

Designs: 20fr, Sada Village, Mayotte. 65fr, Old Iconi Palace, Grand Comoro. 85fr, Nioumatchoua Island, Moheli.

1971, May 3 Photo. *Perf. 13*

C32 AP10 15fr dk bl & multi .15 .15
C33 AP10 20fr multi .22 .15
C34 AP10 65fr grn & multi .45 .22
C35 AP10 85fr bl & multi .55 .30

Engr.

C36 AP11 100fr brn red, grn & vio bl 1.00 .50
Nos. C32-C36 (5) 2.37 1.32

See Nos. 107-110, C45-C49, C53, C62-C64. For overprints and surcharges see Nos. 143, C69, C71, C73, C76-C77, C79-C80, C82, C84.

Flower Type of Regular Issue

Flowers: 60fr, Hibiscus schizopetalus. 85fr, Acalypha sanderii.

1971, July 19 Photo. *Perf. 13*
Size: 27x48mm

C37 A25 60fr grn, ver & yel .60 .30
C38 A25 85fr grn, red & yel .75 .45

For surcharge see No. C75.

Mural, Moroni Airport — AP12

Designs: 85fr, Mural in Arrival Hall, Moroni Airport. 100fr, View of Moroni Airport.

1972, Mar. 30 Photo. *Perf. 13*

C39 AP12 65fr gray & multi .32 .28
C40 AP12 85fr gray & multi .48 .28

Engr.

C41 AP12 100fr brn, bl & slate grn .80 .40
Nos. C39-C41 (3) 1.60 .96

New airport in Moroni.

Eiffel Tower and Moroni Telephone Exchange — AP13

Design: 75fr, Frenchman and Comoro Islander talking on telephone, radio tower and beacons.

1972, Apr. 24

C42 AP13 35fr dl red & gray .18 .15
C43 AP13 75fr dk car, vio & bl .35 .18

First radio-telephone connection between France and Comoro Islands.

ARCHIPEL DES COMORES

CHASSE SOUS MARINE

RF 70F POSTE AERIENNE

Underwater Spear-fishing — AP14

1972, July 5 Engr. *Perf. 13*

C44 AP14 70fr vio bl, brt grn & mar .55 .40

For surcharge see No. C78.

Types of 1971

1972, Nov. 15 Photo.

Designs: 20fr, Cape Sima. 35fr, Bambao Palace. 40fr, Domoni Palace. 60fr, Gomajou Peninsula. 100fr, Map of Anjouan Island.

C45 AP10 20fr brn & multi .15 .15
C46 AP10 35fr dk grn & multi .22 .18
C47 AP10 40fr bl & multi .28 .20
C48 AP10 60fr grnsh blk & multi .38 .30

Engr.

C49 AP11 100fr mar, bl & sl grn .75 .50
Nos. C45-C49 (5) 1.78 1.33

Pres. Said Mohamed Cheikh (1904-70) — AP15

1973, Mar. 16 Photo. *Perf. 13*

C50 AP15 20fr multi .15 .15
C51 AP15 35fr multi .25 .15

For overprints see Nos. C70, C72.

No. C24 Surcharged

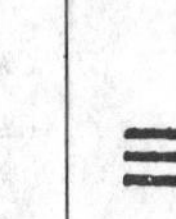

120F

Mission Internationale pour l'étude du Cœlacanthe

1973, Apr. 30 Engr. *Perf. 13*

C52 A19 120fr on 90fr multi .85 .65

Intl. Commission for Coelacanth Studies.

Map of Grand Comoro AP16

1973, June 28 Engr. *Perf. 13*

C53 AP16 135fr vio, bl & dk brn 1.25 .80

See Nos. C65, C68. For surcharges see Nos. C90-C92.

Karthala Volcano AP17

1973, July 16 Photo. *Perf. 13x12½*

C54 AP17 120fr multi .85 .65

Eruption of Karthala, Sept. 1972.
For surcharge see No. C89.

Armauer G. Hansen — AP18

Design: 150fr, Nicolaus Copernicus (1473-1543), Polish astronomer.

1973, Sept. 5 Engr. *Perf. 13*

C55 AP18 100fr brn, dk bl & sl grn .85 .65
C56 AP18 150fr grnsh bl, vio bl & choc 1.25 .75

Cent. of the discovery of the Hansen bacillus, the cause of leprosy.
For overprint and surcharge see Nos. C81, C93.

1983, Sept. 30 **Photo.**
C57 AP19 200fr blk & multi 1.40 1.00

Souvenir Sheet

C58 AP19 100fr blk & multi .90 .90

For overprint see No. C87.

Order of the Star of Anjouan — AP20

Said Omar ben Soumeth — AP21

1974, Jan. 7 **Photo.** ***Perf. 13***
C59 AP20 500fr brn, bl & gold 3.00 2.50

For overprint see No. C95.

Perf. 13x13½, 13½x13
1974, Jan. 31

Design: 135fr, Grand Mufti Said Omar, horiz.

C60 AP21 135fr blk & multi .80 .65
C61 AP21 200fr blk & multi 1.40 1.00

For overprint and surcharge see Nos. C85, C88.

Types of 1971-73

Designs (Views on Mayotte): 20fr, Moya Beach. 35fr, Chiconi. 90fr, Port Mamutzu. 120fr, Map of Mayotte.

1974, Aug. 31 **Photo.** ***Perf. 13***

C62 AP10 20fr bl & multi	.15	.15
C63 AP10 35fr grn & multi	.25	.20
C64 AP10 90fr multi	.60	.50
Engr.		
C65 AP16 120fr ultra & grn	.75	.60
Nos. C62-C65 (4)	1.75	1.45

Jet Take-off — AP22

1975, Jan. 10 **Engr.** ***Perf. 13***
C66 AP22 135fr multi .90 .65

First direct route Moroni-Hahaya-Paris.
For surcharge see No. C86.

Rotary Emblem, Meeting House, Map — AP23

1975, Feb. 23 **Photo.** ***Perf. 13***
C67 AP23 250fr multi 1.65 1.25

Rotary Intl., 70th anniv., Moroni Rotary Club, 10th anniv.
For surcharge see No. C94.

Map Type of 1973

Design: 230fr, Map of Moheli, horiz.

1975, May 26 **Engr.** ***Perf. 13***
C68 AP16 230fr ocher, ol grn & bl 1.65 1.25

STATE OF COMORO

Issues of 1968-75 Surcharged and Overprinted with Bars and: "ETAT COMORIEN" in Black, Silver, Red or Orange

1975 **Printing & Perfs. as Before**

C69 AP10 10fr on 20fr #C62	.15	.15
C70 AP15 20fr (S)	.20	.15
C71 AP10 30fr on 35fr (R) #C63	.25	.20
C72 AP15 35fr (S)	.30	.22
C73 AP10 40fr (O)	.38	.25
C74 A19 50fr	.45	.30
C75 A25 75fr on 60fr	.70	.45
C76 AP10 75fr on 60fr	.70	.45
C77 AP10 75fr on 65fr (O)	.70	.45
C78 AP14 75fr on 70fr	.70	.45
C79 AP11 100fr #C36	.90	.60
C80 AP11 100fr #C49	.90	.60
C81 AP18 100fr	.90	.60
C82 AP10 100fr on 85fr (O)	.90	.60
C83 A25 100fr on 85fr	.90	.60
C84 AP10 100fr on 90fr	.90	.60
C85 AP21 100fr on 135fr (S)	.90	.60
C86 AP22 100fr on 135fr	.90	.60
C87 AP19 200fr (S)	1.75	1.25
C88 AP21 200fr (S)	1.75	1.25
C89 AP17 200fr on 120fr	1.75	1.25
C90 AP16 200fr on 120fr	1.75	1.25
C91 AP16 200fr on 135fr	1.75	1.25
C92 AP16 200fr on 230fr	1.75	1.25
C93 AP18 400fr on 150fr	4.00	2.50
C94 AP23 400fr on 250fr	4.00	2.50
C95 AP20 500fr	4.50	3.25
Nos. C69-C95 (27)	34.73	23.62

See postage section for airmail stamps that are part of joint postage/airmail sets.

Rotary Emblem, Landscape AP26

1979, July 31 **Litho.** ***Perf. 13x12½***
C107 AP26 400fr multi 3.00 1.65

Rotary International.

IYC Emblem, Mother and Child — AP27

1979, July 31 ***Perf. 13x13½***
C108 AP27 250fr multi 1.65 1.25

Intl. Year of the Child. See No. CB1. For surcharges see Nos. C121, C202.

Dimadjou Dispensary, Map of Southern Africa, Emblem AP28

1980, Feb. 23 **Litho.** ***Perf. 12½***
C109 AP28 100fr shown .50 .30
C110 AP28 260fr Globe, Concorde, emblem 1.40 .65

Rotary International, 75th anniv. and Moroni Rotary Club, 15th anniv. (100fr).
For surcharges see Nos. C119-C120.

First Transatlantic Flight, 50th Anniversary — AP29

1980, May 30 **Litho.** ***Perf. 13***
C111 AP29 200fr multi 1.00 .70

No. C111 Surcharged in Blue

1981, Feb. **Litho.** ***Perf. 13***
C112 AP29 30fr on 200fr multi .20 .20

The Dove and the Rainbow, by Picasso — AP30

Picasso Birth Centenary: 70fr, Still Life on a Sideboard. 150fr, Studio with Plaster Head. 250fr, Bowl and Pot, vert. 500fr, The Red Tablecloth.

1981, June 30 **Litho.** ***Perf. 12½***

C113 AP30 40fr multi	.16	.15
C114 AP30 70fr multi	.25	.15
C115 AP30 150fr multi	.65	.35
C116 AP30 250fr multi	1.10	.55
C117 AP30 500fr multi	2.00	1.10
Nos. C113-C117 (5)	4.16	2.30

For surcharge see No. C118.

#C114, C109-C110, CB1 Surchd.

1981, Nov. **Litho.** ***Perf. 12½, 13***

C118 AP30 10fr on 70fr multi	.15	.15
C119 AP28 10fr on 100fr multi	.15	.15
C120 AP28 50fr on 260fr multi	.20	.15
C121 AP27 50fr on 200fr+30fr multi	.20	.15
Set value	.54	.32

Manned Flight Bicentenary — AP31

Balloons. 100fr, 200fr, 300fr, 500fr vert.

1983, Apr. 20 **Litho.** ***Perf. 13***

C122 AP31 100fr Montgolfiere, 1783	.40	.20
C123 AP31 200fr Lunardi, 1784	.80	.40
C124 AP31 300fr Blanchard and Jeffries, 1785	1.10	.60
C125 AP31 400fr Giffard, 1852	1.60	.80
Nos. C122-C125 (4)	3.90	2.00

Souvenir Sheet

C126 AP31 500fr Paris Siege, 1870 2.00 1.00

For overprint see No. 602.

Pre-Olympic Year Sailing — AP32

1983, June 30 **Litho.** ***Perf. 13***

C127 AP32 150fr Type 470	.60	.30
C128 AP32 200fr Flying Dutchman	.80	.40
C129 AP32 300fr Type 470, diff.	1.10	.40
C130 AP32 400fr Finn	1.60	.75
Nos. C127-C130 (4)	4.10	1.85

Souvenir Sheet

C131 AP32 500fr Solding 2.25 1.10

For overprint and surcharge see Nos. 603, C206.

1984 Summer Olympics — AP33

1984, July 10 **Litho.** ***Perf. 13***

C132 AP33 60fr Basketball	.25	.15
C133 AP33 100fr Basketball, diff.	.40	.20
C134 AP33 165fr Basketball, diff.	.65	.35
C135 AP33 175fr Baseball, horiz.	.70	.35
C136 AP33 200fr Baseball, horiz.	.80	.40
Nos. C132-C136 (5)	2.80	1.45

Souvenir Sheet

C137 AP33 500fr Basketball, diff. 2.00 1.00

Nos. C132-C134 vert.

Development Conference — AP34

1984, July 2 **Litho.** ***Perf. 13***
C138 AP34 475fr Tools for development 1.60

Audubon Bicentenary — AP35

1985, Jan. 15 **Litho.** ***Perf. 13***

C139 AP35 100fr Hirundo rustica, vert.	.28
C140 AP35 125fr Icterus galbula, vert.	.35
C141 AP35 150fr Buteo lineatus	.40
C142 AP35 500fr Sphyropieus varius	1.40
Nos. C139-C142 (4)	2.43

Moroni Port Missile Defense — AP36

Design: No. C146, Ngome Ntsoudjini Scout troop.

1985, May 20 **Litho.** ***Perf. 13x12½***
C145 AP36 200fr multi .55
C146 AP36 200fr multi .55

PHILEXAFRICA '85, Lome. Nos. C145-C146 printed se-tenant with center labels picturing map of Africa or UAPT emblem.
For surcharges see Nos. C207-C208.

Natl. Flag, Sun, Outline Map of Islands — AP37

1985, July 6

C147 AP37 10fr multi .15
C148 AP37 15fr multi .15
C149 AP37 125fr multi .35
C150 AP37 300fr multi .75
Nos. C147-C150 (4) 1.40

Natl. independence, 10th anniv.

Runners — AP38

1985, Nov. 12

C151 AP38 250fr shown .65
C152 AP38 250fr Mining .65

PHILEXAFRICA '85, Lome, Togo, Nov. 16-24. Nos. C151-C152 printed se-tenant with center label picturing map of Africa or UAPT emblem.

For surcharges see Nos. C204-C205.

Air Transport Union, UTA, 50th Anniv. — AP39

1985, Dec. 30 Litho. *Perf. 13*

C153 AP39 25fr F-AOUL seaplane .15 .15
C154 AP39 75fr Camel driver, DC-9 .20 .15
C155 AP39 100fr Noratlas and Heron DC-4s .35 .16
a. Souv. sheet of 3, #C153-C155, perf. 12½ .55 .55
C156 AP39 125fr UTA cargo plane .42 .22

Size: 40x52mm

Perf. 12½x13

C157 AP39 1000fr Aircraft, 1935-1985 3.75 1.75
a. Souv. sheet of 2, #C156-C157, perf. 12½ 3.25 3.25
Nos. C153-C157 (5) 4.87 2.43

Halley's Comet — AP40

Comets, astronomers and probes.

1986, Mar. 7 *Perf. 13*

C158 AP40 125fr Edmond Halley, Giotto probe .65 .32
C159 AP40 150fr Giacobini-Zinner, 1959 .80 .40
C160 AP40 225fr Encke, 1961 1.25 .60
C161 AP40 300fr Bradfield, 1980 1.65 .80
C162 AP40 450fr Planet A probe 2.50 1.25
Nos. C158-C162 (5) 6.85 3.37

1986 World Cup Soccer Championships, Mexico — AP41

Various soccer plays.

1986, June 11 Litho. *Perf. 13*

C163 AP41 125fr multi .70 .35
C164 AP41 210fr multi 1.25 .60
C165 AP41 500fr multi 2.75 1.40
C166 AP41 600fr multi 3.50 1.10
Nos. C163-C166 (4) 8.20 3.45

Tennis at the 1988 Summer Olympics — AP42

Various players.

1987, Jan. 28 Litho. *Perf. 13½*

C167 AP42 150fr multi .82 .40
C168 AP42 250fr multi 1.40 .70
C169 AP42 500fr multi 2.75 1.40
C170 AP42 600fr multi 3.25 1.65
Nos. C167-C170 (4) 8.22 4.15

For overprints and surcharge see Nos. C183-C186, C203.

World Wildlife Fund — AP43

Various pictures of the mongoose lemur.

1987, Feb. 18 *Perf. 13*

C171 AP43 75fr multi, vert. .40 .20
C172 AP43 100fr multi .55 .28
C173 AP43 125fr multi .70 .35
C174 AP43 150fr multi .82 .40
Nos. C171-C174 (4) 2.47 1.23

1988 Winter Olympics, Calgary AP44

1987, Apr. 10 Litho. *Perf. 13½*

C175 AP44 150fr Slalom .82 .40
C176 AP44 225fr Ski jumping 1.25 .62
C177 AP44 500fr Women's giant slalom 2.75 1.40
C178 AP44 600fr Luge 3.25 1.65
Nos. C175-C178 (4) 8.07 4.07

AP45

Aviation History AP46

Designs: 200fr, Inventors Didier Daurat and Raymond Vanier with 1935 Air Blue F-ANR1. 300fr, Farman biplane, 1st scheduled airmail delivery, Paris-LeMans-St. Nazaire, Aug. 17, 1918. 500fr, Bleriot aircraft, 1st scheduled airmail delivery, Villacoublay-Vendome-Poitiers-Pauillac, Oct. 15, 1913. 1000fr, Henri Pequet and his aircraft, Feb. 18, 1911.

1987, Dec. 29 Litho. *Perf. 13*

C179 AP45 200fr multi 1.30 .65
C180 AP45 300fr multi 1.95 1.00
C181 AP45 500fr multi 3.25 1.65

Perf. 12½x13

C182 AP46 1000fr multi 6.50 3.25
Nos. C179-C182 (4) 13.00 6.55

Airmail history exposition, Allahabad.

Nos. C167-C170 Ovptd. in Red for 1988 Olympic Tennis Champions

Overprint includes name of athlete and "Medaille d'or / Seoul" or "Medaille / d'argent / Seoul."

1988, Nov. Litho. *Perf. 13½*

C183 AP42 150fr "Miloslav Mecir / (Tchec.)" .95 .48
C184 AP42 250fr "Tim Mayotte / (U.S.A.)" 1.60 .80
C185 AP42 500fr "Steffi Graf / (R.F.A.)" 3.25 1.60
C186 AP42 600fr "Gabriela Sabatini / (Argentine)" 3.85 1.95
Nos. C183-C186 (4) 9.65 4.83

Early Aviators and Aircraft — AP47

Designs: 100fr, Alberto Santos-Dumont (1873-1932), and *Bagatelle,* 1st documented power flight in Europe, Oct. 23, 1906. 150fr, Wright Brothers and *Flyer A.* 200fr, Louis Bleriot (1872-1936) and *Bleriot XI,* 1st crossing of the English Channel in a heavier-than-air craft, July 25, 1909. 300fr, Henri Farman (1874-1958) and Voisin biplane, 1st fixed-route 1-kilometer circular flight, Jan. 13, 1908. 500fr, Gabriel (1880-1973) and Charles (1882-1912) Voisin, established 1st biplane factory (1908), and Voisin biplane. 800fr, Roland Garros (1888-1918), 1st trans-Mediterranean flight, Sept. 23, 1913.

1988, Dec. 7 Litho. *Perf. 13*

C187 AP47 100fr pur .65 .32
C188 AP47 150fr brt lil rose .95 .48
C189 AP47 200fr blk 1.30 .65
C190 AP47 300fr dark yel org 1.90 .95
C191 AP47 500fr dark blue 3.20 1.60
C192 AP47 800fr lt olive grn 5.10 2.55
Nos. C187-C192 (6) 13.10 6.55

For surcharge see No. C209.

Souvenir Sheet

Space Achievements — AP48

Design: World Philatelic Programs stamp collecting emblem, Soviet satellite and Edmond Halley.

1988 Litho. *Perf. 13½*

C193 AP48 750fr multi 5.00 5.00

Nos. C10[...]
C145-C14[...]

1989 Litho.

C202 AP27 5fr on 250fr #[...]
C203 AP42 25fr on 250fr #C16[...]
C204 AP38 50fr on 250fr #C151
C205 AP38 50fr on 250fr #C152 .3[...]
C206 AP32 150fr on 200fr #C128 1.05 .5[...]
C207 AP36 150fr on 200fr #C145 1.05 .52
C208 AP36 150fr on 200fr #C146 1.05 .52
C209 AP47 150fr on 200fr #C189 1.05 .52
Nos. C202-C209 (8) 5.23 2.74

Nos. C204-C205 and C207-C208 printed se-tenant with labels between.

World Cup Soccer, Championships, Italy — AP50

Various soccer plays and map of Italy.

1990, June Litho. *Perf. 13*

C210 AP50 75fr multicolored .60 .30
C211 AP50 150fr multicolored 1.20 .60
C212 AP50 500fr multicolored 3.75 1.90
C213 AP50 1000fr multicolored 8.00 4.00
Nos. C210-C213 (4) 13.55 6.80

Souvenir Sheet

Garry Kasparov, Anatoly Karpov, Russian Chess Champions — AP51

Litho. & Embossed

1991, Aug. 5 *Perf. 13½*

C214 AP51 1500fr gold & multi

World Chess Championships.

1992 Summer Olympics, Barcelona AP52

Litho. & Embossed

1992, July 28 *Perf. 13½*

C215 AP52 1500fr gold & multi 24.00 12.00

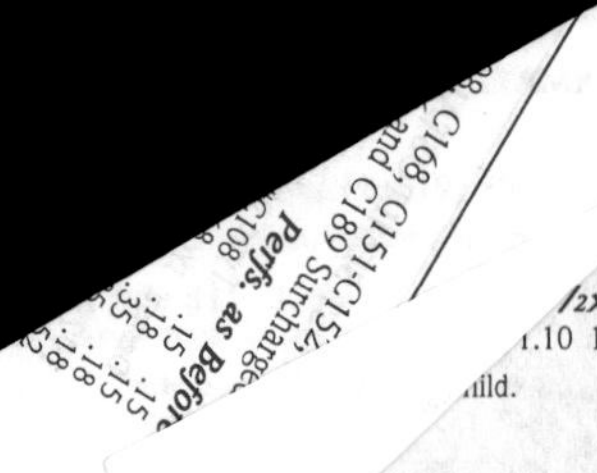

1.10 1.10

…hild.

…E DUE STAMPS

Anjouan Mosque D1

Coelacanth D2

1950 Unwmk. Engr. *Perf. 14x13*

J1	D1	50c deep green	.20	.20
J2	D1	1fr black brown	.20	.20

1954

J3	D2	5fr dk brown & green	.28	.28
J4	D2	10fr gray & red brown	.38	.38
J5	D2	20fr indigo & blue	.60	.60
		Nos. J3-J5 (3)	1.26	1.26

Hibiscus — D3

Designs: 2fr, 15fr, 40fr, 50fr, vertical.

1977, Nov. 19 Litho. *Perf. 13½*

J6	D3	1fr shown	.15	.15
J7	D3	2fr Pineapple	.15	.15
J8	D3	5fr White butterfly	.15	.15
J9	D3	10fr Chameleon	.15	.15
J10	D3	15fr Blooming banana	.15	.15
J11	D3	20fr Orchids	.15	.15
J12	D3	30fr Allamanda cathartica	.15	.15
J13	D3	40fr Cashews	.15	.15
J14	D3	50fr Custard apple	.16	.15
J15	D3	100fr Breadfruit	.35	.16
J16	D3	200fr Vanilla	.65	.35
J17	D3	500fr Ylang ylang	1.60	.80
		Set value	3.35	1.80

OFFICIAL STAMPS

Comoro Flag — O1

Perf. 13x12½

1979-85 Litho. Unwmk.

O1	O1	5fr multi	.15	.15
O2	O1	10fr multi	.15	.15
O3	O1	20fr multi	.15	.15
O4	O1	30fr multi	.18	.15
O5	O1	40fr multi	.25	.16
O6	O1	60fr multi ('80)	.22	.16
O7	O1	75fr multi ('85)	.20	.15
O8	O1	100fr multi	.50	.35
		Nos. O1-O8 (8)	1.80	
		Set value		1.00

See Nos. 526-530.

Pres. Said Mohamed Cheikh (1904-1970) — O2

…0-85

…9	O2	100fr multi	.35	.25
…10	O2	125fr multi ('85)	.35	.22
O11	O2	400fr multi	1.40	1.00
		Nos. O9-O11 (3)	2.10	1.47

CONGO DEMOCRATIC REPUBLIC

ˌde–mə–ˈkra–tik ri–ˈpə–blik of ˈkäŋ–(ˌ)gō

LOCATION — Central Africa
GOVT. — Republic
AREA — 895,348 sq. mi. (estimated)
POP. — 22,480,000 (est. 1971)
CAPITAL — Kinshasa (Leopoldville)

Congo was an independent state, founded by Leopold II of Belgium, until 1908 when it was annexed to Belgium as a colony. Congo became an independent republic in 1960. The name was changed to Republic of Zaire, Oct. 28, 1971. See Zaire in Vol. 5 for later issues.

100 Centimes = 1 Franc
100 Sengi = 1 Li-Kuta,
100 Ma-Kuta = 1 Zaire (1967)

Catalogue values for all unused stamps in this country are for Never Hinged items.

Belgian Congo Flower Issue of 1952-53 Overprinted or Surcharged **CONGO**

Perf. 11½

1960, June 6 Photo. Unwmk.

Flowers in Natural Colors

Size: 21x25½mm

Granite Paper

323	A86	10c dp plum & ocher	.15	.15
324	A86	10c on 15c red & yel grn	.15	.15
325	A86	20c grn & gray	.15	.15
326	A86	40c grn & sal	.15	.15
327	A86	50c on 60c bl grn & pink	.15	.15
328	A86	50c on 75c dp plum & gray	.15	.15
329	A86	1fr car & yel	.15	.15
330	A86	1.50fr vio & ap grn	.15	.15
331	A86	2fr ol grn & buff	.15	.15
332	A86	3fr ol grn & pink	.15	.15
333	A86	4fr choc & lil	.15	.15
334	A86	5fr dp plum & lt bl grn	.15	.15
335	A86	6.50fr dk car & lil	.22	.15
336	A86	8fr grn & lt yel	.32	.15
337	A86	10fr dp plum & pale ol	.45	.15
338	A86	20fr vio bl & dl sal	.90	.35

Overprinted **CONGO**

Size: 22x32mm

339	A86	50fr dp plum & gray bl	4.75	2.25
340	A86	100fr grn & buff	8.25	4.00
		Nos. 323-340 (18)	16.69	8.85

Nos. 324, 327-328 exist without "CONGO" overprint but with surcharge.

Belgian Congo Animal Issue, Nos. 306-317, Overprinted or Surcharged in Red, Blue, Black or Brown **CONGO**

341	A92	10c bl & brn (R)	.15	.15
342	A93	20c red org & sl (Bl)	.15	.15
343	A92	40c brn & bl (Bk)	.15	.15
344	A93	50c brt ultra, red & sep (R)	.15	.15
345	A92	1fr brn, grn & blk (Br)	.15	.15
346	A93	1.50fr blk & org yel (R)	.15	.15
347	A92	2fr crim, blk & brn (Bl)	.15	.15
348	A93	3.50fr on 3fr blk, gray & lil rose (Bk)	.15	.15
349	A92	5fr brn, dk brn & brt grn (Br)	.15	.15
350	A93	6.50fr bl, brn & org yel (R)	.18	.15
a.		Black overprint	.32	.15
351	A92	8fr org brn, ol bis & lil (Br)	.20	.15
352	A93	10fr multi (R)	.30	.15
		Set value	1.40	.90

Same Overprint on Belgian Congo No. 318

1960

353	A94	50c gldn brn, ocher & red brn	.40	.40

Same Overprint and Surcharge of New Value on Belgian Congo Nos. 321-322

Inscription in French

354	A95	3.50fr on 3fr gray & red	.40	.32

Inscription in Flemish

355	A95	3.50fr on 3fr gray & red	.40	.32
		Nos. 353-355 (3)	1.20	1.04

Map of Congo A93a

1960 Photo. *Perf. 11½*

356	A93a	20c brown	.15	.15
357	A93a	50c rose red	.15	.15
358	A93a	1fr green	.15	.15
359	A93a	1.50fr red brn	.15	.15
360	A93a	2fr rose car	.15	.15
361	A93a	3.50fr lilac	.15	.15
362	A93a	5fr brt bl	.15	.15
363	A93a	6.50fr gray	.20	.15
364	A93a	10fr orange	.32	.15
365	A93a	20fr ultra	.50	.24
		Set value	1.70	.90

Congo's Independence.
For overprints see Nos. 371-380.

Flag, People and Broken Chain — A94

1961 Unwmk. *Perf. 11½*

Flag in Blue and Yellow

366	A94	2fr rose vio	.15	.15
367	A94	3.50fr vermilion	.15	.15
368	A94	6.50fr yel brn	.15	.15
369	A94	10fr brt grn	.24	.15
370	A94	20fr car rose	.42	.30
		Nos. 366-370 (5)	1.11	
		Set value		.62

Signing of the Independence Agreement by Belgium, Jan. 4, 1959.

Nos. 356-365 Overprinted in Blue, Black or Red: "Conference Coquilhatville Avril Mai 1961"

1961

371	A93a	20c brn (Bl)	.40	.40
372	A93a	50c rose red (Bk)	.40	.40
373	A93a	1fr grn (R)	.40	.40
374	A93a	1.50fr red brn (Bl)	.40	.40
375	A93a	2fr rose car (Bk)	.40	.40
376	A93a	3.50fr lil (Bl)	.40	.40
377	A93a	5fr brt bl (R)	.40	.40
378	A93a	6.50fr gray (R)	.40	.40
379	A93a	10fr org (Bk)	.40	.40
380	A93a	20fr ultra (R)	.40	.40
		Nos. 371-380 (10)	4.00	4.00

Coquilhatville Conf., Apr.-May, 1961.

Pres. Joseph Kasavubu A95

Kasavubu and Map of Congo A96

Design: 10fr, 20fr, 50fr, 100fr, Kasavubu in uniform and map.

Perf. 11½

1961, June 30 Unwmk. Photo.

Portrait and Inscription in Dark Brown

381	A95	10c yellow	.15	.15
382	A95	20c dp rose	.15	.15
383	A95	40c bl grn	.15	.15
384	A95	50c salmon	.15	.15
385	A95	1fr lilac	.15	.15
386	A95	1.50fr lt brn	.15	.15
387	A95	2fr brt grn	.15	.15
388	A96	3.50fr rose pink	.15	.15
389	A96	5fr gray	1.10	.15
390	A96	6.50fr ultra	.30	.15
391	A96	8fr olive	.52	.15
392	A95	10fr lt vio	.70	.15
393	A95	20fr orange	.70	.15
394	A95	50fr lt bl	1.10	.30
395	A95	100fr ap grn	1.65	.50
		Nos. 381-395 (15)	7.27	
		Set value		1.96

First anniversary of independence.

Nos. 381-387, 389 and 392 Overprinted: "REOUVERTURE du PARLEMENT JUILLET 1961"

1961

Portrait and Inscription in Dark Brown

396	A95	10c yellow	.15	.15
397	A95	20c dp rose	.15	.15
398	A95	40c bl grn	.15	.15
399	A95	50c salmon	.28	.20
400	A95	1fr lilac	.28	.20
401	A95	1.50fr lt brn	.70	.60
402	A95	2fr brt grn	.70	.60
403	A96	5fr gray	.70	.60
404	A95	10fr lt vio	.85	.70
		Nos. 396-404 (9)	3.96	3.35

Congolese parliament re-opening, July, 1961.

Dag Hammarskjold and Map of Africa with Congo — A97

Malaria Eradication Emblem and Mosquito — A98

1962, Jan. 20 Photo. *Perf. 11½*

Gray Background

405	A97	10c dk brn	.15	.15
406	A97	20c Prus bl	.15	.15
407	A97	30c brown	.15	.15
408	A97	40c dk bl	.15	.15
409	A97	50c brn red	.15	.15
410	A97	3fr ol grn	1.65	1.10
411	A97	6.50fr dk vio	.55	.35
412	A97	8fr red brn	.65	.45
		Nos. 405-412 (8)	3.60	
		Set value		2.20

Souvenir Sheets

Imperf

413	A97	25fr blk brn	2.75	2.75
a.		Overprint in green	1.00	1.00

Nos. 405-413 issued in memory of Dag Hammarskjold, Secretary General of the United Nations, 1953-61.

No 413a is overprinted "30 Juin 1962" on stamp and "2eme Anniversaire de l'Independance" on sheet margin. Issued June 30, 1962.

For overprints see Nos. 417-424.

1962, June 15

Granite Paper

414	A98	1.50fr yel, blk & dk red	.15	.15
415	A98	2fr yel grn, brn & bl grn	.28	.15
416	A98	6.50fr ultra, blk & mar	.15	.15
		Set value	.48	.30

WHO drive to eradicate malaria.

Nos. 405-412 Overprinted in Blue, Purple, Black or Carmine

"Paix, Travail, Austerite ..,
C. ADOULA
11 juillet 1962

1962, Oct. 15

Gray Background

417	A97	10c dk brn (Bl)	.15	.15
418	A97	20c Prus bl (P)	.15	.15
419	A97	30c brn (Bk)	.15	.15
420	A97	40c dk bl (C)	.15	.15
421	A97	50c brn red (Bl)	1.10	.50
422	A97	3fr ol grn (P)	.15	.15
423	A97	6.50fr dk vio (Bk)	.20	.15
424	A97	8fr red brn (C)	.28	.15
		Set value	2.00	.95

Reorganization of Adoula administration.

Canceled to Order

Starting in 1963, values in the used column are for "canceled to order" stamps. Postally used copies sell for much more.

A99

1963, Jan. 28	Engr.	*Perf. 10½x13*		
425	A99	2fr dull purple	.90	1.00
426	A99	4fr red	.15	.15
427	A99	7fr dark blue	.15	.15
428	A99	20fr slate green	.20	.15
		Nos. 425-428 (4)	1.40	1.45

Congo's 1st participation at the UPU Cong., New Delhi, Mar. 1963.

For overprints see Nos. 468-471.

Shoebill — A100

Birds: 10c, Pelicans. 20c, Crested guinea fowl, horiz. 30c, Openbill. 40c, White-bellied storks, horiz. 2fr, Marabou. 3fr, Greater flamingos, horiz. 4fr, Congolese peacock. 5fr, Hartlaub ducks, horiz. 6fr, Secretary bird. 7fr, Black-casqued hornbill, horiz. 8fr, Sacred ibis and nest. 10fr, Crowned crane, horiz. 20fr, Saddle-bill stork, horiz.

1963	Unwmk.	Photo. *Perf. 11½*		
429	A100	10c pink, ultra & ocher	.15	.15
430	A100	20c rose red, bl & blk	.15	.15
431	A100	30c grn, ocher & blk	.15	.15
432	A100	40c gray, org & blk	.15	.15
433	A100	1fr brn, emer & gray	.15	.15
434	A100	2fr gray, red & ind	1.10	.32
435	A100	3fr ol grn, blk & rose	.15	.15
436	A100	4fr car rose, vio bl & grn	.15	.15
437	A100	5fr lake, lt bl & blk	.15	.15
438	A100	6fr pur, yel & blk	1.10	.32
439	A100	7fr bl grn, blk & ind	.15	.15
440	A100	8fr yel, org & blk	.15	.15
441	A100	10fr bl, blk & rose	.15	.15
442	A100	20fr cit, red & blk	.30	.15
		Set value	3.35	1.30

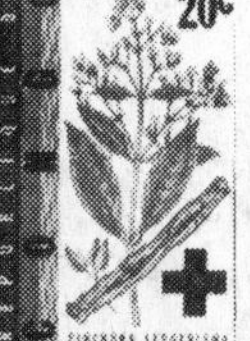

Cinchona Ledgeriana A101

Red Cross Nurse A102

Designs: 10c, 30c, 5fr, Strophanthus sarmentosus.

Perf. 12½x13½, 13½x12½

1963, May 25	Engr.	Unwmk.		
		Cross in Red		
443	A101	10c vio & dl grn	.15	.15
444	A101	20c magenta & bl	.15	.15
445	A101	30c grn & org	.15	.15
446	A101	40c bl & vio	.15	.15
447	A101	5fr ol & rose claret	.15	.15
448	A101	7fr org & blk	.15	.15
449	A102	9fr gray olive & red	.15	.15
450	A102	20fr purple & red	1.10	.65
		Set value	1.55	1.00

International Red Cross centenary.

A souvenir sheet of three contains imperf. 58fr, 7fr, and 20fr stamps similar to Nos. 447, 448 and 450, but in changed colors. Size: 109x75mm. Value $10.

Men Joining Hands and Map of Congo — A103

1963, June 29		Photo. *Perf. 11½*		
451	A103	4fr multi	.85	.30
452	A103	5fr multi	.15	.15
453	A103	9fr multi	.15	.15
454	A103	12fr multi	.18	.15
		Nos. 451-454 (4)	1.33	
		Set value		.50

Issued to celebrate national reconciliation.

Bulldozer and Kabambare Sewer, Leopoldville — A104

Designs: 30c, 5fr, 12fr, Excavator and blueprint. 50c, 9fr, Building Ituri road.

1963, July 1		Engr. Unwmk.		
455	A104	20c multi	.15	.15
456	A104	30c multi	.15	.15
457	A104	50c multi	.15	.15
458	A104	3fr multi	.85	.32
459	A104	5fr multi	.15	.15
460	A104	9fr multi	.15	.15
461	A104	12fr multi	.15	.15
		Set value	1.35	.72

Issued to publicize aid to Congo by the European Economic Community.

Leopoldville Airport N'Djili A105

Design: 5fr, 7fr, 50fr, Tail assembly and airport.

1963, Nov. 30		Photo. *Perf. 11½*		
462	A105	2fr gray, yel & red brn	.15	.15
463	A105	5fr mag, vio & yel	.15	.15
464	A105	6fr bl, yel & dk brn	.85	.35
465	A105	7fr multi	.22	.15
466	A105	30fr lil, yel & ol	.35	.24
467	A105	50fr multi	.40	.25
		Nos. 462-467 (6)	2.12	1.29

Issued to publicize Air Congo.

For surcharge see No. 606.

Nos. 425-428 Overprinted with Silver Frame on Three Sides and Black Inscription: "15e anniversaire / 10 DECEMBRE 1948 / DROITS DE L'HOMME / 10 DECEMBRE 1963"

Engraved and Typographed

1963, Dec. 10		*Perf. 10½x13*		
468	A99	2fr dull purple	.15	.15
469	A99	4fr red	.15	.15
470	A99	7fr dark blue	.18	.18
471	A99	20fr slate green	.20	.20
		Set value	.52	.52

Universal Declaration of Human Rights, 15th anniv.

Nos. 468-471 exist with side date panels transposed ("1963" at left, "1948" at right). Value, each $3.50.

Laboratory Technician and Atomic Emblem — A106

Designs: 1.50fr, 60fr, University. 8fr, 75fr, First African nuclear reactor. 25fr, 100fr, University and crest.

1964, Feb. 1		Photo. *Perf. 14x12½*		
472	A106	50c multi	.15	.15
473	A106	1.50fr multi	.15	.15
474	A106	8fr multi	1.65	1.50
475	A106	25fr multi	.15	.15
476	A106	30fr multi	.20	.15
477	A106	60fr multi	.35	.30
478	A106	75fr multi	.50	.50
479	A106	100fr multi	.65	.55
a.		Souv. sheet of 3	2.25	2.25
		Nos. 472-479 (8)	3.80	3.45

Lovanium University, Leopoldville, 10th anniv.

No. 479a contains 3 imperf. multicolored stamps: 20fr, design as 50c; 30fr, as 8fr; 100fr.

Belgian Congo Issues of 1952-59 Overprinted "REPUBLIQUE DU CONGO" and Surcharged in Black on Overprinted Metallic Panels

1964		*Perf. 11½*		
480	A93	1fr on 20c red org & sl (#307)	.15	.15
481	A86	2fr on 1.50fr (#273)	1.40	.90
482	A93	5fr on 6.50fr (#315)	.22	.15
483	A86	8fr on 6.50fr (#278)	.25	.15

Republic Issues of 1960-61 Surcharged in Black of Overprinted Metallic Rectangles or Ovals

No.	Type			
484	A86	1fr on 6.50fr (#335)	.15	.15
485	A93	1fr on 20c (#342)	.15	.15
486	A86	2fr on 1.50fr (#330)	.15	.15
487	A95	3fr on 20c (#382)	.15	.15
488	A95	4fr on 40c (#383)	.15	.15
489	A93	5fr on 6.50fr ("Congo" red) (#350)	.22	.15
a.		"Congo" black	.22	.15
490	A93a	6fr on 6.50fr (#363)	.22	.15
491	A93a	7fr on 20c (#356)	.32	.18
		Nos. 480-491 (12)	3.53	
		Set value		2.15

Pole Vault A107

Sports: 7fr, 20fr, Javelin, vert. 8fr, 100fr, Hurdling.

Perf. 11½

1964, July 13		Unwmk. Photo.		
		Granite Paper		
492	A107	5fr gray, dk brn & car	.15	.15
493	A107	7fr rose, vio & emer	.85	.35
494	A107	8fr org, yel, red brn & vio bl	.15	.15
495	A107	10fr bl, vio brn & mag	.15	.15
496	A107	20fr gray grn, red brn & ver	.15	.15
497	A107	100fr lil, dk brn & grn	.85	.20
a.		Souv. sheet of 3	3.50	3.50
		Nos. 492-497 (6)	2.30	
		Set value		.80

18th Olympic Games, Tokyo, Oct. 10-25. No. 497a contains 3 imperf. stamps (20fr orange & dark brown, pole vault; 30fr citron and dark brown, hurdling; 100fr dull green and dark brown, javelin). Sheet issued Sept. 10.

National Palace, Leopoldville A108

1964, Sept. 15				
		Granite Paper		
498	A108	50c lil rose & bl	.15	.15
499	A108	1fr bl & lil rose	.15	.15
500	A108	2fr brn red & vio	.15	.15
501	A108	3fr emer & red	.15	.15
502	A108	4fr org & vio bl	.15	.15
503	A108	5fr gray vio & emer	.15	.15
504	A108	6fr sep & org	.15	.15
505	A108	7fr gray ol & red brn	.15	.15
506	A108	8fr rose red & vio bl	1.45	.32
507	A108	9fr vio bl & rose red	.15	.15
508	A108	10fr brn ol & grn	.15	.15
509	A108	20fr bl & brn org	.15	.15
510	A108	30fr dk car rose & grn	.15	.15
511	A108	40fr ultra & dk car rose	.22	.15
512	A108	50fr brn org & grn	.30	.15
513	A108	100fr slate & ver	.55	.15
		Set value	3.35	1.15

For overprints and surcharges see Nos. 574-577, 593-598, 609-615, 670-671, 673-674, 676-677, 680, 684-687.

Pres. John F. Kennedy (1917-63) A109

1964, Dec. 8		Photo. *Perf. 13½*		
514	A109	5fr dk bl & blk	.15	.15
515	A109	6fr rose cl & blk	.15	.15
516	A109	9fr brn & blk	.15	.15
517	A109	30fr pur & blk	.28	.15
518	A109	40fr dl grn & blk	1.65	.50
519	A109	60fr red brn & blk	.45	.20
		Nos. 514-519 (6)	2.83	
		Set value		.90

Souvenir Sheet

No.	Type			
520	A109	150fr blk & mar	2.00	2.00

Rocket and Unisphere A110

Basketball A111

Engraved and Typographed

1965, Mar. 1		Unwmk. *Perf. 12*		
521	A110	50c lil & blk	.15	.15
522	A110	1.50fr bl & lil	.15	.15
523	A110	2fr red brn & brt grn	.15	.15
524	A110	10fr brt grn & dk red	.65	.40
525	A110	18fr vio bl & brn	.15	.15
526	A110	27fr rose red & grn	.22	.15
527	A110	40fr gray & org	.32	.15
		Set value	1.40	.80

New York World's Fair, 1964-65.

1965, Apr.		Photo. *Perf. 13½*		

Designs: 6fr, 40fr, Soccer, horiz. 15fr, 60fr, Volleyball.

No.	Type			
528	A111	5fr blk, grnsh bl & ocher	.15	.15
529	A111	6fr blk, bl gray & crim	.15	.15
530	A111	15fr blk, org & yel grn	.15	.15
531	A111	24fr blk, rose lil & brt grn	.20	.15
532	A111	40fr blk, brt grn & ultra	1.10	.40
533	A111	60fr blk, bl & red lil	.35	.15
		Nos. 528-533 (6)	2.10	
		Set value		.80

First African Games, Leopoldville, Mar. 31-Apr. 7, 1965.

For surcharges see Nos. 604-605.

Earth and Satellites A112

Designs: 9fr, 15fr, 20fr, 40fr, Satellites at left, globe at right.

Perf. 14x14½

1965, June 28		Photo. Unwmk.		
534	A112	6fr blk, sal & vio	.15	.15
535	A112	9fr blk, lt grn & gray	.15	.15
536	A112	12fr org, gray & blk	.15	.15
537	A112	15fr grn, ultra & blk	.15	.15
538	A112	18fr blk, lt grn & gray	1.00	.28
539	A112	20fr blk, sal & vio	.15	.15
540	A112	30fr grn, ultra & blk	.22	.15
541	A112	40fr org, gray & blk	.30	.15
		Nos. 534-541 (8)	2.27	
		Set value		.80

Cent. of the ITU.

Congolese Paratrooper and Parachutes A113

1965, July 5		*Perf. 13x14*		
542	A113	5fr brt bl & brn	.15	.15
543	A113	6fr org & brn	.15	.15
544	A113	7fr br grn & brn	.40	.18
545	A113	9fr brt pink & brn	.15	.15
546	A113	18fr lem & brn	.15	.15
		Set value	.72	.46

Fifth anniversary of independence.

Matadi Harbor and ICY Emblem — A114

Designs (ICY Emblem and): 8fr, 25fr, Katanga mines. 9fr, 60fr, Tshopo Dam, Stanleyville.

1965, Oct. 25 Photo. *Perf. 13x14*

547 A114	6fr ultra, blk & yel	.15	.15
548 A114	8fr org red, blk & bl	.15	.15
549 A114	9fr bl grn, blk & brn org	.15	.15
550 A114	12fr car rose, blk & gray	.75	.30
551 A114	25fr ol, blk & rose red	.18	.15
552 A114	60fr gray, blk & org	.35	.15
	Nos. 547-552 (6)	1.73	
	Set value		.62

International Cooperation Year, 1965.

For overprints and surcharges see Nos. 559-560, 607-608.

Soldiers Giving First Aid — A115

The Army Serving the Country: 7fr, Bridge building. 9fr, Feeding child. 19fr, Maintenance of telegraph lines. 20fr, House building. 30fr, Soldier and flag. (19fr, 20fr, 30fr, vert.)

Perf. 12½x13, 13x12½

1965, Nov. 17

553 A115	5fr sal, brn & red	.15	.15
554 A115	7fr yel & grn	.15	.15
555 A115	9fr ol & brn	.15	.15
556 A115	19fr brt grn & brn	.60	.35
557 A115	20fr lt bl & brn	.15	.15
558 A115	30fr multi	.22	.15
	Nos. 553-558 (6)	1.42	
	Set value		.68

See Nos. 582-586. For surcharges see Nos. 602, 678-679, 683.

Nos. 551-552 Overprinted with UN Emblem and "6e Journée Météorologique Mondiale / 23.3.66." on Metallic Strip

1966, Mar. 23 Photo. *Perf. 13x14*

559 A114	25fr ol & blk	.70	.35
560 A114	60fr gray & blk	.70	.52

6th World Meteorological Day.

Woman's Head and Goat — A116

Designs: 10fr, Sculptured heads. 12fr, Sitting figure and two heads, vert. 53fr, Figure with earrings and kneeling woman with bowl, vert.

Perf. 11½x13, 13x11½

1966, Apr. 23 Litho. Unwmk.

561 A116	10fr red, blk & gray	.15	.15
562 A116	12fr grn, blk & bl	.15	.15
563 A116	15fr dp bl, blk & lil	.15	.15
564 A116	53fr dp rose, blk & vio bl	1.00	.85
	Nos. 561-564 (4)	1.45	1.30

Intl. Negro Arts Festival, Dakar, Senegal, Apr. 1-24.

Pres. Joseph Desiré Mobutu and Fishing Industry A117

Pres. Mobutu and: 4fr, Pyrethrum harvest. 6fr, Building industry. 8fr, Winnowing rice. 10fr, Cotton harvest. 12fr, Banana harvest. 15fr, Cacao harvest. 24fr, Pineapple harvest. No. 573a, Pres. Mobutu without cap, and men rolling up sleeves.

1966, May 1 Photo. *Perf. 11½*

565 A117	2fr dk brn & dk bl	.15	.15
566 A117	4fr dk brn & org	.15	.15
567 A117	6fr dk brn & ol	.65	.55
568 A117	8fr dk brn & brt grnsh bl	.15	.15
569 A117	10fr dk brn & brn red	.15	.15
570 A117	12fr dk brn & vio	.15	.15
571 A117	15fr dk brn & lt ol grn	.15	.15
572 A117	24fr dk brn & lil rose	.20	.15
	Set value	1.25	1.05

Souvenir Sheet

Perf. 11x11½

573	Sheet of 4	.70	.70
a.	A117 15fr red, black & ultra	.15	.15

Lt. Gen. Joseph Desiré Mobutu, Pres. of Congo, and publicizing the "Back to Work" campaign.

For surcharges see Nos. 601, 603, 616, 619-624, 672, 675, 681-682.

Nos. 510-513 Overprinted

1966, June 13 *Perf. 11½*

574 A108	30fr dk car rose & grn	.65	.65
575 A108	40fr ultra & dk car rose	.65	.65
576 A108	50fr brn org & grn	.70	.70
577 A108	100fr slate & ver	.70	.70
	Nos. 574-577 (4)	2.70	2.70

Inauguration of WHO Headquarters, Geneva.

Soccer Player — A118

Designs: 30fr, Two soccer players. 50fr, Three soccer players. 60fr, Jules Rimet Cup, soccer ball and globe.

1966, July 25 Photo. *Perf. 14*

578 A118	10fr ocher, vio & brt grn	.15	.15
579 A118	30fr brt rose lil, vio & ap grn	.22	.15
580 A118	50fr ap grn, Prus bl & tan	.85	.85
581 A118	60fr brt grn, dk brn & gold	.42	.35
	Nos. 578-581 (4)	1.64	1.50

World Cup Soccer Championship, Wembley, England, July 11-30.

For overprints see Nos. 587-590.

Army Type of 1965

The Army Serving the Country: 2fr, Soldiers giving first aid. 6fr, Feeding child. 10fr, House building, vert. 18fr, Bridge building. 24fr, Soldier and flag, vert.

1966, Aug. 8 *Perf. 12½x13, 13x12½*

582 A115	2fr ver, ind & red	.15	.15
583 A115	6fr ultra red brn	.15	.15
584 A115	10fr yel grn & red brn	.40	.35
585 A115	18fr car rose & vio	.15	.15
586 A115	24fr multi	.15	.15
	Set value	.78	.66

Nos. 578-581 Overprinted in Black, Carmine or Green: "FINALE / ANGLETERRE-ALLEMAGNE / 4-2"

1966, Nov. 14 Photo. *Perf. 14*

587 A118	10fr pair, B and C	.28	.28
588 A118	30fr pair, B and G	.90	.80
589 A118	50fr pair, B and C	1.40	1.25
590 A118	60fr pair, B and C	1.70	1.50
	Nos. 587-590 (4)	4.28	3.83

England's victory in the World Soccer Cup Championship. The two colors of the overprint alternate in the sheets.

Souvenir Sheets

Pres. John F. Kennedy — A119

1966, Dec. 28 Engr. *Perf. 13*

591 A119	150fr brown	2.75	2.75
592 A119	150fr slate	2.75	2.75

Issued in memory of Pres. John F. Kennedy. No. 591 has slate green, No. 592 deep orange marginal design. Two imperf. sheets exist: 150fr brown with violet blue margin and 150fr slate with lilac margin. Size: 65x76mm. Value $4.25 each.

Nos. 498-503 Surcharged in Black, Red or Maroon

5 K

4e Sommet OUA
KINSHASA
du 11 au 14 - 9 - 67

1967, Sept. 11 Photo. *Perf. 11½*

593 A108	1k on 2fr	.15	.15
a.	Inverted overprint	6.00	
594 A108	3k on 5fr	.15	.15
595 A108	5k on 4fr	.15	.15
596 A108	6.60k on 1fr (R)	.22	.15
a.	Inverted overprint	4.75	
597 A108	9.60k on 50c	.35	.25
a.	Inverted overprint	4.75	
598 A108	9.80k on 3fr (M)	.50	.35
	Nos. 593-598 (6)	1.52	
	Set value		1.00

Souvenir Sheet

Map of Africa, Torch — A120

599 A120	50k grnsh bl, blk & red	1.50	1.50

4th meeting of the Org. for African Unity, Kinshasa (Leopoldville), Sept. 9-11.

No. 599 in other colors was not a postal issue.

Souvenir Sheet

Horn Blower and EXPO Emblem — A121

1967, Sept. 28 Engr. *Perf. 11½*

600 A121	50k dk brn	1.65	1.65

EXPO '67, International Exhibition, Montreal, Apr. 28-Oct. 27, 1967.

Nos. 565-566 and 582 Overprinted: "NOUVELLE CONSTITUTION 1967" and Surcharged with New Value on Metallic Panel in Magenta or Brown

Perf. 11½, 12½x13

1967, Oct. 9 Photo.

601 A117	4k on 2fr (M)	.15	.15
602 A115	5k on 2fr (B)	.20	.15
603 A117	21k on 4fr (M)	.85	.65
	Nos. 601-603 (3)	1.20	.95

Promulgation of the Constitution, June 4, 1967.

Nos. 528 and 530 Surcharged with New Value and Overprinted: "1ere Jeux Congolais / 25/6 au 2/7/1967 / Kinshasa"

1967, Oct. 16 Photo. *Perf. 13½*

604 A111	1k on 5fr multi	.15	.15
605 A111	9.60k on 15fr multi	.50	.50

First Congolese Games, Kinshasa, June 25-July 2, 1967.

No. 465 Surcharged with New Value and Overprinted: "1er VOL BAC / ONE ELEVEN / 14/5/67"

1967, Oct. 16 *Perf. 11½*

606 A105	9.60k on 7fr multi	.65	.15

1st flight of the BAC 111 in the service of Air Congo, May 14, 1967.

Nos. 547 and 549 Surcharged in Red or Black: "JOURNEE MONDIALE / DE L'ENFANCE / 8-10-67"

1968, Feb. 10 Photo. *Perf. 13x14*

607 A114	1k on 6fr (R)	.15	.15
608 A114	9k on 9fr (B)	.50	.50

Intl. Children's Day. The surcharge is on a rectangle printed in metallic ink.

Nos. 498, 504 and 501 Surcharged in Blue or Red: "Année Internationale / du Tourisme 24-10-1967"

1968, Feb. 10 *Perf. 11½*

609 A108	5k on 50c lil rose & bl (Bl)	.18	.18
610 A108	10k on 6fr sepia & org (R)	.40	.40
611 A108	15k on 3fr emer & red (R)	.55	.55
	Nos. 609-611 (3)	1.13	1.13

International Tourist Year. The surcharge is on a rectangle printed in metallic ink.

Nos. 500, 498 and 502 Surcharged in Black, Violet Blue or Gold

1968, July Photo. *Perf. 11½*

612 A108	1k on 2fr	.15	.15
613 A108	2k on 50c (VBl)	.15	.15
614 A108	2k on 50c (G)	.15	.15
615 A108	9.60k on 4fr	.40	.40
	Set value	.67	.67

The surcharge on No. 612 consists of a black rectangle and new denomination in upper right corner; the surcharge on No. 613 has a violet blue rectangle with denomination printed in white on it; on No. 614 the rectangle is gold and the denomination black; on No. 615 the rectangle is black and the denomination white.

No. 565 Surcharged in White on Black Rectangle

1968, Oct. Photo. *Perf. 11½*

616 A117	10k on 2fr dk brn & dk bl	.40	.15

Leopard
A122

1968, Nov. 5 Litho. *Perf. 10½*
617 A122 2k brt grnsh bl & blk .15 .15
618 A122 9.60k red & blk .40 .15
Set value .15

Mobutu Type of 1966 Surcharged

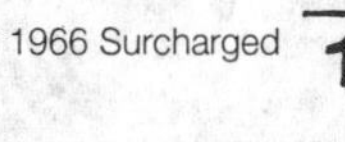

1968, Dec. 20 Photo. *Perf. 11½*
619 A117 15s on 2fr sep & brt bl .15 .15
620 A117 1k on 6fr sep & brn .15 .15
621 A117 3k on 10fr sep & emer .15 .15
622 A117 5k on 12fr sep & org .15 .15
623 A117 20k on 15fr sep & brt grn .60 .42
624 A117 50k on 24fr sep & brt lil 1.65 1.10
Nos. 619-624 (6) 2.85
Set value 1.80

Human Rights
Flame — A123

1968, Dec. 30 *Perf. 12½x13*
625 A123 2k lt ultra & brt grn .15 .15
626 A123 9.60k grn & dp car .35 .22
627 A123 10k brt lil & brn .35 .22
628 A123 40k org brn & pur 1.40 1.00
Nos. 625-628 (4) 2.25 1.59

International Human Rights Year.

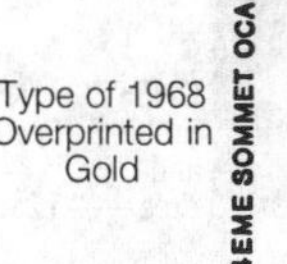

Type of 1968
Overprinted in
Gold

1969, Jan. 27 Photo. *Perf. 12½x13*
629 A123 2k ap grn & red brn .15 .15
630 A123 9.60k rose & emer .35 .22
631 A123 10k gray & ultra .35 .22
632 A123 40k grnsh bl & pur 1.40 1.00
Nos. 629-632 (4) 2.25 1.59

4th summit meeting of OCAM (Organisation Communitee Afrique et Malgache), Kinshasa, Jan. 27.

Kinshasa Fair Emblem and Cotton
Boll — A124

Designs (Fair Emblem and): 6k, Copper. 9.60k, Coffee. 9.80k, Diamond. 11.60k, Oil palm fruits.

1969, May 2 Photo. *Perf. 12½x13*
633 A124 2k brt pur, gold & red lil .15 .15
634 A124 6k grn, gold & bl grn .22 .22
635 A124 9.60k brn, gold & lt brn .35 .15
636 A124 9.80k ultra & gold .35 .32
637 A124 11.60k hn brn, gold & brn .45 .45
Nos. 633-637 (5) 1.52 1.29

Kinshasa Fair, Limete, June 30-July 21.

Fair Entrance, Emblem — A125

Designs (Fair Emblem and): 3k, Gecomin Mining Co. Pavilion. 10k, Administration Building. 25k, Pavilion of the Organization for African Unity.

1969, June 30 Photo. *Perf. 11½*
Granite Paper
638 A125 2k brt rose lil & gold .15 .15
639 A125 3k blue & gold .15 .15
640 A125 10k lt ol grn & gold .32 .25
641 A125 25k copper red & gold .75 .65
Nos. 638-641 (4) 1.37 1.20

Kinshasa Fair, Limete, June 30-July 21.

Congo
Arms — A126

Pres.
Mobutu — A127

1969, July-Sept. Litho. *Perf. 14*
642 A126 10s org & blk .15 .15
643 A126 15s ultra & blk .15 .15
644 A126 30s brt grn & blk .15 .15
645 A126 60s brt rose lil & blk .15 .15
646 A126 90s dp bis & blk .15 .15

Perf. 13
647 A127 1k sky bl & multi .15 .15
648 A127 2k org & multi .15 .15
649 A127 3k multi .15 .15
650 A127 5k brt rose & multi .15 .15
651 A127 6k ultra & multi .15 .15
652 A127 9.60k multi .22 .15
653 A127 10k lt lil & multi .32 .15
654 A127 20k yel & multi .65 .32
655 A127 50k multi 1.65 .70
656 A127 100k fawn & multi 3.00 1.25
Set value 6.50 3.10

Well Driller, by Oscar Bonnevalle — A128

Paintings: 4k, Preparation of cocoa, by Jean Van Noten. 8k, Dock workers, by Constantin Meunier. 10k, Poultry shop, by Henri Evenepoel. 15k, Steel industry, by Constantin Meunier.

Perf. 13x14, 14x13 (8k)
1969, Dec. 15 Litho.
Size: 41x41mm
657 A128 3k multi .15 .15
658 A128 4k multi .15 .15

Size: 28x41mm
659 A128 8k multi .25 .22

Size: 41x41mm
660 A128 10k multi .42 .32
661 A128 15k multi .85 .50
Nos. 657-661 (5) 1.82 1.34

50th anniv. of the ILO.

Souvenir Sheet

Adoration of the Kings, by
Rubens — A129

1969, Dec. Engr. *Perf. 13*
662 A129 50k red lilac 1.50 1.50

Issued for Christmas 1969.

Pres.
Mobutu,
Map and
Flag of
Congo
A130

1970, June 30 Litho. *Perf. 13½x13*
663 A130 10s multi .15 .15
664 A130 90s pur & multi .15 .15
665 A130 1k brn & multi .15 .15
666 A130 2k multi .15 .15
667 A130 7k multi .24 .15
668 A130 10k multi .35 .22
669 A130 20k multi .70 .50
Set value 1.50 1.05

10th anniversary of independence.

Issues of 1964-1966
Surcharged

0,20 K

Perf. 11½, 12½x13, 13x12½
1970, Sept. 24 Photo.
670 A108 10s on 1fr (#499) .15 .15
671 A108 20s on 2fr (#500) .15 .15
672 A117 20s on 2fr (#565) .15 .15
673 A108 30s on 3fr (#501) .15 .15
674 A108 40s on 4fr (#502) .15 .15
675 A117 40s on 4fr (#566) .15 .15
676 A108 60s on 7fr (#505) .70 .52
677 A108 90s on 9fr (#507) .70 .52
678 A115 90s on 9fr (#555) .15 .15
679 A115 1k on 7fr (#554) .15 .15
680 A108 1k on 6fr (#504) .15 .15
681 A117 1k on 12fr (#570) .70 .52
682 A117 2k on 24fr (#572) .15 .15
683 A115 2k on 24fr (#586) .15 .15
684 A108 3k on 30fr (#510) .70 .52
685 A108 4k on 40fr (#511) .15 .15
686 A108 5k on 50fr (#512) 1.65 1.10
687 A108 10k on 100fr (#513) .70 .50
Set value 6.30 4.60

Telecommunications Building,
Geneva — A131

Designs: 2k, 6.60k, UPU Headquarters, Bern. 9.80k, 10k, 11k, UN Headquarters, NY.

1970, Oct. 24 Photo. *Perf. 11½*
688 A131 1k pink & grn .15 .15
689 A131 2k org & grn .15 .15
690 A131 6.60k grnsh bl & rose car .22 .15
691 A131 9.60k yel & vio bl .30 .15
692 A131 9.80k lt ultra & brn .30 .15
693 A131 10k lt pur & brn .30 .18
694 A131 11k rose & brn .35 .22
Nos. 688-694 (7) 1.77
Set value .90

ITU; new UPU Headquarters, Bern; 25th anniv. of the UN.

Pres. Mobutu, Congolese Flag and
Arch — A132

1970, Nov. 24 Litho. *Perf. 13*
695 A132 2k yel & multi .15 .15
696 A132 10k bl & multi .40 .25
697 A132 20k red & multi .85 .55
Nos. 695-697 (3) 1.40 .95

Fifth anniversary of new government.

Apollo 11 in
Flight
A133

Designs: 2k, Astronaut and spacecraft on moon. 7k, Pres. Mobutu decorating astronauts' wives. 10k, Pres. Mobutu with Neil A. Armstrong, Col. Edwin E. Aldrin, Jr. and Lt. Col. Michael Collins. 30k, Armstrong, Aldrin and Collins in space suits.

1970, Dec. 24 *Perf. 13x13½*
698 A133 1k bl & blk .15 .15
699 A133 2k brt pur & blk .15 .15
700 A133 7k dl org & blk .30 .20
701 A133 10k rose red & blk .32 .25
702 A133 30k grn & blk 1.00 .70
Nos. 698-702 (5) 1.92 1.45

Visit of US Apollo 11 astronauts and their wives to Kinshasa.

Metopodontus Savagei — A134

Designs: Various insects of Congo.

1971, Jan. 25 Photo. *Perf. 11½*
703 A134 10s dl rose & multi .15 .15
704 A134 50s gray & multi .15 .15
705 A134 90s multi .15 .15
706 A134 1k citron & multi .15 .15
707 A134 2k gray grn & multi .15 .15
708 A134 3k lt vio & multi .15 .15
709 A134 5k bl & multi .40 .25
710 A134 10k multi .65 .42
711 A134 30k grn & multi 1.65 1.00
712 A134 40k ocher & multi 2.00 1.25
Nos. 703-712 (10) 5.60
Set value 3.25

Colotis Protomedia — A135

Designs: Various butterflies and moths of Congo.

1971, Feb. 24
713 A135 10s lt ultra & multi .15 .15
714 A135 20s choc & multi .15 .15
715 A135 70s dp org & multi .15 .15
716 A135 1k vio bl & multi .15 .15
717 A135 3k multi .15 .15
718 A135 5k dk grn & multi .32 .20
719 A135 10k multi .52 .32
720 A135 15k emer & multi .85 .50
721 A135 25k yel & multi 1.10 .70
722 A135 40k multi 2.00 1.25
Nos. 713-722 (10) 5.54 3.72

UN Emblem, Racial
Unity — A136

1971, Mar. 21 Photo. *Perf. 11½*

723 A136 1k lt grn & multi .15 .15
724 A136 4k gray & multi .15 .15
725 A136 5k lt lil & multi .15 .15
726 A136 10k lt bl & multi .32 .20
Set value .60 .42

Intl. year against racial discrimination.

Hypericum Bequaertii A137

Flowers: 4k, Dissotis brazzae. 20k, Begonia wollastonii. 25k, Cassia alata.

1971, May 24 Litho. *Perf. 14*

727 A137 1k multi .15 .15
728 A137 4k multi .20 .15
729 A137 20k multi .85 .32
730 A137 25k multi 1.10 .65
Nos. 727-730 (4) 2.30 1.27

Obelisk at N'sele, Pres. Mobutu — A138

1971, May 20 Photo. *Perf. 11½*

731 A138 4k gold & multi .15 .15

4th anniversary of the People's Revolutionary Movement.

Radar Station A139

Designs: 1k, Waves. 6k, Map of Africa with telecommunications network.

1971, June 25 Photo. *Perf. 11½*

732 A139 1k rose & multi .15 .15
733 A139 3k yel & multi .15 .15
734 A139 6k lt bl & multi .25 .15
Set value .42 .27

3rd World Telecommunications Day, May 17 (1k); opening of satellite telecommunications ground station, Kinshasa, June 30 (3k); Pan-African telecommunication system (6k).

Grass Monkeys A140

Designs: 20s, Moustached monkeys, vert. 70s, De Brazza's monkeys. 1k, Yellow baboons. 3k, Pygmy chimpanzee, vert. 5k, Mangabeys, vert. 10k, Owlfaced monkeys. 15k, Diana monkeys. 25k, Black-and-white colobus, vert. 40k, L'Hoest's monkeys, vert.

1971, Aug.

735 A140 10s vio & multi .15 .15
736 A140 20s lt bl & multi .15 .15
737 A140 70s ocher & multi .15 .15
738 A140 1k gray & multi .15 .15
739 A140 3k rose & multi .22 .15
740 A140 5k brn & multi .52 .15
741 A140 10k multi .90 .22
742 A140 15k multi 1.65 .48
743 A140 25k brt bl & multi 2.75 .75
744 A140 40k red & multi 3.75 .95
Nos. 735-744 (10) 10.39
Set value 2.80

Hotel Inter-Continental, Kinshasa — A141

1971, Oct. 2 Photo. *Perf. 13*

745 A141 2k silver & multi .15 .15
746 A141 12k gold & multi .42 .15
Set value .20

Man Reading — A142

Designs: 2.50k, Open book and abacus. 7k, Five letters surrounding symbolic head.

1971, Oct. 24

747 A142 50s multi .15 .15
748 A142 2.50k multi .15 .15
749 A142 7k multi .42 .15
Set value .57 .26

Fight against illiteracy.

Succeeding issues are listed in Vol. 5 under Zaire.

SEMI-POSTAL STAMPS

Women Carrying Food, Wheat Emblem, and Tractor SP22

1963, Mar. 21 Photo. *Perf. 14x13*

B48 SP22 5fr + 2fr multi .15 .15
B49 SP22 9fr + 4fr multi .30 .15
B50 SP22 12fr + 6fr multi .32 .22
B51 SP22 20fr + 10fr multi 1.65 1.50
Nos. B48-B51 (4) 2.42 2.02

FAO "Freedom from Hunger" campaign.

CONGO PEOPLE'S REPUBLIC

'pē–pəls ri–'pə–blik of 'käŋ–(,)gō

(ex-French)

LOCATION — West Africa at equator
GOVT. — Republic
AREA — 132,046 sq. mi.
POP. — 1,740,000 (est. 1984)
CAPITAL — Brazzaville

The former French colony of Middle Congo became a member state of the French Community on November 28, 1958, and achieved independence on August 15, 1960. For some years before 1958, the colony was joined with three other French territories to form French Equatorial Africa. Issues of Middle Congo (1907-1933) are listed under that heading.

100 Centimes = 1 Franc

Catalogue values for all unused stamps in this country are for Never Hinged items.

Allegory of New Republic A7

1959 Unwmk. Engr. *Perf. 13*

89 A7 25fr brn, dp claret, org & ol .30 .15

1st anniv. of the proclamation of the Republic.

Imperforates
Most stamps of the Republic of the Congo exist imperforate in issued and trial colors, and also in small presentation sheets in issued colors.

C.C.T.A. Issue
Common Design Type

1960 Unwmk. *Perf. 13*

90 CD106 50fr dl grn & plum .60 .55

President Fulbert Youlou — A8

Flag, Map and UN Emblem — A9

1960

91 A8 15fr grn, blk & car .16 .15
92 A8 85fr indigo & car .70 .35

1961, Mar. 11 *Perf. 13*
Flag in Green, Yellow & Red

93 A9 5fr vio brn & dk bl .15 .15
94 A9 20fr org & dk bl .20 .15
95 A9 100fr grn & dk bl 1.00 .90
Nos. 93-95 (3) 1.35 1.20

Congo's admission to United Nations.

Rainbow Runner A10

Designs (fish): 50c, 3fr, Rainbow runner. 1fr, 2fr, Sloan's viperfish. 5fr, Hatchet fish. 10fr, A deep-sea fish.

1961, Nov. 28 Engr.

96 A10 50c brn, ol grn & salmon .15 .15
97 A10 1fr bl grn & sepia .15 .15
98 A10 2fr ultra, sep & dk grn .15 .15
99 A10 3fr dk bl, grn & salmon .15 .15
100 A10 5fr red brn, grn & blk .20 .15
101 A10 10fr blue & red brn .20 .15
Set value .68 .55

Brazzaville Market — A11

1962, Mar. 23 Unwmk. *Perf. 13*

102 A11 20fr blk, red & grn .16 .15

Abidjan Games Issue
Common Design Type

Designs: 20fr, Boxing. 50fr, Running, finish line.

1962, July 21 Photo. *Perf. 12½x12*

103 CD109 20fr car, brt pink, brn & blk .18 .15
104 CD109 50fr car, brt pink, brn & blk .40 .30
Nos. 103-104,C7 (3) 1.48 1.07

Common Design Types pictured in section at front of book.

African-Malgache Union Issue
Common Design Type

1962, Sept. 8

105 CD110 30fr multi .38 .38

Waves Around Globe — A11a

Design: 100fr, Orbit patterns around globe.

1963, Sept. 19 *Perf. 12½*

106 A11a 25fr org, grn & ultra .25 .20
107 A11a 100fr lt red brn, bl & plum .90 .70

Issued to publicize space communications.

King Makoko's Collar — A12

Unwmk.

1963, Oct. 21 Engr. *Perf. 13*

108 A12 10fr shown .15 .15
109 A12 15fr Kebekebe mask .16 .15
Set value .15

UNESCO Emblem, Scales and Tree — A12a

1963, Dec. 10 Unwmk. *Perf. 13*

110 A12a 25fr grn, dk bl & brn .22 .16

15th anniv. of the Universal Declaration of Human Rights.

Barograph and WMO Emblem A12b

1964, Mar. 23 Engr.

111 A12b 50fr grn, red brn & ultra .42 .42

Fourth World Meteorological Day.

Mechanic with Machine — A13

1964, Apr. 8

112 A13 20fr grnsh bl, mag & dk brn .22 .15

Training of technicians.

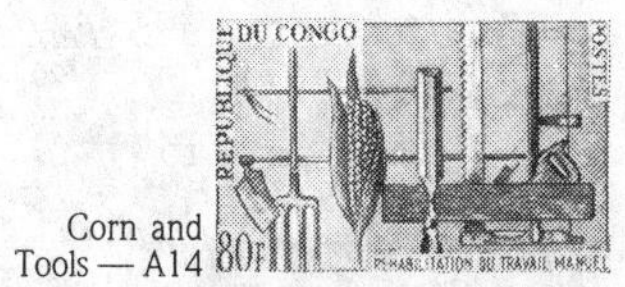
Corn and Tools — A14

1964, Apr. 24 Unwmk. *Perf. 13*
113 A14 80fr brn, grn & brn car .65 .35

Importance of manual labor.

Diaboua Ballet — A15

Kébékébé Dance — A16

Carved Figure — A17

1964, May 8 Engr.
114 A15 30fr multi .35 .20
115 A16 60fr multi .60 .40

1964, May 22
116 A17 50fr brn red & sepia .42 .35

Classroom A18

1964, May 26
117 A18 25fr dk brn, red & blue .22 .15

Issued to publicize education.

Type of Air Post Issue, 1963, Inscribed: "1er ANNIVERSAIRE DE LA REVOLUTION/FETE NATIONALE/15 AOUT 1964"

1964, Aug. 15 Photo. *Perf. 13x12*
118 AP5 20fr lt bl, red, ocher, dk brn & grn .18 .15

1st anniv. of the revolution and Natl. Feast Day, Aug. 15.

Fire Squid — A19

Design: 15fr, Johnson's deep-sea angler (fish).

1964, Oct. 20 Engr. *Perf. 13*
119 A19 2fr ver, lt grn & brn .15 .15
120 A19 15fr vio, lt ol grn & dp cl .22 .15
Set value .20

Cooperation Issue
Common Design Type

1964, Nov. 7 Unwmk. *Perf. 13*
121 CD119 25fr car, brt grn & dk brn .22 .16

Communications Emblems — A20

1965, Jan. 1 Litho. *Perf. 12½x13*
122 A20 25fr ol, red brn & blk .25 .16

Issued to commemorate the establishment of the national postal administration.

Sitatunga A21

Dancer on Stilts A22

Design: 20fr, Elephant, horiz.

1965, Mar. 15 Engr. *Perf. 13*
123 A21 15fr redsh brn, dl grn & bl .20 .15
124 A21 20fr blk, dp bl & sl grn .20 .15
125 A22 85fr lil & multi .70 .60
Nos. 123-125 (3) 1.10 .90

Pres. Alphonse Massamba-Debat — A23

1965-66 Photo. *Perf. 12x12½*
126 A23 20fr dk brn, grn & yel .16 .15
127 A23 25fr brn, bl grn, emer & blk ('66) .22 .15
128 A23 30fr brn, bl grn, org & blk ('66) .25 .15
Nos. 126-128 (3) .63
Set value .34

Soccer Player — A24

Designs: 25fr, Games' emblem (map of Africa and runners). 50fr, Field ball player. 85fr, Runner. 100fr, Bicyclist.

1965, July 17 Photo. *Perf. 12½*
Size: 28x28mm
129 A24 25fr blk, red, yel & grn .16 .15
Size: 34x34mm
130 A24 40fr yel grn & multi .30 .20
131 A24 50fr red & multi .32 .20
132 A24 85fr blk & multi .55 .35
133 A24 100fr yel & multi .65 .42
a. Min. sheet of 5, #129-133 3.00 3.00
Nos. 129-133 (5) 1.98 1.32

1st African Games, Brazzaville, July 18-25.

Arms of Congo — A25

1965, Nov. 15 Litho. *Perf. 12½x13*
134 A25 20fr multi .20 .15

Cooperative Village A26

Design: 30fr, Gymnastic drill team with streamers.

1966, Feb. 18 *Perf. 12½x13*
135 A26 25fr multi .20 .15
136 A26 30fr multi .25 .16

Sculptured Mask — A27

Designs: 30fr, Weaver, painting. 85fr, String instrument, painting, horiz.

Perf. 13x12½, 12½x13
1966, Apr. 9 Photo.
137 A27 30fr multi .25 .15
138 A27 85fr multi .70 .42
139 A27 90fr multi .80 .45
Nos. 137-139 (3) 1.75 1.02

Issued to publicize the International Negro Arts Festival, Dakar, Senegal, Apr. 1-24.

Men and Clocks — A28

1966, Apr. 15 *Perf. 12½x13*
140 A28 70fr pale brn, ocher & dk brn .75 .30

Issued to publicize the introduction of the shorter work day (less lunch time, earlier quitting time).

WHO Headquarters, Geneva A29

1966, May 3 Photo. *Perf. 12½x13*
141 A29 50fr org yel, vio & bl .25 .16

Inauguration of the WHO Headquarters, Geneva.

Church of St. Peter Claver A30

Women's Basketball A31

1966, June 15 Photo. *Perf. 13x12½*
142 A30 70fr multi .70 .30

1966, July 15 Engr. *Perf. 13*

Sport: 1fr, Women's volleyball, horiz. 3fr, Women's field ball, horiz. 5fr, Athletes of various races. 10fr, Torch bearer. 15fr, Soccer and gold medal of First African Games.

143 A31 1fr ultra, choc & ol .15 .15
144 A31 2fr choc, grn & bl .15 .15
145 A31 3fr dk grn, dk car & choc .15 .15
146 A31 5fr sl, emer & choc .15 .15
147 A31 10fr dl bl, dk grn & vio .16 .15
148 A31 15fr vio, car & choc .20 .15
Set value .61 .42

Jules Rimet Cup and Globe — A32

1966, July 15 Photo. *Perf. 12½x12*
149 A32 30fr brt red, gold, blk & bl .35 .18

8th World Soccer Cup Championship, Wembley, England, July 11-30.

Savorgnan de Brazza School A33

1966, Sept. 15 Photo. *Perf. 12½x12*
150 A33 30fr dk pur, grn, yel & blk .25 .15

Pointe-Noire Railroad Station — A34

1966, Oct. 15 Engr. *Perf. 13*
151 A34 60fr grn, red & brn .60 .22

Student with Microscope A35

Balumbu Mask A36

1966, Nov. 28 Engr. *Perf. 13*
152 A35 90fr brn, grn & ind .80 .50

20th anniv. of UNESCO.

1966, Dec. 12 Engr. *Perf. 13*

Masks: 10fr, Kuyu. 15fr, Bakwélé. 20fr, Batéké.

153 A36 5fr car rose & dk brn .15 .15
154 A36 10fr Prus bl & brn .15 .15
155 A36 15fr sep, dl org & dk bl .16 .15
156 A36 20fr dp bl & multi .20 .15
Nos. 153-156 (4) .66
Set value .32

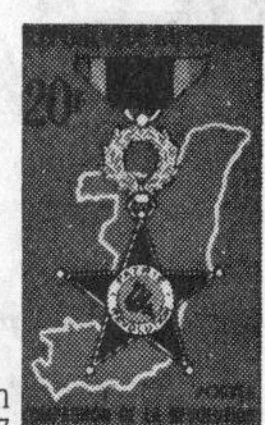
Order of the Revolution and Map — A37

Learning the Alphabet A38

Design: 45fr, Harvesting and loading sugar cane, and sugar mill.

Perf. 12x12½, 12½x12
1967, Mar. 15 Photo.
157 A37 20fr org & multi .20 .15
158 A38 25fr blk, ocher & dk car .20 .15
159 A38 45fr blk, yel grn & lt bl .40 .20
Nos. 157-159 (3) .80 .50

Issued to honor the members of the Order of the Revolution (20fr); to publicize the literacy campaign (25fr); to publicize, sugar production (45fr).

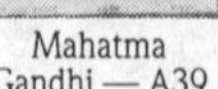

Mahatma Gandhi — A39

Fruit Vendor — A40

1967, Apr. 21 **Engr.** ***Perf. 13***

160 A39 90fr bl & blk .70 .40

Issued in memory of Mohandas K. Gandhi (1869-1948), Hindu nationalist leader.

1967, June **Photo.** ***Perf. 13x12½***

Dolls: 5fr, "Elegant Lady." 25fr, Woman pounding saka-saka. 30fr, Mother and child.

161 A40 5fr gold & multi .15 .15
162 A40 10fr yel grn & multi .15 .15
163 A40 25fr lt ultra & multi .20 .15
164 A40 30fr multi .25 .16
Nos. 161-164 (4) .75
Set value .48

ITY Emblem, Village and Waterfall A41

1967, July 5 **Engr.** ***Perf. 13***

165 A41 60fr rose cl, org & ol grn .55 .35

Issued for International Tourist Year, 1967.

Symbols of Cooperation A42

Arms of Brazzaville A43

Europafrica Issue, 1967

1967, July 20 **Photo.** ***Perf. 12x12½***

166 A42 50fr multi .42 .20

1967, Aug. 15 **Litho.** ***Perf. 12½x13***

167 A43 30fr yel & multi .30 .15

Fourth anniversary of the revolution.

UN Emblem, Dove and People — A44

Boy and UNICEF Emblem — A45

1967, Oct. 24 **Photo.** ***Perf. 13x12½***

168 A44 90fr bl, dk brn, red brn & yel .90 .50

Issued for United Nations Day, Oct. 24.

1967, Dec. 11 **Engr.** ***Perf. 13***

169 A45 90fr mar, blk & ultra .80 .42

21st anniv. of UNICEF.

Albert Luthuli, Dove and Globe — A46

1968, Jan. 29 **Engr.** ***Perf. 13***

170 A46 30fr brt grn & ol bis .25 .16

Albert Luthuli (1899-1967) of South Africa, winner of 1960 Nobel Peace Prize.

Arms of Pointe Noire — A47

1968, Feb. 20 **Litho.** ***Perf. 12½x13***

171 A47 10fr brt pink & multi .15 .15

Motherhood A48

Mayombe Viaduct A49

1968, May 25 **Engr.** ***Perf. 13***

172 A48 15fr dk car rose, sky bl & blk .16 .15

Issued for Mother's Day.

1968, June 24

173 A49 45fr maroon, slate grn & bl .35 .16

A50

1968, July 29 **Photo.** ***Perf. 13x12½***

174 A50 5fr Daimler, 1889 .15 .15
175 A50 20fr Berliet, 1897 .20 .16
176 A50 60fr Peugeot, 1898 .55 .30
177 A50 80fr Renault, 1900 .75 .40
178 A50 85fr Fiat, 1902 .80 .45
Nos. 174-178,C67-C68 (7) 5.45 3.01
Nos. 174-178 (5) 2.45 1.46

Tanker, Refinery and Map of Area Served — A50a

1968, July 30 ***Perf. 12½***

179 A50a 30fr multi .25 .15

Issued to commemorate the opening of the Port Gentil (Gabon) Refinery, June 12, 1968.

UN Emblem and Tree of Life — A51

1968, Nov. 28 **Engr.** ***Perf. 13***

180 A51 25fr dk grn, red & dp lil .25 .15

20th anniv. of WHO.

Development Bank Issue

Common Design Type

1969, Sept. 10 **Engr.** ***Perf. 13***

181 CD130 25fr car rose, grn & ocher .22 .15
182 CD130 30fr bl, grn & ocher .25 .15
Set value .20

Bicycle A52

Designs (Bicycles and Motorcycles): 75fr, Hirondelle. 80fr, Folding bicycle. 85fr, Peugeot. 100fr, Excelsior Manxman. 150fr, Norton. 200fr, Brough Superior "Old Bill." 300fr, Matchless and N.L.G.-J.A.P.S.

1969, Oct. 6 **Engr.** ***Perf. 13***

183 A52 50fr multi .40 .20
184 A52 75fr multi .60 .28
185 A52 80fr multi .65 .30
186 A52 85fr multi .70 .35
187 A52 100fr multi .85 .42
188 A52 150fr multi 1.10 .60
189 A52 200fr multi 2.00 .75
190 A52 300fr multi 2.75 1.25
Nos. 183-190 (8) 9.05 4.15

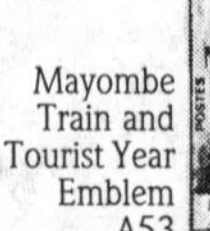

Mayombe Train and Tourist Year Emblem A53

Design: 40fr, Train and Mbamba Tunnel, vert.

Perf. 13x12½, 12½x13

1969, Oct. 20 **Photo.**

191 A53 40fr multi .38 .18
192 A53 60fr multi .45 .20

Issued for African Tourist Year.

Loutete Cement Works — A54

Loutete Cement Works: 15fr, Mixing tower, vert. 25fr, Cable transport, vert. 30fr, General view of plant.

1969, Dec. 10 **Engr.** ***Perf. 13***

193 A54 10fr dk gray, rose cl & dk ol .15 .15
194 A54 15fr Prus bl, red brn & pur .15 .15
195 A54 25fr mar, brn & Prus bl .20 .15
196 A54 30fr vio brn, ultra & blk .22 .15
a. Min. sheet of 4, #193-196 .80 .80
Nos. 193-196 (4) .72
Set value .40

ASECNA Issue

Common Design Type

1969, Dec. 12

197 CD132 100fr dull brown .90 .42

Pineapple Harvest and ILO Emblem A55

Design: 30fr, Worker at lathe and ILO emblem.

1969, Dec. 20 **Engr.** ***Perf. 13***

198 A55 25fr bl, olive & brn .20 .15
199 A55 30fr rose red, choc & slate .22 .15

50th anniv. of the ILO.

SOTEXCO Textile Plant, Kinsoundi A56

Designs: 20fr, Women in spinnery. 25fr, Hand-printing textiles. 30fr, Checking woven cloth.

1970, Jan. 20

200 A56 15fr grn, blk & lil .15 .15
201 A56 20fr plum, car & sl grn .15 .15
202 A56 25fr bl, slate & brn .20 .15
203 A56 30fr gray, car rose & brn .25 .15
Nos. 200-203 (4) .75
Set value .42

Hotel Cosmos, Brazzaville A57

1970, Jan. 30

204 A57 90fr sl grn, bl & red brn .65 .30

The status of the three sets for Kennedy, etc., Summer Olympics, and Baroque paintings is not certain.

Linzolo Church — A58

Diosso Gorge — A59

Design: 90fr, Foulakari waterfall.

1970 **Engr.** ***Perf. 13***

205 A58 25fr multi .16 .15
206 A59 70fr multi .40 .18
207 A59 90fr multi .55 .22
Nos. 205-207 (3) 1.11 .55

Issue dates: 25fr, Feb. 10; others, Feb. 25.

Volvaria Esculenta — A60

Mushrooms: 10fr, Termitomyces entolomoides. 15fr, Termitomyces microcarpus. 25fr, Termitomyces aurantiacus. 30fr, Termitomyces mammiformis. 50fr, Tremella fuciformis.

1970, Mar. 31 **Photo.** ***Perf. 13***

208 A60 5fr multi .15 .15
209 A60 10fr multi .15 .15
210 A60 15fr multi .16 .15
211 A60 25fr multi .30 .15
212 A60 30fr multi .35 .18
213 A60 50fr multi .45 .30
Nos. 208-213 (6) 1.56
Set value .88

Laying Coaxial Cable — A61

Design: 30fr, Full view of rail car; 3 cable layers on railway roadbed.

1970, Apr. 30 Engr. *Perf. 13*

214 A61 25fr dk brn & multi .22 .15
215 A61 30fr brn & multi .25 .15

Issued to publicize the laying of the coaxial cable linking Brazzaville and Pointe Noire.
For surcharges see Nos. 263-264.

UPU Headquarters Issue
Common Design Type

1970, May 20

216 CD133 30fr dk pur, gray & mag .30 .15

Mother Feeding Child — A62

Dag Hammarskjold, UN Emblem — A63

Design: 90fr, Mother nursing infant.

1970, May 30 Photo.

217 A62 85fr vio bl & multi .65 .38
218 A62 90fr lil & multi .70 .40

Issued for Mother's Day.

1970, June 20 Engr. *Perf. 13*

UN Emblem and: No. 220, Trygve Lie, horiz. No. 221, U Thant, horiz.

219 A63 100fr scar, dk red & dk pur .80 .50
220 A63 100fr dk red, ultra & ind .80 .50
221 A63 100fr grn, emer & dk red .80 .50
a. Souv. sheet of 3, #219-221 3.00 3.00
Nos. 219-221 (3) 2.40 1.50

25th anniv. of the UN and to honor its Secretaries General.

Brillantaisia Vogeliana A64

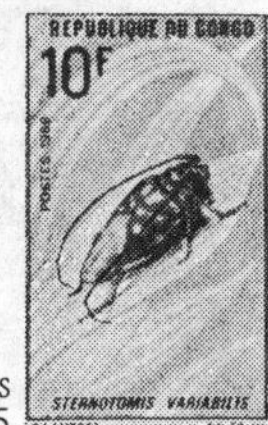

Sternotomis Variabilis — A65

Designs (Plants and Beetles): 2fr, Plectranthus decurrens. 3fr, Myrianthemum mirabile. 5fr, Connarus griffonianus. 15fr, Chelorrhina polyphemus. 20fr, Metopodontus savagei.

Perf. 12½x12, 12x12½

1970, June 30 Photo.

222 A64 1fr dk grn & multi .15 .15
223 A64 2fr multi .15 .15
224 A64 3fr indigo & multi .15 .15
225 A64 5fr lemon & multi .15 .15
226 A65 10fr lilac & multi .15 .15
227 A65 15fr orange & multi .15 .15
228 A65 20fr multi .18 .15
Set value .68 .50

For surcharge see No. 288.

Stegosaurus A66

Prehistoric Fauna: 20fr, Dinotherium, vert. 60fr, Brachiosaurus, vert. 80fr, Arsinoitherium.

1970, July 20

229 A66 15fr dl grn, ocher & red brn .16 .15
230 A66 20fr lt bl & multi .20 .15
231 A66 60fr lt bl & multi .50 .18
232 A66 80fr lt bl & multi .75 .35
Nos. 229-232 (4) 1.61 .83

Mikado 141, 1932 — A67

Locomotives: 60fr, Steam locomotive 130+032, 1947. 75fr, Alsthom BB 1100, 1962. 85fr, Diesel BB BB 302, 1969.

1970, Aug. 20 Engr. *Perf. 13*

233 A67 40fr mag, bl grn & blk .40 .20
234 A67 60fr blk, bl & grn .55 .25
235 A67 75fr red, bl & blk .65 .30
236 A67 85fr car, sl grn & ocher .80 .38
Nos. 233-236 (4) 2.40 1.13

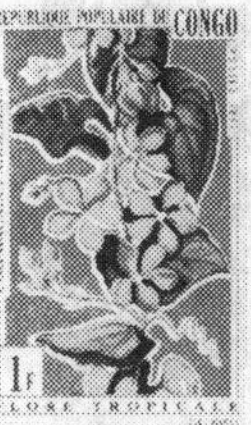

Cogniauxia Padolaena — A68

Green Night Adder — A69

Tropical Flowers: 2fr, Celosia cristata. 5fr, Plumeria acutifolia. 10fr, Bauhinia variegata. 15fr, Poinsettia. 20fr, Thunbergia grandiflora.

1971, Feb. 10 Photo. *Perf. 12x12½*

237 A68 1fr lil & multi .15 .15
238 A68 2fr yel & multi .15 .15
239 A68 5fr ultra & multi .15 .15
240 A68 10fr yel & multi .15 .15
241 A68 15fr multi .22 .15
242 A68 20fr dk red & multi .25 .15
Set value .78 .48

Perf. 12x12½, 12½x12

1971, June 26 Photo.

Reptiles: 10fr, African Egg-eating snake, horiz. 15fr, Flap-necked chameleon. 20fr, Nile crocodile, horiz. 25fr, Rock python, horiz. 30fr, Gaboon viper. 40fr, Brown house snake, horiz. 45fr, Jameson's mamba.

243 A69 5fr multi .15 .15
244 A69 10fr multi .15 .15
245 A69 15fr multi .16 .15
246 A69 20fr red & multi .20 .16
247 A69 25fr grn & multi .25 .20
248 A69 30fr multi .35 .25
249 A69 40fr bis & multi .35 .30
250 A69 45fr multi .42 .35
Nos. 243-250 (8) 2.03 1.71

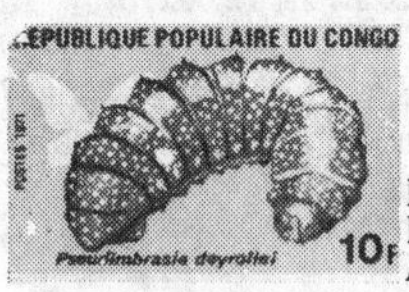

Pseudimbrasia Deyrollei A70

Caterpillars: 15fr, Bunaea alcinoe, vert. 20fr, Epiphora vacuna ploetzi. 25fr, Imbrasia eblis. 30fr, Imbrasia dione, vert. 40fr, Holocera angulata.

1971, July 3 *Perf. 13*

251 A70 10fr ver, blk & grn .15 .15
252 A70 15fr multi .16 .15
253 A70 20fr yel grn, blk & ocher .22 .18
254 A70 25fr multi .25 .20
255 A70 30fr red, blk & yel .35 .25
256 A70 40fr bl, blk & org .50 .38
Nos. 251-256 (6) 1.63 1.31

Boy Scout — A70a

Scouts, Lord Baden-Powell — A70b

Designs: c, Scout facing left. d, Scout facing forward. e, Lord Baden-Powell.

Embossed on Metallic Foil

1971, July 14 *Die Cut Perf. 10½*

256A A70a 90fr Block of 4, #b.-e, silver
256F A70b 1000fr gold

No. 256F is airmail.

Cymothoe Sangaris A71

Butterflies and Moths: 40fr, Papilio dardanus, vert. 75fr, Iolaus timon. 90fr, Papilio phorcas, vert. 100fr, Euchloron megaera.

Perf. 12½x12, 12x12½

1971, Oct. 15

257 A71 30fr yel & multi .35 .20
258 A71 40fr grn & multi .42 .30
259 A71 75fr multi .70 .42
260 A71 90fr multi .90 .60
261 A71 100fr ultra & multi 1.10 .80
Nos. 257-261 (5) 3.47 2.32

Black and White Men Working Together — A72

1971, Oct. 30 *Perf. 13x12½*

262 A72 50fr org & multi .35 .16

Intl. Year Against Racial Discrimination.

REPUBLIQUE POPULAIRE DU CONGO 30F
INAUGURATION DE LA LIAISON COAXIALE 18-11-71

Nos. 214-215 Surcharged

1971, Nov. 18 Engr. *Perf. 13*

263 A61 30fr on 25fr multi .25 .16
264 A61 40fr on 30fr multi .35 .20

Inauguration of cable service between Brazzaville and Pointe Noire. Words of surcharge arranged differently on No. 264.

Map of Congo — A73

1971, Dec. 31 Photo. *Perf. 12½x13*

265 A73 30fr bl & multi .22 .16
266 A73 40fr yel grn & multi .25 .15
267 A73 100fr gray & multi .70 .38
Nos. 265-267 (3) 1.17 .69

"Labor, Democracy, Peace."

Lion — A74

Animals: 2fr, African elephants. 3fr, Leopard. 4fr, Hippopotamus. 5fr, Gorilla, vert. 20fr, Potto. 30fr, De Brazza's monkey. 40fr, Pygmy chimpanzee, vert.

1972, Jan. 31 Engr. *Perf. 13*

268 A74 1fr grn & multi .15 .15
269 A74 2fr dk red & multi .15 .15
270 A74 3fr red brn & multi .15 .15
271 A74 4fr vio & multi .15 .15
272 A74 5fr brn & multi .15 .15
273 A74 20fr org & multi .20 .16
274 A74 30fr ocher & multi .35 .18
275 A74 40fr Prus bl & multi .42 .30
Set value 1.25 .90

WHO, 25th Anniv. — A75

Perf. 12½x13, 13x12½

1973, June 30 Typo.

276 A75 40fr WHO Emblem .20 .15
277 A75 50fr WHO emblem, horiz. .25 .15
Set value .24

Kronenbourg Brewery A76

Designs (Brewery Trademark and): 40fr, Laboratory. 75fr, Vats and controls. 85fr, Automatic control room. 100fr, Pressure room. 250fr, Bottling plant.

1973, July 15 Engr. *Perf. 13*

278 A76 30fr red & multi .16 .15
279 A76 40fr red & multi .20 .15
280 A76 75fr red & multi .38 .20
281 A76 85fr red & multi .55 .25
282 A76 100fr red & multi .70 .40
283 A76 250fr red & multi 1.50 .70
Nos. 278-283 (6) 3.49 1.85

Kronenbourg Brewery, Brazzaville.

Golwe Locomotive, 1935 — A77

Locomotives: 40fr, Diesel, 1935. 75fr, Diesel Whithcomb, 1946. 85fr, Diesel CC200.

1973, Aug. 1 Engr. *Perf. 13*

284 A77 30fr indigo & multi .25 .16
285 A77 40fr vio bl & multi .35 .16
286 A77 75fr multi .60 .25
287 A77 85fr multi .65 .35
Nos. 284-287 (4) 1.85 .92

No. 225 Surcharged with New Value, 2 Bars, and Overprinted in Ultramarine: "SECHERESSE SOLIDARITE AFRICAINE"

1973, Aug. 16 Photo. *Perf. 12½x12*

288 A64 100fr on 5fr multi .55 .38

African solidarity in drought emergency.

African Postal Union Issue

Common Design Type

1973, Sept. 12 Engr. *Perf. 13*

289 CD137 100fr bl grn, vio & brn .50 .25

Bees, Beehive, Honeycomb A78

1973, Dec. 10 Engr. *Perf. 13*

290 A78 30fr sl grn, dk red & bl .18 .15
291 A78 40fr sl bl, sl grn & lt grn .22 .15

"Work and economy."

Family, UN and FAO Emblems A79

Designs: 40fr, Grain, emblems. 100fr, Grain, emblems, vert.

1973, Dec. 10

292 A79 30fr dk car & dk brn .18 .15
293 A79 40fr dk grn, yel & ind .22 .15
294 A79 100fr grn, brn & org .55 .35
Nos. 292-294 (3) .95
Set value .52

World Food Program, 10th anniversary.

Amilcar Cabral, Cattle and Child — A80

1974, July 15 Engr. *Perf. 13*

295 A80 100fr multi .50 .35

First death anniversary of Amilcar Cabral (1924-1973), leader of anti-Portuguese guerrilla activity in Portuguese Guinea.

Félix Eboué, Cross of Lorraine A81

1974, Aug. 31 Litho. *Perf. 13*

296 A81 30fr bl & multi .16 .15
297 A81 40fr brt pink & multi .22 .15
Set value .24

Félix A. Eboué (1884-1944), Governor of Chad, first colonial governor to join Free French in WWII, 30th death anniversary.

Pineapples A82

1974, Nov. 12

298 A82 30fr shown .16 .15
299 A82 30fr Bananas .16 .15
300 A82 30fr Safous .16 .15
301 A82 40fr Avocados .22 .15
302 A82 40fr Mangos .22 .15
303 A82 40fr Papaya .22 .15
304 A82 40fr Orange .22 .15
Nos. 298-304 (7) 1.36
Set value .86

Charles de Gaulle and Conference Building — A83

1974, Nov. 25 Engr. *Perf. 13*

305 A83 100fr multi .50 .35

Brazzaville Conference, 25th anniversary.

George Stephenson and Various Locomotives — A84

1974, Dec. 15

306 A84 75fr slate green & olive .38 .22

George Stephenson (1781-1848), English inventor and railroad founder.

UDEAC Issue

Presidents and Flags of Cameroun, CAR, Congo, Gabon and Meeting Center — A84a

1974, Dec. 8 Photo. *Perf. 13*

307 A84a 40fr gold & multi .22 .15

See note after Cameroun No. 595.
See No. C195.

Irish Setter — A85

Designs: Dogs.

1974, Dec. 15 Photo. *Perf. 13x13½*

308 A85 30fr shown .22 .15
309 A85 40fr Borzoi .30 .15
310 A85 75fr Pointer .50 .22
311 A85 100fr Great Dane .65 .38
Nos. 308-311 (4) 1.67 .90

1974, Dec. 15

Designs: Cats.

312 A85 30fr Havana chestnut .22 .15
313 A85 40fr Red Persian .30 .15
314 A85 75fr Blue British .50 .22
315 A85 100fr African serval .65 .38
Nos. 312-315 (4) 1.67 .90

Labor Party Flags and People — A86

Design: 40fr, Hands holding flowers and tools.

1974, Dec. 31 Engr. *Perf. 13x12½*

316 A86 30fr red & multi .16 .15
317 A86 40fr red & multi .22 .15
Set value .20

5th anniversary of Congolese Labor Party and of introduction of red flag.

Symbols of Development — A87

U Thant and UN Headquarters — A88

Paul G. Hoffman and UN Emblem A89

Perf. 13x12½, 12½x13

1975, Feb. 28 Litho.

318 A87 40fr multi .20 .15
319 A88 50fr light blue & multi .22 .15
320 A89 50fr yellow & multi .22 .15
Nos. 318-320 (3) .64 .45

National economic development.

Map of China and Mao Tse-tung — A90

1975, Mar. 9 Engr. *Perf. 13*

321 A90 75fr multi .40 .25

25th anniv. of the PRC.

Woman Breaking Bonds, Women's Activities, Map of Congo — A91

1975, June 20 Litho. *Perf. 12½*

322 A91 40fr gold & multi .25 .15

Revolutionary Union of Congolese Women, URFC, 10th anniversary.

CARA Soccer Team — A92

Design: 40fr, Team captain and manager receiving trophy, vert.

1975, July 15 Litho. *Perf. 12½*

323 A92 30fr multi .18 .15
324 A92 40fr multi .22 .15

CARA team, winners of African Soccer Cup 1974.

Citroen, 1935 — A93

Designs: Early autombiles.

1975, July 17 *Perf. 12*

325 A93 30fr shown .16 .15
326 A93 40fr Alfa Romeo, 1911 .22 .15
327 A93 50fr Rolls Royce, 1926 .25 .20
328 A93 75fr Duryea, 1893 .40 .30
Nos. 325-328 (4) 1.03 .80

Tipoye Transport — A94

1975, Aug. 5

329 A94 30fr shown .15 .15
330 A94 40fr Dugout canoe .20 .15
Set value .21

Traditional means of transportation.

Raising Red Flag — A95

1975, Aug. 15

331 A95 30fr shown .16 .15
332 A95 40fr National Conference .22 .15

2nd anniv. of installation of popular power (30fr) and 3rd anniv. of Natl. Conf. (40fr).

Line Fishing — A96

Woman Pounding "Foufou" — A97

Traditional Fishing: 30fr, Trap fishing, horiz. 60fr, Spear fishing. 90fr, Net fishing, horiz.

1975, Aug. 31 **Litho.** *Perf. 12*

333 A96 30fr multi .16 .15
334 A96 40fr multi .22 .15
335 A96 60fr multi .35 .20
336 A96 90fr multi .45 .35
Nos. 333-336 (4) 1.18 .85

1975, Sept. 5

Household Tasks: No. 338, Woman chopping wood. 40fr, Woman preparing manioc, horiz.

337 A97 30fr multi .16 .15
338 A97 30fr multi .16 .15
339 A97 40fr multi .22 .15
Nos. 337-339 (3) .54
Set value .34

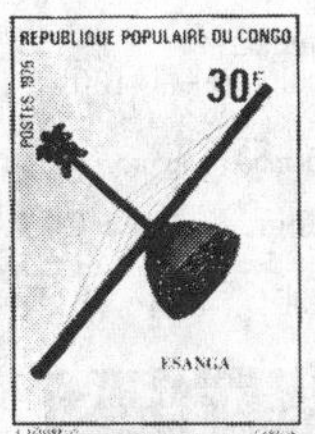
Musical Instruments — A98

1975, Sept. 20 *Perf. 12½*

340 A98 30fr Esanga .16 .15
341 A98 40fr Kalakwa .22 .15
342 A98 60fr Likembe .35 .22
343 A98 75fr Ngongui .40 .25
Nos. 340-343 (4) 1.13 .77

Dzeke (Congolese) Shell Money A99

Ancient Money: No. 346, like No. 344. Nos. 345, 347, Okengo, Congolese, iron bar. 40fr, Gallic coin, c. 60 B.C. 50fr, Roman denarius, 37 B.C. 60fr, Danubian coin, 2nd cent. B.C. 85fr, Greek stater, 4th cent. B.C.

1975-76 **Engr.** *Perf. 13*

344 A99 30fr red & multi .16 .15
345 A99 30fr vio & multi .16 .15
346 A99 35fr ol & multi .20 .15
347 A99 35fr dk car rose & multi .20 .15
348 A99 40fr Prus bl & brn .22 .15
349 A99 50fr Prus bl & ol .25 .16
350 A99 60fr dk grn & brn .35 .22
351 A99 85fr mag & sl grn .42 .25
Nos. 344-351 (8) 1.96 1.38

Nos. 346-347 inscribed "1976" and issued Mar. 1976; others issued Oct. 5, 1975.

Moschops — A100

Pre-historic Animals: 70fr, Tyrannosaurus. 95fr, Cryptocleidus. 100fr, Stegosaurus.

1975, Oct. 15 **Litho.** *Perf. 13*

352 A100 55fr multi .30 .20
353 A100 75fr multi .40 .22
354 A100 95fr multi .50 .35
355 A100 100fr multi .55 .38
Nos. 352-355 (4) 1.75 1.15

Albert Schweitzer (1875-1965), Medical Missionary — A101

1975, Oct. 15 **Engr.**

356 A101 75fr ol, brn & red .40 .25

Alexander Fleming A102

Designs: No. 358, André Marie Ampère. No. 359, Clement Ader.

1975, Nov. 15 **Engr.** *Perf. 13*

357 A102 60fr brn, grn & blk .35 .20
358 A102 95fr blk, red & grn .50 .38
359 A102 95fr red, blue & indigo .50 .38
Nos. 357-359 (3) 1.35 .96

Fleming (1881-1955), developer of penicillin; Ampère (1775-1836), physicist; Ader (1841-1925), aviation pioneer.

UN Emblem "ONU" and "30" — A103

1975, Dec. 20 **Engr.** *Perf. 13*

360 A103 95fr car, ultra & grn .50 .38

United Nations, 30th anniversary.

Women's Broken Chain — A104

Design: 60fr, Equality between man and woman, globe, IWY emblem.

1975, Dec. 20 **Litho.** *Perf. 12½*

361 A104 35fr mag, ocher & gray .20 .15
362 A104 60fr ultra, brn & blk .35 .22

International Women's Year, 1975.

Pres. Marien Ngouabi, Flag and Workers — A105

Echo of the P.C.T. A106

Perf. 12½x12, 13x12½

1975, Dec. 31

363 A105 30fr multi .16 .15
364 A106 35fr multi .20 .15
Set value .20

6th anniversary of the Congolese Labor Party (P.C.T.). See No. C215.

A.G. Bell and 1876 Telephone A107

1976, Apr. 25 **Litho.** *Perf. 12½x13*

365 A107 35fr yel, brn & org brn .20 .15

Cent. of 1st telephone call by Alexander Graham Bell, Mar. 10, 1876. See No. C229.

Women Selling Fruit and Vegetables A108

1976, Sept. 19 **Litho.** *Perf. 12½x13*

366 A108 35fr shown .20 .15
367 A108 60fr Market scene .35 .20

Congolese Coiffure — A109

Designs: Various women's hair styles.

1976, Oct. 10 **Litho.** *Perf. 13*

368 A109 35fr multi .20 .15
369 A109 60fr multi .35 .22
370 A109 95fr multi .50 .35
371 A109 100fr multi .55 .38
Nos. 368-371 (4) 1.60 1.10

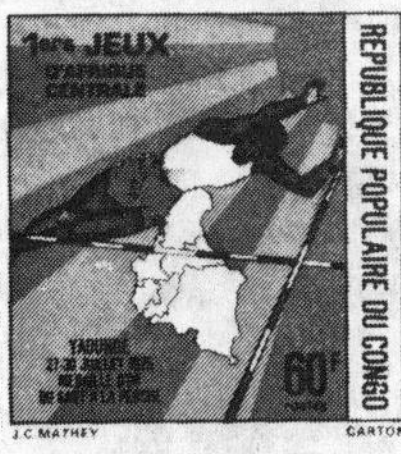
Pole Vault, Map of Central Africa A110

Design: 95fr, Long jump and map of Central Africa.

1976, Oct. 25 *Perf. 12½*

372 A110 60fr yel & multi .25 .18
373 A110 95fr yel & multi .38 .28

Gold medalists, 1st Central African Games, Yaoundé, July 27-30, 1975. See Nos. C230-C231.

Antelope A111

1976, Oct. 27 **Litho.** *Perf. 12½*

Size: 36x36mm

374 A111 5fr shown .15 .15
375 A111 10fr Buffalos .15 .15
376 A111 15fr Hippopotamus .15 .15
377 A111 20fr Wart hog .15 .15
378 A111 25fr Elephants .15 .15
Set value .43 .31

1976, Dec. 8

Designs: Birds.

Size: 26x36mm

379 A111 5fr Saddle-bill storks .15 .15

Size: 36x36mm

380 A111 10fr Malachite kingfisher .15 .15
381 A111 20fr Crowned cranes .15 .15
Set value .22 .18

Bicycling, Map of Participants A112

Heliotrope A113

1976, Dec. 21 **Photo.** *Perf. 12½x13*

382 A112 35fr shown .20 .15
383 A112 60fr Fieldball .35 .22
384 A112 80fr Running .42 .35
385 A112 95fr Soccer .50 .38
Nos. 382-385 (4) 1.47 1.10

First Central African Games, Libreville, Gabon, June-July 1976.

1976, Dec. 23 **Photo.** *Perf. 12½x13*

Flowers: 5fr, Water lilies. 15fr, Bird-of-paradise flower.

386 A113 5fr multi .15 .15
387 A113 10fr multi .15 .15
388 A113 15fr multi .20 .15
Set value .39 .17

Torch and Olive Branches A114

1976, Dec. 25 **Litho.** *Perf. 12½x13*

389 A114 35fr multi .15 .20

National Pioneer Movement.

The Spirit of '76 A115

Designs: 125fr, Pulling down George III statue. 150fr, Battle of Princeton. 175fr, Generals of Revolutionary War. 200fr, Burgoyne's surrender at Saratoga. 500fr, Battle of Lexington.

1976, Dec. 29 **Litho.** *Perf. 14*

390 A115 100fr multi .65 .25
391 A115 125fr multi .80 .35
392 A115 150fr multi .90 .38
393 A115 175fr multi 1.10 .50
394 A115 200fr multi 1.25 .55
Nos. 390-394 (5) 4.70 2.03

Souvenir Sheet

395 A115 500fr multi 3.25 1.40

American Bicentennial.

Dugout Canoe Race — A116

Design: 60fr, 2-man dugout canoes.

1977, Mar. 27 Litho. *Perf. 13x13½*

396 A116 35fr multi .22 .15
397 A116 60fr multi .38 .22

Dugout canoe races on Congo River.

Lilan Goua — A117

Fresh-water Fish: 15fr, Liko ko. 25fr, Liyan ga. 35fr, Mbessi. 60fr, Mongandza.

1977, June 15 Litho. *Perf. 12½*

398 A117 10fr multi .15 .15
399 A117 15fr multi .15 .15
400 A117 25fr multi .16 .15
401 A117 35fr multi .22 .15
402 A117 60fr multi .38 .22
Nos. 398-402 (5) 1.06
Set value .58

Traditional Headdress — A118

1977, June 30 Litho. *Perf. 12½*

403 A118 35fr shown .20 .15
404 A118 60fr Leopard cap .35 .22

See Nos. C234-C235.

Bondjo Wrestling — A119

Designs: 40fr, 50fr, Bondjo wrestling (different). 40fr, horiz.

1977, July 15

405 A119 25fr multi .15 .15
406 A119 40fr multi .20 .16
407 A119 50fr multi .25 .20
Nos. 405-407 (3) .60 .51

"Schwaben" LZ 10, 1911 — A120

Zeppelins: 60fr, "Viktoria Luise." LZ 11, 1913. 100fr, LZ 120. 200fr, LZ 127. 300fr, "Graf Zeppelin II" LZ 130.

1977, Aug. 5 Litho. *Perf. 11*

408 A120 40fr multi .22 .15
409 A120 60fr multi .40 .20
410 A120 100fr multi .65 .22
411 A120 200fr multi 1.25 .55
412 A120 300fr multi 2.00 .80
Nos. 408-412 (5) 4.52 1.92

History of the Zeppelin. Exist imperf. See No. C236.

Coat of Arms and Rising Sun — A121

1977, Aug. 15

413 A121 40fr multi .20 .16

14th anniversary of the revolution.

Victor Hugo and The Hunchback of Notre Dame — A122

Designs (Hugo and): 60fr, Les Miserables. 100fr, Les Travailleurs de la Mer (octopus).

1977, Aug. 20 Engr. *Perf. 13*

414 A122 35fr multi .20 .15
415 A122 60fr multi .35 .22
416 A122 100fr multi .55 .40
Nos. 414-416 (3) 1.10 .77

Victor Hugo (1802-1885), French novelist.

Mao Tse-tung A123

Lithographed; Gold Embossed

1977, Sept. 9 *Perf. 12x12½*

417 A123 400fr red & gold 2.25 1.60

Chairman Mao Tse-tung (1893-1976), Chinese Communist leader, 1st death anniv.

Peter Paul Rubens A124

1977, Sept. 20 Gold Embossed

418 A124 600fr gold & lt bl 3.25 2.50

Peter Paul Rubens (1577-1640), painter.

Child Leading Blind Woman Across Street A125

1977, Oct. 22 Litho. *Perf. 12½x13*

419 A125 35fr multi .20 .15

World Health Day: To see is life.

Paul Kamba and Records A126

1977, Oct. 29

420 A126 100fr multi .55 .25

Paul Kamba (1912-1950), musician.

Trajan Vuia and Flying Machine — A127

Designs: 75fr, Louis Bleriot and plane. 100fr, Roland Garros and plane. 200fr, Charles Lindbergh and Spirit of St. Louis. 300fr, Tupolev Tu-144. 500fr, Lindbergh and Spirit of St. Louis over ship in Atlantic.

1977, Nov. 18 Litho. *Perf. 14*

421 A127 60fr multi .30 .18
422 A127 75fr multi .35 .22
423 A127 100fr multi .50 .22
424 A127 200fr multi 2.00 .50
425 A127 300fr multi 1.50 .70
Nos. 421-425 (5) 4.65 1.82

Souvenir Sheet

426 A127 500fr multi 2.75 1.25

History of aviation.

Elizabeth II and Prince Philip A128

Design: 300fr, Elizabeth II wearing Crown.

1977, Dec. 21

427 A128 250fr multi 1.20 .65
428 A128 300fr multi 1.50 .70

25th anniv. of the reign of Queen Elizabeth II. See #C239. For overprints see #468-469, C244.

King Baudouin A129

Design: No. 430, Charles de Gaulle.

1977, Dec. 21

429 A129 200fr multi 1.25 .65
430 A129 200fr multi 1.25 .65

King Baudouin of Belgium and Charles de Gaulle, president of France.

Ambete Sculpture — A130

Congolese art: 85fr, Babembe sculpture.

1978, Feb. 18 Engr. *Perf. 13*

431 A130 35fr lt brn & multi .20 .15
432 A130 85fr lt grn & multi .45 .35

St. Simon, by Rubens A131

Rubens Paintings: 140fr, Duke of Lerma. 200fr, Madonna and Saints. 300fr, Rubens and his Wife Helena Fourment. 500fr, Farm at Laeken.

1978, Mar. 7 Litho. *Perf. 13½x14*

433 A131 60fr gold & multi .40 .16
434 A131 140fr gold & multi .90 .30
435 A131 200fr gold & multi 1.25 .45
436 A131 300fr gold & multi 2.00 .65
Nos. 433-436 (4) 4.55 1.56

Souvenir Sheet

437 A131 500fr gold & multi 3.25 1.40

Peter Paul Rubens, 400th birth anniv.

Pres. Ngouabi and Microphones A132

Designs: 60fr, Ngouabi at his desk, horiz. 100fr, Portrait.

Perf. 12½x13, 13x12½

1978, Mar. 18 Litho.

438 A132 35fr multi .20 .15
439 A132 60fr multi .35 .22
440 A132 100fr multi .55 .40
Nos. 438-440 (3) 1.10 .77

Pres. Marien Ngouabi, 1st death anniv.

Ferenc Puskas and Argentina '78 Emblem — A133

Players and Emblem: 75fr, Giacinto Facchetti. 100fr, Bobby Moore. 200fr, Raymond Kopa. 300fr, Pele. 500fr, Franz Beckenbauer.

1978, Apr. 4 *Perf. 14x13½*

441 A133 60fr multi .35 .20
442 A133 75fr multi .40 .22
443 A133 100fr multi .50 .25
444 A133 200fr multi 1.25 .60
445 A133 300fr multi 1.50 .75
Nos. 441-445 (5) 4.00 2.02

Souvenir Sheet

446 A133 500fr multi 2.50 1.00

11th World Cup Soccer Championship, Argentina, June 1-25.
For overprints see Nos. 481-486.

Pearl S. Buck and Chinese Women — A134

Nobel Prize winners: 75fr, Fridtjof Nansen, refugees and Nansen passport. 100fr, Henri Bergson, book and flame. 200fr, Alexander Fleming and Petri dish. 300fr, Gerhart Hauptmann and book. 500fr, Henri Dunant and Red Cross Station.

1978, Apr. 29

447 A134 60fr multi .40 .22
448 A134 75fr multi .45 .25
449 A134 100fr multi .60 .30
450 A134 200fr multi 1.40 .65
451 A134 300fr multi 1.75 .90
Nos. 447-451 (5) 4.60 2.32

Souvenir Sheet

452 A134 500fr multi 3.25 1.40

African Buffalos A135

Endangered animals and Wildlife Fund Emblem: 35fr, Okapi, vert. 85fr, Rhinoceros. 150fr, Chimpanzee, vert. 200fr, Hippopotamus. 300fr, Buffon's kob, vert.

1978 *Perf. 14½*

453 A135 35fr multi .22 .16
454 A135 60fr multi .40 .20
455 A135 85fr multi .55 .28
456 A135 150fr multi .90 .40
457 A135 200fr multi 1.40 .60
458 A135 300fr multi 1.90 .80
Nos. 453-458 (6) 5.37 2.44

Issue dates: 35fr, Aug. 11. Others, July 11.

Emblem, Young People, Gun and Fist — A136

1978, July 28 *Perf. 12½*

459 A136 35fr multi .20 .15

11th World Youth Festival, Havana, July 28-Aug. 5.

Pyramids and Camels — A137

Seven Wonders of the Ancient World: 50fr, Hanging Gardens of Babylon. 60fr, Statue of Zeus, Olympia. 95fr, Colossus of Rhodes. 125fr, Mausoleum of Halicarnassus. 150fr, Temple of Artemis, Ephesus. 200fr, Lighthouse, Alexandria. 300fr, Map of Eastern Mediterranean showing locations. (50fr, 60fr, 95fr, 125fr, 200fr, vertical.)

1978, Aug. 12 **Litho.** *Perf. 14*

460 A137 35fr multi .22 .15
461 A137 50fr multi .35 .16
462 A137 60fr multi .40 .20
463 A137 95fr multi .60 .30
464 A137 125fr multi .80 .38
465 A137 150fr multi 1.00 .45
466 A137 200fr multi 1.25 .55
467 A137 300fr multi 2.00 .80
Nos. 460-467 (8) 6.62 2.99

Nos. 427-428 Overprinted in Silver: "ANNIVERSAIRE DU COURONNEMENT 1953-1978"

1978, Sept. **Litho.** *Perf. 14*

468 A128 250fr multi 1.40 .50
469 A128 300fr multi 1.60 .65

25th anniversary of corporation of Queen Elizabeth II. See No. C244.

Kwame Nkrumah and Map of Africa — A138

1978, Sept. 23 **Litho.** *Perf. 13x12½*

470 A138 60fr multi .35 .16

Nkrumah (1909-72), Pres. of Ghana.

Wild Boar Hunt — A139

Local hunting and fishing: 50fr, Fish smoking. 60fr, Hunter with spears and dog, vert.

1978 **Litho.** *Perf. 12*

471 A139 35fr multi .22 .16
472 A139 50fr multi .35 .22
473 A139 60fr multi .40 .25
Nos. 471-473 (3) .97 .63

Issue dates: 35fr, 60fr, Oct. 5; 50fr, Oct. 10.

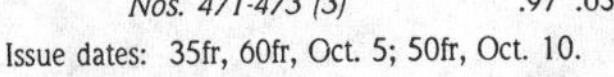

View of Kalchreut, by Dürer — A140

Paintings by Dürer: 150fr, Elspeth Tucher, vert. 250fr, "The Great Piece of Turf," vert. 350fr, Self-portrait, vert.

1978, Nov. 23 **Litho.** *Perf. 14*

474 A140 65fr multi .42 .28
475 A140 150fr multi 1.00 .70
476 A140 250fr multi 1.60 1.10
477 A140 350fr multi 2.25 1.50
Nos. 474-477 (4) 5.27 3.58

Albrecht Dürer (1471-1528), German painter.

Basketmaker — A141

Productive Labor: 90fr, Woodcarver. 140fr, Women hoeing field.

1978, Nov. 18 **Litho.** *Perf. 12½*

Size: 25x36mm

478 A141 85fr multi .60 .40
479 A141 90fr multi .60 .40

Size: 27x48mm

Perf. 12

480 A141 140fr multi .90 .65
Nos. 478-480 (3) 2.10 1.45

Nos. 441-446 Overprinted in Silver:
a. "1962 VAINQUEUR: BRESIL"
b. "1966 VAINQUEUR: / GRANDE BRETAGNE"
c. "1970 VAINQUEUR: / BRESIL"
d. "1974 VAINQUEUR: / ALLEMAGNE (RFA)"
e. "1978 VAINQUEUR: / ARGENTINE"
f. "ARGENTINE-PAYS BAS 3-1/25 juin 1978"

1978, Nov. *Perf. 14x13½*

481 A133 (a) 60fr multi .40 .25
482 A133 (b) 75fr multi .50 .35
483 A133 (c) 100fr multi .65 .45
484 A133 (d) 200fr multi 1.40 .90
485 A133 (e) 300fr multi 2.00 1.40
Nos. 481-485 (5) 4.95 3.35

Souvenir Sheet

486 A133 (f) 500fr multi 3.50

Winners, World Soccer Cup Championships 1962-1978.

Heart and Charts A142

1978, Dec. 16 **Engr.** *Perf. 13*

487 A142 100fr multi .65 .45

Fight against hypertension.

Party Emblem and Road — A143

1978, Dec. 31 **Litho.** *Perf. 12½x12*

488 A143 60fr multi .40 .25

Congolese Labor Party, 9th anniversary.

Capt. Cook, Polynesians and House — A144

Capt. James Cook (1728-1779): 150fr, Island scene. 250fr, Polynesian longboats. 350fr, Capt. Cook's ships off Hawaii.

1979, Jan. 16 *Perf. 14½*

489 A144 65fr multi .38 .28
490 A144 150fr multi 1.00 .70
491 A144 250fr multi 1.60 1.10
492 A144 350fr multi 2.25 1.50
Nos. 489-492 (4) 5.23 3.58

Pres. Marien Ngouabi — A145

1979, Mar. 18 **Litho.** *Perf. 12*

493 A145 35fr multi .22 .15
494 A145 60fr multi .40 .25

Assassination of President Ngouabi, 2nd anniv.

"1979," IYC Emblem, Child A146

A146a

1979 **Litho.** *Perf. 12½x13*

495 A146 45fr multi .30 .20
496 A146 75fr multi .50 .35

Souvenir Sheet

Perf. 14½

496A A153a 250fr multi

International Year of the Child.
Issued: 45fr, 75fr, Apr. 30. 250fr, Sept. 5.

Pottery Vases and Solanum — A147

Design: 150fr, Mail runner, Concorde, train, UPU emblem, envelope.

1979, June 8 **Litho.** *Perf. 13*

497 A147 60fr multi .40 .22

Engr.

498 A147 150fr multi 1.00 .60

Philexafrique II, Libreville, Gabon, June 8-17. Nos. 497, 498 each printed in sheets of 10 with 5 labels showing exhibition emblem.

Rowland Hill, Diesel Locomotive, Germany No. 78 — A148

Designs (Rowland Hill and): 100fr, Old steam locomotive and France No. B10. 200fr, Diesel locomotive and US No. 245. 300fr, Steam locomotive and England-Australia First Aerialpost vignette, 1919. 500fr, Electric train, Concorde and Middle Congo No. 75.

1979, June *Perf. 14*

499 A148 65fr multi .42 .28
500 A148 100fr multi .65 .45
501 A148 200fr multi 1.40 .90
502 A148 300fr multi 2.00 1.25
Nos. 499-502 (4) 4.47 2.88

Souvenir Sheet

503 A148 500fr multi 3.50

Sir Rowland Hill (1795-1879), originator of penny postage.

Salvador Allende, Flags, Demonstrators — A149

1979, July 21 **Litho.** *Perf. 12½*

504 A149 100fr multi .65 .45

Salvador Allende, president of Chile.

Old Man Telling Stories — A150

1979, July 28

505 A150 45fr multi .30 .20

Story telling as education.

Handball Players A151

Designs: 75fr, Players and ball (vert.). 250fr, Pres. Ngouabi, cup on map of Africa, player.

1979, July 31 **Litho.** *Perf. 12½*

Size: 40x30mm, 30x40mm

506 A151 45fr multi .30 .20
507 A151 75fr multi .50 .35

Size: 22x40mm

Perf. 12x12½

508 A151 250fr multi 1.60 1.25

Marien Ngouabi Handball Cup.

Map and Flag of Congo A152

1979, Aug. 15

509 A152 50fr multi .35 .22

16th anniversary of revolution.

Souvenir Sheet

Virgin and Child, by Dürer A153

1979, Aug. 13 *Perf. 13½*

510 A153 500fr red brn & lt grn 3.50

Albrecht Dürer (1471-1528), German engraver and painter.

Bach and Contemporary Instruments — A155

Design: No. 512, Albert Einstein, astronauts on moon.

1979, Sept. 10 *Perf. 13½*

511 A155 200fr multi 1.40 .90
512 A155 200fr multi 1.40 .90

Yoro Fishing Port — A156

1979, Sept. 26 **Litho.** *Perf. 12½*

513 A156 45fr shown .30 .20
514 A156 75fr Port at night .50 .35

Mukukulu Dam — A157

1979, Oct. 5 *Perf. 12½x12*

515 A157 20fr multi .15 .15
516 A157 45fr multi .30 .20

Emblem, Control Tower, Jets — A158

1979, Dec. 12 **Litho.** *Perf. 12½*

517 A158 100fr multi .65 .50

ASECNA (Air Safety Board), 20th anniv.

Congolese Labor Party, 10th Anniversary A159

1979, Dec. 31

518 A159 45fr multi .30 .15

A160

A161

1980, Mar. 30 **Litho.** *Perf. 12½*

519 A160 45fr multi .30 .25
520 A160 95fr multi .60 .45

Post Office, 15th Anniversary.

1980, May 5

521 A161 100fr multi .55 .25

Visit of Pope John Paul II.

Rotary International, 75th Anniversary — A162

1980, May 10 **Litho.** *Perf. 12½*

522 A162 150fr multi 1.00 .50

Pointe Noire Foundry A163

1980, June 18 **Litho.** *Perf. 12½*

523 A163 30fr shown .16 .15
524 A163 35fr Different view .18 .15
Set value .18

Claude Chappe, Tower A164

1980, June 21 **Litho.** *Perf. 12½*

525 A164 200fr multi 1.10 .55

Claude Chappe (1763-1805), French engineer.

Mossaka Harbor — A165

1980, June 23

532 A165 45fr shown .25 .15
533 A165 90fr Different view .50 .22

Papilio Dardanus (Front and Back) — A167

Human Rights Emblem, People — A169

July 31st Hospital — A168

1980, July 12 **Litho.** *Perf. 12½*

534 A167 5fr shown .15 .15
535 A167 15fr Kalima aethiops .15 .15
536 A167 20fr Papilio demodocus .16 .15
537 A167 60fr Euphaedra .42 .16
538 A167 90fr Hypolimnas misippus .65 .25
Nos. 534-538 (5) 1.53
Set value .56

Souvenir Sheet

539 A167 300fr Charaxes smaragdalis 2.25

1980, July 31

540 A168 45fr multi .25 .15

1980, Aug. 2

541 A169 350fr shown 2.00 1.00
542 A169 500fr Man breaking chain 2.50 2.50

Human Rights Convention, 32nd anniv.

Citizens and Congolese Arms — A170

1980, Aug. 15 *Perf. 12½*

543 A170 75fr shown .40 .20
544 A170 95fr Dove on flag, fists, vert. .50 .25
545 A170 150fr Dove holding Congolese arms .80 .40
Nos. 543-545 (3) 1.70 .85

August 13-15th Revolution, 17th anniv.

Coffee and Cocoa Trees on Map of Congo — A171

Coffee and Cocoa Day: 95fr, Branches, map of Congo.

1980, Aug. 18 *Perf. 13½x13*

546 A171 45fr multi .22 .15
547 A171 95fr multi .50 .25

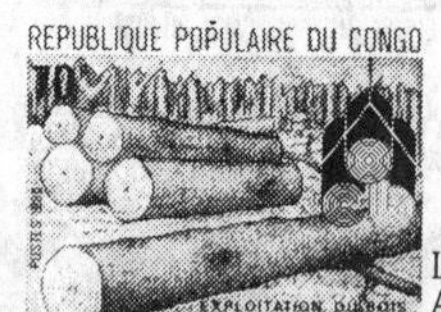

Logging A172

1980, Aug. 28

548 A172 70fr shown .40 .20
549 A172 75fr Wood transport .40 .20

Pres. Neto of Angola, 1st Death Anniv. — A173

Lark — A174

1980, Sept. 11

550 A173 100fr multi .55 .25

1980, Sept. 17

Designs: Birds.

551 A174	45fr multi, horiz.	.30	.15
552 A174	75fr multi, horiz.	.55	.25
553 A174	90fr multi, horiz.	.60	.30
554 A174	150fr multi	1.00	.50
555 A174	200fr multi	1.40	.65
556 A174	250fr multi	1.60	.80
a	Souv. sheet of 6, #551-556	7.00	
	Nos. 551-556 (6)	5.45	2.65

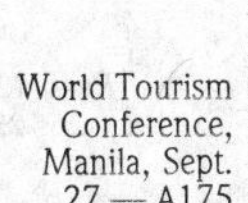

World Tourism Conference, Manila, Sept. 27 — A175

1980, Sept. 27 Litho. *Perf. 13½x13*

557 A175	100fr multi	.55	.25

First Day of School Term — A176

1980, Oct. 2 Photo. *Perf. 13*

558 A176	50fr multi	.25	.15

First House in Brazzaville — A177

Brazzaville Centenary: 65fr, First native village. 75fr, Old Town Hall, 1912. 150fr, View from bank of Bacongo, 1912. 200fr, Meeting of explorer Savorgnan de Brazza and chief Makoko, 1880.

1980, Oct. 3 Litho. *Perf. 12½*

559 A177	45fr multi	.25	.15
560 A177	65fr multi	.35	.18
561 A177	75fr multi	.40	.20
562 A177	150fr multi	.80	.40
563 A177	200fr multi	1.10	.55
	Nos. 559-563 (5)	2.90	1.48

Boys on Bank of Congo River — A178

1980, Oct. 30

564 A178	80fr shown	.42	.20
565 A178	150fr Djoue Bridge	.80	.40

Revolutionary Stadium and Athletes — A179

1980, Nov. 20 *Perf. 13x12½*

566 A179	60fr multi	.35	.16

Rebuilt Railroad Bridge over Congo River A180

1980, Nov. 29 *Perf. 13x13½*

567 A180	75fr multi	.40	.20

Mangoes, Loudima Fruit Packing Station A181

1980, Dec. 2 *Perf. 13*

568 A181	10fr shown	.15	.15
569 A181	25fr Oranges	.15	.15
570 A181	40fr Citrons	.20	.15
571 A181	85fr Mandarins	.45	.22
	Nos. 568-571 (4)	.95	
	Set value		.44

African Postal Union, 5th Anniversary — A182

1980, Dec. 24 *Perf. 13½*

572 A182	100fr multi	.55	.25

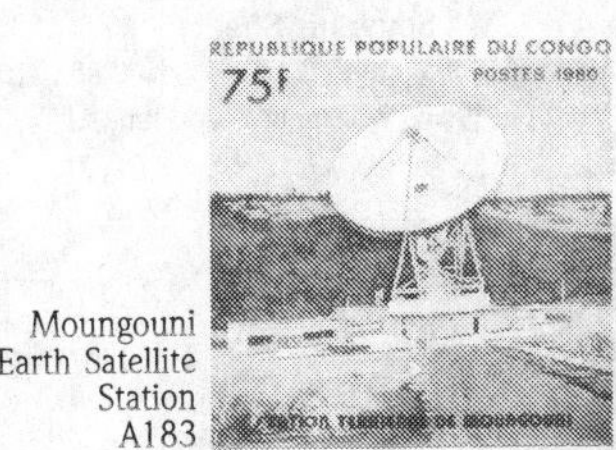

Moungouni Earth Satellite Station A183

1980, Dec. 30 *Perf. 12½*

573 A183	75fr multi	.40	.20

Hertzian Wave Communication, Brazzaville — A184

1980, Dec. 30 *Perf. 12½x12*

574 A184	150fr multi	.80	.40

1980 African Handball Champion Team — A185

Perf. 12½x13, 13x12½

1981, Jan. 26 Litho.

575 A185	100fr Receiving cup, vert.	.55	.25
576 A185	150fr shown	.80	.40

Pres. Denis Sassou-Nguesso — A186

1981, Feb. 5 Litho. *Perf. 12½*

577 A186	45fr multi	.25	.15
578 A186	75fr multi	.40	.20
579 A186	100fr multi	.55	.25
	Nos. 577-579 (3)	1.20	.60

Columbia Space Shuttle Orbiting Earth A187

Space Conquest: 100fr, Luna 17, 1970. 200fr, 300fr, 500fr, Columbia space shuttle, 1981.

1981, May 4 Litho. *Perf. 14x13½*

580 A187	100fr multi	.55	.25
581 A187	150fr multi	.80	.40
582 A187	200fr multi	1.10	.55
583 A187	300fr multi	1.60	.80
	Nos. 580-583 (4)	4.05	2.00

Souvenir Sheet

584 A187	500fr multi	2.50	1.40

For overprint see No. 725.

Fight Against Apartheid — A188

Twin Palm Tree of Louingui — A189

1981, May 5 Litho. *Perf. 12½*

585 A188	100fr deep blue	.55	.25

1981, May 22 *Perf. 12x12½*

586 A189	75fr multi	.40	.20

13th World Telecommunications Day — A190

1981, June 6 *Perf. 12½*

587 A190	120fr multi	.60	.30

Rubber Extraction — A191

1981, June 27 *Perf. 13*

588 A191	50fr shown	.25	.15
589 A191	70fr Sap draining	.40	.16

Intl. Year of the Disabled A192

1981, June 29 Engr.

590 A192	45fr multi	.25	.15

See No. B7.

Bird Trap — A194

Designs: Animal traps. 10fr vert.

1981, July

596 A194	5fr multi	.15	.15
597 A194	10fr multi	.15	.15
598 A194	15fr multi	.15	.15
599 A194	20fr multi	.15	.15
600 A194	30fr multi	.15	.15
601 A194	35fr multi	.20	.15
	Set value	.69	.38

Mausoleum of King Maloango — A195

1981, July 4 Litho. *Perf. 12½*

602 A195	75fr shown	.40	.20
603 A195	150fr Mausoleum, portrait	.80	.40

Prince Charles and Lady Diana, Coach A196

Royal wedding: Couple and coaches.

1981, Sept. 1 Litho. *Perf. 14½*

604 A196	100fr multi	.55	.25
605 A196	200fr multi	1.10	.55
606 A196	300fr multi	1.60	.80
	Nos. 604-606 (3)	3.25	1.60

Souvenir Sheet

607 A196	400fr multi	2.25	1.10

World Food Day — A197

1981, Oct. 16 Litho. *Perf. 13½x13*

608 A197	150fr multi	.80	.55

12th World UPU Day — A198

1981, Oct. 24 Engr. *Perf. 13x12½*

609 A198	90fr multi	.50	.22

Royal Guard A199

1981, Oct. 31 Litho. *Perf. 12½x13*
610 A199 45fr multi .22 .15

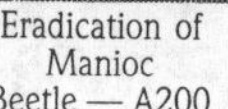
Eradication of Manioc Beetle — A200

Natl. Red Cross — A201

1981, Nov. 18 Litho. *Perf. 12½*
611 A200 75fr multi .40 .20

1981, Nov. 18 *Perf. 13*
612 A201 10fr Bandaging patient .15 .15
613 A201 35fr Treating child .15 .15
614 A201 60fr Drawing well water .35 .16
Nos. 612-614 (3) .65
Set value .31

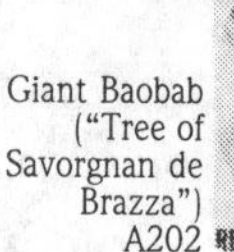

Giant Baobab ("Tree of Savorgnan de Brazza") A202

1981, Dec. 19 Litho. *Perf. 13*
615 A202 45fr multi .22 .15
616 A202 75fr multi .40 .20

Fetish Figure — A203

Designs: Various carved figures.

1981, Dec. 19 *Perf. 13x12½*
617 A203 15fr multi .15 .15
618 A203 25fr multi .15 .15
619 A203 45fr multi .22 .15
620 A203 50fr multi .25 .15
621 A203 60fr multi .35 .16
Nos. 617-621 (5) 1.12
Set value .54

Caves of Bangou A204

1981, Dec. 29 *Perf. 13x13½*
622 A204 20fr multi .15 .15
623 A204 25fr multi .15 .15
Set value .24 .15

King Makoko and His Queen, Ivory Sculptures by R. Engongodzo A205

Perf. 13½x13, 13x13½
1982, Feb. 27 Litho.
624 A205 25fr Woman, vert. .15 .15
625 A205 35fr Woman, diff., vert. .15 .15
626 A205 100fr shown .55 .25
Nos. 624-626 (3) .85
Set value .42

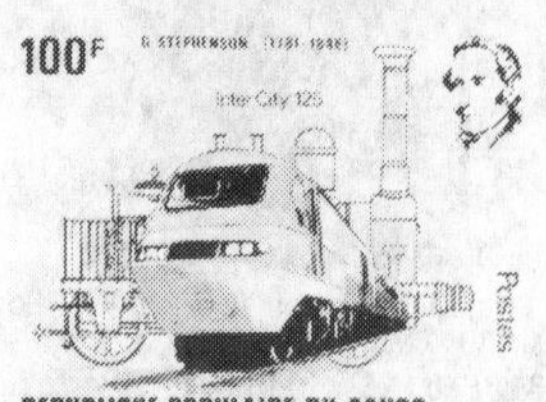
George Stephenson (1781-1848) and Inter City 125, Gt. Britain — A206

Locomotives: 150fr, Sinkansen Bullet Train, Japan. 200fr, Advanced Passenger Train, Gt. Britain. 300fr, TGV-001, France.

1982, Mar. 2 Litho. *Perf. 12½*
627 A206 100fr multi .55 .25
628 A206 150fr multi .80 .40
629 A206 200fr multi 1.10 .55
630 A206 300fr multi 1.60 .80
Nos. 627-630 (4) 4.05 2.00

Scouting Year A207

1982, Apr. 13 Litho. *Perf. 13*
631 A207 100fr Looking through binoculars .55 .25
632 A207 150fr Reading map .80 .40
633 A207 200fr Helping woman 1.10 .55
634 A207 300fr Crossing rope bridge 1.60 .80
Nos. 631-634 (4) 4.05 2.00

Souvenir Sheet
635 A207 500fr Hiking, horiz. 3.00 1.75

For overprint see No. 726.

Franklin Roosevelt A208

1982, June 12 Litho. *Perf. 13*
636 A208 150fr shown .80 .40
637 A208 250fr Washington 1.40 .65
638 A208 350fr Goethe 2.00 .90
Nos. 636-638 (3) 4.20 1.95

21st Birthday of Princess Diana, July 1 — A209

1982, June 12 *Perf. 14*
639 A209 200fr Candles 1.10 .55
640 A209 300fr "21" 1.60 .80

Souvenir Sheet
641 A209 500fr Diana 2.50 1.40

5-Year Plan, 1982-1986 A210

Perf. 13x12½, 12½x13
1982, June 19
642 A210 60fr Road construction .25 .15
643 A210 100fr Communications, vert. .40 .20
644 A210 125fr Operating room equipment, vert. .50 .22
645 A210 150fr Hydroelectric power, vert. .65 .30
Nos. 642-645 (4) 1.80 .87

ITU Plenipotentiary Conference, Nairobi — A211

1982, June 26 *Perf. 13*
646 A211 300fr multi 1.60 .80

Nos. 604-607 Overprinted in Blue: "NAISSANCE ROYALE 1982"

1982, July 30 *Perf. 14½*
647 A196 100fr multi .55 .25
648 A196 200fr multi 1.10 .55
649 A196 300fr multi 1.60 .80
Nos. 647-649 (3) 3.25 1.60

Souvenir Sheet
650 A196 400fr multi 2.25 1.10

Birth of Prince William of Wales, June 21.

Nutrition Campaign — A212

1982, July 24 Litho. *Perf. 12½*
651 A212 100fr multicolored .55 .25

WHO African Headquarters, Brazzaville — A213

1982, July 24 Litho. *Perf. 12½*
652 A213 125fr multicolored .65 .35

TB Bacillus Centenary — A214

1982, Aug. 7 *Perf. 12½x12*
653 A214 250fr Koch, bacillus 1.40 .65

Pres. Sassou-Nguesso and 1980 Simba Prize — A215

1982, Oct. 20 Litho. *Perf. 13*
654 A215 100fr multi .55 .25

Turtles — A216

Various turtles and tortoises.

1982, Dec. 1
655 A216 30fr multi .16 .15
656 A216 45fr multi .22 .15
657 A216 55fr multi .30 .15
Nos. 655-657 (3) .68
Set value .35

Boy Gathering Coconuts — A217

Nest in Tree Trunk — A218

1982, Dec. 11
658 A217 100fr multi .55 .25

1982, Dec. 29 *Perf. 12½*
659 A218 40fr shown .20 .15
660 A218 75fr Nests in palm tree .40 .20
661 A218 100fr Woven nest on thorn branch .55 .25
Nos. 659-661 (3) 1.15 .60

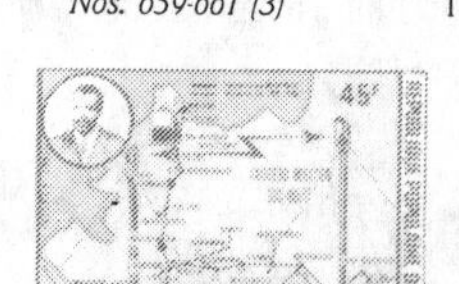
Hertzian Wave Communication Network — A219

1982, Dec. 30 *Perf. 13x12½*
662 A219 45fr multi .22 .15
663 A219 60fr multi .35 .16
664 A219 95fr multi .50 .25
Nos. 662-664 (3) 1.07 .56

30th Anniv. of Customs Cooperation Council — A220

1983, Jan. 26 Litho. *Perf. 12½x13*
665 A220 100fr Headquarters .55 .25

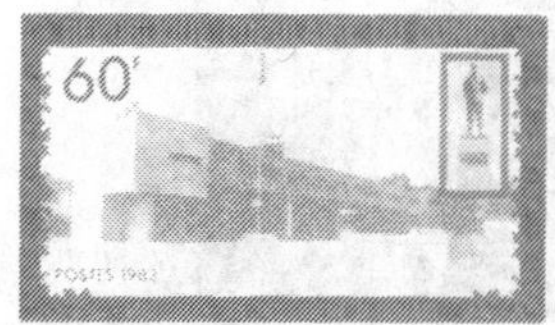

Mausoleum of Pres. Marien Ngouabi — A221

1983, Feb. 8 *Perf. 13*

666 A221 60fr multi .35 .16
667 A221 80fr multi .42 .20

Ironsmiths — A222

1983 *Perf. 12½*

668 A222 45fr shown .22 .15
669 A222 150fr Weaver, vert. .80 .40

Issue dates: 45fr, Mar. 5; 150fr, Feb. 24.

Carved Chess Pieces, by R. Engongonzo — A223

Various pieces.

1983, Feb. 26 *Perf. 13*

670 A223 40fr multi .22 .15
671 A223 60fr multi .35 .16
672 A223 95fr multi .50 .25
Nos. 670-672 (3) 1.07 .56

Easter 1983 A224

Raphael drawings. 200fr, 400fr vert.

1983, Apr. 20 **Litho.** *Perf. 13*

673 A224 200fr Transfiguration study 1.10 .55
674 A224 300fr Deposition from Cross 1.60 .80
675 A224 400fr Christ in Glory 2.00 1.10
Nos. 673-675 (3) 4.70 2.45

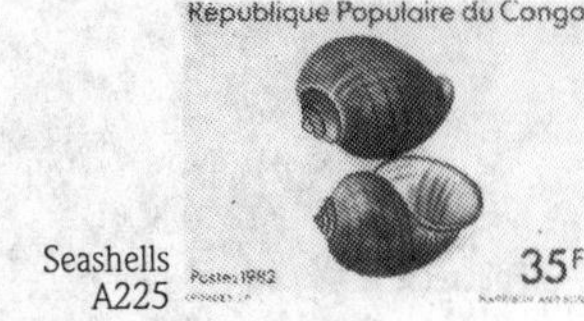

Seashells A225

1983 **Litho.** *Perf. 15x14*

675A A225 25fr multi
676 A225 35fr multi .15 .15
677 A225 65fr multi .16 .15

Dated 1982.

A226 A227

Various traditional combs.

1983, May *Perf. 14*

678 A226 30fr multi .15 .15
679 A226 70fr multi .18 .15
680 A226 85fr multi .22 .15
Nos. 678-680 (3) .55
Set value .27

Perf. 12½x13

1983, Aug. 10 **Litho & Engr.**

681 A227 60fr multi .16 .15
682 A227 100fr multi .25 .15
Set value .22

20th anniv. of revolution.

Centenary of the Arrival of Christian Missionaries — A228

Churches and Clergymen: 150fr, A. Carrie, Church of the Sacred Heart, Loango, vert. 250fr, Msgr. Augouard; St. Louis, Liranga; St. Joseph, Linzolo.

1983, Aug. 23 *Perf. 12½*

683 A228 150fr multi .40 .20
684 A228 250fr multi .65 .35

Local Flowers — A229

1984, Jan. 20 **Litho.** *Perf. 12½*

685 A229 5fr Liana thunderaie, vert. .15 .15
686 A229 15fr Bougainvillea .15 .15
687 A229 20fr Anthurium, vert. .15 .15
688 A229 45fr Allamanda .15 .15
689 A229 75fr Hibiscus, vert. .20 .15
Set value .47 .32

35th Anniv. of World Peace Council A230

1984, Mar. 31 **Litho.** *Perf. 13x12½*

690 A230 50fr multi .15 .15
691 A230 100fr multi .30 .15
Set value .22

Anti-Nuclear Arms Campaign — A231

1984, May 31 **Litho.** *Perf. 12x12½*

692 A231 200fr Explosion, victims .60 .30

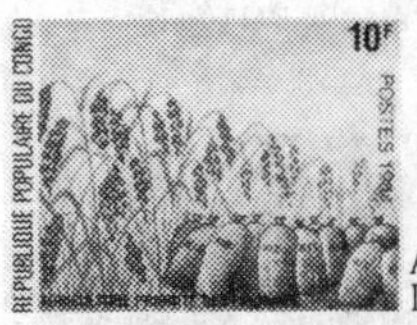

Agriculture Day — A232

Perf. 13x13½, 13½x13

1984, June 30 **Litho.**

693 A232 10fr Rice .15 .15
694 A232 15fr Pineapples .15 .15
695 A232 60fr Manioc, vert. .16 .15
696 A232 100fr Palm tree, map, vert. .32 .16
Set value .58 .34

Congress Palace — A233

1984, July 27 *Perf. 13*

697 A233 60fr multi .16 .15
698 A233 100fr multi .30 .15
Set value .23

Chinese-Congolese cooperation.

CFCO-Congo Railways, 50th Anniv. A234

1984, July 30 *Perf. 13½*

699 A234 10fr Loulombo Station .15 .15
700 A234 25fr Les Bandas Chinese Labor Camp .15 .15
701 A234 125fr "50" .40 .20
702 A234 200fr Admin. bldg. .60 .30
Nos. 699-702 (4) 1.30
Set value .60

Locomotives — A235

Ships on the Congo River — A236

1984, Aug. 24 *Perf. 12½*

703 A235 100fr CC 203 .30 .15
704 A236 100fr Tugboat .30 .15
705 A235 150fr BB 103 .45 .22
706 A236 150fr Pusher tugboat .45 .22
707 A235 300fr BB-BB 301 .90 .45
708 A236 300fr Dredger .90 .45
709 A235 500fr BB 420 L'Eclair 1.50 .75
710 A236 500fr Cargo ship 1.50 .75
Nos. 703-710 (8) 6.30 3.14

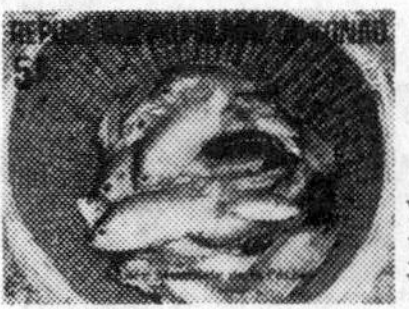

World Fisheries Year — A237

1984, Oct. 16 *Perf. 13½*

711 A237 5fr Basket of fish .15 .15
712 A237 20fr Net fishermen in boat .15 .15
713 A237 25fr School of fish .15 .15
714 A237 40fr Net fisherman .15 .15
715 A237 55fr Trawler .15 .15
Set value .42 .28

Anti-polio Campaign — A238

M'Bamou Palace Hotel, Brazzaville — A239

1984, Oct. 30

716 A238 250fr Disabled men, hand .65 .35
717 A238 300fr Target, disabled women, horiz. .80 .42

1984, Dec. 15 *Perf. 14½*

718 A239 60fr multi .16 .15
719 A239 100fr multi .25 .15
Set value .22

Fauna A240

1984, Dec. *Perf. 15x14½*

720 A240 30fr Pangolin .15 .15
721 A240 70fr Bat .20 .15
722 A240 85fr Civet cat .22 .15
Nos. 720-722 (3) .57
Set value .27

Congo River Logging A241

1984, Dec. *Perf. 13½x13*

723 A241 60fr Log raft, crew hut .16 .15
724 A241 100fr Tugboat pushing logs .25 .15
Set value .22

Souvenir Sheets

Nos. 584, 635 Ovptd. with Exhibition in Black or Green

1985, Mar. 8 *Perf. 14x13½, 13*

725 A187 500fr TSUKUBA EXPO '85 1.40 .65
726 A207 500fr ITALIA '85 emblem, ROME (G) 1.40 .65

See Nos. C336-C337.

Zonocerus Variegatus — A242

1985, Mar. 15 *Perf. 13*

727 A242 125fr multi .35 .16

Burial of a Teke Chief — A243

1985, Apr. 30 ***Perf. 12½***
728 A243 225fr multi .65 .32

Edible Fruit — A244

1985, June 15 ***Perf. 13½***
729 A244 5fr Trichoscypha acuminata, vert. .15 .15
730 A244 10fr Aframomum africanum .15 .15
731 A244 125fr Gambeya lacuurtiana .35 .16
732 A244 150fr Landolphia jumelei .40 .20
Set value .85 .46

Sizes: #729, 22x36mm, #731, 36x22mm.

Lions Club Intl., 30th Anniv. — A245

1985, June 25 ***Perf. 12½***
733 A245 250fr Flag, District 403B .65 .35

Russian Soldier, Kremlin, Fall of Berlin A246

1985, July 27 ***Perf. 12***
734 A246 60fr multi .16 .15

Defeat of Nazi Germany, end of World War II, 40th anniv.

Lady Olave Baden-Powell, Girl Guides Founder — A247

Anniversaries and events: 150fr, Girl Guides, 75th anniv. 250fr, Jacob Grimm, fabulist; Sleeping Beauty. 350fr, Johann Sebastian Bach, composer; European Music Year, St. Thomas Church organ, Leipzig. 450fr, Queen Mother, 85th birthday, vert. 500fr, Statue of Liberty, cent., vert.

1985, Aug. 26 ***Perf. 13***
735 A247 150fr multi .45 .22
736 A247 250fr multi .80 .40
737 A247 350fr multi 1.10 .55
738 A247 450fr multi 1.25 .60
739 A247 500fr multi 1.50 .70
Nos. 735-739 (5) 5.10 2.47

PHILEXAFRICA '85, Lome, Togo, Nov. 16-24 — A248

1985, Oct. 10 ***Perf. 13x12½***
740 A248 250fr shown .90 .45
741 A248 250fr Airport, postal van .90 .45

Nos. 740-741 printed se-tenant with center label picturing map of Africa or UAPT emblem.

Mushrooms — A249

1985, Dec. 14 **Litho.** ***Perf. 13***
742 A249 100fr Coprinus, vert. .38 .20
743 A249 150fr Cortinarius .55 .25
744 A249 200fr Armillariella mellea .75 .38
745 A249 300fr Dictyophora 1.10 .55
746 A249 400fr Crucibulum vulgare 1.50 .70
Nos. 742-746 (5) 4.28 2.08

Arbor Day — A250

Children's Hoop Races — A251

1986, Mar. 6 ***Perf. 13½***
747 A250 60fr Planting sapling .32 .16
748 A250 200fr Map, lifecycle diagram 1.10 .55

1986, Apr. 30 ***Perf. 12½***
749 A251 5fr Two boys .15 .15
750 A251 10fr One boy .15 .15
751 A251 60fr Three boys, horiz. .32 .16
a. Souvenir sheet of 3, Nos. 749-751 .45 .28
Set value .43 .26

A252

A253

1986, June 5 **Litho.** ***Perf. 13½***
752 A252 60fr Garbage disposal .32 .16
753 A252 125fr Dumping garbage .75 .38

Intl. Environment Day.

1986, July 15 **Litho.** ***Perf. 13x12½***

Traditional Modes of Transporting Goods: 5fr, Basket on head, child in sling carrier. 10fr, Child in carrier on hip, large basket strapped to forehead. 60fr, Man carrying load on shoulder.

754 A253 5fr multi .15 .15
755 A253 10fr multi .15 .15
756 A253 60fr multi .32 .16
Set value .43 .26

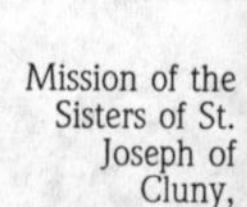

Mission of the Sisters of St. Joseph of Cluny, Cent. — A254

1986, Aug. 19 **Litho.** ***Perf. 12½x13***
757 A254 230fr multi 1.40 .70

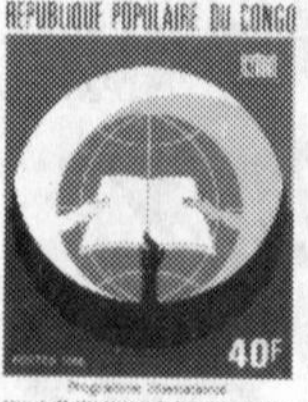

A255

A256

1986, Aug. 30 **Litho.** ***Perf. 13½***
758 A255 40fr multi .22 .15
759 A255 60fr multi .35 .18
760 A255 100fr multi .60 .30
Nos. 758-760 (3) 1.17 .63

UNESCO intl. communications development program.

1986, Sept. 15 **Litho.** ***Perf. 13½***
761 A256 100fr multi .60 .30

Intl. Peace Year.

World Food Day — A257

1986, Oct. 16
762 A257 75fr Food staples .40 .20
763 A257 120fr Mother feeding child .80 .40

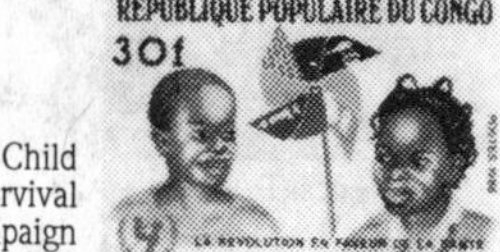

UN Child Survival Campaign A258

Mothers, children and pinwheels in various designs.

1986, Oct. 27
764 A258 15fr multi, vert. .15 .15
765 A258 30fr multi .16 .15
766 A258 70fr multi, vert. .38 .20
Nos. 764-766 (3) .69
Set value .33

A258a

A259

1986, Dec. 5 **Litho.** ***Perf. 12x12½***
766A A258a 100fr multi .65 .32

27th Soviet Communist Party congress.

1987, Feb. 10 **Litho.** ***Perf. 13½***
767 A259 30fr multi .16 .15
768 A259 45fr multi .25 .15
769 A259 75fr multi .40 .20
770 A259 120fr multi .65 .32
Nos. 767-770 (4) 1.46 .82

Election of President Sassou-Nguesso, head of the Organization of African States.

Traditional Wedding A260

1987, Feb. 18 **Litho.** ***Perf. 12½x13***
771 A260 5fr multi .15 .15
772 A260 15fr multi .15 .15
773 A260 20fr multi .15 .15
Set value .25 .16

The Blue Lake — A261

1987, July 16 ***Perf. 12½***
774 A261 5fr multi .15 .15
775 A261 15fr multi .15 .15
776 A261 75fr multi .42 .22
777 A261 120fr multi .68 .35
Nos. 774-777 (4) 1.40
Set value .66

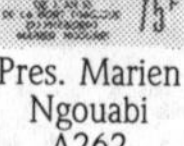

Pres. Marien Ngouabi A262

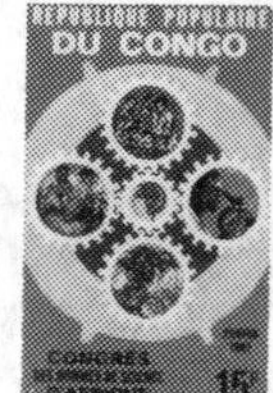

Congress of African Scientists A263

1987, July 16 ***Perf. 13***
778 A262 75fr multi .42 .22
779 A262 120fr multi .68 .35

Tenth death anniv.

1987, Sept. 10 ***Perf. 13x12½***
780 A263 15fr multi .15 .15
781 A263 90fr multi .60 .30
782 A263 230fr multi 1.55 .78
Nos. 780-782 (3) 2.30 1.23

4th African Games, Nairobi — A264

1987, Oct. 30 ***Perf. 12½***
783 A264 75fr multi .55 .28
784 A264 120fr multi .88 .45

Raoul Follereau (1903-1977), Philanthropist A265

1987, Oct. 20 ***Perf. 13½***
785 A265 120fr multi .88 .45

Cure leprosy.

FAO, 40th Anniv. — A266

1987, Nov. 17 *Perf. 12½*

786 A266 300fr multi 2.15 1.10

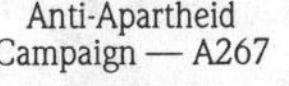

Anti-Apartheid Campaign — A267

Nelson Mandela — A268

Perf. 13½x15, 14½x15

1987, Sept. 21 **Litho.**

787	A267	60fr multi	.42	.20
788	A268	240fr multi	1.75	.88

Natl. UNICEF Vaccination Campaign A269

Africa Fund A270

Perf. 13½x14½, 14½x13½

1987, Sept. 28

789	A269	30fr Inoculating adults, horiz.	.22	.15
790	A269	45fr shown	.32	.16
791	A269	500fr Inoculating children, horiz.	3.50	1.75
		Nos. 789-791 (3)	4.04	2.06

No. 791 is airmail.

1987, Sept. 28 *Perf. 13½x15*

792	A270	25fr multi	.18	.15
793	A270	50fr multi	.36	.18
794	A270	70fr multi	.50	.25
		Nos. 792-794 (3)	1.04	.58

Self-sufficiency in Food Production by the Year 2000 — A271

1987, Nov. 20 **Litho.** *Perf. 13½*

795	A271	20fr multi	.15	.15
796	A271	55fr multi	.40	.20
797	A271	100fr multi	.72	.35
		Nos. 795-797 (3)	1.27	.70

Simon Kimbangu (b. 1887), Founder of the Church of Christ on Earth — A272

1987, Nov. 28 *Perf. 12½*

798	A272	75fr Kimbangu, vert.	.55	.28
799	A272	120fr Kimbangu, parrot, vert.	.85	.42
800	A272	240fr Kimbanguist Church, Nkamba	1.70	.85
a.		Souvenir sheet of 3, #798-800	3.10	1.55
		Nos. 798-800 (3)	3.10	
		Set value		.52

October Revolution, Russia, 70th Anniv. A273

Design: Lenin inspecting revolutionary troops, Red Square, from an unspecified painting.

1988, Feb. 19 **Litho.** *Perf. 12½x12*

801	A273	75fr multi	.50	.25
802	A273	120fr multi	.80	.40

African Writers Opposing Apartheid — A274

Intl. Fund for Agricultural Development (IFAD), 10th Anniv. — A275

1988, Apr. 6 **Litho.** *Perf. 13½*

803	A274	15fr multi	.15	.15
804	A274	60fr multi	.45	.22
805	A274	75fr multi	.52	.25
		Nos. 803-805 (3)	1.12	.62

1988, Apr. 30

806 A275 240fr multi 1.70 .85

Invention of the Telegraph by Samuel Morse, 150th Anniv. (in 1987) — A276

1988, Apr. 28

807	A276	90fr Morse, vert.	.65	.32
808	A276	120fr shown	.85	.42

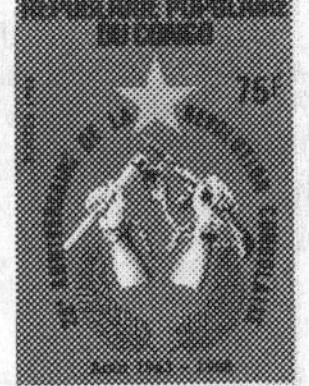

A277

A278

1988, Sept. 20 **Litho.** *Perf. 13½*

809	A277	5fr Eucalyptus trees, Brazzaville	.15	.15
810	A277	10fr Stop cutting down trees	.15	.15
		Set value	.15	.15

Fight against desertification.

1988, Aug. 12 **Litho.** *Perf. 13½*

Campaigns: No. 812, Return to the Land Campaign (farming). 120fr, Self-sufficiency in food production.

811	A278	75fr shown	.52	.25
812	A278	75fr multi	.52	.25
813	A278	120fr multi	.82	.40
		Nos. 811-813 (3)	1.86	.90

Congo Revolution, 25th anniv.

Yoro Fishing Village A279

1988, Sept. 1

814	A279	35fr shown	.24	.15
815	A279	40fr Liberty Place	.28	.15

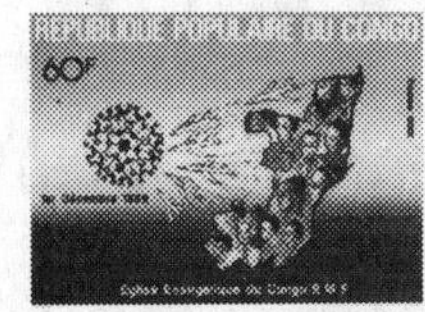

Intl. Day for the Fight Against AIDS — A280

1988, Dec. 1 **Litho.** *Perf. 13½*

816	A280	60fr shown	.38	.20
817	A280	75fr Emblem	.48	.25
818	A280	180fr Modified UN emblem, campaign emblem	1.15	.58
		Nos. 816-818 (3)	2.01	1.03

Natl. Committee for the Fight Against AIDS and Evangelical Anglican Church of Congo anti-AIDS campaign.

February 5 Movement, 10th Anniv. A281

1989, Apr. 21 **Litho.** *Perf. 13½*

819	A281	75fr Rally	.45	.22
820	A281	120fr Pres. Sassou-Nguesso, natl. achievements	.72	.35

UN Declaration of Human Rights, 40th Anniv. (in 1988) A282

1989, May 19 *Perf. 13*

821	A282	120fr multi	.78	.40
822	A282	350fr multi	2.25	1.15

Marien Nguabi, Founder of Congo Labor Party A282a

1989, July 31 **Litho.** *Perf. 12½x13*

822A A282a 240fr red & yellow 1.70 .85

Red Cross and Red Crescent Societies, 125th Annivs. A283

Designs: 120fr, Dunant, emblem, Congo Red Cross.

1989, Sept. 19 **Litho.** *Perf. 13*

823	A283	75fr shown	.48	.25
824	A283	120fr multicolored	.78	.40

No. 824 is airmail.

Organization of African Unity, 25th Anniv. — A284

1989, Oct. 19 **Litho.** *Perf. 12½*

825 A284 120fr multicolored .78 .40

African Development Bank, 25th Anniv. A285

1989, Dec. 22 **Litho.** *Perf. 12½x13*

826	A285	75fr multicolored	.55	.28
827	A285	120fr multicolored	.85	.42

WHO, 40th Anniv. (in 1988) A286

1989, Dec. 28 **Litho.** *Perf. 12½*

828	A286	60fr shown	.42	.20
829	A286	75fr Blood donation, vert.	.55	.28

See Nos. 846-847 for overprints.

Congo Labor Party (PCT), 20th Anniv. — A287

1989, Dec. 22 **Litho.** *Perf. 13x12½*

830	A287	75fr multicolored	.55	.28
831	A287	120fr multicolored	.85	.42

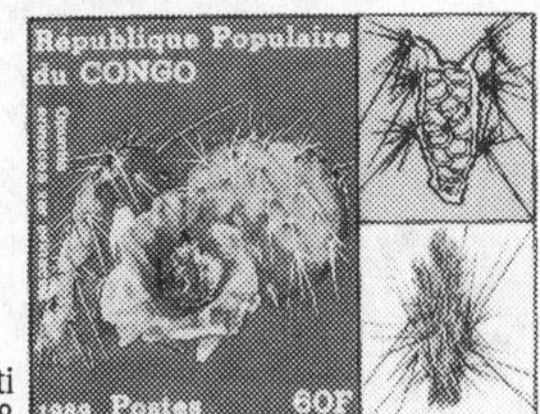

Cacti A288

Perf. 12½x13, 13x12½

1989, Nov. 22

832 A288 35fr *Opuntia phaeacantha discata* .25 .15
833 A288 40fr *Opuntia ficus indica* .28 .15
834 A288 60fr *Opuntia erinacea* .42 .22
835 A288 75fr *Opuntia rufida* .55 .28
836 A288 120fr *Opuntia leptocaulis* .85 .42
Nos. 832-836 (5) 2.35 1.22

Souvenir Sheet

Perf. 12½

837 A288 220fr *Opuntia compresa* 1.60 .80

Nos. 832-833, 835 and 837 vert. No. 837 contains one 32x40mm stamp.

1992 Winter Olympics, Albertville A289

1989, Dec. 22 *Perf. 12½*

838 A289 75fr Ice dancing .52 .26
839 A289 80fr Nordic skiing .55 .28
840 A289 100fr Speed skating .70 .35
841 A289 120fr Luge .85 .42
842 A289 200fr Alpine skiing 1.40 .70
843 A289 240fr Ice hockey 1.70 .85
844 A289 400fr Ski jumping 2.80 1.40
Nos. 838-844 (7) 8.52 4.26

Souvenir Sheet

Perf. 13

845 A289 500fr Bobsled 3.50 1.75

No. 845 contains one 32x40mm stamp.

Nos. 828-829 Ovptd. "NOTRE PLANETE, NOTRE SANTE PENSER GLOBALEMENT AGIR LOCALEMENT" in 3 or 5 Lines

1989, Dec. 28 *Perf. 12½*

846 A286 60fr multicolored .42 .20
847 A286 75fr multicolored .55 .28

Health care for everyone.

Intl. Literacy Year — A290

1990, June 26 **Litho.** *Perf. 13½*

848 A290 75fr bl, blk & yel .55 .28

Birds — A291

Designs: 25fr, Tourterelle des bois. 50fr, Fauvette pitchou, vert. 70fr, Faucon crecerelle, vert. 150fr, Perroquet gris, vert.

1990, July 10

849 A291 25fr multicolored .18 .15
850 A291 50fr multicolored .36 .18
851 A291 70fr multicolored .50 .25
852 A291 150fr multicolored 1.10 .55
Nos. 849-852 (4) 2.14 1.13

Dance Masks — A292

Flowering Plants — A293

1990, July 24 *Perf. 13*

853 A292 120fr Mondo .85 .42
854 A292 360fr Bapunu 2.60 1.30
855 A292 400fr Kwele 2.90 1.45
Nos. 853-855 (3) 6.35 3.17

1990, Sept. 15 **Litho.** *Perf. 12½*

856 A293 30fr Tournesol (sunflower) .25 .15
857 A293 45fr Cassia alata, horiz. .35 .18
858 A293 75fr Oeillette (opium poppy) .60 .30
859 A293 90fr Acalypha sanderil .70 .35
Nos. 856-859 (4) 1.90 .98

1992 Summer Olympics, Barcelona — A294

1990, June 28 **Litho.** *Perf. 13½*

860 A294 100fr Street scene, vert. .80 .40
861 A294 150fr shown 1.20 .60
862 A294 200fr Sailing, diff. 1.60 .80
863 A294 240fr Marketplace 1.90 .95
864 A294 350fr Harbor 2.80 1.40
865 A294 500fr Monument, vert. 4.00 2.00
Nos. 860-865 (6) 12.30 6.15

Souvenir Sheet

866 A294 750fr Cathedral, vert. 6.00 3.00

Nos. 864-865 airmail. Nos. 860-865 exist in miniature sheets of 1.

Royal Necklaces A295

1990, Aug. 18 **Litho.** *Perf. 13½*

867 A295 75fr shown .65 .32
868 A295 100fr Necklace, diff. .85 .42

Boy Scouts Observing Nature — A296

Scout: 35fr, Photographing butterfly, Euphaedra eusimoides. 40fr, Picking mushrooms, Armillaria mellea. 75fr, Drawing butterfly, Palla decius. 80fr, Using magnifying glass, Kallima ansorgei. 500fr, Using microscope, Cortinarius speciocissimus. 600fr, Feeding butterfly, Graphium illyris. 750fr, Photographing mushrooms, Volvariella bombycina.

1991, June 8 **Litho.** *Perf. 13½*

869 A296 35fr multicolored .30 .15
870 A296 40fr multicolored .35 .18
871 A296 75fr multicolored .65 .32
872 A296 80fr multicolored .70 .35
873 A296 500fr multicolored 4.15 2.10
874 A296 600fr multicolored 4.85 2.45
a. Min. sheet of 4, #869, 871-872, 874 11.00 5.50
Nos. 869-874 (6) 11.00 5.55

Souvenir Sheet

875 A296 750fr multicolored 6.20 3.10

Nos. 869-874 exist in souvenir sheets of 1. Nos. 873-875 are airmail.

Medicinal Plants — A297

Designs: 15fr, Ocimum viride. 20fr, Kalanchoe pinnata, vert. 30fr, Euphorbia hirta. 60fr, Catharanthus roseus, vert. 75fr, Bidens pilosa, vert. 100fr, Brillantaisia patula, vert. 120fr, Cassia occidentalis, vert.

1991, Jan. 30 **Litho.** *Perf. 11½*

876 A297 15fr multicolored .15 .15
877 A297 20fr multicolored .15 .15
878 A297 30fr multicolored .22 .15
879 A297 60fr multicolored .45 .22
880 A297 75fr multicolored .55 .28
881 A297 100fr multicolored .75 .38
882 A297 120fr multicolored .90 .45
Nos. 876-882 (7) 3.17 1.78

Mushrooms A298

1991, Mar. 25 **Litho.** *Perf. 13*

883 A298 30fr Amanita rubescens .24 .15
883A A298 45fr Cathelasma imperiale .38 .18
883B A298 75fr Amanita caesarea .60 .30
883C A298 90fr Boletus regius .75 .38
883D A298 120fr Pluteus cervinus 1.00 .50
883E A298 150fr Boletus chrysenteron 1.20 .60
883F A298 200fr Agaricus arvensis 1.60 .80
Nos. 883-883F (7) 5.77 2.91

A number has been reserved for a souvenir sheet with this set.

African Tourism Year — A299

1991, Apr. 15 **Litho.** *Perf. 13½*

884 A299 75fr shown .55 .30
885 A299 120fr Zebra, map .90 .45

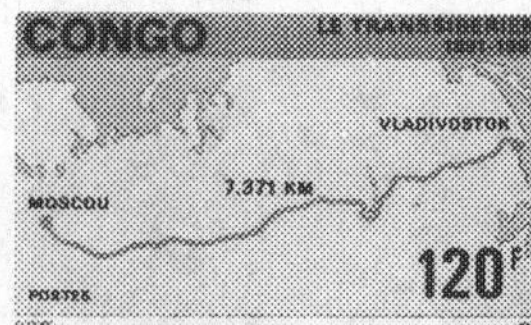

Allegory of New Republic — A300

1991, May 13 **Litho.** *Perf. 13*

888 A300 15fr blue .15 .15
890 A300 30fr brt grn .22 .15
893 A300 60fr org yel .42 .22
894 A300 75fr brt pink .52 .28
898 A300 120fr dk brown .85 .42
Nos. 888-898 (5) 2.16 1.22

This is an expanding set. Numbers will change if necessary.

Trans-Siberian Railroad, Cent. — A301

1991, June 6 **Litho.** *Perf. 13*

899 A301 120fr Map .90 .45
900 A301 240fr Map, train 1.80 .90

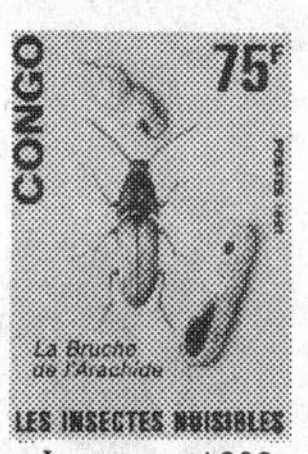

Telecom 91 — A302

1991, June 29 **Litho.** *Perf. 13*

901 A302 75fr multi .55 .30
902 A302 120fr multi, vert. .90 .45

6th World Forum and Exposition on Telecommunications, Geneva, Switzerland.

Insects — A303

A304

1991, July 2 *Perf. 12½*

903 A303 75fr Peanut beetle .55 .30
904 A303 120fr Centaur, horiz. .90 .45
905 A303 200fr Coffee beetle 1.50 .75
906 A303 300fr Goliath beetle 2.20 1.10
Nos. 903-906 (4) 5.15 2.60

1991, July 16 **Litho.** *Perf. 12½*

907 A304 75fr Water conservation .55 .28

Amnesty Intl., 30th Anniv. A305

Designs: 40fr, Candle, sun, vert. 75fr, "30," broken chains, vert.

1991, Aug. 13 *Perf. 13½*

908 A305 40fr multicolored .30 .15
909 A305 75fr multicolored .55 .28
910 A305 80fr multicolored .60 .30
Nos. 908-910 (3) 1.45 .73

Congo Postage Stamps, Cent. — A306

Designs: 75fr, Similar to French Congo #1. 120fr, Similar to French Congo #35. 240fr, Similar to Congo Republic #89. 500fr, Similar to French Congo #1, 35 and Congo Republic #89.

Perf. 13x13½

1991, Aug. **Litho. & Engr.**

911 A306 75fr beige & dk grn .55 .28
912 A306 120fr beige, dk grn & brn .90 .45
913 A306 240fr multicolored 1.75 .90
914 A306 500fr multicolored 3.70 1.85
a. Strip of 4, #911-914 6.90 3.45

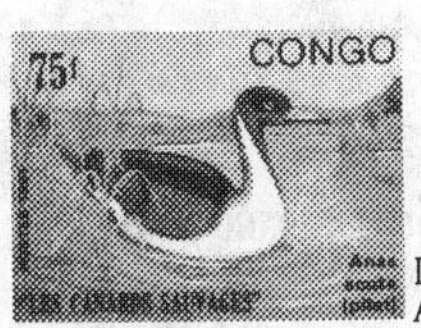

Ducks A307

1991, Aug. 8 Litho. *Perf. 12½*

915 A307 75fr Anas acuta .55 .28
916 A307 120fr Somateria mollissima, vert. .90 .45
917 A307 200fr Anas clypeata, vert. 1.50 .75
918 A307 240fr Anas platyrhynchos 1.80 .90
Nos. 915-918 (4) 4.75 2.38

Automobiles and Space — A308

Designs: 35fr, Ferrari 512S by Pininfarina. 40fr, Vincenzo Lancia, Lancia Stratos by Bertone. 75fr, Maybach Zeppelin type 12, Wilhelm Maybach. 80fr, Mars Observer, 1992. 500fr, Magellan probe surveying Venus. 600fr, Magnification of Sun, Ulysses probe. 750fr, Crew of Apollo 11.

1991, Aug. 23 Litho. *Perf. 13½*

919 A308 35fr multicolored .28 .15
920 A308 40fr multicolored .32 .16
921 A308 75fr multicolored .60 .30
922 A308 80fr multicolored .65 .32
923 A308 500fr multicolored 4.00 2.00
924 A308 600fr multicolored 4.75 2.35
Nos. 919-924 (6) 10.60 5.28

Souvenir Sheet

925 A308 750fr multicolored 5.90 2.95

Nos. 923-925 are airmail. No. 925 contains one 60x42mm stamp.

Butterflies — A309

1991, Aug. 31 *Perf. 11½*

926 A309 75fr Petit bleu .60 .30
927 A309 120fr Charaxe .95 .48
928 A309 240fr Papillon feuille, vert. 1.90 .95
929 A309 300fr Papillon de l'oranger, vert. 2.40 1.20
Nos. 926-929 (4) 5.85 2.93

Celebrities and Organizations — A310

Designs: 100fr, Bo Jackson, baseball and football player. 150fr, Nick Faldo, golfer. 200fr, Rickey Henderson, Barry Bonds, baseball players. 240fr, Gary Kasparov, World Chess Champion. 300fr, Starving child, Lions and Rotary Clubs emblems. 350fr, Wolfgang Amadeus Mozart. 400fr, De Gaulle, Churchill. 500fr, Jean-Henri Dunant, founder of Red Cross. 750fr, De Gaulle, vert.

1991, Sept. 2 *Perf. 13½*

930 A310 100fr multicolored .80 .40
931 A310 150fr multicolored 1.20 .60
932 A310 200fr multicolored 1.60 .80
933 A310 240fr multicolored 1.90 .95
934 A310 300fr multicolored 2.40 1.20
935 A310 350fr multicolored 2.75 1.40
936 A310 400fr multicolored 3.20 1.60
937 A310 500fr multicolored 4.00 2.00
Nos. 930-937 (8) 17.85 8.95

Souvenir Sheet

938 A310 750fr multicolored 5.90 2.95

Nos. 936-938 are airmail. No. 938 contains one 35x50mm stamp.

Gen. Charles de Gaulle in Africa — A311

Designs: 120fr, De Gaulle, Free French flag, vert. 240fr, De Gaulle, Appeal of Brazzaville, 1940.

Perf. 13½x13, 13x13½

1991, Sept. 2

939 A311 75fr multicolored .60 .30
940 A311 120fr multicolored .95 .45
941 A311 240fr multicolored 1.90 .95
Nos. 939-941 (3) 3.45 1.70

A312

Paintings — A313

1991, Oct. 12 *Perf. 11½*

942 A312 75fr multicolored .60 .30
943 A313 120fr multicolored .95 .45

REPUBLIQUE POPULAIRE DU CONGO 20F

Discovery of America, 500th Anniv. (in 1992) — A314

Designs: 20fr, Portrait of Christopher Columbus by Sebastian Del Pombo. 35fr, Portrait of Columbus. 40fr, Portrait of Columbus facing right. 55fr, Santa Maria. 75fr, Nina. 150fr, Pinta. 200fr, Arms and signature of Columbus.

1991, May 30 *Perf. 13*

944 A314 20fr multicolored .15 .15
945 A314 35fr multicolored .28 .15
946 A314 40fr multicolored .30 .15
947 A314 55fr multicolored .45 .22
948 A314 75fr multicolored .60 .30
949 A314 150fr multicolored 1.20 .60
950 A314 200fr multicolored 1.60 .80
Nos. 944-950 (7) 4.58 2.37

Primates A315

1991, Dec. 13 Litho. *Perf. 13*

951 A315 30fr Cercopithecus diana .24 .15
952 A315 45fr Pan troglodytes .38 .18
953 A315 60fr Theropithecus gelada .48 .24
954 A315 75fr Papio hamadryas .60 .30
955 A315 90fr Macaca nemestrina .75 .38
956 A315 120fr Gorilla gorilla 1.00 .50
957 A315 240fr Mandrillus sphinx 1.95 1.00
Nos. 951-957 (7) 5.40 2.75

Nos. 953-957 are vert. A number has been reserved for a souvenir sheet with this set.

Anniversaries and Events A316

Designs: 50fr, Launching of Sputnik II with dog, Laika, 1957. 75fr, Mahatma Gandhi and Martin Luther King, Jr. 1964. 120fr, Launching of Meteosat and ERS-1 over Europe and Africa. 240fr, Maybach Zeppelin automobile and Ferdinand von Zeppelin, 75th death anniversary. 300fr, Konrad Adenauer, 25th death anniversary and opening of the Brandenburg Gate, 1989. 500fr, Pope John Paul II's visit to Africa. 600fr, Elvis Presley, American entertainer.

1992, Feb. 4 Litho. *Perf. 13½*

959 A316 50fr multicolored .38 .20
960 A316 75fr multicolored .58 .30
961 A316 120fr multicolored .95 .48
962 A316 240fr multicolored 1.90 .95
963 A316 300fr multicolored 2.35 1.15
964 A316 500fr multicolored 3.90 2.00
a. Souvenir sheet of 3, #960, 963-964 11.50 5.75
Nos. 959-964 (6) 10.06 5.08

Souvenir Sheet

965 A316 600fr multicolored 4.70 2.35

Nos. 959-964 exist in souvenir sheets of 1. Nos. 962, 964-965 are airmail.

Explorers — A317 Birds — A318

Genoa '92: 75fr, Juan de la Cosa, nautical chart. 95fr, Martin Alonso Pinzon, astrolabe. 120fr, Alonso de Ojeda, hour glass. 200fr, Vicente Yanez Pinzon, sun dial. 250fr, Bartholomew Columbus, quadrant.

1992, Oct. 21 Litho. *Perf. 13*

966 A317 75fr multicolored .60 .30
967 A317 95fr multicolored .75 .38
968 A317 120fr multicolored 1.00 .50
969 A317 200fr multicolored 1.60 .80
970 A317 250fr multicolored 2.00 1.00
Nos. 966-970 (5) 5.95 2.98

A number has been reserved for a souvenir sheet with this set.

1992, Oct. 21

Designs: 60fr, Sagittarius serpentarius. 75fr, Ephippiorhynchus senegalensis. 120fr, Bugeranus carunculatus. 200fr, Ardea melanocephala. 250fr, Phoenicopterus ruber roseus.

972 A318 60fr multicolored .48 .24
973 A318 75fr multicolored .60 .30
974 A318 120fr multicolored 1.00 .50
975 A318 200fr multicolored 1.60 .80
976 A318 250fr multicolored 2.00 1.00
Nos. 972-976 (5) 5.68 2.84

A number has been reserved for a souvenir sheet with this set.

Wild Cats — A319

1992, Nov. 21 Litho. *Perf. 13*

978 A319 45fr Panthera leo .35 .15
979 A319 60fr Panthera tigris .50 .25
980 A319 75fr Lynx lynx .60 .30
981 A319 95fr Caracal caracal .80 .40
982 A319 250fr Leopardus pardalis 2.00 1.00
Nos. 978-982 (5) 4.25 2.10

Souvenir Sheet

983 A319 400fr Acinonyx jubatus 3.25 1.75

No. 983 contains one 32x40mm stamp.

1992 Winter Olympics, Albertville — A320

1992 Summer Olympics, Barcelona — A321

Gold medalists: 150fr, N. Mishkutyonok, A. Dmitriev, pairs figure skating, Unified team. 200fr, I. Appelt, H. Winkler, G. Haldacher, T. Schroll, 4-man bobsled, Austria. 500fr, Gunda Niemann, speed skating, Germany. 600fr, Bjorn Daehlie, cross-country skiing, Norway. 750fr, Alberto Tomba, giant slalom, Italy.

1992, Dec. 21 Litho. *Perf. 13½*

984 A320 150fr multicolored 1.20 1.20
985 A320 200fr multicolored 1.60 1.60
986 A320 500fr multicolored 4.00 4.00
987 A320 600fr multicolored 4.75 4.75
Nos. 984-987 (4) 11.55 11.55

Souvenir Sheet

988 A320 750fr multicolored 6.00 6.00

Nos. 986-988 are airmail. No. 988 contains one 35x50mm stamp. Name on No. 987 spelled incorrectly.

1992, Dec. 21

Barcelona landmarks, Olympic event: 75fr, Steeple of La Sagrada Familia, baseball. 100fr, The Muse, Palace of Music, running. 150fr, Cupola interior, long jump. 200fr, St. Paul Hospital, pole vault. 400fr, Sculpture, by Miro, shot put. 500fr, Galley, Maritime Museum, table tennis. 750fr, La Sagrada Familia, tennis.

989 A321 75fr multicolored .60 .30
990 A321 100fr multicolored .80 .40
991 A321 150fr multicolored 1.20 .60
992 A321 200fr multicolored 1.60 .80
993 A321 400fr multicolored 3.20 3.20
994 A321 500fr multicolored 4.00 4.00
Nos. 989-994 (6) 11.40 9.30

Souvenir Sheet

995 A321 750fr multicolored 6.00 6.00

Nos. 993-995 are airmail.

Christmas — A321a

Paintings: 95fr, The Madonna of the Grand Duke, by Raphael. 200fr, The Madonna with a Book, by Botticelli. 250fr, The Madonna Carondelet, by Fra Bartolommeo. 400fr, Madonna and Child, by Raphael.

1992, Dec. 20 Litho. *Perf. 12½*

995A A321 95fr multicolored .70 .35
995B A321 200fr multicolored 1.50 .75
995C A321 250fr multicolored 1.90 .95
Nos. 995A-995C (3) 4.10 2.05

Souvenir Sheet

995D A321 400fr multicolored 3.00 1.50

Nos. 995A-995D were not available until late 1993.

Birds of Prey — A322

A323

1993, Jan. 15 Litho. *Perf. 12½x13*

996 A322 45fr Charognard .38 .20
997 A322 75fr Vulture .65 .32
998 A322 120fr Eagle 1.00 .50
Nos. 996-998 (3) 2.03 1.02

1993, Dec. 21 Litho. *Perf. 13½*

Traditional ceramics.

999 A323 45fr Liloko .35 .18
1000 A323 75fr Mbeya .60 .30
1001 A323 120fr Jug with ladles, Mbeya 1.00 .50
Nos. 999-1001 (3) 1.95 .98

Wild Animals — A325

Designs: 60fr, Damaliscus lunatus. 75fr, Gazella granti. 95fr, Equus quagga. 120fr, Panthera pardus. 200fr, Syncerus caffer. 250fr, Hippopotamus ampibius. 350fr, Panthera leo.

1993, Feb. 20 Litho. *Perf. 13*

1008 A325 60fr Damaliscus lunatus .50 .25
1009 A325 75fr Gazella granti .60 .30
1010 A325 95fr Equus quagga .80 .40
1011 A325 120fr Panthera pardus 1.00 .50
1012 A325 200fr Syncerus caffer 1.65 .85
1013 A325 250fr Hippopotamus amphibius 2.00 1.00
1014 A325 300fr Necrosyrtes monachu
1015 A325 350fr Panthera leo 3.00 1.50
Nos. 1008-1015 (7) 9.55 4.80

Wild Flowers — A326

Designs: 75fr, Hibiscus schizopetalus. 95fr, Pentas lanceolata. 120fr, Ricinus communis. 200fr, Delonix regia. 250fr, Stapelia gigantea.

1993, May 20 Litho. *Perf. 12½*

1016 A326 75fr multicolored *1.65 .80*
1017 A326 95fr multicolored *2.00 1.00*
1018 A326 120fr multicolored *2.50 1.25*
1019 A326 200fr multicolored *4.25 2.00*
1020 A326 250fr multicolored *5.50 2.75*
Nos. 1016-1020 (5) *15.90 7.80*

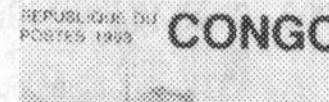

Deep Sea Submersibles A327

1993, June 25

1021 A327 75fr Transport PC-1202 *1.65 .80*
1022 A327 95fr J. Sea Link 1 *2.00 1.00*
1023 A327 120fr Nemo *2.50 1.25*
1024 A327 200fr Robot *4.25 2.25*
1025 A327 250fr Alvin *5.50 2.75*
Nos. 1021-1025 (5) *15.90 8.05*

A number has been reserved for a souvenir sheet with this set.

Protection of Nature A335

Designs: 50fr, Choeropsis liberiensis. 90fr, Hyemoschus aquaticus. 205fr, Taurotragus euryceros, vert. 300fr, Redunca redunca, vert.

1994, Aug. 27 Litho. *Perf. 12½*

1063 A335 50fr multicolored *.22 .15*
1064 A335 90fr multicolored *.42 .20*
1065 A335 205fr multicolored *.95 .55*
1066 A335 300fr multicolored *1.40 .70*
Nos. 1063-1066 (4) *2.99 1.60*

Intl. Year of the Family — A337

1995, Jan. 28 Litho. *Perf. 12½*

1072 A337 90fr shown *.42 .20*
1073 A337 205fr African map, child *.95 .48*
1074 A337 300fr Family, native huts *1.40 .70*
Nos. 1072-1074 (3) *2.77 1.38*

Insects — A338

1994 Litho. *Perf. 12½*

1075 A338 90fr Tarantula *.42 .20*
1076 A338 205fr Spider *.95 .48*
1077 A338 240fr Ladybug *1.10 .55*
Nos. 1075-1077 (3) *2.47 1.23*

Souvenir Sheet

1078 A338 400fr Bee *1.90 .90*

Rotary Intl., 90th Anniv. A339

Designs: 90fr, Polio victim. No. 1080, Playing ball with children. No. 1081, Children with food. 300fr, Delivering polio vaccine.

1500fr, Paul Harris, Rotary emblem.

1996, Feb. 6 Litho. *Perf. 14*

1079 A339 90fr multicolored .35 .20
1080 A339 205fr multicolored .80 .40
1081 A339 205fr multicolored .80 .40
1082 A339 300fr multicolored 1.25 .50
Nos. 1079-1082 (4) 3.20 1.50

Souvenir Sheet

1083 A339 1500fr multicolored 6.00 3.00

SEMI-POSTAL STAMPS

Anti-Malaria Issue
Common Design Type

1962, Apr. 7 Engr. *Perf. 12½x12*

B3 CD108 25fr + 5fr bister .42 .42

Freedom from Hunger Issue
Common Design Type

1963, Mar. 21 Unwmk. *Perf. 13*

B4 CD112 25fr + 5fr vio bl, bl grn & brn .40 .40

Boy Suffering from Sleeping Sickness — SP1

Fight Against Communicable Diseases; 40fr+5fr, Examination, treatment, vert.

1981, June 6 Litho. *Perf. 13*

B5 SP1 40fr + 5fr multi .25 .15
B6 SP1 65fr + 10fr multi .40 .20

IYD Type of 1981

1981, June 29 *Perf. 12½*

B7 A192 75fr + 5fr multi .42 .20

AIR POST STAMPS

Olympic Games Issue
French Equatorial Africa No. C37 Surcharged in Red Like Chad No. C1

1960 Unwmk. Engr. *Perf. 13*

C1 AP8 250fr on 500fr grnsh blk, blk & sl 3.50 3.50

17th Olympic Games, Rome, Aug. 25-Sept. 11.

Helicrysum Mechowiam — AP1

Flowers: 200fr, Cogniauxia podolaena. 500fr, Thesium tencio.

1961, Sept. 28 Engr. *Perf. 13*

C2 AP1 100fr grn, lil & yel .90 .60
C3 AP1 200fr bl grn, yel & brn 1.75 .80
C4 AP1 500fr brn red, yel & sl grn 4.00 1.75
Nos. C2-C4 (3) 6.65 3.15

Air Afrique Issue
Common Design Type

1961, Nov. 25 Unwmk. *Perf. 13*

C5 CD107 50fr lil rose, sl grn & grn .40 .35

Loading Timber, Pointe-Noire Harbor — AP2

1962, June 8 Photo. *Perf. 12½x12*

C6 AP2 50fr multi .40 .35

Opening of the Intl. Fair and Exhib., Pointe-Noire, June 8-11.

Abidjan Games — AP3

Costus Spectabilis — AP4

1962, July 21 *Perf. 12x12½*

C7 AP3 100fr Basketball .90 .62

1963 Unwmk. *Perf. 13*

Design: 250fr, Mountain acanthus.

C8 AP4 100fr multi .90 .55
C9 AP4 250fr multi 2.25 1.25

REPUBLIQUE DU CONGO 100F MAIRIE DE BRAZZAVILLE POSTE AERIENNE

Brazzaville City Hall and Pres. Fulbert Youlou — AP4a

1963, Aug. Photo. *Perf. 13x12*

C10 AP4a 100fr multi 37.50 37.50

African Postal Union Issue
Common Design Type

1963, Sept. 8 *Perf. 12½*

C13 CD114 85fr pur, ocher & red .60 .42

Air Afrique Issue, 1963
Common Design Type
Perf. 13x12

1963, Nov. 19 Unwmk. Photo.

C14 CD115 50fr multi .42 .35

Liberty Place, Brazzaville — AP5

1963, Nov. 28

C15 AP5 25fr multi .22 .16

See No. 118.

Europafrica Issue
Common Design Type

1963, Nov. 30 *Perf. 12x13*

C16 CD116 50fr gray, yel & dk brn .55 .38

Timber Industry — AP6

1964, May 12 Engr. *Perf. 13*

C17 AP6 100fr grn, brn red & blk .80 .45

Chiefs of State Issue

Map and Presidents of Chad, Congo, Gabon and CAR — AP6a

1964, June 23 Photo. *Perf. 12½*

C18 AP6a 100fr multi .80 .45

See note after Central African Republic No. C19.

Europafrica Issue, 1964

EUROPAFRIQUE Sunburst, Wheat, Cogwheel and Globe — AP7

1964, July 20 *Perf. 12x13*
C19 AP7 50fr yel, Prus bl & mar .42 .25

See note after Cameroun No. 402.

Hammer Thrower, Olympic Flame and Stadium — AP8

50fr, 100fr, vert.

1964, July 30 **Engr.** *Perf. 13*
C20 AP8 25fr shown .22 .15
C21 AP8 50fr Weight lifter .42 .30
C22 AP8 100fr Volleyball .80 .65
C23 AP8 200fr High jump 1.60 1.25
a. Min. sheet of 4, #C20-C23 4.00 4.00
Nos. C20-C23 (4) 3.04 2.35

Issued for the 18th Olympic Games, Tokyo, Oct. 10-25, 1964.

Communications Symbols — AP8a

1964, Nov. 2 **Litho.** *Perf. 12½x13*
C24 AP8a 25fr dl rose & dk brn .25 .20

See note after Chad No. C19.

Town Hall, Brazzaville — AP9

1965, Jan. 30 **Photo.** *Perf. 12½*
C25 AP9 100fr multi .80 .42

Coupling Hooks — AP10

1965, Feb. 27 **Photo.** *Perf. 13x12*
C26 AP10 50fr multi .42 .25

Economic Europe-Africa Association.

Breguet Dial Telegraph, ITU Emblem and Telstar — AP11

1965, May 17 **Engr.** *Perf. 13*
C27 AP11 100fr dk bl, ocher & brn .90 .55

Cent. of the ITU.

Pope John XXIII (1881-1963), St. Peter's Cathedral AP12

Perf. 12½x13
1965, June 26 **Photo.** **Unwmk.**
C28 AP12 100fr gldn brn & multi .80 .60

Pres. John F. Kennedy — AP13

Log Rolling — AP14

Portraits: 25fr on 50fr, Patrice Lumumba, premier of Congo Republic (ex-Belgian). 50fr, Sir Winston Churchill. 80fr, Barthélémy Boganda, premier of Central African Republic.

1965, June *Perf. 12½*
C29 AP13 25fr on 50fr dk brn & red .25 .25
a. Surcharge omitted 15.00 15.00
C30 AP13 50fr dk brn & yel grn .60 .60
C31 AP13 80fr dk brn & bl .80 .80
C32 AP13 100fr dk brn & org yel 1.00 1.00
a. Min. sheet of 4, #C29-C32 3.50 3.50
Nos. C29-C32 (4) 2.65 2.65

A second miniature sheet contains one each of Nos. C29a, C30-C32. Value, $30.

Issue dates: 25fr, 80fr, June 25, 50fr, 100fr, No. C32a, June 26.

1965, Aug. 14 **Engr.** *Perf. 13*
C33 AP14 50fr grn, brn & red brn .50 .25

Issued to publicize national unity.

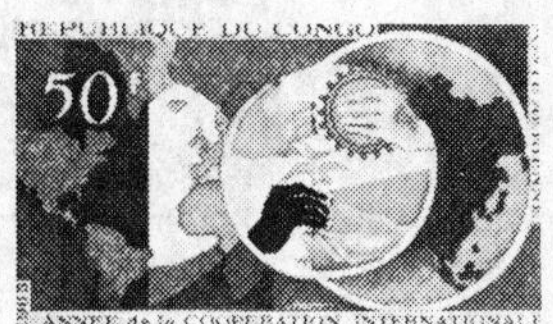

World Map and Symbols of Agriculture and Industry — AP15

1965, Oct. 18 **Engr.** *Perf. 13*
C34 AP15 50fr dk bl, blk, brn & org .50 .35

International Cooperation Year, 1965.

Abraham Lincoln — AP16

1965, Dec. 15 **Photo.** *Perf. 13*
C35 AP16 90fr pink & multi .70 .42

Centenary of death of Abraham Lincoln.

Charles de Gaulle, Torch and Map of Africa — AP17

1966, Feb. 28 **Engr.** *Perf. 13*
C36 AP17 500fr dk red, dk grn & dk red brn 9.00 7.50

22nd anniv. of the Brazzaville Conf.

D-1 Satellite over Brazzaville Space Tracking Station — AP18

Grain, Atom Symbol and Map of Africa and Europe — AP19

1966, May 15 **Engr.** *Perf. 13*
C37 AP18 150fr blk, dl red & bl grn 1.25 .60

1966, July 20 **Photo.** *Perf. 12x13*
C38 AP19 50fr multi .55 .35

See note after Gabon No. C46.

Pres. Massamba-Debat and President's Palace — AP20

3rd anniv. of the Revolution: 30fr, Robespierre and storming of the Bastille. 50fr, Lenin and storming of the Winter Palace.

1966, Aug. 15 **Photo.** *Perf. 12x12½*
C39 AP20 25fr multi .20 .15
C40 AP20 30fr multi .22 .15
C41 AP20 50fr multi .40 .20
a. Souv. sheet of 3, #C39-C41 1.00 1.00
Nos. C39-C41 (3) .82
Set value .40

Air Afrique Issue, 1966

Common Design Type

1966, Aug. 31 **Photo.** *Perf. 13*
C42 CD123 30fr lil, lem & blk .30 .15

Dr. Albert Schweitzer — AP21

1966, Sept. 4 **Photo.** *Perf. 12½*
C43 AP21 100fr red, blk, bl & lil .80 .55

Issued to honor Dr. Albert Schweitzer (1875-1965), medical missionary.

AP22 AP23

1966, Dec. 26 **Photo.** *Perf. 13*
C44 AP22 100fr Crab, microscope and pagoda .80 .42

9th Intl. Anticancer Cong., Tokyo. Oct. 23-29.

1967 **Photo.** *Perf. 13*

Birds: 50fr, Social Weaver. 75fr, European Bee-eater. 100fr, Lilac-breasted roller. 150fr, Regal sunbird. 200fr, Crowned cranes. 250fr, Secretary bird. 300fr, Knysna touraco.

C45 AP23 50fr multi .65 .25
C46 AP23 75fr multi .90 .38
C47 AP23 100fr multi 1.10 .55
C48 AP23 150fr multi 1.40 .75
C49 AP23 200fr multi 1.90 .90
C50 AP23 250fr multi 2.25 1.25
C51 AP23 300fr multi 2.75 1.50
Nos. C45-C51 (7) 10.95 5.58

Issued: Nos. C45-C47, Feb. 13; others, June 20.

Shackled Hands AP24

1967, May 24 **Photo.** *Perf. 12½x13*
C52 AP24 500fr multi 4.50 2.00

Issued for African Liberation Day.

Sputnik 1, Explorer 6 and Earth — AP25

Space Craft: 75fr, Ranger 6, Lunik 2 and moon. 100fr, Mars 1, Mariner 4 and Mars. 200fr, Gemini, Vostok and earth.

1967, Aug. 1 **Engr.** *Perf. 13*
C53 AP25 50fr multi .40 .22
C54 AP25 75fr multi .60 .35
C55 AP25 100fr multi .80 .55
C56 AP25 200fr multi 1.60 1.10
Nos. C53-C56 (4) 3.40 2.22

Space explorations.

African Postal Union Issue, 1967

Common Design Type

1967, Sept. 9 Engr. *Perf. 13*

C57 CD124 100fr ver, ol & emer .80 .45

Boy Scouts, Tents and Jamboree Emblem — AP26

Design: 70c, Borah Peak, Idaho; tents, Scout sign and Jamboree emblem.

1967, Sept. 29

C58 AP26 50fr multi .38 .20
C59 AP26 70fr multi .55 .25

12th Boy Scout World Jamboree, Farragut State Park, ID, Aug. 1-9.

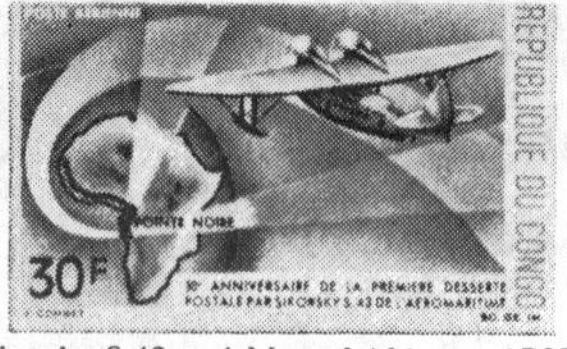

Sikorsky S-43 and Map of Africa — AP27

1967, Oct. 2 Photo. *Perf. 13*

C60 AP27 30fr multi .30 .16

30th anniv. of the 1st airmail connection by Aeromaritime Lines from Casablanca to Pointe-Noire.

Men of Four Races Dancing on Globe — AP28

1968, Feb 8 Engr. *Perf. 13*

C61 AP28 70fr dk brn, ultra & emer .60 .35

Friendship among peoples.

The Oath of the Horatii, by Jacques Louis David — AP29

Paintings: 25fr, On the Barricades, by Delacroix. No. C63, Grandfather and Grandson, by Ghirlandajo, vert. No. C64, The Demolition of the Bastille, by Hubert Robert. 200fr, Negro Woman Arranging Peonies, by Jean F. Bazille.

1968 Photo. *Perf. 12x12½, 12½x12*

C62 AP29 25fr multi .20 .15
C63 AP29 30fr multi .35 .20
C64 AP29 30fr multi .22 .15
C65 AP29 100fr multi .90 .55
C66 AP29 200fr multi 2.00 1.25
Nos. C62-C66 (5) 3.67 2.30

Issue dates: Nos. C62, C64, Aug. 15. Nos. C63, C65-C66, Mar. 20.
See Nos. C78-C81, C111-C115.

Early Automobile Type

1968, July 29 Photo. *Perf. 13x12½*

C67 A50 150fr Ford, 1915 1.40 .65
C68 A50 200fr Citroen, 1922 1.60 .90

Europafrica Issue

Square Knot — AP30

1968, July 20 Photo. *Perf. 13*

C69 AP30 50fr multi .38 .16

5th anniv. of the economic agreement between the European Economic Community and the African and Malgache Union.

Martin Luther King, Jr. — AP31

Robert F. Kennedy — AP32

1968, Aug. 5 *Perf. 12½*

C70 AP31 50fr lt grn, Prus grn & blk .38 .16

1968, Sept. 30 Photo. *Perf. 13x12½*

C71 AP32 50fr dp car, ap grn & blk .42 .20

Running — AP33

Olympic Rings and: 20fr, Soccer, vert. 60fr, Boxing, vert. 85fr, High jump.

1968, Dec. 27 Engr. *Perf. 13*

C72 AP33 5fr emer, brt bl & choc .15 .15
C73 AP33 20fr dk bl, brn & dk grn .16 .15
C74 AP33 60fr mar, brt grn & choc .50 .25
C75 AP33 85fr blk, car rose & choc .65 .35
Nos. C72-C75 (4) 1.46
Set value .73

19th Olympic Games, Mexico City, Oct. 12-27.

PHILEXAFRIQUE Issue

G. De Gueidan, by Nicolas de Largillière AP34

1968, Dec. 30 Photo. *Perf. 12½*

C76 AP34 100fr pink & multi .90 .70

Issued to publicize PHILEXAFRIQUE, Philatelic Exhibition, in Abidjan, Feb. 14-23. Printed with alternating pink label.
See Nos. C89-C93.

2nd PHILEXAFRIQUE Issue

Common Design Type

Design: 50fr, Middle Congo No. 72 and Pointe-Noire harbor.

1969, Feb. 14 Engr. *Perf. 13*

C77 CD128 50fr car rose, sl grn & bis brn .50 .42

Painting Type of 1968.

Paintings: 25fr, Battle of Rivoli, by Carle Vernet. 50fr, Battle of Marengo, by Jacques Augustin Pajou. 75fr, Battle of Friedland, by Horace Vernet. 100fr, Battle of Jena, by Charles Thevenin.

1969, May 20 Photo. *Perf. 12x12½*

C78 AP29 25fr vio bl & multi .25 .16
C79 AP29 50fr cop red & multi .50 .35
C80 AP29 75fr grn & multi .70 .35
C81 AP29 100fr brn & multi 1.10 .50
Nos. C78-C81 (4) 2.55 1.36

Bicentenary of birth of Napoleon I.

Ernesto Ché Guevara — AP35

1969, June 10 Photo. *Perf. 12½*

C82 AP35 90fr brn, org & blk .70 .38

Issued in memory of Ernesto Ché Guevara (1928-1967), Cuban revolutionist.

Doll, Train and Space Toy — AP36

1969, June 20 Engr. *Perf. 13*

C83 AP36 100fr mag, org & gray .80 .42

International Toy Fair, Nuremberg, Germany.

Europafrica Issue, 1969

Ribbon Tied Around Bar — AP37

1969, Aug. 5 Photo. *Perf. 13x12*

C84 AP37 50fr bl grn, lil & blk .35 .20

See note after Chad No. C11.

Armstrong, Aldrin and Collins — AP38

Painter, Poto-Poto School — AP39

Souvenir Sheet

Design: No. C85b, Blast-off from Moon.

Embossed on Gold Foil

1969, Sept. 15 *Imperf.*

C85 Sheet of 2 14.00 14.00

See note after Algeria No. 427. No. C85 contains one each of Nos. C85a and C85b with simulated perforations. Size: 65x52mm.

1970, Feb. 20 Engr. *Perf. 13*

Designs: 150fr, Sculpture lesson (man, infant and sculpture). 200fr, Potter working on vase.

C86 AP39 100fr multi .55 .25
C87 AP39 150fr multi .80 .40
C88 AP39 200fr multi .90 .65
Nos. C86-C88 (3) 2.25 1.30

Painting Type (Philexafrique) of 1968

Paintings: 150fr, Child with Cherries, by John Russell. 200fr, Erasmus, by Hans Holbein the Younger. 250fr, "Silence" (head), by Bernardino Luini. 300fr, Scene from the Massacre of Scio, by Delacroix. 500fr, The Capture of Constantinople by the Crusaders, by Delacroix.

1970 Photo. *Perf. 12½*

C89 AP34 150fr lil & multi 1.40 .60
C90 AP34 200fr multi 1.60 .80
C91 AP34 250fr brn & multi 1.90 1.00
C92 AP34 300fr multi 2.50 1.10
C93 AP34 500fr brn & multi 3.50 1.90
Nos. C89-C93 (5) 10.90 5.40

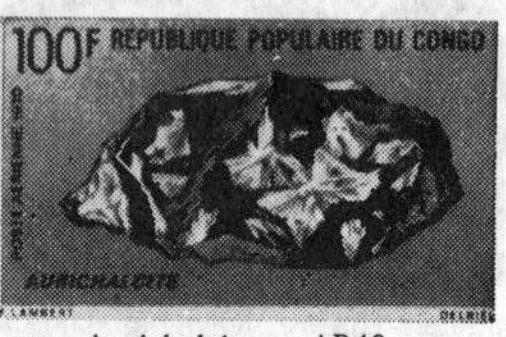

Aurichalcite — AP40

1970, Mar. 20

C94 AP40 100fr shown .75 .38
C95 AP40 150fr Dioptase 1.25 .55

Lenin — AP41

Karl Marx — AP42

1970, June 25 Photo. *Perf. 12½*

C96 AP41 45fr shown .35 .15
C97 AP41 75fr Lenin, seated .50 .22

Centenary of the birth of Lenin (1870-1924), Russian communist leader.

1970, July 10 Engr. *Perf. 13*

Design: No. C99, Friedrich Engels.

C98 AP42 50fr emer, dk brn & dk red .38 .20
C99 AP42 50fr ultra, dk brn & dk red .38 .20

Karl Marx (1818-1883) and Friedrich Engels (1820-1895), German socialist writers.

Otto Lilienthal's Glider, 1891 — AP43

Designs: 50fr, "Spirit of St. Louis," Lindbergh's first transatlantic solo flight, 1927. 70fr, Sputnik 1, first satellite in space. 90fr, First man on the moon, Apollo 11, 1969.

1970, Sept. 5 Engr. *Perf. 13*

C100 AP43 45fr dp car, bl & ol bis .38 .20
C101 AP43 50fr emer, sl grn & brn .38 .20
C102 AP43 70fr brt bl, ol bis & dp car .55 .25
C103 AP43 90fr brn, bl & ol gray .75 .38
Nos. C100-C103 (4) 2.06 1.03

Forerunners of space exploration.

Saint on Horseback — AP44

Marilyn Monroe and NYC — AP45

Designs from Stained Glass Windows, Brazzaville Cathedral: 150fr, Saint with staff. 250fr, The Elevation of the Host, from rose window.

1970, Dec. 10 Photo. *Perf. 12½*

C104 AP44 100fr multi	.50	.28
C105 AP44 150fr multi	.90	.45
C106 AP44 250fr multi	1.50	.80
a. Souv. sheet of 3, #C104-C106	3.00	3.00
Nos. C104-C106 (3)	2.90	1.53

Christmas 1970.

1971, Mar. 16 Engr. *Perf. 13*

Portraits: 150fr, Martine Carol and Paris. 200fr, Erich von Stroheim and Vienna. 250fr, Sergei Eisenstein and Moscow.

C107 AP45 100fr brt grn, red brn & ultra	.65	.25
C108 AP45 150fr brn, brt lil & ultra	1.10	.40
C109 AP45 200fr choc & ultra	1.40	.60
C110 AP45 250fr brt grn, brn vio & ultra	1.60	.65
Nos. C107-C110 (4)	4.75	1.90

History of motion pictures.

Painting Type of 1968

Paintings: 100fr, Christ Carrying Cross, by Paolo Veronese. 150fr, Christ on the Cross, Burgundian School, 1500, vert. 200fr, Descent from the Cross, by Rogier van der Weyden. 250fr, Christ Laid in the Tomb, Flemish School, 1500, vert. 500fr, Resurrection, by Hans Memling, vert.

1971, Apr. 26 Photo. *Perf. 13*

C111 AP29 100fr grn & multi	.60	.30
C112 AP29 150fr grn & multi	.90	.40
C113 AP29 200fr grn & multi	1.25	.60
C114 AP29 250fr grn & multi	1.50	.75
C115 AP29 500fr grn & multi	3.25	1.65
Nos. C111-C115 (5)	7.50	3.70

Easter 1971.

Map of Africa and Telecommunications System — AP46

1971, June 18 Photo. *Perf. 12½*

C116 AP46 70fr bl, gray & dk brn	.42	.20
C117 AP46 85fr bl, lil rose & dk brn	.50	.25
C118 AP46 90fr grn, yel & dk brn	.55	.30
Nos. C116-C118 (3)	1.47	.75

Pan-African telecommunications system.

Globe and Waves AP47

1971, June 19

C119 AP47 65fr lt bl & multi	.40	.18

3rd World Telecommunications Day.

Japanese Mask and Play — AP48

Olympic Torch and Rings — AP49

Design: 150fr, Japanese and African women, symbolic leaves.

1971, June 28 Engr. *Perf. 13*

C120 AP48 75fr lil, blk & mag	.55	.25
C121 AP48 150fr dk brn, brn red & red lil	1.00	.55

PHILATOKYO '71 International Stamp Exhibition, Tokyo, Apr. 20-30.

13th World Boy Scout Jamboree, Japan, gold foil 1000fr airmail and silver foil souv. sheet of four 90fr, issued July 14. Nos. 71C01-71C02.

1971, July 20 Engr. *Perf. 13*

Design: 350fr, Olympic rings and various sports, horiz.

C122 AP49 150fr multicolored	1.10	.60
C123 AP49 350fr multicolored	2.50	1.10

Pre-Olympic Year, 1971.

Scout Emblem, Japanese Dragon and African Carved Canoe — AP50

Designs (Boy Scout Emblem and): 90fr, Japanese mask and African boy, vert. 100fr, Japanese woman and African drummer, vert. 250fr, Congolese mask.

1971, Aug. 25

C124 AP50 85fr multi	.65	.30
C125 AP50 90fr multi	.70	.35
C126 AP50 100fr multi	.80	.40
C127 AP50 250fr multi	2.00	.90
Nos. C124-C127 (4)	4.15	1.95

13th Boy Scout World Jamboree, Asagiri Plain, Japan, Aug. 2-10.

Olympic Rings and Running — AP51

Designs (Olympic Rings and): 85fr, Hurdles. 90fr, Weight lifting, boxing, discus, running, javelin. 100fr, Wrestling. 150fr, Boxing.

1971, Sept. 30

C128 AP51 75fr plum, bl & dk brn	.45	.20
C129 AP51 85fr scar, sl & dk brn	.50	.22
C130 AP51 90fr vio bl & dk brn	.60	.30
C131 AP51 100fr brn & slate	.65	.35
C132 AP51 150fr grn, red & dk brn	1.10	.55
Nos. C128-C132 (5)	3.30	1.62

75th anniv. of the 1t modern Olympic Games.

Congo No. C36 and de Gaulle — AP52

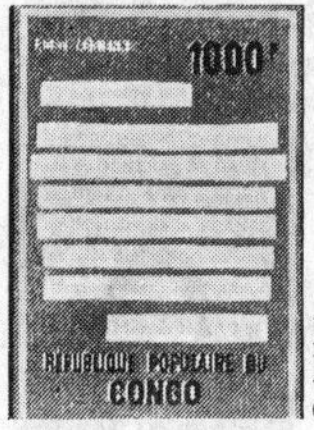

Pres. Marien Ngouabi's Tribute to de Gaulle — AP53

Design: No. C135, Charles de Gaulle.

1971, Nov. 9

C133 AP52 500fr slate grn & multi	3.25	3.25

Lithographed; Gold Embossed
Perf. 12½

C134 AP53 1000fr gold, grn & red	8.50	8.50
C135 AP53 1000fr gold, grn & red	8.50	8.50
a. Pair, #C134-C135	17.50	17.50

Charles de Gaulle (1890-1970), president of France.

African Postal Union Issue, 1971
Common Design Type

Design: 100fr, Allegory of Congo Republic (woman) and UAMPT Building, Brazzaville.

1971, Nov. 13 Photo. *Perf. 13x13½*

C136 CD135 100fr bl & multi	.70	.38

Flag of Congo Republic and "Revolution" — AP54

1971, Nov. 30

C137 AP54 100fr red & multi	.65	.35

8th anniversary of revolution.

Workers and Flag — AP55

Design: 40fr, Flag of Congo Republic and sun.

1971, Dec. 31 Photo. *Perf. 13x12½*

C138 AP55 30fr multi	.16	.15
C139 AP55 40fr red & multi	.22	.15
Set value		.22

2nd anniv. of founding of Congolese Labor Party (#C138), and adoption of red flag (#C139).

Book Year Emblem — AP56

1972, June 3 Litho. *Perf. 12½*

C140 AP56 50fr red, grn & yel	.25	.15

International Book Year 1972.

Congolese Soccer Team — AP57

Design: No. C142, Captain of winning team and cup, vert.

1973, Feb. 22 Photo. *Perf. 13*

C141 AP57 100fr ultra, red & blk	.65	.42
C142 AP57 100fr red, yel & blk	.65	.42

Girl Holding Bird, Environment Emblem — AP58

1973, Mar. 5 Engr.

C143 AP58 85fr org, slate grn & bl	.42	.25

UN Conference on Human Environment, Stockholm, Sweden, June 5-16, 1972.

Miles Davis — AP59

Designs: 140fr, Ella Fitzgerald. 160fr, Count Basie. 175fr, John Coltrane.

1973, Mar. 5 Photo. *Perf. 13x13½*

C144 AP59 125fr multi	.65	.35
C145 AP59 140fr multi	.70	.38
C146 AP59 160fr multi	.90	.42
C147 AP59 175fr multi	1.00	.50
Nos. C144-C147 (4)	3.25	1.65

Black American jazz musicians.

Olympic Rings, Hurdling — AP60

Designs (Olympic Rings and): 150fr, Pole vault, vert. 250fr, Wrestling.

1973, Mar. 15 Engr. *Perf. 13*

C148 AP60 100fr lil rose & vio	.65	.35
C149 AP60 150fr emer & vio	1.00	.50
C150 AP60 250fr bl & magenta	1.60	.90
Nos. C148-C150 (3)	3.25	1.75

20th Olympic Games, Munich, Aug. 26-Sept. 11, 1972.

Refinery and Storage Tanks, Djéno — AP61

Designs: 230fr, Off-shore drilling platform, vert. 240fr, Workers assembling drill, vert. 260fr, Off-shore drilling installation.

1973, Mar. 20

C151 AP61 180fr red, bl & indigo 1.10 .55
C152 AP61 230fr red, bl & blk 1.40 .65
C153 AP61 240fr red, ind & brn 1.50 .80
C154 AP61 260fr red, bl & blk 1.75 .90
Nos. C151-C154 (4) 5.75 2.90

Oil installations, Pointe-Noire.

Astronauts, Landing Module and Lunar Rover on Moon — AP62

1973, Mar. 31

C155 AP62 250fr multi 1.60 1.00

Apollo 17 US moon mission, Dec. 7-19, 1972.

ITU Emblem, Symbols of Communications AP63

1973, May 24 Engr. *Perf. 13*

C156 AP63 120fr multi .55 .25

5th International Telecommunications Day.

White Horse, by Delacroix — AP64

Designs: Paintings by Eugene Delacroix.

1973, June 30 Photo. *Perf. 13*

C157 AP64 150fr shown .90 .90
C158 AP64 250fr Lion sleeping 1.50 1.25
C159 AP64 300fr Lion and tiger 1.75 1.50
Nos. C157-C159 (3) 4.15 3.65

See Nos. C169-C171.

Copernicus and Heliocentric System — AP65

1973, June 30 Engr.

C160 AP65 50fr multi .30 .22

500th anniversary of the birth of Nicolaus Copernicus (1473-1543), Polish astronomer.

Plane, Ship, Rocket, Village, Sun and Clouds — AP66

1973, July

C161 AP66 50fr red & multi .25 .20

Cent. of intl. meteorological cooperation.

Pres. Marien Ngouabi — AP67

1973, Aug. 12 Photo. *Perf. 13*

C162 AP67 30fr multi .16 .15
C163 AP67 40fr aqua & multi .20 .15
C164 AP67 75fr red & multi .42 .20
Nos. C162-C164 (3) .78
Set value .37

10th anniversary of independence.

Stamps, Album, African Woman AP68

Designs: 40fr, No. C167, Stamps in shape of map of Congo, album, globe. No. C168, Like 30fr.

1973, Aug. 12

C165 AP68 30fr pur & multi .16 .15
C166 AP68 40fr multi .20 .15
C167 AP68 100fr dk brn & multi .50 .38
C168 AP68 100fr ocher & multi .50 .38
Nos. C165-C168 (4) 1.36 1.06

Nos. C165, C168 for the 10th anniv. of the revolution, Nos. C166-C167 the Intl. Philatelic Exhib., Brazzaville.

Painting Type of 1973 Inscribed "EUROPAFRIQUE"

Designs: Details from "Earth and Paradise," by Jan Brueghel, the Elder.

1973, Oct. 10 Photo. *Perf. 13*

C169 AP64 100fr Spotted hyena .65 .50
C170 AP64 100fr Leopard and lion .65 .50
C171 AP64 100fr Elephant and creatures .65 .50
Nos. C169-C171 (3) 1.95 1.50

US and Russian Spacecraft Docking — AP69

Design: 80fr, US and USSR spacecraft docked in space and emblems of 1975 joint space mission.

1973, Oct. 15 Engr. *Perf. 13*

C172 AP69 40fr bl, red & brn .22 .15
C173 AP69 80fr red, grn & bl .42 .25

Planned joint US and Soviet space missions.
For overprint see No. C251.

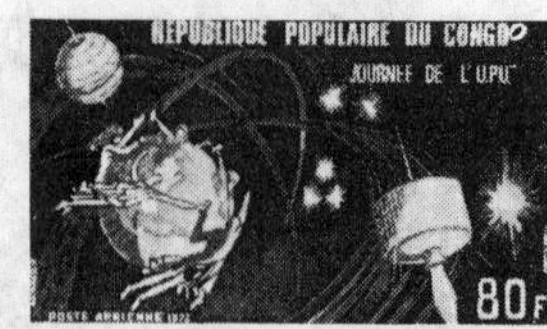

UPU Monument, Satellites, Big Dipper — AP70

1973, Nov. 20 Engr. *Perf. 13*

C174 AP70 80fr vio bl & lt bl .42 .22

Universal Postal Union Day.

Astronauts Working in Space — AP71

Design: 40fr, Spacecraft and Skylab docking in space.

1973, Nov. 30

C175 AP71 30fr ultra, sl grn & choc .16 .15
C176 AP71 40fr mag, org & sl grn .22 .16

Skylab, first space laboratory.

Goalkeeper, Soccer — AP72

Design: 100fr, Soccer player kicking ball.

1973, Dec. 20

C177 AP72 40fr sl grn, sepia & brn .20 .16
C178 AP72 100fr pur, red & slate grn .65 .38

World Soccer Cup, Munich, 1974.

John F. Kennedy (1917-1963) AP73

1973, Dec. 20 Photo. *Perf. 12½*

C179 AP73 150fr ultra, gold & blk .80 .50

Runners — AP74 Flag over Map of Congo — AP75

1973, Dec. 20 Engr. *Perf. 13*

C180 AP74 40fr sl grn, red & brn .22 .16
C181 AP74 100fr red, sl grn, & brn .65 .38

2nd African Games, Lagos, Nigeria.

1973, Dec. 31 Photo.

C182 AP75 40fr dp grn & multi .20 .15

4th anniversary of Congolese Labor Party and of the Congo Red Flag.

Soccer and Games Emblem — AP76

1974, June 20 Photo. *Perf. 13*

C183 AP76 250fr multi 1.40 .90

World Cup Soccer Championship, Munich, June 13-July 7.

Astronauts Yuri A. Gagarin and Alan B. Shepard — AP77

Designs: 30fr, Space, globe, Russian and American flags with names of astronauts who perished in space. 100fr, Alexei Leonov and Neil A. Armstrong in space and on moon.

1974, June 30 Engr. *Perf. 13*

C184 AP77 30fr red, ultra & brn .16 .15
C185 AP77 40fr red, bl & brn .22 .15
C186 AP77 100fr car, grn & brn .65 .40
Nos. C184-C186 (3) 1.03 .70

For overprint see No. C254.

Soccer Game Superimposed on Ball — AP78 Link-up Emblem, Stages of Link-up — AP79

1974, July 31 Photo. *Perf. 13*

C187 AP78 250fr multi 1.40 .90

Germany's victory in World Cup Soccer Championship.

1974, Aug. 8 Engr. *Perf. 13*

Design: 300fr, Spacecraft docking over globe, horiz.

C188 AP79 200fr pur, bl & red 1.10 .80
C189 AP79 300fr multi 1.60 1.10

Russo-American space cooperation.
For overprint see No. C255.

Symbols of Communications, UPU Emblem — AP80

1974, Aug. 10

C190 AP80 500fr blk & red 2.00 1.50

Centenary of Universal Postal Union.
For surcharge see No. C194.

Lenin and Pendulum Trace Pattern — AP81

1974, Sept. 16 **Engr.** ***Perf. 13***
C191 AP81 150fr multi .80 .55

Lenin (1870-1924).

Churchill and Order of the Garter AP82

Marconi and Wireless Telegraph AP83

1974, Oct. 1 **Litho.** ***Perf. 13***
C192 AP82 200fr lt grn & multi 1.10 .65
C193 AP83 200fr lt ultra & multi 1.10 .65

Birth centenaries of Sir Winston Churchill (1874-1965), statesman; and of Guglielmo Marconi (1874-1937), Italian electrical engineer and inventor.

No. C190 Surcharged in Violet Blue with New Value, 2 Bars and: "9 OCTOBER 1974"

1974, Oct. 9
C194 AP80 300fr on 500fr multi 1.60 1.10

Universal Postal Union Day.

UDEAC Issue

Presidents and Flags of Cameroun, CAR, Gabon and Congo — AP83a

1974, Dec. 8 **Photo.** ***Perf. 13***
C195 AP83a 100fr gold & multi .55 .40

See note after Cameroun No. 595.

Regatta at Argenteuil, by Monet — AP84

Impressionist Paintings: 40fr, Seated Dancer, by Degas. 50fr, Girl on Swing, by Renoir. 75fr, Girl with Straw Hat, by Renoir. All vertical.

1974, Dec. 15
C196 AP84 30fr gold & multi .22 .16
C197 AP84 40fr gold & multi .25 .20
C198 AP84 50fr gold & multi .42 .35
C199 AP84 75fr gold & multi .45 .38
Nos. C196-C199 (4) 1.34 1.09

National Fair — AP85

1974, Dec. 20
C200 AP85 30fr multi .16 .15

National Fair, Aug. 24-Sept. 8.

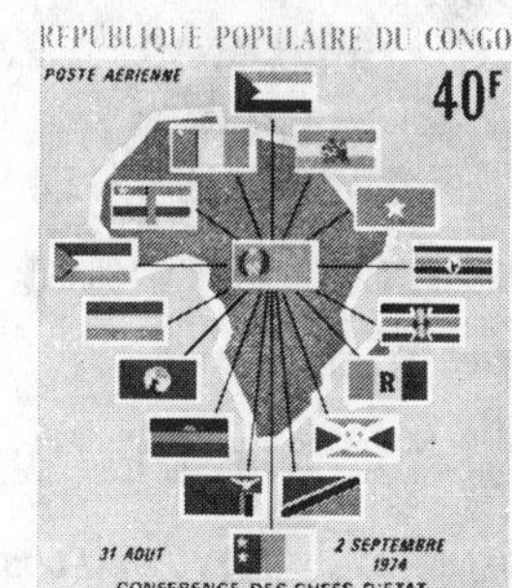

Flags of Participating Nations, Map of Africa — AP86

1974, Dec. 20 ***Perf. 13***
C201 AP86 40fr ultra & multi .25 .16

Conference of Chiefs of State of Central and East Africa, Brazzaville, Aug. 31-Sept. 2.

"Five Weeks in a Balloon," by Jules Verne AP87

Design: 50fr, "Around the World in 80 Days," by Jules Verne.

1975, June 30 **Litho.** ***Perf. 12½***
C202 AP87 40fr multi .22 .15
C203 AP87 50fr multi .25 .16

Jules Verne (1828-1905), French science fiction writer, 70th death anniversary.

Paris-Brussels Train, 1890 — AP88

Design: 75fr, Santa Fe, 1880.

1975, June 30
C204 AP88 50fr ocher & multi .25 .16
C205 AP88 75fr lt bl & multi .40 .22

Soyuz and Apollo-Soyuz Emblem AP89

Design: 100fr, Apollo and emblem.

1975, July 20 **Litho.** ***Perf. 12½***
C206 AP89 95fr org, blk & mag .50 .35
C207 AP89 100fr vio, bl & blk .55 .40

Apollo Soyuz space test project (Russo-American space cooperation), launching July 15; link-up, July 17.

For overprints see Nos. C252-C253.

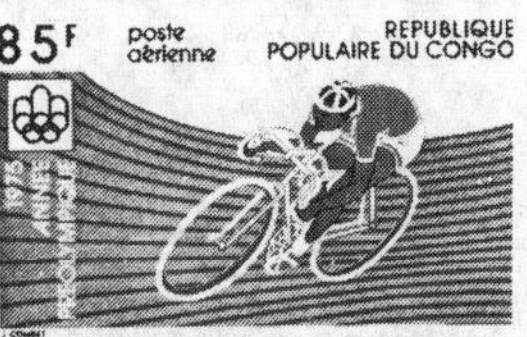

Bicycling and Montreal Olympic Emblem — AP90

Designs (Montreal Olympic Emblem and): 40fr, Boxing, vert. 50fr, Basketball, vert. 95fr, High jump. 100fr, Javelin. 150fr, Running.

Perf. 12½x13, 13x12½

1975, Oct. 30 **Photo.**
C208 AP90 40fr multi .22 .15
C209 AP90 50fr red & multi .25 .16
C210 AP90 85fr bl & multi .45 .35
C211 AP90 95fr org & multi .50 .38
C212 AP90 100fr multi .55 .40
C213 AP90 150fr multi .80 .60
Nos. C208-C213 (6) 2.77 2.04

Pre-Olympic Year 1975.

Map of Africa, Sports and Flags — AP91

Workers and Flag — AP92

1975, Dec. 20 **Litho.** ***Perf. 12½***
C214 AP91 30fr multi .15 .15

10th anniversary of first African Games, Brazzaville.

1975, Dec. 31 **Litho.** ***Perf. 12½***
C215 AP92 60fr multi .35 .20

Congolese Labor Party (P.C.T.), 6th anniv.

Alphonse Fondere — AP93

Historic Ships: 5fr, like 30fr. 40fr, Hamburg, 1839. 15fr, 50fr, Gomer, 1831. 20fr, 60fr, Great Eastern, 1858. 95fr, J.M. White II, 1878.

1976 **Engr.** ***Perf. 13***
C216 AP93 5fr multi .15 .15
C217 AP93 10fr multi .15 .15
C218 AP93 15fr multi .15 .15
C219 AP93 20fr multi .15 .15
C220 AP93 30fr multi .16 .15
C221 AP93 40fr multi .20 .16
C222 AP93 50fr multi .25 .20
C223 AP93 60fr multi .35 .22
C224 AP93 95fr multi .50 .38
Set value 1.75 1.25

Issued: #C216-C219, May; #C220-C224, Mar. 7.

Europafrica Issue 1976

Peasant Family, by Louis Le Nain — AP94

Paintings: 80fr, Boy with Top, by Jean B. Chardin. 95fr, Venus and Aeneas, by Nicolas Poussin. 100fr, The Rape of the Sabine Women, by Jacques Louis David.

1976, Mar. 20 **Litho.** ***Perf. 12½***
C225 AP94 60fr gold & multi .35 .20
C226 AP94 80fr gold & multi .42 .30
C227 AP94 95fr gold & multi .50 .38
C228 AP94 100fr gold & multi .55 .40
Nos. C225-C228 (4) 1.82 1.28

Nos. C225-C228 printed in sheets of 8 stamps and horizontal gutter with commemorative inscription.

Telephone Type of 1976

1976, Apr. 25 **Litho.** ***Perf. 12½x13***
C229 A107 60fr pink, maroon & crim .35 .22

Sports Type of 1976

Designs: 150fr, Runner and map of Central Africa. 200fr, Discus and map.

1976, Oct. 25 ***Perf. 12½***
C230 A110 150fr multi .60 .45
C231 A110 200fr multi .80 .55

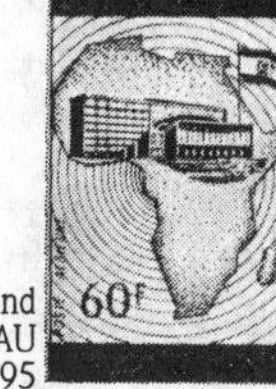

Map of Africa, Flag and OAU Headquarters — AP95

1976, Dec. 16 **Typo.** ***Perf. 13x14***
C232 AP95 60fr multi .35 .22

13th anniv. of the Organization for African Unity.

Europafrica Issue

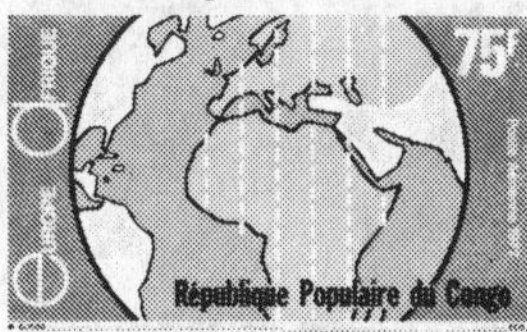

Map of Europe and Africa — AP96

1977, June 28 **Litho.** ***Perf. 13***
C233 AP96 75fr multi .40 .35

Headdress Type of 1977

1977, June 30 ***Perf. 12½***

Designs: 250fr, Two straw caps. 300fr, Beaded cap.

C234 A118 250fr multi 1.40 1.00
C235 A118 300fr multi 1.60 1.25

Zeppelin Type of 1977
Souvenir Sheet

Design: 500fr, LZ 127 over US Capitol.

1977, Aug. 5 **Litho.** ***Perf. 11***
C236 A120 500fr multi 2.50 1.00

No. C236 exists imperf.

Checkerboard AP97

1977, Aug. 20 **Engr.** ***Perf. 13***
C237 AP97 60fr red & blk .35 .22

Lomé Convention on General Agreement on Tariffs and Trade (GATT).

Newton, Intelsat Satellite and Classical "Planets" — AP98

1977, Aug. 25
C238 AP98 140fr multi .75 .60

Isaac Newton (1642-1727), natural philosopher and mathematician.

Elizabeth II Type of 1977
Souvenir Sheet

Design: 500fr, Royal family on balcony.

1977, Dec. 21 Litho. *Perf. 14*
C239 A128 500fr multi 2.50 1.00

For overprint see No. C244.

Mallard
AP99

Birds: 75fr, Purple heron, vert. 150fr, Reed warbler, vert. 240fr, Hoopoe, vert.

Perf. 13x12¹/₂, 12¹/₂x13

1978, May 22
C240 AP99 65fr multi .35 .22
C241 AP99 75fr multi .40 .20
C242 AP99 150fr multi .80 .42
C243 AP99 240fr multi 1.25 .65
Nos. C240-C243 (4) 2.80 1.49

Souvenir Sheet
No. C239 Overprinted in Silver: "ANNIVERSAIRE DU / COURONNEMENT / 1953-1978"

1978, Sept. Litho. *Perf. 14*
C244 A128 500fr multi 2.75 1.10

25th anniv. of coronation of Elizabeth II.

Philexafrique II-Essen Issue
Common Design Types

Designs: No. C245, Leopard and Congo No. C243. No. C246, Eagle and Wurttemberg No. 1.

1978, Nov. 1 Litho. *Perf. 12¹/₂*
C245 CD138 100fr multi .65 .40
C246 CD139 100fr multi .65 .40
a. Pair, #C245-C246 1.30 1.00

Map of Africa, Satellites — AP100

Map of Africa and People — AP101

1978, Nov. 25 Engr. *Perf. 13*
C247 AP100 100fr multi .65 .40

Pan-African Telecommunications Network, PANAFEL.

1979, Aug. 2 Litho. *Perf. 12¹/₂*
C248 AP101 45fr multi .30 .20
C249 AP101 75fr multi .50 .35

5th Conference of Panafrican Youth Movement, Brazzaville, Aug. 2-7.

Abala Peasant Woman
AP102

1979, Aug. 20
C250 AP102 150fr multi 1.00 .60

Nos. C173, C206-C207, C186, C189 Overprinted "ALUNISSAGE APOLLO XI / JUILLET 1969" and Emblem

Perf. 13, 12¹/₂

1979, Nov. 5 Engr., Litho.
C251 AP69 80fr multi .55 .35
C252 AP89 95fr multi .60 .40
C253 AP89 100fr multi .65 .42
C254 AP77 100fr multi .65 .42
C255 AP79 300fr multi 2.00 1.40
Nos. C251-C255 (5) 4.45 2.99

Apollo 11 moon landing, 10th anniversary.

Runner, Olympic Rings — AP103

Pre-Olympic Year: 100fr, Boxing. 200fr, Fencing, vert. 300fr, Soccer. 500fr, Moscow '80 emblem, vert.

1979 Litho. *Perf. 13¹/₂*
C256 AP103 65fr multi .40 .20
C257 AP103 100fr multi .60 .30
C258 AP103 200fr multi 1.10 .60
C259 AP103 300fr multi 2.00 .90
C260 AP103 500fr multi 3.00 1.50
Nos. C256-C260 (5) 7.10 3.50

Cross-Country Skiing — AP104

Lake Placid '80 Emblem and: 60fr, Slalom. 200fr, Ski jump, 350fr, Downhill skiing, horiz. 500fr, Woman skier.

1979, Dec *Perf. 14¹/₂*
Size: 24x42mm, 42x24mm
C261 AP104 40fr multi .25 .18
C262 AP104 60fr multi .40 .28
C263 AP104 200fr multi 1.40 .90
C264 AP104 350fr multi 2.25 1.50

Size: 31¹/₂x46¹/₂mm
Perf. 14
C265 AP104 500fr multi 3.50 2.25
Nos. C261-C265 (5) 7.80 5.11

13th Winter Olympic Games, Lake Placid, NY, Feb. 12-24, 1980.

Overprinted with Names of Winners

1980, Apr. 28
C266 AP104 40fr Zimiatov .20 .15
C267 AP104 60fr Moser-Proell .32 .16
C268 AP104 200fr Tomanen 1.10 .55
C269 AP104 350fr Stock 1.75 .90
C270 AP104 500fr Stenmark-Wenzel 2.50 1.40
Nos. C266-C270 (5) 5.87 3.16

Long Jump, Olympic Rings
AP105

Olympic rings and long jump scenes. Nos. C266, C268-C269 vert.

1980, May 2 Litho. *Perf. 14¹/₂*
C271 AP105 75fr multi .40 .20
C272 AP105 150fr multi .80 .40
C273 AP105 250fr multi 1.40 .65
C274 AP105 350fr multi 1.90 .90
Nos. C271-C274 (4) 4.50 2.15

Souvenir Sheet
C275 AP105 500fr multi 2.75 1.40

22nd Summer Olympic Games, Moscow, July 19-Aug. 3.
For overprints see Nos. C292-C296.

Stadium, Mascot, Madrid Club Emblem — AP106

Stadium, Mascot and Club Emblem: 75fr, Zaragoza. 100fr, Madrid Athletic Club. 150fr, Valencia. 175fr, Spain. 250fr, Barcelona.

1980, June 23 Litho. *Perf. 14x13¹/₂*
C276 AP106 60fr multi .35 .16
C277 AP106 75fr multi .42 .20
C278 AP106 100fr multi .30 .30
C279 AP106 150fr multi .90 .45
C280 AP106 175fr multi 1.00 .80
Nos. C276-C280 (5) 2.97 1.91

Souvenir Sheet
C281 AP106 250fr multi 1.50 .80

World Soccer Cup 1982.
For overprints see Nos. C298-C303.

Adoration of the Shepherds — AP107

Rembrandt Paintings: 100fr, The Burial. 200fr, Christ at Emmaus. 300fr, Annunciation, vert. 500fr, Crucifixion, vert.

1980, July 4 *Perf. 12¹/₂*
C282 AP107 65fr multi .35 .20
C283 AP107 100fr multi .55 .25
C284 AP107 200fr multi 1.10 .55
C285 AP107 300fr multi 1.60 .80
C286 AP107 500fr multi 2.75 1.25
Nos. C282-C286 (5) 6.35 3.05

Albert Camus (1913-1960), Writer — AP108

Design: 150fr, Jacques Offenbach (1819-1880), composer, vert.

1980, July 5 Engr. *Perf. 13*
C287 AP108 100fr multi .60 .30
C288 AP108 150fr multi .90 .45

Raffia Dancing Skirts
AP109

Traditional Dancing Costumes: 300fr, Tam-tam dancers, vert. 350fr, Masks.

1980, Aug. 6 Litho. *Perf. 13¹/₂*
C289 AP109 250fr multi 1.40 .65
C290 AP109 300fr multi 1.60 .80
C291 AP109 350fr multi 1.90 .90
Nos. C289-C291 (3) 4.90 2.35

Nos. C271-C275 Overprinted with Winner and Country

1980, Nov. 14 Litho. *Perf. 14¹/₂*
C292 AP105 75fr multi .40 .20
C293 AP105 150fr multi .80 .40
C294 AP105 250fr multi 1.40 .65
C295 AP105 350fr multi 2.00 .90
Nos. C292-C295 (4) 4.60 2.15

Souvenir Sheet
C296 AP105 500fr multi 2.75 1.40

REPUBLIQUE POPULAIRE DU CONGO

The Studio by Picasso
AP109a

1981, July 4 *Perf. 12¹/₂*
C296A AP109a 100fr shown .55 .25
C296B AP109a 150fr Landscape .80 .40
C296C AP109a 200fr Cannes Studio 1.10 .55
C296D AP109a 300fr Still Life 1.60 .80
C296E AP109a 500fr Still Life, diff. 2.75 1.25
Nos. C296A-C296E (5) 6.80 3.25

1st Seminar on Petroleum, Gas and Energy Alternatives, Brazzaville
AP109b

1981 Litho. *Perf. 12¹/₂*
C296F AP109b 75fr multicolored

Numbers have been reserved for two additional values in this set. The editors would like to see the 100fr and 150fr stamps.

1350th Anniv. of Mohamed's Death at Medina — AP110

1982, July 17 Litho. *Perf. 13*
C297 AP110 400fr Medina Mosque minaret 2.25 1.10

Nos. C276-C281 Overprinted with Finalists and/or Scores in Black on Silver

1982, Oct. 7 Litho. *Perf. 14x13¹/₂*
C298 AP106 60fr multi .35 .16
C299 AP106 75fr multi .40 .20
C300 AP106 100fr multi .55 .25
C301 AP106 150fr multi .80 .40
C302 AP106 175fr multi .90 .45
Nos. C298-C302 (5) 3.00 1.46

Souvenir Sheet
C303 AP106 250fr multi 1.40 .65

30th Anniv. of Amelia Earhart's Transatlantic Flight — AP111

1982, Dec. 4 Engr. *Perf. 13*
C304 AP111 150fr multi .80 .40

Wind Surfing
AP112

Various wind surfing scenes, 1984 Olympic Games, 100fr, 300fr, 400fr vert.

1983, June 4 Litho. *Perf. 13*

C305 AP112 100fr multi .45 .22
C306 AP112 200fr multi 1.00 .50
C307 AP112 300fr multi 1.50 .70
C308 AP112 400fr multi 2.00 1.00
Nos. C305-C308 (4) 4.95 2.42

Souvenir Sheet

C309 AP112 500fr multi 7.50 1.40

For overprint see No. C336.

Manned Flight Bicentenary
AP113

Various balloons.

1983, June 7

C310 AP113 100fr Montgolfiere, 1783 .40 .20
C311 AP113 200fr Flesselles, 1784 .80 .40
C312 AP113 300fr Auguste Piccard, 1931 1.25 .60
C313 AP113 400fr Don Piccard 1.65 .90
Nos. C310-C313 (4) 4.10 2.10

Souvenir Sheet

C314 AP113 500fr Mail transport balloon, 1870 2.50 1.40

For overprint see No. C337.

Christmas 1983
AP114

Various Virgin and Child Paintings by Botticelli.

1984, Jan. 21 Litho. *Perf. 13*

C315 AP114 150fr multi .45 .22
C316 AP114 350fr multi 1.10 .60
C317 AP114 500fr multi 1.60 .80
Nos. C315-C317 (3) 3.15 1.62

Vase of Flowers, by Manet (1832-83)
AP115

Paintings: 200fr, Small Holy Family, by Raphael. 300fr, La Belle Jardiniere, by Raphael. 400fr, Virgin of Loretto, by Raphael. 500fr, Portrait of Richard Wagner (1813-83), by Giuseppe Tivoli.

1984, Feb. 24 Litho. *Perf. 13*

C318 AP115 100fr multi .30 .15
C319 AP115 200fr multi .60 .30
C320 AP115 300fr multi .80 .40
C321 AP115 400fr multi 1.25 .60
C322 AP115 500fr multi 1.59 .70
Nos. C318-C322 (5) 4.54 2.15

1984 Summer Olympics — AP116

1984, Mar. 31 *Perf. 13*

C323 AP116 45fr Judo, vert. .15 .15
C324 AP116 75fr Judo, diff. .20 .15
C325 AP116 150fr Wrestling .45 .22
C326 AP116 175fr Fencing .55 .25
C327 AP116 350fr Fencing, diff. 1.10 .55
Nos. C323-C327 (5) 2.45 1.32

Souvenir Sheet

C328 AP116 500fr Boxing 1.50 .70

1984 Summer Olympic Gold Medalists — AP117

Sailing/yachting: 100fr, Stephan Van Den Berg, Netherlands, Windglider Class, vert. 150fr, US, Soling Class. 200fr, Spain, 470 Class. 500fr, US, Flying Dutchman Class, vert.

1984, Dec. 18 Litho. *Perf. 13*

C329 AP117 100fr multi .38 .20
C330 AP117 150fr multi .60 .28
C331 AP117 200fr multi .70 .38
C332 AP117 500fr multi 2.00 .90
Nos. C329-C332 (4) 3.68 1.76

Virgin and Child, by Giovanni Bellini (c. 1430-1516) — AP118

Religious paintings: 100fr, Holy Family, by Andrea del Sarto (1486-1530), vert. 400fr, Virgin with Angels, by Cimabue (c. 1240-1302), vert.

1985, Feb. 12 Litho. *Perf. 13*

C333 AP118 100fr multi .25 .15
C334 AP118 200fr multi .55 .25
C335 AP118 400fr multi 1.00 .50
Nos. C333-C335 (3) 1.80 .90

Christmas 1984.

Souvenir Sheets
Nos. C309, C314 Ovptd. with Exhibition in Blue or Green

1985, Mar. 8 *Perf. 13*

C336 AP112 500fr OLYMPHILEX '85 / LAUSANNE (B) 1.40 .65
C337 AP113 500fr MOPHILA '85 / HAM - BURG (G) 1.40 .65

Audubon Birth Bicentenary — AP119

Illustrations of North American bird species by Audubon. Nos. C338-C339 vert.

1985, Apr. 11 *Perf. 13½*

C338 AP119 100fr Passiformes fringillidae .25 .15
C339 AP119 150fr Eudocimus ruber .40 .20
C340 AP119 200fr Buteo jamaicensis .55 .25
C341 AP119 350fr Camptorhynchus labradorius .90 .45
Nos. C338-C341 (4) 2.10 1.05

PHILEXAFRICA '85, Lome — AP120

Youths in public service activities.

1985, May 20 *Perf. 13*

C342 AP120 200fr Community health care .55 .25
C343 AP120 200fr Agriculture .55 .25
a. Pair, #C342-C343 + label 1.10 .75

Admission to UN, 25th Anniv. — AP121

1985, Aug. 13

C344 AP121 190fr multi .60 .28

Christmas — AP123

Paintings: 100fr, The Virgin and the Infant Jesus, by David. 200fr, Adoration of the Magi, by Hieronymus Bosch (1450-1516). 400fr, Virgin and Child, by Van Dyck.

UN, 40th Anniv. — AP122

1985, Oct. 25 *Perf. 12½*

C345 AP122 180fr Rainbow, emblem .60 .30

1985, Dec. 20 Litho. *Perf. 13*

C346 AP123 100fr multi .40 .18
C347 AP123 200fr multi .70 .38
C348 AP123 400fr multi 1.50 .75
Nos. C346-C348 (3) 2.60 1.31

Nos. C346-C347 vert.

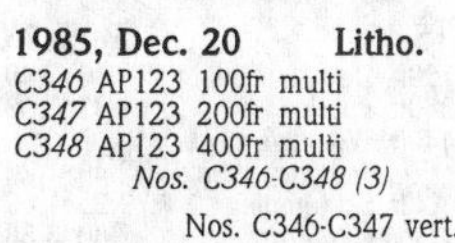

Halley's Comet — AP124

1986, Feb. 17

C349 AP124 125fr Halley, comet .68 .35
C350 AP124 150fr West's Comet, 1976 .82 .40
C351 AP124 225fr Ikeya Seki's Comet, 1965 1.25 .62
C352 AP124 300fr Trajectory diagram 1.65 .82
C353 AP124 350fr Comet, Vega probe 2.00 1.00
Nos. C349-C353 (5) 6.40 3.19

Nos. C350-C351 vert.

Cosmos-Frantel Hotel — AP125

1986, May 1 *Perf. 13½*

C354 AP125 250fr multi 1.40 .70

1986 World Cup Soccer Championships, Mexico — AP126

Various soccer plays.

1986, July 22 Litho. *Perf. 13*

C355 AP126 150fr multi .90 .45
C356 AP126 250fr multi 1.50 .75
C357 AP126 440fr multi 2.75 1.40
C358 AP126 600fr multi 3.75 1.10
Nos. C355-C358 (4) 8.90 3.70

Air Africa, 25th Anniv. — AP127

1986, Nov. 29 Litho. *Perf. 13½*

C359 AP127 200fr multi 1.10 .55

1988 Winter Pre-Olympics, Calgary — AP128

1986, Dec. 15 *Perf. 13*

C360 AP128 150fr Downhill skiing .80 .40
C361 AP128 250fr Bobsled 1.35 .68
C362 AP128 440fr Women's cross-country skiing 2.40 1.20
C363 AP128 600fr Ski jumping 3.25 1.60
Nos. C360-C363 (4) 7.80 3.88

Nos. C361-C362 vert.

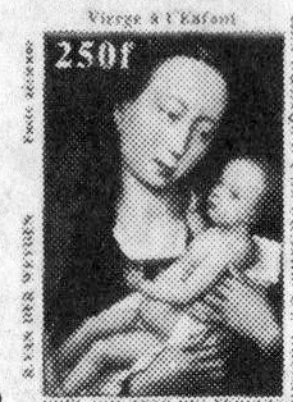

Christmas — AP129

Paintings by Rogier van der Weyden (c.1399-1464): 250fr, Virgin and Child. 440fr, The Nativity. 500fr, Virgin with Carnation.

1986, Dec. 23 *Perf. 13½*

C364 AP129 250fr multi 1.35 .68
C365 AP129 440fr multi 2.40 1.20
C366 AP129 500fr multi 2.75 1.35
Nos. C364-C366 (3) 6.50 3.23

Crocodiles, World Wildlife Fund — AP130

1987, Jan. 22 *Perf. 13*

C367 AP130 75fr Osteolaemus tetraspis .40 .20
C368 AP130 100fr Crocodylus cataphractus .55 .28
C369 AP130 125fr Osteolaemus tetraspis, diff. .68 .35
C370 AP130 150fr Crocodylus cataphractus, diff. .80 .40
Nos. C367-C370 (4) 2.43 1.23

1988 Summer Olympics, Seoul — AP131

1987, July 11 **Litho.** *Perf. 13*

C371 AP131 100fr Backstroke .70 .35
C372 AP131 200fr Freestyle 1.50 .75
C373 AP131 300fr Breaststroke 2.25 1.10
C374 AP131 400fr Butterfly 2.75 1.40
Nos. C371-C374 (4) 7.20 3.60

Souvenir Sheet

C375 AP131 750fr Start of event 5.25 2.75

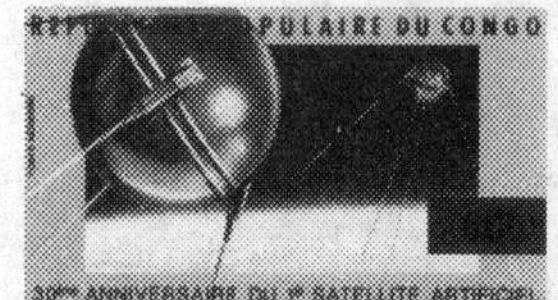

Launch of Sputnik, First Artificial Satellite, 30th Anniv. — AP132

1987, June 5 *Perf. 12½x12*

C376 AP132 60fr multi .42 .20
C377 AP132 240fr multi 1.75 .85

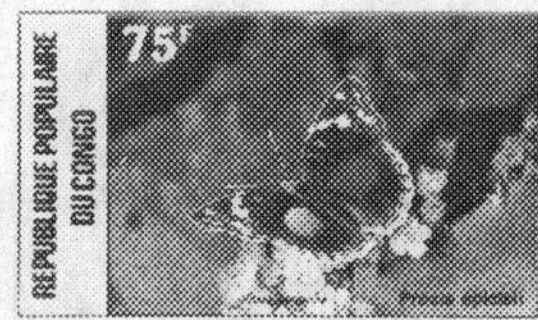

Butterflies — AP133

1987, Sept. 4 *Perf. 12½*

C378 AP133 75fr Precis epicleli .50 .25
C379 AP133 120fr Deilephila nerii .80 .40
C380 AP133 450fr Euryphene senegalensis 3.00 1.50
C381 AP133 550fr Precis almanta 3.75 1.10
Nos. C378-C381 (4) 8.05 3.25

Coubertin, Eternal Flame and Greece No. 125 — AP134

Cameo portrait, athletes and stamps: 120fr, Runners, France No. 198. 350fr, Congo Republic No. C22, hurdler. 600fr, High jump, Congo Republic No. C75.

1987, Nov. 4

C382 AP134 75fr shown .55 .28
C383 AP134 120fr multi .88 .45
C384 AP134 350fr multi 2.50 1.25
C385 AP134 600fr multi 4.25 2.15
Nos. C382-C385 (4) 8.18 4.13

Pierre de Coubertin (1863-1937), promulgator of the modern Olympics.

Arrival of Schweitzer in Lambarene, 75th Anniv. — AP135

1988, Apr. 17 **Litho.** *Perf. 12½*

C386 AP135 240fr multi 1.70 .85

Dr. Albert Schweitzer (1875-1965), Nobel Peace Prize winner of 1952, founded Lambarene Hospital, Gabon, in 1913.

1988 Summer Olympics, Seoul — AP136

Pentathlon: 75fr, Swimming. 170fr, Cross-country running, vert. 200fr, Shooting. 600fr, Equestrian. 700fr, Fencing.

1988, June 10 **Litho.** *Perf. 13*

C387 AP136 75fr multi .50 .25
C388 AP136 170fr multi 1.15 .58
C389 AP136 200fr multi 1.35 .68
C390 AP136 600fr multi 4.00 2.00
Nos. C387-C390 (4) 7.00 3.51

Souvenir Sheet

C391 AP136 750fr multi 5.00 2.50

Elimination Matches, 1990 World Cup Soccer Championships — AP137

Various athletes and cities in Italy.

1989, June 15 **Litho.** *Perf. 13*

C392 AP137 75fr Bari .45 .22
C393 AP137 120fr Rome .72 .35
C394 AP137 500fr Florence 3.00 1.50
C395 AP137 550fr Naples 3.25 1.65
Nos. C392-C395 (4) 7.42 3.72

PHILEXFRANCE '89 — AP138

Paintings: 300fr, Storming of the Bastille, July 14, 1789, from a gouache by J.P. Houel. 400fr, Eiffel Tower, by G. Seurat.

1989, June 22

C396 AP138 300fr multi 1.80 .90
C397 AP138 400fr multi 2.40 1.20

French revolution, bicent. (300fr); Eiffel Tower, cent. (400fr).

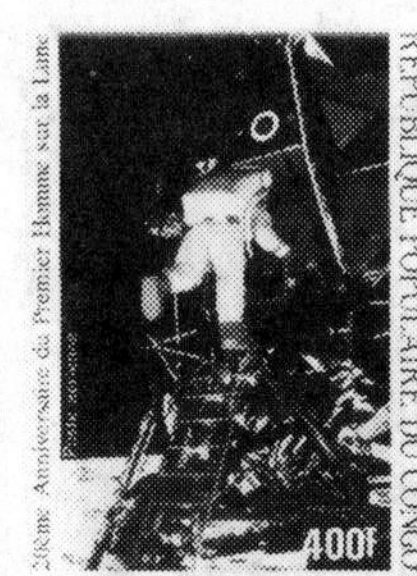

First Moon Landing, 20th Anniv. AP139

Man's first step on the Moon: No. C398, Astronaut on ladder. No. C399, Conducting experiments on the Moon's surface.

1989, June 22

C398 AP139 400fr multi 2.50 1.25
C399 AP139 400fr multi 2.50 1.25

World Cup Soccer Championships, Italy — AP140

Various soccer plays and architecture.

1990, June 8 **Litho.** *Perf. 13*

C400 AP140 120fr multicolored .95 .48
C401 AP140 240fr multicolored 1.85 .95
C402 AP140 500fr multicolored 3.85 1.95
C403 AP140 600fr multicolored 4.65 2.35
Nos. C400-C403 (4) 11.30 5.73

Pan African Postal Union, 10th Anniv. — AP141

1991, Jan. 10 **Litho.** *Perf. 13½*

C404 AP141 60fr shown .48 .24
C405 AP141 120fr Emblem .95 .48

1992 Winter Olympics, Albertville AP142

1991, June 8 **Litho.** *Perf. 13½*

C406 AP142 120fr Ice hockey 1.15 .58
C407 AP142 300fr Speed skating 2.90 1.45

Litho. & Embossed

C408 AP142 1500fr Slalom skiing

Numbers have been reserved for souvenir sheets in this set.

1992 Summer Olympics, Barcelona AP143

Designs: No. C411, Equestrian. No. C412, Long jump.

1992 **Litho. & Embossed** *Perf. 13½*

C411 AP143 1500fr gold & multi

Souvenir Sheet

C412 AP143 1500fr gold & multi

Anniversaries AP144

Designs: 90fr, Victor Schoelcher, missionary, death cent. 205fr, Martin Luther King, civil rights reformer, 25th death anniv. 300fr, Claude Chappe (1763-1805), bicent. of visual telegraph.

1993 **Litho.** *Perf. 14*

C413 AP144 90fr multicolored *.40 .20*
C414 AP144 205fr multicolored *.95 .50*
C415 AP144 300fr multicolored *1.40 .70*
Nos. C413-C415 (3) *2.75 1.40*

AIR POST SEMI-POSTAL STAMPS

Hathor Pillar — SPAP1

Unwmk.

1964, Mar. 9 Engr. *Perf. 13*

CB1 SPAP1 10fr + 5fr vio & chnt .18 .15
CB2 SPAP1 25fr + 5fr org brn & slate grn .30 .22
CB3 SPAP1 50fr + 5fr slate grn & brn red .55 .45
Nos. CB1-CB3 (3) 1.03 .82

UNESCO world campaign to save historic monuments in Nubia.

POSTAGE DUE STAMPS

Messenger — D6

MH. 1521 Broussard Plane — D7

Early Transportation: 1fr, Litter. 2fr, Canoe. 5fr, Bicyclist. 10fr, Steam locomotive. 25fr, Seaplane.

Unwmk.

1961, Dec. 4 Engr. *Perf. 11*

J34 D6 50c ultra, ol bis & red .15 .15
J35 D6 1fr red brn, red & grn .15 .15
J36 D6 2fr grn, ultra & brn .15 .15
J37 D6 5fr pur & gray brn .15 .15
J38 D6 10fr bl, grn & chocolate .25 .25
J39 D6 25fr bl, dk grn & dk brn .55 .55

Modern transportation: 1fr, Land Rover. 2fr, River boat transporting barge. 5fr, Trailer-truck. 10fr, Diesel locomotive. 25fr, Boeing 707 jet plane.

J40 D7 50c ultra, olive bis & red .15 .15
J41 D7 1fr red & grn .15 .15
J42 D7 2fr ultra, grn & brn .15 .15
J43 D7 5fr pur & gray brn .15 .15
J44 D7 10fr dk grn & chocolate .25 .25
J45 D7 25fr bl, dk grn & sepia .55 .55
Set value 2.00 2.00

The two types of each value in Nos. J34-J45 (early and modern transportation) were printed tête bêche, se-tenant at the base.

Flowers — D8

Flowers: 2fr, Phaeomeria magnifica. 5fr, Millettia laurentii. 10fr, Tuberose. 15fr, Pyrostegia venusta. 20fr, Hibiscus.

1971, Mar. 25 Photo. *Perf. 12x12½*

J46 D8 1fr multi .15 .15
J47 D8 2fr multi .15 .15
J48 D8 5fr pink & multi .15 .15
J49 D8 10fr dk grn & multi .15 .15
J50 D8 15fr multi .16 .16
J51 D8 20fr multi .25 .25
Set value .66 .66

Flowers and Fruit — D9

1986, June 5 Litho. *Perf. 13*

J52 D9 5fr Passiflora quadrangulares .15 .15
J53 D9 10fr Cannaceae, vert. .15 .15
J54 D9 15fr Ananas comosus, vert. .15 .15
Set value .21 .15

OFFICIAL STAMPS

Coat of Arms — O1

1968-70 Unwmk. Typo. *Perf. 14x13*

O1 O1 1fr multi ('70) .15 .15
O2 O1 2fr multi ('70) .15 .15
O3 O1 5fr multi ('70) .15 .15
O4 O1 10fr multi ('70) .20 .15
O5 O1 25fr emer & multi .16 .15
O6 O1 30fr red & multi .20 .15
O7 O1 50fr multi ('70) .60 .30
O8 O1 85fr multi ('70) 1.10 .60
O9 O1 100fr multi ('70) 1.40 .70
O10 O1 200fr multi ('70) 2.00 1.50
Nos. O1-O10 (10) 6.11 4.00

CORFU

kȯr-'fü

LOCATION — An island in the Ionian Sea opposite the Greek-Albanian border
GOVT. — A department of Greece
AREA — 245 sq. mi.
POP. — 114,620 (1938)
CAPITAL — Corfu

In 1923 Italy occupied Corfu (Kerkyra) during a controversy with Greece over the assassination of an Italian official in Epirus. Italy again occupied Corfu in 1941-43.

100 Centesimi = 1 Lira
100 Lepta = 1 Drachma

ISSUED UNDER ITALIAN OCCUPATION

Watermark

Wmk. 140- Crown

Italian Stamps of 1901-23 Overprinted **CORFÙ**

1923, Sept. 20 Wmk. 140 *Perf. 14*

N1 A48 5c green 2.00 2.00
N2 A48 10c claret 2.00 2.00
N3 A48 15c slate 2.00 2.00
N4 A50 20c brown orange 2.00 2.00
N5 A49 30c orange brown 2.00 2.00
N6 A49 50c violet 2.00 2.00
N7 A49 60c blue 2.00 2.00
N8 A46 1 l brown & green 2.00 2.00
Nos. N1-N8 (8) 16.00 16.00

Italian Stamps of 1901-23 Surcharged **CORFÙ Lepta 25**

1923, Sept. 24

N9 A48 25 l on 10c claret 8.00 5.00
N10 A49 60 l on 25c blue 4.00
N11 A49 70 l on 30c org brn 4.00
N12 A49 1.20d on 50c violet 6.00 5.00
N13 A46 2.40d on 1 l brn & grn 6.00 5.00
N14 A46 4.75d on 2 l grn & org 4.00
Nos. N9-N14 (6) 32.00

Nos. N10, N11, N14 were not placed in use.

Issue for Corfu and Paxos

Nos. N15-N34, NC1-NC12, NJ1-NJ11 and NRA1-NRA3 have been extensively counterfeited, some with forged cancellations.

Stamps of Greece, 1937-38, Overprinted in Black **CORFU**

Perf. 12x13½, 12½x12, 13½x12

1941, June 5 Wmk. 252

N15 A69 5 l brn red & blue 4.00 3.00
N16 A70 10 l bl & brn red (On 397) 1.50 1.25
N17 A70 10 l bl & brn red (On 413) 50.00 50.00
N18 A71 20 l black & grn 1.00 1.00
N19 A72 40 l green & blk 1.50 1.50
N20 A73 50 l brown & blk 2.00 2.00
N21 A74 80 l ind & yel brn 2.00 2.00
N22 A67 1d green 2.50 2.00
N23 A84 1.50d green 6.50 6.00
N24 A75 2d ultra 1.65 1.25
N25 A67 3d red brown 2.25 2.00
N26 A76 5d red 3.00 2.00
N27 A77 6d olive brown 3.00 3.00
N28 A78 7d dark brown 3.00 2.50
N29 A67 8d deep blue 2.75 2.00
N30 A79 10d red brown 40.00 32.50
N31 A80 15d green 5.00 4.50
N32 A81 25d dark blue 4.50 4.00
N33 A84 30d orange brown 14.00 11.00
N34 A67 100d carmine lake 25.00 22.50
Nos. N15-N34 (20) 175.15 156.00

AIR POST STAMPS

Greece Nos. C37 and C26-C35, Overprinted Like Nos. N15-N34

Perf. 12½x13, 13x12½, 13½x12½

1941, June 5 Unwmk.

NC1 D3 50 l dk brown 2.50 2.50
NC2 AP16 1d red 52.50 37.50
NC3 AP17 2d gray blue 3.00 3.00
NC4 AP18 5d violet 3.00 3.00
NC5 AP19 7d deep ultra 3.00 3.00
NC6 AP20 10d bister brn (On C26) 75.00 50.00
NC7 AP20 10d brown org (On C35) 17.50 12.50
NC8 AP21 25d rose 18.00 19.00
NC9 AP22 30d dark green 16.00 19.00
NC10 AP23 50d violet 21.00 22.50
a. Double overprint 150.00
NC11 AP24 100d brown 375.00 250.00

On No. C36

Serrate Roulette 13½

NC12 D3 50 l violet brown 12.50 10.00
a. On No. C36a

POSTAGE DUE STAMPS

Postage Due Stamps of Greece, 1913-35 Overprinted Like Nos. N15-N34

1941, June 5 Unwmk.

Serrate Roulette 13½

NJ1 D3 10 l carmine 1.00 1.00
NJ2 D3 25 l ultra 1.00 1.00
NJ3 D3 80 l lilac brown 75.00 60.00

Perf. 12½x13, 13½x12½

NJ4 D3 1d lt bl (On J80) 200.00 137.50
NJ5 D3 2d light red 1.50 1.10
NJ6 D3 5d gray 5.00 4.50
NJ7 D3 10d gray green 3.00 3.00
NJ8 D3 15d red brown 3.00 3.00
NJ9 D3 25d light red 3.00 3.00
NJ10 D3 50d orange 4.00 4.00
NJ11 D3 100d slate green 95.00 60.00

Corfu Italian and Greek Occupation stamps can be mounted in the Scott Greece album.

POSTAL TAX STAMPS

Greece Nos. RA61-RA63, Overprinted Like Nos. N15-N34

1941, June 5 Unwmk. *Perf. 13½x12*

NRA1 PT7 10 l brt rose, *pale rose* .75 .75
NRA2 PT7 50 l gray grn, *pale grn* .75 .50
NRA3 PT7 1d dull blue, *lt bl* 4.00 3.50
Nos. NRA1-NRA3 (3) 5.50 4.75

Stamps overprinted "CORFU" were replaced by Italian stamps overprinted "Isole Jonie." (See Ionian Islands.)

COSTA RICA

ˌkäs-tə-ˈrē-kə

LOCATION — Central America between Nicaragua and Panama
GOVT. — Republic
AREA — 19,344 sq. mi.
POP. — 2,450,226 (1984)
CAPITAL — San Jose

8 Reales= 100 Centavos= 1 Peso
100 Centimos= 1 Colon (1900)

Catalogue values for unused stamps in this country are for Never Hinged items, beginning with Scott 238 in the regular postage section, Scott C117 in the air post section, Scott CE1 in the air post special delivery section, Scott E1 in the special delivery section, and Scott RA1 in the postal tax section.

Watermarks

Wmk. 215- Small Star in Shield, Multiple

Wmk. 229- Wavy Lines

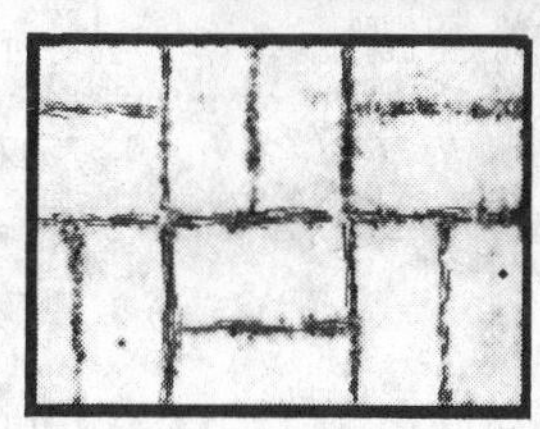

Wmk. 334- Rectangles

Values for unused stamps are for examples with original gum as defined in the catalogue introduction. Very fine examples of Nos. 1-22 will have perforations just clear of the design on one or more sides due to the placement of the stamps on the plates and to imperfect perforating methods.

Coat of Arms — A1

1863 Unwmk. Engr. *Perf. 12*

1 A1 ½r blue .60 1.00
a. ½r light blue .60 1.00
b. Pair, imperf. horiz. *1,500.*

2	A1	2r scarlet	1.25	1.75
3	A1	4r green	15.00	15.00
4	A1	1p orange	30.00	30.00
		Nos. 1-4 (4)	46.85	47.75

The ½r was printed from two plates. The second is in light blue with little or no sky over the mountains.

Imperforate copies of Nos. 1-2 are corner copies from poorly perforated sheets.

Nos. 1-3 Surcharged in Red or Black:

1 cto. (a) — 1 *cto.* (b) — 2 cts. (c)

5 cts. U.P.U. (d) — 20 CTS U.P.U. (e)

1881-82

Red or Black Surcharge

7	A1(a)	1c on ½r ('82)	2.50	
a.		On No. 1a	10.00	
8	A1(b)	1c on ½r ('82)	10.00	
9	A1(c)	2c on ½r, #1a	2.50	
a.		On No. 1	6.00	
12	A1(c)	5c on ½r	6.00	
13	A1(d)	5c on ½r ('82)	60.00	
14	A1(d)	10c on 2r (Bk) ('82)	70.00	
15	A1(e)	20c on 4r ('82)	225.00	

Overprints with different fonts and "Oficial" were never placed in use, and are said to have been surcharged to a dealer's order. The ½r surcharged "DOS CTS" is not a postage stamp.

Postally used copies of Nos. 7-15 are rare. Fake cancellations exist.

Counterfeits exist of surcharges on #7-15.

Gen. Prospero Fernández
A6

President Bernardo Soto Alfaro
A7

1883, Jan. 1

16	A6	1c green	1.25	.80
17	A6	2c carmine	1.25	.90
18	A6	5c blue violet	20.00	1.00
19	A6	10c orange	100.00	7.00
20	A6	40c blue	1.25	1.25
		Nos. 16-20 (5)	123.75	10.95

Unused copies of 40c usually lack gum.

For overprints see Nos. O1-O20, O24, Guanacaste 1-38, 44.

1887

21	A7	5c blue violet	6.00	.50
22	A7	10c orange	2.00	1.00

Unused copies of 5c usually lack gum.

For overprints see Nos. O22-O23, Guanacaste 42-43, 45.

A8

A9

1889

Black Overprint

23	A8	1c rose	2.75	1.00
24	A9	5c brown	2.75	1.00

Vertical and inverted overprints are fakes.

For overprints see Guanacaste Nos. 47-54.

President Soto Alfaro
A10 A11

A12

A13

A14

A15

A16

A17

A18

A19

1889 ***Perf. 14-16 & Compound***

25	A10	1c brown	.35	.45
a.		Horiz. pair, imperf. vert	60.00	
b.		Imperf. pair	75.00	
c.		Horiz. or vert. pair, imperf. btwn.	70.00	
26	A11	2c dark green	.35	.45
a.		Imperf., pair	30.00	
b.		Vert. pair, imperf. horiz.	40.00	
c.		Horiz. pair, imperf. btwn.	40.00	
27	A12	5c orange	.45	.35
a.		Imperf., pair	85.00	
b.		Horiz. pair, imperf. btwn.	70.00	
28	A13	10c red brown	.40	.35
a.		Vert. or horiz. pair, imperf. btwn.	70.00	
29	A14	20c yellow green	.30	.35
a.		Vert. pair, imperf. horiz.	60.00	
b.		Horizontal pair, imperf. btwn.	60.00	
30	A15	50c rose red	1.00	
		Telegram cancel		.75
31	A16	1p blue	1.25	
		Telegram cancel		.75
32	A17	2p dull violet	6.00	
a.		2p slate	6.00	
		Telegram cancel		4.00
33	A18	5p olive green	20.00	
		Telegram cancel		10.00
34	A19	10p black	85.00	
		Telegram cancel		52.50
		Nos. 25-34 (10)	115.10	

Nos. 30-34 normally were used on telegrams and most copies were peeled off of the forms and sold by the government.

For overprints see Nos. O25-O30, Guanacaste 55-67.

Arms of Costa Rica
A20 A21

A22

A23

A24

A25

A26

A27

A28

A29

1892 ***Perf. 12-15 & Compound***

35	A20	1c grnsh blue	.30	.40
36	A21	2c yellow	.30	.40
37	A22	5c red lilac	.30	.25
a.		5c violet	45.00	.28
38	A23	10c lt green	.75	.35
a.		Horiz. pair, imperf. btwn.	52.50	
39	A24	20c scarlet	10.00	.22
a.		Horiz. pair, imperf. btwn.		37.50
40	A25	50c gray blue	4.75	3.25
41	A26	1p green, *yel*	1.00	.75
42	A27	2p brown red, *lilac*	2.50	.80
a.		2p rose red, *pale lil*	10.00	.80
43	A28	5p dk blue, *blue*	2.00	.80
44	A29	10p brown, *pale buff*	25.00	4.00
a.		10p brown, *yellow*	7.00	
		Nos. 35-44 (10)	46.90	11.22

Imperfs. of Nos. 35-44 are proofs.

For overprints see Nos. O31-O36.

Statue of Juan Santamaría
A30

Juan Mora Fernández
A31

View of Port Limón — A32

Braulio Carillo ("Branlio" on stamp) — A33

National Theater — A34

José M. Castro — A35

Birris Bridge — A36

Juan Rafael Mora — A37

Jesús Jiménez — A38

Coat of Arms — A39

1901, Jan. ***Perf. 12-15½***

45	A30	1c green & blk	.50	.30
a.		Horiz. pair, imperf. btwn.		
46	A31	2c vermilion & blk	.60	.30
47	A32	5c gray blue & blk	.75	.30
a.		Vert. pair, imperf. btwn.		110.00
48	A33	10c ocher & blk	1.65	.35
49	A34	20c lake & blk	10.00	.22
a.		Vert. pair, imperf. btwn.	110.00	
50	A35	50c dull lil & dk bl	4.00	1.10
51	A36	1col ol bis & blk	50.00	2.75
52	A37	2col car rose & dk grn	11.00	2.75
53	A38	5col brown & blk	50.00	2.75
54	A39	10col yel grn & brn red	22.50	2.25
		Nos. 45-54 (10)	151.00	13.07

The 2c exists with center inverted.

Nos. 45-57 in other colors are private reprints made in 1948. They have little value.

For surcharge and overprints see Nos. 58, 78, O37-O44.

Remainders

In 1914 the government sold a large quantity of stamps at very much less than face value. The lot included most regular issues from 1901 to 1911 inclusive, postage due stamps of 1903 and official stamps of 1901-03. These stamps were canceled with groups of thin parallel bars. The higher valued used stamps, such as Nos. 64, 65-68a, sell for much less than the values quoted which are for stamps with regular postal cancellations. A few sell for much higher prices.

José M. Cañas — A40

Julián Volio — A41

Eusebio Figueroa Oreamuno — A42

1903 ***Perf. 13½, 14, 15***

55	A40	4c red vio & blk	1.75	.80
56	A41	6c olive grn & blk	7.00	2.25
57	A42	25c gray lil & brn	15.00	.28
		Nos. 55-57 (3)	23.75	3.33

See note on private reprints following No. 54.

For overprints see Nos. 81, O45-O47.

No. 49 Surcharged in Black:

1905

58	A34	1c on 20c lake & blk	.60	.55
a.		Inverted surcharge	10.00	10.00
b.		Diagonal surcharge	.60	.55

Specimens surcharged in other colors are proofs.

Statue of Juan Santamaria A43

Juan Mora Fernández A44

José M. Cañas A45

Mauro Fernández A46

Braulio Carrillo — A47

Julián Volio — A48

Eusebio Figueroa Oreamuno — A49

José M. Castro — A50

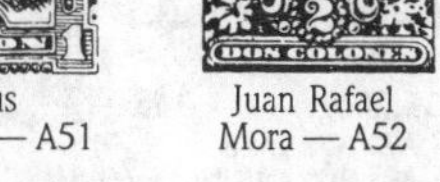

Jesús Jiménez — A51

Juan Rafael Mora — A52

Perf. 11x14, 14 (1c, 5c, 10c, 25c)

1907 **Unwmk.**

No.	Type	Description	Unused	Used
59	A43	1c red brn & ind	.80	.30
a.		Perf. 11x14	16.00	1.50
60	A44	2c yel grn & blk	.90	.30
a.		Perf. 14	.90	.30
61	A45	4c car & indigo	10.00	2.00
a.		Perf. 14	400.00	37.50
62	A46	5c yel & dull bl	1.75	.15
a.		Perf. 11x14	40.00	1.00
63	A47	10c blue & blk	2.00	.50
a.		Perf. 11x14	20.00	1.00
64	A48	20c olive grn & blk	25.00	5.00
a.		Perf. 14	25.00	5.00
65	A49	25c gray lil & blk	2.00	2.00
a.		Perf. 11x14	50.00	30.00
66	A50	50c red lil & blue	45.00	25.00
a.		Perf. 14	75.00	30.00
67	A51	1col brown & blk	20.00	20.00
a.		Perf. 14	20.00	20.00
68	A52	2col claret & grn	100.00	65.00
a.		Perf. 14	200.00	110.00
		Nos. 59-68 (10)	207.45	120.25
		Nos. 59a-68a (10)	846.90	236.30

Imperforate copies of the above set are either proofs or from unfinished sheets, which were placed on the market in London. A few were postally used. The 1c, 2c, 5c, 20c, 50c, 1 col and 2 col exist with center inverted.

Nos. 59-68 exist with papermaker's watermark.

For overprints see Nos. 77, 79-80, 82-84, O48-O55, O60-O64.

Statue of Juan Santamaria A53

Juan Mora Fernández A54

José M. Cañas — A55

Mauro Fernández — A56

Braulio Carrillo — A57

Julián Volio — A58

Eusebio Figueroa Oreamuno A59

Jesús Jiménez A60

1910 ***Perf. 12***

No.	Type	Description	Unused	Used
69	A53	1c brown	.20	.20
70	A54	2c dp green	.25	.20
71	A55	4c scarlet	.25	.20
72	A56	5c orange	.75	.20
73	A57	10c deep blue	.25	.20
74	A58	20c olive grn	.25	.20
75	A59	25c dp violet	8.00	.55
76	A60	1col dk brown	.50	.50
		Nos. 69-76 (8)	10.45	2.25

For overprints and surcharge see Nos. 111C-111J, B1, C2, O56-O59.

No. 60a Overprinted in Red *1911*

1911 ***Perf. 14***

No.	Type	Description	Unused	Used
77	A44	2c yel grn & blk	1.50	1.00
a.		Inverted overprint	5.00	5.00
b.		Double overprint, both inverted	42.50	

Stamps of 1901-07 Overprinted in Red or Black *** 1911 ***

No.	Type	Description	Unused	Used
78	A30	1c grn & blk (R)	.85	.55
a.		Black overprint	32.50	18.00
b.		Inverted overprint		
79	A43	1c red brn & ind (Bk)	.70	.40
a.		Inverted overprint	4.25	3.50
b.		Double overprint	5.00	5.00
80	A44	2c yel grn & blk (Bk)	.70	.40
a.		Inverted overprint	3.50	3.50
b.		Dbl. ovpt., one as on No. 77	40.00	25.00
c.		Double overprint, one inverted	13.00	13.00
d.		Pair, one stamp No. 77	25.00	18.00
e.		Perf. 11x14	40.00	20.00

No. 55 Overprinted in Black **Habilitado 1911**

No.	Type	Description	Unused	Used
81	A40	4c red vio & blk	1.00	.65

Stamps of 1907 Overprinted in Blue, Black or Rose **Habilitado 1911**

Perf. 14, 11x14 (#83, 84)

No.	Type	Description	Unused	Used
82	A46	5c yel & bl (Bl)	1.10	.20
a.		"Habilitada"	3.25	2.50
b.		"2911"	5.50	3.25
c.		Roman "I" in "1911"	3.00	2.00
d.		Double overprint	5.00	5.00
e.		Inverted overprint	5.50	3.75
f.		Black overprint	—	2.00
g.		Triple overprint	5.50	
h.		Vert. pair, imperf. horiz.	37.50	
83	A47	10c bl & blk (Bk)	4.00	1.40
a.		As #83, Roman "I" in "1911"	7.00	5.00
c.		As #83, double overprint	19.00	11.50
d.		Perf. 14	45.00	1.10
84	A47	10c bl & blk (R)	7.50	7.50
a.		Roman "I" in "1911"	15.00	14.00
c.		Perf. 14	19.00	11.50
		Nos. 77-84 (8)	17.35	12.10

Many counterfeits of overprint exist.

A61

A62

A63

Telegraph Stamps Surcharged in Rose, Blue or Black

1911 ***Perf. 12, 14, 14x11***

No.	Type	Description	Unused	Used
86	A61	1c on 10c bl (R)	.25	.20
a.		"Coereos"	7.75	5.50
b.		Inverted surcharge		
87	A61	1c on 10c bl (Bk)	*175.00*	*100.00*
88	A61	1c on 25c vio (Bk)	.25	.20
a.		"Coereos"	7.75	5.50
b.		Pair, one without surcharge	19.00	
c.		Double surcharge	7.75	
e.		Double surch., one inverted	11.50	
89	A61	1c on 50c red brn (Bl)	.40	.40
a.		Inverted surcharge	5.00	5.00
b.		Double surcharge	4.25	
90	A61	1c on 1col brn (R)	.40	.40
91	A61	1c on 5col red (Bl)	.70	.55
92	A61	1c on 10col dk brn (R)	.90	.70
93	A62	2c on 5c brn org (Bk)	2.75	1.90
a.		Inverted surcharge	*7.75*	*3.75*
b.		"Correos" inverted	*15.00*	
c.		Double surcharge	7.75	
94	A62	2c on 10c bl (R)	100.00	
a.		Perf. 14	*300.00*	
b.		"Correos" inverted		
c.		As "b," perf. 14		
95	A62	2c on 50c cl (Bk)	.40	.50
a.		Inverted surcharge	3.75	3.25
b.		Double surcharge	11.50	
c.		Perf. 14	50.00	20.00
96	A62	2c on 1col brn (Bk)	.70	.70
a.		Inverted surcharge	11.50	
b.		Double surcharge	15.00	
97	A62	2c on 2col car (Bk)	.60	.60
a.		Inverted surcharge	7.00	5.00
b.		"Correos" inverted	7.75	5.50
c.		Double surcharge		
d.		Perf. 14	25.00	15.00
98	A62	2c on 5col grn (Bk)	.65	.65
a.		Inverted surcharge	9.00	7.00
b.		"Correos" inverted	*15.00*	*4.25*
c.		Perf. 14	5.00	2.00
99	A62	2c on 10col mar (Bk)	.80	.65
a.		"Correos" inverted		
b.		Perf. 14	5.00	3.00
100	A63	5c on 5c org (Bl)	.40	.25
a.		Double surcharge	7.00	7.00
b.		Inverted surcharge	7.00	5.00
c.		Pair, one without surcharge	16.00	

Counterfeits exist of Nos. 87, 94 and all minor varieties. Used copies of No. 94 with target cancels are counterfeits.

Nos. 93-99 exist with papermaker's watermark.

Coffee Plantation A64

1921, June 17 **Litho.** ***Perf. 11½***

No.	Type	Description	Unused	Used
103	A64	5c bl & blk	1.50	1.50
a.		Tête bêche pair	3.00	3.00
b.		Imperf., pair	10.50	
c.		As "a," imperf.	27.50	

Centenary of coffee raising in Costa Rica.

Liberty with Torch of Freedom — A65

1921 **Typo.** ***Perf. 11***

No.	Type	Description	Unused	Used
104	A65	5c violet	.60	.40
a.		Imperf.	50.00	

Cent. of Central American independence.

For overprint see No. 111.

Juan Mora and Julio Acosta A66

1921, Sept. 15 ***Perf. 11½***

No.	Type	Description	Unused	Used
105	A66	2c orange & blk	.85	.80
106	A66	3c green & blk	.85	.80
107	A66	6c scarlet & blk	1.10	.90
108	A66	15c dk blue & blk	2.75	2.75
109	A66	30c orange brn & blk	4.50	4.50
		Nos. 105-109 (5)	10.05	9.75

Centenary of Central American independence. Issue requested by Costa Rican Philatelic Society. Authorized by decree calling for 2,000 of 30c and 5,000 each of other values. Many more were printed illegally including imperforates, color changes and inverted centers.

Each sheet of 20 (4x5) contains 5 tête-bêche pairs.

Simón Bolívar — A67

1921 **Engr.** ***Perf. 12***

No.	Type	Description	Unused	Used
110	A67	15c deep violet	.30	.20

For overprint No. 110a see set following No. 111. For surcharge see No. 148

No. 104 Overprinted **CORREOS 1922**

1922 ***Perf. 11***

No.	Type	Description	Unused	Used
111	A65	5c violet	.50	.40
a.		Inverted overprint	10.00	
b.		Double overprint	15.00	

Stamps of 1910-1921 Overprinted in Blue, Red, Black or Gold

1922 ***Perf. 12***

No.	Type	Description	Unused	Used
111C	A53	1c brown (Bl)	.20	.20
111D	A54	2c deep green (R)	.20	.20
111E	A55	4c scarlet	.20	.20
111F	A56	5c orange	.45	.35
111G	A57	10c deep blue (R)	.45	.35
111H	A67	15c deep violet (G)	2.00	1.50
		Nos. 111C-111H (6)	3.50	2.80

Inverted overprints occur on all values. Counterfeits exist.

No. 72 Overprinted

1923

No.	Type	Description	Unused	Used
111J	A56	5c orange	.60	.60
k.		"VD." for "UD."	*60.00*	*60.00*

Jesús Jiménez — A68

1923, June 18 **Litho.** ***Perf. 11½***

No.	Type	Description	Unused	Used
112	A68	2c brown	.20	.20
113	A68	4c green	.20	.20
114	A68	5c blue	.30	.20
115	A68	20c carmine	.30	.25
116	A68	1col violet	.35	.35
		Nos. 112-116 (5)	1.35	1.20

Pres. Jesús Jiménez (1823-98).

Nos. 112-116, imperf, were not regularly issued. Value, set $2.

For overprints see Nos. O65-O69.

National Monument A70

Harvesting Coffee — A71

Banana Growing — A73

General Post Office — A74

Columbus Soliciting Aid of Isabella — A75

Christopher Columbus A76

Columbus at Cariari — A77

Map of Costa Rica — A78

Manuel M. Gutiérrez — A79

1923-26 Engr. *Perf. 12*

117 A70	1c violet		.15	.15
118 A71	2c yellow		.26	.15
119 A73	4c deep green		.52	.30
120 A74	5c light blue		.90	.15
121 A74	5c yellow grn ('26)		.26	.15
122 A75	10c red brn		1.65	.15
123 A75	10c car rose ('26)		.35	.15
124 A76	12c carmine rose		5.25	1.75
125 A77	20c deep blue		7.00	.60
126 A78	40c orange		6.75	1.50
127 A79	1col olive green		1.90	.60
	Nos. 117-127 (11)		24.99	5.65

See Nos. 151-156. For surcharges and overprints see Nos. 136-140, 147, 189, 218, C2.

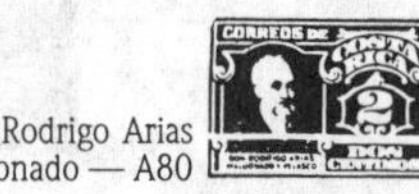
Rodrigo Arias Maldonado — A80

1924 *Perf. 12½*

128 A80	2c dark green	.15	.15
a.	Perf. 14	.15	.15

See No. 162.

Map of Guanacaste A81

Mission at Nicoya — A82

1924 Litho. *Perf. 12*

129 A81	1c carmine rose	.30	.20
130 A81	2c violet	.30	.20
131 A81	5c green	.30	.20
132 A81	10c orange	2.00	.50
133 A82	15c light blue	.65	.42
134 A82	20c gray black	1.10	.70
135 A82	25c light brown	1.50	1.25
	Nos. 129-135 (7)	6.15	3.47

Centenary of annexation of Province of Guanacaste to Costa Rica.

Exist imperf. Value, set, $35.

Stamps of 1923 Surcharged:

a

b

1925

136 A74(a)	3c on 5c lt blue	.20	.15
137 A75(a)	6c on 10c red brn	.28	.25
138 A78(a)	30c on 40c orange	.52	.40
139 A79(b)	45c on 1col ol grn	.90	.50
a.	Double surcharge		
	Nos. 136-139 (4)	1.90	1.30

No. 124 Surcharged

═10   10═

1926

140 A76	10c on 12c car rose	1.00	.30

College of San Luis, Cartago — A83

Chapui Asylum, San José — A84

Normal School, Heredia — A85

Ruins of Ujarrás — A86

1926 Unwmk. Engr. *Perf. 12½*

143 A83	3c ultra	.15	.15
144 A84	6c dark brown	.32	.20
145 A85	30c deep orange	.75	.25
146 A86	45c black violet	2.00	.85
	Nos. 143-146 (4)	3.22	1.45

For surcharges see Nos. 190-190D, 217.

No. 124 Surcharged in Black:

1928, Jan. 7 *Perf. 12*

147 A76	10c on 12c car rose	4.00	4.00

Issued in honor of Col. Charles A. Lindbergh during his Good Will Tour of Central America.

The surcharge has been privately reprinted using an original die. They can be distinguished by distinct dots under the "10s." All errors and inverted surcharges are reprints.

No. 110 Surcharged **5   5**

1928

148 A67	5(c) on 15c dp violet	.15	.15
a.	Inverted surcharge	25.00	

Type I — A88

CORREOS 5 CENTIMOS — Type II

CORREOS 5 CENTIMOS — Type III

CORREOS 5 CENTIMOS — Type IV

CORREOS 5 CENTIMOS — Type V

Surcharge Typo. (I-V) & Litho. (V)

1929 *Perf. 12½*

149	A88 5c on 2col car (I)	.28	.18
a.-d.	Types II-V	.28	.18

Telegraph Stamp Surcharged for Postage as in 1929, Surcharge Lithographed

1929

150 A88	13c on 40c deep grn	.15	.15
a.	Inverted surcharge	.85	.70

Excellent counterfeits exist of No. 150a.

Types of 1923-26 Issues Dated "1929"
Imprint of Waterlow & Sons

1930 Size: 26x21½mm *Perf. 12½*

151 A70	1c dark violet	.15	.15
155 A74	5c green	.15	.15
156 A75	10c carmine rose	.35	.15
	Nos. 151-156 (3)	.65	
	Set value		.24

Juan Rafael Mora — A89

1931

157 A89	13c carmine rose	.20	.15

For surcharge see No. 209.

Seal of Costa Rica Philatelic Society ("Octubre 12 de 1932") A90

1932, Oct. 12 *Perf. 12*

158 A90	3c orange	.22	.15
159 A90	5c dark green	.35	.22
160 A90	10c carmine rose	.40	.25
161 A90	20c dark blue	.50	.32
	Nos. 158-161 (4)	1.47	.94

Phil. Exhib., Oct. 12, 1932. See #179-183.

Maldonado Type of 1924

1934 *Perf. 12½*

162 A80	3c dark green	.15	.15

Red Cross Nurse — A91

1935, May 31 *Perf. 12*

163 A91	10c rose carmine	.32	.15

50th anniv. of the founding of the Costa Rican Red Cross Society.

Air View of Cartago — A92

Miraculous Statuette and View of Cathedral A93

Vision of 1635 — A94

1935, Aug. *Perf. 12½*

164 A92	5c green	.15	.15
165 A93	10c carmine	.30	.15
166 A92	30c orange	.45	.20
167 A94	45c dark violet	1.10	.35
168 A93	50c blue black	1.75	.75
	Nos. 164-168 (5)	3.75	1.60

Tercentenary of the Patron Saint, Our Lady of the Angels, of Costa Rica.

Map of Cocos Island — A95

1936, Jan. 29 *Perf. 14, 11½ (25c)*

169 A95	4c ocher	.20	.15
170 A95	8c dark violet	.28	.15
171 A95	25c orange	.30	.15
172 A95	35c brown vio	.45	.15
173 A95	40c brown	.60	.20
174 A95	50c yellow	.60	.50
175 A95	2col yellow grn	8.00	6.00
176 A95	5col green	20.00	12.00
	Nos. 169-176 (8)	30.43	19.30

Exist imperf. Value, set, $40.

For surcharges see Nos. 196-200, C55-C56.

Map of Cocos Island and Ships of Columbus A96

1936, Dec. 5 *Perf. 12*

177 A96	5c green	.15	.15
178 A96	10c carmine rose	.15	.15
	Set value	.24	.15

For overprints see Nos. 247, O80-O81.

Seal of Costa Rica Philatelic Society ("Diciembre 1937") — A97

1937

179 A97 2c dark brown .15 .15
180 A97 3c black .15 .15
181 A97 5c green .15 .15
182 A97 10c orange red .18 .15
Nos. 179-182 (4) .63 .60

Souvenir Sheet

Imperf

183 Sheet of 4 .45 .45
a. A97 2c dark brown .15 .15
b. A97 3c black .15 .15
c. A97 5c green .15 .15
d. A97 10c orange red .15 .15

Phil. Exhib., Dec. 1937.

Purple Guaria Orchid, National Flower — A98

Tuna A99

Native with Donkey Carrying Bananas A101

Designs: 3c, Cacao pod. 10c, Coffee harvesting.

1937-38 Wmk. 229 *Perf. 12½*

184 A98 1c green & vio ('38) .28 .15
185 A98 3c chocolate ('38) .15 .15

Unwmk. *Perf. 12*

186 A99 2c olive gray .18 .15
187 A101 5c dark green .20 .15
188 A101 10c carmine rose .28 .18
Nos. 184-188 (5) 1.09
Set value .54

National Exposition.

No. 125 Overprinted in Black **1938**

1938 Unwmk. *Perf. 12*

189 A77 20c deep blue .32 .15

No. 146 Surcharged in Red:

a

b

c

d

e **15 Cts.**

1940 *Perf. 12½*

190 A86(a) 15c on 45c black vio .40 .20
190A A86(b) 15c on 45c black vio .40 .20
190B A86(c) 15c on 45c black vio .40 .20
190C A86(d) 15c on 45c black vio .52 .25
190D A86(e) 15c on 45c black vio .40 .15
Nos. 190-190D (5) 2.12 1.00

#190D exists with inverted surcharge. Value, $5.

Allegory A103

Overprinted "Dia Panamericano de la Salud / 2 Diciembre 1940" and Arc

1940, Dec. 2 Engr. *Perf. 12*

191 A103 5c green .20 .15
192 A103 10c rose carmine .22 .15
193 A103 20c deep blue .55 .18
194 A103 40c brown 1.10 .80
195 A103 55c orange yellow 2.25 .95
Nos. 191-195 (5) 4.32 2.23

Pan-American Health Day. See #C46-C54. Exist without overprint.

Stamps of 1936 Surcharged in Black:

15 CENTIMOS 15

1941 *Perf. 14, 11½*

196 A95 15c on 25c orange .22 .20
197 A95 15c on 35c brn vio .22 .20
198 A95 15c on 40c brown .22 .20
199 A95 15c on 2col yel grn .22 .20
200 A95 15c on 5col green .40 .35
Nos. 196-200 (5) 1.28 1.15

Nos. 196-200 exist with surcharge inverted. Value, $5 a set.

National Stadium A104

Engr.; Flags Typo. in Natl. Colors

1941, May 8 *Perf. 12½*

201 A104 5c green .75 .20
a. Flags omitted 60.00
202 A104 10c orange .60 .20
203 A104 15c car rose .90 .30
204 A104 25c dk blue 1.00 .42
205 A104 40c chestnut 4.00 1.25
206 A104 50c purple 5.00 1.50
207 A104 75c red orange 8.00 3.00
208 A104 1col dk carmine 15.00 6.00
Nos. 201-208 (8) 35.25 12.87

Caribbean and Central American Soccer Championship. See #C57-C66, C121-C123.

No. 157 Surcharged in Black **5 Céntimos 5**

1941 *Perf. 12*

209 A89 5c on 13c car rose .15 .15

Cleto González Viquez — A105

Design: 5c, José Rodriguez.

1941-45 Engr. *Perf. 12½*

210 A105 3c dp orange .16 .15
210A A105 3c dp plum ('43) .16 .15
210B A105 3c carmine ('45) .16 .15
211 A105 5c dp violet .20 .15
211A A105 5c brown blk ('43) .20 .15
Nos. 210-211A (5) .88
Set value .54

See No. 256.

Old University of Costa Rica — A106

New National University A107

1941, Aug. 26 *Perf. 12*

212 A106 5c green .35 .15
213 A107 10c yellow org .38 .15
214 A106 15c lilac rose .50 .15
215 A107 25c dull blue .75 .20
216 A106 50c fawn 3.00 1.25
Nos. 212-216 (5) 4.98 1.90

National University, founded in 1940. See Nos. C74-C80.

Nos. 144, 189 Surcharged in Black or Red

15 CENTIMOS 15

1942 *Perf. 12½, 12*

217 A84 5c on 6c dk brn .18 .15
218 A77 15c on 20c dp bl (R) .24 .15

Nos. 217-218 exist with inverted surcharge. Value, each $5.

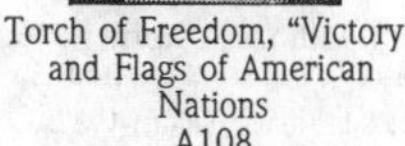

Torch of Freedom, "Victory" and Flags of American Nations A108

Juan Mora Fernández A109

1942, Sept. 25 *Perf. 12*

219 A108 5c rose .20 .15
220 A108 5c yellow grn .20 .15
221 A108 5c purple .20 .15
222 A108 5c dp blue .20 .15
223 A108 5c red orange .20 .15
Nos. 219-223 (5) 1.00
Set value .50

For overprints see Nos. 238-241.

1943-47 Engr.

Designs: 2c, Bruno Carranza. 3c, Tomas Guardia. 5c, Manuel Aguilar. 15c, Francisco Morazan. 25c, Jose M. Alfaro. 50c, Francisco M. Oreamuno. 1col, Jose M. Castro. 2col, Juan Rafael Mora.

224 A109 1c red lilac .15 .15
225 A109 2c black .15 .15
226 A109 3c deep blue .15 .15
227 A109 5c brt blue grn .15 .15
a. 5c bright green ('47) .15 .15
228 A109 15c scarlet .20 .15
229 A109 25c brt ultra 1.00 .15
230 A109 50c dp violet 2.00 .45
231 A109 1col black brown 3.00 1.50
232 A109 2col deep orange 4.00 2.00
Nos. 224-232 (9) 10.80 4.85

See Nos. 344-368, C81-C91A, C124-C127, C154-C158, C179-C181, C768-C772, C790-C794, C854-C858. For surcharges see Nos. C154-C158, C182, C184-C185.

View of San Ramón A118

1944, Jan. 19

233 A118 5c dark green .15 .15
234 A118 10c orange .15 .15
235 A118 15c rose pink .24 .15
236 A118 40c gray black .90 .45
237 A118 50c deep blue 1.50 .75
Nos. 233-237 (5) 2.94
Set value 1.40

100th anniv. of the founding of the City of San Ramón. See Nos. C94-C102.

Catalogue values for unused stamps in this section, from this point to the end of the section, are for Never Hinged items.

Nos. 220-223 Overprinted in Red or Black

La entrevista de los Presidentes De la Guardia y Picado contribuirá a afianzar la unidad Continental. 18 setiembre 1944

1944, Sept. 18

238 A108 5c yel green .15 .15
239 A108 5c purple (R) .15 .15
240 A108 5c dp blue (R) .15 .15
241 A108 5c red orange .15 .15
Set value .48 .40

Amicable settlement of a boundary dispute with Panama. This overprint also exists on No. 219.

Mauro Fernández (1844-1905), Statesman — A119

Unwmk.

1945, July 21 Engr. *Perf. 14*

242 A119 20c deep green .25 .15

For surcharge see No. 246.

Coffee Harvesting A120

1945, Oct. 9 *Perf. 12*

243 A120 5c dk green & blk .15 .15
244 A120 10c orange & blk .18 .15
245 A120 20c car rose & blk .22 .20
Nos. 243-245 (3) .55
Set value .40

No. 242 Surcharged in Red Brown

1946 Unwmk. *Perf. 14*

246 A119 15c on 20c dp green .20 .15

Exists with inverted surcharge. Value, $5.

No. O80 Overprinted in Red **CORREOS 1947**

1947, Mar. 19 *Perf. 12*

247 A96 5c green .15 .15

Exist with inverted overprint. Value, $5.

Cervantes — A121

A122

Wmk. 215

1947, Nov. 10 Engr. *Perf. 14*

249 A121 30c deep blue .20 .15
250 A121 55c deep carmine .35 .30

400th anniv. of the birth of Miguel de Cervantes Saavedra, novelist, playwright and poet.

1947, Aug. 26 Unwmk. *Perf. 12*

251 A122 5c brt green .15 .15
252 A122 10c car rose .15 .15
253 A122 15c ultra .20 .18
254 A122 25c orange red .25 .25
255 A122 50c lilac .50 .35
Nos. 251-255,C160-C167 (13) 6.59 5.65

Franklin D. Roosevelt. For surcharges see Nos. C224-C226.

Small Portrait Type of 1941

Design: 3c, Bishop Bernardo A. Theil.

1948 *Perf. 12½*

256 A105 3c deep ultra .15 .15

Old University of Costa Rica — A123

1953, June 25 Litho. *Perf. 12*
Black Surcharge

257 A123 5c on 10c green .15 .15

Revenue Stamp Surcharged in Red or Blue — A124

1955-56 Unwmk. Engr. *Perf. 12*

258 A124 5c on 2c emerald .15 .15
259 A124 15c on 2c emer (Bl) .18 .15
260 A124 15c on 2c emer ('56) .18 .15
Nos. 258-260,C341-C344 (7) 1.54
Set value 1.00

For surcharges see #C341-C344, C431-C433.

Justo A. Facio A125

Anglo-Costa Rican Bank A126

1960, Apr. 20 Photo. *Perf. 13½*

261 A125 10c brown red .15 .15

Centenary of the birth (in 1859) of Prof. Justo A. Facio. Exists imperf.

Nos. RA12-RA15 Surcharged in Red

1963
10
CENTIMOS

1963, Mar.

262 PT3 10c on 5c dk car .16 .15
263 PT3 10c on 5c sepia .16 .15
264 PT3 10c on 5c dull grn .16 .16
265 PT3 10c on 5c blue .16 .15
Nos. 262-265 (4) .64 .61

1963 Unwmk. *Perf. 13½*

266 A126 10c gray .15 .15

Centenary of the Anglo-Costa Rican Bank.

Arms of San José — A127

Alberto M. Brenes Mora — A128

Coats of Arms: 35c, Cartago. 50c, Heredia. 55c, Alajuela. 65c, Guanacaste. 1col, Puntarenas. 2col, Limon.

1969, Sept. 14 Litho. *Perf. 14x13½*

267 A127 15c multicolored .15 .15
268 A127 35c multicolored .15 .15
269 A127 50c gray & multi .15 .15
270 A127 55c buff & multi .16 .20
271 A127 65c multicolored .24 .25
272 A127 1col pink & multi 1.00 .25
273 A127 2col multicolored 1.00 .50
Nos. 267-273 (7) 2.85 1.65

1976, Mar. 1 Litho. *Perf. 10½*

274 A128 1col violet blue .25 .20
Nos. 274,C653-C657 (6) 2.80 2.25

Prof. Alberto Manuel Brenes Mora, botanist, birth centenary.

Map of Costa Rica, Reader with Book — A129

1978, July 17 Litho. *Perf. 13½*

275 A129 50c multicolored .15 .15

National five-year literacy plan.

A130

A131

1983, May 17 Litho. *Perf. 13x13½*

276 A130 10c multicolored .15 .15
277 A130 50c multicolored .15 .15
278 A130 10col multicolored .70 .25
Set value .80 .35

World Communications Year.

1983, May 30 Litho. *Perf. 10½*

279 A131 20col black 1.40 .50

First World Congress of Human Rights, 1982.

UPU Membership Centenary — A132

1983, June 30 Litho. *Perf. 16*

280 A132 3col #17, monument .75 .15
281 A132 10col #20, headquarters 1.50 .28

French Alliance Centenary — A133

1983, July 21 Litho. *Perf. 11*

282 A133 12col Scene in San Jose, by Christina Fournier .85 .28

Christmas 1983 — A134

Nativity tableau in continuous design. Illustration reduced.

1983, Dec. 5 Litho. *Perf. 13½*

283 A134 1.50col multi .15 .15
284 A134 1.50col multi .15 .15
285 A134 1.50col multi .15 .15
Set value .30 .15

Costa Rican Gardens Association.

Fishery Development Administration — A135

1983, Dec. 19 Litho. *Perf. 13½*

286 A135 8.50col multi .56 .18

Local Birds — A136

1984, Jan. 9 Litho. *Perf. 13½*

287 A136 10c Quetzal .20 .15
288 A136 50c Cyanerpes cyaneus .20 .15
289 A136 1col Turdus grayi .20 .15
290 A136 1.50col Momotus momota .20 .15
291 A136 3col Colibri thalassinus .50 .15
292 A136 10col Notiochelindon cyanoleuca 1.50 .15
Nos. 287-292 (6) 2.80
Set value .35

Dated 1983. 10c, 1.50col, 3col vert.

José Joaquin Mora, Hero of 1856 Independence Campaign A137

Paintings, Juan Santamaria Museum, San José: 1.50col, Pancha Carrasco. 3 col, Death of Juan Santamaria, horiz. 8.50col, Juan Rafael Mora Porras.

1984, Apr. 10 Litho. *Perf. 10½*

293 A137 50c multi .15 .15
294 A137 1.50col multi .15 .15
295 A137 3col multi .15 .15
296 A137 8.50col multi .18 .15
Set value .34 .20

For surcharge see No. 440.

Jesus Bonilla Chavarria, Composer — A138

Musicians and Composers: 5col, Benjamin Gutierrez (b. 1937). 12col, Pilar Jimenez (1835-1922). 13col, Jose Daniel Zuniga Zeledon (1889-1981).

1984, May 30 Litho. *Perf. 13½*

297 A138 3.50col blk & lil .15 .15
298 A138 5col blk & pink .15 .15
299 A138 12col blk & grn .24 .15
300 A138 13col blk & yel .26 .15
Set value .68 .22

Figurines, Jade Museum — A139

1984 Summer Olympics — A140

1984, June 27 Litho. *Perf. 13½*

301 A139 4col Man (pendant) .15 .15
302 A139 7col Seated man .15 .15
303 A139 10col Dish, horiz. .20 .15
Nos. 301-303 (3) .50
Set value .15

1984, July 27

304 A140 1col Basketball .15 .15
305 A140 8col Swimming .15 .15
306 A140 11col Bicycling .22 .15
307 A140 14col Running .28 .15
308 A140 20col Boxing .40 .15
309 A140 30col Soccer .60 .16
Nos. 304-309 (6) 1.80
Set value .50

Public Street Lighting Centenary — A141

1984, Aug. 9 Litho. *Perf. 10½*

310 A141 6col Street scene by Luis Chacon .15 .15

10th Natl. Stamp Exhibition, Sept. 10-16 A142

1984, Sept. 10 Litho. *Perf. 10½*

311 A142 10col Natl. monument .20 .15
312 A142 10col Juan Mora Fernandez monument .20 .15
a. Min. sheet, 2 each #311-312 1.50
Set value .15

Natl. Arms — A143

1984, Oct. 29 Engr. *Perf. 14x13½*

313 A143 100col dk green 6.00 3.00
314 A143 100col yel org 6.00 3.00

Detail from Sistine Virgin by Raphael
A144 A145

1984, Dec. 7 Litho. *Perf. 10½*

315 A144 3col multi .15 .15
316 A145 3col multi .15 .15
a. Pair, #315-316 .15 .15

20th Intl. Bicycle Race, Costa Rica — A146

1984, Dec. 19 Litho. *Perf. 13½*
317 A146 6col multi .28 .28

Intl. Youth Year A147

1985, Jan. 31 *Perf. 10½*
322 A147 11col IYY emblem, #C476 .45 .45

Scouting Movement, 75th anniv.

Labor Monument, San Jose — A148

Natl. values: 11col, Freedom of speech- wooden hand printing press. 13col, Neutrality- dove, natl. flag, outline map.

1985, Feb. 28
323 A148 6col shown .28 .28
324 A148 11col bl, blk & yel .44 .44
325 A148 13col multi .52 .52

Size: 68x38mm
326 A148 30col Nos. 323-325 1.15 1.15
Nos. 323-326 (4) 2.39 2.39

Natl. Red Cross Cent., UN 40th Anniv. A149

1985, May 3 *Perf. 10½*
327 A149 3col No. 163 .15 .15
328 A149 5col No. C120, vert. .25 .25

Club Emblem A150

1st Club Pres., Ricardo Saprissa Ayma — A151

Design: No. 330, Hands holding soccer ball.

1985, July 16 *Perf. 10½*
329 A150 3col multi .15 .15
330 A150 3col multi .15 .15
a. Pair, #329-330 .30 .30
331 A151 6col multi .28 .28
Nos. 329-331 (3) .58 .58

Saprissa Soccer Club, 50th Anniv.

Orchids — A152

1985, Dec. 3
332 A152 6col Brassia arcuigera .42 .42
333 A152 6col Encyclia peraltensis .42 .42
334 A152 6col Maxillaria especie .42 .42
a. Strip of 3, #332-334 2.00 .90
335 A152 13col Oncidium turialbae .90 .90
336 A152 13col Trichopilia marginata .90 .90
337 A152 13col Stanhopea ecornuta .90 .90
a. Strip of 3, #335-337 4.00 1.80
Nos. 332-337 (6) 3.96 3.96

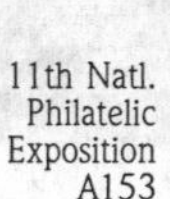

11th Natl. Philatelic Exposition A153

1985, Dec. 3 Litho. *Perf. 13½*
338 A153 20col No. C41 .80 .20

Christmas 1985 — A153a

1985, Dec. 12 Litho. *Perf. 10½*
338A A153a 3col multi .15 .15

Compulsory Education, Cent. — A154

Designs: 3col, Primary school, horiz. 30col, Mauro Fernandez Acuna, founder.

1986, Feb. 28 *Perf. 13½*
339 A154 3col pale yel & brn .15 .15
340 A154 30col pale pink & brn 1.20 .30
Set value .35

Agriculture Students — A155

1986, Mar. 21 *Perf. 10½*
341 A155 10col shown .40 .15
342 A155 10col IDB emblem .40 .15
343 A155 10col Capo Bianco fisherman .40 .15
a. Strip of 3, #341-343 1.20 1.20
Set value .30

Inter-American Development Bank Annual Governors' Assembly, San Jose.

Presidents Type of 1943

Designs: Nos. 344, 349, 354, 359, 364, Francisco J. Orlich Bolmarcich, 1962-66.
Nos. 345, 350, 355, 360, 365, Jose Joaquin Trejos Fernandez, 1966-70.
Nos. 346, 351, 356, 361, 366, Daniel Oduber Quiros, 1974-78.
Nos. 347, 352, 357, 362, 367, Rodrigo Carazo Oido, 1978-82.
Nos. 348, 353, 358, 363, 368, Luis Alberto Monge Alvarez, 1982-86.

1986, May 12 Litho. *Perf. 10½*
344 A109 3col turq blue .35 .15
345 A109 3col turq blue .35 .15
346 A109 3col turq blue .35 .15
347 A109 3col turq blue .35 .15
348 A109 3col turq blue .35 .15
a. Strip of 5, #344-348 *3.50 3.50*
349 A109 6col yel brn .70 .15
350 A109 6col yel brn .70 .15
351 A109 6col yel brn .70 .15
352 A109 6col yel brn .70 .15
353 A109 6col yel brn .70 .15
a. Strip of 5, #349-353 *7.00 7.00*
354 A109 10col brn org 1.25 .15
355 A109 10col brn org 1.25 .15
356 A109 10col brn org 1.25 .15
357 A109 10col brn org 1.25 .15
358 A109 10col brn org 1.25 .15
a. Strip of 5, #354-358 *12.00 12.00*
359 A109 11col slate gray 1.40 .15
360 A109 11col slate gray 1.40 .15
361 A109 11col slate gray 1.40 .15
362 A109 11col slate gray 1.40 .15
363 A109 11col slate gray 1.40 .15
a. Strip of 5, #359-363 *13.00 13.00*
364 A109 13col olive 1.50 .15
365 A109 13col olive 1.50 .15
366 A109 13col olive 1.50 .15
367 A109 13col olive 1.50 .15
368 A109 13col olive 1.50 .15
a. Strip of 5, #364-368 *15.00 15.00*
Nos. 344-368 (25) 26.00
Set value 2.35

1986 World Cup Soccer Championships, Mexico — A156

1986, May 30 Litho. *Perf. 13½*
369 A156 1col Players .20 .15
370 A156 1col Character trademark, vert. .20 .15
371 A156 4col as No. 370 .85 .15
372 A156 6col as No. 369 1.25 .15
373 A156 11col Players, diff. 2.50 .15
Nos. 369-373 (5) 5.00
Set value .33

Intl. Peace Year — A157

Gold Museum, Central Bank of Costa Rica — A158

Peace in many languages: a, "Hoa binh," etc. b, "Vrede," etc. c, "Pace," etc.

1986, July 31 Litho. *Perf. 10½*
374 Strip of 3 .55 .15
a.-c. A157 5col, any single .18 .15

1986, Sept. 19 *Perf. 13½*

Designs: Various undescribed works of Pre-Columbian art.

375 Strip of 5 1.10 .30
a.-e. A158 6col any single .22 .15
376 Strip of 5 2.25 .60
a.-e. A158 13col any single .45 .15

A159

Fauna and Flora — A160

1986, Dec. 16 Litho. *Perf. 13x13½*
377 A159 2col Centurio senex .15 .15
378 A159 3col Glossophaga soricina .15 .15
379 A159 4col Ectophylla alba .15 .15
380 A159 5col Ectophylla alba, diff. .35 .15
381 A159 6col Agalychnis callidryas .45 .15
382 A159 10col Dendrobates pumilio .75 .15
383 A159 11col Hyla ebraccata .80 .15
384 A159 20col Phyllobates lugubris 1.50 .18
Nos. 377-384 (8) 4.30
Set value .64

Souvenir Sheet

Perf. 12½x12
385 A160 50col Agalychnis callidryas, diff. *50.00 7.00*

Natl. Science and Technology Day — A161

Mural (detail), by Francisco Amighetti, Clorito Picado Social Security Clinic.

1987, July 31 Litho. *Perf. 10½*
386 A161 8col multi *3.50* .15

Natl. Museum, Cent. — A162

Artifacts: No. 387a, Dowel-shaped figure of a man. No. 387b, Ape-like carved stone figurine. No. 387c, Polished stone ritual figure. No. 387d, Carved granite capital. No. 387e, Two-legged pot. No. 388a, Bowl. No. 388b, Sculpture. No. 388c, Water jar.

1987, Aug. 7
387 Strip of 5 1.60 .40
a.-e. A162 8col any single .32 .15
388 Strip of 3 1.80 .45
a.-c. A162 15col any single .60 .15
Nos. 387-388 (2) 3.40 .85

Horse-drawn Wagon — A163

1987, Oct. 26
389 A163 20col shown .78 .20
390 A163 20col Street in old San Jose .78 .20
391 A163 20col Provincial coat of arms .78 .20
Nos. 389-391 (3) 2.34 .60

City of San Jose, 250th anniv. Rotary Club, 60th anniv.

Columbus Day — A164

1987, Oct. 26 *Perf. 10½*

392 A164 30col Map, 16th cent. 1.15 .30

Day of the Race; 495th anniv. of Columbus's departure from Palos, Spain, on first journey to the New World.

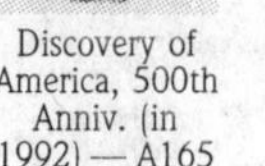

Discovery of America, 500th Anniv. (in 1992) — A165

Pres. Oscar Arias, 1987 Nobel Peace Prize Winner — A166

Maps of Honduras, Nicaragua, Costa Rica and Panama, believed to be Asia by Columbus: No. 393, Costa Rica, 16th cent. No. 394, Map of "Asia" by Bartholomeu Columbus (1461-1514).

1987, Nov. 20 Litho. *Perf. 13½*

393 A165 4col yel & dk red brn .16 .15
394 A165 4col yel & dk red brn .16 .15
a. Pair, #393-394 .32 .15

1987, Dec. 2 *Perf. 10½*

395 A166 10col multi .30 .15

Two Houses, a Watercolor by Fausto Pacheco (1899-1966) — A167

1987, Dec. 22 Litho. *Perf. 10½*

396 A167 1col multi .15 .15

Intl. Year of Shelter for the Homeless.

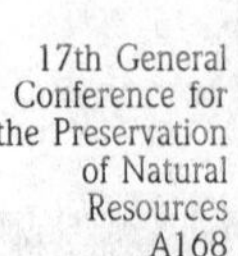

17th General Conference for the Preservation of Natural Resources A168

1988, Feb. 1 Litho. *Perf. 13½*

397 A168 5col Green turtle .20 .15
398 A168 5col Emblem, golden toad .20 .15
399 A168 5col Blue butterfly .20 .15
Nos. 397-399 (3) .60
Set value .15

Intl. Red Cross and Red Crescent Organizations, 125th Annivs. — A169

1988, Apr. 18 Litho. *Perf. 10½*

400 A169 30col lt blue & dark red 1.00 .25

North and South Campaign A170

1988, June 6 Photo. *Perf. 11½*
Granite Paper

401 A170 18col Adult education .60 .15
402 A170 20col Cultural radio programs .68 .18

Cultural cooperation with Liechtenstein. See Liechtenstein #886-887. For overprint see #C921.

A171

A172

1988, June 27 Litho. *Perf. 10½*

403 A171 3col dk blue, dark red & yel .15 .15

Anglo-Costa Rican Bank, 125th anniv.

1988, Sept. 16 Litho. *Perf. 13½*

404 A172 25col Character trademark .68 .18
405 A172 25col Games emblem .68 .18
a. Pair, #404-405 1.40 .40

1988 Summer Olympics, Seoul.

Girls' High School, Cent. — A173

1988, Oct. 17 Litho. *Perf. 10½*

406 A173 10col Student, courtyard .28 .15

A174

A175

1988, Nov. 18

407 A174 10col gray, greenish bl & red brn .25 .15

Educator Omar Dengo (1888-1928) and the Teachers' College, Heredia.

1988, Nov. 28 *Perf. 13½*

Design: Indian glass-bead and lion-tooth necklace.

408 A175 4col multi .15 .15

Discovery of America, 500th anniv. (in 1992).

A176

A177

1988, Dec. 26 Litho. *Perf. 10½*

409 A176 2col Observation tower .15 .15

Natl. Meteorological Institute, cent. For surcharge see No. 439.

1989, Feb. 28

Designs: Indigenous flora.

410 A177 5col *Eschweilera costaricensis* .15 .15
411 A177 10col *Heliconia wagneriana* .25 .15
412 A177 15col *Heliconia lophocarpa* .38 .15
413 A177 20col *Aechmea magdalenae* .50 .15
414 A177 25col *Psammisia ramiflora* .62 .16
415 A177 30col *Passiflora vitifolia* .75 .20
Nos. 410-415 (6) 2.65
Set value .68

A178

A179

1989, July 1 Litho. *Perf. 10½*

416 A178 30col Nation at Arms .75 .20

French Revolution, bicent.

1989, Aug. 28 Litho. *Perf. 13½*

417 A179 10col Sugar mill .25 .15

Grecia County, 151st anniv.
For overprints see Nos. RA106-RA109.

America Issue — A180

UPAE emblem and pre-Columbian stone carvings: 50col, Three-footed bench for grinding corn. 100col, Sphere.

Perf. 12½x12
Litho. & Engr.

1989, Oct. 12 Wmk. 334

418 A180 50col multi 1.20 .30
419 A180 100col multi 2.45 .62

For overprint see No. C916.

A181

A182

Perf. 10½

1989, Oct. 23 Litho. Unwmk.

420 A181 10col Orchid .25 .15

"100 Years of Democracy" summit of Presidents.

Perf. 13½

1989, Nov. 27 Litho. Unwmk.

421 A182 18col Map, H.F. Pittier, emblem .42 .15

Natl. Geographic Institute, cent.
For surcharge see No. 452.

America Issue — A183

Pre-Columbian gold frog figurine and facing portraits of Ferdinand V and Isabella I on gold coin struck by Spain from 1476 to 1516.

1989, Dec. 4 *Perf. 10½*

422 A183 4col multicolored .15 .15

Discovery of America, 500th anniv. (in 1992).

Natl. Theater, Cent. A184

Perf. 10½

1990, Feb. 27 Litho. Unwmk.

423 A184 5col *Coffee Allegory* .15 .15

World Cup Soccer Championships, Italy — A185

1990, June 1 Litho. *Perf. 10½*

424 A185 5col multicolored .22 .15

Univ. of Costa Rica, 50th Anniv. A187

1990, Aug. 24 Litho. *Perf. 10½*

426 A187 18col multicolored .40 .15

Education, Democracy, Peace — A188

Litho. & Engr.

1990, Oct. 31 *Perf. 12½*

427 A188 100col shown 1.10 .55
428 A188 200col Flag as map 2.25 1.10
429 A188 500col National arms 5.25 2.75
Nos. 427-429 (3) 8.60 4.40

For overprints see Nos. 448, C920.

Hospitals — A190

America Issue — A191

Designs: No. 431, St. Vincent de Paul Hospital, Heredia. No. 432, Natl. Psychiatric hospital.

1990, Dec. 18 Engr. *Perf. 13x12½*

431 A190 50col multicolored 1.10 .28
432 A190 100col multicolored 2.25 .55

1990, Dec. 21 Litho. *Perf. 10½*

433 A191 18col Ara macao .36 .15
434 A191 18col Ara ambigua .36 .15
a. Pair, #433-434 .75 .20
435 A191 24col Cassia grandis .48 .15
436 A191 24col Tabebuia ochracea .48 .15
a. Pair, #435-436 1.00 .25
Nos. 433-436 (4) 1.68
Set value .48

Costa Rica-Panama Border Treaty, 50th Anniv. — A192

Designs: a, Flags, national arms. b, Presidents. c, Map.

1991, May 24 Litho. *Perf. 10½*
437 A192 10col Strip of 3, #a.-c. .70 .18

Discovery of America, 500th Anniv. (in 1992) — A193

1991, Oct. 11 Litho. *Perf. 13½*
438 A193 4col multicolored .15 .15

Nos. 409, 296 Surcharged

3.00
COLONES

1
Colón

1991, Oct. 21 Litho. *Perf. 10½*
439 A176 1col on 2col #409 .15 .15
440 A137 3col on 8.50col #296 .15 .15
Set value .15 .15

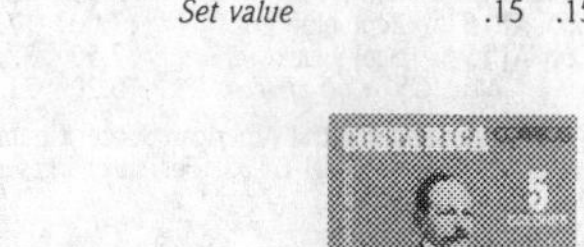

Former Presidents, Supreme Court of Justice — A194

Designs: a, Benito Serrano Jimenez. b, Luis Davila Solera. c, Fernando Baudrit Solera. d, Alejandro Alvarado Garcia.

Perf. 14½x13½
1992, Feb. 28 Litho.
441 A194 5col Strip of 4, #a.-d. 1.40 .35

DINADECO, Natl. Directorate of Community Development, 25th Anniv. — A195

1992, Apr. 28 Litho. *Perf. 10½*
442 A195 15col multicolored 1.05 .28

Compare with No. C505.

A196

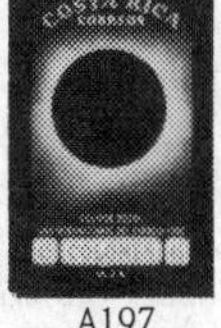

A197

1992, May 26 Litho. *Perf. 13½*
443 A196 15col lake & black 1.05 .28

Dr. Solon Nunez Frutos, public health pioneer.

1992, July 17 Litho. *Perf. 13*

Solar Eclipse: a, Total eclipse. b, Post Office Bldg. during eclipse. c, Partial eclipse.

444 A197 45col Strip of 3, #a.-c. 3.25 .80

A198

A199

1992, Aug. 14 Litho. *Perf. 13½*
445 A198 35col multicolored .85 .22

Interamerican Institute for Agricultural Cooperation, 50th anniv.

1992, Nov. 5 Litho. *Perf. 10½*
446 A199 2col Waterfall .15 .15
447 A199 15col Coastline .22 .15
Set value .27 .15

Cocos Island, 450th anniv. of discovery.

No. 427 Ovptd. "CENTENARIO / DE LIMON"

Litho. & Engr.
1992, Nov. 27 *Perf. 12½*
448 A188 100col black & blue 1.45 .35

America Issue — A200

1992, Dec. 15 Litho. *Perf. 10½*
449 A200 15col Anolis townsendi .22 .15
450 A200 35col Pinaroloxias inornata .85 .22
Set value .28

Natl. Theater A201

Detail from painting "Allegory of Fine Arts," by Roberto Fontana.

1993, Jan. 29 Litho. *Perf. 10½*
451 A201 20col multicolored .28 .15

5
colones

No. 421 Surcharged

1993, Mar. 26 Litho. *Perf. 13½*
452 A182 5col on 18col multi .16 .15

Protection of the Dolphin A202

1993, May 17 Litho. *Perf. 10½*
453 A202 10col Delphinus delphis .15 .15
454 A202 20col Stenella coeruleoalbus .28 .15
Set value .21

Costa Rican Civil Service, 40th Anniv. — A203

1993, May 28 Litho. *Perf. 13½*
455 A203 5col multicolored .15 .15

Costa Rican Chamber of Industries, 50th Anniv. A204

1993, July 15 *Perf. 10½*
456 A204 45col multicolored .65 .32

School of Communication Sciences, University of Costa Rica, 25th Anniv. — A205

1993, Aug. 19 Litho. *Perf. 13½*
457 A205 20col black, blue & red .28 .15

Protection of the Tropical Rain Forest — A206

1993, Aug. 27 *Perf. 10½*
458 A206 2col Passiflora vitifolia .15 .15
459 A206 35col Gurania megistantha .50 .25
Set value .53 .26

Social Guarantees and Labor Code, 50th Anniv. A207

1993, Sept. 14 Litho. *Perf. 10½*
460 A207 20col multicolored .42 .22

A208

A209

1993, Oct. 25 Litho. *Perf. 13½*
461 A208 45col multicolored .90 .45

Intl. Assoc. of Professional Custom-House Agents, 15th Congress.

1993, Nov. 26 *Perf. 10½*
462 A209 20col multicolored .42 .22

Miguel Angel Castro Carazo (1893-1960), educator and humanitarian.

A211

A212

1993, Dec. 23 Litho. *Perf. 10½*
464 A211 20col multicolored .40 .20

Law School of Costa Rica, 150th anniv.

1994, Mar. 8 Litho. *Perf. 13*
465 A212 20col Natl. Theater .40 .20

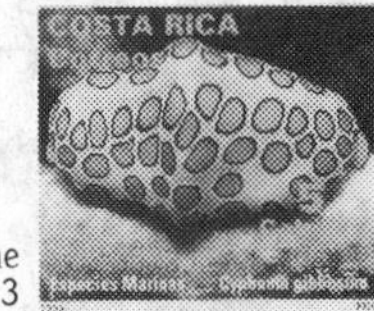

Marine Life — A213

Designs: 5col, Cyphoma gibbosum. 10col, Ophioderma rubicundum. 15col, Myripristis jacobus. 20col, Holocanthus passer. 35col, Paranthias furcifer. 45col, Tubastraea coccinea. 50col, Acanthaster planci. 55col, Ocypode. 70col, Arothron meleagris. 100col, Thalassoma lucasanum.

Litho. & Embossed
1994, Apr. 29 *Perf. 12½x12*
466 A213 5col multicolored .15 .15
467 A213 10col multicolored .20 .15
468 A213 15col multicolored .28 .15
469 A213 20col multicolored .38 .20
470 A213 35col multicolored .65 .32
471 A213 45col multicolored .85 .42
472 A213 50col multicolored .95 .48
473 A213 55col multicolored 1.10 .55
474 A213 70col multicolored 1.40 .70
Nos. 466-474 (9) 5.96 3.12

Souvenir Sheet
Perf. 13
475 A213 100col multicolored 2.00 2.00

America Issue A214

Illustrations from 19th century Book of Figueroa: a, Man on horseback. b, Back of ox carrying bundles.

1994, Dec. 19 Litho. *Perf. 10½*
476 A214 20col Pair, #a.-b. + label .90 .45

No. 476 is a continuous design.

Rotary Intl., 90th Anniv. — A215

1995, Mar. Litho. *Perf. 13½*
477 A215 20col multicolored .45 .25

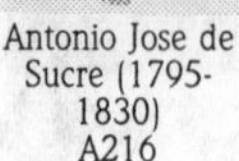

Antonio Jose de Sucre (1795-1830)
A216

Guanacaste Institute, 50th Anniv.
A217

Design: 30col, Jose Marti (1853-95).

1995 Litho. *Perf. 10½*

478	A216	10col multicolored	.15	.15
479	A216	30col multicolored	.50	.25

1995 *Perf. 13½*

480	A217	50col green, black & bister	.80	.40

SEMI-POSTAL STAMPS

No. 72 Surcharged in Red

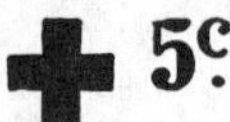

1922 Unwmk. *Perf. 12*

B1	A56	5c + 5c orange	.50	.20

Issued for the benefit of the Costa Rican Red Cross Society. In 1928, owing to a temporary shortage of the ordinary 5c stamp, No. B1 was placed on sale as a regular 5c stamp, the surtax being disregarded.

Discus Thrower — SP1

Trophy — SP2

Parthenon SP3

1924 Litho. *Imperf.*

B2	SP1	5c dark green	1.50	2.00
B3	SP2	10c carmine	1.50	2.00
B4	SP3	20c dark blue	3.50	3.00
a.		Tête bêche pair	14.00	16.00

Perf. 12

B5	SP1	5c dark green	1.50	2.00
B6	SP2	10c carmine	1.50	2.00
B7	SP3	20c dark blue	3.00	3.50
a.		Tête bêche pair	14.00	16.00
		Nos. B2-B7 (6)	12.50	14.50

These stamps were sold at a premium of 10c each, to help defray the expenses of athletic games held at San José in Dec. 1924.

AIR POST STAMPS

Airplane — AP1

Perf. 12½

1926, June 4 Unwmk. Engr.

C1	AP1	20c ultramarine	2.00	.35

No. 123 Overprinted

CORREO AEREO

1930, Mar. 14 *Perf. 12*

C2	A75	10c carmine rose	1.00	.15

Inverted or double overprints are fakes.

AP3

1930-32 *Perf. 12½*

C3	AP3	5c on 10c dk brn ('32)	.15	.15
C4	AP3	20c on 50c ultra	.15	.15
C5	AP3	40c on 50c ultra	.30	.15
		Nos. C3-C5 (3)	.60	
		Set value		.30

The existence of genuine inverted or double surcharges of Nos. C3-C5 is in doubt.

Telegraph Stamp Overprinted

Correo Aereo

1930, Mar. 19

C6	AP3	1col orange	1.50	.30

No. O79 Surcharged in Red

1930, Mar. 11

C7	O7	8c on 1col lilac & blk	.45	.35
C8	O7	20c on 1col lilac & blk	.60	.45
C9	O7	40c on 1col lilac & blk	1.25	.90
C10	O7	1col on 1col lilac & blk	1.75	1.25
		Nos. C7-C10 (4)	4.05	2.95

AP6

AP7

Red Surcharge on Revenue Stamps

1931-32 *Perf. 12*

C11	AP6	2col on 2col gray grn	25.00	25.00
C12	AP6	3col on 5col lil brn	25.00	25.00
C13	AP6	5col on 10col gray blk	25.00	25.00
		Nos. C11-C13 (3)	75.00	75.00

There were two printings of this issue which were practically identical in the colors of the stamps and the surcharges.

Nos. C11 and C13 have the date "1929" on the stamp, No. C12 has "1930."

Black Overprint on Telegraph Stamp

1932, Mar. 8 *Perf. 12½*

C14	AP7	40c green	1.50	.30
a.		Inverted overprint	18.00	

Mail Plane about to Land — AP8

Allegory of Flight — AP9

1934, Mar. 14 *Perf. 12*

C15	AP8	5c green	.15	.15
C16	AP8	10c car rose	.15	.15
C17	AP8	15c chocolate	.35	.15
C18	AP8	20c dp blue	.40	.15
C19	AP8	25c dp orange	.50	.15
C20	AP8	40c olive blk	.90	.15
C21	AP8	50c gray blk	.60	.15
C22	AP8	60c org yel	1.25	.18
C23	AP8	75c dull vio	1.75	.45
C24	AP9	1col dp rose	1.40	.15
C25	AP9	2col lt blue	1.50	.60
C26	AP9	5col black	4.00	4.00
C27	AP9	10col red brn	6.50	6.50
		Nos. C15-C27 (13)	19.45	12.93

Stamps Nos. C15 to C27 with holes punched through were for use of government officials.

See Nos. C216-C219. For overprints see Nos. C67-C73, C92-C93, C103-C116, CO1-CO13.

Airplane over Poás Volcano — AP10

1937, Feb. 10

C28	AP10	1c black	.15	.15
C29	AP10	2c brown	.15	.15
C30	AP10	3c dk violet	.15	.15
		Set value	.36	.30

First Fair of Costa Rica.

Puntarenas AP11

National Bank — AP12

Perf. 12, 12½

1937, Dec. 15 Unwmk.

C31	AP11	2c black gray	.15	.15
C32	AP11	5c green	.15	.15
C33	AP11	20c deep blue	.28	.22
C34	AP11	1.40col olive brn	2.75	2.75
		Nos. C31-C34 (4)	3.33	3.27

1938, Jan. 11 Wmk. 229 *Perf. 12½*

C35	AP12	1c purple	.15	.15
C36	AP12	3c red org	.15	.15
C37	AP12	10c car rose	.15	.15
C38	AP12	75c brown	1.50	1.50
		Set value	1.74	1.70

Nos. C31-C38 commemorate the Natl. Products Exposition held at San José, Dec. 1937.

Airport Administration Building, La Sabana AP13

1940, May 2 Engr. Unwmk.

C39	AP13	5c green	.15	.15
C40	AP13	10c rose pink	.15	.15
C41	AP13	25c lt blue	.15	.15
C42	AP13	35c red brown	.22	.22
C43	AP13	60c red org	.35	.35
C44	AP13	85c violet	1.00	.85
C45	AP13	2.35col turq grn	5.50	5.50
		Nos. C39-C45 (7)	7.52	7.37

Opening of the Intl. Airport at La Sabana.

Duran Sanatorium AP14

Overprinted "Dia Panamericano de la Salud / 2 Diciembre 1940" and Bar in Black

1940, Dec. 2 *Perf. 12*

C46	AP14	10c scarlet	.15	.15
C47	AP14	15c purple	.15	.15
C48	AP14	25c lt blue	.28	.24
C49	AP14	35c bister brn	.45	.40
C50	AP14	60c pck green	.55	.55
C51	AP14	75c olive	1.25	1.40
C52	AP14	1.35col red org	5.50	5.50
C53	AP14	5col sepia	24.00	24.00
C54	AP14	10col red lilac	92.50	92.50
		Nos. C46-C54 (9)	124.83	124.89

Pan-American Health Day. Exist without overprint. Few copies of C53-C54 were sold for postal purposes, nearly all having been obtained by philatelic speculators.

No. 174 Surcharged in Black or Blue

AEREO
Aviación Panamericana
Dic. 17 1940
15 CENTIMOS 15

1940, Dec. 17 *Perf. 14*

C55	A95	15c on 50c yel (Bk)	.50	.45
C56	A95	30c on 50c yel (Bl)	.50	.45

Pan-American Aviation Day, proclaimed by President F. D. Roosevelt.

The 15c surch. exists on #171, value $30.

International Soccer Game at National Stadium — AP15

1941, May 8 *Perf. 12*

C57	AP15	15c red	.75	.15
C58	AP15	30c dp ultra	.85	.25
C59	AP15	40c red brown	.85	.35
C60	AP15	50c purple	1.25	.75
C61	AP15	60c brt green	1.50	.85
C62	AP15	75c yel org	2.50	1.40
C63	AP15	1col dull vio	4.25	4.25
C64	AP15	1.40col rose	8.75	8.75
C65	AP15	2col blue grn	17.00	17.00
C66	AP15	5col black	37.50	37.50
		Nos. C57-C66 (10)	75.20	71.25

Caribbean and Central American Soccer Championship. See Nos. C121-C123. For surcharges see Nos. C145-C147.

Air Post Stamps of 1934 Overprinted or Surcharged in Black with New Values and Bars

Mayo 1941
Tratado Limítrofe
Costa Rica - Panamá

1941, June 2

C67	AP8	5c on 20c dp bl	.18	.15
C68	AP8	15c on 20c dp bl	.22	.18
C69	AP8	40c on 75c dl vio	.32	.22
C70	AP9	65c on 1col dp rose	.60	.50
C71	AP9	1.40col on 2col lt bl	3.00	3.00
C72	AP9	5col black	11.00	11.00
C73	AP9	10col red brn	12.50	12.50
		Nos. C67-C73 (7)	27.82	27.55

Issued in commemoration of the settlement of the Costa Rica-Panama border dispute.

Nos. C67-C73 are found with hyphen omitted in overprint. Nos. C67-C69 with inverted overprint.

University Types of 1941

1941, Aug. 26 *Perf. 12*

C74	A107	15c salmon	.22	.15
C75	A106	30c lt blue	.32	.15
C76	A107	40c orange	.38	.28
C77	A106	60c turq green	.48	.40
C78	A107	1col violet	1.90	1.90
C79	A106	2col black	4.75	4.75
C80	A107	5col sepia	15.00	15.00
		Nos. C74-C80 (7)	23.05	22.63

Portrait Type of 1943-47

Designs: 40c, Manuel Aguilar. No. C83, Francisco Morazan. No. C83A, Jose R. De Gallegos. 50c, Jose M. Alfaro. 60c, Francisco M. Oreamuno. 65c, Jose M. Castro. 85c, Juan Rafael Mora. 1col, Jose M. Montealegre. 1.05col, Braulio Carrillo. 1.15col, Jesus Jimenez. 1.40col, Bruno Carranza. 2col, Tomas Guardia.

1943-45 Engr.

C81	A109	10c rose pink	.15	.15
C82	A109	40c blue	.20	.15
C82A	A109	40c car rose	.20	.15

C83 A109 45c magenta .30 .22
C83A A109 45c black .18 .15
C84 A109 50c turq grn 1.50 .18
C84A A109 50c red org .28 .18
C85 A109 60c brt ultra .40 .15
C85A A109 60c brt grn .18 .15
C86 A109 65c scarlet .75 .22
C86A A109 65c brt ultra .20 .18
C87 A109 85c dp org .90 .30
C87A A109 85c dull pur 1.10 .38
C88 A109 1col black 1.10 .40
C88A A109 1col scarlet .45 .18
C88B A109 1.05col bis brn .60 .40
C89 A109 1.15col red brn 1.50 1.40
C89A A109 1.15col green 2.00 1.10
C90 A109 1.40col dp vio 2.25 1.90
C90A A109 1.40col org yel 1.40 1.25
C91 A109 2col black 3.50 1.10
C91A A109 2col ol grn 1.10 .28
Nos. C81-C91A (22) 20.24 10.57

Issued: #C82A, C83A, C84A, C85A, C86A, C87A, C88A, C88B, C89A, C90A, C91A, 1945. See #C124-C127, C179-C181. For surcharges see #C154-C158, C182, C184-C185.

Nos. C26-C27 Overprinted in Red or Blue

Legislacion Social
15 Setiembre 1943

1943, Sept. 16
C92 AP9 5col black (R) 3.00 2.25
C93 AP9 10col red brown (Bl) 6.00 4.00

Mercury and Plane — AP31

1944, Jan. 19
C94 AP31 10c red org .15 .15
C95 AP31 15c dk car .18 .15
C96 AP31 40c brt ultra .30 .22
C97 AP31 45c dp red lil .35 .28
C98 AP31 60c turq grn .48 .40
C99 AP31 1col dk red brn 1.10 .80
C100 AP31 1.40col gray blk 6.00 5.00
C101 AP31 5col violet 16.00 15.00
C102 AP31 10col black 52.50 52.50
Nos. C94-C102 (9) 77.06 74.50

City of San Ramón founding, 100th anniv.
Very few copies of the 5col or 10col stamps were sold for postal purposes, nearly all having been obtained by philatelic speculators.

No. CO10 With Additional Overprint in Black

1944

1944, Nov. 22
C103 AP9 1col deep rose .70 .35
a. Blue overprint 55.00

Nos. CO1-CO13 Overprinted in Carmine or Black

1945, Jan. 12 Unwmk. *Perf. 12*
C104 AP8 5c green .60 .55
C105 AP8 10c car rose (Bk) .60 .55
C106 AP8 15c chocolate .60 .55
C107 AP8 20c deep blue .35 .32
C108 AP8 25c dp org (Bk) .60 .60
C109 AP8 40c ol blk .35 .32
C110 AP8 50c gray blk .60 .60
C111 AP8 60c org yel (Bk) .90 .32
C112 AP8 75c dull violet .75 .60
C113 AP9 1col dp rose (Bk) .75 .32
C114 AP9 2col light blue 4.75 4.50
C115 AP9 5col black 6.00 5.50
C116 AP9 10col red brn (Bk) 9.00 8.25
Nos. C104-C116 (13) 25.85 22.98

#C104 exists inverted & overprinted in black.

Catalogue values for unused stamps in this section, from this point to the end of the section, are for Never Hinged items.

AP32

Telegraph Stamps Overprinted in Black or Carmine

1945, Feb. 28 Unwmk. *Perf. 12½*
C117 AP32 40c green (C) .25 .15
C118 AP32 50c ultra (C) .30 .15
C119 AP32 1col orange (Bk) .65 .40
Nos. C117-C119 (3) 1.20 .70

#C117 exists with inverted overprint. Value, $5.

Florence Nightingale and Edith Cavell AP33

1945 Engr.
C120 AP33 1col black & car .75 .50

60th anniv. of the Costa Rican Red Cross Soc. For surcharge see No. C183.

Soccer Type of 1941
Inscribed: "Febrero 1946"

1946, May 13 *Perf. 12*
C121 AP15 25c green .75 .60
C122 AP15 30c dull yellow .75 .60
C123 AP15 55c deep blue .90 .60
Nos. C121-C123 (3) 2.40 1.80

Portrait Type of 1943-47

Designs: 25c, Aniceto Esquivel. 30c, Vicente Herrera. 55c, Prospero Fernandez. 75c, Bernardo Soto.

1946, May 12
C124 A109 25c blue .20 .15
C125 A109 30c red brown .25 .20
C126 A109 55c plum .40 .30
C127 A109 75c blue green .60 .40
Nos. C124-C127 (4) 1.45 1.05

Hospital of St. John of God — AP38

1946, June 24 Unwmk. *Perf. 12½*
Center in Black
C128 AP38 5c yel grn .15 .15
C129 AP38 10c dk brown .15 .15
C130 AP38 15c carmine .15 .15
C131 AP38 25c dk blue .16 .16
C132 AP38 30c dp org .32 .24
C133 AP38 40c olive grn .16 .16
C134 AP38 50c violet .28 .28
C135 AP38 60c dk sl grn .60 .55
C136 AP38 75c brown .48 .40
a. Horiz. pair, imperf. btwn. 100.00
C137 AP38 1col blue .60 .32
C138 AP38 2col brn org .90 .70
C139 AP38 3col dk vio brn 1.75 1.75
C140 AP38 5col yellow 2.25 2.25
Nos. C128-C140 (13) 7.95 7.26

Rafael Iglesias — AP39

Designs: 3col, Ascensión Esquivel. 5col, Cleto González Viquez. 10col, Ricardo Jiménez Oreamuno.

1947, Jan. 15 Wmk. 215 *Perf. 14*
Center in Black
C141 AP39 2col blue 1.10 .80
C142 AP39 3col dp car 1.65 1.10
C143 AP39 5col dk green 2.50 1.65
C144 AP39 10col orange 4.75 3.00
Nos. C141-C144 (4) 10.00 6.55

Nos. C121-C123 Surcharged in Black

Habilitado para
₡ 0.15
Decreto Nº 16 de
28 de abril de 1947

1947, May 5 Unwmk. *Perf. 12*
C145 AP15 15c on 25c green .90 .75
C146 AP15 15c on 30c dull yel .90 .75
C147 AP15 15c on 55c dp blue .90 .75
Nos. C145-C147 (3) 2.70 2.25

Exist with inverted surcharge.

Columbus in Cariari AP43

1947, May 19 Engr. *Perf. 12½*
Center in Black
C148 AP43 25c green .24 .15
C149 AP43 30c dp ultra .24 .15
C150 AP43 40c red orange .35 .15
C151 AP43 45c violet .45 .24
C152 AP43 50c brt carmine .50 .20
C153 AP43 65c brown org 1.40 .70
Nos. C148-C153 (6) 3.18 1.59

For surcharges see Nos. C178, C220-C223.

Nos. C84A, C85A, C127, C88A, and C88B Surcharged with New Value in Black or Red

1947, June 3 *Perf. 12*
C154 A109 15c on 50c red org .25 .15
C155 A109 15c on 60c brt grn (R) .25 .15
C156 A109 15c on 75c bl grn (R) .25 .15
C157 A109 15c on 1col scar .30 .15
C158 A109 15c on 1.05col bis brn .25 .15
Nos. C154-C158 (5) 1.30
Set value .63

#C155 is known with black surcharge. Value, $10. #C156 with inverted surcharge. Value, $10.

Early Steam Locomotive AP44

1947, Nov. 10 *Perf. 12½*
C159 AP44 35c bl grn & blk 1.00 .25

Electric railroad to the Pacific coast, 50th anniv.

Roosevelt Type of Regular Issue

1947, Aug. 26 *Perf. 12*
C160 A122 15c green .15 .15
C161 A122 30c car rose .15 .15
C162 A122 45c red brown .22 .20
C163 A122 65c org yel .25 .22
C164 A122 75c blue .32 .22
C165 A122 1col ol grn .50 .38
C166 A122 2col black 1.25 1.00
C167 A122 5col scarlet 2.50 2.25
Nos. C160-C167 (8) 5.34 4.57

For surcharges see Nos. C224-C226.

National Theater AP46

Rafael Iglesias AP47

1948, Jan. 26 *Perf. 12½*
Center in Black
C168 AP46 15c brt ultra .15 .15
C169 AP46 20c red .18 .15
C170 AP47 35c dk green .25 .22
C171 AP46 45c purple .35 .25
C172 AP46 50c carmine .35 .25
C173 AP46 75c red vio .75 .75
C174 AP46 1col olive 1.40 1.10
C175 AP46 2col red brn 2.25 1.50
C176 AP47 5col org yel 3.50 3.25
C177 AP47 10col brt bl 8.00 6.00
Nos. C168-C177 (10) 17.18 13.62

50th anniversary of National Theater.

No. C150 Surcharged in Carmine

HABILITADO
PARA
₡ 0.35

1948, Apr. 21
C178 AP43 35c on 40c .35 .35

Exists with surcharge inverted.

Portrait Type of 1943-47

Designs: 5c, Salvador Lara. 15c, Carlos Duran.

1948 Engr. *Perf. 12*
C179 A109 5c sepia .32 .15
C180 A109 10c olive brown .32 .15
C181 A109 15c violet .32 .15
Nos. C179-C181 (3) .96
Set value .26

Nos. C88B, C120, C89A and C90A Surcharged in Carmine or Black

1824-1949
125 Aniversario
de la Anexión
Guanacaste
₡ 0.55

Perf. 12½, 12
1949, Aug. 28 Unwmk.
C182 A109 35c on 1.05col bis brn .18 .15
C183 AP33 50c on 1col blk & car .30 .25
a. 2nd & 3rd lines both read "125 Aniversario" 6.75 6.75
C184 A109 55c on 1.15col grn .48 .40
C185 A109 55c on 1.40col org yel (Bk) .48 .38
Nos. C182-C185 (4) 1.44 1.18

125th anniv. of the annexation of the province of Guanacaste.
Overprint differs on No. C183, with "Guanacaste" in capitals, and lower case "a" in "Anexión."
The variety "I" for "i" in "Anexion" is found on Nos. C182, C184 and C185.

Symbols of UPU — AP48

1950, Jan. 11 Photo. *Perf. 11½*
C186 AP48 15c lilac rose .15 .15
C187 AP48 25c chalky blue .15 .15
C188 AP48 1col gray green .32 .15
Nos. C186-C188 (3) .62
Set value .20

75th anniv. of the UPU.

Battle of El Tejar, Cartago AP49

Occupation of Limón — AP50

Bull (Cattle Raising) — AP51

Designs: 25c, Lucha ranch. 35c, Trenches of San Isidro Battalion. 55c and 75c, Observation post. 80c and 1col, Dr. Carlos Luis Valverde.

Inscribed: "Guerra de Liberacion Nacional 1948"

Engraved; Center Photogravure
1950, July 20 *Perf. 12½*
Center in Black
C189 AP49 15c brt car .15 .15
C190 AP50 20c dull green .20 .15
C191 AP49 25c dull blue .24 .15
C192 AP49 35c chestnut .28 .15
C193 AP49 55c lilac .55 .20
C194 AP49 75c red org .90 .32

C195	AP50	80c gray	.90	.50
C196	AP50	1col org yel	1.25	.55
		Nos. C189-C196 (8)	4.47	2.17

2nd anniv. of the War for Natl. Liberation.

Inscribed: "Feria Nacional Agricola Ganadera e Industrial Cartago 1950"

1950, July 27

Designs: 1c, 10c, 2col, Bull. 2c, 30c and 3col, Tuna fishing. 3c and 65c, Pineapple. 5c, 50c and 5col, Bananas. 45c, 80c and 10col, Coffee picker.

Center in Black

C197	AP51	1c brt green	.15	.15
C198	AP51	2c brt blue	.15	.15
C199	AP51	3c chocolate	.15	.15
C200	AP51	5c dp ultra	.15	.15
C201	AP51	10c green	.15	.15
C202	AP51	30c purple	.20	.15
C203	AP51	45c vermilion	.22	.15
C204	AP51	50c blue gray	.35	.15
C205	AP51	65c dk blue	.40	.20
C206	AP51	80c dp rose	.85	.55
C207	AP51	2col org yel	2.25	1.65
C208	AP51	3col blue	5.00	4.00
C209	AP51	5col carmine	7.25	6.00
C210	AP51	10col dp claret	7.25	6.00
		Nos. C197-C210 (14)	24.52	19.60

National Agricultural, Livestock and Industrial Fair, Cartago, 1950.
For surcharge see No. RA1.

Queen Isabella I and Caravels of Columbus AP52

Unwmk.

1952, Mar. 4 Engr. *Perf. 13*

C211	AP52	15c carmine	.25	.15
C212	AP52	20c orange	.45	.15
C213	AP52	25c ultra	.70	.15
C214	AP52	55c dp green	2.25	.24
C215	AP52	2col violet	4.25	.45
		Nos. C211-C215 (5)	7.90	1.14

500th anniversary of the birth of Queen Isabella I of Spain.

Mail Plane Type of 1934

1952-53 *Perf. 12*

C216	AP8	5c blue	.32	.15
C217	AP8	10c green	.32	.15
C218	AP8	15c car rose ('53)	.38	.15
C219	AP8	35c purple	1.00	.20
		Nos. C216-C219 (4)	2.02	
		Set value		.50

Nos. C149-C151, C153 Surcharged in Red: "HABILITADO PARA CINCO CENTIMOS 1953"

1953, Apr. 24 *Perf. 12½*

Center in Black

C220	AP43	5c on 30c dp ultra	1.00	.85
C221	AP43	5c on 40c red org	.15	.15
C222	AP43	5c on 45c vio	.15	.15
C223	AP43	5c on 65c brn org	.20	.15
		Nos. C220-C223 (4)	1.50	1.30

Nos. C161-C163 Surcharged in Black

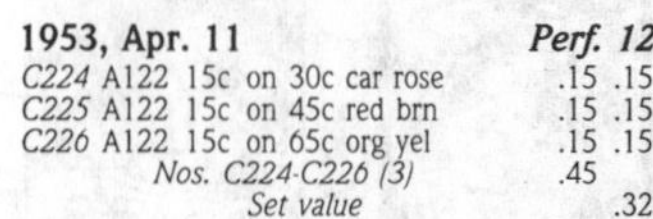

1953, Apr. 11 *Perf. 12*

C224	A122	15c on 30c car rose	.15	.15
C225	A122	15c on 45c red brn	.15	.15
C226	A122	15c on 65c org yel	.15	.15
		Nos. C224-C226 (3)	.45	
		Set value		.32

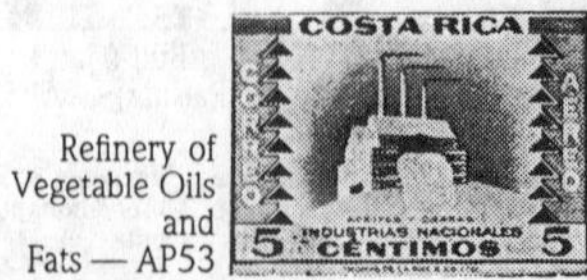
Refinery of Vegetable Oils and Fats — AP53

Industries: 10c, Pottery. 15c, Sugar. 20c, Soap. 25c, Lumber. 30c, Matches. 35c, Textiles. 40c, Leather. 45c, Tobacco. 50c, Preserving. 55c, Canning. 60c, General. 65c, Metals. 75c, Pharmaceuticals. 80c, Pharmaceuticals. 1col, Paper. 2col, Rubber. 3col, Airplane maintenance. 5col, Marble. 10col, Beer.

Engraved; Center Photogravure

1954-59 Unwmk. *Perf. 13x12½*

Center in Black

C227	AP53	5c red	.15	.15
C228	AP53	10c dk blue	.15	.15
C229	AP53	15c green	.15	.15
C230	AP53	20c violet	.15	.15
C231	AP53	25c magenta	.15	.15
C232	AP53	30c purple	.30	.18
C233	AP53	35c red vio	.15	.15
C234	AP53	40c black	.25	.15
C235	AP53	45c dk green	.50	.20
C236	AP53	50c vio brown	.32	.15
C237	AP53	55c yellow	.22	.15
C238	AP53	60c brown	.60	.30
C239	AP53	65c carmine	.70	.45
C240	AP53	75c violet	1.10	.40
C240A	AP53	80c pur & gray	.52	.45
C241	AP53	1col blue	.32	.18
a.		Imperf., pair	80.00	
C242	AP53	2col rose pink	1.00	.55
C243	AP53	3col ol grn	1.50	.90
C244	AP53	5col black	2.25	.75
C245	AP53	10col yellow	6.50	5.00
		Nos. C227-C245 (20)	16.98	10.71

Issue dates: 30c, 35c, 60c, 65c, 75c, 2col, 3col, Oct. 20. 80c, Oct. 2, 1959. Others, Sept. 1.
See #C252-C255. For surcharges and overprint see #C314-C315, C334-C336, RA2, RA11.

Globe, Rotary Emblem — AP54

Map of Costa Rica — AP55

Designs: 25c, Hand protecting boy. 40c, 2col, Hospital. 45c, Globe and palm leaves. 60c, Lighthouse.

1956, Feb. 7 Engr. *Perf. 12*

C246	AP54	10c green	.15	.15
C247	AP54	25c dk blue	.15	.15
C248	AP54	40c dk brown	.35	.28
C249	AP54	45c brt red	.24	.20
C250	AP54	60c dk red vio	.28	.24
C251	AP54	2col yel org	.70	.50
		Nos. C246-C251 (6)	1.87	1.52

50th anniv. of Rotary Intl. (in 1955).

Industries Type of 1954

Designs as in 1954.

Engraved; Center Photogravure

1956, Feb. 17 *Perf. 12*

Center in Black

C252	AP53	5c ultra	.15	.15
C253	AP53	10c vio blue	.15	.15
C254	AP53	15c org yel	.15	.15
C255	AP53	75c red org	.30	.16
		Nos. C252-C255 (4)	.75	
		Set value		.34

1957, June 21 Engr. *Perf. 13½x13*

Designs: 10c, Map of Guanacaste. 15c, Inn. 20c, House of Santa Rosa. 25c, Gen. Jose Manuel Quiros. 30c, Old Presidential Palace. 35c, Joaquin Bernardo Calvo. 40c, Luis Molina. 45c, Gen. Jose Joaquin Mora. 50c, Gen. Jose Maria Canas. 55c, Juan Santamaria monument. 60c, National monument. 65c, Antonio Vallerriestra. 70c, Ramon Castilla y Marquesado. 75c, San Carlos fortress. 80c, Francisco Maria Oreamuno. 1col, Pres. Juan Rafael Mora.

C256	AP55	5c lt blue	.15	.15
C257	AP55	10c green	.15	.15
C258	AP55	15c dp orange	.15	.15
C259	AP55	20c lt brown	.24	.15
C260	AP55	25c vio blue	.24	.15
C261	AP55	30c violet	.35	.15
C262	AP55	35c car rose	.35	.15
C263	AP55	40c slate	.35	.15
C264	AP55	45c rose red	.40	.16
C265	AP55	50c ultra	.40	.16
C266	AP55	55c ocher	.70	.16
C267	AP55	60c brt car	.55	.24
C268	AP55	65c carmine	.60	.24
C269	AP55	70c orange yel	.75	.30
C270	AP55	75c emerald	.70	.28
C271	AP55	80c dk brown	.80	.35
C272	AP55	1col black	.85	.35
		Nos. C256-C272 (17)	7.73	3.44

Centenary of War of 1856-57.

Cleto Gonzalez Viquez AP56

Highway and Gonzalez Viquez AP57

Designs: 10c, Ricardo Jimenez Oreamuno. 20c, Puntarenas wharf and Jimenez. 35c, Post and Telegraph Bldg. and Jimenez. 55c, Pipeline and Gonzalez Viquez. 80c, National Library and Gonzalez Viquez. 1col, Electric train and Jimenez. 2col, Gonzales and Jimenez.

1959, Nov. 23 Engr. *Perf. 13½*

C274	AP56	5c car & ultra	.15	.15
C275	AP56	10c red & gray	.15	.15

Perf. 13½x13

C276	AP57	15c dk bl grn & blk	.15	.15
C277	AP57	20c car & brn	.15	.15
C278	AP57	35c rose lil & bl	.15	.15
C279	AP57	55c olive & vio	.25	.18
C280	AP57	80c ultra	.40	.30
C281	AP57	1col orange & mar	.40	.28
C282	AP57	2col gray & mar	1.00	.75
		Nos. C274-C282 (9)	2.80	
		Set value		1.84

For surcharge and overprint see #C337, C339.

Soccer — AP58

Designs: Various soccer scenes.

Perf. 13½

1960, Mar. 7 Unwmk. Photo.

C283	AP58	10c black	.15	.15
C284	AP58	25c ultra	.15	.15
C285	AP58	35c red orange	.15	.15
C286	AP58	50c red brown	.20	.15
C287	AP58	85c Prus green	.65	.50
C288	AP58	5col dp claret	2.00	2.00
		Nos. C283-C288 (6)	3.30	3.10

Souvenir Sheet

Imperf

C289	AP58	2col blue	1.00	1.00

3rd Pan-American Soccer Games, San José, Mar. 1960.
Nos. C283-C288 exist imperf.

WRY Uprooted Oak Emblem — AP59

1960, Apr. 7 Unwmk. *Perf. 11½*

Granite Paper

C290	AP59	35c vio bl, blk & yel	.20	.15
C291	AP59	85c black & brt pink	.40	.32

Refugee Year, July 1, 1959-June 30, 1960.

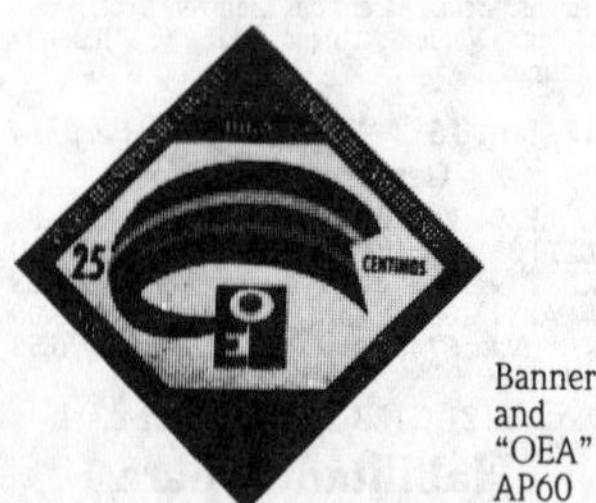
Banner and "OEA" AP60

Designs: 35c, "OEA" in oval. 55c, Clasped hands. 2col, "OEA" and map of Americas. 5col, Flags forming bird. 10col, Map of Costa Rica, flags and "OEA."

1960, Aug. 15 Litho. *Perf. 10*

C292	AP60	25c black & multi	.15	.15
a.		Multi, impression sideways	45.00	
C293	AP60	35c multicolored	.32	.30
a.		Pair, imperf. between	45.00	
C294	AP60	55c multicolored	.50	.40
C295	AP60	5col multicolored	3.00	2.75
C296	AP60	10col black & multi	5.00	4.00
		Nos. C292-C296 (5)	8.97	7.60

Souvenir Sheet

Imperf

C297	AP60	2col multicolored	2.25	2.25

Pan-American Conf., San Jose, Aug. 15.

St. Louisa de Marillac and Orphanage AP61

St. Vincent de Paul — AP62

Designs: 25c, St. Vincent and old seminary. 50c, St. Louisa and sickroom. 1col, St. Vincent and new seminary.

1960, Oct. 26 Engr. *Perf. 14x13½*

C298	AP61	10c green	.15	.15
C299	AP61	25c carmine	.15	.15
C300	AP61	50c dk blue	.22	.15
C301	AP61	1col brown org	.40	.32
C302	AP62	5col brown	2.00	1.65
		Nos. C298-C302 (5)	2.92	2.42

300th anniv. of the deaths of St. Vincent (1581?-1660) and St. Louisa (1591-1660). Exist imperf.

Runner AP63

Sports: 2c, Woman swimmer. 3c, Bicyclist. 4c, Weight lifter. 5c, Woman tennis player. 10c, Boxers. 25c, Soccer player. 85c, Basketball player. 1col, Baseball batter. 5col, Romulus and Remus statue. 10col, Pistol marksman.

Perf. 13½x14

1960, Dec. 14 Photo. Unwmk.

Designs in Black

C303	AP63	1c brt yel	.15	.15
C304	AP63	2c lt ultra	.15	.15
C305	AP63	3c dp rose	.15	.15
C306	AP63	4c yellow	.15	.15
C307	AP63	5c brt yel grn	.15	.15
C308	AP63	10c pink	.15	.15
C309	AP63	25c lt bl grn	.15	.15
C310	AP63	85c lilac	.90	.75
C311	AP63	1col gray	1.10	.90
C312	AP63	10col lt vio	9.00	7.25
		Nos. C303-C312 (10)	12.05	9.95

Souvenir Sheets

Perf. 14x13½, Imperf.

C313	AP63	5col multi	3.50	3.50

17th Olympic Games, Rome, Aug. 25-Sept. 11.
Nos. C303-C312 exist imperf.

No. C255 Surcharged and Overprinted in Blue or Ultramarine: "XV Campeonato Mundial de Beisbol de Aficionados"

Engraved and Photogravure

1961, Apr. 21 *Perf. 12*

Center in Black

C314	AP53	25c on 75c red org (Bl)	.20	.15
C315	AP53	75c red orange (U)	.55	.22

15th Amateur Baseball Championships.

Alberto Brenes C.
AP64

Miguel Obregon
AP65

Portraits: No. C317, Manuel Aguilar. No. C318, Agustin Gutierrez L. No. C319, Vicente Herrera.

1961, June 12 Photo. *Perf. 12*

C316 AP64 10c deep claret .15 .15
C317 AP64 10c blue .15 .15
C318 AP64 25c bright violet .15 .15
C319 AP64 25c gray .15 .15
Set value .38 .34

First Continental Congress of Lawyers, San José, June 11-15. Exist imperf.
See Nos. C330-C333.

1961, July 19 Litho. *Perf. 13½*

C320 AP65 10c Prussian green .15 .15

Birth centenary of Prof. Miguel Obregon L. Exists imperf.

UN Food and Agriculture Organization
AP66

UN day (UN Organizations): 20c, WHO. 25c, ILO. 30, ITU. 35c, World Meteorological Organization. 45c, UNESCO. 85c, ICAO. 5col, "United Nations" holding the world. 10col, Int. Bank for Reconstruction and Development.

Perf. 11½

1961, Oct. 24 Unwmk. Engr.

C321 AP66 10c lt grn .15 .15
C322 AP66 20c orange .15 .15
C323 AP66 25c Prus grn .18 .15
C324 AP66 30c dk bl .18 .15
C325 AP66 35c car rose .85 .20
C326 AP66 45c violet .30 .18
C327 AP66 85c blue .65 .50
C328 AP66 10col dk sl grn 4.75 4.00
Nos. C321-C328 (8) 7.21 5.48

Souvenir Sheet

Imperf

C329 AP66 5col ultra 2.75 2.75

For overprint see No. C338.

Portrait Type of 1961

Portraits: No. C330, Dr. José Maria Soto Alfaro. No. C331, Dr. Elias Rojas Roman. No. C332, Dr. Andres Saenz Llorente. No. C333, Dr. Juan José Ulloa Giralt.

1961 Photo. *Perf. 13½*

C330 AP64 10c bl grn .15 .15
C331 AP64 10c violet .15 .15
C332 AP64 25c dk gray .20 .15
C333 AP64 25c dp claret .20 .15
Set value .58 .40

9th Congress of Physicians of Central America and Panama.

Nos. C229, C236 and C280 Surcharged in Black, Orange or Red

Engraved; Center Photogravure

1962 *Perf. 13x12½, 13½x13*

C334 AP53 10c ("10") on 15c .15 .15
C334A AP53 10c ("c0.10") on 15c (R) .15 .15
C335 AP53 25c on 15c .16 .15
C336 AP53 35c on 50c (O) .25 .16

Engr.

C337 AP57 85c on 80c (R) .70 .55
Nos. C334-C337 (5) 1.41 1.16

Nos. C324 and C282 Overprinted in Red: "II CONVENCION FILATELICA CENTROAMERICANA SETIEMBRE 1962"

1962, Sept. 12 *Perf. 11½, 13½x13*

C338 AP66 30c dark blue .48 .38
C339 AP57 2col gray & mar 1.50 1.10

2nd Central American Phil. Convention.

Revenue Stamp Surcharged with New Values and "CORREO AEREO" in Red

1962 Engr. *Perf. 12*

C341 A124 25c on 2c emer .15 .15
C342 A124 35c on 2c emer .15 .15
C343 A124 45c on 2c emer .25 .22
C344 A124 85c on 2c emer .48 .40
Nos. C341-C344 (4) 1.03 .92

Arms and Malaria Eradication Emblem — AP67

1963, Feb. 14 Photo. *Perf. 11½*

C345 AP67 25c brt rose .15 .15
C346 AP67 35c brn org .16 .15
C347 AP67 45c ultra .28 .20
C348 AP67 85c bl grn .45 .38
C349 AP67 1col dk bl .60 .50
Nos. C345-C349 (5) 1.64 1.38

WHO drive to eradicate malaria.

Central American Tapir
AP68

Designs: 5c, Paca. 25c, Jaguar. 30c, Ocelot. 35c, Whitetail deer. 40c, Manatee. 85c, White-throated capuchin monkey. 5col, White-lipped peccary.

Perf. 13½

1963, May Unwmk. Photo.

C354 AP68 5c yel ol & brn .15 .15
C355 AP68 10c orange & sl .15 .15
C356 AP68 25c blue & yel .18 .15
C357 AP68 30c lt yel grn & brn .32 .20
C358 AP68 35c bis & red brn .45 .15
C359 AP68 40c emer & sl bl .55 .25
C360 AP68 85c green & blk .85 .40
C361 AP68 5col gray grn & choc 4.75 2.75
Nos. C354-C361 (8) 7.40 4.20

Stamp of 1863 and Packet "William Le Lacheur"
AP69

1963, June 26 Litho.

C362 AP69 25c dl rose & chlky bl .15 .15
C363 AP69 2col gray bl & org 1.25 .75
C364 AP69 3col bister & emer 2.50 1.40
C365 AP69 10col dl grn & ocher 7.00 4.25
Nos. C362-C365 (4) 10.90 6.55

Centenary of Costa Rica's stamps.

Souvenir Sheets

Stamps of 1863 and San José Postmark — AP70

Perf. 13½, Imperf.

1963, June 26 Unwmk.

C366 AP70 5col bl, red, grn & org 3.50 3.50

Cent. of Costa Rica's stamps.
In 1968 copies of No. C366 were overprinted "2-4 Agosto 1968" and "III Exposicion Filatelica Nacional / 'Costa Rica 68'." Value $6.

Issue of 1863 and: 2col, Recaredo Bonilla Carrillo, Postmaster, 1862-63. 3col, Burros, overland mail transport, 1839. 10col, Burro railway car.

Animal Type of 1963 Surcharged in Red

Designs: 10c on 1c, Little anteater. 25c on 2c, Gray fox. 35c on 3c, Armadillo. 85c on 4c, Great anteater.

1963, Sept. 14 Photo. *Perf. 13½*

C367 AP68 10c on 1c brt grn & org brn .20 .15
C368 AP68 25c on 2c org yel & ol grn .20 .15
C369 AP68 35c on 3c bluish grn & brn .28 .15
C370 AP68 85c on 4c dp rose & dk brn .52 .22
Nos. C367-C370 (4) 1.20
Set value .48

Copies of #C370 exist without surcharge.

Pres. Kennedy — AP71

Ancestral Figure — AP72

Portraits- Presidents: 25c, Francisco J. Orlich, Costa Rica. 30c, Julio A. Rivera, El Salvador. 35c, Miguel Ydigoras F., Guatemala. 85c, Dr. Ramon Villeda M., Honduras. 1col, Luis A. Somoza, Nicaragua. 3col, Roberto F. Chiari, Panama.

1963, Dec. 7 Unwmk. *Perf. 14*

Portraits in Black Brown

C371 AP71 25c vio brn .15 .15
C372 AP71 30c brt lil rose .15 .15
C373 AP71 35c ocher .15 .15
C374 AP71 85c gray bl .32 .22
C375 AP71 1col org brn .32 .25
C376 AP71 3col lt ol grn 1.65 1.10
C377 AP71 5col gray 2.25 1.65
Nos. C371-C377 (7) 4.99 3.67

Meeting of Central American Presidents with Pres. John F. Kennedy, San José, Mar. 18-20, 1963.

1963-64 Photo. *Perf. 12*

Ancient Art: 5c, Dog, horiz. 10c, Ornamental stool, horiz. 25c, Male figure. 30c, Ceremonial dancer. 35c, Ceramic vase. 50c, Frog. 55c, Bell. 75c, Six-limbed figure. 85c, Seated man. 90c, Bird-shaped jug. 1col, Twin human beaker, horiz. 2col, Alligator, horiz. 3col, Twin-tailed lizard. 5col, Figure under arch. 10col, Polished stone figure.

C378 AP72 5c lt yel grn & Prus grn .15 .15
C379 AP72 10c buff & dk grn .15 .15
C380 AP72 25c rose & dk brn .15 .15
C381 AP72 30c ocher & Prus grn ('64) .20 .15
C382 AP72 35c sal & sl grn .20 .15
C383 AP72 45c lt bl & dk brn .20 .15
C384 AP72 50c dl bl & dk brn .30 .15
C385 AP72 55c yel grn & dk brn .40 .15
C386 AP72 75c ocher & dk red brn .40 .15
C387 AP72 85c yel & red brn 1.10 .35
C388 AP72 90c cit & red brn 1.40 .35
C389 AP72 1col lt bl & dk brn .80 .25
C390 AP72 2col buff & dk grn 1.25 .45
C391 AP72 3col yel grn & dk brn 4.25 .70
C392 AP72 5col cit & sep 4.25 1.25
C393 AP72 10col rose lil & sl grn 6.75 3.00
Nos. C378-C393 (16) 21.95 7.70

For surcharges and overprint see Nos. C395, C397-C378, C400, C426-C428.

Flags of Central American States — AP73

Alfredo Gonzalez F. — AP74

1964 *Perf. 14*

C394 AP73 30c bl, gray, red & blk .32 .25

Central American Independence issue. For surcharge see No. C396.

Nos. C381, C394 and C387 Surcharged ₡ 0.05

1964, Oct. *Perf. 12, 14*

C395 AP72 5c on 30c .15 .15
C396 AP73 15c on 30c .15 .15
C397 AP72 15c on 85c .15 .15
Set value .22 .18

No. C388 Surcharged: "C 0.15 / CONFERENCIA POSTAL / DE PARIS - 1864"

1964 *Perf. 12*

C398 AP72 15c on 90c cit & red brn .15 .15

Paris Postal Conference.

1965, June Photo. *Perf. 12*

C399 AP74 35c dk blue green 3.00 .15

50th anniv. of the National Bank and honoring Alfredo Gonzalez F., 1st governor of the bank.

No. C390 Overprinted: "75 ANIVERSARIO / ASILO CHAPUI / 1890-1965"

1965, Aug. 14 Unwmk. *Perf. 12*

C400 AP72 2col buff & dk grn 1.00 .60

75th anniv. of Chapui Asylum, San José.

Girl, FAO Emblem and Hands Holding Grain — AP75

Church of Nicoya — AP76

Designs (FAO Emblem and): 15c, Map of Costa Rica and silos, horiz. 50c, World population chart and children. 1col, Plane over map of Costa Rica, horiz.

1965 Litho. *Perf. 14*

C401 AP75 15c lt brn & blk .15 .15
C402 AP75 35c blk & yel .15 .15
C403 AP75 50c ultra & dk grn .20 .15
C404 AP75 1col grn, blk & sil .38 .20
Nos. C401-C404 (4) .88
Set value .53

FAO "Freedom from Hunger" campaign.

1965, Dec. 20 *Perf. 13½x14*

Designs: 5c, Leonidas Briceno B. 15c, Scroll dated "25 de Julio de 1964." 35c, Map of Guanacaste and Nicoya peninsula. 50c, Dancing couple. 1col, Map showing local products.

C405 AP76 5c red brn & blk .15 .15
C406 AP76 10c bl & gray .15 .15
C407 AP76 15c bis & slate .15 .15
C408 AP76 35c blue & slate .15 .15
C409 AP76 50c gray & vio bl .22 .15
C410 AP76 1col buff & slate .50 .35
Set value 1.00 .72

Acquisition of the Nicoya territory.

Runner and Olympic Rings
AP77

Pres. Kennedy Speaking in San José Cathedral
AP78

Olympic Rings and Emblem: 10c, Bicyclists. 40c, Judo. 65c, Basketball. 80c, Soccer. 1col, Hands holding torches, and Mt. Fuji.

1965, Dec. 23 *Perf. 13x13½*

C411 AP77 5c bis & multi .15 .15
C412 AP77 10c lt lil & multi .15 .15
C413 AP77 40c multi .15 .15
C414 AP77 65c lem & multi .24 .15
C415 AP77 80c tan & multi .35 .20
C416 AP77 1col multi .48 .28
a. Souv. sheet of 2 3.00 3.00
Nos. C411-C416 (6) 1.52
Set value .84

18th Olympic Games, Tokyo, Oct. 10-25, 1964. No. C416a contains two 1col stamps, one like No. C416, the other with gray background replacing yellow orange. Sheet also exists imperf, same value.

Perf. 13½x13, 13x13½

1965, Dec. 23 Litho. Unwmk.

Designs: 45c, Friendship 7 capsule circling globe, and Kennedy, horiz. 85c, Kennedy and John, Jr. 1col, Curtis-Lee Mansion and flame from Kennedy grave, Arlington, Va.

C417	AP78	45c brt bl & lil	.18	.15
C418	AP78	55c org & brt bl	.25	.18
C419	AP78	85c gray, dk brn & red brn	.40	.25
C420	AP78	1col multi	.48	.30
a.		Souv. sheet of 2	1.10	1.10
		Nos. C417-C420 (4)	1.31	.88

President John F. Kennedy (1917-63). No. C420a contains two 1col stamps, one like No. C420, the other with green background replacing dark blue. Sheet also exists imperf, same value.

For surcharges see Nos. C429-C430.

Firemen with Hoses — AP79

Designs: 5c, Fire engine "Knox," horiz. 10c, 1866 fire pump. 35c, Fireman's badge. 50c, Emblem and flags of Confederation of Central American Fire Brigades.

1966, Mar. 12 Litho. *Perf. 11*

C421	AP79	5c black & red	.28	.15
C422	AP79	10c bister & red	.35	.15
C423	AP79	15c blk, red brn & red	.52	.18
C424	AP79	35c black & yel	.90	.24
C425	AP79	50c dk blue & red	1.90	.35
		Nos. C421-C425 (5)	3.95	1.07

Centenary of San José Fire Brigade.

Nos. C381, C383, C386 and C418-C419 Surcharged

C0.15 a C 0.50 b

1966 Photo. *Perf. 12*

C426	AP72(a)	15c on 30c	.15	.15
C427	AP72(a)	15c on 45c	.15	.15
C428	AP72(a)	35c on 75c	.20	.15

Litho. *Perf. 13x13½*

C429	AP78(a)	35c on 55c	.20	.15
C430	AP78(b)	50c on 85c	.35	.20
		Nos. C426-C430 (5)	1.05	
		Set value		.60

Revenue Stamps (Basic Type of A124) Surcharged

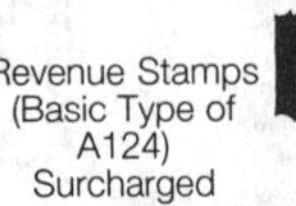

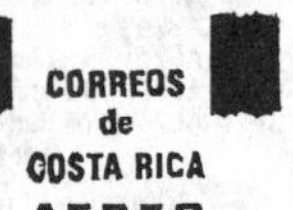

CORREOS de COSTA RICA AEREO 15

1966, Dec. Engr. *Perf. 12*

C431	A124	15c on 5c blue	.15	.15
C432	A124	35c on 10c claret	.16	.15
C433	A124	50c on 20c rose red	.25	.15
		Nos. C431-C433 (3)	.56	
		Set value		.30

Central Bank of Costa Rica — AP80

1967, Mar. Litho. *Perf. 11*

C434	AP80	5c brt grn	.15	.15
C435	AP80	15c brown	.15	.15
C436	AP80	35c scarlet	.20	.15
		Set value	.37	.23

Power Lines — AP81

Telecommunications Building, San Pedro — AP82

Electrification Program: 15c, Telephone Central. 25c, La Garita Dam. 35c, Rio Mache Reservoir. 50c, Cachi Dam.

1967, Apr. 24 Litho. *Perf. 11*

C437	AP81	5c dk gray	.15	.15
C438	AP82	10c brt rose	.15	.15
C439	AP81	15c brn org	.15	.15
C440	AP82	25c brt ultra	.15	.15
C441	AP82	35c brt grn	.18	.15
C442	AP82	50c red brn	.32	.18
		Set value	.84	.52

Chondrorhyncha Aromatica AP83

Institute Emblem AP84

Orchids: 10c, Miltonia endresii. 15c, Stanhopea cirrhata. 25c, Trichopilia suavis. 35c, Odontoglossum schlieperianum. 50c, Cattleya skinneri. 1col, Cattleya dowiana. 2col, Odontoglossum chiriquense.

1967, June 15 Engr. *Perf. 13x13½*

Orchids in Natural Colors

C443	AP83	5c multicolored	.15	.15
C444	AP83	10c olive & multi	.30	.15
C445	AP83	15c multicolored	.30	.15
C446	AP83	25c multicolored	.60	.15
C447	AP83	35c dull vio & multi	.60	.15
C448	AP83	50c brown & multi	.75	.15
C449	AP83	1col vio & multi	2.00	.32
C450	AP83	2col dk ol bis & multi	3.25	.65
		Nos. C443-C450 (8)	7.95	
		Set value		1.54

Issued for the University Library.

1967, Oct. 6 Litho. *Perf. 13x13½*

C451	AP84	50c vio bl, lt bl & bl	.20	.18

Inter-American Agriculture Institute, 25th anniv.

Church of Solitude — AP85

LACSA Emblem — AP86

Costa Rican Churches: 10c, Basilica of Santo Domingo, Heredia. 15c, Cathedral of Tilaran. 25c, Cathedral of Alajuela. 30c, Mercy Church. 35c, Basilica of Our Lady of Angels. 40c, Church of St. Raphael, Heredia. 45c, Ujarras ruins. 50c, Ruins of parish church, Cartago. 55c, Cathedral of San José. 65c, Parish church, Puntarenas. 75c, Church of Orosi. 80c, Cathedral of St. Isidro, the General. 85c, St. Ramon Church. 90c, Church of the Abandoned. 1col, Coronado Church. 2col, Church of St. Teresita. 3col, Parish Church, Heredia. 5col, Carmelite Church. 10col, Limon Cathedral.

1967, Dec. 15 Engr. *Perf. 12½*

C452	AP85	5c green	.15	.15
C453	AP85	10c blue	.15	.15
C454	AP85	15c lilac	.15	.15
C455	AP85	25c dl yel	.15	.15
C456	AP85	30c org brn	.20	.15
C457	AP85	35c lt bl	.25	.15
C458	AP85	40c dp org	.25	.15
C459	AP85	45c dl bl grn	.25	.15
C460	AP85	50c olive	.30	.20
C461	AP85	55c brown	.30	.20
C462	AP85	65c car rose	.55	.25
C463	AP85	75c sepia	.60	.30
C464	AP85	80c yellow	1.10	.40
C465	AP85	85c vio blk	1.25	.40
C466	AP85	90c emerald	1.25	.55
C467	AP85	1col slate	1.00	.30
C468	AP85	2col brt grn	4.75	1.65
C469	AP85	3col orange	6.75	2.75
C470	AP85	5col vio blue	6.75	2.75
C471	AP85	10col carmine	8.25	4.00
		Nos. C452-C471 (20)	34.40	14.95

See Nos. C561-C576.

Perf. 13x13½, 13½x13

1967, Dec. 12 Litho. & Engr.

Design: 45c, LACSA emblem and jet, horiz. 50c, Decorated wheel and anniversary emblem.

C472	AP86	40c ultra, grnsh bl & gold	.15	.15
C473	AP86	45c blk, pale grn, ultra & gold	.18	.15
C474	AP86	50c blue & multi	.20	.18
		Nos. C472-C474 (3)	.53	.48

20th anniv. (in 1966) of Lineas Aereas Costaricenses, LACSA, Costa Rican Airlines.

Scout Directing Traffic AP87

Runner AP88

Designs: 25c, Campfire under palm tree. 35c, Flag of Costa Rica, Scout flag and emblem. 50c, Encampment, horiz. 65c, Photograph of first Scout troop, horiz.

1968, Mar. 15 *Perf. 13*

C475	AP87	15c lt bl, blk & lt brn	.15	.15
C476	AP87	25c lt ultra, vio bl & org	.16	.15
C477	AP87	35c blue & multi	.24	.15
C478	AP87	50c multicolored	.28	.20
C479	AP87	65c sal, dk bl & brn	.40	.24
		Nos. C475-C479 (5)	1.23	
		Set value		.72

Costa Rican Boy Scouts, 50th anniversary.

1968, Jan. 17 Litho. *Perf. 10x11*

Sports: 40c, Women's running. 55c, Boxing. 65c, Bicycling. 75c, Weight lifting. 1col, High diving. 3col, Rifle shooting.

C481	AP88	30c multi	.15	.15
C482	AP88	40c multi	.16	.15
C483	AP88	55c multi	.24	.16
C484	AP88	65c lil & multi	.30	.16
C485	AP88	75c multi	.30	.16
C486	AP88	1col multi	.35	.24
C487	AP88	3col multi	1.50	.90
		Nos. C481-C487 (7)	3.00	1.92

19th Olympic Games, Mexico City, Oct. 12-27.

Philatelic Exhibition Emblem — AP89

1969, June 5 Litho. *Perf. 11x10*

C488	AP89	35c multicolored	.15	.15
C489	AP89	40c pink & multi	.15	.15
C490	AP89	50c lt blue & multi	.18	.15
C491	AP89	2col multicolored	.65	.48
		Nos. C488-C491 (4)	1.13	
		Set value		.78

4th Natl. Philatelic Exhib., San José, June 5-8.

ILO Emblem AP90

1969, Oct. 29 Litho. *Perf. 10*

C492	AP90	35c bl grn & blk	.18	.15
C493	AP90	50c scarlet & blk	.27	.15
		Set value		.25

50th anniv. of the ILO.

Soccer — AP91

Stylized Crab — AP92

Designs: 65c, Soccer ball, map of North and Central America. 85c, Soccer player. 1col, Two players in action.

1969, Nov. 23 Litho. *Perf. 11x10*

C494	AP91	65c gray & multi	.24	.16
C495	AP91	75c multicolored	.24	.16
C496	AP91	85c multicolored	.30	.20
C497	AP91	1col pink & multi	.35	.24
		Nos. C494-C497 (4)	1.13	.76

Issued to publicize the 4th Soccer Championships (CONCACAF), Nov. 23-Dec. 7.

1970, May 14 Litho. *Perf. 12½*

C498	AP92	10c blk & lil rose	.15	.15
C499	AP92	15c blk & yel	.15	.15
C500	AP92	50c blk & brn org	.20	.15
C501	AP92	1.10col blk & emer	.50	.20
		Set value	.80	.40

10th Inter-American Cancer Cong., May 22-29.

Costa Rica No. 124, Magnifying Glass and Stamps — AP93

Design: 2col, Father and son with stamps and album.

1970, Sept. 14 Litho. *Perf. 11*

C502	AP93	1col ultra, brn & car rose	.95	.20
C503	AP93	2col blk, pink & ultra	1.10	.50

The 5th National Philatelic Exhibition.

EXPO Emblem and Costa Rican Cart — AP94

Designs (EXPO Emblem and): 10c, Japanese floral arrangement, vert. 35c, Pavilion and Tower of the Sun. 40c, Japanese tea ceremony. 45c, Woman picking coffee, vert. 55c, Earth seen from moon, vert.

1970, Oct. 22 Litho. *Perf. 13x13½*

C504	AP94	10c multi	.15	.15
C505	AP94	15c grn & multi	.15	.15
C506	AP94	35c bl & multi	.15	.15
C507	AP94	40c gray & multi	.20	.15
C508	AP94	45c multi	.20	.15
C509	AP94	55c blk & multi	.20	.15
		Nos. C504-C509 (6)	1.05	
		Set value		.62

EXPO '70 International Exhibition, Osaka, Japan, Mar. 15-Sept. 13.

Escazu Valley, by Margarita Bertheau — AP95

Paintings: 25c, "Irazu," by Rafael A. Garcia, vert. 80c, Shore landscape, by Teodorico Quiros. 1col,

"The Other Face," by Cesar Valverde. 2.50col, Mother and Child, by Luis Daell, vert.

1970, Nov. 4 Litho. Perf. 12½

C510	AP95	25c multi	.65	.32
C511	AP95	45c multi	.65	.32
C512	AP95	80c multi	1.00	.52
C513	AP95	1col multi	1.00	.60
C514	AP95	2.50col multi	2.00	1.00
		Nos. C510-C514 (5)	5.30	2.76

Arms of Costa Rica, 1964 — AP96

National Theater — AP97

Various Coats of Arms, dated: 10c, Nov. 27, 1906. 15c, Sept. 29, 1848. 25c, Apr. 21, 1840. 35c, Nov. 22, 1824. 50c, Nov. 2, 1824. 1col, Mar. 6, 1824. 2col, May 10, 1823.

1971, Feb. 10 Litho. Perf. 14x13½

C515	AP96	5c buff & multi	.20	.15
C516	AP96	10c multi	.20	.15
C517	AP96	15c yel & multi	.24	.15
C518	AP96	25c pink & multi	.28	.15
C519	AP96	35c multi	.32	.16
C520	AP96	50c rose & multi	.35	.16
C521	AP96	1col beige & multi	.40	.20
C522	AP96	2col multi	.80	.40
		Nos. C515-C522 (8)	2.79	
		Set value		1.30

1971, Apr. 14 Litho. Perf. 11

C523	AP97	2col plum	.38	.30

Organization of American States meeting.

José Matias Delgado, Manuel José Arce AP98

Flag of Costa Rica — AP99

Independence Leaders: 10c, Miguel Larreinaga and Manuel Antonio de la Cerda, Nicaragua. 15c, José Cecilio del Valle, Dionisio de Herrera, Honduras. 35c, Pablo Alvarado and Florencio del Castillo, Costa Rica. 50c, Antonio Larrazabal and Pedro Molina, Guatemala. 2col, Costa Rica coat of arms.

1971, Sept. 14 Perf. 13

C524	AP98	5c multi	.15	.15
C525	AP98	10c multi	.15	.15
C526	AP98	15c gray, brn & blk	.15	.15
C527	AP98	35c multi	.15	.15
C528	AP98	50c multi	.15	.15
C529	AP99	1col multi	.20	.15
C530	AP99	2col multi	.40	.32
		Set value	1.00	.78

Central American independence, sesqui.

Soccer Federation Emblem AP100

Children of the World AP101

1971, Dec. 6

C531	AP100	50c multi	.15	.15
C532	AP100	60c multi	.15	.15
		Set value		.20

50th anniv. of Soccer Federation of Costa Rica.

1972, Jan. 11 Perf. 12½

C533	AP101	50c multi	.15	.15
C534	AP101	1.10col red & multi	.30	.25

25th anniv. (in 1971) of UNICEF.

Tree of Guanacaste AP102

Designs: 40c, Hermitage, Liberia. 55c, Petroglyphs, Rincón Brujo. 60c, Painted head, sculpture from Curubandé, vert.

1972, Feb. 28 Perf. 11

C535	AP102	20c brn, ol & brt grn	.15	.15
C536	AP102	40c brn & ol	.15	.15
C537	AP102	55c blk & brn	.15	.15
C538	AP102	60c blk, buff & ver	.20	.15
		Nos. C535-C538 (4)	.65	
		Set value		.44

Bicentenary of the founding of the city of Liberia, Guanacaste.

Farm and Family AP103

Inter-American Exhibitions AP104

Designs: 45c, Cattle, dairy products and meat, horiz. 50c, Kneeling figure with plant. 10col, Farmer and map of Americas.

1972, June 30 Litho. Perf. 12½

C539	AP103	20c multi	.15	.15
C540	AP103	45c multi	.15	.15
C541	AP103	50c dp yel, grn & blk	.15	.15
C542	AP103	10col brn, org & blk	1.75	1.00
		Nos. C539-C542 (4)	2.20	
		Set value		1.20

30th anniversary of the Inter-American Institute of Agricultural Sciences.

1972, Aug. 26 Litho. Perf. 13

C543	AP104	50c org & brn	.15	.15
C544	AP104	2col bl & vio	.38	.30

4th Interamerican Philatelic Exhibition, EXFILBRA, Rio de Janeiro, Aug. 26-Sept. 2.

First Book Printed in Costa Rica — AP105

Intl. Book Year: 50c, 5col, National Library, horiz.

1972, Dec. 7 Litho. Perf. 12½

C545	AP105	20c brt bl	.15	.15
C546	AP105	50c gold & multi	.15	.15
C547	AP105	75c multi	.15	.15
C548	AP105	5col multi	.95	.75
		Nos. C545-C548 (4)	1.40	
		Set value		1.00

Road to Irazú Volcano AP106

1972-73 Perf. 11x11½, 11½x11

C549	AP106	5c like 20c	.15	.15
C550	AP106	15c Coco-Culebra Bay	.15	.15
C551	AP106	20c shown	.15	.15
C552	AP106	25c like 15c	.15	.15
C553	AP106	40c Manuel Antonio Beach	.15	.15
C554	AP106	45c Tourist Office emblem	.15	.15
C555	AP106	50c Lindora Lake	.15	.15
C556	AP106	60c San Jose P.O., vert.	.18	.15
C557	AP106	80c like 40c	.22	.18
C558	AP106	90c like 45c	.22	.18
C559	AP106	1col like 50c	.22	.18
C560	AP106	2col like 60c	.45	.35
		Set value	1.95	1.50

Tourism year of the Americas.

Issue dates: 20c, 25c, 80c, 90c, 1col and 2col, Dec. 26, 1972. Others, Mar. 21, 1973.

No. C555 exists eith inverted center, used only.

Church Type of 1967

Designs as before.

1973, July 16 Engr. Perf. 12½

C561	AP85	5c sl grn	.15	.15
C562	AP85	10c olive	.15	.15
C563	AP85	15c orange	.15	.15
C564	AP85	25c brown	.15	.15
C565	AP85	30c rose claret	.15	.15
C566	AP85	35c violet	.15	.15
C567	AP85	40c brt grn	.15	.15
C568	AP85	45c dull yel	.18	.15
C569	AP85	50c rose mag	.18	.15
C570	AP85	55c blue	.18	.15
C571	AP85	65c black	.24	.18
C572	AP85	75c rose red	.24	.18
C573	AP85	80c yel grn	.24	.18
C574	AP85	85c lilac	.28	.24
C575	AP85	90c brt pink	.28	.24
C576	AP85	1col dk blue	.28	.24
		Nos. C561-C576 (16)	3.15	
		Set value		2.20

Human Rights Flame AP107

OAS Emblem AP108

1973, Dec. 10 Photo. Perf. 10½

C577	AP107	50c black & red	.15	.15

25th anniversary of the Universal Declaration of Human Rights.

1973, Dec. 17 Litho. Perf. 10½

C578	AP108	20c dk bl & dp car	.15	.15

25th anniv. of the OAS.

Joaquin Vargas Calvo — AP109

AP110

1974, Jan. 14

C579	AP109	20c shown	.15	.15
C580	AP109	20c Alejandro Monestel	.15	.15
C581	AP109	20c Julio Mata	.15	.15
C582	AP109	60c Julio Fonseca	.18	.15
C583	AP109	2col Rafael A. Chaves	.45	.32
C584	AP109	5col Manuel M. Gutierrez	1.10	.90
		Nos. C579-C584 (6)	2.18	
		Set value		1.50

Costa Rican composers honored by the National Symphony Orchestra.

Revenue Stamps Overprinted "Habilitado para Correo Aereo"

1974, Apr. 5 Engr. Perf. 12

C585	AP110	50c brown	.15	.15
C586	AP110	1col violet	.22	.15
C587	AP110	2col orange	.42	.25
C588	AP110	5col olive	1.65	1.25
		Nos. C585-C588 (4)	2.44	1.80

Telephone Building, San Pedro — AP111

EXFILMEX 74 Emblem — AP112

Designs: 65c, Rio Macho Control, horiz. 85c, Turbines, Rio Macho Center. 1.25col, Cachi Dam and reservoir, horiz. 2col, I.C.E. Headquarters.

1974, July 30 Litho. Perf. 10½

C589	AP111	50c gold & multi	.15	.15
C590	AP111	65c gold & multi	.20	.15
C591	AP111	85c gold & multi	.25	.15
C592	AP111	1.25col gold & multi	.30	.20
C593	AP111	2col gold & multi	.50	.30
		Nos. C589-C593 (5)	1.40	.95

25th anniversary of Costa Rican Electrical Institute (I.C.E.).

1974, Aug. 22 Perf. 13

C594	AP112	65c green	.16	.15
C595	AP112	3col lilac rose	.60	.42

5th Inter-American Philatelic Exhibition, EXFILMEX-74 UPU, Mexico City, Oct. 26-Nov. 3.

Map of Costa Rica, 4-S Emblem AP113

Design: 50c, Young harvesters and 4-S emblem.

1974, Oct. 7 Litho. Perf. 12x11

C596	AP113	20c brt grn	.15	.15
C597	AP113	50c multi	.15	.15
		Set value	.25	.15

25th anniversary of 4-S Clubs of Costa Rica (similar to US 4-H Clubs).

Roberto Brenes Mesen AP114

"Life Insurance" AP115

Designs: 85c, "Love and Death," manuscript, horiz. 5col, Hands of writer.

1974, Oct. 14 Litho. Perf. 10½

C598	AP114	20c blk & brn	.15	.15
C599	AP114	85c blk & red	.22	.16
C600	AP114	5col blk & red brn	1.10	.85
		Nos. C598-C600 (3)	1.47	1.16

Birth centenary of Roberto Brenes Mesen, educator and writer.

1974, Oct. 30 Perf. 14

Designs: 20c, Ricardo Jiménez Oreamuno and Tomás Soley Güell, horiz. 50c, Harvest Insurance (hand holding shovel; horiz.). 85c, Maritime insurance (hand holding paper boat). 1.25col, INS emblem. 2col, Workers rehabilitation (arm with crutch). 2.50col, Workers' Compensation (hand holding wrench). 20col, Fire insurance (hands protecting house).

C601	AP115	20c multi	.15	.15
C602	AP115	50c multi	.15	.15
C603	AP115	65c multi	.15	.15
C604	AP115	85c multi	.16	.15
C605	AP115	1.25col multi	.25	.16
C606	AP115	2col multi	.42	.25
C607	AP115	2.50col multi	.55	.42
C608	AP115	20col multi	4.25	4.25
		Nos. C601-C608 (8)	6.08	5.68

Costa Rican Insurance Institute (Instituto Nacional de Seguros, INS), 50th anniversary.

For surcharges see Nos. C721-C722.

WPY Emblem — AP116

Oscar J. Pinto F. — AP117

1974, Nov. 13 Litho. *Perf. 11x11½*

C609 AP116 2col vio bl & red .42 .25

World Population Year.

1974, Dec. 2 *Perf. 13*

Designs: 50c, Alberto Montes de Oca D., champion sharpshooter. 1col, Eduardo Garnier, sports promoter. O. J. Pinto, introducer of soccer.

C610 AP117 20c gray & dk bl .15 .15
C611 AP117 50c gray & dk bl .15 .15
C612 AP117 1col gray & dk bl .25 .15
Nos. C610-C612 (3) .55
Set value .30

First Central American Olympic Games, held in Guatemala, 1973.

Mormodes Buccinator AP118

Masdevallia Ephippium AP119

Designs: Orchids.

Perf. 10½, 13½

1975, Mar. 7 Litho.

C613 AP118 25c *shown* .40 .15
C614 AP118 25c *Gongora clavi-odora* .40 .15
C615 AP119 25c *shown* .40 .15
C616 AP119 25c *Encyclia spondiadum* .40 .15
a. Block of 4, #C613-C616 1.60 1.00
C617 AP118 65c *Lycaste skinneri alba* .90 .20
C618 AP118 65c *Peristeria elata* .90 .20
C619 AP119 65c *Miltonia roezelii* .90 .20
C620 AP119 65c *Brassavola digby-ana* .90 .20
a. Block of 4, #C617-C620, 10½ 4.00 2.00
b. Block of 4, #C617-C620, 13½ 20.00
C621 AP118 80c *Epidendrum mirabile* 1.25 .30
C622 AP118 80c *Barkeria lin-dleyana* 1.25 .30
C623 AP119 80c *Cattleya skinneri* 1.25 .30
C624 AP119 80c *Sobralia macrantha* 1.25 .30
a. Block of 4, #C621-C624 5.50 2.50
C625 AP118 1.40col *Lycaste cruenta* 1.50 .35
C626 AP118 1.40col *Oncidium obry-zatum* 1.50 .35
C627 AP119 1.40col *Gongora armeniaca* 1.50 .35
C628 AP119 1.40col *Sievekingia suavis* 1.50 .35
a. Block of 4, #C625-C628 7.00 4.00

Perf. 13½

C629 AP118 1.75col *Hexisea imbri-cata* 1.50 .35
C630 AP118 2.15col *Warcewic-zella discolor* 1.50 .35
C631 AP119 2.50col *Oncidium kramerianum* 2.50 .55
C632 AP119 3.25col *Cattleya dowi-ana* 3.00 .65
Nos. C613-C632 (20) 24.70 5.90

5th National Flower Exhibition.

Nos. C613-C628 were printed in both perforations on two different papers: dull finish and shiny. Nos. C629-C632 were printed on shiny paper.

Most copies of Nos. C617-C620, perf 10½, were surcharged.

For overprints and surcharges see Nos. C715-C720, C723-C728.

Radio Club Emblem AP120

Members' Flags and Emblem AP121

Design: 2col, Federation emblem.

1975, Apr. 16 Litho. *Perf. 13½*

C633 AP120 1col blk & red lil .45 .15
C634 AP121 1.10col multi .55 .18
C635 AP120 2col blk & bl .90 .27
Nos. C633-C635 (3) 1.90 .60

16th Central American Radio Amateurs' Convention, San José, May 2-4.

Nicoya Beach — AP122

Designs: 75c, Driving cattle. 1col, Colonial Church, Nicoya. 3col, Savannah riders, vert.

1975, Aug. 1 Litho. *Perf. 13½*

C636 AP122 25c gray & multi .15 .15
C637 AP122 75c gray & multi .25 .15
C638 AP122 1col gray & multi .30 .18
C639 AP122 3col gray & multi .90 .75
Nos. C636-C639 (4) 1.60 1.23

Sesqui. of annexation of Nicoya District.

Costa Rica #158 AP123

Designs (Type A90 of 1932): No. C641, #159. No. C642, #160. No. C643, #161.

1975, Aug. 14 Litho. *Perf. 12*

C640 AP123 2.20col blk & org .42 .35
C641 AP123 2.20col blk & dk grn .42 .35
C642 AP123 2.20col blk & car rose .42 .35
C643 AP123 2.20col blk & dk bl .42 .35
a. Block of 4, #C640-C643 1.75 1.75

6th Natl. Phil. Exhib., San José, Aug. 14-17.
For surcharges see Nos. C885-C892.

IWY Emblem — AP124

1975, Oct. 9 Litho. *Perf. 10½*

C644 AP124 40c vio bl & red .15 .15
C645 AP124 1.25col blk & ultra .20 .15
Set value .22

International Women's Year 1975.

UN Emblem — AP125

UN, 30th Anniv.: 60c, UN General Assembly, horiz. 1.20col, UN Headquarters, NY.

1975, Oct. 24 *Perf. 12*

C646 AP125 10c bl & blk .15 .15
C647 AP125 60c multi .15 .15
C648 AP125 1.20col multi .20 .15
Set value .40 .31

The Visitation, by Jorge Gallardo AP126

"20-30" Club Emblem AP127

Paintings by Jorge Gallardo: 1col, Nativity and Star. 5col, St. Joseph in his Workshop, Virgin and Child.

1975, Nov. 3 *Perf. 10½*

C649 AP126 50c multi .16 .15
C650 AP126 1col multi .28 .15
C651 AP126 5col multi 1.00 .70
Nos. C649-C651 (3) 1.44 1.00

Christmas 1975.

1976, Jan. 16 Litho. *Perf. 12*

C652 AP127 1col multi .15 .15

"20-30" Club of Costa Rica, 20th anniv.

Quercus Brenessi Trel AP128

"Literary Development" AP129

Plants: 30c, Maxillaria albertii schecht. 55c, Calathea brenessi standl. 2col, Brenesia costaricensis schlecht. 10col, Philodendron brenesii standl.

1976, Mar. 1 *Perf. 10½*

C653 AP128 5c multi .15 .15
C654 AP128 30c multi .15 .15
C655 AP128 55c multi .15 .15
C656 AP128 2col tan & multi .35 .20
C657 AP128 10col multi 1.75 1.40
Nos. C653-C657 (5) 2.55 2.05

Prof. Alberto Manuel Brenes Mora, botanist, birth centenary.

1976, Apr. 9 Litho. *Perf. 16*

Designs: 1.10col, Man holding book, stylized. 5col, Costa Rican flag emanating from book, horiz.

C658 AP129 15c multi .15 .15
C659 AP129 1.10col multi .15 .15
C660 AP129 5col multi .90 .70
Nos. C658-C660 (3) 1.20 1.00

Publishing in Costa Rica.

Postrider, 1839 AP130

Costa Rica No. 13, Post Office AP131

Designs: 65c, Costa Rica No. 14 and Post Office. 85c, Costa Rica No. 15 and Post Office. 2col, UPU Monument, Bern, vert.

1976, May 24 *Perf. 10½*

C661 AP130 20c apple grn & blk .15 .15
C662 AP131 50c bister & multi .15 .15
C663 AP131 65c multi .15 .15
C664 AP131 85c multi .16 .15
C665 AP130 2col blk & lt bl .35 .28
Nos. C661-C665 (5) .96
Set value .64

Cent. of UPU (in 1974).

Nos. C662-C664 exist without the surcharges on reproductions of Nos. 13-15.

Telephones, 1876 and 1976 — AP132

Designs: 2col, Wall telephone. 5col, Alexander Graham Bell.

1976, June 28

C666 AP132 1.60col lt bl & blk .28 .20
C667 AP132 2col multi .35 .20
C668 AP132 5col yel & blk .90 .70
Nos. C666-C668 (3) 1.53 1.10

Centenary of first telephone call by Alexander Graham Bell, Mar. 10, 1876.

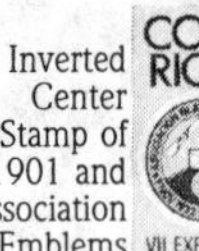

Inverted Center Stamp of 1901 and Association Emblems AP133

Design: 5col, 1901 stamp between Costa Rican Philatelic Society and Interamerican Philatelic Federation emblems.

1976, Nov. 11 Litho. *Perf. 10½*

C669 AP133 50c multi .15 .15
C670 AP133 1col multi .16 .15
C671 AP133 2col multi .35 .20
Nos. C669-C671 (3) .66
Set value .37

Souvenir Sheet

Perf. 12, Imperf.

C672 AP133 5col multi .90 .90

7th Natl. Phil. Exhib. and 9th Plenary Assembly of the Interamerican Phil. Fed. (FIAF), San José, Nov. 1976.

No. C670 exists in colors of No. C671.

"Seeing Eye" and Map of Costa Rica — AP134

Amadeo Quiros Blanco — AP135

1976, Nov. 22 *Perf. 16*

C673 AP134 35c blk & bl .15 .15
C674 AP135 2col multi .35 .20
Set value .28

General Audit Office, 25th anniversary.

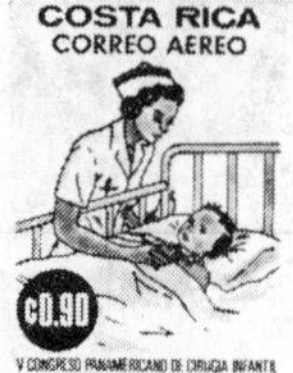

Nurse Attending Child — AP136

LACSA Circling Globe — AP137

Design: 1.10col, National Children's Hospital, horiz.

1976, Nov. 29

C675 AP136 90c multi .16 .15
C676 AP136 1.10col multi .20 .16

5th Panamerican Congress of Pediatric Surgery and 12th Congress of Pediatrics.

1976, Dec. 1 *Perf. 10½*

Designs: 1.20col, Route map. 3col, LACSA emblem and Costa Rican flag.

C677 AP137 1col multi .16 .15
C678 AP137 1.20col multi .20 .15
C679 AP137 3col multi .52 .30
Nos. C677-C679 (3) .88 .60

Costa Rican Air Lines (LACSA), 30th anniversary.

Boston Tea Party AP138

US Bicent.: 5col, Declaration of Independence. 10col, Ringing Liberty Bell to announce Independence, vert.

1976, Dec. 24

C680 AP138 2.20col multi .38 .28
C681 AP138 5col multi .90 .70
C682 AP138 10col multi 1.75 1.40
Nos. C680-C682 (3) 3.03 2.38

Tree of Guanacaste AP139

Felipe J. Alvarado AP140

Designs (Rotary Emblem and): 60c, Dr. Paul Blanco Cervantes Hospital, horiz. 3col, Map of Costa Rica, horiz. 10col, Paul Harris.

1977, Mar. 31 **Litho.** *Perf. 16*

C683 AP139 40c multi .15 .15
C684 AP140 50c multi .15 .15
C685 AP139 60c multi .15 .15
C686 AP139 3col multi .70 .42
C687 AP140 10col multi 2.00 1.40
Nos. C683-C687 (5) 3.15 2.27

Rotary Club of San José, 50th anniversary.

Boruca Cloth AP141

Design: 1.50col, Painted wood ornament.

1977, Feb. 22

C688 AP141 75c multi .15 .15
C689 AP141 1.50col multi .28 .15
Set value .24

Natl. Artisan & Small Industry Program.

Juana Pereira AP142

Alonso de Anguciana de Gamboa AP143

Designs: 1col, First Church of Our Lady of the Angels, horiz. 1.10col, Our Lady of the Angels (gold sculpture). 1.25col, Crown of Our Lady of the Angels.

1977, June 6 **Litho.** *Perf. 10½*

C690 AP142 50c multi .15 .15
C691 AP142 1col multi .16 .15
C692 AP142 1.10col multi .20 .15
C693 AP142 1.25col multi .24 .16
Nos. C690-C693 (4) .75
Set value .47

50th anniv. of the coronation of Our Lady of the Angels, patron saint of Costa Rica.

1977, July 4 **Litho.** *Perf. 10½*

Designs: 75c, Church of Esparza. 1col, Statue of Our Lady of Candlemas. 2col, Statue of Diego de Artieda y Chirino.

C694 AP143 35c multi .15 .15
C695 AP143 75c multi .15 .15
C696 AP143 1col multi .16 .15
C697 AP143 2col multi .35 .28
Nos. C694-C697 (4) .81
Set value .56

400th anniv. of the founding of Esparza.
For surcharge see No. C883.

CARE Emblem and Child — AP144

Design: 1col, CARE emblem and soybeans, horiz.

1977, Sept. 14 **Litho.** *Perf. 16*

C698 AP144 80c multi .15 .15
C699 AP144 1col multi .16 .15
Set value .20

20th anniversary of CARE (relief organization) in Costa Rica.

Institute's Emblem — AP145

First Map of Americas, 1540 AP146

1977, Oct. 21 **Litho.** *Perf. 16*

C700 AP145 50c blk & multi .15 .15
C701 AP146 1.40col blk & multi .24 .20
Set value .27

Hispanic Cultural Institute of Costa Rica, 25th anniversary.

Mercy Church, by Ricardo Ulloa B. — AP147

Health Ministry Emblem — AP148

Paintings: 1col, Christ, by Floria Pinto de Herrero. 5col, St. Francis and the Birds, by Louisa Gonzalez Y Saenz.

1977, Nov. 9 **Litho.** *Perf. 10½*

C702 AP147 50c multi .15 .15
C703 AP147 1col multi .16 .15
C704 AP147 5col multi .90 .70
Nos. C702-C704 (3) 1.21 1.00

1977, Nov. 16 *Perf. 16*

C705 AP148 1.40col multi .24 .20

Creation of Ministry of Health.

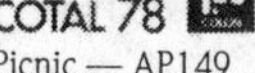

Picnic — AP149

San Martin — AP150

Designs: 50c, Weaver. 2col, Beach scene. 5col, Fruit and vegetable market. 10col, Swans on lake.

1978, Mar. 21 **Litho.** *Perf. 10½*

C706 AP149 50c blk & multi .15 .15
C707 AP149 1col blk & multi .16 .15
C708 AP149 2col blk & multi .35 .20
C709 AP149 5col blk & multi .90 .70
C710 AP149 10col blk & multi 1.90 1.40
Nos. C706-C710 (5) 3.46 2.60

Conf. of Latin American Tourist Organizations.

1978, Aug. 7 **Litho.** *Perf. 10½*

C711 AP150 5col multi 1.00 .65

Gen. José de San Martin (1778-1850), soldier and statesman, fought for South American independence.

Geographical Institute Emblem — AP151

University Federation Emblem — AP152

1978, Aug. 28 **Litho.** *Perf. 12½*

C712 AP151 5col multi .85 .60

Pan-American Geography and History Institute, 50th anniversary. Exists imperf.

1978, Sept. 18 *Perf. 11*

C713 AP152 80c ultra .15 .15

Central American University Federation, 30th anniversary.

Emblems AP153

1978, Oct. 24 *Perf. 16*

C714 AP153 2col aqua, blk & gold .32 .24

6th Interamerican Philatelic Exhibition, Argentina 78, Buenos Aires, Oct. 1978.

Nos. C629-C631 Overprinted: "50 Aniversario del / primer vuelo de PAN AM / en Costa Rica / 1928-1978"

1978, Nov. 1 **Litho.** *Perf. 13½*

C715 AP118 1.75col multi .30 .20
C716 AP118 2.15col multi .35 .25
C717 AP119 2.50col multi .42 .30
Nos. C715-C717 (3) 1.07 .75

1st Pan Am flight in Costa Rica, 50th anniv.

Nos. C629-C631 Overprinted: "50 Aniversario de la / visita de Lindbergh a / Costa Rica 1928-1978"

1978, Nov. 1

C718 AP118 1.75col multi .30 .20
C719 AP118 2.15col multi .35 .25
C720 AP119 2.50col multi .45 .30
Nos. C718-C720 (3) 1.10 .75

50th anniversary of Lindbergh's visit.

Nos. C603 and C607 Surcharged with New Value, 4 Bars and: "Centenario del / Asilo Carlos / Maria Ulloa / 1878-1978"

1978, Nov. 8 *Perf. 14*

C721 AP115 50c on 65c multi .15 .15
C722 AP115 2col on 2.50col multi .32 .24

Asilo Carlos Maria Ulloa, birth centenary.

No. C617-C620, C630-C631 Surcharged with New Value and 4 Bars

Perf. 10½, 13½

1978, Nov. 13 **Litho.**

C723 AP118 50c on 65c .15 .15
C724 AP118 50c on 65c .15 .15
C725 AP119 50c on 65c .15 .15
C726 AP119 50c on 65c .15 .15
a. Block of 4, #C723-C726 .60 .40
C727 AP118 1.20col on 2.15col .35 .15
C728 AP119 2col on 2.50col .52 .24
Nos. C723-C728 (6) 1.47
Set value .66

#C723-C726, perf. 13½, value $20, unused, $10, used, each. #C726a, unused, $350.

Star over Map of Costa Rica AP154

"Flying Men," Chorotega AP155

1978, Nov. 13 *Perf. 10½*

C729 AP154 50c blue & blk .15 .15
C730 AP154 1col rose lil & blk .15 .15
C731 AP154 5col orange & blk .90 .60
a. Strip of 3, #C729-C731 1.25

Christmas 1978. #C729-C731 printed in sheets of 100 and se-tenant in sheet of 15 (3x5).

1978, Nov. 20 *Perf. 11½*

Designs: 1.20col, Oviedo giving his History of Indies to Duke of Calabria, horiz. 10col, Lord of Oviedo's coat of arms.

C732 AP155 85c multi .15 .15
C733 AP155 1.20col blk & lt bl .20 .15
C734 AP155 10col multi 1.90 1.25
Nos. C732-C734 (3) 2.25 1.55

500th birth anniv. of Gonzalo Fernandez de Oviedo, 1st chronicler of Spanish Indies.

Msgr. Domingo Rivas AP156

San José Cathedral AP157

1978, Dec. 6 *Perf. 16, 13½ (20col)*

C735 AP156 1col black & indigo .15 .15
C736 AP157 20col multicolored 3.50 3.25

Centenary of the Cathedral of San José.

View of Coco Island — AP158

Designs: 2.10, 3, 5 col, various views of Coco Island. 10col, Installation of memorial plaque, people and flag. 5, 10col vert.

1979, Apr. 30 **Litho.** *Perf. 10½*

C737 AP158 90c multi .22 .15
C738 AP158 2.10col multi .50 .24
C739 AP158 3col multi .70 .38
C740 AP158 5col multi 1.25 .60

C741	AP158	10col multi	2.25	1.25
a.		Souv. sheet of 5, #C737-C741	5.00	4.00
		Nos. C737-C741 (5)	4.92	2.62

Visit of Pres. Rodrigo Carazo Odio to Coco Island, June 24, 1978, in the interest of national defense.

Shrimp
AP159

Designs: 85c, Mahogany snapper. 1.80col, Corvina. 3col, Crayfish. 10col, Tuna.

1979, May 14 Litho. *Perf. 13½*

C742	AP159	60c multi	.15	.15
C743	AP159	85c multi	.15	.15
C744	AP159	1.80col multi	.35	.22
C745	AP159	3col multi	.52	.40
C746	AP159	10col multi	1.75	1.25
		Nos. C742-C746 (5)	2.92	2.17

Marine life protection.

Hungry Nestlings, IYC Emblem — AP160

Microwave Transmitters, Mt. Irazu — AP161

1979, May 24 *Perf. 11*

C747	AP160	1col multi	.38	.18
C748	AP160	2col multi	.75	.38
C749	AP160	20col multi	7.50	5.00
		Nos. C747-C749 (3)	8.63	5.56

International Year of the Child.

1979, June 28 Litho. *Perf. 14*

Design: 1col, Arenal Dam, horiz.

C750	AP161	1col multi	.20	.15
C751	AP161	5col multi	1.00	.70

Costa Rican Electricity Institute, 30th anniversary.

Costa Rica No. 1 and Rowland Hill
AP162

Design: 10col, Penny Black and Hill.

1979, July 16 *Perf. 13*

C752	AP162	5col lil rose & bl gray	1.00	.70
C753	AP162	10col dl bl & blk	1.75	1.25

Sir Rowland Hill (1795-1879), originator of penny postage.

Poverty, by Juan Ramon Bonilla — AP163

National Sculpture Contest: 60c, Hope, by Hernan Gonzalez. 2.10col, Cattle, by Victor M. Bermudez, horiz. 5col, Bust of Clorito Picado, by Juan Rafael Chacon. 20col, Mother and Child, by Francisco Zuniga.

1979, July 16 Litho. *Perf. 12*

C754	AP163	60c multi	.15	.15
C755	AP163	1col multi	.22	.15
C756	AP163	2.10col multi	.38	.28
C757	AP163	5col multi	1.10	.75
C758	AP163	20col multi	4.25	3.50
		Nos. C754-C758 (5)	6.10	4.83

Danaus Plexippus — AP164

Butterflies: 1col, Phoebis philea. 1.80col, Rothschildia. 2.10col, Prepona omphale. 2.60col, Marpesia marcella. 4.05col, Morpho cypris.

1979, Aug. 31 Litho. *Perf. 13½*

C759	AP164	60c multi	*1.90*	.30
C760	AP164	1col multi	*3.75*	.30
C761	AP164	1.80col multi	*5.75*	.50
C762	AP164	2.10col multi	*7.50*	.50
C763	AP164	2.60col multi	*7.50*	1.00
C764	AP164	4.05col multi	*11.00*	1.50
		Nos. C759-C764 (6)	*37.40*	4.10

SOS Emblem, Houses
AP165

Children's Drawings: 5col, 5.50col, Landscapes, diff.

1979, Sept. 18

C765	AP165	2.50col multi	.50	.35
C766	AP165	5col multi	1.00	.70
C767	AP165	5.50col multi	1.10	.80
		Nos. C765-C767 (3)	2.60	1.85

SOS Children's Villages, 30th anniversary.

President Type of 1943

Presidents of Costa Rica: 60c, Rafael Iglesias C. 85c, Ascension Esquivel Ibarra. 1col, Cleto Gonzalez Viquez. 2col, Ricardo Jimenez Oreamuno.

1979, Oct. 8 Litho. *Perf. 13½*

C768	A109	10c dk blue	.15	.15
C769	A109	60c dull pur	.15	.15
C770	A109	85c red org	.16	.15
C771	A109	1col red org	.20	.15
C772	A109	2col brown	.40	.28
a.		Strip of 5, #C768-C772	1.10	.75
		Nos. C768-C772 (5)	1.06	
		Set value		.68

Printed in sheets of 100 and se-tenant in sheets of 25 (5x5).

See Nos. C790-C794.

Holy Family, Creche
AP167

Reforestation
AP168

1979, Nov. 16 Litho. *Perf. 12½*

C773	AP167	1col multi	.20	.15
C774	AP167	1.60col multi	.35	.24

Christmas 1979.

1980, Jan. 14 Litho. *Perf. 11*

C775	AP168	1col multi	.16	.15
C776	AP168	3.40col multi	.55	.40

Anatomy Lesson, by Rembrandt
AP169

1980, Feb. 7 Litho. *Perf. 10½*

C777	AP169	10col multi	2.50	1.25

Legal medicine teaching in Costa Rica, 50th anniversary.

Rotary Intl., 75th Anniv. — AP170

Gulf of Nicoya, Satellite Photo — AP171

1980, Feb. 26 *Perf. 16*

C778	AP170	2.10col multi	.32	.24
C779	AP170	5col multi	.80	.60

1980, Mar. 10 Litho. *Perf. 12½*

C780	AP171	2.10col Puerto Limon	.32	.24
C781	AP171	5col shown	.80	.60

14th Intl. Symposium on Remote Sensing of the Environment, San José, Apr. 23-30. Exist imperf.

Soccer, Moscow '80 Emblem — AP172

Poas Volcano — AP173

1980, Apr. 16 Litho. *Perf. 10½*

C782	AP172	1col shown	*.16*	.15
C783	AP172	3col Bicycling	*12.00*	.50
C784	AP172	4.05col Baseball	*6.00*	.75
C785	AP172	20col Swimming	*15.00*	3.25
		Nos. C782-C785 (4)	*33.16*	4.65

22nd Summer Olympic Games, Moscow, July 19-Aug. 3.

1980, May 14 Litho. *Perf. 10½*

C786	AP173	1col shown	.16	.15
C787	AP173	2.50col Cahuita Beach	.40	.28

National Parks Service, 10th anniversary.

José Maria Zeledon Brenes, Score — AP174

Design: 10col, Manuel Maria Gutierrez.

1980, June 25 Litho. *Perf. 12½*

C788	AP174	1col multi	.16	.15
C789	AP174	10col multi	1.50	1.25

National anthem composed by Brenes (words) and Gutierrez (music). Exist imperf.

President Type of 1943

Presidents of Costa Rica: 1col, Alfredo Gonzalez F. 1.60col, Federico Tinoco G. 1.80col, Francisco Aguilar B. 2.10col, Julio Acosta G. 3col, Leon Cortes C.

1980, Aug. 14 Litho. *Perf. 11*

C790	A109	1col dk red	.16	.15
C791	A109	1.60col slate bl	.24	.16
C792	A109	1.80col brown	.28	.20
C793	A109	2.10col dl grn	.32	.24
C794	A109	3col dk pur	.48	.32
		Nos. C790-C794 (5)	1.48	1.07

8th Natl. Phil. Exhib. — AP175

Fruits — AP176

1980, Sept. 11 *Perf. 13½*

C795	AP175	5col multi	.80	.60
C796	AP175	20col multi	3.25	2.75

1980, Sept. 24 *Perf. 10½*

C797	AP176	10c shown	.15	.15
C798	AP176	60c Cacao	.15	.22
C799	AP176	1col Coffee	.16	.15
C800	AP176	2.10col Bananas	.32	.24
C801	AP176	3.40col Flowers	.55	.40
C802	AP176	5col Sugar cane	.80	.20
		Nos. C797-C802 (6)	2.13	1.36

Giant Tree, by Jorge Carvajal
AP177

Virgin and Child, by Raphael
AP178

Paintings: 2.10col, Secret Look, by Rolando Cubero. 2.45col, Consuelo, by Fernando Carballo. 3col, Volcano, by Lola Fernandez. 4.05col, attending Mass, by Francisco Amighetti.

1980, Oct. 22 Litho. *Perf. 10½*

C803	AP177	1col multi	.16	.15
C804	AP177	2.10col multi	.32	.24

Size: 28x30mm

C805	AP177	2.45col multi	.40	.32

Size: 22x36mm

C806	AP177	3col multi	.48	.35
C807	AP177	4.05col multi	.65	.48
		Nos. C803-C807 (5)	2.01	1.54

1980, Nov. 11 *Perf. 13½*

Christmas 1980: 10col, Virgin and Child and St. John, by Raphael.

C808	AP178	1col multi	.16	.15
C809	AP178	10col multi	1.50	1.50

Juan Santamaria International Airport — AP179

1980, Dec. 11 Litho. *Perf. 10½*

Sizes: 30x30mm, 31x25mm (1.30col), 25x32mm (2.60col)

C810	AP179	1col Caldera Harbor	.16	.15
C811	AP179	1.30col shown	.20	.16
C812	AP179	2.10col Rio Frio Railroad Bridge	.32	.24
C813	AP179	2.60col Highway to Colon	.40	.32
C814	AP179	5col Huetar post office	.80	.60
		Nos. C810-C814 (5)	1.88	1.47

Paying your taxes means progress.

For surcharge see No. C884.

Repertorio Americano Cover, J. Garcia Monge and Signature
AP180

1981, Jan. 2 Litho. *Perf. 10½*

C815	AP180	1.60col multi	.24	.16
C816	AP180	3col multi	.48	.32

Birth centenary of J. Garcia Monge, founder of Repertorio Americano journal.

Arms of Aserri (Site of Cornea Bank) AP181

Harpia Harpyja AP182

1981, Jan. 28 Litho. *Perf. 13½*

C817 AP181	1col	shown	.16	.15
C818 AP181	1.80col	Eye	.28	.20
C819 AP181	5col	Rojas	.80	.60
		Nos. C817-C819 (3)	1.24	.95

Establishment of human cornea bank, founded by Abelardo Rojas.

1980, Dec. 23 *Perf. 11*

C820 AP182	2.10col	shown	.75	.24
C821 AP182	2.50col	Ara macao	1.00	.32
C822 AP182	3col	Felis concolor	1.25	.35
C823 AP182	5.50col	Ateles geoffrovi	2.50	.65
		Nos. C820-C823 (4)	5.50	1.56

Medical and Surgical Clinic — AP183

1981, Apr. 8 Litho. *Perf. 10½*

C824 AP183	5c	shown	.15	.15
C825 AP183	10c	Physiology class	.15	.15
C826 AP183	50c	Medical school, A. Chavarria (1st dean)	.15	.15
C827 AP183	1.30col	Music school	.15	.15
C828 AP183	3.40col	Carlos Monge Alfaro Library	.20	.16
C829 AP183	4.05col	R.F. Brenes, rector (1952-1961), vert.	.24	.20
		Set value	.67	.57

University of Costa Rica, 40th anniversary.

Mail Transport by Horse AP184

1981, May 6 Litho. *Perf. 10½*

C830 AP184	1col	shown	.16	.15
C831 AP184	2.10col	Train, 1857	.32	.24
C832 AP184	10col	Mail carriers, 1858	1.50	1.25
		Nos. C830-C832 (3)	1.98	1.64

Heinrich von Stephan (1831-97), UPU founder.

13th World Telecommunications Day — AP185

1981, May 18 *Perf. 11*

C833 AP185	5col	multi	.80	.60
C834 AP185	25col	multi	4.00	2.75

Bishop Bernardo Thiel AP186

Juan Santamaria AP187

1981, June 8 Litho. *Perf. 10½*

C835		Strip of 5, stained glass windows	.50	.40
a.		AP186 1col Sts. Peter & Paul	.15	.15
b.		AP186 1col St. Vincent de Paul	.15	.15
c.		AP186 1col Death of St. Joseph	.15	.15
d.		AP186 1col Archangel Michael	.15	.15
e.		AP186 1col Holy Family	.15	.15
C836 AP186	2col	shown	.20	.15

Consecration of Bernardo Augusto Thiel as Bishop of San Jose.

1981, June 26 *Perf. 13½*

C837 AP187	1col	shown	.15	.15
C838 AP187	2.45col	Alajuela Cathedral, horiz.	.25	.15
		Set value		.21

Alajuela province.

Potters — AP188

1981, July 10 Litho. *Perf. 10½*

C839 AP188	15c	shown	.15	.15
C840 AP188	1.60col	Bricklayers	.15	.15
C841 AP188	1.80col	Farmers	.15	.15
C842 AP188	2.50col	Fishermen	.16	.15
C843 AP188	3col	Nurse, patient	.20	.16
C844 AP188	5col	Children, traffic policeman	.40	.24
		Nos. C839-C844 (6)	1.21	
		Set value		.72

Model of New Natl. Archives AP189

Natl. Archives Centenary: 1.40col, Leon Fernandez Bonilla, founder, vert. 2col, Arms, vert. 3col, St. Thomas University, former headquarters.

1981, Aug. 24 Litho. *Perf. 13½*

C845 AP189	1.40col	multi	.15	.15
C846 AP189	2col	multi	.16	.15
C847 AP189	3col	multi	.20	.16
C848 AP189	3.50col	multi	.24	.20
		Nos. C845-C848 (4)	.75	
		Set value		.54

Men Reaching for Sun, Map AP190

1981, Sept. 9 Litho. *Perf. 11*

C849 AP190	1col	Man in wheelchair, stairs, vert.	.30	.15
C850 AP190	2.60col	Man reaching for scale, vert.	.75	.15
C851 AP190	10col	shown	3.00	.52
		Nos. C849-C851 (3)	4.05	
		Set value		.70

Intl. Year of the Disabled.

World Food Day — AP191

1981, Oct. 16 Litho. *Perf. 10½*

C852 AP191	5col	multi	.40	.24
C853 AP191	10col	multi	.70	.52

President Type of 1943

President of Costa Rica: 1col, Rafael A. Calderon Guardia, 1940. 2col, Teodoro Picado Michalski, 1944. 3col, José Figueres Ferrer, 1953. 5col, Otilio Ulate Blanco, 1949. 10col, Mario Echandi Jimenez, 1958.

1981, Dec. 7 Litho. *Perf. 13½*

C854 A109	1col	pink	.15	.15
C855 A109	2col	orange	.16	.15
C856 A109	3col	green	.20	.16
C857 A109	5col	dk bl	.35	.24
C858 A109	10col	blue	.70	.52
		Nos. C854-C858 (5)	1.56	1.22

Bar Assoc. of Costa Rica Centenary (1981) — AP192

1982, Mar. 22 Litho. *Perf. 13½*

C859 AP192	1col	Emblem, horiz.	.15	.15
C860 AP192	2col	E. Figueroa, 1st pres.	.15	.15
C861 AP192	20col	Bar building, horiz.	1.25	.60
		Nos. C859-C861 (3)	1.55	
		Set value		.72

National Progress AP193

1982 *Perf. 10½*

C862 AP193	95c	Housing	.15	.15
C863 AP193	1.15col	Agricultural fair	.15	.15
C864 AP193	1.45col	Education	.15	.15
C865 AP193	1.65col	Drinkable water	.15	.15
C866 AP193	1.80col	Rural medical care	.15	.15
C867 AP193	2.10col	Recreational areas	.15	.15
C868 AP193	2.35col	Natl. Theater Square	.15	.15
C869 AP193	2.60col	Communications	.15	.15
C870 AP193	3col	Electric railroad	.15	.15
C871 AP193	4.05col	Irrigation	.16	.15
		Set value	1.15	.88

Issue dates: 1.80col, 2.10col, 2.60col, 3col, 4.05col, May 5; others, June 16.

City of Alajuela Bicentenary AP194

Perez Zeledon County, 50th Anniv. (1981) AP195

Designs: 5col, Central Park Fountain. 10col, Juan Santamaria Historical and Cultural Museum, horiz. 15col, Church of Christ of Esquipulas. 20col, Monsignor Esteban Lorenzo de Tristan, 25col, Father Juan Manuel Lopez del Corral.

1982, Aug. 9

C872 AP194	5col	multi	.28	.16
C873 AP194	10col	multi	.55	.28
C874 AP194	15col	multi	.80	.60
C875 AP194	20col	multi	1.10	.60
C876 AP194	25col	multi	1.40	.80
		Nos. C872-C876 (5)	4.13	2.44

1982, Aug. 30

Designs: 10c, Saint's Stone. 50c, Monument to Mothers. 1col, Pedro Perz Zeledon. 1.25col, St. Isidore Labrador Church. 3.50col, Municipal Building, horiz. 4.25col, Arms.

C877 AP195	10c	multi	.15	.15
C878 AP195	50c	multi	.15	.15
C879 AP195	1col	multi	.15	.15
C880 AP195	1.25col	multi	.15	.15
C881 AP195	3.50col	multi	.20	.15
C882 AP195	4.25col	multi	.24	.16
		Set value	.72	.50

Nos. C695 and C813 Surcharged

1982, Oct. 28 Litho. *Perf. 10½*

C883 AP143	3col	on 75c multi	.20	.15
C884 AP179	5col	on 2.60col multi	.32	.16

Nos. C640-C643 Surcharged and Overprinted: "IX EXPOSICION FILATELICA - 1982"

1982, Oct. 28 *Perf. 12*

C885 AP123	8.40col	on #C640	.48	.40
C886 AP123	8.40col	on #C641	.48	.40
C887 AP123	8.40col	on #C642	.48	.40
C888 AP123	8.40col	on #C643	.48	.40
C889 AP123	9.70col	on #C640	.60	.48
C890 AP123	9.70col	on #C641	.60	.48
C891 AP123	9.70col	on #C642	.60	.48
C892 AP123	9.70col	on #C643	.60	.48
		Nos. C885-C892 (8)	4.32	3.52

9th Natl. Stamp Exhibition.

TB Bacillus Centenary — AP196

Pan-American Blood Donors' Society, 7th Cong. — AP197

1982, Nov. 19 *Perf. 13½*

C893 AP196	1.50col	Koch	.15	.15
C894 AP196	3col	Koch, slide	.16	.15
C895 AP196	3.30col	Health Ministry	.20	.15
		Nos. C893-C895 (3)	.51	
		Set value		.28

1982, Nov. 25 *Perf. 11*

C896 AP197	30col	Natl. Blood Assoc. emblem	1.50	1.00
C897 AP197	50col	Cong. emblem	2.50	1.50

AP198

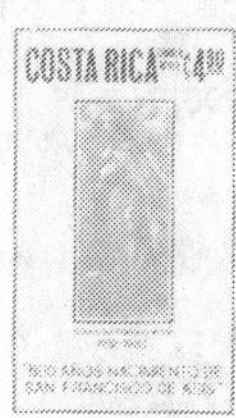

AP199

1982, Dec. 13 Litho. *Perf. 10½*

C898 AP198	8.40col	Emblem, horiz.	.40	.20
C899 AP198	9.70col	Emblem, diff.	.48	.24
C900 AP198	11.70col	Handshake, horiz.	.60	.28
C901 AP198	13.05col	Emblem, diff., horiz.	.65	.32
		Nos. C898-C901 (4)	2.13	1.04

Inter-Governmental Migration Committee, 30th anniv.

1983, Jan. 3 *Perf. 16*

Designs: 4.80col, St. Francis of Assisi, (1182-1226), by El Greco. 7.40col, Portrait, diff.

C902 AP199	4.80col	multi	.24	.15
C903 AP199	7.40col	multi	.35	.15
		Set value		.20

For surcharges see Nos. C908-C911.

Visit of Pope John Paul II — AP200

Bolivar, by Francisco Zuniga Chavarria — AP201

1983, Mar. 1 Litho. *Perf. 10½*

C904 AP200	5col	multi	*1.75*	.15
C905 AP200	10col	multi	*1.75*	.40
C906 AP200	15col	multi	*4.25*	.60
		Nos. C904-C906 (3)	*7.75*	1.15

1983, July 22 Litho. *Perf. 16*

C907 AP201	10col	multi	.55	.20

Nos. C902-C903 Surcharged

1983, Sept. 23 Litho. *Perf. 16*

C908 AP199 10c on 4.80col .15 .15
C909 AP199 50c on 4.80col .15 .15
C910 AP199 1.50col on 7.40col .15 .15
C911 AP199 3col on 7.40col .15 .15
Set value .45 .20

LACSA Costa Rica Airlines, 40th Anniv. — AP202

Various childrens' drawings.

1986, Dec. 12 Litho. *Perf. 13½*

C912 AP202 1col Adriana E. Hidalgo .40 .15
C913 AP202 7col Osvaldo A.G. Vega 2.75 .15
C914 AP202 16col David V. Rodriguez 6.25 .18
Nos. C912-C914 (3) 9.40
Set value .30

Roman Macaya Lahmann, Aviation Pioneer AP203

1988, Sept. 26 Litho. *Perf. 10½*

C915 AP203 10col multi .28 .15

No. 418 Ovptd. **LEY 7097 CORREO AEREO**

1990, Nov. 5

C916 A180 50col multicolored 1.10 .28

Bagging Coffee Beans — AP204

Perf. 10½

1990, Nov. 16 Litho. Unwmk.

C917 AP204 50col multicolored 1.10 .28

AP205

AP206

1990, Dec. 6

C918 AP205 50col blue & black 1.10 .28

First postage stamps, 150th anniv.

1991, Mar. 25 Litho. *Perf. 10½*

Design: Banana Picker, 1897, by Alleardo Villa.

C919 AP206 30col multicolored .65 .16

National Theater.

No. 428 Overprinted **Aéreo EXFILCORI '91**

Litho. & Engr.

1991, Sept. 13 *Perf. 12½*

C920 A188 200col on #428 4.50 1.10

12th Natl. Philatelic Exposition.

No. 402 Overprinted CENTENARIO DEL BALONCESTO CORREO AEREO

1991, Oct. 11 Litho. *Perf. 11½*

Granite Paper

C921 A170 20col multicolored 1.40 .35

Basketball, cent.

Social Security Administration, 50th Anniv. — AP207

1991, Nov. 1 Litho. *Perf. 13½*

C922 AP207 15col multicolored 1.05 .28

La Poesia by Vespaciano Bignami — AP208

1992, Jan. 24 Litho. *Perf. 10½*

C923 AP208 35col multicolored 2.50 .65

National Theater.

Discovery of America, 500th Anniv. — AP209

Columbus' ships: a, Nina. b, Santa Maria. c, Pinta.

1992, Oct. 8 Litho. *Perf. 13½*

C924 AP209 45col Strip of 3, #a.-c. 2.00 .50

Intl. Arts Festival — AP210

1993, Mar. 15 Litho. *Perf. 13½*

C925 AP210 45col multicolored .65 .16

Telecommunications Institute, 30th Anniv. — AP211

1993, Nov. 25 Litho. *Perf. 13½*

C926 AP211 45col multicolored .90 .45

Ministry of the Interior, 150th Anniv. AP212

1994, Mar. 8 Litho. *Perf. 10½*

C927 AP212 45col multicolored .90 .45

Intl. Year of the Family — AP213

1994, May 5 Litho. *Perf. 10½*

C928 AP213 45col multicolored .90 .45

AIR POST SPECIAL DELIVERY STAMPS

Catalogue values for unused stamps in this section are for Never Hinged items.

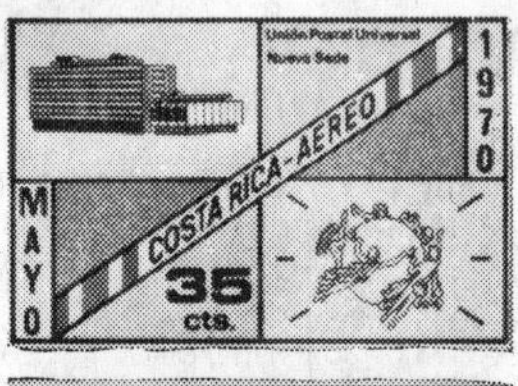

UPU Headquarters and Monument, Bern — APSD1

Perf. 10x11

1970, May 20 Litho. Unwmk.

CE1 APSD1 35c multi .20 .15
CE2 APSD1 60c multi .30 .15

Opening of the UPU Headquarters in Bern. The red and black label attached to the 60c is inscribed "EXPRES." Values are for stamps with label attached.

Stamps with labels removed were used for regular airmail.

AIR POST OFFICIAL STAMPS

Air Post Stamps of 1934 Overprinted in Red **OFICIAL**

1934 Unwmk. *Perf. 12*

CO1 AP8 5c green .20 .20
CO2 AP8 10c car rose .20 .20
CO3 AP8 15c chocolate .35 .35
CO4 AP8 20c deep blue .55 .55
CO5 AP8 25c deep org .55 .55
CO6 AP8 40c olive blk .60 .60
CO7 AP8 50c gray blk .60 .60
CO8 AP8 60c org yel .75 .75
CO9 AP8 75c dull vio .75 .75
CO10 AP9 1col deep rose 1.10 1.10
CO11 AP9 2col light blue 3.50 3.50
CO12 AP9 5col black 6.50 6.50
CO13 AP9 10col red brown 7.75 7.75
Nos. CO1-CO13 (13) 23.40 23.40

For overprints see Nos. C103-C116.

SPECIAL DELIVERY STAMPS

Catalogue values for unused stamps in this section are for Never Hinged items.

Winged Letter SD1

Unwmk.

1972, Mar. 20 Litho. *Perf. 11*

E1 SD1 75c brown & red .18 .15
E2 SD1 1.50col blue & red .38 .25

1973 *Perf. 11x12*

E3 SD1 75c green & red .18 .15

1973, Nov. 5 Litho.

E4 SD1 75c lilac & orange .95 .55

Concorde SD2

1976, May 17 Litho. *Perf. 16*

E5 SD2 1col vermilion & multi .18 .15

SD3

SD4

1979, June 15 Litho. *Perf. 12½*

E6 SD3 2col multi .38 .25

1980, Dec. 18 Litho. *Perf. 12½*

E7 SD4 2col multi .38 .25

1982, Dec. 20 Litho. *Perf. 11*

E8 SD4 4col multi .38 .25

POSTAGE DUE STAMPS

D1

D2

1903 Unwmk. Engr. *Perf. 14*

Numerals in Black

J1 D1 5c slate blue 5.00 .90
J2 D1 10c brown orange 5.00 .65
J3 D1 15c yellow green 2.00 1.75
J4 D1 20c carmine 2.25 1.65
J5 D1 25c slate gray 3.00 1.75
J6 D1 30c brown 4.50 2.50
J7 D1 40c olive bister 4.50 2.50
J8 D1 50c red violet 4.50 2.00
Nos. J1-J8 (8) 30.75 13.70

1915 Litho. *Perf. 12*

J9 D2 2c orange .15 .15
J10 D2 4c dark blue .15 .15
J11 D2 8c gray green .40 .40
J12 D2 10c violet .16 .16
J13 D2 20c brown .20 .20
Nos. J9-J13 (5) 1.06 1.06

OFFICIAL STAMPS

Values for unused stamps are for examples with original gum as defined in the catalogue introduction. Very fine examples of Nos. O1-O24 will have perforations just clear of the design on one or more sides.

Official stamps, to about 1915, normally were not canceled when affixed to official mail. Occasionally they were canceled in a foreign country of destination. Used values are for favor-canceled specimens or for stamps without gum.

Regular Issues Overprinted

Overprinted in Red, Black, Blue or Green **Oficial**

1883-85 Unwmk. *Perf. 12*

O1 A6 1c green (R) 1.25 1.00
O2 A6 1c green (Bk) 1.25 1.00
O3 A6 2c carmine (Bk) 1.50 1.25
O4 A6 2c carmine (Bl) 1.65 1.40
O5 A6 5c blue vio (R) 3.25 2.75
O6 A6 10c orange (G) 4.25 3.50
O7 A6 40c blue (R) 4.25 3.50
Nos. O1-O7 (7) 17.40 14.40

Overprinted **OFICIAL**

1886

O8 A6 1c green (Bk) 1.00 1.00
O9 A6 2c carmine (Bk) 1.50 1.50
O10 A6 5c blue vio (R) 15.00 10.00
O11 A6 10c orange (Bk) 15.00 10.00
Nos. O8-O11 (4) 32.50 22.50

Overprinted **OFICIAL**

O12 A6 1c green (Bk) .90 .90
O13 A6 2c carmine (Bk) 1.25 1.25
O14 A6 5c blue vio (R) 15.00 10.00
O15 A6 10c orange (Bk) 15.00 10.00
Nos. O12-O15 (4) 32.15 22.15

Nos. O8-O11 and O12-O15 exist se-tenant in vertical pairs.

Overprinted in Black **Oficial**

O16 A6 5c blue vio 35.00 25.00
O17 A6 10c orange — 225.00

Overprinted **OFICIAL.**

1887

O18 A6 1c green .50 .50
O19 A6 2c carmine .45 .45
O21 A6 10c orange 20.00 12.00
c. Double overprint 30.00
O22 A7 5c blue vio 5.00 2.25
O23 A7 10c orange .45 .45
c. Double overprint 25.00
O24 A6 40c blue .45 .45
Nos. O18-O24 (6) 26.85 16.10

Overprinted "OFICAL"

O18a A6 1c green
O19a A6 2c carmine *10.00 10.00*
O22a A7 5c blue violet *10.00*
O23a A7 10c orange *10.00 2.75*
O24a A6 40c blue *12.00 12.00*
Nos. O18a-O24a (4) 42.00

Dangerous counterfeits exist of Nos. O18a-O24a.

Without Period

O18b A6 1c green .65 .65
O19b A6 2c carmine .65 .65
O22b A7 5c blue violet 2.50 2.50
O23b A7 10c orange .95
Nos. O18b-O23b (4) 4.75

Nos. O18b-O23b are from a separate plate. No. O21 exists without period (position 32). These must be collected in pairs.

Issues of 1889-1901 Overprinted **OFICIAL**

1889 *Perf. 14, 15*

O25 A10 1c brown .20 .20
O26 A11 2c dk green .20 .20
O27 A12 5c orange .20 .20
O28 A13 10c red brown .20 .20
O29 A14 20c yellow grn .20 .20
O30 A15 50c rose red 1.00 1.00
Nos. O25-O30 (6) 2.00 2.00

1892

O31 A20 1c grnsh blue .24 .24
O32 A21 2c yellow .24 .24
O33 A22 5c violet .24 .24
O34 A23 10c lt green 1.00 1.00
O35 A24 20c scarlet .16 .15
O36 A25 50c gray blue .50 .50
Nos. O31-O36 (6) 2.38 2.37

1901-02

O37 A30 1c green & blk .35 .35
O38 A31 2c ver & blk .35 .35
O39 A32 5c gray bl & blk .35 .35
O40 A33 10c ocher & blk .60 .60
O41 A34 20c lake & blk .85 .85
O42 A35 50c lilac & dk bl 2.75 2.75
O43 A36 1col ol bis & blk 8.00 8.00
Nos. O37-O43 (7) 13.25 13.25

No. 46 Overprinted in Green **PROVISORIO OFICIAL**

1903

O44 A31 2c ver & blk 2.25 2.25
b. "PROVISIORO" 6.00 6.00
d. Inverted overprint 6.00 4.00
f. As "b," inverted 10.00 8.00

Counterfeit overprints exist.

Regular Issue of 1903 Overprinted Like Nos. O25-O43

1903 *Perf. 14, 12½x14*

O45 A40 4c red vio & blk 1.10 1.10
O46 A41 6c ol grn & blk 1.25 1.25
O47 A42 25c gray lil & brn 8.00 4.50
Nos. O45-O47 (3) 10.35 6.85

Counterfeit overprints exist.

Regular Issue of 1907 Overprinted **OFICIAL**

1908 *Perf. 14*

O48 A43 1c red brn & ind .15 .15
O49 A44 2c yel grn & blk .15 .15
O50 A45 4c car & ind .15 .15
O51 A46 5c yel & dull bl .15 .15
O52 A47 10c blue & blk .90 .90
O53 A49 25c gray lil & blk .16 .16
O54 A50 50c red lil & bl .28 .28
O55 A51 1col brown & blk .70 .70
Nos. O48-O55 (8) 2.64 2.64

Various varieties of the overprint and basic stamps exist.

Imperf examples of Nos. O48, O49, O53 were found in 1970.

Regular Issue of 1910 Overprinted in Black **OFICIAL 15 VI · 1917**

1917

O56 A56 5c orange .22 .22
a. Inverted overprint 3.00 2.50
O57 A57 10c deep blue .18 .18
a. Inverted overprint

No. 74 Surcharged **OFICIAL ✱15✱ CENTIMOS**

1920 Red Surcharge *Perf. 12*

O58 A58 15c on 20c olive grn .50 .50

Nos. 72, 61, 59, 65-67 Surcharged or Overprinted **1921 – 22**

A56

OFICIAL
O60

A43

OFICIAL

1921 Black Surcharge *Perf. 12*

O59 A56 10c on 5c orange .30 .24
a. "10 CTS." inverted 16.00

Perf. 14

O60 A45 4c car & indigo .28 .28
a. "1291" for "1921" 11.00
O61 A43 6c on 1c red brn & ind .40 .40
O62 A49 20c on 25c gray lil & blk .40 .40

Overprinted like No. O60

O63 A50 50c red lil & bl 1.50 1.50
O64 A51 1col brn & blk 2.75 2.75
Nos. O59-O64 (6) 5.63 5.57

Nos. O60 to O64 exist with date and new values inverted. These may be printer's waste but probably were deliberately made.

Regular Issue of 1923 Overprinted **OFICIAL**

1923 *Perf. 11½*

O65 A68 2c brown .22 .22
O66 A68 4c green .15 .15
O67 A68 5c blue .22 .22
O68 A68 20c carmine .15 .15
O69 A68 1col violet .30 .30
Nos. O65-O69 (5) 1.04 1.04

Nos. O65 to O69 exist imperforate but were not regularly issued in that condition.

O7

1926 Unwmk. Engr. *Perf. 12½*

O70 O7 2c ultra & blk .15 .15
O71 O7 3c mag & blk .15 .15
O72 O7 4c lt bl & blk .15 .15
O73 O7 5c grn & blk .15 .15
O74 O7 6c ocher & blk .15 .15
O75 O7 10c rose red & blk .15 .15
O76 O7 20c ol grn & blk .15 .15
O77 O7 30c red org & blk .15 .15
O78 O7 45c brown & blk .18 .18
O79 O7 1col lilac & blk .28 .28
Set value 1.10 1.10

See #O82-O94. For surcharges see #C7-C10.

Regular Issue of 1936 Overprinted in Black **OFICIAL**

1936 Unwmk. *Perf. 12*

O80 A96 5c green .15 .15
O81 A96 10c carmine rose .15 .15
Set value .16 .16

Type of 1926

1937 *Perf. 12½*

O82 O7 2c vio & blk .15 .15
O83 O7 3c bis brn & blk .15 .15
O84 O7 4c rose car & blk .15 .15
O85 O7 5c ol grn & blk .15
O86 O7 8c blk brn & blk .15
O87 O7 10c rose lake & blk .15
O88 O7 20c ind & blk .15 .15
O89 O7 40c red org & blk .20 .20
O90 O7 55c dk vio & blk .28
O91 O7 1col brn vio & blk .24 .24
O92 O7 2col gray bl & blk .48 .48
O93 O7 5col dl yel & blk 2.50 2.50
O94 O7 10col blue & blk 16.00 16.00
Nos. O82-O94 (13) 20.75

Nine stamps of this series exist with perforated star (2c, 3c, 4c, 20c, 40c, 1col, 2col, 5col, 10col). These were issued to officials for postal purposes. Unpunched copies were sold to collectors but had no franking power. Values for unused are for unpunched.

POSTAL TAX STAMPS

Catalogue values for unused stamps in this section are for Never Hinged items.

Most postal tax issues were to benefit the Children's Village and were obligatory on all mail during Dec.

No. C198 Surcharged in Red: "Sello de Navidad Pro-Ciudad de Los Niños 5 5"

Engraved; Center Photogravure

1958 Unwmk. *Perf. 12½*

RA1 AP51 5c on 2c brt bl & blk .15 .15

Similar Surcharge in Green on Type of 1954

Design: Like No. C228, pottery.

RA2 AP53 5c on 10c dk bl & blk .35 .15
a. Inverted surcharge 7.50

Father Edward J. Flanagan — PT1

Father Peralta — PT2

Paintings: No. RA4, Boy by El Greco. No. RA5, Boy by Jose Ribera. No. RA6, Girl by Amadeo Modigliani.

Perf. 13½

1959, Nov. 25 Unwmk. Photo.

RA3 PT1 5c green .25 .20
RA4 PT1 5c dl gray vio .25 .20
RA5 PT1 5c olive .25 .20
RA6 PT1 5c lilac rose .25 .20
Nos. RA3-RA6 (4) 1.00 .80

Exist imperf.

1960 Litho. *Perf. 14*

Designs: No. RA8, Girl by Renoir. No. RA9, Boys with cups by Velazquez. No. RA10, Singing children, sculpture by F. Zuñiga.

RA7 PT2 5c chocolate .25 .20
RA8 PT2 5c dp org .25 .20
RA9 PT2 5c plum .25 .20
RA10 PT2 5c grysh bl .25 .20
Nos. RA7-RA10 (4) 1.00 .80

Exist imperf.

#C229 Surcharged Like #RA1-RA2

Engraved; Center Photogravure

1961 *Perf. 13x12½*

RA11 AP53 5c on 15c grn & blk .22 .15

Nicolas, Son of Rubens — PT3

Boys in Workshop — PT4

Designs: No. RA13, Madonna by Bellini. RA14, Angel playing stringed instrument by Melozzo. RA15, Msgr. Rubén Odio H.

1962 Photo. *Perf. 13½*

RA12 PT3 5c dark carmine .25 .20
RA13 PT3 5c sepia .25 .20
RA14 PT3 5c dull green .25 .20
RA15 PT3 5c blue .25 .20
Nos. RA12-RA15 (4) 1.00 .80

For surcharges see Nos. 262-265.

Type of 1962, Inscribed "1963"
Designs as before

1963 Photo. *Perf. 13½*

RA16 PT3 5c sepia (RA12) .25 .15
RA17 PT3 5c ultra (RA13) .25 .15
RA18 PT3 5c dk car (RA14) .25 .15
RA19 PT3 5c black (RA15) .25 .15
Nos. RA16-RA19 (4) 1.00 .60

1964 Litho. *Perf. 12½*

Designs: No. RA21, Two playing boys. No. RA22, Teacher and children. No. RA23, Priest with boys.

RA20 PT4 5c bright green .25 .15
RA21 PT4 5c rose lilac .25 .15
RA22 PT4 5c blue .25 .15
RA23 PT4 5c brown .25 .15
Nos. RA20-RA23 (4) 1.00 .60

Brother Casiano de Madrid PT5

Christmas Ornaments PT6

Designs: No. RA25, National Children's Hospital. No. RA26, Poinsettia. No. RA27, Santa Claus with children (diamond).

1965, Dec. 10 Litho. *Perf. 10*

RA24 PT5 5c red brn .18 .15
RA25 PT5 5c green .18 .15
RA26 PT5 5c red .18 .15
RA27 PT5 5c ultra .18 .15
Nos. RA24-RA27 (4) .72 .60

1966 Litho. *Perf. 11*

RA28 PT6 5c shown .18 .15
RA29 PT6 5c Angel .18 .15
RA30 PT6 5c Church .18 .15
RA31 PT6 5c Reindeer .18 .15
Nos. RA28-RA31 (4) .72
Set value .32

General Post Office, San José — PT7

1967, Mar. **Litho.** ***Perf. 11***
RA32 PT7 10c blue .15 .15

No. RA32 was issued as a postal tax stamp to be used by organizations normally allowed free postage. On Dec. 15, 1972, it was authorized for use as an ordinary postage stamp.

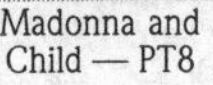

Madonna and Child — PT8

Star of Bethlehem, Mother and Child — PT9

1967 **Litho.** ***Perf. 11***
RA33 PT8 5c ol grn .15 .15
RA34 PT8 5c dp lil rose .15 .15
RA35 PT8 5c brt bl .15 .15
RA36 PT8 5c grnsh bl .15 .15
Set value .48 .40

1968, Dec. **Litho.** ***Perf. 12½***
RA37 PT9 5c gray .15 .15
RA38 PT9 5c rose red .15 .15
RA39 PT9 5c dk rose brn .15 .15
RA40 PT9 5c bis brn .15 .15
Set value .48 .40

Madonna and Child — PT10

Christ Child, Star — PT11

1969, Dec. **Litho.** ***Perf. 12½***
RA41 PT10 5c dk bl .15 .15
RA42 PT10 5c orange .15 .15
RA43 PT10 5c brn red .15 .15
RA44 PT10 5c bl grn .15 .15
Set value .20 .20

1970, Dec. **Litho.** ***Perf. 12½***
RA45 PT11 5c brt pur .15 .15
RA46 PT11 5c lil rose .15 .15
RA47 PT11 5c olive .15 .15
RA48 PT11 5c ocher .15 .15
Set value .20 .20

Christ Child and "PAX" — PT12

Madonna and Child — PT13

1971, Nov. 29
RA49 PT12 10c dk bl .15 .15
RA50 PT12 10c orange .15 .15
RA51 PT12 10c brown .15 .15
RA52 PT12 10c green .15 .15
Set value .28 .20

1972, Nov. 30 ***Perf. 11x11½***
RA53 PT13 10c dk bl .15 .15
RA54 PT13 10c brt red .15 .15
RA55 PT13 10c lilac .15 .15
RA56 PT13 10c green .15 .15
Set value .28 .20

Madonna and Child — PT14

Boys Eating Cake, by Murillo — PT15

1973, Nov. 30 **Litho.** ***Perf. 12½***
RA57 PT14 10c purple .15 .15
RA58 PT14 10c car rose .15 .15
RA59 PT14 10c gray .15 .15
RA60 PT14 10c org brn .15 .15
Set value .28 .20

1974, Nov. 25 ***Perf. 13***

Paintings: No. RA62, Virgin and Child, with St. John, by Raphael. No. RA63, Maternity, by Juan R. Bonilla. No. RA64, Praying Child, by Reynolds.

RA61 PT15 10c brt pink .15 .15
RA62 PT15 10c rose lil .15 .15
RA63 PT15 10c dk gray .15 .15
RA64 PT15 10c vio bl .15 .15
Set value .24 .20

See No. RA110.

"Happy Dreams," by Sonia Romero — PT16

Virgin and Child, by Hans Memling — PT17

Paintings: No. RA66, Virgin with Carnation, by Leonardo da Vinci. No. RA67, Children with Tortoise, by Francisco Amighetti. No. RA68, Boy with Pigeon, by Picasso.

1975, Nov. 25 **Litho.** ***Perf. 10½***
RA65 PT16 10c gray .15 .15
RA66 PT16 10c red lil .15 .15
RA67 PT16 10c org brn .15 .15
RA68 PT16 10c brt bl .15 .15
Set value .20 .20

1976, Nov. 24 **Litho.** ***Perf. 10½***

Paintings: No. RA70, Boy with Sombrero, by Auguste Renoir. No. RA71, Meditation (Boy), by Floria Pinto de Herrero. No. RA72, Gaston de Mezerville (boy), by Lolita Zeller de Peralta.

RA69 PT17 10c rose lil .15 .15
RA70 PT17 10c rose car .15 .15
RA71 PT17 10c gray .15 .15
RA72 PT17 10c vio bl .15 .15
Set value .20 .20

Boy's Head, by Amparo Cruz — PT18

Boy with Kite — PT19

Paintings: No. RA74, Girl's head, by Rubens. No. RA75, Girl and infant, by Cristina Fournier. No. RA76, Mariano Goya, by Goya.

1977, Nov. **Litho.** ***Perf. 10½***
RA73 PT18 10c gray ol .15 .15
RA74 PT18 10c rose red .15 .15
RA75 PT18 10c brt ultra .15 .15
RA76 PT18 10c brt rose lil .15 .15
Set value .20 .20

1978, Nov. 20 **Litho.** ***Perf. 12½***

Designs: Nos. RA78-RA79, Girl flying kite.

RA77 PT19 10c magenta .15 .15
RA78 PT19 10c slate .15 .15
RA79 PT19 10c lilac .15 .15
RA80 PT19 10c vio bl .15 .15
Set value .20 .20

Boy Leaning on Tree — PT20

Boy on Swing — PT21

1979, Nov. 19 **Litho.** ***Perf. 12½***
RA81 PT20 10c blue .15 .15
RA82 PT20 10c orange .15 .15
RA83 PT20 10c magenta .15 .15
RA84 PT20 10c green .15 .15
Set value .20 .20

1980, Nov. 18 **Litho.** ***Perf. 12½***
RA85 PT21 10c brt bl .15 .15
RA86 PT21 10c brt yel .15 .15
RA87 PT21 10c crim rose .15 .15
RA88 PT21 10c brt grn .15 .15
Set value .20 .20

Boy Riding Toy Car — PT22

Youth Running Machine — PT23

1981, Nov. 19 **Litho.** ***Perf. 11***
RA89 PT22 10c blue .15 .15
RA90 PT22 10c green .15 .15
RA91 PT22 10c red .15 .15
RA92 PT22 10c orange .15 .15
Set value .20 .20

1982, Nov. 19 **Litho.** ***Perf. 10½***
RA93 PT23 10c red .15 .15
RA94 PT23 10c gray .15 .15
RA95 PT23 10c purple .15 .15
RA96 PT23 10c grnsh bl .15 .15
Set value .20 .20

Youths Working on Wheelchair — PT24

Girl on Bicycle — PT25

1983, Nov. 24 **Litho.** ***Perf. 16***
RA97 PT24 10c red .15 .15
RA98 PT24 10c orange .15 .15
RA99 PT24 10c ultra .15 .15
RA100 PT24 10c green .15 .15
Set value .20 .20

Christmas 1983.

1984, Nov. 20 **Litho.** ***Perf. 10½***
RA101 PT25 10c violet .15 .15

Christmas 1984.

Taking a Child in Out of the Cold — PT26

Depressed Child — PT27

1985, Dec. 1 **Litho.** ***Perf. 13***
RA102 PT26 10c dull brn .20 .15

Christmas 1985.

1986, Dec. 1 **Litho.** ***Perf. 10½***
RA103 PT27 10c lemon .15 .15

Christmas stamps, 25th anniv.; Christmas 1986.

Christmas — PT28

Teaching Children — PT29

1987, Dec. 1 **Litho.** ***Perf. 10½***
RA104 PT28 10c dk ol bis & brt bl .15 .15

No postal tax stamp was issued for 1988.

1989, Dec. 1 **Litho.** ***Perf. 13½***
RA105 PT29 1col blue, blk & brt apple grn .15 .15

Christmas 1989.

No. 417 Ovptd. in Red, Blue, Green, or Orange

LEY 7157
PRO-CIUDAD
DE LOS
NIÑOS 1990

1990, Nov. 16 **Litho.** ***Perf. 13½***
RA106 A179 10col multi (R) .25 .15
RA107 A179 10col multi (Bl) .25 .15
RA108 A179 10col multi (G) .25 .15
RA109 A179 10col multi (O) .25 .15
Nos. RA106-RA109 (4) 1.00
Set value .24

Art Type of 1974

Design: 10col, Praying Child, by Reynolds.

1991, Nov. 18 **Litho.** ***Perf. 10½***
RA110 PT15 10col dark ultra .70 .18

Boy in Workshop — PT30

Children's Village — PT31

1992, Dec. 1 **Litho.** ***Perf. 10½***
RA111 PT30 10col red .15 .15

Christmas.

1993, Nov. 17
RA112 PT31 10col multicolored .22 .15

Christmas.

Christmas — PT32

1994, Nov. 23 **Litho.** ***Perf. 10½***
RA113 PT32 11col lilac & slate .15 .15

GUANACASTE

ˌgwä–nə–ˈkästā

(A province of Costa Rica)

LOCATION — Northwestern coast of Central America
AREA — 4,000 sq. mi. (approx.)
POP. — 69,531 (estimated)
CAPITAL — Liberia

Residents of Guanacaste were allowed to buy Costa Rican stamps, overprinted "Guanacaste," at a discount from face value because of the province's isolation and climate, which makes it difficult to keep mint stamps. Use was restricted to the province.

Counterfeits of most Guanacaste overprints are plentiful.

Very fine examples of Nos. 1-54 will have perforations just clear of the design on one or more sides.

On Issue of 1883
Overprinted Horizontally in Black

16mm **Guanacaste**

1885 Unwmk. *Perf. 12*

1	A6	1c green	3.00	3.00
2	A6	2c carmine	3.00	3.00
a.		"Gnanacaste"	*150.00*	
3	A6	10c orange	15.00	15.00
a.		"Gnanacaste"	*500.00*	

Same Overprint in Red

4	A6	1c green	3.00	3.00
a.		"Gnanacaste"	*150.00*	
b.		Overprinted in black & red	*250.00*	
5	A6	5c blue violet	15.00	3.00
a.		"Gnanacaste"	*350.00*	
6	A6	40c blue	15.00	15.00

Overprinted Horizontally in Black

17½mm **Guanacaste**

7	A6	1c green	5.00	5.00
8	A6	2c carmine	5.00	5.00
9	A6	5c blue violet	25.00	5.00
10	A6	10c orange	25.00	15.00
11	A6	40c blue	40.00	40.00

Same Overprint in Red

12	A6	5c blue violet	40.00	15.00
13	A6	40c blue	*2,000.*	

Overprinted Horizontally in Black

18½mm- c **Guanacaste**

14	A6	2c carmine	10.00	7.00
15	A6	10c orange	60.00	50.00

Same Overprint in Red

16	A6	1c green	6.00	7.00
a.		Double ovpt., one in blk	125.00	
17	A6	5c blue violet	35.00	7.00
18	A6	40c blue	50.00	50.00

Same Overprint, Vertically in Black

19	A6	1c green	*4,000.*	
20	A6	2c carmine	*3,500.*	
21	A6	5c blue violet	400.00	150.00
22	A6	10c orange	75.00	40.00

Guanacaste *e* GUANACASTE *f* GUANACASTE *g* GUANACASTE *h* GUANACASTE *i*

Overprinted Type e, Vertically

23	A6	1c green	250.00	200.00
24	A6	2c carmine	200.00	175.00
25	A6	5c blue violet	200.00	50.00
26	A6	10c orange	60.00	45.00

Overprinted Type f, Vertically

27	A6	1c green	500.00	300.00
28	A6	2c carmine	250.00	200.00
29	A6	5c blue violet	400.00	100.00
30	A6	10c orange	70.00	60.00

Overprinted Type g, Vertically

31	A6	1c green	600.00	225.00
32	A6	2c carmine	400.00	225.00
33	A6	5c blue violet	375.00	125.00
34	A6	10c orange	150.00	125.00

Overprinted Type h, Vertically

35	A6	1c green	250.00	100.00
36	A6	2c carmine	125.00	80.00
37	A6	5c blue violet	175.00	75.00
38	A6	10c orange	35.00	25.00

The authenticity of Costa Rica Nos. 16-19 with overprint "i" has not been established.

On Issues of 1883-87

Overprinted Horizontally in Black **Guanacaste**

1888-89

42	A7	5c blue violet	15.00	3.00

Overprinted Horizontally in Black **Guanacaste**

43	A7	5c blue violet	15.00	3.00

Overprinted Horizontally in Black **Guanacaste**

44	A6	2c carmine	3.00
45	A7	10c orange	3.00

Inverted overprints are fakes.

On Issue of 1889
Overprinted Like Nos. 7-13, Horizontally

1889

47	A8	2c blue	20.00

Vertically

48	A8	2c blue (c)	250.00
49	A8	2c blue (e)	60.00
51	A8	2c blue (f)	100.00
52	A8	2c blue (g)	250.00
54	A8	2c blue (h)	100.00

Nos. 47-54 are overprinted "Correos." Copies without "Correos" are known postally used, and are valued the same as Nos. 47-54, unused.

Dangerous counterfeits exist of Nos. 1-54.

On Nos. 25-33

Overprinted Horizontally in Black **GUANACASTE**

1889 *Perf. 14 and 15*

55	A10	1c brown	5.00	3.00
56	A11	2c dk grn	3.00	1.50
57	A12	5c orange	4.00	1.50
58	A13	10c red brn	4.00	1.50
59	A14	20c yel grn	1.00	1.50
60	A15	50c rose red	1.50	1.50
61	A16	1p blue	2.50	2.50
62	A17	2p violet	5.00	5.00
63	A18	5p ol grn	35.00	30.00
		Nos. 55-63 (9)	61.00	48.00

Overprinted "GUAGACASTE"

60a	A15	50c rose red	*300.00*	
61a	A16	1p blue	*300.00*	80.00
62a	A17	2p violet	*350.00*	80.00
63a	A18	5p olive green	*500.00*	80.00

Overprinted Horizontally in Black **GUANACASTE**

64	A10	1c brown	2.00	1.50
a.		Vert. pair, imperf. between		
65	A11	2c dark green	2.00	1.50
66	A12	5c orange	2.00	1.50
67	A13	10c red brown	2.00	1.50
		Nos. 64-67 (4)	8.00	6.00

CRETE

'krēt

LOCATION — An island in the Mediterranean Sea south of Greece
GOVT. — A department of Greece
AREA — 3,235 sq. mi.
POP. — 336,150 (1913)
CAPITAL — Canea

Formerly Crete was a province of Turkey. After an extended period of civil wars, France, Great Britain, Italy and Russia intervened and declaring Crete an autonomy, placed it under the administration of Prince George of Greece as High Commissioner. In October, 1908, the Cretan Assembly voted for union with Greece and in 1913 the union was formally effected.

40 Paras = 1 Piaster
4 Metallik = 1 Grosion (1899)
100 Lepta = 1 Drachma (1900)

Issued Under Joint Administration of France, Great Britain, Italy and Russia

British Sphere of Administration District of Heraklion (Candia)

A1

A2

Handstamped

1898 Unwmk. *Imperf.*

1	A1	20pa violet	400.00	275.00

1898 Litho. *Perf. 11½*

2	A2	10pa blue	8.00	2.50
a.		Horiz. pair, imperf. btwn.		
b.		Imperf., pair	250.00	
3	A2	20pa green	8.00	2.50
a.		Imperf., pair	250.00	

1899

4	A2	10pa brown	8.00	2.50
a.		Horiz. pair, imperf. btwn.		
b.		Imperf., pair	250.00	
5	A2	20pa rose	8.00	2.50
a.		Imperf., pair	250.00	

Used values for Nos. 2-5 are for stamps canceled by the straight-line "Heraklion" town postmark. Stamps canceled with any other postmark used for postal duty are scarce and worth much more.

Counterfeits exist of Nos. 1-5.

Reprints exist of Nos. 2-5.

Russian Sphere of Administration District of Rethymnon

Coat of Arms
A3 A4

1899 Handstamped *Imperf.*

10	A3	1m green	6.50	4.50
11	A3	2m black	6.50	4.50
12	A3	2m rose	250.00	200.00
13	A4	1m blue	75.00	17.00

Nos. 10-13 exist on both wove and laid papers. Counterfeits exist.

Poseidon's Trident
A5 A5a

1899 Litho. *Perf. 11½*

With Control Mark Overprinted in Violet

Without Stars at Sides

14	A5	1m orange	80.	60.
15	A5	2m orange	80.	60.
16	A5	1gr orange	80.	60.
17	A5	1m green	80.	60.
18	A5	2m green	80.	60.
19	A5	1gr green	80.	60.
20	A5	1m yellow	80.	60.
21	A5	2m yellow	80.	60.
22	A5	1gr yellow	80.	60.
23	A5	1m rose	80.	60.
24	A5	2m rose	80.	60.
25	A5	1gr rose	80.	60.
26	A5	1m violet	80.	60.
27	A5	2m violet	80.	60.
28	A5	1gr violet	80.	60.
29	A5	1m blue	80.	60.
30	A5	2m blue	80.	60.
31	A5	1gr blue	80.	60.
32	A5	1m black	1,250.	1,050.
33	A5	2m black	1,200.	1,050.
34	A5	1gr black	1,200.	1,050.

With Stars at Sides

35	A5a	1m blue	25.00	15.00
36	A5a	2m blue	7.00	5.25
37	A5a	1gr blue	4.50	3.25
38	A5a	1m rose	50.00	40.00
39	A5a	2m rose	7.00	5.25
40	A5a	1gr rose	4.50	3.25
41	A5a	1m green	22.50	15.00
42	A5a	2m green	7.00	5.25
43	A5a	1gr green	4.50	3.25
44	A5a	1m violet	22.50	15.00
45	A5a	2m violet	7.00	5.25
46	A5a	1gr violet	4.50	4.25
		Nos. 35-46 (12)	166.00	120.00

Nearly all of Nos. 14 to 46 may be found without control mark, with double control marks and in various colors.

Counterfeits exist of Nos. 14-46.

Issued by the Cretan Government

Hermes — A6

Hera — A7

Prince George of Greece — A8

Talos — A9

Minos — A10

St. George and the Dragon — A11

1900, Mar. 1 Engr. *Perf. 14*

50	A6	1 l violet brown	.25	.25
51	A7	5 l green	1.25	.25
52	A8	10 l red	1.65	.25
53	A7	20 l carmine rose	4.75	1.10
		Nos. 50-53 (4)	7.90	1.85

See #64-71. For overprints and surcharges see #54-63, 72-73, 85, 88, 93, 97-99, 108, 111.

Overprinted **ΠΡΟΣΩΡΙΝΟΝ**

Red Overprint

54	A8	25 l blue	2.00	.80
55	A6	50 l lilac	2.25	1.25
56	A9	1d gray violet	12.00	10.00
57	A10	2d brown	24.00	24.00
58	A11	5d green & blk	85.00	85.00
		Nos. 54-58 (5)	125.25	121.05

Black Overprint

59	A8	25 l blue	2.00	.85
60	A6	50 l lilac	2.00	1.25
61	A9	1d gray violet	10.00	4.50
a.		Inverted overprint	*500.00*	*500.00*
62	A10	2d brown	22.50	14.00
63	A11	5d green & blk	45.00	45.00
		Nos. 59-63 (5)	81.50	65.60

1901

Without Overprint

64	A6	1 l bister		.85
65	A7	20 l orange	4.50	.85
66	A8	25 l blue	8.25	.45
67	A6	50 l lilac	27.50	22.50
68	A6	50 l ultra	12.50	11.00
69	A9	1d gray violet	27.50	22.50
70	A10	2d brown	8.75	7.75
71	A11	5d green & blk	8.75	7.75
		Nos. 64-71		65.70
		Nos. 65-71	89.50	

No. 64 is a revenue stamp that was used for postage for a short time. Unused, it can only be considered as a revenue.

Types A6 to A8 in olive yellow, and types A9 to A11 in olive yellow and black are revenue stamps.

See note following No. 53.

Surcharges with the year "1922" on designs A6, A8, A9, A11, A13, A15-A23 and D1 are listed under Greece.

No. 66 Overprinted in Black **ΠΡΟΣΩΡΙΝΟΝ**

1901

72	A8	25 l blue	30.00	.85
a.		First letter of ovpt. invtd.	300.00	200.00

No. 65 Surcharged in Black **5**

1904, Dec.

73	A7	5 l on 20 l orange	4.50	.85
a.		Without "5" at right	100.00	50.00

Mycenaean Seal — A12

Britomartis (Cortyna Coin) — A13

Prince George — A14

Kydon and Dog (Cydonia Coin) — A15

Triton (Itanos Coin) — A16

Ariadne (Knossos Coin) — A17

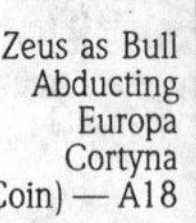

Zeus as Bull Abducting Europa Cortyna Coin) — A18

Palace of Minos Ruins, Knossos A19

Arkadi Monastery and Mt. Ida — A20

1905, Feb. 15

No.	Type	Description	Unused	Used
74	A12	2 l dull violet	2.00	.45
75	A13	5 l yellow grn	4.50	.45
76	A14	10 l red	4.50	.45
77	A15	20 l blue grn	4.50	.85
78	A16	25 l ultra	6.00	.85
79	A17	50 l yellow brn	7.00	5.50
80	A18	1d rose car & dp brn	50.00	50.00
81	A19	3d orange & blk	35.00	35.00
82	A20	5d ol grn & blk	14.00	13.00
		Nos. 74-82 (9)	127.50	106.55

For overprints see Nos.86-87, 89, 91-92, 94-95, 104, 106, 109-110, 112-113, 115-120.

The so-called revolutionary stamps of 1905 were issued for sale to collectors and, so far as can be ascertained, were of no postal value whatever.

A. T. A. Zaimis — A21

Prince George Landing at Suda A22

1907, Aug. 28

No.	Type	Description	Unused	Used
83	A21	25 l blue & blk	35.00	1.10
84	A22	1d green & blk	8.25	8.25

Administration under a High Commissioner. For overprints see Nos. 90, 105, 107.

Stamps of 1900-1907 Overprinted in Black ΕΛΛΑΣ

1908, Sept. 21

No.	Type	Description	Unused	Used
85	A6	1 l violet brn	.65	.65
86	A12	2 l dull violet	.65	.65
87	A13	5 l yellow grn	.65	.65
88	A8	10 l red	1.10	.65
89	A15	20 l blue grn	4.25	.85
90	A21	25 l blue & blk	9.25	.85
91	A17	50 l yellow brn	9.25	2.50
92	A18	1d rose car & dp brn	55.00	55.00
93	A10	2d brown	8.75	8.75
94	A19	3d orange & blk	27.50	27.50
95	A20	5d ol grn & blk	24.00	24.00
		Nos. 85-95 (11)	141.05	122.05

This overprint exists inverted and double, as well as with incorrect, reversed, misplaced and omitted letters. Similar errors are found on the Postage Due and Official stamps with this overprint.

Hermes by Praxiteles — A23

1908

No.	Type	Description	Unused	Used
96	A23	10 l brown red	2.25	.85
a.		Pair, one without overprint	8.00	
b.		Inverted overprint	15.00	
c.		Double overprint	15.00	

Nos. 96 and 114 were not regularly issued without overprint.

For overprints see Nos. 103, 114.

No. 53 Surcharged ΕΛΛΑΣ ΠΡΟΣΟΡΙΝΟΝ 5 5

1909

No.	Type	Description	Unused	Used
97	A7	5 l on 20 l car rose	100.00	100.00

Forgeries exist of No. 97.

On No. 65

No.	Type	Description	Unused	Used
98	A7	5 l on 20 l orange	1.75	1.75
a.		Inverted surcharge		

Overprinted on Nos. 64, J1 ΕΛΛΑΣ ΠΡΟΣΟΡΙΝΟΝ

No.	Type	Description	Unused	Used
99	A6	1 l bister	1.65	1.65
100	D1	1 l red	1.65	1.65

No. J4 Surcharged ΕΛΛΑΣ 2 ΠΡΟΣΩΡΙΝΟΝ

No.	Type	Description	Unused	Used
101	D1	2 l on 20 l red	1.65	1.65
b.		Inverted surcharge	10.00	
c.		Second letter of surcharge "D" instead of "P"	30.00	30.00

No. J4 Surcharged ΕΛΛΑΣ 2 ΠΡΟΣΩΡΙΝΟΝ

No.	Type	Description	Unused	Used
102	D1	2 l on 20 l red	1.65	1.65

Overprinted in Black:

ΕΛΛΑΣ a ΕΛΛΑΣ b

ΕΛΛΑΣ c

No.	Type	Description	Unused	Used
103	A23(a)	10 l brown red	4.50	.85
a.		Inverted overprint	40.00	
104	A15(a)	20 l blue grn	5.25	.85
105	A21(c)	25 l blue & blk	5.50	1.65
106	A17(a)	50 l yellow brn	10.00	5.25
107	A22(b)	1d green & blk	10.00	10.00
108	A10(a)	2d brown	10.00	10.00
109	A19(b)	3d orange & blk	77.50	72.50
110	A20(b)	5d ol grn & blk	24.00	24.00
		Nos. 103-110 (8)	146.75	125.10

Stamps of 1900-08 Overprinted in Red or Black ΕΛΛΑΣ

1909-10

No.	Type	Description	Unused	Used
111	A6	1 l violet brown	.45	.25
112	A12	2 l dull violet	.45	.30
113	A13	5 l yellow green	.45	.25
114	A23	10 l brown red (Bk)	.85	.25
115	A15	20 l blue green	3.00	.65
116	A16	25 l ultra	3.50	.65
117	A17	50 l yellow brn	8.50	6.50
118	A18	1d rose car & dp brn (Bk)	52.50	52.50
119	A19	3d orange & blk	45.00	45.00
120	A20	5d ol grn & blk	35.00	35.00
		Nos. 111-120 (10)	149.70	141.35

POSTAGE DUE STAMPS

D1

1901 Unwmk. Litho. *Perf. 14*

No.	Type	Description	Unused	Used
J1	D1	1 l red	.25	.25
J2	D1	5 l red	.65	.45
J3	D1	10 l red	1.10	.45
J4	D1	20 l red	1.40	1.10
J5	D1	40 l red	13.00	13.00
J6	D1	50 l red	13.00	13.00
J7	D1	1d red	13.00	13.00
J8	D1	2d red	13.00	13.00
		Nos. J1-J8 (8)	55.40	54.25

For overprints and surcharges see Nos. 100-102, J9-J26.

Surcharged in Black Ι ΔΡΑΧΜΗ

1901

No.	Type	Description	Unused	Used
J9	D1	1d on 1d red	10.00	10.00

Overprinted ΕΛΛΑΣ

1908

No.	Type	Description	Unused	Used
J10	D1	1 l red	.45	.45
J11	D1	5 l red	.85	.85
J12	D1	10 l red	.85	.85
J13	D1	20 l red	2.25	2.25
J14	D1	40 l red	8.75	8.75
J15	D1	50 l red	8.75	8.75
J16	D1	1d red	92.50	92.50
J17	D1	1d on 1d red	8.75	8.75
J18	D1	2d red	13.00	13.00
		Nos. J10-J18 (9)	136.15	136.15

Nos. J10-J18 exist with inverted overprint. Counterfeits of No. J16 exist.

Overprinted ΕΛΛΑΣ

1910

No.	Type	Description	Unused	Used
J19	D1	1 l red	.45	.25
J20	D1	5 l red	1.40	.25
J21	D1	10 l red	.85	.45
J22	D1	20 l red	3.50	1.40
J23	D1	40 l red	8.75	8.75
J24	D1	50 l red	11.00	11.00
J25	D1	1d red	22.50	22.50
J26	D1	2d red	22.50	22.50
		Nos. J19-J26 (8)	70.95	67.10

OFFICIAL STAMPS

O1

O2

Unwmk.

1908, Jan. 14 Litho. *Perf. 14*

No.	Type	Description	Unused	Used
O1	O1	10 l dull claret	15.00	2.25
O2	O2	30 l blue	35.00	2.25

Nos. O1-O2 exist imperf.

Overprinted ΕΛΛΑΣ

No.	Type	Description	Unused	Used
O3	O1	10 l dull claret	15.00	2.25
a.		Inverted overprint	55.00	
O4	O2	30 l blue	35.00	2.25
a.		Inverted overprint	60.00	

Overprinted ΕΛΛΑΣ

1910

No.	Type	Description	Unused	Used
O5	O1	10 l dull claret	2.25	2.25
O6	O2	30 l blue	2.25	2.25

Nos. O5-O6 remained in use until 1922, nine years after union with Greece.

CROATIA

krō-'ā-sh(ē–ə

LOCATION — Southeastern Europe
GOVT. — Independent state
AREA — 44,453 sq. mi.
POP. — 7,000,000 (approx.)
CAPITAL — Zagreb

The Independent Croatian State of 1941-45 became part of the Yugoslav Federation in 1945.

Croatia declared its independence in 1991.

100 Paras = 1 Dinar
100 Banica = 1 Kuna
100 Paras = 1 Dinar (1991)
1 Kuna = 100 Lipa (1994)

Catalogue values for unused stamps in this country are for Never Hinged items, beginning with Scott 100 in the regular postage section, Scott B100 in the semi-postal section, Scott C1 in the airmail section and Scott RA20 in the postal tax section.

Watermark

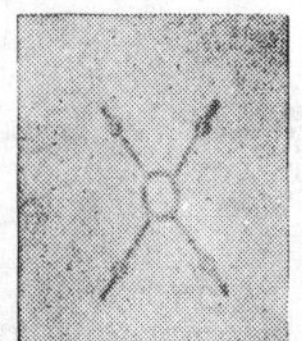

Wmk. 278- Network Connecting Circles

Yugoslavia Nos. 143 to 148B Overprinted in Black

NEZAVISNA DRŽAVA HRVATSKA IIIIII

Perf. 12½

1941, Apr. 12 Unwmk. Typo.

No.	Type	Description	Unused	Used
1	A16	50p orange	1.00	*2.25*
2	A16	1d yellow grn	1.00	*2.75*
3	A16	1.50d red	1.00	*1.25*
4	A16	2d deep magenta	1.00	*1.75*
5	A16	3d dull red brn	1.75	*4.75*
6	A16	4d ultra	1.75	*5.25*
7	A16	5d dark blue	2.75	*5.75*
8	A16	5.50d dk violet brn	2.75	*6.25*
		Nos. 1-8 (8)	13.00	*30.00*

The overprint exists inverted on Nos. 1-6; double on Nos. 2, 3 and 5.

NEZAVISNA DRŽAVA HRVATSKA

Yugoslavia Nos. 142 to 154 Overprinted in Black

1941, Apr. 21

No.	Type	Description	Unused	Used
9	A16	25p black	.15	*.30*
10	A16	50p orange	.15	*.30*
11	A16	1d yellow grn	.15	*.30*
12	A16	1.50d red	.15	*.30*

13 A16 2d deep magenta .15 .65
14 A16 3d dull red brn .15 .90
15 A16 4d ultra .30 1.00
16 A16 5d dark blue .50 1.00
17 A16 5.50d dk violet brn .50 1.25
18 A16 6d slate blue .60 1.75
19 A16 8d sepia 1.00 1.75
20 A16 12d brt violet 1.20 2.75
21 A16 16d dull violet 1.25 3.25
22 A16 20d blue 1.50 3.75
23 A16 30d bright pink 2.25 5.75
Nos. 9-23 (15) 10.00 25.00

The overprint exists inverted on Nos. 9-11, 17 and 20; double on Nos. 9, 12 and 17.

Yugoslavia Nos. 147, 148 Surcharged in Black

1941, May 16

24 A16 1d on 3d dull red brn .20 .30
25 A16 2d on 4d ultra .20 .30

The overprint exists inverted and double on Nos. 24-25.

Postage Due Stamps of Yugoslavia, Nos. J28, J30 to J32, Overprinted in Black

1941, May 17

26 D4 50p violet .15 .25
27 D4 2d deep blue .30 .50
28 D4 5d orange .30 .50
29 D4 10d chocolate .40 .75
Nos. 26-29 (4) 1.15 2.00

Counterfeit overprints on Nos. 1-29 are plentiful.

Imperforates

Nearly all Croatian stamps, from No. 30 through 80, B3 through B76, J6 through J25, O1 through O24 and RA1 through RA7 exist imperforate.

Ozalj Castle — A1

Designs: 50b, City of Jajce. 75b, Old Warasdin. 1k, Velebit Mountains. 1.50k, Zelanjak. 2k, Zagreb Cathedral. 3k, Osjek Cathedral. 4k, Drina River. No. 38, Konjica. No. 39, Zemun. 6k, Dubrovnik. 7k, Save River. 8k, Sarajevo. 10k, Plitvice. 12k, Klis Fortress, Split. 20k, Hvar. 30k, Syrmia. 50k, Senj. 100k, Banjaluka (without "F.I.").

1941-43 Unwmk. Photo. *Perf. 11.*

Ordinary Paper

30 A1 25b henna .15 .15
31 A1 50b slate blue .15 .15
32 A1 75b dk olive grn .15 .15
33 A1 1k Prussian green .15 .15
34 A1 1.50k deep green .15 .15
35 A1 2k carmine lake .15 .15
36 A1 3k brown red .15 .15
37 A1 4k deep ultra .15 .15
38 A1 5k black .50 .45
39 A1 5k blue .15 .15
40 A1 6k lt olive brn .15 .15
41 A1 7k orange red .15 .15
42 A1 8k chestnut .15 .15
43 A1 10k dark plum .25 .15
44 A1 12k olive brown .35 .25
45 A1 20k golden brown .25 .15
46 A1 30k black brown .35 .20
47 A1 50k dk slate green .55 .25
48 A1 100k violet .80 1.50
Set value 3.75 3.75

Nos. 31, 35 and 43 exist on thin to pelure paper. Shades of all values exist.

For overprints and surcharge see #49-51, 53.

Tête bêche Pairs

30a A1 25b .15 .30
31a A1 50b .15 .30
33a A1 1k .30 .55
34a A1 1.50k .30 .35
35a A1 2k .20 .30
37a A1 4k .20 .35
38a A1 5k 1.75 3.00
40a A1 6k .20 .35
41a A1 7k .20 .35
42a A1 8k .65 .90
43a A1 10k 1.25 1.50
45a A1 20k 1.25 1.50
46a A1 30k .90 1.50
47a A1 50k 4.50 8.75
Nos. 30a-47a (14) 12.00 20.00

Types of 1941 Overprinted in Brown or Green

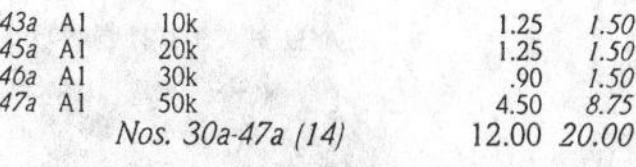

1942, Apr. 9

49 A1 2k dark brown .15 .25
50 A1 5k dark carmine .25 .35
51 A1 10k dark blue green (G) .30 .60
Nos. 49-51 (3) .70 1.20

First anniversary of Croatian independence.

Banjaluka ("F.I." at upper right) — A20

1942, June 13

52 A20 100k violet 1.50 2.50

Banjaluka Philatelic Exhibition.

No. 35 Surcharged in Red Brown with New Value and Bar

1942, June 23

53 A1 25b on 2k carmine lake .15 .22
a. Tête bêche pair .30 .60

Trakoscan Castle — A21

Catherine Zrinski — A23

Design: 12.50k, Citadel of Veliki Tabor.

1943

Pelure Paper

54 A21 3.50k brown carmine .30 .30
55 A21 12.50k violet black .30 .30

No. 54 exists on ordinary paper.

1943, June 7 Engr. *Perf. 12½*

Designs: 2k, Fran Krsto Frankopan. 3.50k, Peter Zrinski.

Various Frames

56 A23 1k dark blue .15 .15
57 A23 2k dark olive green .15 .15
58 A23 3.50k dark red .15 .25
Set value .30 .40

Rugjer Boscovich A26

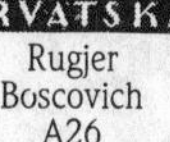

Ante Pavelich A27

1943, Dec. 13 *Perf. 11*

59 A26 3.50k copper red .15 .25
60 A26 12.50k dk violet brn .25 .35

Rugjer Boscovich (1711-1787). Serbo-Croat mathematician and physicist.

1943-44 Litho. *Perf. 12½, 14*

61 A27 25b orange ver .15 .15
62 A27 50b Prus blue .15 .15
63 A27 75b olive green .15 .15
64 A27 1k lt green .15 .15
65 A27 1.50k dull gray vio .15 .15
66 A27 2k rose lake .15 .15
67 A27 3k rose brown .15 .15
68 A27 3.50k bright blue .15 .15
a. 3.50k dark blue, perf. 11½ 1.10 2.00
69 A27 4k brt red violet .15 .15
70 A27 5k ultra .15 .15
71 A27 8k orange brn .15 .15
72 A27 9k rose pink .15 .15
73 A27 10k violet brn .15 .15
74 A27 12k dk olive bis .15 .15
75 A27 12.50k gray black .15 .15
76 A27 18k dull brown .15 .15
77 A27 32k dark brown .15 .15
78 A27 50k grnsh blue .15 .15
79 A27 70k orange .25 .30
80 A27 100k violet .45 .50
Set value 2.00 3.00

Nos. 61 and 63 measure 20½x26mm. Nos. 62 and 64-80 measure 22x27½mm.

Issue dates: 2k, 1943; No. 68a, June 13, 1943, Pavelich's birthday; others, 1944.

"Labor Day 1945" — A28

1945 Photo. *Perf. 11½*

81 A28 3.50k red brown .15 .90

Catalogue values for unused stamps in this section, from this point to the end of the section, are for Never Hinged items.

Nos. RA20, RA20a Surcharged in Black and Gold

1991, Nov. 21 Litho. *Perf. 14*

100 PT10 4d on 1.20d #RA20 .45
a. Perf. 11x10½ .45

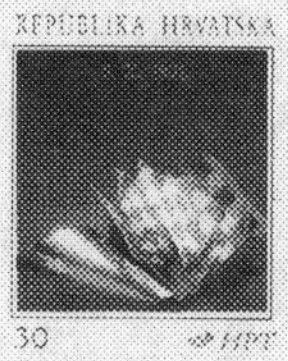

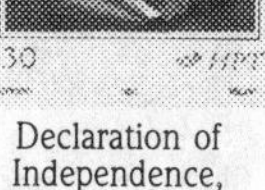

Declaration of Independence, Oct. 8, 1991 — A35

Christmas — A36

1991, Dec. 10 *Perf. 12*

101 A35 30d multicolored 2.00

1991, Dec. 11 *Perf. 12*

Creche figures of the Holy Family from Kosljun Monastery, Krk.

102 A36 4d multicolored .75

No. RA21 Surcharged in Black and Gold

1992, Jan. 3 *Perf. 10½x11*

103 PT11 20d on 1.70d #RA21 .50

Croatian Arms — A37

1992, Jan. 15 *Perf. 11x10½*

104 A37 10d multicolored .20
a. Perf. 14 .20

See No. RA22.

1992 Winter Olympics, Albertville — A38

1992, Feb. 4 *Perf. 11x10½*

105 A38 30d multicolored 2.00

Croatian Cities and Landmarks A39

A39a

A39b

Designs: 6d, Knin. 7d, Eltz Castle, Vukovar. 20d, Church, Ilok. 30d, Starcevic Street, Gospic. 45d, Rector's Palace, Dubrovnik. 50d, St. Jakov's Cathedral, Sibenik. 100d, Vinkovci. 200d, Pazin, vert. No. 118, Beli Monastery. No. 119, Krapina. 500d, Slavonski Brod. 1000d, Varazdin. 2000d, Karlovac. 5000d, Zadar, vert. 10,000d, Vis.

1992-94 *Perf. 14*

107 A39 6d multicolored .15
108 A39 7d multicolored .25
112 A39 20d multicolored .25
a. Perf. 11x10½ 1.05
113 A39 30d multicolored .75
114 A39 45d multicolored 1.50
115 A39 50d multicolored 1.65
116 A39a 100d multicolored .45
117 A39a 200d multicolored .35
118 A39 300d multicolored 4.00
119 A39b 300d multicolored 1.00
122 A39a 500d multicolored 1.25
123 A39a 1000d multicolored 1.90
123A A39a 2000d multicolored 2.25
123B A39a 5000d multicolored 2.50
123C A39a 10,000d multicolored 4.50
Nos. 107-123C (15) 22.75

Issue dates: 6d, Apr. 18. 7d, Apr. 8. No. 112, Feb. 28. No. 112a, Sept. 9. 30d, May 21. 45d, Apr. 14. 50d, Apr. 28. No. 118, June 26. 100d, Dec. 14, 1992. No. 119, 500d, Feb. 9, 1993. 1000d, Mar. 16, 1993. 200d, Apr. 22, 1993. 2000d, May 20, 1993. 5000d, Sept. 24, 1993. 10,000d, 2/22/94.

This is an expanding set. Numbers may change.

Statue of King Tomislav — A40

1992, May 5 Engr. *Perf. 12½ Horiz.*

Coil Stamp

124 A40 10d dark green .25

Railroad Station, Zagreb, Cent. — A41

1992, June 30 Litho. *Perf. 14*

125 A41 30d multicolored .75

Matica, Society of Knowledge and Literacy, 150th Anniv. — A42

1992, July 8

126 A42 20d red, gold & black .35

Bishop Josip Juraj Strossmayer, Founder A43

1992, July 9
127 A43 30d multicolored *.45*

Croatian Academy of Arts and Sciences, 125th anniv., in 1991.

1992 Summer Olympics, Barcelona — A44

Design: 105d, Abstract design.

1992, July 25
128 A44 40d shown *.50*
129 A44 105d multicolored *1.25*

Flowers — A45

Designs: 30d, Edraianthus pumilio. 85d, Degenia velebitica, vert.

1992, July 28
130 A45 30d multicolored *.40*
131 A45 85d multicolored *1.05*

Wildlife — A46

Designs: 40d, Monticola solitarius. 75d, Elaphe situla.

1992, July 31
132 A46 40d multicolored *.50*
133 A46 75d multicolored *.90*

Discovery of America, 500th Anniv. — A47

Europa: 30d, 60d, Sailing ship. 75d, 130d, Indian in Chicago, by Ivan Mestrovic (1883-1962).

1992 Litho. ***Perf. 14***
134 A47 30d multicolored *.35*
135 A47 60d multicolored *.75*
136 A47 75d red & black *.90*
137 A47 130d red, blk & gold *1.60*
Nos. 134-137 (4) *3.60*

Issue dates: 30d, 75d, July 31; others, Sept. 4.

A48

A49

1992, Oct. 2
138 A48 40d multicolored *.35*
139 A48 130d multi, diff. *1.05*

Declaration of Croatian Literary Language, 25th Anniv. (#133). Spelling reform by Dr. Ivan Broz, cent. (#134).

1992, Oct. 16
140 A49 90d multicolored *.60*

City of Samobor, 750th Anniv.

Gift of the St. Juraj Church by Archbishop Mucimir, 1100th Anniv. — A50

1992, Oct. 30
141 A50 60d multicolored *.40*

Reign of King Bela IV, 750th Anniv. — A51

1992, Nov. 16 Litho. ***Perf. 14***
142 A51 180d multicolored *.95*

Christmas — A52

1992, Dec. 7
143 A52 80d multicolored *.40*

Blaz Lorkovic (1839-1892), Scientist — A53

Kolo Literature Review, 150th Anniv. — A54

1992, Dec. 21
144 A53 250d multicolored *.85*

1992, Dec. 22
145 A54 300d multicolored *1.15*

Ivan Bunic-Vucic (1592-1658) — A55

1992, Dec. 29
146 A55 350d multicolored *1.30*

Nikola Tesla (1856-1943), Physicist — A56

1993, Jan. 30
147 A56 250d multicolored *.70*

Self-Portrait, by Ferdo Quiquerez (1845-1893) A57

1993, Feb. 10
148 A57 100d multicolored *.25*

Wildlife — A58

1993, Feb. 23 Litho. ***Perf. 14***
149 A58 500d Cervus elaphus *1.15*
150 A58 550d Haliaeetus albicilla *1.30*

Self-Portrait, by Zlatko Sulentic (1893-1971) A59

1993, Mar. 17
151 A59 350d multicolored *.65*

Lipik Health and Convalescent Home, Cent. — A60

1993, Apr. 22 Litho. ***Perf. 14***
152 A60 400d multicolored *.75*

Ivan Goran Kovacic (1913-1943), Author — A61

1993, Apr. 24
153 A61 200d multicolored *.35*

59th PEN Congress, Dubrovnik A62

1993, Apr. 24
154 A62 800d multicolored *1.25*

Ivan Kukuljevic (1816-89), Politician, Historian, Writer — A63

1993, May 2 Litho. ***Perf. 14***
155 A63 500d multicolored *.75*

Croatian Natl. Theatre, Split, Cent. — A64

Pag, 500th Anniv. — A65

1993, May 6 Litho. ***Perf. 14***
156 A64 600d multicolored *.85*

1993, May 18
157 A65 800d multicolored *.95*

Croatian Membership in United Nations, 1st Anniv. — A66

1993, May 22
158 A66 500d multicolored *.60*

Europa A67

Contemporary paintings by: 700d, Ivo Dulcic (1916-75). 1000d, Miljenko Stancic (1926-77). 1100d, Ljubo Ivançic (b. 1925).

1993, June 5
159 A67 700d multicolored *.75*
160 A67 1000d multicolored *1.00*
161 A67 1100d multicolored *1.10*
a. Miniature sheet, 2 each #159-161 *5.75*
Nos. 159-161 (3) *2.85*

Intl. Art Biennial, Venice — A68

Works of art by: 250d, Milivoj Bijelic. 600d, Ivo Dekovic. 1000d, Zeljko Kipke.

1993, June 10 Litho. ***Perf. 14***
162 A68 250d multicolored *.25*
a. Souvenir sheet of 4 *1.00*
163 A68 600d multicolored *.75*
a. Souvenir sheet of 4 *3.00*
164 A68 1000d multicolored *1.00*
a. Souvenir sheet of 4 *4.00*
Nos. 162-164 (3) *2.00*

1993 Mediterranean Games — A69

1993, June 15 Litho. *Perf. 14*
165 A69 700d multicolored .75

Adolf Waldinger (1843-1904), Painter — A70

1993, June 16
166 A70 300d multicolored .30

Famous Croatian Battles A71

1993, July 6 Litho. *Perf. 14*
167 A71 800d Krbavskom, 1493 .65
168 A71 1300d Sisak, 1593 1.05

Miroslav Krleza (1893-1981), Writer — A72

1993, July 7
169 A72 400d multicolored .35

Croatian Membership in UPU, 1st Anniv. — A73

1993, July 20 Litho. *Perf. 14*
170 A73 1800d multicolored 1.40

Vlaho Paljetak (1893-1944), Composer — A74

1993, Aug. 7
171 A74 500d multicolored .35

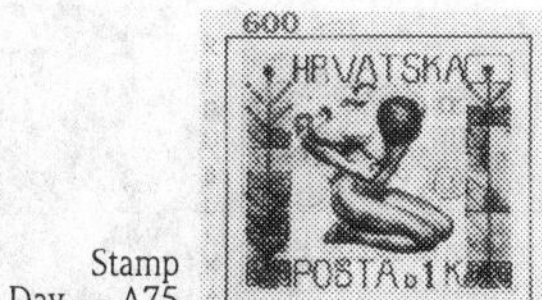

Stamp Day — A75

1993, Sept. 9 Litho. *Perf. 14*
172 A75 600d multicolored .35

Map of Istria, 1620 — A76

1993, Sept. 20
173 A76 2200d multicolored 1.10

Incorporation of Istria, Rijeka and Zadar into Croatia, 50th anniv.

Tadija Smiciklas (1843-1914), Historian — A77

1993, Oct. 1
174 A77 800d black, gold & red .40

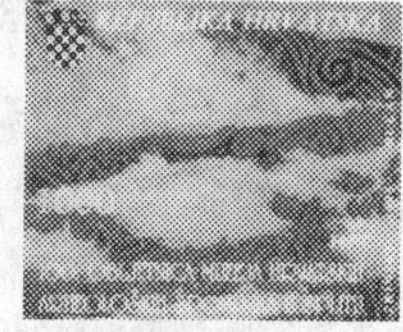
Archaelogical Museum, Split, Cent. — A78

1993, Oct. 27
175 A78 1000d multicolored .45

A79

REPUBLIKA HRVATSKA 900

A80

1993, Nov. 17 Litho. *Perf. 14*
176 A79 3000d multicolored 1.40

Uprising of 13th Pioneer Battalion, Villefranche-de-Rouergue, France, 50th anniv.

1993, Nov. 18

Design: 900d, Josip Eugen Tomic (1843-1906), writer.

177 A80 900d multicolored .40

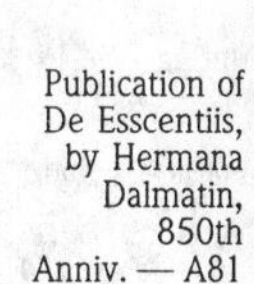
Publication of De Esscentiis, by Hermana Dalmatin, 850th Anniv. — A81

1993, Nov. 30
178 A81 1000d multicolored .45

Christmas — A82

Paintings: 1000d, Christmas at the Front, by Miroslav Sutej. 4000d, Birth of Christ, 15th cent. fresco, Marienkirch of Dvigrad.

1993, Dec. 3
179 A82 1000d multicolored .40
180 A82 4000d multicolored 1.75

Organized Skiing in Croatia, Cent. — A83

1993, Dec. 15
181 A83 1000d multicolored .40

Croatian Natl. Guard, 125th Anniv. — A84

1993, Dec. 22
182 A84 1100d multicolored .45

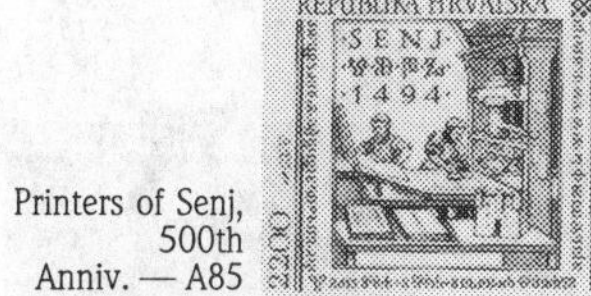

Printers of Senj, 500th Anniv. — A85

1994, Jan. 29
183 A85 2200d multicolored .95

1994 Winter Olympics, Lillehammer A86

1994, Feb. 12
184 A86 4000d multicolored 1.75

Dinosaurs from Western Istria — A87

Designs: a, 2400d, Iguanodons. b, 4000d, Map, skeleton.

1994, Mar. 7
185 A87 Pair, #a.-b. 2.75

Nos. 185a-185b are a continuous design.

Zora Dalmatinska Magazine, 150th Anniv. — A88

1994, Mar. 15
186 A88 800d multicolored .40

Croatian University, Zagreb, 325th Anniv. — A89

Design: 2200d, University building, Emperor Leopold I's seal, vice-chancellor's chain.

1994, Apr. 19 Litho. *Perf. 14*
187 A89 2200d multicolored 1.00

Protect the Environment A90

ILO, 75th Anniv. A91

1994, Apr. 22 Litho. *Perf. 14*
188 A90 3800d Canis lupus 1.75

1994, May 2
189 A91 1000d multicolored .50

Europa

A92 A93

European inventions, discoveries: 3800d, Faust Vrancic (1551-1617), parachute. 4000d, Slavoljub Penkala (1871-1922), fountain pen.

1994, May 16
190 A92 3800d multicolored 1.75
191 A93 4000d multicolored 1.90

A94

A95

1994, June 3
192 A94 2.40k Iris croatica 1.10
193 A94 4k Colchicum visianii 1.90

1994, June 7

Design: 1d, Drazen Petrovic (1964-93), basketball player.

194 A95 1d multicolored .50

Tourism in Croatia, 150th Anniv. — A96

Designs: 80 l, Plitvice Lakes Natl. Park. 1k, Waterfalls, Krka River. 1.10k, Kornati Islands Natl. Park. 2.20k, Kopacki Trscak nature reserve. 2.40k Sailboats, Opatijska Riviera resort. 3.80k, Brijuni islands. 4k, Trakoscan castle, Zagorje.

1994, June 15 Litho. *Perf. 14*

196 A96 80 l multicolored *.40*
197 A96 1k multicolored *.45*
198 A96 1.10k multicolored *.50*
200 A96 2.20k multicolored *1.00*
201 A96 2.40k multicolored *1.10*
206 A96 3.80k multicolored *1.75*
207 A96 4k multicolored *1.90*
a. Min. sheet of 7, #196-198, 200-201, 206-207 + 2 labels *7.25*
Nos. 196-207 (7) *7.10*

Issued: 80 l, 1k, 1.10k, 2.20k, 2.40k, 3.80k, 4k, 6/15/94. This is an expanding set. Numbers may change.

Croatian Musicians A97

Designs: 1k, Kresimir Baranovic (1894-1975), composer, vert. 2.20k, Vatroslav Lisinski (1819-54), composer, vert. 2.40k, Pauline Liederbuch (b.1644), harpist.

1994, June 20

211 A97 1k multicolored *.45*
212 A97 2.20k multicolored *1.00*
213 A97 2.40k multicolored *1.10*
Nos. 211-213 (3) *2.55*

Croatian Fraternal Union, Cent. — A98

1994, Aug. 15 Litho. *Perf. 14*

214 A98 2.20k multicolored *1.10*

A99

A100

1994, Aug. 31

215 A99 80 l multicolored *.40*

Intl. Year of the Family.

1994, Sept. 10

216 A100 1k multicolored *.50*

Intl. Olympic Committee, cent.

Visit of Pope John Paul II — A101

1994, Sept. 10

217 A101 1k multicolored *.50*

No. 217 printed with se-tenant label.

Antoine de Saint-Exupery (1900-44), Aviator, Author A102

1994, Sept. 20

218 A102 3.80k multicolored *1.90*

13th Intl. Congress on Early Christian Archeology A103

1994, Sept. 23

219 A103 4k multicolored *2.00*

No. 219 printed with se-tenant label.

Modern Croatian Paintings A104

Designs: 2.40k, Still Life with Fruits and Basket, by Marino Tartaglia, 1926. 3.80k, In the Park, by Milan Steiner, c. 1918. 4k, Self-portrait, by Vilko Gecan, 1929.

1994, Oct. 12

220 A104 2.40k multicolored *1.25*
221 A104 3.80k multicolored *1.90*
222 A104 4k multicolored *2.00*
Nos. 220-222 (3) *5.15*

Ivan Belostenec (1594-1675), Writer & Lexicographer A105

1994, Nov. 9

223 A105 2.20k multicolored *1.10*

City of Zagreb, Zagreb Bishopric, 900th Anniv. A106

Designs: No. 224a, 1k, Zagreb exchange building, designed by V. Kovacic, S. Penkala's airplane, Cibona office tower, designed by Hrzic, Pitesa and Serbetic. b, 1k, Maxi Cat, by Zlatko Grgic, Zagreb School of Animated Film. c, 1k, St. Mark's Church, Gradec; photo of gas lantern, by Toso Dabac. d, 4k, Late Gothic bishop's staff, Valvasor's view of Zagreb.

13.50k, Zagreb street scene, Penkala's airplane, vert.

1994, Nov. 16

224 A106 Strip of 4, #a.-d. *3.50*

Souvenir Sheet

225 A106 13.50k multicolored *6.75*

No. 224 is a continuous design. No. 225 contains one 24x48mm stamp.

Christmas A107

Design: 1k, Epiphany, by unknown sculptor.

1994, Dec. 1 Litho. *Perf. 14*

226 A107 1k multicolored *.50*

Virgin Mary's Sanctuary, Loreto, 700th Anniv. A108

Design: 4k, The Moving of the Holy House, by Giovanni Battista Tiepolo.

1994, Dec. 10

227 A108 4k multicolored *1.90*

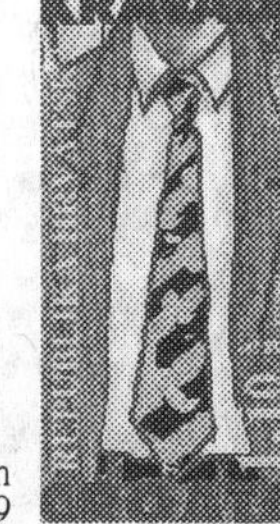

Necktie in Croatia — A109

Tie designs: 1.10k, Businessman's, 1995. 3.80k, English Dandy, 1810. 4k, Croatian soldier, 1630.

1995, Jan. 19 Litho. *Perf. 14*

228 A109 1.10k multicolored *.40*
229 A109 3.80k multicolored *1.40*
230 A109 4k multicolored *1.50*
a. Souvenir sheet of 3, #228-230 *3.30*
Nos. 228-230 (3) *3.30*

Croatian Monasteries — A110

Designs: 1k, Jesuit Monastery, Zagreb, 350th anniv. 2.40k, Franciscan Monastery, Visovac, 550th anniv.

1995, Feb. 16

231 A110 1k multicolored *.35*
232 A110 2.40k multicolored *.90*

Hunting Dogs — A111

Designs: 2.20k, Istrian short-haired. 2.40k, Posavinian. 3.80k, Istrian wire-haired.

1995, Mar. 9 Litho. *Perf. 14*

233 A111 2.20k multicolored *.90*
234 A111 2.40k multicolored *.95*
235 A111 3.80k multicolored *1.50*
Nos. 233-235 (3) *3.35*

Town of Split, 1700th Anniv. — A112

Designs: No. 236a, 1k, Drawing of reconstruction of Diocletian's Palace. b, 2.20k, "Split Harbour," by Emanuel Vidovic, 1937. c, 4k, Modern view of town, bust of Marko Marulic by Ivan Mestrovic.

13.40k, Buildings, vert.

1995, Apr. 20 Litho. *Perf. 14*

236 A112 Strip of 3, #a.-c. *3.00*

Souvenir Sheet

237 A112 13.40k multicolored *5.50*

No. 237 contains one 24x48mm stamp.

World Team Handball Championships, Iceland — A113

1995, May 4

238 A113 4k multicolored *1.65*

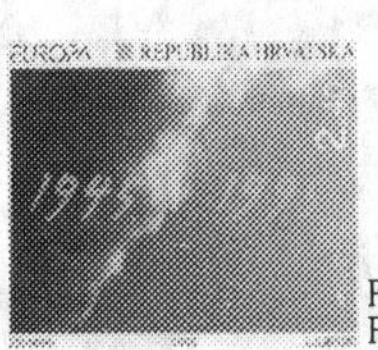

Peace & Freedom — A114

Europa: 2.40k, Clearing storm clouds. 4k, Hands of angel, by Francisco Robba.

1995, May 9

239 A114 2.40k multicolored *1.00*
240 A114 4k multicolored *1.65*

Anti-Austria Demonstrations, 150th Anniv. — A115

1995, May 15

241 A115 1.10k multicolored *.45*
242 A115 3.80k multicolored *1.50*

Croatian surrender to British forces at Bleiburg, 50th anniv. (#242).

Independence Day — A116

1995, May 30 Litho. *Perf. 14*

243 A116 1.10k multicolored *.45*

Croatian Sculptures at Venice Biennial, 1995 — A117

Designs: 2.20k, Installation (a part), by Martina Kramer. 2.40k, Paracelsus Paraduchamps, by Mirko Zrinscak, vert. 4k, Shadows, by Goran Petercol.

1995, June 8 **Litho.** ***Perf. 14***

244	A117	2.20k	multicolored	.90
245	A117	2.40k	multicolored	1.00
246	A117	4k	multicolored	1.65

St. Anthony of Padua (1195-1231) — A118

1995, June 13

247	A118	1k	multicolored	.40

Marine Life — A119

1995, June 29 **Litho.** ***Perf. 14***

248	A119	2.40k	Caretta caretta	.95
249	A119	4k	Tursiops truncatus	1.65

Liberation of the City of Knin — A120

1995, Aug. 5 **Litho.** ***Perf. 14***

250	A120	1.30k	multicolored	.50

Krka River Hydroelectric Power Plant, Cent. — A121

1995, Aug. 28

251	A121	3.60k	multicolored	1.40

Stamp Day — A122

1995, Sept. 9 **Litho.** ***Perf. 14***

252	A122	1.30k	multicolored	.50

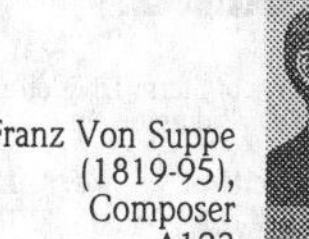

Franz Von Suppe (1819-95), Composer A123

1995, Sept. 15

253	A123	6.50k	multicolored	2.50

Liberation of Petrinja from Turkish Rule, 400th Anniv. A124

1995, Sept. 21

254	A124	2.20k	multicolored	.85

Croatian Music — A125

Composers, conductors: 1.20k, Ivo Tijardovic (1895-1976). 1.40k, Lovro Von Matacic (1899-1985). 6.50k, Jakov Gotovac (1895-1982).

1995, Sept. 23

255	A125	1.20k	multicolored	.45
256	A125	1.40k	multicolored	.55
257	A125	6.50k	multicolored	2.50
			Nos. 255-257 (3)	3.50

Herman Bollé (1845-1926), Architect — A126

Designs: 2.40k, Izidor Krsnjavi (1845-1927), painter. 3.60k, Croatian National Theatre, cent.

1995, Oct. 14 **Litho.** ***Perf. 14***

258	A126	1.80k	multicolored	.65
259	A126	2.40k	multicolored	.90
260	A126	3.60k	multicolored	1.40
			Nos. 258-260 (3)	2.95

Croatian Towns — A127

1995, Oct. 20

261	A127	1k	Bjelovar	.40
262	A127	1.30k	Osijek, vert.	.50
263	A127	1.40k	Cakovec, vert.	.55
264	A127	2.20k	Rovinj	.85
265	A127	2.40k	Korcula	.90
266	A127	3.60k	Zupanja	1.40
			Nos. 261-266 (6)	4.60

UN, FAO, 50th Anniv. — A128

Design: No. 268, "5, 0" in form of cracker, FAO.

1995, Oct. 24

267	A128	3.60k	multicolored	1.40
268	A128	3.60k	multicolored	1.40
a.			Pair, #267-268	2.80

Croatian Scientists — A129

Designs: 1k, Spiro Brusina (1845-1908). Bogoslav Sulek (1816-95). 6.50k, Front of European language dictionary, published by Faust Vrancic (1551-1617).

1995, Oct. 30

269	A129	1k	multicolored	.40
270	A129	2.20k	multicolored	.85
271	A129	6.50k	multicolored	2.50
			Nos. 269-271 (3)	3.75

Institute for Blind Children, Cent. — A130

1995, Nov. 23 **Litho.** ***Perf. 14***

272	A130	1.20k	multicolored	.45

Christmas A131

1995, Dec. 1

273	A131	1.30k	multicolored	.50

Maroc Polo's Return from China, 700th Anniv. A132

1995, Dec. 7

274	A132	3.60k	multicolored	1.30

Liberated Towns A133

1995, Dec. 16

275	A133	20 l	Hrvatska Kostajnica	.15
276	A133	30 l	Slunj	.15
277	A133	50 l	Gracac	.20
278	A133	1.20k	Drnis, vert.	.45
279	A133	6.50k	Glina	2.50
280	A133	10k	Obrovac, vert.	3.75
			Nos. 275-280 (6)	7.20

Incunabula — A134

Designs: 1.40k, Lectionary of Bernardin of Split. 3.60k, Spovid Opcena (General Confession).

1995, Dec. 28

281	A134	1.40k	multicolored	.55
282	A134	3.60k	multicolored	1.30

SEMI-POSTAL STAMPS

Types of Yugoslavia, 1941, Overprinted in Gold "NEZAVISNA / DRZAVA / HRVATSKA"

Perf. 11½

1941, May 10 **Unwmk.** **Engr.**

B1	SP80	1.50d + 1.50d bl blk	7.25	13.00
B2	SP81	4d + 3d choc	7.25	13.00

Five thousand sets of Yugoslavia Nos. 142-154 were overprinted "NEZAVISNA DRZAVA HRVATSKA 10. IV. 1941" and small shield in red or blue, in 1941. Sold for double face value. Value, set, $225.

Costume of Sinj, Dalmatia — SP1

Soldiers with Arms of the Axis States — SP4

Designs (Costumes): 2k+2k, Travnik, Bosnia. 4k+4k, Turopolje, Croatia.

1941, Oct. 12 **Photo.** ***Perf. 10½x10***

B3	SP1	1.50k + 1.50k Prus bl & red	.20	.35
B4	SP1	2k + 2k ol brn & red	.30	.45
B5	SP1	4k + 4k brn lake & red	.45	1.10
		Nos. B3-B5 (3)	.95	1.90

The surtax aided the Croatian Red Cross. Sheets of 20 stamps and 5 labels.

1941, Dec. 3 ***Perf. 11***

B6	SP4	4k + 2k blue	.90	2.00

The surtax was used for Croatian Volunteers in the East.

Model Plane — SP5

Model Plane — SP6

Designs: 3k+3k, Boy with model plane. 4k+4k, Model seaplane in flight.

1942, Mar. 25

B7	SP5	2k + 2k sepia	.20	.35
B8	SP6	2.50k + 2.50k dl grn	.30	.60
B9	SP5	3k + 3k brn car	.35	.70
B10	SP6	4k + 4k dp bl	.50	1.00
		Nos. B7-B10 (4)	1.35	2.65

Nos. B7-B10 were issued in sheets of 25 and in sheets of 24 plus label.

Souvenir Sheets

Perf. 11

B11	Sheet of 2	14.00	22.50
a.	SP5 2k+8k brown carmine	5.25	9.00
b.	SP5 3k+12k deep blue	5.25	9.00

Imperf

B12	Sheet of 2	14.00	22.50
a.	SP5 2k+8k deep blue	5.25	9.00
b.	SP5 3k+12k brown carmine	5.25	9.00

The sheets measure 125x110mm.

Aviation Exposition of Zagreb. The surtax aided society of Croatian Wings (Hrvatska Krila).

Nos. B11-B12 exist with colors of stamps and inscriptions transposed.

Boy Trumpeters SP10

Triumphal Arch SP11

Mother and Child — SP12

1942, July 5 *Perf. 11½*

B13 SP10	3k + 1k lake	.35	*.60*
B14 SP11	4k + 2k dk brn	.40	*.75*
B15 SP12	5k + 5k dp bl grn	.50	*.90*
	Nos. B13-B15 (3)	1.25	*2.25*

The surtax was for national welfare.

Matthew Gubec
SP13

Ante Starcevich
SP14

SP15

1942, Nov. 22 *Perf. 14½*

B16 SP13	3k + 6k dark red	.15	*.30*
B17 SP14	4k + 7k sepia	.15	*.30*

Souvenir Sheets

Perf. 12, Imperf.

B18 SP15	5k + 20k dull blue	7.25	*8.25*

Heroes of Senj, May 9, 1937. Nos. B16-B17 were printed in sheets of 16 + 9 labels, each bearing a hero's name. The surtax aided the Natl. Youth Soc.

Sestine
Peasant — SP16

Croatian Labor
Corpsman — SP20

Designs: 3k+1k, Slavonian peasant. 4k+2k, Bosnian peasant. 10k+5k, Dalmatian peasant. 13k+6k, Sestine peasant.

1942, Oct. 4 *Perf. 11½*

B20 SP16	1.50k + 50b org brn & red	.40	*.75*
B21 SP16	3k + 1k dl pur & red	.40	*.75*
B22 SP16	4k + 2k dp bl & red	.50	*1.00*
B23 SP16	10k + 5k dk ol bis & red	.70	*1.50*
B24 SP16	13k + 6k rose lake & red	1.50	*3.00*
	Nos. B20-B24 (5)	3.50	*7.00*

The surtax aided the Croatian Red Cross.
Issued in sheets of 24 stamps plus label.

1943, Jan. 17 **Wmk. 278** *Perf. 11*

Designs: 3k+3k, Corpsman with wheelbarrow. 7k+4k, Corpsman plowing.

B25 SP20	2k + 1k ol gray & sepia	.95	*1.90*
B26 SP20	3k + 3k brn & sepia	.95	*1.90*
B27 SP20	7k + 4k gray bl & sepia	.95	*1.90*
	Nos. B25-B27 (3)	2.85	*5.70*

The surtax aided the State Labor Service (Drzavna Radna Sluzba). Issued in sheets of 9.

Arms of Zagreb
and "Golden
Bull" — SP23

1943, Mar. 23 **Unwmk.**

B28 SP23	3.50k (+ 6.50k) bril ultra	.60	*1.65*

700th anniversary of Zagreb's "Golden Bull," a Magna Carta of civic rights and privileges granted to the city in 1242 by King Bela because the Croats annihilated Tartar hordes at Grobnik.

Issued in sheets of 8 with marginal inscriptions.

Ante
Pavelich — SP24

Sailor at Sea of
Azov — SP26

1943, Apr. 10 *Perf. 14*

B29 SP24	5k + 3k copper red	.15	*.30*
B30 SP24	7k + 5k dark green	.15	*.30*

Surtax aided the National Youth Society.

Issued in sheets of 100, and in miniature sheets of 16 stamps + 9 labels.

Souvenir Sheets

1943, May 17 ***Perf. 12, Imperf.***

B31 SP24	12k + 8k dp ultra	4.50	*7.25*

1943, July 1 *Perf. 11*

Designs: 2k+1k, Flier at Sevastopol and Rzhev. 3.50k+1.50k, Infantrymen at Stalingrad. 9k+4.50k, Panzer Division at Don River.

B33 SP26	1k + 50b grn	.15	*.15*
B34 SP26	2k + 1k dk red	.15	*.15*
B35 SP26	3.50k + 1.50k dk bl	.15	*.15*
B36 SP26	9k + 4.50k chestnut	.15	*.15*
	Nos. B33-B36 (4)		*.60*
	Set value	.35	

Souvenir Sheets

Perf. 11, Imperf.

B37	Sheet of 4	.90	*2.50*
a.	SP26 1k+50b dark blue	.20	*.30*
b.	SP26 2k+1k green	.20	*.30*
c.	SP26 3.50k+1.50k dk red brown	.20	*.30*
d.	SP26 9k+4.50k bluish black	.20	*.30*

Issued to honor the Croatian Legion which fought with the Germans in Russia.

The surtax aided the Croatian Legion.

St. Mary's
Church and
Cistercian
Cloister,
Zagreb, in
1650
SP31

1943, Sept. 12 **Engr.** *Perf. 14½*

B39 SP31	18k + 9k dl gray vio	.80	*1.65*

Souvenir Sheet

Perf. 12½

B40 SP31	18k + 9k blk brn	3.50	*6.00*

Croatian Phil. Soc. Exhibition at Zagreb.

No. B39 Overprinted in Red

HRVATSKO MORE
8. IX.
1943.

1943, Sept. 12

B41 SP31	18k + 9k dl gray vio	3.00	*5.00*

Return to Croatia of the Dalmatian and Croatian coasts.

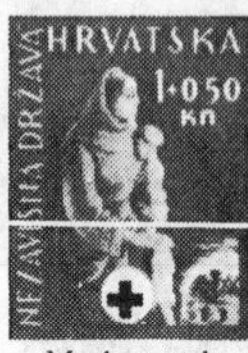

Mother and
Children
SP33

Nurse and
Patient
SP34

1943, Oct. 3 **Litho.** *Perf. 11*

Cross in Red

B42 SP33	1k + 50b bl grn	.15	*.20*
B43 SP33	2k + 1k bril car	.15	*.20*
B44 SP33	3.50k + 1.50k brt bl	.15	*.20*
B45 SP34	8k + 3k red brn	.15	*.20*
B46 SP34	9k + 4k yel grn	.15	*.30*
B47 SP33	10k + 5k dp vio	.20	*.35*
B48 SP34	12k + 6k brt ultra	.25	*.45*
B49 SP33	12.50k + 6k dk brn	.40	*.70*
B50 SP34	18k + 8k brn org	.50	*.90*
B51 SP34	32k + 12k dk gray	.90	*1.50*
	Nos. B42-B51 (10)	3.00	*5.00*

The surtax aided the Croatian Red Cross.

Post Horn and
Arms — SP35

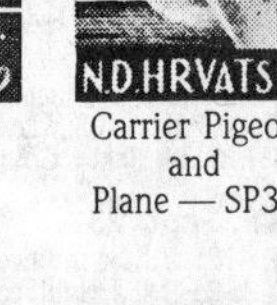

Carrier Pigeon
and
Plane — SP36

Mercury
SP37

Winged Wheel
SP38

1944, Feb. 3

B52 SP35	7k + 3.50k ol bis & red	.15	*.15*
B53 SP36	16k + 8k bl & dk bl	.15	*.18*
B54 SP37	24k + 12k red & rose red	.15	*.28*
B55 SP38	32k + 16k gray & red	.30	*.55*
	Nos. B52-B55 (4)		*1.16*
	Set value	.60	

The surtax benefited communications and railway employees. Sheets of 9.

St. Sebastian
SP39

War Invalids
SP40

Statue of Ancient
Croatian
King — SP41

Death of King Peter
Svacic, 1097 — SP42

1944, Feb. 15

B56 SP39	7k + 3.50k org red & rose car	.15	*.20*
B57 SP40	16k + 8k yel grn & dk grn	.15	*.30*
B58 SP41	24k + 12k yel brn & red	.15	*.30*
B59 SP42	32k + 16k bl & dk bl	.30	*.60*
	Nos. B56-B59 (4)	.75	*1.40*

The surtax aided wounded war victims.

Issued in sheets of eight stamps, with marginal inscriptions and a central label picturing St. Sebastian.

Black Legion in
Combat — SP43

Guarding the
Drina — SP44

Jure
Francetich — SP45

1944, May 22 **Photo.** ***Imperf.***

B60 SP43	3.50k + 1.50k brn red	.15	.15
B61 SP44	12.50k + 6.50k slate bl	.15	.15
B62 SP45	18k + 9k olive brn	.15	.15
	Set value	.25	.25

Third anniversary of Croatian independence.

The surtax aided the National Youth Society. Sheets of 20.

Perf. 14½

B63 SP45	12.50k + 287.50k int blk	1.75	*9.00*

Issued to commemorate Jure Francetich.

Labor Corpsmen
Marching — SP46

Corpsman
Digging — SP47

Designs: 18k+9k, Officer instructing corpsman. 32k+16k, Pavelich reviewing Labor Corps. Sheets of 8 plus label.

Perf. 11, 12½, 14½

1944, Aug. 20 **Engr.**

B65 SP46	3.50k + 1k dk red	.15	.15
B66 SP47	12.50k + 6k sepia	.15	.15
B67 SP47	18k + 9k dk bl	.15	.20
B68 SP47	32k + 16k gray grn	.15	.20
	Set value	.30	.50

Souvenir Sheet

Perf. 12½

B69 SP47	32k + 16k dk brn, *cr*	1.25	2.50

The surtax aided the State Labor Service (Drzavna Radna Sluzba).

Palm Leaf — SP51

1944, Nov. 12 **Litho.** *Perf. 11*

B70 SP51	2k + 1k dl grn & red	.15	.15
B71 SP51	3.50k + 1.50k car lake & red	.15	.15
B72 SP51	12.50k + 6k ind & red	.15	.20
	Nos. B70-B72 (3)		.50
	Set value	.25	

The surtax aided the Croatian Red Cross. Sheets of 16.

Men of
Storm
Division
SP52

Designs: 70k+70k, Soldiers of Storm Division in action. 100k+100k, Storm Division emblem.

1944 **Unwmk.** **Litho.** *Perf. 11*

B73 SP52	50k + 50k brick red	35.00	*75.00*
B74 SP52	70k + 70k sepia	35.00	*75.00*
B75 SP52	100k + 100k chlky, pale & dp bl	35.00	*75.00*
	Nos. B73-B75 (3)	105.00	*225.00*

Souvenir Sheet

B76	Sheet of 3	650.00	*1,000.*
a.	SP52 50k + 50k brick red		
b.	SP52 70k + 70k sepia		
c.	SP52 100k + 100k chalky, pale & deep blue		

Nos. B76a to B76c are inscribed "O. A." in brick red at right below design. The sheet measures 216x132mm. The surtax aided the First Croatian Storm Division. Counterfeits are plentiful.

Postman
SP55

Telephone Line Repairman
SP56

Designs; 24k+12k, Switchboard operator. 50k+25k, 100k+50k, Postman delivering parcel. Sheets of 8.

1945 **Photo.**

B77 SP55 3.50k + 1.50k sl gray .15 *.15*
B78 SP56 12.50k + 6k brn car .15 *.15*
B79 SP56 24k + 12k dk grn .15 *.20*
B80 SP56 50k + 25k brn vio .15 *.30*
Nos. B77-B80 (4) *.80*
Set value .40

Souvenir Sheet

B81 SP56 100k + 50k dp brn 1.75 *3.50*

The surtax on Nos. B77-B81 aided employees of the P.T.T.

Catalogue values for unused stamps in this section, from this point to the end of the section, are for Never Hinged items.

Famous Croatians — SP60

Designs: No. B100, Ban Josip Jelacic (1801-59). No. B101, Dr. Ante Starcevic (1823-96). 7d + 3d, Stjepan Radic (1871-1928).

1992 **Litho.** ***Perf. 11x10½***

B100 SP60 4d +2d multi *.45*
B101 SP60 4d +2d multi *.50*

Perf. 14

B102 SP60 7d +3d multi *.40*
Nos. B100-B102 (3) *1.35*

Issue dates: No. B100, Feb. 1. No. B101, Mar. 4. No. B102, Apr. 2. This is an expanding set. Numbers may change.

The surcharge on Nos. B100-B102 was initially an obligatory tax on all internal and overseas mail. From May 15, 1992, these stamps were valid for postage at their 6d or 10d face values.

AIR POST STAMPS

Catalogue values for unused stamps in this section are for Never Hinged items.

Airplane, Zagreb Cathedral and Port of Dubrovnik — AP1

Designs: No. C2, Airplane over ruins of Diocletian's Palace, Split. No. C3, Coat of arms, aiplane, Zagreb Cathedral and Pula amphitheatre. No. C4, Paper Airplane Made from Picture of Osijek Cathedral.

1991-92 **Litho.** ***Perf. 11x10½***

C1 AP1 1d multicolored *.15*
a. Perf. 14 *.15*
C2 AP1 2d multicolored *.25*
a. Perf. 14 *.25*
C3 AP1 3d multicolored *.40*
C4 AP1 4d multicolored *.30*
Nos. C1-C4 (4) *1.10*

Issue dates: No. C1, Sept. 9. No. C1a, June 24, 1992. No. C2, Oct. 9. No. C2a, 1992. No. C3, Nov. 20. No. C4, Feb. 14, 1992.

POSTAGE DUE STAMPS

Yugoslavia Nos. J28-J32 Overprinted in Black

1941, Apr. 26 **Unwmk.** ***Perf. 12½***

J1 D4 50p violet .20 *.30*
a. 50p rose violet 4.00 *6.00*
J2 D4 1d deep magenta .20 *.30*
J3 D4 2d deep blue 5.25 *9.00*
J4 D4 5d orange .60 *.90*
J5 D4 10d chocolate 2.75 *4.50*
Nos. J1-J5 (5) 9.00 *15.00*

The overprint on the 50p exists inverted. Counterfeit overprints exist.

D1

D2

1941, Sept. 12 **Litho.** ***Perf. 11***

J6 D1 50b carmine lake .15 *.20*
J7 D1 1k carmine lake .15 *.20*
J8 D1 2k carmine lake .15 *.40*
J9 D1 5k carmine lake .20 *.45*
J10 D1 10k carmine lake .35 *.60*
Nos. J6-J10 (5) 1.00 *1.85*

1943 ***Perf. 11½, 12x12½, 12½***

Size: 24x24mm

J11 D2 50b lt blue & gray .15 .15
J12 D2 1k lt blue & gray .15 .15
J13 D2 2k lt blue & gray .15 *.15*
J14 D2 4k lt blue & gray .15 *.20*
J15 D2 5k lt blue & gray .15 *.20*
J16 D2 6k lt blue & gray .15 *.20*
J17 D2 10k blue & indigo .15 *.30*
J18 D2 15k blue & indigo .15 *.30*
J19 D2 20k blue & indigo .50 *.80*
Nos. J11-J19 (9) *2.45*
Set value 1.35

1942, July 30 ***Perf. 10½, 11½***

Size: 25x24¼mm

J20 D2 50b lt blue & gray .15 *.15*
J21 D2 1k lt blue & gray .15 *.15*
J22 D2 2k lt blue & gray .20 *.30*
J23 D2 5k lt blue & gray .15 *.25*
J24 D2 10k lt blue & blue .30 *.50*
J25 D2 20k lt blue & blue .55 *.90*
Nos. J20-J25 (6) 1.50 *2.25*

OFFICIAL STAMPS

Croatian Coat of Arms
O1 O2

Perf. 10½, 11½

1942-43 **Unwmk.** **Litho.**

Ordinary Paper

O1 O1 25b rose lake .15 .15
O2 O1 50b slate blk .15 .15
O3 O1 75b gray grn .15 .15
O4 O1 1k orange brn .15 .15
O5 O1 2k turq blue .15 *.15*
O6 O1 3k vermilion .15 .15
O7 O1 4k brown vio .15 .15
O8 O1 5k ultra .20 *.35*
a. Thin paper 4.50 *2.00*
O9 O1 6k brt violet .15 .15
O10 O1 10k lt green .15 .15
O11 O1 12k brown rose .15 *.15*
O12 O1 20k dark blue .15 *.15*
O13 O2 30k brn vio & gray .15 *.15*
O14 O2 40k vio blk & gray .15 *.15*
O15 O2 50k brn lake & gray .30 *.35*
O16 O2 100k black & pink .30 *.35*
Set value 1.70 *2.35*

1943-44 **Thin Paper** ***Perf. 11½***

O17 O1 25b claret .15 .15
O18 O1 50b gray .15 .15
O19 O1 75b dull green .15 .15
O20 O1 1k orange brn .15 .15
O21 O1 2k slate blue .15 .15
O22 O1 3.50k car rose .15 .15
a. Ordinary paper 4.50 *8.50*
O23 O1 6k brt red vio .15 .15
O24 O1 12.50k deep orange .15 .15
a. Ordinary paper 3.00 *5.50*
Set value .40 .65

POSTAL TAX STAMPS

Nurse and Soldier — PT1

Wounded Soldier — PT2

Unwmk.

1942, Oct. 4 **Litho.** ***Perf. 11***

RA1 PT1 1k olive grn & red .20 *.30*

The tax aided the Croatian Red Cross. Issued in sheets of 24 plus label.

1943, Oct. 3

RA2 PT2 2k blue & red .15 *.20*

The tax aided the Croatian Red Cross.

Ruins — PT3

Wounded Soldier — PT4

1944, Jan. 1 **Photo.** ***Perf. 12***

RA3 PT3 1k dk slate green .15 *.15*
RA4 PT4 2k carmine lake .15 *.15*
RA5 PT4 5k black .15 *.15*
RA6 PT4 10k deep blue .15 *.25*
RA7 PT4 20k brown .30 *.45*
Set value .65 *.85*

Catalogue values for unused stamps in this section, from this point to the end of the section, are for Never Hinged items.

Interior of Zagreb Cathedral — PT10

1991, Apr. 1 **Litho.** ***Perf. 14***

RA20 PT10 1.20d black & gold *.40*
a. Perf. 11x10½ *.40*
b. Perf. 11 *.40*

Worker's Fund. No. RA20 was required on mail during April 1991.

For surcharges see Nos. 100, 100a.

Shrine of the Virgin, 700th Anniv. — PT11

1991, May 16 ***Perf. 10½x11***

RA21 PT11 1.70d multicolored *.55*

Workers' Fund. No. RA21 was required on mail May 16-31, 1991.

Croatian Arms Type of 1992

1991, July 1 ***Perf. 11x10½***

RA22 A37 2.20d multicolored *1.15*

No. RA22 was required on mail during July 1991.

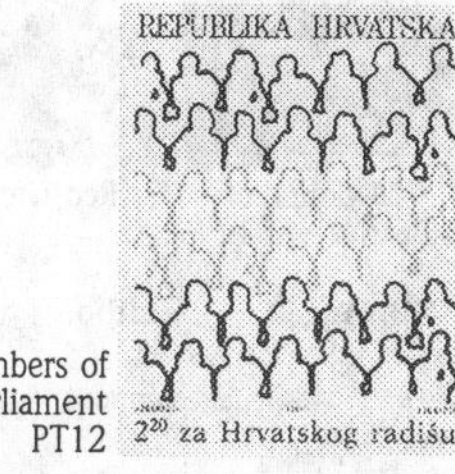

Members of Parliament PT12

1991, Aug. 1 ***Perf. 11x10½***

RA23 PT12 2.20d multicolored *1.15*

Worker's Fund. No. RA23 was required on mail during Aug. 1991.

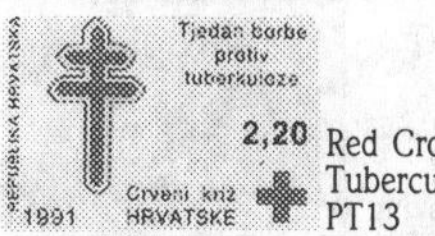

Red Cross and Tuberculosis PT13

1991, Sept 14 ***Perf. 11***

RA24 PT13 2.20d blue & red *.70*

Required on mail Sept. 14-21, 1991.

Re-erection of Ban Josip Jelacic Equestrian Statue, Zagreb — PT14

1991, Nov. 1 ***Perf. 11x10½***

RA25 PT14 2.20d multicolored *.40*
a. Imperf. *.70*

Worker's Fund. No. RA25 was required on mail during Nov. 1991.

"VUKOVAR" with Barbed Wire — PT16

1992, Jan. 1 **Litho.** ***Perf. 11x10½***

RA32 PT16 2.20d black & brown *.30*
a. Imperf. *.55*

Vukovar Refugee's Fund. No. RA32 was required on mail during Jan. 1992.

Red Cross PT17

Red Cross and Solidarity PT18

1992 ***Perf. 11***

RA33 PT17 3d red & black .15
RA34 PT18 3d red & black .15

Issue dates: No. RA33, May 8. No. RA34, June 1.
No. RA33 was required on mail May 8-15, 1992; No. RA34, June 1-7, 1992.

Madonna of Bistrica — PT19

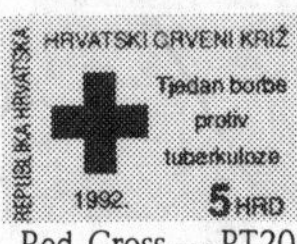
Red Cross — PT20

1992, Aug. 1 **Litho.** ***Perf. 14***

RA35 PT19 5d blue & gold .15

No. RA35 was required on mail, Aug. 1-8, 1992.

1992, Sept. 21 **Litho.** ***Perf. 11***

RA36 PT20 5d black & red .25

Required on mail Sept. 21-28, 1992.

St. George Slaying Dragon — PT21

1992, Nov. 4 ***Perf. 14***

RA37 PT21 15d multicolored .15

Cancer Research League. No. RA37 was required on mail Nov. 4-11, 1992.
See No. RA43.

Red Cross — PT22

1993, May 8 **Litho.** ***Rough Perf. 11***

RA38 PT22 80d black & red .20

No. RA38 was required on mail May 8-15, 1993.

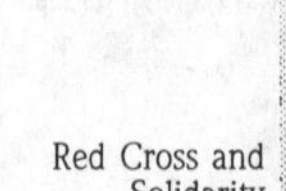

Red Cross and Solidarity PT23

1993, June 1

RA39 PT23 100d black & red 1.10

No. RA39 was required on mail June 1-7, 1993.

Cardinal Stepinac (1898-1960) — PT24

1993, July 15 **Litho.** ***Perf. 14***

RA40 PT24 150d multicolored .20

Required on mail July 15-22, 1993.

Zrinski-Frankopan Foundation — PT25

Design: 200d, Gen. Peter Zrinski (1621-1671), Politician and Fran Krsto Frankopan, Count of Tersat (1643-1671), Poet.

1993, Aug. 12 **Litho.** ***Perf. 14***

RA41 PT25 200d gray & blue .20

Required on mail Aug. 12-19, 1993.

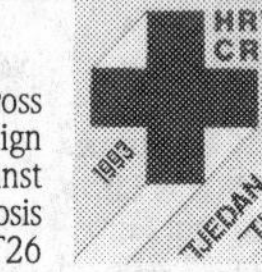
Red Cross Campaign Against Tuberculosis PT26

1993, Sept. 14 **Litho.** ***Perf. 11***

RA42 PT26 300d gray, red & black .20

Required on mail Sept. 14-21, 1993.

St. George Slaying Dragon Type of 1992

1993, Oct. 11 **Litho.** ***Perf. 14***

RA43 PT21 400d multicolored .25

Cancer Research League. Required on mail Oct. 11-31, 1993.

Save the Children of Croatia — PT27

1993, Nov. 1 ***Perf. 13½x14***

RA44 PT27 400d multicolored .25

Required on mail Nov. 1-30, 1993.

Croatian Red Cross — PT28

1994, May 5 **Litho.** ***Perf. 11***

RA45 PT28 500d multicolored .25

Required on mail May 8-15, 1994.

Red Cross Solidarity PT29

Ludberg Church PT30

1994, May 5 **Litho.** ***Perf. 11***

RA46 PT29 50 l multicolored .25

Required on mail June 1-7, 1994.

1994, July 15 ***Perf. 14***

RA47 PT30 50 l multicolored .25

Required on mail July 15-22, 1994.

Save the Children of Croatia — PT31

St. George Slaying Dragon — PT32

1994, Aug. 16 **Litho.** ***Perf. 14***

RA48 PT31 50 l multicolored .25

Required on mail Aug. 16-29, 1994.

1994, Sept. 1

RA49 PT32 50 l multicolored .25

Cancer Research League. Required on mail Sept. 1-8, 1994.

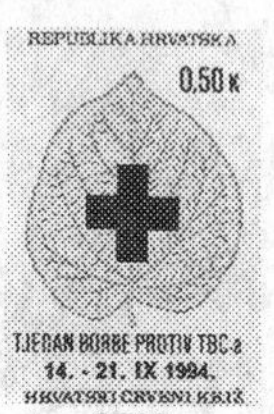
PT33

PT34

1994, Sept. 14 ***Perf. 11***

RA50 PT33 50 l black, green & red .40

Red Cross Campaign against Tuberculosis. Required on mail Sept. 14-21, 1994.

1994, Oct. 15 **Litho.** ***Perf. 14***

RA51 PT34 50 l multicolored .30

Town of Slavonski Brod, 750th anniv.

Homage to Olympia, by Ivan Lackovic PT35

Intl. Olympic Committee, Cent. — PT36

Designs: a, Tennis. b, Soccer. c, Basketball. d, Team handball. e, Canoeing, kayaking. f, Water polo. g, Track and field. h, Gymnastics.

1994, Nov. 2 **Litho.** ***Perf. 14***

RA52 PT35 50 l Pair, #a.-b. 1.40

Miniature Sheets

RA53 PT36 50 l Sheet of 8, #a.-h. *5.75*
RA54 PT36 50 l Sheet of 8, #a.-h. *5.75*

Nos. RA52b, RA53a, RA53d-RA53e, RA53h, RA54b-RA54c, RA54f-RA54g have IOC centennial emblem. Others have emblem of Croation Olympic Committee.
Required on mail Nov. 2-15, 1994.

CUBA

'kyü–bə

LOCATION — The largest island of the West Indies; south of Florida
GOVT. — Former Spanish possession
AREA — 44,206 sq. mi.
POP. — 6,743,000 (est. 1960)
CAPITAL — Havana

Formerly a Spanish possession, Cuba made several unsuccessful attempts to gain her freedom, which finally led to the intervention of the US in 1898. In that year under the Treaty of Paris, Spain relinquished the island to the US in trust for its inhabitants. In 1902 a republic was established and the Cuban Congress took over the government from the military authorities.

8 Reales Plata = 1 Peso
100 Centesimos = 1 Escudo or Peseta (1867)
1000 Milesimas = 100 Centavos = 1 Peso

Catalogue values for unused stamps in this country are for Never Hinged items, beginning with Scott 402 in the regular postage section, Scott B3 in the semi-postal section, Scott C38 in the airpost section, Scott CB1 in the airpost semi-postal section, Scott E15 in the special delivery section, and Scott RA1 in the postal tax section.

Pen cancellations are common on the earlier stamps of Cuba. Stamps so canceled sell for very much less than those with postmark cancellations.

Watermarks

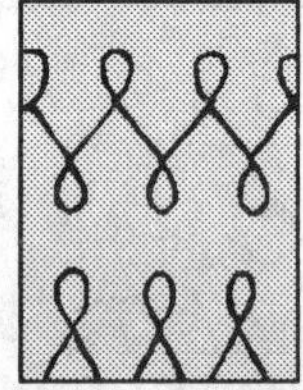
Wmk. 104- Loops

Wmk. 105- Crossed Lines

Wmk. 106- Star

Wmk. 229- Wavy Lines

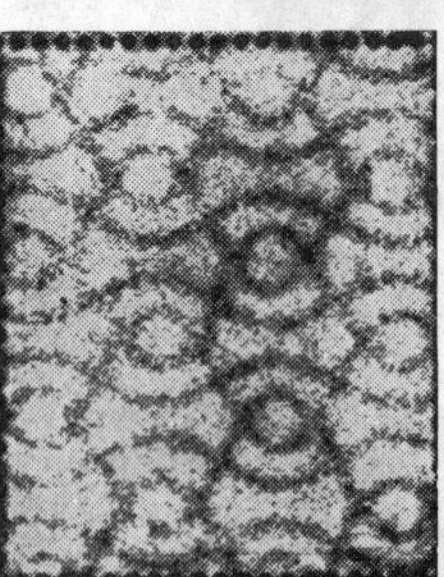
Wmk. 320

Wmk. 321- "R de C"

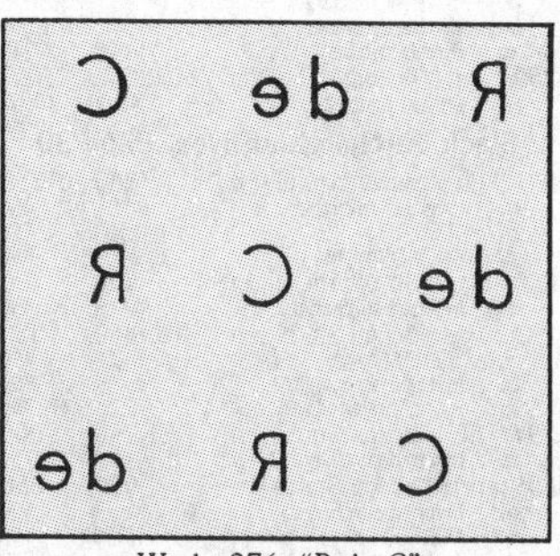

Wmk. 376- "R de C"

Issued under Spanish Dominion

Used also in Puerto Rico: Nos. 1-3, 9-14, 17-21, 32-34, 35A-37, 39-41, 43-45, 47-49, 51-53, 55-57.
Used also in the Philippines: Nos. 2-3.
Identifiable cancellations of those countries will increase the value of the stamps.

Queen Isabella II — A1

Blue Paper

1855 **Typo.** **Wmk. 104** ***Imperf.***

1	A1	½r p blue green	40.00	4.00
2	A1	1r p gray green	40.00	3.00
3	A1	2r p carmine	225.00	11.00
4	A1	2r p orange red	800.00	15.00
		Nos. 1-4 (4)	1,105.	33.00

See Nos. 9-14. For surcharges see Nos. 5-8, 15.

Counterfeit surcharges are plentiful.

Nos. 3-4 Surcharged **Y ¼**

1855-56

5	A1	¼r p on 2r p carmine	750.00	225.00
6	A1	¼r p on 2r p org red		325.00

Surcharged **Y ¼**

7	A1	¼r p on 2r p carmine	550.00	100.00
a.		Without fraction bar		350.00
8	A1	¼r p on 2r p org red	750.00	190.00
a.		Without fraction bar		500.00

The "Y¼" surcharge met the "Ynterior" rate for delivery within the city of Havana.

Rough Yellowish Paper

1856 **Wmk. 105**

9	A1	½r p grnsh blue	9.00	1.40
10	A1	1r p green	600.00	12.50
a.		1r p emerald	1,800.	15.00
11	A1	2r p orange red	250.00	16.00

White Smooth Paper

1857 **Unwmk.**

12	A1	½r p blue	4.50	.65
13	A1	1r p gray green	4.00	.65
a.		1r p pale yellow green	6.75	1.50
14	A1	2r p dull rose	17.50	3.00
		Nos. 12-14 (3)	26.00	4.30

Surcharged **Y¼**

1860

15	A1	¼r p on 2r p dl rose	190.00	67.50
a.		1 of ¼ inverted	225.00	140.00

Queen Isabella II
A2 A3

1862-64 ***Imperf.***

16	A2	¼r p black	21.00	10.00
17	A3	¼r p blk, *buff* ('64)	21.00	10.00
18	A3	½r p green ('64)	4.75	.70
19	A3	½r p grn, *pale rose* ('64)	11.00	3.00
20	A3	1r p bl, *sal* ('64)	4.75	1.00
a.		Diagonal half used as ½r p on cover		100.00
21	A3	2r p ver, *buff* ('64)	27.50	7.75
		Nos. 16-21 (6)	90.00	32.45

No. 17 Overprinted in Black **66**

1866

22	A3	¼r p black, *buff*	65.00	22.50

Exists with handstamped "1866."

A5 A6

1866

23	A5	5c dull violet	47.50	22.50
24	A5	10c blue	1.75	1.00
25	A5	20c green	1.65	1.00
26	A5	40c rose	11.00	9.00
		Nos. 23-26 (4)	61.90	33.50

Stamps Dated "1867"

1867 ***Perf. 14***

27	A5	5c dull violet	35.00	13.00
28	A5	10c blue	6.00	1.00
a.		Imperf., pair	18.00	6.00
29	A5	20c green	6.00	1.00
a.		Imperf., pair	40.00	65.00
30	A5	40c rose	12.50	7.50
		Nos. 27-30 (4)	59.50	22.50

Stamps Dated "1868"

1868

31	A6	5c dull violet	20.00	8.25
32	A6	10c blue	3.75	1.75
a.		Diagonal half used as 5c on cover		100.00
33	A6	20c green	7.50	3.50
a.		Diagonal half used as 10c on cover		125.00
34	A6	40c rose	14.00	8.00
		Nos. 31-34 (4)	45.25	21.50

Nos. 31-34 Overprinted in Black **HABILITADO POR LA NACION.**

1868

35	A6	5c dull violet	55.00	25.00
35A	A6	10c blue	55.00	25.00
36	A6	20c green	55.00	25.00
37	A6	40c rose	55.00	25.00
		Nos. 35-37 (4)	220.00	100.00

1869 **Stamps Dated "1869"**

38	A6	5c rose	45.00	12.00
39	A6	10c red brown	4.25	1.75
a.		Diagonal half used as 5c on cover		75.00
40	A6	20c orange	8.50	2.75
41	A6	40c dull violet	35.00	8.25
		Nos. 38-41 (4)	92.75	24.75

Nos. 38-41 Ovptd. Like Nos. 35-37

42	A6	5c rose	140.00	32.50
43	A6	10c red brown	52.50	20.00
44	A6	20c orange	42.50	27.50
45	A6	40c dull violet	65.00	27.50
		Nos. 42-45 (4)	300.00	107.50

"Espana"
A8 A9

1870 ***Perf. 14***

46	A8	5c blue	140.00	50.00
47	A8	10c green	3.25	1.00
a.		Diagonal half used as 5c on cover		100.00
48	A8	20c red brown	3.25	1.00
a.		Diagonal half used as 10c on cover		100.00
49	A8	40c rose	200.00	27.50

1871

50	A9	12c red lilac	21.00	9.00
a.		Imperf., pair	60.00	60.00
51	A9	25c ultra	2.75	.90
a.		Imperf., pair	30.00	30.00
b.		Diagonal half used as 12c on cover		140.00
52	A9	50c gray green	2.75	.90
a.		Imperf., pair	47.50	32.50
b.		Diagonal half used as 25c on cover		140.00
53	A9	1p pale brown	27.50	9.00
a.		Imperf., pair	47.50	47.50
		Nos. 50-53 (4)	54.00	19.80

King Amadeo — A10

1873 ***Perf. 14***

54	A10	12½c dark green	37.50	14.00
55	A10	25c gray	2.75	1.10
a.		Diagonal half used as 12½c on cover		82.50
56	A10	50c brown	1.60	1.40
a.		Imperf., pair	40.00	40.00
b.		Half used as 25c on cover		82.50
57	A10	1p red brown	250.00	45.00
a.		Diagonal half used as 50c on cover		225.00

"España"
A11

Coat of Arms
A12

1874

58	A11	12½c brown	14.00	6.50
59	A11	25c ultra	1.10	1.10
a.		Diagonal half used as 12½c on cover		82.50
60	A11	50c dp violet	1.90	1.10
61	A11	50c gray	1.90	1.10
a.		Diagonal half used as 25c on cover		82.50
62	A11	1p carmine	82.50	32.50
a.		Imperf., pair	190.00	190.00
		Nos. 58-62 (5)	101.40	42.30

1875

63	A12	12½c lt violet	1.25	.65
a.		Imperf., pair	35.00	
64	A12	25c ultra	.60	.50
a.		Imperf., pair	35.00	
b.		Diagonal half used as 12½c on cover		75.00
65	A12	50c blue green	.60	.50
a.		Imperf., pair	35.00	
b.		Diagonal half used as 25c on cover		50.00
66	A12	1p brown	8.00	5.00
a.		1p dk brown	8.00	5.00
b.		Half used as 50c on cover		85.00
		Nos. 63-66 (4)	10.45	6.65

King Alfonso XII
A13 A14

1876

67	A13	12½c green	2.25	.55
68	A13	25c gray	.75	.35
a.		Diagonal half used as 12½c on cover		80.00
69	A13	50c ultra	.75	.45
a.		Imperf., pair	11.50	
70	A13	1p black	8.50	3.75
a.		Imperf., pair	27.50	
		Nos. 67-70 (4)	12.25	5.10

1877

71	A14	10c lt green	35.00	
72	A14	12½c gray	7.50	1.40
a.		Imperf., pair	20.00	
73	A14	25c dk green	.55	.45
a.		Imperf., pair	20.00	
74	A14	50c black	.55	.45
a.		Imperf., pair	20.00	
b.		Half used as 25c on cover		80.00
75	A14	1p brown	25.00	17.50
		Nos. 71-75 (5)	68.60	

No. 71 was not placed in use.

Stamps Dated "1878"

1878

76	A14	5c blue	.50	.45
77	A14	10c black	60.00	
78	A14	12½c brown bis	3.50	1.40
a.		12½c gray bister	2.25	1.10
79	A14	25c dp green	.40	.25
b.		Diagonal half used as 12½c on cover		60.00
80	A14	50c dk blue grn	.40	.25
81	A14	1p carmine	11.00	6.00
		Nos. 76-81 (6)	75.80	

No. 77 was not placed in use.

Imperf., Pairs

76a	A14	5c blue	20.00
77a	A14	10c black	150.00
78b	A14	12½c brown bister	20.00
79a	A14	25c deep green	20.00
80a	A14	50c dk blue green	20.00
81a	A14	1p carmine	40.00

Stamps Dated "1879"

82	A14	5c slate black	.75	.40
83	A14	10c orange	125.00	65.00
84	A14	12½c rose	.75	.40
85	A14	25c ultra	.55	.40
a.		Diagonal half used as 12½c on cover		75.00
b.		Imperf., pair	40.00	30.00
86	A14	50c gray	.50	.35
a.		Diagonal half used as 25c on cover		75.00
87	A14	1p olive bister	22.00	12.50
		Nos. 82-87 (6)	149.55	79.05

A15

A16

A17

1880

88	A15	5c green	.40	.15
89	A15	10c lake	60.00	
90	A15	12½c gray	.40	.15
91	A15	25c gray blue	.40	.15
a.		Diagonal half used as 12½c on cover		75.00
92	A15	50c brown	.50	.15
a.		Half used as 25c on cover		75.00
93	A15	1p yellow brn	7.50	3.00
		Nos. 88-93 (6)	69.20	

No. 89 was not placed in use.

1881

94	A16	1c green	.40	.15
95	A16	2c lake	32.50	
96	A16	2½c olive bister	.75	.30
97	A16	5c gray blue	.40	.15
98	A16	10c yellow brown	.45	.15
99	A16	20c dark brown	7.50	5.00
		Nos. 94-99 (6)	42.00	

No. 95 was not placed in use.

1882

100	A17	1c green	.50	.35
101	A17	2c lake	3.00	.35
102	A17	2½c dk brown	6.50	2.25
103	A17	5c gray blue	3.00	.75
a.		Diagonal half used as 2½c on cover		75.00
104	A17	10c olive bister	.50	.15
105	A17	20c red brown	77.50	32.50
		Nos. 100-105 (6)	91.00	36.35

See #121-131. For surcharges see #106-120.

Issue of 1882 Surcharged or Overprinted in Black, Blue or Red:

a

b

c

d

e

1883

Type "a"

106	A17	5 on 5c (R)	1.75	.90
a.		Triple surcharge		
b.		Double surcharge	3.25	3.25
c.		Inverted surcharge	2.50	2.50
d.		Without "5" in surcharge	7.25	7.25
e.		Dbl. surch., types "a" & "d"		
107	A17	10 on 10c (Bl)	1.75	.90
a.		Inverted surcharge		
b.		Double surcharge	2.75	
108	A17	20 on 20c	22.50	19.00
a.		"10" instead of "20"	50.00	50.00
b.		Double surcharge		

Type "b"

109	A17	5 on 5c (R)	1.75	.90
a.		Inverted surcharge	2.50	2.50
b.		Double surcharge	3.50	

No.	Type	Description	Unused	Used
110	A17	10 on 10c (Bl)	2.75	1.50
a.		Inverted surcharge	3.50	3.50
b.		Double surcharge		
111	A17	20 on 20c	25.00	18.00
a.		Double surcharge		
b.		Dbl. surch., types "b" & "c"		

Type "c"

No.	Type	Description	Unused	Used
112	A17	5 on 5c (R)	1.75	1.10
a.		Inverted surcharge		
b.		Dbl. surch., types "c" & "d"	4.25	
113	A17	10 on 10c (Bl)	4.25	1.75
a.		Inverted surcharge		
b.		Double surcharge		
114	A17	20 on 20c	35.00	18.00
a.		"10" instead of "20"	90.00	90.00
b.		Double surcharge		
c.		Dbl. surch., types "a" & "c"		

Type "d"

No.	Type	Description	Unused	Used
115	A17	5 on 5c (R)	1.75	1.10
a.		Inverted surcharge	2.50	2.50
b.		Double surcharge		
116	A17	10 on 10c (Bl)	4.25	1.75
a.		Inverted surcharge		
b.		Double surcharge		
117	A17	20 on 20c	60.00	25.00
a.		Dbl. surch., types "a" & "d"		

Type "e"

No.	Type	Description	Unused	Used
118	A17	5c gray blue (R)	2.75	1.65
a.		Double overprint	4.50	
119	A17	10c olive bis (Bl)	4.25	3.50
a.		Double overprint		
120	A17	20c red brown	72.50	32.50
a.		Double overprint		
		Nos. 106-120 (15)	242.00	127.55

Handstamped overprints and surcharges are counterfeits.

Type of 1882

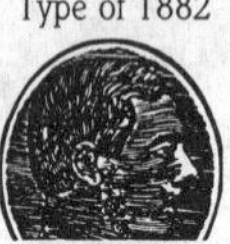

Original

1st retouch

2d retouch

The differences between the stamps of 1882 and the various retouches are as follows:

Original state: The medallion is surrounded by a heavy line of color of nearly even thickness, touching the horizontal line below the word "Cuba" (or "Filipinas," "Puerto Rico", as the case may be); the opening in the hair above the temple is narrow and pointed.

1st retouch: The line around the medallion is thin, except at the upper right, and does not touch the horizontal line above it; the opening in the hair is slightly wider and a trifle rounded; the lock of hair above the forehead is shaped like a broad "V" and ends in a point; there is a faint white line below it, which is not found on the stamps in the original state. Owing to wear of the plate the shape of the lock of hair and the width of the white line below it vary.

2nd retouch: The opening in the hair forms a semi-circle; the lock above the forehead is nearly straight, having only a slight wave, and the white line is much broader than before.

1883-86

No.	Type	Description	Unused	Used
121	A17	1c grn, 2nd retouch	1.25	.15
122	A17	2½c olive bister	.32	.15
124	A17	2½c violet	.32	.15
a.		2½c red lilac ('85)	.40	.15
b.		2½c ultramarine	110.00	42.50
125	A17	5c gray bl, 1st retouch	1.25	.15
126	A17	5c gray bl, 2nd retouch	4.00	1.00
a.		Diagonal half used as 2½c on cover		30.00
127	A17	10c brn, 1st retouch	1.65	.50
a.		Diagonal half used as 5c on cover		30.00
128	A17	20c olive bister	11.50	2.75
		Nos. 121-128 (7)	20.29	4.85

1888

No.	Type	Description	Unused	Used
129	A17	2½c red brown	2.25	1.25
130	A17	10c blue	1.25	.80
a.		Diagonal half used as 5c on cover		
131	A17	20c brnsh gray	11.00	4.75
		Nos. 129-131 (3)	14.50	6.80

King Alfonso XIII
A18 A19

1890-97

No.	Type	Description	Unused	Used
132	A18	1c gray brn	11.00	4.25
133	A18	1c ol gray ('91)	7.00	.90
134	A18	1c ultra ('94)	2.00	.35
135	A18	1c dk vio ('96)	1.00	.16
136	A18	2c slate blue	4.25	1.00
137	A18	2c lil brn ('91)	1.00	.35
138	A18	2c rose ('94)	17.50	2.50
139	A18	2c claret ('96)	6.00	.60
140	A18	2½c emerald	7.00	1.75
141	A18	2½c salmon ('91)	21.00	4.25
142	A18	2½c lilac ('94)	1.75	.24
143	A18	2½c rose ('96)	.70	.15
144	A18	5c olive gray	.70	.52
145	A18	5c emer ('91)	.90	.45
146	A18	5c sl blue ('96)	.35	.15
147	A18	10c brn vio	1.75	.60
148	A18	10c claret ('91)	1.25	.45
149	A18	10c emer ('96)	2.00	.16
150	A18	20c dk vio	.80	.52
151	A18	20c ultra ('91)	11.00	4.25
152	A18	20c red brn ('94)	17.50	4.25
153	A18	20c vio ('96)	17.50	5.25
154	A18	40c org brn ('97)	35.00	10.50
155	A18	80c lil brn ('97)	45.00	14.00
		Nos. 132-155 (24)	213.95	57.60

Imperf., Pairs

No.	Type	Description	Unused	Used
134a	A18	1c ultramarine	150.00	
138a	A18	2c rose	150.00	
142a	A18	2½c lilac	150.00	
145a	A18	5c emerald	150.00	
148a	A18	10c claret	150.00	
152a	A18	20c red brown	200.00	

1898

No.	Type	Description	Unused	Used
156	A19	1m orange brn	.15	.15
157	A19	2m orange brn	.15	.15
158	A19	3m orange brn	.15	.15
159	A19	4m orange brn	3.25	1.40
160	A19	5m orange brn	.15	.15
161	A19	1c black vio	.15	.15
162	A19	2c dk blue grn	.15	.15
163	A19	3c dk brown	.15	.15
164	A19	4c orange	9.75	3.50
165	A19	5c car rose	.70	.16
a.		Imperf., pair	100.00	
166	A19	6c dk blue	.15	.15
a.		Imperf., pair	100.00	
167	A19	8c gray brown	.70	.35
168	A19	10c vermilion	.70	.35
169	A19	15c slate green	3.25	.35
170	A19	20c maroon	.40	.16
171	A19	40c dark lilac	1.65	.35
172	A19	60c black	1.65	.35
173	A19	80c red brown	11.00	7.00
174	A19	1p yel green	11.00	7.00
175	A19	2p slate blue	16.00	7.00
		Nos. 156-175 (20)	61.25	29.17

Nos. 156-160 were issued for use on newspapers. For surcharges see Nos. 176-189C, 196-200.

Issued under Administration of the United States

Puerto Principe Issue

Issues of Cuba of 1898 and 1896 Surcharged:

HABILITADO 1 cent. — a

HABILITADO 1 cents. — b

HABILITADO 2 cents. — c

HABILITADO 2 cents. — d

HABILITADO 3 cents. — e

HABILITADO 3 cents. — f

HABILITADO 5 cents. — g

HABILITADO 5 cents. — h

HABILITADO 5 cents. — i

HABILITADO 5 cents. — j

HABILITADO 3 cents. — k

HABILITADO 3 cents. — l

HABILITADO 10 cents. — m

Types a, c, d, e, f, g and h are 17½mm high, the others are 19½mm high.

Black Surcharge On Nos. 156, 157, 158 and 160

1898-99

No.	Type	Description	Unused	Used
176	(a)	1c on 1m org brn	45.00	30.00
177	(b)	1c on 1m org brn	45.00	35.00
a.		Broken figure "1"	75.00	65.00
b.		Inverted surcharge		200.00
d.		As "a," inverted		250.00
178	(c)	2c on 2m org brn	22.50	18.00
a.		Inverted surcharge	250.00	50.00
179	(d)	2c on 2m org brn	40.00	35.00
a.		Inverted surcharge	350.00	100.00
179B	(k)	3c on 1m org brn	300.00	175.00
c.		Double surcharge	1,500.	750.00
179D	(l)	3c on 1m org brn	*1,500.*	*675.00*
e.		Double surcharge	—	—
179F	(e)	3c on 2m org brn		*1,500.*

Value is for copy with minor faults.

No.	Type	Description	Unused	Used
179G	(f)	3c on 2m org brn	—	*2,000.*

Value is for copy with minor faults.

No.	Type	Description	Unused	Used
180	(e)	3c on 3m org brn	27.50	30.00
a.		Inverted surcharge		*100.00*
181	(f)	3c on 3m org brn	75.00	75.00
a.		Inverted surcharge		*200.00*
182	(g)	5c on 1m org brn	700.00	200.00
a.		Inverted surcharge		*500.00*
183	(h)	5c on 1m org brn	*1,300.*	*500.00*
a.		Inverted surcharge		*700.00*
184	(g)	5c on 2m org brn	750.00	250.00
185	(h)	5c on 2m org brn	1,500.	500.00
186	(g)	5c on 3m org brn		165.00
a.		Inverted surcharge		700.00
187	(h)	5c on 3m org brn		400.00
a.		Inverted surcharge		1,000.
188	(g)	5c on 5m org brn	70.00	60.00
a.		Inverted surcharge	400.00	200.00
b.		Double surcharge		—
189	(h)	5c on 5m org brn	350.00	250.00
a.		Inverted surcharge		400.00
b.		Double surcharge		—

The 2nd printing of Nos. 188-189 has shiny ink. Values are for the 1st printing.

No.	Type	Description	Unused	Used
189C	(i)	5c on 5m org brn		*7,500.*

Black Surcharge on No. P25

No.	Type	Description	Unused	Used
190	(g)	5c on ½m bl grn	250.00	75.00
a.		Inverted surcharge	500.00	150.00
b.		Pair, right stamp without surcharge		500.00

Value for No. 190b is for pair with unsurcharged copy at right. Exists with unsurcharged stamp at left.

No.	Type	Description	Unused	Used
191	(h)	5c on ½m bl grn	300.00	90.00
a.		Inverted surcharge		200.00
192	(i)	5c on ½m bl grn	550.00	200.00
a.		Dbl. surch., one diagonal		*11,500.*
193	(j)	5c on ½m bl grn	700.00	300.00

Red Surcharge on No. 161

No.	Type	Description	Unused	Used
196	(k)	3c on 1c blk vio	60.00	35.00
a.		Inverted surcharge		300.00
197	(l)	3c on 1c blk vio	125.00	55.00
a.		Inverted surcharge		300.00
198	(i)	5c on 1c blk vio	20.00	25.00
a.		Inverted surcharge		125.00
b.		Surcharge vert. up		*3,500.*
c.		Double surcharge	*400.00*	*600.00*
d.		Dbl. invtd. surch.		—

No. 198b exists reading down.

No.	Type	Description	Unused	Used
199	(j)	5c on 1c blk vio	50.00	50.00
a.		Inverted surcharge		250.00
b.		Vertical surcharge		*2,000.*
c.		Double surcharge	1,000.	600.00
200	(m)	10c on 1c blk vio	20.00	*50.00*
a.		Broken figure "1"	40.00	*100.00*

Black Surcharge on Nos. P26-P30

No.	Type	Description	Unused	Used
201	(k)	3c on 1m bl grn	350.	350.
a.		Inverted surcharge		450.
b.		"EENTS"	550.	450.
c.		As "b," inverted		850.
202	(l)	3c on 1m bl grn	500.	400.
a.		Inverted surcharge		850.
203	(k)	3c on 2m bl grn	850.	350.
a.		"EENTS"	1,250.	450.
b.		Inverted surcharge		850.
c.		As "a," inverted		950.
204	(l)	3c on 2m bl grn	1,250.	600.
a.		Inverted surcharge		750.
205	(k)	3c on 3m bl grn	900.	350.
a.		Inverted surcharge		500.
b.		"EENTS"	1,250.	450.
c.		As "b," inverted		700.
206	(l)	3c on 3m bl grn	1,200.	550.
a.		Inverted surcharge		700.
211	(i)	5c on 1m bl grn		1,800.
a.		"EENTS"	—	2,500.
212	(j)	5c on 1m bl grn		2,500.
213	(i)	5c on 2m bl grn		1,800.
a.		"EENTS"	—	1,900.
214	(j)	5c on 2m bl grn		1,900.
	(i)	5c on 3m bl grn		500.
a.		"EENTS"		1,000.
216	(j)	5c on 3m bl grn	—	1,000.
217	(i)	5c on 4m bl grn	*2,500.*	900.
a.		"EENTS"	*3,000.*	1,500.
b.		Inverted surcharge		*2,000.*
c.		As "a," inverted		2,000.
218	(j)	5c on 4m bl grn		*1,500.*
a.		Inverted surcharge		*2,000.*
219	(i)	5c on 8m bl grn	*2,500.*	1,250.
a.		Inverted surcharge		1,500.
b.		"EENTS"	—	1,800.
c.		As "b," inverted		2,500.
220	(j)	5c on 8m bl grn		2,000.
a.		Inverted surcharge		2,500.

CUBA

United States Nos. 279, 267, 279B, 268, 281, 282C and 283 Surcharged in Black

1 c. de PESO.

1899 Wmk. 191 *Perf. 12*

No.	Type	Description	Unused	Used
221	A87	1c on 1c yel grn	5.25	.35
222	A88	2c on 2c car	5.75	.40
a.		2c on 2c red	6.50	.30
c.		Inverted surcharge	*3,500.*	*3,500.*
223	A88	2½c on 2c carmine	3.50	.45
a.		2½c on 2c red	4.00	1.60
224	A89	3c on 3c pur	10.00	1.75
a.		Period btwn. "B" and "A"	30.00	30.00
225	A91	5c on 5c bl	10.00	2.00
226	A94	10c on 10c brn, type I	20.00	6.50
b.		"CUBA" omitted	*4,000.*	*4,000.*
226A	A94	10c on 10c brn, type II	*6,000.*	
		Nos. 221-226 (6)	54.50	11.45

The 2½c was sold and used as a 2c stamp.

Excellent counterfeits of this and the preceding issue exist, especially inverted and double surcharges.

Issues of the Republic under US Military Rule

Statue of Columbus
A20

Royal Palms
A21

"Cuba"
A22

Ocean Liner
A23

Cane Field — A24

1899 Engr. Wmk. 191C *Perf. 12*

No.	Type	Description	Unused	Used
227	A20	1c yel grn	3.50	.15
228	A21	2c carmine	3.50	.15
a.		2c scarlet	3.50	.15
b.		Booklet pane of 6 ('02)	*2,000.*	

229 A22 3c purple 3.50 .16
230 A23 5c blue 3.50 .20
231 A24 10c brown 11.00 .50
Nos. 227-231 (5) 25.00 1.16

No. 228b was issued by the Republic.

Issues of the Republic

No. 229 Surcharged in Carmine

1902, Sept. 30

232 A22 1c on 3c purple 1.00 .50
a. Inverted surcharge 150.00 150.00
b. Surcharge sideways (numeral horizontal)
c. Double surcharge 200.00 200.00

Counterfeits of the errors are plentiful.

Re-engraved

The re-engraved stamps of 1905-07 may be distinguished from the issue of 1899 as follows:

ORIGINAL RE-ENGRAVED

1c- The ends of the label inscribed "Centavo" are rounded instead of square.
2c- The foliate ornaments, inside the oval disks bearing the numerals of value, have been removed.
5c- Two lines forming a right angle have been added in the upper corners of the label bearing the word "Cuba."
10c- A small ball has been added to each of the square ends of the label bearing the word "Cuba."

1905 Unwmk. *Perf. 12*

233 A20 1c green 1.65 .15
234 A21 2c rose 1.10 .15
a. Booklet pane of 6 135.00
236 A23 5c blue 32.50 1.00
237 A24 10c brown 3.00 .45
Nos. 233-237 (4) 38.25 1.75

Maj. Gen. Antonio Maceo — A26

1907

238 A26 50c gray bl & blk 1.00 .75

Bartolomé Masó A27

Máximo Gómez A28

Julio Sanguily A29

Ignacio Agramonte A30

Calixto García A31

José M. Rodriquez y Rodriquez (Mayia) A32

Carlos Roloff — A33

1910, Feb. 1

239 A27 1c grn & vio .75 .15
a. Center inverted 150.00 *150.00*
240 A28 2c car & grn 1.50 .15
a. Center inverted 500.00 *500.00*
241 A29 3c vio & bl 1.00 .20
242 A30 5c bl & grn 14.00 .80
243 A31 8c ol & vio 1.00 .32
244 A32 10c brn & bl 6.25 .65
a. Center inverted 750.00
245 A26 50c vio & blk 1.50 .48
246 A33 1p slate & blk 7.00 4.00
Nos. 239-246 (8) 33.00 6.75

1911-13

247 A27 1c green .45 .15
248 A28 2c car rose .60 .15
a. Booklet pane of 6 ('13) 75.00
250 A30 5c ultra 1.50 .15
251 A31 8c ol grn & blk .90 .60
252 A33 1p black 4.25 2.00
Nos. 247-252 (5) 7.70 3.05

Map of Cuba — A34

1914-15

253 A34 1c green .42 .15
a. Booklet pane of 6 80.00
254 A34 2c car rose .60 .15
a. Booklet pane of 6 80.00
255 A34 2c red ('15) 1.25 .15
a. Booklet pane of 6 80.00
256 A34 3c violet 4.00 .30
257 A34 5c blue 5.75 .15
258 A34 8c ol grn 4.50 .60
259 A34 10c brown 8.50 .30
260 A34 10c ol grn ('15) 10.00 .45
261 A34 50c orange 65.00 8.75
262 A34 1p gray 90.00 20.00
Nos. 253-262 (10) 190.02 31.00

Imperf. pairs, value each $100 to $500.

Gertrudis Gómez de Avellaneda, Cuban Poetess (1814-73) A34a

1914

263 A34a 5c blue 10.50 5.00

José Martí A35

Máximo Gómez A36

José de la Luz Caballero — A37

Calixto García — A38

Ignacio Agramonte A39

Tomás Estrada Palma A40

José A. Saco A41

Antonio Maceo A42

Carlos Manuel de Céspedes — A43

1917-18 Unwmk. *Perf. 12*

264 A35 1c bl grn .80 .15
a. Booklet pane of 6 37.50
b. Booklet pane of 30 250.00
265 A36 2c rose .60 .15
a. Booklet pane of 6 50.00
b. Booklet pane of 30 210.00
266 A36 2c lt red ('18) .60 .15
a. Booklet pane of 6 50.00
267 A37 3c violet 1.00 .15
a. Imperf. pair 275.00
b. Booklet pane of 6 50.00
268 A38 5c dp bl 2.00 .15
269 A39 8c red brn 4.75 .15
270 A40 10c yel brn 2.50 .15
271 A41 20c gray grn 9.50 1.00
272 A42 50c dl rose 11.00 1.00
273 A43 1p black 11.00 1.00
Nos. 264-273 (10) 43.75
Set value 3.50

1925-28 Wmk. 106 *Perf. 12*

274 A35 1c bl grn 1.25 .15
a. Booklet pane of 30 325.00
275 A36 2c brt rose 1.10 .15
a. Booklet pane of 6 70.00
b. Booklet pane of 30 325.00
276 A38 5c dp bl 2.25 .15
277 A39 8c red brn ('28) 4.50 .50
278 A40 10c yel brn ('27) 5.25 .60
279 A41 20c olive grn 8.25 1.00
Nos. 274-279 (6) 22.60 2.55

1926 *Imperf.*

280 A35 1c blue green 1.10 .95
281 A36 2c brt rose 1.00 .80
282 A38 5c deep blue 1.65 1.65
Nos. 280-282 (3) 3.75 3.40

See Nos. 304-310. For overprint and surcharge see Nos. 317-318, 644.

Arms of Republic A44

1927, May 20 Unwmk. *Perf. 12*

283 A44 25c violet 7.25 3.00

25th anniversary of the Republic.
For surcharges see Nos. 355, C3.

Tomás Estrada Palma — A45

Designs: 2c, Gen. Gerardo Machado. 5c, Morro Castle. 8c, Havana Railway Station. 10c, Presidential Palace. 13c, Tobacco Plantation. 20c, Treasury Building. 30c, Sugar Mill. 50c, Havana Cathedral. 1p, Galician Clubhouse, Havana.

1928, Jan. 2 Wmk. 106

284 A45 1c deep green .32 .20
285 A45 2c brt rose .32 .20
286 A45 5c deep blue .95 .30
287 A45 8c lt red brn 1.50 .75
288 A45 10c bister brn .80 .50
289 A45 13c orange 1.25 .50
290 A45 20c olive grn 1.50 .65
291 A45 30c dk violet 2.75 .50
292 A45 50c carmine rose 4.50 1.75
293 A45 1p gray black 9.00 4.00
Nos. 284-293 (10) 22.89 9.35

Sixth Pan-American Conference.

Capitol, Havana A55

1929, May 18

294 A55 1c green .25 .40
295 A55 2c carmine rose .25 .35
296 A55 5c blue .38 .50
297 A55 10c bister brn .75 .60
298 A55 20c violet 2.50 2.50
Nos. 294-298 (5) 4.13 4.35

Opening of the Capitol, Havana.

Hurdler — A56

1930, Mar. 15 Engr.

299 A56 1c green .55 .25
300 A56 2c carmine .55 .25
301 A56 5c deep blue .80 .25
302 A56 10c bister brn 1.25 .80
303 A56 20c violet 5.40 2.50
Nos. 299-303 (5) 8.55 4.05

2nd Central American Athletic Games.

Types of 1917 Portrait Issue
Flat Plate Printing

1930-45 Wmk. 106 Engr. *Perf. 10*

304 A35 1c blue green .85 .25
a. Booklet pane of 6 50.00
b. Booklet pane of 30
305 A36 2c brt rose 160.00 75.00
a. Booklet pane of 6 1,200.
305B A37 3c dk rose vio ('42) 2.25 .30
c. Booklet pane of 6 42.50
306 A38 5c dk blue 2.75 .20
306A A39 8c red brn ('45) 2.75 .25
307 A40 10c brown 2.75 .25
a. 10c yellow brown ('35) 3.50 .75
307B A41 20c olive grn ('41) 4.75 .75
Nos. 304-307B (7) 176.10 77.00

Nos. 305 and 305B were printed for booklet panes and all copies have straight edges.
For surcharge see No. 644.

Rotary Press Printing

308 A35 1c blue grn 1.10 .15
309 A36 2c brt rose 1.10 .15
a. Booklet pane of 50
310 A37 3c violet 1.50 .15
a. 3c dull violet ('38) 1.10 .15
b. 3c rose violet ('41) 1.10 .15
c. Booklet pane of 50
Set value .30

Flat plate stamps measure 18½x21½mm; rotary press, 19x22mm.

The Mangos of Baragua — A57

War Memorial — A61

Battle of Mal Tiempo A58

Battle of Coliseo A59

Maceo, Gómez and Zayas — A60

Perf. 12½

1933, Apr. 23 Photo. Wmk. 229

312 A57 3c dk brown	.65	.15
313 A58 5c dk blue	.65	.25
314 A59 10c emerald	1.90	.25
315 A60 13c red	1.90	.65
316 A61 20c black	3.75	2.00
Nos. 312-316 (5)	8.85	3.30

War of Independence and dedication of the "Soldado Invasor" monument.

Types of 1917 Issues with Carmine or Black Overprint Reading Up or Down

GOBIERNO REVOLUCIONARIO 4-9-1933

Rotary Press Printing

Wmk. 106

1933, Dec. 23 Engr. *Perf. 10*

317 A35 1c blue green (C)	.30	.15

With Additional Surcharge of New Value and Bars

318 A37 2c on 3c vio (Bk)	.30	.15

Establishment of a revolutionary junta.

Dr. Carlos J. Finlay — A62

1934, Dec. 3 Engr. *Perf. 10*

319 A62 2c dark carmine	.45	.15
320 A62 5c dark blue	1.00	.35

Cent. of the birth of Dr. Carlos J. Finlay (1833-1915), physician-biologist who found that a mosquito transmitted yellow fever.

Pres. José Miguel Gómez — A63

Gómez Monument — A64

1936, May *Perf. 10*

322 A63 1c green	.28	.15
323 A64 2c carmine	.65	.15

Unveiling of a monument to Gen. José Miguel Gómez, ex-president.

Matanzas Issue

Map of Cuba A65

Designs: 2c, Map of Free Zone. 4c, S. S. "Rex" in Matanzas Bay. 5c, Ships in Matanzas Bay. 8c, Caves of Bellamar. 10c, Valley of Yumuri. 20c, Yumuri River. 50c, Ships Leaving Port.

Perf. 12½

1936, May 5 Photo. Wmk. 229

324 A65 1c blue green	.20	.15
325 A65 2c red	.30	.15
326 A65 4c claret	.65	.20
327 A65 5c ultra	.55	.20
328 A65 8c orange brn	1.25	.50
329 A65 10c emerald	1.00	.50
330 A65 20c brown	2.50	1.75
331 A65 50c slate	4.00	2.50
Nos. 324-331,C18-C21,CE1,E8 (14)	24.08	13.58

Exist imperf. Value 20% more.

"Peace and Work" A73

Máximo Gómez Monument — A74

Torch — A75

"Independence" — A76

"Messenger of Peace" — A77

1936, Nov. 18 *Perf. 12½*

332 A73 1c emerald	.20	.15
333 A74 2c crimson	.24	.15
334 A75 4c maroon	.30	.15
335 A76 5c ultra	1.00	.40
336 A77 8c dk green	1.65	.80
Nos. 332-336,C22-C23,E9 (8)	7.64	3.32

Maj. Gen. Máximo Gómez, birth centenary.

Sugar Cane — A78

Primitive Sugar Mill — A79

Modern Sugar Mill — A80

Wmk. 106

1937, Oct. 2 Engr. *Perf. 10*

337 A78 1c yellow green	.35	.22
338 A79 2c red	.25	.15
339 A80 5c bright blue	.35	.28
Nos. 337-339 (3)	.95	.65

Cuban sugar cane industry, 400th anniv.

Argentine Emblem — A81

Mountain Scene (Bolivia) — A82

Arms of Brazil — A83

Canadian Scene — A84

Camilo Henriquez (Chile) — A85

Gen, Francisco de Paula Santander (Colombia) — A86

Natl. Monument (Costa Rica) — A87

Autograph of José Martí (Cuba) — A88

Columbus Lighthouse (Dominican Rep.) A89

Juan Montalvo (Ecuador) A90

Abraham Lincoln (US) A91

Quetzal and Scroll (Guatemala) A92

Arms of Haiti — A93

Francisco Morazán (Honduras) — A94

Fleet of Columbus — A95

Wmk. 106

1937, Oct. 13 Engr. *Perf. 10*

340 A81 1c dp green	.35	.42
341 A82 1c green	.35	.42
342 A83 2c carmine	.35	.42
343 A84 2c carmine	.35	.42
344 A85 3c violet	1.00	1.25
345 A86 3c violet	1.00	1.25
346 A87 4c bister brn	1.10	1.50
347 A88 4c bister brn	2.00	2.50
348 A89 5c blue	1.00	1.25
349 A90 5c blue	1.00	1.25
350 A91 8c citron	7.00	8.50
351 A92 8c citron	1.75	2.00
352 A93 10c maroon	1.75	2.00
353 A94 10c maroon	1.75	2.00
354 A95 25c rose lilac	17.50	21.00
Nos. 340-354,C24-C29,E10-E11 (23)	76.25	85.68

Nos. 340-354 were sold by the Cuban PO for 3 days, Oct. 13-15, during which no other stamps were sold. They were postally valid for the full face value. Proceeds from their three-day sale above 30,000 pesos were paid by the Cuban POD to the Assoc. of American Writers and Artists. Remainders were overprinted "SVP" (Without Postal Value).

No. 283 Surcharged in Green

1937, Nov. 19 Unwmk. *Perf. 12*

355 A44 10c on 25c violet	6.75	1.40

Centenary of Cuban railroads.

Ciboney Indian and Cigar — A96

Cigar and Globe — A97

Tobacco Plant and Cigars — A98

1939, Aug. 28 Wmk. 106 *Perf. 10*

356 A96 1c yellow green	.15	.15
357 A97 2c red	.30	.15
358 A98 5c brt ultra	.60	.15
Nos. 356-358 (3)	1.05	
Set value		.20

General Calixto García A99 A100

1939, Nov. 6 *Perf. 10, Imperf.*

359 A99 2c dark red	.30	.15
360 A100 5c deep blue	.60	.28

Birth centenary of General Garcia.

Gonzalo de Quesada — A101

1940, Apr. 30 Engr. *Perf. 10*

361 A101 2c rose red	.38	.22

Pan American Union, 50th anniversary.

Rotary Club Emblem, Cuban Flag and Tobacco Plant — A102

Lions Emblem, Cuban Flag and Royal Palms — A103

1940, May 18 Wmk. 106 *Perf. 10*

362 A102 2c rose red .65 .48

Rotary Intl. Convention held at Havana.

1940, July 23

363 A103 2c orange vermilion .95 .48

Lions International Convention, Havana.

Dr. Nicolás J. Gutiérrez A104

1940, Oct. 28

364 A104 2c orange ver .40 .25
365 A104 5c blue .50 .30
a. Sheet of four, imperf., unwmkd. 2.50 2.50
b. As "a," black overprint ('51) 3.00 3.00

100th anniv. of the publication of the 1st Cuban Medical Review, "El Repertorio Medico Habanero."

No. 365a contains 2 each of Nos. 364-365 imperf. and sold for 25c.

For overprint see No. C43A.

In 1951 No. 365a was overprinted in black: "50 Aniversario Descubrimiento Agente Transmisor de la Flebre Amarilla por el Dr. Carlos J. Finlay Honor a los Martires de la Ciencia 1901 1951." The overprint is illustrated over No. C43A, but does not include the plane and "Correo Aereo."

Major General Guillermo Moncada — A105

Moncada Riding into Battle A106

1941, June 25

366 A105 3c dk brown, *buff* .70 .18
367 A106 5c bright blue .70 .35

Maj. Gen. Guillermo Moncada (1841-96).

Globe Showing Western Hemisphere — A107

"Labor: Wealth of America" — A109

Maceo, Bolívar, Juárez, Lincoln and Arms of Cuba A108

Tree of Fraternity, Havana — A110

Statue of Liberty — A111

Perf. 10, Imperf.

1942, Feb. 23 Wmk. 106

368 A107 1c emerald .16 .15
369 A108 3c orange brown .20 .15
370 A109 5c blue .35 .15
371 A110 10c red violet .80 .38
372 A111 13c red 1.00 .65
Nos. 368-372 (5) 2.51 1.48

Spirit of Democracy in the Americas.
The imperforate varieties are without gum.

Ignacio Agramonte Loynaz — A112

Rescue of Sanguily by Agramonte A113

1942, Apr. 10 *Perf. 10*

373 A112 3c bister brn .45 .22
374 A113 5c brt blue, *bluish* .85 .32

100th anniv. of the birth of Ignacio Agramonte Loynaz, patriot.

"Unmask the Fifth Columnists" — A114

"Be Careful, The Fifth Column is Spying on You" — A115

"Destroy it. The Fifth Column is like a Serpent" — A116

"Fulfill your Patriotic Duty by Destroying the Fifth Column" — A117

"Don't be Afraid of the Fifth Column. Attack it" — A118

1943, July 5

375 A114 1c dk blue grn .22 .15
376 A115 3c red .32 .15
377 A116 5c brt blue .38 .15
378 A117 10c dull brown .95 .32
379 A118 13c dull rose vio 1.90 .95
Nos. 375-379 (5) 3.77 1.72

General Eloy Alfaro and Flags of Cuba and Ecuador A119

1943, Sept. 20

380 A119 3c green .70 .15

General Eloy Alfaro of Ecuador, 100th birth anniv.

Retirement Security A120

1943, Nov. 8 Wmk. 106 *Perf. 10*

381 A120 1c yellow green .30 .15
382 A120 3c vermilion .35 .15
383 A120 5c bright blue .40 .22

1944, Mar. 18

384 A120 1c bright yel grn .75 .30
385 A120 3c salmon .90 .30
386 A120 5c light blue 1.50 .75
Nos. 381-386 (6) 4.20 1.87

Half the proceeds from the sale of Nos. 381-386 were used for the Communications Ministry Employees' Retirement Fund.

Portrait of Columbus — A121

Bartolomé de Las Casas — A122

First Statue of Columbus at Cárdenas — A123

Discovery of Tobacco A124

Columbus Sights Land A125

1944, May 19

387 A121 1c dk yel grn .18 .18
388 A122 3c brown .30 .18
389 A123 5c brt blue .40 .18
390 A124 10c dk violet 1.00 .60
391 A125 13c dk red 2.00 1.00
Nos. 387-391,C36-C37 (7) 4.83 2.49

450th anniv. of the discovery of America.

Major General Carlos Roloff — A126

Americas Map and 1st Brazilian Postage Stamps — A127

1944, Aug. 21

392 A126 3c violet .28 .18

Maj. Gen. Carlos Roloff, 100th birth 4anniv.

1944, Dec. 20 Engr.

393 A127 3c brown orange .85 .32

Cent. of the 1st postage stamps of the Americas, issued by Brazil in 1843.

Seal of the Society — A128

Luis de las Casas and Luis Maria Penalyer A129

1945, Oct. 5 Wmk. 106 *Perf. 10*

394 A128 1c yellow green .15 .15
395 A129 2c scarlet .22 .15
Set value .18

Sesquicentenary of the founding of the Economic Society of Friends of the Country.

Aged Couple A130

1945, Dec. 27

396 A130 1c dk yellow grn .25 .15
397 A130 2c scarlet .40 .15
398 A130 5c cobalt blue .75 .18

1946, Mar. 26

399 A130 1c brt yellow grn .50 .15
400 A130 2c salmon pink .40 .15
401 A130 5c light blue .60 .25
Nos. 396-401 (6) 2.90
Set value .79

See note after No. 386.

Catalogue values for unused stamps in this section, from this point to the end of the section, are for Never Hinged items.

Gabriel de la Concepcion Valdés Plácido A131

1946, Feb. 5

402 A131 2c scarlet .90 .18

Cent. of the death of the poet Gabriel de la Concepcion Valdés.

Manuel Marquez Sterling — A132

Globe and Cross — A133

1946, Apr. 30

403 A132 2c scarlet .90 .18

Founding of the Manuel Marquez Sterling Professional School of Journalism, 3th anniv.

1946, July 4 **Engr.**

404 A133 2c scarlet, *pink* .85 .18

80th anniv. of the Intl. Red Cross.

Cow and Milkmaid — A134

Franklin D. Roosevelt — A135

1947, Feb. 20 **Wmk. 106** ***Perf. 10***

405 A134 2c scarlet .75 .15

1947 National Livestock Exposition.

1947, Apr. 12

406 A135 2c vermilion .28 .15

2nd anniv. of the death of Franklin D. Roosevelt.

Antonio Oms Sarret and Aged Couple A136

1947, Oct. 20

407 A136 1c dp yellow grn .15 .15

408 A136 2c scarlet .20 .15

409 A136 5c lt blue .45 .40

Nos. 407-409 (3) .80 .70

See note after No. 386.

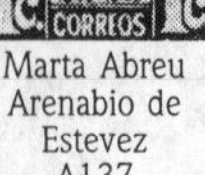

Marta Abreu Arenabio de Estevez A137

"Charity" A138

Marta Abreu Monument, Santa Clara A139

"Patriotism" A140

1947, Nov. 29

410 A137 1c dp yellow grn .20 .15

411 A138 2c scarlet .30 .15

412 A139 5c brt blue .50 .25

413 A140 10c dk violet 1.00 .50

Nos. 410-413 (4) 2.00 1.05

Birth cent. of Marta Abreu Arenabio de Estevez, philanthropist and humanitarian.

Armauer Hansen A141

1948, Apr. 9

414 A141 2c rose carmine .75 .15

International Leprosy Congress, Havana.

Mother and Child — A142

1948, Oct. 15 **Engr.**

415 A142 1c yellow grn .32 .15

416 A142 2c scarlet .45 .15

417 A142 5c brt blue .95 .20

Nos. 415-417 (3) 1.72

Set value .40

See note after No. 386.

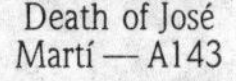

Death of José Martí — A143

Martí Rowing to Shore — A144

1948, Nov. 10 **Wmk. 106** ***Perf. 10***

418 A143 2c scarlet .35 .15

419 A144 5c brt blue .80 .18

50th anniversary of the death of José Martí, patriot (in 1945).

Tobacco Picking — A145

Liberty Carrying Flag and Cigars — A146

Cigar and Arms of Cuba — A147

1948, Dec. 6

Size: 22½x26mm

420 A145 1c green .15 .15

421 A146 2c rose car .25 .15

422 A147 5c brt blue .35 .15

Nos. 420-422 (3) .75

Set value .18

Cuba's tobacco industry. See Nos. 445-447. For overprints and surcharge see Nos. 448-451, 512.

Equestrian Statue of Gen. Antonio Maceo — A148

Sword Salute to Maceo — A149

Designs: 2c, Portrait of Maceo. 5c, Mausoleum, El Cacahual. 10c, East to West invasion. 20c, Battle of Peralejo. 50c, Declaration of Baragua. 1p, Death of Maceo at San Pedro.

1948, Dec. 15 **Wmk. 229** ***Perf. 12½***

423 A148 1c blue green .18 .18

424 A148 2c red .18 .18

425 A148 5c blue .32 .18

426 A149 8c black & brown .45 .30

427 A149 10c brown & bl grn .45 .20

428 A149 20c blue & car 1.90 .90

429 A149 50c car & ultra 3.00 2.00

430 A149 1p black & violet 6.25 2.75

Nos. 423-430 (8) 12.73 6.69

Birth cent. (in 1945) of Maceo.

Symbol of Pharmacy A150

Morro Lighthouse A151

1948, Dec. 28 ***Perf. 10***

431 A150 2c rose carmine .75 .15

1st Pan-American Congress of Pharmacy, Havana, Dec. 1948.

1949, Jan. 17 **Wmk. 229** ***Perf. 12½***

432 A151 2c carmine .75 .15

Centenary (in 1944) of the erection of the Morro Lighthouse.

Jagua Castle, Cienfuegos A152

1949, Jan. 27 **Wmk. 106** ***Perf. 10***

433 A152 1c yellow green .40 .15

434 A152 2c rose red .80 .20

200th anniv. of the construction of Jagua Castle and the cent. of the publication of the 1st newspaper in Cienfuegos.

Manuel Sanguily y Garritt — A153

Map of Isle of Pines — A154

1949, Mar. 31

435 A153 2c rose red .35 .15

436 A153 5c blue .75 .22

Manuel Sanguily y Garritt (1848-1925), cabinet member, editor, author.

1949, Apr. 26

437 A154 5c blue .90 .70

20th anniv. of the recognition of Cuban ownership of the Isle of Pines.

Ismael Cespedes — A155

1949, Sept. 28

438 A155 1c yellow green .40 .15

439 A155 2c scarlet .40 .15

440 A155 5c brt blue .90 .20

Nos. 438-440 (3) 1.70

Set value .40

See note after No. 386.

Gen. Enrique Collazo — A156

Enrique José Varona — A157

1950, Feb. 28 **Engr.** ***Perf. 10***

441 A156 2c scarlet .50 .15

442 A156 5c brt blue 1.00 .20

Centenary (in 1948) of the birth of General Enrique Collazo.

1950, Feb. 28

443 A157 2c scarlet .40 .15

444 A157 5c brt blue .80 .20

Centenary of the birth of Enrique José Varona, writer and patriot.

Tobacco Types of 1948

1950, June 20 **Re-engraved**

Size: 21x25mm

445 A145 1c green .40 .15

446 A146 2c rose red .40 .15

447 A147 5c blue .60 .16

Nos. 445-447 (3) 1.40

Set value .32

The re-engraved stamps show slight differences in many minor details.

For overprints and surcharge see #448-451, 512.

No. 446 Overprinted in Black

BANCO NACIONAL DE CUBA
INAUGURACION 27 ABRIL 1950

1950, Apr. 27

448 A146 2c rose red .75 .20

Natl. Bank of Cuba opening, Apr. 27, 1950.

Re-engraved Tobacco Types of 1950 Overprinted in Carmine

U.P.U
1874
1949

1950, May 18

449 A145 1c yellow green .15 .15

450 A146 2c lilac rose .20 .15

451 A147 5c light blue .38 .15

Nos. 449-451 (3) .73

Set value .30

75th anniv. (in 1949) of the UPU.

No. 451 exists with surcharge inverted.

Manuel Balanzategui, Antonio L. Pausa and Train Wreck
A158

Fernando Figueredo
A159

1950, Sept. 21 **Engr.**

452 A158 1c yellow grn .35 .15
453 A158 2c scarlet .35 .15
454 A158 5c brt blue .75 .20
Nos. 452-454 (3) 1.45
Set value .40

1951, Mar. 17 **Wmk. 106** ***Perf. 10***

455 A159 1c green .40 .15
456 A159 2c scarlet .40 .15
457 A159 5c brt blue .75 .15
Nos. 455-457 (3) 1.55
Set value .31

Three-fourths of the proceeds from the sale of these stamps were used for the Communication Ministry Employees' Retirement Fund.

See Nos. 474, C51-C56, E15. For surcharges see Nos. 474, C51-C56, E15.

Miguel Teurbe Tolón and Flag — A160

Narciso Lopez — A161

Emilia Teurbe Tolón Sewing Flag — A162

Cuban Flag — A163

Engraved and Lithographed

1951, July 3 **Wmk. 229** ***Perf. 13***

458 A160 1c Prus grn, ultra & red .24 .15
459 A161 2c red & gray blk .35 .15
460 A162 5c ultra & red .75 .28
461 A163 10c rose vio, bl & red 1.25 .40
Nos. 458-461,C41-C43,E13 (8) 9.89 3.18

Centenary of adoption of Cuba's flag.

Clara Louise Maass and Hospitals — A164

Hospitals: Lutheran Memorial, Newark, N.J. and Las Animas, Havana.

Wmk. 106

1951, Aug. 24 **Engr.** ***Perf. 10***

462 A164 2c scarlet .90 .20

75th anniv. of the birth of Clara Louise Maass, (1876-1901), American nurse and martyr in yellow fever fight.

Airmail Type and

José Raul Capablanca
A165

Capablanca Club, Havana
A166

Wmk. 229

1951, Nov. 1 **Photo.** ***Perf. 13***

463 A165 1c blue grn & org 2.25 .38
464 AP27 2c rose car & dk brn 2.75 .75
465 A166 5c black & dp ultra 5.25 1.25
Nos. 463-465,C44-C46,E14 (7) 39.75 7.38

Jose Raul Capablanca, World Chess titlist (1921). Value imperf., set of 7 pairs, $1,500.

Antonio Guiteras Holmes — A167

Guiteras Preparing Social Legislation
A168

Fort of the Morrillo
A169

Wmk. 106

1951, Oct. 22 **Engr.** ***Perf. 10***

466 A167 1c yellow green .22 .15
467 A168 2c rose carmine .40 .15
468 A169 5c deep blue .65 .15
Nos. 466-468,C47-C49 (6) 4.62 1.50

16th anniv. of the Action of the Morrillo and to honor Antonio Guiteras Holmes, who was killed there.

Souvenir sheets containing stamps similar to Nos. 466-468, but in different colors, are listed as Nos. C49a-C49b.

Poinsettia
A170

Maj. Gen. José Maceo
A171

1951, Dec. 1 **Engr. and Typo.**

469 A170 1c green & car 1.75 .25
470 A170 2c rose car & grn 2.00 .38

See Nos. 498-499.

1952, Feb. 6 **Engr.**

471 A171 2c yellow brown .40 .15
472 A171 5c indigo .90 .15

Birth centenary of Maceo.

See note after No. C49.

Isabella I — A172

Receipt of Autonomy — A173

1952, Feb. 22

473 A172 2c bright red .60 .15

500th anniv. of the birth of Queen Isabella I of Spain.

Souvenir sheets containing 2c stamps of type A172 are listed as Nos. C50a-C50b.

Type of 1951 Surcharged in Green

1952, Mar. 18

474 A159 10c on 2c yel brn 1.25 .25

Perf. 12½

1952, May 27 **Wmk. 106** **Engr.**

Designs: 2c, Tomas Estrada Palma and Luis Estevez Romero. 5c, Barnet, Finlay, Guiteras and Nuñez. 8c, Capitol. 20c, Map, Central Highway. 50c, Sugar Mill.

Centers in Black

475 A173 1c dk green .22 .15
476 A173 2c dk carmine .28 .15
477 A173 5c dk blue .32 .15
478 A173 8c dk brown car .55 .15
479 A173 20c dk olive grn 1.40 .40
480 A173 50c dp orange 2.75 .80
Nos. 475-480,C57-C60,E16 (11) 12.27 4.05

50th anniv. of the Republic of Cuba.

Hands Holding Coffee Beans
A174

Designs: 2c, Map and man picking coffee beans. 5c, Farmer with pan of beans.

1952, Aug. 22 **Wmk. 229** ***Perf. 13½***

481 A174 1c green .40 .15
482 A174 2c rose red .75 .15
483 A174 5c dk vio bl & aqua 1.00 .20
Nos. 481-483 (3) 2.15 .50

Bicentenary of coffee cultivation.

Col. Charles Hernandes y Sandrino
A175

Alonso Alvarez de la Campa
A176

1952, Oct. 7 **Wmk. 106** ***Perf. 10***

484 A175 1c yellow grn .20 .15
485 A175 2c scarlet .35 .15
486 A175 5c blue .40 .15
487 A175 8c black 1.10 .30
488 A175 10c brown red 1.10 .30
489 A175 20c brown 4.00 2.50
Nos. 484-489,C63-C72,E17 (17) 30.95 16.10

See note after No. 457.

Frame Engraved; Center in Black

1952, Nov. 27

Portraits: 2c, Carlos A. Latorre. 3c, Anacleto Bermudez. 5c, Eladio G. Toledo. 8c, Angel Laborde. 10c, Jose M. Medina. 13c, Pascual Rodriguez. 20c, Carlos Verdugo.

490 A176 1c green .25 .15
491 A176 2c carmine .50 .15
492 A176 3c purple .60 .15
493 A176 5c blue .60 .15
494 A176 8c bister brn 1.25 .32
495 A176 10c orange brn 1.00 .28
496 A176 13c lilac rose 2.00 .40
497 A176 20c olive grn 3.00 .70
Nos. 490-497,C73-C74 (10) 12.85 3.90

Execution of 8 medical students. 81st anniv.

Christmas Type of 1951
Dated "1952-1953"

Frame Engr.; Center Typo.

1952, Dec. 1

Centers: Tree.

498 A170 1c yel grn & car 4.00 1.00
499 A170 3c vio & dk grn 4.00 1.00

Birthplace of José Martí — A177

Marti at St. Lazarus Quarry — A178

Designs: No. 501, Court martial. No. 502, artiano house, Havana. No. 504, El Abra ranch, Isle of Pines. No. 505, Symbols, "Marti the Poet." No. 506, Marti and Bolivar statue, Caracas. No. 507, At desk in New York. No. 508, House where revolutionary party was formed. No. 509, First issue of "Patria."

1953 **Engr.** ***Perf. 10***

500 A177 1c dk grn & red brn .15 .15
501 A177 1c dk grn & red brn .15 .15
502 A177 3c purple & brn .25 .15
503 A178 3c purple & brn .25 .15
504 A177 5c dp bl & dk brn .40 .18
505 A178 5c ultra & brn .40 .18
506 A178 10c red brn & blk 1.00 .38
507 A178 10c dk brn & blk 1.00 .38
508 A178 13c dk ol grn & dk brn 1.65 .80
509 A177 13c dk ol grn & brn 1.65 1.00
Nos. 500-509,C79-C89 (21) 25.50 11.98

Centenary of birth of José Marti.

Rafael Montoro Valdez — A179

Francisco Carrera Justiz — A180

1953, Mar. 5

510 A179 3c dark violet .35 .15

Rafael Montoro Valdez, statesman, birth cent.

1953, Mar. 9

511 A180 3c rose red .25 .15

Francisco Carrera Justiz, educator, statesman.

No. 446 Surcharged with New Value

1953, June 16

512 A146 3c on 2c rose red .60 .15

Board of Accounts Bldg., Havana — A181

1953, Nov. 3 **Engr.**

513 A181 3c blue .20 .15
Nos. 513,C90-C91 (3) 2.85 1.27

1st Intl. Cong. of Boards of Accounts, Havana, Nov. 2-9.

Miguel Coyula Llaguno — A182

Communications Assoc. Flag — A183

Designs: 3c, 8c, Enrique Calleja Hensell. 10c, Antonio Ginard Rojas.

1954 **Dated 1953**

514 A182 1c green .22 .15
515 A182 3c rose red .22 .15
516 A183 5c blue .90 .15
517 A182 8c brn car 1.40 .32
518 A182 10c brown 2.25 .50
Nos. 514-518,C92-C95,E19 (10) 15.81 8.92

Nos. 515 and 517 show the same portrait, but inscriptions are arranged differently.

See note after No. 457.

José Marti — A184

Maximo Gomez — A184a

Portraits: 3c, José de la Luz Caballero. 4c, Miguel Aldama. 5c, Calixto Garcia. 8c, Ignacio Agramont. 10c, Tomas Estrada Palma. 13c, Carlos J. Finlay. 14c, Serafin Sanchez. 20c, José Antonio Saco. 50c, Antonio Maceo. 1p, Carlos Manuel de Cespedes.

1954-56 **Wmk. 106** ***Perf. 10***

519 A184 1c green .25 .15
520 A184a 2c rose car .25 .15
521 A184 3c violet .25 .15
521A A184 4c red lil ('56) .30 .15
522 A184a 5c slate bl .35 .15
523 A184a 8c car lake .50 .15
524 A184 10c sepia .50 .15
525 A184 13c org red .75 .15

525A A184a 14c gray ('56) 1.00 .15
526 A184 20c olive 1.50 .15
527 A184a 50c org yel 2.50 .25
528 A184a 1p orange 5.00 .38
Nos. 519-528 (12) 13.15
Set value 1.35

See Nos. 674-680. For surcharges see Nos. 636, 641-643.

Maj. Gen. José M. Rodriguez — A185

Design: 5c, Gen. Rodriguez on horseback.

1954, June 8 Engr. *Perf. 12½*
Center in Dark Brown

529 A185 2c dark carmine .65 .15
530 A185 5c deep blue 1.40 .20

Cent. of the birth of Maj. Gen. José Maria Rodriguez (in 1851).

Gen. Batísta Sanatorium A186

1954, Sept. 21 Wmk. 106 *Perf. 10*

531 A186 3c deep blue .30 .15

See No. C107.

Santa Claus — A187

Maria Luisa Dolz — A188

1954, Dec. 15

532 A187 2c dk grn & car 4.00 .38
533 A187 4c car & dk grn 3.50 .38

Christmas 1954.

1954, Dec. 23

534 A188 4c deep blue4 .25 .15

Cent. of the birth of Maria Luisa Dolz, educator and defender of women's rights. See No. C108.

Cuban Flag and Scouts Saluting — A189

1954, Dec. 27 *Perf. 12½*

535 A189 4c dark green .75 .15

Issued to publicize the national patrol encampment of the Boy Scouts of Cuba.

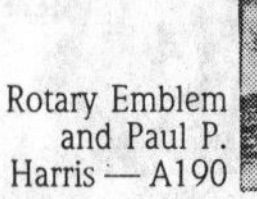

Rotary Emblem and Paul P. Harris — A190

1955, Feb. 23 Engr. Wmk. 106

536 A190 4c blue .75 .15

Rotary International, 50th anniversary. See No. C109.

Maj. Gen. Francisco Carrillo — A191

Portrait: 5c, Gen. Carrillo standing.

1955, Mar. 8 *Perf. 10*

537 A191 2c brt red & dk bl .40 .15
538 A191 5c dk bl & dk brn .75 .15
Set value .20

Cent. of the birth of Maj. Gen. Francisco Carrillo (1851-1926).

Stamp of 1885 and Convent of San Francisco A192

Designs (including 1855 stamp): 4c, Volanta carriage. 10c, Havana, 19th century. 14c, Captain general's residence.

1955, Apr. *Perf. 12½*

539 A192 2c lil rose & dk grnsh bl .75 .16
540 A192 4c ocher & dk grn 1.00 .16
541 A192 10c ultra & dk red 2.25 .90
542 A192 14c grn & dp org 5.50 1.00
Nos. 539-542,C110-C113 (8) 17.75 6.07

Cent. of Cuba's 1st postage stamps.

Maj. Gen. Mario G. Menocal — A193

Gen. Emilio Nuñez — A194

Portraits: 10c, J. G. O. Gomez. 14c, A. Sanchez de Bustamente.

1955, June 22

543 A193 2c dark green .50 .15
544 A194 4c lilac rose .60 .15
545 A193 10c deep blue 1.00 .24
546 A194 14c gray violet 2.00 .35
Nos. 543-546,C114-C116,E20 (8) 14.35 6.39

See note after No. 457.

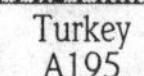

Turkey A195

Gen. Emilio Nuñez A196

1955, Dec. 15 Engr.

547 A195 2c slate grn & dk car 3.75 .38
548 A195 4c rose lake & brt grn 3.75 .30

Christmas 1955.

1955, Dec. 27

549 A196 4c claret .50 .15
Nos. 549,C127-C128 (3) 3.00 1.05

Cent. of the birth of Gen. Emilio Nunez, Cuban revolutionary hero.

Francisco Cagigal de la Vega (1695-1777) A197

Julian del Casal A198

1956, Mar. 27 *Perf. 12½*

552 A197 4c rose brn & slate bl .50 .15

Cuban post bicent. See No. C129.

1956, May 2

Portraits: 4c, Luisa Perez de Zambrana. 10c, Juan Clemente Zenea. 14c, José Joaquin Palma.

Portraits in Black

553 A198 2c green .24 .15
554 A198 4c rose lilac .30 .15
555 A198 10c blue .60 .15
556 A198 14c violet .75 .18
Nos. 553-556,C131-C133,E21 (8) 8.64 3.28

See note after No. 457.

Victor Muñoz — A199

Masonic Temple, Havana — A200

1956, May 13

557 A199 4c brn & grn .25 .15

Issued in honor of Victor Munoz (1873-1922), founder of Mother's Day in Cuba. See No. C134.

1956, June 5

558 A200 4c blue .50 .15

See No. C135.

Virgin of Charity, El Cobre — A201

"The Cry of Yara" — A202

1956, Sept. 8 *Perf. 12½*

559 A201 4c brt bl & yel .40 .15

Issued in honor of Our Lady of Charity of Cobre, patroness of Cuba. See No. C149.

1956, Oct. 10

560 A202 4c dk grn & brn .25 .15

Cuba's independence from Spain.

Raimundo G. Menocal — A203

The Three Wise Men — A204

1956, Dec. 3 Wmk. 106 *Perf. 12½*

561 A203 4c dk brn .25 .15

Cent. of the birth of Prof. Raimundo G. Menocal, physician.

1956, Dec. 1

562 A204 2c red & slate grn 2.00 .60
563 A204 4c slate grn & red 2.00 .40

Christmas 1956.

The first value column gives the catalogue value of an unused stamp, the second that of a used stamp.

Martin Morua Delgado A205

Boy Scouts at Campfire A206

1957, Jan. 30

564 A205 4c dark green .25 .15

Delgado, patriot, birth cent.

1957, Feb. 22 Wmk. 106 *Perf. 12½*

565 A206 4c slate grn & red .45 .18

Cent. of the birth of Lord Baden-Powell, founder of the Boy Scouts. See No. C152.

"The Blind," by M. Vega — A207

Paintings: 4c, "The Art Critics" by M. Melero. 10c, "Volanta in Storm" by A. Menocal. 14c, "The Convalescent" by L. Romañach.

1957, Mar. Engr. *Perf. 12½*
Side and Lower Inscriptions in Dark Brown

566 A207 2c olive green .22 .15
567 A207 4c orange red .28 .15
568 A207 10c olive green .40 .25
569 A207 14c ultra .55 .25
Nos. 566-569,C153-C155,E22 (8) 8.65 3.10

See note after No. 457.

Emblem of Philatelic Club of Cuba A208

Juan F. Steegers A209

1957, Apr. 24

570 A208 4c ocher, blue & red .30 .15

Issued for Stamp Day, Apr. 24, and the National Philatelic Exhibition. See No. C156.

1957, Apr. 30

571 A209 4c blue .25 .15

Juan Francisco Steegers y Perera (1856-1921), dactyloscopy pioneer. See No. C157.

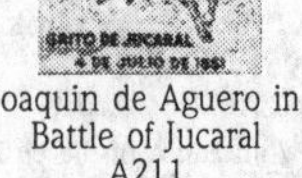

Victoria Bru Sanchez A210

Joaquin de Aguero in Battle of Jucaral A211

1957, June 3 Wmk. 106 *Perf. 12½*

572 A210 4c indigo .25 .15

1957, July 4

573 A211 4c dk grn .25 .15

Issued to honor Joaquin de Aguero, Cuban freedom fighter and patriot. See No. C162.

Boy, Dogs and Cat — A212

Col. Rafael Manduley del Rio — A213

1957, July 17

574 A212 4c Prus grn 1.00 .30

Mrs. Jeanette Ryder, founder of the Humane Society of Cuba. See Nos. C163-C163a.

1957, July 31

575 A213 4c Prus grn .25 .15

Issued to honor Col. Manduley del Rio, patriot, on the cent. of his birth (in 1856).

Palace of Justice A214

1957, Sept. 2 Engr. *Perf. 12½*

576 A214 4c blue gray .25 .15

Opening of the new Palace of Justice in Havana. See No. C165.

Generals of the Liberation A215

1957, Sept. 26

577 A215 4c dl grn & red brn .50 .15
578 A215 4c dl bl & red brn .50 .15
579 A215 4c rose & brn .50 .15
580 A215 4c org yel & brn .50 .15
581 A215 4c lt vio & brn .50 .15
Nos. 577-581 (5) 2.50
Set value .50

Generals of the army of liberation.

1st Publication Printed in Cuba — A216

Patio — A217

1957, Oct. 18 Wmk. 106 *Perf. 12½*

582 A216 4c slate blue .25 .15
Nos. 582,C167-C168 (3) 1.75 .65

José Marti National Library.

1957, Nov. 19

583 A217 4c red brn & grn .25 .15
Nos. 583,C173-C174 (3) 2.35 .95

Cent. of the 1st Cuban Normal School.

Trinidad, Founded 1514 — A218

Fortifications, Havana, 1611 — A219

Views: 10c, Padre Pico street, Santiago de Cuba. 14c, Church of Our Lady, Camaguey.

1957, Dec. 17 Engr. *Perf. 12½*

584 A218 2c brn & ind .18 .15
585 A219 4c sl grn & brn .25 .15
586 A219 10c sep & red .75 .20
587 A219 14c grn & dk red .65 .15
Nos. 584-587,C175-C177,E23 (8) 7.33 2.91

See note after No. 457.

Nativity — A220

1957, Dec. 20

588 A220 2c multi 1.75 .50
589 A220 4c multi 1.75 .38

Christmas 1957.

Dayton Hedges and Ariguanabo Textile Factory A221

1958, Jan. 30 Wmk. 106 *Perf. 12½*

590 A221 4c blue .25 .15

Issued to honor Dayton Hedges, founder of Cuba's textile industry. See No. C178.

Dr. Francisco Dominguez Roldan — A222

José Ignacio Rivero y Alonso — A223

1958, Feb. 21

591 A222 4c green .25 .15

Roldan (1864-1942), who introduced radiotherapy and physiotherapy to Cuba.

1958, Apr. 1

592 A223 4c light olive grn .25 .15

José Ignacio Rivero y Alonso, editor of Diario de la Marina, 1919-44. See No. C179.

Map of Cuba and Mail Route, 1756 A224

1958, Apr. 24 *Perf. 12½*

593 A224 4c dk grn, aqua & buff .30 .15

Issued for Stamp Day, Apr. 24 and the National Philatelic Exhibition. See No. C180.

Maj. Gen. José Miguel Gomez A225

Nicolas Ruiz Espadero A226

1958, June 6 Wmk. 106 *Perf. 12½*

594 A225 4c slate .25 .15

Maj. Gen. José Miguel Gomez, President of Cuba, 1909-13. See No. C181.

1958, June 27 *Perf. 12½*

Indigo Emblem

Musicians: 4c, Ignacio Cervantes. 10c, José White. 14c, Brindis de Salas.

595 A226 2c brown .28 .15
596 A226 4c dk gray .28 .15
597 A226 10c ol grn .40 .15
598 A226 14c red .55 .20

Green Emblem

Physicians: 2c, Tomas Romay Chacon. 4c, Angel Arturo Aballi. 10c, Fernando Gonzalez del Valle. 14c, Vicente Antonio de Castro.

599 A226 2c brown .32 .15
600 A226 4c gray .55 .20
601 A226 10c dk car .40 .18
602 A226 14c dk bl .55 .22

Red Emblem

Lawyers: 2c, Jose Maria Garcia Montes. 4c, Jose A. Gonzalez Lanuza. 10c, Juan B. Hernandez Barreiro. 14c, Pedro Gonzalez Llorente.

603 A226 2c sepia .28 .15
604 A226 4c gray .40 .20
605 A226 10c olive grn .48 .15
606 A226 14c slate blue .55 .20
Nos. 595-606 (12) 5.04
Set value 1.78

For surcharges see Nos. 629-631.

Carlos de la Torre — A227

1958, Aug. 29 Engr. Wmk. 321

607 A227 4c violet blue .30 .15
Nos. 607,C182-C184 (4) 7.80 4.55

Dr. Carlos de la Torre y Huerta (1858-1950), naturalist. For surcharge see No. 632.

Poey's "Memorias" Title Page — A228

Felipe Poey — A229

1958, Sept. 26 Wmk. 106

608 A228 2c blk & lt vio .35 .15
609 A229 4c brn blk .45 .15
Nos. 608-609,C185-C191,E26-E27 (11) 47.30 18.05

Felipe Poey (1799-1891), naturalist.

Theodore Roosevelt — A230

Cattleyopsis Lindenii Orchid — A231

1958, Oct. 27 *Perf. 12½*

610 A230 4c gray grn .30 .15

Theodore Roosevelt, birth cent. See #C192.

Engraved and Photogravure

1958, Dec. 16 Wmk. 321 *Perf. 12½*

Christmas: 4c, Oncidium Guibertianum Orchid.

611 A231 2c multi 1.75 .50
612 A231 4c multi 2.00 .50

For surcharge see No. 633.

Flag and Revolutionary A232

Gen. Adolfo Flor Crombet (1848-95) A233

Engr. & Typo.

1959, Jan. 28 Wmk. 321

613 A232 2c car rose & gray .15 .15

Day of Liberation, Jan. 1, 1959.

1959, Mar. 18 Engr. Wmk. 106

614 A233 4c slate green .30 .15

For surcharge see No. 634.

Maria Teresa Garcia Montes A234

Carlos Manuel de Cespedes A235

1959, Nov. 11 *Perf. 12½*

615 A234 4c brown .20 .15

Issued to honor Maria Teresa Garcia Montes (1880-1930), founder of the Musical Arts Society. See No. C198. For surcharge see No. 635.

1959, Oct. 10 Wmk. 106 *Perf. 12½*

Presidents: No. 617, Salvador Cisneros Betancourt. No. 618, Manuel de Jesus Calvar. No. 619, Bartolomé Maso. No. 620, Juan B. Spotorno. No. 621, Tomas Estrada Palma. No. 622, Francisco Javier de Céspedes. No. 623, Vicente Garcia.

616 A235 2c slate blue .32 .15
617 A235 2c green .32 .15
618 A235 2c dp vio .32 .15
619 A235 2c org brn .32 .15
620 A235 4c dk car .40 .20
621 A235 4c dp brn .40 .20
622 A235 4c dk gray .40 .20
623 A235 4c dk vio .40 .20
Nos. 616-623 (8) 2.88 1.40

Issued to honor former Cuban presidents.

No. B3 Surcharged in Red: "HABILITADO PARA / 2¢"

1960

624 SP2 2c on 2c + 1c car & ultra .50 .15

See No. C199.

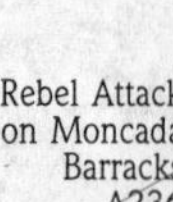

Rebel Attack on Moncada Barracks
A236

Designs: 2c, Rebels disembarking from "Granma." 10c, Battle of the Uvero. 12c, Map of Cuba and rebel ("The Invasion").

1960, Jan. 28 Wmk. 320

625 A236 1c gray ol, bl & ver .16 .15
626 A236 2c bl, gray ol & brn .22 .15
627 A236 10c bl, gray ol & red .42 .15
628 A236 12c brt bl, brn & grn .60 .15
Nos. 625-628,C200-C202 (7) 6.40 2.60

First anniversary of revolution.

Stamps of 1956-59 Surcharged with New Value in Carmine or Silver

1960, Feb. 3

629 A226 1c on 4c dk gray & ind .35 .15
630 A226 1c on 4c gray & grn .55 .25
631 A226 1c on 4c gray & red .35 .15
632 A227 1c on 4c vio bl .35 .15
633 A231 1c on 4c multi (S) .90 .50
634 A233 1c on 4c slate grn .32 .15
635 A234 1c on 4c brown .35 .15
636 A184a 2c on 14c gray .45 .15
Nos. 629-636,C203-C204 (10) 5.12 2.25

Tomas Estrada Palma Statue, Havana
A237

17th Olympic Games, Rome, Aug. 25-Sept. 11
A238

Statues: 2c, Mambi Victorioso (Battle of San Juan Hill), Santiago de Cuba. 10c, Marta Abreo de Estevez. 12c, Ignacio Agramonte, Camaguey.

Perf. 12½

1960, Mar. 28 Wmk. 321 Engr.

637 A237 1c brn & dk bl .20 .15
638 A237 2c grn & red .30 .15
639 A237 10c choc & red .75 .15
640 A237 12c gray ol & vio 1.00 .20
Nos. 637-640,C206-C208 (7) 6.10 2.15

See note after No. 386

Nos. 521A, 522 and 525 Surcharged "HABILITADO / PARA / 2¢" in Violet Blue, Red or Black

1960 Wmk. 106 *Perf. 10*

641 A184 2c on 4c red lil (VB) .50 .15
642 A184a 2c on 5c sl bl (R) .60 .15
643 A184 2c on 13c org red .75 .22

No. 307B Surcharged "HABILITADO / 10¢"

644 A41 10c on 20c ol grn .50 .15
Nos. 641-644 (4) 2.35
Set value .54

Perf. 12½

1960, Sept. 22 Engr. Wmk. 321

645 A238 1c Sailboats .15 .15
646 A238 2c Marksman .25 .15

For souvenir sheet see No. C213a.

Camilo Cienfuegos and View of Escolar
A239

1960, Oct. 27 Litho. Unwmk.

647 A239 2c brn, bl, grn & red .15 .15

1st anniv. of the death of Camilo Cienfuegos, revolutionary hero.

Morning Glory
A240

Tobacco and Christmas Hymn
A241

1960 Litho. *Perf. 12½*

648 A240 1c red .55 .50
649 A241 1c Tobacco .75 .75
650 A241 1c Mariposa .75 .75
651 A241 1c Guaiacum .75 .75
652 A241 1c Coffee .75 .75
a. Block of 4, #649-652 4.50
653 A240 2c ultra .75 .75
654 A241 2c Tobacco 2.00 2.00
655 A241 2c Mariposa 2.00 2.00
656 A241 2c Guaiacum 2.00 2.00
657 A241 2c Coffee 2.00 2.00
a. Block of 4, #654-657 12.00
658 A240 10c ocher 2.25 2.00
659 A241 10c Tobacco 5.50 5.00
660 A241 10c Mariposa 5.50 5.00
661 A241 10c Guaiacum 5.50 5.00
662 A241 10c Coffee 5.50 5.00
a. Block of 4, #659-662 35.00
Nos. 648-662 (15) 36.55 34.25

Issued for Christmas 1960.

Nos. 648-662 were printed in three sheets of 25. Nine stamps of type A240 form a center cross, stamps of type A241 form a block of four in each corner with the musical bars joined in an oval around the floral designs.

"Public Capital for Economic Benefit" — A242

Designs: 2c, Chart and symbols of agriculture and industry. 6c, Cogwheels.

Perf. 11½

1961, Jan. 10 Unwmk. Photo.

663 A242 1c yel, blk & org .20 .15
664 A242 2c bl, blk & red .20 .15
665 A242 6c yel, red org & blk .50 .25
Nos. 663-665,C215-C218 (7) 4.40 2.45

Issued to publicize the conference of underdeveloped countries, Havana.

Jesus Menéndez and Sugar Cane — A243

1961, Jan. 22 Litho. *Perf. 12½*

666 A243 2c dk grn & brn .20 .15

Jesus Menéndez, leader in sugar industry.

Same Overprinted in Red: "PRIMERO DE MAYO 1961 ESTAMOS VENCIENDO"

1961, May 2

667 A243 2c dk grn & brn .30 .25

Issued for May Day, 1961.

Dove and UN Emblem
A244

1961, Apr. 12 Litho. *Perf. 12½*

668 A244 2c red brn & yel grn .30 .15
669 A244 10c emer & rose lil .50 .20
a. Souv. sheet, #668-669, imperf. 1.00
Nos. 668-669,C222-C223 (4) 1.70 .80

15th anniv. (in 1960) of the UN.

Maceo Stamp of 1907 and 1902 Simulated Cancel
A245

Stamp Day: 1c, Revolutionary 10c stamp of 1874 and 1868 "cancel." 10c, No. 613 and "cancel."

1961, Apr. 24 Unwmk.

670 A245 1c dull rose & dk grn .18 .15
671 A245 2c salmon & dk grn .18 .15
672 A245 10c pale grn, car rose & blk .38 .22
Nos. 670-672 (3) .74 .52

For overprint see No. 681.

Hand Releasing Dove — A246

1961, July 26 *Perf. 12½*

673 A246 2c blk, red, yel & gray .30 .15

26th of July (1953) movement, Castro's revolt against Fulgencio Batista.

Burelage on back consisting of wavy lines and diagonal rows of "CUBA CORREOS" in pale salmon.

Portrait Type of 1954

Designs: Same as before. On the 2c, "1833" is replaced by "?".

Wmk. 321 (Nos. 674, 676); Unwmkd.
Perf. 12½ (Nos. 674, 676); Rouletted
1961-69 Engr.

674 A184 1c brown red
675 A184 1c lt blue ('69)
676 A184a 2c slate green
677 A184a 2c yel grn ('69)
678 A184 3c org ('64)
679 A184 13c brn ('64)
680 A184 20c lilac ('69)

Issue dates: Nos. 674, 676, Aug. 1, 1961. Nos. 678-679, Dec. 7, 1964. Others, Sept. 1969.

For Nos. 675, 677-680, see embargo note following No. 702.

No. 672 Ovptd. in Red

primera
exposición
filatélica
oficial
oct. 7-17. 1961

Perf. 12½

1961, Oct. 7 Litho. Unwmk.

681 A245 10c pale grn, car rose & blk

1st Official Phil. Exhib., Havana, Oct. 7-17.

Education Year — A247

Designs: One letter (per stamp) of "CUBA," book and various quotations by Jose Marti about the virtues of literacy.

1961, Nov. 22

682 A247 1c pale grn, red & blk
683 A247 2c blue, red & blk
684 A247 10c vio, red & blk
685 A247 12c org, red & blk

A248

Christmas
A249

Designs: 1c, Snails. 2c, Birds, vert. 10c, Butterflies.

1961, Dec. 1

686 A248 1c Polymita flammulata
687 A249 1c Polymita fulminata
688 A249 1c Polymita nigrofasciata
689 A249 1c Polymita fuscolimbata
690 A249 1c Polymita roseolimbata
a. Block of 5 + label, Nos. 686-690
691 A248 2c Cuban grassquit
692 A249 2c Cuban macaw
693 A249 2c Cuban trogon
694 A249 2c Bee hummingbird
695 A249 2c Ivory-billed woodpecker
a. Block of 5 + label, Nos. 691-695
696 A248 10c Othreis toddi
697 A249 10c Uranidia boisduvalii
698 A249 10c Phoebis avellaneda
699 A249 10c Phaloe cubana
700 A249 10c Papilio gundlachianus
a. Block of 5 + label, Nos. 696-700

Stamps of the same denomination printed se-tenant in sheets of 20 stamps plus 5 labels picturing bells and star. Stamps of Type A249 are arranged in blocks of 4; Type A248 stamps and labels form a cross in sheet.

See Nos. 760-774, 912-926, 1025-1039, 1179-1193, 1303-1317, 1464-1478 and 1572-1586.

3rd Anniv. of the Revolution — A250

1962, Jan. 3

701 A250 1c multi
702 A250 2c multi

See Nos. C226-C228.

Importation Prohibited

Cuban stamps issued after No. 673 have not been valued because the embargo on trade with Cuba, proclaimed Feb. 7, 1962, by President Kennedy, prohibits the importation from any country of stamps of Cuban origin, used or unused.

Natl. Militia
A251

Silhouettes of militiamen and women and their peace-time occupations: 1c, Farmer. 2c, Welder. 3c, Seamstress.

1962, Feb. 26

703 A251 1c blue grn & blk
704 A251 2c deep blue & blk
705 A251 10c brt org & blk

Bay of Pigs Invasion, 1st Anniv. — A252

1962, Apr. 17

706 A252 2c multi
707 A252 3c multi
708 A252 10c multi

1st West Indies Packet A253

1962, Apr. 24

709 A253 10c red & gray

Stamp Day. See No. E32.

Intl. Labor Day — A254

1962, May 1

710 A254 2c ocher & blk
711 A254 3c ver & blk
712 A254 10c greenish blue & blk

Natl. Sports Institute (INDER) Emblem and Athletes A255

1962, July 25 **Wmk. 321**

713 A255 1c Judo
714 A255 1c Discus
715 A255 1c Gymnastics
716 A255 1c Wrestling
717 A255 1c Weight lifting
718 A255 2c Roller skating
719 A255 2c Equestrian
720 A255 2c Archery
721 A255 2c Bicycling
722 A255 2c Bowling
723 A255 3c Power boating
724 A255 3c One-man kayak
725 A255 3c Swimming
726 A255 3c Sculling
727 A255 3c Yachting
728 A255 9c Soccer
729 A255 9c Volleyball
730 A255 9c Baseball
731 A255 9c Basketball
732 A255 9c Tennis
733 A255 10c Boxing
734 A255 10c Underwater fishing
735 A255 10c Model-plane flying
736 A255 10c Pistol shooting
737 A255 10c Water polo
738 A255 13c Paddleball
739 A255 13c Fencing
740 A255 13c Sports Palace
741 A255 13c Chess
742 A255 13c Jai alai

Stamps of the same denomination printed se-tenant in sheets of 25. Various combinations possible.

9th Anniv. of the Revolution A256

Attack on Moncada Barracks: Abel Santamaria and: 2c, Barracks under siege. 3c, Children at Moncada School.

1962, July 26

743 A256 2c brn car & dark ultra
744 A256 3c dark ultra & brn car

8th World Youth Festival for Peace and Friendship, Helsinki, July 28-Aug. 6 — A257

1962, July 28

745 A257 2c Dove, emblem
746 A257 3c Hand grip, emblem
a. Min. sheet of 2, Nos. 745-746, imperf.

9th Central American and Caribbean Games, Kingston, Jamaica, Aug. 11 - 25 — A258

1962, Aug. 27

747 A258 1c Boxing
748 A258 2c Tennis
749 A258 3c Baseball
750 A258 13c Fencing

A259

First Natl. Congress of the Federation of Cuban Women — A260

1962, Oct. 1

751 A259 9c rose, blk & grn
752 A260 13c blk, grn & lt blue

Latin American University Games — A261

1962, Oct. 13 **Wmk. 106**

753 A261 1c Running
754 A261 2c Baseball
755 A261 3c Basketball
756 A261 13c World map

World Health Organization Campaign to Eradicate Malaria — A262

Designs: 1c, Magnified specimen of the parasitic protozoa, microscope. 2c, Swamp and mosquito. 3c, Chemist's structural formulas for quinine, cinchona plant.

1962, Dec. 14

757 A262 1c multi
758 A262 2c multi
759 A262 3c multi

Christmas Type of 1961

Designs: 2c, Reptiles. 3c, Insects, vert. 10c, Rodents.

1962, Dec. 21 **Unwmk.**

760 A248 2c Epicrates angulifer
761 A249 2c Cricosaurus typica
762 A249 2c Anolis equestris
763 A249 2c Tropidophis wrighti
764 A249 2c Cyclura macleayi
a. Block of 5 + label, Nos. 760-764
765 A248 3c Cubispa turquino
766 A249 3c Chrysis superba
767 A249 3c Essostruta roberto
768 A249 3c Hortensia conciliata
769 A249 3c Lachnopus argus
a. Block of 5 + label, Nos. 765-769
770 A248 10c Monophyllus cubanus
771 A249 10c Capromys pilorides
772 A249 10c Capromys pre-hensilis
773 A249 10c Atopogale cubana
774 A249 10c Capromys prehensilis
a. Block of 5 + label, Nos. 770-774

Christmas 1962. See note after No. 700.

Soviet Space Flights — A263

Spacecraft and cosmonauts: 1c, Vostok 1, Yuri A. Gagarin, Apr. 12, 1961. 2c, Vostok 2, Gherman S. Titov, Aug. 6-7, 1961. 3c, Vostok 3, Andrian G. Nikolaev, Aug. 11-15, 1962, and Vostok 4, Pavel R. Popovich, Aug. 12-15, 1962. 9c, Vostok 5, Valery F. Bykovsky, June 14-19, 1963. 13c, Vostok 6, Valentina V. Tereshkova, June 16-19, 1963.

1963-64 **Wmk. 321**

775 A263 1c ultra, red & yel
776 A263 2c grn, yel & rose lake
777 A263 3c yel, vio & ver
778 A263 9c red, dark vio & yel
779 A263 13c dark blue green, dull red brown & yel

Issue dates: 1c, 2c, 3c, Feb. 26. Others, Aug. 15, 1964.

Attack of the Presidential Palace, 6th Anniv. A264

Designs: 9c, Guerillas attacking palace. 13c, Four student leaders. 30c, Jose A. Echeverria, Menelad Mora.

1963, Mar. 13

780 A264 9c dark red & blk
781 A264 13c chalky blue & sep
782 A264 30c org & grn

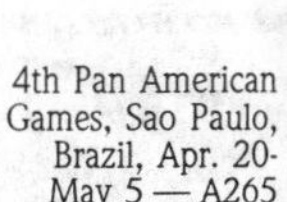

4th Pan American Games, Sao Paulo, Brazil, Apr. 20-May 5 — A265

1963, Apr. 20

783 A265 1c Baseball
784 A265 13c Boxing

Stamp Day A266

Design: 3c, Mask mailbox, 19th cent. 10c, Mask mailbox at the Plaza de la Catedral, Havana.

1963, Apr. 25

785 A266 3c black & dark org
786 A266 10c black & pur

See Nos. 828-829, 956-957 and 1102-1103.

Labor Day — A267

1963, May 1

787 A267 3c shown
788 A267 13c Four workers

Intl. Children's Week, June 1-7 A268

1963, June 1

789 A268 3c blue blk & bister brn
790 A268 30c blue blk & red

Ritual Effigy — A269

Broken Chains at Moncada — A270

Taino Civilization artifacts: 3c, Wood-carved throne, horiz. 9c, Stone-carved figurine.

1963, June 29

791 A269 2c org & red brn
792 A269 3c ultra & red brn
793 A269 9c rose & gray

Montane Anthropology Museum, 60th anniv.

1963, July 26

Designs: 2c, Attack on the Presidential Palace. 3c, The insurrection. 7c, Strike of April 9. 9c, Triumph of the revolution. 10c, Agricultural reform and nationalization of industry. 13c, Bay of Pigs victory.

794 A270 1c pink & blk
795 A270 2c lt blue & vio brn
796 A270 3c lt vio & brn
797 A270 7c apple green & rose
798 A270 9c olive bister & rose vio
799 A270 10c beige & sage grn
800 A270 13c pale org & slate blue

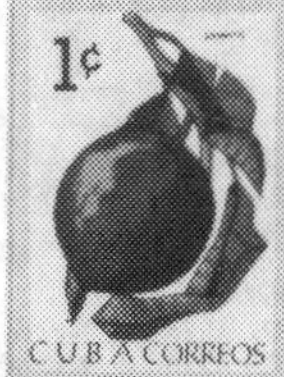

Indigenous Fruit — A271

1963, Aug. 19

801 A271 1c Star apple
802 A271 2c Cherimoya
803 A271 3c Cashew nut
804 A271 10c Custard apple
805 A271 13c Mangoes

Geometric Shapes — A272

View of a Town — A273

Designs: No. 806, Circle, triangle, square, vert. No. 807, Roof, window, vert. No. 808, View of a town. No. 809, View of a town in blue. No. 810, View of a town in olive bister and red. No. 811, Circle, triangle, vert. No. 812, House, roof and doorway, vert. No. 813, House, girders.

1963, Sept. 29 **Unwmk.**

806 A272 3c multi
807 A272 3c multi
808 A273 3c multi
809 A273 3c multi
810 A273 13c multi
811 A272 13c multi
812 A272 13c multi
813 A272 13c multi

7th Intl. Congress of the Intl. Union of Architects.

Ernest Hemingway (1899-1961), American Author — A274

Hemingway and: 3c, The Old Man and the Sea. 9c, For Whom the Bell Tolls. 13c, Hemingway Museum (former residence), San Francisco de Paula, near Havana.

1963, Dec. 5 **Wmk. 321**

814 A274 3c brn & lt blue
815 A274 9c sage grn & pink
816 A274 13c blk & yel grn

Natl. Museum, 50th Anniv. A275

Works of art: 2c, El Zapateo (Dance), by Victor P. Landaluze. 3c, Abduction of the Mulatto Women, by Carlos Enriquez, vert. 9c, Greek Panathean amphora, vert. 13c, My Beloved (bust of a young woman), by Jean Antoine Houdon, vert.

1964, Mar. 19 **Unwmk.**

817 A275 2c multi
818 A275 3c multi
819 A275 9c multi
820 A275 13c multi

General Strike on Apr. 9, 6th Anniv. — A276

Rebel leaders: 2c, Bernardo Juan Borrell. 3c, Marcelo Salado. 10c, Oscar Lucero. 13c, Sergio Gonzalez.

1964, Apr. 9

821 A276 2c blk, yel grn & dull org
822 A276 3c blk, red & dull org
823 A276 10c blk, pur & beige
824 A276 13c blk, brt blue & beige

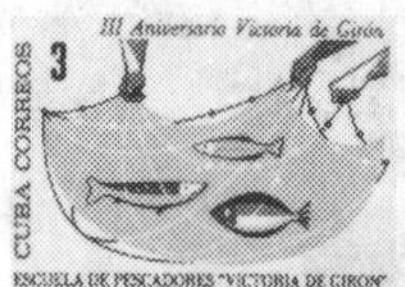

Bay of Pigs Invasion, 3rd Anniv. — A277

Designs: 3c, Fish in net. 10c, Victory Monument. 13c, Fallen eagle, vert.

1964, Apr. 17

825 A277 3c multi
826 A277 10c multi
827 A277 13c multi

Stamp Day Type of 1963

Stamp Day 1964: 3c, Vicente Mora Pera, 1st postal director. 13c, Unissued provisional stamp, 1871.

1964, Apr. 24

828 A266 3c ocher & dull lil
829 A266 13c dull vio & lt olive grn

Labor Day — A278

Diplomatic Relations with China — A279

1964, May 1

830 A278 3c Industry
831 A278 13c Agriculture

1964, May 15

Designs: 1c, China Monument, Havana. 2c, Cuban and Chinese farmers. 3c, Natl. flags.

832 A279 1c multi
833 A279 2c org brn, blk & apple grn
834 A279 3c multi

15th UPU Congress, Vienna, May-June A280

1964, May 29

835 A280 13c Hemispheres on world map
836 A280 30c Heinrich von Stephan
837 A280 50c UPU Monument, Bern

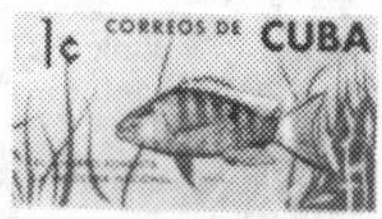

Development of Natl. Industry A281

1964, June 16

838 A281 1c Fish
839 A281 2c Cow
840 A281 13c Chickens

Merchant Fleet — A282

1964, June 30

841 A282 1c Rio Jibacoa
842 A282 2c Camilo Cienfuegos
843 A282 3c Sierra Maestra
844 A282 9c Bahia de Siguanea
845 A282 10c Oriente

Unification of Viet Nam — A283

Designs: 2c, Vietnamese guerrilla, American soldier. 3c, Northerner and southerner shaking hands over map of united Viet Nam. 10c, Ox-drawn plow, machinised harvester. 13c, Natl. flags and profiles of Cuban and Vietnamese farmers.

1964, July 20

846 A283 2c multi
847 A283 3c multi
848 A283 10c multi
849 A283 13c multi

11th Anniv. of the Revolution A284

1964 Summer Olympics, Tokyo, Oct. 10-25 A285

Designs: 3c, Raul Gomez Garcia and poem. 13c, Cover of La Historia Me Absolvera, by Fidel Castro.

1964, July 25

850 A284 3c red, tan & blk
851 A284 13c multi

1964, Oct. 10 **Wmk. 376** ***Perf. 10***

852 A285 1c Gymnastics
853 A285 2c Rowing
854 A285 3c Boxing
855 A285 7c Running, horiz.
856 A285 10c Fencing, horiz.
857 A285 13c Foil, cleats, oar, boxing glove, sun, horiz.

Satellite and Globe A286

Satellite and Partial Globe A287

No. C31 and Partial Globe A288

Various satellites and rockets.

1964, Oct. 15

858 A286 1c shown
859 A287 1c shown
860 A287 1c Globe LL
861 A287 1c Globe UR
862 A287 1c Globe UL
a. Block of 5 + label, Nos. 858-862
863 A286 2c Spacecraft and globe
864 A287 2c Globe LR
865 A287 2c Globe LL
866 A287 2c Globe UR
867 A287 2c Globe UL
a. Block of 5 + label, Nos. 863-867
868 A286 3c Satellite and globe
869 A287 3c Globe LR
870 A287 3c Globe LL
871 A287 3c Globe UR
872 A287 3c Globe UL
a. Block of 5 + label, Nos. 868-872
873 A286 9c Satellite and globe, diff
874 A287 9c Globe LR
875 A287 9c Globe LL
876 A287 9c Globe UR
877 A287 9c Globe UL
a. Block of 5 + label, Nos. 873-877
878 A286 13c Satellite and globe, diff.
879 A287 13c Globe LR
880 A287 13c Globe LL
881 A287 13c Globe UR
882 A287 13c Globe UR
a. Block of 5 + label, Nos. 878-882
883 A288 50c blk & lt grn
a. Souvenir sheet of one, Wmk. 321

Experimental Cuban postal rocket flight, 25th anniv. Stamps of the same denomination printed se-tenant in sheets of 20 stamps and 5 inscribed labels. Stamps of Type A287 arranged in blocks of 4 with a complete globe in center of block; Type A286 stamps and labels form a cross in center of sheet. Inscribed "1939-Cohete Postal Cubano-1964."

No. 883a contains one 46x28mm stamp.

Type of A288 Ovptd. in Silver

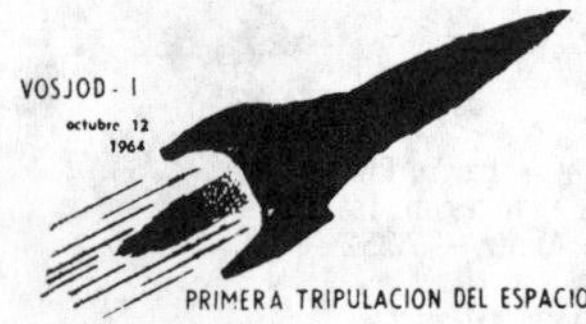

1964, Oct. 17 **Unwmk.**

884 A288 50c dark red brown & lt grn

No. 884 not issued without overprint.

40th Death Anniv. of Lenin — A289

Havana Zoo — A290

Designs: 13c, Lenin Mausoleum, horiz. 30c, Lenin, star, hammer and sickle.

1964, Nov. 7 **Wmk. 376**

885 A289 3c org & blk
886 A289 13c pur, pink & blk
887 A289 30c blue & blk

1964, Nov. 25

888 A290 1c Leopard, horiz.
889 A290 2c Elephant
890 A290 3c Fallow deer
891 A290 4c Kangaroo, horiz.
892 A290 5c Lions, horiz.
893 A290 6c Eland, horiz.
894 A290 7c Zebra, horiz.
895 A290 8c Hyena, horiz.
896 A290 9c Tiger, horiz.
897 A290 10c Guanaco, horiz.
898 A290 13c Chimpanzees, horiz.
899 A290 20c Peccary, horiz.
900 A290 30c Raccoon
901 A290 40c Hippopotamus, horiz.
902 A290 50c Tapir, horiz.
903 A290 60c Dromedary
904 A290 70c Bison, horiz.
905 A290 80c Black bear
906 A290 90c Water buffalo, horiz.

Size: 47x32mm

907 A290 1p Deer in nature park, horiz.

Heroes of the 1895 War of Independence — A291

1964, Dec. 7

908 A291 1c Jose Marti
909 A291 2c Antonio Maceo
910 A291 3c Maximo Gomez
911 A291 13c Calixto Garcia

Christmas Type of 1961

Designs: 2c, Coral. 3c, Jellyfish. 10c, Starfish and sea-urchins.

1964, Dec. 18

912 A248 2c Dwarf cup coral
913 A249 2c Eusmilia fastigiata
914 A249 2c Acropora palmata
915 A249 2c Acropora profilera
916 A249 2c Diploria labyrinthiformis
a. Block of 5 + label, Nos. 912-916
917 A248 3c Condylactis gigantea
918 A249 3c Physalia physalis
919 A249 3c Aurelia aurita
920 A249 3c Linuche unguiculata
921 A249 3c Cassiopea frondosa
a. Block of 5 + label, Nos. 917-921
922 A248 10c Neocrinus blakei
923 A249 10c Eucidaris tribuloidas
924 A249 10c Tripneutes
925 A249 10c Ophiocoma echinata
926 A249 10c Oreaster celiculatus
a. Block of 5 + label, Nos. 922-926

Christmas 1964. See note after No. 700.

Dr. Tomas Romay (1764-1849), Physician and Scientist — A292

Romay Monument — A293

Designs: 2c, First vaccination against smallpox. 3c, Portrait and treatise on vaccination.

1964, Dec. 21

927 A292 1c blk & olive brn
928 A292 2c blk & tan
929 A293 3c olive & dark red brown
930 A293 10c bister & blk

Second Declaration of Havana — A294

Map of Latin America and ripples or map of Cuba and peasant breaking shackles under text from the Declaration of Havana: No. 931a, 932a "Visperas de su muerte..." No. 931b, 932b, "Un continente, que juntos suponen representos..." No. 931c, 932c, "Y no se ocultaran ni el gobierna..." No. 931d, 932d, "Millones de mulatos latinamericanos que saben..." No. 931e, "A labran la tierra en condiciones..."

1964, Dec. 23

931 Strip of 5
a.-e. A294 3c any single
932 Strip of 5
a.-e. A294 13c any single

Nos. 931-932 printed in sheets of 25 (5x5).

Dioramas in New Cuban Postal Museum — A295

1965, Jan. 4

Yellow & Black Border

933 A295 13c Maritime Post
934 A295 30c Insurrection Post

Souvenir Sheet

Imperf

935 Sheet of 2
a. A295 13c like #933, blue & blk border
b. A295 30c like #934, blue & blk border

Stamps in #935 have simulated perforations; buff margin is inscribed "PRECIO 50c" LR.

Fishing Fleet A296

1965, May 1

936 A296 1c Schooner
937 A296 2c Omicron
938 A296 3c Victoria
939 A296 9c Cardenas
940 A296 10c Sigma
941 A296 13c Lambda

Intl. Women's Day — A297

1965, Mar. 8

942 A297 3c Lidia Doce
943 A297 13c Clara Zetkin

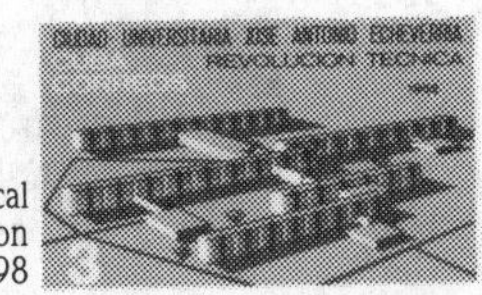

Technical Revolution A298

Designs: 3c, Jose Antonio Echeverria University School. 13c, Stylized symbols of science and research, molecular structure and satellite dish.

1965, Mar. 31

944 A298 3c tan, blk & dark red brn
945 A298 13c multi

Cosmonauts, Rocket — A299

Designs: 30c, Cosmonauts Pavel I. Balyayev, Aleksei A. Leonov taking first space walk.

1965, Apr. 2

946 A299 30c dark blue, blk & brn
947 A299 50c brt pink & blue blk

Flight of Voskhod 2, the first man to walk in space, Mar. 17.

Abstract Wood Carving by Eugenio Rodriguez — A300

Abraham Lincoln — A301

Paintings in the Natl. Museum, Havana: 3c, Garden with Sunflowers, by Victor Manuel. 10c, Abstract, by Wilfredo Lam, horiz. 13c, Children, by Enrique Ponce, horiz.

1965, Apr. 12

948 A300 2c multi

Size: 35x46mm

949 A300 3c multi

Size: 46x35mm

950 A300 10c multi

Size: 43x37mm

951 A300 13c multi

1965, Apr. 15

Designs: 1c, Log cabin, birth site, horiz. 2c, Memorial, Washington, DC, horiz. 3c, Monument, Washington, DC. 13c, Portrait, quote.

952 A301 1c yel bister, red brn & gray
953 A301 2c lt blue & dark blue
954 A301 3c red org, blk & blue blk
955 A301 13c org, blk & blue blk

Stamp Day Type of 1963

Stamp Day 1965: 3c, 18th Cent. postmarks and packet. 13c, No. C16 and airplanes over capital.

1965, Apr. 24

956 A266 3c sep & dark org
957 A266 13c brt blue, sal rose & blk

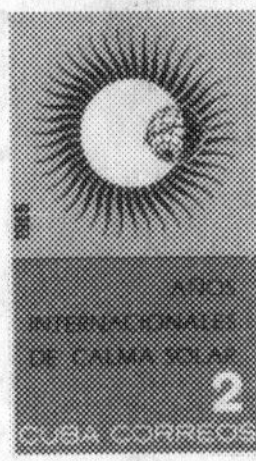

Intl. Quiet Sun Year — A302

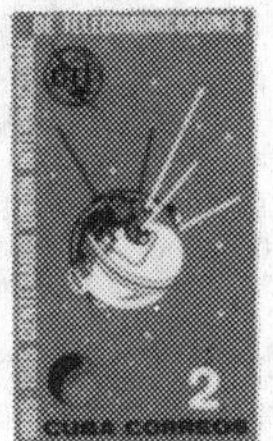

Intl. Telecommunications Union, Cent. — A303

1965, May 10

958 A302 1c Sun, Earth's magnetic pole, horiz.
959 A302 2c Sun Year emblem
960 A302 3c Earth's magnetic field, horiz.
961 A302 6c Atmospheric currents, horiz.
962 A302 30c Solar rays on planet surface
963 A302 50c Effect on satellite orbits, horiz.
a. Souv. sheet of one, imperf.
b. As "a," changed colors

Stamps in Nos. 963a-963b have simulated perforations.

Stamp in No. 963b is blue blk, Prus blue, org yel & red. Issued Oct. 10 for the Philatelic Space Exhibition, Havana, Oct. 10-17.

1965, May 17

964 A303 1c Station, horiz.
965 A303 2c Satellite
966 A303 3c Telstar, horiz.
967 A303 10c Telstar, receiving station
968 A303 30c ITU emblem, horiz.

9th Communist World Youth and Students Congress — A304

1965, June 10

969 A304 13c Flags of Cuba and Algeria, emblem
970 A304 30c Flags, guerrillas

Matias Perez, Cuban Aeronautics Pioneer A305

1965, June 23

971 A305 3c pink & blk
972 A305 13c dull vio & blk, diff.

Flowers and Maps of Their Locations — A306

1965, July 20

973 A306 1c Rosa canina, Europe
974 A306 2c Chrysanthemum hortorum, Asia
975 A306 3c Strelitzia reginae, Africa
976 A306 4c Dahlia pinnata, No. America
977 A306 5c Cattleya labiata, So. America
978 A306 13c Grevillea banksii, Oceania
979 A306 30c Brunfelsia nitida, Cuba

1st Natl. Games A307

1965, July 25

980 A307 1c Swimming
981 A307 2c Basketball
982 A307 3c Gymnastics
983 A307 30c Hurdling

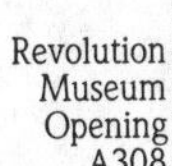

Revolution Museum Opening A308

1965, July 26

984 A308 1c Anti-tank guns
985 A308 2c Tanks
986 A308 3c Bazookas
987 A308 10c Uniform, guerillas
988 A308 13c Compass, yacht Granma

A309

1965, Aug. 20

989 A309 1c Finlay's signature
990 A309 2c Anopheles mosquito
991 A309 3c Portrait
992 A309 7c Microscope
993 A309 9c Portrait, diff.
994 A309 10c Monument
995 A309 13c Discussing theory with doctors

Carlos J. Finlay (1833-1915), discovered transmission of yellow fever via anopheles mosquito. Nos. 990-995 vert.

Butterflies A310

1965, Sept. 22 **Unwmk.**

996 A310 2c Dismorphia cubana
997 A310 2c Anetia numidia briarea
998 A310 2c Carathis gortynoides
999 A310 2c Hymenitis cubana
1000 A310 2c Eubaphe heros
a. Strip of 5, Nos. 996-1000
1001 A310 3c Lycorea ceres demeter
1002 A310 3c Eubaphe disparitis
1003 A310 3c Siderone nemesis
1004 A310 3c Syntomidopsis variegata
1005 A310 3c Ctenuchidia virgo
a. Strip of 5, Nos. 1001-1005
1006 A310 13c Prepona antimache crossina
1007 A310 13c Sylepta reginalis
1008 A310 13c Chlosyne perezi perezi
1009 A310 13c Anaea clytemnestra iphigenia
1010 A310 13c Anetia cubana
a. Strip of 5, Nos. 1006-1010

Cuban Mint, 50th Anniv. A311

Coins (obverse and reverse).

1965, Oct. 13

1011 A311 1c 20 centavos, 1962
1012 A311 2c 1 peso, 1934
1013 A311 3c 40 centavos, 1962
1014 A311 8c 1 peso, 1915
1015 A311 10c Marti peso, 1953
1016 A311 13c 20 pesos, 1915

Tropical Fruit — A312

1965, Nov. 15 *Perf. 12½*

1017 A312 1c Oranges
1018 A312 2c Custard apples
1019 A312 3c Papayas
1020 A312 4c Bananas
1021 A312 10c Avocado
1022 A312 13c Pineapple
1023 A312 20c Guavas
1024 A312 50c Marmalade plums

Christmas Type of 1961

Birds.

1965, Dec. 1

1025 A248 3c Icterus galbula
1026 A249 3c Passerina ciris
1027 A249 3c Setophaga ruticillar
1028 A249 3c Dendroica tusca
1029 A249 3c Pheucticus ludovicianus
a. Block of 5 + label, Nos. 1025-1029
1030 A248 5c Pyranga olivacea
1031 A249 5c Dendroica dominica
1032 A249 5c Vermivora pinus
1033 A249 5c Protonotaria citrea
1034 A249 5c Wilsonia citrina
a. Block of 5 + label, Nos. 1030-1034
1035 A248 13c Passerina cyanea
1036 A249 13c Anas discors
1037 A249 13c Aix sponsa
1038 A249 13c Spatula clypeata
1039 A249 13c Nycticorax hoactli
a. Block of 5 + label, Nos. 1035-1039

Christmas 1965. See note after No. 700.

Intl. Athletic Competition, Havana, 7th Anniv. — A313

1965, Dec. 11 **Wmk. 376** *Perf. 10*

1040 A313 1c Hurdling
1041 A313 2c Discus
1042 A313 3c Shot put
1043 A313 7c Javelin
1044 A313 9c High jump
1045 A313 10c Hammer throw
1046 A313 13c Running

Fish in the Natl. Aquarium A314

1965, Dec. 5 **Unwmk.** *Perf. 12½*

1047 A314 1c Echeneis naucrates
1048 A314 2c Katsuwonus pelamis
1049 A314 3c Abudefduf saxatilis
1050 A314 4c Istiophorus
1051 A314 5c Epinephelus striatus
1052 A314 10c Lutianus analis
1053 A314 13c Ocyurus chrysurus
1054 A314 30c Holocentrus ascensionis

Andre Voisin (d. 1964), French Naturalist A315

1965, Dec. 21 **Wmk. 376**

1055 A315 3c shown
1056 A315 13c Portrait, flags, microscope, plant

Transportation — A316

1965, Dec. 30

1057 A316 1c Skoda bus, Czechoslovakia
1058 A316 2c Ikarus bus, Hungary
1059 A316 3c Leyland bus, G.B.
1060 A316 4c TEM-4 locomotive, USSR
1061 A316 7c BB-69.000 locomotive, France
1062 A316 10c Remolcador tugboat, DDR
1063 A316 13c 15 de Marzo freighter, Spain
1064 A316 20c Ilyushin 18 jet, USSR

A317

7th Anniv. of the Revolution A318

1966, Jan. 2

1065 A317 1c Guerrillas
1066 A317 2c Commander and tank
1067 A317 3c Sailor, patrol boat
1068 A318 10c Jet aircraft
1069 A318 13c Rocket

Conference of Asian, African and South American Countries, Havana A319

1966, Jan. 3

1070 A319 2c Emblem at R
1071 A319 3c Emblem at L
1072 A319 13c Emblem at center

Guardalabarca Beach — A320

1966, Feb. 10

1073 A320 1c shown
1074 A320 2c Gran Piedra mountain
1075 A320 3c Guama Village
1076 A320 13c Soroa waterfall, vert.

11th Medical and 7th Natl. Dental Congresses A321

1966, Feb. 28 **Wmk. 376**

1077 A321 3c multi
1078 A321 13c multi, diff.

Folk Art A322

1966, Feb. 28 **Unwmk.**

1079 A322 1c Afro-cuban ritual puppet
1080 A322 2c Sombreros
1081 A322 3c Ceramic vase
1082 A322 7c Lanterns, lamp
1083 A322 9c Table lamp
1084 A322 10c Shark, wood sculpture
1085 A322 13c Snail-shell necklace, earrings

Nos. 1079-1083 vert.

Chelsea College, by Canaletto A323

Ceramics and paintings in the National Museum: 1c, Ming vase. 3c, Portrait of a Lady, by Goya. 13c, Portrait of Fayum, bas-relief. Nos. 1086, 1088-1089 vert.

1966, Mar. 31 **Wmk. 376**

1086 A323 1c multi
1087 A323 2c multi
1088 A323 3c multi
1089 A323 13c multi

First Man in Space, 5th Anniv. A324

Designs: 1c, Konstantin Eduardovich Tsiolkovsky (1857-1935), Soviet rocket and space sciences pioneer. 2c, Cosmonauts in training, vert. 3c, Yuri Gagarin, rocket, Earth. 7c, Cosmonauts Nikolaev and Popovich, vert. 9c, Tereshkova and Bykovsky. 10c, Komarov, Feoktistov and Yegarov. 13c, Leonov taking first space walk.

1966, Apr. 12

1090 A324 1c multi
1091 A324 2c multi
1092 A324 3c multi
1093 A324 7c multi
1094 A324 9c multi
1095 A324 10c multi
1096 A324 13c multi

Bay of Pigs Invasion, 5th Anniv. A325

1966, Apr. 17

1097 A325 2c Tank
1098 A325 3c Burning ship, plane crash
1099 A325 9c Tank in ditch
1100 A325 10c Soldier, gunners
1101 A325 13c Operations map

Stamp Day Type of 1963

Designs: 3c, Cuban Postal Museum interior. 13c, No. 613 and stamp collector.

1966, Apr. 24

1102 A266 3c sage grn & sal rose
1103 A266 13c brn, sal rose & blk

Stamp Day 1966. 1st Anniv. of the Cuban Postal Museum (No. 1102); 1st anniv. of the Cuban Philatelic Federation (No. 1103).

Flowers and Symbols of Industry — A326

1966, May 1

1104 A326 2c Anvil
1105 A326 3c Machete
1106 A326 10c Hammer
1107 A326 13c Hemisphere, gearwheel

Labor Day.

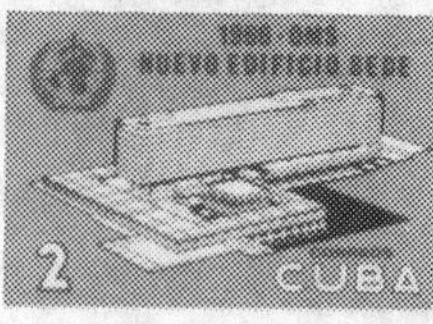

Opening of the World Health Organization Headquarters, Geneva — A327

Views of WHO headquarters and emblem or emblem on flag.

1966, May 3

1108 A327 2c blk & yel org
1109 A327 3c blk, lt blue & yel org
1110 A327 13c blk, lt blue & yel org

10th Central American and Caribbean Games, Puerto Rico, June 11-25 A328

1966, June 11

1111 A328 1c Running, vert.
1112 A328 2c Rifle shooting
1113 A328 3c Baseball, vert.
1114 A328 7c Volleyball, vert.
1115 A328 9c Soccer, vert.
1116 A328 10c Boxing, vert.
1117 A328 13c Basketball, vert.

Progress in Education A329

Designs: 1c, Makarenko School, Playa de Tarara. 2c, Natl. Literacy Campaign Museum. 3c, Lantern, literacy campaign emblem for 1961. 10c, Frank Pais education team in the mountains. 13c, Farmer, factory worker.

1966, June 15

1118 A329 1c grn & blk
1119 A329 2c yel, olive bister & blk
1120 A329 3c brt blue, lt blue & blk
1121 A329 10c golden brn, brn & blk
1122 A329 13c multi

1st Graduating class of Makarenko School (1c), 5th anniv. of the Natl. Literacy Campaign (3c), 4th anniv. of agricultural and industrial trade education (13c).

12th Congress of the Cuban Labor Organization — A330

1966, Aug. 12

1123 A330 3c multi

Sea Shells — A331

1966, Aug. 25 **Unwmk.**

1124 A331 1c Liguus flammellus
1125 A331 2c Cypraea zebra
1126 A331 3c Strombus pugilis
1127 A331 7c Aequipecten muscosu
1128 A331 9c Liguus fasciatus crenatus
1129 A331 10c Charonia variegata
1130 A331 13c Liguus fasciatus archeri

Breeding Messenger Pigeons A332

1966, Sept. 18 **Wmk. 376**

1131 A332 1c shown
1132 A332 2c Timer
1133 A332 3c Coops
1134 A332 7c Breeder tending coops
1135 A332 9c Pigeons in yard
1136 A332 10c Two men, message

Size: 47x32mm

1137 A332 13c Baracoa to Havana championship flight, July 26, 1959

Provincial and Natl. Coats of Arms, Map of Cuba — A333

17th World Chess Olympiad, Havana — A334

1966, Oct. 10

1138 A333 1c Pinar del Rio
1139 A333 2c Havana
1140 A333 3c Matanzas
1141 A333 4c Las Villas
1142 A333 5c Camaguey
1143 A333 9c Oriente

Size: 30x48mm

1144 A333 13c National arms

1966, Oct. 18

1145 A334 1c Pawn
1146 A334 2c Rook
1147 A334 3c Knight
1148 A334 9c Bishop
1149 A334 10c Queen, games, horiz.
1150 A334 13c King and emblem, horiz.

Souvenir Sheet

Imperf

1151 A334 30c Capablanca Vs. Lasker, 1914, horiz.

No. 1151 contains one 49½x31mm stamp.

Cuban-Soviet Diplomatic Relations — A335

1966, Nov. 7

1152 A335 2c Lenin Hospital
1153 A335 3c Oil tanker, world map
1154 A335 10c Workers, gearwheels
1155 A335 13c Agriculture

2nd Song Festival A336

Cuban composers and their compositions.

1966, Nov. 18

1156 A336 1c Amadeo Roldan
1157 A336 2c Eduardo Sanchez de Fuentes
1158 A336 3c Moises Simons
1159 A336 7c Jorge Anckermann
1160 A336 9c Alejandro G. Caturla
1161 A336 10c Eliseo Grenet
1162 A336 13c Ernesto Lecuona

Viet Nam War — A337

Flag of Viet Nam and: 2c, US aircraft discharging bombs, dead cattle. 3c, Gas mask and victims. 13c, US bombs, women and children.

1966, Nov. 23

1163 A337 2c multi
1164 A337 3c multi
1165 A337 13c multi

10th Anniv. of Successful Revolution Campaigns — A338

Revolution leaders and scenes of the insurrection.

1966, Nov. 30

1166 A338 1c Antonio Fernandez
1167 A338 2c Candido Gonzalez
1168 A338 3c Jose Tey
1169 A338 7c Tony Aloma
1170 A338 9c Otto Paralleda
1171 A338 10c Juan Manuel Marquez
1172 A338 13c Frank Pais

Intl. Leisure Time and Recreation Seminar A339

1966, Dec. 2

1173 A339 3c shown
1174 A339 9c World map, stopwatch, eye
1175 A339 13c Earth, clock, emblem

1st Natl. Telecommunications Forum — A340

1966, Dec. 12

1176 A340 3c shown
1177 A340 10c Satellite in orbit
1178 A340 13c Shell, satellite
a. Souv. sheet of 3, #1176-1178, imperf,

No. 1178a sold for 30c.

Christmas Type of 1961

1966, Dec. 20 **Unwmk.**

1179 A248 1c Cypripedium eurylochus
1180 A249 1c Cattleya speciosissima
1181 A249 1c Cattleya mendelii majestica
1182 A249 1c Cattleya trianae amesiana
1183 A249 1c Cattleya labiata macfarlanei
a. Block of 5 + label, Nos. 1179-1183
1184 A248 3c Cypripedium morganiae burfordense
1185 A249 3c Cattleya Countess of Derby
1186 A249 3c Cypripedium hookerae volunteanum
1187 A249 3c Cattleya warscewiczii reginae burfordense
1188 A249 3c Cypripedium stonei cannartae
a. Block of 5 + label, Nos. 1184-1188
1189 A248 13c Cattleya mendelii Duchess of Montrose
1190 A249 13c Oncidium macranthum
1191 A249 13c Cypripedium stonei platytoenium
1192 A249 13c Cattleya dowiana aurea
1193 A249 13c Laelia anceps
a. Block of 5 + label, Nos. 1189-1193

Christmas 1966. See note after No. 700.

8th Anniv. of the Revolution — A341

1967, Jan. 2

1194 A341 3c Liberation, 1959
1195 A341 3c Agrarian Reform, 1960
1196 A341 3c Education, 1961
1197 A341 3c Agriculture, 1965
a. Strip of 4, Nos. 1194-1197
1198 A341 13c Rodin's Thinker, Planning, 1962
1199 A341 13c Organization, 1963
1200 A341 13c Economy, 1964
1201 A341 13c Solidarity, 1966
a. Strip of 4, Nos. 1198-1201

Nos. 1198-1201 vert.

Spring, by Jorge Arche — A342

Paintings in the Natl. Museum: 1c, Coffee Machine, by Angel Acosta Leon, vert. 2c, Country People, by Eduardo Abela, vert. 13c, Still-life, by Amelia Pelaez, vert. 30c, Landscape, by Gonzalo Escalante.

1967, Feb. 27

1202 A342 1c multi
1203 A342 2c multi
1204 A342 3c multi
1205 A342 13c multi
1206 A342 30c multi

Natl. Events, Mar. 13, 1957 A343

1967, Mar. 13 **Wmk. 376**

1207 A343 3c Attack on Presidential Palace

Size: 41x28mm

1208 A343 13c Landing of Corynthia
1209 A343 30c Cienfuego revolt

Evolution of Man — A344

Prehistoric men: 2c, Australopithecus. 3c, Pithecanthropus erectus. 4c, Sinanthropus pekinensis. 5c, Neanderthal man. 13c, Cro-magnon man carving tusk. 20c, Cro-magnon man painting petroglyph.

1967, Mar. 31 **Unwmk.**

1210 A344 1c multi
1211 A344 2c multi
1212 A344 3c multi
1213 A344 4c multi
1214 A344 5c multi
1215 A344 13c multi
1216 A344 20c multi

Stamp Day A345

Carriages.

1967, Apr. 24

1217 A345 3c Victoria
1218 A345 9c Volante
1219 A345 13c Quitrin

EXPO '67, Montreal, Apr. 28-Oct. 27 A346

1967, Apr. 28

1220 A346 1c Cuban pavilion
1221 A346 2c Space exploration
1222 A346 3c Petroglyph, hieroglyph
1223 A346 13c Agriculture, computer technology
1224 A346 20c Athletes

Botanical Gardens, Sequicentennial A347

Flowering plants.

1967, May 30

1225 A347 1c Eugenia malaccencis
1226 A347 2c Jacaranda filicifolia
1227 A347 3c Coroupita guianensis
1228 A347 4c Spathodea campanulata
1229 A347 5c Cassia fistula
1230 A347 13c Plumieria alba
1231 A347 20c Erythrina poeppigiana

Natl. Ballet — A348

1967, June 15

1232 A348 1c Giselle
1233 A348 2c Swan Lake
1234 A348 3c Don Quixote
1235 A348 4c Calaucan
1236 A348 13c Swan Lake
1237 A348 20c Nutcracker

Intl. Ballet Festival, Havana.

5th Pan American Games, Winnipeg, Canada, July 22-Aug. 7 — A349

1st Conference of Latin American Solidarity Organization (OLAS) — A350

1967, July 22

1238 A349 1c Baseball, horiz.
1239 A349 2c Swimming, horiz.
1240 A349 3c Basketball
1241 A349 4c Gymnastic rings
1242 A349 5c Water polo
1243 A349 13c Weight lifting, horiz.
1244 A349 20c Javelin

1967, July 28 **Wmk. 376**

Portrait of representative, map of South American homeland: No. 1245, Camilo Torres, Colombia. No. 1246, Luis de la Puente Uceda, Peru. No. 1247, Luis A. Turcios Lima, Guatemala. No. 1248, Fabricio Ojeda, Venezuela.

1245 A350 13c pale grn, blk & red
1246 A350 13c lil, blk & red
1247 A350 13c dark chalky blue, blk & red
1248 A350 13c golden brn, blk & red

Portrait of Sonny Rollins, by Alan Davie A351

Bathers, by Gustave Singier A352

Modern Art: No. 1250, Twelve Selenities, by Felix Labisse. No. 1251, Night of the Drinker, by Friedensreich Hundertwasser. No. 1252, Figure, by Mariano. No. 1253, All-Souls, by Wilfredo Lam. No. 1254, Darkness and Cracks, by Antonio Tapies. No. 1256, Torso of a Muse, by Jean Arp. No. 1257, Figure, by M.W. Svanberg. No. 1258, Oppenheimer's Information, by Erro. No. 1259, Where Cardinals Are Born, by Max Ernst. No. 1260, Havana Landscape, by Portocarrero. No. 1261, EG 12, by Victor Vasarely. No. 1262, Frisco, by Alexander Calder. No. 1263, The Man with the Pipe, by Picasso. No. 1264, Abstract Composition, by Sergei Poliakoff. No. 1265, Painting, by Bram van Velde. No. 1266, Sower of Fires, by R. Matta. No. 1267, The Art of Living, by Rene Magritte. No. 1268, Poem, by Joan Miro. No. 1269, Young Tigers, by Jean Messagier. No. 1270, Painting, by M. Vieira da Silva. No. 1271, Live Cobra, by Pierre Alechinsky. No. 1272, Stalingrad, by Asger Jorn. 30c, Warriors, by Edouard Pignon. 50c, Cloister, a mural at the exhibition representing the Salon de Mayo pictures.

1967, July 29 **Unwmk.**

1249 A351 1c shown
1250 A351 1c multi
1251 A351 1c multi
1252 A351 1c multi
1253 A351 1c multi
a. Strip of 5, Nos. 1249-1253

Sizes: 36½x54mm, 36½x53mm, 36½x45mm, 36½x41mm

1254 A352 2c multi
1255 A352 2c shown
1256 A352 2c multi
1257 A352 2c multi
1258 A352 2c multi
a. Strip of 5, Nos. 1254-1258

Sizes: 36½x54mm, 36½x40mm, 36½x42mm, 36½x49mm

1259 A352 3c multi
1260 A352 3c multi
1261 A352 3c multi
1262 A352 3c multi
1263 A352 3c multi
a. Strip of 5, Nos. 1259-1263

Sizes: 35x15mm, 35x67mm, 35x46½mm, 35x55mm

1264 A352 4c multi
1265 A352 4c multi
1266 A352 4c multi
1267 A352 4c multi
1268 A352 4c multi
a. Strip of 5, Nos. 1264-1268

Sizes: 49x32mm, 49x35mm, 49x46mm

1269 A351 13c multi
1270 A351 13c multi
1271 A351 13c multi
1272 A351 13c multi
a. Strip of 4, Nos. 1269-1272

Size: 54x32mm

1273 A351 30c multi

Souvenir Sheet

Imperf

1274 A351 50c multi

Salon de Mayo Art Exhibition, Havana. No. 1274 contains one 88x45mm stamp with simulated perforations. Issued Oct. 7.

World Underwater Fishing Championships — A353

1967, Sept. 5

1275 A353 1c Green moray
1276 A353 2c Octopus
1277 A353 3c Great barracuda
1278 A353 4c Blue shark
1279 A353 5c Spotted jewfish
1280 A353 13c Sting ray
1281 A353 20c Green turtle

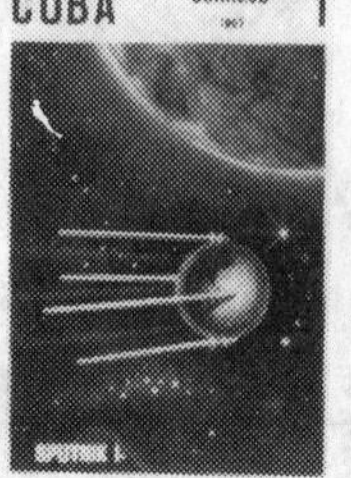

Soviet Space Program — A354

1967, Oct. 4 **Wmk. 376**

1282 A354 1c Sputnik 1
1283 A354 2c Lunik 3
1284 A354 3c Venusik
1285 A354 4c Cosmos
1286 A354 5c Mars 1
1287 A354 9c Electron 1 & 2
1288 A354 10c Luna 9
1289 A354 13c Luna 10
a. Souv. sheet of 8, #1282-1289, imperf.

Stamps in #1289a have simulated perfs.

50th Anniv. of the October Revolution, Russia — A355

Paintings: 1c, Storming the Winter Palace, by Sokolov, Skalia and Miasnikov. 2c, Lenin Addressing Congress, by W.A. Serov. 3c, Lenin, by H.D. Nalbandian. 4c, Lenin Explaining Electrification Map, by L.A. Schmatko. 5c, Dawn of the Five-Year Plan, by J.D. Romas. 13c, Kusnetzkroi Steel Furnace No. 1, by P. Kotov. 30c, Victory, by A. Krivonogov.

1967, Nov. 7 **Unwmk.**

1290 A355 1c 64x36mm
1291 A355 2c 48x36mm
1292 A355 3c
1293 A355 4c 48x36mm
1294 A355 5c 50x36mm
1295 A355 13c 36x50mm
1296 A355 30c 50x36mm

Castle of the Royal Forces, Havana A356

Historic architecture: 2c, Iznaga Tower, Trinidad, vert. 3c, Castle of Our Lady of the Angels, Cienfuegos. 4c, St. Francis de Paula Church, Havana. 13c, St. Francis Convent, Havana. 30c, Castle del Morro, Santiago de Cuba.

1967, Nov. 7 **Wmk. 376**

Sizes: 26x47mm (1c), 41x29mm (3c, 4c), 38½x31mm (13c)

1297 A356 1c multi
1298 A356 2c multi
1299 A356 3c multi
1300 A356 4c multi
1301 A356 13c multi
1302 A356 30c multi

Christmas Type of 1961

Birds.

1967, Dec. 20

1303 A248 1c Struthia camelus australis
1304 A249 1c Chysolophus pictus
1305 A249 1c Ciconia ciconia ciconia
1306 A249 1c Balearica pavonina
1307 A249 1c Dromiceius novaehollandiae
a. Block of 5 + label, Nos. 1303-1307
1308 A248 3c Anodorhynchus hyacinthus
1309 A249 3c Psittacus erithacus
1310 A249 3c Domicella garrula
1311 A249 3c Ramphastos sulfuratus
1312 A249 3c Kakatoe galerita galerita
a. Block of 5 + label, Nos. 1308-1312
1313 A248 13c Phoenicopterus ruber
1314 A249 13c Pelecanus erythrorhynchos
1315 A249 13c Alopochen aegyptiacus
1316 A249 13c Dendronessa galericulata
1317 A249 13c Chenopsis atrata
a. Block of 5 + label, Nos. 1313-1317

Christmas 1967. See note after No. 700.

Ernesto "Che" Guevara (1928-1967), Revolution Leader A356a

1968, Jan. 3

1318 A356a 13c blk, dark red & buff

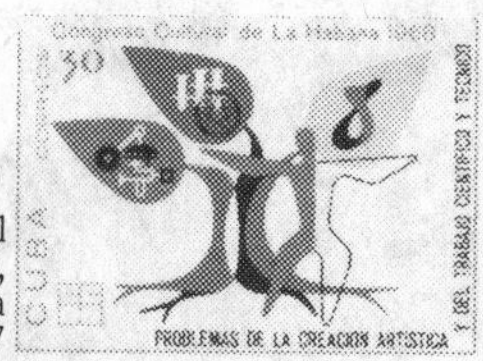

Cultural Congress, Havana A357

Abstract designs: No. 1319, Independence fostering culture. No. 1320, Integral formation of man. No. 1321, Responsibility of intellectuals. No. 1322, Relationship between culture and the mass media. No. 1323, The arts versus science and technology. Nos. 1319-1322 vert.

1968, Jan. 4

1319 A357 3c multi
1320 A357 3c multi
1321 A357 13c multi
1322 A357 13c multi
1323 A357 30c multi

Canaries and Breeding Cycles — A358

1968, Apr. 13

1324 A358 1c F.C.C. 4016
1325 A358 2c A.C.C. 774
1326 A358 3c A.C.C. 122
1327 A358 4c F.C.C. 4477
1328 A358 5c A.C.C. 117
1329 A358 13c A.N.R. 1175
1330 A358 20c A.C.C. 777

Stamp Day — A359

Paintings: 13c, The Village Postman, by J. Harris. 30c, The Philatelist, by G. Sciltian.

1968, Apr. 24 **Unwmk.**

1331 A359 13c multi
1332 A359 30c multi

World Health Organization, 20th Anniv. A360

1968, May 10 **Wmk. 376**

1333 A360 13c Nurse, mother, child
1334 A360 30c Surgeons

Intl. Children's Day — A361

1968, June 1

1335 A361 3c multi

Seville Camaguey Flight, 35th Anniv. — A362

1968, June 20

1336 A362 13c Plane Four Winds
1337 A362 30c Capt. Berberan, Lt. Collar, pilots

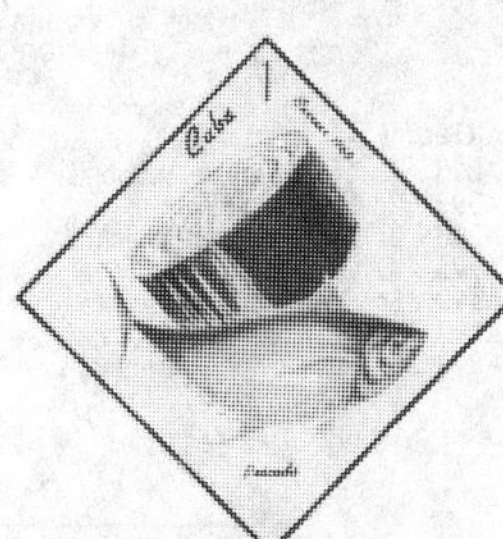

Natl. Food Production — A363

1968, June 29

1338 A363 1c Yellow tuna, can
1339 A363 2c Cow, dairy products
1340 A363 3c Rooster, eggs
1341 A363 13c Rum, sugar cane
1342 A363 20c Crayfish, box

Attack of Moncada Barracks, 15th Anniv. A364

1968, July 26

Size: 43x29mm (13c)

1343 A364 3c Siboney farmhouse
1344 A364 13c Assault route, Santiago de Cuba
1345 A364 30c Students, school

Committee for the Defense of the Revolution, 8th Anniv. — A365

1968, Sept. 28

1346 A365 3c multi

Guerilla Day A366

Che Guevara and: 1c, Rifleman and "En Cualquier Lugar..." 3c, Machine gunners and "Crear tres muchos Viet Nam." 9c, Silhouette of battalion and "Este Tipo De Lucha..." 10c, Guerillas cheering and "Hoy aquilatamos..." 13c, Map of Caribbean, So. America and "Hasta La Victoria Siempre."

1968, Oct. 8

1347 A366 1c gold, brt blue grn & blk
1348 A366 3c gold, org brn blk
1349 A366 9c multi
1350 A366 10c gold, lt olive grn & blk
1351 A366 13c gold, red org & blk

Cuban War of Independence, Cent. — A367

Independence fighters and scenes.

1968, Oct. 10 **Unwmk.**

1352 A367 1c C.M. de Cespedes, broken wheel
1353 A367 1c E. Betances, horsemen, flag
1354 A367 1c I. Agramonte, Clavellinas Monument
1355 A367 1c A. Maceo, Baragua Protest
1356 A367 1c J. Marti, horsemen
a. Strip of 5, Nos. 1352-1356
1357 A367 3c M. Gomez, The Invasion
1358 A367 3c J.A. Mella, declaration
1359 A367 3c A. Guiteras, El Morrillo monument
1360 A367 3c A. Santamaria, attack on Moncada Barracks
1361 A367 3c F. Paiz memorial
a. Strip of 5, Nos. 1357-1361
1362 A367 9c J. Echeverria, student protest
1363 A367 13c C. Cienfuegos, insurrection
1364 A367 30c Che Guevara, 1st Declaration of Havana

Souvenir Sheet

The Burning of Bayamo, by J.E. Hernandez Giro — A368

1968, Oct. 18 *Imperf.*

1365 A368 50c multi

Natl. Philatelic Exhibition, independence cent. Stamp in No. 1365 has simulated perforations.

19th Summer Olympics, Mexico City, Oct. 12-27 — A369

1968, Oct. 21 *Perf. 12½*

1366 A369 1c Parade of athletes
1367 A369 2c Women's basketball, vert.
1368 A369 3c Hammer throw, vert.
1369 A369 4c Boxing
1370 A369 5c Water polo
1371 A369 13c Pistol shooting

Size: 32x50mm

1372 A369 30c Mexican flag, calendar stone

Souvenir Sheet

Imperf

1373 A369 50c Running

Stamp in #173 has simulated perforations.

Civilian Activities of the Armed Forces A370

1968, Dec. 2 **Wmk. 376** *Perf. 12½*

1374 A370 3c Crop dusting
1375 A370 9c Che Guevara's Brigade
1376 A370 10c Road building
1377 A370 13c Plowing, harvesting

San Alejandro School of Painting, Sesquicentennial — A371

Paintings: 1c, Manrique de Lara's Family, by Jean Baptiste Vermay, vert. 2c, Seascape, by Leopoldo Romanach. 3c, Wild Cane, by Antonio Rodriguez, vert. 4c, Self-portrait, by Miguel Melero, vert. 5c, The Lottery List, by Jose Joaquin Tejada. 13c, Portrait of Nina, by Armando B. Menocal, vert. 30c, Landscape, by Esteban B. Chartrand. 50c, Siesta, by Guillermo Collazo.

1968, Dec. 30 **Unwmk.**

Sizes: 38x48mm (1c, 3c), 39x50mm (4c, 13c), 53x36mm (30c)

1378 A371 1c multi
1379 A371 2c multi
1380 A371 3c multi
1381 A371 4c multi
1382 A371 5c multi
1383 A371 13c multi
1384 A371 30c multi

Souvenir Sheet

Imperf

1385 A371 50c multi

No. 1385 contains one 52x41½mm stamp that has simulated perforations.

10th Anniv. of the Revolution A372

1969, Jan. 3 **Wmk. 376** *Perf. 12½*

1386 A372 13c multi

Villaclarenos Rebellion, Cent. — A373

1969, Feb. 6

1387 A373 3c Gutierrez and Sanchez

Women's Day — A374

Design: Mariana Grajales, rose and statue.

1969, Mar. 8

1388 A374 3c multi

Cuban Pioneers and Young Communists Unions — A375

1969, Apr. 4

1389 A375 3c Pioneers
1390 A375 13c Young Communists

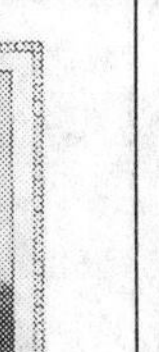

Guaimaro Assembly, Cent. A376

1969, Apr. 10

1391 A376 3c dark brn

The Postman, by Jean C. Cazin A377

Paintings: 30c, Portrait of a Young Man, by George Romney.

1969, Apr. 24 **Unwmk.**

1392 A377 13c multi

Size: 35½x43½mm

1393 A377 30c multi

Stamp Day.

Agrarian Reform, 10th Anniv. A378

1969, May 17 **Wmk. 376**

1394 A378 13c multi

Marine Life A379

1969, May 20 **Unwmk.**

1395 A379 1c Petrochirus bahamensis
1396 A379 2c Stenopus hispidus
1397 A379 3c Panulirus argus
1398 A379 4c Callinectes sapidus
1399 A379 5c Gecarcinus ruricola
1400 A379 13c Macrobrachium carcinus
1401 A379 30c Carpilius coralinus

Intl. Labor Organization, 50th Anniv. — A380

1969, June 6 **Wmk. 376**

1402 A380 3c shown
1403 A380 13c Blacksmith breaking chains

Paintings in the Natl. Museum — A381

Designs: 1c, Flowers, by Raul Milian, vert. 2c, Annunciation, by Antonia Eiriz. 3c, Factory, by Marcelo Pogolotti, vert. 4c, Territorial Waters, by Luis Martinez Pedro, vert. 5c, Miss Sarah Gale, by John Hoppner, vert. 13c, Two Women Wearing Mantilla, by Ignacio Zuloaga. 30c, Virgin and Child, by Francisco de Zurburan.

1969, June 15 **Unwmk.**

1404 A381 1c 39x59mm
1405 A381 2c
1406 A381 3c 39½x49mm
1407 A381 4c 39½x43mm
1408 A381 5c 39½x45½mm
1409 A381 13c 38x41½mm
1410 A381 30c 39x45mm

Broadcasting Institute — A382

1969, July 5 **Wmk. 376**

1411 A382 3c shown
1412 A382 13c Hemispheres, tower
1413 A382 1p Waves on graph

Fish A383

1969, July 20 **Unwmk.**

1414 A383 1c Apogon maculatus
1415 A383 2c Bodianus rufus
1416 A383 3c Microspathodon chrysurus
1417 A383 4c Gramma loreto
1418 A383 5c Chromis marginatus
1419 A383 13c Myripristis jacobus
1420 A383 30c Nomeus gronovii, vert.

Natl. Film Industry, 10th Anniv. — A384

1969, Aug. 5 **Wmk. 376**

1421 A384 1c Poster
1422 A384 3c Documentaries
1423 A384 13c Cartoons
1424 A384 30c Entertainers

Napoleon in Milan, by Andrea Appiani — A385

Paintings in the Napoleon Museum, Havana: 2c, Hortensia de Beauharnais, by Francois Gerard. 3c, Napoleon as First Consul, by J.B. Regnault. 4c, Elisa Bonaparte, by Robert Lefevre. 5c, Napoleon Planning Coronation Ceremony, by J.G. Vibert, horiz. 13c, Napoleon as Cuirassier Corporal, by Jean Meissonier. 30c, Napoleon Bonaparte, by LeFevre.

1969, Aug. 20 **Unwmk.**

1425 A385 1c
1426 A385 2c 41½x55mm
1427 A385 3c 45½x56mm
1428 A385 4c 43x62½mm
1429 A385 5c 63x47½mm
1430 A385 13c 43x62½mm
1431 A385 30c 45x59½mm

See Nos. 2448-2453.

Cuba's Victory at the 17th World Amateur Baseball Championships, Santo Domingo — A386

1969, Sept. 11

1432 A386 13c multi

No. 1432 printed se-tenant with inscribed label listing finalists.

Alexander von Humboldt (1769-1859), German Naturalist — A387

1969, Sept. 14

1433 A387 3c Surinam eel
1434 A387 13c Night ape
1435 A387 30c Condors

World Fencing Championships, Havana — A388

Designs: 1c, Ancient Egyptians in combat. 2c, Roman gladiators. 2c, Viking and Norman. 4c, Medieval tournament. 5c, French musketeers. 13c, Japanese samurai. 30c, Mounted Cubans, War of Independence. 50c, Modern fencers.

1969, Oct. 2

1436 A388 1c multi
1437 A388 2c multi
1438 A388 3c multi
1439 A388 4c multi
1440 A388 5c multi
1441 A388 13c multi
1442 A388 30c multi

Souvenir Sheet

Imperf

1443 A388 50c multi

Stamp in No. 1443 has simulated perforations.

Natl. Revolutionary Militia, 10th Anniv. — A389

1969, Oct. 26 **Wmk. 376**

1444 A389 3c multi

Disappearance of Maj. Camilo Cienfuegos, 10th Anniv. — A390

1969, Oct. 28

1445 A390 13c multi

Agriculture — A391

1969, Nov. 2 **Unwmk.**

1446 A391 1c Strawberries, grapes
1447 A391 1c Onions, asparagus
1448 A391 1c Rice
1449 A391 1c Banana
1450 A391 3c Pineapple, vert.
1451 A391 3c Tobacco, vert.
1452 A391 3c Citrus fruits, vert.
1453 A391 3c Coffee, vert.
1454 A391 3c Rabbits, vert.
1455 A391 10c Pigs, vert.
1456 A391 13c Sugar cane
1457 A391 30c Bull

Stamps of the same denomination printed se-tenant in strips.

Sporting Events — A392

1969, Nov. 15

1458 A392 1c 2nd Natl. Games
1459 A392 2c 11th Anniv. Games
1460 A392 3c Barrientos Commemorative, vert.
1461 A392 10c 2nd Olympic Trials, vert.
1462 A392 13c 6th Socialist Bicycle Race, vert.
1463 A392 30c 6th Capablanca Memorial Chess Championships, vert.

Christmas Type of 1961

Flowering plants.

1969, Dec. 1

1464 A248 1c Plumbago capensis
1465 A249 1c Petrea volubilis
1466 A249 1c Clitoria ternatea
1467 A249 1c Duranta repens
1468 A249 1c Ruellia tuberosa
a. Block of 5 + label, Nos. 1464-1468
1469 A248 3c Turnera ulmifolia
1470 A249 3c Thevetia peruviana
1471 A249 3c Hibiscus elatus
1472 A249 3c Allamanda cathartica
1473 A249 3c Cosmos sulphureus
a. Block of 5 + label, Nos. 1469-1473
1474 A248 13c Delonix regia
1475 A249 13c Neriun oleander
1476 A249 13c Cordia sebestena
1477 A249 13c Lochnera rosea
1478 A249 13c Jatropha integerrima
a. Block of 5 + label, Nos. 1474-1478

Christmas 1969. See note after No. 700.

Zapata Swamp Fauna A393

1969, Dec. 15

1479 A393 1c Trelanorhynus variabilis
1480 A393 2c Hyla insulsa
1481 A393 3c Atractosteus tristoechus
1482 A393 4c Capromys nana
1483 A393 5c Crocodylus rhombifer
1484 A393 13c Amazona leucocephala
1485 A393 30c Agelaius phoeniceus assimilis

Nos. 1482, 1484-1485 vert.

Tourism — A394

1970, Jan. 25 **Wmk. 376**

1486 A394 1c Jibacoa Beach
1487 A394 3c Trinidad City
1488 A394 13c Santiago de Cuba
1489 A394 30c Vinales Valley

Medicinal Plants — A395

1970, Feb. 10 **Unwmk.**

1490 A395 1c Guarea guara
1491 A395 3c Ocimum sanctum
1492 A395 10c Canella winterana
1493 A395 13c Bidens pilosa
1494 A395 30c Turnera ulmifolia
1495 A395 50c Picramnia pentandra

11th Central American and Caribbean Games, Panama, Feb. 28-Mar. 14 — A396

1970, Feb. 28 **Wmk. 376**

1496 A396 1c Weight lifting
1497 A396 3c Boxing
1498 A396 10c Gymnastics
1499 A396 13c Running
1500 A396 30c Fencing

Souvenir Sheet

Imperf

1501 A396 50c Baseball

No. 1501 contains one 50x37mm stamp that has simulated perforations.

EXPO '70, Osaka, Japan, Mar. 15-Sept. 13 — A397

1970, Mar. 15

1502 A397 1c Enjoying life
1503 A397 2c Improving on nature, vert.
1504 A397 3c Better living standard
1505 A397 13c Intl. cooperation, vert.
1506 A397 30c Cuban pavilion

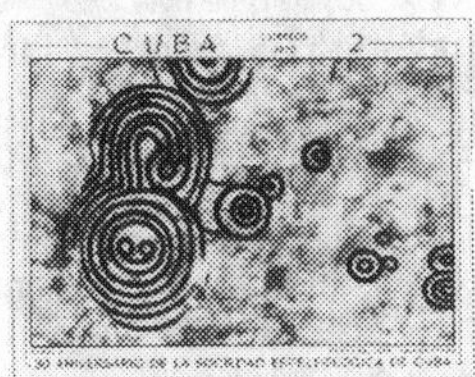

Speleological Soc., 30th Anniv. — A398

Petroglyphs in Cuban caves: 1c, Ambrosio Cave, Varadero Matanzas. 2c, Cave No. 1, Punta del Este, Isle of Pines. 3c, Pichardo Cave, Cubitas Camaguey Mountains. 4c, Ambrosio Cave, diff. 5c, Cave No. 1, diff. 13c, Garcia Ribiou Cave, Havana. 30c, Cave No. 2, Punta del Este.

1970, Mar. 28 Unwmk.

Sizes: 29x45mm (1c, 3c, 4c, 13c)

1507 A398 1c multi
1508 A398 2c shown
1509 A398 3c multi
1510 A398 4c multi
1511 A398 5c multi
1512 A398 13c multi
1513 A398 30c multi

Aviation Pioneers A399

1970, Apr. 10

1514 A399 3c Jose D. Blino
1515 A399 13c Adolfo Teodore

Lenin Birth Centenary — A400

Paintings and quotes: 1c, Lenin in Kazan, by O. Vishniakov. 2c, Young Lenin, by V. Prager. 3c, Second Socialist Party Congress, by Y. Vinagradov. 4c, First Manifesto, by F. Golubkov. 5c, First Day of Soviet Power, by N. Babasiuk. 13c, Lenin in Smolny, by M. Sokolov. 30c, Autumn in Gorky, by A. Varlamov. 50c, Lenin at Gorky, by N. Bashkakov.

1970, Apr. 22

Sizes: 67½x46mm (1c, 4c, 5c)

1516 A400 1c multi
1517 A400 2c shown
1518 A400 3c multi
1519 A400 4c multi
1520 A400 5c multi
1521 A400 13c multi
1522 A400 30c multi

Souvenir Sheet

Imperf

1523 A400 50c multi

No. 1523 contains one 48x46mm stamp that has simulated perforations.

Stamp Day — A401

1970, Apr. 24

1524 A401 13c The Letter, by J. Arche

Size: 30x44mm

1525 A401 30c Portrait of A Cadet, Anonymous

Da Vinci's Anatomical Drawing, Earth, Moon — A402

1970, May 17 Wmk. 376

1526 A402 30c multi

World Telecommunications Day.

Ho Chi Minh (1890-1969), President of North Viet Nam — A403

1970, May 19 Unwmk.

1527 A403 1c Vietnamese fisherman

Size: 32x44mm

1528 A403 3c Two women
1529 A403 3c Plowing field

Size: 33x45mm

1530 A403 3c Teacher, students in air-raid shelter
1531 A403 3c Nine women in paddy

Size: 34x41½mm

1532 A403 3c Camouflaged machine shop

Size: 34x39mm

1533 A403 13c shown

Cuban Cigar Industry A404

1970, July 5

1534 A404 3c Plantation, Eden cigar band
1535 A404 13c Factory, El Mambi band
1536 A404 30c Packing cigars, Lopez Hermanos band

Projected Sugar Production: Over 10 Million Tons — A405

1970, July 26

1537 A405 1c Cane-crushing
1538 A405 2c Sowing and crop dusting
1539 A405 3c Cutting sugar cane
1540 A405 10c Transporting cane
1541 A405 13c Modern cutting machine
1542 A405 30c Intl. Brigade, cane cutters, vert.
1543 A405 1p Sugar warehouse

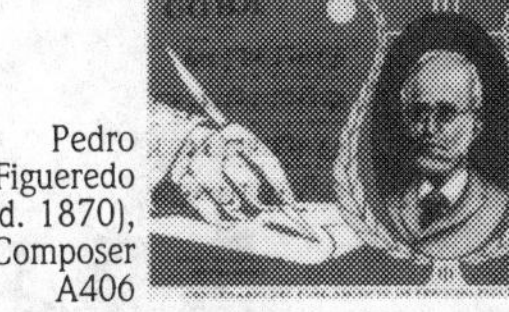

Pedro Figueredo (d. 1870), Composer A406

Versions of the Natl. Anthem.

1970, Aug. 17

1544 A406 3c 1868 Version
1545 A406 20c 1898 Version

Women's Federation, 10th Anniv. — A407

1970, Aug. 23

1546 A407 3c multi

Militia, by Servando C. Moreno — A408

Paintings in the Natl. Museum: 2c, Washerwomen, by Aristides Fernandez. 3c, Puerta del Sol, Madrid, by L. Paret Y Alcazar. 4c, Fishermen's Wives, by Joaquin Sorolla. 5c, Portrait of a Woman, by Thomas de Keyser. 13c, Mrs. Edward Foster, by Sir Thomas Lawrence. 30c, Tropical Gypsy, by Victor M. Garcia.

1970, Aug. 31

1547 A408 1c shown

Size: 45x41mm

1548 A408 2c multi
1549 A408 3c multi

Size: 40x41mm

1550 A408 4c multi

Size: 38x45½mm

1551 A408 5c multi
1552 A408 13c multi
1553 A408 30c multi

See Nos. 1640-1646, 1669-1675, 1773-1779.

Havana Declaration, 10th Anniv. — A409

1970, Sept. 2

1554 A409 3c Jose Marti Square

Committee for the Defense of the Revolution, 10th Anniv. A410

1970, Sept. 28

1555 A410 3c multi

39th Sugar Technician's Assoc. (ATAC) Conference — A411

1970, Oct. 11

1556 A411 30c multi

Wildlife A412

1970, Oct. 20

1557 A412 1c Numida meleagris galeata
1558 A412 2c Dendrocygna arborea
1559 A412 3c Phasianus colchicus torquatus
1560 A412 4c Zenaida macroura macroura
1561 A412 5c Colinus virginianus cubanensis
1562 A412 13c Sus scrofa
1563 A412 30c Odocoileus virginianus

Black-magic Feast, by M. Puente — A413

Afro-Cuban folk paintings: 3c, Hat Dance, by V.P. Landaluze. 10c, Los Hoyos Conga Dance, by Domingo Ravenet. 13c, Climax of the Rumba, by Eduardo Abela.

1970, Nov. 5

Sizes: 36x48½mm (3c, 13c), 44½x44mm (10c)

1564 A413 1c shown
1565 A413 3c multi
1566 A413 10c multi
1567 A413 13c multi

Road Safety Week A414

1970, Nov. 15

1568 A414 3c Zebra, road signs
1569 A414 9c Prudence the Bear

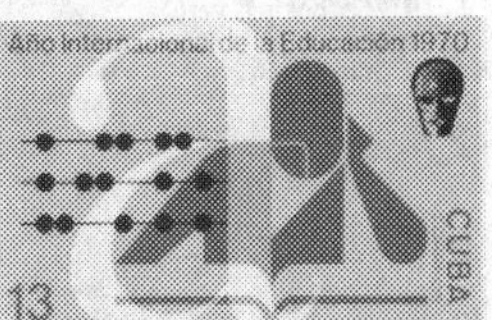

Intl. Education Year — A415

1970, Nov. 20

1570 A415 13c Abacus, "a"
1571 A415 30c Cow, microscope

Christmas Type of 1961

Birds.

1970, Dec. 1

1572 A248 1c Dives atroviolaceus
1573 A249 1c Glaucidium siju siju
1574 A249 1c Todus multicolor
1575 A249 1c Xiphidiopicus percussus percussus
1576 A249 1c Ferminia cerverai
a. Block of 5 + label, Nos. 1572-1576
1577 A248 3c Teretistris fornsi
1578 A249 3c Myadestes elisabeth elisabeth
1579 A249 3c Polioptila lembeyei
1580 A249 3c Vireo gundlachii gundlachii
1581 A249 3c Teretistris fernandinae
a. Block of 5 + label, Nos. 1577-1581
1582 A248 13c Torreornis inexpectata inexpectata
1583 A249 13c Chondrohierax wilsonii
1584 A249 13c Accipiter gundlachi
1585 A249 13c Starnoenas cyanocephala
1586 A249 13c Aratinga euops
a. Block of 5 + label, Nos. 1582-1586

Christmas 1970. See note after No. 700.

Camilo Cienfuegos Military Academy A416

1970, Dec. 2

1587 A416 3c multi

7th Congress of the Intl. Organization of Journalists A417

1971, Jan. 4

1588 A417 13c multi

World Meteorology Day — A418

1971, Feb. 16

Size: 39½x35½mm (3c)

1589 A418 1c Class, weather chart, computer, vert.
1590 A418 3c Weather map
1591 A418 8c Equipment, vert.
1592 A418 30c shown

6th Pan American Games, Cali, Colombia — A419

1971, Feb. 20

1593 A419 1c Emblem, vert.
1594 A419 2c Women's running, vert.
1595 A419 3c Rifle shooting
1596 A419 4c Gymnastics, vert.
1597 A419 5c Boxing, vert.
1598 A419 13c Water polo
1599 A419 30c Baseball

Porcelain and Mosaics in the Metropolitan Museum, Havana — A420

Designs: 1c, Parisian vase, 19th cent. 3c, Mexican bowl, 17th cent. 10c, Parisian vase, diff. 13c, Colosseum, Italian mosaic, 19th cent. 20c, Mexican bowl, 17th cent. 30c, St. Peter's Square, Italian mosaic, 19th cent.

1971, Mar. 11

Sizes: 34½x53mm (1c, 10c), 46x53mm (3c), 42x48mm (20c)

1600 A420 1c multi
1601 A420 3c multi
1602 A420 10c multi
1603 A420 13c shown
1604 A420 20c multi
1605 A420 30c multi

See Nos. 1699-1705.

Natl. Child Centers, 10th Anniv. — A421

1971, Apr. 10

1606 A421 3c multi

Manned Space Flight 10th Anniv. — A422

Cosmonauts in training.

1971, Apr. 12

1607 A422 1c multi
1608 A422 2c multi, diff.
1609 A422 3c multi, diff.
1610 A422 4c multi, diff.
1611 A422 5c multi, diff.
1612 A422 13c multi, diff.
1613 A422 30c multi, diff.

Souvenir Sheet

Imperf

1614 A422 50c multi

Stamp in #1614 has simulated perf.

Bay of Pigs Invasion, 10th Anniv. A423

1971, Apr. 17

1615 A423 13c multi

Stamp Day — A424

Packets: 13c, Jeune Richard attacking the Windsor Castle, 1807. 30c, Orinoco.

1971, Apr. 24

1616 A424 13c multi
1617 A424 30c multi

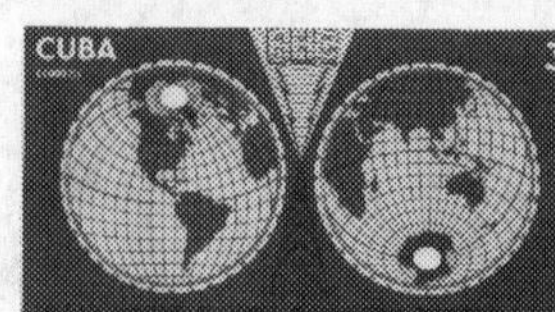

Cuban Intl. Broadcast Service, 10th Anniv. — A425

1971, May 1 **Wmk. 376**

1618 A425 3c multi
1619 A425 50c multi

Orchids A426

1971, May 15

1620 A426 1c Cattleya skinnerii
1621 A426 2c Vanda hibrida
1622 A426 3c Cypripedium collossum
1623 A426 4c Cypripedium gloucophyllum
1624 A426 5c Vanda tricolor
1625 A426 13c Cypripedium mowgh
1626 A426 30c Cypripedium solum

See Nos. 1677-1683 and 1780-1786.

Enrique Loynaz del Castillo (b. 1861), Composer — A427

1971, June 5 **Wmk. 376**

1627 A427 3c Portrait, Invasion Hymn

Bee Keeping — A428

1971, June 20 **Unwmk.**

1628 A428 1c Egg, larvae, pupa
1629 A428 3c Worker
1630 A428 9c Drone
1631 A428 13c Defense of hive
1632 A428 30c Queen

Children's Drawings — A429

1971, Aug. 30

Size: 45x39mm

1633 A429 1c Sailboat
1634 A429 3c The Little Train

Sizes: 45½x35½mm (9c, 13c), 47x37½mm (10c)

1635 A429 9c Sugar Cane Cutter
1636 A429 10c Return of the Fishermen
1637 A429 13c The Zoo

Size: 47x42mm

1638 A429 20c House and Garden

Size: 31½x50mm

1639 A429 30c Landscape

Art Type of 1970

Paintings in the Natl. Museum: 1c, St. Catherine of Alexandria, by F. Zurburan. 2c, The Cart, by Federico Americo. 3c, St. Christopher and Child, by J. Bassano. 4c, Little Devil, by Rene Portocarrero. 5c, Portrait of a Woman, by Nicolas Maes. 13c, Phoenix, by Raul Martinez. 30c, Sir William Pitt, by Thomas Gainsborough.

1971, Sept. 20

1640 A408 1c 31x55mm
1641 A408 2c 48x37mm
1642 A408 3c 31x55mm
1643 A408 4c 37x48mm
1644 A408 5c 37x48mm
1645 A408 13c 39x48½mm
1646 A408 30c 39x48½mm

Sport Fishing — A431

1971, Oct. 30

1647 A431 1c Albula vulpes
1648 A431 2c Seriola species
1649 A431 3c Micropterus salmoides
1650 A431 4c Coryphaena hippurus
1651 A431 5c Megalops atlantica
1652 A431 13c Acanthocybium solandri
1653 A431 30c Makaira ampla

19th World Amateur Baseball Championships — A432

1971, Nov. 22 **Wmk. 376**

1654 A432 3c shown
1655 A432 1p Globe as baseball

Execution of Medical Students, Cent. A433

Paintings: 3c, Dr. Fermin Valdez Dominguez, anonymous. 13c, Execution of the Medical Students, by M. Mesa. 30c, Capt. Federico Capdevila, anonymous.

1971, Nov. 27 **Unwmk.**

Size: 61 1/2x46mm (13c)

1656 A433 3c multi
1657 A433 13c multi
1658 A433 30c multi

Spindalis Zena Pretrei A434

Birds: 1c, Falco sparverius sparverioides vigors. 2c, Glaucidium siju siju. 3c, Priotelus temnurus temnurus. 4c, Saurothera merlini merlini. 5c, Nesoceleus fernandinae. 30c, Mimocichla plumbea rubripes. 50c, Chlorostilbon ricordii ricordii and Archilochus colubris. Nos. 1659-1663 vert.

1971, Dec. 10

1659 A434 1c multi
1660 A434 2c multi
1661 A434 3c multi
1662 A434 4c multi
1663 A434 5c multi
1664 A434 13c shown
1665 A434 30c multi

Size: 55 1/2x29mm

1666 A434 50c multi

Death centenary of Ramon de la Sagra, naturalist.

Cuba's Victory at the World Amateur Baseball Championships — A435

1971, Dec. 8 **Wmk. 376**

1667 A435 13c multi

UNICEF, 25th Anniv. — A436

1971, Dec. 11

1668 A436 13c multi

Art Type of 1970

Paintings in the Natl. Museum: 1c, Arrival of an Ambassador, by Vittore Carpaccio. 2c, Senora Malpica, by G. Collazo. 3c, La Chorrera Tower, by Esteban Chartrand. 4c, Creole Landscape, by Carlos Enriquez. 5c, Sir William Lemon, by George Romney. 13c, Landscape, by Henry Cleenewerk. 30c, Valencia Beach, by Joaquin Sorolla y Bastida.

1972, Jan. 25 **Unwmk.**

1669 A408 1c 50x33mm
1670 A408 2c 27 1/2x52mm
1671 A408 3c 50x33mm
1672 A408 4c 35x43mm
1673 A408 5c 35x43mm
1674 A408 13c 43x33mm
1675 A408 30c 43x33mm

Academy of Sciences, 10th Anniv. — A437

1972, Feb. 20 **Wmk. 376**

1676 A437 13c Capitol Type of 1929

Orchid Type of 1971

1972, Feb. 25 **Unwmk.**

1677 A426 1c Brasso cattleya sindorossiana
1678 A426 2c Cypripedium doraeus
1679 A426 3c Cypripedium exul
1680 A426 4c Cypripedium rosy dawn
1681 A426 5c Cypripedium champolliom
1682 A426 13c Cypripedium bucolique
1683 A426 30c Cypripedium sullanum

Eduardo Agramonte (1849-1872), Physicist A438

1972, Mar. 8

1684 A438 3c Portrait by F. Martinez

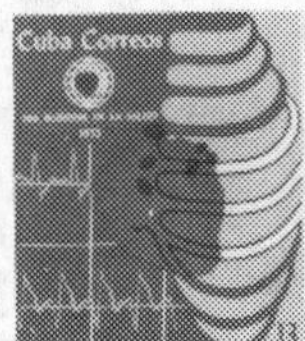

World Health Day — A439

1972, Apr. 7 **Wmk. 376**

1685 A439 13c multi

Soviet Space Program — A440

1972, Apr. 12 **Unwmk.**

1686 A440 1c Sputnik 1
1687 A440 2c Vostok 1
1688 A440 3c Valentina Tereshkova
1689 A440 4c Alexei Leonov
1690 A440 5c Lunokhod 1, moon vehicle
1691 A440 13c Linking Soyuz capsules
1692 A440 30c Victims of Soyuz 11 accident

Stamp Day — A441

Designs: 13c, Postmaster-Gen. Vicente Mora Pera, by Ramon Loy. 30c, Soldier's Letter, Cuba to Venezuela, 1897.

1972, Apr. 24

1693 A441 13c shown

Size: 48x39mm

1694 A441 30c multi

Labor Day — A442

Jose Marti, Ho Chi Minh — A443

3rd Conference Against War in Indo-China, May 19 — A444

1972, May 1 **Wmk. 376**

1695 A442 3c multi

1972, May 19

1696 A443 3c shown
1697 A444 13c shown
1698 A443 30c Roses, conference emblem

Metropolitan Museum Type of 1971

Portraits: 1c, Salvador del Muro, by J. Del Rio. 2c, Luis de las Casas, by Del Rio. 3c, Cristopher Columbus, anonymous. 4c, Tomas Gamba, by V. Escobar. 5c, Maria Galarraga, by Escobar. 13c, Isabel II, by Federico Madrazo. 30c, Carlos II, by Miguel Melero.

1972, May 25 **Unwmk.**

Size: 34x43 1/2mm

1699 A420 1c multi
1700 A420 2c multi
1701 A420 3c multi
1702 A420 4c multi
1703 A420 5c multi

Size: 34x51 1/2mm

1704 A420 13c multi
1705 A420 30c multi

Children's Songs Competition, Natl. Library A445

1972, June 5 **Wmk. 376**

1706 A445 3c multi

Thoroughbred Horses — A446

1972, June 30 **Unwmk.**

1707 A446 1c Tarpan
1708 A446 2c Kertag
1709 A446 3c Creole
1710 A446 4c Andalusian
1711 A446 5c Arabian
1712 A446 13c Quarter horse
1713 A446 30c Pursang

Frank Pais (d. 1957), Educator, Revolutionary — A447

1972, July 26 **Wmk. 376**

1714 A447 13c blk & red

1972 Summer Olympics, Munich, Aug. 26-Sept. 10 — A448

1972, Aug. 26 **Unwmk.**

1715 A448 1c Athlete, emblems, vert.
1716 A448 2c "M," boxing
1717 A448 3c "U," weight lifting
1718 A448 4c "N," fencing
1719 A448 5c "I," rifle shooting
1720 A448 13c "C," running
1721 A448 30c "H," basketball

Souvenir Sheet

Imperf

1722 A448 50c Gymnastics

Stamp in No. 1722 has simulated perforations.

Intl. Hydrological Decade — A449

Landscapes: 1c, Tree Trunks, by Domingo Ramos. 3c, Cyclone, by Tiburcio Lorenzo. 8c, Vinales, by Ramos. 30c, Forest and Brook, by Antonio R. Morey, vert.

1972, Sept. 20

1723 A449 1c multi
1724 A449 3c multi
1725 A449 8c multi
1726 A449 30c multi

Butterflies from the Gundlach Collection — A450

1972, Sept. 25

1727 A450 1c Papilio thoas oviedo
1728 A450 2c Papilio devilliers
1729 A450 3c Papilio polixenes polixenes
1730 A450 4c Papilio androgeus epidaurus
1731 A450 5c Papilio cayguanabus
1732 A450 13c Papilio andraemon hernandezi
1733 A450 30c Papilio celadon

A451

Miguel de Cervantes Saavedra (1547-1616), Spanish Author — A452

Paintings by A. Fernandez: 3c, In La Mancha, vert. 13c, Battle with Wine Skins. 30c, Don Quixote de La Mancha, vert. 50c, Scene from Don Quixote, by Jose Moreno Carbonero.

1972, Sept. 29
Size: 34½x46mm (3c, 30c)

1734 A451 3c multi
1735 A451 13c shown
1736 A451 30c multi

Souvenir Sheet
Perf. 12½ on 3 Sides

1737 A452 50c shown

Guerrilla Day, 5th Anniv. A453

1972, Oct. 8

1738 A453 3c Ernesto "Che" Guevara
1739 A453 13c Tamara "Tania" Bunke
1740 A453 30c Guido "Inti" Peredo

Traditional Musical Instruments A454

1972, Oct. 25

1741 A454 3c Abwe (rattles)
1742 A454 13c Bonko enchemiya (drum)
1743 A454 30c Iya (drum)

MATEX '72, 3rd Natl. Philatelic Exhibition, Matanzas — A455

1972, Nov. 18 **Wmk. 376**

1744 A455 13c No. 467
1745 A455 30c No. C49

Nos. 1744-1745 printed se-tenant with insribed labels picturing Type A232, emblem of the Cuban Philatelic Federation.

Historic Ships A456

1972, Nov. 30 **Unwmk.**

1746 A456 1c Viking long boat, 6th-9th cent.
1747 A456 2c Caravel, 15th cent., vert.
1748 A456 3c Galleass, 16th cent.
1749 A456 4c Galleon, 17th cent., vert.
1750 A456 5c Clipper, 19th cent.
1751 A456 13c Steam packet, 19th cent.

Size: 52½x29mm.

1752 A456 30c Atomic icebreaker Lenin, 20th cent.

UNESCO Save Venice Campaign — A457

1972, Dec. 8

1753 A457 3c Lion of St. Mark
1754 A457 13c Bridge of Sighs, vert.
1755 A457 30c St. Mark's Cathedral

Cuba, World Amateur Baseball Champion in 1972 — A458

Sport Events, 1972 — A459

1972, Dec. 15

1756 A458 3c Umpire

1972, Dec. 22

1757 A459 1c shown
1758 A458 2c Pole vault
1759 A458 3c like No. 1756
1760 A458 4c Wrestling
1761 A458 5c Fencing
1762 A458 13c Boxing
1763 A458 30c Marlin

Barrientos Memorial Athletics Championships, 11th Amateur Baseball Championships, Cerro Pelado Intl. Tournament, Central American and Caribbean Fencing Tournament, Giraldo Cordova Tournament, Ernest Hemingway Natl. Fishing Contest.

No. 1759 inscribed "XI serie nacional de beisbol aficionado."

Medals Won by Cubans at the 1972 Summer Olympics, Munich A460

Designs: 1c, Bronze medal, Women's 100-meter. 2c, Bronze, women's relay. 3c, Gold, 54kg boxing. 4c, Silver, 81kg boxing. 5c, Bronze, 51kg boxing. 13c, Gold, 87kg boxing. 30c, Gold, silver cup, heavyweight boxing. 50c, Bronze medal, basketball.

1973, Jan. 28

1764 A460 1c multi
1765 A460 2c multi
1766 A460 3c multi
1767 A460 4c multi
1768 A460 5c multi
1769 A460 13c multi
1770 A460 30c multi

Souvenir Sheet
Imperf

1771 A460 50c multi

Stamp in No. 1771 has simulated perforations.

A461 A462

Portrait by A.M. Esquivel.

1973, Feb. 10

1772 A461 13c multi

Gertrudis Gomez de Avellaneda (1814-1873), poet.

Art Type of 1970

Paintings in the Natl. Museum: 1c, Bathers in the Lagoon, by C. Enriquez. 2c, Still-life, by W.C. Heda. 3c, Gallantry, by P. Landaluze. 4c, Return in the Late Afternoon, by C. Troyon. 5c, Elizabetta Mascagni, by F.X. Fabre. 13c, The Picador, by De Lucas Padilla, horiz. 30c, In the Garden, by Arburu Morell.

1973, Feb. 28
Sizes: 36x46mm, 46x36mm

1773 A408 1c multi
1774 A408 2c multi
1775 A408 3c multi
1776 A408 4c multi
1777 A408 5c multi
1778 A408 13c multi
1779 A408 30c multi

Orchid Type of 1971

1973, Mar. 26

1780 A426 1c Dendrobium hybrid
1781 A426 2c Cypripedium exul
1782 A426 3c Vanda miss. joaquin rose marie
1783 A426 4c Phalaenopsis schilleriana
1784 A426 5c Vanda gilbert tribulet
1785 A426 13c Dendrobium hybrid, diff.
1786 A426 30c Arachnis catherine

1973, Apr. 7 **Wmk. 376**

1787 A462 10c multi, *buff*

World Health Day. World Health Organization, 25th anniv.

Anti-Polio Campaign — A463

1973, Apr. 9 **Unwmk.**

1788 A463 3c multi

Soviet Space Program A464

1973, Apr. 12

1789 A464 1c Soyuz rocket launch, vert.
1790 A464 2c Luna 1, Moon
1791 A464 3c Luna 16 taking-off from Moon, vert.
1792 A464 4c Venus 7
1793 A464 5c Molnia 1, vert.
1794 A464 13c Mars 3
1795 A464 30c Radar observation ship, Yuri Gagarin

Stamp Day A465

Postmarks: 13c, Santiago de Cuba, 1760. 30c, Havana, 1760.

1973, Apr. 24

1796 A465 13c multi
1797 A465 30c multi

See Nos. 1888-1891.

Portrait by A. Espinosa — A466

1973, May 11

1798 A466 13c multi

Maj.-Gen. Ignacio Agramonte (1841-1873).

Birthplace, Torun, and Inventions — A467

Copernicus Monument, Warsaw — A468

1973, May 25

1799 A467 3c shown
1800 A467 13c Copernicus, spacecraft
1801 A467 30c Manuscript, Frombork Tower

Souvenir Sheet
Perf. 12½ on 3 Sides

1802 A468 50c shown

500th anniversary of the birth of Nicolaus Copernicus (1473-1543), Polish astronomer.

Improvement of School Education — A469

1973, June 12 **Wmk. 376**

1803 A469 13c multi

Cattle — A470

1973, June 28 **Unwmk.**
1804 A470 1c Jersey
1805 A470 2c Charolaise
1806 A470 3c Creole
1807 A470 4c Swiss
1808 A470 5c Holstein
1809 A470 13c Santa gertrudis
1810 A470 30c Brahman

A471

A472

1973, July 10 **Wmk. 376**
1811 A471 13c multi

10th Communist Festival of Youths and Students, East Berlin.

1973, July 26 **Unwmk.**
1812 A472 3c Siboney Farm, Santiago de Cuba
1813 A472 13c Moncada Barracks
1814 A472 30c Revolution Plaza, Havana

20th anniv. of the Revolution.

10th Anniv. of the Revolutionary Navy A473

1973, Aug. 3 **Wmk. 376**
1815 A473 3c Midshipman, missile frigate

Interior, by Manuel Vicens A474

Paintings in the Natl. Museum: 1c, Amalia of Saxony, by J.K. Rossler. 3c, Margarita of Austria, by J. Pantoja de la Cruz. 4c, City Hall Official, anonymous. 5c, View of Santiago de Cuba, by Hernandez Giro. 12c, The Catalan, by J.J. Tejada. 30c, Alley in Guayo, by Tejada.

1973, Aug. 30 **Unwmk.**
Sizes: 26½x41mm (1c, 3c), 28½x39mm (4c, 13c, 30c)
1816 A474 1c multi
1817 A474 2c multi
1818 A474 3c multi
1819 A474 4c multi
1820 A474 5c multi
1821 A474 13c multi
1822 A474 30c multi

WMO Emblem, Paintings by J. Madrazo A475

1973, Sept. 4
1823 A475 8c Spring
1824 A475 8c Summer
1825 A475 8c Fall
1826 A475 8c Winter

World Meteorogical Organization, cent. Nos. 1823-1826 printed se-tenant in strips of 4; frame reversed on 2nd and 4th stamp in strip.

A476

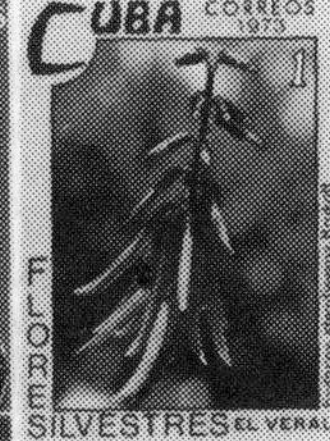

A477

27th World and 1st Pan American Weight Lifting Championships: Various weightlifting positions.

1973, Sept. 12
1827 A476 1c shown
1828 A476 2c multi, diff.
1829 A476 3c multi, diff.
1830 A476 4c multi, diff.
1831 A476 5c multi, diff.
1832 A476 13c multi, diff.
1833 A476 30c multi, diff.

1973, Sept. 28

Flowering plants.

1834 A477 1c Erythrina standleyana
1835 A477 2c Lantana camara
1836 A477 3c Canavalia maritima
1837 A477 4c Dichromena colorata
1838 A477 5c Borrichia arborescens
1839 A477 13c Anguria pedata
1840 A477 30c Cordia sebestena

8th World Trade Union Congress, Varna, Bulgaria A478

1973, Oct. 5 **Wmk. 376**
1841 A478 13c multi

Cuban Natl. Ballet, 25th Anniv. — A479

Sea Shells — A480

1973, Oct. 28 **Unwmk.**
1842 A479 13c gold & brt ultra

1973, Oct. 29
1843 A480 1c Liguus fasciatus fasciatus
1844 A480 2c Liguus fasciatus guitarti
1845 A480 3c Liguus fasciatus whartoni
1846 A480 4c Liguus fasciatus angelae
1847 A480 5c Liguus fasciatus trinidadense
1848 A480 13c Liguus blainianus
1849 A480 30c Liguus vittatus

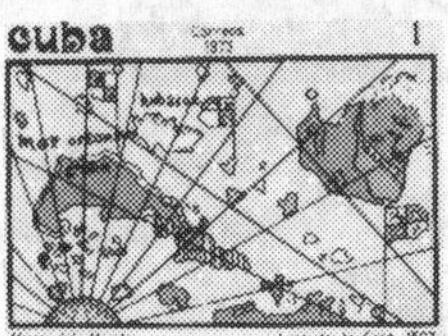

Maps of Cuba A481

1973, Oct. 29
1850 A481 1c Juan de la Cosa, 1502
1851 A481 3c Ortelius, 1572
1852 A481 13c Bellini, 1762
1853 A481 40c 1973

15th Anniversary of the Revolution — A482

1974, Jan. 2
1854 A482 1c No. 625
1855 A482 3c No. 626
1856 A482 13c No. C200
1857 A482 40c No. C201

Woman, by F. Ponce de Leon — A483

Amilcar Cabral — A484

Portraits in the Camaguey Museum: 3c, Mexican Girls, by J. Arche. 8c, Young Woman, by A. Menocal. 10c, Mulatto Woman Drinking from Coconut, by L. Romanach. 13c, Head of an Old Man, by J. Arburu.

1974, Jan. 10
1858 A483 1c multi
1859 A483 3c multi
1860 A483 8c multi
1861 A483 10c multi
1862 A483 13c multi

1974, Jan. 20
1863 A484 13c multi

Amilcar Cabral, Guinea-Bissau freedom fighter, 1st death anniv.

Lenin, by I.V. Kosmin — A485

12th Central American and Caribbean Games, Santo Domingo — A486

1974, Jan. 21
1864 A485 30c multi

50th death anniv. of Lenin.

1974, Feb. 8
1865 A486 1c Emblem
1866 A486 2c Javelin
1867 A486 3c Boxing
1868 A486 4c Baseball, horiz.
1869 A486 13c Basketball, horiz.
1870 A486 30c Volleyball, horiz.

Portrait by F. Martinez — A487

Portrait of a Man, by J.B. Vermay — A488

1974, Feb. 27
1871 A487 13c multi

Carlos M. de Cespedes (d. 1874), patriot.

1974, Mar. 7

Paintings in the Natl. Museum: 2c, The Wet Nurse, by C.A. Van Loo. 3c, Cattle in River, by R. Morey. 4c, Village, by Morey. 13c, Faun and Bacchus, by Rubens. 30c, Young Woman Playing Cards, by R. Madrazo.

1872 A488 1c shown
1873 A488 2c multi
1874 A488 3c multi
1875 A488 4c multi
1876 A488 13c multi
1877 A488 30c multi

Council for Mutual Economic Assistance (COMECON), 25th Anniv. — A489

1974, Mar. 15
1878 A489 30c Comecon building, Moscow

Visit of Leonid I. Brezhnev to Cuba, Jan. 28-Feb. 3 — A490

1974, Mar. 28
1879 A490 13c Jose Marti, Lenin, flags
1880 A490 30c Brezhnev, Fidel Castro

Science Fiction A491

Paintings by A. Sokolov.

1974, Apr. 12
1881 A491 1c Martian Crater
1882 A491 2c Fiery Labyrinth
1883 A491 3c Amber Wave
1884 A491 4c Flight Through Space
1885 A491 13c Planet in Nebula
1886 A491 30c World of Two Suns

Cosmonauts Day.

UPU, Cent. A492

1974, Apr. 15
1887 A492 30c Letter, 1874

Stamp Day Type of 1973

Postmarks.

1974, Apr. 24

1888 A465 1c Havana
1889 A465 3c Matanzas
1890 A465 13c Trinidad
1891 A465 20c Guana Vacoa

18th Sports Congress of Friendly Armies — A493

1974, May 5 **Wmk. 376**

1892 A493 3c multi

Felipe Poey (1799-1891), Naturalist — A494

Designs: 1c, 4c, Butterflies. 2c, 13c, Sea shells. 3c, 30c, 50c, Fish.

1974, May 26 ***Perf. 12½x12***

1893 A494 1c Eumaeus atala atala
1894 A494 2c Pineria terebra
1895 A494 3c Chaetodon sedentarius
1896 A494 4c Eurema dina dina
1897 A494 13c Hemitrochus fuscolabiata
1898 A494 30c Eupomacentrus partitus

Souvenir Sheet

Imperf

1899 A494 50c Apogon binotatus

Stamp in #1899 has simulated perforations.

Havana Philharmonic Orchestra, 50th Anniv. — A495

Designs: 1c, Antonio Mompo and cello. 3c, Cesar Perez Sentenat and piano. 5c, Pedro Mercado and trumpet. 10c, Pedro Sanjuan and Havana Philharmonic emblem. 13c, Roberto Ondina and flute.

1974, June 8 ***Perf. 12½***

1900 A495 1c multi
1901 A495 3c multi
1902 A495 5c multi
1903 A495 10c multi
1904 A495 13c multi

Garden Flowers — A496

1974, June 12

1905 A496 1c Heliconia humilis
1906 A496 2c Anthurium andraeanum
1907 A496 3c Canna generalis
1908 A496 4c Alpinia purpurata
1909 A496 13c Gladiolus grandiflorus
1910 A496 30c Amomum capitatum

A497

A498

World Amateur Boxing Championships: Emblem and various boxers.

Perf. 12x12½

1974, Aug. 24 **Litho.** **Unwmk.**

1911 A497 1c multi
1912 A497 3c multi
1913 A497 13c multi

1974, Aug. 28 ***Perf. 13***

Extinct birds.

1914 A498 1c Dodo
1915 A498 3c Ara de Cuba (parrot)
1916 A498 8c Passenger pigeon
1917 A498 10c Moa
1918 A498 13c Great auk

Pres. Salvador Allende of Chile (d. 1973) A499

1974, Sept. 11

1919 A499 13c multi

Wildflowers A500

Model Aircraft A501

1974, Sept. 14 ***Perf. 13x12½***

1920 A500 1c Suriana maritima
1921 A500 3c Cassia ligustrina
1922 A500 8c Flaveria linearis
1923 A500 10c Stachytarpheta jamaicensis
1924 A500 13c Bacopa monnieri

1974, Sept. 22 ***Perf. 12½***

1925 A501 1c shown
1926 A501 3c Sky diving
1927 A501 8c Glider
1928 A501 10c Crop dusting
1929 A501 13c Commercial aviation

Civil Aeronautic Institute, 10th anniv. Nos. 1927-1929 horiz.

History of Cuban Baseball A502

1974, Oct. 3 ***Perf. 13***

1930 A502 1c Indians playing ball
1931 A502 3c 1st Official game, 1874
1932 A502 8c Emilio Sabourin
1933 A502 10c Umpire, players, 1974
1934 A502 13c Latin-American Stadium, Havana

Nos. 1930-1932 vert.

Mambi 10c Stamp (Revolutionary Junta Issue), Cent. — A503

1974, Oct. 10

1935 A503 13c multi

16th Conference of Customs Organizations of Socialist Countries — A504

1974, Oct. 15

1936 A504 30c Comecon Building, Moscow

Disappearance of Major Camilo Cienfuegos, 15th Anniv. — A505

Wmk. 376

1974, Oct. 28 **Litho.** ***Perf. 13***

1937 A505 3c multi

8th World Mining Conference — A506

1974, Nov. 3

1938 A506 13c multi

Petroleum Institute, 15th Anniv. A507

1974, Nov. 20

1939 A507 3c multi

Intersputnik Earth Station Opening — A508

1974, Nov. 30 **Unwmk.**

1940 A508 3c shown
1941 A508 13c Satellite, satellite dish
1942 A508 1p Satellite, flags

Philatelic Federation, 10th Anniv. A509

1974, Nov. 30 ***Perf. 12½x13***

1943 A509 30c multi

Souvenir Sheet

Mercury — A510

1974, Dec. 6 ***Imperf.***

1944 A510 50c multi

4th Natl. Phil. Exhib., Havana.

1st World Peace Congress, 25th Anniv. — A511

1974, Dec. 16 **Wmk. 376** ***Perf. 13***

1945 A511 30c *F. Joliot-Curie,* by Picasso

Ruben Martinez Villena (b. 1899), Revolutionary — A512

1974, Dec. 20 **Unwmk.**

1946 A512 3c red org & yel

Souvenir Sheet

Cuban Victories, 1st Amateur Boxing Championships — A513

1975, Jan. 6 **Litho.** ***Imperf.***

1947 A513 50c Trophy

The World, by Marcelo Pogolotti A514

Paintings in the Natl. Museum: 2c, *The Silk-Cotton Tree,* by Henry Cleenewerk. 3c, *Landscape,* by Guillermo Collazo. 5c, *Still-life,* by Francisco

Peralta. 13c, *Maria Wilson,* by Federico Martinez, vert. 30c, *The Couple,* by Mariano Fortuny.

1975, Jan. 20 *Perf. 13*
1948 A514 1c multi
1949 A514 2c multi
1950 A514 3c multi
1951 A514 5c multi
1952 A514 13c multi
1953 A514 30c multi

Intl. Women's Year A515

1975, Feb. 6
1954 A515 13c multi

Fishing Industry — A516

Various fish and fishing vessels.

1975, Feb. 22
1955 A516 1c Long-finned tuna
1956 A516 2c Tuna
1957 A516 3c Mediterranean grouper
1958 A516 8c Hake
1959 A516 13c Prawn
1960 A516 30c Lobster

Minerals — A517

1975, Mar. 15 Litho. *Perf. 13x12½*
1961 A517 3c Nickel
1962 A517 13c Copper
1963 A517 30c Chromium

Cosmonaut's Day — A518

Perf. 13x12½, 12½x13
1975, Apr. 12
1964 A518 1c Cosmodrome
1965 A518 2c Probe, vert.
1966 A518 3c Eclipse
1967 A518 5c Threshold to Space
1968 A518 13c Mean Moon of Mars
1969 A518 30c Cosmonaut's view of Earth

The future of space.

Stamp Day A519

Various covers.

1975, Apr. 24 *Perf. 13*
1970 A519 3c multi
1971 A519 13c multi
1972 A519 30c multi

Victory Over Fascism, 30th Anniv. A520

Design: Raising red flag over Reichstag, Berlin.

1975, May 9 *Perf. 13x12½*
1973 A520 30c multi

A521

Works in the Decorative Art Museum — A522

Designs: 1c, Sevres porcelain vase, vert. 2c, Meissen porcelain statue *Shepherdess and Dancers,* vert. 3c, Chinese porcelain dish *Lady with Parasol.* 5c, Chinese screen detail *The Phoenix,* vert. 13c, *Allegory of Music,* by Francois Boucher (1703-70), vert. 30c, *Portrait of a Lady,* by L. Tocque, vert. 50c, *The Swing,* by Hubert Robert (1733-1808).

Perf. 12½x13, 13x12½
1975, May 10
1974 A521 1c multi
1975 A521 2c multi
1976 A521 3c shown
1977 A521 5c multi
1978 A521 13c multi
1979 A521 30c multi

Souvenir Sheet

Perf. 13x12½ on 3 Sides

1980 A522 50c shown

No. 1980 contains one 25x39mm stamp.

Intl. Children's Day A523

Wmk. 376

1975, May 31 Litho. *Perf. 13*
1981 A523 3c multi

Indigenous Birds — A524

1975, June 18 **Unwmk.**
1982 A524 1c *Vireo gundlachi*
1983 A524 2c *Gymnoglaux lawrenci*
1984 A524 3c *Aratingo eoups*
1985 A524 5c *Staroenas cyanocephala*
1986 A524 13c *Chondrohierax wilsoni*
1987 A524 30c *Cyanolimnas cerverai*

See #2121-2125, 2180-2182, C276-C276.

Scientific Investigation Center, 10th Anniv. — A525

1975, July 1 *Perf. 12½*
1988 A525 13c multi

Irrigation and Drainage Commission, 25th Anniv. — A526

1975, Aug. 2 *Perf. 13*
1989 A526 13c multi

Afforestation A527

1975, Aug. 20
1990 A527 1c *Cedrela mexicana*
1991 A527 3c *Swietenia mahagoni*
1992 A527 5c *Calophyllum brasiliense*
1993 A527 13c *Hibiscus tiliaceus*
1994 A527 30c *Pinus caribaea*

Cuban Women's Federation, 15th Anniv. — A528

1975, Aug. 23
1995 A528 3c multi

Intl. Conference on the Independence of Puerto Rico — A529

1975, Sept. 5 **Litho.**
1996 A529 13c multi

A530

A531

7th Pan American Games, Mexico: Aztec calendar stone and various athletes.

1975, Sept. 20 *Perf. 12½x13*
1997 A530 1c Baseball
1998 A530 3c Boxing
1999 A530 5c Basketball
2000 A530 13c High jump
2001 A530 30c Weight lifting

Souvenir Sheet

Imperf

2002 A530 50c Stone, emblem

1975, Sept. 28 *Perf. 12½x13*
2003 A531 3c multi

Revolutionary Defense Committees (CDR), 15th anniv.

Friendship Among the Peoples Institute, 15th Anniv. A532

1975, Oct. 8 *Perf. 12½x13*
2004 A532 3c multi

Natl. Bank, 25th Anniv. A533

Designs: 1-peso coins and banknotes identified by serial numbers.

1975, Oct. 13 *Perf. 13x12½*
2005 A533 13c Coin, 1915
2006 A533 13c C882736A, 1934
2007 A533 13c A000387A, 1946
2008 A533 13c 933906, 1964
2009 A533 13c K000000, 1976
a. Strip of 5, Nos. 2005-2009

Locomotives — A534

1975, Oct. 28 Unwmk. *Perf. 12½*
2010 A534 1c *La Junta,* 1837
2011 A534 3c Steam engine 2-8-0 *No. 12*
2012 A534 5c Diesel TEM 4 *No. 51010*

2013 A534 13c Diesel DVM 9 *1-7 55*
2014 A534 30c Diesel M 62K *No. 61601*

Railway history.

Development of the Textile Industry — A535

1975, Nov. 10 ***Perf. 13x12½***
2015 A535 13c Bobbins, flag, loom operator

Veterinary Medicine A536

Parasites and host species.

1975, Nov. 25 **Litho.** ***Perf. 13***
2016 A536 1c *Haemonchus,* lamb
2017 A536 2c *Ancylostoma caninum,* dog
2018 A536 3c *Dispharynx nasuta,* rooster
2019 A536 5c *Gasterophilus intestinalis,* horse
2020 A536 13c *Ascaris lumbricoides,* pig
2021 A536 30c *Boophilus microplus,* bull

Manuel Ascunce Domenech Educational Detachment A537

1975, Nov. 27 **Litho.**
2022 A537 3c multi

Development of Agriculture and Animal Husbandry — A538

1975, Dec. 15 **Litho.** ***Perf. 13x12½***
2023 A538 13c Irrigation

1st Communist Party Congress — A539

Perf. 12½x13, 13x12½
1975, Dec. 17
2024 A539 3c "1," revolutionaries, vert.
2025 A539 13c shown
2026 A539 30c Party leaders

8th Latin-American Obstetrics and Gynecology Congress — A540

1976, Jan. 24 ***Perf. 13***
2027 A540 3c multi

Paintings in Natl. Museums A541

Designs: 1c, *Seated Woman,* by Victor Manuel, vert. 2c, *Garden,* by Santiago Rusinol. 3c, *Guadalquivir River,* by Manuel Barron y Carrillo. 5c, *Self-portrait,* by Jan Havicksz Steen, vert. 13c, *Portrait of a Woman,* by Louis Michel Van Loo, vert. 30c, *La Chula,* by Jose Arburu Morell, vert.

1976, Jan. 30 ***Perf. 13, 12½ (3c, 30c)***
Sizes: 29x40mm (1c, 5c, 13c), 40x29mm (2c), 44x27mm (3c), 27x44mm (30c)
2028 A541 1c multi
2029 A541 2c multi
2030 A541 3c multi
2031 A541 5c multi
2032 A541 13c multi
2033 A541 30c multi

10th Cong. of Ministers from Socialist Communications Organizations, Feb. 12, Havana — A542

1976, Feb. 12 **Litho.** ***Perf. 13***
2034 A542 13c multi

Hunting Dogs A543

1976, Feb. 20
2035 A543 1c American foxhound
2036 A543 2c Labrador retriever
2037 A543 3c Borzoi
2038 A543 5c Irish setter
2039 A543 13c Pointer
2040 A543 30c Cocker spaniel

Socialist Constitution — A544

1976, Feb. 24 ***Perf. 12½***
2041 A544 13c Natl. flag, arms, anthem

Chess Champions — A545

Designs: 1c, Ruy Lopez Segura and chessboard. 2c, Francois Philidor and frontispiece of his book, *Analysis of the Game of Chess.* 3c, Wilhelm Steinitz and knight. 13c, Emanuel Lasker and king. 30c, Jose Raul Capablanca learning to play chess as a small boy.

1976, Mar. 15 ***Perf. 13x12½***
2042 A545 1c multi
2043 A545 2c multi
2044 A545 3c multi
2045 A545 13c multi
2046 A545 30c multi

Havana Radio Intl. Broadcasts, 15th Anniv. — A546

1976, Mar. 26
2047 A546 50c multi

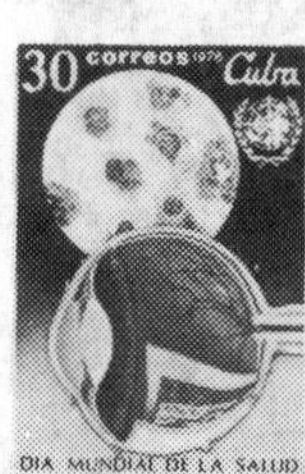

World Health Day — A547

Child Care Centers, 15th Anniv. — A548

1976, Apr. 7
2048 A547 30c multi

1976, Apr. 10 ***Perf. 12½x13***
2049 A548 3c multi

1st Manned Space Flight, 15th Anniv. A549

1976, Apr. 12 ***Perf. 13***
2050 A549 1c Gagarin, lift-off
2051 A549 2c V. Tesreshkova, rockets
2052 A549 3c A. Leonov's space walk, vert.
2053 A549 5c Spacecraft, vert.
2054 A549 13c Spacecraft, diff., vert.
2055 A549 30c Space link-up

Bay of Pigs Invasion, 15th Anniv. A550

Perf. 13x12½, 12½x13
1976, Apr. 17
2056 A550 3c shown
2057 A550 13c Bomber, pilot
2058 A550 30c Soldiers exulting, vert.

Natl. Militia, 17th anniv. (3c); Air Force, 15th anniv. (13c); proclamation of the socialist revolution, 15th anniv. (30c).

Nat. Assoc. of Small Farmers (ANAP), 15th Anniv. A551

1976, May 17 ***Perf. 13x12½***
2059 A551 3c multi

1976 Summer Olympics, Montreal — A552

1976, May 25 ***Perf. 12½x13***
2060 A552 1c Volleyball
2061 A552 2c Basketball
2062 A552 3c Long jump
2063 A552 4c Boxing
2064 A552 5c Weight lifting
2065 A552 13c Judo
2066 A552 30c Swimming

Souvenir Sheet

Imperf

2067 A552 50c Character trademark (otter)

See Nos. 2106, 2112.

Modern Secondary Schools A553

1976, June 12 **Litho.** ***Perf. 13***
2068 A553 3c red, pale grn & blk

Indigenous Birds — A554

1976, June 15 ***Perf. 13x12½***
2069 A554 1c *Teretistris fornsi*
2070 A554 2c *Glaucidium siju*
2071 A554 3c *Nesoceleus fernandinae*
2072 A554 5c *Todus mutlicolor*
2073 A554 13c *Accipiter gundlachi*
2074 A554 30c *Priotelus temnurus*

EXPO '76, USSR A555

1976, July 5 ***Perf. 12½x13, 13x12½***
2075 A555 1c Anatomical scanning device
2076 A555 3c Child, doe
2077 A555 10c Cosmonauts
2078 A555 30c Tupolev supersonic jet

Public health and industrial safety (1c), environmental protection (3c), space exploration (10c) and modern transportation (30c). Nos. 2075-2077 vert.

Death Cent. of "El Inglesito" — A556

1976, Aug. 4 *Perf. 13*

2079 A556 13c Henry M. Reeve

Portrait of J. Dabour, by G. Collazo — A557

Paintings by Collazo: 2c, *The Art Lovers,* horiz. 3c, *The Patio.* 5c, *Coconut Tree.* 13c, *New York Studio,* horiz. 30c, *R. Emelina Collazo.*

Perf. 13, 12½x13 (5c, 30c), 13x12½ (13c)

1976, Sept. 2

Sizes: 33x44mm, 44x33mm (2c), 31x46mm (5c, 30c), 46x31mm (13c)

2080 A557 1c multi
2081 A557 2c multi
2082 A557 3c multi
2083 A557 5c multi
2084 A557 13c multi
2085 A557 30c multi

Camilo Cienfuegos Military Schools, 10th Anniv. A558

1976, Sept. 23 *Perf. 13*

2086 A558 3c multi

Development of the Merchant Marine — A559

Various cargo and passenger ships.

1976, Oct. 2 *Perf. 12½*

2087 A559 1c multi
2088 A559 2c multi
2089 A559 3c multi
2090 A559 5c multi
2091 A559 13c multi
2092 A559 30c multi

8th Intl. Health Film Festival of Socialist Countries, Havana — A560

1976, Oct. 4 *Perf. 13x12½*

2093 A560 3c multi

5th Intl. Ballet Festival, Havana A561

Scenes from ballets. 2c, 5c, 13c, 30c vert.

1976, Nov. 6 *Perf. 13*

2094 A561 1c *Apollo*
2095 A561 2c *The River and the Forest*
2096 A561 3c *Giselle*
2097 A561 5c *Oedipus Rex*
2098 A561 13c *Carmen*
2099 A561 30c *Vital Song*

3rd Military Games A562

1976, Nov. 25 *Perf. 13*

2100 A562 3c multi

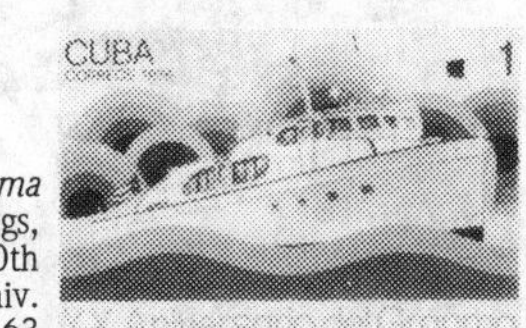

Granma Landings, 20th Anniv. A563

1976, Dec. 2 *Perf. 13x12½*

2101 A563 1c Landing craft
2102 A563 3c Landing force
2103 A563 13c Castro, soldiers
2104 A563 30c Globe, rifles

Souvenir Sheet

Cuban Landscape, by F. Cadava — A564

1976, Dec. 8 *Perf. 13x13½*

2105 A564 50c multi

CIENFUEGOS '76, 5th natl. phil. exhib.

Summer Olympics Type of 1976 and

Victory of Cuban Athletes at the Montreal Games — A565

1976, Dec. 10 *Perf. 12½x13*

2106 A565 1c Volleyball
2107 A565 2c Hurdles
2108 A565 3c Running (starting blocks)
2109 A565 8c Boxing
2110 A565 13c Running (finish line)
2111 A565 30c Judo

Souvenir Sheet

Imperf

2112 A552 50c like No. 2063

Paintings in the Natl. Museum A566

Designs: 1c, *Golden Cross Inn,* by S. Scott. 3c, *Portrait of a Man,* by J.C. Verspronck, vert. 5c, *Venetian Landscape,* by Francesco Guardi. 10c, *Valley Corner,* by H. Cleenewerck, vert. 13c, *F. Xaviera Paula,* anonymous, vert. 30c, *F. de Medici,* by C. Allori, vert.

Perf. 13, 12½x13 (3c, 10c, 30c), 12½ (13c)

1977, Jan. 18

Sizes: 40x29mm, 27x42mm (3c, 10c, 30c), 27x43½mm (13c)

2113 A566 1c multi
2114 A566 3c multi
2115 A566 5c multi
2116 A566 10c multi
2117 A566 13c multi
2118 A566 30c multi

Rural Transport A567

1977, Feb. 15 *Perf. 13*

2119 A567 3c multi

Constitution of Popular Government — A568

1976, Dec. 1 *Perf. 13x12½*

2120 A568 13c multi

Bird Type of 1975

1977, Feb. 25 *Perf. 13*

2121 A524 1c *Xiphidiopicus percussus*
2122 A524 4c *Tiaris canora*
2123 A524 10c *Dives atroviolaceus*
2124 A524 13c *Ferminia cerverai*
2125 A524 30c *Mellisuga helenae*

Lenin Park Aquarium, Havana A569

1977, Mar. 15

2126 A569 1c *Chichlasoma meeki*
2127 A569 3c *Barbus tetrazona tetrazona*
2128 A569 5c *Cyprinus carpio*
2129 A569 10c *Betta splendens*
2130 A569 13c *Pterophyllum scalare,* vert.
2131 A569 30c *Hemigrammus caudovittatus*

Sputnik (1st Artificial Satellite), 20th Anniv. — A570

Designs: 1c, DDR No. 370, *Sputnik.* 3c, Hungary No. 1216, *Luna 16.* 5c, North Korean Intl. Geophysical Year 10-won stamp of 1958, *Cosmos.* 10c, Poland No. 822, *Sputnik 3.* 13c, Yugoslavia No. 870, Earth, Moon. 30c, Cuba No. 866, Earth, Moon. 50c, Russia No. 2021, *Sputnik.*

1977, Apr. 12 *Perf. 13x12½*

2132 A570 1c multi
2133 A570 3c multi
2134 A570 5c multi
2135 A570 10c multi
2136 A570 13c multi
2137 A570 30c multi

Souvenir Sheet

Imperf

2138 A570 50c multi

No. 2138 has simulated perfs.

Antonio Maria Romeu (1876-1955), Composer — A571

1977, May 10 **Litho.** *Perf. 13*

2139 A571 3c multi

See No. C251.

Flowering Plants — A572

1977, May 31

2140 A572 1c *Hibiscus rosa sinensis*
2141 A572 2c *Nerium oleander*
2142 A572 5c *Allamanda cathartica*
2143 A572 10c *Pelargonium zonale*

Dr. Juan Tomas Roig (b. 1877), botanist. See Nos. C252-C254.

Fire Prevention Week A573

1977, June 20

2144 A573 1c shown
2145 A573 2c Horse-drawn fire pump, diff.
2146 A573 6c Early motorized vehicle
2147 A573 10c Modern truck
2148 A573 13c Turntable-ladder truck
2149 A573 30c Crane vehicle

Natl. Decorations (Ribbons and Medals of Honor) — A574

1977, July 26 *Perf. 12x12½*

2150 A574 1c shown
2151 A574 3c multi, diff.

See Nos. C255-C256.

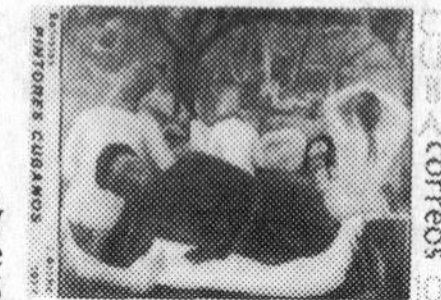

Paintings by Jorge Arche A575

Perf. 13x12½, 12½x13 (10c), 13 (5c)
1977, Aug. 25
Sizes: 26x38mm, 29x40mm (5c), 38x26mm (10c)

2152 A575 1c *Portrait of Mary*
2153 A575 3c *Jose Marti*
2154 A575 5c *Portrait of Aristides*
2155 A575 10c *Bathers*

Nos. 2152-2154 vert. See Nos. C257-C259.

4th Military Spartakiad (Summer Sports) — A576

1977, Sept. 10 *Perf. 13*

2156 A576 1c Boxing
2157 A576 3c Volleyball
2158 A576 5c Parachuting
2159 A576 10c Running

See Nos. C260-C261.

Intl. Airmail Service, 50th Anniv. A577

Designs: 1c, Biplane and No. C62. 2c, Three-engine plane and Cuba-Key West 1st flight cancel, Oct. 28, 1927. 5c, Flying boat and intl. airmail service 1st flight cachet. 10c, Jet aircraft and Havana-Madrid cachet, Apr. 26, 1948.

1977, Oct. 27 Litho. *Perf. 12x12½*

2160 A577 1c multi
2161 A577 2c multi
2162 A577 5c multi
2163 A577 10c multi

See Nos. C263-C264.

October Revolution, Russia, 60th Anniv. — A578

1977, Nov. 7 *Perf. 13x12½*

2164 A578 3c Cruiser *Aurora*
2165 A578 13c Lenin, Flags
2166 A578 30c Hammer, sickle, symbols of agriculture, technology

Felines, Havana Zoo — A579

1977, Nov. 24 Litho. *Perf. 13*

2167 A579 1c Cat
2168 A579 2c Black panther
2169 A579 8c Puma
2170 A579 10c Leopard

See Nos. C266-C267.

Martyrs of the Revolution, 20th Death Annivs. — A580

1977, Dec. 2 *Perf. 12½x12*

2171 A580 3c Cienfuegos Uprising
2172 A580 20c Siege on the Presidential Palace

See No. C268.

Intl. Measurement System — A581

1977, Dec. 9

2173 A581 3c multi

Havana University, 250th Anniv. — A582

1978, Jan. 5 *Perf. 13x12½*

2174 A582 3c multi

See Nos. C270-C271.

Landscape with Figures, by J. Pilliment A583

Paintings in the Natl. Museum of Art: 1c, *Seated Woman*, by R. Mandrazo, vert. 4c, *Girl*, by J. Sorolla, vert. 10c, *The Cow*, by E. Abela.

Perf. 12x12½, 13 (4c, 6c, 10c)
1978, Feb. 20
Sizes: 27x42mm, 29x40mm (4c), 40x29mm (6c, 10c)

2175 A583 1c multi
2176 A583 4c multi
2177 A583 6c shown
2178 A583 10c multi

See Nos. C273-C274.

Frontier Troops, 15th Anniv. — A584

1978, Mar. 5 *Perf. 13*

2179 A584 13c multi

Bird Type of 1975

Perf. 13, 12½x12 (4c)
1978, Mar. 10 Size: 42x27mm

2180 A524 1c *Myadestes elisabeth*
2181 A524 4c *Palioptila lembeyei*
2182 A524 10c *Teretistris fernandinae*

Name of bird inscribed below vignette. See Nos. C275-C276.

Cosmonaut's Day — A585

1978, Apr. 12 *Perf. 13*

2183 A585 1c Intercosmos, vert.
2184 A585 2c Luna 24
2185 A585 5c Venus 9, vert.
2186 A585 10c Cosmos

See Nos. C278-C279.

9th World Trade Unions Congress, Prague A586

1978, Apr. 16

2187 A586 30c ver, deep brn & blk

Cactus Flowers — A587

1978, May 15 *Perf. 12½x13 (1c), 13*

2188 A587 1c *Melocactus guitarti*
2189 A587 4c *Leptocereus wrightii*
2190 A587 6c *Opuntia militaris*
2191 A587 10c *Cylindropuntia hystrix*

Natl. Botanical Gardens. See #C281-C282.

Lenin Park Aquarium, Havana A588

1978, June 15 *Perf. 13*

2192 A588 1c *Barbus arulios*
2193 A588 4c *Hiphessobrycon flammeus*
2194 A588 6c *Poecilia reticulata*
2195 A588 10c *Colis lalia*

See Nos. C286-C287.

MEDELLIN '78, 13th Central American and Caribbean Games — A589

1978, July 1

2196 A589 1c Basketball, vert.
2197 A589 3c Boxing, vert.
2198 A589 5c Weight lifting, vert.
2199 A589 10c Fencing

See Nos. C288-C289.

Attack on Moncada Barracks, 25th Anniv. — A590

1978, July 26

2200 A590 3c multi

See Nos. C290-C291.

World Youth and Students Festival, Havana A591

Natl. flags and views of host cities.

1978, July 28

2201 A591 3c Prague, 1947
2202 A591 3c Budapest, 1949
2203 A591 3c Berlin, 1951
2204 A591 3c Bucharest, 1953
2205 A591 3c Warsaw, 1955
a. Strip of 5, Nos. 2201-2205

See Nos. C292-C297.

Young Workers' Army, 5th Anniv. — A592

1978, Aug. 3

2206 A592 3c multi

Tuna Industry A593

1978, Aug. 30 *Perf. 12½x12*

2207 A593 1c Tuna boat
2208 A593 2c Processing ship
2209 A593 5c Shrimp boat
2210 A593 10c Inshore stern trawler

See Nos. C298-C299.

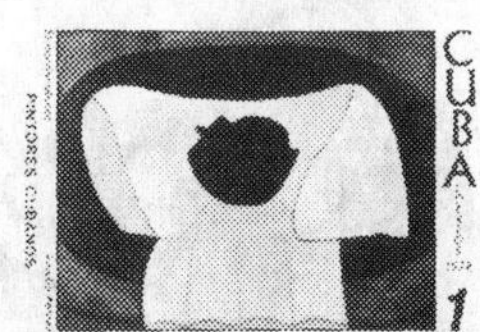

Paintings by Amelia Pelaez del Casal (1896-1968) — A594

Perf. 13x12½, 13 (3c, 6c), 12½x13

1978, Sept. 15

2211 A594 1c *The White Mantle*
2212 A594 3c *Still-life with Flowers*, vert.
2213 A594 6c *Women*, vert.
2214 A594 10c *Fish*, vert.

See Nos. C301-C303.

African Fauna, Havana Zoo A595

1978, Oct. 20 ***Perf. 13***

2215 A595 1c Rhinoceros
2216 A595 4c Okapi, vert.
2217 A595 6c Mandrill
2218 A595 10c Giraffe, vert.

See Nos. C307-C308.

Natl. Ballet, 30th Anniv. A596

1978, Oct. 28 ***Perf. 13x12½***

2219 A596 3c *Grande Pas de Quatre*

See Nos. C309-C310.

A597 A598

Flowers of the Pacific: Various species.

1978, Nov. 30 **Litho.** ***Perf. 13***

2220 A597 1c multi
2221 A597 4c multi
2222 A597 6c multi
2223 A597 10c multi

See Nos. C311-C312.

1979, Jan. 1 ***Perf. 12½x13 (3c), 13***

2224 A598 3c Castro, soldier
2225 A598 13c Industry
2226 A598 1p Flag, globe, flame

Triumph of the Revolution, 20th anniv.

Doves and Pigeons — A599

1979, Jan. 30 ***Perf. 13***

2227 A599 1c *Starnoenas cyanocephala*
2228 A599 3c *Geotrygon chysia*
2229 A599 7c *Geotrygon caniceps*
2230 A599 8c *Geotrygon montana*
2231 A599 13c *Columba leucocephala*
2232 A599 30c *Columba inornata*

Paintings in the Natl. Museum of Art — A600

Designs: 1c, *Genre Scene*, by David Teniers. 3c, *Arrival of Spanish Troops*, by J. Louis Meissonier. 6c, *A Joyful Gathering*, by Sir David Wilkie. 10c, *A Robbery*, by E. De Lucas Padilla. 13c, *Tea Time*, by R. Madrazo, vert. 30c, *Peasants in Front of a Tavern*, by Adriaen van Ostade.

1979, Feb. 20

2233 A600 1c multi
2234 A600 3c multi
2235 A600 6c multi
2236 A600 10c multi
2237 A600 13c multi
2238 A600 30c multi

See Nos. 2262-2267, C317.

Marine Flora — A601

1979, Mar. 20

2239 A601 3c *Nymphaea capensis*
2240 A601 10c *Nymphaea ampla*
2241 A601 13c *Nymphaea coerulea*
2242 A601 30c *Nymphaea rubra*

All are incorrectly inscribed "Nymphaca."

A602 A603

1979, Mar. 24

2243 A602 3c multi

Cuban film industry, 20th anniv.

1979, Apr. 12

2244 A603 1c Rocket launch
2245 A603 4c Soyuz
2246 A603 6c Salyut
2247 A603 10c Link-up
2248 A603 13c Soyuz, Salyut
2249 A603 30c Parachute landing

Cosmonaut's Day. See No. C315.

6th Summit Meeting of Non-Aligned Countries — A604

1979, Apr. 17

2250 A604 3c Understanding, cooperation
2251 A604 13c Fight colonialism
2252 A604 30c New world economic order

House of the Americas Museum, 20th Anniv. — A605

1979, Apr. 28 ***Perf. 13x12½***

2253 A605 13c Cuna Indian tapestry

Agrarian Reform, 20th Anniv. — A606

1979, May 17 ***Perf. 12½x12***

2254 A606 3c multi

Souvenir Sheet

The Party, by Jules Pascin — A607

1979, May 18 ***Perf. 13***

2255 A607 50c multi

PHILASERDICA '79 phil. exhib., Sofia.

Nocturnal Butterflies A608

1979, May 25

2256 A608 1c *Eulepidotis rectimargo*
2257 A608 4c *Othreis materna*
2258 A608 6c *Noropsis hieroglyphica*
2259 A608 10c *Heterochroma*
2260 A608 13c *Melanchroia regnatrix*
2261 A608 30c *Attera gemmata*

Art Type of 1979

Paintings by Victor Emmanuel Garcia (d. 1969): 1c, *Main Avenue, Paris*. 3c, *Portrait of Enmita*. 6c, *San Juan River, Matanzas*. 10c, *Woman Carrying Hay*. 13c, *Still-life with Vase*. 30c, *Street at Night*. Nos. 2262-2267 vert.

1979, June 15

2262 A600 1c multi
2263 A600 3c multi
2264 A600 6c multi
2265 A600 10c multi
2266 A600 13c multi
2267 A600 30c multi

See No. C317.

World Peace Council, 30th Anniv. A609

1979, June 29 ***Perf. 12½x13***

2268 A609 30c multi

1980 Summer Olympics, Moscow — A610

1979, July 30 ***Perf. 13x12½***

2269 A610 1c Wrestling
2270 A610 4c Boxing
2271 A610 6c Women's volleyball
2272 A610 10c Shooting
2273 A610 13c Weight lifting
2274 A610 30c High jump

Roses — A611 A612

1979, Aug. 20 ***Perf. 13***

2275 A611 1c *Rosa eglanteria*
2276 A611 2c *Rosa centifolia anemonoides*
2277 A611 3c *Rosa indica vulgaris*
2278 A611 5c *Rosa eglanteria punicea*
2279 A611 10c *Rosa sulfurea*
2280 A611 13c *Rosa muscosa alba*
2281 A611 20c *Rosa gallica purpurea velutina*

1979, Aug. 30

2282 A612 13c multi

Council for Mutual Economic Assistance, 30th anniv.

Cubana Airlines, 50th Anniv. A613

Various aircraft.

1979, Oct. 8

2283 A613 1c Ford trimotor
2284 A613 2c Sikorsky S-38
2285 A613 3c Douglas DC-3
2286 A613 4c Douglas DC-6
2287 A613 13c Ilyushin IL-14
2288 A613 40c Tupolev TU-104

Disappearance of Camilo Cienfuegos, 20th Anniv. — A614

1979, Oct. 28

2289 A614 3c multi

Reinoso, Sugar Cane and Blossom A615

1979, Nov. 12

2290 A615 13c multi

Sugar Cane Research Institute, 15th anniv., and sesquicentennial of the birth of Alvaro Reinoso.

Zoo Animals A616

1979, Nov. 15

2291 A616 1c Chimpanzees
2292 A616 2c Leopards
2293 A616 3c Deer
2294 A616 4c Lion cubs
2295 A616 5c Bear cubs
2296 A616 13c Squirrels
2297 A616 30c Pandas
2298 A616 50c Tiger cubs

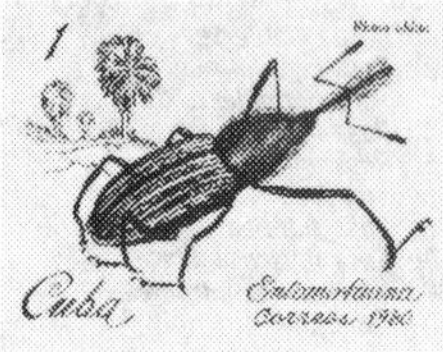

Insects A617

1980, Jan. 25

2299 A617 1c *Rhina oblita*
2300 A617 5c *Odontocera josemartii*, vert.
2301 A617 6c *Pinthocoelium columbinum*
2302 A617 10c *Calasoma splendida*, vert.
2303 A617 13c *Homophileurus cubanus*, vert.
2304 A617 30c *Heterops dimidiata*, vert.

1980 Summer Olympics, Moscow — A618

1980, Feb. 20 ***Perf. 12½***

2305 A618 1c Weight lifting
2306 A618 2c Shooting
2307 A618 5c Javelin
2308 A618 6c Wrestling
2309 A618 8c Judo
2310 A618 10c Running
2311 A618 13c Boxing
2312 A618 30c Women's volleyball

Souvenir Sheet

Imperf

2313 A618 50c Mischa character

No. 2313 contains one 32x40mm stamp.

Paintings in the Natl. Museum A619

Designs: 1c, *The Oak Trees*, by Henry Joseph Harpignies, vert. 4c, *Family Reunion*, by Willem van Mieris. 6c, *Domestic Fowl*, by Melchior De Hondecoeter, vert. 9c, *Innocence*, by William A. Bougereau, vert. 13c, *Venetial Scene II*, by Michele Marieschi. 30c, *Spanish Peasant Woman*, by Joaquin Dominguez Bequer, vert.

Perf. 12½, 13 (9c, 30c), 12½x13 (13c)

1980, Mar. 11

Sizes: 29x40mm, 40x29mm (4c), 28x42mm (9c, 30c), 38x26mm (13c)

2314 A619 1c multi
2315 A619 4c multi
2316 A619 6c multi
2317 A619 9c multi
2318 A619 15c multi
2319 A619 30c multi

Souvenir Sheet

LONDON '80 — A620

1980, Apr. 1 ***Perf. 13***

2320 A620 50c *Malvern Hall*, by John Constable

Intercosmos Program — A621

1980, Apr. 12

2321 A621 1c Emblem, flags
2322 A621 4c Astrophysics
2323 A621 6c Satellite communications
2324 A621 10c Meteorology
2325 A621 13c Biology and medicine
2326 A621 30c Surveying satellite

Cuban Postage Stamps, 125th Anniv. — A622

1980, Apr. 24 ***Perf. 12½***

2327 A622 30c Nos. 1, 7 and 613

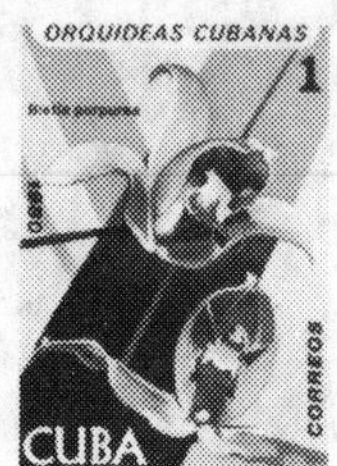

Orchids — A623

1980, May 20 ***Perf. 13***

2328 A623 1c *Bletia purpurea*
2329 A623 4c *Oncidium leiboldii*
2330 A623 6c *Epidendrum cochleatum*
2331 A623 10c *Cattleyopsis lindenii*
2332 A623 13c *Encyclia fucata*
2333 A623 30c *Encyclia phoenicea*

Marine Mammals A624

1980, June 20

2334 A624 1c *Tursiops truncatus*
2335 A624 3c *Megaptera novaeangliae*, vert.
2336 A624 13c *Ziphius cavirostris*
2337 A624 30c *Monachus tropicalis*

Urban Reform Campaign, 20th Anniv. — A625

Nationalization of Foreign Industry, 20th Anniv. — A626

Perf. 13x12½, 12½x13

1980, July 26

2338 A625 3c multi
2339 A626 13c multi

Moncada Program.

Colonial Copperware A627

Perf. 12½, 12½x13 (13c)

1980, July 29

Sizes: 27x43½mm, 38x26mm (13c)

2340 A627 3c Wine pitcher, 19th cent.
2341 A627 13c Oil jar, 18th cent.
2342 A627 30c Lidded pitcher, 19th cent.

Cuban Women's Federation, 20th Anniv. — A628

1980, Aug. 23 ***Perf. 13***

2343 A628 3c multi

Souvenir Sheet

ESPAMER '80, Madrid — A629

Design: *Clotilde Passing Through the Country Garden*, by Joaquin Sorolla y Bastida.

1980, Aug. 29

2344 A629 50c multi

Postage stamps of Spain, 130th anniv.

1st Havana Declaration, 20th Anniv. — A630

1980, Sept. 2

2345 A630 13c multi

Construction of Naval Vessels in Cuba, 360th Anniv. — A631

Ships under construction: 1c, *Our Lady of Atocha*, galleon, 1620. 3c, *El Rayo*, warship, 1749. 7c, *Santisima Trinidad*, 1769. 10c, *Santisima Trinidad*, diff., 1805, vert. 13c, Steamships *Congreso* and *Colon*, 1851. 30c, Cardenas and Chullima shipyards.

1980, Sept. 15

2346 A631 1c multi
2347 A631 3c multi
2348 A631 7c multi
2349 A631 10c multi
2350 A631 13c multi
2351 A631 30c multi

A633

A634

1980, Sept. 26 ***Perf. 13***

2354 A633 13c multi

Fidel Castro's 1st speech before the UN General Assembly, 20th anniv.

1980, Sept. 28 ***Perf. 13x12½***

2355 A634 3c multi

Revolutionary defense committees, 20th anniv.

Souvenir Sheet

ESSEN '80, 49th Intl. Philatelic Federation Congress — A635

Painting: *Portrait of a Lady*, by Ludger Tom Ring The Younger.

1980, Oct. 2 **Litho.** ***Perf. 13***
2356 A635 50c multi

Early Locomotives — A636

1980, Oct. 15
2357 A636 1c Josefa
2358 A636 2c Chaparra Sugar Co. No. 22
2359 A636 7c Steam storage locomotive
2360 A636 10c 2-4-2 locomotive
2361 A636 13c 2-4-0 locomotive
2362 A636 30c Oil combustion engine, 1909

Lighthouses A637

1980, Oct. 30
2363 A637 3c Roncali, San Antonio
2364 A637 13c Jagua, Cienfuegos
2365 A637 30c Maisi Point, Guantanamo

See Nos. 2440-2442, 2553-2555, 2614-2616.

Victory of Cuban Athletes at the 1980 Summer Olympics, Moscow — A638

1980, Nov. 10 **Litho.** ***Perf. $12^1/_2$x12***
2366 A638 13c Bronze medals
2367 A638 30c Silver medals
2368 A638 50c Gold medals

Nos. 2366-2368 each printed se-tenant with label containing statistical data.

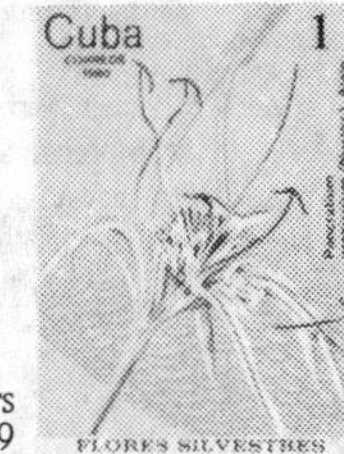

Wildflowers A639

1980, Nov. 20 ***Perf. 13***
2369 A639 1c *Pancratium arenicolum*
2370 A639 4c *Urechites lutea*
2371 A639 6c *Solanum elaegnifolium*
2372 A639 10c *Hamelia patens*
2373 A639 13c *Morinda royoc*
2374 A639 30c *Centrosema virginianum*

Souvenir Sheet

7th Natl. Stamp Exhibition — A640

1980, Nov. 22
2375 A640 50c Mail train

2nd Communist Party Congress — A641

1980, Dec. 17
2376 A641 3c shown
2377 A641 13c Industry, communication
2378 A641 30c Athletics, elderly, education

Paintings in the Natl. Museum of Art — A642

Designs: 1c, *Lady Mayo*, by Anton Van Dyck, vert. 6c, *The Spinner*, by Giovanni Battista Piazzeta, vert. 10c, *Daniel Collyer*, by Francis Cotes, vert. 13c, *Palm Gardens, Mallorca*, by Santiago Rusinol Prats. 20c, *Landscape with Roadway and Houses*, by Frederick Waters Watts. 50c, *Landscape with Sheep*, by Jean-Francois Millet.

1981, Jan. 20
2379 A642 1c multi
2380 A642 6c multi
2381 A642 10c multi
2382 A642 13c multi
2383 A642 20c multi
2384 A642 50c multi

See Nos. 2510-2515.

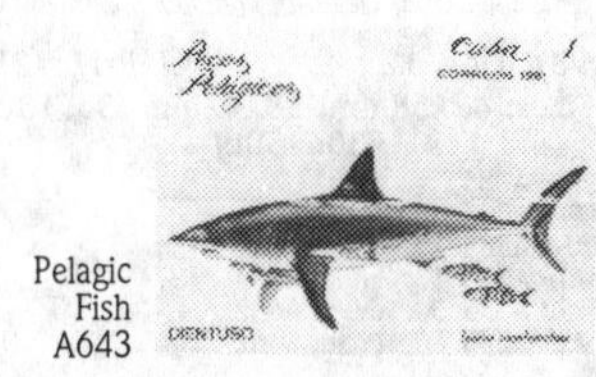

Pelagic Fish A643

1981, Feb. 25
2385 A643 1c *Isurus oxyrhynchus*
2386 A643 3c *Lampris regius*
2387 A643 10c *Istiophorus platypterus*
2388 A643 13c *Mola mola*, vert.
2389 A643 30c *Coruphaena hippurus*
2390 A643 50c *Tetrapturus albidus*

1982 World Cup Soccer Championships, Spain — A644

Globe and various soccer players.

1981, Mar. 20 ***Perf. $12^1/_2$***
2391 A644 1c multi
2392 A644 2c multi
2393 A644 3c multi
2394 A644 10c multi, vert.
2395 A644 13c multi, vert.
2396 A644 50c multi

Souvenir Sheet
Perf. 13
2397 A644 1p Soccer ball, flag

No. 2397 contains one 40x32mm stamp.

Opening of the 1st Kindergarten, 20th Anniv. — A645

1981, Apr. 10 ***Perf. 13***
2398 A645 3c multi

1st Man in Space, 20th Anniv. A646

Designs: 1c, Jules Verne, Russian scientist Konstantin E. Tsiolkovski, and Sergei P. Korolev, designer of the 1st Soviet spacecraft, vert. 2c, Yuri Gagarin, 1st man in space. 3c, Valentina Tereshkova, 1st woman in space, and *Vostok 6*. 5c, Aleksei A. Leonov, 1st man to walk in space. 13c, Konstantin Feoktistov, Boris Yegorov and Vladimir Komarov, *Voskhod I* crew, 1st 3-man orbital flight. 30c, Valeri Ryumen and Leonid Popov, set a space endurance record. 50c, Arnaldo Tamayo, 1st Cuban cosmonaut, and Soviet cosmonaut Yuri Romanenko on joint space flight, vert.

1981, Apr. 12 ***Perf. $12^1/_2$***
2399 A646 1c multi
2400 A646 2c multi
2401 A646 3c multi
2402 A646 5c multi
2403 A646 13c multi
2404 A646 30c multi
2405 A646 50c multi

A647

1981, Apr. 19 **Litho.** ***Perf. 13***
2406 A647 3c multi, vert.
2407 A647 13c multi, vert.
2408 A647 30c multi

Creation of armed forces (DAAFAR) (3c), Bay of Pigs Invasion, 20th Anniv. (13c), Proclamation of the socialist revolution (30c).

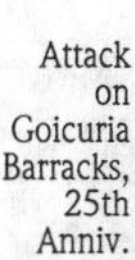

Attack on Goicuria Barracks, 25th Anniv. A648

1981, Apr. 29
2409 A648 3c multi

Natl. Assoc. of Small Farmers (ANAP), 20th Anniv. A649

1981, May 17
2410 A649 3c multi

Souvenir Sheet

WIPA '81 — A650

1981, May 22 **Litho.**
2411 A650 50c Austria No. 643

Fighting Cocks — A651

Perf. $12^1/_2$x13, 13x$12^1/_2$
1981, May 25
2412 A651 1c Canelo, vert.
2413 A651 3c Cenizo
2414 A651 7c Blanco, vert.
2415 A651 13c Pinto, vert.
2416 A651 30c Giro
2417 A651 50c Jabao, vert.

Ministry of the Interior, 20th Anniv. — A652

1981, June 6 ***Perf. 13***
2418 A652 13c multi

Footnotes near stamp listings often refer to other stamps of the same design.

Souvenir Sheet

Mother and Child, by Zlatka Dabova — A653

1981, June 14
2419 A653 50c gold, sil & blk

Bulgaria, 1300th anniv. BULGARIA '81 phil. exhib.

Horse-drawn Carriages — A654

1981, June 25
2420 A654 1c Streetcar
2421 A654 4c Bus
2422 A654 9c Breake
2423 A654 13c Landau
2424 A654 30c Phaeton
2425 A654 50c Funeral coach

House in the Country, by Mario Caridad — A655

1981, July 15 *Perf. 12½*
2426 A655 30c multi

Intl. Year of the Disabled.

Sandinistas, 25th Anniv. — A656

1981, July 23 *Perf. 13*
2427 A656 13c multi

State Institutions, 20th Annivs. — A657

1981, July 26 *Perf. 12½*
2428 A657 3c multi
2429 A657 13c multi, diff.
2430 A657 30c multi, diff.

Institute for Sports, Physical Education and Recreation (3c); Radio Havana (13c); and Ministry of Foreign Trade (MINCEX) (30c).

Carlos J. Finlay and Cent. of His Theory of Biological Vectors — A658

1981, Aug. 14 *Perf. 13*
2431 A658 13c multi

Nonaligned Countries Movement, 20th Anniv. — A659

1981, Sept. 1
2432 A659 50c multi

Horses — A660

Illustration reduced. Nos. 2433-2437 vert.

1981, Sept. 15 *Perf. 13*
Size: 29x40mm
2433 A660 1c multi
2434 A660 3c multi, diff.
2435 A660 8c multi, diff.
2436 A660 13c multi, diff.
2437 A660 30c multi, diff.

Size: 68x27mm
Perf. 12½
2438 A660 50c Herd

Souvenir Sheet

Idyll in a Tea House, by Kitagawa Utamaro — A661

1981, Oct. 9 *Perf. 13*
2439 A661 50c multi

PHILATOKYO '81.

Lighthouse Type of 1980

1981, Oct. 15 **Litho.**
2440 A637 3c North Rock
2441 A637 13c Lucrecia Point
2442 A637 40c East Guano

Jose Marti Natl. Library, 80th Anniv. — A662

Sugar mills, lithographs from *Los Ingenios,* by Eduardo Laplante (b. 1818): 3c, Flor de Cuba, 1838. 13c, El Progreso, 1845. 30c, Santa Teresa, 1847.

1981, Oct. 18 *Perf. 12½x12*
2443 A662 3c multi
2444 A662 13c multi
2445 A662 30c multi

Pablo Picasso (b. 1881) and No. 1263 A663

1981, Oct. 25 *Perf. 12½x13*
2446 A663 30c multi

Souvenir Sheet

ESPAMER '81, Buenos Aires — A664

1981, Nov. 13 *Perf. 13*
2447 A664 1p Packet

Art Type of 1969

Paintings in the Napoleon Museum: 1c, *Napoleon in Coronation Costume,* anonymous. 3c, *Napoleon with Landscape in the Background,* by Jean Horace Vernet. 10c, *Bonaparte in Egypt,* by Edouard Detaille. 13c, *Napoleon on Horseback,* by Hippolyte Bellange. 30c, *Napoleon in Normandy,* by Bellange. 50c, *Death of Napoleon,* anonymous.

1981, Dec. 1 *Perf. 12½*
Sizes: 42x58mm, 58x42mm (3c, 13c, 30c, 50c)
2448 A385 1c multi
2449 A385 3c multi, horiz.
2450 A385 10c multi
2451 A385 13c multi, horiz.
2452 A385 30c multi, horiz.
2453 A385 50c multi, horiz.

Napoleon Museum, 20th anniv.

25th Annivs. A665

1981, Dec. 2 *Perf. 13*
2454 A665 3c Revolutionaries, vert.
2455 A665 20c Marksman
2456 A665 1p Yacht *Granma*

November 30th insurrection (3c); creation of the revolutionary armed forces (20c); and disembarking of revolutionary forces (1p).

Fauna — A666

1981, Dec. 14 **Litho.** *Perf. 12½x12*
2457 A666 1c Hummingbird
2458 A666 2c Parakeet
2459 A666 5c Hutia
2460 A666 20c Almiqui
2461 A666 35c Manatee
2462 A666 40c Crocodile

Fernando Ortiz, Folklorist, Birth Cent. A667

1981, Dec. 20 *Perf. 12½x13*
2463 A667 3c Portrait by Jorge Arche y Silva
2464 A667 10c Hanging idol
2465 A667 30c Arara drum
2466 A667 50c Chango statue

Literacy Campaign, 20th Anniv. — A668

1981, Dec. 25 *Perf. 12½x12*
2467 A668 5c Conrado Benitez
2468 A668 5c Manuel Asunce

Printed se-tenant.

A669

1982 World Cup Soccer Championships, Spain — A670

Various athletes.

1982, Jan. 15 *Perf. 13*
2469 A669 1c multi, vert.
2470 A669 2c multi, vert.
2471 A669 5c multi, vert.
2472 A669 10c multi, vert.
2473 A669 20c shown
2474 A669 40c multi
2475 A669 50c multi, vert.

Souvenir Sheet
2476 A670 1p shown

No. 2476 contains one 32x40mm stamp.

10th World Trade Unions Congress, Havana — A671

1982, Feb. 10 **Litho.**

2477 A671 30c Lazaro Pena, delegate

Butterflies — A672

1982, Feb. 25 ***Perf. 12½***

2478 A672 1c *Euptoieta hegesia*
2479 A672 4c *Metamorpha stelenes insularis*
2480 A672 5c *Heliconius charithonius ramsdeni*
2481 A672 20c *Phoebis avellaneda*
2482 A672 30c *Hamadryas ferox diasia*
2483 A672 50c *Marpesia eleuchea*

Exports — A673

Designs: 3c, Sugar (processing plant). 4c, Lobster (fishing boat). 6c, Canned fruits. 7c, Agricultural machinery. 8c, Nickel (passenger jet, industrial complex, car). 9c, Rum. 10c, Coffee. 30c, Fresh fruit. 50c, Tobacco. 1p, Cement. Nos. 2489-2493 vert.

Perf. 12x12½, 12½x12

1982, Feb. 26

2484 A673 3c lt grn
2485 A673 4c car rose
2486 A673 6c dull blue
2487 A673 7c brt org
2488 A673 8c brt vio
2489 A673 9c slate
2490 A673 10c dull red brn
2491 A673 30c bister
2492 A673 50c orange
2493 A673 1p olive bister

Tulips A674

1982, Mar. 30 ***Perf. 12½x13***

2494 A674 1c Greenland
2495 A674 3c Mariette
2496 A674 8c Ringo
2497 A674 20c La Tulipe Noire
2498 A674 30c Jewel of Spring
2499 A674 50c Orange Parrot

Communist Youth Organization, 20th Anniv. — A675

1982, Apr. 4 ***Perf. 13***

2500 A675 5c multi

2nd UN-Pacific Congress on the Peaceful Use of Outer Space A676

1982, Apr. 12

2501 A676 1c *Mars*
2502 A676 3c *Venera*
2503 A676 6c *Salyut-Soyuz* link-up
2504 A676 20c *Lunokhod* moon vehicle
2505 A676 30c *Venera* with heat shield
2506 A676 50c *Cosmos*

Cover A677

1982, Apr. 24 ***Perf. 12½x12***

2507 A677 20c Havana-Veracruz
2508 A677 30c Havana-Tampico

Stamp Day. English post office, 1842-1877 (20c); and French post office, 1862-1877 (30c).

Broadcasting and Television Institute (ICRT), 20th Anniv. — A678

1982, May 24 ***Perf. 12x12½***

2509 A678 30c multi

Art Type of 1981
With Larger Type

Paintings in the Natl. Museum of Art: 1c, *Portrait of a Youth* (girl), by Jean B. Greuze, vert. 3c, *Procession in Brittany*, by Jules Breton. 9c, *Landscape*, by Jean Piliment. 20c, *Late Afternoon*, by William A. Bourgueran, vert. 30c, *Tiger*, by Ferdinand V.E. Delacroix. 40c, *The Chair*, by Wilfredo Lam, vert.

Perf. 13, 13x12½ (3c), 12x12½ (20c, 40c), 12½x12 (30c)

1982, May 31 **Litho.**

2510 A642 1c 29x40mm
2511 A642 3c 46x36mm
2512 A642 9c 40x29mm
2513 A642 20c 27x42mm
2514 A642 30c 42x27mm
2515 A642 40c 27x42mm

Souvenir Sheet

PHILEXFRANCE '82 — A679

1982, June 7 ***Perf. 13***

2516 A679 1p Steamship *Louisiana* at St. Nazaire

DEPORFILEX '82 — A680

1982, June 10 ***Perf. 13x12½***

2517 A680 20c Hurdler, No. 300

Reptiles A681

1982, June 15 ***Perf. 13***

2518 A681 1c *Pseudemys decussata*
2519 A681 2c *Tropidophis pardalis*
2520 A681 3c *Crocodylus rhombifer*
2521 A681 20c *Cyclura nubila*
2522 A681 30c *Anolis allisonis*
2523 A681 50c *Alsophis cantherigerus*

George Dimitrov (1882-1949), Bulgarian Prime Minister — A682

1982, June 18

2524 A682 30c multi

Koch, Bacillus A683

1982, July 18

2525 A683 20c multi

Discovery of the tubercle bacillus by Dr. Robert Koch, cent.

14th Central American and Caribbean Games — A684

1982, Aug. 1

2526 A684 1c Baseball
2527 A684 2c Boxing
2528 A684 10c Water polo
2529 A684 20c Javelin
2530 A684 35c Weight lifting
2531 A684 50c Volleyball

Hydraulic Development Plan, 20th Anniv. — A685

Designs: 5c, Fruit, *Eichornia crassipes*, ship. 20c, Arid soil, *Nymphaea alba*, irrigation and reservoir systems.

1982, Aug. 9

2532 A685 5c multi
2533 A685 20c multi

Souvenir Sheet

DEPORFILEX '82, Intl. Stamp and Coin Exhibition — A686

1982, Aug. 10 **Litho.**

2534 A686 1p Cuco, character trademark

14th Central American and Caribbean Games.

Namibia Day A687

1982, Aug. 26

2535 A687 50c multi

1982 World Cup Soccer Championships, Spain — A688

Various athletes.

1982, Aug. 30

2536 A688 5c multi
2537 A688 20c multi
2538 A688 30c multi
2539 A688 50c multi

Also exist in miniature sheets of 16 + 9 labels containing 4 each Nos. 2536-2539 in blocks of 4.

Natl. Folklore Ensemble, 20th Anniv. A689

Paintings by V.P. Landaluze.

1982, Sept. 10

2540 A689 20c *Little Devil*, vert.
2541 A689 30c *Day of Kings*

Prehistoric Fauna A690

1982, Sept. 15 **Litho.**

2542 A690 1c *Ornimegalonyx oteroi*, vert.
2543 A690 5c *Crocodylus rhombifer*
2544 A690 7c *Aquila borrasi*, vert.
2545 A690 20c *Geocapromys columbianus*
2546 A690 35c *Megalocnus rodens*, vert.
2547 A690 50c *Nesophontes micrus*

15th Death Anniv. of Che Guevara — A691

1982, Oct. 8 ***Perf. 13x12½***

2548 A691 20c multi

Discovery of America, 490th Anniv. — A692

1982, Oct. 12 ***Perf. 13***

2549 A692 5c shown
2550 A692 20c *Santa Maria*, vert.
2551 A692 35c *Pinta*, vert.
2552 A692 50c *Nina*, vert.

Lighthouse Type of 1980

1982, Oct. 25

2553 A637 5c Jutias Caye
2554 A637 20c Paredon Grande Caye
2555 A637 30c Morro Santiago de Cuba

George Washington, 250th Birth Anniv. — A693

Designs: Quotations and anonymous oil paintings, 18th-19th cent.

1982, Oct. 29 ***Perf. 12x12½***

2556 A693 5c multi
2557 A693 20c multi, diff.

Souvenir Sheet

8th Natl. Philatelic Exposition, Ciego de Avila — A694

1982, Nov. 13

2558 A694 1p Paddle steamer *Almendares*

8th Congress of the Cuban Philatelic Federation, Nov. 13-22.

Lenin Natl. Park, 10th Anniv. A695

1982, Dec. 28

2559 A695 5c multi

Chess Champion Jose Raul Capablanca and King — A696

1982, Dec. 29

2560 A696 5c shown
2561 A696 20c Rook
2562 A696 30c Knight
2563 A696 50c Queen
a. Bklt. pane of 4, Nos. 2560-2563

Exist in sheets of 4+2 labels picturing chessmen.

USSR, 60th Anniv. A697

1982, Dec. 30 ***Perf. 13x12½***

2564 A697 30c multi

World Communications Year — A698

1983, Jan. 24 **Litho.** ***Perf. 13***

2565 A698 20c multi

No. 507 and Birthplace — A699

1983, Jan. 28 ***Perf. 13x12½***

2566 A699 5c multi

Jose Marti (b. 1853), writer, revolution leader.

1984 Summer Olympics, Los Angeles — A700

1983, Jan. 31 ***Perf. 13***

2567 A700 1c Javelin
2568 A700 5c Volleyball
2569 A700 6c Basketball
2570 A700 20c Weight lifting
2571 A700 30c Wrestling
2572 A700 50c Boxing

Souvenir Sheet

Perf. 13½x13

2573 A700 1p Judo

No. 2573 contains one 32x40mm stamp.

Radio Rebelde, 25th Anniv. — A701

1983, Feb. 24 ***Perf. 13***

2574 A701 20c multi

Karl Marx, Death Cent. A702

1983, Mar. 14

2575 A702 30c multi

1st Manned Balloon Flight, Bicent. — A703

Various balloons.

1983, Mar. 30

2576 A703 1c multi
2577 A703 3c multi
2578 A703 5c multi
2579 A703 7c multi
2580 A703 30c multi
2581 A703 50c multi

Souvenir Sheet

2582 A703 1p Jose D. Blino

No. 2582 contains one 32x40mm stamp.

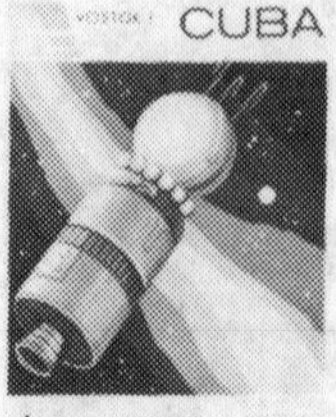

Cosmonauts' Day — A704

1983, Apr. 12 **Litho.**

2583 A704 1c *Vostok 1*
2584 A704 4c Satellite *Frances D1*
2585 A704 5c *Mars 2*
2586 A704 20c *Soyuz*
2587 A704 30c Meteorological satellite
2588 A704 50c Intercosmos satellite

Stamp Day A705

1983, Apr. 24

2589 A705 20c Havana-Key West cover
2590 A705 30c Spain-Havana cover

1st Intl. airmail services.

Souvenir Sheet

TEMBAL '83, Basel — A706

1983, May 21 ***Perf. 13½x13***

2591 A706 1p Weasel

Simon Bolivar, Liberator of South America A707

1983, July 24 ***Perf. 12½x13***

2592 A707 5c Jose Rafael de las Heras
2593 A707 20c Bolivar

Attack of Moncada Barracks, 30th Anniv. A708

Designs: 5c, Jose Marti, Moncada barracks. 20c, Abel Santamaria, Jose Luis Tasende and Boris Luis Santa Coloma, martyrs, vert. 30c, *History Will Absolve Me*, declaration of Fidel Castro, vert.

1983, July 26 ***Perf. 13***

2594 A708 5c multi
2595 A708 20c multi
2596 A708 30c multi

Souvenir Sheet

Alberto Santos-Dumont (1873-1932) — A709

1983, July 29 *Perf. 13x13½*

2597 A709 1p Dumont's aircraft

BRASILIANA '83, Rio; 140th anniv. of 1st stamp issued in the Americas.

9th Pan American Games, Caracas — A710

1983, Aug. 14 *Perf. 13x12½*

2598 A710 1c Weight lifting
2599 A710 2c Volleyball
2600 A710 3c Baseball
2601 A710 20c High jump
2602 A710 30c Basketball
2603 A710 50c Boxing

Port, by Claude Joseph Vernet — A711

1983, Sept. 5

2604 A711 30c multi

French alliance, cent.

Pres. Salvador Allende of Chile (d. 1973) — A712

1983, Sept. 12

2605 A712 20c multi

1st Congress of Farmers at Arms, 25th Anniv. — A713

1983, Sept. 21 *Perf. 12½x12*

2606 A713 5c multi

Raphael, 500th Birth Anniv. — A714

1983, Sept. 30 **Litho.** *Perf. 13*

2607 A714 1c *Girl with Veil*
2608 A714 2c *The Cardinal*
2609 A714 5c *Francesco M. Della Rovere*
2610 A714 20c *Portrait of a Youth*
2611 A714 30c *Magdalena Doni*
2612 A714 50c *La Fornarina*

State Quality Seal A715

1983, Oct. 14

2613 A715 5c multi

Lighthouse Type of 1980

1983, Oct. 20

2614 A637 5c Carapachibey
2615 A637 20c Cadiz Bay
2616 A637 30c Gobernadora Point

Turtles A716

1983, Nov. 15

2617 A716 1c *Eretmochelys imbricata*
2618 A716 2c *Lepidochelys kempi*
2619 A716 5c *Chrysemys decussata*
2620 A716 20c *Caretta caretta*
2621 A716 30c *Chelonia mydas*
2622 A716 50c *Dermochelys coriacea*

World Communications Year — A717

1983, Nov. 23

2623 A717 1c Bell's Gallow Frame, telephone
2624 A717 5c Telegram, airmail
2625 A717 10c Satellite, satellite dish
2626 A717 20c Television, radio
2627 A717 30c 24th Communications conf.

Nos. 319 and 990 A718

1983, Dec. 3 *Perf. 13x12½*

2628 A718 20c multi

See note after No. 320.

Flowers, Birds — A719

Flowers — A720

1983, Dec. 20 *Perf. 13*

2629 A719 5c *Opuntia dillenii*
2630 A719 5c *Euphorbia podocarpifolia*
2631 A719 5c *Dinema cubincola*
2632 A719 5c *Guaiacum officinale*
2633 A719 5c *Magnolia cubensis*
a. Strip of 5, Nos. 2629-2633
2634 A719 5c *Jatropha angustifolia*
2635 A719 5c *Cochlospermum vitifolium*
2636 A719 5c *Tabebuia lepidota*
2637 A719 5c *Kalmiella ericoides*
2638 A719 5c *Jatropha integerrima*
2639 A719 5c *Melocactus actinacanthus*
2640 A719 5c *Cordia sebestana*
2641 A719 5c *Tabernae - montana apoda*
2642 A719 5c *Lantana camara*
2643 A719 5c *Cordia gerascanthus*
a. Block of 10, Nos. 2634-2643
2644 A719 5c *Tiaris canora*
2645 A719 5c *Phaethon lepturus*
2646 A719 5c *Myadestes elisabeth*
2647 A719 5c *Saurothera merlini*
2648 A719 5c *Polioptila lembeyei*
a. Strip of 5, Nos. 2644-2648
2649 A719 5c *Mellisuga helenae*
2650 A719 5c *Mimus polyglottos*
2651 A719 5c *Todus multicolor*
2652 A719 5c *Amazona leucocephala*
2653 A719 5c *Ferminia cerverai*
2654 A719 5c *Pelecanus occidentalis*
2655 A719 5c *Melanerpes superciliaris*
2656 A719 5c *Mimocichla plumbea*
2657 A719 5c *Aratinga euops*
2658 A719 5c *Sturnella magna*
a. Block of 10, Nos. 2649-2658

Souvenir Sheets

2658B A719 100c *Hedychium coronarium*
2658C A719 100c *Priotelus temnurus*

1983, Dec. 30 *Perf. 12½*

2659 A720 60c Tobacco
2660 A720 70c Lily
2661 A720 80c Mariposa
2662 A720 90c Orchid

25th Anniv. of the Revolution — A721

1983, Dec. 31 **Litho.** *Perf. 13*

2663 A721 5c shown
2664 A721 20c Flags, Santa Clara Rlwy. tracks

25th Anniv. of the Revolution — A722

1984, Jan. 8

2665 A722 20c Guevara, Castro
2666 A722 20c Star
2667 A722 20c PCC emblem, workers

Printed se-tenant.

Lenin, 60th Death Anniv. A723

1984, Jan. 21 *Perf. 12½x12*

2668 A723 30p Spasski Tower, Russia Nos. 295, 265

Cuban Labor Union, 45th Anniv. A724

1984, Jan. 28 *Perf. 13*

2669 A724 5c multi

Butterflies — A725

1984, Jan. 31 *Perf. 13x12½*

2670 A725 1c *Ixias balice*
2671 A725 2c *Phoebis avellaneda*
2672 A725 3c *Anthocaris sara*
2673 A725 5c *Victorina*
2674 A725 20c *Heliconius cydno cydnides*
2675 A725 30c *Parides gundlachianus calzadillae*
2676 A725 50c *Catagramma sorana*

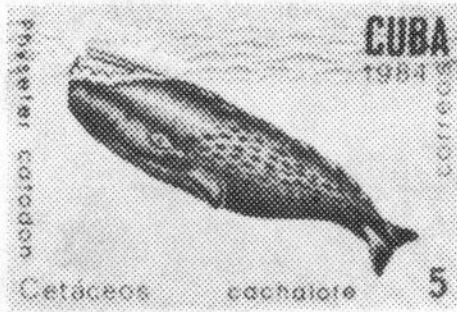

Marine Mammals — A726

Perf. 12x12½, 12½x12

1984, Feb. 15

2677 A726 1c *Grampus griseus*, vert.
2678 A726 2c *Delphinus delphis*, vert.
2679 A726 5c *Physeter catodon*
2680 A726 6c *Stenella plagiodon*, vert.
2681 A726 10c *Pseudorca crassidens*
2682 A726 30c *Tursiops truncatus*, vert.
2683 A726 50c *Megaptera novaeangliae*

Augusto C. Sandino (1893-1934), Nicaraguan Revolutionary — A727

1984, Feb. 21 *Perf. 13*

2684 A727 20c multi

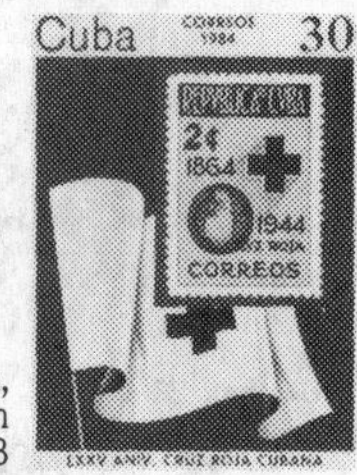

Red Cross in Cuba, 75th Anniv. — A728

1984, Mar. 10

2685 A728 30c Flag, No. 404

Cuban Film Industry, 25th Anniv. A729

1984, Mar. 24

2686 A729 20c multi

Caribbean Flowers — A730

1984, Mar. 29

2687 A730 1c *Brownea grandiceps*
2688 A730 2c *Couroupita guianensis*
2689 A730 5c *Triplaris surinamensis*
2690 A730 20c *Amherstia nobilis*
2691 A730 30c *Plumieria alba*
2692 A730 50c *Delonix regia*

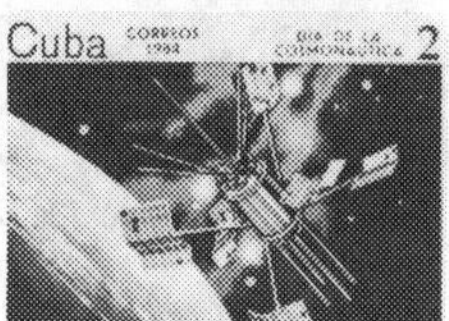

Cosmonauts' Day — A731

1984, Apr. 12

2693 A731 2c *Electron 1,* 1964
2694 A731 3c *Electron 2,* 1964
2695 A731 5c *Intercosmos 1,* 1969
2696 A731 10c *Mars 5,* 1974
2697 A731 30c *Soyuz,* 1969
2698 A731 50c USSR-Bulgaria space flight, 1979

Souvenir Sheet

Perf. 12½

2699 A731 1p *Luna 1,* 1959

No. 2699 contains one 32x40mm stamp.

Mothers' Day — A732

1984, Apr. 19 ***Perf. 13***

2700 A732 20c Red roses
2701 A732 20c Pink roses

Stamp Day — A733

Designs: Mural, by R. Rodriguez Radillo (details).

1984, Apr. 24 ***Perf. 13x12½***

2702 A733 20c Mexican runner
2703 A733 30c Egyptian boatman

See Nos. 2787-2788, 2860-2861, 3025-3026, 3122-3123, 3213-3214.

Souvenir Sheet

ESPANA '84, Madrid — A734

1984, Apr. 27 ***Perf. 13x13½***

2704 A734 1p Clipper ship

Women's Basketball, 1984 Summer Olympics A735

1984, May 5 ***Perf. 13***

2705 A735 20c multi

Agrarian Reform Act, 25th Anniv. A736

1984, May 17 ***Perf. 13½x13***

2706 A736 5c multi

Banco Popular de Ahorro, 1st Anniv. — A737

1984, May 18 ***Perf. 13***

2707 A737 5c multi

Antiguan Locomotives — A738

1984, June 11 ***Perf. 12½x12***

2708 A738 1c multi
2709 A738 4c multi, diff.
2710 A738 5c multi, diff.
2711 A738 10c multi, diff.
2712 A738 30c multi, diff.
2713 A738 50c multi, diff.

Souvenir Sheet

19th UPU Congress, HAMBURG '84 — A739

1984, June 19 ***Perf. 13x13½***

2714 A739 1p Nos. 73, 232

Intl. Olympic Committee, 90th Anniv. — A740

1984, June 23 ***Perf. 13***

2715 A740 30c Coubertin, torch-bearer

Children's Day A741

1984, July 15 ***Perf. 12½x13***

2716 A741 5c multi

1984 Summer Olympics, Los Angeles — A742

1984, July 28 ***Perf. 13***

2717 A742 1c Wrestling
2718 A742 3c Discus
2719 A742 5c Volleyball
2720 A742 20c Boxing
2721 A742 30c Basketball
2722 A742 50c Weight lifting

Souvenir Sheet

Perf. 12½

2723 A742 1p Baseball

No. 2723 contains one 32x40mm stamp.

Emilio Roig de Leuchsenring (1889-1964), Historian — A743

1984, Aug. 8 ***Perf. 13***

2724 A743 5c multi

Friendship Games, Aug. 18-26, Havana A744

1984, Aug. 18

2725 A744 3c Volleyball
2726 A744 5c Women's volleyball
2727 A744 8c Water polo
2728 A744 30c Boxing

Cattle Breeding A745

1984, Sept. 20

2729 A745 2c Artificial pastures
2730 A745 3c Cuban carib
2731 A745 5c Charolaise, vert.
2732 A745 30c Cuban cebu, vert.
2733 A745 50c White-udder

Souvenir Sheet

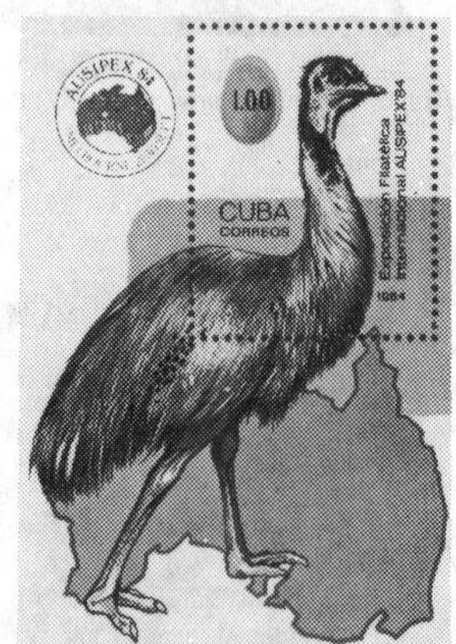

AUSIPEX '84, Sept. 21-30, Melbourne — A746

1984, Sept. 21 ***Perf. 12½***

2734 A746 1p Emu

Fauna — A747

1984, Oct. 10 ***Perf. 13***

2735 A747 1c *Polymita*
2736 A747 2c *Solenodon cubanus*
2737 A747 3c *Alsophis cantherigerus*

2738 A747 4c *Osteopilus septentrionalis*
2739 A747 5c *Mellisuga helenae*
2740 A747 10c *Capromys melanurus*
2741 A747 30c *Todus multicolor*
2742 A747 50c Parrots (cotorra)

Souvenir Sheet

ESPAMER '85, Havana — A748

1984, Oct. 12
2743 Sheet of 4+2 labels
a. A748 5c Ferdinand, Isabella
b. A748 20c Departure from Palos
c. A748 30c *Nina, Pinta, Santa Maria*
d. A748 50c Landing in America

Columbus Day.

Souvenir Sheet

9th Natl. Phil. Exhibition, Oct. 20-28, Santiago de Cuba — A749

1984, Oct. 20 *Perf. 12½*
2744 A749 1p multicolored

Natl. Revolutionary Militia, 25th Anniv. A750

1984, Oct. 26 *Perf. 12½x13*
2745 A750 5c multi

Disappearance of Camilo Cienfuegos, 25th Anniv. — A751

1984, Oct. 28 *Perf. 13x12½*
2746 A751 5c multi

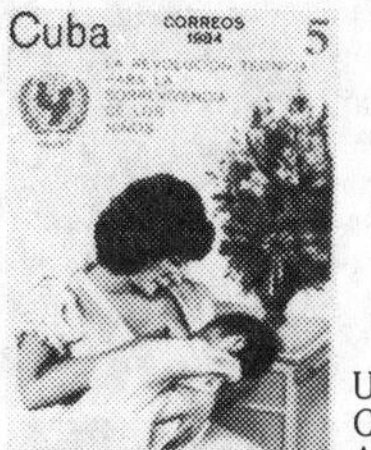

UN Child Survival Campaign A752

1984, Nov. 11 *Perf. 13*
2747 A752 5c Breast-feeding

Classic Automobiles — A753

1984, Nov. 25
2748 A753 1c 1909 Morgan
2749 A753 2c 1922 Austin
2750 A753 5c 1903 De Dion-Bouton
2751 A753 20c 1908 Ford Model T
2752 A753 30c 1885 Benz
2753 A753 50c 1910 Benz

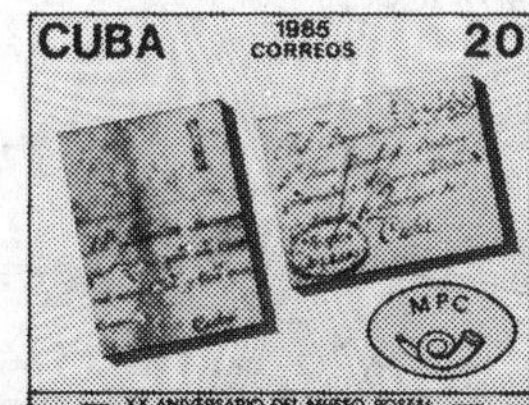

Postal Museum, 20th Anniv. — A754

1985, Jan. 2 *Perf. 13x12½*
2754 A754 20c multi

Portrait of Celia Sanchez, by E. Escobedo — A755

1985, Jan. 11 *Perf. 13*
2755 A755 5c multi

Celia Sanchez (1920-1980), party leader.

PORTO '85, Intl. Pigeon Exhibition A756

1985, Jan. 23
2756 A756 20c multi

1986 World Cup Soccer Championships, Mexico — A757

Athletes and Flags of previous host nations.

1985, Jan. 25
2757 A757 1c Chile, 1962
2758 A757 2c Great Britain, 1966
2759 A757 3c Mexico, 1970
2760 A757 4c Federal Republic of Germany, 1974
2761 A757 5c Argentina, 1978
2762 A757 30c Spain, 1982
2763 A757 50c Sweden, 1958

Souvenir Sheet

Perf. 12½

2764 A757 1p Mexico, 1986

No. 2764 contains one 40x32mm stamp.

Bacanao Natl. Park — A758

Dinosaurs.

1985, Feb. 14 *Perf. 13x12½*
2765 A758 1c Pteranodon
2766 A758 2c Brontosaurus
2767 A758 4c Iguanodontus
2768 A758 5c Estegosaurus
2769 A758 8c Monoclonius
2770 A758 30c Corythosaurus
2771 A758 50c Tyrannosaurus

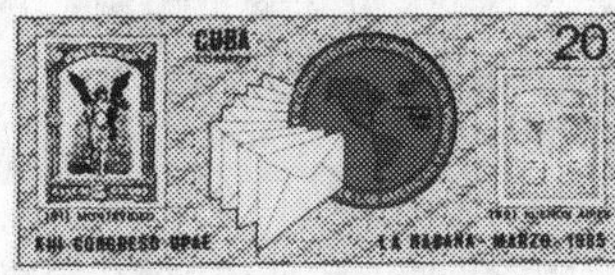

13th Congress of the Postal Unions of the Americas, Havana — A759

Design: Uruguay #196, congress emblem and Brazil #287. Illustration reduced.

1985, Mar. 11 *Perf. 12½x12*
2772 A759 20c multi

ESPAMER '85 A760

Indian activities: 1c, Playing ball. 2c, Medicine man preparing calumet and other ritual items. 5c, Net and spear fishing. 20c, Potter. 30c, Hunting. 50c, Hollowing-out canoe, decorating paddle. 1p, Cooking.

1985, Mar. 19 *Perf. 12½x13*
2773 A760 1c multi
2774 A760 2c multi
2775 A760 5c multi
2776 A760 20c multi
2777 A760 30c multi
2778 A760 50c multi

Souvenir Sheet

Perf. 12½

2779 A760 1p multi

No. 2779 contains one 32x40mm stamp.
An imperf. souvenir sheet exists containing Nos. 2773-2779.

Cosmonauts' Day — A761

Designs: 2c, Spacecraft orbiting Moon. 3c, Two spacecraft. 10c, Space walkers linked. 13c, Space walkers welding. 20c, *Vostok 2*. 50c, *Lunayod 1* moon vehicle.

1985, Apr. 12 *Perf. 13x12½*
2780 A761 2c multi
2781 A761 3c multi
2782 A761 10c multi
2783 A761 13c multi
2784 A761 20c multi
2785 A761 50c multi

12th Youth and Students Festival, Moscow — A762

1985, Apr. 19 *Perf. 13*
2786 A762 30c Lenin Mausoleum

Stamp Day Type of 1984

Mural, by R. Rodriguez Radillo (1967), details: 20c, Roman charioteer (courier of *Cursus Publicus*). 35c, Medieval nobleman, monks (monastic messenger mail).

1985, Apr. 24 *Perf. 13x12½*
2787 A733 20c multi
2788 A733 35c multi

Mothers' Day — A763

1985, May 2 *Perf. 13*
2789 A763 1c Peonies
2790 A763 4c Carnations
2791 A763 5c Dahlias
2792 A763 13c Roses
2793 A763 20c Roses, diff.
2794 A763 50c Tulips

50th Death Anniv. of Antonio Guiteras and Carlos Aponte, Revolutionaries — A764

1985, May 9 *Perf. 12½x12*
2795 A764 5c multi

End of WWII, 40th Anniv. A765

1985, May 10
2796 A765 5c shown
2797 A765 20c Soviet memorial, Berlin-Treptow
2798 A765 30c Dove

Souvenir Sheet

ARGENTINA '85, Buenos Aires — A766

1985, June 5 *Perf. 13½x13*

2799 A766 1p *Vulture gryphus*

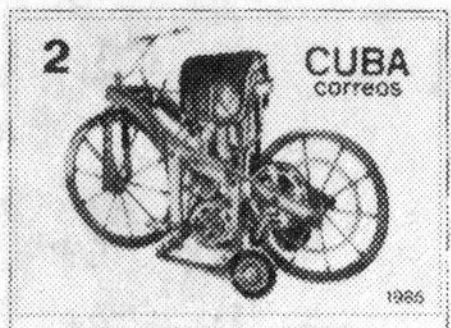

Motorcycle, Cent. — A767

1985, June 28 *Perf. 13*

2800 A767 2c 1885 Daimler
2801 A767 5c 1910 Kaiser Tricycle
2802 A767 10c 1925 Fanomobile
2803 A767 30c 1926 Mars A20
2804 A767 50c 1936 Simson BSW

Development of Health Care Since the Revolution — A768

1985, July 18 *Perf. 12½x12*

2805 A768 5c Hospitals

Federation of Cuban Women (FMC), 25th Anniv. — A769

1985, Aug. 23

2806 A769 5c multi

No. 2807 printed se-tenant with label picturing federation emblem.

Universiade Games, Japan — A770

1985, Aug. 27 *Perf. 13*

2807 A770 50c multi

1st Havana Declaration, 25th Anniv. — A771

1985, Sept. 2

2808 A771 5c Jose Marti statue, revolutionaries

Souvenir Sheet

ITALIA '85 — A772

1985, Sept. 25 *Perf. 12½*

2809 A772 1p Roman galley

Revolutionary Defense Committees (CDR), 25th Anniv. — A773

1985, Sept. 28 *Perf. 13*

2810 A773 5c multi

Aquarium Fish A774

1985, Sept. 30 **Litho.**

2811 A774 1c *Centropyge argi*
2812 A774 3c *Holacanthus tricolor*
2813 A774 5c *Chaetodon capistratus*
2814 A774 10c *Chaetodon sedentarius*
2815 A774 20c *Chaetodon ocellatus*
2816 A774 50c *Holacanthus ciliaris*

Communist Party Central Committee, 20th Anniv. — A775

1985, Oct. 1

2817 A775 5c multi

Souvenir Sheet

EXFILNA '85 — A776

1985, Oct. 18

2818 A776 1p Spain No. C45, Cuba No. 387

UN, 40th Anniv. — A777

1985, Oct. 24

2819 A777 20c multi

Sites on the UNESCO World Heritage List A778

Designs: 2c, Plaza Vieja, 16th cent. 5c, Royal Army Castle, c. 1558. 20c, Havana Cathedral, c. 1748. 30c, Captains-General Palace (Havana City Museum), 1776. 50c, The Temple, 1827.

1985, Nov. 25

2820 A778 2c multi
2821 A778 5c multi
2822 A778 20c multi
2823 A778 30c multi
2824 A778 50c multi

1986 World Cup Soccer Championships, Mexico — A779

Various athletes.

1986, Jan. 20

2825 A779 1c multi
2826 A779 4c multi
2827 A779 5c multi
2828 A779 10c multi
2829 A779 30c multi
2830 A779 50c multi

Souvenir Sheet

Perf. 13½x13

2831 A779 1p multi

No. 2831 contains one 32x40mm stamp.

3rd Communist Party Congress, Havana — A780

1986, Feb. 4 *Perf. 13*

2832 A780 5c shown
2833 A780 20c Party and natl. flags, emblem

Natl. Sports Institute (INDER), 25th Anniv. A781

1986, Feb. 23

2834 A781 5c multi

A782 A783

1986, Feb. 23

2835 A782 5c multi

Ministry of Domestic Trade, 25th anniv.

1986, Feb. 25 *Perf. 12½x12*

Exotic flowers in the Botanical Gardens.

2836 A783 1c *Tecomaria capensis*
2837 A783 3c *Michelia champaca*
2838 A783 5c *Thunbergia grandiflora*
2839 A783 8c *Dendrobium phalaenopsis*
2840 A783 30c *Allamanda violacea*
2841 A783 50c *Rhodactus bleo*

Gundlach and Birds A784

1986, Mar. 14 **Litho.** *Perf. 13½x13*

2842 A784 1c *Agelaius assimilis*
2843 A784 3c *Dendroica pityophila*
2844 A784 7c *Myiarchus sagrae*
2845 A784 9c *Dendroica petechia gundlachi*
2846 A784 30c *Geotrygon caniceps*
2847 A784 50c *Colaptes auratus chrysocaulosus*

Juan Cristobal Gundlach (d. 1896), ornithologist.

Pioneers Youth Organization, Founded by Jose Marti, 25th Anniv. — A785

1986, Apr. 3 *Perf. 13*

2848 A785 5c Induction

150th Birth Anniv. of Maximo Gomez — A786

1986, Apr. 4

2849 A786 20c multi

A787

A788

1986, Apr. 10 *Perf. 12½*
2850 A787 5c multi

Kindergartens, 25th anniv.

1986, Apr. 12 *Perf. 13x13½*

1st Man in Space, 25th Anniv.: 1c, *Vostok* and rocket designer Sergei Korolev. 2c, Yuri Gagarin, *Vostok 1.* 5c, Valentina Tereshkova, *Vostok 6.* 20c, *Salyut-Soyuz* space link. 30c, Capsule landing. 50c, *Soyuz* rocket launch. 1p, Konstantin Tsiolkovski (1857-1935), rocket scientist.

2851 A788 1c multi
2852 A788 2c multi
2853 A788 5c multi
2854 A788 20c multi
2855 A788 30c multi
2856 A788 50c multi

Souvenir Sheet

Perf. 12½

2857 A788 1p multi

No. 2857 contains one 32x40mm stamp.

Natl. Flag and No. 2407 — A789

1986, Apr. 19 *Perf. 13*
2858 A789 5c shown
2859 A789 20c Banners, natl. crest

Bay of Pigs invasion, 25th anniv. (5c); Proclamation of Socialist Revolution, 25th anniv. (20c).

Stamp Day Type of 1984

Mural, by R. Rodriguez Radillo (1967), details.

1986, Apr. 24 *Perf. 13x12½*
2860 A733 20c Mail coach, 18th-19th cent.
2861 A733 30c Pony Express

Radio Havana, 25th Anniv. — A790

1986, May 1
2862 A790 5c multi

EXPO '86, Vancouver — A791

Locomotives: 1c, *Stourbridge Lion,* 1829, US. 4c, Stephenson's *Rocket,* 1829, GB. 5c, 1st Russian locomotive, 1845. 8c, Seguin's locomotive, 1830, France. 30c, 1st Canadian locomotive, 1836. 50c, Urban locomotive, Belgian Grand Central Rlwy., 1872. 1p, US locomotive pulling Cuban sugar train, 1837.

1986, May 2 Litho. *Perf. 12½x12*
2863 A791 1c multi
2864 A791 4c multi
2865 A791 5c multi
2866 A791 8c multi
2867 A791 30c multi
2868 A791 50c multi

Souvenir Sheet

Perf. 13x13½

2869 A791 1p multi

No. 2869 contains one 40x32mm stamp.

Assoc. of Small Farmers, (ANAP), 25th Anniv. A792

1986, May 17 *Perf. 13*
2870 A792 5c multi

Intl. Peace Year A793

1986, June 2
2871 A793 30c multi

Ministry of the Interior (MININT), 25th Anniv. — A794

1986, June 6
2872 A794 5c multi

Martin Luther King, Jr. A795

1986, June 27 *Perf. 13½x13*
2873 A795 20c multi

Bonifacio Byrne (d. 1936), Poet A796

1986, July 5 *Perf. 13*
2874 A796 5c multi

Cuban Union of Writers and Artists (UNEAC), 25th Anniv. — A797

Sandanista Movement in Nicaragua (FSLN), 25th Anniv. — A798

1986, July 10 *Perf. 13x12½*
2875 A797 5c multi

1986, July 23 *Perf. 13x12*

Design: Augusto Cesar Sandino and Carlos Fonseca.

2876 A798 20c multi

Ministry of Transportation, 25th Anniv. — A799

1986, Aug. 1 *Perf. 13*
2877 A799 5c multi

7th University Games of Central America and the Caribbean — A800

1986, Aug. 9
2878 A800 20c multi

Souvenir Sheet

STOCKHOLMIA '86 — A801

Designs: a, 2c Mambi Revolutionary stamp of 1897. b, Sweden Type A7, cancellation.

1986, Aug. 28 *Perf. 12½*
2879 A801 Sheet of 2
a.-b. 50c multi

Nonaligned Countries Movement, 25th Anniv. — A802

1986, Sept. 1 *Perf. 13½x13*
2880 A802 50c multi

Orchids — A803

1986, Sept. 15 *Perf. 12½*
2881 A803 1c *Cattleya hardyana*
2882 A803 4c *Brassolaelio cattleya*
2883 A803 5c *Phalaenopsis marget moses*
2884 A803 10c *Laelio cattleya prism palette*
2885 A803 30c *Phalaenopsis violacea*
2886 A803 50c *Disa uniflora*

Latin American History A804

Pre-Columbian artifacts: No. 2887, Mayan dwelling and votive jade sculpture. No. 2888, Inca vase and Tiahuanacu sun gate (Bolivia). No. 2889, Spain No. C47, discovery of America 500th anniv. emblem, scroll. No. 2890, Diaguitan duck-shaped pitcher and Pucara de Quitor ruins (Chile). No. 2891, San Agustin Archaeological Park megaliths and Quimbayan sculpture (Colombia). No. 2892, Moler grinding stone and Chorotega ceramic figurine. No. 2893, Tabaco idol and Indian dwelling (Cuba). No. 2894, Spain No. C38. No. 2895, Taino dwelling and chair (Dominica). No. 2896, Tolita statue and Ingapirca Castle ruins. No. 2897, Maya vase and Tikal Temple (Guatemala). No. 2898, Copan ruins and Maya idol. No. 2899, Spain No. C37. No. 2900, Chichen Itza Temple and Zapotecan urn (Mexico). No. 2901, Punta de Zapote megaliths and Ometepe ceramic figurine. No. 2902, Tonosi lidded ceramic bowl and Barriles monoliths. No. 2903, Ruins at Machu-Picchu and Inca statue (Peru). No. 2904, Spain No. C49. No. 2905, Teepees and triangular sculpture (Puerto Rico). No. 2906, Fertility statue from Santa Ana and Santo Domingo Cave.

1986, Oct. 12 *Perf. 13*
2887 A804 1c multi
2888 A804 1c multi
2889 A804 1c multi
2890 A804 1c multi
2891 A804 1c multi
a. Strip of 5, Nos. 2887-2891
2892 A804 5c multi
2893 A804 5c multi
2894 A804 5c multi
2895 A804 5c multi
2896 A804 5c multi
a. Strip of 5, Nos. 2892-2896
2897 A804 10c multi
2898 A804 10c multi
2899 A804 10c multi
2900 A804 10c multi
2901 A804 10c multi
a. Strip of 5, Nos. 2897-2901
2902 A804 20c multi
2903 A804 20c multi
2904 A804 20c multi
2905 A804 20c multi
2906 A804 20c multi
a. Strip of 5, Nos. 2902-2906

Discovery of America, 500th anniv. (in 1992). See Nos. 2966-2985, 3065-3084, 3253-3272, 3463-3466.

Intl. Brigades, Spain, 50th Anniv. — A805

1986, Oct. 14 *Perf. 12½x12*
2907 A805 30c multi

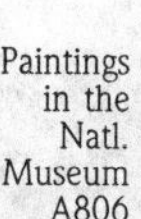

Paintings in the Natl. Museum A806

Designs: 2c, *Two Children,* by Gutierrez de la Vega, vert. 4c, *Sed,* by Jean-Georges Vibert. 6c, *Virgin and Child,* by Niccolo Abbate, vert. 10c, *Bullfight,* by Eugenio de Lucas Velazquez. 30c, *The Five Senses,* anonymous. 50c, *Arrival at Thomops Castle,* by Jean Louis Ernest.

1986, Nov. 5 *Perf. 13*

2908 A806 2c multi
2909 A806 4c multi
2910 A806 6c multi
2911 A806 10c multi
2912 A806 30c multi
2913 A806 50c multi

Anniversaries A807

1986, Dec. 2 Litho. *Perf. 12¹/₂*

2914 A807 5c *Granma*

Size: 26x38mm

2915 A807 20c Soldier, rifle, flag

Granma Landings, 30th anniv. (5c); Revolutionary Armed Forces, 30th anniv. (20c).

Scholarship Program, 25th Anniv. A808

1986, Dec. 22 *Perf. 13*

2916 A808 5c Guevara, students

Natl. Literacy Campaign, 25th Anniv. — A809

1986, Dec. 25 *Perf. 13x12¹/₂*

2917 A809 5c Marti, man learning to write

Siege of La Plata, 30th Anniv. A810

1987, Jan. 17 *Perf. 12¹/₂x12*

2918 A810 5c Map, revolutionaries

Paintings in the Natl. Museum A811

Designs: 3c, *Gypsy,* by Joaquin Sorolla, vert. 5c, *Sir Walter Scott,* by Sir John W. Gordon, vert. 10c, *Farm Meadows,* by Alfred de Breanski. 20c, *Still-life,* by Isaac van Duynen. 30c, *Landscape with Figures,* by Francesco Zuccarelli. 40c, *The Failure* (defeated bullfighter), by Ignacio Zuloaga, vert.

1987, Feb. 5 *Perf. 13*

2919 A811 3c multi
2920 A811 5c multi
2921 A811 10c multi
2922 A811 20c multi
2923 A811 30c multi
2924 A811 40c multi

Siege of the Presidential Palace, 30th Anniv. — A812

1987, Mar. 13 *Perf. 12¹/₂x12*

2925 A812 5c Palace, van, Echeverra

Lazarus Ludwig Zamenhof and Russia Type A77 — A813

1987, Mar. 16 *Perf. 13¹/₂x13*

2926 A813 30c multi

Esperanto, cent.

Souvenir Sheet

EXFILNA '87, 10th Natl. Stamp Exposition, Holguin — A814

1987, Mar. 28 *Perf. 13x13¹/₂*

2927 A814 1p Nos. 552, C129

25th Anniv. and 5th Cong. of the Youth Communist League (U.J.C.) — A815

1987, Apr. 4 *Perf. 13*

2928 A815 5c multi

Intercosmos, 20th Anniv. — A816

1987, Apr. 12 Litho. *Perf. 12¹/₂x12*

2929 A816 3c *Intercosmos 1*
2930 A816 5c *Intercosmos 2*
2931 A816 10c *TD*
2932 A816 20c *Cosmos 93*
2933 A816 30c *Molniya*
2934 A816 50c *Vostok 3*

Souvenir Sheet

Perf. 13¹/₂x13

2935 A816 1p Rocket, *Vostok 3*

No. 2935 contains one 32x40mm stamp.

Stamp Day A817

Stamped covers and canceled stamps.

1987, Apr. 24 *Perf. 13*

2936 A817 30c Havana, 1890
2937 A817 50c Santiago de Cuba, 1869

Mothers' Day — A818

Various dahlias and roses.

1987, May 2

2938 A818 3c multi
2939 A818 5c multi
2940 A818 10c multi
2941 A818 13c multi
2942 A818 30c multi
2943 A818 50c multi

Bone-lengthening Procedure (Femur in Frame) — A819

1987, May 4

2944 A819 5c multi

ORTOPEDIA '87, medical congress for orthopedists from Spanish and Portuguese-speaking countries, Havana.

Cuban Broadcasting and Television Institute, 25th Anniv. — A820

1987, May 24 *Perf. 13*

2945 A820 5c multi

Battle of Uvero, 30th Anniv. A821

1987, May 28 *Perf. 13¹/₂x13*

2946 A821 5c Views of monument, Sierra Maestra Mts.

CAPEX '87 — A822

Natl. flags, stamps and 19th cent. mail carriers pictured on cigarette cards: 3c, Messenger, llamas and Bolivia Type A9. 5c, Early p.o., automobile and France Type A17. 10c, Messengers riding elephants and Thailand Type A2. 20c, Messenger riding camel and stamp of Egypt, 1879. 30c, Mail troika and stamp of Russia. 50c, Post rider and stamp of Indo-China. 1p, Post rider and Mambi Revolutionary stamp.

1987, June 15 *Perf. 12¹/₂x13*

2947 A822 3c multi
2948 A822 5c multi
2949 A822 10c multi
2950 A822 20c multi
2951 A822 30c multi
2952 A822 50c multi

Souvenir Sheet

Perf. 13¹/₂x13

2953 A822 1p multi

No. 2953 contains one 32x40mm stamp.

Dinosaur Exhibits, Bacanao Natl. Park A823

1987, June 25 *Perf. 13*

2954 A823 3c multi
2955 A823 5c multi
2956 A823 10c multi
2957 A823 20c multi
2958 A823 35c multi
2959 A823 40c multi

Frank Pais (d. 1957), Teacher and Student Leader A824

1987, July 30 *Perf. 12¹/₂x12*

2960 A824 5c Pais, Rafael Maria Mendive University

10th Pan American Games, Indianapolis — A825

1987, Aug. 8

2961 A825 50c multi

Printed se-tenant with inscribed label picturing the 1991 Havana Games character trademark.

Siege of Cienfuegos, 30th Anniv. — A826

1987, Sept. 5 *Perf. 13*
2962 A826 5c Memorial

Souvenir Sheet

HAFNIA '87, Denmark — A827

1987, Sept. 16 *Perf. 13½x13*
2963 A827 1p Danish mailman, 1887, Type A6

Souvenir Sheet

ESPAMER '87, La Coruna, Oct. 2-12 — A828

1987, Oct. 2
2964 A828 1p La Coruna Port, 1525

20th Heroic Guerrillas Day — A829

1987, Oct. 8 *Perf. 12½x12*
2965 A829 50c Coins, #1364

Latin American History Type of 1986

Indians and birds: No. 2966, Tehuelche Indian of Argentina and *Habia rubica.* No. 2967, *Ramphastos cuvieri* and Tibirica Indian of Brazil. No. 2968, Spain No. C31 and discovery of America 500th anniv. emblem. No. 2969, *Vulture gryphus* and Lautaro Indian of Chile. No. 2970, Calarca Indian of Colombia and *Opisthocomus hoazin.* No. 2971, *Priotelus temnurus* and Hatuey Indian of Cuba. No. 2972, *Columbigallina passerina* and Enriquillo Indian of the Dominican Republic. No. 2973, Spain No. 427. No. 2974, *Semnornis ramphastinus* and Ruminahui Indian of Ecuador. No. 2975, *Pharomachrus mocinno* and Tecum Uman Indian of Guatemala. No. 2976, Anacaona Indian of Haiti and *Aramas guarauna.* No. 2977, Lempira Indian of Honduras and *Diglossa baritula.* No. 2978, Spain No. C42. No. 2979, *Onychorhinchus mexicanus* and Cuauhtemoc Indian of Mexico. No. 2980, *Setofaga picta* and Nicarao Indian of Nicaragua. No. 2981, *Rupicola peruviana* and Atahualpa Indian of Peru. No. 2982, Atlacatl Indian of El Salvador and *Bluteo jamaicensis.* No. 2983, Spain No. 432. No. 2984, Abayuba Indian of Uruguay and *Phytotoma rutila.* No. 2985, Guaycaypuro Indian of Venezuela and *Ara arauna.*

1987, Oct. 12 *Perf. 13*
2966 A804 1c multi
2967 A804 1c multi
2968 A804 1c multi
2969 A804 1c multi
2970 A804 1c multi
a. Strip of 5, Nos. 2966-2970
2971 A804 5c multi
2972 A804 5c multi
2973 A804 5c multi
2974 A804 5c multi
2975 A804 5c multi
a. Strip of 5, Nos. 2971-2975
2976 A804 10c multi
2977 A804 10c multi
2978 A804 10c multi
2979 A804 10c multi
2980 A804 10c multi
a. Strip of 5, Nos. 2976-2980
2981 A804 20c multi
2982 A804 20c multi
2983 A804 20c multi
2984 A804 20c multi
2985 A804 20c multi
a. Strip of 5, Nos. 2981-2985

Discovery of America, 500th anniv. (in 1992). *Vultur* is spelled incorrectly on No. 2969.

October Revolution, Russia, 70th Anniv. — A830

1987, Nov. 7 *Perf. 12½x12*
2986 A830 30c Soviet spacecraft, Russia No. 379

Cuban Railway, 150th Anniv. — A831

Stamps on stamps.

1987, Nov. 19 *Perf. 13x12½*
2987 A831 3c No. 453
2988 A831 5c No. 1061
2989 A831 10c No. 2010
2990 A831 20c No. 2011
2991 A831 35c No. 2360
2992 A831 40c No. 2361

Souvenir Sheet
Perf. 13x13½
2993 A831 1p No. 355

No. 2993 contains 40x32mm one stamp.
An imperf. sheet containing Nos. 2987-2992 exists, inscribed to promote the 17th Pan American Railway Congress.

San Alejandro Art School, 170th Anniv. — A832

Paintings: 1c, *Landscape,* by Domingo Ramos. 2c, *Portrait of Rodriguez Morey,* by Eugenio Gonzalez Olivera. 5c, *Wagons,* by Eduardo Morales. 10c, *Portrait of Elena Herrera,* by Armando Menocal, vert. 30c, *Rape of Dejanira,* by Miguel Melero, vert. 50c, *The Card Player,* by Leopoldo Romanach.

Perf. 13x12½, 12½x13
1988, Jan. 12
2994 A832 1c multi
2995 A832 2c multi
2996 A832 5c multi
2997 A832 10c multi
2998 A832 30c multi
2999 A832 50c multi

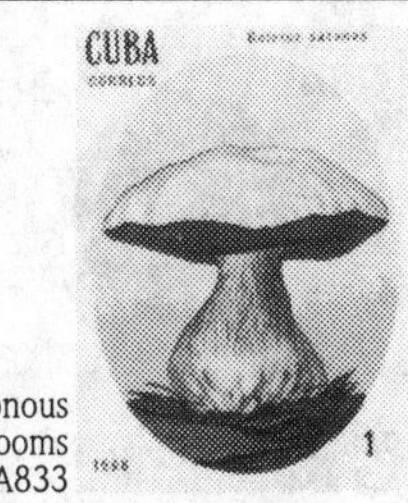
Poisonous Mushrooms A833

1988, Feb. 15 *Perf. 13*
3000 A833 1c *Boletus satanas*
3001 A833 2c *Amanita citrina*
3002 A833 3c *Tylopilus felleus*
3003 A833 5c *Paxillus involutus*
3004 A833 10c *Inocybe patouillardii*
3005 A833 30c *Amanita muscaria*
3006 A833 50c *Hypholoma fascicu-lare*

Radio Rebelde, 30th Anniv. — A834

1988, Feb. 24 *Perf. 12½x12*
3007 A834 5c multi

Monuments A835

1988 **Litho.** *Perf. 13*
3008 A835 5c Mario Munoz, Santiago de Cuba
3009 A835 5c Frank Pais Memorial, eternal flame

Battle fronts, 30th annivs. Issue dates: No. 3008, Mar. 5. No. 3009, Mar. 11.

Mothers' Day — A836

1988, Mar. 30
3010 A836 1c Red roses
3011 A836 2c Pale pink roses
3012 A836 3c Daisies
3013 A836 5c Dahlias
3014 A836 13c White roses
3015 A836 35c Carnations
3016 A836 40c Pink roses

Cosmonauts' Day — A837

1988, Apr. 12
3017 A837 2c *Gorizont*
3018 A837 3c *Mir-Kvant* space link
3019 A837 4c *Signo 3*
3020 A837 5c Mars, space probe
3021 A837 10c *Phobos*
3022 A837 30c *Vega*
3023 A837 50c Spacecraft

Souvenir Sheet
Perf. 13½x13
3024 A837 1p Spacecraft, diff.

No. 3024 contains one 32x40mm stamp.

Stamp Day Type of 1984

Mural, by R. Rodriguez Radillo (1967) details: 30c, Mail coach, telegraph operator. 50c, Passenger pigeon.

1988, Apr. 24 *Perf. 13x12½*
3025 A733 30c multi
3026 A733 50c multi

Institute for Research on Sugar Cane and Byproducts (ICIDCA), 25th Anniv. — A838

1988, May 23 *Perf. 12½x12*
3027 A838 5c multi

Cubana Airlines Transatlantic Flights — A839

1988, May 25
3028 A839 2c Madrid, 1948
3029 A839 4c Prague, 1961
3030 A839 5c Berlin, 1972
3031 A839 10c Luanda, 1975
3032 A839 30c Paris, 1983
3033 A839 50c Moscow, 1987

Souvenir Sheet

FINLANDIA '88 — A840

1988, June 1 *Perf. 12½*
3034 A840 1p Steam packet *Furst Menschikoff*

Postal Union of the Americas and Spain (UPAE) Conference on Stamps of the Americas, Havana — A841

Illustration reduced.

1988, June 20 *Perf. 12½x12*
3035 A841 20c multi

Beetles A842

1988, June 30 *Perf. 13*
3036 A842 1c *Megasoma elephas fabricus*
3037 A842 3c *Platycoelia flavoscutellata ohaus,* vert.

3038 A842 4c *Plusiotis argenteola bates*
3039 A842 5c *Heterosternus oberthuri ohaus*
3040 A842 10c *Odontotaenius zodiacus truqui*
3041 A842 35c *Chrysophora chrysochlora la treille*, vert.
3042 A842 40c *Phanaeus leander waterhouse*

Jose Raul Capablanca (1888-1942), Chess Champion — A843

Perf. 12½x13, 13x12½

1988, July 15

3043 A843 30c Chessmen, vert.
3044 A843 40c J. Corza, Capablanca
3045 A843 50c Lasker, Capablanca
3046 A843 1p Winning configuration, 1921, vert.
3047 A843 3p Portrait by E. Valderrama, vert.
3048 A843 5p Chessmen, Capablanca

Souvenir Sheets

3049 Sheet of 2
  a. A843 30c No. 464, vert.
  b. like No. 3043, size: 32x40mm
3050 Sheet of 2
  a. A843 40c No. 465
  b. like No. 3044, size: 40x32mm
3051 Sheet of 2
  a. A843 50c No. C44
  b. like No. 3045, size: 40x32mm
3052 Sheet of 2
  a. A843 1p No. 464, vert.
  b. like No. 3046, size: 32x40mm
3053 Sheet of 2
  a. A843 3p No. C46, vert.
  b. like No. 3047, size: 32x40mm
3054 Sheet of 2
  a. A843 5p No. C45, vert.
  b. like No. 3048, size: 32x40mm

Attack on Moncada Barracks, 35th Anniv. A844

1988, July 26 ***Perf. 13***

3055 A844 5c blk, yel ocher & red

Souvenir Sheet

PRAGA '88 — A845

1988, Aug. 26 ***Perf. 12½***

3056 A845 1p Czechoslovakia No. 45

Czechoslovakian postage stamps, 70th anniv.

Revolutionary Invasion Force, 30th Anniv. — A846

1988, Aug. 31 ***Perf. 12½x12***

3057 A846 5c multi

World Marxist Review, 30th Anniv. A847

1988, Sept. 1 ***Perf. 13***

3058 A847 30c multi

Locomotives A848

1988, Sept. 19 ***Perf. 12½x13***

3059 A848 20c Stephenson's *Rocket*, 1837
3060 A848 30c Miller, US, 1839
3061 A848 50c *La Junta*
3062 A848 1p J.G. Brill trolley, US, 1922
3063 A848 2p TEM 4K, USSR, c. 1960
3064 A848 5p CAP 9 electric, c. 1988

Latin American History Type of 1986

Natl. arms and patriots: No. 3065, San Martin, Argentina. No. 3066, M.A. Padilla, Bolivia. No. 3067, No. 390 and discovery of America 500th anniv. emblem. No. 3068, Tiradentes, Brazil. No. 3069, O'Higgins, Chile. No. 3070, A. Narino, Colombia. No. 3071, Marti, Cuba. No. 3072, No. 391 and emblem. No. 3073, Duarte, Dominican Republic. No. 3074, Sucre, Ecuador. No. 3075, M.J. Arce, El Salvador. No. 3076, Dessalines, Haiti. No. 3077, No. C36 and emblem. No. 3078, Hidalgo, Mexico. No. 3079, J.D. Estrada, Nicaragua. No. 3080, Diaz, Paraguay. No. 3081, F. Bolognesi, Peru. No. 3082, No. C37 and emblem. No. 3083, Artigas, Uruguay. No. 3084, Bolivar, Venezuela.

1988, Oct. 12 ***Perf. 13***

3065 A804 1c multi
3066 A804 1c multi
3067 A804 1c multi
3068 A804 1c multi
3069 A804 1c multi
  a. Strip of 5, Nos. 3065-3069
3070 A804 5c multi
3071 A804 5c multi
3072 A804 5c multi
3073 A804 5c multi
3074 A804 5c multi
  a. Strip of 5, Nos. 3070-3074
3075 A804 10c multi
3076 A804 10c multi
3077 A804 10c multi
3078 A804 10c multi
3079 A804 10c multi
  a. Strip of 5, Nos. 3075-3079
3080 A804 20c multi
3081 A804 20c multi
3082 A804 20c multi
3083 A804 20c multi
3084 A804 20c multi
  a. Strip of 5, Nos. 3080-3084

Discovery of America, 500th anniv. (in 1992).

Havana Museum, 20th Anniv. — A849

Design: Captain-General's Palace and Maces of Municipal Havana.

1988, Oct. 16 Litho. ***Perf. 12½x12***

3085 A849 5c multi

Anniversaries — A850

1988, Oct. 28 ***Perf. 13***

3086 A850 5c *Swan Lake*
3087 A850 5c Theater in 1838 and 1988
  a. Pair, Nos. 3086-3087

Natl. Ballet, 40th anniv. (No. 3086); Grand Theater of Havana, 150th anniv. (No. 3087).

Intl. Literacy Year A851

1988, Dec. 5

3088 A851 5c multi

UN Declaration of Human Rights, 40th Anniv. — A851a

1988, Dec. 10

3088A A851a 30c multi

Battle of Santa Clara, 30th Anniv. A852

1988, Dec. 28 ***Perf. 13x12½***

3089 A852 30c Monument, Che Guevara Plaza

30th Anniv. of the Revolution — A853

1989, Jan. 1 ***Perf. 13***

3090 A853 5c multi
3091 A853 20c multi
3092 A853 30c multi
3093 A853 50c multi

Edible Mushrooms — A854

1989, Jan. 10

3094 A854 2c *Pleurotus levis*
3095 A854 3c *Pleurotus floridanus*
3096 A854 5c *Amanita caesarea*
3097 A854 10c *Lentinus cubensis*
3098 A854 40c *Pleurotus ostreatus* (brown)
3099 A854 50c *Pleurotus ostreatus* (yellow)

2c, 3c, 5c, 40c, 50c, vert.

Souvenir Sheet

INDIA '89 — A855

1989, Jan. 20

3100 A855 1p Indian River Post, 1858

Central Organization of Cuban Trade Unions (CTC), 50th Anniv. — A856

1989, Jan. 28 ***Perf. 12½***

3101 A856 5c No. 2477, CTC emblem

Butterflies A857

1989, Feb. 15

3102 A857 1c *Metamorpho dido*
3103 A857 3c *Callithea saphhira*
3104 A857 5c *Papilio zagreus*
3105 A857 10c *Mynes sestia*
3106 A857 30c *Papilio dardanus*
3107 A857 50c *Catagranma sorana*

1990 World Cup Soccer Championships, Italy — A858

Various athletes.

1989, Mar. 15 ***Perf. 13***

3108 A858 1c multi
3109 A858 3c multi, diff.
3110 A858 5c multi, diff.
3111 A858 10c multi, diff.
3112 A858 30c multi, diff.
3113 A858 50c multi, diff.

Souvenir Sheet

Perf. 12½

3114 A858 1p multi, diff., horiz.

No. 3114 contains one 40x32mm stamp.

Natl. Revolutionary Police (PNR), 30th Anniv. — A859

1989, Mar. 23 ***Perf. 13***

3115 A859 5c multi

Cosmonauts' Day — A860

Spacecraft and rocket mail covers: 1c, *Zodiac* and cover, Australia 1934. 3c, Lighthouse and cover, India, 1934. 5c, Cover, England, 1934. 10c, *Icarus* and cover, The Netherlands, 1935. 40c, *La Douce France* and cover, France, 1935. 50c, Rocket mail cover, Cuba, 1939.

1989, Apr. 12
3116 A860 1c multi
3117 A860 3c multi
3118 A860 5c multi
3119 A860 10c multi
3120 A860 40c multi
3121 A860 50c multi

Stamp Day Type of 1984

Details of mural by R. Rodriguez Radillo (1967): 30c, Mail coach, satellite dish. 50c, Galleon, longboats, train, passenger pigeon, horses.

1989, Apr. 24 Litho. ***Perf. 13x12½***
3122 A733 30c multi
3123 A733 50c multi

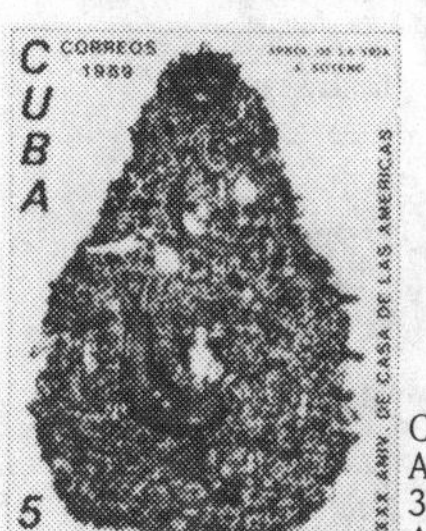

Casa de Las Americas, 30th Anniv. A861

1989, Apr. 28 ***Perf. 12½x13***
3124 A861 5c multi

BULGARIA '89 — A862

1989, May 1 ***Perf. 12½***
3125 A862 1p Bulgaria No. 346

58th FIP Congress and 101st anniv. of Bulgarian Railways.

Cuban Postal Code A863

1989, May 5 ***Perf. 13***
3126 A863 5c multi

Mothers' Day — A864

Perfume bottles and flowers.

1989, May 10
3127 A864 1c Habano, tobacco
3128 A864 3c Violeta, violets
3129 A864 5c Mariposa, mariposa
3130 A864 13c Coral Negro, roses
3131 A864 30c Ala Alonso, jasmine
3132 A864 50c D'Man, lemon blossoms

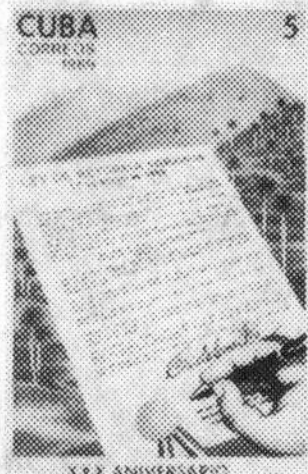

Agrarian Reform Law, 30th Anniv. — A865

1989, May 17 ***Perf. 12x12½***
3133 A865 5c multi

Council for Mutual Economic Assistance (CAME), 40th Anniv. A866

1989, June 1 Litho. ***Perf. 12½x13***
3134 A866 30c multi

13th World Communist Youth and Student Festival, Pyongyang — A867

1989, July 1 Litho. ***Perf. 12½***
3135 A867 30c multi

Souvenir Sheet

Rouget de Lisle Singing La Marseillaise, by Pils — A868

1989, July 7 ***Perf. 13***
3136 A868 1p multi

PHILEXFRANCE '89, French revolution bicent. and Cuban revolution 30th anniv.

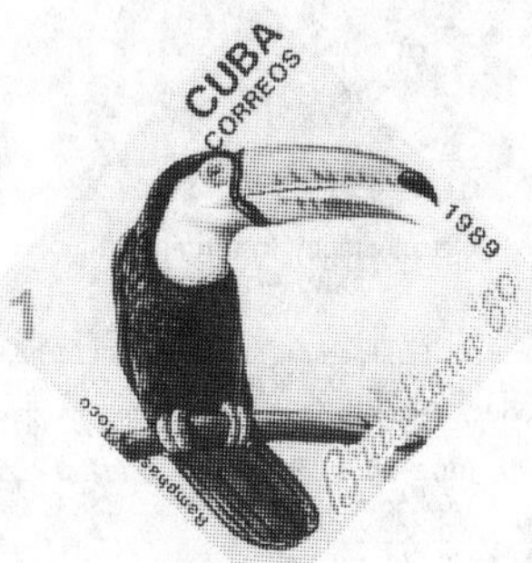

BRASILIANA '89 — A869

Exotic birds. (Illustration reduced.)

1989, July 28 Litho. ***Perf. 12½***
3137 A869 1c *Ramphastos toco*
3138 A869 3c *Agamia agami*
3139 A869 5c *Eudocimus ruber*
3140 A869 10c *Psophia leucoptera*
3141 A869 35c *Harpia harpyja*
3142 A869 50c *Cephatopterus ornatus*

Warships A870

1989, Sept. 29 Litho. ***Perf. 12½***
3143 A870 1c *El Fenix*
3144 A870 3c *Triunfo*
3145 A870 5c *El Rayo*
3146 A870 10c *San Carlos*
3147 A870 30c *San Jose*
3148 A870 50c *San Genaro*

America Issue — A871

UPAE emblem and pre-Columbian art: 5p, Stone carving, Indians in dugout canoe. 20p, Petroglyph, Indian drawing on stone wall.

1989, Oct. 12 ***Perf. 12½x12***
3149 A871 5c multi
3150 A871 20c multi

Latin American History A872

Writers and orchids: No. 3151, Domingo Sarmiento (1811-1888), Argentine educator, and *Govenia utriculata.* No. 3152, Joaquim Maria Machado de Assis (1839-1908), Brazilian novelist, and *Laelia grandis.* No. 3153, Salvador No. 69 and discovery of America anniv. emblem. No. 3154, Jorge Isaacs (1837-1895), Colombian novelist, and *Cattleya trianae.* No. 3155, Alejo Carpentier, Cuban writer, and *Cochleanthes discolor.* No. 3156, Pablo Neruda (1904-1973), Chilean poet, and *Oxalis adenophylla.* No. 3157, Pedro Urena, Dominican writer, and *Epidendrum fragrans.* No. 3158, Salvador No. 86 and anniv. emblem. No. 3159, Juan Montalvo (1832-1889), Ecuadorian satirist, and *Miltonia vexillaria.* No. 3160, Miguel Asturias (1899-1974), Guatemalan writer awarded the 1966 Lenin Peace Prize and 1967 Nobel Prize for literature, and *Odontoglossum rossii.* No. 3161, Jose C. del Valle, Honduran writer, and *Laelia anceps.* No. 3162, Alfonso Reyes (1889-1959), Mexican poet, and *Laelia anceps alba.* No. 3163, Salvador No. 87 and anniv. emblem. No. 3164, Ruben Dario (1867-1917), Nicaraguan poet, and *Brassavola acaulis.* No. 3165, Belisario Porras (1856-1942), president of Panama, and *Pescatorea celina.* No. 3166, Ricardo Palma (1833-1919), Peruvian writer, and *Coryanthes leucocorys.* No. 3167, Eugenio Maria de Hostos (1839-1903), Puerto Rican writer, and *Guzmania berteroniana.* No. 3168, Salvador No. 88 and anniv. emblem. No. 3169, Jose E. Rodo (1872-1917), Uruguayan philosopher, essayist, and *Cypella hebertii.* No. 3170, Romulo Gallegos, Venezuelan writer, and *Cattleya mossiae.*

1989, Oct. 27 Litho. ***Perf. 13***
3151 A872 1c multicolored
3152 A872 1c multicolored
3153 A872 1c multicolored
3154 A872 1c multicolored
3155 A872 1c multicolored
a. Strip of 5, Nos. 3151-3155
3156 A872 5c multicolored
3157 A872 5c multicolored
3158 A872 5c multicolored
3159 A872 5c multicolored
3160 A872 5c multicolored
a. Strip of 5, Nos. 3156-3160
3161 A872 10c multicolored
3162 A872 10c multicolored
3163 A872 10c multicolored
3164 A872 10c multicolored
3165 A872 10c multicolored
a. Strip of 5, Nos. 3161-3165
3166 A872 20c multicolored
3167 A872 20c multicolored
3168 A872 20c multicolored
3169 A872 20c multicolored
3170 A872 20c multicolored
a. Strip of 5, Nos. 3166-3170

Discovery of America 500th anniv. (in 1992).

Disappearance of Camilo Cienfuegos, 30th Anniv. — A873

1989, Oct. 28
3171 A873 5c multicolored

Founding of the City of Trinidad, 475th Anniv. A874

1989, Nov. 6 ***Perf. 12½x13***
3172 A874 5c multicolored

Paintings in the Natl. Museum A875

Designs: 1p, *Familiar Scene,* by Antoine Faivre. 2p, *Flowers,* by Emile Jean Horace Vernet (1789-1863). 5p, *The Judgement of Paris,* by Charles Le Brun (1619-1690). 20p, *Outskirts of Nice,* by Eugene Louis Boudin (1824-1898). 30p, *Portrait of Sarah Bernhardt,* by G.J.V. Clairin. 50p, *Fishermen in Port,* by C.J. Vernet.

Perf. 12½, 12½x13 (30p)
1989, Nov. 20 Litho.
Size of 30p: 36x46mm
3173 A875 1c multicolored
3174 A875 2c multicolored
3175 A875 5c multicolored
3176 A875 20c multicolored
3177 A875 30c multicolored
3178 A875 50c multicolored

11th Pan-American Games, Havana, 1991 — A876

1989, Dec. 15 Litho. ***Perf. 12½***
3179 A876 5c Cycling
3180 A876 5c Fencing
3181 A876 5c Water polo
3182 A876 5c Shooting
3183 A876 5c Archery
3184 A876 20c Tennis, vert.
3185 A876 30c Swimming, vert.
3186 A876 35c Diving, vert.
3187 A876 40c Field hockey
3188 A876 50c Basketball, vert.

Jose Marti's *Golden Age,* Cent. — A877

1989, Dec. 20 ***Perf. 13***

3189 A877 5c scar, light blue & blk

Cuban Postal Museum, 25th Anniv. — A878

1990, Jan. 2 ***Perf. 13x12½***

3190 A878 5c *Almendares*
3191 A878 30c Mail train

Speleological Soc., 50th Anniv. — A879

(Illustration reduced).

1990, Jan. 15 ***Perf. 12½***

3192 A879 30c multicolored

1990 World Cup Soccer Championships, Italy — A880

Various Italian architecture and athletes: No. 3193a, Dribbling (in red and blue). No. 3193b, Heading (in red and green). No. 3193c, Kicking (in green). 10c, Goalie catching ball. 30c, Dribbling, diff. 50c, Kicking, diff. 1p, Goalie catching ball, diff.

1990, Jan. 30 **Litho.** ***Perf. 12½***

3193 Strip of 3
a.-c. A880 5c any single
3194 A880 10c multicolored
3195 A880 30c multicolored
3196 A880 50c multicolored

Souvenir Sheet

3197 A880 1p multicolored

No. 3193 has a continuous design picturing The Colosseum.

1992 Summer Olympics, Barcelona — A881

1990, Feb. 20 **Litho.** ***Perf. 12½***

3198 A881 1c Baseball
3199 A881 4c Running
3200 A881 5c Basketball
3201 A881 10c Women's volleyball
3202 A881 30c Wrestling
3203 A881 50c Boxing

Souvenir Sheet

3204 A881 1p High jump

Nos. 3198-3201 and 3203 are vert.
No. 3204 contains one 40x32mm stamp.

75th Universal Esperanto Congress — A882

1990, Mar. 7

3205 A882 30c Tower of Babel

No. 3205 printed se-tenant with inscribed label publicizing the congress.

Souvenir Sheet

1992 Winter Olympics, Albertville — A883

1990, Mar. 30 **Litho.** ***Perf. 13***

3206 A883 1p multicolored

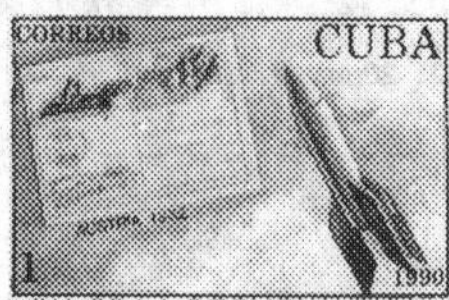

Cosmonauts' Day — A884

Spacecraft and rocket mail covers: 1c, Austria, 1932. 2c, Germany, 1933. 3c, Netherlands, 1934. 10c, Belgium, 1935. 30c, Yugoslavia, 1935. 50c, United States, 1936.

1990, Apr. 12 ***Perf. 12½***

3207 A884 1c multicolored
3208 A884 2c multicolored
3209 A884 3c multicolored
3210 A884 10c multicolored
3211 A884 30c multicolored
3212 A884 50c multicolored

Stamp Day Type of 1984

Details of mural by R. Rodriguez Radillo (1967): 30c, Train station. 50c, Jet aircraft in flight.

1990, Apr. 24 ***Perf. 13x12½***

3213 A733 30c multicolored
3214 A733 50c multicolored

Labor Day, Cent. A885

1990, Apr. 30 ***Perf. 13***

3215 A885 5c multicolored

Souvenir Sheet

Great Britain No. 1 on Cover — A886

1990, May 3

3216 A886 1p multicolored

Stamp World London '90, Penny Black 150th anniv.

Penny Black, 150th Anniv. A887

Portraits of Sir Rowland Hill and stamps of Great Britain.

1990, May 6 **Litho.** ***Perf. 12½x12***

3217 A887 2c No. 1
3218 A887 3c No. 2
3219 A887 5c Type A5
3220 A887 10c No. 5
3221 A887 30c First day postmark
3222 A887 50c 5 #1 on Mulready envelope

Celia Sanchez Manduley (1920-1980) A888

1990, May 9 ***Perf. 12½x13***

3223 A888 5c multicolored

Ho Chi Minh (1890-1969), Vietnamese Communist Party Leader — A889

1990, May 19 ***Perf. 12½***

3224 A889 50c multicolored

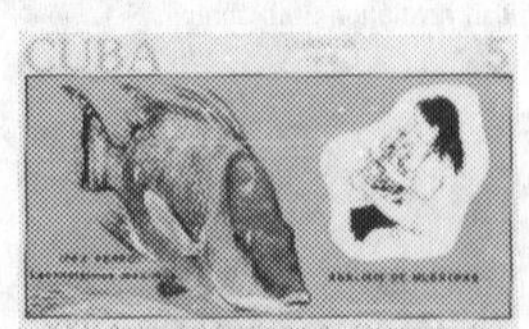

Oceanography Institute, 25th Anniv. — A890

Designs: 5c, Specimen analysis and *Lachnolaimus maximus.* 30c, Research ship, fish, coral reef. 50c, Specimen collection and *Panulirus argus.*

1990, June 18 **Litho.** ***Perf. 12½***

3225 A890 5c multicolored
3226 A890 30c multicolored
3227 A890 50c multicolored

5th Latin American Botanical Conference A891

1990, June 25 **Litho.** ***Perf. 12½***

3228 A891 3c Banara minutiflora
3229 A891 5c Oplonia nannophylla
3230 A891 10c Jacquinia brunnescens
3231 A891 30c Rondeletia brachycarpa
3232 A891 50c Rondeletia odorata

Tourism A892

1990, June 30

3233 A892 5c Wind surfing
3234 A892 10c Spear fishing
3235 A892 30c Deep sea fishing
3236 A892 40c Hunting

Nos. 3233, 3236 vert.

Art Treasures A893

Designs: 5c, "La Flauta Del Dios Pan." 20c, "Un Pastor." 50c, "Ganimedes." 1p, "Venus Anadiomena."

1990, July 20

3237 A893 5c multicolored
3238 A893 20c multicolored
3239 A893 50c multicolored
3240 A893 1p multicolored

Birds A894

1990, Aug. 24 **Litho.** ***Perf. 13***

3241 A894 2c Podiceps cristatus
3242 A894 3c Gallirallus australis
3243 A894 5c Nestor notabilis
3244 A894 10c Xenicus longipes
3245 A894 30c Cracticus torquatus
3246 A894 50c Prostemadera novaeseelandiae

Souvenir Sheet

3247 A894 1p Kiwi

New Zealand '90. No. 3247 contains one 39x31mm stamp.

8th UN Congress on Crime Prevention — A895

1990, Aug. 27 Litho. *Perf. 12½*
3248 A895 50c blue, silver & red

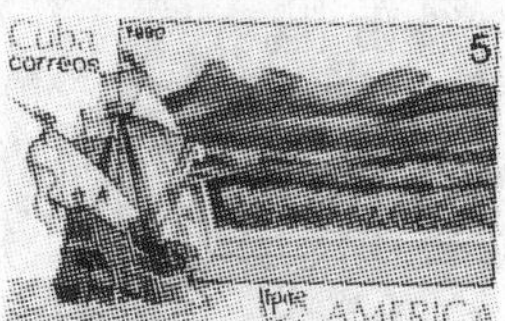

Discovery of America, 500th Anniv. (in 1992) — A896

1990, Oct. 12 Litho. *Perf. 12½*
3249 A896 5c Ship, shore
3250 A896 20c Columbus, village

Cuban Television, 40th Anniv. A897

1990, Oct. 12 Litho. *Perf. 13*
3251 A897 5c multicolored

Nationalization of Railroads, 30th Anniv. — A898

1990, Oct. 13 *Perf. 13x12½*
3252 A898 50c multicolored

Latin American History Type of 1986

Latin American stamps or flags and costumes: No. 3253, Argentina. No. 3254, Bolivia. No. 3255, Argentina No. 91. No. 3256, Colombia. No. 3257, Costa Rica. No. 3258, Cuba. No. 3259, Chile. No. 3260, Dominican Republic No. 110. No. 3261, Ecuador. No. 3262, El Salvador. No. 3263, Guatemala. No. 3264, Mexico. No. 3265, Puerto Rico No. 133. No. 3266, Nicaragua. No. 3267, Panama. No. 3268, Paraguay. No. 3269, Peru. No. 3270, El Salvador No. 103. No. 3271, Puerto Rico. No. 3272, Venezuela.

1990, Oct. 27 *Perf. 12½*
3253 A804 1c multicolored
3254 A804 1c multicolored
3255 A804 1c multicolored
3256 A804 1c multicolored
3257 A804 1c multicolored
a. Strip of 5, Nos. 3253-3257
3258 A804 5c multicolored
3259 A804 5c multicolored
3260 A804 5c multicolored
3261 A804 5c multicolored
3262 A804 5c multicolored
a. Strip of 5, Nos. 3258-3262
3263 A804 10c multicolored
3264 A804 10c multicolored
3265 A804 10c multicolored
3266 A804 10c multicolored
3267 A804 10c multicolored
a. Strip of 5, Nos. 3263-3267
3268 A804 20c multicolored
3269 A804 20c multicolored
3270 A804 20c multicolored
3271 A804 20c multicolored
3272 A804 20c multicolored
a. Strip of 5, Nos. 3268-3272

Discovery of America, 500th anniv. (in 1992).

11th Jai Alai World Championships A899

1990, Nov. 14 Litho. *Perf. 12½*
3273 A899 30c multicolored

No. 3273 printed with se-tenant label.

11th Pan American Games, Havana — A900

1990, Nov. 15 Litho. *Perf. 12½*
3274 A900 5c Judo
3275 A900 5c Sailing
3276 A900 5c Kayak
3277 A900 5c Rowing
3278 A900 5c Equestrian
3279 A900 10c Table tennis
3280 A900 20c Men's gymnastics, vert.
3281 A900 30c Baseball, vert.
3282 A900 35c Team handball, vert.
3283 A900 50c Soccer, vert.

See Nos. 3311-3320.

A901

Butterflies — A902

1990, Nov. 20 Litho. *Perf. 13*
3284 A901 5c Boxing
3285 A901 30c Baseball
3286 A901 50c Volleyball

16th Central American and Caribbean Games, Mexico.

1991, Jan. 25 Litho. *Perf. 12½*
3287 A902 2c Chioides marmorosa
3288 A902 3c Composia fidelissima
3289 A902 5c Danaus plexippus
3290 A902 10c Hypolimnas misippus
3291 A902 30c Hypna iphigenia
3292 A902 50c Hemiargus ammon

Jose Luis Guerra Aguiar (1914-1990), Director of Postal Museum — A903

1991, Feb. 17 Litho. *Perf. 12½*
3293 A903 5c multicolored

A904

A905

1991, Feb. 20
3294 A904 1c Long jump
3295 A904 2c Javelin
3296 A904 3c Field hockey
3297 A904 5c Weight lifting
3298 A904 40c Cycling
3299 A904 50c Gymnastics

Souvenir Sheet

3300 A904 1p Torchbearer

1992 Summer Olympics, Barcelona.

1991, Apr. 12 Litho. *Perf. 13*

1st Man in Space, 30th anniv.: 5c, Yuri Gagarin. No. 3302, Cosmonaut Y. Romanenko. No. 3303, Cosmonaut A. Tamayo. No. 3304, Mir space station. No. 3305, Mir space station, docked Soyuz, earth. 50c, Soviet space shuttle Buran.

3301 A905 5c multicolored
3302 A905 10c multicolored
3303 A905 10c multicolored
a. Pair, #3302-3303
3304 A905 30c multicolored
3305 A905 30c multicolored
a. Pair, #3304-3305
3306 A905 50c multicolored

Proclamation of the Socialist Revolution, 30th Anniv. — A906

Design: 50c, Ship, jet on fire.

1991, Apr. 19 *Perf. 12½*
3307 A906 5c multicolored
3308 A906 50c multicolored

Bay of Pigs invasion, 30th anniv., No. 3308.

Stamp Day — A907

Details from mural by R. Rodriguez Radillo: 30c, Rocket lift-off. 50c, Dish antenna, horiz.

Perf. 12½x13, 13x12½

1991, Apr. 24
3309 A907 30c multicolored
3310 A907 50c multicolored

11th Pan American Games Type of 1990

1991, May 15 Litho. *Perf. 12½*
3311 A900 5c Volleyball
3312 A900 5c Rhythmic gymnastics
3313 A900 5c Synchronized swimming
3314 A900 5c Weight lifting
3315 A900 5c Baseball
3316 A900 10c Bowling
3317 A900 20c Boxing
3318 A900 30c Running
3319 A900 35c Wrestling
3320 A900 50c Karate

Nos. 3311-3315 & 3317 are vert.

Airships A908

Designs: 5c, First ellipsoidal, 1784, J.B.M. Meusnier. 10c, First with steam engine, 1852, H. Giffard. 20c, First with gas engine, 1872, P. Haenlein. 30c, First with gasoline engine, 1896, H. Wolfert. 50c, First rigid aluminum, 1897, D. Schwarz. 1p, LZ-129 Hindenburg, 1936, F. von Zeppelin.

1991, July 1 Litho. *Perf. 13*
3321 A908 5c multicolored
3322 A908 10c multicolored
3323 A908 20c multicolored
3324 A908 30c multicolored
3325 A908 50c multicolored
3326 A908 1p multicolored

Espamer '91, Buenos Aires, Argentina.

Simon Bolivar A909

1991, June 22 Litho. *Perf. 12½x13*
3327 A909 50c multicolored

Amphictyonic Cong. of Panama, 165th anniv.

Birds A910

Designs: 45c, Melanerpes superciliaris. 50c, Myadestes elisabeth. 2p, Priotelus temnurus. 4p, Tiaris canora. 5p, Campephilus principalis. 10p, Amazona leucocephala, horiz. 16.45p, Mellisuga helenae, horiz.

Perf. 12½x13, 13x12½

1991, July 15
3328 A910 45c multicolored
3329 A910 50c multicolored
3330 A910 2p multicolored
3331 A910 4p multicolored
3332 A910 5p multicolored
3333 A910 10p multicolored
3334 A910 16.45p multicolored

Tourism — A911

Designs: No. 3335, Varadero Beach, vert. No. 3336, Cayo Largo, vert. No. 3337, Artillerymen at fortress San Carlos de la Cabana. No. 3338, Tres Reyes del Morro Castle.

1991, July 30
3335 A911 20c multicolored
3336 A911 20c multicolored
3337 A911 30c multicolored
3338 A911 30c multicolored

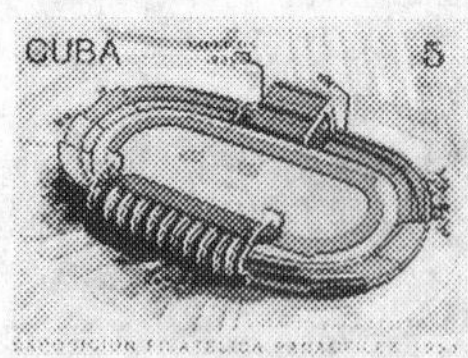

Panamfilex '91
A912

11th Pan American Games venues: 5c, Pan American Stadium. 20c, Swimming venue. 30c, Multisports center. 50c, Velodrome. 1p, Havana City Coliseum and Sports Center.

1991, Aug. 4 Litho. ***Perf. 12½***

3339 A912 5c multicolored
3340 A912 20c multicolored
3341 A912 30c multicolored
3342 A912 50c multicolored

Souvenir Sheet

3343 A912 1p multicolored

No. 3343 contains one 40x32mm stamp.

Paintings
A913

Designs: 5c, Kataoka Dengoemon Takafusa, by Utagawa Kuniyoshi. 10c, Evening Walk, by Hosoda Eishi. 20c, Courtesans, by Torii Kiyonaga. 30c, Conversation, by Utamaro. 50c, Bridge at Inaribashi, by Hiroshige. 1p, On the Terrace, by Kiyonaga.

1991, Sept. 9 Litho. ***Perf. 12½x13***

3344 A913 5c multicolored
3345 A913 10c multicolored
3346 A913 20c multicolored
3347 A913 30c multicolored
3348 A913 50c multicolored
3349 A913 1p multicolored

Phila Nippon '91, Tokyo.

Souvenir Sheet

1992 Winter Olympics, Albertville — A914

1991, Sept. 25 Litho. ***Perf. 12½***

3350 A914 1p multicolored

Cuban Communist Party, 4th Congress — A915

1991, Oct. 10

3351 A915 5c shown
3352 A915 50c Congress symbol

Discovery of America, 500th Anniv. (in 1992) — A916

Designs: 5c, Columbus, Vicente and Martin Pinzon. 20c, Santa Maria, Nina and Pinta.

1991, Oct. 12

3353 A916 5c multicolored
3354 A916 20c multicolored

Jose Marti
A917

1991, Oct. 15 ***Perf. 13x12½***

3355 A917 50c multicolored

Publication of "Simple Verses," cent.

Latin American History
A918

Stamps or musicians and instruments: No. 3356, Julian Aguirre, Argentina, charango. No. 3357, Eduardo Caba, Bolivia, antara. No. 3358, Chile #2. No. 3359, Heitor Villalobos, Brazil, resonator trumpet. No. 3360, Guillermo Uribe-Holguin, Colombia, drum. No. 3361, Miguel Failde, Cuba, claves. No. 3362, Enrique Soro, Chile, drum. No. 3363, Chile #57. No. 3364, Segundo L. Moreno, Ecuador, xylophone. No. 3365, Ricardo Castillo, Guatemala, marimba. No. 3366, Carlos Chavez, Mexico, guitar. No. 3367, Luis A. Delgadillo, Nicaragua, maracas. No. 3368, Chile #69. No. 3369, Alfredo De Saint-Malo, Panama, mejorana. No. 3370, Jose Asuncion Flores, Paraguay, harp. No. 3371, Daniel Alomia, Peru, flute. No. 3372, Juan Morell y Campos, Puerto Rico, cuatro. No. 3373, Chile #72. No. 3374, Eduardo Farini, Uruguay, drums. No. 3375, Juan V. Lecuna, Venezuela, cuatro, diff.

1991, Oct. 27 ***Perf. 13***

3356 A918 1c multicolored
3357 A918 1c multicolored
3358 A918 1c multicolored
3359 A918 1c multicolored
3360 A918 1c multicolored
a. Strip of 5, #3356-3360
3361 A918 5c multicolored
3362 A918 5c multicolored
3363 A918 5c multicolored
3364 A918 5c multicolored
3365 A918 5c multicolored
a. Strip of 5, #3361-3365
3366 A918 10c multicolored
3367 A918 10c multicolored
3368 A918 10c multicolored
3369 A918 10c multicolored
3370 A918 10c multicolored
a. Strip of 5, #3366-3370
3371 A918 20c multicolored
3372 A918 20c multicolored
3373 A918 20c multicolored
3374 A918 20c multicolored
3375 A918 20c multicolored
a. Strip of 5, #3371-3375

Discovery of America, 500th anniv. in 1992 (Nos. 3358, 3363, 3368, 3373).

Jose Marti Pioneers Organization, 1st Congress — A919

1991, Oct. 29

3376 A919 5c multicolored

Toussaint L'Ouverture (1743-1803)
A920

1991, Nov. 20 ***Perf. 12½x13***

3377 A920 50c multicolored

Haitian Revolution, Bicent.

Cuban Revolutionary Armed Forces, 35th Anniv. — A921

Design: 50c, Landing of the Granma expedition, 35th anniv., vert.

Perf. 12½x12, 12x12½

1991, Dec. 2 Litho.

3378 A921 5c multicolored
3379 A921 50c multicolored

Gen. Ignacio Agramonte (1841-1873), Revolutionary Hero
A922

1991, Dec. 23 Litho. ***Perf. 12½x13***

3380 A922 5c multicolored

Souvenir Sheet

1992 Winter Olympics, Albertville — A923

1992, Jan. 15 ***Perf. 13***

3381 A923 1p multicolored

1992 Summer Olympics, Barcelona
A924

1992, Jan. 20 Litho. ***Perf. 13x12½***

3382 A924 3c Table tennis
3383 A924 5c Handball
3384 A924 10c Shooting
3385 A924 20c Long jump, vert.
3386 A924 35c Judo
3387 A924 50c Fencing

Souvenir Sheet

Perf. 12½

3388 A924 100c Rhythmic gymnastics, vert.

No. 3388 contains one 32x40mm stamp.

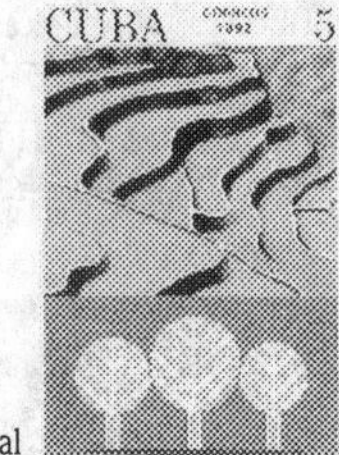

Environmental Protection — A925

1992, Feb. 10 ***Perf. 13***

3389 A925 5c Terraced hillsides
3390 A925 20c Save the whales
3391 A925 35c Ozone hole over Antarctica
3392 A925 40c Nuclear disarmament

Dogs
A926

1992, Mar. 10 Litho. ***Perf. 13x12½***

3393 A926 5c Boxer
3394 A926 10c Great dane
3395 A926 20c German shepherd
3396 A926 30c Various breeds
3397 A926 35c Doberman pinscher
3398 A926 40c Fox terrier
3399 A926 50c Poodle

Souvenir Sheet

Perf. 12½

3400 A926 1p Bichon frise, vert.

No. 3400 contains one 32x40mm stamp.
Nos. 3401-3404 will not be assigned.

Union of Young Communists, 30th Anniv. — A928

1992, Apr. 4 Litho. ***Perf. 13***

3405 A928 5c multicolored

Cuban Revolutionary Party, Cent. — A929

1992, Apr. 10 *Perf. 13x12½*

3406 A929 5c multicolored
3407 A929 50c multicolored

Discovery of America, 500th Anniv. — A930

1992, Apr. 14 *Perf. 12½*

3408 A930 5c Landing at Bariay
3409 A930 20c Landing at San Salvador

Granada '92 Philatelic Exhibition A931

Views of the Alhambra, Granada: 5c, With Sierra Nevada mountains beyond. 10c, Arches at sunset. 20c, Interior architecture. 30c, Patio, fountain of lions. 35c, Bedroom. 50c, View of Albaicin.

1992, Apr. 17 *Perf. 13*

3410 A931 5c multicolored
3411 A931 10c multicolored
3412 A931 20c multicolored
3413 A931 30c multicolored
3414 A931 35c multicolored
3415 A931 50c multicolored

La Bodeguita Del Medio Restaurant, 50th Anniv. A932

1992, Apr. 26

3416 A932 50c multicolored

Fish A933

1992, May 15 **Litho.** *Perf. 12½*

3417 A933 5c Holacanthus isabelita
3418 A933 10c Equetus lanceolatus
3419 A933 20c Acanthurus coeruleus
3420 A933 30c Abudefduf saxatilis
3421 A933 50c Micropathodon chrysurus

Orchids — A934

1992, June 20 **Litho.** *Perf. 12½*

3422 A934 3c Cattleya hibrida
3423 A934 5c Phalaenopsis
3424 A934 10c Cattleyopsis lindenii
3425 A934 30c Bletia purpurea
3426 A934 35c Oncidium luridum
3427 A934 40c Vanda hibrida

Soroa Orchid Garden, 40th anniv.

Mellisuga Helenae A935

1992, July 7 *Perf. 13*

3428 A935 5c Sitting on nest
3429 A935 10c Wings extended
3430 A935 20c Sitting on branch
3431 A935 30c In flight

World Wildlife Fund.

Tourism A936

1992, July 15 **Litho.** *Perf. 12½*

3432 A936 10c Guardalavaca Beach
3433 A936 20c Bucanero Hotel
3434 A936 30c Sailing ship, Havana
3435 A936 50c Varadero Beach

Souvenir Sheet

Expo '92, Seville — A937

1992, July 27 **Litho.** *Perf. 13*

3436 A937 1.50p multicolored

1992 Summer Olympics, Barcelona A938

Athlete, sport: 5c, Eligio (Kid Chocolate) Sardinas, boxing. 35c, Ramon Fonst, fencing. 40c, Sergio Martinez, cycling. 50c, Martin Dihigo, baseball.

1992, July 20 **Litho.** *Perf. 12½x13*

3437 A938 5c multicolored
3438 A938 35c multicolored
3439 A938 40c multicolored
3440 A938 50c multicolored

Olymphilex '92.

Discovery of America, 500th Anniv. A939

Designs: 5c, Alvarez Cabral. 10c, Alonso Pinzon. 20c, Alonso de Ojeda. 30c, Amerigo Vespucci. 35c, Prince Henry the Navigator. 40c, Bartolomeu Dias. 0p, Columbus' fleet, vert.

1992, Sept. 18 **Litho.** *Perf. 12½*

3441 A939 5c multicolored
3442 A939 10c multicolored
3443 A939 20c multicolored
3444 A939 30c multicolored
3445 A939 35c multicolored
3446 A939 40c multicolored

Souvenir Sheet

Perf. 13

3447 A939 1p multicolored

Genoa '92. No. 3447 contains one 32x40mm stamp.

1992 Summer Olympics Medal Winners, Barcelona A940

Medals and participants in events: No. 3448, Bronze, 4x100-meter relay, women's high jump, and women's 800-meter. No. 3449, Gold, high jump, women's discus. No. 3450, Silver, 4x400-meter relay, bronze, discus. No. 3451, Gold and silver, boxing. No. 3452, Gold, baseball. No. 3453, Gold, women's volleyball. No. 3454, Gold, silver, and bronze, judo. No. 3455, Gold and bronze, Greco-Roman and freestyle wrestling. No. 3456, Silver and bronze, fencing, silver, weight lifting.

1992, Sept. 24 **Litho.** *Perf. 13*

3448 A940 5c multicolored
3449 A940 5c multicolored
3450 A940 5c multicolored
3451 A940 20c multicolored
3452 A940 20c multicolored
3453 A940 20c multicolored
3454 A940 50c multicolored
3455 A940 50c multicolored
3456 A940 50c multicolored

6th World Track and Field Cup, Havana A941

1992, Sept. 24 **Litho.** *Perf. 13*

3457 A941 5c High jump
3458 A941 20c Javelin
3459 A941 30c Hammer throw
3460 A941 40c Long jump, vert.
3461 A941 50c Hurdles, vert.

Souvenir Sheet

3462 A941 1p Women's relay

No. 3462 contains one 40x32mm stamp.

Latin American History Type of 1986

Discovery of America: No. 3463a, Columbus, Queen Isabella. b, Columbus at Rabida Monastery. c, Columbus, pointing up, outlining his plan. d, Columbus, with scroll, before Salamanca Council. e, Departure of Columbus' fleet from Palos.

No. 3464a, Three ships stopping at Canary Islands. b, Columbus speaking to crew. c, Land sighted, Oct. 12, 1492. d, Columbus landing in New World. e, Meeting natives.

No. 3465a, Grounding of Santa Maria at Hispanola. b, Arrival of Nina at Palos. c, Columbus welcomed in Barcelona. d, Columbus describes his voyage to Ferdinand and Isabella. e, Departure of fleet from Cadiz on second voyage.

No. 3466a, King and Queen welcome Columbus. b, Fleet on Columbus' third voyage. c, Columbus deported from Hispanola to Spain as prisoner. d, Columbus on ship, fourth voyage. e, Death of Columbus, May 20, 1506 in Valladolid.

1992, Oct. 3 *Perf. 13*

3463 A804 1c Strip of 5, #a.-e.
3464 A804 5c Strip of 5, #a.-e.
3465 A804 10c Strip of 5, #a.-e.
3466 A804 20c Strip of 5, #a.-e.

Jose Maria Chacon y Calvo (1892-1969), Historian — A942

1992, Oct. 29 *Perf. 13*

3467 A942 30c multicolored

Churches — A943

Designs: 5c, Basilica of Nuestra Senora de la Caridad del Cobre. 20c, Santa Maria del Rosario Church. 30c, Espiritu Santo Church. 50c, Santo Angel Custodio Church.

1992, Nov. 10 **Litho.** *Perf. 12½*

3468 A943 5c multicolored
3469 A943 20c multicolored
3470 A943 30c multicolored
3471 A943 50c multicolored

Development of the Diesel Engine — A944

1993, Jan. 20 **Litho.** *Perf. 12½*

3472 A944 5c Truck
3473 A944 10c Automobile
3474 A944 30c Tugboat
3475 A944 40c Locomotive
3476 A944 50c Tractor

Souvenir Sheet

3477 A944 1p Rudolf Diesel

No. 3477 contains one 40x32mm stamp. Rudolf Diesel, 80th anniv. of death (#3477).

Davis Cup Tennis Competition — A945

Various tennis players in action.

Perf. 12x12½, 12½x12

1993, Feb. 10 **Litho.**

3478 A945 5c multi, vert.
3479 A945 20c multi, vert.
3480 A945 30c multi, vert.
3481 A945 35c multicolored
3482 A945 40c multicolored

Souvenir Sheet

Perf. 12½

3483 A945 1p multicolored

No. 3483 contains one 40x32mm stamp.

Scientists A946

Designs: 3c, Pierre-Paul-Emile Roux (1853-1933), bacteriologist. 5c, Carlos J. Finlay (1833-1915), suggested mosquito as carrier of yellow fever. 10c, Ivan Petrovich Pavlov (1849-1936), physiologist, investigated conditioned reflexes. 20c, Louis Pasteur, chemist, developer of pasteurization. 30c, Santiago Ramon y Cajal (1852-1934), histologist, isolated the neuron. 35c, Sigmund Freud, psychoanalyst. 40c, Wilhelm Conrad Roentgen, physicist, discoverer of x-ray. 50c, Joseph Lister, surgeon, introduced principle of antisepsis. 1p, Robert Koch, bacteriologist, developer of tuberculin, vert.

1993, Mar. 3 **Litho.** *Perf. 12½*

3484 A946 3c multicolored
3485 A946 5c multicolored
3486 A946 10c multicolored
3487 A946 20c multicolored
3488 A946 30c multicolored
3489 A946 35c multicolored
3490 A946 40c multicolored

3491 A946 50c multicolored

Souvenir Sheet

3492 A946 1p multicolored

Bicycles
A947

Bicycles designed by: 3c, Leonardo da Vinci, 15th cent. 5c, Karl Von Drais de Sauerbrun, 1813. 10c, Ernest Michaux, 1856. 20c, James Starley, 1869. 30c, Harry Lawson, 1879. 35c, Guaso (Cuba), 1992.

1993, Apr. 14 *Perf. 13*

3493 A947 3c multicolored
3494 A947 5c multicolored
3495 A947 10c multicolored
3496 A947 20c multicolored
3497 A947 30c multicolored
3498 A947 35c multicolored

Cuban Natl. Museum, 80th Anniv.
A948

Paintings by Joaquin Sorolla y Bastida (1863-1923): 3c, Child Eating Watermelon, 1920, vert. 5c, Valencian Fisherwomen, 1909. 10c, Regattas. 20c, Contadina, 1889. 40c, Summer, 1904. 50c, Boats on the Ocean, 1908.

1993, May 29 Litho. *Perf. 13x12½*

3499 A948 3c multicolored

Perf. 12½x13

3500 A948 5c multicolored
3501 A948 10c multicolored
3502 A948 20c multicolored
3503 A948 40c multicolored
3504 A948 50c multicolored

Water Birds
A949

Perf. 12½, 13x12½ (5, 30c)

1993, June 15

3505 A949 3c Jacana spinosa
3506 A949 5c Ardea herodias, vert.
3507 A949 10c Himantopus mexicanus
3508 A949 20c Nycticorax nycticorax
3509 A949 30c Grus canadensis, vert.
3510 A949 50c Aramus guarauna

Brasiliana '93. Nos. 3506, 3510 are 27x44mm.

Anniversaries — A950

Designs: No. 3511, Jose Marti, Moncada Barracks. No. 3512, "History Will Absolve Me," declaration of Fidel Castro, Marti. No. 3513, Jose Marti, Rafael M. Mendive, vert. No. 3514, Carlos Manuel de Cespedes, gear wheels.

1993, July 26 Litho. *Perf. 13*

3511 A950 5c multicolored
3512 A950 5c multicolored
3513 A950 5c multicolored
3514 A950 5c multicolored

Attack on Moncada Barracks, 40th anniv. (#3511). Declaration of Fidel Castro, 40th anniv. (#3512). Birth of Jose Marti, 140th anniv. (#3513). Declaration of the Ten Years' War, 125th anniv. (#3514).

Flowers from Cienfuegos Botanical Gardens — A951

1993, Aug. 20

3515 A951 3c Sedum allantoides
3516 A951 5c Heliconia caribaea
3517 A951 10c Anthurium andraeanum
3518 A951 20c Pseudobombax ellipticum
3519 A951 35c Ixora coccinea
3520 A951 50c Callistemon specious

Bangkok '93, Intl. Philatelic Exhibition — A952

Butterflies: 3c, Battus devillievs. 5c, Anteos maerula. 20c, Ascia monuste evonima. 30c, Junonia coenia. 35c, Anartia jatrophae guantanamo. 50c, Hypolimnas misippus.

1993, Sept. 10 Litho. *Perf. 13*

3521 A952 3c multicolored
3522 A952 5c multicolored
3523 A952 20c multicolored
3524 A952 30c multicolored
3525 A952 35c multicolored
3526 A952 50c multicolored

Endangered Species — A953

1993, Oct. 12 Litho. *Perf. 13*

3527 A953 5c Phoenicopterus ruber
3528 A953 50c Ajaia ajaja

Latin American Revolutionaries
A954

Flags, map and: No. 3529, Simon Bolivar. No. 3530, Jose Marti. No. 3531, Benito Juarez, Mexican President. No. 3532, Ernesto "Che" Guevara.

1993, Oct. 27 Litho. *Perf. 13*

3529 A954 50c multicolored
3530 A954 50c multicolored
3531 A954 50c multicolored
3532 A954 50c multicolored
a. Block of 4, #3529-3532

17th Central American and Caribbean Games, Ponce, Puerto Rico — A955

1993, Nov. 10 Litho. *Perf. 12½*

3533 A955 5c Swimming
3534 A955 10c Pole vault
3535 A955 20c Boxing
3536 A955 35c Gymnastics, vert.
3537 A955 50c Baseball, vert.

Souvenir Sheet

3538 A955 1p Basketball

No. 3538 contains one 40x32mm stamp.

Mariana Grajales (1808-93), Patriot — A956

Peter I. Tchaikovsky (1840-93), Composer — A957

1993, Nov. 27 *Perf. 13*

3539 A956 5p multicolored

1993, Nov. 30

3540 A957 5c Portrait
3541 A957 20c Swan Lake Ballet
3542 A957 30c Statue
3543 A957 50c Museum, horiz.

A958

A959

1994, Jan. 1 Litho. *Perf. 13*

3544 A958 5c multicolored

35th anniv. of the Revolution.

1994, Jan. 1

Various soccer players.

3545 A959 5c multicolored
3546 A959 20c multicolored
3547 A959 30c multicolored
3548 A959 35c multicolored
3549 A959 40c multicolored
3550 A959 50c multicolored

Souvenir Sheet

3551 A959 1p multicolored

1994 World Cup Soccer Championships, US. No. 3551 contains one 40x31mm stamp.

Cats
A960

1994, Feb. 15 Litho. *Perf. 12½*

3552 A960 5c Blue Persian
3553 A960 10c Havana
3554 A960 20c Maine coon
3555 A960 30c Blue British shorthair
3556 A960 35c Bicolor Persian
3557 A960 50c Gold chinchilla

Souvenir Sheet

Perf. 13

3558 A960 1p Abyssinian, vert.

No. 3558 contains one 30x38mm stamp.

Medicinal Plants — A961

Designs: 5c, Salvia officinalis. 10c, Aloe barbadensis. 20c, Helianthus annuus. 30c, Matricaria chamomilla. 40c, Calendula officinalis. 50c, Tilia platyphyllos.

1994, Mar. 30 Litho. *Perf. 12½*

3559 A961 5c multicolored
3560 A961 10c multicolored
3561 A961 20c multicolored
3562 A961 30c multicolored
3563 A961 40c multicolored
3564 A961 50c multicolored

Carriages — A962

Designs: 5c, Public coach, 1860. 10c, Coach of Ferdinand VII, Maria Louisa. 30c, Louis XV-style coach. 35c, Elizabeth II gala day's coach. 40c, Catalina II's summer coach. 50c, Volanta habanera.

1994, Apr. 20 *Perf. 12½x12*

3565 A962 5c multicolored
3566 A962 10c multicolored
3567 A962 30c multicolored
3568 A962 35c multicolored
3569 A962 40c multicolored
3570 A962 50c multicolored

No. 3570 is 68x37mm.

Aquaculture — A963

Designs: 5c, Crassostrea rhizophorae. 20c, Cardisoma guanhumi. 30c, Tilapia melanopleura. 35c, Hippospongia lachne. 40c, Panulirus argus. 50c, Cyprinus carpio.

1994, May 10 Litho. *Perf. 12½*

3571 A963 5c multicolored
3572 A963 20c multicolored
3573 A963 30c multicolored
3574 A963 35c multicolored
3575 A963 40c multicolored
3576 A963 50c multicolored

Intl. Olympic Committee, Cent. — A964

1994, June 23 Litho. *Perf. 12½*

3577 A964 5c Flag, runners
3578 A964 30c Flag, world map
3579 A964 50c Flag, Olympic flame

Scientists
A965

Designs: 5c, Michael Faraday (1791-1867), physicist. 10c, Marie Curie (1867-1934), physical chemist. 20c, Pierre Curie (1859-1906), chemist. 30c, Albert Einstein (1879-1955), physicist, mathematician. 40c, Max Planck (1858-1947), theoretical physicist. 50c, Otto Hahn (1879-1968), physical chemist.

1994, July 20 Litho. *Perf. 12½*

3580 A965 5c multicolored
3581 A965 10c multicolored
3582 A965 20c multicolored
3583 A965 30c multicolored
3584 A965 40c multicolored
3585 A965 50c multicolored

Cactus Flowers A966

Designs: 5c, Opuntia dillenii. 10c, Opuntia millspaughii, vert. 30c, Leptocereus santamarinae. 35c, Pereskia marcanoi. 40c, Dendrocereus nudiflorus, vert. 50c, Pilocereus robinii.

1994, Aug. 15 Litho. *Perf. 12½*

3586 A966 5c multicolored
3587 A966 10c multicolored
3588 A966 30c multicolored
3589 A966 35c multicolored
3590 A966 40c multicolored
3591 A966 50c multicolored

Souvenir Sheet

2nd Spanish-Cuban Philatelic Exhibition, Havana — A967

Design: 1p, Cuban postal rocket, #C31.

1994, Sept. 18

3592 A967 1p multicolored

Experimental postal rocket flight, 55th anniv.

Dogs A968

1994, Sept. 20

3593 A968 5c Rough collie
3594 A968 20c American cocker spaniel
3595 A968 30c Dalmatian
3596 A968 40c Afghan hound
3597 A968 50c English cocker spaniel

Cayo Largo Island A969

Fauna: 15c, Carpilius corallinus. 65c, Cyclura nubila, vert. 75c, Pelecanus occidentalis. 4p, Chelonia mydas.

1994, Sept. 30 Litho. *Perf. 12½*

3598 A969 15c multicolored
3599 A969 65c multicolored
3600 A969 75c multicolored
3601 A969 1p multicolored

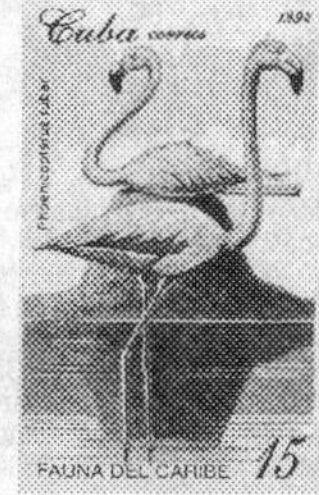

A970 A971

1994, Oct. 28

3602 A970 15c multicolored

Camilo Cienfuegos Gorriaran, revolutionary, 35th anniv. of disappearance.

1994, Oct. 30

Fauna of the Caribbean: 10c, Epinephelus flavolimbatus, horiz. No. 3604, Phoenicopterus ruber. No. 3605, Aetobatus narinari. No. 3606, Istiophorus platypterus, horiz. No. 3607, Tursiops truncatus, horiz. No. 3608, Pelecanus occidentalis.

3603 A971 10c multicolored
3604 A971 15c multicolored
3605 A971 15c multicolored
3606 A971 15c multicolored
3607 A971 65c multicolored
3608 A971 65c multicolored

ICAO, 50th Anniv. A972

1994, Nov. 9

3609 A972 65c multicolored

Zoological Garden, Havana, 55th Anniv. — A973

1994, Nov. 14 Litho. *Perf. 13*

3610 A973 15c Bronze monument
3611 A973 65c Ara chloroptera
3612 A973 75c Carduelis carduelis

Cuban Philatelic Federation, 30th Anniv. A974

1994, Nov. 20

3613 A974 15c multicolored

America Issue A975

Postal transportation: 15c, 18th Cent. Spanish galleon, maritime postal service, vert. 65c, 19th Cent. postal rider, insurgent postal service.

1994, Dec. 12

3614 A975 15c multicolored
3615 A975 65c multicolored

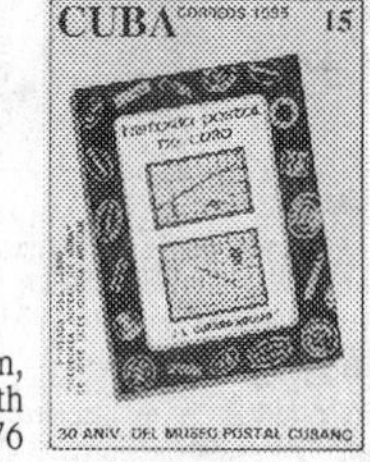

Postal Museum, 30th Anniv. — A976

1995, Jan. 2

3616 A976 15c multicolored

Lizards A977

Designs: 15c, Anolis baracoae. 65c, Sphaerodactylus ramsdeni. 75c, Leiocephalus raviceps. 85c, Sphaerodactylus ruibali. 90c, Anolis ophiolepis. 1p, Sphaerodactylus armasi.

1994, Nov. 30 Litho. *Perf. 12½*

3617 A977 15c multicolored
3618 A977 65c multicolored
3619 A977 75c multicolored
3620 A977 85c multicolored
3621 A977 90c multicolored
3622 A977 1p multicolored

Cuban War of Independence, Cent. — A978

1995, Feb. 24 Litho. *Perf. 12½*

3623 A978 15c Jose Marti, flag

Pan American Games, Mar del Plata, Argentina A979

1995, Mar. 11 Litho. *Perf. 13*

3624 A979 10c Boxing, vert.
3625 A979 15c Weight lifting, vert.
3626 A979 65c Volleyball, vert.
3627 A979 75c Wrestling
3628 A979 85c Baseball
3629 A979 90c High jump

National Aquarium, 35th Anniv. A980

Fish: 10c, Holacanthus cillaris. 15c, Hypoplectrus guttavarius. 65c, Anisotremus virginicus. 75c, Amblycirrhitus pinos. 85c, Pomaacanthus paru. 90c, Acanthurus coeruleus.

1995, Apr. 28 Litho. *Perf. 13*

3630 A980 10c multicolored
3631 A980 15c multicolored
3632 A980 65c multicolored
3633 A980 75c multicolored
3634 A980 85c multicolored
3635 A980 90c multicolored

FAO, 50th Anniv. A981

1995, Apr. 7 Litho. *Perf. 13*

3636 A981 75c multicolored

First Cuban Postage Stamp, 140th Anniv. — A982

Designs: 15c, No. 1. 65c, Ornamental letter drop, envelope.

1995. Apr. 24 Litho. *Perf. 12½*

3637 A982 15c black & blue green
3638 A982 65c multicolored

Jose Marti, Death Cent. A983

Designs: 15c, Marti killed in combat, signature, portrait. 65c, Landing of Marti, Cuban patriots on Playitas beach. 75c, Montecristi Manifesto signed in Domincan Republic, Marti. 85c, Meeting of Marti, Maceo, Gomez at La Mejorana Farm. 90c, Marti's mausoleum, Santiago, Cuba, vert.

Perf. 12½x13, 13x12½

1995, May 19

3639 A983 15c multicolored
3640 A983 65c multicolored
3641 A983 75c multicolored
3642 A983 85c multicolored
3643 A983 90c multicolored

Antonio Maceo (1845-96), Revolutionary — A984

1995, June 14 Litho. *Perf. 12½*

3644 A984 15c multicolored

Butterflies A985

Designs: 10c, Dione vanillae. 15c, Eunica tatila. 65c, Melete salacia. 75c, Greta cubana. 85c, Eurema daira. 90c, Phoebis sennae.

1995, June 20 *Perf. 12½x13*

3645 A985 10c multicolored
3646 A985 15c multicolored
3647 A985 65c multicolored
3648 A985 75c multicolored
3649 A985 85c multicolored
3650 A985 90c multicolored

World War II Combat Planes
A986

Designs: 10c, Supermarine "Spitfire," Great Britain. 15c, IL-2, Russia. 65c, Curtiss P-40, US. 75c, Messerschmitt Bf-109, Germany. 85c, Morane-Sauinier 406, France.

1995, July 30 Litho. *Perf. 12½*
3651 A986 10c multicolored
3652 A986 15c multicolored
3653 A986 65c multicolored
3654 A986 75c multicolored
3655 A986 85c multicolored

A987

A988

1995, Aug. 6 Litho. *Perf. 12½*
3656 A987 15c multicolored

Ernesto Lecuona, composer, pianist, birth cent.

1995, Aug. 10
Color of Horse or Horses
3657 A988 10c golden brown, white
3658 A988 15c white, horiz.
3659 A988 65c dark brown, white
3660 A988 75c red brown
3661 A988 85c tan
3662 A988 90c white

Singapore '95.

Souvenir Sheet

Beijing Intl. Stamp & Coin Expo '95 — A989

Illustration reduced.

1995, Aug. 28 *Perf. 13*
3663 A989 50c multicolored

1996 Summer Olympics, Atlanta — A990

1995, Sept. 25 Litho. *Perf. 13*
3664 A990 10c Wrestling
3665 A990 15c Weight lifting
3666 A990 65c Women's volleyball
3667 A990 75c Women's athletics
3668 A990 85c Baseball
3669 A990 90c Women's judo

Souvenir Sheet
3670 A990 1p Boxing

No. 3670 contains one 30x36mm stamp.

Cuban Sugar Industry, 400th Anniv.
A991

Paintings from "Los Ingenios," by Edouard Laplante, 1852: 15c, Steam train, sugar factory. 65c, Sugar factory, tower, bridge.

1995, Oct. 3
3671 A991 15c multicolored
3672 A991 65c multicolored

UN, 50th Anniv.
A992

1995, Oct. 24 Litho. *Perf. 13*
3673 A992 65c multicolored

Zoological Gardens, Havana
A993

Designs: 10c, Panthera leo, vert. 15c, Equus grevyi. 65c, Pongo pygmaeus, vert. 75c, Elephas maximus. 85c, Sciurus vulgaris. 90c, Procyon lotor.

1995, Oct. 30 Litho. *Perf. 13*
3674 A993 10c multicolored
3675 A993 15c multicolored
3676 A993 65c multicolored
3677 A993 75c multicolored
3678 A993 85c multicolored
3679 A993 90c multicolored

UNESCO, 50th Anniv. — A994

UNESCO World Culture and National Heritage sites: 65c, Santa Clara de Asis Convent. 75c, San Francisco de Asis Minor Basilica.

1995, Nov. 4
3680 A994 65c multicolored
3681 A994 75c multicolored

Orchids — A995

Designs: 40c, Bletia patula. 45c, Galeandra beyrichii. 50c, Vanilla dilloniana. 65c, Macradenia lutescens. 75c, Oncidium luridum. 85c, Ionopsis utricularioides.

1995, Nov. 10 *Perf. 12½*
3682 A995 40c multicolored
3683 A995 45c multicolored
3684 A995 50c multicolored
3685 A995 65c multicolored
3686 A995 75c multicolored
3687 A995 85c multicolored

Motion Pictures, Cent. — A996

1995, Dec. 7 *Perf. 13*
3688 A996 15c Lumiere Brothers
3689 A996 15c Marilyn Monroe
3690 A996 15c Marlene Dietrich
3691 A996 15c Vittorio DeSica
3692 A996 15c Charlie Chaplin
3693 A996 15c Greta Garbo
3694 A996 65c Humphrey Bogart
3695 A996 75c Montaner
3696 A996 85c Cantinflas

Souvenir Sheet

4th Cuban-Spanish Philatelic Exhibition, Havana — A997

Illustration reduced.

1995, Dec. 11 Litho. *Perf. 13*
3697 A997 1p multicolored

America Issue — A998

1995, Dec. 12
3698 A998 15c Centurus superciliaris
3699 A998 65c Todus multicolor

Generals Who Died in 1895 War — A999

Designs: No. 3700, Alfonso Goulet Goulet, Francisco Adolfo Crombet Ballon. No. 3701, Jesus Calvar O, Jose Guillermo Moncada, Tomas Jordan. No. 3702, Francisco Borrero Lavadi, Francisco Inchaustegui Cabrera.

1995, Dec. 20 *Perf. 12½*
3700 A999 15c multicolored
3701 A999 15c multicolored
3702 A999 15c multicolored
a. Strip of 3, #3700-3702

Island of Coco Cay, Jardines del Rey — A1000

Bird, scenic view: 10c, Sterna antillarum, aerial view of island. 15c, Eudocimus albus, people on beach. 45c, Spindalis zena, couple on steps of resort complex. 50c, Turdus plumbeus, resort. 65c, Mimus polyglottos, resort. 75c, Phoenicopterus ruber, couple in pool at resort.

1995, Dec. 23
3703 A1000 10c multicolored
3704 A1000 15c multicolored
3705 A1000 45c multicolored
3706 A1000 50c multicolored
3707 A1000 65c multicolored
3708 A1000 75c multicolored

Patriots — A1001

Designs: 15c, Carlos M. de Céspedes (1819-74). 65c, José Marti (1853-95). 75c, Antonio Maceo (1845-96). 1.05p, Ignacio Agramonte (1841-73). 2.05p, Máximo Gómez (1836-1905). 3p, Calixto Garcia (1839-98).

1996, Jan. 10
3709 A1001 15c green
3710 A1001 65c blue
3711 A1001 75c carmine
3712 A1001 1.05p lilac
3713 A1001 2.05p brown
3714 A1001 3p light brown

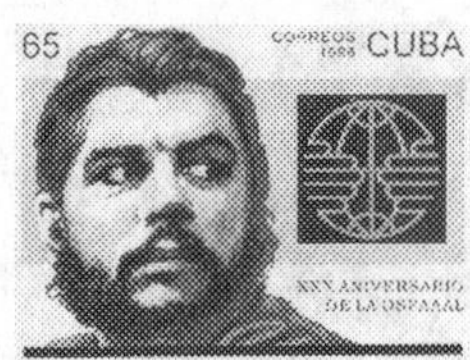

Organization of Solidarity of the Peoples of Africa, Asia and Latin America (OSPAAAL), 30th Anniv. — A1002

1996, Jan. 14
3715 A1002 65c multicolored

Scientists — A1003

Designs: 10c, Leonardo da Vinci (1452-1519). 15c, Mikhail V. Lomonosov (1711-65), atmospheric scientist. 65c, James Watt (1736-1819), engineer, inventor. 75c, Guglielmo Marconi (1874-1937), physicist. 85c, Charles R. Darwin (1809-82), naturalist.

1996, Jan. 30 Litho. *Perf. 12½*
3716 A1003 10c multicolored
3717 A1003 15c multicolored
3718 A1003 65c multicolored
3719 A1003 75c multicolored
3720 A1003 85c multicolored

SEMI-POSTAL STAMPS

Curie Issue
Common Design Type
Wmk. 106

1938, Nov. 23 Engr. *Perf. 10*

B1	CD80	2c + 1c salmon	2.25	.90
B2	CD80	5c + 1c deep ultra	2.25	1.10

40th anniv. of the discovery of radium by Pierre and Marie Curie. Surtax for the benefit of the Intl. Union for the Control of Cancer.

Catalogue values for unused stamps in this section, from this point to the end of the section, are for Never Hinged items.

"Agriculture" Supporting "Industry" SP2

Engr., Center Typo.

1959, May 7 Wmk. 321 *Perf. 12½*

B3 SP2 2c + 1c car & ultra .35 .15

Agricultural reforms. See No. CB1. For surcharges see Nos. 624, C199.

Nurse SP3

Perf. 12½, Imperf.

1959, Sept. 22 Photo. Wmk. 229

B4 SP3 2c + 1c crimson rose .30 .15

AIR POST STAMPS

Seaplane over Havana Harbor AP1

Wmk. 106

1927, Nov. 1 Engr. *Perf. 12*

C1 AP1 5c dark blue 2.25 .20

For overprint see No. C30.

Type of 1927 Issue Overprinted

LINDBERGH
FEBRERO 1928

1928, Feb. 8

C2 AP1 5c carmine rose 1.25 1.25

No. 283 Surcharged in Red

CORREO AEREO NACIONAL
10¢ 10¢

1930, Oct. 27 Unwmk.

C3 A44 10c on 25c violet 1.25 1.25

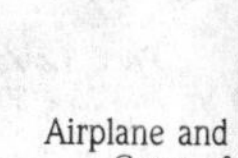

Airplane and Coast of Cuba — AP3

For Foreign Postage

1931, Feb. 26 Wmk. 106 *Perf. 10*

C4	AP3	5c green	.38	.15
C5	AP3	10c dk blue	.38	.15
C6	AP3	15c rose	.75	.28
C7	AP3	20c brown	.75	.15
C8	AP3	30c dk violet	1.10	.18
C9	AP3	40c dp orange	2.50	.35
C10	AP3	50c olive grn	3.00	.35
C11	AP3	1p black	4.50	.90
		Nos. C4-C11 (8)	13.36	2.51

See No. C40. For surcharges see Nos. C16-C17, C203, C225.

Airplane AP4

For Domestic Postage

1931-46

C12	AP4	5c rose vio ('32)	.30	.15
a.		5c brown violet ('36)	.30	.15
C13	AP4	10c gray blk	.30	.15
C14	AP4	20c car rose	2.25	.75
C14A	AP4	20c rose pink ('40)	.95	.18
C15	AP4	50c dark blue	3.75	.75
		Nos. C12-C15 (5)	7.55	1.98

See #C130. For overprints see #C31, E29-E30.

Type of 1931 Surcharged in Black

PRIMER TREN AEREO
INTERNACIONAL. 1935
O'Meara y du Pont + 10cts.

1935, Apr. 24 *Perf. 10*

C16 AP3 10c + 10c red 7.25 6.00
a. Double surcharge 110.00

Imperf

C17 AP3 10c + 10c red 18.00 19.00

Matanzas Issue

Air View of Matanzas AP5

Designs: 10c, Airship "Macon." 20c, Airplane "The Four Winds." 50c, Air View of Fort San Severino.

Perf. 12½

1936, May 5 Photo. Wmk. 229

C18	AP5	5c violet	.38	.25
C19	AP5	10c yel org	.75	.38
C20	AP5	20c green	2.50	1.50
C21	AP5	50c greenish slate	4.50	3.00
		Nos. C18-C21 (4)	8.13	5.13

Exist imperf. Value 20% more.

"Lightning" AP9

Allegory of Flight AP10

1936, Nov. 18

C22 AP9 5c violet 1.00 .22
C23 AP10 10c org brn 1.25 .35

Major Gen. Maximo Gomez, birth cent.

Flat Arch (Panama) — AP11

Carlos Antonio López (Paraguay) — AP12

Inca Gate, Cuzco (Peru) AP13

Atlacatl (Salvador) AP14

José Enrique Rodó (Uruguay) — AP15

Simón Bolívar (Venezuela) — AP16

Wmk. 106

1937, Oct. 13 Engr. *Perf. 10*

C24	AP11	5c red	4.25	4.25
C25	AP12	5c red	4.25	4.25
C26	AP13	10c blue	5.00	5.00
C27	AP14	10c blue	5.00	5.00
C28	AP15	20c green	5.50	6.25
C29	AP16	20c green	5.50	6.25
		Nos. C24-C29 (6)	29.50	31.00

For the benefit of the Assoc. of American Writers and Artists. See note after No. 354.

Type of 1927 Overprinted in Black

1913 1938
ROSILLO
Key West-Habana

1938, May Wmk. 106

C30 AP1 5c dk org 2.00 1.10

1st airplane flight from Key West to Havana, made by Domingo Rosillo, 1913.

Type of 1931-32 Overprinted

EXPERIMENTO DEL
COHETE
Postal
AÑO DE 1939

1939, Oct. 15

C31 AP4 10c emerald 14.00 5.00

Issued in connection with an experimental postal rocket flight held at Havana.

Sir Rowland Hill, Map of Cuba and First Stamps of Britain, Spanish Cuba and Republic of Cuba — AP17

1940, Nov. 28 Engr. Wmk. 106

C32 AP17 10c brown 2.00 1.25

Souvenir Sheet

Unwmk. *Imperf.*

C33 Sheet of 4 10.00 10.00
a. AP17 10c light brown 2.50 1.00

Cent. of the 1st postage stamp.
Sheet sold for 60c.
No. C33 exists with each of the four stamps overprinted in black: "Exposicion de la ACNU/24 de Octubre de 1951/Dia de las Naciones" and "Historia de la Aviacion" in lower margin. Value, $60.
For overprints see Nos. C39, C211.

Poet José Heredia and Palms — AP18

Heredia and Niagara Falls — AP19

1940, Dec. 30 Wmk. 106

C34 AP18 5c emerald 1.00 .90
C35 AP19 10c greenish slate 2.00 1.25

Death cent. of José Maria Heredia y Campuzano (1803-39), poet and patriot.

First Cuban Land Sighted by Columbus AP20

Columbus Lighthouse AP21

1944, May 19

C36 AP20 5c olive green .30 .15
C37 AP21 10c slate black .65 .20
Set value .27

450th anniv. of the discovery of America.

Catalogue values for unused stamps in this section, from this point to the end of the section, are for Never Hinged items.

Conference of La Mejorana (Meceo, Gomez and Marti) AP22

1948, May 21 Wmk. 229 *Perf. 12½*

C38 AP22 8c org yel & blk 1.40 .60

50th anniv. of the start of the War of 1895.

Souvenir Sheet
No. C33 Overprinted in Ultramarine

1948, May 21 Unwmk. *Imperf.*

C39 AP17 Sheet of 4 7.50 7.00

The overprint is applied in the center of the four 10c stamps, so that a portion falls on each.
American Air Mail Soc. Convention, Havana, May 21 to 23, 1948. The sheets sold for 60c each.

Type of 1931

1948, June 15 Wmk. 106 *Perf. 10*

C40 AP3 8c orange brown 1.25 .20

Narciso Lopez Landing at Cárdenas — AP23

Flag on Cuban Fort — AP24

Flag on Morro Castle, Havana — AP25

Engraved and Lithographed

1951, July 3 Wmk. 229 *Perf. 13*

C41	AP23	5c ol grn, ultra & red	.90	.20
C42	AP24	8c red brn, bl & red	1.40	.20
C43	AP25	25c gray blk, bl & red	2.00	1.25
		Nos. C41-C43 (3)	4.30	1.65

Centenary of adoption of Cuba's flag.

Souvenir Sheet

Illustration reduced.

1951, Aug. 24 Unwmk. *Imperf.*
C43A Sheet of 4 6.00 5.00

50th anniv. of the discovery of the cause of yellow fever by Dr. Carlos J. Finlay, and to honor the martyrs of science.

Postage Type and

Resignation Play of Dr. Lasker AP26

Capablanca Making "The Exact Play" — AP27

Wmk. 229

1951, Nov. 1 Photo. *Perf. 13*
C44 AP26 5c shown 3.00 .50
C45 AP27 8c shown 5.00 .75
C46 A165 25c Capablanca 9.00 2.00
Nos. C44-C46 (3) 17.00 3.25

30th anniv. of the winning of the World Chess title by José Raul Capablanca.

Morrillo Types of Regular Issue

Wmk. 106

1951, Nov. 22 Engr. *Perf. 10*
C47 A167 5c violet .70 .15
C48 A168 8c dp grn .90 .15
C49 A169 25c dk brn 1.75 .75
a. Souv. sheet of 6, black brown, perf. 13 30.00 30.00
b. Souv. sheet of 6, grn, imperf. 125.00 125.00
Nos. C47-C49 (3) 3.35 1.05

Nos. C49a and C49b contain one each of the 1c, 2c and 5c of types A167-A169 and of the 5c, 8c and 25c airmail stamps of types A167-A169. Sheets are unwatermarked and measure 124x133mm.

Isabella Type of Regular Issue, 1952

1952, Feb. 22
C50 A172 25c purple 2.00 .80
a. Souv. sheet of 2, perf. 11 12.50 12.50
b. Souv. sheet of 2, imperf. 15.00 15.00

Nos. C50a and C50b contain one each of a 2c of type A172 and a 25c air-mail stamp of type A172. In No. C50a, the 2c and marginal inscriptions are brown carmine; the 25c, dark blue. In No. C50b, the 2c and marginal inscriptions are dark blue; the 25c, brown carmine. Sheets measure 108x18mm.

Type of Regular Issue of 1951 Surcharged in Various Colors

5¢

AEREO

1952, Mar. 18

Color: Yellow Brown
C51 A159 5c on 2c .50 .15
C52 A159 8c on 2c (C) 1.00 .15
C53 A159 10c on 2c (Bl) 1.00 .15
C54 A159 25c on 2c (V) 1.50 1.00
C55 A159 50c on 2c (C) 5.00 2.00
C56 A159 1p on 2c (Bl) 12.50 7.50
Nos. C51-C56 (6) 21.50 10.95

Country School AP32

Entrance, University of Havana AP33

Designs: 10c, Presidential Mansion, 25c, Banknote.

Perf. 12½

1952, May 27 Wmk. 106 Engr.

Centers Various Shades of Green
C57 AP32 5c dk pur .40 .15
C58 AP33 8c dk red .60 .15
C59 AP32 10c dp blue 1.25 .20
C60 AP32 25c dk vio brn 2.00 1.00
Nos. C57-C60 (4) 4.25 1.50

Foundation of the Republic of Cuba, 50th anniv.

Plane and Map — AP34

Agustín Parlá — AP35

1952, July 22 Engr. *Perf. 10*
C61 AP34 8c black .90 .55
a. Souv. sheet, 8c deep blue 10.00 10.00
b. Souv. sheet, 8c deep green 10.00 10.00
C62 AP35 25c ultra 2.50 1.65
a. Souv. sheet, 25c deep blue 10.00 10.00
b. Souv. sheet, 25c deep green 10.00 10.00

30th anniv. of the Key West-Mariel flight of Agustin Parla.

The four souvenir sheets are perf. 11.

Col. Charles Hernandes y Sandrino — AP36

1952, Oct. 7
C63 AP36 5c orange .50 .15
C64 AP36 8c brt yel grn .50 .15
C65 AP36 10c dk brown .65 .15
C66 AP36 15c dk Prus grn 1.25 .50
C67 AP36 20c aqua 1.65 .65
C68 AP36 25c crimson 1.25 .65
C69 AP36 30c dk vio bl 3.25 1.65
C70 AP36 45c rose lilac 3.25 2.25
C71 AP36 50c indigo 2.00 1.65
C72 AP36 1p bister 6.50 3.25
Nos. C63-C72 (10) 20.80 11.05

Three-fourths of the proceeds from the sale were used for the Communications Ministry Employees' Retirement Fund.

Entrance, University of Havana — AP37

F. V. Dominguez, M. Estebanez and F. Capdevila — AP38

1952, Nov. 27 Engr.; Center Typo.
C73 AP37 5c ind & dk blue .90 .35
C74 AP38 25c org & dk grn 2.75 1.25

81st anniv. of the execution of 8 medical students.

AP39

Lockheed Constellation Airliners AP40

1953, May 22 Engr.
C75 AP39 8c orange brn .42 .15
C76 AP39 15c scarlet 1.65 .24

Typographed and Engraved
C77 AP40 2p dp green & dk brn 27.50 10.00
C78 AP40 5p blue & dk brn 35.00 16.00
Nos. C75-C78 (4) 64.57 26.39

See #C120-C121. For surcharge see #C224.

Page of Manifesto of Montecristi AP42

House of Maximo Gomez AP43

Designs: No. C79, Marti in Kingston, Jamaica, No. C80, With Workers in Tampa, Florida. No. C83, Marti addressing liberating army. No. C84, Portrait. No. C85, Dos Rios obelisk. No. C86, Marti's first tomb. No. C87, Present tomb. No. C88, Monument in Havana. No. C89, Martian forge.

1953 Engr. *Perf. 10*
C79 AP42 5c dk car & blk .30 .15
C80 AP43 5c dk car & blk .30 .15
C81 AP43 8c dk green & blk .75 .18
C82 AP42 8c dk green & blk .75 .18
C83 AP43 10c dk blue & dk car 1.50 .50
C84 AP42 10c dk blue & dk car 1.50 .50
C85 AP42 15c violet & gray 1.25 .90
C86 AP42 15c violet & gray 1.25 .90
C87 AP42 25c brown & car 3.00 1.25
C88 AP42 25c brown & car 3.00 1.25
C89 AP43 50c yellow & bl 5.00 2.50
Nos. C79-C89 (11) 18.60 8.46

Cent. of the birth of José Marti.

Board of Accounts Building — AP44

Design: 25c, Plane above Board of Accounts Bldg.

1953, Nov. 3
C90 AP44 8c rose carmine .90 .22
C91 AP44 25c dk gray grn 1.75 .90

1st Intl. Cong. of Boards of Account, Havana, Nov. 2-9, 1953.

Miguel Coyula Llaguno — AP45

Antonio Ginard Rojas — AP46

Designs: 10c, Gregorio Hernandez Saez. 1p, Communications Association Flag.

1954
C92 AP45 5c dark blue .32 .15
C93 AP46 8c red violet .40 .25
C94 AP46 10c orange .85 .35
C95 AP45 1p black 6.00 6.00
Nos. C92-C95 (4) 7.57 6.75

See note after No. C72.

Four-engine Plane and Cane Field — AP47

Plane and Harvesters Cutting Cane — AP48

Designs in Lower Triangle: 10c, Tractor pulling loaded wagons. 15c, Train of sugar cane. 20c, Modern mill. 25c, Evaporators. 30, Sacks of sugar. 40c, Loading sugar on ship. 45c, Ox cart. 50c, Primitive sugar mill. 1p, Alvaro Reinoso.

1954, Apr. 27 Engr.
C96 AP47 5c yellow green .40 .15
C97 AP48 8c brown .90 .15
C98 AP48 10c dark green 1.00 .18
C99 AP48 15c henna brn .50 .40
C100 AP48 20c blue .70 .65
C101 AP48 25c scarlet 1.00 .65
C102 AP48 30c lilac rose 1.75 .95
C103 AP48 40c deep blue 2.00 1.25
C104 AP48 45c violet 4.00 2.50
C105 AP48 50c brt blue 3.00 1.65
C106 AP47 1p dk gray blue 5.50 3.25
Nos. C96-C106 (11) 20.75 11.78

For surcharges see Nos. C204.

Sanatorium Type of Regular Issue

1954, Sept. 21 Wmk. 106 *Perf. 10*
C107 A186 9c deep green 1.00 .50

Dolz Type of Regular Issue, 1954

1954, Dec. 23
C108 A188 12c carmine 1.00 .50

Rotary Type of Regular Issue, 1955

1955, Feb. 23
C109 A190 12c carmine 1.00 .50

Stamps of 1855 and 1905, Palace of Fine Arts AP52

Designs (including 2 stamps): 12c, Plaza de la Fraternidad. 24c, View of Havana. 30c, Plaza de la Republica.

1955, Apr. 24 *Perf. 12½*
C110 AP52 8c dk grnsh bl & grn 1.25 .50
C111 AP52 12c dk ol grn & red 1.50 .35
C112 AP52 24c dk red & ultra 1.75 1.00
C113 AP52 30c dp org & brn 3.75 2.00
Nos. C110-C113 (4) 8.25 3.85

Cent. of Cuba's 1st postage stamps.

Mariel Bay — AP53

Views: 12c, Varadero beach. 1p, Vinales valley.

1955, June 22 Wmk. 106
C114 AP53 8c dk car & dk grn .75 .30
C115 AP53 12c dk ocher & brt bl 1.00 .25
C116 AP53 1p dk grn & ocher 6.00 4.00
Nos. C114-C116 (3) 7.75 4.55

See note after No. C72.

Map of Crocier's 1914 Flight — AP54

Design: 30c, Crocier in plane.

1955, July 4 *Perf. 10*

C117 AP54 12c red & dk grn		.60	.20
C118 AP54 30c dk grn & mag		2.25	.60

35th anniv. of the death of Jaime Gonzalez Crocier, aviation pioneer.

Cuban Museum, Tampa, Fla. — AP55

1955, July 1 **Engr.** *Perf. 12½*

C119 AP55 12c red & dk brn	1.25	.35

Cent. of Tampa's incorporation as a town.

Lockheed Type of 1953

Typographed and Engraved

1955, Sept. 21 **Wmk. 106**

C120 AP40 2p bl & ol grn	17.50	8.50
C121 AP40 5p dp rose & ol grn	37.50	16.50

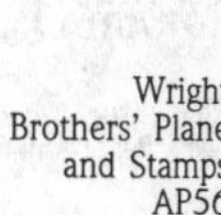

Wright Brothers' Plane and Stamps AP56

Designs: 12c, Spirit of St. Louis. 24c, Graf Zeppelin. 30c, Constellation passenger plane. 50c, Convair jet fighter.

Engraved and Photogravure

1955, Nov. 12 Wmk. 106 *Perf. 12½*

Inscription and Plane in Black

C122 AP56 8c car & bl	1.00	.35
C123 AP56 12c yel grn & car	2.25	.70
C124 AP56 24c vio & car	7.00	2.50
C125 AP56 30c bl & red org	6.00	3.25
C126 AP56 50c ol grn & red org	8.00	4.00
a. Souvenir sheet of 5	27.50	27.50
Nos. C122-C126 (5)	24.25	10.80

International Centenary Philatelic Exhibition in Havana, Nov. 12-19, 1955.

No. C126a is printed on thick paper and measures 140x178mm. It contains one each of Nos. C122-C126 with the background of each stamp printed in a different color from the perforated stamps.

"Three Friends" and Gen. Emilio Nuñez AP57

Design: 12c, Landing on the Cuban Coast.

1955, Dec. 27 **Engr.** **Unwmk.**

C127 AP57 8c ultra & dk car	1.00	.40
C128 AP57 12c grn & dk red brn	1.50	.50

Gen. Emilio Nu
ñez, Cuban revolutionary hero, birth cent.

Post Type of Regular Issue, 1956

Design: 12c, Bishop P. A. Morell de Santa Cruz (1694-1768).

1956, Mar. 27 **Wmk. 106**

C129 A197 12c dk brn & grn	.90	.30

Plane Type of 1931-46

1956 **Engr.** *Perf. 10*

C130 AP4 50c greenish blue	2.00	1.00

Portrait Type of Regular Issue, 1956.

1956, May 2 *Perf. 12½*

Portraits: 8c, Gen. Julio Sanguily. 12c, Gen. José Maria Aguirre. 30c, Col. Ernesto Ponts Sterling.

Portraits in Black

C131 A198 8c brown	.75	.20
C132 A198 12c dull yellow	1.25	.20
C133 A198 30c indigo	2.25	1.50
Nos. C131-C133 (3)	4.25	1.90

See note after No. C72.

Mother and Child — AP60

Masonic Temple Havana — AP61

1956, May 13 Wmk. 106 *Perf. 12½*

C134 AP60 12c ultra & red	1.00	.25

Issued in honor of Mother's Day 1956.

1956, June 5

C135 AP61 12c olive green	.60	.20

Pigeon — AP62

Gundlach Hawk — AP63

Birds: 8c, Wood duck. 19c, Herring gulls. 24c, White pelicans. 29c, Common merganser. 30c, Quail. 50c, Herons (great white, great blue and Wurdemann's). 1p, Northern caracara. 2p, Middle American jacana. 5p, Ivory-billed woodpecker.

1956

C136 AP62 8c blue	.40	.18
C137 AP62 12c gray blue	5.50	.15
C138 AP63 14c green	1.10	.25
C139 AP63 19c redsh brn	.80	.55
C140 AP63 24c lilac rose	.95	.55
C141 AP62 29c green	1.25	.55
C142 AP62 30c dk ol bis	1.50	.80
C143 AP63 50c slate blk	3.00	1.10
C144 AP63 1p dk car rose	4.75	2.25
C145 AP62 2p rose violet	10.50	4.25
C146 AP63 5p brt red	24.00	8.75
Nos. C136-C146 (11)	53.75	19.38

See Nos. C205, C235-C237. For surcharges and overprints see #C147, C151, C197, C209-C210

Inauguración
Edificio Club
Filatélico de la
República de Cuba
Julio 13 de 1956.

8¢

Type of 1956 Surcharged

Design: 24c, White pelicans.

1956, July 13

C147 AP63 8c on 24c deep org	.75	.35

Opening of the new building of the Cuba Philatelic Club, Havana, July 14, 1956.

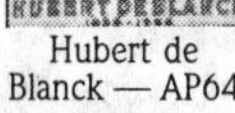

Hubert de Blanck — AP64

Church of Our Lady of Charity — AP65

1956, July 6

C148 AP64 12c ultra	.70	.25

Hubert de Blanck (1856-1932), composer.

1956, Sept. 8

C149 AP65 12c green & car	.90	.40
a. Souvenir sheet of 2, imperf.	8.00	7.00

Issued in honor of Our Lady of Charity of Cobre, patroness of Cuba.

No. C149a contains one each of Nos. 559 and C149. No. C149a exists with yellow of No. 559 omitted.

Benjamin Franklin AP66

1956, Oct. 5 **Engr.** *Perf. 12½*

C150 AP66 12c red brn	1.00	.40

Type of 1956 Surcharged in Blue

Design: 2p, Middle American jacana.

1956, Oct. 26 **Wmk. 106**

C151 AP62 12c on 2p dk gray	1.00	.75

Issued in honor of the 12th Inter-American Press Association Conference, Havana.

Lord Baden-Powell — AP67

1957, Feb. 22

C152 AP67 12c slate	1.50	.35

Centenary of the birth of Lord Baden-Powell, founder of the Boy Scouts.

Hanabanilla Waterfall AP68

Designs: 12c, Sierra de Cubitas. 30c, Puerto Boniato.

1957, Mar. 29

C153 AP68 8c blue & red	.75	.20
C154 AP68 12c green & red	1.20	.25
C155 AP68 30c ol grn & dk pur	2.00	1.00
Nos. C153-C155 (3)	3.95	1.45

See note after No. 457.

Philatelic Club, Havana AP69

Fingerprint AP70

1957, Apr. 24 Wmk. 106 *Perf. 12½*

C156 AP69 12c yel, grn & brn	1.00	.25

Stamp Day, and the Natl. Phil. Exhib.

1957, Apr. 30

C157 AP70 12c claret brown	1.00	.20

Birth cent. (in 1856) of Juan Francisco Steegers y Perera, dactyloscopy pioneer.

Baseball Player — AP71

1957, May 17 Wmk. 106 *Perf. 12½*

C158 AP71 8c shown	1.00	.35
C159 AP71 12c Ballerina	1.75	.40
C160 AP71 24c Girl diver	2.50	1.00
C161 AP71 30c Boxers	3.50	1.50
Nos. C158-C161 (4)	8.75	3.25

Issued to honor young Cuban athletes.

Joaquin de Aguero AP72

Jeanette Ryder AP73

1957, July 4

C162 AP72 12c indigo	1.00	.25

Issued to honor Joaquin de Aguero, Cuban freedom fighter and patriot.

1957, July 17

C163 AP73 12c dk red brn	1.00	.35
a. Pair, #574, C163	2.00	1.00

Mrs. Jeanette Ryder, founder of the Humane Society of Cuba.

José M. de Heredia y Girard — AP74

John Robert Gregg — AP75

1957, Aug. 16 **Engr.** **Wmk. 106**

C164 AP74 8c dk blue vio	.50	.25

José Maria de Heredia y Girard (1842-1905), Cuban born French poet.

Justice Type of Regular Issue, 1957

1957, Sept. 2 *Perf. 12½*

C165 A214 12c green	1.00	.50

1957, Oct. 1

C166 AP75 12c dark green	.95	.35

90th anniv. of the birth of John Robert Gregg, inventor of the Gregg shorthand system.

D. Figarola Caneda — AP76 José Marti National Library — AP77

1957, Oct. 18 Wmk. 106 *Perf. 12½*

C167 AP76 8c ultra .55 .25
C168 AP77 12c chocolate .95 .25

José Marti National Library.

Map of Cuba and UN Emblem — AP78

1957, Oct. 24

C169 AP78 8c dk green & brn .60 .20
C170 AP78 12c car rose & grn .85 .40
C171 AP78 30c ind & brt pink 2.00 .90

Issued for United Nations Day, 1957.

Map of Cuba and Florida — AP79

1957, Oct. 28

C172 AP79 12c dk red brn & bl .85 .40

30th anniv. of airmail service from Key West to Havana.

Type of Regular Issue, 1957 and

Stairway and Bell Tower — AP80

Design: 12c, Facade of Normal School.

1957, Nov. 19 Engr. *Perf. 12½*

C173 A217 12c indigo & ocher .85 .20
C174 AP80 30c dk car & gray 1.25 .60

View Types of Regular Issue, 1957

Views: 8c, El Viso Fort, El Caney. 12c, Sancti Spiritus Church. 30c, Concordia Bridge, Matanzas.

1957, Dec. 17 *Perf. 12½*

C175 A218 8c dk gray & red .75 .28
C176 A219 12c brown & gray 1.00 .28
C177 A218 30c red brn & bl gray 1.50 .95
Nos. C175-C177 (3) 3.25 1.51

See note after No. C72.

Hedges Types of Regular Issue, 1958

Design: 8c, Dayton Hedges and Matanzas rayon factory.

1958, Jan. 30 Wmk. 106 *Perf. 12½*

C178 A221 8c green 1.00 .40

Diario de la Marina Building — AP81

1958, Apr. 1

C179 AP81 29c black 3.50 2.00

Jose Ignacio Rivero y Alonso, editor of the newspaper, Diario de la Marina.

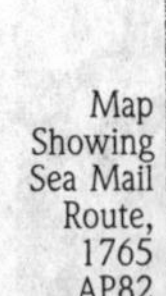

Map Showing Sea Mail Route, 1765 AP82

1958, Apr. 24 Wmk. 106 *Perf. 12½*

C180 AP82 29c dk bl aqua & buff 2.50 1.25

Issued for Stamp Day, Apr. 24, and the National Philatelic Exhibition.

Gen. Gomez in Battle — AP83 Snail (Polymita Picta) — AP84

1958, June 6 Engr.

C181 AP83 12c slate green .80 .25

Issued in honor of Maj. Gen. José Miguel Gomez, President of Cuba, 1909-13.

1958, Aug. 29 Wmk. 321 *Perf. 12½*

Fossils: 12c, Megalocnus Rodens. 30c, Ammonite.

C182 AP84 8c gray, red & yel 1.50 .90
C183 AP84 12c brn, *yel grn* 2.50 1.50
C184 AP84 30c grn, *pink* 3.50 2.00
Nos. C182-C184 (3) 7.50 4.40

Centenary of the birth of Dr. Carlos de la Torre, naturalist.

Papilio Caiguanabus AP85 Cuban Sea Bass AP86

Designs: 12c, Teria gundlachia. 14c, Teria ebriola. 19c, Nathalis felicia. 29c, Butter Hamlet. 30c, Tattler.

1958, Sept. 26 Wmk. 106 *Perf. 12½*

C185 AP85 8c multicolored 1.75 .50
C186 AP85 12c emer, blk & org 2.00 .50
C187 AP85 14c multicolored 3.00 .75
C188 AP85 19c bl, blk & yel 3.75 1.00
C189 AP86 24c multicolored 4.50 1.00
C190 AP86 29c blk, brn & ultra 7.00 1.25
C191 AP86 30c blk, yel grn & sep 8.00 1.75
Nos. C185-C191 (7) 30.00 6.75

Felipe Poey (1799-1891), naturalist.

Battle of San Juan Hill, 1898 — AP87

Perf. 12½

1958, Oct. 27 Wmk. 106 Engr.

C192 AP87 12c black brown 1.00 .30

Birth centenary of Theodore Roosevelt.

UNESCO Building, Paris — AP88

Design: 30c, "UNESCO" and map of Cuba.

1958, Nov. 7

C193 AP88 12c dk slate grn 1.00 .40
C194 AP88 30c dp ultra 2.25 1.35

UNESCO Headquarters in Paris opening, Nov. 3.

Postal Notice of 1765 — AP89 Musical Arts Building — AP90

Design: 30c, Administrative postal book of St. Cristobal, Havana, 1765.

1959, Apr. 24 Wmk. 321 *Perf. 12½*

C195 AP89 12c Prus blue & sep .65 .25
C196 AP89 30c sepia & Prus bl 1.25 .85

Issued for Stamp Day, Apr. 24, and the National Philatelic Exhibition.

Type of 1956 Surcharged with New Value, Bar and "ASTA" Emblem in Dark Blue

1959, Oct. 17 Wmk. 321 *Perf. 12½*

C197 AP63 12c on 1p emer 1.00 .40

Issued to publicize the meeting of the American Soc. of Travel Agents, Oct. 17-23.

Perf. 12½

1959, Nov. 11 Wmk. 106 Engr.

C198 AP90 12c yellow green 1.00 .25

40th anniversary of the Musical Arts Society.

No. CB1 Surcharged in Red: "HABILITADO PARA / 12c"

Engr. & Typo.

1960 Wmk. 321 *Perf. 12½*

C199 SPAP1 12c on 12 + 3c car & grn 1.50 .75

Type of Regular Issue, 1960.

Designs: 8c, Battle of Santa Clara. 12c, Rebel forces entering Havana. 29c, Bank-note changing hands ("Clandestine activities in the cities").

Perf. 12½

1960, Jan. 28 Wmk. 320 Engr.

C200 A236 8c bl, gray ol & sal 1.00 .25
C201 A236 12c gray ol & ocher 1.50 .25
C202 A236 29c gray & car 2.50 1.50
Nos. C200-C202 (3) 5.00 2.00

Nos. C9 and C104 Surcharged "12c" in Red

1960, Feb. 3 Wmk. 106

C203 AP3 12c on 40c dp org .75 .30
C204 AP48 12c on 45c vio .75 .30

Pigeon Type of 1956

1960, Feb. 12 Wmk. 321

C205 AP62 12c brt blue grn .50 .15

Statue Type of Regular Issue, 1960.

Statues: 8c, José Marti, Matanzas. 12c, Heroes of the Cacarajicara, Pinar del Rio. 30c, Cosme de la Torriente, Isle of Pines, horiz.

1960, Mar. 28 *Perf. 12½*

C206 A237 8c gray & car .60 .25
C207 A237 12c blue & car 1.00 .25
C208 A237 30c violet & brn 2.25 1.00
Nos. C206-C208 (3) 3.85 1.50

See note after No. 386.

Type of 1956 and No. C33 Overprinted in Dark Blue

1960, Apr. 24 Wmk. 321 *Perf. 12½*

C209 AP62 8c orange yel .30 .20
C210 AP62 12c cerise .50 .20

Souvenir Sheet

C211 AP17 Sheet of 4 20.00 20.00

Stamp Day, Apr. 24, 1960, and Natl. Phil. Exhib.
No. C211 has added marginal inscription in dark blue for cent. of the ¼r on 2r (No. 15).

Type of Olympic Games Issue, 1960

Perf. 12½

1960, Sept. 22 Wmk. 321 Engr.

C212 A238 8c Boxer .40 .20
C213 A238 12c Runner .60 .40
a. Souvenir sheet of 4 3.00

17th Olympic Games, Rome, Aug. 25-Sept. 11. No. C213a contains one each imperf. of types of Nos. 645-646 and Nos. C212-C213 in dark blue.

No. C3 and Flight Symbols of 1930, 1960 AP91

1960, Oct. 30 Litho. Unwmk.

C214 AP91 8c multicolored 2.00 1.50

30th anniv. of national air mail service.

Sword of Sheaf of Wheat — AP92

Designs: 12c, Two workers, horiz. 30c, Three maps, horiz. 50c, Hand inscribed "Peace" in 5 languages.

1961, Jan. 10 Photo. *Perf. 11½*

Granite Paper

C215 AP92 8c multicolored .30 .20
C216 AP92 12c multicolored .45 .20
C217 AP92 30c black & red 1.25 .50
C218 AP92 50c blk, bl & red 1.50 1.00
Nos. C215-C218 (4) 3.50 1.90

Conf. of Underdeveloped Countries, Havana.

José Marti and "Declaration of Havana" AP93

Background in Spanish, English or French.

1961, Jan. 28 Litho. *Perf. 12½*

C219 AP93 8c pale grn, blk & red 1.00 .60
C220 AP93 12c org yel, blk & pale vio 1.50 1.00
C221 AP93 30c pale bl, blk & pale brn 2.50 1.50
a. Souvenir sheet of 3 6.50 6.50
Nos. C219-C221 (9) 15.00 9.30

Declaration of Havana, Sept. 1, 1960.

Sheets of 25 are imprinted in margin "E" for Spanish, "I" for English or "F" for French.

No. C221a contains one each of Nos. C219-C221, imperf. The 8c has background in Spanish, the 12c in English and the 30e in French.

UN Type of 1961

1961, Apr. 12 Unwmk. *Perf. 12½*

C222 A244 8c dp car & yel .30 .15
C223 A244 12c brt ultra & org .60 .30
a. Souv. sheet of 2, #C222-C223, imperf. 2.00

Nos. C76 and C7 Surcharged

HABILITADO PARA 8 cts.

Wmk. 106

1961, Oct. 1 Engr. *Perf. 10*

C224 AP39 8c on 15c No. C76
C225 AP3 8c on 20c No. C7

Revolution Anniv. Type of 1962

Perf. 12½

1962, Jan. 3 Litho. Unwmk.

C226 A250 8c multi
C227 A250 12c multi
C228 A250 30c multi

1st Sugarcane Harvest in Socialist Cuba, 1st Anniv. — AP94

1962, Jan. 16

C229 AP94 8c salmon pink & dark brn
C230 AP94 12c bluish lil & blk

Importation Prohibited

Cuban stamps issued after No. C230 have not been valued because the embargo on trade with Cuba, proclaimed Feb. 7, 1962, by President Kennedy, prohibits the importation from any country of stamps of Cuban origin, used or unused.

Intl. Radio Service AP95

1962, Mar. 26 Wmk. 321

C231 AP95 8c multi
C232 AP95 12c multi
C233 AP95 30c multi
C234 AP95 1p multi

Bird Type of 1956

1962, July 20 Engr. Wmk. 321

C235 AP63 1p like #C144, royal blue
C236 AP62 2p like #C145, dark red
C237 AP63 5p like #C146, rose lake

PRAGA '62 — AP96

1962, Aug. 18 Litho.

C238 AP96 31c Czechoslovakia No. 1080

Souvenir Sheet

Imperf

C239 AP96 31c like No. C238

No. C239 contains one 60x35½mm stamp.

Achievements of the Revolution — AP97

1966, July 26 Wmk. 376 *Perf. 12½*

C240 AP97 1c Agrarian reform
C241 AP97 2c Industrialization
C242 AP97 3c Urban reform
C243 AP97 7c Eradication of unemployment
C244 AP97 9c Education
C245 AP97 10c Public health
C246 AP97 13c Excerpt from *La Historia Me Absolvera,* by Castro

Camaguey-Seville Flight, 35th Anniv. — AP98

1971, Jan. 12 Unwmk.

C247 AP98 13c Aircraft
C248 AP98 30c Map, Lieut. Menendez Palaez

Havana-Santiago de Chile Direct Air Service, 1st Anniv. — AP99

1972, June 26 Wmk. 376

C249 AP99 25c multi

6th Congress of Latin American and Caribbean Exporters of Sugar, Havana — AP100

Perf. 12½x12

1977, Feb. 28 Unwmk.

C250 AP100 13c multi

Composer Type of 1977

1977, May 10 *Perf. 13*

C251 A571 13c Jorge Ankerman and score

Flower Type of 1977

1977, May 31

C252 A572 13c *Caesalpinia pulcherrima*
C253 A572 30c *Catharanthus roseus*

Souvenir Sheet

Perf. 13½x13

C254 A572 50c Juan Tomas Roig

No. C254 contains one 32x40mm stamp.

Natl. Decorations Type of 1977

1977, July 26 *Perf. 12x12½*

C255 A574 13c multi, diff.
C256 A574 30c multi, diff.

Art Type of 1977

Paintings by Jorge Arche: 13c, *My Wife and I,* vert. 30c, *Domino Players.* 50c, *Self-portrait,* vert.

1977, Aug. 25 *Perf. 13x12½*

Size: 26x38mm

C257 A575 13c multi

Size: 40x29mm

Perf. 13

C258 A575 30c multi

Souvenir Sheet

Perf. 13½x13

C259 A575 50c multi

No. C259 contains one 32x40mm stamp.

Spartakiad Type of 1977

1977, Sept. 10 *Perf. 13*

C260 A576 13c Grenade-throwing
C261 A576 30c Rifle-shooting, horiz.

10th Heroic Guerrilla's Day AP101

1977, Oct. 8 *Perf. 12½x13*

C262 AP101 13c Guerrilla fighters

Airmail Service Type of 1977

1977, Oct. 27 *Perf. 12x12½*

C263 A577 13c Havana-Mexico cachet
C264 A577 30c Havana-Prague cachet

Souvenir Sheet

Adoration of the Magi, by Rubens — AP102

1977, Nov. 18 *Perf. 13*

C265 AP102 50c multi

Ruben's 400th birth anniv.

Havana Zoo Type of 1977

1977, Nov. 24

C266 A579 13c Tiger
C267 A579 30c Lion

Revolution Martyrs Type of 1977

1977, Dec. 2 *Perf. 12½x12*

C268 A580 13c *Corynthia* landing

Pan American Health Organization (OPS), 75th Anniv. — AP103

1977, Dec. 2

C269 AP103 13c multi

Havana University Type of 1978

1978, Jan. 5 *Perf. 13x12½*

C270 A582 13c Crossed sabres, university
C271 A582 30c University, statue, crowd

Portrait of Jose Marti (b. 1853), by A. Menocal — AP104

1978, Jan. 28

C272 AP104 13c multi

Art Type of 1978

Paintings in the Nat. Museum of Art: 13c, *El Guadalquivir,* by M. Barrow. 30c, *Portrait of H.E. Ridley,* by J.J. Masqueries, vert.

1978, Feb. 20 *Perf. 12½x12, 13*

Sizes: 42x27mm, 29x40mm

C273 A583 13c multi
C274 A583 30c multi

Bird Type of 1975

1978, Mar. 10 *Perf. 12½x12, 13*

Size: 42x27mm, 27x42mm

C275 A524 13c *Torreornis inexpectata,* horiz.
C276 A524 30c *Ara tricolor*

Baragua Protest, Cent. — AP105

1978, Mar. 15 *Perf. 13x13½*

C277 AP105 13c *Antonio Maceo,* by A. Melero

Cosmonaut's Day Type of 1978

1978, Apr. 12 *Perf. 13*

C278 A585 13c *Venus 10*

Size: 36x46mm

Perf. 12½x13

C279 A585 30c *Lunokhod 2,* vert.

SOCFILEX '78, Budapest — AP106

1978, May 7 *Perf. 13x12½*

C280 AP106 30c Parliament, Hungary No. 217

Cactus Type of 1978

1978, May 15 *Perf. 13*

C281 A587 13c *Rhodocactus cubensis*
C282 A587 30c *Harrisia taetra*

World Telecommunications Day — AP107

1978, May 17

C283 AP107 30c multi

Organization of African Unity, 15th Anniv. — AP108

1978, May 25 *Perf. 13x12½*
C284 AP108 30c multi

Souvenir Sheet

CAPEX '78, Toronto — AP109

1978, June 9 *Perf. 13x13½*
C285 AP109 50c *Niven, Wales,* by G.H. Russell

Aquarium Type of 1978

1978, June 15 *Perf. 13*
C286 A588 13c *Carassias auratus,* vert.
C287 A588 30c *Symphysodon aequifasciata axelrodi*

MEDELLIN Games Type of 1978

1978, July 1
C288 A589 13c Volleyball
C289 A589 30c Running

Attack on Moncada Type of 1978

1978, July 26
C290 A590 13c Soldiers bearing rifles
C291 A590 30c Stylized dove, banners

Youth Festival Type of 1978

Natl. flags and views of host cities.

1978, July 28
C292 A591 13c Moscow, 1957
C293 A591 13c Vienna, 1959
C294 A591 13c Helsinki, 1962
C295 A591 13c Sofia, 1968
C296 A591 13c Berlin, 1973
a. Strip of 5, Nos. C292-C296

Size: 46x36mm

Perf. 13x12½

C297 A591 30c Havana, 1978

Tuna Industry Type of 1978

1978, Aug. 30 *Perf. 12½x12*
C298 A593 13c Stern trawler
C299 A593 30c Refrigerator ship

Demand, as well as supply, determine a stamp's market value.

Souvenir Sheet

PRAGA '78 — AP110

1978, Sept. 8 *Perf. 13*
C300 AP110 50c *Marina,* by A. Brandeis

Art Type of 1978

Paintings by Amelia Pelaez del Casal (1896-1968).

1978, Sept. 15 *Perf. 12x12½, 13*
C301 A594 13c *Yellow Flowers,* vert.
C302 A594 30c *Still-life in Blue,* vert.

Souvenir Sheet

Perf. 13½x13

C303 A594 50c *Portrait of Amelia,* by L. Romanach, vert.

No. C303 contains one 32x40mm stamp.

Socialist Communication Organizations Congress (OSS), 20th Anniv. — AP111

1978, Sept. 25 *Perf. 13*
C304 AP111 30c multi

Souvenir Sheet

EXFILNA '78, 6th Natl. Philatelic Exposition — AP112

1978, Oct. 10 *Imperf.*
C305 AP112 50c 1st Postal Card, issued in 1878

No. C305 has simulated perfs.

Intl. Anti-Apartheid Year — AP113

1978, Oct. 16 *Perf. 12½*
C306 AP113 13c multi

Zoo Type of 1978

1978, Oct. 20 *Perf. 13*
C307 A595 13c *Acinonyx jubatos*
C308 A595 30c *Loxodonta africana,* vert.

Natl. Ballet Type of 1978

1978, Oct. 28 *Perf. 12½x13*
C309 A596 13c *Giselle,* vert.
C310 A596 30c *Genesis,* vert.

Pacific Flora Type of 1978

1978, Nov. 30 *Perf. 13*
C311 A597 13c multi, diff.
C312 A597 30c multi, diff.

25th Death Anniv. of Julius and Ethel Rosenberg, American Communists Executed for Espionage — AP114

1978, Dec. 20
C313 AP114 13c multi

Julio A. Mella (d. 1929) AP115

1979, Jan. 10
C314 AP115 13c multi

Cosmonaut's Day Type of 1979
Souvenir Sheet

1979, Apr. 12 *Perf. 13½x13*
C315 A603 50c Orbital complex

No. C315 contains one 32x40mm stamp.

Intl. Year of the Child — AP116

1979, June 1 *Perf. 13x12½*
C316 AP116 13c multi

Art Type of 1979

1979, June 15 *Perf. 13½x13*
C317 A600 50c *Portrait of Victor Emmanuel Garcia,* by J. Arche, vert.

No. C317 contains one 32x40mm stamp.

CARIFESTA '79, Festival of Caribbean Peoples, Havana AP117

1979, July 16 *Perf. 12½x13*
C318 AP117 13c multi

10th World Universiade Games, Mexico City — AP118

1979, Sept. 1 *Perf. 13x12½*
C319 AP118 13c grn, pale grn & gold

6th Conference of Nonaligned Countries — AP119

1979, Sept. 3
C320 AP119 50c Convention Palace

Sir Rowland Hill (d. 1879), Originator of Penny Postage — AP120

1979, Sept. 4 *Perf. 13½x13*
C321 AP120 30c Hill, casket

SOCFILEX '79, Bucharest — AP121

Illustration reduced.

1979, Oct. 25 *Perf. 12½*
C322 AP121 30c Romania No. 683, flags

Intl. Radio Consultative Committee (CCIR), 50th Anniv. — AP122

1979, Nov. 30 *Perf. 12½x12*
C323 AP122 30c Ground receiving station

1st Soviet-Cuban Joint Space Flight — AP123

1980, Sept. 23 *Perf. 12½*
C324 AP123 13c multi
C325 AP123 30c multi

Capt. Mariano Barberan, Lt. Joaquin Collar, and Their Airplane Cuatro Vientos. AP124

1993, June 11 Litho. *Perf. 13*
C326 AP124 30c multicolored
1st Flight Seville-Camaguey, 60th anniv.

AIR POST SEMI-POSTAL STAMP

Catalogue values for unused stamps in this section are for Never Hinged items.

Farm Couple and Factory SPAP1

Engr. & Typo.
1959, May 7 Wmk. 321 *Perf. 12½*
CB1 SPAP1 12c + 3c car & grn 1.25 .50
Agricultural reforms. See No. C199.

AIR POST SPECIAL DELIVERY STAMPS

Matanzas Issue

Matanzas Harbor APSD1

Perf. 12½
1936, May 5 Photo. Wmk. 229
CE1 ASPD1 15c light blue 2.50 1.25
Exists imperf. Value $5 unused, $2.50 used.

SPECIAL DELIVERY STAMPS

Issued under US Administration

US No. E5 Surcharged in Red

CUBA.
10c.
de PESO

1899 Wmk. 191 *Perf. 12*
E1 SD3 10c on 10c blue 130.00 100.00
a. No period after "CUBA" 450.00 400.00

Issues of the Republic under US Military Rule

Special Delivery Messenger SD2

Inscribed: "Immediata"

1899 Wmk. U S-C (191C) Engr.
E2 SD2 10c orange 45.00 15.00

Issues of the Republic
Inscribed: "Inmediata"

1902 *Perf. 12*
E3 SD2 10c orange 1.00 .75

J. B. Zayas — SD3

1910 Unwmk.
E4 SD3 10c orange & blue 11.00 3.25
a. Center inverted 725.00

Airplane and Morro Castle — SD4

1914, Feb. 24 *Perf. 12*
E5 SD4 10c dark blue 15.00 1.25

1927 Wmk. Star (106)
E6 SD4 10c deep blue 12.00 .50

1935 *Perf. 10*
E7 SD4 10c blue 12.00 .40

Matanzas Issue

Mercury SD5

Wmk. Wavy Lines (229)
1936, May 5 Photo. *Perf. 12½*
E8 SD5 10c deep claret 3.00 1.25
Exists imperf. Value $0 unused, $2.50 used.

"Triumph of the Revolution" SD6

1936, Nov. 18
E9 SD6 10c red orange 2.00 1.10
Maj. Gen. Máximo Gómez (1836-1905).

Temple of Quetzalcoatl (Mexico) SD7

Ruben Dario (Nicaragua) SD8

Wmk. 106
1937, Oct. 13 Engr. *Perf. 10*
E10 SD7 10c dp org 4.25 4.25
E11 SD8 10c dp org 4.25 4.25
Issued for the benefit of the Association of American Writers and Artists. See note after No. 354.

Letter and Symbols of Transportation SD9

1945, Oct. 30
E12 SD9 10c olive brown 2.00 .20

Governor's Building, Cárdenas SD10

Engraved and Lithographed
1951, July 3 Wmk. 229 *Perf. 13*
E13 SD10 10c hn brn, ultra & red 3.00 .55
Cent. of the adoption of Cuba's flag.

Chess Type of Regular Issue, 1951

1951, Nov. 1 Photo.
E14 A166 10c dk grn & rose brn 12.50 1.75

Catalogue values for unused stamps in this section, from this point to the end of the section, are for Never Hinged items.

Type of Regular Issue of 1951 Surcharged in Red Violet

10¢
E. ESPECIAL

Wmk. 106
1952, Mar. 18 Engr. *Perf. 10*
E15 A159 10c on 2c yel brn 3.00 .95

Arms and Bars from National Hymn — SD12

Roseate Tern — SD13

1952, May 27 *Perf. 12½*
E16 SD12 10c dp org & bl 2.50 .75
Republic of Cuba founding, 50th anniv.

Type of Air Post Stamps of 1952 Inscribed: "Entrega Especial"

1952, Oct. 7 *Perf. 10*
E17 AP36 10c pale olive grn 3.00 1.50
Three-fourths of the proceeds from the sale of No. E17 were used for the Communications Ministry Employees' Retirement Fund.

1953, July 28
E18 SD13 10c blue 2.75 .75

Gregorio Hernandez Saez SD14

Felix Varela SD15

1954, Feb. 23
E19 SD14 10c olive green 3.25 .90

1955, June 22 *Perf. 12½*
E20 SD15 10c brn car 2.50 .95
See note after No. E17.

Portrait Type of Regular Issue, 1956
Inscribed: "Entrega Especial"
Portrait: 10c, Jose Jacinto Milanes.

1956, May 2 Wmk. 106
E21 A198 10c dk car rose & blk 2.50 .75
See note after No. E17.

Painting Type of Regular Issue, 1957,
Inscribed: "Entrega Especial"
Painting: 10c, "Yesterday" by E. Garcia Cabrera.

1957, Mar. 15 Engr. *Perf. 12½*
E22 A207 10c dk brn & turq bl 3.25 .85
See note after No. E17.

View Type of Regular Issue, 1957,
Inscribed: "Entrega Especial."
View: 10c, Independence square, Pino del Rio.

1957, Dec. 17
E23 A218 10c dk pur & brn 2.25 .75
See note after No. E17.

View in Havana and Messenger SD16

1958, Jan. 10 Engr.
E24 SD16 10c blue 1.50 .55
E25 SD16 20c green 2.00 .65
See Nos. E28, E31.

Fish Type of Air Post Issue, 1958,
Inscribed "Entrega Especial."
Fish: 10c, Blackfish snapper. 20c, Mosquitofish.

1958, Sept. 26 Wmk. 106 *Perf. 12½*
E26 AP86 10c blk, bl, pink & yel 4.00 2.00
E27 AP86 20c blk, ultra & pink 12.50 9.00
See note after No. C191.

Messenger Type of 1958

1960 Wmk. 321 *Perf. 12½*
E28 SD16 10c brt vio 1.75 .50

Plane Type of Air Post Issue, of 1931-46,
Surcharged in Black or Red:
"HABILITADO ENTREGA ESPECIAL 10¢"

1960 Wmk. 106 *Perf. 10*
E29 AP4 10c on 20c car rose 1.40 .50
E30 AP4 10c on 50c grnsh bl (R) 1.10 .50

Messenger Type of 1958

1961, June 28 Wmk. 321 *Perf. 12½*
E31 SD16 10c orange 1.75 .65

West Indies Packet Type of 1962
Perf. 12½

1962, Apr. 24 Litho. Unwmk.
E32 A253 10c buff, dull ultra & brn

POSTAGE DUE STAMPS

Issued under Administration of the United States

Postage Due Stamps of the US Nos. J38, J39, J41 and J42 Surcharged in Black like Nos. 221-226A

1899 Wmk. 191 *Perf. 12*
J1 D2 1c on 1c dp claret 45.00 5.25
J2 D2 2c on 2c dp claret 45.00 5.25
a. Inverted surcharge 2,500.
J3 D2 5c on 5c dp claret 45.00 5.25
J4 D2 10c on 10c dp claret 27.50 2.50
Nos. J1-J4 (4) 162.50 18.25

Issues of the Republic

D1

1914 Unwmk. Engr. *Perf. 12*

J5 D1 1c carmine rose 6.50 1.00
J6 D1 2c carmine rose 8.00 1.00
J7 D1 5c carmine rose 12.00 2.00
Nos. J5-J7 (3) 26.50 4.00

1927-28

J8 D1 1c rose red 3.50 .70
J9 D1 2c rose red 5.50 .70
J10 D1 5c rose red 6.50 1.00
Nos. J8-J10 (3) 15.50 2.40

NEWSPAPER STAMPS

Issued under Spanish Dominion

N1

N2

1888 Unwmk. Typo. *Perf. 14*

P1 N1 ½m black .20 .25
P2 N1 1m black .20 .30
P3 N1 2m black .20 .30
P4 N1 3m black 1.50 1.00
P5 N1 4m black 1.90 2.00
P6 N1 8m black 7.25 8.50
Nos. P1-P6 (6) 11.25 12.35

1890

P7 N2 ½m red brown .45 .60
P8 N2 1m red brown .45 .60
P9 N2 2m red brown .75 .90
P10 N2 3m red brown .95 1.00
P11 N2 4m red brown 7.25 5.25
P12 N2 8m red brown 7.25 5.25
Nos. P7-P12 (6) 17.10 13.60

1892

P13 N2 ½m violet .15 .30
P14 N2 1m violet .15 .30
P15 N2 2m violet .15 .30
P16 N2 3m violet .95 .30
P17 N2 4m violet 3.50 1.75
P18 N2 8m violet 7.50 2.75
Nos. P13-P18 (6) 12.40 5.70

1894

P19 N2 ½m rose .15 .30
a. Imperf. pair 22.50
P20 N2 1m rose .40 .30
P21 N2 2m rose .45 .30
P22 N2 3m rose 1.75 1.25
P23 N2 4m rose 3.00 1.50
P24 N2 8m rose 5.25 3.75
Nos. P19-P24 (6) 11.00 7.40

1896

P25 N2 ½m blue green .15 .28
P26 N2 1m blue green .15 .28
P27 N2 2m blue green .15 .28
P28 N2 3m blue green 2.50 1.50
P29 N2 4m blue green 5.25 7.00
P30 N2 8m blue green 9.50 10.00
Nos. P25-P30 (6) 17.70 19.34

For surcharges see Nos. 190-193, 201-220.

POSTAL TAX STAMPS

Catalogue values for unused stamps in this section are for Never Hinged items.

Mother and Child — PT1

Nurse with Child — PT2

Wmk. Star. (106)

1938, Dec. 1 Engr. *Perf. 10*

RA1 PT1 1c bright green 1.25 .20

The tax benefited the National Council of Tuberculosis fund for children's hospitals. Obligatory on all mail during December and January. This note applies also to Nos. RA2-RA4, RA7-RA10, RA12-RA15, RA17-RA21.

1939, Dec. 1

RA2 PT2 1c orange vermilion .75 .20

"Health" Protecting Children — PT3

1940, Dec. 1

RA3 PT3 1c deep blue .75 .20

Mother and Child — PT4

Victory — PT5

1941, Dec. 1

RA4 PT4 1c olive bister .75 .20

1942-44

RA5 PT5 ½c orange .30 .15
RA6 PT5 ½c gray ('44) .45 .15

Issue dates: No. RA5, July 1, 1942. No. RA6, Oct. 3, 1944.

Type of 1941 Overprinted "1942" in Black

1942, Dec. 1

RA7 PT4 1c salmon .80 .25
a. Inverted overprint 60.00 50.00

As PT3 — PT6

As PT4 — PT7

1943, Dec. 1

RA8 PT6 1c brown .75 .20

1949, Dec. 9

RA9 PT7 1c blue .50 .20

Type of 1949 Inscribed: "1950"

1950, Dec. 1 Engr.

RA10 PT7 1c rose red .50 .15

Proposed Communications Building
PT8 PT10

Woman Holding Child Aloft — PT9

Child — PT11

1951, June 5 Wmk. 106 *Perf. 10*

RA11 PT8 1c violet .75 .15

The tax was to help build a new Communications Building. This note applies also to Nos. RA16, RA34, RA43.

1951, Dec. 1

RA12 PT9 1c violet blue .45 .15
RA13 PT9 1c brown carmine .45 .15
RA14 PT9 1c olive bister .45 .15
RA15 PT9 1c deep green .45 .15
Nos. RA12-RA15 (4) 1.80
Set value .20

1952, Feb. 8

RA16 PT10 1c dark blue .30 .15

See Nos. RA34, RA43.

1952, Dec. 1

RA17 PT11 1c rose carmine .75 .15
RA18 PT11 1c yellow green .75 .15
RA19 PT11 1c blue .75 .15
RA20 PT11 1c orange .75 .15
Nos. RA17-RA20 (4) 3.00
Set value .50

Hands Reaching for Lorraine Cross — PT12

Child's Head, Lorraine Cross — PT13

1953, Dec. 1 *Perf. 9½*

RA21 PT12 1c rose carmine .50 .15

1954, Nov. 1 *Perf. 9½x10*

RA22 PT13 1c rose red .75 .20
RA23 PT13 1c violet .75 .20
RA24 PT13 1c bright blue .75 .20
RA25 PT13 1c emerald .75 .20
Nos. RA22-RA25 (4) 3.00 .80

The tax benefited the Natl. Council of Tuberculosis fund for children's hospitals. Obligatory on all mail during Nov., Dec., Jan. & Feb. This note applies also to #RA26-RA33, RA35-RA42.

Rose and Watering Can — PT14

Child and Protective Hands — PT15

1955, Nov. 1

RA26 PT14 1c red orange .75 .15
RA27 PT14 1c red lilac .75 .15
RA28 PT14 1c bright blue .75 .15
RA29 PT14 1c orange yellow .75 .15
Nos. RA26-RA29 (4) 3.00
Set value .50

1956, Nov. 1

RA30 PT15 1c rose red .75 .15
RA31 PT15 1c yellow brown .75 .15
RA32 PT15 1c bright blue .75 .15
RA33 PT15 1c emerald .75 .15
Nos. RA30-RA33 (4) 3.00
Set value .50

Building Type of 1952

1957, Jan. 18 *Perf. 10*

RA34 PT10 1c rose red .30 .15

Mother and Child by Silvia Arrojo Fernandez
PT16

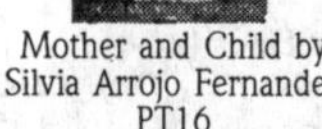
National Council of Tuberculosis
PT17

Wmk. 321

1957, Nov. 1 Engr. *Perf. 10*

RA35 PT16 1c dull rose .65 .15
RA36 PT16 1c bright blue .65 .15
RA37 PT16 1c gray .65 .15
RA38 PT16 1c emerald .65 .15
Nos. RA35-RA38 (4) 2.60
Set value .50

1958

RA39 PT17 1c rose red .35 .15
RA40 PT17 1c red brown .35 .15
RA41 PT17 1c gray .35 .15
RA42 PT17 1c emerald .35 .15
Nos. RA39-RA42 (4) 1.40
Set value .50

Building Type of 1952

1958 Wmk. 321

RA43 PT10 1c rose red .30 .15

CYRENAICA

ˌsir-ə-ˈnā-ə-kə

LOCATION — In northern Africa bordering on the Mediterranean Sea
GOVT. — Former Italian colony
AREA — 75,340 sq. mi.
POP. — 225,000 (approx. 1934)
CAPITAL — Bengasi (Benghazi)

Cyrenaica was incorporated into the kingdom of Libya in 1951.

100 Centesimi = 1 Lira
1000 Milliemes = 1 Pound (1950)

Catalogue values for unused stamps in this country are for Never Hinged items, beginning with Scott 65 in the regular postage section, Scott J1 in the postage due section.

Used values in italics are for postally used stamps. CTO's or stamps with fake cancels sell for about the same as unused, hinged stamps.

Watermark

Wmk. 140- Crown

Propaganda of the Faith Issue

Italy Nos. 143-146 Overprinted **CIRENAICA**

1923, Oct. 24 Wmk. 140 *Perf. 14*

1 A68 20c ol grn & brn org 1.10 *5.50*
2 A68 30c claret & brn org 1.10 *5.50*
3 A68 50c vio & brn org .90 *4.50*
4 A68 1 l bl & brn org .90 *4.50*
Nos. 1-4 (4) 4.00 *20.00*

Fascisti Issue

Italy Nos. 159-164 Overprinted in Red or Black **CIRENAICA**

1923, Oct. 29 Unwmk. *Perf. 14*

5 A69 10c dk grn (R) 1.00 *4.50*
6 A69 30c dk vio (R) 1.00 *4.50*
7 A69 50c brn car 1.00 *4.50*

Wmk. 140

8 A70 1 l blue 1.00 *4.50*
9 A70 2 l brown 1.00 *4.50*
10 A71 5 l blk & bl (R) 1.00 *7.50*
Nos. 5-10 (6) 6.00 *30.00*

Manzoni Issue

Italy Nos. 165-170 Overprinted in Red **CIRENAICA**

1924, Apr. 1 *Perf. 14*

11 A72 10c brn red & blk .65 *5.00*
12 A72 15c bl grn & blk .65 *5.00*
13 A72 30c blk & slate .65 *5.00*
14 A72 50c org brn & blk .65 *5.00*
15 A72 1 l bl & blk 5.00 *32.50*
a. Double overprint 110.00 275.00
16 A72 5 l vio & blk 130.00 *575.00*
Nos. 11-16 (6) 137.60 *627.50*

Vertical overprints on Nos. 11-14 are essays. On Nos. 15-16 the overprint is vertical at the left.

Victor Emmanuel Issue

Italy Nos. 175-177 Overprinted **CIRENAICA**

1925-26 Unwmk. *Perf. 11*

17 A78 60c brn car .15 *2.00*
18 A78 1 l dark blue .20 *2.00*
19 A78 1.25 l dk bl ('26) .65 *6.00*
a. Perf. 13½ 55.00 *150.00*
Nos. 17-19 (3) 1.00 *10.00*

Issue dates: Nov. 1925, July 1926.

Saint Francis of Assisi Issue

Italian Stamps of 1926 Overprinted **CIRENAICA**

1926, Apr. 12 Wmk. 140 *Perf. 14*

20 A79 20c gray grn .85 *3.00*
21 A80 40c dk vio .85 *3.00*
22 A81 60c red brn .85 *3.00*

Overprinted in Red **Cirenaica**

Unwmk.

23 A82 1.25 l dk bl, perf. 11 .85 3.00
24 A83 5 l + 2.50 l ol grn 2.25 5.50
Nos. 20-24 (5) 5.65 17.50

Volta Issue

Type of Italy 1927, Overprinted **Cirenaica**

1927, Oct. 10 Wmk. 140 *Perf. 14*

25 A84 20c purple 2.00 7.50
26 A84 50c dp org 2.50 5.00
27 A84 1.25 l brt bl 3.00 7.50
Nos. 25-27 (3) 7.50 20.00

#25 exists with overprint omitted. See Italy.

Monte Cassino Issue

Types of 1929 Issue of Italy, Overprinted in Red or Blue **CIRENAICA**

1929, Oct. 14

28 A96 20c dk grn (R) 1.25 5.00
29 A96 25c red org (Bl) 1.25 5.00
30 A98 50c + 10c crim (Bl) 1.25 7.50
31 A98 75c + 15c ol brn (R) 1.25 7.50
32 A96 1.25 l + 25c dk vio (R) 2.00 7.50
33 A98 5 l + 1 l saph (R) 2.00 7.50

Overprinted in Red **Cirenaica**

Unwmk.

34 A100 10 l + 2 l gray brn 2.00 10.00
Nos. 28-34 (7) 11.00 50.00

Royal Wedding Issue

Type of Italian Stamps of 1930 Overprinted **CIRENAICA**

1930, Mar. 17 Wmk. 140

35 A101 20c yel grn .45 2.00
36 A101 50c + 10c dp org .35 2.50
37 A101 1.25 l + 25c rose red .35 3.00
Nos. 35-37 (3) 1.15 7.50

#35 exists with overprint omitted. See Italy.

Ferrucci Issue

Types of Italian Stamps of 1930, Overprinted in Red or Blue **Cirenaica**

1930, July 26

38 A102 20c violet (R) .45 1.50
39 A103 25c dk grn (R) .45 1.50
40 A103 50c black (R) .45 1.50
41 A103 1.25 l dp bl (R) .45 1.50
42 A104 5 l + 2 l dp car 1.90 3.00
Nos. 38-42 (5) 3.70 9.00

Virgil Issue

Types of Italian Stamps of 1930 Overprinted in Red or Blue

CIRENAICA

1930, Dec. 4

43 A106 15c vio blk .30 1.50
44 A106 20c org brn (Bl) .30 1.50
45 A106 25c dk grn .30 1.25
46 A106 30c lt brn (Bl) .30 1.50
47 A106 50c dl vio .30 1.25
48 A106 75c rose red (Bl) .30 1.50
49 A106 1.25 l gray bl .30 1.50

Unwmk.

50 A106 5 l + 1.50 l dk vio 1.65 6.00
51 A106 10 l + 2.50 l ol brn (Bl) 1.65 6.00
Nos. 43-51 (9) 5.40 22.00

Saint Anthony of Padua Issue

Types of Italian Stamps of 1931 Overprinted in Blue or Red

CIRENAICA

1931, May 7 Wmk. 140

52 A116 20c brown (Bl) .55 2.00
53 A116 25c green (R) .55 2.00
54 A118 30c gray brn (Bl) .55 2.00
55 A118 55c dl vio (Bl) .55 2.00
56 A120 1.25 l slate bl (R) .55 2.00

Overprinted like Nos. 23-24 in Red or Black

Unwmk.

57 A121 75c black (R) .55 2.00
58 A122 5 l + 2.50 l dk brn 1.65 7.25
Nos. 52-58 (7) 4.95 19.25

Carabineer A1

1934, Oct. 16 Photo. Wmk. 140

59 A1 5c dk ol grn & brn 1.50 4.00
60 A1 10c brn & blk 1.50 4.00
61 A1 20c scar & indigo 1.50 4.00
62 A1 50c pur & brn 1.50 4.00
63 A1 60c org brn & ind 1.50 4.00
64 A1 1.25 l dk bl & grn 1.50 4.00
Nos. 59-64 (6) 9.00 24.00

2nd Colonial Art Exhibition held at Naples. See Nos. C24-C29.

Catalogue values for unused stamps in this section, from this point to the end of the section, are for Never Hinged items.

Autonomous State

Senussi Warrior A2 A3

Perf. 12½

1950, Jan. 16 Unwmk. Engr.

65 A2 1m dark brown .15 .15
66 A2 2m rose car .15 .15
67 A2 3m orange .15 .15
68 A2 4m dark green .55 .65
69 A2 5m gray .15 .15
70 A2 8m red orange .15 .30
71 A2 10m purple .15 .30
72 A2 12m red .20 .35
73 A2 20m deep blue .20 .30
74 A3 50m choc & ultra 1.40 3.00
75 A3 100m bl blk & car rose 4.00 8.50
76 A3 200m vio & pur 5.25 12.00
77 A3 500m dk grn & org 17.50 30.00
Nos. 65-77 (13) 30.00 56.00

SEMI-POSTAL STAMPS

Many issues of Italy and Italian Colonies include one or more semipostal denominations. To avoid splitting sets, these issues are generally listed as regular postage unless all values carry a surtax.

Holy Year Issue

Italian Semi-Postal Stamps of 1924 Overprinted in Black or Red

CIRENAICA

1925, June 1 Wmk. 140 *Perf. 12*

B1 SP4 20c + 10c dk grn & brn 1.00 3.00
B2 SP4 30c + 15c dk brn & brn 1.00 3.00
B3 SP4 50c + 25c vio & brn 1.00 3.00
B4 SP4 60c + 30c dp rose & brn 1.00 3.00
B5 SP8 1 l + 50c dp bl & vio (R) 1.00 3.00
B6 SP8 5 l + 2.50 l org brn & vio (R) 1.00 3.00
Nos. B1-B6 (6) 6.00 18.00

Colonial Institute Issue

"Peace" Substituting Spade for Sword — SP1

1926, June 1 Typo. *Perf. 14*

B7 SP1 5c + 5c brown .20 1.50
B8 SP1 10c + 5c olive grn .20 1.50
B9 SP1 20c + 5c blue grn .20 1.50
B10 SP1 40c + 5c brown red .20 1.50
B11 SP1 60c + 5c orange .20 1.50
B12 SP1 1 l + 5c blue .20 1.50
Nos. B7-B12 (6) 1.20 9.00

Surtax for Italian Colonial Institute.

Types of Italian Semi-Postal Stamps of 1926 Overprinted like Nos. 17-19

1927, Apr. 21 Unwmk. *Perf. 11*

B13 SP10 40c + 20c dk brn & blk .80 3.50
B14 SP10 60c + 30c brn red & ol brn .80 3.50
B15 SP10 1.25 l + 60c dp bl & blk .80 3.50
B16 SP10 5 l + 2.50 l dk grn & blk 1.25 4.50
Nos. B13-B16 (4) 3.65 15.00

The surtax on these stamps was for the charitable work of the Voluntary Militia for Italian National Defense.

Allegory of Fascism and Victory — SP2

1928, Oct. 15 Wmk. 140 *Perf. 14*

B17 SP2 20c + 5c bl grn .50 2.50
B18 SP2 30c + 5c red .50 2.50
B19 SP2 50c + 10c purple .50 2.50
B20 SP2 1.25 l + 20c dk bl .50 2.50
Nos. B17-B20 (4) 2.00 10.00

46th anniv. of the Societa Africana d'Italia. The surtax aided that society.

Types of Italian Semi-Postal Stamps of 1926 Overprinted in Red or Black like Nos. 52-56

1929, Mar. 4 Unwmk. *Perf. 11*

B21 SP10 30c + 10c red & blk .85 3.50
B22 SP10 50c + 20c vio & blk .85 3.50
B23 SP10 1.25 l + 50c brn & bl 1.00 5.00
B24 SP10 5 l + 2 l ol grn & blk (Bk) 1.00 5.00
Nos. B21-B24 (4) 3.70 17.00

Surtax for the charitable work of the Voluntary Militia for Italian Natl. Defense.

Types of Italian Semi-Postal Stamps of 1926 Overprinted in Black or Red like Nos. 52-56

1930, Oct. 20 *Perf. 14*

B25 SP10 30c + 10c dk grn & bl grn (Bk) 3.75 10.00
B26 SP10 50c + 10c dk grn & vio 3.75 10.00
B27 SP10 1.25 l + 30c ol brn & red brn 3.75 10.00
B28 SP10 5 l + 1.50 l ind & grn 11.00 32.50
Nos. B25-B28 (4) 22.25 62.50

Surtax for the charitable work of the Voluntary Militia for Italian Natl. Defense.

Sower — SP3

1930, Nov. 27 Photo. Wmk. 140

B29 SP3 50c + 20c ol brn .75 4.00
B30 SP3 1.25 l + 20c dp bl .75 4.00
B31 SP3 1.75 l + 20c green .75 4.00
B32 SP3 2.55 l + 50c purple 1.25 4.00
B33 SP3 5 l + 1 l dp car 1.25 4.00
Nos. B29-B33 (5) 4.75 20.00

25th anniv. of the Italian Colonial Agricultural Institute. The surtax was for the aid of that institution.

AIR POST STAMPS

Air Post Stamps of Tripolitania, 1931, Overprinted in Blue like Nos. 38-42

1932, Jan. 7 Wmk. 140 *Perf. 14*

C1 AP1 50c rose car .35 .15
C2 AP1 60c dp org 1.50 8.00
C3 AP1 80c dl vio 1.50 8.00
Nos. C1-C3 (3) 3.35 16.15

Air Post Stamps of Tripolitania, 1931, Overprinted in Blue

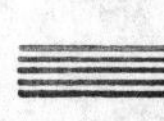

1932, May 12

C4 AP1 50c rose car .45 .25
C5 AP1 80c dull violet 2.00 10.00

This overprint was also applied to the 60c, Tripolitania No. C9. The overprinted stamp was never used in Cyrenaica, but was sold at Rome in 1943 by the Postmaster General for the Italian Colonies. Value $4.

Arab on Camel — AP2

Airplane in Flight AP3

1932, Aug. 8 Photo.

C6 AP2 50c purple .70 .15
C7 AP2 75c brn rose 1.65 2.75
C8 AP2 80c deep blue 1.65 2.75
C9 AP3 1 l black .25 .15
C10 AP3 2 l green .50 1.50
C11 AP3 5 l deep car 1.00 4.50
Nos. C6-C11 (6) 5.75 11.80

For surcharges and overprint see #C20-C23.

Graf Zeppelin Issue

Zeppelin and Clouds forming Pegasus AP4

Zeppelin and Ancient Galley — AP5

Zeppelin and Giant Bowman AP6

1933, Apr. 15

C12 AP4 3 l dk brn 4.00 35.00
C13 AP5 5 l purple 4.00 35.00
C14 AP6 10 l dp grn 4.00 60.50
C15 AP5 12 l deep blue 4.00 85.00
C16 AP4 15 l carmine 4.00 72.50
C17 AP6 20 l black 4.00 100.00
Nos. C12-C17 (6) 24.00 388.00

North Atlantic Crossing Issue

Airplane Squadron and Constellations AP7

1933, June 1

C18 AP7 19.75 l grn & dp bl 10.00 250.00
C19 AP7 44.75 l red & indigo 10.00 250.00

Type of 1932 Overprinted and Surcharged

1934-XII
PRIMO VOLO DIRETTO
ROMA - BUENOS-AYRES
TRIMOTORE "LOMBARDI-MAZZOTTI"

1934, Jan. 20

C20	AP3	2 l on 5 l org brn	1.40	*27.50*
C21	AP3	3 l on 5 l yel grn	1.40	*27.50*
C22	AP3	5 l ocher	1.40	*27.50*
C23	AP3	10 l on 5 l rose	1.40	*27.50*
		Nos. C20-C23 (4)	5.60	*110.00*

For use on mail to be carried on a special flight from Rome to Buenos Aires.

Transport Plane — AP8

Venus of Cyrene — AP9

1934, Oct. 9

C24	AP8	25c sl bl & org red	1.50	*4.00*
C25	AP8	50c dk grn & ind	1.50	*4.00*
C26	AP8	75c dk brn & org red	1.50	*4.00*
a.		Imperf.	185.00	
C27	AP9	80c org brn & ol grn	1.50	*4.00*
C28	AP9	1 l scar & ol grn	1.50	*4.00*
C29	AP9	2 l dk bl & brn	1.50	*4.00*
		Nos. C24-C29 (6)	9.00	*24.00*

2nd Colonial Arts Exhib. held at Naples.

AIR POST SEMI-POSTAL STAMPS

King Victor Emmanuel III — SPAP1

Wmk. 104

1934, Nov. 5 Photo. *Perf. 14*

CB1	SPAP1	25c + 10c gray grn	1.25	*5.00*
CB2	SPAP1	50c + 10c brn	1.25	*5.00*
CB3	SPAP1	75c + 15c rose red	1.25	*5.00*
CB4	SPAP1	80c + 15c brn blk	1.25	*5.00*
CB5	SPAP1	1 l + 20c red brn	1.25	*5.00*
CB6	SPAP1	2 l + 20c brt bl	1.25	*5.00*
CB7	SPAP1	3 l + 25c pur	10.50	*40.00*
CB8	SPAP1	5 l + 25c org	10.50	*40.00*
CB9	SPAP1	10 l + 30c dp vio	10.50	*40.00*
CB10	SPAP1	25 l + 2 l dp grn	10.50	*40.00*
		Nos. CB1-CB10 (10)	49.50	*190.00*

65th birthday of King Victor Emmanuel III and the non-stop flight, Rome-Mogadiscio.

AIR POST SEMI-POSTAL OFFICIAL STAMP

Type of Air Post Semi-Postal Stamps, 1934, Overprinted Crown and "SERVIZIO DI STATO" in Black

1934, Nov. 5 Wmk. 140 *Perf. 14*

CBO1	SPAP1	25 l + 2 l cop red		*1,150.*

POSTAGE DUE STAMPS

Catalogue values for unused stamps in this section are for Never Hinged items.

D1

Perf. 12½

1950, July 1 Unwmk. Engr.

J1	D1	2m dark brown	10.00	*25.00*
J2	D1	4m deep green	10.00	*25.00*
J3	D1	8m scarlet	10.00	*25.00*
J4	D1	10m vermilion	10.00	*25.00*
J5	D1	20m orange yel	10.00	*25.00*
J6	D1	40m deep blue	10.00	*25.00*
J7	D1	100m dark gray	10.00	*25.00*
		Nos. J1-J7 (7)	70.00	*175.00*

CZECHOSLOVAKIA

ˌche-kə-slō-ˈvä-kē-ə

LOCATION — Central Europe
GOVT. — Republic
AREA — 49,355 sq. mi.
POP. — 15,395,970 (1983)
CAPITAL — Prague

The Czechoslovakian Republic consists of Bohemia, Moravia and Silesia, Slovakia and Ruthenia (Carpatho-Ukraine). In March 1939, a German protectorate was established over Bohemia and Moravia, as well as over Slovakia which had meanwhile declared its independence. Ruthenia was incorporated in the territory of Hungary. These territories were returned to the Czechoslovak Republic in 1945, except for Ruthenia, which was ceded to Russia. Czechoslovakia became a federal state on Jan. 2, 1969.

On Jan. 1, 1993 Czechoslovakia separated into Slovakia and the Czech Republic.

See Volume 5 for the stamps of Slovakia.

100 Haleru = 1 Koruna

Catalogue values for unused stamps in this country are for Never Hinged items, beginning with Scott 142 in the regular postage section, Scott B144 in the semi-postal section, Scott C19 in the air post section, Scott EX1 in the personal delivery section, Scott J58 in the postage due section, Scott O1 in the officials section, and Scott P14 in the newspaper section.

Watermarks

Wmk. 107- Linden Leaves (Vertical)

Czechoslovakia stamps can be mounted in the Scott Czechoslovakia album.

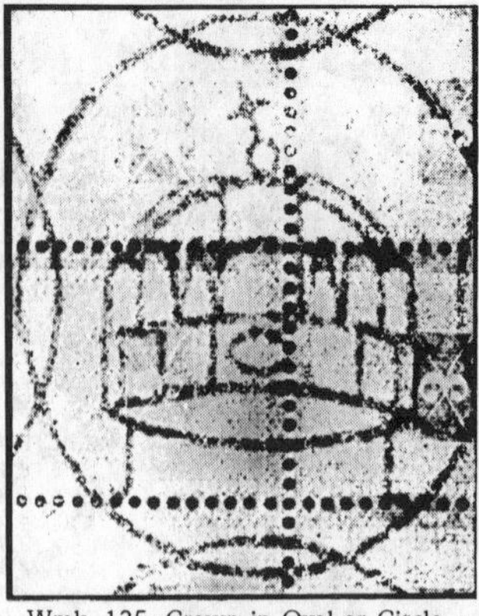
Wmk. 135- Crown in Oval or Circle, Sideways

Wmk. 136

Wmk. 136a

Wmk. 341- Striped Ovals

Stamps of Austria overprinted "Ceskoslovenska Republika," lion and "Cesko Slovensky Stat," "Provisorni Ceskoslovenska Vlada" and Arms, and "Ceskoslovenska Statni Posta" and Arms were made privately. A few of them were passed through the post but all have been pronounced unofficial and unauthorized by the Postmaster General.

During the occupation of part of Northern Hungary by the Czechoslovak forces, stamps of Hungary were overprinted "Cesko Slovenska Posta," "Ceskoslovenska Statni Posta" and Arms, and "Slovenska Posta" and Arms. These stamps were never officially issued though copies have passed the post.

Hradcany at Prague — A1

1918-19 Unwmk. Typo. *Imperf.*

1	A1	3h red violet	.15	.15
2	A1	5h yellow green	.15	.15
3	A1	10h rose	.15	.15
4	A1	20h bluish green	.15	.15
5	A1	25h deep blue	.20	.15
6	A1	30h bister	.25	.15
7	A1	40h red orange	.25	.15
8	A1	100h brown	.85	.15
9	A1	200h ultra	1.40	.15
10	A1	400h purple	1.65	.15

On the 3h-40h "Posta Ceskoslovenska" is in white on a colored background; on the higher values the words are in color on a white background.

The 25h in ultramarine was not valid for postage.

Nos. 1-6 exist as tete-beche gutter pairs.

See #368, 1554, 1600. For surcharges see #B130, C1, C4, J15, J19-J20, J22-J23, J30.

Perf. 11½, 13½

13	A1	5h yellow green	.30	.20
a.		Perf. 11½x10½	1.10	.30
14	A1	10h rose	.25	.15
15	A1	20h bluish green	.25	.15
a.		Perf. 11½	.50	.25
16	A1	25h deep blue	.25	.15
a.		Perf. 11½	1.40	.60
20	A1	200h ultra	2.75	.15
		Nos. 1-10,13-16,20 (15)	9.00	
		Set value		1.00

All values of this issue exist with various private perforations and copies have been used on letters.

The 3, 30, 40, 100 and 400h formerly listed are now known to have been privately perforated.

A2

Type II - Sun behind cathedral. Colorless foliage in foreground.

Type III - Without sun. Shaded foliage in foreground.

Type IV - No foliage in foreground. Positions of buildings changed. Letters redrawn.

1919 *Imperf.*

23	A2	1h dark brown (II)	.15	.15
25	A2	5h blue green (IV)	.20	.15
27	A2	15h red (IV)	.25	.25
29	A2	25h dull violet (IV)	.20	.15
30	A2	50h dull violet (II)	.20	.15
31	A2	50h dark blue (IV)	.20	.15
32	A2	60h orange (III)	.65	.25
33	A2	75h slate (IV)	.50	.15
34	A2	80h olive grn (III)	.65	.25
36	A2	120h gray black (IV)	1.00	.25
38	A2	300h dark green (III)	4.00	.25
39	A2	500h red brown (IV)	2.00	.25
40	A2	1000h violet (III)	9.00	1.40
a.		1000h bluish violet	19.00	3.00
		Nos. 23-40 (13)	19.00	
		Set value		3.30

Perf. 11½, 13½, 13½x11½

1919-20

41	A2	1h dk brown (II)	.15	.15
42	A2	5h blue grn (IV), perf. 13½	.15	.15
a.		Perf. 11½	20.00	7.50
43	A2	10h yellow grn (IV)	.25	.15
a.		Imperf.	19.00	17.50
b.		Perf. 11½	15.00	1.25
44	A2	15h red (IV)	.15	.15
a.		Perf. 11½x10½	15.00	5.00
b.		Perf. 11½x13½	35.00	10.00
c.		Perf. 13½x10½	77.50	20.00
45	A2	20h rose (IV)	.30	.15
a.		Imperf.	55.00	40.00
46	A2	25h dull vio (IV), perf. 11½	.60	.20
a.		Perf. 11½x10½	20.00	.60
b.		Perf. 13½x10½	25.00	14.00
47	A2	30h red violet (IV)	.20	.15
a.		Imperf.	95.00	77.50
b.		Perf. 14x13½	300.00	50.00
c.		30h deep violet	.20	.15
d.		As "c," perf. 14x13½	300.00	50.00
e.		As "c," imperf.	200.00	150.00
50	A2	60h orange (III)	.45	.15
a.		Perf. 14x13½	20.00	10.00
53	A2	120h gray black (IV)	5.75	3.00
		Nos. 41-53 (9)	8.00	
		Set value		3.60

Nos. 43a, 45a and 47a were imperforate by accident and not issued in quantities as were Nos. 23 to 40.

Rouletted stamps of the preceding issues are said to have been made by a postmaster in a branch post office at Prague, or by private firms, but without authority from the Post Office Department.

The 50, 75, 80, 300, 500 and 1000h have been privately perforated.

Unlisted color varieties of types A1 and A2 were not officially released, and some are printer's waste.

For surcharges see Nos. B131, C2-C3, C5-C6, J16-J18, J21, J24-J29, J31, J42-J43.

Pres. Thomas Garrigue Masaryk — A4

1920 *Perf. 13½*

61	A4	125h gray blue	1.00	.15
a.		125h ultramarine	40.00	25.00
62	A4	500h slate, *grysh*	4.00	2.00
a.		Imperf.	25.00	
63	A4	1000h blk brn, *brnsh*	7.00	3.50
		Nos. 61-63 (3)	12.00	5.65

Nos. 61, 61a, 63 imperf. were not regularly issued.

For surcharge see No. B131.

Carrier Pigeon with Letter — A5

Czechoslovakia Breaking Chains to Freedom — A6

Hussite Priest — A7

Agriculture and Science — A8

1920 *Perf. 14*

No.	Type	Description	Unused	Used
65	A5	5h dark blue	.15	.15
a.		Perf. 13½	65.00	17.50
66	A5	10h blue green	.15	.15
a.		Perf. 13½	50.00	21.00
67	A5	15h red brown	.15	.15
68	A6	20h rose	.15	.15
69	A6	25h lilac brown	.15	.15
70	A6	30h red violet	.15	.15
71	A6	40h red brown	.15	.15
a.		Tête bêche pair	2.75	1.75
b.		Perf. 13½	.45	.15
72	A6	50h carmine	.30	.15
73	A6	60h dark blue	.35	.15
a.		Tête bêche pair	6.25	4.00
b.		Perf. 13½	2.75	.35

Photo.

No.	Type	Description	Unused	Used
74	A7	80h purple	.35	.20
75	A7	90h black brown	.60	.35

Typo.

No.	Type	Description	Unused	Used
76	A8	100h dark green	.60	.15
77	A8	200h violet	1.00	.15
78	A8	300h vermilion	2.50	.15
a.		Perf. 14x13½	6.00	.50
79	A8	400h brown	6.75	.85
80	A8	500h deep green	8.00	.85
a.		Perf. 14x13½	67.50	8.00
81	A8	600h deep violet	11.00	.85
a.		Perf. 14x13½	250.00	10.00
		Nos. 65-81 (17)	32.50	
		Set value		4.00

No. 69 has background of horizontal lines.
Imperfs. were not regularly issued.
Nos. 71 and 73 exist as tete-beche gutter pairs.
For surcharges and overprint see Nos. C7-C9, J44-J56.

1920-25 *Perf. 14*

No.	Type	Description	Unused	Used
82	A5	5h violet	.15	.15
a.		Tête bêche pair	2.00	1.40
b.		Perf. 13½	1.00	.60
83	A5	10h olive bister	.15	.15
a.		Tête bêche pair	3.75	2.50
b.		Perf. 13½	.35	.15
84	A5	20h deep orange	.15	.15
a.		Tête bêche pair	30.00	10.50
b.		Perf. 13½	6.00	.90
85	A5	25h blue green	.15	.15
86	A5	30h deep violet ('25)	2.25	.15
87	A6	50h yellow green	.35	.15
a.		Tête bêche pair	32.50	27.50
b.		Perf. 13½	16.00	2.75
88	A6	100h dark brown	.55	.15
a.		Perf. 13½	25.00	.30
89	A6	150h rose	3.50	.75
a.		Perf. 13½	62.50	1.40
90	A6	185h orange	1.25	.15
91	A6	250h dark green	3.50	.30
		Nos. 82-91 (10)	12.00	
		Set value		1.50

Imperfs. were not regularly issued.
Nos. 82-84, 87 exist as tete-beche gutter pairs.

Type of 1920 Issue Redrawn

Type I - Rib of leaf below "O" of POSTA is straight and extends to tip. White triangle above book is entirely at left of twig. "P" has a stubby, abnormal appendage.

Type II - Rib is extremely bent; does not reach tip. Triangle extends at right of twig. "P" like Type I.

Type III - Rib of top left leaf is broken in two. Triangle like Type II. "P" has no appendage.

1923 *Perf. 14, 14x13½*

No.	Type	Description	Unused	Used
92	A8	100h red, *yellow*, III, perf. 14x13½	1.25	.15
a.		Type I, perf. 14	2.25	.15
b.		Type I, perf. 14x13½	2.75	.15
c.		Type II, perf. 14	2.25	.15
d.		Type II, perf. 14x13½	2.75	.15
e.		Type III, perf. 14	14.00	.15
93	A8	200h blue, *yellow*, II, perf. 14	6.00	.15
a.		Type II, perf. 14x13½	12.50	.25
b.		Type III, perf. 14	9.50	.28
c.		Type III, perf. 14x13½	52.50	.52
94	A8	300h violet, *yellow*, I, perf. 14	5.25	.15
a.		Type II, perf. 14	42.50	.40
b.		Type II, perf. 14x13½	87.50	.55
c.		Type III, perf. 14x13½	10.50	.15
d.		Type III, perf. 14	24.00	.35
		Nos. 92-94 (3)	12.50	
		Set value		.25

President Masaryk
A9 A10

Perf. 14x13½, 13½

1925 **Photo.** **Wmk. 107**
Size: 19½x23mm

No.	Type	Description	Unused	Used
95	A9	40h brown orange	1.00	.15
96	A9	50h olive green	1.90	.15
97	A9	60h red violet	2.25	.15
		Nos. 95-97 (3)	5.15	
		Set value		.30

Distinctive Marks of the Engravings.

I, II, III - Background of horizontal lines in top and bottom tablets. Inscriptions in Roman letters with serifs.

IV- Crossed horizontal and vertical lines in the tablets. Inscriptions in Antique letters without serifs.

I, II, IV - Shading of crossed diagonal lines on the shoulder at the right.

III - Shading of single lines only.

I - "T" of "Posta" over middle of "V" of "Ceskoslovenska." Three short horizontal lines in lower part of "A" of "Ceskoslovenska."

II - "T" over right arm of "V." One short line in "A."

III - "T" as in II. Blank space in lower part of "A."

IV - "T" over left arm of "V."

Wmk. Horizontally (107)
Engr.
I. First Engraving
Size: 19¾x22½mm

No.	Type	Description	Unused	Used
98	A10	1k carmine	1.25	.15
99	A10	2k deep blue	3.00	.26
100	A10	3k brown	5.75	.65
101	A10	5k blue green	1.90	.45
		Nos. 98-101 (4)	11.90	1.51

Wmk. Vertically (107)
Size: 19¼x23mm

No.	Type	Description	Unused	Used
101A	A10	1k carmine	140.00	5.25
101B	A10	2k deep blue	175.00	17.50
101C	A10	3k brown	525.00	17.50
101D	A10	5k blue green	5.00	2.00

II. Second Engraving
Wmk. Horizontally (107)
Size: 19x21½mm

No.	Type	Description	Unused	Used
102	A10	1k carmine	57.50	.50
103	A10	2k deep blue	4.75	.25
104	A10	3k brown	5.75	.50
		Nos. 102-104 (3)	68.00	1.25

III. Third Engraving
Size: 19-19½x21½-22mm
Perf. 10

No.	Type	Description	Unused	Used
105	A10	1k carmine rose	1.75	.15
a.		Perf. 14	17.50	.15

IV. Fourth Engraving
Size: 19x22mm

1926 *Perf. 10*

No.	Type	Description	Unused	Used
106	A10	1k carmine rose	1.25	.15

Perf. 14

No.	Type	Description	Unused	Used
108	A10	3k brown	7.00	.15
		Set value		.20

There is a 2nd type of No. 106: with long mustache. Same values. See No. 130.

Karlstein Castle — A11

1926, June 1 **Engr.** *Perf. 10*

No.	Type	Description	Unused	Used
109	A11	1.20k red violet	.48	.40
110	A11	1.50k car rose	.32	.15
111	A11	2.50k dark blue	4.00	.35
		Nos. 109-111 (3)	4.80	.90

See Nos. 133, 135.

Karlstein Castle — A12

Pernstein Castle — A13

Orava Castle A14

Masaryk A15

Strahov Monastery A16

Hradcany at Prague A17

Great Tatra — A18

1926-27 **Engr.** **Wmk. 107**

No.	Type	Description	Unused	Used
114	A13	30h gray green	1.25	.15
115	A14	40h red brown	.50	.15
116	A15	50h deep green	.50	.15
117	A15	60h red vio, *lil*	.85	.15
118	A16	1.20k red violet	4.00	1.50

Perf. 13½

No.	Type	Description	Unused	Used
119	A17	2k blue	.90	.15
a.		2k ultramarine	3.00	.50
120	A17	3k deep red	1.75	.15
121	A18	4k brown vio ('27)	4.00	.50
122	A18	5k dk green ('27)	17.00	3.00
		Nos. 114-122 (9)	30.75	5.90

No. 116 exists in two types. The one with short, straight mustache at left sells for several times as much as that with longer wavy mustache.
See Nos. 137-140.

Coil Stamps
Perf. 10 Vertically

No.	Type	Description	Unused	Used
123	A12	20h brick red	.75	.40
a.		Vert. pair, imperf. horiz.	100.00	
124	A13	30h gray green	.50	.15
a.		Vert. pair, imperf. horiz.	100.00	
125	A15	50h deep green	.25	.15
		Nos. 123-125 (3)	1.50	.70

See No. 141.

1927-31 **Unwmk.** *Perf. 10*

No.	Type	Description	Unused	Used
126	A13	30h gray green	.25	.15
127	A14	40h deep brown	.70	.15
128	A15	50h deep green	.20	.15
129	A15	60h red violet	.70	.15
130	A10	1k carmine rose	1.10	.15
131	A15	1k deep red	.75	.15
132	A16	1.20k red violet	.40	.15
133	A11	1.50k carmine ('29)	.55	.15
134	A13	2k deep green ('29)	.50	.15
135	A11	2.50k dark blue	5.50	.30
136	A14	3k red brown ('31)	.60	.15
		Nos. 126-136 (11)	11.25	
		Set value		.90

No. 130 exists in two types. The one with longer mustache at left sells for several times as much as that with the short mustache.

1927-28 *Perf. 13½*

No.	Type	Description	Unused	Used
137	A17	2k ultra	.85	.15
138	A17	3k deep red ('28)	1.90	.65
139	A18	4k brown violet ('28)	6.00	1.00
140	A18	5k dark green ('28)	6.25	.50
		Nos. 137-140 (4)	15.00	2.30

Coil Stamp

1927 *Perf. 10 Vertically*

No.	Type	Description	Unused	Used
141	A12	20h brick red	.50	.15

Catalogue values for unused stamps in this section, from this point to the end of the section, are for Never Hinged items.

Hradec Castle — A19

Brno Cathedral — A25

Masaryk — A27

10th anniv. of Czech. independence: 40h, Town Hall, Levoca. 50h, Telephone exchange, Prague. 60h, Town of Jasina. 1k, Hluboka Castle. 1.20k, Pilgrims' House, Velehrad. 2.50k, Great Tatra. 5k, Old City Square, Prague.

1928, Oct. 22 *Perf. 13½*

No.	Type	Value	Color	Unused	Used
142	A19	30h	black	.15	.15
143	A19	40h	red brown	.20	.15
144	A19	50h	dark brown	.25	.15
145	A19	60h	orange red	.25	.15
146	A19	1k	carmine	.30	.20
147	A19	1.20k	brown vio	.75	.50
148	A25	2k	ultra	.85	.50
149	A19	2.50k	dark blue	2.00	1.25
150	A27	3k	dark brown	1.75	.80
151	A25	5k	deep violet	2.50	1.90
			Nos. 142-151 (10)	9.00	5.75

From one to three sheets each of Nos. 142-148, perf 12½, appeared on the market in the early 1950's.

Coat of Arms — A29

1929-37 *Perf. 10*

No.	Type	Value	Color	Unused	Used
152	A29	5h	dark ultra ('31)	.15	.15
153	A29	10h	bister brn ('31)	.15	.15
154	A29	20h	red	.15	.15
155	A29	25h	green	.15	.15
156	A29	30h	red violet	.15	.15
157	A29	40h	dk brown ('37)	.22	.15
a.			40h red brown ('37)	1.00	.15

Coil Stamp

Perf. 10 Vertically

No.	Type	Value	Color	Unused	Used
158	A29	20h	red	.20	.15
			Set value	.75	.45

For overprints see Bohemia and Moravia Nos. 1-5, Slovakia 2-6.

St. Wenceslas A30

Founding St. Vitus' Cathedral A31

Design: 3k, 5k, St. Wenceslas martyred.

1929, May 14 *Perf. 13½*

No.	Type	Value	Color	Unused	Used
159	A30	50h	gray green	.50	.15
160	A30	60h	slate violet	.75	.15
161	A31	2k	dull blue	1.50	.45
162	A30	3k	brown	1.75	.25
163	A30	5k	brown violet	8.75	2.75
			Nos. 159-163 (5)	13.25	3.75

Millenary of the death of St. Wenceslas.

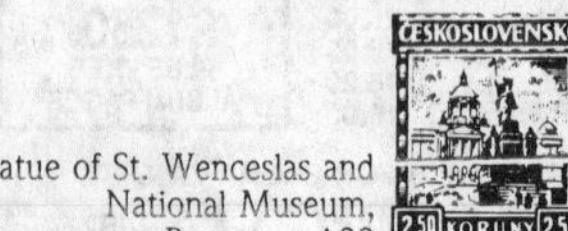

Statue of St. Wenceslas and National Museum, Prague — A33

1929 *Perf. 10*

No.	Type	Value	Color	Unused	Used
164	A33	2.50k	deep blue	.65	.15

Brno Cathedral A34

Tatra Mountain Scene A35

Design: 5k, Old City Square, Prague.

1929, Oct. 15 *Perf. 13½*

No.	Type	Value	Color	Unused	Used
165	A34	3k	red brown	2.50	.15
166	A35	4k	indigo	4.50	.60
167	A35	5k	gray green	6.00	.35
			Nos. 165-167 (3)	13.00	1.10

See No. 183.

A37

Type I

Type II

Two types of 50h:

I - A white space exists across the bottom of the vignette between the coat, shirt and tie and the "HALERU" frame panel.

II - An extra frame line has been added just above the "HALERU" panel which finishes off the coat and tie shading evenly.

1930, Jan. 2 *Perf. 10*

No.	Type	Value	Color	Unused	Used
168	A37	50h	myrtle green (II)	.15	.15
a.			Type I	.90	.15
169	A37	60h	brown violet	.60	.15
170	A37	1k	brown red	.25	.15
			Nos. 168-170 (3)	1.00	
			Set value		.15

See No. 234.

Coil Stamp

1931 *Perf. 10 Vertically*

No.	Type	Value	Color	Unused	Used
171	A37	1k	brown red	1.50	.75

President Masaryk — A38

St. Nicholas' Church, Prague — A39

1930, Mar. 1 *Perf. 13½*

No.	Type	Value	Color	Unused	Used
175	A38	2k	gray green	.85	.30
176	A38	3k	red brown	1.50	.30
177	A38	5k	slate blue	4.50	2.00
178	A38	10k	gray black	9.00	4.00
			Nos. 175-178 (4)	15.85	6.60

Eightieth birthday of President Masaryk.

1931, May 15

No.	Type	Value	Color	Unused	Used
183	A39	10k	black violet	10.50	2.50

Krivoklat Castle — A40

Krumlov Castle — A42

Design: 4k, Orlik Castle.

1932, Jan. 2 *Perf. 10*

No.	Type	Value	Color	Unused	Used
184	A40	3.50k	violet	2.25	.90
185	A40	4k	deep blue	2.75	.40
186	A42	5k	gray green	3.00	.40
			Nos. 184-186 (3)	8.00	1.70

A43

A44

Miroslav Tyrs — A45

1932, Mar. 16

No.	Type	Value	Color	Unused	Used
187	A43	50h	yellow green	.45	.15
188	A43	1k	brown carmine	.85	.15
189	A44	2k	dark blue	8.00	.45
190	A44	3k	red brown	14.00	.45
			Nos. 187-190 (4)	23.30	1.20

1933, Feb. 1

No.	Type	Value	Color	Unused	Used
191	A45	60h	dull violet	.28	.15

Miroslav Tyrs (1832-84), founder of the Sokol movement; and the 9th Sokol Congress (#187-190).

First Christian Church at Nitra A46 A47

1933, June 20

No.	Type	Value	Color	Unused	Used
192	A46	50h	yellow green	.45	.15
193	A47	1k	carmine rose	4.50	.25
			Set value		.33

Prince Pribina who introduced Christianity into Slovakia and founded there the 1st Christian church in A.D. 833.

All gutter pairs are vertical.

Bedrich Smetana, Czech Composer and Pianist, 50th Death Anniv. — A48

1934, Mar. 26 **Engr.** *Perf. 10*

No.	Type	Value	Color	Unused	Used
194	A48	50h	yellow green	.40	.15

Consecration of Legion Colors at Kiev, Sept. 21, 1914 — A49

Ensign Heyduk with Colors A51

Legionnaires A52

Design: 1k, Legion receiving battle flag at Bayonne.

1934, Aug. 15 *Perf. 10*

No.	Type	Value	Color	Unused	Used
195	A49	50h	green	.35	.15
196	A49	1k	rose lake	.50	.15
197	A51	2k	deep blue	2.25	.25
198	A52	3k	red brown	3.50	.25
			Nos. 195-198 (4)	6.60	
			Set value		.60

20th anniv. of the Czechoslovakian Legion which fought in WWI.

Antonin Dvorák, (1841-1904), Composer — A53

1934, Nov. 22

No.	Type	Value	Color	Unused	Used
199	A53	50h	green	.30	.15

Pastoral Scene — A54

1934, Dec. 17 *Perf. 10*

No.	Type	Value	Color	Unused	Used
200	A54	1k	claret	.50	.15
a.			Souv. sheet of 15, perf. 13½	250.00	225.00
b.			As "a," single stamp	8.50	7.00
201	A54	2k	blue	1.75	.35
a.			Souv. sheet of 15, perf. 13½	850.00	850.00
b.			As "a," single stamp	37.50	32.50

Centenary of the National Anthem.

Nos. 200a & 201a have thick paper, darker shades, no gum. Forgeries exist.

President Masaryk A55 A56

1935, Mar. 1

No.	Type	Value	Color	Unused	Used
202	A55	50h	green, *buff*	.28	.15
203	A55	1k	claret, *buff*	.52	.15
204	A56	2k	gray blue, *buff*	1.40	.30
205	A56	3k	brown, *buff*	2.75	.30
			Nos. 202-205 (4)	4.95	
			Set value		.76

85th birthday of President Masaryk. See No. 235.

Monument to Czech Heroes at Arras, France — A57

1935, May 4

No.	Type	Value	Color	Unused	Used
206	A57	1k	rose	.55	.15
207	A57	2k	dull blue	1.50	.18
			Set value		.38

20th anniversary of the Battle of Arras.

Gen. Milan Stefánik — A58

Sts. Cyril and Methodius — A59

1935, May 18

No.	Type	Value	Color	Unused	Used
208	A58	50h	green	.20	.15

1935, June 22

No.	Type	Value	Color	Unused	Used
209	A59	50h	green	.15	.15
210	A59	1k	claret	.32	.15
211	A59	2k	deep blue	1.25	.28
			Nos. 209-211 (3)	1.72	
			Set value		.38

Millenary of the arrival in Moravia of the Apostles Cyril and Methodius.

Masaryk A60

Statue of Macha, Prague A61

1935, Oct. 20 *Perf. 12½*
212 A60 1k rose lake .15 .15

No. 212 exists imperforate. See No. 256. For overprints see Bohemia and Moravia Nos. 9-10, Slovakia 12.

1936, Apr. 30
213 A61 50h deep green .15 .15
214 A61 1k rose lake .30 .15
Set value .15

Karel Hynek Macha (1810-1836), Bohemian poet.

Jan Amos Komensky (Comenius) — A61a

Pres. Eduard Benes — A62

Gen. Milan Stefánik — A63

1936
215 A61a 40h dark blue .15 .15
216 A62 50h dull green .15 .15
217 A63 60h dull violet .15 .15
Set value .35 .15

See #252, 255. For overprints see Bohemia and Moravia #6, 8, Slovakia 7, 9-11.

Castle Palanok near Mukacevo — A64

Town of Banska Bystrica — A65

Castle at Zvikov — A66

Ruins of Castle at Strecno — A67

Castle at Cesky Raj — A68

Palace at Slavkov (Austerlitz) — A69

Statue of King George of Podebrad — A70

Town Square at Olomouc — A71

Castle Ruins at Bratislava — A72

1936, Aug. 1
218 A64 1.20k rose lilac .15 .15
219 A65 1.50k carmine .15 .15
220 A66 2k dark blue green .15 .15
221 A67 2.50k dark blue .28 .15
222 A68 3k brown .32 .15
223 A69 3.50k dark violet 1.40 .35
224 A70 4k dark violet .60 .15
225 A71 5k green .55 .15
226 A72 10k blue 1.50 .35
Nos. 218-226 (9) 5.10
Set value 1.15

For overprints and surcharge see Nos. 237-238, 254A, Bohemia and Moravia 11-12, 14-19, Slovakia 13-14, 16-23.

President Benes — A73

Soldiers of the Czech Legion — A74

1937, Apr. 26 Unwmk. *Perf. 12½*
227 A73 50h deep green .15 .15

For overprints see Nos. 236, Slovakia 8.

1937, June 15
228 A74 50h deep green .15 .15
229 A74 1k rose lake .26 .15
Set value .15

20th anniv. of the Battle of Zborov.

Cathedral at Prague — A75

Jan Evangelista Purkyne — A76

1937, July 1
230 A75 2k green .60 .15
231 A75 2.50k blue .90 .30

16th anniv. of the founding of the "Little Entente."

1937, Sept. 2
232 A76 50h slate green .16 .15
233 A76 1k dull rose .18 .15
Set value .15

150th anniv. of the birth of Purkyne, Czech physiologist.

Masaryk Types of 1930-35

1937, Sept. *Perf. 12½*
234 A37 50h black .15 .15

With date "14.IX. 1937" in design

235 A56 2k black .35 .15
Set value .15

Death of former President Thomas G. Masaryk on Sept. 14, 1937.

International Labor Bureau Issue

Stamps of 1936-37 Overprinted in Violet or Black **B.I.T.1937**

1937, Oct. 6 *Perf. 12½*
236 A73 50h dp green (Bk) .28 .30
237 A65 1.50k carmine (V) .38 .40
238 A66 2k dp green (V) .60 .65
Nos. 236-238 (3) 1.26 1.35

Bratislava Philatelic Exhibition Issue

Souvenir Sheet

A77

1937, Oct. 24 *Perf. 12½*
239 A77 Sheet of 2 1.25 .85
a. 50h dark blue .38 .32
b. 1k brown carmine .38 .32

The stamps show a view of Poprad Lake (50h) and the tomb of General Milan Stefanik (1k).

No. 239 overprinted "Liberation de la Tchechoslovaquie, 28-X-1945" etc., was sold at a philatelic exhibition in Brussels, Belgium.

St. Barbara's Church, Kutna Hora — A79

Peregrine Falcon, Sokol Emblem — A80

1937, Dec. 4
240 A79 1.60k olive green .15 .15

For overprints see Bohemia and Moravia Nos. 13, Slovakia 15.

1938, Jan. 21
241 A80 50h deep green .25 .15
242 A80 1k rose lake .35 .15
Set value .15

10th Intl. Sokol Games. Imperf. copies of No. 242 are essays. Nos. 241-242 se-tenant with labels sell slightly higher.

Legionnaires

A81 A82

Legionnaire — A83

1938
243 A81 50h deep green .15 .15
244 A82 50h deep green .15 .15
245 A83 50h deep green .15 .15
Set value .30 .15

20th anniv. of the Battle of Bachmac, Vouziers and Doss Alto. #243-245 se-tenant with label sell slightly higher.

Jindrich Fügner, Co-Founder of Sokol Movement — A84

1938, June 18 *Perf. 12½*
246 A84 50h deep green .15 .15
247 A84 1k rose lake .15 .15
248 A84 2k slate blue .42 .15
Set value .60 .15

10th Sokol Summer Games. Nos. 246-248 se-tenant with labels sell slightly higher.

View of Pilsen — A85

Cathedral of Kosice — A86

1938, June 24
249 A85 50h deep green .15 .15

Provincial Economic Council meeting, Pilsen. For overprint see Bohemia & Moravia #7.

1938, July 15 *Perf. 12½*
250 A86 50h deep green .15 .15

Kosice Cultural Exhibition.

Prague Philatelic Exhibition Issue

Souvenir Sheet

Vysehrad Castle - Hradcany A87

1938, June 26 *Perf. 12½*
251 A87 Sheet of 2 4.00 3.00
a. 50h dark blue 1.50 1.50
b. 1k deep carmine 1.50 1.50

Stefánik Type of 1936

1938, Nov. 21
252 A63 50h deep green .20 .15

Allegory of the Republic — A89

1938, Dec. 19 **Unwmk.**
253 A89 2k lt ultra .28 .15
254 A89 3k pale brown .32 .15

20th anniv. of Independence. See No. B153.

"Wir sind frei!"

Stamps of Czechoslovakia, 1918-37, overprinted with a swastika in black or red and "Wir sind frei!" were issued locally and unofficially in 1938 as Czech authorities were evacuating and German authorities arriving. They appeared in the towns of Asch, Karlsbad, Reichenberg-Maffersdorf, Rumburg, etc.

The overprint, sometimes including a surcharge or the town name (as in Karlsbad), exists on many values of postage, air post, semi-postal, postage due and newspaper stamps.

No. 226 Surcharged in Orange Red

Otvorenie slovenského snemu 18.I. 1939

1939, Jan. 18 Unwmk. *Perf. 12½*
254A A72 300h on 10k blue .75 3.50

Opening of the Slovakian Parliament.

View of Jasina — A89a

Perf. 12½

1939, Mar. 15 Engr. Unwmk.
254B A89a 3k ultra 12.50 *25.00*

Inauguration of the Carpatho-Ukraine Diet, Mar. 2, 1939.
Printed for use in the province of Carpatho-Ukraine but issued in Prague at the same time.
Used value is for red commemorative cancel.

Stefánik Type of 1936

1939 Engr. *Perf. 12½*
255 A63 60h dark blue 17.50 *25.00*

Used exclusively in Slovakia.

Masaryk Type of 1935 with hyphen in Cesko-Slovensko

1939, Apr. 23
256 A60 1k rose lake .15 .15

Linden Leaves and Buds — A90

1945 Photo. *Perf. 14*
256A A90 10h black .15 .15
257 A90 30h yellow brown .15 .15
258 A90 50h dark green .15 .15
258A A90 60h dark blue .15 .15

Engr.
(Buds Open)
Perf. 12½

259 A90 60h blue .15 .15
259A A90 80h orange ver .15 .15
260 A90 1.20k rose .15 .15
261 A90 3k violet brown .15 .15
262 A90 5k green .15 .15
Set value .45 .45

Thomas G. Masaryk — A91

Coat of Arms — A92

1945-46 Photo. *Perf. 12*
262A A91 5h dull violet ('46) .15 .15
262B A91 10h orange yel ('46) .15 .15
262C A91 20h dk brown ('46) .15 .15
263 A91 50h brt green .15 .15
264 A91 1k orange red .15 .15
265 A91 2k chalky blue .25 .25
Set value .60 .53

1945 *Imperf.*
266 A92 50h olive gray .15 .15
267 A92 1k brt red vio .15 .15
268 A92 1.50k dk carmine .15 .15
269 A92 2k deep blue .15 .15
269A A92 2.40k henna brn .30 .20
270 A92 3k brown .15 .15
270A A92 4k dk slate grn .15 .15
271 A92 6k violet blue .25 .15
271A A92 10k sepia .38 .20
Set value 1.25 .75

Nos. 266-217A exist in 2 printings. Stamps of the 1st printing are on thin, hard paper in sheets of 100; those of the 2nd printing on thick, soft wove paper in sheets of 200.

Staff Capt. Ridky (British Army) — A93

Dr. Miroslav Novak (French Army) — A94

Capt. Otakar Jaros (Russian Army) — A95

Staff Capt. Stanislav Zimprich (Foreign Legion) — A96

2nd Lt. Jiri Kral (French Air Force) — A97

Josef Gabcik (Parachutist) — A98

Staff Capt. Alois Vasatko (Royal Air Force) — A99

Private Frantisek Adamek (British Colonial Service) — A100

Perf. 11½x12½

1945, Aug. 18 Engr.
272 A93 5h intense blue .15 .15
273 A94 10h dark brown .15 .15
274 A95 20h brick red .15 .15
275 A96 25h rose red .15 .15
276 A97 30h purple .15 .15
277 A98 40h sepia .15 .15
278 A99 50h dark olive .15 .15
279 A100 60h violet .15 .15
280 A93 1k carmine .15 .15
281 A94 1.50k lake .15 .15
282 A95 2k ultra .15 .15
283 A96 2.50k deep violet .15 .15
284 A97 3k sepia .15 .15
285 A98 4k rose lilac .15 .15
286 A99 5k myrtle green .20 .15
287 A100 10k brt ultra .65 .16
Set value 1.80 .90

Flags of Russia, Great Britain, US and Czechoslovakia A101

View of Banská Bystrica A102

Patriot Welcoming Russian Soldier, Turciansky A103

Ruins of Castle at Sklabina A104

Czech Patriot, Strecno — A105

1945, Aug. 29 Photo. *Perf. 10*
288 A101 1.50k brt carmine .15 .15
289 A102 2k brt blue .15 .15
290 A103 4k dark brown .30 .30
291 A104 4.50k purple .30 .30
292 A105 5k deep green .75 .75
Nos. 288-292 (5) 1.65 1.65

National uprising against the Germans.
A card contains one each of Nos. 288-292 on thin cardboard, ungummed. Size: 148x210mm. Sold for 50k.

Stefánik · Benes · Masaryk
A106 A107 A108

1945-47 Engr. *Perf. 12, 12½*
293 A106 30h rose violet .15 .15
294 A107 60h blue .15 .15
294A A106 1k red org ('47) .15 .15
295 A108 1.20k car rose .15 .15
295A A108 1.20(k) rose lil ('46) .15 .15
296 A106 2.40(k) rose .15 .15
297 A107 3k red violet .16 .15
297A A108 4k dark blue ('46) .15 .15
298 A108 5k Prus green .16 .15
299 A107 7k gray .18 .15
300 A106 10k gray blue .45 .15
300A A106 20k sepia ('46) .90 .18
Set value 2.30 .72

1945 Photo. *Perf. 14*
301 A108 50h brown .15 .15
302 A106 80h dark green .15 .15
303 A107 1.60(k) olive green .15 .15
304 A108 15k red violet .55 .15
Set value .73 .25

Statue of Kozina and Chod Castle, Domazlice — A109

Red Army Soldier — A110

1945, Nov. 28 Engr. *Perf. 12½*
305 A109 2.40k rose carmine .15 .15
306 A109 4k blue .20 .15

250th anniv. of the death of Jan Sladky Kozina, peasant leader.

1945, Mar. 26 Litho. *Imperf.*
307 A110 2k crimson rose .38 .35
308 A110 5k slate black 1.75 1.50
309 A110 6k ultramarine .45 .42
Nos. 307-309 (3) 2.58 2.27

Souvenir Sheet

1945, July 16
Gray Burelage

310 Sheet of 3 3.00 2.50
a. A110 2k crimson rose .40 .30
b. A110 5k slate black .40 .30
c. A110 6k ultramarine .40 .30

Return of Pres. Benes, Apr., 1945.

Clasped Hands A112

Karel Havlícek Borovsky A113

1945 *Rouletted 12½*
311 A112 1.50k brown red 2.50 2.50
312 A112 9k red orange .55 .60
313 A112 13k orange brown .75 .75
314 A112 20k blue 2.00 2.00
Nos. 311-314 (4) 5.80 5.85

1946, July 5 Engr. *Perf. 12½*
315 A113 1.20k gray black .18 .18

Borovsky (1821-56), editor and writer.

Old Town Hall, Brno — A114

Hodonin Square — A115

Perf. 12½x12, 12x12½

1946, Aug. 3 Engr. Unwmk.
316 A114 2.40k deep rose .18 .15
317 A115 7.40k dull violet .32 .15
Set value .21

See No. B159.

President Eduard Benes — A116

1946, Oct. 28
318 A116 60h indigo .15 .15
319 A116 1.60k dull green .15 .15
320 A116 3k red lilac .15 .15
321 A116 8k sepia .22 .15
Set value .44 .20

Flag, Symbols A117

Saint Adalbert A118

1947, Jan. 1 *Perf. 12½*
322 A117 1.20k Prus green .15 .15
323 A117 2.40k deep rose .15 .15
324 A117 4k deep blue .32 .15
Nos. 322-324 (3) .62
Set value .20

Czechoslovakia's two-year reconstruction and rehabilitation program.

1947, Apr. 23
326 A118 1.60k gray .48 .28
327 A118 2.40k rose carmine .80 .65
328 A118 5k blue green 1.00 .42
Nos. 326-328 (3) 2.28 1.35

950th anniv. of the death of Saint Adalbert, Bishop of Prague.

Grief — A119

Allegorical Figure — A120

1947, June 10 Engr.
329 A119 1.20k black .30 .25
330 A119 1.60k slate black .38 .38
331 A120 2.40k brown violet .48 .48
Nos. 329-331 (3) 1.16 1.11

Destruction of Lidice, 5th anniversary.

World Federation of Youth Symbol — A121

Thomas G. Masaryk — A122

1947, July 20
332 A121 1.20k violet brown .30 .15
333 A121 4k slate .35 .15

World Youth Festival held in Prague, July 20-Aug. 17.

1947, Sept. 14
334 A122 1.20k gray blk, *buff* .16 .15
335 A122 4k blue blk, *cream* .40 .15
Set value .25

Death of Masaryk, 10th anniv.

Msgr. Stefan Moyses — A123

1947, Oct. 19

336	A123	1.20k rose violet	.16	.15
337	A123	4k deep blue	.35	.18
		Set value		.28

150th anniversary of the birth of Stefan Moyses, first Slovakian chairman of the Slavic movement.

"Freedom from Social Oppression" A124

1947, Oct. 26 Photo. *Perf. 14*

338	A124	2.40k brt carmine	.20	.20
339	A124	4k brt ultra	.35	.15

30th anniversary of the Russian revolution of October, 1917.

Benes A125

"Czechoslovakia" Greeting Sokol Marchers A126

1948, Feb. 15 Photo.

Size: 17½x21½mm

340	A125	1.50k brown	.15	.15

Size: 19x23mm

341	A125	2k deep plum	.15	.15
342	A125	5k brt ultra	.15	.15
		Set value	.26	.15

1948, Mar. 7 Engr. *Perf. 12½*

343	A126	1.50k brown	.15	.15
344	A126	3k rose carmine	.15	.15
345	A126	5k blue	.30	.15
		Set value	.50	.20

The 11th Sokol Congress.

King Charles IV — A127

St. Wenceslas, King Charles IV — A128

1948, Apr. 7

346	A127	1.50k black brown	.15	.15
347	A128	2k dark brown	.15	.15
348	A128	3k brown red	.18	.15
349	A127	5k dark blue	.38	.15
		Nos. 346-349 (4)	.86	
		Set value		.33

600th anniv. of the foundation of Charles University, Prague.

Czech Peasants in Revolt — A129

Jindrich Vanicek — A130

Unwmk.

1948, May 14 Photo. *Perf. 14*

350	A129	1.50k dk olive brown	.15	.15

Centenary of abolition of serfdom.

1948, June 10 Engr. *Perf. 12½*

Designs: 1.50k, 2k, Josef Scheiner.

351	A130	1k dark green	.15	.15
352	A130	1.50k sepia	.15	.15
353	A130	2k gray blue	.18	.15
354	A130	3k claret	.26	.15
		Set value	.60	.35

11th Sokol Congress, Prague, 1948.

Frantisek Palacky & F. L. Rieger — A131

Miloslav Josef Hurban — A132

1948, June 20 Unwmk.

355	A131	1.50k gray	.15	.15
356	A131	3k brown carmine	.18	.15
		Set value		.16

Constituent Assembly at Kromeriz, cent.

1948, Aug. 27 *Perf. 12½*

Designs: 3k, Ludovit Stur. 5k, Michael M. Hodza.

357	A132	1.50k dark brown	.15	.15
358	A132	3k carmine lake	.15	.15
359	A132	5k indigo	.25	.15
		Nos. 357-359 (3)	.55	
		Set value		.26

Cent. of 1848 insurrection against Hungary.

Eduard Benes A133

Czechoslovak Family A134

1948, Sept. 28

360	A133	8k black	.20	.15

President Eduard Benes, 1884-1948.

1948, Oct. 28 *Perf. 12½x12*

361	A134	1.50k deep blue	.15	.15
362	A134	3k rose carmine	.20	.16
		Set value	.28	.23

Czechoslovakia's Independence, 30th anniv.

Pres. Klement Gottwald — A135

1948-49 *Perf. 12½*

Size: 18½x23½mm

363	A135	1.50k dk brown	.15	.15
364	A135	3k car rose	.25	.15
a.		3k rose brown	.40	.15
365	A135	5k gray blue	.22	.15

Size: 23½x29mm

366	A135	20k purple	1.10	.15
		Nos. 363-366 (4)	1.72	
		Set value		.27

See Nos. 373, 564, 600-604.

Souvenir Sheet

1948, Nov. 23 Unwmk. *Imperf.*

367	A135	30k rose brown	3.50	2.75

52nd birthday of Pres. Klement Gottwald (1896-1953).

Hradcany Castle Type of 1918
Souvenir Sheet

1948, Dec. 18

368	A1	10k dk blue violet	1.25	.90

1st Czechoslovak postage stamp, 30th anniv.

Czechoslovak and Russian Workmen Shaking Hands — A138

Lenin — A139

1948, Dec. 12 *Perf. 12½*

369	A138	3k rose carmine	.20	.15

5th anniv. of the treaty of alliance between Czechoslovakia and Russia.

1949, Jan. 21 Engr. *Perf. 12½*

370	A139	1.50k violet brown	.25	.15
371	A139	5k deep blue	.25	.20

25th anniversary of the death of Lenin.

Gottwald Type of 1948 Inscribed: "UNOR 1948" and

Gottwald Addressing Meeting — A140

1949, Feb. 25 Photo. *Perf. 14*

372	A140	3k red brown	.15	.15

Perf. 12½

Engr.

Size: 23½x29mm

373	A135	10k deep green	.60	.25
		Set value		.30

1st anniv. of Gottwald's speech announcing the appointment of a new government. No. 372 exists in a souvenir sheet of 1. It was not sold to the public.

A141

A142

Designs (Writers): 50h, P. O. Hviezdoslav. 80h, V. Vancura. 1k, J. Sverma. 2k, Julius Fucik. 4k, Jiri Wolker. 8k, Alois Jirasek.

1949 Photo. *Perf. 14*

374	A141	50h violet brown	.15	.15
375	A141	80h scarlet	.15	.15
376	A141	1k dk olive green	.15	.15
377	A141	2k brt blue	.38	.15

Perf. 12½

Engr.

378	A141	4k violet brown	.38	.15
379	A141	8k brown black	.48	.15
		Nos. 374-379 (6)	1.69	
		Set value		.30

1949, May 20

Designs: 3k, Stagecoach and Train. 5k, Postrider and post bus. 13k, Sailing ship and plane.

380	A142	3k brown carmine	1.40	1.40
381	A142	5k deep blue	.70	.40
382	A142	13k deep green	1.40	.75
		Nos. 380-382 (3)	3.50	2.55

75th anniv. of the UPU.

Reaping — A143

Communist Emblem and Workers — A144

Workman, Symbol of Industry — A145

Perf. 12½x12, 12x12½

1949, May 24 Unwmk.

383	A143	1.50k deep green	.60	.60
384	A144	3k brown carmine	.30	.30
385	A145	5k deep blue	.60	.60
		Nos. 383-385 (3)	1.50	1.50

No. 384 for the ninth meeting of the Communist Party of Czechoslovakia, May 25, 1949.

Bedrich Smetana and Natl. Theater, Prague — A146

Aleksander Pushkin — A147

1949, June 4 *Perf. 12½x12*

386	A146	1.50k dull green	.20	.15
387	A146	5k deep blue	.55	.20
		Set value		.28

125th anniv. of the birth of Bedrich Smetana, composer.

1949, June 6 *Perf. 12x12½*

388	A147	2k olive gray	.32	.25

150th anniversary of the birth of Aleksander S. Pushkin.

Frederic Chopin and Conservatory, Warsaw — A148

1949, June 24 *Perf. 12½x12*

389	A148	3k dark red	.35	.20
390	A148	8k violet brown	.90	.50

Cent. of the death of Frederic F. Chopin.

Globe and Ribbon — A149

Zvolen Castle — A150

1949, Aug. 20 *Perf. 12½x12*

391	A149	1.50k violet brown	.25	.20
392	A149	5k ultra	.60	.40

50th Prague Sample Fair, Sept. 11-18, 1949.

Starting in 1949, commemorative stamps which are valued in italics were issued in smaller quantities than those in the balance of the set and sold at prices higher than face value.

1949, Aug. 28 *Perf. 12½*

393	A150	10k rose lake	.80	.15

Early Miners — A151

Miner of Today — A152

Design: 5k, Mining Machine.

1949, Sept. 11 *Perf. 12½*

No.	Type	Value / Color	Unused	Used
394	A151	1.50k sepia	.90	.55
395	A152	3k carmine rose	4.25	1.50
396	A151	5k deep blue	3.50	1.50
		Nos. 394-396 (3)	8.65	3.55

700th anniv. of the Czechoslovak mining industry; 150th anniv. of the miner's laws.

Construction Workers — A153

Joseph V. Stalin — A154

1949, Dec. 11 *Perf. 12½*

No.	Type	Value / Color	Unused	Used
397	A153	1k shown	2.50	.75
398	A153	2k Machinist	1.50	.38

2nd Trade Union Congress, Prague, 1949.

1949, Dec. 21 **Unwmk.**

Design: 3k, Stalin facing left.

Cream Paper

No.	Type	Value / Color	Unused	Used
399	A154	1.50k greenish gray	*1.25*	*.60*
400	A154	3k claret	*3.50*	*1.40*

70th birthday of Joseph V. Stalin.

Skier — A155

Efficiency Badge — A156

Engr., Photo. (3k)

1950, Feb. 15 *Perf. 12½, 13½*

No.	Type	Value / Color	Unused	Used
401	A155	1.50k gray blue	2.00	.75
402	A156	3k vio brn, *cr*	2.00	1.25
403	A155	5k ultramarine	*2.50*	*1.50*
		Nos. 401-403 (3)	*6.50*	*3.50*

51st Ski Championship for the Tatra cup, Feb. 15-26, 1950.

Vladimir V. Mayakovsky, Poet, 20th Death Anniv. — A157

1950, Apr. 14 **Engr.** *Perf. 12½*

No.	Type	Value / Color	Unused	Used
404	A157	1.50k dark brown	*2.25*	*1.10*
405	A157	3k brown red	2.25	.85

See Nos. 414-417, 422-423, 432-433, 464-465, 477-478.

Soviet Tank Soldier and Hradcany A158

Designs: 2k, Hero of Labor medal. 3k, Two workers (militiamen) and Town Hall, Prague. 5k, Text of government program and heraldic lion.

1950, May 5

No.	Type	Value / Color	Unused	Used
406	A158	1.50k gray green	.42	.20
407	A158	2k dark brown	.90	.70
408	A158	3k brown red	.32	.20
409	A158	5k dark blue	.52	.16
		Nos. 406-409 (4)	*2.16*	*1.26*

5th anniv. of the Czechoslovak People's Democratic Republic.

Factory and Young Couple with Tools A159

Designs: 2k, Steam shovel. 3k, Farmer and farm scene. 5k, Three workers leaving factory.

1950, May 9 **Engr.**

No.	Type	Value / Color	Unused	Used
410	A159	1.50k dark green	.90	.75
411	A159	2k dark brown	*1.00*	*.75*
412	A159	3k rose red	.45	.35
413	A159	5k deep blue	.45	.35
		Nos. 410-413 (4)	*2.80*	*2.20*

Canceled to Order

The government philatelic department started about 1950 to sell canceled sets of new issues. Values in the second ("used") column are for these canceled-to-order stamps. Postally used copies are worth more.

Portrait Type of 1950

Design: S. K. Neumann.

1950, June 5 **Unwmk.** *Perf. 12½*

No.	Type	Value / Color	Unused	Used
414	A157	1.50k deep blue	.15	.15
415	A157	3k violet brown	*.95*	*.75*

Stanislav Kostka Neumann (1875-1947), journalist and poet.

1950, June 21

Design: Bozena Nemcova.

No.	Type	Value / Color	Unused	Used
416	A157	1.50k deep blue	*1.25*	*.75*
417	A157	7k dark brown	.30	.20

Bozena Nemcova (1820-1862), writer.

Liberation of Colonies — A160

Designs: 2k, Allegory, Fight for Peace. 3k, Group of Students. 5k, Marching Students with flags.

1950, Aug. 14

No.	Type	Value / Color	Unused	Used
418	A160	1.50k dark green	.15	.15
419	A160	2k sepia	*.85*	*.55*
420	A160	3k rose carmine	.16	.15
421	A160	5k ultra	.40	.35
		Nos. 418-421 (4)	*1.56*	*1.20*

2nd International Students World Congress, Prague, Aug. 12-24, 1950.

Portrait Type of 1950

Design: Zdenek Fibich.

1950, Oct. 15

No.	Type	Value / Color	Unused	Used
422	A157	3k rose brown	*.90*	*.55*
423	A157	8k gray green	.35	.20

Centenary of the birth of Zdenek Fibich, musician.

Miner, Soldier and Farmer A161

Czech and Soviet Soldiers A162

1950, Oct. 6

No.	Type	Value / Color	Unused	Used
424	A161	1.50k slate	*.60*	*.60*
425	A162	3k carmine rose	.30	.30

Issued to publicize Czech Army Day.

Prague Castle, 16th Century A163

Prague, 1493 — A164

Designs: 3k, Prague, 1606. 5k, Prague, 1794.

1950, Oct. 21 *Perf. 14*

No.	Type	Value / Color	Unused	Used
426	A163	1.50k black	3.25	3.00
427	A164	2k chocolate	3.25	3.00
428	A164	3k brown carmine	3.25	3.00
429	A164	5k gray	3.25	3.00
a.		Block of 4, #426-429	17.50	16.00

See Nos. 434-435.

Communications Symbols — A165

1950, Oct. 25 *Perf. 12½*

No.	Type	Value / Color	Unused	Used
430	A165	1.50k chocolate	.15	.15
431	A165	3k brown carmine	*.85*	*.30*
		Set value		*.35*

1st anniv. of the foundation of the Intl. League of P.T.T. Employees.

Portrait Type of 1950

Design: J. Gregor Tajovsky.

1950, Oct. 26

No.	Type	Value / Color	Unused	Used
432	A157	1.50k brown	*1.00*	*.60*
433	A157	5k deep blue	*.65*	*.30*

10th anniversary of the death of J. Gregor Tajovsky (1874-1940), Slovakian writer.

Scenic Type of 1950

Design: Prague, 1950.

1950, Oct. 28

No.	Type	Value / Color	Unused	Used
434	A164	1.50k indigo	.35	.15
a.		Souvenir sheet of 4, imperf.	12.50	10.00
435	A164	3k brown carmine	*.65*	*.50*

Czech and Soviet Steel Workers A166

1950, Nov. 4 **Unwmk.**

No.	Type	Value / Color	Unused	Used
436	A166	1.50k chocolate	.30	.20
437	A166	5k deep blue	*.65*	*.48*

Issued to publicize the 2nd meeting of the Union of Czechoslovak-Soviet Friendship.

Dove by Picasso — A167

1951, Jan. 20 **Photo.** *Perf. 14*

No.	Type	Value / Color	Unused	Used
438	A167	2k deep blue	*4.00*	*2.75*
439	A167	3k rose brown	2.50	1.75

1st Czechoslovak Congress of Fighters for Peace, held in Prague.

Julius Fucik — A168

1951, Feb. 17 **Engr.** *Perf. 12½*

No.	Type	Value / Color	Unused	Used
440	A168	1.50k gray	.42	.30
441	A168	5k gray blue	*1.10*	*.75*

Drop Hammer — A169

Installing Gear — A170

1951, Feb. 24

No.	Type	Value / Color	Unused	Used
442	A169	1.50k gray blk	.15	.15
443	A170	3k violet brn	.15	.15
444	A169	4k gray blue	*.65*	*.48*
		Nos. 442-444 (3)	*.95*	
		Set value		*.60*

Women Machinists A171

Apprentice Miners A172

Designs: 3k, Woman tractor operator. 5k, Women of different races.

1951, Mar. 8 **Photo.** *Perf. 14*

No.	Type	Value / Color	Unused	Used
445	A171	1.50k olive brown	.22	.15
446	A171	3k brown car	*.90*	*.52*
447	A171	5k blue	.40	.15
		Nos. 445-447 (3)	*1.52*	*.82*

International Women's Day, Mar. 8.

1951, Apr. 12 **Engr.** *Perf. 12½*

No.	Type	Value / Color	Unused	Used
448	A172	1.50k gray	*.45*	*.24*
449	A172	3k red brown	.15	.15
		Set value		*.31*

Plowing — A173

Collective Cattle Breeding — A174

1951, Apr. 28 **Photo.** *Perf. 14*

No.	Type	Value / Color	Unused	Used
450	A173	1.50k brown	.50	.50
451	A174	2k dk green	*.75*	*.65*

Tatra Mountain Recreation Center A175

Mountain Recreation Centers: 2k, Beskydy (Beskids). 3k, Krkonose (Carpathians).

1951, May 5 **Engr.** *Perf. 12½*

No.	Type	Value / Color	Unused	Used
452	A175	1.50k deep green	.20	.15
453	A175	2k dark brown	*.75*	*.50*
454	A175	3k rose brown	.30	.15
		Nos. 452-454 (3)	*1.25*	*.80*

Issued to publicize the summer opening of trade union recreation centers.

Klement Gottwald and Joseph Stalin A176

Factory Militiaman A177

Red Army Soldier and Partisan A178

Marx, Engels, Lenin and Stalin A179

1951 Unwmk. *Perf. 12½*

455	A176	1.50k olive gray	.65	.25
456	A177	2k red brown	.22	.15
457	A178	3k rose brown	.22	.15
458	A176	5k deep blue	2.00	1.40
459	A179	8k gray	.60	.25
		Nos. 455-459 (5)	3.69	2.20

30th anniv. of the founding of the Czechoslovak Communist Party.

A180 A181

Design: 1k, 2k, Antonin Dvorák. 1.50k, 3k, Bedrich Smetana.

1951, May 30

460	A180	1k redsh brown	.25	.15
461	A180	1.50k olive gray	.70	.32
462	A180	2k dk redsh brn	.85	.70
463	A180	3k rose brown	.25	.15
		Nos. 460-463 (4)	2.05	1.32

International Music Festival, Prague.

Portrait Type of 1950

1951, June 21

Portrait: Bohumir Smeral (facing right).

464	A157	1.50k gray	.45	.35
465	A157	3k rose brown	.40	.15

10th anniv. of the death of Bohumir Smeral, political leader.

1951, June 21

466	A181	1k shown	.65	.28
467	A181	1.50k Discus	.45	.28
468	A181	3k Soccer	1.10	.28
469	A181	5k Skier	2.25	1.25
		Nos. 466-469 (4)	4.45	2.09

Issued to honor the 9th Congress of the Czechoslovak Sokol Federation.

Scene from "Fall of Berlin" A182

Scene from "The Great Citizen" A183

1951, July 14

470	A182	80h rose brown	.30	.20
471	A183	1.50k dark gray	.30	.20
472	A182	4k gray blue	1.25	.75
		Nos. 470-472 (3)	1.85	1.15

International Film Festival, Karlovy Vary, July 14-29, 1951.

Alois Jirásek — A184

"Fables and Fate" A185

Design: 4k, Scene from "Reign of Tabor."

1951, Aug. 23 Engr. *Perf. 12½*

473	A184	1.50k gray	.35	.15
474	A184	5k dark blue	1.65	1.25

Photo.

Perf. 14

475	A185	3k dark red	.35	.15
476	A185	4k dark brown	.35	.18
		Nos. 473-476 (4)	2.70	1.73

Cent. of the birth of Alois Jirásek, author.

Portrait Type of 1950

Design: Josef Hybes (1850-1921), co-founder of Czech Communist Party.

1951, July 21 Engr.

477	A157	1.50k chocolate	.15	.15
478	A157	2k rose brn	.55	.35
		Set value		.45

"Ostrava Region" — A186

Mining Iron Ore — A187

1951, Sept. 9

479	A186	1.50k dk brown	.15	.15
480	A187	3k rose brown	.15	.15
481	A186	5k deep blue	1.10	.90
		Nos. 479-481 (3)	1.40	
		Set value		1.02

Miner's Day, Sept. 9, 1951.

Soldiers on Parade — A188

Designs: 1k, Gunner and field gun. 1.50k, Klement Gottwald. 3k, Tankman and tank. 5k, Aviators.

Perf. 14 (80h, 5k), 12½

Photo. (80h, 5k), Engr.

1951, Oct. 6

Inscribed: "Den CS Armady 1951"

482	A188	80h olive brown	.25	.22
483	A188	1k dk olive grn	.25	.22
484	A188	1.50k sepia	.40	.22
485	A188	3k claret	.50	.22
486	A188	5k blue	1.10	.75
		Nos. 482-486 (5)	2.50	1.63

Issued to publicize Army Day, Oct. 6, 1951.

Stalin and Gottwald A189

Lenin, Stalin and Soldiers A190

1951, Nov. 3 Engr. *Perf. 12½*

487	A189	1.50k sepia	.15	.15
488	A190	3k red brown	.16	.15
489	A189	4k deep blue	1.10	.40
		Nos. 487-489 (3)	1.41	
		Set value		.50

Issued to publicize the month of Czechoslovak-Soviet friendship, 1951.

Peter Jilemnicky A191

Ladislav Zapotocky A192

1951, Dec. 5 Unwmk.

491	A191	1.50k redsh brown	.24	.15
492	A191	2k dull blue	.48	.35

Peter Jilemnicky (1901-1949), writer.

1952, Jan. 12 *Perf. 11½*

493	A192	1.50k brown red	.15	.15
494	A192	4k gray	.45	.45

Centenary of the birth of Ladislav Zapotocky, Bohemian socialist pioneer.

Jan Kollar — A193

Lenin and Lenin Hall — A194

1952, Jan. 30 Unwmk. *Perf. 11½*

495	A193	3k dark carmine	.15	.15
496	A193	5k violet blue	.65	.50
		Set value		.55

Jan Kollar (1793-1852), poet.

1952, Jan. 30 *Perf. 12½*

497	A194	1.50k rose carmine	.15	.15
498	A194	5k deep blue	.65	.35
		Set value		.43

6th All-Russian Party Conf., 40th anniv.

Emil Holub and African — A195

Gottwald Metallurgical Plant — A196

1952, Feb. 21 *Perf. 11½*

499	A195	3k red brown	.50	.30
500	A195	5k gray	1.75	1.10

Death of Emil Holub, explorer, 50th anniv.

1952, Feb. 25 Photo. *Perf. 14*

Designs: 2k, Foundry. 3k, Chemical plant.

501	A196	1.50k sepia	.25	.15
502	A196	2k red brown	1.00	.60
503	A196	3k scarlet	.15	.15
		Nos. 501-503 (3)	1.40	
		Set value		.75

Student, Soldier and Worker — A197

Youths of Three Races — A198

1952, Mar. 21 Unwmk. *Perf. 14*

504	A197	1.50k blue	.15	.15
505	A198	2k olive black	.22	.15
506	A197	3k lake	.85	.50
		Nos. 504-506 (3)	1.22	
		Set value		.65

International Youth Day, Mar. 25, 1952.

Similar to Type of 1951

Portrait: Otakar Sevcik.

1952, Mar. 22 Engr. *Perf. 12½*

507	A184	2k choc, *cr*	.50	.40
508	A184	3k rose brn, *cr*	.15	.15

Otakar Sevcik, violinist, birth cent.

Jan A. Komensky A199

Industrial and Farm Women A200

1952, Mar. 28

509	A199	1.50k dk brown, *cr*	1.25	.60
510	A199	11k dk blue, *cr*	.25	.15

360th anniv. of the birth of Jan Amos Komensky (Comenius), teacher and philosopher.

1952, Mar. 8

511	A200	1.50k dp blue, *cr*	1.00	.50

International Women's Day Mar. 8, 1952.

Woman and Children A201

Antifascist A202

1952, Apr. 12

512	A201	2k chocolate, *cr*	.75	.40
513	A201	3k dp claret, *cr*	.16	.15
		Set value		.46

Intl. Conf. for the Protection of Children, Vienna, Apr. 12-16, 1952.

1952, Apr. 11 Photo. *Perf. 14*

514	A202	1.50k red brown	.15	.15
515	A202	2k ultra	.60	.45
		Set value		.50

Day of International Solidarity of Fighters against Fascism, Apr. 11, 1952.

Harvester — A203

Design: 3k, Tractor and Seeders.

1952, Apr. 30

516 A203	1.50k	deep blue	.90	.65
517 A203	2k	brown	.20	.15
518 A203	3k	brown red	.20	.15
		Nos. 516-518 (3)	*1.30*	*.95*

Youths Carrying Flags A204

1952, May 1

519 A204	3k	brown red	.55	.40
520 A204	4k	dk red brown	.70	.60

Issued to publicize Labor Day, May 1, 1952.

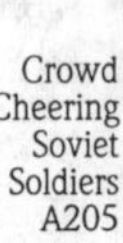

Crowd Cheering Soviet Soldiers A205

1952, May 9

521 A205	1.50k	dark red	.60	.50
522 A205	5k	deep blue	*1.25*	*1.00*

Liberation of Czechoslovakia from German occupation, 7th anniversary.

Children A206 — J. V. Myslbek A207

Design: 3k, "Pioneer" teaching children.

1952, May 31 Engr. *Perf. 12½*

523 A206	1.50k	dk brn, *cr*	.15	.15
524 A206	2k	Prus grn, *cr*	.90	.45
525 A206	3k	rose brn, *cr*	.15	.15
		Nos. 523-525 (3)	*1.20*	
		Set value		*.55*

International Children's Day May 31, 1952.

1952, June 2

Design: 8k, Allegory, "Music."

526 A207	1.50k	red brown	.20	.15
527 A207	2k	dark brown	.95	.95
528 A207	8k	gray green	.15	.15
		Nos. 526-528 (3)	*1.30*	*1.25*

Joseph V. Myslbek (1848-1922), sculptor.

Beethoven A208 — House of Artists A209

1952, June 7 Unwmk. *Perf. 11½*

529 A208	1.50k	sepia	.35	.25
530 A209	3k	red brown	.35	.25
531 A208	5k	indigo	*1.25*	*.75*
		Nos. 529-531 (3)	*1.95*	*1.25*

International Music Festival, Prague, 1952.

Lidice, Symbol of a New Life — A210

1952, June 10 *Perf. 12½*

532 A210	1.50k	dk violet brn	.15	.15
533 A210	5k	dark blue	.75	.50
		Set value		*.55*

Destruction of Lidice, 10th anniversary.

Jan Hus — A211 — Bethlehem Chapel — A212

1952, July 5

534 A211	1.50k	brown	.15	.15
535 A212	3k	red brown	.15	.15
536 A211	5k	black	*.85*	*.65*
		Nos. 534-536 (3)	*1.15*	*.95*

550th anniv. of the installation of Jan Hus as pastor of Bethlehem Chapel, Prague.

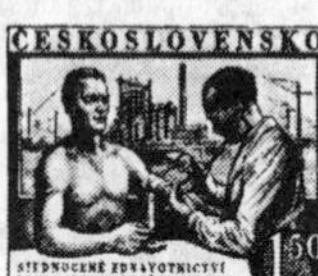

Doctor Examining Patient — A213

Design: 2k, Doctor, Nurse, Mother and child.

1952, July 31

537 A213	1.50k	dark brown	.70	.50
538 A213	2k	blue violet	.16	.15
539 A213	3k	rose brown	.16	.15
		Nos. 537-539 (3)	*1.02*	
		Set value		*.60*

Czechoslovakia's Unified Health Service.

Relay Race — A214

1952, Aug. 2 *Perf. 11½*

540 A214	1.50k	shown	.65	.35
541 A214	2k	Canoeing	*1.75*	*.75*
542 A214	3k	Cycling	.35	.35
543 A214	4k	Hockey	*2.25*	*2.00*
		Nos. 540-543 (4)	*5.00*	*3.45*

Issued to publicize Czechoslovakia's Unified Physical Education program.

F. L. Celakovski A215 — Mikulas Ales A216

1952, Aug. 5 *Perf. 12½*

544 A215	1.50k	dark brown	.15	.15
545 A215	2k	dark green	.75	.50
		Set value		*.55*

Centenary of the death of Frantisek L. Celakovski, poet and writer.

Perf. 11x11½

1952, Aug. 30 Engr. Unwmk.

546 A216	1.50k	dk gray grn	.35	.25
547 A216	6k	red brown	*2.00*	*1.50*

Birth centenary of Mikulas Ales, painter.

17th Century Mining Towers — A217 — Jan Zizka — A218

Designs: 1.50k, Coal Excavator. 2k, Peter Bezruc mine. 3k, Automatic coaling crane.

1952, Sept. 14 *Perf. 12½*

548 A217	1k	sepia	.85	.50
549 A217	1.50k	dark blue	.15	.15
550 A217	2k	olive gray	.15	.15
551 A217	3k	violet brown	.18	.15
		Nos. 548-551 (4)	*1.33*	
		Set value		*.67*

Miners' Day, Sept. 14, 1952. No. 550 also for the 85th anniv. of the birth of Peter Bezruc (Vladimir Vasek), poet.

1952, Oct. 5 Engr. *Perf. 11½*

Inscribed: ". . . . Armady 1952,"

Designs: 2k, Fraternization with Russians. 3k, Marching with flag.

552 A218	1.50k	rose lake	.15	.15
553 A218	2k	olive bister	.15	.15
554 A218	3k	dk car rose	.15	.15
555 A218	4k	gray	*1.10*	*.85*
		Nos. 552-555 (4)	*1.55*	
		Set value		*1.00*

Issued to publicize Army Day, Oct. 5, 1952.

Souvenir Sheet

Statues to Bulgarian Partisans and to Soviet Army — A219

1952, Oct. 18 Unwmk. *Perf. 12½*

556 A219	Sheet of 2	65.00	17.50
a.	2k deep carmine	20.00	5.75
b.	3k ultramarine	20.00	5.75

National Philatelic Exhibition, Bratislava, Oct. 18-Nov. 2, 1952.

Danube River, Bratislava — A220

1952, Oct. 18

557 A220	1.50k	dark brown	.15	.15

National Philatelic Exhibition, Bratislava.

Conference with Lenin and Stalin — A221 — Worker and Nurse Holding Dove and Olive Branch — A222

1952, Nov. 7

558 A221	2k	brown black	*1.00*	*.75*
559 A221	3k	carmine	.15	.15

35th anniv. of the Russian Revolution and to publicize Czechoslovak-Soviet friendship.

1952, Nov. 15 Photo. *Perf. 14*

560 A222	2k	brown	.85	.50
561 A222	3k	red	.15	.15

Issued to publicize the first State Congress of the Czechoslovak Red Cross.

Matej Louda, Hussite Leader, Painted by Mikulas Ales A223

Design: 3k, Dragon-killer Trutnov, painted by Ales.

1952, Nov. 18 Engr. *Perf. 11½*

562 A223	2k	red brown	.20	.15
563 A223	3k	grnsh gray	.30	.15
		Set value		*.16*

Mikulas Ales, painter, birth cent.

Gottwald Type of 1948-49

1952, June 2 Unwmk. *Perf. 12½*

Size: 19x24mm

564 A135	1k	dark green	.15	.15

"Peace" Flags — A224 — Dove by Picasso — A225

1952, Dec. 12 Photo. *Perf. 14*

565 A224	3k	red brown	.25	.15
566 A224	4k	deep blue	.80	.50
		Set value		*.55*

Issued to publicize the Congress of Nations for Peace, Vienna, Dec. 12-19, 1952.

1953, Jan. 17

Design: 4k, Czech Family.

567 A225	1.50k	dark brown	.15	.15
568 A225	4k	slate blue	.60	.30
		Set value		*.35*

2nd Czechoslovak Peace Congress.

Smetana Museum — A226

Design: 4k, Jirásek Museum.

1953, Feb. 10 Engr. *Perf. 11½*

569 A226	1.50k	dk violet brn	.15	.15
570 A226	4k	dark gray	*1.00*	*.65*
		Set value		*.70*

Prof. Zdenek Nejedly, 75th birth anniv.

Martin Kukucin A227 — Jaroslav Vrchlicky A228

Designs: 2k, Karel Jaromir Erben. 3k, Vaclav Matej Kramerius. 5k, Josef Dobrovsky.

1953, Feb. 28

571 A227	1k	gray	.15	.15
572 A228	1.50k	olive	.15	.15
573 A228	2k	rose lake	.15	.15
574 A228	3k	lt brown	.20	.15
575 A228	5k	slate blue	*1.10*	*1.10*
		Set value	*1.50*	*1.40*

Issued to honor Czech writers and poets: 1k, 25th anniv. of death of Kukucin. 1.50k, birth cent. of Vrchlicky. 2k, cent. of completion of "Kytice" by Erben. 3k, birth bicent. of Kramerius. 5k, birth bicent. of Dobrovsky.

Militia A229 — Gottwald A230

Design: 8k, Portraits of Stalin and Gottwald and Peoples Assembly.

Perf. 13½x14

1953, Feb. 25 Photo. Unwmk.

576 A229 1.50k deep blue .15 .15
577 A230 3k red .15 .15
578 A229 8k dark brown *1.10 .75*
Nos. 576-578 (3) *1.40*
Set value *.88*

5th anniv. of the defeat of the attempt to reinstate capitalism.

Book and Torch — A231

Design: 3k, Bedrich Vaclavek.

1953, Mar. 5 Engr. *Perf. 11½*

579 A231 1k sepia *.70 .50*
580 A231 3k orange brown .15 .15

Bedrich Vaclavek (1897-1943), socialist writer.

Stalin Type of 1949
Inscribed "21 XII 1879-5 III 1953"

1953, Mar. 12

581 A154 1.50k black .25 .15

Death of Joseph Stalin, Mar. 5, 1953.

Mother and Child — A232

Girl Revolutionist — A233

1953, Mar. 8

582 A232 1.50k ultra .15 .15
583 A233 2k brown red *.75 .35*
Set value *.40*

International Women's Day.

Klement Gottwald — A234

1953, Mar. 19

584 A234 1.50k black .15 .15
585 A234 3k black .15 .15
Set value .15

Souvenir Sheet

Imperf

586 A234 5k black 2.25 1.75

Death of Pres. Klement Gottwald, Mar. 14, 1953.

Josef Pecka, Ladislav Zapotocky and Josef Hybes A236

1953, Apr. 7 Unwmk. *Perf. 11½*

587 A236 2k lt violet brn .15 .15

75th anniversary of the first congress of the Czech Social Democratic Party.

Cyclists — A237

1953, Apr. 29

588 A237 3k deep blue .45 .25

6th International Peace Bicycle Race, Prague-Berlin-Warsaw.

Medal of "May 1, 1890" A238

Designs: 1.50k, Lenin and Stalin. 3k, May Day Parade. 8k, Marx and Engels.

Engraved and Photogravure

1953, Apr. 30 *Perf. 11½x11, 14*

589 A238 1k chocolate *1.00 .70*
590 A238 1.50k dark gray .15 .15
591 A238 3k carmine lake .15 .15
592 A238 8k dk gray green .25 .15
Nos. 589-592 (4) *1.55*
Set value *.95*

Issued to publicize Labor Day, May 1, 1953.

Sowing Grain — A239

1953, May 8 Photo. *Perf. 14*

593 A239 1.50k shown .30 .15
594 A239 7k Reaper *.95 .75*

Socialization of the village.

Dam — A240

Welder — A241

Design: 3k, Iron works.

1953, May 8 *Perf. 11½*

595 A240 1.50k gray *.52 .45*
596 A241 2k blue gray .15 .15
597 A240 3k red brown .15 .15
Nos. 595-597 (3) *.82*
Set value *.55*

Josef Slavik — A242

Leos Janacek — A243

1953, June 19

598 A242 75h dp gray blue *.42 .15*
599 A243 1.60k dark brown .85 .15
Set value *.22*

Issued on the occasion of the International Music Festival, Prague, 1953.

Gottwald Type of 1948-49

Perf. 12½ (15h, 1k), 11½ (20h, 3k)

1953

600 A135 15h yellow green .15 .15
601 A135 20h dk violet brn .20 .15
602 A135 1k purple .60 .15
603 A135 3k brown car .15 .15
604 A135 3k gray .65 .15
Nos. 600-604 (5) 1.75
Set value .25

Nos. 600-604 vary slightly in size.

Pres. Antonin Zapotocky — A244

1953, June 19 Photo. *Perf. 14*

605 A244 30h violet blue .45 .15
606 A244 60h cerise .25 .15
Set value .15

Julius Fucik A245

Book and Carnation A246

1953, Sept. 8 Engr. *Perf. 12½*

607 A245 40h dk violet brn .22 .15
608 A246 60h pink *.40 .25*
Set value *.30*

10th anniv. of the death of Julius Fucik, Communist leader executed by the Nazis.

Miner and Flag — A247

Design: 60h, Oil field and workers.

1953, Sept. 10 *Perf. 11½*

609 A247 30h gray .20 .15
610 A247 60h brown vio *.75 .50*
Set value *.55*

Miner's Day, Sept. 10, 1953.

Volleyball Game — A248

Motorcyclist — A249

Design: 60h, Woman throwing javelin.

1953, Sept. 15

611 A248 30h brown red *1.50 1.50*
612 A249 40h dk violet brn 3.00 .85
613 A248 60h rose violet 3.00 .85
Nos. 611-613 (3) 7.50 *3.20*

Hussite Warrior — A250

Pres. Antonin Zapotocky — A251

Designs: 60h, Soldier presenting arms. 1k, Red army soldiers.

1953, Oct. 8

614 A250 30h brown .28 .15
615 A250 60h rose lake .65 .15
616 A250 1k brown red *1.25 .70*
Nos. 614-616 (3) *2.18 1.00*

Issued to publicize Army Day, Oct. 3, 1953.

1953 Unwmk. *Perf. 11½, 12½*

617 A251 30h violet blue .26 .15
618 A251 60h carmine rose .50 .15
Set value .15

No. 617 is perf. 11½ and measures 19x23mm, No. 618 perf. 12½ and 18½x23½mm.

See No. 780.

Charles Bridge and Prague Castle — A252

Korean and Czech Girls — A253

1953, Aug. 15 Engr. *Perf. 11½*

619 A252 5k gray 2.25 .15

1953, Oct. 11 *Perf. 11x11½*

620 A253 30h dark brown 3.00 1.50

Czechoslovakia's friendship with Korea.

Flags, Hradcany Castle and Kremlin — A254

Designs: 60h, Lomonosov University, Moscow. 1.20k, Lenin Ship Canal.

1953, Nov. 7

621 A254 30h dark gray *1.10 .75*
622 A254 60h dark brown 1.25 .85
623 A254 1.20k ultra 2.25 1.50
Nos. 621-623 (3) *4.60 3.10*

Czechoslovak-Soviet friendship month.

Emmy Destinn, Opera Singer — A255

National Theater, Prague — A256

Portrait: 2k, Eduard Vojan, actor.

1953, Nov. 18 *Perf. 14*

624 A255 30h blue black .85 .40
625 A256 60h brown .25 .15
626 A255 2k sepia *2.25 .65*
Nos. 624-626 (3) *3.35 1.20*

Natl. Theater founding, 70th anniv.

Josef Manes — A257

Vaclav Hollar — A258

1953, Nov. 28 *Perf. 11x11½*

627 A257 60h brown carmine .35 .15
628 A257 1.20k deep blue *1.10 .52*

Issued to honor Josef Manes, painter.

1953, Dec. 5

Portrait: 1.20k, Head framed, facing right.

629 A258 30h brown black .20 .15
630 A258 1.20k dark brown *.80 .45*

Vaclav Hollar, artist and etcher.

Leo N. Tolstoi — A259

1953, Dec. 29 **Unwmk.**
631 A259 60h dark green .20 .15
632 A259 1k chocolate 1.10 .65

Leo N. Tolstoi, 125th birth anniv.

Locomotive A260

Design: 1k, Plane loading mail.

Engraved, Center Photogravure

1953, Dec. 29 *Perf. 11½x11*
633 A260 60h brn org & gray vio .45 .25
634 A260 1k org brn & brt bl 1.25 .75

Lenin — A261

Lenin Museum, Prague — A262

1954, Jan. 21 **Engr.** *Perf. 11½*
635 A261 30h dark brown .45 .15
636 A262 1.40k chocolate 1.00 .90

30th anniversary of the death of Lenin.

Klement Gottwald — A263

Design: 2.40k, Revolutionist with flag.

Perf. 11x11½, 14x13½

1954, Feb. 18
637 A263 60h dark brown .30 .15
638 A263 2.40k rose lake 4.25 1.50

25th anniversary of the fifth congress of the Communist Party in Czechoslovakia.

Gottwald Mausoleum, Prague — A264

Gottwald and Stalin A265

Design: 1.20k, Lenin & Stalin mausoleum, Moscow.

1954, Mar. 5 *Perf. 11½, 14x13½*
639 A264 30h olive brown .20 .15
640 A265 60h deep ultra .26 .15
641 A264 1.20k rose brown 1.25 .85
Nos. 639-641 (3) 1.71 1.15

1st anniv. of the deaths of Stalin and Gottwald.

Two Runners — A266

Group of Hikers — A267

Design: 1k, Woman swimmer.

1954, Apr. 24 *Perf. 11½*
642 A266 30h dark brown 1.75 .75
643 A267 80h dark green 5.75 3.50
644 A266 1k dk violet blue 1.10 .70
Nos. 642-644 (3) 8.60 4.95

Nurse — A268

Designs: 15h, Construction worker. 40h, Postwoman. 45h, Ironworker. 50h, Soldier. 75h, Lathe operator. 80h, Textile worker. 1k, Farm woman. 1.20k, Scientist and microscope. 1.60k, Miner. 2k, Physician and baby. 2.40k, Engineer. 3k, Chemist.

1954 *Perf. 12½x12, 11½x11*
645 A268 15h dark green .22 .15
646 A268 20h lt violet .28 .15
647 A268 40h dark brown .40 .15
648 A268 45h dk gray blue .15 .15
649 A268 50h dk gray green .28 .15
650 A268 75h deep blue .28 .15
651 A268 80h violet brown .28 .15
652 A268 1k green .55 .15
653 A268 1.20k dk violet blue .28 .15
654 A268 1.60k brown blk .95 .15
655 A268 2k orange brown 1.25 .15
656 A268 2.40k violet blue 1.00 .15
657 A268 3k carmine 1.40 .15
Nos. 645-657 (13) 7.32
Set value .75

Antonin Dvorák — A269

Prokop Divis — A270

Portraits: 40h, Leos Janacek. 60h, Bedrich Smetana.

1954, May 22 *Perf. 11x11½*
658 A269 30h violet brown .85 .20
659 A269 40h brick red 1.40 .20
660 A269 60h dark blue .90 .16
Nos. 658-660 (3) 3.15 .56

"Year of Czech Music," 1954.

1954, June 15
661 A270 30h gray .15 .15
662 A270 75h violet brown .65 .50

200th anniv. of the invention of a lightning conductor by Prokop Divis.

Slovak Insurrectionist A271

Anton P. Chekhov A272

Design: 1.20k, Partisan woman.

1954, Aug. 28 *Perf. 11½*
663 A271 30h brown orange .18 .15
664 A271 1.20k dark blue .80 .75

Slovak national uprising, 10th anniv.

1954, Sept. 24
665 A272 30h dull gray grn .15 .15
666 A272 45h dull gray brn .90 .65

50th anniv. of the death of Chekhov, writer.

Soviet Representative Giving Agricultural Instruction A273

Designs: 60h, Soviet industrial instruction. 2k, Dancers (cultural collaboration).

1954, Nov. 6 *Perf. 11½x11*
667 A273 30h yellow brown .15 .15
668 A273 60h dark blue .20 .15
669 A273 2k vermilion 1.25 1.25
Nos. 667-669 (3) 1.60 1.55

Czechoslovak-Soviet friendship month.

Jan Neruda — A274

Portraits: 60h, Janko Jesensky. 1.60k, Jiri Wolker.

1954, Nov. 25 *Perf. 11x11½*
670 A274 30h dark blue .85 .15
671 A274 60h dull red 1.40 .50
672 A274 1.60k sepia .35 .18
Nos. 670-672 (3) 2.60 .83

Issued to honor Czechoslovak poets.

View of Telc — A275

Views: 60h, Levoca. 3k, Ceske Budejovice.

1954, Dec. 10 **Engr. & Photo.**
673 A275 30h black & bis .35 .15
674 A275 60h brown & bis .35 .15
675 A275 3k black & bis 2.00 1.50
Nos. 673-675 (3) 2.70 1.80

Pres. Antonin Zapotocky A276

Attacking Soldiers A278

1954, Dec. 18 **Engr.** *Perf. 11½*
676 A276 30h black brown .45 .15
677 A276 60h dark blue .25 .15

Souvenir Sheet

Imperf

678 A276 2k deep claret 5.00 3.00

70th birthday of Pres. Antonin Zapotocky. See Nos. 829-831.

1954, Oct. 3 *Perf. 11½*

Design: 2k, Soldier holding child.

679 A278 60h dark green .32 .15
680 A278 2k dark brown 1.00 .95

Army Day, Oct. 6, 1954.

Woman Holding Torch — A279

Comenius University Building — A280

Design: 45h, Ski jumper.

1955, Jan. 20 **Engr.**
681 A279 30h red 1.90 .25

Engraved and Photogravure

682 A279 45h black & blue 2.50 .16

First National Spartacist Games, 1955.

1955, Jan. 28 **Engr.** *Perf. 11½*

Design: 75h, Jan A. Komensky medal.

683 A280 60h deep green .20 .15
684 A280 75h chocolate .90 .45

35th anniversary of the founding of Comenius University, Bratislava.

Czechoslovak Automobile A281

Designs: 60h, Textile worker. 75h, Lathe operator.

1955, Mar. 15 **Unwmk.**
685 A281 45h dull green .65 .45
686 A281 60h dk violet blue .15 .15
687 A281 75h sepia .35 .15
Nos. 685-687 (3) 1.15
Set value .55

Woman Decorating Soviet Soldier — A282

Stalin Memorial, Prague — A283

Designs: 35h, Tankman with flowers. 60h, Children greeting soldier.

1955, May 5 **Engr.** *Perf. 11½*
688 A282 30h blue .25 .15
689 A282 35h dark brown .75 .50
690 A282 60h cerise .25 .15

Photo.

691 A283 60h sepia .40 .15
Nos. 688-691 (4) 1.65
Set value .65

10th anniv. of Czechoslovakia's liberation.

Music and Spring — A284

Foundry Worker — A285

Design: 1k, Woman with lyre.

1955, May 12 **Engr. & Photo.**
692 A284 30h black & pale blue .35 .25
693 A284 1k black & pale rose 1.10 1.00

International Music Festival, Prague, 1955.

1955, May 12 **Engr.**

Design: 45h, Farm workers.

694 A285 30h violet .15 .15
695 A285 45h green *.60 .45*
Set value *.50*

Issued to publicize the third congress of the Trade Union Revolutionary Movement.

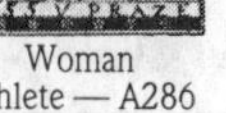

Woman Athlete — A286 Jakub Arbes — A287

Designs: 60h, Dancing couple. 1.60k, Athlete.

1955, June 21

696 A286 20h violet blue *.65 .35*
697 A286 60h green .25 .15
698 A286 1.60k red .65 .24
Nos. 696-698 (3) *1.55 .74*

Issued to publicize the first National Spartacist Games, Prague, June-July, 1955.

1955

Portraits: 30h, Jan Stursa. 40h, Elena Marothy-Soltesova. 60h, Josef Vaclav Sladek. 75h, Alexander Stepanovic Popov. 1.40k, Jan Holly. 1.60k, Pavel Josef Safarik.

699 A287 20h brown .25 .15
700 A287 30h black .25 .15
701 A287 40h gray green .75 .15
702 A287 60h black .50 .15
703 A287 75h claret *1.10 .70*
704 A287 1.40k black, *cr* .50 .18
705 A287 1.60k dark blue .50 .15
Nos. 699-705 (7) *3.85*
Set value *1.20*

Various anniversaries of prominent Slavs.

Girl and Boy of Two Races — A288 Costume of Ocova, Slovakia — A289

1955, July 20

706 A288 60h violet blue .30 .15

5th World Festival of Youth in Warsaw, July 31-Aug. 14.

1955, July 25

Regional Costumes: 75h, Detva man, Slovakia. 1.60k, Chodsko man, Bohemia. 2k, Hana woman, Moravia.

Frame and Outlines in Brown

707 A289 60h orange & rose *8.25 5.75*
708 A289 75h orange & lilac *4.75 3.00*
709 A289 1.60k blue & orange *8.25 4.75*
710 A289 2k yellow & rose *9.00 6.50*
Nos. 707-710 (4) *30.25 20.00*

Carp A290

Designs: 30h, Beetle. 35h, Gray Partridge. 1.40k, Butterfly. 1.50k, Hare.

1955, Aug. 8 **Engr. & Photo.**

711 A290 20h sepia & lt bl 1.10 .15
712 A290 30h sepia & pink .65 .15
713 A290 35h sepia & buff .65 .15
714 A290 1.40k sepia & cream *2.75 2.00*
715 A290 1.50k sepia & lt grn .65 .25
Nos. 711-715 (5) *5.80 2.70*

Tabor A291

Designs: 45h, Prachatice. 60h, Jindrichuv Hradec.

1955, Aug. 26 **Engr.**

716 A291 30h violet brown .20 .15
717 A291 45h rose carmine *.75 .60*
718 A291 60h sage green .20 .15
Nos. 716-718 (3) *1.15*
Set value *.70*

Issued to publicize the architectural beauty of the towns of Southern Bohemia.

Souvenir Sheet

Various Views of Prague — A292

1955, Sept. 10 **Engr.** ***Perf. 14x13½***

719 A292 Sheet of 5 22.50 20.00
a. 30h gray black 3.75 3.50
b. 45h gray black 3.75 3.50
c. 60h rose lake 3.75 3.50
d. 75h rose lake 3.75 3.50
e. 1.60k gray black 3.75 3.50

International Philatelic Exhibition, Prague, Sept. 10-25, 1955. Size: 145x110mm. Exists imperf., value $40.

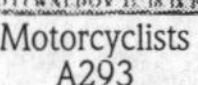

Motorcyclists A293 Workers, Soldier and Pioneer A294

1955, Aug. 28

720 A293 60h violet brown 2.25 .50

30th International Motorcycle Races at Gottwaldov, Sept. 13-18, 1955.

1955, Oct. 6 **Unwmk.** ***Perf. 11½***

Army Day: 60h, Tanks and planes.

721 A294 30h violet brown .25 .15
722 A294 60h slate *1.25 1.25*

Hans Christian Andersen — A295

Portraits: 40h, Friedrich von Schiller. 60h, Adam Mickiewicz. 75h, Walt Whitman.

1955, Oct. 27

723 A295 30h brown red .15 .15
724 A295 40h dark blue *.95 .65*
725 A295 60h deep claret .15 .15
726 A295 75h greenish black .30 .15
Nos. 723-726 (4) *1.55*
Set value *.85*

Issued in honor of these four poets and to mark the 100th anniversary of the publication of Walt Whitman's "Leaves of Grass."

Railroad Bridge A296

Designs: 30h, Train crossing bridge. 60h, Train approaching tunnel. 1.60k, Miners' housing project.

Inscribed: "Stavba Socialismu"

1955, Dec. 15

727 A296 20h dull green .25 .20
728 A296 30h violet brown .25 .15
729 A296 60h slate .25 .15
730 A296 1.60k carmine rose .50 .15
Nos. 727-730 (4) 1.25
Set value .35

Issued to publicize socialist public works.

Hydroelectric Plant — A297 Jewelry — A298

2nd Five Year Plan: 10h, Miner with drill. 25h, Building construction. 30h, Harvester. 60h, Metallurgical plant.

Inscribed: "Druhy Petilety Plan 1956-1960."

1956, Feb. 20 ***Perf. 11½x11***

731 A297 5h violet brown .20 .15
732 A297 10h gray black .20 .15
733 A297 25h dk car rose .20 .15
734 A297 30h green .20 .15
735 A297 60h violet blue .20 .15
Nos. 731-735 (5) 1.00
Set value .25

1956, Mar. 17 ***Perf. 11x11½***

736 A298 30h shown .22 .15
737 A298 45h Glassware *3.75 2.00*
738 A298 60h Ceramics .65 .15
739 A298 75h Textiles .22 .15
Nos. 736-739 (4) *4.84 2.45*

Products of Czechoslovakian industries.

Karlovy Vary (Karlsbad) A299 "We Serve our People" A300

Various Spas: 45h, Marianske Lazne (Marienbad). 75h, Piestany. 1.20k, Tatry Vysne Ruzbachy (Tatra Mountains).

1956, Mar. 17

740 A299 30h olive green 1.10 .25
741 A299 45h brown .85 .20
742 A299 75h claret *6.00 4.00*
743 A299 1.20k ultra .42 .15
Nos. 740-743 (4) *8.37 4.60*

Issued to publicize Czechoslovakian spas.

1956, Apr. 9 **Photo.** ***Perf. 11x11½***

Designs: 60h, Russian War Memorial, Berlin. 1k, Tank crewman with standard.

744 A300 30h olive brown .28 .15
745 A300 60h carmine rose .28 .15
746 A300 1k ultra *4.75 3.00*
Nos. 744-746 (3) *5.31 3.30*

Exhibition: "The Construction and Defense of our Country," Prague, Apr., 1956.

Cyclists — A301 Girl Basketball Players — A302

Athletes and Olympic Rings — A303

Engraved and Photogravure

1956, Apr. 25 **Unwmk.** ***Perf. 11½***

747 A301 30h green & lt blue *2.50 .20*
748 A302 45h dk blue & car 1.00 .20
749 A303 75h brown & lemon 1.00 .20
Nos. 747-749 (3) *4.50 .60*

9th Intl. Peace Cycling Race, Warsaw-Berlin-Prague, May 1-15, 1956 (No. 747). 5th European Womens' Basketball Championship (No. 748). Summer Olympics, Melbourne, Nov. 22-Dec. 8, 1956 (No. 749).

Mozart — A304 Home Guard — A305

Designs: 45h, Josef Myslivecek. 60h, Jiri Benda. 1k, Bertramka House, Prague. 1.40k, Xaver Dusek (1731-1799) and wife Josepha. 1.60k, Nostic Theater, Prague.

1956, May 12 **Engr.**

Design in Gray Black

750 A304 30h bister .60 .50
751 A304 45h gray green *11.00 8.50*
752 A304 60h pale rose lilac .40 .15
753 A304 1k salmon 1.00 .30
754 A304 1.40k lt blue 2.25 .25
755 A304 1.60k lemon .60 .15
Nos. 750-755 (6) *15.85 9.85*

200th anniv. of the birth of Wolfgang Amadeus Mozart and to publicize the International Music Festival in Prague.

1956, May 25

756 A305 60h violet blue .60 .15

Issued to commemorate the first meeting of the Home Guard, Prague, May 25-27, 1956.

Josef Kajetan Tyl — A306 River Patrol — A307

Portraits: 20h, Ludovit Stur. 30h, Frana Sramek. 1.40k, Karel Havlicek Borovsky.

1956, June 23

757 A306 20h dull purple .55 .15
758 A306 30h blue .30 .15
759 A306 60h black .30 .15
760 A306 1.40k claret *2.75 1.40*
Nos. 757-760 (4) *3.90 1.85*

Issued to honor various Czechoslovakian writers. See Nos. 781-784, 873-876.

1956, July 8 *Perf. 11x11½*

Design: 60h, Guard and dog.

761 A307 30h ultra	.85	.26
762 A307 60h green	.16	.15
Set value		.31

Issued to honor men of Frontier Guard.

Type of 1956 and

Steeplechase — A308

1956, Sept. 8 Unwmk. *Perf. 11½*

763 A308 60h indigo & bister	*1.75*	*.40*
764 A308 80h brown vio & vio	1.00	.15
765 A303 1.20k slate & orange	.75	.20
Nos. 763-765 (3)	*3.50*	*.75*

Steeplechase, Pardubice, 1956 (No. 763). Marathon race, Kosice, 1956 (No. 764). Olympic Games, Melbourne, Nov. 22-Dec. 8 (No. 765).

Woman Gathering Grapes — A309

Fishermen A310

Designs: 35h, Women gathering hops. 95h, Logging.

1956, Sept. 20 **Engr.**

766 A309 30h brown lake	.25	.15
767 A309 35h gray green	.25	.20
768 A310 80h dark blue	.45	.15
769 A310 95h chocolate	*1.50*	*1.40*
Nos. 766-769 (4)	*2.45*	*1.90*

Issued to publicize natural resources.

European Timetable Conf., Prague, Nov. 9-13 — A311

A312

Locomotives: 10h, 1846. 30h, 1855. 40h, 1945. 45h, 1952. 60h, 1955. 1k, 1954.

1956, Nov. 9 Unwmk. *Perf. 11½*

770 A311 10h brown	1.25	.15
771 A312 30h gray	.50	.15
772 A312 40h green	3.00	.15
773 A312 45h brown car	*14.00*	*9.50*
774 A312 60h indigo	.50	.15
775 A312 1k ultra	1.00	.15
Nos. 770-775 (6)	*20.25*	*10.25*

Costume of Moravia — A313

Regional Costumes (women): 1.20k, Blata, Bohemia. 1.40k, Cicmany, Slovakia. 1.60k, Novohradsko, Slovakia.

1956, Dec. 15 *Perf. 13½*

776 A313 30h brn, ultra & car	1.90	.60
777 A313 1.20k brn, car & ultra	1.50	.15
778 A313 1.40k brn, ocher & ver	*3.75*	*1.75*
779 A313 1.60k brn, car & grn	1.90	.40
Nos. 776-779 (4)	*9.05*	*2.90*

See Nos. 832-835.

Zapotocky Type of 1953

1956, Oct. 7 Unwmk. *Perf. 12½*

780 A251 30h blue	.30	.15

Portrait Type of 1956

Portraits: 15h, Ivan Olbracht. 20h, Karel Toman. 30h, F. X. Salda. 1.60k, Terezia Vansova.

1957, Jan. 18 Engr. *Perf. 11½*

781 A306 15h dk red brn, *cr*	.20	.15
782 A306 20h dk green, *cr*	.20	.15
783 A306 30h dk brown, *cr*	.20	.15
784 A306 1.60k dk blue, *cr*	.38	.15
Nos. 781-784 (4)	.98	
Set value		.26

Issued in honor of Czechoslovakian writers.

Kolin Cathedral A315

Views: No. 786, Banska Stiavnica. No. 787, Uherske Hradiste. No. 788, Karlstein. No. 789, Charles Bridge, Prague. 1.25k, Moravska Trebova.

1957, Feb. 23

785 A315 30h dk blue gray	.15	.15
786 A315 30h rose violet	.15	.15
787 A315 60h deep rose	.35	.15
788 A315 60h gray green	.35	.15
789 A315 60h brown	.26	.15
790 A315 1.25k gray	*1.25*	*1.25*
Nos. 785-790 (6)	*2.51*	
Set value		*1.50*

Issued to commemorate anniversaries of various towns and landmarks.

Komensky Mausoleum, Naarden — A316

Jan A. Komensky — A317

Farm Woman — A318

Old Prints: 40h, Komensky teaching. 1k, Sun, moon, stars and earth.

Perf. 11½x11, 14 (A317)

1957, Mar. 28 Engr. Unwmk.

791 A316 30h pale brown	.24	.15
792 A316 40h dark green	.24	.15
793 A317 60h chocolate	*1.25*	*.75*
794 A316 1k carmine rose	.45	.15
Nos. 791-794 (4)	*2.18*	
Set value		*1.00*

300th anniv. of the publication of "Didactica Opera Omnia" by J. A. Komensky (Comenius). No. 793 issued in sheets of four.

1957, Mar. 22 *Perf. 11½*

795 A318 30h lt blue green	.35	.15

3rd Cong. of Agricultural Cooperatives.

Cyclists A319

Woman Archer A320

Boxers — A321

Rescue Team A322

Perf. 11½x11, 11x11½

1957, Apr. 30

796 A319 30h sepia & ultra	.25	.15
797 A319 60h dull grn & bis	*1.50*	*1.25*
798 A320 60h gray & emer	.25	.15
799 A321 60h sepia & org	.25	.15
800 A322 60h violet & choc	.25	.15
Nos. 796-800 (5)	*2.50*	
Set value		*1.50*

10th Intl. Peace Cycling Race, Prague-Berlin-Warsaw (#796-797). Intl. Archery Championships (#798). European Boxing Championships, Prague (#799). Mountain Climbing Rescue Service (#800).

Jan V. Stamic — A323

Musicians: No. 802, Ferdinand Laub. No. 803, Frantisek Ondricek. No. 804, Josef B. Foerster. No. 805, Vitezslav Novak. No. 806, Josef Suk.

1957, May 12 *Perf. 11½*

801 A323 60h purple	.25	.15
802 A323 60h black	.25	.15
803 A323 60h slate blue	.25	.15
804 A323 60h brown	.25	.15
805 A323 60h dull red brn	.60	.15
806 A323 60h blue green	.25	.15
Nos. 801-806 (6)	1.85	
Set value		.45

Spring Music Festival, Prague.

Josef Bozek — A324

School of Engineering — A325

Portraits: 60h, F. J. Gerstner. 1k, R. Skuhersky.

1957, May 25

807 A324 30h bluish black	.15	.15
808 A324 60h gray brown	.25	.15
809 A324 1k rose lake	.25	.15
810 A325 1.40k blue violet	.55	.15
Nos. 807-810 (4)	1.20	
Set value		.30

School of Engineering in Prague, 250th anniv.

Pioneer and Philatelic Symbols — A326

Design: 60h, Girl and carrier pigeon.

Engraved and Photogravure

1957, June 8 *Perf. 11½*

811 A326 30h olive grn & org	.50	.15

Engr. *Perf. 13½*

812 A326 60h brn & vio bl	*1.25*	*1.00*

Youth Philatelic Exhibition, Pardubice.

"Grief" A327

Motorcyclists A328

Design: 60h, Rose, symbol of new life.

1957, June 10

813 A327 30h black	.25	.15
814 A327 60h blk & rose red	*.55*	*.22*
Set value		*.32*

Destruction of Lidice, 15th anniversary.

1957, July 5 *Perf. 11½*

815 A328 60h dk gray & blue	.60	.15

32nd International Motorcycle Race.

Karel Klic — A329

Josef Ressel — A330

1957, July 5

816 A329 30h gray black	.15	.15
817 A330 60h violet blue	.24	.15
Set value		.15

Klic, inventor of photogravure, and Ressel, inventor of the ship screw.

Chamois — A331

Gentian A332

Designs: 30h, Brown bear. 60h, Edelweiss. 1.25k, Tatra Mountains.

1957, Aug. 28 Engr. *Perf. 11½*

818 A331 20h emer & brnsh gray .60 .35
819 A331 30h lt blue & brn .50 .15
820 A332 40h gldn brn & vio bl .75 .15
821 A332 60h yellow & grn .35 .15

Size: 48x28½mm

822 A332 1.25k ol grn & bis *1.50 1.25*
Nos. 818-822 (5) 3.70
Set value *1.80*

Tatra Mountains National Park.

"Marycka Magdonova" A333

Man Holding Banner of Trade Union Cong. A334

Engraved and Photogravure

1957, Sept. 15 Unwmk. *Perf. 11½*

823 A333 60h black & dull red .30 .15

90th birthday of Petr Bezruc, poet and author of "Marycka Magdonova."

1957, Sept. 28 Engr.

824 A334 75h rose red .38 .15

4th Intl. Trade Union Cong., Leipzig, Oct. 4-15.

Television Transmitter and Antennas — A335

Design: 60h, Family watching television.

1957, Oct. 19 Engr. *Perf. 11½*

825 A335 40h dk blue & car .20 .15
826 A335 60h redsh brown & emer .24 .15
Set value .15

Issued to publicize the television industry.

Worker, Globe and Lenin A336

Design: 60h, Worker, factory, hammer and sickle.

1957, Nov. 7 *Perf. 12x11½*

827 A336 30h claret .20 .15
828 A336 60h gray blue .24 .15
Set value .15

Russian Revolution, 40th anniversary.

Zapotocky Type of 1954 dated: 19 XII 1884-13 XI 1957

1957, Nov. 18 Unwmk. *Perf. 11½*

829 A276 30h black .15 .15
830 A276 60h black .22 .15
Set value .15

Souvenir Sheet

Imperf

831 A276 2k black 1.00 .75

Death of Pres. Antonin Zapotocky.

Costume Type of 1956

Regional Costumes: 45h, Pilsen woman, Bohemia. 75h, Slovacko man, Moravia. 1.25k, Hana woman, Moravia. 1.95k, Teshinsko woman, Silesia.

1957, Dec. 18 Engr. *Perf. 13½*

832 A313 45h brn, bl & dk red 2.50 1.00
833 A313 75h dk brn, red & grn 1.75 .80
834 A313 1.25k dk brn, scar & ocher 2.50 .75
835 A313 1.95k sepia, bl & ver *3.00 2.00*
Nos. 832-835 (4) *9.75 4.55*

A337 A338

Designs: 30h, Radio telescope and observatory. 45h, Meteorological station in High Tatra. 75h, Sputnik 2 over Earth.

1957, Dec. 20 *Perf. 11½*

836 A337 30h violet brn & yel 1.75 .70
837 A338 45h sepia & lt bl .45 .35
838 A337 75h claret & blue 2.50 1.00
Nos. 836-838 (3) 4.70 2.05

IGY, 1957-58. No. 838 also for the launching of Sputnik 2, Nov. 3, 1957.

Girl Skater — A339

Litomysl Castle — A340

Designs: 40h, Canoeing. 60h, Volleyball. 80h, Parachutist. 1.60k, Soccer.

1958, Jan. 25 Engr. *Perf. 11½x12*

839 A339 30h rose violet 1.25 .25
840 A339 40h blue .25 .15
841 A339 60h redsh brown .25 .15
842 A339 80h violet blue *1.50 .50*
843 A339 1.60k brt green .45 .15
Nos. 839-843 (5) *3.70 1.20*

Issued to publicize various sports championship events in 1958.

1958, Feb. 10 *Perf. 11½*

Design: 60h, Bethlehem Chapel.

844 A340 30h green .20 .15
845 A340 60h redsh brown .20 .15
Set value .15

80th anniversary of the birth of Zdenek Nejedly, restorer of Bethlehem Chapel.

Giant Excavator — A341

Jewelry — A342

Peace Dove and: 60h, Soldiers, flame and banner, horiz. 1.60k, Harvester and rainbow, horiz.

1958, Feb. 25

846 A341 30h gray violet & yel .20 .15
847 A341 60h gray brown & car .25 .15
848 A341 1.60k green & dull yel .50 .15
Nos. 846-848 (3) .95
Set value .21

10th anniv. of the "Victorious February."

Engraved and Photogravure

1958 Unwmk. *Perf. 11½*

Designs: 45h, Dolls. 60h, Textiles. 75h, Kaplan turbine. 1.20k, Glass.

849 A342 30h rose car & blue .15 .15
850 A342 45h rose red & pale lil .20 .15
851 A342 60h violet & aqua .15 .15
852 A342 75h ultra & salmon *1.10 .75*
853 A342 1.20k blue grn & pink .28 .15
Nos. 849-853 (5) *1.88*
Set value *1.00*

Issued for the Universal and International Exposition at Brussels.

King George of Podebrad A343

Design: 60h, View of Prague, 1628.

1958, May 19 Engr.

854 A343 30h carmine rose .35 .15
855 A343 60h violet blue .30 .15
Set value .15

Issued to publicize the National Archives Exhibition, Prague, May 15-Aug. 15.

"Towards the Stars" — A344

Women of Three Races — A345

Boy, Girl and Globes A346

1958, May 26

856 A344 30h carmine rose *.75 .35*
857 A345 45h rose violet .20 .15
858 A346 60h blue .18 .15
Nos. 856-858 (3) *1.13 .65*

The Soc. for Dissemination of Political and Cultural Knowledge (#856). 4th Cong. of the Intl. Democratic Women's Fed. (#857). 1st World Trade Union Conf. of Working Youths, Prague, July 14-20 (#858).

Grain, Hammer and Sickle A347

Atomic Reactor A348

Design: 45h, Map of Czechoslovakia, hammer and sickle.

1958, May 26

859 A347 30h dull red .16 .15
860 A347 45h green .16 .15
861 A348 60h dark blue .20 .15
Nos. 859-861 (3) .52
Set value .17

11th Congress of the Czech Communist Party and the 15th anniv. of the Russo-Czechoslovakian Treaty.

Karlovy Vary A349

Various Spas: 40h, Podebrady. 60h, Marianske Lazne. 80h, Luhacovice. 1.20k, Strbske Pleso. 1.60k, Trencianske Teplice.

1958, June 25

862 A349 30h rose claret .15 .15
863 A349 40h redsh brown .15 .15
864 A349 60h gray green .15 .15
865 A349 80h sepia .20 .15
866 A349 1.20k violet blue .32 .15
867 A349 1.60k lt violet *1.10 .80*
Nos. 862-867 (6) *2.07*
Set value *1.15*

Telephone Operator A350

Pres. Novotny A351

Design: 45h, Radio transmitter.

1958, June 20

868 A350 30h black & brn org .25 .15
869 A350 45h black & lt grn .35 .20
Set value .28

Conference of Postal Ministers of Communist Countries, Prague, June 30-July 9.

1958-59 *Perf. 12½*

870 A351 30h brt violet blue .20 .15
b. Perf. 11½ .20 .20
870A A351 30h lt violet ('59) *.80 .50*
871 A351 60h carmine rose .22 .15

Perf. 11½

Redrawn

871A A351 60h rose red .20 .15
Nos. 870-871A (4) *1.42*
Set value *.70*

On No. 871 the top of the "6" turns down; on No. 871A it is open.

Czechoslovak Pavilion, Brussels — A352

1958, July 15 Engr. & Photo.

872 A352 1.95k lt blue & bis brn .90 .15

Czechoslovakia Week at the Universal and International Exhibition at Brussels.

Portrait Type of 1956

Portraits: 30h, Julius Fucik. 45h, G. K. Zechenter 60h, Karel Capek. 1.40k, Svatopluk Cech.

1958, Aug. 20 Engr. *Perf. 11½*

873 A306 30h rose red .25 .15
874 A306 45h violet *1.25 .50*
875 A306 60h dk blue gray .15 .15
876 A306 1.40k gray .50 .15
Nos. 873-876 (4) *2.15*
Set value *.75*

Death anniversaries of four famous Czechs.

The Artist and the Muse — A353

1958, Aug. 20 *Perf. 14*

877 A353 1.60k black 2.75 1.25

85th birthday of Max Svabinsky, artist and engraver.

Children's Hospital, Brno A354

Designs: 60h, New Town Hall, Brno. 1k, St. Thomas Church. 1.60k, View of Brno.

1958, Sept. 6 Unwmk. *Perf. 11½*

Size: 40x23mm

878 A354 30h violet .15 .15
879 A354 60h rose red .20 .15
880 A354 1k brown .45 .15

Perf. 14

Size: 50x28mm

881 A354 1.60k dk slate grn *1.90 1.75*
Nos. 878-881 (4) *2.70 2.20*

Natl. Phil. Exhib., Brno, Sept. 9.
No. 881 sold for 3.10k, including entrance ticket to exhibition. Issued in sheets of four.

Lepiota Procera — A355

Children on Beach — A356

Mushrooms: 40h, Boletus edulis. 60h, Krombholzia rufescens. 1.40k, Amanita muscaria L. 1.60k, Armillariella mellea.

1958, Oct. 6 *Perf. 14*

882 A355 30h dk brn, grn & buff .25 .15
883 A355 40h vio brn & brn org .25 .15
884 A355 60h black, red & buff .25 .15
885 A355 1.40k brown, scar & grn .75 .25
886 A355 1.60k blk, red brn & ol *2.75 1.10*
Nos. 882-886 (5) *4.25 1.80*

1958, Oct. 24 Unwmk. *Perf. 14*

Designs: 45h, Mother, child and bird. 60h, Skier.

887 A356 30h blue, yel & red .15 .15
888 A356 45h ultra & carmine .24 .15
889 A356 60h brown, blue & yel .35 .15
Nos. 887-889 (3) .74
Set value .30

UNESCO Headquarters in Paris opening, Nov. 3.

Bozek's Steam Car of 1815 A357

Designs: 45h, "Präsident" car of 1897. 60h, "Skoda" sports car. 80h, "Tatra" sedan. 1k, "Autocar Skoda" bus. 1.25k, Trucks.

Engraved and Photogravure

1958, Dec. 1 *Perf. 11½x11*

890 A357 30h vio blk & buff .50 .15
891 A357 45h ol & lt ol grn .38 .15
892 A357 60h ol gray & sal .55 .15
893 A357 80h claret & bl grn .38 .15

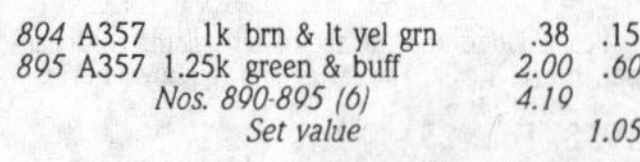

894 A357 1k brn & lt yel grn .38 .15
895 A357 1.25k green & buff *2.00 .60*
Nos. 890-895 (6) *4.19*
Set value *1.05*

Issued to honor the automobile industry.

Stamp of 1918 and Allegory — A358

1958, Dec. 18 Engr. *Perf. 11x11½*

896 A358 60h dark blue gray .28 .15

40th anniv. of the 1st Czechoslovakian postage stamp.

Ice Hockey A359

Sports: 30h, Girl throwing javelin. 60h, Ice hockey. 1k, Hurdling. 1.60k, Rowing. 2k, High jump.

1959, Feb. 14 *Perf. 11½x11*

897 A359 20h dk brown & gray .26 .15
898 A359 30h red brn & org brn .26 .15
899 A359 60h dk bl & pale grn .20 .15
900 A359 1k maroon & citron .38 .15
901 A359 1.60k dull vio & lt bl .55 .15
902 A359 2k red brn & lt bl *1.75 1.00*
Nos. 897-902 (6) *3.40*
Set value *1.30*

Congress Emblem — A360

"Equality of All Races" — A361

Design: 60h, Industrial and agricultural workers and emblem.

1959, Feb. 27 *Perf. 11½*

903 A360 30h maroon & lt blue .15 .15
904 A360 60h dk blue & yellow .16 .15
Set value .15

4th Agricultural Cooperative Cong. in Prague.

1959, Mar. 23

Designs: 1k, "Peace." 2k, Mother and Child: "Freedom for Colonial People."

905 A361 60h gray green .18 .15
906 A361 1k gray .25 .15
907 A361 2k dk gray blue *1.25 .50*
Nos. 905-907 (3) *1.68*
Set value .64

10th anniversary of the signing of the Universal Declaration of Human Rights.

Girl Holding Doll — A362

Frederic Joliot Curie — A363

Designs: 40h, Pioneer studying map. 60h, Pioneer with radio. 80h, Girl pioneer planting tree.

1959, Mar. 28 Engr. & Photo.

908 A362 30h violet bl & yel .20 .15
909 A362 40h indigo & ultra .20 .15
910 A362 60h black & lilac .15 .15
911 A362 80h brown & lt green .30 .15
Nos. 908-911 (4) .85
Set value .45

10th anniv. of the Pioneer organization.

1959, Apr. 17 Engr.

912 A363 60h sepia .75 .25

Frederic Joliot Curie and the 10th anniversary of the World Peace Movement.

"Reaching for the Moon" — A364

Town Hall Pilsen — A365

1959, Apr. 17

913 A364 30h violet blue .95 .25

2nd Cong. of the Czechoslovak Assoc. for the Propagation of Political and Cultural knowledge.

1959, May 2

Designs: 60h, Part of steam condenser turbine. 1k, St. Bartholomew's Church, Pilsen. 1.60k, Part of lathe.

914 A365 30h lt brown .15 .15
915 A365 60h violet & lt grn .20 .15
916 A365 1k violet blue .30 .15
917 A365 1.60k black & yellow *1.25 .85*
Nos. 914-917 (4) *1.90*
Set value *1.05*

2nd Pilsen Stamp Exhib. in connection with the centenary of the Skoda (Lenin) armament works.

Factory and Emblem A366

Inscribed: "IV Vseodborovy sjezd, 1959"

1959, May 13

918 A366 30h shown .15 .15
919 A366 60h Dam .20 .15
Set value .15

4th Trade Union Congress.

Zvolen Castle A367

1959, June 13

920 A367 60h gray olive & yel .30 .15

Regional Stamp Exhibition, Zvolen, 1959.

Frantisek Benda — A368

Aurel Stodola — A369

Portraits: 30h, Vaclav Kliment Klicpera. 60h, Karel V. Rais. 80h, Antonin Slavicek. 1k, Peter Bezruc.

1959, June 22 *Perf. 11½x11*

921 A368 15h violet blue .15 .15
922 A368 30h orange brown .15 .15
923 A369 40h dull green .15 .15
924 A369 60h dull red brn .25 .15
925 A369 80h dull violet .25 .15
926 A368 1k dark brown .25 .15
Nos. 921-926 (6) 1.20
Set value .35

View of the Fair Grounds A370

Designs: 60h, Fair emblem and world map. 1.60k, Pavilion "Z."

Inscribed: "Mezinarodni Veletrh Brne 6.-20.IX. 1959"

Engraved and Photogravure

1959, July 20 Unwmk. *Perf. 11½*

927 A370 30h lilac & yellow .15 .15
928 A370 60h dull blue .25 .15
929 A370 1.60k dk blue & bister .40 .15
Nos. 927-929 (3) .80
Set value .20

International Fair at Brno, Sept. 6-20.

Revolutionist and Flag — A371

Slovakian Fighter — A372

Design: 1.60k, Linden leaves, sun and factory.

Perf. 11½

1959, Aug. 29 Unwmk. Engr.

930 A371 30h black & rose .16 .15
931 A372 60h carmine rose .25 .15
932 A371 1.60k dk blue & yel .45 .15
Nos. 930-932 (3) .86
Set value .20

Natl. Slovakian revolution, 15th anniv. and Slovakian Soviet Republic, 40th anniv.

Alpine Marmots A373

1959, Sept. 25 Engr. & Photo.

933 A373 30h shown .35 .15
934 A373 40h Bison .50 .15
935 A373 60h Lynx, vert. 1.00 .15
936 A373 1k Wolf *1.75 .80*
937 A373 1.60k Red deer .75 .15
Nos. 933-937 (5) *4.35 1.40*

Tatra National Park, 10th anniv.

Lunik 2 Hitting Moon and Russian Flag A374

1959, Sept. 23 *Perf. 11½*

938 A374 60h dk red & lt ultra .85 .25

Issued to commemorate the landing of the Soviet rocket on the moon, Sept. 13, 1959.

Stamp Printing Works, Peking
A375

1959, Oct. 1

939 A375 30h pale green & red .20 .15

10 years of Czechoslovakian-Chinese friendship.

Haydn — A376

Great Spotted Woodpecker — A377

Design: 3k, Charles Darwin.

1959, Oct. 16 Engr. *Perf. 11½*

940 A376 60h violet black .45 .15
941 A376 3k dark red brown *1.10 .52*

150th death anniv. of Franz Joseph Haydn, Austrian composer, and 150th birth anniv. of Charles Darwin, English naturalist.

1959, Nov. 16 *Perf. 14*

Birds: 30h, Blue tits. 40h, Nuthatch. 60th, Golden oriole. 80h, Goldfinch. 1k, Bullfinch. 1.20k, European kingfisher.

942 A377 20h multicolored .42 .15
943 A377 30h multicolored .42 .15
944 A377 40h multicolored *1.65 1.00*
945 A377 60h multicolored .42 .15
946 A377 80h multicolored .42 .20
947 A377 1k multicolored .42 .15
948 A377 1.20k multicolored .85 .50
Nos. 942-948 (7) *4.60 2.30*

Nikola Tesla
A378

Designs: 30h, Alexander S. Popov. 35h, Edouard Branly. 60h, Guglielmo Marconi. 1k, Heinrich Hertz. 2k, Edwin Howard Armstrong and research tower, Alpine, N. J.

Engraved and Photogravure

1959, Dec. 7 *Perf. 11½*

949 A378 25h black & pink *.50 .15*
950 A378 30h black & orange .15 .15
951 A378 35h black & lt vio .16 .15
952 A378 60h black & blue .20 .15
953 A378 1k black & lt grn .25 .15
954 A378 2k black & bister *1.50 .42*
Nos. 949-954 (6) *2.76*
Set value *.75*

Issued to honor inventors in the fields of telegraphy and radio.

Gymnast — A379

2nd Winter Spartacist Games: 60h, Skier. 1.60k, Basketball players.

1960, Jan. 20 *Perf. 11½*

955 A379 30h salmon pink & brn .50 .15
956 A379 60h lt blue & blk .20 .15
957 A379 1.60k bister & brn .30 .25
Nos. 955-957 (3) 1.00
Set value .45

1960, June 15 Unwmk.

Designs: 30h, Two girls in "Red Ball" drill. 60h, Gymnast with stick. 1k, Three girls with hoops.

958 A379 30h lt grn & rose claret .15 .15
959 A379 60h pink & black .25 .15
960 A379 1k ocher & vio bl .45 .15
Nos. 958-960 (3) .85
Set value .32

2nd Summer Spartacist Games, Prague, June 23-July 3.

River Dredge Boat
A380

Ships: 60h, River tug. 1k, Tourist steamer. 1.20k, Cargo ship "Lidice."

1960, Feb. 22 *Perf. 11½*

961 A380 30h slate grn & sal .45 .15
962 A380 60h maroon & pale bl .15 .15
963 A380 1k dk violet & yel .45 .15
964 A380 1.20k lilac & pale grn *.60 .90*
Nos. 961-964 (4) *1.65 1.35*

Ice Hockey Players — A381

Design: 1.80k, Figure skaters.

1960, Feb. 27

965 A381 60h sepia & lt blue .30 .25
966 A381 1.80k black & lt green *3.25 2.50*

8th Olympic Winter Games, Squaw Valley, Calif., Feb. 18-29, 1960.

1960, June 15 Unwmk.

Designs: 1k, Running. 1.80k, Women's gymnastics. 2k, Rowing.

967 A381 1k black & orange .42 .16
968 A381 1.80k black & sal pink 1.00 .25
969 A381 2k black & blue *1.65 .95*
Nos. 967-969 (3) *3.07 1.36*

17th Olympic Games, Rome, Aug. 25-Sept. 11.

Trencin Castle — A382

Castles: 10h, Bezdez. 20h, Kost. 30h, Pernstein. 40h, Kremnica. 50h, Krivoklát castle. 60h, Karlstein. 1k, Smolenice. 1.60k, Kokorin.

1960-63 Engr. *Perf. 11½*

970 A382 5h gray violet .15 .15
971 A382 10h black .15 .15
972 A382 20h brown org .25 .15
973 A382 30h green .16 .15
974 A382 40h brown .16 .15
974A A382 50h black ('63) .16 .15
975 A382 60h rose red .25 .15
976 A382 1k lilac .30 .15
977 A382 1.60k dark blue .60 .15
Nos. 970-977 (9) 2.18
Set value .45

1961, Oct. Wmk. 341

977A A382 30h green 1.50 .15

Lenin — A383

Soldier Holding Child — A384

1960, Apr. 22 Unwmk.

978 A383 60h gray olive .40 .20

90th anniversary of the birth of Lenin.

1960, May 5 Engr. & Photo.

Designs: No. 980, Child eating pie. No. 981, Soldier helping concentration camp victim. No. 982, Welder and factory, horiz. No. 983, Tractor driver and farm, horiz.

979 A384 30h maroon & lt blue .25 .15
980 A384 30h dull red .20 .15
981 A384 30h green & dull blue .20 .15
982 A384 60h dk blue & buff .35 .15
983 A384 60h redsh brn & yel grn .35 .15
Nos. 979-983 (5) 1.35
Set value .35

15th anniversary of liberation.

Steelworker — A385

Design: 60h, Farm woman and child.

1960, May 24

984 A385 30h maroon & gray .16 .15
985 A385 60h green & pale blue .28 .15
Set value .15

1960 parliamentary elections.

Red Cross Nurse Holding Dove
A386

Fire Fighters
A387

1960, May 26 Unwmk.

986 A386 30h brown car & bl .16 .15
987 A387 60h dk blue & pink .28 .15
Set value .15

3rd Congress of the Czechoslovakian Red Cross (No. 986), and the 2nd Fire Fighters' Congress (No. 987).

Hand of Philatelist with Tongs and Two Stamps
A388

Design: 1k, Globe and 1937 Bratislava stamp (shown in miniature on 60h).

1960, July 11 *Perf. 11½*

988 A388 60h black & dull yel .40 .15
989 A388 1k black & blue .60 .15
Set value .18

Issued to publicize the National Stamp Exhibition, Bratislava, Sept. 24-Oct. 9.

See Nos. C49-C50.

Stalin Mine, Ostrava-Hermanovice
A390

Viktorin Cornelius, Lawyer
A391

Designs: 20h, Power station, Hodonin. 30h, Gottwald iron works, Kuncice. 40h, Harvester. 60h, Oil refinery.

1960, July 25

992 A390 10h black & pale grn .16 .15
993 A390 20h maroon & lt bl .16 .15
994 A390 30h indigo & pink .16 .15
995 A390 40h green & pale lilac .16 .15
996 A390 60h dk blue & yel .20 .15
Nos. 992-996 (5) .84
Set value .30

Issued to publicize the new five-year plan.

1960, Aug. 23 Engr.

Portraits: 20h, Karel Matej Capek-Chod, writer. 30h, Hana Kvapilova, actress. 40h, Oskar Nedbal, composer. 60h, Otakar Ostrcil, composer.

997 A391 10h black .20 .15
998 A391 20h red brown .20 .15
999 A391 30h rose red .25 .15
1000 A391 40h dull green .35 .15
1001 A391 60h gray violet .25 .15
Nos. 997-1001 (5) 1.25
Set value .45

See Nos. 1037-1041.

Skoda Sports Plane Flying Upside Down
A392

1960, Aug. 28 Engr. & Photo.

1002 A392 60h violet blue & blue .75 .15

1st aerobatic world championships, Bratislava.

Constitution and "Czechoslovakia" — A393

1960, Sept. 18

1003 A393 30h violet bl & pink .20 .15

Proclamation of the new socialist constitution.

Workers Reading Newspaper
A394

Man Holding Newspaper — A395

1960, Sept. 18

1004 A394 30h slate & ver .15 .15
1005 A395 60h black & rose .22 .15
Set value .15

Day of the Czechoslovak Press, Sept. 21, 1960, and 40th anniv. of the Rudé Právo paper.

Globes and Laurel A396

1960, Sept. 18 **Engr.**
1006 A396 30h dk blue & bister .25 .15

World Federation of Trade Unions, 15th anniv.

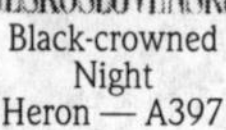

Black-crowned Night Heron — A397

Doronicum Clusii (Thistle) — A398

Birds: 30h, Great crested grebe. 40h, Lapwing. 60h, Gray heron. 1k, Graylag goose, horiz. 1.60k, Mallard, horiz.

Engraved and Photogravure

1960, Oct. 24 **Unwmk.** ***Perf. 11½***

Designs in Black

1007 A397 25h pale vio blue .15 .15
1008 A397 30h pale citron .50 .15
1009 A397 40h pale blue .25 .15
1010 A397 60h pink .35 .15
1011 A397 1k pale yellow .50 .15
1012 A397 1.60k lt violet *2.00 1.00*
Nos. 1007-1012 (6) *3.75*
Set value *1.45*

1960, Nov. 21 **Engr.** ***Perf. 14***

Flowers: 30h, Cyclamen. 40h, Primrose. 60h, Hen-and-chickens. 1k, Gentian. 2k, Pasqueflower.

1013 A398 20h black, yel & grn .25 .15
1014 A398 30h black, car rose & grn .32 .15
1015 A398 40h black, yel & grn .32 .15
1016 A398 60h black, pink & grn .32 .15
1017 A398 1k black, bl, vio & grn .55 .15
1018 A398 2k black, lil, yel & grn *2.25 1.00*
Nos. 1013-1018 (6) *4.01*
Set value *1.50*

Alfons Mucha — A399

1960, Dec. 18 **Engr.** ***Perf. 11½x12***
1019 A399 60h dk blue gray .30 .15

Day of the Czechoslovak Postage Stamp and birth cent. of Alfons Mucha, designer of the 1st Czechoslovakian stamp (Type A1).

Rolling-mill Control Bridge — A400

Athletes with Flags — A401

Designs: 30h, Turbo generator. 60h, Ditch-digging machine.

1961, Jan. 20 **Unwmk.** ***Perf. 11½***
1020 A400 20h blue .15 .15
1021 A400 30h rose .15 .15
1022 A400 60h brt green .22 .15
Nos. 1020-1022 (3) .52
Set value .15

Third Five-Year Plan.

Perf. 11x11½, 11½x11

1961, Feb. 20 **Engr. & Photo.**

Designs: No. 1024, Motorcycle race, horiz. 40h, Sculling, horiz. 60h, Ice skater. 1k, Rugby. 1.20k, Soccer. 1.60k, Long-distance runners.

1023 A401 30h rose red & bl .20 .15
1024 A401 30h dk blue & car .20 .15
1025 A401 40h dk gray & car .35 .15
1026 A401 60h lilac & blue .30 .15
1027 A401 1k ultra & yel .30 .15
1028 A401 1.20k green & buff .50 .15
1029 A401 1.60k sepia & salmon *2.00 1.00*
Nos. 1023-1029 (7) *3.85*
Set value *1.45*

Various sports events.

Exhibition Emblem A402

Rocket Launching A403

1961, Mar. 6 **Engr.** ***Perf. 11½***
1030 A402 2k dk blue & red 1.25 .15

"Praga 1962" International Stamp Exhibition, Prague, Sept. 1962.

1961, Mar. 6 **Engr. & Photo.**

Designs: 30h, Sputnik III, horiz. 40h, As 20h, but inscribed "Start Kosmicke Rakety k Venusi - 12.II.1961". 60h, Sputnik I, horiz. 1.60k, Interplanetary station, horiz. 2k, Similar to type A404, without commemorative inscription.

1031 A403 20h violet & pink .35 .15
1032 A403 30h dk green & buff .50 .15
1033 A403 40h dk red & yel grn .35 .15
1034 A403 60h violet & buff .25 .15
1035 A403 1.60k dk bl & pale grn .35 .15
1036 A403 2k mar & pale bl *1.90 1.10*
Nos. 1031-1036 (6) *3.70*
Set value *1.55*

Issued to publicize Soviet space research.

Portrait Type of 1960

Portraits: No. 1037, Jindrich Mosna. No. 1038, Pavol Orszagh Hviezdoslav. No. 1039, Alois Mrstik. No. 1040, Joza Uprka. No. 1041, Josef Hora.

1961, Mar. 27 ***Perf. 11½***
1037 A391 60h green .20 .15
1038 A391 60h dark blue .20 .15
a. "ORSZACH" instead of "ORSZAGH" *30.00 15.00*
1039 A391 60h dull claret .20 .15
1040 A391 60h gray .20 .15
1041 A391 60h sepia .20 .15
Nos. 1037-1041 (5) 1.00
Set value .25

Man Flying into Space A404

1961, Apr. 13
1042 A404 60h car & pale bl .35 .15
1043 A404 3k ultra & yel *2.00 .60*
Set value *.65*

1st man in space, Yuri A. Gagarin, Apr. 12, 1961. See No. 1036.

Flute Player — A405

Blast Furnace and Mine, Kladno — A406

1961, Apr. 24 **Engr.**
1044 A405 30h shown .25 .15
1045 A405 30h Dancer .38 .15
1046 A405 60h Lyre player .25 .15
Nos. 1044-1046 (3) .88
Set value .35

Prague Conservatory of Music, 150th anniv.

1961, Apr. 24
1047 A406 3k dull red .75 .15

Marching Workers — A407

Woman with Hammer and Sickle — A408

Klement Gottwald Museum A409

Designs: No. 1050, Lenin Museum. No. 1051, Crowd with flags. No. 1053, Man saluting Red Star.

1961, May 10
1048 A407 30h dull violet .15 .15
1049 A409 30h dark blue .15 .15
1050 A409 30h redsh brown .15 .15
1051 A407 60h vermilion .20 .15
1052 A408 60h dark green .20 .15
1053 A408 60h carmine .20 .15
Nos. 1048-1053 (6) 1.05
Set value .30

Czech Communist Party, 40th anniversary.

Puppet — A410

Designs: Various Puppets.

Engraved and Photogravure

1961, June 20 **Unwmk.** ***Perf. 11½***
1054 A410 30h ver & yel .15 .15
1055 A410 40h sepia & bluish grn .20 .15
1056 A410 60h vio bl & sal .20 .15
1057 A410 1k green & lt blue .20 .15
1058 A410 1.60k mar & pale vio *1.25 .35*
Nos. 1054-1058 (5) *2.00*
Set value *.55*

Woman, Map of Africa and Flag of Czechoslovakia — A411

1961, June 26
1059 A411 60h red & blue .25 .15

Issued to publicize the friendship between the people of Africa and Czechoslovakia.

Map of Europe and Fair Emblem A412

Designs (Fair emblem and): 60h Horizontal boring machine, vert. 1k, Scientists' meeting and nuclear physics emblem.

1961, Aug. 14 ***Perf. 11½***
1060 A412 30h dk bl & pale grn .15 .15
1061 A412 60h green & pink .25 .15
1062 A412 1k vio brn & lt bl .35 .15
Nos. 1060-1062 (3) .75
Set value .20

International Trade Fair, Brno, Sept. 10-24.

Sugar Beet, Cup of Coffee and Bags of Sugar A413

Charles Bridge, St. Nicholas Church and Hradcany A414

1961, Sept. 18 **Unwmk.** ***Perf. 11½***
1063 A413 20h shown .15 .15
1064 A413 30h Clover .15 .15
1065 A413 40h Wheat .15 .15
1066 A413 60h Hops .20 .15
1067 A413 1.40k Corn .35 .15
1068 A413 2k Potatoes *1.25 .55*
Nos. 1063-1068 (6) *2.25*
Set value *.85*

1961, Sept. 25
1069 A414 60h violet bl & car .70 .15

26th session of the Governor's Council of the Red Cross Societies League, Prague.

Orlik Dam and Kaplan Turbine A415

Designs: 30h, View of Prague, flags and stamps. 40h, Hluboká Castle, river and fish. 60h, Karlovy Vary and cup. 1k, Pilsen and beer bottle. 1.20k, North Bohemia landscape and vase. 1.60k, Tatra mountains, boots, ice pick and rope. 2k, Ironworks, Ostrava Kuncice and pulley. 3k, Brno and ball bearing. 4k, Bratislava and grapes. 5k, Prague and flags.

1961 **Unwmk.** ***Perf. 11½***

Size: 41x23mm

1070 A415 20h gray & blue *.25 .22*
1071 A415 30h vio blue & red *.18* .15
1072 A415 40h dk blue & lt grn *.40 .25*
1073 A415 60h dk blue & yel *.30 .18*
1074 A415 1k maroon & green .55 .45
1075 A415 1.20k green & pink *.55* .35
1076 A415 1.60k brown & vio bl .90 .52
1077 A415 2k black & ocher 1.10 .85
1078 A415 3k ultra & yel *1.50 .65*
1079 A415 4k purple & sal *2.00 1.10*

Perf. 13½
Engr.
Size: 50x29mm

1080 A415 5k multicolored *20.00 16.00*
Nos. 1070-1080 (11) 27.73 20.72

"PRAGA 1962 World Exhib. of Postage Stamps," Aug. 18-Sept. 2, 1962. No. 1080 was printed in sheet of 4.

Globe A416

Engraved and Photogravure

1961, Nov. 27 *Perf. 11½*
1081 A416 60h red & ultra .28 .15

Issued to publicize the Fifth World Congress of Trade Unions, Moscow, Dec. 4-16.

Orange Tip Butterfly — A417

Bicyclists — A418

Designs (butterflies): 20h, Zerynthia hypsipyle Sch. 30h, Apollo. 40h, Swallowtail. 60h, Peacock. 80h, Mourning cloak (Camberwell beauty). 1k, Underwing (moth). 1.60k, Red admiral. 2k, Brimstone (sulphur).

1961, Nov. 27 **Engr.**
1082 A417 15h multicolored .35 .15
1083 A417 20h multicolored .50 .15
1084 A417 30h multicolored .75 .15
1085 A417 40h multicolored .75 .18
1086 A417 60h multicolored .75 .25
1087 A417 80h multicolored 1.00 .25
1088 A417 1k multicolored 1.00 .25
1089 A417 1.60k multicolored 1.40 .35
1090 A417 2k multicolored *3.50 1.25*
Nos. 1082-1090 (9) *10.00* 2.98

Printed in sheets of ten.

Engraved and Photogravure

1962, Feb. 5 **Unwmk.** *Perf. 11½*

Sports: 40h, Woman gymnast. 60h, Figure skaters. 1k, Woman bowler. 1.20k, Goalkeeper, soccer. 1.60k, Discus thrower.

1091 A418 30h black & vio bl .18 .15
1092 A418 40h black & yel .18 .15
1093 A418 60h slate & grnsh bl .25 .15
1094 A418 1k black & pink .25 .15
1095 A418 1.20k black & green .25 .15
1096 A418 1.60k blk & dull grn *1.40* .60
Nos. 1091-1096 (6) *2.51*
Set value .90

Various 1962 sports events.
No. 1095 does not have the commemorative inscription.

Karel Kovarovic — A419

Frantisek Zaviska and Karel Petr A420

Designs: 20h, Frantisek Skroup. 30h, Bozena Nemcova. 60h, View of Prague and staff of Aesculapius. 1.60k, Ladislav Celakovsky. 1.80k, Miloslav Valouch and Juraj Hronec.

1962, Feb. 26 **Engr.**
1097 A419 10h red brown .15 .15
1098 A419 20h violet blue .15 .15
1099 A419 30h brown .15 .15
1100 A420 40h claret .15 .15
1101 A419 60h black .20 .15
1102 A419 1.60k slate green .52 .15
1103 A420 1.80k dark blue .60 .15
Set value 1.50 .40

Various cultural personalities and events.

Miner and Flag A421

1962, Mar. 19 **Engr. & Photo.**
1104 A421 60h indigo & rose .25 .15

30th anniv. of the miners' strike at Most.

"Man Conquering Space" — A422

Soviet Spaceship Vostok 2 — A423

Designs: 40h, Launching of Soviet space rocket. 80h, Multi-stage automatic rocket. 1k, Automatic station on moon. 1.60k, Television satellite.

1962, Mar. 26
1105 A422 30h dk red & lt blue .25 .15
1106 A422 40h dk blue & sal .25 .15
1107 A423 60h dk blue & pink .25 .15
1108 A423 80h rose vio & lt grn .60 .15
1109 A422 1k indigo & citron .35 .15
1110 A423 1.60k green & buff *1.75 .75*
Nos. 1105-1110 (6) *3.45*
Set value *1.15*

Issued to publicize space research.

Polar Bear — A424

Zoo Animals: 30h, Chimpanzee. 60h, Camel. 1k, African and Indian elephants, horiz. 1.40k, Leopard, horiz. 1.60k, Przewalski horse, horiz.

1962, Apr. 24 **Unwmk.** *Perf. 11½*
Design and Inscriptions in Black
1111 A424 20h grnsh blue .25 .15
1112 A424 30h violet .25 .15
1113 A424 60h orange .25 .15
1114 A424 1k green .50 .15
1115 A424 1.40k carmine rose .50 .20
1116 A424 1.60k lt brown *1.75 .90*
Nos. 1111-1116 (6) *3.50*
Set value *1.40*

Child and Grieving Mother — A425

Klary's Fountain, Teplice — A426

Design: 60h, Flowers growing from ruins of Lezáky.

1962, June 9 **Engr. & Photo.**
1118 A425 30h black & red .30 .15
1119 A425 60h black & dull bl .35 .15
Set value .15

20th anniversary of the destruction of Lidice and Lezáky by the Nazis.

1962, June 9
1120 A426 60h dull grn & yel .35 .15

1,200th anniversary of the discovery of the medicinal springs of Teplice.

Malaria Eradication Emblem, Cross and Dove A427

Soccer Goalkeeper A428

Design: 3k, Dove and malaria eradication emblem.

1962, June 18
1121 A427 60h black & crimson .16 .15
1122 A427 3k dk blue & yel *1.25 .60*

WHO drive to eradicate malaria.

1962, June 20 **Unwmk.** *Perf. 11½*
1123 A428 1.60k green & yellow 1.10 .15

Czechoslovakia's participation in the World Cup Soccer Championship, Chile, May 30-June 17. See No. 1095.

Soldier in Swimming Relay Race A429

"Agriculture" A430

Designs: 40h, Soldier hurdling. 60h, Soccer player. 1k, Soldier with rifle in relay race.

1962, July 20
1124 A429 30h green & lt ultra .15 .15
1125 A429 40h dk purple & yel .15 .15
1126 A429 60h brown & green .20 .15
1127 A429 1k dk blue & sal pink .35 .15
Nos. 1124-1127 (4) .85
Set value .25

2nd Summer Spartacist Games of Friendly Armies, Prague, Sept., 1962.

1962 **Engr.** *Perf. 13½*

Designs: 60h, Astronaut in capsule. 80h, Boy with flute, horiz. 1k, Workers of three races, horiz. 1.40k, Children dancing around tree. 1.60k, Flying bird, horiz. 5k, View of Prague, horiz.

1128 A430 30h multicolored 1.50 .90
1129 A430 60h multicolored .65 .55
a. Miniature sheet of 8 *15.00 12.50*
1130 A430 80h multicolored 2.25 1.25
1131 A430 1k multicolored 3.25 2.25
1132 A430 1.40k multicolored 3.25 2.25
1133 A430 1.60k multicolored *4.25 3.50*
Nos. 1128-1133 (6) *15.15 10.70*

Souvenir Sheet

1134 A430 5k multicolored *12.00 10.00*
a. Imperf. *35.00 30.00*

"PRAGA 1962 World Exhib. of Postage Stamps," Aug. 18-Sept. 2, 1962. No. 1133 also for FIP Day, Sept. 1. Printed in sheets of 10.

No. 1129a contains 4 each of Nos. 1128-1129 and 2 labels arranged in 2 rows of 2 se-tenant pairs of Nos. 1128-1129 with label between. Sold for 5k, only with ticket.

No. 1134 contains one 51x30mm stamp. Sold only with ticket.

Children in Day Nursery and Factory A431

Sailboat and Trade Union Rest Home, Zinkovy — A432

Engraved and Photogravure

1962, Oct. 29 **Unwmk.** *Perf. 11½*
1135 A431 30h black & lt blue .20 .15
1136 A432 60h brown & yellow .20 .15
Set value .15

Cruiser "Aurora" — A433

1962, Nov. 7
1137 A433 30h black & gray bl .15 .15
1138 A433 60h black & pink .20 .15
Set value .15

Russian October revolution, 45th anniv.

Cosmonaut and Worker — A434

Lenin — A435

1962, Nov. 7
1139 A434 30h dark red & blue .15 .15
1140 A435 60h black & dp rose .20 .15
Set value .15

40th anniversary of the USSR.

Symbolic Crane — A436

Designs: 40h, Agricultural products, vert. 60h, Factories.

1962, Dec. 4
1141 A436 30h dk red & yel .15 .15
1142 A436 40h gray blue & yel .20 .15
1143 A436 60h black & dp rose .30 .15
Nos. 1141-1143 (3) .65
Set value .25

Communist Party of Czechoslovakia, 12th cong.

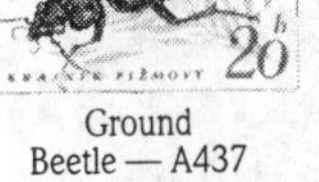

Ground Beetle — A437

Table Tennis — A438

Beetles: 30h, Cardinal beetle. 60h, Stag beetle, vert. 1k, Great water beetle. 1.60k, Alpine longicorn, vert. 2k, Ground beetle, vert.

1962, Dec. 15 Engr. *Perf. 14*

No.	Type	Description	Unused	Used
1144	A437	20h multicolored	.22	.15
1145	A437	30h multicolored	.22	.15
1146	A437	60h multicolored	.22	.15
1147	A437	1k multicolored	.65	.16
1148	A437	1.60k multicolored	1.00	.30
1149	A437	2k multicolored	2.25	1.25
		Nos. 1144-1149 (6)	4.56	
		Set value		1.90

Engraved and Photogravure

1963, Jan. *Perf. 11½*

Sports: 60h, Bicyclist. 80h, Skier. 1k, Motorcyclist. 1.20k, Weight lifter. 1.60k, Hurdler.

No.	Type	Description	Unused	Used
1150	A438	30h black & dp grn	.18	.15
1151	A438	60h black & orange	.18	.15
1152	A438	80h black & ultra	.18	.15
1153	A438	1k black & violet	.25	.15
1154	A438	1.20k black & pale brn	.30	.20
1155	A438	1.60k black & carmine	.40	.20
		Nos. 1150-1155 (6)	1.49	
		Set value		.68

Various 1963 sports events.

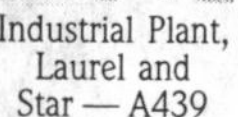

Industrial Plant, Laurel and Star — A439

Symbol of Child Welfare Home — A440

Industrial Plant and Symbol of Growth — A441

1963, Feb. 25 Unwmk. *Perf. 11½*

No.	Type	Description	Unused	Used
1156	A439	30h carmine & lt bl	.15	.15
1157	A440	60h black & car	.20	.15
1158	A441	60h black & red	.20	.15
		Nos. 1156-1158 (3)	.55	
		Set value		.15

15th anniv. of the "Victorious February" and 5th Trade Union Cong.

Artists' Guild Emblem — A442

Juraj Jánosik — A443

Eduard Urx — A444

National Theater, Prague — A445

Designs: No. 1163, Woman reading to children. No. 1164, Juraj Pálkovic. 1.60k, Max Svabinsky.

Engr. & Photo.; Engr. (A444)

1963, Mar. 25 Unwmk. *Perf. 11½*

No.	Type	Description	Unused	Used
1159	A442	20h black & Prus bl	.15	.15
1160	A443	30h car & lt bl	.15	.15
1161	A444	30h carmine	.15	.15
1162	A445	60h dl red brn & lt bl	.15	.15
1163	A444	60h green	.15	.15
1164	A444	60h black	.25	.15
1165	A444	1.60k brown	.52	.15
		Set value	1.25	.35

Various cultural personalities and events.

Boy and Girl with Flag A446

Television Transmitter A447

Engraved and Photogravure

1963, Apr. 18 *Perf. 11½*

No.	Type	Description	Unused	Used
1166	A446	30h slate & rose red	.20	.15

The 4th Congress of Czechoslovak Youth.

1963, Apr. 25

Design: 40h, Television camera, mast and set, horiz.

No.	Type	Description	Unused	Used
1167	A447	40h buff & slate	.20	.15
1168	A447	60h dk red & lt blue	.25	.15
		Set value		.15

Czechoslovak television, 10th anniversary.

Rocket to the Sun A448

Designs: 50h, Rockets and Sputniks leaving Earth. 60h, Spacecraft to and from Moon. 1k, 3k, Interplanetary station and Mars 1. 1.60k, Atomic rocket and Jupiter. 2k, Rocket returning from Saturn.

1963, Apr. 25

No.	Type	Description	Unused	Used
1169	A448	30h red brn & buff	.15	.15
1170	A448	50h slate & bluish grn	.20	.15
1171	A448	60h dk green & yel	.25	.15
1172	A448	1k dk gray & sal	.45	.15
1173	A448	1.60k gray brn & lt grn	.75	.20
1174	A448	2k dk purple & yel	2.50	.75
		Nos. 1169-1174 (6)	4.30	
		Set value		1.20

Souvenir Sheet

Imperf

No.	Type	Description	Unused	Used
1175	A448	3k Prus grn & org red	3.00	2.50

No. 1175 issued for 1st Space Research Exhib., Prague, Apr. 1963.

Studio and Radio A449

Design: 1k, Globe inscribed "Peace" and aerial mast, vert.

1963, May 18 Unwmk. *Perf. 11½*

No.	Type	Description	Unused	Used
1176	A449	30h choc & pale grn	.15	.15
1177	A449	1k bluish grn & lilac	.30	.15
		Set value		.15

40th anniversary of Czechoslovak radio.

Tupolev Tu-104B Turbojet A450

Design: 1.80k, Ilyushin Il-18 Moskva.

1963, May 25

No.	Type	Description	Unused	Used
1178	A450	80h violet & lt bl	.35	.15
1179	A450	1.80k dk blue & lt grn	.75	.15
		Set value		.15

40th anniversary of Czechoslovak airlines.

9th Cent. Ring, Map of Moravian Settlements — A451

Woman Singing — A452

Design: 1.60k, Falconer, 9th cent. silver disk.

1963, May 25

No.	Type	Description	Unused	Used
1180	A451	30h lt green & blk	.18	.15
1181	A451	1.60k dull yel & blk	.45	.15
		Set value		.15

1100th anniversary of Moravian empire.

1963, May 25 Engr.

No.	Type	Description	Unused	Used
1182	A452	30h bright red	.40	.15

60th anniversary of the founding of the Moravian Teachers' Singing Club.

Kromeriz Castle and Barley — A453

Centenary Emblem, Nurse and Playing Child — A454

Engraved and Photogravure

1963, June 20 Unwmk. *Perf. 11½*

No.	Type	Description	Unused	Used
1183	A453	30h slate grn & yel	.30	.15

Natl. Agricultural Exhib. and 700th anniv. of Kromeriz.

1963, June 20

No.	Type	Description	Unused	Used
1184	A454	30h dk gray & car	.40	.15

Centenary of the International Red Cross.

Bee, Honeycomb and Emblem — A455

Liberec Fair Emblem — A456

1963, June 20

No.	Type	Description	Unused	Used
1185	A455	1k brown & yellow	.40	.15

19th Intl. Beekeepers Cong., Apimondia, 1963.

1963, July 13

No.	Type	Description	Unused	Used
1186	A456	30h black & dp rose	.35	.15

Liberec Consumer Goods Fair.

Town Hall, Brno — A457

Cave, Moravian Karst — A458

Design: 60h, Town Hall tower, Brno.

1963, July 29

No.	Type	Description	Unused	Used
1187	A457	30h lt blue & maroon	.18	.15
1188	A457	60h pink & dk blue	.25	.15
		Set value		.15

International Trade Fair, Brno.

1963, July 29

Designs: No. 1190, Trout, Hornad Valley. 60h, Great Hawk Gorge. 80h, Macocha mountains.

No.	Type	Description	Unused	Used
1189	A458	30h brown & lt bl	.20	.15
1190	A458	30h dk bl & dull grn	.20	.15
1191	A458	60h green & blue	.20	.15
1192	A458	80h sepia & pink	.22	.15
		Nos. 1189-1192 (4)	.82	
		Set value		.30

Blast Furnace — A459

1963, Aug. 15 Unwmk. *Perf. 11½*

No.	Type	Description	Unused	Used
1193	A459	60h blk & bluish grn	.25	.15

30th Intl. Cong. of Iron Founders, Prague.

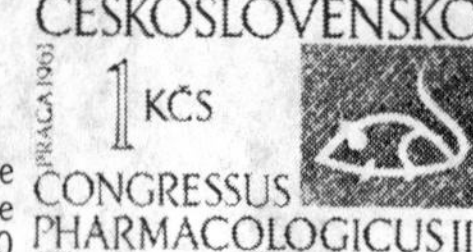

White Mouse A460

1963, Aug. 15

No.	Type	Description	Unused	Used
1194	A460	1k black & carmine	.40	.15

2nd Intl. Pharmacological Cong., Prague.

Farm Machinery for Underfed Nations — A461

Wooden Toys — A462

1963, Aug. 15 Engr.

No.	Type	Description	Unused	Used
1195	A461	1.60k black	.40	.15

FAO "Freedom from Hunger" campaign.

1963, Sept. 2 Engr. *Perf. 13½*

Folk Art (Inscribed "UNESCO"): 80h, Cock and flowers. 1k, Flowers in vase. 1.20k, Janosik, Slovak hero. 1.60k, Stag. 2k, Postilion.

No.	Type	Description	Unused	Used
1196	A462	60h red & vio bl	.25	.15
1197	A462	80h multi	.35	.20
1198	A462	1k multi	.45	.25
1199	A462	1.20k multi	.45	.18
1200	A462	1.60k multi	.45	.18
1201	A462	2k multi	2.50	1.00
		Nos. 1196-1201 (6)	4.45	1.96

Sheets of 10.

Canoeing — A463

Tree and Star — A464

Sports: 40h, Volleyball. 60h, Wrestling. 80h, Basketball. 1k, Boxing. 1.60k, Gymnastics.

Engraved and Photogravure

1963, Oct. 26 *Perf. 11½*

No.	Type	Description	Unused	Used
1202	A463	30h indigo & grn	.25	.15
1203	A463	40h red brn & lt bl	.25	.15
1204	A463	60h brn red & yel	.25	.15

1205 A463 80h dk pur & dp org .25 .15
1206 A463 1k ultra & dp rose .25 .15
1207 A463 1.60k vio bl & ultra 2.00 1.00
Nos. 1202-1207 (6) 3.25 1.75

1964 Olympic Games, Tokyo.

1963, Dec. 11 Unwmk. *Perf. 11½*

Design: 60h, Star, hammer and sickle.

1208 A464 30h bis brn & lt bl .15 .15
1209 A464 60h carmine & gray .20 .15
Set value .15

Russo-Czechoslovakian Treaty, 20th anniv.

Atom Diagrams Surrounding Head — A465

Chamois — A466

1963, Dec. 12 Engr.

1210 A465 60h dark purple .40 .15

3rd Congress of the Association for the Propagation of Scientific Knowledge.

1963, Dec. 14 *Perf. 14*

Animals: 40h, Alpine ibex. 60h, Mouflon. 1.20k, Roe deer. 1.60k, Fallow deer. 2k, Red deer.

1211 A466 30h multi .50 .25
1212 A466 40h multi .55 .35
1213 A466 60h brown, yel & grn .70 .30
1214 A466 1.20k multi .75 .25
1215 A466 1.60k multi 1.25 .35
1216 A466 2k multi 4.00 2.00
Nos. 1211-1216 (6) 7.75 3.50

Figure Skating — A467

Ice Hockey — A468

Designs: 80h, Skiing, horiz. 1k, Field ball player.

Engraved and Photogravure

1964, Jan. 20 Unwmk. *Perf. 11½*

1217 A467 30h violet bl & yel .15 .15
1218 A467 80h dk blue & org .15 .15
1219 A467 1k brown & lilac .35 .15
Nos. 1217-1219 (3) .65
Set value .25

Intl. University Games (30h, 80h) and the World Field Ball Championships (1k).

1964, Jan. 20

1220 A468 1k shown .85 .35
1221 A468 1.80k Toboggan 1.00 .60
1222 A468 2k Ski jump 2.50 2.25
Nos. 1220-1222 (3) 4.35 3.20

9th Winter Olympic Games, Innsbruck, Jan. 29-Feb. 9, 1964.

Magura Rest Home, High Tatra — A469

Design: 80h, Slovak National Insurrection Rest Home, Low Tatra.

1964, Feb. 19 Unwmk. *Perf. 11½*

1223 A469 60h green & yellow .20 .15
1224 A469 80h violet bl & pink .20 .15
Set value .15

Skiers and Ski Lift A470

Designs: 60h, Automobile camp, Telc. 1k, Fishing, Spis Castle. 1.80k, Lake and boats, Cesky Krumlov.

1964, Feb. 19 Engr. & Photo.

1225 A470 30h dk vio brn & bl .15 .15
1226 A470 60h slate & car .25 .15
1227 A470 1k brown & olive .40 .15
1228 A470 1.80k slate grn & org .65 .25
Nos. 1225-1228 (4) 1.45
Set value .45

Moses, Day and Night by Michelangelo — A471

Designs: 60th, "A Midsummer Night's Dream," by Shakespeare. 1k, Man, telescope and heaven, vert. 1.60k, King George of Podebrad (1420-71).

1964, Mar. 20

1229 A471 40h black & yel grn .20 .15
1230 A471 60h slate & car .20 .15
1231 A471 1k black & lt blue .35 .15
1232 A471 1.60k black & yellow .45 .15
a. Souvenir sheet of 4 ('88) 2.00 2.00
Nos. 1229-1232 (4) 1.20
Set value .35

400th anniv. of the death of Michelangelo (40h); 400th anniv. of the birth of Shakespeare (60h); 400th anniv. of the birth of Galileo (1k); 500th anniv. of the pacifist efforts of King George of Podebrad (1.60k).

No. 1232a for PRAGA '88.

Yuri A. Gagarin — A472

Astronauts: 60h, Gherman Titov. 80h, John H. Glenn, Jr. 1k, Scott M. Carpenter, vert. 1.20k, Pavel R. Popovich and Andrian G. Nikolayev. 1.40k, Walter M. Schirra, vert. 1.60k, Gordon L. Cooper, vert. 2k, Valentina Tereshkova and Valeri Bykovski, vert.

1964, Apr. 27 Unwmk. *Perf. 11½*

Yellow Paper

1233 A472 30h black & vio bl .50 .25
1234 A472 60h dk grn & dk car .25 .15
1235 A472 80h dk car & vio .50 .20
1236 A472 1k ultra & rose vio .25 .25
1237 A472 1.20k ver & ol gray .50 .35
1238 A472 1.40k black & dl grn 1.25 .50
1239 A472 1.60k pale pur & Prus grn 3.00 1.50
1240 A472 2k dk blue & red 1.00 .40
Nos. 1233-1240 (8) 7.25 3.60

World's first 10 astronauts.

Creeping Bellflower A473

Film "Flower" and Karlovy Vary Colonnade A474

Flowers: 80h, Musk thistle. 1k, Chicory. 1.20k, Yellow iris. 1.60k, Gentian. 2k, Corn poppy.

1964, June 15 Engr. *Perf. 14*

1241 A473 60h dk grn, lil & org 1.25 .25
1242 A473 80h blk, grn & red lil 1.25 .25
1243 A473 1k vio bl, grn & pink 1.25 .45
1244 A473 1.20k black, yel & grn 1.25 .30
1245 A473 1.60k violet & grn 1.25 .40
1246 A473 2k vio, red & grn 4.50 2.00
Nos. 1241-1246 (6) 10.75 3.65

Engraved and Photogravure

1964, June 20 Unwmk. *Perf. 13½*

1247 A474 60h black, blue & car 1.25 .15

14th Intl. Film Festival at Karlovy Vary, July 4-19.

Silesian Coat of Arms — A475

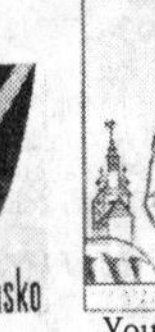

Young Miner of 1764 — A476

1964, June 20 *Perf. 11½*

1248 A475 30h black & yel .25 .15

150th anniv. of the Silesian Museum, Opava.

1964, June 20

1249 A476 60h sepia & lt grn .25 .15

Mining School at Banska Stiavnica, bicent.

Skoda Fire Engine A477

1964, June 20

1250 A477 60h car rose & lt bl .35 .15

Voluntary fire brigades in Bohemia, cent.

Gulls, Hradcany Castle, Red Cross — A478

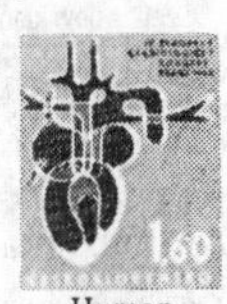

Human Heart — A479

1964, July 10

1251 A478 60h car & bluish gray .35 .15

4th Czechoslovak Red Cross Congress at Prague.

1964, July 10

1252 A479 1.60k ultra & car .60 .15

4th European Cardiological Cong. at Prague.

Partisans, Girl and Factories — A480

Battle Scene, 1944 — A481

Design: 60h, Partisans and flame.

Engraved and Photogravure

1964, Aug. 17 Unwmk. *Perf. 11½*

1253 A480 30h brown & red .15 .15
1254 A480 60h dk blue & red .20 .15
1255 A481 60h black & red .20 .15
Nos. 1253-1255 (3) .55
Set value .15

20th anniv. of the Slovak Natl. Uprising; No. 1255, 20th anniv. of the Battles of Dukla Pass.

Hradcany at Prague — A482

Discus Thrower and Pole Vaulter — A483

Design: 5k, Charles Bridge and Hradcany.

1964, Aug. 30 *Perf. 11½x12*

1256 A482 60h black & red .48 .15

Souvenir Sheet

Engr. *Imperf.*

1257 A482 5k deep claret 1.90 1.50

Millenium of the Hradcany, Prague.
No. 1257 stamp size: 30x50mm.

Engraved and Photogravure

1964, Sept. 2 *Perf. 13½*

Designs: 60h, Bicycling, horiz. 1k, Soccer. 1.20k, Rowing. 1.60k, Swimming, horiz. 2.80k, Weight lifting, horiz.

1258 A483 60h multi .35 .25
1259 A483 80h multi .50 .25
1260 A483 1k multi .50 .25
1261 A483 1.20k multi .60 .30
1262 A483 1.60k multi .75 .35
1263 A483 2.80k multi 4.00 2.00
Nos. 1258-1263 (6) 6.70 3.40

Issued to commemorate the 18th Olympic Games, Tokyo, Oct. 10-25. Sheets of 10.

Miniature Sheet

Space Ship Voskhod I, Astronauts and Globe — A484

1964, Nov. 12 Unwmk. *Perf. 11½*

1264 A484 3k dk bl & dl lil, *buff* 4.50 3.50

Russian 3-man space flight of Vladimir M. Komarov, Boris B. Yegorov and Konstantin Feoktistov, Oct. 12-13.

Steam Engine and Atomic Power Plant — A485

Diesel Engine "CKD Praha" — A486

1964, Nov. 16 Engr.

1265 A485 30h dull red brown .15 .15

Engraved and Photogravure

1266 A486 60h green & salmon .20 .15
Set value .25 .15

Traditions and development of engineering; No. 1265 for 150th anniv. of the First Brno Engineering Works, No. 1266 for the engineering concern CKD Praha.

European Redstart — A487

Birds: 60h, Green woodpecker. 80h, Hawfinch. 1k, Black woodpecker. 1.20k, European robin. 1.60k, European roller.

1964, Nov. 16 Litho. *Perf. 10½*

1267 A487	30h multicolored	.15	.15
1268 A487	60h black & multi	.25	.15
1269 A487	80h multicolored	.50	.15
1270 A487	1k multicolored	.50	.25
1271 A487	1.20k lt vio bl & blk	.35	.25
1272 A487	1.60k yellow & blk	1.25	.60
	Nos. 1267-1272 (6)	3.00	
	Set value		1.30

Dancer A488

"In the Sun" Pre-school Children A489

Designs: 60h, "Over the Obstacles," teenagers. 1k, "Movement and Beauty," woman flag twirler. 1.60k, Runners at start.

Engraved and Photogravure

1965 Unwmk. *Perf. 11½*

1273 A488	30h red & lt blue	.15	.15

Perf. 11½x12

1274 A489	30h vio bl & car	.15	.15
1275 A489	60h brown & ultra	.20	.15
1276 A489	1k black & yellow	.25	.15
1277 A489	1.60k maroon & gray	.60	.24
	Nos. 1273-1277 (5)	1.35	
	Set value		.50

3rd Natl. Spartacist Games. Issue dates: No. 1273, Jan. 3. Nos. 1274-1277, May 24.

Mountain Rescue Service — A490

Arms and View, Beroun — A491

Designs: No. 1279, Woman gymnast. No. 1280, Bicyclists. No. 1281, Women hurdlers.

1965, Jan. 15 Unwmk. *Perf. 11½*

1278 A490	60h violet & blue	.22	.15
1279 A490	60h maroon & ocher	.22	.15
1280 A490	60h black & carmine	.22	.15
1281 A490	60h green & yellow	.22	.15
	Nos. 1278-1281 (4)	.88	
	Set value		.20

Mountain Rescue Service (#1278); 1st World Championship in Artistic Gymnastics, Prague, Dec. 1965 (#1279); World Championship in Indoor Bicycling, Prague, Oct. 1965 (#1280); "Universiada 1965," Brno (#1281).

1965, Feb. 15

Designs: No. 1283, Town Square, Domazlice. No. 1284, Old and new buildings, Frydek-Mystek. No. 1285, Arms and view, Lipnik. No. 1286, Fortified wall, City Hall and Arms, Policka. No. 1287, View and hops, Zatek. No. 1288, Small fortress and rose, Terezin.

1282 A491	30h vio bl & lt bl	.15	.15
1283 A491	30h dull pur & yel	.15	.15
1284 A491	30h slate & gray	.15	.15
1285 A491	30h green & bis	.15	.15
1286 A491	30h brown & tan	.15	.15
1287 A491	30h dk blue & cit	.15	.15
1288 A491	30h black & rose	.15	.15
	Nos. 1282-1288 (7)	1.05	
	Set value		.35

Nos. 1282-1287 for 700th anniv. of the founding of various Bohemian towns; No. 1288 the 20th anniv. of the liberation of the Theresienstadt (Terezin) concentration camp.

Sun's Corona A492

Space Research: 30h, Sun. 60h, Exploration of the Moon. 1k, Twin space craft, vert. 1.40k, Space station. 1.60k, Exploration of Mars, vert. 2k, USSR and US Meteorological collaboration.

Perf. 12x11½, 11½x12

1965, Mar. 15

1289 A492	20h rose & red lilac	.25	.15
1290 A492	30h rose red & yel	.25	.15
1291 A492	60h bluish blk & yel	.25	.15
1292 A492	1k purple & pale blue	.50	.15
1293 A492	1.40k black & salmon	.50	.20
1294 A492	1.60k black & pink	.50	.20
1295 A492	2k bluish blk & lt bl	*1.50*	*1.00*
	Nos. 1289-1295 (7)	*3.75*	
	Set value		*1.75*

Space research; Nos. 1289-1290 also for the Intl. Quiet Sun Year, 1964-65.

Frantisek Ventura, Equestrian; Amsterdam, 1928 — A493

Czechoslovakian Olympic Victories: 30h, Discus, Paris, 1900. 60h, Running, Helsinki, 1952. 1k, Weight lifting, Los Angeles, 1932. 1.40k, Gymnastics, Berlin, 1936. 1.60k, Double sculling, Rome, 1960. 2k, Women's gymnastics, Tokyo, 1964.

1965, Apr. 16 *Perf. 11½x12*

1296 A493	20h choc & gold	.22	.15
1297 A493	30h indigo & emer	.22	.15
1298 A493	60h ultra & gold	.22	.15
1299 A493	1k red brn & gold	.35	.22
1300 A493	1.40k dk sl grn & gold	.75	.60
1301 A493	1.60k black & gold	.80	.60
1302 A493	2k maroon & gold	1.10	.45
	Nos. 1296-1302 (7)	3.66	2.32

Astronauts Virgil Grissom and John Young — A494

Designs: No. 1304, Alexei Leonov floating in space. No. 1305, Launching pad at Cape Kennedy. No. 1306, Leonov leaving space ship.

1965, Apr. 17 *Perf. 11x11½*

1303 A494	60h slate bl & lil rose	.25	.15
1304 A494	60h vio blk & blue	.25	.15
1305 A494	3k slate bl & lil rose	1.50	1.00
1306 A494	3k vio blk & blue	1.50	1.00
	Nos. 1303-1306 (4)	3.50	2.30

Issued to honor American and Soviet astronauts. Printed in sheets of 25; one sheet contains 20 No. 1303 and 5 No. 1305, the other sheet contains 20 No. 1304 and 5 No. 1306.

Russian Soldier, View of Prague and Guerrilla Fighters A495

Designs: No. 1308, Blast furnace, workers and tank. 60h, Worker and factory. 1k, Worker and new constructions. 1.60k, Woman farmer, new farm buildings and machinery.

1965, May 5 Engr. *Perf. 13½*

1307 A495	30h dk red, blk & ol	.15	.15
1308 A495	30h multicolored	.15	.15
1309 A495	60h vio bl, red & blk	.24	.15
1310 A495	1k dp org, blk & brn	.38	.15
1311 A495	1.60k yellow, red & blk	.70	.20
	Nos. 1307-1311 (5)	1.62	
	Set value		.46

20th anniv. of liberation from the Nazis.

Slovakian Kopov Dog A496

Dogs: 40h, German shepherd. 60h, Czech hunting dog with pheasant. 1k, Poodle. 1.60k, Czech terrier. 2k, Afghan hound.

1965, June 10 *Perf. 12x11½*

1312 A496	30h black & red org	.35	.15
1313 A496	40h black & yellow	.35	.15
1314 A496	60h black & ver	.25	.15
1315 A496	1k black & dk car rose	.80	.15
1316 A496	1.60k black & orange	.50	.25
1317 A496	2k black & orange	1.50	.65
	Nos. 1312-1317 (6)	3.75	
	Set value		1.25

World Dog Show at Brno and the International Dog Breeders Congress, Prague.

UN Headquarters Building, NY — A497

Designs: 60h, UN Emblem and inscription. 1.60k, ICY emblem.

1965, June 24 *Perf. 12x11½*

1318 A497	60h dk red brn & yel	.18	.15
1319 A497	1k ultra & lt blue	.35	.15
1320 A497	1.60k gold & dk red	.50	.35
	Nos. 1318-1320 (3)	1.03	
	Set value		.45

20th anniv. of the UN and the ICY, 1965.

Trade Union Emblem A498

1965, June 24 Engr.

1321 A498	60h dk red & ultra	.25	.15

20th anniv. of the Intl. Trade Union Federation.

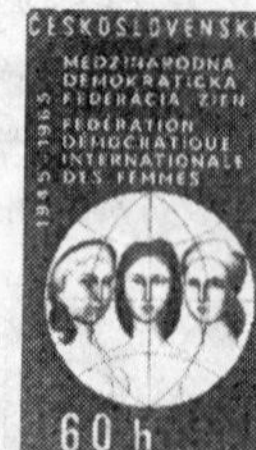

Women and Globe — A499

1965, June 24 *Perf. 11½x12*

1322 A499	60h violet blue	.25	.15

20th anniv. of the Intl. Women's Federation.

Children's House (Burgraves' Palace), Hradcany — A500

Matthias Tower — A501

1965, June 25 *Perf. 11½*

1323 A500	30h slate green	.20	.15
1324 A501	60h dark brown	.25	.15
	Set value		.15

Issued to publicize the Hradcany, Prague.

Marx and Lenin — A502

1965, July 1 Engr. & Photo.

1325 A502	60h car rose & gold	.20	.15

6th conf. of Postal Ministers of Communist Countries, Peking, June 21-July 15.

Joseph Navratil — A503

Jan Hus — A504

Gregor Johann Mendel A505

Costume Jewelry A506

Bohuslav Martinu A507

Seated Woman and University of Bratislava A508

ITU Emblem and Communication Symbols — A509

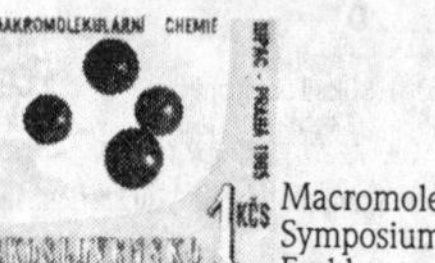

Macromolecular Symposium Emblem — A510

Design: No. 1327, Ludovit Stur (diff. frame).

1965 Unwmk. *Perf. 11½*

1326 A503	30h black & fawn	.15	.15
1327 A503	30h black & dull grn	.15	.15
1328 A504	60h black & crimson	.20	.15
1329 A505	60h vio bl & red	.20	.15
1330 A506	60h purple & gold	.20	.15
1331 A507	60h black & orange	.20	.15
1332 A508	60h brn, *yel*	.20	.15
1333 A509	1k orange & blue	.35	.15
1334 A510	1k black & dp org	.35	.15
	Nos. 1326-1334 (9)	2.00	
	Set value		.45

No. 1326, Navratil (1798-1865), painter; No. 1327, Stur (1815-56), Slovak author and historian;

No. 1328, the 550th anniv. of the death of Hus, religious reformer;
No. 1329, cent. of publication of Mendel's laws of inheritance; No. 1330 publicizes the "Jablonec 1965" costume jewelry exhib.; No. 1331, Martinu (1890-1959), composer; No. 1332, 500th anniv. of the founding of the University of Bratislava as Academia Istropolitana; No. 1333, cent. of the ITU; No. 1334, Intl. Symposium on Macromolecular Chemistry, Prague, Sept. 1-8.

"Young Woman at her Toilette," by Titian — A512

Help for Flood Victims — A513

Rescue of Flood Victims A514

Miniature Sheet

1965, Aug. 12

1336 A512	5k multicolored	3.75	2.00

Hradcany Art Gallery. #1336 contains one stamp.

1965, Sept. 6 **Engr.**

1337 A513	30h violet blue	.15	.15

Engraved and Photogravure

1338 A514	2k dk ol grn & ol	.65	.45

Help for Danube flood victims in Slovakia.

Dotterel A515

Mountain Birds: 60h, Wall creeper, vert. 1.20k, Lesser redpoll. 1.40k, Golden eagle, vert. 1.60k, Ring ouzel. 2k, Eurasian nutcracker, vert.

1965, Sept. 20 **Litho.** ***Perf. 11***

1339 A515	30h	multi	.24	.15
1340 A515	60h	multi	.24	.15
1341 A515	1.20k	multi	.32	.15
1342 A515	1.40k	multi	.75	.25
1343 A515	1.60k	multi	.60	.30
1344 A515	2k	multi	1.40	1.25
		Nos. 1339-1344 (6)	3.55	2.25

Levoca — A516

Medicinal Plants — A517

Views of Towns: 10h, Jindrichuv Hradec. 20h, Nitra. 30h, Kosice. 40h, Hradec Králové. 50h, Telc. 60h, Ostrava. 1k, Olomouc. 1.20k, Ceske Budejovice. 1.60k, Cheb. 2k, Brno. 3k, Bratislava. 5k, Prague.

Engraved and Photogravure

1965-66 ***Perf. 11½x12***

Size: 23x19mm

1345	A516	5h	black & yel	.15	.15
1346	A516	10h	ultra & ol bis	.15	.15
1347	A516	20h	black & lt bl	.15	.15
1348	A516	30h	vio bl & lt grn	.15	.15
1348A	A516	40h	dk brn & lt bl ('66)	.15	.15
1348B	A516	50h	black & ocher ('66)	.16	.15
1348C	A516	60h	red & gray ('66)	.22	.15
1348D	A516	1k	pur & pale grn ('66)	.30	.15

Perf. 11½x11

Size: 30x23mm

1349	A516	1.20k	slate & lt bl	.35	.15
1350	A516	1.60k	indigo & yel	.45	.15
1351	A516	2k	sl grn & pale yel	.55	.15
1352	A516	3k	brown & yellow	.75	.15
1353	A516	5k	black & pink	1.25	.15
			Nos. 1345-1353 (13)	4.78	
			Set value		.82

1965, Dec. 3 **Engr.** ***Perf. 14***

1354 A517	30h	Coltsfoot	.20	.15
1355 A517	60h	Meadow saffron	.25	.15
1356 A517	80h	Corn poppy	.35	.15
1357 A517	1k	Foxglove	.60	.20
1358 A517	1.20k	Arnica	.50	.25
1359 A517	1.60k	Cornflower	.75	.40
1360 A517	2k	Dog rose	*3.75*	*1.50*
		Nos. 1354-1360 (7)	*6.40*	*2.80*

Strip of "Stamps" — A518

Engraved and Photogravure

1965, Dec. 18 ***Perf. 11½***

1361 A518	1k dark red & gold	2.75	2.25

Issued for Stamp Day, 1965.

Romain Rolland (1866-1944), French Writer — A519

Symbolic Musical Instruments & Names of Composers — A520

Portraits: No. 1362, Stanislav Sucharda (1866-1916), sculptor. No. 1363, Ignac Josef Pesina (1766-1808), veterinarian. No. 1365, Donatello (1386-1466), Italian sculptor.

1966, Feb. 14 **Engr.** ***Perf. 11½***

1362 A519	30h deep green	.15	.15
1363 A519	30h violet blue	.15	.15
1364 A519	60h rose lake	.20	.15
1365 A519	60h brown	.20	.15
	Nos. 1362-1365 (4)	.70	
	Set value		.20

1966, Jan. 15 **Engr. & Photo.**

1366 A520	30h black & gold	.30	.20

Czech Philharmonic Orchestra, 70th anniv.

Figure Skating Pair A521

Designs: No. 1368, Man skater. No. 1369, Volleyball player, spiking, vert. 1k, Volleyball player, saving, vert. 1.60k, Woman skater. 2k, Figure skating pair.

1966, Feb. 17

1367 A521	30h	dk car rose	.15	.15
1368 A521	60h	green	.20	.15
1369 A521	60h	carmine & buff	.20	.15
1370 A521	1k	vio & lt bl	.30	.15
1371 A521	1.60k	brown & yellow	.40	.15
1372 A521	2k	blue & grnsh bl	*2.00*	*.40*
		Nos. 1367-1372 (6)	3.25	
		Set value		*.75*

#1367-1368, 1371-1372 for the European Figure Skating Championships, Bratislava; #1369-1370 for the World Volleyball Championships.

Souvenir Sheet

Girl Dancing — A522

1966, Mar. 21 **Engr.** ***Imperf.***

1373 A522	3k slate bl, red & bl	1.75	1.50

Cent. of the opera "The Bartered Bride" by Bedrich Smetana.

"Ajax" 1841 A523

Locomotives: 30h, "Karlstejn" 1865. 60h, Steam engine, 1946. 1k, Steam engine with tender, 1946. 1.60k, Electric locomotive, 1964. 2k, Diesel locomotive, 1964.

1966, Mar. 21 ***Perf. 11½x11***

Buff Paper

1374 A523	20h	sepia	.30	.15
1375 A523	30h	dull violet	.30	.15
1376 A523	60h	dull purple	.30	.15
1377 A523	1k	dark blue	.50	.15
1378 A523	1.60k	dk blue grn	.60	.20
1379 A523	2k	dark red	*3.00*	*.90*
		Nos. 1374-1379 (6)	*5.00*	
		Set value		*1.45*

European Perch A524

Fish: 30h, Brown trout, vert. 1k, Carp. 1.20k, Northern pike. 1.40k, Grayling. 1.60k, Eel.

Perf. 13x13½, 13½x13

1966, Apr. 22 **Litho.** **Unwmk.**

1380 A524	30h	multi	.25	.15
1381 A524	60h	multi	.35	.15
1382 A524	1k	multi	.50	.15
1383 A524	1.20k	multi	.50	.20
1384 A524	1.40k	multi	.85	.25
1385 A524	1.60k	multi	*2.75*	*1.10*
		Nos. 1380-1385 (6)	*5.20*	*2.00*

Intl. Fishing Championships, Svit, Sept. 3-5.

WHO Headquarters, Geneva — A525

Engraved and Photogravure

1966, Apr. 25 ***Perf. 12x11½***

1386 A525	1k dk blue & lt blue	.40	.15

Opening of the WHO Headquarters, Geneva.

Symbolic Handshake and UNESCO Emblem — A526

1966, Apr. 25 ***Perf. 11½***

1387 A526	60h bister & olive gray	.15	.15

20th anniv. of UNESCO.

Prague Castle Issue

Belvedere Palace and St. Vitus' Cathedral — A527

Crown of St. Wenceslas, 1346 — A528

Design: 60h, Madonna, altarpiece from St. George's Church.

1966, May 9 **Engr.** ***Perf. 11½***

1388 A527	30h dark blue	.20	.15

Engraved and Photogravure

1389 A527	60h blk & yel bis	.50	.15
	Set value		.25

Souvenir Sheet

Engr.

1390 A528	5k multi	2.75	2.50

See Nos. 1537-1539.

Tiger Swallowtail A529

Butterflies and Moths: 60h, Clouded sulphur. 80h, European purple emperor. 1k, Apollo. 1.20k, Burnet moth. 2k, Tiger moth.

1966, May 23 **Engr.** ***Perf. 14***

1391 A529	30h	multi	.22	.15
1392 A529	60h	multi	.45	.15
1393 A529	80h	multi	.45	.15
1394 A529	1k	multi	.45	.20
1395 A529	1.20k	multi	.90	.25
1396 A529	2k	multi	*2.25*	*1.25*
		Nos. 1391-1396 (6)	*4.72*	*2.15*

Sheets of ten.

Flags of Russia and Czechoslovakia — A530

Designs: 60h, Rays surrounding hammer and sickle "sun." 1.60k, Girl's head and stars.

Engraved and Photogravure

1966, May 31 *Perf. 11½*

1397 A530	30h dk bl & crim	.15	.15
1398 A530	60h dk bl & red	.20	.15
1399 A530	1.60k red & dk bl	.50	.15
	Nos. 1397-1399 (3)	.85	
	Set value		.18

13th Congress of the Communist Party of Czechoslovakia.

Dakota Chief — A531

Designs: 20h, Indians, canoe and tepee, horiz. 30h, Tomahawk. 40h, Haida totem poles. 60h, Kachina, good spirit of the Hopis. 1k, Indian on horseback hunting buffalo, horiz. 1.20k, Calumet, Dakota peace pipe.

1966, June 20

Size: 23x40mm

1400 A531	20h vio bl & dp org	.18	.15
1401 A531	30h blk & dl org	.18	.15
1402 A531	40h blk & lt bl	.18	.15
1403 A531	60h grn & yel	.22	.15
1404 A531	1k pur & emer	.22	.15
1405 A531	1.20k vio bl & rose lil	.35	.28

Perf. 14

Engr.

Size: 23x37mm

1406 A531	1.40k multi	*1.65*	*.90*
	Nos. 1400-1406 (7)	*2.98*	
	Set value		*1.50*

Cent. of the Náprstek Ethnographic Museum, Prague, and "The Indians of North America" exhibition.

Model of Molecule — A532

Engraved and Photogravure

1966, July 4 Unwmk. *Perf. 11½*

1407 A532	60h blk & lt bl	.20	.15

Czechoslovak Chemical Society, cent.

"Guernica" by Pablo Picasso — A533

1966, July 5

Size: 75x30mm

1408 A533	60h blk & pale bl	1.25	1.25

30th anniversary of International Brigade in Spanish Civil War.

Sheets of 15 stamps and 5 labels inscribed "Picasso-Guernica 1937."

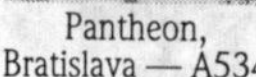

Pantheon, Bratislava — A534

Atom Symbol and Sun — A535

Designs: No. 1410, Devin Castle and Ludovit Stur. No. 1411, View of Nachod. No. 1412, State Science Library, Olomouc.

1966, July 25 **Engr.**

1409 A534	30h dl pur	.16	.15
1410 A534	60h dk bl	.22	.15
1411 A534	60h green	.22	.15
1412 A534	60h sepia	.22	.15
	Nos. 1409-1412 (4)	.82	
	Set value		.20

No. 1409, Russian War Memorial, Bratislava; No. 1410, the 9th cent. Devin Castle as symbol of Slovak nationalism; No. 1411, 700th anniv. of the founding of Nachod; No. 1412, the 400th anniv. of the State Science Library, Olomouc.

Engraved and Photogravure

1966, Aug. 29 *Perf. 11½*

1413 A535	60h blk & red	.20	.15

Issued to publicize Jachymov (Joachimsthal), where pitchblende was first discovered, "cradle of the atomic age."

Brno Fair Emblem — A536

Olympia Coin and Olympic Rings — A537

1966, Aug. 29

1414 A536	60h blk & red	.20	.15

8th International Trade Fair, Brno.

1966, Aug. 29

Design: 1k, Olympic flame, Czechoslovak flag and Olympic rings.

1415 A537	60h blk & gold	.18	.15
1416 A537	1k dk bl & red	.50	.30
	Set value		.35

70th anniv. of the Olympic Committee.

Missile Carrier, Tank and Jet Plane A538

1966, Aug. 31

1417 A538	60h blk & apple grn	.30	.15

Issued to commemorate the maneuvers of the armies of the Warsaw Pact countries.

Mercury A539

Designs: 30h, Moravian silver thaler, 1620, reverse and obverse, vert. 1.60k, Old and new buildings of Brno State Theater. 5k, International Trade Fair Administration Tower and postmark, vert.

1966, Sept. 10

1418 A539	30h dk red & blk	.25	.15
1419 A539	60h org & blk	.25	.15
1420 A539	1.60k blk & brt grn	.75	.25
	Nos. 1418-1420 (3)	1.25	
	Set value		.38

Souvenir Sheet

1421 A539	5k multi	2.50	2.50

Brno Philatelic Exhibition, Sept. 11-25. No. 1421 contains one 30x40mm stamp.

First Meeting in Orbit — A540

Designs: 30h, Photograph of far side of Moon and Russian satellite. 60h, Photograph of Mars and Mariner 4. 80th, Soft landing on Moon. 1k, Satellite, laser beam and binary code. 1.20k, Telstar over Earth and receiving station.

1966, Sept. 26 *Perf. 11½*

1422 A540	20h vio & lt grn	.15	.15
1423 A540	30h blk & sal pink	.15	.15
1424 A540	60h slate & lilac	.25	.15
1425 A540	80h dk pur & lt bl	.25	.15
1426 A540	1k blk & vio	.30	.15
1427 A540	1.20k red & bl	*1.65*	*.45*
	Nos. 1422-1427 (6)	*2.75*	
	Set value		*.95*

Issued to publicize American and Russian achievements in space research.

Badger A541

Game Animals: 40h, Red deer, vert. 60h, Lynx. 80h, Hare. 1k, Red fox. 1.20k, Brown bear, vert. 2k, Wild boar.

1966, Nov. 28 Litho. *Perf. 13½*

1428 A541	30h multi	.18	.15
1429 A541	40h multi	.20	.15
1430 A541	60h multi	.25	.15
1431 A541	80h multi *(europaens)*	.35	.15
a.	80h multi *(europaeus)*	4.75	3.50
1432 A541	1k multi	.45	.20
1433 A541	1.20k multi	.45	.25
1434 A541	2k multi	*2.75*	*1.50*
	Nos. 1428-1434 (7)	*4.63*	*2.55*

The sheet of 50 of the 80h contains 40 with misspelling "europaens" and 10 with "europaeus."

"Spring" by Vaclav Hollar, 1607-77 A542

Paintings: No. 1436, Portrait of Mrs. F. Wussin, by Jan Kupecky (1667-1740). No. 1437, Snow Owl by Karel Purkyne (1834-1868). No. 1438, Tulips by Vaclav Spála (1885-1964). No. 1439, Recruit by Ludovít Fulla (1902-1980).

1966, Dec. 8 Engr. *Perf. 14*

1435 A542	1k black	4.50	4.25
1436 A542	1k multicolored	2.75	2.25
1437 A542	1k multicolored	2.75	2.25
1438 A542	1k multicolored	2.75	2.25
1439 A542	1k multicolored	*22.50*	*19.00*
	Nos. 1435-1439 (5)	*35.25*	*30.00*

Printed in sheets of 4 stamps and 2 labels. The labels in sheet of No. 1435 are inscribed "Vaclav Hollar 1607-1677" in fancy frame. Other labels are blank.

See No. 1484.

Symbolic Bird — A543

Engraved and Photogravure

1966, Dec. 17 *Perf. 11½*

1440 A543	1k dp blue & yel	.65	.65

Issued for Stamp Day.

Youth — A544

1967, Jan. 16 *Perf. 11½*

1441 A544	30h ver & lt bl	.18	.15

5th Cong. of the Czechoslovak Youth Org.

Symbolic Flower and Machinery A545

1967, Jan. 16

1442 A545	30h carmine & yel	.18	.15

6th Trade Union Congress, Prague.

Parents with Dead Child — A545a

1967, Jan. 16 *Perf. 11½*

1442A A545a	60h black & salmon	.25	.15

"Peace and Freedom in Viet Nam."

View of Jihlava and Tourist Year Emblem A546

Views and Tourist Year Emblem: 40h, Spielberg Castle and churches, Brno. 1.20k, Danube, castle and churches, Bratislava. 1.60k, Vlatava River bridges, Hradcany and churches, Prague.

1967, Feb. 13 Engr. *Perf. 11½*

Size: 40x23mm

1443 A546	30h brown violet	.15	.15
1444 A546	40h maroon	.15	.15

Size: 75x30mm

1445 A546	1.20k violet blue	.40	.16
1446 A546	1.60k black	*1.10*	*.50*
	Nos. 1443-1446 (4)	1.80	
	Set value		*.76*

International Tourist Year, 1967.

Black-tailed Godwit — A547

Birds: 40h, Shoveler, horiz. 60h, Purple heron. 80h, Penduline tit. 1k, Avocet. 1.40k, Black stork. 1.60k, Tufted duck, horiz.

1967, Feb. 20 Litho. *Perf. 13½*

1447 A547	30h multi	.15	.15
1448 A547	40h multi	.24	.15
1449 A547	60h multi	.24	.15
1450 A547	80h multi	.50	.15
1451 A547	1k multi	.50	.20
1452 A547	1.40k multi	.32	.20
1453 A547	1.60k multi	*2.50*	*1.00*
	Nos. 1447-1453 (7)	*4.45*	
	Set value		*1.80*

Solar Research and Satellite — A548

Space Research: 40h, Space craft, rocket and construction of station. 60h, Man on moon and orientation system. 1k, Exploration of solar system and rocket. 1.20k, Lunar satellites and moon photograph. 1.60k, Planned lunar architecture and moon landing.

Engraved and Photogravure

1967, Mar. 24 *Perf. 11½*

1454 A548	30h	yel & dk red	.15	.15
1455 A548	40h	vio bl & blk	.15	.15
1456 A548	60h	lilac & grn	.15	.15
1457 A548	1k	brt pink & sl	.18	.15
1458 A548	1.20k	lt violet & blk	.30	.18
1459 A548	1.60k	brn lake & blk	*1.10*	*.60*
		Nos. 1454-1459 (6)	*2.03*	
		Set value		*1.00*

Gothic Painting, by Master Theodoric A549

Designs: 40h, "Burning of Master Hus," from Litomerice Hymnal. 60h, Modern glass sculpture. 80h, "The Shepherdess and the Chimney Sweep," Andersen fairy tale, painting by J. Trnka. 1k, Section of pressure vessel from atomic power station. 1.20k, Three ceramic figurines, by P. Rada. 3k, Montreal skyline and EXPO '67 emblem.

1967, Apr. 10 **Engr.** *Perf. 14*

Size: 37x23mm

1460 A549	30h	multi	.15	.15
1461 A549	40h	multi	.15	.15
1462 A549	60h	multi	.16	.15
1463 A549	80h	multi	.22	.15
1464 A549	1k	multi	.25	.22
1465 A549	1.20k	multi	*1.10*	*.60*
		Nos. 1460-1465 (6)	*2.03*	*1.42*

Souvenir Sheet

Perf. 11½

Size: 40x30mm

1466 A549	3k	multi	1.75	1.50

EXPO '67, International Exhibition, Montreal, Apr. 28-Oct. 27, 1967.

Canoe Race A550

Women Playing Basketball — A551

Designs: No. 1468, Wheels, dove and emblems of Warsaw, Berlin, Prague. 1.60k, Canoe slalom.

Perf. 12x11½, 11½x12

1967, Apr. 17 **Engr. & Photo.**

1467 A550	60h	black & brt bl	.20	.15
1468 A550	60h	black & salmon	.20	.15
1469 A551	60h	black & grnsh bl	.20	.15
1470 A551	1.60k	black & brt vio	*1.25*	*.50*
		Nos. 1467-1470 (4)	*1.85*	
		Set value		*.68*

No. 1467, 5th Intl. Wild-Water Canoeing Championships; No. 1468, 20th Warsaw-Berlin-Prague Bicycle Race; No. 1469, Women's Basketball Championships; No. 1470, 10th Intl. Water Slalom Championships.

"Golden Street" — A552

Designs: 60h, Interior of Hall of King Wenceslas. 5k, St. Matthew, from illuminated manuscript, 11th century.

1967, May 9 *Perf. 11½x11*

1471 A552	30h	rose claret	.20	.15
1472 A552	60h	bluish black	.45	.15
		Set value		.20

Souvenir Sheet

Perf. 11½

1473 A552	5k	multicolored	2.75	2.50

Issued to publicize the Castle of Prague.

Stylized Lyre with Flowers — A553

Old-New Synagogue, Prague — A554

1967, May 10 *Perf. 11½*

1474 A553	60h	dull pur & brt grn	.28	.15

Prague Music Festival.

1967, May 22 *Perf. 11½*

Designs: 30h, Detail from Torah curtain, 1593. 60h, Prague Printer's emblem, 1530. 1k, Mikulov jug, 1804. 1.40k, Memorial for Concentration Camp Victims 1939-45, Pincas Synagogue (menorah and tablet). 1.60k, Tombstone of David Gans, 1613.

1475 A554	30h	dull red & lt bl	.15	.15
1476 A554	60h	blk & lt grn	.20	.15
1477 A554	1k	dk bl & rose lil	.25	.15
1478 A554	1.20k	dk brn & mar	.40	.15
1479 A554	1.40k	black & yellow	.40	.15
1480 A554	1.60k	green & yel	*5.00*	*2.75*
		Nos. 1475-1480 (6)	*6.40*	*3.50*

Issued to show Jewish relics. The items shown on the 30h, 60h and 1k are from the State Jewish Museum, Prague.

"Lidice" A555

Prague Architecture A556

1967, June 9 **Unwmk.** *Perf. 11½*

1481 A555	30h	black & brt rose	.20	.15

25th anniversary of the destruction of Lidice by the Nazis.

1967, June 10 **Engr. & Photo.**

1482 A556	1k	black & gold	.45	.20

Issued to publicize the 9th Congress of the International Union of Architects, Prague.

Peter Bezruc A557

1967, June 21

1483 A557	60h	dull rose & blk	.25	.15

Centenary of the birth of Peter Bezruc, poet and writer.

Painting Type of 1966

Design: 2k, Henri Rousseau (1844-1910), self-portrait.

1967, June 22 **Engr.** *Perf. 11½*

1484 A542	2k	multicolored	1.75	1.25

Praga 68, World Stamp Exhibition, Prague, June 22-July 7, 1968. Printed in sheets of 4 stamps (2x2), separated by horizontal gutter with inscription and picture of Natl. Gallery, site of Praga 68.

View of Skalitz — A558

Designs: No. 1486, Mining tower and church steeple, Pribram. No. 1487, Hands holding book and view of Presov.

1967, Aug. 21 **Engr.** *Perf. 11½*

1485 A558	30h	violet blue	.15	.15
1486 A558	30h	slate green	.15	.15
1487 A558	30h	claret	.15	.15
		Set value	.25	.15

Issued to commemorate anniversaries of the towns of Skalitz, Pribram and Presov.

Colonnade and Spring, Karlovy Vary and Communications Emblem — A559

1967, Aug. 21 **Engr. & Photo.**

1488 A559	30h	violet bl & gold	.28	.15

Issued to commemorate the 5th Sports and Cultural Festival of the Employees of the Ministry of Communications, Karlovy Vary.

Ondrejov Observatory and Galaxy — A560

1967, Aug. 22 **Engr.**

1489 A560	60h	vio bl, rose lil & sil	.75	.25

13th Cong. of the Intl. Astronomical Union.

Orchid — A561

Flowers from the Botanical Gardens: 30h, Cobaea scandens. 40h, Lycaste deppei. 60h, Glottiphyllum davisii. 1k, Anthurium. 1.20k, Rhodocactus. 1.40k, Moth orchid.

1967, Aug. 30 **Litho.** *Perf. 12½*

1490 A561	20h	multicolored	.15	.15
1491 A561	30h	pink & multi	.15	.15
1492 A561	40h	multicolored	.25	.15
1493 A561	60h	lt blue & multi	.30	.15
1494 A561	1k	multicolored	.50	.18
1495 A561	1.20k	lt yellow & multi	.60	.30
1496 A561	1.40k	multicolored	*1.75*	*.45*
		Nos. 1490-1496 (7)	*3.70*	
		Set value		*1.25*

Red Squirrel A562

Animals from the Tatra National Park: 60h, Wild cat. 1k, Ermine. 1.20k, Dormouse. 1.40k, Hedgehog. 1.60k, Pine marten.

Engraved and Photogravure

1967, Sept. 25 *Perf. 11½*

1497 A562	30h	black, yel & org	.25	.15
1498 A562	60h	black & buff	.25	.15
1499 A562	1k	black & lt blue	.32	.15
1500 A562	1.20k	brn, pale grn & yel	.50	.15
1501 A562	1.40k	black, pink & yel	.60	.18
1502 A562	1.60k	black, org & yel	*2.50*	*1.00*
		Nos. 1497-1502 (6)	*4.42*	
		Set value		*1.55*

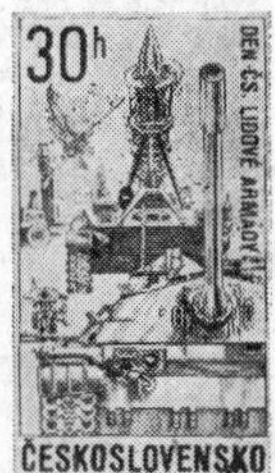

Rockets and Weapons — A563

1967, Oct. 6 **Engr.** *Perf. 11½*

1503 A563	30h	slate green	.30	.15

Day of the Czechoslovak People's Army.

Cruiser "Aurora" Firing at Winter Palace A564

Designs: 60h, Hammer and sickle emblems and Red Star, vert. 1k, Hands reaching for hammer and sickle, vert.

1967, Nov. 7 **Engr. & Photo.**

1504 A564	30h	black & dk car	.15	.15
1505 A564	60h	black & dk car	.15	.15
1506 A564	1k	black & dk car	.20	.15
		Set value	.38	.18

Russian October Revolution, 50th anniv.

The Conjurer, by Frantisek Tichy A565

Paintings: 80h, Don Quixote, by Cyprian Majernik. 1k, Promenade in the Park, by Norbert Grund. 1.20k, Self-portrait, by Peter J. Brandl. 1.60k, Saints from Jan of Jeren Epitaph, by Czech Master of 1395.

1967, Nov. 13 **Engr.** *Perf. 11½*

1507 A565	60h	multi	.25	.20
1508 A565	80h	multi	.25	.20
1509 A565	1k	multi	.50	.40
1510 A565	1.20k	multi	.50	.40
1511 A565	1.60k	multi	*4.50*	*3.75*
		Nos. 1507-1511 (5)	*6.00*	*4.95*

Sheets of 4. See Nos. 1589-1593, 1658-1662, 1711-1715, 1779-1783, 1847-1851, 1908-1913, 2043-2047, 2090-2093, 2147-2151, 2265-2269, 2335-2339, 2386-2390, 2437-2441, 2534-2538, 2586-2590, 2634-2638, 2810-2813, 2843-2847, 2872-2874, 2908-2910, 2936-2938.

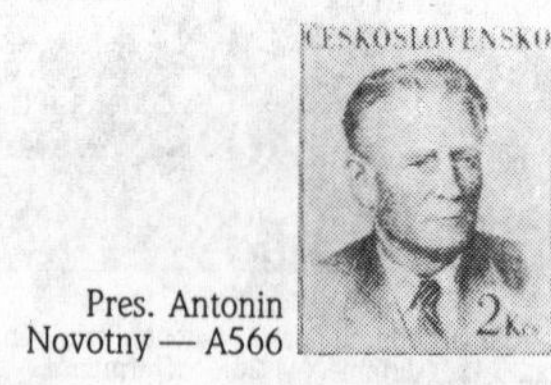

Pres. Antonin Novotny — A566

1967, Dec. 9 **Engr.** ***Perf. 11½***

1512	A566	2k blue gray	.90	.15
1513	A566	3k brown	1.40	.15
		Set value		.15

Czechoslovakia Nos. 65, 71 and 81 of 1920 — A567

1967, Dec. 18

1514	A567	1k maroon & silver	.95	.75

Issued for Stamp Day.

Symbolic Flag and Dates — A568

1968, Jan. 15 **Engr.** ***Perf. 11½***

1515	A568	30h red, dk bl & ultra	.25	.15

50th anniversary of Czechoslovakia.

Figure Skating and Olympic Rings — A569

Designs (Olympic Rings and): 1k, Ski course. 1.60k, Toboggan chute. 2k, Ice hockey.

1968, Jan. 29 **Engr. & Photo.**

1516	A569	60h blk, yel & ocher	.18	.15
1517	A569	1k ol grn, lt bl & lem	.24	.15
1518	A569	1.60k blk, lil & bl grn	.42	.18
1519	A569	2k blk, ap grn & lt bl	*1.25*	*.55*
		Nos. 1516-1519 (4)	*2.09*	*1.03*

10th Winter Olympic Games, Grenoble, France, Feb. 6-18.

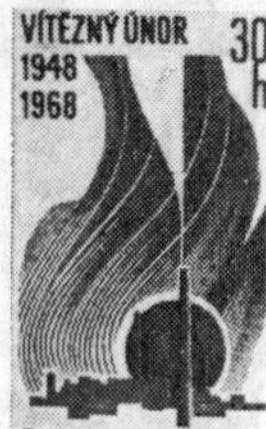

Factories and Rising Sun — A570

Design: 60h, Workers and banner.

1968, Feb. 25 ***Perf. 11½x12***

1520	A570	30h car & dk bl	.15	.15
1521	A570	60h car & dk bl	.18	.15
		Set value		.15

20th anniversary of February Revolution.

Map of Battle of Sokolow — A571

Human Rights Flame — A572

1968, Mar. 8 ***Perf. 11½***

1522	A571	30h blk, brt bl & car	.25	.15

Engr.

1523	A572	1k rose carmine	.65	.30
		Set value		.35

25th anniv. of the Battle of Sokolow, Mar. 8, 1943, against the German Army, No. 1522; Intl. Human Rights Year, No. 1523.

Janko Kral and Liptovsky Mikulas — A573

Karl Marx — A574

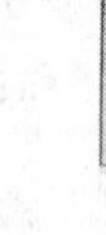

Girl's Head — A575

Arms and Allegory — A576

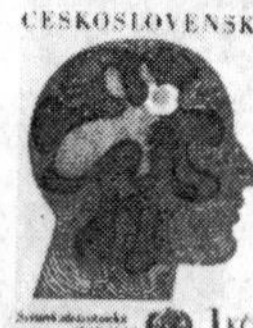

Head — A577

1968, Mar. 25 **Engr.**

1524	A573	30h green	.15	.15
1525	A574	30h claret	.15	.15

Engraved and Photogravure

1526	A575	30h dk red & gold	.15	.15
1527	A576	30h dk blue & dp org	.15	.15
1528	A577	1k multicolored	.50	.20
		Nos. 1524-1528 (5)	1.10	
		Set value		.40

The writer Janko Kral and the Slovak town Liptovsky Mikulas (No. 1524); 150th anniv. of the birth of Karl Marx (No. 1525); cent. of the cornerstone laying of the Prague Natl. Theater (No. 1526); 150th anniv. of the Prague Natl. Museum (No. 1527); 20th anniv. of WHO (1k).

Symbolic Radio Waves A578

Design: No. 1530, Symbolic television screens.

1968, Apr. 29 ***Perf. 11½***

1529	A578	30h blk, car & vio bl	.15	.15
1530	A578	30h blk, car & vio bl	.15	.15
		Set value		.15

45th anniv. of Czechoslovak broadcasting (#1529), 15th anniv. of television (#1530).

Olympic Rings, Mexican Sculpture and Diver — A579

Olympic Rings and: 40h, Runner and "The Sanctification of Quetzalcoatl." 60h, Volleyball and Mexican ornaments. 1k, Czechoslovak and Mexican Olympic emblems and carved altar. 1.60k, Soccer and ornaments. 2k, View of Hradcany, weather vane and key.

1968, Apr. 30

1531	A579	30h black, bl & car	.15	.15
1532	A579	40h multi	.16	.15
1533	A579	60h multi	.25	.15
1534	A579	1k multi	.35	.15
1535	A579	1.60k multi	.50	.20
1536	A579	2k black & multi	*2.00*	*.55*
		Nos. 1531-1536 (6)	*3.41*	
		Set value		*1.05*

Issued to publicize the 19th Olympic Games, Mexico City, Oct. 12-27.

Prague Castle Types of 1966

Designs: 30h, Tombstone of Bretislav I. 60h, Romanesque door knocker, St. Wenceslas Chapel. 5k, Head of St. Peter, mosaic from Golden Gate of St. Vitus Cathedral.

1968, May 9 ***Perf. 11½***

1537	A527	30h multicolored	.15	.15
1538	A527	60h black, red & cit	.20	.15
		Set value		.15

Souvenir Sheet

Engr.

1539	A528	5k multicolored	2.50	2.50

Pres. Ludvik Svoboda — A580

1968-70 **Engr.** ***Perf. 11½***

1540	A580	30h ultramarine	.15	.15
1540A	A580	50h green ('70)	.15	.15
1541	A580	60h maroon	.15	.15
1541A	A580	1k rose car ('70)	.30	.15
		Nos. 1540-1541A (4)	.75	
		Set value		.20

Shades exist of No. 1541A.

"Business," Sculpture by Otto Gutfreund — A581

Cabaret Performer, by Frantisek Kupka A582

Designs (The New Prague): 40h, Broadcasting Corporation Building. 60h, New Parliament. 1.40k, Tapestry by Jan Bauch "Prague 1787." 3k, Presidential standard.

Engr. & Photo.; Engr. (2k)

1968, June 5

1542	A581	30h black & multi	.18	.15
1543	A581	40h black & multi	.18	.15
1544	A581	60h dk brown & multi	.24	.15
1545	A581	1.40k dk brown & multi	.60	.15
1546	A582	2k indigo & multi	*1.75*	*1.75*
1547	A581	3k black & multi	.75	.50
		Nos. 1542-1547 (6)	*3.70*	*2.85*

1968, June 21 ***Perf. 11½***

Designs (The Old Prague): 30h, St. George's Basilica. 60h, Renaissance fountain. 1k, Villa America-Dvorak Museum, 18th cent. building. 1.60k, Emblem from the House of Three Violins, 18th cent. 2k, Josefina, by Josef Manes. 3k, Emblem of Prague, 1475.

1548	A581	30h green, gray & yel	.20	.15
1549	A581	60h dk vio, ap grn & gold	.20	.15
1550	A581	1k black, lt bl & pink	.30	.15
1551	A581	1.60k slate grn & multi	.55	.20
1552	A582	2k brown & multi	*1.25*	*1.25*
1553	A581	3k blk, yel, bl & pink	1.25	.30
		Nos. 1548-1553 (6)	*3.75*	*2.20*

Nos. 1542-1553 publicized the Praga 68 Philatelic Exhibition. Nos. 1542-1545, 1547-1551, 1553 issued in sheets of 15 + 15 labels with Praga 68 emblem and inscription. Nos. 1546, 1552 issued in sheets of 4 (2x2) with one horizontal label between top and bottom rows showing Praga 68 emblem.

Souvenir Sheet

View of Prague and Emblems — A583

Engraved and Photogravure

1968, June 22 ***Imperf.***

1554	A583	10k multicolored	3.75	3.50

Praga 68 and 50th anniv. of Czechoslovak postage stamps. Sold only together with a 5k admission ticket to the Praga 68 philatelic Exhibition.

Madonna with the Rose Garlands, by Dürer A584

1968, July 6 ***Perf. 11½***

1555	A584	5k multicolored	3.75	2.25

FIP Day, July 6. Issued in sheets of 4 (2x2) with one horizontal label between, showing Praga 68 emblem.

Stagecoach on Rails A585

Design: 1k, Steam and electric locomotives.

1968, Aug. 6

1556 A585 60h multicolored .32 .15
1557 A585 1k multicolored .45 .18

No. 1556: 140th anniv. of the horse-drawn railroad Ceské Budejovice to Linz; No. 1557: cent. of the Ceské Budejovice to Plzen railroad.

6th Intl. Slavonic Cong. in Prague — A586

1968, Aug. 7 ***Perf. 11½***

1558 A586 30h vio blue & car .50 .15

Ardspach Rocks and Ammonite — A587

Designs: 60h, Basalt formation and frog skeleton fossil. 80h, Rocks, basalt veins and polished agate. 1k, Pelecypoda (fossil shell) and Belanske Tatra mountains. 1.60k, Trilobite and Barrande rock formation.

1968, Aug. 8

1559 A587 30h black & citron .15 .15
1560 A587 60h black & rose cl .16 .15
1561 A587 80h black, lt vio & pink .20 .15
1562 A587 1k black & lt blue .25 .15
1563 A587 1.60k black & bister *1.40* *.65*
Nos. 1559-1563 (5) *2.16*
Set value *1.00*

Issued to publicize the 23rd International Geological Congress, Prague, Aug. 8-Sept. 3.

Raising Slovak Flag A588

Design: 60h, Slovak partisans, and mountain.

1968, Sept. 9 **Engr.** ***Perf. 11½***

1564 A588 30h ultra .15 .15
1565 A588 60h red .20 .15
Set value .15

No. 1564 for the Slovak Natl. Council, No. 1565 the 120th anniv. of the Slovak national uprising.

Flowerpot, by Jiri Schlessinger (age 10) — A589

Drawings by Children in Terezin Concentration Camp: 30h, Jew and Guard, by Jiri Beutler (age 10). 60h, Butterflies, by Kitty Brunnerova (age 11).

Engraved and Photogravure

1968, Sept. 30 ***Perf. 11½***

Size: 30x23mm

1566 A589 30h blk, buff & rose lil .15 .15
1567 A589 60h black & multi .18 .15

Perf. 12x11½

Size: 41x23mm

1568 A589 1k black & multi .30 .15
Nos. 1566-1568 (3) .63
Set value .25

30th anniversary of Munich Pact.

Arms of Regional Capitals — A590

Arms of Prague — A591

1968, Oct. 21 ***Perf. 11½***

1569 A590 60h Banská Bystrica .15 .15
1570 A590 60h Bratislava .15 .15
1571 A590 60h Brno .15 .15
1572 A590 60h Ceské Budejovice .15 .15
1573 A590 60h Hradec Králové .15 .15
1574 A590 60h Kosice .15 .15
1575 A590 60h Ostrava (horse) .15 .15
1576 A590 60h Plzen .15 .15
1577 A590 60h Ustí nad Labem .15 .15

Perf. 11½x16

1578 A591 1k shown .75 .25
Nos. 1569-1578 (10) 2.10
Set value .80

#1578 issued in sheets of 10. See #1652-1657, 1742-1747, 1886-1888, 2000-2001.

Flag and Linden Leaves A592

Bohemian Lion Breaking Chains (Type SP1 of 1919) — A593

Design: 60h, Map of Czechoslovakia, linden leaves, Hradcany in Prague and Castle in Bratislava.

1968, Oct. 28 ***Perf. 12x11½***

1579 A592 30h dp blue & magenta .20 .15
1580 A592 60h blk, gold, red & ultra .20 .15
Set value .15

Souvenir Sheet

Engr.

Perf. 11½x12

1581 A593 5k red 2.50 2.25

Founding of Czechoslovakia, 50th anniv.

Ernest Hemingway A594

Cinderlad A595

Caricatures: 30h, Karel Capek (1890-1938), writer. 40h, George Bernard Shaw. 60h, Maxim Gorki. 1k, Pablo Picasso. 1.20k, Taikan Yokoyama (1868-1958), painter. 1.40k, Charlie Chaplin.

Engraved and Photogravure

1968, Nov. 18 ***Perf. 11½x12***

1582 A594 20h black, org & red .15 .15
1583 A594 30h black & multi .15 .15
1584 A594 40h black, lilac & car .15 .15
1585 A594 60h black, sky bl & grn .15 .15
1586 A594 1k black, brn & yel .28 .15
1587 A594 1.20k black, dp car & vio .30 .18
1588 A594 1.40k black, brn & dp org *1.50* *.50*
Nos. 1582-1588 (7) *2.68*
Set value *1.05*

Cultural personalities of the 20th cent. and UNESCO. See Nos. 1628-1633.

Painting Type of 1967

Czechoslovakian Art: 60h, Cleopatra II, by Jan Zrzavy (1890-1977). 80h, Black Lake (man and horse), by Jan Preisler (1872-1918). 1.20k, Giovanni Francisci as a Volunteer, by Peter Michal Bohun (1822-1879). 1.60k, Princess Hyacinth, by Alfons Mucha (1860-1939). 3k, Madonna and Child, woodcarving, 1518, by Master Paul of Levoca.

1968, Nov. 29 **Engr.** ***Perf. 11½***

1589 A565 60h multi .38 .24
1590 A565 80h multi .38 .38
1591 A565 1.20k multi 1.10 .60
1592 A565 1.60k multi .75 .85
1593 A565 3k multi *4.50* *3.50*
Nos. 1589-1593 (5) *7.11* *5.57*

Sheets of 4.

1968, Dec. 18 **Engr. & Photo.**

Slovak Fairy Tales: 60h, The Proud Lady. 80h, The Ruling Knight. 1k, Good Day, Little Bench. 1.20k, The Spellbound Castle. 1.80k, The Miraculous Hunter. The designs are from illustrations by Ludovit Fulla for "Slovak Stories."

1594 A595 30h multi .15 .15
1595 A595 60h multi .16 .15
1596 A595 80h multi .22 .15
1597 A595 1k multi .30 .15
1598 A595 1.20k multi .30 .15
1599 A595 1.80k multi *1.50* *.65*
Nos. 1594-1599 (6) *2.63*
Set value *1.00*

Czechoslovakia Nos. 2 and 3 — A596

1968, Dec. 18

1600 A596 1k violet bl & gold .75 .65

50th anniv. of Czechoslovakian postage stamps.

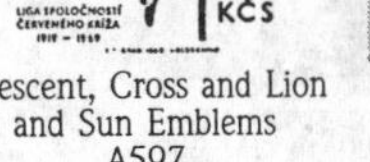

Crescent, Cross and Lion and Sun Emblems A597

ILO Emblem A598

Design: 60h, 12 crosses in circles forming large cross.

1969, Jan. 31 ***Perf. 11½***

1601 A597 60h black, red & gold .20 .15
1602 A597 1k black, ultra & red .35 .15
Set value .20

No. 1601: 50th anniv. of the Czechoslovak Red Cross. No. 1602: 50th anniv. of the League of Red Cross Societies.

1969, Jan. 31

1603 A598 1k black & gray .28 .15

50th anniv. of the ILO.

Cheb Pistol — A599

Historical Firearms: 40h, Italian pistol with Dutch decorations, c. 1600. 60h, Wheellock rifle from Matej Kubik workshop c. 1720. 1k, Flintlock pistol, Devieuxe workshop, Liege, c. 1760. 1.40k, Duelling pistols, from Lebeda workshop, Prague, c. 1835. 1.60k, Derringer pistols, US, c. 1865.

1969, Feb. 18

1604 A599 30h black & multi .15 .15
1605 A599 40h black & multi .16 .15
1606 A599 60h black & multi .16 .15
1607 A599 1k black & multi .24 .15
1608 A599 1.40k black & multi .35 .15
1609 A599 1.60k black & multi *1.25* *.48*
Nos. 1604-1609 (6) *2.31*
Set value *.85*

Bratislava Castle, Muse and Book — A600

Designs: No. 1611, Science symbols and emblem (Brno University). No. 1612, Harp, laurel and musicians' names. No. 1613, Theatrical scene. No. 1614, Arms of Slovakia, banner and blossoms. No. 1615, School, outstretched hands and woman with linden leaves.

1969, Mar. 24 **Engr.** ***Perf. 11½***

1610 A600 60h violet blue .20 .15

Engraved and Photogravure

1611 A600 60h black, gold & slate .20 .15
1612 A600 60h gold, blue, blk & red .20 .15
1613 A600 60h black & rose red .20 .15
1614 A600 60h rose red, sil & bl .20 .15
1615 A600 60h black & gold .20 .15
Nos. 1610-1615 (6) 1.20
Set value .30

50th anniv. of: Komensky University in Bratislava (#1610); Brno University (#1611); Brno Conservatory of Music (#1612); Slovak Natl. Theater (#1613); Slovak Soviet Republic (#1614); cent. of the Zniev Gymnasium (academic high school) (#1615).

Baldachin-top Car and Four-seat Coupé of 1900-1905 — A601

Designs: 1.60k, Laurin & Klement Voiturette, 1907, and L & K touring car with American top, 1907. 1.80k, First Prague bus, 1907, and sectionalized Skoda bus, 1967.

1969, Mar. 25 **Engr. & Photo.**

1616 A601 30h blk, lil & lt grn .15 .15
1617 A601 1.60k blk, org brn & lt bl .40 .20
1618 A601 1.80k multi *1.25* *.75*
Nos. 1616-1618 (3) *1.80* *1.10*

Peace, by Ladislav Guderna — A602

1969, Apr. 21 ***Perf. 11***

1619 A602 1.60k multi .50 .35

20th anniv. of the Peace Movement. Issued in sheets of 15 stamps and 5 tabs.

Horse and Rider, by Vaclav Hollar — A603

Old Engravings of Horses: 30h, Prancing Stallion, by Hendrik Goltzius, horiz. 80h, Groom Leading Horse, by Matthäus Merian, horiz. 1.80k, Horse and Soldier, by Albrecht Dürer. 2.40k, Groom and Horse, by Johann E. Ridinger.

Perf. 11x11½, 11½x11

1969, Apr. 24

Yellowish Paper

1620 A603 30h dark brown .20 .15
1621 A603 80h violet brown .20 .15
1622 A603 1.60k slate .40 .15
1623 A603 1.80k sepia .40 .25
1624 A603 2.40k multi *2.75* .70
Nos. 1620-1624 (5) 3.95 *1.40*

M. R. Stefánik as Astronomy Professor and French General
A604

1969, May 4 Engr. *Perf. 11½*

1625 A604 60h rose claret .20 .15

Gen. Milan R. Stefánik, 50th death anniv.

St. Wenceslas Pressing Wine, Mural by the Master of Litomerice
A605

Design: No. 1627, Coronation banner of the Estates, 1723, with St. Wenceslas and coats of arms of Bohemia and Czech Crown lands.

1969, May 9 Engr. *Perf. 11½*

1626 A605 3k multicolored 1.50 1.40
1627 A605 3k multicolored 1.50 1.40

Issued to publicize the art treasures of the Castle of Prague. See Nos. 1689-1690.

Caricature Type of 1968

Caricatures: 30h, Pavol Orszagh Hviezdoslav (1849-1921), Slovak writer. 40h, Gilbert K. Chesterton (1874-1936), English writer. 60h, Vladimir Mayakovski (1893-1930), Russian poet. 1k, Henri Matisse (1869-1954), French painter. 1.80k, Ales Hrdlicka (1869-1943), Czech-born American anthropologist. 2k, Franz Kafka (1883-1924), Austrian writer.

Engraved and Photogravure

1969, June 17 *Perf. 11½x12*

1628 A594 30h black, red & blue .15 .15
1629 A594 40h black, blue & lt vio .15 .15
1630 A594 60h black, rose & yel .15 .15
1631 A594 1k black & multi .28 .15
1632 A594 1.80k blk, ultra & ocher .35 .18
1633 A594 2k blk, yel & brt grn *1.50* .50
Nos. 1628-1633 (6) 2.58
Set value .95

Issued to honor cultural personalities of the 20th century and UNESCO.

"Music," by Alfons Mucha — A606

Paintings by Mucha: 60h, "Painting." 1k, "Dance." 2.40k, "Ruby" and "Amethyst."

1969, July 14 *Perf. 11½x11*

Size: 30x49mm

1634 A606 30h black & multi .15 .15
1635 A606 60h black & multi .15 .15
1636 A606 1k black & multi .18 .15

Size: 39x51mm

1637 A606 2.40k black & multi *1.40 1.10*
Nos. 1634-1637 (4) *1.88*
Set value *1.30*

Alfons Mucha (1860-1930), painter and stamp designer (Type A1).

Pres. Svoboda and Partisans
A607

Design: No. 1639, Slovak fighters and mourners.

1969, Aug. 29 *Perf. 11*

1638 A607 30h ol grn & red, *yel* .15 .15
1639 A607 30h vio bl & red, *yel* .15 .15
Set value .24 .15

25th anniversary of the Slovak uprising and of the Battle of Dukla.

Tatra Mountain Stream and Gentians
A608

Designs: 60h, Various views in Tatra Mountains. No. 1644, Mountain pass and gentians. No. 1645, Houses, Krivan Mountain and autumn crocuses.

1969, Sept. 8 Engr. *Perf. 11*

Size: 71x33mm

1640 A608 60h gray .22 .15
1641 A608 60h dark blue .22 .15
1642 A608 60h dull gray vio .22 .15

Perf. 11½

Size: 40x23mm

1643 A608 1.60k multi .40 .18
1644 A608 1.60k multi *1.50* .50
1645 A608 1.60k multi .40 .18
Nos. 1640-1645 (6) 2.96
Set value *1.05*

20th anniv. of the creation of the Tatra Mountains Natl. Park. Nos. 1640-1642 are printed in sheets of 15 (3x5) with 5 labels showing mountain plants. Nos. 1643-1645 issued in sheets of 10.

Bronze Belt Ornaments
A609

Archaeological Treasures from Bohemia and Moravia: 30h, Gilt ornament with 6 masks. 1k, Jeweled earrings. 1.80k, Front and back of lead cross with Greek inscription. 2k, Gilt strap ornament with human figure.

Engraved and Photogravure

1969, Sept. 30 *Perf. 11½x11*

1646 A609 20h gold & multi .15 .15
1647 A609 30h gold & multi .15 .15
1648 A609 1k red & multi .20 .15
1649 A609 1.80k dull org & multi .35 .20
1650 A609 2k gold & multi *1.75* .40
Nos. 1646-1650 (5) 2.60
Set value .80

"Mail Circling the World"
A610

1969, Oct. 1 Engr. *Perf. 12*

1651 A610 3.20k multi 1.40 .90

16th UPU Cong., Tokyo, Oct. 1-Nov. 14. Issued in sheets of 4.

Coat of Arms Type of 1968

Engraved and Photogravure

1969, Oct. 25 *Perf. 11½*

1652 A590 50h Bardejov .16 .15
1653 A590 50h Hranice .16 .15
1654 A590 50h Kezmarok .16 .15
1655 A590 50h Krnov .16 .15
1656 A590 50h Litomerice .16 .15
1657 A590 50h Manetin .16 .15
Nos. 1652-1657 (6) .96
Set value .30

Painting Type of 1968

Designs: 60h, Requiem, 1944, by Frantisek Muzika. 1k, Resurrection, 1380, by the Master of the Trebon Altar. 1.60k, Crucifixion, 1950, by Vincent Hloznik. 1.80k, Girl with Doll, 1863, by Julius Bencur. 2.20k, St. Jerome, 1357-67, by Master Theodorik.

1969, Nov. 25 *Perf. 11½*

1658 A565 60h multi .25 .22
1659 A565 1k multi .25 .22
1660 A565 1.60k multi .35 .30
1661 A565 1.80k multi .65 .55
1662 A565 2.20k multi *2.50 2.25*
Nos. 1658-1662 (5) *4.00 3.54*

Sheets of 4.

Symbolic Sheet of Stamps — A611

1969, Dec. 18 *Perf. 11½x12*

1663 A611 1k dk brn, ultra & gold .40 .40

Issued for Stamp Day 1969.

Ski Jump — A612

Designs: 60h, Long distance skier. 1k, Ski jump and slope. 1.60k, Woman skier.

1970, Jan. 6 *Perf. 11½*

1664 A612 50h multi .15 .15
1665 A612 60h multi .15 .15
1666 A612 1k multi .20 .15
1667 A612 1.60k multi *1.00* .32
Nos. 1664-1667 (4) *1.50*
Set value .52

Intl. Ski Championships "Tatra 1970."

Ludwig van Beethoven — A613

Portraits: No. 1669, Friedrich Engels (1820-95), German socialist. No. 1670, Maximilian Hell (1720-92), Slovakian Jesuit and astronomer. No. 1671, Lenin, Russian Communist leader. No. 1672, Josef Manes (1820-71), Czech painter. No. 1673, Comenius (1592-1670), theologian and educator.

1970, Feb. 17 Engr. *Perf. 11x11½*

1668 A613 40h black .15 .15
1669 A613 40h dull red .15 .15
1670 A613 40h yellow brn .15 .15
1671 A613 40h dull red .15 .15
1672 A613 40h brown .15 .15
1673 A613 40h black .15 .15
Set value .65 .30

Anniversaries of birth of Beethoven, Engels, Hell, Lenin and Manes, 300th anniv. of the death of Comenius, and to honor UNESCO.

Bells
A614

Designs: 80h, Machine tools and lathe. 1k, Folklore masks. 1.60k, Angel and Three Wise Men, 17th century icon from Koniec. 2k, View of Orlik Castle, 1787, by F. K. Wolf. 3k, "Passing through Koshu down to Mishima" from Hokusai's 36 Views of Fuji.

Engraved and Photogravure

1970, Mar. 13 *Perf. 11½x11*

Size: 40x23mm

1674 A614 50h multi .15 .15
1675 A614 80h multi .18 .15
1676 A614 1k multi .25 .15

Size: 50x40mm

Perf. 11½

1677 A614 1.60k multi .45 .30
1678 A614 2k multi .60 .35
1679 A614 3k multi *1.65 1.00*
Nos. 1674-1679 (6) *3.28 2.10*

EXPO '70 Intl. Exhib., Osaka, Japan, Mar. 15-Sept. 13, 1970. Nos. 1674-1676 issued in sheets of 50, Nos. 1677-1679 in sheets of 4.

Kosice Townhall, Laurel and Czechoslovak Arms — A615

1970, Apr. 5 *Perf. 11*

1680 A615 60h slate, ver & gold .25 .15

Government's Kosice Program, 25th anniv.

"The Remarkable Horse" by Josef Lada — A616

Lenin — A617

Paintings by Josef Lada: 60h, Autumn, 1955, horiz. 1.80k, "The Water Sprite." 2.40k, Children in Winter, 1943, horiz.

1970, Apr. 21 *Perf. 11½*

1681 A616 60h black & multi .18 .15
1682 A616 1k black & multi .35 .15
1683 A616 1.80k black & multi .45 .20
1684 A616 2.40k black & multi *1.50* .65
Nos. 1681-1684 (4) *2.48 1.15*

1970, Apr. 22

Design: 60h, Lenin without cap, facing left.

1685 A617 30h dk red & gold .15 .15
1686 A617 60h black & gold .18 .15
Set value .33 .15

Lenin (1870-1924), Russian communist leader.

Fighters on the Barricades — A618

Design: No. 1688, Lilac, Russian tank and castle.

1970, May 5 *Perf. 11x11½*

1687	A618	30h dull pur, gold & bl	.15	.15
1688	A618	30h dull grn, gold & red	.15	.15
		Set value	.25	.15

No. 1687: 25th anniv. of the Prague uprising. No. 1688: 25th anniv. of the liberation of Czechoslovakia from the Germans.

Prague Castle Art Type of 1969

Designs: No. 1689, Bust of St. Vitus, 1486. No. 1690, Hermes and Athena, by Bartholomy Springer (1546-1611), mural from White Tower.

1970, May 7 **Engr.** *Perf. 11½*

1689	A605	3k maroon & multi	1.75	1.50
1690	A605	3k lt blue & multi	1.75	1.50

Compass Rose, UN Headquarters and Famous Buildings of the World — A619

Engraved and Photogravure

1970, June 26 *Perf. 11*

1691	A619	1k black & multi	.25	.20

25th anniv. of the UN. Issued in sheets of 15 (3x5) and 5 labels showing UN emblem.

Cannon from 30 Years' War and Baron Munchhausen — A620

Historical Cannons: 60h, Cannon from Hussite war and St. Barbara. 1.20k, Cannon from Prussian-Austrian war, and legendary cannoneer Javurek. 1.80k, Early 20th century cannon and spaceship "La Colombiad" (Jules Verne). 2.40k, World War I cannon and "Good Soldier Schweik."

1970, Aug. 31 *Perf. 11½*

1692	A620	30h black & multi	.15	.15
1693	A620	60h black & multi	.15	.15
1694	A620	1.20k black & multi	.35	.15
1695	A620	1.80k black & multi	.35	.18
1696	A620	2.40k black & multi	*1.65*	*.65*
		Nos. 1692-1696 (5)	*2.65*	
		Set value		*1.00*

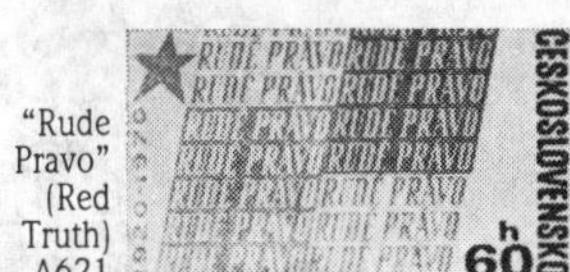

"Rude Pravo" (Red Truth) A621

1970, Sept. 21 *Perf. 11½x11*

1697	A621	60h car, gold & blk	.15	.15

50th anniv. of the Rude Pravo newspaper.

"Great Sun" House Sign and Old Town Tower Bridge, Prague — A622

Designs: 60h, "Blue Lion" and Town Hall Tower, Brno. 1k, Gothic corner stone and Town Hall Tower, Bratislava. 1.40k, Coat of Arms and Gothic Tower, Bratislava, and medallion. 1.60k, Moravian Eagle and Gothic Town Hall Tower, Brno. 1.80k, "Black Sun" and "Green Frog" house signs and New Town Hall, Prague.

1970, Sept. 23 *Perf. 11x11½*

1698	A622	40h black & multi	.15	.15
1699	A622	60h black & multi	.15	.15
1700	A622	1k black & multi	.26	.15
1701	A622	1.40k black & multi	*1.75*	*.52*
1702	A622	1.60k black & multi	.45	.16
1703	A622	1.80k black & multi	.55	.20
		Nos. 1698-1703 (6)	*3.31*	
		Set value		*1.10*

Germany-Uruguay Semifinal Soccer Match — A623

Designs: 20h, Sundisk Games' emblem and flags of participating nations. 60h, England-Czechoslovakia match and coats of arms. 1k, Romania-Czechoslovakia match and coats of arms. 1.20k, Brazil-Italy, final match and emblems. 1.80k, Brazil-Czechoslovakia match and emblems.

1970, Oct. 29 *Perf. 11½*

1704	A623	20h blk & multi	.15	.15
1705	A623	40h blk & multi	.15	.15
1706	A623	60h blk & multi	.16	.15
1707	A623	1k blk & multi	.30	.15
1708	A623	1.20k blk & multi	.35	.15
1709	A623	1.80k blk & multi	*1.75*	*.45*
		Nos. 1704-1709 (6)	*2.86*	
		Set value		*.75*

9th World Soccer Championships for the Jules Rimet Cup, Mexico City, May 30-June 21.

Congress Emblem — A624

1970, Nov. 9 **Engr. & Photo.**

1710	A624	30h blk, gold, ultra & red	.20	.15

Congress of the Czechoslovak Socialist Youth Federation.

Painting Type of 1967

Paintings: 1k, Seated Mother, by Mikulas Galanda. 1.20k, Bridesmaid, by Karel Svolinsky. 1.40k, Walk by Night, 1944, by Frantisek Hudecek. 1.80k, Banska Bystrica Market, by Dominik Skutecky. 2.40k, Adoration of the Kings, from the Vysehrad Codex, 1085.

1970, Nov. 27 **Engr.** *Perf. 11½*

1711	A565	1k multi	.25	.25
1712	A565	1.20k multi	.35	.35
1713	A565	1.40k multi	.40	.40
1714	A565	1.80k multi	.50	.45
1715	A565	2.40k multi	*2.25*	*2.25*
		Nos. 1711-1715 (5)	*3.75*	*3.70*

Sheets of 4.

Radar — A625

Designs: 40h, Interkosmos 3, geophysical satellite. 60h, Molniya meteorological satellite. 1k, Astronaut and Vostok satellite. No. 1720, Interkosmos 4, solar research satellite. No. 1720A, Space satellite (Sputnik) over city. 1.60k, Two-stage rocket on launching pad.

1970-71 **Engr. & Photo.** *Perf. 11*

1716	A625	20h blk & multi	.15	.15
1717	A625	40h blk & multi	.15	.15
1718	A625	60h blk & multi	.15	.15
1719	A625	1k blk & multi	.25	.15
1720	A625	1.20k blk & multi	.35	.15
1720A	A625	1.20k blk & multi ('71)	.35	.15
1721	A625	1.60k blk & multi	*1.40*	*.35*
		Nos. 1716-1721 (7)	*2.80*	
		Set value		*.80*

Issued to publicize "Interkosmos," the collaboration of communist countries in various phases of space research. Issue dates: No. 1720A, Nov. 15, 1971; others, Nov. 30, 1970.

Face of Christ on Veronica's Veil — A626

Slovak Ikons, 16th-18th Centuries: 60h, Adam and Eve in the Garden, vert. 2k, St. George and the Dragon. 2.80k, St. Michael, vert.

1970, Dec. 17 **Engr.** *Perf. 11½*

Cream Paper

1722	A626	60h multi	.18	.15
1723	A626	1k multi	.28	.25
1724	A626	2k multi	.52	.48
1725	A626	2.80k multi	*1.65*	*1.65*
		Nos. 1722-1725 (4)	*2.63*	*2.53*

Sheets of 4.

Carrier Pigeon Type of 1920 — A627

Engraved and Photogravure

1970, Dec. 18 *Perf. 11x11½*

1726	A627	1k red, blk & yel grn	.50	.50

Stamp Day.

Song of the Barricades, 1938, by Karel Stika — A628

Designs (Czech and Slovak Graphic Art): 50h, Fruit Grower's Barge, 1941, by Cyril Bouda. 60h, Moon (woman) Searching for Lilies of the Valley, 1913, by Jan Zrzavy. 1k, At the Edge of Town (working man and woman), 1931, by Koloman Sokol. 1.60k, Summer, 1641, by Vaclav Hollar. 2k, Gamekeeper and Shepherd of Orava Castle, 1847, by Peter M. Bohun.

Engr. & Photo.; Engr. (40h, 60h, 1k)

1971, Jan. 28 *Perf. 11½*

1727	A628	40h brown	.15	.15
1728	A628	50h black & multi	.15	.15
1729	A628	60h slate	.15	.15
1730	A628	1k black	.30	.15
1731	A628	1.60k black & buff	.48	.16
1732	A628	2k black & multi	*1.25*	*.32*
		Nos. 1727-1732 (6)	*2.48*	
		Set value		*.75*

Saris Church A629

Bell Tower, Hronsek A630

Designs: 1k, Roofs and folk art, Horácko. 2.40k, House, Jicin. 3k, House and folk art, Melnik. 3.60k, Church of St. Bartholomew, Chrudim. 5k, Watch Tower, Nachod. 5.40k, Baroque house, Posumavi. 6k, Cottage, Orava. 9k, Cottage, Turnov. 10k, Old houses, Liptov. 14k, House and wayside bell stand. 20k, Houses, Cicmany.

Engraved and Photogravure

1971-72 *Perf. 11½x11, 11x11½*

1733	A630	1k multi	.25	.15
1734	A629	1.60k multi	.45	.15
1735	A630	2k multi	.55	.15
1736	A629	2.40k multi	.65	.15
1736A	A630	3k multi ('72)	.85	.15
1737	A629	3.60k multi	1.00	.15
1737A	A630	5k multi ('72)	1.25	.15
1738	A629	5.40k multi	1.25	.15
1739	A630	6k multi	1.50	.15
1740	A630	9k multi	2.25	.25
1740A	A629	10k multi ('72)	2.75	.25
1741	A629	14k multi	3.25	.22
1741A	A629	20k multi ('72)	5.00	.75
		Nos. 1733-1741A (13)	21.00	
		Set value		2.00

Nos. 1736A, 1738, 1740 are horizontal.
See No. 2870.

Coat of Arms Type of 1968

1971, Mar. 26 *Perf. 11½*

1742	A590	60h Zilina	.16	.15
1743	A590	60h Levoca	.16	.15
1744	A590	60h Ceska Trebova	.16	.15
1745	A590	60h Uhersky Brod	.16	.15
1746	A590	60h Trutnov	.16	.15
1747	A590	60h Karlovy Vary	.16	.15
		Nos. 1742-1747 (6)	.96	
		Set value		.30

"Fight of the Communards and Rise of the International" — A631

Design: No. 1749, World fight against racial discrimination, and "UNESCO."

1971, Mar. 18 *Perf. 11*

1748	A631	1k multicolored	.28	.18
1749	A631	1k multicolored	.28	.18

No. 1748 for cent. of the Paris Commune. No. 1749 for the Year against Racial Discrimination. Issued in sheets of 15 stamps and 5 labels.

A632

A633

Design: Edelweiss, mountaineering map and equipment.

1971, Apr. 27 *Perf. 11½x11*

1750	A632	30h multicolored	.18	.15

50th anniversary of Slovak Alpine Club.

1971, Apr. 27 *Perf. 11½*

1751	A633	30h Singer	.18	.15

50th anniversary of Slovak Teachers' Choir.

Abbess' Crosier, 16th Century A634

Design: No. 1753, Allegory of Music, 16th century mural.

1971, May 9

1752 A634 3k gold & multi 1.50 1.25
1753 A634 3k blk, dk brn & buff 1.50 1.25

See Nos. 1817-1818, 1884-1885, 1937-1938, 2040-2041, 2081-2082, 2114-2115, 2176-2177, 2238-2239, 2329-2330, 2384-2385, 2420-2421.

Lenin — A635

Designs: 40h, Hammer and sickle allegory. 60h, Raised fists. 1k, Star, hammer and sickle.

1971, May 14 *Perf. 11*

1754 A635 30h blk, red & gold .15 .15
1755 A635 40h blk, ultra, red & gold .15 .15
1756 A635 60h blk, ultra, red & gold .15 .15
1757 A635 1k blk, ultra, red & gold .30 .15
Set value .62 .20

Czechoslovak Communist Party, 50th anniv.

Star, Hammer-Sickle Emblems — A636

Design: 60h, Hammer-sickle emblem, fist and people, vert.

Perf. 11½x11, 11x11½

1971, May 24 **Engr. & Photo.**

1758 A636 30h blk, red, gold & yel .15 .15
1759 A636 60h blk, red, gold & bl .20 .15
Set value .28 .15

14th Congress of Communist Party of Czechoslovakia.

Ring-necked Pheasant — A637

Designs: 60h, Rainbow trout. 80h, Mouflon. 1k, Chamois. 2k, Stag. 2.60k, Wild boar.

1971, Aug. 17 *Perf. 11½x11*

1760 A637 20h orange & multi .15 .15
1761 A637 60h lt blue & multi .15 .15
1762 A637 80h yellow & multi .15 .15
1763 A637 1k lt green & multi .18 .15
1764 A637 2k lilac & multi .45 .18
1765 A637 2.60k bister & multi *1.90 .65*
Nos. 1760-1765 (6) *2.98*
Set value *1.00*

World Hunting Exhib., Budapest, Aug. 27-30.

Diesel Locomotive A638

Gymnasts and Banners A639

1971, Sept. 2 *Perf. 11x11½*

1766 A638 30h lt bl, blk & red .15 .15

Cent. of CKD, Prague Machine Foundry.

1971, Sept. 2 *Perf. 11½x11*

1767 A639 30h red brn, gold & ultra .15 .15

50th anniversary of Workers' Physical Exercise Federation.

Road Intersections and Bridge — A640

1971, Sept. 2 **Engr. & Photo.**

1768 A640 1k blk, gold, red & bl .28 .15

14th World Highways and Bridges Congress. Sheets of 25 stamps and 25 labels printed se-tenant with continuous design.

Chinese Fairytale, by Eva Bednarova — A641

Designs: 1k, Tiger and other animals, by Mirko Hanak. 1.60k, The Miraculous Bamboo Shoot, by Yasuo Segawa, horiz.

Perf. 11½x11, 11x11½

1971, Sept. 10

1769 A641 60h multi .20 .15
1770 A641 1k multi .35 .15
1771 A641 1.60k multi .85 .25
Nos. 1769-1771 (3) 1.40
Set value .45

Bratislava BIB 71 biennial exhibition of illustrations for children's books.

Apothecary Jars and Coltsfoot A642

Intl. Pharmaceutical Cong.: 60h, Jars and dog rose. 1k, Scales and adonis vernalis. 1.20k, Mortars and valerian. 1.80k, Retorts and chicory. 2.40k, Mill, mortar and henbane.

1971, Sept. 20 *Perf. 11½x11*

Yellow Paper

1772 A642 30h multi .15 .15
1773 A642 60h multi .15 .15
1774 A642 1k multi .30 .15
1775 A642 1.20k multi .42 .15
1776 A642 1.80k multi .70 .22
1777 A642 2.40k multi *1.50 .45*
Nos. 1772-1777 (6) *3.22*
Set value *1.00*

Painting Type of 1967

Paintings: 1k, "Waiting" (woman's head), 1967, by Imro Weiner-Král. 1.20k, Resurrection, by Master of Vyssi Brod, 14th century. 1.40k, Woman with Pitcher, by Milos Bazovsky. 1.80k, Veruna Cudova (in folk costume), by Josef Mánes. 2.40k, Detail from "Feast of the Rose Garlands," by Albrecht Dürer.

1971, Nov. 27 *Perf. 11½*

1779 A565 1k multi .32 .32
1780 A565 1.20k multi .45 .45
1781 A565 1.40k multi .55 .55
1782 A565 1.80k multi .70 .70
1783 A565 2.40k multi *2.25 2.25*
Nos. 1779-1783 (5) *4.27 4.27*

Sheets of 4.

Workers Revolt in Krompachy, by Julius Nemcik — A643

1971, Nov. 28 *Perf. 11x11½*

1784 A643 60h multi .20 .15

History of the Czechoslovak Communist Party.

Wooden Dolls and Birds — A644

Folk Art and UNICEF Emblem: 80h, Jug handles, carved. 1k, Horseback rider. 1.60k, Shepherd carrying lamb. 2k, Easter eggs and rattle. 3k, "Zbojnik," folk hero.

1971, Dec. 11 *Perf. 11½*

1785 A644 60h multi .20 .15
1786 A644 80h multi .28 .15
1787 A644 1k multi .40 .15
1788 A644 1.60k multi .60 .15
1789 A644 2k multi 1.25 .38
1790 A644 3k multi 2.25 .55
Nos. 1785-1790 (6) 4.98
Set value 1.25

25th anniv. of UNICEF.

Runners, Parthenon, Czechoslovak Olympic Emblem A645

Designs: 40h, Women's high jump, Olympic emblem and plan for Prague Stadium. 1.60k, Cross-country skiers, Sapporo '72 emblem and ski jump in High Tatras. 2.60k, Discus thrower, Discobolus and St. Vitus Cathedral.

1971, Dec. 16 **Engr. & Photo.**

1791 A645 30h multi .15 .15
1792 A645 40h multi .15 .15
1793 A645 1.60k multi .45 .20
1794 A645 2.60k multi 1.75 .65
Nos. 1791-1794 (4) 2.50
Set value .85

75th anniversary of Czechoslovak Olympic Committee (30h, 2.60k); 20th Summer Olympic Games, Munich, Aug. 26-Sept. 10, 1972 (40h); 11th Winter Olympic Games, Sapporo, Japan, Feb. 3-13, 1972 (1.60k).

Post Horns and Lion — A646

1971, Dec. 17 *Perf. 11x11½*

1795 A646 1k blk, gold, car & bl .30 .15

Stamp Day.

Figure Skating A647

"Lezáky" A648

Designs (Olympic Emblems and): 50h, Ski jump. 1k, Ice hockey. 1.60k, Sledding, women's.

1972, Jan. 13 *Perf. 11½*

1796 A647 40h pur, org & red .15 .15
1797 A647 50h dk bl, org & red .16 .15
1798 A647 1k mag, org & red .32 .15
1799 A647 1.60k bl grn, org & red *1.25 .30*
Nos. 1796-1799 (4) *1.88*
Set value *.50*

11th Winter Olympic Games, Sapporo, Japan, Feb. 3-13.

1972, Feb. 16

Designs: No. 1801, Boy's head behind barbed wire, horiz. No. 1802, Hand rising from ruins. No. 1803, Soldier and banner, horiz.

1800 A648 30h blk, dl org & red .15 .15
1801 A648 30h blk & brn org .15 .15
1802 A648 60h blk, yel & red .15 .15
1803 A648 60h sl grn & multi .15 .15
Set value .50 .20

30th anniv. of: destruction of Lezáky (No. 1800) and Lidice (No. 1802); Terezin concentration camp (No. 1801); Czechoslovak Army unit in Russia (No. 1803).

Book Year Emblem A649

Steam and Diesel Locomotives A650

1972, Mar. 17 *Perf. 11½x11*

1804 A649 1k blk & org brn .30 .15

International Book Year 1972.

1972, Mar. 17 *Perf. 11½x11*

1805 A650 30h multi .20 .15

Centenary of the Kosice-Bohumin railroad.

"Pasture," by Vojtech Sedlacek — A651

Designs: 50h, Dressage, by Frantisek Tichy. 60h, Otakara Kubina, by Vaclav Fiala. 1k, The Three Kings, by Ernest Zmetak. 1.60k, Woman Dressing, by Ludovit Fulla.

1972, Mar. 27 *Perf. 11½x11*

1806 A651 40h multi .15 .15
1807 A651 50h multi .15 .15
1808 A651 60h multi .18 .15
1809 A651 1k multi .30 .18
1810 A651 1.60k multi *.85 .85*
Nos. 1806-1810 (5) *1.63*
Set value *1.45*

Czech and Slovak graphic art. 1.60k issued in sheets of 4. See #1859-1862, 1921-1924.

Ice Hockey A652

Design: 1k, Two players.

1972, Apr. 7 *Perf. 11*

1811 A652 60h blk & multi .18 .15
1812 A652 1k blk & multi .35 .15
Set value .20

World and European Ice Hockey Championships, Prague.
For overprint see Nos. 1845-1846.

Bicycling, Olympic Rings and Emblem — A653

1972, Apr. 7

1813 A653	50h shown		.20	.15
1814 A653	1.60k Diving		.60	.15
1815 A653	1.80k Canoeing		.70	.15
1816 A653	2k Gymnast		*1.40*	*.48*
	Nos. 1813-1816 (4)		*2.90*	
	Set value			*.76*

20th Olympic Games, Munich, Aug. 26-Sept. 11.

Prague Castle Art Type of 1971

Designs: No. 1817, Adam and Eve, column capital, St. Vitus Cathedral. No. 1818, Czech coat of arms (lion), c. 1500.

1972, May 9 *Perf. 11½*

1817 A634	3k blk & multi	*2.25*	*1.75*
1818 A634	3k blk, red, sil & gold	1.25	.75

Sheets of 4.

Andrej Sladkovic (1820-1872), Poet — A654

Portraits: No. 1820, Janko Kral (1822-1876), poet. No. 1821, Ludmilla Podjavorinska (1872-1951), writer. No. 1822, Antonin Hudecek (1872-1941), painter. No. 1823, Frantisek Bilek (1872-1941), sculptor. No. 1824, Jan Preisler (1872-1918), painter.

1972, June 14 *Perf. 11*

1819 A654	40h pur, ol & bl	.15	.15
1820 A654	40h dk grn, bl & yel	.15	.15
1821 A654	40h blk & multi	.15	.15
1822 A654	40h brn, grn & bl	.15	.15
1823 A654	40h choc, grn & org	.15	.15
1824 A654	40h grn, sl & dp org	.15	.15
	Set value	.72	.30

Men with Banners — A655

1972, June 14 *Perf. 11x11½*

1825 A655	30h dk vio bl, red & yel	.15	.15

8th Trade Union Congress, Prague.

Art Forms of Wire A656

Ornamental Wirework: 60h, Plane and rosette. 80h, Four-headed dragon and ornament. 1k, Locomotive and loops. 2.60k, Tray and owl.

1972, Aug. 28 *Perf. 11½x11*

1826 A656	20h sal & multi	.15	.15
1827 A656	60h multi	.20	.15
1828 A656	80h pink & multi	.28	.15
1829 A656	1k multi	.40	.15
1830 A656	2.60k rose & multi	*1.40*	*.45*
	Nos. 1826-1830 (5)	*2.43*	
	Set value		*.75*

"Jiskra" A657

Engr. & Photo.

1972, Sept. 27 *Perf. 11½x11*

Size: 40x22mm

Multicolored Design on Blue Paper

1831 A657	50h shown	.15	.15
1832 A657	60h "Mir"	.20	.15
1833 A657	80h "Republika"	.25	.15

Size: 48x29mm

Perf. 11x11½

1834 A657	1k "Kosice"	.30	.15
1835 A657	1.60k "Dukla"	.45	.15
1836 A657	2k "Kladno"	*1.75*	*.55*
	Nos. 1831-1836 (6)	*3.10*	
	Set value		*.95*

Czechoslovak sea-going vessels.

Hussar, 18th Century Tile — A658

1972, Oct. 24 *Perf. 11½x11*

1837 A658	30h shown	.15	.15
1838 A658	60h Janissary	.15	.15
1839 A658	80h St. Martin	.20	.15
1840 A658	1.60k St. George	.45	.15
1841 A658	1.80k Nobleman's guard	.50	.15
1842 A658	2.20k Slovakian horseman	*1.75*	*.60*
	Nos. 1837-1842 (6)	*3.20*	
	Set value		*1.00*

Horsemen from 18th-19th century tiles or enamel paintings on glass.

Worker, Flag Hoisted on Bayonet A659

Star, Hammer and Sickle A660

1972, Nov. 7 *Perf. 11x11½*

1843 A659	30h gold & multi	.15	.15
1844 A660	60h rose car & gold	.15	.15
	Set value	.23	.15

55th anniv. of the Russian October Revolution (30h); 50th anniv. of the Soviet Union (60h).

Nos. 1811-1812 Overprinted in Violet Blue or Black

CSSR
MAJSTROM
SVETA

1972 *Perf. 11*

1845 A652	60h multi (VBl)	5.25	4.50
1846 A652	1k multi (Bk)	5.25	4.50

Czechoslovakia's victorious ice hockey team. The overprint on the 60h is in Czech and reads CSSR/MISTREM/SVETA; the overprint on the 1k (shown) is in Slovak.

Painting Type of 1967

Designs: 1k, "Nosegay" (nudes and flowers), by Max Svabinsky. 1.20k, Struggle of St. Ladislas with Kuman nomad, anonymous, 14th century. 1.40k, Lady with Fur Hat, by Vaclav Hollar. 1.80k, Midsummer Night's Dream, 1962, by Josef Liesler. 2.40k, Pablo Picasso, self-portrait.

1972, Nov. 27 **Engr. & Photo.**

1847 A565	1k multi	.55	.35
1848 A565	1.20k multi	.70	.50
1849 A565	1.40k blk & cream	.85	.65
1850 A565	1.80k multi	1.10	1.00
1851 A565	2.40k multi	*2.50*	*2.50*
	Nos. 1847-1851 (5)	*5.70*	*5.00*

Sheets of 4.

Goldfinch — A661

Songbirds: 60h, Warbler feeding young cuckoo. 80h, Cuckoo. 1k, Black-billed magpie. 1.60k, Bullfinch. 3k, Song thrush.

1972, Dec. 15

Size: 30x48½mm

1852 A661	60h yel & multi	.16	.15
1853 A661	80h multi	.22	.15
1854 A661	1k lt bl & multi	.22	.15

Engr.

Size: 30x23mm

1855 A661	1.60k multi	.35	.15
1856 A661	2k multi	.45	.20
1857 A661	3k multi	*2.50*	*.75*
	Nos. 1852-1857 (6)	*3.90*	
	Set value		*1.35*

Post Horn and Allegory — A662

1972, Dec. 18 **Engr. & Photo.**

1858 A662	1k blk, red lil & gold	.30	.30

Stamp Day.

Art Type of 1972

1973, Jan. 25 *Perf. 11½x11*

Designs: 30h, Flowers in Window, by Jaroslav Grus. 60h, Quest for Happiness, by Josef Balaz. 1.60k, Balloon, by Kamil Lhotak. 1.80k, Woman with Viola, by Richard Wiesner.

1859 A651	30h multi	.15	.15
1860 A651	60h multi	.15	.15
1861 A651	1.60k multi	.45	.15
1862 A651	1.80k multi	*1.25*	*.60*
	Nos. 1859-1862 (4)	*2.00*	
	Set value		*.88*

Czech and Slovak graphic art.

Tennis Player — A663

Figure Skater — A664

Torch and Star — A665

1973, Feb. 22 *Perf. 11*

1863 A663	30h vio & multi	.15	.15
1864 A664	60h blk & multi	.15	.15
1865 A665	1k multi	.30	.15
	Nos. 1863-1865 (3)	*.60*	
	Set value		*.27*

80th anniversary of the tennis organization in Czechoslovakia (30h); World figure skating championships, Bratislava (60h); 3rd summer army Spartakiad of socialist countries (1k).

Star and Factories — A666

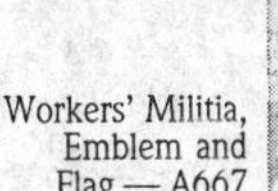

Workers' Militia, Emblem and Flag — A667

1973, Feb. 23

1866 A666	30h multi	.15	.15
1867 A667	60h multi	.15	.15
	Set value	.22	.15

25th anniversary of the Communist revolution in Czechoslovakia and of the Militia.

Capt. Jan Nalepka, Major Antonin Sochor and Laurel A668

Designs (Torch and): 40h, Evzen Rosicky, Mirko Nespor and ivy leaves. 60h, Vlado Clementis, Karol Smidke and linden leaves. 80h, Jan Osoha, Josef Molak and oak leaves. 1k, Marie Kuderikova, Jozka Jaburkova and rose. 1.60k, Vaclav Sinkule, Eduard Urx and palm leaf.

1973, Mar. 20 *Perf. 11½x11*

Yellow Paper

1868 A668	30h blk, ver & gold	.15	.15
1869 A668	40h blk, ver & grn	.15	.15
1870 A668	60h blk, ver & gold	.15	.15
1871 A668	80h blk, ver & gold	.20	.15
1872 A668	1k blk, ver & grn	.28	.15
1873 A668	1.60k blk, ver & sil	*.60*	*.18*
	Nos. 1868-1873 (6)	*1.53*	
	Set value		*.56*

Fighters against and victims of Fascism and Nazism during German Occupation.

Virgil I. Grissom, Edward H. White, Roger B. Chaffee — A669

Designs: 20h, Soviet planetary station "Venera." 30h, "Intercosmos" station. 40h, Lunokhod on moon. 3.60k, Vladimir M. Komarov, Georgi T. Dobrovolsky, Vladislav N. Volkov, Victor I. Patsayev. 5k, Yuri A. Gagarin.

1973, Apr. 12 *Perf. 11½x11*

Size: 40x22mm

1874 A669	20h multi	.15	.15
1875 A669	30h multi	.15	.15
1876 A669	40h multi	.15	.15

Engr.

Perf. 11½

Size: 49x30mm

1877 A669	3k multi	1.25	.55
1878 A669	3.60k multi	1.65	1.10
1879 A669	5k multi	*3.75*	*3.50*
	Nos. 1874-1879 (6)	*7.10*	*5.60*

In memory of American and Russian astronauts.

Radio — A670

Telephone and Map of Czechoslovakia A671

Television — A672

1973, May 1 *Perf. 11½x11*

1880 A670	30h blk & multi	.15	.15
1881 A671	30h lt bl, pink & blk	.15	.15
1882 A672	30h dp bl & multi	.15	.15
	Set value	.27	.15

Czechoslovak anniversaries: 50 years of broadcasting (No. 1880); 20 years of telephone service to all communities (No. 1881); 20 years of television (No. 1882).

Coat of Arms and Linden Branch — A673

1973, May 9 *Perf. 11x11½*

1883 A673 60h red & multi .20 .15

25th anniv. of the Constitution of May 9.

Prague Castle Art Type of 1971

Designs: No. 1884, Royal Legate, 14th century. No. 1885, Seal of King Charles IV, 1351.

1973, May 9 *Perf. 11½*

1884 A634 3k blue & multi .85 1.00
1885 A634 3k gold, grn & dk brn 1.25 1.75

Sheets of 4.

Coat of Arms Type of 1968

1973, June 20

1886 A590 60h Mikulov .15 .15
1887 A590 60h Zlutice .15 .15
1888 A590 60h Smolenice .15 .15
Nos. 1886-1888 (3) .45
Set value .24

Coats of arms of Czechoslovakian cities.

Heraldic Colors of Olomouc and Moravia A674

Anthurium A675

1973, Aug. 23 **Engr. & Photo.**

1889 A674 30h multi .15 .15

University of Olomouc, 400th anniv.

1973, Aug. 23 *Perf. 11½*

Sizes: 60h, 1k, 2k, 30x50mm.; 1.60k, 1.80k, 3.60k, 23x39mm.

1890 A675 60h Tulips .75 .75
1891 A675 1k Rose .35 .25
1892 A675 1.60k shown .35 .20
1893 A675 1.80k Iris .35 .20
1894 A675 2k Chrysanthemum *2.25 2.25*
1895 A675 3.60k Cymbidium .75 .35
Nos. 1890-1895 (6) *4.80 4.00*

Flower Show, Olomouc, Aug. 18-Sept. 2. 60h, 1k, 2k issued in sheets of 4, others in sheets of 10.

Hunting Dogs A676

1973, Sept. 5

1896 A676 20h Irish setter .15 .15
1897 A676 30h Czech terrier .15 .15
1898 A676 40h Bavarian hunting dog .15 .15
1899 A676 60h German pointer .24 .15
1900 A676 1k Cocker spaniel .32 .15
1901 A676 1.60k Dachshund *1.00 .25*
Nos. 1896-1901 (6) *2.01*
Set value .62

50th anniversary of the Czechoslovak United Hunting Organization.

St. John, the Baptist, by Svabinsky — A677

Works by Max Svabinsky: 60h, "August Noon" (woman). 80h, "Marriage of True Minds" (artist and muse). 1k, "Paradise Sonata I" (Adam dreaming of Eve). 2.60k, Last Judgment, stained glass window, St. Vitus Cathedral.

1973, Sept. 17 **Litho. & Engr.**

1902 A677 20h black & pale grn .15 .15
1903 A677 60h black & buff .15 .15

Engr.

1904 A677 80h black .25 .18
1905 A677 1k slate green .30 .22
1906 A677 2.60k multi *1.50 1.25*
Nos. 1902-1906 (5) *2.35 1.95*

Centenary of the birth of Max Svabinsky (1873-1962), artist and stamp designer. 20h and 60h issued in sheets of 25; 80h and 1k se-tenant in sheets of 4 checkerwise; 2.60k in sheets of 4.

Trade Union Emblem — A678

1973, Oct. 15 **Engr. & Photo.**

1907 A678 1k red, bl & yel .25 .15

8th Congress of the World Federation of Trade Unions, Varna, Bulgaria.

Painting Type of 1967

Designs: 1k, Boy from Martinique, by Antonin Pelc. 1.20k, "Fortitude" (mountaineer), by Martin Benka. 1.80k, Rembrandt, self-portrait. 2k, Pierrot, by Bohumil Kubista. 2.40k, Ilona Kubinyiova, by Peter M. Bohun. 3.60k, Virgin and Child (Veveri Madonna), c. 1350.

1973, Nov. 27 *Perf. 11½*

1908 A565 1k multi, vio bl inscriptions *1.75 1.10*
a. 1k multi, black inscriptions *15.00 14.00*
1909 A565 1.20k multi *1.75 1.10*
1910 A565 1.80k multi .48 .30
1911 A565 2k multi .75 .45
1912 A565 2.40k multi .75 .45
1913 A565 3.60k multi 1.00 .60
Nos. 1908-1913 (6) *6.48 4.00*

Sheets of 4. Nos. 1910-1913 printed se-tenant with gold and black inscription on gutter.

Central background bluish gray on No. 1908, light bluish green on No. 1908a.

Postilion — A679

1973, Dec. 18

1914 A679 1k gold & multi .25 .20

Stamp Day 1974 and 55th anniversary of Czechoslovak postage stamps. Printed with 2 labels showing telephone and telegraph.

Bedrich Smetana — A681

Pablo Neruda, Chilean Flag — A682

"CSSR" — A680

Comecon Building, Moscow — A683

1974, Jan. 1

1915 A680 30h red, gold & ultra .15 .15

5th anniversary of Federal Government in the Czechoslovak Socialist Republic.

1974, Jan. 4 *Perf. 11x11½*

1916 A681 60h shown .16 .15
1917 A681 60h Josef Suk .16 .15
1918 A682 60h shown .16 .15
Nos. 1916-1918 (3) .48
Set value .24

Smetana (1824-84), composer; Suk (1874-1935), composer, and Pablo Neruda (Neftali Ricardo Reyes, 1904-73), Chilean poet.

1974, Jan. 23

1919 A683 1k gold, red & vio bl .25 .15

25th anniversary of the Council of Mutual Economic Assistance (COMECON).

Symbols of Postal Service — A684

1974, Feb. 20 *Perf. 11½*

1920 A684 3.60k multi .95 .45

BRNO '74 National Stamp Exhibition, Brno, June 8-23.

Art Type of 1972

Designs: 60h, Tulips 1973, by Josef Broz. 1k, Structures 1961 (poppy and building), by Orest Dubay. 1.60k, Bird and flowers (Golden Sun-Glowing Day), by Adolf Zabransky. 1.80k, Artificial flowers, by Frantisek Gross.

1974, Feb. 21 *Perf. 11½x11*

1921 A651 60h multi .15 .15
1922 A651 1k multi .30 .16
1923 A651 1.60k multi .45 .20
1924 A651 1.80k multi .90 .32
Nos. 1921-1924 (4) 1.80 .83

Czech and Slovak graphic art.

Oskar Benes and Vaclav Prochazka A685

Portraits: 40h, Milos Uher and Anton Sedlacek. 60h, Jan Hajecek and Marie Sedlackova. 80h, Jan Sverma and Albin Grznar. 1k, Jaroslav Neliba and Alois Hovorka. 1.60k, Ladislav Exnar and Ludovit Kukorelli.

1974, Mar. 21 *Perf. 11½x11*

1925 A685 30h indigo & multi .15 .15
1926 A685 40h indigo & multi .15 .15
1927 A685 60h indigo & multi .15 .15
1928 A685 80h indigo & multi .20 .15
1929 A685 1k indigo & multi .26 .15
1930 A685 1.60k indigo & multi .75 .22
Nos. 1925-1930 (6) 1.66
Set value .54

Partisan commanders and fighters.

"Water, the Source of Energy" A686

Symbolic Designs: 1k, Importance of water for agriculture. 1.20k, Study of the oceans. 1.60k, "Hydrological Decade." 2k, Struggle for unpolluted water.

1974, Apr. 25 **Engr.** *Perf. 11½*

1931 A686 60h multi .15 .15
1932 A686 1k multi .22 .20
1933 A686 1.20k multi .35 .30
1934 A686 1.60k multi .45 .40
1935 A686 2k multi 1.50 1.50
Nos. 1931-1935 (5) 2.67 2.55

Hydrological Decade (UNESCO), 1965-1974. Sheets of 4.

Allegory Holding "Molniya," and Ground Station A687

Sousaphone A688

1974, Apr. 30 **Engr. & Photo.**

1936 A687 30h vio bl & multi .15 .15

"Intersputnik," first satellite communications ground station in Czechoslovakia.

Prague Castle Art Type of 1971

Designs: No. 1937, Golden Cock, 17th century locket. No. 1938, Glass monstrance, 1840.

1974, May 9 **Engr.** *Perf. 11½*

1937 A634 3k gold & multi 1.40 1.25
1938 A634 3k blk & multi 1.40 1.25

Sheets of 4.

Engraved and Photogravure

1974, May 12 *Perf. 11x11½*

1939 A688 20h shown .15 .15
1940 A688 30h Bagpipe .15 .15
1941 A688 40h Violin, by Martin Benka .15 .15
1942 A688 1k Pyramid piano .30 .15
1943 A688 1.60k Tenor quinton, 1754 .80 .25
Set value 1.30 .55

Prague and Bratislava Music Festivals. The 1.60k also commemorates 25th anniversary of Slovak Philharmonic Orchestra.

Child — A689

1974, June 1 *Perf. 11½*

1944 A689 60h multi .15 .15

Children's Day. Design is from illustration for children's book by Adolf Zabransky.

Globe, People and Exhibition Emblems A690

Design: 6k, Rays and emblems symbolizing "Oneness and Mutuality."

1974, June 1

1945	A690	30h multi	.15	.15
1946	A690	6k multi	1.50	1.00

BRNO 74 Natl. Stamp Exhib., Brno, June 8-23. Sheets of 16 stamps and 14 labels.

Resistance Fighter — A691

Actress Holding Tragedy and Comedy Masks — A692

1974, Aug. 29 ***Perf. 11½***

1947	A691	30h multi	.15	.15

Slovak National Uprising, 30th anniversary.

1974, Aug. 29

1948	A692	30h red, sil & blk	.15	.15

Bratislava Academy of Music and Drama, 25th anniversary.

Slovak Girl with Flower — A693

1974, Aug. 29

1949	A693	30h multi	.15	.15

SLUK, Slovak folksong and dance ensemble, 25th anniversary.

Hero and Leander A694

Design: 2.40k, Hero watching Leander swim the Hellespont. No. 1952, Leander reaching shore. No. 1953, Hero mourning over Leander's body. No. 1954, Hermione, Leander's sister. No. 1955, Mourning Cupid. Designs are from 17th century English tapestries in Bratislava Council Palace.

1974-76

1950	A694	2k multi	1.65	1.25
1951	A694	2.40k multi	1.75	1.25
1952	A694	3k multi	2.25	1.75
1953	A694	3k multi	.75	.65
1954	A694	3.60k multi	2.50	2.00
1955	A694	3.60k multi	1.00	.90
		Nos. 1950-1955 (6)	9.90	7.80

Issue dates: Nos. 1950-1951, Sept. 25, 1974. Nos. 1952, 1954, Aug. 29, 1975. Nos. 1953, 1955, May 9, 1976.

Soldier Standing Guard, Target, 1840 — A695

Painted Folk-art Targets: 60h, Landscape with Pierrot and flags, 1828. 1k, Diana crowning champion marksman, 1832. 1.60k, Still life with guitar, 1839. 2.40k, Salvo and stag in flight, 1834. 3k, Turk and giraffe, 1831.

1974, Sept. 26 ***Perf. 11½***

Size: 30x50mm

1956	A695	30h black & multi	.15	.15
1957	A695	60h black & multi	.15	.15
1958	A695	1k black & multi	.22	.15

Engr.

Perf. 12

Size: 40x50mm

1959	A695	1.60k green & multi	.42	.35
1960	A695	2.40k sepia & multi	.70	.60
1961	A695	3k multi	*2.25*	*2.25*
		Nos. 1956-1961 (6)	*3.89*	*3.65*

UPU Emblem and Postilion — A696

UPU Cent. (UPU Emblem and): 40h, Mail coach. 60h, Railroad mail coach, 1851. 80h, Early mail truck. 1k, Czechoslovak Airlines mail plane. 1.60k, Radar.

Engraved and Photogravure

1974, Oct. 9 ***Perf. 11½***

1962	A696	30h multi	.15	.15
1963	A696	40h multi	.15	.15
1964	A696	60h multi	.15	.15
1965	A696	80h multi	.20	.15
1966	A696	1k multi	.28	.15
1967	A696	1.60k multi	1.00	.22
		Nos. 1962-1967 (6)	1.93	
		Set value		.67

Sealed Letter — A697

Post Rider — A699

Stylized Bird — A698

Postal Code Symbol — A698a

Designs: 20h, Post Horn, Old Town Bridge Tower. No. 1971, Carrier pigeon. No. 1979, Map of Czechoslovakia with postal code numbers.

1974, Oct. 31 ***Perf. 11½x11***

1968	A699	20h multi	.15	.15
1969	A697	30h brn, bl & red	.15	.15
1970	A699	40h multi	.15	.15
1971	A697	60h bl, yel & red	.16	.15
		Set value	.39	.20

See No. 2675.

Coil Stamps

1975 **Photo.** ***Perf. 14***

1976	A698	30h brt bl	.15	.15
1977	A698	60h carmine	.18	.15
		Set value		.20

1976 ***Perf. 11½***

1978	A698a	30h emer	.15	.15
1979	A698a	60h scar	.15	.15
		Set value	.23	.15

Nos. 1976-1979 have black control number on back of every fifth stamp.

Ludvik Kuba, Self-portrait, 1941 A700

Paintings: 1.20k, Violinist Frantisek Ondricek, by Vaclav Brozik. 1.60k, Vase with Flowers, by Otakar Kubin. 1.80k, Woman with Pitcher, by Janko Alexy. 2.40k, Bacchanalia, c. 1635, by Karel Skreta.

1974, Nov. 27 **Engr.** ***Perf. 11½***

1980	A700	1k multi	.32	.25
1981	A700	1.20k multi	.48	.30
1982	A700	1.60k multi	.55	.40
1983	A700	1.80k multi	.55	.50
1984	A700	2.40k multi	2.25	2.00
		Nos. 1980-1984 (5)	4.15	3.45

Czech and Slovak art. Sheets of 4.

See Nos. 2209-2211, 2678-2682, 2721-2723, 2743, 2766-2768.

Post Horn A701

Engraved and Photogravure

1974, Dec. 18 ***Perf. 11x11½***

1985	A701	1k multicolored	.30	.20

Stamp Day.

Still-life with Hare, by Hollar — A702

Designs: 1k, The Lion and the Mouse, by Vaclav Hollar. 1.60k, Deer Hunt, by Philip Galle. 1.80k, Grand Hunt, by Jacques Callot.

1975, Feb. 26 ***Perf. 11½x11***

1988	A702	60h blk & buff	.15	.15
1989	A702	1k blk & buff	.24	.15
1990	A702	1.60k blk & yel	.45	.18
1991	A702	1.80k blk & buff	1.00	.50
		Nos. 1988-1991 (4)	1.84	
		Set value		.80

Hunting scenes from old engravings.

Guns Pointing at Family — A703

Young Woman and Globe — A704

Designs: 1k, Women and building on fire. 1.20k, People and roses. All designs include names of destroyed villages.

1975, Feb. 26 ***Perf. 11***

1992	A703	60h multi	.18	.15
1993	A703	1k multi	.28	.15
1994	A703	1.20k multi	.32	.15
		Nos. 1992-1994 (3)	.78	
		Set value		.27

Destruction of 14 villages by the Nazis, 30th anniversary.

1975, Mar. 7 ***Perf. 11½x11***

1995	A704	30h red & multi	.15	.15

International Women's Year 1975.

Little Queens, Moravian Folk Custom A705

Folk Customs: 1k, Straw masks (animal heads and blackened faces), Slovak. 1.40k, The Tale of Maid Dorothea (executioner, girl, king and devil). 2k, Drowning of Morena, symbol of death and winter.

1975, Mar. 26 **Engr.** ***Perf. 11½***

1996	A705	60h blk & multi	.20	.20
1997	A705	1k blk & multi	.35	.35
1998	A705	1.40k blk & multi	.50	.50
1999	A705	2k blk & multi	1.25	1.25
		Nos. 1996-1999 (4)	2.30	2.30

Sheets of four.

Coat of Arms Type of 1968

Engraved and Photogravure

1975, Apr. 17 ***Perf. 11½***

2000	A590	60h Nymburk	.15	.15
2001	A590	60h Znojmo	.15	.15
		Set value		.15

Coats of arms of Czechoslovakian cities.

Czech May Uprising — A706

Liberation by Soviet Army — A707

Czechoslovak-Russian Friendship — A708

Engr. & Photo.; Engr. (A707)

1975, May 9

2002	A706	1k multi	.25	.15
2003	A707	1k multi	.25	.15
2004	A708	1k multi	.25	.15
		Nos. 2002-2004 (3)	.75	
		Set value		.36

30th anniv. of the May uprising of the Czech people and of liberation by the Soviet Army; 5th anniv. of the Czechoslovak-Soviet Treaty of Friendship, Cooperation and Mutual Aid.

Adolescents' Exercises — A709

Designs: 60th, Children's exercises. 1k, Men's and women's exercises.

Engraved and Photogravure

1975, June 15 *Perf. 12x11½*

2005 A709 30h lil & multi .15 .15
2006 A709 60h multi .15 .15
2007 A709 1k vio & multi .25 .15
Nos. 2005-2007 (3) .55
Set value .27

Spartakiad 1975, Prague, June 26-29. Nos. 2005-2007 each issued in sheets of 30 stamps and 40 labels, showing different Spartakiad emblems.

Datrioides Microlepis and Sea Horse — A710

Tropical Fish (Aquarium): 1k, Beta splendens regan and pterophyllum scalare. 1.20k, Carassius auratus. 1.60k, Amphiprion percula and chaetodon sp. 2k, Pomacanthodes semicirculatus, pomocanthus maculosus and paracanthorus hepatus.

1975, June 27 *Perf. 11½*

2008 A710 60h multi .18 .15
2009 A710 1k multi .35 .15
2010 A710 1.20k multi .42 .16
2011 A710 1.60k multi .52 .20
2012 A710 2k multi *1.75* *.50*
Nos. 2008-2012 (5) *3.22* *1.16*

Pelicans, by Nikita Charushin — A711

Book Illustrations: 30h, The Dreamer, by Lieselotte Schwarz. 40h, Hero on horseback, by Val Muntenau. 60h, Peacock, by Klaus Ensikat. 80h, Man on horseback, by Robert Dubravec.

1975, Sept. 5

2013 A711 20h multi .15 .15
2014 A711 30h multi .15 .15
2015 A711 40h multi .15 .15
2016 A711 60h multi .15 .15
2017 A711 80h multi *.40* *.20*
Set value *.65* *.48*

Bratislava BIB 75 biennial exhibition of illustrations for children's books.
Nos. 2013-2017 issued in sheets of 25 stamps and 15 labels with designs and inscriptions in various languages.

Strakonice, 1951 A712

Designs: Motorcycles.

1975, Sept. 29 *Perf. 11½*

2018 A712 20h shown .15 .15
2019 A712 40h Jawa 250, 1945 .15 .15
2020 A712 60h Jawa 175, 1935 .15 .15
2021 A712 1k ITAR, 1921 .30 .18
2022 A712 1.20k ORION, 1903 .35 .20
2023 A712 1.80k Laurin & Klement, 1898 1.65 .40
Nos. 2018-2023 (6) 2.75
Set value .95

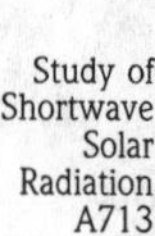

Study of Shortwave Solar Radiation A713

Soyuz-Apollo Link-up in Space — A714

Designs: 60h, Study of aurora borealis and Oréol satellite. 1k, Study of ionosphere and cosmic radiation. 2k, Copernicus, radio map of the sun and satellite.

1975, Sept. 30

2024 A713 30h multi .15 .15
2025 A713 60h yel, rose red & vio .18 .15
2026 A713 1k bl, yel & vio .30 .18
2027 A713 2k red, vio & yel .45 .20

Engr.

2028 A714 5k vio & multi *2.50* *2.50*
Nos. 2024-2028 (5) *3.58* *3.18*

International cooperation in space research. No. 2028 issued in sheets of 4.
The design of No. 2026 appears to be inverted.

Slovnaft, Petrochemical Plant — A715

Designs: 60h, Atomic power station. 1k, Construction of Prague subway. 1.20k, Construction of Friendship pipeline. 1.40k, Combine harvesters. 1.60k, Apartment house construction.

Engraved and Photogravure

1975, Oct. 28

2029 A715 30h multi .15 .15
2030 A715 60h multi .15 .15
2031 A715 1k multi .30 .15
2032 A715 1.20k multi .35 .15
2033 A715 1.40k multi .40 .15
2034 A715 1.60k multi *.75* *.40*
Nos. 2029-2034 (6) *2.10*
Set value *.88*

Socialist construction, 30th anniversary. Nos. 2029-2034 printed se-tenant with labels.

Pres. Gustav Husak — A716

1975, Oct. 28 **Engr.**

2035 A716 30h ultra .15 .15
2036 A716 60h rose red .15 .15
Set value .21 .15

Prague Castle Art Type of 1971

Designs: 3k, Gold earring, 9th century. 3.60k, Arms of Premysl Dynasty and Bohemia from lid of leather case containing Bohemian crown, 14th century.

1975, Oct. 29

2040 A634 3k blk, grn, pur & gold *.75* *.75*
2041 A634 3.60k red & multi *2.00* *2.00*

Sheets of 4.

Miniature Sheet

Ludvik Svoboda, Road Map, Buzuluk to Prague, Carnations — A717

1975, Nov. 25

2042 A717 10k multi 12.00 12.00

Pres. Ludvik Svoboda, 80th birthday.
Exists imperf., value $55.

Art Type of 1967

Paintings: 1k, "May 1975" (Woman and doves for 30th anniv. of peace), by Zdenek Sklenar. 1.40k, Woman in national costume, by Eugen Nevan. 1.80k, "Liberation of Prague," by Alena Cermakova, horiz. 2.40k, "Fire 1938" (woman raising fist), by Josef Capek. 3.40k, Old Prague, 1828, by Vincenc Morstadt.

1975, Nov. 27 **Engr.** *Perf. 11½*

2043 A565 1k blk, buff & brn .26 .26
2044 A565 1.40k multi .30 .30
2045 A565 1.80k multi .60 .52
2046 A565 2.40k multi .95 .95
2047 A565 3.40k multi 1.75 1.50
Nos. 2043-2047 (5) 3.86 3.53

Sheets of 4.

Carrier Pigeon — A718

Engraved and Photogravure

1975, Dec. 18 *Perf. 11½*

2048 A718 1k red & multi .28 .15

Stamp Day 1975.

Frantisek Halas — A719

Wilhelm Pieck — A720

Frantisek Lexa — A721

Jindrich Jindrich — A722

Ivan Krasko — A723

1976, Feb. 25 *Perf. 11½*

2049 A719 60h multi .15 .15
2050 A720 60h multi .15 .15
2051 A721 60h multi .15 .15
2052 A722 60h multi .15 .15
2053 A723 60h multi .15 .15
Nos. 2049-2053 (5) .75
Set value .38

Halas (1901-49), poet; Pieck (1876-1960), pres. of German Democratic Republic; Lexa (1876-1960), professor of Egyptology; Jindrich (1876-1967), composer and writer; Krasko (1876-1958), Slovak poet. No. 2051 printed in sheets of 10, others in sheets of 50.

Ski Jump, Olympic Emblem A724

Designs (Winter Olympic Games Emblem and): 1.40k, Figure skating, women's. 1.60k, Ice hockey.

1976, Mar. 22 *Perf. 12x11½*

2054 A724 1k gold & multi .25 .15
2055 A724 1.40k gold & multi .32 .18
2056 A724 1.60k gold & multi *.42* *.25*
Nos. 2054-2056 (3) *.99* *.58*

12th Winter Olympic Games, Innsbruck, Austria, Feb. 4-15.

Javelin and Olympic Rings — A725

Designs (Olympic Rings and): 3k, Relay race. 3.60k, Shot put.

1976, Mar. 22 *Perf. 11½*

2057 A725 2k multi .65 .20
2058 A725 3k multi .95 .32
2059 A725 3.60k multi *1.40* *.65*
Nos. 2057-2059 (3) *3.00* *1.17*

21st Olympic Games, Montreal, Canada, July 17-Aug. 1.

Table Tennis — A726

1976, Mar. 22 *Perf. 11x12*

2060 A726 1k multi .30 .15

European Table Tennis Championship, Prague, Mar. 26-Apr. 4.

Symbolic of Communist Party A727

Worker, Derrick, Emblem A728

1976, Apr. 12 *Perf. 11x12*

2061 A727 30h gold & multi .15 .15
2062 A728 60h gold & multi .15 .15
Set value .23 .15

15th Congress of the Communist Party of Czechoslovakia.

Radio Prague Orchestra — A729

Dancer, Violin, Tragic Mask — A730

Actors — A731

Folk Dancers — A732

Film Festival — A733

1976, Apr. 26 *Perf. 11½*

2063 A729 20h gold & multi .15 .15
2064 A730 20h pink & multi .15 .15
2065 A731 20h lt bl & multi .15 .15
2066 A732 30h blk & multi .15 .15
2067 A733 30h vio bl, rose & grn .15 .15
Set value .30 .25

Czechoslovak Radio Symphony Orchestra, Prague, 50th anniv. (No. 2063); Academy of Music and Dramatic Art, Prague, 50th anniv. (No. 2064); Nova Scena Theater Co., Bratislava, 30th anniv. (No. 2065); Intl. Folk Song and Dance Festival, Straznice, 30th anniv. (No. 2066); 20th Intl. Film Festival, Karlovy Vary (No. 2067).

Hammer and Sickle
A734 A735

Design: 6k, Hammer and sickle, horiz.

1976, May 14

2068 A734 30h gold, red & dk bl .15 .15
2069 A735 60h gold, red & dp car .25 .15
Set value .17

Souvenir Sheet

2070 A735 6k red & multi 1.50 1.50

Czechoslovak Communist Party, 55th anniv. #2070 contains a 50x30mm stamp.

Ships in Storm, by Frans Huys (1522-1562)
A736

Old Engravings of Ships: 60h, by Václav Hollar (1607-77). 1k, by Regnier Nooms Zeeman (1623-68). 2k, by Francois Chereau (1680-1729).

Engraved and Photogravure

1976, July 21 *Perf. 11x11½*

2071 A736 40h buff & blk .15 .15
2072 A736 60h gray, buff & blk .15 .15
2073 A736 1k lt grn, buff & blk .30 .15
2074 A736 2k lt bl, buff & blk *1.25 .40*
Nos. 2071-2074 (4) *1.85*
Set value .60

"UNESCO"
A737

1976, July 30 *Perf. 11½*

2075 A737 2k gray & multi .50 .45

30th anniversary of UNESCO. Sheets of 10.

Souvenir Sheet

Hands Holding Infant, Globe and Dove
A738

1976, July 30

2076 Sheet of 2 6.75 6.00
a. A738 6k multi 3.00 2.50

European Security and Cooperation Conference, Helsinki, Finland, 2nd anniv.

Merino Ram — A739

Couple Smoking, WHO Emblem and Skull — A740

Designs: 40h, Bern-Hana milk cow. 1.60k, Kladruby stallion Generalissimus XXVII.

1976, Aug. 28 *Perf. 11½x12*

2077 A739 30h multi .15 .15
2078 A739 40h multi .15 .15
2079 A739 1.60k multi .35 .18
Set value .50 .28

Bountiful Earth Exhibition, Ceske Budejovice, Aug. 28-Sept. 12.

1976, Sept. 7 *Perf. 12x11½*

2080 A740 2k multi .75 .40

Fight against smoking, WHO drive against drug addiction. Printed in sheets of 10 (2x5) with WHO emblems and inscription in margin.

Prague Castle Art Type of 1971

Designs: 3k, View of Prague Castle, by F. Hoogenberghe, 1572. 3.60k, Faun and Satyr, sculptured panel, 16th century.

1976, Oct. 22 **Engr.** *Perf. 11½*

2081 A634 3k multi 2.00 2.00
2082 A634 3.60k multi .75 .50

Sheets of 4.

Guernica 1937, by Imro Weiner-Kral
A741

1976, Oct. 22

2083 A741 5k multi 1.25 .60

40th anniv. of the Intl. Brigade in Spain.

Zebras
A742

Designs: 20h, Elephants, vert. 30h, Cheetah. 40h, Giraffes, vert. 60h, Rhinoceros. 3k, Bongos, vert.

Engraved and Photogravure

1976, Nov. 3 *Perf. 11½x11, 11x11½*

2084 A742 10h multi .15 .15
2085 A742 20h multi .15 .15
2086 A742 30h multi .15 .15
2087 A742 40h multi .15 .15
2088 A742 60h multi .15 .15
2089 A742 3k multi 1.25 .50
Set value 1.75 .78

African animals in Dvur Kralove Zoo.

Art Type of 1967

Paintings of Flowers: 1k, by Peter Matejka. 1.40k, by Cyril Bouda. 2k, by Jan Breughel. 3.60k, J. Rudolf Bys.

1976, Nov. 27 **Engr.** *Perf. 11½*

2090 A565 1k multi .80 .60
2091 A565 1.40k multi 1.00 .80
2092 A565 2k multi 1.65 1.25
2093 A565 3.60k multi .90 .75
Nos. 2090-2093 (4) 4.35 3.40

Sheets of 4. Emblem and name of Praga 1978 on horizontal gutter.

Postrider, 17th Century, and Satellites — A743

1976, Dec. 18 **Engr. & Photo.**

2094 A743 1k multi .25 .15

Stamp Day 1976.

Ice Hockey — A744

Arms of Vranov — A745

Designs: 1k, Biathlon. 1.60k, Ski jump. 2k, Downhill skiing.

1977, Feb. 11 *Perf. 11½*

2095 A744 60h multi .15 .15
2096 A744 1k multi .30 .15
2097 A744 1.60k multi *1.25 .24*
2098 A744 2k multi .55 .32
Nos. 2095-2098 (4) *2.25 .86*

6th Winter Spartakiad of Socialist Countries' Armies.

1977, Feb. 20

Designs: Coats of Arms of Czechoslovak towns.

2099 A745 60h shown .15 .15
2100 A745 60h Kralupy & Vltavou .15 .15
2101 A745 60h Jicin .15 .15
2102 A745 60h Valasske Mezirici .15 .15
Nos. 2099-2102 (4) .60
Set value .24

See Nos. 2297-2300.

Window, Michna Palace — A746

Prague Renaissance Windows: 30h, Michna Palace. 40h, Thun Palace. 60h, Archbishop's Palace, Hradcany. 5k, St. Nicholas Church.

1977, Mar. 10

2103 A746 20h multi .15 .15
2104 A746 30h multi .15 .15
2105 A746 40h multi .15 .15
2106 A746 60h multi .15 .15
2107 A746 5k multi *1.75 .75*
Nos. 2103-2107 (5) *2.35*
Set value *.98*

PRAGA 1978 International Philatelic Exhibition, Prague, Sept. 8-17, 1978.

Children, Auxiliary Police
A747

1977, Apr. 21 *Perf. 11½*

2108 A747 60h multi .15 .15

Auxiliary Police, 25th anniversary.

Warsaw, Polish Flag, Bicyclists
A748

Congress Emblem
A749

Designs: 60h, Berlin, DDR flag, bicyclists. 1k, Prague, Czechoslovakian flag, victorious bicyclist. 1.40k, Bicyclists on highways, modern views of Berlin, Prague and Warsaw.

1977, May 7

2109 A748 30h multi .15 .15
2110 A748 60h multi .16 .15
2111 A748 1k multi *.48 .25*
2112 A748 1.40k multi .35 .20
Nos. 2109-2112 (4) *1.14*
Set value *.58*

30th International Bicycle Peace Race Warsaw-Prague-Berlin.

1977, May 25 *Perf. 11½*

2113 A749 30h car, red & gold .15 .15

9th Trade Union Congress, Prague 1977.

Prague Castle Art Type of 1971

Designs: 3k, Onyx footed bowl, 1350. 3.60k, Bronze horse, 1619.

1977, June 7 **Engr.**

2114 A634 3k multi 1.10 1.00
2115 A634 3.60k multi 1.65 1.50

Sheets of 4.

French Postrider, 19th Century, PRAGA '78 Emblem
A750

Postal Uniforms: 1k, Austrian, 1838. 2k, Austrian, late 18th century. 3.60k, Germany, early 18th century.

1977, June 8 Engr. & Photo.

2116 A750 60h multi .15 .15
2117 A750 1k multi .26 .15
2118 A750 2k multi .45 .18
2119 A750 3.60k multi *1.90* *.75*
Nos. 2116-2119 (4) *2.76*
Set value *1.05*

PRAGA 1978 International Philatelic Exhibition, Prague, Sept. 8-17, 1978.
Nos. 2116-2119 issued in sheets of 50 and sheets of 4 with 4 labels and horizontal gutter.

Coffeepots, Porcelain Mark
A751

Mlada Boleslav Costume
A752

Czechoslovak Porcelain and Porcelain Marks: 30h, Urn. 40h, Vase. 60h, Cup and saucer, jugs. 1k, Candlestick and plate. 3k, Cup and saucer, coffeepot.

1977, June 15

2120 A751 20h multi .15 .15
2121 A751 30h multi .15 .15
2122 A751 40h multi .15 .15
2123 A751 60h multi .15 .15
2124 A751 1k multi .25 .15
2125 A751 3k multi *1.10* *.65*
Nos. 2120-2125 (6) *1.95*
Set value *1.00*

1977, Aug. 31 Engr. *Perf. 11½*

PRAGA Emblem and Folk Costumes from: 1.60k, Vazek. 3.60k, Zavadka. 5k, Belkovice.

2126 A752 1k multi .25 .25
2127 A752 1.60k multi *2.00 2.00*
2128 A752 3.60k multi .75 .70
2129 A752 5k multi .85 .85
Nos. 2126-2129 (4) *3.85 3.80*

Issued in sheets of 10 and in sheets of 8 plus 2 labels showing PRAGA '78 emblem.

Old Woman, Devil and Spinner, by Viera Bombova
A753

Book Illustrations: 60h, Bear and tiger, by Genadij Pavlisin. 1k, Coach drawn by 4 horses (Hans Christian Andersen), by Ulf Lovgren. 2k, Bear and flamingos (Lewis Carroll), by Nicole Claveloux. 3k, King with keys, and toys, by Jiri Trnka.

1977, Sept. 9 Engr. & Photo.

2130 A753 40h multi .15 .15
2131 A753 60h multi .15 .15
2132 A753 1k multi .25 .15
2133 A753 2k multi .50 .18
2134 A753 3k multi *1.75* *.50*
Nos. 2130-2134 (5) *2.80*
Set value *.88*

Prize-winning designs, 6th biennial exhibition of illustrations for children's books, Bratislava.

Globe, Violin, Doves, View of Prague — A754

1977, Sept. 28 *Perf. 11½*

2135 A754 60h multi .18 .15

Congress of International Music Council of UNESCO, Prague and Bratislava.

Souvenir Sheets

"For a Europe of Peace"
A755

Designs: 1.60k, "For a Europe of Cooperation." 2.40k, "For a Europe of Social Progress."

1977, Oct. 3

2136 Sheet of 2 .75 .60
a. A755 60h multi .25 .25
2137 Sheet of 2 1.75 1.25
a. A755 1.60k multi .50 .50
2138 Sheet of 2 2.50 2.00
a. A755 2.40k multi .80 .80

2nd European Security and Cooperation Conference, Belgrade. Nos. 2136-2138 each contain 2 stamps and 2 blue on buff inscriptions and ornaments.

S. P. Korolev, Sputnik I Emblem — A756

Sailors, Cruiser Aurora — A757

Designs: 30h, Yuri A. Gagarin and Vostok I. 40h, Alexei Leonov. 1k, Neil A. Armstrong and footprint on moon. 1.60k, Construction of orbital space station.

1977, Oct. 4

2139 A756 20h multi .15 .15
2140 A756 30h multi .15 .15
2141 A756 40h multi .15 .15
2142 A756 1k multi .28 .15
2143 A756 1.60k multi .80 .25
Set value 1.30 .50

Space research, 20th anniv. of 1st earth satellite.

1977, Nov. 7

2144 A757 30h multi .15 .15

60th anniv. of Russian October Revolution.

"Russia," Arms of USSR, Kremlin
A758

"Science"
A759

1977, Nov. 7

2145 A758 30h multi .15 .15

55th anniversary of the USSR.

1977, Nov. 17

2146 A759 3k multi .75 .35

Czechoslovak Academy of Science, 25th anniversary.

Art Type of 1967

Paintings: 2k, "Fear" (woman), by Jan Murdoch. 2.40k, Jan Francisci, portrait by Peter M. Bohun. 2.60k, Vaclav Hollar, self-portrait, 1647. 3k, Young Woman, 1528, by Lucas Cranach. 5k, Cleopatra, by Rubens.

1977, Nov. 27 Engr. *Perf. 11½*

2147 A565 2k multi .40 .35
2148 A565 2.40k multi *2.50 2.25*
2149 A565 2.60k multi 1.75 1.50
2150 A565 3k multi .70 .65
2151 A565 5k multi 1.10 1.00
Nos. 2147-2151 (5) *6.45 5.75*

Sheets of 4.

View of Bratislava, by Georg Hoefnagel — A760

Design: 3.60k, Arms of Bratislava, 1436.

1977, Dec. 6

2152 A760 3k multi 1.90 1.50
2153 A760 3.60k multi .90 .65

Sheets of 4. See Nos. 2174-2175, 2270-2271, 2331-2332, 2364-2365, 2422-2423, 2478-2479, 2514-2515, 2570-2571, 2618-2619.

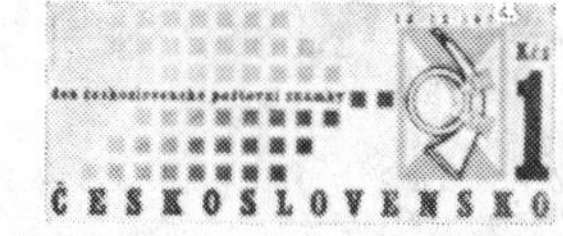

Stamp Pattern and Post Horn — A761

1977, Dec. 18 Engr. & Photo.

2154 A761 1k multi .25 .15

Stamp Day.

Zdenek Nejedly — A762

Karl Marx — A763

1978, Feb. 10 *Perf. 11½*

2155 A762 30h multi .15 .15
2156 A763 40h multi .15 .15
Set value .18 .15

Zdenek Nejedly (1878-1962), musicologist and historian; Karl Marx (1818-1883), political philosopher.

Civilians Greeting Guardsmen — A764

Intellectual, Farm Woman and Steel Worker, Flag — A765

1978, Feb. 25

2157 A764 1k gold & multi .25 .15
2158 A765 1k gold & multi .25 .15
Set value .20

30th anniv. of "Victorious February" (No. 2157), and Natl. Front (No. 2158). See note after 2190.

Yuri A. Gagarin, Vostok I — A766

10k Coin, 1964, and 25k Coin, 1965 — A767

Design: 30h, 3.60k, like No. 2140.

Engraved; Overprint Photogravure (Blue and carmine on 30h, green and lilac rose on 3.60k)

1978, Mar. 2 *Perf. 11½x12*

2159 A766 30h dk red .25 .25
2160 A766 3.60k vio bl *4.50 4.00*

Capt. V. Remek, 1st Czechoslovakian cosmonaut on Russian spaceship Soyuz 28, Mar. 2-9.

1978, Mar. 14 Engr. & Photo.

Designs: 40h, Medal for Culture, 1972. 1.40k, Charles University medal, 1948. 3k, Ferdinand I medal, 1568. 5k, Gold florin, 1335.

2161 A767 20h sil & multi .15 .15
2162 A767 40h sil & multi .15 .15
2163 A767 1.40k gold & multi *2.00* *.30*
2164 A767 3k gold & multi .65 .38
2165 A767 5k gold & multi 1.00 .50
Nos. 2161-2165 (5) *3.95*
Set value *1.30*

650th anniversary of Kremnica Mint.

Tire Tracks and Ball — A768

Congress Emblem — A769

1978, Mar. 15

2166 A768 60h multi .15 .15

Road safety.

1978, Apr. 16 *Perf. 11½*

2167 A769 1k multi .25 .15

9th World Trade Union Cong., Prague 1978.

Shot Put and Praha '78 Emblem — A770

Designs: 1k, Pole vault. 3.60k, Women runners.

1978, Apr. 26

2168 A770 40h multi .15 .15
2169 A770 1k multi .32 .15
2170 A770 3.60k multi 1.25 .75
Nos. 2168-2170 (3) 1.72
Set value .90

5th European Athletic Championships, Prague 1978.

Ice Hockey — A771

Designs: 30h, Hockey. 2k, Ice hockey play.

1978, Apr. 26

2171	A771	30h	multi	.15	.15
2172	A771	60h	multi	.15	.15
2173	A771	2k	multi	.40	.18
		Nos. 2171-2173 (3)		.70	
		Set value			.35

5th European Ice Hockey Championships and 70th anniversary of Bandy hockey.

Bratislava Type of 1977

Designs: 3k, Bratislava, 1955, by Orest Dubay. 3.60k, Fishpound Square, Bratislava, 1955, by Imro Weiner-Kral.

1978, May 9 Engr. *Perf. 11½*

2174	A760	3k	multi	1.10	1.00
2175	A760	3.60k	multi	1.65	1.50

Sheets of 4.

Prague Castle Art Type of 1971

Designs: 3k, King Ottokar II, detail from tomb. 3.60k, Charles IV, detail from votive panel by Jan Ocka.

1978, May 9

2176	A634	3k	multi	.75	.50
2177	A634	3.60k	multi	2.00	2.00

Sheets of 4.

Ministry of Post, Prague A772

Engraved and Photogravure

1978, May 29 *Perf. 12x11½*

2178	A772	60h	multi	.15	.15

14th session of permanent COMECOM Commission (Ministers of Post and Telecommunications of Socialist Countries).

Palacky Bridge A773

Prague Bridges and PRAGA '78 Emblem: 40h, Railroad bridge. 1k, Bridge of May 1. 2k, Manes Bridge. 3k, Svatopluk Cech Bridge. 5.40k, Charles Bridge.

1978, May 30

2179	A773	20h	blk & multi	.15	.15
2180	A773	40h	blk & multi	.15	.15
2181	A773	1k	blk & multi	.25	.15
2182	A773	2k	blk & multi	.50	.25
2183	A773	3k	blk & multi	.70	.35
2184	A773	5.40k	blk & multi	3.00	1.00
		Nos. 2179-2184 (6)		4.75	
		Set value			1.80

PRAGA 1978 International Philatelic Exhibition, Prague, Sept. 8-17.

St. Peter and Apostles, Clock Tower, and Emblem — A774

Town Hall Clock, Prague, by Josef Manes, and PRAGA '78 Emblem: 1k, Astronomical clock. 2k, Prague's coat of arms. 3k, Grape harvest (September). 3.60k, Libra. 10k, Arms surrounded by zodiac signs and scenes symbolic of 12 months, horiz. 2k, 3k, 3.60k show details from design of 10k.

1978, June 20 *Perf. 11½x11*

2185	A774	40h	multi	.15	.15
2186	A774	1k	multi	.28	.15
2187	A774	2k	multi	.50	.20
2188	A774	3k	multi	*2.00*	*.75*
2189	A774	3.60k	multi	.75	.25
		Nos. 2185-2189 (5)		*3.68*	*1.50*

Souvenir Sheet

Perf. 12x12

2190	A774	10k	multi	7.00	7.00

PRAGA'78 Intl. Philatelic Exhibition, Prague, Sept. 8-17. No. 2190 contains one 50x40mm stamp. Sheet exists imperf.

A non-valid souvenir sheet contains 4 imperf. copies of No. 2157. Sold only with PRAGA ticket.

Folk Dancers — A775

1978, July 7 *Perf. 11½x12*

2191	A775	30h	multi	.15	.15

25th Folklore Festival, Vychodna.

Overpass and PRAGA Emblem A776

Designs (PRAGA Emblem and): 1k, 2k, Modern office buildings (diff.). 6k, Old and new Prague. 20k, Charles Bridge and Old Town, by Vincent Morstadt, 1828.

1978 *Perf. 12x11½*

2192	A776	60h	blk & multi	.15	.15
2193	A776	1k	blk & multi	.26	.15
2194	A776	2k	blk & multi	.52	.25
2195	A776	6k	blk & multi	2.75	1.10
		Nos. 2192-2195 (4)		3.68	1.65

Souvenir Sheet

Engr.

2196	A776	20k	multi	6.50	6.50

PRAGA 1978 Intl. Phil. Exhib., Prague, Sept. 8-17. No. 2196 also for 60th anniv. of Czechoslovak postage stamps. No. 2196 contains one 61x45mm stamp.

Issue dates: Nos. 2192-2195, Sept. 8; No. 2196, Sept. 10.

Souvenir Sheet

Apollo's Companion, by Titian A777

Design: No. 2197b, King Midas. Stamps show details from "Apollo Flaying Marsya" by Titian.

1978, Sept. 12 *Perf. 11½*

2197		Sheet of 2		6.75	6.75
a.	A777	10k	multi	3.00	3.00
b.	A777	10k	multi	3.00	3.00

Titian (1488-1576), Venetian painter. No. 2197 with dark blue marginal inscription "FIP" was sold only with entrance ticket to PRAGA Philatelic Exhibition.

Exhibition Hall — A778

Engraved and Photogravure

1978, Sept. 13 *Perf. 11½x11*

2198	A778	30h	multi	.15	.15

22nd International Engineering Fair, Brno.

Postal Newspaper Service — A779

TV Screen, Headquarters and Logo — A780

Newspaper, Microphone A781

1978, Sept. 21 *Perf. 11½*

2199	A779	30h	multi	.15	.15
2200	A780	30h	multi	.15	.15
2201	A781	30h	multi	.15	.15
		Set value		.24	.15

Postal News Service, 25th anniv.; Czechoslovakian television, 25th anniv.; Press, Broadcasting and Television Day.

Sulky Race A782

Pardubice Steeplechase: 10h, Falling horses and jockeys at fence. 30h, Race. 40h, Horses passing post. 1.60k, Hurdling. 4.40k, Winner.

1978, Oct. 6 *Perf. 12x11½*

2202	A782	10h	multi	.15	.15
2203	A782	20h	multi	.15	.15
2204	A782	30h	multi	.15	.15
2205	A782	40h	multi	.15	.15
2206	A782	1.60k	multi	.38	.22
2207	A782	4.40k	multi	1.75	.80
		Nos. 2202-2207 (6)		2.73	
		Set value			1.25

Woman Holding Arms of Czechoslovakia A783

1978, Oct. 28 *Perf. 11½*

2208	A783	60h	multi	.15	.15

60th anniversary of independence.

Art Type of 1974

Paintings: 2.40k, Flowers, by Jakub Bohdan (1660-1724). 3k, The Dream of Salas, by Ludovit Fulla, horiz. 3.60k, Apostle with Censer, Master of the Spissko Capitals (c. 1480-1490).

1978, Nov. 27 Engr.

2209	A700	2.40k	multi	.60	.45
2210	A700	3k	multi	.70	.65
2211	A700	3.60k	multi	2.50	2.00
		Nos. 2209-2211 (3)		3.80	3.10

Slovak National Gallery, 30th anniversary.

Musicians, by Jan Könyves — A784

Slovak Ceramics: 30h, Janosik on Horseback, by Jozef Franko. 40h, Woman in Folk Costume by Michal Polasko. 1k, Three Girls Singing, by Ignac Bizmayer. 1.60k, Janosik Dancing, by Ferdis Kostka.

Engraved and Photogravure

1978, Dec. 5 *Perf. 11½x12*

2212	A784	20h	multi	.15	.15
2213	A784	30h	multi	.15	.15
2214	A784	40k	multi	.15	.15
2215	A784	1k	multi	.30	.15
2216	A784	1.60k	multi	1.00	.25
		Set value		1.50	.48

Alfons Mucha and his Design for 1918 Issue — A785

1978, Dec. 18 *Perf. 11½*

2217	A785	1k	multi	.25	.15

60th Stamp Day.

COMECON Building, Moscow — A786

1979, Jan. 1 *Perf. 11½*

2218	A786	1k	multi	.25	.15

Council for Mutual Economic Aid (COMECON), 30th anniversary.

Woman's Head and Grain — A787

Woman, Workers, Child, Doves — A788

1979, Jan. 1

2219	A787	30h	multi	.15	.15
2220	A788	60h	multi	.16	.15
		Set value		.24	.15

United Agricultural Production Assoc., 30th anniv. (30h); Czechoslovakian Federation, 10th anniv. (60h).

Soyuz 28, Rockets and Capsule — A789

Designs: 60h, Astronauts Aleksei Gubarev and Vladimir Remek on launching pad, vert. 1.60k, Soviet astronauts J. Romanenko and G. Grecko, Salyut 6 and recovery ship. 2k, Salyut-Soyuz orbital complex, post office in space and Czechoslovakia No. 2153. 4k, Soyuz 28, crew after landing and trajectory map, vert. 10k, Gubarev and Remek,

Intercosmos emblem, arms of Czechoslovakia and USSR.

1979, Mar. 2
2221 A789 30h multi .15 .15
2222 A789 60h multi .20 .15
2223 A789 1.60k multi .50 .15
2224 A789 2k multi 1.90 .50
2225 A789 4k multi .80 .50
Nos. 2221-2225 (5) 3.55
Set value 1.20

Souvenir Sheet

2226 A789 10k multi 4.00 4.00

1st anniv. of joint Czechoslovak-Soviet space flight. Size of No. 2226: 76x93mm (stamp 39x55mm). No. 2226 has Cyrillic inscription, No. 2455a does not. No. 2226 exists imperf.

Alpine Bellflowers A790

Stylized Satellite, Dial, Tape A791

Mountain Flowers: 20h, Crocus. 30h, Pinks. 40h, Alpine hawkweed. 3k, Larkspur.

1979, Mar. 23 *Perf. 11½*
2227 A790 10h multi .15 .15
2228 A790 20h multi .15 .15
2229 A790 30h multi .15 .15
2230 A790 40h multi .15 .15

Perf. 14

2231 A790 3k multi 1.40 .75
Nos. 2227-2231 (5) 2.00
Set value 1.00

Mountain Rescue Service, 25th anniversary.

The 3k exists perf. 11½.

1979, Apr. 2
2232 A791 10h multi .15 .15

Telecommunications research, 30th anniv.

Artist and Model, Dove, Bratislava Castle — A792

Cog Wheels, Transformer and Student — A793

Musical Instruments, Bratislava Castle — A794

Pioneer Scarf, IYC Emblem — A795

Red Star, Man, Child and Doves — A796

1979, Apr. 2
2233 A792 20h multi .15 .15
2234 A793 20h multi .15 .15
2235 A794 30h multi .15 .15
2236 A795 30h multi .15 .15
2237 A796 60h multi .16 .15
Set value .48 .25

Fine Arts Academy, Bratislava, 30th anniv.; Slovak Technical University, 40th anniv.; Radio Symphony Orchestra, Bratislava, 30th anniv.; Young Pioneers, 30th anniv. and IYC; Peace Movement, 30th anniversary.

Prague Castle Art Type of 1971

Designs: 3k, Burial crown of King Ottokar II. 3.60k, Portrait of Mrs. Reitmayer, by Karel Purkyne.

1979, May 9 *Perf. 11½*
2238 A634 3k multi 1.75 1.65
2239 A634 3.60k multi .85 .75

Sheets of 4.

Arms of Vlachovo Brezi, 1538 — A797

Animals in Heraldry: 60h, Jesenik, 1509 (bear and eagle). 1.20k, Vysoke Myto, 1471 (St. George slaying dragon). 1.80k, Martin, 1854 (St. Martin giving coat to beggar). 2k, Zebrak, 1674 (mythological beast).

1979, May 25 *Perf. 11½x12*
2240 A797 30h multi .15 .15
2241 A797 60h multi .15 .15
2242 A797 1.20k multi .28 .15
2243 A797 1.80k multi *1.00 .30*
2244 A797 2k multi .40 .18
Nos. 2240-2244 (5) *1.98*
Set value *.70*

Forest, Thriving and Destroyed A798

Designs: 1.80k, Water. 3.60k, City. 4k, Cattle. All designs show good and bad environment, separated by exclamation point; Man and Biosphere emblem.

1979, June 22 **Engr.** *Perf. 11½*
2245 A798 60h multi .15 .15
2246 A798 1.80k multi .32 .25
2247 A798 3.60k multi *1.75 .75*
2248 A798 4k multi .75 .40
Nos. 2245-2248 (4) *2.97 1.55*

Man and Biosphere Program of UNESCO.

Blast Furnace — A799

Engraved and Photogravure

1979, Aug. 29 *Perf. 11x11½*
2249 A799 30h multi .15 .15

Slovak National Uprising, 35th anniversary.

Frog and Goat A800

Book Illustrations (IYC Emblem and): 40h, Knight on horseback. 60h, Maidens. 1k, Boy with sled following rooster. 3k, King riding flying beast.

1979, Aug. 30 *Perf. 11½x11*
2250 A800 20h multi .15 .15
2251 A800 40h multi .15 .15
2252 A800 60h multi .16 .15
2253 A800 1k multi .30 .15
2254 A800 3k multi *1.75 .50*
Nos. 2250-2254 (5) *2.51*
Set value *.78*

Prize-winning designs, 7th biennial exhibition of illustrations for children's books, Bratislava; International Year of the Child. Printed with labels showing story characters.

"Bone Shaker" Bicycles, 1870 A801

Bicycles from: 20h, 1978. 40h, 1910. 60h, 1886. 3.60k, 1820.

1979, Sept. 14 *Perf. 12x11½*
2255 A801 20h multi .15 .15
2256 A801 40h multi .15 .15
2257 A801 60h multi .15 .15
2258 A801 2k multi .50 .20
2259 A801 3.60k multi 2.00 .65
Nos. 2255-2259 (5) 2.95
Set value 1.00

Bracket Clock, 18th Century — A802

Designs: 18th century clocks.

1979, Oct. 1 *Perf. 11½*
2260 A802 40h multi .15 .15
2261 A802 60h multi .15 .15
2262 A802 80h multi .85 .25
2263 A802 1k multi .25 .15
2264 A802 2k multi .50 .20
Nos. 2260-2264 (5) 1.90
Set value .70

Art Type of 1967

Paintings: 1.60k, Sunday by the River, by Alois Moravec. 2k, Self-portrait, by Gustav Mally. 3k, Self-portrait, by Ilia Yefimovic Repin. 3.60k, Horseback Rider, by Jan Bauch. 5k, Dancing Peasants, by Albrecht Dürer.

1979, Nov. 27 **Engr.** *Perf. 12*
2265 A565 1.60k multi .40 .28
2266 A565 2k multi .45 .42
2267 A565 3k multi .60 .55
2268 A565 3.60k multi 3.25 3.25
2269 A565 5k multi 1.10 1.00
Nos. 2265-2269 (5) 5.80 5.50

Bratislava Type of 1977

Designs: 3k, Bratislava Castle on the Danube, by L. Janscha, 1787. 3.60k, Bratislava Castle, stone engraving by Wolf, 1815.

1979, Dec. 5
2270 A760 3k multi .70 .65
2271 A760 3.60k multi 1.90 1.90

Stamp Day — A803

Engraved and Photogravure

1979, Dec. 18 *Perf. 11½x12*
2272 A803 1k multi .25 .15

Electronic Circuits — A804

Designs: 50h, Satellite dish. 2k, Airplane. 3k, Computer punch tape.

1979-80 **Photo.** *Perf. 11½x12*

Coil Stamps

2273 A804 50h red .15 .15
2274 A804 1k brown .25 .15
2275 A804 2k green ('80) .50 .20
2276 A804 3k lake ('80) .70 .25
Nos. 2273-2276 (4) 1.60
Set value .60

The 1k comes in two shades.

Runners and Dove A805

Engraved and Photogravure

1980, Jan. 29 *Perf. 12x11½*
2289 A805 50h multi .15 .15

50th Intl. Peace Marathon, Kosice, Oct. 4.

Downhill Skiing — A806

1980, Jan. 29 *Perf. 11½x12*
2290 A806 1k shown .24 .15
2291 A806 2k Speed skating .80 .30
2292 A806 3k Four-man bobsled .65 .28
Nos. 2290-2292 (3) 1.69 .73

13th Winter Olympic Games, Lake Placid, NY, Feb. 12-24.

Basketball — A807

1980, Jan. 29 *Perf. 11½*
2293 A807 40h shown .15 .15
2294 A807 1k Swimming .25 .15
2295 A807 2k Hurdles 1.75 .40
2296 A807 3.60k Fencing .75 .35
Nos. 2293-2296 (4) 2.90 1.05

22nd Olympic Games, Moscow, July 19-Aug. 3.

Arms Type of 1977

1980, Feb. 20 *Perf. 11½*
2297 A745 50h Bystrice Nad Pernstejnem .15 .15
2298 A745 50h Kunstat .15 .15
2299 A745 50h Rozmital Pod Tremsinem .15 .15
2300 A745 50h Zlata Idka .15 .15
Set value .48 .24

Theatrical Mask — A808

Slovak National Theater, Actors — A809

1980, Mar. 1
2301 A808 50h multi .15 .15
2302 A809 1k multi .25 .15
Set value .15

50th Jiraskuv Hronov Theatrical Ensemble Review; Slovak National Theater, Bratislava, 60th anniversary.

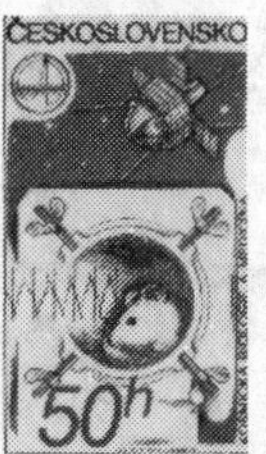

Mouse in Space, Satellite — A810

Police Corps Banner, Emblem — A811

Intercosmos: 1k, Weather map, satellite. 1.60k, Intersputnik television transmission. 4k, Camera, satellite. 5k, Czech satellite station, 1978, horiz. 10k, Intercosmos emblem, horiz.

Perf. 11½x12, 12x11½

1980, Apr. 12

2303 A810 50h multi .15 .15
2304 A810 1k multi .25 .15
2305 A810 1.60k multi 1.75 .20
2306 A810 4k multi .75 .40
2307 A810 5k multi 1.00 .50
Nos. 2303-2307 (5) 3.90 1.40

Souvenir Sheet

2308 A810 10k multi 3.25 2.50

Intercosmos cooperative space program.

1980, Apr. 17 *Perf. 11½*

2309 A811 50h multi .15 .15

National Police Corps, 35th anniversary.

Lenin's 110th Birth Anniversary — A812

Design: #2311, Engels's 160th birth anniv.

1980, Apr. 22

2310 A812 1k tan & brn .25 .15
2311 A812 1k lt grn & brn .25 .15
Set value .20

Old and Modern Prague, Czech Flag, Bouquet A813

Boy Writing "Peace" A814

Pact Members' Flags, Dove A815

Czech and Soviet Arms, Prague and Moscow Views A816

1980, May 6 *Perf. 12x11½*

2312 A813 50h multi .15 .15
2313 A814 1k multi .25 .15
2314 A815 1k multi .25 .15
2315 A816 1k multi .25 .15
Nos. 2312-2315 (4) .90
Set value .35

Liberation by Soviet army, 35th anniv.; Soviet victory in WWII, 35th anniv.; Signing of Warsaw Pact (Bulgaria, Czechoslovakia, German Democratic Rep., Hungary, Poland, Romania, USSR), 25th anniv.; Czechoslovak-Soviet Treaty of Friendship, Cooperation and Mutual Aid, 10th anniv.

Souvenir Sheet

UN, 35th Anniv. A817

1980, June 3 **Engr.** *Perf. 12*

2316 Sheet of 2 2.75 2.75
a. A817 4k multicolored 1.25 1.25

Athletes Parading Banners in Strahov Stadium, Prague, Spartakiad Emblem A818

Engraved and Photogravure

1980, June 3 *Perf. 12x11½*

2317 A818 50h shown .15 .15
2318 A818 1k Gymnast, vert. .25 .15
Set value .15

Spartakiad 1980, Prague, June 26-29.

Aechmea Fasciata — A819

A820

1980, Aug. 13 *Perf. 12*

2319 A819 50h *Gerbera Jamesonii* .15 .15
2320 A819 1k *Aechmea fasciata* 1.65 .25
2321 A819 2k *Strelitzia reginae* .70 .25
2322 A819 4k *Paphiopedilum* 1.40 .50
Nos. 2319-2322 (4) 3.90 1.15

Olomouc and Bratislava Flower Shows.

1980, Sept. 24 *Perf. 11½x12*

Designs: Folktale character embroideries.

2323 A820 50h Chad girl .15 .15
2324 A820 1k Punch and dog .25 .15
2325 A820 2k Dandy and Posy .48 .20
2326 A820 4k Lion and moon 2.50 .75
2327 A820 5k Wallachian dance 1.00 .40
Nos. 2323-2327 (5) 4.38 1.65

National Census A821

1980, Sept. 24 *Perf. 12x11½*

2328 A821 1k multi .25 .15

Prague Castle Type of 1971

Designs: 3k, Old Palace gateway. 4k, Armorial lion, 16th century.

1980, Oct. 28 *Perf. 12*

2329 A634 3k multi 2.00 1.90
2330 A634 4k multi .75 .65

Sheets of 4.

Bratislava Type of 1977

Designs: 3k, View across the Danube, by J. Eder, 1810. 4k, The Old Royal Bridge, by J.A. Lantz, 1820.

1980, Oct. 28

2331 A760 3k multi 2.00 1.90
2332 A760 4k multi .75 .65

10th Anniversary of Socialist Youth Federation — A822

1980, Nov. 9 *Perf. 12x11½*

2333 A822 50h multi .15 .15

No. 2137 Overprinted in Red: 3. / MEZINARODNI VELETRH ZNAMEK / ESSEN '80

1980, Nov. 18

2334 A755 1.60k multi *14.00 14.00*

Czechoslovak Day/ ESSEN '80, 3rd International Stamp Exhibition, No. 2334 has overprinted red marginal inscription.

Art Type of 1967

Designs: 1k, Pavel Jozef Safarik, by Jozef B. Klemens. 2k, Peasant Revolt mosaic, Anna Podzemma. 3k, St. Lucia, 14th century statue. 4k, Waste Heaps, by Jan Zrzavy, horiz. 5k, Labor, sculpture by Jan Stursa.

1980, Nov. 27 **Engr.** *Perf. 12*

2335 A565 1k multi 1.10 1.10
2336 A565 2k multi 2.25 2.25
2337 A565 3k multi .50 .50
2338 A565 4k multi .85 .85
2339 A565 5k multi 1.00 1.00
Nos. 2335-2339 (5) 5.70 5.70

Stamp Day — A823

Engraved and Photogravure

1980, Dec. 18 *Perf. 11½x12*

2340 A823 1k multi .25 .15

7th Five-year Plan, 1981-1985 A824

1981, Jan. 1 *Perf. 11½*

2341 A824 50h multi .15 .15

International Year of the Disabled — A825

1981, Feb. 24

2342 A825 1k multi .25 .15

Landau, 1800 A826

1981, Feb. 25 *Perf. 12x11½*

2343 A826 50h shown .15 .15
2344 A826 1k Mail coach, 1830 .26 .25
2345 A826 3.60k Mail sled, 1840 *4.00 1.75*
2346 A826 5k 4-horse mail coach, 1860 1.00 1.00
2347 A826 7k Open carriage, 1840 1.50 1.50
a. Sheet of 4 *15.00 12.00*
Nos. 2343-2347 (5) *6.91 4.65*

WIPA '81 Intl. Philatelic Exhibition, Vienna, Austria, May 22-31. No. 2347a issued May 10.

Wolfgang Amadeus Mozart — A827

Famous Men: No. 2348, Joesph Hlavka (1831-1908). No. 2349, Juraj Hronec (1881-1959). No. 2350, Jan Sverma (1901-44). No. 2351, Mikulas Schneider-Trnavsky (1881-1958). No. 2352, B. Bolzano (1781-1848). No. 2353, Dimitri Shostakovich, composer. No. 2354, George Bernard Shaw, playwright.

1981, Mar. 10 *Perf. 11½*

2348 A827 50h multi .18 .15
2349 A827 50h multi .18 .15
2350 A827 50h multi .18 .15
2351 A827 50h multi .18 .15
2352 A827 1k multi .80 .25
2353 A827 1k multi .35 .15
2354 A827 1k multi .35 .15
2355 A827 1k multi .35 .15
Nos. 2348-2355 (8) 2.57
Set value .79

Souvenir Sheet

Yuri Gagarin A828

1981, Apr. 5 *Perf. 12*

2356 Sheet of 2 5.50 4.00
a. A828 6k multicolored 2.25 2.00

20th anniv. of 1st manned space flight.

Workers and Banner A829

1981, Apr. 6 *Perf. 12x11½*

2357 A829 50h shown .15 .15
2358 A829 1k Hands holding banner .26 .15
2359 A829 4k Worker holding banner, vert. 1.00 .35
Nos. 2357-2359 (3) 1.41
Set value .49

Czechoslovakian Communist Party, 60th anniv.

Congress Emblem, View of Prague A830

1981, Apr. 6

2360 A830 50h shown .15 .15
2361 A830 1k Bratislava .25 .15
Set value .15

16th Communist Party Congress.

Agriculture Museum, 90th Anniv. A831

Natl. Assembly Elections A832

1981, May 14 *Perf. 11½x12*
2362 A831 1k multi .25 .15

1981, June 1
2363 A832 50h multi .15 .15

Bratislava Type of 1977

Designs: 3k, Bratislava Castle, by G.B. Probst, 1760. 4k, Grassalkovic Palace, by C. Bschor, 1815.

1981, June 10 *Perf. 12*
2364 A760 3k multi 2.00 2.00
2365 A760 4k multi .75 .50

Uran and Red October Hotels A833

Successes of Socialist Achievements Exhibition: 1k, Brno-Bratislava Highway, Jihlava. 2k, Nuclear power station, Jaslovske Bohunice.

1981, June 10 *Perf. 12x11½*
2366 A833 80h multi .20 .15
2367 A833 1k multi .25 .15
2368 A833 2k multi .50 .20
Nos. 2366-2368 (3) .95
Set value .38

Border Defense Units, 30th Anniv. — A834

Civil Defense, 30th Anniv. — A835

Army Cooperation, 30th Anniv. — A836

Rysy Youth Mountain Climbing Contest A837

Engraved and Photogravure

1981, July 11 *Perf. 11½*
2369 A834 40h multi .15 .15
2370 A835 50h multi .15 .15
2371 A836 1k multi .25 .15
2372 A837 3.60k multi .90 .32
Nos. 2369-2372 (4) 1.45
Set value .52

30th Natl. Festival of Amateur Puppet Ensembles — A838

1981, July 2 *Perf. 11½*
2373 A838 2k Punch and Devil .48 .20

Souvenir Sheet

Guernica, by Pablo Picasso — A839

1981, July 2 Engr. *Perf. 11½x12*
2374 A839 10k multi 3.75 3.25

Picasso's birth centenary; 45th anniv. of Intl. Brigades in Spain.

Cat Holding Flower, by Etienne Delessert — A840

8th Biennial Exhibition of Children's Book Illustrations (Designs by): 50h, Albin Brunovsky, vert. 1k, Adolf Born. 2k, Vive Tolli. 10k, Suekichi Akaba.

Engraved and Photogravure

1981, Sept. 5 *Perf. 11½*
2375 A840 50h multi .15 .15
2376 A840 1k multi .24 .15
2377 A840 2k multi .42 .20
2378 A840 4k multi .95 .45
2379 A840 10k multi 4.00 2.00
Nos. 2375-2379 (5) 5.76 2.95

Prague Zoo, 50th Anniv. — A841

1981, Sept. 28 *Perf. 11½x12*
2380 A841 50h Gorillas .15 .15
2381 A841 1k Lions .25 .15
2382 A841 7k Przewalski's horses 1.65 .80
Nos. 2380-2382 (3) 2.05 1.10

Anti-smoking Campaign — A842

1981, Oct. 27 *Perf. 12*
2383 A842 4k multi 1.00 .60

No. 2383 se-tenant with label.

Prague Castle Art Type of 1971

Designs: 3k, Carved dragon, Palais Lobkovitz, 16th cent. 4k, St. Vitus Cathedral, by J. Sember and G. Dobler, 19th cent.

1981, Oct. 28
2384 A634 3k multi .65 .65
2385 A634 4k multi 2.00 2.00

Sheets of 4.

Art Type of 1967

Designs: 1k, View of Prague, by Vaclav Hollar (1607-1677). 2k, Czechoslovak Academy medallion, engraved by Otakar Spaniel (1881-1955). 3k, Jihoceska Vysivka, by Zdenek Sklenar (b. 1910). 4k, Still Life, by A.M. Gerasimov (1881-1963). 5k, Standing Woman, by Pablo Picasso (1881-1973).

1981, Nov. 27 Engr. *Perf. 12*
2386 A565 1k multi 2.25 2.25
2387 A565 2k multi .50 .50
2388 A565 3k multi .75 .75
2389 A565 4k multi 1.00 1.00
2390 A565 5k multi 1.25 1.25
Nos. 2386-2390 (5) 5.75 5.75

Sheets of 4. Sheets of No. 2390 exist with center gutter inscribed with Philexfrance 82 and FIP emblems. Value, $15.

Stamp Day — A843

Engraved and Photogravure

1981, Dec. 18 *Perf. 11½x12*
2391 A843 1k Engraver Edward Karel .25 .15

Russian Workers' Party, Prague Congress, 70th Anniv. — A844

1982, Jan. 18 *Perf. 12*
2392 A844 2k Lenin .50 .35
a. Sheet of 4 5.50 5.00

No. 2392 issued in sheet of 8.

1982 World Cup Soccer A845

Designs: Various soccer players.

1982, Jan. 29 *Perf. 12x11½*
2393 A845 1k multi .25 .15
2394 A845 3.60k multi .70 .35
2395 A845 4k multi 1.40 .50
Nos. 2393-2395 (3) 2.35 1.00

10th World Trade Union Congress, Havana — A846

Arms of Hrob — A847

1982, Feb. 10 *Perf. 11½*
2396 A846 1k multi .25 .15

1982, Feb. 10 *Perf. 12x11½*

Arms of various cities.

2397 A847 50h shown .15 .15
2398 A847 50h Nove Mesto Nad Metuji .15 .15
2399 A847 50h Trencin .15 .15
2400 A847 50h Mlada Boleslav .15 .15
Set value .48 .20

See Nos. 2499-2502, 2542-2544, 2595-2597, 2783-2786.

50th Anniv. of the Great Strike at Most — A848

1982, Mar. 23 *Perf. 11½*
2401 A848 1k multi .25 .15

60th Intl. Railway Union Congress A849

1982, Mar. 23 *Perf. 12x11½*
2402 A849 6k Steam locomotive, 1922, electric, 1982 1.50 .75

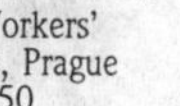

10th Workers' Congress, Prague A850

George Dimitrov A851

1982, Apr. 15
2403 A850 1k multi .25 .15

1982, May 1
2404 A851 50h multi .15 .15

A852

10th Lidice Intl. Children's Drawing Contest — A853

Engravings: 40h, The Muse Euterpe Playing a Flute, by Crispin de Passe (1565-1637). 50h, The Lute Player, by Jacob de Gheyn (1565-1629). 1k, Woman Flautist, by Adriaen Collaert (1560-1618). 2k, Musicians in a Hostel, by Rembrandt (1606-1669). 3k, Hurdygurdy Player, by Jacques Callot (1594-1635).

1982, May 18 *Perf. 11½x12*
2405 A852 40h multi .15 .15
2406 A852 50h multi .15 .15
2407 A852 1k multi .25 .15
2408 A852 2k multi .48 .20
2409 A852 3k multi .90 .60
Nos. 2405-2409 (5) 1.93 1.25

1982, May 18
2410 A853 2k multi 1.00 1.00

Issued in sheets of 6.

40th Anniv. of Lidice Destruction of Lidice and Lezaky — A854

1982, June 4 *Perf. 11½*
2411 A854 1k Girl, rose .25 .15
2412 A854 1k Hands, barbed wire .25 .15

Souvenir Sheet

UN Disarmament Conference — A855

1982, June 4 *Perf. 12*
2413 Sheet of 2 7.50 6.00
a. A855 6k Woman holding doves 3.50 2.75

Souvenir Sheet

2nd UN Conference on Peaceful Uses of Outer Space, Vienna, Aug. 9-21 — A856

1982, Aug. 9 **Engr. & Photo.**

2414 Sheet of 2 7.50 7.00
a. A856 5k multi 3.50 3.00

Krivoklat Castle A857

1982, Aug. 31 ***Perf. 12x11½***

2415 A857 50h shown .15 .15
2416 A857 1k Statues (Krivoklat) .26 .15
2417 A857 2k Nitra Castle .52 .24
2418 A857 3k Pottery, lock (Nitra) .75 .35
a. Souv. sheet of 4, #2415-2418 2.50 2.00
Nos. 2415-2418 (4) 1.68
Set value .75

50th Anniv. of Zizkov Hill Natl. Monument — A858

1982, Sept. 16

2419 A858 1k multi .25 .15

Prague Castle Art Type of 1971

Designs: 3k, St. George and the Dragon, 1373. 4k, Tomb of King Vratislav I, 10th cent.

1982, Sept. 28 ***Perf. 12***

2420 A634 3k multi 2.00 .65
2421 A634 4k multi .75 .75

Sheets of 4.

Bratislava Type of 1977

Designs: 3k, Paddle steamer, Parnik, 1818. 4k, View from Bridge, 19th cent.

1982, Sept. 29

2422 A760 3k multi 2.00 .65
2423 A760 4k multi .75 .75

European Danube Commission — A859

1982, Sept. 29 ***Perf. 11½x12***

2424 A859 3k Steamer, Bratislava Bridge .75 .35
a. Souvenir sheet of 4 6.50 5.25
2425 A859 3.60k Ferry, Budapest .95 .50
a. Souvenir sheet of 4 8.50 7.00

16th Communist Party Congress — A860

1982, Oct. 28 ***Perf. 12x11½***

2426 A860 20h Agriculture .15 .15
2427 A860 1k Industry .25 .15
2428 A860 3k Engineering .75 .35
Nos. 2426-2428 (3) 1.15
Set value .50

30th Anniv. of Academy of Sciences — A861

1982, Oct. 29 ***Perf. 11½***

2429 A861 6k Emblem 1.50 .75

65th Anniv. of October Revolution A862

Design: 1k, 60th anniv. of USSR.

1982, Nov. 7 ***Perf. 12x11½***

2430 A862 50h multi .15 .15
2431 A862 1k multi .25 .15
Set value .20

Jaroslav Hasek, Writer, Sculpture by Josef Malejovsky — A863

Sculptures: 2k, Jan Zrzavy, freedom fighter, by Jan Simota. 4.40k, Leos Janacek, composer, by Milos Axman. 6k, Martin Kukucin, freedom fighter, by Jan Kulich. 7k, Peaceful Work, by Rudolf Pribis.

Engraved and Photogravure

1982, Nov. 26 ***Perf. 11½x12***

2432 A863 1k multi .24 .15
2433 A863 2k multi .48 .20
2434 A863 4.40k multi 1.00 .50
2435 A863 6k multi 1.25 .70
2436 A863 7k multi 3.00 1.50
Nos. 2432-2436 (5) 5.97 3.05

Art Type of 1967

Paintings: 1k, Revolution in Spain, by Josef Sima (1891-1971). 2k, Woman Dressing, by Rudolf Kremlicka (1886-1932). 3k, The Girl Bride, by Dezider Milly (1906-1971). 4k, Performers, by Jan Zelibsky (b. 1907). 5k, The Complaint of the Birds, by Emil Filla (1882-1953).

1982, Nov. 27 ***Perf. 12***

2437 A565 1k multi 1.00 .25
2438 A565 2k multi 2.00 .50
2439 A565 3k multi .75 .75
2440 A565 4k multi 1.00 1.00
2441 A565 5k multi 1.25 1.00
Nos. 2437-2441 (5) 6.00 3.50

Stamp Day — A864

1982, Dec. 8 ***Perf. 11½***

2442 A864 1k Engraver Jaroslav Goldschmied (1890-1977) .25 .15

A865

A866

1983, Jan. 10 **Engr.** ***Perf. 12x11½***

2443 A865 50h dark blue .15 .15

Pres. Gustav Husak, 70th birthday. See No. 2686.

1983, Feb. 24 **Engr. & Photo.**

Designs: 50h, Jaroslav Hasek (1882-1923), writer. 1k, Julius Fucik (1903-1943), antifascist martyr. 2k, Martin Luther (1483-1546). 5k, Johannes Brahms (1833-1897), composer.

2444 A866 50h multi .15 .15
2445 A866 1k multi .25 .15
2446 A866 2k multi .45 .18
a. Souvenir sheet of 4 *12.00* *9.00*
2447 A866 5k multi 1.10 .45
Nos. 2444-2447 (4) 1.95
Set value .78

Nordposta '83 Intl. Stamp Exhibition, Hamburg. No. 2446a issued Nov. 1.

Workers Marching — A867

Family — A868

1983, Feb. 25 ***Perf. 11½***

2448 A867 50h multi .15 .15
2449 A868 1k multi .26 .15
Set value .15

35th anniv. of "Victorious February" (50h), and Natl. Front (1k).

World Communications Year — A869

Perf. 11½, 12x11½ (2k)

1983, Mar. 16

2450 A869 40h multi .15 .15
2451 A869 1k multi .25 .15
2452 A869 2k multi .45 .20
2453 A869 3.60k multi .90 .40
Nos. 2450-2453 (4) 1.75
Set value .75

Various wave patterns. 2k, 40x23mm; 3.60k, 49x19mm.

7th World Ski-jumping Championships A870

1983, Mar. 16 ***Perf. 11½***

2454 A870 1k multi .25 .15

Souvenir Sheet

5th Anniv. of Czechoslovak-USSR Intercosmos Cooperative Space Program — A871

1983, Apr. 12 ***Perf. 12***

2455 Sheet of 2 14.00 7.00
a. A871 10k multi 6.00 3.00

See No. 2226.

Protected Species A872

1983, Apr. 28 ***Perf. 12x11½***

2456 A872 50h Butterfly, violets .15 .15
2457 A872 1k Water lilies, frog .25 .15
2458 A872 2k Pine cones, crossbill .48 .20
2459 A872 3.60k Herons .90 .38
2460 A872 5k Gentians, lynx 1.00 .38
2461 A872 7k Stag 5.25 1.50
Nos. 2456-2461 (6) 8.03 2.76

A873

A874

Soviet Marshals.

1983, May 5 ***Perf. 11½***

2462 A873 50h Ivan S. Konev .15 .15
2463 A873 1k Andrei I. Sheremenko .25 .15
2464 A873 2k Rodion J. Malinovsky .48 .20
Nos. 2462-2464 (3) .88
Set value .33

30th anniv. of Czechoslovak-Soviet defense treaty.

1983, July 13 ***Perf. 12***

2465 A874 2k multi .50 .20
a. Souvenir sheet of 4 5.00 4.00

World Peace and Life Congress, Prague. No. 2465 issued in sheets of 8.

Emperor Rudolf II by Adrian De Vries (1560-1626) A875

Art treasures of the Prague Castle: 5k, Kinetic relief, Timepiece, Rudolf Svoboda.

1983, Aug. 25 ***Perf. 11½***

2466 A875 4k multi 1.00 .40
2467 A875 5k multi 1.25 .50

See Nos. 2518-2519, 2610-2611, 2654-2655, 2717-2718, 2744-2745, 2792-2793.

ČESKOSLOVENSKO
50 h

9th Biennial of Illustrations for Children and Youth — A876

Illustrators: 50h, Oleg K. Zotov, USSR. 1k, Zbigniew Rychlicki, Poland. 4k, Lisbeth Zwerger, Austria. 7k, Antonio Dominques, Angola.

1983, Sept. 9 **Engr. & Photo.**

2468 A876 50h multi .15 .15
2469 A876 1k multi .26 .15
2470 A876 4k multi 1.00 .40
2471 A876 7k multi 1.75 .70
a. Souv. sheet of 4, #2468-2471 3.50 2.50
Nos. 2468-2471 (4) 3.16 1.40

World Communications Year — A877

Emblems and aircraft.

1983, Sept. 30 ***Perf. 11½***

2472 A877 50h red & black .15 .15
2473 A877 1k red & black, vert. .25 .15
2474 A877 4k red & black 1.00 .75
Nos. 2472-2474 (3) 1.40
Set value .90

60th anniv. of the Czechoslovak Airlines.

16th Party Congress Achievements — A878

1983, Oct. 20 *Perf. 12x11½*

2475 A878 50h Civil engineering construction .15 .15
2476 A878 1k Chemical industry .25 .15
2477 A878 3k Health services .75 .40
Nos. 2475-2477 (3) 1.15
Set value .55

Bratislava Type of 1977

Designs: 3k, Two sculptures, Viktor Tilgner (1844-96). 4k, Mirbachov Palace, 1939, by Julius Schubert (1888-1947).

1983, Oct. 28 *Perf. 12*

2478 A760 3k multi 2.00 .65
2479 A760 4k multi 1.00 1.00

Natl. Theater, Prague, Centenary — A879

1983, Nov. 8 **Engr.** *Perf. 11½*

2480 A879 50h Natl. Theater building .15 .15
2481 A879 2k State Theater, Natl. Theater .50 .20
Set value .25

Messenger of Mourning, by Mikolas Ales — A880

Designs: 2k, Genius, theater curtain by Vojtech Hynais (1854-1925). 3k, Music, Lyric drawings by Frantisek Zenisek (1849-1916). 4k, Symbolic figure of Prague, by Vaclav Brozik (1851-1901). 5k, Hradcany Castle, by Julius Marak (1832-1899).

1983, Nov. 18 **Engr.**

2482 A880 1k multi 1.40 .30
2483 A880 2k multi 2.75 .60
2484 A880 3k multi .75 .65
2485 A880 4k multi 1.00 .85
2486 A880 5k multi 1.25 1.00
Nos. 2482-2486 (5) 7.15 3.40

Warrior with Sword and Shield, Engraving, 17th Cent. — A881

Engravings of Costumes: 50h, Bodyguard of Rudolf II, by Jacob de Gheyn (1565-1629). 1k, Lady with Lace Collar, by Jacques Callot (1592-1635). 4k, Lady, by Vaclav Hollar (1607-77). 5k, Man, by Antoine Watteau (1684-1721).

Engraved and Photogravure

1983, Dec. 2 *Perf. 11½x12*

2487 A881 40h multi .15 .15
2488 A881 50h multi .15 .15
2489 A881 1k multi .25 .15
2490 A881 4k multi .75 .40
2491 A881 5k multi 2.25 .75
Nos. 2487-2491 (5) 3.55
Set value 1.35

Stamp Day — A882

1983, Dec. 18

2492 A882 1k Karl Seizinger (1889-1978), #114 .25 .15

Czechoslovak Federation, 15th Anniv. — A883

1984, Jan. 1 *Perf. 11½*

2493 A883 50h Bratislava, Prague Castles .20 .15

35th Anniv. of COMECON A884

1984, Jan. 23

2494 A884 1k Headquarters, Moscow .25 .15

1984 Winter Olympics A885

1984, Feb. 7 *Perf. 12x11½*

2495 A885 2k Cross-country skiing .50 .25
2496 A885 3k Hockey .75 .30
a. Souvenir sheet of 4 3.75 3.00
2497 A885 5k Biathlon 1.25 .50
Nos. 2495-2497 (3) 2.50 1.05

Intl. Olympic Committee, 90th Anniv. — A886

1984, Feb. 7 *Perf. 11½x12*

2498 A886 7k Rings, runners, torch 1.75 .70

City Arms Type of 1982

1984, Mar. 1 *Perf. 12x11½*

2499 A847 50h Kutna Hora .15 .15
2500 A847 50h Turnov .15 .15
2501 A847 1k Martin .25 .15
2502 A847 1k Milevsko .25 .15
Nos. 2499-2502 (4) .80
Set value .30

Intercosmos Space Program — A887

Resistance Heroes — A888

Various satellites. Nos. 2503-2507 se-tenant with labels showing flags.

1984, Apr. 12 *Perf. 11½x12*

2503 A887 50h multi .15 .15
2504 A887 1k multi .16 .15
2505 A887 2k multi .35 .20
2506 A887 4k multi .75 .40
2507 A887 5k multi 1.40 .50
Nos. 2503-2507 (5) 2.81 1.40

1984, May 9 *Perf. 11x11½*

Designs: 50h, Vendelin Opatrny (1908-44). 1k, Ladislav Novomesky (1904-44). 2k, Rudolf Jasiok (1919-44). 4k, Jan Nalepka (1912-43).

2508 A888 50h multi .18 .15
2509 A888 1k multi .25 .15
2510 A888 2k multi .50 .20
2511 A888 4k multi 1.00 .35
Nos. 2508-2511 (4) 1.93
Set value .70

Music Year — A889

1984, May 11 *Perf. 11½*

2512 A889 50h Instruments .15 .15
2513 A889 1k Organ pipes, vert. .25 .15
Set value .15

Bratislava Type of 1977

Designs: 3k, Vintners' Guild arms, 19th cent. 4k, View of Bratislava (painting commemorating shooting competition, 1827).

1984, June 1 *Perf. 12*

2514 A760 3k multi .75 .75
2515 A760 4k multi 1.00 1.00

Issued in sheet of 4.

Central Telecommunications Building, Bratislava — A890

1984, June 1 *Perf. 11½*

2516 A890 2k multi .45 .15

A891

A893

1984, June 12 *Perf. 12*

2517 A891 5k UPU emblem, dove, globe 1.75 1.25

1984 UPU Congress. Issued in sheet of 4 with and without Philatelic Salon text.

Prague Castle Type of 1983

Designs: 3k, Crowing rooster, St. Vitus Cathedral, 19th cent. 4k, King David from the Roundnice, Book of Psalms illuminated manuscript, Bohemia, 15th cent.

1984, Aug. 9 **Engr. & Photo.**

2518 A875 3k multi .65 .40
2519 A875 4k multi .90 .65

1984, Aug. 28 *Perf. 11½x12*

Playing cards.

2520 A893 50h Jack of Spades, 16th cent. .15 .15
2521 A893 1k Queen of spades, 17th cent. .25 .15
2522 A893 2k 9 of hearts, 18th cent. .50 .25
2523 A893 3k Jack of clubs, 18th cent. .75 .35
2524 A893 5k King of hearts, 19th cent. 1.25 .60
Nos. 2520-2524 (5) 2.90 1.50

Slovak Natl. Uprising, 40th Anniv. A894

1984, Aug. 29 *Perf. 12x11½*

2525 A894 50h Family, factories, flowers .15 .15

Battle of Dukla Pass (Carpathians), 40th Anniv. — A895

1984, Sept. 8 *Perf. 11½x12*

2526 A895 2k Soldiers, flag .40 .15

1984 Summer Olympics A896

1984, Sept. 9 *Perf. 12x11½*

2527 A896 1k Pole vault .20 .15
2528 A896 2k Bicycling .40 .20
2529 A896 3k Rowing .60 .35
2530 A896 5k Weight lifting 1.00 .45
a. Souv. sheet of 4, #2527-2530 2.00 1.75
Nos. 2527-2530 (4) 2.20 1.15

16th Party Congress Goals and Projects A897

1984, Oct. 28 *Perf. 12x11½*

2531 A897 1k Communications .16 .15
2532 A897 2k Transportation .32 .20
2533 A897 3k Transgas pipeline .50 .30
a. Souvenir sheet of 3 2.50 2.00
Nos. 2531-2533 (3) .98 .65

Art Type of 1967

Paintings: 1k, The Milevsky River, by Karel Stehlik (b. 1912). 2k, Under the Trees, by Viktor Barvitius (1834-1902). 3k, Landscape with Flowers, by Zolo Palugyay (1898-1935). 4k, King in Palace, Visehrad Codex miniature, 1085. 5k, View of Kokorin Castles, by Antonin Manes. Nos. 2534-2537 horiz.; issued in sheets of 4.

1984, Nov. 16 *Perf. 11½*

2534 A565 1k multi .85 .25
2535 A565 2k multi 1.10 .50
2536 A565 3k multi .65 .65
2537 A565 4k multi .85 .85
2538 A565 5k multi 1.10 1.00
Nos. 2534-2538 (5) 4.55 3.25

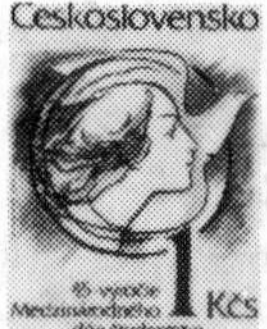

Students' Intl., 45th Anniv. — A898

Birth Cent., Antonin Zapotocky — A899

1984, Nov. 17

2539 A898 1k Head, dove .20 .15

Engr. & Photo.

1984, Dec. 18 *Perf. 11½*

2540 A899 50h multi .15 .15

Stamp Day — A900

1984, Dec. 18 *Perf. 11½x12*

2541 A900 1k Engraver Bohumil Heinz (1894-1940) .20 .15

City Arms Type of 1982

1985, Feb. 5 *Perf. 12x11½*

2542 A847 50h Kamyk nad Vltavou .15 .15
2543 A847 50h Havirov .15 .15
2544 A847 50h Trnava .15 .15
Set value .24 .15

University of Applied Arts, Prague, Centenary — A901

1985, Feb. 6 *Perf. 11½x12*
2545 A901 3k Art and Pleasure, sculpture .60 .30

Trnava University, 350th Anniv. — A902

1985, Feb. 6 *Perf. 11½x12*
2546 A902 2k Town of Trnava .40 .20

Military Museum Exposition A903

1985, Feb. 7 *Perf. 11½x12, 12x11½*
2547 A903 50h Armor, crossbow, vert. .15 .15
2548 A903 1k Medals, vert. .20 .15
2549 A903 2k Biplane, spacecraft .40 .18
Nos. 2547-2549 (3) .75
Set value .33

UN 40th Anniv., Peace Year 1986 A905

(Vladimir I. Lenin (1870-1924), 1st Chairman of Russia — A904)

1985, Mar. 15 **Engr.** *Perf. 12*
2550 A904 2k multi .50 .30

No. 2550 printed in sheets of 6.

1985, Mar. 15
2551 A905 6k UN, Peace Year emblems *1.75 1.50*

Issued in sheets of 4.

A906 A907

Engraved and Photogravure
1985, Apr. 5 *Perf. 11½*
2552 A906 4k Natl. arms, twig, crowd .80 .40

Kosice govt. plan, Apr. 5, 1945.

1985, Apr. 5
2553 A907 50h Natl. arms, flag, soldiers .15 .15

Natl. Security Forces, 40th anniv.

Halley's Comet, INTERCOSMOS Project Vega — A908

Design: Emblem, space platform, interstellar map, intercept data.

1985, Apr. 12 *Perf. 12x11½*
2554 Sheet of 2 *7.50 6.75*
a. A908 5k multicolored *1.75 1.50*

Project Vega, a joint effort of the USSR, France, German Democratic Republic, Austria, Poland, Bulgaria and CSSR, was for the geophysical study of Halley's Comet, Dec. 1984-Mar. 1986.

European Ice Hockey Championships, Prague, Apr. 17-May 3 — A909

1985, Apr. 13
2555 A909 1k Hockey players, emblem .20 .15

No. 2555 Ovptd. "CSSR MISTREM SVETA" in Violet Blue

1985, May 31 *Perf. 12x11½*
2556 A909 1k multi *2.75 2.75*

Natl. Chess Org., 80th Anniv. — A910

1985, Apr. 13 *Perf. 11½*
2557 A910 6k Emblem, game board, chessmen .90 .50

Anniversaries — A911

1985, May 5 *Perf. 11½x12*
2558 A911 1k May Uprising, 1945 .15 .15
2559 A911 1k Soviet Army in CSSR, 1945 .15 .15
2560 A911 1k Warsaw Treaty, 1950 .15 .15
2561 A911 1k Czech-Soviet Treaty, 1970 .15 .15
Nos. 2558-2561 (4) .60
Set value .45

Spartakiad '85, Strahov Stadium, Prague, June 27 — A912

Designs: 50h, Gymnasts warming up with rackets and balls. 1k, Rhythmic gymnastics floor exercise, Prague Castle.

1985, June 3 *Perf. 11½, 11½x12*
2562 A912 50h multi .15 .15

Size: 53x22mm

2563 A912 1k multi .18 .15
Set value .25 .15

WWII Anti-Fascist Political Art A913

Drawings and caricatures: 50h, Fire, and From the Concentration Camp, by Joseph Capek (1887-1945). 2k, The Conference on Disarmament in Geneva, 1927 and The Prophecy of Three Parrots, 1933, by Frantisek Bidlo (1895-1945). 4k, The Unknown Warrior to Order, 1936, and The Almost Peaceful Dove, 1937, by Antonin Pelc (1895-1967).

1985, June 4 *Perf. 12x11½*
2564 A913 50h multi .15 .15
2565 A913 2k multi .28 .18
2566 A913 4k multi .60 .40
Nos. 2564-2566 (3) 1.03 .73

Helsinki Conference on European Security and Cooperation, 10th Anniv. — A914

1985, July 1 **Engr. & Photo.**
2567 A914 7k multi 1.50 1.00
a. Souvenir sheet of 4 7.00 7.00

An imperf. souv. sheet similar to No. 2567a was issued June 1, 1988 for FINLANDIA '88 and PRAGA '88.

12th World Youth Festival, Moscow A915

1985, July 2
2568 A915 1k Kremlin, youths .18 .15

A916 A918

1985, Sept. 3 *Perf. 11½*
2569 A916 50h multi .15 .15

Federation of World Trade Unions, 40th anniv.

Bratislava Type of 1977

Designs: 3k, Castle and river, lace embroidery by Elena Holeczyova (1906-1983). 4k, Pottery cups and mugs, 1600-1500 B.C.

1985, Sept. 4 **Engr.** *Perf. 12*
2570 A760 3k multi .55 .45
2571 A760 4k multi .75 .60

Issued in sheets of 4.

Engraved and Photogravure
1985, Sept. 5 *Perf. 11½*

Children's book illustrations: 1k, Rocking Horse, by Kveta Pacovska, USSR. 2k, Fairies, by Gennadij Spirin, USSR. 3k, Butterfly and Girl, by Kaarina Kaila, Finland. 4k, Boy and Animals, by Erick Ingraham, US.

2572 A918 1k multi .15 .15
2573 A918 2k multi .28 .18
2574 A918 3k multi .45 .25
2575 A918 4k multi .60 .35
a. Souv. sheet of 4, #2572-2575 3.50 2.75
Nos. 2572-2575 (4) 1.48 .93

10th biennial of illustrations.

5-Year Development Plan — A919

1985, Oct. 28 *Perf. 12x11½*
2576 A919 50h Construction machinery .15 .15
2577 A919 1k Prague subway, map .15 .15
2578 A919 2k Modern textile spinning .28 .22
Nos. 2576-2578 (3) .58
Set value .40

16th Communist Party Congress goals.

Prague Castle — A920 A921

Engr., Engr. & Photo. (3k)
1985, Oct. 28 *Perf. 12*
2579 A920 2k Presidential Palace Gate, 1768 .30 .22
2580 A920 3k St. Vitus' Cathedral .45 .38

Sheets of 6.

Engraved and Photogravure
1985, Nov. 23 *Perf. 11½x12*

Glassware: 50h, Pitcher, Near East, 4th cent. 1k, Venetian pitcher, 16th cent. 2k, Bohemian goblet, c. 1720. 4k, Harrachov Bohemian vase, 18th cent. 6k, Jablonec Bohemian vase, c. 1900.

2581 A921 50h multi .15 .15
2582 A921 1k multi .15 .15
2583 A921 2k multi .28 .22
2584 A921 4k multi .60 .42
2585 A921 6k multi .90 .70
Nos. 2581-2585 (5) 2.08 1.64

Arts and Crafts Museum, Prague, cent.

Art Type of 1967

Designs: 1k, Young Woman in a Blue Gown, by Jozef Ginovsky (1800-1857). 2k, Lenin on the Charles Bridge, Prague, 1952, by Martin Sladky (b. 1920). 3k, Avenue of Poplars, 1935, by Vaclav Rabas (1885-1954). 4k, The Martyrom of St. Dorothea, 1516, by Hans Baldung Grien (c. 1484-1545). 5k, Portrait of Jasper Schade van Westrum, 1645, by Frans Hals (c. 1581-1666).

1985, Nov. 27 **Engr.** *Perf. 12*
2586 A565 1k multi *1.25 1.00*
2587 A565 2k multi .35 .35
2588 A565 3k multi .55 .45
2589 A565 4k multi .75 .60
2590 A565 5k multi .90 .75
Nos. 2586-2590 (5) *3.80 3.15*

Sheets of 4.

Bohdan Roule (1921-1960), Engraver — A922

Engraved and Photogravure
1985, Dec. 18 *Perf. 11½x12*
2591 A922 1k multicolored .16 .15

Stamp Day 1985.

(ČESKOSLOVENSKO — Intl. Peace Year — A923)

1986, Jan. 2
2592 A923 1k multi .16 .15

Philharmonic Orchestra, 90th Anniv. — A924

EXPO '86, Vancouver — A925

1986, Jan. 2 *Perf. 11½*
2593 A924 1k Victory Statue, Prague .16 .15

1986, Jan. 23 *Perf. 11½*

Design: Z 50 LS monoplane, Cenyerth Prague-Kladno locomotive, Sahara Desert rock drawing, 5th-6th cent. B.C.

2594 A925 4k multicolored .60 .40

City Arms Type of 1982

1986, Feb. 10 *Perf. 12x11½*

Size: 42x54mm

2595 A847 50h Myjava .15 .15
2596 A847 50h Vodnany .15 .15
2597 A847 50h Zamberk .15 .15
Set value .25 .20

17th Natl. Communist Party Congress, Prague, Mar. 24 — A926

1986, Mar. 20 *Perf. 11½*

2598 A926 50h shown .15 .15
2599 A926 1k Industry .18 .15
Set value .25 .15

Natl. Communist Party, 65th Anniv. — A927

1986, Mar. 20 *Perf. 12x11½*

2600 A927 50h Star, man, woman .15 .15
2601 A927 1k Hammer, sickle, laborers .18 .15
Set value .25 .15

Natl. Front Election Program A928

1986, Mar. 28

2602 A928 50h multi .15 .15

Karlovy Vary Intl. Film Festival, 25th Anniv. — A929

1986, Apr. 3 *Perf. 11½*

2603 A929 1k multi .18 .15

A930 A931

1986, Apr. 8 **Engr. & Photo.**

2604 A930 1k multi .18 .15

Spring of Prague Music Festival.

1986, Apr. 25

2605 A931 50h multi .15 .15

Prague-Moscow air service, 50th anniv.

Intl. Olympic Committee, 90th Anniv. — A932

1986, May 12 *Perf. 11½x12*

2606 A932 2k multi .30 .20

1986 World Cup Soccer Championships, Mexico — A933

1986, May 15 *Perf. 12x11½*

2607 A933 4k multi .60 .40

Women's World Volleyball Championships, Prague — A934

1986, May 19

2608 A934 1k multi .18 .15

Souvenir Sheet

Intl. Philatelic Federation, FIP, 60th Anniv. — A935

1986, June 3 **Engr.** *Perf. 12*

2609 A935 20k multi 4.50 3.50

Exists imperf. and with perforations between stamps omitted.

Prague Castle Type of 1983

Designs: 2k, Jewelled funerary pendant, 9th cent. 3k, Allegory of Blossoms, sculpture by Jaroslav Horejc (1886-1983), St. Vitus' Cathedral.

1986, June 6 **Engr.** *Perf. 12*

2610 A875 2k multi .32 .30
2611 A875 3k multi .70 .45

UN Child Survival Campaign — A937

Toys.

Engraved and Photogravure

1986, Sept. 1 *Perf. 11½*

2612 A937 10h Rooster .15 .15
2613 A937 20h Horse and rider .15 .15
2614 A937 1k Doll .24 .16
2615 A937 2k Doll, diff. .48 .32
2616 A937 3k Tin omnibus, c. 1910 .75 .50
Nos. 2612-2616 (5) 1.77
Set value 1.05

UNICEF, 40th anniv.

Registration, Cent. — A938

1986, Sept. 2 *Perf. 11½x12*

2617 A938 4k Label, mail coach .60 .45

Bratislava Type of 1977

1986, Sept. 11 **Engr.** *Perf. 12*

2618 A760 3k Sigismund Gate .55 .38
2619 A760 4k St. Margaret, bas-relief .70 .52

Sheets of four.

Owls — A939

Engraved and Photogravure

1986, Sept. 18 *Perf. 11½*

2620 A939 50h Bubo bubo .15 .15
2621 A939 2k Asio otus .32 .25
2622 A939 3k Strix aluco .50 .35
2623 A939 4k Tyto alba .65 .50
2624 A939 5k Asio flammeus .80 .65
Nos. 2620-2624 (5) 2.42 1.90

Souvenir Sheet

Intl. Brigades in Spain — A940

Theater curtain: Woman Savaged by Horses, 1936, by Vladimir Sychra (1903-1963), Natl Gallery, Prague.

1986, Oct. 1 **Engr.** *Perf. 12*

2625 Sheet of 2 3.00 2.75
a. A940 5k multi 1.25 1.00

Locomotives and Streetcars — A941

Engraved and Photogravure

1986, Oct. 6 *Perf. 12x11½*

2626 A941 50h KT-8 .15 .15
2627 A941 1k E458.1 .16 .15
2628 A941 3k T466.2 .48 .30
2629 A941 5k M152.0 .80 .52
Nos. 2626-2629 (4) 1.59 1.12

Paintings in the Prague and Bratislava Natl. Galleries A942

Designs: 1k, The Circus Rider, 1980, by Jan Bauch (b. 1898). 2k, The Ventriloquist, 1954, by Frantisek Tichy (1896-1961). 3k, In the Circus, 1946, by Vincent Hloznik (b. 1919). 6k, Clown, 1985, by Karel Svolinsky (1896-1986).

1986, Oct. 13 **Engr.** *Perf. 12*

2630 A942 1k multi .18 .15
2631 A942 2k multi .38 .30
2632 A942 3k multi .52 .42
2633 A942 6k multi 1.10 .90
Nos. 2630-2633 (4) 2.18 1.77

Art Type of 1967

Designs: 1k, The Czech Lion, May 1918, by Vratislav H. Brunner (1886-1928). 2k, Boy with Mandolin, 1945, by Jozef Sturdik (b. 1920). 3k, Metra Building, 1984, by Frantisek Gross (1909-1985). 4k, Portrait of Maria Maximiliana at Sternberk, 1665, by Karel Skreta (1610-1674). 5k, Adam and Eve, 1538, by Lucas Cranach (1472-1553).

1986, Nov. 3 **Engr.** *Perf. 12*

2634 A565 1k multi *.20 .15*
2635 A565 2k multi *.40 .28*
2636 A565 3k multi *.60 .38*
2637 A565 4k multi *.80 .55*
2638 A565 5k multi *1.00 .65*
Nos. 2634-2638 (5) *3.00 2.01*

Sheets of 4.

Stamp Day — A943

Design: V.H. Brunner (1886-1928), stamp designer, and No. 88.

Photo. & Engr.

1986, Dec. 18 *Perf. 11½x12*

2639 A943 1k multicolored .15 .15

World Cyclocross Championships, Jan. 24-25, Central Bohemia — A944

1987, Jan. 22 *Perf. 11½*

2640 A944 6k multi 1.00 .60

Czechoslovakian Bowling Union, 50th Anniv. — A945

1987, Jan. 22 *Perf. 11½*

2641 A945 2k multi .35 .20

State Decorations — A946

Designs: 50h, Gold Stars of Socialist Labor and Czechoslovakia. 2k, Order of Klement Gottwald. 3k, Order of the Republic. 4k, Order of Victorious February. 5k, Order of Labor.

1987, Feb. 4 *Perf. 12x11½*

2642 A946 50h multi .15 .15
2643 A946 2k multi .35 .22
2644 A946 3k multi .50 .45
2645 A946 4k multi .70 .40
2646 A946 5k multi .85 .50
Nos. 2642-2646 (5) 2.55 1.72

Butterflies A947

1987, Mar. 4

2647	A947	1k Limenitis populi	.15	.15
2648	A947	2k Smerinthus ocellatus	.30	.22
2649	A947	3k Pericallia matronula	.45	.30
2650	A947	4k Saturnia pyri	.60	.38
		Nos. 2647-2650 (4)	1.50	1.05

Natl. Nuclear Power Industry A948

1987, Apr. 6

2651 A948 5k multi .75 .50

11th Revolutionary Trade Union Movement Congress, Apr. 14-17, Prague — A949

1987, Apr. 7 *Perf. 11½*

2652 A949 1k multi .15 .15

Souvenir Sheet

INTERCOSMOS, 10th Anniv. — A950

Design: Cosmonauts Alexei Gubarev of the USSR and Vladimir Remek of Czechoslovakia, rocket and emblem.

1987, Apr. 12 **Engr.** *Perf. 12*

2653	Sheet of 2	3.50	3.50
a.	A950 10k multi	1.75	1.75
b.	Souv. sheet of 4, litho. & engr., imperf.	*7.00*	*7.00*

No. 2653b issued Nov. 15, 1987.

Prague Castle Art Treasures Type of 1983

Designs: 2k, Three Saints, stained-glass window detail, c. 1870, St. Vitus Cathedral, by Frantisek Sequens (1830-1896). 3k, Coat of Arms, New Land Rolls Hall, 1605.

1987, May 9 *Perf. 11½*

2654	A875	2k multi	.30	.20
2655	A875	3k dk red, slate gray & yel org	.45	.30

Nos. 2654-2655 each printed in sheets of 6.

PRAGA '88 A951

Photo. & Engr.

1987, May 12 *Perf. 12x11½*

2656	A951	3k Telephone, 1894	.50	.32
2657	A951	3k Postal van, 1924	.50	.32
2658	A951	4k Locomotive tender, 1907	.75	.42
2659	A951	4k Tram, 1900	.75	.42
2660	A951	5k Steam roller, 1936	.85	.52
		Nos. 2656-2660 (5)	3.35	2.00

Printed in sheets of 8 + 2 labels picturing telephone or vehicles. Nos. 2657-2658 also printed in sheets of 4 + label picturing vehicles.

Destruction of Lidice and Lezaky, 45th Anniv. — A952

Drawings: No. 2661, When the Fighting Ended, 1945, by Pavel Simon. No. 2662, The End of the game, 1945, by Ludmila Jirincova.

1987, June *Perf. 11½*

2661	A952	1k blk, cerise & vio	.15	.15
2662	A952	1k blk, gold, pale lil & cerise	.15	.15
		Set value		.20

Union of Czechoslovakian Mathematicians and Physicists, 125th Anniv. — A953

Designs: No. 2663, Prague Town Hall mathematical clock, Theory of Functions diagram. No. 2664, J.M. Petzval (1807-1891), J. Strouhal (1850-1922) and V. Jarnik (1897-1970). No. 2665, Geographical measurement from A.M. Malletta's book, 1672, earth fold and Brownian motion diagrams.

1987, July 6 *Perf. 11½x12*

2663	A953	50h multi	.15	.15
2664	A953	50h multi	.15	.15
2665	A953	50h multi	.15	.15
		Set value	.30	.25

A954

A955

Award-winning illustrations.

1987, Sept. 3 *Perf. 11½*

2666	A954	50h Asun Balzola, Spain	.15	.15
2667	A954	1k Frederic Clement, France	.20	.15
2668	A954	2k Elzbieta Gaudasinska, Poland	.40	.26
a.		Souv. sheet of 2 + label	.80	.60
2669	A954	4k Marija Lucija Stupica, Yugoslavia	.80	.52
		Nos. 2666-2669 (4)	1.55	1.08

11th Biennial of Children's Book Illustration, Sept. 11-Oct. 30, Bratislava.

1987, Sept. 23

2670 A955 50h Eternal flame, flower .15 .15

Theresienstadt Memorial for the victims from 23 European countries who died in the Small Fortress, Terezin, a Nazi concentration camp.

Socialist Communications Organization, 30th Anniv. — A956

1987, Sept. 23

2671 A956 4k Emblem, satellite, dish receiver .65 .40

Jan Evangelista Purkyne (1787-1869), Physiologist A957

1987, Sept. 30

2672 A957 7k multicolored 1.10 .75

ČESKOSLOVENSKO

Views of Bratislava A958

Designs: 3k, Male and female figures supporting an oriel, Arkier Palace, c. 1552. 4k, View of Bratislava from Ware Conterfactur de Stadt Presburg, from an engraving by Hans Mayer, 1563.

1987, Oct. 1 **Engr.** *Perf. 12*

2673	A958	3k multicolored	.52	.35
2674	A958	4k multicolored	.70	.45

Printed in sheets of 4 with Bratislava Castle (from Mayer's engraving) between.

See Nos. 2719-2720, 2763-2764, 2800-2801.

Type of 1974

Photo. & Engr.

1987, Nov. 1 *Perf. 12x11½*

2675 A699 1k Post rider .15 .15

PRAGA '88, Aug. 26-Sept. 4, 1988. No. 2675 printed se-tenant with label picturing exhibition emblem.

October Revolution, Russia, 70th Anniv. A959

Establishment of the Union of Soviet Socialist Republics, 65th Anniv. — A960

1987, Nov. 6 *Perf. 12x11½*

2676	A959	50h multicolored	.15	.15
2677	A960	50h multicolored	.15	.15
		Set value	.15	.15

Art Type of 1974

Paintings in national galleries: 1k, Enclosure of Dreams, by Kamil Lhotak (b. 1912). 2k, Tulips, by Ester Simerova-Martincekova (b. 1909). 3k, Triptych with Bohemian Landscape, by Josef Lada (1887-1957). 4k, Accordion Player, by Josef Capek (1887-1945). 5k, Self-portrait, by Jiri Trnka (1912-1969).

1987, Nov. 18 **Engr.** *Perf. 12*

2678	A700	1k multi	.18	.15
2679	A700	2k multi	.38	.22
2680	A700	3k multi	.55	.32
2681	A700	4k multi	.75	.45
2682	A700	5k multi	.95	.60
		Nos. 2678-2682 (5)	2.81	1.74

Czech and Slovak art. Issued in sheets of 4.

69th Stamp Day — A961

Portrait of Jacob Obrovsky (1882-1949), stamp designer, Bohemian Lion (Type SP1), sketch of a lion and PRAGA '88 emblem.

Photo. & Engr.

1987, Dec. 18 *Perf. 11½x12*

2683 A961 1k multicolored .15 .15

No. 2683 printed in sheet of four with eight labels se-tenant with stamps, inscribed "100 Years of the National Philatelic Movement in Czechoslovakia" in Czech. The four labels between the "blocks of six" are blank.

Czechoslovak Republic, 70th Anniv. — A962

1988, Jan. 1 *Perf. 12x11½*

2684 A962 1k Woman, natl. arms, linden branch .15 .15

Natl. Front, 40th Anniv. — A963

1988, Feb. 25 *Perf. 11½*

2685 A963 50h multicolored .15 .15

Husak Type of 1983

Photo. & Engr.

1988, Jan. 10 *Perf. 12x11½*

2686 A865 1k brt rose & dk carmine .15 .15

Olympics — A965

1988, Feb. 1 *Perf. 11½x12*

2687	A965	50h Ski jumping, ice hockey	.15	.15
2688	A965	1k Basketball, soccer	.18	.15
2689	A965	6k Discus, weight lifting	1.00	.85
		Nos. 2687-2689 (3)	1.33	1.15

Exist in souv. sheets of 2, imperf. between and in souv. sheets of 2, imperf.

Victorious February, 40th Anniv. — A966

Design: Statue of Klement Gottwald by Rudolf Svoboda.

1988, Feb. 25 *Perf. 11½*

2690 A966 50h multicolored .15 .15

No. 2690 exists in a souvenir sheet of two No. 2690 and two postally invalid copies of No. 637, imperf. Sheet exists imperf.

Classic Automobiles — A967

1988, Mar. 1 *Perf. 12x11½*

2691	A967	50h 1914 Laurin & Klement	.15	.15
2692	A967	1k 1902 Tatra NW Type B	.28	.18
2693	A967	2k 1905 Tatra NW Type E	.55	.35
2694	A967	3k 1929 Tatra 12 Normandie	.85	.55
2695	A967	4k 1899 Meteor	1.10	.72
a.		Bklt. pane, 2 3k, 3 4k + label		
		Nos. 2691-2695 (5)	2.93	1.95

Postal Museum, 70th Anniv. A968

Praga '88 emblem and: 50h, Postman, Malostranske Namesti Square p.o., Prague, c. 1742, and Velka Javorina television transmitter, 1979. 1k, Telecommunications Center, Mlada Boleslav, 1986, and Carmelite Street p.o., Prague, c. 1792. 2k, Prague 1 (1873) and Bratislava 56 (1984) post offices. 4k, Communications Center, Prachatice (1982), postman and Maltetske Nameski Square p.o., Prague, c. 1622.

1988, Mar. 10

2696	A968	50h multi	.15	.15
2697	A968	1k multi	.22	.16
2698	A968	2k multi	.42	.28
2699	A968	4k multi	.90	.60
a.		Souv. sheet, 2 each #2698-2699	3.75	2.00
		Nos. 2696-2699 (4)	1.69	1.19

In No. 2699a the top pair of Nos. 2698-2699 is imperf. at top and sides.

A969

A970

1988, Mar. 29 ***Perf. 11½***
2700 A969 50h multicolored .15 .15

Matice Slovenska Cultural Assoc., 125th anniv.

1988, May 12 **Photo. & Engr.**

PRAGA '88. (Exhibition emblem and aspects of the Museum of Natl. Literature, Prague): 1k, Gate and distant view of museum. 2k, Celestial globe, illuminated manuscript, bookshelves and ornately decorated ceiling. 5k, Illuminated "B" and decorated binder of a medieval Bible. 7k, Celestial globe, illuminated manuscript, Zodiacal signs (Aries and Leo), view of museum.

2701 A970 1k multicolored .25 .15
a. Souvenir sheet of 4 1.25 .60
2702 A970 2k multicolored .50 .28
a. Souvenir sheet of 4 2.50 1.25
2703 A970 5k multicolored 1.25 .75
a. Souvenir sheet of 4 6.50 3.00
2704 A970 7k multicolored 1.50 .80
a. Souvenir sheet of 4 7.25 3.25
b. Souv. sheet of 4, imperf., #2701-2704 3.50 2.50
Nos. 2701-2704 (4) 3.50 1.98

PRAGA '88 — A971

Exhibition emblem and fountains, Prague.

1988, June 1 ***Perf. 11½x12***
2705 A971 1k Waldstein Palace .25 .16
2706 A971 2k Old town square .52 .25
2707 A971 3k Charles University .80 .40
2708 A971 4k Prague Castle 1.10 .52
a. Souv. sheet of 4, #2705-2708 2.75 1.75
Nos. 2705-2708 (4) 2.67 1.33

Souvenir Sheet

Soviet-US Summit Conference on Arms Reduction, Moscow — A972

Design: The capital, Washington, and the Kremlin, Moscow.

1988, June 1 ***Perf. 12x11½***
2709 A972 4k blue blk, dark red & gold 2.25 1.25

Exists imperf.

PRAGA '88 A973

Exhibition emblem and modern architecture, Prague: 50h, Trade Unions Central Recreation Center. 1k, Koospol foreign trade company. 2k, Motol Teaching Hospital. 4k, Culture Palace.

1988, July 1 ***Perf. 12x11½***
2710 A973 50h multicolored .15 .15
2711 A973 1k blk, lt blue & bister .24 .15
2712 A973 2k multicolored .45 .26
a. Souv. sheet, 2 1k, 2 2k + 4 labels, imperf. 1.75
2713 A973 4k multicolored .95 .52
a. Souv. sheet, 2 50h, 2 4k + 4 labels, imperf. 2.50
Nos. 2710-2713 (4) 1.79 1.08

Souvenir Sheet

PRAGA '88 — A974

Design: Exhibition emblem and Alfons Mucha (1860-1939), designer of first Czech postage stamp.

1988, Aug. 18 **Engr.** ***Perf. 12***
2714 A974 Sheet of 2 3.00 1.75
a. 5k multicolored 1.50 .85

Czech postage stamps, 70th anniv.

Souvenir Sheets

PRAGA '88 A975

Paintings: 5k, *Turin, Monte Superga,* by Josef Navratil (1798-1865), Postal Museum, Prague.

Details of *Bacchus and Ariadne,* by Sebastiano Ricci (1659-1734), Natl. Gallery, Prague: No. 2716a, Ariadne. No. 2716b, Bacchus and creatures.

1988
2715 Sheet of 2 2.75 1.50
a. A975 5k multi 1.50 .85
2716 Sheet of 2 5.50 3.25
a.-b. A975 10k any single 2.75 1.50

Issue dates: 5k, Aug. 19. 10k, Aug. 26. No. 2716 exists with emblem and inscription "DEN F.I.P. JOURNEE DE LA FEDERATION INTERNATIONALE DE PHILATELIE."

Prague Castle Type of 1983

Painting: 2k, Pottery jug, 17th cent. 3k, *St. Catherine with Angel,* 1580, by Paolo Veronese.

1988, Sept. 28 **Engr.** ***Perf. 12***
2717 A875 2k shown .95 .52
2718 A875 3k multi 1.25 .70

Issued in sheets of 6.

Bratislava Views Type of 1987

Designs: 3k, *Hlavne Square, circa 1840* an etching by R. Alt-Sandman, 1840. 4k, *Ferdinand House, circa 1850,* a pen-and-ink drawing by V. Reim.

1988, Oct. 19
2719 A958 3k multicolored .95 .52
2720 A958 4k multicolored 1.25 .70

Issued in sheets of 4.

Art Type of 1974

Paintings in natl. galleries: 2k, *With Bundles,* 1931, by Martin Benka (1888-1971). 6k, *Blue Bird,* 1903, by Vojtech Preissig (1873-1944). 7k, *A Jaguar Attacking a Rider,* c. 1850, by Eugene Delacroix (1798-1863).

1988, Nov. 17 **Engr.** ***Perf. 12***
2721 A700 2k multicolored .30 .15
2722 A700 6k multicolored .90 .40
2723 A700 7k multicolored 1.05 .45
Nos. 2721-2723 (3) 2.25 1.00

Czech and Slovak art. Issued in sheets of 4.

Stamp Day — A978

Design: 1k, Jaroslav Benda (1882-1970), illustrator and stamp designer.

Photo. & Engr.

1988, Dec. 18 ***Perf. 11½x12***
2724 A978 1k multicolored .15 .15

Paris-Dakar Rally — A979

Trucks: 50h, Earth, Motokov Liaz. 1k, Liaz, globe. 2k, Earth, Motokov Tatra. No. 607. 4k, Map of racecourse, turban, Tatra.

1989, Jan. 2 ***Perf. 12x11½***
2725 A979 50h multicolored .15 .15
2726 A979 1k multicolored .15 .15
2727 A979 2k multicolored .26 .15
2728 A979 4k multicolored .52 .26
Nos. 2725-2728 (4) 1.08
Set value .50

Czechoslovakian Federation, 20th Anniv. — A980

1989, Jan. 1
2729 A980 50h multicolored .15 .15

Jan Botto (1829-1881) A981

Taras Grigorievich Shevchenko (1814-1861) A982

Jean Cocteau (1889-1963) A983

Charlie Chaplin (1889-1977) A984

Jawaharlal Nehru (1889-1964) and "UNESCO" — A985

Famous men: No. 2732, Modest Petrovich Musorgsky (1839-1881).

Photo. & Engr.

1989, Mar. 9 ***Perf. 12x11½***
2730 A981 50h brn blk & lt blue green .15 .15
2731 A982 50h shown .15 .15
2732 A982 50h multicolored .15 .15
2733 A983 50h red brn, grnh blk & org brn .15 .15
2734 A984 50h blk, int blue & dark red .15 .15
2735 A985 50h brn blk & lt yel green .15 .15
Set value .45 .30

Shipping Industry A986

1989, Mar. 27
2736 A986 50h *Republika* .15 .15
2737 A986 1k *Pionyr,* flags .15 .15
2738 A986 2k *Brno,* flags .22 .15
2739 A986 3k *Trinec* .32 .18
2740 A986 4k Flags, mast, *Orlik* .45 .25
2741 A986 5k *Vltava,* communication hardware .55 .32
Nos. 2736-2741 (6) 1.84 1.20

Pioneer Organization, 40th Anniv. — A987

Photo. & Engr.

1989, Apr. 20 ***Perf. 11½***
2742 A987 50h multi .15 .15

Art Type of 1974

Details of *Feast of Rose Garlands,* 1506, by Albrecht Durer, Natl. Gallery, Prague: a, Virgin and Child. b, Angel playing mandolin.

1989, Apr. 21 **Engr.** ***Perf. 12***

Miniature Sheet

2743 Sheet of 2 4.75 2.50
a.-b. A700 10k any single 2.50 1.25

Prague Castle Art Type of 1983

Designs: 2k, Bas-relief picturing Kaiser Karl IV, from Kralovske tomb by Alexander Colin (c. 1527-1612). 3k, Self-portrait, by V.V. Reiner (1689-1743).

1989, May 9 **Photo. & Engr.**
2744 A875 2k dark red, sepia & buff .30 .16
2745 A875 3k multi .45 .24

Printed in sheets of 6.

Souvenir Sheet

PHILEXFRANCE '89, French Revolution Bicent. — A988

1989, July 14 **Engr.** ***Perf. 12***
2746 A988 5k brt blue, blk & dk red .75 .35

Haliaeetus albicilla A989

Photo. & Engr.

1989, July 17 ***Perf. 12x11½***
2747 A989 1k multicolored .15 .15

World Wildlife Fund — A990

Toads and newts.

1989, July 18 *Perf. 11½x12*
2748 A990 2k *Bombina bombina* .30 .15
2749 A990 3k *Bombina variegata* .45 .16
2750 A990 4k *Triturus alpestris* .60 .22
2751 A990 5k *Triturus montandoni* .75 .28
Nos. 2748-2751 (4) 2.10 .81

Slovak Folk Art Collective, 40th Anniv. — A991

1989, Aug. 29 *Perf. 12x11½*
2752 A991 50h multicolored .15 .15

Slovak Uprising, 45th Anniv. — A992

Photo. & Engr.
1989, Aug. 29 *Perf. 11½x12*
2753 A992 1k multicolored .15 .15

A993

A994

Award-winning illustrations.

1989, Sept. 4 *Perf. 11½*
2754 A993 50h Hannu Taina, Finland .15 .15
2755 A993 1k Aleksander Aleksov, Bulgaria .15 .15
2756 A993 2k Jurgen Spohn, West Berlin .25 .15
2757 A993 4k Robert Brun, Czechoslovakia .50 .25
a. Souvenir sheet of 2 1.20 .60
Nos. 2754-2757 (4) 1.05
Set value .50

12th Biennial of Children's Book Illustration, Bratislava.

1989, Sept. 5 **Engr.** *Perf. 11½x12*
Poisonous mushrooms.
2758 A994 50h *Nolanea verna* .15 .15
2759 A994 1k *Amanita phalloides* .15 .15
2760 A994 2k *Amanita virosa* .30 .15
2761 A994 3k *Cortinarius orellanus* .45 .22
2762 A994 5k *Galerina marginata* .75 .38
Nos. 2758-2762 (5) 1.80
Set value .88

Bratislava Views Type of 1987

Views of Devin, a Slavic castle above the Danube, Bratislava.

1989, Oct. 16 **Engr.** *Perf. 12*
2763 A958 3k Castle, flower 1.65 .75
2764 A958 4k Castle, urn 2.25 1.25

Printed in sheets of 4.

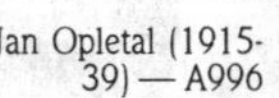
Jan Opletal (1915-39) — A996

Photo. & Engr.
1989, Nov. 17 *Perf. 12x11½*
2765 A996 1k multicolored .15 .15

Intl. Student's Day. Funeral of Opletal, a Nazi victim, on Nov. 15, 1939, sparked student demonstrations that resulted in the closing of all universities in occupied Bohemia and Moravia.

Art Type of 1974

Paintings in Natl. Galleries: 2k, *Nirvana*, c. 1920, by Anton Jasusch (1882-1965). 4k, *Winter Evening in Town*, c. 1907, by Jakub Schikaneder (1855-1924), horiz. 5k, *The Bakers*, 1926, by Pravoslav Kotik (1889-1970), horiz.

1989, Nov. 27 **Engr.** *Perf. 12*
2766 A700 2k multicolored 1.10 .65
2767 A700 4k multicolored 2.25 1.25
2768 A700 5k multicolored 2.75 1.65
Nos. 2766-2768 (3) 6.10 3.55

Printed in sheets of 4.

Stamp Day — A997

Design: Portrait of Cyril Bouda, stamp designer, art tools and falcon.

Photo. & Engr.
1989, Dec. 18 *Perf. 11½x12*
2769 A997 1k multicolored .15 .15

A998

A999

Photo. & Engr.
1990, Jan. 8 *Perf. 11½x12*
2770 A998 1k multicolored .15 .15

UNESCO World Literacy Year. Printed se-tenant with inscribed label picturing UN and UNESCO emblems.

1990, Jan. 9 *Perf. 11½*

Famous men: No. 2771, Karel Capek, writer. No. 2772, Thomas G. Masaryk. 1k, Lenin. 2k, Emile Zola, French writer. 3k, Jaroslav Heyrovsky (1890-1987), chemical physicist. 10k, Bohuslav Martinu (1890-1959), composer.

2771 A999 50h multicolored .15 .15
2772 A999 50h multicolored .15 .15
2773 A999 1k multicolored .16 .15
2774 A999 2k multicolored .32 .18
2775 A999 3k multicolored .48 .25
2776 A999 10k multicolored 1.65 .88
Nos. 2771-2776 (6) 2.91
Set value 1.50

Nos. 2771 and 2775-2776 inscribed "UNESCO."

Pres. Vaclav Havel A1000

Handball Players A1001

1990, Jan. 9 *Perf. 12x11½*
2777 A1000 50h red, brt vio & blue .15 .15

See Nos. 2879, 2948.

1990, Feb. 1 *Perf. 11½*
2778 A1001 50h multicolored .15 .15

1990 Men's World Handball Championships, Czechoslovakia.

Flora — A1002

A1003

Photo. & Engr.
1990, Mar. 1 *Perf. 11½*
2779 A1002 50h *Antirrhinum majus* .15 .15
2780 A1002 1k *Zinnia elegans* .16 .15
2781 A1002 3k *Tigridia pavonia* .45 .25

Perf. 12x12½
2782 A1002 5k *Lilium candidum* .80 .45
Nos. 2779-2782 (4) 1.56
Set value .84

City Arms Type of 1982

Photo. & Engr.
1990, Mar. 28 *Perf. 12x11½*
2783 A847 50h Prostejov .15 .15
2784 A847 50h Bytca .15 .15
2785 A847 50h Sobeslav .15 .15
2786 A847 50h Podebrady .15 .15
Set value .30 .20

1990, Apr. 16 *Perf. 11½x12*
2787 A1003 1k brn vio, rose & buff .20 .15

Visit of Pope John Paul II.

World War II Liberation A1004

Photo. & Engr.
1990, May 5 *Perf. 11½*
2788 A1004 1k multicolored .20 .15

Souvenir Sheet

150th Anniv. of the Postage Stamp — A1005

1990, May 6 **Engr.** *Perf. 12*
2789 A1005 7k multicolored 1.25 .65

Stamp World London 90.

World Cup Soccer Championships, Italy — A1006

Photo. & Engr.
1990, May 8 *Perf. 11½*
2790 A1006 1k multicolored .15 .15

Free Elections A1007

1990, June 1
2791 A1007 1k multicolored .15 .15

Prague Castle Type of 1983

1990, June 6, 1990 **Engr.**
2792 A875 2k Gold and jeweled hand .35 .18
2793 A875 3k Medallion .52 .26

Art treasures of Prague Castle. Printed in sheets of 6.

Helsinki Conference, 15th Anniv. — A1008

Perf. 12x11½
1990, June 21 **Photo & Engr.**
2794 A1008 7k multicolored 1.10 .60

Dr. Milada Horakova A1009

1990, June 25 *Perf. 12x11½*
2795 A1009 1k multicolored .15 .15

Intercanis Dog Show, Brno A1010

Designs: 50h, Poodles, 1k, Afghan hound, Irish wolfhound, greyhound. 4k, Czech terrier, bloodhound, Hannoverian hound. 7k, Cavalier King Charles Spaniel, cocker spaniel, American cocker spaniel.

1990, July 2
2796 A1010 50h multicolored .15 .15
2797 A1010 1k multicolored .16 .15
2798 A1010 4k multicolored .60 .32
2799 A1010 7k multicolored 1.10 .55
Nos. 2796-2799 (4) 2.01 1.17

Bratislava Art Type of 1987

1990 **Engr.** *Perf. 12*
2800 A958 3k Ancient Celtic coin .52 .28
2801 A958 4k Gen. Milan Stefanik .70 .32

Issue dates: 3k, Sept. 29. 4k, July 21. Printed in sheets of 4.

Grand Pardubice Steeplechase, Cent. — A1011

Photo. & Engr.
1990, Sept. 7 *Perf. 12x11½*
2802 A1011 50h multicolored .15 .15
2803 A1011 4k multi, diff. .70 .36
Set value .41

Protected Animals A1012

Litho. & Engr.

1990, Oct. 1 *Perf. 12x11*

2804 A1012 50h Marmota marmota .15 .15
2805 A1012 1k Felis silvestris .16 .15
2806 A1012 4k Castor fiber .65 .35
2807 A1012 5k Plecotus auritus .85 .42
Nos. 2804-2807 (4) 1.81 1.07

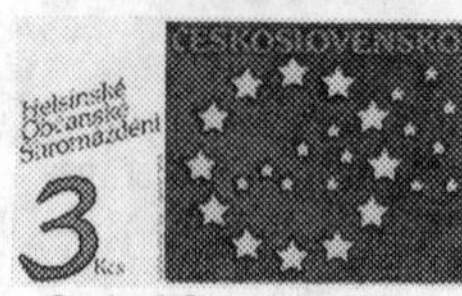

Conf. of Civic Associations, Helsinki — A1013

Perf. 12x11½

1990, Oct. 15 **Litho. & Engr.**

2808 A1013 3k blue, gold & yel .50 .30

Československo Christmas — A1014

Photo. & Engr.

1990, Nov. 15 *Perf. 11½x12*

2809 A1014 50h multicolored .15 .15

Art Type of 1967

Works of art: 2k, Krucemburk by Jan Zrzavy (1890-1977), horiz. 3k, St. Agnes of Bohemia from the St. Wenceslas Monument, Prague by Josef V. Myslbek (1848-1922). 4k, The Slavs in their Homeland by Alfons Mucha (1860-1939). 5k, St. John the Baptist by Auguste Rodin (1840-1917).

1990, Nov. 27 **Engr.** *Perf. 11½*

2810 A565 2k multicolored .32 .18
2811 A565 3k multicolored .50 .28
2812 A565 4k multicolored .60 .32
2813 A565 5k multicolored .80 .45
Nos. 2810-2813 (4) 2.22 1.23

Karel Svolinsky (1896-1986), Vignette from No. 1182 — A1016

1990, Dec. 18 **Photo. & Engr.**

2814 A1016 1k multicolored .15 .15

Stamp Day.

A1017

A1018

1991, Jan. 10 *Perf. 11½*

2815 A1017 1k multicolored .15 .15

European Judo Championships, Prague.

1991, Jan. 10

Design: A. B. Svojsik (1876-1938), Czech Scouting Founder.

2816 A1018 3k multicolored .30 .15

Scouting in Czechoslovakia, 80th Anniv.

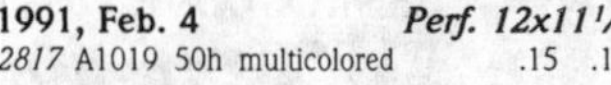

Bethlehem Chapel, Prague, 600th Anniv. — A1019

1991, Feb. 4 *Perf. 12x11½*

2817 A1019 50h multicolored .15 .15

Wolfgang Amadeus Mozart (1756-1791), Old Theatre — A1020

1991, Feb. 4

2818 A1020 1k multicolored .15 .15

Steamship Bohemia, 150th Anniv. — A1021

1991, Feb. 4 *Perf. 11½x12*

2819 A1021 5k multicolored .50 .25

Famous Men — A1022

Designs: No. 2820, Antonin Dvorak (1841-1904), composer. No. 2821, Andrej Kmet (1841-1908), botanist. No. 2822, Jaroslav Seifert (1901-1986), poet, Nobel laureate for Literature. No. 2823, Jan Masaryk (1886-1948), diplomat. No. 2824, Alois Senefelder (1771-1834), lithographer.

1991, Feb. 18 *Perf. 12x11½*

2820 A1022 1k multicolored .18 .15
2821 A1022 1k multicolored .18 .15
2822 A1022 1k multicolored .18 .15
2823 A1022 1k multicolored .18 .15
2824 A1022 1k multicolored .18 .15
Nos. 2820-2824 (5) .90
Set value .50

#2820-2824 printed with se-tenant labels. See No. 2831.

Europa — A1023

A1024

Photo. & Engr.

1991, May 6 *Perf. 11½x12*

2825 A1023 6k blk, bl & red .60 .30

Photo. & Engr.

1991, May 10 *Perf. 11½x12*

2826 A1024 1k multicolored .15 .15

General Exhibition in Prague, cent.

Antarctic Treaty, 30th Anniv. A1025

1991, May 20 *Perf. 12x11½*

2827 A1025 8k multicolored .80 .40

Castles — A1026

Scenic Views — A1027

1991, June 3 *Perf. 11½*

2828 A1026 50h Blatna .15 .15
2829 A1026 1k Bouzov .15 .15
2830 A1026 3k Kezmarok .30 .15
Set value .45 .22

Famous Men Type

Design: Jan Palach (1948-1969), Student.

Photo. & Engr.

1991, Aug. 9 *Perf. 12x11½*

2831 A1022 4k black .40 .20

Printed se-tenant with label.

Photo. & Engr.

1991, Aug. 28 *Perf. 11½*

2832 A1027 4k Krivan mountains .40 .20
2833 A1027 4k Rip mountain .40 .20

A1028

A1029

Illustrations by: 1k, Binette Schroeder, Germany. 2k, Stasys Eidrigevicius, Poland.

Photo. & Engr.

1991, Sept. 2 *Perf. 11½*

2834 A1028 1k multicolored .15 .15
2835 A1028 2k multicolored .15 .15
Set value .25 .15

13th Biennial Exhibition of Children's Book Illustrators, Bratislava.

1991, Sept. 27 **Engr.** *Perf. 11½*

Design: Father Andrej Hlinka (1864-1938), Slovak nationalist.

2836 A1029 10k blue black 1.15 .55

Art of Prague and Bratislava — A1030

Designs: No. 2837, Holy Infant of Prague. No. 2838, Blue Church of Bratislava.

1991, Sept. 30

2837 A1030 3k multicolored .35 .18
2838 A1030 3k multicolored .35 .18

Flowers — A1031

Christmas — A1033

Photo. & Engr.

1991, Nov. 3 *Perf. 12x11½*

2839 A1031 1k Gagea bohemica .15 .15
2840 A1031 2k Aster alpinus .20 .15
2841 A1031 5k Fritillaria meleagris .50 .25
2842 A1031 11k Daphne cneorum 1.10 .55
Nos. 2839-2842 (4) 1.95 1.10

Art Type of 1967

Paintings: 2k, Everyday Homelife by Max Ernst. 3k, Lovers by Auguste Renoir. 4k, Head of Christ by El Greco. 5k, Coincidence by Ladislav Guderna. 7k, Two Maidens by Utamaro.

1991, Nov. 3 **Engr.** *Perf. 11½*

2843 A565 2k multicolored .22 .15
2844 A565 3k multicolored .32 .16
2845 A565 4k multicolored .45 .22
2846 A565 5k multicolored .55 .28
2847 A565 7k multicolored .78 .40
Nos. 2843-2847 (5) 2.32 1.21

1991, Nov. 19

2848 A1033 50h multicolored .15 .15

Stamp Day — A1034

Design: Martin Benka (1888-1971), stamp engraver.

Photo. & Engr.

1991, Dec. 18 *Perf. 11½x12*

2849 A1034 2k multicolored .20 .15

1992 Winter Olympics, Albertville — A1035

1992, Jan. 6 *Perf. 11½*

2850 A1035 1k Biathlon .15 .15

Photo. & Engr.

1992, May 21 *Perf. 11½*

2851 A1035 2k Tennis .22 .15

1992 Summer Olympics, Barcelona.

Souvenir Sheet

Jan Amos Komensky (Comenius), Educator — A1036

1992, Mar. 5 **Engr.**

2852 A1036 10k multicolored 1.00 1.00

World Ice Hockey Championships, Prague and Bratislava — A1037

1992, Mar. 31 **Photo. & Engr.**

2853 A1037 3k multicolored .34 .18

Traffic Safety A1038

1992, Apr. 2

2854 A1038 2k multicolored .22 .15

Expo '92, Seville — A1039

1992, Apr. 2

2855 A1039 4k multicolored .45 .22

Discovery of America, 500th Anniv. A1040

1992, May 5 **Engr.**

2856 A1040 22k multicolored 2.65 1.30

Europa. Printed in sheets of 8.

Czechoslovak Military Actions in WWII — A1041

Designs: 1k, J. Kubis and J. Gabcik, assassins of Reinhard Heydrich, 1942. 2k, Pilots flying for France and Great Britain. 3k, Defense of Tobruk. 6k, Capture of Dunkirk, 1944-45.

1992, May 21 Engr. *Perf. 12x11½*

2857 A1041 1k multicolored	.15	.15
2858 A1041 2k multicolored	.22	.15
2859 A1041 3k multicolored	.32	.16
2860 A1041 6k multicolored	.65	.32
Nos. 2857-2860 (4)	1.34	
Set value		.64

A1042

A1043

Photo. & Engr.

1992, June 10 *Perf. 11½*

2861 A1042 2k multicolored .22 .15

Czechoslovakian Red Cross.

1992, June 30

2862 A1043 1k multicolored .15 .15

Junior European Table Tennis Championships, Topolcany.

Beetles — A1044

1992, July 15

2863 A1044 1k Polyphylla fullo	.15	.15
2864 A1044 2k Ergates faber	.22	.15
2865 A1044 3k Meloe violaceus	.32	.16
2866 A1044 4k Dytiscus latissimus	.42	.20
Nos. 2863-2866 (4)	1.11	
Set value		.53

The 1k exists with denomination omitted.

Troja Castle A1045

1992, Aug. 28 Engr. *Perf. 11½*

2867 A1045 6k shown	.65	.32
2868 A1045 7k Statue of St. Martin, vert.	.75	.38
2869 A1045 8k Lednice Castle	.90	.45
Nos. 2867-2869 (3)	2.30	1.15

Chrudim Church Type of 1971

Photo. & Engr.

1992, Aug. 28 *Perf. 11½x11*

2870 A629 50h multicolored .15 .15

Postal Bank — A1045a

Photo. & Engr.

1992, Aug. 28 *Perf. 11½x12*

2870A A1045a 20k multicolored 2.25 1.10

Antonius Bernolak, Georgius Fandly A1046

Photo. & Engr.

1992, Oct. 6 *Perf. 12x11½*

2871 A1046 5k multicolored .55 .28

Slovakian Educational Society, bicent.

Cesky Krumlov — A1046a

Photo. & Engr.

1992, Oct. 19 *Perf. 11½x12*

2871A A1046a 3k brick red & brown .35 .18

See No. 2890.

Painting Type of 1967

Paintings: 6k Old Man on a Raft, by Koloman Sokol. 7k, Still Life of Grapes and Raisins, by Georges Braque, horiz. 8k, Abandoned Corset, by Toyen.

Perf. 11½x12, 12x11½

1992, Nov. 2 Engr.

2872 A565 6k multicolored	.65	.32
2873 A565 7k multicolored	.75	.38
2874 A565 8k multicolored	.90	.45
Nos. 2872-2874 (3)	2.30	1.15

Christmas — A1047

Photo. & Engr.

1992, Nov. 9 *Perf. 12x11½*

2875 A1047 2k multicolored .22 .15

Jindra Schmidt (1897-1984), Graphic Artist and Engraver — A1048

Photo. & Engr.

1992, Dec. 18 *Perf. 11½x12*

2876 A1048 2k multicolored .22 .15

Stamp Day.

On January 1, 1993, Czechoslovakia split into Czech Republic and Slovakia. Czech Republic listings continue here. Slovakia can be found in Volume 5.

CZECH REPUBLIC

AREA — 30,449 sq. mi.
POP. — 10,311,831 est. 1992

Natl. Arms — A1049

1993, Jan. 20 Photo. & Engr. *Perf. 11*

2877 A1049 3k multicolored .33 .16

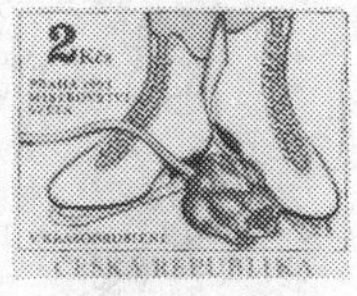

1993 World Figure Skating Championships, Prague — A1050

1993, Feb. 25 *Perf. 11½x11*

2878 A1050 2k multicolored .22 .15

Havel Type of 1990 Inscribed "Ceska Republika"

Photo. & Engr.

1993, Mar. 2 *Perf. 12x11½*

2879 A1000 2k vio, vio brn & blue .22 .15

St. John Nepomuk, Patron Saint of Czechs, 600th Death Anniv. A1051

1993, Mar. 11

2880 A1051 8k multicolored .90 .45

See Germany No. 1776; Slovakia No. 158.

Holy Hunger, by Mikulas Medek — A1052

1993, Mar. 11 *Perf. 11½*

2881 A1052 14k multicolored 1.20 .60

Europa.

Sacred Heart Church, Prague A1053

1993, Mar. 30 Engr. *Perf. 11½*

2882 A1053 5k multicolored .45 .22

Brevnov Monastery, 1000th Anniv. — A1054

Perf. 12x11½

1993, Apr. 12 Litho. & Engr.

2883 A1054 4k multicolored .38 .18

1993 Intl. Junior Weight Lifting Championships, Cheb — A1055

Photo. & Engr.

1993, May 12 *Perf. 11½*

2884 A1055 6k multicolored .55 .28

Clock Tower and Church, Brno — A1056

1993, June 16 Engr. *Perf. 12x11½*

2885 A1056 8k multicolored .75 .38

Brno, 750th anniv.

Arrival of St. Cyril and St. Methodius, 1130th Anniv. — A1057

1993, June 22 Photo. & Engr.

2886 A1057 8k multicolored .75 .38

See Slovakia No. 167.

Souvenir Sheet

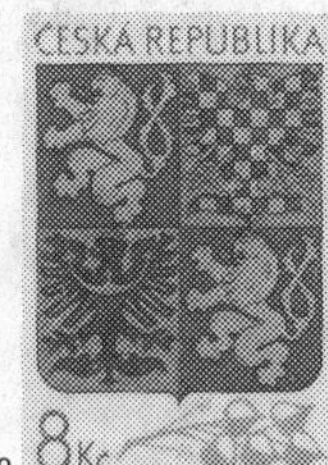

State Arms — A1058

1993, June 22 *Perf. 11½*

2887 A1058 8k Sheet of 2 1.45 .75

Architecture Type of 1992 Inscribed "Ceska Republika" and

A1059

Cities: 1k, Ceske Budejovice. 2k, Usti Nad Labem. #2890, like #2871A. #2890A, Brno. 5k, Plzen. 6k, Slany. 7k, Ostrava. 8k, Olomouc. 10k, Hradec Kralove. 20k, Prague. 50k, Opava.

Perf. 12x11½, 11½x12

1993-94 Photo. & Engr.

2888	A1059	1k deep claret & org	.15	.15
2889	A1059	2k red violet & blue	.18	.15
2890	A1046a	3k gray blue & red	.28	.15
		Complete booklet, 5 #2890	1.40	
2890A	A1059	3k dark blue & red	.25	.15
		Complete booklet, 5 #2890A	1.25	
2891	A1059	5k bluish green & brn	.48	.24
2891A	A1059	6k green & org yel	.70	.35
2891B	A1059	7k black brown & grn	.75	.38
2892	A1059	8k deep violet & yel	.75	.38
2893	A1059	10k olive gray & red	.95	.48
2894	A1059	20k red & blue	1.90	.95
2895	A1059	50k brown & green	4.75	2.35
		Nos. 2888-2895 (11)	11.14	5.73

Issued: No. 2890A, 3/30/94; 6k, 10/1/94; 7k, 11/23/94; others, 7/1/93. This is an expanding set. Numbers may change.

Czech Republic and Slovakia stamps can be mounted in the Scott annual Czech Republic and Slovakia supplement.

World Rowing Championships, Racice — A1060

Photo. & Engr.

1993, Aug. 18 *Perf. 11½*

2901 A1060 3k multicolored .32 .16

A1061

Trees — A1062

Famous men: 2k, August Sedlacek (1843-1926), historian. 3k, Eduard Cech (1893-1960), mathematician.

1993, Aug. 26 *Perf. 12x11½*

2902 A1061 2k multicolored .22 .15
2903 A1061 3k multicolored .32 .16

1993, Oct. 26 *Perf. 11½*

2904 A1062 5k Quercus robur .55 .28
2905 A1062 7k Carpinus betulus .75 .38
2906 A1062 9k Pinus silvestris 1.00 .50
Nos. 2904-2906 (3) 2.30 1.16

Christmas — A1063

A1064

Photo. & Engr.

1993, Nov. 8 *Perf. 11½*

2907 A1063 2k multicolored .18 .15

Art Type of 1967 Inscribed "CESKA REPUBLIKA"

Paintings: 9k, Strahovska Madonna, by Po Roce, 1350. 11k, Composition, by Miro, horiz. 14k, Field of Green, by Van Gogh, horiz.

1993 **Engr.** *Perf. 11½x12*

2908 A565 9k multicolored .55 .28

Perf. 12x11½

2909 A565 11k multicolored 1.00 .50
2910 A565 14k multicolored 1.25 .65
Nos. 2908-2910 (3) 2.80 1.43

Issued: 11k, 14k, Nov. 8; 9k, Dec. 15.

Photo. & Engr.

1994, Jan. 19 *Perf. 11½*

2911 A1064 2k multicolored .20 .15

Intl. Year of the Family.

Jan Kubelik (1880-1940), Composer A1065

Photo. & Engr.

1994, Jan. 19 *Perf. 11½*

2912 A1065 3k multicolored .25 .15

UNESCO A1065a

Designs: 2k, Voltaire (1694-1778), philosopher. 6k, Georgius Agricola (1494-1555), mineralogist, humanist.

1994, Feb. 2 *Perf. 12x11½*

2913 A1065a 2k multicolored .16 .15
2914 A1065a 6k multicolored .48 .25

A1066

A1067

Photo. & Engr.

1994, Feb. 2 *Perf. 11½*

2915 A1066 5k multicolored .40 .20

1994 Winter Olympics, Lillehammer.

Photo. & Engr.

1994, May 4 *Perf. 11½*

Europa (Marco Polo and): No. 2916, Stylized animals, Chinese woman. No. 2917, Stylized animals.

2916 A1067 14k multicolored 1.10 .55
2917 A1067 14k multicolored 1.10 .55
a. Pair, #2916-2917 2.25 1.10

A1068

A1070

Architectural Sights — A1069

1994, May 18

2918 A1068 5k Eduard Benes .40 .20

1994, May 18

UNESCO: 8k, Houses at the square, Telc. 9k, Cubist house designed by Chochol, Prague.

2919 A1069 8k multicolored .65 .32
2920 A1069 9k multicolored .75 .35

Photo. & Engr.

1994, June 1 *Perf. 11½*

2921 A1070 2k Children's Day .18 .15

Dinosaurs A1071

Perf. 11½x11, 11x11½

1994, June 1 **Litho.**

2922 A1071 2k Stegosaurus .18 .15
2923 A1071 3k Apatosaurus .28 .15
2924 A1071 5k Tarbosaurus, vert. .45 .22
Nos. 2922-2924 (3) .91 .52

A1072

A1073

Photo. & Engr.

1994, June 1 *Perf. 11½x11*

2925 A1072 8k multicolored .75 .38

1994 World Cup Soccer Championships, US.

1994, June 15 *Perf. 11x11½*

2926 A1073 2k multicolored .18 .15

12th Pan-Sokol Rally, Prague.

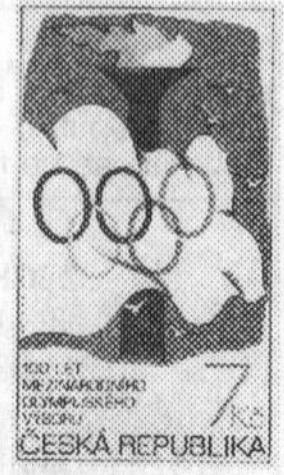

Intl. Olympic Committee, Cent. — A1074

1994, June 15

2927 A1074 7k multicolored .65 .32

UPU, 120th Anniv. A1075

1994, Aug. 3 **Engr.** *Perf. 11½*

2928 A1075 11k multicolored 1.25 .65

Songbirds — A1076

Designs: 3k, Saxicola torquata. 5k, Carpodacus erythrinus. 14k, Luscinia svecica.

Photo. & Engr.

1994, Aug. 24 *Perf. 11x11½*

2929 A1076 3k multicolored .32 .16
2930 A1076 5k multicolored .55 .28
2931 A1076 14k multicolored 1.65 .80
Nos. 2929-2931 (3) 2.52 1.24

Historic Race Cars — A1077

Photo. & Engr.

1994, Oct. 5 *Perf. 11½*

2932 A1077 2k 1900 NW .22 .15
2933 A1077 3k 1908 L&K .35 .18
Complete booklet, 5 #2933 1.65
2934 A1077 9k 1912 Praga 1.00 .50
Nos. 2932-2934 (3) 1.57 .83

Christmas — A1078

Photo. & Engr.

1994, Nov. 9 *Perf. 11½*

2935 A1078 2k multicolored .22 .15

Art Type of 1967 Inscribed "CESKA REPUBLIKA"

Engraving or paintings: 7k, Stary Posetilec A Zena, by Lucas Van Leyden. 10k, Moulin Rouge, by Henri de Toulouse-Lautrec. 14k, St. Vitus Madonna, St. Vitus Cathedral, Prague.

1994, Nov. 9 **Engr.** *Perf. 12*

2936 A565 7k multicolored .75 .38
2937 A565 10k multicolored 1.00 .50
2938 A565 14k multicolored 1.40 .70
Nos. 2936-2938 (3) 3.15 1.58

Nos. 2936-2938 printed in sheets of 4.

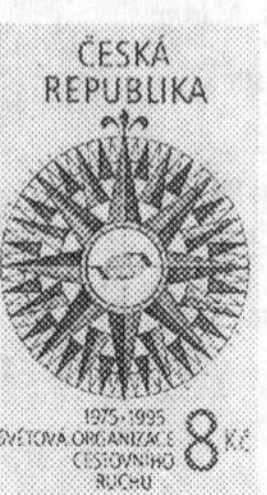

World Tourism Organization, 20th Anniv. A1079

Czech Stamp Production A1080

Photo. & Engr.

1995, Jan. 2 *Perf. 11x12*
2939 A1079 8k green blue & red .75 .38

1995, Jan. 20
2940 A1080 3k Design N1 .30 .15

Czech Republic & European Union Association Agreement A1081

Perf. 13½x12½

1995, Jan. 20 **Litho.**
2941 A1081 8k multicolored .75 .38

Famous Men A1082

Designs: 2k, Johannes Marcus Marci (1595-1667). 5k, Ferdinand Peroutka (1895-1978). 7k, Premysl Pitter (1895-1976).

Photo. & Engr.

1995, Feb. 1 *Perf. 12x11*
2942 A1082 2k multicolored .18 .15
2943 A1082 5k multicolored .45 .22
2944 A1082 7k multicolored .65 .32
Nos. 2942-2944 (3) 1.28 .69

Theater Personalities — A1083

Designs: No. 2945, Jiri Voskovec (1905-81). No. 2946, Jan Werich (1905-80). No. 2947, Jaroslav Jezek (1906-42). 22k, Caricatures of Voskovec, Werich, and Jezek with piano.

1995 **Photo. & Engr.** *Perf. 12x11*
2945 A1083 3k multicolored .30 .15
Complete booklet, 3 #2945 .90
2946 A1083 3k multicolored .30 .15
Complete booklet, 3 #2946 .90
2947 A1083 3k multicolored .30 .15
Complete booklet, 3 #2947 .90
a. Strip of 3, #2945-2947 .90 .45
Complete booklet, 2 #2947a 1.80
Nos. 2945-2947 (3) .90 .45

Souvenir Sheet
Photo.
Perf. 12

2947B A1083 22k yellow & black 2.00 1.00

Issued: 3k, 3/15; 22k, 9/20.

Havel Type of 1990 Inscribed "Ceska Republika"

Photo. & Engr.

1995, Mar. 22 *Perf. 12x11½*
2948 A1000 3.60k blue, vio & mag .30 .15
Complete booklet, 5 #2948 1.50

Rural Architecture A1084

1995, Mar. 22 *Perf. 11½*
2949 A1084 40h shown .15 .15
2950 A1084 60h Homes, diff. .15 .15
Set value .15 .15

European Nature Conservation Year — A1085

1995, Apr. 12
2951 A1085 3k Bombus terrestris .20 .15
Complete booklet, 5 #2951 1.00
2952 A1085 5k Mantis religiosa .40 .20
Complete booklet, 5 #2952 2.00
2953 A1085 6k Calopteryx splendens .45 .22
Complete booklet, 5 #2953 2.25
Nos. 2951-2953 (3) 1.05 .57

Peace & Freedom A1086

Photo. & Engr.

1995, May 3 *Perf. 11½*
2954 A1086 9k Rose, profiles .70 .35
2955 A1086 14k Butterfly, profiles 1.10 .55

Europa.

Natural Beauties in Czech Republic A1087

Designs: 8k, "Stone Organ" scenic mountain. 9k, Largest sandstone bridge in Europe.

Photo. & Engr.

1995, May 3 *Perf. 11½*
2956 A1087 8k multicolored .65 .32
2957 A1087 9k multicolored .70 .35

Children's Day — A1088

Photo. & Engr.

1995, June 1 *Perf. 11½*
2958 A1088 3.60k multicolored .35 .15

First Train from Vienna to Prague, 150th Anniv. A1089

Designs: 3k, Chocen Tunnel. 9.60k, Entering Prague.

1995, June 21
2959 A1089 3k multicolored .25 .15
Complete booklet, 5 #2959 1.25
2960 A1089 9.60k multicolored .85 .42

World Wrestling Championships, Prague — A1090

Photo. & Engr.

1995, Sept. 6 *Perf. 11½*
2961 A1090 3k multicolored .30 .15

Cartoon Characters — A1091

Designs: 3k, Man playing violin, woman washing, by Vladimir Rencin. 3.60k, Angel, naked man, by Vladimir Jiranek. 5k, Circus trainer holding ring for champagne cork to pop through, by Jiri Sliva.

1995, Sept. 6
2962 A1091 3k multicolored .30 .15
2963 A1091 3.60k multicolored .35 .15
2964 A1091 5k multicolored .45 .25
Nos. 2962-2964 (3) 1.10 .55

SOS Children's Villages, 25th Anniv. — A1092

1995, Sept. 20 **Litho.** *Perf. 13½x13*
2965 A1092 3k multicolored .35 .15

A1093

Design: 2.40k, Gothic. 3k, Secession. 3.60k, Romance. 9.60k, Renaissance Portal. 14k, Baroque.

1995 **Photo. & Engr.** *Perf. 12x11½*
2966 A1093 2.40k red & green .30 .15
2967 A1093 3k green & blue .35 .15
2968 A1093 3.60k purple & green .45 .20
2969 A1093 9.60k blue & red .95 .50
2970 A1093 14k green & purple 1.60 .80
Nos. 2966-2970 (5) 3.65 1.80

Issued: 9.60k, 9/27; 2.40k, 14k, 10/11; 3k, 3.60k, 10/25.

UN, 50th Anniv. A1094

1995, Oct. 11 **Litho.** *Perf. 12x11½*
2971 A1094 14k multicolored 1.60 .80

Wilhelm Röntgen (1845-1923), Discovery of the X-Ray, Cent. — A1095

1995, Oct. 11 **Photo. & Engr.**
2972 A1095 6k blk, buff & bl vio .75 .35

Art Type of 1967 Inscribed "CESKA REPUBLIKA"

Designs: 6k, Parisiene, by Ludek Marold. 9k, Vase of Flowers, by J.K. Hirschely. 14k, Portrait of J. Malinskeho, by Antoinín Machek.

1995, Nov. 8 *Perf. 12*
2973 A565 6k multicolored .75 .35
2974 A565 9k multicolored 1.00 .50
2975 A565 14k multicolored 1.60 .80
Nos. 2973-2975 (3) 3.35 1.65

Nos. 2973-2975 printed in sheets of 4.

Christmas — A1096

1995, Nov. 8 *Perf. 11½*
2976 A1096 3k multicolored .35 .15
Complete booklet, 3 #2976 1.05

SEMI-POSTAL STAMPS

Nos. B1-B123 were sold, in sets only, at 1½ times face value at the Philatelists' Window of the Prague P.O. for charity benefit. They were available for ordinary postage.

Almost all stamps between Nos. B1-B123 are known with misplaced or inverted overprints and/or in pairs with one stamp missing the overprint.

The overprints of Nos. B1-B123 have been well forged.

Austrian Stamps of 1916-18 Overprinted in Black or Blue

a — POŠTA ČESKOSLOVENSKÁ 1919

1919 *Perf. 12½*
B1 A37 3h brt violet .20 .25
B2 A37 5h lt green .20 .25
B3 A37 6h dp orange (Bl) .60 .50
B4 A37 6h dp orange (Bk) *1,050.* *1,050.*
B5 A37 10h magenta .60 .75
B6 A37 12h lt blue .60 .65
B7 A42 15h dull red .20 .25
B8 A42 20h dark green .20 .25
a. 20h green 110.00 70.00
B9 A42 25h blue .30 .40
B10 A42 30h dull violet .30 .40
B11 A39 40h olive grn .30 .40
B12 A39 50h dk green .30 .40
B13 A39 60h dp blue .30 .40
B14 A39 80h orange brn .30 .40
B15 A39 90h red violet .70 .75
B16 A39 1k car, *yel* (Bl) .50 .60
B17 A39 1k car, *yel* (Bk) 125.00 100.00
B18 A40 2k light blue 1.90 1.90
a. 2k dark blue 2,250. 1,750.
B19 A40 3k carmine rose 50.00 27.50
a. 3k claret 850.00 775.00
B20 A40 4k yellow grn 15.00 8.25
a. 4k deep green 40.00 26.00
B21 A40 10k violet 200.00 110.00
a. 10k deep violet 225.00 125.00
b. 10k black violet 240.00 135.00

The used value of No. B18a is for copies which have only a Czechoslovakian cancellation. Some of the copies of Austria No. 160 which were officially overprinted with type "a" and sold by the post office, had previously been used and lightly canceled with Austrian cancellations. These canceled-before-overprinting copies, which were postally valid, sell for about one-fourth as much.

Granite Paper

B22 A40 2k light blue 2.00 2.00
B23 A40 3k carmine rose 7.25 6.00

The 4k and 10k on granite paper with this overprint were not regularly issued.

Excellent counterfeits of Nos. B1-B23 exist.

Austrian Newspaper Stamps Overprinted

b — POŠTA ČESKOSLOVENSKÁ 1919

Imperf

On Stamp of 1908

B26 N8 10h carmine 1,400. 1,400.

On Stamps of 1916

B27 N9 2h brown .15 .15
B28 N9 4h green .22 .22
B29 N9 6h deep blue .15 .15
B30 N9 10h orange 2.75 2.75
B31 N9 30h claret 1.10 1.10
Nos. B27-B31 (5) 4.37 4.37

Austrian Special Handling Stamps Overprinted in Blue or Black

Stamps of 1916 Overprinted

c — POŠTA ČESKOSLOVENSKÁ 1919

Perf. 12½

B32 SH1 2h claret, *yel* (Bl) 27.50 25.00
B33 SH1 5h dp grn, *yel* (Bk) *1,650.* *1,100.*

Stamps of 1917 Overprinted

d

POŠTA ČESKOSLOVENSKÁ 1919

No.	Type	Description	Unused	Used
B34	SH2	2h cl, *yel* (Bl)	.25	.35
a.		Vert. pair, imperf. btwn.	*175.00*	
B35	SH2	2h cl, *yel* (Bk)	60.00	35.00
B36	SH2	5h grn, *yel* (Bk)	.25	.25

Austrian Air Post Stamps, #C1-C3, Overprinted Type "c" Diagonally

No.	Type	Description	Unused	Used
B37	A40	1.50k on 2k lil	210.00	165.00
B38	A40	2.50k on 3k ocher	210.00	165.00
B39	A40	4k gray	950.00	775.00

1919

Austrian Postage Due Stamps of 1908-13 Overprinted Type "b"

No.	Type	Description	Unused	Used
B40	D3	2h carmine	*3,000.*	*2,750.*
B41	D3	4h carmine	20.00	15.00
B42	D3	6h carmine	11.00	8.00
B43	D3	14h carmine	75.00	35.00
B44	D3	25h carmine	40.00	20.00
B45	D3	30h carmine	350.00	300.00
B46	D3	50h carmine	900.00	825.00

Austria Nos. J49-J56 Overprinted Type "b"

No.	Type	Description	Unused	Used
B47	D4	5h rose red	.20	.30
B48	D4	10h rose red	.20	.30
B49	D4	15h rose red	.20	.30
B50	D4	20h rose red	2.00	1.50
B51	D4	25h rose red	1.25	1.00
B52	D4	30h rose red	.50	.50
B53	D4	40h rose red	2.00	1.75
B54	D4	50h rose red	400.00	350.00

Austria Nos. J57-J59 Overprinted Type "a"

No.	Type	Description	Unused	Used
B55	D5	1k ultra	12.50	10.00
B56	D5	5k ultra	55.00	35.00
B57	D5	10k ultra	225.00	225.00

Austria Nos. J47-J48, J60-J63 Overprinted Type "c" Diagonally

No.	Type	Description	Unused	Used
B58	A22	1h gray	27.50	17.50
B59	A23	15h on 2h vio	140.00	110.00
B60	A38	10h on 24h blue	100.00	85.00
B61	A38	15h on 36h vio	1.00	1.00
B62	A38	20h on 54h org	100.00	85.00
B63	A38	50h on 42h choc	1.00	1.00

Hungarian Stamps Ovptd. Type "b"

1919 Wmk. 137 *Perf. 15*

On Stamps of 1913-16

No.	Type	Description	Unused	Used
B64	A4	1f slate	2,000.	1,850.
B65	A4	2f yellow	3.50	2.50
B66	A4	3f orange	45.00	25.00
B67	A4	6f olive green	4.50	4.50
B68	A4	50f lake, *bl*	1.25	1.00
B69	A4	60f grn, *sal*	50.00	20.00
B70	A4	70f red brn, *grn*	2,000.	1,500.

On Stamps of 1916

No.	Type	Description	Unused	Used
B71	A8	10f rose	350.00	250.00
B72	A8	15f violet	165.00	125.00

On Stamps of 1916-18

No.	Type	Description	Unused	Used
B73	A9	2f brown orange	.15	.15
B74	A9	3f red lilac	.16	.15
B75	A9	5f green	.15	.15
B76	A9	6f grnsh blue	.60	.60
B77	A9	10f rose red	1.40	2.25
B78	A9	15f violet	.22	.22
B79	A9	20f gray brown	5.50	5.00
B80	A9	25f dull blue	.80	.75
B81	A9	35f brown	6.75	6.75
B82	A9	40f olive green	1.75	1.50

Overprinted Type "d"

No.	Type	Description	Unused	Used
B83	A10	50f red vio & lil	.80	.80
B84	A10	75f brt bl & pale bl	.75	.75
B85	A10	80f yel grn & pale grn	1.10	1.10
B86	A10	1k red brn & cl	1.40	1.40
B87	A10	2k ol brn & bis	5.50	5.50
B88	A10	3k dk vio & ind	37.50	37.50
B89	A10	5k dk brn & lt brn	140.00	90.00
B90	A10	10k vio brn & vio	1,500.	1,000.

Overprinted Type "b"

On Stamps of 1918

No.	Type	Description	Unused	Used
B91	A11	10f scarlet	.22	.22
B92	A11	20f dark brown	.28	.28
B93	A11	25f deep blue	1.40	1.25
B94	A12	40f olive grn	1.50	1.25
B95	A12	50f lilac	67.50	25.00

On Stamps of 1919

No.	Type	Description	Unused	Used
B96	A13	10f red	7.00	6.00
B97	A13	20f dk brn	*2,750.*	*2,750.*

Same Overprint On Hungarian Newspaper Stamp of 1914

Imperf

No.	Type	Description	Unused	Used
B98	N5	(2f) orange	.20	.30

Same Overprint On Hungarian Special Delivery Stamp

Perf. 15

No.	Type	Description	Unused	Used
B99	SD1	2f gray grn & red	.25	.35

Same Ovpt. On Hungarian Semi-Postal Stamps

No.	Type	Description	Unused	Used
B100	SP3	10f + 2f rose red	.52	.60
B101	SP4	15f + 2f violet	.90	.90
B102	SP5	40f + 2f brn car	7.00	3.50
		Nos. B98-B102 (5)	8.87	5.65

Hungarian Postage Due Stamps of 1903-18 Overprinted Type "b"

1919 Wmk. 135 *Perf. 11½, 12*

No.	Type	Description	Unused	Used
B103	D1	50f green & black	*525.00*	*525.00*

Wmk. Crown (136, 136a)

Perf. 11½x12, 15

No.	Type	Description	Unused	Used
B104	D1	1f green & black	*500.00*	*500.00*
B105	D1	2f green & black	*275.00*	*275.00*
B106	D1	12f green & black	*2,500.*	*2,500.*
B107	D1	50f green & black	150.00	150.00

Wmk. Double Cross (137)

Perf. 15

On Stamps of 1914

No.	Type	Description	Unused	Used
B110	D1	1f green & black	425.00	400.00
B111	D1	2f green & black	225.00	225.00
B112	D1	5f green & black	600.00	600.00
B113	D1	12f green & black	*1,750.*	*1,750.*
B114	D1	50f green & black	150.00	150.00

On Stamps of 1915-18

No.	Type	Description	Unused	Used
B115	D1	1f green & red	175.00	140.00
B116	D1	2f green & red	1.00	.80
B117	D1	5f green & red	12.50	10.00
B118	D1	6f green & red	1.50	1.50
B119	D1	10f green & red	.60	.60
B120	D1	12f green & red	2.00	2.00
B121	D1	15f green & red	7.50	5.00
B122	D1	20f green & red	1.00	1.00
B123	D1	30f green & red	45.00	35.00
		Nos. B115-B123 (9)	246.10	195.90

Excellent counterfeits of Nos. B1-B123 exist.

Bohemian Lion Breaking its Chains — SP1

Mother and Child — SP2

Perf. 11½, 13½ and Compound

1919 Typo. Unwmk.

Pinkish Paper

No.	Type	Description	Unused	Used
B124	SP1	15h gray green	.15	.15
B125	SP1	25h dark brown	.15	.15
a.		25h light brown	*10.00*	
B126	SP1	50h dark blue	.15	.15

Photo.

Yellowish Paper

No.	Type	Description	Unused	Used
B127	SP2	75h slate	.15	.15
B128	SP2	100h brn vio	.15	.15
B129	SP2	120h vio, *yel*	.15	.15
		Set value	.30	.48

Nos. B124-B126 commemorate the 1st anniv. of Czechoslovak independence. Nos. B127-B129 were sold for the benefit of Legionnaires' orphans. Imperforates exist.

See No. 1581.

Regular Issues of Czechoslovakia Surcharged in Red:

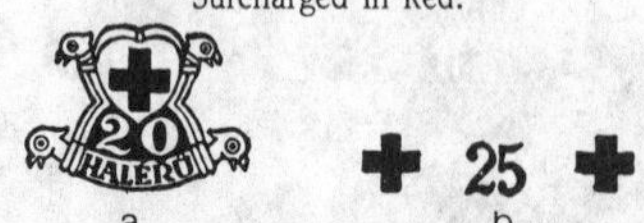

a b

1920 *Perf. 13½*

No.	Type	Description	Unused	Used
B130	A1(a)	40h + 20h bister	.70	1.10
B131	A2(a)	60h + 20h green	.70	1.10
B132	A4(b)	125h + 25h gray bl	1.40	2.75
		Nos. B130-B132 (3)	2.80	4.95

President Masaryk — SP3

Wmk. Linden Leaves (107)

1923 Engr. *Perf. 13½x14½*

No.	Type	Description	Unused	Used
B133	SP3	50h gray green	.75	.65
B134	SP3	100h carmine	1.25	.70
B135	SP3	200h blue	4.00	4.25
B136	SP3	300h dark brown	4.25	4.50
		Nos. B133-B136 (4)	10.25	10.10

5th anniv. of the Republic.

The gum was applied through a screen and shows the monogram "CSP" (Ceskoslovenska Posta). These stamps were sold at double their face values, the excess being given to the Red Cross and other charitable organizations.

International Olympic Congress Issue

Semi-Postal Stamps of 1923 Overprinted in Blue or Red

1925

No.	Type	Description	Unused	Used
B137	SP3	50h gray green	5.00	5.00
B138	SP3	100h carmine	8.50	8.50
B139	SP3	200h blue (R)	57.50	57.50
		Nos. B137-B139 (3)	71.00	71.00

These stamps were sold at double their face values, the excess being divided between a fund for post office clerks and the Olympic Games Committee.

Sokol Issue

Semi-Postal Stamps of 1923 Overprinted in Blue or Red

1926

No.	Type	Description	Unused	Used
B140	SP3	50h gray green	3.75	4.25
B141	SP3	100h carmine	3.75	4.25
B142	SP3	200h blue (R)	17.00	18.00
a.		Double overprint		
B143	SP3	300h dk brn (R)	27.50	30.00
		Nos. B140-B143 (4)	52.00	56.50

These stamps were sold at double their face values, the excess being given to the Congress of Sokols, June, 1926.

Catalogue values for unused stamps in this section, from this point to the end of the section, are for Never Hinged items.

Midwife Presenting Newborn Child to its Father; after a Painting by Josef Manes

SP4 SP5

1936 Unwmk. Engr. *Perf. 12½*

No.	Type	Description	Unused	Used
B144	SP4	50h + 50h green	.50	.45
B145	SP5	1k + 50h claret	.85	.75
B146	SP4	2k + 50h blue	2.00	1.90
		Nos. B144-B146 (3)	3.35	3.10

"Lullaby" by Stanislav Sucharda

SP6 SP7

1937 *Perf. 12½*

No.	Type	Description	Unused	Used
B147	SP6	50h + 50h dull green	.48	.35
B148	SP6	1k + 50h rose lake	1.00	.70
B149	SP7	2k + 1k dull blue	1.90	1.40
		Nos. B147-B149 (3)	3.38	2.45

President Masaryk and Little Girl in Native Costume — SP8

1938 *Perf. 12½*

No.	Type	Description	Unused	Used
B150	SP8	50h + 50h deep green	.42	.48
B151	SP8	1k + 50h rose lake	.48	.55

Souvenir Sheet

Imperf

No.	Type	Description	Unused	Used
B152	SP8	2k + 3k black	3.00	3.50

88th anniv. of the birth of Masaryk (1850-1937).

Allegory of the Republic Type

Souvenir Sheet

1938 *Perf. 12½*

No.	Type	Description	Unused	Used
B153	A89	2k (+ 8k) dark blue	2.50	2.50

The surtax was devoted to national relief for refugees.

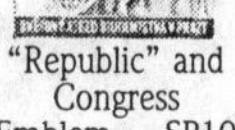

"Republic" and Congress Emblem — SP10

St. George Slaying the Dragon — SP11

1945 Engr.

No.	Type	Description	Unused	Used
B154	SP10	1.50k + 1.50k car rose	.16	.15
B155	SP10	2.50k + 2.50k blue	.25	.20

Students' World Cong., Prague, Nov. 17, 1945.

1946

No.	Type	Description	Unused	Used
B156	SP11	2.40k + 2.60k car rose	.20	.15
B157	SP11	4k + 6k blue	.45	.20

Souvenir Sheet

Imperf

No.	Type	Description	Unused	Used
B158	SP11	4k + 6k blue	.75	.75

1st anniv. of Czechoslovakia's liberation. The surtax aided WW II orphans.

Old Town Hall Type of 1946

Souvenir Sheet

1946, Aug. 3 *Imperf.*

No.	Type	Description	Unused	Used
B159	A114	2.40k rose brown	.70	.60

Brno Natl. Stamp Exhib., Aug., 1946.

The sheet was sold for 10k.

"You Went Away" — SP14

"You Remained Ours" — SP15

"You Came Back" — SP16

1946, Oct. 28 Photo. *Perf. 14*

No.	Type	Description	Unused	Used
B160	SP14	1.60k + 1.40k red brn	.42	.50
B161	SP15	2.40k + 2.60k scarlet	.20	.26
B162	SP16	4k + 4k deep blue	.38	.48
		Nos. B160-B162 (3)	1.00	1.24

The surtax was for repatriated Slovaks.

Barefoot Boy — SP17

Woman and Child — SP18

Designs: 2k+1k, Mother and child. 3k+1k, Little girl.

Perf. 12½

1948, Dec. 18 Unwmk. Engr.

B163	SP17	1.50k + 1k rose lilac	.20	.15
B164	SP17	2k + 1k dp blue	.15	.15
B165	SP17	3k + 1k rose car	.18	.22
		Nos. B163-B165 (3)	.53	
		Set value		.38

The surtax was for child welfare.

Labels alternate with stamps in sheets of Nos. B163-B165.

1949, Dec. 18 *Perf. 12½*

Design: 3k+1k, Man lifting child.

B166	SP18	1.50k + 50h gray	*2.50*	*1.25*
B167	SP18	3k + 1k claret	*4.50*	*1.75*

The surtax was for child welfare.

Dove Carrying Olive Branch
SP19 SP20

1949, Dec. 18

B168	SP19	1.50k + 50h claret	*3.25*	*1.25*
B169	SP20	3k + 1k rose red	*3.25*	*1.50*

The surtax was for the Red Cross.

AIR POST STAMPS

Nos. 9, 39-40, 20, and Types of 1919 Surcharged in Red, Blue or Green:

1920 Unwmk. *Imperf.*

C1	A1	14k on 200h (R)	7.75	15.00
a.		Inverted surcharge	125.00	
C2	A2	24k on 500h (Bl)	21.00	30.00
a.		Inverted surcharge	175.00	
C3	A2	28k on 1000h (G)	21.00	30.00
a.		Inverted surcharge	175.00	
b.		Double surcharge	175.00	
		Nos. C1-C3 (3)	49.75	75.00

Perf. 14, 14x13½

C4	A1	14k on 200h (R)	14.00	14.00
a.		Perf. 14x13½	55.00	52.50
C5	A2	24k on 500h (Bl)	32.50	32.50
a.		Perf. 14x13½	77.50	77.50
C6	A2	28k on 1000h (G)	25.00	25.00
a.		Inverted surcharge	110.00	110.00
b.		Perf. 14	425.00	350.00
		Nos. C4-C6 (3)	71.50	71.50
		Nos. C1-C6 (6)	121.25	146.50

Excellent counterfeits of the overprint are known.

Stamps of 1920 Surcharged in Black or Violet:

1922, June 15

C7	A8	50h on 100h dl grn	1.50	1.50
a.		Inverted surcharge	175.00	
b.		Double surcharge	200.00	
C8	A8	100h on 200h vio	2.00	3.25
a.		Inverted surcharge	175.00	
C9	A8	250h on 400h brn (V)	5.00	7.50
a.		Inverted surcharge	175.00	
		Nos. C7-C9 (3)	8.50	12.25

Fokker Monoplane
AP3

Smolik S 19
AP4

Smolik S 19 — AP5

Fokker over Prague — AP6

1930, Dec. 16 Engr. *Perf. 13½*

C10	AP3	50h deep green	.15	.15
C11	AP3	1k deep red	.25	.25
C12	AP4	2k dark green	.60	.55
C13	AP4	3k red violet	1.25	1.00
C14	AP5	4k indigo	1.00	.80
C15	AP5	5k red brown	1.50	1.50
C16	AP6	10k vio blue	3.50	3.50
a.		10k ultra	6.25	6.50
C17	AP6	20k gray violet	4.50	3.00
		Nos. C10-C17 (8)	12.75	10.75

Two types exist of the 50h, 1k and 2k, and three types of the 3k, differing chiefly in the size of the printed area. A "no hill at left" variety of the 3k exists.

Imperf. copies of Nos. C10-C17 are proofs.

Perf. 12

C10a	AP3	50h deep green	1.90	1.90
C11a	AP3	1k deep red	18.00	18.00
C12a	AP4	2k dark green	14.00	14.00
C14a	AP5	4k indigo	6.00	6.25
C15a	AP5	5k red brown	*525.00*	
C17a	AP6	20k gray violet	4.00	3.00

Perf. 12x13½, 13½x12

C11b	AP3	1k deep red	2.75	2.75
C12b	AP4	2k dark green	9.25	9.25
C17b	AP6	20k gray violet	*425.00*	

Type of 1930 with hyphen in Cesko-Slovensko

1939, Apr. 22 *Perf. 13½*

C18	AP3	30h rose lilac	.15	.15

Catalogue values for unused stamps in this section, from this point to the end of the section, are for Never Hinged items.

Capt. Frantisek Novak — AP7

Plane over Bratislava Castle — AP8

Plane over Charles Bridge, Prague — AP9

1946-47 *Perf. 12½*

C19	AP7	1.50k rose red	.20	.15
C20	AP7	5.50k dk gray bl	.35	.15
C21	AP7	9k sepia ('47)	.90	.15
C22	AP8	10k dl grn	.80	.45
C23	AP7	16k violet	1.10	.35
C24	AP8	20k light blue	1.25	.35
C25	AP9	24k dk bl, *cr*	.90	.90
C26	AP9	24k rose lake	1.75	.75
C27	AP9	50k dk gray bl	3.25	1.50
		Nos. C19-C27 (9)	10.50	4.75

No. C25 was issued June 12, 1946, for use on the first Prague-New York flight.

Nos. C19-C24, C26-C27 Surcharged with New Value and Bars in Various Colors

1949, Sept. 1 *Perf. 12½*

C28	AP7	1k on 1.50k (Bl)	.15	.15
C29	AP7	3k on 5.50k (C)	.25	.15
C30	AP7	6k on 9k (Br)	.35	.15
C31	AP7	7.50k on 16k (C)	.50	.18
C32	AP8	8k on 10k (G)	.50	.28
C33	AP8	12.50k on 20k (Bl)	.75	.30
C34	AP9	15k on 24k rose lake (Bl)	1.75	.55
C35	AP9	30k on 50k (Bl)	1.25	.60
		Nos. C28-C35 (8)	5.50	2.36

Karlovy Vary (Karlsbad) — AP10

1951, Apr. 2 Engr. *Perf. 13½*

C36	AP10	6k shown	2.00	.52
C37	AP10	10k Piestany	2.00	.75
C38	AP10	15k Marienbad	4.00	.52
C39	AP10	20k Silac	*5.25*	*3.00*
		Nos. C36-C39 (4)	*13.25*	*4.79*

View of Cesky Krumlov — AP11

Views: 1.55k, Olomouc. 2.35k, Banska Bystrica. 2.75k, Bratislava. 10k, Prague.

1955 *Perf. 11½*

Cream Paper

C40	AP11	80h olive green	1.10	.15
C41	AP11	1.55k violet brn	1.10	.35
C42	AP11	2.35k violet blue	1.75	.20
C43	AP11	2.75k rose brown	2.50	.35
C44	AP11	10k indigo	3.50	1.50
		Nos. C40-C44 (5)	9.95	2.55

Issue dates: 10k, Feb. 20. Others, Mar. 28.

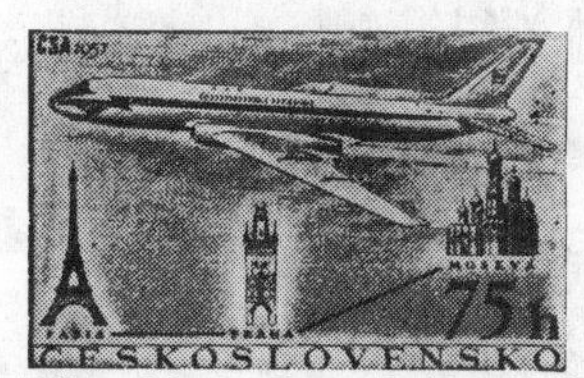

Airline: Moscow-Prague-Paris — AP12

Design: 2.35k, Airline: Prague-Cairo-Beirut-Damascus.

Engraved and Photogravure

1957, Oct. 15 Unwmk. *Perf. 11½*

C45	AP12	75h ultra & rose	.50	.15
C46	AP12	2.35k ultra & org yel	1.00	.20

Planes at First Czech Aviation School, Pardubice
AP13

Design: 1.80k, Jan Kaspar and flight of first Czech plane, 1909.

1959, Oct. 15

C47	AP13	1k gray & yel	.20	.15
C48	AP13	1.80k blk & pale bl	.95	.15
		Set value		.20

50th anniv. of Jan Kaspar's 1st flight Aug. 25, 1909, at Pardubice.

Mail Coach, Plane and Arms of Bratislava — AP14

Design: 2.80k, Helicopter over Bratislava.

1960, Sept. 24 Unwmk. *Perf. 11½*

C49	AP14	1.60k dk bl & gray	*2.00*	*.95*
C50	AP14	2.80k grn & buff	*3.00*	*1.50*

Issued to publicize the National Stamp Exhibition, Bratislava, Sept. 24-Oct. 9.

AP15

AP16

Designs: 60h, Prague hails Gagarin. 1.80k, Gagarin, rocket and dove.

1961, June 22

C51	AP15	60h gray & car	.20	.15
C52	AP15	1.80k gray & blue	.55	.20
		Set value		.25

No. C51 commemorates Maj. Gagarin's visit to Prague, Apr. 28-29; No. C52 commemorates the first man in space, Yuri A. Gagarin, Apr. 12, 1961.

1962, May 14 Engr. *Perf. 14*

Designs ("PRAGA" emblem and): 80h, Dove and Nest of Eggs. 1.40k, Dove. 2.80k, Symbolic flower with five petals. 4.20k, Five leaves.

C53	AP16	80h multicolored	.40	.22
C54	AP16	1.40k blk, dk red & bl	1.25	1.00
C55	AP16	2.80k multicolored	2.00	1.75
C56	AP16	4.20k multicolored	3.00	2.50
		Nos. C53-C56 (4)	6.65	5.47

PRAGA 1962 World Exhibition of Postage Stamps, Aug. 18-Sept. 2, 1962.

Vostok 5 and Lt. Col. Valeri Bykovski
AP17

Design: 2.80k, Vostok VI and Lt. Valentina Tereshkova.

1963, June 26

C57	AP17	80h slate bl & pink	.38	.15
C58	AP17	2.80k dl red brn & lt bl	.85	.25

Space flights of Valeri Bykovski, June 14-19, and Valentina Tereshkova, first woman astronaut, June 16-19, 1963.

PRAGA 1962 Emblem, View of Prague and Plane — AP18

Designs: 60h, Istanbul '63 (Hagia Sophia). 1k, Philatec Paris 1964 (Ile de la Cité). 1.40k, WIPA 1965 (Belvedere Palace, Vienna). 1.60k, SIPEX 1966 (Capitol, Washington). 2k, Amphilex '67 (harbor and old town, Amsterdam). 5k, PRAGA 1968 (View of Prague).

Engraved and Photogravure

1967, Oct. 30 *Perf. 11½*

Size: 30x50mm

C59	AP18	30h choc, yel & rose	.15	.15
C60	AP18	60h dk grn, yel & lil	.16	.15
C61	AP18	1k blk, brick red & lt bl	.26	.15
C62	AP18	1.40k vio, yel & dp org	.38	.16
C63	AP18	1.60k ind, tan & lil	.42	.26
C64	AP18	2k dk grn, org & red	.60	.35

Size: 40x50mm

C65	AP18	5k multi	*2.75*	*2.25*
		Nos. C59-C65 (7)	*4.72*	*3.47*

PRAGA 1968 World Stamp Exhibition, Prague, June 22-July 7, 1968. No. C59-C64 issued in sheets of 15 stamps and 15 bilingual labels. No.

C65 issued in sheets of 4 stamps and one center label.

Glider L-13 — AP19

Airplanes: 60h, Sports plane L-40. 80h, Aero taxi L-200. 1k, Crop-spraying plane Z-37. 1.60k, Aerobatics trainer Z-526. 2k, Jet trainer L-29.

1967, Dec. 11

C66	AP19	30h multi	.15	.15
C67	AP19	60h multi	.15	.15
C68	AP19	80h multi	.20	.15
C69	AP19	1k multi	.24	.15
C70	AP19	1.60k multi	.38	.20
C71	AP19	2k multi	*1.25*	*.55*
		Nos. C66-C71 (6)	*2.37*	
		Set value		*1.00*

Charles Bridge, Prague, and Balloon — AP20

Astronaut, Moon and Manhattan — AP21

Designs: 1k, Belvedere, fountain and early plane. 2k, Hradcany, Prague, and airship.

1968, Feb. 5 Unwmk. *Perf. 11½*

C72	AP20	60h multicolored	.24	.15
C73	AP20	1k multicolored	.35	.20
C74	AP20	2k multicolored	.65	.55
		Nos. C72-C74 (3)	1.24	.90

PRAGA 1968 World Stamp Exhibition, Prague, June 22-July 7, 1968.

1969, July 21

Design: 3k, Lunar landing module and J. F. Kennedy Airport, New York.

C75	AP21	60h blk, vio, yel & sil	.20	.15
C76	AP21	3k blk, bl, ocher & sil	1.00	.75

Man's 1st landing on the moon, July 20, 1969, US astronauts Neil A. Armstrong and Col. Edwin E. Aldrin, Jr., with Lieut. Col. Michael Collins piloting Apollo 11.

Nos. C75-C76 printed with label inscribed with names of astronauts and European date of moon landing.

TU-104A over Bitov Castle AP22

Designs: 60h, IL-62 over Bezdez Castle. 1.40k, TU-13A over Orava Castle. 1.90k, IL-18 over Veveri Castle. 2.40k, IL-14 over Pernstejn Castle. 3.60k, TU-154 over Trencin Castle.

1973, Oct. 24 Engr. *Perf. 11½*

C77	AP22	30h multi	.15	.15
C78	AP22	60h multi	.15	.15
C79	AP22	1.40k multi	.26	.15
C80	AP22	1.90k multi	.38	.20
C81	AP22	2.40k multi	*2.75*	*.85*
C82	AP22	3.60k multi	.52	.30
		Nos. C77-C82 (6)	*4.21*	*1.80*

50 years of Czechoslovakian aviation.

Old Water Tower and Manes Hall — AP23

Designs (Praga 1978 Emblem, Plane Silhouette and): 1.60k, Congress Hall. 2k, Powder Tower, vert. 2.40k, Charles Bridge and Old Bridge Tower. 4k, Old Town Hall on Old Town Square, vert. 6k, Prague Castle and St. Vitus' Cathedral, vert.

Engraved and Photogravure

1976, June 23 *Perf. 11½*

C83	AP23	60h ind & multi	.15	.15
C84	AP23	1.60k ind & multi	.35	.15
C85	AP23	2k ind & multi	.45	.15
C86	AP23	2.40k ind & multi	.50	.25
C87	AP23	4k ind & multi	.90	.32
C88	AP23	6k ind & multi	3.25	.85
		Nos. C83-C88 (6)	5.60	1.87

PRAGA 1978 International Philatelic Exhibition, Prague, Sept. 8-17, 1978.

Zeppelin, 1909 and 1928 — AP24

Designs (PRAGA '78 Emblem and): 1k, Ader, 1890, L'Eole and Dunn, 1914. 1.60k, Jeffries-Blanchard balloon, 1785. 2k, Otto Lilienthal's glider, 1896. 4.40k, Jan Kaspar's plane, Pardubice, 1911.

1977, Sept. 15 *Perf. 11½*

C89	AP24	60h multi	.15	.15
C90	AP24	1k multi	.32	.15
C91	AP24	1.60k multi	.50	.15
C92	AP24	2k multi	.70	.22
C93	AP24	4.40k multi	*2.25*	*.75*
		Nos. C89-C93 (5)	*3.92*	*1.42*

History of aviation.

SPECIAL DELIVERY STAMPS

Doves — SD1

1919-20 Unwmk. Typo. *Imperf.*

E1	SD1	2h red vio, *yel*	.15	.15
E2	SD1	5h yel grn, *yel*	.15	.15
E3	SD1	10h red brn, *yel* ('20)	.38	.38
		Set value	.50	.50

For overprints and surcharge see Nos. P11-P13.

1921 White Paper

E1a	SD1	2h red violet	3.00
E2a	SD1	5h yellow green	2.75
E3a	SD1	10h red brown	52.50
		Nos. E1a-E3a (3)	58.25

It is doubted that Nos. E1a-E3a were regularly issued.

PERSONAL DELIVERY STAMPS

Catalogue values for unused stamps in this section are for Never Hinged items.

PD1

Design: No. EX2, "D" in each corner.

1937 Unwmk. Photo. *Perf. 13½*

EX1	PD1	50h blue	.25	.30
EX2	PD1	50h carmine	.25	.30

PD3

1946 *Perf. 13½*

EX3	PD3	2k deep blue	.35	.35

POSTAGE DUE STAMPS

D1

1918-20 Unwmk. Typo. *Imperf.*

J1	D1	5h deep bister	.15	.15
J2	D1	10h deep bister	.15	.15
J3	D1	15h deep bister	.15	.15
J4	D1	20h deep bister	.15	.15
J5	D1	25h deep bister	.18	.15
J6	D1	30h deep bister	.30	.15
J7	D1	40h deep bister	.32	.25
J8	D1	50h deep bister	.32	.15
J9	D1	100h blk brn	1.25	.15
J10	D1	250h orange	4.75	1.40
J11	D1	400h scarlet	6.50	1.40
J12	D1	500h gray grn	2.50	.20
J13	D1	1000h purple	3.50	.25
J14	D1	2000h dark blue	15.00	.60
		Nos. J1-J14 (14)	35.22	
		Set value		4.75

For surcharges see Nos. J32-J41, J57.

Nos. 1, 33-34, 10 Surcharged in Blue

100 DOPLATIT

1922

J15	A1	20h on 3h red vio	.35	.16
J16	A2	50h on 75h slate	.95	.20
J17	A2	60h on 80h olive grn	.30	.15
J18	A2	100h on 80h olive grn	.50	.15
J19	A1	200h on 400h purple	.70	.15
		Nos. J15-J19 (5)	2.80	.81

Same Surcharge on Nos. 1, 10, 30-31, 33-34, 36, 40 in Violet

1923-26

J20	A1	10h on 3h red vio	.15	.15
J21	A1	20h on 3h red vio	.15	.15
J22	A1	30h on 3h red vio	.15	.15
J23	A1	40h on 3h red vio	.22	.15
J24	A2	50h on 75h slate	1.40	.15
J25	A2	60h on 50h dk vio ('26)	2.75	1.25
J26	A2	60h on 50h dk bl ('26)	2.75	1.50
J27	A2	60h on 75h slate	1.25	.15
J28	A2	100h on 80h ol grn	40.00	.75
J29	A2	100h on 120h gray blk	1.40	.15
J30	A1	100h on 400h pur ('26)	.80	.15
J31	A2	100h on 1000h dp vio ('26)	1.75	.25
		Nos. J20-J31 (12)	52.77	4.95

Postage Due Stamp of 1918-20 Surcharged in Violet

50

1924

J32	D1	50h on 400h scar	1.00	.15
J33	D1	60h on 400h scar	3.00	.70
J34	D1	100h on 400h scar	2.00	.20
		Nos. J32-J34 (3)	6.00	1.05

Postage Due Stamps of 1918-20 Surcharged with New Values in Violet as in 1924

1925

J35	D1	10h on 5h bister	.15	.15
J36	D1	20h on 5h bister	.15	.15
J37	D1	30h on 15h bister	.25	.15
J38	D1	40h on 15h bister	.32	.15
J39	D1	50h on 250h org	1.10	.20
J40	D1	60h on 250h org	1.40	.50
J41	D1	100h on 250h org	3.50	.35
		Nos. J35-J41 (7)	6.87	
		Set value		1.28

Stamps of 1918-19 Surcharged with New Values in Violet as in 1922

1926 *Perf. 14, 11½*

J42	A2	30h on 15h red	.70	.35
J43	A2	40h on 15h red	.52	.15

On #J44-J49 On #J50-J56

1926 Violet Surcharge *Perf. 14*

J44	A8	30h on 100h dk grn	.15	.15
J45	A8	40h on 200h violet	.24	.15
J46	A8	40h on 300h ver	.95	.26
a.		Perf. 14x13½		30.00
J47	A8	50h on 500h dp grn	.50	.15
a.		Perf. 14x13½	2.50	
J48	A8	60h on 400h brown	1.00	.16
J49	A8	100h on 600h dp vio	2.50	.35
a.		Perf. 14x13½	30.00	1.25
		Nos. J44-J49 (6)	5.34	1.22

1927 Violet Overprint

J50	A6	100h dark brown	.65	.15
a.		Perf. 13½	*275.00*	15.00

Surcharged with New Value in Violet

J51	A6	40h on 185h org	.18	.15
J52	A6	50h on 20h car	.24	.15
a.		50h on 50h carmine (error)		*30,000.*
J53	A6	50h on 150h rose	.30	.15
a.		Perf. 13½	12.50	2.00
J54	A6	60h on 25h brown	.42	.20
J55	A6	60h on 185h orange	.55	.15
J56	A6	100h on 25h brown	.60	.20
		Nos. J50-J56 (7)	2.94	
		Set value		.77

No. J52a is known only used.

No. J12 Surcharged in Violet **200**

1927 *Imperf.*

J57	D1	200h on 500h gray grn	3.25	2.50

Catalogue values for unused stamps in this section, from this point to the end of the section, are for Never Hinged items.

D5

1928 *Perf. 14x13½*

J58	D5	5h dark red	.15	.15
J59	D5	10h dark red	.15	.15
J60	D5	20h dark red	.15	.15
J61	D5	30h dark red	.15	.15
J62	D5	40h dark red	.15	.15
J63	D5	50h dark red	.15	.15
J64	D5	60h dark red	.15	.15
J65	D5	1k ultra	.22	.15
J66	D5	2k ultra	.65	.15
J67	D5	5k ultra	1.10	.15
J68	D5	10k ultra	2.00	.15
J69	D5	20k ultra	4.50	.15
		Nos. J58-J69 (12)	9.52	
		Set value		.85

D6

1946-48 Photo. *Perf. 14*

J70	D6	10h dark blue	.15	.15
J71	D6	20h dark blue	.15	.15
J72	D6	50h dark blue	.15	.15
J73	D6	1k carmine rose	.15	.15
J74	D6	1.20k carmine rose	.28	.15
J75	D6	1.50k carmine rose ('48)	.35	.15
J76	D6	1.60k carmine rose	.40	.15
J77	D6	2k carmine rose ('48)	.40	.15
J78	D6	2.40k carmine rose	.75	.15
J79	D6	3k carmine rose	1.00	.15
J80	D6	5k carmine rose	1.65	.15
J81	D6	6k carmine rose ('48)	2.00	.15
		Nos. J70-J81 (12)	7.43	
		Set value		.60

D7

D8

1954-55 Engr. *Perf. 12½, 11½*

No.	Design	Value	Description	Unused	Used
J82	D7	5h	gray green ('55)	.15	.15
J83	D7	10h	gray green ('55)	.15	.15
J84	D7	30h	gray green	.15	.15
J85	D7	50h	gray green ('55)	.15	.15
J86	D7	60h	gray green ('55)	.18	.15
J87	D7	95h	gray green	.35	.15
J88	D8	1k	violet	.35	.15
J89	D8	1.20k	violet ('55)	.35	.15
J90	D8	1.50k	violet	.70	.15
J91	D8	1.60k	violet ('55)	.45	.15
J92	D8	2k	violet	.85	.15
J93	D8	3k	violet	1.10	.15
J94	D8	5k	violet ('55)	1.40	.22
			Nos. J82-J94 (13)	6.33	
			Set value		.82

Perf. 11½ stamps are from a 1963 printing which lacks the 95h, 1.60k, and 2k.

Stylized Flower — D9

Designs: Various stylized flowers.

Engraved and Photogravure

1971-72 *Perf. 11½*

No.	Design	Value	Description	Unused	Used
J95	D9	10h	vio bl & pink	.15	.15
J96	D9	20h	vio & lt bl	.15	.15
J97	D9	30h	emer & lil rose	.15	.15
J98	D9	60h	pur & emer	.15	.15
J99	D9	80h	org & vio bl	.15	.15
J100	D9	1k	dk red & emer	.25	.15
J101	D9	1.20k	grn & org	.20	.15
J102	D9	2k	blue & red	.42	.15
J103	D9	3k	blk & yel	.48	.15
J104	D9	4k	brn & ultra	.85	.15
J105	D9	5.40k	red & lilac	1.00	.20
J106	D9	6k	brick red & org	1.40	.30
			Nos. J95-J106 (12)	5.35	
			Set value		1.00

All except 5.40k issued in 1972.

OFFICIAL STAMPS

Catalogue values for unused stamps in this section are for Never Hinged items.

Coat of Arms — O1

1945 Unwmk. Litho. *Perf. 10½x10*

No.	Design	Value	Description	Unused	Used
O1	O1	50h	dp slate grn	.15	.15
O2	O1	1k	dp bl vio	.15	.15
O3	O1	1.20k	plum	.22	.15
O4	O1	1.50k	crimson rose	.15	.15
O5	O1	2.50k	bright ultra	.22	.15
O6	O1	5k	dk vio brn	.28	.22
O7	O1	8k	rose pink	.42	.38
			Nos. O1-O7 (7)	1.59	
			Set value		.85

Redrawn

1947 Photo. *Perf. 14*

No.	Design	Value	Description	Unused	Used
O8	O1	60h	red	.15	.15
O9	O1	80h	dk olive grn	.15	.15
O10	O1	1k	dk lilac gray	.15	.15
O11	O1	1.20k	dp plum	.15	.15
O12	O1	2.40k	dk car rose	.15	.15
O13	O1	4k	brt ultra	.15	.15
O14	O1	5k	dk vio brn	.18	.18
O15	O1	7.40k	purple	.32	.28
			Set value	.92	.85

There are many minor changes in design, size of numerals, etc., of the redrawn stamps.

NEWSPAPER STAMPS

Windhover — N1

1918-20 Unwmk. Typo. *Imperf.*

No.	Design	Value	Description	Unused	Used
P1	N1	2h	gray green	.15	.15
P2	N1	5h	green ('20)	.15	.15
a.			5h dark green	.40	.15
P3	N1	6h	red	.38	.28
P4	N1	10h	dull violet	.15	.15
P5	N1	20h	blue	.15	.15
P6	N1	30h	gray brown	.15	.15
P7	N1	50h	orange ('20)	.24	.18
P8	N1	100h	red brown ('20)	.40	.28
			Set value	1.30	1.00

Nos. P1-P8 exist privately perforated.

For surcharges and overprints see Nos. P9-P10, P14-P16.

Stamps of 1918-20 Surcharged in Violet

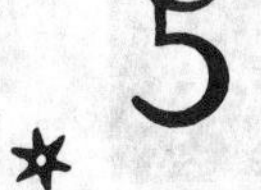

1925-26

No.	Design	Description	Unused	Used
P9	N1	5h on 2h gray green	.60	.38
P10	N1	5h on 6h red ('26)	.42	.38

Special Delivery Stamps of 1918-20 Overprinted in Violet

NOVINY

1926

No.	Design	Description	Unused	Used
P11	SD1	5h apple grn, *yel*	.20	.18
a.		5h dull green, *yellow*	.50	.40
P12	SD1	10h red brn, *yel*	.15	.15

With Additional Surcharge of New Value

No.	Design	Description	Unused	Used
P13	SD1	5h on 2h red vio, *yel*	.35	.60
		Nos. P11-P13 (3)	.70	.93

Catalogue values for unused stamps in this section, from this point to the end of the section, are for Never Hinged items.

Newspaper Stamps of 1918-20 Overprinted in Violet

1934

No.	Design	Value	Description	Unused	Used
P14	N1	10h	dull violet	.15	.15
P15	N1	20h	blue	.15	.15
P16	N1	30h	gray brown	.18	.22
			Set value	.28	.32

Overprinted for use by commercial firms only.

Carrier Pigeon — N2

1937 *Imperf.*

No.	Design	Value	Description	Unused	Used
P17	N2	2h	bister brown	.15	.15
P18	N2	5h	dull blue	.15	.15
P19	N2	7h	red orange	.15	.15
P20	N2	9h	emerald	.15	.15
P21	N2	10h	henna brown	.15	.15
P22	N2	12h	ultra	.15	.15
P23	N2	20h	dark green	.15	.15
P24	N2	50h	dark brown	.15	.15
P25	N2	1k	olive gray	.15	.15
			Set value	.54	.47

For overprint see Slovakia Nos. P1-P9.

Bratislava Philatelic Exhibition Issue

Souvenir Sheet

1937 *Imperf.*

No.	Design	Description	Unused	Used
P26	N2	10h henna brn, sheet of 25	4.00	4.50

Newspaper Delivery Boy — N4

1945 Unwmk. Typo. *Imperf.*

No.	Design	Value	Description	Unused	Used
P27	N4	5h	dull blue	.15	.15
P28	N4	10h	red	.15	.15
P29	N4	15h	emerald	.15	.15
P30	N4	20h	dark slate green	.15	.15
P31	N4	25h	bright red vio	.15	.15
P32	N4	30h	ocher	.15	.15
P33	N4	40h	red orange	.15	.15
P34	N4	50h	brown red	.15	.15
P35	N4	1k	slate gray	.15	.15
P36	N4	5k	deep vio blue	.15	.15
			Set value	.60	.55

CZECHOSLOVAK LEGION POST

The Czechoslovak Legion in Siberia issued these stamps for use on its mail and that of local residents. Forgeries exist.

Urn and Cathedral at Irkutsk — A1

Armored Railroad Car — A2

Sentinel — A3

Lion of Bohemia — A4

1919 Litho. *Perf. 11½*

No.	Design	Description	Unused	Used
1	A1	25k carmine	14.00	
a.		Imperf.	14.00	
2	A2	50k yellow green	14.00	
a.		Imperf.	14.00	
3	A3	1r red brown	32.50	
a.		Imperf.	32.50	
		Nos. 1-3 (3)	60.50	
		Nos. 1a-3a (3)	60.50	

Originals of Nos. 1-3 and 1a-3a have yellowish gum. Ungummed remainders, which were given a white gum, exist imperforate and perforated 11½ and 14. Value per set, $3.

Embossed

Perce en Arc in Blue

No.	Design	Description	Unused	Used
4	A4	(25k) blue & rose	2.50	

Two types: I- 6 points on star-like mace head at right of goblet; large saber handle; measures 19½x24¾mm. II- 5 points on mace head; small saber handle; measures 20x25mm.

No. 4 Overprinted

1920

1920

No.	Design	Description	Unused	Used
5	A4	(25k) bl & rose	7.00	

Both types of No. 4 received overprint.

No. 5 Surcharged with New Values in Green

2

No.	Design	Value	Description	Unused	Used
6	A4	2k	bl & rose	25.00	
7	A4	3k	bl & rose	25.00	
8	A4	5k	bl & rose	25.00	
9	A4	10k	bl & rose	25.00	
10	A4	15k	bl & rose	25.00	
11	A4	25k	bl & rose	25.00	
12	A4	35k	bl & rose	25.00	
13	A4	50k	bl & rose	25.00	
14	A4	1r	bl & rose	25.00	
			Nos. 6-14 (9)	225.00	

BOHEMIA AND MORAVIA

Catalogue values for unused stamps in this country are for never hinged items, beginning with Scott 20 in the regular postage section, Scott B1 in the semi-postal section, Scott J1 in the postage due section, Scott O1 in the official section, and Scott P1 in the newspaper section.

German Protectorate

Stamps of Czechoslovakia, 1928-39, Overprinted in Black

BÖHMEN u. MÄHREN

ČECHY a MORAVA

Perf. 10, 12½, 12x12½

1939, July 15 Unwmk.

No.	Design	Value	Description	Unused	Used
1	A29	5h	dk ultra	.15	*.20*
2	A29	10h	brown	.15	*.20*
3	A29	20h	red	.15	*.20*
4	A29	25h	green	.15	*.20*
5	A29	30h	red vio	.15	*.20*
6	A61a	40h	dk bl	2.50	*4.75*
7	A85	50h	dp grn	.15	*.20*
8	A63	60h	dl vio	2.50	*4.75*
9	A60	1k	rose lake (212)	.75	*1.75*
10	A60	1k	rose lake (256)	.30	*.85*
11	A64	1.20k	rose lilac	3.00	*6.25*
12	A65	1.50k	carmine	2.50	*4.75*
13	A79	1.60k	olive grn	2.50	*4.75*
a.			"Mähnen"	16.00	*27.50*
14	A66	2k	dk bl grn	1.10	*1.75*
15	A67	2.50k	dk bl	3.00	*4.50*
16	A68	3k	brown	3.00	*4.75*
17	A70	4k	dk vio	3.50	*5.00*
18	A71	5k	green	3.50	*5.75*
19	A72	10k	blue	4.75	*9.50*
			Nos. 1-19 (19)	33.80	*60.30*

The size of the overprint varies, Nos. 1-10 measure 17½x15½mm, Nos. 11-16 19x18mm, Nos. 17 and 19 28x17½mm and No. 18 23½x23mm.

Catalogue values for unused stamps in this section, from this point to the end of the section, are for never hinged items.

Linden Leaves and Closed Buds — A1

1939-41 Photo. *Perf. 14*

No.	Design	Value	Description	Unused	Used
20	A1	5h	dark blue	.15	.15
21	A1	10h	blk brn	.15	.15
22	A1	20h	crimson	.15	.15
23	A1	25h	dk bl grn	.15	.15
24	A1	30h	dp plum	.15	.15
24A	A1	30h	golden brn ('41)	.15	.15
25	A1	40h	orange ('40)	.15	.15
26	A1	50h	slate grn ('40)	.15	.15
			Set value	.50	.50

See Nos. 49-51.

Castle at Zvikov — A2

Karlstein Castle — A3

St. Barbara's Church, Kutna Hora — A4

Cathedral at Prague — A5

Brno Cathedral — A6

Town Square, Olomouc — A7

1939 Engr. *Perf. 12½*

No.	Design	Value	Description	Unused	Used
27	A2	40h	dark blue	.15	.15
28	A3	50h	dk bl grn	.15	.15
29	A4	60h	dl vio	.15	.15
30	A5	1k	dp rose	.15	.15
31	A6	1.20k	rose lilac	.40	*.65*
32	A6	1.50k	rose car	.15	.15
33	A7	2k	dk bl grn	.15	.15
34	A7	2.50k	dark blue	.15	.15
			Set value	1.10	*1.10*

No. 31 measures 23½x29½mm, No. 42 measures 18½x23mm.

See #52-53, 53B. For overprints see #60-61.

Zlin — A8

Iron Works at Moravská Ostrava — A9

Prague — A10

1939-40

No.	Type	Denom.	Color	Unused	Used
35	A8	3k	dl rose vio	.18	.15
36	A9	4k	slate ('40)	.15	.15
37	A10	5k	green	.40	.38
38	A10	10k	lt ultra	.30	.65
39	A10	20k	yel brn	.90	1.25
			Nos. 35-39 (5)	1.93	2.58

Types of 1939 and

Neuhaus — A11

Lainsitz Bridge near Bechyne — A14

Pernstein Castle — A12

Samson Fountain, Budweis — A15

Pardubice Castle — A13

Kromeriz — A16

Wallenstein Palace, Prague — A17

1940 **Engr.** ***Perf. 12½***

No.	Type	Denom.	Color	Unused	Used
40	A11	50h	dk bl grn	.15	.15
41	A12	80h	dp bl	.25	.40
42	A6	1.20k	vio brn	.38	.25
43	A13	2k	gray grn	.20	.15
44	A14	5k	dk bl grn	.20	.15
45	A15	6k	brn vio	.20	.25
46	A16	8k	slate grn	.20	.35
47	A17	10k	blue	.45	.30
48	A10	20k	sepia	1.10	1.50
			Nos. 40-48 (9)	3.13	3.50

No. 42 measures 18½x23mm; No. 31, 23½x29½mm.

Types of 1939-40

1941

No.	Type	Denom.	Color	Unused	Used
49	A1	60h	violet	.15	.15
50	A1	80h	red org	.15	.15
51	A1	1k	brown	.15	.15
52	A5	1.20k	rose red	.15	.15
53	A4	1.50k	lil rose	.15	.15
53A	A13	2k	light blue	.15	.15
53B	A6	2.50k	ultra	.15	.15
53C	A12	3k	olive	.20	.15
			Set value	.98	1.05

Nos. 49-51 show buds open. Nos. 52 and 53B measure 18¾x23½mm and have no inscriptions below design.

For overprints see Nos. 60-61.

Antonin Dvorák — A18

1941, Aug. 25 **Engr.** ***Perf. 12½***

No.	Type	Denom.	Color	Unused	Used
54	A18	60h	dull lilac	.15	.15
55	A18	1.20k	sepia	.26	.26

Antonin Dvorák (1841-1904), composer.
Labels alternate with stamps in sheets of #54-55.

Farming Scene A19

Factories A20

1941, Sept. 7 **Photo.** ***Perf. 13½***

No.	Type	Denom.	Color	Unused	Used
56	A19	30h	dk red brn	.15	.15
57	A19	60h	dark green	.15	.15
58	A20	1.20k	dk plum	.20	.25
59	A20	2.50k	sapphire	.25	.40
			Set value	.65	

Issued to publicize the Prague Fair.

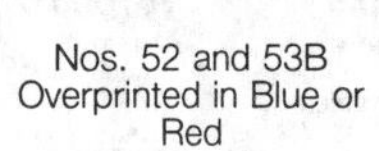

Nos. 52 and 53B Overprinted in Blue or Red

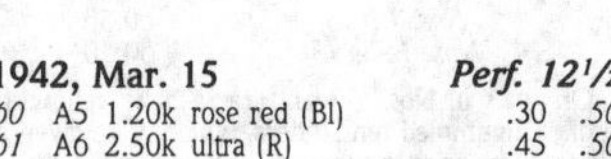

1942, Mar. 15 ***Perf. 12½***

No.	Type	Denom.	Color	Unused	Used
60	A5	1.20k	rose red (Bl)	.30	.50
61	A6	2.50k	ultra (R)	.45	.50

3rd anniv. of the Protectorate of Bohemia and Moravia.

Adolf Hitler A21

17th Century Messenger A22

1942 **Photo.** ***Perf. 14***

Size: 17½x21½mm

No.	Type	Denom.	Color	Unused	Used
62	A21	10(h)	gray blk	.15	.15
63	A21	30(h)	bister brn	.15	.15
64	A21	40(h)	slate blue	.15	.15
65	A21	50(h)	slate grn	.15	.15
66	A21	60(h)	purple	.15	.15
67	A21	80(h)	org ver	.15	.15

Perf. 12½

Engr.

Size: 18x21mm

No.	Type	Denom.	Color	Unused	Used
68	A21	1k	dl brn	.15	.15
69	A21	1.20(k)	carmine	.15	.15
70	A21	1.50(k)	claret	.15	.20
71	A21	1.60(k)	Prus grn	.15	.50
72	A21	2k	light blue	.15	.25
73	A21	2.40(k)	fawn	.15	.25

Size: 18½x24mm

No.	Type	Denom.	Color	Unused	Used
74	A21	2.50(k)	ultra	.15	.25
75	A21	3k	olive grn	.15	.25
76	A21	4k	brt red vio	.15	.25
77	A21	5k	myrtle grn	.15	.25
78	A21	6k	claret brn	.15	.25
79	A21	8k	indigo	.15	.25

Size: 23½x29¾mm

No.	Type	Denom.	Color	Unused	Used
80	A21	10k	dk gray grn	.15	1.00
81	A21	20k	gray vio	.30	1.00
82	A21	30k	red	.75	1.50
83	A21	50k	deep blue	1.50	3.00
			Set value	3.75	

1943, Jan. 10 **Photo.** ***Perf. 13½***

No.	Type	Denom.	Color	Unused	Used
84	A22	60h	dark rose violet	.15	.15

Stamp Day.

Scene from "Die Meistersinger" — A23

Richard Wagner — A24

Scene from "Siegfried" — A25

1943, May 22

No.	Type	Denom.	Color	Unused	Used
85	A23	60h	violet	.15	.15
86	A24	1.20k	carmine rose	.15	.15
87	A25	2.50k	deep ultra	.15	.20
			Set value	.26	.40

Richard Wagner (1813-83).

St. Vitus' Cathedral, Prague — A26

Adolf Hitler — A27

1944, Nov. 21 **Engr.** ***Perf. 12½***

No.	Type	Denom.	Color	Unused	Used
88	A26	1.50k	dull rose brn	.15	.15
89	A26	2.50k	dull lilac blue	.15	.25
			Set value	.22	

1944

No.	Type	Denom.	Color	Unused	Used
90	A27	4.20k	green	.20	.50

SEMI-POSTAL STAMPS

Catalogue values for unused stamps in this section are for never hinged items.

Nurse and Wounded Soldier — SP1

Red Cross Nurse and Patient — SP2

Perf. 13½

1940, June 29 **Photo.** **Unwmk.**

No.	Type	Denom.	Color	Unused	Used
B1	SP1	60h + 40h	indigo	.55	.60
B2	SP1	1.20k + 80h	deep plum	.70	.65

Surtax for German Red Cross.
Labels alternate with stamps in sheets of #B1-B2.

1941, Apr. 20

No.	Type	Denom.	Color	Unused	Used
B3	SP2	60h + 40h	indigo	.38	.60
B4	SP2	1.20k + 80h	dp plum	.38	.65

Surtax for German Red Cross.
Labels alternate with stamps in sheets of #B3-B4.

Old Theater, Prague — SP3

Mozart — SP4

1941, Oct. 26

No.	Type	Denom.	Color	Unused	Used
B5	SP3	30h + 30h	brown	.15	.15
B6	SP3	60h + 60h	Prus grn	.15	.15
B7	SP4	1.20k + 1.20k	scar	.24	.45
B8	SP4	2.50k + 2.50k	dk bl	.45	.55
			Nos. B5-B8 (4)	.99	1.30

150th anniversary of Mozart's death.

Labels alternate with stamps in sheets of Nos. B5-B8. The labels with Nos. B5-B6 show two bars of Mozart's opera "Don Giovanni." Those with Nos. B7-B8 show Mozart's piano.

Adolf Hitler — SP5

Nurse and Soldier — SP6

1942, Apr. 20 **Engr.** ***Perf. 12½***

No.	Type	Denom.	Color	Unused	Used
B9	SP5	30h + 20h	dl brn vio	.15	.15
B10	SP5	60h + 40h	dl grn	.15	.15
B11	SP5	1.20k + 80h	dp claret	.15	.15
B12	SP5	2.50k + 1.50k	dl bl	.15	.35
			Set value	.50	

Hitler's 53rd birthday.

1942, Sept. 4 ***Perf. 13½***

No.	Type	Denom.	Color	Unused	Used
B13	SP6	60h + 40h	deep blue	.15	.15
B14	SP6	1.20(k) + 80(h)	dp plum	.15	.15
			Set value	.15	.15

The surtax aided the German Red Cross.

Emperor Charles IV — SP7

Peter Parler — SP8

John the Blind, King of Bohemia — SP9

Adolf Hitler — SP10

1943, Jan. 29

No.	Type	Denom.	Color	Unused	Used
B15	SP7	60h + 40h	violet	.15	.15
B16	SP8	1.20k + 80h	carmine	.15	.15
B17	SP9	2.50k + 1.50k	vio bl	.15	.20
			Set value	.20	.42

The surtax was for the benefit of the German wartime winter relief.

1943, Apr. 20 **Engr.** ***Perf. 12½***

No.	Type	Denom.	Color	Unused	Used
B18	SP10	60h + 1.40k	dl vio	.15	.15
B19	SP10	1.20k + 3.80k	carmine	.15	.25
			Set value	.20	

Hitler's 54th birthday.

Deathmask of Reinhard Heydrich — SP11

Eagle and Red Cross — SP12

1943, May 28 **Photo.** ***Perf. 13½***

No.	Type	Denom.	Color	Unused	Used
B20	SP11	60h + 4.40k	black	.30	.40

No. B20 exists in a miniature sheet containing a single copy. It was given to officials attending Heydrich's funeral.

1943, Sept. 16 ***Perf. 13***

No.	Type	Denom.	Color	Unused	Used
B21	SP12	1.20k + 8.80k	blk & car	.15	.15

The surtax aided the German Red Cross.

Native Costumes SP13

Nazi Emblem, Arms of Bohemia, Moravia SP14

1944, Mar. 15 *Perf. 13½*

B22 SP13	1.20(k) + 3.80(k) rose lake	.15	.15
B23 SP14	4.20(k) + 10.80(k) golden brn	.15	.15
B24 SP13	10k + 20k saph	.16	*.30*
	Set value	.30	

Fifth anniversary of protectorate.

Adolf Hitler — SP15

Bedrich Smetana — SP16

1944, Apr. 20

B25 SP15	60h + 1.40k olive blk	.15	.15
B26 SP15	1.20k + 3.80k slate grn	.15	.20
	Set value	.15	.30

1944, May 12 **Engr.** *Perf. 12½*

B27 SP16	60h + 1.40k dk gray grn	.15	.15
B28 SP16	1.20k + 3.80k brn car	.15	.20
	Set value	.15	.30

Bedrich Smetana (1824-84), Czech composer and pianist.

PERSONAL DELIVERY STAMPS

PD1

1939-40 **Unwmk.** **Photo.** *Perf. 13½*

EX1 PD1	50h indigo & blue ('40)	.45	*.80*
EX2 PD1	50h carmine & rose	.55	*1.10*

POSTAGE DUE STAMPS

Catalogue values for unused stamps in this section are for never hinged items.

D1

1939-40 **Unwmk.** **Typo.** *Perf. 14*

J1	D1	5h dark carmine	.15	.15
J2	D1	10h dark carmine	.15	.15
J3	D1	20h dark carmine	.15	.15
J4	D1	30h dark carmine	.15	.15
J5	D1	40h dark carmine	.15	.15
J6	D1	50h dark carmine	.15	.15
J7	D1	60h dark carmine	.15	.15
J8	D1	80h dark carmine	.15	.15
J9	D1	1k bright ultra	.15	*.30*
J10	D1	1.20k brt ultra ('40)	.22	*.32*
J11	D1	2k bright ultra	.80	*.90*
J12	D1	5k bright ultra	.80	*1.00*
J13	D1	10k bright ultra	1.25	*1.65*
J14	D1	20k bright ultra	3.25	*4.25*
		Nos. J1-J14 (14)	7.67	*9.62*

OFFICIAL STAMPS

Catalogue values for unused stamps in this section are for never hinged items.

Numeral O1

Eagle O2

1941, Jan. 1 **Unwmk.** **Typo.** *Perf. 14*

O1	O1	30h ocher	.15	.15
O2	O1	40h indigo	.15	.15
O3	O1	50h emerald	.15	.15
O4	O1	60h slate grn	.15	.15
O5	O1	80h org red	.65	.20
O6	O1	1k red brn	.25	.15
O7	O1	1.20k carmine	.25	.15
O8	O1	1.50k dp plum	.45	.15
O9	O1	2k brt bl	.45	.15
O10	O1	3k olive	.45	.15
O11	O1	4k red vio	.80	.45
O12	O1	5k org yel	2.00	.90
		Nos. O1-O12 (12)	5.90	
		Set value		2.00

1943, Feb. 15

O13	O2	30(h) bister	.15	.15
O14	O2	40(h) indigo	.15	.15
O15	O2	50(h) yel grn	.15	.15
O16	O2	60(h) dp vio	.15	.15
O17	O2	80(h) org red	.15	.15
O18	O2	1k chocolate	.15	.15
O19	O2	1.20(k) carmine	.15	.15
O20	O2	1.50(k) brn red	.15	.20
O21	O2	2k lt bl	.15	.20
O22	O2	3k olive	.15	.20
O23	O2	4k red vio	.15	.20
O24	O2	5k dk grn	.15	*.35*
		Set value	1.00	1.50

NEWSPAPER STAMPS

Catalogue values for unused stamps in this section are for never hinged items.

Carrier Pigeon

N1 N2

1939 **Unwmk.** **Typo.** *Imperf.*

P1	N1	2h ocher	.15	.15
P2	N1	5h ultra	.15	.15
P3	N1	7h red orange	.15	.15
P4	N1	9h emerald	.15	.15
P5	N1	10h henna brown	.15	.15
P6	N1	12h dark ultra	.15	.15
P7	N1	20h dark green	.15	*.25*
P8	N1	50h red brown	.15	*.35*
P9	N1	1k greenish gray	.15	*.35*
		Set value	.95	*1.60*

No. P5 Overprinted in Black **GD-OT**

1940

P10	N1	10h henna brown	.15	*.30*

Overprinted for use by commercial firms.

1943, Feb. 15

P11	N2	2(h) ocher	.15	.15
P12	N2	5(h) light blue	.15	.15
P13	N2	7(h) red orange	.15	.15
P14	N2	9(h) emerald	.15	.15
P15	N2	10(h) henna brown	.15	.15
P16	N2	12(h) dark ultra	.15	.15
P17	N2	20(h) dark green	.15	.15
P18	N2	50(h) red brown	.15	.15
P19	N2	1k slate green	.15	*.25*
		Set value	.50	.81

Bohemia and Moravia stamps can be mounted in the Scott Czechoslovakia album or Germany album part 2.

1997 Vol. 2 Number Changes

Number in 1996 Catalogue	Number in 1997 Catalogue
Argentina	
1752-1754	1751-1753
1756-1757	1754-1755
1760-1761	1756-1757
1763-1764	1758-1759
Austria	
2d, 4c	Added
6c, 10b	Added
12a, 17a, 25a	Added
27a, 30a	Added
56a	Added
J6a	J6a, J6b
Lombardy-Venetia	
12b	Added
Azerbaijan	
394a	394b
Belarus	
27	25
29-30	26-27
32-37	28-33
39-40G	34-40B
Belgian Congo	
5b	Added
26a	Added
29a	Added
Belgium	
38b	Added
J1a	Footnoted
Brazil	
59a, 66a	Added
73a, 75a, 77a	Added
81a, 84a	Added
89	90a, 90b
153b	Added
2449	2452
2450	2451
2451	2450
2452	2449
C3b, C9b	Added
Caroline Islands	
20a, 20b	Added
Central Africa	
1088a, 1089a	Footnoted
China	
1a, 2a, 3a	Added
4a	Added
7a, 8a	7c, 8b
7a, 7b, 8a, 9a, 9b	Added
22i, 22p	Added
36b	Added
25a, 28f, 29b, 30f	Added
31d, 32b, 33d, 35c, 37b	Added
47e, 47f	Added
50b, 53b, 67b	Added
98b	Added
102c, 102d, 102e	Added
104c, 105c	Added
110b, 112b, 113b, 117c, 119a	Added
125b, 127c	Added
2876a	Deleted
2876b, 2876c	2876a, 2876b
2N114	2N114a
2N114a	2N114
3N32	3N32a
3N32a	3N32
5N21	5N21a
5N21a	5N21
6N2	6N2a
6N2a	6N2
6N53	6N53a
6N53a	6N53
7N23	7N23a
7N23a	7N23
7N31	7N31a
7N31a	7N31
Costa Rica	
63	63a
63a	63
C632a	Deleted
Guanacaste	
45a	Deleted
Czechoslovakia	
B119a	Footnoted

Index and Identifier

All page numbers shown are those in this Volume 1B.

Postage stamps that do not have English words on them are shown in the Identifier which begins on page 940.

Illustrated Identifier

This section pictures stamps or parts of stamp designs that will help identify postage stamps that do not have English words on them.

Many of the symbols that identify stamps of countries are shown here as well as typical examples of their stamps.

See the Index and Identifier on the previous pages for stamps with inscriptions such as "sen," "posta," "Baja Porto," "Helvetia," "K.S.A.", etc.

Linn's Stamp Identifier is now available. The 144 pages include more 2,000 inscriptions and over 500 large stamp illustrations. Available from Linn's Stamp News, P.O. Box 29, Sidney, OH 45365-0029.

HEADS, PICTURES AND NUMERALS

GREAT BRITAIN

Great Britain stamps never show the country name, but, except for postage dues, show a picture of the reigning monarch.

Victoria

Edward VII George V Edward VIII

George VI

Elizabeth II

Some George VI and Elizabeth II stamps are surcharged in annas, new paisa or rupees. These are listed under Oman.

Silhouette (sometimes facing right, generally at the top of stamp)

The silhouette indicates this is a British stamp. It is not a U.S. stamp.

VICTORIA

Queen Victoria

INDIA

Other stamps of India show this portrait of Queen Victoria and the words "Service" and "Annas."

AUSTRIA

YUGOSLAVIA

(Also BOSNIA & HERZEGOVINA if imperf.)

BOSNIA & HERZEGOVINA

Denominations also appear in top corners instead of bottom corners.

HUNGARY

Another stamp has posthorn facing left

BRAZIL

AUSTRALIA

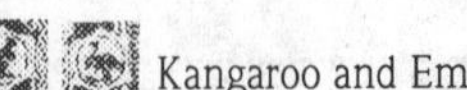

Kangaroo and Emu

GERMANY

Mecklenburg-Vorpommern

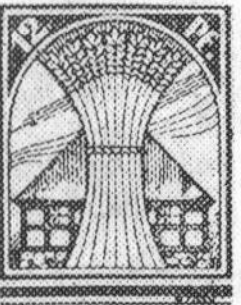

SWITZERLAND

ORIENTAL INSCRIPTIONS

CHINA

中 中

Any stamp with this one character is from China (Imperial, Republic or People's Republic). This character appears in a four-character overprint on stamps of Manchukuo. These stamps are local provisionals, which are unlisted. Other overprinted Manchukuo stamps show this character, but have more than four characters in the overprints. These are listed in People's Republic of China.

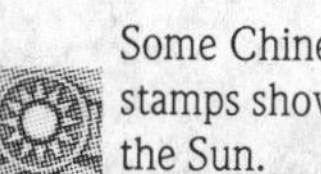

Some Chinese stamps show the Sun.

中華民國郵票

Most stamps of Republic of China show this series of characters.

Stamps with the China character and this character are from People's Republic of China. 人

中国人民邮政

Calligraphic form of People's Republic of China

Chinese stamps without China character

REPUBLIC OF CHINA

PEOPLE'S REPUBLIC OF CHINA

Mao Tse-tung

MANCHUKUO

Temple

The first 3 characters are common to many Manchukuo stamps.

Emperor Pu-Yi

The last 3 characters are common to other Manchukuo stamps.

Orchid Crest

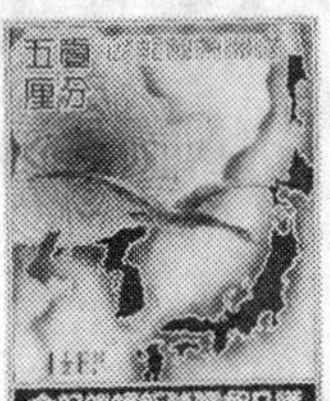
Manchukuo stamp without these elements

JAPAN

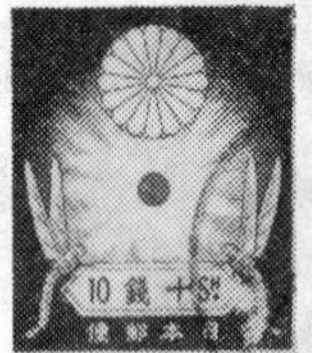

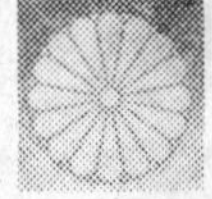
Chrysanthemum Crest

Country Name

Japanese stamps without these elements

RYUKYU ISLANDS

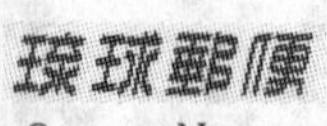
Country Name

PHILIPPINES (Japanese Occupation)

Country Name

NORTH BORNEO (Japanese Occupation)

Indicates Japanese Occupation

Country Name

MALAYA (Japanese Occupation)

Indicates Japanese Occupation

Country Name

BURMA (Japanese Occupation)

Indicates Japanese Occupation

シャン Country Name

Other Burma Japanese Occupation stamps without these elements

Burmese Script

KOREA

These two characters, in any order, are common to stamps from the Republic of Korea (South Korea) or the unlisted stamps of the People's Democratic Republic of Korea (North Korea).

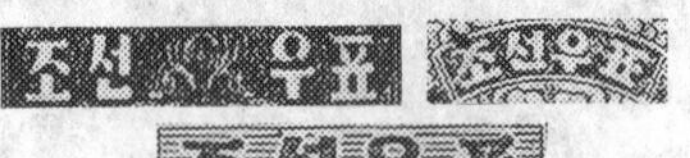
This series of four characters can be found on the stamps of both Koreas.

Yin Yang appears on some stamps.

대한민국 우표

Indicates Republic of Korea (South Korea)

THAILAND

Country Name

King Prajadhipok and Chao P'ya Chakri

CENTRAL AND EASTERN ASIAN INSCRIPTIONS

INDIA - FEUDATORY STATES

Alwar

Bhor

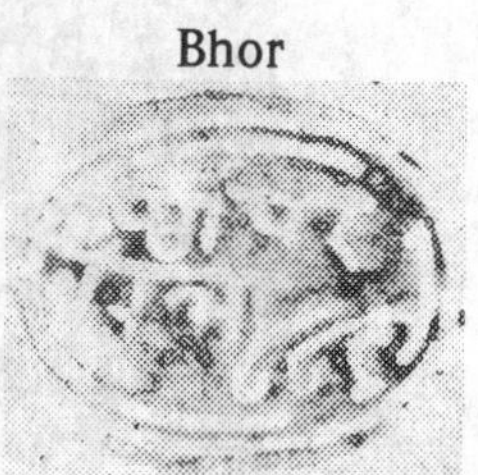

Bundi

milar stamps come with fferent designs in corners ıd differently drawn daggers t center of circle).

Faridkot

Hyderabad

Similar stamps exist with straight line frame around stamp, and also with different central design which is inscribed "Postage" or "Post & Receipt."

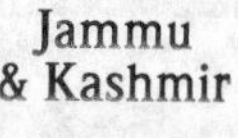

Jammu & Kashmir

Indore

Jhalawar

Nowanuggur

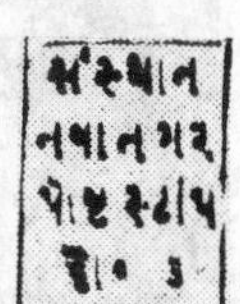

Rajpeepla

Soruth

BANGLADESH

NEPAL

Similar stamps are smaller, have squares in upper corners and have five or nine characters in central bottom panel.

TANNU TUVA

ISRAEL

GEORGIA

ARMENIA

The four characters are found somewhere on pictorial stamps. On some stamps only the middle two are found.

ARABIC INSCRIPTIONS

AFGHANISTAN

Many early Afghanistan stamps show Tiger's head, many of these have ornaments protruding from outer ring, others show inscriptions in black.

Arabic Script

Mosque Gate & Crossed Cannons

BAHRAIN

EGYPT

IRAN

Country Name

Note Crown

Lion with Sword

JORDAN

LEBANON

Similar types have denominations at top and slightly different design.

LIBYA

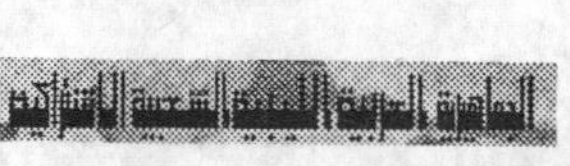

Country Name in various styles

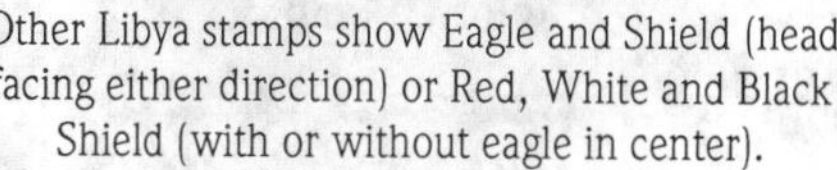

Other Libya stamps show Eagle and Shield (head facing either direction) or Red, White and Black Shield (with or without eagle in center).

SAUDI ARABIA

Note Tughra (Central design)

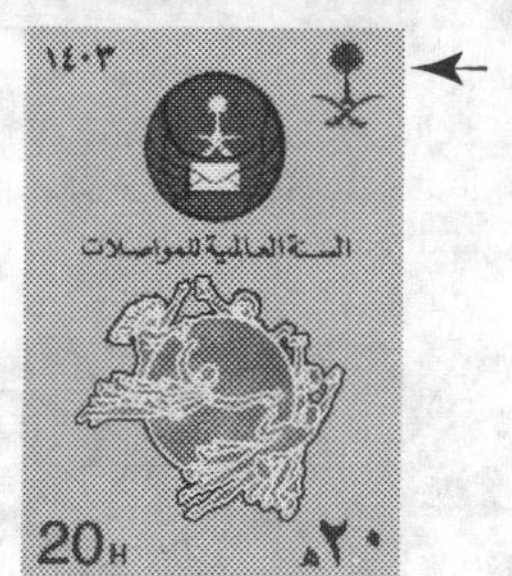

Palm Tree and Swords

SYRIA

THRACE

YEMEN

PAKISTAN - Bahawalpur

Country Name in top panel, star and crescent

TURKEY

Star & Crescent

Tughra (similar tughras can be found on stamps of Afghanistan and Saudi Arabia)

Mohammed V

Mustafa Kemal

Plane, Star and Crescent

TURKEY IN ASIA

Other Turkey in Asia pictorials show star & crescent.

GREEK INSCRIPTIONS

GREECE

Country Name in various styles (Some Crete stamps overprinted with the Greece country name are listed in Crete.)

Lepta

ΔΡΑΧΜΗ ΔΡΑΧΜΑΙ ΛΕΠΤΟΝ

Drachma Drachmas Lepton

Abbreviated Country Name ΕΛΛ

Other forms of Country Name

No country name

CRETE

Country Name

These words are on other stamps

Grosion

Crete stamps with a surcharge that have the year "1922" are listed under Greece.

EPIRUS

Country Name

IONIAN ISLANDS

CYRILLIC INSCRIPTIONS

RUSSIA

Postage Stamp

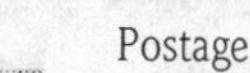

Imperial Eagle

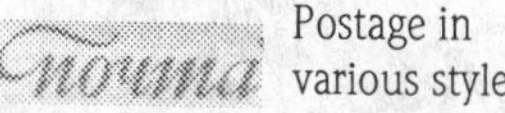

Postage in various styles

Abbreviation for Kopeck

Abbreviation for Ruble

Russia

Abbreviation for Russian Soviet Federated Socialist Republic

Abbreviation for Union of Soviet Socialist Republics

RUSSIA - Army of the North

"OKCA"

RUSSIA - Wenden

RUSSIAN OFFICES IN THE TURKISH EMPIRE

These letters appear on other stamps of the Russian offices.

The unoverprinted version of this stamp and a similar stamp were overprinted by various countries (see below).

ARMENIA

FAR EASTERN REPUBLIC

Country Name

SOUTH RUSSIA

Country Name

FINLAND

Circles and Dots on stamps similar to Imperial Russia issues

BATUM

Forms of Country Name

TRANSCAUCASIAN FEDERATED REPUBLICS

Abbreviation for Country Name

KAZAKHSTAN

Country Name

KYRGYZSTAN

Counrty Name

ROMANIA

TADJIKISTAN

Counrty Name & Abbreviation

UKRAINE

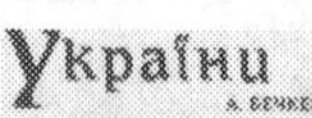

Country Name in various forms

The trident appears on many stamps, usually as an overprint.

Abbreviation for Ukrainian Soviet Socialist Republic

WESTERN UKRAINE

Abbreviation for Country Name

AZERBAIJAN

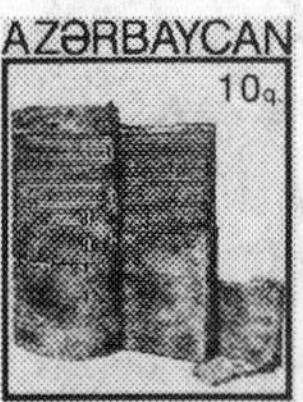

Country Name

АССР

Azerbaijan Soviet Socialist Republic

MONTENEGRO

ЦРНА ГОРА

Country Name in various forms

Abbreviation for country name

No country name (A similar Montenegro stamp without country name has same vignette.)

SERBIA

Country Name in various forms

Abbreviation for country name

YUGOSLAVIA

Showing country name

No Country Name

MACEDONIA

Country Name

BULGARIA

Country Name

Stotinka

Postage

Abbreviation for Stotinki

Stotinki (plural)

Country Name in various forms and styles

Н Р България

Н Р България

No country name

Abbreviation for Lev, leva

MONGOLIA

Country name in one word

Tugrik in Cyrillic

Country name in two words

Mung in Cyrillic

Mung in Mongolian

Tugrik in Mongolian

Arms

No Country Name

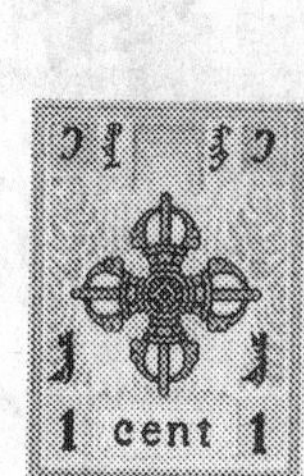

INDEX TO ADVERTISERS – 1997 VOLUME 2

1997 VOLUME 2 DEALER DIRECTORY YELLOW PAGE LISTINGS

This section of your Scott Catalogue contains advertisements to help you conveniently find what you need, when you need it...!

Accessories

BROOKLYN GALLERY COIN & STAMP
8725 4th Avenue
Brooklyn, NY 11209
718-745-5701
718-745-2775 FAX

H & S ROGG
P.O. Box 1076
Port Richey, FL 34673-1076
813-848-7697

Aerophilately

HENRY GITNER PHILATELISTS INC.
P.O. Box 3077-S
Middletown, NY 10940
914-343-5151 or 800-947-8267
914-343-0068 FAX

Albums

VIDIFORMS COMPANY INC.
Showgard House
110 Brenner Drive
Congers, NY 10920
914-268-4005
914-268-5324 FAX

Accessories

Albums & Accessories

THE KEEPING ROOM
P.O. Box 257
Trumbull, CT 06611-0257
203-372-8436

PJC COLLECTIBLES
377 Doat Street
Buffalo, NY 14211
716-891-8155 TELEPHONE & FAX

Andorra-French

JOE HARRIS
P.O. Box 13430
Baltimore, MD 21203
410-732-4791

Appraisals

UNIQUE ESTATE APPRAISALS
1937 NE Broadway
Portland, OR 97232
503-287-4200 or 800-646-1147

Approvals

THE STAMP ACT
Rt. 1 P.O. Box 93
East Orland, ME 04431
800-743-7832

Approvals Personalized - Worldwide & U.S.

THE KEEPING ROOM
P.O. Box 257
Trumbull, CT 06611-0257
203-372-8436

Approvals - Worldwide

ROSS WETREICH INC.
P.O. Box 1300
Valley Stream, NY 11582-1300
516-825-8974

Approvals Worldwide - Collections

S. R. L. STAMPS
P.O. Box 296
Huguenot, NY 12746
914-856-3429 TELEPHONE & FAX

Argentina - Ducks

METROPOLITAN STAMP CO. OF CHICAGO, INC.
P.O. Box 1133
Chicago, IL 60690-1133
815-439-0142
815-439-0143 FAX

Argentina - First Day Covers

VICTOR R. OSTOLAZA
Casilla #4338
Lima 100
PERU
511-476-2102 FAX

Argentina - New Issues

VICTOR R. OSTOLAZA
Casilla #4338
Lima 100
PERU
511-476-2102 FAX

Asia

ALLKOR STAMP COMPANY
Box 1346
Port Washington, NY 11050
516-883-3296 TELEPHONE & FAX

REGENCY STAMPS, LTD.
Le Chateau Village #106
10411 Clayton Road
St. Louis, MO 63131
800-782-0066
314-997-2231 FAX

MICHAEL ROGERS, INC.
199 E. Welbourne Ave.
Winter Park, FL 32789
407-644-2290
407-645-4434 FAX

Asia

THE STAMP ACT
P.O. Box 1136
Belmont, CA 94002
415-592-3315
415-508-8104 FAX
BChang@IX.NETCOM.COM
Internet address

SOUTHEAST STAMPS
P.O. Box 6768
Shreveport, LA 71106

Approvals - Worldwide

Auctions

Auction House

B TRADING CO.
114 Quail Street
Albany, NY 12206
518-465-3497 TELEPHONE & FAX

REGENCY PHILATELIC AUCTIONS, LTD.
Le Chateau Village #106
10411 Clayton Road
St. Louis, MO 63131
800-782-0066
314-997-2231 FAX

Auctions

CEE-JAY STAMP AUCTIONS, INC.
P.O. Box 321
Waldorf, MD 20604
800-360-2022
301-705-7255 FAX

CHARLES G. FIRBY AUCTIONS
6695 Highland Road Suite #107
Waterford, MI 48327
810-666-5333
810-666-5020 FAX

STAMP CENTER / DUTCH COUNTRY AUCTIONS
4115 Concord Pike
Wilmington, DE 19803
302-478-8740
302-478-8779 FAX

Auctions - Public

ALAN BLAIR STAMPS / AUCTIONS
5520A Lakeside Avenue
Richmond, VA 23228
800-689-5602 TELEPHONE & FAX

Austria

JOSEPH EDER
P.O. Box 5517
Hamden, CT 06518
203-281-0742
203-230-2410 FAX

HENRY GITNER PHILATELISTS INC.
P.O. Box 3077-S
Middletown, NY 10940
914-343-5151 or 800-947-8267
914-343-0068 FAX

JOE HARRIS
P.O. Box 13430
Baltimore, MD 21203
410-732-4791

HUNGARIA STAMP EXCHANGE
P.O. Box 3024
Andover, MA 01810
508-682-0242
508-794-2567 FAX

R. SCHNEIDER
Box 23049
Belleville, IL 62223
618-277-8543
618-277-1050 FAX

Baltic States

HENRY GITNER PHILATELISTS INC.
P.O. Box 3077-S
Middletown, NY 10940
914-343-5151 or 800-947-8267
914-343-0068 FAX

JOE HARRIS
P.O. Box 13430
Baltimore, MD 21203
410-732-4791

SCOTT®

CATALOGUE TABS

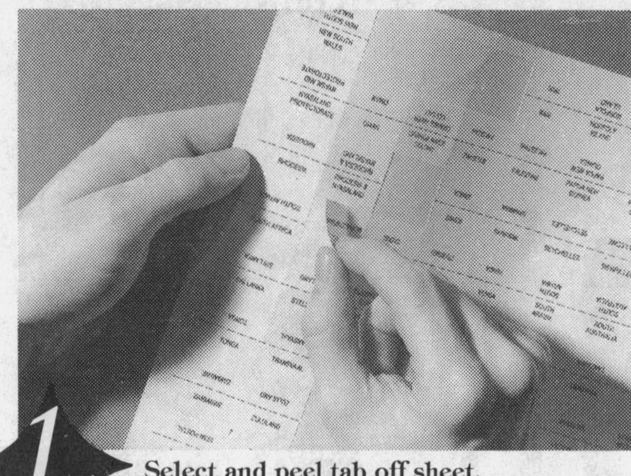

1\. Select and peel tab off sheet.

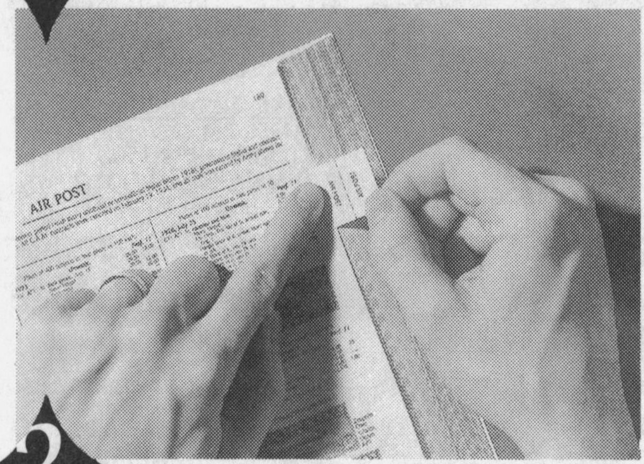

2\. Affix a portion of the tab to the appropriate page. Fold tab in half at the dotted line.

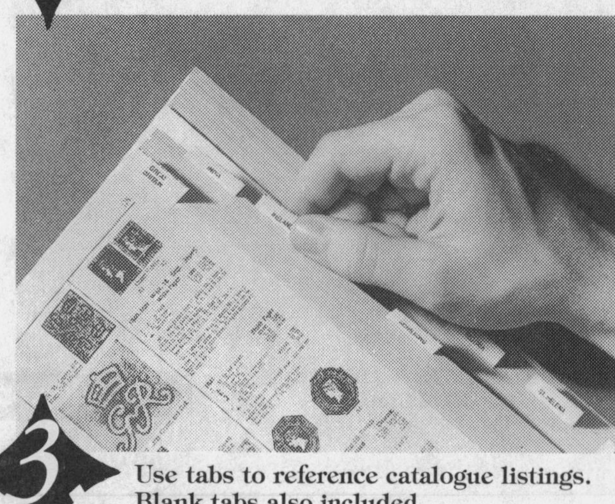

3\. Use tabs to reference catalogue listings. Blank tabs also included.

Scott Catalogue Tabs make looking up listings as easy as 1-2-3!

Tabs are sold for each volume of the catalogue, plus the Specialized and the Classic.

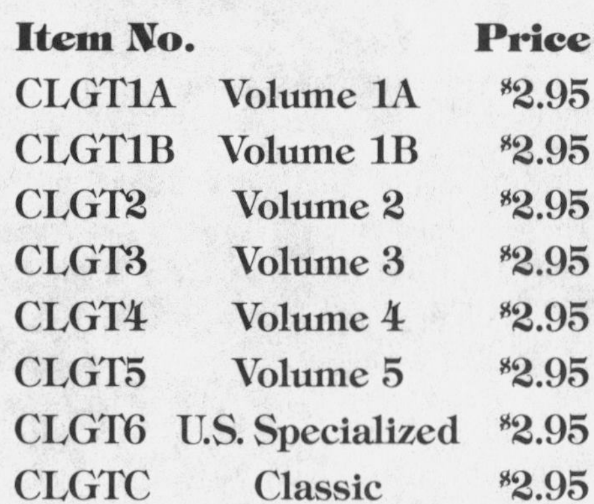

Item No.		Price
CLGT1A	Volume 1A	$2.95
CLGT1B	Volume 1B	$2.95
CLGT2	Volume 2	$2.95
CLGT3	Volume 3	$2.95
CLGT4	Volume 4	$2.95
CLGT5	Volume 5	$2.95
CLGT6	U.S. Specialized	$2.95
CLGTC	Classic	$2.95

Available from your favorite dealer or direct from:

Scott Publishing Co.
P.O. Box 828
Sidney OH 45365-0828

Belgium

HENRY GITNER PHILATELISTS INC.
P.O. Box 3077-S
Middletown, NY 10940
914-343-5151 or 800-947-8267
914-343-0068 FAX

JOE HARRIS
P.O. Box 13430
Baltimore, MD 21203
410-732-4791

Belgium & Colonies

BROOKSIDE STAMPS
P.O. Box 412
Worthington, OH 43085
614-436-0524

Belgium - New Issues

BELGIUM STAMP AGENCY IN NORTH AMERICA
One Unicover Center
Cheyenne, WY 82008-0026
800-443-4225
800-628-3123 FAX

Brazil - First Day Covers

VICTOR R. OSTOLAZA
Casilla #4338
Lima 100
PERU
511-476-2102 FAX

Brazil - New Issues

VICTOR R. OSTOLAZA
Casilla #4338
Lima 100
PERU
511-476-2102 FAX

Bulgaria

HUNGARIA STAMP EXCHANGE
P.O. Box 3024
Andover, MA 01810
508-682-0242
508-794-2567 FAX

Chile - First Day Covers

VICTOR R. OSTOLAZA
Casilla #4338
Lima 100
PERU
511-476-2102 FAX

Chile - New Issues

VICTOR R. OSTOLAZA
Casilla #4338
Lima 100
PERU
511-476-2102 FAX

Buying

China

JUNO STAMPS
1765 Juno Avenue
St. Paul, MN 55116
800-714-3469
612-699-2510 FAX

MICHAEL ROGERS, INC.
199 E. Welbourne Avenue
Winter Park, FL 32789
407-644-2290
407-645-4434 FAX

China - New Issues

CHINA STAMP AGENCY IN NORTH AMERICA
One Unicover Center
Cheyenne, WY 82008-0003
800-443-4225
800-628-3123 FAX

Collections

BOB & MARTHA FRIEDMAN STAMPS
624 Homestead Place
Joliet, IL 60435
815-725-6666
708-241-1532 FAX

DR. ROBERT FRIEDMAN & SONS STAMPS & COINS
7451 S. Woodward #108
Woodridge, IL 60517-2665
708-241-1515
708-241-1532 FAX

HENRY GITNER PHILATELISTS INC.
P.O. Box 3077-S
Middletown, NY 10940
914-343-5151 or 800-947-8267
914-343-0068 FAX

Covers

JUDNICK POSTCARDS & COVERS
P.O. Box 12248
Columbus, OH 43212-0248
614-278-9399

Czechoslovakia

HUNGARIA STAMP EXCHANGE
P.O. Box 3024
Andover, MA 01810
508-682-0242
508-794-2567 FAX

SOCIETY FOR CZECHOSLOVAK PHILATELY, INC.
Tom Cossaboom, SCP Secretary
Box 25332
Scott Air Force Base, IL 62225
USA

Discount Supplies

VERUS DISCOUNT STAMP CO.
P.O. Box 187
West Chicago, IL 60186
708-896-8938

Duck Stamps

METROPOLITAN STAMP CO. OF CHICAGO
P.O. Box 1133
Chicago, IL 60690-1133
815-439-0142
815-439-0143 FAX

TRENTON STAMP & COIN CO.
1804 RT. 33
Trenton, NJ 08690
800-446-8664
609-587-8664 FAX

Duck Stamps - Foreign

METROPOLITAN STAMP CO. OF CHICAGO
P.O. Box 1133
Chicago, IL 60690-1133
815-439-0142
815-439-0143 FAX

Europe

REGENCY STAMPS, LTD.
Le Chateau Village #106
10411 Clayton Road
St. Louis, MO 63131
800-782-0066
314-997-2231 FAX

France

JOSEPH EDER
P.O. Box 5517
Hamden, CT 06518
203-281-0742
203-230-2410 FAX

German Area

R. SCHNEIDER
Box 23049
Belleville, IL 62223
618-277-8543
618-277-1050 FAX

Germany

JOSEPH EDER
P.O. Box 5517
Hamden, CT 06518
203-281-0742
203-230-2410 FAX

Great Britain

NOVA PHILATELIC SALES
Box 161
Lakeside, N.S. B3T 1M6
CANADA
902-826-2165

Inverted Centers - World

MARTIN SELLINGER
Box 47
White Plains, NY 10602
914-948-4246
914-682-7384 FAX

Japan

GEORGE C. BAXLEY
P.O. Box 807
Alamogordo, NM 88311
505-437-8707
505-434-1571 FAX

Latin America

BROOKSIDE STAMPS
P.O. Box 412
Worthington, OH 43085
614-436-0524

Literature

JAMES BENDON LTD.
PO Box 6484
3307 Limassol
CYPRUS
+357 5 311228 FAX
bendon@dial.cylink.com.cy e-mail

Lots & Collections

DAVE ALLEGO
P.O. Box 13
Ambridge, PA 15003-0013
412-266-4255

BOB & MARTHA FRIEDMAN STAMPS
624 Homestead Place
Joliet, IL 60435
815-725-6666
708-241-1532 FAX

DR. ROBERT FRIEDMAN & SONS STAMPS & COINS
7451 S. Woodward #108
Woodridge, IL 60517-2665
708-241-1515
708-241-1532 FAX

Mail Bid Sales

CONNEXUS
P.O. Box 130
Tryon, NC 28782
704-859-5882
704-859-2702 FAX

JUNO STAMPS
1765 Juno Avenue
St. Paul, MN 55116
800-714-3469
612-699-2510 FAX

QUEST INTERNATIONAL
P.O. Box 139A,
Thames Ditton,
Surrey, KT7 OER
UNITED KINGDOM
44-181-398-7740
44-181-398-4661 FAX

Mail Order

ALMAZ CO., DEPT. VY
P.O. Box 100-812
Vanderveer Station
Brooklyn, NY 11210
718-241-6360 TELEPHONE & FAX

B & D HOBBIES
P.O. Box 4
Gladstone, OR 97027
503-656-3149

BOB BECK
Box 3209 Harbourtown Station
Hilton Head Island, SC 29928
803-671-3241

Mail Order

LOG HOUSE PHILATELIST
Box 267 Harju Road
Grand Marais, MI 49839

ROBERT'S STAMP EXCHANGE
P.O. Box 362
Carpentersville, IL 60110
708-695-6568

SHARI'S STAMPS
104-3 Old Highway 40 #130
O'Fallon, MO 63366
800-382-3597

Middle East - Arab

THE PERFECT PERF
P.O. Box 16127
Pittsburgh, PA 15242
412-429-1618
412-561-0660 FAX

Mounts

VIDIFORMS COMPANY INC.
Showgard House
110 Brenner Drive
Congers, NY 10920
914-268-4005
914-268-5324 FAX

New Issues

DAVIDSON'S STAMP SERVICE
P.O. Box 20502
Indianapolis, IN 46220
317-255-9408

New Issues - Retail

BOMBAY PHILATELIC CO., INC.
P.O. Box 7719
Delray Beach, FL 33482-7719
561-499-7990
561-499-7553 FAX

STANLEY M. PILLER
3351 Grand Ave.
Oakland, CA 94610
510-465-8290
510-465-7121 FAX

Mail Sales

New Issues

New Issues - Scandinavia

NORDICA
P.O. Box 284
Old Bethpage, NY 11804
516-931-3485 TELEPHONE & FAX
NordicaD@aol.com e-mail

Postcards

JUDNICK POSTCARDS & COVERS
P.O. Box 12248
Columbus, OH 43212-0248
614-278-9399

Proofs & Essays

HENRY GITNER PHILATELISTS INC.
P.O. Box 3077-S
Middletown, NY 10940
914-343-5151 or 800-947-8267
914-343-0068 FAX

E. JOSEPH MCCONNELL INC.
P.O. Box 683
Monroe, NY 10950
914-496-5916
914-782-0347 FAX

Publications / Collector

AMERICAN PHILATELIST
Dept. TZ
P.O. Box 8000
State College, PA 16803
814-237-3803
814-237-6128 FAX

GLOBAL STAMP NEWS
P.O. Box 97
Sidney, OH 45365-0097
513-492-3183
513-492-6514 FAX

MEKEEL'S WEEKLY STAMP NEWS
Box 5050-sy
White Plains, NY 10602
800-MEKEEL-1
914-997-7261 FAX

Ryukyus

GEORGE C. BAXLEY
P.O. Box 807
Alamogordo, NM 88311
505-437-8707
505-434-1571 FAX

Safes - Stamps

KINGSBERY MANUFACTURING CORP.
715 West Zavala Street
Crystal City, TX 78839
800-445-0763

Stamp Shows

ATLANTIC COAST EXHIBITIONS
Division of Beach Philatelics
P.O. Box 150
Virginia Beach, VA 23458-0150
804-425-8566 TELEPHONE & FAX

CONNECTICUT STAMP SHOWS
Box 5050-sy
White Plains, NY 10602
800-MEKEEL-1
914-997-7261 FAX

HIGHTSTOWN SECOND SATURDAY BOURSE
Monmouth St.(RTE.633) opposite
Ramada Inn
Exit 8 New Jersey Turnpike
Hightstown, NJ 08520

AL SOTH
P.O. Box 22081
Milwaukie, OR 97269
503-794-0956

STAMP STORES

Arizona

B.J.'S STAMPS / BARBARA J. JOHNSON
6342 W. Bell Road
Glendale, AZ 85308
602-878-2080
602-412-3456 FAX

California

ASHTREE STAMP & COIN
2410 N. Blackstone
Fresno, CA 93703
209-227-7167

BREWART STAMPS
1015 N. Euclid
Anaheim, CA 92801
714-533-0400
714-533-2701

BROSIUS STAMP & COIN
2105 Main Street
Santa Monica, CA 90405
310-396-7480

FISCHER - WOLK PHILATELICS
24771 "G" Alicia Parkway
Laguna Hills, CA 92653
714-837-2932

HERB'S STAMP CENTER
11748 Washington Place
West Los Angeles, CA 90066
310-397-3883

KENRICH CO.
9418-A Las Tunas Drive
Temple City, CA 91780
818-286-3888
818-286-6035 FAX

NATICK STAMPS & HOBBIES
405 S. Myrtle Avenue
Monrovia, CA 91016
818-305-7333
818-305-7335 FAX

STANLEY M. PILLER
3351 Grand Ave.
Oakland, CA 94610
510-465-8290
510-465-7121 FAX

THE STAMP GALLERY
1515 Locust Street
Walnut Creek, CA 94596
510-944-9111

STAMPCRAFT
P.O. Box 2425
Santa Clara, CA 95055
800-245-5389
408-241-4440 FAX

Colorado

ACKLEY'S ROCKS & STAMPS
3230 N. Stone Ave.
Colorado Springs, CO 80907
719-633-1153

AURORA STAMPS & COINS
9818 E. Colfax Ave.
Aurora, CA 80010
303-364-3223

SHOWCASE STAMPS
3865 Wadsworth Blvd.
Wheat Ridge, CO 80033
303-425-9252
303-425-7410 FAX

Connecticut

MILLER'S STAMP SHOP
41 New London Turnpike
Uncasville, CT 06382
203-848-0468 TELEPHONE & FAX

SILVER CITY COINS & J & B STAMPS
41 Colony Street
Meriden, CT 06451
203-235-7634

Delaware

AUREL STAMP SHOPPE
Bobby Leiter
104 Market Street
Bridgeville, DE 19933-1127
302-337-7855

Florida

ARLINGTON STAMP & COIN CO.
1350 University Blvd., North
Jacksonville, FL 32211-5226
904-743-1776

BEACH STAMP & COIN
971 E. Eau Gallie Blvd.
and Highway A1A Suite G
Melbourne Beach, FL 32937
407-777-1666

CLARK'S CORNER
4223 Bee Ridge Road
Sarasota, FL 34233
941-377-6909
941-377-6604 FAX

CORBIN STAMP & COIN
115-A East Brandon Blvd.
Brandon, FL 33511
813-651-3266

HAUSER'S COIN & STAMP
3425 S. Florida Ave.
Lakeland, FL 33803
941-647-2052
941-644-5738 FAX

HUGO'S STAMP EMPORIUM
P.O. Box 5527
Lake Worth, FL 33466
407-966-7517

INTERCONTINENTAL / RICARDO DEL CAMPO
7379 Coral Way
Miami, FL 33155-1402
305-264-4983
305-262-2919 FAX

Georgia

Florida

JACK'S COINS & STAMPS
801 Northlake Blvd.
North Palm Beach, FL 33408
407-844-7710

JERRY SIEGEL / STAMPS FOR COLLECTORS
1920 E. Hallandale Beach Blvd.
Suite 507
Hallandale, FL 33009
954-457-0422 TELEPHONE & FAX

NEW ENGLAND STAMP
4987 Tamiami Trail East
Village Falls Professional Ctr.
Naples, FL 33962
941-732-8000
941-732-7701 FAX

ST. JOHN'S STAMP SHOP
2 Aviles Street
St. Augustine, FL 32084
904-829-9673

THE STAMP PLACE
576 First Avenue North
St. Petersburg, FL 33701
813-894-4082

WINTER PARK STAMP SHOP
199 E. Welbourne Ave.
Suite 201
Winter Park, FL 32789
800-845-1819
407-628-0091 FAX

Georgia

STAMPS UNLIMITED OF GEORGIA
133 Carnegie Way
Room 250
Atlanta, GA 30303
404-688-9161

Illinois

DON CLARK'S STAMPS
937 1/2 W. Galena Blvd.
Aurora, IL 60506
630-896-4606

DR. ROBERT FRIEDMAN & SONS STAMPS & COINS
7451 S. Woodward #108
Woodridge, IL 60517-2665
708-241-1515
708-241-1532 FAX

H.C. STAMP & COIN CO.
10 Crystal Lake Plaza
Crystal Lake, IL 60014
815-459-3940

MARSHALL FIELD'S STAMP DEPT.
111 N. State Street
Chicago, IL 60602
312-781-4237

ROSEMOOR STAMP & COIN CO.
2021 Ridge Road
Homewood, IL 60430
708-799-0880

STAMP KING / RICHARD E. DREWS AUCTIONS
7139 W. Higgins Road
Chicago, IL 60656
312-775-2100
312-792-9116 FAX

WHITE HOUSE JEWELERS
54 N. Main
Canton, IL 61520
309-647-2777

Florida

STAMP STORES

Indiana

J & J COINS & STAMPS
7019 Calumet Avenue
Hammond, IN 46324
219-932-5818

KNIGHT STAMP & COIN COMPANY
301 Main Street
Hobart, IN 46342
800-634-2646

VILLAGE STAMP AND COIN
40 E. Cedar
Zionsville, IN 46077
317-873-6762

Kentucky

COLLECTORS STAMPS LTD.
4012 DuPont Circle #313
Louisville, KY 40207
502-897-9045

TREASURE ISLAND COINS & STAMPS
232 W. Broadway
Louisville, KY 40202
502-583-1222

Maryland

BALTIMORE COIN & STAMP EXCHANGE INC.
10194 Baltimore National Pike
Unit 104
Ellicott City, MD 21042
410-418-8282
410-418-4813 FAX

BULLDOG STAMP CO.
4641 Montgomery Ave.
Bethesda, MD 20814
301-654-1138

STAMP & COIN WORLD
511-A Delaware Avenue
Towson, MD 21286
410-828-4465 or 800-452-4560
410-828-4560 FAX

Massachusetts

FALMOUTH STAMP & COIN
11 Town Hall Square
Falmouth, MA 02540
508-548-7075 or 800-341-3701

J & N FORTIER
484 Main Street
Worcester, MA 01608
508-757-3657

KAPPY'S COINS & STAMPS
534 Washington St.
Norwood, MA 02062
617-762-5552
617-762-3292 FAX

Michigan

AMERICA'S STAMP STOP
23333 Orchard Lake Rd.
Farmington, MI 48336
810-474-4460

BIRMINGHAM COIN AND JEWELRY
1287 S. Woodward
Birmingham, MI 48009
810-642-1234
810-642-4207 FAX

Michigan

MEL COON STAMPS
3833 Twelve Mile
Berkley, MI 48072
810-398-6085
810-398-4549 FAX

THE MOUSE AND SUCH
696 N. Mill Street
Plymouth, MI 48170
313-454-1515

Minnesota

CROSSROADS STAMP SHOP
2211 West 54th Street
Minneapolis, MN 55419-1515
612-928-0119

JW STAMP COMPANY
5300 250th Street
Saint Cloud, MN 56301
320-252-2996

Missouri

KNIGHT'S COINS & STAMPS
323 South Avenue
Springfield, MO 65806
417-862-3018

REGENCY STAMPS, LTD.
Le Chateau Village #106
10411 Clayton Road
St. Louis, MO 63131
800-782-0066
314-997-2231 FAX

Nebraska

TUVA ENTERPRISES
209 So. 72nd Street
Omaha, NE 68114
402-397-9937

New Hampshire

BRUNELLE STAMPS & COINS
25 East Broadway
Derry, NH 03038
603-432-2658
603-437-7279 FAX

New Jersey

AALLSTAMPS
38 N. Main Street
P.O. Box 249
Milltown, NJ 08850
908-247-1093
908-247-1094 FAX

A.D.A. STAMP CO., INC.
910 Boyd Street
Toms River, NJ 08753
908-240-1131
908-240-2620 FAX

BERGEN STAMPS & COLLECTABLES
717 American Legion Dr.
Teaneck, NJ 07666
201-836-8987

CHARLES STAMP SHOP
47 Old Post Road
Edison, NJ 08817
908-985-1071
908-819-0549 FAX

COLONIAL COINS & STAMPS
1865 Rt. #35
Wall Township, NJ 07719
908-449-4549

New Jersey

FAIRIDGE STAMP INC.
447 Broadway
Westwood, NJ 07675
201-666-8869

RON RITZER STAMPS, INC.
Millburn Mall
2933 Vauxhall Road
Union, NJ 07088
908-687-0007 TELEPHONE & FAX

SCRIVENER'S STAMPS & COLLECTIBLES
178 Maplewood Avenue
P.O. Box 1035
Maplewood, NJ 07040
201-762-5650
201-762-6709 FAX

TRENTON STAMP & COIN CO.
1804 RT. 33
Trenton, NJ 08690
800-446-8664
609-587-8664 FAX

New York

B.B.C. STAMP & COIN INC.
185 East Main St.
P.O. Box 2141
Setauket, NY 11733-0715
516-751-5662

CHAMPION STAMP CO.
432 West 54th Street
New York, NY 10019
212-489-8130
212-581-8130 FAX

JOHN'S COINS, CARDS & STAMPS INC.
36 West 34th Street
2nd Floor
New York, NY 10001
212-244-2646

LINCOLN COIN & STAMP
33 West Tupper Street
Buffalo, NY 14202
716-856-1884

SUBURBAN STAMPS, COINS AND COLLECTIBLES
120 Kreischer Road
North Syracuse, NY 13212
315-452-0593

VILLAGE STAMPS & COINS
22 Oriskany Blvd.
Yorkville Plaza
Yorkville, NY 13495
315-736-1007 or 800-490-1007

North Dakota

THE COLLECTOR'S DEN / L.V. FISCHER
P.O. Box 9303
Fargo, ND 58106-9303
701-241-7747 TELEPHONE & FAX

Ohio

CROWN & EAGLE
5303 N. High Street
Columbus, OH 43214
614-436-2042

FEDERAL COIN INC.
39 The Arcade
Cleveland, OH 44114
216-861-1160
216-861-5960 FAX

Ohio

HILLTOP STAMP SERVICE
P.O. Box 626
Wooster, OH 44691
330-262-5378

J L F STAMP STORE
3041 E. Waterloo Road
Akron, OH 44312
330-628-8343

LAZARUS STAMP DEPT.
141 S. High St.
5th Floor
Columbus, OH 43215
614-463-3214

THE LINK STAMP CO.
3461 E. Livingston Ave.
Columbus, OH 43227
614-237-4125 or 800-546-5726

NEWARK STAMP COMPANY
49 North Fourth Street
Newark, OH 43055
614-349-7900

Oregon

AL'S STAMP & COIN
2132 West 6th
Eugene, OR 97402
503-343-0091

UNIQUE ESTATE APPRAISALS
1937 NE Broadway
Portland, OR 97232
503-287-4200 or 800-646-1147

Pennsylvania

KAUFMANN'S STAMP DEPT.
400 Fifth Ave.
Pittsburgh, PA 15219
412-232-2598

LARRY LEE STAMPS
322 S. Front Street
Wormleysburg, PA 17043
717-763-7605

PENNSYLVANIA STAMP CO.
229 Sixth Street
McKeesport, PA 15132
800-545-6604

PHILLY STAMP & COIN CO. INC.
1804 Chestnut Street
Philadelphia, PA 19103
215-563-7341
215-563-7382 FAX

WORLD OF STAMPS & COINS
Route 611
Fountain Court Mall
Bartonsville, PA 18321
717-688-9829

Rhode Island

PODRAT COIN [illegible]CHANGE INC.
769 Hope Str[illegible]
Providence[illegible] 02906
401-861-7[illegible]40
401-27[illegible]3032 FAX

Tennessee

HERRON HILL, INC.
5007 Black Road
Suite 140
Memphis, TN 38117-4505
901-683-9644

STAMP STORES

Texas

ALAMO HEIGHTS STAMP SHOP
1201 Austin Hwy
Suite 128
San Antonio, TX 78209
800-214-9526
800-495-5255 FAX

AUSTIN STAMP & COIN
13107 F M 969
Austin, TX 78724
512-276-7793

DALLAS STAMP GALLERY
1002 North Central Expressway
Suite 501
Richardson, TX 75080
800-759-9109
214-669-4742 FAX

Virginia

ALAN BLAIR STAMPS / AUCTIONS
5520A Lakeside Avenue
Richmond, VA 23228
800-689-5602 TELEPHONE & FAX

CENTURY STAMPS & COINS
6436 Brandon Ave.
Springfield, VA 22150
703-569-0739

KENNEDY'S STAMPS & COINS
7059 Brookfield Plaza
Springfield, VA 22150
703-569-7300

LATHEROW & CO. INC.
5054 Lee Highway
Arlington, VA 22207
703-538-2727

PRINCE WILLIAM STAMP & COIN CO.
14011-H St. Germain Dr.
Centreville, VA 22020
703-830-4669

Washington

HIDDEN TREASURES INC.
9960 NW Silverdale Way #11
Silverdale, WA 98383
360-692-1999 or 800-322-1993
360-698-1905 FAX

TACOMA MALL BLVD. COIN & STAMP
5225 Tacoma Mall Blvd. E-101
Tacoma, WA 98409
206-472-9632

THE STAMP & COIN PLACE
1310 Commercial
Bellingham, WA 98225
360-676-8720
360-647-6947 FAX

West Virginia

DAVID HILL LTD.
6433 U.S. Route 60 E
Barboursville, WV 25504
304-736-4383

Wisconsin

HERITAGE STAMPS
11400 W. Bluemound Rd.
Milwaukee, WI 53226-4049
800-231-6080
414-369-0741 FAX

JIM LUKES' STAMP & COIN
815 Jay Street
P.O. Box 1780
Manitowoc, WI 54221
414-682-2324

Supplies

VIDIFORMS COMPANY INC.
Showgard House
110 Brenner Drive
Congers, NY 10920
914-268-4005
914-268-5324 FAX

Supplies & Accessories

BEACH PHILATELICS
P.O. Box 150
Virginia Beach, VA 23458-0150
804-425-8566 TELEPHONE & FAX

GLOBAL STAMP & COIN
460 Ridge Street
Lewiston, NY 14092
800-368-4328
716-754-8513 FAX

Supplies - Mail Order

GOPHER SUPPLY CO.
1973 Sloan Place #20
Maplewood, NJ 55117
612-771-8840 or 800-815-3868
612-486-8441 FAX

STAMPCRAFT
P.O. Box 2425
Santa Clara, CA 95055
800-245-5389
408-241-4440 FAX

Supplies - Stamps & Coins

M.A. STORCK CO.
652 Congress Street
Portland, ME 04104
800-734-7271

Topicals

GERSON - REITER INC.
610 SW Alder Street
Suite 500
Portland, OR 97205
503-228-5233
503-228-5288 FAX

Topicals - Beatles

BICK INTERNATIONAL
P.O. Box 854
Van Nuys, CA 91408
818-997-6496
818-988-4337 FAX

Topicals - Biology

EASTERN SHORE STAMP CO.
P.O. Box 298
Fruitland, MD 21826
410-742-7221

Topicals - Butterflies

HENRY GITNER PHILATELISTS INC.
P.O. Box 3077-S
Middletown, NY 10940
914-343-5151 or 800-947-8267
914-343-0068 FAX

Topicals - Churchill

BICK INTERNATIONAL
P.O. Box 854
Van Nuys, CA 91408
818-997-6496
818-988-4337 FAX

Topicals - Columbus

MR. COLUMBUS
Box 1492
Frankenmuth, MI 48734

Topicals - France

E. JOSEPH MCCONNELL INC.
P.O. Box 683
Monroe, NY 10950
914-496-5916
914-782-0347 FAX

Topicals - Miscellaneous

DISCOUNT TOPICALS
P.O. Box 74-7435
Rego Park, NY 11374
212-726-8075

MEKEEL'S WEEKLY STAMP NEWS
Box 5050-sy
White Plains, NY 10602
800-MEKEEL-1
914-997-7261 FAX

MINI - ARTS
Estherville, IA 51334
712-362-4710

Topicals – Miscellaneous

SCOTT 1996 SUPPLEMENT SCHEDULE

Some of the supplements listed may not be produced due to the small number of new issues released.
Scott supplements are available from your favorite dealer or direct from Scott Publishing Co.

February

International Part 30A	830P194
International Part 30B	830P294

March

American	170S095
Minuteman	180S095
Minuteman U.N.	181S095
National	100S095
Pony Express	178S095
Stars & Stripes	176S095
U.N. Imprint Blocks	552S095
U.N. Singles	551S095

April

Marshall Islands	111MA95
Micronesia	111MI95
Palau	111PA95
U.S. 20th Century B/4	140S095
U.S. Booklet Panes	101S095
U.S. Commem. Blocks	120S095
U.S. Commem. Singles	130S095
U.S. Duck Blocks	N/A
U.S Federal & State Duck	N/A
U.S. PNC Comprehensive	114S095
U.S. PNC Simplified	113S095
U.S. PNC Singles	117S095
U.S. Postal Cards	110S095
U.S. Postal Stationery	105S095
U.S. Regular/Air Plate Block	125S095
U.S. Small Panes	118S095

May

Albania	601S095
Austria	300S095
British Europe	203S095
Bulgaria	602S095
Canada	240S095
Channel Islands	202S095
Croatia	603S095
France	310S095
Germany	315S095
Great Britain	200S095
Ireland	201S095
Master Canada	245S095
Monaco & French Andorra	333S095
Macedonia	604S095
Romania	605S095
Slovenia	606S095
St. Pierra & Miquelon	607S095

June

Bahrain	560S095
Egypt	608S095
Greece	320S095
Israel Singles	500S095
Israel Tabs	501S095
Jordan	609S095
Korea	515S095
Kuwait	623S095
Lebanon	610S095
Syria	612S095
UAE	613S095
Yemen	614S095
U.S. Hingeless	100SH95
U.S. Platinum	199S095

July

Afghanistan	N/A
Bangladesh	702S095
Bhutan	610S095
Brunei	N/A
Burma	N/A
India	613S095
Italy	325S095
Japan	510S095
Laos	619S095
Malaysia	620S095
Nepal	618S095
Pakistan	673S095
Portugal	340S095
Portugal Colonies	341S095
San Marino	328S095
Spain & Spanish Andorra	355S095
Sri Lanka	622S095
Turkey	505S095
Vatican City	375S095

August

Baltic States	361S095
Belgium	303S095
Czech Republic	307S095
Fiji	624S395
French Polynesia	625S095
FSAT	626S095
Hungary	323S095
Indonesia	627S095
Kiribati	628S095
Luxembourg	330S095
Nauru	629S095
Netherlands	335S095
New Caledonia	630S095
Philippines	631S095
Pitcairn Islands	632S095
Poland	338S095
Russia	360S095
Samoa	633S095
Solomon Islands	634S095
Tonga	635S095
Tuvalu	636S095
Vanuatu	637S095
Wallis & Futuna	638S095

September

Argentina	642S095
Australia	210S095
Australia Depend	211S095
New Zealand Depend.	221S095
Bolivia	643S095
Brazil	644S095
Chile	645S095
Colombia	646S095
Costa Rica	647S095
Dominican Republic	648S095
Ecuador	649S095
Guatemala	650S095
Haiti	651S095
Honduras	652S095
Mexico	430S095
New Zealand	220S095
New Zealand Depend.	221S095
Nicaragua	711S095
Panama	653S095
Paraguay	654S095
Peru	655S095
Salvador	656S095
Uruguay	657S095
Venezuela	658S095

October

Barbados,Trinadad,Tobago	261S795
Botswana	661S095
British Africa	270S095
British Orient	275S095
Dominica	261S495
Grenada	261S895
Guyana	261S595
Kenya	662S095
Leeward Islands	261S195
Liberia	663S095
Malawi	664S095
Mauritius	665S095
Namibia	666S095
Nigeria	667S095
North & West Caribbean	261S095
People's Republic China	520S095
Republic of China	530S095
Seychelles	668S095
South Atlantic	261S395
St. Lucia	261S995
St. Vincent	261S695
Sudan	670S095
Swaziland	671S095
Zimbabwe	672S095

November

Algeria	674S095
Benin	675S095
Burkina Faso	676S095
Burundi	677S095
Cameroun	678S095
Central Africa	679S095
Chad	680S095
Comoro Islands	681S095
Congo	682S095
Djibouti	683S095
Equatorial Guinea	684S095
Ethiopia	685S095
Gabon	686S095
Guinea	687S095
Guinea-Bissau	712S095
Ivory Coast	688S095
Madagascar	689S095
Mali	690S095
Mauritania	691S095
Morocco	692S095
Niger	693S095
Rwanda	694S095
Senegal	696S095
Somalia	697S095
St. Thomas & Prince	695S095
Togo	696S095
Tunisia	697S095
Zaire	696S095
Zambia	697S095

December

Eritrea	710S095
Gambia	703S095
Ghana	704S095
Lesotho	705S095
Maldives	706S095
Sierra Leone	707S095
Tanzania	708S095
Uganda	709S095

Scott Publishing Co.
P.O. Box 828
Sidney OH 45365
1-800-572-6885

Topicals - Worldwide

United Nations

BEACH PHILATELICS
P.O. Box 150
Virginia Beach, VA 23458-0150
804-425-8566 TELEPHONE & FAX

United States

BEACH PHILATELICS
P.O. Box 150
Virginia Beach, VA 23458-0150
804-425-8566 TELEPHONE & FAX

BOB & MARTHA FRIEDMAN STAMPS
624 Homestead Place
Joliet, IL 60435
815-725-6666
708-241-1532 FAX

DR. ROBERT FRIEDMAN & SONS STAMPS & COINS
7451 S. Woodward #108
Woodridge, IL 60517-2665
708-241-1515
708-241-1532 FAX

United States - Plate Blocks

BEACH PHILATELICS
P.O. Box 150
Virginia Beach, VA 23458-0150
804-425-8566 TELEPHONE & FAX

United States - Price Lists

ROBERT E. BARKER
P.O. Box 888063
Dunwoody, GA 30356
800-833-0217
770-671-8918 FAX

United States Stamps & Covers - Supplies

QUALITY STAMPS
22669 Remington Court
Elkhart, IN 46514-4675

Vietnam - North

ALLKOR STAMP COMPANY
Box 1346
Port Washington, NY 11050
516-883-3296 TELEPHONE & FAX

Want Lists

GERSON - REITER INC.
610 SW Alder Street
Suite 500
Portland, OR 97205
503-228-5233
503-228-5288 FAX

CHARLES P. SCHWARTZ
P.O. Box 165
Mora, MN 55051
612-679-4705

Want Lists - Worldwide

HERB'S STAMP CENTER
11748 Washington Place
West Los Angeles, CA 90066
310-397-3883

ST. JOHN'S STAMP SHOP
2 Aviles Street
St. Augustine, FL 32084
904-829-9673

Wanted - Estates

BOB & MARTHA FRIEDMAN STAMPS
624 Homestead Place
Joliet, IL 60435
815-725-6666
708-241-1532 FAX

DR. ROBERT FRIEDMAN & SONS STAMPS & COINS
7451 S. Woodward #108
Woodridge, IL 60517-2665
708-241-1515
708-241-1532 FAX

TOWN & COUNTRY STAMPS LTD.
P.O. Box 13542-S
St. Louis, MO 63138
314-869-7063
314-869-7851 FAX

Wanted To Buy

BOB & MARTHA FRIEDMAN STAMPS
624 Homestead Place
Joliet, IL 60435
815-725-6666
708-241-1532 FAX

DR. ROBERT FRIEDMAN & SONS STAMPS & COINS
7451 S. Woodward #108
Woodridge, IL 60517-2665
708-241-1515
708-241-1532 FAX

Western Europe

EDWARD J. MCKIM
1373 Isabelle
Memphis, TN 38122

Wholesale

HENRY GITNER PHILATELISTS INC.
P.O. Box 3077-S
Middletown, NY 10940
914-343-5151 or 800-947-8267
914-343-0068 FAX

Wholesale Collections

A.D.A. STAMP CO., INC.
910 Boyd Street
Toms River, NJ 08753
908-240-1131
908-240-2620 FAX

Wholesale Philatelic & Numismatic Accessories

ECONOMICAL WHOLESALE CO.
6 King Philip Road
Worcester, MA 01606
508-853-3127

HARRY EDELMAN
111-37 Lefferts Blvd.
P.O. Box 20140
So. Ozone Park, NY 11420
718-641-2710
718-641-0737 FAX

M. C. CLAYTON
290 East Grand Avenue
S. San Francisco, CA 94080
415-873-7577
415-873-7573 FAX

CHARLES R. HEISLER INC.
500 Oak Grove Drive
Lancaster, PA 17601
800-784-6886
717-299-2366 FAX

LEDO SUPPLY CO.
P.O. Box 1749
Sandpoint, ID 83864
800-257-8331

Wholesale Philatelic & Numismatic Accessories

M.A. STORCK CO.
652 Congress Street
Portland, ME 04104
800-734-7271

POLLARD COIN & STAMP SUPPLY CO., INC.
5220 E. 23rd Street
Indianapolis, IN 46218
317-547-1306
317-547-1311 FAX

SCOTT WESTERN
5670 Schaefer Ave. No. L
Chino, CA 91710
909-590-5030
909-465-6368 FAX

Wholesale Supplies

DOUBLE J. STAMPS
P.O. Box 1127
Arlington Heights, IL 60006
847-843-8700
847-843-2878 FAX

JOHN VAN ALSTYNE STAMPS & SUPPLIES
1787 Tribute Rd. Suite J
Sacramento, CA 95815
916-565-0600
916-565-0539 FAX

Worldwide

DAVE ALLEGO
P.O. Box 13
Ambridge, PA 15003-0013
412-266-4255

AMERICAN STAMP & COIN CO.
7225 N. Oracle Rd.
Suite #102
Tucson, AZ 85704
520-297-3456

MEL COON STAMPS
3833 Twelve Mile
Berkley, MI 48072
810-398-6085
810-398-4549 FAX

GERSON - REITER INC.
610 SW Alder Street
Suite 500
Portland, OR 97205
503-228-5233
503-228-5288 FAX

HERITAGE STAMPS
11400 W. Bluemound Rd.
Milwaukee, WI 53226-4049
800-231-6080
414-369-0741 FAX

MARLIN LARSON
217 Country Garden Lane
San Marcos, CA 92069
619-744-1435
619-744-5119 FAX

MCMILLAN & WIFE
2740 Sarver Lane
San Marcos, CA 92069
619-744-1435
619-744-5119 FAX

EDWARD J. MCKIM
1373 Isabelle
Memphis, TN 38122

Worldwide - Price Lists

HALL'S STAMPS (ITEX)
P.O. Box 8095
Spokane, WA 99203
509-838-1903 TELEPHONE & FAX

Worldwide - Romania

GEORGE ARGHIR, PHILATELISTS
Detunata Str. 17-27
P.O. Box 521
RO-3400 Cluj-Napoca 9
ROMANIA
40-64-414036 TELEPHONE & FAX

Worldwide - Year Sets

BOMBAY PHILATELIC CO., INC.
P.O. Box 7719
Delray Beach, FL 33482-7719
561-499-7990
561-499-7553 FAX

HENRY GITNER PHILATELISTS INC.
P.O. Box 3077-S
Middletown, NY 10940
914-343-5151 or 800-947-8267
914-343-0068 FAX

WALLACE STAMPS
Box 82
Port Washington, NY 11050
516-883-5578

Worldwide